KU-364-078

CATALOGUE

OF

THE LONDON LIBRARY

SUPPLEMENT

1920–1928

CATALOGUE

OF

THE LONDON LIBRARY

ST. JAMES'S SQUARE, LONDON

SUPPLEMENT

1920-1928

BY

C. T. HAGBERG WRIGHT, LL.D.

AND

C. J. PURNELL, M.A.

LONDON

1929

Printed in Great Britain by
NEILL & CO., LTD., EDINBURGH.

THE
LONDON LIBRARY
ST. JAMES'S SQUARE, S.W. 1

London Library,

St. James's Square, S.W. 1.

The London Library contains over 400,000 volumes. Standard Works of current literature and older and rarer volumes, in various languages, are added from time to time to the number of over 7000 a year. The collection is thoroughly representative, selected from the literatures of many countries and embracing works on almost every subject. While primarily intended for the supply of serious literature, the Library does not wholly exclude works of fiction. All Members have free access to the shelves.

Fifteen volumes at a time are allowed to Country Members; Ten to residents in London. The annual subscription is four guineas, and there is an entrance fee of three guineas. The composition for life membership varies according to age. For every extra guinea per annum, an additional number of Volumes may be had at the rate of five Volumes at one time of old Works.

Fourteen days are allowed for the perusal of new Books (*i.e.* Books published within the last twelve months), and one month for Books of older date.

The Reading Rooms, which are open daily from Ten to Six, are furnished with Dictionaries and Encyclopædias, English and Foreign Periodicals, and with the current literary papers.

The Library is closed three days at Easter and three days at Christmas, on Whit-Monday and August Bank Holiday.

Subscribers are admitted on the recommendation of a Member, subject to the approval of the Committee.

C. T. HAGBERG WRIGHT,

Secretary and Librarian.

1928.

NOTE

THIS SUPPLEMENT contains all the books added to the Library from the time the last Supplement to the Catalogue was going through the press in 1920 up to the middle of 1928. It includes, among other collections, the Allan Library, consisting of some Incunabula, early Reformation literature, etc.; the late Mr. H. B. Irving's library of criminology, presented by Mrs. Irving; a large number of miscellaneous books bequeathed by the late Miss Hastings and the late Mr. C. Ll. Davies; and Armenian books bequeathed by the late Mr. F. C. Conybeare.

References to books, the main entries of which are included in the Catalogue, 2 vols., 1913–14, or in Supplement 1, 1920, etc., are preceded by †. *E.g.* **Luther (Martin)**, *see* †ULENBERG (C.) Gesch., B1, 1836.

† before an alternative heading in square brackets denotes the British Museum form, where it differs from that adopted by the London Library. Many alternative forms already given in the 1913 Catalogue are here omitted.

PLACE OF PUBLICATION.—Much space has been saved by omitting systematically the names of certain places of publication which frequently recur. For example:—

Berlin	*is omitted where titles of works are in*			German
Bucuresci	,,	,,	,,	Roumanian
Buda-Pesth	,,	,,	,,	Hungarian
Christiania	,,	,,	,,	Norwegian
Copenhagen	,,	,,	,,	Danish
Lisbon	,,	,,	,,	Portuguese
London	,,	,,	,,	English
Madrid	,,	,,	,,	Spanish
Paris	,,	,,	,,	French
Reykjavík	,,	,,	,,	Icelandic
Rome	,,	,,	,,	Italian
Stockholm	,,	,,	,,	Swedish

The following are abbrevs. of places of publn. :—

A.	=Amsterdam	N.Y.	=New York
B'ham.	=Birmingham	O.	=Oxford
C.	=Cambridge	П.	=Petrograd
D.	=Dublin	Phila.	=Philadelphia
E.	=Edinburgh	С.-П.	=St. Petersburg
L.	=Leipzig	St.	=Stuttgart
Liv'l.	=Liverpool	Str.	=Strassburg
M'ter.	=Manchester	W.	=Washington

The explanation of other symbols and abbreviations will be found in the main Catalogue, but some of the more common abbreviations, with a few additional ones, are given overleaf.

Several volumes which are described as "wanting" in the Catalogue have been acquired, and therefore it is necessary to consult both the Catalogue and its Supplements. It is the intention of the Committee to continue to complete imperfect sets, and any gift by Members of missing volumes would be welcomed.

The price of this Supplement to Members is £2, 2s. net. To non-members, £3, 10s. net.

The price of Supplement 1 (1913–20) to Members is £1, 1s. net. To non-members, £1, 10s. net.

The price of the Subject-Index (vol. 2, 1923) to Members is £2, 5s. To non-members, £3, 3s.

SHORT LIST OF ABBREVIATIONS

In the great majority of cases the contractions used are, it is hoped, clear from the context. A more complete list is given in the 1913 edition of the Catalogue.

In inflected languages, where the terminations are variable according to context, one form alone is given below.

The following endings, among others, are systematically omitted:—

able, ais[se], al[e], atic, ation[s], ationes, ensis, etical, iensis, ieux[se], inaire, inal[e], inary, ion[s], ional[e], ique, isch, ische, ition[s], lich[e], ory, ous, ural, ution

A

A. = Auflage; Ausgabe
a. = about; alla; andere; annum; another; author
Abhdl. d. k. s. Ges. d. Wiss. = Abhandlungen der königlich sächsischen Gesellschaft der Wissenschaften
a.c. = another copy
a.c.b.w.h. = another copy bound with his [her]
acc. = accession; according; account; accedit, accedunt, accessit; accurante
ahd. = althochdeutsche

B

B. = Band; Bind
b. = baron; behalf; bis; birth; born; bound
B.M. = British Museum
b.w. = bound with
b.w.h. = bound with his [her]

C

c. = central; century; circa; comte; conte; contra; cura
C.E.f.I.P. = Carnegie Endowment for Internat. Peace
C. f. Bibl. = Centralblatt für Bibliothekswesen
C.I. of Wash. = Carnegie Institution of Washington
coll. = collated; collection, &c.
C.S.E.Lat. = Corpus scriptorum ecclesiasticorum Latinorum

D

D [d] = Deel
d. = daughter; deacon; diaconus; der, die, das, &c.; died; duke, duchess

E

E. = East; Eastern
e. = earl; emperor; episcopus; ein, eine, &c.
E.E.T.S. = Early English Text Society
E.S. = extra series
ét. = étude
étr. = étrangers

F

f. = family; foreign; français; from
fl. = flourished
f.p.c. = for private circulation
f.p.d. = for private distrib.

G

G. é. de la Fr. = Grands écrivains de la France
Ges. = Gesellschaft
Gr. écr. fr. = Grands écrivains français
G.S. = Geological Survey

H

H. = Hälfte; Heft
h. = her, his
H.E. = Bibliothèque de l'Ecole des Hautes Etudes
H.M.S.O. = H.M. Stationery Office
Hss. = Handschriften

I

i. = ihre
I.R.A.O. = Imp. Russ. Arch. Obschestvo
I.R.G.O. = Imperat. Russ. Geog. Obschestvo
I.R.I.O. = Imperat.Russ.Istor. Obschestvo

J

j. = jusqu'à
Jhdt. = Jahrhundert
Jhrg. = Jahrgang

K

K. = Kaiserlich; Königlich.
k. = king, kotet
Kl. = Klasse

L

L. = Lieferung
Lit.V.in St. = Literarischer Verein in Stuttgart

M

m. = marchioness; maréchal; marquis; mein, &c.; minister; monachus
Ma. [M.-A.] = Mittelalter
Min. des Aff. Etrang. = Ministère des Affaires Etrangères
M. Tud. A. = Magyar Tudományos Akademia

N

N. = North; Nozze
n. = nach; new, neu, nouveau; northern
n.d. = no date
n.ed. = new edition
n.e.t. = not earlier than
n.p. = no place [of publication]
N.S. = new series

O

o. = other
o.e. = other essays
o.p. = other poems
or. = orationes; oriental
o.s. = other stories
o.t. = other tales
O.T.F. = Oriental Translation Fund

P

P. = Pamphlet
p. = part, parts, partie; père; poems; pour; prince
pag. cont. = pagination continued
p.c. = per cura
p.p. = privately printed
ps. [pss.] = pseudonym[s]
p. serv. = per servire; pour servir

Q

q. = queen; quibus

R

r. = reign, règne, royal; rex, rey
rewr. = rewritten

S

s. = saint; sein; series; seu, sive; siècle, secolo; son, sa, ses; sobre; sur
S.C. to Knowledge = Smithsonian Contributions to Knowledge
S.d.A.T.F. = Société des anciens textes français
S. de l'Hist. de France = Société de l'Histoire de France
sec. = secolo; secondo, secundum; secretario, secretary; secrète; secula
sep. = separate
S.I. = Smithsonian Institution
Smlg. = Sammlung
St. = saint; study; studies
sub-t. = sub-title

T

T. = Theil
t. = title; tome, tomo, tomus; touchant, touching
tp. = title-page
tr. = translated, &c.

U

ü. = über
u. = und

V

v. = volume; von
var. = various
v.p. = various places [of publication]

W

W. = Wissenschaften
w. = west, western; with
w.h. = with his [her]
w. sel. f. h. = with selections from his [her]
w. sep. tp. = with separate title-page
w.t. = with title

Z

z. = zum, zur, &c.
zw. = zwischen

CORRIGENDA

PAGE	COL.	LINE	
88	1	18*	*Delete* [BERTRAND (ALOYSIUS), *dit Louis*].
88	1	12*–14*	*Transfer* Œuvres poét. &c. *to separate heading* **Bertrand (Aloysius)**.
88	1	4*, 5*	*Transfer see* SPRIETSMA (C.) &c. *to separate heading* **Bertrand (Aloysius)**.
196	1	18*	*Transfer* Les hommes de la route *to heading* **Chamson (André)**.
218	1	40	*For* P2566 *read* P2556.
528	2	36	*For* 1, 2 *read* 2, 3.
567	2	31, 32*	*Transfer entry* **Lévy (Isidore)** &c. *to* p. 568, col. 1.

* Counted from the bottom of the column upwards.

CATALOGUE

FOR 1919/20–1927/28

A

A. (A.), *ps.* Tritheism &c. [*pref. signed* A. A.], *see* SOUTH (R.)

A. (C. B.) Parnaso venezolano: sel. compos. poét. col. por C. B. A., 2ª ed. 2t, 1918, *see* PARNASO.

A. (H.) *The hist. of S. Elizabeth, 1632, *see* HAWKINS (H.)

A. (H. D. M.) *A sober &c. disc. conc. interest of words in prayer &c., 1661, *see* SOBER.

A. (*le sieur* **J.**), *see* AYMON (JEAN).

A. (P. L.) Geonomia armena, 1881, *see* ALISHANIAN (L.)

A. (R.) Vindiciæ pietatis, 1667, *see* ALLEINE (R.)

A. (T.) Abridgment des touts cases reportez alarge p. Mons. Plowden &c.; comp. &c. p. T. A. [*i.e.* T. Ashe], 1600?, *see* PLOWDEN (E.)

A. (T.) Hist. of the Azores, 1813, *see* ASHE (*Capt.* T.)

A. (T. R.) Cat. of books chiefly theolog. coll. by T. R. A., *n.d.*, *see* ALLAN LIBRARY.
Cat. of coll. of Bibles &c. formed by T. R. A., 1883, *see* ALLAN LIBRARY.

A. (W.) Life of Mr. Paschal [*by Mme.* G. Perrier], w. h. letters rel. to Jesuits; tr. by W. A[ndrews], 2v, 1744, *see* PASCAL (B.)

Aahmes, *Egyptian queen*, *see* NAVILLE (E.) La reine A., 1921–22.

Aakjaer (Jeppe). Vredens Børn. 2et opl. s8º. 1905

Aarbøger. Aarbøger for nord. Oldkyndighed, 1867–76, *see* KONGELIGT NORD. OLDSKRIFT-SELSKAB.

Aaron ben Elijah, *Karaite.* Libri coronæ legis, id est Comm. in Pentateuchum Karaitici. Ed., Lat. vertit & illust. J. G. L. Kosegarten. 4º. Jenæ. 1824

Aarskatalog [ÅRSKATALOG]. Aarskatalog over norsk litt. 1924–27. Forsynet med register av G. E. Raabe. 8º. Oslo. 1925–28

Aarssens (Frans van). [AERSSEN]. Verbaal van de ambassade van A., Joachimi & Burmania naar Engeland, 1625. [Hist. Genoots. Werken, N.S., 10]. 8º. Utrecht. 1867

Aasen (Ivar). Norsk gramm. 8º. [1899]

A. B. The golden archer; bk. of sonnets, by A. B., 1920, *see* GOLDEN.

Abadie (*Lt.-Col.* **Maurice**). Afrique Cent. La Colonie du Niger. Préf. de M. Delafosse. la8º. 1927
Opérations au Levant. Les 4 sièges d'Aïntab (1920–21). 8º. 1922
Les races du Haut-Tonkin de Phong-Tho à Long-Son. Préf. de P. Pelliot. 4º. 1924

Abad Pérez (D. Jorge).
Devocionario Muzárabe. s8º. Toledo. 1903

Abarbanel, *see* ISAAC, *ben Judah, Abravanel.*

Abas, *Mar, called Katina* [MARIBAS; *sometimes identified w. Moses of Choren*]. Extraits de la chron. de Maribas Kaldoyo (Mar Abas Katina?): essai par F. Macler. [Extr. du Journ. Asiat.; P2791]. 8º. 1903
see CARRIÈRE (A.) Moïse de Khoren & les généal. patriarc., 1891.
,, MARR (N. YA.) Араб. извлеч. изъ сир. хрон. Марибаса, 1902.

Abati (Antonio), *see* MARINELLA (L.) 2 brevi novelle di L. M. e A. A., 1854.

Abati (Giuseppe de), *see* PALAZZI. I palazzi &c. che non sono più del re; di G. de A. [&c.], 1921.

Abati (Joaquin), *see* ARNICHES (C.) & J. A. Las grandes fortunas, 1920.

Abaza (Konstantin Konstantinovich). Казаки: Донцы, Уральцы, Кубанцы, Терцы. 8º. С.-П. 1890

Abba (Giuseppe Cesare), *see* BULFERETTI (D.) G. C. A., 1838–1910, versi e prose, 1924.

Abbadessa (Giuseppe). Le aspirazioni ital. nei canti dei poeti irredenti, *see* SOCIETÀ SICILIANA. Archivio &c., N.S., 43, 1921.

Abbadie (François), *see* DAX. Le Livre noir & les Etabl. de D.; [*ed., w. intr. &c. by*] F. A., 1902.

Abbadie (Jacques). Le triomphe de la providence &c.; ou l'ouverture des sept seaux; la 1e partie de l'Apocalypse expliquée &c. 4t *in* 2v. s8º. Amsterdam. 1723

'Abbas, *Efendi*, *see* 'ABD UL-BAHĀ IBN BAHĀ ULLĀH.

Abbati (H.)
The unclaimed wealth. Intr. by J. A. Hobson. 8º. [1924]

Abbatt (William). The colloquial who's who. Authors &c who have used pen-names &c., 1600–1924. 2v. 8º. N.Y. 19

Abbey (Edwin Austin), *R.A.*, *see* LUCAS (E. V.) E. A rec. of h. life &c., 2v, 1921.

Abbo [*surnamed* CERNUUS], *monk of St. Germain.* De Parisiaco libri 3. Ex M. G. H. recudi fecit G. H. P [Scr. rerum Germ. in usum schol.] 8º. Hannoveræ. 1

Abbot (Charles Greeley). *Works in* Smithsonian Inst. Misc. c
Distrib. of energy over the sun's disk, 1926. [78.]
On periodicity in solar variation, 1918. [69.]
Provisional solar-constant values, Aug. 1920–Nov. 1924, 1925. [77.]
Solar variation & forecasting, 1925. [77.]
see SMITHSONIAN INSTITUTION. Annals of Astrophys. Observ. of the S. I., v4, by C. G. A. &c., 1922.

—— **F. E. Fowle, & L. B. Aldrich.** Distrib. of energy in the spectra of the sun & stars, 1923, *see* SMITHSONIAN INSTIT. Misc. coll^{s}., 74, 1925.

—— **& A. F. Moore.** Obs. of the total solar eclipse of May 20, 1919, *see* SMITHSONIAN INSTIT. Misc. coll., v71, 1920.

Abbot (George), *bp. of* (1) *Lichfield & Coventry*, (2) *of London*, (3) *abp. of Canterbury.* The reasons wh. Dr. Hill has brought for the upholding of papistry unmasked. pl. [*No more publ^{d}.*] s4º. 1604

Abbot (Leonard Harris), *see* MOORE (A. F.) & L. H. A. The brightness of the sky, 1920.

Abbot (Robert), *bp. of Salisbury, 1560–1617.* A defence of the Reformed Catholicke of W. Perkins. pl, 2, *b. in* 1v. s4º. 1606–7
A mirrour of Popish subtilties. P. Spence, &c. [*Imperf.*] s4º. 1594

Abbotsford Club.
Miscellany. Ed. J. Maidment. v1. 4º. E. 1837
see BUCKINGHAM, *The fam. of.* Compota domest., 1443 &c.; [ed. W. B. D. D. Turnbull], 1836.
,, DEGORE. Sire Degarre: romance, 13th c., 1849.
,, DRUMMOND (J.) Mem^{s}. of Sir E. Cameron &c., 1842.
,, EDINBURGH. Liber Conventus S. Katherine Senensis prope E., 1841.
,, FIFE, *Synod of.* Eccles. records: sels. f. minutes of S. of F., 1611–87. 1837.
see HUME (D.) De familia Humia Wedderburn., 1839.
,, LANARK. Eccles. records: sels. f. reg. of presbytery of L., 1623–1709, 1839.
,, SAINT ANDREWS. Eccles. records: sels. f. minutes St. A. & Cupar, 1641–98, 1837.
,, —— Liber offic. curie metrop. S. A. sentent., 1845.

Abbott (Edith) & S. P. Breckinridge. Admin. of the aid-to-mothers law in Illinois, 1921, *see* UNITED STATES: LABOUR.
Abbott (Edwin Abbott). Flatland. Intr. by G. Garnett. 3rd ed. rev. la8°. O. 1926
"Righteousness" in the Gospels, *see* BRIT. ACADEMY. Procs., 1917–18.
—— & *Sir* **J. R. Seeley.** Eng. lessons. [repr.] s8°. 1917
Abbott (Evelyn), *see* WRIGHT (*Sir* R. S.) Golden treasury of anc. Greek poetry, 2nd ed., rev. by E. A., 1889.
Abbott (Frank Frost) & A. C. Johnson. Municip. admin. in the Roman Emp. 8°. Princeton. 1926
Abbott (George Frederick). Greece & the Allies, 1914–22. Pref. by Adm. M. Kerr. s8°. [1922]
Thucydides: st. in hist. reality. 8°. 1925
Under the Turk in Constantinople; Sir J. Finch's embassy, 1674–81. Foreword by Visct. Bryce. 8°. 1920
Abbott (J. H. M.), *see* MACQUARIE (*Maj.-Gen.* L.) The Macquarie Book [*by A. &c.*], 1921.
Abbott (*Col.* **James).** The T'Hakoorine. A tale of Maandoo. [*Verse*]. s8°. 1841
" " ....2nd ed., *w.t.* *The legend of Maandoo. 8°. 1893
Abbott (Thomas Kingsmill), *see* DUBLIN UNIV.: TRINITY COLLEGE. Cat. of Irish MSS.; comp. by A. &c., 1921.
Abbott (Wilbur Cortez). Col. John Scott of Long Island, 1634?–96. 8°. New Haven, *Yale.* 1918
Abbott-Smith (G.) A manual Greek lexicon of the New Test. 8°. E. 1922
'Abd al-Ḥaqq *al-Badīsī.* [*Abū Muḥammad 'Abd al-Haqq &c.*] El-Maqṣad (Vies des saints du Rif); tr. annot. de G. S. Colin, *see* MISSION SCIENT. DU MAROC. Archives, v26, 1926.
'Abd Allāh ibn Abī Zaid, *al-Ḳairuwānī, see* IBN ABŪ ZAYD.
'Abd Allah ibn 'Umar Muḥammad ibn 'Alí, *al Baidhāwí.* Hist. Sinensis. Lat. reddita ab A. Mullero. Nunc una cum additamentis ed. ab autoris filio Q. A. Mullero. Acc. Itineraria duo, Comm. alphab., Basilicon Sin., Nomenclator geograph. [*w. sep. pagins.*] s4°. Jenæ. 1689
'Abd Allāh Muḥammad ibn 'Umar al-Makkí, *al-Āṣafí, Ulughkání.* An Arabic hist. of Gujarat. Ed. Sir E. D. Ross. [Ind. Texts Ser.] 2v. 8°. 1910–21
'Abd al-Rahmān ibn Ḥasan, *al-Jabartī.* Merveilles biograph. & hist. ou chroniques du cheikh Abd-el-R. Tr. par Chefik Mansour Bey, Abdulaziz Kalil Bey &c. 9t. la8°. Le Caire. 1888–96
'Abd al Razzaq ibn Najaf Kulī, *see* KAJARS. *Dynasty of the K., tr. f. Pers. MS. [*of A.*] by Sir H. Jones Brydges, 1833.
'Abd el Ḥaqq, *see* 'ABD AL-ḤAQQ.
Abdou, *Cheikh, see* MUHAMMAD ABDU, *Sheikh.*
Abdruck des Passawischen Vortrags, 1552, *see* PASSAU.
'Abd ul-Bahā ibn Bahā Ullāh, *called Abbas Efendi.* [*A traveller's narr. to illustrate the Bab episode. In Persian*]. 8°. 1308[=1890]
see ESSLEMONT (J. E.) Bahā'u'llāh & the new era, 1923.
Abdul Hamid, *maulavi, see* BANKIPORE. Cat. of Arabic & Pers. MSS., v5 i, ii, 10, prep. by A. H., 1920–26.
Abdullah (Achmed), *see* ACHMED ABDULLAH.
'Abd Ullāh ibn Muḥammad ibn Husan, *see* CHRISTENSEN (A.) Xavāss-i-āyāt: ms. persan trait. la magie des versets du Coran [*by* 'A. U. ibn M. ibn H.], 1920–21.
Abdul Muqtadir, *maulavi, see* BANKIPORE. Cat. of Arabic & Pers. MSS. in Or. Publ. Lib. at B.; v6–9, 11, prep. by A. M., 1918–27.
see O'CONNOR (V. C. S.) An Eastern library; w. 2 cats. of its Persian &c. MSS. comp. by Abdul M. &c., 1920.
'Abd ul-Rashīd ibn 'Abd ul-Ghafūr, *Ḥusainī.* Gram. pers. præcepta quas lexico pers. R. præf. ed. Dr. Splieth. la8°. Halis. 1846
A'Beckett (Gilbert Abbott).
The comic Blackstone. n. ed. s8°. 1856
Abeghian (Manuk).
Der armen. Volksglaube. Dissert. 8°. L. 1899
Abel (Carl).
Die engl. Verba d. Befehls. [P2507]. 8°. 1878
Zur ägypt. Etymologie. [P2589]. 8°. 1878
Zur ägypt. Kritik. [P2589]. 8°. 1878
see POTT (A. F.) Allgem. Sprachwiss. u. C. A. Aegypt. Sprachstudien, 1886.
Abel (F. M.), *see* VINCENT (L. H.) & E. J. H. MACKAY. Hébron; par V. & M. avec collab. de F. M. A., 1923.
Abel (Othenio).
Lehrbuch d. Paläozoologie. la8°. Jena. 1920

Abélard (Pierre).
The letters of A. & Heloise. Tr. C. K. Scott Moncrieff. Pref. letter by G. Moore. 4°. 1925
Philos. Schr. Hrsg. B. Geyer. [Beitr. z. Gesch. d. Phil. d. M.-a., 21, i–iii]. 8°. Münster. 1919–27
1, Die logica, "Ingredientibus": i, Die Glossen zu Porphyrius; ii, Die Glossen zu den Kategorien; iii, Die Glossen zu Περὶ ἑρμηνείας.
see BITTCHER (C. F. H.) Comm. de P. A. theol. systematica, 1844.
" BORNEMANN (J. A.) Anselmus & A., 1840.
see FRERICHS (J. H. F.) Comm. de P. A. doct. dogm. & morali, 1827.
" GOLDHORN (D. J. H.) De summis princ. theol. A., 1836.
" JORISSEN (Th.) Hist. Karakters, 1, A. en Heloise, 1912.
" MOORE (G.) Héloïse & A. [*fiction*], 2v, 1921; 1925; 2nd impr., 1926.
" THOLUCK (F. A. G.) Disput. de T. Aquinate & A. interp. N. Test., 1842.
" VACANDARD (E.) A., sa lutte avec St. Bernard &c., 1881.
Abelin (Johann Gottfried) [*ps.* ARLANIBÆUS (PHILIPPUS)]. Arma Suecica; descr. belli quod Gustavus Adolphus c. Ferdinandi II exercitum gessit. [*& Contin. b. together*]. s4°. Frankfort. 1631–32
Aben Yachya, *see* JACHIADES (J.)
Aberbrothoc, *see* ARBROATH.
Aberconway (Charles Benjamin Bright M'Laren, *1st baron*), *of Bodnant.* The basic industries of Gt. Brit. la8°. 1927
Abercrombie (John), *horticulturist.*
The gardener's pocket dictionary. 3v. s8°. 1786
see MAWE (T.) & J. A. Every man his own gardener, 1829.
Abercrombie (Lascelles).
An essay tow. a theory of art. s8°. 1922
The idea of great poetry. 8°. 1925
Principles of Eng. prosody. p1, The elements. 8°. 1923
Romanticism. 8°. 1926
The theory of poetry. 8°. 1924
Thomas Hardy: a crit. study. [n. ed.] s8°. [1919]
Abercrombie (Patrick).
The preservation of rural England. la8°. 1926
see DONCASTER. D. regional planning scheme: rep. prep. by P. A. &c., 1922.
" KENT. East K. regional planning scheme, prelim. survey; prep. by P. A. &c., 1925.
—— **S. Kelly & A. Kelly.** Dublin of the future. The new town plan. [Civics Inst. of Ireland, 1]. fol. Liv'l. 1922
Abercromby (David).
Fur academicus. s8°. Amstelodami. 1689
A moral disc. of the power of interest. 2nd ed. s8°. 1691
Abercromby (*Hon.* **John).** A proposed chronol. arrangement of the drinking cup &c. in Britain. [*From* Soc. of Antiq., Scotl. Proc., v38]. 8°. [E.] 1904
Aberdeen. Extr. f. Council Register of A. [Ed. J. Stuart. Scot. Burgh Rec. Soc.] 2[v.] 1,1625–42. 2,1643–1747. la8°. E. 1871–72
Proc. at presentation to A. Grammar School of statue of Lord Byron. [Addr. by H. J. C. Grierson]. [P2718]. 8°. Aberdeen. 1923
UNIVERSITY.
Aberdeen Univ. studies. No. 86, 94, 97, 105. 8°. Aberdeen. 1922–28
Aberdeen Univ. Library Bulletin, v4–6, Dec. 1918–Jan. 1928. [86, 97, 105.]
Bibliography of the Gordons, by J. M. Bulloch, sect. 1, 1924. [94.]
Aberdeen (George Hamilton-Gordon, *4th earl of***).** Award upon meaning of Ld. A.'s letter, Sept. 1843, by J. Ricord, in controv. w. R. Charlton claiming lands in Honolulu. [P2776]. 8°. Honolulu. 1844
see BALFOUR (*Lady* F.) The life of G. 4th earl of A., 2v, 1923.
Aberdeen & Temair (Ishbel Maria, *marchioness of*), *wife of 1st marquis, see* ABERDEEN & TEMAIR (J. C. G., *1st marq.*) "We twa," 2v, 1925.
Aberdeen & Temair (John Campbell Gordon, *1st marq.*) **& Ishbel M.,** *marchioness of* **A. & T.** "We twa." Remins. 2v. 8°. [1925]
Åberg (Nils Fritiof). The Anglo-Saxons in Eng. dur. early cents. aft. invasion. la8°. Uppsala. 1926
La civilisation énéolith. dans la Péninsule Ibér. la8°. Uppsala. [1921]
Das nord. Kulturgebiet in Mitteleuropa währ. d. jüng. Steinzeit. 2[v], 1, Text, 2, Tafeln. 8°. Uppsala. 1918
Studier öfver d. yngre stenåldern i Norden och Västeuropa. la8°. Norrköping. 1912

Aberigh-Mackay (Geo. R.)
Notes on West. Turkistan. 8º. Calcutta. 1875

Abert (Hermann), *see* JAHN (O.) W. A. Mozart, neubearb. v. H. A., 6.A., 2T., 1923.

Abert (Josef Friedrich).
Aus Würzburgs Vergangenheit. 8º. Würzburg. 1922

Abetti (Giorgio), *see* FILIPPI (F. DE) Rel. scientif. d. Spediz. Ital. de F. nell'Himàlaia &c., s1, v1, Astronomia &c.; [*by*] G. A. &c., 1925.

Abfertigung u. Widerlegung, zweier Jesuit. schmähl. Lästerschrifften, gest. d. d. Würtemberg. Theologen, 1587, *see* WÜRTEMBERG.

Abgarus, *king of Edessa.*
see CARRIÈRE (A.) A. legend in Moses of Khoren's Hist.; tr. into Arm., 1898.
„ DASHEAN (H.) Sh. bibliog. st[s]. &c., *in Armenian*, v2, 1901.
„ HEINE (J. E. C.) Diss. de Christi ad A. epistola, 1759.
see LABUBNA. Lettre d'Abgar, ou hist. de la convers. des Edesséens par L., 1868.
„ SCHENCKE (J. C.) De Christi scriptis, 1787.
„ SCHULTZ (G.) De Epist. Xti ad A., 1706.

Abgrall (*l'abbé* **J. M.**) Architecture bretonne, diocèse de Quimper. 8º. Quimper. 1904

Abhandlung. *Abhandlung ü. d. ältere scandinav. Gesch. v. d. Cimbrern u. d. scand. Gothen, 2T, 1781, *see* WEDEL-JARLSBERG (*b.* F. W. AF).
*Abhandlung v. Schlafe d. Seelen nach d. Tode als e. Widerleg. d. Sch. d. T. Seidels. s8º. Halberstadt. 1754
see also SCHREIBEN. Schreiben an d. ungen. Verf. d. Abhandl. &c., 1754.

Abhedānanda, *Svāmī.*
How to be a Yogi. 6th ed. San Francisco. *n.d.*

Abhidhamma Pitaka, *see* PUGGALA-PAÑÑATTI. Designat. of human types [4th wk. of the A.P.]; tr. B. C. Law, 1924.

Abicht (Johann Heinrich).
De rationis in theologia vi &c. 8º Lipsiæ. 1790

Ableiges (Jacques d'), *fl. 14c.*, *see* FRANCE. Grand Coutumier de F. [*comp. by J. d'A.*], 1868.

Abney (*Sir* **William de Wiveleslie**), *see* BARNET. B. bk. of photography, 1898.

Abomilech, *see* WILLIAM, *of Salisbury, ps.* *Chron. of A., king of the Isles, 1820.

Aboth. The Ethics of the Fathers coll. by Nathan the Babylonian A.D. 200. Tr. w. [text &] intr. to the Talmud [by R. Y., *i.e.* R. Young]. s8º. E. [1852 ?]

About (Edmond F. V.)
Madelon. 5e éd. s8º. 1868
Les mariages de Paris. s8º. 1899
„ „ Intr. par E. Faguet. s8º. *Nelson.* [1911]
Le nez d'un notaire. s8º. *Nelson.* [1913]
Trente & quarante. Tr. by Lord Newton. Intr. by T. Gibson Bowles. 8º. 1899

Aboyne, *earls of*, *see* BULLOCH (J. M.) The earls of A., 1908.

Abraham *Astapattzi.* Nerbolean. [Praise of see of Echmiadzin. *In Armenian*]. s8º. K.-polis. 1807

Abraham *ben Meir Aben Ezra* [IBN EZRA]. Comm. on Canticles. Ed., w. tr., by H. J. Mathews. s8º. 1874
Comm. on Isaiah. Ed. & tr. by M. Friedländer. [Soc. of Heb. Lit. Publ[s]. 2 & 3]. 2v. 8º. 1873
Decalogus cum comm. Rabbi Aben Ezra & Lat. vers. S. Munsteri [*b.w.* ELIJAH *ben Asher*. Cap. cantici, 1527]. s8º. Basileæ *J. Froben.* 1527

Abraham III [*of Crete*], *catholicus of Echmiadzin.* Mon hist. & celui de Nadir, Chah de Perse (1870), *see* BROSSET (M. F.) Coll. d'hist. arm., t2, 1876.

Abraham, *Ecchellensis.* Linguæ Syriacæ, sive Chaldaicæ, perbrevis institutio [*in Syriac*]. s8º. Romæ. 1628

Abraham, *bp. of Ephesus, 6th cent.* Homélies [*Grec & Lat.*], *see* MARY, *the Virgin.* Homélies mariales byz., éd. &c. M. Jugie, 1922.

Abraham, *bp. of Mamigona.* [A. bp. of M. & his letter to Vatchagan. *In Armenian.* Ed. B. Sargisean. P2811]. 8º. Venetik. 1899

Abraham, *the patriarch* [ABRAM; ABRAMO]. The life, & surprising adv[s]., miracles &c. of A.; first related by Caab-Ekbaar &c., *see* WALDRON (F.G.), Shakspearean misc., 1802.
The Testament of A. Tr. w. intr. &c. by G. H. Box. App. cont. tr. f. Coptic version of Test. of Isaac & Jacob, by S. Gaselee. s8º. 1927
see JAY (S.) Tragedies of sin; w. remarques on the life of A., 1689.
„ SYMSON (A.) Tripatriarchicon [*poem*], 1705.

Abraham, *the Patriarch, ps.* Liber de creatione, & Cabalistinis, Hebraicè Sepher Iezira, authore Abrahamo, *see* PISTORIUS (J.) Artis Cabalist. t1, 1587.

Abraham Jaghel *ben Hananiah de' Galicchi.* Doctrina salutaris &c. juxta exemplar Rabbinicum Amstelodam. s8º. Helmstadii. 1704

Abraham (Carl), *see* FERENCZI (S.) Psycho-analysis & war neuroses; by S. F., C. A. &c., 1921.

Abraham (George Dixon).
On Alpine heights & British crags. 8º. [1919]

Abraham (Gerald E. H.) Borodin: the composer & h. music. With refs. to Balakirev, Moussorgsky &c. s8º. 1927

Abraham (James Johnston). My Balkan log. 8º. 1921

Abraham (May E.) & A. L. Davies. The law rel. to factories & workshops. 3rd ed. 8º. 1901

Abraham Maimon, *see* MAIMON (ABRAHAM).

Abrahams (Aleck). Life & works of W. Robinson, topographer &c., w. Indices to Hist. &c. of Edmonton [*& h. o. works*] by J. Ardagh. s8º. 1925

Abrahams (Israel).
By-paths in Hebraic bookland. 8º. Phila. 1920
Campaigns in Palestine f. Alexander the Gr. [Brit. Acad. Schweich Lect., 1922]. 8º. 1927
Poetry & religion. Foreword by Sir A. Quiller-Couch. [A. Davis Mem. Lect., 1920]. s8º. [1920]
Studies in Pharisaism & the Gospels. 2nd ser. 8º. C. 1924

Abramovich (Nikolai Yaklovich) [*ps.* KADMIN (N.)] Исторія русской поэзіи. 2T. la8º. Москва. 1914–15

Abramowski (Edouard). Le subconscient normal. 8º. 1914

Abramus (Bartholomæus), *bp. of Aria*, *see* FLORENCE, *Council of.* Acta; interp. B. A., 1526.

Abranches (Dunshee de). Governos e congressos da Republ. do Brazil (1899–1917). v1. 8º. S. Paulo. 1918

Abrantès (Laure Junot, *duchesse* **d').** Autobiography & recoll. [Tr.] n. ed. [*w. 2nd tp*: The home & court life of Napoleon]. 4v. 8º. 1893
see CHANTEMESSE (R.) Le roman inconnu de la duchesse d'A., 1927.

Abravanel (Isaac ben Judah), *see* ISAAC, *ben Judah, Abravanel.*

Abravanel (Leon). De amore dialogi tres: a J. C. Saraceno Lat. don., *see* PISTORIUS (J.) Artis Cabalist. t1, 1587.

Abrégé. *Abrégé chronolog. de l'hist. de Pologne, 1763, *see* SCHMID (F. A.)
*Abrégé de l'hist. de Provence, 1837, *see* PROVENCE.

Abreu (Bartholomeu Paes de), *see* PAES DE ABREU (B.)

Abril (Manuel). Fernando A. de Sotomayor. 8º. [1920]
Ramon Casas. 8º. [1919]
—— & R. Baroja. Aguafortistas. 8º. [1920]

Abschied der gesandten Augspurg. Confession, zum Colloquio inn Wormbs, 1557, *see* WORMS.

Abstimmung (Die) in Oberschlesien, 1921, *see* OBERSCHLESIEN.

Abstract. *Abstract of proc. for support. civil rights of prot.-dissenters, 1796, *see* DISSENTERS.
*Abstract (An) of what is nec. to be known conc. the Constit. Unigenitus &c. [*by D.* ***], tr., 1724, *see* UNIGENITUS.

Abū 'Abdallah al Ḥusain ibn Mansoûr, *al Ḥallâj, surnamed Abū al Moghîth*, *see* ḤALLAJ.

Abū 'Abdallah Muḥammad ibn al-Ṭayyib, *see* MUHAMMAD AL-QÂDIRÎ.

Abū 'Abd Allah Sa'īdī, *see* IBN 'ASKAR.

Abū 'Alī al-Muḥassin al-Tanūkhī.
The table-talk of a Mesopotamian judge, being 1st part of the Nishwār al-Muḥāḍarah. Ed. D. S. Margoliouth. [Or. Tr. Fund, N.S., 27]. 8º. 1921
„ „ Tr. f. Arabic by D. S. Margoliouth. [Or. Tr. Fund, N.S., 28]. 8º. 1922

Abudacnus (Josephus). Hist. Jacobitarum &c. cum annot. J. Nicolai. Vulg. S. Havercampus. 8º. Lugd. Batav. 1710

Abū Dulaf. [ABU-DOLEF; †MIS'AR IBN AL-MUHALHIL (ABŪ D.), *al-Yanbū'ī*], *see* GRIGOREV (V. V.) Объ Абу-Долефѣ &c., 1872.

Abu'l Abbas Ahmad, *see* AHMAD IBN MUḤAMMAD *al-Yaqouby.*

Abu'l Abbas Ahmad el-Khadir ben 'Alī Ghailan, *see* GHAILAN.

Abu 'l-'Ala [ABULOLA; †AḤMAD IBN 'ABD ALLĀH IBN SULAIMĀN (ABŪ AL-'ALĀ), *al-Tanūkhi, al Ma'arrī*], *see* NICHOLSON (R. A.) St[s]. in Islamic poetry. [The meditations of Ma'arrī &c. (*text & tr.*)], 1921.

Abulfaraj. [GREGORIUS BARHEBRÆUS.] Chronicon Syriacum e cod. Bodl. descr., vertit, notisque illustr. P. J. Bruns. Ed. G. G. Kirsch. 2t (1, *Lat. tr.*; 2, *Syr. text*). s4º. Lipsiæ. 1789

Abulfaraj [*continued*]. Chronicon Syr. e codd. MSS. emend. &c. [*in Syriac*]. 8°. Parisiis. 1890

Abulfeda [†ISMĀ'ĪL IBN 'ALĪ ('IMĀD AL-DĪN ABŪ AL-FIDĀ), *prince of Hamat*]. A gen. descr. of Arabia; tr., 1718, *see* ARVIEUX (L. D'), Travels, 2nd ed., 1732.
see HUDSON (J.) *ed.* Geog. vet. scriptores Gr. min., v3, 1712.
„ ROMMEL (D. C. V.) A. Arabiæ descr., 1802.

Abu'l-Qāsim Maḥmūd b. 'Umar az-Zamakhsharī, *1074–1143, see* †KORAN. The Qoran; w. comm. of the Imám Aboo al-Qásim &c., entitled "The Kashsháf" &c., 2v, 1856–9.

Abū-Mansūr 'abd-al-Kāhir ibn Tāhir, *al Baghdādī* (*d. 1037*). Moslem schisms & sects (Al-Fark Bain al-Firak). Tr. by K. C. Seelye. [Columbia Univ., Or. st., 15]. pl. 8°. N.Y. 1920

Abū Muḥammad 'Abd al-Ḥaqq &c., *see* 'ABD AL-ḤAQQ, *al-Bādisī*.

Abū Muḥammad b. Abū Zayd, *see* IBN ABŪ ZAYD.

Abushkah [ABOUCHKA], *see* PAVET DE COURTEILLE (A. J. B. DE) Dict. turk-oriental [*founded on Turk. orig. known as A.*], 1870.

Abusiger (Hector). Epistola Terentiana ad L. Danæum. [*b. w.* Gerlach (S) Hyperaspistes, 1581]. s4°. Tubingæ. 1581

Abuzé (L') en court. [Lyon, typographe indéterm., vers 1484]. Not. de E. Droz. [Livres à grav. imp. à Lyon au 15e siècle, 2]. 4°. Lyon. [1925]

Abyssinia. The Royal Chron. of A., 1769–1840. Tr. & notes by H. Weld-Blundell. la8°. C. 1922

***Academia:** or, The humours of the Univ. of Oxford, 1716, *see* D'ANVERS (A.)

Academia das Sciencias de Lisboa, *see* ACADEMIA REAL DAS SCIENCIAS DE LISBOA.

Academia Provincial de Bellas Artes de Barcelona, *see* GUDIOL (J.) El pintor L. Borrassá, 1926.

Academia Real das Sciencias de Lisboa. [ACADEMIA DAS SCIENCIAS DE LISBOA].
see BARRETO (J. F.) Rel da embaixada a França em 1641 &c., 1918.
„ COLLECÇÃO de opusc. reimpr. rel. a hist. d. navegações &c. dos Portuguezes, t1, 1875.
„ DALGADO (S. R.) Gloss. luso-asiático, v2, 1921.
see EANNES DE ZURARA (G.) Crónica da tomada de Ceuta por João I; publ. F. M. Esteves Pereira, 1915.
„ FERREIRA DE VASCONCELLOS (J.) Comédia Eufrosina, 1918.

Academia Româna. Analele Acadamiei Române. Seria 2, t32–43. Ser. 3, t1. [*Each t. has 4p* (Partea Administ. si Desbat.; Mem. Secț. Ist.; Mem. Secț. Lit.; Mem. Secț. Științifice. Partea Admin., Ser. 3, t1 *wanting*, Mem. Ist., t40–43 *wanting*; Mem. Secț. Lit., t34, 39–43, s3, t1 *wanting*, Mem. Științif., t40–43 *wanting*]. 4°. 1910–23

Biblioteca Acad. Rom. Cat. mss. românești; întocmit de J. Bianu & R. Caracaș. t2, Numerele 301–728. 8°. 1913

Biblioteca Acad. Rom. Creșterea colecțiunilor, 1909–15. 4°. Ploesti &c. 1909–15

Bull. de la Sect. Histor. Année 3—t12 (1915–22). 8° Bucarest. 1915–25
11, Congrès de Byzantinologie de Bucarest, Mém.

Discursuri de recepțiune, 21–33, 44–57. [44–57 *in* 2v.] 4° & la8°. București. 1900–23

Publicațiunile Fondului Vasile Adamachi, t4–8. la8°. București 1910–16; t6 & 8 *have tp*s. *as below* :—
VI, 39, Cercetări orig. despre pelagra in România, de A. Babeș & V. Bușilă, 1915.
VIII, 46, Pescăria & pescuitul in România, de Gr. Antipa, 1916.

see ANTIPA (GR.) Dunărea & problemele ei &c., 1921.
„ —— Problemele evol. poporului Roman, 1919.
„ BIANU (J.) & N. Hodoș. Bibliogr. român. veche 1508–1830, t2; ed. A. R., 1905–10.
„ DRAGANU (N.) Doua mss. vechi Cod. Todorescu & Cod. Martian, 1914.
„ FILITTI (I. C.) Domniile române sub Regulam. Organic, 1834–48, 1915.
„ HURMUZAKI (E. DE). Doc. priv. la ist. Românilor, cul. de E. de H., v14–19, 1911–22.
„ IORGA (N.) Ist. poporului frances, 1919.
see IORGA (N.) Izvoarele contemp. asupra mişcării lui Tudor Vladimirescu, 1921.
„ —— Scurtă istorie a Slavilor Răsăriteni Rusia & Polonia, 1919.
„ ISTRATI (C. I.) Studiu rel. la o nomenclatură gen. în chimia organică, 1913.
„ LIVY. Istoria, tr. de N. Locusteanu și I. S. Petrescu, t4, 5, 1911–15.
„ NISTOR (I.) Der nat. Kampf in d. Bukowina, 1919.
„ —— Românii & Rutenii in Bucovina, 1915.
„ PANTU (Z. C.) Orchidaceele din România, 1916.

Academia Româna [*continued*].
see PASCU (G.) Sufixele Românesti, 1916.
„ PONI (P.) Statistica raželsilor, 1921.
„ ROMSTORFER (K. A.) Cetatea Sucevii, 1913.
„ STEFANELLI (T. V.) Doc. din vechiul ocolal Câmpulungului Moldovenesc, 1915.
see TOCILESCU (GR. G.) Mon. epigr. și sculptu. ale Mus. Nat. de Antichitati din Bucuresci, 1902–08.

Academici Eterei, *see* ACCADEMICI ETEREI.

Académie. *Académie univ. des jeux, avec des instruct. faciles pour apprendre à les bien jouer. n. éd., augm. 2p [*in 1v*]. s8°. Amsterdam. 1760

Académie Celtique. Table des publs., 1894, *see* SOCIÉTÉ NAT. DES ANTIQ. DE FRANCE.

Académie d'Arras [*form.* SOC. ROY. POUR L'ENCOUR. DES SCIS. &C.], *see* ARRAS. Cartul. de l'abbaye de St.-Vaast d'A.; publ., au nom de l'Acad. d'Arras par M. Van Drival, 1875.

Académie de Mâcon, *see* MÂCON. Cartul. de St.-Victor de M.; publ. par C. Ragut, 1864.

Académie des Beaux-Arts, *see* SOUBIES (A.) Les membres de l'A. des B.-A., s4, 1876–1901, 1917.

Académie des Belles-Lettres de Marseille, *see* LAUTARD (J. B.) Hist. de l'Acad. de M., 1726–1826, 2p, 1826–29.

Académie des Inscriptions & Belles-Lettres. Fonds d'épigraphie grecque. Fondation du Duc de Loubat, *see* DURRBACH (F.), *ed.* Inscrs. de Délos: comptes des Hiéropes, 1926.

Hist. & mém. de l'Institut. [*Cont. as* Mém. de l'Institut]. t41, 42. 4°. 1920–22
Collignon (M.) L'emplacement du Cécropion à l'Acropole d'Athènes, 1920. [41.]
Cordier (H.) Annales de l'Hôtel de Nesle, 1920. [41.]
Cuq (E.) Les nouv. fragments du code de Hammourabi &c., 1920. [41.]
Dieulafoy (M.) La mosquée d'Hassân, 1922. [42.]
Foucart (P. F.) Le culte des héros chez les Grecs, 1922. [42.]
—— Un décret athénien rel. aux combattants de Phylé, 1922. [42.]
Fournier (P.) Les colls. canon. rom. de Grégoire VII, 1920. [41.]
Huart (C.) Les Ziyârides, 1922. [42.]

Mémoires conc. l'Asie Or. (Inde, Asie Cent., Extrême Or.). Publ. sous la dir. de MM. Senart, Chavannes, Cordier. t2, 3. 4°. 1916–19
Chavannes (E.) Le jet des dragons, 1919. [3.]
Coedes (G.) A propos d'une stèle d'Angkor-Vat, 1916. [2.]
Foucher (A.) Les représent. de Jâtaka dans l'art bouddh., 1919. [3.]
Hackin (J.) Les scènes figurées de la vie du Buddha &c., 1916. [2.]
Pelliot (P.) Le Chou king en caractères anc. &c., 1916. [2.]

Mémoires présentés par divers savants. 4°. 1923
s1, Sujets divers d'érudition, t13i.
Audollent (A.) Les tombes gallo-rom. à inhum. des Martres-de-Veyre, 1923. [I, 13i.]
Bonnel de Mézières (A.) Rech. sur l'emplacement de Ghana & sur le site de Tekrour, 1923. [I, 13i.]
Formigé (J.) Le prétendu cirque romain d'Orange, 1923. [I, 13i.]
—— Rem. div. sur les théâtres rom. à propos de ceux d'Arles & d'Orange, 1923. [I, 13i.]
Glotz (G.) Le droit des gens dans l'antiq. grecque, 1923. [I, 13i.]
Michon (E.) Un décret du dème de Cholargos rel. aux Thesmophories, 1923. [I, 13i.]
Sidersky (D.) Et. sur la chronologie assyro-babylon., 1923. [I, 13i.]

see CHARTES & diplômes rel. à l'hist. de France, *in progress*.
„ SANDALGIAN (J.) Inscr. cunéiformes urart., mém. prés. à l'Acad., 1900.

FONDATION PIOT. Fondation E. Piot. Monuments & méms. t23–28. fol. 1918–26
Bénédite (G.) Amon & Toutânkhamon (Musée Egypt. du Louvre). [24.]
—— Cueillette du lis & le "lirinon." [25.]
—— Tête de princesse de la fam. d'Akhounaten. [27.]
Blum (A.) Ms. inéd. du 13e S. de la "Bible des pauvres." [28.]
Boreux (C.) Stèle-table d'offrandes de Senpou. [25.]
Blochet (E.) Peintures des mss. pers. de la Coll. Marteau à la Bibl. Nat. [23.]
Bréhier (L.) Miniatures des "Homélies" du moine Jacques &c. [24.]
Capart (J.) L'art égypt. & la loi de frontalité. [26.]
Champollion (J. F.) Lettre à M. Dacier rel. à l'alphabet des hiéroglyphes, 1822. [25.]
Charbonneaux (J.) 3 armes d'apparat du Palais de Mallia. [28.]
Chassinat (E.) Tête en grès rouge du roi Didoufrî. [25.]
Couissin (P.) Statuette de femme acrobate du Musée de Rennes, 1925–26. [28.]

Académie des Inscriptions & Belles-Lettres [*continued*].

Cumont (F.) L' " Aphrodite à la tortue " de Doura-Europos. [27.]
—— Culte égypt. & le mysticisme de Plotin. [25.]
—— " Le sacrifice du tribun rom. Terentius " & les Palmyréniens à Doura. [26.]
Daressy (G.) Représ. égypt. du pèsement d. actions. [25.]
Demangel (R.) Un nouvel alabastre du peintre de Pasiadès. [26.]
Deonna (W.) 3 têtes antiq. du Musée d'Art &c. à Genève. [27.]
Deschamps (P.) Légende arturienne à la cath. de Modène. [28.]
Diehl (C.) Sur quelq. étoffes coptes du Louvre. [25.]
Drioton (E.) Un second prophète d'Onouris. [25.]
Dugas (C.) Un plat rhodo-ionien trouvé à Delos. [28.]
Durrieu (*cte.* P.) Légende du roi Mercie dans un livre d'heures du 15e s. [24.]
—— Une " Pitié de Notre-Seigneur," tableau franç. (Louvre). [23.]
Dussaud (R.) La digue du lac de Homs. [25.]
Enlart (C.) Un tissu persan du 10e s. découv. à St.-Josse. [24.]
Foucart (G.) Le vaisseau d'or d'Amon-Râ. [25.]
Fougères (G.) T. Homolle, 1848–1925. [28.]
Gabrici (E.) Vaso campano à pittura policroma rappr. Sileno e le ninfe. [24.]
Gauthier (H.) Sur une tombe à Athribis du Delta. [25.]
Hackin (J.) Sculptures gréco-bouddh. du Kapisa. [28.]
Heuzey (L.) Le péplos des femmes grec. [24.]
Homolle (T.), *see* FOUGÈRES (G.)
Lacau (P.) Statues " guérisseuses " dans l'anc. Egypte. [25.]
Lechat (H.) Dolorosa, tête grecque (Musée de Lyon). [23.]
Lefebvre (G.) Bas-relief grec dans un tombeau égypt. [25.]
Marquet de Vasselot (J. J.) Ivoire chrét. réc. acquis par le Musée de Louvre. [28.]
Merlin (A.) Statuette de terre cuite peinte trouvée à Carthage (Musée du Bardo). [24.]
Michon (E.) Isis, Horus & Serapis accomp. de Dionysos, bas-relief. [25.]
—— Tête de jeune homme de la frise du Parthénon (Louvre). [23.]
Montet (P.) L'art phénicien au 18e siècle av. J.-C. [27.]
—— Égyptiens à Byblos. [25.]
Moret (A.) Fragm. du mastaba de Shery, prêtre. [25.]
Morgan (J. J. M. de). Prem. temps de l'Égypte. [25.]
Naville (E.) La reine Aahmes. [25.]
Nicole (G.) Vase du style de Meidias, Ensérune. [27.]
Pasiadès, see DEMANGEL (R.)
Perdrizet (P.) Antiq. de Leontopolis. [25.]
Pézard (M.) Nouv. stèle de Séti Ier. [25.]
Picard (C.) Portrait d'homme inconnu, tête de bronze trouvée dans Délos. [24.]
—— Tête féminine du Musée d'Alexandrie. [28.]
Poinssot (L.) & R. Lantier. Mosaïques de la " maison d'Ariadne," à Carthage. [27.]
Pottier (E.) L'Égypte & la plastique grecque. [25.]
—— Replique de la " Vénus de Médicis." [23.]
Reinach (S.) 2 nouv. statues d'Aphrodite. [27.]
—— Statuette en bronze trouvée en 1913 à Bavai. [28.]
Rostovtsev (M.) Statuette d'un cavalier de la coll. de Mme J. D. Rockefeller. [28.]
—— Trouvaille de l'époque gréco-sarmate de Kertch &c. [26.]
Sottas (H.) Statuettes funéraires, 18e dynastie. [25.]
Tafrali (O.) Fresques de l'église St.-Nicolas de Courtéa-de-Argeš. [23.]
Thureau-Dangin (F.) Statuettes de Tello. [27.]
Urseau (C.) Tombe de l'évêque Ulger à la cath. d'Angers. [28.]
Vitry (P.) Un fragm. du tombeau de St. Lazare d'Autun au Musée du Louvre. [26.]
—— La " Vierge d'Isenheim." [27.]
Weill (R.) Figurines funéraires. [25.]

see DURRIEU (*cte.* P.) La miniature flamande, 1415–1530, 1921.
,, WADDINGTON (W. H.) Rec. gén. d. monnaies grecques d'Asie mineure, 2e éd., t1i, 1925.

Académie des Sciences. Annuaire, 1920–28. s8°. [1920–28]
Comptes rendus hebdomadaires, t167–184. 4°. 1918–27
see POINCARÉ (H.) Œuvres ; publ. P. Appell, t1, 1928.

Académie des Sciences, Arts & Belles-Lettres de Dijon, *see* BOURGOGNE. Chartes de communes &c. en B. ; publ. l'Acad. Imp. des Scis. &c. de D. par J. Garnier, 3t, 1867–77 ; intr. de J. G. &c., 1918.
see CHAUME (*l'abbé* M.) Origs. du duché de Bourgogne, p1, 2i, 1925–27.

Académie des Sciences, Belles-Lettres & Arts de Lyon, *see* LYONS. Cartul. lyonnais : docs. inéd. &c., 2t, 1885–93.

Académie des Sciences Morales & Politiques. [INSTITUT NATIONAL DES SCIENCES & ARTS, SCIENCES M. & P. *One of the 5 wh. form the* Institut de France.] Compte rendu. t91, 92 (1919), 80e–87e année (1920–27) [*2v to each year*]. 8° [1919–27]
see SEILLIÈRE (E.) Une acad. à l'époque romant., 1926.

Académie Française.
see BARTHOU (L.) Disc. (*on* H. Roujon), 1919.
,, —— Réponse au disc. de J. Bédier (*on* E. Rostand), 1921.
,, BÉDIER (J.) Disc., 1921.
,, BERTRAND (L. M. E.) Disc., 1926.
,, CAMBON (J.) Disc., 1919.
,, CHEVRILLON (A.) Disc., 1921.
,, CUREL (*vte.* F. DE). Disc., 1919.
,, DESCHANEL (P.) Disc., 1900.
,, ESTAUNIÉ (E.) Disc., 1925.
,, FLERS (R. DE). Disc., 1921.
,, FOCH (*mar.* F.) Disc., 1920.
,, GAUTIER (P.) Anthol. de l'A. F., 1820–1920, t1, 2, 1921.
see GOYAU (G.) Disc. &c., 1923.
,, HANOTAUX (G.) Rép. au disc. de P. Valéry, 1927.
,, HAUSSONVILLE (G. P. O. DE C., *cte.* D'). Visite du Czar Pierre le Gr. en 1717, Séance oct. 1896, 1896.
,, JOFFRE (*mar.* J. J. C.) Disc., 1919.
,, JONNART (C. C. A.) Disc., 1925.
,, LYAUTEY (*gén.* H.) Disc., 1921.
,, NOLHAC (P. DE). Disc., 1923.
,, REVON (M.) & P. BILLOTEY. L'Acad. Franç., 1895–1920, 1922.
,, ROBERT (H.) Disc., 1924.
,, VALÉRY (P.) Disc., 1927.

Académie Nationale des Sciences, Arts & Belles-Lettres de Caen. Mémoires. n. sér. t1. 8°. Caen. 1925
see PRENTOUT (H.) Les états provinciaux de Normandie, t1, 1925. [n.s., 1]

Académie Royale d'Architecture. Procès-verbaux, 1671–1793. Publ. par H. Lemonnier. [Soc. de l'Hist. de l'Art Franç.] t6-9, 1744–93. 8°. 1920–26

Académie Royale de Belgique.
Annuaire, 1914–25. 80e–91e ann. [1915–19 *in* 1v.] s8°. Brux. 1914–25
,, ,, Tables des notices biog. publ. dans l'Annuaire, 1835–1914 ; par F. Leuridant. s8°. Brux. 1919
Bull. de la classe des lettres & des sciences morales & polit., 1914, 1919–26. [1915–18 *not published*]. 8° Brux. 1914–26
,, ,, Tables gén. des Bull., 1899–1910 ; par F. Leuridant & J. Perrée. 8°. Brux. 1919
,, ,, Tables gén. des Bull., 1911–1914 ; par F. Leuridant. 8°. Brux. 1919
Bulletin de la Comm. Royale d'Hist., *see* COMM. ROYALE D'HIST. DE BELGIQUE.
Bulletins de la Classe des Beaux-Arts, t7, 1925. 8° Brux. 1925
Compte rendu de la céléb. du 150e anniv. de l'Acad. 8° Brux. 1922
BIBLIOTHÈQUE. Cat. des livres de la Bibl. de l'Acad. Royale. 2p [*in* 4v. p2i–iii *pagin. contin.*] 8°. Brux. 1881–90
Cat. onomast. des accroissements de la Bibl. Par F. Leuridant & J. Perrée. Beaux-arts, 1890–1914 [*b. w.* Lettres &c. *below*]. 8°. Brux. 1919
,, ,, Lettres & scis. mor. & polit., 1887–1914. 8°. Brux. 1919
,, ,, Sciences, 1883–1914. 8°. Brux. 1919
REFERENCES.
see BIGWOOD (G.) Le régime juridique &c. du commerce de l'argent dans la Belg. du m.â., 2p, 1921–22.
,, BIOGRAPHIE Nationale, t22, 23, 1914–24.
see COMMISSION ROYALE D'HIST. DE BELGIQUE.
,, LE NAIN (L.) Vie acad., 1914–18, 1919.
,, LEURIDANT (F.) Une éduc. de prince au 18e. s. : Charles J. de Ligne, 1923.

Académie Royale de Peinture & de Sculpture. Le salon de 1725. Compte rendu de l'expos. faite au Salon Carré du Louvre. Publ. avec notes &c. par G. Wildenstein. [Soc. de l'Hist. de l'Art Fr.] s8°. 1924

Academy of Political Science, N.Y. Proceedings, v8–11, 12i ; v12, No. 1, *has t.* Internat. problems & rels. : addresses &c. : ed. J. T. Shatwell &c. 8°. 1918–26

Acandia (Giorgio d'), *see* VAINA (E.) Nazione albanese ; 2a ed. aum. d'uno scr. di G. d'A. su V., 1917.

***Acanthologie,** ou dict. epigrammatique, 1817, *see* FAYOLLE (F. J. M.)

Acarie (*Mme.* Barbe), *see* MARIE, *de l'Incarnation.*

Acarisio (Alberto), *see* ACCARIGI (A.)

Accademia de' Filergiti, *see* MARCHESI BUONACCORSI (G. V.) Mem. st. dell' ant. &c. Accad. de' F., di Forli, 1741.

Accademia degl' Incogniti. Le glorie de gli Incogniti ; overo gli huomini ill. s4°. Venetia. 1647

Accademia della Crusca, *see* RAZZOLINI (L.) &c. Bibl. dei testi di lingua a stampa citati d. Accad. d. C., 1878.

Accademia Difettuosa. Rime. s8°. [Bologna. 1717]

Accademia Etrusca, *Cortona.* Saggi di dissert. accad. pubbl. lette nell' Accad. Etr. t1–4 [t1 *in* 2p, *b. separately*; t2 *b. w.* t1i; t4 *b. w.* t1ii]. la8°. 1735–43

Accademia Pontaniana, *see* MINIERI RICCIO (C.) Cenno stor. d. A. P., 1876.

Accademici Eterei. Rime de gli A. E. [*b. w.* Bembo (P.) Giunta, 1563]. s4°. [Padova. 1567]

Accademici Infecondi, *Rome.* Le pompe funebri celeb. da signori A. I. per la morte d. Elena L. Cornara. la8°. Padova. 1686

Accadia (C. Dentice di), *see* DENTICE DI ACCADIA (C.)

Accarigi (Alberto) [*Acarisio*], *see* SANSOVINO (E.) *ed.* Osserv. d. lingua volg., 1562.

**Accentuated* list of Brit. Lepidoptera, 1858, *see* LEPIDOPTERA.

Acciaiuoli (Niccolà), *grand seneschal of Naples, see* PALMERIUS (M.) La vita di N. A., 1588.

Acciajuoli (*card.* Filippo). *Réponse [*attrib. to F. de Almada e Mendonça*] à la Rel. envoyée par le Card. Torregiani aux ministres étr. à Rome, de l'expulsion du Card. A.; tr. [*w. the* Relation], *see* PORTUGAL. Rec. de decrets &c., Suite, 1760.

see CUNHA (L. DA). Carta ao Card A. para sahir da Corte de Lisboa, 1760.

Acciarini (Tideo), *see* LO PARCO (F.) T. A., umanista marchigiano d. sec. 15, con s. Carmina &c., 1920.

Accolti (Bernardo), *Aretino, 1465–1535.* Verginia. Comedia, con un cap. della Madonna. nuov. corr. & ristamp. s8°. Vinegia. 1535

Account.

*Account of a seminary at Epsom &c., 1783, *see* EPSOM.

*Account (An) of sufferings of persecuted protestants in Salzburg, 1732, *see* SALZBURG.

*Account of the grand masonic procession, at laying foundation-stone of 1st building in London-Street, 1824, *see* GLASGOW.

*Account (An) of the progress of the reform of manners in Eng. &c., 11th ed., 1703, *see* ENGLAND.

*Account of the remark. revival of the work of God in Cornwall, 1814, *see* CORNWALL.

*Account (An) of the rise &c. of the Soc. for Discharge &c. of persons imprisoned for small debts, 6th ed., 1783, *see* SOCIETY FOR THE DISCHARGE &C.

*Account (An) of the trans. of the late King James in Ireland, 1689, 1690, *see* JAMES II.

*Genuine (A) acc. of some trans. in the E. Indies, 1753, *see* EAST INDIES.

*Short acc. of the 1st settlement of Virginia, Maryland &c. by the English, 1735, 1922, *see* SHORT.

***Acetaria:** A discourse of sallets, 1699, *see* EVELYN (J.)

Acevedo (Eduardo). Manual de hist. Uruguaya. [*t2 & 3 have t.* Hist. del Uruguay]. 3t. 8°. Montevideo. 1916–19

Acharian (R.), *see* ADJARIAN (H.)

Acheson (Arthur). Shakespeare's lost years in London, 1586–92. John Florio as Falstaff &c. 8°. 1920

Shakespeare's sonnet story, 1592–98. With an app. incl. a mon. on the Crosse Inn & the Tavern of Oxford, by E. T. Leeds. 8°. 1922

Achilles Tatius, *the Rhetorician.* Dell' amore di Leucippe & di Clitophonte. Tr. d. lingua greca nella ital. [*by* F. A. Coccio]. s8°. Vinegia. 1578

Achilli (Giovanni Giacinto), *see* EARDLEY (*Sir* C. E.) Imprisonment &c. of G. A., 1850.

Achmed Abdullah. The trail of the beast. s8°. [1921]

Acier (Jacques Galiot de Genouillac, *seigneur* **d'),** *see* GALIOT DE GENOUILLAC (J.)

Acker (Paul). Les deux cahiers. s8°. [1912]

Ackeret (Jakob). Das Rotorschiff u. s. physikal. Grundlagen. Vorwort v. L. Prandtl. 8°. Göttingen. 1925

Ackerman (Phyllis), *Ph.D.*

Wallpaper, its hist., design & use. 8°. 1923

Ackermann (Alfred S. E.) Popular fallacies. 3rd ed., w. intr. by Sir R. Gregory. 8°. 1923

Scientific paradoxes & problems &c. Intr. by C. V. Boys. 8°. 1925

Ackermann (Rudolph), *see* COMBE (W.) *Hist. of Abbey Ch. of St. Peter's Westminster, 2v, 1812.

Acland (Eleanor). Dark side out. s8°. [1921]

Acland (Hugh Dyke). Illust. of the Vaudois, views, engr. by E. Finden f. drawings by H. D. A.; w. descr. [by A. H. D.] la8°. 1831

Acland (John E.), *see* DORSET COUNTY MUSEUM. Guide, comp. by J. E. A., 13th ed., 1911.

Acoluth (Andreas). Obadias Armenus cum anal. vocum Armen. gramm. s4°. Lipsiæ. 1680

Acorn, *ps.* English timber & its econ. conversion. [Rider's Techn. ser., No. 10]. 2nd ed. s8°. *n.d.*

Acosta (Gabriel).

Comm. quinque in lib. Vet. Test. fol. Lugduni. 1641

Acosta (Joseph d'). De natura novi orbis libri 2, & De promulgatione Evangelii apud barbaros, libri 6. s8°. Coloniæ Agrippinæ. 1596

Acosta (Uriel) [*form.* GABRIEL ACOSTA *or* D'ACOSTA]. Schriften. Mit Einl., Übertrag. &c., hrsg. C. Gebhardt. [Bibl. Spinozana, t2]. 8°. A. 1922

Acqua (Carlo dell'). Del piede Liutprando detto anche Aliprando o Liprando, *see* REGIA DEP. DI STORIA PATRIA. Misc., t21, 1883.

Acremant (Germaine).

La hutte d'acajou. s8°. [1924]

Acres (W. Marston). London & Westminster in hist. & lit. s8°. [1923]

Notes on the hist. & lit. assoc. of London. s8°. 1922

Acs (Károly). Ungar., deut., ital., roman., böm.-slowak. u. serb. Gespräche. s8°. Pest. 1859

***Act** (An) at Oxford: comedy, 1704, *see* BAKER (TH.)

Acta.

*Acta causæ rituum seu ceremoniarum Sinensium: complect. Mandatum Caroli Maigrot &c. s8°. Coloniæ Agrip. 1715

Acta colloquii in comitiis Imperii Ratisponæ habiti, 1541, *see* BUCER (M.)

Acta Comitialia Hung. Sopronensia &c., 1681, *see* SOPRON.

Acta conventus Thorun., 1645, *see* THORN.

Acta et decreta 2[æ] synodi prov. Ultraject., 1763, 1764, *see* UTRECHT.

Acta et diplomata e R. Tabulario Veneto; st. & opera A. S. Minotto, v2, sect. 3, *see* TREVISO. Codex Trivisianus, 996–1318, 1874–75.

Acta et epist. rel. Transylvaniæ &c., v1, 1914, *see* VERESS (A.) *ed.*

Acta gen. octavę Synodi, 1526, *see* FLORENCE, *Council of.*

Acta historico-ecclesiastica; oder, Nachrichten v. d. neuesten Kirchengesch. [B1, *w. add*[l]. *tp.*, Acta eccl., *ed. by* J. C. Colerus: B2–20 *ed. by* J. C. & W. E. Bartholomæi]. 20B (120 T. & Anhänge). s8°. Weimar. 1734–58.

„ „ Beyträge zu d. Actis. 3B. s8°. Weimar. 1746–58

„ „ Allgem. Register ü. d. 20 Bde d. Act. u. 3 Bde d. Beyträge. s8°. Weimar. 1765–66

„ Nova Acta hist.-eccl.; oder Sammlung zu den neuest. Kirchengesch. [*Ed.* J. C. Bartholomæi]. 12B. s8°. Weimar. 1758–74

„ „ Allgem. Reg. (Repert. d. neu. Kirchengesch.), T1. s8°. Weimar. 1790

„ Acta hist.-eccl. nostri temp. [*Contin. of* Nova Acta hist.-eccles. *Ed.* C. W. Schneider]. Bde 1–11. s8°. Weimar. 1774–86

Acta hist.-eccl.; Acten, Urkunden u. Nachr. z. neuesten Kirchengesch. [B1–2, *ed.* C. W. Schneider: B3, *ed.* J. S. Schröter]. [*Contin. of* Acta hist.-eccl.] 3B. s8°. Weimar. 1788–93

Acta Iberica SS. tergemin. martyrum Speusippi Eleusippi Meleusippi. Explic., ed. & Ross. vertit N.Marr. [Отт. изъ Зап. Вост. Отд. И. Р. Арх. Общ., t17]. la8°. С.–П. 1906

Acta Imperii ined. sec. 13 & 14: Urkunden &c., B2, 1885, *see* WINKELMANN (E.) *ed.*

*Acta martyrum eorum videlicet qui hoc sæc. &c., 1556, *see* CRESPIN (J.)

*Acta oder geschicht wie es uff dem gesprech in Zürich ergangen ist &c., 1523, *see* ZÜRICH.

Acta publ., d. Neundten Electorat betreff., 1693, *see* ELECTORAT.

Acta Sanctorum, quæ coll. J. Bollandus.

„ „ Novembris coll. digesta illust. ab H. Delehaye & P. Peeters. t4, fol. Brux. 1925

„ „ De prosec. operis Bollandiani quod Acta Sanct. inscrib. [*signed* J. B. Boone *& others*]. 8°. Brussels. 1838

see KOHLER (C.) Mélanges p.s. à l'hist. de l'Orient lat. &c., *for indexes to the A. S.*, 1906.

„ MABILLON (J.) Præfationes in Acta Sanctorum Ord. S. Benedicti &c., 1724.

Acta Sanctorum martyrum orient. et occident.; S. E. Assemanus rec. &c., 2p, 1748, *see* MARUTAS, *St.*

Actes. [Actes de la dispute &c.] Acts of the dispute & conf., Paris, 1566, betw. 2 doctors of Sorbon [S. Vigor & C. de Saintes] & 2 ministers of the Reformed Church [J. de l'Espine & H. Du Rosier]. Tr. J. Golburne. 8°. 1602

Actes & doc[s]. de la Conférence Germano-Polonaise, tenue à Vienne du 30 avr. au 30 août 1924. 8°. Vienne. [1925]

*Actes, mémoires &c. conc. la paix d'Utrecht, 6t, 1714–15, *see* UTRECHT.

Action (L') française [*newspaper*].

see GWYNN (D.) The "Action Française" condemnation, 1928.

„ MAURRAS (C.) Le démocratie relig.: l'A. fr. & la relig. cath. &c., 1921.

Acton (*Rev.* **Edward**), *see* Graham (P.A.) Iwerne Minster, w. contrib^{s}. by H. S. Bower, E.A. &c., 1923.

Acton (John E. E. Dalberg-Acton, *1st baron*). The history of freedom in antiquity. [P2598]. 4°. Bridgenorth, 1877

Sendschreiben an e. deut. Bischof d. Vatican. Concils, Sept. 1870. [P2695]. 8°. Nördlingen. [1870]

see Drew (*Mrs.* M.) A., Gladstone &c., 1924.

,, Ketteler (W. E. v.) Die Minorität auf d. Concil: Antw. auf A.'s Sendschreiben, 1870.

Actors.

*Actors by daylight; or pencillings in the pit. v1, 8°. 1838

Acts [*see also* Acta; Actes].

*Acts (The) of Adonis the Great, 1820, *see* Adonis, *the Great.*

*Acts of the dispute & conference, Paris, 1566, 1602, *see* Actes.

Acts of 30 & 43 Geo. III, rel. to dist. in Chelsea, called Hans Town, 1807, *see* Hans Town.

Principall acts of the Assembly of the Kirk of Scot., 1639–1858, *see* Church of Scotland.

Acuña (Cristoval de). Novo descobr. do gr. Rio das Amazonas, 1641, *see* Instituto Hist. e Geog. Brazil. Revista, t28, 1865.

Acworth (Angus Whiteford). Financial reconstr. in England, 1815–22. 8°. 1925

Acworth (Mary), *aft. wife of T. T. Busk, see* Busk (*Mrs.* M.)

Acworth (William Mitchell). Hist. sketch of state railway ownership. s8°. 1920

Ad. *Ad persecutores Anglos pro catholicis &c., 1589, *see* Allen (W.) *card.*

*Ad Regis Galliae consiliarios, exhortatio; tr., 1561, *see* Gallia.

Adæus. Liturgia sanct. apostol. Adæi & Maris, cui acc. 2 aliæ in quibusdam festis &c. dicendæ. [*In Syriac*]. 4°. Urmiæ. 1890

Adair (Cecil). Grandmamma over the sea. s8°. [1926]

Adair (Edward Robert). Sources for the hist. of the Council in 16th & 17th c^{s}. [Helps for students of hist., No. 51]. s8°. 1924

William Thomas, *see* Pollard (A. F.) Tudor studies, 1924.

Adalbert, *abp. of Magdeburg, see* Regino, *Prumiensis.* Chron. cum cont. Treverensi [*by* A.]; rec. F. Kurze, 1890.

Adam, *le Bossu* [Adam de la Hale le Bochu d'Aras]. Canchons u. Partures. Hrsg. v. R. Berger. B1, Canchons. [Roman. Bibl., 17]. s8°. Halle a. S. 1900

Le jeu de la feuillée & Le jeu de Robin & Marion. Tr. par. E. Langlois. [Poèmes & récits. de la vieille France, 1]. s8°. 1923

Le jeu de Robin & Marion, suivi du Jeu du pèlerin. Ed. E. Langlois. [Class. franç. du m. â.] s8°. 1924

Adam, *abbot of Eynsham.* [Evesham; *form. a monk of the household of St. Hugh, bp. of Lincoln*; Adamus, *of the monastery of St. Augustine at Canterbury.*] The Revelation to the Monk of Evesham, 1196. Ed. E. Arber. [Eng. repr^{s}. *b.w.* Howell (J.) Instructions &c., 1868]. s8°. [1869]

Adam, *the patriarch.* Adam girq. [Adam book. *In Armenian*]. s8°. [K. Polis. 1799]

*Le mystère d'Adam. Drame relig. du. 12e siècle. Texte & tr. nouv. par H. Chamard. s8°. 1925

see Clug (C. G.) De baptismo A. comm. &c., 1747.

,, Regenfus (V. H.) Diss. de philos. A., 1715.

Adam, *de Saint Victor, see* Analecta hymnica medii ævi, B54, 55, Die Sequenzen d. Thesaurus Hymnologicus H. A. Daniels &c., T2, Liturg. Prosen, insbes. die d. A. v. St. V. zugeschrieb. &c., 1915–22.

Adam (Frank), *F.R.G.S.* Clans, septs & regt^{s}. of Scot. Highlands. 2nd ed. 8°. E. 1924

Adam (Hargrave Lee). The police encyclopædia. Pref. by Sir R. Anderson. 8v. 8°. [1920 ?]

Adam (James), *architect, see* Bolton (A. T.) The architecture of R. & J. A., 1922.

Adam (James), *fellow of Emmanuel Coll., Cambridge.* The nuptial number of Plato: its solution &c. 8° 1891

Adam (Johannes). Übers. u. Glossar d. altspan. Poema del Cid, *see* Roman. Forschungen, B32, 1913.

Adam (Juliette), *see* Mustafa Kamel, *pasha.* Lettres égypt. franç. addr. à Mme. J. A., 1895–1908, *n.d.*

Adam (Leonhard). Nordwestamerik. Indianerkunst. [Orbis pictus; hrsg. P. Westheim, B17]. la8°. [1923 ?]

Adam (Paul).

Le lion d'Arras. [Le temps & la vie]. s8°. [1920]

Notre Carthage. Préf. du Gén. Mangin. s8°. 1922

Adam (Robert), *architect.*

see Bolton (A. T.) Archit. & decor. of R. A. & Sir J. Soane (1758–1837), 1920.

,, —— The architecture of R. & J. A., 1922.

Adam (William), *of Matlock Bath.* The gem of the Peak, or Matlock Bath &c.: tour f. Derby to Matlock. s8°. 1843

Adama van Scheltema (C. S.)

Eenzame liedjes. 6e dr. s8°. Rotterdam. 1921

Uit stilte en strijd. 4e dr. s8°. Rotterdam. 1918

Van zon en zomer. 4e dr. s8°. Rotterdam. 1915

Adami (Vittorio). La magistratura dei confini n. ant. domini di casa Savoia, *see* Regia Deput. Misc., t48, 1915.

Adamkiewicz (Albert). Die Eigenkräfte d. Stoffe, d. Gesetz v. d. " Erhaltung d. Materie" u. d. Wunder im Weltall. [Bibl. f. Philos., B17]. 8°. 1920

Adamov (E. A.)

Европейские державы и Греция в эпоху мировой войны &c. Под редакц. &c. Е. А. А. 8°. Москва. 1922

Константинополь и Проливы. [Европ. державы и Турция во время Мир. Войны]. Под ред. Е. А. А. 2т. la8°. Москва. 1925–26

Adamović (Lujo).

Die Pflanzenwelt Dalmatiens. 8°. L. 1911

Adams, *The family of, of Massachusetts.* A cycle of Adams letters, 1861–65. Ed. W. C. Ford. 2v. 8°. 1921

Adams (*Lt.-Col.* **Archibald**). The Western Rajputana States: Marwar, Sirohi, Jaisalmir. 2nd ed. 8°. 1900

Adams (Arthur Barto). Marketing perishable farm products 8°. N.Y., *Columbia Univ.* 1916

Adams (Brooks).

The emancip. of Mass. rev. & enl. ed 8°. N.Y. [1919]

see Adams (Henry). The degradation of the democratic dogma; intr. by B. A., 1919.

Adams (Charles Francis), *U.S. minister at the court of St. James's.* An address on the life &c. of W. H. Seward &c. la8°. Albany. 1873

Adams (Charles Francis), *the younger; 2nd son of C. F. A.; 1835–1915.*

The Trent affair. [P2707]. la8°. Boston. [Mass.] 1912

see Adams, *Fam. of.* A cycle of A. letters, 1861–65, 2v, 1921.

Adams (Clement). Chancellor's voyage to Muscovy; being A.'s Angl. navig. ad Muscovitas (1630). Added, De moneta Russica (1630) [*w. sep. tp. & pagin.*] Tr^{s}. by J. M'Crindle; ed. E. Goldsmid. [Bibl. curiosa.] s8°. *p.p.*, E. 1886

Adams (Douglas). Skating. With ch. by Miss L. Cheetham & N. G[oodman?]. s8°. 1890

Adams (Edwin Plimpton). Smithsonian math. formulæ &c., *see* Smithsonian Institution. Misc. coll^{s}., v74, No. 1, 1922.

Adams (Eleanor Nathalie). Old Eng. scholarship, 1566–1800. Diss. [Yale st^{s}. in Eng., 55]. 8°. New Haven, *Yale.* 1917

Adams (Elmer Cleveland) & W. D. Foster.

Heroines of mod. progress. [Reissued]. s8°. N.Y. 1921

Adams (Ephraim Douglass).

Great Britain & Amer. Civil War. 2v. 8°. 1925

The influence of Grenville on Pitt's for. policy, 1787–98. [C. I. of Wash. Publ. 13]. la8°. Wash. 1904

Adams (George Burton).

The Brit. Empire & a League of peace. [P2466]. 8°. N.Y. 1919

Constitut. hist. of England. 8°. [1920]

Council & courts in Anglo-Norman Eng. [Yale Hist. Publs. St., 5]. 8°. New Haven, *Yale,* 1926

Origin of the Eng. constit. enl. ed. 8°. New Haven, *Yale.* 1920

An outline sketch of Eng. constit. hist. s8°. New Haven, *Yale.* 1918

Adams (George Plimpton).

Idealism & the mod. age. 8°. New Haven, *Yale.* 1919

Adams (Hannah).

An abridgment of the hist. of New Eng. s8°. 1806

Adams (Henry), *essayist, 3rd son of C. F. Adams, U.S. Minister, 1838–1912.* [Adams (H. Brooks)].

*Democracy. An Amer. novel. s8°. 1882

The degradation of the democratic dogma. Intr. by B. Adams. s8°. N.Y. 1919

Letters to a niece & Prayer to the Virgin of Chartres. With a niece's mem^{s}. by M. La Farge 8°. 1920

Mont-Saint-Michel & Chartres. [Mass. Hist. Soc.] la8°. 1919

see Adams, *Fam. of.* A cycle of A. letters, 1861–65, 2v, 1921.

Adams (Herbert).

The Queen's Gate mystery. s8°. [1927]

The secret of Bogey House. s8°. [1924]

Adams (James Truslow).
The founding of New England. 8°. Boston [U.S.] [1921]
Revolut. New England, 1691–1776. 8°. Boston [U.S.] [1923]
Adams (*Sir* John), *M.A., B.Sc.* Educ. movements & methods. [*By var. wrs.*] Intr. by J. A. s8°. [1924]
Errors in school. s8°. 1927
Mod. developments in educat. practice. s8°. 1922
Adams (John), *president of the U.S.* Defence of the constitutions of govt. of the U.S. agst. the attack of Turgot. n. ed. 3v. 8°. 1794
Adams (Joseph) [*ps.* "CORRIGEEN"]. Salmon & trout angling. Foreword by Marq. of Hartington. 8°. [1923]
Adams (Joseph Quincey). Chief pre-Shakespearian dramas. Sel. of plays illust. hist. of Eng. drama down to Shakespeare. 8°. [1925]
Life of W. Shakespeare. 8°. 1923
see HERBERT (*Sir* HENRY). Dramatic records (1623–73), 1917.
Adams (Percy Walter Lewis). Hist. of the Douglas family & th. descendants. s4°. Bedford. 1921
Hist. of the Jukes family of Cound, Shropshire &c. 8°. Tunstall. [1927]
Adams (Randolph Greenfield).
Hist. of the foreign policy of the U.S. 8°. N.Y. 1924
Polit. ideas of the Amer. Revol., 1765–75. Thesis [Univ. of Penn.] s8°. Durham, N.C. 1922
Adams (*Mrs.* Sarah), *née Flower, see* STEPHENSON (H. W.) The author of Nearer, my God, to Thee: S. F. A., 1922.
Adams (Thomas), *D.D., preacher at Willington &c.* A comm. upon the 2nd Epistle wr. by St. Peter. fol. 1633
Workes. fol. 1629
Adams (Thomas Sewall) & H. L. Sumner.
Labor problems. A text book. 8°. N.Y. 1920
Adams (William Davenport), *son of W. H. D. Adams.* Eng. epigrams. Sel. & arr., w. intr. &c. by W. D. A. s8°. 1878
Songs of society f. Anne to Victoria. Ed., w. notes &c. by W. D. A. s8°. 1880
Adams (William Henry Davenport).
Windsor Castle & the waterway thither. la8°. 1880
Adamson (*Sir* John Ernest). The individual & the environment; theory of education as adjustment. 8°. 1921
Adamson (John William). A guide to the hist. of educ. [*b. w.* Cunningham (W.) Mons. of E. mun. life, 1920]. s8°. 1920
Short hist. of educ. [repr.] 8°. C. 1922
Adamus, *Bremensis.* Hamburg. Kirchengesch. [*Lat.*] Hrsg. B. Schmeidler. [Scr. rerum Germ.] 3e A. 8°. Hannover. 1917
Adamus (Melchior). *The life & death of M. Luther. [Presented in an Eng. dresse by T. Hayne]. s4°. 1641
Vitæ Germanorum theologorum. s8°. Francofurti. 1653
Adcock (Arthur St. John).
The Bookman treasury of living poets. Ed. A. 8°. [1926]
Gods of mod. Grub Street: impresss. of contemp. authors, [*w.*] portraits. s8°. [1923]
Addaeus, *see* THADDAEUS.
Adderbury, *Oxon.* A. "Rectoria," *see* Hobson (T. F.), *ed.*
Addereth, *see* ADRETH.
Addington (Samuel). Catal. of library of S.A., sold by Sotheby, May 1886. [*MS. prices*]. [P2747]. 8°. [1886]
Addison (*Rt. Hon.* Christopher).
The betrayal of the slums. s8°. 1922
Politics f. within, 1911–18, incl. records of a gt. national effort. Foreword by Ld. Carson. 2v. 8°. 1924
Addison (James Thayer). Chinese ancestor worship. s8°. [1926]
Addison (*Rt. Hon.* Joseph).
Works. 4v. 4°. B'ham. 1761
Works. Notes by R. Hurd. Adds. coll. & ed. by H. G. Bohn. [repr.] 6v. s8°. *Bohn.* 1900–02
Cato, *see* INCHBALD (*Mrs.* E.) Brit. theatre, v8, 1808.
,, *see* NEW English theatre, v10, 1777.
Crit. on Paradise lost; w. remarks on the versific. of Milton, by S. Johnson. [Ed. T. Park]. s8°. 1805
Days w. Sir Roger de Coverley. Repr. f. the "Spectator." Illust. by H. Thomson. [3rd ed.] s8°. [1892]
The evidences of the Xtn. relig. &c. s8°. 1730
A letter f. Italy to C., Lord Halifax, 1701; w. Mourning muse of Alexis, by Congreve, 1695 &c. [P2868]. s8°. 1709
Poet. works. Collated by T. Park. s8°. 1807
Remarks on several parts of Italy &c., 1701–03. 3rd ed. s8°. 1726
4th ed. s8°. 1733
Sels. f. "A.'s papers contrib. to "Spectator." Intr. & notes by T. Arnold. s8°. O. 1883
Il Tamburo. Parafrasi in versi sciolti d. tr. dal Sig. Des Touches. [*Suppressed by ord. of the Inquisition of Rome, w. damnatory decree, dated 1750, in MS.*] 8°. Firenze. 1750
see DOBRÉE (B.) Essays in biog., 1680–1726, 1925.
,, FREEHOLDER (THE), or Polit. essays; [by J. A.], 1716.

Addison (Lancelot), *dean of Lichfield.* The primitive instit., or, a disc. of catechizing. s8°. 1674
Addleshaw (William Percy).
Cathedral Church of Exeter. [n. & rev. ed.] s8°. 1921
Address.
*Address (An) to Protestants &c., 1692, *see* PENN (W.)
*Address to the people on death of Pr. Charlotte (1817), *see* SHELLEY (P. B.)
*A modest address to the Commons of Gt. Brit. &c., 1756, *see* MODEST.
Addresses. Addresses pres. f. the Court of Common Council to the king, resoluts. &c., 1778, *see* LONDON: CIVIC INSTIT.
Addyman (Frank Thornton), *see* COLEMAN (J. B.) & F. T. A. Pract. agric. chemistry, n. impr., 1913.
Adel, *Yorks.* Registers of the parish ch. of Adel, 1606–1812, & mon. inscrs. Ed. G. D. Lumb. [Thoresby Soc., 5]. 8°. Leeds. 1895
Adelardus *Bathensis.* Quæstiones naturales; tr. H. Gollancz, *see* BERACHYA. Dodi ve-nechdi, 1920.
Adeline (Jules). A.'s art dictionary. Tr. & enl. 8°. 1891
Adelmann (Helene). Aus. m. Kinderzeit. 2e A. 8°. 1897
Adelphi (The).
Ed. J. M. Murry. v1 (June–Dec. 1923). 8°. 1923
Adelung (Friedrich v.) *Rapports entre la langue sanscrit & la langue russe. Prés. à l'Acad. Imp. Russe. [P2701]. 4°. St. Pétersbourg. 1811
Adelung (Johann Christoph), *see* HUMBOLDT (W. v.) Berichtig. &c. z. 1.Abschn, d. 2. B. d. Mithridates [*by* J. C. A.], 1817.
Aden, Gulf of. Red Sea & Gulf of Aden pilot, 7th ed. & Suppl., 1912–22, *see* ADMIRALTY.
Adeney (John Howard).
The Jews of Eastern Europe. s8°. 1921
Adiaphora. *De adiaphoris Scoti τοῦ τυχόντος aphorismi. [*Attrib. to* (1) Sir James Sempill, (2) David Calderwood]. s8°. *n.p.* 1622
Adjarian (Hratcheay) [ACHARIAN (R.)].
Провинціал. словарь армянскаго языка. [*In Armenian.* Эминскій этнограф. сборникъ изд. при Лазаревскомъ Инст. Восточ. Языковъ, вып. 9]. la8°. Tiflis. 1913
[St. Mesrop & the invention of writing. Hist. of sources &c. *In Armenian.* Banaser *publ.* P2817]. 8°. Paris. 1907
see MANANDEAN (Y.) & H. A. Rec. martyrol. of Armenians, 1903.
Adjemean (Mkrtitch).
Vahagn. [*Armenian poem*]. s8°. K. Polis. 1871
Adler (Alfred). The practice & theory of individual psychology. Tr. P. Radin. 8°. 1924
Adler (Caspar) [AQUILA (CASPAR)], *see* HILLINGER (J. G.) Memoria Aquilina: Leben d. C. A., nebst dessen Erbaul. Catechismo, 1731.
Adler (Emanuel), *see* HANUSCH (F.) Regelung d. Arbeitsverhältnisse im Kriege; v. E. A. &c., 1927.
Adler (Felix). Reconstruction of the spiritual ideal. Hibbert Lects., 1923. s8°. N.Y. 1924
Adler (Friedrich). Ortszeit, Systemzeit, Zonenzeit u. d. ausgezeichn. Bezugssystem d. Electrodynamik. Unters. ü. d. Lorentzsche u. Einsteinsche Kinematik. 8°. Wien. 1920
Adler (Fritz). Aus Stralsunds Vergangenheit. [Pommersche Heimatkunde, B3, 4]. 2T. s8°. Greifswald. 1922–23
Adler (Georg) Fr. Nietzsche. [*Extr. f.* Nord u. Süd. B56, H168]. [P2478]. 8°. Breslau. 1891
Adler (Jacob Georg Christian), *see* LORCK (J.) Bibl. Biblica &c. ed. J. G. C. A., 1787.
Adler (Michael). Brit. Jewry: book of honour, [1914–18]. Ed. M. A. Organiser, M. R. G. Freeman. 4°. 1922
***Administration** (The) of Ireland, 1920, 1921, *see* IRELAND.
Admiralty.
Coll. of all such statutes &c. as rel. to the A., Navy &c. down to 14th year of George II. 4°. 1742
The Euxine, f. Russ. survey of 1836. [A. chart]. folded 8°. 1853
NAVAL INTELLIGENCE DIVISION. *The words "A handbook of" or "A manual of" have been omitted f. following titles.*
Alsace-Lorraine [*& Atlas, fol.*]. 8°. 1920
Arabia. v1. s8°. [1920]
Belgian Congo. 8°. [1920]
Bulgaria. s8°. [1920]
NAVAL INTELLIGENCE DIVISION [*continued*].
German East Africa. s8°. 1920
,, ,, Suppl., Hygiene &c. s8°. 1923
Greece. v1. s8°. [1920]
Kenya Colony (Brit. E. Africa), and the K. Protectorate (Prot. of Zanzibar). s8°. [1920]
Libya. s8°. [1920]
Macedonia &c. s8°. [1920]
Mesopotamia &c., Geol. of. 8°. [1920]
Mexico. [Maps *in case*]. s8°. [1919]

Admiralty [*continued*].

NAVAL INTELLIGENCE DIVISION [*continued*].
Netherlands India (Dutch East Indies). 8°. [1920]
Norway & Sweden. s8°. [1920]
Portuguese East Africa. 8°. 1920
Portuguese Nyasaland. s8°. [1920]
Roumania. s8°. [1920]
Serbia, Montenegro, Albania & adj. parts of Greece. s8°. 1920
Siberia & Arctic Russia. v1. s8°. [1920]
Syria including Palestine. s8° [1920]
Turanians & Pan-Turanianism. 8°. [1921]
Turkey in Europe. s8°. [1920]
Uganda Protectorate. s8°. [1920]
Vocabularies: Eng., Arabic, Persian, Turk., Armenian, Kurdish, Syriac. s8°. 1920
Vocabularies: Eng., German, Magyar, Serbian, Bulgar, Rouman., Greek, Turkish. s8°. 1920

PILOTS.
The word pilot has been omitted from following titles.
Africa. 3p. *&* Suppl^s. 2, 6; [p1 & 3, 8th ed.; p2, 7th ed.] 8°. 1915–22
Alaska (S.-E.) 8°. 1920
„ „ Suppl. 1. 8°. 1921
Arctic. 3v *&* Suppl^s. 4, 6; [v1, 2, 3rd ed.; v3, 2nd ed.] 8°. 1915–22
Australia. 5v *&* Suppl^s. 4, 5. 8°. 1914–22
„ Notices to mariners, 1922, rel. to A. p., v5. 8°. [1922]
Baltic. 3p *&* Suppl. 6, 7; [p1 & 2, 5th ed.; p1, form. publ. as the Danish pilot, orig. comp. by Adm. Zahrtmann]. 8°. 1912–22
„ Notices to mariners rel. to B. p., p1. 8°. [1922]
Bay of Bengal. 5th ed. *&* Suppl. 1. 8°. 1921–22
Bay of Biscay, *&* Suppl. 1. 8°. 1921–22
Bering Sea & Strait, *&* Suppl. 1. 8°. 1920–22
Black Sea. 7th ed. *&* Suppl. 2. 8°. 1920–22
British Columbia. 2v *&* Suppl. 6; [v1, 4th ed.] 8°. 1913–22
„ „ Notices to mariners, 1922, rel. to B.C. p. 8°. [1922]
Central America. West coasts of C. Amer. & U.S. 3rd ed. *&* Suppl. 5. 8°. 1916–22
„ „ Notices to mariners, 1916. 8°. 1916
Channel. 3p *&* Suppl^s. 2, 4 & 5; [p1, 11th ed.; p2, 8th ed.] 8°. 1917–22
China Sea. 5v *&* Suppl^s. 6 & 7. 8°. 1912–22

PILOTS [*continued*].
Eastern Archipelago. 3v [v1, 2, 3rd ed.; v3, 2nd ed.] *&* Suppl^s. 1, 5, 6. 8°. 1911–22
„ „ Notices to mariners, 1921–22. 8°. [1921–22]
England, West coast. 6th ed. *&* Suppl. 6. 8°. 1910–20
„ „ Notices to mariners, 1920, 1921. 8°. [1920–21]
India. West coast of I. 6th ed. *&* Suppl. 2. 8°. 1919–22
Indian Ocean (South). Orig. comp. by H. A. Moriarty. 3rd ed. *&* Suppl. 6. 8°. 1911–21
„ „ Notices to mariners, 1921, 1922. 8°. [1921–22]
Irish coast. 7th ed. 8°. 1922
Japan. 2nd ed. *&* Suppl. 6. 8°. 1914–22
Korea. East coasts of K. & Siberia & Sea of Okhotsk, *&* Suppl. 7. 8°. 1913–22
Mediterranean. 5v. [v1–4, 5th ed.] *&* Suppl. 2, 3, 5–7. 8°. 1913–22
Newfoundland & Labrador. 5th ed. 2v. *&* Suppl. 4. 8°. 1917–22
New Zealand. 9th ed. *&* Suppl. 3. 8°. 1919–22
North Sea. 4p. [p1, 2, 7th ed.; p3, 4, 8th ed.] *&* Suppl. 6. 8°. 1914–22
„ „ Notices to mariners, 1922. 8°. [1922]
Norway. 3p. [p1, 5th ed.; p2, 4th ed.] *&* Suppl^s. 4, 6. 8°. 1914–22
Nova Scotia (S.-E. coast) & Bay of Fundy. 7th ed., 1921. 8°. 1922
Pacific Islands. 5th ed. 3v. *&* Suppl^s. 1–3. 8°. 1918–22
Red Sea & Gulf of Aden. 7th ed. *&* Suppl. 1. 8°. 1921–22
St. Lawrence. 8th ed. 2v. *&* Suppl. 5. 8°. 1916–22
Scotland, West coast. 7th ed. 2v. *&* Suppl. 1. 8°. 1921–22
South Amer. 3p. [p1, 6th ed.; p2, 11th ed.] *&* Suppl. 5 & 6. 8°. 1911–22
„ „ Notices to mariners, 1921. 8°. [1921]
Spain, West coasts of S. & Portugal, *&* Suppl. 1. 8°. 1921–22
United States, East coast of U.S. 3rd ed. 2v. *&* Suppl. 1. 8°. 1921–22
West Indies. 3v. [v1, 2, 7th ed.; v3, 2nd ed.] *&* Suppl. 1, 6. 8°. 1912–22
„ „ Notices to mariners, 1922. 8°. [1922]
Yangtse Kiang. Comp. by T. H. Tizard, *&* Suppl. 5. 8°. 1914–28
see JUTLAND, BATTLE OF. Battle of J., 30th May–1st June 1916: offic. despatches &c., 1920.

Admonitions of an Egyptian sage; [ed.] A. H. Gardiner, 1909, *see* EGYPTIAN.

Adney (Frances) *see* ROERICH (N. C.) "The messenger" (R.'s paintings): 7 articles by F. A. &c., 1925.

Adonis, *the Great, ps.* *The acts of Adonis the Great, king of Bull. [*A satire on King George IV.*] [P425]. 8°. [1820 ?]

Adonts (Nikolai Georgevich).
Арменія въ епоху Юстиніана. [Тексты и разыск. по арм.-груз. філол., (С.-П. Унив.), кн. 11] la8°. С.-П. 1908
Начал. исторія Арменіи у Себеоса &c. [Отт. изъ т8 Визант. временн. P2804]. la8°. С.-П. 1901

Adorna, *The family of, see* ROSSI (B. DE') Istoria genealog. &c. d. case A. &c., 1719.

Adreth (Solomon ben), *see* SOLOMON, *ben Abraham ben Adreth, 1235–1310.*

Adrian II, *pope.* Epistolæ, *see* DÜMMLER (E. L.), *ed.* Epist. Merow. et Karol. ævi, t4, 1925.

Adrian IV, *pope, see* EGGERS (A.) Die Urkunde Hadrians IV, f. Heinr. II v. Eng. ü. d. Besetzung Irlands, 1922.

Adrian VI, *pope.*
Eyn Bepstlich Breve dem radt czu Bamberg gesand widder den Luther. [*Foll^d. by note by Luther*]. [P2539]. s4°. *n.p.* 1523
Breve ad Fridericum Saxoniæ ducem, adv. Lutherum. s8°. *n.p. n.d.* [1523 ?]
Legatio A. ad Conventum Nuremberg. a. 1522 missa. Resp. principum. Gravamina centum &c. [*Pref. by Luther*]. Denuo recusum. s4°. Vittembergæ. 1538
Was der ausszug zū Bepstlicher hailigkeit verordnet, derhalb geratschlagt hat, volgt hernach. [P2539]. s4°. *n.p. n.d.* [1523 ?]
*Wie der Hailig vater Bapst Adrianus eingeriten ist zu Rom, 28 Aug. 1522, 1522, *see* GENGENBACH (P.)

Adriani (Giovanni Battista), *Professore di Storia.* Della vita e d nunziature del Card. P. Santa Croce; per cura di G.A. [A. Cicarelli De orig., antiq. &c. illust. domus Sanctacruciæ—P. card. Sanctacrucii De vita atque rebus gestis, 1514–67—Nunziatura di P. Santa Croce al re dei Romani, 1548], *see* REGIA DEP. DI STORIA PATRIA. Misc., t5, 1868.

Adshead (Stanley Davenport).
Town planning & town development. 8°. [1923]

Adshead (W. P.) Exper. séances; rep. by W. P. A., *see* SMEDLEY (A.) Some reminisc., 1900.

Advance in co-education: articles by var. a^s., 1919, *see* WOODS (A.) *ed.*

Adventures. *Adventures (The) of a gentleman in search of a horse &c., 1836, *see* STEPHEN (*Sir* G.)

***Advertisements** for Ireland (1623): descr. of State of I. in r. of James I; ed. G. O'Brien, 1923, *see* IRELAND.

Advertiser's A.B.C. (The). Standard advertisement directory, 1921. Compiled &c. by T. B. Browne, Ltd. la8°. 1921

Advice. *Advice to officers of the British Army [*Attrib. to* F. Grose *and also to* John Williamson]. 6th ed. s8°. 1783
*Some seasonable advice f. an honest sailor, 1746, *see* VERNON (*adm.* E.)

Advocate.
*The advocate of conscience liberty. s8°. *n.p.* 1673

Adye (*Maj.-Gen. Sir* **John).**
Soldiers & others I have known. 8°. 1925

Adye (*Gen. Sir* **John Miller).**
The Brit. army in 1875. [P2602]. 8°. 1876
The defence of Cawnpore, by the troops under Maj.-Gen. C. A. Windham. 8°. 1858

Adye (Willett L.) The hist. of the pr. Greek text of the N.T. [P2561]. 8°. Southampton. 1865

Adzarean (H.), *see* ADJARIAN (H.)

Ægean civilizations: lect., 1925, *see* LUNN (*Sir* H. S.) *ed.*

Aegerter (Emmanuel), *see* JOACHIM, *abbot of Fiore.* L'évangile eternel; préc. d'une biog. par E. A., 2t, 1928.

Ægidius, *Corboliensis, see* VIEILLARD (C.) Gilles de Corbeil, 1140–1224 ?, 1909.

Ægidius, *of Lessines, see* BIRKENMAJER (A.) Verm. Unters. (Brief R. Kilwardbys u. die Streitschrift A.'s, 1277), 1922.

Ælfric, *abbot, called Grammaticus.*
Selected homilies. Ed. H. Sweet. 2nd ed. s8°. O. 1901
see BIBLE: ANGLO-SAXON. The old Eng. version of the Heptateuch, A.'s Treatise on O. & N. Test. & h. Pref. to Genesis &c.; ed. &c. S. J. Crawford, 1922.
see BIBLIOTHEK d. angelsächs. Prosa, B9, Die Hirtenbriefe A. in altengl. u. lat. Fassung; hrsg. mit. Übers. &c. v. B. Fehr, 1914.
„ —— B10, Exameron anglice [*attr. to A.*]; ed. w. tr. &c. by S. J. Crawford, 1921

Aellen (Hermann). Schweizerisches Zeitgenossen-Lexikon. Hrsg. A. unter Mitarbeit v. W. J. Meyer &c. 8°. Bern. 1921

Ælred, *abbot of Rievaulx, Saint.* [AILRED]. Opera omnia, ope & studio R. Gibboni. Add. Anon. rithmi de laude virginitatis. s4°. Duaci. 1531
see POWICKE (F. M.) A. of R. & h. biog. W. Daniel, 1922.

Aelst (Peter Coeck van), *see* COECK (P.), *of Aelst.*

Æmilius (Georgius). *Evangelia quæ Dominicis & aliis festis diebus leguntur heroico carmine reddita. s8°. Coloniæ. 1554
see CHYTRÆUS (D.) De morte & vita æterna [*foll^d. by* Imagines mortis illust. epigr. G. Æ.]. 1581.

Æneas, *Gazæus.* Theophrastus sive de animarum immortalitate, *Gr. & Lat.*, 1559, *see* THEOLOGI. Theolog. aliquot Græc. libri 1560.

Æneas, *Tacticus.* Æ. T. [On the defence of fortified positions &c.]—Asclepiodotus [Tactics]—Onasander [The general]. [Texts] w. Eng. tr. by members of the Illinois Greek Club. [Loeb Class. Lib.] s8°. 1923

Æ. on siegecraft. Crit. ed. [& tr.] by L. W. Hunter. Rev., w. add. by S. A. Handford. 8°. O. 1927

Æneas, *the Trojan.* Eneas: roman du 12e s. Ed. J. J. Salverda de Grave. [Class. fr. du m-a., 44]. s8°. 1925

Æpinus (Franz Albert). Metaphysicæ ad theolog. applic. compendium. Ed. 3a aucta. s8°. Rostochii. 1728

Aeppli (Fritz), *see* ÄPPLI (F.)

Aereboe (Friedrich). Einfl. d. Krieges auf d. landwirtschaftl. Produkt. in Deutschland. [C.E. for Internat. Peace]. la8°. St. 1927

Die Landwirtschaft u. d. Krieg, 2T, *see* KAISER-WILHELM-DANK. Kriegsschr., H49, 67, 68, 1916.

Aeronautics. Complete aeronautics; [*by var. as.*], v1, 1920, *see* WINCHESTER (C.), *ed.*

Æschines, *the orator.* Discours. Texte établi & tr. par V. Martin & G. de Budé. [Coll. des univs. de France]. t1. 8°. 1927

Orationes [*in Greek*], *see* ORATORES. Orationes horum rhetorum &c., p1, 1513.

see DOBSON (W. S.), *ed.* Oratores Attici, t12, A., t16, Demosthenis & A. interpret. Lat., 1828.

Æschylus.

Æschylus. Rec. J. Scholefield. Ed. 2a. 8°. Cantab. 1830

Tragædiæ selectæ Æschyli, Sophoclis, Euripidis. Cum dupl. interpret. Latina, una ad verbũ, altera carmine. Ennianæ interpret. locorũ aliquot Euripidis. s8°. *n.p. H. Stephanus.* 1567

TRANSLATIONS.

A. With Eng. tr. H. W. Smyth. [Loeb Class. Lib.] 2[v]. s8°. 1922–26

Eschyle. Texte établi & tr. par P. Mazon. [Coll. des univs. de France]. 2t. 8°. 1920–25

Agamemnon of Æ. & the Bacchanals of Euripides, w. passages f. lyric &c. poets of Greece. Tr. H. H. Milman. s8°. 1865

Agamemnon. Freely tr. by A. Platt. s8°. [1911]

The Agamemnon of A. Tr. into Eng. rhyming verse, w. explan. notes by G. Murray. s8°. [1920]

Les Choéphores d'Eschyle. [Tr. & Essai de mise en scène par P. Claudel]. la8°. 1920

The Choëphoroe. Tr. into Eng. rhyming verse by G. Murray. s8°. [1923]

TRANSLATIONS [*continued*].

Les Euménides d'Eschyle. [Tr. *w.* Note *by* P. Claudel]. 2e. éd. la8°. 1920

Eumenides. Tr. into rhyming verse by G. Murray. 8°. [1925]

The Oresteia of A. Gk. text as arr. for performance at Cambridge, w. Eng. verse tr. by R. C. Trevelyan. s8°. C. 1920

Prometheu acorrentado; tr. portug. por Pedro II, imp. do Brazil, *see* INSTITUTO HIST. &c. BRAZIL. Rev., t67, 68, 1906–7.

Prometheus bound. Repr. in Eng. & expl. by E. G. Harman. 8°. 1920

REFERENCES.

see DINDORF (C. W.) Poet. scenic. Græc. fabulæ &c., ed. 5a. 1869.

„ FLAXMAN (J.) Class. compositions: tragedies of E., engr. by Piroli, 1870.

„ HOERNLE (E. S.) Problem of the Agamemnon: crit. of Dr. Verrall's theory &c., 1921.

„ —— The recognition scene in the Choephoroe, 1922.

„ SMYTH (H. W.) Æschylean tragedy, 1924.

Æsop. [ÄSOP; ÆSOPUS; ESOPE; ESOPO; ESOPUS; ISOPO].

Fabulæ Æsopi Græcè & Latinè, nunc denuo selectæ. Eae item quas Avienus carm. expr. Acc. Ranarum & murium pugna Homero asscr. s8°. Amstelodami. 1672

Habentur hoc volumine hæc, videlicet. Vita [a Maximo Planude composita], & Fabellæ [146] Æsopi cum interpret. lat. &c.—Gabriæ fabellæ &c.—Phurnutus de natura deorum—Palæphatus de non credendis historiis—Heraclides Ponticus de Allegoriis apud Homerum—Orî Apollinis Niliaci hieroglyphica — Coll. proverbiorum Tarrhæi & Didymi &c. [Ed. Aldus Pius Manutius. *Gr. & Lat.*] fol. [Venetiis, apud Aldum. 1505]

Only Æsop & Babrius [Gabrias] are furnished w. a Lat. tr. by the editor; the other works are in Gr.

TRANSLATIONS.

Fables. [Tr.], w. applic. [by J. Croxall]. 8°. 1722

Sel. fables of E. & o. fabulists. [*w.* Life by Meziriac, & An essay on the fable by R. Dodsley]. 8°. B'ham. *Baskerville.* 1764

Fables of Æ. &c., w. applic. by S. Croxall. 22nd ed. s8°. 1825

Fables. New version by T. James, illust. by J. Tenniel. s8°. 1852

Arakq Ezoubos (Fables of Æsop). Tr. by Minas V. Bjshkcan. s8°. Venice. 1886

[*Sel. fables in Persian*]. s8°. [Teheran]. 1311 [=1893]

Æsop [*continued*].

TRANSLATIONS [*continued*].

Ysopet-Avionnet: The Lat. & French texts. Ed. K. McKenzie & W. A. Oldfather. [Illinois, Univ. of. Studies in lang. &c., v5 iv]. la8°. Urbana. [1921]

see CORROZET (G.) Le Comte du Rossignol [& Fables du très anc. E.], 1924.

see FREYTAG (F. G.) Narr. M. Planudae de insigni Æ. deform., 1717.

„ GILCHRIST (J. B.) The oriental fabulist, polyglot trs. into Hindoostanee &c., 1803.

Æsquillus (Publius) *ps.*, *see* FLACIUS (M.) *Illyricus.*

Æsquillus (Publius), *der Societet Jesu Baccalaureus, ps.* Eygentliche &c. Beschreybung dess heylig. Röm. u. Cathol. Hafenkäss. Reymenweiss verfasset &c. durch P. A. s4°. *n.p.* 1618

Æthiopicæ [ÆTHIOPICARUM], *Chaldeæ, seu Æthiopicæ linguæ institutiones, 1630, *see* CHALDEÆ.

Rerum Æthiop. scr. occid. ined. a sæc. 16 ad 19, v15, 1917, *see* BECCARI (C.)

Æthiopicum. *Alphabetum Æ. &c., 1631, *see* ALPHABETUM.

Æthiopische Marienhymnen, 1919, *see* GROHMANN (A.), *ed.*

Ætna. L'Etna. Poème. Texte établi & tr. par J. Vessereau. [Coll. des univs. de France]. 8°. 1923

Afanasevich (Xénia), *see* ATANASSIEVITCH (X.)

Afan de Ribera (Fulgencio). La virtud al uso y mística à la moda. Asunto y tema Alex. Giron instruy. á su hijo. s8°. 1820

Affarosi (Camillo). Notizie istor. di Reggio di Lombardia &c. p1 [*no more publ.*] 4°. Padova. 1755

Affelmann (Johann). Progr. in prælectiones publ. de Jubilæo Evangel. [P483]. s4°. Rostochii. 1617

Affo (Ireneo). Istoria d. città &c. di Guastalla. 4t. 4°. Guastalla. 1785–87

*Vita de Pierluigi Farnese duca di Parma &c. [Ed. P. Litta]. 8°. Milano. 1821

Afghan. The third Afghan war, 1919. Gen. Staff. Br., Army H.Q., India. 8°. 1926

Afghan, *ps.* The wanderings of Asaf. s8°. 1923

Afghanistan. Narr. of events in A., 1872–Apr. 1874 (Cabul précis, chap. 9 & 10); Apr. 1874–May 1875. [3 pagins.] fol. [?1874–5]

Aflalo (Frederick George).

Sunshine & sport in Florida & W. Indies. 8°. 1907

Afrahat, *surnamed the Persian sage.* [APHRAATES]. Girq Zgon. [Book called Wise. Discourses *wrongly attrib. to Jacob, patr. of Nisibis. In Armenian.* Ed. Yohanean]. 8°. K.-polis. 1824

Afremov (Ivan Fedorovich).

Историч. обозрѣніе Тульской губ. Ч1. 8°. Москва. 1850

Africa.

A. pilot, 3p & suppls. 2, 6, 1915–22, *see* ADMIRALTY.

Imperial map of S.A. Comp. J. Wood. [5p]. folded s8°. Cape Town. [1900] Ermelo. Nylstroom. Ladysmith. Wakkerstroom. Lydenburg.

Outline of a vocab. of langs. in W. & C. Africa comp. for the Niger Exped. [Afr. Civiliz. Soc.] s. obl. 8°. 1841

UNION OF SOUTH AFRICA.

Journal of the Dept. of Agriculture (1904–26). [*No more publ.*] [*Publ. suspended* Sept. 1914–March 1920]. 8°. Pretoria. 1904–26

Publ. under var. titles, as under:—

Transvaal (The) agric. journal. Issued by Agric. Dept., v3–9 (Oct. 1904–Oct. 1910).

UNION OF SOUTH AFRICA [*contd.*]

Agric. journal of the Union of South Africa, v1–8 (Feb. 1911–Aug. 1914).

Journal of the Dept. of Agric., v1–12 (April 1920–Sept. 1926).

Monthly bulletin of Union statistics. No. 1–72 (1922–27). [No. 1, 4–6, 9, 10 *wanting*]. fol. Pretoria. [1922–27]

Official Year Book. No. 3–8, 1919–25. Statistics for 1910–25. 8°. Pretoria. 1920–27

Select docs. rel. to the unific. of S.A., 2v, 1924, *see* NEWTON (A. P.) *ed.*

Aftalion (Albert). Effect of the War upon French textile industry & Effect &c. upon Fr. commercial policy, *see* GIDE (C.) *ed.* Effects of the War upon Fr. econ. life, 1923.

Les fondements du socialisme. [Bibl. gén. d'écon. polit.] 8°. 1923

L'industrie textile en France pend. la Guerre. [C. E. for Int. Peace]. la8°. [1924]

Monnaie, prix & change. 8°. 1927

Agacino y Martinez (Eugenio). Manuel pract. del marino mercante. 2a ed. 8°. Cadiz. 1912

Agapetus, *deacon of S. Sophia, 6c., see* DASHEAN (H.) Sh. bibliog. sts. &c., *in Armenian*, v2, 1901.

Agas (Ralph). [AGGAS]. London in the reign of Elizabeth. Fac-simile of map by A., 1560. By E. Weller. folded 8º.*n.d.*
„ „ [*a. c. b. w.* Rocque (J.) Survey of London, 1748]. folded fol. *n.d.*

Agate (James Evershed). Alarums & excursions. s8º. 1922
The contemporary theatre, 1924. Intr. by N. Coward. s8º. 1925
„ „ ......1925. Intr. by C. E. Montague. 8º. 1926
Responsibility. A novel. s8º. 1919

Agathangelus, *historian.* [Hist. of the Armenians. *In Armenian.* Ed. G. Ter-Mkrttchean & St. Kanayeantz. (Historians of Arm.; ed. St. Malkhasean, v. lii)]. la8º. Tiflis. 1909

Agathangelus, *of St. Theresa, Monk.* Chron. of events, 1623–1733, rel. to settlement of order of Carmelites in Mesopotamia (Bassora). Wr. by A. of St. T. & others. Ed. w. tr. &c. by Sir H. Gollancz. 8º. O. 1927

Agathias [A. MYRINAEUS; A. MYRINENSIS], *see* LEAF (W.) Byzantine Pleiad [A. &c.], 1920.

Agathon, *ps., see* MASSIS (H.)

Ageorges (Joseph). Une famille française au 19e s.: les Pagès & les Bordes-Pagès. 8º. Tourcoing. 1920

Aggas (Ralph), *see* AGAS.

Aghnides (Nicolas Prodromos). Mohammedan theories of finance; w. an intr. to Mohamm. law & a bibliog. 8º. N.Y., *Columbia Univ.* 1916

Agius de Soldanis (Giovanni Pietro Francesco). Della lingua punica usata da Maltesi &c. [*Foll. by* Nuova scuola di gramm. *w. sep. tp. &* Diz. punico-maltese]. s8º. Roma. 1750

Agnel (G. Arnaud d'), *see* ARNAUD D'AGNEL (G.)

***Agnes de Castro:** tragedy, 1696, *see* COCKBURN (C.)

Agniashvili. [National tales. *In Georgian.* Coll. by A. Bk. 1. P2806]. s8º. [Tiflis. 1890]

Agop (Joannes).
Gramm. Latina Armenice expl. s4º. Romæ. 1675
Puritas Haygica; seu, gramm. Armenica. s4º. Romæ. 1675

Agostini (Alberto M. de). I miei viaggi n. Terra del Fuoco. [*Plates b. separately*]. 4º. Torino. [1923]

Agostino, *di Duccio, see* DUCCIO (AGOSTINO DI).

Agostino (Erminia dell'), *see* DELL' AGOSTINO (E.)

Agoult (*la comtesse* Maria C. S. d'). Mémoires, 1833–54. Intr. de D. Ollivier. s8º. [1927]

Agra & Oudh, *United Provinces of.* Gen. rep. on public instruction in U. P. of A. & O. for year ending 31st March 1919, 1920, 1922, 1924. fol. Allahabad. 1919–24
Hist. of services of gazetted officers attached to U. P. Corr. up to 1st July 1920–27. [1920–22, *2p. to each year*; 1923–25, *7p. to each year*; 1926–27, *12p. to each year. p8 wanting*]. 8º. Allahabad [*&* Calcutta]. 1920–27
Rep. on admin. of U. P. of A. & O., 1919/20–1925/26. fol. & 8º. Allahabad *&* Lucknow. 1921–27
The U. P. Code, w. chronol. table & index. 5th ed. 3v. la8º. Calcutta. 1922

Agreda (Marie de) [†MARIA FERNANDEZ CORONEL, *de Agreda*]. La Cité mystique de Dieu. Vie de la Vierge Marie révélée par elle-même à M. de A. Tr. par Croset. 2e éd. rev. & corr. 6t. s8º. 1862
Vie divine de la V. M.; abrégé de La Cité Myst. par B. A. de Cæsare. Tr. J.-A. Boullan. 7e éd. s8º. 1884

Agreement. *Agreement betw. the present & former gov.: or, a disc. of this monarchy, 1689, *see* FULLWOOD (F.)

Agricol (Magne), *ps., see* HAITZE (P. J. DE).

Agricola (Daniel). Passio Domini nostri J. Christi secundum seriem quattuor evangelist. &c. [*Precd. by* Directorium in dū. pass. articulos, 1513; *b. w.* POSTILLÆ. Postille majores &c., 1514]. s4º. [Basileæ. A. P. de Langendorff. 1514]

Agricola (Georgius), *the elder, see* DARMSTÆDER (E.) G. A., 1494–1555, 1926.

Agricola (Germanus). Die sittl. Staatsidee im Wirtschaftsleben. la8º. München. 1924

Agricola (Gnæus Julius), *see* MOTHERSOLE (J.) A.'s road into Scotland, 1927.

Agricola (Ignatius). Historia prov. Soc. Jesu Germaniæ super (1541–1640). 5p. fol. Augustæ Vindel. 1727–54
Only p1, 2 (1727–29) *by* I. Agricola; p3 *by* A. Flotto; p4 & 5 *by* F. X. Kropf; *& a section of* p5 *by* P. Weitenauer; p3–5 *wanting.*

Agricola (Johann), *of Eisleben, see* ELWERT (E.) De antinomia I. A., 1836.
see WEWETZER (A.) De Antinomismo J. A., diss. 1829.
„ WITZEL (G.) Acta v.d. vergebung d. Sunden, 1537.

Agricola (Martin). Musica instrument. deudsch, 1528 u. 1545, z. Teil facs. A. [Gesellsch. f. Musikforsch., Publ. 20]. 8º. L. 1896

Agricola (Michael), *bp. of Åbo.* Käsikirja & messu. Julkaisseet E. N. Setälä & K. B. Wiklund. [Mon. ling. Fennicæ, 1]. la8º. Helsingissä. 1893

Agricola (Theophilus), *ps.* [*i.e.* GEORG MAYER ?] Kurtze antwurt auff das Büchlein so Mathias Flacius Illyricus wider Caspar Schwenckfeldt hat inn Druckh lassen ausgehn. s4º. [Augsburg ?] 1556

Agricultural. *Agricult. co-op. in its applic. to the farmer in Brit. Emp. [Survey, ed. K. Walter.] Intr. by Sir H. Plunkett. 8º. 1925
Agricult. research in 1925, 1926, *see* ROYAL AGRIC. SOC.

Agricultural & Horticultural Society of India.
Transactions. v1. 8º. Serampore. 1829

Agricultural Economics Research Institute, *Oxford, see* FITZ-RANDOLPH (H. E.) & M. D. HAY. Rural indust. of Eng. & Wales; survey on behalf of A.E.R.I., 3v, 1926–27.

Agricultural journal of India (The).
v14, 15, 17–19 (1919, 20, 22–24). la8º. Calcutta. 1919–24

Agricultural journal of the Union of S. Africa, Feb. 1911–Aug. 1914, *see* AFRICA: UNION OF S.A. Journal of Dept. of Agric.

Agricultural Research Institute, *Pusa.* Bulletin Nos. 44–153 [Nos. 64, 72, 76, 77, 80, 86, 90, 92, 95, 98, 99, 120, 121, 129 & 135 *wanting*]. la8º. 1915–24
Previous Nos. possessed by the Library have been catalogued separately. See references in Supplement, 1913–20.
Scientific reports, 1919/20–1923/24. la8º. Calcutta. 1920–24

Agrippa (Henricus Cornelius).
De incertitudine & vanitate scientiarū & artium declamatio. s8º. apud Antverpiam. 1531
„ „ denuo ab autore recogn. & aucta. s8º. *n.p.* 1544
In Artem brevem R. Lullii comm. s8º. Coloniæ. 1533

Agronomes. Agronomes (Les) latins: Caton, Varron, Columelle, Palladius avec la tr. en Fr. [*by — Antoine*]; publ. sous la dir. de M. Nisard. [*Lat. & Fr.*] la8º. 1877

Agrûmyja masry maktûba bil lisân el masry we ma'ha amsila. 8º. Felôrensa. 1904

Aguado Bleye (Pedro).
Manual de hist. de España. 2a ed., aument. 2t. 8º. Bilbao. 1918
„ „ ....3a ed. t1. 8º. Bilbao. 1922

Aguilar (Grace). The days of Bruce. s8º. *n.d.*

Aguilar y Cuadrado (Rafael). La Catedral de Sigüenza. [*Text in Span., Fr. & Eng.*] s8º. Barcelona. [1927 ?]
Guadalajara-Alcalá de Henares. [Art in Spain, 2. Hisp. Soc. of Amer.] s8º. Barcelona. *n.d.*

Aguilera y López (José).
Col. de poesías sel. castellanas. 8a ed. s8º. Granada. 1901

Aguilo (Juan Cabre), *see* CABRE AGUILO (J.)

Aguirre (Domingo de). Tratado hist.-legal d. Real Palacio ant. y su quarto nuevo de Barcelona. [*Folld. by h.* Discursus super officiis &c. *w. sep. pagin.*] fol. Vienna de Austria. 1725

Aguirre (Francesco de), *see* LATTES (A.) F. de A. e S. Maffei, 1909.

Aharon, *see* AARON.

Aharonian (Avetis). Dans les ténèbres: nouvelle, *see* ŒUVRES LIBRES, 50, 1925.

Ahasuerus, *the wandering Jew, see* JEW. *Kurtze beschreibung &c. v. e. Juden mit Namen A. 1602, 1925.

Ahikar. The story of A. f. the Syriac, Arab., Arm., Ethiopic, O. Turk., Gk. & Slav. versions. By F. C. Conybeare, J. R. Harris, A. S. Lewis. 2nd ed. enl. 8º. C. 1913
see DASHEAN (H.) Sh. bibliog. sts. &c., *in Armenian,* v2, 1901.
„ NÖLDEKE (T.) Untersuch. z. Achiqar-Roman, 1913.
„ REINACH (T.) Un conte babylonien dans le litt. juive: le roman d'A., 1899.

Ahlgren (Ernst).
Samlade skrifter. 6b. s8º. [1918–20]
1, Från Skåne—Folkliv och småberättelser, 4e uppl.
2, Berättelser och utkast—Efterskörd, 4e uppl.
3, Pengar, 6e uppl. 4, Fru Marianne, 6e uppl.
5, Moderd, av E. A. & A. Lundegård, 4e uppl.
6, Dramatik, av E. A. & A. Lundegård.
7, Studier och brottstycken, utg. av A. Lundegård.

Ahlqvist (August Engelbrekt). Die Kulturwörter d. westfinn. Sprachen. [Forsch. aus d. Gebiete d. ural-alta. Spr., T2]. Deut. umgearb. A. 8º. Helsingfors. 1875

Aḥmad *al-Wanscharīsī.* La pierre de touche des fétwas: choix de consultations jurid. des faqîhs du Maghreb, 2t, *see* MISSION SCIENT. DU MAROC. Archives, v12, 13, 1908–9.

Aḥmad b. Muḥammad al-Ğarādī, *see* BURCHARDT (H.) Aus d. Jemen: B.'s letzte Reise durch Südarabien; [*wr. in Arabic by* A. b. M.]; bearb. [*w. Germ. tr.*] v. E. Mittwoch, 1926.

Aḥmad Djemal *Pasha.*
Mem. of a Turkish statesman, 1913–1919. 8°. [1922]

Aḥmad Emin, *see* EMIN (AHMED).

Aḥmad ibn 'Abdallah. [AHMET BEN-ABDALA]. Epist. theol. de libero arbitrio ad Dn. de Aquila scr. Ed. &c. à Z. Grapio. Annexæ 2 disput. &c. [P2671]. s4°. Rostochii. *n.d.*

Aḥmad ibn 'Abd Allāh, *al-Ḳalkashandī, called Ibn Abī Ghuddah, see* GAUDEFROY-DEMOMBYNES (M.) La Syrie à l'époque des Mamelouks d'ap. les a[s]. arabes [*i.e.* Qalqachandi &c.], 1923.

Aḥmad ibn Fartua, *Iman.* Hist. of first 12 years of the reign of Mai Idris Alooma of Bornu (1571–83), w. the "Diwan of the Sultans of Bornu" & "Girgam" of the Magumi. Tr. w. intr. & notes by H. R. Palmer. 8°. Lagos. 1926

Aḥmad ibn Fudhlān [IBN FOSZLAN]. Ibn-Foszlan's u. a. Araber Berichte ü. die Russen ält. Zeit. Text u. Übers. &c.; nebst 3 Beilagen v. C. M. Frähn. [Kais. Akad. d. Wiss.] 4°. S[t].P. 1823

Aḥmad ibn Ḥusain (Abū al-Jaiyib) *called al-Mutanabbi.* Montenebbi, d. grösste arab. Dichter. Übers. v. J. von Hammer. 8°. Wien. 1824

Aḥmad ibn Khālid [AḤMED BEN KHÂLÉD ENNÊṢIRI ESSLÂOUI]. Kitab elistiqṣa &c. pl, 2, 4ii; tr. E. Fumey, A. Graulle &c., *see* MISSION SCIENT. DU MAROC. Archives, t10, 30, 31, 1907.

Aḥmad ibn Muḥammad, *al-Yamanī, al-Shirwānī.* Nafḥat[u] l'-Yaman: "Breezes f. Yemen." [Arabic stories &c.] Tr., w. philol. & crit. notes by D. C. Phillott. pl. 8°. Calcutta. 1907

Aḥmad ibn Muḥammad al-Yaqouby (Abu'l Abbas) *al-Malouy.* Touḥfat al-Qouḍḍât [*text & tr.*], *see* MISSION SCIENT. DU MAROC. Archives, v15, 1909.

Aḥmad ibn 'Umar, *Niẓāmī, 'Arūzī, of Samarkand* [NIDHÁMÍ-I-'ARÚDÍ]. The Chahár Maqála ("four discourses"). Tr. by E. G. Browne. [*Repr. f.* Journal of R.A.S., 1899]. 8°. Hertford. 1899

Aḥmad ibn Yaḥyā, *al-Balāḏurī* [AḤMAD IBN JĀBIR]. Origins of the Islamic state; tr., w. notes of Kitâb Futûh al-Buldân of al-Balâdhuri, by F. C. Murgotten. [Columbia Univ. St[s]. in hist. &c., 68]. p2, 8°. N.Y. 1924

Aḥmad ibn Yaḥyā, *called Ibn Faḍl Allāh, al-'Umari, see* IBN FADL ALLAH, *al-'Umari.*

Ahmad Rustem *Bey.* [AHMED RUSTEM *Bey*].
The World War & Turco-Armenian q. s8°. [Berne]. *n.d.*

Aḥmad Tambi Marakkayar, *Muhi-ud-Din, see* MARJORIBANKS (N.E.) & A.T.M. Rep. on Indian labour emigr. to Ceylon & Malaya, 1917.

Aḥmad Vetik.
[Turkish lexicon. *In Turkish*]. 8°. [1293=1876]

Ahmed, *see* AHMAD.

Aho (Juhani), *ps.* [*i.e.* JUHANI BROFELDT].
Domen. Skådespel. Öfvers. af H. Nohrström. s8°. Helsingfors. [1908]
Hafnet i lugn. Spånor 5. Öfvers. af E. Snellman. s8°. Helsingfors. [1912]
Om jaktområden och jaktvård. [P2427]. s8°. Helsingfors. [1902]
Schweres Blut. Roman. [Uebertr. G. Schmidt]. s8°. Dresden. [1920]

Aicard (Jean). Le rire de Maurin des Maures. s8°. [1923]

Aichel (Otto). Kausale St. z. ontogenet. &c. Geschehen am Kiefer, *see* KÖN.-PREUSS. AKAD. Abh., Phys.-math. Klasse, 1918.

Aide-mémoire. Aide-mémoire to milit. sc. Ed. by a Comm. of the Corps of R.E. [*i.e.* G. G. Lewis &c]. 2nd ed., corr. la8°. 1853–62

Aigrain (R.), *see* BAUDRILLART (A.), A. VOGT &c. Dict. d'hist. & de géog. ecclés.; publ. sous la dir. de A. B. &c., t3, 1924.

Aigrefeuille (Charles d'). Hist. de Montpellier. n. éd., publ. M. de La Pijardière. [Soc. des Bibl. Languedociens]. 4t. 4°. Montpellier. 1875–82

Aigremont (Maugis d'), *see* MAUGIS *d' Aigremont.*

Aikhenvald (Yuly Isævich).
Двѣ жены, Толстая и Достоевская. Матеріалы Комм. А. 8°. Берлинъ. 1925
Силуэты рус. писателей. t2, 3, нов. литература. (2, изд. 5[oe]; 3, изд. 4[oe]). 8°. Берлин. 1923
Этюды о западныхъ писателяхъ. la8°. Москва. 1910

Aikin (Edmund). Designs for villas & o. rural bldgs., w. intr. essay. 4°. 1808

Aikin (John), *M.D.* *The woodland companion; or, a descr. of Brit. trees. 3rd ed. corr. s8°. 1820

—— & Mrs. Barbauld.
Evenings at home. 10th ed. 6v. s8°. 1814

Aikin (William A.) Eng. vowel-sounds. Intr. by R. Bridges. H. W. Fowler on 'ing.' [S.P.E. Tract, 26]. 8°. O. 1927
The voice. 8°. 1920

Aikman (Henry G.), *ps.* [*i.e.* HAROLD HUNTER ARMSTRONG]. Zell. s8°. [1921]

Aikman (James). An hist. acc. of covenanting in Scotland, 1556 to 1638. 8°. E. 1848

Ailred, *see* ÆLRED.

Aimé-Martin (Louis), *ed.*, *see* JESUITS. Lettres édif. & cur. conc. l'Asie &c., 4t, 1838–43.

Aimery (Christiane). Le masque du devoir. Roman. s8°. 1923

Aimoinus, *monach. Floriac.*, *see* LABBE (P.) De script. eccles. quos attigit R. Bellarminus dissert., t2, Diatriba de A., 1660.

Ainslie (Douglas).
Adventure, social & literary. 8°. [1922]
The song of the Stewarts. Prelude. 8°. E. 1909

Ainslie (James Robert). Physiography of S. Nigeria & forest flora. [Oxford Forestry Mem., 5]. la8°. O. 1926

Ainsworth (Henry). The communion of saints. s8°. 1641

Ainsworth (Robert). The most nat. & easy way of institution, domestic educ. &c. 2nd ed. [P2668]. 8°. 1736

Ainsworth (William Harrison).
Guy Fawkes. Ill. by G. Cruikshank. 8°. *n.d.*
Mervyn Clitheroe. n. ed. s8°. 1865
The Star-Chamber. s8°. *n.d.*
The Tower of London. 8°. [1840]

Ainsworth-Davis (James Richard). Crops & fruits. Intr[s]. by Sir E. Geddes & S. Machin. [Resources of the Emp., v1i]. 4°. 1924
Meat, fish, & dairy produce. Intr. by Sir G. Campbell. [Resources of the Emp., v1ii]. 4°. 1924
Principles of agriculture. s8°. [1924]

Ainu. Uwepekere, A. stories tr. w. text, 1924, *see* BATCHELOR (J.)

Air Ministry.
King's regul. & Air Co. instructions for R.A.F. 2v. 8°. 1924
The R.A.F. as a career. [Air publ. 1100]. 8°. 1925

Aird (Gustavus). *Genealogy of the fam. of Douglas of Mulderg & Robertson of Kindeace. 8°. Dingwall. 1895

Airlie, *The house of, see* WILSON (W.) House of A., 2v, 1924.

Airlie (David Ogilvy, *6th earl*), *see* OGILVY (D.)

Airlie (Mabell, *countess of*). In Whig society, 1775–1818. Comp. f. corr. of Eliz., Vtess. Melbourne & Emily Lamb, Ctess. Cowper, aft. Vtess. Palmerston 8°. 1921
Lady Palmerston & her times. 2v. 8°. 1922

Airy (*Sir* **George Biddell).** Acc. of the Northumberland equatoreal & dome, Cambridge Observatory. 4°. C. 1844

Aiston (G.), *see* HORNE (G.) & G. A. Savage life in C. Australia, 1924.

Aita (Antonio). Retratos imaginarios. s8°. Buenos Aires. 1917

Aitchison (George). Unknown Brighton. 8°. [1926]

Aitchison (Leslie). Engineering steels. 8°. 1921

Aitken (Edward Hamilton) [*ps.* EHA], *see* SCINDE. Gazetteer, vol. A; comp. by E. H. A., 1907.

Aiton (Arthur Scott). Antonio de Mendoza, 1st viceroy of New Spain. 8°. Durham, *Carolina.* 1927

Aix de La Chaise (François d'), *see* LE NOBLE (P.) *Hist. du père La C., 2p, 1719.
see PETRE (E.) Antwort an Pater la Chaisen, 1688.

Aix-en-Provence. *Aix anc. & mod., descr., préc. de l'hist. [*by* J. F. P****]. 2e éd. s8°. Aix. 1833
Musée d'Aix, pl, Mon[s]. archéol., sculptures & objets de curiosité, par H. Gibert. s8°. Aix. 1882
Recueil des historiens de la France, Pouillés, t8, Prov[s]. d'A. &c., 1923, *see* RECUEIL.

Aiyar (R. Sathyanatha). Hist. of the Nayaks of Madura. Ed. w. intr. & notes by S. K. Aiyangar. 8°. [Madras]. 1924

Aizman (David Yakoblevich).
Ледоходъ, *see* SBORNIK. Сб. товар. "Знаніе," 5, 1905.

Ajalbert (Jean). Le bouquet de Beauvais, ou 2 années à la manufacture nat. de tapisseries (1917–19). s8°. [1921]
Dix années à Malmaison, 1907–17. Préf de L. Bérard. s8°. 1920

Ajbar machmuâ (col. de tradiciones). Crónica anón del s. XI. Tr. y anot. por E. Lafuente y Alcántara [*w. text*]. [R. Acad. de la Hist. Col. de obras aráb. de hist. &c., t1]. la8°. 1867

Ajmere-Merwara. Rep. on admin. of A.-M., 1917/18—1923/24. fol. Calcutta. 1919–25

Ajtay (Jozsef).
A választási reform. [P2393]. 8°. Budapest. 1908
——, **B. Jancsó & A. Kovács.** The Transylvanian q. [East Europ. problems. No. 15–18. P2567]. s8°. 1921

Akbar, *emperor of Hindustan, see* Du Jarric (P.) A. & the Jesuits: missions to A.; tr. &c. C. H. Payne, 1926.

Akeley (Carl Ethan). In brightest Africa. 8°. 1924

Akenside (Mark).
Poet. works. Collated by T. Park. 2v. s8°. 1805
" " [Life by A. Dyce. Aldine ed.] s8°. 1886
see Williams (I. A.) 7 18th cent. bibliogs., M. A. &c., 1924.

Akerman (John Yonge) [*ps.* Paul Pindar].
Wiltshire tales. s8°. 1853

Akhmatova (Anna). Anno Domini 1921. s8°. Petropolis. 1921
Бѣлая стая. Стихотворенія. s8°. П. 1917
Forty-seven love poems. Tr. N. Duddington. 8°. 1927
У самого моря. s8°. П. 1921
Четки, стихи. s8°. Берлинъ. [1921]

Akhnaton, *k. of Egypt, see* Bissing (F. W. v.) Denkmäler d. Kunst Amenophis IV, 1914.
see Weigall (A. E. P.) Life & times of A., n. & rev. ed., 1922.

Akhsharumov (Dmitry Dmitrievich), *1823–1910.*
Изъ моихъ воспоминаній (1849–51). 8°. С.-П. 1905

Akimov (Vladimir Petrovich) [Makhnovets (V. P.)].
Мат. для характ. развитія Р. Соц.-дем. Р. П. [P2715]. s8°. Женева. 1905

Akinean (Nerses) [Cyrion, catholikos of Georgia (574–610). *In Armenian*]. s8°. Vienna. 1910
Timotheos Kouz (*Ælurus*). [*With app.* Timotheos I of Alexandria. *In Armenian.* P2809]. s8°. Vienna. 1909

Akins (Thomas B.), *ed., see* Nova Scotia. *Sels. f. publ. docs., 1869.

Akkar, *ps., see* Racca (C.)

Aksakov (Konstantin Sergeevich).
О русскихъ глаголахъ. [P2399]. la8°. Москва. 1855

Aksakov (Sergyei Timofeevich).
Собраніе сочиненій 6t. [t2 *wanting*]. 8°. Москва. 1902–13
Chron. of a Russian family. Tr. M. C. Beverley. Intr. by Prince Mirsky. 8°. [1924]
A Russian gentleman. Tr. J. D. Duff. s8°. [1923]
A Russian schoolboy. Tr. J. D. Duff. s8°. [1924]

Akselrod (Pavel Borisovich).
Красное знамя въ Россіи. [P2716]. s8°. Женева. 1900
Къ вопросу о соврем. задъчахъ и тактикѣ русск. соц.-демократовъ. [P2716]. s8°. Женева. 1898

Akten z. Gesch. d. bair. Bauernaufstandes, 1705–6, 3T, 1912–15, *see* Riezler (S.) & C. v. Wallmenich.

Akuraters (Jānis) [Akurater].
Novellen. [Lett. Lit., B4]. 8°. Riga. [1921]
see Blaumanis (R.). Builders of new Rome & o. Lettish tales; [*by*] R. B., J. A. &c.; tr., 1924.

Alacoque (Marguerite Marie) [Al-Coq]. *see* Bougaud (E.) Revels. of the sacred heart to M. M. & hist. of h. life; tr., 2nd., 1890.

Ála flekks saga, *see* Lygisǫgur. Drei l.; hrsg. A. Lagerholm, 1927.

Alagona (Petrus).
Theologicæ summæ comp. s8°. Herbipoli. 1620

Alain, *ps., see* Chartier (E.)

Alais [Alez]. Iugement & canon. Avec le serment d'approb. du synode nat. des églises reformées de France tenu à Alez és Cevennes, Oct. 1620, du synode tenu à Dordrecht 1618–19. s4°. Amsterdam. 1621

Alamán (Lucas). Hist de Méjico desde 1808. 2p *in* 5t [li–iv]. 8°. Méjico. 1849–52
see Peña y Reyes (A. de la) L. A., 1924.

Alamanni (Antonio), *1460–1528.* Sonetti, *see* Burchiello, *ps.* I sonetti del B. &c., 1552.

Alamanni (Luigi), *the elder, 1495–1556.*
La coltivazione. s8°. London. 1780
Opere toscane. [Elegie, Egloghe, sonetti, Favole &c.] s8°. Lugd. *Gryphius.* 1532

Åland. *(The) Åland q. & rights of Finland. Mem. by Finnish jurists [P2518]. la8°. Helsingfors. 1920
Convention rel. à la non-fortific. & à la neutralis. des Iles d'A. [*No tp.* P2687]. fol. *n.p.* [1921]

Alander (Pehr Gustaf). De relig. Xtna in Vestrogotiam intro-ducta. Disq. Pars prior. s4°. Upsaliæ. [1839]

Alano (*il card.* **Guglielmo**), *see* Allen (W.) *card.*

Alanus, *de Insulis.* "*Doctor Universalis*" [Alanus *Autisio-dorensis*]. Opere moralia &c.; Opera et studio. C. de Visch. fol. Antverpiae. 1654
Regulæ de sacra theologia, *see* Mingarelli (G. L.) Anec-dotorum fasc., 1756.

Alarcos, *Count.* Romance del conde A., c. 1520. With intr. & var. readings, ed. H. Thomas [Early Span. ballads in B.M, 2]. 8°. 1927

Alas (Leopoldo), [*ps.* Clarin].
El señor y lo demás, son cuentos. s8°. *n.d.*

Al-Asha, *see* Maimun ibn Kais.

Alaska. S.-E. A. pilot *&* Suppl. 1, 1920–21, *see* Admiralty.

Alazard (Jean).
L'abbé L. Strozzi, corr. artist. de Mazarin &c. 8°. 1924
Pérugin. Biog. crit. [Les gr. artistes]. 8°. 1927

Alba (Carlos Maria Fitz-James Stuart y Portocarrero, *16th duke* **de),** *9th duke of Berwick.* Cat. de las col. del Palacio de Liria. Publ. la Duquesa de A. la8°. 1898

Alba (Jacobo Stuart Fitz-James, *17th duke* **de),** *10th duke of Berwick.*
Cat. de la col. de pinturas del Duque. Por A. M. de Barcia. sm. fol. 1911
Cat. de las miniaturas y pequeños retratos pert. al Duque. Por J. Ezquerra del Bayo. 4p. 1924
Discurso. [Docs. y notas. Contestacion d. Conde de Romanones. Real Acad. de Bellas Artes de S. Fernando]. [*& o. papers*]. la8°. 1924
El Mariscal de Berwick: bos-quejo biog. la8°. 1925
Noticias hist. y geneal. de los estados de Montijo y Teba. Publ. A. la8°. 1915
see Fuensalida (G. G. de). Corr. de F., embaj. en Alemania &c., 1496–1509; publ. A., 1907.

Alba (María del Pilar Teresa Cayetana de Silva Alvarez de Toledo, *duchess* **de),** *see* Ezquerra del Bayo (J.), La Duquesa de A. y Goya, 1928.

Alba (Maria del Rosario, *duchess* **de),** *wife of 16th Duke, see* Alba (C. M. F. S. y P., *16th Duke*). Cat. de las col. del Palacio de Liria, publ la Duquesa, 1898.
see Columbus (C.) Nuevas autogr. de C. Colon; publ. la Duq. de Berwick y de A., 1902.

Al-Baghdādī, *see* Abū-Manṣūr 'Abd-al-Kāhir ibn-Ṭāhir.

Albalat (Antoine). L'art d'écrire. 6e éd. 8°. 1900
Formation du style. 2e éd. s8°. 1902
Souvs. de la vie litt. n. éd., augm. s8°. 1924

Alban, *Saint & martyr, see* Edward, *the Confessor.* La estoire de St. Ædward, w. MS. of The life of St. A.; intr. by M. R. James, 1920.

Albanaise. *Gramm. albanaise. Par. P. W. [Trübner's Coll.] 8°. London. 1887

Albanès (*l'abbé* **Joseph Hyacinthe).** Gallia christiana novis-sima. Hist. des archevêchés, évêchés & abbayes de France. Accomp. des doc. rec. dans les registres du Vatican &c. Compl. &c. par U. Chevalier.
t1–7. 4°. 1, Montbéliard, 2–7, Valence. 1899–1920
1, Aix, Apt, Fréjus, Gap, Riez & Sisteron [*& Instrumenta w. sep. pagin.*], 1899.
2, Marseille (évêques, prévots, statuts), 1899.
3, Arles (Archevêques, conciles, prévots, statuts), 1900.
4, Saint-Paul-Trois-Châteaux (évêques, prévots), 1909.
5, Toulon (évêques, prévots), 1911.
6, Orange (évêques, prévots), 1916.
7, Avignon (évêques, archevêques, prévots), 1920.

Albanese (Domenico Tommaso), *see* Marciano (G.) Descr. d. prov. d'Otranto; con aggiunte del D. T. A., 1855.

Albanesi (*Mme.* **E. Maria).** The white in the black. s8°. [1926]

Albani (*card.* **Annibale),** *bp. of Sabina, see* Menologion. Menol. Græc. &c.; st. &c. A. A. &c., 3p, 1727.

Albania. A hdbk. of Serbia, A. &c., 1920, *see* Admiralty.

Albano (Joseph). Four sonnets w. Portug. prose-tr. [P2520]. 8°. Fortalexiæ. 1918

Albany, *London.* A hist. of A., 1920, *see* Civis, *ps.*

Albany, *New York.* Proc. at laying of stone of New Capitol, 24th June 1871. 8°. Albany. 1871

Albany (Helen, *duchess of*). Partics., plan &c. of the estate Claremont, seat of Duchess of A. Sale by Knight, Frank & Rutley, 27th July 1922. fol. 1922

Albarracin. Carta de poblacion de la ciudad S. Maria de A.; Riba y Garcia, *see* Coleccion de docs. para el est. de la hist. de Aragon, t10, 1915.

Albaspinæus (Gabriel), *bp. of Orleans, see* L'Aubespine (G. de).

Albee (John). Remembrances of Emerson. 8°. 1903

Albemarle (Isabella, *ctss. of*), *see* Isabella, *de Fortibus.*

Alber (Erasmus) [†ALBERUS (ERASMUS)]. Vom Underscheid der Evangel. u. Papist. Mess &c. s4°. *n.p.* [1539]
see KÖRNER (E.) E. A.: d. Kämpferleben e. Gottesgelehrten aus Luthers Schule, 1910.
Albericus, *Monachus Casinensis, the younger.* Storia d. visione del mon. A.; pubbl. e tr., *see* CANCELLIERI (F.) Osserv. &c., s. l'origin. d. Div. Comm., 1814.
Albert, *cardinal, archduke of Austria, governor of the Netherlands. see* BELGIQUE. Jurisprudentia heroica, demonstr. in comm. ad. edictum Pr. A. &c. emulgat. 1616, 1668.
,, HAUTECLOCQUE (*le cte.* G. DE). Arras &c. s. A. &c., 1873.
Albert I, *duke of Bavaria.* De oorlogen van A. met de Friezen in de laaste jaren der 14e eeuw. Naar onuitg. bescheiden door E. Verwijs. [Hist. Genoots. te Utrecht. Werken, N.S., 8]. 8°. Utrecht. 1869
Albert V, *duke of Bavaria, see* HARTIG (O.) Die Gründung d. Münchener Hofbibl. durch Albrecht V &c., 1917.
Albert, *king of the Belgians, see* BEYENS (*le b.* E.) Le roi Albert, 1919.
Albert, *of Bohemia, see* LEIDINGER (G.) Untersuch. z. Passauer Geschichtschreibung, 1915.
Albert III, *bp. of Halberstadt, c.* 1316–90 [ALBERT *von Sachsen*; *A. v. Rückmarsdorf*], *see* HEIDINGSFELDER (G.) A. v. Sachsen, s. Lebensgang u. s. Komm. z. Nikomach. Ethik d. Aristotles, 1921.
Albert, *abp. of Magdeburg* [*A. of Brandenburg*], *see* LUTHER (M.) An den durchleucht. Fürsten &c. A., 1532.
Albert, *abp. of Magdeburg, abp.-elector of Mainz, Cardinal, see* MENNEL (J.) De inclito actu eccl. Aug. celebrato 1518 [*at install. of A., as a Cardinal*], 1518.
Albert I, *prince of Monaco.* Coll. de doc^s. hist. [*&* Mem^s.] publ. par ordre de le Pr. A. de M.
see FONTENAY LE MARMION. Cartulaire; publ. G. Saige, 1895.
,, LABANDE (L. H.) Avignon au 15e siècle, 1920.
,, MONACO. Inventaires du Palais de M., 1604–1731; publ. &c. par L. H. Labande, 1918.
,, SAINT-PONS. Chartrier de l'abbaye de St.-P., 1913.
see INSTITUT DE PALÉONTOLOGIE HUMAINE. Fondation A. I.
Albert, *duke of Prussia, Grand Master of the Teutonic Order.* Bekenntnisschr.; hrsg. F. Spitta., *see* ARCHIV F. REFORMATIONSGESCH., Jhrg. 6, 1909.
see TSCHACKERT (P.) Herzog A. v. P. als reform. Persönlichkeit, 1894.
Albert, *king of Saxony, see* JOHN GEORGE, *Duke of Saxony.* König A. v. Sachsen, 1922.
Albert Frederick Arthur George, *duke of York, see* NEW ZEALAND. Royalty in N.Z.: visit of T.R.H. the Duke & Duchess of Y., 1927.
Albert (Edward). Kirk o' Field. s8°. [1925]
Albert (F. R.) Der Briefwechsel H. v. Einsiedel mit Luther, Melanchthon, Spalatin &c. Aus Hss. dargestellt v. F.R.A. [Quellen &c. aus d. Gesch. d. Reformationsjhdts., B7]. 8°. L. 1908
Albert (Honoré T. P. J. d'), *duc de Luynes, see* LUYNES.
Albert (Peter Paul). Achthundert Jahre Freiburg im Breisgau, 1120–1920. 4°. Freiburg im Br. 1920
Der Meister E. S., s. Name, s. Heimat u. s. Ende: Funde u. Vermutungen. la8°. Str. 1911
see BEYERLE (K.) Kultur d. Abtei Reichenau [v. P. P. A. &c., hrsg. K. B.], 2 Halbb., 1925.
Albertanus, *Judex* [BRIXIENSIS], *see* BOSTOCK (J. K.) A. Brix. in Germany, 1924.
Albertazzi (Adolfo). Top. s8°. [1922]
Alberti (*gen.* **Adriano).** L'Italia e la fine d. Guerra Mondiale. p2 (Villa Giusti). [Min. d. Guerra]. la8°. 1924
Vittorio Veneto, p1, La lotta sul Grappa. Sunto estr. d. pubbl. L'It. e la fine d. Guerra. [Min. d. Guerra]. la8°. 1924
Alberti (Annibale) & R. Cessi. La politica mineraria d. Repubblica Veneta. [Minist. d. Econ. Naz.] 8°. 1927
Alberti (C. E. R.) H. Pestalozzi, *see* VIRCHOW (R.) & F. v. HOLTZENDORFF. Samml., H79, 1869.
Alberti (Fabio degli). De sacris utensilibus. fol. Romæ. 1783
Sacræ Rotæ Romanæ decisiones a F. de A. coll., 1783, *see* ROTA ROMANA.
Alberti (Girolamo). Dispacci al Senato Veneto 1673, matrimonio di M. B. E. d'Este con G. Stuart. [*Ed.* C. Soranzo & F. Silvestre. Nozze Lawley-Wiel. N122; 135]. 8°. Venezia. 1890
Alberti (Joannes). Periculum crit., in quo loca quædam cum Vet. ac Novi Fœderis, tum Hesychii & aliorum, illust. &c. s8°. Lugd. Batav. 1727
Alberti (Leon Battista). Congiura di S. Porcari; tr., *see* MANZI (G.) Testi, 1816.
see VENTURI (A.) L. B. A.: 26 riprod. con testo e cat., 1923.
Alberti (Valentin). Ausführl. Gegen-Antwort auff P. J. Speners Vertheid, s. u. d. Pietisten Unschuld. [P443]. s4°. L. 1696
Kurtz &c. Bedencken ü. 12 papist. Religions-Fragen &c. [*b. w.* Fecht (J.) Hist. Coll. Emmending., 1694]. s8°. L. [1693]
Kurtze Erinnerungen, betr. das Gespräch v. d. Relig. zweg geb. Lutheraner. [*b. w.* Fecht (J.) Hist. Coll. Emmending., 1694]. s8°. L. 1691
Alberti di Villanova (*il conte* **Francesco).** Grand dict. français-ital. [*&* ital.-fr.] 2^e ed. 2t. 4°. Milan. 1840–41
Nuovo dizion. portat. ital.-francese e fr.-ital. compend. da quello d'A. per G. Martinelli. 7a ed. riv. da M. Santagnello. s8°. Londra. 1853
Albertina. Doubletten d. Kupferstichsamml. A. in Wien. Eng. Schabkunstblätter d. 18. Jhdts. &c. Versteig. 20–22 Nov. 1923 [durch] Gilhofer & Ranschburg. 4°. Wien. [1923]
Französ. Kupferstiche d. 18. Jhdts. aus d. Dubletten d. Kupferstichsamml. A. in Wien &c. Versteig. 13–16 Nov. 1922 durch C. G. Boerner. 4°. L. [1922]
Handzeichnungen alter Meister aus d. A. u. aus Privatbesitz, N. F., 1922, *see* MEDER (J.)
Albertini (Eugène). La composition dans les ouvrages philos. de Sénèque. [Ecoles Franç. d'Athènes & de Rome, fasc. 127]. la8°. 1923
Les divisions admin. de l'Espagne romaine. 8°. 1923
Albertini (Luigi), *see* BIANCHI (A. G.) Il Senatore L. A., 191[illegible]
Albertinus (Arnaldus). Tractatus de agnoscendis assertionbus catholicis & hæreticis s4°. Venetris. 1571
Albertis (Fabius de), *see* ALBERTI (FABIO DEGLI).
Alberts (Wilhelm). Gustav Frenssen. 8°. 1922
Albertus, *Magnus, bp. of Ratisbon.* De animalibus lib. 26. Nach d. Cölner Urschrift. Hrsg. v. H. Stadler. [Beitr. z. Gesch. d. Phil. d. Ma., 16]. B2. Buch 13–26. 8°. Münster. 1920
Girg Eraneloyn A. [The Book of Albert, called Paradise of the soul. Tr. fr. Lat. into Armenian by Mkhithar Vardapet of Sebaste (Sivas)]. s8°. Venice. 1729
see STRUNZ (F.) A. M.: Weisheit u. Naturforsch. im M.-A., 1926.
Albery (William). A parliamentary hist. of Horsham, 1295–1885. Intr. by H. Belloc. 8°. 1927
Albini (Giuseppe), *see* DANTE ALIGHIERI. Lectura D., Il c. 20 del Paradiso letto da G. A., 1912.
Albion (Robert Greenhalgh). Forests & sea power: timber probl. of the R.N., 1652–1862. [Harvard Econ. St., 29]. 8°. Camb. [U.S.] 1926
Albizzi, *The family of, see* BROSCH (M.) A. u. Medici, 1908.
Albizzi (Antonio). Decem principia doctrinæ Christ. s8°. Campidoni. 1612
see VENETA. Squitinio d. liberta v. [*attr. to A.*], 1612.
Albo (Joseph), *see* JOSEPH, *Albo.*
Albon (*le marq.* **d').** Cartul. gén. de l'ordre du Temple, 1119?–50. Fasc. compl. cont. table &c. 4°. 1922.
Alborghetti (Gio. Jacopo) [*ps.* LOGILDO MEREO]. Le ingiuste gelosie, pastorale. [Nozze Caracciolo-Caracciolo]. [N125]. 8°. Nap. 1717
Serenata a 3 voci. [Nozze Pinto-Malaspina]. [N125]. 8°. *n.p.* [*c.* 1717]
Il trionfo d. grazia: drama sacro. [N125]. 8°. Piacenza. 1717
Albornotius (Ægidius), *card., abp. of Toledo.* Sel^s. f. Ordinances of A. (*tr.*), *see* EMERTON (E.) Humanism & tyranny, 1925.
Albornoz y Menduiña (Claudio Sánchez-), *see* SÁNCHEZ-ALBORNOZ Y MENDUIÑA (C.)
Albrecht (Arthur Emil). Internat. Seamen's Union of America, *see* UNITED STATES: LABOR, Bull. 342, 1923.
Albrecht (Gerhard), *see* GRUNDRISS D. SOZIALÖKONOMIK, Abt. 9, Soziale System d. Kapitalismus, T1, mit Beitr. v. G. A. &c., 1926.
Albrecht (Otto). Luthers Katechismen. [Verein f. Ref.-Gesch. Schr., Jhrg. 33 (Nr. 121/22)]. 8°. L. 1915
Albright (Evelyn May). Dramatic publication in Eng., 1580–1640. [Mod. Lang. Assoc. of Amer.] 8°. N.Y. 1927
Albright (W. F.) Excavations &c. at Tell el-Ful (Gibeah of Saul), *see* AMER. SCHOOLS OF OR. RESEARCH. Annual, v4, 1924.
Albrizzi (Giovanni Battista). Relaz. di Bergamo, 1745. Con note [*by* A. Marcello. Nozze Peregalli-Albrizzi. N123]. la8°. Venezia. 1856

Albucius (Aurelius) [ALBUZIO (A.)]. A. Alciati in Stellam & Longovalliũ defensio. [P2541]. s8°. Basileæ. 1529

Album. Album reprod. obrazów z wystawy w Pałacu Łazienkowskim, 1919, see WARSAW.

Album v. Autographen d. westphäl. Friedensschlusses, 1849, see WESTPHÄLISCH.

Albuquerque, *The family of*, see SANTA MARIA JABOATAM (A. de) Cat. gen. das princ. fams. proced. de A. &c., 1889.

Albus (Joannes Jacobus). Theses theolog. De syncera ac solida verbi Dei &c. interpret. [P2607]. s4°. Ingolstadii. 1588

Alcæus, *of Mitylene* [ALKÄOS]. Ἀλκαίου Μέλη. Fragm. of the lyrical poems. Ed. E. Lobel. 8°. O. 1927

see DIEHL (E.) Anthol. lyrica, v1, 1925.

„ „ Suppl. lyricum, 3e A., 1917.

„ DIELS (H.) De Alcæi voto, 1920.

„ LYRA Græca; ed. & tr. by J. M. Edmonds, v1, A. &c., 1922.

Alcais (Abel). Figures & récits de Carthage chrét., 2e & 3e siècles. s8°. 1908

Alcalà Galiano (Antonio), *1789–1865*. Memorias. Publ. por su hijo. 2t. 8°. 1886

Alcalde del Rio (H.), H. Breuil & L. Sierra. Les cavernes de la région Cantabrique (Espagne). [Peintures &c. des cavernes paléolith., publ. s. l. ausp. d'Albert I de Monaco]. fol. Monaco. 1911

Alcamenes, *Greek sculptor, fl. 5th cent. B.C.*, see WALDSTEIN (*Sir* C.) A. & the establ. of class. type in Gr. art, 1926.

Alcandre [*Attrib. formerly to the princesse de Conti, more recently to the duc de Bellegarde*].

*L'Alcandre ou les amours du roy Henry le Grand, par M.L.P.D.C., see HENRY III, *King of Fr.* Rec. de div. pièces, 1664.

Alcántara (Emilio Lafuente y), see LAFUENTE Y ALCÁNTARA (E.)

Alcázar (Baltasar del). Poesías. [Letras esp.; publ. J. Hurtado &c., 2]. s8°. [1925]

Alcazar (Ludovico ab). Vestigatio arcani sensus in Apocalypsi. Adj. opusc. de sacris ponderibus &c. [*w. sep. pagin.*] fol. Lugduni. 1618

Alcenius (Carolus Alexander). De scholis Fenniæ post reform. eccl. comm. s8°. Helsingforsiæ. 1848

—— **& August Schauman.** De scholis Fenniæ ante reform. eccl. Dissert. acad. p1–5 propon. C. A. A., A. S. [*& others*]. s4°. Helsingforsiæ. 1848–49

Alciatus (Andreas). De quinque pedum præscriptione liber unus. De magistratibus &c. liber unus. [P2541]. s8°. Lugdioni. 1529

Libellus de ponderibus & mensuris. Item Budæi quædam de eadem re.—Item P. Melanchthonis, de iisdem sententia. Alciati quoque & P. Melanchthonis in laudem juris civilis, orationes duæ. [P2541]. s8°. Haganoæ. 1530

see ALBUCIUS (A.) A. A. in Stellam & Longovallium defensio, 1529.

„ VIARD (P. E.) André Alciat, 1492–1550, 1926.

Alcibiades, see FRIEDLÄNDER (P.) Der grosse A.: e. Weg zu Plato, 2T, 1921–23.

Alcidamas [ALKIDAMAS]. A. contra dicendi magistros [*in Greek*], see ORATORES, Orationes horum rhetorum &c., p3, 1513.

Alcinous. Liber de doctrina Platonis, see IAMBLICHUS *of Chalcis.* De mysteriis &c., 1497.

Alciphron. A.: letters f. the country & the town &c. Tr. F. A. Wright, w. intr. & notes. [Broadway trs.] s8°. [1923]

Alcman [ALKMAN], see LYRA. Lyra Græca; ed. & tr. by J. M. Edmonds, v1, A. &c., 1922.

Alcocer y Martinez (Mariano). Anales universitarios. Hist. de la Univ. de Valladolid. 4t. la8°. Valladolid. 1918–22

1, Libro de Bezerro que compuso V. Velázquez de Figueroa (1757), con notas por M.A.M. Los estatutos en Latin tr. por F. Fernandez Moreno. Con introd. d. C. Valverde y Valverde, 1918.

2, Bulas apostól. y privilegios reales, transcr. y notas por M A.M., 1919.

3, Expedientes de provisiones de cátedras, orden. y anot. por M.A.M., 1921.

4, Hacienda univ. y jurisdicción del rector, por M.A.M., 1922.

Cat. razonado de obras impr. en Valladolid, 1481–1800. la8°. Valladolid. 1926

Alcock (Frederick James). Mt. Albert map-area. [Canada, Geolog. Survey]. 8°. Ottawa. 1926

Reed-Wekusko map-area, N. Manitoba. [Canada: Geol. Survey. P2512]. 8°. Ottawa. 1920

Alcock (*Sir* Rutherford), *K.T.S.* Notes on med. hist. & statistics of Brit. legion of Spain. 8°. 1838

Alcuin Club.

A. C. Collections. [v] 2–4, 18, 19, 23. *var. sizes.* 1899–1920

see DEARMER (P.) Illusts. of the Liturgy: drawings by C. O. Skilbeck &c., 1912. [19.]

„ FRERE (W. H.) Expos. de la Messe f. La Legende dorée of Jean de Vignay, 1899. [2.]

„ FRERE (W. H.) Pontifical services illust. f. miniatures of 15th & 16th cent., 2v, 1901. [3, 4.]

„ GRAHAM (R.), *ed.* Chantry certificates & Edwardian inventories for Oxfordshire, 1920. [23.]

„ RATIONALE of ceremonial, 1540–43; notes &c. by C. S. Cobb, 1910. [18.]

A. C. Tracts. [v] 6, 11, 15, 16. la8°. 1906–25

„ ATCHLEY (E. G. C. F.) The people's prayers: use of Litany, 1906. [6.]

„ BISHOP (W. C.) The Mozarabic & Ambrosian rites, 1924. [15.]

„ GASELEE (S.) The Uniats & th. rites, 1925. [16.]

„ WYATT (E. G. P.) English or Roman use? 1913. [11.]

Alcuinus [ALBINUS]. Epistolæ, see †DÜMMLER (E. L.), ed. Epist. Merow. et Karol. ævi, t4, 1925.

Opera de nova coll. &c. Cura & studio Frobenii. 2t *in* 3v. [t1 i, ii *b. sep.*; t2 i, ii *b. together*]. fol. mon. S. Emmerami typogr. 1777

see GRIEVE (A.) Willibrord, missionary, 691–739; incl. tr. of the Vita Willibrordi by A. of York, 1923.

„ LORENTZ (F.) Life of A.; tr., 1837.

Aldanov (M. A.), see LANDAU-ALDANOV.

Aldao (Eugenio Carré), see CARRÉ ALDAO (E.)

Aldborough. *Hist. of A. &c., 1853, see TURNER (T. S.)

Alden, *publishers.* Oxford guide. Enl. ed. s8°. O. 1905

Alden (Percy), see LABOUR & industry: lects. by P. A. &c., 1920.

Alder (Robert). Wesleyan missions. s8°. 1842

Alder (William Fisher). The isle of vanishing men: advents. in cannibal land. 8°. [1922]

Alderfirst of Ababrelton, *ps.* Britannia Magna. [P2846]. 8°. 1884

Alderman (H. M.) The charm of old Surrey. 8°. [1927]

Aldersey, *The family of*, see BRIDGEMAN (C. G. O.) Genealog. acc. of fam. of A. of Aldersey & Spurstow, Co. Chester, 1899.

Aldersmith (H.), see DAVIDSON (D.) & H. A. The Great Pyramid, v1, 1924.

Aldhelm, *St., bp. of Sherborn.* Opera. Ed. R. Ehwald. [Mon. Germ. Hist., A. a., t15]. 4°. Berolini. 1919

The riddles of A.: text & verse tr. &c. by J. H. Pitman. [Yale Sts. in English, 67]. 8°. New Haven. 1925

Aldington (Richard). A book of "Characters" f. Theophrastus, J. Hall, Sir T. Overbury, N. Breton &c. Compiled & tr. by R. A., w. intr. &c. [Broadway Trans.] 8°. [1924]

A fool i' the forest. A phantasmagoria. 8°. [1925]

French comedies of the 18th c. Regnard, The residuary legatee—Lesage, Turcaret &c.—Marivaux, The game of love &c.—Destouches, The conceited count. Tr. R. A., w. intr. &c. [Broadway Trs.] 8°. [1923]

French studies & reviews. 8°. [1926]

Voltaire. s8°. 1925

Aldini (*il conte* Antonio), see ZANOLINI (A.) A. A. ed i suoi tempi, v1, 1864.

Aldobrandini (Nicolò Papadopoli), see PAPADOPOLI (*il conte* N.)

Áldor (Imre). Dósa György s a parasztlázadás 1514–ben. [P2394]. s8°. 1899

Kossuth Lajos élete és pályája. 2lk kiadás. s8°. 1892

Aldrich (Annie Charlotte Catharine), see †CHILDAR (C.), *ps.*

Aldrich (John Merton), see VAN DUZEE (M. C.), F. R. COLE & J. M. A. The dipterous genus Dolichopus &c., 1921.

Aldrich (Loyal Blaine).

The melikeron, see SMITHSONIAN INST. Misc. coll., v72, 1922.

The reflecting power of clouds, 1919, see S. I. Misc. coll., v69, 1921.

The Smithsonian eclipse exped. of June 8, 1918, 1919, see S. I. Misc. coll., v69, 1921.

see S. I. Annals of Astrophys. Observ. of the S. I.; v4, by L. B. A. &c., 1922.

„ S. I. Distrib. of energy in the spectra of the sun & stars, by L. B. A. &c., 1923.

Aldrich (*Mrs.* Thomas Bailey), *form.* *Lilian Woodman.* Crowding memories. 8°. [1921]

Aldrich-Blake (*Dame* Louisa Brandreth), see RIDDELL (G. A. R., *1st b.*) Dame L. A.-B., 1926.

Aldridge (Henry R.) The national housing manual. 4°. 1923

Aldridge (William), *see* Holdsworth (W.) & W. Aldridge. Natural short-hand &c., 1768.
Aldrovandi (Ulisse), *see* Toni (G. B. de). Spigolature A., &c., 1922.
Aldwell (Samuel William Hemphill).
Wingfield. s4°. Ipswich. [1926]
Aleandro (*card.* **Girolamo),** *the elder, b. 1480.* Die Depeschen, d. A. vom Wormser Reichstage 1521. Übers. u. erläut. v. P. Kalkoff. [Verein f. Ref.-gesch. Schr., Jhrg. 4, Nr. 17]. 8°. Halle. 1886
Aleandro (Girolamo), *the younger, see* Peiresc (N. de). Corr. inéd. avec. A. &c., 1819.
Aleardi (Aleardo). Canti. 7ª ed. s8°. Firenze. 1889
Due lettere ined. [1857. *Facs.* Nozze Ridolfi-Benini. N123]. la8°. [Rovigo. 1886]
Alecis (Guillaume), *see* Cons (L.) L'auteur de la farce de Pathelin [? G. A.], 1926.
Aleïchem (Scholem). Le conseil, *see* Œuvres libres, 52, 1925.
Aleksandrov (Vladimir Stepanovich).
Народный писенныкъ зъ найкращихъ украин. писень. s8°. Харькивъ. 1887
Alekseev (Gleb).
Мертвый бѣгъ повѣсть. s8°. въ Берлинѣ. 1923
Alekseev (Konstantin S.), *see* Stanislavsky (K.), *ps.*
Alekseev (Petr Alekseevich).
Рѣчь. [P2716]. s8°. Женева. 1889
Aleman (Mateo). *Hist. de Guzman d'Alfarache. Tr. M. Lesage. 2t. s8°. Maestricht. 1787
The rogue, or, The life of Guzman de Alfarache. Done into Eng. by J. Mabbe, 1623. Intr. by J. Fitzmaurice-Kelly. [Tudor Trans., s2, v2–5]. 4v. s4°. 1924
Alemany Bolufer (José). Dicc. enciclop. ilust. de la lengua esp. Publ. J. A. B. [*2p. in 1v. sep. pagin.*] s8°. Barcelona. *n.d.*
La geografía de la península Ibérica en los escr. árabes. la8°. Granada. 1921
Tratado de la formación de palabras en la lengua castellana: la deriv. y la compos. 8°. 1920
Alembert (Jean le Rond d'). An acc. of the destruction of Jesuits in France. s8°. 1771
see Diderot (D.) Entretien entre D. & d'A., 1921.
Alencar Araripe (Tristão de). Exped. do Ceará em auxilio do Piauhi e Maranhão [1823], *see* Instituto Hist. e Geog. Brazil. Revista, t48, 1885.
Guerra civil do Rio-Grande do Sul, *see* Instituto Hist. e Geog. Brazil. Revista, t43, 45–47, 1880–84.
Alençon (Robert II, *seign.* **de),** *see* Robert II, *de Bellême.*
Alenda y Mira (Jenaro). Rel. de solemnidades y fiestas públ. de España. t1. la8°. 1903
Alenitsin (Vladimir Dmitrievich).
О путешествіи Дженкинсона въ Хиву. [I. R. G. O. Записки по отдѣл. этнограф., 6ii]. 8°. С.–П. 1880
Alenius (Carolus Gust. Bernh.) Diss. statum polit. & relig. in Lapponia Pitensi præs. delin. s4°. Aboæ. [1769]
Aleramo (Sibilla). Amo, dunque sono. 8°. Milano. 1927
Una donna. n. ed. s8°. Milano. 1919
Il passaggio. s8°. Milano. 1919
*S. Aleramo. [*By* ***. Uomini d. giorno, N44]. la8°. Milano. 1921
Ales (Alexander de), *called Doctor Irrefragabilis, see* Alexander, *de Ales.*
Alès (Anatole).
Les moines imprimeurs. [P2859]. 8°. 1873
Alesius (Alexander). Comm. in Evang. Johannis a. 1552. s8°. Basileæ. *J. Oporinus.* [1553]
Diligens refutatio errorum, quos sparsit nuper A. Osiander in libro: De unico mediatore Christo. s8°. Witebergæ, *I. Luft.* 1552
Responsio ad Cochlei calumnias. s8°. *n.p. n.d.* [1535 ?]
Alessandria, *Piedmont.* Alcuni capit. ined. d. statuti di A.; [*ed. A. Lattes*], *see* Regia Dep. di Storia Patria. Misc. t38, 1902.
Alessio (Alberto), *see* Filippi (F. de). Rel. scientif. d. Spediz. Ital. de F. nell' Himàlaia &c., s1, v1, Astronomia &c.; [*by*] G. Abetti, A. A. &c., 1925.
Alessio Robles (Vito).
Bibliog. de Coahuila, hist. y geog. 8°. Mexico. 1927
Aletheia. *The Aletheia: spirit of truth, 1899, *see* Mace (A. G.)
Alethes (Clerophilus), *ps., see* Constable (—).
Aletophilus, *Germanus, ps., see* Lyser (J.)

Alexander, *de Ales, called Doctor Irrefragabilis* [Ales (Alex. de); Hales (Alex. de)]. Univ. theologiæ summa in 4 partes distrib. 4p. fol. Venetiis. 1576
Each part has sep. tp. dated 1575.
Alexander [*of Battenberg*], *prince; prince of Bulgaria f. 1879 to 1886; aft. Graf v. Hartenau, see* Hartenau (A. J., *Graf* v.)
Alexander, *van Bruchsal* [Bruxal; Brugsal], *see* Hill (G. F.) A. of Bruchsal, 1925.
Alexander, *Franciscan friar, see* Gilson (J. P.) Friar A. & h. hist. interp. of the Apocalypse, 1922.
Alexander, *grammaticus* [A., *de Villedieu*]. Massa compoti, *see* Bacon (R.) Op. ined., fasc. 6, 1926.
Alexander, *the Great, king of Macedon.*
Buik (The) of A. By J. Barbour, Ed., w. intr., notes & glossary. w. Fr. origs., by R. L. G. Ritchie. [S.T.S., N.S., 12, 17, 21]. v1–3. 8°. E. 1921–27
Ἱστόρια Ἀ. Die armen. Übers. d. Alexander-Biog. (Pseudo-Callisthenes) zurückgeführt v. R. Raabe. [P2808]. 8°. L. 1896
Letter to Aristotle [*O. Eng. & Lat.*], *see* Rypins (S.), *ed.*, 1924.
Patmouthiun Alekhsandri. [Hist. of A. *in Armenian*]. 8°. i Venetik. 1842
see Armstrong (E. C.) Authorship of Vengement Alixandre &c., 1926.
,, Callisthenes. Hist. Alex. Magni; recensio vet., ed. G. Kroll, v1, 1926.
see Dashean (H.) Sts. of Pseudo-Callisthenes' Life of A.; *in Arm.*, 1892.
,, Edwards (B.) Classif. of MSS. of Vengement Alixandre, 1926.
,, Ehrenberg (V.) A. u. Ägypten, 1926.
,, Hill (G. F.) A. the Gt. & the Persian lion-gryphon, 1923.
,, Köpp (F.) Üb. Bildnis A. d. Gr., 1892.
,, Smith (V. A.) Early hist. of India &c., incl. the invasion of A. the Gt., 1904; 08; 14; 24.
Alexander III, *pope, see* Larcena (J.) Séjour à Sens du pape A. III (1163–5), 1925.
Alexander VI, *pope* [Roderico Lenzuoli Borgia].
see Du Boulay (N.) *Vies des papes A. VI & Léon X; par D. B., 1751.
,, Mathew (A. H.) Life & times of R. B., Pope A. VI, 1924.
,, Portigliotti (G.) I Borgia: Ales. I &c., 1921; tr., 1928.
,, Rodocanachi (E.) Hist. de Rome: une cour princière au Vatican: A. VI &c., 1925.
,, Schnitzer (J.) P. Delfin, 1444–1525: Kirchenreform A. VI &c., 1926.
Alexander VII, *pope* [Fabio Chigi].
see *Rome exactly descr. as to the state, under A. VII, 1664.
,, Viva (D.) Damnatæ theses ab A. VII &c., 1749.
Alexander VIII, *pope, see* Möring (C.) A. papa VIII pseudonymus, 1690.
see Viva (D.) Damnatæ theses ab Alex. VII, Innocentio XI, & A. VIII, 1749.
Alexander I, *emperor of Russia.*
Истор. док. изъ царствованія А. I. [Международная библ., 24]. 2oe изд. s8°. Лейпцигъ. *n.d.*
,, [*a. ed.* Собраніе мат., 7]. 2oe изд. s8°. Лейпцигъ. *n.d.*
Corresp. avec sa sœur la Gr.-Duchesse Catherine, 1805–18. [Publ. avec intr. par] Grand-Duc Nicolas Mikhaïlowitch. la8°. St. Pétersbourg. 1910
see Bogdanovich (M. I.) Исторія царствов. Имп. А. I. 6т, 1869–71
see Kuplevasky (N. O.) Манифестъ А. I. 1816 о переимен. финлянд. правит. совѣта, 1910.
,, Lloyd (H. E.) Alex. 1, sketch of h. life &c., 1826.
,, Nicholas Mikhailovich. L'emp. A.I: essai d'étude hist., t1, 1912.
,, Waliszewski (K.) La Russie il y a 100 ans: le règne d'A. Ier, 1801-25, 3t, 1923–25.
Alexander II, *emperor of Russia.*
Восплачь русскій народъ! о А. [P2749]. 8°. Москва. 1881
*Мат. для ист. гоненія студентовъ при А. II. [Междун. Библ., т31]. 2oe изд. s8°. Лейпцигъ *n.d.*
Покушеніе на жизнь Имп. [P2749]. fol. sheet. С.–П. 1881
Послѣднія минуты жизни А. II. [P2749]. 8°. С.–П. 1881
see Cardonne (C. de). L'emp. A. II., 1855–81, 1883.
see Corti (E. C.) Alex. v. Battenberg, s. Kampf mit d. Zaren &c., 1920.
,, Kolosov (A.) А. II. его личность &c., 1902.
,, Paléologue (G. M.) Le roman trag. de l'Emp. A. II, 1923.
,, —— Tragic romance of A.; tr., 1926.
Alexander III, *emperor of Russia.*
see Corti (E. C.) Alex. v. Battenberg, s. Kampf mit d. Zaren &c., 1920.
see Daudet (E.) L'avant-dernier Romanoff, A. III, 1920.

Alexander III [*continued*].
see Kolosov (A.) A. III., его личность &c., 1902.
,, Pobedonostsev (K. P.) Письма П. к А. III, т1, 1925.
see Tsebrikova (M.) Письмо А. II., 1898.

Alexander *a Sancta Teresia prof. of theology, Louvain.* Confut. justificationis praxeos. [P2659]. s8º. Ypris. 1683

Alexander, *de Villa Dei, see* Alexander, *grammaticus.*

Alexander (Alexander), *F.R.G.S.* A wayfarer's log. 8º. 1919

Alexander (Ann). *Facts rel. to the state of children employed by chimney sweepers as climbing boys. 2nd ed. [P2825]. s8º. York. 1817

Alexander (Archibald Browning Drysdale). The shaping forces of mod. religious thought. 8º. Glasgow. 1920

Alexander (*Maj.* **Arthur Charles Bridgeman).** Jutland: plea for a Naval General Staff. 8º. 1923

Alexander (*Mrs.* **Francis),** *see* Libro d'oro (Il), Venice, 1623; golden book, tr. Mrs. F. A., 1905.

Alexander (Frederick Matthias). Constructive conscious control of the individual. Intr. by J. Dewey. s8º. [1924]
Man's supreme inheritance. Intr. by Prof. J. Dewey. [2nd ed. rev.] 8º. [1918]

Alexander (George Glover). The admin. of justice in criminal matters (in England & Wales). [*&* Suppl. (1919) *pagin. cont.*] 8º. C. 1915
Archdeacon Paley as a jurist. [Repr. f. Journal of Comp. Legisl. &c., v18. P2466]. 8º. 1918

Alexander (Hartley Burr). The problem of metaphysics &c. 8º. N.Y. 1902
see Mythology of all races, v11, Latin America; by A., 1920.

Alexander (Natalis), *see* Alexandre (Noël).

Alexander (Philip Frederick). The earliest voyages, 1519–1617. Ed. P. F. A. [Camb. travel bks.] 8º. C. 1916

Alexander (Ruth). Thirst. s8º. [1925]

Alexander (Samuel), *Fellow of Lincoln College.* Space, time, & deity. Gifford Lects., 1916–18. 2v. 8º. 1920
,, ,, [repr.] 2v. 8º. 1927
Spinoza & time. Afterword by Vsct. Haldane. [Arthur Davis Mem. Lect.] s8º. [1921]

Alexander (*Sir* **Wm.),** *aft. earl of Stirling, see* Stirling (W. A., *earl of*).

Alexandra Fedorovna, *empress consort of Nicholas II, emp.*
Письма къ Николаю II. Переводъ съ англ. В. Д. Набокова. [*in Russian & Eng.*] 2t. 8º. Берлинъ. 1922
Letters of the Tsaritsa to the Tsar, 1914–16. Intr. by Sir B. Pares. 8º. [1923]
see Dehn (*Mme.* L.) The real Tsaritsa, 1922.
,, Nicholas II, *emp.* Переписка Н. и Александры Романовых, 1914–17, т3—5 с предисл. М. Н. Покровского, 1923–27.
,, Omessa (Ch.) & H. Omessa. La dern. Tsarine, 1920.
,, Poliakoff (V.) The tragic bride: story of the Empress A., 1927.

Alexandre (Noël) [Natalie Alexander].
*Apol. d. Dominicains missionnaires de la Chine: ou, rép. au liv. du P. le Tellier: & à l'éclairc. du P. le Gobien. Par un relig. doct. &c. [*i.e.* N. A.] [*Folld. by* Doc. controv. & apol. Dominican. confirm. *w. sep. tp. & pagin.*] s8º. Cologne. 1699
Works in Migne (J. P.) Theol. cursus, 1859–62.
De cultu sanctorum. [14.]
De justa bonorum temporal. ab eccles. possessione—Apolog. pro Joanne XXII—De investituris episc. & abbat., (J. P.) *ed.* [18.]
Works in Migne [*contd.*]
De Noachidarum præceptis—De præceptis moral. legis Mosaicæ *&* o. *dissert*s. [15.]
De oratione Dominica. [17.]
De symbolo fidei—De symbolo Apostolorum. [6.]
De tradit. non scriptis. [26.]
Tract. de peccatis. [11.]
see Daniel (G.) Litt. ad R. P. A. Thomist. doct. cum doct. S. J. compar., 1700.
,, Spanheim (F.) Hist. imag., adv. N. A., 1686.

Alexandrina. *Collectanea A., 1925, *see* Powell (J. U.)

Alexi (Joannes). Gramm. Daco-Romana sive Valachica, Latinitate donata, aucta, &c. 8º. Viennæ. 1826

Alexia [*Le Clerc*], *Blessed.* Mutter A. Le C.: Leben &c., *see* Hubert (W. E.) Lebensbilder kath. Erzieher, B6, 1897.

Alexinsky (Gregor). Du Tsarisme au communisme. La Révol. russe, ses causes & s. effets. s8º. 1923

Alexis, *Saint.* *La vie de St. A.: poème du 11e s. Texte crit. de G. Paris. [Class. fr. du m. a.] s8º. 1911

Alexis Mikhailovich, *emp. of Russia, 1645–6.*
Собраніе писемъ царя А. М. Иждивеніемъ К. I. Солдатенкова. Изд. П. Бартеневъ. 8º. Москва. 1856

Alexis (Paul), *see* Deffoux (L.) & E. Zavie. Le groupe de Médan: P. A. &c., 1920.

Alez, *see* Alais.

Alfaric (Prosper). L'évolution intell. de St. Augustin. [t]1. la8º. 1918
1, Du Manichéisme au Néoplatonisme.
see Fides, *of Agen, St.* La chanson de Ste Foy, t2, intr. & comm. par P. A., 1926.

Alferius (Ogerius). Indice d. Cron. astesi (Muratori, R. I. S., XI) di O. A. &c., comp. C. Merkel &c., *see* Regia Dep. di Storia Patria. Misc., t23, App., 1884.

Alfieri (*il conte* **Vittorio).** Il misogallo—Del principe e delle lettere. Pref. di R. B. Crivelli. s8º. Milano. [1919]
Rime ined. 4º. Italia. 1809
Tragedie. 6v. 8º. Firenze. 1820–21
Vita, rime e scr. min. *Ed.* M. Scherillo. s8º. Milano. 1917
see Gustarelli (A.) V. A., v1, Vita, 1917.
,, Teza (E.) Del Saule A. tr. in Armeno d. P. Bagratuni, 1895.

Alfonso V, *king of Aragon & Naples.* *Il Padiglione di re Alfonso, versi; [*ed.* P. Rajna]. [Nozze D'Ancona-Cardoso. N122]. 8º. Firenze. 1904
see Faraglia (N. F.) Storia d. lotta tra A. V d'A. e Renato d'Angiò, 1908.

Alfonso X [Alphonso X, *the Wise, king of Castile & Leon*].
see Huidekoper (C.) Die Süden Don Alfonsos d. Weisen: Roman; übertr., 1923.
,, Real Acad. Española. Discursos &c. 7. centen. del nacim. del rey A. [*by* J. Ribera &c.], 1921.
,, Ribero (J.) La musica de las cantigas [*forming v3 of* Cantigas de Santa Maria *of A.*], 1922.
,, Trend (J. B.) A. the Sage &c., 1926.

Alfonso II [*d'Este*], *duke of Ferrara, see* Este (A. II).

Alfonso V, *king of Portugal.* Ordenaçoens do Sen. Rey D. A. V, 5 livros, 1792, *see* Portugal. Coll. da legisl. &c.

Alfonso XIII, *k. of Spain.*
see Blasco-Ibañez (V.) A. XIII démasqué; tr., 1924.
,, —— A. XIII unmasked; [tr.], 1925.
,, Maura Gamazo (G.) Hist. crit. del reinado de A. XIII dur. la regencia de María Cristina de Austria, 2t, 1919–25.
,, Meynadier (R.) Les étapes de la royauté d'A. XIII, 1914.

Alfonso (Luis). Murillo. s8º. Barcelona. 1886

Alfonsus *a Cartagena, see* Alonso, *de C.*

Alford (Henry), *dean of Canterbury, see* Elliot (E. B.) Apocalypsis A., 1852.

Alford (Violet). Peeps at Eng. folk-dances. 8º. 1923

Alfræði Íslenzk. Islandsk encyklopædisk litt. Udg. ved. Kr. Kålund. [Samfund til u. af g. l., 45.] [rimtol] 3, Landslýsingar M. Fl. 8º. 1917–18

Alfred, *the Great, king of England.*
see Anderton (H. O.) The song of A.: [*epic poem*], 1912.
,, Bibliothek d. angel-sächs. Prosa: B11, A.'s Bearb. d. Solil. d. Augustinus; hrsg. W. Endter, 1922.
see Browne (G. F.) King A.'s books, 1920.
,, Lees (B. A.) A. the Gt., repr., 1919.
,, Pauli (R.) Life of A., tr.; app., A.'s Orosius, tr. Thorpe, 1902.
,, Pye (H. J.) A.: poem, 1801.

Alfredus, *Anglicus* [A. v. Sareshel]. De motu cordis. Hrsg. &c. v. C. Baeumker. [Beitr. z. Gesch. d. Philos. d. M.-a., B23i–ii]. 8º. Münster i. W. 1923

Algazzali [†Muḥammad ibn Muḥammad, *al Ghazzālī*]. Mishkāt al-Anwār ("The niche for lights"). Tr. w. intr. by W. H. T. Gairdner. [Roy. As. Soc. Monogr., v19.] 8º. 1924
see Carra de Vaux (*Bar.* B.) Gazali, 1902.

Algemeene. De alg. Belydenissen d. vereen. Vlaamsche &c. Doopgezinde, 1739, *see* Baptists.

Algeri. *Istoria degli stati di A., Tunisi, Tripoli e Marocco. Tr. d. lingua ingl. s8º. Londra. 1754

Algeria. *How we fared in A. [By C. H.] 8º. 1875

Algérie. Inscr. lat. de l'Algérie. t1. fol. 1922
1, I. de la Proconsulaire; rec. & publ. par S. Gsell.
Musées & colls. archéolog. de l'A. & de la Tunisie. [Descr. de l'Afrique du Nord, Min. de l'Instr. Publ. &c.] 4º. 1921–24
Musée Africain du Louvre; par A. Héron de Villefosse.
Musée Alaoui, 2e Suppl. par. M. A. Merlin & R. Lantier.
Musée de Cherchel: Suppl. par M. Durry.

Alghero. Statuti dei Gremi artigiani di A., con nota di A. Pino-Branca, *see* Regia Deput. Misc., t51, 1924.

Alha [Alh-khand]. The lay of A. Saga of Rajput chivalry. Partly tr. by W. Waterfield. Intr. & abstracts by Sir G. Grierson. 8º. O. 1923

Al-Ḥallâj, *see* Ḥallâj.

Alhoy (P. Maurice) & L. Lurine. Les prisons de Paris, hist., types &c. éd. illust. la8°. 1846

Alice, *princess of Gt. Brit. & Ireland &c.* Letters to H.M. the Queen. New &c. ed. w. mem. by Princess Christian. 8°. 1885

Alidosi (Giov. Niccolò Pasquali). Li riformatori d. stato di libertà di Bologna, 1466–1614. Fameglie, arme &c. s8°. Bologna. 1614

Aliénor, *see* Eleanor.

'Alī ibn 'Isā, *see* Bowen (H.). Life &c. of 'A., 1928.

Alington (Cyril Argentine).

The count in Kensington. s8°. 1926

Elementary Christianity. s8°. 1927

Mr. Evans. A cricketo-detective story. s8°. 1922

Strained relations. s8°. 1922

Twenty years; development of the Party system between 1815–1835. 8°. O. 1921

Alione (Giovanni Giorgio), *see* Maccheronee di 5 poeti ital. del sec. 15: G. G. A. &c., 1864.

Aliprando, *king of the Lombards, see* Liudprandus.

Aliquis, *ps.* Landlords, Land laws &c. in Scotland, 1881, *see* Scotland.

Aliquot constitutiones &c. apost., 1700, *see* Constitutiones.

Aliscans, chanson de geste, *see* Guessard (F.) Anc. poëtes, t10, 1870.

Alishanian (Leonce). *Geonomia Armena col. rapp. alla mostra Veneto-Arm., nell' occas. del 3. Congr. Geog. Internaz. [*signed* P. L. A.; P2792]. 8°. Venezia. 1881

Alison (*Sir* Archibald), *1st bart.*

Hist. of Europe, 1789–1815. 9th ed. 12v. & Index. 8°. 1853–56

„ „ Atlas, constr. &c. under dir. of A., by A. K. Johnston, w. vocab. &c. obl. 8°. E. 1855

„ „ ....libr. ed. obl. 8°. E. 1875

Alison (William Pulteney). Obs. on the reclamation of waste lands &c. [P2554]. 8°. E. 1850

Alisov (Petr Fedoseevich).

Третье отдѣленіе Трагико-водевильная сцена. [P2389]. s8°. Берлинъ. 1903

'Ali Ṭabari. The book of relig. & empire. Def. &c. of Islām, wr. w. assist. of the Caliph Mutawakkil, 847–61. Tr. &c. A. Mingana. 8°. M'ter. 1922

Alix [*Le Clerc*], *see* Alexia.

Alix (Frédéric). Un moine bibliophile au 17e s., Pierre Pecquet. [P2404]. 8°. 1912

Al-Jabartī, *see* 'Abd al Raḥmān ibn Ḥasan, *al-J.*

Alker (Ernst). Phillip Hafner, ein altwiener Komödiendichter. [Theater u. Kultur, B9]. s8°. Wien. 1923

All. *All about postal matters in Egypt, 1898, *see* Egypt.

Allacci (Leone) [Leo Allatius], *1586–1696.*

De utriusque eccles. occident. & orient. in dogmate de purgatorio perpetua consensione, *see* Migne (J. P.) *ed.* Theol. cursus, t18, 1862.

Græciæ orthodoxæ tomus primus [-secundus] in quo cont. scr., Nicephorus Blemmida, J. Veccus [*& others*]. De process. spiritus sancti. *Gr. & Lat.* 2t. s4°. Romæ. 1652–59

Joannes Henricus Hottingerus fraudis, & imposturæ manifestæ convictus. s8°. Romæ. 1661

see Antiquitates. Eccles. Orient. antiq. L. A. &c., 1682.

„ Veiel (E.) Exercit. de eccl. Græc. hodierna, L.A. opposita, 1666.

Allahabad. General Missionary Conf. held in A., 1872–3, 1873, *see* Missionary Conference.

Allan Library. *A catalogue of books chiefly theological coll. by T. R. A. In usum amicorum. [*2 copies interleaved with MS. adds. supplementing one another; one copy w.* Suppl. *pagin. cont.*] 8°. *n.d.*

Catalogue of a coll. of Bibles &c. formed by T. R. A. In usum amicorum. [*Interleaved, w. MS. adds. b. w. h.* Cat. of books, *n.d.*] 8°. 1883

see Harmer (E. G.) *Coins & medals of A. L., 1888.

„ Wesley (J.) Wesley, the man &c., w. acc. of A. L., 1891.

Allan (Alexander). Hunting the sea otter. 8°. 1910

Allan (C. Wilfrid), *see* Scarborough (W.) Coll. of Chinese proverbs; rev. & enl. by add. of 600 proverbs by C. W. A., 1926.

Allan (John). Hdbk. for pop. use in testing doct. of unitarianism. s8°. Glasgow. *n.d.*

Allan (John Harrison). A pictor. tour in the Mediterranean. fol. 1843

Allan (Percy). The drought antidote, artesian resources of N.S.W. [Paper, Sydney Univ. Engin. Soc.] 8°. [1906]

Allan (Thomas Robinson). Cat. of books chiefly theolog. [*&* Bibles] coll. by T. R. A., *n.d.*–1883, *see* Allan Library.

Allard (Carolus). Regni Poloniæ, Lithuaniæ &c. tabula. *folded* s8°. Amstelo Bat. [1670 ?]

Allard (Louis). La comédie de mœurs en France au 19e siècle. t1, 1795–1815. 8°. Cambridge, *Mass.* 1923

Allard (Paul). Les esclaves chrét. jusqu'à la fin de la domin. rom. en occident. 5e éd., refondue. s8°. 1914

Allard (Roger). Luc A. Moreau. Reprods. [&] ét. crit. s8°. [1920]

Marie Laurencin. Reprods. [&] ét. crit. s8°. [1921]

R. de La Fresnaye. Reprods. [&] notice. s8°. 1922

Allardyce (Paul).

"Stops," or, how to punctuate. [19th impr.] s8°. [1920]

Allbutt (*Sir* Thomas Clifford). Greek medicine in Rome, w. o. hist. essays. [Fitzpatrick Lects., 1909–10]. 8°. 1921

Science in the school. 3 letters. [P2709]. 8°. 1917

see Sudhoff (C.) Essays on hist. of med.; pres. to S.; by Sir T. C. A. &c., 1923.

Allcroft (Arthur Hadrian). The circle & the cross. [Repr. f. Arch. Journal, v77–80.] v1, The circle. 8°. 1927

Downland pathways. Pref. by E. V. Lucas. 8°. 1924

Alldeutsche Verband (Der), *see* Zwanzig Jahre alldeut. Arbeit &c.; hrsg. v. d. Hauptleitung d. A. V., 1910.

Allegri (Alessandro). Rime e prose. 8°. Amsterdamo. 1754

Alleine (Joseph) [Aleine], *1634–68.*

An alarme to unconverted sinners. Annexed, cases of conscience [*sep. pagin.*] s8°. 1691

Christian letters (1659–64), *see* Life *below*, 1672.

Earail dhurachdach. Eidir-theangaicht'o'n Bheurla le J[ohn] S[mith]. s8°. Inbhirneis. 1802

Extracts f. works, *see* Wesley (J.) Xtn. lib., v24, 25, 1753.

The life & death of J. A. [*By var. as.* Introd. *by* R. Baxter. *Folld. by* Sermon at funeral of J. A., by G. Newton & Christian letters, by J. A., *each w. sep. pagins.*] s8°. 1672

see Jackson (T.) Lib. of Xtn. biog., v3, 1838.

„ Newton (G.) A sermon, funeral of J. A., 1672.

Alleine (Richard). Instructions about heart-work. s8°. 1681

*Vindiciæ pietatis: or a vindic. of godliness. By R. A. s8°. 1667

Allemagne. Docs. diplom.: docs. rel. aux négoc. conc. les garanties de securité contre une agression de l'A., 1924, *see* France. Min. des Affaires Etr.

Allemagne (Henry René d'). Les accessoires du costume & du mobilier. 3t. 4°. 1928

Allemande. *Uniformes (Les) de l'armée a., 1877, *see* Uniformes.

Allemane (*Mlle.*), *see* Balde (J.)

Allemann (Rudolf Siegfried), *see* Mentzel (O. F.) Life at the Cape in mid-18th c.: biog. of R. S. A. (1784); tr., 1919.

Allen & Hanburys, *Ltd., see* Cripps (E. C.) Plough Court: story of a notable pharmacy, 1715–1927, 1927.

Allen (*Rev. Dr.*) An acc. of the behaviour of James Maclaine f. h. condemn. to h. execution, Oct. 1750. 3rd ed. [P2828]. s8°. 1750

Allen (Barten Wilcockson), A. H. Gray &c. A corner-stone of reconstruction: working for social purity among men. s8°. 1919

Allen (Carl Ferdinand). Gesch. d. dän. Sprache im Herzogthum Schleswig u. Südjütland. 2T. 8°. Schleswig. 1857–58

Allen (Carleton Kemp). Law in the making. 8°. O. 1927

Allen (Eugene Thomas), *see* Day (A. L.) & E. T. A. Volcanic activity &c. of Lassen Peak, 1925.

Allen (Glover Morrill). Birds & th. attributes. 8°. [1926]

Allen (Grant). The tidal Thames. Cat. of drawings of W. L. Wyllie. Exhib. at Fine Art Soc. [P2404]. 8°. [1884]

see Harrison (F.) G. A., 1848–1899, address, 1899.

Allen (*Maj. Gen.* Henry Tureman), *U.S. Army.* My Rhineland journal. 8°. 1924

Allen (Herbert), *see* Victoria & Albert Museum. H. A. coll. of Eng. porcelain; by B. Rackham, 2nd ed., 1923.

Allen (Herbert Warner). Wines of France. 8°. [1924]

Allen (Hervey). Israfel: life & times of E. A. Poe, 2v. la8°. 1927

Allen (*Sir* Hugh Percy), *see* Hull (A. E.) *ed.* Dict. of mod. music &c., 1924.

Allen (*Mrs* Ida Cogswell Bailey).

On cooking—menus—service. s8°. 1924

Allen (J. W.) The polit. conceptions of Luther, *see* Pollard (A. F.) Tudor studies, 1924.

Allen (James) *Inghamite minister,* **& Christopher Batty.** A coll. of hymns for those that seek &c. redemption. 2nd ed. w. App. [*wanting*]. s8°. Kendal. 1761

Allen (James Lane). Flute & violin, & o. Kentucky tales. s8°. E. 1892
A Kentucky cardinal & Aftermath. Illust. by H. Thomson. s8°. 1901
s8°. [1920]
The Kentucky warbler.
Allen (John Ernest), see HIRST (F. W.) & J. E. A. Brit. War budgets, 1926.
Allen (Joseph), *of Greenwich Hospital.* Life of Nelson. s8°. 1857
Allen (*Commandant* **Mary S.**), *O.B.E.* The pioneer policewoman. Ed. & arr. by J. H. Heyneman. 8°. 1925
Allen (Percy). Berry: the heart of France. 8°. 1923
The stage life of Mrs. Stirling: w. sketches of 19th c. theatre. Intr. by Sir F. R. Benson. 8°. [1922]
Allen (Percy S.), *of Sydney, Australia.* Stewart's hand-book of Pacific Islands. Guide, w. bibliog. 8°. Sydney. 1920
Allen (Percy Stafford). Erasmus' services to learning. [From Proc[s]. of Brit. Acad. P2818, 2821]. 8°. [1925]
Allen (Thomas William).
Homer: origins & transmission. 8°. O. 1924
see HOMER. ILIAD. The Homeric catalogue of ships; ed. w. commentary by T. W. A., 1921.
Allen (William), *ps., see* SEXBY (E.)
Allen (William), *cardinal.* *Ad persecutores Anglos pro catholicis domi forisque persecutionem sufferentibus, contra libellum [*by* W. Cecil, Lord Burghley], inscr. Justitia Britannica. Tr. in Lat. s8°. *n.p., n.d.* [1589?]
Duo edicta Elizabethae contra sacerdotes Soc. Jesu &c. Una cum Apologia G. Alani pro iisdem sacerdotibus &c. Add. ejusdem G. A. consolatio ad afflictos Catholicos Angliæ. s8°. Augustæ Trevir. 1583
see FITZ-HERBERT (N.) De antiq. & contin. Cath. relig. in Anglia & De Alani card. vita libellus, 1608.
„ FULKE (W.) A confutation of a treatise made by W. A. &c., *c.* 1586.
„ —— 2 treatises agst. the papistes; 1, ans. of Xtn protestant to challenge of a Popish Cath. [W. A. abp. of Mechlin], 2p, 1577.
Allen (William), *controversial writer.* *The danger of enthusiasm discov., in an epistle to the Quakers. s8°. 1674
Allen (William), *F.R.S., of Lichfield, Sussex,* 1770–1843, *see* SHERMAN (J.) Mem. of W. A., 1851.
Allen (William E. D.) Beléd-es-Siba: sketches &c. of travel & hist. s8°. 1925
The Caucasus, *see* BUCHAN (J.) *ed.* Nations: Baltic & C. States, 1923.
Allenby (*Field Marshal Sir* **Edmund Henry Hynman),** *1st Visc.*
see EGYPTIAN EXPEDIT. FORCE. Brief record of the advance of the E.E. Force, under A., July 1917 to Oct. 1918, 2nd ed., 1919.
„ GILBERT (*Maj.* V.) Romance of last crusade: w. A. to Jerusalem, 1924.
see MASSEY (W. T.) A.'s final triumph, 1920.
„ MORISON (J. L.) A.'s 1st attempt on Jerusalem, 1919.
„ SAVAGE (R.) A. of Armageddon, 1925.
Allende Salazar (Angel). Biblioteca del Bascófilo. Cat. gen. de obras ref. á las prov. de Vizcaya, Guipúzcoa, Álava y Navarra. la8°. 1887
Allendy (René). Les rêves & leur interprét. psychanalyt. s8°. 1926
Allerton Mauleverer. The registers of A. M., Co. York [1562–1812]. Transcr. by F. W. Slingsby. [Yorks. Par. Reg. Soc., 31]. 8°. *p.p.* 1908
Allery (Pietro de Lucas, *conte* **della Roche d'),** *see* ROCHE D'ALLERY (P. DE L., *conte* DELLA).
Allestree (Richard), *D.D.* [ALLESTRY].
Eighteen sermons. fol. 1669
see WHOLE DUTY OF MAN, & *o. wks., sometimes attrib. to R. A.*
Alletz (Pons Augustin). *Dict. des Conciles. Coll. des canons &c. s8°. 1761
*Dict. theol. Adj. Summarium S. Script. librorum & Conciliorum gen. &c. In Lat. serm. conv. ed. alt. rev. s8°. Augustæ Vindelic. 1762
see ESCARTIN Y CARRERA (F. A.) Pintura de la hist. de la iglesia &c. [? *tr. of* Alletz (P. A.) Tableau &c.], 7t, 1796.
Alley (Jerome). The judge, occ. by the death of Lord Clare. A poem. s8°. 1803
Alley (Leavitt). Report of trial of L. A., for murder of A. Ellis. Rep. by F. F. Heard. 8°. Boston [*Mass.*] 1875

Alley (William), *bp. of Exeter.* Πτωχομουζεῖον. The poore mans librarie. Rapsodial upon the 1st Ep. of Peter. Corr. 2t *in* 1v. fol. 1571
Alleyn (Edward), *see* SHAKESPEARE ASSOC. Papers on S. &c., w. papers on E. A., 1927.
Alleyne (John), *see* BOND (F. B.) Hill of vision: forecast of the Gt. War &c. f. automatic wr[s]., 1909–18, of J. A., 1919.
Allgemeine Bibliothek der biblischen Litteratur. Von J. G. Eichborn. 10B. s8°. Le. 1787–1800.
Allgemeine Staatengeschichte.
Abt. 1, *see* GESCHICHTE D. EUROP. STAATEN.
Abt. 2, *see* GESCHICHTE D. AUSSEREUROP. STAATEN.
Abt. 3, *see* DEUTSCHE LANDESGESCHICHTEN.
Allgood (*Maj.-Gen.* **George).**
China war, 1860. Letters & journals. obl. 4°. 1901
Allgood (Henry G. C.). Hist. of Bethnal Green, to 1680, Repr., N. East. Leader. s8°. 1894
All Hallows, *London Wall.* The registers of christenings &c. of Allhallows, 1559–1675. [Ed. E. B. Jupp & R. Hovenden]. 4°. *p.p.* 1878
Alliance Assurance Company, *see* SCHOOLING (*Sir* W.) A. A., 1824–1924, 1924.
Allier (Raoul). La psychologie de la conversion chez les peuples non-civilisés. 2t. 8°. 1925
Allies (*Miss* **Mary H.)**
Thomas Will. Allies, 1813–1903. s8°. 1924
Allies (Thomas William), *see* ALLIES (*Miss* M. H.) T. W. A., 1813–1903, 1924.
Allinga (Petrus). Fax dissidii extincta. [*b. w.* Schoock (M.) Exercitat., 1663]. s4°. Amstelædami. 1682
Allingham (E. G.) Romance of the rostrum: life of H. Stevens & hist. of 38 King St., w. acc. of famous sales there &c. Pref. by Ld. Rothschild. 8°. 1924
Allingham (*Mrs.* **Helen),** *wife of W. Allingham, see* PATERSON (A. H.) Homes of Tennyson; painted by A., 1905.
Allingham (Hugh). Ballyshannon. s8°. Londonderry. 1879
Allinson (May). Dressmaking in Mass., *see* UNITED STATES: LABOUR. Bull., 193, 1916.
Allison (John M. S.) Thiers & the French monarchy. 8°. [1926]
Allison (William)
"My kingdom for a horse!" Recoll. 8°. 1919
Allison (William Henry). Inventory of unpubl. material for Amer. relig. hist. in Protestant Church archives &c. [C. I. of Wash. Publ., 137]. la8°. Wash. 1910
Allix (Pierre) [PETER ALIX, *D.D.*] Remarks upon the eccles. hist. of the anc. churches of the Albigenses. s4°. 1692
Remarks upon the eccles. hist. of the anc. churches of Piedmont. s4°. 1690
Allmers (Hermann). Marschenbuch. Land-u. Volksbilder aus d. Marschen d. Weser u. Elbe. 8°. Gotha. 1858
Allo (E. Bernard). Saint Jean: l'Apocalypse. la8°. 1921
Alloggio (Sabino). Saggi non finiti. 8°. Milano. [1927]
Allon (Henry).
Mem. of the Rev. James Sherman. 2nd ed. 8°. 1863
Allonville (Charles Auguste Louville d', *marq.* **de),** *see* LOUVILLE (C. A. d'A., *marq.* DE).
Allori (Agnolo), *called Il Bronzino.* Sonetti di A. ed altre rime ined. di più insigni poeti. [*Ed.* D. Moreni]. la8°. Firenze. 1823
see SCHULZE (H.) Die Werke A. B.'s, 1911.
Allotte de la Fuÿe (François Maurice). Monnaies grec. Coll. du Col. A. de la F., 1e [& 2e] vente, 17–21 fév., 4–5 mai, 1925. [*Illust.*] la8°. [1925]
Allotte de la Fuÿe (Marguerite).
Jules Verne, sa vie, s. œuvre. [2e ed.] s8°. [1928]
The lord of death. Play. Tr. L. N. Parker. s8°. 1923
Allport (Herbert R.)
Abraham Lincoln. s8°. [1923]
Casual Club papers, 1907, 1910, 1912, 1915. [s1–4]. s8°. *p.p.* 1907–15
Henry of Navarre & o. papers. s8°. *p.p.* [1920]
Macaulay. s8°. *p.p.* 1917
Oliver Cromwell & Good-bye to Garynahine. s8°. *p.p.* 1922
see CHRISTIAN (E. B. V.) H. R. A. & h. Casual Club papers, 1924.
Allwood (Montagu C.)
Carnations for every garden &c. 8°. [1926]
Allwörden (Heinrich von).
Hist. Michælis Serveti &c. s4°. Helmstadii. [1727]
Allyn (Richard). Narr. of the victory obt. by the Eng. & Dutch fleet comm. by Adm. Russell over that of France, near La-Hogue, 1692, & acc. drawn up by Sir C. Shovel's dir., w. lists of the fleets. Added 2 letters wr. by Adm. Russell & Sir R. Delaval. 8°. 1744

Almada e Mendonça (F. de), *see* ACCIAJUOLI (*card.* F.) *Réponse [*attrib. to F. de A. e M.*] à la Rel. envoyée par le Card. T. &c., 1760.

Almagià (Roberto). L'Italia di G. A. Magini e la cartografia dell' Italia nei sec. 16 & 17. fol. Napoli. 1922

Al-Malouy, *see* AḤMAD IBN MUḤAMMAD *al-Yaqouby*.

Almanacco italiano. Enciclopedia popolare. v28, 32. s8º. Firenze. 1922–27

Almanach de Gotha. 1804, 54ᵉ–78ᵉ années, 1817–41, 158ᵉ–165ᵉ années (1921–28). s8º. Gotha. [1803–1928]

Almanach de la cour, de la ville & des dépts., 1835. s8º. 1835

Almanach des gourmands. 3ᵉ année. s8º. 1805

Almanach national: annuaire off. de la Rép. Fr., 1915–19. 8º. Nancy. [1919]

Alma-Tadema (*Sir* Lawrence), *R.A.* Exhib. of the works of Sir L. A.-T. Winter Exhib., 1913. [R.A.] [P2429]. 8º. 1913

Almedingen (Martha Edith).
The Catholic Ch. in Russia to-day. s8º. 1923

Almeida (Fortunato de).
Hist. de Portugal. t1–4. 8º. Coimbra. 1922–26

Almeida (João Ferreira d'), *see* FERREIRA D'ALMEIDA (J.)

Almeida (Pedro Taques de), *see* TAQUES (P.)

Almenas (*conde* de las), *see* LAS ALMENAS (*conde* DE).

Alméras (Henri d'). Le petit Capet dans sa prison du Temple, *see* ŒUVRES LIBRES, No. 33, 1924.
Un procès de faux & d'envoûtement au m. â., [Robert d'Artois], *see* ŒUVRES LIBRES, No. 76, 1927.
La vie paris. sous la République de 1848. 8º. [1921]

Almieri (Ginevra degli), *see* DEGLI ALMIERI (G.)

Almosen [ALMUSSEN]. Pfaltzgrave Friderichs Christl Almussen Ordnung, 1574, *see* FREDERICK III, *Elector Palatinate.*

Almqvist (Carl Jonas Ludwig). Folklivsberättelser. 8º. [1927]
Sara Videbeck & The chapel. Tr. A. B. Benson. s8º. N.Y. 1919
Törnrosens bok. Utg. av O. Holmberg [& A. Werin]. [Saml. skr., under red. av F. Böök.] 13B *in* 5v. s8º. [1921]

Al-Mufaḍḍal, *see* MUFAḌḌAL IBN MUḤAMMAD, *al-Ḍabbī.*

Almussen, *see* ALMOSEN.

Alnwick Castle. *Illusts. of A. &c., 1857?, *see* HARTSHORNE (C. H.)

Aloisio (Nicola d'). F. M. Martini. [Uomini del giorno, N. 17]. la8º. Milano. 1919

Alongi (Giuseppe). La Camorra. [Bibl. antrop.-giurid., s2, v13]. 8º. Torino. 1890

Alonso, *de Cartagena, bp. of Burgos* [ALFONSUS], *1384–1456.*
Regum Hisp., Roman. imperat. &c. anacephalæosis, *see* HISPANICA. Rer. Hisp. scr., t2, 1597.
see BIRKENMAJER (A.) Verm. Unters. (Streit d. A. mit L. Bruni Aretino), 1922.

Alonso (Aurelio Martin), *see* MARTIN ALONSO (A.)

Alonso (B. Sánchez), *see* SÁNCHEZ ALONSO (B.)

Alonso Cortés (Narciso), *see* CORTÉS (N. A.)

Alonso del Real (J.), *see* CALDERON DE LA BARCA (P.) C. segun sus obras &c.; por J. A. del R., 1881.

Aloui, *Musée.* Musées & colls. archéolog. de l'Algérie &c., 1921–22, *see* ALGÉRIE.

Aloysius [GONZAGA], *Saint, see* GONZAGA (A.)

Alpæus (Jacobus). Disputationes, *see* DU MOULIN (P.) Thesaurus disputat., v2, 1661.

Alpen (Heinrich Simon van). Gesch. u. Litt. d. Heidelberg. Katechismus &c. [Anhang. z. d. öffentl. Katechisationen, T3ii]. 8º. Frankfurt am Main. 1800

Alpenrosen: e Schweizer-Almanach, 1811–31 [1817, 1826–28 *missing*]. Hrsg. v. Kuhn, Meisner &c. s8º. Bern. [1811–31]

Alpertus, *Monachus, S. Symphoriani Mettensis.* De diversitate temporum. Inleiding v. C. Pijnacker Hordijk; uitg. door A. Hulshof. [Hist. Genoots. Werken, s3, 37]. 8º. A. 1916

Alpha of the Plough, *ps., see* GARDINER (A. G.)

Alphabetical. An alphabet. arrangement of Wesleyan Methodist ministers &c., 1847–1900, *see* WESLEYAN METHODIST.

Alphabetum.
The alphabets below publ. at Rome were issued by the Sac. Congreg. de Prop. Fide *& generally cont. the* Orat. Dominic.

*A. Æthiopicum &c. s8º. Romæ. 1631
A. Æthiopicum. s8º. Romæ. 1789
*A. Arabicum. 8º. Romæ. 1592
*A. Arabicum. s8º. Romæ. 1715
,, ,, [*a. ed.*] s8º. Romæ. 1797
*A. Armenum. s8º. Romæ. 1673
*A. Armenum. s8º. Romæ. 1784
*A. Barmanum. [*Ed.* G. C. Amaduzzi. *a. c. b. w.* Alphab. Tangut., 1773]. s8º. Romæ 1776

Alphabetum [*continued*].
*A. Barmanum, ed. altera emend. s8º. Romæ. 1787
*A. Bœmicum. s8º. Pragæ. 1718
*A. Brammhanicum [*b. w.* Alphabetum Tangut., 1773]. s8º. Romæ. 1771
*A. Chaldaicum ant. Estranghelo dictum &c. s8º. Romæ. 1636
*A. Græcum. [*Ed.* G. C. Amaduzzi]. s8º. Romæ. 1771
*A. Grandonico - Malabaricum sive Samscrudonicum [*b. w.* Alphabetum Tangut., 1773]. s8º. Romæ. 1772
*A. Hebraicum; addito Samaritano & Rabbinico &c. s8º. Romæ. 1771
*A. Ibericum, sive Georgianum. s8º. Romæ. 1629
*A. Persicum. s8º. Romæ. 1783
*A. Syro-Chaldæum. s8º. Romæ. 1797
*A. Tangutanum sive Tibetanum. s8º. Romæ. 1773

Alpha Delta Phi Fraternity. The A. D. Phi. [Catalogue of the Fraternity], 1832–82. la8º. [N.Y.: Boston pr.] 1882
,, ,, [1832–99]. la8º. N.Y. 1899
A. D. Phi. Reunion dinner, 1875. [P2598]. 8º. N.Y. *p.p.* 1876
A. D. Phi. [Songs]. la8º. N.Y. 1881

Alphen (Hieronymus Simons van), *see* DRAKENBORCH (A.) Oratio fun. in ob. H. S. v. A., 1743.

***Alphonus,** King of Aragon, 1599, 1926, *see* GREENE (R.)

Alpine Club. Exhib. of Swiss coloured prints, Dec. 1924. Catalogue. [P2785]. 8º. 1924

Alpine Club of Canada, *see* CANADIAN A. JOURNAL.

Alpine Journal (The). By members of the Alpine Club. v16–20. 8º. 1893–1901

Al-Qâdirî, *see* MUHAMMAD AL-QÂDIRÎ.

Alsace-Lorraine. A manual of A.-L., 1920, *see* ADMIRALTY.

Alsario dalla Croce (Vincenzo). Vesuvius ardens. 8º. 1632

Alsop (Christine Magolier), 1805–79.
Memorials. Compiled by M. Braithwaite. s8º. 1881

Alsop (Vincent). *The mischief of impositions, agst. a disc. [by Stillingfleet] The mischief of separation. 2nd ed. [P2653]. s4º. 1680
see CLAGETT (W.) *A reply to The mischief of impos., 1681.

Alst (Peter Coecke van), *see* COECK (P.)

Alstedius (Joannes Henricus) [ALSTED (JOHANN HEINRICH)].
Consiliarius acad. & schol. Acc. Consilium de copia rerum & verborum. 8º. Argentorati. 1610
Physica harmonica. Tertiâ curá s8º. Herbornæ. 1616
see CHAMIER (D.) Panstratiæ cath. corpus, t5, De sacramentis & De ecclesia; studio J. H. A., 1630.

Alt (Albrecht). Die griech. Inschr. d. Palaestina Tertia westl. d. 'Araba. [Wiss. Veröff. d. deut.-türk. Denkmalschutz-Kommandos; hrsg. Wiegand, H2]. fol. 1921

Alt (Jacob), *see* ALT (R.) Samml., 1921.

Alt (Rudolf). Samml. v. 21 orig.-Aquarellen v. R. Alt u. 6 Aquarellen v. J. Alt. Versteig., Gilhofer & Ranschburg, 1921. [P2699]. 4º. Wien. [1921]

Altaich [NIEDERALTAICH]. Annales Altahenses maiores; ex rec. W. de Giesebrecht &c. [Scr. rer. Germ. in usum schol.] ed. 2ª. Rec. E. L. B. ab Oefele. 8º. Hannoverae. 1891

Altamirano (Ignacio Manuel).
Paisejes y leyendas de Mexico. s1. 8º. México. 1884

Altamira y Crevea (Rafael).
Arte y realidad. s8º. Barcelona. 1921
Cuestiones mod. de historia. s8º. 1904
Epítome de hist. de España. 8º. 1927
Spanish drama as an elem. of moral educ., *see* ROY. SOC. OF LIT. Essays, N.S., v5, 1925.
see CHAPMAN (C. E.) Hist. of Spain; founded on A., 1925.

Altaner (Berthold), *see* JORDAN, *of Saxony.* Briefe, Beitr. z. Gesch. d. Frömmigkeit im 13. Jhdt., v. B. A., 1925.

Altan Tobchi.
Алтанъ Тобчи. Монгольская лѣтопись въ подлинномъ текстѣ и переводѣ, &c.; переводъ Галсана Гомбоева [*ed.* P. S. Savelev], *see* Imp. Russ. Arch. Obsch. Труды восточ. отд., ч 6, 1858.

Al-Tanūkhī, *see* ABU 'ALĪ AL-MUḤASSIN AL-TANŪKHĪ.

Altbergamaskische Sprachdenkmäler (9–15 Jhdt), 1893, *see* LORCK (J. E.) *ed.*

Altdorfer (Albrecht).
see BALDASS (L.) A. A.: Studien ü. d. Entwicklungsfaktoren im Werke d. Künstlers, 1923.
,, FRIEDLÄNDER (M. J.) A. A., 1924.
see FRIEDLÄNDER (M. J.) A. A. Landschafts Radierungen, 1906.
,, WALDMANN (E.) A. A., 1923.
,, WOLF (G. J.) A. [Künstler-Monogr.], 1925.

Alte. *Alte u. neue Zeugnisse v. Zustande d. Seelen nach diesem Leben. [*Incl.* Boehmens gründl. Eröffnung]. s8º. *n.p. n.d.*

Alte Orient (Der). Hrsg. v. d. Vorderasiat. Gesellschaft. Jhrg. 13, 17, 18, 21–25. 8°. L. 1920–26
Friedrich (J.) Aus d. hethit. Schrifttum, 2H, 1925. [24, 25.]
Grapow (H.) Vergleiche u. a. bildl. Ausdrücke im Ägypt., 1920. [21.]
Jeremias (A.) Babylon. Dichtungen &c., 1925. [25.]
Jirku (A.) Der Kampf um Syrien-Palästina, 1926. [25.]
——Wanderungen d. Hebräer im 3. u. 2. vorchr. Jahrt., 1924. [24.]
Landsberger (B.) Assyr. Handelskolonien in Kleinasien, 1925 [24.]
Langdon (S.) Ausgrabungen in Babylonien seit 1918; üb., 1927. [26.]
Luschan (F. v.) Entst. u. Herkunft d. ion. Säule, 1912. [13.]
Meissner (B.) Assyrische Jagden, 1911. [13.]
Prášek (J. V.) Kyros der Grosse, 1912. [13.]
Rusch (A.) Die Stellung d. Orisis im theolog. System v. Heliopolis, 1924. [24.]
Sachs (C.) Altägypt. Musikinstrumente, 1920. [21.]
Schäfer (H.) Sinn u. Aufgaben d. Berliner Ägypt. Museums, 1920. [22.]
Sethe (K. H.) Die Ägyptologie, 1921. [23.]
Weber (O.) Altoriental. Siegelbilder, 2B, 1922. [17, 18.]
Zimmern (H.) Babylon. Hymnen u. Gebete, 2e Auswahl, 1911. [13.]
—— Das babylon. Neujahrsfest, 1926. [25.]
—— Hethit. Gesetze aus Boghazköi (um 1300 v. Chr.), 1922. [23.]
„ „ Beihefte. H1–11. 8°. L. 1924–27
For later No^s^. see MORGENLAND, H12 &c.
Baumgärtel (E.) Dolmen u. Mastaba, 1926. [6.]
Bell (H. I.) Juden u. Griechen im röm. Alexandreia, 1926. [9.]
Ehrenberg (V.) Alexander u. Ägypten, 1926. [7.]
Gressmann (H.) Die hellenist. Gestirnrelig., 1925. [5.]
Hartmann (R.) Die Welt d. Islams, 1927. [11.]
Hopfner (T.) Orient u. griech. Philos., 1925. [4.]
Köster (A.) Schiffahrt &c. d. östl. Mittelmeeres, 1924. [1.]
Preisendanz (C.) Akephalos d. kopflose Gott, 1926. [8.]
Schubart (W.) Die Griechen in Ägypten, 1927. [10.]
Vogt (J.) Röm. Politik in Ägypten, 1924. [2.]
Weber (W.) Der Prophet u. s. Gott: St. z. 4. Ekloge Vergils, 1925. [3.]

Alten (W. von).
Max Slevogt. [Knackfuss, 116]. la8°. Bielefeld. 1926

Alten-Eck (Christian), *see* DASSOV (TH.) Comam Hebræorum licit. & interdict., 1695.

Altenrath (Georg). Catechismus ubiquitisticus. s8°. Franckfurt. 1614

Alter (Franz Carl).
Über Georgian. Litteratur. s8°. Wien. 1798
Ueber die Samskrdam. Sprache. s8°. Wien. 1799

Altertum (Vom) zur Gegenwart. Die Kulturzusammenhänge in d. Hauptepochen u. auf d. Hauptgebieten. Skizzen v. F. Boll, A. Curtius *& others*. 8°. L. 1919

Altes u. neues aus d. Schatz theolog. Wissenschaften, 1701, *see* UNSCHULDIGE NACHRICHTEN V. ALT. U. NEU. THEOL. SACHEN.

Altes (J. Korthals-), *see* KORTHALS-ALTES (J.)

Altham (Michael). *Some queries to Protestants answ. &c. [P2664]. s4°. 1686

Althorp (John Charles Spencer, *visct.*), *3rd e. Spencer, 1782–1845, see* UNITED IRELAND. U. I. on S. &c., 1888.

Alting (Henricus). Hist. Eccles. Palatinæ, *see* MIEG (J. R.) Monumenta, 1701.

Altkatholiken. Beschlüsse d. 2ten Synode d. A. d. deut. Reiches, Bonn, 1875. [P2691]. 8°. Bonn. 1875
*Verhandl. d. A.-Versamml., Nürnberg &c., Dec. 1871. [P2694]. 8°. München. 1872
Verhandl. d. 2. A.-Congr. zu Köln. 8°. Köln. 1872

Altman (S.), *see* ROYAL MAIL LINE. Gesch. d. Wanderungen; verfasst v. S. A., 8. erweit. A., 1926.

Altmann (Julius). Runen finn. Volkspoesie. Gesammelt u. üb. v. J. A. s8°. L. 1856

Altnordische Saga-Bibliothek. Hrsg. v. G. Cederschiöld, [F. Jonsson] &c. H16, 17. 8°. Halle (Saale). 1921–27
see LYGISOGUR. Drei lygisogur; hrsg. Å. Lagerholm, 1927. [17.]
„ VATNSDOELA SAGA; hrsg. W. H. Vogt, 1921. [16.]

Altolaguirre y Duvale (Angel de) & A. Bonilla y San Martín. Indice gen. de los papelas del Consejo de Indias, 6t, *see* COLECCIÓN de docs. inéd. de Ultramar, s2, t14–19, 1923–26.

Alton-Shée (*le cte.* Edmond d').
Mes mémoires, 1826–48. 2p. 8°. 1869
Souvs. de 1847 & de 1848 p. f. suite à Mes méms. 8°. [1879]

Altorfinae. *Epitome emblematum Acad. A., 1602, *see* HULSIUS (L.)

Altorientalische Gesellschaft.
Mitteilungen, B1, i, iii. 8°. L. 1925
see EBELING (E.) Liebeszauber im alt. Or., 1925. [1i.]
„ SCHLOBIES (H.) Akkad. Wettergott in Mesopotamien, 1925. [1iii.]

Altoviti, *Family of, see* PASSERINI (L.) Geneal. &c. d. fam. A., 1871.

Altsiona. Альціона. кн. 1. 2^oe^ изд. s4°. Москва. 1914

Altus (Henricus). Donatio Constantini, facta (ut ajunt) Sylvestro papæ. s4°. Helmestadi. 1703

Alumni Cantabrigienses: biog. list of students &c., Cambridge, to 1900, p1, 4v, 1922–27, *see* VENN (J.) & J. A. VENN.

Alva (Fernando Alvarez de Toledo, *duke of***),** *see* BELGÆ. Libellus supplex B. per Albani tyran. ejectorum, 1570.

Alvares (Didacus), *abp. of Trani.* De auxiliis Divinæ gratiæ & humani arbitrii viribus & libertate &c., libri 12. fol. Romæ. 1610

Alvares de Andrade (Thomé), *see* THOMÉ *de Jesus*.

Alvares de Araujo (Francisco Manoel). Viagem de explor. dos rios das Velhas e San Francisco, *see* INSTITUTO HIST. & GEOG. BRAZIL. Rev., t39, 1876.

Álvarez (Abelardo Merino), *see* MERINO ÁLVAREZ (A.)

Alvarez (Alejandro). Le droit internat. de l'avenir. [Inst. Amér. de Droit Internat.] la8°. Wash. 1916
Internat. law &c. f. the point of view of the Amer. Cont.: lect. &c., 1916–18, incl. st. of the univ^s^. of Latin Amer. & U.S. [C. E. f. Int. Peace]. la8°. Wash. 1922
The Monroe doctrine &c. [C. E. for Int. Peace]. la8°. N.Y. 1924

Alvarez de Arenales (*Gen.* **Juan Antonio),** *see* ARENALES (*Gen.* J. A. A. DE).

Alvarez de Colmenar (Juan). Les delices de l'Espagne & du Portugal. 5t. [*pagin. cont.*] s8°. Leide. 1707

Alvarez de Paz (Jacobus), *jesuit, see* *THRONUS justitiæ &c. ex 4 S. J. patribus desumptus: A. de Paz &c., 1624.

Alvarez Pereira (Nuno), *constable of Portugal; 1360–1431*
Chronica do condestabre de Portugal Dom N. A. P. [*sometimes attrib. to F. Lopez*]. Com revisao, pref. e notas por Mendes des Remedios. s8°. Coimbra. 1911

Álvarez Quintero (Serafín) & Joaquín Álvarez Quintero. Four plays. Eng. by Helen & Harley Granville-Barker. The women have their way—A hundred years old—Fortunato—The lady from Alfaqueque. 8°. 1927
Los Galeotes, comedia. s8°. 1917

Alvarus (Emmanuel). De instit. gramm. pro Illyricis accomodata &c. s8°. Romæ. 1637

Alveld (Augustin), *see* LONICER (J.) Contra Romanistam fratrem A. A., 1520.
see VELTKIRCH (I.) Confut. Libelli F. A. A., 1520.

Alverdes (Friedrich). Social life in the animal world. [Tr. K. C. Creasy]. 8°. [1927]

Alves (José Luiz). Os claustros e o clero no Brazil, *see* INSTITUTO HIST. E GEOG. BRAZIL. Revista, t57, 1894.

Alves de Lima y Silva (Luis), *duque de Caxias, see* CAXIAS.

Alvord (Clarence Walworth). The Illinois country, 1673–1818. [Centennial hist., v1]. 8°. Springfield. 1920

Al-Wanscharīsī (Aḥmad), *see* **Aḥmad** *al-Wanscharīsī.*

Alymantius Francus (Theophilus), *see* FRANCUS (T. A.)

Alypius, *Stylites, Saint, the Cionite, see* DELEHAYE (H.) Saints stylites, 1923.

Alzona (Encarnación). Some French contemp. opinions of the Russ. Revol. of 1905. [Columbia Univ., St. in hist. &c., 100ii]. 8°. N.Y. 1921

Amadas. Amadas & Ydoine. Roman du 13e s. Ed. J. R. Reinhard. [Class. fr. du m. â.] s8°. 1926

Amade (Jean). Anthologie catalane. s1, Les poètes roussillonnais, avec intr., bibliog., tr. franç. &c. par A. s8°. Perpignan. 1908

Amadeus [*of Savoy*], *prince of Achaia.* Statuta Soc. S. Iohannis Bapt. Augustæ Taurin., 1389, ed. A. Ceruti, *see* REGIA DEP. DI STORIA PATRIA. Misc., t11, 1870.

Amadeus VI, *of Savoy* [CONTE VERDE]. Nuova ediz. degli statuti del 1379 di A. VI di S.; [*ed.*] C. Nani, *see* REGIA DEP. DI STORIA PATRIA. Misc., t22, 1884.
see DUFOUR (A. H.) & F. RABUT. Renonciat. du Comte A. VI de S. au mariage arrêté entre lui & la Pcsse. Jeanne de Bourgogne, 1878.
„ GABOTTO (F.) L'età d. Conte Verde in Piemonte (1350–83), 1895.

Amadis, *de Gaula, see* TENREIRO (R. M.) Libros de caballerías, sel. por T., 1924.

Amador de Los Rios (José).
Poesías. Prólogo de J. Valera. 8°. 1880
Toledo pintoresca. la8°. 1845
—— **& J. de Dios de la Rada y Delgado.** Hist. de la villa y corte de Madrid. 4t. fol. 1860–64

Amador de los Rios (Rodrigo). Inscripciones árabes de Cordoba prec. de estudio de la Mezquita-Aljama. 2ª ed. s8º. 1880
Inscripciones árabes de Sevilla, prec. de una carta-pról. d. J. Amador de los Rios. 8º. 1875
Amaduzzi (Giovanni Cristofano) [AMADUTIUS (J. C.)] Alphabetum Barmanorum; [*ed.* G. C. A.], 1776; 1787, *see* ALPHABETUM.
*Alphabetum Græcum; [*ed.* G. C. A.], 1771, *see* ALPHABETUM.
Amalarius (F.), *abp. of Treves, see* COCHLÆUS (J.) Speculum missæ ex antiquiss. Patribus coll., 1572.
Amama (Sixtinus). Anti-barbarus biblicus, libro quarto auctus. Acc. variæ dissert. & orat. & resp. ad censuras M. Marsenni. s4º. Franequeræ. 1656
Censura Vulgatæ atque à Tridentinis canonizatæ vers. 5 lib. Mosis. s4º. Franckeræ Fris. 1620
Amanda, *Tante, see* TANTE AMANDA.
Åman-Nilsson (G.)
Lord Byron och det sekelgamla förtalet. 8º. [1915]
Amante (Bruto). Giulia Gonzaga e il movimento relig. femm. nel sec. 16. 8º. Bologna. 1896
Amarilla Etrusca, *ps., see* BANDETTINI LANDUCCI (T.)
Amat (Felice), *abp. of Palmyra* [*ps.* MELATO (M. P.); PADUA (MACARIO)]. Ecclesiæ Jesu-Christi ichnographia. [*b. w. h.* Meditationes, 1833]. s8º. Barcinone. 1830
Meditationes [in Palmyræ ruinas]. s8º. Barcinone. 1833
Obs. pacificas sobre la potestad ecles. 3p. *in* 2t. 8º. Barcelona. 1817–22
Seis cartas [& carta 7ª] à Irénico, ideas de los derechos del hombre &c. [*b. w. h.* Obs., p3, 1822]. 8º. Barcelona. 1817
Amat de Graveson (Ignace Hyacinthe). Epistolæ apolog. pro doctrina SS. Augustini & Thomæ de gratia se ipsa efficaci. [*Ed.* F. G. Caratinus]. s8º. Veronæ. 1737
Epistolæ scr. in quibus doctrina de gratia &c. contra Scholæ Thomisticæ adversarios asseritur. Classis 1ª [vols. 2 & 3 *wanting*]. s4º. Romæ. 1728
Amat di San Filippo (Pietro). Della schiavitù &c. in Sardegna, *see* REGIA DEP. DI STORIA PATRIA. Misc., t33, 1895.
Storia econ. d. Sardegna, *see* REGIA DEP. DI STORIA PATRIA. Misc., t39, 1903.
see BIANCO (A.) Planisferio, 1436, *n.d.*
Amateur photographer (The). v50, 51 (July 1925–June 1926). 4º. 1925–26
Amati (Basilio). Delle origini Romagnuole. s8º. Forli. 1831
Amatucci (Aurelio Giuseppe). Dalle rive del Nilo ai lidi del "Mar nostro." 2v. s8º. Bari. 1909–10
1, Oriente e Grecia. 2, Cartagine e Roma.
L'Eneide di Virgilio e la Sicilia, *see* SOCIETÀ SICIL. Arch., n.s., 45, 1924.
Ambedkar (B. R.) Evolution of prov. finance in Brit. India. Foreword by E. R. A. Seligman. 8º. 1925
Amblimont (Bèatrix Stéphanie Renart de Fuchsamberg d'), *see* LÂGE DE VOLUDE (*la marq.* B. S. DE).
Amboyna. True &c. narr.; or (2nd p. of A.) of injuries &c., 1665, *see* DARELL (J.)
Ambrogio, *da Paullo* [AMBROISE, *de Paullo*]. Cronaca milanese, 1476–1515; ed. A. Ceruti, *see* REGIA DEP. DI STORIA PATRIA. Misc., t13, 1871.
Ambrose, *Saint, bp. of Milan.* Opera. Ex ed. Romana. 5t *in* 2v. [*pagin. of t1 & 2 contin.*] fol. Parisiis. 1632
Opera. Studio ord. S. Benedicti e S. Mauri. 2t. fol. Parisiis. 1686–90
The App. *to* t2 *cont*ˢ. Vita *&* Varii tractatus suppos. *w. sep. pagin*ˢ.
Ambrose (Isaac). Extracts f. works, *see* WESLEY (J.) Xtn. lib., v13–15, 1752.
Ambrose (*Capt.* **John).** The defence made by J. A., late capt. of H.M. ship The Rupert, at the court-martial on board The London, Sept 23 &c., with sentence. By a Gentleman of the Inner-Temple. [P608]. s8º. 1745
Ambrosius (Ernst), *see* GÜNTHER (F.) Der Harz, 3. A. bearb. v. E. A., 1924.
Ambrosius (Samuel), *ed., see* *NOVI ECCLESIAST.-SCHOLAST. ANNALES &c., 1793–95.
Ambrun (P.), *ps.* Rép. à l'Histoire crit. du Vieux Test., 1678, *see* †SIMON (R.) Hist. crit., v2, 1685.
Ambulator; or pocket companion round London. 6th ed. [ed. R. Lobb]. s8º. 1793
,, ,, ...11th ed. s8º. 1811
Amdrup (G.), *captain in the Danish navy, see* THALBITZER (W.) *ed.* The Ammassalik Eskimo, p1, Results of G. A.'s exped., 1898–1900 &c., 1914.

Ameer Ali, *Syed.* Persian culture, *see* PERSIA SOCIETY. Lectures, 1913.
The spirit of Islâm: w. life of Prophet. [Rev. ed.] 8º. [1922]
Amelia, *queen of Portugal* [MARIE AMÉLIE LOUISE HÉLÈNE, *consort of Ch. I of Portugal*], *see* CORPECHOT (L.) Mem. of Queen A., 1915.
Amélineau (E.) Prolégom. à l'ét. de la relig. égypt. [H. E.: Sci. relig., v30]. p2. 8º. 1916
Amelot de la Houssaye (Abraham Nicolas de). Petrus Suavis Polanus in Hist. Conc. Tridentini opere &c. defensus. [P2647]. s4º. Curiæ Narisc. 1686
Amelroy, *Barons of* [AMMERZODE], *see* BOX (J.) Chron. of the castle of A., w. notices of its anc. barons, 1870.
Am Ende (J. G.), *see* ENDE (J. G. AM).
Amendola (Giovanni). Il patto di Roma. Scr. di G. A., G. A. Borgese, U. Ojetti, A. Torre, con pref. di F. Ruffini. s8º. 1919
Amendola (Giov. Batt.), *1848–87, see* SAPORI (F.) Maestri, No. 20, 1920.
Åmen-em-àpt, *son of Kanekht* [AMENEMOPE; AMENOPHIS].
The teaching of A.; Egypt. text & tr. &c., 1924, *see* BUDGE (*Sir* E. A. T. W.)
,, ,, [Tr. &c.] by F. Ll. Griffith, *see* JOURNAL OF EG. ARCH., v12, 1926.
Das Weisheitsbuch d. A., aus d. Papyrus 10474 d. B. M. hrsg. &c. v. H. O. Lange, *see* KONG. DANSKE VIDENSK. SELSKAB. Hist.-filol. Medd., B11, 1925.
Amenemhēt, *the scribe, see* GARDINER (A. H.) The tomb of A., 1915.
Amenemope [AMENOPHIS], *see* ÅMEN-EM-ÀPT.
Amenhotpe, *see* HUY, *Nubian viceroy.*
Amenta (Niccolò), *see* ZAGARIA (R.) Vita e opere di N. A., 1659–1719, 1913.
America.
America's merchant marine, 1920, *see* BANKERS TRUST CO., *N.Y.*
Congresso Internacional de Hist. de A., 1922. Annaes, v1, *see* INSTITUTO HIST. &c. BRAZIL. Revista, tomo esp., 1925.
*Hist. of North America, cont. acc. of 1st settlements &c., & intr. s8º. 1757
Mod. atlas of A. &c., 1905, *see* PHILIPS' *publ. firm.*
Procˢ. & debates of Brit. Parliaments resp. N. Amer., v1, 2, 1542–1702, 1924–27, *see* STOCK (L. F.), *ed.*
*Prophetic voices ab. A., *n.d., see* PROPHETIC.
*Reds in Amer., 1924, *see* WHITNEY (R. M.)
Relaciones hist. de A., sig. 16, 1916, *see* SERRANO Y SANZ (M.), *ed.*
South A. pilot, 3p, Suppl. 5, 6, *&* Not. to mariners, 1911–22, *see* ADMIRALTY.
West coasts of C. Amer. & U.S. pilot, 3rd ed., *&* Suppl. 5, *&* Not. to mariners, 1916–22, *see* ADMIRALTY.
Américains. *Recherches philos. sur les A., 2t, 1771, *see* PAUW (C.)
American.
Amer. & Brit. verse, 1920, *see* YALE REVIEW.
Amer. ballads & songs, 1922, *see* POUND (L.), *ed.*
Amer. (The) Commission on conditions in Ireland. Interim rep. [P2530]. 8º. 1921
Amer. for. policy, based upon statements of presidˢ. &c. Intr. by N. M. Butler. [C.E. f. Int. Peace]. 2nd ed. la8º. Wash. 1920
Amer. social hist. as rec. by Brit. travellers [1789–1922], 1924, *see* NEVINS (A.), *ed.*
Arbitration treaties among Amer. nations to 1910, 1924, *see* MANNING (W. R.), *ed.*
Letters on the Amer. Revol., 1774–76, 1925, *see* WILLARD (M. W.), *ed.*
Mod. Amer. poetry, 1921, *see* UNTERMEYER (L.)
Orig. pr. records of Amer. vessels captured, 1803–11 &c. [Sold 7th April 1926], Amer. Art Assoc. [P2855]. 8º. N.Y. [1926]
Represent. poems, Amer. & Eng., 1886, *see* LATHROP (G. P.)
Seventy Amer. hist. nuggets. Fr. the Library of a N.Y. collector. To be sold, Feb. 1920, Anderson Gall. [P2856]. 8º. N.Y. 1920
Short (A) hist. of Amer. lit.; ed. W. P. Trent, J. Erskine &c., 1924, *see* CAMBRIDGE HIST. OF ENG. LIT.
Sources & docˢ. illust. the Amer. Revol., 1764–88 &c., 1923, *see* MORISON (S. E.), *ed.*
Specimens of Amer. poetry, w. crit. & biogr. notice, 1839, *see* KETTELL (S.)
*Thousand (A) Amer. men of mark of to-day. 8º. Chicago. 1916
Treasury (The) of Amer. sacred song, 1896, *see* HORDER (W. G.), *ed.*
Two centˢ. growth of Amer. law, 1701–1901; by Members of Yale Law School, 1901, *see* YALE UNIV.
American Academy in Rome. Papers & monographs. v1, 2, 4, 5. 8º. Rome. 1919–25
see BRYAN (W. R.) Italic hut urns &c., 1925. [4.]
,, HOLLAND (L. A.) Faliscans in prehist. times, 1925. [5.]
,, PETERSON (R. M.) Cults of Campania, 1919. [1.]
,, TAYLOR (L. R.) Local cults in Etruria, 1923. [2.]

American Academy of Arts & Letters, *see* LOWELL (J. R.) Commem. of cent. of birth of L., 1919.

American Academy of Political & Social Science [*Philadelphia*]. Annals, 1904–18. v23–78 [*b. in* 28v. 26i, 27i, 35ii, 36i, ii, 45, 51, 67, 76 *wanting*]. la8°. Phila. 1904–18
„ „ 25th Anniversary index, 1890–1916. [Suppl. to *& b. w.* March 1916]. la8°. Phila. 1916
„ „ ....Suppl^s. 8°. Phila. 1896–1927
see LUCAS (A. F.) Legal minimum wage in Mass, 1927.
„ PATTEN (S. N.) Theory of social forces, 1896.
Foreign policy of U.S.: polit. and commercial Addresses, Apr. 1899. 8°. Phila. 1899

American almanac (The) & repository of useful knowledge. 1830, 1832–33, 1844–49. 9v *in* 6. s8°. Boston. 1830–49

American almanac & treasury of facts. 1878–89. s8°. N.Y. 1878–89

American annals of education & instruction for 1831–32. Ed. W. C. Woodbridge. Contin. of Amer. journ. of educ. v1, 2. 8°. Boston. 1831–32

American Antiquarian Soc., *Worcester, Mass.* Proceedings at Worcester, June 2nd, 1868. [P2623]. 8°. Worc. [Mass.] 1868

American Association for the Advancement of Science. Proc., 1887–1908. [v36–58, 56–57 *in 1v*]. 8°. Salem. 1888–1908

American Association for Internat. Conciliation, *see* INTERNATIONAL CONCILIATION, 1923–.

American blue-book of biography. Prominent Americans of 1915. Ed. &c. T. W. Herringshaw. 8°. Chicago. 1915

American Citizen (An), *ps.* Philos. of plan of salvation, 1847, *see* WALKER (J. B.)

American Folk-Lore Society. Memoirs. v15, 2p. 8°. Cambridge, Mass. 1923
see PARSONS (E. C.) Folk-lore f. the Cape Verde Islands, 2p, 1923. [15.]

American Geographical Society.
see BOWMAN (I.) The Andes of Southern Peru; publ. by the A. G. S., 1920.
„ JOHNSON (D. W.) Battlefields of the World War &c., 1921.
„ MALLORY (W. H.) China: land of famine, 1926.
„ MUSIL (A.) Arabia Deserta, 1927.
„ —— The middle Euphrates, 1927.
„ —— The Northern Ḥeğâz, 1926.
„ *SHORT acc. of 1st settlement of prov^s. of Virginia &c., 1735, 1922.
„ WRIGHT (J. K.) Geog. lore of time of Crusades, 1925.

American Historical Association.
Annual report, 1917; 1918, v1, 2; 1919, v1, 2; 1920, v1. 8°. Wash. 1920–25
1918, ii, *cont.* Autobiog. of M. van Buren; ed. J. C. Fitzpatrick.
1919, ii, *cont.* Austin papers; ed. E. C. Barker, 2v.

American historical review (The). v25–32 (Oct. 1919–July 1927). la8°. N.Y. 1920–27

American Institute of International Law.
Acta final de la sesion de la Habana, 22–27 enero, 1917. la8°. Habana. 1917
Actas, mem. y proyectos de las sesiones de la Habana, 22–27 enero, 1917. la8°. N.Y. 1918
Declar. of the rights & duties of nations—Offic. comment—Constit. & by-laws—Officers & members. [P2676]. 8°. *n.p.* [1916]
Inst. Amér. de Droit Internat.: hist., notes, opinions. la8°. Wash. 1916
Procès-verb. de la prem. sess. tenue à Washington, 29 déc. 1915–8 jan. 1916. 8°. N.Y. 1916
see ALVAREZ (A.) Le droit internat. de l'avenir, 1916.
„ ROOT (E.) The Declar. of the rights &c. of nations, adopted by the A.I. of I.L.: addr., Apr. 27, 1916.
„ SCOTT (J. B.) The Recommend^s. of Habana, adopted by the A.I. of I.L., Jan. 23, 1917: addr. & c. by J. B. S., 1917.

American Institute of Mining Engineers.
Transactions. v34–70, 72–74 (1903–26). 8°. N.Y. 1904–27
„ „ Gen. index, v36–55 (1905–16). 8°. N.Y. 1918

American Journal of archaeology.
Ser. 2, v23–31 (1919–27). 8°. Concord, N.H. [1919–27]
see ART STUDIES, v1, 1923.
„ KELSEY (F. W.) Excav. at Carthage, 1925, 1926.

American journal of international law. Analytical index to A. j. of i. law & Suppl^s., v1–14, 1907–20, & Proc^s. of Amer. Soc. of I. Law, 1907–20. Prep. by G. A. Finch. la8°. Wash. 1921
see UNITED STATES: FOR. AFFAIRS. Diplom. corr. betw. U.S. & bellig. govt^s. rel. to neutral rights &c., 3v, 1915–17. [Suppl., v9–11].

American journal of philology. v40–48. la8°. Baltimore. 1919–27

American Library Association. Educat. list. Books for schools establ. by Army Educ. Comm. [P2420]. s8°. Paris. 1919
see MUDGE (I. G.) New guide to reference books, 1923.

American (The) miscellany of pop. tales &c. by transatlantic authors. 2v. 8°. 1840

American missionary register. By Z. Lewis. v1. 8°. N.Y. 1821

American Museum (The): or, annual register of fugitive pieces, anc. & mod., for 1798. 8°. Phila. 1799

American Museum of Natural History. Handbook ser. Nos. 1–4, 7, 8, 10–12. s8°. N.Y. 1917–25
see GODDARD (P. E.) Indians of Northwest Coast, 1924. [10.]
„ —— Indians of the Southwest, 2nd ed., 1921. [2.]
„ KROEBER (A. L.) People of the Philippines, 1919. [8.]
„ LUCAS (F. A.) Animals of the past, 1920. [4.]
„ MEAD (C. W.) Old civilizations of Inca land, 1924. [11.]
„ NICHOLS (J. T.) Fishes of vicinity of New York City, 1918. [7.]
„ SPINDEN (H. J.) Anc. civilizations of Mexico &c., 1917. [3.]
„ WHITLOCK (H. P.) Story of minerals, 1925. [12.]
„ WISSLER (C.) N. Amer. Indians of the plains, 2nd ed., 1920. [1.]
see NATURAL HISTORY: Journal of the Amer. Mus., v21–27, 1921–27.

American Philosophical Society. List. [P2737]. 8°. [Phila.] 1922
Transactions. v2. 8°. Phila. 1838
see DU PONCEAU (P. E.) Diss. on the Chinese system of writing &c., 1838. [2.]

American (The) political science review. v13–21 (1919–27). la8°. Baltimore. 1919–27
„ „ Gen. index (v1–20), & to Proc. of Amer. Pol. Sc. Assoc., 1904–14. 8°. [Baltimore]. 1927

American Red Cross. Trench fever. Rep. of Comm. Prep. by R. P. Strong. la8°. 1918

American (The) register: review of hist., polit. & lit. [Ed. R. Walsh]. v1. 8°. Phila. 1817

American (The) review of hist. & politics. v1–4i *in* 2v. 8°. London., *Phila. pr.* 1811–12
2*i*, 3*ii*, 4*i have append. w. sep. pagin.*

American Schools of Oriental Research. [AMER. SCHOOL OF O. R. IN JERUSALEM]. Annual. Ed. B. W. Bacon. v4, 5 (for 1922–24). la8°. New Haven. 1924–25

American Social Science Assoc. Reconstruction after the War. Journal, v4, 1918, *see* NATIONAL INSTIT. OF SOC. SCI.

American Society for the Excavation of Sardis. Publ., v1, 10, 1922–26, *see* SARDIS.

American Society of International Law, *see* AMER. JOURNAL OF INTERNAT. LAW. Analyt. index, v1–14, &[to] Proc^s. of A. Soc. of I. Law, 1907–20; prep. by G. A. Finch, 1921.

American year book (The). Record of events &c., 1919. Ed. F. G. Wickware. 8°. N.Y. 1920

Americana, 1925, *see* MENCKEN (H. L.), *ed.*

Americanists. INTERNAT. CONGRESS OF A. Crón. del 11° Congr. Internat. de A., Mexico, 1895, escr. por E. de Olavarria y Ferrari. 8°. Mexico. 1896
Internat. Congress of A. Proc. of 19th Congr., Wash., 1915. Ed. F. W. Hodge. la8°. Wash. 1917

Americano (Un), *ps.* Discursos sobre una constit. relig.; su autor un Americano, 1820, *see* Llorente (J. A.)

Americans. National portrait gallery of disting. Americans, 4v, 1865, *see* NATIONAL.

Amérique. Carte des possessions angl. & franç. du Continent de l'Amér. Sept. [Maps, 7]. folded fol. Amsterdam &c. 1755

Ames (William), *D.D.* [AMESIUS (GUILIELMUS)].
Anti-synodalia scripta, Remonstrantes in Synodo Dordracena &c. s8°. A. 1633
„ „ ......[*a. ed.*] s8°. A. 1646
Bellarminus enervatus. [Disputationes anti-B.] 4t *in* 1v. s8°. A. 1629
„ „ ed. nova recog. s8°. A. 1630
Coronis ad collationem Hagiensem, adv. Remonstrantium 5 articulos de div. prædestinatione &c. ed. noviss. [*b. w. h.* Anti-synodalia scr., 1646]. s8°. A. 1650
De conscientia &c. libri V. s4°. A. 1630
„ „ ed. nova. s8°. A. 1643
De conscientia &c. libri 5. ed. nov. [*b. w. h.* Medulla theologica, 1650]. s8°. A. 1650
Disceptatio de circulo pontificio &c., Item ejusdem Disq. theolog., Orationes duæ &c. [*b. w. h.* Anti-synodalia scr., 1646]. s8°. A. 1644
Diss. theolog. de 2 quæst. controv. 1, De reconciliatione per mortem Christi. 2, De electione &c. s4°. Roterodami Batav. 1615
Medulla theologica. ed. noviss. s8°. A. 1650
Philosophemata [*b. w. h.* De conscientia, 1643]. s8°. Lugd. Batav. 1643

Ames (William) [*continued*].

Puritanismus Angl. &c. [*b. w. h.* Medulla theolog., 1650]. s8º. A. 1658

Rescriptio ad N. Grevinchovii resp. quod opposuit dissert. De redemptione gen. &c. s4º. A. 1615

„ „ ed altera emend. [*b. w. h.* Anti-synodalia scr., 1646]. s8º. Hardervici. 1645

see Bradshaw (W.) *Puritanismus Anglicanus; *tr. w. pref. by W. A.*, ann. discept. de circulo pontificio [*by W. A.*], 1610.

„ Eaton (N.) G. A. sententia de orig. sabbati &c., 1653; 1658.

„ Ryssen (L. van). Veritas de lusu aleæ, a G. A. defensa, 1660.

Amet (Jacques).
Le Jutland, bataille navale du 31 mai 1916. 8º. [1923]

Ametrano (Scipione), *ps.*, see Capece (Bruto).

Amfilokhy, *Archimandrite*. О греч. кондакарѣ 12–13 в. Моск. Синод. библ. &c. [I. Akad. Nauk. Зап., т16]. 8º С.-П, 1869

Amfiteatrov (Aleksandr Valentinovich).
Господа Обмановы. Глава 2 & 3. [P2499]. s8º. Berlin. *n.d.*–1903
Зачарованная степь. 8º. Ревель. [1921]

Amherst (Hugh Amherst, *4th earl*). Cat. of pr. bks. &c., prop. of Earl of A. &c. & 3rd portion of Melville papers. Sold by Sotheby, May 1926. [Illust. P2857]. 8º. 1926

Amherst (*Lt.-Gen.* William), *c. 1732–81.* Journal in Amer., 1758–60. [Ed.] w. intr. by J. C. Webster. 8º. [1927]

Amherst of Hackney (William Amherst Tyssen-Amherst, *1st baron*). Hand-list of coll. of books & MSS. belong. to Ld. A. of H. Compiled by S. de Ricci. la8º. C. 1906

Ami (L') du lettré, 1923. [Assoc. des Courriér. Litt.] s8º. [1923]

Amiani (Pietro Maria).
Mem. istor. d. cittá di Fano. 2p. fol. Fano. 1751

Amiati (Antonietta). Cosimo I e i frati di S. Marco, see Archivio stor. ital. Anno, 81, 1925.

Amic (Auguste). Hist. de Masséna. 8º. 1864

Amic (Henri). Un bon garçon. Roman. s8º. [1921]

Ami Chand, see Omichund.

Amici (F. Nicola). Enrico Ferri. la8º. Milano. 1920

Amicis (Edmondo de). Spagna. 8ª ed. 8º. Firenze. 1883

Amicus Hiberniæ, *ps.*, see Barrington (J. T.)

Amiel (A. Traber-), see Traber-Amiel (A.)

Amiel (Denys). Monsieur & Mme. Un-tel: comédie, see Œuvres libres, 55, 1926.

—— **& A. Obey.** La souriante Madame Beudet: pièce, see Revue (La) hebdomadaire. Suppl.: coll. nouv., No. 7, 1922.

Amiel (Henri Fréd.)

Fragm. d'un journal intime. éd. nouv., augm. de fragm. inéd. & préc. d'une intr. par B. Bouvier. 3t. 8º. [1922]

Journal intime; tr. w. notes &c., by Mrs. H. Ward. n. ed. 8º. 1889

Philine: fragm. inéd. du Journal intime. Publ. B. Bouvier. Intr. par E. Jaloux. [Écr. intimes]. 8º. 1927

Principes gén. de pédagogie. Publ. avec intr. par L. Bopp. 8º. 1925

see Bopp (L.) H. F. A., 1926.

„ Brooks (Van W.) Malady of the ideal: Obermann, M. de Guérin, & A., 1913.

„ Seillière (*b.* E. A. A. L.) A. Vinet; app. s. A., 1925.

„ Thibaudet (A.) Intérieurs: A. &c., 1924.

Aminson (Henrik), see Strengnaees. Bibl. Templi Cathedralis S.; descr. ab. H. A., 1863.

Amira (Alessandro). Storia d. soggiorno di Carlo XII in Turchia. Pubbl. N. Iorga. 8º. Bucarest. 1905

Amira (Carl v.) Die german. Todesstrafen, see Kön. Akad. d. W. zu München, Abhdlgn., B31, 1922.
Die "grosse Bilderhs. v. Wolframs Willehalm," see Kön. Akad. d. W. zu München. Phil. Kl., Sitz., 1917.
Die Neubauersche Chronik, see Kön. Akad. d. W. zu München. Phil. Kl., Sitz., 1918.

'Amīr ibn Muhammad, *al-Ru'āmī*. Hist. Jemanae sub Hasano Pasha, quam e cod. MS. Arab. ed. &c. A. Rutgers [*Lat. tr., notes & index only, without Arabic text*]. s4º. Lugd. Bat. 1838

Amis. *Le roi Flore & la belle Jeanne—Amis & Amiles; adaptés par G. Michaut, 1923, see Flore, *le roi*.

Amling (Wolfgang). Ein Christl. Trostpredigt [*on Job I, 21*], v. d. Herrn Joachim Ernsten, Fürsten zu Anhalt. s4º. Zerbst. 1587
see Hoym (C. von). Erinnerungsschrifft &c. Verantwortung [*by John George; drawn up by W. A.*], 1597.

Ammann (Hans Jakob). H. J. Ammann, genannt d. Thalwyler Schärer, u. s. Reise ins Gelobte Land. [Text, 1630. Ed. A. F. Ammann. Pref. &c. by A. Waldburger]. 4º. Zürich. 1919

Ammers-Küller (Jo van).
Maskerade. 2e dr. 8º. Rotterdam. 1920

Ammerzode, see Amelroy.

Ammianus Marcellinus. Rerum gest. libri sup. Rec. C. U. Clark adjuv. L. Traube & G. Heraeo. v2, pl. 8º. Berolini. 1915
The Roman hist. Tr. C. D. Yonge. [repr.] s8º. *Bohn.* 1911
see Ensslin (W.) Zur Geschichtschr. u. Weltanschauung d. A. M., 1923.
„ Thornell (G.) Ad. Scr. Hist. Aug. & A. M., 1927.

Ammirato (Scipione), *the elder*. Albero e ist. d. famiglia de Conti Guidi, con l'agg. di S. Ammirato il G[iovane]. fol. Firenze. 1640

Ammirato (Scipione), *the younger*, see Ammirato (S.), *the elder*.

Ammon (Christoph Fr. v.)
Nova opuscula theolog. s8º. Gottingæ. 1803
Summa theolog. Christ. ed. 2ª. corr. 8º. Erlangæ. 1808

Ammon (Johann Christoph). Kernhaffter Auszug d. besten &c. Schrifften &c. aus allen Theilen d. theolog. Wiss. aus d. 40B. d. Unschuldigen Nachrichten. 5T [T5, Fortsetzung &c. *Foll*[d]. *by* A. Wolffens & G. Fr. Rogalls Hell leuchtender Spiegel d. Lehrer u. Prediger &c.] s8º. Roth. 1745–58

Ammonius (Clement), see Boissardus (J. J.) Bibl. chalcograph.; cont. *by* C. A., 1650–54.

***Amoenitates** lit. Friburgenses, 3 fasc., 1775–76, see Riegger (J. A. S. v.)

Amomo, *ps.* Rime toscane d'Amomo per Madama Charlotta d'Hisca. s8º. Parigi. 1535

Amonn (Alfred), see Wirtschaftstheorie. Beiträge z. W.; hrsg. K. Diehl, T1, Volkseinkommen &c.: wiss. Gutachten v. A. A. &c., 1926.

—— **& M. v. Bernatzky.** Währungsreform in d. Tschechoslowakei u. in Sowjet-Russl. [V. f. Sozialpol., B165iv]. 8º. München. 1924

Amor. *Theatrum amoris divini &c., 1655, see Theatrum.

Amoretti (Giovanni Vittorio). G. Boine e la lett. ital. contemp. [Veröff. d. Roman. Auslandsinst., Bonn, B2]. s8º. Bonn. 1922

Amoros (Bernard), *monk, of St.-Flour* [Amorosus (B.)].
Canzoniere provenzale. Intr. di G. Bertoni. [Coll. Friburgensia, N.S., fasc. 11, 12]. 2[v.] (1, Complemento Cámpori. 2, Sez. Riccardiana.) la8º. Friburgo (Sviz.) 1911

Amort (Eusebius), see Erhard (T. A.) Polycrates Gersen. contra scutum Kempense; apol. contra E. A., 1729.

Amory (Thomas C.) Milit. services & life of Maj.-Gen. J. Sullivan, of the Amer. Revol. army. 8º. Boston. 1868

Amos (Flora Ross). Early theories of transl. [Columbia Univ. St[s]. in Eng. &c. lit.] s8º. N.Y. 1920

Amos (Sheldon). The science of law. 9th ed. s8º. 1909

Amours. *Amours (Les) de Mr. Vieux Bois, *n.d.*, see Bois (*Mr.* V.), *ps.*
*Amours des grands hommes de France. [*b. w.* Galardi (P. F. de) Tyrannie heureuse, 1671]. pl, 2. s8º. 1676

Ampelius (Lucius). Liber memorialis, see Florus (L. A.) Rerum Romanar. libri IV, 1583.
see Florus (L. A.) L. A. F., Cl. Salmasius add. L. A., 1638.

Ampère (Jean Jacques), see Launay (L. de). Un amoureux de Mme. Récamier; journal de J. J. A., 1927.

Amphilochius, *Saint, bp. of Iconium* [*A. Iconiensis*]. Epistola ad Seleucum de recta studiorum ac vitæ ratione, vers. Iambicis scr. Græcolat. Interp. & ed. A. W. Cunone. Add. Gregorii Naz. carmine 33 de libris biblicis, rec. I. B. Bernholdi. [*b. w.* Dietelmair (J. A.) Hist. dogm. de descensu Xti ad inferos, 1741]. s8º. Altorphii. 1740

Amsdorff (Nicolaus von).

Antwort, Glaub &c. auff das Interim. [P2440]. s4º. [Magdeburg ?]. 1548

Auff die künstliche &c. Oration so D. Ziegler zu Leiptzig am Oster montag widder die bestendigen Lutherischen recitirt hat. Antwort [P2440]. s4º. Magdeburgk. *M. Lotther.* 1549

Das D. Pfeffinger seine missethat &c. leugnet überzeugt wird, das er die Kirchen Christi zustort &c. [P2442]. s4º. [Magdeburg]. 1559

Das in der Schrifft ausdrücklich verkündigt ist, Das die Röm. Kirche vom Christl. glauben abfallen, Christum &c. verleugnen sol. [P2468]. s4º. [Ihena]. 1555

Ein gut newe Jar den grossen Herrn in dieser Welt geschanckt. [P2468]. s4º. [Ihena]. 1554

*Die haubt artickel durch welche Christenheyt bysshere verfuret worden ist &c. s4º. Wittemberg. 1522

„ „ [*a. ed.*: Hauptartickel]. s4º. [Wittemberg ?] 1523

Das itzund die rechte zeit sey, Christum &c. zu bekennen &c. [P2468]. s4º. *n.p.* 1551

Ein kurtzer vnterricht auff D. Georgen Maiors Antwort, das er nit vnschůldig sey. s4º. Basel. 1552

see Luther (M.) Exempel einen Christl. Bischoff (N. v. A.) zu weihen, 1542.

„ Pfeffinger (J.) Antwort, u. Confut. d. Schwermerey N. v. A., 1558.

Amsterdam.
Amsterd. Pegasus. Liedekens door M. C[ampanus], J. J. C[olevelts], J. R[obbertsens], A. P. C[raen].— obl. s8º. t'Amstelredam. 1627
Cat. des peintures du Musée de l'Etat à A. par A. Bredius. 3e éd., rev. s8º. Amsterdam. 1891
Cat. van de Bibl. d. Vereen. Doopgezinde Gemeente te A. [*Pref. signed* S. Muller]. [3p & Suppl. *in* 1v.] 8º. Amsterdam. 1854–60
Lyste der naamen & woonplaatsen van de Makelaars, &c. [P2614]. s8º. A. 1784
Lyste van de capiteinen, luitenants &c. over de 60 Vaandelen Burgers binnen de Stad A. [P2614]. s8º. A. 1784
Naamen en woonplaatsen d. residenten, agenten, consuls &c. resid. binnen A. [P2614]. s8º. A. 1784
Naamen en woonplaatsen van de Assuradeurs &c. [P2614]. s8º. A. 1784
Naamen en woonplaatsen van de professoren in het Illustre Athenæum, Hortus Medicus, en Coll. Chirurgicum &c. [P2614]. s8º. A. 1784
Naamregister van alle de Kooplieden &c. d. stad A. &c. [P2614]. s8º. A. 1784

UNIVERSITY LIBRARY.
De incunabelen en de Nederland. uitg. tot 1540 in de Bibl. d. Univ. van A. Beschr. door C. P. Burger. 2d (d2 met Aanhangsel : De Amsterdam. uitg. tot 1578). 8º. 's-Gravenhage. 1919–23

Amsterdam (Johann), *see* LUTHER (M.) Etliche warhafft. weissagung u. spruche d. M. Luthers, durch J. A. zusamengebr., 1552.

Amsterdamsche Almanak voor Koophandel en Zeevaert, 1831, 1839, 1848. s8º. A. [1831–48]

Amstutz (Noah Steiner). Hdbk. of photo-engraving ; enl. & rev. of Jenkins' Man. of p. ; w. suppl. chs. by F. E. Ives & S. H. Horgan. 3rd ed. 8º. Chicago. 1907

Amthor (Christoph Heinrich). *Hist. &c. Untersuchung d. Uhrsachen [sic] durch welche d. zw. Dennemarck u. Schweden vorgefall. Streitigkeiten &c. sich entsponnen &c. Von e. Dännemärcker übergeben. s4º. [Copenhagen]. 1715

Amthor (Georg Michael). De apostasia. 8º. Coburgi. 1823

Amu, *river.* *Аму и Узбой. [P2396]. 8º. Самара. [1879]

Amundsen (Roald). My life as an explorer. 8º. 1927
My Polar flight. 8º. [1925]

Amyraut (Moyse). Discours de l'estat des fidèles après la mort. s4º. Saumur. 1646
Discourse conc. divine dreams mention'd in Scripture. Tr. J. Lowde. s8º. 1676

Amzalak (Moses Bensabat).
David Nieto : notícia biobibliog. 4º. Lisboa. 1923
A tipografia hebraica em Portugal no sec. 15. 4º. Coimbra. 1922

Anacreon.
Opera Græce : cum Lat. vers. &c. indice. [*Ed.* M. Maittaire. *Only 100 copies printed*]. 4º. Londini. 1725
Carmina &c. ed. 3ª. s8º. Argentorati. 1786
Les odes d'A. et de Sapho en vers franç. par le poëte Sans Fard [*w. text*]. s8º. Rotterdam. 1712
see DIEHL (E.) Anthol. lyrica, v1, 1925.
„ LYRA. Lyra Græca ; ed. & tr. by J. M. Edmonds, v2, A. &c., 1924.

Anagnostopulos (G. P.) Tsakon. Grammatik. Geleitwort v. E. Schwyzer. [Texte &c. z. Byz.-Neugriech. Philologie, Beiheft, Nr. 5]. 8º. 1926

Anais das bibliotecas e arquivos. Ser. 2, v1–5. la8º. 1920–24

Analecta. Analecta Græca hactenus non ed. &c., 1688, *see* COTELERIUS (J. B.) Eccles. Gr. mon., t4, 1688.
*Analecta sacra & mira de rebus Catholic. in Hibernia &c., 3p, 1617–19, *see* ROTH (D.)

Analecta Bollandiana. t34–44. la8º. Brux. 1915–26
see CHEVALIER (U.) Repert. hymnolog. &c (extr. des A. B.], 1892–1912.

Analecta hymnica medii ævi. [v]54, 55. 8º. L. 1915–22
Die Sequenzen d. Thesaurus Hymnologicus H. A. Daniels &c. T2i, Liturg. Prosen d. Übergangsstiles u. d. 2en Epoche, insbes. die d. Adam v. St. Victor zugeschrieb. &c. hrsg. v. C. Blume u. H. Bannister. [54.]
T2ii, Liturg. Prosen 2er Epoche auf Feste d. Heiligen ; nebst Anhange : Hymnodie d. Gelderlandes u. d. Haarlemer Gebietes aus HSS. &c. hrsg. v. C. Blume. [55.]
Ein Jahrtausend latein. Hymnendichtung ; aus d. A. hymnica, 2t, 1909, *see* DREVES (G. M.)

Analysis. *Analysis (An) of the moral & relig. sentiments cont. in Sopho &c., 1755, *see* ANDERSON (G.)
Analysis operum S. S. Patrum & script. eccles., 18t, 1780–96, *see* SCHRAM (D.)

Anamnesis. 'Ανάμνησις juris quod in approb. pontificibus imperatores habuerunt, &c., 1562, *see* PONTIFICES.

Ānanda Āchārya, *Śrī.*
The book of the cave : Gaurisankarguhā. 8º. 1919
Snow-birds. 8º. 1919

Ananda Ranga, *Pilāi.*
Diary. Tr. Ed. H. Dodwell. v7–11. 8º. Madras. 1919–27

Ananias, *of Narek.* [Book of confession (10c.) *In Armenian. Ed.* Miaban. *Extr. f. Ararat,* 1892. P2792]. 8º. Vagharshapat. 1892

Ananias, *of Shirak* (*7c.*), *see* AUCHER (P.) Anc. weights &c. *by* A. &c., *in Armenian,* 1821.

Ananias, *the translator.* [A. the Tr. & his lit. works (On Jonah & John the Baptist). *In Armenian.* Ed. B. Sargisean. P2811]. 8º. Venetik. 1899

Ananikian (Mardiros H.), *see* MYTHOLOGY of all races, v7, Armenian ; by M. H. A., 1925.

***Ananoun** zamanakagrouthiun : [anon. chron. (7c.) *partly comp. by* Andreas ?] ; ed. B. Sargisean, 1904, *see* ARMENIAN.

Anaphora, *see* EUCHOLOGION. Anaphora of St. Basil, St Gregory & St. Cyril &c. *Copt. & Arab.*, 1736.

Anarchy. *Complete grammar (The) of a., 1918, *see* COMPLETE.

Anastasius, *bibliothecarius.* De vitis Roman. pontif. : cum notis. 4t [*each vol. has 2 pagin.*] fol. Romæ. 1718–35
see PERELS (E.) Papst Nikolaus I u. A. B., 1920.

Anastasius, *Sinaita, presbyter.* Sermo III De hominis creatione, *see* CHRYSOSTOM, *St.* In Ninivit. poenitent. homilia &c., 1764.

Anatolia. Inquiries in A. Rep. of Interallied Inquiry Mission, rep. of M. Gheri &c. [1919–22]. [P2712]. 8º. Lausanne. [1922]

Anatolian studies ; pres. to Sir W. M. Ramsay ; ed. W. H. Buckler &c., 1923, *see* RAMSAY (*Sir* W. M.)

Anatomy. *Anatomy (The) of Simon Magus, 1700, *see* SIMON MAGUS.

Ancel (Jacques). Manuel hist. de la q. d'Orient (1792–1923) 8º. 1923
Peuples & nations des Balkans. s8º. 1926
Les travaux & les jours de l'armée d'Orient, 1915–18. s8º. 1921

Ancelet-Hustache (Jeanne). Mechtilde de Magdebourg, 1207–82 : ét. de psych. relig. 8º. 1926

Ancelot (Jacques Arsène P. F.)
Vie de Chateaubriand. la8º. 1856

Anchel (Robert). La commém. des rois de France à Paris pend. la Restauration, *see* SOCIÉTÉ DE L'HIST. DE PARIS &c., Mém., t47, 1924.

Anchieta (José d'). Sermão, 1568, *see* INSTITUTO HIST. E GEOG. BRAZIL. Revista, t54, 1891.

Anciens poëtes (Les) de la France, 10t, 1859–70, *see* GUESSARD (F.), *ed.*

Ancient [ANTIENT].
*Ancient (The) & mod. hist. of the Balearick Islands ; tr., 1716, *see* DAMETO (J.) & V. MUT.
Ancient records of Assyria & Babylonia, v1, 2, 1926–27, *see* LUCKENBILL (J. D.), *ed.*
*Antient (The) & mod. hist. of the city of York &c., 1730, *see* GENT (T.)

Ancient Egypt. Ed. F. Petrie. 1916, 1917, 1920–26. la8º. 1916–26

***Ancilla's** share, 1924, *see* ROBINS (*Miss* ELIZ.)

Ancillon (J. P. Friedrich).
Glauben u. Willen in d. Philos. [P2471]. 8º. 1824
Zur Vermittlung d. Extreme i. d. Meinungen. 2T [in 1B.] 8º. 1828–31
T1, Gesch. u. Politik. T2, Philos. u. Poesie.

Ancillon (Louis Frédéric). Judicium de judiciis c. argumentum Cartes. pro existentia Dei. 8º. Berolini. 1792

Ancona (Eligio). Hist. de Yucatán. Ed. M. Heredia Argüelles. 2a ed. 4t. 8º. Barcelona. 1889

Ancona (Paolo d'). La miniatura fiorentina (sec. 11–16). 2v. (1, Testo e tavole. 2, Catalogo descritt.) fol. Firenze. 1914
La miniature ital. du 10e au 16e siècle. Tr. P. Poirier. fol. 1925

Ancora (Gaetano d'). Guida ragionata per le antichità e per le curiosità naturali di Pozzuoli &c. 8º. Napoli. 1792

Ancren Rule, *see* DYMES (D. M. E.) The orig. lang. of the A. R., 1924.

Ancyranum, *Monumentum, see* AUGUSTUS (C. J. C. O.), *emp. of Rome.*

Ander (Peter Justus). Über Ursprung &c. d. Rhaeto-Roman. Spr. 8º. Chur. 1862

Anderdon (J. H.), *see* Weston (A. A.) Cat. of engr. portraits, formed by J. H. A., 1904.

Andersen (Hans Christian), *the Novelist.*

Eventyr. ny, krit. Udg. med Komm. ved H. Brix & A. Jensen. 5B. s8°. 1919

Der Improvisator. Übers. H. Denhardt. s8°. L. [1890 ?]

Kun en Spillemand. 2[en] Udg. 2D. [*in* 1v.] s8°. 1854

Märchen. Für d. Jugend ausgewählt v. H. Heller. s8°. Nürnberg. [1915]

Märchen. 2B. 8°. L. 1923

Nur ein Geiger. Übers. G. Fink. s8°. St. 1848

Only a fiddler & o. t. Tr. M. Howitt. 3v. [*in* 1]. 8°. 1845

Sämtl. Märchen. 16[e] A. s8°. L. [1920]

Tales for children. Tr. by A. Wehnert & C. Peachey. *n. ed.* 8°. 1872

Il violinista. Tr. B. Sperani. 8°. Milano. 1879

see Reumert (E.) H. A. the man; tr., 1927.

Andersen (Johannes C.) 100 represent. New Zealand books. [Alex. Turnbull Lib. Bull. 1]. [P2834]. 8°. Wellington, N.Z. 1925

Andersen (Vilh.) Adam Oehlenschläger et Livs Poesi. [3v.] la8°. 1899–1900
1, Ungdom. 2, Mandom og Alderdom. 3, Eftermaele.
Paludan-Müller. 2B. 8°. København. 1910

Anderson (*Surgeon*), *see* Firminger (W. K.) Diaries of 3 surgeons [A. &c.], 1909.

Anderson (*Dame* **Adelaide Mary).** Humanity & labour in China: indust. visit, 1923–26. 8°. 1928
Women in the factory, 1893–1921. 8°. 1922

Anderson (Alan Orr). Early sources of Scot. hist., 500–1286. Coll. & ed. by A. O. A. 2v. 8°. E. 1922

Anderson (Alex. Grant), *Medical officer of health, Rochdale, see* Rochdale. Rep. on housing conditions &c., 1911.

Anderson (Arthur P. Moore-), *see* Moore-Anderson (A. P.)

Anderson (*Hon. Mrs.* **Caroline Dorothea).** Pract. relig. exempl. by letters & life of R. Anderson. s8°. 1845

Anderson (David), *of Glasgow.* Cat. of mod. pictures &c., prop. of D. A., Hon. Mrs. B. M. Denison &c., sold by Christie, May 13, 1927. [Illust.] 8°. 1927

Anderson (Dice Robins). Edmund Randolph, *see* Bemis (S. F.), *ed.* Amer. Secr. of State, v2, 1927.

Anderson (Ernest Masson), *see* Richey (J. E.), G. V. Wilson & E. M. A. Econ. geology of Ayrshire coalfields, 2v, 1925.

Anderson (George), *of Glasgow* [*ps.* Cyclops].
Art of skating. s8°. Glasgow. 1852
" " ....2nd ed. s8°. 1868

Anderson (George), *of Inverness,* **& Peter Anderson.** Guide to Highlands & islands of Scotland &c. s8°. 1834

Anderson (George), *of the Tron Ch., Edinb.* *An analysis of the moral &c. sentiments in wr. of Sopho & Hume, *wrongly attrib. to G. A.*, 1755, *see* Bonar (J.)
An estimate of the profit & loss of relig.: w. refs. to Essays on morality &c. [*by* H. Home, Ld. Kames]. 8°. E. 1753

Anderson (*Sir* **George),** *C.I.E.*, **& M. Subedar.** The development of an Indian policy (1818–1858). [Last days of the Company, 1]. 8°. 1921

Anderson (H. M.) Kelston of Kells. s8°. E. 1927

Anderson (James), *LL.D., of Monk's Hill, Aberdeenshire.* An acc. of the pres. state of the Hebrides & W. coasts of Scot. &c. [w. app.] 8°. E. 1785

Anderson (James Drummond), *see* Punjab: Govt. Publ. Custom. law of the Muzaffargarh distr., comp. by A., 1926.

Anderson (James R.), *see* Glasgow. The burgesses & guild-brethren of G., 1573–1750, ed. J. R. A., 1923–25.

Anderson (John), *of Dumbarton.* A defence of the church govt. &c. of the Presbyterians. n. ed. rev. 8°. E. 1820

Anderson (John), *fugitive slave.* Story of the life of J. A. Ed. H. Twelvetrees. s8°. 1863

Anderson (John Corbet). Short chron. conc. parish of Croydon, Surrey. 8°. 1882

Anderson (John George Clark). Pontica. [Rep. of work in 1899, pl. Repr. f. journal of Hellenic St., v20. P2516]. la8°. 1900

Anderson (*Lt.-Col.* **Joseph).**
Recoll[s]. of a Peninsular veteran. 8°. 1913

Anderson (Madge). Heroes of the puppet stage. 8°. [1924]

Anderson (Nels). The hobo: sociology of the homeless man. 8°. Chicago. [1923]

Anderson (Nicolai). Studien z. Vergleichung d. indogerm. u. finn.-ugr. Sprachen. [*no tp., book begins at page* 49]. 8°. [Dorpat. 1879]

Anderson (Peter), *of Inverness, see* Anderson (G.) & P. A. Guide to Highlands &c., 1834.

Anderson (R.), *architect.* Examples of the municipal, commercial & street archit. of France & Italy, 12–15 cent. fol. [1870–75]

Anderson (Robert), *of the Madras C. Service.* Rudiments of Tamuḻ grammar. la8°. 1821

Anderson (Robert), *of Trinity Chapel, Brighton,* 1795–1843, *see* Anderson (*Hon.* C. D.) Pract. relig. exempl. by letters & life of R. A., 1845.

Anderson (*Sir* **Robert),** *LL.D., see* Moore-Anderson (A. P.) Sir R. A., 1919.

Anderson (*Sir* **Robert Rowand),** *see* Scottish. Examples of Scottish architecture f. 12th to 17th c.: reprod[s].; ed. Sir R. R. A. &c., 1921.

Anderson (Roger Charles), *F.R.G.S., see* Anderson (Romola) & R. C. A. The sailing-ship, 1926.
see Rigging. A treatise on r., *c.* 1625; ed. R. C. A., 1921.

Anderson (Romola) & R. C. Anderson.
The sailing-ship: 6000 yrs. of hist. 8°. [1926]

Anderson (Sherwood).
The triumph of the egg. [repr.] s8°. N.Y. 1921

Anderson (Vladimir Maksimilian).
Старообрядчество и сектантство. Истор. очеркъ. 8°. С.–П. *n.d.*

Anderson (Walter). Der Chalifenmünzfund v. Kochtel, mit Beitr. v. R. Vasmer, *see* Dorpat Univ. Acta &c., B, v7, 1927.

Anderson (William), *M.Inst.C.E.*
Conversion of heat into work. 8°. 1887

Anderson (William), *misc. writer.* The Scot. nation: surnames, families, biog. hist. 3v. la8°. E. 1862–3

Andersson (Aksel). Paul Schwenke. [Särtryck ur Nord. Tidskrift för Bok-& Biblioteksväsen, 1922]. [P2702]. la8°. [Upsala. 1922]
Upsala Univ. Biblioteks om-och tillbyggnad åren 1913–17. [P2416]. la8°. Uppsala. 1919

Anderton (Basil). Sketches f. a library window. [Justus Lipsius &c.] 8°. C. 1922

Anderton (H. Orsmond).
Early Eng. music. Pref. by R. R. Terry. s8°. 1920
Granville Bantock. s8°. 1915
The song of Alfred. [*Epic poem*]. 8°. 1912

Andler (Charles).

Nietzsche, sa vie & sa pensée. [t] 1, 2, 3, 5, [t2, 2e éd.] 8°. 1920–22
1, Précurseurs; 2, Jeunesse; 3. Pessimisme esthét.; 5, N. & le transformisme intellect.

Le Pangermanisme colonial (1888–1914). Préf. par C. A. Textes tr. par L. Simonnot. 8°. 1916

Le Pangermanisme continental (1888–1914). Textes tr. par L. Marchand, G. Bianquis &c. Préf. par C. A. 8°. 1915

Le Pangermanisme philosoph. (1800–1914). Textes tr. M. Aboucaya &c. Préf. par C. A. 8°. 1917

Andocides. Orationes [*in Greek*], *see* Oratores. Orationes, p2, 1513.
see Dobson (W. S.) *ed.* Oratores Attici, t1, Antiphon & A., t13, Antiphonis, A. &c. interpret. Lat., 1828.

Andonian (Aram), *see* Naim *Bey.* Memoirs: Turkish offic. doc[s]. rel. to Armenians; comp. by A. A., 1920.

Andoyer (Henri), *see* Hanotaux (G.) Hist. de la nation franç., t14, Hist. des sciences, v1, Mathémat., mécanique &c. par H. A. &c., 1924.

Andrade (Edward Neville da Costa).
The structure of the atom. 8°. 1923

Andrae (August). Französ. Belege zu Wanderanekdoten &c., *see* Romanische Forsch., B34, 1915.

Andrae (Walter). Der Anu-Adad-Tempel in Assur. [Deut. Or.-Gesell., Wiss. Veröff., 10]. fol. L. 1909
Die Festungswerke v. Assur. [Deut. Or.-Gesell., Wiss. Veröff., 23]. [2B]. (1, Textband; 2, Tafelband). fol. L. 1913
Hatra. Nach Aufnahmen v. Mitgliedern d. Assur-Exped. d. Deut. Or.-Gesell. [Deut. Or.-Gesell., Wiss. Veröff., 9, 21]. 2T in 1v. fol. L. 1908–12
Die Stelenreihen in Assur. [Deut. Or.-Gesell., Wiss. Veröff., 24]. fol. L. 1913

Andrássy (*Graf* **Julius),** *the elder,* 1823–90. Gróf Andrássy G. beszédei. 2k (1847–71). 8°. 1891–93
see Andrassy (J.), *the younger.* Bismarck, A. &c., 1927.

Andrássy (*Graf* **Julius),** *the younger,* 1860– .

A Magyar állam. 2k. la8°. Budapest. 1901–5

Az 1867-iki kiegyezésröl. 8°. 1896

Bismarck, Andrassy & their successors. 8°. 1927

Diplomacy & the War. Tr. J. H. Reece. 8°. 1921

Diplomatie u. Weltkrieg. 8°. 1920

André (*Major* **John**), *see* †SEWARD (*Miss* A.) Poet. wks., v2 (Monody on A. & Letters by A.), 1810.

André (Louis), *see* BOURGEOIS (E.) & L. A. Les sources de l'hist. de France : 17e s., 1610–1715, t3–5, 1923–26.

André (Marius). La fin de l'empire espagnol d'Amérique. Préf. de C. Maurras s8°. [1922]

Das wahre Abenteuer d. C. Columbus. Übertr. v. J. Eckardt. s8°. Wien. 1927

André (*capt.* **P. J.**) [PIERRE REDAN]. L'Islam Noir : confréries relig. islam. en Afr. occid. &c. Préf. de J. Carde. s8°. 1924

André (R. Ed.), *see* SAINT-SAUVEUR (H.) Les beaux jardins de France ; introd. de R. E. A., 1922.

André (Valère), *see* ANDREAS (VALERIUS), *Desselius.*

Andréadès (A.) La destr. de Smyrne & les dern. atrocités turques en Asie Mineure (sep.–nov. 1922). [P2682]. 8°. Athènes. 1923

Le montant du budget de l'Emp. Byzantin. [Extr. de La Rev. des Ét. Gr., t34, 1921]. [P2703]. la8°. 1922

La population angl. 8°. Ferrara. [1922]

Andreæ (G.) The dawn of juvenile lit. in England. 8°. Amsterdam. 1925

Andreae (Jacob), *called Schmidtlein.* [SMIDELINUS (J.).]

Acta colloquii Montis Belligartensis, 1586. Præside Friderico com. Wirtembergico &c. Inter J. A. & T. Bezam. [Pref. by Frederick, count of Wurtemberg]. s4°. Tubingæ. 1594

Assertio piæ &c. doctr. de personali unione qua resp. ad T. Beze Placidum &c. resp. ad J. Brentii argumenta &c. s4°. Tubingæ. 1565

Collatio catholicæ &c. fidei de persona Christi & sacra ejus cœna cum disput. I.A. hab. Wittembergæ a. LXXX. [Repetitio doct. Lutheri]. [P2504]. s4°. Neapoli Nemetum. 1582

Confutatio disputat. J. J. Grynæi de Cœna Domini Heidelbergæ 4 April. 1584 propos. s4°. Tubingæ. 1584

Disput. de electione &c. divina. Præs. J. A., A. Kommerellus resp. [P2626]. s4°. Tubingæ. 1574

Oratio de incarnatione Filii Dei, contra errores Zwinglianorum & Calvinist. [P2504]. s4°. Tubingæ. 1586

Prima disput. c. errores Calvinistarum, de baptismo. Præs. J. A., def. G. Otho. [P2673]. s4°. Tubingæ. 1588

*Solida refut. compil. Cinglianæ & Calvin. &c. Conscr. per theologos Wirtembergicos. fol. Tubingæ. 1584

Von d. Erbsünde &c. [P2665]. s4°. [Eisleben]. 1573

see ANDREÆ (J. V.) Fama Andreana reflorescens sive J. A. vitæ &c. recitatio, 1630.

see BEUMLER (M.) Ad J. A. triplex scriptum &c. 1586.

,, BREMEN. *Antwort d. Diener Gôttl. Worts in d. Kirchen &c. zu B. auf J. A. Widerlegung &c., 1583.

,, CAROLUS (A. D.) Wirtenberg. Unschuld durch Prüfung dessen, was G. Arnold, bevorab v. J. A. aufgez. u. s. Kirchen-u. Ketzer-Hist. einverleibt hat, 1708.

,, FLACIUS (M.) Defensio de originali peccato &c. á J. Andraea aed., 1575.

,, HEERBRAND (J.) Oratio funebris de vita & obitu J. A., 1590.

,, INGOLSTADT. *Disp. de majestate Christi, adv. impias J. A. theses, 1564.

,, LATOMUS (B.) De docta simplicitate primæ Ecclesiæ &c. adv. insult. J. A., 1559.

,, NASE (J.) Examen chartaceæ Lutheran. Concordiæ &c. [*against J. A.*], 1581.

,, PAREUS (D.) Rettung der zur Newstadt a. d. H. getr. Bibel wider J. A. &c., 1592.

,, STAPHYLIUS (F.) *elder.* Prodromus &c., adv. J. S., 1563.

,, STURMIUS (J.) Epist. apolog. contra J. A., 1581.

,, VIA (J. A.) Jugis eccl. cathol. sacrificii &c. : def. c. calumnias J. A. S., 1570.

Andreæ (Johann Valentin). Fama Andreana reflorescens sive J. Andreae vitæ, funeris, scriptorum &c. recitatio. [Leich predigt durch L. Osiandrum—Olea Andreana, *w. sep. tp.*] s8°. Argentorati. 1630

see HAFENREFFER (M.) Doct. Christ. summa, contr. à J. V. A., 1614.

Andreae (Wolffgang Ludwig). Cometa nuperus an & quæ mala præsignificare credendus sit ? &c. Praes. J. C. Sturmius. [P447]. s4°. Altdorfi. [1681]

Andrea Guardi, *see* GUARDI (A.)

Andreas, *Presbyter, Ratisbonensis* [ANDREAS V. REGENSBURG], *see* WAHL (J.) A.v. R., e. Geschichtsschr. d. 15. Jhdts., 1882.

Andreas (Valerius), *Desselius, see* NÈVE (F.) Valère André, 1846.

Andreas (Willy). Russ. Diplomatie u. Politik Fr. Wilhelms IV. v. Preussen, 1927, *see* KÖNIGL. - PREUSS. AKAD. Abhandl., Phil.-hist. Kl., 1926.

Andree (Richard). Handatlas. Ergänzungsband. fol. L. 1922, *see* KOHN (A.) & R. A. Sibirien u. das Amurgebiet, 2B, 1876.

Andreev (Ivan Dmitr.), *ed., see* SAINT PETERSBURG : UNIV. Отчетъ о состочніи &c. С.–П. унив. за 1913, 1914.

Andreev (Leonid Nikolaevich).

Анатэма. Трагич. представленіе. 8°. Berlin. *n.d.*

Анфиса. Драма. 8°. Berlin. *n.d.*

Губернаторъ. Повѣсть. 8°. Berlin. *n.d.*

Екатерина Ивановна. Драма [*b. w. h.* Анфиса, *n.d.*] 8°. Berlin. *n.d.*

Жизнь Василія Ѳивеискаго—Красный смѣхъ—Воръ, *see* SBORNIK. Сб. товар. "Знаніе" 1, 3, 5, 1904–5.

Изъ дневника, *see* RUSSKII. P. сборникъ, 1920.

Книга о Леониде Андреве. Воспоминания М. Горького &c. 8°. П. 1922

Красный смѣхъ. [*a. c. b. w. h.* Губернаторъ, *n.d.*] 8°. Berlin. *n.d.*

Мысль, Драма. 8°. Berlin. *n.d.*

Надсмертное—Возвратъ. Два разсказа.[*a. c. b. w. h.* Губернаторъ, *n.d.*] 8°. Berlin. *n.d.*

Не убій. Драма. [*b. w. h.* Анфиса, *n.d.*] 8°. Berlin. *n.d.*

Прекрасныя Сабинянки. [*b. w. h.* Анфиса, *n.d.*] 8°. Berlin. *n.d.*

Происшествіе — Попугаи. Двѣ пьесы [*b. w. h.* Мысль *n.d.*] 8°. Berlin. *n.d.*

Профессоръ Сторицынъ, Драма [*b. w. h.* Мысль, *n.d.*]. 8°. Berlin. *n.d.*

Разсказъ о семи повѣшенныхъ. [*a. c. b. w. h.* Губернаторъ, *n.d.*] 8°. Berlin. *n.d.*

Сынъ человѣческій. [*b. w. h.* Анатэма, *n.d.*] 8°. Berlin. *n.d.*

Тотъ, кто получаетъ пощечины. Представленіе. [*a. c. b. w. h.* Мысль, *n.d.*] 8°. Берлинъ. *n.d.*

У окна. [P2719]. 8°. С.–П. 1906

TRANSLATIONS.

Anathema. Tragedy. Tr. H. Bernstein. s8°. N.Y. 1910

Il Belgio vivrà ! Dramma. [Tr.] Markoff e L. E. Morselli. 8°. *n.d.*

The dark. Tr. L. A. Magnus & K. Walter. 8°. Richmond. 1922

Le rire rouge. La guerre en Mandchourie. Tr. S. Persky. s8°. [1905]

Samson in chains : posthumous tragedy. Auth. tr. & pref. by H. Bernstein. s8°. [1923]

Les sept pendus. La vie d'un pope. Tr. par S. Persky & A. Touchard. s8°. 1911

To the stars. Drama. Tr. by M. Magnus. s8°. 1921

see ROERICH (N. C.) "The messenger" (R.'s paintings) : 7 articles by F. Adney, L. A. &c., 1925.

André-Hesse (Germaine). Anna Karénine, manucure ; nouvelle, *see* ŒUVRES libres, 67, 1926.

Andrei Vladimirovich, *see* ANDREW VLADIMIROVICH.

Andréossi (*le cte* **Antoine François**). Constantinopel u. d. Bosporus von Thrazien in 1812–14, u. 1826. Aus d. Franz. üb. v. Dr. Bergk. 8°. L. 1828

André-Pontier (L.) Hist. de la pharmacie. la8°. 1900

Andres (Juan Francisco). Vida de San Orencio obispo de Aux. Transl. de sus reliquias a Huesca. s4°. Zaragoça. 1648

Andrew, *Saint, abp. of Caesarea.* [Comm. on the Apocalypse. By A. & Arethas. Tr. into Armenian by Nerses, *abp. of Tarsus*]. s8°. Yerousalem. 1855

Andrew II, *king of Hungary* [ENDRE], *see* GAAL (M.) II. Endre Magyar király, 1903.

Andrew Vladimirovich [ROMANOV], *grand duke, b.* 1879. Дневник 1915 г. Ред. В. П. Семенникова. 8°. Ленинград 1925

Andrew (G. W.) Fuel. Ed. G. W. A., [*w.*] sections by H. Louis, A. W. Eastlake &c. Intrs. by Sir E. Geddes & Sir R. A. Hadfield. [Resources of the Empire, v4]. 4°. 1924

Andrewes (Lancelot), *bp. of Winchester.*

The pattern of catechistical doctrine ; expos. of the Ten Commandments &c. 4°. 1650

Preces privatæ Græcè & Latinè. s8°. O. 1675

Private devotions & Manual for the sick. s8°. *Pickering.* 1839

96 sermons, 5th ed. ; added, a sermon, Aug. 1606. fol. 1661

17 sermons on the Nativity. n. ed. 8°. [1890]

Tortura Torti, sive ad Matthæi Torti [*i.e. Card. Bellarmino*] librum responsio. s4°. Londini. 1609

Andrews (Alfred). Genealogy & eccles. hist. [of New Britain]. 8°. Chicago. 1867

Andrews (Charles McLean). The colon. background of the Amer. Revol. 8°. New Haven. 1924

Guide to the materials for Amer. hist. to 1783 in the Public Rec. Office. 2v. [C. I. of Wash. Publ., 90A]. la8°. Wash. 1912–14

Hist. development of mod. Europe, 1815–97. Student's ed. 2v. *in* 1 [*sep. pagin*s.]. 8°. N.Y. 1900

Andrews (Ethan Allen), *see* FREUD (W.) Lat.-Eng. lex.; founded on lex. of F., w. add. by A., 1862.

Andrews (F. H.) Ancient Chinese figured silks, excav. by Sir A. Stein &c. [Repr. f. Burlington Mag., 1920. P2508]. 4º. 1920

Andrews (Herbert), *see* BECK (C.) & H. A. Photographic lenses, 1903.

Andrews (Irene Osgood) & M. A. Hobbs. Econ. effects of the World War upon women & children in Gt. Brit. [Carnegie Endowment f. Internat. Peace. Prelim. econ. studies]. 2nd (rev.) ed. la8º. N.Y. 1921

Andrews (John), *LL.D.* The day of alarm; view of the spirit &c. of men in France. 8º. [1803]

An essay on republican principles &c. [P2515]. 8º. 1783

Andrews (John), *LL.B., vic. of Marden, Kent.* The Scripture-doct. of divine grace. 2nd ed. s8º. 1769

Andrews (John Bertram). Anthrax, 1917; 1920, *see* UNITED STATES: LABOUR. Bull. 205, 267, 1920.

Andrews (Roy Chapman). On the trail of anc. man: field work of the Cent. Asiatic Expeds. [1922, 23, 25]. Intr. &c. by H. F. Osborn. la8º. N.Y. 1926

Andrews (Samuel J.) The life of our Lord upon the earth. n. & rev. ed. 8º. E. 1892

Andrews (William).
Famous frosts & frost fairs in Gt. Brit. 8º. 1887

Andrievich (Vladimir Kallistrat.) Сибирь въ xix ст. (1796–1819). 2ч *in* 1v. 8º. С.-П. 1889

Androclus, *ps., see* WARD (W. J.)

Andronicus [*Comnenus*], *see* FULLER (T.), *D.D.* Andronicus or the unfortunate politician, 1646.

Andrović (Johann). Gramm. d. lingua jugo-slava (serbo-croata). [Manuali Hoepli]. 2ª ed. s8º. Milano. 1920

Anecdotes. *A. of Mr. Hogarth &c., 1803; 1811; 1813, *see* HOGARTH (W.)

Anet (Claude), *ps.* [*i.e.* J. SCHOPFER].
Adolesence, nouvelle, *see* ŒUVRES libres, 53, 1925.
Ariane, jeune fille russe. s8º. 1920
Ariane. Tr. G. Chapman. s8º. 1927
Les bergeries. s8º. [1904]
Feuilles persanes. [Cahiers verts, 32]. s8º. 1924
,, ,, [*a. ed.*] s8º. 1924
La fille perdue: pièce, *see* ŒUVRES libres, 35, 1924.
La fin d'un monde. s8º. 1925
Nadia, *see* ŒUVRES libres, 13, 1922.
Notes sur l'amour. s8º. 1908
Notes sur l'amour en Russie, *see* ŒUVRES libres, 9, 1922.
Petite ville. n. éd. s8º. 1921
Quand la terre trembla. . . . s8º. 1921
La rive d'Asie. [6e éd.] s8º. 1927
Théâtre. Mademoiselle Bourrat—La fille perdue. s8º. 1924

Anetzi (Mekhithar), *see* MEKHITHAR, *Anetzi.*

Angas (Lawrence Lee Bazley). Germany & h. debts: reparation problem &c. s8º. 1923
Reparations, trade & foreign exchange s8º. 1922

Ange. *Ange (L') conducteur dans la dévotion chrétienne &c., 1780, *see* CORET (J.)

Angeberg (*cte.* **d'),** *ps.* [*i.e.* JAKÒB LEONARD CHODZKO]. Recueil des traités, conventions &c. conc. la Pologne, 1762–1862. 8º. 1862

Angel. *Angel's (An) message, 1858, *see* FAWCETT (*Miss* J.)

Angel (Manuel Uribe), *see* URIBE ANGEL (M.)

Angela [*Merici*], *St., foundress of the Ursulines, see* HUBERT (W. E.) Levensbilder kath. Erzieher, B3, 1891.
see MONICA, *Sister.* A. M. & h. teaching idea, 1474–1540, 1927.

Angelbertus, *see* ANGILBERTUS.

Angeli (Bonaventura), *historian.* Hist. d. cittá de Parma, & descr. del fiume Parma. s4º. Parma. 1591

Angeli (Luigi). Mem. biograf. di uomini ill. Imolesi &c. 8º. Imola. 1828
Mem. stor. sull'Ordine Aureato, Con note &c. del P. Giacchieri. 3ª ed. 8º. 1841

Angelico (*Frà*).
see DOUGLAS (L.) Fra A., 2nd ed., 1902.
,, MASON (J.) Fra A., 1907.
,, PAPINI (R.) Fra Giov. A., 1925.
,, SCHNEIDER (E.) Fra A. da Fiesole, 1387–1455, 1924.

Angelino (P. De Kat). Mudras auf Bali: Handhaltungen d. Priester. Zeichn. v. T. de Kleen. [Kulturen d. Erde, B15]. 4º. Hagen i. W. 1923

Angell (Norman), *ps.* [*i.e.* N. ANGELL LANE]. The fruits of victory. Sequel to "The great illusion." s8º. [1921]
The public mind. s8º. [1926]
see WAR & PEACE: a N.A. monthly, v1, 2, 1913–14.

Angelo (Henry). Reminisc., w. mems. of h. father & friends. 2v. 8º. 1828–30

Angelomus, *Monachus.* Enarrat. in Cantica Canticorum. [P2544]. s8º. Coloniæ. 1531

Angelon (Manuel). Crón. de la prov. de Barcelona, 1870, *see* ESPAÑA. Crón. gen., v3, 1865 &c.

Angeloni (Francesco), *di Terni.* Hist. di Terni. [3p *&* Vite de' santi &c. di T., *pagin. cont.*] la8º. 1646

Angelos (Christophoros) [ANGELUS (C.)] Enchiridium de statu hodiern. Graecorum. Graecè conscr., cum vers. Lat. & annotat. cura G. Fehlavii. s4º. Lipsiæ. 1676
Status & ritus eccl. Graecae, Graecè descr. à C. A. Lat. conv. à G. Ehelavio &c. s8º. Francofurto. 1655

Angelsächsiche Lesebuch mit Glossar versehen, 1915, *see* KLUGE (F.), *ed.*

Angelus [CARLETUS], *de Clavasio.* Summa Angelica de casibus Conscientie. s4º. Parisiis. 1502
519 numbered leaves, preceded by 7 unnumbered cont. Prologue &c. (the first of which is missing) & followed by 14 unnumbered (sig. VV 1–8, XX 1–6) cont. the Rubrice &c.

Angelus *a S. Francisco* [N. MASON]. Certamen Seraphicum prov. Angliae pro sancta Dei eccl., in quo declar. quomodo fratres minores Angli certarunt &c. [App. de missionibus. Cat. script. Anglorum ex ord. fratrum Min.] s4º. Duaci. 1649

Angelus Silesius (Johannes), *ps., see* SCHEFFLER (JOHANN).

Anger (Helmut). Die wicht. geograph. Lit. ü. d. Russ. Reich seit 1914 in russ. Spr. la8º. Hamburg. 1926

Angerville (Mouffle d'), *see* MOUFFLE D'ANGERVILLE.

Anghiari (Gerolamo Maggi d'), *see* MAGGI (GIROLAMO).

Angilbertus, *miles* [ANGELBERTUS]. Rhythmus de pugna Fontanetica, *see* NITHARDUS. Hist. libri 3; rec. E. Müller, ed. 3ª, 1907.

Angioletti (G. B.) Il giorno d. giudizio. 3ª ed. riv. Intr. di C. Linati. s8º. Torino. 1928

Angiol'eri (Cecco). Nuovi sonetti; *ed.* A. F. Massèra, *see* MONACI (E.) Studj romanzi, v13, 1917.
Sonnets. Done into Eng. doggerel by C. H. M. D. Scott. s8º. *p.p.* 1925

Anglade (Joseph). Hist. sommaire de la Litt. méridionale au m. âge. 8º. 1921
Les troubadours de Toulouse. s8º. Toulouse. 1928

Anglas (J.) Depuis Darwin. s8º. 1924

Anglemont (Edouard d'), *see* ASSE (E.) Les petits romantiques: E. d'A. &c., 1900.

Anglemont (*capt.* **Lucien Delahaye d'),** *see* DELAHAYE D'ANGLEMONT (L.)

Angler's (An) garland, 1920, *see* PARKER (E.), *ed.*

Angleterre. Etat de l'A. au comm. de 1822. [*Tr. of an Eng. govt. publ.* The state of the nation]. Tr. P. A. D[ufau] & J. G[uadet]. 8º. 1822
,, ,, *For a. ed., see* CONSTANT (B.) &c. Mél. polit. &c., t3, 1829.
*Hist. des révolutions d'A. sous Jacques II jusqu'au couronnement de Guillaume III. s8º. Amsterdam. 1689

Angli [ANGLORUM; ANGLOS]. *Ad persecutores Anglos pro catholicis &c., 1589, *see* ALLEN (W.) *card.*
*Metamorphosis Anglorum sive mutationes variæ regum, regni, rerumque Angliæ Ex var. mon. & auctor. contextum &c. s8º. [The Hague?]. 1653

Anglia. *Elenchus motuum nuperorum in A. &c., 1649, *see* BATE (G.)

Anglia. Zeitschrift für engl. Philologie.
B44–51 [Neue Folge B32–39]. 8º. Halle a. S. 1920–27
,, ,, Beiblatt: Mitteilungen ü. engl. Spr. u. Litt.; hrsg. v. M. F. Mann, Jahrg. 30–38. 8º. Halle a. S. 1919–27

Anglican. Anglican essays: princs. &c. of the A. Communion as Catholic & Reformed. By Abp. of Armagh, R. H. Murray, G. G. Coulton, Archdeacon of Chester (ed.) &c. 8º. 1923

Anglican Evangelical Group Movement. Liberal evangelicanism. Pamphlets by V. F. Storr, B. H. Streeter &c. 1–53, *in* 2v]. s8º. [1923–4]

Anglicarum. Rerum A. scr. post Bedam præcipui, nunc primum ed., 1596, *see* SAVILE (*Sir* H.), *ed.*

Anglo-American year book.
Directory & guide to London. s8º. [1913]

Anglo-Belgian Union, *see* ROYAL ACADEMY. Exhib. of Flemish & Belgian art, 1300–1900, organiz. by the A.-B. U., 2nd ed., 1927.

Anglo-Catholic Congress. Report of the 1st A.-C. Congress, London, 1920. Pref. by D. Stone. 8º. 1920

Anglo-French review (The). v1-4 (Feb. 1919–Dec. 1920). [*No more publ.*] 8°. [1919–20]

Anglo-Hellenic League (The). [*Publications*]. No. 2–56, *in* 3v., No. 37 in P2248 ; Nos. 16, 22, 25 & 40 *are wanting* ; No. 21 *not issued*]. s8°. [1913–28]

Anglo-Italian review (The). v4–5 (May 1919–Feb. 1920). s8°. *&* 8°. [1919–20]

Anglo-Japanese. *Problem (The) of the A.-J. alliance. [P2484]. 8°. [1920]

Anglo-Norman. Cambridge A.-N. texts. Poem on the Assumption ; ed. J. P. Strachey—Poem on the Day of Judgment ; ed. H. J. Chaytor—Divisiones mundi ; ed. O. H. Prior. [Pref. &c. by O. H. Prior. Camb. A.-N. Soc.] 8°. C. 1924

Anglo-Saxon. *A.-S. & Norse poems, 1922, *see* KERSHAW (N.), *ed.*

Anglo-Saxon Chronicle. An A.-S. C. Ed. E. Classen & F. E. Harmer. [Mod. Lang. Texts, Eng. ser.] s8°. M'ter. 1926

*Chron. Saxon. Ed. & Lat. fecit E. Gibson. 4°. Oxonii. 1692

Anglo-South American Handbook, 1921, 1922, incorp. Mexico & C. Amer. Ed. W. H. Koebel. s8°. 1921–22

Angmering, *Sussex.* Parish registers. First book, 1562–1687. Ed. E. W. D. Penfold. [Sussex Rec. Soc., v18]. 8°. 1913

Angoso (Angel), *architect.*
Salamanque. [L'Esp. architect. & mon.] 4°. [1927]

Angoulême, *The family of, see* BUCKINGHAM, *The fam. of.* Compota domestica familiarum de B. & d'A., 1443, 52, 63 ; [ed. W. B. D. D. Turnbull], 1836.

Angoulême (*la duchesse* d'). Narr. of journey of Louis XVI &c. to Varennes—Priv. mem. of what passed in the Temple &c. ; tr., *see* FRENCH REVOLUTION. Royal memˢ. &c., 1823.

Anguillara (Luigi), *see* LEGRÉ (L.) La botanique en Provence au 16ᵉ s. : L. A. &c., 1901.

Angus, *The family of, see* FRASER (*Sir* W.) The Douglas book, v2, A. memˢ., 1885.

Angus (Joseph). The voluntary system : reply to Lect. of Dr. Chalmers. 8°. 1839

Angus (S.) The mystery-religions & Xtianity. 8°. 1925

Anguttara-Nikāya. Bk. of the numerical sayings [*one of the* Suttapitakas]. p2 ; tr. A. D. Jayasundere. Ed. F. L. Woodward. [Buddhist Suttas]. 8°. Madras. 1925

Anhalt. Das die 42 Anhalt. Argument, wider d. Ubiquisten Trewme, noch fest stehen. Verantwortung vff d. 4. Cap. d. Apol. v. T. Kirchner, N. Selnecker u. M. Chemnitio verfasset. Gestelt durch d. Kirchendiener i. A. &c. s4°. Zerbst. 1584

*Repetitio brevis orthod. confessionis quam amplect. eccl. princ. A. &c. Item : De mysterio Incarn. Verbi & unionis hypostaticæ, contra Ubiquitatem, assertio catholica. s4°. Neapoli Casimiriana. 1581

*Streit u. Zweispalt der Anhalt. u. Luther. Theologen, ü. d. erklerung d. Wort Christi, Matth. 28. Von e. Liebhaber d. Christlichen Warheit beschrieben. [P2437]. s4°. L. *J. Beyer.* 1585

Añíbarro y Rives (Manuel Martínez), *see* MARTÍNEZ AÑÍBARRO Y RIVES (M.)

Anima. *Opus novū maximū & insigne super epistolas totius quadragesime quod dicitur anima fidelis. [219 *leaves* +10 *pages Tabula*]. s8°. [Parisiis]. *J. Petit.* 1501

Animadversiones. *A. in hist. theol. dogmat. &c. de divina gratia a S. Maffaejo elaboratam, 1749, *see* MAFFEI (*il march* F. S.)

Animadversions. *A. upon Dr. Sherlock's bk. ; Vindic. of the Trinity &c., 1693, *see* SOUTH (R.)

***Animal** magnetism : farce, 1792, *see* INCHBALD (*Mrs.* E.)

Animals' Defender, *see* ZOOPHILIST & ANIMALS' DEFENDER.

Anisimova (Mariya). Стихи. s8°. Римъ. 1920

Anissia. Ma vie : récit dicté par un paysanne [A.] à T. A. Kuzminskaya, 1923, *see* KUZMINSKAYA (T. A.)

Anker (Jean). Die Vererbung d. Haarfarbe beim Dachshunde, *see* KONG. DAN. VID. SELSK. Biol. Medd., 4, 1923–25.

Anker(Kurt). Kronprinz Wilhelm. [P2406]. s8°. 1919

Ankermann (Bernhard), *see* CHANTEPIE DE LA SAUSSAYE (P. D.) Lehrbuch d. Religionsgesch. ; 4ᵉ A., in Verbindung mit B. A. &c., 2B, 1925.

Anna, *consort of Elector August I, of Saxony, daughter of Christian III, of Denmark, see* STURMHOEFEL (C. H.) Kurfürstin A. v. Sachsen : polit. &c. Lebensbild, 1905.

Anna, *mother of Virgin Mary* [HANNA], *see* BUDGE (*Sir* E. A. T. W.) Legends of Our Lady Mary & h. mother H. ; tr. f. Ethiopic MSS. by B., 1922.

Anna, *empress of Russia, see* MITTAG (J. G.) Merkw. Leben u. Thaten A. Ivanownae, 1741.

Annaes da Confer. Interest. de Ensino Prim. (1921), 1922, *see* BRAZIL : GOVT. PUBLICATIONS.

Annales.
Annales Danici medii ævi. Ed. novam curavit E. Jørgensen. Udg. af Selskabet for udg. af kilder til Dansk hist. 4°. København. 1920

Annales Egmundani, *see* EGMOND OF ZEE.
Annales Fuldenses &c., 1891, *see* FULDA.
Annales Marbacences, 1907, *see* MARBACH.
Annales maximi Coloniensis, *see* COLONIENSIS.
Annales regni Franc. (741–829), qui dic. A. Laurissenses maj. & Einhardi, 1895, *see* FRANCI.
Annales Vedastini, *see* SAINT-VAAST, *Abbey, Arras.*
Annales Xantenses, *see* XANTEN.
*Novi eccles.-Scholast. annales &c. ; ed. S. Ambrosius, 3v, 1793–95, *see* *NOVI.

Annales de la propagation de la foi. Rec. périod. des lettres des évéques & des missionaires, & de tous les doc. rel. aux missions. Coll. suite aux Lettres édifiantes. [1822–83]. t1–55 [52 *wanting*]. 8°. Lyon. 1841–83
,, ,, Table, 1822–53, 1853–74 [2v]. 8°. Lyon. 1853–74
For Eng. ed. see ANNALS OF THE PROPAG. &C.

Annales des sciences naturelles. Zoologie & paléontologie. s10, t2–10. 8°. 1918–27

Annales historiques de la Révolution Française. Organe de la Soc. des Etudes Robespierristes. n. sér., t1–4, 1924–27. 8°. Reims. 1924–27

Annales patriotiques & litt. de la France & affaires polit. de l'Europe. Journal libre, par un Soc. d'écrivains patriotes, & dir. par M. Mercier &c. 3 Oct. 1789—7 Nov. 1795. [11v.] s4°. 1789–95

Annali. Annali genovesi di Caffaro e dei suoi contin., 1923–25, *see* CAFFARUS.

Annals. Annals of Newgate, or malefactors register, 4v, 1776, *see* VILLETTE (J.)
Martin's Annals of crime, or New Newgate calendar, v1, 2, 1837–38, *see* MARTIN (A.)

Annals (The) & magazine of natural history. Ser. 9, v4–20. 8°. 1920–27

Annals of archæology & anthropology. Issued by the Institute of Arch. [Univ. of Liverpool]. Ed. J. L. Myres &c. v1–14. la8°. Liv'l. 1908–27

Annals of the propagation of the faith. Coll. of letters f. bishops & missionaries &c. Contin. of Lettres édifiantes. v1–22 [v20–22 *imperfect*]. 8°. [v1 & 2, Paris ; v3–22, D.]. 1838–59
,, ,, ...[*a. issue*]. v1–6. 8°. 1839–45
These vols. correspond to vols. 2–8 of the Paris & Dublin ed. above.
,, ,, ...Retrospective ser. v1. 8°. 1839
For French ed., to 1883, see ANNALES DE LA PROPAG. &C.

Annand (James), *see* MACCALLUM (J. L.) J. A. : a tribute, 1908.

Annandale, *The earldom &c. of, see* FRASER (*Sir* W.) The A. family book of the Johnstones, Earls & Marquises of A., 2v, 1894.

Annandale (Thomas Nelson), *ed.* Zoolog. results of tour in Far East, *see* ASIATIC SOC. OF BENGAL. Mems., v6, 1925.

Annat (François), *Jesuit, see* NOUET (J.), F. A. &c. Responses aux Lettres Provinc. &c., 1668.

Anne [*of Brittany*], *q. consort of* (i) *Charles VIII,* (ii) *Louis XII, kings of France, see* BRETAIGNE. Récit des funérailles d'A. de B., 1858.

Anne [*Bullen*], *q. c. of Henry VIII, k. of Eng.* [ANNE BOLEYN]. Acc. (An) of Queen A. B. From a MS. in writing of Sir R. Twysden, 1623. [P2877]. 8°. [1815?]
see CARLES (L. DE). Poème s. la mort d'A. B., 1927.
,, SERGEANT (P. W.) Life of A. B., 1923.

Anne [*of Denmark*], *q. c. of James I of England.* *Account of last moments of A., 27th March 1619, *see* ABBOTSFORD CLUB. Misc. v1, 1837.

Anne, *queen of Gt. Brit. & Ireland, see* MARY II. Letters of 2 queens [M. II & A.] ; ed. B. Bathurst, 1924.
see STATE PAPERS. Calendar, Domestic Ser. [of r. of A.], v2, 1703–4, 1924.

Anne, *consort of William IV of Orange, d. 1759, see* WILLIAM IV, *of Orange.* Eng. corr. v. Pr. W. IV & Pr. Anna, 1734–43, 1924.

Anne Mary [*of Brandenburg-Anspach*], *consort of Christopher, Duke of Wirtemberg, see* CELL (E.) Oratio funebris &c., 1592.

Annesley (Samuel), *LL.D., Minister of St. Giles, Cripplegate.* Casuistical morning exercise. By ministers in London, preached in Oct. 1689. [Coll. & ed. by S. A.] v4 [*tp. wanting*]. 4º. 1690

The life & funeral sermon of the Rev. T. Brand. [*tp. wanting*]. s8º. [1692]

The morning-exercise at Cripple-gate: or several cases of conscience, by ministers, Sept. 1661. s4º. 1661

Annin (Robert Edwards). Woodrow Wilson. 8º. N.Y. 1924

Anno, *St., abp. of Cologne.* Poetæ anon. Teuton. Rhythmus de S. Annone archi-ep. Colon. Acc. versio Lat & notæ J. Schilteri & obs. J. G. Scherzii, *see* SCHILTER (J.) Thesaurus antiq., t1, 1728.

Annotations upon books of O. & N. Test., 1645; 2nd ed., 2v, 1651, *see* BIBLE. COMPL. TEXTS.

Annuaire. Nouvel ann. de France; réd. par A. Bret, [1836?], *see* NOUVEL.

Annuaire de la noblesse de France. Fondé par B. d'Hauterive & cont. s. la dir. du Vte. A. Révérend. Année 80–84 (1923–27). s8º. 1924–28

Annuaire du monde musulman. Rédigé par L. Massignon. Année 1 (1923). Préf. de A. de Châtelier. la8º. [1924]

Annuaire généalog. de la noblesse de France, 6e année, 1914, *see* REX.

Annuaire général de la France & de l'étranger, 1925, 1926. [Soc. d'Études &c. écon.] 6e, 7e année[s]. 8º. 1925–26

Annuaire International de Statistique. Publ. par l'Office de l'Inst. Internat. de Statist. [p] 4, 5. la8º. La Haye. 1921–21
4, Mouvt. de la pop. (Amérique).
5, Etat & mouvt. de la pop. (Afr., Asie, Océanie).

Annual charities register & digest. 30th ed. & 33rd ed. 8º. 1921–25

Annual register.
Annual register (The). 1920–26. [New Series]. 8º. 1921–27

Annuario statistico italiàno. [Ufficio Centrale di Statistica]. s2, v7, 1917–18, 8, 1919–21. 4º. 1919–25

Annunzio (Gabriele d'), *ps.* [*i.e.* GAETANO RAPAGNATTO].

Canto novo: intermezzo (1881–83). [Poesie.] Ed. defin. s8º. Milano. 1896
Contemplazione della morte. [4a. impr.] s8º. Milano. 1920
Contro uno e contro tutti. s8º. 1919
Le elegie romane. n. impr. [*b. w. h.* Laudi, lib. 3, 4, 1916]. 8º Milano. [1911]
Le faville del maglio. t1, Il venturiero senza ventura &c. s8º. Milano. 1924
Giovanni episcopo. 2a ed. 8º. Napoli. 1899
L'innocente. 7a ed. s8º. Milano. 1897
Juvenilia. s8º. Firenze. 1925
Laudi del cielo, del mare, della terra e degli eroi. 4 lib. *in* 2v. 8º. [Milano. 1914–16]
1, Maia. 2, Elettra. 3, Alcione. 4, Merope.
Notturno. s8º. Milano. 1921
Parole al popolo &c., 1920, *see* FIUME. La reggenza ital. d. Carnaro, 1920.
Per l'Italia degli Italiani. la8º. Milano. 1923
La Pisanella. Commedia volta in verso ital. d. E. Janni. s8º. Milano. [1919]
Le Vergini delle Rocce. 4a. ed. s8º. Milano. 1896

TRANSLATIONS.
Aspects de l'inconnu. La Léda sans cygne, suivi d'un Envoi à la France. Tr. A. Doderet. 3e éd. 8º. 1922
Italy or death. From the "Vedetta d'Italia," Sep. 10 & 12, 1919. Tr. & notes by H. Furst. [P2574]. s8º. Fiume. [1919]
Nocturne. Tr. A. Doderet. 8º. [1923]
Tales of my native town. [Tr.] Intr. by J. Hergesheimer. s8º. [1920]
see BORGESE (G. A.) Risurrezioni (L'op. poet. di G. d'A. &c.), 1922.
,, FRACASSINI (G.) G. d'A., 1916.
,, FLORA (F.) D'A., 1926.
,, HERFORD (C. H.) G. d'A., 1920.
,, MACDONALD (J. N.) A polit. escapade: Fiume & d'A., 1921.
,, PASQUARIS (G. M.) G. d'A., 1923.
,, SERRA (R.) Scritti ined. (Di G. d'A. e di 2 giornalisti), 1923.
,, TORSIELLO (I. E.) Gli ulimi giorni di Fiume Dannunziana, 1921.

Annusson (Juri), *see* UNITED STATES: EDUC. Public instr. in Estonia; by J. A.; tr., 1926.

Anodos, *ps., see* COLERIDGE (M. E.)

***Anomaliae:** desultory essays on misc. subjects, 1798, *see* WATKINS (W.)

***Anonimalle** chronicle (The), 1333–81, f. a MS. wr. at St. Mary's Abbey, York. Ed. V. H. Galbraith. [M'ter. Univ. Publ., Hist. Ser., 45]. 8º. M'ter. 1927

Anonimo, *di Utopia, ps., see* LANDI (O.)

Anonymus [ANONYMI]. Anonymi Belae Regis notarii, hist. Hungarica, 1772, *see* HUNGARICA.

*Anonymi diss. de pace & concordia eccl., 1630, *see* HALES (J.)

Anon. Mellic. de script. eccles, 1716, *see* MELLICENSIS.

Another gentleman with a duster, *ps.* *Is Coué a foe to Xty?, 1923, *see* COUÉ (E.)

Anrich (Gustav). Die Strassburger Reformation: Rede. [V. f. Ref.-gesch. Schr., Jhrg. 36 (Nr. 130)]. 8º. L. 1918
see NICHOLAS, *St.* Hagios N.: Der hlg. N. in d. griech. Kirche; Texte u. Untersuch. v. G. A., 2B, 1913–17.

Ansaldo (Giovanni), C. Ariaghi *& others.* Che cos'è l'Inghilterra. s8º. Torino. 1924

Anscharius, *Saint, abp. of Hamburg & Bremen, see* REMBERT, *St.* S. Anscharii vita gemina, per S. R. & Gualdonem, 1677.

Anschütz (Gerhard), *see* HANDBUCH d. Politik; hrsg. G. A. &c., 3e A., 6B, 1920–26.

Anschütz (Hugo). Der Kampf d. Saarbeamten unter d. Völkerbundsregierung. 8º. Frankfurt. 1922

Ansell (Charles), *the elder.* A treatise on friendly societies &c. 8º. 1835

Anselm, *St., abp. of Canterbury.*

Opera, nec non Eadmeri Hist. novorum &c. labore G. Gerberon. [Eadmeri Hist. *&c. has sep. pagin.*] 2a ed. aucta. fol. Lutetiæ. 1721
Anselmi in omnes Pauli epitolas enarrat. fol. Coloniæ. 1533
Cur Deus homo. [*fol. 1a* Anshelmi præfatio in librũ Cur Deus Homo, incipit feliciter; *fol. 30b ends* . . . qui est benedictus in secula. Amen]. fol. *n.p.* [Strasburg, *Geo. Husner,* c. 1473]
Cur Deus homo: added a sel. f. h. letters. 8º. [1889]
Devotions. [Tr.] Ed. C. C. J. Webb. [Lib. of Devotions]. s8º. 1903
Le rationalisme chrétien à la fin du 11e siècle, ou Monologium & Proslogium de S. A., sur l'essence divine. Tr. H. Bouchitté. 8º. 1842
Stimulus amoris, Soliloquium jubileum, Super resolutione an missame celebrare aut non, *see* AUGUSTINE, *Saint,* Manuale &c., 1506.
Theologia, comm. & disput. illustr. auctore J. Saenz de Aguirre. ed. nova. 3t. fol. Romæ. 1688–90
see BILLROTH (J. G. F.) De A. C. proslogio & monologio diss., 1832.
,, BORNEMANN (J. A.) A. & Abaelardus, 1840.
,, CHARMA (A.) St. Anselme, 1853.
,, MÖHLER (J. A.) Life of St. A.; tr. H. Rymer, 1842.
,, RIBBECK (A. F.) A. C. doctr. de S. Spiritu, 1838.
,, ROTHE (P. C.) De vita & gestis A., 1840.
,, VEDER (G. R.) Diss. de A., 1832.
,, ZIJNEN (F. P. J. S.) Spec. hist.-dogmat. quo A. & Calvini placita de redemtione inter se conf., 1852.

Anselmus, *Laudunensis Eccl. diaconus.* Systemat. Sentenzen. Hrsg. &c. v. F. P. Bliemetzrieder. [Beitr. d. Gesch. d. Phil. d. M.-a., B18ii, iii]. T1, Texte. 8º. Münster. 1919

Anselmus, *de Ysalguerio, see* ISALGUIER (A. D').

Ansgar, *St.* [†ANSCHARIUS (*St.*), *abp. of Hamburg & Bremen*]. *see* REMBERT, *St.* Vita A.; rec. G. Waitz, 1884.
,, —— A., apostle of the North, 801–865; tr. C. H. Robinson, 1921.

Ansiedelung (Die) v. Europäern in d. Tropen. [V. f. Sozialpol., B147v]. 8º. München. 1915
5, Die deut. Kolonisten im brasil. Staate Espirito Santo; v. E. Wagemann.

Anson (*Maj.-Gen. Sir* **Archibald Edward Harbord).** About myself & others, 1745–1920. 8º. 1920

Anson (Elizabeth G.) & F. Anson. Mary Hamilton, aft. Mrs. J. Dickenson, at court &c., f. letters &c., 1756–1816. Ed. E. & F. A. 8º. 1925

Anson (Florence), *see* ANSON (E. G.) & F. A., *edd.* Mary Hamilton, 1925.

Anson (George Anson, *baron*). Voyage round the world, 1740–4. Comp. by R. Walter. 15th ed. 4º. 1776

Anson (L.) Numismata Graeca. Greek coin-types. 6p. [*b. in* 3v]. 4º. 1911–16
,, ,, ... Gen. guide-index. [*b. w.* v1]. 4º. 1910

Anson (*Rt. Hon. Sir* **Wm. Reynell),** *bart.* Law & custom of the constitution. 5th ed. by M. L. Gwyer. v1. 8º. O. 1922
A memoir. [*By var. wrs.*] Ed. H. H. Henson. 8º. O. 1920
Principles of the law of contract. 16th ed., by M. L. Gwyer. 8º. O. 1923

Ansono, *see* SANO DI PIETRO.

Anspach (Eliz. *margravine of*), *see* LEY (H.) Die litterar. Tätigkeit d. Lady Craven, 1904.

Anspach (L. E. F.) & A. M. Coutanche. Dictionary of Anglo-Belgian law. 2p [*in 1v*]. la8º. 1920

Anstey (Christopher). The New Bath Guide. Repr., Cayme Press. 8º. Kensington. 1927
A paraphrase of 13th chap. of 1st Corinthians. [P2568]. sfol. 1779

Anstey (F.), *ps.*
The last load: stories & essays. s8º. [1925]

Anstruther, *The family of, see* ANSTRUTHER (A. W.) Hist. of the fam. of A., 1923.

Anstruther (Arthur Wellesley).
Hist. of the family of Anstruther. 4°. E. 1923

Anstruther (Philip), *Major-Gen. of the Madras Artillery.* Mem. recomm. a light eighteen-pounder gun. [P2602]. s8°. [1840]
A proposal for increasing the strength of the "Indian Army," &c. [P2485]. s8°. Madras. 1839

Answer [ANSWERE].
*A. to A letter conc. the Kings going f. Holdenby &c., 1647, *repr.*, *see* CHARLES I, *k. of Gt. Brit.*
*Answer (An) to some things cont. in Dr. Hicks's Christian priesthood &c., 1709, *see* HANCOCK (J.)
*Answere (An) to certain scandalous papers, 1606, *see* CECIL (*Sir R.*)
*Answer (An) to the Provinciall Letters &c., 1659, *see* PASCAL (B.)
*Answer (An) to the Scotch Presbyt. eloquence, 1789, *see* RIDPATH (G.)

Antefoker, *vizier of Sesostris I, see* DAVIES (N. DE G.) Tomb of A., & of h. wife, Senet, 1920.

Anthiaume (*l'abbé* **Albert).**
Un ancêtre du Borda au Havre : l'Ecole Royale de Marine, 1773–5. Préf. de l'Amiral Didelot. 8°. 1920
Cartes marines, constructions navales, voyages de découverte, chez les Normands, 1500–1650. Préf. de l'Amiral Buchard. 2t. 8°. 1916
Evolution &c. de la sc. nautique en France & princ. chez les Normands. Préf. de l'Amiral Buchard. 2t. 8°. 1920
Le navire : sa construct. en France & princ. chez les Normands. 8°. 1922
Le navire : sa propulsion en France & princ. chez les Normands. 8°. 1924
La science astronom. & naut. au m. âge chez les Normands. [Soc. Havraise d'Et[s]. Div.] 8°. Le Havre. 1919
L'astrolabe-quadrant du Musée de Rouen &c. 8°. 1910

Anthologia. Anthologia lyrica, 2v, 1925, *see* DIEHL (E.) *ed.*

Anthologia Graeca.
A. G. epigrammatum Palatina cum Planudea. Ed. H. Stadtmueller. v3i. s8°. L., *Teubner.* 1906
TRANSLATIONS.
Epigramme der Gr. Anthologie ausgewählt u. verdeutscht v. J. G. Regis. s8°. St. 1856
Anthologie Grecque. Tr., avec notices biog. &c. [*by* F. Dübner]. 2t. s8°. 1863
The girdle of Aphrodite : the compl. love-poems of the Palat. Anthol. Tr. by F. A. Wright, w. an intr. [Broadway Tr[s].] s8°. 1923
The poets of the Gr. A. Companion vol. to The girdle of Aphrodite. Tr. F. A. Wright, w. biog. & crit. pref[s]. [Broadway Tr[s].] s8°. [1924]
see LUMB (T. W.) Notes, 1920.

Anthologia Latina. Anthologiæ latinæ suppl. Rec. M. Ihm. v1. s8°. L., *Teubner.* 1895
1, Damasi Epigrammata, acc. Pseudodamasiana &c.
Anthologia latina, s. Poesis lat. suppl. Ed. F. Buecheler & A. Riese. p2, fasc. 3. s8°. L. 1926
p2, Carmina lat. epigraphica, conlegit F. Buecheler, fasc. 3, Suppl. ; curavit E. Lommatzsch.

Anthologie.
A. catalane, s1, 1908, *see* AMADE (J.), *ed.*
A. de la litt. roumaine ; tr. &c., 1920, *see* IORGA (N.) & S. GORCEIX, *edd.*
A. de la nouv. poésie franç. éd. rev. & augm. 11e éd. s8°. [1926]
A. des écrivains de la Guerre, 1919, *see* FAGE (A.)
A. des écrivains morts à la Guerre, 1914–18. Publ. par l'Assoc. des Écrivains Combattants. Intr. de [L. Bérard]. 2t. (1, Préf. de H. Malherbe ; 2, Préf. de J. Germain). 8°. Amiens. 1924
A. des poètes lyr. franç., 1911, *see* SAROLEA (C.), *ed.*
A. du théâtre fr. au m. âge, 1925, *see* GASSIES DES BRULIES (G.)

Anthology. Anthology of friendship, repr., 1920, *see* CARPENTER (E.) *ed.*
Anthology of magazine verse, 1926, *see* BRAITHWAITE (W. S.) *ed.*
Anthology (An) of mod. verse, 1921 ; 8th ed., 1922, *see* METHUEN (A.)

Anthony, *Saint, the monk, of Egypt, see* ATHANASIUS, *Saint, Patriarch of Alexandria.* Vita S. A. eremitæ, 1611.
see REITZENSTEIN (R.) Des Athanasius Werk ü. d. Leben d. A., 1914.

Anthony, *Saint, of Padua.*
see GILLIAT-SMITH (E.) St. A., acc. to h. contemp., 1926.
,, SCHLAGER (P.) Der heilige A. v. P. in Kunst u. Legende, 1923.

Anthony Ulric, *Duke of Brunswick.* Fifty reasons or motives why the Roman Catholick apostolick religion ought to be preferr'd to all sects & which induced A. U. to abjure Lutheranism, &c. s8°. Antwerp. 1715

Anthony (Henry Bowen), *see* BROWN UNIVERSITY. A. memorial : cat. of Harris Coll. of Amer. poetry [pres. to Library of B. Univ. by H. B. A.], 1886.

Anthony (Joseph). The gang. s8°. [1922]

Anthony (Katharine). Catherine the Great. 8°. [1926]
Margaret Fuller : a psycholog. biog. [2nd impr.] s8°. [1922]

Anthony (Raoul Louis Ferd.), *see* ROHAN-CHABOT (—). Angola & Rhodesia, 1912–14, t4, fasc. 1, Mammifères [par R. A. &c.], 1923.

Anthony (Susan B.), *see* HISTORY of woman suffrage, v3, 4, ed. S. B. A. &c., 1886–1902.

Anthropological Institute of Gt. Britain [ROYAL ANTH. INST.]
Journal. v50–57. la8°. [1920–27]
Occas. papers. No. 6, 8. la8°. 1924–27
see FRANKFORT (H.) St[s]. in early pottery of the Near East, 2p, 1924–27. [6, 8.]

Anthropologie (L'). t30–37. la8°. 1920–27
t37 *cont[s]*. Atlas : Aïnou &c. par G. Montandon.

Anthropos : ethnolog. Bibliothek.
B2ii–v, 3i. 8°. Münster i. W. 1920–27
see BIEBER (F. J.) Kaffa : e. altkuschit. Volkstum in Inner-Afrika, B1, 2, 1920. [2ii, iii.]
,, BOLLIG (P. L.) Bewohner d. Truk-Inseln, 1927. [3i.]
,, HOFMAYR (W.) Die Schilluk, 1925. [2v.]
,, KLEINTITSCHEN (P. A.) Mythen &c. e. Melanesierstammes, 1924. [2iv.]

Anti (Carlo). *Works in* REALE ACCAD. D. LINCEI. Mon. ant.
Athena marina e alata, 1920. [26.]
Esplor. arch. n. Licia e n. Panfilia, 1923. [29.]
Monumenti Policletei, 1920. [26.]

Antididagma, seu Christ. et Cathol. religionis per Canonicos Metropol. Eccles Colonien. propugnatio &c., 1544, *see* COLOGNE.

Antidote. *Antidote au Congrès de Rastadt, 1798, *see* PRADT (D. D. DE).

Antiguedad. *De la antiguedad &c. d. Bascuenze en España &c., 1728, *see* LARRAMENDI (M. DE).

Anti-Jacobin, *ps.* New lights on Jacobinism, abs. f. Robison's Hist. of free masonry, w. app. cont. acc. of Voltaire's behaviour on his death-bed, & a letter from J. H. Stone. [P2515]. 8°. B'ham. 1798

Anti-Jacobin (The), or Weekly examiner. Poetry of the A.-J. Ed. w. intr. & notes by L. Rice-Oxley. [Percy Repr.] 8°. O. 1924

Antike Denkmäler. Hrsg. v. K. Deut. Archäolog. Institut. B3, H2–5. lafol. 1913–26

Antilogia Papae, scripta vet. authorum, 1555, *see* WEISSENBURGER (W.)

Antimaco (Giulio), *ed., see* ORVIETO. Cronaca d'O., 1342–63, 1845.

Anti-Maynooth. Proc. of A.-M. conf. 1845, 1845, *see* THELWALL (A. S.) *ed.*

Antink (Margo Scharten-), *see* SCHARTEN-ANTINK (M.)

Antinoos, *see* MARCONI (P.) A., saggio sull' arte dell' eta Adriana, 1923.

Antiochenum. Monumentum Antioch, *see* AUGUSTUS, *emp.*

Antiochus, *of Ascalon, fl. B.C. 80, see* STRACHE (H.) Eklektizismus d. A. v. A., 1921.

Antiochus [STRATIG], *monk.*
Плѣненіе Іерусалима Персами въ 614 г. Груз. текстъ, изслѣд., изд., перевелъ и араб. извлеч. приложилъ Н. Марръ [*Georgian text & Russ. tr. have sep. pagin[s]. Arabic has sep. tp.* (*1907*) *& pagin.* Тексты и раз по арм.-груз. филол., кн. 9]. la8°. С.-П. 1909

Antipa (Gregor). Dunărea, & problemele ei ştiinţifice, econ. & polit. [Acad. Română, Studii & cercetări, 6]. la8°. Bucureşti. 1921
Pescăria & pescuitul in România, *see* ACADEMIA ROMÂNA. Publ. Fond. V. Adamachi, t8, 1916.
Problemele evoluţiei poporului Român. [Acad. Româna, Studii & cercetări, 3]. la8°. Cartea Românească. 1919

Antiphon, *the Orator.* Discours, suivis des fragm[s]. d'Antiphon le Sophiste. Texte établi & tr. par L. Gernet. [Coll. des univ[s]. de France]. 8°. 1923
see DOBSON (W. S.) *ed.* Oratores Attici, t1, A. &c., t13, A. &c. interpret. Lat. 1828.

Antiphon, *Sophista, see* ANTIPHON, *the Orator.* Disc., suivis des fragm[s]. d'A. le Sophiste, 1923.

Antiphonaire, *see* ANTIPHONARIUM.

Antiphonale. Antiphonale Missarum S. Gregorii, 9–10 s., cod. 239 de la Bibl. de Laon. [Paléogr. Musicale, 10]. 4°. Tournai (Belg.). 1909
Antiphonale Missarum S. Gregorii, 10e s., cod. 47 de la Bibl. de Chartres. [Paléogr. Mus., 11]. 4°. Tournai (Belg.). 1912

Antiphonale [*continued*].
Antiphonale officii monastici écrit par le B. Hartker. No. 390–91 de la Bibl. de St.-Gall. [Paléogr. Mus., 1]. 4°. Solesmes. 1900
Le codex 121 de la Bibl. d'Einsiedeln (10–11s.) Antiphonale missarum S. Gregorii. [Paléogr. Mus., 4]. 4°. Solesmes. 1894
Antiphonarium [Antiphonaire]. Antiphonaire monastique, 12ᵉ s. Cod. 601 de la Bibl. Capitul. de Lucques. [Paléogr. Mus., 9]. 4°. Tournai (Belgique). 1906
Antiphonarium Ambrosianum du Musée Brit. (12ᵉ s.) Cod. Add. 34209. [Paléogr. Mus., 5, 6]. 2p. 4°. Solesmes. 1896
Antiphonarium tonale Missarum 11ᵉ s., cod. H. 159 de la Bibl. de l'École de Méd. de Montpellier. Phototypies. [Paléogr. Mus., 8]. 4°. Tournai (Belgique). 1901–5
***Antiquarian** & topogr. cabinet: views of objects of curiosity in Gt. Brit. &c., 10v, 1807–11, *see* Storer (J. S.) & J. Greig.
Antiquarian itinerary (The): specimens of architecture, w. o. vestiges of antiquity in Gt. Brit. 7v. s8°. 1815–18
Antiquarian repertory (The), v4, 1784, *see* Grose (F.)
Antiquaries journal (The), 1921–, *see* Society of Antiquaries of London.
Antiquissimum. *A. verissimum seu consensus priscæ eccl. doctorum cum Aug. Conf. &c., 1658, *see* Augsburg Confess.
Antiquitates. Ecclesiae Or. antiq. clariss. vir. Card. Barberini, E. Allatii, J. Morini &c. dissert. Praef. est J. Morini vita. s8°. Lipsiæ. 1682
Antiquities. *A. (The) of London & Westminster, by N. B., 1722, *see* Bailey (N.)
Antiquity. The claim of antiquity, w. annot. list of bks. Issued by Councils of the Socˢ. for Prom. of Hellenic & Roman Stˢ. & of Class. Assoc. s8°. 1922
Anti-Saloon League. Year book, 1918–25. Compiled & ed. E. H. Cherrington. s8°. Westerville, Ohio. [1918–25]
see Cherrington (E. H.) Hist. of the A.-S. L., 1913.
Anti-slavery Convention, 1843, *see* Brit. & For. Anti-slavery Soc.
Antithesis. *Antithesis Christi & Antichristi &c., 1578, *see* Rosarius (S.)
***Anti-Volkna,** 1762, *see* Frederick II, *king of Prussia.*
Antoine (André Léonard).
Mes souvenirs sur le Théâtre Antoine & s. l'Odéon. s8°. 1928
" Mes souvenirs " sur le Théâtre-Libre. s8°. 1921
see Waxman (S. M.) A. & the Théâtre-Libre, 1926.
Antoine (André Paul) & M. Léry. Les chevaux de bois, comédie, *see* Œuvres (Les) libres, 27, 1923.
Antoine (Paul Gabriel) [Antonius (Paulus Gabriel)]. De obligationibus spec. certorum statuum & offic. De sacris Xtn. ritibus, *see* Migne (J. P.) *ed.* Theol. cursus, t16, 19, 1859.
Theologia moralis. 4°. Romæ. 1748
Antologia. Antologia de los mej. poetas castellanos, 1913, *see* Mesa y Lopez (R.)
Antologia de poetas líricos castellanos, t14, 1916, *see* Menéndez y Pelayo (M.)
Antologia portuguesa. Organiz. por A. de Campos. s8°. Paris. 1920–26
see Barros (J. de) & D. de Couto. Prim. dec. da Asia, 1921.
„ Bernardes (M.) Nova floresta &c., 2v, 1920–21.
„ Cacegas (L. de). Vida de D. Fr. Bartolomeu dos Mártyres Fr. L. de Souza, t1, 1921.
„ Camoens (L. de). C. lírico, 3v, 1923–25; 2ª ed., v1, 1925.
„ Eça de Queiroz. Selecta, 2v, 1922–23.
„ Fernandez Trancoso (G.) Hist. de proveito exemplo, 1923.
„ Figueiredo (A. de). A. de F., 1923.
„ Gil (A.) Prosa e verso, 1923.
„ Guerra Junqueiro (A.) Verso e prosa, 1921.
„ Herculano (A.) Quadros lit. da hist. medieval, 1921.
„ Lopes (F.) Cron. de D. Pedro e D. Fernando [&] D. João I, 3v, 1921–22.
„ Lopes Vieira (A.) Verso e prosa, 1925.
„ Lucena (J. de). Vida do F. de Xavier, 2v, 1921.
„ Paladinos da linguagem, 3v, 1922–26.
Antommarchi (C. Francesco). Mémˢ., ou, Les derniers moments de Napoléon. 2t. [t2 *wants tp.*] 8°. 1825
Anton, *Dalmatin, see* Truber (P.) Hauptartickel christl. Lehre, in d. crobat. verdolm., *by A. D. &c.*, 1562.
Anton I, *catholicos of Georgia, 18c.* [Georgian gram. *In Georgian*]. la8°. Tiflis. 1885
Anton (Augustin). De Pathmo Lutheri in arce Warteburg animadv. adv. card. Pallavicinum. Ed. 5a. [*ed.* P. Anton. P2627]. s4°. Halae Magdeb. 1710
„ „ Ed. noviss. [*ed.* P. Anton. P442]. s4°. Halae Magdeb. 1730

Anton (Paul) [Antonius (P.)]. Concilii Tridentini adeoque et pontificiorum doctrina s8°. Halae Magdeb. 1738
Programmata. Acc. J. D. Herrnschmidii progr. festiva. Rec. J. A. Maier. s8°. Halae. 1735
Antona-Traversi (Camillo), *see* Deledda (G.) & C. A.-T. Le lierre, 1928.
—— **& A. Ottolini.** Ugo Foscolo. 4v. la8°. Milano. 1927–28
Antonelli (Alessandro). Mem. del regno di Napoli. Rivol. del 1820. 8°. Aquila. 1848
Antonelli (Etienne). Bolshevist Russia. 8°. 1920
Principes d'économie pure. La théorie de l'échange sous le régime de la libre concurrence. 8°. 1914
Antonelli (Giuseppe), *see* Ferrara. Indice dei mss. d. Civica Bibl. di F., pl, 1884.
Antonello, *da Messina* [Antonio], *see* Berenson (B.) 3 essays in method: (A possible & imposs. A.), 1927.
Antonesco (Eftimie), *ed., see* Roumains. Les sacrifices r. pend. la Guerre; ed. E. A., 1919.
Antonin, *le Pieux, see* Antoninus (T. A. F. B. P.), *emp.*
Antonini (*l'abbé* **Annibale).**
Dict. italien, latin & françois. pl. 4°. 1743
Antonini (Giacomo). Il teatro contemp. in Italia. s8°. Milano. 1927
Antoninus, *St., abp. of Florence, 1389–1459.* [Summa. *fol. 1*: *blank*; *fol. 2a*: Proemium in secundam partem summe; *fol. 3b*: Tabula; *fol. 5a*: Incipit secunda pars summe maioris fratris Anthonini archiepiscopi florentini. *Ends fol. 307b*: Hic finis 2e pt. sum̄e; *fol. 308a*: Registrum &c.] fol. [Venetiis. *Leonardus Wild de Ratisbona.* 1481]
No tp., catchwords, or foliation; signatures a, b, d, e, i, n, in tens; c, f, g, h, k–m, o—&, 9, 4, A–L in eights: 308 leaves. Initials in red filled in by hand. Orig. binding w. chain.
Antoninus (Titus Aurelius Fulvius Bojonius Pius), *emperor of Rome, see* Lacourt-Gayet (G.) Antonin le Pieux & son temps, 1888.
***Antonio** & Mellida & A.'s revenge, 1602, 1921, *see* Marston (J.)
Antonio, *de Lebrixa, the Elder.* De bello Navariensi libri 2. Rerum a Ferdinando et Elis. &c. gestarum dec. 2, *see* Hispanica. Rer. Hisp. scr., t2, 1579.
Antonio Maria, *da Vicenza &* **Joannes,** *a Rubino.* Lexicon Bonaventurianum philosophico-theolog. Opera &c. Ant. M. A. Vicetia & J. a Rubino. la8°. Venetiis. 1880
Antonio de Sangroniz (José). Marruecos: condiciones fisicas, &c. s8°. 1921
Antonius Arimathæensis, *ps., see* Grabe (Joseph).
Antonius, *a Sancta Maria Angelorum.* Scotus Aristotelicus seu philosophia peripat. ad mentem subtilis J. Duns Scoti. 2t. fol. Lisbonæ. 1747–59
Antonius (Paulus Gabriel), *see* Antoine (P. G.)
Antonius (Petrus), *Finariensis.* De dignitate principum liber, *see* Tritheim (J.) Res gestæ Friderici Palatini elect., 1602.
Antoniutti (Pietro), 1732–1827, *see* Narducci (L.) Notizie biogr. d. P. A., 1884.
Antonovich (Vladimir Bonifatevich) & M. P. Dragomanov.
Истор. пѣсни малорусск. народа съ объясненіями В. А. & М. Д. t1, 2i [*in* 1v]. 8°. Кіевъ. 1874–75
Antony, *metropolitan of Kiev.*
Словарь къ твореніямъ Достоевскаго &c. s8°. Софія. 1921
Antrobus (Florence Caroline Mathilde, *Lady*). Guide to Amesbury & Stonehenge. [P2711]. s8°. Amesbury. [1900]
Antsiferov (N.), *see* Blok (A.) Об Александре Блоке: статьи Н. А. &c., 1921.
Antwerp [Antverpiensis; Anvers].
Cat. of Plantin-Moretus Museum, by M. Rooses. 3rd Eng. ed. s8°. Antwerp. 1921
Confessio ministrorum J.C. in eccl. A. quæ Augustanæ Conf. adsentitur. [*b. w.* Antwerp. Ministrorum adhort., 1566.] s8°. *n.p.* [Antverpiæ ?] 1567
Ministrorum J.C. in eccl. A., quæ Augustanæ Confess. adsentitur, adhort. ad seriam pœnitentiam &c. s8°. *n.p.* [Antverpiæ ?] 1566
La peinture ancienne au Musée royal des Beaux-Arts d'A. Préc. d'un Guide histor. & crit. par P. de Mont. 4°. Bruxelles. 1914
Antwort. A. d. alliierten &c. Mächte [*ed.* U. Rauscher], 1919, *see* Versailles, *Treaty of.*
*Antwort d. Diener Göttl. Worts in d. Kirchen &c. zu Bremen auf J. Andreae vermeinte Widerlegung &c., 1583, *see* Bremen.
Anuario internacional, 1927–28. Inglat. y Amér. Lat. Red. por J. A. Hunter. s8°. Londres. [1927]
Anuchin (Dmitry Nikolaevich), *see* Uvarova (*Ctss.* P. S.) Сборникъ статей въ честь гр. П. С. У., 1885–1915; *intr. by D. N. A.*, 1916.
Anville (J. B. B. d') [†Bourguignon d'Anville (Jean Bapt.)]
L'empire de Russie s8°. 1772

Anzeigung u. bekantnus des Glaubens u. der lere, so die adpellierenden Stende Key. Maiestet auff yetzigen tag zu Augspurg öberantwurt habend, 1530, *see* AUGSBURG.

Anzengruber (Ludwig) [*ps.* LUDWIG GRUBER].
Werke. Mit biog. Einleitung. 8B. [*in* 2*v*.] s8°. *n.d.*

Anziani (Niccolò). D. Bibl. Mediceo-Laurenziana di Firenze. [P2837]. la8°. Firenze. 1872

Anzilotti (Antonio). *Works in* ARCHIVIO STOR. ITAL.
Un amico napoletano di G. P. Vieusseux : bar. G. Savarese, 1921. [79i.]
Il tramonto d. Stato cittadino, 1924. [82i.]
V. Gioberti e il fallimento d. guerra federale, 1920. [78ii.]

Aosta. Cartulaire de l'évêché d'Aoste (13e s.) ; publ. J.-A. Duc, *see* REGIA DEP. DI ST. PAT. Misc., t23, 1884.
Livre des cens de l'évêché d'A. (1305) ; publ. J. A. Duc, *see* REGIA DEP. DI ST. PAT. Misc., t35, 1898.

Aparisi y Guijarro (Antonio).
Le roi d'Espagne. Tr. [P2830]. 8°. 1869

***Ape (L') patria** : racc. storica, Ravenna [*attrib. to Rasi ?*], 1845, *see* RAVENNA.

Apelles [APELLE]. Apelleisches, 1910, *see* SIX (J.)

Apellus (Johannes). *De actionibus ex Institut. Justiniani. [P2541]. s8°. Wittembergæ. 1526

Apert (Eugène). La croissance. s8°. 1921

Apesteguy (Bernard Joseph), *see* CHIQUITO DE CAMBO, *ps.*

***Aphorismi** doct. Jesuit. &c., 1608, *see* JESUITS.

Aphthonius, *Sophista.* Progymnasmata. Ed. H. Rabe. Acc. anonymi Aegypt., Sopatri &c. fragm. [Rhetores Graec., v10]. s8°. L. *Teubner.* 1926

Apicius (Coelius). De re coquinaria. Ed. C. Giarratano & F. Vollmer. s8°. L., *Teubner.* 1922
see VOLLMER (F.) St. zu d. röm. Kochbuche v. A., 1920.

Apin (Siegmund Jacob). Hist. nat. de veritate Scr. S. testimonium. s8°. Altorfi Norimb. 1717
Unvorgreiffl. Gedancken wie man sowohl alte als neue Dissertationes sammlen u. e. guten Indicem darüber halten soll. s4°. Nürnberg. 1719

Apionus, *ps.* *The Bolshevists of anc. hist., 1924, *see* BOLSHEVISTS.

Apocrypha. Apocrypha. Tr. 1611, rev. 1894. la8°. C. 1895
Apocrypha, hoc est narr. de Christo, Maria, Ioseph, &c. ; ed. Gr.-Lat. a M. Neandro, *see* LUTHER (M.) Catechesis parva &c., 1567.
[Apoc. acts of the Apostles. *In Armenian.* Ed. Q. A. Tchraqean]. s8°. Venetik. 1904
[Apoc. books of the N. Test. *In Armenian*]. 8°. Venetik. 1898
[Apoc. books of the O. Test. *Ed.* S. Hovsekheantz. *In Armenian*]. s8°. Venetik. 1896
Books of the A., w. crit. &c. obs., by Charles Wilson. 8°. E. 1801
Codex apoc. Novi Test., t1, 2, 1719, *see* FABRICIUS (J. A.)
Epistula apostol., *see* EPISTOLA.
Excluded books of the N. Test. Tr. J. B. Lightfoot, M. R. James, H. B. Swete &c. Intr. by J. A. Robinson. 8°. [1927]
James (M. R.) Apoc. N. T., w. o. narr^s. & fragm^s. Tr. M. R. J. s8°. O. 1924
—— *ed.* Latin infancy gospels : new text, w. parallel vers. f. Irish. 8°. C. 1927
see DASHEAN (H.) [Doct. of the Apostles, Apoc. bk. of canons &c. *In Armenian*], 1896.
„ FINDLAY (A. F.) Byways : st^s. in uncanon. Gospels & Acts, 1923.
„ MÖLLING (C. J.) Pseudo-Vet. Test., 1707.
„ PELLICANUS (C.) Comm. Bibliorum &c., t5, 1538.
„ RAINOLDS (J.) Censura libr. apoc. Vet. Test. adv. pontificios, impr. R. Bellarminum, 2t, 1611.
„ TISCHENDORF (L. F. C.) De evangel. A. orig. &c., 1851.
„ VETTER (P.) Die armen. apokr. Apostelakten (*in Gr. & Arm.*), 1901–2?.

Apollinaire (Guillaume).
Alcools. Poèmes, 1898–1913. 4e éd. s8°. 1920
La femme assise. 5e éd. s8°. 1920
Les peintres cubistes. 10e éd. s8°. [1922]
see ROUVEYRE (A.) Souv^s. de mon commerce : Gourmont, A., Moréas, &c., 1921.

Apollinarius, *bp. of Laodicea, see* RAVEN (C. E.) Apollinarianism, 1923.

Apollo. A journal of the arts. Ed. R. S. Glover. v1–6 (Jan. 1925–Dec. 1927). 4°. 1925–27

Apollo. *Il natal d'A., 1775, *see* MATTEI (S.)

Apollodorus, *Atheniensis.* Bibliotheca, *see* MYTHOGRAPHI GRAECI ; ed. R. Wagner, ed. 2^a., v1, 1926.
Bibliothek d. A. Übers. v. J. G. Meusel. Vorrede v. H. Klotz. 8°. Halle. 1768
The Library. [Text]. w. tr. by Sir J. G. Frazer. [Loeb Class. Lib.] 2v. s8°. 1921

Apollon. Аполлонъ. 1916, 1917. No^s. 1–3[? *no more publ.*] 4°. С.-П. 1916–17

Apollonii (Gulielmus). A consid. of certaine controversies agitated in Eng. conc. the govt. of the Ch. of God. s8°. 1645

Apollonio (Ferdinando).
Delle campane di S. Marco. la8°. Venezia. 1909

Apollonius, *Alexandrinus, Dyscolus.* A. D. quae supersunt. Rec., apparat. crit., comm., indices adj. R. Schneider & G. Uhlig. [Gramm. Graeci, p2, v1i, ii, 2, 3]. v1i, ii, 2, 3. 8°. L., *Teubner.* 1878–1910
Hist. comment. liber. Gr. & Lat. Cum notis G. Xylandri & J. Meursii, Emend. &c. L. H. Teucherus. 8°. Lips. 1792

Apollonius, *Pergaeus.* A. P. quae Graece extant, cum comment. ant. Ed. & Latine interpr. I. L. Heiberg. 2v. s8°. L., *Teubner.* 1891–93

Apollonius, *Rhodius.* The Argonautica. Bk. 3. Ed. M. M. Gillies. 8°. C. 1928
The tale of the Argonauts. Tr. A. S. Way. [Temple Classics]. s8°. 1901

Apollonius, *the senator, d. c. 185, see* †CONYBEARE (F. C.) The Apology & Acts of A. &c., [tr.] w. notes, 1894.
see HARNACK (C. G. A.) Der Process d. Christen A., 1893.

Apollonius, *Tyaneus, see* MEYER (E.) Kl. Schr., B2 (A. v. T. u. d. Biog. des Philostratos), 1924.

Apollonius, *Tyrius* [APOLONIO]. Die altfranzös. Prosavers. d. A.-Romans ; hrsg. C. B. Lewis, *see* ROMANISCHE FORSCH., B34, 1915.
Libro de Apolonio. An old Span. poem. Ed. C. C. Marden. p2, Grammar, notes, & vocab. [Elliott Monographs, 11–12]. 8°. Princeton, N. J. 1922

Apologia.
*Apologia doctrinæ eor. qui vulgo appellantur Waldenses &c., 1538, *see* WALDENSES.
Apologia modesta & Christiana ad acta conventus 15 Theologorum Torgæ nuper habiti, 1575, *see* TORGAU.
Apologia oder Verantwortung d. christl. Concordien Buchs, 1583, *see* KIRCHNER (T.), N. SELNECCER & M. CHEMNITZ.
*Apologia od. Verantworttungsschrifft d. Evangel. Kirchen in England &c. [Vorrede *signed* M. Harnisch.] s8°. Newstadt a. d. Hardt. 1589
*Apologia pro conf. sive declar. sententiæ eorum qui voc. Remonstrantes, 1629, *see* EPISCOPIUS (S.)

Apology [APOLOGIE].
*Apologie cathol. contre les libelles &c., 1585, *see* L'ALLOUETTE (E. DE).
*Apologie d. Dominicains missionn. de la Chine, 1699, *see* ALEXANDRE (N.)
*Apology (An) for the Church hist. of Eng., 1500–1688, 1742, *se* TOOTELL (H.)
*Apology (An) for the clergy of Bristol in petitioning an Act of Parl. for their better &c. maintenance [? *by Benjamin Bayly.* P2669]. s8°. 1712

Apophthegmata. Üb. d. kopt.-sa 'id. Apophthegmata Patrum Aegypt. &c., 1918, *see* HOPFNER (T.)

Apostles. Apocryphal acts of the A. (*in Armenian*), 1904, *see* APOCRYPHA.
Armen. apokr. Apostelakten, p1, 2 (*in Gr. & Arm.*), 1901–2, *see* VETTER (P.)
Epistula apostol., *see* EPISTOLA.

Apostles' Creed. Belydenisse d. Christel. Geloofs &c. [*w. comm. by J. Szlichting*]. s4°. *n.p.* 1643
Confessio fidei Christ. ed. nom. eccles. Polon. [*w. comm.* by J. Szlichting, *b. w.* Apostles' Creed. Belydenisse, 1643]. s4°. *n.p.* 1642
„ „ ....s8°. *n.p.* 1651

Apostol (Paul). Soviet Russia : legal & econ. condit^s. of indust. &c. activity. [*By*] P. A., Count W. N. Kokovtzoff &c. s8°. [1924]

Apostolic [APOSTOLICAL ; APOSTOLICÆ]. The Apostolic Fathers. [Tr. by Abp. Wake], w. intr. by Dr. Burton. [Anc. & Mod. Lib. of Theolog. Lit.] 2p. 8°. [1888–89]
1, Epistles of SS. Clement of Rome & Barnabas, & the Shepherd of Hermas. 2, Epistles of St. Ignatius & St. Polycarp [& Essay on the right use of Fathers, by W. Reeves].
„ „ ....[*a. ed.*] 2v. s8°. E. 1909
[Doct. of the Apostles, Canons &c. : comm. & text ; *in Armen.*], 1896, *see* DASHEAN (H.)

Apostolic [*continued*].
The genuine epistles of the apostolical Fathers Barnabas—Clement—Ignatius—Polycarp—the Shepherd of Hermas &c., tr. 1719, *see* WAKE (W.)
CONSTITUTIONES APOSTOLICAE.
Canones S. Apostol., *Gr. & Lat.*, *see* THEOLOGI. Theolog. aliquot Græc. libri, 1560.
De Constit. Apost. B. Clemente Romano auctore libri 8 Io. Carolo Bovio interprete. s8°. Parisiis. 1564
see BURNET (G.) Vindic. of Ch. of Scot. *foll*[d]. *by* Obs. on the 1st & 2nd Canons commonly ascr. to the Apostles, 1673.
„ WERNSDORF (G.) Diss. de Constit. Apost. orig., c. G. Whistonum, 1739.

Apparatus. Apparatus Biblicus, 1723, *see* LAMY (B.)
*Apparatus brevis ad theologiam & jus Canon., 1751, *see* FAURE (J. B.)

Appasamy (A. J.), *see* STREETER (B. H.) & A. J. A. The Sadhu, 1921.

Appeal.
*Appeal (An) on behalf of Brit. subjects in &c. the River Plate. [P2832]. 8°. 1846
*Appeal (An) to the candid &c. members of the Establ. Church conc. irregular preaching, 1786, *see* CREIGHTON (J.)
*Appeal (An) to the Protest[s]. of Gt. Brit. & Ir., on Rom. Cath. q. in reply to address by C. Butler. [P524, *a.c. b.w.* Butler (C.), Address, 2nd. ed., 1813]. 8°. 1813
*Appeal (An) to the public whether a Calvinist can &c., 1780, *see* TAYLOR (T.)

Appel (Carl). Festschrift f. C. A. zu s. 70. Geburtstage am 17. Mai 1927, *see* ZEITSCHRIFT F. ROMAN. PHILOL., B47, 1927.

Appell (Johann Wilhelm), *see* COLONNA (F.) Dream of Poliphilus: facs. of woodcuts, 1499; w. not. & descr. by A., 1888.

Appendini (Francesco Maria).
De præstantia &c. ling. Illyricæ diss. s8°. Ragusii. 1806
Gramm. d. lingua Illirica. s8°. Ragusa. 1808

Apperley (Charles James) [*ps.* NIMROD]. Nimrod's hunting remin. &c. n. ed. w. intr. by W. Shaw Sparrow. 4°. [1926]

Appia (Georges Ant. J. Ed.) G. Appia, pasteur & prof. en Italie & à Paris, 1827–1910. Souv[s]. réunis par sa famille. 2t. 8°. [1923?–25]

Appian, *of Alexandria* [APPIANUS]. Roman. hist. quæ sup. Græce & Lat. cum ind. la8°. Parisiis, *Didot*. 1840

Appius Claudius Pulcher, *see* CLAUDIUS PULCHER (A.)

Appleby (H. N.), *see* GREAT WESTERN PORTS; produced &c. by H. N. A., 1927.
see SOUTH WALES PORTS; produced by H. N. A., 1924.

Appleton (Daniel) & Co., *publishers.* The cyclopædia of Amer. biography. New enl. ed. of A.'s cyclop. of Amer. biog.; orig. ed. J. G. Wilson &c. Ed. J. E. Homans, w. intr. by R. Johnson. v8, 9. 8°. N.Y. 1918–22
see OVERTON (G. M.) Portrait of a publisher & 1st 100 yrs. of Hse. of A., 1825–1925, 1925.

Appleton (Lewis). Mem. of Henry Richard. s8°. 1889

Appleton (Reginald Bainbridge). The elements of Greek philos. f. Thales to Aristotle. s8°. [1922]
Euripides the idealist. s8°. 1927

Appleton (Thomas Gold).
Life & letters. Prep. by S. Hale. s8°. N.Y. 1885

Appleton (William Archibald), *Sec. to Gen. Federation of Trade Unions.* Trade unionism. s8°. [1924]
Trade unions. s8°. [1925]
What we want & where we are. s8°. [1921]

Appleton (William Worthen), *see* OVERTON (G. M.) Portrait of a publisher [*i.e.* W. W. A.], 1925.

Appleyard (John Whittle), *Wesleyan missionary in S. Africa*, *see* SMITH (T.) Mem. of J. W. A., 1881.

Appleyard (Rollo). Relation betw. the "bight," "span," & "dip" of catenaries. [P2490]. 8°. 1920

Äppli (Fritz). Die wicht. Ausdrücke f. d. Tanzen i. d. roman. Sprachen. [Zeitschr. f. roman. Philol. Beih. 75]. 8°. Halle. 1925

Apponyi (Albert, *Gróf*), *b. 1846*. Apponyi A. beszédei. 2[lk]. kiadás. 2k., 1872–95. 8°. 1897
Hungarian foreign policy. [P2567]. s8°. 1921
The Peace-treaty proposed to Hungary. [P2567]. s8°. 1920

Apponyi (Rudolf, *Gróf*). Vingt-cinq ans à Paris (1826–52). Journal du R. A. Publ. par E. Daudet. t4, 1844–52. 8°. 1926

Appuhn (Charles), *see* BIBLIOTHÈQUE & MUSÉE DE LA GUERRE. Cat. du fonds allem.; réd. par J. Dubois avec collab. de C. A., t1–3, 1921–22.

Aprile (Francesco). Della cronologia univ. d. Sicilia libri tre. sfol. Palermo. 1725

Apsley House, *London*. Descr. & hist. cat. of the coll. of pictures & sculpture at Apsley House. By E. Wellington. 2v. 4°. 1901

Apthorp (East). Disc. on prophecy. 2v. 8°. 1786

Apukhtin (Aleksei Nikolaevich).
Между смертью и жизнью. [P2392]. s8°. Москва. 1917

Apuleius, *Barbarus* [APULEIUS (SEXTUS); PSEUDO-APULEIUS]. The herbal of A. B. f. early 12th-cent. MS. (MS. Bodl. 130). [Facsimile]. Descr. by R. T. Gunther. [Roxburghe Club]. 4°. O. 1926
Herbarius, *see* CORPUS medicorum Lat., v4, 1927.

Apuleius (Lucius), *Madaurensis.* Opera omnia. Curâ Petri Colvii cum ejusdem notis. [*w. sep. tp. & pagin.*] s8°. Lugd. Batav. 1588
Apologie—Florides. Texte établi & tr. par P. Vallette. [Coll. des univ[s]. de France]. 8°. 1924
see RAPHAEL, *the painter.* La favola di Psiche disegnata da R., colla spiegaz. in ottava rima, 1774.

Aqua Blanca (Peter de), *bp. of Hereford*, *see* PETER *de Aqua Blanca.*

Aquila *of Sinope* [AQUILA, *ponticus*], *see* DATHE (J. A.) & S. F. N. MORUS. Disput. in A. reliquias interpret. Hoseæ, 1757.

Aquila (Caspar), *see* ADLER (C.)

Aquilano (Serafino) [AQUILA (SERAFINO DELL'); CIMINELLI (S. DE); †CIMINO (S.)], *1466–1500*. Opere, con molte cose aggionte di novo. Sonetti 165, Egloghe 3, Epistole 7 &c. s8°. [Vinegia. *Bindoni &c.* 1529]

Aquinas (Thomas) *Saint* [†THOMAS, *Aquinas*].
St. T. A.; papers, 6th centenary of canonizat., Manchester, 1924. By A. Whitacre, V. McNabb, A. E. Taylor & *others.* 8°. O. 1925
Vera S. Thomæ A. sententia de infallib. Rom. pontif. refut. eorum quæ R. Bianchi scripsit. [P2691]. 8°. Neapoli. 1870

QUODLIBETA.
[Quæstiones seu de duodecim quodlibet. *f1. blank. f2–4 table. Beg. f. 5*[a] [*red*] Summa de quolibet Thome Aq̄natis fratris &c. *Ends f. 136*[a] [*red*] Beati Thome Aquinatis quodlibeta duodecim expliciūt feliciter p̱ Joanneꝫ sensenschmid]. fol. [Nurmberge. *J. Sensenschmidt*, 1474].
*136ff. No tp., pagin. or sign. [*1–4; a–c in tens; d 1–8; e–n in tens; o 1–4]. Capitals blank.*

SUMMA.
*Quinque novi indices generales [Summæ S. Thomæ]. s8°. Lugduni. 1623
[Summæ theologiæ]. Secundus liber secunde partis. fol. [Venetiis p. Franciscum de Hailbrun (*i.e.* Franz Renner) & Nicolaū de Frankfordia socios, 1475].
323 printed leaves; no tp., pagin. or signatures; 1a blank; 1b–8b Tabulæ questionum &c.; *9a–323b text, beg.* Incipit liber &c.
Totius summæ conclusiones. s8°. Antverpiæ. 1614

TRANSLATIONS.
The Summa contra gentiles. Lit. tr. by the Eng. Dominican Fathers. Books 1, 2. 2v. 8°. 1923–24
Summa theologica. Tr. by Fathers of the Eng. Dominican Prov. 3p *in* 19 No[s]. *or* vol[s]. [I, 1–3; IIi, 1–3; IIii, 1–6; III, 1–7; *each no. w. sep. tp. & pagin.* pl, no. 1, 2nd rev. ed.] 8°. 1912–22
„ 2nd rev. ed. pl, no. 3 (QQ 75–119) [*in* 2v.] 8°. 1922

REFERENCES.
see ALAGONA (P.) Theolog. summæ compend., 1620.
„ BENTIVOGLIO (P.) Compendii Theologiæ T. Aquinatis, 1585.
„ BIRKENMAJER (A.) Verm. Unters. (Brief d. Pariser Artistenfakult. ü. d. Tod d. hl. T.), 1922.
„ BRIAS (C. DE). Thomistarum triumphus, t1, 2, 1672–3.
„ CARBONE DE COSTACCIARO (L.) Compend. totius summæ theolog. T. A., 1609.
„ DEURWERDERS (F.) Militia angelica T. A., 1659.
„ DORSCHAEUS (J. G.) T. A. exhib. confessor veritatis evang., 1656.
„ GALLO (J.) De laudibus T. A. oratio, 1563.
„ GILSON (F.) Philos. of St. T. A.; auth. tr., 1924.
„ —— St. Thomas d'A., 3e éd., 1925.
„ GRABMANN (M.) Die echten Schriften d. T. v. A., 1920.
„ GREDT (J.) Elem. philos. Aristotelico-Th., ed. 3[a], 2v, 1921–22.
„ KLING (C. F.) Descr. Summæ theolog. T. A., 1846.
„ KOCH (J.) Durandus de S. Porchiano: Forsch. z. Streit um T. v. A. zu Beg. d. 14. J., Tl, 1927.
„ MACEDO (F.) Collationes doctr. S. Thomæ, & Scoti, 1680.
„ MAYOL (J.) Summa moralis doctr. Thomisticæ circa Decalogum &c., 1861.
„ RADA (J. DE) Controversiæ theolog. inter S. Thomam & Scotum, 1599.
„ RANST (F. VAN) Veritas in medio: seu D. Thomas propositiones versantes a Baianis usque ad Quesnellianas prædamnans, 1715.
„ REGINALD (A.) Doct. T. A. tria principia &c., 1670.

Aquinas (Thomas) [*continued*].

see Reiser (A.) Vindiciæ evangelico-Thomisticæ &c., 1669.
,, Requesenius (J. M.) Sel. disp. in primam secundæ divi T., 1659.
,, Taylor (A. E.) St. T. A. as a philosopher, 1924.
,, Tholuck (F. A. G.) Disput. de T. A. & Abaelardo interp. N. Test., 1842.
see Tractatus sollennis de arte &c. predicandi ex script. Thome de A. &c. recoll., 1483.
,, Wicksteed (P. H.) Reactions betw. dogma & philos. illust. f. works of S. T. A., 1920.
,, Wigandt (M.) Tribunal confessariorum &c.; dogmata T. A. &c. opera M. W., 1724.

Arabia. *Arabia seu Arabum vicinarumq; gentium orientalium leges, ritus, mores, instit. & hist. [*By* Gabriel Sionita &c. *Added* W. Drechsler, Hist. Arabum. *b. w.* Trigault (N.) Regni Chin. descr., 1639]. s8°. Amsterdami. 1635
A hdbk. of A., 1920, *see* Admiralty: Naval Intell. Div.

Arabian Nights. A. N. Tr. into French by M. Galland, & now done into Eng. f. last Paris ed. 4v. [*tps. of v2 & 4 torn. tp. & pp. 1–10 of v3 wanting*]. s8°. 1787
A. N. Tr. E. W. Lane. Intr. by J. Jacobs. Illust. by F. Brangwyn. 6v. s8°. 1896
A. N. Sel. f. Lane's tr. Oxf. ed. s8°. O. 1915
A. N. entertainments. Sel. & ed. A. Lang. n. impr. s8°. 1921
Le livre des mille nuits & une nuit. [Tr. du Dr. J. C. Mardrus. Illust. par facs. des miniatures &c.] 8t. la4°. [1908–12]

Arabicum. *Alphabetum A., 1592, *see* Alphabetum.

Arachiel, *see* Arakel.

Aragão e Vasconcellos (Antonio Luiz de Brito), *see* Brito Aragão e Vasconcellos.

Aragon (Henry). La vigne dans l'antiquité. Légendes &c. du "dieu de la vigne" &c. 8°. Toulouse. 1916

Aragon (Louis). Le paysan de Paris. 2e éd. s8°. [1926]

Aragona (Tullia d').
Rime d. T. di A., et di diversi a lei. s8°. Vinegia. 1547

Arakel, *of Siunik.* Pages choisies: Visions de l'enfer & du ciel—Le livre d'Adam; tr. préc. d'une ét. &c., *see* Tchobanian (A.) La roseraie d'Arménie, t1, 1918.

Arakel, *of Tabriz* [A. of Tauriz; Araqel (*Vartapet*)]. Livre d'hist. trait. des évènements de l'Arménie (1604–68); [*tr.*], *see* Brosset (M. F.) Coll. d'histor. arm., t1, 1874.
Patmouthiun. [Hist. *in Armenian.* 3rd ed.] 8°. Vagharshapat. 1896

Aram (Eugene). The trial & life of E. A., w. letters & poems &c. s8°. Richmond. 1832
Trial of E. A. for the murder of D. Clark &c. 13th ed. [P2825]. s8°. Knaresbrough. *n.d.*
see Bristow (W.) *The genuine acc. of the trial of E. A., 11th ed., 1815.
,, Scatcherd (N.) "Gleanings" after E. A., 1836.
,, —— Mem. of E. A. &c., 2nd ed., 1838.

Aramaic. A. papyri of 5th c. B.C.; ed., w. tr. &c. by A. Cowley, 1923, *see* Cowley (A. E.)

Aramäische Papyrus aus Elephantine, 1911, *see* Ungnad (A.)

Aramis, *ps.* *Monkraven: the story of h. betrayal. 3v. s8°. 1886

Aranha (José Pereira da Graça). Canaan. Tr. M. J. Lorente. Pref. by G. Ferrero. s8°. [1921]

Arano (Annibale).
C. Cressini: pittore. s8°. Torino. [1924?]
R. Weiss: pittore. s8°. Torino. [1923]

Araquistain (Luis).
El Archipiélago Maravilloso. Aventuras. s8°. [1923]
El peligro yanqui. s8°. 1921

Ararat. [*Monthly mag. in Armenian*]. Nov. 1892–Mar. 1893. [P2807]. 1895–98 [*in* 2v. Mar., May, Oct. part of Nov. & Dec. 1895, Mar., May & June 1896 *wanting*]. 8°. & 4°. Vagharshapat. 1892–98
,, ,, ,, 1914–July 1917 [Jan., Aug., Oct.–Dec. 1914, Jan., Sept., Oct. 1915, Sept.–Dec. 1916, & Jan.–May 1917 *wanting*]. la8°. Etchmiadzine. 1914–17

Araratsky (V.) Подвиги царизма. Кровавые февральскіе дни въ Баку [*a. c. in* P2715]. 8°. Женева. 1905

Arason (Jón). Relig. digte; udg. af F. Jonsson, *see* Kongeligt Dan. Vid. Selsk., Hist.-fil. Med., B2, 1918–19.

Aratus. A.; w. Eng. tr. by G. R. Mair, 1921, *see* Callimachus.

Araujo (Francisco Manoel Alvares de), *see* Alvares de Araujo (F. M.)

Arbaud (Joseph d'). La bête du Vaccarès. [*Fr. & Prov.*] Préf. de C. Maurras. [Cahiers verts, 64]. s8°. 1926

Arbaumont (Jules d'), *see* Vignory. Cartul. du prieuré de St.-Etienne de V.; publ. avec intr. &c. par J. d'A., 1882.

Arbeau (Thoinot), *ps.*, *see* Tabourot (J.)

Arbeiter-Rat (Der). Organ d. Arbeiterräte Deutschlands. Jahr. 1. Nr. 27. [P2417]. 4°. [1919]

Arbeitsgesetzbuch (Das) Sowjetrusslands; hrsg. &c. H. Freund, 1923, *see* Russia: Sov. Rep.

Arbelet (Paul). La jeunesse de Stendhal. 2t. 8°. 1919
1, Grenoble, 1783–99. 2, Paris-Milan, 1799–1802.
Stendhal épicier ou les infortunes de Mélanie. s8°. [1926]

Arbeo, *episc. Frisingensis, see* Cyrinus.

Arber (Agnes) [*Mrs.* E. A. Newell Arber]. Water plants: aquatic angiosperms. la8°. 1920

Arblay (*Mme.* d') [†Burney (Frances), *aft. D'Arblay*].
see Büttner (C.) Die Sprache in Evelina, 1924.
,, Johnson (R. B.), *ed.* F. B. & the Burneys, 1926.
,, Masefield (M.) Story of F. B., 1927.

Arborio (*card.* Mercurino), *conte di Gattinara.* Hist. vite & gest. per dom. magnum cancellarium (M. A.), con note &c. *ed.* C. Bornate, *see* Regia Deput. Miscellanea, t48, 1915.
Testamento [1529]; ed. V. Promis, *see* Regia Dep. di Storia Patria. Misc., t18, 1879.

Arbroath [Aberbrothoc]. Liber S. Thome de Aberbrothoc. Reg. abbacie de A. [Ed. C. Innes & P. Chalmers. Bannatyne Club]. 2p. 4°. E. 1848–56
1, Reg. vetus, 1178–1329. 2, Reg. nigrum, 1329–1536.

Arbusow (Leonid). Wolter v. Plettenberg u. d. Untergang d. Deut. Ordens in Preussen. [Verein f. Ref.-gesch. Jhrg. 36 (Nr. 131)]. 8°. L. 1919

Arbuthnot, *The family of.* Inventory of A. titles, 1206–1483, f. MS. of G. Home, *see* Maidment (J.) & R. Pitcairn. Nugæ derelictæ, 1822.
see Arbuthnot (*Mrs.* P. S.-M.) Mems. of the Arbuthnots of Kincardineshire & Aberdeenshire, 1920.

Arbuthnot (Alexander), *see* Maitland (*Sir* R.) The Maitland 4°. MS. cont. poems by Sir R. M., A., &c., 1920.

Arbuthnot (George). Herzegovina; or Omer Pacha & the Xtn. rebels. With a brief acc. of Servia &c. s8°. 1862

Arbuthnot (John), *M.D.* The hist. of John Bull—Epitaph on Don Francisco, *see* Miscellany (A) of the wits, 1920.
see Teerink (H.) Hist. of John Bull: re-issued f. orig. pamphlets (Law is a bottomless pit &c.), 1712, w. investig. into composition &c., 1925.

Arbuthnot (*Mrs.* P. S.-M.) Mem. of the Arbuthnots of Kincardineshire & Aberdeenshire. la8°. [1920]

Arc (Jeanne d').

*La hist. de la Poncella de Francia [1512], *see* Revue hispan., t66, 1926.
Procès de condamnation de J. d'A. Texte, tr. & notes [par] P. Champion. 2t. (1, Texte lat.; 2, Intr., tr. & notes). 8°. 1920–21
Saint Joan of Orleans: scenes f. the 15th cent. Mystère du Siège d'Orléans; sel. &c. J. Evans, 1926, *see* Orleans.
see Auriac (J. E. d') La véritable J. d'A., 1920.
,, Delteil (J.) Jeanne d'A., 1925.
,, Denis (L.) La vérité sur J. d'A., 1910.
,, Du his (C.) Opusc. hist. rel. a J. D. (1610), 1856.
,, France (A.) Life of J. of A.; tr. W. Stephens, repr., 2v, 1924.
,, Luce (S.) J. d'A. à Domremy, 1886.
,, Paine (A. B.) Joan of Arc, 2v, 1925.
see Péguy (C. P.) Le mystère de la charité de J., 2t, 1910–26.
,, Porché (F.) La vierge au grand cœur, ou la mission &c. de J. d'A. [*play*], 1925.
,, Prutz (H. G.) Die Briefe J. d'A., 1914.
,, —— Neue Stud., 1917.
,, —— Zur Gesch. d. Jungfrau: d. Loire-Feldzug, 1429 — Krönungszug n. Rheims, 1920–23.
,, Quenedey (L.) Prison de J. d'A. à Rouen, 1923.
,, Rudler (G.) Michelet, historien de J. d'A., 2t, 1926.
,, Schiller (J. C. F. v.) Die Jungfrau v. Orleans: Tragödie, 1861.
,, Shaw (G. B.) Saint Joan: a chronicle play, 1924.
,, Voltaire. La Pucelle, the Maid of Orleans: poem; n. tr., rev. &c. by E. Dowson, 2v, 1899.

Arcadia, *Rome, see* Zappi (G. B. F.) Rime, p2, Alcuni rime di celeb. poeti dell' A. di R., 1773.

Arcadios, *of the monastery of Vatopedi, deacon, see* Athos. Cat. of Greek MSS. in mon. of Vatopedi on Mt. A.; by S. Eustratiades & A., 1924.

Arcana. *Arcana soc. Jesu publ. bono vulgata &c., 1635, *see* Schoppe (C.)

Arcangelo, *da Borgo-nuovo, see* **Archangelo** [*Pozzo*], *da Borgo-nuovo.*

Arcanum, *ps.* *The blot on Parliament & the cleansing. s8°. 1923

Arceval (Julio) *ps.?*, *see* MADARIAGA (S. DE). A. y los Ingleses, 1925.

Archæologia Cambrensis. Journal of the Cambrian Arch. Assoc. s6, v20, s7, v1–7. 8°. 1920–27

Archæological & hist. coll^s. rel. to Co. of Renfrew, 2v, 1885–90, *see* RENFREW.

Archæological Institute of America. Investigations at Assos. Drawings &c. of buildings &c. discov. dur. excav^s., 1881–83, by J. T. Clark, F. H. Bacon &c. Ed. w. notes by F. H. Bacon. [pl. *no more publ.*] fol. 1902

see ART & ARCHÆOLOGY, v2, 3, 1915–16.

Archæology [*see also* ARCHÉOLOGIE]. *How to observe in a.: suggestions to travellers &c., 1920, *see* BRITISH MUSEUM.

The year's work in a., 1921, 1922, *see* CONGRESS OF ARCHÆOL. SOCIETIES.

Archambault (Thomas). Cat. des reliques de l'Empereur, prov. de S^te. Hélène, coll. de A. Vente, Drouot, Avril 1924. [P2859]. 8°. 1924

Archangelo [*Pozzo*], *da Borgo-Nuovo.* Interpret. in selectiora Cabalistarum dogmata, ex comm. J. Pici Mirandulani excerpta, *see* PISTORIUS (J.) Artis Cabalist. t1, 1587.

Archanz (L'), *see* LARCHANZ.

Archbold (William Arthur Jobson). Outlines of Indian constit. hist. (Brit. period). 8°. 1926

Archdekin (Richard) [ARSDEKIN]. Præcipuæ controversiæ fidei &c. ac resolutiones theolog. s8°. Lovanii. 1671

Theologia tripartita &c., ed. 5a. v1. s8°. Antverpiæ. 1682

Vitæ &c. S. Patricii. Cum brevi notitia Hiberniæ & prophetia S. Malachiæ [*b. w. h.* Præcipuæ controversiæ, 1671]. s8°. Lovanii. 1671

Archéologie. Comptes rendus du Congrès Internat. d'Ar. Classique. 2e session. la8°. le Caire. 1909

Archer (Dorothy). Corsica, the scented isle. 8°. [1924]

Archer (Frederick James), *see* HUMPHRIS (E. M.) Life of Fred A., 2nd ed., 1923.

Archer (Richard Lawrence).

Secondary educ. in the 19th c. 8°. C. 1921

Archer (William). The old drama & the new. 8°. 1923

The Peace-President [Wilson]. s8°. [1919]

Three plays [Martha Washington—Beatriz Juana—Lidia]. Note by B. Shaw. 8°. [1927]

W. A. as rationalist. Coll. of h. writings. Ed. w. crit. notice by J. M. Robertson. 8°. [1925]

—— **& H. Granville Barker.** A national theatre: scheme & estimates. la8°. 1907

Archibald (Edith J.) Life and letters of Sir E. M. Archibald. Foreword by Sir R. L. Borden. 8°. Toronto. 1924

Archibald (*Sir* Edward Mortimer), *see* ARCHIBALD (E. J.) Life & letters of Sir E. M. A., 1924.

Archibald (John), *see* KENT. East K. regional planning scheme, prelim. survey; prep. f. the Comm. by P. Abercrombie & J. A., 1925.

Archieratikon. Древне-грузинскій архіератиконъ. [*Liturgy of St. James*]. Груз. текстъ, изд, &c. К. С. Кекелидзе. la8°. Тифлисъ. 1912

The Georgian version of the liturgy of St. James. [Tr.] by F. C. Conybeare & O. Wardrop. [Extr. de la Revue de l'Orient chrét., t19]. 8°. Paris. 1915

Archilochus [ARCHILOCHOS].

see DIEHL (E.) Suppl. lyricum, 3e A., 1917.

,, HUDSON-WILLIAMS (T.) Early Greek elegy: fragm^s. of A. &c., 1926.

Archimedes. Opera omnia cum comm. Eutocii. Iterum ed. J. L. Heiberg. s8°. L., *Teubner*. 1910–15

Œuvres compl. Tr., avec intr. par P. Ver Eecke. la8°. 1921

see CZWALINA (A.) A., 1925.

,, HEATH (*Sir* T. L.) A. [Pioneers of progress], 1920.

Archinto (Alberico), *Cardinal.* Bibliothecæ A. cat. Publicè prostabit Romæ, 1760. 3p *in* 1v. s8°. Romæ. 1760

Architectural & Archæological Society for Co. of Buckingham, *see* PIPE ROLLS. Cal. of P. R. for Bucks. & Beds., 1189–99; by G. H. Fowler &c., 1923.

Architectural Association School. A book of design by senior students. Intr. essays by R. Atkinson &c. 4°. 1924

Archiv für d. gesamte Psychologie. B36. 8°. L. 1917

Archiv für das Studium d. neueren Sprachen u. Literaturen. Hrsg. L. Herrig &c. B1–152 (1–100, Neu. Ser. 1–52). 8°. Elberfeld &c. 1846–1927

B11, 13, 15–19, 21, 22, 24, 37 *wanting.* B25iii, iv, 27ii–iv, 28i, 29ii, iii, 31i, ii *wanting.* *These vols. also lack title pages & indexes.* B140 *has* Deut. Sonderheft, *w. sep. tp. &c.*

Archiv für Geschichte der Medizin: hrsg. v. d. Puschmann-Stiftung an d. Univ. Leipzig unter Redaktion v. K. Sudhoff. B10–19. la8°. L. 1917–27

15, Karl Sudhoff zum 70. Geburtstage [Festschrift]; hrsg. E. Ebstein u. R. Stein.

Archiv für Geschichte der Philosophie. B32–38 (Neue Folge, 25–31). 8°. 1918–27

,, ,, ...Beilagen. 8°. 1914–25

see LÖWENHEIM (L.) Die Wissenschaft Demokrits, 1914. [26iv.]

,, STEIN (W.) Nietzsche u. d. bild. Kunst, 1925. [30i, ii.]

,, UXKULL-GYLLENBAND (W., *Graf*). Griech. Kultur-Entstehungslehren, 1924. [36iii, iv.]

Archiv für Litteratur-u. Kirchengesch. d. Mittel Alters. Hrsg. v. H. Denifle u. F. Ehrle. B1–7 [*no more publ.*] 8°. 1885–1900

Archiv für Reformationsgesch. Texte u. Untersuchungen. In Verbindung mit d. Verein f. Reformationsgesch, hrsg. v. W. Friedensburg. Jhrg. 1–11 (1903/04–1914). 8°. 1904–14

,, ,, ...Ergänzungsband 1–4. 8°. 1906–11

see HEGLER (A.) Beitr. z. Gesch. d. Mystik in d. Reformationszeit, 1906. [1.]

,, HELT (G.) Briefwechsel, 1907. [2.]

,, WOTSCHKE (T.) Briefw. d. Schweizer mit d. Polen, 1908. [3.]

,, ZERENER (H.) St. ü. d. beginn. Eindringen d. Luther. Bibelübers. in d. deut. Lit., 1911. [4.]

Archiv für Religionswissenschaft vereint mit d. Beiträgen z. Religionswiss. d. Religionswiss. Gesellschaft in Stockholm. Hrsg. O. Weinrich &c. B23–25. 8°. L. 1925–27

B25 *cont^s.* Systemat. Verzeichnis, B1–25, *w. sep. tp. & pagin.*

Archiv für Stamm-u. Wappenkunde. Jahr. 1–14 (1900–1914). la8°. Kahla &c. 1901–14

Jahr. 1, *h. t.* Der Wappensammler &c.

,, 2, 3, *h. t.* Wellers Archiv f. Stamm-u. Wappenkunde.

,, 10–14, *h. t.* Roland. Verein zur Förderung d. Stamm-, Wappen-u. Siegelkunde. Monatsschrift.

Archiv für systematische Philosophie. Neue Folge der Philosoph. Monatshefte. B25–30. 8°. 1920–27

,, ,, ...Beilagen. 8°. 1924–25

see MOSZKOWSKI (A.) Abbau d. "Unendlich," 1925. [19i, ii.]

,, STICKERS (J.) Die absolute Vereindeutlichung d. philos. Terminologie, 1924. [28iii, iv.]

Archives.

Archives dépt. de la Manche, *see* MONT-MOREL. Cartul. de Mont-M., 1878.

Archives hist. du Maine, *see* SOCIÉTÉ DES ARCHIVES HIST. DU MAINE.

Archives hist. & ecclés de la Picardie &c., 1842, *see* ROGER (P. A.), *ed.*

Archives municipales de Bordeaux, 1867–90, *see* BORDEAUX.

Archives marocaines, 1904 &c., *see* MISSION SCIENT. DU MAROC.

Archivio glottologico italiano. Dir. da G. I. Ascoli. 2v. 8°. 1873–76

v1 *cont^s.* Saggi ladini, di G. I. Ascoli.

Archivio storico italiano.

Anno 76–85. la8°. Firenze. 1918–27

In the list below only the "Documenti," "Memorie orig." & "Necrologie" have been indexed.

Amiati (A.) Cosimo I e i frati di S. Marco. [Anno 81.]

Anzilotti (A.) Un amico napolet. di G. P. Vieusseux: bar. G. Savarese. [Anno 79, v1.]

—— Il tramonto d. Stato cittadino. [Anno 82, v1.]

—— V. Gioberti e il fallimento d. guerra federale. [Anno 78, v2.]

Arnolfi, *fam. of, see* Dorini (U.)

Barbadoro (B.) Beni demaniali, Firenze. [Anno 85, v2.]

Bartoli (C.), *see* Mancini (G.)

Bernardy (A. A.) La missione di B. Franklin a Parigi &c., 1776–86. [Anno 78, v1.]

Boccaccio (G.), *see* Nicolini.

Bononio, *st, see* Falce (A.)

Branca (M.) Contesa per Sardegna tra Pisa e Genova. [Anno 78, v1.]

Bresslau (H.) Necrologia. [Anno 85, v1.]

Cessi (R.) "Maone" medioevali. [Anno 77, v1.]

Chiappelli (A.) Maestri e scuole in Pistoia fino al sec. 14. [Anno 78, v1.]

Chiappelli (L.) L'età longobardo e Pistoia. [Anno 79, v1.]

—— Formaz. storica d. comune cittadino in Italia, p2. [Anno 85, v1.]

—— Una lettera mercant. del 1330, 1924. [Anno 82, v1.]

Cipolla (Carlo). Necrologia. [Anno 76, v2]

Coen (A.) Necrologia, A. C. [Anno 79, v2.]

Dante Alighieri, *see* Del Lungo (I.); Levi (C.); Maggini (F.); Mazzoni (G.); Panella (A.); Sapori (A.); Solmi (A.).

Del Lungo (I.) Il "giusto giudicio" imprecato da Dante. [Anno 79, v1.]

—— Vicende d'un' impostura erudita &c. [Anno 78, v1.]

Doria (A.) Un Giobertiano di Toscana: V. Salvagnoli &c. [Anno 80.]

Dorini (U.) Carte d. fam. Arnolfini. [Anno 82, v2.]

Archivio storico italiano [*continued*].
Este (Alfonso II d') *duke of Ferrara*, see Lazzari (A.)
Falce (A.) Contrib. alla diplom. di Tuscia. [Anno 83, v1.]
—— Doc. ined. d. duchi &c. di Tuscia. [Anno 85, v1, 2.]
—— La Vita ratbertiana di S. Bononio &c. [Anno 83, v1.]
Ferrara (M.) 2 sonetti contro il Savonarola. [Anno 80.]
Fiorilli (C.) I dipintori a Firenze nell' arte dei medici &c. [Anno 78, v2.]
Fiorini (V.) Necrologia, V. F. [Anno 84, v1.]
Foresti (A.) Viaggi di F. Petrarca dall' Italia ad Avignone. [Anno 78, v1.]
Franklin (B.), *see* Bernardy (A. A.)
Frati (C.) L. Scarabelli &c. [Anno 77, v1.]
Galiani (F.), *see* Nicolini (F.)
Gioberti (V.), *see* Anzlotti (A.)
—— *see* Rubertis (A. de).
Giordani (P.), *see* Frati (C.)
Gitti (A.) Eudossia e Genserico. [Anno 83, v2.]
Landogna (F.) Maestri & scol. pisani n. Studio di Bologna (12–14c.) [Anno 84, v1.]
Lazzari (A.) I "ricordi di governo" di Alfonso II d'Este &c. [Anno 78, v1.]
Leicht (P. S.) Elem. rom. nella costituz. longobarda. [Anno 81.]
—— Romani e germani in un giuram. carolingio. [Anno 85, v1.]
Levi (C.) Dante "dramatis persona." [Anno 79, v1.]
Levi (E.) Troveri ed abbazie. [Anno 83, v1.]
Luiso (F. P.) Biog. di Bonagiunta Orbicciani. [Anno 85, v2.]
Lupi (C.) Necrologia. [Anno 77, v1.]
Luzio (A.) Riforme a. statuto di Carlo Alberto. [Anno 84, v1.]
Maggini (F.) La mostra dantesca alla Laurenziana di Firenze. [Anno 79, v1.]
Mancini (G.) Contrib. dei Cortonesi a. coltura ital. [Anno 79, v2.]
—— Cosimo Bartoli (1503–72). [Anno 76, v2.]
—— Gregorio Tifernate. [Anno 81.]
—— G. Tortelli cooperatore di Niccolò V nel fondare la Bibl. Vaticana. [Anno 78, v2.]
—— Necrologia. [Anno 83, v1.]
Mazzoni (G.) Il nome di Dante e le 2 società ital. intitolate da lui. [Anno 79, v1.]
Montanelli (G.), *see* Rubertis (A. de).
Naldini (L.) La "tallia militum societatis tallie tuscie" &c. [Anno 78, v1.]
Nicholas V, *pope*, *see* Mancini (G.)
Nicolini (F.) La famiglia del Abate Galiani. [Anno 76, v2.]
—— Lettera di G. Boccaccio a Fr. de' Bardi. [Anno 82, v2.]
—— Per la biog. di G.-B. Vico. [Anno 83, v2.]
Novati (F.) Necrologia F. N. [Anno 76, v1.]
Orbicciani (Bonagiunta), *see* Luiso (F. P.)
Ottokar (N.) L'istit. d. priorato a Firenze. [Anno 82, v1.]
Panella (A.) Commem. di P. Villari, e bibl. [Anno 76, v2.]
—— Crisi di reg. d'un comune merid. [*i.e.* Aquila]. [Anno 81.]
—— Firenze e il sec. crit. d. fortuna di Dante. [Anno 79, v1.]
—— L'Italia e la q. rom. [1858–59]. [Anno 80.]
Pardi (G.) Disegno d. storia demografica di Livorno, 1918. [Anno 76, v1.]
Pernice (A.) Episodio d. valore toscano n. guerre di Valacchia. [Anno 83, v1.]
Petrarch, *see* Foresti (A.)
Pieraccini (P.) Note di demografia fiorentina. [Anno 83, v2.]
Pieri (P.) La quest. di Malta e il gov. napoletano (1798–1803), 1927. [Anno 85, v1.]
—— Taranto nel 1799 e Mgr. Capecelatro, 1924. [Anno 82, v1.]
Quazza (R.) La lotta diplomat. tra Genova e la Spagna. [Anno 78, v1.]
Ratberto, *benedictine*, *see* Falce (A.)
Rodolico (N.) Alla vigilia d. Repubbl. napol. d. 1799. [Anno 80.]
Rubertis (A. de). V. Gioberti e la Costituente di G. Montanelli. [Anno 79, v2.]
—— V. Gioberti e la vertenza tosco-piemont. d. Lunigiana. [Anno 85, v2.]
Russo (R.) Polit. d. Vaticano n. Dieta di Ratisbona, 1630. [Anno 84, v1.]
Santini (P.) Ant. riforme superstiti dei Costituti fiorentini. [Anno 79, v2.]
Sapori (A.) Beneficenza d. compagnie mercant. del trecento. [Anno 83, v2.]
—— Compagnie d. Bardi &c. in Inghilterra, sec. 13 e 14. [Anno 80.]
—— Rassegna crit.: pubbl. dantesche ital. del centenario. [Anno 79, v1.]
Savarese (*il b.* G.), *see* Anzilotti (A.)
Scarabelli (L.), *see* Frati (C.)
Schiaffini (A.) Chiese non parrocch. nel M.E. [Anno 81.]
—— "Parochia" e "Plebs." [Anno 80.]
Schiaparelli (L.) Note paleog. [Anno 82, v1, 2, 84, v1.]
Schipa (M.) Nobili e popolani in Napoli nel medioevo. [Anno 83, v1.]
Sella (P.) Costituz. d. Stato d. Chiesa. [Anno 85, v2.]
—— Costituz. per la Romagna pubbl. Cesena, 1289. [Anno 83, v2.]

Archivio storico italiano [*continued*].
Sestan (E.) Ricerche int. primi podestà toscani. [Anno 82, v2.]
Sforza (G.) Necrologia, G. S. [Anno 82, v2.]
Solmi (A.) Stato e chiesa nel pensiero di Dante. [Anno 79, v1.]
Tocco (V. di). Prog. di confed. ital. (1572), 1924. [Anno 82, v1.]
Tortelli (G.), *see* Mancini (G.)
Vieusseux (G. P.), *see* Anzilotti (A.)
Vigo (P.) Necrologia. [Anno 78, v1.]
Villari (Pasquale), *see* Panella (A.)
Vincentiis (E. de). Caduta d. monarchia borbon. in un' op. ined. di L. Bianchini. [Anno 83, v2.]
Zdekauer (L.) Necrologia, L. Z. [Anno 82, v2.]

Archivio storico per la Dalmazia. Pubbl. mensile fondata da A. Cippico. v1–4 (Apr. 1926–Marzo 1928). la8º. 1926–28

Archivio veneto. Anno 3. 8º. Venezia. 1873
see Sanuto (M.) La spediz. di Carlo viii in It., 1873.

Archivo bibliografico hispano-americano. Publ. V. Suárez. t15. 8º. Madrid. 1925

Archivo General de Indias, *Seville*. Catalogo: cuadro gen. de la documentación. [Por P. Torres Lanzas y G. Latorre. Publ. del Centro Oficial de Estud. Amer. Bibl. Colon. Amer., t1]. 8º. Sevilla 1918
Catálogo de legajos del A. G. de I. Por P. Torres Lanzas. [Publ. del Centro Oficial de Estud. Amer. Bibl. Colon. Amer., t2, 6, 8]. la8º. Sevilla. 1919–22
Secciones 1 & 2 & Suppl., Patronato y Contaduria gen. del Consejo de Indias. [2.]
Sección 3 & Contin., Casa de la Contratación de las Indias. [6, 8.]
Documentos, *see* Museu Paulista. Annaes, t1, 1922.
Relación descript. de los mapas, planos &c. exist. en el A. G. de I. Por P. Torres Lanzas. [De la Revista de Arch., Bibl. y Museos]. s8º. Sevilla. 1897–1906
Filipinas, 1897.
Guatemala, 1903.
México y Floridas, t2, 1900.
Panamá, Santa Fe y Quito, 1904.
Perú y Chile, 1906.
see Latorre (G.) Rel. geogr. de Indias, [2t], 1919–20.

Archivo historico portuguez. v1–4, 6–8. la8º. Lisboa. 1903–10

Arcoleo (Giorgio), *see* Dante Alighieri. Lectura D.: G. Boccaccio; conf. da G. A., 1913.

Arconati Visconti (Costanza), *see* Malvezzi (A.) Il risorgimento ital. in un carteggio di patrioti lombardi, 1821–60; lettere ined. di A. A. V. &c., 1924.

Arco-Valley (*Graf* Anton), *b. 1897*. Der Prozess gegen A. A.-V. der den bayer. Ministerpräsidenten K. Eisner erschossen Lat. Hrsg. v. H. Freiherrn v. Pranckh. [P2407]. 8º. München. 1920

Arctic. A. pilot, 3v & Suppl[s]. 4, 6, 1915–22, *see* Admiralty.

Arctopolitanus (Gabriel). Diss. hist. de orig. ac relig. Fennonum. Praes. F. Törner. [P2641]. s4º. Upsaliæ. [1728]

Arcudius (Petrus) [Arkoudios (Petros)]. De purgatorio igne, adv. Barlaam. [*Gr. & Lat.* Ed. P. Ligaridius]. s4º. Romæ. 1637
Utrum detur purgatorium & an illud sit per ignem. [*b. w. h.* De purgatorio igne, 1637]. s4º. Romæ. 1632

Ardant du Picq (*Col.* Charles) [†Ardant du Picq (Charles Jean Jacques Joseph)]. Battle studies: anc. & mod. Tr. f. 8th ed. by J. H. Greely & Maj. R. C. Cotton. s8º. N.Y. 1921

Ardashir, *see* Artaxerxes.

Ardavín (Luis Fernández), *see* Fernández Ardavín (L.)

Ardel (Henri). La faute d'autrui. s8º. [1920]

Arden of Feversham, *see* Cust (L.) A. of F., 1920.

Arden (Albert Henry). Progressive grammar of Telugu. la8º. Madras. 1873

Arden (Clive). Sinners in heaven. s8º. 1923

Arden (*Miss* Juliette).
Cole, A.D. 200–1920 Tercentenary ed. la8º. 1920

Ardenne (*Baron* Armand von). Die Befreiung v. Galizien, *see* Kaiser-Wilhelm-Dank. Kriegsschr., H66, 1916.
Kämpfe nach d. Winterschlacht an d. Masurischen seen &c., *see* Kaiser-Wilhelm-Dank. Kriegsschr., H62, 1916.

Ardenne de Tizac (Jean Henri d') [*ps.* Jean Viollis, *q. v. for h. novels*]. Les animaux dans l'art chinois. 50 planches, intr. &c. par H. d'A. de T. fol. [1923]
L'art chinois classique. la8º. 1926

Arderne (John). De arte phisicali & de cirurgia (1412). Tr. Sir D'Arcy Power. [Wellcome Hist. Medical Mus. Research st[s]., No. 1]. la8º. 1922

Ardingly, *Sussex*. Parish registers, 1558–1812. Ed. G. W. E. Loder. [Sussex Rec. Soc., v17]. 8º. 1913

Arditi (Giacomo). Corografia fisica e storia d. Prov. di Terra d'Otranto. la8º. Lecce. 1879–85

Ardizio (Curzio), *d. 1606*. Rime ined. [*Ed.* A. Saviotti. Nozze Palazzi-Giannuzzi-Savelli. N. 140]. la8°. [Pesaro. 1892]

Ardouin-Dumazet (Victor Eugene).
Voyage en France, s54, 60–6; [54, 4e éd.; 60–62, 3e éd.; 63, 4e éd.] s8°. 1919–21
54, Normandie: 2, Normandie centrale, 1921.
60, Les Provinces délivrées: 1, Haute Alsace, 1919.
61, „ „ 2, Basse-Alsace, 1919.
62, „ „ 3, Lorraine, 1920.
63, Normandie: 3, Normandie Orientale, 1921.
64, Banlieue Parisienne: 1, Région sud-est & est, 1921.
65, „ „ 2, „ nord & nord-est, 1921.
66, „ „ 3, „ ouest & sud-ouest, 1921.

Ardzrouni, *Family of, see* THOMAS, *Ardzr.* Hist. des A. (10 c.); tr. Brosset, 1874.

Ardzrouni (Thomas), *see* THOMAS *Ardzrouni.*

Ardzrouni (Vahan). Zantakht. [Plague. *In Armenian.* P2802]. s8°. Vagharshapat. 1897

Areitio (Darío de), *see* VIZCAYA, DIPUTACIÓN DE. Biblioteca: ensayo de un cat. de la sección Vascongada por D. de A., 1919.

Arenales (*Gen.* **Juan Antonio Alvarez de)**, *see* URIBURU (J. E.) Hist. del Gen. A., 1770–1831, 1924.

Arenas (Manuel Núñez de), *see* NÚÑEZ DE ARENAS (M.)

Arend (Heinrich Conrad). Diss. de colloquiis charitativis sæc. 16. per Germaniam irrito eventu institutis. Sub mod. J. F. Buddei. s4°. Jenæ. [1719]

Arend (Maximilian August). Gluck. 8°. 1921

Arène (Edouard).
Nice autrefois. Souvs. de 50 ans. la8°. Nice. 1910

Arensberg (Walter Conrad). Burial of Francis Bacon & h. mother in Lichfield Chapter House; commun. conc. Rosicrucians. la8°. Pittsburgh, Penn. 1924
Secret grave of Francis Bacon at Lichfield. [P2732]. 8°. 1923

Arent (Leonora). Electric franchises in N.Y. City. 8°. N.Y., *Columbia Univ.* 1919

Aresi (Paolo), *bp. of Tortona, see* KIESLING (J. R.) De insanabili Eccl. Rom. c. aq. transsubst. &c. scepticismo, contra P. A., 1772.

Aretæus, *see* CORPUS. Corpus medic. Græc.; ed. Acad. Berol., v2, A. ed. C. Hude, 1923.

Arethas, *bp. of Cæsarea, see* ANDREW, *St., abp. of Cæsarea.* Comm. on the Apocalypse by A. & Aretas; tr. into Armenian by Nerses of Tarsus, 1855.
see EUTHYMIUS I, *patr. of Constantinople.* Homélies &c., & s. oraison funèbre par A. (c. 921), 1922.

Aréthuse. Revue trimestr. [d'art & d'archéol.] Dir. par J. Babelon &c. année[s] 1–4. la8°. 1923–27

Aretin (Johann Christoph Anton Maria, *Baron* **von).** Über die frühesten universalhistor. Folgen d. Erfindung d. Buchdruckerkunst. [*With facsimile*]. 4°. München. 1808

Aretino (Bernardo Accolti), *see* ACCOLTI (B.) *Aretino.*

Aretino (Leonardo) [†BRUNI (L.) *Aretino*]. Hist. Florent. pop. libri 12, & Rerum suo temp. gest. comm.; a cura di E. Santini e C. di Pierro, *see* MURATORI (L. A.) Rerum Ital. Script., t19iii, 1914–26.
see BIRKENMAJER (A.) Verm. Unters. (Streit d. Alonso v Cartagena mit A.), 1922.

Aretino (Pietro). Lettere scr. a P. A. Emendate p. c. di T. Landoni [*&* G. Vanzolini]. 2v. *in* 4. s8°. Bologna. 1873–75
Each vol. has 2nd tp. which is a facs. of that pr. in 1551.
see HUTTON (E.) P. A., the scourge of princes, 1922.

Aretius (Benedictus). Examen theolog. ed. 4a [*b. w. h.* Sermones tres 1578]. s8°. Lausannæ. 1588
Sermones tres de Coena Dei. s8°. Lausannæ. 1578

Aretz (Gertrude, *see* KIRCHEISEN (G.)

Arevalo (Faustino). Hymnodia Hispanica &c. Præm. dissert. de hymnis eccl. Acc. app. de festo convers. Gothorum, Breviarii Quignon. fata, censura hymn. Santolii Victorini. 4°. Romæ. 1786

Arévalo Salto (Felipe).
Aristocracia de sangre. Novela. s8°. *n.d.*

Arexy (Gaston).
Les jeux de hasard, loteries & Paris &c. s8°. 1923

Arezzo. Doc. per la storia d. città di Arezzo nel m. evo. Racc. p. c. U. Pasqui. [Doc. di st. ital., v11, 13]. 2v. 4°. Firenze. 1899–1916
1, Cod. diplomat., 650 ?–1180. 2, Cod. diplomat, 1180–1337.

Arezzo (Claudio Mario). Hisp. chorographia, *see* HISPANICA. Rer. Hisp. scr., t1, 1579.

Arfe, *The family of, see* SÁNCHEZ CANTÓN (F. J.) Los Arfes, escultores de plata &c., 1501–1603, 1920.

Argence (Theo), *see* MONATTE (P.) T. A. & A. HERCLET. Left wing trade-unionism in France, 1922.

Argensola (Bartolomé L. de) [†LEONARDO Y ARGENSOLA (B.)] Prim. parte de los anales de Aragon que prosigue los del Secretario G. Çurita, desde 1516 [–1520]. fol. Çaragoça. 1630

Argensola (Lupercio L. de). Pour une éd. des A. [*texts; ed.* R. Foulché-Delbosc], *see* REVUE HISPAN., t48, 1920.

Argenson (*le marq.* **d').** Autour d'un ministre de Louis XV [*i.e.* le comte d'Argenson]. Lettres intimes inéd. 8°. 1923

Argenson (Marc Pierre, *comte* **d')**, 1696–1764, *see* ARGENSON (*le marq.* D'). Aut. d'un ministre de Louis XV [*i.e.* le cte. d'A.], 1923.

Argentan (Louis François d'), *see* BERNIÈRES LOUVIGNY (J. DE). Le Chrestien intérieur &c. tirez des écrits par un solitaire [*i.e.* L. Fr. d'A.], 1689–90.

Argentina. La A.: est. físico, etnogr., polit. &c. [H. E. C.] 10a ed. s8°. Buenos Aires. [1926 ?]

Argentoratum, *see* STRASSBURG.

Argentré (Charles Duplessis de), *see* DU PLESSIS D'ARGENTRÉ (C.), *bp. of Tulle.*

Arghún Khán, *Ilkhán of Persia.* 2 mongol. Orig.-Briefen d. Könige v. Persien A. u. Öldshäitu an Philipp d. Schönen. [*w. text & Germ. tr.*] v. I. J. Schmidt. [P519]. 8°. St. Petersburg. 1824

Argonaut, *ps.* *Arts of rowing &c., 1866, *see* BRICKWOOD (E. D.)

Arguedas (Alcides).
Hist. gén. de la Bolivie. Tr. S. Dilhan. la8°. 1923

Argyll (Archibald Campbell, *1st marq. of***).** Speech, 25 June 1646, w. papers of the Commissioners for Scotland &c. 8°. 1646

Arhakial, *see* ARAKEL.

Ari (*Frodi*) [ARE *Frode*; ARIUS MULTISCIUS; THORGILSSON ARI]. Islands Landnamabok. Vers. Lat., lects. var. &c. illust. [*by J. Finnsson*]. s4°. Hauniæ. 1774

Ariaghi (Carlo), *see* ANSALDO (G.), C. A. *& o.* Che cos'è l'Inghilterra, 1924.

Ariana, *Musée de l'.*
Cat. officiel. Par G. Sidler. 8°. Genève. 1905

Arias Montano (Benito). Communes &c. Heb. ling. idiotismi —Liber Joseph, sive De arcano sermone *& o. wks., see* BIBLE. Biblia sacra, t8, 1572.
Libri 2 Paralipomenon, Hebraice, cum interlineari vers. Xantis Pagnini. s8°. Ex Off. Plantin. 1611
see BELL (A. F. G.) B. A. M., 1922.

Arichandra, *king of Ayodhya, see* HARISCHANDRA.

Aringhus (Paulus). Abgebildetes, unterird. Rom. Übers. C. Bauman. s8°. Arnheim. 1668

Ariosto (Lodovico).
Lirica. A cura di G. Fatini. [Scr. d'It., 95]. 8°. Bari. 1924
ORLANDO FURIOSO.
O. F. Con le annot. &c. di G. Ruscelli [*w. sep. tp.* (1562)], la vita dell' autore descr. da G. B. Pigna &c. la8°. Venetia. 1558
O. F. [*Engr. by P. Lapi*]. 4t. s8°. Londra. 1781
O. F., prec. da alc. pensieri di V. Gioberti. 2a ed. 2v. 8°. Firenze. 1849
O. F., illust. da G. Doré, con pref. di G. Carducci. fol. Milano. 1899
TRANSLATIONS.
Roland le furieux. Tr. F. de Rosset. Ensemble la suitte de ceste hist. [*w. sep. tp. dated* 1623 *& sep. pag.*] s4°. 1625
TRANSLATIONS [*continued*].
Roland Furieux. Tr. M. d'Ussieux. 3t. 8°. 1775–6
O. F., tr. w. notes by J. Hoole. n. ed. 5v. 8°. 1799
O. F., tr. W. S. Rose. [repr.] 2v. s8°. *Bohn.* 1900
Supposes: comedie; Engl. by G. Gascoygne (1566), *see* ADAMS (J. Q.) Chief pre-Shakespearian dramas, 1925.
see CROCE (B.) A., Shakespeare e Corneille, 1920; tr., 1920.
„ EDWARDS (E. W.) The Orlando Furioso & its predecessor, 1924.
„ FATINI (G.) Su la fortuna e l'autenticità d. liriche di L. A., 1924.

Arishima (Takérô). Cette femme-là. Roman jap. contemp. Tr. inéd. de M. Yoshitomi & A. Maybon. s8°. [1926]

Aristarchus, *Grammaticus, see* WECKLEIN (N.) Über Zenodot u. A., 1919.

Aristarchus, *Samius, see* HEATH (T. L.) The Copernicus of antiquity: A. of S., 1920.

Aristeas, *officer at the court of Ptolemy Philadelphus.* De legis divinæ ex Hebraica lingua in Graecam tr., per Septuaginta interpretes hist. Cum conversione Lat. autore M. Garbitio. [*Ed.* S. Schardius. 2 *pagins.*] s8°. Basileæ. [1561]
see FÉVRIER (J. G.) Date &c. de la lettre d'A. à Philocrate, 1924.
„ HODY (H.) Contra hist. A. de 70 interpret. diss., 1684.

Aristides, *Saint, of Athens.* [Sermones 2 ex Arm. vers. tr. patres Mechit. *Arm. & Lat. a. c. in* P2812]. 8°. Venetiis. 1878

Aristides (Ælius). A. de laudibus Athenarum ; de laud. urbis Romæ [*in Greek*], *see* ORATORES. Orationes, p3, 1513.
Libri rhetorici 2. Ed. G. Schmid. [Rhetores Gr., v5]. s8°. L., *Teubner.* 1926

Aristokratii. *Объ аристократіи, 1874, *see* RUSSIA.

Aristophanes, *the poet.*
Comœdiæ undecim Gr. & Lat. Cum emend. præcipue J. Scaligeri. Acc. Fragmenta. s8°. Lugd. Batov. 1625
Comœdias ed. T. Bergk. v1, 2 [1, ed. 2ª corr]. s8°. Lips. *Teubner.* 1918–21
LYSISTRATA.
Lysistrate. Erklärt v. U. v. Wilamowitz-Moellendorff. 8°. 1927
TRANSLATIONS.
Comedies: Clouds, Plutus, Frogs, Birds. Tr. w. notes [by R. Cumberland]. 8°. 1812
The comedies of A. Ed., tr. & expl. by B. B. Rogers. v1–3. 8°. 1910–16
1, Acharnians, Knights ; 2, Clouds, Wasps ; 3, Peace, Birds.
Aristophanes. With Eng. tr. of B. B. Rogers. [Loeb Class. Lib.] 3v. s8°. 1924
Aristophane. Texte établi par V. Coulon & tr. par H. Van
TRANSLATIONS [*continued*].
Daele. [Coll. des univˢ. de France]. t1, 2. 8°. 1923–24
1, Les Acharniens — Les cavaliers — Les nuées ; 2, Les guêpes—La paix.
A. in Eng. verse. By A. S. Way. v1. 8°. 1927
Birds & Frogs. Tr. into rhymed Eng. verse w. intr. essay &c. by M. MacGregor. la8°. 1927
see DINDORF (C. W.) Poet. scenic. Græc. fabulæ &c., ed. 5ª, 1869.
„ FRERE (*Rt. Hon.* J. H.) Works, 2nd ed., v3, Trˢ. f. A. &c., 1874.
„ HARMAN (E. G.) Birds of A. consid. in rel. to Athenian politics, 1920.
„ HOLZINGER (C. v.) Die Aristophaneshss. d. Wiener Hofbibl., B2, 1912.
„ WALKER (R. J. B.) Essay on the date of A.'s Ecclesiazusæ, 1925.

Aristotelian Society. Proceedings. N.S., 18–27. 8°. 1918–27
Suppl. vol. 3–6. 8°. 1923–26
3, Relativity, logic & mysticism: papers, A.S., the Mind Assoc. & the Scots Philosoph. Club, Durham, July 1923.
4, Concepts of continuity: papers &c., A.S. & the Mind Assoc., Univ. Coll., Reading, July 11–14, 1924.
5, Philosophy & metaphysics: paper & symposia, A.S., the Mind Assoc. & the Oxford Philos. Soc., Oxf., July 1925.
6, Methods of analysis: symposia, A.S. & Mind Assoc., Camb., July 1926.

Aristotle.
DE ANIMA.
Comm. Collegii Conimbric. in 3 lib. De anima 3ª ed. Græci contextus Lat. è regione respond. s4°. Coloniæ. 1600
DE COELO.
Comm. Coll. Conimbric. in 4 lib. De coelo. 4ª ed. partim Gr. contextus Lat. è regione respond. ed. [*b. w.* Comm. in Lib. Physicorum, 1599–1600]. s4°. Coloniæ. 1600
DE GENERATIONE & CORRUPTIONE.
Comm. Coll. Conimbric. in lib. De g. & c. 2ª ed. Gr. contextus Lat. è regione respond. s4°. Moguntiæ. 1599
On coming-to-be & passing-away (De g. & c.) Rev. text, w. intr. & comm. by H. H. Joachim. 8°. O. 1922
DE REPUBLICA ATHENIENSIUM.
Athen. Resp. Rec. F. G. Kenyon. s8°. Oxonii. [1920]
ELENCHI, *see also* TOPICA, *below.*
ETHICA.
Ethics. Illus. w. essays & notes by Sir A. Grant. 4th ed. rev. v1. 8°. 1885
In lib. Ethic. ad Nicom. aliquot Conimbric. cursus disput. 4ª Germ. ed. corr. [*b. w.* Comm. in 3 lib. De anima, 1600]. s4°. Coloniæ. 1600
METAPHYSICA.
M. Recog. W. Christ. n. impr. corr. s8°. L. *Teubner.* 1916
M. Rev. text w. intr. & comm. by W. D. Ross. 2v. 8°. O. 1924
METEOROLOGICA.
Comm. Coll. Conimbric. in lib. Meteor. [*b. w.* Comm. in lib. De generatione, 1599]. s4°. Coloniæ. 1600
Meteorolog. libri 4. Rec., ind. verborum add. F. H. Fobes. 8°. Cantab. Mass. 1919
ORGANON.
Comm. Coll. Conimbric. in univ. dialecticam, num in Germania ed. [De interpretatione *has sep. pagin.*] 2p *in* 1v. s4°. Coloniæ Agrippinæ. 1607
PARVA NATURALIA.
Comm. Coll. Conimbric. in lib. qui parva naturalia appelantur [*b. w.* Comm. in 3 lib. De anima, 1600]. s4°. Coloniæ. 1600
PHYSICA.
Comm. Coll. Conimbric. in octo lib. Physic. qui Gr. contextus Lat. è regione respondenti, ed. 2p *in* 1v. s4°. Coloniæ. 1599–1600
POETICA.
De arte poet. lib. Rec. &c. J. Vahlen. 8° Berolini. 1874
POLITICA.
Politic. libri 8, cum vet. tr. Guilelmi de Moerbeka. Rec. F. Susemihl. 8°. Lips. 1872
TOPICA.
Topica cum libro de sophist. elenchis. Eschedis I. Strache ed. M. Wallies. s8°. Lipsiæ, *Teubner.* 1923
TRANSLATIONS.
Works. Tr. under editorship of J. A. Smith & W. D. Ross. v2, 3i, iv, 7, 9, 10, 11. 8°. O. 1908–27

Aristotle [*continued*].
TRANSLATIONS [*continued*].
2ii, iii, De Cælo ; by J. L. Stocks—De generatione & corruptione ; by H. H. Joachim. 3i, Meteorologica ; by E. W. Webster. 3iv, Parva naturalia ; by J. I. Beare & G. R. T. Ross. 7, Problemata ; by E. S. Forster. 9, Ethica Nicomachea ; by W. D. Ross —Magna moralia ; by St. G. Stock—Ethica Eudemia—De virtutibus et vitiis ; by J. Solomon. 10, Politica ; by B. Jowett—Œconomica ; by E. S. Forster—Atheniensium Respublica ; by Sir F. G. Kenyon. 11, Rhetorica ; by W. Rhys Roberts—De rhetorica ad Alexandrum ; E. S. Forster—De poetica ; I. Bywater.
DE REPUBLICA ATHENIENSIUM.
Constit. d'Athènes. Texte établi & tr. par G. Mathieu & B. Haussoullier. [Coll. des univˢ. de France]. 8°. 1922
ETHICA.
Nicomachean ethics. Tr. w. notes by J. E. C. Welldon. [repr.] s8°. 1902
The Nicomachean Ethics. [Text], w. Eng. tr. by H. Rackham. [Loeb Class. Lib.] s8°. 1926.
PHYSICA.
Physique. Texte établi & tr. par H. Carteron. [Coll. des univ. de Fr.] t1, 1–4. 8°. 1926
POETICA.
On the art of poetry. Tr. by I. Bywater. Pref. by G. Murray. s8°. O. 1920
Poetica Arab. interp. Abu Bashar, *see* MARGOLIOUTH (D. S.), *ed.* Analecta, 1887.
Poetics.—" Longinus " on The sublime. [Texts, w. Eng. tr. by W. H. Fyfe].—Demetrius on Style. [Text, w. Eng. tr. by W. R. Roberts. Loeb Class. Lib.] s8°. 1927
see RHETORICA, *below.* Rettorica e Poetica ; tr. in lingua vulg. fiorent. da B. Segni, 1549.
POLITICA.
Treatise on government. Tr. W. Ellis. 8°. 1888
RHETORICA.
Rettorica e Poetica. Tr. in lingua vulgare fiorentina da B. Segni. 8°. Firenze. 1549
The " art " of rhetoric. [Text], w. Eng. tr. by J. H. Freese. [Loeb Class. Lib.] s8°. 1926
Rhetoric. Tr. w. Hobbes' anal.
RHETORICA [*continued*].
&c. Also the Poetic. Tr. T. Buckley. s8°. *Bohn.* 1883
SPURIOUS WORKS.
The book of the Apple. Ed. in Persian & Eng. by D. S. Margoliouth. [*Extr. f.* Journ. of Roy. Asiatic Soc., 1892]. 8°. 1892
Über d. reine Gute (Liber de causis). Im Auftr. d. Görres-Gesells. bearb. v. O. Bardenhewer. [*b. w.* Aristotle. Bk. of the apple, 1892]. 8°. Freiburg i. B. 1882
see ABÉLARD (P.) Philos. Schr., 1ii, Die Glossen zu den Kategorien, 1921.
„ ARNIM (H. v.) Die 3 Ethiken, 1924.
„ —— Z. Entstehungsgesch. d. A. Politik, 1924.
„ BOCCIUS (A. B.) Princ. Aristot. & Cartes. collatio, 1685.
„ BRITISH MUSEUM. PR. BOOKS. Catalogue: A., 1884.
„ BURNET (J.) A., lect., 1924.
„ CONYBEARE (F. C.) [Exam. of writings of David the Invincible, tr. of A.; App., A. De Deo, *in Arm.*], 1893.
„ ELIAS. Komm. in A. Kategorias versio armenica ed. J. Manandean, 1911.
„ GRANT (*Sir* A.) The Ethics of A., essays & notes, v1, 1857.
„ GREDT (J.) Elem. philos. A.-Thomasticæ, ed. 3ª, 2v, 1921–22.
„ HEIDINSFELDER (G.) Albert v. Sachsen, s. Lebensgang u. s. Komm. z. Nikomach. Ethick d. A., 1921.
„ KAPPES (M.) A.-Lex., term. tech., 1894.
„ KNOGLER (C.) Disput. de habitibus morum ex lib. 7 ad Nicomachum conscr., 1595.
„ MARGOLIOUTH (D. S.) The Homer of A., 1923.
„ NEWMAN (J. H.) Poetry, w. ref. to A.'s Poetics ; ed. A. S. Cook, 1891.
„ RICHARDS (H. P.) Aristotelica, 1915.
„ ROSS (W. D.) A., 1923.
„ SCHEGKIUS (J.) Admonitio de comment. suis in Topica A. &c., 1585.
„ SIGER, *v. Brabant.* Neuaufgefund. Quaestionen S.'s zu d. Werken A.'s, hrsg. M. Grabmann, 1924.
„ STOCKS (J. L.) Aristotelianism, 1926.
„ WITTMANN (M.) Die Ethik. d. A., 1920.

Arithmetics. *Earliest a. in English. [E. E. T. S. E. S. 118], 1922, *see* STEELE (R. R.)

Arizcun (J. M. Florit y), *see* FLORIT Y ARIZCUN.

Arkheograficheskaya Kommissiya, *see* IMPERATORSKAYA ARKH. KOMM.

Arkhieratikon, *see* ARCHIERATIKON.

Arkhiv Russkoi Revolyutsii. Архивъ русской революціи. Изд. Г. В. Гессеномъ. t1–17. s4°. Берлинъ. [1920–26]

Arkoudios (Petros), *see* ARCUDIUS (P.)

Arkwright (*Sir* Richard), 1732–92, *see* CRABTREE (J. H.) R. A. [Pioneers of progress], 1923.
see UNWIN (G.) S. Oldknow & the Arkwrights, 1924.

Arkwright (Richard), *son of Sir R. Arkwright* ; *1755–1843, see* UNWIN (G.) S. Oldknow & the Arkwrights, 1924.

Arland (Marcel). Etienne. 6ᵉ éd. s8°. [1924]

Arlanibaeus (Philippus), *ps., see* ABELIN (JOHANN GOTTFRIED).

Arlen (Michael), *ps.* [*i.e.* M. KOUYOUMDCAN].

The green hat. [2nd impr.] 8°. [1924]
May Fair. 8°. [1925]
"Piracy." s8°. [1922]
" [8th imp.] s8°. [1924]
These charming people. s8°. [1923]
Young men in love. s8°. [1927]

Arles. Pars actorum Conc. Arel., *see* GALLIA. *Vet. aliq. G. theol. scripta, 1586.
see RECUEIL. R. des historiens de la France, Pouillés, t8, Provs. d'A. &c., 1923.

Armada. Nat. A. Tercentenary Commem., 1888. Catalogue of loan coll., Plymouth. 8°. Plymouth. 1888

Armagnac (M. M. d'). La vie & les entretiens d'une femme du monde au 18e s., d'ap. les souvs. &c. de B. C. de M. de Montaugé, 1762–97. Docs. fournis par la Ctsse. de Lagrèze-Champol. Préf. de Mgr. Baudrillart. s8°. [1924]

Arman de Caillavet (*Mme.* **Albert),** *see* POUQUET (J. M.) Le salon de Mme. de A. de C., 1926.

Armandus *de Bellovisu.* Sacrarum litt. prof. eximius A. De declaratione difficilium terminorum tam theologicalium q̄ philosophie ac logice. [*b. w.* Marchesinus (J.) Mamotrectus, 1479]. s4°. [offic. H. Quentell civis Colon. 1502] *sig.* A–R *in sixes,* S1–4 & T1–5.

Armandy (André). Rapa-nui. s8°. 1923

Armbruster (Charles Hubert). Initia Amharica. An intr. to spoken Amharic. p3. la8°. C. 1920
3, Amharic-Eng. vocabulary w. phrases. v1, H–S.

Armbruster (Ludwig), *see* ROTTER (E.), L. A. &c. Die Biene in Ägypten, 1921.

Armées (Les) franç. dans la gr. Guerre, 1923–4, *see* FRANCE: MINISTÈRE DE LA GUERRE.

Armena. Conciliationis eccles. Armenae, 2p, 1658–90, *see* GALANO (C.)
*Gramm. della ling. a. &c., 1879, *see* GRAMMATICA.

Armengaud (Jean Germain Désiré). Les galeries publiques de l'Europe: Rome. fol. 1859

Armenia [ARMENIAN; ARMYANSKAGO].
N.B.—*Anonymous Armenian books are included under this heading.*
*Ananoun zamanakagrouthiun. [Anon. chron. (7c) *partly comp. by* Andreas? Ed. B. Sargisean; *b. w.* George, *of Pisidia.* Vetzoreayq, 1900]. 8°. Venetik. 1904
[Armenian book of prayers. *Unidentified. Tp. wanting*]. s8°. *n.p. n.d.*
*Armenian pop. songs tr. into Eng. [*w. text*]. 2nd ed. [*a. c. in* P2810]. 8°. Venice. 1867
Banq Khratoutz. [Maxims of the anc. philosophers; *in Armenian.* Soferq Hayk., v1]. s8°. i Venetik. 1853
*Grqoyk, nouagaran. [Manual or book of canticles. *In Armenian*]. s8°. K.-polis. 1794
[Karg tprouthean. Order of A. Ch., *cont. singer's part of offices. In Armenian*]. s8°. i Venetik. 1834
[*Lamentations for the ills of the land of Arm. & Martyrdom of St. V. *In Armenian.* Soferq Hayk., v13] s8°. i Venetik. 1854
Mashtotz. [Ritual of the Armenian Ch. *In Armenian*]. 8°. Venetik. 1831
Mashtotz. [Ritual for ordin. of clergy, deacons &c. *In Armenian*]. la8°. i Vagharshapat. 1876
Notarq Hayotz [1393–1467. Coll. &c. L. Firlalemean Tosbetzi. *In Armenian; b. w.* Philo *Judaeus.* Sermons. (*In Arm.*) 1892]. 8°. K.-Polis. 1892
[Order of consecration &c. of catholics & patriarch of all Armenia. *In Armenian*]. la8°. i Vagharshapat. 1876
Parl. Debates, H. of Lords, Nov. 13, 1918; H. of C., Oct. 23–Nov. 18, 1918; Armenia, 1918, *see* PARLIAMENT.
Patmouthiun Hayoy: [Hist. of the Armenians. *In Arm.*], 3v, 1784–86, *see* TCHAMTCHEAN (M.)
[Ritual of ordination of a bishop of the A. Church. *In Armenian*]. la8°. i Vagharshapat. 1876
Sharakan (Arm. hymnal), 1664 &c., *see* SHARAKAN.
Собранie актовъ относящ. къ обозрѣнію исторіи армянскаго народа. 3ч. 4°. Москва. 1833–38
Soferq Haykakanq. [Armenian books, v1–22]. s8°. i Venetik. 1853–61
Catalogued separately under following headings:—

Armenia: Banq.	[1.]	Isaac, *patr. of Arm.*	[2.]
Armenia: Lamentations.	[13.]	James, *of Nisibis.*	[22.]
Bartholomew.	[19.]	John, *Deacon.*	[3, 5, 17.]
Benik.	[21.]	Nerses, *Parthian.*	[6, 7.]
Chrysostom.	[4.]	Nerses, *Shnorhali.*	[14, 16.]
Elisha.	[18.]	Shushan.	[9.]
Goriun.	[11.]	Simeon, *bp.*	[20.]
Gregory, *Illum.*	[10.]	Sisianos.	[12.]
Gregory, *Skevratzi.*	[15.]	Thaddæus.	[8.]

Armenia [*continued*].
Tonatzoytz. [Armenian Church calendar or directory. *In Armenian*]. s8°. Echmiadzin. 1774
" " ....s8°. i Venetik. 1782
Zamakargouthiun. [Breviary of Arm. Church. *In Armenian*]. s8°. Amstelrodam. 1705
Zamakargouthiun. [Hours of the A. Church: Psalms, Breviary, Calendar. *In Armenian*]. 4°. Yerousalem. 1889

Armenian National Delegation.
Memorandum on the Armenian question. 8°. [1918]

Armenie. *Hist. litt. de l'Arménie anc., siècles 4–13, *in Armenian,* 2nd ed., 1886, *see* ZARBHANALEAN (K.)

Armenien. Deutschland u. A., 1914–18: Sammlung diplomat. Aktenstücke, 1919, *see* LEPSIUS (J.) *ed.*

Arméniennes. *Etudes a. en Europe, siècle 14–19, *in Armenian,* 1895, *see* ZARBHANALEAN (K.)

Armenier. *Zur Urgesch. d. A., 1854, *see* LAGARDE (P. A. de).

Armenii. Armeniorum de Trinitate &c. confessio A. P. interp. Una cum explic. &c. [*a. c. b. w.* Flacius (M.) Def. sanae doctr. &c., 1570]. s8°. Witebergæ. 1570

Armenum. *Alphabetum A., 1673, *see* ALPHABETUM.

Armfelt (*Count* **Gustaf Mauritz),** *see* DAUDET (E.) Un drame d'amour à la cour de Suède, 1784–95 [Baron d'A. & M. de Rudenschold], 1913.
see TEGNÉR (E.) G. M. A.: st. ur A.'s efterlemnade papper &c., 3[B], [1883–7].

Armin (Th.) Das heut. Mexiko. 8°. L. 1865

Arminian (The) magazine. Wesleyan-Methodist (The) Magazine. v108–114 (s6, v9–15). 8°. 1885–91

Arminius, *prince of the Cherusci, see* SPIEGEL (F. T.) A. vita & res gest., 1679.

Arminius (Jacobus) [HERMANNS (J.)]
Opera theolog. nunc denuò conjunctim recusa. s4°. Francofurti. 1635
Disc. on the priesthood of Christ. deliv. 1603 at Leyden. Tr. M. Martindale. [P527]. 8°. York. 1815
Disputationes. Præm. oratio de vita &c. auctoris. 2p. *in* 1v. s8°. Lugd. Bat. 1610
Epistola ad Hippolytum &c. necnon articuli &c. s8°. Delphis Batav. 1613
Examen modestum libelli, quem G. Perkinsius ed. De prædestinationis modo &c. Add. Analysis cap. 9 ad Roman. s8°. Lugd. Bat. 1612
J. A. Amica, cum F. Junio de prædestinatione, collatio. s8°. Lugd. Bat. 1613
Orationes, itemque tractatus insigniores &c. ed. 2a recogn. s8°. Lugd. Bat. 1613
Quelques poésies [*Latin*]. Publ. &c. H. de Vries de Heekelingen. 8°. La Haye. 1925
Theses theol. de natura Dei. s8°. Lugd. Bat. 1603
see BRANDT (C.) Hist. vitæ J. A. &c. 1724.
" EPISCOPIUS (S.) Popish labyrinth, as also the life & death of J. A., 1673.
" HARRISON (A. W.) Beginnings of Arminianism, to the synod of Dort, 1926.

Arminius (Wilhelm), *form. W. H. Schultze.* "Und setzet ihr nicht d. Leben ein." Gesch. aus d. Befreiungskriegen. 3e A. 8°. St. [1913?]

Armistead (Wilson). A tribute for the Negro. 8°. M'ter. 1848

Armistice. Prelim. hist. of the A.; tr., 1924, *see* GERMANY: GOVT. PUBLS.

Armitage (Francis Paul).
Diet & race. Anthropol. essays. 8°. 1922

Armitage (Harold). Francis Chantrey. s8°. [1915]

Armitage (William James), *archdeacon of Halifax, N.S.* Story of the Canadian revision of the Prayer Book. Foreword by S. P. Matheson, abp. s8°. C. 1922

Armont (Paul) & M. Gerbidon. Alain, sa mère & sa maîtresse, comédie, *see* ŒUVRES libres, 12, 1922.
Une petite sans importance, *see* ŒUVRES libres, 78, 1927.

Armourers & Brasiers, *Company of, see* ELLIS (H. D.) Sh. descr. of anc. silver plate belonging to W. Co. of A. & B. 1892.

Armstrong College, *Newcastle-upon-Tyne.* [UNIV. OF DURHAM]. Calendar, 1925–1927. s8°. Newcastle-upon-Tyne. 1925–27

Armstrong (Archibald), *jester.*
A banquet of jests & merry tales. 8°. 1889

Armstrong (Charles Wicksteed). The mystery of existence. Added, Brief st. of sex problem. [2nd ed.] s8°. 1920
Survival of the unfittest. s8°. [1927]

Armstrong (Edward Cooke). A. Marshall Elliott. [Elliott Monogr., 15. P2731]. 8°. Princeton, N.J. 1923
The authorship of Vengement Alixandre & of Venjance Alixandre. [Elliott Monogr., 19]. 8°. Princeton, N.J. 1926

Armstrong (Edward Frankland), *ed.* Chemistry in the 20th cent. [*By var. wrs.*] la8°. 1924

Armstrong (George). Map of Palestine, f. surveys. Comp. by G. A. & rev. by Sir C. W. Wilson & C. R. Conder. [Pal. Expl. F.; *b. w.* Warren (Sir C.) Plans &c., *n.d.*] lafol. 1890

Armstrong (Hamilton Fish). The new Balkans. Intr. by A. C. Coolidge. 8º. 1927

Armstrong (Harold).

Turkey in travail: birth of a new nation. 8º. [1925]

Armstrong (Harold Hunter), *see* AIKMAN (HENRY G.) *ps.*

Armstrong (Henry Edward).

James Dewar, 1842–1923. Lecture. [P2738]. 8º. 1924

Armstrong (Herbert Rowse). Trial of H. R. A. Ed. F. Young. [Notable Brit. Trials]. 8º. E. [1927]

Armstrong (John), *physician.*

Poet. works. Collated by T. Park. s8º. 1807

see WILLIAMS (I. A.) 7 18th cent. bibliog[s]., J. A. &c., 1924.

Armstrong (S. F.).

Brit. grasses & th. employment in agric. 8º. C. 1917

Armstrong (Wallace Edwin).

Rossel Island: ethnolog. study. 8º. C. 1928

Army. The British A. &c., 1892, *see* STANHOPE (E.)

Army Council, *see* HEWETT (*Sir* J. P.) Rep. for A. C. on Mesopotamia, 1919.

Army List (The), *see* LIST (A) of the officers of the Army &c., 1784–1867.

Army List (Monthly). Jan. 1921, Jan. & July 1922, Jan. & July 1923, Jan. & July 1924, July 1925. s8º. 1921–25

„ „ Half-yearly Suppl., June 1923. s8º. 1923

Army List (Quarterly), for quarter ending Mar. 1916, Sept. 1916, June 1921. 8º. 1916–21

Army Quarterly (The), w. which is incorp. The United Service magazine. v1–15 (Oct. 1920–Jan. 1928). 8º. [1920–28]

Armyanskago, *see* ARMENIA.

Armytage (Duncan). Christianity in the Rom. world. 8º. 1927

Armytage (Percy), *C.V.O.*

By the clock of St. James's. 8º. [1927]

Arnalda, sive captiva victrix [1570], 1910, *see* COBHAM (C. D.)

Arnaldi (Ulrico). La scatola dei sogni. s8º. Milano. 1926

Arnaud (François Thomas Marie de Baculard d'), *see* BACULARD D'ARNAUD.

Arnaud (Raoul). La débâcle financ. de la Révol.: Cambon (1756–1820), d'ap. des docs. inéd. s8º. 1926

Arnaud d'Agnel (G.), *see* BOUCHES-DU-RHÔNE; encyclop. départ., t3, Temps mod., par A., 1920.

—— & E. Isnard. Monticelli: sa vie & s. œuvre, 1824–86. Préc. des appréc. de G. Geffroi, T. Duret &c. 4º. 1926

Arnauld (Antoine), *doctor of the Sorbonne.*

De la calomnie ou instruction du procès entre les Jésuites & leur adversaires &c., *see* JESUITS. *Morale prat. &c., 12e éd., t8, 1716.

*L'esprit de M. A., partic. de l'Apologie pour les catholiques, 2p, 1684, *see* JURIEU (P.)

Hist. de Dom Jean Palafox &c., *see* JESUITS. *Morale prat., t4, 1718.

Hist. de la persécution de 2 saints évêques par les Jésuites &c., 2e ed., *see* JESUITS. *Morale prat. &c., t5, 1717.

*Hist. des differens entre les missionaires Jésuites & ceux des ordres de St. Dominique & de St. François &c., 1735, *see* JESUITS. *Morale prat., t6, 7, 1735.

*La morale pratique des Jésuites, 2e ed. 8t (t3–8 *by* A. Arnauld), 1682–1735, *see* JESUITS.

*Nouv. défense de la tr. du Nouv. Test. imprimée à Mons; contre le livre de M. Mallet. 8º. Cologne. 1680

„ Contin. s8º. Cologne. 1682

Plaidoyé pour l'Univ. de Paris, demanderesse contre les Jésuites defendeurs 12 & 13 Juillet 1594. s8º. 1594

*Réponse à la lettre d'une personne de condition touch. les règles de la conduite des SS. PP. &c. 1683, *see* LE MAISTRE DE SACY (I. L.) Les Enluminures &c., 1683.

*Théologie morale des Jésuites & nouv. casuistes &c. [? by A. A.], 1666, *see* JESUITS.

*Très-humble remontrance à Messire H. de Precipiano archevêque de Malines sur son decret du 15 Jan. 1695 port. défense de lire &c. De la fréquente communion par A. Arnauld. [*b. w.* Quesnel (P.) Hist. abr. de M. Arnauld, 1695]. s8º. *n.p.* 1695

see BOURGEOIS (J.) Rel. de M. B. pour la défense du livre De la fréq. communion, par A., 1695.

„ CLAUDE (J.) Cath. doctr. of the Eucharist, in ans. to A., 1684.

„ QUESNAL (P.) *Hist. abregée de la vie &c. de M. Arnauld, 1695.

—— & P. Nicole. *Logica, sive ars cogitandi. E 3a apud Gallos ed. rec. & aucta in Lat. versa. s8º. Lond'ni. 1677

Arndius (Josua). Lexicon antiq. eccl. s4º. Gripswaldiæ. 1669

Manuale legum Mosaic. 3p *in* 1v. s8º. Gustrovi. 1666

Arndt (Bruno). Marianne. Roman. s8º. Trier. 1921

Arndt (Erich). Das Weib zu Nain. Mit Bildern v. K. Ritter. s8º. München. [1921]

Arndt (Ernst Moritz). *Was bedeutet Landsturm u. Landwehr? (*facs.* 1813), *see* FREYTAG (G.) Bilder, B5, 1925.

Arndt (Johann) [ARNDTIUS (J.)]

De vero Christianismo libri 4 olim Lat. redditi nunc rev. &c. cura &c. A. W. Bœmi. Acc. nov. præf. de vita & scr. Arndtianis. 2t. 8º. Londini. 1708

De vero Christianismo liber l. In Tamulicum conv. B. Schulzius. s8º. Halæ Magd. 1751

Libellus precum relig. dictus Hortulus paradisiacus. In Tamul. conv. R. Schulzius. 4p. *in* 1v. [*3 tp[s]. & pagin[s].*] s8º. Halæ Magdeb. 1749–50

True Christianity. Ed. W. Jacques. [Tr.] 2v. [v2 *wanting*]. 8º. 1815–17

see WINTER (F. J.) J. A., d. Verf. d. Wahren Christentums, 1911.

Arne (Thomas Augustine). Heart of oak. [*b. w.* Corelli (A.) Twelve concertos, *n.d.*] 4º. *n.d.*

Arnell (Charles John).

Poets of the Wight. Anthology. 8º. Newport. 1922

Arneth (Joseph). Die ant. Gold- u. Silber- Monumente, 1850, *see* KAIS.-KÖN. MÜNZ- U. ANT.-KABINET ZU WIEN.

Die Cinque-Cento Cameen u. Arb. d. B. Cellini u. s. Zeitg., 1858, *see* KAIS.-KÖN. MÜNZ- U. ANT.-KABINET ZU WIEN.

Arneudo (Giuseppe Isidore). Diz. esegetico tecnico &c. per le arti graf. spec. tipografia. [3v]. 8º. Torino. [1917–25]

Arniches (Carlos).

Los caciques: farsa cómica. 2a. ed. s8º. 1920

—— & J. Abati.

Las grandes fortunas. Farsa cómica. s8º. 1920

Arnim (*countess* **v.**), *née Beauchamp.*

*The enchanted April. s8º. 1922

*Introduction to Sally. 8º. 1926

*Love. s8º. 1925

*Vera. By a. of "Elizabeth & h. German garden." s8º. 1921

Arnim (Bettina v.) Bettinas Briefwechsel mit Goethe. Hrsg. R. Steig. s8º. L. 1922

see GOETHE (J. W. v.) Briefwechsel mit e. Kinde [*i.e.* B. v. A.], 3T, 1920.

—— & G. v. Arnim. Leben d. Hochgräfin Gritta v. Rattenzuhausbeiuns. Hrsg. O. Mallon. s8º. 1926

Arnim (Gisela v.), *see* ARNIM (B. v.) & G. v. A. Leben d. Hochgräfin Gritta v. Rattenzuhausbeiuns, 1926.

Arnim (Hans v.) *Works in* KAIS. AKAD. D. WISS. ZU WIEN. Sitz.

Die 3 aristotel. Ethiken, 1925. [202.]

Sprachl. Forsch. zur Chronol. der Platon. Dialoge, 1912. [169.]

Z. Entstehungsgesch. d. aristotel. Politik, 1924. [200.]

Stoicorum vet. fragm. coll. A. v4, Ind. conscr. M. Adler. 8º. L. 1924

Xenophons Memorabilien u. Apologie d. Sokrates, *see* KONG. DAN. VID. SELSK. Hist.-fil. Med., B8, 1923–4.

Arning (Wilhelm). Vier Jahre Weltkrieg in Deutsch-Ostafrika. 8º. Hannover. [1919]

Arnobius, *Afer.* Adversus gentes libri 7. [D. Heraldi animadv., T. Canteri notæ, G. Stewechii electa, G. Elmenhorstii obs., *ed.* A. Thysius, *each w. sep. pagin.*] ed. nov. s4º. Lugd. Bat. 1651

Arnold (Bernhard). Sappho, *see* VIRCHOW (R.) & F. v. HOLTZENDORFF. Vorträge, H118, 1871.

Arnold (Carl Franklin). Die Ausrottung d. Protestantismus in Salzburg unter Erzbischof Firmian &c. [Verein f. Ref.-gesch. Schr., Jhrg. 18, Nr. 67, 69]. 2H. 8º. Halle. 1900–1

Arnold (Christoph). Linguæ Latinæ ornatus, quem congessit itemque J. M. Dilherri ad locos inventionis rhetor. manuductionem [*sep. tp. & pagin.*] illi adstruxit C. A. ed. 3a. s8º. Norimbergæ. 1668

Arnold (Edward Carleton). Brit. waders. 4º. C. 1924

Arnold (*Sir* Edwin), *see* BHAGAVADGĪTĀ. The song celestial, or B., tr. [into verse] by A., 1889.

Arnold (F. H.) Petworth: hist. & antiq[s]. s8º. Petworth. 1864

Arnold (Gottfried) [ARNOLDUS (GOTHOFREDUS)].

Hist. & descr. theologiæ myst. s8º. Francofurti. 1702

Unpartheyische Kirchen-u. Ketzer-Historien bis 1688. Bey d. neuen Aufl. verbessert &c. 3B. (B3 *has* 2 Abschnitt *w. sep. pag.*) fol. Schaffhausen. 1740–2

see CAROLUS (A. D.) Wirtenberg. Unschuld, durch christl. Prüfung dessen, was G. A. einverleibt hat, 1708.

„ CYPRIAN (E. S.) Allgem. Anmerck. ü. G. A. Kirchen-u. Ketzer-Hist., 1700.

„ FERBER (J. J.) Exercit. 2a de fanat., G. A. Kirchen-Hist. oppos., 1711.

„ FEUSTKING (F. C.) Diss. qua G. A. anistoresias in re sacra convictum, 1719.

„ KIESSLING (G. N.) Th. Munzeri doctr. & facta & G. A. lapsus, 1708.

Arnold (Hans), *hypnotist.* Verkehr mit d. jenseit. Welt ohne Medien. [P2480]. 8º. L. 1900

Arnold (Hugh).
The glass in Balliol College chapel. [P2589]. 8°. [O.] *n.d.*

Arnold (John), *see* GILES (J.) Tryal of J. G. for attempt to assassinate J. A., 1681.

Arnold (Julean Herbert). Commercial hdbk. of China. By J. A. &c. 2v. 8°. Wash. 1919–20

Arnold (Lilian). Draped idols. s8°. [1923]
The second wife. [2nd impr.] s8°. [1924]

Arnold (Matthew).
God & the Bible. pop. ed. s8°. 1888
Selected poems. s8°. 1902
Unpubl. letters. Ed. A. Whitridge. [Yale, Mather Mem. Publ. Fund]. s8°. New Haven, *Yale.* 1923
see GRIERSON (H. J. C.) Ld. Byron: A. & Swinburne, 1920.
,, HOUGHTON (R. E. C.) Infl. of classics on the poetry of A., 1923.
,, HUDSON (W. H.) Studies in interpret.; Keats, Clough, M. A., 1896.

Arnold (Nicolaus) [†ARNOLDUS (N.)]
Lux in tenebris. ed. 2ª. s4°. Franekeræ. 1665
Religio Sociniana, seu Catechesis Racoviana major refutata. s4°. Franequeræ. 1654

Arnold (Paula), *see* KELLNER (L.), P. A. &c. Austria of the Austrians &c., 1914.

Arnold (Robert Franz). Allgemeine Bücherkunde z. neu. deut. Literaturgesch. 2e, neu bearbt. &c. A. 8°. 1919
Das deut. Drama. In Verbindung mit J. Bab, A. Ludwig, F. Michael &c.; hrsg. R. F. A. la8°. München. 1925

Arnold (Thomas), *D.D., head master of Rugby.* Poetry of common life. Sels., w. pref. by T. A. s8°. 1844
see CAMPBELL (R. J.) T. A., 1927.
,, STRACHEY (L.) Eminent Victorians, 1920.

Arnold (*Sir* Thomas Walker). The Caliphate. 8°. O. 1924
Survivals of Sasanian & Manichaean art in Persian painting. [Charlton lect.] s4°. O. 1924

Arnold (William Harris).
Ventures in book collecting. 8°. N.Y. 1923

Arnold-Forster (*Rt. Hon.* Hugh O.)
A hist. of England. 8°. [1915?]
see HALIBURTON (A. L. H.) Army organiz.: A.-F. scheme, 1905.

Arnold-Foster (*Mrs.* Mary). Studies in dreams, w. foreword by Dr. M. Prince. 8°. [1921]

Arnoldi (Caspar Friedrich). Sepulchra Hebræorum. Præs. C. F. A., resp. D. Kleselius. [P431]. s4°. Wittenbergæ. [1695]
Signa crucis Hebrææ gentis &c. Præs. T. Dassovio. [P431] s4°. Wittenbergæ. [1695]

Arnoldus, *abbot of Lübeck.* Chron. Slavorum. Ex rec. I. M. Lappenbergii. Rec. fecit G. H. Pertz. [Scr. rerum Germ. in usum schol.] 8°. Hannoveræ. 1868

Arnoldus (Gothofredus), *see* ARNOLD (G.)

Arnolfini, *The family of, see* DORINI (U.) Le carte della fam. A. acq. dal R. Arch. di Stato di Lucca, 1924.

Arnould (*Mlle.* Sophie), *see* GONCOURT (E. DE) & J. DE GONCOURT. S. A. d'ap. sa corr. & s. méms. inéd., éd. déf., 1922.

Arnoux (Alexandre).
Le cabaret. 8e éd. s8°. [1927]
Le chiffre. [14e éd.] s8°. 1926
Écoute s'il pleut. Roman. s8°. [1923]
Huon de Bordeaux. Mélodrame féerique. s8°. [1922]
Indice 33. [8e éd.] s8°. [1927]
Petite lumière & l'ourse. Féerie. s8°. 1923
Suite variée. [Cahiers verts, 55]. s8°. 1925

Arnoux (Jacques d'). Paroles d'un revenant. Préf. de H. Bordeaux. s8°. [1925]

Arnoux (Jean), *see* DU MOULIN (P.) Bouclier de la foy, déf. de la confess. de foy des égl. ref. de Fr., contre A., 1870.
see DU MOULIN (P.) The buckler of the faith; or a defence &c. against M. A., 1623.

Arnstädt (Friedrich August). François Rabelais u. s. Traité d'éduc. mit bes. Berücksicht. d. pädagog. Grundsätze Montaigne's, Locke's &c. 8°. L. 1872

Aronovich (A. M.), *see* GERNET (M. N.) Преступный мир Москвы: сборник статей А. М. А. &c., 1924.

Aronson (Moses Judah). La philos. morale de J. Royce. 8°. 1827

Arpe (Peter Friedrich). Themis Cimbrica, sive de Cimbrorum &c. antiq. institutis comm. s4°. Hamburgi. 1737

Arpi (Mario d'). Le Mexique. Vers. franç. de P. Dermée. la8°. Bergame. [1924]

Arragel (Moses), *of Guadalfajara, see* BIBLE: SPANISH. O. T.; tr. into Castilian by M. A. (1422–33?), 2v, 1918–21.

Arras. Arras 1917. [Kriegsberichte aus d. Gr. Hauptquartier, H28]. [P2502]. 8°. St. 1917

Arras [*continued*].
Cartul. de Notre-Dame-des-Ardents à A. [Publ.] L. Cavrois. 8°. Arras. 1876
Cartul. de Saint-Vaast d'A. Rédige au 12e s. par Guimann. Publ., au nom de l'Acad. d'Arras par M. Van Drival. 8°. Arras. 1875
Traité d'A., 23 déc., 1482 (Paris, 1483) facs. &c., *see* PICOT (E.) & H. STEIN. Recueil, 1923.

Arrest. *A. du Parl. de Thoulouse contre la prétendue déclar. de foy de Mr. de Candales, 1616, *see* TOULOUSE.

Arrhenius (Claudius) [ORNHJÄLM]. Hist. Sueonum Gothorumq. eccl. libri 4 priores [-12 cent.] s4°. Stockholmiæ. 1689
see REMBERT, *St.* S. Anscharii vita &c.; ed. C. A., 1677.

Arrhenius (Svante August). Chemistry in mod. life. Tr. & rev. by C. S. Leonard. 8°. 1926
Der Lebenslauf d. Planeten. Nach d. 4. Auflage, übers. v. B. Finkelstein. 8°. L. 1919

Arrian (Flavius). A. de expedit. Alex. Magni hist. libri 8. Ex B. Vulcanii nova interpret. Alexandri vita ex Plut. Ejusdem libri 2 de fortuna vel virtute Alexandri. [*Gr. & Lat. 2 pagins.*] fol. [Geneva]. *H. Stephanus.* 1575
L'Inde. Texte établi & tr. par P. Chantraine. [Coll. des Univ. de France]. 8°. 1927

Arrigon (Louis Jules). La jeune captive: Aimée de Coigny, Dsse. de Fleury &c. s8°. 1921

Arrivabene (Lodovico). Della orig. de'cavaglieri del Tosone &c.: dialoghi 2. 8°. Mantoa. 1589

Arros, *ps., see* ROSSATO (A.)

Arrowsmith (John), *Regius Prof. of Divinity, Camb.* The Covenant-avenging sword. Sermon. [P2662]. s4°. 1643

Arrowsmith (Richard Staines). The prelude to the Reformation. Eng. church life f. age of Wycliffe to breach w. Rome. [Sts. in Ch. hist.] s8°. 1923

Ars memorativa: reprod. Druck d. A. Sorg, Augsburg, 1490, aus e. venez. Werk d. J. P.; Vorwort v. E. Weil, 1922, *see* PUBLICIUS (JACOBUS).

Ars (Eusèbe de Brémond d'), *see* BRÉMOND D'ARS (E. DE).

Arsandaux (M. L.) Evasion, *see* ŒUVRES libres, No. 79, 1928.

Ars Asiatica. Sous le patronage de l'Ecole Franç. de l'Extrème-Orient. Publ. sous la dir. de V. Goloubew. t1–4. fol. 1914–22
see CHAVANNES (E.) Six mons. de la sculpture chin., 1914. [2.]
,, —— & R. PETRUCCI. La peinture chin. au Musée Cernuschi, 1914. [1.]
,, PARMENTIER (H.) Sculptures chames, Tourane, 1922. [4.]
,, RODIN (A.), A. COOMARASWAMY &c. Sculptures çivaïtes, 1921. [3.]

Arsenev (Konstantin Ivanovich), 1789–1865, *see* PEKARSKY (P. P.) О жизни &c. А., 1871.

Arsenev (Nikolai). Жажда подлиннаго бытія: пессимизмъ и мистика. 8°. Берлинъ *n.d.*

Arsenev (Vladimir K.) In d. Wildnis Ostsibiriens: Forschungsreisen im Ussurigebiet. Übers. F. Daniel. 2B. 8°. [1924]
Russen u. Chinesen in Ostsibirien. Übers. F. Daniel. 8°. [1926]

Arsenev (Yury Vasilevich). Новыя данныя о службѣ Николая Спаѳарія въ Россіи 1671–1708. [P2516; 2532]. la8°. Москва. 1900
Описаніе Москвы и Моск. госуд. xvii в. [P2532]. 8°. Москва. 1911
see SPATHARY (N. G.) Списокъ посольства въ Китай, 1906.

Arsenius, *Saint, called the Great, see* THEODORE, *Studita, St.* Enkomion auf d. hlgn. A., *Greek,* 1920.

Årskatalog, *see* AARSKATALOG.

Arsky (R.) Le contrôle ouvrier. [P2392]. s8°. *n.p. n.d.*

Arstal (Axel), *see* RUGE (S.) & A. A. Norwegen, 3e A., 1913.

Arsy (Jean Louis d'). Le grand dict. françois-flamen &c. Item une gramm. franç. [& Het groote woorden-boeck] [2p *in* 1v.] s4°. Utrecht. 1643

Art.
Art (L') de conserver sa santé, comp. par l'Ecole de Salerne; tr., 1766, *see* SCHOLA SALERNITANA.
Art (L') d'enluminure. Traité du 14e siècle tr. du Latin avec notes &c. par L. Dimier. s8°. 1927
,, ,, *Lat. text;* ed. Lecoy de la Marche, *see* SOC. NAT. DES ANTIQ. DE FR. Mém., s5, t7, 1886.
Art (L') lyonnais, expos., 1925, *see* LYON.
*Art (The) of speaking in publick. [Tr. f. the French.] 2nd ed. s8°. 1727
*Masterpieces of mod. German a., 2v, c. 1885, *see* GERMAN.
Outline of art, 1923, *see* ORPEN (*Sir* W.), *ed.*
*Whole (The) art of dying, 1705, *see* WHOLE.

Art (L'). t4–7. lafol. 1876

Art amateur (The), devoted to art in the household. v27–37. fol. N.Y. 1892–97

Art & archaeology. Publ. by the Arch. Inst. of Amer. v2, 3, July 1915–June 1916. 8º & la8º. Baltimore. 1915–16

Art & letters. Illust. quarterly. Ed. F. Rutter &c. v1–3 (1917–20). [*No more publ.*] la8º. 1917–20

Art (L') de vérifier les dates [*By M. F. d'Antine, C. Clémencet & V. Durand*]. 3e éd. [*cont. & publ.*] par un religieux Bénédictin de S. Maur [F. Clément]. 3t. fol. 1783–87

Art (L') et les artistes, *see* ZULOAGA (I.) I. Z, 1925.

Art (L') flamand & hollandais, anc. & mod. Études & docs. publ. sous la dir. de P. Buschmann. s1. 4º. Brux. [1904]

Art in America. An illust. magazine. Ed. F. F. Sherman. v8–15. la8º. N. York. 1920–27

Art studies, medieval, renaissance & mod. Ed. by members of the Depts. of the Fine Arts at Harvard & Princeton Univs. [Amer. journ. of Archaeology, Extra No.] [v1]. fol. 1923–4

Artabasda (Nicolaus) [ARTAVASDE; RHABDAS]. 2 lettres arithmét. (texte grec & tr.), *see* TANNERY (P.) Méms. scient., t4, 1920.

Artashir, *see* ARTAXERXES.

Artaxerxes I [BABAKAN], *shah of Persia, 224–241.* [ARDASHIR; ARTASHIR PAPAKAN]. Artashir Babakan Karnamak. [*Tr. f. Pahlavi into Armenian by* H. Thireaqean]. 8º. Paris. 1906

see †MÜLLER (F.) Beitr. z. K. d. Kārnāmak i Artaχšir i Pāpakān, 1897.

Arte (L'). Anno 22–30, 1919–27. fol. 1919–27

Arte español. Revista de la Soc. de Amigos del Arte. Año 1–16, 1912–27 (t1–8). [t4–6 *incomplete*]. la8º. [1912–27]

Artefeuil (Louis Ventre, *seigneur* **de la Touloubre,** *dit*). *Hist. héroïque & univ. de la noblesse de Provence. 4t [t3, Suppl. *w. 2 pagins.*; t4, Suppl. 2, *incl.* Tables armoriales *by* Vte. de Roziere (Blois, 1901) *w. 2 pagins.*] s4º. Avignon. 1776–1901

Artevelde, *The family of.* Cartul. hist. & généalog. des Artevelde. [*Ed.*] par N. de Pauw. [Acad. Roy. des Scis. &c. de Belg. Comm. Roy. Hist.] 4º. Brux. 1920

Arthinean (Hovh.), *see* ARTIGNAN (JOHANNES).

Arthur, *king of Britain.*

see BERRY (C. W.) King Arthur: [*play*], 1923.
,, BINYON (L.) Arthur: tragedy, 1923.
,, BLACKMORE (*Sir* R.) Prince Arthur: Poem, 1714.
,, BOULENGER (J.) Romans de la Table Ronde, t4, La mort d'A. &c., 1923.
,, BROWN (A. C. L.) Iwain: st. in origs. of A. romance, 1903.
,, BRUCE (J. D.) Evol. of A. romance to 1300, 2v, 1923.
,, CHAMBERS (*Sir* E. K.) A. of Britain, 1927.
,, JEAN, *a. of Rigomer.* Les merveilles de Rigomer: altfr. Artusroman, 1908–15.
,, JONES (W. L.) King A. in hist. &c., 2nd ed., 1914.
see KITTREDGE (G. L.) A. & Gorlagon, 1903.
,, KLOSE (M.) Der Roman v. Claris u. Laris in s. Bezieh. z. altfranz. Artusepik &c., 1916.
,, LELAND (J.) Assertion of King A.; tr. by R. Robinson f. L.'s Assertio inclytissimi A., w. Lat. orig.; ed. &c. W. E. Mead, 1925.
,, ROBINSON (J. A.) 2 Glastonbury legends: King A. &c., 1926.
,, SNELL (F. J.) King A.'s country, 1926.
,, WESTON (J. L.) King A. & h. knights, 1899.
,, ZENKER (R.) Forsch. z. Artusepik, 1, 1921.

Arthur (Anne Knox). An embroidery book. 8º. 1920

Arthur (*Sir* George), *Bart.*
Life of Lord Kitchener. 3v. 8º. 1920
Sarah Bernhardt. 8º. [1923]
Story of the Household cavalry. By Sir G. A. assist. by Capt. Shennan. v3. la8º. 1926
see MAURICE (*Maj.-Gen. Sir* F. B.) & *Sir* G. A. Life of Ld. Wolseley, 1924.

Arthur (William), *Wesleyan Minister.*
The life of Gideon Ouseley. s8º. 1876
A mission to the Mysore. s8º. 1847
The Modern Jove; a review of the speeches of Pio Nono. s8º. 1873
The tongue of fire. 11th ed. s8º. 1857
The tongue of fire [*in Tamil*]. s8º. 1884

***Arti** (Le) che vanno per via n. città di Venezia, 1803, *see* ZOMPINI (G.)

Artickel. Artickel d. fürgenumen Concilium betreffend von Karolo V &c., 1533, *see* CHARLES V, *Emperor.*
*Etlich Artickel gottes lob, und d. heyl. Röm. Reichs, u. d. gantzen Teutschen Nation ere u. gemeynan nutz belangend. Ein christl. verwarnung. s4º. [Hagenaw. 1521]
,, ,, ...[*a. ed.*]. s4º. [Strassburg. 1521]

Artickel [*continued*].
*Dye Grundtl. u. rechten haupt Artickl aller Baurschafft u. Hyndersessen &c. (*facs.* 1525), *see* FREYTAG (G.) Bilder, B3ii, 1924.

Articles of the Church of England. Articles of relig., Edward VI & Elizabeth [*6 versions in parallel cols. By Dr. Burney*]. 4º. 1811
The faith, doct. & relig. professed &c. in Eng. &c., in the 39 articles. s4º. C. 1691
see WELCHMAN (E.) The 39 articles; tr., 13th ed., 1823.

Articuli.
A. de quibus egerunt per visitatores in reg. Saxoniæ, *see* SAXONY. Visit. of Saxon Ref. Church, 1527–28; *ed.* R. Laurence, 1839.
A. juxta quos regitur Eccl. regni Ungariæ, 1667, *see* HUNGARIA.
A. visitat. eccl.: Xtni. de Sacra Cœna &c. relig. Zwinglio-Calvin. [1594] decursi &c., 1662, *see* HEINRICI (D.)
*Tredecim a. fidei Iudæorum, 1529, *see* MAIMONIDES.

Articulus. *Articulus de Justificatione, 1732, *see* NEUMEISTER (E.)

Artigas (Miguel) Don L. de Góngora y Argote. [Real Acad. Esp.]. la8º. 1925

Artignan (Johannes) [ARTHINEAN (HOVH.)] Plantes de la Bible d'ap. la vers. armén. du 5e siècle. [*In Armenian*]. s8º. K. polis. 1913

Artikel, *see* ARTICKEL.

Artillery. *Our artillery: a plea f. its better tech. educ. By A General Officer. [P2489]. 8º. 1875

Artiñano (Gervasio de) [ARTIÑANO Y DE GALDÁCANO (G. DE)]. La arquitectura naval esp. (en madera). Conf., 1914. sfol. 1920

Artist, The. Illust. monthly record. v21–23. la8º. 1898

Artner (Carl Andreas).
Arbor consanguinitatis &c. [P2633]. s4º. Lipsiæ. 1699

Artois. Plan & cartes d. villes d'A., *n.d.*, *see* BEAULIEU (S. DE).

Artois (*comte* d'), *see* CHARLES X, *king of France.*

Artopœus (Henricus), *see* HESSELS (J.) Tractatus pro invocat. Sanctorum c. H. A. &c., 1568.

Artopoeus (Johann Christoph). Disput. de abdicatione Caroli V. imp. Præs. U. Obrechto. [P2641]. s4º. Argentorati. 1676

Artopoeus (Johann Georg). Elenchus errorum a Justino c. res Judaicas admiss., 1695, *see* SCHLÄGER (C. J.) Diss. fasc., 1742.

Arts & Crafts Exhibition Society.
Cat. of the 1st Exhibition. s8º. 1888

Artus (Louis). Ma grandmère Lancelot, nouvelle, *see* ŒUVRES libres, 17, 1922.
La Présidente, *see* ŒUVRES libres, 80, 1928.

Artusi (Pellegrino). La scienza in cucina &c. 6a ed. 8º. Firenze. 1902

Arunachalam (*Sir* Ponnambalam). Light f. the East: letters on gñanam, the divine knowledge. Ed. E. Carpenter. s8º. [1927]

Arundel (Thomas Howard, *2nd earl of*), 1585–1646, *see* HERVEY (M. F. S.) Life, corresp. & colls. of T. H., 1921.
see PRIDEAUX (H.) Marmora Oxon., ex A. &c., 1676.

Arundell (Dennis Drew). H. Purcell. s8º. 1927

Arup (Erik). Danmarks hist. [B1]. la8º. 1925

Arusmont (Frances d'), *see* WRIGHT (F.), *aft. Mme. d'Arusmont.*

Arvali, *fratelli, see* MARINI (G. L.) Atti &c. de F. a., 2p, 1795.

Arvari, *The family of, see* ERVARI.

Arvieux (Laurent d'). The travels of the Chev. d'A. in Arabia; wr. by himself, & publ. by Mr. de la Roque. Add., Descr. of Arabia, by Ishmael Abulfeda. Done into Eng. by an eminent hand. [Descr. &c. *has sep. tp. dated* 1718]. 2nd ed. s8º. 1732

Arz (*Generaloberst* Artur).
Zur Gesch. d. Grossen Krieges, 1914–18. 8º. Wien. 1924

As. *As they are: French polit. portraits; by ***; tr. W. Katzin, 1924, *see* CEUX qui nous mènent, 1922; tr., 1924.

Asafev (Boris Vladimirovich), *see* GOSUDARSTV. INST. ISTORII ISKUSSTV. Музыка и музыкал. быт старой России, t1, [*by* B. V. A. &c.], 1927.

Asatir (The). Samaritan book of the "Secrets of Moses." With the Pitron or Samaritan comm. & S. story of the death of Moses. Publ. w. intr., tr. & notes by M. Gaster. [O.T.F., N.S., 26]. 8º. 1927

Asbaje (Juana Ines de), *see* JUANA INES [DE ASBAJE], *de la Cruz.*

Asbjörnsen (Peter Christen) & J. I. Moe. Norwegian fairy tales, f. coll. of A. & M. Tr. H. & J. Gade. 8º. N.Y. 1924

Asbury (Francis), *bp. of Meth.-Episc. Ch. in U.S.; 1745–1816.* An extract f. journal of F. A., 1771–78. v1. s8°. Phila. 1792
see BRIGGS (F. W.) Bishop A., 1879.
„ COKE (T.) & F. A. Doctrines of M. Episc. Ch., 1798.
„ STRICKLAND (W. P.) The pioneer bishop: A., 1858; 1860.

***Ascanius,** or the young adventurer, 1745–46, 1802, *see* GRIFFITHS (R.)

Ascargorta (Juan de). Manual de confessores ad mentem Scoti. 6ª impr. corr. s8°. Madrid. 1764

Ascenscius (Jodocus Badius), *see* BADIUS (J.)

Ascension, *island.* The just vengeance of heaven exemplify'd in a journal found by Capt. Mawson, on the isl. of A., 1730?, *see* MAWSON (*Capt.*)

Aschaffenburg (Gustav). Das Verbrechen u. s. Bekämpfung. 3e verb. A. 8°. Heidelberg. 1923

Ascham (Anthony), *Eng. ambass. at Madrid.* The process & pleadings in the court of Spain upon the death of A. A. &c. killed by J. Guillim &c. [Tr. *Foll. by MS. copy of Milton's despatches reg. A. A. b. w.* Hurtado de Mendoza (A.) Fiestas, 1670]. s4°. 1651

Ascham (Roger). The scholemaster. Ed. w. notes by J. E. B. Mayor. s8°. 1863

Aschehoug (H.) & Co.
Forlag, 1872–1922. Jubilæumskatalog. 8°. 1922

Asclepiodotus, *wr. on milit. tactics.* Tactics: text, w. Eng. tr. by members of the Illinois Greek Club [Loeb Class. Lib], 1923, *see* ÆNEAS, *Tacticus.*

Ascoli (Georges). La Grande-Bretagne dev. l'opin. franç. [1339–1600. App. Poème sur la mort d'Anne Boleyn, par L. de Carles—Poèmes publ. à l'occas. de la mort de Marie Stuart &c.] 8°. 1927

Ascoli (Graziadio Isaia), *see* ARCHIVIO GLOTTOLOGICO ITAL., dir. da G. I. A., 2v, 1873–76.

Asconius Pedianus (Quintus) [ASCONIO PEDIANO]. Commentarii. Rec. C. Giarratano. [Coll. di testi e mon. Romani; publ. E. Pais &c.] la8°. 1920
Orationum Ciceronis quinque enarratio. Rec. &c. A. C. Clark. s8°. O. [1907]

Ash (Edward C.) Dogs: hist. & development. 2v. 4°. 1927

Ashbee (Charles Robert).
Craftmanship in compet. industry. 8°. [1908]
Mod. Eng. silverwork. 4°. [*Essex House Pr.* 1909]
A Palestine notebook, 1918–23. 8°. 1923
see JERUSALEM, 1920–22: rec. of Pro-J. Co.; ed. A., 1924.

Ashby (Arthur W.) & P. G. Byles.
Rural education. Pref. by [A. L. Smith]. s8°. O. 1923

Ashby (Douglas).
Things seen in Switzerland in summer. s8°. 1928

Ashby (Thomas).
Antiquæ statuæ urbis Romæ [*by* G. B. de' Cavalieri, 1569], *see* BRIT. SCHOOL AT ROME. Papers, v9, 1920.
Dessins inéd. de Carlo Labruzzi [Extr., Ecole fr. de Rome, Mélanges, t23]. [P2837]. la8°. Rome. 1903
The Palazzo Odescalchi, *see* BRIT. SCHOOL AT ROME. Papers, v9, 1920.
The Roman Campagna in classical times. 8°. 1927
Turner's visions of Rome. 4°. 1925
La villa dei Quintilii. [Estr. da "Ausonia," 1909, fasc. 1]. la8°. 1910

Ashcroft (James), *see* HOLDEN (W.) The trial & convict. of J. A., W. H. &c. for murder of M. Marsden &c. 1817.

Ashdown (A. Millicent).
A complete system of nursing. [repr.] 8°. 1921

Ashdowne (William). *The distinction betw. the ordin. & extraordin. gifts of the Holy Spirit. By an impartial hand. [P490]. 8°. 1767

Ashe (A. W.) & H. G. T. Boorman. Chemicals. Intr. by Sir E. Geddes, Sir M. Muspratt & R. G. Perry. [Resources of the Empire, v7]. 4°. 1924

Ashe (Jonathan). The masonic manual; or, Lects. on freemasonry. 2nd ed. s8°. 1825
„ „ ......With annots. &c. by G. Oliver. n. ed., re-ed. by J. E. Cox. s8°. 1870

Ashe (*Capt.* Thomas). *Hist. of the Azores or Western islands. [*Dedic.* signed T. A. *i.e.* T. Ashe]. 4°. 1813

Ashe (Thomas), *of Gray's Inn, see* PLOWDEN (E.) Abridgment des touts les cases reportez alarge per Mons. P. &c.; composee &c. p. T. A., 1600?

Asher (Adolph). A bibliograph. essay on the Scriptores rerum German. 4°. 1843

Asher (George Michael). Sketch of Henry Hudson, the navigator. [P2623]. 8°. Brooklyn. 1867

Asheshov (Nikolai Petrovich). Софья Перовская. Мат. для биографии, &c. 8°. П. 1920

Ashford (Mary).
see HOLROYD (E.) Obs. upon the case of A. Thornton, tried for murder of M. A., 1819.
„ THORNTON (A.) Affecting case of M. A. incl. trial of A. T. for murder of M. A., 1817.

Ashik (Anton Baltazarevich). Воспорское царство съ его палеограф. и надгробн. памятниками. [*Some plates mutilated*]. 3ч *in* 1v. 4°. Одесса. 1848–49

Ashley Library, *see* WISE (T. J.) The A. Library: cat. of pr. books, MSS. &c. coll. by T. J. W., 9v, 1922–27.

Ashley (*Miss* Annie), *M.A., see* GRIER (*Miss* L.) & A. A. Brit. labour &c., 1921.

Ashley (Percy Walter Llewellyn). Mod. tariff hist.: Germany—U.S.—France. 3rd ed. 8°. 1920

Ashley (*Sir* William James).
The bread of cur forefathers. 8°. O. 1928
Econ. organis. of England. 9th impr. 8°. 1925
The tariff problem.
4th ed. w. add. ch. of 2nd ed. & intr. of 3rd ed. s8°. 1920

Ashmead-Bartlett (Ellis).
The tragedy of Central Europe. 8°. [1923]

Ashmole (Bernard). Hygieia on Acropolis & Palatino, *see* BRIT. SCHOOL AT ROME. Papers, v10, 1927.

Ashmole (Elias). Diary & will of E. A. Ed. & extended f. orig. MS. by R. T. Gunther. [Old Ashm. repr. 2]. s8°. O. 1927
see HUMPHREYS (A. L.) E. A., 1925.
„ TUCKETT (J. E. S.) Dr. R. Rawlinson & the masonic entries in A.'s diary, 1912.

Ashton (Arthur Jacob). As I went on my way. 8°. [1924]

Ashton (Harry). Madame de la Fayette. la8°. C. 1922

Ashton (James), *see* MEW (J.) & J. A. Drinks of the world, 1892.

Ashton (John), *antiquary.* The adv. & discourses of Capt. J. Smith. Newly ordered by J. A. 8°. 1883
Florizel's folly. s8°. 1899

Ashton (Leigh).
Intr. to the study of Chinese sculpture. 4°. 1924

Ashton (Thomas Southcliffe). Iron & steel in the indust. revolution. [Univ. of M'ter. Econ. hist. ser., No. 11]. 8°. M'ter. 1924

Ashton (William). The evol. of a coast-line: Barrow to Aberystwyth & the Isle of Man. 8°. 1920

Ashton & Mitchell, *Messrs., see* BRERETON (A.) Walk down Bond St.: house of A. & M., 1820–1920, 1920.

Ashton-Wolfe (H.) The underworld: reminisc. 8°. [1926]

Ashwell (George) [ASHWELLO; ASHEVELLO].
De Socino et Socinianismo dissert. s8°. Oxoniæ. 1680

Asia. Offic. guide to Eastern Asia. Prep. by Dept. of Railways, Tokyo. v1–5 [1, 5, 2nd ed.] s8°. Tokyo. 1914–20
1, Chosen & Manchuria, Siberia. 2, South-West. Japan. 3, North-East. Japan. 5, East Indies, incl. Philippine Isl. &c.

Asiatic Society of Bengal.
Memoirs. v6. 4°. Calcutta. 1925
6, Zoolog. results of a tour in the Far East; ed. N. Annandale.
see GRIERSON (G. A.) The Ōrmurī or Bargistā lang., 1918.
„ MELLO (F. DE) & J. F. ST. A. FERNANDES. Révision des champignons appart. au genre Nocardia, 1919.

Asiatic Society of Japan. Transactions. v44i, ii, 45–49ii, s2, v1–4. 8°. Yokohama & Tokyo. 1916–27.
The following have sep. tps. &c.:—
44ii, Becker (J. E. de). Elements of Japanese law.
45i, Tokutomi (I.) Life of Shoin Yoshida; tr. H. E. Coleman.
45ii, Kato (S.) The Warongo or Jap. Analects.
46ii, 49i, Heike monogatari; tr. A. L. Sadler.
47, Cat. of lib. of As. Soc. of J.
49ii, Holtom (D. C.) Polit. philos. of mod. Shinto.
s2, v1, Suppl., Kato (G.) St. of develop. of relig. ideas as illust. by Jap. phallicism.
v4, Meh Tse, Soc. teachings; tr. L. Tomkinson.

Asiatique. Mythologie a. illust., 1928, *see* MYTHOLOGIE.

Asie-Mineure. Mém. sur les nationalités en A.-M. [Turc Yourdou. P2712]. 8°. Genève. 1919

Asin Palacios (Miguel). Islam & the Divine Comedy. Tr. & abr. by H. Sunderland. 8°. 1926
see JESUS CHRIST. Logia & agrapha Domini Jesu apud Moslem. script. usitata; coll., vertit &c. M. A. et P., fasc. 2, 1926.

Asioli (Bonifazio). Trattato di armonia. 4°. Milano. [1813]

Askenazy (Szymon).
Dantzig & Poland. Tr. W. J. Rose. 8°. [1921]

Askham Richard. The registers of Askham Richard, 1579–1812. Transcr. & ed. F. W. Slingsby. [Yorks. Parish Reg. Soc., 31. *b. w.* Allerton Mauleverer. Reg., 1908]. 8°. *p.p.* 1908

Asklund (Bror), *see* HEDIN (S.) S. Tibet: researches, 1906–8, v9iii, Zur Geol. v. Ost-Pamir, v. B. A., 1922.

Askwith (Edward Harrison).
A course of pure geometry. 8°. C. 1921

Askwith (George Ranken Askwith, *1st baron*).
Industrial problems & disputes. 8°. 1920

Askwith (Herbert). Young Orland. [8th ed.] 8°. [1927]

Aslan (Kevork). Armenia & the Armenians. Tr. P. Crabitès, w. pref. s8°. N.Y. 1920

Aslin (Mary S.), *see* ROTHAMSTED EXPERIMENTAL STATION: LIBRARY. Cat. of pr. bks. on agric., 1471–1840; notes by A., 1926.

Asloan (John). The Asloan MS.: a misc. in prose & verse. Ed. W. A. Craigie. [Scottish Text Soc., N.S., 14, 16]. 2v. 8°. E. 1923–25

Asoka, *emperor of India, see* BHANDARKAR (D. R.) Asoka, 1925.
see CORPUS inscr. Indicarum, n. ed., v1, Inscr. of A., 1925.
„ HYDERABAD Arch. Series, No. 1, New Asokan edict of Maski, 1915.

Asolik (Stephan), *see* STEPHANUS, *of Taron.*

Aspects. *Aspects of Jewish life & thought, *see* BENAMMI, *ps.* Letters, s1, 1922.

Aspern (Carl). Illust. Gesch. d. europ. Krieges 1914[–18]. [Habbels Kriegschronik]. B6–10. 8°. Regensburg. [1916–19]

Aspinall (Arthur).
Lord Brougham & the Whig party. 8°. M'ter. 1927

Aspneas (Georgios K.) Πολιτικὴ ἱστορία τῆς νεωτέρας Ἑλλάδος, 1821–1921. T1, 2 (–1900). 8°. ἐν Ἀθήναις 1922–23

Aspremont. La chanson d'A., 12e siècle. Ed. L. Brandin. [Class. fr. du M. A.] t2. s8°. 1920
La chanson d'A. d'ap. un poème du 13e siècle. [Ed.] L. Brandin. Préf. de J. Bédier. 8°. [1924]

Asquith (Cyril), *see* CHALMERS (D.) & C. A. Outlines of constit. law, 1922.

Asquith (Emma Alice Margaret), *wife of Earl of Oxford & Asquith.* Autobiography. 2v. 8°. 1920[–22]
Lay sermons. s8°. [1927]
Places & persons. [2nd impr.] 8°. [1925]
see PAIN (B. E. O.) Marge Askinforit, 1920.

Asquith (*Rt. Hon.* Herbert Henry), *earl of Oxford & Asquith.*
50 yrs. of Parliament. 2v. 8°. [1926]
The genesis of the War. 8°. 1923
Studies & sketches. 8°. 1924

Assam. The coloniz. of waste-lands in A., official corr. &c. [P2592]. 8°. Calcutta. 1899
*Earthquake in Bengal & A., 1897, *see* BENGAL.

Assas (Manuel de). Crón. de la prov. de Santander, 1867, *see* ESPAÑA. Crón. gen., v10, 1865, &c.

Asse (Eugéne). Les petits romantiques. A. Fontaney—J. Polonius—L'indépend. de la Grèce & les poètes de la Restauration—J. de Rességuier—E. d'Anglemont. 8°. 1900

Asselineau (Charles).
L'enfer du bibliophile. [P2588]. s8°. 1860

Assemanus (Josephus Aloysius) [ASSEMANI (JOS. MOYSES)].
Codex liturgicus eccl. univ. in 15 lib., in quo cont. libri rituales, missales, pontificales, officia, dypticha &c. eccl. Occid. & Or. [*Gr., Arabic, Coptic, Syriac &c. & Lat.* 13t. *in* 12]. s4°. Romæ. 1749–66
1–6, Codex liturgicus &c. lib. 1–4, p. 1–3; 7, Missale Alexandrinum Sancti Marci; 8–13, Codex liturgicus &c. lib. 8, p. 1–6. *No more published.*
Comm. de ecclesiis earum reverentia, et asylo &c. Acc. Josephi de Bonis De oratoriis publicis ac Fortunati a Brixia De oratoriis domesticis. fol. Romæ. 1766
De Catholicis seu patriarchis Chaldæorum et Nestor. comm. 4°. Romæ. 1775
De ritibus sacris, *see* MIGNE (J. P.) *ed.* Theol. cursus, t26, 1859.
De sacris ritibus, *see* LANGUET DE LA VILLENEUVE DE GERGY (J. J.) De vero eccles. sensu, 1757.
De synodo diœcesana dissert. s4°. Romæ. 1776
Diss. de unione, & communione eccl. 4°. Romæ. 1770
see MISSAL. Missale Alexandrinum S. Marci &c. J. A. A. rec., 1754.

Assemanus (Josephus Simonius). De Bonifacio ac Redempto episcopis: Deque presbytero Eutichio, diss. s4°. Romæ. 1745

Assembly of Divines, *see* DIVINES.

Assertion. *A. (An) of the gov. of the Ch. of Scotland &c., 1644, *see* GILLESPIE (G.)

Assigny (Louis Troya d'), *see* TROYA D'ASSIGNY (L.)

Assize Rolls. Earliest Lincoln. A. R., 1202–9, 1926, *see* LINCOLNSHIRE.

Assmus (Burghard). Das Damenregiment im Vatikan u. Privatleben d. Päpste. [Coll. "Purpur u. Sünde"; hrsg. v. B. A., 2]. s8°. [1903]

Asso (Ignacio de), *see* ASSO Y DEL RIO (I. J. DE).

Associated Societies for the Care & Maintenance of Infants.
Rep. of proc. of the conf. on child adoption. [P2754]. 8°. [1920]
Rep. of sel. comm. app. to examine child adoption. [P2754]. 8°. [1920]

Association Anglo-Arménienne, *see* HAÏASDAN, LE, 1888–92.

Association des Écrivains Combattants, *see* ANTHOLOGIE des écrivains morts à la Guerre, 1914–18, 2t, 1924.

Association des Ets. Grecques, *see* MILLIET (P.) Rec. M., t1, 1921.

Association for the Preservation of the Memorials of the Dead in Ireland. [*aft.* THE IRISH MEMORIALS ASSOC., *incorp.* THE DUBLIN PARISH REGISTER SOCIETY].
Journal. v10, 11 (1917–25). 8°. D. 1920–25
„ „ Parish reg. sect., 1921–25. 8°. D. 1925

Association (L') Internat. des Travailleurs, *see* GUILLAUME (J.) Karl Marx, Pangermaniste & L'A. I. des T., 1915.

Association of Assistant Masters in Secondary Schools (Incorporated). Mem. on the teaching of English. [P2690]. s8°. C. 1923

Association of Men of Kent & Kentish Men, *see* PLOMER (H. R.) Kentish feast, 1916.

Association of Special Libraries & Information Bureaux. Rep. of procs. of 2nd confer., 1925. 8°. 1926

Association Patriotique Arménienne, *see* HAÏASDAN, LE, 1888–92

Assonica (Petrus). Breves chronicæ Bergom. [Manfredi Zenunonis, P. A. &c. 1117–1512]; nunc. primum ed. cura I. Finazzi, *see* REGIA DEP. DI STORIA PATRIA. Misc., t5, 1868.

Asso y del Rio (Ignacio Jordan de). Hist. de la economía polit. de Aragon. 8°. Zaragoza. 1798

Assyria. Ancient records of A. & Babylonia, v1, 2, 1926–27, *see* LUCKENBILL (D. D.) *ed.*

Astapattzi (Abraham), *see* ABRAHAM *Astapattzi.*

Astarloa y Aguirre (Pablo Pedro de). Apología de la lengua Bascongada &c., en respuesta á los reparos propuestos [*by* J. Traggia] &c. 8°. 1803

Astbury (John), *see* PRICE (R. K.) A., Whieldon & Ralph Wood figures, & Toby jugs, 1922.

Astell (Mary). *Essay in defence of the female sex, 3rd ed., 1697, *sometimes attrib. to M. A., see* †DRAKE (*Mrs.*)

Aster, *pseud.* The bridge of light: a message f. the unseen. s8°. 1899

Aster (Ernst v.), *see* DESSOIR (M.) *ed.* Lehrbuch d. Philos., B1, Gesch. d. P.; v. E. v. A. &c., 1925.

Asterisk, *ps.* *Gone native. Tale of the South Seas. s8°. 1924

Asti. Cronachette astesi [*Latin*]; ed. V. Promis, *see* REGIA DEP. DI STORIA PATRIA. Misc., t9, 1870.

Astle (Thomas). The origin & progress of writing. 2nd ed., w. adds. fol. 1803

Aston (Anthony), *see* NICHOLSON (W.) A. A., stroller &c. app. A's suppl. to Cibber's Lives &c., 1920.

Aston (E. A.) An Irish constituent convention. [P2385]. s8°. D. [1919]

Aston (Francis William). Isotopes. 8°. 1922

Aston (*Maj.-Gen. Sir* George Grey), *K.C.B.* Defence of the Empire, *see* BUCHAN (J.) *ed.* Nations of to-day, Gt. Brit., v2, 1923.

Astorga (Emanuel d'), *see* VOLKMANN (H.) E. d'A., 2B, 1911–22.

Astorga (Manuel), *see* VEGA INCLAN (M. DE LA), J. DE CASTRO Y LOPEZ & M. A. Rel. hist. de la últ. campaña de Marq. del Duero, 1874.

Astruc (Jean), *see* LODS (A.) J. A. & la crit. bibl., 1924.

Atanagi (Dionigi). De le rime di diversi nobili poeti toscani. Racc. da D. A., libro primo (& secondo). [2v]. s8°. Venetia. 1565

Atanassievitch (Xénia). La doct. métaphys. & géométr. de Bruno. 8°. Belgrade. 1923

Atcharian (H.), *see* ADJARIAN (H.)

Atchison (*Capt.* Thomas). Petition to the King, submitted to The Duke of Wellington 14th Jan. 1829. [*b. w. h.* Trial, 1825]. 8°. 1829
Statement of A. in def. of his milit. integrity. [P2593]. s8°. 1834
Trial, by a gen. Court Martial at Malta. 8°. 1825

Atchley (Edward Godfrey Cuthbert Frederick). "He that readeth the Epistle." Reissue of The parish clerk &c. 8°. O. 1927
The people's prayers. [Alcuin Club Tracts, 6]. la8°. 1906

Athalaric, *king of Italy, see* NEUBOUR (G. P. A.) Diss. qua regis A. edictum de elig. papa illustratur, 1740.

Athanasian Creed (The).
Rep. of the Comm. of bishops on the revis. of the A. C. Introd. & notes by Charles John, bp. of Glouc. &c. [P519]. 8°. 1872
see EDEN (R.) The A. C.; facts & suggest. incl. a new tr., 1872.
,, IRONS (W. J.) Athanasius contra mundum: a letter &c., 1872.
see RADCLIFFE (J.) The conf., called the creed of St. A. 1844.
,, STANLEY (A. P.) The A. C., Ritual Comm. &c., 1871.
,, SWAINSON (C. A.) The A. C. & its usages in the Eng. Ch. &c., 1870.
,, WATERLAND (D.) Crit. hist. of the A. c., 1870.

Athanasius, *Saint, patriarch of Alexandria.*
De incarnatione Verbi Dei. Tr. w. introd. &c. by H. Bindley. s8°. [1887]
Festal letters, Syriac version. Ed. W. Cureton. [Soc. for the Publ. of Or. Texts]. la8°. 1848
Interpretatio Psalmorum [*w. text in Gr. & Lat.*] fol. Patavii. 1777
Orations against the Arians. [Anc. & Mod. Lib. of Theolog. Lit.] 8°. [1889]
Sel. treatises in controv. w. the Arians. Tr. by J. H. Newman. 2nd ed. 2v. s8°. 1881
[Sermons, letters & controv. works. *In Armenian.* Ed. E. Tayetzi]. 8°. i Venetik. 1899
Vita S. Antonii a D. A. Græce scr. e cod. Boico ed. Cum D. Hœschelii interpret. & notis. s4°. Augustæ Vindel. 1611
see BELL (H. I.) Jews &c. in Egypt: J. troubles in Alex. & the A. controv., 1924.
,, REITZENSTEIN (R.) A.'s Werk ü. d. Leben des Antonius, 1914.
,, SCHWARTZ (E.) Der sog. Sermo major de fide d. A., *w. text*, 1924.

Athanasius, *son of Nikita, see* NIKITIN (A.)

Athanasius, *of Nisibis, see* SEVERUS, *pat. of Antioch.* The 6th bk. of sel. letters, in Syriac vers. of A. of N., 4p, 1902–4.

Athenæum (The). 1920–21 (Jan. Feb. only of 1921). 4°. 1920.
[From Feb. 19, 1921, The Athenæum was incorporated w. The Nation, *q.v.*]

Athenæum Club, *London.*
Rules & list of members, 1906. s8°. 1906
see WARD (T. H.) Hist. of the A., 1824–1925, 1926.
,, WAUGH (F. G.) The A. C. & its associations, 1894; 1897.

Athenæus, *Naucratita.* Dipnosophistarum libri xv. Rec. G. Kaibel. 3v. s8°. *Teubner.* L. 1923–25
Deipnosophists. Lit. tr. by C. D. Yonge. 3v. s8°. *Bohn.* 1854
The Deipnosophists. [Text] w. Eng. tr. by C. B. Gulick [Loeb Class. Lib.] v1. s8°. 1927

Athenagoras [A. *Atheniensis*; ATENAGORA].
Apologia pro Christianis. Ejusdem, De resurrectione mortuorum. Uterque Græcè & Latinè. s8°. *n.p.* [Paris] *H. Stephanus.* 1557.
Apologia pro Christianis, 1559—De mortuorum resurrect., *Gr. & Lat.*, 1560, *see* THEOLOGI. Theologorum aliquot Græc. libri, 1560.
Della risurrezione de' morti. Tr. G. Faletti con un' orazione d. Natività di Cristo comp. da G. F. 8°. Verona [1735]
Disc. sur la resurrection des morts. Tr. par L. Reiner. s8°. Breslau. 1753
see RAU (J. J.) Diatribe de philos. Justini & A., 1733.

Athenian. *Athenian (The) Oracle &c., by a Member of the Athenian Soc., 1704; Suppl., 1710, *see* WESLEY (S.)
*Athenian Sport: or, 2000 paradoxes. By a Member of the Athenian Soc., *see* DUNTON (J.)

Athenian Society, *see* WESLEY (S.) The Athenian Oracle, 1704–10.

Athens. ACROPOLIS MUSEUM. Catalogue. v2, Sculpture & arch. fragments, by S. Casson, w. section upon terracottas, by D. Brooke. s8°. C. 1921

Atherley-Jones (Llewellyn Archer).
Looking back: remin. of a polit. career. 8°. 1925

Atherton (Gertrude Franklin). Black oxen. s8°. 1923
The crystal cup. s8°. [1925]
The immortal marriage. s8°. [1927]
Sisters-in-law. s8°. 1921

Atherton (John), *bp. of Waterford & Lismore, see* BERNARD (N.) Penitent death of J. A., executed 5 Dec. 1640, 2nd ed., 1642.

Atholl, *Earldom of, see* ROBERTSON (J. A.) Comitatus de Atholia, 1860.

Atholl (John Stewart, *4th earl*), *chancellor of Scotland; d. 1578.* Inventar of ye gudis & geir delivrit be J. Flemig to my lord A., 1578, *see* MAIDMENT (J.) & R. PITCAIRN. Nugæ derelictæ, 1822.

Athos. Actes de l'A., 1, Actes de Xenophon. Publ. L. Petit. [Βυζάντινα χρον. No. 1. P2789]. la8°. С.-П. 1903

Athos. Cat. of the Greek MSS. in lib. of the Laura on Mt. A., w. notices f. o. libraries. By Spyridon, monk & S. Eustratiades. [Harvard Theolog. St., 12. *2nd tp. in Greek*]. 4°. Camb., *Harvard.* 1925
Cat. of the Greek MSS. in lib. of the mon. of Vatopedi on Mt. A. By S. Eustratiades & Arcadios, deacon. [Harvard Theolog. St[s]., 11. *2nd tp. in Greek*]. 4°. Camb., *Harvard.* 1924
see MARR (N. YA.) Агіограф. мат. по груз. рукописямъ Ивера, 2ч, 1900–1.

Atkey (Bertram). Smiler Bunn—gentleman crook. s8°. [1923]

Atkins (Gaius Glenn).
Mod. relig. cults & movements. 8°. [1924]

Atkins (Henry Gibson).
Hist. of German versification. s8°. [1923]

Atkins (John William Hey), *see* OWL (THE) & THE NIGHTINGALE; ed. w. intr., texts &c. by A., 1922.

Atkins (Samuel Elliott) & W. H. Overall.
Some acc. of the W. Co. of Clockmakers. la8°. *p.p.* 1881

Atkinson (Christopher Thomas).
Marlborough & rise of Brit. Army. 8°. N.Y. 1921
The Seventh Division, 1914–18. 8°. 1927

Atkinson (Edward), *writer on polit. economy.*
Facts & figures. Basis of econ. sc. 8°. Boston. 1904

Atkinson (Edward Dupré).
Dromore, an Ulster diocese. s8°. Dundalk. 1925

Atkinson (*Surgeon* **Edward Leicester),** *see* LEIPER (R. T.) & E. L. A. Parasitic worms, 1914–20.

Atkinson (G. W. E.), *see* WALKER (J. T.) Map of Turkestan, comp. under orders of J. T. W., chiefly by G. W. E. A., 1883.

Atkinson (Geoffroy). The extraord. voyage in French lit. bef. 1700. [Columbia Univ. St[s].] s8°. N.Y. 1920
The extraord. voyage in French lit., 1700–20. 8°. Paris. 1922
La litt. géograph. franç. de la Renaiss. 4°. 1927
Relations de voyages du 17e siècle & l'évol. des idées &c. s8°. [1924]

Atkinson (George Francis). Relation of plants to environment. Lect[s]., Cornell Univ. 8°. Ithaca, N.Y. 1904

Atkinson (John), *D.D.* The beginnings of the Wesleyan movement in America. 8°. N.Y. 1896

Atkinson (Meredith), *ed.* Australia; economic & polit. studies. By var. writers. s8°. Melbourne. 1920

Atkinson (Robert), *see* †ROYAL IRISH ACADEMY. Book of Ballymote; w. intr., anal. &c. by R. A., 1887.

Atkinson (Robert), *F.R.I.B.A., see* ARCHITECTURAL ASSOC. SCHOOL. Book of design; intr. essays by R. A. &c., 1924.

—— & H. Bagenal.
Theory & elements of architecture. v1, pl. la8°. [1926]

Atkinson (Solomon). The effects of the new syst. of free trade upon our shipping, colonies & commerce, in a lett. to W. Huskisson. [P448]. 8°. 1827

Atkinson (Thomas Dinham).
Eng. architecture. 5th ed. s8°. [1918]

Atkinson (W. A.) Knaresborough & its manor houses. [P2770]. s8°. Knaresborough. 1924

Atlantic Monthly (The).
v123–140 (Jan. 1919–Dec. 1927). 8°. Boston. 1919–27

Atlas. Mod. a. of America &c., 1905, *see* PHILIPS', *publ. firm.*

Atlas, The, a general newspaper & journal of literature. v1–10, May 21, 1826–Dec. 27, 1835. [*tp[s]. & indexes to v2 & 3 wanting*]. fol. 1826–35

Atley (John), *see* BETHELL (T.) A letter to J. A., preacher &c. to J. Wesley, 1788.

Atmore (Charles). The Methodist memorial; lives &c. of preachers. Introd. w. acc. of state of religion &c. & a hist. of Methodism. 8°. Bristol. 1801
see CHANDLER (S.) Hist. of persecution; app. on recent persecutions, by C. A., 1813.

Attambelos I, *of Characene, see* HILL (G. F.) Attambelos I, 1922.

Attenborough (Frederick Levi). The laws of the earliest Eng. kings. Ed. & tr. by F. L. A. 8°. C. 1922

Attersoll (William). A comm. upon Numbers. fol. 1618
The pathway to Canaan: or an expos. upon the 20 & 21 chaps. [*& a cont. called*: The hist. of Balak K. & Balaam or an expos. uppon the 22–25 chaps.] of Numbers. [2p *in* 1v.] s4°. 1609–10

Attici. Oratores A., 16t, 1828, *see* DOBSON (W. S.), *ed.*

Attila, *king of the Huns, see* ROHT (R.) A. Hunnorum rex, 1671.

Attischen Grabreliefs (Die): hrsg. v. A. Conze. B4, Text; B4, Tafeln. fol. 1911–22

Attlee (Clement Richard). The social worker. s8°. 1920

Attorney-at-Law, *ps.* *Pract. instrs. on the law of landlords & tenants &c. 8°. Chicago. 1872

Attree (*Col.* **Frederick William Town),** *see* SUSSEX. Notes of p. m. inq. taken in S.; abstr. & tr. by A., 1912.

Aubanel (Théodore), *see* VINCENT (J.) T. A., la vie & l'homme, le poète, 1924.

Auberlen (Carl August). The divine revelation. Mem. of a. Tr. by A. B. Paton. 8°. E. *Clark.* 1867

Le prophète Daniel et l'Apocalypse de S. Jean. Tr. de la 2e éd. par H. de Rougemont. 8°. Lausanne. 1880

Aubernon (*Mme.*), *1825–99, see* DU BLED (V.) La société franç. dep. cent ans, s2, Mme. A. & s. amis, 1924.

Auberon (Reginald). The nineteen hundreds. 8°. [1922]

Aubert, *de Puycibot, see* JAUSBERT.

Aubert (*Commandant* **Auguste).** Les Vauclusiens, dict. biograph. s8°. Avignon. 1890

Aubert (Louis), *see* FENAYROU (G.) *G. F. [*murder of L. A. by G. F.*], *n.d.*

Aubert (Marcel). La sculpture franç. du moyen âge & de la Renaissance. la8°. 1926

Aubert (Théodore). L'affaire Conradi. Plaidoirie pour A. Polounine devant Tribunal de Lausanne, 14 & 15 nov. 1923. [Procès du Bolchévisme]. 8°. Genève. 1924

Bolshevism's terrible record: an indictment. s8°. 1924

Aubert de Versé (Noël) [*le sieur* A. D. V.] *L'avocat des protestans dans lequel on justifie la séparation des protestans d'avec l'Eglise Rom., c. les objections d. S. Nicole, Brueys & Ferrand. s8°. Amsterdam. 1686

Aubert de Vitry (François Jean Philibert). *Obs. d'un journaliste sur "Du système polit. suivi par le ministère"; par Chateaubriand. [P2553]. 8°. 1818

Auberteuil (Michel René Hilliard d'), *see* HILLIARD D'AUBERTEUIL.

Aubertin (Charles), *see* DANGUY (R.) Gr. vins de Bourgogne; par R. D. avec collab. de C. A., 1892.

Aubigné (Théodore Agrippa d'). *La confession de M. de Sancy, *see* HENRY III, *k. of Fr.* Rec. de div. pièces, 1664.

Hist. univ. Suppl. Publ. J. Plattard. [S. de l'H. de F.] 8°. 1925

Mémoires, 1557–1622, *see* BUCHON (J. A. C.) Choix de chroniques &c., 1884.

Aubin (Eugène).

Le Maroc d'aujourd'hui. 9e éd. 8°. 1922

Aubin (Hermann), Th. Frings *& others.* Gesch. d. Rheinlandes. Von H. A., Th. Frings, J. Hansen &c. [Hrsg. v. d. Ges. f. rhein. Gesch.] 2B. 8°. Essen. 1922

Aubin (Nicolas). *The devil in disguise: or, Rome run a roving. [Hist. of the devils of Loudun. Tr.] s8°. 1710

Aubry (G. Jean-). Eugène Boudin, d'après des docs. inédits. 4°. 1922

see CONRAD (J.) Life & letters, by G. J.-A., 2v, 1927.

Aubry (Octave).

Couleur de sang. s8°. [1928]

,, ,, : heures d' Espagne, *see* ŒUVRES libres, 58, 1926.

Les femmes & le 18 Brumaire, *see* ŒUVRES libres, 74, 1927.

Le roi perdu (Louis XVII retrouvé). Mém. inéd. du Comte de Vaisons (1786–1873). Publ. [*or rather wr. by*] O. A. [Le roman dans l'hist.] 8°. 1924

Le roman de Napoléon Bonaparte & Joséphine. s8°. [1927]

Aucassin & Nicolette. A. & N.: chantefable du 13e siècle. Ed. M. Roques. [Class. fr. du m. âge, 41]. s8°. 1925

A. & N. Eng. by A. Lang. [repr.] s8°. 1910

Of A. & N. Tr. in prose & verse, w. Amabel & Amoris, by L. Housman. s8°. 1925

Aucher (Jean Bapt.) [AUGEREAN (MKRTTCH)], *see* AVEDICHIAN (G.), KH. SIURMELEAN & J. B. A. New dict. of Armenian, 2v, 1836–37.

Aucher (Paschal) [†AUKERIAN (HAROUTIUN)]. *A brief acc. of the Mechitaristican Soc. founded on the isl. of St. Lazaro. [Tr. by A. Goode. P505]. s8°. Venice. 1835

[Explan. of anc. weights & measures, by Epiphanius, Moses of Khoren & Ananias of Shirak. *In Armenian*]. 8°. i Venetik. 1821

Auckland, *New Zealand.* Municipal &c. handbook of A. Ed. J. Barr. s8°. Auckland. 1922

Aucour (Jean Barbier d'), *see* BARBIER D'AUCOUR (J.)

Auctions-Katalog, *see* KATALOG.

Auctores. Auctores Lat. ling. &c., notae D. G., 1585, *see* GODEFROY (D.)

Audax, *bp. of Asti, c. 904–26* [AUDACE], *see* CIPOLLA (C.) Di A. e di due doc. ined., 1889.

Aude (Edouard). Le Musée d'Aix-en-Provence. s8°. [1921]

Audiat (Gabriel). Charles Le Goffic. [2e éd.] s8°. [1922]

Audiat (Pierre). L'Aurélia de Gérard de Nerval. [Bibl. G. de Nerval]. 8°. 1926

La biographie de l'œuvre litt. la8°. 1924

Audiau (Jean). La pastourelle dans la poésie occitane du m.-â. Textes publ. & tr., avec intr. &c. par J. A. s8°. 1923

Audiguier (Vital d'), *sieur de la Ménor.* *A tragi-comicall hist. of our times, under the borrowed names of Lisander & Calista. [*Sometimes attrib. to G. de Coste*]. [Tr. W. D.] fol. 1627

Audin (Marius). Le livre, s. illust., sa décor. Préf. de L. Pichon. 8°. 1926

Audollent (Auguste). Les tombes gallo-rom. à inhumation des Martres-de-Veyre, *see* ACAD. DES INSCR. &c. Méms. &c., s1, t13i, 1923.

Audot (Louis Eustache). La cuisinière de la campagne &c. 60e ed. s8°. 1882

Audouin (Edward), *see* POITIERS. Rec. de docs. conc. la commune &c. de P., t1, par E. A., 1923.

Audouin-Dubreuil (Louis), *see* HAARDT (G. M.) & L. A.-D. Le raid Citroën: prem. trav. du Sahara, 1923.

Audoux (Marguerite). L'atelier de Marie-Claire. Roman. s8°. [1920]

Marie Claire's workshop. Tr. F. S. Flint. s8°. 1920

Audsley (George Ashdown), *LL.D.* The organ of the 20th cent. 8°. 1919

The ornamental arts of Japan. 2v. fol. 1882–4

Audubert-Boussat (Maurice). Dans le vent d'autan, *see* ŒUVRES libres, No. 72, 1927.

Audubon (John James). Delineations of Amer. scenery & character; intr. by F. H. Herrick. 8°. 1926

Auer (Max). Bruckner. 8°. Zürich. [1923]

Auerbach (Felix). The Zeiss works. Tr. fr. 2nd ed. by S. F. Paul & F. J. Cheshire. 8°. [1904]

Auerbach (Mathias). Mitleid u. Charakter. [Bibl. f. Phil.; hrsg. v. L. Stein, B20]. 8°. 1921

Auffenberg-Komarów (Moritz *Frhr.* **v.)** Aus Österreichs Höhe u. Niedergang. 8°. München. 1921

Aufhauser (Johannes B.) Buddha u. Jesus in i. Paralleltexten, *see* KLEINE TEXTE, 157, 1926.

Augapfel (Julius). Babylon. Rechtsurkunden Artaxerxes I u. Darius II, 1917, *see* KAIS. AKAD. D. WISS. ZU WIEN. Denkschr., B59, 1917.

Augé (Claude), *ed.*,

see LAROUSSE. L. mensuel illust., t1–5, *n.d.*

,, ——. Petit L. illust., 1922.

Augé-Laribé (Michel). Agric. & food supply in France dur. the War. Agric., by M. A.-L. Food supply, by P. Pinot. [C. E. for Internat. Peace. Tr. & abr. ser.] 8°. New Haven, *Yale.* 1927

L'agric. pend. la Guerre. [C. E. f. Int. Peace. Sér. fr.] la8°. [1925]

Augenscheinliche. *A. Erweisung, dass die Formula Concordiae &c. 1603, *see* FORMULA CONCORDIAE.

Augerean (Mkrttch), *see* AUCHER (J. B.)

Augier (G. V. Émile).

Les effrontés: comédie en 5 actes. n. éd. s8°. 1893

Augouard (Prosper Philippe), *see* WITTE (*b.* J. DE). Un explorateur & un apôtre du Congo franç.: Mgr. A.; sa vie par J. de W., &c. 1924.

Augsburg [AUGUSTA; AUGSPURG].

Abschiedt d. Röm. Keys. Maiest. &c. uff d. Reichstag zu Augspurg uffgericht, A.D. 1548, 1548–49, *see* CHARLES V., *emp. of Germany.*

Acta Comiciorum Augustæ ex litteris Philippi, Jonæ & aliorum ad M.L. Hrsg. G. Berbig. [Quellen &c. aus d. Gesch. d. Reformationsjhdts., B2]. 8°. Halle (Saale). 1907

Auszschreiben an die Röm. Kaiserl. Maiestaten. Von Burgermaister u. Ratgeben A., Abthůung der Päpstt. Mess &c. s4°. [Augsburg. 1537]

Bekandtnuss der vier Frey u. Reichstätt, Strassburg, Costantz, Memmingen u. Lindaw, uff dem Reichstag zu Augspurg im XXX Jar gehalten, 1531, *see* STRASSBURG.

Formula Reformationis per Cæsaream Maiest. Statibus Eccles in comitiis A., 1548, *see* CHARLES V, *emp.*

Notitia de libris usque ad a. 1500 impr. in Bibl. monast. SS. Udalricum & Afram Aug. ext., 2p, 1788–89, *see* BRAUN (P. I.)

Der röm. Kaiserl. Maiestat. erclärung, 1548, *see* CHARLES V, *emp. of Germany.*

Augsburg [*continued*].
Röm. Kayserl. Maiest. u. gemeiner Stende des heil. Reichs Ordnüge, auff jungst zu A. &c. gehalt. Reichsstägen gemacht 1538, *see* CHARLES V, *Emp. of Germany*.
Urkundenbuch zu d. Gesch. d. Reichstages zu A., 1530, 2B, 1833–35, *see* FÖRSTEMANN (C. E.)

Augsburg Confession [AUGSPURGISCHE CONFESSION. *Arranged chronologically*].
Anzeigung u. bekantnus des Glaubens u. der lere, so die adpelliereden Stende Key. M. auff yetzigen tag zu Augspurg överantwurt habend. [*Signed* Johanns Hertzog zů Saxen *& others*.] s4°. *n.p.* 1530
Confessio fidei exhibita Carolo V in Comiciis Augustæ a. 1530. Add. est Apologia [*by Melanchthon*.] s8°. Witebergæ. *G. Rhau.* 1531
„ „ Beide, Deudsch u. Lat. [2p. *in* 1v]. s4°. Wittebergæ. *G. Rhaw.* [1531]
The German part has sep. tp. & signatures, its title is : Conf. odder Bekantnus des Glaubens Fürsten u Stedte &c.
„ „ [*Latin part only*.] s4°. Wittebergæ. [*G. Rhau*]. 1531
Confessio relig. Christianæ 1530, per legatos Argentorati &c., 1531, *see* STRASSBURG.
Confessio odder Bekantnus des Glaubens etlicher Fürsten u. Stedte, uberantwort Keiserl. Maiestat, auff dem Reichstag gehalten zu Augspurg 1530. [*Tr. by* J. Jonas] *&* Apologia der Confessio [*by* P. Melanchton ; *w. sep. tp.*] s8°. Wittemberg. [*G. Rhaw.* 1533]
Confessio fidei exhibita Carolo V in Comiciis Augustæ. Add. est Apologia Conf. dilig. recog. s4°. Vitebergæ. *G. Rhau.* 1540
„ „ [*a. ed.*] s8°. [Vitebergæ. *G. Rhau.* 1542]
Abtrucke der verwarungsschrift, der Chur u. Fürsten &c. d. Augspurg. Conf. Eynungs verwandten, Irer yetzigen Kriegssrüstung halben, an Keyserl. Mayestat aussgangen u. beschehen. [P2439]. s4°. [Nuremberg. *Joh. v. Berg & Ulrich Neuber*]. 1546
Confessio fidei exhib. Carolo V *&* Apologia, *see* CONFESSIONES fidei Xtnæ 3, 1553.
Confessio fidei Græcè redd. a P. Dolscio. s8°. Basileæ. [1559]
Causæ cur electores, principes, &c. Aug. Conf. conjuncti status ad Concilium a Pio IIII Tridenti indictum, non accedant &c. Item Resp. datum legatis pontificis in conventu Naumburg. a. 1561. s8°. Vitebergæ. 1564
„ „ una cum aliis materiis. [P2643]. s4°. Helmstadii. 1664
*Gründtlicher bericht u. warhafftige erklerungh warumb die Chur u. Fürsten &c. d. Augsp. Conf., das Tridentisch Concilium nith haben besuechen wollen. s4°. *n.p.* 1564
Einhellige Bekentnis vieler Theol. &c. d. alt. Augs. Conf. &c., 1572, *see* MELISSANDER (C.)
Concordia. Christl. widerholete, Bekentnüs Churfürsten, Fürsten u. Stende Augspurg. Conf., u. derselben Theologen Lere u. Glaubens. Mit angeheffter, erklerung etl. Artickel, bey welchen nach M. Luthers absterben disputation u. streit vorgefallen. [App. : Verzeichnüs d. Zeugnissen heil. Schr. &c. 1580 ; *w. sep. tp. & pagin.*] fol. Dresden. 1581
Grundl. warhafft. Hist. v. d. Augsburg. Confession. Item v. d. Concordia 1536. Gestellet durch Theologen. [*b. w.* Kirchner (T.), N. Selneccer & M. Chemnitz. Apologia 1583.] fol. L. 1584
*Augspurg. Conf. auff gnädig. Befehl d. churfürstl. Durchl. zu Brandenburgk. Auss unterschied. Exemplarn nachgedruckt &c. s4°. Franckfurt. 1636
*Antiq. verissimum seu consensus priscæ eccl. doctorum cum Aug. Conf. sociis, ab antiq. theologo. [*b. w.* Himmel (J.) Syntagma, 1650]. s4°. Wittebergæ. 1658
Concordia Christl. wiederholte Bekäntniss Chur-Fürsten u. Stände Augspurg. Conf. &c. Mit. e. Anhange [Hist. theol. Einl. zu d. Symbol. Schr., v. H. Pipping, *w. sep. tp. & pagin.*] s4°. L. 1703
Concordia pio &c. consensu repetita conf. fidei & doctr. electorum, principum &c. Imperii &c. E J. Mülleri & M. S. Mülleri MS., curaque ed. a P. Müllero. s4°. Lipsiæ. 1705
Die unveränderte Augspurg. Conf., deutsch u. lat. Mit Vorbericht hrsg. v. G. W. Panzer. s8°. Nürnberg. 1782
Conf. August. In usum schol. cur. G. B. Winer. s8°. Erlangæ. 1825
Conf. August. a. 1540 a Melanchthone ed. variata illa. Accur. redd. &c. a M. Webero. [P558]. 4°. Halis. 1830
Conf. fidei August. a. 1530 Imp. Carolo V. exhib., postea a. 1540 recogn. & aucta. Ed. H. Heppe. 8°. Cassellis Catt. 1855
Die Augsburg. Konfession, lat. u. deut., kurz erläut. v. T. Kolde. Mit 5 Beilagen. 8°. Gotha. 1896
Die unveränderte A. Konf., deut. u. lat. &c. Krit. A. v. P. Tschackert. 8°. L. 1901
see ANTWERP. Ministrorum J.C. in eccl. Antverp., quæ A.C. adsentitur, adhortatio, 1566.
„ ERYTHRÆUS (V.) Aug. confess. &c., 3p., 1565–67.
„ JOHN GEORGE, *d. of Sax.* Solida decisio 4 A.C. controv. cap. &c., 1624.
„ LEODIUS (A. F.) Harmonia Confess. August., 1573.
„ MYLIUS (G.) Augustanæ conf. explic., 1596.
„ RIBINI (J.) Memor. Aug. Conf. in regno Hungar., 2v, 1787–89.
„ SUPPLICATIONES, Erklärungen u. Prot., der Churf. Fürsten u. Stände d. A.C. verwandt, 1579.

Augsburg Confession [*continued*].
see WÜRTTEMBERG. Acta &c. theolog. Wirtemb. & patriarchæ Hieremiæ, 1576–81, de A.C., 1584.
„ ZÖCKLER (O.) Die A. Conf. &c. hist. untersucht v. O. Z., 1870.

Augur, *ps.*, *see* POLIAKOFF (V.)

August Wilhelm, *prince of Prussia ; 1722–58, see* FREDERICK II, *king of Prussia.* Briefwechsel mit s. Bruder, A. W., 1927.

Augusta, *empress of Germany, see* TSCHUDI (C.) A., Tysk Keiserinde, 1912.

Augustana Confessio, *see* AUGSBURG CONFESSION.

Augusti (Johann Christian Wilhelm).
Hist. ecclesiast. epitome. 8°. Lipsiæ. 1834
see THEOLOG. MONATSCHRIFT ; hrsg. A., 1801, 1802.

Augustine *Saint, abp. of Canterbury.*
see COLLINS (W. E.) Begin. of Eng. Xty. : St. A., 1898.
„ GASQUET (F. A.) Mission of St A. &c., 1924.
„ HOWORTH (*Sir* H. H.) St. A. of C., 1913.

Augustine, *Saint, bp. of Hippo.* [AURELIUS AUGUSTINUS].
Operum tomus septimus recog. & emend. s4°. Venetiis. 1570
Operum t1[-10]. 11t. fol. Parisiis 1679-1700
Each vol., except 4 & 11, has an Appendix *w. sep. pagin. t1 & 2 ; 6 & 7, & 8 & 9 are b. together. t3 has 2p. v11 is not numbered & cont.* Vita Augustini *&* Index gen. *to the 10v. & App*[s].
Opera. Rec. P. Knöll. [Corpus Script. Eccles. Lat., 63]. sect. 1, pars 3. 8°. Vindobonæ. 1922
Ad Optatum episc. Milevit. de natura &c. animæ &c. [*b. w.* Op., t11, 1700.] fol. Viennæ. 1733
[Ad virgines de sobrietate & ebrietate—De quatuor virtutibus caritatis—De contritione cordis. *Begins* Augustinus ad virgines de sobrietate & ebrietate incipit felicit. *Ends* Finitus est liber seu tractatus beati Augustini episc. ypon. de cōtricōne cordis cū ceteris tractatulis eiusdem &c.] s4°. *n.p.* [Lauingen ? 1472]
[*29 leaves, without regist. or pagin. ; 24 lines to a full page. Part of a larger collect.* (*76 leaves*) *cont. in add. to the above* : De anima & spiritu. De ebrietate. De vanitatibus seculi ; De vita christiana.]
Ain andechtiger &c. Tractat von üppigkait der welt ; neülich auss Latein in Teütsch gebracht [durch e. Doctor zu Augspurg]. s4°. Augspurg. [*Silvanus Otmar*]. 1519
De catechizandis rudibus liber. [Text], tr., intr. & comm. Dissert. by J. P. Christopher. 8°. Wash. 1926
De ciuitate dei [*Begins fol. 17*[a]. Aurelii Augustini ēpi de ciuitate dei liber primus feliciter incipit. *Ends fol. 302b.* A.A. opus de ciuitate dei feliciter explicit : confectuꝫ uenetijs ab egregio & diligēti magistro Nicolao ienson Petro mozenicho principe : Anno a natiuitate domini milesimo quadringētesimo septuagesimo quinto : sexto nonas octobres]. sfol. [Venetiis. *N. Jenson.* 1475]
302 ff. f1 blank ; ff 2[a]*–15*[b] *rubrica ; f16 blank ; without tp., signatures, catchwords or pagin. ; double columns, 46 lines each ; fol. 17*[a] *illuminated.*
De civitate Dei contra paganos libri xxii. Ed., w. intr. & app[s]. by J. E. C. Welldon. 2v. 8°. 1924
De spiritu et littera—De periculis contingentibus circa sacramentum eucharistiæ—De suffragiis missæ. s4°. *n.p.* [Cologne : *printer of Dictys*]. *n.d.* [15 cent.]
40 leaves, the first, a blank, is wanting. Beg. on fol. 2[a]. Incipit prologus beati augustini episcopi de spiritu et littera. *Ends on fol. 40b.* Explicit. de suffragiis misse.
De vita christiana. s4°. *n.p.* [Speier, *Printer of Postilla scolastica super Apocalypsin*]. *n.d.* [15 cent.]
Manuale beati Augustini [*ascr.*] de aspiratiōe hōis ad deū. Stimulus amoris b. Anselmi. Soliloquium jubileū b. Anselmi Anselmus super resolutione pusillanimis cōscientie dubitātis an missam celebrare expediat aut nō. Bonaventura de ꝑparatione ad missam. s8°. [*Colonie per Martinū de Werdena.* 1506]
Meditationes Divi Augustini Episc. Hipponensis. [Soliloquia—Encheridion *& o. opuscula. Foll*[d]. *by* Meditationes S. Bernardi *& o. opuscula. 8 leaves prelim. matter : ff. 1, 2,* Masellus Beneventanus Rev. p. D. Hieronymo podio, *f. 3,* Liber ad lectorem *& summary of vol.* In hoc divino volumine &c. *ff. 3b–8a,* Tabula. *f. 9a,* Medit. Augustini. *f. 119b & 120a & b blank. f. 121,* S. Bernardi Meditationes &c. *ending on f. 184b ; f. 185,* Registrum]. s4°. *n.p.* [1475 ?]
185 leaves, without tp., pagin., or signatures. 30 lines to a full page.
Regule, *see* JOANNES FRANCISCUS *Brixianus.* Habes isto vol. 4 regulas &c., 1510.
[Sermones duo de resurrectione futura mortuorum]. [*b. w. h.* De spiritu et littera &c., *n.d.*] s4°. *n.p.* [*Cologne : printer of Dictys*]. *n.d.* [15 cent.]
32 leaves. Beg. on fol. 1[a]. Incipit sermo btī Augustini epī de resurrectione futura mortuorum. *Ends on fol. 32a* : Explicit sermo scd's btī Augustini epī de resur. mortuorum.
Soliloquia. s8°. Viennæ Austriæ. 1642
TRANSLATIONS.
The city of God. Tr. by J. H[ealey], 1610. v1. 8°. [1890]
City of God. [Abr. & tr., w. pref.] by F. R. M. Hitchcock. [Tr. of Xtn. lit., s2.] s8°. 1922

Augustine [*continued*].
TRANSLATIONS [*continued*].
[Confessions.] The Kernell, or Extr. f. hist. p. of Conf. s8°. Paris. 1638
Confessions. Tr., & w. notes, by W. Wats, D.D. s8°. 1650
Confessions—Méditations; tr., *see* BUCHON (J. A. C.) Choix d'ouvr. myst., 1840.
Confessions. Tr. E. B. Pusey. [Everyman's Lib.] s8°. [1907]
Confessions. Tr. w. notes & intr. by C. Bigg. 11th ed. s8°. [1923]
Confessions. Texte établi & tr. par P. de Labriolle. [Coll. des univs. de France.] 2t. 8°. 1925–26
The Enchiridion. s8°. [1887]
[Soliloquies]. Alfred d. Gr. Bearb. d. S.; hrsg. v. W. Endter, *see* BIBL. D. ANGELSÄCHS. PROSA, B11, 1922.
Soliloques. Tr. P. de Labriolle. Intr. de B. Groethuysen. [Ecrits intimes]. 8°. 1927
see ALFARIC (P.) L'évol. intell. de St. A., t1, 1918.
„ BARRY (M. I.) St. A., the orator: rhetor. qualities of A.'s Sermones ad populum, 1924.
„ BATIFFOL (P.) Catholicisme de St. A., 2e éd., 2t, 1920.
„ BERTI (G. L.) Augustinianum systema de gratia, vindicatum &c., 1747.
„ BERTRAND (L. M. E.) Autour de St. A., 1921.
„ BOYER (C.) Christianisme & Néo-platonisme dans la formation de St. A., 1920.
„ BRIAS (C. DE). Thomistarum triumphus, i.e. Augustini & Thomæ concordia, t1, 2, 1672–73.
„ BUTLER (E. C.) Western mysticism: teaching of A. &c. on contemplation &c., 1922; 2nd ed., 1927.
„ DANEAU (L.) Paratitla in D. Aurelii Augustini tomos duos præcipuos, nimirum 6 & 7, 1578.
„ DONATUS (L.) Oratio pro glorios. doct. eccles. A. solennitate, c. 1482.
„ FIGGIS (J. N.) Polit. aspects of S. A.'s "City of God," 1921
„ FRONTEAU (J.) Antithesis A. & Calvini, 1651.
„ HARDY (G.) Le "De civitate Dei" source princ. du "Disc. sur l'hist. univ.", 1913.
„ HOLL (C.) A.'s innere Entwicklung, 1923.
„ MONCEAUX (P.) Hist. litt. de l'Afr. chrét., t7, St. A. & le Donatisme, 1923.
„ MONTGOMERY (W.) St. A.: aspects of h. life & thought, 1924.
„ NORIS (E.) Hist. Pelagiana &c. add. Vindiciis A., 1673.
„ OTTLEY (R. L.) St. in the Confessions of St. A., 1919.
„ POSSIDIUS, *St.* S. A. A. Hipp. episc. vita, 1764.
„ SCHUBERT (A.) A.'s Lex-æterna-Lehre, 1924.
„ STANISLAUS *a Placentia*. A. & Scoti de gratia Xti consensus, 2v, 1768.
„ SUTCLIFFE (M.) The unmasking of a masse-monger; or, the vindic. of St. A.'s Confessions, 1626.

Augustinian [AUGUSTINIANI]. Chapters of the A. canons, 1922, *see* SALTER (H. E.) *ed.*
Synodi Augustinianorum de libertate monachorum sententia. [*2 leaves without pagin. or sign. Decor. border to tp.*] [P2539]. s4°. Wittemberg. [1522]

Augustin-Thierry (A.), *see* THIERRY (A. A)

Augustinus [KASENBORT] *Moravus.* [*A. Olomucensis*]. Epistole cōtra perfidiam Valdensium, ejusdem bine littere de heresi Vald., *see* WALDENSES. In hoc vol. haec cont. &c., 1512.

Augustus II, *duke of Brunswick-Luneburg, see* HILDEBRAND (J.) Augusta Caes. Octav. Augusti & Augusti ducis B. & L., 1662.

Augustus II, *king of Poland, der Starke* [FREDERICK AUGUSTUS I, *elector of Saxony, 1670–1733*], *see* GURLITT (C.) August d. Starke, 2B, 1924.
see †HALLENDORF (C.) Konung A. politik åren 1700–1, 1898.
„ KIRCHHOFF (A.) Die Anfänge kirchl. Toleranz in Sachsen; A. der Starke u. die Reformierten, 1872.
„ †POLLNITZ (C. L., *Frhr.* v.) *Des galanten Sachsens T2, 1735.

Augustus Albert Francis Xavier Benedict, *prince of Saxony, see* SAXONY (F. A. X., *pr. of*).

Augustus (Caius Julius Cæsar Octavianus), *emperor of Rome.*
Monumentum Ancyranum. Ed. E. G. Hardy. s8°. O. 1923
Monumentum Antiochenum. Die neugefund. Aufzeichnung d. Res gestæ. Hrsg. u. erläut. v. W. M. Ramsay u. A. v. Premerstein. [Klio, Beiheft 19]. 8°. L. 1927
Res gestæ divi A.; w. Eng. tr. by F. W. Shipley. [Loeb Class. Lib.], *see* VELLIUS PATERCULUS (C.) Comp., 1924.
see CORDINGLEY (R. A.) & I. A. RICHMOND. The Mausoleum of A., 1927.
„ DESSAU (H.) Gesch. d. röm. Kaiserzeit, B1, 1924.
„ HILDEBRAND (J.) Augusta Cæsaris Octav. Augusti &c., 1662.
see HOLMES (T. R. E.) The architect of the Rom. Emp., 1928.
„ KORNEMANN (E.) Mausoleum u. Tatenbericht A., 1921.
„ MOMMSEN (T.) Comment. ludorum sæc. quint., imp. A., 1890.
„ PLEW (J.) Quellenuntersuchungen z. Gesch. d. Kaisers Hadrian, nebst Anhange ü. d. Mon. Ancyr., 1890.
„ †SANDYS (*Sir* J. E.) Latin epigraphy (app., Mon. Ancyr.), 1919.

Aukerian (Haroutiun), *see* AUCHER (PASCHAL).

Aulard (François V. Alphonse).
Études & leçons sur la Révol. franç. s8. 8°. 1921
„ „ ......s9. 8°. 1924
Hist. polit. de la Révol. franç. 5e éd., 2e tir. 8° 1921
Paris sous le premier Empire. [Coll. de doc. rel. à l'hist. de Paris]. 3t. la8°. 1912–23
Le patriotisme français, de la Renaissance à la Révolution. s8°. 1921

Auld (*Lt.-Col.* **Samuel James Mason) & D. R. Edwardes-Ker.** Pract. agricult. chemistry. 2nd ed. 8°. 1921

Aulnoy (*Mme.* **d'**) *d. 1705* [*Countess* D'ANOIS &c.] Memoirs of the Court of Eng. In 2 parts. Now made English, to wh. is added The Lady's pacquet of letters. s8°. 1707
„ „ ......Tr. Mrs. W. H. Arthur. Ed. & rev. w. notes by G. D. Gilbert. [Broadway Trans.] [2nd impr.] 8°. [1927]
Rel. du voyage d'Esp. [1679–80]; publ. R. Foulché-Delbosc, *see* REVUE HISPAN., t67, 1926.
„ FOULCHÉ-DELBOSC (R.) Mme. d'A. & l'Espagne, 1926.

Ault (Norman). Elizabethan lyrics. Chosen by N. A. 8°. 1925
Life in anc. Britain. Social & econ. develop. to Roman Conquest. s8°. 1920
17th cent. lyrics f. orig. texts. 8°. 1928

Ault (Warren Ortman).
Priv. jurisdiction in Eng. 8°. New Haven, *Yale.* 1923

Aumale (Henri, *duc* **d'),** *1822–97* [†HENRY EUGENE PHILIP LOUIS [*d'Orleans*], *duc* D'AUMALE]. Hist. of the princes de Condé in the 16th & 17th cs. Tr. R. B. Borthwick. 2v. 8°. 1872
see VALLERY-RADOT (R.) Le duc d'A., d'ap. sa corr. avec Cuvillier-Fleury, t1, 1840–71, 1922.

Aumonier (Stacy).
The baby grand & o. s. s8°. 1926
Heartbeat. s8°. [1922]
Miss Bracegirdle & others. s8° [1923]
One after another. s8°. [1920]
Overheard: 15 tales. s8°. [1924]
The Querrils. s8°. [1919]

Aumont (J. M. Tourneur-), *see* TOURNEUR-AUMONT (J. M.)

Aungervyle Society. Reprints. [*Each w. sep. tp. & pagin.*] 2s. 8°. *p.p.* E. 1881–4
Garland (A) of old hist. ballads, 1600–1762, 1881. [1.]
Goldsmid (E.) Chron. table of dram. wks. perf. in France, p1, 1200–1599, 1883. [2.]
Hamilton (*Lady* A.) Key to "Epics of the T'on"; [*by* J. D. Barnett], 1883. [2.]
Hentzner (P.) Journey into England, 1598; ed. H. Walpole (1797), 1881. [1.]
Heywood (T.) A marriage triumphe (1613), 1884. [2.]
Jones (*Sir* W.) Indian game of chess, & Burmha game of chess &c. by H. Cox, 1883. [2.]
Jourdan (S.) Disc. of the Barmudas &c. (1610), 1884. [2.]
Ludlow (E.) Imprisonment &c. of Charles I &c., 1882. [1.]
Lupton (D.) London & the countrey carbonadoed (1632), 1883. [2.]
Marvell (A.) *Flagellum parliament., 1661–78, 1881. [1.]
Octavian, *emp.* Romance of O., abr. by J. J. Conybeare (1809); ed. &c. E. M. Goldsmid, 1882. [1.]
Ossian. Fragms. of anc. poetry coll. in Highlands &c. (1760), 1881. [1.]
Parliament. Mystery of the good old cause &c. (1660), 1883. [2.]
Percy (T.), *bp.* The hermit of Warkworth (1771), 1883. [2.]
[Political]. 2 polit. squibs, 1660–90, 1883. [2.]
[Russian]. R. invasion of Poland, 1563; tr., 1884. [2.]
Secundus (J.) Kisses: fragms. &c. on the kiss (1803), 1884. [2.]
Shelley (P. B.) Addr. to people on death of Pr. Charlotte (1817), 1883. [2.]
[Tories.] *Proper lessons for the T. (1716), 1883. [2.]
Urban VIII, *pope.* *Passionate remonstrance &c. (1641), 1884. [2.]

Aurangzib, *see* SARKAR (J.) Hist. of A., v4, 5, 1919–24.

Aurbach (Christian Wilhelm). Diss. de eloquentia inepta T. Munzeri. [P484]. s4°. Vitembergæ. 1716

Aurea. *Biblia aurea, 1475; 1495, *see* RAMPEGOLLIS (A. DE).

Aurel, *ps.* [*i.e. Mme.* ALFRED MORTIER]. Le précis de l'ardeur, *see* ŒUVRES libres, 31, 1924.

Aureli (Aurelio). La gloria d'amore, spettacolo festivo fatto rappres. dal Duca di Parma sopra l'acque. Per sponsali del Princ. Odoardo con pessa Dorotea Sofia di Neoburgo. Poesia d'A. A. [*w. la. folded plates*]. s4°. Parma. 1690

Aurelia, *ps., see* MACE (A. G.)

Aurelius Antoninus (Marcus), *called the Philosopher, emperor of Rome.*
Ad se ipsum. Rec. &c. I. H. Leopold. s8°. O. [1908]
De rebus suis libri 12. [*Gr. & Lat.*] Comm. &c. illust. Studio T. Gataker. s4°. Cantab. 1652

Aurelius Antoninus [*continued*].

TRANSLATIONS.

Meditations. Tr. J. Collier, *see* TERTULLIAN. Apology; tr., 1889.

Meditations. Tr., w. notes by M. Casaubon, 2nd ed., 1635. [Ed. W. H. D. Rouse. Temple Classics]. [2nd ed.] s8º. 1905

Pensées. Tr. de Joly. s8º. 1803

TRANSLATIONS [*continued*].

Pensées. Texte établi & tr. par A. I. Trannoy. Préf. d'A. Puech. [Coll. des univs. de France]. 8º. 1925

Thoughts. Tr. G. Long. rev. ed. s8º. 1886

„ „ s8º. *Bohn.* 1901

see SEDGWICK (H. D.) M. A., 1921.

Aurelius Augustinus, *see* AUGUSTINE, *Saint.*

Auriac (Jules Eugène d'). La véritable Jeanne d'Arc. 8º. 1920

Aurificus (Nicolaus), *see* BUONFIGLI (*le père* NICCOLÓ AURIFICO).

Aurigemma (Salvatore). Iscr. con dedica alla Domina Caelestis in Sabrata—Notizie archeolog. s. Tripolitania, *see* ITALY: MIN. D. COLONIE. Not. arch., Anno 1, 1915.

Aurigny (Gilles d') [DAVRIGNY; *ps. le Pamphile*]. Trente Psalmes du royal prophete David; tr. de Latin en rithme fr. par G. Davrigny. [*b. w.* Marot (C.) Pseaulmes, 1548]. s8º. Lyon. 1549

Auriol (Charles), *see* CAMPREDON (*Gén.* J. D. M. DE), *ed.* Docs. milit.: défense du Var &c., 1889.

Aurivillius (Carl). Diss. ad sacras literas & philol. orientalem pertin. Cum præf. J. D. Michaelis. 8º. Goettingæ. 1790

Aurner (Nellie Slayton).

Caxton, mirrour of 15th-cent. letters. 8º. 1926

Hengest: early Eng. hero legend. 8º. Iowa. 1918

Aurobindo (Ghose), *see* CHATTERJEE (B. C.) Gandhi or Aurobindo?, 1921.

Aurogallus (Matthaeus). De Hebræis urbium, locorum &c. nominibus. [*b. w.* Bible: Psalms. Psalterium Hebr., 1533]. s8º. Wittenbergæ. [1526]

Ausbildungsvorschrift f. d. Nachrichtentruppe. H1–4 [*in* 1v.] 8º. 1924–5

Auserlesene. *Auserlesene Lebensbeschr. heiliger Seelen &c., 1733–43, *see* TERSTEEGEN (G.)

Auserlesene theolog. Bibl., 1780–92, *see* DÖDERLEIN (J. C.)

Ausonius (Decimus Magnus). Omnia opera nuper maxima diligentia recognita atque excusa. s8º. [Florentiæ, *sumptu Philippi Juntae.*] 1517

Works. With Eng. tr. by H. G. E. White. [Loeb Class. Lib.] v2. s8º. 1921

Aussaresses (François) & H. Gauthier-Villars. La vie privée d'un prince allemand au 17e s. L'électeur palat. Charles-Louis (1617–80). s8º. [1926]

***Aussführlicher** u. gründtl. Bericht: Was sich bey vergangner Belager &c. d. Statt Magdeburg verloffen, 1631, *see* MAGDEBURG.

Austen (*Major* Ernest Edward), *see* BRIT. MUSEUM OF NAT. HIST.: ZOOLOGY. The house-fly; by E. E. A., 1920.

Austen (Jane).

[Novels. St. Martin's libv.] 10v. s8º. 1908–1910

1, 2, Pride & prejudice. 3, 4, Sense & sensibility. 5, Northanger Abbey. 6, Persuasion. 7, 8, Emma. 9, 10, Mansfield Park.

Novels. Text based on collation of early eds. by R. W. Chapman, w. notes &c. 5v. 8º. O. 1923

„ „ 2nd ed. 5v. 8º. O. 1926

1, Sense & sensibility; 2, Pride & prejudice; 3, Mansfield Park [*& Lovers' vows*]; 4, Emma; 5, Northanger Abbey—Persuasion.

*Emma. 3v. s8º. 1816

„ n. ed. s8º. 1870

„ Intr. by A. Dobson. [repr.] s8º. 1898

Lady Susan. Repr. f. the MS. s8º. O. 1925

Love & friendship, & o. early works. Pref. by G. K. Chesterton. s8º. 1922

Mansfield Park. n. ed. s8º. 1870

*Northanger Abbey: & Persuasion 4v. s8º. 1818

„ „ n. ed. s8º. 1870

Northanger Abbey & Persuasion. Intr. by A. Dobson. [repr.] s8º. 1921

Persuasion. 2 chapters pr. f. J. A.'s autograph. s8º. O. 1926

[Sanditon]. Fragm. of a novel, wr. Jan.–March 1817. s8º. O. 1925

Sense & sensibility. n. ed. s8º. 1870

The Watsons. Intr. by A. B. Walkley. s8º. 1923

„ „ A fragm. by J. A., concluded by L. Oulton. s8º. [1923]

„ „ A fragm. s8º. O. 1927

see AUSTEN-LEIGH (J. E.) Mem. of J. A., 1926.

„ AUSTEN-LEIGH (M. A.) Personal aspects of J. A., 1920.

„ *MARY HAMILTON; by a niece of the late Miss A., 1927.

„ SPURGEON (C. F. E.) J. A., 1927.

„ VILLARD (L.) Jane Austen; tr. V. Lucas, w. a new study of J. A. by R. B. Johnson, 1924.

Austen (Wilfrid Abernethy Evers). Fabric & finance: structure & endowments of the Ch. of Eng. &c. s8º. 1922

The structure & endowments of the Church of Eng. [P2503]. s8º. 1921

Austen-Leigh (James Edward). Mem. of Jane Austen. [Repr. of 2nd ed., 1871]. Intr., notes &c. by R. W. Chapman. s8º. O. 1926

Austen-Leigh (Mary Augusta).

Personal aspects of Jane Austen. 8º. 1920

Austen-Leigh (Richard Arthur), *see* LEIGH (R. A. A.-).

Austin (Alfred), *poet laureate.*

Russia before Europe. 8º. 1876

Austin (Bertram) & W. F. Lloyd. The secret of high wages. Foreword by W. T. Layton. 8º. [1926]

Austin (Elaine), *see* SHAW (*Sir* W. N.) Man. of meteorology; by S. w. assist. of E. A., v1, 2, 1926–28.

Austin (H. Evans). Law rel. to laundries, institutions under Factory &c. Act, 1901 & 1907, w. intr., notes &c. 8º. 1907

Austin (Herbert Henry), *ed.*, *see* AUSTIN (*Maj.* T.) "Old stick-leg": extr. f. diaries, 1926.

Austin (James Curtiss). The significant name in Terence. [Univ. of Illinois. Sts. in lang. &c., v7iv]. 8º. Urbana. 1922

Austin (John), *Roman Catholic writer* [*ps.* WILLIAM BIRCHLEY].

*The Christian moderator, or persecution for religion condemned. 4th ed. s8º. 1652

*Devotions. First part: in the ant. way of offices; w. psalms &c. 4th ed. corr. s8º. Roan. 1685

„ ....Reformed by a person of quality [S. Hopton] & publ. by G. Hickes. 4th ed. s8º. 1712

Austin (John Osborne). The ancestral dict. [*descendants of L. Latham*]. Ed. J. O. A. 8º. Central Falls. [1891]

Austin (Moses) & S. F. Austin. Austin papers [1789–1827: materials coll. by M. & S. F. A.]; ed. E. C. Barker, 2v, *see* AMERICAN HIST. ASSOC. Ann. rep., 1919, v2, 1924.

Austin (Richard). Social decay & regeneration. Intr. by H. Ellis. 8º. 1921

Austin (Robert S.), *see* HARRISON (A. M.) & R. S. A. Some Tuscan cities, 1924.

see —— & ——. Some Umbrian cities, 1925.

Austin (Stephen F.), *see* AUSTIN (M.) & S. F. A. A. papers, 1789–1827, 2v, 1924.

Austin (*Maj.* Thomas). "Old stick-leg." Extr. f. diaries of Maj. T. A. Arr. by Brig.-Gen. H. H. Austin. 8º. [1926]

Austin (William), *of Lincoln's Inn.* Devotionis Augustinianæ flamma, or, certaine devout, &c. meditations. Set forth by Anne Austin. 2nd ed. [*w. add. engr. tp.*] sfol. 1637

Australasia. Picturesque atlas of A., 3v, 1886, *see* GARRAN (*Hon.* A.)

Australasian Association for the Advancement of Science.

Reports of 1st [–7th] meeting[s], 1888–98. Ed. A. Liversidge &c. [7v.] 8º. Sydney. [1889–98]

Australia.

*Australia in Palestine, 1919, *see* GULLETT (H. S.) & C. BARRETT, *edd.*

A. pilot, 5v, suppls. 4, 5, *&* Not. to mariners rel. to A. p., v5, 1914–22, *see* ADMIRALTY.

Hist. records of A. s1, v12–19, 21–26; s3, v1–5; s4, sect. A, v1. 8º. 1919–25

s1, Governors' despatches to & f. Eng., v12–19, 21–26, 1825–48.

s3, Despatches &c. rel. to settlement of the states. v1, Port Phillip, Victoria, 1803–4—Tasmania, 1803–12. v2–4, Tasmania, 1812–25. v5, Tasmania, 1825–27, Northern territory, 1823–27, Western port, Victoria, 1826–27.

s4, Legal papers. Sect. A, v1, 1786–1827.

Official directory & almanac of Australia, 1883. 8º. Sydney. 1883

Poetry in Australia, 1923, *see* LINDSAY (N.)

COMMONWEALTH OF A.

Bureau of Census & Statistics.

Commonwealth demography, 1919, 1920 & prev. yrs. Prep. by G. H. Knibbs. fol. Melbourne [1920–21]

COMMONWEALTH OF A. [*contd.*].

Finance. Summary of f. statistics, 1911/12–1920/21. fol. Melbourne. [1922]

Offic. hist. of Australia in the War, v1, 2, 7, 8, 12. 8º. Sydney. 1921–24

see BEAN (C. E. W.) Story of Anzac, 1914–15, 2v, 1921–24. [1, 2.]

„ —— & H. S. GULLETT. Photographic record of the War, 1923. [12.]

„ CUTLACK (F. M.) A. Flying Corps in the War, 1914–18, 1923. [8.]

„ GULLETT (H. S.) A. Imp. Force in Sinai &c., 1914–18, 1923. [7.]

Official year book of the C. of A., 1920–23. Nos. 13–16. Prep. by G. H. Knibbs &c. [Bureau of Census & Statistics]. 8º. Melbourne. [1920–23]

Parliamentary Debates, 1920–26 (26th Feb. 1920–13th Aug. 1926). la8º. [Melbourne]. 1920–26

„ Index 1920/21–1926. [6v]. la8º. [Melbourne]. 1922–26

Australian. Illust. A. encyclopaedia. Ed. A. W. Jose & H. J. Carter. 2v. la8°. Sydney. 1925–26

Australian Museum, *Sydney, see* NORTH (A. J.) Descr. cat. of nests & eggs of birds in Australia &c., 1889.

Austria [AUSTRIA-HUNGARY: AUSTRIAN].
Austria-Hungary's effort to exterminate h. Jugoslav subjects. Speeches &c. [P2584]. s8°. 1917
Austrian Red Book. Offic. files pert. to pre-war hist. [Tr.], pl, 28 June to 23 July 1914. 8°. [1920]
Austria's Peace offer 1916–17; ed. G. de Manteyer, 1921, *see* MANTEYER (G. DE).
The Emperor's manifesto, 1701, *see* LEOPOLD I.
Secret treaties of A.-Hungary, 1879–1914, v1, 2, 1920–21, *see* PRIBRAM (A. F.)

Austria (Caterina, *Infanta of*), *see* CATHERINE [*of Spain*], *consort of Charles Emanuel I, d. of Savoy.*

***Austriaca** Austeritas, &c. 1671, *see* TÖKÖLY (I.) *count.*

Auswahl. Auswahl hist. Stücke aus hebrä. Schriftstellern. Mit Texte, Übers. u. Anm. 8°. 1840

Auswärtiges Amt. Die diplomat. Akten d. A. A., 1871–1914, T1–5i, 1923–26, *see* SCHWERTFEGER (B.)
Die grosse Politik d. europ. Kabinette, 1871–1914, 1922–26, *see* GROSSE.

Autenrieth (Johann Heinrich Friedrich v.) Ansichten ü. Natur-u. Seelenleben. Hrsg. v. H. F. Autenrieth. 8°. St. 1836
Ueb. d. Menschen u. s. Hoffnung e. Fortdauer. 8°. Tübingen. 1825

Autenrieth (Otto).
Die 3 kommenden Kriege. Eine milit.-polit. Prophezeiung. 5e A. [P2407]. 8°. Naumburg. [1919]
„ „ ....[*a. ed.*] s8°. Naumburg a. S. 1921

***Auteur (L')** du système, 1825, *see* LA GERVAISAIS (*marq.* DE).

Authentic [AUTHENTICK].
*Authentic (An) acc. of the late exped. to Bretagne, 1747, *see* LESTOCK (*adm.* R.)
*Authentic detail of particulars rel. to the late Duchess of Kingston 1788, *see* KINGSTON (*duchess of*).
*Authentic mem[s]. of the Portuguese Inquisition, 1761, *see* PORTUGUESE.
*Authentic report of the discuss., Rome 1872, &c., conc. the coming of St. Peter to Rome; tr. W. Arthur, 1872, *see* RESOCONTO.
*Authentick copy of last will & test. of R******, E——l of O*****, 1745, *see* WALPOLE (*Sir* R.)

Author (The). Organ of the Soc. of Authors (Incorporated). v30–37. 4°. 1920–27

***Authorship.** A guide to literary technique. By a well-known author. s8°. [1922]

Autié (Léonard), *see* BORD (G.) La fin de 2 légendes; L'affaire Léonard &c., 1909.

Autin (Albert). L'anathème. 4e éd. s8°. [1921]

Auto. *Relacion del auto partic. de fé de la Inquisit. de Sevilla, 1723, 1723, *see* SEVILLA.

Autograph prices current. Compiled & ed. by A. J. Herbert. v5, 6, Aug. 1919–July 1922. 8°. [1919–22]

Autographen. Album v. A. d. westphäl. Friedensschlusses (1648), 1849, *see* WESTPHÄLISCH.

Automathes, *see* KIRKBY (J.) *Capacity & extent of the human understanding exempl. in case of A., 1745.

Autos portugueses de G. Vicente y de la escuela Vicentina, 1922, *see* VICENTE (G.)

Autos de fé. Relacion de los a. de fé, Valladolid, Cordova y Zaragoza, 1723, *see* VALLADOLID.

Autran (Charles). Phéniciens. Contrib. à l'hist. ant. de la Méditerranée. 4°. 1920
Sumérien & Indo-Européen: l'aspect morpholog. de la question. 4°. 1925

Auvergne. Coutumes de la prov. d'A., 4t, 1784–6, *see* DU MOULIN (C.) *ed.*

Auvergne-Lauraguais (*le card.* **Hugues Robert Jean Charles de La Tour d'),** *see* LA TOUR D'AUVERGNE-LAURAGUAIS.

Auvray (Louis), *see* BELLIER DE LA CHAVIGNERIE (E.) Dict. gén. des artistes de l'école franç.; continué par L. A., 2t, Suppl. *&* Table topog., 1882–7.

Auxiliary Hospitals, 1916, *see* BRITISH RED CROSS &c.

Avadānas, *see* MÜLLER (F. W. K.) Uigurica, 3, Uigur. A.-Bruchstücke (1–8), 1922.
see PRZYLUSKI (J.) Légende de l'emp. Açoka (A.-Avadāna) dans les textes ind. & chin., 1923.

A-Valle (Carlo) [†VALLE (CARLO A)]. Elogio di Paolo Sarpi. [P2841]. 8°. Alessandria. 1867
see LESSONA (M.) & C. A. Diz. univ. di scienze, lettere ed arti, 1875.

Avebury (John Lubbock, *1st baron*).
Ants, bees & wasps. 10th ed. s8°. 1890
Fifty years of science. Address, Brit. Assoc., 1881. 5th ed. s8°. 1890
The life-work of Ld. A, 1834–1913. Essays by Sir B. Mallet, Sir A. Keith &c. Ed Hon. Mrs. A. Grant Duff. s8°. 1924
On Brit. wild flowers in rel. to insects. s8°. 1882

Aved (Jacques André Joseph), *see* WILDENSTEIN (G.) Le peintre A. sa vie & son œuvre, 2v, 1922.

Avedichian (Gabriel) [AVETIQEAN].
[Armenian grammar, *in Armenian*]. 8°. i Venetik. 1815
—— **Kh. Siurmelean & J. B. Aucher.** [New dict. of Armenian. *In Armenian*]. 2v. 4°. i Venetik. *San Lazar.* 1836–37

Aveline (William Talbot), *F.G.S.* Geol. of parts of Notts. & Derbyshire. [Mem. of G. Survey]. 2nd ed. 8°. 1879
Geol. of parts of Notts., Yorks. & Derbyshire. [Mem. of G. Survey]. 2nd ed. 8°. 1880
Geol. of the country around Nottingham. [Mem. of G. Survey]. 2nd ed. 8°. 1880
see RAMSAY (*Sir* A. C.), W. T. A. & E. HULL. Geol. of parts of Wilts. &c., 1858.
—— **& T. McK. Hughes.** Geology of country around Kendal &c. [Mem. of G. Survey]. 2nd ed. 8°. 1898

Aveling (Francis). Directing mental energy. 8°. 1927

Avenarius (Ferdinand). Gedichte. s8° München. 1923
Max Klinger als Poet. Mit e. Briefe Klingers u. e. Beitr. v. H. W. Singer. Kriegsausgabe. la8°. München. [1917]
Die Weltkarikatur in d. Völkerverhetzung. 3e A. v. "Bild als Narr." 8°. München. 1921

Avenarius (Joannes), *see* HABERMANN (J.)

Avenarius (Richard). Philosophie als Denken d. Welt. [*b. w.* Payot (J.) L'éduc. de la volonté, 1895]. 8°. L. 1876

Avencebrol [IBN GEBIROL; SALOMO BEN JEHUDA IBN GEBIROL; AVICEBRON &c.] Sel. relig. poems. Tr. into Eng. verse by I. Zangwill f. crit. text ed. I. Davidson. [*with text.* Jew. Publ. Soc. of Amer.] s8°. Phila. 1923

Avenel (*vte.* **Georges d').** Les revenus d'un intellectuel de 1200 à 1913. s8°. [1922]

Aventinus (Joannes). Chron. Schir., *see* CONRADUS, *Schir.*, Chron. Schir., 1716.

Aventures. *Aventures, Les, de Pomponius, 1724, *see* LABADIE (—).

Averdunk (Heinrich) & J. Müller-Reinhard. G. Mercator u. d. Geographen unter s. Nachkommen, 1914, *see* PETERMANNS MITT. Ergnzb., 39, 1915.
—— **& W. Ring.** Gesch. d. Stadt Duisburg. 8°. Essen. 1927

Avesnes, *ps.* [*i.e. le comte* LOUIS DE BLOIS].
L'île heureuse. [7e éd.] s8°. [1920]

Aveteantz (Stephannos Dschnthloumean). Sirakarkadsch. [Coll. of Arm., Pers. & Ind. songs. *In Armenian.* Ed. A. P2816]. s8°. i Kalkatha. 1830

Avetiqean (Gabriel), *see* AVEDICHIAN (G.)

Avezac (M. P. d') [AVEZAC-MACAYA (M. A. D'); *ps.* UN GÉOGRAPHE BIBLIOPHILE]. *Martin Hylacomylus Waltzemüller &c. Notes &c. par un géographe bibliophile [*i.e.* M. P. d'A. Extr. des Annales des Voyages, 1866]. 8°. 1867

Avicenna [ABUGALIUS FILIUS SINÆ &c.]
see CARRA DE VAUX (*bar.* B.) Avicenne, 1900.
„ MARGOLIOUTH (D. S.) Analecta orient. ad Poeticam Aristoteleam [Poetica A. &c.]; ed. D. M., 1887.
„ —— Avicenna, 1914.

Avienus (Rufus Festus). Ora maritima (Periplus Massil. sæc. VI. a. C.) Ed. A. Schulten. [Fontes Hisp. antiq., fasc. 1]. 8°. Barcinone. 1922

Avila (Diego de), *see* THOMAS, *a Jesu.*

Avila (Sanchez de), *see* DÁVILA (S.)

Avondo (Vittorio), *see* THOVEZ (E.) L'opera pittorica di V. A.: 28 tavole con intr., 1912.

Avraamki letopis. Лѣтописный сборникъ, имен. лѣт. Авраамки. [Полное соб. русс. лѣтоп. изд. Археогр. Ком., т16]. 4°. С.-П. 1889

Avvakum Petrovich, *protopop, 1621–81.* Житие А., им самим написанное, *see* VERSTI. Версты, N. 1, 1926.
Life of the Archpriest A. by himself. Tr. J. Harrison & H. Mirrlees. s8°. 1924

***Avviso** di Parnaso nel q. si racc. la pouertà &c., 1621, *see* VENETIA.

Awakener, The. v1 (Nov. 16, 1912–Nov. 29, 1913). fol. 1912–13

Awaloff-Bermondt (Pavel Mikhailovich), *see* BRAATZ (K. W. v.) Fürst A. P. Lieven im Kampfe gegen d. balt. Separatismus &c. u. d. A.-B. Affäre, 1926.

Awdeley (John), *see* VILES (E.) & F. J. FURNIVALL, *edd.* Rogues & vagabonds of Shakespeare's youth ; A.'s " Fraternitye of vacabondes " &c., 1907.
Awdlay (John), *chantry priest.* Alia cantalena de S. Maria. 8°. Long Crendon. 1926
Axelrod (Alexandre). L'œuvre économ. des Soviets. [Préf. d'E. Bernstein]. 8°. [1920]
Axon (William Edward Armitage).
Echoes of old Lancashire. 8°. 1899
Axtrez (Jean Marie Joseph Alfred Piales d'), *see* PIALES D'AXTREZ (J. M. J. A.)
Ayala (Balthazar). De jure et officiis bellicis et discip. militari libri 3. 2v. la8°. Wash. 1912
1, [Text] ; ed. J. Westlake. 2, The tr., by J. P. Bate.
Aydie (Odet d'), *seigneur de Lescun, comte de Comminges, see* JAURGAIN (J. DE). 2 Comtes de Comminges béarnais au 15e s. : O. d'A. &c., 1919.
Aye, *d'Avignon.* A. d'A., chanson de geste, *see* GUESSARD (F.) Anc. poëtes, t6, 1861.
Ayer (Edward E.) Cat. of the E. E. A. ornitholog. library ; by J. T. Zimmer, 2p, 1926, *see* FIELD COLUMBIAN MUSEUM. Zoolog. ser., v16, 1926.
Ayer (N. W.) & Sons, *publishers.* American newspaper annual. Cat. of Amer. newspapers, 1885, 1920. la8°. Phila. 1885–1920
Aygalliers (A. Wautier d'), *see* WAUTIER D'AYGALLIERS (A.)
Ayling (Stephen), *see* †STIRLING-MAXWELL (*Sir* W.), *ed.* *Examples of ornamental heraldry of 16th c. [photolithography by S. A.], 2s, 1867–8.
Aylmer, *The family of.* Pedigree of family of A. of Eng. & Irel. Compiled by J. E. F. Aylmer. With add. notes by F. A. A. 4°. 1909
Aylmer (James Evans Freke), *see* AYLMER, *family of.* Pedigree of family of A. ; compiled by J. E. F. A. &c., 1909.
Ayloffe (*Sir* Joseph), *bart.* An hist. descr. of an anc. painting at Cowdary in Sussex, seat of Visc. Montague. [P2699]. 4°. 1778
Aymard (Camille). Bolchevisme ou Fascisme ? . . . Français, il faut choisir. s8°. [1926]
Aymé (Marcel). Aller retour. 2e éd. s8°. [1927]
Aymon (Jean). Mon. de la relig. des Grecs et de la fausseté de plus. confessions de foi des Chrétiens orient. s4°. à La Haye. 1708
Tableau de la cour de Rome. s8°. La Haye. 1707
Aymonier (Etienne).
Hist. de l'ancien Cambodge. 8°. Strasbourg. [1921]
Aynard (Joseph). Les poëtes lyonnais, précurseurs de la Pléiade. Maurice Scève—Louise Labé—Pernette du Guillet. Intr. &c. de J. A. 8°. 1924
Ayrshire. *Ballads & songs of A. [s1]. 8°. Ayr. 1846

Ayrton (*Mrs.* Hertha), *wife of Prof. W. E. Ayrton, form. Marks, see* SHARP (E.) H. A., 1854–1923, 1926.
Ayrût (Lûtfi Yûssef), *see* ROBERTSON (F. E.) Arabic vocab. for Egypt : Arabic by L. Y. A., 1898.
Ayscough (*Mrs.* Florence). A Chinese mirror. la8°. [1925]
Fir-flower tablets. Poems tr. f. Chinese by F. A. Eng. versions by A. Lowell. 8°. 1922
Ayscough (John), *ps.* [*i.e. Mgr.* F. BICKERSTAFFE-DREW].

Abbotscourt.	s8°. 1919	Pages from the past.	8°. 1922
Faustula.	s8°. 1912	The story of Oscar.	s8°. [1925]
Mariquita.	s8°. 1922		

Aytoun (Wm. Edmondstoune) [*ps.* T. PERCY JONES]. The ballads of Scotland. Ed. A. 2nd ed. rev. 2v. s8°. E. 1859
Lays of the Scot. cavaliers & o. p. Intr. by H. Morley. s8°. 1891
The life & times of Richard I. s8°. 1840
Poems. [Oxf. ed.] s8°. O. 1921
Ayusawa (Iwao Frederick). Internat. labour legisl. [Columbia Univ. Stud., 91, ii]. 8°. N.Y. 1920
Ayvazovsqi (Gabriel). [On the pronunc. of *gh* & *l. In Armenian.* P2812]. 8°. Venetik. 1852
Ayyar (P. V. Jagadīsa), *see* JAGADĪSA AYYAR (P. V.)
Ayyar (S. N. Chandrasekhara), *see* CHANDRASEKHARA AYYAR (S. N.)
Ayyar (T. V. Ramakrishna), *see* RAMAKRISHNA AYYAR (T. V.)
Azarian (Stephen). Eccl. Armeniæ traditio de Romani pontificis primatu jurisdict. &c. 8°. Romæ. 1870
Azeglio (Massimo d'). M. d'Azeglio alla Guerra dell' Indipendenza nel '48. Doc. ined. [Note &c. di G. Sforza]. 8°. Modena. 1911
Vita italiana. Bozzetti. Intr. di M. Tabarrini. s8°. 1910
Azevedo (*Conde* de). Catálogo da livraria que pert. aos Condes de A. e de Samodæs. Red. por J. dos Santos. 2p. 4°. Porto. 1921–22
Azevedo (Francisco de), *see* WESSELS (C.) Early Jesuit travellers in C. Asia, 1603–1721 [app. A.'s acc. of journ. to Tibet (1631–32)], 1924.
Aziatskoe Muzei, *see* IMPERATORSKAYA AKAD. NAUK.
Aznar (Francisco). Indumentaria española : doc. (7c.–). Publ. F. A. 2a ed. fol. [1881]
Azores. *Hist of the A., 1813, *see* ASHE (*Capt.* T.)
Azorin, *ps., see* MARTINEZ RUIZ (J.)
Azzi (Carlo).
Vocab. domestico ferrarese-ital. 8°. Ferrara. 1857 [1867]
Azzurrinio (Bernardino). Chronica breviora aliaque mon. faventina [*includ.* Vite dei 4 santi protettori di Faenza] ; a B. A. coll. ; a cura di A. Messeri, v1, *see* MURATORI (L. A.) Rerum Ital. scr., t28iii, 1905–21.

B

B* (*le baron* de).** La dernière heure des Turcs &c. Tr. du B*** par M. L. de S., *see* SEVELINGES (C. L. DE).
B. (*Baronin*). Auctions-kat. e. Samml. v. Mobiliaren, Kupferstichen &c. aus d. BesitzeB., 1920, *see* KATALOG.
B. (*Mdlle.* de), *see* BEAUMONT (*Mdlle.* DE).
B. (A.) *Covent Garden drollery, 1672, 1928, *see* COVENT G.
B. (A.) *Gloria Britannica : acc. of the Royal Navy &c., 1696, *see* GLORIA.
B. (A.) The golden archer ; bk. of sonnets, 1920, *see* GOLDEN.
B. (A.), *writer on art.* A. John : [plates, w. descr. signed A. B.], 1923, *see* JOHN (A. E.)
P. Nash : [plates, w. descr. &c. signed A. B.] 1923, *see* NASH (P.)
B. (B.) *A strange Delilah, 1921, *see* STRANGE.
B. (C. E.) More leaves f. the commonplace book of C. E. B., 1907, *see* BATES (C. E.)
B. (D.) *Vies des papes Alexandre VI & Léon X, 1751, *see* DU BOULAY (N.)
B. (D.), *P.* A reformation of a catholike deformed ; by W. Perkins ; made by D. B. P., 2p, 1604, *see* BISHOP (W.), *bp. of Chalcedon.*
B. (E.), H. W. Fowler & A. Clutton-Brock.
Metaphor. [S. P. E. Tract No. 11]. 8°. 1922
B. (G.) *Index to Muir's Sanskrit texts, pl, 2, comp. by G. B., 1861, *see* MUIR (J.)
B. (G.) *Situation (The) in Ireland, *signed* G. B., 1920, *see* IRELAND, ANON. WORKS.

B. (H.) "Crossing the Bar" &c., tr., 1890, *see* TENNYSON.
B. (H.), *a. of* Political sketches, *see* DOYLE (J.) Key &c., 1839.
B. (I.) *English expositor, 1641, *see* BULLOKAR (J.)
B. (I.) *Herefordshire orchards, 1724, *see* BEALE (J.)
B. (J.) *From the Lune to the Neva, 1879, *see* BENSON (J.)
B. (J.) *Scenes f. the lives of Robson & Redpath, 1857, *see* ROBSON (W. J.)
B. (L. C.) *Topogr. & hist. guide to Corfe Castle, Dorset, *n.d.*, *see* CORFE CASTLE.
B. (N.) *The antiqs. of London & Westminster, 1722, *see* BAILEY (N.)
B. (P. de). Annales ; tr., 1625, *see* BELLIGENT (PIERRE DE).
B. (P. O.) Istoria di Pescia, 1784, *see* BALDASSERONI (P. O.)
B. (R.) *A catechism & conf. of faith, 1740, *see* BARCLAY (R.)
B. (R.), *gent.* *Hist. (The) of Virginia, 1722, *see* BEVERLEY (R.)
B. (R.), *of Lincolne's Inne, see* BELING (R.)
B. (S.) *Hist. apologet., ou déf. des libertez des égl. réform. de Fr. [Epitre *signed* S. B.], 1688, *see* GAUTIER (F. DE).
B. (T.) *An end to controv. betw. the Rom. Cath. & Protest. relig., 1654, *see* BAYLY (T.)
B. (T. M.) *Newark as a publishing town, 1898, *see* BLAGG (T. M.)
B. (W.) Ten learned personages lately converted (in France) ; tr. by W. B., 1601, *see* FRANCE.
B. (W.), *M.A.* *Four cent. of sel. hymns, 1668, *see* BARTON (W.)

B. (W. B.) Statistics of Prot. miss. socs., 1874, *see* BOYCE (W. B.)

B. (W. H.) New metr. version of Ps. &c., 1848, *see* BIBLE: Ps.

B. (X.) Sir C. Holmes: [*intr. signed* X. B.], 1924, *see* HOLMES (*Sir* C. J.)

Baader (Franz Xaver v.)

see CARRIERE (M.) Vom Geist, Schwert u. Handschlag für F. B., 1841.
„ HAMBERGER (J. W. F.) Cardinalpunkte d. B. Philos., 1855.
„ HOFFMANN (F.) B. als Begründer d. Philos. d. Zukunft, 1856.
see HOFFMANN (F.) B. in s. Verhältniss zu Hegel u. Schelling &c., 1850.
„ LUTTERBACK (J. A. B.) Lebensepochen B.'s u. Charakteristik s. Systems d. Philos., 1860.

Baasch (Ernst).
Gesch. Hamburgs, 1814–1918. 2B. 8°. Gotha. 1924–25

Baaz (Johan), *the elder, bp. of Wexiö* [†BAAZIUS (J.), *the elder*]. Inventarium Eccl. Sueo-Gothorum. s4°. Lincopiæ. 1642

Bab (Julius). Die deut. Kriegslyrik 1914–1918: e. krit. Bibliog. 8°. Stettin. 1920
see ARNOLD (R. F.) *ed.* Das deut. Drama; in Verb. mit J. B. &c., 1925.

Babakan (Artaxerxes), *see* ARTAXERXES I.

Baba Tahir, *see* TAHIR.

Babbitt (Irving). Democracy & leadership. 8°. [1924]
Rousseau & romanticism. 8°. Boston. 1919

Babel (Antony). La Bessarabie: ét. hist. &c. 8°. 1926

Babel (Isaak). Рассказы. s8°. Москва. [1925]

Babelon (Ernest). Cat. de la Coll. de Luynes. Monnaies grecques. [Bibl. Nat. Dépt. des Medailles &c.] [t]1, 2. [Planches *in case, sep.*] la8°. 1924–26
Traité des monnaies grecques & rom. p2, t4, fasc. 1, 2. s4°. 1926–27
p2, Descr. hist. t4, fasc. 1, 2.
see TUNISIE. Atlas archéolog. de la T.; accomp. d'un texte rédigé par E. B. &c., 1893–1913.
„ WADDINGTON (W. H.) Rec. gén. d. monnaies grecques d'Asie min., cont. par E. B. &c., 2e éd., t1i, 1925.

Babelon (Jean). Jacopo da Trezzo & la constr. de l'Escurial. Les arts à la cour de Philippe II, 1519–89. [Bibl. de l'Ec. des H. Et. Hispan., fasc. 3]. la8°. Bordeaux. 1922
see ARÉTHUSE: revue; dir. J. B. &c., 1923–.

Babenroth (A. Charles). Eng. childhood: Wordsworth's treatment of childhood. [Columbia Univ. Sts. in Eng. &c. lit.] 8°. N.Y. 1922

Babenstuber (Ludwig). Diss. ostend. P. Quesnellium & Jansenistas errores suos injuste tribuere scholae S. Thomae. [P443]. s4°. Augustæ Vindel. 1720

Baber [BĀBUR]. [MUḤAMMAD BĀBAR (ZAHĪR AL-DĪN), *emp. of Hindustan*]. Mems. New tr. of the Bābur-nama, incorpor. Leyden & Erskine's of 1826 A.D., by A. S. Beveridge. 2v. [*pagin. cont.*] 8°. [1917–21]
Mems. Tr. by J. Leyden & W. Erskine. Annot. & rev. by Sir L. King. 2v. s8°. O. 1921
see PANTUSOV (N. N.) Фергана по зап. Б., 1880.

Babeş (A.) & V. Buşilă. Cercetări orig. despre pelagra in România, *see* ACADEMIA ROMÂNA. Publ. Fond. V. Adamachi, t6, 1915.

Babet, *ps., see* NORMONT (E., *ctsse.* DE).

Babeuf (François Noël), *see* ESPINAS (A.) Phil. soc. du 18e s. (B. & le Babouvisme), 1898.

Babin (Evgenii). Как организовать ротную ячейку. 2e изд. [P2455]. s8°. Киев. 1919

Babinger (Franz). Stambuler Buchwesen im 18 Jhdt. [P2501]. 4°. L.1919.

Babington (Anthony), *see* MARY, *queen of Scots*. M. & the B. plot; ed. J. H. Pollen, 1922.

Babington (Gervase), *bp. of* (1) *Llandaff,* (2) *Exeter,* (3) *Worcester.* Works. [Ed. M. Smith]. fol. 1637
Comfortable notes upon the bookes of Exodus & Leviticus &c. 2p. *in* 1v. s4°. 1604

Babington (Percy L.)
Bibliog. of the writings of J. A. Symonds. 8°. 1925

Babrius. Gabriæ fabellæ &c., *see* ÆSOP, 1505.

Babukic (Věkoslav). Grundzüge d. Ilir. Gram. Mit e. Vorrede v. R. Fröhlich. s8°. Wien. 1839

Babylon. *The romaunce of the Sowdone of Babyloyne & of Ferumbras his sone, 1854, *see* FIERABRAS.

Babylonian. B. (The) epic of creation, 1923, *see* LANGDON (S.)
B. hist. texts rel. to capture &c. of Babylon; tr., 1924, *see* SMITH (S.) *tr.*

Bac (Ferd.) Le mariage de l'Imp. Eugénie. s8°. [1928]

Baccaglini (Alessandro). La legislaz. ital. sul credito agrario, *see* ITALY: MINISTERO DI AGRIC. &c. Annali d. cred., 1911.

Baccarini (Domineco), *see* SAPORI (F.) Maestri, No. 25, 1921.

Baccelli (Alfredo), *see* LUCA (P. DE). A. B., 1920.

Bacchelli (Riccardo).
Il diavolo al Pontelungo. 2v. 8°. Milano. 1927

Bacchi della Lega (Alberto). Bibliog. dei vocab. ne' dialetti Ital. racc. e poss. da G. Romagnoli. 8°. Bologna. 1876
see RAZZOLINI (L.) & A. B. D. L. Bibl. dei testi di lingua a stampa citati d. Accad. d. Crusca, 1878.

Bacchylides [BACCHILIDE]. Odi e frammenti. Testo greco, tr. e note a cura di N. Festa. s8°. Firenze. 1898
„ „ ....[*a. ed.*] s8°. Firenze. 1916
see DIEHL (E.) Suppl. lyricum, 3e A., 1917.
„ LYRA Græca, ed. & tr. J. M. Edmonds, v3, 1927.

Bacci (Orazio). La Toscana alla fine del Granducato: conf. di O. B., *see* TOSCANA.
see DANTE ALIGHIERI. Lectura D.: c. 11 dell' Inferno letto da O. B., 1915.

Bacci (Pietro Jacopo). Vita di S. Filippo Neri. 8°. Roma. 1859

Bach (Adolf), *ed., see* GOETHE (J. W. v.) Goethes Rheinreise, 1774, 1923.

Bach (Johann Sebastian).

Cantata texts, sacred & secular. With reconstruct. of the Leipzig Liturgy of h. period [& intr. &c.] by C. S. Terry. la8°. 1926
Matthäus-Passion: Oratorium. Klavierauszug [Ed. Peters]. la8°. L. *n.d.*
Passionsmusik nach d. Evang. Matthäi cap. 26 & 27. s8°. L. *n.d.*
Das wohltemperirte Clavier. 48 preludes & fugues. C. Halle's ed. [2v]. fol. *n.d.*
see FORKEL (J. N.) J. S. B., h. life, art & work; tr., w. notes &c. by C. S. Terry, 1920.
see FULLER-MAITLAND (J. A.) The "48" B.'s Wohltemp. Clavier, Bk 1, 2, 1925.
„ —— Keyboard suites of B., 1925.
„ GRACE (H.) The organ works of B., 1922.
„ RIEMANN (H.) Anal. of B.'s Wohltemperirtes Clavier; tr., 1890.
„ TERRY (C. S.) Bach's chorals, p3, 1921.
„ WHITTAKER (W. G.) Fugit. notes on cantatas & motets of B., 1925.

Bach (W. C.) Decimarum &c. tabula. A tithing table &c. [*b. w.* Spelman (*Sir* H.) Tithes, 1646]. s4°. 1635

Bachaumont (L. P. de) [†PETIT DE BACHAUMONT (LOUIS)].
see DU HAUSSET (*Mme.*) Méms., & extr. des Méms. de B., 1762–82; avec notices &c., par F. Barrière, 1882.
„ MÉMOIRES secrets de B.; rev. &c. par P. L. Jacob [*abr. ed.*], 1874.

Bache (Alexander Dallas).
Report on educ. in Europe. 8°. Phila. 1839

Bachelier (Louis). Le jeu, la chance & le hasard. s8°. 1924

Bachelin (Henri). J. K. Huysmans. s8°. 1926

Bachelin-Deflorenne (Antoine).
La science des armoiries. 8°. 1880

Bacheller (Irving).
A man for the ages. [*A. Lincoln. Fiction*]. s8°. 1920
The trumpets of God. s8°. [1927]

***Bachelor (The)** of the Albany, 1927, *see* SAVAGE (M.)

Bachhofer (Ludwig). Chinesische Kunst. s8°. Breslau. 1923

Bachi (Riccardo). L'alimentazione e la polit. annonaria in Italia. Con app. di G. Zingali. [C. E. for Internat. Peace. Storia econ. &c. d. Guerra Mondiale. Ser. Ital.] la8°. Bari. 1926

Bachiacca (Il) [UBERTINI (FRANCESCO D'ALBERTINO)], *see* TINTI (M.) Il Bachiacca, 1925.

Bachiarius, *monachus, see* MACINERNY (M. H.) St. Mochta & B., 1924.

Bachmann (Adolf). Böhmen u. s. Nachbarländer unter Georg v. Podiebrad, 1458–61 u. d. Königs Bewerbung um d. deut. Krone. 8°. Prag. 1878
Works ed. A. B. in FONTES RERUM AUSTRIAC.
Briefe u. Acten z. österr.-deut. Gesch. im Zeit. K. Friedrich III, 1885. [44.]
Urkunden u. Actenstücke z. österreich. Gesch. (1440–71), 1879. [42.]
Urkundl. Nachträge z. österr.-deut. Gesch. im Zeit. K. Friedrich III, 1892. [46.]

Bachmann (Paul). Über Gauss' Zahlentheoret. Arbeiten, *see* GAUSS (C. F.) Werke, B10ii, Abh. 1, 1922.

Bachmann (Paul) [PAULUS, *Abt zur Alden Zellen*]. Ein Schnoptuchlein auff Luthers Geyfer u. unlust. s4°. [Dressden. *Wolffgang Stöckel*]. 1533

Bachmann (Walter). Kirchen u. Moscheen in Armenien u. Kurdistan. [Deut. Orient-Gesell., Wiss. Veröffentl., 25]. fol. L. 1913

——, **C. Watzinger & T. Wiegand.** Petra. Mit e. Beiträge v. K. Wulzinger. [Wiss. Veröffentl. d. deut.-türk. Denkmalschutz-Kommandos; hrsg. v. T. Wiegand, H3]. fol. 1921

Bachmann (Zacharias), *see* RIVANDER (Z.) *ps.*

Bachowski (Władysław) & M. Treter. Wystawa miniatur i sylwetek we Lwowie, 1912. wydanie 2^{e}, uzupełnione, z 20 reprod. &c. 8°. Lwowie. [1912]

Back (Friedrich). Mittelrhein. Kunst: Beitr. z. Gesch. d. Malerei u. Plastik im 14. & 15. Jhdt. 4°. Frankfurt a. M. 1910

Backhouse, *The family of, see* FOSTER (J.) Descendants of John B., of Moss Side, Lancs., 1894.

Backhouse (John), *yeoman, see* FOSTER (J.) Descendants of J. B., 1894.

Backmeister (Lucas), *see* BACMEISTER (L.)

Backus (Isaac), *D.D.* Hist. of New-England; w. partic. ref. to the Baptists. 3v. [v2 & 3 *have tp.* A Church hist. of New-Eng.] 8°. Boston. Mass. 1777–96

Policy, as well as honesty, forbids the use of secular force in relig. affairs. [*b. w. h.* Hist. of New-Eng., v1, 1777]. 8°. Boston, Mass. 1779

Backwell (H. F.), *of Nigerian admin. service, see* HAUSALAND. Occup., 1900–4; tr., ed. w. intr. by H. F. B., 1927.

Bacmeister (Lucas) [BACKMEISTER (L.)] De morte Caroli V, *see* LACKMANN (A. H.) De edendis L. Lossii &c. epist., 1719.

Bacolla (A.) La musique en Turquie & traits biogr. s. G. Donizetti. Tr. G. D. [P2860]. la8°. Cple. 1911

Tableaux pour la coincidence des dates &c. pour l'Orient. 2e éd. la8°. Cple. 1910

Bacon, *The family of, see* RYE (W.) The false pedigree &c. of f. of B., 1919.

Bacon (Alban Francis Langley).
The wanderings of a temporary warrior. 8°. 1922

Bacon (Alice, *lady*), *viscountess St. Albans, née Barnham, aft. Lady Underhill, see* BUNTEN (A. C.) Life of A. B., 1919.

Bacon (*Lady* **Ann),** *see* ARENSBERG (W. C.) Burial of Francis B. & h. mother in Lichfield Chapter House, 1924.

Bacon (Benjamin Wisner).
The apostolic message. 8°. N.Y. 1925
The beginnings of Gospel story: inq. into sources &c. of Mark. 8°. New Haven, *Yale.* 1920
The Gospel of Mark: compos. &c. 8°. New Haven, *Yale.* 1925

Bacon (Charlotte). The Grays. s8°. [1922]

Bacon (Edward Denny), *see* BIBLIOTHECA. Bibl. Lindesiana, v7, Cat. of philatelic library of the Earl of Crawford; by E. D. B., 1911; Suppl., 1926.

Bacon (Francis), *viscount St. Albans, baron Verulam.*

Works. Ed. J. Spedding, R. L. Ellis, & D. D. Heath. v1–7. 8°. 1889–1901
Certaine miscellany works [*each w. sep. tp.: pagin. cont.*] Publ. by W. Rawley. [*b. w. h.* Essayes, 1632]. s4°. 1629
1. Considerations touching a warre w. Spaine.
2. An advertisement touching an holy warre.
3. An offer to King James, of a digest to be made of the lawes of Eng.
4. The hist. of the reigne of Henry VIII.

Essayes. Newly enlarged. s4°. 1632
Essays. With a table of the colours of good & evil. Added, The wisdom of the Antients. [Eng. by Sir A. Gorges]. [3p.] s8°. 1680
Essays. s8°. 1755
Essays. Intr. &c. by F. Storr & C. H. Gibson. 11th impr. s8°. 1918
New Atlantis, tr., *see* MORLEY (H.) Ideal commonwealths, 1885.
Of the advancement & proficience of learning. Interpreted by G. Wats. sfol. O. 1640
,, ,, ...s8°. 1808
Sylva sylvarum: or, a naturall historie. [*Foll*^{d}. *by h.* New Atlantis, *w. sep. tp. & pagin.*] s. fol. 1627
see ARENSBERG (W. C.) Burial of F. B. & h. mother in Lichfield Chapter House &c., 1924.
,, —— Secret grave of F. B. at Lichfield, 1923.
,, BROAD (C. D.) The philos. of F. B., 1926.
,, BURLINGTON FINE ARTS CLUB. Cat. of exhib. of Eliz. art in conjunc. w. tercent. of F. B., 1926.
,, DAWBARN (C. Y. C.) Uncrowned: story of Queen Elizabeth & the early life of F. B.; suppl. notes, 1923.
,, HICKSON (*Col.* S. A. E.) The prince of poets &c. [Shakespeare-B.], 1926.
,, LAING (F. H.) Lord B.'s philos. examined &c., 1877.
,, LEVINE (I.) F. B., 1561–1626, 1925.
,, TAYLOR (A. E.) F. B., lect., 1926.
,, WHITE (*Sir* W. HALE-) B., Gilbert & Harvey, 1927.
,, WOODWARD (P.) Sir F. B., 1920.

Bacon (Francis Henry), *see* ARCHÆOLOGICAL INST. OF AMER. Investig^{s}. at Assos: drawings of buildings &c. disc., 1881–83, by J. T. Clark, F. H. B. &c.; ed. w. notes by F. H. B., pl, 1902.

Bacon (Janet Ruth). Voyage of the Argonauts. 8°. [1925]

Bacon (Leonard Woolsey).
Mem. of Emily Bliss Gould. s8°. N.Y. [1879]

Bacon (*Adm. Sir* **Reginald Hugh Spencer),** *K.C.B.*
The Jutland scandal. 8°. [1924]

Bacon (Robert). For better relations w. our Latin Amer. neighbours: journey to S. Amer. 2p. *in* 1v. [p1, Eng. text. p2, Span.] [C. E. f. Int. Peace. 2nd ed. of publ^{s}., Nos. 7 & 8]. la8°. Wash. 1916

Bacon (Roger).

Opera hactenus ined. Fasc. IV–VI. 8°. O. 1913–26
4, Liber secundus Communium naturalium, De celestibus.
5, Secretum secretorum cum glossis & notulis; ed. R. Steele. Acc. versio anglicana ex Arabico ed. per A. S. Fulton, versio vetusta Anglo-Norman, nunc prim. ed.
6, Compotus. Acced. Compotus Rob. Grossecapitis & Massa compoti Alex. de Villa Dei. Ed. R. Steele.

The famous hist. of Fryer B. Ed. E. Goldsmid. [Bibl. curiosa]. 2v. s8°. *p.p.* E. 1886
see STEELE (R. R.) R. B. & the state of science in the 13th cent., 1921.

Bacon (*Lieut.* **Thomas).**
First impr^{s}. &c. f. nature in Hindostan. 2v. 8°. 1837

Bacot (Jacques). Le Tibet révolté. Vers Népémakö, la terre promise des Tibétains. 8°. 1912
see GUIMET. Bulletin archéolog., 2, Asie &c.: Missions Pelliot & B., 1921.
,, WOOLF (H. I.) 3 Tibetan mysteries: Tchrimekundan &c.; tr. f. Fr. version of J. B., 1924.

Bacourt (Pierre de) & J. W. Cunliffe. French lit. dur. the last half-century. s8°. 1923

Baculard d'Arnaud (François Thomas Marie de), *1718–1805, see* LA VILLEHERVÉ (B. DE) F.-T. de B. d'A.: s. théâtre & s. théories dramat., 1920.

Badberger (Martial) & Ursicinus Dröling. Tract. de jure, & justitia una cum parergis ex 3. libro Sentent. juxta mentem J. Duns Scoti. Praes. A. Holzmann. s8°. Passavii. 1720

Baddeley (*Mrs.* **Emma).** [Coll. of prints made by Mrs. B., presented to the London Library by J. F. B. Arranged, mounted & bound as below]. 61v. atlas fol. *n.d.*

Aeronautics, 1.
Battles, 1.
Caricatures, 1.
Miscellaneous, 1.
Portraits, English, 24.
,, , Foreign, 10
,, , Groups, 1.
,, , Unidentified, 1.
Topographical.
English counties, 5.
Foreign, 3.
Ireland, Scotland & Wales, 1.
London, 8.
,, Churches, 2.
,, Plans, 1.
,, Westminster, 1.

Baddeley (John Frederick).
Russia in the "eighties." Sport & politics. 8°. 1921
see MATHER (L. E.) *ed.* The Rt. Hon. Sir W. Mather, 1838–1920; [*by var. a.*, J. F. B. &c.], 1925.

Baddeley (*Sir* **John James).** Aldermen of Cripplegate Ward, w. acc. of the office. la8°. [1901]
Cripplegate. *p.f.p.c.* 8°. 1921
The Guildhall. 3rd ed. 8°. 1905

Baddeley (M. J. B.) & C. S. Ward, *edd.*, Thorough Guide Series.

Devon (N.) & N. Cornwall. By C. S. W. 8th ed. rev. s8°. 1924
Devon (S.) & S. Cornwall. 6th ed. rev. s8°. 1902
Scotland. The Highlands. s8°. 1888
Wales (N.) 10th ed., rev. 2p. s8°. [1924]

Baddeley (Thomas), *see* RICHARDSON (J.) Popery unmasked; ans. to T. B.'s Sure way &c., 1825.

Baddeley (Welbore St. Clair).
Hist. of Cirencester. 8°. Cirencester. 1924
see HARE (A. J. C.) & ST. C. B. Sicily, 1905.

Bade (Josse), *see* BADIUS (J.)

Badeley (Edward), *barrister.*
*Consider. on divorce. By a barrister. 8°. 1857

Baden. Regesten d. Markgrafen v. B. u. Hachberg 1050–1515. Hrsg. v. d. Bad. Hist. Comm. B1, 3, 4. 4°. Innsbruck. 1892–1915
1, Markgrafen v. B., 1050–1428. Markgrafen v. Hachberg 1218–1428; bearb. v. R. Fester.
3, Markgrafen v. B., 1431 (1420)–1543; bearb. v. H. Witte, mit Reg. v. F. Frankhauser.
4, Markgrafen v. B., 1453–1475; bearb. v. A. Krieger.

Baden, *Switzerland.* Die disputacion vor den xij orten einer lobl. eidtgnoschafft nālich Bern, Lutzern, Ury, Schvuytz Undervualden &c. von wegen der einigkeit in christl. glauben in iren landen &c., 1526, zů Badē. [*Between Eck & others. Comp. by T. Murner*]. s4°. Lutzern. *T. Murner.* 1527
Ein gleidt so die froñen Christenl. Eydgenossen nachbemelter ọrter, Bern, Lucern, Uri, Schwytz, Unterwalden, Zug u. Glaris U. Zwinglin uff die Collation oder Disputation, im Mey a. &c. xxvi. zů Baden gehalten worden zugeschickt haben &c. s4°. *n.p. n.d.* [Luzern?. 1527?]

Baden (Bernard, *margrave of***),** *see* BERNARD, *margrave of B.*

Baden (Max, *prince of***),** *see* MAX, *prince of Baden.*

Baden-Powell (*Major* **Baden Fletcher Smyth).** Cat. of coll. of aeronautical books &c. prop. of B.-P. Sold by Hodgson, 23 June 1923. [P2858]. 8°. 1923

Baden-Powell (*Lt.-Gen. Sir* **Robert Stephenson Smyth).**
Pig-sticking or hog-hunting. [rev. & enl. ed.] 8°. 1924

Bader (Augustin), *see* BOSSERT (G.) A. B. v. Augsburg &c. nach d. Prozessakten v. 1530, 1913–14.

Bader (*Mlle.* **Clarisse).**
Women in anc. India. [Tr. M. E. R. Martin]. 8°. 1925

Badger (Geo. Percy).
Descr. of Malta. 2nd ed. s8°. Valletta. 1851

Badische Historische Commission, *see* Regesta episc. Constant. B3, 1913–26.

Badischer Kunstgewerbe-Verein. Alte u. neue Fächer aus d. Wettbewerbung u. Austellung zu Karlsruhe, 1891. [*w.* Vorwort v. H. Götz. Der Fächer: geschichtl. Skizze v. M. Rosenberg]. fol. [1891]

Badischer und Württembergischer Schwarzwaldverein, *see* SCHWARZWALD (DER) in Farbenphotographien, 1911.

Badius (Jodocus), *Ascensius, see* RENOUARD (P.) Bibliog. des imprs. & des œuvres de J. B. A., impr. & humaniste, 1462–1535, 3t, 1908.

Badius (Johannes). Gründliche &c. Ableynung d. Vermeynten Antwort C. Ulenbergii wider zwo Schrifften J. B. eyngewendet &c. [*b. w.* Heidelberg. Bekanntnuss &c., 1592]. s4°. Herborn. 1592

Badley (John Haden).
Bedales, a pioneer school. 8°. [1923]
School talks in peace & war. s8°. O. 1920

Badmaev (Petr Aleksandrovich), *see* SEMENNIKOV (V. P.) За кулисами царизма: архив Б., 1925.

Badminton Library (The) of Sports & Pastimes.
Cricket. n. ed. by P. F. Warner. s8°. 1920

Bâdshâh Nâmah, *see* BANKIPORE. Reprods. of illusts. f. 3 Persian MSS. [B.-N. &c.] in Publ. Libr. at B., 1920.

Badsworth, *ps.* [*i.e.* A. LINDSAY LISTER].
*Laws & principles of bridge. s8°. N.Y. 1903

Baedeker (Carl).
FRANCE.
Northern F. 5th ed. s8°. L. 1909
Southern F., incl. Corsica. 6th rev. ed. s8°. L. 1914
GREECE. 3rd ed. s8°. 1905
ITALY.
1, N. Italy. 14th ed. s8°. 1913
2, C. Italy & Rome. 13th ed. s8°. 1900
" " 15th ed. s8°. 1909
3, S. Italy & Sicily. 14th ed. s8°. 1903
MEDITERRANEAN, includ. Madeira, the Canary Isls., Morocco, Algeria &c. s8°. 1911
SPAIN & PORTUGAL. 2nd ed. s8°. 1901
" " 4th ed. s8°. 1913
SÜDBAYERN, Tirol, Salzburg, Ober-u. Nieder-Österreich &c. 35e A. s8°. L. 1912
SWITZERLAND & adj. portions of Italy, Savoy & Tyrol. 23rd ed. s8°. 1909
" " 25th ed. s8°. 1913

Baena (Juan Alfonso de). Cancionero. Reprod. in facs. f. MS. in Bibl. Nat. Foreword by H. R. Lang. [Hispanic Soc. of Amer.] fol. N.Y. 1926

Baer (C. H.), *see* VÖLKERKRIEG (DER). Chronik d. Ereignisse; bearb. C. H. B., B22–28, 1920–23.

Baer (Carl Ernst v.) Lebensgesch. Cuvier's. Hrsg. L. Stieda. [*Extr. fr.* Archiv. f. Anthrop., B24]. 4°. [Braunschweig. 1896]
Welche Auffassung d. leb. Natur ist d. richtige? [P2470]. 8°. 1862

—— & Gr. v. Helmersen. Beiträge z. Kenntniss d. Russ. Reiches &c. B18i. 8°. St. Petersb. 1856
Bode (A.) Verbreitungs-Gränzen d. wicht. Holzgewächse d. Europ. Russlands, 1856. [18.]

Baer (Joseph) & Co., *booksellers.* Cat. theol. cathol. [727 & Bilderatlas]. 8°. & la8°. Frankfurt a. M. [1926]
Codices manuscripti. Incunabula xylogr. & typogr. Cat. 675. la8°. Frankfurt a. M. 1921
Frankfurter Bücherfreund. B11. 8°. Frankfurt a. Main. 1913
Incunabula typogr. [3p. *in* 1v]. la 8°. Frankfurt a.M. *n.d.*-[1928]

Baerlein (Henry).
The birth of Yugoslavia. 2v. 8°. [1922]
Box o' lights. s8°. [1923]
A difficult frontier (Yugoslavs & Albanians). s8°. [1922]
Here are dragons s8°. [1925]
The house of the fighting-cocks. s8°. [1922]
The march of the 70 thousand. 8°. [1926]

Baert (Alex. Balthasar Fr. de Paule de). Extr. du journal d'un voyage fait 1784 dans la p. mérid. de la Russie, *see* MÉMOIRES hist. &c. s. les pays entre la Mer Noire &c., 3p, 1797.

Baertsoen (Albert), *see* FIERENS-GEVAERT (H.) A. B., 1910.

Baerwald (Hermann), *see* BÄRWALD (H.)

Baethgen, *see* BÄTHGEN.

Baez (Cecilio). Le Paraguay, s. évol. hist. &c. 8°. 1927

Bagdad. Notice sur le chemin de fer de Bagdad &c., 1916, *see* FRANCE: STATE DEPTS., MIN. DE LA GUERRE.

Bagehot (Walter).
Biog. studies. Ed. R. H. Hutton. 2nd ed. 8°. 1889
The Eng. constitution. [repr.] s8°. 1920
Literary studies. Ed. R. H. Hutton. 4th ed. 2v. 8°. 1891

Bagenal, *The family of* [BAGNALL; BAGNOLD], *see* BAGENAL (P. H.) Vicissitudes, 1530–1800, 1925.

Bagenal (Hope), *see* ATKINSON (R.) & H. B. Theory & elem. of architecture, v1, p1, 1926.

Bagenal (Philip H.) Vicissitudes of an Anglo-Irish family [*i.e.* Bagenal], 1530–1800. la8°. 1925

Bagger (Eugene Szeheres). Francis Joseph, emp. of Austria. 8°. N.Y. 1927

Baggs (Charles Michael), *bp. of Pella.* The ceremonies of the Holy Week at Rome. 3rd ed. [P524]. 8°. Rome. 1854

Bagguley (William H.), *F.L.A., see* MARVELL (A.) A. M., 1621–78 &c.; ed. W. H. B., 1922.

Baghdādī,, *see* ABŪ-MANSŪR 'ABD-AL-KĀHIR IBN-TĀHIR, *al B.*

Bagley (William Chandler), *see* BEARD (C. A.) & W. C. B. Hist. of Amer. people, rev. ed., 1924.

Baglione (Giovanni). Le vite de' pittori, sculptori &c., 1572–1642. 8°. 1642

Bagnall, *The family of, see* BAGENAL.

Bagnall-Bull (E.)
The Ukraine; the granary of Europe. [P2485]. *f.p.c.* [1920]

Bagnold, *The family of, see* BAGENAL.

Bagoes Hoembarå & Mantri Koripan: Balineesch gedicht; tekst & vertaling bewerkt door R. v. Eck, *see* BIJDRAGEN tot de taal &c. v. Ned. Ind., volg. 3, d11, 1876.

Bagot (Christopher Neville). The celeb. case of Bagot *v.* Bagot, Ir. Prob. Court, Apr. to May, 1878. [Disputed will of C. N. B. *b. w.* Rachel (*Mme.*) Life &c., 1868]. 2nd ed. 8°. *n.d.*

Bagot (Daniel).
Protestant catechism. 27th thousand. s8°. [1840?]

Bagot (Richard). The Gods decide. s8°. 1919
Lakes of Northern Italy. [3rd ed., rev.] s8°. [1924]

Bagshaw (J. F. C.) Practical banking. With chaps. by C. F. Hannaford & W. H. Peard. 8°. 1920

Bagster (Samuel) & Sons, *publishers.*
The analyt. Greek lex. s4°. 1852

Bahā 'u 'llāh [MIRZA ḤUSAIN 'ALĪ], *see* ESSLEMONT (J. E.) Bahā 'u 'llāh & the new era, 1923.

Bahil (Matthias). Tristiss. eccl. Hungariæ Protest. facies. Traurige Abbildung d. protest. Gemeinden in Ungarn &c. [*Lat. & Germ.*] s8°. Bregæ. 1747

Bahlow (Ferd.) Johann Knipstro. [Verein f. Ref.-gesch. Schr., Jhrg. 16, Nr. 62]. 8°. Halle. 1898

Bahnsen (Julius Friedrich August).
Beitr. z. Charakterologie &c. 2B [*in* 1v]. 8°. L. 1867
Der Widerspruch im Wissen u. Wesen d. Welt. 2e A. 2B [*in* 1v]. 8°. L. 1882

Bahr (Hermann). Der Meister. Komödie. s8°. 1904

Bähr (Johann Friedrich) & N. A. Bähr. Biga orat. secul. 1, De hist. &c. librorum symbol. Eccl. Evang. in Pommerania. 2, De hist. &c. ordin. Eccl. Pommeran. [P426]. s4°. Gryphiswaldiæ. 1736

Bähr (Nicolaus Albert), *see* BÄHR (J. F.) & N. A. B. Biga orat., 1736.

Bahrdt (Carl Friedrich). Apparatus crit. ad. interpr. Vet. Test. congestus. v1 [*no more publ.*] s8°. Lipsiæ. 1775
Systema theol. Lutheranæ orthodoxum. [App. [*sep. pagin.*] De eccl. ejusque ratione ad rem publ.] 8°. Halæ. 1785
see GÖZE (J. M.) B. Verdeutsch. d. N. T. keine Übers., 1773.

Bährens (Emil). Poetæ Latini minores. Post Æm. B. iterum rec. F. Vollmer. v2ii. s8°. L., *Teubner.* 1923
2ii, Ovidi Nux—Consolatio ad Liviam—Priapea.

Baier (A. H.) Symbolik d. christl. Confessionen &c. B1, S. d. röm. kathol. Kirche. 2 Abth. [*pagin. cont. no more publ.*] 8°. Greifswald. 1854

Baier (Johann Jacob). Ausführl. Nachricht v. Altdorff. Andere A. s4°. Nürnberg. 1717

Baier (Johann Wilhelm) [BAIERUS (J. G.)], *the elder*.
Collatio doctrinæ pontific. & protest., disput. 28. Ed. alt. s4°. Jenæ. [1686]
Compend. theologiæ hist. &c. s8°. Francofurti. 1699
Compend. theologiæ moralis. s8°. Jenæ. 1698
Compend. theologiæ positivæ &c. s8°. Lipsiæ. 1717
„ „ [*a. ed.*] s8°. Lipsiæ. 1750
„ „ sec. ed. 1694, cur., vitam B[1]. &c. adj. E. Preuss. s8°. Berolini. 1864
De excidio Sodomæ. [P1015]. s4°. [Jenæ. 1695]
Diss. qua Concilii Nicæni primi auctoritas &c. à crimin. D. Zwickeri & C. Sandii defenditur. s8°. Jenæ. [1671]
„ „ Rev. & aucta. s4°. Jenæ. 1695
Diss. qua dialogi Erbermanniani inter Lutherum & Arium, fictitiis ejus Trophæis inserti, excutiuntur. Præs. S. Niemanno. [P440]. s4°. Jenæ. [1673]
see LANGE (J. M.) Ad Compend. theol. mor. suppl., 1700.
„ REUSCH (J. P.) Annot. in J. G. B. Compend. theol. posit., 1757.

Baier (Johann Wilhelm) [BAIERUS], *the younger*. De informatione catechetica aphorismi, ad præf. catechismorum B. Lutheri. s8°. Vinariæ. 1698
Trias quæstionum ad diluvii sacram hist. s4°. [Altdorff]. 1610

Baiern [BAYERN]. Akten z. Gesch. d. bair. Bauernaufstandes, 1705–6, 3T, 1912–15, *see* RIEZLER (S.) & C. v. WALLMENICH.
Alte Kunst in Bayern ; hrsg. v. Landesamt f. Denkmalpflege. H1–10. la8°. Augsburg. 1924–26
see ECKARDT (A.) Alt. Kunstgewerbe in Unterfranken, 1925. [6.]
„ GRÖBER (C.) Oberpfälz. Burgen u. Schlösser, 1925. [8.]
„ —— Die Plastik in d. Oberpfalz, 1924. [5.]
„ —— Unterfränk. Burgen, 1924. [4.]
„ MADER (F.) Oberpfälz. Klöster u. Wallfahrtskirchen, 1924. [1.]
„ —— Passau, 1925. [7.]
„ —— Stadt-u. Dorfkirchen d. Oberpfalz, 1926. [10.]
„ RITZ (J. M.) Unterfränk. Barockschlösser, 1925. [9.]
„ —— Unterfränk. Dorf, 1924. [3.]
„ RÖTTGER (B. H.) Unterfränk. Stadt, 1924. [2.]
Bayerische Chroniken d. 14. Jhdts. Hrsg. G. Leidinger. [Scr. rerum Germ. in usum schol.] 8°. Hannoveræ. 1918
Chronica de gestis princip.—Chron. Ludovici imp. IV—Chron. de ducibus Bavariæ.
Die Bayern im Grossen Kriege, 1914–18. Hrsg. v. Bayer. Kriegsarchiv. [Tafeln &c. *b. separately*]. 8°. München. 1923
Frankreichs Saarpolitik: d. Saar Interpellation im bayer. Landtag am 14. u. 15. Feb. 1922. [P2755]. 8°. München. 1922

Baigne. Cartul. de l'abbaye de St-Etienne de Baigne. [Publ. &c.] par l'abbé Cholet. [Soc. Arch. &c. de la Charente. Cartul. de l'Angoumois, t1]. 4°. Angoulême. 1867

Baikie (James). The Amarna age. Pref. by S. A. Cook. 8°. 1926
Century of excav. in land of Pharaohs. 8°. [1924]
Egyptian papyri & papyrus hunting. 8°. 1925

Baikov (Feodor Isakovich). Voyage d'un ambassadeur à la Chine, 1653, *see* BERNARD (J. F.) *ed.* Recueil, t4, 1718 ; 1732.

Baildon (Joshua) *tr.*, *see* MEXIA (P.) Rarities, 1651.

Bailey (*Maj.* C. T. P.)
Knives & forks. Sel. &c. w. intr. by B. s4°. 1927

Bailey (Cyril). The legacy of Rome. Essays by C. Foligno, E. Barker, H. S. Jones &c. Ed. C. B., w. intr. by Rt. Hon. H. H. Asquith. s8°. O. 1923
The mind of Rome. Contrib[s]. by C. B., J. Bell &c. Ed. C. B. s8°. O. 1926

Bailey (Edward Battersby), *see* GEOLOG. SURVEY OF SCOT. Mem. Tertiary &c. geol. of Mull, Loch Aline &c. ; by E. B. B. &c., 1924.

Bailey (George Cyril). The complete airman. 8°. [1920]

Bailey (Henry Christopher).
Barry Lefroy. s8°. [1919]
Call Mr. Fortune. 2nd ed. s8°. [1924]
The fool. s8°. [1921]
Knight at arms. s8°. [1924]
The merchant prince. s8°. [1926]
Mr. Fortune's practice. s8°. [1923]
Mr. Fortune's trials. s8°. [1925]
The plot. s8°. [1922]
The rebel. s8°. [1923]

Bailey (J.B.) Hist. of the churches in the rural deanery of Maryport &c. 8°. Cockermouth. 1920

Bailey (John Cann).
Continuity of letters. 8°. O. 1923
Poetry & commonplace: Warton lect., *see* BRIT. ACAD. Proc., v9, 1919–20.
Some polit. ideas & persons. s8°. 1921
The unpopularity of Landor, *see* ROY. SOC. OF LIT. Essays, N.S., v5, 1925.
Walt Whitman. [Eng. Men of Letters]. 8°. 1926
see CAVENDISH (*Lady* FRED.) Diary ; ed. J. B., 2v, 1927.

Bailey (Liberty Hyde). The apple tree. s8°. N.Y. 1922
Cultivated evergreens, U.S. & Canada. [*By var. wr*[s].] Ed. L. H. B. la8°. 1923
The pruning-manual. 18th ed., rev. &c. of Pruning-bk. (1898). 8°. N.Y. 1919

Bailey (Nathan).
*The antiqs. of London & Westminster. By N. B. s8°. 1722

Bailey (T. Grahame). Gram. of the Shina (Ṣiṇā) lang. [Roy. As. Soc. Prize Publ. Fund, v8]. 8°. 1924
Linguistic studies f. the Himalayas: gram. of 15 H. dialects. [R. As. Soc. Monogr[s]., 17]. 8°. 1915

Bailey (Temple). The trumpeter swan. s8°. [1921]

Bailey (Thomas), *sub-dean of Wells*, *see* BAYLY (T.)

Baillet (Jules). Inscr[s]. grec. & lat. des tombeaux des rois ou syringes à Thèbes, fasc. 1, *see* INSTITUT FRANÇ. D'ARCH. ORIENT. DU CAIRE. Mém., t42, 1926.

Baillie (James Black). Studies in human nature. 8°. 1921
see LABOUR & industry: lect[s]. by P. Alden, J. B. B. &c., 1920.
„ MUIRHEAD (J. H.) *ed.* Contemp. Brit. philos.: statements by J. B. B. &c., s1, 1924.

Baillie (Joanna). De Monfort, *see* INCHBALD (*Mrs.* E.) Brit. theatre, v24, 1808.
see CARHART (M. S.) Life & work of J. B., 1923.

Baillie (John), *D.D.*, *vicar of Wyvenhoe*.
A memoir of A. L. Newton. 16th ed. s8°. 1871

Baillie (Robert) [BAYLIE], *Principal of Glasgow University*, *see* COTTON (J.) The way of congreg. churches cleared, f. aspersions of B., 1648.

Baillie-Saunders (Margaret). Becky & Co. s8°. [1920]
Dimity Hall. s8°. [1925]
McBride's first wife. s8°. [1921]
Mr. Churchwarden—and Lady. 3rd ed. s8°. [1927]
Roof-tops. 2nd ed. s8°. [1927]

Bailly (Anatole). Dict. grec-français, réd. avec conc. de É. Egger. 10e éd. rev. la8°. *n.d.*

Bailly (Auguste). *Works in* Œuvres libres.
L'amazone captive, 1925. [51.]
L'amour & M. Charibot, 1924. [42.]
La Carcasse & le Tord-Cou, roman, 1923. [26.]
Estelle, jeune fille d'autrefois, 1927. [75.]
L'homme né de la chair, 1923. [20.]
Mikou, jeune fille d'aujourd'hui, 1926. [67.]
Saint-Esprit, 1926. [57.]

Bailly (Edmond). La légende de diamant. 7 récits du monde Celtique. s8°. 1909

Bailly (Jean Sylvain), see FERNAND-LAURENT (C. J.) J. S. B., prem. maire de Paris, 1927.

Bailo (Luigi). Ant. e nuovi nomi d. vie d. Treviso. [Nozze Lutti-Felissent. N. 135]. la8°. Treviso. 1885
L'istit. d. Monte di pietà in Treviso, 1496 [Nozze Palazzi-Cipollato. N. 129]. la8°. Treviso. 1885
—— **& G. Biscaro.** Della vita e d. opere di Paris Bordon. la8°. Treviso. 1900

Bailward (William Amias).
The slippery slope & o. p. on social subjects. 8°. 1920

Bain (A. Watson), *ed.* The modern teacher. Essays on educ. aims & methods [*by var. a.*] Intr. by W. H. Hadow. 8°. [1921]

Bain (Francis William). The substance of a dream. Tr. f. MS. by B. s8°. [1919]

Bainbridge (Lucy Seaman). One of the pioneer women in medicine [C. A. Seaman]. [P2576]. 8°. 1921

Bainbridge (William).
Law of mines & minerals. 8°. 1841

Bainbridge (William Seaman). Rep. on pres. cond. in the Ruhr & Rhineland. [P2719]. 8°. N.Y. 1923

Baine (Paul), *see* BAYNES (P.)

Baines (Edward), *the elder*. Hist., directory &c. of Lancaster. Dir. dept. by W. Parson. 2v. 8°. Liv'l. 1824–25

Baines (Edward), *rector of Bluntisham, Hunts.*, *see* MACGHEE (R. J.) Ch. of Rome: her pres. moral theology; *ed.* E. B., 1853.

Baines (Sir Edward). The social, educat. & relig. state of the manufacturing districts, 2 letters to Sir R. Peel &c. 8°. 1843

Baines (J. W.) *see* BRADLEY (A. G.), A. C. CHAMPNEYS & J. W. B. Hist. of Marlborough College, rev., 1923.

Baines (Sir Jervoise Athelstane). Ethnography. With list of wks. on Ind. e. by W. Siegling. [Grundr. d. indo-ar. Phil., B2, H5]. la8°. Str. 1912

Baines (Peter Augustin) *bp. of Siga*, *see* POTCHETT (W.) Popery unchanged, comm. on sermon by bp. of Siga, 1826.

Baines (Thomas), *of Liverpool, printer*. Lancashire & Cheshire, past & pres. With acc. of the rise &c. of manufactures &c. by W. Fairbairn [*w. sep. pagin.*] 2v. 4°. 1868–69

Bainville (Jacques). Hist. de France. [14e éd.] s8°. 1924

Baird (Charles Washington). A chapter on liturgies. Pref. & app. by T. Binney. s8°. 1856

Baird (*Gen. Sir* **David**), *Bart.*, *see* THORNTON (L. H.) Light & shade in bygone India [career of Sir D. B.], 1927.
see WILKIN (*Capt.* W. H.) Life of Sir D. B., 1912.

Baird (William), *of Auchmeddan.* Genealog. mem. of the Duffs. [Pref. by L. D. G. Duff]. 8°. *p. f. p. c.* Aberdeen. 1869

Baird (William), *F.S.A.Scot.* Annals of Duddingston & Portobello. 8°. E. 1898.

Baireuth (*Die Markgrafin* **v.**) Eine preuss. Königstochter: Denkwürdigk. Hrsg. J. Armbruster. s8°. Ebenhausen. 1925

Baius (Michael), *see* BAY (M. DE).

Bajanov (V.) Каменноугольная промышленность за 1920. la8°. Москва. 1920

Bajer (Joannes Guilielmus), *see* BAIER (J. W.)

Baker (Alfred Thomas), *Litt.D.* Saints' lives wr. in Anglo-French: th. hist. &c. importance, *see* ROY. SOC. OF LIT. Essays, N.S., v4, 1924.

Baker (Amy J.) [*Mrs.* MAYNARD CRAWFORD]. The king's passion. s8°. [1920]
The one step. s8°. [1926]

Baker (Augustine). Inner life & writings of Dame G. More. Rev. & ed. by B. Weld-Blundell. v1. s8°. 1910

Baker (Bernard Granville). Waveney. 8°. [1924]

Baker (Charles), *see* SLESSER (*Sir* H.) & C. B. Trade union law, 2nd ed., 1926.

Baker (Charles Henry Collins).
Crome. Intr. by C. J. Holmes. 4°. [1921]
Dutch painting of the 17th cent. [" The Studio "]. 8°. 1926
Lely & Kneller. s8°. [1922]
see HOLMES (*Sir* C. J.) & C. H. C. B. Making of the Nat. Gallery, 1824–1924, 1924.
see LECONFIELD (C. H. W., *3rd b.*) Cat. of Petworth coll. of pictures in poss. of Ld. L.; by C. H. C. B., 1920.

Baker (Charles Whiting). Government control & operat. of industry in Gt. Brit. & the U.S. dur. the World War. [C. E. f. Int. Peace]. la8°. N.Y. 1921

Baker (David Erskine). Biographia dramatica. n. ed. corr. & cont. fr. 1764 to 1782. 2v. 8°. 1782

Baker (Dwight Condo). T'ai Shan, sacred Eastern peak of China. s8°. Shanghai. 1925

Baker (Elizabeth). Chains, *see* Plays of to-day, v1, 1925.

Baker (Ernest A.) The Highlands w. rope & rucksack. 8°. 1923
Hist. of the Eng. novel. The age of romance; f. beginnings to the Renaissance. 8°. 1924
The public library. 8°. 1922
The uses of libraries. [*Lect*s. *by var. wr*s.] Ed. E. A. B. 8°. 1927

Baker (G. P.) Sulla the fortunate. 8°. [1927]

Baker (George Pierce). Dramatic technique. 8°. [1921]

Baker (Henry Dunster). Brit. India: w. notes on Ceylon &c., 1915, *see* UNITED STATES: CONSULAR REPORTS.

Baker (Henry Frederick).
Principles of geometry. 4v. 8°. C. 1922–25

Baker (Oliver).
Black jacks & leather bottells. 4°. [1921]

Baker (Philip J. Noel). Disarmament. 8°. 1926
The Geneva Protocol for the pacific settlement of internat. disputes. 8°. 1925
The League of Nations at work. 8°. [1926]

Baker (Ray Palmer), *Ph.D.* A hist. of Eng.-Canadian lit. to the Confederation. 8°. Camb. [U.S.] 1920

Baker (Ray Stannard). Woodrow Wilson & world-settlement, wr. f. h. unpubl. & pers. material. 3v. la8°. 1923
Woodrow Wilson: life & letters. [v1, 2]. 8°. 1928
1, 1856–90. 2, 1890–1910.

Baker (*Sir* **Richard).** Meditations &c. upon the first Psalm; the penitential Ps. &c. (first pr. 1639–1640). n. ed. Introd. by A. B. Grosart. s8°. 1882

Baker (T. H.) Notes on St. Martin's Church & Parish, [Salisbury]. 8°. Salisbury. 1906

Baker (Thomas), *dramatist.* *An act at Oxford. A comedy. By a. of the Yeoman o' Kent. s4°. 1704
Tunbridge-Walks: a comedy. [P2865]. s8°. 1764

Baker (Thomas), *of St. John's Coll., Cambridge.* Reflections upon learning. s8°. 1699

Bakharev (V.) Какъ держать себя на допросахъ изд 2е. [P2716]. s8°. Женева. 1902

Bakhuizen van den Brink (Reiner Cornelis), 1810–65. Vondel met Roskam en Rommelpot. 3e druk. 8°. 'S-Gravenhage. 1886

Bakker (Ina Boudier-), *see* BOUDIER-BAKKER (I.)

Bakst (Lev Samoilovich). Сѣровъ и я въ Греціи дорожныя записи. 8°. [Берлинъ]. 1923

Bakunin (Mikhail Aleksandrovich).
Всесвѣтный революц. союзъ. [L'alliance univ. P2824]. s8°. Genève. 1888
М. А. Бакунинъ. 1. Статья А. И. Герцена о Бакунинѣ. 2. Біограф. очеркъ М. Драгоманова. 3. Рѣчи и Воззванія. s8°. *n.p.* 1906
Письма Б. къ Герцену и Огареву. Съ біограф. введеніемъ М. П. Драгоманова. s8°. С.–П. 1906
M. B.'s Beichte a. d. Peter-Pauls-Festung an Zar Nikolaus I. [Übers. besorgte L. Keneth]. Veröffentl. K. Kersten. Vorwort v. W. Polonski. 8°. 1926
see HERZEN (A.) М. Б. и польское дѣло, *n.d.*
,, HUCH (R.) M. B. u. d. Anarchie, 1923.
,, KORNILOV (A. A.) Годы странствий М. Б., 1925.
,, — Молодые годы М. Б., 1915.
,, POLONSKY (V.) М. А. Б. t1, 1922.
,, STEKLOV (YU.) М. А. Б., жизнь и деятельность. 4т, 1920–27.

Balaban (Majer). Die Judenstadt v. Lublin. la8°. 1919

Balabanov (Angelica). Erinnerungen u. Erlebnisse. 8°. 1927

Balabanov (M.) Царская Россия 20 века. 8°. Харьков. 1927

Balaguer (P. Bohigas), *see* BOHIGAS BALAGUER (P.)

Balaguer (Victor). Obras poét. Con prólogo de R. G. de la Rosa. [Bibl. univ.: Col. de los mejores as., t57]. s8°. 1915

Balaton, *lake.* Resultate d. wissenschaftl. Erforschung d. Balatonsee. 4°. Wien *&* Budapest. 1920
B1ii, Hydrographie v. E. von Cholnoky. [Anhang. Grundwässer, v. G. Rigler 1911, *b. w.* T2].
B3i §2. B. Környékének archæologiája. [*in Hungarian.*] 4°. Budapest. 1920
,, ,, Topog. u. geolog. atlas, T2. [Entworfen v. L. v. Loczy]. [*b. w.* T1]. obl.fol. Budapesten. 1920

Balbinus (Bohuslaus Aloysius). Diss. apolog. pro lingua Slavonica, præcipue Bohemica. 8°. Pragæ. 1775
Epitome hist. rerum Bohemic. Boleslav. hist. &c. Adj.: libri duo (6 & 7) de antiq. Boleslav. eccl. collegio &c. [3p. *in* 1v. *sep. pagin*s.] fol. Pragæ. 1673–77
Miscell. hist. regni Bohemiæ. Item hist. brevis temp. &c. Dec 1. Lib. 1–8; Dec. 2. Lib. 1–2 [*in* 3v.] fol. Pragæ. 1679–88
Decas 2, lib. 2, Tabularium Bohemo-genealog. *in* 4p.

Balbo (*il conte* **Cesare),** *see* PASSAMONTI (E.) C. B. e la rivol. del 1821 in Piemonte, 1926.

Balbo (*il conte* **Prospero),** *see* BOGINO (G. L.), P. B. &c. Lettere a Ferrari, 1883.

Balbuena (Bernardo de), *bp. of Porto Rico.* Siglo de oro en las selvas de Erífile. [*&* Grandeza Mejicana, *w. sep. pag.*] s8°. 1821

Balcarres papers, *see* MARY, *of Lorraine, q. consort of James V.* Foreign corr. w. M. de L., f. the B. p., 2v, 1923–25.

Balcarres (Alexander Lindsay, *1st earl of*); *1618–59.*
Works in MAIDMENT (J.) *ed.* Hist. fragms., p3, 1833.
Acc. of any accession the Earl of B. had to the late engagement, 1649.
Instructs. to A., Earl of B. [& Passeport en faveur de B.], 1654.
Letter to Charles II, 1653.
Proposals submitted to Charles II, 1654.

Balch (Herbert E.) The caves of Mendip. s8°. 1926

Balch (Thomas). Internat. courts of arbitration. 4th ed. w. introd. &c., by T. W. Balch. 4°. Phila. 1912
,, ,, ...7th ed., ed. T. W. Balch. la8°. Phila. 1916

Bald (Robert). Gen. view of the coal trade of Scotland; added, Inq. into condit. of women who carry coals &c. 8°. E. 1808

Baldass (Ludwig). Albrecht Altdorfer: St. ü. d. Entwicklungsfaktoren im Werke d. Künstlers. 4°. Wien. 1923
Die Gemälde d. Lucas van Leyden. s8°. Wien. 1926
Der Künstlerkreis Maximilians. la8°. Wien. 1923

Baldasseroni (Prospero Omero). *Istoria d. città di Pescia e d. Valdinievole. s4°. Pescia. 1784

Baldauf (Richard).
Der Mönch v. St. Gallen. [Historie u. Kritik. 1]. 8°. L. 1903

Balde (Jean) *ps.* [*i.e. Mlle.* ALLEMANE].
Le goéland. s8°. [1926]
La survivante. s8°. [1923]
La vigne & la maison. s8°. [1922]

Baldensperger (Fernand).
Orientations étrangères chez H. de Balzac. la8°. 1927
Sensibilité musicale & romantisme. s8°. 1925
see RHÉNANIE, LA: conférences, *by* F. B. &c., 1922.

Balder (Johannes). Conflictus de B. Georgio martyre, adv. C. C. Sandium. Præs. J. Paschio. [P596]. s4°. Wittenbergæ. [1685]

Balderston (Katharine C.)
Hist. & sources of Percy's Memoir of Goldsmith. s8°. C. 1926
Baldeschi (Elia Colini-), *see* COLINI-BALDESCHI (E.)
Baldesi (Gino). Dalle antiche corporazioni al mod. sindacalismo. s8°. Milano. 1924
Baldinotti (Tommaso), *1429–1501*, *see* CHITI (A.) T. B. poeta pistoiese: vita e rime, 1898.
Baldricus, *abbot of Bourgueil*, *see* BALDRICUS, *abp. of Dol.*
Baldricus, *abp. of Dol.* [BAUDRI DE BOURGUEIL]. Œuvres poét. Ed. crit. publ. d'ap. le ms. du Vatican par P. Abrahams. la8°. 1926
see LEHMANN (P.) Pseudo-ant. Lit. des M.-A. [Anh., Heroiden d. B. de Bourgueil], 1927.
Baldry (Alfred Lys). Contemp. figure painters. Ed. G. Holme. [The Studio]. la8°. [1925]
Balduin (François) [BALDUINUS (F.)]. Responsio [*by F. B.*] ad Calvinum & Bezam pro F. Balduino. Cum refut. calumniarum de Scriptura &c. [*With an address to the reader on the controversy betw. Calvin & F. B. by* Michael Fabricius]. 8°. Coloniæ. 1564
Balduin (Friedrich) [†BALDUINUS (F.)].
Adventus Christi typicus. s8°. Wittebergæ. 1621
*Ausführl. u. gründl. Wiederlegung d. deut. Arian. Catechismi, z. Rackaw in Polen a. 1608 gedr. Durch d. Theolog. Fac. zu Wittenberg. [*b. w. h.* Solida refut., 1620]. s8°. Wittenberg. 1619
Comm. in omnes epistolas Pauli &c. Acc. Summa Univ. theologiæ, Index Balduinianus gener. aut J. Aleario. [*sep. tp. & pagin.*] s4°. Francofurti. 1564
De disput. Lutheri cum diabolo in controv. de privatâ missâ. s8°. Islebii. 1605
Disput. de hæreticis, & quomodo sint coercendi. Resp. N. Albano. [P2632]. s4°. Witebergæ. 1608
Hyperaspistes Lutheri, adv. orationem N. Serarii, in qua disserit, utrum verum sit Lutherum, diabolo magistro & doctore usum esse. s4°. Lipsiæ. 1603
In tres postremos prophetas Haggæum, Zachariam, Malachiam comm. Una cum textu Græco-Lat. s8°. Wittebergæ. 1610
Ein Leichpredigt bey d. Leichbegängnuss G. Mylii. [P2613]. s4°. Wittemberg. 1607
Passio typica, seu lib. typorum Vet. Test. [*b. w. h.* Adventus Christi typicus, 1621]. 2 lib. s8°. Wittebergæ. 1614–16
Solida refutatio catechismi Ariani, qui Rackoviæ in Polonia a. 1608 excusus &c. Eruta & nom. Fac. Theol. in Acad. Witteberg. ed., jam in lat. serm. tr. s8°. Wittebergæ. 1620
see BECANUS (M.) De communione sub utraq. specie disput. M. B. ed. à F. B., 1610.
,, SCHMID (S.) In Prophetas minores comm. cum F. B. In tres poster. prophetas comment., 1698.
Balduin (Gottlieb). Exarchatus hist. diss. Sub præs. Æ. Strauchii. [P432]. s4°. Wittebergæ. [1661]
Baldung (Hans) [BALDUNG-GRIEN], *see* SCHMITZ (H.) H. B. (Knackfuss), 1922.
Baldwin Locomotive Works.
*Hist. of B. L. Works, 1831–1907. 8°. Phila. 1907
Baldwin (Bird Thomas), *see* TERMAN (L. M.) Genetic studies of genius; by L. M. T., assisted by B. T. B. &c., 1925.
Baldwin (Dane Lewis), L. N. Broughton, *& others.* A concordance to the poems of John Keats. [C. I. of Wash.] 4°. Wash. 1917
Baldwin (George), *Brit. Consul in Egypt.* Polit. recoll^s. rel. to Egypt, w. narr. of Brit. campaign in 1801. 8°. 1801
Baldwin (Matthias W.), *founder of Baldwin Locomotive Works*, *see* BALDWIN LOCOMOTIVE WORKS. Hist., 1831–1907, 1907.
Baldwin (Oliver). Six prisons & two revolutions: adv. in Trans-Caucasia & Anatolia, 1920–21. 8°. [1925]
Baldwin (Simeon Eben.) The Hartford Convention. [*Repr. fr.* N. Haven Hist. Soc., v9. P2589]. 8°. New Haven. 1918
Baldwin (*Rt. Hon.* Stanley).
The classics & the plain man. Pres. addr., Class. Assoc., 1926. [P2847]. 8°. 1926
On England & o. addresses. 8°. [1926]
Peace & goodwill in industry. 3 speeches, March 1925. s8°. [1925]
The preservation of anc. cottages. W. a note by T. Hardy. [R. Soc. of Arts]. 8°. [1927]
see NATIONAL UNIONIST ASSOC. Looking ahead &c., w. 3 speeches by S. B., 1924.
Bale (John), *bp. of Ossory.* Acta Romanorum Pontificum, ad temp. Pauli IV, ex J. B. maiore Catal. Anglic. Script. desumpta. s8°. Francofurti ad Moenum. 1567
Balearick Islands. *The anc. & mod. hist. of the B. I.; tr., 1716, *see* DAMETO (J.) & V. MUT.
Balemann (Henric. Ditericus).
Diss. de jure civium originar. s8°. Altorfii. 1746
Balen. Die B.-Dichtungen u. i. Quellen, 1918, *see* VETTERMANN (E.)
Balentz (B.) Cat. complet de la librairie B. B. [*In Armenian*]. 5th ed. [*b. w. h.* Short cat., 1894]. s8°. K.-polis. 1902
[Short cat. of books on sale by B. *In Armenian*]. s8°. K.-polis. 1894
Balet (Leo). Der Frühholländer Geertgen tot Sint Jans. 8°. Haag. 1910
Baleus (Joannes), *ps.*, *see* STENIUS (SIMON).
Balfour MSS. Letters &c. rel. to Gt. Brit. [& Ireland] dur. reign of James I, f. B. MSS., *see* ABBOTSFORD CLUB. Misc., v1, 1837.
Balfour (Alexander Hugh Bruce, *6th baron*), *of Burleigh*, *see* BALFOUR (*Lady* F.) Mem. of Ld. B. of B., K.T., 1925.
Balfour (Andrew) & H. H. Scott.
Health problems of the Empire. [Brit. Empire, 5]. 8°. [1924]
Balfour (Arthur James Balfour, *1st earl of.*)
Essays, speculative & political. 8°. [1920]
Opinions & argument f. speeches & addresses, 1910–27. 8°. [1927]
Theism & thought: st. in familiar beliefs. 2nd course of Gifford Lect^s., 1922–23. 8°. [1923]
see NEEDHAM (J.) *ed.* Science, religion & reality; [by] Earl B. &c., 1925.
,, RAYMOND (E. T.) Mr. B.: a biog., 1920.
Balfour (*Lady* Frances). The life of George, 4th earl of Aberdeen. 2v. 8°. [1923]
Mem. of Lord Balfour of Burleigh, K.T. 8°. [1925]
Balfour (*Rt. Hon.* Gerald William). The Ear of Dionysius: scripts. [*Extr. f.* Soc. for Psych. Res., Proc., v29. P2423] 8°. 1917
Balfour (Graham).
Life of R. L. Stevenson. 2nd ed. 2v. 8°. 1901
Balfour (*Hon.* James Moncreiff).
Recent happenings in Persia. 8°. E. 1922
Balfour (John Hutton).
Manual of botany. 5th ed. 8°. E. 1875
Balfour (M. Melville).
London pride. Songs of the City. s8°. [1927]
Balfour (Robert, *5th baron*), *of Burleigh*; *d. 1757.* *Mem. rel. to B. *w.* App., 1821, *see* MAIDMENT (J.) & R. PITCAIRN. Nugæ derel., 1822.
Balfour-Browne (Frank).
Conc. the habits of insects. 8°. C. 1925
Insects. [Home Univ. Lib.] s8°. [1927]
***Balkanization** of agric.: agrarian ref. in Hungary &c., 1921, *see* HUNGARY.
Balkan review (The). Ed. Crawfurd Price. v1–4 (Feb. 1919–Jan. 1921). s8°. 1919–21
Bal Krishna, *M.A., Ph.D.* Commercial rel^s. betw. India & England, 1601–1757. [London Sch. of Econ^s. St^s. in econ^s. &c., No. 67]. 8°. 1924
***Ball** (The); or, a glance at Almack's, 1829, *see* YATES (G.)
Ball (Arthur E.), *see* WOOD (H. G.) & A. E. BALL. Tom Bryan: a mem., 1922.
Ball (Charles James). The Book of Job; rev. text & version. Pref. by C. F. Burney. 8°. O. 1922
Shumer & Shem: philological coincidences &c., 1915, *see* BRIT. ACAD. Proc^s., 1915–16.
Ball (Eustace Alfred Reynolds), *F.R.G.S.*, *see* BLACK, *publ.* Guides: Cairo of to-day; by E. A. R.-B., 4th ed., 1925.
Ball (Francis Elrington).
The judges in Ireland, 1221–1921. 2v. 8°. [1926]
Ball (Hugo). Byzantin. Christentum: 3 Heiligenleben [*i.e.* J. Klimax, Dionysius Areopagita, Symeon d. Stylit]. 8°. München. 1923
Zur Kritik d. deut. Intelligenz. 8°. Bern. 1919
Ball (John), *M.R.I.A.* Ball's Alpine Guides. [3v]. s8°. 1873
East Switzerland.
Pass of St. Gothard & the Ital. lakes.
South Tyrol &c.
Ball (John), *Puritan divine.* A friendly triall of the grounds tending to separation, stinted Liturgie & set form of Prayer &c. s4°. C. 1640
Ball (Katherine M.)
Decorative motives of orient. art. 4°. [1927]
Ball (Oona Howard), *wife of Sidney Ball.* Sidney Ball, memories & impressions. 8°. O. 1923

Ball (*Sir* **Robert Stawell).**
The cause of an ice age. 2nd ed. s8°. 1892
Pop. guide to the heavens. 83 plates &c. 3rd ed. 8°. 1910
Story of the heavens. n. & rev. ed. 8°. 1893

Ball (Robert Stawell), *son of Sir R. S. Ball.*
Natural sources of power. 8°. 1908

Ball (Sidney), *see* BALL (O. H.) S. B., mem. & impress., 1923.

Ball (Walter William Rouse).
Mathematical recreations & essays. 9th ed. 8°. 1920
String figures. 2nd ed. s8°. C. 1921

Ballad Society. Love poems & humourous ones, 1614–19. Put forth by F. J. Furnivall. [11. *a. c. b. w.* Capt. Cox, h. ballads &c., 1871]. la8°. Hertford. 1874

Ballads.
*Ballads and songs of Ayrshire, s1, 1846, *see* AYRSHIRE.
*Book (A) of favourite mod. b. Illust. la8°. 1860
Bundle (A) of b.; ed. H. M., 1891, *see* MORLEY (H.)
Cavalier & Puritan b. &c., 1640-60, 1923, *see* ROLLINS (H. E.), *ed.*
Garland (A) of old hist. b[s]., 1600–1752, *see* AUNGERVYLE Soc. Reprints, s1, 1881.

Ballantine (Wm.), *serjeant-at-law.* Some experiences of a barrister's life. n. & rev. ed. (the 5th). s8°. 1882

Ballantyne (Andrew), *Methodist missionary at Bwaidoga, see* JENNESS (D.) & A. B. The North. D'Entrecasteaux, 1920.

Ballantyne (James Robert).
Gram. of the Mahratta lang. 4°. E. 1839

Ballard (Adolphus) & James Tait, *edd.*
Brit. borough charters, 1216–1307. 8°. C. 1923

Ballard (*Brig.-Gen.* **Colin Robert).**
Military genius of A. Lincoln. 8°. O. 1926
Napoleon: an outline. 8°. [1924]

Ballard (*Vice-Adm.* **George Alexander).**
America & the Atlantic. 8°. [1923]
Influence of the sea on the polit. hist. of Japan. 8°. 1921
Rulers of the Indian Ocean. la8°. 1927

Ballard (Philip Boswood).
The changing school. 2nd impr. 8°. 1926
Group tests of intelligence. 2nd & rev. ed. s8°. 1923
Mental tests. 3rd impr. s8°. [1923?]
The new examiner. 2nd impr. 8°. 1924

Ballarini (Sante), *violin maker, see* GISALBERTI (A.)

Ballerini (Antonio). Jus & officium episcop. in ferendo suffragio pro infallibilitate Rom. pontif. ed. alt. [P2691]. 8°. Ratisbonæ. 1870

Ballerini (Girolamo), *see* BALLERINI (P.) & G. B. De vi &c. primatûs Roman. pontif. &c., 1860.

Ballerini (Pietro). De potestate eccles. summ. pontificum & conciliorum gen. liber. Una cum vindiciis auct. pontif. contra opus J. Febronii. [*b. w. h.* De vi &c. primatus Rom. pontif., 1770]. s4°. Augustæ Vindel. 1770
De vi ac ratione primatus Roman. pontificum & de ipsorum infallibilitate. s4°. Augustæ Vindel. 1770
—— **& G. Ballerini.** De vi ac ratione primatûs Roman. pontif., App., De infallibilitate pontif. &c.—De potestate eccles. summorum pontif. & concil. gen., *see* MIGNE (J. P.), *ed.* Theologiæ cursus, t3, 1860.

Ballester (Rafael).
Bibliografia de la hist. de España. 8°. Gerona. 1921

Ballesteros (Mercedes Gaibros de), *see* GAIBROIS DE BALLESTEROS (M.)

Ballesteros Robles (Luis).
Dicc. biográfico matritense. la8°. 1912

Ballesteros y Beretta (Antonio). Hist. de España y su infl. en la hist. univ. t1–4i. la8°. Barcelona. 1919–26
Sevilla en el siglo 13. la8°. 1913

Ballet. Ballet de la délivrance de Renaud, *see* PRUNIÈRES (H.) Ballet de cour en France &c., 1914.

Ballet (Claude Louis Auguste), *see* CASTAING (E. S.) Affaire C.; préc. de not. sur B., 2e éd., 1823.

Ballet (Daniel Hippolyte), *see* CASTAING (E. S.) Affaire C.; préc. de not. sur B., 2e éd., 1823.

Ballhausen (Carl). Die 3 engl.-holländ. Seekriege, 1652–74; sowie d. schwed.-holländ. Seekrieg, 1658–59. Bl. la8°. Haag. 1923

Ballhausen (Lucius, *Frhr.* **v.)**
Bismarck-Erinnerungen. 4.–6. A. 8°. St. 1921

Ballhorn (Friedrich). Alphabete orient. u. occident. Sprachen. 8e verm. A. la8°. L. 1859
„ „ ....10[e] A. 8°. L. 1870

Ballin (Albert), *1857–1918, see* HULDERMANN (B.) A. B., 1922; tr. W. J. Eggers, 1922.

Ballmann (Adolph Joseph), *see* RICHTER (A. F.) & A. J. B. Illyr.-deut. &c. Handwörterbuch, 2T, 1839–40.

Ballmann (Erich), *see* STRAHL (H.) & E. B. Embryonalhüllen u. Plazenta v. Putorius furo, 1915.

Ballot (*Mlle.* **Marie Juliette).** Les laques d'Extrême-Or., Chine & Japon. 8°. 1927
see MARQUET DE VASSELOT (J. J.) & B. Chin. ceramics, 1922.

Balls (William Lawrence). The cotton plant in Egypt. 8°. 1919

Ballu (Albert).
Les ruines de Timgad (antique Thamugadi). la8°. 1897

Ballymote, *Book of.* The book of Ballymote: pieces in Irish lang., compiled 15th c.; w. intr., anal. &c. by R. Atkinson. [Roy. Ir. Acad.] fol. D. 1887

Balmashev (S. V.), *see* KARPOVICH (P. V.) К. & Б. передъ судомъ, 1902.

Balme (Joshua Rhodes).
Letters on the Amer. Republ. enl. ed. s8°. [1864]

Balmerino (Arthur Elphinstone, *6th baron*), *see* KILMARNOCK (W. B., *4th e. of*). Trials of K. & B. for high treason, 1746, w. lives &c., 1746.

Balmont (Konstantin Dmitrievich).
Даръ землѣ. s8°. Парижъ. 1921
Поэзия как волшебство. s8°. Москва. 1922
Сонеты солнца, меда, и луны. s8°. Берлинъ. [1921]

Balogh (Arthur).
Tanulmányok az alkotmánypolitika köréböl. 8°. 1895

Baloghy (Ernö).
A magyar Kultura és a nemzetiségek. 8°. 1908

Balparda (Gregorio de). Hist. crít. de Vizcaya y de sus fueros. tl. 8°. 1924

Balsamo-Crivelli (Gustavo), *see* GIOBERTI (V.) & G. MASSARI. G.-M., carteggio, 1838–52; pubbl. e annot. da G.B.-C., 1920.

Balsamo Crivelli (Riccardo).
Boccaccino racconto. 8°. Bari. 1920
La fiaba di Calugino. 8°. Bari. 1926

Balshaw (H. C. L.) A Spanish reader. s8°. 1918

Baltasar, *Armenian scribe.* Talaran phogrik. [Small song-book *In Armenian*]. s8°. *n.p. n.d.*

Baltazar (Pierre) [BALTHASAR], *see* MARTIN (C.) Généalogies &c. des forestiers & comtes de Flandre: ornées de portraicts &c. par P. B., 1580.

Balthasar (Jacob Heinrich). Diss. de zelo Pomeranorum adv. Reformatos &c. [P441]. s4°. Gryphiswaldiæ. 1722
Hist. d. Torgischen Buchs, als d. nähesten Entwurfs d. Berg. Concordien-Buchs &c. 6 St. *in* 1v. s4°. Greifswald & L. 1741–44

Balthasar (Pierre), *see* BALTAZER (P.)

Baltic. B. pilot, 3p, Suppl. *&* Not., 1912–22, *see* ADMIRALTY.

Baltser (Osvald). Къ ист. общ.-государств. строя Польши. Переводъ съ польскаго подъ редак. Н. В. Ястребова. [*b. w.* Kutshev (S.) Очеркъ, 1907]. 8°. С.–П. 1908

Baltus (Jean François). *Réponse à l'Hist. des Oracles de Mr. de Fontenelle &c. 2e éd. s8°. Strasbourg. 1709
*Suite de la réponse à l'Hist. des Oracles. s8°. Amsterdam. 1709

Baltzer (Johann), *see* LÜBECK. Bau -u. Kunstdenkmäler, T3, 4i, ii; bearb. v. J. B. &c., 1920–28.

Baluchistan. Admin. rep. of the B. Agency, 1917/8–1925/26 fol. Calcutta. 1919–27

Baluze (Etienne). Vitæ Paparum Avenion. 1305–94. n. éd., d'ap. les mss. &c. par G. Mollat. t3–4. 8°. Paris. 1921–22

Balyasny (M.) Чего ждать отъ русскаго національизма. [Оттискъ изъ "Ладо." P2452]. 8°. С.-П. 1911

Balzac (*Mme.* **Eveline),** *née Rzewuska, wife of (1) V. Hanski, (2) H. de Balzac, see* LÉGER (C.) Eve de Balzac d'ap. des docs. inéd., 1926.

Balzac (Honoré de).
Contes philosoph. Intr. par P. Bourget. [Coll. Gallia]. s8°. Londres. [1913]
Le cousin Pons. [Les parents pauvres]. s8°. *n.d.*
Illusions perdues. 3[t]. s8°. [1924–25]
Le père Goriot. [Notice biog. par H. Duvernois]. s8°. Londres. *Dent.* [1907]
La recherche de l'absolu. s8°. *n.d.*

TRANSLATIONS.
[La comédie humaine]. Tr. E. Sedgwick, [W. Walton, G. B Ives &c. Ed. defin. *Japan*

TRANSLATIONS [*continued*].
paper. Plates in 2 states]. 11v [v10 *wanting*]. 8°. *for subs.* 1897
About Catherine de Medici. [Tr. C. Bell]. [repr.] s8°. [1925]
Eugénie Grandet. [Tr. E. Marriage. Pref. by G. Saintsbury]. [repr.] s8°. [c. 1907]
Old Goriot. [Tr. E. Marriage. Pref. by G. Saintsbury]. [repr.] s8°. [1908]
The wild ass's skin. [Tr. E. Marriage]. [repr.] s8°. 1908

Balzac (Honoré de) [*continued*].
TRANSLATIONS [*continued*].
see BALDENSPERGER (F.) Orientations étrangères chez H. de B., 1927.
„ BARNES (H. E.) St. of variations betw. ed[s]. of B.'s Les Chouans, 1923.
„ BENJAMIN (R.) La prodig. vie d'H. de B., 1925.
„ CLOUZOT (H.) & R.-H. VALENSI. Le Paris de la Comédie humaine—(B. & ses fournisseurs), 1926.
see FLOYD (J. H.) Women in the life of B., 1921.
„ GIGLI (G.) B. in Italia, 1920.
„ LÉGER (C.) Ève de B. d'ap. des docs. inéd., 1926.
„ LUDWIG (E.) Kunst u. Schicksal (B. &c.), 1927.

Balzac (Jean Louis Guez *sieur* **de)** [J. L. GUEZIUS BALZACIUS]. Aristippus. Being a disc. conc. the court. Eng. by R. W. s8°. 1659.

Balzani (Ugo). Di alcuni doc. rel. al ritrov. d. cadavere di P. Sarpi. [Estr., R. Accad. dei Lincei, Cl. di sci. morale &c., v4. P2837]. la8°. Roma. 1895

Bambagiuoli (Graziuolo de') [BAMBAGLIOLI]. Il commento piú antico e la piú ant. versione lat. d. Inferno. P. c. d. A. Fiammazzo. 8°. Udine. 1892

Bampfylde (John). Poet. works. Collated by T. Park. [*b. w.* Moore (J. H.). Poet. works, 1808]. s8°. 1808.

Banachevitch (Nicolas).
Jean Bastier de La Péruse (1529–54). 8°. 1923

Banaser. [Revue archéol., hist. &c. Publ. sous la dir. de K. J. Basmadjian. *in Armenian*]. 1899, no. 4, 1900, no. 1, 1902–1907 [1902, no. 1 *in* P2811 ; 1906, no. 3 *wanting*]. 8°. Paris. 1899–1907

Banat. Mém. prés. à la Conf. de la Paix. L'unité du Banat, situation écon. du Banat. [Déleg. des Souabes du Banat]. [P2501]. 4°. 1919

Bancel (A. Daudé-), *see* DAUDÉ-BANCEL (A.)

Bancels (J. Larguier des), *see* LARGUIER DES BANCELS (J.)

Banchelli (Umberto F.) Le mem. di un Fascista, 1919–22. s8°. Firenze. 1922

Banchi (Luciano), *see* SENESE. Statuti S. ; publ. p. c. di F.-L. Polidori [& L. B.], 1863–67.

Banckes (Richard) [BANKS]. Religion & reason adjusted &c. w. app. of objections. [*b. w.* Stebbing (H.) A defence, 1718.] 2nd ed. [*2 pagin*]. s8°. 1696

Bancks (Charles Gerard Winstanley). Hartley thr. the ages. 8°. Hartley. 1927

Banco Urquijo, *see* ESPAÑA. La riqueza y el progreso de E. ; ed. por el B. U., 1924.

Bancroft (George), *historian.*
Hist. of the U.S. author's last rev. 6v. 8°. N.Y. 1883–85
Joseph Reed : a hist. essay. [*a. c. in* P2623]. 8°. N.Y. 1867
Lit. & hist. miscell. 8°. N.Y. 1855
see GREENE (G. W.) Nathanael Greene. An exam. conc. N. G., in v9 of B.'s Hist. of U.S., 1866.
„ SCHUYLER (G. L.) Corr. upon B.'s Hist. 1867.

Bancroft (Hubert Howe).
Hist. de Méjico. 8°. San Francisco. 1887

Bancroft (Nathaniel William). The Bengal Horse artillery of the olden time ; w. sk. of Sutlej campaign. [P2602]. 2nd ed. 8°. Simla. 1900

Bancroft (Richard), *bp. of London ; abp. of Canterbury.* Daungerous positions &c., publ. &c. within this Iland of Brytaine under pretence of Reformation &c. s8°. 1593

Bancroft (*Sir* Squire B.) Empty chairs. 8°. 1925

Bandelier (Adolph Francis Alphonse) & Fanny Ritter Bandelier, *edd.*, *see* HACKETT (C. W.) *ed.* Hist. doc[s]. rel. to New Mexico &c., v1, 2, 1923–26.

Bandello (Matteo), *bp. of Agen.* Le 5e tome des Hist. tragiques ; par F. de Bel-leforest (*sic*), 1582 ; tr. 1608, *see* GOLLANCZ (I.) Sources of Hamlet, 1926.
Rime : pubbl. L. Costa. 8°. Torino. 1816
Tragical tales. Tr. G. Fenton. Intr. by R. L. Douglas. Modernized & ed. by H. Harris. [Broadway trans.] 8°. [1924]
see FISCHER (R.) Quellen zu Romeo u. Julia (B., Brooke (*Eng. & Germ.*) &c.), 1922.

Bandettini Landucci (Teresa) [AMARILLI ETRUSCA]. Poesie estemporanee. t1, 2 [*tp. of t2 damaged*]. 8°. Lucca. 1835

Bandinelli (R. Bianchi), *see* BIANCHI BANDINELLI (R.)

Bandini (Angelo Maria). A. M. B. in Piemonte : diario di viaggio, nov. 1778 ; *ed.* A. Beccaria, *see* REGIA DEPUT. Miscellanea, t45, 1910.
Fasciculus rerum Græc. eccl. exhib. tract. Basilii Magni de Synisactis, Necephori Callisti Xanthopuli sermonem in M. Magdalenam &c. Græce, cura A. M. Bandini. [Gr. Eccl. vet mon. ex Bibl. Medicea]. 8°. Florentiæ. 1764

Bandini (Angelo Maria) [*continued*].
Vita di A. Vespucci (1745). Comm. da G. Uzielli. Bibl. d. opere conc. P. Toscanelli & A. V. per G. Fumagalli. sfol. Firenze. 1898
see CIPOLLA (C.) A. M. B. a Verona (1778), 1913.

Bandini (Carlo). Spoleto. [Italia art. 85]. la8°. Bergamo. [1922 ?]

Bandtkie (Jerzy Samuel). De primis Cracoviæ in arte typogr. incunabulis diss. s4°. Cracoviæ. 1812

Banerjea (Pramathanath). A study of Ind. economics. 2nd ed. rev. & enl. s8°. 1915

Banerjea (*Sir* Surendranath). A nation in making : remin. of 50 years of public life. 8°. 1925

Banerjee (Gauranga Nath). Hellenism in anc. India. 2nd ed. rev. & enl. 8°. Calcutta. 1920

Banerji (Nripendra Chandra). The ideal of Swaraj in educ. & govt. Intr. by C. F. Andrews. s8°. Madras. 1921

Banerji (R. D.), *M.A.* The Pālas of Bengal. [*Extr. f.* As. Soc. of Bengal, Mem., v5. P2751]. 4°. Calcutta. 1915
The temple of Śiva, at Bhumara, *see* INDIA : ARCH. SURVEY. Mem. 16, 1924.

Banff, *county of.* Records of the co. of B., 1660–1760. Comp. by J. Grant. W. intr. by A. & H. Tayler. [New Spalding Club]. 4°. Aberdeen. 1922

Banfield (E. J.) Last leaves f. Dunk Island ; intr. by A. H. Chisholm. s8°. [Sydney]. 1925
My tropic isle. [2nd ed.] 8°. [1912]
Tropic days. 8°. [1918]

Bang (A. Chr). Hans Nielsen Hauge og hans samtid. 3e opl. 8°. 1910
Den norske kirkes historie. la8°. 1912

Bang (Herman). Excentriske Noveller. s8°. 1914
Værker i Mindeudgave. 2[et] Oplag. 6B. s8°. 1920–21
1, Ved Vejen—Det hvide Hus—Det graa Hus—Sommerglæder. 2, Fortællinger. 3, Haabløse Slægter—Stuk. 4, Tine—Ludvigsbakke. 5, Mikaël—De uden Fædreland. 6, Digte—To Sørgespil—Ti Aar—Theater.

Bang (Thomas) [BANGIUS]. Exercit. de ortu & progr. literarum &c. s4°. Cracoviæ. 1691

Bang (Willy). Materialien zur Kunde d. ält. eng. Dramas. Begründet u. hrsg. v. W. B. B34ii, iii. 4°. Louvain. 1912–13
Crawford (C.) The Marlowe Concordance [p2, 3], 1912–13. [34ii, iii.]
Vom Kökturk. z. Osman., Mittlg., 1–4, *see* KÖN. PREUSS. AKAD. D. WISS. Abhdl. (Phil.-hist. Klasse), 1917, 1919, 1921.
—— **& J. Marquart.** Osttürk. Dialektstudien, 1914, *see* KÖN. GESELLS. D. WISS. ZU GÖTT. Abhlgn., N.F., B13, 1914.

Bangay (R. D.) Elem. princ[s]. of wireless telegraphy. 11th impr. 2p [*in 1v. sep. tp[s]. & pagin[s].*] s8°. 1923

Bange (Ernst Friedrich). Peter Flötner. [Meister d. Graphik, B14]. sfol. L. [1916]

Bangius (Thomas), *see* BANG (T.)

Bangor. Diocese of Bangor in the 16th c.: digest of reg. of the bishops, 1512–1646. Comp. w. intr. by A. I. Pryce. 8°. Bangor. 1923

Bangs (Heman), 1790–1869, *Wesleyan minister.* The autobiog. & journal of the Rev. H. B. ; w. introd. by Bp. Janes. Ed. by h. daughters [*w. a* memorial of Mrs. Sally Burritt Bangs, *w. sep. pag.*] s8°. N.Y. 1872

Bangs (Nathan). A hist. of the Methodist Episc. church [*var. ed[s].*] 4v. s8°. N.Y. 1845–56
see STEVENS (A.). Life & times of N. B., 1863.

Banholzer (P.), *see* HOFMAYR (W.) Die Schilluk : nach. P. B., 1925.

Banister (Thomas). *Britain & h. colonial dependencies &c. [*MS. add[n]. by a.*] [P2832]. 8°. 1844

Bankers' Clearing House, London. Report, 1920–27 [*no tp.*] la8°. [1921–28]

Bankers Trust Company, *New York.* America's merchant marine. [Publ. by B. T. Co.] s8°. N.Y. 1920

Bankes (Viola). Shadow-show. s8°. [1921]

Bankipore. Cat. of Arabic & Persian MSS. in the Oriental Public Library at B. Prep. by Maulavi Abdul Muqtadir [v5, 10 by Maulavi Abdul Hamid. 12, by Maulavi Muinuddin Nadwi.] v5–12 [5 *in* 2p].
5, Tradition, 2p. 6, History. 7, Ind. hist. 8, Biog., romances &c. 9, Persian MSS. ; philology & sciences. 10, Theology. 11, Persian MSS. ; sciences (cont.) & arts. 12, Arabic MSS. Biog.
Reproductions of illust[s]. f. 3 Persian MSS. [Bâdshâh Nâmah—Shah Nîmah—Tîmûr-Nâmah] in Or. Publ. Lib. at B. Prep. by Wali-ud-din Khuda Bakhsh. [Descr. list & Reprod[s]. *b. together*]. fol. *n.p.* [1920]

Bankrotstvo. *Банкротство буржуазныхъ идеаловъ. [P848]. s8°. [Москва]. 1905

Banks (Elizabeth L.) School for John & Mary. s8°. 1925

Banks (John Shaw). Christianity & the science of religion. [Fernley Lect.] 8°. 1880

Our Indian Empire: its rise &c. s8°. 1889

Banks (*Rt. Hon. Sir* **Joseph**), *bart.*, *see* HERMANNSSON (H.) B. & Iceland, 1928.

Banks (Nathan). A revision of the Nearctic termites, w. notes by T. E. Snyder. [S.I. U.S. Nat. Mus.; Bull., 108]. 8°. Wash. 1920

Banks (Theodore Howard), *Jr.* Wild geese. [Yale Ser. of Younger Poets]. s8°. New Haven, *Yale*. 1921

Banks (*Sir* **Thomas Christopher**), *bart.* Hist. of the family of Marmyun, office of King's champion &c. 4°. 1817

Bannatyne Club.

see ARBROATH. Liber S. Thome de Aberbrothoc, 1178–1536, 2p, 1848–56.

,, COURCELLES (—). Extr. f. despatches, 1586–87, 1828.

,, DRYBURGH. Liber S. Marie de D., 1847.

,, FERRERIUS (J.) Hist. Abbatium de Kynlos &c., 1839.

see MELROSE ABBEY. Chron. de Mailros; ed. J. Stevenson, 1835.

,, MORTON, *Earldom of.* Reg. Honoris de M., 2v, 1853.

,, SAINT ANDREWS. Liber cartarum Prioratus S. Andree, 1841.

,, SCOTLAND. Papers rel. to the regalia of S., 1829.

,, SOLTRE. Reg. Domus de S. &c., 1861.

Bannerman (D. Douglas). The scripture doct. of the church. Cunningham Lects. 8°. E. 1887

Bannerman (David Armitage). The Canary Islands. la8°. 1922

Bannister (Arthur Thomas). The cathedral ch. of Hereford. [Sts. in church hist.] 8°. [1924]

see HEREFORD. Descr. cat. of MSS. in H. Cath. Library; compiled by A. T. B., 1927.

,, —— Diocese of H.: institutions, 1539–1900; comp. by A. T. B. 1923.

Bannister (Henry Marriott), *see* VATICAN LIBRARY. Monumenti Vatic. di paleografia musicale lat.; racc. e ill. da E. M. B., 1913.

Banting (William). Letter on corpulence. 3rd. ed. 8°. 1864

Bantock (Granville Ransome), *see* ANDERTON (H. O.) G. B. [Living masters of music], 1915.

Banzarov (Dordji). Изъ писемъ Д. Б. [1847–52], съ пред. &c. П. С. Савельева, *see* IMP. RUSS. ARCH. OBSCH. Труды Восточ. отд., ч3, 1858.

Bapp (Carl). Aus Goethes griech. Gedankenwelt: G. & Heraklit &c. [Das Erbe d.Alten, Reihe 2, H6]. 8°. L. 1921

Bapst (Germain).

Etudes sur l'étain dans l'antiq. & au m. â. 8°. 1884

Baptismal. *Baptismal bonds renewed, by O. H., *M.A.*, 1687, *see* HEYWOOD (O.)

Baptist [BAPTISTS]. De algemeene Belydenissen d. vereen. Vlaamsche, Vriesche, en Hooghduitsche Doopsgezinde Gemeinte Godts &c. Door I. P. S. [*Foll. by* Het oprecht verbondt v. eenigheyt—Vereenig. van de princ. Artijkelen —Laatste byvoegsel (1626), 1740, *each w. sep. tp. & pagin.*] s8°. Rotterdam. 1739

Baptist (The) Confession of faith. Pref. by C. H. Spurgeon. s8°. 1855

A confession of faith put forth by elders &c. of Xtns. baptized upon profession in London & country. s8°. 1677

Baptist Mission Press, *Calcutta.*

Specimen of printing types. 8°. Calcutta. 1826

Baptist Missionary Soc. *Christian miss. in the East & West, in conn. w. B. M. S., 1792–1872, 1873, *see* UNDERHILL (E. B.)

Periodical accounts. 6v. [v3 *wanting*]. 8°. Clipstone, *aft.* London. 1800–10

see COX (F. A.) Hist. of Baptist Mission. Soc., 2v, 1842.

Baptist (The) record & Biblical repository. v1. 8°. 1844

Barabino (Nicolò), *1832–91*, *see* SAPORI (F.) Maestri dell' arte, No. 4, 1919.

Baracca (Francesco), *see* MASCARDI (M.) Vita di F. B., 1925.

Barach (Carl Sigmund). Kleine philosoph. Schriften. (Hieronymus Hirnhaim—Nominalismus vor Roscellin—Die Wiss. als Freiheitsthat, *each w. sep. pagin.*) 8°. Wien. 1878

Barahona (Diego). Glosa a la obra de Jorge Manrrique. [Hispanic Soc. of America]. 8°. *n.p.* 1541 [facs. repr. *De Vinne Press.* 1902]

Baranov (A.) Словарь Монгольскихъ терминовъ. [Мат. по Маньчжурiи &c. B11, 36]. [2p *in* 1v.] la8°. Харбинъ. 1907–11

Barat (L.), *see* DUMAS (G.) Traité de psychologie; avec collab. de L. B. &c., t1, 1923.

Baratta (Mario). Cesare Battisti—Confine orient. d'Italia—G. Mazzini ed il confine orient. d'It., *see* QUADERNI geograf., N.1, 3, 7, 1918–19.

Barbadoro (Bernardino).

see DAMI (L.) & B. B. Firenze di Dante, 1921.

,, FIORENTINA. Consigli d. Rep. F.: per c. di B. B., 1921.

Barbagallo (Corrado), *see* FERRERO (G.) & C. B. Roma antica, 3v, 1921–22.

Barbari (Sacopo de), *see* BORENIUS (T.) 4 early Ital. engr., 1923.

Barbarini (*il card.* **Antonio**), *see* BARBERINO.

Barbaro (Daniello). Exquisitæ in Porphirium comment. s8°. Venetiis. 1542

Barbarus (Hermolaus), *Patriarch of Aquileia*, *see* MELANCHTHON (P.) Elementorum rhetorices libri 2, adj. Epistolæ Pici & H. B. &c., 1547.

Barbauld (*Mrs.*), *1743–1825*, *see* AIKIN (J.) & *Mrs.* B. Evenings at home, 1814.

Barbavara (Francesco), *see* MAIOCCHI (R.) F. B. dur. la reggenza di Caterina Visconti, 1898.

Barbeau (Marius) & E. Sapir. Folk songs of French Canada. la8°. New Haven, *Yale*. 1925

Barbellion (W. N. P.), *ps.* [*i.e.* B. F. CUMMINGS].

Enjoying life & o. lit. remains. s8°. 1919

,, ,, ...[2nd impr.] s8°. 1919

A last diary. Pref. by A. J. Cummings. s8°. 1920

Barber (Edwin Atlee). Mexican maiolica in coll. of Hisp. Soc. of America. 8°. N.Y. 1915

Spanish glass in coll. of Hisp. Soc. of Amer. s8°. N.Y. 1917

Barber (Eric Arthur), *see* BURY (J. B.) Hellenistic age; by J. B. B., E. A. B. &c., 1923.

see POWELL (J. U.) & E. A. B., *edd.* New chapters in hist. of Greek lit., 1921.

Barber (Margaret H.) A British nurse in Bolshevik Russia, Apr. 1916–Dec. 1919. [P2431]. s8°. 1920

Barber (Marshall Albert), *see* DARLING (S. T.), M. A. B. &c. Hookworm & malaria research in Malaya &c., 1920.

Barber (Robert). [A book of psalmody, cont. variety of tunes &c.; *no tp.*] 8°. [1727?]

Psalm singer's choice companion. [*b. w. h.* Bk. of psalmody]. 8°. 1727

Barbèra (Piero). La Toscana alla fine del Granducato: conf. di P. B. &c., 1909, *see* TOSCANA.

Barberino (*il card.* **Antonio**) [BARBARINI], *see* URBAN VIII, *pope.* *Passionate remonstrance upon late procs. &c., w. reply of Card. de B. (*satire*, 1641), 1884.

Barberino (*il card.* **Francesco**), *the elder*, *see* ANTIQUITATES. Eccles. Orient. antiq. B. &c., 1682.

Barbey (Bernard).

Le cœur gros. [Les cahiers verts, 45]. s8°. 1924

Barbey d'Aurevilly (Jules A.).

Disjecta membra. Les textes. 2t. 8°. 1925

see BORDEAUX (H.) Le Walter Scott normand, B. d'A., 1925.

Barbi (Michele). Studi Danteschi. [*By var. authors*]. Dir. da M. B. v1–12. 8°. Firenze. 1920–27

Studi sul Canzoniere di Dante, con nuove indagini sulle raccolte di ant. rime ital. 8°. Firenze. 1915

Barbier (Paul). Eng. infl. on the French vocab. [S. P. E. Tract No. 7, 13]. [2p]. 8°. O. 1921–23

Barbiera (Raffaello).

Ideali e caratteri dell' ottocento. 8°. Milano. 1926

Nella gloria e nell' ombra. 8°. Milano. 1926

Voci e volti del passato (1800–1900). s8°. Milano. 1920

Barbier d'Aucour (Jean). *Onguant pour la brûlure; ou le secret pour empescher aux Jésuites de bruler des livres, 1683, *see* LE MAISTRE DE SACY (I. L.) Les Enluminures &c., 1683.

Barbier de Meynard (Charles Adrien Casimir). Dict. géog., hist. & litt. de la Perse &c. extr. du Mòdjem el-Bouldan de Yaqout &c. la8°. 1861

Barbier de Montault (Xavier). Traité liturg. &c. des Agnus Dei. 3e éd. [P2506]. 8°. Rome. 1865

Barbieri (Guiseppe), *see* †CENTONAJO, *messer.* Novelletta, piacevole [*by G. B.*], *n.d.*

Barbosa (Duarte). Book of D. B. Acc. of countries bordering on the Indian Ocean &c., compl. about 1518. Tr., ed. &c. M. L. Dames. [Hakluyt Soc., s2, v49]. 8°. 1921

see TEMPLE (*Sir* R. C.) Some comments on B. (as ed. by M. L. Dames), 1923.

Barbosa (José). Cat. chronolog., hist., genealog. &c. das rainhas de Portugal &c. 8º. 1727

Barbour (George Freeland).
Life of Alex. Whyte, D.D. 8º. 1923

Barbour (John), *see* ALEXANDER, *the Gt.* Buik of A., by J. B.; ed. Ritchie, v1–3, 1921–27.

Barbusse (Henri).
Les enchaînements. 2t. s8º. [1925]
Jésus. s8º. [1927]
Light. Tr. F. Wray. s8º. 1919
Paroles d'un combattant. Articles &c., 1917–20. s8º. [1920]
Trois films: Force—L'au-dela—Le crieur. s8º. [1926]
Under fire. Tr. F. Wray. [Intr. by B. Rhys. Everyman's Lib.] s8º. [1926]
see MAXE (J.) Cahiers de l'anti-France, 4, "Clarté," s. initiateurs, R. Lefèbvre &c.; 5, "Clarté," séminaire des apprentis dictateurs, 1922.

Barbuto (Rustico), *see* RUSTICO DI FILIPPO.

Barcia (Angel M. de), *see* ALBA (J. S. F., *Duke* DE). Cat. de la col. de pinturas del D., por B., 1911.

Barckhausen (Henri Auguste), *ed., see* BORDEAUX. Archives municip., 1878–90.

Barclay (John), *minister of the Berean Assembly in Edinburgh.*
The Psalms paraphr. acc. to the N. T. interpret. &c. [v2, A select coll. of new orig. spirit. songs &c. *No gen. tp.*] [2v]. s8º. E. 1776

Barclay (John), *poet, a. of the Argenis.* [BARCLAIUS (GUILELMUS)]. Argenis. Nunc primum illust. [*by* L. G. Bugnotius, *w. life of the a.*] 8º. Lugd. Bat. 1664
The mirror of minds: or Barclay's Icon animorum. Engl. by T. May. s8º. 1633

Barclay (John M.) Digest of rules of H. of Repres., *see* UNITED STATES. Constit., add. B.'s Digest., 1871.

Barclay (Robert), *the elder.* An apology for the true Xtian divinity, as held forth by Quakers. s4º. 1678
*A catechism & conf. of faith. By R. B. 6th ed. s8º. 1740
*Serious consid. on absolute predestination. Extr. f. a late a. [*i.e.* R. B., *by* J. Wesley. P2533]. s8º. Bristol. 1741
see KEITH (G.) The standard of the Quakers examined, or an ans. to the Apology of R. B., 1702.

Barclay (*Sir* Thomas). The French judicial system. [Repr. f. Jurid. Rev. P2849]. 8º. 1926

Barclay (William).
Banffshire. [Camb. County Geographies]. s8º. C. 1922
Schools & schoolmasters of Banffshire. Foreword by Sir G. A. Smith. la8º. Banff. 1925

Barclay (William) [BARCLAIUS], *professor of Civil Law at Angers.* De potestate Papæ. s8º. [London?]. 1609
see BELLARMINO (*il card.* R. E. R.) Tract. de potestate pontificis adv. W. B., 1610.

Barclay (William Singer).
The land of Magellan. 8º. [1926]

Barclays Bank, Ltd., *see* MATTHEWS (P. W.) Hist. of B. B., Ltd.; ed. A. W. Tuke, 1926.

Barcyǹska (*Countess* Helene). Love's last reward. s8º. [1920]
Tesha. s8º. [1923]

Barðarson (Guðmundur G.) Om d. marine Molluskfauna ved Vestkysten af Island, *see* KONG. DAN. VID. SELSK. Biol. Medd., B2, 1919–20.
Stratigraph. survey of pliocene deposits at Tjörnes, Iceland, *see* KONG. DAN. VID. SELSK. Biol. Medd., 4, 1923–25.

Bardavíu Ponz (Vicente). Hist. de la ant. villa de Albalate del Arzobispo. 8º. Zaragoza. 1914

Bardenhewer (Otto). Gesch. d. altkirchl. Lit. B4. 8º. Freiburg im Breisgau. 1924
4, Das 5te Jhdt., mit Einschluss d. syr. Lit. d. 4ten Jhdt.

Bardi, *The family of, see* SAPORI (A.) Compagnie d. B. &c. in Inghilt. n. sec. 13 e 14, 1922.

Bardi (Pietro). La poesia di Wordsworth (1770–1808). [Bibl. di cultura mod.] 8º. Bari. 1922

Bardin (J. B.) Hist. du pays de Septême (Isère). 2e éd. 8º. Vienne. 1905

Bardina (Sofiya Illarionovna), *see* STEPNIAK (S.), *ps.* *C. H. Б., 1883; 1900.

Bardola (C.) Sonets, *see* ROMANISCHE FORSCHUNGEN, B32, 37, 1913–17.

Bardo Thödol. The Tibetan Book of the Dead [B. T.]: after-death exper. on the Bardo plane acc. to Lāma Kazi Dawa-Samdup's Eng. rendering. By W. Y. Evans-Wentz. Foreword by Sir J. Woodroffe. 8º. 1927

Bardoux (Jacques). L'ouvrier Anglais d'aujourd'hui. 8º. 1921

Bardy (Gustave). Paul de Samosate: ét. hist. [Spicilegium sacrum. Lovan. Ets. & docs., fasc. 4]. la8º. Louvain. 1923

Bare (Maurice de). Les meunières du Moulin Rouge, *see* ŒUVRES LIBRES, 48, 1925.

Bareilles (Bertrand).
Le drame oriental. D'Athènes à Angora. s8º. 1923
Un Turc à Paris 1806–11: voyage & mission de Mouhib Effendi ambass. du Sultan Selim III. [P2711]. s8º. 1920

Barennes (Jean), *see* BIRON (R.) & J. B. Un prince anglais, card.-légat au 16e s., R. Pole, 1923.

Barentonius (Gulielmus Postellus), *see* POSTEL (GUILLAUME).

Baret (Michael). An hipponomie, or, the vineyard of horsemanship, devided into 3 bks. [*4 pagins. tp. &c. wanting*]. 8º. 1618

Baretti (Giuseppe), *see* NEUMAN (H.) & G. B. Dict. of Span. & Eng., 4th ed., 2v, 1823.

Barfield (Owen). History in Eng. words. s8º. [1926]

Barfod (H. P. B.). H.M. Kong Christian IX. 2B *in* 1. 4º. København. 1888–1906

Bargagli (Scipione). I trattenimenti dove da vaghe donne e da giovani huomini rappresentati sono honesti &c. giuochi: narrate novelle; e cantate alcune amorose canzonette. s4º. Venetia, *Giunti.* 1592

Bargagli-Petrucci (Fabio). Storia delle arti decor. e applic. v1. la8º. Bologna. [1926?]

Bargilliat (Michel). Prælect. juris canon. ed. 30a ab auct. recog. &c. 2t. s8º. Parisiis. 1915

Barham (Rich. Harris).
Ingoldsby legends. compl. ed. [3s *in* 1v]. s8º. 1889

Barhydt (David Parish).
Indust. exchanges & social remedies &c. s8º. N.Y. 1849

Bariatinsky (*princess* Anatole Marie).
Character as revealed by handwriting. s8º. [1924]
My Russian life 8º. 1923

Barić (Andria).
Slovica Serbsko-ilirsk. jezika. 2º izd. 8º. Splietu. 1860

Barichella (Vittorio).
Andrea Palladio e la sua scuola. 4º. Lonigo. 1880

Barignano (Pietro), *see* RUSCELLI (G.) Rime di div. autori bresciani: P. B. &c., 1553.

Barillon (Henry de), *bp. of Luçon.* Ordonnances synodales du dioceze de Luçon. s8º. Paris. 1685

Baring (*Hon.* Maurice), *4th son of 1st baron Revelstoke.*
C. 8º. [1924]
,, ...[n. impr.] 8º. [1924]
Cat's cradle. 8º. [1925]
Coll. poems. 8º. [1925]
Daphne Adeane. 8º. [1926]
,, ,, [n. impr.] 8º. [1926]
Dead letters. [*repr. w. adds.*] 8º. [1925]
Diminutive dramas. 2nd impr. s8º. [1919]
French lit. s8º. [1927]
Half a minute's silence & o. stories. 8º. [1925]
Hildesheim. 4 pastiches. 8º. 1924
His Majesty's embassy & o. plays. 8º. [1923]
In memoriam A. Herbert, Capt. Lord Lucas, killed, Nov. 3 1916. [*Poem*]. 8º. O. 1917
Overlooked. s8º. 1922
Oxford book of Russian verse. Chosen by M. B. s8º. O. 1924
Passing by. s8º. [1921]
Poems: 1914–19. s8º. [1920]
Punch & Judy & o. e. 8º. [1924]
The puppet show of memory. 8º. 1922
R.F.C. H.Q., 1914–18. s8º. 1920
Round the world in any number of days. s8º. 1919
Tinker's leave. s8º. [1927]
A triangle. s8º. [1923]

Baring-Gould (Sabine).
Brittany. [Little Guides]. s8º. 1902
Early reminiscences, 1834–64. 8º. [1923]
The Evangelical revival. 8º. [1920]
Further reminiscences, 1864–94. 8º. [1925]
Germany. By S. B.-G., w. collab. of A. Gilman. Rev. & enl. by J. McCabe. [Story of the Nations]. [10th impr. (2nd ed.)] 8º. [1921]
Yorkshire oddities. 4th ed. 2v *in* 1. 8º. 1880

Baringius (Melchior Laurentius).
De ascetis dissert. [P2743]. s4º. Helmestadi. 1672

Barja (César).
Libros y autores mod. [Lit. española]. s8º. [1924]

Barkas (Thomas P.) An acc. of Miss Wood's mediumship, see SMEDLEY (A.) Some reminisc., 1900.

Barker (*Capt.* D. Wilson), *see* WILSON-BARKER (*Capt.* D.)

Barker (Ernest), *M.A.*
The Crusades. [World's manuals]. s8º. 1923
National character. 8º. [1927]

Barker (Harley Granville). [GRANVILLE-BARKER (H. G.)].
The exemplary theatre. 8º. 1922
From Henry V to Hamlet. [From Procs. of Brit. Acad. P2821]. 8º. [1925]
On translating plays, *see* ROY. SOC. OF LIT. Essays, N.S., v5, 1925.
Prefaces to Shakespeare. s1. 8º. 1927
The secret life. Play. s8º. 1923

Barker (Harley Granville, [*continued*].

Some tasks for dramatic scholarship, *see* ROY. SOC. OF LIT. Essays, N.S., v3, 1923.

The Voysey inheritance, *see* PLAYS of to-day, v1, 1925.

see ARCHER (W.) & H. G. B. A national theatre, 1907.

,, HOUSMAN (L.) & G. B. Prunella, 1925.

Barker (Helen Granville-), *wife of Harley Granville Barker.* Ada. s8º. 1923

Barker (J. Ellis). Cancer, how it is caused &c. Intr. by Sir W. A. Lane. 8º. [1924]

Good health & happiness. Intr. by Sir W. A. Lane. s8º. [1927]

[Mod. Germany, her problems &c. *Tr. into Japanese*]. 8º. [1921]

Barker (Joseph), *1806–1875.* The life of Joseph Barker. Wr. by himself. Ed. J. T. Barker. s8º. 1880

Barker (William Gideon Michael Jones). Hist. &c. of Wensleydale & the valley of the Yore. 2nd ed. 8º. 1856

Barkey (Nicolaus). Bibliotheca Hagana, 1768–77, *see* BIBLIOTHECA.

see BIBLIOTHECA Bremensis nova, 1760–67.

,, MUSEUM Haganum hist.-philol.-theologicum &c., 1774–80.

,, SYMBOLÆ litt. Haganæ, 1777–81.

Barkhausen (Heinrich).

Elektronen-Röhren. 2. umgearb. A. B1. 8º. L. 1924

Barking. Ordinale & customary of the Benedictine nuns of Barking Abbey. [Wr. at instance of S. Felton, abbess]. Ed. w. pref. by J. B. L. Tolhurst. [Henry Bradshaw Soc., 65]. v1. 8º. 1927

Barkly (Sir Henry) *K.C.B.* Arnald de Berkeley. [Repr. f. Trans. of Bristol &c. Arch. Soc., v16. P2705]. 8º. [Bristol. 1892]

The Berkeleys of Cobberley. [Repr. f. Trans. of Bristol &c. Arch. Soc., v17. P2705]. 8º. [Bristol. 1893]

The earlier house of Berkeley. [Repr. f. Trans. of Bristol &c. Arch. Soc., v8. P2705]. 8º. [Bristol. 1884]

On fallibility of Domesday in reg. to " ancient demesne." [*Extr.* P2702]. 4º. *n.p. n.d.*

Remarks on the Liber Niger of the Exchequer. [Repr. f. Trans. of Bristol &c. Arch. Soc., v14. P2705]. 8º. [Bristol. 1890]

Barkworth (Arthur Bromby Wilson-), *see* WILSON-BARKWORTH (A. B.)

Barlaam & Josaphat. Б. и І. Груз. текстъ, съ перевод. и пред. изд. А. Хахановъ. [Лазар. Инст. Вост. Яз. Труды, вып. 9. P2803]. 8º. Москва. 1902

see MARR (N. YA.) Агіограф матер. по груз. рукописямъ Ивера, ч2, житіе Св. В. Сирокавказскаго, 1901.

,, —— Мудрость Балавара, груз. версія душепол. ист. о В. и І., 1889.

,, OTTO II, *bp. of Freising.* Der Laubacher B., 1913.

Barlow (George), [*ps.* JAMES HINTON]. A lost mother. la8º. 1892

Barlow (Jane). Between doubting & daring. Verses. s8º. O. 1916

From the East unto the West. s8º. 1898

Barlow (Jerome), *see* ROY (W.) & J. B. *Rede me & be nott wrothe &c., 1528; ed. E. Arber, 1871.

Barlow (John), *minister of the Word.* An expos. of the 1st & 2nd chap. of the latter Episte [*sic*] of Paul to Timothie. [*Foll*^{d}. *by* A disc. of spiritual steadfastness &c. The true guide to glory &c., & o. sermons, *w. sep. tp*^{s}. *& pagin.*] sfol. 1632

Barlow (Percival). The general hist. of Europe; &c. fol. [1791 ?]

Barlow (Thomas), *bp. of Lincoln.* Brutum fulmen, or the bull of Pope Pius V. [dat. 27 April 1570] conc. the damnation of Q. Elizabeth with obs. &c. [*wants tp.*] s4º. 1681

*A few plain reasons why a Protestant of the Ch. of Eng. should not turn R.C. [P2661]. s4º. 1688

Popery: or the principles &c. appr. by the Ch. of Rome. s8º. 1679

Barlow (Thomas Lambert), *see* MACNAIR (J. F. A.) & T. L. B. Oral trad. f. the Indus, 1908.

Barlow (William), *bp. of Chichester; d. 1568.* Dialogue on the Lutheran factions [1531]. With introd. on Anglican Orders by J. R. Lunn. s8º. 1897

see BARNES (A. S.) Bp. Barlow & Anglican orders, 1922.

Barlow (Wm.), *bp. of (1) Rochester, (2) Lincoln.* The summe and substance of the Conference, wh. it pleased H.M. to have w. clergie at Hampton Court Jan. 14, 1603. Added, some copies untrue. s4º. 1604

Barmanum. *Alphabetum Barmanum &c., 1776; 1787, *see* ALPHABETUM.

Barnabas, *Saint.*

see APOSTOLIC. The Apostolic Fathers; [tr.], v1, 1888; 1909.

,, COTELERIUS (J. B.), *ed.*, SS. patrum B^{ae} &c. opera, 2v, 1724.

,, LIETZMANN (H.) Hdbh. z. N.T.; Ergänzungsband, 3, Der B.-brief, erkl. v. H. Windisch, 1920.

see ROBINSON (J. A.) B., Hermas &c., 1920.

,, WAKE (W.) The genuine epistles of the apostol. Fathers, B. &c.; tr., 1719.

Barnabei (Felice). Scavi di antichità nel territorio falisco (Narce &c.), *&* Atlante, *see* REALE ACCAD. D. LINCEI. Mon. ant., v4, 1894.

Barnard (*The Lady* Anne), *see* FAIRBRIDGE (D.) Lady A. B. at Cape of Good Hope, 1797–1802, 1924.

Barnard (Edward), *historian.* The new, impartial &c. hist. of England, to end of pres. year [1789]. [*Incomplete. tp. &c. mutilated*]. fol. [1790 ?]

Barnard (Francis Pierrepont). Edward IV's French exped. of 1475: leaders & th. badges, MS. 2. M. 16. College of Arms. Ed. F. P. B. s4º. O. 1925

Ital. jettons. [Repr. f. Num. chron., s4, v20]. 8º. 1920

Mediæval England. A new ed. of B.'s Companion to Eng. hist. Ed. H. W. C. Davis. 8º. O. 1924

Barnard (Harry). Chats on Wedgwood ware. 8º. [1924]

Barnard (Howard Clive). The French tradition in educ., Ramus to Mme. Necker de Saussure. s8º. C. 1922

Barnard (John), *D.D., rector of Waddington.* Theologo-Historicus or, the life of Peter Heylin, D.D. Wr. to correct errors of [*Rev. G. Vernon*]: also an ans. to Baxter's accusations of Dr. H. s8º 1683

Barnard (Nicolas), *dean of Ardagh, see* BERNARD (N.)

Barnave (Antoine Pierre Joseph Marie), see HEIDENSTAM (O. G. de). Letters of Marie Antoinette, Fersen & B.; tr., 1926.

Barnefield (George), *see* CARPENTER (E.) & G. B. Psychology of Shelley, 1925.

Barnes (Arthur Stapylton). Bishop Barlow & Anglican orders: st. of orig. doc^{s}. 8º. 1922

Barnes (Bertie Frank), *see* GWYNNE-VAUGHAN (*Dame* H. C. I.) & B. F. B. Structure &c. of fungi, 1927.

Barnes (Eleanor C.), *aft. wife of Sir Alfred Yarrow.* Alfred Yarrow, h. life & work. 8º. 1923

,, ,, ...2nd impr. 8º. 1924

Barnes (Ernest William), *bp. of Birmingham.* Should such a faith offend? Sermons &c. 8º. 1927

Barnes (*Rt. Hon.* George Nicoll). From workshop to War Cabinet. Intr. by D. Lloyd George. s8º. 1924

Industrial conflict, the way out. s8º. 1924

see SOLANO (E. J.) *ed.* Labour as an internat. problem: essays by G. N. B. &c., 1920.

Barnes (*Major* Harry).

Housing, the facts & the future. 8º. 1923

Barnes (Harry Elmer).

see LAIDLER (H. W.) & N. THOMAS, *edd.* New tactics in soc. conflict: symposium, by H. E. B. &c., 1926.

,, MERRIAM (C. C.) & H. E. B., *edd.* Hist. of polit. theories, recent times; contrib. by students of W. A. Dunning, 1924.

Barnes (Helen Elcessor). Study of the variations betw. orig. & standard ed^{s}. of Balzac's Les Chouans. 8º. Chicago. [1923]

Barnes (J. H.) Sugar & the sugarcane in Gurdaspur dist., *see* AGRIC. RES. INST., Pusa, Bull. 69, 1918.

Barnes (J. S.). Il futuro stato d'Albania, *see* QUADERNI geograf, N. 8, 1919.

Barnes (*Rt. Hon. Sir* John Gorell), *1st baron Gorell, see* GORELL (*Rt. Hon. Sir* J. G. B., *1st b.*)

Barnes (*Dame* Juliana) [†BERNERS (JULYANA)]. A treatyse of fysshynge wyth an angle, 1496. Ed. " Piscator." [Bibl. curiosa]. s8º. *p.p.* E. 1885

see HODGKIN (J.) Proper terms: meanings of phrases in " The book of St. Albans " [by J. B.], 1486, 1909.

Barnes (Lionel Hickman), *see* CHALMERS (D.) & L. H. B. Student's guide to Roman law, 1907.

Barnes (Matthew). What is pure French, by B. *&* Note on " As to," by H. W. Fowler. [S.P.E. Tract No. 8]. 8º. 1922

Barnes (Robert), *Chaplain of Henry VIII.* Vitæ Roman. pontif., quos Papas vocamus. s8º. Witebergæ. *I. Clug.* 1536

Barnes (*Hon.* Ronald Gorell), *see* GORELL (R. G. B., *3rd b.*).

Barnes (William), *B.D.* Hwomely rhymes. A 2nd coll. of poems in Dorset dial. s8º. 1859

Poems of rural life, in the Dorset dial. 3 coll. [1, 4th ed.; 2, 2nd ed.] s8º. 1862–66

Barnes (William Emery). Brian Walton, ed. of the London Polyglot, *see* WARD (*Sir* A. W.) In memoriam, 1924.

Barnes (William H.) Hist. of the 39th Congress of the U.S. 8º. N.Y. 1868

Barnes-Grundy (Mabel). Three people. s8º. [1926]

Barnestapolius (Obertus) *ps.* [*i.e.* ROBERT TURNER ?]. Maria Stuarta, martyr Eccl., innocens à cæde Darleana vindice O. B. [*b. w.* Scotus (R) Summarium rationum &c., 1588]. s8º. Ingolstadii. 1588

Barnet. B. Book of photography. Articles by W. de W. Abney &c. 8º. Barnet. 1898

Barnett (Ada). The joyous adventurer. s8º. [1923]

Barnett (Edward de Barry). Explosives. 8º. 1919

Barnett (*Lt.-Col.* George Henry).
With the 48th Div. in Italy. 8º. E. 1923

Barnett (Herbert).
Glympton: hist. of an Oxfordshire manor. 8º. O. 1923
„ „ [*a. issue*, Oxf. Rec. Soc., v5]. 8º. O. 1923

Barnett (J. Davies). Key to " Epics of the T'on " [*by* Lady A. Hamilton], *see* AUNGERVYLE SOC. Reprints, s2, 1883.

Barnett (Lionel David). Alphab. guide to Sinhalese folklore f. ballad sources. [Repr. f. " Ind. Antiq."]. 4º. Bombay. 1917

Barnett (Samuel Augustus).
The service of God; sermons, &c. 8º. 1897

Barnett (T. Ratcliffe).
Border by-ways & Lothian lore. 8º. E. [1925]
The Road to Rannoch & the Summer Isles 8º. E. [1924]

Barneveld (Jan van Olden) [OLDENBARNEVELT]. Verhooren (1618), *see* HISTORISCH GENOOTS. TE UTRECHT. Berigten, 2ii, 1850.

Barneville (Pierre de). Tiburce. s8º. [1922]

Barney (Laura Clifford). God's heroes. Drama. la8º. [1910]

Barney (R. W.), *see* BRIT. ANTARCTIC EXPED., 1910–13: Zoology, v3, Crustacea, p5; by B., 1915–23.

Barnham (Alice), *see* BACON (A., *lady*), *viscountess St. Albans.*

Barnich (Georges). Le bilan de la Ruhr &c. 8º. Brux. 1924

Barnicoat (Constance), *aft. wife of Julian Grande, see* GRANDE.

Barnouw (Adriaan Jacob). Holland under Q. Wilhelmina. Foreword by E. W. Bok. 8º. N.Y. 1923
Vondel. [Gt. Hollanders; ed. E. W. Bok]. 8º. 1925

Bärnreither (Josef Maria). Grundfragen d. soz. Versicherung in Österreich. [P2418]. 8º. Wien. 1908

Barns (Robert), *Chaplain of Henry VIII, see* BARNES (R.)

Barns (Thomas Alexander). Across the great craterland to the Congo. Intr. by J. W. Gregory. 8º. 1923
Tales of the ivory trade. s8º. [1923]
The wonderland of the E. Congo. Intr. by Sir H. H. Johnston. la8º. [1922]

Barnwell (James G.) Autograph letters & hist. docs., estate of J. G. B. Sold, May 1921; S. V. Henkels. [P2747]. 8º. Phila. [1921]

Barocelli (Pietro). Albintimilium, *see* REALE ACCAD. D. LINCEI. Mon. ant., v29, 1923.

Baroche (*Mme.* Jules). Second Empire: notes & souvenirs. Préf. de M. F. Masson. la8º. 1921

Barockmuseum, *Vienna, see* VIENNA.

Baroda. Hdbk. of the B. Library dept., 1921; 4th ed., 1926, *see* DUTT (N. M.)
Library system of the B. State, 3rd ed., 1924, *see* DUTT (N. M.)
Select. f. the hist. recs. of the hered. minister of B., 1922, *see* GUPTE (B. A.)

Baroja (Pío).
El amor, el dandysmo y la intriga. [Mem. de un hombre de acción]. s8º. [1922]
Los amores tardíos. [Agonías de n. tiempo]. s8º. [1927]
César o nada. [Las ciudades]. s8º. [1920]
La Ciudad de la Niebla. s8º. Lond. *Nelson.* [1912]
„ „ ....s8º. [1920]
La dama errante. s8º. [1920]
Entretenimientos. 8º. 1926
La feria de los discretos. s8º. 1917
Las figuras de cera. [Mem. de un hombre de acción]. s8º. [1924]
El gran torbellino del mundo. [Agonías de n. tiempo]. s8º. [1926]
El laberinto de las sirenas. s8º. [1923]
El mundo es ansí. [Las ciudades]. s8º. 1919
La nave de los locos. [Mem. de un hombre de acción]. s8º. [1925]
La sensualidad pervertida. s8º. [1920]
Las veleidades de la fortuna. [Agonías de n. tiempo]. s8º. [1926]
La Veleta de Gastizar. [Mem. de un hombre de acción]. 2a ed. s8º. 1927
Vidas sombrías. s8º. *n.d.*

Baroja (Ricardo), *see* ABRIL (M.) & R. B. Aguafortistao, 1920.

Baron (M.), T. Junghanns & H. Schindler. Die Muttersprache. Ausg. A. Lesebuch. T4, neu bearb. v. B., J. u. S. 15e A. 8º. L. 1904

Barone (Enrico). La storia militare d. nostra guerra. Fino a Caporetto. 8º. Bari. 1919

Barone (Nicola). Paleografia latina diplomatica &c. [& Atlante di facsimili, folio]. 8º. Napoli. 1923

Baronian (Sukias) [PARONEAN (S.)] [The council of Chalcedon & the Armenian church. *In Armenian. Extr. f.* Banaser. P2817]. 8º. Paris. 1902

Baronius (*cardinal* Caesar).
Parænesis ad rempublicam Venetam, *see* PAUL V, *pope.* Controversiæ, 1607.
see CASAUBON (I.) De rebus sacris &c. exercit. 16 ad B. proleg. in Annales & primam p. de J. Christi nativ., vita, &c., 1615.
„ KORTHOLT (C.), *the elder.* Disq. anti-Baronianæ &c., 1708.
see MARTYROLOGIUM. Martyrologium Rom. &c., auctore C. B., 1597.
„ OTTE (J. H.) Exam. perpetui in Annales C. B. cent. 1–3, 3p, 1676.
„ TRIBBECHOV (A.) Exercit. ad B. Annales, 1708.

Barozzi (Giacomo) *called Il Vignola.* Memorie e studi int. a J. B. [*by* A. G. Spinelli, A Sorbelli &c.] pubbl. n. 4. cent. d. nascita p. c. d. Com. prep. alle onoranze. la8º. Vignola. 1908
see WARE (W. R.) The Amer. Vignola, pl, 1904.
„ WILLICH (H.) G. B. da V., 1906.

Barozzi (Nicolò) & G. Berchet. *Delle accoglienze ai principi di Savoia fatte d. Veneziani, 1367–1722. [P2835]. 8º. Venezia. 1868

Barr (James), *B.D.* The Scottish Church q. s8º. 1920

Barr (John). The city of Auckland, N.Z., 1840–1920: prec. by a Maori hist. of Auckland Isthmus, by G. Graham. 8º. Auckland. 1922
see AUCKLAND. Municipal &c. hdbk. of A., *ed.* J. B., 1922.

Barrachin (—). Coll. B.: antiquités, monnaies; vente, Hôtel Drouot, déc. 1924. la8º. [1924]

Barral (*le cte.* E. de), *ed., see* BARRAL (P. A. A. O., *vte.* DE). Souv. de guerre &c. (1812–15), 1925.

Barral (Philippe Anne Amédée Octave, *vicomte* de). Souv. de guerre & de captivité d'un page de Napoléon (1812–15). Publ. par le cte. E. de Barral. s8º. [1925]

Barrau-Dihigo (L.), *see* FOULCHÉ-DELBOSC (R.) & L. B.-D. Manuel de l'Hispanisant, t1, 2, 1920–25.
see PARIS (G.) Cat. de la bibl. G. P.; par. L. B.-D., livr. 1, 1912.

Barré (Aimé), *see* LEBIEZ (P.) & A. B. *Murder of Mme. Gillet by P. L. & A. B., n.d.*

Barré (Henri), *see* BOUCHES-DU-RHÔNE; encyclop. départ.; publ. sous la dir. de P. Masson, 1913– .

Barre (Joseph). Vie de M. le Marq. de Fabert, Maréchal de France. 2t. s8º. 1752

Barrême (François). Comptes-faits, ou tarif gén. des monnoies. n. éd. s8º. Amsterdam. 1774

Barrès (Jean Bapt. Aug.), *1784–1849.* Mem. of a Napoleonic officer, J. B. B. [1804–35]. Ed., w. intr. by M. Barrès. Tr. B. Miall. 8º. [1925]
Souv. d'un officier de la Grande Armée [1804–35]. Publ. par M. Barrès. s8º. [1923]

Barrès (Maurice).
L'âme française & la Guerre. [t12]. s8º. 1920
12, Les tentacules de la pieuvre.
Les bastions de l'Est: Colette Baudoche. n. éd. augm. &c. s8º. [1923]
Les bastions de l'Est. Le génie du Rhin. s8º. [1921]
Chron. de la Grande Guerre. [t] 1–4, 1 fév.–31 mai 1915. 8º. [1920–21]
Dante, Pascal & Renan. s8º. [1923]
Une enquête aux pays du Levant. 2[t]. s8º. [1923]
Faut-il autoriser les congrégations? s8º. [1924]
Un jardin sur l'Oronte. s8º. [1922]
Les maîtres. [14e éd.] s8º. [1927]
Le mystère en pleine lumière. [31e éd.] s8º. [1926]
La politique rhénane. Discours parl. s8º. 1922
Pour la haute intelligence franç. Préf. de C. Moureu. s8º. [1925]
Scènes & doctrines du nationalisme. [Ed. défin.] 2t. s8º. [1925]
Taine et Renan: pages perdues, rec. & commentées par V. Giraud. s8º. 1922
see BARRÈS (J. B. A.) Souv. d'un officier de la Grande Armée [1804–35]; publ. par M. B., 1923: tr., 1925.
„ BENJAMIN (R.) Le soliloque de M. B., 1923.
„ BERTRAND (L. M. E.) Disc. pour la récept. de L. B. [*on* M. B.], 1926.
„ BORDEAUX (H.) Le retour de B. à sa terre & à ses morts, 1924.
„ —— Voyageurs d'Orient, t2, B. &c., 1926.
„ BRÉMOND (H.), M.B., 1924.

Barrès (Maurice [*continued*].
see DIETZ (J.) M.B., 1927.
„ FAURE-BIGUET (J. N.) M. B.: son œuvre, 1924.
„ GAULTIER (P.) Maîtres de la pensée franç., 1921.
„ GIRAUD (V.) Les maîtres de l'heure : M. B., 1922.
see THARAUD (J.) &c. Un grand maître n'est plus, 1927.
„ ——Mes années chez B.,1928.
„ THIBAUDET (A.) Les princes lorrains [B. &c.], 1924.
„ —— La vie de M. B., 3e éd., 1921.

Barret (George), *the elder, see* BODKIN (T.) 4 Irish landscape painters, G. B. &c., 1920.

Barreto (João Franco). Relação da embaixada a França em 1641. [Rel. da viag. que fiz. F. de Mello &c.] Reimpr. com noticias e docs. por C. Roma du Bocage e E. Prestage. [Acad. das Sci. de Lisboa. Prim. embaixadas de João IV]. 8°. Coimbra. 1918

Barrett (Alfred), *Wesleyan Minister.*
Christ in the storm. s8°. 1859
Essay on the pastoral office. 8°. 1839
The ministry & polity of the Xtn. Church &c. s8°. 1854

Barrett (Charles), *see* GULLETT (H. S.) & C. B. Australia in Palestine, 1919.

Barrett (Eaton Stannard). [*ps.* POLYPUS]. The heroine. Intr. by W. Raleigh. s8°. 1909

Barrett (Florence Elizabeth), *wife of Sir W. F. Barrett.* Conception control. Foreword by Abp. of Canterbury. s8°. 1922

Barrett (Walter), *ps.* [*i.e.* JOSEPH A. SCOVILLE]. The old merchants of New York City. s1–4. s8°. N.Y. 1865–68

Barrett (*Sir* Wm. Fletcher) & T. Besterman.
The divining-rod. 8°. [1926]

Barrey (Lodowick) [*i.e.* DAVID OGE BARRY], *d. 1610, see* LAWRENCE (W. J.). The mystery of L. B., 1917.

Barreyre (Jean). Le navire aveugle. [Coll. des Amis des Lettres fr.] s8°. [1925]

Barri (Giacomo).
The painters voy. to Italy. Engl. by W. L. s8°. 1679

Barrie (*Sir* James Matthew).
Alice sit-by-the-fire. [Plays]. s8°. 1924
Courage. [Rectorial addr., St. Andrews Univ., 1922]. s8°. [1922]
Dear Brutus. s8°. 1926
A kiss for Cinderella. s8°. [1920]
Margaret Ogilvy. By h. son [*i.e.* Sir J. M. B.] s8°. [1921]
Mary Rose. s8°. 1924
The old lady shows her medals. [The new word—Barbara's wedding—A well-remembered voice]. s8°. [1921]
Quality Street : a comedy. s8°. 1925
„ „ ....[repr.] s8°. 1925
The twelve-pound look, & o. plays. s8°. [1921]
see WALBROOK (H. M.) J. M. B. & the theatre, 1922.

Barrière (Marcel). Le mauvais éros, roman, *see* ŒUVRES libres, 30, 1923.

Barrili (Anton Giulio).
Una notte d'estate e altre novelle. s8°. Milano. 1921
Se fossi re ! s8°. Milano. 1921

Barringer (Leslie). Gerfalcon. s8°. [1927]

Barrington (E.), *ps.* [*i.e. Mrs.* L. ADAMS BECK, *née* MORESBY].
The chaste Diana. The romance of the 1st "Polly Peacham." s8°. [1923]
The exquisite Perdita. s8°. [1926]
The gallants. [Stories &c.] 8°. [1924]
Glorious Apollo. s8°. [1926]
The house of fulfilment. s8°. 1927
"The ladies." [Stories &c.] 8°. 1927
The ninth vibration & o. s. s8°. Toronto. 1922
The splendour of Asia. s8°. [1927]
The way of stars. s8°. [1925]

Barrington (*Mrs.* Emilie I.), *see* BARRINGTON (*Mrs.* RUSSELL).

Barrington (*Sir* Jonah).
Recolls. Intr. by G. Birmingham. s8°. D. *n.d.*

Barrington (*Col.* Joseph Thomas) [*ps.* AMICUS HIBERNIAE].
England on the defensive. 8°. 1881
*Ireland a nation. By Amicus Hiberniae. [P2590]. 8°. 1908

Barrington (Michael). David Arnot. s8°. [1927]

Barrington (*Mrs.* Russell). [*Mrs.* EMILIE I. BARRINGTON, *form. Wilson*]. A St. Luke of the 19th cent. [*Fiction*]. s8°. [1922]
The servant of all : pages f. the life of J. Wilson. 2v. 8°. 1927

Barrington (*Hon.* Shute), *bp. of* (1) *Llandaff,* (2) *Salisbury,* (3) *Durham, see* BOWYER (W.) Crit. conjectures &c. on the New Test. ; by W. B., Bp. B. &c., 4th ed., 1812.

Barron (Douglas Gordon). Castle of Dunnottar & its hist., w. descr. of bldgs. by W. M. Mackenzie & G. P. H. Watson. 4°. E. 1925

Barron (Edward). The royal wanderer, or mem. of Caroline. 8°. 1820

Barros (João de) & D. de Couto. B. [v] 1. Prim. dec. da Asia. [Antologia portug.]. 2a ed. s8°. Paris. 1921

Barroso (Francisco Diez), *see* DIEZ BARROSO (F.)

Barrow (George), *F.G.S.*
Geol. of the Cheadle Coal-field. [Mem. of G. Survey]. 8°. 1903
Geol. of the Isles of Scilly, w. petrolog. notes by J. S. Flett. [Mem. of G. S.] 8°. 1906
Geol. of N. Cleveland. [Mem. of G. Survey]. 8°. 1888
see FOX-STRANGWAYS (C. E.) A. G. CAMERON & G. B. Geol. of country around Northallerton &c., 1886.
„ —— C. REID & G. B. Geol. of Eskdale &c., 1885.
„ —— & G. B. Geol. of country betw. Whitby & Scarborough &c., 1915.
see REID (C.), G. B. &c. Geol. of co. around Padstow & Camelford, 1910.
„ ——, —— Geol. of co. around Tavistock & Launceston, 1911.
„ ——, —— Geol. of Dartmoor, 1912.
„ USSHER (W. A. F.), G. B. &c. Geol. of co. around Bodmin & St. Austell, 1909.

——, W. Gibson *& others.* Geol. of the co. around Lichfield, incl. N. parts of S. Staffs & Warwick coalfields ; w. contrib. f. J. B. Hill *& others* [Mem. of G. Survey]. 8°. 1919

—— & L. J. Wills. Records of London wells. [Mem. of G. Survey]. 8°. 1913

——, J. S. G. Wilson & E. H. C. Craig. Geol. of the co. round Blair Atholl &c. [G. S. of Scot. Mem.] 8°. 1905

Barrow (Isaac), *D.D.* Sermon upon the Passion, Good Friday, 1677. s8°. 1682
Several sermons agst. evil-speaking. [*b. w. h.* Sermon, 1682. 2 *pagins.*] s8°. 1678
The usefulness of mathemat. learning. Lects. &c. 8°. 1734

Barry (David Oge), *d. 1610, see* BARREY (L.)

Barry (Florence V.) A century of children's books. s8°. [1922]

Barry (Frank Russell).
Christianity & psychology. Lects. s8°. 1923

Barry (Ian). Specul. in economics. 8°. 1925

Barry (*Sister* M. Inviolata). St. Augustine, the orator : st. of rhetorical qualities of A.'s Sermones ad populum. Diss. [Cath. Univ. of Amer., Patristic Sts., v6]. 8°. Wash. 1924

Barry (William Francis), *D.D.* Memories & opinions. 8°. [1926]
The Turks, Cardinal Newman, & the Council of Ten [*Repr. fr.* Nineteenth Century, 1919. P2418]. 8°. 1919

Barsony (Georgius), *bp. of Grosswardein.* [BARSONY DE LOVAS BERENY (G.)]. Veritas toti mundo declarata : Sacram Maj. non obligari ad tolerandos in Ungaria Lutheranos &c., 1681. [*b. w.* Kellio (M.) Extractus brevis, 1721]. s8°. [Tyrnaviæ? 1721?]
see CZIPKES (G.) Molimen Sisyphium ; Frustaneitas conatus istius G. B., 1672.

Barstow (George Eames). The Chino-Japanese imbroglio. [P2484]. 8°. Five Ways. [1919?]

Bart (Jean), *see* MALO (H.) Les corsaires dunkerquois & J. B., t2, 1662–1702, 1914.

Bartels (Adolf). Die besten deut. Romane : 12 Listen, mit Einleitung. 6e A. s8°. L. 1919
Die deutsche Dichtung d. Gegenwart. 8°. L. 1921

Bartenstein (Johann Christoph). Diss. de bello Carolo V a Mauritio Saxon. elect. illato &c. Praes. J. H. Boeclero. [P484]. s4°. Argentorati. [1709]

Barter (S.) Woodwork. Pref. by G. Ricks. 8°. [1892]

Bartet (Etienne). La Tramontane : notes sur l'Italie. Préf. de H. Bidou. 8°. [1919]

Barth (Christian Gottlob). Biblia Historia, &c. [Tr. into Finnish]. s8°. Helsingissä. 1858
Biblia Sâdsi. Bible stories tr. into Akra-lang. f. 80th German ed. s8°. Calw. 1854
Mawu-agbalea me nya. Bible-stories tr. into Ewe-lang. s8°. St. 1858
Wiisкümmend kaks Piibli Luggu wannast Test. &c. [*Bible stories in Esthonian*]. s8°. Tartus. 1860

Barth (Franciscus Josephus). De statuto principis (gallicè Titre legal), *see* MIGNE (J. P.) *ed.* Theol. cursus, t16, 1859.

Barth (Hans). Bibliogr. d. schweizer Gesch. bis ende 1913, B3, 1915, *see* QUELLEN z. SCHWEIZER GESCH., N. F., Abt. 4, B3, 1915.
Osteria. Guida spirit. d. osterie Ital. da Verona a Capri. Tr. di G. Bistolfi. Pref. di G. D'Annunzio. n. ed. riv. & ampl. s8°. Firenze. [1921]

Barth (Heinrich), *see* PETERMANN (A. H.) Acc. of exped. to C. Africa, under B. &c., 1850–53, 1854.

Barth (Johann Matthæus). Exerc. de inspiratis recentior. Praes. G. Wernsdorfio. [P426]. s4°. Vittembergæ. [1715]

Barth (M. E. Auguste), *member of the Institut Français &c.* Œuvres. t3-5. 8º. 1917-27
3-5, Comptes rendus &c., 1872-1911, bibliog., index.

Barth (Paul). Die Philosophie d. Gesch. als Soziologie. 3e u. 4e erw. A. T1, Grundleg. u. krit. Übers. 8º. L. 1922

Barth (Theodor). Polit. Porträts. Neue A. besorgt v. E. Feder. la8º. [1923]

Barthe (Nicolas Thomas). Les fausses infidélités, *see* THÉÂTRE choisi du 18e s., t2, 1914.

Barthel (Ernst). Polargeometrie. [Bibl. f. Philos.; hrsg. v. L. Stein, B16]. 8º. 1919

Barthélemy (Anatole J. B. A. de). Privilèges de l'église & de la ville de Tréguier. [*Extr.* P2463]. 8º. *n.d.*

Barthélemy (*le cte.* **Edouard M. de),** *see* MONTMARTRE. Recueil des chartes de l'abbaye royale de M.; publ. & annoté par E. de B., 1883.

Barthélemy (Jean Jacques), *see* BÉRENGER (L. P.) *D'Anacharsis [*of* J. J. B.], ou Lettres d'un troubadour sur cet ouvrage &c., 1789.

Barthélemy (Joseph). Le gouvernement de la France. s8º. 1919
Le vote des femmes. 8º. 1920

Barthélemy (P. Sauvaire, *marq. de*). Mon vieil Annam: ses hommes. Contes &c. 8º. 1927

Bartholameu [FERNANDEZ], *dos Martyres, abp. of Braga, see* BARTHOLOMEU.

Barthold (W.) Zur Gesch. d. Christentums in Mittel-Asien bis z. mongol. Erob. Verm. deut. Bearb. hrsg. v. R. Stübe. [P2811]. 8º. Tübingen. 1901

Bartholeyns (A. O'D.)
Chimes for the times &c. [P2420]. s8º. 1919

Bartholinus (Albertus). Liber de scriptis Danorum, Norwag. & Island. &c., *see* MOLLER (J.) Bibl. septentr. eruditi, 1699.

Bartholinus (Thomas), *the elder.* De Cruce Christi hypomnemata 4. [*b. w.* Lipsius (J.) De Cruce, 1670]. s8º. Amstelodami. 1670

Bartholomæi (Johann Christian) & Wilhelm Ernst Bartholomæi, *edd., see* *ACTA Historico-Eccl. *&* Nova acta &c., 1734-86.

Bartholomæis (Vincenzo de). Avanzi di un canzoniere provenzale del sec. 13—Ritmo volgare lucchese del 1213, *see* MONACI (E.) Studj romanzi, v12, 1915.

Bartholomæo (Paulinus a Sancto), *see* PAOLINO *da San Bartolommeo.*

Bartholomeu [FERNANDEZ], *dos Martyres, abp. of Braga.* [†BARTHOLAMEU], *see* CACEGAS (L. DE). Vida de B. dos M.; reform. &c. L. de Souza, 3t, 1890; 2a ed., t1, 1921.

Bartholomew, *Saint & Apostle.* [Martyrdom of B., Oskeantz & Souqiasantz &c. *In Armenian.* Soferq Hayk., v19]. s8º. i Venetik. 1854

Bartholomew (Augustus Theodore), *see* CAMBRIDGE. St. JOHN, COLL. OF. Samuel Butler Coll.: cat. & comm. by H. F. Jones & A. T. B., 1921.

Bartholomew (I. G.) The cause of evil. 8º. 1927

Bartholomew (John George). An atlas of economic geography. Intr. by L. W. Lyde. 4º. 1914
Handy refer. atlas of London & suburbs. 4th ed. 8º. E. 1921
The Oxford advanced atlas. 2nd ed. rev. fol. 1924
see TIMES (THE). Survey atlas of the world; prep. under dir. of J. G. B., 1922.

Bartholoni (Jean). Wagner & le recul du temps. Lettre-préf. de L. Barthou. s8º. [1924]

Bartholus (Johannes Baptista).
Institut. juris Canonici. s4º. Ausugii. 1749

Barthou (Louis).
Disc. de réception [*on* H. Roujon. Acad. Fr., 6 fév. 1919. P2819]. s8º. 1919
Le gén. Hugo, 1773-1828: lettres & docs. inéd. 8º. [1926]
Lamartine, orateur. 8º. 1918
Le politique. s8º. [1923]
Rachel. 8º. 1926
Réponse au discours de J. Bédier [sur E. Rostand]. s8º. 1921
see CEUX. *Ceux qui nous mènent: L. B. &c., par ***, 1922; tr., 1924.
„ ROBERT (H.) Disc. pour la récept. de H. R. (Réponse de L. B.), 1924.

"Bartimeus," *ps.* [*i.e.* L. A. DA COSTA RICCI].
An awfully big adventure. s8º. [1919]
Great security. [repr.] s8º. [1925]
The navy eternal. s8º. [1918]
Seaways. s8º. [1923]
*Unreality. s8º. [1920]

Bartlett (Adelaide). Trial of A. B. Ed. Sir J. Hall. 8º. E. [1927]

Bartlett (Frederick Charles).
Psychology & prim. culture. s8º. C. 1923

Bartlett (Henrietta Collins). Mr. William Shakespeare: orig. & early eds. of quartos & folios, source books & contemp. notices. 8º. New Haven, *Yale.* 1922

Bartlett (Jeffrey). Hymns & songs of praise &c. Added, New garden of spiritual flowers. s8º. 1710

Bartlett (John R.) Pier Antonio Gariazzo & h. works: 124 reprods., w. introd. by J. R. B. 4º. Milan. [1926]

Bartlett (John Russell). Personal narr. of explor. & incidents in Texas, New Mexico &c. conn. w. the U.S. & Mexican Boundary Comm., 1850-53. 2v. 8º. 1854

Bartlett (William Henry).
see PARDOE (J. S. H.) Beauties of the Bosphorus; drawings by W. H. B., 1839.
„ STEBBING (H.) Christian in Palestine; illust. by W. H. B., 1847.
„ WILLIS (N. P.) Canadian scenery illust. by W. H. B., 2v, 1842.

Bartoccini (Renato). Guida di Lepcis (Leptis Magna). s8º. [1927]
Guida di Sabratha. s8º. [1927]

Bartold (Vasily Vladimirovich).
Историко-географ. обзоръ Ирана. la8º. С.-П. 1903
Отчетъ о поѣздкѣ въ Среднюю Азію, 1893-4. [Имп. Акад. Наукъ, Записки, s8, t1iv]. la8º. С.-П. 1897
Улугбекъ и его время. [Imp. Akad. Nauk. Mém., s8, t13v]. la8º. П. 1918

Bartoli (Alfonso). Gli Horrea Agrippiana e la diaconia di S. Teodoro, *see* REALE ACCAD. D. LINCEI. Mon. ant., v27, 1921.

Bartoli (Cosimo), *see* MANCINI (G.) C. B., 1503-72, 1918.

Bartoli (Pietro Santi), *see* SANTI BARTOLI (P.)

Bartolozzi (Francesco). Cat. of loan coll. of engravings &c. by F. B. &c. Intr. by A. W. Tuer. 8º. 1883

Bartolus, *de Saxoferrato.* De Guelphis *&* Tract. de tyrannia [*tr.*], *see* EMERTON (E.) Humanism & tyranny, 1925.

Barton (Bernard). Poems. 3rd ed. w. add. s8º. 1822

Barton (*Sir* **Dunbar Plunket),** *Bart.*
Bernadotte & Napoleon, 1763-1810. 8º. 1921
Bernadotte, prince & king, 1810-44. 8º. 1925

——, C. Benham & F. Watt.
The story of our Inns of Court. 8º. [1924]

Barton (F. R.) Nickel coinage. s8º. [1927]

Barton (Frank Townend). Cattle, sheep & pigs: pract. breeding &c. 2nd ed. 8º. [1920]

Barton (George Aaron). Sumerian business & admin. docs., to dyn. of Agade. [Penn. Univ. Babyl. Sect., v9, No. 1]. 4º. Phila. 1915

Barton (George Burnett). Poets & prose writers of New South Wales. 8º. Sydney. 1866

Barton (Jean-François, *baron* **de Montbas),** *see* MONTBAS.

Barton (William), *M.A.* The book of Psalms in metre. Newly tr. by W. B. s8º. 1705
*Four centuries of select hymns. By W. B. s8º. *Parkhurst.* 1668
Six centuries of sel. hymns &c., w. a catechism, the Canticles & a catal. of vertuous women. 4th ed. s8º. 1688
Two centuries of sel. hymns coll. out of the Psalms. By W. B. s8º. 1672

Barton (William Eleazar).
Life of Abraham Lincoln. 2v. 8º. [1925]
The soul of Abraham Lincoln. 8º. N.Y. [1920]

Bartrum (Joseph P.)
The Psalms, newly paraphrased. s8º. Boston [Mass.] 1833

Bartsch (Paul). A monograph of American shipworms. [S. I. U.S. Nat. Mus. Bull. 122]. 8º. Wash. 1922

Bartsch (Rudolf Hans).
Die Gesch. von d. Hannerl. u. i. Liebhabern. s8º. L. [1913]
Lukas Rabesam. s8º. L. 1922
Unerfüllte Geschichten. s8º. L. 1917

Baruch. Die Apokalypsen d. Esra u. d. B. &c.; hrsg. B. Violet, 1924, *see* EZRA.

Baruch (Bernard Mannes). The making of the reparation & econ. sections of the Treaty. 8º. N.Y. [1920]

Baruch (S.) Spinoza. [*Extr. fr.* Hebrew Union College Monthly. P2412]. 8º. [Cincinnati. 1914]

Baruzi (Jean). Saint Jean de la Croix & le problème de l'expérience myst. 8º. 1924

Bärwald (Hermann). Das Baumgartenberger Formelbuch; hrsg. v. H. B., *see* FONTES RERUM AUSTRIAC., B25, 1866.

Barwick (John), *dean of St. Paul's.* *Querela Cantabrig.: or, a remonstrance for banished members of the Univ. of Camb. s8º. *n.p.* 1647
„ „ [*a. ed. b. w.* Ryves (B.) Mercurius rusticus, 1865]. s8º. 1865

Bary (Helen V.) Child welfare, *see* UNITED STATES: LABOUR. Children's bureau, Publ. 127, 1923.

Barye (Antoine Louis), *see* SAUNIER (C.) B. [Maîtres de l'art mod.], 1925.

Basan (Pierre François). Dict. des graveurs anc. & mod. 2p. s8°. 1767

Bas-Berry (Le): revue mensuelle illust. d'hist., d'archéologie &c. t1, 2. 8°. Chateauroux. 1875–76

Baschet (Armand). Les archives de Venise. la8°. 1857

Baschmakoff (Alexandre). *Mém. sur le mouv. communiste en Bulgarie, 1921–22. Par A. B. off. [P2719]. 8°. [1923]

Bascuenze. *De la antiguedad y univ. del B. en España &c., 1728, *see* LARRAMENDI (M. DE).

Bascule, *ps.* Advanced auction bridge. 2nd ed. s8°. 1916
Royal spades auction bridge. s8°. 1913

Basden (George Thomas).
Among the Ibos of Nigeria. 8°. 1921

Basdevant (Jules), *see* FRANCE. MINISTÈRE DES AFF. ETR. Traités &c. en vigueur entre la France & les puissances étr; rec. prép. par J. B., t3, 4, 1920–22.

Basel. Bekantnuss unsers heyligen Christl. gloubens, wie es di Kilch zu Basel haltet [*signed* Heinrich Rythiner]. 4°. [Basel. 1534]
„ „ [*a. issue beg.*:—] Bekanthnus unseres &c. [*b. w. issue above*]. fol. [Basel. 1534]
„ „ [*a. issue beg.*:—] Bekanthnus unseres &c. [*b. w. issue* above]. fol. [Basel. 1534]
Theologica theoremata &c. in Basil. Acad. &c., 1589, *see* GRYNÆUS (J. J.)
see RABEL (E.) Papyrusurkunden d. Öffentl. Bibl. d. Univ. zu B., 1917.

Basevi (George), *see* BOLTON (A. T.) Archit. educ. &c., w. ref. to G. B., 1924.

Basevi (William Henry Francis).
The burial of the dead. s8°. 1920

Bashford (Henry Howarth) [*ps.* PETER HARDING].
The plain girl's tale. s8°. [1919]

Bashford (Herbert) & H. Wagner. A man unafraid: st. of J. C. Frémont. 8°. San Francisco. [1927]

Bashkirtseff (Marie), *see* BOREL (P.) Le visage inconnu de M. B., 1925.
„ CAHUET (A.) Moussia, ou la vie &c. de M. B., 1926.

Basil, *Saint, the Great; abp. of Cæsarea in Cappadocia.*
Ayn kurtzer [doch artlicher] Tractat des fürtreff. Kriech. u. hayligē lerers Basilij Magni v. erwölāg des aynen lebens ausz zwayen, durch W. Rämē newlich ausz Latein in Teütsch gepracht. s4°. [Augspurg, *S. Grimm & M. Wirsung*]. 1522
Contra Eunomium de Spiritu Sancto lib. III interp. G. Trapezuntio, *see* FLORENCE, *Council of.* Acta, 1526.
[Homilies on the 6 days of creation. *In Armenian*]. 8°. i Venetik. 1830
Letters. With Eng. tr. by R. J. Deferrari. [Loeb Class. Lib.] v1. s8°. 1926
Regula S. B. [tr. T. Ruffinus], *see* JOANNES FRANCISCUS *Brixianus.* Habes isto vol. 4 regulas &c., 1510.
Tract. de synisactis, Græce, *see* BANDINI (A. M.) Fasc. rer. Gr. eccles., 1764.
see EUCHOLOGION. Anaphora of St. B. &c., *Copt. & Arab.*, 1736.
„ LIBANIUS. Opera, v11, Epist. 840–1544, una cum B. cum L. commercio epist., 1922.
„ POT (C. W. v. D.) Specimen theolog. de B., 1835.

Basil I, *the Macedonian, emp. of Constantinople.*
see LEO III, *emp. of the East.* Manual of later Rom. law; founded upon Procheiros Nomos of B. I. &c., 1927.
„ VASILEV (A. A.) Византія и Арабы, В. І. &c., 867–959, 1902.

Basil, *Maleinos, higoum. of Kymina, see* MICHAEL, *Maleinos, St.* Vie & office, suiv. du Traité ascét. de B. texte grec [*& Lat. tr. of Pontanus*], publ. par L. Petit, 1903.

Basile (Carlo Emanuele). L'erede. 8°. Milano. 1923

Basile (Giovanni Batt.) Il Pentamerone. Tr. dall' ant. dial. napol. e corr. di note da B. Croce. 2v. 8°. Bari. 1925

Basilevsky (B.), *see* BAZILEVSKY (B.)

Baskervile (John), *see* BASKERVILLE (J.)

Baskerville Club. [*Publications*]. No. 1. Handlist. 8°. C. 1904

Baskerville (John).
see BASKERVILLE CLUB, No. 1, Handlist [*f. wh. Straus & Dent's J. B. was aft. developed*], 1904.
„ CAVE (T.) J. B., 1706–75, the printer, h. ancestry, 1923.

Basketmakers' Company, *London.* Records of the B. C. Comp. by H. H. Bobart. 8°. 1911

Basmadjian (K. J.) [BASMADSCHEAN]. Ani. [*In Armenian & French*]. folded. s8°. [Paris. 1904]
Chron. de l'hist. d'Arménie. [Extr. de la Révue de l'Orient chret., t19]. la8°. 1915
[F. Müller: Obituary not. *In Armenian.* P2798]. la8°. Venetik. 1898

Basnage de Beauval (Jacques). Hist. de la relig. des églises réf., avec une hist. des erreurs de l'Eglise Rom. 2t. s8°. Rotterdam. 1690
Traité des préjugez faux & légitimes, ou rép. aux lettres &c. de 4 prélats. Mrs. de Noailles, Colbert, Bossuet, & Nesmond. 3t [*in* 1v. *pagin. contin.*] s8°. Delft. 1701
see BOSSUET (J. B.) Déf. de l'Hist. des variations, contre la rép. de M. B., 1727.

Basnin (Vasily Nikolaevich), *ed.*, *see* SICHEVSKY ( ). Зап. о кит. границѣ, 1846, 1875.

Bass (John Foster) & H. G. Moulton. America & the balance sheet of Europe. 2nd printing. 8°. N.Y. 1922

Bassano. Matricola d. congregazione di M. V. d. Pace e di San Paolo apostolo in B. 1450. [Ed. O. Chilesotti]. la8°. [Bassano. 1887]

Bassano, *Mantovano, see* MACCHERONEE di 5 poeti ital. del sec. 15: B. M. &c., 1864.

Bassano (Vincenzo Giustiniani, *march.* **di).** Disc. sopra la musica de' suoi tempi, 1628. [Nozze Banchi-Brini. N122]. 8°. Lucca. 1878

Bassanti (Vincenzio), *see* GIORGI (C.) Della storia del P. G. Savonarola [*sometimes attrib. to B.*], 1782.

Basse-Fontaine. Cartul. de l'abbaye de Basse-Fontaine—Chartes de Beauvoir. [Publ. &c.] par l'abbé Lalore. [Coll. des cartul. du dioc. de Troyes, t3]. 8°. 1878

Bassermann-Jordan (Ernst v.) Die Gesch. d. Zeitmessung u. d. Uhren. Hrsg. v. E. v. B.-J. B1, Lief. B, E. 4°. 1920
see BORCHARDT (L.) Die altägypt. Zeitmessung, 1920. [1B.]
„ DRECKER (J.) Die Theorie d. Sonnenuhren, 1925. [1E.]

Basset (René). Man. de langue kabyle (dial. zouaoua). s8°. 1887
Mille & un contes, récits & légendes arabes. 3t. la8°. 1924–27

Basset (Thomas), *see* SANCROFT (W.) *abp. of Canterbury.* Proc. & tryal in case of abp. of Canterbury &c. [ed. T. B. & T. Fox.], 1689.

Bassi (Martino). Dispareri in materia d'architettura &c. Annotaz. da F. B. Ferrari. 4°. Milano. 1771

Bassi (Ugo), *see* GUALTIERI (L.) Memorie di U. B., 1861.

Bassler (Ray Smith), *see* CANU (F.) & R. S. B. Bryozoa &c., 1918–23.

Bassompierre (*le maréchal* **François de),** *see* WILLIAMS (H. N.) A gallant of Lorraine: F., Seigneur de B. &c., 1579–1646, 2v, 1921.

Bastable (Charles Francis). The commerce of nations. 9th ed., rev. by T. E. Gregory. 8°. [1923]

Baste (Eugène Pierre), *see* GRANGE (EUGÈNE), *ps.*

Bastelaer (René van), *see* VAN BASTELAER (R.)

Bastier de la Péruse (Jean), *see* LA PÉRUSE (J. B. DE).

Bastille, *Paris.* Docs., *see* LINGUET (S. N. H.) Méms. &c., 1884.

Bastingius (Jeremias). An expos. or comm. upon the Catechisme, taught in the Low Countries &c. Tr. out of Lat. 5th ed. 8°. 1614

Bastwick (John). The letany of J. B., doctor of phisicke. pl. [*no more publ.*] s4°. *n.p.* 1637

Bataille (Henry).
L'enfance éternelle, roman, *see* ŒUVRES LIBRES, 7, 1922.
La forêt, *see* ŒUVRES libres, 1, 1921.
Notre image, pièce, *see* ŒUVRES libres, 11, 1922.
Le phalène. éd. déf. s8°. 1921
La quadrature de l'amour. 8°. 1920
Théâtre compl. [t] 1–8. s8°. [1922–27]
1, La lépreuse—L'holocauste. 2, Le masque—L'enchantement. 3, Résurrection—Maman Colibri. 4, La marche nuptiale—Poliche. 5, La femme nue—Le scandale. 6, La vierge folle—Le songe d'un soir d'amour—La déclaration. 7, Le phalène. 8, L'enfant de l'amour—Notre image.
Vers préférés. s8°. [1923]
see BLANCHART (P.) H. B., s. œuvre &c., 1922.

Bataillon (Lionel), *see* FEBVRE (L.) Geogr. intr. to hist., by L. F. in collab. w. L. B., 1925.

Batard-Razelière (A.), *see* BOUCHES-DU-RHÔNE: encyclop. départ., t9, par A. B.-R. &c., 1922.

Batault (Georges). Le problème juif. s8°. [1921]

Batavia. Dagh-Register gehonden int Casteel Batavia vant passerende daer ter plaetse als over geheel Nederlandts India. 1679–81. Uitg. v. F. de Haan. 3d. la8°. Batavia. 1909–19

Batavia [*continued*].
Dutch papers: extr. f. the "Dagh register" [espec. conc. Siam], 1624–42. [Tr. Vajirañāṇa Nat. Lib.] la8°. Bangkok. 1915
Naam-boekje van de Heeren der Hooge Ind. Regeeringe &c., enz. op B. [P2614]. s8°. A. 1784
Oud Batavia: gedenkboek uitg. v. het Bat. Genootschap. 2d. la8°. Batavia. 1922
„ „ Platen album. [d. 3]. sm. fol. Batavia. 1923

Bataviaasch Genootschap van Kunsten en Wetenschappen. *see* BATAVIA. Oud B., gedenkboek, uitg. v. het Genootschap, 3d, 1922–3.
„ TIJDSCHRIFT VOOR IND. TAAL-, LAND-EN VOLKENKUNDE, uitg. door het B. G. v. K. e. W., 1853–95.

Batchelor (John). Ainu life & lore: echoes of a departing race. 8°. Tokyo. [1927]
Uwepekere or Ainu fireside stories. Tr. by J. B. [*w.* Ainu text]. s8°. Tokyo. [1924]

Bate (George), *M.D.* [*ps.* VERIDICUS (THEODORUS)]. Abrégé des dern. mouvemens d'Angleterre &c. [*abridgm. of the* Elenchus motuum &c.] s8°. Anvers. 1651
*Elenchus motuum nuperorum in Anglia, simul ac juris regii & parlament. brevis ennarr. A. 2455. [*Pref. signed* Th. Veridicus]. s8°. Lutetiæ Paris. 1649

Bate (John), *Wesleyan minister.* Six thousand illustr. of moral & relig. truths. 11th ed. 8°. *n.d.*

Bate (Percy H.)
The Eng. Pre-Raphaelite painters. [2nd ed.] 8°. 1901
Mod. Scot. portrait painters. Intr. essay by P. B. 4°. E. 1910

Bateman (Somerset). Simon de Montfort. s8°. B'ham. 1923

Bates (Charles Ellison). *More leaves f. the commonplace book of C. E. B. s8°. 1907

Bates (Elisha). The doctrines of Friends. s8°. Leeds. 1829

Bates (F. A.) Graves memoirs of the Civil War. Compiled f. 17th cent. records by F. A. B. 4°. E. 1927

Bates (Jean Victor). Sir Edward Carson, Ulster leader. Intr. by Rt. Hon. A. J. Balfour. s8°. 1921

Bates (William), *D.D.*
A funeral-sermon for R. Baxter. 2nd ed. s8°. 1692

Bates (William), *song writer.* Coll. of songs sung at Vauxhall by Mr. Vernon. Composed by W. B. fol. 1769

Bateson (William). Essays & addresses; w. acc. of h. life by B. Bateson. 8°. C. 1928

Bath, *Somersetshire.* Accounts of the Chamberlains of the City of Bath, 1568–1602. Ed. F. D. Wardle. [Somerset Record Soc., v38]. *p. f. s. o.* 8°. 1923
*Original Bath guide. [enl. & impr.] s8°. Bath. [1845]

Bath & West & S. Counties Society. Journal. s5, v15. 8°. 1921

Bath York-House Catch Club. *A selection of catches, glees, &c. s8°. 1804

Bath (John Alex. Thynne, *4th marq. of*), *see* †BOYLE (M. L.) Biog. cat. of portraits at Longleat, seat of the Marq. of B., 1881.

Bath (William Pulteney, *earl of*), *see* WAGER (*Adm. Sir* C.) Orig. letters to an honest sailor [*i.e.* Adm. Vernon, f. Sir C. W., W. P., &c.], 1746.

Bäthgen (Friedrich). Sindban, oder d. sieben weisen Meister. Syr. u. Deutsch. [P2600]. 8°. L. 1879

Batho (Edith C.)
The Ettrick Shepherd. [J. Hogg, *w. bibliog.*] 8°. C. 1927
The life of Christ in the ballads, *see* ENGLISH ASSOC. Essays &c., v9, 1924.

Bathory (István), *king of Poland.* Rationes curiæ Steph. Báthory hist. Hung. & Transylvan. illust. (1576–86). Ed. A. Veress. [Mon. Hung. in Polonia (1575–1668), v1. Fontes rer. Hung., t3]. la8°. Budapest. 1918

Bathurst (*Hon.* **Allen Benjamin),** *see* MARY II, *q. of Gt. Brit. &c.* Letters of 2 queens; [ed.] B., 1924.

Bathurst (Benjamin), *see* HALL (*Sir* J.) Four famous mysteries: story of Mr. Bathurst, &c., 1922.

Bathurst (Charles), *see* BLEDISLOE (C. B., *baron*).

Bathurst (Seymour Henry Bathurst, *7th earl*). Rep. on MSS. of E. B., *see* HISTORICAL MSS. COMM. Bathurst, 1923.

Batiffol (Louis).
Le card. de Retz. [Figures du passé]. 8°. [1927]
see CARNAVALET. Les gr. salons litt., 17e & 18e siècles; par L. B. &c., 1928.

Batiffol (Pierre). Catholicism & Papacy: Anglican & Russian difficulties. Auth. tr. by O. R. Vassall-Phillips. s8°. [1926]
Le catholicisme de St. Augustin. 2e éd. 2[t]. s8°. 1920
Le siège apostolique, 359–451. 2e éd. s8°. 1924
L'église & le droit de guerre. 2e éd. s8°. 1920

Bátky (Zsigmund) & K. Kogutowicz. Ethnograph. map of Hungary. atlas fol. Budapest. 1919
„ „ ....Index. s8°. Budapest. 1919

Batlle (Joan Bta.), *bookseller.*
L'arxiu: cat. 2. [P2800]. s8°. Barcelona. 1900

Baton (Antoine). Les merveilleuses légendes de nos vieilles prov. Rec. A. B. 4°. 1927

Batowski (Zygmunt).
Norblin. [Nauka i sztuka, t13]. 8°. Lwów. [1911]

Batsell (Walter Russell). U.S. & the system of mandates, *see* INTERNAT. CONCILIATION, No. 213, 1925.

Batsford (Herbert). English mural mons. & tombstones. Coll. of photographs: sel. by H. B., w. intr. by W. H. Godfrey. 8°. [1916]

Battaglia (Otto Forst-), *see* FORST-BATTAGLIA (O.)

Battaglini (Nicolò). Il consiglio e lo statuto di Torcello. Con app. 8°. Venezia. 1874
Torcello antica e mod. 8°. Venezia. 1871

Battandier (Albert). Le card. J. B. Pitra, évèque de Porto, bibliothécaire de la Sainte Eglise. la8°. 1893

Battelli (Guido). Lodovico Cardi, detto Il Cigoli. [Piccola coll. d'arte, 38]. s8°. Firenze. [1922]

Batten (Edmund Chisholm). Henry VII in Somersetshire. [*From* Roy. Arch. Soc., N.S., v5. P2862]. 8°. [1878]

Batten (H. Mortimer).
The badger, afield & underground. 8°. 1923
Inland birds. Intr. by Sir H. Maxwell. 8°. 1923

Battenberg (*princess* **Marie** *of*), *see* ERBACH-SCHÖNBERG (*princess* M. *of*).

Battersby (Caryl).
The song of the golden bough & o. p. 8°. 1898

Battersby (George), *see* WILKINSON (N.), D. HERD &C. The trial of N. W. &c., for the murder of G. B., 1816.

Battersea (Constance, *Lady*), *wife of Cyril Flower, 1st baron B.*
Reminiscences. 8°. 1922
Thoughts in verse. s8°. Norwich. [1920]

Batteville (Jean de), *see* WATTEVILLE (J. DE).

Batthyan (Ignatius de), *count, bp. of Transylvania.* Leges eccl. regni Hungariæ &c. adjac. opera &c. I. de B. coll. & ill. 3t. Albæ Carolinæ & Claudiopoli. 1785–1827

Batthyány (*graf* **Ludwig).** *Graf. L. B. Von einem Deutsch-Ungar. [P2588]. s8°. Grimma. 1850

Battistella (Antonio). L'abbazia di Moggio. 8°. Udine. 1903
La Repubblica di Venezia ne' suoi undici secoli di storia. Con pref. di A. Fradeletto. 8°. Venezia. 1921

Battisti (Carlo). Die Mundart von Valvestino. Reiseber, *see* KAIS. AKAD. D. W. ZU WIEN. Sitzb., B174, 1915.

Battisti (Cesare). Il Trentino, con un'app. su l'Alto Adige. [*Biog. of C. B. by* L. F. de Magistris]. 3a ed. 8°. Novara. 1919
see BARATTA (M.) C. B., geografo-martire, 1918.

Battistini (Mario). I medici e la medicina in Volterra nel medioevo. 8°. Castelfiorentino. 1922

Battle. *Battle (The) of Craignilder: anc. Gallovidian ballad; arr. w. intr. &c. by Capt. Denniston. s8°. E. 1832

Battles. *Battles (The) of Talavera, poem, 8th ed., 1810, *see* CROKER (*Rt. Hon.* J. W.)

Batton (Achatius). Wilhelm v. Rubruk u. s. Sendung i. d. Land d. Tataren. [Frankiskan. St., Beiheft 6]. 8°. Münster in W. 1921

Battorich (C.) The martyrdom of Croatia. [East Europ. problems, No. 7. P2567]. s8°. 1920

Battus (Bartholomæus). De justificatione hominis libri 3. [*b. w.* Calixtus (G.) Epitome theol. &c., 1647]. s8°. Gryphiswaldi. 1656

Batty (*Mrs.* **Beatrice Braithwaite),** *see* BRAITHWAITE-BATTY (*Mrs.* B.)

Batty (Christopher), *see* ALLEN (J.) & C. B. Coll. of hymns, 1761.

Batty (*Capt.* **Robert).** German scenery f. drawings made 1820. [*Descr. notes in Eng. & Fr.*] la8°. 1823
Scenery of the Rhine, Belgium & Holland f. drawings by B. [*Descrs. in Eng. & Fr.*] la8°. 1826

Battye (J. S.), *Litt.D.* W. Australia: hist. to [1900]. 8°. O. 1924

Baturin (N.) Очерк ист. социал-демократии в России. перепечат. со 2го изд. 8°. Москва. 1922

Batyushkov (Konstantin Nikolaevich).
Сочиненія. изд. 5ое. la8°. С.-П. 1887

Batyushkov (Pompei Nikolaevich).
Бессарабія: истор. описаніе. 8°. С.-П. 1892

Batz (*le baron* **Jean de),** *see* BORD (G.) La fin de 2 légendes; L'affaire Léonard-Le B. de B., 1909.

Batz de Castro (Violante de), *see* SAINT-ROMAIN (V.)

Bau. Bau- u. Kunstdenkmale in Dalmatien, 1927, *see* IVEKOVIĆ (C. M.)

Die Bau- u. Kunstdenkmäler v. Westfalen, hrsg. v. A. Ludorff, 1906–12, *see* WESTFALEN.

Bau (Mingchien Joshua). The foreign rel^s^. of China: hist. & survey. rev. & enl. ed. 8°. [1922]

Mod. democracy in China. s8°. Shanghai. 1923

Bauche (Henri). Le langage populaire. Gram. & dict. du Français de Paris. s8°. 1920

see LORDE (A. DE) & H. B. Les drames du Grand-Guignol, t1, 1924.

Baud-Bovy (Daniel).

Le Berceau des Serbes. Photographies de F. Boissonnas; Intr. de D. B.-B. [L'image de la Serbie.] 4°. Genève. 1919

The cradle of the Servians. Photographs of F. Boissonnas; Intr. by D. B.-B. 4°. Geneva. 1919

L'Epire berceau des Grecs. 100 héliogr^s^. de F. Boissonnas. Intr. &c. de D. B.-B. [L'image de la Grèce]. 4°. Genève. 1915

Peasant art in Switzerland. Tr. A. Palliser. [Publ. by The Studio]. la8°. 1924

Peintres genevois, 1702–1849. 2s. 4°. [Genève]. 1903–4 1, Liotard—Huber—Saint-Ours—De La Rive. 2, Töpffer—Massot—Agasse.

Salonique, la ville des belles églises. Héliogravures de F. Boissonnas; Préf. de D. B.-B. [L'image de la Grèce]. 4°. Genève. 1919

Baudeau (Nicolas). Analyse de l'ouvrage du Pape Benoît XIV sur les béatific. & canonis., *see* MIGNE (J. P.) *ed.* Theol. cursus, t8, 1860.

Baudelaire (Charles P.)

Amœnitates Belgicæ. Ms. inéd., publ. avec intr. par P. Dufay. la8°. 1925

Les fleurs du mal—Petits poèmes en prose—Les paradis artificiels. Tr. A. Symons. 8°. 1925

Journaux intimes. Fusées, Mon cœur mis à nu. Préf. par Ad. Van Bever. s8°. 1920

Œuvres complètes. Notice, notes & eclairc. de J. Crepet. [t1–3]. 8°. 1922–25 1, Les fleurs du mal—Les épaves. 2, Curiosités esthét. 3, L'art romantique.

see FLOTTES (P.) B. l'homme & le poète, 1922.

„ NICOLSON (*Hon.* H.) Swinburne & B., 1926.

„ RAYNAUD (E.) C. B., ét. biog., essai de bibliog. &c., 1922.

„ REYNOLD (G. DE). C. B., 1920.

„ SYMONS (A.) C. B.: a study, 1920.

„ THIBAUDET (A.) Intérieurs; B. &c., 1924.

Baudier (Michel). Hist. de l'administ. du card. Ximenès, grand ministre d'Estat en Espagne. s4°. 1635

Baudissin (Klaus, *Graf* v.) G. A. Wallis, Maler aus Schottland, 1768–1847. la8°. Heidelberg. 1924

Bauditz (Gustav Sophus). Komedie paa Kronborg—Sent Foraar—Junisol—Landsbybørn—Matthieus Hare. s8°. 1914

Baudius (Dominicus). Lib. tres de induciis belli Belgici, 1609–1621. [*b. w.* Pareus (D.) Hist. Palatina, 1633]. s8°. Lugd. Bat. 1629

see BRANDT (C.) Hist. vitæ Arminii acc. Baudii in Arminii obit. epicedia, 1724.

Baudouin (Charles). [BAUDOUIN (LOUIS C.)].

Études de psychanalyse. 8°. Neuchatel. [1922]

The power within us. Tr. E. & C. Paul. s8°. [1923]

Studies in psychoanalysis. Tr. E. & C. Paul. 8°. [1922]

Suggestion & autosuggestion. 2e éd. 8°. 1921

Suggestion & autosuggestion: based upon investig^s^. made by the New Nancy School. Tr. E. & C. Paul. 8°. [1920]

„ „ .... [repr.] 8°. 1921

„ „ [3rd impr.] 8°. [1921]

Tolstoi: the teacher. Tr. F. Rothwell. With doc^s^. supplied by P. Biroukof. s8°. 1923

Baudri, *de Bourgueil, 1046–1130*, *see* BALDRICUS, *abp. of Dol.*

Baudrier (Henri Louis), *1815–84.* Bibliog. lyonnaise: recherches s. les imprimeurs, libraires &c. de Lyon au 16^e^ s. Publ. & contin. par J. Baudrier. 12s. [s12 publ. par H. de Terrebasse]. la8°. Lyon. 1895–1921

s9 *incl^s^.* Table gen. s1–9.

Baudrier (Julien), *see* BAUDRIER (H. L.) Bibliog. lyonnaise; publ. & contin. par J. B., 12s, 1895–1921.

Baudrillart (Alfred). L'enseignement cathol. dans la France contemp. Et^s^. & discours. 8°. 1910

Lettres d'un pèlerin [dans le Levant & en Terre Sainte en 1923]. 8°. 1924

see JONNART (C. C. A.) Disc. pour la récept. de C. J. (Rép. de A. B.), 1925.

——, A. Vogt, U. Rouzies, &c. Dict. d'hist. & de géog. eccl. Publ. sous la dir. de A. B. &c. t3, Anforaria-Arfons. la8°. 1924

Baudry de Lozières (*Général* Louis Narcisse). *Voyage à la Louisiane & sur l'Amér. septentr., 1794–98 par B. D. 8°. 1802

Bauer (*Oberst*), *see* BAUER (MAX).

Bauer (Adolf). Die Herkunft d. Bastarnen, 1918, *see* KAISERL. AKAD. D. WISS. ZU WIEN. Sitz., B185, 1918.

Vom Griechentum z. Christentum. 2e veränd. A. hrsg. v. W. A. Bauer. s8°. L. 1923

Bauer (B.)

Das Frauenkloster Lichtenthal. 8°. Baden-Baden. 1896

Bauer (Carl). Die Beziehungen Calvins zu Frankfurt a. M. [Verein f. Ref.-Gesch. Schr., Jhrg. 38 (Nr. 133).] 8°. L. 1920

Luther u. d. Papst. [Verein f. Ref.-Gesch. Schr., Jhrg. 27 (Nr. 100).] 8°. L. 1910

Bauer (Carl Ludwig). De lectione Thucydidis. Exerc. def. C. L. B., assumto C. Naumanno. [P445]. s4°. Lipsiae. [1753]

Bauer (Franz Xaver).

Proklos v. Konstantinopel. 8°. München. 1919

Bauer (Georg Lorenz).

Entwurf e. Hermeneutik d. Alten u. N. Test. 8°. L. 1799

Bauer (Hans). Die Tempora im Semit. 8°. L. 1910

Bauer (Johann Carl Valentin). Consp. theologiæ Turcarum Mochamm. Praes. H. G. Reime. [P2671]. s4°. Jenæ. 1720

Bauer (Ludwig). Tagebuch aus Genua. s8°. Basel. [1922]

Bauer (Marion) & E. Peyser. How music grew. Intr. by W. J. Henderson. 8°. N.Y. 1925

Bauer (Max). Der grosse Krieg in Feld u. Heimat. 3^e^ A. 8°. Tübingen. 1922

Konnten wir d. Krieg vermeiden &c.? [P2406]. s8°. [1919]

Bauer (Otto).

The Austrian revolution. Tr. H. J. Stenning. 8°. [1925]

Bauer (Stephan). Internat. labor legisl. & the Soc. of nations; tr., *see* UNITED STATES: LABOUR. Bull. 254, 1919.

Untersuch. ü. d. Lebenskosten in d. Schweiz; mit Beitr. v. E. Ackermann &c. hrsg. v. S. B., *see* UNTERSUCHUNGEN üb. Preisbildung, Abt. C., 5, 1917.

Bauer (Walter). Die Evangelien, II, Joannes; erklärt v. W. B., *see* LIETZMANN (H.) *ed.* Hbch. z. N.T., B2ii, 1912; 2^e^ A., B6, 1925.

see LIETZMANN (H.) *ed.* Hbch z. N. Test.; in Verbindung mit W. B. &c., B1–4, 1910–19; Ergänzungsband 2, Briefe d. Ignatius v. Antiocha u. d. Polykarpbrief; erkl. v. W. B., 1920.

Bauer Landauer (Ignacio). Don Fr. de Benavides. cuatralvo de las galeras de España. [La marina esp. en el siglo XVI]. la8°. 1921

Bauernkalendar. (*facs.* 14 Jhdt.), *see* FREYTAG (G.) Bilder, B2, 1924.

Baugency [BEAUGENCY]. Cartul. de l'abbaye de Notre-Dame de Baugency. Publ. par G. Vignat. [Soc. Arch. &c. de l'Orléanais. Mém., t16, fasc. 1. *no tp.*] la8°. [Orléans. 1879]

Baum (Johann Wilhelm).

Franz Lambert v. Avignon, &c. s8°. Str. 1840

Baum (Julius). Altschwäb. Kunst. 4°. Augsburg. 1923

Baum (Paull Franklin).

The princ. of Eng. versific. 8°. Camb. [U.S.] 1922

Baumann (Arthur A.) The last Victorians. 8°. 1927

Baumann (Carl). Das Postwesen in Basel unter d. kaufmänn. Direktorium, 1682–1798. 8°. Weinfelden. 1927

Baumann (Émile). Job le prédestiné. s8°. 1922

Baumann (H.), *see* MURET (E.) & D. H. SANDERS. Encyclop. Eng.-Germ. & Germ.-Eng. dict., p2, Germ.-Eng., n. ed. by B., 1913.

Baumann (Johann Julius). Elem. d. Philosophie. 8°. L. 1891

Handbuch d. Moral &c. [*b. w. h.* Philos. als Orientirung, 1872]. 8°. L. 1879

Philosophie als Orientirung ü. die Welt. 8°. L. 1872

Sechs Vorträge aus d. Gebiete d. prakt Philos. [*a. c. in* P2461]. s8°. L. 1874

Baumbach (Rudolf). Lieder e. fahrenden Gesellen. s8°. St. 1921

Trug-Gold, Erzählung a. d. 17 Jhdt. 7^e^ Aufl. d. Tasch.-A. s8°. 1910

Zlatorig. Eine Alpensage. s8°. St. 1921

Baumeister (Friedrich Christian).

Exercit. academ. & scholast. s4°. Lipsiæ. [1741]

Baumer (Edward).

The early days of the Sun Fire Office. 8°. 1910

Baumgärtel (Elise). Dolmen u. Mastaba, *see* ALTE ORIENT, Beih. 6, 1926.

Baumgarten (Hermann). Karl V. u. d. deut. Reformation. [Verein f. Ref.-gesch. Schr., Jhrg. 7, Nr. 27]. 8°. Halle. 1889

Baumgarten (Otto). Geistige u. sittl. Wirkungen d. Krieges in Deut. Von O. B., E. Förster, A. Rademacher, W. Flitner. [C. E. for Internat. Peace]. la8°. St. 1927

Baumgarten (Otto) [*continued*].
Der Krieg u. d. Bergpredigt, *see* DEUTSCHE Reden in schwerer Zeit, 24, 1915.
see LÜDINGHAUSEN (B. G. H. H. R. F. *Frhr.* v.) Schuld am deut. Zusammenbruch; hrsg. O. B., 1919.
„ WEISS (J.) Die Schriften d. N. Test.; neu übers. u. erklärt v. O. B. &c., 2e A., 2B, 1907–8; 3e A., 4B, 1917–18.

Baumgarten (Siegmund Jacob).
Erläut. d. klein. Catechismi M. Luthers. 3. A. durchges. &c. v. J. G. Kirchner. 8o. Halle. 1764
Nachrichten v. merkwürdigen Büchern. 12B *in* 5v [B12, Register]. s8o. Halle. 1752–58
Programmata cum app. epistolarum. Coll. & dig. G. C. Bakius. s8o. Halæ Magdeb. 1740
Sammlung e. Bedenken d. theol. Facultät zu Halle. 4T. s8o. Halle. 1747–1751
Theolog. Bedencken. 7 Samml. *in* 2v; [Samml. 1–4, 2. Aufl.] s8o. Halle. 1744–50
Theolog. Gutachten. 2 Samml. *in* 1v. s8o. Halle. 1753–55
Theses theolog. elem. doctrinæ sanctioris ad ductum breviarii dogmat. J. A. Freylinghausen complexæ. ed. 3a. s8o. Halæ. 1758
see LÜDEKE (J. F.) Tabulæ synopticæ in Theses theol. S. J. B., 1760.
„ NACHRICHTEN von e. Hallischen Bibl., 1748–51.

Baumgartenberger (Das) Formelbuch; e. Quelle z. Gesch. d. XIII. Jhdt.; hrsg. v. H. Bärwald, *see* FONTES RERUM AUSTRIAC., B25, 1866.

Baumgarten- Crusius (Artur).
Deutsche Heerführung im Marnefeldzug 1914. 8o. 1921

Baumgarten-Crusius (Ludwig Friedrich Otto).
De theologia Scoti. [P2655]. 4o. Jenæ. 1826

Baumgartner (Milton D.) Dryden's rel. to Germany in 18th cent., *see* NEBRASKA UNIV. Univ. studies, v14, 1914.

Bäumker (Clemens). Petrus de Hibernia, u. s. Disput. vor König Manfred, *see* KÖN. AKAD. D. WISS. ZU MÜNCHEN. Phil. Kl., Sitz., 1920.
—— **& B. Sartorius v. Waltershausen.** Frühmittelalt. Glossen d. angebl. Jepa z. Isagoge d. Porphyrius. [Beitr. z. Gesch. d. Philos. d. M-a's, B24i]. 8o. Münster i. W. 1924

Baumstark (Anton). Gesch. d. syr. Lit. mit Ausschluss d. chr.-palästin. Texte. s4o. Bonnæ. 1922
see ORIENS CHRISTIANUS, hrsg. unter Schriftleit. v. A. B., Jahrg. 1, 2, 1901–2.

Baun (Friedrich). J. A. Bengel, d. Vater d. schwäb. Pietismus (1687–1752). 4.A. [P2617]. s8o. St. 1922

Baup (Charles). Précis des faits qui ont amené &c. la démission de la majorité des pasteurs &c. de l'église de Vaud, en 1845. Accomp. des docs. 8o. Lausanne. 1846

Baur (F. W. de), *see* BAWR (F. W. DE).

Baur (Ferdinand Christian v.) Comparatur Eusebius Cæsar. cum Herodoto Halicarnass. [P426]. s4o. Tubingæ. [1834]
De Ebionitarum orig. & doct., ab Essenis repetenda. [P2594]. s4o. Tubingæ. [1831]

Baur (Gustav Adolf Ludwig). De Anicio M. S. Boëthio Xtnæ doct. assertore. [P2759]. 8o. Darmstadii. 1861
Ueb. die Bedeut. d.hist. Continuität. Festrede. 4o. Giessen. 1857

Baur (*Oberstleut.* H.)
Deut. Eisenbahner im Weltkrieg, 1914–18. la8o. St. 1927

Bausset (*le card.* Louis François de).
Hist. de Bossuet. 2e éd. rev. 4t. Versailles. 1819

Bautier (Pierre), *see* DESTRÉE (J.) & P. BAUTIER. Heures dites da Costa (16c.), 1924.

Bavaria. Chronicæ Bavaricæ sæc. 14, *see* BAIERN. Bayer. Chron., 1918.

Baverstock (J. H.) Some acc. of Maidstone, Kent. Added, genealog. tables of the Bosville fam. la8o. 1832

Bawr (F. W. de) [BAUR]. [6 plans of movts. of armies, sieges &c. dur. the Seven Years War, 1758 &c. Maps, 7]. folded fol. La Haye. 1765–66

Bax (Clifford). Inland far: bk. of thoughts & imprs. 8o. 1925
Polite satires. The unknown hand—The volcanic island—Square pegs. s8o. 1922
Up stream. Drama. s8o. 1922

Bax (Ernest Belfort).
The real, the rational, & the alogical. 8o. 1920

Baxter (Andrew). *Enq. into the nature of the human soul. 2nd ed. 2v. s8o. 1737

Baxter (Evelyn V.) & L. J. Rintoul. Some Scot. breeding duck: their arrival & dispersal. 8o. E. 1922

Baxter (George), *see* LEWIS (C. T. C.) G. B., the picture printer, 1924; Suppl., Price list, 1924.

Baxter (*Mrs.* Margaret), *wife of Richard Baxter, see* BAXTER (R.) Mems. of M. B. &c., 1826.

Baxter (Matthew). Methodism. With recoll. of the Rev. R. Eckett &c. s8o. 1865

Baxter (Richard).
Add. notes on the life & death of Sir M. Hale. [*b. w.* Burnet (G.) Life of Sir M. Hale, 1682]. s8o. 1682
Against the revolt to a foreign jurisdiction. 2p *in* 1v [*pagin. cont.*] s8o. 1691
Apology against the modest exceptions of T. Blake & the digression of G. Kendall. Added animadversions on a late dissert. of L. Colvinus, *alias* L. Molinæus & an admonition of W. Eyre. With Mr. Crandon's Anatomy for satisfaction of Mr. Caryl [*each w. sep tp. & pagin.*] s4o. 1654
Autobiography, being the Reliquiæ Baxterianæ abr. f. the folio (1696). Intr. apps. &c. by J. M. L. Thomas. 8o. 1925
Catholick communion defended agst. both extreams. 5p. [*each w. sep. pagin.; 1, 2, & 3 sep. tps.*] *in* 1v. s4o. 1684
1, The dangerous schismatick. 2, Animadv. on Mr. Raphson's book. 3, Survey of defender of Dr. Stillingfleet. 4, Reasons of communion w. parish-churches. 5, Reasons: J. Owen's 12 arguments.
Certain disput. of right to sacraments &c. agst. assault of T. Blake &c. [*tp. wanting*]. s4o. 1657
A Christian directory or A Summ of pract. theologie & cases of conscience. 2nd ed. fol. 1678
Church-hist. of the govt. of bishops & their councils &c. abbrev. 8o. 1681
The cure of church-divisions. 3rd ed. s8o. 1670
A defence of the principles of love necessary to the unity &c. of Christians. [2p *in* 1v]. s8o. 1671
Extract of R. Baxter's aphorisms of justification. Publ. J. Wesley. 2nd ed. [P2533]. s8o. 1745
„ „ ....3rd ed. [P2537]. s8o. 1784
Five disputs. of church-govt. & worship. s4o. 1659
Full & easie satisfaction which is the true & safe religion. s8o. 1674
A key for catholicks, to open the jugling of the Jesuits &c. 2p. [*in* 1v. *pagin. cont.*] s4o. 1659
The last work of a believer. s8o. 1862
Mem. of Mrs. M. Baxter &c. s8o. 1826
More proofs of infants church-membership & th. right to baptism &c. Confut. of M. Tombes h. arguments, of the forgeries of H. Danvers &c. s8o. 1675
More reasons for the Xtn. religion. s8o. 1672
Naked Popery; or the naked falshood of a book called the Catholick naked truth or the Puritan convert. wr. by W. H. s4o. 1677
The Nonconformists plea for peace &c. s8o. 1679
*A petition for peace: w. the reformation of the liturgy. s4o. 1661
Practical works. 4v. lafol. 1707
The reformed pastor. Ed. by W. Brown. n. ed. s8o. [1862]
*Roman tradition examined in the point of transubstantiation. In ans. to A rational discourse &c. [*b. w. h.* Naked Popery &c., 1677]. s4o. *n.p.* 1676
The safe religion or 3 disput. for the reformed Catholicke relig. agst. popery. s8o. 1657
The Saints everlasting rest. 9th ed. rev. s4o. 1662
„ „ ....n. ed. 2v. 8o. 1887
„ „ *for a. ed., see* WESLEY (J.) Xtn. lib., v37, 1754.
The successive visibility of the Church of which the Protestants are the soundest members. Def. against W. Johnson &c. s8o. 1660
Treatise of episcopacy confuting diocesan churches, prelacy &c. [2p *in* 1v]. s4o. 1681
The true & only way of concord of all Christian churches. [3p *in* 1v. 2 *pagins.*] s8o. 1680
La vusch da Dieu chi clama ils pecchiaduors a poenitentia. Verti in noss Rumansch tras J. H. Dorta. s8o. Scuol. 1700
see BARNARD (J.) Theologico-Historicus; also ans. to B.'s accus. of Dr. Heylin, 1683.
„ BATES (W.), *D.D.* A funeral-sermon for R. B., w. acc. of h. life, 2nd ed., 1692.
„ CAVE (T.) J. Baskervile, 1706–75—R. B., 1615–91, & Kidderminster parish church, 1923.
„ LADELL (A. R.) R. B., puritan & mystic, 1925.
„ POWICKE (F. J.) Life of R. B., 1615–91, 1924.
„ —— The Rev. R. B. under the cross (1662–91), 1927.
„ SHERLOCK (W.) *A disc. about church unity &c., ans. to B. &c., 1681.

Bay (Jens Christian).
Echoes of R. L. Stevenson. s8o. Chicago. 1920

Bay (Michel de) [†BAIUS (M.)], *1513–89*. Opera, cum bullis pontificum &c.; studio A. P. [*i.e.* Gabriel Gerberon]. 2p *in* 1v. s4o. Coloniæ Agripp. 1696
De meritis operum libri 2. De prima hominis justicia &c., lib. 2. De sacramentis, contra Calvinum tract. s8o. Lovanni. 1565
see BERTI (G. L.) Augustinianum systema de gratia vindic. sive refut. libr. Bajanismus &c., 1747.
„ RANST (F. VAN). Veritas in medio &c.; imserta vita B., 1715.

Bayan (George). Armenian proverbs &c. tr. into Eng. [*w. texts*]. s8°. Venise. 1909

Bayard [†Du Terrail (Pierre), *seigneur de Bayard*].
see Guyard de Berville (—). Hist. de B., n. éd., 1809.
,, Mailles (J. de). *Hist. de chev. B. &c., 1616.

Bayard (Emile). L'art de reconnaître la céramique, franç. & étr. 10e éd. s8°. 1924
L'art de reconnaître les tableaux anc., les écoles & les styles. s8°. 1921

Bayard (Jean Émile).
The Latin Quarter. Tr. P. Mitchell. 8°. [1926]
Montmartre, w. remin. of artists & writers. Tr. R. Anningson & T. Davies. 8°. [1926]

Baye (*le baron* **Joseph de).** En Géorgie. [Extr. de la Revue de Géog. P2807]. 8°. 1898
L'œuvre de V. Wasnetzoff dev. l'école mod. de peinture en Russie. 2e éd. 8°. 1896

Bayer (Gottlieb Siegfried) [Bayerus (Theophilus S.)] De horis Sinicis & cyclo horario comm. Acc. ejusdem Parergon Sinicum de calendariis Sinicis &c. [P2701]. 4°. Petropoli. 1735
,, ,, [*a. c. b. w.* Ihre (J.) Scripta vers. Ulphilanum, 1773].
Museum Sinicum, in quo Sin. linguæ et litt. ratio explicatur. 2t. (t2, Lexicon &c.) 8°. Petropoli. 1730

Bayerische, *see* Baiern.

Bayes (*Mr.*) *ps., see* Parker (Sam.), *bp. of Oxford.*

Bayeux. Ordinaire & coutumier de l'église cath. de B. (13e s.). Publ. U. Chevalier. 8°. 1902

Bayle (Pierre). Dict. hist. & crit. 5e éd. rev. &c. avec vie de l'a. par Des Maizeaux. 4t. fol. Amsterdam. 1740
*Nouv. lettres de l'a. de la Crit. gén. de l'Hist. du Calvinisme de Mr. Maimbourg. 2t. s8°. Ville-Franche. 1685

Bayle (X. Torau-), *see* Torau-Bayle (X.)

Bayley (John Arthur). *Remin. of school & army life, 1839–59. s8°. 1875

Bayley (Percy E. G.), *see* Tregarthen (G.) Australian Commonwealth; add. chap. by B., 1924.

Bayley (R. Child). The complete photographer. 5th ed., rev. & partly rewr. 8°. [1914]

Bayley (Thomas), *sub-dean of Wells, see* Bayly (T.)

Baylie (Tho.), *see* Bayly (T.)

Baylis (Harry A.) Nemertinea—Oligochæta, *see* Brit. Antarctic Exped., 1910–13. Zoology, v2, 1914–20.
see British Mus. of Nat. Hist.: Zoology. Synopsis of families &c. of Nematoda, by H. A. B. &c., 1926.

Baylis (Harry James). Minucius Felix. 8°. 1928

Baylis (Lilian Mary), *see* Hamilton (C.) & L. M. B. The Old Vic, 1926.

Bayliss (W. D.), *see* MacNair (J. F. A.) Prisoners their own warders &c.; ass. by W. D. B., 1889.

Bayly (Benjamin), *rector of St. James's, Bristol.* *An apology for the clergy of Bristol &c. [? by B. B.], 1712, *see* Apology.

Bayly (Richard), *see* White (F.) A replie to Jesuit Fisher's answere &c.; annexed a Conf. of R. B[ayly?]. w. [F. W.], 1624.

Bayly (Thomas), *D.D., Subdean of Wells.* [Baylie]. Certamen religiosum: or, a conf. betw. Charles King of Eng. & Henry, late marq. of Worcester, conc. religion, 1646. s8°. 1649
*An end to controversie betw. the R.C. & Protestant religions. By T. B. s4°. Doway. 1654

Bayly (Thomas Haynes). You can't marry your grandmother. Comedy. [P2583]. s8°. *Webster. n.d.*

Bayne (Paul), *see* **Baynes (Paul).**

Bayne (Peter). Eng. Puritanism, *see* Church of England. Docs. rel. to settlement of C. of E., 1662, &c., 1862.

Baynes (Norman Hepburn). The Byzantine Empire. [Home Univ. Lib.] s8°. [1925]
The Historia Augusta: its date & purpose. s8°. O. 1926
Israel am. the nations. 8°. 1927

Baynes (Paul) [Baine; Bayne]. Comm. upon the 1st & 2nd chaps. of Colossians &c. [*w. sep. tp.* Lectures &c., *& sep. pagin.*] s4°. 1634
Comm. upon the 1st chap. of Ephesians &c. 8°. 1618
Comm. upon Ephesians. 5th ed., Added, Life of the a. &c. sfol. 1658

Baynes (Robert Hall). Lyra Anglicana: hymns & sacred songs. [12th ed.] s8°. 1879

Bayreuth, *see* Baireuth.

Bazil (Osvaldo). Parnaso antillano. Compil. de poetas de Cuba, Puerto Rico y S. Domingo. s8°. Barcelona. [1916]
Parnaso dominicano. Compil. de los mejores poetas de S. Domingo. s8°. Barcelona. [1916]

Bazin (Hippolyte). Les monuments de Paris. Préf. d'A. Theuriet. Dessins de N. Dias. la8°. [1904]

Bazin (René) [*ps.* Bernard Seigny].
Baltus le Lorrain. s8°. 1926
Charles de Foucauld, explorateur du Maroc, ermite au Sahara. 8°. [1921]
Charles de Foucauld, hermit & explorer. Tr. P. Keelan. 8°. 1923
Le Conte du Triolet. s8°. 1924
Il était quatre petits enfants. s8°. 1923
Notes d'un amateur de couleurs. [2e éd.] s8°. [1920]
,, ,, [5e éd.] s8°. [1920]
Stéphanette. s8°. [1923]

Bazlee (John). Sel. coll. of Psalms & hymns. 2nd ed., w. suppl. s8°. *Gilbert.* 1770

Bazmavep hantisaran [*Monthly Journal, in Armenian*], 51st–59th years (1893–1902) & Apr. 1906, May 1909 & Nov.–Dec. 1913 [*b. in* 8v.] la8°. Venetik. 1893–1913

Bazzoni (Augusto). Uno storiografo cesareo del sec. 18 [*G. B. Comazzi*], see Regia Dep. di Storia Patria. Misc., t33, 1895

B* D***.** *Voyage à la Louisiane, 1794–98, 1802, *see* Baudry de Lozières (*Gén.* L. N.)

Beach (Rex). Padlocked. 3rd ed. s8°. [1927]
Rainbow's end. s8°. 1916

Beaconsfield (Benjamin Disraeli, *earl of*).
Coningsby; or, The new generation. *n. impr.* s8°. 1919
Endymion. n. impr. (1912). reissue. s8°. 1919
Novels & tales. Coll. ed. n. ed. 10v. s8°. 1871–81
1, Lothair.
2, Coningsby.
3, Sybil.
4, Tancred.
5, Venetia.
6, Henrietta Temple.
7, Contarini Fleming—The rise of Iskander.
8, Alroy—Ixion in heaven—The infernal marriage—Popanilla.
9, The young duke—Count Alarcos.
10, Vivian Grey.
,, ,, [Hughenden ed.] n. impr. (1912–18). reissue. 11v. s8°. 1919
Sybil. n. impr. (1919). reissue. s8°. 1920
Wit & wisdom of B. n. ed. s8°. 1883
see Clarke (*Rt. Hon. Sir* E. G.) B. D., 1804–81, 1926.
,, Maurois (A.) Vie de D., 16e éd., 1927.
,, Meynell (W.) The man D., rev. ed., 1927.
,, Monypenny (W. F.) Life of B. D., earl of B., v5, 6, by G. E. Buckle, 1920.
,, Murray (D. L.) D., 1927.
,, Punch. B. Disraeli in cartoons, n. ed., 1881.
,, Raymond (E. T.) Disraeli: the alien patriot, 1925.
,, Schmitz (O. A. H.) Die Kunst d. Politik [*on* Ld. B.], 1911.
,, Somervell (D. C.) D. & Gladstone, 1925.

Beadle (Erastus F.) To Nebraska in '57: a diary, *see* New York Publ. Lib. Bull., v27, 1923.

Beadnell (Hugh John Llewellyn). The wilderness of Sinai: 2 years' explor. Foreword by D. G. Hogarth. 8°. 1927

Beagloic (Concobar o), *see* Begly (C.)

Beale (Dorothea), *see* Shillito (E. H.) D. B., Princ. of Cheltenham Ladies' Coll., 1858–1906, 1920.

Beale (John). *Herefordshire orchards, 1724, *see* Bradley (R.) New improvements, 4th ed., 1724.

Beale (Mary), *née* Cradock, *1632–97, see* Milner-Gibson-Cullum (G.) M. B., 1918.

Beals (Carleton).
Rome or death: story of Fascism. s8°. 1923

Beamish (A. E.) & W. G. Beamish.
Lawn tennis for ladies. s8°. [1924]

Beamish (W. G.), *see* Beamish (A. E.) & W. G. B.

Beamont (William). An acc. of the Roman station at Wilderspool, in Appleton, Cheshire [P2404]. 8°. Warrington. 1876.
Henry IV. P1. An attempt to connect some Cheshire persons &c. w. Shakespeare's drama. [P2428]. 8°. Chester. 1876
Mem. of T. Robson. [P2404]. 8°. Warrington. 1886
Notes of Eng. judges &c., 1, W. Garnet. [P2428]. 8°. *f.p.c.* Warrington. 1883

Bean (Charles Edwin Woodrow). The story of Anzac, 1914–15. [Offic. hist. of Australia in the War, v1, 2]. 2v. 8°. Sydney. 1921–24

—— & H. S. Gullett. Photographic record of the War; annot. by C. E. W. B. & H. S. G. [Offic. hist. of Australia in the War, v12]. 8°. Sydney. 1923

Bean (William Jackson).
Ornamental trees for amateurs. 8°. 1925
Shrubs for amateurs. 8°. 1924

Beard (Charles Austin).
American gov. & politics. 4th ed. rev. 8°. N.Y. 1924
An econ. interpret. of the constitution of the U.S. 8°. N.Y. 1925
see Breasted (J. H.), J. H. Robinson & C. A. B. Outlines of Europ. hist., 2p, *n.d.*
see Robinson (J. H.) & C. A. B. Development of mod. Europe, 2v, w. Suppl., 1907–18.

Beard (Charles Austin) & M. R. Beard. Hist. of the United States. s8°. N.Y. 1922
Rise of American civilization. 2v. 8°. 1927
—— **& W. C. Bagley.** Hist of the American people. rev. ed. [repr.] 8°. N.Y. 1924

Beard (Mary Ritter), *wife of C. A. Beard, see* BEARD (C. A.) & M. R. B.

Beard (Thomas). The theatre of God's judgements, or a coll. of histories &c. conc. the judgements of God. Tr. out of French & augm. [*pages 461 & 462 supplied in MS.*] s4°. 1597

Beardmore (John). Cat. of the coll. of arms & armour, formed by J. B. Sold by Christie, July 1921. [*Illust.*] 8°. 1921

Beardsley (Aubrey). Early work. Pref. note by H. C. Marillier. [repr.] 4°. 1912
Later work. [repr.] 4°. 1912
Uncollected work of A. B., w. intr. by C. L. Hind. 4°. 1925
see BURDETT (O.) The B. period, 1925.

Beardsley (Wilfred Attwood).
Infinite constructions in Old Spanish. 8°. N.Y. 1921

Beasley (Pierce) [PIARAS BEASLAI]. Michael Collins & the making of a new Ireland. 2v. 8°. [1926]

Beatianus (Augustinus) [BEAZZANO (AGOSTINO)]. De le cose volgari et latine del B. [Sonetti &c.] s8°. [Venetia. 1538]

Beatillo (Antonio). Hist. di Bari. 8°. Napoli. 1637

Beatrice. *Tale (The) of Beatrice. Tr. f. Middle Dutch by P. Geyl. [Dutch Lib., 4]. s8°. The Hague. 1927

Beatson (*Maj.-Gen.* **Finlay Cochrane).** Wellington: the crossing of the Gaves & the Battle of Orthez. 8°. 1925
With Wellington in the Pyrenees, 1813. 8°. [1914]

Beattie (James). An essay on the nature &c. of truth in opposition to sophistry & scepticism. 8°. E. 1777
Letter to the Rev. Hugh Blair, on the improvement of Psalmody in Scotland. [P2586]. s8°. E. 1829
Poet. works. Coll. by T. Park. [*b. w.* Goldsmith (O.) Poet. wks., 1805]. s8°. 1805

Beattie (William), *of Glasgow.* Cat. of mod. pictures & drawings of W. B., A. H. Glen-Coats &c. Sold by Christie, July 11, 1924. [*Illust.* P2748]. 8°. 1924

Beattie (William), *M.D.*
Switzerland. Illust. by W. H. Bartlett. 2v. 4°. 1839

Beatty (Arthur). W. Wordsworth. 8°. Madison. 1922

Beatty (Charles). Journal of a two-months' tour among frontier inhabitants of Pensylvania [*sic*] & W. of the Aleghgeny Mtns., *see* EDWARDS (J.) Acc. of life of D. Brainerd, 1798.

Beatty (Herbert Macartney).
A brief hist. of education. s8°. 1922

Beaty (John Owen). John Esten Cooke, Virginian. [Columbia Univ. St[s]. in Eng. &c. lit.] 8°. N.Y. 1922
see HUBBELL (J. B.) & J. O. B. Intr. to poetry, 1922.

Beauberon (Nicolas François Le Clerc de), *see* LE CLERC DE BEAUBERON.

Beauchamp, *The family of.* 2 registers form. belonging to the family of Beauchamp of Hatch. Ed. Sir H. C. Maxwell-Lyte. [Somerset Rec. Soc., v35]. s4°. *p. f. s. o.* 1920

Beauchamp (Alphonse de). Hist. de la guerre de la Vendée & des Chouans. 3t. 8°. 1806
Hist. des malheurs &c. de Pie VII sous le règne de Napoléon. s8°. 1814

Beauchamp (Kathleen), *aft. wife of J. Middleton Murry, see* MANSFIELD (K.) *ps.*

Beauchamp (Richard de), *5th earl of Warwick, see* †WARWICK (R. DE B., *5th e.*)

Beauchampe. *B.: or, the Kentucky tragedy, 1843, *see* SIMMS (W. G.)

Beauclerk (Helen).
The green lacquer pavilion. [5th impr.] 8°. 1926

Beaudouin (Mondry). Étude du dialecte chypriote mod. et médiéval. Thèse. 8°. 1883

Beaufé's (Jacques), *see* JARRIGE (P.) A further discovery &c., 2, Calumnies of B. refuted, 1658.

Beauford (William). Antient topog. of Ireland &c., *see* VALLANCEY (C.) Coll., v3, 1783.
Druidism revived—Orig. & lang. of the Irish & the learning of the Druids, 1781, *see* VALLANCEY (C.) Coll., v2, 1781.

Beaufort (Henry Adelbert Wellington FitzRoy Somerset, *9th duke of*). Cat. of old Eng. lacquer furniture, property of B., & old Eng. &c. furniture &c. property of 5th marq. of Hertford &c. Sold by Christie, June 1921. [*Illust.*] 8°. 1921

Beaufort (Henry Somerset, *1st duke of*) [*form. 3rd marq. of Worcester*], *see* BAYLY (T.) Certamen religiosum: conf. betw. Charles K. of Eng. & H. late marq. of W., 1646, 1649.

Beaufort (Thomas Richard). Pictures & how to clean them, added, Notes on restoration work. s8°. [1926]

Beaugency, *see* BAUGENCY.

Beaulieu (Louis Le Blanc de), *see* LE BLANC DE BEAULIEU (L.)

Beaulieu (Luke de). *The Holy Inquisition. s8°. 1681

Beaulieu (Sébastien de), *sieur de Pontault* [BEAULIEU LE DONJON; †PONTAULT (S. DE)]. *Plan & cartes d. villes d'Artois. obl.8°. *n.p. n.d.*
Plans & profiles d. princ. villes de Bourgogne. obl.8°. *n.d.*
Plans & profiles d. princ. villes de Flandre. obl.8°. *n.d.*

Beaumanoir (Henri Charles de), *Marquis de Lavardin, see* SFONDRATI (*il card.* C.) *Legatio Rom. M. L. &c., 1688.

Beaumarchais. Œuvres compl. 6t. 8°. 1821
see KITE (E. S.) B. & the War of Amer. Indep., 2v, 1918.
„ RIVERS (J.) Figaro: the life of B., 1922.
„ VALLES (*vte.* H. C. B. T. M. DE). B. magistrat, 1928.

Beaumont (*Mdlle.* **de),** *dame proselyte de l'Église de Rome, see* LENFANT (J.) Preservatif contre la réunion avec le Siège de Rome, contre le livre [Rép. aux raisons &c., 1718] de Mlle. de B. &c., 1723.

Beaumont (A.) Heroic story of the Czecho-Slovak legions. [P2403]. 8°. Prague. 1919

Beaumont (*Mrs.* **Agnes),** *d. 1720, see* JACKSON (T.) Lib. of Xtn. biog., v4, 1838.

Beaumont (Arthur James), *see* BEAUMONT (AUG.) Ambassadors, 1836.

Beaumont (Augustus). Ambassadors: what do we pay them for? [*Case of Dr. A. J. Beaumont imprisoned in France*]. [P2782]. 8°. 1836

Beaumont (Cyril W.)
Hist. of Harlequin. Pref. by S. Sitwell. la8°. 1926

Beaumont (Francis) & J. Fletcher.
Best plays. Intr. &c. by J. St. L. Strachey. [v]1. s8°. 1887
The chances, *see* INCHBALD (*Mrs.* E.) Brit. theatre, v6, 1808.
Dram. works; collated w. former ed[s]. & corr.; w. notes & engravings. [Ed. G. Colman]. 10v. 8°. 1778
Rule a wife & have a wife, *see* INCHBALD (*Mrs.* E.) Brit. theatre, v6, 1808.
see OLIPHANT (E. H. C.) The plays of B. & F.: attempt to determine th. respective shares &c., 1927.
„ WITHINGTON (R.) "F. S., which is to say . . ." [*phrase in* Knight of the burning pestle], 1925.

Beaumont (George Frederick).
Hist. of Coggeshall, in Essex. 8°. 1890

Beaumont (J. A. B.) Travels in Buenos Ayres & the adj. prov. of the Rio de la Plata. 8°. 1828

Beaumont (Joseph), *barrister at law.* The life of the Rev. J. Beaumont, *M.D.* 8°. 1856

Beaumont (Joseph), *M.D., 1813–55.* Mem. of Mrs. Mary Tatham. s8°. 1838
see BEAUMONT (Jos.), *barrister at law.* The life of Rev. J. B., 1856.

Beaumont (*ctsse.* **Pauline Marie M. F. U. de),** *see* BEAUNIER (A.) Le roman d'une amitié: J. Joubert & P. de B., 1924.

Beaumont (Roberts). Carpets & rugs. la8°. 1924
Colour in woven design. 8°. 1890

Beaumont (Saunier de), *see* SAUNIER DE BEAUMONT.

Beaunier (André). Le dernier jour, *see* ŒUVRES libres, 15, 1922.
La folle jeune fille. s8°. 1922
Irene exigeante, *see* ŒUVRES (Les) libres, 25, 1923.
Le roman d'une amitié: J. Joubert & P. de Beaumont. s8°. 1924 [1923]

Beaurieu (Gaspard Guillard de) [†GUILLARD DE BEAURIEU], *see* LEGOUIS (E.) G. G. de B. & son Élève de la nature, 1763, 1925.

Beauties of English poets. [Byron &c. *Eng. & Armenian*]. s8°. Venice. 1852

Beauvais.
Cartul. de l'Hôtel-Dieu de B. [Publ. &c.] V. Leblond. [Soc. Acad. de l'Oise. Doc[s]., t4]. la8°. 1919
Cartul. de la maladrerie de Saint-Lazare. [*Ed.*] V. Leblond. [Soc. Acad. de l'Oise. Docs., t7]. la8°. 1922
Censier de l'Hôtel-Dieu de B., 1316. [Publ.] Dr. Leblond. [Extr. du Bull. philol. & hist., 1917. P2469]. 8°. 1919
Obituaire de l'Hôtel-Dieu de B., 1292. [Publ.] Dr. Leblond. [Extr. du Bull. philol. & hist., 1917. P. 2469]. 8°. 1919

Beauverie (Jean Jules) & L. Faucheron. Atlas colorié de la flore alpine. Par B. & F. d'ap. Hegi & Dunzinger. 8°. 1906

Beauvilliers (Paul Hippolyte de), *duc de St. Aignan, 1684–1776.* Portraits & caractères de la cour d'Esp., 1718–21; *ed.* J. de Boislisle, *see* SOC. DE L'HIST. DE FR. Ann.-Bull., 1925.

Beauvoir. Chartes de B.; [publ. &c.] par l'abbé Lalore, *see* Basse-Fontaine. Cartulaire, 1878.

Beaverbrook (*Rt. Hon.* **William Maxwell Aitken,** *1st baron*).
Politicians & the press. s8°. 1926

Beazley (John Davidson). Attic red-figured vases in Amer. museums. la8°. Cambridge [U.S.] 1918
Attische Vasenmaler des rotfigur. Stils. 8°. Tübingen. 1925
The Lewes House coll. of ancient gems [*property of E. P. Warren*]. la8°. O. 1920
see Corpus vasorum antiquorum. Gt. Brit., fasc. 3, Oxford, Ashmolean Museum; by J. D. B., 1927.

Bebel (August). Будущее общество. Переводъ. [P2458]. 8°. Москва. 1918

Bebel (Baltasar).
Adv. præexistentiam animarum, errorem C. Sandii, &c. [*b. w.* Sandius (C.) Tract., 1671]. s8°. Argentorati. 1675
Examen disquis. de statu &c. animarum postquam discesserunt a corporibus. s8°. Argentorati. 1671
Hypomnema apologeticum, *see* Dannhauer (J. C.) Nuncius, 1664.
see Disquisitiones theol. de anima sep. &c., a [B. B., &c.], 2p, 1730.
„ Dury (J.) Consult. irenic. Προδιόρθωσις, inter J. C. Dannhawerum, B. B. & J. D., 1664.
„ Fasciculus rar. &c. scr. theol., de animæ statu, a B. &c., 1692.

Bebelius (Henricus). Liber hymnorum in metra noviter redactorum.—Apologia & defensio poetice ac oratorie maiestatis.—Brevis expositio terminorum in hymnis &c.—Annot. eiusdem in quasdam vocabulorum interpret. Mammetracti [*i.e.* J. Marchesinus]. s4°. [Tübingen. 1501]
[*The hymns are paged 1–32. The preliminary & annotative portions are without pagin. Signatures 1, & a–f in 8; g in 4; h in 8; h8 wanting*].
Opusculum de instit. puerorum, una cum apologia, poetices contra æmulos. Item. Opusc. qui auctores legendi sint ad compar. eloquentiæ.—Comœdia de opt. studio scholasticorum. Item. Oratio de util. eloquentiæ, Apol. contra adversarios. [*Without pagin. Sigs. Aa, A–D, Bb–Dd.* s4°. [Argentorati. 1513]

Bebenbergius (Lupoldus), *bp. of Bamberg, see* Egloffstein (L. de).

Becanus (Martin), *Jesuit* [*ps.* Novus Homo].
Opera omnia aliquot tractatibus posthumis aucta &c. [Analogia Vet. & Novi Test. *w. sep. tp. & pagin.*] 2t *in* 1v [*pagin. contin.*] fol. Moguntiæ. 1649
Analogia Vet. ac Nov. Test. s8°. Moguntiæ. 1620
Compendium manualis controv. huius temp. de fide ac relig. s8°. Parisiis. 1632
De communione sub utraq. specie disp. M. B. cum notis. Una cum confess. J. Hussi, ed. à F. Balduino. s8°. Wittebergæ. 1610
De triplici sacrificio, naturæ, legis, gratiæ libelli tres. s8°. Moguntiæ. 1610
Quæstiones Batavicæ. [*b. w. h.* De tripl. sacrificio, 1610]. s8°. Moguntiæ. 1611
*Supplic. ad Imperatorem, reges, &c., super causis Generalis Concilii convocandi. Contra Paulum V. [*Dedic. signed:* Novus Homo]. [*b. w.* Clemangiis (N. de) Opera, 1613]. s4°. Londini. 1613
Tractatus scholast. de libero arbitrio. [*b. w. h.* De triplici sacrificio, 1610]. s8°. Moguntiæ. 1613
see Harris (R.) Concordia Anglic. de primatu eccles. regio; adv. B. De dissidio Angl., 1612.
„ Musæus (J.) Collegium controv. B. &c. oppos., 1701.
„ Sonntag (C.) Stricturæ Anti-B. adv. lib. 1 Manualis controv., 1708.

Beccari (Camillo). Rerum Æthiop. scr. occid. ined. a sæc. 16 ad 19; cur. C. B., v15, Index analyt. la8°. 1917

Beccari (Odoardo). Asiatic palms—Lepidocaryeæ. [Annals of Roy. Botanic Garden, Calcutta, 12ii]. p3, & Plates, p3. 4°. & fol. Calcutta, 1918–21

Beccaria (Augusto). A. M. Bandini in Piemonte, nov. 1778, *see* Regia Deput. Misc., t45, 1910.

Beccaria (Cesare) [†Beccaria Bonesana (*il march.* C.)].
*Dei delitti e d. pene. 4°. Brescia. 1807
see Phillipson (C.) 3 criminal law reformers: B. &c., 1923.

Béchamp (Pierre Jacques Antoine), *see* Hume (E. D.) B. or Pasteur?, 1923.

Becher (E.), *see* Frey (M. v.), *ed.* Abhandlgn. ü. d. Speichel v. E. B. &c. (1851), 1890.

Becher (Erich), *see* Dessoir (M.) *ed.* Lehrbuch d. Philos., B2, P. in i. Einzelgebieten; v. E. B. &c., 1925.

Bechhofer-Roberts (Carl Eric). In Denikin's Russia & the Caucasus, 1919–20. s8°. Glasgow. [1921]
The literary renaissance in America. s8°. [1923]

Bechhofer-Roberts (Carl Eric) [*continued*].
A wanderer's log, India, the Far East, Russia &c. 8°. [1922]
see Reckitt (M. B.) & C. E. B. Meaning of national guilds, 2nd rev. ed., 1920.

Bechmann (Friedemann). Ad Instit. catecheticas C. Dieterici annot. uberiores. Præf. De orig. & auctor. catechismi præm. I. F. Buddeus. s4°. Francof. 1707
Theologia polemica. Præf. I. F. Buddei. s4°. Jenæ. 1719

Bechmann (Johann Volckmar). Exercit. de jure viarum. ed. nov. [P2746]. s4°. Halæ Magd. 1730

Bechstein (Ludwig).
Märchenbuch. Holzschnitten v. L. Richter. 4e A. 8°. L. 1877

Bechtel (Friedrich). Die griech. Dialekte. 3B. la8°. 1921–24

Becius (Johannes), *see* Zanchius (H.) Theses de iis quæ de J. C. post union. præd. &c.; præs. H. Z., def. J. B., 1582.

Beck (*Mrs.* **Adams**), *see* Barrington (E.), *ps.*

Beck (Adolf). A. B. (1877–1904). Ed. E. R. Watson. [Notable Brit. trials]. 8°. [1924]

Beck (Carl), *dean of Reutlingen.*
Zeittafeln für die Dogmengesch. 8°. Tübingen. 1864

Beck (Caspar Achatius) [Beckius], *see* Schmid (L. C.) Disput. de oblig. ad cedendum in via publ.; sub præs. C. A. B., 1728.

Beck (Christian Daniel) [Beckius]. Comm. hist. decretorum relig. Xtnæ & Formulæ Lutheriæ. 8°. Lipsiæ. 1801

Beck (Conrad), & H. Andrews.
Photographic lenses. 2nd ed. 8°. [1903]

Beck (Erich). Die russ. Kirche. Gesch., Lehre u. Liturgie &c. 8°. Bühl i. Baden. 1922

Beck (Hermann). Kaspar Klee v. Gerolzhofen. [V. f. Ref.-gesch. Schr., Jhrg. 19. Nr. 71]. 8°. Halle. 1901

Beck (James Montgomery). Constit. of the U.S. Pref. by Earl of Balfour. [Gray's Inn Lect^s.] s8°. [1922]
Constit. of the U.S., yesterday, to-day—& to-morrow? 8°. [1924]
The passing of the new freedom. s8°. N.Y. [1920]

Beck (James Sigismund). The principles of crit. philos. sel. f. wks. of Kant & expounded by J. S. B. Tr. 8°. 1797

Beck (Josef). Die Geschichts-Bücher d. Wiedertäufer in Oesterr.-Ungarn &c., 1526–1785, *see* Fontes rerum Austr., B43, 1883.

Beck (Joseph). *A contin. of the hist. narr. [*by Sir C. Reed*] of the Irish Society, 1864–78. [*b. w.* Reed (Sir C.) Hist. narr., 1865]. s8°. *n. p.* [1878]

Beck (Matthias Friedrich), *see* Luhn (J. B.) M. F. B. memoria, 1703.

Beck (Michael). Versio Lutheri Megalandri in 330 dictis Vet. Test. à M. A. H. F[rancke] auct. [9] disq. vindicata. Sub præs. M. B. [*Each disq. has diff. respondent & sep. tp., pagin. contin.*] s4°. [Ulmæ]. 1696–98

Beck (Ulrich Sebastian). Obs. de subscriptione Augustanæ Confess. [P2642]. s4°. *n.p.* [1730]

Becke (*Maj.* **Archibald Frank**).
What to apply in tactical problems. s8°. 1909

Becker (Aug.), *see* Becker (Phil. Aug.)

Becker (August), *novelist.* Die Pfalz u. d. Pfälzer. Mit e. Anhang v. K. A. Becker. 3. A. 8°. Neustadt a. d. Haardt. 1924

Becker (Carl).
Paul Gerhardt, &c. 2te verm. A. s8°. L. [c. 1853]

Becker (Carl Wilhelm), *see* Hill (G. F.) B. the counterfeiter, 2p, 1924–25.

Becker (*Col.* **G.**) Les confins franco-suisses & le Traité de Versailles. Blocus continental. la8°. Nancy. 1922
Trois conférences sur Ludendorff, chef d'Armée. Réunion des forces—Évolutions—Conduite de la bataille. 8°. Nancy. 1920

Becker (J. E. de). Elem. of Jap. law, *see* Asiatic Soc. of Japan. Trans., v44ii, 1916.

Becker (Josef). Textgesch. Liudprands v. Cremona. [Quellen &c. z. lat. Philol. d. M.A., B3ii]. 8°. München. 1908

Becker (Philipp August).
Bonaventure des Periers, *see* Kais. Akad. d. W. in Wien. Sitzb., B200, 1924.
Christophle de Longueil, s. Leben u. s. Briefwechsel. [Veröff. d. Roman. Auslandsinst., Bonn, B5]. 8°. Bonn. 1924
C. Marot: s. Leben u. s. Dichtung. la8°. München. 1926
C. Marots Liebeslyrik, 1917, *see* Kais. Akad. d. Wiss in Wien. Sitzb., B184, 1918.
C. Marots Psalmenübers., *see* Kön.-Sächs. Gesells. Berichte, Phil.-hist. Cl., B72, 1920.
Mellin de Saint-Gelais, *see* Kais. Akad. d. W. in Wien. Sitzb., B200, 1924.

Becker (Walter). Die Sage v. d. Höllenfahrt Christi in d. altfranz. Lit., *see* ROMAN. FORSCH., B32, 1913.

Becket (Thomas), *Saint.*

see GARNIER, *de Pont Sainte-Maxence.* La vie de St. T., poème hist. du 12e s.; publ. E. Walberg, 1922.
,, HUTTON (W. H.) T. B., n. ed., rev. &c., 1926.
,, L'HUILLIER (A.) St. T. de Cantorbéry, 2t, 1891–2.
see MASON (A. J.) What became of the bones of St. T., 1920.
,, RYE (W.) Some new facts in life of St. T., connected w. Norfolk, 1924.
,, STAPLETON (T.) Tres Thomæ &c., 1588.

Beckett (Francis). T. Brahe's Uraniborg & Stjerneborg on the island of Hveen. Drawings by C. Christensen, text by F. B. [*Dan. & Eng.*] fol. Copenhagen. 1921

Beckford, *The family of.*
see BRITTON (J.) Graph. &c. illust. of Fonthill Abbey, w. heraldical &c. notices of the B. fam., 1823.
,, GREGORY (W.) The B. fam.: remin. of Fonthill Abbey &c., 2nd ed., 1898.

Beckford (William), *of Fonthill Abbey.* Biogr. memoirs of extraord. painters. n. ed. s8o. 1824

Beckius (Christian Daniel), *see* BECK (C. D.)

Beckmann (Johann). Dagboek v. z. reis door Nederland in 1762 [*in German*]; medged. door G. W. Kernkamp, *see* HISTORISCH GENOOTS. Bijdr., d33, 1912.

Beckwith (Martha Warren), *see* HALEOLE (S. N.) The Hawaiian romance of Laieikawai; w. intr. & tr. by M. W. B., 1919.

Becman (Christian). Oratio de barbarie, &c. super. temp. [P483]. s4o. Anbergæ. 1617

Becon (Thomas), *see* XENOPHON. Gnomologiæ &c.; sententiæ ex prob. aut. excerptæ per T. B. 1559.

Becque (Henry).

Conférences, notes d'album, poésies, corr. [Œ. compl., 7]. [6e éd.] 8o. 1926
Querelles litt. [Œ. compl., 5]. s8o. 1925
Souvs. d'un auteur dramat. [Œ. compl., 6]. 8o. 1926
see GOT (A.) H. B., sa vie & s. œ., 1920.
,, SÉE (E.) H. B. ou servitude & grandeur dram., 1926.

Becquer (Gustavo Adolfo). Obras. 5a ed. 3t. s8o. 1904
Twenty poems. [Tr.], w. intr. note by R. Croft-Cooke. s8o. O. 1927

Bedale (E. M.) Effects of posture & rest, *see* INDUST. FATIGUE RESEARCH BD. Rep. 29, 1924.

Beddard (Frank Evers). Animal coloration. 8o. 1892

Beddoes (W. F.)
The management of English woodlands. 8o. [1919]

Beddow (Bruce). The golden milestone. s8o. [1925]

Bede [†BEDA, *The Venerable*].

Eccl. hist. gentis Anglorum libri 5. s8o. Coloniæ Agrippinæ. 1601
Eccl. hist. of the Eng. nation. Tr. J. Stevens. Add. Life of the a. s8o. 1723
Hist. eccl. gentis Anglorum, Hist. abbatum & Epist. ad Ecgberctum cum Epist. Bonifacii ad Cudberthum. Cura G. H. Moberly. s8o. Oxonii. 1869
see GEHLE (H.) Disput. de B. vita & scriptis, 1838.
,, LEHMANN (P.) Wert u. Echtheit e. B. abgesproch. Schrift, 1919.

Bedell (William), *bp. of Kilmore & Ardagh.* A letter to J. Waddesworth upon controv. betw. Papists & Protestants. Added Prospectus of Christian Institute & an address [*sep. pagin.*] 8o. 1827
see BEDELL (W.), *son of bp. B.* Life of Bishop B., 1871.
,, BURNET (G.) *Life of W. B., & letters betw. J. Waddesworth & W. B., 1685.
,, JACKSON (T.) Lib. of Xtn. biog., v8, W. B., by G. Burnet, 1838.
,, WADDESWORTH (J.) Letters betw. Spain & England &c., betw. J. W. & W. B., 1624.

Bedell (William), *d. 1670, son of bp. Bedell.* Life of Bp. Bedell, *see* MAYOR (J. E. B.) Camb. in the 17th cent., p3, 1871.

Bedenken [BEDENCKEN].

*Bedencken auf das Interim &c., 1548, *see* OSIANDER (A.)
Bedencken das diese Proposition &c.; gestellet durch d. Predigen zu Mansfelt, 1553, *see* MANSFELD.
*Bedencken d. Theologen zu Braunschweigk &c., 1571, *see* BRAUNSCHWEIG.
Bedencken (Christlichs) u. Motiven dess Herrn Ernst Fr. &c., 1590, *see* ERNEST FREDERICK, *Margrave of Baden.*

Bedford. Roll of Justices in Eyre at B., 1202 [&] 1227; [ed.] G. H. Fowler, *see* BEDFORDSHIRE HIST. REC. SOC. Publs., v1, 3, 1913–16.

Bedford (Herbrand Arthur Russell, *11th duke of*). Our home army in 1909 & 1913. [Repr. f. Morning Post]. [P2495]. 8o. 1910

Bedford (T.), *see* INDUST. FATIGUE RESEARCH BD. Reps. 11, 18; by T. B. &c., 1921–22.

Bedfordshire. Cal. of Feet of Fines for B., 1192–1272; ed. G. H. Fowler, 1919, *see* BEDFORDSHIRE HIST. REC. SOC. Publs., v6, 1919.
Cal. of Pipe Rolls of r. of Rich. I, 1189–99, 1923, *see* BEDFORDSHIRE HIST. REC. SOC. Publs., v7, 1923.

Bedfordshire Historical Record Society.
Publications. v1–11. 8o. Aspley Guise. 1913–27
v7, *publ. in conjunct. w.* Architect. &c. Soc. for Co. of Bucks., & *cont.* Cal. of Pipe Rolls of reign of Rich. I for Bucks. & Beds., 1189–99; by G. H. Fowler & M. W. Hughes.
v10, *cont.* Digest of charters pres. in Cartulary of the Priory of Dunstable; by G. H. Fowler.
Quarto memoirs. v1. fol. Aspley Guise. 1922
see FOWLER (G. H.) Beds. in 1086: anal. &c. of Domesday Bk., 1922. [1.]

Bédier (Joseph).

Discours de récept. à l'Acad. Fr. sur l'œuvre d'E. Rostand. s8o. 1921
Les légendes épiques. 2e éd., rev. & corr. 4t. 8o. 1914–21
see BARTHOU (L.) Rép. au disc. de B., 1921.
,, CHANSON (LA) DE ROLAND; publ. & tr. par J. B., 1924; comm. par J. B., 1927.
see *CHÂTELAINE (LA) de Vergy: conte du 13e siècle; publ. & tr. J. B., 1927.
,, HANOTAUX (G.) Hist. de la nation franç., t12, Hist. des lettres, v1, Des origines à Ronsard; par J. B. &c., 1921.

Bedloe (William) [BEDLOW]. The exam. of W. B., rel. to the Popish Plot, taken by Sir F. North. [P525]. sfol. 1680
A faithful acc. of the sickness, death & burial of Capt. W. B. [*signed T. S. No tp.* P525]. sfol. 1680
Narr. &c. of the horrid Popish plot. [*a.c. in* P525]. sfol. 1679

Bednar (F.), *ed., see* REFORMACNI sbornik., 1, 1921.

Bedny (Demyan), *ps.* Богатырскій бой. [P2697]. 8o. [Москва]. 1921
Песни прошлого. [P2697; 2750]. 8o. [Москва]. 1920

Bedrock: a quarterly review of scientific thought. v3, no. 1 (April 1914). [*no more publ.*] 8o. 1914

Bedrossian (Matthias) [PETROSEAN (M.)].
New dict. Armenian-Eng. 8o. Venice. 1875–79

Bedwell (Cyril Edward Albert).
A brief hist. of the Middle Temple. 8o. 1909

Beebe (Charles William).

The Arcturus adventure: acc. of New York Zoolog. Soc.'s 1st oceanographic exped. la8o. N.Y. 1926
The edge of the jungle. [2nd impr.] 8o. 1922
Galápagos: world's end. Publ. New York Zoolog. Soc. la8o. N.Y. 1924
The log of the sun: chron. of nature's year. la8o. N.Y. 1906
,, ,, ... 8o. [1927]
A monograph of the pheasants. [N.Y. Zoolog. Soc.] 4v. fol. 1918–22
Pheasant jungles. 8o. N.Y. 1927
Tropical wild life in Brit. Guiana. By C.W.B., G. I. Hartley & P. G. Hawes. Intr. by T. Roosevelt. [N.Y. Zoolog. Soc.] v1. [*no more publ.*] 8o. N.Y. 1917
see BEEBE (M. C.) & C. W. B. Our search for a wilderness, 1910.

Beebe (Mary Blair) & C. W. Beebe. Our search for a wilderness: 2 ornitholog. exped. to Venezuela & Brit. Guiana. 8o. 1910

Beecham (John). An essay on the constit. of Wesleyan Methodism. [P449]. 8o. 1850

Beecham (John Charles). The yellow spider. s8o. [1921]

Beecheno (F. R.) Notes on Norwich Castle. 8o. Norwich. 1888

Beeching (Henry Charles), *dean of Norwich.* The character of Shakespeare, *see* BRIT. ACADEMY. Proc., 1917–18.

Beekman (A. A.) Nederland als Polderland: beschr. van d. eigenaardigen toestand der belangrijkste helft van ons land. 2e druk. 8o. Zutphen. *n.d.*

Beelen-Bertholff (*baron* **de**). Berichte d. ersten Agenten Österr. in d. Verein. Staaten v. Amerika, Baron de B.-B., 1784–9; hrsg. v. H. Schlitter, *see* FONTES RERUM AUSTRIAC., B45ii, 1891.

Beenken (Hermann). Bildhauer d. 14 Jhdts. am Rhein u. in Schwaben. la8o. L. 1927
Roman. Skulptur in Deutschland (11. u. 12. Jhdt.) [Hdbch. d. Kunstgesch.; hrsg. G. Biermann]. la8o. L. 1924

Beer (Adolf), *see* JOSEPH II, *emp.* J. II u. Graf Ludwig Cobenzl: ihr Briefwechsel; hrsg. v. A. B. & J. Fiedler, 2B, 1901.

Beer (Carl). Gesch. Böhmens mit bes. Berücksichtigung d. Gesch. d. Deutschen in Böhmen. s8o. Reichenberg. [1921]

Beer (E. S. de), *see* DE BEER (E. S.)

Beer (Fritz). Die Einsteinsche Relativitätstheorie. 6 Vorträge. 5e A. [*b. w.* Einstein (A.) Äther &c., 1920]. 8o. Wien. 1920

Beer (Georg), *prof. in Heidelberg.* Welches war d. älteste Relig. Israels? 8°. Giessen. 1927

Beer (George Louis). G. L. B., a tribute. [*by var. writers.* Foreword by Col. E. M. House]. 8°. N.Y. 1924

Beer (Max).
Allgemeine Gesch. d. Sozialismus u. d. soz. Kämpfe. 5T. s8°. 1919–23
1, Altertum. 2, Mittelalter. 3, Neuere Zeit, 14–18 Jhdt. 4, Zeit v. 1750–1860. 5, Neueste Zeit bis 1920.
Hist. of Brit. socialism. v2. 8°. 1920
The life & teaching of Karl Marx. Tr. T. C. Partington & H. J. Stenning. s8°. [1921]
The pioneers of land reform. T. Spence [The real rights of man], W. Ogilvie [The right of property in land], T. Paine [Agrarian justice]. Introd. by M. B. s8°. 1920
Social struggles & socialist forerunners. Tr. H. J. Stenning. s8°. [1924]
Social struggles & thought (1750–1860). Tr. H. J. Stenning. s8°. [1925]
Social struggles in antiquity. Tr. H. J. Stenning. s8°. [1922]
Social struggles in the Middle Ages. Tr. H. J. Stenning, & rev. by the a. s8°. [1924]

Beer (*Mrs.* Rachel). Cat. of pictures &c., the prop. of Mrs. R. B. Sold by Christie, July 22, 1927. [*Illust.* P2873]. 8°. 1927

Beer (Thomas). The mauve decade: Amer. life at the end of the 19th cent. 8°. 1926
Stephen Crane: st. in Amer. letters. Intr. by J. Conrad. 8°. 1924

Beer (William). Checklist of American periodicals, 1741–1800. [Amer. Antiq. Soc.] [P2737]. 8°. Mass. 1923

Beerbohm (Max). And even now. 8°. 1920
Herbert Beerbohm Tree; memories [*by var. a.*] coll. by M. B. 8°. [1921]
see Lynch (B.) M. B. in perspective, 1921.

Beerfelde (*Hauptmann* von). Wer sind die Schuldigen am Weltkrieg-Völkermord? [P2408; P2522]. 8°. [1918]

Beermann (Sigismund). Evangelicæ rei integritas Hardtiana in negotio Jonæ. s8°. Wolffenbuttelæ. 1721

Beernhäuter. *Der erste Beernhäuter, sampt Simplicissimi Gauckeltasche, 1670, *see* Grimmelshausen (H. J. C. v.)

Beers (Clifford Whittingham). A mind that found itself. Autobiography. 8°. 1908

Beers (Rudolf), *see* Garcia (Z.) Bibl. patrum Latin. Hisp.; nach d. Aufzeichnungen B., 1915.

Beerski (P. Jeannerat de), *see* Jeannerat de Beerski (P.)

Bees. *The natural hist. of b.; tr., 1744, *see* Réaumur (R. A.)

Bees (Nikos A.) [ΒΈΗΣ]. Der französ.-mittelgr. Ritterroman "Imberios u. Margarona" u. d. Gründungssage d. Daphniklosters, Äthen. 8°. 1924
Die Inschriftenaufzeichnung d. Kodex Sinaiticus Gr. 508 u. d. Maria-Spiläotissa-Klosterkirche bei Sille (Lykaonien). 8°. 1922

Beeson (Charles Henry). Isidor-Studien. [Quellen &c. z. lat. Philol. d. M.-A., B4ii]. 8°. München. 1913

Beet (Joseph Agar). Comm. on Romans. 7th ed. s8°. 1890
The credentials of the gospel. 19th Ternley Lect. 8°. 1889
The new life in Christ. 8°. 1895
Through Christ to God, a study in sci. theology. 8°. 1892

Beetham (Bently), *F.Z.S.* Among our banished birds. 8°. 1927

Beethoven (Ludwig van).
Works: *Rondo, Andante, Sonata &c. var. ed.; works have sep. tp. & pagin.* 4°. *n.p. n.d.*
Beethoven, 1770–1827. [*By var. as. Extr. f.* Music & Letters. v8]. la8°. [1927]
Berichte d. Zeitgenossen, Briefe &c. Gesamm. u. erl. v. A. Leitzmann. 2B. s8°. L. 1921
Sämtl. Briefe. Hrsg. E. Kastner. Verm. &c. Neuausg. v. F. Kapp. 8°. L. [1923]
see Behrend (W.) L. van B.'s pianoforte sonatas; tr., 1927.
" Bekker (P.) B., 1922.
" Fouque (O.) Révolutionnaires de la musique, 1882.
" Frimmel (T. v.) Neue Beethoveniana, n. A., 1890.
see Hadow (W. H.) B., 1917.
" Hevesy (A. de). B.: vie intime, 1926.
" Ludwig (E.) Kunst u. Schicksal (B. &c.), 1927.
" Marliave (J. de). Les quatuors de B., 1925.
" Naumann (E.) L. van B., Vortrag, 1870.
" Newman (E.) The unconscious B., 1927.
" Pfordten (H. *Frhr.* v. d.) B., 1922.
" Sullivan (J. W. N.) B., h. spiritual development, 1927.
" Thayer (A. W.) Life of B.; ed. Krehbiel, 3v. 1921.
" Turner (W. J.) B., 1927.

Beeton (Isabella Mary).
Dict. of every-day cookery. 35th thousand. 8°. *n.d.*

Beeton (Samuel O.), *see* Dowty (A. A.) & S. O. B. The coming K——, *n.d.*

Beeton's Christmas Annual, *see* Dowty (A. A.) & S. O. Beeton. The coming K——, *n.d.*

Beets (A.), *see* Vries (M. de) &c. *edd.* Woordenboek d. Nederl. taal, d7i; bewerkt door A. B., 1926.

Beets (Nicolaas) [*ps.* Hildebrand].
Camera obscura. 16e druk. s8°. Haarlem. 1886
Gedichten. [Jubilé-uitg.] 8e dr. 5d. *in* 1v. [d5, 4e dr.] s8°. Leiden. *n.d.*

Beevor (*Sir* Hugh Reeve), *5th bart.* Norfolk woodlands. [Repr. f. Trans. of Norfolk &c. Nat. Soc. v11. P2773]. 8°. *n.p.* [1924]

Beevor (Ralph Jermy), *see* Felsted School. Alumni Felsted. ed. R. J. B., 1921.

***Befreiung** Ostpreussens, *see* Weltkrieg (Der), 1914 bis 1918, B2, 1925.

Begbie (Harold).
Broken lights: varieties of Xtn. opinion. 8°. [1926]
An English family. s8°. [1919]
The latest thing. s8°. [1920]
Life of William Booth. 2v. 8°. 1920
The ways of laughter. s8°. [1921]

Begbie (Peter James). Supernat. illusions. 2v [*in* 1]. 8°. 1851

Beger (Eusebius). De advocatia imperatoris Judaica &c. s4°. Tubingæ. 1748

Begg (Robert Burns). Witchcraft in Kinross-shire: criminal trials at Crook of Devon in 1662. s8°. *p.f.p.c.* Kinross. *n.d.*

Beggi (F. O.) The papal criminal history &c. With Venice, its martyrdom &c. [*sep. pagin.*] s8°. 1862

Beginnings (The) of Xty., pl, v1–3, 1920–26, *see* Foakes-Jackson (F. J.) & K. Lake, *edd.*

Begley (John). The dioc. of Limerick, 16 & 17 c. 8°. D. 1927

Begly (Connor). [Beagloic (Concobar o)]. Engl.-Irish dict. [By B. & H. MacCurtin]. 4°. Ab. Pairis. [Paris]. 1732

Begtrup (Holger), H. Lund & P. Manniche. Folk high schools of Denmark & the develop. of a farming community. Intr. by Sir M. Sadler. s8°. 1926

Béguinot (Augusto) & A. Vaccari. Contrib. [*&* 2° contrib.] alla flora d. Libia. [Min. d. Affari Esteri]. 8°. 1912–13

Bégule (Lucien). L'église Saint-Maurice, anc. cath. de Vienne en Dauphiné, son arch., sa décor. Accomp. d'une notice hist. par J. Bouvier. 4°. 1914
Incrustations décorat. des cathédrales de Lyon & de Vienne. 4°. Lyon. 1905

Beham (Barthel). Kupferstiche u. Holzschnitte v. B. u. H. S. Beham u. A. Dürer &c. Versteig. durch G. G. Boerner, Leipzig. [P2699]. 4°. L. [1921]

Beham (Hans Sebald), *see* Beham (B.) Kupferstiche u. Holzschnitte &c., 1921.

Beham (Joannes Ferdinandus) [Behamb]. Notitia Hungariæ antiquo-mod. Berneggeriana, perpetuis observat. condecorata &c. [2 p. *in* 1v.] s8°. Argentorati. 1676

Behem, *see* Bohemia.

Behn (Aphra). Poems upon sev. occasions: w. A voyage to the island of love [*w. sep. pagin.*] s8°. 1684
*The ten pleasures of marriage. [Wr. by A. Marsh, 1682] & 2nd pt. The confession of the new married couple [1683]. Attrib. to A. B. Intr. J. Harvey. [Navarre Soc.] *p.p.* 8°. 1922

Behr (H. von). Bei d. fünften Reserve-Div. im Weltkriege. Tagebuch-Aufzeichnungen. 8°. 1919

Behr (Johann Adam).
Catechismus in emblematibus. s4°. Augspurg. 1718

Behrend (William). Ludwig van Beethoven's pianoforte sonatas. Tr. I. Lund. Intr. by A. Cortot. s8°. 1927

Behrens (Edward Beddington). The Internat. Labour Office (League of Nations): survey of problems of internat. admin. Foreword by H. J. Laski. s8°. 1924

Behrens (Gustav), *see* Kaiserl. Deut. Arch. Inst. German. Denkmäler d. Frühzeit, T1, Denkmäler d. Wangionengebietes; bearbt. v. G. B., 1923.

Behring Sea. B. S. & Strait pilot, *&* Suppl. 1, 1920–22, *see* Admiralty.

Behrs (Sergei Andreev.) Воспоминанія о Л. Н. Толстомъ. [P643] s8°. Смоленскъ. 1893

Behula: the Indian "Pilgrim's progress." Tr. f. Bengali by D. C. Sen, by J. W. Petavel & K. C. Sen. Foreword by Sir A. Mookerjee. s8°. Calcutta. 1923

Beibitz (Joseph Hugh). Belief, faith, & proof. Intr. by bp. Gore. s8°. 1922

Beidavæus (Abdalla), *see* 'Abd Allah ibn 'Umar Muḥammad ibn 'Ali *al Baïdhâwî.*

Beier (Adrian), *prof. of law at Jena.* De sigillo confessionis. [P436]. s4°. Lipsiæ. 1724

Beil (Ludwig). Martin. Roman. s8º. 1919

Bein (Alex.) Die Staatsidee Alex. Hamiltons. [Hist. Zeitschrift. Beih. 12]. 8º. München. 1927

Beit (Sir Otto). Cat. of the coll. of pottery & porcelain of O. B. fol. 1916

Japanese colour-prints &c. in coll. of Sir O. B. [By J. Brinckmann & E. F. Strange]. 4º. *p.p.*, *Chiswick Press.* 1924

Beiträge [BEYTRÄGE]. *Beiträge zu W. Hogarth's Lebensbeschr. &c., 1783, *see* NICHOLS (JOHN).

Beyträge zu d. Actis historico-eccl. &c., 1746–58, *see* ACTA HISTORICO-ECCL. &c.

Beiträge zur deut. Literaturwissenschaft; hrsg. v. E. Elster. Nr. 15. 8º. Marburg. 1919

see KERN (O.) Johann Rist als weltlicher Lyriker, 1919. [15.]

Beiträge zur englischen Philologie. Hrsg. M. Förster. H5, 6. 8º. L. 1926–7

see *COURT of sapience; krit. Textausg. v. R. Spindler, 1927. [6.]

„ SCHNIPPEL (E.) Die engl. Kalenderstäbe, 1926. [5.]

Beiträge z. Geschichte d. deutschen Sprache u. Literatur. B43–51; hrsg. v. W. Braune. 8º. Halle a. S. 1918–27

Beiträge z. Geschichte d. Philosophie d. Mittelalters. Hrsg. v. C. Bäumker. 8º. Münster. 1918–27

B16, 18ii, iii, 20iii–vi, 21i–iii, 22i–iv, 23i–v, 24i–vi, 25iii–iv, 26i.

see ABÉLARD (P.) Philos. Schr., 1i–iii, 1919–27. [21i–iii.]

„ ALBERTUS, *Magnus.* De animalibus lib. 26; hrsg. H. Stadler, B2, 1920. [16.]

„ ALFREDUS, *Anglicus.* De motu cordis; hrsg. &c. C. Baeumker, 1923. [23i–ii.]

„ ANSELMUS, *Laudunensis.* Systemat. Sentenzen; hrsg. v. F. P. Bliemetzrieder, T1, 1919. [18ii, iii.]

„ BÄUMKER (C.), & SARTORIUS v. WALTERSHAUSEN. Glossen d. Jepa z. Isagoge d. Porphyrius, 1924. [24i.]

„ BIRKENMAJER (A.) Verm. Unters. z. Gesch. d. mittelalt. Philos., 1922. [20v.]

„ ECKHART (*Meister*). Lat. Rechtfertigungsschrift E.'s; hrsg. v. A. Daniels, 1923. [23v.]

„ GARNERIUS, *de Rochefort.* *Contra Amaurianos; hrsg. v. C. Bäumker, 1926. [24v–vi.]

„ GRABMANN (M.) Die echten Schr. d. Thomas v. Aquin, 1920. [22i, ii.]

„ GUNDISALVI (D.) Von d. Hervorgange d. Welt (De processu mundi); hrsg. v. G. Bülow, 1925. [24iii.]

„ HEIDINGSFELDER (G.) Albert v. Sachsen, s. Lebensgang &c., 1921. [22iii, iv.]

„ KOCH (J.) Durandus de S. Porciano O. P.: Forsch. z. Streit um Thomas v. Aquin zu Beg. d. 14. Jhdts, T1, 1927. [26i.]

„ LUYCKX (B. A.) Erkenntnislehre Bonaventuras, 1923. [23iii, iv.]

„ MÜLLER (H. F.) Dionysios, Proklos, Plotinos, 1918. [20iii–iv.]

„ ROSENMÖLLER (B.) Relig. Erkenntnis nach Bonaventura, 1925. [25iii, iv.]

„ SCHUBERT (A.) Augustins Lex-aeterna-Lehre, 1924. [24ii.]

„ SPETTMANN (H.) Die Psychologie d. J. Pecham, 1919. [20vi.]

Beiträge zur Kunde steiermärk. Geschichtsquellen. 1864–1906, *see* HISTORISCHER VEREIN F. STEIERMARK.

Beiträge z. Philosophie d. deut. Idealismus. Im Auftrage d. Deut. Philos. Gesellschaft &c. Hrsg. A. Hoffmann &c. B1–3 (1918–25). 8º. Erfurt. 1918–26.

—— Beiheft, *see* BINDER (J.) Luthers Staatsauffassung, 1924.

Beitz (Egid). Das heilige Trier. la8º. Augsburg. 1927

Beitzke (Hermann). Über d. Familie Rheinen. [*no tp. b. w.* Roland. Vereinsbeilage, 1912–14]. la8º. *n.d.*

Bekandtnus, *see* BEKENNTNISS.

Bekäntniss, *see* BEKENNTNISS.

Beke (Charles Tilstone). On the origin of the Gallas. From Rep. of Brit. Assoc., 1847. [*b. w.* Tutschek (C. & L.) Dict., 1844–45]. 8º. 1848

Bekenntniss [BEKANNTNUSS &c., *see also* GLAUBENSBEKANTNUS].

Bekandtnuss der vier Frey u. Reichstätt, Strassburg, Costantz &c., 1531, *see* STRASSBURG.

Bekanntnuss d. Theologen u. Kirchendiener Heidelberg &c. 1592, *see* HEIDELBERG.

*Bekantnuss d. waaren Glaubens &c., 1644, *see* HELVETIA: CONFESSIO HELVETICA.

*Bekantnuss unsers heyl. Christl. glouhens, wie es di Kilch zu Basel haltet, 1534, *see* BASEL.

*Bekenntnisse van dem Sacramente des lives u. blodes Christi &c., 1534, *see* BRAUNSCHWEIG.

Bekentnis von d. ewig. Gnadenwahl &c. Gottes z. Seligkeit; gest. d. die theol. Facultet zu Wittenberg, 1597, *see* WITTENBERG.

Christl. Glaubens-Bekentnus d. waffenlosen Mennonisten, 1664, *see* MENNONISTEN.

*Einhellige Bekentnis vieler Theol. &c., 1572, *see* MELISSANDER (C.).

Bekenntniss [*continued*].

Kirchen-Ordnung u. Glaubens-Bekäntniss &c., 1711, *see* FRANCE. La discipline eccl.

Kurtz Bekentnis u. Artickel v. heil. Abendmal &c. zu Torgaw, 1574, *see* TORGAU.

Bekenntnisschriften. B. (Die) d. altprotestant. Kirche Deutschlands; hrsg. H. L. J. Heppe, 1855, *see* HEPPE (H. L. J.)

B. (Die) d. evang.-reformirten Kirche, 1847, *see* BÖCKEL (E. G. A.)

Beketova (M. A.) Александр Блок, біограф. очерк s8º. П. 1922

Bekker (Betje), *see* WOLFF (ELIZ.)

Bekker (Paul). Beethoven. 8º. St. 1922

Bekoev (Georg) [BEKOJEFF]. Das Ossenland. [*Russ. & German*]. Über. v. H. v. Busch. s8º. 1924

Beksics (Gusztáv).

A dualismus. Története, Közjogi értelme és nemzeti förekvéseink. 8º. 1892

A magyar doctrinairek. s8º. 1882

A román kérdés és a fajok harcza Európában és Magyarországon. 8º. 1895

Kemény Zsigmond a forradalom s a kiegyeyés. 2ik kiadás. 8º. 1883

Magyarország jövöje az ujabb nemzeti elhelyezkedés alapján. [P2393]. 8º. 1900

Mátyás Király birodalma és Magyarország jövöje. 8º. 1905

Bel (Matěj) [BELIUS (MATHIAS)]. Compendium Hungariæ geograph. in partes 4 divisum. ed. 4a, auctior & corr. [2p *in* 1v. *pagin. cont.*] s8º. Posonii. 1792

„ „ *For Suppl.*, *see* COMPENDIOLUM regn. Slavoniæ &c., 1792.

De vet. litt. Hunno-Scythica exercit. s8º. Lipsiæ. 1718

Hungariæ antiq. & novæ prodromus, cum specimine &c. fol. Norimbergæ. 1723

Bela [BELÆ]. Anon. Belæ Regis notar. hist. Hungarica, 1772, *see* HUNGARICA.

Belaiew (Ivan S.), *see* BELYAEV.

Belaiew (*Col.* N. T.), *C.B.* Crystallis. of metals. Lect., 1922. Pref. by H. C. H. Carpenter. s8º. [1923]

Начало Руси: лекція. [P2824]. s8º. Лондонъ. 1925

О Булатѣ и Харалугѣ. [Rec. d'ét. déd. à la mém. de N. P. Kondakov, tir. à part]. 4º. Prague. 1926

О древн. &c. русс. мѣрахъ. [Semin. Kondakov. Rec. tir. à part]. la8º. Prague. 1927

Belando (Nicolas de Jesus).

Manual para sacerdotes. s8º. Valencia. 1773

Belcari (Feo). Prose. Racc. & pubbl. da O. Gigli. [Bibl. class. sacra &c., sec. 15, t1–5]. 5t. s8º. 1843–44

Contents as under [*each w. sep. tp.*]

1, Vita d. B. Giov. Colombibi da Siena, riv. &c. d. O. Rainaldi.

2, Parte d. vita d'Alcuni Gesuati, riv. &c. O. Rainaldi—Vita di Frate Egidio, pubbl. O. Gigli.

3, Lettere, pubbl. D. Moreni—2 trattati d. B. Jacopone da Todi, volgariz. da F. B.—Trattato di Riccardo da S. Vittore de quattro gradi d. carità volgariz—Il prato spirituale [*by* J. Moschus], volgariz. di F. B.

4, 5, Il prato spirituale, *continued.*

Belcher (*Maj.* Ernest Albert) & J. A. Williamson. Migration within the Empire. [Brit. Empire: survey; ed. H. Gunn, v12]. 8º. [1924]

Belcher (Henry) *of Whitby.* Illust. of scenery on Whitby & Pickering railway, f. drawings by G. Dodgson. With descr. by H. B. 8º. 1836

Beldam (Joseph). Summary of laws affecting Protestant Dissenters. s8º. 1827

Belethus (Joannes). Rationale divin. officiorum (12c.), *see* DURANDUS (G.) Rationale, 1859.

Beletsky (S. P.) Григорий Распутин. la8º. П. 1923

Belfast. *Hist. collections rel. to the town of B. [to 1801]. 8º. Belfast. *G. Berwick.* 1817

Belfast & Prov. of Ulster directory, 1917. 8º. Belfast. 1917

Belfast Natural Hist. & Philos. Society. Spec. meeting rel. to mummies f. Thebes. [F. the "Northern Whig," 24. Oct. P2800]. s8º. Belfast. 1850

Belgae. *Libellus supplex Imp. Majestati cæterisque principibus, &c., nomine Belgarum ex inferiori Germania, Evangel. religionis causa per Albani ducis tyrannidem ejectorum, in comitiis Spirensibus exhib. s8º. [Antverp ?]. 1570

Belgicus. *Mercurius Belgicus, 1685, *see* MERCURIUS.

Belgiojosa (*la pssa.* Cristina di), *see* THIERRY (A. A.) La princesse B., 1926.

Belgiojoso (Carlo).

Republicani e Sforzeschi (1447–50). 2v. s8º. 1864

Belgique [Belge ; Belgium].
Archives de l'état à Vienne &c., 1924, *see* Laenen (J.), *ed.*
Archives de l'État en B. pend. la Guerre, 1914–18. Annuaire publ. sous J. Cuvelier. 8º. [Renaix]. 1914–18
La Belgique illust., 2t, 1878–82, *see* Van Bemmel (*b.* E. P. P.)
Campagnes coloniales Belges, 1914–18. [Ministère de la Défense Nat.] t1. la8º. Brux. 1927
Commission for Relief in B.: statist. review of operations, 1914–19 [1925], *see* Gay (G. I.)
*Confessio sive declaratio sententiæ pastorum, qui in Foederato Belgio Remonstrantes vocantur. s4º. Herder-Wiici. 1622
Constit. de la B., suivie de la loi élect. [P505]. s8º. Brux.[1831]
Ecclesiarum Belgic. confessio, interp. J. Revio; & Catechesis; interp. F. Sylburgio [*Gr. & Lat.*] s8º. Amstelodami. 1638
Exposition de l'art belge; organ. par L. Bénédite &c. au Musée du Jeu de Paume à Paris, mai-juil. 1923, *see* Bénédite (L.)
German (The) army in Belgium: the White Bk. of May 1915; tr. E. N. Bennett, 1921, *see* Deutsch. D. Weissbuch II &c.
Germ. legisl. for B., 17s. & Ind^s., 1915–19, *see* Huberich (C. H.) & A. Nicol-Speyer, *edd.*
Inventaires des archives de la Belg. publ. par. ordre de Gouvt.
see Nelis (H.) Chambres des comptes de Flandre & de Brabant &c., 1914.
„ —— Chambre des comptes de Lille: cat. des chartes du sceau de l'audience, t1 (1385–1586), 1915.
„ —— Invent. des archives de l'Univ. de Louvain &c., 1817–35, 1917.
„ Verkooren (A.) Invent. des chartes & cartul. du Luxembourg, t2–4, 1915–17.
„ —— Inventaire des chartes &c. des duchés de Brabant & de Limbourg &c., p1, t1–7, 1910–17.
„ Verriest (L.) Inventaire du fonds de la cour des mortemains de Hainaut, 1915.
Inventaires sommaires des archives de l'État en Belg.
see Hoop (A. d') Inventaire gén. des archives eccl. du Brabant, t2, 3, 1914–22.
Jurisprudentia heroica, sive de jure Belg. circa nobilit. &c. demonstr. in comm. ad edictum Pr. Alberti &c. emulgat. 14. Dec. 1616. [*Edict. in Dutch & Fr.* Comm. *by* P. Christinæus ?] fol. Brux. 1668
*Letter on the B. Revolution; tr., 1831, *see* Van de Weyer (S.)
Nouv. carte phys. & routière du roy. de la B. folded s8º. Bruxelles. 1836
Rapports & doc. d'enquête. [Comm. d'Enquête sur les Viol. des Règles du Droit des Gens &c.] 4v [v1 & 3 *in* 2t, *w. sep. tp. & pagin.*] la8º. Brux. 1921–23
1, Attentats commis par les troupes allemandes pend. l'invas. &c. de la Belgique.
2, Déport. des ouvriers belges & traitements infligés aux prisonniers de guerre &c.
3, Mesures prises par les Allemands à l'ég. de l'indust. belge pend. l'occup.
4, Mesures législ., judic. &c. prises par les Allemands.
The second Belgian Grey Book. p1 & p2 (sect. 10). [P2749]. 8º. 1925

Belgrano (Luigi Tommaso). Della dedizione dei Genovesi a Luigi XII di Francia, *see* Regia Dep. di Storia Patria. Misc., t1, 1862.
Storia coloniale dell' epoca ant., med. e mod. Riprod. d. 2a ed. del Manuale di storia d. colonie. s8º. Firenze. 1916

Belgrano (*General* Manuel), *see* Mitre (B.) Hist. de B. &c., 4t, 1927–28.

Belgrave (C. Dalrymple).
Siwa, the oasis of Jupiter Ammon. 8º. [1923]

Belhaven (*Hon.* Ralph Gerard Alex. Hamilton, *Master of*). War diary, 1914–18. 8º. 1924

Belii [Byelii]. Бѣлый терроръ или выстрѣлъ 4 Апрѣля 1865 г. [*b. w.* Panaev. Новгородское возмущеніе въ 1831, 1874]. 3е изд. s8º. Лейпцигъ. *n.d.*

Belii (Andrei).
Возвратъ (повѣсть). s8º. Берлинъ. 1922
Глоссалолія: поэма о звукѣ. s8º. Берлинъ. 1922
Записки чудака. 2т. s8º. Москва. 1922
Котик Летаев. s8º. П. 1922
Королевна и рыцари. Сказки. s8º. 1919
Первое свиданіе, поэма. s8º. П. 1921
Петербургъ, Романъ 2ч. s8º. Берлинъ. 1922
Послѣ разлуки. Берлинскій песенник. s8º. П. [1922]
Путевыя замѣтки. т1. Сицимя и Тунисъ. s8º. Москва. 1922
Серебряный голубь. Романъ. 2ч. s8º. Берлинъ. 1922
Сирин ученого варварства (По поводу книги В. Иванова "Родное и Вселенское." [P2580]. s8º. Берлин. 1922
Стихи о Россіи. s8º. Берлинъ. 1922
Стихотворенія. s8º. Берлинъ. 1923
Христос воскрес. s8º. П. 1918

Beling (Richard) [*ps.* Irenaeus (Philopater)]. *Vindiciarum Catholic. Hiberniæ lib. duo [Rerum in Hibernia gestarum, 1641–49 synops.—Confut. libelli quem P. King, in Catholicos Hiberniæ proceres publ. *2 pagin.*] s8º. Parisiis. 1650
see Sidney (*Sir* P.) Countesse of Pembrokes Arcadia, added 6th booke by R. B., 1633.

Belinsky (V. G.), *see* Byelinsky.

Belius (Matthias), *see* Bel (Matěj).

Belknap (Jeremy), *D.D.* The hist. of New-Hampshire. 3v. 8º. Phila. & Boston, Mass. 1784–92

Bell (A. H.), *see* Cockfield (W. E.) & A. H. B. Whitehorse district, Yukon, 1926.

Bell (Aubrey F. G.)
Baltasar Gracián. [Hispanic Soc. of Amer.] s8º. 1921
Benito Arias Montano. [Hisp. Soc. of Amer., 5]. s8º. O. 1922
Contemp. Spanish lit. 8º. 1926
Diogo do Couto. [Hisp. Soc. of Amer.] s8º. O. 1924
Fernam Lopez. [Hisp. Soc. of Amer.] s8º. O. 1921
Francisco Sanchez, El Brocense. [Hisp. Soc. of Amer.] s8º. 1925.
Gaspar Corrêa. [Hisp. Soc. of Amer.] s8º. O. 1924
Gil Vicente. [Hisp. Soc. of Amer.] s8º. 1921
In Portugal. 8º. 1912
Juan Ginés de Sepúlveda. [Hisp. Soc. of Amer.] s8º. 1925
Luis de Camões. [Hisp. Soc. of Amer.] s8º. 1923
Luis de Leon: st. of the Spanish Renaissance. 8º. O. 1925
The Oxford book of Portuguese verse, 12th–20th c. Chosen by B. s8º. O. 1925
Portuguese bibliography. [Hisp. Soc. of America]. s8º. O. 1922
Portuguese literature. 8º. O. 1922
Spanish Galicia. s8º. 1922
see Elton (O.), A. F. G. B. &c. James Fitzmaurice-Kelly, 1924.

Bell (C. C.), *see* Bell (H. I.) & C. C. B. Welsh poems of 20th cent., 1925.

Bell (*Sir* Charles). The hand: as evincing design. 8º. 1834

Bell (*Sir* Charles Alfred).
English-Tibetan colloquial dict. 2nd ed. s8º. Calcutta. 1920
Grammar of colloq. Tibetan. 2nd ed. s8º. Calcutta. 1919
Tibet, past & present. 8º. O. 1924

Bell (Charles Francis). Designs by I. Jones for masques & plays at Court: descr. cat. of drawings &c.; intr. & notes by P. Simpson & C. F. B., *see* Walpole Soc., v12, 1924.

Bell (Charles Frederic Moberly), *see* Copplestone (B.) M. B. & h. times, 1925.

Bell (Clive) [A. C. H. Bell].
Landmarks in 19th cent. painting. 8º. 1927
Since Cézanne. s8º. 1922

Bell (Edward), *M.A., Trinity Coll., Cambridge.* Early architecture in W. Asia: Chaldæan, Hittite, Assyrian, Persian. s8º. 1924
Hellenic architecture, genesis & growth. s8º. 1920
Prehellenic architecture in the Ægean. 8º. 1926
see Macmillan (*Sir* F.) Net bk. Agreement 1899 &c., incl. narr. of dispute betw. Times Book Club & Publishers' Assoc., by E. B., 1924.

Bell (Edward Price). The American officers' club in London (9 Chesterfield Gdns.) [P2380]. 4º. 1918
The war of democracy. Lord Haldane states Britain's case. [P2415]. s4º. *n.d.*
World chancelleries: sentiments &c. by fam. statesmen. Intr. by C. Coolidge. 8º. Chicago. 1926

Bell (*Mrs.* G. H.), *see* Travers (John).

Bell (George Kennedy Allen), *dean of Canterbury.*
Docs. on Xtn. unity, 1920–24. Ed. G. K. A. B. s8º. 1924
see Stockholm. The S. Conf., 1925: offic. rep.; ed. G. K. A. B., 1926.

Bell (*Miss* Gertrude Margaret Lowthian).
Letters. Sel. & ed. Lady Bell. 2v. 8º. 1927
*Safar Nameh. Persian pictures. s8º. 1894

Bell (H. I.) & C. C. Bell. Welsh poems of the 20th cent. in Eng. verse, w. essay on Welsh poetry by H. I. B. 8º. Wrexham. 1925

Bell (Harold Idris). Jews & Xtns. in Egypt: Jewish troubles in Alexandria & the Athanasian controv. Illust. by texts f. Greek papyri in Brit. Mus. Ed. H. I. B., w. 3 Coptic texts ed. W. E. Crum. la8º. 1924
Juden u. Griechen im röm. Alexandreia, *see* Alte Orient, Beih. 9, 1926.

Bell (Henry Thomas Mackenzie). Half hours w. represent. novelists of the 19th c., w. brief biog. & intr. &c. 3v. 8º. 1927
Sel. poems. s8º. [1921]

Bell (Herbert C.), D. W. Parker *& others.* Guide to Brit. West Indian archive materials, in London & in the Isl^s., for the hist. of the U.S. [C. I. of Wash.] la8º. Wash. 1926

Bell (James), *major in the East York Militia.* View of univ. hist., lit., & the sev. schools of painting to 1842. Tables founded on G. G. Bredow & Sir M. van Bree. 5th ed., enl. &c. lafol. 1842

Bell (James), *prebendary of Wells.* Queen Elizabeth & a Swedish princess: acc. of visit of Princess Cecilia in 1565, f. orig. MS. of J. B. [Ed. E. Seaton. Haslewood bks.] 8°. 1926

Bell (*Miss* Jane), *see* HILL (T.) Cause of truth defended: 2 trials of H. for defamation of character of Miss B., 1827.
see HILL (REV. T.) Facts conn. w. prosecut. of T. H. for defaming charac. of J. B., 1832.

Bell (John), *of Antermony.* Travels f. St. Petersburg to var. parts of Asia. 2v. 8°. E. 1788
v2 conts. Journal of Mr. de Lange, 1721–22.

Bell (John), *D.D., Rector of Bainton.* New Pantheon; or, hist. dict. of the gods &c. 2v. 4°. 1790

Bell (John Keble) [*ps.* HOWARD (KEBLE)].
An author in wonderland. 8°. 1919
"The fast lady." [3rd impr.] s8°. [1925]
Lord Babs. s8°. 1927
My motley life. 8°. 1927
Paradise Island. s8°. [1926]

Bell (Malcolm).
Sir E. Burne-Jones, a record & review. 4°. 1892

Bell (*Col.* Mark Sever). Armenia. [P2593]. s8°. D. 1891

Bell (*Mrs.* Mary I. M.), *formerly Ottley.*
Short hist. of the Papacy. 8°. [1921]

Bell (Richard), *B.D.* Origin of Islam in its Xtn. environment. Gunning Lect., 1925. 8°. 1926

Bell (Robert), *a. of "The Life of Canning."* Anc. poems, ballads & songs of the peasantry of Eng. Ed. R. B. s8°. 1862

Bell (Robert), *M.D.* Remin. of an old physician. 8°. 1924

Bell (Thomas), *of Barnwell, Northamptonshire.* The ruins of Liveden; w. notices of fam. of Tresham, & its conn. w. the Gunpowder Plot &c. 4°. 1847

Bell (Thomas), *Protestant writer.*
The downefall of Poperie. [P2660]. s4°. 1604
T. Bels motives conc. Rom. faith &c. 2nd ed. corr. [P2660]. s4°. C. 1605

Bell (Walter Andrew), *see* HAYES (A. O.) & W. A. B. South. part of the Sydney coal field, Nova Scotia, 1923.

Bell (Walter George).
The Great Fire of London in 1666. 8°. 1920
The Great Plague in London in 1665. 8°. [1924]
More about unknown London. s8°. 1921
The Tower of London. s8°. 1921
Unknown London. [2nd ed.] s8°. 1920

Bellamintes, *pseud.* Mém. de F. H. comte de Seckendorff. [*b. w.* Canstein (C. H. v.) Das Muster, Lebens-Beschr. Speners, 1740]. s8°. Amsterdam. 1739

Bellamy (Daniel), *the elder.* The young ladies miscellany: or, youths' innocent & rational amusement. [*includ.* The Cambrian patriot, by E. Holdsworth; tr. D. B. *Each play has sep. tp. pagin. cont.*] s8°. 1723

Bellamy (John), *see* LEE (S.) A letter to J. B. on h. n. tr. of the Bible, 1821.
see TODD (H. J.) Vindic. of our auth. tr. of the Bible: occ. by object. by B. &c., 1819.
,, WHITTAKER (J. W.) Enquiry into the interp. of the Hebrew Script. w. remarks on B.'s new tr., 1819.

Bellarmino (*il card.* Roberto F. R.), *abp. of Capua* [*ps.* MATTHAEUS TORTUS].
Apologia pro responsione sua ad librum Iacobi Magnæ Brit. reg.: Triplici nodo triplex cuneus. In qua apologia refellitur præfatio monitoria regis ejusdem. Acc. eadem ipsa responsio quæ sub nomine M. Torti prodierat. 2p. s4°. Romæ. 1609
Conciones. Habitæ Lovanii ante annos c. quadraginta. s4°. Cameraci. 1617
De æterna felicitate sanctorum libri 5. s8°. Romæ. 1616
De ascensione mentis in Deum per scalas rerum creatarum &c. s8°. Viennæ Austriæ. 1679
De libro, quem Lutherani vocant Concordiæ. s8°. Ingolstadii. 1585
De scriptoribus eccl. liber vnus. Cum brevi Chronologia usque ad 1612 [*w. sep. pagin.*] s8°. Coloniæ Agripp. 1613
,, ,, [*a. ed.*] s4°. Coloniæ. 1684
De septem verbis a Christo in cruce prolatis lib. duo. s8°. Antverpiæ. 1618
Disputat. de controversiis Christ. fidei adv. hujus temp. hæreticos tomus secundus. [Controversia 1–5 *in* 3v, *each w. sep. pagin.*] s8°. Ingolstadii. 1589
,, ,, t. primus [-quartus]. ed. nov. opera J. Vitzk. 4t. *in* 2v. fol. Pragæ. 1721
*Doctrina Xtna. Armenice in Lat. versa & publ. à T. Petræo. s8°. Amstelodami. 1667

Bellarmino [*continued*].
Responsio ad libellum inscr.: Responsio ad epistolam, *see* PAUL V *pope.* Controversiæ, 1607.
Responsio ad libellum inscr.: Tractatus &c. circa valorem excommunicat. Joh. Gersonis, 1606, *see* PAUL V *pope.* Controversiæ, 1607.
Tractatus de potestate summi pontificis in rebus temporalibus ad. Gul. Barclaium. s8°. Coloniæ Agrippinæ. 1610
The joys of the blessed. Tr. by T. Foxton. With essay by Addison. s8°. 1722
see AMES (W.) Bellarminus enervatus, 4t, 1629; ed. nova, 1630.
,, ANDREWES (L.) *bp.* Tortura Torti s. ad Ti. lib. resp., 1609.
,, DORSCHÆUS (J. G.) T. Aquinas exhib. confessor veritatis evang. [in] tomis 4 R. B. exam., 1656.
,, DU SAUSSAY (A.) Insignis libri de script. eccles. B. contin., 1500–1600, 1684.
,, FULIGATTI (J.) Vita R. B., 1631.
,, GRETSER (J.) Controvers. R. B. defensio, 2t, 1607–9.
,, HOË (M.) Apologeticus contra R. B. judicium pro Concordiæ libro, 1605.
,, HUBER (S.) Antibellarminus; confut. eorum quæ adv. Xtnam. fidem disputavit R. B., 1607-9.
see LABBE (P.) De script. eccles. quos attigit R. B., 2t, 1660.
,, MARSILIO (G.) Defensio. adv. quod scripsit B. &c., 1607.
,, POLANUS (A.) De æterna Dei prædestinatione &c. à R. B. depravationibus asserta, 1600.
,, RAINOLDS (J.) Censura libr. apocryph. Vet Test. adv. pontificios, impr. R. B., 2t, 1611.
,, RAITZ V. FRENTZ (E.) Der ehrw. Kard. R. B., 1921.
,, RUHEL (C.) Dogmata &c. de papa e B. libris de Rom. pontif., 1604.
,, RULE (W. H.) Celebr. Jesuits, v2, 1853.
,, SARPI (P.) Apologia adv. opposit. factas ab card. B. &c., 1606.
,, SHARP (J.) Cursus theologicus &c.: ad B. argumenta resp., 1620.
,, WHITAKER (W.), *D.D.* Disput. de S. Scriptura, contra. R. B. &c., 1588.
,, —— Disp. de sacra Script.; contra papistas, imprimis R. B., 1590.
,, WÜRTEMBERG. Abfertigung u. Wider legung 2 Lästerschr., eines durch R. B. unter dem Tittel Iudicium de libro Concordiæ, 1587.

Bellaud ( ), *M.D.* Essai sur la langue armén. 8°. 1812

Belle Assemblée (La), or, Bell's Court & fashionable magazine. v1–7, 1806–9 [v2 *wanting*]. N.S., v1–8, 1810–13 [v5 *wanting, some portraits wanting*]. 8°. 1806–13
v7 *has* Suppl.: Night thoughts by Young, 1810.

Belle (Edmond Bouchié de), *see* BOUCHIÉ DE BELLE (E.)

Bellecour (*Madame* Rose Perrine) [*dite Mlle.* BEAUMÉNARD & *Mlle.* GOGO], *see* GINISTY (P.) Mlle. Gogo, 1730–99, 1913.

Bellefond (Nicolas Villault, *sieur* de), *see* VILLAULT (N.)

Bellefonds (A. Linant de), *see* LINANT DE BELLEFONDS (A.)

Bellelli (Fulgenzio), *see* BERTI (G. L.) Augustin. systema de gratia vindic., sive refut. libr. Bajanismus &c. in scr. B. &c., 1747.

Bellem (*Madame* de) [JEANNE PINAUT], *see* KALKEN (F. v.) Mme. de B., la "Pompadour des Pays-Bas," 1923.

Bellême (Robert II de), *see* ROBERT II DE B., *seign. d'Alençon.*

Bellemo (Eugenio). La pesca dei Chioggiotti &c. [P2844]. s8°. [Chioggia. 1908]

Bellerby (J. R.) Control of credit as a remedy for unemployment. 8°. 1923
Monetary stability. 8°. 1925

Bellermann (Johann Joachim).
Hdbch. d. bibl. Literatur. 4T *in* 2v. s8°. Erfurt. 1796–99

Bellessort (André). Essai sur Voltaire. 8°. 1925
La Pérouse. s8°. [1926]
Reflets de la vieille Amérique. s8°. 1923
Sainte-Beuve & le 19e siècle. [3e éd.] 8°. 1927

Bellet (Charles Félix). Les orig. des églises de France, & les fastes épiscopaux. n. éd., suiv. d'une étude sur le cursus & la critique. 8°. 1898

Bellet (Daniel). Le commerce allemand. [2e éd.] s8°. 1916

Bellevüe (*le marq.* de). Ploërmel, ville & sénéchaussée. 8°. 1915

Bellew (Henry Walter).
The history of Káshgharia. s4°. Calcutta. 1875
Inq. into ethnography of Afghanistan. Prep. for 9th Int. Cong. of Orientalists. 8°. Woking. 1891

Bellezza (Paolo). Curiosità manzoniane. s8°. Milano. [1923]
La satira del citatore, *see* ROMANISCHE FORSCH., B34, 1915.

Belli (Luigi), *1844–1919*, *see* SAPORI (F.) Maestri dell' arte, No. 18, 1919.

Belli (Pietrino), *Signore di Grinzane*, *see* RONDOLINO (F.) P. B., sua vita e suoi scritti, 1890.

Belliberone (Nicolaus Franciscus Clericus a), *see* LE CLERC DE BEAUBERON (N. F.)

Bellican (Theopald von), *see* GERLACHER (T.), *von Billican.*

Bellier de La Chavignerie (Emile). Dict. gén. des artistes de l'école franç. : architectes, peintres, sculpteurs, &c. Cont. par L. Auvray. 2t, Suppl. *&* Table topog. la8º. 1882–87

Belligent (Pierre de), *see* CAMDEN (W.) Annales, true hist. of Eliz. [tr. f. the Fr. of P. de B. by A. Darcie], 1625.

Bellingham (John) & N. Hubin. Patent (1679) of J. B. & N. H. ; manufacture of window glass. [P2501]. la8º. 1857

Bellini, *The family of, see* PAOLETTI (P.) Raccolta di doc. ined., f1, I. Bellini, 1894.

Bellini (Bernardo), *see* TOMMASÉO (N.) & B. B. Diz. d. lingua ital., 4v, 1861–79.

Bellini (Giovanni), *see* FOGOLARI (G.) G. B., 1921.

Bellini (Lorenzo), *1643–1704.* La Bucchereide. [Ed. C. Téoli. Bibl. rara, v27]. s8º. Milano. 1863

Bellini (Vincenzo), *musical composer.* Memorie e lettere [*&* Biografia.] A cura di F. Florime. s8º. Firenze. 1882

Bellius (Martinus), *ps., see* CHÂTEILLON (S.)

Bellman (Carl Michael). Skrifter. Standardupplaga utg. av Bellmanssällskapet. v1–3. s8º. 1921–25
1, Fredmans epistlar. 2, Fredmans sänger. 3, Bacchanaliska qwäden & En stuf rim.

Bellman (Harold). The building society movement. Intr. by Sir J. Stamp. s8º. [1927]

Bello (Andrés). Odes of B., Olmedo & Heredia. Intr. by E. C. Hills. [Hisp. Soc. of Amer.] s8º. N.Y. 1920

Bello (Luis). Ensayos e imaginaciones sobre Madrid. s8º. 1919

Bello (Pietrino), *see* BELLI (P.)

Belloc (Alexis). Les postes franç. : recherches hist. &c. 8º. 1886

Belloc (Hilaire).

The aftermath, or, Gleanings f. a busy life ; Caliban's Guide to letters—Lambkin's remains. [2nd ed.] s8º. 1920
Battle of Blenheim. s8º. 1922
The campaign of 1812 & the retreat from Moscow. s8º. [1924]
Companion to Wells's Outline of hist. 4º. 1926
The contrast. 8º. 1923
The cruise of the "Nona." 8º. 1925
Danton. [pop. ed.] s8º. *n.d.*
Economics for Helen. [2nd ed.] s8º. [1924]
" " [3rd ed.] s8º. [1924]
The emerald of Catherine the Great. s8º. [1926]
Europe & the Faith. 8º. 1920
The highway & its vehicles. Ed. G. Holme. 4º. 1926
Hist. of England. v1–3. 8º. [1925–28]
" " 2nd ed. v1. 8º. [1926]
The House of Commons & monarchy. s8º. [1920]
The Jews. 8º. [1922]
Lambkin's remains, *for 2nd ed. see* The aftermath &c. *above.*
Many cities. 8º. 1928
The mercy of Allah. s8º. 1922
Miniatures of French hist. 8º. [1925]
Mr. Belloc still objects to Mr. Wells's "Outline of History." s8º. 1926
Mr. Petre. With 22 drawings by G. K. Chesterton. [2nd impr.] s8º. [1925]
Mrs. Markham's new hist. of England. la8º. *Cayme Press.* 1926
On. s8º. [1923]
Paris. 3rd ed. s8º. [1912]
The path to Rome. 4th ed. s8º. [1916]
The road. 8º. 1923
Short talks w. the dead & others. 8º. *Cayme Press,* Kensington. 1926
Sonnets & verse. 8º. [1923]
see GRANT (W. A.) The topog. of Stane Street : crit. review of "The Stane St." of H. B., 1922.
" LAND & WATER, Oct. 17, 1914–Dec. 28, 1916, *War articles by H. B. &c.,* 1914–16.
" MANDELL (C. C.) & E. SHANKS. H. B., 1916.
" WELLS (H. G.) Mr. B. objects to "The outline of history," 1926.

Belloni (Ant.) Curzio Gonzaga, rimatore d. sec. 16. [Estr. d. Propugnatore, n.s., v4]. 8º. Bologna. 1891

Bellori (Giovanni Pietro). Le pitture antiche del sepolcro de' Nasonii n. via Flaminia disegnate &c. da P. Santi Bartoli, descr. &c. da G. P. B. fol. 1680

Bellorini (Egidio). Giovanni Berchet. s8º. Messina. [1917]

Bellot (Hugh Hale Leigh). Texts illust. constit. of Supreme Court of U.S. & Court of Internat. Justice. Intr. by B. [Grotius Soc. Publs., No. 8]. 8º. 1921

Bellotto (Bernardo), *called Canaletto, see* CANALETTO.

Bellows (John). Dict. for the pocket, Fr.-Eng., Eng.-Fr. 2nd ed. s8º. [1883]

Bellows (Max). Dict. of German & Eng., Eng. & German. Rev. C. Sherwood &c. 8º. 1912

Bellows (William). A visit to Alsace. [P2585]. s8º. [1922]

Belloy (Pierre de), *see* L'ALLOUETTE (E. DE). *Apologie cathol. contre les libelles, &c. [*also ascr. to P. de B.*], 1585.

Bell's Court & fashionable magazine, 1806–13, *see* BELLE ASSEMBLÉE (LA).

Bell's Weekly messenger, July 3, 1815. [*b. w.* v29, 1824]. fol. 1815

***Bellum** grammaticale, 1580, *see* GUARNA (A.)

Bellus (Julius) [*ps.* PHILIPPUS HONORIUS], *see* POLONIA. Respublica Poloniæ &c. div. aut. [J. B. &c.] 1627.

Belmont (August).
Letters, speeches &c. of A. B. *p.p.* la8º. [N.Y.] 1890

Belmont (Perry). National isolation an illusion : interdependence of U.S. & Europe. 8º. N.Y. 1925

Beloch (Julius) [BELOCH (CARL JULIUS)]. Griech. Geschichte. 2te neugest. A. B3i, ii, B4i, ii. 8º. 1922–27
La popolaz. d'Italia nei sec. 16–18, *see* †INSTITUT INTERN. DE STATIST. Bull., t3, 1888.
Röm. Gesch. bis z. Beginn d. punisch. Kriege. 8º. 1926

Belokurov (Sergei Alekseevich). Юрій Крижаничъ въ Россіи (1659–77). [Имп. Общ. Ист. при Москов. Унив.] [*2 pagin.*] la8º. Москва. 1901

Belon (Pierre), *1517–64, see* LEGRÉ (L.) La botanique en Provence au. 16e s. : L. Anguillara &c., 1901.

Beloruss (M.) [BYELORUSS]. Рабочіе и интеллигенція. [P2387]. s8º. Женева. 1904

Belot (Adolphe).
Mlle. Giraud, ma femme. 29e éd. s8º. 1870

Belot (Gustave).
Études de morale positive. 2e éd. rev. & augm. 2t. 8º. 1921

Belov (Evgeny) [БѢловъ].
Казань. Нижній Новгородъ. Кострома. 8º. Москва. 1913

Belov (Vadim Mikhailovich). Белая печать. 8º. П. 1922

Below (Georg V.) Das ältere deut. Städtewesen u. Bürgertum. 3. A. la8º. Bielefeld. 1925
Deut. Reichspolitik einst u. jetzt. 8º. Tübingen. 1922
Die ital. Kaiserpolitik d. deut. Ma. mit bes. Hinblick auf d. Politik Friedr. Barbarossas. [Hist. Zeitschr. Beiheft 10]. 8º. München. 1927
Probleme d. Wirtschaftsgesch. 2.A. 8º. Tübingen. 1926

Belt (Richard). *A review of the B. trial. [B. *v.* Lawes]. By an Outsider ; w. sk. of the life of B. [P2827]. 8º. [1882]

Beltramelli (Antonio). Il cantico. 3a ristampa. s8º. [1925]
Il passo dell' ignota. s8º. Milano. 1927
Ravenna la taciturna. s8º. Firenze. 1907

Beltran Masses (Federico) [FEDERICO BELTRAN], *see* FRANCÉS (J.) F. B. M., 1920.

Beltrán y Rózpide (Ricardo). Compendio de hist. de España. 6a ed., con notas &c. por R. Beltrán y González. 2t. 8º. 1921–22

Beltrán y Villagrasa (Pio). Interpretación del usatge "Solidus Aureus." [Publ. en el "Mem. Numism. Esp., junio 1921]. [P2702]. la8º. 1921

Belyaev (Ivan Dmitrievich) [†BYELYAEV].
Исторія Новгорода великаго отъ древнѣйшихъ временъ до паденія. [Разсказы, кн. 2, изд. 2oe]. s8º. Москва. 1866
Крестьяне на Руси. 4oe изд. la8º. Москва. 1903
О географ. свѣдѣніяхъ въ древней Россіи, *see* IMPERAT. RUSS. GEOG. OBSCH. Записки, кн. 6, 1852.

Belyaev (Ivan Stepanovich) [BYELYAEV].
Практич. курсъ изученія древней русской скорописи для чтенія рукописей xv–xviii ст. la8º. Москва. 1907

Belyaev (*Col.* **N. T.**), *see* BELAIEW.

Belydenis. *Singaleesch b. boekje, 1742, *see* SINGALEESCH.

Belydenisse [BELYDENISSEN]. De algemeene Belydenissen d. vereenigde Vlaamsche, Vriesche &c., Doopgezinde, 1739, *see* BAPTIST.
*Belydenisse des Christel. Geloofs &c., 1643, *see* APOSTLES' CREED.
De nederlandsche Geloofsbelijdenis (Belydenisse d. gheloofs), 1562, 1864, *see* NEDERLANDSCHE.

Bembo (Giovanni) [†BEMBUS (J.)], *1473–1545.* Autobiog. (1536). Hrsg. T. Mommsen. [Aus d. Sitz. d. k. Akad. d. Wiss., 1861, B1. P2872]. 8º. [München. 1861]

Bembo (*il card.* **Pietro**), *bp. of* (1) *Gubbio,* (2) *Bergamo.* Giunta fatta al Ragionamento degli articoli et de verbi. s4º. [Modona. 1563]
Rime. [*&* Stanze, *w. sep. sign. fol. 1* (*blank*) *wanting*]. 8º. [Vinegia. 1530]
see SANSOVINO (F.) *ed.* Osserv. d. lingua volg. &c., 1562.

Bembridge School, *see* WHITEHOUSE (J. H.) *ed.* Bembridge ; by members of B. S., 1923.

Bemis (George).
see BIGELOW (G. T.) & G. B. Report of trial of A. Rogers for murder of C. Lincoln, 1844.
" WEBSTER (J. W.) Report of case of W. indicted for murder of G. Parkman ; by G. B., 1850.

Bemis (Samuel Flagg). The Amer. Secretaries of State & th. diplomacy. Ed. S. F. B. v1–3. 8°. N.Y. 1927
1, Hist. intr.; by J. B. Scott—R. R. Livingston; by M. L. Bonham—J. Jay; by S. F. Bemis.
2, T. Jefferson; by S. F. Bemis—E. Randolph; by D. R. Anderson—T. Pickering; by H. J. Ford—J. Marshall; by A. J. Montague.
3, J. Madison; by C. E. Hill—R. Smith; by C. C. Tansill—J. Monroe; by J. W. Pratt.
Jay's treaty: st. in commerce & diplomacy. 8°. N.Y. 1923
Pinckney's Treaty: America's advantage f. Europe's distress, 1783–1800. 8°. Baltimore, *U.S.* 1926

Bemporad. B.'s concise guide to Florence, 1920, *see* Waterfield (*Mrs.* L. D.)

Bemrose (H. Cheney), *see* Smith (S. C. K.) & H. C. B. Wright of Derby, 1922.

Bena (Amalrich v.), *see* Garnerius, *de Rochefort.* *Contra Amaurianos (13c.); hrsg. v. C. Bäumker, 1926.

Benac (Gaston), *see* Chiquito de Cambo, G. B. & E. Vogt. La pelote basque, 1924.

Ben Adreth, *see* Solomon, *ben Abraham ben Adreth, 1235–1310.*

Benaglio (Marc' Antonio). Relaz. d. carestia e d. peste di Bergamo e suo territ., 1629 e 1630; publ. G. Finazzi, *see* Regia Dep. di Storia Patria. Misc., t6, 1865.

Benalúa (*conde* **de**), *Duque de San Pedro de Galatino.* Memorias. t1, 1867–75. 8°. [1924]

Benamati (Giov. Batt.) *Servita.*
Ist. della città di Guastalla. 8°. Parma. 1674

Bénard (*le commandant* **Charles**).
Un été chez les Samoyèdes, juil.–oct. 1914. s8°. [1921]

Benario (Michael Smilg-), *see* Smilg-Benario (M.)

Ben Assher, *ps.* *A nomad in North America. 8°. 1927

Benavente (Jacinto).
El hijo de Polichinela: comedia. 8°. 1927
La noche iluminada. 8°. 1927
Teatro. t22–31. [22, 4ª ed.; 23, 24, 2ª ed.] s8°. 1918–25
Plays. Tr. w. intr. by J. G. Underhill. auth. ed. 4s. s8°. N.Y. 1921–24
1, His widow's husband—The bonds of interest—The evil doers of good—La Malquerida.
2, No smoking — Princess Bebé — The governor's wife—Autumnal roses.
3, The prince who learned everything out of books—Saturday night—In the clouds—The truth.
4, The school of princesses—A lady—The magic of an hour—Field of ermine.
see Lázaro (A.) J. B., de su vida y de su obra, 1925.
„ Starkie (W.) J. B., 1924.

Benavides (Alfonso de). Relatio quam Philippo IV exhibuit J. Santander. Per manus A. de B., custodis prov. & convers. Novi Mexico. In qua agitur de magnis thesauris inibi detectis. [Tr.] s8°. Salisburgi. 1634

Benavides (Diego de), *3rd marq. of Solera, see* Vincencio de Vidania (D.) F. de Benavides: servicios heredados &c. y los de su hijos, D. de B. &c., 1696.

Benavides (Francisco de), *cuatralvo de galeras, 16 cent., see* Bauer Landauer (I.) Don F. de B., cuatralvo de las galeras de Esp., 1921.

Benavides (Francisco de), *2nd marq. of Solera, see* Vincencio de Vidania (D.) F. de B.: servicios heredados &c., 1696.

Benavides (Luis de), *4th marq. de Solera, see* Vincencio de Vidania (D.) F. de Benavides: servicios &c. y los de su hijos, L. de B. &c., 1696.

Benbow (William). Crimes of the clergy, w. App., The scourge of Ireland. 8°. 1823

Benckendorf (*count* **Aleksandr Konstantinovich**), *see* Marchand (R.) Un livre noir: diplomatie d'avant-guerre, 1910–14, t2, Corresp. d'Isvolsky & de B. &c., 1923.

Benckendorff (*Count* **Paul**). Last days at Tsarskoe Selo: last sojourn of Emp. & Empress of Russia at T. S., 1917. Tr. M. Baring. s8°. 1927

Benco (Silvio). Gli ultimi anni d. domin. austriaca a Trieste. 3p. s8°. Milano. 1919

Benda (Julien). Les Amorandes. s8°. 1922
La croix de roses. Préc. d'un dialogue d'Eleuthère avec l'a. [Cahiers verts, 17]. s8°. 1923
Lettres à Mélisande. 8°. 1925
La trahison des clercs. [Cahiers verts, s2, t6]. s8°. 1927

Bender (Ewald).
Die Kunst Ferd. Hodlers. Bl. 8°. Zürich. 1923
Das Leben Ferd. Hodlers. Mit 3 Beitr. v. H. Bahr, R. Breuer, u. P. Modrow. s8°. Zürich. 1921

Bender (Harold Herman).
The home of the Indo-Europeans. s8°. Princeton. 1922

Bendinelli (Goffredo).
Works in Reale Accad. d. Lincei. Mon. ant.
Antichità Tudertine del Museo Naz. di Villa Giulia, 1914. [23.]
Bronzi votivi italici d. Museo di Villa Giulia, 1920. [26.]
Monumenta Lanuvina, 1921. [27.]
Il mon. sepolcr. d. Aureli al viale Manzoni in Roma, 1922. [28.]
Il mon. sotterr. di Porta Maggiore in Roma, 1926. [31.]
Tomba con vasi &c. (5c B.C.) nella necrop. di Todi, 1916. [24.]

Bendsen (Bende). Die nordfries. Sprache nach d. Moringer Mundart. [Anbang]. Hrsg. M. de Vries. 8°. Leiden. 1860

Bendz (Ernst).
Joseph Conrad: an appreciation. 8°. Gothenburg. 1923

Benedek (*Feldzeugmeister* **Ludwig v.**), *see* Krauss (A.) Moltke, B. u. Napoleon, 1901.

Benedetti (Bart.) Int. alle rel. commerciali di Venezia e di Norimberga. [P2852]. 8°. Venezia. 1863

Benedetti (Leonardo de-). Luigi Carini. la8°. Milano. [1920]

Benedetto, *da Majano, see* Dussler (L.) B. da M., 1924.

Benedetto (Luigi Foscolo). Mme. de Warens, la "Maman" de Rousseau. s8°. Firenze. [1922]
see Polo (M.) Il milione; a cura di L. F. B., 1928.

Benedict, *Saint, abbot of Monte Casino.* Regula, *see* Joannes Franciscus *Brixianus.* Habes isto vol. 4 regulas &c., 1510.
Rule of St. B. Tr. w. intr. by Card. Gasquet. s8°. 1925

Benedict IX, *pope.*
see Mittler (T.) De schismate in Eccl. Rom. sub pontif. B. IX, 1835.
„ Poole (R. L.) B. IX & Gregory VI, 1917.

Benedict XI, *pope, see* Boniface VIII, *pope.* Acta inter B. VIII, B. XI & Phil. regem, 1614.

Benedict XII, *pope.* Benoit XII, 1334–42: lettres closes, patentes &c. se rapp. à la France, [publ.] par G. Daumet. [Ecoles Franç. d'Athènes & de Rome]. 4°. 1920

Benedict XIII, *pope, see* Bollati di Saint-Pierre (F. E.) Frammento (Articuli super substractione B. XIII), 1882.
see Klemm (J. C.) Concil. a B. XIII in Laterano habiti examen, 1729–30.

Benedict XIII, *antipope, see* Luna (P. de).

Benedict XIV, *pope.*
De festis Jesu Christi & B. Mariæ, libri 2, *see* Migne (J. P.) *ed.* Theol. cursus, t26, 1859.
De Missæ sacrificio, *see* Migne (J. P.) *ed.* Theol. cursus, t23, 1860.
De synodo diœcesana, *see* Migne (J. P.) *ed.* Theol. cursus, t25, 1860.
The diocesan synod: chapters f. "De synodo diœcesana." Sel. & done into Eng. by W. R. V. Brade, w. 2 apps. by C. E. Douglas. s8°. 1926
Lettres par lesquelles, il établit F. de Saldanha visiteur &c. de la c^ie^ de Jesus &c., *see* Portugal. Recueil de decrets apostol. &c., pl, 1758.
see Baudeau (N.) Anal. de l'ouvr. du p. B. XIV sur les béatifications &c., 1860.
„ Dens (P.) Theol. moralis &c.; acc. epitome ex operibus B. XIV &c., 1832.
„ Zech (F. X.) Rigor moderatus doctr. pontif. circa usuras à B. XIV per epist. encycl. episc. Ital. trad. &c., & Epist. encycl., 1859.

Benedict XV, *pope, see* Van den Heuvel (J.) Statesmanship of B. XV; tr., 1923.

Benedict (Francis Gano), W. R. Miles, P. Roth & H. M. Smith. Human vitality & efficiency under prolonged restricted diet. [C. I. of Wash. Publ., 280]. la8°. Wash. 1919

Benedict (Russell). Illust. catal. of acts & laws of the colony &c. of New York &c. Coll. made by R. B., to be sold Feb. 1922, Amer. Art Assoc. la8°. N.Y. [1922]

Benedict (William A.) & H. A. Tracy. Hist. of Sutton, Mass., 1704–1876. 8°. Worcester, *U.S.* 1878

Benedictbeuern, *see* Fragmenta Burana; hrsg. v. W. Meyer, 1901.

Benedictines. *Vetus disciplina monastica, seu coll. auctorum ord. S. Benedicti max. partem ined., qui ante 600 fere annos per Italiam, Galliam atque Germaniam de monastica disciplina tractarunt. Prodit nunc primum opera & studio **Presbyteri [*i.e.* Marquardi Herrgott]. 4°. Parisiis. 1726
see Ghent. Annals of the Eng. B. of Ghent, 1894.
„ Paléographie musicale: principaux mss. de chant grégorien &c. publ. par les B. de Solesmes, 11v, 1900–12.

Benedictinum. Ceremoniale Benedictinum &c., 1610, *see* Bursfeld, *monastery of.*

Benedictsen (Åge Meyer) & A. Christensen. Les dialectes d'Awromān & de Pāwā: textes, avec une esq. de gramm., *see* Kongeligt Dan. Vid. Selsk. Hist.-fil. Med, B6, 1921–22.

Benedictus, *canon S. Petri, see* Lanciani (R.) Itin. di Einsie l n e l'ord. di B., 1890.

Benedikt (Rudolf). Chemistry of the coal-tar colours. Tr. w. add. by E. Knecht. s8°. 1886

Bénédite (Georges). Amon & Toutânkhamon (Musée Egypt. du Louvre), see ACAD. DES INSCR. Fond. Piot. Mon., t24, 1920.
La cueillette du lis & le "lirinon," see ACAD. DES INSCR.: FOND. PIOT. Mon. &c., t25, 1921–22.
Sur une tête de princesse de la fam. d'Akhounaten, see ACAD. DES INSCR. &c. Fond. Piot. Mons. &c., t27, 1924.

Bénédite (Léonce), *conservateur au Musée du Luxembourg.*
Expos. de l'art belge; org. par L. B. &c. au Musée du Jeu de Paume à Paris, 1923. la8°. Brux. 1923
Expos. de l'art suisse du 15e au 19e siècle. Org. par L. B. &c. au Musée du Jeu de Paume, juin 1924. 8°. [1924]

Benedito (Manuel), see FRANCÉS (JOSÉ). M. B., 1920.

Benefield (Barry). The chicken-wagon family. s8°. N.Y. 1925

Benelli (Sem).
L'amorosa tragedia: poema dram. in 3 atti. 8°. Milano. 1925
La Gorgona. Dramma. 7a impr. s8°. Milano. [1919]

Beneš (Edvard). Détruisez l'Autriche-Hongrie! Le martyre des Tchéco-Slovaques à travers l'hist. [P2419]. s8°. [1916]

Beneshevich (Vladimir Nikolaevich). Обозрѣніе трудовъ по Славяновѣдѣнію, состав. А. Л. Бемомъ, М. Г. Долобко &c. подъ ред. В. Н. Бенешевича. 1912. [Имп. Акад. Наукъ.] выпускъ 1. 8°. С.-П. 1913

Benett (William). The ethical aspects of evolution. 8°. O. 1908
Freedom & liberty. 9°. 1920

Benevolensky (Ar.)
Ради чего и въ имя чего? [P846]. s8°. С.-П. 1890

Benezet (Anthony). Views of Amer. slavery taken a century ago. A. B., J. Wesley. s8°. Phila. 1858

Bénézit (Emmanuel). Dict. crit. &c. des peintres, sculpteurs &c. Par un groupe d'écrivains sous la dir. de E. B. t3, L–Z. 8°. [1923]

Benfey (Theodore). A Sanskrit-Engl. dict. 8°. 1866

Bengal.
GOVT. PUBL.
Bengal Code. Suppl. to 4th ed. Bengal acts, 1915–23. la8°. Calcutta. 1924
B. local statutory rules & orders, 1924. [3rd ed.] 3v. la8°. Calcutta. 1925–26
Bibliog. of B. records, 1632–1858. 8°. Calcutta. 1925
Bibliog. of B. records, 1756–1858. Comp. by B. Record Room. [P2818]. 8°. *n.p.* 1924
Cat. of Eng. records, 1758–1858, pres. in Hist. Rec. Room of B. 4°. Calcutta. 1922
Hist. of services of gazetted officers. Corr. to 1st July 1920–27. 8°. Calcutta. 1920–27 2p *for each year.*
Letter copy book of the Supervisor of Rajshahi at Nator, 1769–72. Ed. B. Record Room. la8°. Calcutta. 1925
Press list of anc. doc. pres. in Secretariat Record Room. s3, Controlling Comm. of Commerce, 1771–76. 2v. fol. Calcutta. 1919–21
Proc. of the Comm. of Circuit at Krishnagar & Kasimbazar [Dacca, Rangpur &c.] v1–8, 10 June to 18 Feb. 1773. fol. Calcutta. 1926–27
Proc. of the Controlling Council of Revenue at Murshidabad, 27th Sept. 1770–2nd Mar. 1774. Ed. w. intr. &c. by W. K. Firminger. [Records of Govt. of B.] v1–12 [7 *in* 2p]. fol. Calcutta. 1919–24
Select index to gen. letters f. Court of Directors in the Judicial Department, 1795–1854. 2v. la8°. Calcutta. 1924–26
Sel. index to gen. letters to & f. the Court of Directors in the Revenue &c. depts., [1765]–1858. v1–4. la8°. Calcutta. 1926–27
ANON. WORKS &c.
*Earthquake in Bengal & Assam. Repr. f. the "Englishman." 8°. Calcutta. 1897
List of officers of the B. army, 1758–1834, p1, 1927, see HODSON (V. C. P.)

Bengal, *Bay of.* B. of B. pilot, 5th ed., & Suppl. 1, 1921–22, see ADMIRALTY.

Bengal district records.
Chittagong. v1, 1760–73. 4°. Calcutta. 1920–26
Dinajpur. v2, 1786–88. 4°. Calcutta. 1924
Midnapur. v3, 1771–74, v4, 1770–74. Letters received. 4°. Calcutta. 1925–26
Rangpur. v2–5, 1779–87 [v1, 2. Ed. W. K. Firminger]. 4°. Calcutta. 1920–27

Bengal, past & present. Journal of the Calcutta Hist. Soc. v8–30 (1914–25). 4°. Calcutta. [1914–25]

Bengel (Ernest Gottlieb von). Opuscula acad. Ed. indicesque adj. J. G. Pressel. 8°. Hamburgi. 1834

Bengel (Johann Albrecht), *1687–1752.*
Abriss d. so genannten Brüdergemeine &c. 2T. *in* 1v. s8°. St. 1751
Apparatus crit. ad Nov. Test. Ed. 2a auct. & emend. cur. P. D. Burkio. 4°. Tubingæ. 1763
Erklärte Offenbarung Johannis aus d. revid. Grund-Text übersetzt &c. 3e A. s8°. St. 1758
Gnomon Novi Test. ed. 3a, per E. Bengelium cur., 5° recusa, adjuv. J. Steudel. la8°. Londini. 1862

Bengel (Johann Albrecht) [*continued*].
Sechzig erbaul. Reden ü. d. Offenbarung Johannis. s8°. St. 1748
„ n. A. s8°. St. 1771
see BAUN (FR.) J. A. B. d. Vater d. schwäb. Pietismus, 1922.
see BURK (J. C. F.) J. A. B.'s Leben u. Wirken, 1831.
„ —— Mem. of J. A. B.; tr., 1842.
„ LÖBER (G. F.) Obs. ad hist. vitæ & mortis J. C., 1767.

Bengescu (Gheorghe). Despre activit. lit. ai fam. Golescu, see ACADEMIA ROM. Disc., 52, 1923.

Benham (Charles), *barrister*, see BARTON (*Sir* D. P.), C. B. &c. Story of our Inns of Court, 1924.

Benham (Daniel). Memoirs of James Hutton; annals of h. life & conn. w. the United Brethren. 8°. 1856

Benham (William Gurney).
Book of quotations. [n. ed., enl. & rev.] 8°. 1924
Cassell's classified quotations. 8°. 1921

Beni (Paolo), *1552–1625.* Rime varie. Racc. &c. d. Cavalcanti. 8°. Padova. [1614]

Benians (Sylvia). From Renaissance to Revolution: polit. development of Europe &c. 8°. [1923]

Benik, *Vardapet.* [HOVHANNES *Vanandetzi*]. [Prayers (13 cent.) *In Armenian.* Soferq Hayk., v21]. s8°. i Venetik. 1861

Beningha (Sikko), see BENNINGE (S.)

Benitez de Lugo (Cajetanus). Concursus Dei prævius &c. efficax &c. Vera etiam Christi gratia illuminans &c. atque à Jansenii & Quesnellii erroribus vindicata. Disput. theol. 5t. s4°. Romæ. 1737

Benjamin, *ben Mordecai, ps.*, see TAYLOR (HENRY).

Benjamin (L. N.) The St. Albans raid: investig. into charges agst. Lt. B. H. Young &c., 1864, before Judge Coursol &c. 8°. Montreal. 1865

Benjamin (René).
Antoine déchainé, see ŒUVRES libres, 3, 1921.
La farce de la Sorbonne. [P2435]. s8°. [1911]
Les justices de paix. Bois orig. de G. Bruyer. [Le livre de demain, 14]. 8°. *n.d.*
Les plaisirs du hasard. Comédie. s8°. [1922]
La prodigieuse vie d'H. de Balzac. s8°. [1925]
Le soliloque de Maurice Barrès, see ŒUVRES libres, 29, 1923.
Taureaux & méridionaux, choses vues, see ŒUVRES (Les) libres, 19, 1923.

Benjamin (S. G. W.)
Persia. [Story of the nations]. 2nd ed. 8°. 1889

Benn (*Sir* Ernest John Pickstone).
The confessions of a capitalist. la8°. [1925]
If I were a labour leader. [2nd impr.] 8°. 1926

Benn (*Sir* John Williams), see GARDINER (A. G.) J. Benn & the progressive movement. 8°. 1925

Benn (*Capt.* William Wedgwood). In the side shows. 8°. 1919

Benner (Johann Hermann). Dissert. de noxa homiletica Zinzendorfiana. Præs. J. H. B., resp. G. C. Hess. [P2632]. s4°. Gissæ. [1744]
Notitia salutis. [3p *in* 1v. pagin. contin.] s8°. Gissæ. 1765
Noxa catechetica Zinzendorfiana locis quibusdam obs. s4°. Gissæ. 1743

Bennet (George).
Olam Haneshamoth, intermediate state &c. 8°. Carlisle. 1800
see MONTGOMERY (J.) Journal of voyages &c. by D. Tyerman & G. B., 1821–29, 2v, 1831.

Bennet (James Henry). Winter & spring in the Mediterranean. 5th ed. 8°. 1875

Bennet (Robert Ames). Waters of conflict. s8°. [1926]

Bennet (Thomas), *D.D.* An answer to the dissenters' pleas for separation, or abridgm. of London cases. 3rd ed. C. 1701
An essay on the 39 articles of religion. s8°. 1715

Bennett (Alfred Gordon). The valley of paradise. s8°. [1922]

Bennett (Alfred Rosling). London & Londoners in the eighteen-fifties & sixties. 8°. [1924]

Bennett (Charles A.)
A philosoph. study of mysticism. 8°. New Haven, *Yale.* 1923

Bennett (Edward T.)
Spiritualism. Introd. by Sir O. Lodge. s8°. 1906

Bennett (Enoch Arnold).
Clayhanger. 14th & cheaper ed. s8°. 1920
The Clayhanger family: Clayhanger—Hilda Lessways—These twain. s8°. 1925
Elsie & the child. [repr.] s8°. [1924]
The glimpse. n. &c. ed. s8°. 1912
The great adventure: play. 6th ed. s8°. [1923]
Lilian. [repr.] s8°. [1922]
The lion's share. [pop. ed.] s8°. [1927]
Lord Raingo. s8°. [1926]
Mr. Prohack. s8°. [1922]
The reasonable life. s8°. 1907
Riceyman Steps. s8°. [1923]

Bennett (Enoch Arnold) [*continued*].

Things that have interested me. s8°. 1921
*The truth about an author. s8°. 1903
„ „ ....s8°. 1914
What the public wants. Play. [2nd impr.] s8°. [1921]
The woman who stole everything & o. s. s8°. [1927]

see BENNETT (M.) A. B., 1925.
„ SCOTT-MONCRIEFF (C. K.), *ed.* Marcel Proust: an Eng. tribute; by J. Conrad, E. A. B. &c., 1923.
„ SHAW (G. B.) Common sense about the War, *w.* Replies by A. B. &c., 1914.

—— **& E. Knoblock.** Mr. Prohack: comedy. 8°. 1927

Bennett (Ernest Leigh-), *see* LEIGH-BENNETT (E.)

Bennett (Francis James), *F.G.S.* Geology of the co. around Attleborough, Watton & Wymondham. [Mems. of G.S.] 8°. 1884

Geology of the co. around Diss, Eye, Botesdale & Ixworth. [Mems. of G.S.] 8°. 1884

—— **& J. H. Blake,** *F.G.S.*

Geology of the co. betw. & S. of Bury St. Edmunds & Newmarket. Ed., w. add., by W. Whitaker. [Mems. of G.S.] 8°. 1866

Bennett (Frank Selwyn Macaulay). Expecto: essay towards a biol. of the world to come. Foreword by J. Y. Simpson. s8°. Chester. 1926

Bennett (*Hon.* Henry Grey), *see* HULBERT (C.) Candid strictures on "Thoughts on the Protest. ascendancy in Ireland," in a letter to [*its a.*] H. G. B., 1807.

Bennett (Henry Stanley).

The Pastons & their England. 8°. C. 1922

Bennett (Hugh Garner).

The manufacture of leather. 4th impr. 8°. 1920

Bennett (J. W. Wheeler-), *see* WHEELER-BENNETT (J. W.)

Bennett (John Hughes), *M.D.* The present state of medicine. 2nd ed. [P2561]. 8°. E. 1855

see MACGILCHRIST (J.) Remarks on Pres. state of medicine: review of B.'s lect., 1856.

Bennett (Marguerite), *wife of Arnold Bennett.*

Arnold Bennett. 8°. 1925

Bennett (Richard). Cat. of early printed books & illum. MSS. coll. by R. B. la8°. 1900

Bennett (T. P.) Architectural design in concrete. Photographs comp. by F. R. Yerbury. 4°. 1927

Bennett (Thos.) Eng.-Norweg. phrasebook. s8°. *n.d.*

Bennett (William), *of the Society of Friends.* Narr. of a recent journey of 6 weeks in Ireland. s8°. 1847

Bennett (William Henry).

Religion of the Post-Exilic prophets. 8°. E. 1907

Bennetts (Henry Johnson Treloar). Evidence of things not seen. Coll. f. miracles & versions of the Sacrament. 8°. 1920

*The sentimental celibate. By the husband of one wife. s8°. 1922

Benninge (Sicke) [BENINGA; BENINGHA]. De kroniek van S. B., le & 2e deel (Kroniek van van Lemego). Uitg. &c. door J. A. Feith, mit inleiding v. P. J. Blok. [Hist. Genoots. Werken, N.S., 48]. 8°. Utrecht. 1887

Bennion (B.)

The angler in South Africa. s8°. Johannesburg. 1923

Benno, *Cardinal.* Vita & gesta Hildebrandi (Greg. VII), *see* ROSARIUS (S.) Antithesis Christi &c., 1578.

Benno II, *bp. of Osnabrück, see* HINDENBERG (I.) B. II, als Architekt, 1921.

see NORBERT, *St., abp. of Magdeburg.* Vita B. II; rec. H. Bresslau, 1902.

Benoît, *de Sainte-More.* B. de Ste.-M. & le roman de Troie [*w. text*], par A. Joly, *see* †SOC. DES ANTIQ. DE NORMANDIE. Mém., s3, v7, 1869.

Benoit (Fernand). Arles. s8°. Lyon. 1927

Benoit (François). L'architecture: antiquité. la8°. 1911

L'architecture: l'Orient méd. & mod. la8°. 1912

Benoit (Pierre).

Alberte. s8°. [1926]
L'Atlantide. Roman. s8°. [1920]
Axelle. s8°. [1928]
La châtelaine du Liban. Roman. s8°. [1924]
La Chaussée des Géants. Roman. s8°. [1922]
Count Philip. s8°. [1920]
Le lac salé. Roman. s8°. [1921]
The lady of Lebanon. Tr. F. Keyzer. s8°. [1925]
Mademoiselle de la Ferté. s8°. [1923]
L'oublié. Roman. s8°. [1922]
Pour Don Carlos. Roman. s8°. 1920
Le puits de Jacob. Roman. s8°. [1925]
The Queen of Atlantis. s8°. [1920]
Le Roi Lépreux. Roman. s8°. [1927]

Benoit (Pierre) [*continued*].

Les suppliantes. Poèmes. s8°. [1920]
La surprenante aventure du baron de Pradeyles, *see* ŒUVRES libres, 2, 1921.
see BOURGET (P.) Le roman des quatre; [par] P. B., P. B. &c., 2t, 1923–26.

Benolte (Thomas), *Clarenceux King of Arms, see* KENT. Visitations, 1530–31, by T. B. &c.; ed. W. B. Bannerman, pl, 1923.

Benrath (Carl). B. Ochino v. Siena. Beitr. z. Gesch. d. Reformation. 8°. L. 1875

Gesch. d. Reformation in Venedig. [Verein f. Ref.-gesch. Schr., Jhrg. 5, Nr. 18]. 8°. Halle. 1887

Julia Gonzaga. [Verein f. Ref.-gesch. Schr., Jhrg. 16, Nr. 65]. 8°. Halle. 1900

Luther im Kloster, 1505–25. [Verein f. Ref.-gesch. Schr., Jhrg. 23, Nr. 87]. 8°. Halle. a.d.S. 1905

Bense (J. F.) Anglo-Dutch rel., to death of William III: hist. intr. to dict. of Low-Dutch elem. in Eng. vocab. la8°. 1925

Ben Sira, *ps.* ספר בן סירא [P468]. s8°. Livorno. [1828]

Bensley (E. R.), *see* LOPES (J. M.), E. R. B. &c. Nuevo dicc. inglés-esp. y esp.-ingl., 2p, n.d.

Bensly (Edward). Some alter. & errors in success. eds. of the Anat. of melancholy, *see* MADAN (F.) R. Burton &c., 1926.

Benso (Giofredo), *di Santena, see* MANUEL DI SAN GIOVANNI (G.) Tre doc. rig. G. B. di S., mercatante di Chieri n. sec. 16, 1869.

Benson (Arthur Christopher) [*ps. C. Carr; T. B.; J. T.*]

A. C. B. as seen by some friends [*i.e.* M. R. James, S. Gaselee &c. Rev. by E. H. Ryle]. 8°. 1925
The art of the biographer, *see* ROY. SOC. OF LIT. Essays &c., n.s., v6, 1926.
Basil Netherby [*&* The uttermost farthing]. s8°. [1926]
The canon. s8°. [1926]
The child of the dawn. 2nd impr. 8°. 1912
Chris Gascoyne. From the diary of J. Trevor. s8°. 1924
Cressage. s8°. [1927]
Diary. Ed. P. Lubbock. 8°. [1926]
Escape & o. essays. 8°. 1915
The house of Menerdue. s8°. 1925
Life of E. W. Benson, Abp. of Canterbury. 2v. 8°. 1899
Magdalene Coll. Cambridge, its buildings & hist. 8°. C. 1923
Memories & friends. 8°. 1924
The reed of Pan. Eng. renderings of Greek epigrams & lyrics. 8°. 1922
The trefoil: Wellington College, Lincoln, Truro. 8°. 1923

Benson (Edward Frederic).

Across the stream. s8°. 1919
Alan. s8°. [1924]
The climber. pop. ed. s8°. 1912
Colin. s8°. [1923]
Colin II. s8°. [1925]
The Countess of Lowndes Square & o. s. s8°. [1920]
David Blaize & the blue door. s8°. [1927]
David of King's. [repr.] s8°. [1927]
Dodo wonders. s8°. [1921]
Lovers & friends. s8°. [1921]
Lucia in London. s8°. [1927]
Mezzanine. s8°. [1926]
Miss Mapp. s8°. [1922]
Mother. [*Mary Benson, wife of Abp. B.*] 8°. [1925]
Our family affairs, 1867–96. 8°. 1920
Peter. s8°. [1922]
Pharisees & publicans. s8°. [1926]
Queen Lucia. s8°. [1920]
Rex. s8°. [1925]
Robin Linnet. s8°. [1919]
Sir Francis Drake. 8°. [1927]
Visible & invisible. s8°. [1923]

Benson (Edward White), *abp. of Canterbury.*

see BENSON (A. C.) Life of E. W. B., 2v, 1899.

„ ——. The trefoil: Wellington College, Lincoln, & Truro, 1923.

Benson (Edwin). Life in a mediæval city: illust. by York in the 15th c. 8°. 1920

Benson (Eugene).

From the Asolan hills. rev. ed. 8°. Asolo. [1902]

Pater's Marius the Epicurean. [Repr. f. N. Y. Comm. Advertiser]. 8°. Rome. 1885

Benson (Evelyn), *wife of R. H. Benson, of Buckhurst Park, Sussex, see* BENSON (R. H.) & E. B. Cat. of Ital. pictures, 1914.

Benson (George), *D.D., of Great Salkeld.* A paraphrase & notes on the seven Catholic epistles. [v2 *of h.* Paraphrase]. 4°. 1749

A paraphrase & notes on epistles of St. Paul, viz. I & II Thessal., I & II Timothy, Philemon & Titus. 2nd ed., corr. 4°. 1752

Benson (James W.) Time & time-tellers. [repr.] s8°. 1902

Benson (Jane). *From the Lune to the Neva. s8°. 1879

Quaker pioneers in Russia. 8°. 1902

Benson (Joseph), *Wesleyan minister, 1748–1821.*

An apology for the Methodists. s8°. 1801
A defence of the Methodists. s8°. 1793
A farther defence of the Methodists [*b. w. h.* Defence, 1793]. s8°. 1793
Hymns for children &c. Sel. by B. s8°. 1806

Benson (Joseph) [*continued*].
Sermons. 8°. 1802
*A short acc. of the death of Mrs. M. Hutton. 2nd ed. [P2542]. s8°. [Newcastle]. 1777
see MACDONALD (*Rev.* J.) Mem. of Rev. J. B., 1822.
,, TREFFRY (R.) *sen.* Mem. of J. B., 1840.

Benson (Mary), *wife of abp.* *Benson, see* BENSON (E. F.) Mother, 1925.

Benson (Richard Meux). Further letters. Ed. W. H. Longridge. [v2]. s8°. [1920]

Benson (Robert Henry), *of Buckhurst Park, Sussex,* **& E. Benson.** Cat. of Italian pictures at 16, South St., London & Buckhurst, Sussex, coll. by R. & E. B. 4°. *p.p.* 1914
Cat. of portion of coll. of early Chinese porcelain &c., formed by R. H. B., sold by Christie &c., July 1 &c., 1924. [Illust.] 8°. [1924]
see CUST (L.) La collection de R. H. B., 1907.

Benson (Robert Hugh). The queen's tragedy. [repr.] s8°. *n.d.*

Benson (Samuel), *Chaplain of St. Saviour's, Southwark.* A guide to St. Saviour's Church, Southwark. 3rd ed. rev. & enl. s8°. 1885

Benson (Stella). Goodbye, stranger. s8°. 1926
Pipers & a dancer. s8°. 1924
The poor man. s8°. 1922

Benson (William Arthur Smith). Drawing, its hist. & uses. Memoir by Hon. W. N. Bruce. 8°. 1925

Bensusan (Samuel Levy). Velasquez. [Masterpieces in colour. *b. w.* Israels (J.) Rembrandt, 1909]. 8°. [1909]

Bent (Arthur Cleveland). Life histories of N. American gulls & their terns. Order Longipennes. [S.I., U.S. Nat. Mus., Bull. 113]. 8°. Wash. 1921
Life hist. of N. Amer. marsh birds. Orders Odontoglossæ, Herodiones & Paludicolæ. [S.I. U.S. Nat. Mus., Bull. 135]. 8°. Wash. 1926
Life hist. of N. Amer. petrels & pelicans &c. [S.I, U.S. Nat. Mus., Bull. 121]. 8°. Wash. 1922
Life hist. of N. Amer. wild fowl. Order Anseres (part). [S.I., U.S. Nat. Mus., Bull. 126, 130]. 8°. Wash. 1923–25

Bent (James). Life & death of L. Jeffreys, *see* †WESTERN martyrology, 5th ed., 1705.

Bentham (George). Hdbk. of Brit. flora. Rev. by Sir J. D. Hooker. 7th ed. rev. by A. B. Rendle. s8°. 1924
see FITCH (W. H.) & W. G. SMITH. Illust. of Brit. flora: companion to B.'s Hdbk. &c., 1880.

Bentham (Jeremy) [*ps.* SMITH (GAMALIEL)]. Church-of-Englandism & its catechism examined; w. views of the Eng. & Scot. churches &c. [Cat. exam. *beg. sep. pagin.*] 8°. 1818
Plan for an univ. & perpet. peace. Intr. by C. J. Colombos. [Grotius Soc. Publ.] 8°. 1927
Theory of legislation. Tr. f. the French of E. Dumont by R. Hildreth. 4th ed. s8°. 1882
Treatise on judicial evidence, f. MSS. of J. B. by M. Dumont. Tr. 8°. 1825
see PHILLIPSON (C.) 3 criminal law reformers: B. &c., 1923.

Bentham (Thomas). Hist. of Beddington. s8°. 1923

Benthem (Heinrich Ludolf). Neu-eröffneter Engeländ. Kirch- u. Schulen-Staat. Nebst e. Vorrede Mentzers den Nutzen d. Reisen beurtheilend &c. 8°. L. 1732

Bentinck (Charles D.), *D.D.* Dornoch Cathedral & parish, incl. chap. on architect. hist. of the Cath. by W. D. Simpson. 8°. Inverness. 1926

Bentinck (*Lady* **Norah).** The ex-Kaiser in exile. 8°. [1921]
My wanderings & memories. 8°. [1924]

Bentinck (Willem), *heer v. Rhoon, see* HUFFEL (W. C. VAN). W. B. van R., 1725–47, 1923.

Bentivoglio (Giovanni), *see* SIGHINOLFI (L.) L'architett. Bentivolesca in Bologna, 1909.

Bentivoglio (*il card.* **Guido).** Racc. di lettere scr. dal Card. B. in tempo d. sue nuntiature di Francia &c. s8°. 1654

Bentivoglio (Pio). Compendii theologiæ Thomæ Aquinatis. Opera P. B. perfecti. Ed. 1ª. Add. Thomæ vita &c. s8°. Venetiis. 1585

Bentley (John Francis), *see* L'HÔPITAL (W. DE). Westminster Cathedral & its architect [*i.e.* B.], 2v, 1919.

Bentley (Richard), *D.D., Master of Trinity Coll., Cambridge, see* MACKAIL (J. W.) B.'s Milton, 1924.

Bentum (Philipp Christian), *see* MAUL (D.) Leben u. Werke d. Malers C. B., 1915.

Bentwich (Norman de Mattos). Hellenism. 8°. Phila. 1919

Bentzon (Th.), *ps.* Le violon de Job—Sous le masque—Sang-mêlé—Armelle. s8°. 1875

Benua (Aleksandr Nikolaevich), *see* ERNST (S.) A. Б., 1921.

Benvenuti (Cesare), *da Crema.* Tract. de vita & communitate clericorum per 12 sæcula. 2ª ed., ex Ital. in Lat. tr. ab J. Kistler. s4°. Constantiæ. 1736

Benyowsky (*Count* **Moritz August)** [BENYOVSZKY]. Gróf B. M. saját emlékiratai és utleírásai. Fordította Jókai Mór. 2K. 8°. 1888

Benzel (Carl Jesper). Comm. de J. Duraeo, maxime de actis ejus Suecanis. s4°. Helmstadii. [1744]

Benzelius (Henricus). Syntagma dissert. in Acad. Lundensi habitarum. Cum praef. J. E. Kappii. Acc. index. 2t *in* 1v. s4°. Francofurti. 1745

Benzon (R. v. Fischer), *see* FISCHER-BENZON (R. v.)

Beöthy (Ákos). A magyar államiság fejlödése, küzdelmei. 3 kresz. la8°. *n.d.* & 1906

Beowulf.
Anglo-Saxon poems of B. The travellers song & the battle of Finnesburh. Ed. J. M. Kemble. 2nd ed. s8°. 1835
A transl. of the Anglo-Saxon poem of B. With glossary &c. by J. M. Kemble. s8°. 1837
B. A metrical tr. into mod. Eng. by J. R. C. Hall. s8°. C. 1914
Widsith — Beowulf — Finnsburgh — Waldere — Deor. Done into Eng. by C. Scott-Moncrieff. Intr. by Visct. Northcliffe. 8°. 1921
B., & The fight at Finnsburg. Ed., w. intr., bibliog. &c. by F. Klaeber. 8°. Boston [U.S.] 1922
B. Tr. into Eng. rhyming verse, w. intr. & notes by A. Strong. Foreword on "Beowulf & the heroic age" by R. W. Chambers. 8°. 1925
see CHAMBERS (R. W.) B., introd., 1921.
,, FÖRSTER (M.) Die B.-Hs., 1919.
,, WILLIAMS (R. A.) The Finn episode in B., 1924.

Bepstlichen, *see* PÄPSTLICHE.

Ber, *of Bolechow* [BER BIRKENTHAL; BEREK], *1723–1805.* Memoirs. Tr. f. orig. Hebrew MS. w. intr. &c., by M. Vishnitzer. 8°. O. 1922

Ber (Karl Maksimovich). О проектѣ развед. устрицъ у русск. береговъ Балт. Моря. [I. Akad. Nauk. Зап., т1]. 8°. С.-П. 1862

Berachya [†BERECHIAH, *ben Natronai, Nakdan*]. Dodi venechdi (Uncle & nephew). Ed., w. Eng. tr., intr. &c. to wh. is added tr. f. Latin of Adelard of Bath's Quæstiones naturales, by H. Gollancz. 8°. 1920

Béranger (Pierre Jean de).
Chansons. 2t [*in* 1v]. s8°. 1821
Chansons inéd. [*b. w. h.* Chansons, 1821]. s8°. 1828
Musique des chansons de B., airs notés anc. & mod. 10e éd., revue par F. Bérat &c. 8°. 1868
Œuvres compl. cont. les dix chansons nouv. 2t. s8°. 1854–55
Songs. Tr. by a. of the "Exile of Idria," w. sketch of life of B. [by J. G. H. Bourne]. s8°. 1837

Bérard (Edoardo), *see* BÉRARD (P. A. E.)

Bérard (Leon), *see* CEUX. *Ceux qui nous mènent: L. Barthou, L. B. &c., par * * *, 1922; tr., 1924.

Bérard (Pierre Antoine Édouard), *see* CARUTTI (D.) Il Canonico E. D.: cenno commem., 1890.

Bérard (Victor). Intr. à l'Odyssée. 3t. 8°. 1924–25
Ithaque & la Grèce des Achéens. [Navig. d'Ulysse, t1]. 8°. 1927

Béraud (Henri).
Au Capucin Gourmand. s8°. [1925]
Le bois du templier pendu. s8°. 1926
Ce que j'ai vu à Moscou. s8°. 1925
Lazare. Roman. s8°. [1924]
Le martyre de l'obèse. s8°. [1922]
,, *for another ed., see* ŒUVRES libres, 7, 1922.
Le vitriol de lune. s8°. [1922]

Berbice. Naam-lyst d. bestierders, officieren &c. op de colonie de Berbice, Wieronje, Canje en Wicki. [P2614]. s8°. A. 1784

Berbig (Georg). Georg Spalatin u. s. Verhältnis zu M. Luther, 1525. [Quellen &c. aus d. Gesch. d. Reformationsjhdts., B1]. 8°. Halle (Saale). 1906
see QUELLEN U. DARSTELLUNGEN AUS. D. GESCH. D. REFORMATIONSJHDTS.; hrsg. G. B., B1–18, 1906–11.

Berceo (Gonzalo de). Los milagros de Nuestra Señora, 1; hrsg. A. Hämel. [Samml. rom. Übungstexte, 10]. s8°. Halle. 1926
"Prosas." [Vida de S. Domingo de Silos &c. Bibl. econ. de clás. castell.] s8°. Paris. *n.d.*

Berchem (Egon, *Frhr.* **v.)**
Siegel. [Bibl. für Kunst-u. Antiq.-Sammler, B11]. 8°. 1918

Berchem (Max van). Arab. Inschriften, *see* SARRE (F.) & E. HERZFELD. Archäolog. Reise im Euphrat- u. Tigris-Gebiet, B1, 3, 1911.
Mat. pour un Corpus inscr. arabic., p2, 3, *see* INSTITUT FRANÇ. D'ARCH. ORIENT. DU CAIRE. Mém., t25, 29, 43, 44i, 45i, 1909–25.

Berchem (Max van) & E. Fatio. Voyage en Syrie, t2, *see* INSTITUT FRANÇ. D'ARCH. ORIENT. DU CAIRE. Mém., t38, 1915.
Berchet (Giovanni), *see* BELLORINI (E.) G. B., 1917.
Berchet (Guglielmo), *see* BAROZZI (N.) & G. B. *Delle accogl. ai principi di Savoia fatte d. Veneziani, 1367–1722, 1868.
Berchmans (Jan), *Jesuit* [JEAN BERCHMANS, *Saint*], *see* CEPARI (V.) Vita Berchmanni &c., 1630.
Berchmans (Jules), *see* DUGAS (C.), J. B. &c. Le sanctuaire d'Aléa Athéna à Tégée, 1924.
Berck. Docs. p. s. à l'hist. de B., 1913, *see* LHOMEL (G. DE) *ed.*
Bercovici (Konrad).
Around the world in New York. 8º. [1924]
Bercy (Léon de). Montmartre & s. chansons. Poètes & chansonniers. 8º. 1902
Berdan (John Milton).
Early Tudor poetry, 1485–1547. 8º. N.Y. 1920
Berdrow (Wilhelm). Alfred Krupp. 2B. la8º. [1927]
Berdyaev (Nikolai Aleksandrovich) [BERDIAEV].
see KOLPINSKA (A.) I precursori d. Rivoluzione Russa; con L'anima d. Russia, di N. B., 1919.
,, VEKHI. Вѣхи: сборникъ, 1909.
Bereford (*Sir* William de), *Chief Justice of the Common Bench; d. 1326, see* BOLLAND (W. C.) Chief Justice Sir W. B., 1924.
Berek, *of Bolechow, see* BER.
Berendts (Eduard Nikolaevich).
Кое-что о соврем. вопросахъ. [P2446]. 8º. С.-П. 1906
Къ вопросу о правовомъ положенiи Финляндiи. [P2451]. 8º. С.-П. 1910
Berengarius I., *Marchese di Busca* [BERENGARIO; BALENGERI], *see* CIPOLLA (C.) La pergamena orig. del trattato nel 1180 tra B. I. e il comune di Asti, 1900.
Bérenger (Laurent Pierre). *D'Anacharsis, ou Lettres d'un troubadour [*i.e.* L. P. P.] sur cet ouvrage, suiv. de 2 notices analyt. &c. [P2760]. 8º. Amsterdam. 1789
Bérenger-Férand (L. J. B.) Le baron H. Larrey. 8º. [1899]
Berenson (Bernhard). Three essays in method. la8º. O. 1927
The Venetian painters of the Renaissance. 3rd ed. Illust. la8º. N.Y. 1897
see SPECULUM humanæ salvationis: reprod. of Ital. MS. &c., w. disc. of school & date by B. B., 1926.
Berenyi (Paulus P. Jasz-), *see* JASZ-BERENYI (P. P.)
Beresford (John). The godfather of Downing street, Sir G. Downing (1623–84). 8º. [1925]
Gossip of the 17th & 18th c. 8º. [1923]
Beresford (John Davys).
The decoy. s8º. [1927]
An imperfect mother. s8º. 1920
The imperturbable duchess & o. s. s8º. [1923]
The monkey-puzzle. s8º. [1925]
The prisoners of Harlting. s8º. [1922]
Revolution. Novel. s8º. [1921]
Signs & wonders. s8º. Waltham Saint Lawrence. 1921
Unity. s8º. [1924]
Beresford (Leslie) [*ps.* PAN].
The other Mr. North. s8º. [1926]
Beresford (William Carr, *visct.*)
see D'URBAN (*Lt.-Gen. Sir* B.) Rep. of oper. under Sir W. C. B. in the Alemtejo &c. 1811, 1835.
,, NAPIER (*Gen. Sir* W. F. P.) *Strictures on passages in N.'s Hist. of the Peninsular War wh. ref. to Gen. B., 2nd ed., 1835.
Beresford-Hope (*Rt. Hon.* A. J. B.) [†HOPE (ALEX. J. BERESFORD), *aft. Beresford-Hope*]. A popular view of the Amer. Civil War. 2nd ed. [P2593]. 8º. 1861
Beretta (Antonio Ballesteros y), *see* BALLESTEROS Y BERETTA (A.)
Berettini (Pietro), *see* BERRETTINI (P.)
Berezin (Ilya Nikolaevich). Арм. и груз. надписи въ церквахъ Джульфы &c.—Еврейскiя надписи въ Алеппо, *see* IMP. RUSS. ARCH. OBSCH. Труды Восточ. отд., ч4, 1859.
Очеркъ внутренн. устройства Улуса Джучiева, *see* IMPERAT. RUSS. ARCH. OBSCH. Труды Восточ. отд., ч8, 1864.
Bereznyakov (M.), *see* VOLKOV (S.) & M. B. Общiй уставъ росс. желѣзныхъ дорогъ, 1901.
Berg (Arved). Latvia & Russia. s8º. 1920
Berg (Ernst). Das Problem d. Kausalität. [Bibl. f. Philos.; hrsg. v. L. Stein, B19]. 8º. 1920
Berg (Johan August). Sverige framstäldt i taflor. 96 litografier &c. med. text. [*Fr. drawings of* F. C. Kierschou &c.] obl.4º. Göteborg. [1856]
Berg (Johann Peter). Symbolæ litt. ex Haganis factæ Duisburgenses, 1783–84, *see* SYMBOLÆ.
see MUSEUM DUISBURGENSE, 1782–85.
Berg (Joh. Rut.), *see* JESUITS. Epist. Indicæ &c., 1566; 3ª ed., 1570.
Berg (Leo S.) Nomogenesis, or evolution determined by law. Intr. by D'A. W. Thompson. Tr. J. N. Rostovtsow. 8º. 1926
Berg (Nicolaus) [†BERGIUS (N.)]. Exercitatio de statu eccl. & relig. Moscovit. prop. præs. N. B., respond. M. G. Krook. s8º. Holmiæ. 1704
Bergamin (José).
Tres escenas en ángulo recto (1924). 8º. 1925
Bergamo. Ant. Calendarii d. chiesa di B., ed. G. Finazzi, *see* REGIA DEP. DI STORIA PATRIA. Misc., t13, 1871.
Breves chronicæ Bergom. [Manfredi Zenunonis, Petri Assonica &c., 1117–1512]; nunc. primum ed. cura I. Finazzi, *see* REGIA DEP. DI STORIA PATRIA. Misc., t5, 1868.
Bergasse (Nicolas). Réflexions sur l'acte constit. du Sénat, *see* CHATEAUBRIAND (*le vte.* F. R. DE). De Buonaparte &c., 1814.
Bergé (—), *avocat.* Principes de gouv. &c., *see* CONSTANT (B.) &c. Mél. polit. &c., t2, 1829.
Bergé (Adolphe). Dict. persan-franç. &c. s8º. 1868
Bergendal (Kurt), *see* HECKSCHER (E. F.) *ed.* Sveriges ekon. &c. hist. [1914–25]; under medverk. av K. B. &c., d1, 1926.
Bergendorff (Fr.), *see* HANSLIAN (R.) & F. B. Der chem. Krieg, 1925.
Berger (Arnold Erich). Martin Luther in kulturgesch. Darstellung. 3T. [3i, ii]. 8º. 1895–1921
Berger (Christoph Heinrich). Comm. de personis vulgo larvis seu mascheris. [*b. w.* Amthor (C. H.) Untersuchung, 1715]. 4º. Francofurti. [1723]
Berger (Elie), *archivist, see* INNOCENT IV, *pope.* Les registres d'I. IV; publ. par E. B., t4, 1921.
Berger (Friedrich Ludwig von). *Opuscula miscella quædam juris publici. [Comm. de pari, vel dispari forma Boemiæ & Austriæ &c. ubi Goldasti &c. perv. opiniones profligantur; *& o. wks.*] s8º. [Lipsiæ]. 1725
Berger (Paul).
Nestorianismus hæreseos convictus. s4º. Wittenbergæ. 1726
Berger (Wilhelm). Johannes Hus u. König Sigmund. [*a. c. b. w.* Lechler (G. V.) J. Hus, 1889]. 8º. Augsburg. 1871
Berget (Alphonse). Les problèmes de l'Océan. s8º. 1920
Vagues & marées. s8º. [1923]
Bergh (Henry van den), *see* VAN DEN BERGH (H.)
Bergh (Leonard John Vanden), *see* VANDEN BERGH (J. L.)
Berghauer (Joannes Thomas Adalbert). Βιβλιομαχεία: Bibl. Feld-Zug u. Musterung vieler verfälschten Bibelen &c. s4º. Ober-Ammergau. 1746
Berghman (Gustaf Schlegel). Etudes sur la bibliog. elzevir., basées sur l'ouvr. Les Elzevier de A. Willems. la8º. Stockholm. 1885
see WILLEMS (A.) Les Elzevier; suppl. par G. B., 1897.
Berghöffer (Christian Wilhelm). Meyer A. Rothschild, d. Gründer d. Rothschild. Bankhauses. 2ᵉ A. la8º. Fr. am M. 1923
Bergholt (Ernest). Royal auction bridge. s8º. *n.d.*
Bergier (Nicolas Sylvestre). Tractatus hist.-dogmat. de vera religione. Versio Lat. 3t. 4º. Venetiis. 1790
Bergius (Joannes), *chaplain to the Elector of Brandenburg.*
The pearle of peace & concord; or a treat. of pacific. betw. the dissent. churches of Xt. Tr. M. Bohemus. s8º. 1655
Bergk (Theodor), *see* DIEHL (E.) Anthologia lyrica [*n. ed. of B.*], 2v, 1925.
Bergman (Sten).
Through Kamchatka by dog-sled & skis. 8º. 1927
Bergmann (Anton) [*ps.* TONY].
Ernest Staas, advocaat. 17ᵉ dr. 8º. 1919
Bergmann (Carl).
Hist. of reparations. Foreword by Sir J. Stamp. la8º. 1927
Bergmans (Paul). Henry Vieuxtemps. s8º. Turnhout. 1920
Bergner (Heinrich). Naumberg u. Merseburg. [Berühmte Kunststätten, B47]. 2. umgearb. A. s8º. L. 1926
Bergson (Henri).
Durée & simultanéité à propos de la théorie d'Einstein. s8º. 1922
L'évolution créatrice. 11ᵉ éd. 8º. 1912
Matter & memory. Auth. tr. by A. M. Paul & W. S. Palmer. [repr.] 8º. 1919
Mind-energy: lect. & essays. Tr. H. Wildon Carr. 8º. 1920
see CARR (H. W.) "Time" & "history" in contemp. philos., w. spec. ref. to B. &c., 1918.
see GAULTIER (P.) Maîtres de la pensée franç., H. B. &c., 1921.
,, GRANDJEAN (F.) Une révolution dans la philos.: la doctrine de H. B., 2ᵉ éd., 1916.

Bergson (Henri) [*continued*].

see Gunn (J. A.) B. & h. philosophy, 1920.
„ Luce (A. A.) B.'s doctrine of intuition, 1922.
„ Maire (G.) H. B.: s. œuvre, 1926.
„ Nordmann (C.) Notre maître de temps &c.: Einstein ou B.?, 1924.
„ Péguy (C. P.) Œuvres compl., t9, Note conjointe sur M. Descartes préc. de la note sur M. B., 1924.
see Rostrevor (G.) B. & future philosophy, 1921.
„ Solomon (J.) B., 1922.
„ Stephen (K.) The misuse of mind: study of B.'s attack on intellectualism, 1922.
„ Thibaudet (A.) Le Bergsonisme, 3e éd., 2t, 1923.
„ Turquet-Milnes (G.) Some mod. Fr. writers: a study in Bergsonism, 1921.
„ Wheeler (O. A.) B. & education, 1922.

Bergsträsser (Gotthelf), *see* Nöldeke (T.) Gesch. d. Qorāns, 2e A., T3, Gesch. d. Qorāntexts v. G. B., 1926.

Bergsträsser (Ludwig). Gesch. der polit. Parteien in Deutschland. 3e verb. &c. A. s8o. Mannheim. 1924

Berguer (Georges). Some aspects of the life of Jesus f. psycholog. & psycho-analytic point of view. Tr. E. S. & Van W. Brooks. 8o. 1923

Bergwiese (Hans).
Die polit. Parteien Deutschlands. [P2456]. 8o. Hannover.1919

Bericht [Berichten]. *B. von d. Colloquio der zu Quedelburg versam. Theologen, 1585, *see* Quedlinburg.
Gründlicher B. auss heyliger Schrifft &c., 1605, *see* Gründlicher.
Der Königl. Dän. Miss. aus Ost-Indien eingesandter ausführl. Berichten, 1735–60, *see* Dänische Missionarien.

Beridze (V.) Грузинскій глоссарій, *see* Marr (N. Ya.) Мат. по яфет. яз., 6, 1912.

Bering (Vitus) [Beringius].
Florus Danicus. [Repr.] s8o. [Tyrnavia]. 1716

Beringer (François). Les indulgences, leur nature & leur usage. Tr. E. Abt. & A. Feyerstein. 2e éd. 2t. 8o. 1893

Beringer (Joachim) [*ps.* Ursinus (J.)]. Flosculi blasphemiarum ex 3 concionibus super beatific. I. Lojolæ habitis descr. &c. [P597]. s4o. *n.p.* 1612

Beritashvili (Ivane). Tshovelta phiziologia. [*In Georgian*]. [2v. *in* 1.] 8o. Tiflis. 1920–21

Berjeau (Jean Philibert). Essai bibliogr. sur le Speculum humanæ salvationis; indiquant le passage de la xylographie à la typogr. Intr. de l'éd. fac-simile. 4o. Londres. 1862

Berkeley, *The family of, see* Barkly (*Sir* H.) The Berkeleys of Cobberley, 1893.
see Barkly (*Sir* H.) The earlier house of B., 1884.

Berkeley (Arnald de), *see* Barkly (*Sir* H.) A. de B., baron of the Exchequer, 1264, 1892.

Berkeley (Cara).
Some Rom. monuments in the light of hist. 2v. 8o. 1927

Berkeley (George), *bp. of Cloyne.*
The querist, 1735–37. [J. H. Univ. Repr. of econ. tracts. 3p *in* 1v. P2619]. 8o. [Baltimore. 1910]
Siris: virtues of tar water &c. [*b. w.* Walpole (*Sir* R.) Autentick copy of will, 1745]. 2nd ed. 8o. 1744
see Erdmann (B.) B.'s Philos. im Lichte s. wissenschaftl. Tagebuchs, 1919.
„ Johnston (G. A.) Development of B.'s philos., 1923.
„ Levi (A.) La filosofia di G. B., 1922.
„ Metz (R.) G. B.: Leben u. Lehre, 1925.

Berkeley (Miles Joseph), *see* Smith (W. G.) Outlines of Brit. fungology, suppl. [*to* B.'s Outlines], 1891.

Berkh (Vasily Nikolaevich). Царствованіе царя Михаила Θеодоровича и взглядъ на междуцарствіе. 2ч 8o. С.–П. 1832
Царствованіе царя Θеодора Алексѣевича и ист. перваго стрѣлецкаго бунта. 2ч *in* 1v. 8o. С.–П. 1834–35

Berkman (Alexander).
The Bolshevik myth: diary, 1920–22. 8o. [1925]

Berl (Emmanuel). Méditation sur un amour défunt. [Les cahiers verts, 58]. s8o. 1925
Recherches sur la nature de l'amour. [1] La réalité des sentiments. 8o. [1923]

Berlan (Francesco). La introduz. d. stampa in Milano a prop. dei Miraculi de la gloriosa Verzene Maria, 1469. 8o. Veneziæ. 1884

Berlanga y Rosado (Manuel Rodriguez de), *see* Rodriguez de Berlanga y Rosado (M.)

Berlepsch-Valendàs (Hans Eduard v.) Die Gartenstadtbewegung in England. [Sieper (E.) *ed.* Kultur d. mod. Eng., B3]. 8o. München. 1912
Motive d. deut. Architektur d. 16.–18. Jhdts. Hrsg. v. A. Lambert u. E. Stahl. Text v. H. E. v. B. Abtlg. 1, Früh-u. Hochrenaissance, 1500–1650. 100 Tafeln [15, 51, 56, 62, 87–89, 99 *wanting*]. fol. St. 1890

Berlin. Album v. Berlin. 3 Panoramen u. 49 Ansichten. obl.4o. *Globus Verlag.* [1904]
*Corr. p. s. de suite à l'Hist. secrette de la cour de B., 1789, *see* Mirabeau (H. G. R., *cte.* de).
Washington & Berlin. Corr. betw. Count Bernstorff & B. &c., 1916, 1920, *see* Washington.

Berlinische Nachrichten v. Staats-u. gelehrten Sachen. [No.] 1, 30. Junii 1740 (*facs.*), *see* Freytag (G.) Bilder, B5, 1925.

Berlioux (Etienne Félix). Slave trade in Africa in 1872. [Tr.] Pref. by J. Cooper. 8o. 1872

Berlioz (Hector). Instrumentationslehre. Aut. deut. A. v. A. Dörffel. 5e A. 8o. L. 1893
Treatise upon mod. instrumentation & orchestration. Tr. M. C. Clarke. 2nd ed. la8o. 1858
see Fouque (O.) Révolutionnaires de la musique, 1882.
„ Prod'homme (J. G.) H. B., 1803–69, sa vie &c., 1904.
„ Young (F.) Mastersingers &c. [w. essay on H. B.], 2nd ed., 1908.

Berlitz (Maximilian Delphinus). Método-Berlitz para la enseñanza de idiom. mod. Parte española. Con la colab. de B. Collonge. 8a ed. 8o. Berlin. 1905

Berman (Louis), *M.D.*
The glands regulating personality. 8o. N.Y. 1922

Bermondsey. Cat. of prints & drawings in the B. Public Libraries illust. Bermondsey, past & present. Comp. by J. D. Stewart. 8o. 1927

Bermondt (P. Awaloff), *see* Awaloff-Bermondt (P. M.)

Bermudez (João). Breve rel. da embaixada que J. B. trouxe do imp. da Ethiopia, Preste João, 1565, *see* Collecção de opusc. reimpr., t1, 1875.

Bern, *see* Berne.

Bernadotte (*capitaine* **Henry de),** *see* Louvie (P.), *ps.*

Bernal de O'Reilly (Antonio). Bizarria guipuzcoana y sitio de Fuenterrabía, 1474–1638. s8o. San Sebastian. 1872
Practica consular de España. Formulario de cancillerias consulares y col. de decretos &c. la8o. Havre. 1864

Bernanos (Georges). L'imposture. s8o. [1927]
Sous le soleil de Satan. s8o. 1926
The star of Satan. Tr. V. Lucas. s8o. [1927]

Bernanose (Marcel). Les arts décoratifs au Tonkin. 4o. 1922

Bernard, *margrave of Baden, c. 1430–1458, see* Ringholz (O.) Der sel. Markgraf B., 1892.

Bernard, *Saint, abbot of Clairvaux.*
Delle perfezione d. vita spirit. Epistola. Volgar. da N. di Bonifacio. [P2787]. 8o. Bologna. 1856
Life of St. Malachy of Armagh. [Tr., w. intr.] by H. J. Lawlor. [Trans. of Xtn. lit., s5]. s8o. 1920
On consideration. Tr. G. Lewis. s8o. O. 1908
Papst u. Papstthum nach d. Zeichnung d. h. Bernhard v. Clairvaux. Übers. u. Erläut. s. Schr. "De Consideratione," v. J. H. Reinkens. s8o. Münster. 1870
Sel. treatises: De dilig. Deo; ed. W. W. Williams. De grad. humilit. & superb.; ed. B. R. V. Mills. [Camb. patr. texts]. s8o. C. 1926
Theologia didascalico-moralis, ex ipsius scr. coll. s8o. Francofurti. 1700
Traité de la considération: tr., *see* Buchon (J. A. C.) Choix d'ouvr. myst., 1840.
Treatise conc. grace & free will. Tr., w. intr. &c. by W. W. Williams. [Trans. of Xtn. lit., s2, Lat. texts]. s8o. 1920
see Augustine, *Saint, bp. of Hippo.* Meditationes &c., 1475 ?.
„ Butler (E. C.) Western mysticism: teaching of SS. Augustine, B. &c. on contemplation &c., 1922; 2nd ed., 1927.
„ Coulton (G. G.) 5 cent. of religion, v1, St. B. &c., 1923.
„ Goyau (G.) St. B., 1927.
„ Ratisbonne (M. T.) Hist. de B. & de s. siècle, 11e éd., 2t, 1903.
„ Vacandard (*l'abbé* E.) Abélard, sa lutte avec St. B. &c., 1881.

Bernard, *of Compostella, the elder, see* Singer (H.) Die Dekretalensammlung d. B. C. ant., 1914.

Bernard, *Saint, of Menthon, see* Duc (J. A.) A quelle date est mort St. B. de M.?, 1894.
see Fourman (J.) Über d. Sprache d. Mystère de St. B. de M., 1913.

Bernard, *de Ventadour, see* Vossler (C.) Minnesang d. B., 1918.

Bernard (Augustin).
L'Afrique du Nord. [C. E. f. Internat. Peace]. la8o. [1926]

Bernard (Charles de). Nouvelles & mélanges. n. éd. s8°. 1854
La peau du lion & La chasse aux amants. n. éd. [*b. w. h.* Nouv. & mélanges, 1854]. s8°. 1858
Bernard (Claude). La science expérim. 7e éd. s8°. 1925
Bernard (Emile), *see* DUBOIS (U.) & E. B. La cuisine classique, 12e éd., 2t, 1886.
Bernard (Georges). A travers les bouges de Paris, choses vues, *see* ŒUVRES libres, 62, 1926.
Bernard (Jean Frédéric), *ed.* Recueil de voyages au Nord. 10t [t1–4, n. éd.; 5, 6, 3e éd.] s8°. Amsterdam. 1725–38
Bernard (Jean Jacques). Denise Marette, pièce, *see* ŒUVRES libres, 68, 1927.
Le feu qui reprend mal: pièce, *see* REVUE (LA) HEBDOMADAIRE. Suppl.: coll. nouv. &c., No. 5, 1922.
Théâtre. Le feu qui reprend mal—Martine—Le printemps des autres—L'invitation au voyage. s8°. [1925]
Bernard (Jean Marc). Œuvres. 2t. s8°. 1923
1, Sub tegmine fagi—Premiers poèmes—Vers inéd.—La vallée du Rhone, suiv. des Reliquiæ de R. Monier.
2, Petits sentiers de la poésie franc.—Symbolisme & classicisme —Études & portraits.
Bernard (John Henry), *bp. of Ossory, aft. abp. of Dublin, aft. provost of T. C., Dublin, see* BIBLE. PSALMS. Tho Psalter in Lat. & Eng.; intr. by J. H. B., 1911.
Bernard (Luther Lee).
Instinct: st. in social psychology. 8°. [1924]
Bernard (Nicholas), *dean of Ardagh.* The penitent death of a woefull sinner &c., J. Atherton, Bp. of Waterford, executed 5. Dec. 1640. As also Sermon [*w. sep. tp.*] 2nd ed. [*tp. mutilated*]. s8°. 1642
Bernard (Pierre). Étude sur les esclaves & les serfs d'église en France du 6e au 13e s. 8°. 1919
Bernard (Pierre), *magistrat à Béziers.* L'explication de l'Edit de Nantes de M. B. avec nouv. observ. & nouv. édits &c. touch. la religion prétendu réformée, par M. Soulier. 8°. 1683
Bernard (Pierre Joseph).
Œuvres compl. Ed. de Cazin. s8°. [1785?]
Bernard (Richard), *rector of Batcombe, Somerset.* A key of knowledge for the opening of St. Johns mysticall Revelation. [*engraved tp.*] 8°. 1617
Bernard (Tristan) [PAUL, *dit* TRISTAN BERNARD].
L'Anglais tel qu'on le parle. Vaudeville. s8°. 1899
Ce que l'on dit aux femmes, comédie, *see* ŒUVRES libres, 18, 1922.
Le cordon bleu, comédie inéd., *see* ŒUVRES libres, 29, 1923.
Corinne & Corentin. Roman. s8° [1923].
L'enfant prodigue du Vésinet. Roman. s8°. [1921]
Féerie bourgeoise. Roman. s8°. [1924]
Le Prince charmant: comédie, *see* ŒUVRES libres, 2, 1921.
La volonté de l'homme, pièce, *see* ŒUVRES libres, 14, 1922.
Bernardakes (A. N.) Περὶ τοῦ ἐν Ἑλλάδι ἐμπορίου etc. 8°. ἐν Ἀθήναισ. 1885
Bernardes (Manoel), *1644–1710.* B. Nova floresta &c. [Antologia portug.; organiz. por A. de Campos]. 2a ed. 2v. s8°. Paris. 1920–21
Bernardi (Jacopo). Cenni sull' orig. &c. d. stampa n. prov. venete. [P2843]. 4°. Cavarzere. 1887
Commemor. d. G. Veludo. [Estr. d. R. Istit. Veneto, Atti, Ser. 7, t1. P2840]. 8°. Venezia. 1890
Della pubbl. del cartario dell' ant. abbadia d' Oulx fatta da Berta e Rivautella, e del codice Peralda, *see* REGIA DEP. DI STORIA PATRIA. Misc., t20, 1882.
see CARUTTI (D.) Mgr. J. B., 1900.
Bernardini (Oddone), *see* ITALY: MIN. D. LAVORI PUBBL. Porti marit. [Not. racc. da E. Coen-Cagli e O. B.], 1905.
Bernardus, *Cremifan.* [NORICUS], *see* LEIDINGER (G.) B. Noricus, 1917.
Bernardus, *Morlanensis* [BERNARD, *monk of Cluny*]. Hora novissima. Metr. version of portions of Latin poem by B., ent. "De contemptu mundi," w. text, by C. L. Ford. 8°. 1898
Bernardy (Amy A.) La missione di B. Franklin a Parigi &c., 1776–86, *see* ARCHIVIO STORICO ITAL. Anno 78, v1, 1920.
L'ultima guerra turco-veneziana (1714–18). 8°. Firenze. 1902
Bernasconi (Ugo). Arturo Tosi. s8°. Milano. 1925
Bernatzky (M. v.), *see* AMONN (A.) & M. v. B. Wâhrungsreform in d. Tschechoslowakei u. in Sowjet-Russland, 1924.
Bernbaum (Ernest). The drama of sensibility: Eng. sentimental comedy &c., 1696–1780. [Harvard St. in Eng., v3]. 8°. Cambridge, *Harvard.* 1925
The Mary Carleton narratives, 1663–73. A missing chap. in the hist. of the Eng. novel. 8°. O. [1914]
Bernd (Adam) [*ps.* MELODIUS (CHRISTIANUS)], *see* LÖSCHER (V. E.) Kurtze Rettung &c. geg. d. Melodischen Einwürfe, 1729.
Bernd (Christian Samuel Theodor). Wappenbuch d. preuss. Rheinprovinz. Mit Beschreibung [*w. sep. tp. & pagin.*] 2T [*in* 1v]. 8°. Bonn. 1835
„ „ Nachtrag, mit Beschreibung [*w. sep. tp. & pagin. b. w.* Wappenbuch, 1835]. 8°. Bonn. 1842–43
Berne [BERN; BERNN].
Cat. des périodiques suisses, coll. de la Bibl. Nat. à B. [*2nd tp. in Germ.*] 8°. Bümpliz-Bern. 1917
Die disputacion vor den xii orten e. lobl. eidtgnoschafft nälich B., Lutzern &c., 1527, *see* BADEN, *Switzerland.*
Ein gleidt so die frommen Christenliche Eydgenossen nachbemelter örter, B., Lucern &c., 1527?, *see* BADEN, *Switzerland.*
Handlung oder Acta gehaltner Disput. zů B. in üchtland. [*Betw. B. Haller, F. Kolb & others*]. 8°. Zürich, *C. Froschouer,* 1528
*Hier vürt angezeigt dz unchristlich frevel &c. e. lobl. herrschafft von Bern &c., 1528, *see* MURNER (T.)
*Ratschlag halltender Disput. zu Bernn, 1528, *see* RATSCHLAG.
*Von den fier Ketzeren zu Bern verbrant &c., 1509, [1510], *see* MURNER (T.)
Bernegger (Matthias). Hypobolimæa Mariæ camera, seu Idolum Lauretanum dejectum. [P183]. s4°. Argentorati. 1619
Justi Lipsii Politicorum libri secundi [-sexti] capita in aphorismos resoluta, &c. [Append. prima & secunda]. Præs. M. B. [*var. resp.*] 12p [*each w. sep. tp. & signatures*]. s4°. Argentorati. 1616–17
Berneker (Erich).
Russ. Gramm. [Samml. Göschen]. s8°. L. 1897
Slavische Christomathie mit Glossaren. 8°. Str. 1902
Bernhard, *der Grosse, duke of Saxe-Weimar, see* PHILIPPS (J. T.) Hist. of Ernestus of Saxe-Gotha & B. of S.-W. &c., 1740.
Bernhard (Ernst Adolf). Psychische Vorgänge betrachtet als Bewegungen. [Bibl. f. Phil.; hrsg. v. L. Stein, B23]. 8°. 1923
Bernhard (Georg Friedrich). Diarium oder Tag-Register, Zeit d. Auffenthalts M. Lutheri auf d. Veste [*sic*] Coburg, April–Oct. 1530. [P442]. s4°. Coburg. [1730]
Bernhard (Ludwig).
Was wird aus d. Völkerbund? [P2493]. 8°. 1920
Bernhard (Oskar). Planzenbilder auf griech. u. röm. Munzen. [Veröffentl. d. Schweiz. Gesell. f. Gesch. d. Medizin &c.] 8°. Zürich. 1924
Bernhardi (Friedrich A. J. v.) *Bernhardi converted. A comp. study. [P2380]. 4°. [1915]
Deutschlands Heldenkampf, 1914–18. 8°. München. 1922
The new Bernhardi. World power or downfall. s8°. 1915
Vom Kriege d. Zukunft. Nach. d. Erfahrungen d. Weltkrieges. 8°. 1920
Bernhardi (Theodor v.) Aus d. Leben T. v. B.'s. T9. 8°. L. 1906
9, In Spanien u. Portugal: Tagebuchblätter, 1869–71.
Bernhardt (Ernst). Wie Luther in unruhigen Zeiten &c. beruhiget u. tröstet. s8°. Halle. 1831
Bernhardt (Sarah) [*i.e. Mme.* DAMALA, *née* ROSINE BERNHARDT]. Ma double vie. Mém. de S. B. 2t. s8°. 1923
see ARTHUR (*Sir* G.) S. B., 1923.
Bernhardt (Theodor). Lord Palmerston, *see* VIRCHOW (R.) & F. v. HOLTZENDORFF. Vorträge, H107, 1870.
Bernhold (Johann Baltasar). De characteribus pseudoprophetarum in M. Luthero min. obviis. Præses J. B. B., resp. J. G. Graemer. [P2628]. s4°. Altorfii. 1731
Berni (*il conte* Francesco).
Dell' accademia parte 1 [& 2 *in* 1v]. 8°. Ferrara. 1657–58
Il primo, [*&* Il secondo-; *&* Il terzo-] libro dell' opere burlesche di F. B., di G. della Casa, del Varchi, del Mauro, del Bino, del Molza, del Dolce e del Firenzuola [*& others*]. s8°. Londra [t3, Firenze]. 1723
see BETUSSI (G.) Descr. d. Cataio; con l'agg. d. co. F. B., 1669.
Bernia, Il, *ps., see* TELUCCINI (M.), *called Il B.*
Bernier (Etienne Alexandre J. B. M.), *bp. of Orléans, see* MEYER (A.) L'abbé B., apôtre de La Vendée, 1923.
Bernier (Jean).
Hist. de Blois. 3p [*in* 1v. Preuves *have sep. pagin.*] 4°. 1682
Berniera (Giovanni Angelo). Compendium hist. Reformationis. s8°. Londini. 1707
Bernières Louvigny (Jean de). Le Chrestien intérieur. [J. de B. L.] par un solitaire [le P. L.-F. d'Argentan]. Augm. des Pensées de M. de B. L. t1 *in* 2p. [*in* 1v]. s8°. 1689–90
Œuvres spirituelles; 2p *in* 1v. [p1 3e éd.; 2, 2e éd.] s8°. 1687–90

Bernini (Giovanni Lorenzo).
see MUÑOZ (A.) G. L. B., 1925.
,, STEINMANN (E.) Terra-Kotta-modelle B., 1907.
Bernoni (Domenico). Le vicende di Asola. 8°. 1876
Bernoni (Domenico Giuseppe). Dei Torresani, Blado e Ragazzoni, celeb. stampatori a Venezia &c. nel 15 e 16 sec. 8°. Milano. 1890
Bernoulli (Johann), *1744–1807, see* STIEDA (W.) J. B. in s. Bezieh. z. preuss. Herrscherhause u. z. Akad. d. Wiss., 1925.
Bernsau (Heinrich Wilhelm). Theologiæ dogmat. methodo scientifica pertractatæ pars prior. [*in 2 sections*]. Cum præf. C. de. Wolfii. s4°. Lugduni Batav. 1747–55
Bernstein (Aaron). A. v. Humboldt u. d. Geist 2 Jhdte, *see* VIRCHOW (R.) & F. v. HOLTZENDORFF. Samml., H89, 1869.
Bernstein (Eduard).
Die deutsche Revolution, B1 [*no more publ.*] 8°. 1921
Dokumente z. Weltkrieg 1914. Hrsg. E. B. 1, Das deut. Weissbuch. [*repr.*] s8°. 1919
E. B., 1850–72 : Kindheit u. Jugendjahre. 8°. 1926
Ferdinand Lassalle. Eine Würdigung d. Lehrers u. Kämpfers. 8°. 1919
My years of exile. Tr. B. Miall. 8°. [1921]
Die Voraussetzungen d. Sozialismus u. d. Aufgaben d. Sozialdemokratie. neue, verb. &c. A. s8°. St. 1920
Die Wahrheit ü. die Einkreisung Deutschlands. [P2407]. s8°. [1920]
Was ist Sozialismus ? [P2580]. 8°. 1922
Bernstein (*Frau* Elsa), *see* ROSMER (E.) *ps.*
Bernstein (Georg Heinrich). Chrestomathia Syriaca cum Lexico. Pars posterior Lexicon Syr. denuo ed. 8°. Lipsiæ. 1836
Bernstein (Heinrich Agathon). Dagboek v. B.'s laatste reis naar Nieuw-Guinea &c., 1864–65 ; bewerkt door S. van Musschenbrock, *see* BIJDRAGEN tot de taal &c. v. Ned. Ind., volg. 4, d7, 1883.
Bernstein (Henry). Félix, pièce, *see* ŒUVRES libres, 71, 1927.
La galerie des glaces. [Pièce]. s8°. [1926]
Bernstein (Richard). Der Kapp-Putsch u. seine Lehren. [P2410]. 8°. 1920
Bernstorff, *The family of.* Bernstorffske papirer. Udvalgte breve &c. vedrørende familien B., 1732–1835. Udg. af A. Friis. 3B. la8°. København. 1904–13
Bernstorff (Elise, *Gräfin* von). Gräfin E. v. B., 1789–1835. Aus i. Aufzeichnungen. 2B *in* 1v. 8°. 1896
Bernstorff (Johann Heinrich, *Graf.* v.) Deutschland u. Amerika. Erinnerungen aus d. fünfjahr. Kriege. 8°. 1920
My 3 years in America. 8°. [1920]
see WASHINGTON & Berlin : corr. betw. Count B. & Berlin. &c., 1916, 1920.
Bernstorffske papirer, 1732–1835 ; udg. A. Friis, 3B, 1907–13, *see* BERNSTORFF, *The family of.*
Béroalde de Verville (François), *see* SAINEAN (L.) Problèmes litt. du 16ᵉ s., Moyen de parvenir &c., 1927.
Berolzheimer (Ruth). Child welfare in N. Jersey, p2, by R. B. &c., *see* UNITED STATES : LAB. Children's Bur., No. 175, 1927.
Berosus, *the Chaldean, see* SCHNABEL (P.) B. u. d. babylon.-hellen. Lit. (B. Babyloniac. libr. 3 fragm.), 1923.
Béroul, *see* TRISTRAM. Le roman de T. ; par B. ; éd. E. Muret, 1913.
Berquin (Arnaud). The blossoms of morality, by the editor of The looking-glass of the mind [*i.e.* A. B.] Cuts by I. Bewick. 4th ed. s8°. 1806
The children's friend. Sel. f. [L'ami des enfants *of*] M. Berquin. n. ed. s8°. 1805
Berr (Henri). L'évolution de l'humanité ; intr. gén. par H. B., *see* PERRIER (E.) La terre avant l'hist., 1920.
La synthèse en hist. 8°. 1911
Berra (Manuel Orozco y), *see* OROZCO Y BERRA (M.)
Berr de Turique (Julien), *see* BISSON (A.) & J. B. DE T. Trois Anabaptistes, 2ᵉ éd., 1904.
Berrettini (Pietro) [BERETTINI ; PIETRO DA CORTONA], *see* MUÑOZ (A.) P. da C. ; 32 riprod. con testo e cat., 1921.
Berrian (William). Catalogue of books &c. on Mormonism. Coll. by W. B. [P2622]. s8°. 1898
Berridge (John). Sion's songs. s8°. 1785
Whole works. With mem. by R. Whittingham. 2nd ed. w. add. s8°. 1864
Berridge (Walter Sydney). Animal curiosities. 8°. [1922]
Berrington (Joseph), *see* PLOWDEN (C.) Remarks on a bk. entitled Mem. of G. Panzani, prec. by address to Rev. J. B., 1741.
Berrow (Capel).
A lapse of souls in a state of pre-existence. [*a. ed. without preface.* Letters to B. *on larger paper folded*]. 8°. *n.d.*
Berruguete (Alonso Gonzalez), *see* ORUETA Y DUARTE (R. DE). B. y su obra, 1917.
Berry (*le duc* de), *1778–1820.* Cat. of Dutch & Flemish pictures for sale at Christie &c. [P2600]. s8°. 1834
see LUCAS-DUBRETON (J.) Louvel le régicide, 1923.
Berry (Caroline F. L., *duchesse* de). Galerie de la Dsse. de B. Ecole franç. Peintres mod. Ouvrage lithographie sous la dir. de Chev. Bonnemaison. 2t. lafol. 1822
see GUIBOURG (A.) *Relation de l'arrest. de S. A. R., 1832.
Berry (Charles Walter). King Arthur. A simple appreciation. [*Play*]. 8°. 1923
Berry (Edward Wilber). The fossil higher plants from the Canal Zone. [S. I., U.S. Nat. Mus. Bull., 103]. 8°. Wash. 1918
Berry (James). My experiences as an executioner. Ed. H. Snowden Ward. s8°. [1891]
Berry (Jean, *duc* de), *see* DURRIEU (*cte.* P.) Les très belles Heures de Notre Dame du Duc de B., 1922.
Berry (W. Turner), *see* BLADES (W.) Cat. of exhib. in comm. of centenary of W. B. ; comp. by W. T. B., 1924.
Bers (S. A.), *see* BEHRS (S. A.)
Bersaucourt (Albert de). Albert Samain, s. œuvre. s8°. [1925]
Berse (Gaspar) [BARZÉE (G.)], *see* JESUITS. Epist. Indicæ [*by B. &c.*], 1566 ; 3ª ed., 1570.
Bertacchi (Cosimo). L'Armenia, *see* QUADERNI geograf., N. 2, 1918.
Bertacchi (Giovanni). Sensi terreni n. Paradiso di Dante, *see* DANTE : Lectura Dantis, 1915.
Bertanza (Enrico) & Vittorio Lazzarini. Il dialetto veneziano fino a. morte di Dante 1321. Notizie e documenti. la8°. Venezia. 1891
Bertarelli (Achille) & A. Monti. Tre sec. di vita milanese n. doc. iconografici, 1630–1875. fol. Milano. 1927
Bertaud [BERTHAUD]. Chartes de N.-D. de Bertaud, mon. de femmes, de l'ordre des Chartreux, diocèse de Gap. Publ. sous les auspices de la Soc. d'Et. des Hautes-Alpes par P. Guillaume. la8°. Gap. 1888
Bertaut (Jean), *bp. of Sées, see* GRENTE (G.) J. B., abbé d'Aunay &c., 1552–1611, 1903.
Bertaut (Jules). L'étonnante hist. de Pierre Coignard, *see* ŒUVRES libres, No. 77, 1927.
Henry Bordeaux : son œuvre. s8°. [1924]
Le roman nouveau. s8°. [1920]
Voltaire. s8°. [1911]
Bertaux (Emile). Rome. [Villes d'art célèbres]. [3t] 1, 4ᵉ éd. ; 2, 3, 3ᵉ éd., rev. la8°. 1916–24
1, L'antiquité.
2, De l'ère des catacombes à l'avèn. de Jules II.
3, De l'avèn. de Jules II à nos jours.
Bertelli (Dante). J. G. Wirsüng, *see* PADOVA. Monogr. s. Studio di Padova, 1922.
Bertels (John). Bertels' Engelska affärslexikon. Prakt. hand- och uppslagsbok för Eng. handelskorr. Svenskt-Eng., Eng.-Svenskt. 3ᵉ uppl. 8°. [1920]
Berthaud, *see* BERTAUD.
Bertheau (Ernst). Comm. on the Books of Chronicles ; tr. J. Martin, *see* KEIL (C. F.) Comm. on Bk. of Kings &c. ; tr., 2v, 1857.
Berthelot (André). L'Afrique saharienne & soudanaise, ce qu'en ont connu les anciens. s4°. 1927
Berthemet (*Capt.* Henry), *see* TOURNÈS (*Col.* R.) & *Capt.* H. B. La Bataille des Flandres, 1925.
Bertheroy (Jean), *ps.* Les brebis de Mme. Deshoulières. s8°. 1924
Roseline & l'amour. s8°. [1923]
Berthet (Antoine), *see* DUMOLARD (H.) Le véritable J. Sorel [*i.e.* A. B.], 1927.
Berthier (Alfred).
Le poète Savoyard, J.-P. Veyrat, 1810–44. 8°. 1920
Berthold, *of Tuttlingen, fl. 1322–31, see* ERBEN (W.) B. v. T., 1923.
Berthold (Arthur). Meine Ansicht. s8°. St. [1917]
Bertholdus, *Dominican.* Horologiū devotiōis. [*Ends : sig.* h8 *verso* : Explicit Horologium devotionis per me Johannem Landen Colonie. *Woodcuts on front & back of tp.*] s8°. [Colonie. *Joh. Landen.* c. 1498]
66 leaves sig. a–f in eights, g1–10, h1–8.

Bertholet (Alfred).
Hist. of Hebrew civiliz. Tr. A. K. Dallas. 8°. [1926]
Kulturgesch. Israels. la8°. Göttingen. 1919
see CHANTEPIE DE LA SAUSSAYE (P. D.) Lehrbuch d. Religionsgesch., 4e A., hrsg. A. B. &c., 2B, 1925.
Berthoud (Alfred). New theories of matter & the atom. Tr. E. & C. Paul. 8°. [1924]
Berti (Carolina Coronedi), *see* CORONEDI BERTI (C.)
Berti (Giovanni Lorenzo). Augustinianum systema de gratia vindicatum, sive refutatio librorum Banjanismus & Jansenismus in scriptis Bellelli, & Berti. 2p. s4°. Romæ. 1747
Bertie of Thame (Francis Leveson Bertie, *1st b.***)** Diary, 1914–8. Ed. Lady A. Gordon Lennox, w. foreword by Visc. Grey of Falloden. 2v. la8°. [1924]
Bertieri (Raffaello). L'arte di G. Bodoni. Con notizia biog. a cura di G. Fumagalli. 4°. Milano. [1924]
Bertius (Petrus). Theatrum geographiæ vet., t1, *see* PTOLEMY. Geographiæ libri 8, 1619.
see HAGIENSIS. Scripta advers. collat. H.; Lat. fecit P. B., 1615.
Bertling (Ernst August), *ed., see* *THEOLOGISCHE BERICHTE &c., 110 Stücke, 1764–73.
Bertolotti (Antonino). Convenzioni e statuti pell' estirpamento dei berrovieri e de' ladri dal Monferrato &c. nei sec. 13 e 14, *see* REGIA DEP. DI STORIA PATRIA. Misc., t12, 1871.
Bertolotti (Davide). Viaggio ai 3 laghi di Como, Lugano e Maggiore. [*3 pagin.*] s8°. Como. 1825
Bertoni (Giulio). *Works in* MONACI (E.) Studj romanzi.
Discussioni etimolog., 1917. [13.]
Note su Peire d'Auvergne, 1917. [13.]
La "sestina" di Guilhem de Saint Grigori, 1917. [13.]
Sordello e Reforzat, 1915. [12.]
Il Duecento. [Storia Lett. d'Italia]. la8°. Milano. [1910]
Guarino da Verona fra letterati e cortigiani a Ferrara (1429–60). [Bibl. dell' Archiv. Romanicum, s1, v1]. la8°. Ginevra. 1921
Bertram, *Benedictine, of Corbie, see* RATRAMNUS.
Bertram (*Cardinal* **Adolf).** Gesch. d. Bisthums Hildesheim. 3B. la8°. Hildesheim. 1899–1925
Bertram (Anthony). Here we ride. s8°. [1927]
Bertram (*Sir* **Anton) & H. C. Luke.** Rep. of Comm. apptd. by the Gov. of Palestine to inquire into Orthodox Patriarchate of Jerusalem. 8°. O. 1921
Bertram (Carl Julius). Britann. gentium hist. ant. scr. 3: Ricardus Corinensis, Gildas Badonicus, Nennius Banchorensis. Rec. notisque & indice auxit C. B. 8°. Havniæ. 1757
Bertram (Ernst). Heinrich v. Kleist. Rede. 8°. Bonn. 1925
Das Nornenbuch. 8°. L. 1925
Bertram (Ferdinand).
Mein Hamburg. 4T. 8°. Hamburg. [1921–23]
Bertram (James Glass) [*ps*s. W. M. COOPER; L. H. CURZON; ELLANGOWAN]. *The blue ribbon of the Turf. 8°. 1890
*A mirror of the Turf. 8°. 1892
Bertram (Oswald). Gesch. d. Cansteinschen Bibelanstalt in Halle. 8°. Halle. 1863
Bertrand (*le comte*) *ps., see* MONTHOLON (*gén.* C. J. F. T. DE).
Bertrand (*l'abbé* **Antoine-Louis)** [*ps.* A. DE LANTENAY], *see* TAMIZEY DE LARROQUE (P.) Peiresc; suppl. à la not. d'A. de L., 1893.
Bertrand (*le comte* **Henri Gratien),** *see* NAPOLEON I. Recueil de pièces authent. sur le captif de Ste.-Hélène; suivis de lettres de Comte B. &c., 12t, 1821–25.
Bertrand (Joseph Louis François).
Calcul des probabilités. 2e éd. 8°. 1907
Bertrand (Louis M. E.) [BERTRAND (ALOYSIUS), *dit Louis*].
Autour de Saint Augustin. s8°. [1921]
Cardénio, l'homme aux rubans couleur de feu. 18e éd. s8°. 1922
Devant l'Islam. s8°. [1926]
Disc. pour la récept. de L. B. [*on* M. Barrès. Rép. de J. Cambon. Acad. Fr., 25 nov. 1926. P2869]. 4°. 1926
Flaubert à Paris ou le mort vivant. [Cahiers verts, 7]. s8°. 1921
Louis XIV. [63e éd.] s8°. [1923]
Louis XIV. 86e éd. s8°. [1927]
Mlle. de Jessincourt. [5e éd.] s8°. [1917]
Œuvres poét. La volupté &c. Publ. &c. C. Sprietsma. 8°. 1926
Retour d'Egypte, *see* ŒUVRES libres, 53, 1925.
Sainte Thérèse. [39e éd.] s8°. [1927]
Les villes d'or: Algérie & Tunisie romaines. s8°. [1921]
see SPRIETSMA (C.) L. B., 1807–41, 1926.
Bertrand (Thomas Bernard), *see* HAZON (J. A.) Notice des hommes de la Faculté de Médecine de Paris; extr. (en plus gr. partie) du ms. de T. B. B., 1778.
Bertrand de Broussillon (*le comte* **Arthur),** *see* MANS. Cartul. de l'évêché du M., 965–1786; publ. par le comte B. de B., 1908.
Bertuch (Friedrich Justin). Bilderbuch zum Nutzen u. Vergnügen der Jugend. [Porte-feuille instructif &c. *Germ. & French*]. B10. 4°. Wien. 1807
Bertuchi (A. J.) The Island of Rodriguez: a Brit. colony in the Mascarenhas group. 8°. 1923
Beruete y Moret (Aureliano de), *the younger.*
Hist. de la pintura española en el siglo 19. s4°. 1926
Ioaquin Sorolla. 8°. [1919]
Spanish painting. Text by B. y M. Ed. G. Holme. [Studio Spec. No.] la8°. 1921
Velasquez. In the Prado Museum. [Art in Spain, 6. Hispanic Soc.] s8°. Barcelona. *n.d.*
Berühmte Kunststätten. s8°. L. 1908–14
see FISCHER (J. L.) Ulm, 1912. [56.]
,, HAUPT (A.) Lissabon u. Cintra, 1913. [62.]
,, †LAUTERBACH (A.) Warschau, 1918. [66.]
,, LEITSCHUH (F. F.) Bamberg, 1914. [63.]
,, MAYER (A. L.) Segovia, Avila u. El Eskorial, 1913. [61.]
see MAYER (A. L.) Toledo, 1910. [51.]
,, NEUMANN (W.) Riga u. Reval, 1908. [42.]
,, SCHILLMANN (F.) Viterbo u. Orvieto, 1911. [55.]
,, SCHMITZ (H.) Soest, 1908. [45.]
,, SCHRADER (B.) Die röm. Campagna, 1910. [49.]
Bervaldi (Josef), *see* BULIĆ (F.) & J. B. Kron. solinskih biskupa—Kron. spljetskih nadbiskupa, 1912.
Berwick (George). *Hist. coll. rel. to Belfast, *publ. G. B.*, 1817, *see* BELFAST.
Berwick (James Fitzjames, *1st duke of), marshal of France, see* ALBA (J. S. F.-J., *17th duke de*). El Mariscal de B., 1925.
Beryushina (A.)
Почему я стала коммунисткой? [P2722]. s8°. Москва. 1919
Berzeviczy (Albert). Régi emlekek 1853–70. 8°. 1907
Berzsenyi (Dániel), *1776–1836, see* GAAL (M.) B. D., 1898.
Besant (*Mrs.* **Annie).**
Initiation. repr. 8°. 1918
Psychology. [Essays & addresses, v1]. 8°. 1911
A study in karma. s8°. Adyar, Madras. *n.d.*
Thought power. Its control & culture. s8°. 1901
see CLEATHER (A. L.) H. P. BLAVATSKY: a gt. betrayal [*i.e.* Mrs. B. & the Theosoph. Soc.], 1922.
,, LÉVY (E.) Mrs. B. & the pres. crisis in the Theosoph. Soc.; tr., 1913.
Besant (Arthur Digby). Our centenary: hist. of 1st 100 yrs. of the Clerical, Medical & Gen. Life Assurance Soc. s8°. 1924
Besant (G. B.) London Bridge. s8°. [1927]
Besant (*Sir* **Walter).**
The Society of Authors: record. [P2524]. s8°. 1893
—— **& James Rice.** Sir Rich. Whittington. n. ed. s8°. 1905
Bescheiden betref. de prov. organis. d. Holland. lakenbereiders, 1917, *see* POSTHUMUS (N. W.), *ed.*
Beschius (Constantinus Josephus). [BESCHI]. A grammar of the common dialect of the Tamulian language &c. Tr. C. H. Horst. 8°. Vepery. 1806
Gramm. Latino-Tamulica ad usum missionarum S. J. s8°. Trangambariæ. 1738
Beschlüsse d. 2ten Synode d. Altkatholiken d. deut. Reiches, 1875, *see* ALTKATHOLIKEN.
Beschreibendes Verzeichnis d. illum. Hss. in Osterreich, B1–8, 1905–27, *see* WICKHOFF (F.), *ed.*
***Beschrijving** van een exemplar van de Biblia Pauperum &c., 1839, *see* BIBLIA PAUPERUM.
Beselin (Laurentius Christian). In periocham Flavii Josephi de Jesu Christo exercit., præs. J. A. Bosio. [P2637]. s4°. Jenæ. 1673
Beslay (François). *Voyage aux pays rouges. s8°. 1873
Beslière (Jean). Marguerite Fauquenoy. Roman. s8°. [1924]
Besnard (Albert). Sous le ciel de Rome. Intr. de M. Prévost. s8°. [1925]
Besnier (Georges), *see* LEXOVIENNES. Études lex., t1, par G. B. &c., 1915.
Besold (Christoph) [†BESOLDUS (CHRISTOPHORUS)]. Axiomatum philosophiæ Christianæ. p. 1a. [*b. w.* Fulevius (J.) Diss. jurid., 1627]. s8°. Argentorati. 1628
De nuptiis jurid.-polit. discursus. s4°. Tubingæ. 1621
Besongne (Nicolas), *see* FRANCE. L'État de la Fr.; [ed. N. B.], 5t, 1727.
Besplas (Joseph Marie Gros de), *see* GROS DE BESPLAS (J. M.)
Bessarion (*card.* **Joannes),** *abp. of Nice, aft. of Siponto or Manfredonia.* Oratio ad Grçcos, B. interp.; ejusdem epistola de successu Synodi ac de Spiritus Sancti processione, *see* FLORENCE, *Council of.* Acta, 1526.

Besse (Joseph). *Brief acc. of many of the persecutions of Quakers in Exchequer, Eccl. & o. Courts. 8º. 1736
*Vindic. of Brief acc. of many persecutions &c. [by J. B.] shewing fallacy &c. of late Exam. thereof [by T. Hayter]. 8º. 1737
„ „ [*a. ed. b. w. h.* Brief acc. &c., 1736]. 8º. 1741
see HAYTER (T.), *bp.* *Exam. of bk. pr. by Quakers [& ed. J. B.], ent. Brief acc. of many persec. &c., 1741.

Bessel (Friedr. Wilhelm), *see* WATSON (G. N.) Treatise on the theory of B. functions, 1922.

Besses (Luis). Dicc. de argot español. s8º. Barcelona. *n.d.*

Besson (Emmanuel). Le contrôle des budgets en France & à l'étranger. 2e éd. 8º. 1901

Best (The) short stories of 1924, 1925, 1926, 1927, *see* O'BRIEN (E. J.) & J. COURNOS, *edd.*

Best (Elsdon). The Maori. [Polynesian Soc. Mem., v5]. 2v. 8º. Wellington, N.Z. 1924

Best (Harry).
The blind. Their condition &c. in the U.S. 8º. N.Y. 1919

Best (*Hon.* James William). Indian Shikar notes, w. spec. ref. to the C. Prov. 2nd ed. s8º. Allahabad. 1922

Best (Mary Agnes). Thomas Paine. 8º. [1927]

Best (R. H.) & C. K. Ogden. Problem of the continuation school, & its solution in Germany. Intr. by G. Kerschensteiner. 8º. 1914

Besta (Enrico). La cattura dei Veneziani in Oriente &c. [*Extr. f.* Antologia Veneta, v1. P2835]. 8º. Feltre. 1900
Il diritto e le leggi civ. di Venezia [–1205]. 8º. Venezia. 1900
Nuove richerche sul Chronicon Altinate. [Estr. d. Nuovo Archivio Veneto, N.S., v15]. 8º. Venezia. 1908
Tomaso Diplovataccio e l'opera sua. 8º. Venezia. 1903

Bestaux (Eugène).
Bibliographie tchèque. Fasc. 1. 8º. Prague. 1920

Beste (John Richard Digby) [†BEST (J. R.), *aft. J. R. Beste, aft. J. R. Digby Beste*]. *Transalpine memoirs; or, anecdotes &c. of Italy &c. By an Eng. Catholic. [2v. *in* 1]. s8º. Bath. 1826

Besterman (Theodore), *see* BARRETT (*Sir* W. F.) & T. B. The divining-rod, 1926.

***Bestrebungen (Die)** für e. wirtschaftl. Annäherung Deutschlands u. Oesterr.-Ungarns. Hrsg. v. Vorstand d. sozialdemokrat. Partei Deutschl. [P2492]. 8º. 1916

Bestujev (Aleksandr Aleksandrovich), *1797–1837*, *see* BESTUJEV (N. A.) Памяти братьей Б., *n.d.*

Bestujev (Nikolai Aleksandrovich), *1791–1855.* Памяти братьей Бестужевыхъ. Издържки изъ соврем. записокъ Декабристовъ. [*b. w.* Trubetskoi (S. P.) Записки, 1874]. 2ое изд. s8º. Лейпцигъ. *n.d.*

***Besuch** (Ein) bei L. Lateau, 1875, *see* LATEAU (A. L.)

Betendorf (João Felippe). Chronica da missão dos padres da Comp. de Jesus no Maranhão, *see* INSTITUTO HIST. &C. BRAZIL. Rev., t72, 1910.

Beth (Carl). Einfürhrung in d. vergleich. Religionsgesch. [Aus Natur u. Geisteswelt, 658, B.] s8º. L. 1920

Betham-Edwards (*Miss* Matilda). Mid-Victorian mem. With personal sketch by S. Grand. 8º. 1919

Bethe (Erich). Die Ichneutai d. Sophokles, *see* KÖNIGL.-SÄCHS. GESELLS. D. WISS. Berichte, phil.-hist. Kl., B71, 1919.

Bethel (Slingsby). *The interest of princes & states. s8º. 1680
*The providences of God obs. thr. several ages tow. this nation. [*tp. wanting.* P2663]. s4º. [1691?]
*The world's mistake in O. Cromwell &c. s8º. 1668

Bethell (Alfred James).
Cleopatra to Christ. [*Typed notes.* 4v. in 2]. sfol. [1921]

Bethell (*Col.* Henry Arthur).
Modern guns & gunnery. 8º. Woolwich. 1905
„ „ ....[2nd ed.] 8º. Woolwich. 1907
„ „ ....[3rd ed.] 8º. Woolwich. 1910

Bethell (Thomas). A letter to J. Atley, late preacher &c. to J. Wesley. Setting forth his ingratitude &c. [P449]. 8º. 1788

Bethge (Hans).
Deut. Lyrik seit Liliencron. Hrsg. H. B. s8º. L. [1921]
Jens Peter Jacobsen. Ein Versuch. 8º. 1920

Bethleem (Louis).
Romans à lire & romans à proscrire. 8e éd. s8º. 1922

Bethlen (Wolffgangus de). Hist. de rebus Transsylvanicis. ed. 2a. 6v. 8º. Cibinii. 1782–93

Bethmann Hollweg (Theobald v.)
Betrachtungen zum Weltkriege. T2. 8º. 1921
Kriegsreden. Hrsg. &c. F. Thimme. 8º. St. 1919
Reflections on the World War. Tr. G. Young. pl [*no more publd.*] 8º. [1920]

Bethmann Hollweg (Theobald v.) [*continued*].
see KÖTSCHKE (H.) Unser Reichskanzler [*i.e.* T. v. B. H.), s. Leben u. Wirken, 1921.
„ LIEBIG (H. v.) B.-H. &c. (Reichsverderber, T1), 1922.
see LIEBIG (H. v.) Die Politik v. B. H., 1919.
„ PAYER (F.) Von B. H. bis Ebert, 1923.

Béthune (Conon de), *see* QUÈNES *de Béthune.*

Bethune-Baker (James Franklin), *form. J. F. Baker.*
The way of modernism & o. essays. 8º. C. 1927
see MATTHEWS (W. R.), *ed.* King's Coll. lect. on immortality; by J. F. B.-B. &c., 1920.

Betrachtung. *B. v. d. mittl. Zustand d. Seelen; *tr.*, 1703, *see* WHITE (T.)

Betrone (Annibale), *see* PASELLA (G.) A. B., 1920.

Bett (Henry). Johannes Scotus Erigena. 8º. C. 1925

Bettag (Franz). Die Eroberung v. Nowo Georgiewsk. [Schlachten d. Weltkrieges, H4]. 8º. Oldenburg i. O. 1921

Bettany (Frederick George). Stewart Headlam: a biog. 8º. 1926

Bettelheim (Anton), *see* NEUE Österreichische Biog., 1815–1918, geleitet v. A. B., Abt. 1, B1–4, Abt. 2., 1923–27.

Betterton (Thomas). *Life of T. B. [by C. Gildon], w. the judgment of Mons. de St. Evremond upon the Ital. &c. music &c. Added, The amorous widow, a comedy, by B. s8º. 1710
see ODELL (G. C. D.) Shakespeare f. B. to Irving, 2v, 1920.

Bettignies (Louise M. J. H. de).
see REDIER (A. J. L.) La guerre des femmes: L. de B. &c., 1924.
„ —— Story of L. de B.; tr., 1926.

Bettoni-Cazzago (*il conte* Francesco).
see FÈ D'OSTIANI (L. F.) Commem. del Conte F. B., 1901.

Betts (John). The story of the Irish Society. 2nd ed. 8º. 1921

Betussi (Giuseppe). Descr. d. Cataio, luogo d. march. P E. degli Obizi. Con l'agg. d. co. F. Berni. Ristamp. con l'ind. d. p. A. Libanori. 8º. Ferrara. 1669
Ragionamento sopra il Cathaio; luogo d. ill. S. P. E. Obizzi. s4º. Padova. 1673

Beucler (André). Sept francs cinquante la ligne, roman, *see* ŒUVRES libres, 70, 1927.
La ville anonyme. s8º. [1925]

Beugnot (*le cte.* Arthur Auguste). Rapport sur l'instruction publ. [Assemblée Nat. Législ. *no tp.* P2558]. 8º. 1849

Beumelburg (Werner). Douaumont. [Schlachten d. Weltkrieges, B1 (=B8 d. 1. A.)]. 2. A. 8º. Oldenburg. 1925
Loretto. Dargestellt v. W. B., auf Grund e. hist. Studie v. W. Fürstner. [Schlachten d. Weltkrieges, B17]. 8º. Oldenburg i. O. 1927
Ypern, 1914. [Schlachten d. Weltkrieges, B10]. 8º. Oldenburg i. O. 1926

Beumer (Ph. Jak.)
Der kleine Schriftleser. 14e A. 8º. Düsseldorf. *n.d.*

Beumler (Marcus). Ad J. Andreæ triplex scriptum. Falconis complementum &c. [*b. w.* Grabe (J.) Isagoge &c. 1586]. s4º. Neostadii Palatin. 1586

Beurlin (Jacob), *Prof. of theology at Tübingen.* Refutatio Sotici scripti, *see* CHRISTOPH, *Herzog zu Würtemberg.* Confessio, t2, 1561.

Beusch (Gulielmus). Tract. de pactis & contractibus in genere, *see* MIGNE (J. P.), *ed.* Theol. cursus, t16, 1859.

Beusch (Paul). Staatsbetrieb oder Privatbetrieb. [P2409]. 8º. M. Gladbach. 1919

Beuter (Pedro Antonio). Prima [*&* Segunda] parte de la coronica gen. de España y espec. del reyno de Valencia. [*sep. tp. & pagin., tp. of pl. mutilated*]. sfol. Valencia. 1604

Beuthen. Die deut. Stadt B. o/S u. i. nächste Umgeb. Hrsg. v. K. Kasperkowitz im Auftr. d. Magistrats &c. [Monogr. deut. Städte, B15]. la8º. 1925

Bevan (Edwyn Robert). Hellenism & Xty. 8º. [1921]
Hist. of Egypt under the Ptolemaic dynasty. 8º. [1927]
Jerusalem under the high-priests. 5 lect. on period betw. Nehemiah & the New Test. 5th impr. 8º. 1924
Later Greek religion. 8º. 1927
A memoir of Leslie Johnston. s8º. 1921
see BURY (J. B.) Hellenistic age; by J. B. B., E. B. &c., 1923.
—— **& C. Singer.** The legacy of Israel. Essays by Sir G. A. Smith, E. Bevan, F. C. Burkitt &c. Planned by I. Abrahams. Ed. E. R. B. & C. S. Intr. by [A. D. Lindsay]. 8º. O. 1927

Beveridge (William), *bp. of St. Asaph* [BEVEREGIUS (G.)]. Συνοδικόν, sive Pandectæ canonum SS. Apostolorum & conciliorum ab eccl. Græca recept. Guil. B. rec. &c. 2t. lafol. Oxonii. 1672

Beveridge (*Sir* **William Henry).**
The public service in war & in peace. [P2435]. s8°. 1920
see HILL (*Sir* N.) &c. War & insurance, 1927.

Beverley (Robert), *of Virginia.* *The hist. of Virginia. [*Engr. tp. has.* By R. B., gent.]
2nd ed. rev. & enl. 4p [in 1v. *pagin. contin.*] 8°. 1722

Bevir (Joseph Louis). The making of Wellington College. First 16 yrs. of its existence. Intr. by Sir Ian Hamilton. 8°. 1920

Bevis (J. F.) & H. J. Jeffery.
Brit. plants: biology & ecology. 2nd ed. rev. & enl. 8°. [1920]

Bewes (Wyndham Anstis). Romance of the law merchant: intr. to st. of internat. & commerc. law. Foreword by Sir R. Atkin. 8°. 1923

Bewick (John), *see* BEWICK (T.) & J. B. Sel. fables, w. cuts by T. & J. B., 1822.

Bewick (Thomas). Memoir of T. B., wr. by himself, 1822–28. Intr. by S. Image. 8°. [1924]
—— **& J. Bewick.** Select fables. With cuts, by T. & J. B. & others; w. mem. & descr. cat. of wks. 8°. 1822

Bewicke-Copley (Robert G. W.), *baron Cromwell, see* CROMWELL.

Bews (John William). An intr. to the flora of Natal & Zululand. 8°. Pietermaritzburg. 1921

Bewsher (Paul).
"Green balls": adv. of a night-bomber. 8°. 1919

Beyens (*le baron* **Eugène).** Le roi Albert, *see* CAHIERS BELGES, No. 28, 1919.
Le Second Empire vu par un diplom. belge.
2t. 8°. Lille *&* Bruges. 1924–26

Beyer (Absolon Pederssøn). Om Norgis rige (1567), *see* STORM (G.), *ed.* Hist.-top. Skr., 1895.

Beyer (August), *Pastor of Zörbich.* Arcana sacra bibliothec. Dresdensium [& Cont. 1 & 2 *in* 1v. *pagin. cont.*]
8°. Dresdæ. 1738–39
Memoriæ hist.-crit. librorum rariorum. Acc. Evangelii Cosmopololitani notæ ad J. B. Menckenii de charletaneria eruditorum &c. s8°. Dresdæ. 1734

Beyer (Georg). De utili & necessaria autorum juridic. & juris arti inserv. notitia. 2ª ed. s8°. Lipsiæ. 1726
see JENICHEN (G. A.) Contin. Notit. auct. juridic. &c. quam olim evulgavit G. B., 1738.

Beyer (Harald). Søren Kierkegaard. 8°. Oslo. 1925

Beyer (Hermann Wolfgang).
Der syrische Kirchenbau. 4°. 1925

Beyer (Oskar). Die Katakombenwelt. 8°. Tübingen. 1927

Beyerle (Konrad). Die Kultur d. Abtei Reichenau. [Von P. P. Albert, H. Baier &c.; hrsg. K. B.] 2 Halbb. [*pagin. cont.*]
4°. München. 1925

Beyle (Marie Henri) [*ps.* STENDHAL; *&* L. A. C. BOMBET].
The abbess of Castro & o. tales. Tr. C. K. S. Moncrieff. s8°. [1926]
Armance, ou quelques scènes d'un salon de Paris en 1827. Texte établi &c. par R. Lebègue. Préf. de A. Gide. [Œuvres compl.] 8°. *Champion.* 1925
La Chartreuse de Parme. Texte revu sur l'éd. orig. & publ. avec des add. & notes. Préf. A. van Bever. [2ᵉ éd.] 2t. s8°. 1922
The Charterhouse of Parma. [Pref. by Balzac's study of S. &c.] Tr. C. K. Scott-Moncrieff. 2v. s8°. [1926]
Chroniques italiennes. Ed. établie par R. L. Doyon. 2t. s8°. *La Connaissance.* 1921
*De l'amour. s8°. Londres. *n.d.*
„ „ éd. rev. & corr. préc., d'une ét. par Sainte-Beuve. s8°. [1920]
„ „ Texte établi &c. par D. Muller & P. Jourda. Préf. de E. Rey. [Œ. compl.] 2t. 8°. *Champion.* 1926
Hist. de la peinture en Italie. Texte établi &c. avec préf. &c. par P. Arbelet. [Œ. compl.] 2t. 8°. *Champion.* 1924
Journal. Texte établi & annoté par H. Debraye & L. Royer. [Œ. compl.] t1. 8°. *Champion.* 1923 1, 1801–05.
The life of Henri Brulard. Tr. C. A. Phillips. Intr. by H. C. Block. 8°. [1925]
Lucien Leuwen. Texte établi &c. par H. Debraye. Préf. de P. Valéry. [Œ. compl.] 4t. 8°. *Champion.* 1926–27
Une position sociale. Intr. &c. par H. Debraye. 8°. [1927]
Racine & Shakespeare. Texte établi & annoté avec préf. &c. par P. Martino. [Œ. compl.] 2t. 8°. *Champion.* 1925
Rome, Naples & Florence. Texte établi & annoté par D. Muller. Préf. de C. Maurras. [Œ. compl.] 2t. 8°. *Champion.* 1919
„ „ ....s8°. [1925]
Le rouge & le noir. éd. compl., rev. &c. s8°. [1909 ?]
„ „ éd. compl., rev. &c. s8°. [1925]
Scarlet & black. Tr. C. K. Scott-Moncrieff. 2v. s8°. [1927]
Vie de Rossini; suivie des Notes d'un dilettante. Texte établi & annoté, avec préf. &c. par H. Prunières. [Œ. compl.] 2t. 8°. *Champion.* 1922

Beyle (Marie Henri) [*continued*].
see ARBELET (P.) La jeunesse de Stendhal &c., 2t, 1919.
„ —— S. épicier, 1926.
„ BOURGET (P.) Stendhal: discours, 28 juin 1920 à l'inaug. du monument, 1920.
see CHAMPION (E.) Hommage à Stendhal, 1920.
„ DUMOLARD (H.) Le véritable Julien Sorel [*i.e.* H. Berthet], 1927.
„ HAZARD (P.) Vie de Stendhal, 6ᵉ éd., 1927.

Beyrlin (Jacob). Antiquit. quæd. Palat. ex J. Agricolæ viridario &c. coll., *see* MIEG (J. R.) Monumenta, 1701.

Bez (Johann Philipp). Septem primos diaconos, sub præs. D. G. Molleri, exam. subjicit J. P. B.
[P432]. s4°. [Altdorfi. 1696]

Beza (M.) Papers on the Rumanian people & lit. Pref. by M. Gaster. 8°. 1920

Beza (T.) [†BÈZE (THEODORE DE)].
Ad tractat. de ministrorum Evang. gradibus ab H. Saravia ed. T. B. resp. [*b. w. h.* Tract. de vera excomm., 1590].
ed. 2ª. s8°. [Geneva] *Le Preux.* 1593
A briefe & pithy summe of the Christian fayth &c.; tr. f. French by R. Fyll. [*Wanting tp. & 2 last leaves*].
s8°. 1585
Confessio Christ. fidei, & ejusdem collatio cum Papisticis hæresibus. Adj. altera brevis conf. s8°. Genevæ. 1577
Conf. de la foy chrest. cont. la confirm. & la refut. des superstitions. s8°. Geneve, *P. Patac.* 1563
„ „ 6ᵉ éd. revue &c. s8°. Geneve, *F. Jaquy.* 1563
De hypostatica duarum in Christi naturarum unione discept. J. B. cum D. J. Pappo. s8°. Genevæ. 1579
*De Iuvenilibus T. Bezæ poematis epistola ad N. C. qua Maimburgius &c. confut. s8°. Amstelodami. 1683
De vera pronuntiatione Gr. & Latinæ linguæ, comm. primus, de pronunt. Græcæ linguæ T. B. [J. Ceratini De sono literarum —A. Mekerchi De veteri & recta pronunt.—Apologeticum pro vet. ac Germ. ling. Græcæ pronunt. [*by* H. Estiene]—J. Lipsii de recta pronunt. Lat. ling. dialog.]
3p. s8°. [Paris], *H. Stephanus.* 1587
Epicedia, quæ aliquot viri &c. T. Bezæ scr. in ipsius obitum [*Hebr., Gr. & Lat.*] [P2647]. s4°. Genevæ. 1606
Iob expounded by T. B. Tr. s8°. C. [1589 ?]
Poemata varia: Sylvæ — Epitaphia — Icones — Cato — Elegiæ — Epigrammata—Emblemata—Censoribus.
s4°. Genevæ, *P. Chouët.* 1597
Psalmorum Davidis & aliorum prophetarum libri 5; argumentis & Lat. paraphrasi illust. s8°. [Londini], *T. Vautrollerius.* 1580
„ „ [*a. ed.*] s8°. Antverpiæ. *N. Barius.* 1580
Tractatus de vera excommunicatione & christiano Presbyterio, T. Erasti centum mss. thes. oppositus & ed. s8°. Londini. 1590
Vie de J. Calvin. n. éd., publ. &c. par A. Franklin. s8°. 1864
see ANDREÆ (J.) Acta colloquii Montis Belligart. [1587], inter J. A. & T. B., 1594.
„ —— Assertio &c. qua resp. ad prim. partem libri T. Beze &c., 1565.
„ BALDUIN (FRANÇOIS) Resp. ad Calvinum & B., 1564.
„ BIBLE: N. T. GR. Codex T. B.; ed. &c. T. Kipling, 2p, 1793.
„ —— —— Τῆς Καινῆς Διαθήκης ἅπαντα, Lat. à T. B. vers. cum annotˢ., 1559.
„ BRUTUS (S. J.), *ps.* Vindiciæ c. tyrannos, *attrib. to B.*, 1660.
„ CONFESSION. *Conf. oder Bekañtnuss &c. Item Eine Kurtze Conf. T. Beze, 1553.
„ LA FAYE (A. DE). De vita & obitu T. B., 1606.
„ MAROT (C.) *&* T. B. Les pseaumes mis en rime franç., 1563.

Bezobrazov (Vladimir Pavlovich). Народное хозяйство Россiи московск. промышл. областъ. чl [*with* Приложенiя, *w. sep. pagin.*]
la8°. C.-П. 1882

Bezrabotny (J.) Les deux révolutions. [P2396]. 8°. *n.p. n.d.*

Bezzi (Mario), *see* BRITISH MUSEUM OF NAT. HIST.: ZOOLOGY. Bombyliidæ of the Ethiopian region, by M. B., 1924.

Bhagavadgītā.
The Bhagavat-Geeta or dialogues of Krishna & Arjoon in 18 lectures. Sanscrit, Canarese & Eng. parallel colˢ. With app. [*sep. pagin.*] cont. Schlegel's Lat. tr., Notes f. Germ. of Humboldt, [Essay by R. D. Griffith] &c. Ed. J. Garrett. 4°. Bangalore. 1846
Bhagavad-Gītā. Tr. L. D. Barnett. [Temple Classics]. s8°. 1905
La Bhagavadgîtâ. Tr. avec intr. par E. Senart. [Les classiques de l'Orient; publ. V. Goloubew, v6]. 8°. 1922
The song celestial, or Bhagavadgîtâ. Tr. [*into verse*] by E. Arnold. 4th ed. 8°. 1889
see OXLEY (W.) Philos. of spirit, illust. by new vers. of B., 2nd ed., 1903.
„ SAUNDERS (K.) The gospel for Asia, 1928.

Bhámada, *see* VARARUCHI. Pràkrita-Prakásá, or, Prákrit gramm., w. comm. of B. &c., 1854.

Bhandarkar (Devadatta Ramkrishna). Arch. remains & excav. at Nagari, *see* INDIA. ARCH. SURVEY. Mem., No. 4, 1920.
Asoka. [Carmighael Lectures, 1923]. 8°. Calcutta. 1925

Bhandarkar (*Sir* **Ramkrishna Gopal**). Vaiṣṇavism, Śaivism & minor relig. systems. [Grundriss d. Indo-Arischen Philol. u. Alt., B3, H6]. la8°. Strassburg. 1913

Bhasa, *Indian playwright, see* SASTRI (H.) B. & authorship of 13 Trivandrum plays, 1926.

Bhaṭṭa-svāmin. B.-S.'s comm. on Kauṭilya's Artha-śāstra. Ed. K. P. Jayaswal & A. Banerji-Sástri. [*Extr. f.* Bihar &c. Research Soc. Journal, v11 & 12]. la8°. 1925–26

Biadego (Giuseppe).
Borgolecco. [Estr. d. Atti dell' Accad. d'Agric. &c. di Verona, s4, v17. P2621]. 8°. Verona. 1916
Cat. descritt. dei mss. d. Bibl. di Verona [by B.], 1892, *see* VERONA.
La fiorentina famiglia Ervari trapiantata a Verona, il poeta Donato e il pittore Ranuccio. [Estr. da Madonna Verona, a. 9. P2621]. 8°. Verona.1915
Medici Veronesi e una libreria medica del sec. 14. [*Fr.* Atti del. Reale Istit. Ven., t75. P2621]. 8°. Venezia. 1916
Per il primo centenario d. Bibl. Comunale di Verona. Discorso. [P2706]. 8°. Verona. 1892
Storia d. Bibl. Comunale di Verona. 8°. Verona. 1892
Tre documenti Scaligeri rig. Spinetta Malaspina. [Estr. d. Miscellanea di studi storici in onore di G. Sforza]. [P2701]. la8°. Lucca. 1915

Biadene (Leandro).
Ind. d. canzone ital. d. sec. 13. 8°. Asolo. 1896

Biagi (Guido). Biblioteca umanistica: coll. di scr. ined. o rare del 15° sec. e ant. Dir. da G. B. [Ser. 1, 1–2]. la8°. Milano. 1925
La Renaissance en Italie. Architect. & decor., 1e époque. fol. [1921]
see DANTE ALIGHIERI. La Divina Commedia; n. figurazione e nel secolare comm. a cura di G. B., v1, 1924.

Bianca, *dssa. di Monferrato, see* MONFERRATO (B., *dssa.* DI).

Bianchi. Nuove regole per la real Confr. de' B. col titolo della S. Croce, 1768, *see* CONFRATERNITA.

Bianchi (A. G.) Il Senatore L. Albertini. la8°. Milano. 1919

Bianchi (Andrea), *see* BLANC (D.), *ps.*

Bianchi (Martha Dickinson).
Life & letters of Emily Dickinson. 8°. [1924]

Bianchi (Mosè), *1840–1904, see* SAPORI (F.) Maestri dell' arte, No. 17, 1919.

Bianchi (Nicomede). I ducati Estensi, 1815–50. Con doc. ined. 2v. s8°. Torino. 1852

Bianchi (Raymundus), *see* AQUINAS (TH.) Vera S. Th. A. sententia de infallibilitate &c., refut. eorum quæ R. B. scr., 1870.

Bianchi Bandinelli (R.) Clusium: ricerche arch. e topog. su Chiusi &c. en età etrusca, *see* REALE ACCAD. DEI LINCEI. Mon. ant., t30, 1925.

Bianchi-Giovini (Aurelio). Il papa e la sua corte, ricordi ined. d'un carabiniere &c. Pubbl. A. B.-G. [P504]. s8°. 1860

Bianchini (Giuseppe Maria) [BLANCHINUS]. Vindiciæ canonic. scripturarum vulgatæ Lat. ed., fragm. &c. ed. opera J. Blanchini. [*Foll. by* Psalterium duplex cum canticis *w. sep. pagin.*] fol. Romæ. 1740

Bianchini (Ludovico), *see* VINCENTIIS (E. DE). Caduta d. monarchia borbon. in un' op. ined. di L. B., 1925.

Bianco (Andrea). Planisferio, 1436, n. Marciana di Venezia. [*Facs.*] Nota illust. d. c. P. Amat di San Filippo [*Extr. f.* Rivista Marittima]. [P2835]. 8°. *n.d.*

Bianco (Jose). Vida de las instit. polit. s8°. Buenos Aires. 1919

Bianquis (Geneviève). La poésie autrich. de Hofmannsthal à Rilke. 8°. 1926

Bianŭ (Joanŭ C.), *see* ACADEMIA ROMÂNA. Bibl. Acad. R. Cat. mss. românești; intocmit de J. B. &c., t2, 1913.
—— **& N. Hodos.**
Bibliografia româneascǎ veche, 1508–1830. Ed. Acad. Româna. t2, 1717–1808. [*no tp.*] fol. 1905–10

Biarnay (S.) & A. Péretié. Recherches archéolog. au Maroc, *see* MISSION SCIENT. DU MAROC. Archives, v18, 1912.

Biasutti (Renato) & G. Dainelli. I tipi umani, *see* FILIPPI (F. DE). Rel. scientif. d. Spediz. Ital. de F. nell' Himàlaia &c., s2, v9, 1925.

Bibby, *The family of, see* READE (A. L.) The Mellards &c., incl. the B. of Liverpool, 1915.

Biberstein Kazimirski (A. de), *see* KAZIMIRSKI (A. DE B.)

Bibesco (*pcsse.* **Elizabeth),** *wife of Prince Antoine Bibesco, née Asquith.* Balloons. [2nd ed.] s8°. *n.d.*
I have only myself to blame. s8°. 1922

Bibesco (*pcsse.* **M.),** *wife of Pr. Georges V. Bibesco.*
Catherine-Paris. [Les cahiers verts]. s8°. 1927
Les huit paradis. s8°. 1925
Isvor, le pays des saules. 2t. s8°. [1923]
Le perroquet vert. s8°. [1924]

Bibl (Viktor). Kaiser Franz u. s. Erbe. [Der Zerfall Österreichs]. 8°. Wien. 1922
Metternich in neu. Beleuchtung. Sein geheimer Briefwechsel mit Wrede &c. [1831–34]. la8°. Wien. 1928

Bible. *The Bible is arranged as follows:—firstly, Complete Texts in English arranged chronologically, & then gen. comm*[s]*. in alphabetical order, after which the various Books & Divisions of the Bible & Languages follow in one alphabetical order.*

COMPLETE ENGLISH TEXTS, *see also* POLYGLOT *below.*
The Holy Scriptures, tr. by M. Coverdale, 1535. Repr. f. copy in library of the Duke of Sussex. la8°. 1838
The Byble, whych is all the holy Scripture &c., tr. into Englishe by Thomas Matthewe, 1537. [*b. in* 2v]. fol. *T. Raynalde & W. Hyll.* 1549
Imperfect. wanting tp. & most of prelimin. pages as also most of the table of Epistles & Gospels &c. Some pages supplied in MS. The N.T. has sep. tp. & foliation.
The Holy Byble. [*Bishop's Bible. Rev. under the superintendence of abp. Parker. 5 foliations & prelim. matter*]. fol. *J. Walley.* 1575
The Bible. [*Genevan version. tp. & prelim. leaves wanting & otherwise imperfect*]. sfol. *C. Barker.* 1576
[The Bible w. annot. & concord. *tp. wanting, also ff. Ai–iii & Aviii of prelim. (Bk. of C. P.); ff. 217, 344–52, 409; f. Ai of the Tables. Prelim. & Tables have no pagin. N.T. has sep. tp.*] s4°. *C. Barker.* 1585
The Bible. [*Geneva vers. without* Apocrypha; *w.* Tomson's rev. N.T., & F. Junius' Annotat[s]. upon Revelation. *Engr. tp.*] [3p *in* 1v]. s4°. 1599
The Holie Bible tr. &c., w. arguments of the Books &c. [Old Test. & Apoc.] 2v [v2 *has t.* The second tome of the Holie Bible]. 8°. Doway. 1609–10
The Holy Bible. [*Tp. & some prelim. leaves wanting*]. fol. *R. Barker.* 1611
The 1st ed. of King James's Bible, "Authorised" version. "He" Bible.
The Holy Bible. [*Prec. by* Genealogies, map &c. *Foll*[d]*. by* Psalmes, by Sternhold & Hopkins, 1612]. s8°. *R. Barker.* 1612
The first 8°. ed. of King James's version; pr. in Roman type. Fol. A1 wanting before the Genealogies.
The Holy Bible. s4°. *R. Barker.* 1613
The first black-letter ed. of King James's version.
The Holy Bible. [*Prec. by* Bk. of C.P., 1621]. s4°. *Norton & Bill.* 1625
Both titles dated 1625, but colophon has date 1624. Both tps. omit the words: Appointed &c.
The Holy Bible. s4°. C. *Printers to the Univ.* 1637
The Holy Bible. fol. C. *Buck & Daniel.* 1638
Corr. Cambridge Bible, rev. by Ward, Goad of Hadley, Boyse &c.
The Holy Bible. s8°. Amsterdam, *John Canne.* 1647
First Eng. Bible w. full marginal references.
The Holy Bible. s4°. C. *J. Field.* 1668
The N.T. is dated 1666. Sometimes known as the "Preaching Bible." Dedication wanting.
The Holy Bible. Newly tr., w. former tr[s]. compared & revised. [*b. w.* Prayer-Book. Bk. of C.P., 1726]. 4°. O. 1727
The Holy Bible, tr. f. Lat. Vulg. O.T. first publ. at Doway, 1609; N.T. at Rhemes, 1582 &c. 5th ed. rev. & corr. acc. to Clementin ed. 4°. D. 1791
The Holy Bible. la8°. *B. & F. B. S.* 1817
The Holy Bible. An exact repr. of the author. vers., 1611. 4°. O. 1833
The Holy Bible. s8°. O. 1840
The Holy Bible. [Miniature ed.] s8°. Glasgow, *Bryce.* 1896
The Holy Bible. Two-version ed. Auth. Vers. w. diff. of Rev. Vers. pr. in margin. 8°. O. [1899]
Modern reader's (The) Bible. Ed. w. intr. & notes by R. G. Moulton. [repr.] 8°. N.Y. 1912
The Holy Bible. [Rev. version]. [5v]. 8°. O. [1881]–85
The Eng. vers. of the Polyglot Bible. 8°. *Bagster. n.d.*

GENERAL COMMENTARIES &c.
*Annot. upon the Old & New Test. by the joint-labour of certain learned divines. [J. Ley, W. Gouge, M. Casaubon & *others of the Westminster Assembly*]. fol. 1645
" " ....2nd ed., enl. [2v]. fol. 1651
Bible (La) annotée par une soc. de théolog. &c. Anc. Test. t1–3, Les prophètes. la8°. [1881–9 ?]
Bible (La) moralisée conservée à Oxford, Paris & Londres. Reprod. intég. du ms. du 13e s. Accomp. d'une notice par Cte. A. de Laborde. [Soc. Franç. de Reprod[s]. de MSS. &c.] 5t. fol. 1911–27
5, Étude, [par] le comte A. de Laborde.
*Bible (The) of every land, w. spec. n. ed. enl. 4°. *Bagster.* [1860]

Bible [*continued*].
GENERAL COMMENTARIES &c. [*continued*].
Cambridge (The) Bible for Schools & Colleges. Ed. J. J. S. Perowne &c. s8°. C. 1914–25
Ecclesiastes ; A. L. Williams, 1922.
Hebrews, Rev. vers. ; A. Nairne, 1921.
Isaiah ; J. Skinner. [2nd ed., repr.], 2v, 1922–25.
Leviticus, Rev. vers. ; A. T. Chapman & A. W. Streane, 1914.
Expositors Bible (The). Ed. W. Robertson Nicoll. s8°. 1889–90
Isaiah ; G. A. Smith, 5th ed., 2v. 1890.
Pastoral Epistles (The) ; A. Plummer, 2nd ed. 1889.
Helps to the study of the Bible. s8°. O. *n.d.*
International Critical Commentary. Ed. S. R. Driver, A. Plummer, & C. A. Briggs. 8°. E. 1920–27
Daniel ; J. A. Montgomery, 1927.
Galatians ; E. De W. Burton, 1921.
Hebrews ; J. Moffatt, 1924.
Job ; S. R. Driver & G. B. Gray [*2 pagins.*], 1921.
Pastoral Epistles (I & II Timothy & Titus) ; W. Lock, 1924.
Revelation of St. John ; R. H. Charles, 2v, 1920.
Lange (J. P.) Theolog.-homilet. Bibelwerk. Hrsg. v. L. Des Alten Test. 20T [in 8v] ; Des Neven Test. 16T [*in* 6v]. 8°. Bielefeld. 1861–78
Meyer (Heinr. Aug. W.) Crit. & exeget. comm. on the N.T. Tr. rev. by W. P. Dickson & W. Stewart. 8°. E. 1884–91
Matthew, 2v. Mark & Luke, 2v.
Wordsworth (Chr.) The Holy Bible, in A.V. With notes by W. Old Test. v2. la8°. 1867

——: REFERENCES.
see ALBERTI (J.) Periculum crit., loca quædam &c., 1727.
,, AMAMA (S.) Anti-barbarus biblicus, 1656.
,, APIN (S. J.) Hist. nat. de verit. Scripts. testimonium, 1717.
,, ARNOLD (N.) Lux in tenebris, vindic. locorum &c., 1665.
,, ARTIGNAN (J.), *ed.* Plantes de la B. d'ap. la vers. arm. du 5e s. (*in Arm.*), 1913.
,, BECANUS (M.) Analogia Vet. & N. Test., 1620.
,, BILDER-BIBEL. Curieuse 252 Bibl. Kern-Sprüche, 1687.
,, BOHLEN (P. v.) Symbolæ ad interpret. S. Cod. ex ling. Persica, 1822.
,, BONAVENTURA, *St.* Auctoritates utriusque Test., c. 1472.
,, BOYLE (R.) Some consid. t. style of H. Scr., 1668.
,, BOYS (J.) Workes, expos. of Scr. in liturgie, 1622.
,, BRENTZ (J.) Op., t1–7, Commentarii, 1576–88.
,, —— Argumenta & sacræ Scr. summa &c., 1544.
,, BRIGGS (C. A.) The B., Church & reason, 1892.
,, BROUGHTON (H.) Epistle to learned nobilitie t. transl. the B., 1597.
,, BROWN (J.) *of Wamphray.* Libri 2, in priori, Wolzogium, in lib. de interp. Scr. causam orthod. prodid. demon, 1670.
,, BUNTING (H.) Itinerarium, or travels of patriarchs &c., 1623 ; 1705.
,, BUTLER (C.) Horæ biblicæ, 1799 ; 2v, 1807.
,, BÜTTINGHAUSEN (C.) Spec. horarum Heb. & Arab. ut et obs. Biblic., 1758.
,, BUXTORFIUS (J.), *younger.* Exercit. ad hist. 1659.
,, CARPENTER (W. B.) Intr. to st. of the Scr., 1902.
,, CARPZOV (J. B.) Disput. acad., philol., exeget., polem., 1699.
,, CARPZOV (J. G.) A defence of the Hebrew Bible ; tr. M. Marcus, 1729.
,, CARYL (J.) Expos., w. pract. obs. upon Job, 1676–77.
,, CASTELLION (S.) Adnotat. Bibl. Sacr., 1738.
,, CHERUBIN DE SAINT-JOSEPH. Bibl. crit. sacræ circa Sacr. libr. difficultates, 4t, 1704–6.
,, COCCEJUS (J.) Opera, 8t, 1673 75 ; 2t, 1706.
,, COCHLÆUS (J.) De novis ex Hebr. tr. S. Scr. disceptatio, 1544.
,, COHU (J. R.) The Bible & mod. thought, 1920.
,, COX (S.) An expositor's note-book, 1889.
,, CREMER (B. S.) Typologia, 2p, 1727.
,, CROWE (W.) *Exact coll. of Eng. wr. on O. & N. T., 1663.
,, DEYLING (S.) Obs. sacr., p1, 1708 ; 3p, 1735–39.
,, DIODATI (G.) Pious annot. &c. ; tr., 2nd ed., 2p, 1648 ; 3rd ed., 1651.
,, DRUSIUS (J.), *the elder.* Animadvers. libri 2, 1585.
,, —— De quæsitis, 1595.
,, —— Quæstionum Ebraic. libri 3, 1599.
,, DUNS (J.) Bibl. nat. science, 2v, 1863–68.
,, DUPIN (L. E.) Diss. prélim. &c. sur la B., 2t, 1701.
,, —— New hist. of eccl. writers, O. & N. T. &c., 3v, 1723.
,, EPHRAIM, *St., Syrus.* Works [*in Armenian*], 4v, 1836.
,, ESTIENNE (R.) Les censures des théologiens de Paris par lesquelles ils av. cond. les B. impr. par R. E., 1552.
,, FARRAR (J.) Proper names, 2nd ed., 1844.
,, FAWTIER (R.) La B. historiée de la John Rylands Lib., 1924.
,, FOSDICK (H. E.) Mod. use of the B., 2nd ed., 1924.
,, FRANCKE (A. H.) Comm. de scopo libr. V. & N. T., 1724.
,, —— Manuductio ad lect. Scr. S., ed. 2a., 1700.
,, FULEVIUS (J.) Dissert. juridica de sacra Scr., 1628.
,, GEHE (H. C.) Sylloge comm., 1792.
,, GERARD (G.) Institutes of Bibl. crit., 2nd ed., 1808.

Bible [*continued*].
GEN. COMM. : REFERENCES [*continued*].
see GIVEN (J. J.) The truth of Scr. &c., 1881.
,, GOUGH (H.) The N.T. quotations collated w. the O.T., 1855.
,, GREGORY (J.) Works, p1, Notes, 1646–84.
,, GRETSER (J.) Admonitio de bibliis Tigurinis, 1615.
,, GRIER (R.) Ans. to Ward's errata of Prot. Bible, 1812.
,, GROTIUS (H.) Annot. in V. & N. T., 1727.
,, GUPPY (H.) Brief sketch of hist. of transmission of B., 1926.
,, GUTENBERG (J.) The G. Bible, Melk copy, sold, 1926.
,, GUYON (*Mme.* J. M.) La Ste Bible, avec explics. &c., 20t, 1790.
,, HAGEMANN (J. G.) Nachr. v. d. fürnehm. Übersetz. d. Heil. Schr. in a. Spr., 1750.
,, HARDESHEIM (C.) *Consensus orthod. Sacræ Scr. & Vet. Eccl., de sententia &c. verborum Cœnæ Dom., 1578.
,, HARMER (T.) Obs. on passages of Scr., 4v, 1776–87.
,, HARRIS (T. M.) The natural hist. of the B. &c., 1824.
,, HASTINGS (J.), *ed.* Great texts of the B., 20v *&* Index, 1910–19.
,, HEBENSTREIT (C. W.) *Obs. ad moralem Libr. Sacr., 1796.
,, HENDERSON (E.) Bibl. researches &c., in Russia, 1826.
,, HENDEWERK (C. L.) Princ. ethica, in V. & N. T. obvia, 1833.
,, HIRT (J. F.) Varia sacra, 1776.
,, HOTTINGER (J. H.) Thesaurus philol. seu Clavis Scr. &c., 1696.
,, HULDRICH (J. J.) Vindic. pro Bibl. tr. Tigurina, 1616.
,, IKEN (C.) Dissert. philolog.-theol. in div. Sacri Cod. loca, 2v, 1749–70.
,, ISIDORE, *of Pelusium, St.* De interpret. div. Scr. epist. libri 4, 1605.
,, JAMES (T.) A treatise of the corruption of Scr. by the Ch. of Rome, 1611.
,, JOHN RYLANDS LIBRARY. Cat. of exhib. illust. hist. of transmission of the B., 1925.
,, JOHNSON (A.) Hist. acc. of sev. Eng. trans. of the B., 1730.
,, JONGE (B. DE). Theatr. princip. V. & N. T., 1627.
,, KEACH (B.) Τροπολογία ; Scr. metaphors, 1779.
,, KENT (C. F.) Makers & teachers of Judaism, 1911.
,, KILBER (H.) Analysis Bibl., 2a ed., 2t, 1856.
,, KIS (S.) Tabulæ analyt., 1592.
,, KITCHIN (J. G.) B. student in the B. M., 1893.
,, LAMY (B.) Apparatus Bibl., 1723.
,, LE CÈNE (C.) Essay for new tr. of the B. ; tr. H. Ross, 1702.
,, LE MAIRE (N.) Sanctuarium profanis occlusum, 1662.
,, LESTER (G.) Lord Tennyson & the B., 1891.
,, LIBENS (J.) Theses proleg. ad sacr. scr., 1720.
,, LIGHTFOOT (J. B.) Bibl. essays, 2nd ed., 1904.
,, LILIENTHAL (M.) Bibl. exeget. Bibl., 1748.
,, LINDANUS (W. D.) De optimo Scr. interp. gen. lib. 3, 1558.
,, MACGHEE (R. J.) Compl. notes of the Doway B. &c., 1837.
,, MARCHESINUS (J.) *Mamotrectus super B., 1479.
,, MARTIN (G.) Discoverie of corruptions of the Holy Scr., 1582.
,, MARTIN (J.) Explic. de plus. textes difficiles, 1730.
,, MENSCH (H.) Eng. trans. of the B., 1862.
,, MEYER (L.) Philosophia Scr. interpres, ed. J. S. Semler, 1776.
,, MOULTON (W. F.) Hist. of the Eng. B., 2nd ed., 1884.
,, NIEREMBERG (J. E.) De orig. Sacræ Scr. lib. 20, 1641.
,, ORIGEN. In sacras Scr. comm. &c., 2p, 1668.
,, PALUDANUS (J.) Vindiciæ theolog. adv. verbi Dei corruptelas, 1620.
,, PAREUS (D.) Op. theolog. exegetic., 1647.
,, PARKER (J.) The People's B., 25v, 1885–95.
,, PASINI (G.) De præc. SS. Bibl. ling. &c., 1716.
,, PEAKE (A. S.) Comm. on the B. ; ed. P., w. assist. of A. J. Grieve, 1920.
,, PEARSON (J.) &c., *ed.* Critici sacri &c., 9t, 1698.
,, PELLICAN (C.) Comm. Bibliorum, 5t, 1533–8.
,, PENNIMAN (J. H.) Bk. about the Eng. B., 1919.
,, PETRUS *de Rosenheim.* Sacr. literarum memoriale &c., 1544.
,, PFAFF (C. M.) Diss. crit. de genuinis libr. N.T. lectionibus, 1709.
,, PIEPENBRING (C.) Christologie bibl., 1919.
,, PRIDEAUX (H.) Hist. conn. of the O. & N. T. &c., 2v, 1865.
,, RAMBACH (J. J.) Exercit. hermeneut., 1741.
,, —— Instituts. hermeneut. sacræ, 1732.
,, RAMPEGOLLIS (A. DE). Biblia aurea vet. & nov. test. vocitatus, 1475 ; 1495.
,, RAPHEL (G.) Annot. in S. Scr. &c., 2t, 1747 ; ed. nova, 2t, 1750.
,, RECKENBERGER (J. L.) Nexus canon. exeget. nat., 1736.
,, ROBERTS (F.) Clavis Bibliorum, 1675.
,, ROGER (C.) Collation of the S. Scr., 1847.
,, ROHDE (E. S.) Garden-craft in the B. &c., 1927.
,, ROOS (M. F.) Fundamenta psychol. ex S. Scr. coll. &c., 1769.
,, ROTHEN (C.) De libris apparenter deperditis, 1704.
,, ROWSELL (H.) Bibl. stumbling-blocks, 1920.

Bible [*continued*].
GEN. COMM.: REFERENCES [*continued*].
see SAMMLUNG. *S. derjen. Schriften bey Gelegenheit d. wertheim. Bibelwerks &c., 1738.
,, SCHARBAU (H.) Obs. sacræ, 3p, 1759.
,, SCHICKARD (W.) Epitome Bibliorum &c.; accur. B. Raithio, 1663.
,, SCHMID (O.) Über verschied. Eintheil. d. Hlg. Schr. inbes. ü. d. Capitel-Eintheilung S. Langtons im 13 Jhdt., 1892.
,, SCHOFF (W. H.) The ship "Tyre": st. in commerce of the B., 1920.
,, SCHOTT (H. A.) Opuscula, 2t, 1817–18.
,, SEELEN (J. H. v.) Meditat. exeget., 3p, 1730–37.
,, SMITH (G.) The harmony of divine dispensations, 1856.
,, STOBART (*Mrs.* ST. C.) Ancient lights: or, the B. &c. & psychic science, 1923.
,, SURENHUSIUS (G.) Βίβλος καταλλαγῆς in quo concil. loca ex V. & N. T. allegata, 1713.
,, TELLER (J. F.) De apodixi Scr. sacræ, 1773.
,, —— De paradoxia sacra, 1773.
,, TITTMANN (C. C.) Opusc. theol., 1803.
,, TODD (H. J.) Vindic. of auth. tr. of the B. &c., 1819.
,, TOMASI (G. M.) Sacr. Bibliorum vet. tituli, 2p, 1688.
,, TRAIL (W.) Lit. characteristics &c., 1863.
,, TRAPP (I.) Annotations, 5v, 1654–62.
,, VITRINGA (C.) Obs. sacr. lib. 6, 1723.
,, WARD (T.) Errata to the Prot. B., 1688.
,, WESSEL (J.) Fasc. diss. in loca V. & N. T. &c., 1756.
,, WESTWOOD (J. O.) Palæographia sacra pictoria: illust. of anc. vers. of the B., 1843–45.
,, WHISTON (W.) Coll. of records; tr., 2p, 1727.
,, WHITAKER (W.) Disp. de sacr. Scr., 1588–90.
,, WHOWELL (T.) An analogy of the O. & N. T., 2v, 1846.
,, WILDESHAUSEN (J. F.) Bibl. disputat. in V. & N. T., 1736.
,, WILKINSON (W. F.) Personal names in the B., 1866.
,, WINCKLER (J. D.) Animadv. ad varia S. Cod., p1, 1750.
,, WOWER (J.) Syntagma de Gr. & Lat. B. interpret., 1618.
,, WYSS (J. C.) Extract. hist. del V. & N. T., 1719.
,, ZORN (P.) Bibl. antiq. & exeget. in univ. Scr., 1724–25.

Separate Books & Languages other than English.
ACTS, *see also* GOSPELS, *below*, *& var. lang*[s].
see BULLINGER (H.) In A. A. comm. libri 6, 1533; 1535.
,, CADBURY (H. J.) Making of Luke-Acts, 1927.
,, CALIXTUS (G.) In Acta Apostol., 1654.
,, CALVIN (J.) Comm. in Acta Apostol., 1584.
,, —— Comm. upon the A.; tr. C. Fetherstone, 1585; 2v, 1844.
,, CHRYSOSTOM, *Saint.* Comm. on the Acts comp. f. works of C. & Ephraim [*in Armenian*], 1839.
,, COLEMAN (A. M.) Bibl. text of Lucifer of Cagliari (A.), 1927.
,, DIEU (L. DE). Animadv. in A. A., 1634.
,, EPHRAIM, *St., Syrus.* Comm. on the A.: *in Armenian*; ed. N. Akinean, 1921.
,, EVANS (H. H.) S[t]. Paul, author of the A., 1884.
,, FAYE (E. DE). Et. sur les orig[s]. des églises de l'âge apostol., 1909.
,, FOAKES-JACKSON (F. J.) & K. LAKE, *edd.* Beginnings of Xty., p1, A. of the A., v1, 2, 1920–22.
,, GERHARD (J.) Annotat. posthumæ in A. A., 1674.
,, JONAS (J.) Annotationes, 1524.
,, LANGE (J.) Comm. de vita & epist. Pauli, isag. in Acta &c., 1718.
,, LIETZMANN (H.), *ed.* Hdbh. z. N.T., B4i, Die Apostelgesch.; erkl. v. E. Preuschen, 1912.
,, LIMBORCH (P. VAN). Comm. in Acta &c., 1711.
,, LOISY (A.) Les Actes des Apôtres, 1920; tr. nouv., 1925.
,, MAJOR (J. T.) Exeg. locorum diffic. Πραξαποστόλων, 2p, 1647–49.
,, MOMMSEN (T.) & C. G. A. HARNACK. Zu Apostelgesch. 28, 16, 1895.
,, NÖLTING (J. H. V.) Antiq. Damascenæ ex Act. 9, 1-25 illust., 1757.
,, OLSHAUSEN (H.) Bibl. comm. on the Gospels & A.; tr., 4v, 1864–65.
,, PEARSON (J.) Lectiones in A. A. [*in* Opera posthuma, 1687–88].
,, PELLICANUS (C.) In quatuor Evang. & A. A. comm., 1537.
,, RULE (W. H.) Los Hechos &c.; tr. y anot., 1877.
,, STIER (E. R.) Words of the Apostles &c.; tr., 1869.
,, STILL (J. I.) St. Paul on trial, 1923.
,, TIL (S. VAN). Comm. in libros prophet., & A. A. ad annales revocata, 3t, 1744.
,, TRAPP (J.) A comm. upon the A., 1647.
,, VADIANUS (J.) Epitome trium terræ partium, in Actis &c., 1535.
,, WALCH (J. E. I.) Diss. in A. A., 3v, 1761–66.
,, WALTHER (R.) In A. A. homiliæ 175, 1577.
,, WELLHAUSEN (J.) Krit. Anal. d. Apostelgesch., 1914.
,, WHITE (J.) A. A. &c. versio Syr., 2t, 1799–1803.
,, WIKENHAUSER (A.) Die Apostelgesch. u. ihr Geschichtswert, 1921.

Bible [*continued*].
ACTS [*continued*].
see WILSON (J. M.) A. of the A.; tr. f. Codex Bezæ, 1923.
,, ZAHN (T.) Forsch. z. Gesch. d. neutest. Kanons, T9, Die Urausgabe d. Apostelgesch., 1916.
,, —— Komm. z. N.T., B5, Apostelgesch., 2H, 1919.
ALBANIAN.
Ἡ Καινὴ Διαθήκη, δίγλωττος, Γραικικὴ καὶ Ἀλβανητική &c. [The Alban. vers. by E. Mexikos]. Ἐπίστασιᾳ Γρηγορίου Ἀρχιεπισκόπου τῆς Εὐβοίας. [*Mod. Gr. & Albanian*]. 8º. Κορφοι [Corfu]. 1827
ANGLO-SAXON & GOTHIC.
Heptateuchus, Job, & Evang. Nicodemi: Anglo-Sax. Hist. Judith fragm.; Dano-Sax. Ed. E. Thwaites. 8º. O. 1698
Goth. vers. Epist. D. Pauli ad Romanos, ad Cor. 1, ad Ephes. quæ supersunt ex Ambros. Bibl. palimps. ed. C. O. Castilionæus. la8º. Mediolani. 1834
Ðа Halgan Godspel. The A. S. vers. of the Gospels. Ed. B. Thorpe. s8º. 1842
Codex argenteus sive sacr. Evang. vers. Goth. fragmenta. Ed. A. Uppström. sfol. Upsaliæ. 1854–57
The Old Eng. version of the Heptateuch, Ælfric's Treatise on the Old & New Test. & h. Pref. to Genesis. Ed. w. intr. & 3 app[s]., w. a repr. of "A Saxon treatise conc. the Old & New Test., 1st publ. in print by Will. L'Isle of Wilburgham, 1623," & the Vulgate text of the Heptateuch, by S. J. Crawford. [E. E. T. S., 160]. 8º. 1922.
The Lindisfarne Gospels. 3 plates in colour & 36 in monochrome f. Cotton MS. in Brit. Mus. w. pages f. 2 related MSS. Intr. by E. G. Millar. fol. 1923
see BROWN (G. B.) Arts in early Eng., v5, The Gospels of Lindisfarne &c., 1921.
,, CÆDMON. The C. MS.; intr. by Sir I. Gollancz, 1927.
ARABIC, *see also* COPTIC *below.*
[The 4 Gospels in A., w. interlinear Lat. tr. by J. B. Raymundus]. fol. [Romæ. *In typographia Medicea.* 1591]
Without tp., the book beg. at p. 9, pref. & dedic. not published in this ed.
Liber Psalmorum. Ex A. idiomate in Lat. tr. a Victorio Scialac & Gabriele Sionita. [*Arabic & Lat.*] s4º. Romæ. 1614
N. Test. A. ed. T. Erpenio. s4º. Leide. 1616
[*Psalms, Ten Commandments & Lord's Prayer. Ed. S. Negri*]. 8º. *S.P.C.K.* 1725
[New Test. Ed. S. Negri]. 4º. *S.P.C.K.* 1727
[*N.T. Tr. into spoken Arabic by Eli Smith, rev. by C. van Dyck*]. 8º. Beirut. 1860
[*O.T. Tr. by E. Smith & C. van Dyck*]. la8º. Beirut. 1865
[Deuteronomy]. s8º. Lond. 1871
see LAGARDE (P. A. DE). Mater. z. Krit. u. Gesch. d. Pentateuchs, 2B, 1867.
,, PANECIUS (N.) Jacobi Epist. vers. Arab., 1694.
,, RÖDIGER (E.) Comm. de interpret. A. libr. V. T. ex Græca Alex. ducta, 1828.
,, SCHNURRER (C. F.) De Pentateucho Arab. polyglotto, 1780.
,, STORR (G. C.) Diss. de Evang. Arab., 1775.
ARAMAIC, *see also* SONG OF SOLOMON *below.*
see ONKELOS. Thargum, 1546; *& comm*[s].
ARMENIAN.
[N.T. *Ed. T. Vanantetzi.* 2p in 1v]. s8º. [Amsterdam, 1698]
[Psalms. *Foll*[d]. *by* Short calendar, 1733, *w. sep. tp. & pagin.*] s8º. i Venetik. 1748
[Holy Bible. *Ed. J. Zohrab*]. 4º. [Venice]. 1805
[N.T. *in anc. Arm. & mod. Eastern Arm. side by side*]. 8º. [Moscow]. 1834
[Book of Proverbs. *In Arm.*] s8º. Smyrna. 1852
[Bible. *b. in 2v*]. la8º. Venice. 1860
[Gospels]. s8º. Venedik. 1874
[Gospels]. 8º. Jerusalem. 1886
[N.T.] 8º. Venedik. 1888
Zamakargouthiun (Hours, Psalms &c.), 1889, *see* ARMENIAN.
[N.T.] s8º. Lond. 1892
[Psalms]. s8º. Londra. 1892
Книги Паралипоменонъ въ древн. арм. переводѣ. (Ed. princeps). *Ed.* G. Khalatheantz. [Труды по Востоковѣдѣнію, изд. Лазар. Инст. Восточ. яз., вып. 1] la8º. Moskva. 1899
Offenbar. Joh. in e. alt. A. Übers. Hrsg. F. Murad. H1, Text. [P2803]. 8º. Jerusalem. 1905
[Gospel of Mark in Zeythun dialect. P2800]. s8º. K.-polis. 1913
see ACOLUTH (A.) Obadias Armenus cum anal. vocum Armen. gramm., 1680.
,, CONYBEARE (F. C.) The A. version of Revelation; ed. &c. F. C. C., 1907.
,, —— Cod. Pamphili & date of Euthalius, 1895.
,, MACLER (F.) Le texte de l'Evang. armén. d'ap. Matthieu & Marc, 1919.
,, MARR (N. YA.) Замѣтки по текстамъ св. Писанія въ древн. перев. арм. и. груз., 1913.
,, MEILLET (A.) De quelq. évangéliaires arm. accent., 1905.
,, TER-MOVSESEAN (M.) Рукоп. отрывки арм. версіи Ветх. Зав., 1915.
ARMENO-TURKISH.
[*N.T. Turkish in Arm. characters*]. s8º. [St. Petersburg]. 1819
[*N.T. In Arm. characters*]. s8º. Isthanpolta. 1901

Bible [*continued*].
BASUTO.
Testamente e Ncha. [Tr. by E. Casalis & S. Rolland]. 8°. Beerseba. 1856
BATTA (TOBA).
Evang. v. Johannes [Lukas & Genesis], vertaald v. H. N. van der Tuuk. [3v]. 8°. A. 1859
BENGALI.
[Joshua—Esther]. 8°. Serampore. 1809
[N.T.] 8°. Serampore. 1813 [1816]
Gospels acc. to St. Matthew & St. John, in Eng. & B. [Tr. by J. Ellerton]. 8°. Calcutta. 1819
The Holy Bible. [*Wenger's revision*, 7th ed.] 8°. Calcutta. 1885
The N.T. Tr. by C. Bomwetsch. 8°. Calcutta. 1885
BHATNERI [BHUTUNER ; VIRAT &c.]
[Gospels & Acts]. 8°. [Serampore. 1818]
BHUGELKHUNDA [BAGHELI], *see* HINDI, *below*.
BIKANERA [VIKANERA].
The Holy Bible. Tr. by the Serampore missionaries. v5, N.T. [*no more publ.*] s8°. Serampore. 1820
BRETON.
Test. Nevez. Trôet é Brézounek, gant Le Gonidec. s8°. Angoulem. 1827
Bibl. Santel, lekeat e Brezounek gant ann Aotrou Le Gonidec. 2t. la8°. San-Briek. 1866
BULGARIAN.
Новый Завѣтъ. Ново превѣд. отъ П. П. Рылца &c. изд. 2°. 8°. въ Смирнѣ. 1850
Новый Завѣтъ. s8°. Цариградъ. 1872
CANARESE.
The Holy Bible, tr. into C. by Miss. Societies for the Madras Auxil. B. Soc. 4°. Bangalore. 1865
CHALDEE, *see* ARAMAIC.
CHEREMISS.
Святой Еѵангелья. 8°. Питеръ Алашта. 1821
CHINESE.
[N.T. *Morrison's version* (High Wen-li). 2nd ed. 8p *in case*]. s8°. [Canton. 1815]
[Bible in Chinese (High Wen-li). Lassar & Marshman's version.] 5v [*each w. pr. label as below*]. la8°. Serampore. 1817–22
[1], The Pentateuch, 1817.
[2], The Historical Books, 1821.
[3], The Hagiographa, 1818.
[4], The Prophetic Books, 1819.
[5], The New Testament, 1815–22.
Holy Bible in Chinese [High Wen-li]. By Morrison & Milne. 21v [v20, Acts–II Cor. *wanting*]. s8°. [Malacca] *Anglo-Chin. Coll.* 1823
Only v1 bears the translators' names & date of publⁿ. on the printed label. Some volˢ. are reissues.
CHIPPEWA, *see* OJIBWA *below*.
CHRONICLES, *see also* ARMENIAN *above*.
see BERTHEAU (E.) Comm. on Bks. of C. ; tr., 1857.
,, PATRICK (S.) Comm. upon 2 bks. of C. &c., 1706.
COLOSSIANS.
see BAYNES (P.) A comm. upon 1st & 2nd chaps. of C. &c., 1634.
,, BYFIELD (N.) Expos. upon C., 1617.
,, CALIXTUS (G.) Expositio, 1654.
,, ELLICOTT (C. J.) Epistle to Phil., C. &c. : w. comm. & rev. tr., 3rd ed., 1865.
,, FIRMINGER (W. K.) Epistles of St. Paul to the C. &c., w. intr. & notes, 1921.
,, LIETZMANN (H.), *ed.* Hdbh. z. N.T., B3, Die Briefe d. Ap. Paulus, II, An d. K. &c. ; erklärt v. M. Dibelius, 1912.
,, LIGHTFOOT (J. B.) C. & Philemon, 9th ed., 1890.
,, SCHMID (S.) In P. ad C. epist. comm., 1696.
,, WESTCOTT (F. B.) St. Paul's Letter to the C. : paraphrase & expos., 1914.
CONCORDANCES & DICTIONARIES.
*Concordantiæ majores sacræ Bibliæ. [*Follᵈ. by* :—] Alter Concordantiarum tomus, qui est partium indeclinabilium. [By Joannes de Segovia]. [2p in 1v. *Final leaf of p2 imperf.*] 8°. Lugduni *apud S. Gryphium.* 1540
see BAGSTER (S.) *& Sons.* Analyt. Greek lexicon, 1862.
,, BRUDER (C. H.) Ταμιεῖον : concord., ed. ster. 4a, 1888.
,, CRUDEN (A.) C. to the N.T., 1833.
,, —— Conc. to the Scr., 1734.
,, EADIE (J.) New & compl. conc., 1853.
,, GESENIUS (F. H. W.) Heb. lexicon to the O.T. ; tr. C. Leo, 2p, 1825–28.
,, HART (J.) The Port-Royal of Holy Scr., or a new c., 1655.
,, HERREY (R. F.) Two right profit. concordances &c., 1622.
,, HUGO, *de Sancto Charo.* Sacr. Bibl. vulg. ed. concordantiæ ; Luca, 1768 ; 1825.
,, JACKSON (J.) Index Biblicus, 1668.
,, LAMBERT (C. H.) Dicc. de paralelos, conc. y analogias bibl., 1871.
,, NEWMAN (S.) *A conc. to the Holy Scr., 1662.
,, NOLDIUS (C.) Concordantiæ particularum Ebræo-Chaldaic., 1734.
,, TALBOT (M.) An analysis of the H.B., 1800.

Bible [*continued*].
COPTIC, *see also* JOB *below*.
Nov. Test. Ægyptium vulgo Copticum ex MSS. Bodl. descr., cum Vatic. & Paris. contulit & in Lat. vertit D. Wilkins. [*Coptic & Lat.*] 4°. O. 1716
Psalterium in dial. Copt. Memphit. tr. &c. Ed. M. G. Schwartze. 4°. Lips. 1843
4 Evang. Copt. Memphit. Ed. M. G. Schwartze. [N.T. Copt., p1]. 2p. 4°. Lips. 1846–47
[New Test. in C. & Arabic ; ed. by H. Tattam [&] W. Cureton]. 2v [*v1 wanting*]. fol. [London. 1847–52]
Der Pentateuch kopt. Hrsg. P. de Lagarde. 8°. L. *Teubner.* 1867
The Coptic version of the N.T., Sahidic & Thebaic. With crit. apparatus, Eng. tr., register &c. of fragmˢ. [Ed. G. Horner]. v4–7. 8°. O. 1920–24
Gospel of St. John acc. to earliest C. MS. Ed. w. tr. by Sir H. Thompson. [Brit. Sch. of Arch. in Egypt &c.] 4°. 1924
see SCHLEIFER (J.) Sahid. Bibel-Fragm., Brit. Mus., 3, Psalmenfragm., 1914.
,, WESSELY (C.) Sahid. Papyrusfragm. d. paulin. Briefe, 1914.
CORINTHIANS.
see ANSTEY (C.) Paraphrase of 13th chap. of 1st C., 1779.
,, BULLINGER (H.) In poster. P. epist. ad C. comm., 1535.
,, CALIXTUS (G.) Expositio, 1653.
,, CALVIN (J.) Comm. on C., 2v, tr., 1848–49.
,, EDWARDS (T. C.) Comm. on 1st Ep. to the C., 1885.
,, ERASMUS (D.) Verteutschte ausslegung ü. [1 Cor. 14], 1521.
,, GERDES (D.) Meletem. sacra, isag. in c. 15 Epist. I ad C., 1759.
,, GOUDGE (H. L.) Second Ep. to the C. ; intr. &c. by G., 1927.
,, LIETZMANN (H.) Hdbh. z. N.T., B3i, 2, 2e A., 1923.
,, MELANCHTHON (P.) Annot. in Epist. ad Rhom. & ad C., 1523.
,, MUSCULUS (W.) In ambas ad C. Epist. comm., 1566.
,, SAHL (L.) Paraphrasis in prior. Epist. ad. C., 1779.
,, SEMLER (J. S.) Paraph. in l. ad C. Epist., 1770.
,, SIBBES (R.) Comm. upon 2 C. 1, 1655.
,, ULFILAS. U. Gothica versio Epist. ad C. secundæ ; ed. C. O. Castillionæus, 1829.
,, ZWINGLI (U.) Annot. in utranque ad C. epist., 1528.
CREE.
S. Matthew. s8°. London. 1853
CROATIAN.
Pisctole, i Evangelya priko suega Godiscta novo istomacena po razlogu missala dvora Rimskoga. u Slovinschi yezik. fol. v Bnecich. 1715
Sveto Pismo Starog' [& Novog'] Zakona. Sada u Jezik Slavno-Illyricski &c. [*Lat. & Croat*]. 6 svezak. 8°. u Budimu. 1831
A lit. tr. f. the Vulg. by Matia Petar Katančič, a Franciscan.
Chtenya, y Evangeliumi na vsze Nedelye &c. s8°. vu Budimo. 1843
see GJORGI (I.) Vulgatæ Psalmorum ed. Illyrica metaphrasis, 1729.
CURAÇAO.
Ewanhelie di S. Matheo. Pœbl. ab. dir. di C. Conradi. 8°. Curaçao. 1844
CZECH.
[*Bible. Beg. f. a2* (*headline* Poczinase przedmluwa *cut off*) Zadosti welikee byl nieyaky Paulin. kniez pocztiwy. aby mohl rozumieti Pismom swatym. a od tohoto se swieta odtrhnuti y psal k swatemu Ieronymowi, &c.
f. mm8, verso, col. 2. Colophon : Praczy teto a diela. knih tiechto zakona božie konecz včinien gt sstiastnie. &c. A to leta božie° tisyczic° cžtyrzste° osmde sateho osmeho Miesyecze Srpna. *Ends on f. 8* (*of extra leaves which contain table of Epistles & Gospels*), konecz newiete dne ani hodiny]. fol. [Prague. August, 1488]
610 leaves, a1 (*blank ?*) *missing, h1 & mm1 missing ; k6 & x7 are supplied in MS. Double cols. 47 lines ; headlines* (*some cut off*). *Sig. a–g, 10. h, 8. i–z, A, 10. B, 8. C–Z, AA, BB, 10. CC, 8. aa–ll, 10. mm, 8.* (*i–iiii*), *8. Capitals in var. colours. First complete Bohemian Bible.*
Biblj Swatá. [*2nd ed. of the Kralitz Bible of 1579–93*]. 8°. [Kralitz.] 1596
Biblj Swatá, &c. [*3rd ed. of Kralitz Bible. 1199 pp.*] fol. [Kralitz.] 1613
Celý Žaltár. Krále a Proroka Dawida. [*b. w.* Bible : Czech. Nowý Zakon, 1730]. s8°. [Halle ?.] 1730
Nowý Zakon. s8°. [Halle ?.] 1730
Biblia Sacra, to gest : Biblj Swatá. 8°. w. Praze. 1870
see DURICH (F.) De Slavo-Bohemica sacri cod. vers. dissert., 1777.
,, NOWOTNY z LUŽE (F.) Bibl. českých Biblij &c., 1810, c. 1815.
DANIEL.
For ed. in Internat. Crit. Comm. [*by J. A. Montgomery*], *see* BIBLE : GEN. COMM.
[*Daniel in Hebrew. Extr. f.* Aurogallus (M.) Compend. Hebr. &c. gram. [*b. w.* Bible : Psalms. Psalt. Hebr., 1533]. s8°. [Wittembergæ. 1525]

Bible [*continued*].
DANIEL [*continued*].
Daniel sec. Septuaginta ex Tetraplis Origenis ed. e singul. Chisiano cod. annorum supra 800 [*by* Simon de Magistris. *Gr. & Lat.* S. Hippolyti interpret. in D. Apologia sententiæ patrum &c.]. lafol. Romæ. 1772
see AUBERLEN (C. A.) D. et l'Apocalypse de S. Jean ; tr., 1880.
,, BOUTFLOWER (C.) In & around the Bk. of D., 1923.
,, BRIGHTMAN (T.) Workes : expos. of last p. of D. &c., 1644.
,, BROUGHTON (H.) Comm. in D. ; Lat. don., 1599.
,, —— D. his Chaldie visions &c., 1597.
,, BURTON (G.) Essay tow. reconciling the numbers of Daniel & St. John, 1766.
,, CALVIN (J.) Comm^s. on D. ; tr., 2v, 1852–53.
,, DRACONITES (J.) Comm., *w. text*, 1544.
,, DREXEL (H.) D. prophetarum princeps, 1651.
,, GEIER (M.) Comm. in Proverbia &c., 1696.
,, HOCHSTATERUS (J. G.) Disput. Biblica de 2. cap. D., *n.d.*
,, JACHIADES (J.) Paraphrasis in D., 1633.
,, JONAS (J.) Das 7te Cap. D., 1529 ?.
,, JOYE (G.) Exposycion out of P. Melancthon &c., 1550.
,, KEIL (C. F.) Bk. of D. ; tr., 1872.
,, KERKHERDERE (J. G.) Prodromus D., 1711.
,, LOWTH (W.) Comm., 2v, 1726.
,, MÜLLER (D.) De quarta bestia D., cap. 7, diss., 1617.
,, NEWTON (*Sir* I.) Obs. upon D. &c., 1733.
,, PUSEY (E. B.) D. : 9 lects., 3rd ed., 1869.
,, ROOS (M. F.) Expos. of prophesies of D. ; tr., 1811.
,, RULE (W. H.) Hist. expos. of D., 1869.
,, STIFEL (M.) Ein sehr wunderbarl. wortrechnung &c. etl. zalen D., 1553.
,, VÆSARTI (A.) Chron. prophet. & Methodus introd. in veram D. expos., 1682.
,, WAGENSEIL (J. C.) Tela ignea Satanæ ; acc. Mantissa de 70 hebdom. Dan., 1681.
DANISH & NORWEGIAN.
Biblia. Det er deñ gantske Hellige Scrifft paa Danske igen offuerseet oc prentet effter Salige oc Høylofflige ihukommelse, Kong Frederichs II. Befalning. Met Register, Lutheri Fortaler &c. oc V. Theodori Summarier. fol. Kiøbenhaffn. 1589
The second Danish Bible, known as "Frederick II's Bible." 3 pagin^s. colophon of p1 dated 1588. w. woodcuts.
Biblia. [*Rev. H. P. Resen*]. [*1, Gen. to Song of songs*]. s8°. Kiøbinghaffn. 1607
Bibelen. 8°. Christiania. 1871
DEUTERONOMY.
see BUGENHAGEN (J.) Annotationes &c., 1524.
,, FRISCHMUTH (J.) De rege eligendo &c. ex Deut. xvii, 1653.
,, KENNETT (R. H.) D. & the Decalogue, 1920.
,, KITTEL (G.) Sifre zu D., L. 1, 1922.
,, PATRICK (S.) Comm. upon 5th Bk. of Moses, 1700.
DUTCH & FLEMISH, *see also* PSALMS *below*.
De Bibel. Tgeheele Oude ende Nieuwe Testament met grooter naersticheyt naden Latynschen text gecorrigeert, eñ opten cant des boecks die alteratie die hebre-eusche veranderinge &c. Met schoonen figueren ghedruct &c. fol. [Antwerpen, *Willem Vorsterman*. 1528–31]
Colophon of O.T. dated 1528. Tp. of N.T. (Tnyeuvve Testament) dated 1530, colophon, 1531. Woodcuts.
Dat nieuwe testament &c. [*w. woodcuts*]. s8°. Collen. *Ioh. Gymnich*. 1531
Den Bibel met grooter neersticheyt gecorrigeert &c. [*With woodcuts*]. 2p. fol. [Thantwerpē, *Jacob vā Lisuedlt* [*sic*]. 1532
Den Bibel in duyts, verduytst [*by Jan Gheylliaert, f. the German B. of Zürich, 1548–49. N.T. has sep. tp. & foliat.*] s4°. Embden, *S. Mierdman & J. Gheylliert*. 1556
Den Bibel. s4°. [Embden], *Lenaert der Kinderen*. 1563
Repr. of the Menonite Bible of 1560, but without chapter-headings.
Biblia. 8°. [Dort, *Jan Canin*]. 1571–72
Het Nieuwe Test., vertæld volgens de gemeene Lat. overz. 8°. Brussel. 1854
see HINLOPEN (N.) Hist. van de Nederl. Overzettinge des Bybels, &c., 1777.
,, LE LONG (I.) Boek-Zaal d. Nederduitsche Bybels, 1764.
ECCLESIASTES, *see also* BIBLE : GEN. COMM. Camb. B. : Ecclesiastes, by A. L. Williams, 1922.
A paraphrase on the bk. of Eccles. first publ. 1768. Added text of A. V., notes &c. by N. Higgins. 8°. Whitchurch, Salop. *n.d.*
see DRUSIUS (J.) Annot. in Coheleth, 1635.
,, EOBANUS (H.) Psalterium Davidis & Eccl. carm. redd., 1563.
,, GEIER (M.) Comm. in Proverbia & E., 1696.
,, GREGORY II, *pope*. Libri 10 Explan. Eccles., 1791.
,, HENGSTENBERG (E. W.) Comm. on E. &c. ; tr., 1860.
,, JERMIN (M.) Comm. on the booke of E., 1639.
,, MELANCHTHON (P.) Enarr. brevis E., 1850.
,, PATRICK (S.) Bk. of Job, Paraphrase upon E. &c., 1710.
,, PINEDA (J. DE). Comm. in E., 1620.
,, SCHMID (S.) In libr. E. comm., 1691.
,, VARENIUS (A.) Gemmæ Salomonis, 1659.

Bible [*continued*].
EPHESIANS.
see BAYNES (P.) Comm. upon 1st chap. of E., 1618.
,, —— Comm. upon E., 5th ed., 1658.
,, BOYD (R.) In Epist. ad E. prælectiones, 1661.
,, BUCER (M.) Epist. ad Ephesios, 1527.
,, CALIXTUS (G.) Expositio, 1653.
,, CALVIN (J.) Comm. on Galatians & E. ; tr., 1854.
,, DALE (R. W.) E. : its doct. & ethics, 1890.
,, ELLICOTT (C. J.) Epistle to the E. : w. comm. & rev. tr., 4th ed., 1868.
,, LIETZMANN (H.), *ed.* Hdbh. z. N.T., B3, II, An d. E. &c. ; erkl. v. M. Dibelius, 1912.
,, SCHMID (S.) Fasc. disput. s. Epist. ad Eph. &c., 1685.
,, STEVARTIUS (P.) Exegesis in Epist. ad E., 1593.
EPISTLES.
Die Episteln u. Evangelia &c. ; übers, 1733, *see* BIBLE : WEND.
see BENSON (G.) Paraphrase & notes on James, Peter, Jude & John, 1749.
,, BOYS (J.) Workes, expos. of festivall E. &c., 1622.
,, BULLINGER (H.) In omnes Apost. Epist. Pauli 14 &c. comm., 1537.
,, CALVIN (J.) Comm^s. on Cath. E. ; tr., 1855.
,, —— In omnes Pauli epistolas &c., 1565.
,, CAMERARIUS (J.) Notatio figurarum orationis &c., 1556.
,, CREIDE (H.) Meditationes apostolico-epist., 1665.
,, GIUSTINIANO (B.) In omnes Cath. epist. explanat., 1621.
,, GULIELMUS, *Paris.* Postilla super Epistolas &c., 1494 ; 1508.
,, HEMMINGSEN (N.) Comm. in omnes epistolas Apostol., 1579.
,, HYMNI & collectæ, item Evang., Epist., &c., 1573.
,, LUTHER (M.) Ausleg. d. Episteln u. Evang. &c., 1532.
,, MEIER (G.) Homeliæ in Epist. dierum dominic. et festorum, 1563.
,, METTENLEITER (D.) Die sonntägl. Epist. d. kathol. Kirchenjahres, 1856.
,, PISCATOR (J.) Analysis logica 7 epist. apostol., 1597.
,, RULE (W. H.) Los Hechos &c.—Las Epistolas ; tr. y anot., 1877–80.
,, SARGIS *Shnorhali*. [Comm. on the 7 catholic epistles : *in Armenian*], 1743.
,, TRAPP (J.) A comm. upon all the Epistles &c., 1647.
,, WHITBY (D.) Paraph. & comment. on the N.T., v2, Epistles, 1700.
ESKIMO (GREENLAND).
Testamente Nutak, oversat af Paul Egede. s8°. Kiöbenhavn. 1766
Test. Nutak. [*Tr. O. Fabricius*]. s8°. Kiöbenhavnime. 1799
ESKIMO (LABRADOR).
Tamedsa Johannesib Aglangit. s8°. Londonneme, *B.F.B.S.* 1810
ESTHER.
see KEIL (C. F.) The Bk^s. of Ezra, Nehemiah & E. ; tr., 1873.
,, PATRICK (S.) Comm. upon Chron., Esther &c., 1706.
,, ROSSI (G. B. DE). Spec. var. lect. sacri textus & Chaldaica E. add., 1783.
ESTHONIAN.
Meije Issanda Jesusse Kristusse Wastne Testament. s8°. Riga. 1727
Piibli Ramat, se on keik se Jummala Sanna, mis Pühhad Jummala Mehhed &c. 4°. Tallinnas, *J. J. Köler*. 1739
ETHIOPIC.
Psalterium. 4°. Londini. 1815
Novum Test. Æthiopice. Ed. T. P. Platt. s4°. 1830
Vet. Testamenti Æth. tom. 1 & 2 ; ed. & apparatu crit. [*w. sep. pagin.*] instr. A. Dillmann. [Gen. *to* Kings]. 2t. [*in* 1v]. 4°. Lipsiæ. 1853–71
see DORN (B.) De Psalterio Æth. comm., 1825.
,, STAUDACHER (B. A.) Jonas vates, Æth. & Lat., 1706.
EXODUS, *see also* SINHALESE, *below*.
see BABINGTON (G.) Comfortable notes, 1604.
,, JACK (J. W.) Date of the E. in light of external evid., 1925.
,, MINGARELLI (G. L.) Anecd. fasc. (Glossæ super E.), 1756.
,, PATRICK (S.) Comm. upon 2nd Bk. of Moses, 1697.
,, PHILO, *Judæus*. Paralipom. Arm., in Lat. tr. J. B. Aucher, 1826.
,, TETTELBACH (M. H.) Propos. de verbis Jehovæ Exod. 20. Non facies tibi sculptile &c., 1597.
,, WILLET (A.) Hexapla in Exodus [*in his* Hexapla in Genesin. 1632–33.]
EZEKIEL.
see CALVIN (J.) Comm. on 1st 20 chaps. of E. ; tr., 2v, 1849–50.
,, DUJARDIN (E.) Stéphane Mallarmé au prophète E. &c., 1919.
,, GREENHILL (W.) An expos. upon E., [5v], 1649–62.
,, HAFENREFFER (M.) Templum Ezech., 1613.
,, HENGSTENBERG (E. W.) Prophecies of E. ; tr., 1869.
,, KEIL (C. F.) Bibl. comm. on prophecies of E. ; tr., 2v, 1876.
,, LOWTH (W.) Comm., 1723.
,, ŒCOLAMPADIUS (J.) In proph. E. comm., per V. Capiton æditus, 1534.
,, PRADO (H.) & J. B. VILLALPANDO. In E. explanat. &c., 3t, 1596–1604.

Bible [*continued*].

Ezra.

see Howorth (H. H.) Unconvent. views, 2, 1901.
,, Keil (C. F.) The Bk[s]. of E. &c.; tr., 1873.
,, Patrick (S.) Comm. upon Chron., E. &c., 1706.

Fiji.

[Genesis, Exodus, & Psalter. *Tr. begun by J. Hunt & compl. by E. Hazlewood. No tp.*] s8°. [Viwa. 1854]

Finnish, *see also* Karelian, *below.*

Ce Wsi Testamenti. [*Tr. by M. Agricola. With woodcuts. "Correctura" at end in MS.*] s4°. [Stocholmis, *Amundi Lauritzan Poialta*]. 1548

Biblia, Se on: Coco Pyhä Ramattu Suomexi. [*The second F. Bible, but the first Bible pr. in Finland. tp. of N.T. dated* 1683]. s4°. Turusa. 1685

Uusi Testamenti. 8°. Stockholmisa. 1774

see Lilius (C. G.) Animadv. in Fennicam B. vers., 1826.

Fioti.

Minkanda Miazintumwa [Rom.-Rev.] Kifioti kwa N. Westlind. s8°. Mukimbungu. 1891

French, *see also* Compl. Texts &c., *above.*

La Saincte Bible en François, tr. [*by J. de Fèvre*], &c. [*2 foliations: woodcuts*]. fol. Anvers, *Antoine de la Haye.* 1541
3rd ed. of the Antwerp Bible first issued 1530.

La Sainte Bible. [*Repr. of Olivetan's vers.; w. wood-cuts*]. 5t [2–5 *wanting.* 1, *Genesis to Ruth*]. s8°. Lyon [*sic*], *J. de Tournes.* 1553

Le Nouv. Test. [*French & Lat. Foll. by* Recueil d'ancuns mots &c. difficiles]. s8°. *n.p.* 1555

Le Nouv. Test., rev. & corr. sur le Grec, avec annot. &c. par A. Marlorat. s8°. Genève. 1563

La Bible: Vieil & nouv. Test. N.T. rev. & corr. sur le Grec. fol. Geneve, *Pour P. Bernard & C. du Mont.* 1565

La Bible. [*French Genevan vers.; 3 foliations*: 370, 90, 122; *folld. by* Pseaumes par Marot & Beze, Forme des prières ecclés. &c., Confess. de foi &c. *without foliation*]. s8°. *n.p. pour Toussain le Feure.* 1570

La Bible. [*French Genevan vers. A fresh revision*]. 8°. Genève. 1588

Le Nouveau Test. Tr. selon l'éd. Vulgate, avec les differences du Grec. [*De Sacy's version.*] Nouv. ed., revuë &c. 2t (t2, Les Epistres &c.) s8°. Mons. 1672

La Bible. [*French Genevan vers.*] s8°. Amsterdam, *Schippers.* 1678

La Sainte Bible &c. Tr. sur la Vulgate par Mr. Le Maistre de Saci. 2t [*pagin. cont.*] 4°. Mons. 1713

La Sainte Bible. Rev. &c. par D. Martin. Préf. par Mr. L'Enfant. n. éd. 2t. s8°. Hannover. 1728

La Sainte Bible. Tr. nouv. par [E.] de Genoude. 4e éd. corr. 2t. s8°. 1845

Le Nouv. Test. Vers. de J. Fr. Ostervald, rév. par C. F. [*i.e.* C. L. Frossand]. 8°. *Soc. Bibl. de Fr.* 1877

Les Saints Evangiles. Tr. nouv. par H. Lasserre &c. Ed. illustrée. la8°. 1888

La Bible: tr. nouv. [*by*] E. Ledrain. v5, 6, Les prophètes. 8°. 1889–90

Les livres du N.T. Tr., avec intr. gén. & notices par A. Loisy. 8°. 1922

see Gousset (J.) Consid[s]. sur le projet d'une nouv. version franç. de la B., 1698.
,, Reuss (E. W. E.) Fragments litt. & crit. rel. à l'hist. de la B. franç., 1851–66.

Gaelic, *see also* Irish; Psalms, *below.*

Tiomnadh Nuadh &c. s8°. Dun-Eidin, *Paterson.* 1796

Leabhraichean an t-Seann Tiomnaidh. 2 earrann *in* 1v. s8°. E. *S.P.C.K.* 1807

Tiomnadh Nuadh. [*b. w.* Leabhraichean an Seann Tiomnaidh, 1807]. s8°. E. 1813

Leabhraichean an t-Seann Tiomnaidh agus an Tiomnaidh Nuaidh &c. 8°. London. 1867

Galatians.

For ed. in Internat. Crit. Comm. [*by E. De W. Burton*], *see under* Bible: Gen. Comm.

see Calixtus (G.) Expositio, 1653.
,, Calvin (J.) Comm[s]. on G. &c.; tr., 1854.
,, Ellicott (C. J.) Ep. to the G.: w. comm. & rev. tr., 4th ed. 1867.
,, Hoë (M.) Comm. super P. ad G. epist., 1605.
,, Lietzmann (H.), *ed.* Hdbh. z. N.T., B3i, An d. G.; erklärt v. H. L., 1910.
,, Lightfoot (J. B.) Galatians, 7th ed., 1881.
,, Loisy (A.) L'Epitre aux G., 1916.
,, Luther (M.) In epist. P. ad G. comm. &c., 1535.
,, —— Comm. on G.; tr., 1807; 1836; 1864.
,, Olevianus (C.) In Epist. ad G. notæ &c., 1578.
,, Teller (J. F.) J. C. depictum Galatis crucifixum, 1773.

Genesis, *see also* Batta, *above*; Hindustani; Lepcha; Prophetic Books; Sinhalese, *below.*

Genesis cum cathol. espos. ex probatis theologis [F. Vatablus; M. Luther; W. Musculus; I. Calvinus; P. Fagius &c.] excerpta. [2p *in* 1v]. s8°. Morgiis. 1585

Bible [*continued*].

Genesis [*continued*].

Illust[s]. of the Bk. of G. Facsimile of the Ms. Brit. Mus., Egerton, 1894. Intr. by M. R. James [Roxburghe Club]. 4°. O. 1921

see Böhme (J.) Mysterium magnum, or, expos. of 1st Bk. of Moses; tr., 2v, 1924.
,, Bradley (H.) The Cædmonian G., 1920.
,, Calvin (J.) Comm. on G., 2v; tr., 1847–50.
,, Chumnos (G.) O.T. legends f. a Greek poem on G. & Exodus; ed. w. metr. tr. &c. by F. H. Marshall, 1925.
,, Doumergue (E.) Moïse & la G. d'ap. les trav. de E. Naville, 1920.
,, Firnhaber (W.) Disput. Biblica de 15. cap. G., 1598.
,, Gaskell (G. A.) G. interpr. thro' lang. of symbolism, 1925.
,, Gaudenzio (P.) De errore sect.—Conatus in G., 1644.
,, Gerhard (J.) Comm. super G., 1693.
,, Heerbrand (J.) Disput. de polygamia, ex G. 2, 16, 20, 29, 30 cap., 1586.
,, Helmont (F. M. van). Cogit. super 4 priora cap. G., 1697.
,, Hershon (P. I.) G. w. a Talmud. comm. &c., 1883.
,, Kennicott (B.) Two diss., Tree of life &c., 1747.
,, Lagarde (P. A. de). Mater. z. Krit. u. Gesch. d. Pentateuchs, B2 (Die G. arab.), 1867.
,, LeClerc (J.) 12 diss. out of L.'s G.; tr., 1696.
,, Luther (M.) Uber d. Erst Buch Mose &c., 1527.
,, Meintel (J. G.) Probe e. crit. Polyglotten Bibel, 3T, 1761–69.
,, Musculus (W.) In G. comm., 1600.
,, Patrick (S.) Comm. upon 1st Bk. of Moses, called G., 3rd ed., 1704.
,, Philo, *Judæus.* Paralipom. Arm., in Lat. tr. J. B. Aucher, 1826.
,, Rydberg (A. V.) Medeltidens magi—Urpatriarkernas Släkttavla i G. &c., 1921.
,, Sanders (H. A.) & C. Schmidt. Minor Prophets, & the Berlin fragm. of G., 1927.
,, Schmid (S.) Super G. annotat., 1697.
,, Schröder (N. G.) Quatuor prima cap. G. Turcice & Lat.; Schroeder, 1739.
,, Selneccerus (N.) Annot. in G., 1578.
,, Unselt (D. J.) Disput. de chao mundi, c. 1725.
,, Venema (H.) Dissert. sel., t1i, ii, G., 1747–50.
,, Whately (W.) Prototypes &c., out of G., 1640.
,, Willet (A.) Hexapla in G. &c., 1632–33.

Georgian.

[Psalter. *In G. eccles. characters. Imperf. tp. &c. wanting*]. s8°. *n.p.* [c. 1711 ?]

[N.T. *In Georg. Eccles. character. no tp.*] 4°. [Moscow. 1816]

[N.T., *no tp.*] 4°. [St. Petersburg. Russ. B. S. 1818]

[N.T. *Civil character. Repr.*] 8°. Tiflis. 1879

[Pentateuch. *In Georgian Civil character*]. 8°. Tiflis. 1900

4 Evang. vers. G. vet. Ed. V. Beneševič. fasc. 1, 2 [P2805]. 4°. S. Peterbourg. 1909–11

see Hippolytus, *St.* Толкованіе Пѣсни пѣсней, груз. текстъ изд. &c. Н. Марръ, 1901.
,, Marr (N. Ya.) Груз. приписки греч. Евангелія изъ Коридіи, 1911.

German, *see also* Old Testament, *below.*

[Bibel. *F. 2b* (*red*). Hie vahet an das Register über die Bibeln des alten testaments. *f. 3a*: Hie höbet an die Epistel des heyligen priesters sant Iheronimi zů Paulinum von allen götlichen bůchern der hystori; *f. 534a* (*colophon. red*) Diss durchleuchtigost werck der ganczen heyligen geschrifft. genandt die Bibel &c. in Augspurg &c. Umb wöllich volbringung, seye lob. glori und Ere &c.] [*b. in 2v.*] lafol. [Augspurg, *Günther Zainer. n.d.*, 1475–76]
534 leaves, double cols., 58 lines & headline (*foliat. & name of book*). *Ff. 3–424 are numbered I–CCCCXXI, & ff. 425–534, I–Cx; the first leaf is blank & wanting. No sign. The small f. 188 containing Manasses prayer omitted from f. 187b, is not included in the foliat. On f. 258b a note omitted from the text is printed on lower margin. Larger capitals painted in various colours.*
Fourth German Bible.

[Bibel. *Beg. f. 1.* Hie hebet an die Epistel des heyligen priesters sant Iheronimi, &c. *f. 295b*, Ein end hat die weissagūg od' der psalter &c. *f. 296a* (*Part 2*) Hie vahet an dye vorred iheronimi vber das buch der spruch . . . salomonis. *Ends. f. 583, verso, Colophon*: Disz durchleuchtigist werck der gantzen heyligen geschrifft. genant dy bibel . . . Gedruckt durch anthonium Koburger in . . . Nůrenberg Vm̄ wellich volbrīgung. sey lob. glori. & ere der hohen heyligē dryualtigkeit &c., amen.] fol. [Nürenberg, *A. Koburger.* 1483]
583 leaves numbered I to CCCCCLXXXIII; 2 blank leaves between 295 & 296 & blank at end missing; no sigs. double cols. 50 (*sometimes 51*) *lines to col. Woodcuts coloured. Capitals red & blue, some illuminated.*
Ninth German Bible.

[Bibel. *Vol. 2 beg. f. a2.* Hie vahet an die vorred hieronimi über dz bůch der sprüch. *Ends on f. kk8* Diss durchleuch-

Bible [*continued*].
GERMAN [*continued*].
tigest werck der gantzen heyligen geschrift genant die bibel zu teutsch getrukt &c. in Strassburg &c. da lebt unnd regiret gott ewiglich amen].
fol. [Strassburg, *Johann* (*Reinhard*) *Grüninger*. 2nd May 1485]
456 leaves (*numbered with errors, 1-464*), *double cols., 43 lines; headlines. Sig. a–z* (*counting W after V*) *in eights. A–Z* (*omitting W*) *in eights; aa–kk in eights. a blank is wanting.*
Evangelia mit der gloss u. Epistlen Tütsch über das gantz iar allenthalbē darbey, &c. [*tp. imperfect; woodcuts*].
fol. [Strassburg, *Mathis Hüpfuff*. 1512]
Alle Propheten nach Hebraischer sprach verteütschet [*by* Ludwig Haetzer & Hans Denck]. [*157 leaves*].
fol. Augspurg, *S. Ottmar*. 1527
„ „ [*a. ed.*] s8°. [Augspurg, *H. Stainer*]. 1530
Das New Testamēt, so durch L. Emser sāligē v̇teutscht. [*Foll*[d]. *by* Annotationes Hieronimi Emsers, vber Luthers Newe Testamēt ytzt tzum vierden mal vbersehen &c. *w. sep. tp. & pagin.; woodcuts*]. s8°. [Leyptzick, *V. Schumañ*]. 1529
Das Alt Testament teutsch, der vrsprünglichen Hebreyschen warhait nach, auffs trewlichst verdeütscht. [*Pentateuch only. Luther's version; woodcuts*]. s8°. Augspurg, *H. Steyner*. 1530
Die Propheten alle Deudsch. D. Mart. Luth. [*With a pref. to each*]. [2p *in* 1v]. fol. Wittemberg, *Hans Lufft*. 1532
The first complete ed. of Luther's translation of the Prophets.
Biblia, beider Allt unnd Newen Testamenten, fleissig, treulich uñ Christlich, nach alter inn Christlicher kirchen gehabter Translation, mit ausslegunng etlicher dunckeler ort, unnd besserung viler verrückter wort und sprüch, Durch D. Johan Dietenberger, new verdeutscht &c. [*from the Vulgate &c. 578 leaves; w. woodcuts*]. fol. Meyntz, *Peter Jordan*. 1534
Biblia: das ist: die gantze Heilige Schrifft, Deudsch, Auffs new zugericht. D. Mart. Luth.
[3p.] fol. Wittemberg, *Hans Lufft*. 1540–41
p. 1 is dated 1541, p. 2 & 3 (*Das New Testament*) *are dated 1540. From beg. to 2 Kings xvi. the text of p1 is that revised in 1539–40; after that point it is the earlier one. The pages of this ed. are much smaller than those of Lufft's great revised Bible, below.*
„ „ *a. ed. revised by Luther & others, w. same wording but diff. woodcut border to title.* [2p; p1, 350 ff. p2, *wanting*]. lafol. Wittemberg, *Hans Lufft*. 1541
Bibel. Alt u. new Test., durch Johañ Ecken, auf hochteutsch, verdolmetscht. fol. Ingolstat, *S. Weissenhorn*. 1550
[*Genesis–Chronicles. Luther's vers. annot. by J. Salmuth, known as the Crypto-Calvinist. Bible, or Crell's Bible. No tp.; no more published. Some copies have tp.* "Die fünf Bücher Mosis," etc.] fol. [Dresden. 1590–93]
Biblia, vertheutscht &c. durch Johan Piscator &c., T1–4 (Alt. Test.) & Anhang (Apocrypha) [*in* 2v].
4°. Herborn, *C. Raben*. 1602–3
Das newe Test., durch M. Lutherum verteuscht. 8°. Herborn. 1621
Biblia Sacra, nach d. letzten Röm. Sixtiner Ed. durch C. Ulenberg. [*4 pagin*[s].] 8°. Collen, *J. Kreps*. [1630]
Das Newe Test., Trewlich aus d. Griech. ins Teutsche versetzet.
s8°. [Rakow]. 1630
Socinian vers. prep. by T. Crell & I. Stegmann &c., based on Luther's tr., altered for dogmatic purposes.
Das Neue Test., aus d. Grich. übers. [*By the Socinian* J. Felbinger]. s8°. Amsterdam, *C. Cunraden*. 1660
[N.T.] Eine mit d. Grund-Text genauer übereintreff. Übersetz. d. N.T. Ausgefertiget v. C. E. Triller. s8°. Amsterdam. 1703
Biblia Pentapla, Das ist: Die Bücher d. Heilg. Schrift, nach fünf-facher Deutscher Verdolmetschung. 1, Der Römisch-Cathol., durch C. Ulenberg. 2, Der Evang.-Luth. durch M. Luther. 3, Der Evang.-Reform. durch J. Piscator. 4, Der Jüd., im Alt. Test., des J. Athiæ, u. Der Neuen, im N.T., durch J. H. Reitzen. 5, Der Holländ., auf Verordnung d. General-Staaten. Alle mit ihren Vorreden, u. Parallelen &c.
3B. s4°. Wandesbeck bey Hamburg. 1710–12
Only B1 *has gen. tp.*; B2, Das Alte Test., T2; B3, Das Neue Test.
Das N.T. Auffs neue aus d. Grund verteutschet [*by* J. H. Reitz] &c. 2ter Druck. s8°. Franckfurt, *J. F. Regelein*. 1712
Sacra Biblia; nach d. letzten röm. Sixtiner Ed. übers. durch C. Ulenbergium &c. 8°. Bamberg. 1718
[N.T.] Eines abermahligen Versuchs z. Ubersetzung d. Bücher N.T., aus d. Original [*by* Count N. L. Zinzendorf. 2p *in* 1v].
s8°. Büdingen, *J. C. Stöhr*. 1739
Biblia verdeut. v. M. Luther, u. auf Verordn. Ernsts Herzogen z. Sachsen &c. v. etl. Theologen erkläret. [*Foll. by* Confessio, Augsburg, 1530. *With illust*[s]. *& portraits of Dukes of Saxony &c.*] lafol. Nürnberg, *J. A. Endter*. 1768
Die Schriften d. Alten [*&* Neuen] Test. Neu übers. v. J. C. W. Augusti u. W. M. L. de Wette. 5B. 8°. Heidelberg. 1809–14
Die heil. Schr. d. N.T.; übers. v. C. van Ess u. L. van Ess.
4[e] A. 8°. Sulzbach. 1818
Die heil. Schr. d. N.T. Uebers. v. J. H. Kistemaker.
s8°. Münster. 1825

Bible [*continued*].
GERMAN [*continued*].
Evang. sec. Matthæum vers. Francica sæc. 9, & Gothica sæc. 4. Hrsg. J. A. Schmeller. 8°. St. 1827
Die erste deutsche Bibel [c1466]; hrsg. v. W. Kurrelmeyer [Lit. V. in St. 251, 254, 258, 259, 266]. B6–10.
8°. Tübingen, 1909–15
Eine ostdeut. Apostelgesch. d. 14. Jhdts. (aus d. Königsberg. Staatsarchiv, Hs. A. 191). Hrsg. W. Ziesemer.
s8°. Halle (Saale). 1927
——: [LOW GERMAN].
[*f*[*a*]*1 title*]: De Biblie mit vlitigher achtinghe: recht na deme latine in dudesck auerghesettet Mit vorluchtinghę vnde glose: des . . . Nicolai de lyra &c.; *f*[*a*]*1 verso*, [*a*]*2*, [*a*]*3* de delenghe vnde inholdynghe desses bokes; *f*[*a*]*3 verso*–[*a*]*6 verso* de vorrede sunte hieronimi; *f. b1–dd8 Old Testament & Apocrypha; fdd8 verso–qq6 New Testament; qq6 verso blank. f. qq6 colophon:* Deme alweldigheme gade deme hēmelscheme vadere sy vmmetlike danknamicheyt &c. Vnde mit dessen erne bokstaven ghedrucket vnde selichliken vullēbracht vormiddelst Steffen arndes.
fol. [Lubick, *Steffen Arndes*. 19 Nov. 1494]
492 leaves, double cols., 66 lines, headlines. Sig. [*a*] *1–6; b–z, ꝫ, c̄, A–E in eights; F, G in sixes; H, I in eights; K–M in sixes; N, O in eights; P, Q in sixes; R–Z, aa–oo in eights; pp, qq in sixes. Hain 3143.*
Biblia dudesch dat erste [ander] deel. [*Ends*: Hyr endiget sick dat boek der heymeliken openbaringe . . . dar myt ook geendet wert . . . de bibel vor alle andere dudesche Bibelen Lutterer uñ klarer na rechtem warem dudeschem uñ sessicher sprake . . . mit over-Schriften by dem meysten deel der Capittel, und mit figurē de hystorien bedudende &c.
2d. fol. [Halberstad. 1522]
Written in purer Low Saxon dialect than the preced. Bibles of Cologne & Lübeck. C. D. on tp. & elsewhere possibly represent the printer C. Drake. Many of the woodcuts bear the date 1520. Sometimes attrib. to L. Trutebul.
Dath nyge Testament tho dude. [*w. 21 full-page woodcuts by L. Cranach to Bk. of Revelation*].
fol. Vuittemberg. [*Mich. Lotther*. 1528]
Last leaf (*Sign. ee 4*), *wanting, is supplied in Ms.*
De Biblie uth der uthlegginge Doct. M. Luthers yn dyth düdesche ulitich uthgesettet [*by* J. Hoddersen?] mit sundergen underrichtingen [*by* J. Bugenhagen]. fol. Lübeck. 1533
[ff. 94, 127, 75, 118, 70, 149. *The coloph. bears the date* 1 Ap. 1534.
„ „ [*a. issue of the same ed., w. title*]: Biblia: dat ys de gantze Hillige schrifft, Düdesch, Upt nye togerichtet, und mit ulite corrigert D. Mart. Luth. Inn der Keyserliken Stadt Lübeck dorch Ludowich Dyetz gedrückert MDXXXIII. fol. Lübeck. 1533
Biblia: dat ys: de gantze Hillige Schrifft. Vordüdtschet dorch D. Marti. Luth. Uth der lesten Correctur, vorbetert &c. [J. Bugenhagen Pomer (*his expos. on Gen.–Esther, Prov., Eccl., Song of Sol., & Mat.–Acts*)—Summaria aver dat olde Test. (*except Psalms*) dorch M. Vitum Theodorum. [357, 155, 87, 165 *numbered folios in* 2v].
fol. Magdeborch, *Hans Walther*. 1545
Founded on Luther's latest revis. of the text publ. in 1544 in the High-German Bible of H. Lufft, Wittenberg, 1545. The gen. tp. & tps. to De Propheten *&* Dat Nye Testament *have woodcut borders. Init. letters are printed woodcuts. Numerous woodcut illust*[s]. *The comm. by Bugenhagen & Theodorus follow p1* (*fol. 357*) *& are not foliated but have sep. sign*[s].
Biblia, Sassisch. M. Luth. Uppet nye mit flyte dörchgesehn &c. [*Rev. by D. Wolder*]. fol. Hamborch, *J. Lucius d. Jüng*. 1596
——: [SWISS-GERMAN].
Das gantz Nüw Testament recht grüntlich vertütscht. Mit gar gelerten u. richtigen vorreden, Ein gnugsam Register &c.
fol. Zürich, *Christoffel Froschouer*. 1524
Woodcut-border to tp., & woodcuts of Evangelists &c. before each book. First Protestant version in Swiss-German.
Das Alt Testament dütsch, der ursprüngl. Ebreischen waarheyt nach uff das allertrüwlichest verdütschet. [Genesis–Hohelied]. fol. Zürich, *C. Froschouer*. 1525
The vol. cont. Prophets issued in 1529 is wanting & Apocrypha.
Bibel Teütsch. 8°. Zürich, *C. Froschouer*. 1542
——: REFERENCES.
see BECK (M.) Versio Lutheri vindicata, 1696–98.
„ BERGHAUER (J. T. A.) Βιβλιομαχεία: Bibl. Feld-Zug viel. verfälschten Bibelen, 1746.
„ BINDSEIL (H. E.) Verzeichniss d. Orig.-Ausgaben d. Luther. Bibelübers., 1841.
„ BRENTANO (D. v.) Die heil. Schrift d. N.T.; hrsg. D. v. B, 2T *in* 3B., 1790–91.
„ —— Das letzte Wort ü. d. B. Bibelübersetzung, 1793.
„ GIESE (G. C.) Hist. Nachr. v. d. Bibelübersetzung M. Luthers &c., 1771.
„ GÖZ (J. A.) Gesch.-lit. Überblick ü. Luthers Dolmetschung &c. in d. heil. Schr., 1824.

Bible [*continued*].

GERMAN : REFERENCES [*continued*].

see GÖZE (J. M.) Vergleich. d. Orig.-Ausg. d. Uebers. v. Luther, 1517–45 &c., 1777–79.
,, —— Versuch e. Hist. d. niedersächs. Bibeln, 1470–1621, 1775.
,, HAMBURG : STAATS-U. UNIVERSITÄTSBIBL. Die deut. Bibel v. 15. bis 18. Jhdt. : Ausstell., 1922.
,, HERBORN. Trewhertzige &c. Warnung vor d. zu Herborn nachgedr. Deudt. B. &c., 1598.
,, KRAFFT (J. M.) Hist. Nachr. v. d. 1534 in Wittenberg bey H. Lufften gedr. B. Lutheri, 1735.
,, LUTHER (M.) Werke : d. Deutsche Bibel, B4, 5, 1914–23.
,, MAYER (J. F.) Hist. versionis Germ. Bibl. M. Lutheri, 1750 ?.
,, NAST (J.) Hist.-crit. Nachr. v. d. 6 ersten teutschen B.-Ausg., 1767.
,, PALM (J. G.) Hist. d. deut. Bibelübersetzung D. M. Lutheri, 1517–34, 1772.
,, PANZER (G. W.) Ausführl. Beschreib. d. ält. Augsburg. Ausgaben d. B., 1780.
,, †—— Entwurf e. vollst. Gesch. d. deut. Bibelübers. M. Luthers, 1517–81, 1783 ; Zusätze, 1791.
,, —— Litt. Nachr. v. d. allerält. gedr. deut. Bibeln, Nürnberg, 1777.
,, —— Versuch e. kurzen Gesch. d. röm. cath. deut. Bibelübersetzung, 1781.
,, PAREUS (D.) Rettung der z. Newstadt a. d. H. 87 & 91 getruckten Bibel &c., 1592.
,, RAITHIUS (B.) Vindiciæ vers. M. Lutheri labore ed., 1676.
,, RISCH (A.) Luthers Bibelverdeutschung, 1922.
,, SCHMIDT (J. L.) Die göttl. Schr., T1, Gesetze d. Jisraelen, 1735.
,, SEILER (G. F.) Uebers. d. N.T., 2T, 1806.
,, SINNHOLD (J. N.) Ausführl. Hist. d. Wertheim. B., 1735, 1739.
,, STIER (E. R.) Altes u. Neues in deut. B., 1828.
,, WEGNER (G.) Ad M. Lutheri version. B. Germ. obs., 1701.
,, ZELTNER (G. G.) De novis B. version. Germ., 1707.

GIPSY.

Embéo e Majaró Lucas. [*Tr. by George Borrow*].
s8º. [Madrid, *B.F.B.S.*] 1837

GOSPELS, *see also* ARMENIAN ; CHEREMISS ; COPTIC ; GEORGIAN ; GERMAN *above* ; MONGOLIAN ; SINGHALESE ; TAMIL ; WEND *below*.

Θεῖον καὶ ἱερὸν Εὐαγγέλιον. la8º. [Venetiis. 1588]

Evangeliarum quadruplex Lat. vers. antiq., seu vet. Italicæ, in lucem ed. ex cod. manuscr. a J. Blanchino.
2p *in* 4v. fol. Romæ, *A. de Rubeis*. 1749

Bezæ cod. Cantab. : exact copy in ordinary type, Gospels & Acts. Ed., w. intr. &c. by F. H. Scrivener. [*Gr. & Lat.*]
4º. C. 1864

Evangeliarium aus d. Domschatze zu Bamberg, *see* MÜNCHEN. Miniaturen ; hrsg. G. Leidinger, H6, 1914.

The Pepysian Gospel harmony. Ed. M. Goates. [E.E.T.S., 157]. 8º. 1922

see ABBOTT (E. A.) " Righteousness " in the G., 1918.
,, ABRAHAMS (I.) Sts. in Pharisaism & the G., s2, 1924.
,, ÆMILIUS (G.) Evang. heroico carmine reddita, 1554.
,, AGRICOLA (D.) Passio Domini sec. seriem 4 evangel. &c., 1514.
,, BOSSUET (J. B.) Méditations [*in h.* Œ., t9, 10, 1815–16].
,, BOYS (J.) Workes, expos. of festivall G. &c., 1622.
,, BUCER (M.) In sacra quatuor Evang., enarr., 1536.
,, BUGENHAGEN (J.) Annotationes, concordia Evang. &c., 1524.
,, BULLINGER (H.) N.T. hist. Evangel. &c., 1554.
,, BULTMANN (R.) Gesch. d. synopt. Tradition, 1921.
,, BURKITT (F. C.) The G. hist. & its transmission, 1920.
,, CALIXTUS (G.) Quatuor Evang. script. concordia &c., 1624.
,, CALVIN (J.) Comm. on harmony ; tr., 3v, 1845–46.
,, —— Harmonie upon the Evangelists, 1584.
,, CAMERARIUS (J.) Notatio figurarum sermonis in libris 4 Evang., 1572.
,, CANISIUS (P.) Comm. de verbi Dei corruptelis liber primus &c., 1571.
,, CARPENTER (J. E.) The first 3 G., 4th ed., 1906.
,, CRADOCK (S.) The harmony of the four Evang. &c., 1668.
,, CRUM (J. M. C.) Orig. Jerusalem G., 1927.
,, DIEU (L. DE). Animadv. &c. in 4 Evang., 1631.
,, DODGSON (C.) Holzschnitte zu 2 nürnberg. Andachtsbüchern (Evangelia, 1534 &c.), 1909.
,, EBRARD (J. H. A.) G. hist. ; tr., 1863.
,, ECK (J. v.) Christenl. ausslegung d. Evang. &c., T1, 2, 1530.
,, EVANGELISTARION. Ἐυαγγελιστάριον, 1588.
,, GRANT (F. C.) Econ. background of the G., 1926.
,, GRIESBACH (J. J.) Synopsis Evang. &c., 1797.
,, GULIELMUS, *Paris*. Postilla super Evang. &c., 1494 ; 1508.
,, HARDT (H. V. DER). Exegesis loc. difficil., 1761.
,, HEYLYN (J.) Theolog. lectures &c., 1749.
,, HOSKIER (H. C.) The text of Codex Usserianus 2. r2, w. crit. notes &c., 1919.

Bible [*continued*].

GOSPELS [*continued*].

see HUCK (A.) Synopse d. 3 ersten Evang., 1922.
,, HYMNI & collectæ, item Evang. &c., 1573.
,, IMP. AKAD. NAUK. Сборникъ, т97 (Поученія на еванг., 1758 Петровъ), 1921.
,, JONES (M.) The 4 Gs. : th. lit. hist. &c., 1921.
,, JONGE (B. DE). Conciones 3 super E. festorum tot. a., 1616.
,, LE FÈVRE (J.) Comm. initiatorii in 4 Evang., 1526.
,, LIETZMANN (H.), *ed.* Hdbh. z. N.T., B2i ; erkl. v. E. Klostermann &c., 1919.
,, LUTHER (M.) Ausleg. d. Epist. u. Evang. &c., 1532.
,, MALDONATUS (J.) Comm. in 4 Evang., 2t, 1596–97.
,, MEIER (G.) Homel. in Evang. [*in* Op., t3, 1570].
,, MEISNER (B.) Medit. sacræ in Evang. dominic., 1619.
,, MELANCHTHON (P.) In Evang. annot., 1552.
,, METTENLEITER (D.) Sonntägl. Evang. d. kathol. Kirchenjahres, 1856.
,, MIMPRISS (R.) The treasury harmony &c. of the 4 Evang. &c., 1855.
,, MONTEFIORE (C. G.), *ed.* The Synoptic G., 2v, 1927.
,, NEWCOME (W.) An harmony of the G., *in Greek*, 1778.
,, NORTON (A.) Evid. of genuineness of G., 2v, 1847.
,, OLSHAUSEN (H.) Bibl. comm. on the G. &c. ; tr., 4v, 1864–65.
,, OSIANDER (A.) Die gantze evang. hist. &c., 1541.
,, —— Harmoniæ Evang. lib. 3, Gr. & Lat., 1537.
,, OTFRIED *of Weissenburg*. Volumen Evang., 1728.
,, PELLICANUS (C.) In 4 Evang. &c. comm., 1537.
,, PINDER (U.) Speculum passionis &c. cum textu quatuor evãgelistarũ &c., 1507.
,, ROBINSON (E.) A harmony of the 4 G., 1847.
,, RULE (W. H.) Los Cuatro Evanj. ; tr. é ilust. con notas, 1841.
,, SARCERIUS (E.) In Evang. Dominic. postilla, 1541.
,, STANTON (V. H.) The Gs. as hist. docs., p3, 1920.
,, STAPLETON (T.) Promptuarium super Evang. per tot. Quadrages., 1594.
,, —— Promptuarium super E. tot. anni Dominicalia quam de Festis, 2p, 1594.
,, STIER (E. R.) Words of the Lord Jesus ; tr., 8v, 1855–58.
,, STORR (G. C.) Diss. de Evang. Arabicis, 1775.
,, STREETER (B. H.) The 4 Gospels, 1924.
,, SÜSKIND (F. G. v.) Symbol. ad illust. quædam Evang. loca, 3p, 1802–4.
,, THAMER (J. H.) Sched. de orig. &c. pericoparum &c., 1734.
,, THEOPHYLACTUS, *abp. of Achrida*. Opera, t1, Comm. in 4 Evang., 1754.
,, TISCHENDORF (L. F. C.) When were our G. written ? ; tr., 1866 ; 2nd ed., 1867.
,, TISSOT (J. J.) Life of Jesus Christ : compos. f. G., w. notes &c., tr., 2v, 1897.
,, TOWNSON (T.) Discourses on the 4 G. &c., 1778.
,, TRAPP (J.) Comm. upon the 4 Evang. &c., 1647.
,, VERDELLAY (J. DE). Quest. &c. supra evãg. dominic. &c., 1508.
,, WEGLINUS (T.) Prodromus disput. publ. in Johannem cont. proleg. in omnes Evang., 1624.
,, WHITE (J.), *ed.* Sacr. Evang. vers. Syriaca, &c. (*Syr. & Lat.*), 1778.
,, WILSON (M.) Conc. harmony of the 4 G., 1888.
,, WUJEK (J.) Zywot y nauka pana naszego Jesu Christa ; albo Ewang. ze czterech iedna &c., 1597.
,, ZWINGLI (U.) In Evang. hist. de Domino, 1539.

GREEK, *see also* GOSPELS *above* ; NEW TEST. (GREEK) ; OCTATEUCH ; POLYGLOT ; SEPTUAGINT *below*.

Πάντα τὰ κατ' ἐξοχὴν καλούμενα Βιβλία. Sacræ Scr. vet., novæque omnia. [*p1 ed. by* Andreas Asulanus, *p2 by* Federicus Asulanus, *& p3* (*New Test.*) *by* Franciscus Asulanus. ff. 451].
fol. Venetiis, *Aldus & Andreas socer*. 1518

Foliation continuous, but irregular. First ed. of the whole Bible in Greek, except that contained in the Polyglot of Complutum, 1514–17 ; & that was not issued to the public till 1520.

Bibliorum Sacr. Græcus Codex Vaticanus. Auspice Pio IX collatis studiis C. Vercellone & J. Cozza ed. [*Facsimile*].
6t. la4º. Romæ. 1868–81

t6, Auspice Leone XIII cum prolegomenis, comms. & tabulis H. C. Fabiani & J. Cozza ed.

GREEK (MODERN), *see also* ALBANIAN *above*.

Ἡ Καινὴ Διαθήκη : Μαξίμου τοῦ Καλλιουπολίτου μετάφρασις, [*earliest pr. ed. in Mod. Gr.*], 1638, *see* NEW TEST. [GREEK] *below*.

Ἡ Καινὴ Διαθήκη &c. s8º. [London]. 1705

Ἡ Καινὴ Διαθήκη. 8º. ἐν Κανταβριγίᾳ. 1884

GREENLAND DIALECT, *see* ESKIMO *above*.

HABAKKUK.

see GRYNÆUS (J. J.) Hypomnemata in H. libr., 1582.
,, KALINSKY (J. G.) Vaticinia Chabacuci, 1748.

HAGGAI.

see BALDUIN (F.) In 3 postremos prophetas comm., 1610.
,, ROSS (J.) Bp. of Exeter's &c. interp. of H., 1786.

Bible [*continued*].

HEBREW, *see also* DANIEL *above*; POLYGLOT; PSALMS *below*.

חמשה חומשי תורה [*Foll. by the remaining books of the O.T.*] s4°. [Venice, *Daniel Bomberg*. 1521]
D. Bomberg's 2nd 4o. ed.; ed. by orthod. Jews (2 *brothers named Adelkind*), *& intended for Jews.*

Hebraica Biblia Lat. planeque nova Sebast. Munsteri tralatione: adj. insuper e Rabinorum comentariis annotat. &c. [*Heb. & Lat.*] 2t [t2 *has tp.* Vet. Instrumenti t2]. fol. Basileæ, *Ex officina Bebeliana*. 1534–35

[*Hebrew Bible after the ed. of Venice 1548, w. pref. by Jacob ben Chayim &c. Rev. & ed. by J. Buxtorf the elder. No gen. tp. Tp*s. *to var. parts in Hebrew. Foliation contin., but the Jerusalem Targum, The Massorah Magna & the Haphtaroth have sep. foliations.*] [*b. in 3v*]. fol. [*Basel*. 1618–19]
The 6th Rabbinic Bible.

Biblia parva H.-Lat. Dicta insign. Op. &c. H. Opitii. 3a. ed. s8°. Lips. 1689

Biblia, sine punctis &c. Ad Leusden. ed. adornata. [*ed. G. Desmaretz*]. s8°. Amstelædami. 1701

חמשה חומשי תורה. [Pentateuch, Megilloth &c. w. targum of Onkelos]. s8°. [Amsterdam. 1712]

ספר קהלות משה. [*Ed. & pr. by Moses b. Simeon of Frankfort*]. 4v. fol. Amsterdam. 1724–27
מסורה גדולה *in v4 has sep. foliation. The 7th Rabbinic Bible.*

Biblia Heb. sec. ed. Belgicam E. van der Hooght, una cum vers. Lat. S. Schmidii. s4°. Lipsiæ. 1740

Biblia Heb., cum notis & vers. Lat. ad notas crit. facta. Acc. libri Græci qui Deutero-Canonici vocantur. Aut. C. F. Houbigant. 4t. fol. Lutetiæ Paris., *Briasson & Durand*. 1753

Pentateuchus Heb.-Samaritanus charactere Heb.-Chaldaico. Ed. cura B. Blayney. 8°. Oxonii. 1790

Biblia Heb., without points, after text of Kennicott. Notes &c. by B. Boothroyd. 2v. *in* 1. 4°. Pontefract. [1810–16]

Biblia Heb., sec. ult. ed. J. Athiæ a J. Leusden recog., rec. & notis illust. ab E. v. d. Hooght. Ed. nova recog. &c. a Judah D'Allemand. 2t *in* 1v. 8°. Londini. 1825

La Bible, tr. nouv., avec l'héb. en regard. Avec notes &c. par S. Cahen. 18t. 8°. 1831–39

ספר תורה נביאים וכתובים. 8°. Wien. 1874

ספרי הברית החדשה. Hebr. N.T. [Delitzsch's 5th ed.] s8°. [*B.& F.B.S.*] 1883

see MASSORAH.
,, OLD TESTAMENT *below for commentaries.*

HEBREWS, *see also* MATTHEW *below*.
For ed. in Internat. Crit. Comm. [*by J. Moffatt*], *see* BIBLE; GEN. COMM.
see BINNEY (T.) Pract. power of faith &c.: 11th chap. of H., 1830.
,, CALVIN (J.) Comm. on Ep. to the H.; tr., 1853.
,, CARPZOV (J. B.) Sacræ exercit. in S. Pauli epist. ad H., 1750.
,, DERING (E.) 17 lectures upon parte of H., 1583.
,, —— 27 lectures &c., c. 1590.
,, GOUGE (W.) Comm. on Ep. to the H., 2v, 1655.
,, HORN (C.) In Epist. Hebr., 1655.
,, HYPERIUS (A.) Comm., 1584.
,, LIETZMANN (H.), *ed.* Hdbh. z. N.T., B4iii; erkl. v. H. Windisch, 1913.
,, LIMBORCH (P. VAN). Comm. in Acta & in Epist. ad H. &c., 1711.
,, ŒCOLAMPADIUS (J.) In epist. ad H. explan., 1538.
,, OWEN (J.) Works, v18–24, 1862.
,, SCHMID (S.) In epist. ad H. comm., 1698.
,, SCOTT (E. F.) H.: its doctr. & signif., 1922.
,, SYKES (A. A.) Paraphrase &c. upon H., 1755.
,, VAUGHAN (C. J.) Epistle to the H. [*Greek*] w. notes, 1891.

HEPTATEUCH, *see also* ANGLO-SAXON *above*.
see BILLEN (A. V.) Old Lat. texts of the H., 1927.
,, ORIGEN. O.'s Werke, B6, 7, Homilien z. H. in Rufins Übers &c., 2T, 1920–21.

HINDI.
N.T. [*Tr. by the missionaries at Serampore. Tp*s. *in Eng. & Hindi*]. 4°. Serampore. 1811
[Joshua-Esther]. 8°. [Serampore. 1816]
Holy Bible, v4, Prophet. books. 8°. Serampore. 1818
[Matthew to Luke iii, 34 in Awadhi or Kausali dialect]. 8°. [Serampore. 1820]
The Holy Bible, tr. into the Bhugelkhunda [Bagheli] lang. by Serampore missionaries. v5, N.T. [*No more publ.*] 8°. Serampore. 1821
Holy Bible, tr. into Kunouj lang., v5, N.T. [*No more publ.*] 8°. Serampore. 1821
Holy Bible, tr. f. the Hebrew. v2. 8°. Allahabad. 1883
N.T. 8°. Allahabad. 1885
[Gospels. *Pagin. contin., no tp. but each Gospel has pr. slip on wrapper* "St. Matthew (&c.) in Nagree"]. 8°. Serampore. *n.d.*

HINDUSTANI [URDU].
4 priora Geneseos cap. Tr. a B. Schulzio. Ed. J. H. Callenbergius. s8°. Halæ. 1745
Psalterium. Tr. a B. Schultzio. Ed. J. H. Callenbergius. s8°. Halæ. 1747

Bible [*continued*].

HINDUSTANI [URDU] [*continued*].
Liber Danielis &c., Evang. Lucæ, Acta, Rom., Cor., Gal., Eph., Phil., Col., Thess., Tim., Tit., Philem., Hebr.; *b. in 1v, w. sep. tp*s. *in Hindustani & Lat.*] Tr. a B. Schultzio. Ed. J. H. Callenbergius. s8°. Halæ. 1749–50
Epist. Jacobi. Tr. a B. Schultzio. Ed. J. H. Callenbergius. s8°. Halæ. 1750
Petri epist. 1 & 2. Tr. a B. Schultzio. Ed. J. H. Callenbergius. s8°. Halæ. 1750
[Revelation. Tr. B. Schultze]. 8°. [Halle. 1758]
N.T. Tr. H. Martyn. 8°. Serampore. 1814
[Isaiah]. 8°. [Calcutta ?]. 1825
[Proverbs]. 8°. [Calcutta ?]. 1826

HOSEA.
see BURROUGHS (J.) Expos. of chap. 8–9 of H., 1650.
,, DATHE (J. A.) *&* S. F. N. MORUS. Disput. in Aquilæ reliq. interpret. H., 1757.
,, FORIS (F.) Restit. Israel futura, ex H., III, 4, 5, 1712.
,, HARDT (H. V. D.) H. ant. Chaldaicâ Jonathanis paraphrasi &c., 1775.
,, LAMBERT (F.) In Oseam comm., 1525.
,, PAREUS (D.) In H. proph. comm., cum tr., 1616.
,, POCOCK (E.) Comm. on H., 1685.
,, REYNOLDS (E.) Works: Explic. of Chap. XIV of H., 1678.
,, SCHMID (S.) In Hoseam comm., 1687.
,, SCOTT (M.) Message of H., 1921.

HUNGARIAN, *see also* SOLOMON *below*.
Vy̆ Testamentũ Magár ńelweñ, mellét az Gȏrȏg, es Diak ńelwbȏl vyc nnan fordy̆tank &c. [*Tr. by János Erdösi* (*Sylvester*)]. s4°. [Vyszghetben, *Abadi Benedek*. 1541]
First ed. of N.T. in Hungarian.
Bölts Salomon Kíralnac Könyuei. 1, Proverbia. 2, Ecclesiastes. 3, Canticum Cant. 4, Sapientiæ. Magyar nyelven [*by* Gaspar Heltai]. s8°. Colosvarba, *Heltai & Hoffgref*. 1551 [1552]
Bound w. above is Ecclesiasticus, 1551, *q.v.*
Soltar, Magyar nyvelen Heltai Gaspar. [*Tp. & all after fol. 290 wanting*]. s4°. Colosvarat. 1560
A Biblianac másodic része. [Joshua, Judges, Ruth, Samuel & Kings. *Tr. by* Gaspar Heltai]. s4°. Colosvarot, *Heltai*. 1565
Tp., sig. A128 & B128 wanting. First ed. of G. H.'s tr. for use of the Protestants of the Helvetic Confess. in Hungary.
[Az ket Samvel kȏnyueiek, es az ket Kirali kȏnyveknek az Sido nielvnek igassagobol &c. *Tr. by Peter Melius or Juhsz*]. sfol. [Debreczenbe. 1565]
4 leaves prelim. matter, the first being the tp., which is wanting, foll. by 239 leaves of text.
Szent Biblia. Magyar nyelyvre forditatott Caroli Gaspar. [*Foll*d. *by* Soltari, Magyar versekre ford. Molnar, *w. sep. tp. & pagin.*] s8°. Oppenhemiumban. 1612
,, ,, ...[*a. ed.*] s8°. Amstelodamban. 1700
Szent Biblia. Magyarra fordiotta Káldi György Pap. [Oktato intes &c. *at the end has sep. pagin.*] fol. Béchben. [Vienna], *Formika M*. 1626
Uj Test. Görög nyelvböl Magyarrá forditatott &c. Torkos Andras. s8°. Wittembergában. 1736
Szent Biblia. 8°. Ultrajektomban, *Altheer*. 1794
Molnár's revis. of Károli's Bible, 1st pref. dated 1795, 2nd 1794.
Biblia Esmérteti W. J. M. [*i.e.* W. Jankovich Miklos ?]. 8°. [Pesten. 1834]
see BOD (P.) A' Szent Bibl. hist., &c., 1748.
,, VERSEGI (F.) Diss. de vers. Hung. scr. sacr., 1822.

ICELANDIC.
Biblia, þad er, öll Heilög Ritning vtlögd a Norrænu [*Various parts being tr. chiefly f. the Latin by Oddr Gottskálksson, Gissr Einarsson & Gísli Jónsson, rev. & corr. by Guðbrandr Thorláksson, bp. of Hólar & the rest tr. by the latter*]. Med Formalum Doct. Martini Lutheri. fol. a Holum af Jone Jons Syne. 1584
Ff. 295, 192, 124. The first Icelandic Bible.

ILLYRIAN, *see* CROATIAN *above*.

IRISH.
Tiomna Nuadh ar natharruing go Gaoidheilg. Re Huilliam O Domhnuill. s4°. Lunnduin. 1681
Leabhuir na Seitiomna &c. The Books of the O.T. Tr. into Irish by W. Bedel. s4°. 1685
The ed. princ. of the O.T. in Irish.
Tiomna Nuadh Gaoidheilg re V. Domhnuill. s8°. Lunnduin, *R. Ebheringtham*. 1690
An Biobla Naomta. s8°. [D.] 1852

ISAIAH, *see also* HINDUSTANI *above*.
see ABRAHAM *ben Meir Aben Ezra*. Comm. on I.; ed. & tr. M. Friedländer, 2v, 1873.
,, ÆLRED, *abbot of Rievaulx*. Op. omnia, 1531.
,, BUTT (G.) Isaiah versified, 1785.
,, CALVIN (J.) Comm. on I.; tr., 4v, 1850–54.
,, DELITZSCH (F.) Comm. on I.; tr. Driver, 2v, 1890.
,, DURHAM (J.) Christ crucify'd: sermons on 53d ch. of I., 4th ed., 1723.
,, GUNKEL (H.) Ein Vorläufer Jesu [I. 40–55], 1921.
,, HAYMO, *bp. of Halberstadt*. In Esaiam comm. libri 3, 1531.

Bible [*continued*].
ISAIAH [*continued*].
see HENDERSON (E.) Bk. of Prophet I., w. comm. &c., 1840.
,, HYPERIUS (A.) In I. proph. oracula annot., 1574.
,, LOWTH (W.) Comm., 1714.
,, LÜTKEMANN (L.) & A. RAHLFS. Hexaplarische Randnoten zu I. 1–16, 1915.
,, MÜLLER (B.) Cap. 63 Esaiæ in 5 Predigten, 1604.
,, MUSCULUS (W.) In Esaiam comm., 1570.
,, NEUBAUER (A.) 53rd chap. of I., acc. to Jewish interpreters, 2v, 1876–77.
,, ŒCOLAMPADIUS (J.) In Iesaiam &c. comm., 1558.
,, —— In I. hypomnematon libri 6, 1525.
,, ORELLI (C. v.) The prophecies of I.; tr., 1889.
,, SCHMID (S.) Comm. supra prophetias J., 1693.
,, SCHNELL (S.) Disput.: quæ I. Abravanel Hebr. ad cap. 34. Essaiæ scr., 1647.
,, SCHNURRER (C. F.) Disput. ad Es. cap. 27, 1785.
,, —— Obs. ad vaticinia J., 1781.
,, SCOTT (M.) Textual discov. in I. &c., 1927.
,, STOCK (J.) Book of I. in Heb. & Eng., w. notes, 1803.
,, WESSEL (J.) Fasc. dissert. &c., Jes. cap. 54, 1756.
,, ZWINGLI (U.) Complanationis I. fœt. prima, 1529.
ISUBU.
Ekwali ya bwam, e matilabe na Matiyu. s8º. Bimbia, W. Afr. 1846
ITALIAN, *see also* LATIN; PIEDMONTESE *below*.
Biblia in lingua materna con postille & figure, &c. [*Malermi's version*]. fol. Venetiis, *B. de Bendoni*. 1535
Il Nuovo ed Eterno Testamento, in Toscano tr. per M. Theofilo. s8º. Lione. 1551
Il Nuovo Testamento, Lat. & volgare &c. [v1 (*Gospels & Acts*); v2 *wanting*]. s8º. Lyone, *G. Rovillio*. 1558
A revis. of Brucioli's Ital. vers. pr. side by side w. Erasmus' Lat. tr.
La Bibia tr. in lingua volgare &c. [*Rev. & corr. ed. of Brucioli's version. 2 pagin^s.*] 4º. [Geneva], *F. Durone*. 1562
La Bibbia. Nuov. tr. da G. Diodati. [Apoc. & N.T., *w. sep. pagin^s.*] 4º. [Geneva]. 1607
Il Nuovo Test. tr. da G. Diodati. s8º. [Geneva]. 1608
La Sacra Bibbia. Tr. e comm. da G. Diodati. 2ª. ed. sfol. Geneva. 1641
La Santa Biblia in lingua ital. &c. [*Diodati's version*; ed. Mattia d'Erberg]. fol. Colonia. 1712
Bibbia Sacra, sec. la Volgata. Tr. da A. Martini. 8º. Londra. 1828
La Sacra Bibbia. Sec. la tr. di G. Diodati. s8º. Londres. 1874
JAMES, *see also* HINDUSTANI *above*.
see HORN (C.) In Epist. J. &c. expos., 1654.
,, LIETZMANN (H.), *ed.* Hdbh. z. N.T., B4ii; erkl. v. H. Windisch, 1911.
,, MANTON (T.) Pract. comm. on J., 1651.
,, PANECIUS (N.) J. Epist. vers. Arabica, 1694.
,, RENDALL (G. H.) Epist. of St. J. & Judaic Xty., 1927.
,, SCHMID (S.) Fasc. disput^s. Epist. J. &c., 1685.
,, STIER (E. R.) Words of the risen Saviour & comm. on St. J.; tr., 1869.
,, ZWINGLI (U.) Brevis in epist. J. expos. &c., 1533.
JEREMIAH.
Hieremiæ proph. Threni. [*Pref. by P. Melanchthon; b. w.* Psalterium Hebr., 1533]. s8º. [Wittembergæ. 1524]
see CALVIN (J.) Comm^s. on J. &c.; tr., 5v, 1850–55.
,, LOWTH (W.) Comm., 1718.
,, ŒCOLAMPADIUS (J.) In Hier. comm. libri 3, 1533.
,, SCHMID (S.) Comm. in librum J., 2t, 1706.
,, SCHNURRER (C. F.) Observ. ad vaticinia J., 4p, 1793.
,, SKINNER (J.) Prophecy & relig.: life of J., 1922.
,, SMITH (G. A.) Jeremiah, 1923.
,, STEPHEN (D.) J., the prophet of hope, 1923.
,, ZWINGLI (U.) Complanationis J. fœt. prima, 1531.
JOB.
For ed. in Internat. Crit. Comm. [*by S. R. Driver & G. B. Gray*], *see under* BIBLE: GEN. COMM.
Le livre de Job; vers. copte bohaïrique; publ. & tr. par E. Porcher, *see* GRAFFIN (R.) & F. NAU. Patr. or., t18, 1924.
see BALL (C. J.) Book of J., rev. text & version, 1922.
,, BEZA (T.) I. expounded, 1589.
,, BICKELL (G.) Krit. Bearb. d. Iobdialogs, 1892.
,, DELITZSCH (F.) Bibl. comm. on J.; tr., 1866.
,, DEVINE (M.) Story of the book of J., 1921.
,, DREXEL (H.) Iobus div. providentiæ theatrum, 1653.
,, GARNETT (J.) Diss. on J., 1749.
,, GREY (R.) Liber Iobi in vers. metrice div. (*Hebr. & Lat.*), 1742.
,, HASE (T.) De Liviathan J. &c., 1723.
,, HENKE (H. P. C.) Disq. num liber J. c. Odyssea Homeri comparari possit? 1773.
,, HESYCHIUS, *of Jerusalem*. Expos. [*in Arm.*], ed. Tchraqean, 1913.
,, JASTROW (M.) Bk. of J., origin, growth &c., w. n. tr. &c., 1920.
,, KROMAYER (J. A.) Filia matri obstet., de usu ling. Arab. in addisc. Ebræa & explic. Scr. S., in lib. Jobi &c., 1707.
,, LANGHORNE (W.) J.: a poem, 1760.

Bible [*continued*].
JOB [*continued*].
see NICETAS. Catena Græc. patrum in Iob, 1637.
,, ŒCOLAMPADIUS (J.) In Iesaiam, Job &c. comm., 1558–67.
,, PATRICK (S.) Bk. of J. paraphras'd, 1710.
,, RASHI. Comm. Hebr. in prophetas, Hiobum &c.; Lat. versus, 1713.
,, ROSSEEUW SAINT HILAIRE (E. F. A.) Études relig., 1863.
,, SCHMID (S.) In libr. J. comm., 1705.
,, SCHULTENS (A.) Consid. ad nov. vers. libri J. [*in h.* Origines Hebr. &c., 2ª. ed., 1761].
,, —— Op. minora, 1769.
,, STRIGELIUS (V.) Liber Iob, 1575.
JOEL.
see DAVID, *ben J. Kimchi*. Joel &c. c. comm. D. K., 1530.
,, DRACONITES (J.) I. propheta, *Hebr. & Lat.*, 1565.
,, LAMBERT (F.) In J. comm., 1525 ?.
,, POCOCK (E.) A comm. on J., 1691.
JOHN (*Epistles & Gospel*), *see also* BATTA; COPTIC; ESKIMO *above*; KARELIAN; LEPCHA *below*.
see ALESIUS (A.) Comm. in Evang. Joh., 1553.
,, BAUER (W.) Das Johannesevangelium, 2e A., 1925.
,, BRIT. & FOR. BIBLE SOC. St. John iii, 16 in lang. & dialects, &c., 1878; 1925.
,, BULLINGER (H.) In epist. I. expos., 1532
,, —— In Evang. sec. J. comm. libri 10, 1548.
,, BURNEY (C. F.) Aramaic orig. of the 4th Gospel, 1922.
,, CALVIN (J.) Comm. on Gospel acc. to J.; tr., 2v, 1847.
,, —— Comm. upon S. J. [*in h.* Harmonie, 1584].
,, CANDLISH (R. S.) 1st Ep. of J. expounded, 1877.
,, CARPENTER (J. E.) The Johannine writings, 1927.
,, CHARNWOOD (G. R. B., *1st b.*) According to St. J., 1926.
,, CHRYSOSTOM. Comm. on Gospel (*in Armenian*), 1717.
,, CORDIER (B.) Catena patrum Græc. in S. J., 1630.
,, CREUTZIGER (C.) In Evang. J. enarr., 1546.
,, FRANCISCI (A.) Σύνοψσις primi cap. Joh. Evang., 1591.
,, GORE (C.) Epistles of St. J., 1920.
,, GRILL (J.) Untersuch. ü. d. Entstehung d. 4. Evangel., T2, 1923.
,, HENGSTENBERG (E. W.) Comm. on Gospel of J., 2v, 1865.
,, HILDERSAM (A.) 108 lectures on the 4th of J., 1632.
,, HOLLAND (H. S.) The 4th Gospel, 1923.
,, —— Philos. of faith & the 4th Gospel, 1920.
,, HORN (C.) In Epist. J. &c. expos., 1654.
,, HUNNIUS (E.) Op. Lat., t3, 1608.
,, KETTNER (F. E.) Hist. J. de Trinitate, I J. v, 7, 1713.
,, LAMPE (F. A.) Comm., 3t, 1724–26.
,, LIETZMANN (H.), *ed.* Hdbh. z. N.T., B2, Die Evang. II, J.; erkl. v. W. Bauer, 1912; B4ii, Die kathol. Briefe; erkl. v. H. Windisch, 1911.
,, LOISY (A.) Le 4e Evangile; 2e éd. refondue: les épitres dites de J., 1921.
,, MARLORAT (A.) A cathol. &c. expos., 1575.
,, MITTERNACHT (J. S.) Diss. de loco J. XXI, 22 &c., 1665.
,, MUSCULUS (W.) In J. Evang. comm., 1580.
,, NANA, *Syrian vardapet*. Expos. (*in Arm.*); ed. Q. A. Tchraqean, 1920.
,, NOLLOTH (C. F.) Fourth Evangelist, 1925.
,, ŒCOLAMPADIUS (J.) In epist. J. primam demegoriæ 21, 1524: 1525.
,, PROCKSCH (O.) Petrus u. J. bei Marcus u. Matthäus, 1920.
,, SAUNDERS (K.) The gospel for Asia, 1928.
,, SCHEDIUS (J.) Comm. in oraculum J. viii, 25, 1688.
,, SCHMID (S.) Comm. in prim. J. epist., 1707.
,, —— Resolutio cum paraphrasi verb. Evang. Joh. &c., 1699.
,, SIGEL (G.) Explan. prior. 5 cap. primi Evang. J. vers., 1587.
,, SMITH (P. V.) Fourth Gospel, hist. importance, 1926.
,, STANTON (V. H.) The Gospels as hist. doc^s., p3, The 4th G., 1920.
,, STETTINGER (G.) Gesch. d. J. Abschiedsreden; gegen K. Clemen, 1919.
,, SZLICHTING (J.) Notæ in G. Vechneri conc., super initium Evang. J., 1644.
,, THOLUCK (F. A. G.) Comm. on Gospel of St. J.; tr., 1860.
,, TOLETUS (F.) In J. Evang. comm., 1599.
,, WALTHER (R.) Homiliæ &c., 1575.
,, —— In I. Epist. &c. homiliæ 37, 1553.
,, WEGLINUS (T.) Prodromus disput. publ. in J. &c., 1624.
,, WELLHAUSEN (J.) Das Evang. J., 1908.
,, WENDT (H. H.) Die Johannesbriefe u. d. johan. Christentum, 1925.
,, WESTCOTT (B. F.) Epistles of J., Gr., w. notes &c., 1886.
,, WILD (J.) In Jesu Christi secund. J. Evangel. comm., 1558.
,, ZWINGLI (U.) In Evang. hist. &c. & J. Epist. &c., 1539.
JONAH.
see ANANIAS, *the translator*. On J. &c., *in Armenian*; ed. B. Sargisean, 1899.
,, BEERMANN (S.) Evang. rei integritas Hardtiana in negot. J., 1721.
,, KENNEDY (J.) Bk. of J., 1895.
,, MARTIN (A. D.) The Prophet J.: the book & the sign, 1926.

Bible [*continued*].
JONAH [*continued*].
see PATIENCE : an allit. version of J. by the poet of Pearl ; ed. I. Gollancz, 1913.
„ PHILO, *Judæus.* Paralipom. Arm., in Lat. tr. J. B. Aucher, 1826.
„ SIMPSON (W.) The J. legend : interp., 1899.
„ STAUDACHER (B. A.) Jonas vates, Æthiop. & Lat., 1706.
JOSHUA, *see also* HUNGARIAN *above.*
see CALVIN (J.) Comm[s]. on J. ; tr., 1854.
„ HOTTINGER (J. H.) Exercit. Anti-Morinianæ de Pentateucho Samaritano ; acc. Epitome J. &c., 1644.
„ KEIL (C. F.) Comm. on Bk. of J. ; tr., 1857.
„ —— & F. DELITZSCH. J. &c. ; tr., 1865.
„ PATRICK (S.) Comm. on J. &c., 1702.
„ SCHMID (S.) Comm. s. proph. Jesaiæ *&* Annot. in 8 priora cap. J., 1693.
JUDE.
see HORN (C.) In Epist. Joannis 1, 2, 3, & J. expos., 1654.
„ HYPERIUS (A.) Comm. in Pauli Epist. & in Epist. J., 1584.
„ JENKYN (W.) Expos. of J., 1652–54 ; 1656 ; 1839.
„ LIETZMANN (H.), *ed.* Handbuch z. N.T., B4ii ; erkl. v. H. Windisch, 1911.
„ OTES (S.) Explan. of St. J., 1633.
„ ZAHN (T.) Komm. z. N.T., B15 ; ausgelegt v. G. Wohlenberg, 3e A., 1923.
JUDGES.
see KEIL (C. F.) & F. DELITZSCH. Joshua, J. &c. ; tr., 1865.
„ NAUMANN (J. G.) Diss. de Jephtigenia &c., 1712.
„ PATRICK (S.) Comm. on J. &c., 1702.
„ SCHMID (S.) In librum J. comm., 1706.
„ THANCHUM *ben Joseph.* Ad libros V. T. comm., annotat. in loca J. ; Schnurrer, 1791.
KALMUK (WESTERN MONGOLIAN).
[Matthew, Luke & John. Tr. I. J. Schmidt, *each Gospel w. sep. tp. & pagin.*] la8°. [St. Petersburg. 1820 ?]
KARELIAN.
Святой Ювангели Матвѣйста. 8°. Пійтери. [St. P.] 1820
KAUSALI, *see* HINDI *above.*
KIFIOTI, *see* FIOTI *above.*
KINGS, *see also* HUNGARIAN *above.*
see BUGENHAGEN (J.) In Regum duos ult. lib. annot., 1525.
„ BURNEY (C. F.) Notes on Hebrew text of Bk. of K., w. intr. &c., 1903.
„ KEIL (C. F.) Comm. on Bks. of K. ; tr., 2v, 1857.
„ PATRICK (S.) Comm. upon the 2 Bks. of K., 1705.
„ THEOTOKES (N.), *ed.* Σειρὰ 51 ὑπομνηματίστων εἰς τὴν Ὀκτάτευχον καὶ τὰ τῶν βασιλείων, 2t, 1772–73.
KUNOUJ, *see* HINDI *above.*
LAMENTATIONS.
see JARAVA (H.) Los siete psalmos penit., las lamentaciones &c. ; [tr.] H. J., 1556.
LAPP (SWEDISH).
Tat Ajles Tjalog. s4°. Hernösandesne, *C. G. Nordinen.* 1811
The ed. princ. of the complete Bible in Lapp. The N.T. has sep. tp. & pagin.
LATIN VERSIONS, *see also* HEBREW *above* ; POLYGLOT *below.*
[Biblia. *f. 1 blank & wanting. f. 2[a] (red)* Incipit epistola sancti iheronimi ad paulinum prespiterum de omnibus divine historie libris. *f. 4[b] (red)* Incipit prologus in penthateucum moysi. *f. 235[a] (first leaf of t2 red)* Epl'a sancti ieronimi p̄sbiteri ad chroacium et elidorum epōs de libris salomonis. *f. 367[a] (red)* Incipit epl'a beati ieronimi presbiteri ad damasum papam in q̄tuor evengelistas. *f. 462[b], col. 1 End of text.* Et sic est finis. *f. 463[a]* Venerabili viro domino. Iacobo de ysenaco. Menardus solo noīe monachus. *f. 467[a]* Incipit tabula canonum. *Ends on f. 468[b], col. 2* Apocalipsis CCCCLvij. *b. in 2v*].
fol. [Basel, *Bernhard Richel, n.d.* c. 1474]
*No pagin. or foliat. 468 leaves, double cols., 48 lines. Wanting blank at beginning & extra leaf described by Hain (*3041). Errors in capitals at the beg. of Chaps. 4 & 26 of Genesis corrected by pasting the right letter over originals.*
[Biblia. *f. 1a* : Prologus in Genesim. Incipit ep̄la sancti Hieronymi ad Paulinū p̄sbyterꝫ: d'oīb' dīne histoīe libr. Capl̄m 1. Frater Ambrosius &c. *f. 209b* Explicit Psalteriū ; *f. 210a* Ep̄la sancti Hieronymi p̄sbyteri ad Chromatiū & Heliodor' ep̄os : de libr. Salomōis ; *f. 337b, col. 2* Explicit secundus liber Machabeorum. *f. 338a* : Incipit epistola beati Hieronymi ad Damasū papā in qtuor euāgelistas ; *f. 421b, col. 2* Explicit Biblia impressa Venetiis Frācīscū de hailbrun & Nicolaū de frankfordia. *ff. 422a–454a* Incipiunt interp̄tatiōes hebraicorū &c.]
fol. [Venetiis, *Franciscus de Hailbrun & Nicolaus de Frankfordia.* 1475]
454 leaves, without tp., pagin., signat. ; double cols., 51 or 52 lines. The Interpretationes in 3 cols., 54 lines. Headtitles & titles of books are printed. Initials are executed by hand, the large ones illuminated. Hain, 3054.
[Biblia. *f. a2,* Incipit epl'a sācti Hieronymi ad Paulinū p̄b̄rꝫ de oīb' divine historie libris Caplꝫ I. *f. a5,* Incipit liber Genesis qui dicitur hebraice breslth. Capitulum primum.

Bible [*continued*].
LATIN VERSIONS [*continued*].
f. H9, Explicit secundus liber Machabeorum. *f. H10 blank & wanting. f. I1,* Incipit epistola beati Hieronymi ad Damasū papā ī q̄ttuor evangelistas. *f. Q12 colophon* ; Biblia impressa Venetiis opera & impensa N. Ienson Gallici 1476. *R1,* Incipiunt interpretationes hebr. nominum].
fol. [Venetiis, *Nicolaus Jenson.* 1476]
*470 leaves, double cols., 52 lines, sig. a–z in tens ; ꝫ, ?, ꝓ in tens. A–L in tens. M1–12 ; N–P in tens ; Q1–12, R–T in tens ; U–X in eights. Sig. a blank & H10 blank missing. Hain, *3061.*
[Biblia. *f. 1a* Incipit ep̄la sancti hieronimi ad Paulinū presbiter de omnib' divine historie libris. *f. 3b* Incipit liber bresith quem nos genesim dicimus. Capitulum I. *f. 233b, col. 2* Finit psalterium feliciter. *f. 234a* Ep̄la sancti hieronimi p̄sbiteri ad chromatiuꝫ &c. *f. 365b, col. 2* Explicit secundus liber machabeorum. *f. 366a* Incipit ep̄la beati hieronimi p̄sbitēi ad damasū papā ī q̄tuor evāgelistas ; *f. 461b, col. 2* Anno incarnatōis dñice Millesimo quadringentesimo septuagesimo septimo &c. Augusti vero kl' tercio regia ciuitate Nurnbergñ ꝑ Antonium Coburger. *f. 462a* Venerabili viro dño iacobo de ysenaco. Menard' &c. *f. 466a* Incipit canon. *f. 467b* Et sic est finis].
lafol. [Nürnberg, *Antonius Coburger, 30 July.* 1477]
467 leaves ; double cols., 51–53 lines ; no tp., pagin., foliat. or signat. a in twelve ; b–y in tens ; z, & in sixes ; A–M in tens ; N, O in sixes ; P–R in tens ; S, T in eights ; V–Z–aa in tens ; follow six leaves cont. the Epistle of Menardus & the Canones. Hain, 3065. Pollard p. 414. Initials & marg. border on ff. 1 & 234 ; other initials small & large, alternately red & blue.
[Biblia (*Vulgate*) *fragment. Beg.* : Incipit plogus beati ieronimi. In libros regum *&c. containing the 4 books of Kings to Ecclesiasticus chap. 38*]. sfol. [Cologne, *Nicolaus Gotz.* c. 1477]
119 leaves, without headlines, foliation or signatures, but numbered, in writing, 136–244. Sign. p–v in tens ; x 1–8 ; a–d in tens ; e1 are added in a hand of the period.
[Biblia. *Beg. f. a2.* Incipit epistola beati Hieronymi ad Paulinum presbyterum de omnibus divine historie libris. *Ends on f* ℞ *7* Fontibus ex grecis hebreorum quoque libris. Emendata satis &c. Biblia].
fol. *n.p. n.d.* [Nürnberg, *Caspar Hochfeder.* c. 1494]
402 leaves ; double cols., 56 lines ; headlines. Sig. a–z, ꝫ, ?, A–E, 8. F, 6. G, 8. H, 6. J, 8. KK, 6. K–Z, ℞, ℞ *8. 1st & last fol[s]. blank missing. Formerly attrib. to Amerbach of Basel & to Kesler of Basel. *Hain, 3048.*
Biblia cum concordantiis, revisa, correcta & emēdata.
fol. Lugduni, *Jacobus Sacon.* 1512
Biblia Sacra, juxta vet. & consuetā interpret. &c. [*Genesis to Kings*]. s8°. Antvverpiæ [*J. Tibaldæus for F. Birckmann*]. 1526
Sacra Biblia ad LXX. interpretum Fidem tralata.
s4°. Basileæ, *A. Cratander.* 1526
Biblia sacra utriusque Test. Adest index rerum, unà cum Heb. vocum dict. [*Ed.* J. Rudelius. *Woodcuts*].
fol. Coloniæ, *P. Quentel.* 1527
Biblia. Habes in hoc libro, utriusq. instrumenti nova, translationē æditam a . . . S. Pagnino, necnon & librum de interpretamentis hebraicorum, arameorū, græcorumq. nominum . . . Habes & in libri fronte ejusdem ἐπιτομήν &c.
[3p]. 4°. [Lugduni, per Antonium du Ry]. 1528
Tp. bears the date of 1528, but the colophon that of 29 Jan. 1527. First edition of the version of Pagninus. It is said to be the first Bible in which the verses are numbered.
Biblia.—Hebr., Chald., Græca & Lat. nomina restit., cum Lat. interp.—Locorum descr. e cosmographis—Index &c.
lafol. Parisiis, *R. Stephanus.* 1538–40
Prophetæ, Novum Test., 1539 & Hebr. &c. nomina, 1538
have sep. tp[s]. & foliations.
Biblia sacra utriusque Testamenti, & Vetus opera D. Sebast. Munsteri evulgatum. Novum opera D. Eras. Rot. ult. recognitum & æditum. Add. sunt e LXX. versione & Apocryphi libri. [*Pref.* De omnibus S. Scripturæ libris eorumque præstantia, H. Bullingeri expos. 3p *in* 1v].
8°. Tiguri. 1539
Biblia sacra ex Santis Pagnini tralatione, sed ad Hebr. ling. amussim noviss. ita recogn., & scholiis illust. [ed. Michael Servetus]. Acc. Liber interpret. Hebraic., Arab., Græc. nominum. fol. Lugduni. [*Gaspar Trechsel*]. 1542
Biblia Sacros. Testamēti Vet. & Novi, tr. in serm. Lat. [*By L. Juda, T. Bibliander, & P. Cholinus. N. Test. rev. & corr. from the tr. of Erasmus, by R. Gualter, the whole ed. by C. Pellican*]. (De omnibus s. Script. libris, H. Bullingeri expos. —Argumenta in omnia Vet. & Novi Test. capita elegiaco carmine conscripta per R. Gualth.)
3p *in* 1v. fol. Tiguri, *C. Froschoverus.* 1543
First ed. of the Zürich Latin Bible.
Biblia Sacrosancta, tr. [*by Leo Juda & others*] in serm. Lat.
3p. 8°. Tiguri, *C. Froschoverus,* 1544
2nd ed. of the Zürich Bible. Tps. of Apocrypha & N.T. are dated 1543.

Bible [*continued*].
LATIN VERSIONS [*continued*].
Biblia. 8°. Lutetiæ, *R. Stephanus.* 1545
R. Stephanus' second 8°. edition. Zürich version in parallel columns w. the Vulgate.
Biblia ad vetustis. exemplaria nunc recens castigata.—Hebr., Chald., Græca & Lat. nomina restituta, cum Lat. interp., ac locorum e cosmographis descr. &c. fol. Lovanii, *B. Gravius.* 1547
First ed. of the Louvain Bible. The N.T. *&* Hebr. &c. nomina *have sep. foliations.*
Biblia, interprete S. Castalione. Una cum ejusdem annot^s^. [*4 pagin^s^.*] fol. Basileæ, *J. Oporinus.* [1551]
Bibliorum pars prima, id est quinque libri Moschis Lat. rec. ex Heb. facti, brevibusque scholiis illust. ab I. Tremellio & F. Junio. fol. Francofurti ad Mœnum, *A. Wechel.* 1575
Testamenti Vet. Biblia sacra, sive Libri canon., Latini facti ab I. Tremellio & F. Junio &c. Acc. Libri Apocryphi, Lat. redd. a F. Junio & Nov. Test. a Th. Beza in Lat. conv. [*6p w. sep. tp. & pagin.*] s4°. Londini. *H. Middletonus* : *impensis J. H.* 1581
H. Middleton's 2nd ed. in which Beza's vers. of the N.T. f. Gr. is substituted for Tremellius' f. the Syriac : it is pr. in larger type than the rest of the vol. & bears the imprint of Thomas Vautrollerius.
„ „ [*3rd ed.*] s4°. Londini, *H. Midletonus : impensis W. N.* 1585
In this ed. both Tremellius' & Beza's vers. of the N.T. are given side by side.
Biblia Sacra, cum dupl. tr. & scholiis F. Vatabli, à plurimis erroribus repurg. theologorum almae Univ. Salmantic. &c. judicio. 2t. sfol. Salmanticæ. 1584–[86]
t2 *has 5 pagin^s^.* Index Biblicus a J. Harlemio, *has sep. tp. dated* 1585. Approbations dated 1586.
Vet. Test. secundum 70. Latine redditum, & ex auctoritate Sixti V. Pont. Max. ed. [*by card. Carafa : an ancient Lat. vers. completed by F. Nobilius, assisted by bishops Agelius & Laelius, P. Valverda & P. Morinus*]. Add. ind. dictionum hebr., græc. & latin. fol. Romæ, *G. Ferrarius.* 1588
This vers. forms a suppl. to the "Sixtine" or "Roma ι" ed. of the Greek text publ. in 1587.
Biblia sacra Vulgatæ editionis. [Sixti quinti Pont. Max. jussu recognita atque edita. *Further rev. by cardinals Colonna, Allen, & Valverda ; bishops Agelius, & Landus, B. de Miranda, F. Nobili & P. Morinus ; & subsequently by cardinals Toletus, Valiero, & F. Borromeo ; & publ. w. the authority of Clement VIII. App.* Oratio Manassæ, necnon libri duo 3^1^ & 4^1^ Esdræ *w. sep. pagin.*] fol. Romæ, *Ex typogr. Apost. Vatic.* 1592
Biblia Sacra Vulgatæ ed. Sixti Quinti jussu rec. & ed. s4°. Romæ, *Ex typ. Apost. Vaticana.* 1593
Biblia Sacra Vulg. [*Foll. by* Rom. correctionis in Lat. Bibliis ed. Vulg. recog. loca insigniora à F. Luca *w. sep. tp. & pagin.*] fol. Antverpiæ, *J. Moretus.* 1603
Biblia Sacra. Emendat. & locupletior per A. Osiandrum. fol. Tubingæ, *Gruppenbach.* 1606
Biblia Sacra. Præf. Consistorii Theol. in Ducatu Wirtemb. [*Vulgate w. corrections f. the comm^s^. of Lucas Osiander. On back of tp. is a portrait of* Ludwig, Duke of Württemberg & Teck]. s4°. Tubingæ, *P. Gruppenbach.* 1609
Biblia Sacra cum glossa ordin. a Strabo Fuldensi coll., novis PP. Græc. & Lat. explic. locupleta, & postilla N. Lirani, cum addit. Pauli Burgensis episc. & M. Thoringi replicis, theolog. Duacens. studio emend. [*Ed.* Leander de St. Martino]. 6t. fol. Antverpiæ, *J. Meursius.* 1634
Biblia maxima versionum ex linguis oriental. &c. coll. earumque concordia cum Vulgata & ejus expos. lit. cum annot^s^. N. de Lyra, J. Gagnæi, G. Estii, J. Menochii & J. Tirini. Additis proleg. &c. Authore J. de la Haye. 19t *in* 10v [18, 19, Indices]. fol. Lutetiæ Paris. 1660
Biblia Sacra, ex linguis orig. in ling. Lat. tr. à S. Schmidt. s4°. Argentorati, *J. F. Spoor.* 1696
Bibliorum Sacr. Lat. vers. antiq., seu vetus Italica, et cæteræ quæcunque in codd. MSS. & antiq. lib. reperiri potuerunt : quæ cum vulg. Lat. & cum textu Gr. comparantur. Acc. præff., obs. & notæ, indexque nov. &c. opera & studio P. Sabatier. 3t. fol. Remis, *R. Florentain.* 1743–49
t3 has date 1743 on tp., but 1749 in colophon.
Sacra Biblia var. tr., juxta exempl. Antverpiæ impr. 1616, compl. Vulgatam, S. Pagnini ex Hebr., Septuaginta interpr. & Chaldaica paraphr. vers., F. Vatabli tr. &c. [N.T. compl. Vulg., Guidonis Fabricii e Syr. & B. A. Montani tr., insuper D. Erasmi vers.] 4t. fol. Venetiis, *N. Pezzana.* 1747
Vecchio e Nuovo Test. sec. la Volgata. [*With*] tr. in lingua ital. da A. Martini. 4v. la8°. Venezia. 1841–52
Biblia sacra Lat. Hieronymo interp. Ed. instit. Th. Heyse, ad finem perduxit C. de Tischendorf. 8°. Lipsiæ. 1873
Biblia Sacra Vulgatæ ed. Ed. nova versiculis distincta. s8°. Londini. *n.d.*
see AMAMA (S.) Censura Vulg. vers. 5 lib. Mosis, 1620.
„ BIANCHINI (G. M.) Vindiciæ canonic. script. vulg. Lat. &c., 1740.

Bible [*continued*].
LATIN VERSIONS [*continued*].
see BILLEN (A. V.) Old Lat. texts of the Heptateuch, 1927.
„ ESS (L. VAN). Pragmat.-Krit. Gesch. d. Vulg., 1824.
„ GUTENBERG (J.) Gutenbergs erster Druck, Facs. d. ersten Seite, 1855 ?.
„ HOSKIER (H. C.) The text of Codex Usserianus 2, r2, w. crit. notes &c., 1919.
„ JAMES (T.) Bellum Papale, 1678.
„ KAULEN (F.) Gesch. d. Vulg., 1868.
„ —— Hdbch. d. Vulg., 1870.
„ LUCAS (F.) Romanæ correct. in Lat. Bibl. ed. Vulg. loca insigniora, 1603.
„ PLATER (W. E.) & H. J. WHITE. Gram. of the Vulg., 1926.
„ QUENTIN (H.) Mém. sur l'établ. du texte de la Vulg., pl, 1922.
„ VOGEL (A.) Beitr. z. Herstell. d. alt. lat. Übers., 1868.
„ ZIEGLER (L.) Lat. Bibelübers. vor Hieronymus u. d. Itala, 1879.
LEPCHA.
Gospel of John in L. 8°. Calcutta. 1872
Genesis & pt. of Exodus, in Lepshá. 8°. Calcutta. 1874
LETTISH.
Tas Jauns Testaments Muh-su Kunga Jesus Kristus. [*Tr. by* E. Glück *& others, ed. by* J. Fischer]. 4°. Riga. 1685
Biblia, tas irr : Ta ẞwehta Grahmata &c. 8°. Kensbergâ, *J. J. Artunga.* 1739
LEVITICUS. *For ed. in Cambridge Bible* [*by A. T. Chapman &c.*], *see under* BIBLE : GEN. COMM.
see BABINGTON (G.) Comfortable notes, 1604.
„ FRANTZE (W.) Comm. in L., 1696.
„ ISAAC, *ben Judah, Abravanel.* Exordium comm., 1683.
„ PATRICK (S.) Comm. upon 3rd Bk. of Moses, 1698.
LITHUANIAN.
Biblia, Tai esti : Wissas Szwentas Rásztas Séno ir Naujo Testamento &c. [*Tr. by J. J. Quandt & others*]. s8°. Karaláuczuje. 1735
Half-title of Apocrypha is dated 1734.
—— (SAMOGITIAN DIALECT).
Naujas Istatimas Jezaus Christaus Lietuwuszku Leżuwiu iszgulditas par Jozapa Kunigaykszti Giedrayti. s4°. Wilniuje. 1816
The N.T., tr. from the Lat. Vulgate by Pr. Joseph Arnulph Gedroitz.
LUKE, *see also* BATTA *& o. lang^s^. above & below.*
see BODE (C. A.) Evang. sec. L. ex vers. Pers. interpret. in Lat. tr., 1751.
„ BRENTZ (J.) In Evang. sec. L. cap. [24] homiliæ 110, 1552.
„ BULLINGER (H.) In Evang. sec. L. comm. libri 9, 1548.
„ CADBURY (H. J.) Making of Luke-Acts, 1927.
„ CORDIER (B.) Catena 65 Græc. patrum in S. L., 1628.
„ ESTELLA (D. DE). In Evang. sec. L. enarrat., 2t, 1599.
„ EVANS (H. H.) St. Paul, author of Acts & 3rd Gospel, 1884.
„ FLACIUS (M.) Quod locus Lucæ vii &c., 1549.
„ GOGUEL (M.) L'Evang. de Marc. & s. rapp. avec ceux de Mathieu & de L., 1909.
„ LAMBERT (F.) In L. Evang. comm., 1524.
„ LOISY (A.) L'Ev. selon Luc, 1924.
„ OOSTERZEE (J. J. v.) Theolog. &c. comm. on Gospel of St. L. ; tr., 2v, 1862–63.
„ PITMAN (W. H.) Life & works of S. L., 1889.
„ RAGG (L.) St. L. [Westminster Comm.], 1922.
„ RANKE (E.) Fragm. antiq. Evang. L. vers. Lat., 1873.
„ ROBERTSON (A. T.) L. the historian, 1920.
„ ROGERS (N.) True convert, 15th chap. of L., 3p, 1632.
„ SCHMID (S.) Fasc. disput. s. Canticum Zachariæ, 1685.
„ TAYLOR (V.) Behind the 3rd Gospel : Proto-Luke hypothesis, 1926.
„ WAVRE (P. v.) Peregrinus Jerichuntinus, L. 10, 30, 1685.
MALABAR, *see* TAMIL *below.*
MALACHI.
see BALDUIN (F.) In 3 postremos prophetas comm., 1610.
„ BODENSTEIN (A.) Predig ü. M., 1522.
„ BULMERINCQ (A. v.) Einl. in d. Buch d. M., 1926.
„ DAVID, *ben. J. Kimchi.* Joel & M., 1530.
„ SCHUDT (J. J.) De adventu Messiæ ex vaticinio Malach. III, 1 [*in h.* Deliciæ Hebræo-philologicæ &c., 1700].
„ STOCK (R.) Comm. upon M., 1641.
„ TORSHELL (S.) An exercit. upon M., 1670.
MALAGASY.
Ny Teny n'Andriamanitra, Tesitamenta. 8°. An-Tananarivo. 1830
MALAY.
The four Gospels, tr. into Malayan. [*Pref. by* T. Marshall, *Dedic. by* T. Hyde]. 8°. O. 1677
'El Khawlu-' ldjadîd. [*N.T. Tr. by M. Leidekker & others*]. 4°. Amsterdam. 1731
[*Holy Bible. Malay in Arabic characters. Ed. J. M. Mohr & P. v. der Werth*]. [5v]. 8°. Batavia. 1758
MALTO, *see* RAJMAHALI *below.*
MANCHU.
[Matthew. Tr. by S. V. Lipoftsov]. la8°. [St. Petersb. 1822]

Bible [*continued*].

MANX.

Yn Vible Casherick. 2 Lioar. 8°. Whitehaven. 1772–73
The first ed. of the O.T. in Manx, but 2nd issue of v1, the first having been pr. in 1771. It includes 2 books of the Apocrypha, viz. the Wisdom of Solomon & Ecclesiasticus.

Yn Vible Casherick. 8°. London. 1819

MAORI.

Ko tetahi wahanga o te Kawenata Hon. [Mark, Luke, Hebrews–Rev. *only*]. 8°. Paihia. 1840

MARATHI.

[Matthew]. *n.p. n.d.*

see GREENFIELD (W.) Defence of the Serampore M. version of N. Test., 1830.

MARK, *see also* ARMENIAN *& o. langs. above & below.*

see BACON (B. W.) Beginnings of Gospel story, 1920.
,, —— Gospel of M.: comp. & date, 1925.
,, BODE (C. A.) Evang. sec. M. ex vers. Pers. interpret. in Lat. tr., 1751.
,, BULLINGER (H.) In Evang. sec. M. comm., 1545.
,, GOGUEL (M.) L'Evang. de M. & s. rapp. avec ceux de Mathieu & de Luc, 1909.
,, MACLER (F.) Le texte armén. de Matthieu & M., 1919.
,, POSSINUS (P.) Catena Græc. patrum in M., 1673.
,, PROCKSCH (O.) Petrus u. Johannes bei M. u. Matthäus, 1920.
,, RAWLINSON (A. E. J.) St. M.; w. intr., comm. & notes, 1925.
,, WALTHER (R.) M. Evang.: Homiliæ &c., 1577.

MARWARI.

Holy Bible. Tr. into M., v5, N.T. 8°. Serampore. 1821

MATTHEW, *see also* CREE *& o. lang*[s]. *above & below*, *&* PSALMS.

Evangelium sec. M. in lingua Hebr., cum vers. Lat. & annot. Seb. Munsteri. Una cum Epist. Pauli ad Hebræos. s8°. Basileæ, *H. Petri*. [1557]

Parabola de seminatore ex Evang. Matthæi, in 72 Europ. linguas &c. expressa. [Impensis L. L. Bonaparte]. 8°. Lond. 1857

An old Heb. text of M. Tr. &c. H. J. Schonfield. 8°. E. 1927

see BULLINGER (H.) In Evang. sec. M. comm., 1544.
,, CORDIER (B.) & P. POSSINUS. Symbol. in M., 2t, 1546–7.
,, CREMER (B. S.) Naziræus; acc. diss. in loc. M. 2, 23, 1727.
,, FINETTI (B.) Trattato &c.; agg. una difesa del capo 2 di San M., 1756.
,, GOGUEL (M.) L'Evang. de Marc & s. rapp. avec ceux de M. &c., 1909.
,, HUNNIUS (E.). Op. Lat., t3, 1608.
,, JAMES I. Meditatio in cap. 27 Evang. S. M. v. 27–29 &c., 1620.
,, MACLER (F.) Le texte armén. de l'Evang. d'ap. M., 1919.
,, MUSCULUS (W.) In M. comm., 1548.
,, —— In M. comm., 1551; 1567.
,, OLEARIUS (G.) Observ. sacræ ad evang. M., 1743.
,, PISCATOR (J.) Analysis logica Evang. sec. M., 1597.
,, PROCKSCH (O.) Petrus u. Johannes bei Marcus u. M., 1920.
,, RIGGENBACH (E.) Der trinitär. Taufbefehl, M. 28, 19, 1903.
,, SCHMID (S.) Fasc. disput. s. Concionem Xti. M. v, vi, vii, 1685.
,, STRACK (H. L.) & P. BILLERBECK. Komm. z. Neu. Test. aus Talmud &c., B1, M., 1922.
,, THOLUCK (F. A. G.) Comm. on the Sermon on the Mount; tr., 1860.
,, WAKEFIELD (G.) A new tr. of M.; w. notes, 1782.
,, WARD (R.) Theol. questions, dogmat. obs[s]. upon M., 1640.

MEXICAN.

El Evangelio de S. Lucas, del Latin al Mex. ò mejor Nahuatl [*by M. Paz y Sanchez*]. s8°. Londres. 1833

MICAH.

see DRACONITES (J.) M. propheta, *Hebr. & Lat.*, 1565.
,, POCOCK (E.) Comm. on M., 1677.

MOHAWK.

The Gospel acc. to St. J. s8°. *B.F.B.S.* [1804]

The Gospel acc. to St. Luke, tr. by H. A. Hill. s8°. N.Y., *A.B.S.* 1827

MONGOLIAN.

[St. John. *b. w.* St. Matth., 1819]. la8°. [St. Petersburg. 1819 ?]

[St. Matthew]. la8°. [St. Petersburg. 1819]

[Genesis. Tr. by E. Stallybrass &c.] 4°. [Selenginsk. 1833]

MORDVINIAN.

Святой Еѵангелья Лука-гыцъ. 8°. Питеръ Алашта. 1821

MUNDARI.

[Gospels in Mundari, *each w. sep. tp. & pagin.* 4p *in* 1v]. s8°. Calcutta. 1880–82

NAHUM.

see KALINSKY (J. G.) Vaticinia Chabacuci & N., 1748.

NEHEMIAH.

see KEIL (C. F.) The Bk[s]. of Ezra, N. &c.; tr., 1873.
,, PATRICK (S.) Comm. upon Chron., N. &c., 1706.

NEPALESE.

[Matthew I—25, v12. In Palpa. *no tp.*] 8°. [Serampore. 1827]

Gospel acc. to Luke in N. 8°. Calcutta. 1877

NEW TESTAMENT [*English Texts & General Commentaries*]. *For the N.T. in other languages see var. languages above & below.*

The N.T., publ. in 1526. Tr. by W. Tyndale. Repr. w. mem. of h. life &c. by G. Offor. 8°. 1836

Bible [*continued*].

NEW TESTAMENT [*continued*].

The 1st N.T. pr. in the Eng. lang. (1525 or 26). Tr. by W. Tyndale reprod. in facs. w. intr. by F. Fry. s8°. Bristol. 1862

,, ,, ...photo-lithographed f. fragm. in B.M. Ed. E. Arber. s4°. 1871

N.T. A facs. repr. of the Genevan Test., 1557; w. the margin. annot. &c. s4°. Bagster. [1842]

The N.T. tr. out of Latin &c. In the English College of Rhemes [*by W. Allen; R. Bristow; G. Martin & T. Worthington*]. s4°. Rhemes, *John Fogny*. 1582

The N.T., w. notes [*contrived to evade the King's printers' monopoly*]. s8°. 1776

The English Hexapla, exhib. the 6 most important Eng. tr[s]. of the N.T.: Wiclif, 1380; Tyndale, 1534; Cranmer, 1539; Genevan, 1557; Anglo-Rhemish, 1582; Authorized 1611. The orig. text after Scholz &c. [*Gr. & Eng.*] 4°. [1841]

The N.T. tr. by J. Wycliffe c. 1380, pr. f. contemp. MS. &c. s4°. *Pickering*. 1848

The Gospels, Acts, Epistles, & Book of Revelation. A new tr. [by J. N. Darby]. 2nd ed. s8°. *n.d.*

see APOCRYPHA. Excl. bks. of the N.T.; tr. J. B. Lightfoot &c., 1927.
,, ARNAULD (A.) Nouv. déf. de la tr. du N.T. impr. à Mons, 1680.
,, BACON (B. W.) Apostolic message, 1925.
,, BENGEL (J. A.) Apparatus crit., 1763.
,, —— Gnomon N.T., ed. 3a recusa, 1862.
,, BLACKWALL (A.) Auctores sacri, Crit. N.T. &c., 1736.
,, BOWYER (W.) Crit. conjectures &c. on the N.T., coll. f. var. a.[s], 4th ed., 1812.
,, BOX (G. H.) & C. GORE. Divorce in the N.T., 1921.
,, BRENTANO (D. v.), *ed.* Die heil. Schr. d. N.T., 2T, 1790–91.
,, BUCHER (S. F.) Antiq. bibl. ex N.T., 1729.
,, BULLINGER (H.) N.T. hist. evangelica &c., 1554.
,, BURGESS (T.) Remarks on gen. tenour of N.T. reg. nature &c. of J. C., 1831.
,, BURKITT (W.) Expository notes &c. on N.T., *n.d.*
,, CAMERARIUS (J.) Notatio figur. orationis &c., 1572.
,, CANINIUS (A.) Disq. in locos aliq. N.T. obscur., 1602.
,, CHAPMAN (J.) L'auteur du Canon muratorien, *n.d.*
,, CHARLES (R. H.) Teaching of the N.T. on divorce, 1921.
,, COBERN (C. M.) The new archeolog. discov. & th. bearing upon the N.T. &c., 3rd ed., 1918.
,, COKE (T.) Comm. on the N.T., 2v, 1803.
,, CONDER (J.) Literary hist. of the N.T., 1850.
,, CRAMER (L. D.) De bibliologia in N.T. libris, *n.d.*
,, DEISSMANN (G. A.) Licht v. Osten: N.T. u. neuentd. Texte, 4[e] A., 1923.
,, —— Light f. the anc. East; tr. L. R. M. Strachan, 1927.
,, DRUSIUS (J.), *the elder*. Ad voces Hebr. N.T. comm., 1582.
,, EAKIN (F.) Getting acquainted w. the N.T., 1927.
,, EMSER (H.) Annot. uber Luthers naw Test., 1524; 29.
,, ERASMUS (D.) Evangeliæ &c. ex tr. E. cum annot[s]., 1531.
,, ERNESTI (J. A.) Instit. interp. N.T., 1761.
,, FISCHER (C.) Instit. hermeneut. N.T., 1788.
,, FULKE (W.) Text of the N.T., tr. out of Lat. by the Papists at Rhemes, added tr. out of the Greeke &c., 1601.
,, GEORGI (C. S.) Hierocriticus N.T. sive de stylo N.T., 1733.
,, —— Vindiciarum N.T. ab Ebraismis libri 3, 1732.
,, GLASS (S.) Evang. & epistolic. exegesis, 4p, 1647–49.
,, GÖZE (J. M.) Ausführl. Vertheid. d. Complut. griech. N.T., & Fortsetz, 1766–69.
,, —— Bahrdt. Verdeutschung d. N.T. keine Übers. &c., 1773.
,, —— Vertheid. d. Complutens. Bibel, insond. d. N.T., 1765.
,, GROTIUS (H.) De N.T. auctor. liber ab E. Pocock in ling. arab. tr., 1733.
,, HAMMOND (C. E.) Outlines of text. crit., 1872.
,, HAMMOND (H.) Δευτέραι Φροντίδες or a rev. of the paraph. & annot. on the N.T., 1656.
,, HUG (J. L. v.) Introd. to the N.T.; tr. D. Fosdick, 1836.
,, INQUIRY (AN) resp. the orig. copies &c. of N.T., 1822.
,, KENT (C. F.) Work &c. of Apostles, 1920.
,, KNOPF (R.) Einführung in d. N.T., 1919.
,, KORTHOLT (C.) Hist. eccl. N.T., 1697.
,, KREBS (J. T.) Obs. in N.T. e F. Josepho, 1755.
,, KVINOEL (C. T.) Obs. ad N.T. &c., 1794.
,, LANGE (J. P.) Theolog.-homilet. Bibelwerk; Des N.T. 16T, 1861–78.
,, LEIGH (E.) Annot. upon N.T., 1650.
,, LESS (G.) Authenticity &c. of the N.T.; tr. 1804.
,, LIETZMANN (H.) Hdbh. z. N.T., B1–4, 1910–19; 2[e] A., B6, 1925.
,, LOPIS STUNICA (J.) Annot. contra Erasmum in defens. tr. N.T., 1520.
,, MACNEILE (A. H.) Intr. to study of the N.T., 1927.
,, —— N.T. teaching in light of St. Paul's, 1923.
,, MAJUS (J. H.), *elder*. Œconomia judic. divin. sub N.T., 2p, 1717.
,, —— Œconomia temp. N.T., 1708.
,, MALDEN (R. H.) Problems of N.T. to-day, 1923.
,, MELANCHTHON (P.) Op. t1, 2, 1541; Op. p3, 4, 1563–64.

Bible [*continued*].

New Testament [*continued*].

see Michaelis (C. B.) Tract. de var. lectionibus N.T. &c., 1749.
,, Micklem (E. R.) Miracles & the new psychology : healing m. of N.T., 1922.
,, Moffatt (J.) Approach to the N.T., 1921.
,, More (P. E.) The Christ of the N.T., 1924.
,, Moulton (W. F.) Methodist comm. on N.T., 1894.
,, Nairne (A.) Faith of the N.T., 1920.
,, Nösselt (J. A.) Exercitationes, 1803.
,, —— Opusc., fasc. 1–3, 1785–1817.
,, Olearius (J.) De stilo N.T. &c., 1731.
,, Olshausen (H.) Opusc. theolog. ad crisin &c. N.T. pert., 1834.
,, Palairet (E.) Obs. philol. crit. in Nov. Fœd. libros, 1752.
,, Piscator (J.) Comm. in omnes libros N.T., 1621.
,, Postillæ. Postille majores in Epistolas & Evangelias &c., 1514.
,, Rainolds (W.) Refut. of reprehensions &c. by M. Whitaker to deface late Eng. tr. & Cath. annot. of N.T. &c., 1583.
,, Ranke (E.) Spec. cod. N.T. Fuldensis, 1860.
,, Rawlinson (A. E. J.) N.T. doct. of the Christ, 1926.
,, Richardson (J.) Canon of N.T. vindicated &c., 2nd ed., 1701.
,, Robertson (A. T.) Syllabus for N.T. study, 1923.
,, Rouffiac (J.) Rech. s. les caractères du grec dans le N.T. &c., 1911.
,, Schmidt (E.) Opus sacr. : versio N.T. &c., 1658.
,, Scholefield (J.) Hints for an impr. tr. of the N.T., 1836.
,, Scrivener (F. H.) A plain intr. to criticism of the N.T., 1861.
,, Seiler (G. F.) Uebers. d. N.T., 2T, 1806.
,, Semler (J. S.) Neuer Versuch d. Ausleg. &c. d. N.T., 1786.
,, Simonis (J.) Onomasticum N.T. & libr. V. T. Apocr., 1762.
,, Smith (R.) Research papers, *n.d.*—1923.
,, Soden (H. v.) Die Schriften d. N.T. : Untersuch. u. Text, 2T, 1911–13.
,, Stave (E.) Om källorna till 1526 års öfversattning af N.T., 1893.
,, Storr (G. C.) Opusc. acad. ad interpr. libr. sacr., 3v, 1796–1803.
,, Stosch (E. H. D.) Comm. de lib. N.T. canone, 1755.
,, Strack (H. L.) & P. Billerbeck. Komm. z. N.T. aus Talmud u. Midrasch, 3B, 1922–26.
,, Strigelius (V.) Ὑπομνήμα α in libros N.T., 2v, 1565.
,, Symes (J. E.) Evol. of the N.T., 1921.
,, Tholuck (F. A. G.) Disput. de T. Aquinate & Abælardo interp. N.T., 1842.
,, Tittmann (C. C.) De vestigiis Gnosticorum in N.T., 1773.
,, Townsend (G.) The N.T. in chronol. & hist. order, 4th ed., 2v, 1838.
,, Trench (R. C.) Synonyms of the N.T., 7th ed., 1871.
,, Turner (C. H.) The study of the N.T., 1920.
,, Ungarelli (L. M.) Prælect. de N.T., 1847.
,, Vio (T. de). Jentacula : 64 sentent. N.T. expos., 1550.
,, Vorst (J.) De Hebraismis N.T. &c., 1778.
,, Wade (G. W.) N.T. hist., 1922.
,, Wakefield (G.) A new tr. of parts, 1789.
,, Walch (J. G.) Hist. eccl. N.T., 1744.
,, —— Obs. in N. Fœderis libr., 1727.
,, Warfield (B. B.) An introd. to textual crit. of N.T., 1889.
,, Weismann (C. E.) Introd. in memorabilia eccl. hist. sacr. Nov. Test., 2t, 1745.
,, Weiss (J.) Die Schriften d. N.T. ; neu übers. u. erklärt, 3e A. ; hrsg. v. W. Bousset u. W. Heitmüller, 4B, 1917–18.
,, Wesley (J.) Explan. notes [*w. text*], 1755 ; 2nd ed. 1757 ; 4th ed. 1768 ; 11th ed., 2v, 1831.
,, Whitby (D.) Addit. annots. to the N.T., 1710.
,, —— Paraphrase & comm. on the N.T., 2v, 1700–03 ; 2nd ed., 1706.
,, Winzer (J. F.) De dæmonologia in N.T. lib., 1812.
,, Wither (G.) View of the marginal notes of Popish Test. tr., 1588.
,, Zahn (T.) Forschungen z. Gesch. d. neutest. Kanons, T9, 1916.
,, —— Komm. z. N.T., B5, 15, 18i, 1919–24.
,, Zeitschrift f. d. neutestamentl. Wiss. &c., 1900–.

New Testament [Greek], *see also* Gospels *&* Greek *above.*

Novum Instrumentū omne, diligenter ab Erasmo Roterodamo recognitum & emendatum &c. [*Gr. & Lat.*, 2p *in* 1v]. fol. [Basileæ, *J. Froben*]. 1516

Novum Testamentum omne, multo quam antehac diligentius ab Erasmo Roterodamo recognitū, emēdatum ac translatum, una cū annotationibus recognitis &c. [Ratio seu compendium veræ theologiæ, per Erasmum &c. *Gr. & Lat.*] fol. [Basileæ, *J. Frobenius.* 1519]

,, ,, tertio iam ac diligentius ab Erasmo Roterodamo recognitum &c. cum annotationibus. [*Gr. & Lat.*] fol. [Basileæ, *J. Frobenius*]. 1522

,, ,, jam quartum damus, adj. vulgata tr. &c. fol. Basileæ, [*J. Frobenius*]. 1527

,, ,, jam quintum recogn. à Des. Erasmo. fol. Basileæ, [*J. Frobenius*]. 1535

Bible [*continued*].

New Testament [Greek] [*continued*].

Nouum Testamentum Græce. [*Ed.* N. Gerbelius]. s4°. Hagenoæ, *In ædibus Th. Anshelmi.* 1521
First ed. of the Greek text alone, pr. from the second Greek & Latin ed. of Erasmus, 1519, with a few alterations.

Τῆς Καινῆς Διαθήκης ἅπαντα. [*Ed.* R. Estienne]. p2 (Αἱ τοῦ Ἁγίου Παύλου Ἐπιστολαί &c.) s8°. [Lutetiæ, *R. Stephanus.* 1546]

Τῆς Καινῆς Διαθήκης ἅπαντα. Ex Bibl. Regia. [*With the Eusebian Canons &c. Ed.* R. Estienne]. 2p. *in* 1v. fol. Lutetiæ, *R. Stephanus.* 1550

Novum Jesu Christi Test. Cum duplici interpret. D. Erasmi & vet. interpretis : Harmonia item Evangelica &c. 2t. s8°. [Geneva], *R. Stephanus.* 1551
The first Test. in which text is divided into numbered verses.

Τῆς Καινῆς Διαθήκης ἅπαντα. Novum Test., Latine, nunc denuo à T. Beza versum ; cum ejusdem annotat. &c. [*Gr. & Lat.*] fol. Tiguri. 1559

Αἱ τοῦ ἁγίου Παύλου ἐπιστολαί, Αἱ καθολ. ἐπ., Ἀποκάλυψις. s8°. Lutetiæ, *R. Stephanus.* 1568.

Ἡ Καινὴ Διαθήκη. Test. Novum [*Vulgate*]. Interpret. Syriaca N.T., Hebr. typis descr. Lat. serm. reddita, Aut. I. Tremellio, cujus Gramm. Chaldaica & Syra adjecta est. [*w. sep. pagin. Gr., Lat. & Syr.*]. *b. in* 2v. fol. [Genevæ], *H. Stephanus.* 1569

Nov. Test. s8°. Lugd. Batav, *Elzevir.* 1633

N.T. libri omnes recens ed., cum notis &c. R. Stephani, J. Scaligeri, I. Casauboni &c. [*b. w.* Prayer-Book, B. of C.P., 1633]. s8°. Londini, *R. Whittaker.* 1633

Ἡ Καινὴ Διαθήκη, διγλωττος. Διὰ Μαξίμου τοῦ Καλλιουπολίτου γεν. μετάφρασις [*Anc. & Mod. Gr.*] 4°. [Geneva, *P. Aubert*]. [1638]

Nov. Test., cujus Græco contextui respondent interpretationes duæ : una, vetus ; altera Th. Bezæ, ejusdem annots. &c. Acc. J. Camerarii comm. [*w. sep. tp. & pagin.*] fol. Cantabrigiæ, *R. Daniel.* 1642

N.T. libri omnes. ed. nova [*repr. of Buck's ed. b. w.* Bible : Septuagint. V.T. Gr., 1653]. s8°. Londini, *R. Daniel.* 1653

Ἡ Καινὴ Διαθήκη. N.T. cum lect. var. &c. Acc. loca Scripturæ parallela &c. Præm. diss. Studio &c. J. Millii. fol. Oxonii. 1707

Ἡ Καινὴ Διαθήκη, δίγλωττος. [*Anc. & Mod. Gr.*] s8°. Ἄλα τῆς Σαξονίας. 1710

Nov. Test. Gr. e cod. MS. Alexandrino, Mus. Brit., descr. a C. G. Woide. [*Facsimile repr.*] fol. Lond. 1786

Codex Th. Bezæ Evangelia & Apostolorum Acta complectens quadratis literis Græco-Lat. Ed. notasque adj. T. Kipling. 2p [*pagin. cont.*] lafol. Cantab. 1793

Novum Test. Græcum. s8°. Londini. 1828

Nov. Test. Gr. & Lat. C. Lachmann rec. ; P. Buttmannus Gr. lect. auctoritates apposuit. 2v. 8°. Berolini. 1842–50

The Gk. T., w. Eng. notes by S. T. Bloomfield. 5th ed., rev. 2v. 8°. 1843

Τῆς Καινῆς Διαθήκης ἅπαντα. s8°. Καντάβριγία. 1847

Scholia Hellenistica in N.T. Philone et Josepho, Patr. Apost. aliisq. eccles. ant. scr., necnon libris apocryphis maxime depromta. Instr. &c. [E. W. Grinfield]. [2t. *pagin. cont.*] 8°. Londini. 1848

Nov. Test. Sinaiticum, cum Epist. Barnabæ &c. Descr. Æ. F. C. Tischendorf. 4°. Lips. 1863

Nov. Test. Acc. parallela S. Script. loca, vetus capitul. notatio canones Eusebii. [Ed. C. Lloyd, Bp. of Oxford]. s8°. Oxonii. 1869

Cambridge Greek Test. for Schools. s8°. C. 1891
Acts ; ed. J. R. Lumby.

Concordant version. The Sacred Scriptures [*i.e.* N.T.] Restored Gr. text, idiomatic Eng. vers., w. notes &c. 8°. Los Angeles, Cal. [1926]

see Abbott-Smith (G.) Manual Greek lex. of the N.T., 1922.
,, Adye (W. L.) The hist. of the Greek text of the N.T., 1865.
,, Bruder (C. H.) Ταμιεῖον, concordantiæ, ed. ster. 4a. 1888.
,, Clarke (A.) Succinct acc. of princ. eds. of Gr. Test., 1514–1797 &c., 1804.
,, Green (S. G.) Hdbk. to grammar of the Gr. Test., w. vocab., n. impr., rev., 1912.
,, Moulton (J. H.) & G. Milligan. Vocab. of the Gr. Test., p1–6, 1914–26.
,, Nolan (F.) Integrity of the Gr. vulgate, 1815.
,, Radermacher (L.) Neutestamentl. Gram., 1912.
,, Reuss (E. W. E.) Bibl. N.T. Græci, 1872.
,, Schmidt (E.) Op. sacrum posth. : versio N.T. nova ad Gr. verit. emend. &c., 1658.
,, Stolberg (B.) Exercit. de solœcismis &c. Gr. Novi Fœderis dictioni trib., 1688.
,, Turner (C. H.) Early pr. eds. of Gr. T., 1924.
,, Wetstein (J. J.) Ἡ Καινὴ διαθήκη : cum lect. var. & comm. opera &c., J. J. W., 2t, 1751–2.
,, Woide (C. G.) Notitia cod. Alexandr. &c., 1788.

New Testament [Latin], *see also* New Test. [Greek].

Novum Testamentum omne Latina versione [*by D. Erasmus*] oppositum æditioni vulgari sive Germanicæ [*by M. Luther*]. Das gantz Neuw Test. ze Teütsch &c. [*With pref. by J. Zwick. Lat. & German*]. s4°. Zurych, *C. Froschouer.* 1535

Bible [*continued*].
New Testament [Latin] [*continued*].
Novum Test. Lat., ad antiquiss. Græc. exemplaria castigatum & tr. per B. Galterum Delœnum [*i.e.* W. Delaine]. 4°. Londini, *J. Mayler*. 1540
Testamentum Nov. per D. Erasmum noviss. rec. s8°. [Francoforti]. 1551
Nov. Test. Lat. interp. Hieronymo. Ex Cod. Amiatino ed. C. Tischendorf. la8°. Lips. 1850
Codex Fuldensis. N.T. Lat. interpr. Hieronymo. Ed. E. Ranke. 8°. Marburgi. 1868
Nouum Test. Lat., sec. ed. S. Hieronymi. Rec. J. Wordsworth *&* H. J. White. p1, 2i–iii, 3i. 4°. O. 1889–1926
1, 4 Evangelia. 2i, Epist. ad Rom. 2ii, Epist. ad Corinth. 1. 2iii, Epist. ad Corinth. 2. 3i, Actus Apost.
see Irenæus, *St.* N.T. Sancti I.: quotations in the Old Lat. vers.; ed. w. intr[s]. &c. by W. Sanday & C. H. Turner, 1924.
Numbers.
see Attersoll (W.) A comm. upon N., 1618.
,, —— The pathway to Canaan & Hist. of Balak &c., 2p, 1609–10.
,, Cremer (B. S.) Naziræus in Num., cap. 4, 1, &c., 1727.
,, Patrick (S.) Comm. upon 4th Bk. of Moses, 1699.
Obadiah.
see Acoluth (A.) Obadius Armenus, 1680.
,, Jäger (G. F.) Üb. d. Zeitalter O.'s, 1837.
Octateuch.
see Theotokes (N.), *ed.* Σειρὰ 51 ὑπομνηματίστων εἰς τὴν 'Ο. &c., 2t, 1772–73.
Ojibwa.
N.T. Tr. into lang. of O. Indians. s8°. N.Y. 1856
Old Testament, *see also various Books & languages above & below, also* Concordances &c. *above, &* Septuagint *below.*
Die 24 Bücher d. Hl. Schr. Nach d. masoret. Texte. Unter d. Red. v. L. Zunz; übers. v. H. Arnheim, J. Fürst u. M. Sachs. 8°. 1838
Die Schriften d. Alten Test. in Auswahl neu übers. erklärt. v. H. Gressmann, H. Gunkel, M. Haller, H. Schmidt, W. Stärk u. P. Volz. Abtlg. 2, B2, Die grossen Propheten; übers. &c. v. H. Schmidt. 8°. Göttingen. 1915
The O.T.: a new tr. by J. Moffatt. 2v. 8°. [1924]
see Acosta (G.) Comm. quinque in lib. Vet. Test., 1641.
,, Aurivillius (C.) Diss. ad sacras lit. &c., 1790.
,, Bahrdt (C. F.) Apparatus criticus, v1, 1775.
,, Baynes (N. H.) Israel am. the nations, 1927.
,, Bootius (A.) Animadv. sacræ ad text. V.T., 1644.
,, Boyce (W. B.) 6 lect[s]. on higher crit. upon the O.T., 1878.
,, Buddeus (J. F.) Hist. eccl. Vet. Test., 2t, 1715–19.
,, Burney (C. F.) The gospel in the O.T., 1921.
,, Carpzov (J. G.) Intr. ad libros canon. V.T., 3p, 1721–27.
,, Causse (A.) Les plus vieux chants de la B., 1926.
,, Cook (S. A.) A Pre-Massoretic papyrus, 1903.
,, Dathe (J. A.) Opusc. ad crisin & interp. V.T. spect., 1796.
,, Delitzsch (F.) Complutens. Varianten, 1878.
,, —— Die grosse Täuschung: krit. Betracht. zu d. alttest. Berichten, 2T, 1920–21.
,, —— Die Lese-u. Schreibfehler im A.T., 1920.
,, Dieu (L. de). Animadv. in V.T. libros omnes, 1648.
,, Drysdale (A. H.) Early Bible songs, 1890.
,, Duff (A.) Hist. of O.T. crit., 1910.
,, Fabricy (G.) Des titres primitifs de la révélation &c., 2t, 1772.
,, Frazer (*Sir* J. G.) Folk-lore in the O.T., abr. ed., 1923.
,, Funk (G. B.) Symbol. ad interpret. S. Codicis, 1768–69.
,, Geden (J. D.) Doct. of a fut. life in O.T., 2nd ed., 1877.
,, Gordon (A. R.) Prophets of the O.T., 2nd ed., 1919.
,, Gray (G. B.) Sacrifice in the O.T., 1925.
,, Green (S. G.) Hdbk. to O.T. Hebrew, 3rd ed., 1921.
,, Hamilton (G.) Gen. intr. to study of Heb. Scr., 1813.
,, Hävernick (H. A. C.) Gen. intr. to O.T.; tr., 1852.
,, Hengstenberg (E. W.) Hist. of kingdom of God under the O.T.; tr., 2v, 1871–2.
,, Holbein (H.) Icones Vet. Test.: illust[s]. of the O.T., 1830.
,, Isaac, *ben Judah.* Diss. in Lat. versæ à J. Buxtorfio, 1662.
,, Kegel (M.) Away f. Wellhausen: new orientat. in O.T. study; tr., 1924.
,, Keil (C. F.) Manual of hist.-crit. intr. to O.T.; tr., 2v, 1869–70.
,, Kennicott (B.) Ed. Vet. Test. Heb. brevis def., 1782.
,, —— Remarks on sel. pass., 1787.
,, —— 10 annual acc[s]. of collation of Heb. MSS. of O.T., 1760–69, 1770.
,, Kistemaker (J. H.) Comm. de nova exegesi præc. V.T. 1806.
,, Köberle (J.) Die Papyri v. Assuan u. d. A.T., 1908.
,, König (F. E.) Gesch. d. alttest. Religion, 3[e] u. 4[e] A., 1924.
,, —— Theologie d. A.T., 1922.
,, Lange (J. P.) Theolog.-homilet. Bibelwerk; Des A.T. 20T [in 8v], 1861–78.
,, Le Clerc (J.) Sentimens sur l'Hist. crit. du V.T. par R. Simon, 1685.

Bible [*continued*].
Old Testament [*continued*].
see Leusden (J.) Philol. Heb., V.T. Heb., 1739.
,, Majus (J. H.) Œconomia judic. divin., 3p, 1712–14.
,, —— Œconomia temp. V.T., 1706.
,, Marcus (B.) Mykhur Hayen: mistransl. &c. of O.T., 1846.
,, Melanchthon (P.) Op., t1, 1541; Op., p2, 1562.
,, Montefiore (C. G.) The O.T.—& after, 1923.
,, Oesterley (W. O. E.) Immortality & the unseen world: st. in O.T. religion, 1921.
,, Öhler (G. F.) V.T. sententia de rebus futuris, 1846.
,, Orelli (C. v.) The O.T. prophecy &c.; tr., 1889.
,, Origen. O.'s Werke, B6–8, 1920–25.
,, Peake (A. S.) Brotherhood in O.T., 1923.
,, —— The People & the Book, essays, 1925.
,, Peet (T. E.) Egypt & the O.T., 1922.
,, Prosser (J.) Key to Hebrew Script., 1840.
,, Ranke (E.) Par palimpsest. Wirceburg., 1871.
,, Rashi. Comm. Hebr. in libr. Josuæ &c., 1714.
,, Richardson (J.) Obs. & explan. upon the O.T., 1655.
,, Rossi (G. B. de). Apparatus Hebr.-Bibl. &c., 1782.
,, —— Scholia crit., 1798.
,, —— Spec. var. lect. sacri textus &c., 1783.
,, Sands (P. C.) Lit. genius of the O.T., 1924.
,, Sayce (A. H.) Races of the O.T., rev. ed., 1925.
,, Schnurrer (C. F.) Diss. philol.-crit., 1790.
,, Schultens (A.) Op. minora, 1769.
,, Sellin (E.) Der alttest. Prophetismus, 1912.
,, —— Intr. to the O.T.; tr., 1923.
,, Semler (J. S.) Apparatus, 1773.
,, Simon (R.) Hist. crit. V.T.; tr., 1681.
,, Simonis (J.) Onomasticum V.T., 1741.
,, Sinyanki (J. E.) Notes on some passages, 1852.
,, Society for O.T. Study.
,, Taylor (T.) Christ revealed, or the O.T. expl., 1635.
,, Thanchum, *ben Joseph.* Ad libros V.T. comm. &c., 1791.
,, Townsend (G.) The O.T. arr. in hist. & chronolog. order &c., 2nd ed., 2v., 1826.
,, Wesley (I.) Explan. notes upon O.T. [*w. text*], 1765.
,, Whittaker (J. W.) Enq. into interp. of Heb. Scr., 1819.
,, Zeitschrift f. d. alttest. Wissenschaft, 1917–.
Oriya [Orissa].
[Prophets: Isaiah–Malachi]. 8°. [Serampore]. 1809 [1811]
Holy Bible tr. into Ootkula, v3, Poet. books. [*Eng. tp.* 1811; Oriya tp., 1809]. 8°. Serampore. 1811
[Hist. books: Joshua–Esther]. 8°. [Serampore]. 1811 [1814]
[Pentateuch]. 8°. [Serampore]. 1814
O.T. in O. lang. la8°. Cuttack. 1872
N.T. in O. 8°. Cuttack. 1875
Palpa, *see* Nepalese *above.*
Paul & Pauline Epistles.
see also Anglo-Saxon *& o. lang[s]. above & below, & separate Epistles.*
Codex Claromontanus, sive Epistulæ P. omnes Gr. & Lat. ex cod. Paris. Clarom. 6. sæc. ed. C. Tischendorf. 4°. Lipsiæ. 1852
see Anselm, *St.* In S. Pauli epist. enarr., 1533.
,, Balduin (F.) Comm. in omnes epist. P., 1564.
,, Benson (G.) A paraphrase &c. on 6 epist[s]., 2nd ed., 1752.
,, Bugenhagen (J.) Annot. in epist. Pauli, 1524; 1525.
,, —— Ausleg. d. kurtzen Epist. P., 1524–25.
,, Bulcock (H.) The passing & the permanent in St. P., 1926.
,, Bulic (F.) Melita del naufragio di S. P., 1913.
,, Byrne (D.) Brother Saul [*fict.*], 1927.
,, Calvin (J.) Comm. on Philippians, Col. & Thess.; tr., 1851.
,, —— Comm. on Timothy, Titus &c.; tr., 1856.
,, Chrysostom, *Saint.* Comm. on the Epistles of P., *in Armenian*, 2v, 1862.
,, Conybeare (W. J.) & J. S. Howson. Life & epistles of St. P., n. ed., 2v, 1877.
,, Deissmann (G. A.) Paulus, 2. A., 1925.
,, —— P.; tr., 2nd ed., 1926.
,, —— Relig. of Jesus & the faith of P.; tr., 1923.
,, Dobschütz (E. v.) Apostel P., 1, Weltgesch. Bedeut., 1926.
,, Evans (H. H.) St. P., author of Acts &c., 1884.
,, Foakes-Jackson (F. J.) Life of St. P., the man &c., 1927.
,, Giustiniano (B.) In P. epist. explan., 2t, 1612–13.
,, Glover (T. R.) P. of Tarsus, 1925.
,, Godet (F.) Studies; tr., 1889.
,, Harnack (C. G. A. v.) Briefsamml. d. P. &c., 1926.
,, Harrison (P. N.) Probl. of the pastoral epist., 1921.
,, Haymo, *bp. of Halberstadt.* In P. epist. interpretatio, 1529.
,, Heitmüller (W.) Taufe u. Abendmahl bei P., 1903.
,, Herrmann (J. F.) Disput.: testimonia patrum 5 prim. sec. de P. itin. in Hisp., 1740.
,, Hunnius (E.) Op. Lat., t4, 1606.
,, Hyperius (A.) Comm., 1582–84.
,, Iverach (J.) St. Paul, 1890.
,, Knox (W. L.) St. P. & the Church of Jerusalem, 1925.
,, Kopko (P.) Apostolus Bybl. sæc. 14. gramm.-krit. analys., 1912.
,, Lange (J.) Comm. de vita & epist. P. &c., 1718.
,, Lawson (G.) Expos. of the Ep. to the Hebrewes &c., 1662.

Bible [*continu d*].
PAUL AND PAULINE EPISTLES [*continued*].
see LIETZMANN (H.) Petrus u. P. in Rom, 1927.
,, LOCK (W.) St. P. the master-builder, 3rd ed., 1910.
,, LYTTELTON (G., *b.*) Conversion &c. of P., 9th ed., 1799.
,, MACHEN (J. G.) Origin of P.'s religion, 1921.
,, MACNEILE (A. H.) New Test. teaching in light of P.'s, 1923.
,, —— St. P., h. life, letters & Xtn. doctrine, 1920.
,, MEIER (G.) Enarr. epist. S. P. [*in* Op., t1, 1569].
,, —— Vita S. P., 1556; 1732.
,, MELANCHTHON (P.) Declamat. duæ in P. doct., 1522.
,, MUNTZ (W. J. S.) Rome, St. P. & the early church, 1913.
,, MUSCULUS (W.) In Epist. ad Philipp., Colossenses, Thessal. ambas & priman ad Tim. comm., 1565.
,, OLSHAUSEN (H.) Bibl. comm. on Galatians, Ephes., Col. & Thess.; tr., 3rd ed., 1864.
,, OMODEO (A.) P. di Tarso, 1922.
,, PARRY (R. ST. J.) Pastoral epistles, 1920.
,, PEABODY (F. G.) The Apostle P. & the mod. world, 1923.
,, PEARSON (J.) Annales P. [*in* Opera posthuma, 1687–88].
,, PEIRCE (J.) Paraphrase & notes on the Coloss., Philipp. & Hebrews &c., 1733.
,, PISCATOR (J.) Analysis logica epist. P., 1594.
,, ROSS (D. M.) Spiritual genius of St. P., 1925.
,, SCHELLING (F. W. J. v.) De Marcione P. Ep. emendatore, 1795.
,, SCOTT (C. A. A.) Xty. acc. to St. P., 1927.
,, SMYTH (J. P.) Story of St. P.'s life & letters, 1921.
,, SOUTER (A.) Character & hist. of Pelagius' comm. on Epistles of St. P., 1916.
,, SPANHEIM (F.) Diss. hist.: de æra conversionis P. &c., 1679.
,, STILL (J. I.) St. P. on trial, 1923.
,, TEXTS & STUDIES, v9i, ii, Pelagius's expos. of 13 epistles of S. P.; intr. [by A. Souter], 1922–26.
,, THEOPHYLACTUS, *abp. of Achrida.* Opera omnia, t4, Comm. in P., 1755.
,, WENDLER (J. C.) Prodromus bibliothecal bibl., 1721.
,, WESSELY (C.) Sahid. Papyrusfragm. d. paulin. Briefe, 1914.
,, ZIEGLER (L.) Italafragm. d. P. Briefe, 1876.
,, ZWINGLI (U.) In Evang. hist. &c., Epist. P. annot. &c., 1539.
PENTATEUCH, *see also various Books* (GENESIS &C.), *& languages above & below.*
see AARON, BEN E. Libri coronæ legis: comm. in P. Karaitici; ed. J. G. L. Kosegarten &c., 1842.
,, AMAMA (S.) Censura Vulgatæ &c., 1620.
,, BABINGTON (G.) Comfortable notes [*in h.* Wks., 1637].
,, BIBLE: HEBREW. Pentateuchus Heb.-Samarit.; ed. B. Blayney, 1790.
,, CALVIN (J.) Comm. on 4 last bks. of Moses, 4v; tr., 1852–55.
,, CELLARIUS (C.) Horæ Samarit., excerpta P.S. vers. cum Lat. interpret. &c., 1682.
,, DRUSIUS (J.) Ad loca diffic. P. comm., 1617.
,, GERLACH (O. v.) Comm. on the P.; tr., 1860.
,, HARFORD (J. B.) Since Wellhausen: rec. P. crit., 1926.
,, HÄVERNICK (H. A. C.) Hist.-crit. intr. to the P.; tr., 1850.
,, HENGSTENBERG (E. W.) Diss. on genuineness, 2v, 1847.
,, —— Egypt & the Bks. of Moses; tr., 1845.
,, HESSELMAN (B. I.) Språkformen (14 c.), 1927.
,, HOTTINGER (J. H.) Exercit. Anti-Morinianæ de P. Samaritano, 1644.
,, KEIL (C. F.) & F. DELITZSCH. The P.; 3v, 1864–65.
,, KELLY (W.) Lect[s]. introd. to P., 1871.
,, KYLE (M. G.) Moses & the monuments, 1920.
,, LAGARDE (P. A. DE). Mater. z. Krit. u. Gesch. d. P., 2B, 1867.
,, MACDONALD (D.) Introd. to the P., 2v, 1861.
,, MÖLLER (W.) Hist.-krit. Bedenken gegen d. Graf-Wellhausen Hypothese, 1899.
,, NAVILLE (E.) Higher criticism in rel. to the P.; tr., 1923.
,, —— The Law of Moses, 1921.
,, ONKELOS. Thargum ex Chald. in Lat. versa autore P. Fagio, t1, P. 1546.
,, RASHI. Comm. Hebr. in 5 libros Mosis, Lat. versus, 1713.
,, RUTHERFORTH (T.) Letter to Kennicott, &c., 1761.
,, SCHICKARD (W.) Bechinat happeruschim, exam. comm. rabbin., 1621.
,, SCHMIDT (J. L.) Die göttl. Schr., T1, Gesetze d. Jisraelen, 1735.
,, SCHNURRER (C. F.) De P. Arab. polyglotto, 1780.
,, TAYLOR (I.) Consid. on the P., 1863.
,, TERRELL (F. A. H.) *Jehovah & Elohim in P., 1869.
,, TRAPP (J.) Clovis, or comm. upon the P., 1650.
,, WRIGHT (A.) Comm. upon the P., 1662.
,, ZIEGLER (L.) Bruchstücke e. vorhieronym. Übers., 1883.
PERSIAN.
Novum Test. a H. Martyno tr. 4°. Petropoli. 1815
N.T. Tr. H. Martyn &c. 4th ed. 8°. 1837
,, ,, ...6th ed. 8°. 1876
[O.T. Tr. W. Glen]. 8°. London. 1856
see BODE (C. A.) Evang. sec. Marcum [*&* Lucam] ex vers. P. interp. tr. &c., 1751.

Bible [*continued*].
PETER, *see also* HINDUSTANI *above.*
For Apocryphal books, see PETER, *Saint & Apostle.*
see ADAMS (T.) Comm. upon 2nd Epistle wr. by St. P., 1633.
,, ALLEY (W.), *bp.* Πτωχομουζεῖον: rapsodiæ upon 1 Peter, 1571.
,, BULLINGER (H.) In P. epistol. utranque comm., 1533.
,, BYFIELD (N.) Comm. upon 1st 3 chap. of 1st Ep. of P., 1637.
,, GERHARD (J.) Comm. s. P. Epist., 2v, 1641.
,, GOYAU (G.) St. Pierre, 1923.
,, HORN (C.) In Epist. P. I & II expos., 1654.
,, LIETZMANN (H.) Hdbh. z. N.T., B4ii; erkl. v. H. Windisch, 1911.
,, —— P. u. Paulus in Rom, 1927.
,, NIETSCHE (F. A. L.) Epist. P. poster., contra Grotium vindic. &c., 1785.
,, PROCKSCH (O.) P. u. Johannes bei Marcus u. Matthäus, 1920.
,, SPANHEIM (F.) Diss. hist.: de P. in Roman profect. &c., 1679.
,, XAVIER (H.) Hist. S. P., Pers. & Lat., 1639.
,, ZAHN (T.) Komm. z. N.T., B15, ausgelegt v. G. Wohlenberg, 3e A., 1923.
PHILEMON.
see ELLICOTT (C. J.) Philippians &c.: w. comm. & rev. tr., 3rd ed., 1863.
,, FIRMINGER (W. K.) Colossians & P., w. intr. & notes, 1921.
,, LIETZMANN (H.), *ed.* Hdbh. z. N.T., B3ii; erkl. v. M. Dibelius, 1912.
,, LIGHTFOOT (J. B.) Coloss. & P., 9th ed., 1890.
PHILIPPIANS.
see BIGGS (C. R. D.) Epistle of Paul to the P., 1900.
,, CALIXTUS (G.) Expositio, 1654.
,, DAILLÉ (J.) Expos.; tr. J. Sherman, 1841.
,, ELLICOTT (C. J.) Ph.: w. comm. & rev. tr., 3rd ed., 1865.
,, LIETZMANN (H.), *ed.* Hdbh. z. N.T., B3ii; erkl. v. M. Dibelius, 1911.
,, LIGHTFOOT (J. B.) P.: rev. text, notes &c., 1891.
,, STEVARTIUS (P.) Comm. in Epist. ad P., 1595.
,, WIESINGER (J. T. A.) Bibl. comm., 1866.
,, ZWINGLI (U.) Ad Phil. annot. &c., 1531.
PIEDMONTESE.
Test. Neuv.; tr. in lingua piemont. 8°. Londra. 1834
POLISH.
Biblia to iest Księgi Starego y Nowego Test. trudnieyszych, przez D. Iakuba Wuyka. fol. w Krakowie, *w Drukárni Łazárzowéy.* 1599
Biblia Święta. [*Rev. by D. Mikołajewski & J. Turnowski*]. 8°. we Gdansku. 1632
Nowy Test. [*The Dantzig version. Ed. E. Breskott*]. s8°. w Brzegu Slaskim. 1708
Nowy Test. przez X. Jakuba Wuyka przełożony. [Berlin B.S.] s8°. w Poznaniu. 1820
see BIBLE: PSALMS. Zoktarz Dawido, 1539.
POLYGLOT.
Ximenez de Cisneros (*card.* F.) Vetus testamentū multiplici lingua nūc primo impressum . . . Hebraico Greco atq. Chaldaico idiomate. Adiūcta unicuiq. sua latina interpret. 4p–[v5], Novum testamentum grece & latine, subjūg. vocab. &c. [v6], Vocabularium hebraicum & chaldaicū &c. 6v. folio. *in Complutensi univ. A. G. de Brocario.* 1514–17
The cardinal's crest in red on tp.[s] of v1–4 & 6; in black on tp. of v5.
Ἡ Καινὴ Διαθήκη. Test. Nov. Interp. Syr. N.T. Hebr. typ. descr. Eadem Lat. serm. redd. Aut. I. Tremellio, adjecta est. [t1, Evangelia]. fol. [Geneva], *H. Stephanus.* 1569
Biblia sacra Hebraice, Chaldaice, Græce & Latine. Philippi II pietate &c. C. Plantinus excud. [*Ed.* B. Arias Montanus]. 8t. fol. Antverpiæ, *C. Plantinus.* [1569]–72
t6 *cont[s]. vocabularies & grammars, w. sep. tp[s]. & pagin[s].* Lexicon Græcum &c., *no gen. tp.* t8, *var. treatises by Arias &c. each w. sep. tp. & pagin., no gen. tp., first tp. being* Communes &c. Heb. linguæ idiotismi.
Nov. Test. Syr., Ebr., Græcè, Lat., Germ., Bohem., Ital., Hispan., Gallice, Angl., Danicè, Polon.; studio & lab. Eliæ Hutteri. [t1, *Gospels–Acts*]. fol. Noribergæ. 1599
Biblia Sacra quadrilinguia Vet. Test. Hebr. cum vers. Gr. 70 interpr., Lat. S. Schmidii & Germ. Lutheri, accurante C. Reineccio. Acc. præf. S. Deylingii. [Libri apocr. Vet. Test. Græci &c. *w. sep. tp. & pagin.* Biblia Sacra quadrilinguia N.T. Gr. cum vers. Syr., Græca vulg., Lat. & Germ. &c.] [3t]. fol. Lipsiæ. 1747-51
Novi Test. biblia triglotta: Gr., Syr. & Lat.; acc. subsidia crit. Evangelia [*no more publ* .] 4°. Londini. 1828
Lee (S.) Biblia Sacra polyglotta. Acc. prolegomena, auct. Samuele Lee. 3p. 4°. London, *S. Bagster.* 1829–31
O.T. in Hebrew, Greek, Latin & Eng. N.T. in Gr., Lat., Eng. & Portug., with Syriac vers. added.
see LE LONG (J.) *Disc. hist. s. les princ. éd[s]. des Bibles polygl.; par l'a. de la Bibl. Sacræ, 1713.

Bible [*continued*].

PORTUGUESE, *see also* PSALMS *below*.

O Novo Test., tr. pelo J. Ferreira a d'Almeida. s8°. Amster. 1712
Matthew has sep. tp. dated 1711.

Os cinco livros de Moyses.
s4°. Trangambār, *Real Missaõ de Dinamarca.* 1719

Os doze Prophetas menores. [*b. w.* Os livros dogmat., 1744].
4°. Trangambar. 1732

Os livros historicos. Tr. pelo J. F. A. d'Almeida. [*b. w.* Os cinco livros de Moyses, 1719].
s4°. Trangambar, *Real Missaõ de Dinamarca.* 1738

Os livros dogmat. do Velho Test.: Job, Psalmos &c. Tr. J. F. A. d'Almeida. 4°. Trangambar. 1744

Os quatro Prophetas mayores. Tr. J. F. A. d'Almeida &c. [*b. w.* Os livros dogmat., 1744]. 4°. Trangambar. 1751

Prim. parte do N.T.: 4 Evangelistas &c. Tr. J. F. A. d'Almeida, rev. &c. 8°. Trangambar. 1760

O Novo Testamento. Tr. pelo J. Ferreira A. d'Almeida. [*rev. by J. M. Mohr*]. s8°. Batavia. 1773

O Novo T. Tr. ne Indo-P. 8°. Colombo, *Missaõ Wesleyano.* 1852

PROPHETIC BOOKS, *see also* BIBLE: COMPL. TEXTS, *sep. prophets & various lang*[s]. *above & below.*

Facs. of the Wash. MS. of the Minor P. in the Freer coll. & the Berlin fragm. of Genesis. Intr. by H. A. Sanders.
fol. Ann Arbor, Mich. 1927

see BALDUIN (F.) In tres posteriores p. min. comm., 1698.
„ BENNETT (W. H.) Relig. of Post-Exilic prophets, 1907.
„ CALVIN (J.) Comm[s]. on the 12 minor p.; tr., 5v, 1846–49.
„ CAUSSE (A.) Les " pauvres " d'Israël (Prophètes &c.), 1922.
„ CYRIL, *St., patriarch of Alex.* In XII. Prophetas; a J. Pontano Gr. et Lat. ed. &c., 1607.
„ DRUSIUS (J.) Comm. in Prophetas min., 1627.
„ DUHM (B.) The 12 Prophets: version in poet. measures; tr. A. Duff, 1912.
„ HAYMO, *bp.* In XII. prophet. enarr., 1533.
„ KALINSKY (J. G.) Vaticinia Chabacuci & Nachumi & Iesaiæ, Micheæ & Ezechielis oracula &c., 1748.
„ †KUENEN (A.) The prophets &c., in Israel; tr., 1877.
„ LOWTH (W.) Comm. on Daniel & min. p., 2v, 1726.
„ ——Comm. upon larger & lesser P., 3rd ed., 1730; n. ed., 1822.
„ NOWACK (W.) Die kleinen Propheten, 3[e] A., 1922.
„ ŒCOLAMPADIUS (J.) In Iesaiam, Ezechielem, Danielem & Min. p. comm., 1558–67.
„ RASHI. Comm. Heb. in Prophetas; Lat. versus, 1713.
„ ROBINSON (T. H.) Prophecy &c. in anc. Israel; bibliog. by A. S. Peake, 1925.
„ SANDERS (H. A.) & C. SCHMIDT. Minor P. in Freer coll., 1927.
„ SCHMID (S.) In proph. min. comm., 1698.
„ SELLIN (E.) Der alttest. Prophetismus, 1912.
„ TIL (S. VAN). Comm. analyt., 3t, 1744.

PROVERBS, *see also Armenian & o. lang*[s]. *above & below.*

see BOSSUET (J. B.) Œuvres, t2, Libri Salomonis P. &c., cum notis, 1815.
„ DYKES (O.) Royal marriage, K. Lemuel's lesson &c., 1722.
„ GEIER (M.) Comm. in P., 1696.
„ HALL (J.) Salomons divine arts, &c., 1609.
„ MELANCHTHON (P.) Explic. Prov., 1551.
„ PATRICK (S.) Bk. of Job, P. paraphras'd &c., 1710.
„ SCOTT (M.) Textual discov. in P. &c., 1927.

PSALMS, *see also various lang*[s]. *above & below.*

[*German Psalter. Beg. f1*: [D]o dauid ein sun iesse waz in seinem kunigreich do erwelt er im. iiij. mann &c. [*Imperf.*]
8°. [Strassburg, *H. Eggestein.* c. 1475]
78 leaves (a–g in tens; h1–8). 1 leaf cont. end of Ps. 148 & Ps. 149–50, & 20 leaves cont. table are wanting.

Psalterium Davidis cū hymnis. fol. Lips., *M. Lotther.* 1521

Psalterium ex hebreo tr., fratre Felice interprete.
s4°. [Hagonæ, *Thos. Anstelmus.* 1522]

Psalterium. Ab O. Luscinio Lat. redd. [*b. w.* Nachtigall (O.) Allegoriæ, 1524]. s8°. [Augustæ, *Sympertus Ruf.* 1524]

Der ain uñneintzichst Ps. tröstlich in d. Gemain z. d. Zeyt d. Pestilentz zu singen. [*b. w.* Wickner (C.) Das man &c., 1530].
s4°. *n.p. n.d.* [c. 1530]

[Psalterium Hebraicum cum radicibus in margine. Cui acc. capita ex Evang. Matthei versa. s8°. [Lipsiæ. 1533]

Verteutschung aller Ps. wie die Joannes Campensis nach Hebreischer warheit in das latein gebracht hat. [*Tr. by G. Frolich*]. s8°. [Augspurg, *Alexander Weyssenhorn*]. 1534

Ps. in Lat. conversi per J. Draconitem. Item: Sacramenti carnis &c. Christi conf.
s4°. Marpurgi, *Officina E. Cervicorni.* 1536

Zoktarz Dawidow, przez Mistrza Valanthego Wrobla z Poznania na rzecz polska wylozony. [*Lat. & Polish*]. s8°. Cracoviæ. 1539

The whole booke of Ps.; coll. into Eng. meeter by T. Sternhold, J. Hopkins &c. [*tp. mutil., pp. 21, 22, 77 & onwards wanting*]. [*b. w. Bible, C. Barker, 1585*]. s4°. *Assignes of R. Day.* 1585
„ „ [*a. ed.*] w. apt notes to sing them withall. [*Goose on tp.*] 8°. *n.p. n.d.* [c. 1599]
„ „ [*a. ed. b. w.* Bible. The Holy B., 1612]. s8°. 1612
„ „ [*a. ed. b. w.* Bible. Holy B., 1625]. s4°. 1623
„ „ [*a. ed. b. w.* Bible, 1638]. fol. C. 1638

Bible [*continued*].

PSALMS [*continued*].

The whole booke of Ps. [*a. ed.*] s8°. 1639
„ „ [*a. ed.*] 8°. 1641
„ „ [*a. ed. b. w.* Prayer-Bk. Bk. of C. P., 1726]. 4°. 1726
„ „ [*a. ed.*] s8°. 1756
„ „ [*a. ed. b. w.* Prayer-Bk. Bk. of C. P., 1802]. s8°. 1791

Ψαλτήριον. s8°. Ἑνετίησιν. [1628]

The whole booke of Davids Ps., in prose & meetre &c.
s8°. *pr. by W. S.* 1631
„ „ .... s8°. *pr. by T. C.* 1635

The Ps. of David in meeter. By authority of Gen. Assembly of Kirk of Scot. [*b. w.* The Holy Bible, 1668]. s4°. C. 1655

*Harpffen Davids mit Teutschen Saiten bespannet. [*Lat. & Germ. By A. Curtz*]. s8°. Augspurg, *Apergerin.* 1659

Harpffen Davids mit Teutschen Saiten &c. [*Lat. & Germ.* Zum andermal aussgefertiget v. e. auss d. Soc. Jesu].
s8°. Augspurg, *Utzschneider.* 1669

A new vers. of the Ps. fitted to the tunes used in churches. By N. Brady & N. Tate. s8°. Tranquebar. 1717
„ „ [*a. ed. b. w.* Sternhold (T.) & J. Hopkins Bk. of Ps., 1756]. s8°. *Brown.* 1771
„ „ Notes by H. Stebbing. [*b. w.* Prayer Book. B. of C. P., 1838]. s8°. *Bell. n.d.*

Ps. (Les) de David mis en vers françois, revus par le Synode Walon. [*w. tunes*]. n. éd. à laquelle on a joint les Dévotions partic. &c. s8°. à La Haye. 1730

Psalterium cum canticis, *see* ANASTASIUS *bibliothecarius.* De vitis Rom. pontif., t4, 1735.

[*Slavonic Psalter, no tp.*] s8°. [*pr. in* Kievopecherskor Lavrê]. 1747

Boek (Het) d. Ps., nevens christel. Gezangen. [*Foll. by* Kerkboek *without tp., sep. pagin.*] s8°. A. 1779

Sailm Dhaibhidh &c. [*b. w.* Bible: Gælic. Tiomnadh Nuadh, 1796]. s8°. Dun-Eidean, *Stewart,* 1800

Ps. (The) of David in metre. Allowed by the Kirk of Scotland.
s8°. E. 1812

The Ps. in metre, vers. appr. by Ch. of Scot. s8°. E. 1844
„ „ .... [*a. ed.*] s8°. E. 1850

The Bk. of Ps. [*In Hebrew*] by J. S. C. F. Frey. [*b. w. h.* Hebrew gram., 1813]. 8°. 1813

Ps. Syriacè. s8°. Lond. 1825

Ps. Ny Prof-Ofwersättning af Nuwarande Kongl. Bibel-Comm. 4°. Upsala. 1834

New metr. version of the Ps. &c. s8°. 1848

Ps. & hymns for public worship; rev. &c. by J. Turle, 1863, *see* HYMNS.

Psalterium juxta Hebræos Hieronymi e recogn. P. de Lagarde. Acc. Corollarium crit. 8°. Lipsiæ. 1874

Louterell Psalter, 14th cent.; by J. Gage, *see* †VETUSTA monumenta, v6, 1885.

The Ps. chronolog. arranged: an amended vers., w. intr. & notes, by 4 friends [*i.e.* C. T. Arnold, F. E. Kitchener, J. S. Phillpotts, Alex. Potts]. [repr.] 8°. 1891
„ „ The Golden Treasury Psalter, ed. w. briefer notes of The Psalms chronolog. arr. by 4 friends [*i.e.* C. T. Arnold, F. E. Kitchener, J. S. Phillpotts, A. W. Potts]. [repr.] s8°. 1895

The Ps. in Lat. & Eng. Intr. by J. H. Bernard. [s8°. [1911]

The Book of Ps. Jewish version. Sailors' &c. ed.
[2nd impr.] s8°. 1918

Psalterium juxta Hebræos Hieronymi. Ed., w. intr. &c. by J. M. Harden. 8°. 1922

Two East Anglian Psalters at the Bodl. Lib., Oxf. The Ormesby Ps., descr. by S. C. Cockerell. The Bromholm Ps., descr. by M. R. James. [Roxburghe Club]. fol. O. 1926

New version of Ps. [*b. w.* Prayer-Book. B. of C. P., 1801].
s8°. *Reeves. n.d.*

Psalterium Davidis. s8°. Londini. *n.d.*

see ATHANASIUS, *St.* Interpretatio Ps., *Gr. & Lat.*, 1777.
„ AURIGNY (G. D'). 30 Ps.; tr. de Latin par G. D., 1549.
„ BAKER (*Sir* R.) Meditations (1639–40), 1882.
„ BARBER (R.) A book of psalmody, 1727 ?.
„ BARCLAY (J.) The Ps. paraphr. acc. to N.T. interpret. &c., 1776.
„ BARTON (W.) Book of Ps. in metre; tr., 1705.
„ —— Six centuries of sel. hymns &c., 1688.
„ —— Two centuries of sel. hymns &c., 1672.
„ BARTRUM (J. P.) Ps. newly paraphrased, 1833.
„ BEATTIE (J.) Letter on improvement of Psalmody in Scotland, 1829.
„ BECKER (P. A.) C. Marots Psalmenübers, 1920.
„ BEZA (T.) Ps. libri 5, 1580.
„ BIANCHINI (G. M.) Vindiciæ Canonic. Script. & Ps. duplex, 1740.
„ BLACKMORE (*Sir* R.) New vers. of Ps., 1721.
„ BONADE (F.) Eximii prophet. antistitis regia Davidis oracula, per F. B. &c. numeris poëticis exarata, 1531.
„ BOSSUET (J. B.) Œuvres, t1, Liber Ps., add. Canticis, cum notis, 1815.
„ BREITINGER (J. J.) De antiq. Turic. Bibl. Gr. Ps. libro, 1748.
„ *BRIEF (A) & full acc. of Tate's & Brady's n. vers. of the Ps., 1698.

Bible [*continued*].
PSALMS [*continued*].
see BRUNO, *Saint, bp.* Ps. a J. Cochleo restit., 1533.
,, BUCHANAN (G.) Paraphrasis Ps. Davidis poet., 1582 ; 1583 ; 1621.
,, BUGENHAGEN (J.) In librum Ps. interpretatio, 1524.
,, —— Ps., door M. Bucerum verduytscht, *n.d.*
,, BUIST (G.) The Book of Ps. in metre, 1784.
,, BURKE (P. D.) Gnomon Ps., 2t, 1760.
,, BYTHNER (V.) Lyra prophetica Davidis, Ps., 1650.
,, CALVIN (J.) Comm^s. on Ps., 5v ; tr., 1845–49.
,, CAUSSE (A.) Les " pauvres " d'Israël (Prophètes, Ps. &c.), 1922.
,, COCHLÆUS (J.) Wie verkerlich M. Luther den sibenden Psalm verdewtzscht, &c., 1529.
,, COLECCION, de poesías esp., p4, Salmos, 1879.
,, CORDIER (B.) Expos. Patrum in Ps. &c., 3t, 1643–46.
,, CORNERUS (C.) Ps., cum expos. à C. C., 1575.
,, COTTLE (J.) New vers. of Ps. of David, 1801.
,, COTTON (J.) Singing of Ps., 1647.
,, DARBY (C.) Bk. of Ps. in metre, 1704.
,, DELITZSCH (F.) Bibl. comm. on the Ps. ; tr. D. Eaton, 3v, 1887–89.
,, DENHAM (*Sir* J.) Version of Ps., 1714.
,, DENNIS (T.) New vers. in blank verse, 1808.
,, DICKSON (D.) Brief explication, 1654–55.
,, DONNE (J.) A sermon upon Ps. 38, v. 9, 1921.
,, DORN (B.) De Ps. Æthiopico comm., 1825.
,, DOWNES (G.) Glossary to first six Ps., 1823.
,, EMMET (C. W.), C. F. BURNEY, & W. SANDAY. Use of the Ps., 1918.
,, EOBANUS (H.) Ps. Davidis &c. carm. redd., 1563.
,, ERASMUS (D.) Ein fast nutzlich uslegung d. 1. ps., 1520.
,, ERNLE (R. E. P., *1st b.*) Ps. in human life, 2nd ed., 1904.
,, EUTHYMIUS, *Zigabenus.* Comm. in Ps., 1763.
,, FERREIRA D' ALMEIDA (J.) Livro dos Ps. ; tr., 1868.
,, FISHER (J.) Sayinges of David in the 7 penytencyall ps. &c., 1555.
,, FLAMINIO (M. A.) In lib. Ps. explanatio, 1545.
,, GEDDES (A.) New tr. of Bk. of Ps., w. var. readings &c., 1807.
,, GEIER (M.) Comm. in Ps., 1695.
,, GESNER (S.) Comm. in Ps., 1605.
,, GILLINGS (J.) The Ps., metric. arrang. in Tamil, 1891.
,, GJORGI (I.) Vulgatæ Ps. ed. Illyrica metaphr., 1729.
,, GONZAGHI (B.) Ragionamenti s. i 7 peccati mortali & s. i 7 Salmi penit., 1567.
,, GOODE (W.) Entire new vers. of Bk. of Ps., 3rd ed., 1816.
,, HELMORE (T.) Psalter noted *&* Accompanying harmonies [*b. sep.*], 1849 ; 1850.
,, HILDROP (J.) Comm. upon 2nd Ps., 1742.
,, HOLLAND (J.) Psalmists of Britain, 2v, 1843.
,, HORSLEY (S.) Bk. of Ps. ; tr., 4th ed., 1845.
,, IRHAVEN (W. v.) Conject. in Ps. titulos, 1728.
,, JAMES I. Ps. of David ; tr by K. J., 1631 ; 1637 ?.
,, JARAVA (H.) Los siete ps. penit., los quinze ps. &c. ; [tr.], H. J., 1556.
,, KEBLE (J.) *Ps. of David in Eng. verse, 1839.
,, KENNICOTT (B.) Sermon ; w. notes on Ps. 48 & 49, 1765.
,, LAING (D.) Notices reg. metr. vers. of Ps., 1842.
,, LATHAM (H.) Anthologia Davidica, 1846.
,, LE BLANC (T.) Ps. Davidic. analysis, 6t, 1744.
,, LITURGY (A) coll. for use of 1st Episc. Ch. in Boston, w. the Ps., 1785.
,, LOBWASSER (A.) Ps. Davids &c., in Teut. Reymen gebr. durch A. L., 1601 ; 1616 ; 1698.
,, MADAN (M.) Coll. of Ps. &c., 1765.
,, MANT (R.) Book of Ps. in Eng. metr. vers., 1824.
,, MARGARITA. Liber margarita Davitica, 1471 ?.
,, MAROT (C.) Ps. 50 de David ; mis en vers fr. par C. M., 1548.
,, —— & T. BEZA. Les Ps. mis en rime franç., 1563.
,, MELHO (P. DE). Eenige Ps. Davids in Tamul. overgeset, 1755.
,, MERRICK (J.) The Ps. in Eng. verse, 1766.
,, MILBOURNE (L.) Ps. of David ; tr. M., 1698.
,, MILLER (E.) Ps. for the use of churches &c., 1790.
,, MOSSOM (R.) The preacher's tripartite, Ps. XXV &c., 1657.
,, MOWINCKEL (S.) Psalmenstudien, 1, 2, 1921–22.
,, MOZLEY (F. W.) Ps. of the Church : Septuagint comp. w. Heb., 1905.
,, MUSCULUS (W.) In Davidis ps. comm., 1599.
,, NACHTIGALL (O.) Allegoriæ Ps. Davidis &c., 1524.
,, NICOLAUS *de Lyra.* Postilla super Ps. per annum, 1516.
,, NONNOSUS, *abbot.* Ps. Davidis &c., 3p, 1741–42.
,, NOTKER *Labeo.* Ps. David., 1728.
,, PASCHALI (G. C.) Salmi di Davide &c., 1592.
,, PATRICK (S.) Bk. of Job paraphras'd, Bk. of Ps. &c., 4th ed., 1710.
,, PELLICANUS (C.) Ps. C. P. opera elab., 1527.
,, PÉRENNÈS (H.) Les Psaumes ; tr. & comm., 1922.
,, PETERBOROUGH PSALTER. P. Psalter of 14c., descr. by M. R. James, 1921.
,, PETERS (J. P.) Ps. as liturgies, 1922.
,, PHILLIPS (J.) Daveidos or a spec. of Ps. &c., 1698.

Bible [*continued*].
PSALMS [*continued*].
see PRAYER BOOK. Prop. amendments to text of Ps., 1921.
,, RASHI. Comm. Hebr. in Prophetas, Ps. &c. ; Lat. versus, 1713.
,, RAVENSCROFT (T.) Bke. of Ps. &c., w. tunes, 1633.
,, REEVES (J.) Collat. of Heb. & Gr. texts of the Ps., 1800.
,, *REMARKS upon a late pamp. : A brief &c. acc. of Tate's & Brady's n. v. of the Ps., 1699.
,, REUCHLIN (J.) In septem ps. pœnit. interpret. &c., 1512.
,, REYNOLDS (E.) Works : explic. of Ps. 110, 1678.
,, RICIUS (P.) Lepida &c. in ps. Beatus vir. medit., 1519.
,, ROBERTS (F.) Clavis Bibl. ; added metr. vers. of Ps., 1675.
,, ROLLE (R.) In Ps. &c. enarr., 1536.
,, ROLLOCK (R.) Expos. upon some sel. Ps. of David ; tr., 1600.
,, —— In sel. aliquot Ps. D. comm., 1599.
,, ROMAINE (W.) Essay on psalmody &c., 1775.
,, ROUS (F.) *The Ps. of David in Eng. meeter, 1646.
,, SANDAY (W.) & C. W. EMMET. The Ps. explained, 1918.
,, SANDYS (G.) A paraphr. of the Ps. of D., 1676.
,, SAUERLAND (H. V.) & A. HASELOFF. Der Psalter Erzbischof Egberts v. Trier, 1901.
,, SAVONAROLA (G.) Miserere mei deus, mitt auszlegung &c., 1522.
,, SCHMID (S.) Resol. cum paraphrasi Ps. prophet., &c., 1688.
,, SCHRAMB (A.) Pia desideria Davidica, 1707.
,, SCHWICKERIUS (P.) P. S. sita in septem penit. Ps. elucid., 1514.
,, SCOTT (M.) Textual discov. in P. &c., 1927.
,, SERRES (J. DE). Ps. metaphrasis Græca, 1770.
,, SMART (C.) A tr. of the Ps. of David, 1765.
,, SNOY (R.) Ps. David. paraphrasibus ill., 1536 ; 1551.
,, TILING (E.) Disq. de ratione inscript. 15 Ps., cant. adscens., 1765.
,, TOWERS (W. S.) Version of the Ps., 1811.
,, VATABLUS (F.) Annot. in Ps., subj. H. Grotii notis &c., 1767.
,, VONDEL (J. VAN DEN). Werken, d18–20, K. Davids Harpzangen, *n.d.*
,, WATSON (R.) J. Cosin, his opinion &c., metrical Ps. &c., 1684.
,, WATTS (I.) Psalms, imitated in lang. of N.T., 1719 ; 1727 ; 1772.
,, WELCH (A. C.) The Ps. in life, worship & hist., 1926.
,, WELSH (R. E.) & F. G. EDWARDS. Romance of Psalter & hymnal, 1889.
,, WHEATLAND (S.) & T. SYLVESTER. Ps. in heroic verse, 1754.
,, WITHER (G.) Ps. of David tr. into lyrick verse, 1632.
,, ZAPF (G. W.) Ueb. e. Ausg. v. J. de Turrecremata Explan. in Ps., 1803.

PUNJABI.
[Hist. books of O.T. Joshua-Esther]. 8°. Serampore. [1818]
PUSHTU.
Holy Bible, tr. into P. v5, N.T. 8°. Serampore. 1818
RAJASTHANI, *see* BIKANERA ; MARWARI *above.*
RAJMAHALI.
St. John in R. 8°. Agra. 1882
St. Luke in R. 8°. Agra. 1881
RAROTONGAN.
Te Bibilia Tapu ra. la8^o. Lonedona, *B.F.B.S.* 1851
REVELATION [APOCALYPSE], *see also* ARMENIAN *&* *o. lang^s. above & below.*
For ed. in Internat. Crit. Comm., by R. H. Charles, see BIBLE : GEN. COMM.
The Apocalypse in Lat. & French (Bodl. MS. Douce 180). [Reprod. in collotype]. Descr. by M. R. James. [Roxburghe Club]. fol. O. 1922
Commentarius in A. ante centum annos æditus. [*Pref. by M. Luther*]. s8^o. Wittembergæ. 1528
see ABBADIE (J.) Le triomphe de la providence &c., 4t, 1723.
,, ALCAZAR (L. ab). Vestigatio arcani sensus in A., 1618.
,, ALLO (E. B.) St. Jean : l'A., 1921.
,, ANDREW, *St., abp. of Cæsarea.* Comm. on A., tr. into Armenian, 1855.
,, AUBERLEN (C. A.) Daniel et l'A. ; tr., 1880.
,, BENGEL (J. A.) Erklärte Offenb., 1758.
,, —— 60 Reden ü. d. Offenbarung, 1748 ; n. A., 1771.
,, BERNARD (R.) Key for opening of R., 1617.
,, BOSSUET (J. B.) Œuvres, t3, L'A., avec explic. &c., t4, De excidio Babylonis apud S. Joannem, 1815.
,, BRIGHTMAN (T.) Workes, 1644.
,, BROWN (J. AQ.) Jew, the master-key of the A., 1827.
,, BULLINGER (H.) In A., conciones 100, 1557.
,, BURTON (G.) Essay tow. reconciling the numbers of Daniel & St. John, 1766.
,, CARPENTER (J. E.) The Johannine writings, 1927.
,, CHARLES (R. H.) Lect^s. on the A., 1922.
,, CONYBEARE (F. C.) Armenian version of R. ; ed. &c. F. C. C., 1907.
,, CRESSENER (D.) A demonstr. of the first princ. of the Protest. applic. of the A. &c., 1690.
,, DENT (A.) The ruine of Rome &c., 1603.

Bible [*continued*].

REVELATION [*continued*].

see DIEU (L. DE). Apoc. Joh. charact. Syro & Ebr. cum vers. Lat. & notis, 1627.
,, ELLIOT (E. B.) Apoc. Alfordiana &c., 1852.
,, GARRETT (W.) Disc. conc. Antichrist &c., 1680.
,, GEBHARDI (V. C.) De chiliasmo ex A. disq., 1691.
,, GERHARD (J.) Adnotat. in A., ed. 3a, 1712.
,, GILSON (J. P.) Friar Alexander & h. hist. interp. of the A., 1922.
,, GUILD (W.) The sealed book opened, 1656.
,, HEIDEGGER (J. J.) In Joh. Apoc. prophetiam de Babylone magna diatr., 2t, 1687.
,, HOSKIER (H. C.) MSS. of the A., 5p, 1922–24.
,, JANSONIUS (R.) Brevis diss. de visionibus cap. 13 & 17 A., *n.d.*
,, JUNIUS (F.), *the elder*. The A., w. expos. &c., 1596.
,, LOISY (A.) L'A. de Jean, 1923.
,, NEWTON (I.) Obs. upon Daniel & the A., 1733.
,, OMAN (J. W.) Bk. of R., theory of text : rearr. text & tr. : comm., 1923.
,, PAREUS (D.) Comm. upon R., 1644.
,, PEAKE (A. S.) The R. of John, 1920.
,, RAMBACH (J. J.) Betracht. ü. d. 7 Verheiss. &c. (Offenb. 2 & 3), 1733.
,, RIBERA (F. DE). In I. Apoc. comm., 1603.
,, ROBERTS (*Lt.-Col.* F.) The Patmos Record, *n.d.*
,, ROCHA (D. A.) Brevis paraphrasis A., 1653.
,, ROOS (M. F.) Expos. of Daniel, w. compar. ; tr., 1811.
,, ROXAS (A. DE). Comm., 1732.
,, STIFEL (M.) Ein sehr wunderbarlich wortrechnung &c. etl. zalen, 1553.
,, SWEDENBORG (E.) The A. revealed ; tr., 1876.
,, TAYLOR (T.) Christ's victory over the dragon : 12th chap. of R., 1633.
,, TITELMAN (F.) Libri duo de authoritate A., 1530.
,, TRAPP (J.) Comm. upon the R. &c., 1647.
,, WALMESLEY (CH.) Gen. hist. of Xtn. Church reduced f. A., 1771 ; 5th ed., 1812.
,, WHISTON (W.) Essay on the R. of St. J., 1744.
,, ZAHN (T.) Komm. z. Neu. Test., B18, Die Offenbarung d. Johannes ; ausgelegt v. T. Z., H1, 1924.

ROMANS, *see also* PAUL &c. *above*.

see ARMINIUS (J.) Examen libelli add., Analysis cap. 9. ad R., 1612.
,, BEET (J. A.) Comm., 7th ed , 1890.
,, BÖHME (C. F.) Epist. Pauli ad R., Græce, 1806.
,, BORGER (P. A.) Diss. de parte epist. Pauli ad R. parænetica, &c., 1840.
,, BRAIS (E. DE). Epist. ad R. analysis paraphrast., 1707.
,, BUCER (M.) Metaphrases & enarr., t1, in epist. ad R., 1536.
,, BUGENHAGEN (J.) Interpretatio &c., 1527.
,, CALIXTUS (G.) Expositio, 1652.
,, CALVIN (J.) Comm. in Epist. ad R., 1540 ; tr., 1849.
,, DIEU (L. DE). Animadv., 1646.
,, FERME (C.) Log. anal. of R. ; tr., & comm. by A. Melville, in Lat., 1850.
,, HYPERIUS (A.) In D. Pauli ad R. epist. exegema, 1549.
,, LIETZMANN (H.), *ed*. Hdbh. z. N.T., B3, Die Briefe d. Paulus, I, Einführung in d. Textgesch. d. R. ; erkl. v. H. L., 2e A., 1919.
,, LIMBORCH (P. VAN). Comm. in Acta & in Epist. ad R. &c., 1711.
,, MELANCHTHON (P.) Annotat. in Epist. ad R., 1523.
,, —— Commentarii, 1532.
,, MUSCULUS (W.) Comm. in epist. ad R., 1611.
,, MYLIUS (G.) In epist. P. ad R., 1595
,, —— Πρόδρομος disput., 1590.
,, ŒCOLAMPADIUS (J.) In epist. ad R. adnot., 1525.
,, PARR (E.) Plaine expos. upon 8–11 chapters of R., 1618.
,, SCHMIDT (C. F.) Annotationes, 1777.
,, WILD (J.) In sec. Jo. Evang. comm. & P epist. ad R. interp., 1578.

ROMANSCH.

L'Nouf S. Test., huossa da nœf vertieu in R. træs Joann. L. Griti, da Zuoz. &c. 8°. Basel, *G. Decker*. 1640

Da la Biblia. Genesis. Traas J. P. Salutz. s8°. Tury [Zürich], *H. Hamberger*. 1657

La Sacra Bibla : Cun l'agg. dall' Apocrifa. Tschantada, vertida è stamp. in Lingua Rumanscha d'Ingadina Bassa : tras J. A. Vulpio & J. Dorta à Vulpera. [*w. add. engr. tp.* 4 *pagin^s^.*] fol. Scuol. *J. Dorta à Vulpera, juven F.* 1678–79

La S. Bibla, &c. fol. Coira, *Andrea Pfeffer*. 1718
N.T. [*dated 1717*] *is a reprint of ed. of 1648. O.T. & Apocr., tr. by S. Gabriel.*

Il Nouf Test. Tr. in R. d'Engadina Bassa. 8°. Basel. 1812

Bibla. 8°. Coira, *B. Otto for Bibl. Soc.* 1815

Ilg Nief Test. s8°. Cuera. 1820

Il Nouv Test. tr. nel dialect R. d'Engiadina Ota tres J. Menni. s8°. Coira. 1861

see GRÜZMACHER (—). Waldens. Bibel, 1862.

Bible [*continued*].

RUMANIAN.

Думнезеяска Скріптуръ. [*The first ed. of the complete Bible in Rumanian. Tr. by Nicolæ Milescu, a Rumanian chronicler, & others*]. fol. [Bucharest. 1688]

RUSSIAN, *see also* SLAVONIC *below*.

Священныя книги Ветхаго и Новаго Завѣта. 8°. Вѣна. 1889

Святое Евангеліе па русск. и удинск. яз., *see* SBORNIK. Сборн. матер. для опис. Кавказа, 30, 1902.

Священныя книги В. и Н. Завѣта. 8°. Вѣна. 1905

RUTH.

see KEIL (C. F.) & F. DELITZSCH. Joshua, Judges, R. ; tr., 1865.
,, KÖNIGL. GESELLS. D. W. ZU GÖTTINGEN. Nachr., phil.-hist. Kl., 1922 (Rahlfs, Griech. Text d. R.)
,, PATRICK (S.) Comm. on Joshua, R. &c., 1702.
,, SCHMID (S.) Annot. in libell. R., 1696.
,, WERNER (A. C.) Liber R. illust., *Heb. & Lat.*, 1740.

SAMARITAN, *see also* PENTATEUCH *above*.

see CELLARIUS (C.) Horæ S., 1682.
,, RUTHERFORTH (T.) Letter to Kennicott, &c., def. of S. Pentateuch exam., 1761.

SAMUEL, *see also* HUNGARIAN *above*.

see BUGENHAGEN (J.) Annotationes &c., 1524.
,, KEIL (C. F.) & F. DELITZSCH. Bibl. comm. on Bk^s^. of S. ; tr., 1891.
,, PATRICK (S.) Comm. upon the 2 Bks. of S., 1703.
,, SCHMID (S.) In librum prior. [-posterior.] S. comm., 1687.

SANSKRIT.

[Histor. Books. *Tr. W. Carey &c.*] 4°. [Serampore. 1811]

Holy Bible Tr. by Calcutta Bapt. Miss. [Rev. J. Wenger]. v1–3. 8°. Calcutta. 1848–58

N.T. Tr. by Calcutta Bapt. Miss. [*repr.*] 8°. Calcutta. 1886

SANTALI.

Mark [2nd ed.], Luke [2nd ed.], John & Acts [*each w. sep. tp. &c.*] s8°. Calcutta. 1877–85

SCOTTISH, *see also* GAELIC *above*.

St. Matthew, tr. into Lowland Sc. by G. Henderson. s8°. 1862

SECUANA. Bibela [Gen.-Kings II]. 8°. Kuruman. 1853

SEPTUAGINT.

For Lat. translations from the Septuagint, see LATIN *above ; see also* GREEK *&* POLYGLOT *above.*

Ἡ παλαιὰ Διαθήκη κατὰ τοὺς Ἑβδομήκοντα. Vet. Test. juxta S. ex auctor. Sixti V ed. fol. Romæ, *F. Zannetti*. 1587

Vet. Test. Græc. ex vers. S. interp., juxta Exemplar Vatic. Romæ ed. [*Folld. by* Scholia, *w. sep. tp. & pagin.*] s8°. Londini, *R. Daniel*. 1653
First ed. of the LXX. pr. in Eng. Ed. J. Biddle.

Septuaginta interp. t1 [-4]. Ex antiq. MS. Cod. Alexandrino, accurate descr. &c. ed. J. E. Grabe. 4t [*in 2v*]. fol. Oxonii. 1707–20

Vet. Test. ex vers. S. interp., sec. ex. Vatican. Romæ ed. &c. Ed. L. Bos. 4°. Franequeræ, *F. Halma*. 1709

Vet. Test. ex vers. S. interp. olim ad fidem Cod. Alex. emend. &c. a J. E. Grabe. Summa cura ed. J. J. Breitingerus. 4v. 4°. Tiguri Helvet., *J. Heideggerus*. 1730–32

Vet. Test. Gr. e Cod. MS. Alexandrino, qui in Bibl. Musei Brit. asservatur, typis ad similitud. scr. descr. cura H. H. Baber. 3t *in* 5v [1i, ii ; 2i, ii]. lafol. Londini. 1816–21
,, ,, Prolegomena & notæ. lafol. Londini. 1828

Vet. Test. Gr. juxta 70 interp. Textum Vat. ed. &c. C. de Tischendorf. 5^a^ ed. 2t. 8°. L. 1875

Facs. of Wash. MS., 1927, *see* Prophetic Bks. *above*.

The O.T. in Greek, acc. to the text of Codex Vatic. &c. Ed. A. E. Brooke, N. McLean & H. St. J. Thackeray. v2, Later hist. bks., p1, I & II Samuel. 4°. C. 1927

see JOHANNESSOHN (M.) Gebrauch d. Präpositionen in d. S., 1925.
,, RAHLFS (A.) Verzeichnis d. griech. Hss. d. Alt. Test., 1914.
,, THACKERAY (H. ST. J.) S. & Jewish worship, 1921.
,, —— Some aspects of the Gr. O.T., 1927.
,, TOMASI (G. M.) Sacr. Bibliorum vet. tituli, 2p, 1688.
,, VOSSIUS (I.) De S. dissert., 1661–63.
,, WHITE (J.) Plan for new ed. of the LXX, 1779.

SERVIAN.

Нови Завјет. [Das N. Test. ; übers. v. Wuk Steph. Karadschitsch]. 8°. у Бечу. 1847

SIKH, *see* PUNJABI *above*.

SINHALESE.

[Het Heylige Evang. *Tr. W. Konijn. Tp^s^. & pref^s^. wanting*]. 4°. [Colombo. 1739]

[N.T.] Gerevid. &c. door J. J. Fybrants & H. Philipsz. [*Dutch & Sinh. tp^s^.*] 6p *in* 1v. 4°. Colombo. 1771–80
Heyl. Evangelium ; Fybrants & Philipsz, 1780.
Handel. d. Apostelen ; Fybrands & Philipsz, 1771.
Romynen ; Philipsz, 1722.
Cor. & Galat. ; Philipsz, 1773.
Ephesen &c. ; Philipsz, 1776, *& a. issue*, 1775, *b. sep.*
Jacobus &c., mitsgaders d'Openbaringe ; Philipsz, 1776.

Genesis. Overgeset &c. door H. Philipsz. 4°. Colombo. 1783

Exodus. Overgeset &c. door H. Philipsz. 4°. Colombo. 1786

N.T. [*Prep. by W. Tolfrey &c.*] 4°. [Colombo]. 1817

Bible [*continued*].
SINHALESE [*continued*].
Holy B. [*O.T. Gen.-Ezra ii. in 2v, w. pagin. 157, 473, 672 (673–972 wanting). Psalms & Proverbs in 2v. w. sep. tp*s*. & date 1820. Tr. W. Tolfrey &c.*] 4°. Colombo. [1819–23]
SLAVONIC, *see also* PSALMS, RUSSIAN & SERVIAN *above*.
Библія сирѣ книги вѣтхаво й новаго завѣта. [*wanting tp. 5 foliations*]. fol. [Ostrog. 1581]
Библія. [*Rev. of 1581 ed., by Arsenios. tp. in facsimile*]. fol. в' Москвѣ. [1663]
Біблія. [*Repr. of 1663 Bible*]. 5t. 8°. Budæ ?. [1795 ?]
Евангеліе [*Matthew-Acts*] на Славянскомъ и Русскомъ нарѣчіи. 8°. С.-П. 1820
Новый Завѣтъ. s8°. [С.-П. 1849]
Остромирово Евангеліе, 1056–57, *see* PEREVLESSKY (P.) Памятники, 1854.
see KOPKO (P.) Apostolus Bybl. sæc. 14. gramm.-krit. analys., 1912.
SLOVENIAN.
Biblia, Slovenski, tolmazhena, skusi Juria Dalmatina. Bibel, Windisch. [ff. 334, 210, 159. *w. woodcuts*]. fol. Wittemberg. 1584
Svetu pismu Stariga [& Noviga] Testamenta. Id est: Biblia sacra Vet. [& Novi] Test., in Slavo-Carniolicum idioma tr., per Georgium Japel & Blasium Kumerdey. 10p. s8°. Laibach. 1784–1802
SOLOMON, *see also* ECCLESIASTES & PROVERBS *above*.
[A Bölts Kiralnac Könyuci. 1, Proverbia. 2, Ecclesiastes. 3, Canticum Canticorum. 4, Sapientiæ]. [*Imperf.*] s8°. [Kolozsvar, *Helthai Gaspar*. 1552]
Tp. & ff. 8 (sigg. a1, 8), 143 & 144 (sigg. S7, 8) wanting. Sigg. S7, 8 blank except for colophon.
SONG OF SOLOMON.
Paraphrasis Caldayca en los Cantares de Selomoh; con el texto Hebr. y Ladino, tr. en lengua Esp. s8°. Amsterdam. 5461 [1701]
see ABRAHAM, *ben Meir Aben Ezra*. Comm., w. tr., 1874.
,, ANGELOMUS. Enarr. in Cantica, 1531.
,, BARTON (W.) Six cents. of sel. hymns &c., 1688.
,, BRIGHTMAN (T.) Workes: comm. on S. of S. &c., 1644.
,, COTTON (J.) Brief expos., 1642.
,, DILHERR (J. M.) Göttl. Liebesflamme, 1654.
,, HALL (J.), *bp.* Salomons divine arts &c.; w. paraphrase upon the S. of S., 1609.
,, HAYMO, *bp.* Comm. [*in h.* In XII prophet. enarr., 1533].
,, HENRICUS, *de Herph.* Theolog. mysticæ lib. 3, in Cant., 1586.
,, HIPPOLYTUS, *St.* Толкованіе Пѣсни пѣсней, груз. текстъ изд. &c. Н. Марръ, 1901.
,, LAMBERT (F.) In Cant. Cantic. libellum comm., 1524.
,, LUTHER (M.) In Cant. Cantic. enarr., 1539.
,, MASON (J.) Spiritual songs &c., 1685.
,, NONNOSUS, *abbot.* Psalt. Davidis; acc. Cant. Cantic., 3p, 1741–2.
,, PATRICK (S.) Bk. of Job, Song of S. paraphrased &c., 1710.
,, REEVE (J.) Spirit. hymns upon S.'s Song, 1693.
,, RENAN (J. E.) Le Cant. des Cant., tr. avec étude, 5e éd., 1884.
,, SIBBES (R.) Bowels opened, sermons on Canticles, 1641.
,, STUART (A. M.) The Song of Songs, 1860.
,, THEOBALD (Z.) Salomonis Kirchenbraut, 1622.
,, WILLERAM, *abbot of Ebersberg.* In Cant. Cantic. paraphrasis, 1728.
SPANISH.
El Testamento Nuevo. Nueva tr. d. orig. Griego en romance Castellano [*by J. Perez*]. s8°. Venecia, *Iuan Philadelpho*. 1556
La Biblia. Tr. en Español [*by* C. de Reina. *3 pagin*s.]. 4°. [Basel, *T. Guarinus*]. 1569
First complete Spanish Bible.
El Test. Nuevo &c. [*C. de Reina's vers. rev. by C. de Valera*]. s8°. [London]. R. del. Campo. 1596
La Biblia. 2a ed., rev. &c. por C. de Valera. 3p. [*3 foliations*]. fol. Amsterdam, *L. Jacobi*. 1602
Biblia. Tr. de la verdad Hebraica. 8°. Amsterdam, *J. Athias*, 5421 [1661]
Psalmos, Proverbios, Ecclesiastes, y Isaias; tr. por P. Scio de S. Miguel &c. s8°. Paris. 1823
La Sagrada Biblia nuev. tr. de la Vulg. Lat. por F. Torres Amat. t1, 2 del Nuevo Test. 8°. 1823
La Sagrada Biblia nuev. tr. de la Vulg. Lat., por F. Torres Amat. 2a ed. 6t *in* 3v (t6, Notas en forma de diccionario). 8°. 1832–35
La Biblia. Vers. rev. por C. de Valera. n. ed. con emend. la8°. Londres. 1866
El Nuevo Test. Vers. de C. de Valera, rev. 8°. Londres. 1874
Bible (O.T.) Tr. f. Heb. into Castilian by M. Arragel of Guadalfajara (1422–1433 ?). [La Biblia de la Casa de Alba. Roxburghe Club]. 2v. fol. 1918–21
see JARAVA (H.) Los siete psalmos penit., los quinze psalmos, las lamentaciones; [*tr.*], H. J., 1556.
,, RULE (W. H.) Los Cuatro Evanjelios; tr. é ilust. con notas, 1841.

Bible [*continued*].
SPANISH [*continued*].
see RULE (W. H.) Los Hechos de los Apóstoles y las Epíst. à los Rom. y Cor., tr. y anot., 1877.
,, —— Las Epístolas: Gálatas–Revelacion; tr. y anot., 1880.
SUAHILI (SOUTHERN).
Kitabu cha Agano Jipya. s8°. London, *B.& F.B.S.* 1883
SUTO, *see* BASUTO *above*.
SWEDISH, *see also* PSALMS *above*.
Biblia, Thet är all then Helgha Scrifft, pa Swensko. [*6p in 1v. tp*s*. of O.T parts dated 1540*]. fol. Upsala. 15[40]–41
First complete Swedish Bible, known as "Gustavus Vasa's Bible," w. woodcuts.
Thet Gamla Test. s8°. Leyden, *Jacob Marci*. 1633
First 8°. ed. of the so-called Gustavus Adolphus Bible.
Första [—Femte] Mose Bok; [Josua; Domare-Boken; Job; Salomos Ordspråk; Salomos Predikare; Salomos Höga Wisa; Esra; Nehemia; Esther; Psaltaren, *each w. sep. tp. & pagin.*] Ny Prof-Öfwers. af Nuwarande Kongl. Bibel-Comm. 4°. Upsala. 1834–39.
see HESSELMAN (B. I.) Språkformen (14 c.), 1927.
,, SCHINMEIER (J. A.) Schwed. B.-Uebersetzungen u. Ausgaben, 1777–82.
,, STAVE (E.) Om källorna till 1526 [& 1541] års öfversattning af Nya Test., 1893–96.
SYRIAC, *see also* POLYGLOT; PSALMS *above*.
Liber S. Evangelii de Jesu Christo Domino &c. [*Ed.* J. A. Widmanstadius & Moses Mardenas]. s4°. Viennæ, Austriæ. 1555
*St. Paul's epist., the Acts, the epist. of James, Peter, & John have sep. pagin*s*. The Apocalypse is omitted.* Syr. linguæ prima elementa *has sep. tp. & pagin. & is dated at end* 1556.
Novum Test. [*Ed.* G. Le Fèvre de la Boderie. *Syr. in Heb. characters, Gr. & Lat.*] 4°. Parisiis. 1584. [*at end* 1583]
Novum Test. Syr., cum punctis vocalibus & vers. Lat. Matthæi &c. ed. accur. Æ. Gutbirio. Clavis op., Lex., Gramm. Syr. [*w. sep. tp. (dated 1667) & pagin.*] prodit. s8°. Hamburgi. 1664
Codex Syriaco-hexaplaris. Liber quartus Regum e cod. Paris., Jesaias, 12 Prophetæ min., Proverbia, Jobus, Cant., Threni, Ecclesiastes e cod. Mediolan. Ed. &c. H. Middeldorff. 2p *in* 1v. 4°. Berolini. 1735
Cod. Syriaco-Hexaplaris Ambrosiano-Mediolanensis. Ed. & Lat. versus a M. Norberg. 4°. Londini Goth., *C. G. Berling*. 1787
Only one vol., cont. Jeremiah & Ezekiel, publ.
Translatio Syra Pescitto Vet. Test. ex cod. Ambrosiano sec. fere 6 photolith. ed. cur. & adnot. A. M. Ceriani. 2t *in* 1v [*tp. of t2 wanting*]. fol. Mediolani. 1876–83
[N.T. *In anc. Syr. Folld. by* Psalms, *w. sep. tp. & pagin.*] s8°. [N.Y. ?] 1886
[Syriac N.T.] s8°. London, *S. Bagster. n.d.*
see DIEU (L. DE). Apocal. Joh., charact. Syro &c., 1627.
,, JENNINGS (W.) Lex. to the S.N.T., 1926.
,, SCHAAF (C.) Lex. Syr. concordantiale N. Test., 1717.
,, WHITE (J.) Actuum Apostol. et Epistol. versio S., 2t, 1799–1803.
,, —— Sacr. Evangel. vers. S. (*Syr. & Lat.*), 1778.
TAHITI.
Te Evanelia Luka. [*Tr. H. Nott*]. s8°. Moorea, *L.M.S.* 1818
Te Evanelia a Ioane &c. s8°. Huahine, *L.M.S.* 1821
TAMIL.
Biblia Tamulica: Vet. Test., p1[–3]; Studio B. Ziegenbalgii in ling. T. versi. [*p2, 3 studio Z. & B. Schultzii. tp*s*. in Lat. & Tamil*]. 3p *in* 2v. 4°. Trangambariæ. 1723–27
Heyl. Evang. & Handelingen d. Apost., in de T. tale overgebr. 4°. Colombo. 1748
Het nieuw Test. [*Tr. chiefly by P. de Melho. W. pref. in Dutch & Tamil by S. A. Bronsveld & J. J. Fybrands*]. 4°. Colombo. 1759
[*The Psalms in T.*] s8°. [Tranquebar ?. 1785 ?]
Proverbia. [*Lat. & T. tp*s*.*] s8°. Trankenbariæ. 1806
The Malabar N.T. [*Tr. J. P. Fabricius*]. 8°. [Serampore. 1813]
see GILLINGS (J.) Ps. of David metric. arr. in T., 1891.
,, HISTORIÆ. *H. e Scriptis Sacr. sel., 1801.
,, MELHO (P. DE). Eenige Psalmen &c., in T., 1755.
TELUGU.
[New Test.] 8°. Serampore. 1818
N.T. Tr. into T. 8°. Madras. 1884
THESSALONIANS.
see CALIXTUS (G.) Expositio, 1654.
,, ELLICOTT (C. J.) St. Paul's Ep. to the T. [Gr.], w. comm. & rev. tr., 4th ed., 1880.
,, JEWEL (J.) Exposit., 1583.
,, LIETZMANN (H.), *ed.* Hdbh. z. N.T., B3ii; erkl. v. M. Dibelius, 1911.
,, SCLATER (W.) Expos. w. not. upon 1st & 2nd Th., 1630–32.
TIMOTHY, *see also* PAUL &c. *above*.
For ed. in Internat. Crit. Comm. [Pastoral Epistles, by W. Lock], see BIBLE: GEN. COMM.
see BARLOW (J.) Expos. of Chaps. 1 & 2 of T. II &c., 1632.
,, CALVIN (J.) Comm., 1548.
,, CREUTZIGER (C.) Comm., 1540.

Bible [*continued*].
TIMOTHY [*continued*].
see HARRISON (P. N.) Problem of pastoral epist., 1921.
,, LIETZMANN (H.), *ed.* Hdbh. z. N.T., B3, Die Briefe d. Paulus, An T. I, II &c.; erkl. v. M. Dibelius, 1913.
,, NEWTON (*Sir* I.) Two letters : I Tim., iii. 16, 1754.
,, PRYNNE (W.) Unbishoping of T. &c., repr., 1661.
,, WIESINGER (J. T. A.) Bibl. comm., 1866.
TITUS. *For ed. in Internat. Crit. Comm.* [*Pastoral Epistles, by W. Lock*], *see* BIBLE : GEN. COMM.
see BLAU (C. F.) De genuina verb. indole q. P. epist. ad T. scr. præf., 1846.
,, LIETZMANN (H.), *ed.* Hdbh. z. N.T., B3; erkl. v. M. Dibelius, 1913.
,, PRYNNE (W.) Unbishoping of Timothy & T., repr., 1661.
,, TAYLOR (T.) Comm. upon T., 1619.
,, WIESINGER (J. T. A.) Bibl. comm., 1866.
TOBA, *see* BATTA.
TONGAN.
Koe Fuakava Fo'ou. [N.T. Tr. J. E. Moulton]. 8°. Lonitoni. 1880
TSCHEREMISSIAN, *see* CHEREMISS *above*.
TULU.
[N.T. 12p *in* 1v]. 8°. Mangalore. 1842–47
TURKISH.
Test. Nov. Turcice redd. [*Nogai T.*] Op. G. Seaman. s4°. Oxoniæ. 1666
[N.T. (Nogai). Tr. H. Brunton]. 8°. Karass. 1813
[Psalms (Nogai), n. ed. *no pagin.*] s8°. [Astrakhan. 1818]
[N.T. (Osmanli). *Publ. f. MSS. of Ali Bey by J. D. Kieffer*]. 8°. Paris, *B.F.B.S.* 1819
[N.T. (Kirghiz)]. 8°. Astrakhan. 1820
[The Holy Bible in Osmanli]. 4°. Paris, *B.F.B.S.* 1827
[Pentateuch]. 8°. *B. & F.B.S.* [1877]
[N.T. Transcauc. or Azerb. Turk.] 8°. [Leipzig, *B.& F.B.S.*] 1893
see HENDERSON (E.) An appea on the Turk. N.T. pr. at Paris 1819, 1824.
,, NEGRI (S.) Mem. & tract. de vers. N.T. Turc., 1764.
,, SCHRÖDER (N. G.) Quatuor prima cap. Geneseos T. & Lat., 1739.
UDISH.
Святое Еванг. на русск. и убинск. яз., *see* SBORNIK. Сборн. матер. для опис. Кавказа, 30, 1902.
VULGATE, *see* LATIN *above*.
WELSH.
Y Bibl Cyssegr-lan. 8°. Caer-Grawnt, *J. Bentham*, 1746
,, ,, ... s8°. Llundain. 1868
see LLEWELYN (T.) Rem. on Brit. tongue &c. founded on W.B., 1769.
WEND (LOWER).
Das Neue Test., in d. Nieder-Lausitz.-Wend. Spr. übers. &c. v. G. Fabricio. 8°. Kahren. [1709]
To Bôże Piszmo Stârego Test. &c. [*Tr.*] J. F. Frizo. s4°. Choschubusu. 1796
WEND (UPPER).
Das Neue Test. in d. Ober-Lausitz. Wend. Spr. übers. v. M. Frentzeln [*Wend & Germ.*] 8°. Zittau. 1706
Biblia, in d. Ober-Lausitz. Wend. Sprache übers. &c. s4°. Budissin. 1728
Tp. of N.T. dated 1727.
Die Episteln u. Evang. auf alle Sonntage &c. in d. Wend. Spr. übers. [*Germ. & Wend. 2 tp.*] s8°. Budissin 1733
Biblia. [*Revision prep. by J. G. Kühn &c.*] 8°. w Budeschini. 1742
YORUBA.
Ep. to the Romans. Tr. by S. Crowther. s8°. 1850
ZECHARIAH.
see BALDUIN (F.) In 3 postremos proph. comm., 1610.
,, DAVID, *ben J. Kimchi.* Comm. on Z.; tr. A. McCaul, 1837.
,, DRACONITES (J.) Z. propheta, *Hebr. & Lat.*, 1565.
,, KÖSTER (F. B.) Meletemata in Z. cap. 9–14, 1818.
,, MAYER (J. F.) Comm. in Z., 1722.

Biblia. *Biblia aurea, 1475; 1495, *see* RAMPEGOLLIS (A. DE).

Biblia Pauperum. *Beschrijving van een nieuwlings ontdekt exemplaar van de B.P. en de Ars moriendi &c. 8°. 1839

Bibliander (Theodorus). De mysteriis salutiferæ passionis &c. Jesu: libri tres. Adj., oratio D. M. Lutheri de reform. eccl. s4°. Basileæ. [1551]
De ratione communi omnium linguarum & literarū commentarius. s4°. Tiguri. 1548
De ratione temporum, Christianis rebus cognosc. &c. accomodata. Demonstrationum liber alius eodem auctore. s8°. Basileæ. [1551]
Institutionum grammatic. de lingua Heb. liber unus. [*b. w.* Camerarius (J.) Notatio figur. orat. &c., 1556]. s8°. Tiguri. 1535

Bibliófilo aragonés, *ps.*, *see* SÁNCHEZ (J. M.)

Bibliografia. *B. zaragozana del s. 15, 1908, *see* SÁNCHEZ (J. M.)

Bibliografia española. año 19–22 (1919–22). la8°. 1919–23
Continued as Bibliografia gen. española &c., *q.v.*

Bibliografia general española e hispano americana. [año 1–4], 1923–26. la8°. 1925–27
Each año is in 3p b. together, w. sep. tp[s]*. & pagin*[s]*.* 1, Bibliografia. 2, Cronica. 3, Anuncios. Indices *have sep. pagin., no tp. A cont. of* Bibliografia esp., *q.v.*

Bibliographical Institute of the Czechoslovak Republic, *see* ČESKOSLOVENSKÝ ÚSTAV BIBLIOGRAFICKÝ.

Bibliographical Society.
Illustrated monographs. No. 19, 20. 4°. 1923–26
see OSLER (*Sir* W.) Incunabula medica, 1467–80, 1923. [19.]
,, THOMAS-STANFORD (C.) Early ed[s]. of Euclid's Elements, 1926. [20.]
Transactions. v15 (Oct. 1917–March 1919), w. index to v11–15. 8°. 1920
,, ,, s2, v1–7 *see* LIBRARY (THE). s4, v1–7, 1921–27, *incorporating* Trans. of the Bibl. Soc.
,, ,, Suppl. No. 1–5. 8°. O. 1921–26
see DEE (J.) List of MSS. form. owned by Dr. J. D., w. pref. &c. by M. R. James, 1921. [1.]
,, GASELEE (S.) Spanish books in the lib. of Samuel Pepys, 1921. [2.]
,, JAMES (M. R.) Lists of MSS. form. in Peterborough Abbey library, 1926. [5.]
,, JENKINSON (F. J. H.) List of incunabula coll. by G. Dunn arr. to illust. hist. of printing, 1923. [3.]
,, MURPHY (G.) Bibliog. of Eng. character-bks., 1608–1700, 1925. [4.]
Publications.
see BROWN (C.) Register of Middle Eng. relig. & didactic verse, p2, 1920.
,, FORMAN (M. F.) Bibliog. of wr[s]. of G. Meredith, 1922.
,, —— Meredithiana : Suppl., 1924.
,, PLOMER (H. R.) Dict. of printers & booksellers in Eng., Scot. & Ireland, 1668–1725, 1922.
,, POLLARD (A. W.) & G. R. REDGRAVE. Short-title cat. of bks. pr. in Eng. &c., 1475–1640, 1926.
,, WISE (T. J.) Coleridgeiana : Suppl. to bibliog. of C., 1919.
,, —— & S. WHEELER. Bibliog. of writings of W. S. Landor, 1919.

Bibliographical Society of America. *Publications.*
see CHILDS (J. B.) 16th-cent. books, 1925.
,, FISKE (W.) W. F. Memorial : papers, 1919.

Bibliographie.
*B. arménienne [*in Arm.*], 1883, *see* ZARBHANALEAN (K.)
Bibliographie lorraine, 1913–19, 1921, *see* LORRAINE.

Bibliographie der Deutschen Zeitschriften-Literatur.
B41 (1917). 4°. 1918
,, ,, Autoren-Register zu B40, 40A u. 41. [*b. w.* B41]. 4°. 1919
Bibliographie d. deut. Rezensionen. B18 (1913ii). 4°. L. 1914

Bibliographie der fremdsprach. Zeitschriftenliteratur.
B14, 15 (1914iii, iv). 4°. L. 1915–16

Bibliography.
Bibliography of Eng. lang. & lit. 1921. Ed. for Mod. Humanities Research Assoc. by A. C. Paues. 8°. C. 1922
Bibliog. of mod. poetry, w. notes. Compiled by Recorder. [Chapbook, No. 12, v2, June 1920]. 8°. 1920

Biblioteca. Biblioteca bio-bibliog. d. Terra Santa e dell' Oriente Francescano, 1919–27, *see* GOLUBOVICH (G.)
Biblioteca de hist. Vasca. Col. de obras &c. inéd. Ed. S. de Ispizúa. v1–7. 8°. 1919–23
see CAMINO Y ORELLA (J. A.) Hist. de San Sebastián, t1, 1923. [7.]
,, FLORANES (R. DE). Memorias &c. de Vitoria, 1775, 1922. [6.]
,, —— La supresion d. obispado de Alaba &c., 2t, 1919–20. [1, 2.]
,, LANDÁZURI (J. J. DE). Hist. de Guipúzcoa, 2t, 1921. [4, 5.]
,, SALAZAR Y CASTRO (L. DE). Hist. de la casa de Haro, t1, 1920. [3.]
Biblioteca di storia ital. rec., 1800–70, 1913–26, *see* REGIA DEPUTAZ. S. GLI STUDI DI STORIA PATRIA &C.

Biblioteca Ambrosiana, *Milan.*
Guida sommaria. 8°. Milano. 1907
see FRIESEN (O. v.) Codices gotici A., 1927.

Biblioteca dei Maestri Italiani. Guida bibliografica. [Pref. di G. Prezzolini]. 2a ed. s8°. Milano. [1922]

Biblioteca Nacional, *Porto*, *see* ANAIS DAS BIBLIOTECAS E ARQUIVOS, 1920–24.

Biblioteca Oratoriana, *Naples.* I codici ms[s]. d. Bibl. Oratoriana di N. illust. da E. Mandarini. 4°. Napoli. 1897

Bibliotechnoe obozrenie. Библиотечное обозрение. книга 2. 8°. Петроград. 1920

Bibliotheca.
Bibl. Armeno-Georgica, 1–5. la8°. Petropoli. 1911–15
see DIONYSIUS, *Thracian.* Ars gram.; rec. N. Adontz, 1915. [4.]
,, ELIAS, *Aristot. comm.* Komm. in A. Kategorias; ed. J. Manandean, 1911. [1.]
,, JERUSALEM. Синодикъ Крестн. мон.; изд. Н. Марръ, 1914. [3.]
,, KOSTANEANTZ (K.) Лѣтопись на камняхъ, 1913. [2.]
,, TER-MOVSESEAN (M.) Рукоп. отрывки арм. версiи Ветх. Завѣта, 1915. [5.]
Bibliotheca Bremensis nova hist.-phil.-theologica. [Ed. N. Barkey. *Contin. of* Hasé's Bibl. & Symbolæ liter.]
6 classes [*of 3 fasc. each in 3v.*] s8°. Bremæ. 1760–67
Bibl. Carmelitana, 2t, 1752, [repr.], 1927, *see* VILLIERS (C. DE).
Bibl. chemico-mathematica, 2v, 1921, *see* ZEITLINGER (H.) & H. C. SOTHERAN.
Bibl. Cluniacensis, *see* MARRIER (M.) & A. DU CHESNE.
*Bibl. crit. sacræ circa Sacr. libr. difficultates, 4t, 1704–6, *see* CHERUBIN DE SAINT-JOSEPH.
Bibl. Hagana hist.-phil.-theologica, ad contin. Bibl. Bremensis novæ constructa a N. Barkey.
6 classes *in* 6v. s8°. Amstelodami &c. 1768–77
Bibl. hist. hæresiologicæ sel. doct. virorum dissertationes hæret. hæresiumque hist. expon. compl., 1723–29, *see* VOGT (J.)
Bibl. historico-philologico-theologica. [Ed. T. Hase & F. A Lampe].
Classis 1–8 *in* 8v. s8°. Bremæ. 1719–27
Bibl. juris imper. quadripartita &c., 1727, *see* NEUMANN (J. F. W.)
Bibl. Lindesiana.
Cat. of the philatelic library of the Earl of Crawford. By E. D. Bacon. [Philatelic Lit. Soc.] fol. 1911
,, ,, Suppl. [Philatelic Lit. Soc.] fol. 1926
A re-issue of v7 of Bibl. Lindesiana.
Bibl. Lubecensis. [*Ed. by* H. Scharbau, S. G. von Melle & J. H. von Seelen]. 12v *in* 4t. s8°. Lubecæ. 1725–31
Bibl. Patrum Apost. Gr.-Lat., 1699, *see* ITTIG (T.)
Bibl. vet. patrum antiq. script. eccles., 14t, 1765–81, *see* GALLANDIUS (A.)
Maxima bibl. veterum Patrum &c., 28t, 1677–1707, *see* LA BIGNE (M. DE).
Bibliotheca philologica classica. v30–33. 8°. L. 1903–6
Bibliothek. Bibliotheck [*sic*] v. Anzeigen u. Auszügen kl. akad. Schriften theol., philos. &c. Inhalts. Hrsg. Prof. Paulus. 3B *in* 2v. s8°. Jena. 1790–92
Bibliothek wertvoller Novellen u. Erzählungen, 12 B, 1908–12, *see* HELLINGHAUS (O.), *ed.*
Bibliothek d. angelsächs. Prosa. Begründet v. C. W. M. Grien, fortges. v. R. P. Wülker; hrsg. H. Hecht.
B9–11. 8°. Hamburg. 1914–22
9, Die Hirtenbriefe Ælfrics in altengl. u. lat. Fassung; hrsg. mit Übers &c. v. B. Fehr.
10, Exameron anglice or O. E. Hexameron; ed. w. tr. &c. by S. J. Crawford, 1921.
11, König Alfreds d. Grossen Bearb. d. Soliloquien d. Augustinus; hrsg. v. W. Endter.
Bibliothek d. indogerm. Grammatiken. Bearb. v. H. Delbrück &c. B6. 8°. L. 1897
see HÜBSCHMANN (H.) Armen. Gramm., T1, 2 Abt., 1895–97 [6].
Bibliothek für Philosophie. Hrsg. L. Stein. B14–29 [18 *wanting*]. 8°. 1918–26
see AUERBACH (M.) Mitleid u. Charakter, 1921. [20.]
,, ADAMKIEWICZ (A.) Die Eigenkräfte d. Stoffe, 1920. [17.]
,, BARTHEL (E.) Polargeometrie, 1919. [16.]
,, BERG (E.) Problem d. Kausalität, 1920. [19.]
,, BERNHARD (E. A.) Psych. Vorgänge betrachtet als Bewegungen, 1923. [23.]
,, DVORNIKOVIĆ (V.) Die beiden Grundtypen d. Philosophierens, 1918. [15.]
,, ENGEL (M.) Gedanken ü. d. Denken, 1922. [22.]
,, FLEMMING (S.) Willenslehre als Erkenntnisweg, 1917. [14.]
,, HÖFFDING (H.) Bemerk. ü. d. platon. Dialog Parmenides, 1921. [21.]
,, MEYER (M.) Grundskizze zu e. System d. Ethik, 1923. [24.]
,, MOSZKOWSKI (A.) Der Abbau d. "Unendlich," 1925. [27.]
,, STEIN (W.) Nietzsche u. d. bild. Kunst, 1925. [28.]
,, STICKERS (J.) Die absol. Vereindeutl. d. phil. Terminologie, 1924. [25.]
,, UXKULL-GYLLENBAND (W. *Graf*). Griech. Kultur-Entstehungslehren, 1924. [26.]
,, WÄSCHE (H.) Grundzüge zu e. Logik d. Arithmetik, 1926. [29.]
Bibliothekarische Fachbücherei (Die): e. Liste.
[P2872]. 8°. Stettin. 1927
Bibliothèque de l'Ecole des Hautes Etudes. Fasc. 200i, 215, 227–253. 8°. 1912–28
Célébration du cinquantenaire de l'École pratique des H. É. [H. E., 231]. 8°. 1922
Cinquantenaire de l'Ecole pratique des H. É. Mélanges publ. par la section des Sci. hist. & philol. [H. E. 230]. 8°. 1921
see BLOCH (J.) La form. de la langue marathe, 1919. [215.]
,, BLOCH (O.) La pénétr. du français &c., 1921. [232.]
,, BRENOT (A.) Les mots & groupes ïambiques, 1923. [239.]

Bibliothèque de l'Ecole des Hautes Etudes [*continued*].
see BRENOT (A.) Rech. sur l'Ephébie attique &c., 1920. [229.]
,, BRUNEAU (C.) Enquête linguist. s. les patois d'Ardenne, t2, 1926. [248.]
,, BURGER (A.) Les mots de la famille de φύω en grec anc., 1925. [246.]
,, CHAMPOLLION (J. F.) Rec. d'ét. égyptolog. déd. à la mém. de C., 1922. [234.]
,, CONSTANT (G.) La légation du card. Morone près l'Empereur & le Concile de Trente, 1563, 1922. [233.]
,, DECK (S.) La ville d'Eu, 1151–1475, 1924. [243.]
,, FARAL (E.) Les arts poèt. 12e & 13e s., 1924. [238.]
,, FÉVRIER (J. G.) Date, compos. &c. de la lettre d'Aristée à Philocrate, 1925. [242.]
,, HAVET (L.) Texte de l'Orator & sur Isée, 1927. [252.]
,, KURYLOWICZ (J.) Traces de la place du ton en gathique, 1925. [244.]
,, LÉVY (I.) La legende de Pythagore, 1927. [250.]
,, LOT (F.) L'impôt foncier &c., 1928. [253.]
,, MASPERO (J.) Hist. des patriarches d'Alexandrie, 518–616, 1923. [237.]
,, MONOD (G.) Vie & pensée de J. Michelet, 2t, 1923. [235, 236.]
,, NOLHAC (P. DE). Ronsard & l'humanisme, 1921. [227.]
,, PACHTERE (F. G. DE). La table hypothécaire de Veleia, 1920. [228.]
,, PAGÈS (A.) Comm. des poèsies d'A. March, 1925. [247.]
,, PARIS (G.) Cat. de la bibl. G. P.; par L. Barrau-Dihigo, livr. 1, 1912. [200.]
see PICHARD (L.) Tibulle & les auteurs du Corpus Tibull. &c., 1924. [241.]
,, ROSETTI (A.) Rhotacisme en Roumain, 1924. [240.]
,, SKERLJ (S.) Syntaxe du partic. prés. &c. en vieil ital., 1926. [249.]
,, VASUBANDHU. Vijñaptimātratāsiddhi; publ. S. Lévi, pl, 1925. [245.]
,, VIELLIARD (J.) Le Latin des diplômes, 1927. [251.]
SCIENCES RELIG. 22–24ii, 26, 28, 31–33, 35–43. 8°. 1909–27
,, FAYE (E. de). Et. s. les origs. des églises de l'âge apostol., 1909. [23.]
,, ——Origène, v1, 2, 1923–27. [37, 43.]
,, GÉNESTAL (R.) Le privilegium fori en Fr., 2t, 1921–24. [35, 39.]
,, GOGUEL (M.) L'Evangile de Marc &c., 1909. [22.]
,, HARDY (G.) Le "De civitate Dei" source princ. du "Disc. sur l'hist. univ.," 1913. [28.]
,, HERING (J.) La doct. de la chute &c. chez Clément d'Alexandrie, 1923. [38.]
,, HUART (C.) Les saints des Derviches tourneurs, 2t, 1918–22. [32, 36.]
,, KOYRÉ (A.) L'Idée de Dieu chez Descartes, 1922. [33.]
,, LÉVY (I.) Légende de Pythagore, 1926. [42.]
,, MESTRE (E.) Caractères mod. & les Siao tchouan, 1925. [40.]
,, MILLET (G.) L'école grec., l'archit. byz., 1916. [26.]
,, RAYNAUD (G.) Les dieux &c. de l'anc. Guaté., 1925. [41.]
,, ROUFFIAC (J.) Rech. s. les caractères du grec dans le N.T. &c., 1911. [24ii.]
,, TOUTAIN (J.) Les cultes païens dans l'Emp. rom., pl, t3, 1920. [31.]
Bibliothèque de l'Institut Français de Petrograd. t5–7. 8°. 1920–21
see FALCONET (E. M.) Corr. de F. avec Cath. II., 1921. [7.]
,, MAZON (A.) Lexique de la Guerre & de la Révol. en Russie, 1914–18, 1920. [6.]
,, STOGLAV (Le) ou les 100 chapitres, Moscou, 1551; tr. &c. E. Duchesne, 1920. [5.]
Bibliothèque égyptologique. Publ. sous la dir. de G. Maspéro. t25. la8°. 1914
see ROUGÉ (*vte.* O. C. C. E. DE). Œuvres diverses, t5, 1914. [25.]
Bibliothèque Elzivirienne.
see BUSSY-RABUTIN.
,, MARGARET [*de Valois*].
see RABELAIS.
Bibliothèque et Musée de la Guerre. Catalogue méthod. du fonds allemand de la Bibl. Rédigé par J. Dubois. avec collab. de C. Appuhn. Intr. par C. Bloch. [Publs. de la Soc. de l'Hist. de la Guerre, s1]. t1–3. 8°. 1921–22
Bibliothèque Nationale.
ADMINISTRATION & MISC. WORKS.
Cat. [de l'Expos. Orient.] des mss. à peintures, estampes, médailles &c., mai-juin 1925. 8°. [1925]
Cat. des. mss., estampes, médailles &c. exposés, jan.–févr. 1926. 8°. 1926
Choix de chefs-d'œuvre du 15e au 19e siècle. Expos. mai–1 août 1924. s8°. [1924]
see MORTREUIL (T.) La B.N. j. nos jours, 1878.
ANTIQUITIES, MEDALS, &c.
see BABELON (E.) Cat. de la Coll. de Luynes: monnaies grec., t1, 2, 1924–26.
MANUSCRIPTS.
Fac-similés de mss. grecs, lat. & franç. du 5e au 14e siècle exposés dans la Galerie Mazarine. 8°. *n.d.*
Notices & extraits des mss. t41. 4°. 1923
Blochet (E.) Mss. persans & arabes de la coll. Marteau. [41.]
Boethius, *see* Thomas (A.)

Bibliothèque Nationale [*continued*].
MANUSCRIPTS. Notices &c. [*continued*].
Doutrepont (G.) La croisade projetée par Philippe le Bon contre les Turcs. [41.]
Philip III, *duke of Burgundy* [*the Good*], *see* DOUTREPONT (G.)
Thomas (A.) Tr. franç. avec comm. par Maître Pierre de Paris, de la Consolatio philos. de Boèce. [41.]
see BAENA (J. A. DE). Cancionero: reprod. in facs. f. MS. in B.N., 1926.
„ BLOCHET (E.) Enlum. des mss. orient., turcs, arabes, persans de la B.N., 1926.
„ —— Peintures des mss. orientaux de la B.N., 1914–20.
„ —— Peintures des mss. persans de la Col. Marteau à la B.N., 1918–19.
„ CHRONICA. Cronica rímada; reprod. in facs. f. MS. in Bibl. Nat. by A. M. Huntington, 1904.
„ COUDERC (C.) Enluminures des mss. de la B.N., 1927.
„ EXHIBITIONS: Livre ital. Cat. des mss. &c., 1926.
„ HENRY IV, *king of France*. Heures dites de H. IV; reprod. des peintures du ms. latin 1171 de la B.N., *n.d.*
„ LIVRE des merveilles: reprod. des 265 miniatures du ms. franç. 2810, 2t, *n.d.*
„ MARTIN (H.) Joyaux de l'enluminure, 1928.
„ METZ. Coll. Emmery & Cloüet-Buirgnier sur l'hist. de M. & de la Lorraine; publ. H. Omont, 1919.
PRINTED BOOKS.
Cat. gén. des livres imprimés. Auteurs.
t69–90 (Hassebroucq–Le Basque). 8°. 1919–27
PRINTS.
Cat. des ouvr. rel. aux beaux-arts du cabinet des estampes de la B.N., t1, *see* SOC. DE L'HIST. DE L'ART FR. Nouv. arch. &c., n. pér., t11, 1921.
see BLOCHET (E.) Notes sur des peintures hindoues de la B.N., 1926.
„ DUPLESSIS (G.) & G. RIAT &C. Cat. de la coll. des portraits fr. & étrangers, t6, 7, 1907–11.
„ GUIBERT (J.) Dessins du Cabinet Peiresc au C. des Estampes, 1910.

Bibliothèque universelle et Revue Suisse.
t97–[121]. 8°. Lausanne. 1920–27

Bichurin (Jakinth).
Записки о Монголіи. 2t. [*a. c. b. in 1v*]. 8°. С.–П. 1828
Исторія первыхъ четырехъ хановъ изъ дома Чингисова. Переведено съ Китайскаго Мон. Іакинѳомъ. 8°. С.–П. 1829
Исторія Тибета и Хухунора. Переведена съ Китайскаго. 2ч. 8°. С.–П. 1833
Китай, его жители &c. 8°. С.–П. 1840
*Описаніе Тибета въ нынѣшнемъ его состояніи. Переводъ съ Китайскаго. s8°. С.–П. 1828

Bickell (Gustav). Conspectus rei Syrorum litterariæ, add. notis bibliog. &c. 8°. Monasterii. 1871
Krit. Bearb. d. Iobdialogs. [*Extr. f.* Wiener Ztschr. f. d. Kunde d. Morgenl., B6, 7]. 8°. [1892]

Bickerdyke (John) *ps.* [*i.e.* C. H. COOK]. Thames rights & T. wrongs. With notes on the T. Bill of 1894. s8°. Westminster. 1904

Bickerstaffe (Isaac).
The hypocrite. [Dolby's Brit. th.] s8°. 1823
Lionel & Clarissa, *see* INCHBALD (E.) Brit. th., v17, 1808.
Love in a village, *see* INCHBALD (E.) Brit. th., v17, 1808.
Maid of the mill, *see* INCHBALD (E.) Brit. th., v17, 1808.
*The spoil'd child, *see* DUBLIN. Vol. of farces, 1792.

Bickersteth (John Burgon). Hist. of the 6th Cavalry Brigade, 1914–19. Foreword by Sir D. Haig. 8°. [1920]

Bickford (James). Christian work in Australasia &c. s8°. [1878]

Bickham (George), *the younger*. Deliciæ Brit.: or, the curiosities of Kensington, Hampton Court & Windsor Castle &c. 2nd ed. w. adds. s8°. *n.d.* [c. 1750]

Bickley (Francis). Crown colonies of Brit. Amer., *see* BUCHAN (J.), *ed.* Nations, 1923.
Hist. [of Romania], by B. &c., see BUCHAN (J.), *ed.* Nations, 1924.

Bicknell (Beroë A.)
Cases on the law of the constitution. 8°. 1926

Bicknell (C.)
Flowering plants & ferns of the Riviera &c. la8°. 1885

Bicknell (Edward John). Xtn. idea of sin & orig. sin. Pringle-Stuart lect., 1921. 2nd impr. s8°. 1923

Bicknell (John Laurens).
The modern church; a satirical poem. [P2511]. 8°. 1820

Bicknell (W. I.) Illust. London. Engr. by A. H. Payne. Notices by B. 2p. [p2, *no tp.*] s8°. [1846–47]

Biddlecombe (*Sir* George).
The art of rigging. n. ed. rev. & re-comp. by G. B. 8°. 1848

Biddulph (*capt.* Michael Anthony Shrapnel). Assault of Sevastopol. Topogr. sketches. 3p. [P2604]. fol. [1855]
p2 & 3 have title Topogr. sk. of ground bef. Sevastopol &c. p2 *publ. at* Woolwich.

Bidermann (Herm. Ign.) Russ. Umtriebe in Ungarn. Mit Anh. z. Statistik d. ungar. Slaven. [P2398]. 8°. Innsbruck. 1867

Bidermann (Johann Gottlieb). Programmatum lit. sacri, philol., hist. argumenti sylloge. 2v. s8°. Lipsiæ. 1748
v2 has t.: Selecta scholastica. *Each v. has 2 fasc., pagin. contin.*

Bidez (Joseph), *see* UNION ACAD. INTERNAT. Cat. des mss. alchim. grecs, 1924–27.

Bidlo (Yaroslav). Les Polonais et la République Tchécoslovaque. [P2425]. 8°. Prague. 1919

Bidou (Henry), *see* LAVISSE (E.) Hist. de France contemp., t9, La Gr. Guerre; par H. B. &c., 1922.

Bīdpāī. Kilila & Damana. [*In Georgian.* Ed. I. Tchqonias]. la8°. Tiflis. 1886

Bidwell (Percy Wells) & J. I. Falconer. Hist. of agric. in the Northern U.S., 1620–1860. [C. I. of Wash.; Publ. 358]. la8°. Wash. 1925

Bidyabinod (*Pandit* B. B.) Varieties of the Vishṇu image, *see* INDIA. ARCH. SURVEY. Mem[s]. No. 2, 1920.

Bie (Jacques de). Les vrais portraits des rois de France. 2e éd., augm. &c. par H. de Coste. fol. 1637

Bie (Oskar). Der Tanz. 2e verb. A. 8°. 1919

Bieber (Friedrich J.) Kaffa: e. altkuschit. Volkstum in Inner-Afrika. [Anthropos-Bibl., B2ii, iii]. B1, 2. 8°. Münster i. W. 1920–23
1, Einleitung: d. Eigenleben d. Kaffitscho oder Gonga.
2, Das Gemeinleben d. Kaffitscho oder Gonga.

Bieber (Margarete).
Die Denkmäler zum Theaterwesen im Altertum. la8°. 1920

Bieck (Johann Erdmann). Das dreyfache Interim, so in Regenspurg, Augspurg u. Leipzig z. Vereinigung d. päbstl. u. evangl.-luther. Lehre &c. s8°. L. 1721

Biel (Gabriel), *see* BIEL (H. W.) Diss. de B. anti-papista, 1719.

Biel (Hieronymus Wigand). Diss. de G. Biel anti-papista. Præs. G. Wernsdorfio. [P595]. s4°. Vitembergæ. [1719]
Hist. sec. 3. variorum fabulis maculata. Sub præs. J. A. Schmidi. [P432]. s4°. Helmstadii. [1709]

Bielikowicz (Antoni). Słownik polsko-łaciński. 13 zes. [*in* 1v. *pagin. contin.*] 8°. w Krakowie. 1863

Bielohlawek (Anton). Ursachen u. Verlauf d. Kriegsereignisse in Böhmen, 1434. [P2729]. 8°. Braunau. [1894]

Biener (Friedrich August). De Salvii Juliani meritis in edictum prætorium recte æstim. [P2672]. 4°. Lipsiæ. [1809]

Bier (Justus). Das alte Nürnberg in Anlage u. Aufbau. la8°. Nürnberg. 1926

Bierbaum (Max).
Papst Pius XI. Ein Lebens-u. Zeitbild. 8°. [1922]

Bierbaum (Otto Julius). Gesamm. Werke. Hrsg. von M. G. Conrad u. H. Brandenburg.
B1–7. [1, 7, *n.d. no more publ*[d].] s8°. München. 1921–22
1, Gedichte. 2, Pankrazius Graunzer—Stilpe. 3, Studenten-, Künstler-u. Märchengeschichten. 4, Sonderbare Geschichten. 5, 6, Prinz Kuckuck. 7, Reisegeschichten.

Bierce (Ambrose), *1842–1913?*. Letters. Ed. B. C. Pope, w. a mem. by G. Sterling. 8°. San Francisco. 1922

Bierfreund (Theodor). Palemon og Arcite: som bidrag til Shakespearekritiken. s8°. 1891

Biermann (Georg). Louis Corinth. [Knackfuss, 107]. 2[e]. A. la8°. Bielefeld. 1922

Bierstadt (Edward Hale). The great betrayal: Near East problem. With ed. assist. of H. D. Creighton. Foreword by E. Capps. 8°. [1924]

Biervliet (J. J. van), *see* VAN BIERVLIET (J. J.)

Big Bear, *Cree Indian Chief*, *see* CAMERON (W. B.) War trail of B. B.: Canadian N.-W. Rebellion, 1885 &c., 1926.

Bigelow (Erastus B.)
The tariff question, Eng. & U.S. 4°. Boston. 1862

Bigelow (George Tyler) & G. Bemis. Rep. of trial of A. Rogers for murder of C. Lincoln, warden of Mass. State Prison. 8°. Boston, *Mass.* 1844

Bigelow (John). Lest we forget. Gladstone, Morley & the Confederate Loan of 1863. [P2686]. 8°. N.Y. 1905

Bigelow (Poultney). Japan & h. colonies: extr[s]. f. a. diary, 1921. 8°. 1923
Seventy summers. 2v. 8°. 1925

Biggane (Cecil). J. Masefield. s8°. C. 1924

Biggar (Henry Percival). The voyages of the Cabots & Corte-Reals to N. Amer. &c., 1497–1503. [Extr. de Revue Hispan., t10]. la8°. Paris. 1903

Biggs (Charles Richard Davey). Epistle of Paul to the Philippians. [Churchman's Bible]. s8°. 1900

Biggs (T. Hesketh).
The Shwe Dagon Pagoda, Rangoon. s8°. Rangoon. 1895

Bigg-Wither (Reginald Fitzhugh). A short hist. of the Ch. of Russia; its teaching &c. 8°. 1920

Bigham (*Hon.* Clive).
The chief ministers of England, 920–1720. 8°. 1923
The prime ministers of Britain, 1721–1921. 8°. 1922

Bigland (Ralph). Hist., monumental & genealog. coll^s. rel. to Co. of Gloucester. v1, 2 [*as far as p252, i.e.*—Newent]. lafol. 1791–92.
The work is arr. alphabetically acc. to parishes & was never completed by B., but 9 addit. parts were issued, 1870–89, of wh. p4–8 are wanting.
„ „ Contin. p1–3, Newington Bagpath-Willersey. [*Orig. pr. for* Sir T. Phillipps]. Repr. for T. Fitz Roy Fenwick. lafol. [1885–87]
„ „ Contin. p9, Winterbourn-Yate. [Ed. T. FitzRoy Fenwick]. lafol. [1889]

Bignon (François), *see* VULSON (M. DE). Portraits des hommes illust. franç.; desseign. & gravez par B. &c., 1650.

Bigot de Sainte-Croix (Claude Louis). Relaz. d. Piemonte (Mém. hist. sur Savoie &c. sous Ch. Emanuel III & Victor Amédée III); annot. da A. Manno, *see* REGIA DEP. DI STORIA PATRIA. Misc., t16, 1877.

Biguet (J. N. Faure-), *see* FAURE-BIGUET (J. N.)

Bigwood (George). Le régime juridique & écon. du commerce de l'argent dans la Belgique du moyen âge. [Acad. Roy. de Belg. Mém^s., s2, t14]. [2p]. 8°. Brux. [1921–22]

Bihar & Orissa. The B. & O. code. Ed. W. S. Coutts. v3, 4. la8°. Calcutta. 1918–20
„ „ ....Suppl. to v2. la8°. Calcutta. 1920
The B. & O. local statutory rules & orders, 1917. Comp. by W. S. Coutts. 3v. la8°. Patna. 1918–19
„ „ Suppl. 1917–22 [2v. *to each year*]; 1923–25. 2v. la8°. Patna. 1927

Bihar & Orissa Research Society. Journal. v6–13. la8°. Patna. 1920–27
see BHAṬṬA-SVĀMIN. Comm. on Kauṭilya's Artha-Śāstra, 1925–26.

Bihlmans (Alfred). Latvia in the making. [P2848]. 8°. Riga. 1925
see LETTONIE (La); [*by var. a^s.*, A. B. &c.], 1926.

Bijdragen tot de taal-, land- en volkenkunde van Neerlandsch Indië. Tijdschrift van het Koninklijk Inst. voor de Taal &c. v.N. I. volg. 1, d1–4; volg. 2, d1–8; volg. 3, d1–11; volg. 4, d1–10; volg. 5, d1–10; volg. 6, d1–3 (d1–47 d. geheele reeks). d. 76–83. 8°. 's Gravenhage. 1853–1927
The following works form vol^s. of the Bijdragen *or have sep. tp^s.*
Bagoes Hoembarà & Mantri Koripan: Balineesch gedicht; bewerkt door R. v. Eck, 1876. [III, 11.]
Bernstein (H. A.) Dagboek v. B.'s laatste reis naar Nieuw-Guinea &c., 1864–65, 1883. [IV, 7]
Laerne (K. F. van D.) Brazilië en Java: Koffiecultuur, 1885. [IV, 9.]
Nieuw Guinea, onderzocht & beschr. in 1858 door een Ned. Ind. Comm., 1862. [II, 5.]
Van den Berg (L. W. C.) Rechtsbronnen v. Zuid-Sumatra, 1894. [V, 9.]
Verslag d. feestviering v. het 25-jarig bestaan v. het Inst., 1851–76, 1876. [III, 11.]
„ „ Inhoudsopgave, d51–80 (1900–24), met alphabet. register. 8°. 's Gravenhage. 1925

Bilabel (Friedrich). Gesch. Vorderasiens u. Ägyptens, 16.–11. Jhdt. v. Chr. 8°. Heidelberg. 1927
Die ionische Kolonisation. [Philologus, Suppl.-Bd. 14, H1]. 8°. L. 1920
Die klein. Historikerfragm. auf Papyrus; bearb. v. F. B., *see* KLEINE TEXTE, 149, 1922.
see PREISIGKE (F.) Sammelbuch griech. Urkunden aus Ägypten; fortgesetzt v. F. B., B1–3i, 1915–26.

Bilbasov (Vasily Alekseevich). [BILBASSOFF (B. v.)]
Исторія Екатерины Второй. 2т. 8°. Берлинъ. 1900

Bild, Das: Altanten z. Kunst, 1922–24, *see* HAUSENSTEIN (W.), *ed.*

Bilder-Bibel. Curieuse, u. mit 800 Bildern erleuterte 252 Biblische Kern-Sprüche, oder sogen. Kleine Bilder-Bibel &c. obl.8°. Hamburg. 1687

Bilderbuch z. Nutzen u. Vergnügen d. Jugend [*Germ. & Fr.*], B10, 1807, *see* BERTUCH (F. J.)

Bilderdijk (Catharine Wilhelmina) [BILDERDIJK-SCHWEICKHARDT (K. W.)], *wife of W. Bilderdijk.* Dichtwerken. [*b. as* d. 16–18 *of* Bilderdijk (W.) Dichtwerken]. 3d. s8°. Haarlem. 1859–60

Bilderdijk (Willem). Dichtwerken. 15d. s8°. Haarlem. 1856–59
see COSTA (I. DA). De mensch en de dichter W. B., 1859.

Bilfinger (Georg Bernhard). In B. Spinosæ methodum explic. Script. Sacras. Resp. P. Pintzger, 1732. recusa. [P443]. s4°. Jenæ. 1739

Biliński (Leon). Wspomnienia i dokumenty. 2t. (1, 1846–1914. 2, 1915–22). 8°. Warszawa. 1924–25

Biliotti (Eduard) *& Abbé* **Cottret.**
L'île de Rhodes. 8°. Rhodes. 1881

Billardon de Sauvigny (Louis Edme). Constit. des rois des Français, p. s. de suite aux Essais hist. sur les mœurs des Français. 8°. 1792
Essais hist. sur les mœurs des François, ou tr. abr. des chroniques &c. dep. Clovis jusqu'à St. Louis. 5t [t1–3, Grégoire de Tours]. 8°. 1785–92
A made up copy; t1 only is of the 1st ed., & is in 2p, each having sep. pagin. & Table.

Billen (Albert Victor).
The old Latin texts of the Heptateuch. 8°. C. 1927

Biller (Emma).
Markgräfin Barbara v. Brandenburg. 8°. L. 1886

Billerbeck (Paul), *see* STRACK (H. L.) & P. B. Komm. z. Neu. Test. aus Talmud u. Midrasch, 3B, 1922–26.

Billican (Theopald von), *see* GERLACHER (T.), *von Billican.*

Billiet (Joseph), *see* LYON. L'art Lyonnais: exposition, cat. par J. B., 1925.

Billing (*le baron* **Sigismond de).** *L'Espagne & la France. Du mariage d'Isabelle II. [P2830]. 8°. 1843

Billinger (Richard). Über d. Äcker: Gedichte. 8°. 1923

Billioud (Joseph). Les états de Bourgogne aux 14e & 15e s. [Acad. des Sci^s. &c. de Dijon]. la8°. Dijon. 1922

Billotey (Pierre), *see* REVON (M.) & P. B. L'Acad. Franç., 1895–1920, 1922.

Billroth (Joham Gustav Friedrich). De Anselmi Cantuar. proslogio & monologio dissert. 8°. Lipsiæ. [1832]

Billson (Charles James). Leicester memoirs. 8°. Leicester. 1924
Mediæval Leicester. 8°. Leicester. 1920

Billuart (Charles René). *Works in* MIGNE (J. P.) Theol. cursus.
De consensu ad matrimon. requisito, 1860. [25.]
De fine propter quem instituta fuit circumcisio—De intentione ministri sacramentorum, 1841. [21.]
De statu religioso, 1859. [16.]
Tract. de actibus humanis [4p]—Tract. de passionibus, 1861. [11.]
Tractatus de mysteriis Christi & B. Virginis, 1860. [8.]

Billups (Robert S.) & P. L. Jones. Labor cond^s. in the shoe ind. in Mass., 1920–24, *see* UNITED STATES: LABOR. Bull. 384, 1925.

Billy, *the Kid, see* BONNEY (W. H.)

Billy (André). D'homme à homme, *see* ŒUVRES libres, 14, 1922.
La litt. franç. contemp. s8°. 1927
La trentaine, *see* ŒUVRES libres, 5, 1921.

Biloe. Былое, журналъ посвящ. ист. освободительнаго движенія. Годъ 2. Январь-Апрѣлъ [*4 Nos. in 1v*]. la8°. П. 1907

Bilson (John), *see* HOPE (*Sir* W. H. St. J.) & J. B. Architect. descr. of Kirkstall Abbey, 1907.

Bilson (Thomas), *bp. of (1) Worcester, (2) Winchester.* The effect of certaine sermons touching the full redemption of mankind by the death & blood of Christ Jesus &c. s4°. 1599
The perpetual gov. of Christes Church &c. s4°. 1593
The true difference betw. Christian subjection & unchristian rebellion &c. 4p. [*pagin. cont.*] 8°. Oxford. 1585

Bimetallic (The) League. Bimetallic question. Deput. to Prime Minister &c. [P2829.] 8°. M'ter. [1889]
Proc^s. of the Conf., 1888. [*a.c. in* P2829]. 8°. M'ter. 1889

Binder (Heinrich). Was wir als Kriegsberichterstatter nicht sagen durften! s8°. München. 1919

Binder (Johann Wilhelm Friedrich). Diss. de symbolo Nicaeno in concil. Antiocheno secundo adulterato &c. Præs. J. R. Kieslingio. [P426]. s4°. Erlangæ. [1770]

Binding (Rudolf G.) Der Opfergang. Novelle. s8°. L. [1927]

Bindloss (Harold). The broken net. s8°. 1925

Bindseil (H. Ernst). Verzeichniss d. Orig.-Ausgaben der Luther. Bibelübersetzungen &c. [*a.c. in* P2527]. 4°. Halle. 1841

Biner (Joseph). De jure primarum precum & institut., *see* MIGNE (J. P.), *ed.* Theol. cursus, t18, 1862.
Diss. juridica de usuris, *see* MIGNE (J. P.), *ed.* Theol. cursus, t16, 1859.

Binet (Alfred).
On double consciousness. n. ed. 8°. Chicago. 1898
see TERMAN (L. M.) Measurement of intelligence: Stanford revision of B.-Simon intell. scale, repr., 1922.

Binet-Valmer (Gustave). *Works in* ŒUVRES libres.
Antonin Jassard, 1921. [6.]
Le bois qui parle, 1925. [48.]
Cette haine, 1924. [37.]
Ceux qui ne voient pas, 1926. [59.]
Comme on est heureux, 1921. [2.]
Le désir, 1922. [14.]
Les deux vieillards devant la mer, 1924. [33.]
Les fantômes, 1926. [64.]
L'honnêteté déconcertée, 1927. [77.]
Une morte, 1925. [42.]
Parce que tu souffres . . ., 1922. [10.]
Le péché, 1922. [18.]
La pierre dans le miroir, roman, 1923. [23.]
Prosper-Bourguillard, impuissant, présid. du Conseil, 1926. [55.]
Quand ils furent nus, 1925. [52.]
Quatre jeunes filles et le jeune homme incertain, 1927. [70.]
Le taureau, 1923. [28.]
L'enfant qui meurt. 2t. s8°. [1921]
Les jours sans gloire. s8°. [1922]

Bing (Just). H. Ibsens Brand. 8°. *n.d.*

Bing (Li Ung), *see* LI UNG BING.

Bingham (Hiram), *Ph.D.*
Inca land: explor[s]. in Peru. 8°. 1922

Bingham (Joseph). Origines, sive antiq. eccl. In Lat. vertit J. H. Grischovius. Acc. præf. J. F. Buddei. 10t. s4°. Halæ. 1724–29

Bini (Telesforo), *ed.* Rime e prose d. buon sec., tratte da mss. 8°. Lucca. 1852

Binney (Thomas), *1798–1874.*
Illust. of the pract. power of faith &c. Discourses on 11th chap. of Hebrews. 8°. 1830
Sermons on var. occasions, [1837–54]. 8°. *n.d.*
The service of song. 8°. 1848
Sir T. F. Buxton, Bart. Lect. s8°. 1849
see STOUGHTON (J.), *ed.* Mem. of T. B., 1874.

Binning (Thomas Hamilton, *Lord*), *see* HADDINGTON (T. H., *1st earl*).

Binns (Henry Bryan). Hill-tops. s8°. 1921

Binns (Leonard Elliott). Erasmus the reformer. Hulsean Lect[s]., 1921–22. s8°. [1923]

Binsfeld (Peter) [BINSFELDIUS (PETRUS)]. Enchiridion theolog. pastoral. & doctr. 2° rec. & auct. s8°. Augusti Trevir. 1602

Binstead (Herbert Ernest), *see* ENGLISH chairs; intr. by B., 1923.

Binswanger (Ludwig).
Einführ. in d. Probleme d. allgem. Psychologie. la8°. 1922

Binyon (Laurence).
Arthur. Tragedy. 8°. [1923]
Ayuli. Play. s8°. O. 1923
The court painters of the grand Moguls. Hist. intr. & notes by T. W. Arnold. la8°. 1921
The drawings & engravings of W. Blake. Ed. G. Holme. 4°. *The Studio.* 1922
Eng. poetry in its rel. to painting &c., *see* BRIT. ACAD. Proc., 1917–18.
The engraved designs of W. Blake. 4°. 1926
The followers of W. Blake: E. Calvert, S. Palmer, G. Richmond & th. circle. 4°. 1925
Tradition & reaction in mod. poetry. [Eng. Assoc. Pamph. No. 63]. [P2834]. 8°. 1926
see EUMORFOPOULOS (G.) The G. E. coll.: cat. of Chin. frescoes, by L. B., 1927.
„ FRY (R. E.) Chinese art; intr. review &c. by R. F., L. B. &c., 1925.
„ STEIN (*Sir* M. A.) The thousand Buddhas; intr. essay by L. B., 1921.
—— **& J. J. O'B. Sexton.** Japanese colour prints. 4°. 1923

Biographical.
*Biogr. anecdotes of W. Hogarth; & a cat. of h. works, &c., 1781; 1782, *see* NICHOLS (JOHN).
*Biogr. mem[s]. of extraord. painters, n. ed., 1824, *see* BECKFORD (W.)
Biogr. mirrour (The): anc. & mod. Eng. portraits &c., 3v, 1795–1810, *see* HARDING (S.), *publ.*
*Biogr. peerage of Gt. Brit., 1808–9, *see* BRYDGES (*Sir* S. E.)
*Biogr. peerage of Ireland, 1817, *see* BRYDGES (*Sir* S. E.)

Biographie. *Biogr. de tous les ministres dep. la constit. de 1791, j. nos jours. 8°. 1825
*Biogr. gén. des Belges, 1850, *see* ROGER (P. A.)
Biogr. nationale; publ. par l'Acad. Roy. des Sciences &c. de Belgique. t22, 23. [Schott-Stevin]. la8°. Brux. 1914–24
Biogr. univ. [*Michaud*].
For Ital. ed. see DIZIONARIO biog. univ., 5v, 1840–49.

Biographisches Jahrbuch u. deutscher Nekrolog.
B17, 18 (1912–13). 8°. 1915–17
For contin., see DEUT. BIOGRAPH. JAHRBUCH.

Biography. *Biog. of the Brit. stage; lives of actors & actresses. s8°. 1824
see DICT. of nat. Biog., 1912–21; ed. Davis & Weaver, 1927.

Bion, *see* BUCOLIC. Bucoliques grecs; texte & tr. par P. E. Legrand, t2, Moschos, Bion &c., 1927.

Biondelli (Bernardino), *philologist.* Poesie lombarde ined. del sec. 13. Publ. &c. da B. B. la8°. Milano. 1856
Saggio sui dialetti gallo-ital. 8°. Milano. 1853

Biondi (Ernesto), *1855–1917, see* SAPORI (F.) Maestri, No. 23, 1920.

Biondo, *da Forli, see* BLONDUS (F.)

Biorci (Guido). Antichità e prerogative d'Acqui-Staziella, s. istoria profana-eccles. 2t & App. [*App. w. sep. tp. & pagin., b. w. t2*]. la8°. Tortano. [1818–20]

Birabeau (André). *Works in* ŒUVRES libres.
Crime passionnel, 1923. [22.]
La débauche, 1924. [31.]
Un dejeuner de soleil, comédie, 1926. [57.]
Est-ce possible ? comédie, 1924. [38.]
Le parfum de la femme coupable, 1922. [13.]
Petit péché, comédie, 1927. [73.]
Le bébe barbu. s8°. [1920]
La danseuse & le capucin. s8°. [1922]
—— **& R. Wachthausen.** Plaire; comédie, *see* ŒUVRES libres, 63, 1926.

Birch (Eliza).
Poems; added a sel. of hymns. [P2781]. 8°. M'ter. 1800

Birch (*Capt.* **G.)** Sel[s]. f. note-bks. kept by G. B., 1818–21, *see* PUNJAB. P. govt. rec[s]., v9, 1921.

Birch (John Francis). Mem. on national defence. 2nd ed. corr. [P2591]. 8°. 1808

Birch (Thomas), *D.D.* *Inquiry into the share wh. Ch. I had in the trans. of the earl of Glamorgan for bringing over Irish rebels, 1645–46. 8°. 1747
see HOUBRAKEN (J.) & G. VERTUE. Heads of illust. persons of Gt. Brit.; lives by T. B., n. ed., 1813.

Birch (Una) [*aft. Mrs.* POPE-HENNESSY].
Early Chinese jades. 4°. 1923

Birchenough (Charles). Hist. of elem. education in Engl. & Wales f. 1800 to present day. 2nd impr. s8°. 1920

Bircher (Eugen). Beitr. z. Erforsch. d. Schlacht a. d. Marne. H1, Die Schlacht a. Ourcq. 8°. L. 1922
Die Krisis in d. Marneschlacht. la8°. 1927

Birchley (William) [BIRCHLY], *ps., see* AUSTIN (J.), *R.C. writer.*

Birck (Laurits Vilhelm). The theory of marginal value. 8°. 1922

Bird (Henry Edward). Mod. chess & chess masterpieces. 8°. *n.d.*

Bird (J. Malcolm). Relativity & gravit. [*By var. wr[s].*] Ed. J. M. B. s8°. [1921]

Bird (*Sir* **James),** *see* LONDON. Survey of L., v8, Parish of St. Leonard; ed. &c. by Sir J. B., 1922.

Bird (W. Hobart). Anc. mural paintings in the churches of Gloucs. la8°. Gloucester. [1927]

Bird (*Maj.-Gen.* **Wilkinson Dent).**
The direction of war: st. of strategy. 8°. C. 1920

Birds. Pract. hdbk. of Brit. b., 2v, 1920–24, *see* WITHERBY (F. H.), *ed.*

Birdwood (Herbert Mills), *see* BIRDWOOD (*Gen. Sir* W. R.) H. M. B. in India, 1924.

Birdwood (*Gen. Sir* **William Riddell).** H. M. Birdwood in India, *see* WARD (*Sir* A. W.) In memoriam, 1924.

Biren (Ernst Johann), *duke of Courland, see* BIRON (E. J.)

Birger, *Jarl* [BIRGERUS, *dux*], *see* REIN (G.) De loco, quo, arma Tavastis illaturus, appulerit, Birgerus dux, 1833.

Biringucci (Marcello), *see* PIGNOTTI (G.) I pittori Senesi d. fondazione B. &c., 1916.

Birinyi (Louis K.)
The tragedy of Hungary. 8°. Cleveland, Ohio. [1924]

Birkbeck College (*Univ. of London*). B. C. centenary lectures [by Visct. Haldane, Sir W. Ashley & o.] Pref. by J. R. MacDonald. 8°. 1924
Calendar, 1922–23, 1923–24. 8°. [1922–23]

Birkbeck (Rose Katherine), *wife of W. J. Birkbeck.* Life & letters of W. J. Birkbeck. Pref. by Visct. Halifax. 8°. 1922

Birkbeck (William John), *F.S.A., see* BIRKBECK (R. K.) Life & letters of W. J. B., 1923.

Birkeland (Knut B.) The whalers of Akutan: mod. whaling in Aleutian Islands. 8°. New Haven, *Yale.* 1926

Birkeland (Michael), *see* ORDING (F.) Riksarkivar M. B., hans liv og virke, 1919.

Birkenhead (Frederick Edwin Smith, *1st earl***).**
Contemporary personalities. [repr.] 8°. [1924]
Famous trials of history. 8°. [1926]
„ „ 3rd. ed. 8°. [1926]
14 English judges. 8°. [1926]
International law. 6th ed. Ed. R. Moelwyn-Hughes. 8°. 1927
Law, life & letters. 2v. 8°. [1927]
Points of view. 2v. 8°. [1922]
see EPHESIAN, *ps.* Lord B., 1926.

Birkenmajer (Alexander). Verm. Unters. z. Gesch. d. mittelalt. Philos. [Beitr. z. Gesch. d. Phil. d. M.-a., 20v]. 8°. Münster. 1922

Birkenthal (Ber), *see* BER, *of Bolechow.*

Birkett (M. S.) Ferrous metals. Intr[s]. by Sir E. Geddes & A. Dorman. [Resources of the Empire, v8i]. 4°. 1924

Birkhead (Edith). Sentiment & sensibility in the 18th cent. novel, *see* ENG. ASSOC. Essays, v11, 1925.
The tale of terror. Study of the Gothic romance. 8°. 1921

Birkhill (Robert), *ps., see* LOCKHART (D.)

Birkhimer (William E.)
Milit. govt. & martial law. 8°. Wash. 1892

Birkmyre (William). Currency or bi-metallism examined. [P2829]. 8°. Glasgow. 1887

Birley (Robert). The Eng. Jacobins, 1789–1802. Gladstone Mem. Prize Essay, 1924. 8°. 1924

Birmanica. Epigraphia Birmanica, 1919 &c., *see* EPIGRAPHIA.

Birmingham, *see also* KING EDWARD'S SCHOOL.
MUSEUM & ART GALLERY.
Cat. of Loan exhib. of drawings &c. repres. of the bk. illust. of the "Sixties," lent by H. Hartley &c. [P2773]. 8°. 1924
Illust. cat. of perm. coll. of paintings in the Art Gallery & in Aston Hall &c. 8°. B'ham. 1912

Birmingham Public Libraries.
Cat. of the War poetry coll. 8°. B'ham. 1921
Hdbk. to the Commercial library. [P2420]. s8°. B'ham. 1919

Birmingham Small Arms Company [B. S. A.], *see* FROST (G. H.) Munitions of war: work of the B. S. A. &c., 1914–18, 1921.

Birnbaum (Adalbert). Vitruvius u. die griech. Architektur, 1914, *see* KAIS. AKAD. D. WISS. Z. WIEN. Denkschr., B57, 1915.

Birnbaum (Martin). Introductions. Painters, sculptors & graphic artists. 8°. N.Y. 1919

Birnbaum (Salomo). Prakt. Gramm. d. Jidd. Sprache &c. [Hartlebens Bibl. d. Sprachenkunde, T128]. s8°. Wien. [1919]

Birnstingl (H. J.) Sir John Soane. la8°. 1925

Biró (L. A.) Magyar. Sprach-u. Gesangaufnahmen (31. Mitt. d. Phonogr.-Archivs-Komm.), 1913, *see* KAIS. AKAD. D. WISS. Z. WIEN. SITZB., B173, 1914.

Biró (Márton), *bp. of Weszprim.* Enchiridion de fide, hæresiarchis, &c. atque decretis imperat. & regum contra dissipatores Cathol. Eccles. ed. s4°. Jaurini. 1750

Biró (Màtyás), *Dévay.* *Orthographia Ungarica. [Melleklet a Magyar Konyvszemle 1908]. s8°. [Cracoviæ]. 1549. [*repr.* 1908]
see RÉVÉSZ (I.) D. B. M. életrajza, 1863.

Biron (*Sir* **Chartres).** Pious opinions. 8°. [1923]

Biron (Ernst Johann), *duke of Courland* [BIREN; BÜREN (E. J.)], *1690–1772, see* HEMPEL (C. F.) Merkw. Leben d. Grafen. B. &c., 1742.

Biron (*Dom* **Réginald) & J. Barennes.** Un prince anglais, card.-légat au 16e s., R. Pole. 8°. [1923]

Bironius Padanus (Martinus), *see* BIRÓ (MÁRTON).

Birrell (*Rt. Hon.* **Augustine).**
Coll. essays & addresses, 1880–1920. 3v. 8°. 1922
F. Locker-Lampson; w. sel. f. letters & bibliogr. notes on books formerly in Rowfant Lib. Comp. & ed. by A. B. 8°. 1920
More obiter dicta. s8°. 1924
„ „ [n. impr.] s8°. 1924
Nationality & the League of Nations. [Repr. f. Contemp. Rev., 1919. P2739]. 8°. [1919]
Sel. essays, 1884–1907. s8°. [1909]
see MARVELL (A.) A. M., 1621–78, tercent. tributes, by A. B. &c., 1922.

Birt (John). Patristic evenings. 8°. [1846]

Birth control. Medical views on birth control; by H. Crichton-Miller &c., 1926, *see* MARCHANT (*Sir* J.), *ed.*

Biryukov (Pavel Ivanovich). Appeal to humanity, *see* CHERTKOV (V.) Save Russia, 1919.
Л. Н. Толстой: біографія. 3t. s8°. Берлинъ. 1921
The new Russia. [P2381]. s8°. [1919]
see TOLSTOY (*count* L. N.) Love letters; w. st. of autobiog. elements in T.'s work by P. B.; tr., 1923.

Biscaro (Gerolamo), *see* BAILO (L.) & G. B. Della vita &c. di Paris Bordon, 1900.

Biscay, Bay of. B. of B. pilot, & Suppl. 1, 1921–22, *see* ADMIRALTY.

Bischoff (Ernst). Die Entlarvung d. "deutsch-bolschewist. Verschwörung." Vorwort d. P. Scheidemann. Hrsg. B. [P2407]. 8°. 1919

Bischoff (Ferdinand). Old Lemberg laws, *in Armenian, see* KALEMKEAREAN (G.), *tr.* Lemberg codices, 1890.

Bischoffsheim (H. L.) Cat. of Dresden porcelain, objects of art &c. coll. by B., sold by Christie, May 6, 1926. 8°. 1926
Cat. of pictures by old masters coll. by B., sold by Christie, May 7, 1926. 8°. 1926

Bischop (Simon), *see* EPISCOPIUS (S.)

Biscoe (Cecil Earle Tyndale).
Kashmir in sunlight & shade. 8°. 1922

Bishop (John), *of Cheltenham, see* HAMILTON (J. A.) Dict. explan. of 3500 Ital., French &c. musical terms &c., ed. J. B., 47th ed., *n.d.*

Bishop (John), *murderer.* *The hist. of the London Burkers. [J. B. & others]: incl. the life &c. of Eliza Ross, the murderer of Mrs. Walsh. 8°. 1832

Bishop (Joseph Bucklin).
Theodore Roosevelt & h. time. 2v. 8°. 1920

Bishop (Reginald Wm. Snowden). My moorland patients. By a Yorkshire doctor. 8°. 1922

Bishop (William), *bp. of Chalcedon.* A reformation of a catholike deformed: by W. Perkins. Wherein the chiefe controversies in religion are handled. Made by D. B. P. [*i.e.* Dr. Bishop, priest]. 2p *in* 1v. s4°. 1604

Bishop (William Chatterley). The Mozarabic & Ambrosian rites. 4 essays. Ed. C. L. Feltoe. [Alcuin Club Tracts, 15]. s8°. [1924]

Bishops. *Lord bishops none of the Lords bishops, 1640, *see* PRYNNE (W.)

Bisi (Maso). La sorgente. Diario di una signorina (Jeanne H.) s8°. Milano. 1914

Bisinger (Josef). Der Agrarstaat in Platons Gesetzen. [Klio: Beitr. z. alt. Gesch., Beih. 17]. 8°. L. 1925

Biskra. *Biskra & le Sahara constantinois. [Syndicat d'Initiative de Biskra]. s8°. Alger. 1923

Bismarck (Otto, *Fürst* **v.)**
Gesamm. Werke. B1–5, 7–9. [1, 2[e] A.] 4°. [1924–28]
1–5, Polit. Schr.; bearb. H. v. Petersdorff [u. F. Thimme].
7–9, Gespräche, 1854–98; hrsg. u. bearb. W. Andreas.
*B. intime. By a fellow student. Tr. by H. Hayward. s8°. 1890
Bismarck u. d. Nordschlesw. Frage, 1864–79. Diplom. Akten d. Auswärt. Amtes. Hrsg. v. W. Platzhoff, K. Rheindorf, J. Tiedje. Einl. v. W. Platzhoff. 8°. 1925
Erinnerung u. Gedanke. [Gedanken u. Erinn., B3]. 8°. St. 1919
New chapters of B.'s Autobiog. Tr. B. Miall. 8°. [1921]
Polit. Berichte aus Petersburg u. Paris, 1859-62. Hrsg. L. Raschdau. 2B. 8°. 1920
REFERENCES.
see ANDRASSY (J.) B., Andrassy &c., 1927.
„ BALLHAUSEN (L., *Frhr.* v.) Bismarck - Erinnerungen, 1921.
„ BRANDENBURG (E.) Von B. zum Weltkriege, 1924; tr., 1927.
„ CORTI (E. C.) Alex. v. Battenberg, s. Kampf mit d. Zaren u. B., 1920.
„ ECKARDT (J. W. A. v.) Aus d. Tagen v. B.'s Kampf gegen Caprivi: Erinnerungen, 1920.
„ EPPSTEIN (G., *Frhr.* v.) Fürst B. Entlassung, 1920.
„ FREDERICK III, *Germ. emp.* Emperor's diary, 1866 &c.; B.'s rejoinder, 1888.
REFERENCES [*continued*].
see FULLER (J. V.) B.'s diplomacy at its zenith, 1922.
„ GRADENWITZ (O.) B.'s letzter Kampf, 1888–98, 1924.
„ HALLER (J.) B.'s Friedenschlüsse, 1917.
„ HAMMANN (O.) Der missverstandne B., 1921.
„ KULLMANN (E. F. L.) Prozess K. [*for attempted murder of B.*], 1874.
„ LENZ (M.) Kl. hist. Schr., B2, v. Luther z. B., 1920.
„ LUDWIG (E.) B.: Gesch. e. Kampfers, 1927; tr., 1927.
„ —— B.; psycholog. Versuch, 1912.
„ —— Bismarck [3 plays; tr.], 1927.
„ NOLDE (*bar.* B. E.) Петербургская миссия Б., 1859–62, 1925.
„ PLEHN (H.) B.'s auswärtige Politik nach d. Reichsgründung, 1920.
„ RACHFAHL (F.) B.'s Engl. Bündnispolitik., 1922.
„ ROBOLSKY (H.) *B. in Frankfurt, 1885.
„ SCHOLZ (A. v.) Erlebnisse u. Gespräche mit B., 1922.
„ SCHÜSSLER (W.) B.'s Sturz, 1922.
„ STEIN (W.) B.: Leben in Bildern &c., 1915.
„ WAHL (A.) Vom B. d. 70er Jahre, 1920.

Bisschop (William Roosegaarde). The Saar controversy. [Grotius Soc. Publ., No. 2]. 8°. 1924

Bissell (Edward Cone). The historic origin of the Bible. Intr. by R. D. Hitchcock. 8°. E. [1873]

Bisset (Habakkuk). Rolment of courtis. Ed. Sir P. J. Hamilton-Grierson. [Sc. Text Soc., N.S., 10, 13, 18]. 3v. 8°. 1920–26

Bisset-Smith (George Tulloch). The Census & some of its uses &c. Census Act, 1920, &c. 8°. E. 1921

Bissing (Friedrich Wilhelm v.) Beitr. z. Gesch. d. assyr. Skulptur, *see* KÖN. AKAD. D. WISS. Z. MÜNCHEN, Abhdlgn. d. phil. Klasse, B26, 1914.

Das Griechentum u. s. Mission. [Wissensch. u. Bild., Einzeldarst., 169]. s8°. L. 1921

Works in KÖN. AKAD. D. W. ZU MÜNCHEN. Phil. Kl., Sitz.

Beitr. z. Gesch. d. altägypt. Baukunst. [1923]
Die Datierung d. Petrieschen Sinaiinschr. [1920]
Denkmäler z. Gesch. d. Kunst Amenophis IV. [1914]
Ein Hauskauf im 4. Jahrtausend vor Chr. [1920]
Die Reliefs v. Sonnenheiligtum d. Rathures. [1914]
Urspr. u. Wesen d. pers. Kunst. [1927]

Bisso (José). *Works in* ESPAÑA. Crón. gen.

Crón. de la prov. de Alava, 1868. [8.]
Crón. de la prov. de Cádiz, 1868. [5.]
Crón. de la prov. de Málaga, 1869. [9.]
Crón. de la prov. de Murcia, 1870. [11.]
Crón. de la prov. de Sevilla, 1869. [5.]

Bisson (Alexandre).

Les Apaches. Comédie-vaudeville. s8°. 1903
Le bon juge. Comédie. 2e éd. s8°. 1906
Le capitaine Thérèse. Opèra-comique. s8°. 1901
Les erreurs du mariage. Comédie. 2e éd. s8°. 1906
La femme X. . . . Drame. s8°. 1908

—— **& J. Berr de Turique.**
Les trois Anabaptistes. Comédie. 2e éd. s8°. 1904

—— **& G. Livet.** Nick Carter. Pièce. s8°. 1910

—— **& M. Sonal.** Le coup du berger. Vaudeville. s8°. 1911

Bisson de La Roque (F.) Fouilles d'Abou-Roasch (1922–24), 2p —Médamoud (1925–26), 2p, *see* INSTITUT FR. D'ARCH. OR. DU CAIRE. Fouilles, t1, 2, 3i, 4i, 1924–27.

Bisticci (Vespasiano da). The Vespasiano memoirs: lives of illust. men of 15th cent. Tr. W. G. & E. Waters. 8°. 1926

Vite di uomini illustri. Pref. di E. Aubel. v1. s8°. Lanciano. 1911

Vite di uomini illustri del sec. 15. Riv. da L. Frati. [R. Comm. pe'testi di lingua n. Prov. dell' Emilia]. 3v. 8°. Bologna. 1892–3

Bitsilli (P. M.) Россія и Латинство. Статьи П. М. Б., Г. Вернадскаго &c. s8°. Берлинъ. 1923

Этюды о русск. поэзии. s8°. Прага. 1926

Bittcher (C. F. H.) Comm. de P. Abaelardi theol. systematica. [P558]. 4°. Numburgi. [1844]

Bitterauf (Theodor). Zur Entstehungsgesch. d. Bonapartismus, *see* KÖN. AKAD. D. WISS. ZU MÜNCHEN. Phil. Classe, Sitz., 1915.

Bittner (Maximilian). Die heil. Bücher d. Jeziden o. Teufelsanbeter (Kurd. u. Arab.); hrsg. &c. M. B. *&* Nachtrag, 1913, *see* KAIS. AKAD. D. W. IN WIEN. Denkschr., B55, 1917.

Works in KAIS. AKAD. D. WISS. ZU WIEN. Sitzungsber.

Studien z. Laut- u. Formenlehre d. Mehri- Spr. in Südarabien, 4, 5 i–iii, 1914–15. [174, 176, 178.]
Studien z. Šhauri-Spr. in d. Bergen v. Dofâr a. Pers. Meerbusen, [4p], 1916–17. [179, 183.]
Vorstudien z. Gramm. u. z. Wbche. d. Soqoṭri-Spr., 1–3, 1913–18. [173, 186.]

Biuzantatzi (Norayr N.), *see* NORAYR *Biuzantatzi.*

Biver (Paul). Hist. du Château de Meudon. la8°. 1923

Bizari (Pietro). Cyprium bellum, inter Venetos & Selymum gestum. s8°. [Basileæ. 1573]

Pannonicum bellum, sub Max. II & Solymano Turc. gest. Cum epit. rerum in Europa gest., [15]64–73. [*b. w. h.* Cyprium bellum, 1573]. s8°. Basileæ. [1573]

Bizony (Ladislaus). 133 Tage ungar. Bolschewismus. Die Herrschaft Béla Kuns u. Tibor Szamuellys &c. 8°. L. 1920

Bjerre (Andreas).
Psychology of murder. Tr. E. Classen. 8°. 1927

Björck & Börjesson, *booksellers.*
Svensk topografi. [Kat. No. 190]. s8°. [1924]

Björner (Erik Julius). [BIOERNER]. Schediasma hist.-geogr. de Varegis, heroibus Scandianis & primis Russiæ dynastis &c. [*App.* Vita Oddi Jaculatoris ant. carm., *extr. f.* Orvar-Odds saga. *Icelandic, Danish, Lat.*] s8°. Stockholmiæ. 1743

Bjørnson (Bjørnstjerne).
Samlede Digter-Verker. Standardutg. ved F. Bull. 9B. s8°. 1919–20

1, Mindre fortællinger—Mellem Slagene—Synnøve Solbakken—Halte-Hulda—Arne—En Glad Gut.
2, Kong Sverre—Sigurd Slembe—Maria Stuart i Skotland—Jernbanen og Kirkegaarden—Fiskerjenten.
3, Mindre fortællinger—Arnljot Gelline—Sigurd Jorsalfar—Brude-slåtten—En fallit—Redaktoren.
4, Kaptejn Mansana—Magnhild—Kongen—Det ny system—Leonarda.
5, Støv—En hanske—Over ævne, 1—Det flager i byen og på havnen.
6, Geografi og kærlighed—På guds veje—Et stygt barndoms minde—Mors hænder—En dag—Ivar Bye.
7, Absalons hår—Over ævne, 2—Paul Lange og Tora Parsberg —Laboremus—På Storhove—Daglannet.
8, Mary—Når den ny vin blomster—Digte og sange—Fred—Lyset.
9, Varianter.

Arnljot Gelline. 3e opl. s8°. 1884
Artikler og taler. Udg. af C. Collin og H. Eitrem. 2B. 8°. 1912–13
Fortællinger. 3e udg. 2d. s8°. 1881
Maria Stuart i Skotland. 4e udg. s8°. 1879
,, ,, ,, : Darnley. 6e Udg. s8°. 1902

TRANSLATIONS.
Arnljot Gelline. Tr., w. intr. & notes by W. M. Payne. [Scand. classics, v7]. s8°. N.Y. 1917
Mary. [German tr.] s8°. *n.d.*

Björnstjerna (*Grefre* Magnus F. F.)
The Brit. empire in the East. [Tr.] 8°. 1840

Bkah-Hgyur [KAH-GYUR]. Tibetan tales f. Indian sources. Tr. f. Tib. of Kahgyur by F. A. v. Schiefner; [tr.] f. German by W. R. S. Ralston, w. intr. n. ed. by C. A. F. Rhys Davids. [Broadway trans.] 8°. [1926]

Blacam (Aodh de). What Sinn Fein stands for. 8°. D. 1921

Blachos (Angelos). [VLACHOS].
Neugriech. Chrestomathie. s8°. L. 1870
,, ,, ...2e A. s8°. L. 1883

Black. Black book: the tragedy of Pontus, 1914–22. [*Eng. & Fr.* P2682]. 8°. Athens. 1922

Black Book (The) of Winchester, 1925, *see* WINCHESTER.

Black, *publisher.*

B.'s gardening dict. Ed. E. T. Ellis. 8°. 1921

GUIDES.
Cairo of to-day. By E. A. Reynolds-Ball. 4th ed., rev. & enl. s8°. 1905
Dorset, Devon & Cornwall. 11th ed. s8°. E. 1879
,, ,, Ed. A. R. H. Moncrieff. 15th ed. s8°. 1902

GUIDES [*continued*].
Gloucestershire. 5th ed. s8°. E. 1880
Leicester & Rutland. s8°. E. 1884
Trossachs &c. Ed. A. R. H. Moncrieff. 26th ed. s8°. 1903
Wales, North. 7th ed. s8°. E. 1879
,, ,, 23rd ed. s8°. 1907

Black Death, The: compiled f. contemp. sources; tr. C. H. Clarke, 1926, *see* NOHL (J.)

Black Sea. B. S. pilot, 7th ed., *&* Suppl. 2, 1920–22, *see* ADMIRALTY.

*Mem. of a map of the countries betw. B. S. & Caspian &c., 1788, *see* ELLIS (G.)

Black (George Ashton). Hist. of municipal ownership of land on Manhattan Island, to 1844. [Columbia Univ. St. in hist. &c., v1iii]. 8°. N.Y. 1891

Black (George Fraser).
Macpherson's Ossian &c. Bibliog. la8°. N.Y. 1926

Black (Harman). The real 'round S. America. 8°. [1924]

Black (John Bennett). Art of history: st. of 4 gt. historians [Voltaire, Hume, Robertson, Gibbon]. 8°. [1926]

Blackburn (Henry). The Pyrenees. n. ed., rev. 8°. 1881

Blackburn (William J.) Child welfare in N. Jersey, p1, *see* UNITED STATES: LAB. Children's Bur., No. 174, 1927.

Blackburne, *The family of, see* POYNTON (F. J.) Fam. of B., 1874.

Blackburne (Francis), *archdeacon of Cleveland.* Consider. on pres. state of controversy betw. protestants & papists of Gr. Britain & Ireland &c. 8°. 1768

*Mems. of T. Hollis. [2v. v2, Appendix]. 4°. 1780

Blackburne (Ireland), *wife of Thomas Blackburne, see* GREENE (I.)

Blackburne (Richard), *D.D., see* HOBBES (T.) T. H. vita [vitæ Hobbianæ auctarium, *by R. B.*], 1681.

Blackburne (S. S.) Terms & themes of chess problems. n. & enl. ed. &c. w. pref. by A. F. Mackenzie. s8°. 1907

Blacker (J. F.)
The A B C of Eng. salt-glaze stoneware. 8°. [1922]
The A B C of Indian art. 8°. [1922]
The A B C of Japanese art. 2nd ed. 8°. [1922]

Blacker (L. V. S.) On secret patrol in high Asia. 8°. 1922
Blackett (*Sir* Basil Phillott). Mém. sur la superpos. des taxes [*Fr. & Eng.*], 1921, *see* LEAGUE OF NATIONS: COMMISS. ECONOM. &c.
Black-Gate Museum, *Newcastle-upon-Tyne, see* SOC. OF ANTIQ. OF NEWCASTLE. Cat. of inscr. &c. stones, in B.-G. Mus., 1920.
Blackie (John Stuart). The pronunciation of Greek; accent & quantity. 8°. E. 1852
Blackman (Aylward Manley). Luxor & its temples. 8°. [1923]
The rock tombs of Meir. [Arch. Survey of Egypt, 25th mem.]. p4. 4°. 1924
Blackman (Winifred S.) The fellāḥīn of Upper Egypt. Foreword by R. R. Marett. 8°. 1927
Blackmore (Edwin Gordon), *see* OSSINGTON (J. E. D., *visct.*) & *Sir* H. B. W. BRAND. Decisions on points of order, &c.; by E. G. B., 1892.
Blackmore (*Sir* Richard). Creation, poem, *see* PARK (T.) Brit. poets, Suppl., v6, 1808.
A new version of the Psalms of David. s8°. 1721
Prince Arthur. Poem. 4th ed. s8°. 1714
Blackmore (Richard Doddridge). Lorna Doone. [repr.] s8°. *n.d.*
Blackmore (S. Powell). Lawn tennis up-to-date. Pref. by Hon. F. M. B. Fisher. 8°. [1921]
Blackpool. *A new descr. of B. 8°. [1830]
Blackstone (*Sir* William), *Justice of the Court of Common Pleas, see* A'BECKETT (G. A.) The comic B., 1856.
Blackwall Tunnel.
*Descr. of B. T. Repr. f. "London," 1897. obl.8°. 1897
Blackwall (Anthony). Auctores sacri classici def. &c., sive Crit. sacra N. Test. C. Wollius Lat. vertit & Hermeneuticam adj. [*w. sep. tp. & pagin.*] s4°. Lipsiæ. 1736
Blackwelder (Eliot), *geologist, see* WILLIS (B.), E. B. &c. Research in China, 3v. [& atlas], 1906–13.
Blackwell (John), *of Newcastle-upon-Tyne.* *Life of Rev. Alex. Kilham &c. s8°. 1838
Blackwell (Thomas), *the elder, Principal of the Marischal College, Aberdeen.* *Ratio sacra: or an appeal about the reasonableness of revealed relig. s8°. E. 1710
Blackwood (Algernon). Episodes before thirty. 8°. 1923
Tongues of fire & o. sketches. s8°. 1924
—— **& W. Wilson.** The wolves of God & o. fey stories. s8°. [1921]
Blackwood's Magazine. v207–222. 8°. E. 1920–27
Blades (William). Cat. of exhib. in comm. of centenary of W. B., 5–11 Dec. 1924. Compiled by W. T. Berry. 8°. 1924
Biography & typography of W. Caxton. 2nd ed. 8°. 1882
Blado, *The family of, see* BERNONI (D. G.) Dei Torresani, B. &c., 1890.
Blagg (Thomas Mathews). *Newark as a publishing town. By T. M. B[lagg]. Rev. & repr. f. the "Newark Advertiser." *f.p.c.o.* s8°. Newark. 1898
Blagoev (D.) От группы Благоева к "Союзу Борьбы (1886–94). Статьи и воспоминания: К. М. Норинского, В. А. Шелгунова, В. Невского, М. Ольминского. Мат. по делу М. И. Бруснева и Юв. Мельникова &c. [*Ed.* M. Olminsky]. la8°. [Москва]. 1921
Blaine (*Mrs.* Harriet Bailey), *wife of James Gillespie Blaine, form. Stanwood.* Letters [1869–89]. Ed. by H. S. B. Beale. 2v. 8°. N.Y. 1908
Blair (*Rt. Rev. Sir* David Hunter-), *see* HUNTER-BLAIR (*Sir* D.)
Blair (Francis Preston), *the younger, see* CROLY (D. G.) Seymour & B.: th. lives & services, 1868.
Blair (Hugh).
Lectures on rhetoric & belles lettres. 8°. 1823
*Obs. upon An anal. of the moral & relig. sentiments &c. [*b. w.* Kames (H. H.) Essays, 1751]. 8°. E. 1755
Blair (P.), *M.D.* *Thoughts on nature & relig., or an apol. for right of priv. judgment maintained by M. Servetus. s8°. [London ?]. 1774
Blair (Robert). The grave, a poem. [Etchings by L. Schiavonetti f. inventions of W. Blake. *add. engr. tp.*] 4°. 1813
Poet. works of B., Glynn &c. Collated by T. Park. s8°. 1807
Blair (Robert), *minister of St. Andrews.* Life of R. B., cont. h. autiobiog., w. suppl. & cont. of hist. of the times to 1680 by W. Row. Ed. T. M'Crie. [Wodrow Soc., 11]. 8°. E. 1848
Blair (Wilfrid). Sa muse s'amuse. [*Verses*]. 8°. O. 1914
Blaise, *Saint, bp. of Sebaste.* Passio B., *see* JÓNSSON (F.) AM. 623. 4°. Helgensagaer, 1927
Blake, *The family of, see* BLAKE (M. J.) B. family records, 1300–1700, 2s., 1902–5.
see SKEET, *Fam. of.* Hist. of the families of S. &c., 1906.
Blake (George). Young Malcolm. s8°. [1926]

Blake (John Hopwood), *F.G.S.*
Geol. of the co. around E. Dereham. [Mem. of G.S.] 8°. 1888
Geology of the co. around Reading. With contrib. by W. Whitaker. Ed. H. W. Monckton. [Mem. of G.S.] 8°. 1903
Geology of the co. near Yarmouth & Lowestoft. [Mem. of G.S.] 8°. 1890
The water-supply of Berkshire f. underground sources. With contrib. by W. Whitaker. [Mem. of G.S.] 8°. 1902
see BENNETT (F. J.) & J. H. B. Geol. of country betw. & S. of Bury St. Edmunds & Newmarket, 1866.
Blake (John Percy) & A. E. Reveirs-Hopkins. Little books about old furniture. Eng. furniture. n.ed. v1–4. s8°. 1919–20
1, Tudor to Stuart. 2, Period of Q. Anne. 3, Chippendale & h. school; by J. P. B. *alone.* 4, Sheraton period, 1760–1820; by A. E. R.-H. *alone.*
Blake (K. B.), *see* †KALMUS (H. T.) Researches on cobalt &c., p5, by K. & K. B. B., 1916.
Blake (Louisa Brandreth Aldrich-), *see* ALDRICH-BLAKE (L.)
Blake (M. M.) Toddleben's hero. s8°. 1893
Blake (Martin J.) Blake family records, 1300–1600 [–1700]: chronol. cat. w. notes &c. 2s. 8°. 1902–5
*s*2, 1600–1700, *includes* A brief acc. of the 14 anc. families of the town of Galway &c.
Blake (*Adm.* Robert), *see* JOHNSON (S.) Life of R. Savage &c., 1769.
Blake (Thomas), *Puritan Divine.*
see BAXTER (R.) Apol. agst. exceptions of T. B. &c., 1654.
,, —— Cert. disputations of right to sacraments; agst. T. B. &c., 1657.
Blake (Vernon). The art &c. of drawing. 8°. O. 1927
Blake (*Maj.* W. T.) Flying. s8°. [1923]
Flying round the world. 8°. [1923]
Blake (William), *artist.*
Designs for Gray's poems reprod. in monochrome or colour. Intr. by H. J. C. Grierson. atlas fol. 1922
For the sexes. The gates of Paradise. s8°. 1925
Pencil drawings. Ed. G. Keynes. 4°. *Nonesuch Press.* 1927
Poems & prophecies. [Ed. M. Plowman. Everyman's Lib.] s8°. [1927]
Poems, w. spec^{s}. of prose wr. Pref. notice by J. Skipsey. s8°. 1888
Poet. sketches. [1783, Noel Douglas replicas]. 8°. [1926]
Poet. works, lyr. & misc. Ed. w. mem. by W. M. Rossetti. s8°. 1874
,, ,, [Aldine ed. *repr.*] s8°. 1909
Poet. works, incl. the unpubl. French Revol. &c. Ed. w. intr. &c. by J. Sampson. Oxf. ed. s8°. O. 1913
Prophetic writings. Ed. w. intr., gloss. index of symbols &c. by D. J. Sloss & J. P. R. Wallis. 2v. 8°. O. 1926
Writings. Ed. by G. Keynes. 3v. la8°. *Nonesuch Press.* 1925
see BINYON (L.) Drawings & engravings of W. B., 1922.
see BINYON (L.) Engr. designs of W. B., 1926.
,, —— Followers of W. B.: E. Calvert &c., 1925.
,, BLAIR (R.) The grave, a poem: [etchings by L. Schiavonetti f. inventions of W. B.], 1813.
,, BURDETT (O.) W. B. [Eng. men of letters], 1926.
,, BURLINGTON F. A. C. B. centen. exhib., 1927.
,, CLARKE (J. H.) W. B. on the Lord's Prayer, 1927.
,, DAMON (S. F.) W. B., h. philos. & symbols, 1924.
,, FIGGIS (D.) The paintings of W. B., 1925.
,, FLAXMAN (J.) Class. compositions: Theogony &c., engr. by W. B., 1870.
,, GARDNER (C.) W. B., the man, 1919.
,, KEYNES (G. L.) Bibliog. of W. B., 1921.
,, MILTON (J.) On the morning of Christ's nativity: w. illust^{s}. by W. B., 1923.
,, PLOWMAN (M.) Intr. to st. of B., 1927.
,, YOUNG (E.) The complaint & the consolation, w. illust^{s}. by B., 1797.
Blakely (Theophilus Alexander). A letter claiming the orig. invention of an indispensable feature of the Armstrong gun. [P2602]. 8°. 1859
Blaker (Richard). Enter a messenger. s8°. [1926]
The voice in the wilderness. [2nd imp.] s8°. [1922]
Blakeslee (George Hubbard), *ed.* Mexico & the Caribbean. Clark Univ. addr. 8°. N.Y. 1920
Blakeway (George Sheffield). The city of Gloucester, its royal charters of liberties &c. 8°. [Gloucester]. 1924
Blakiston (J. F.) The Jami Masjid at Badaun &c., U.P., *see* INDIA. ARCH. SURVEY. Mem. No. 19, 1926.
Blanc (Dree), *ps.* [*i.e.* ANDREA BIANCHI].
Flôrs di campagne. [P2770]. 8°. Udine. 1904
Blanch (Enrique). Crón. de la prov. de Lérida, 1868, *see* ESPAÑA. Crón. gen., v3, 1865 &c.
Blanchard (Edward Leman), *see* BRADSHAW (G.) Descr. guide to the G. W. Ry.; by E. L. B.; p1, 1845.
Blanchard (Frank Nelson). A revision of the king snakes: Genus Lampropeltis. [S.I., U.S. Nat. Mus., Bull. 114]. 8°. Wash. 1921

Blanchard (Frederic T.)
Fielding, the novelist. 8º. New Haven, *Yale*. 1926

Blanchard (Raoul). Les forces hydro-électriques pend. la Guerre. [C. E. for Int. Peace]. la8º. [1924?]

Blanchart (Paul). François de Curel, s. œuvre. s8º. 1924
Henry Bataille, s. œuvre &c. s8º. 1922

Blanche [*of Montferrat*], *wife of Charles I, d. of Savoy; d. 1509*, *see* Bosio (A.) Notizie sui sepolcri di B. di M. &c., 1870.

Blanche (August).
Banditen. Berättelse. 4. uppl. s8º. Stockholm. [1891]

Blanche (Jacques Emile). Le bracelet tensimétrique. s8º. [1926]
Cahiers d'un artiste. s5, 6 (août 1916–juin 1917). s8º. 1919–20
5, La famille d'Aultreville & les Sommevielle.
6, Les intermédiaires.
Manet. Tr. F. C. de Sumichrast. 8º. 1925
Propos de peintre. sl. 2 [sl, 3e éd.] s8º. 1919–21
1, De David à Degas. Préf. par M. Proust.
2, Dates. Rép. à la préf. de M. Proust.

Blanch é Illa (Narciso). Crón. de la prov. de Gerona, 1865—Albacete, 1866, *see* España. Crón. gen., v3, 11, 1865 &c.

Blanchet (Jules Adrien). Les souterrains-refuges de la France. Contrib. à l'hist. de l'habit. hum. 8º. 1923
see Schlumberger (G. L.) Mélanges off. à G. S.; [Ed. A. B. &c.], 1924.

Blanchet (Léon). Campanella. [Thèse]. 8º. 1920

Blanchinus (Josephus), *see* Bianchini (G. M.)

Blanckenberg (Conrad Gottfried). Das Leben der Glaubigen: P. J. Spener. Leichen-Predigt. [Personalia. Abdanckungs-Rede. Predigt. [P2438]. s4º. *n.p.* 1705

Blanco-Fombona (Rufino).
El conquistador español del s. 16. s8º. [1922]
El hombre de oro. Novela. s8º. *n.d.*
La lámpara de Aladino: noticulas. s8º. 1915

Blanco Meaño (Luis F.) Parnaso boliviano. Sel. antologia de poesías col. por L. F. B. M. Prólogo de R. Bolivar Coronado. s8º. Barcelona. *n.d.*

Blanco Suarez (P.)
Poetas de los siglos 16 y 17. Sel. hecha por P. B. S. 8º. 1923

Bland (Alfred Edward), P. A. Brown & R. H. Tawney. Eng. econ. hist. Sel. docs. Comp. & ed. A. E. B. &c. [repr.] s8º. 1921

Bland (Henry Meade).
Stevenson's California. 8º. San Jose, Cal. [1924]

Bland (Humphry). A treatise of milit. discipline &c. 9th ed. rev. & corr. 8º. 1762

Bland (John Otway Percy). China, Japan & Korea. 8º. 1921
Men, manners & morals in S. America. 8º. 1920

Bland-Sutton (*Sir* John). Orations & addresses. 8º. 1924

Blane (*Sir* Gilbert), *Bart.*, *see* Rolleston (H. D.) Sir G. B., 1916.

Blankenfeld (Johannes), *see* Schnöring (W.) J. B., e. Lebensbild, 1905.

Blanqui (Louis Auguste), *1805–81*, *see* Geffroy (G.) L'enfermé, 2t, 1926.

Blaramberg (Ivan Fedorovich), *1800–78*. Erinnerungen aus d. Leben d. Gen.-Lt. J. v. B. Nach d. Tagebüchern, 1811–71; hrsg. E. v. Sydow. 3B. s8º. 1872–75

Blaringhem (Louis).
Les problèmes de l'hérédité expérim. s8º. 1919

Blasche (Bernhard Heinrich).
Das Böse im Einklange m. d. Weltordnung. 8º. L. 1827
Philosoph. Unsterblichkeitlehre. [*b. w.* Strümpell (L. H.) Herbarts Philos., 1834]. 8º. Erfurt. 1831

Blasco de Lanuza (Vincencio). Hist. eccl. y seculares de Aragon, en que se cont. los annales de Curita &c. 2t. sfol. Çaragoça. 1622

Blasco-Ibañez (Vicente).
A los pies de Venus. s8º. [1926]
En el país del arte. 3 meses en Italia. s8º. Valencia. [1919]
Luna Benamor. Novela. s8º. Valencia. *n.d.*
El militarismo mejicano. s8º. Valencia. [1920]
Novelas de amor y de muerte. s8º. Valencia. [1927]
Novelas de la Costa Azul. s8º. Valencia. [1924]
Oriente. s8º. [1916]
El Papa del mar. Novela. s8º. Valencia. 1925
El paraíso de las mujeres. Novela. s8º. Valencia. [1922]
El préstamo de la difunta. s8º. [1921]
La reina Calafia. s8º. Valencia. 1923
Sangre y arena. Novela. s8º. Valencia. [1919]
La tierra de todos. s8º. Valencia. [1922]
La vuelta al mundo, de un novelista. 3t. 8º. Valencia. 1924–25
Translations.
Alfonso XIII unmasked: the milit. terror in Spain. [Tr. L. Ongley]. 8º. 1925

Blasco-Ibañez (Vicente) [*continued*].
Translations [*continued*].
Alphonse XIII démasqué: la terreur milit. en Espagne. Tr. J. Louvre. s8º. [1924]
Arènes sanglantes. Tr. par G. Hérelle. [20e éd.] s8º. [1921]
Blood & sand. Tr. Mrs. W. A. Gillespie. 8º. [1913]
La bodega (The fruit of the vine). Tr. I. Goldberg. s8º. [1923]
The cabin. Tr. F. H. Snow &c.; w. intr. by J. G. Underhill. s8º. [1919]
The dead command. Tr. F. Douglas. s8º. [1923]
La dévoratrice, *see* Œuvres libres, 76, 1927.
The enemies of women. Tr. I. Brown. s8º. [1922]
Les ennemis de la femme. Tr. A. de Bengoechea. s8º. [1921]
La famille du Docteur Pedraza, nouvelle; tr. J. & M. Caravon, *see* Œuvres (Les) libres, No. 24, 1923.
In the land of art. Tr. F. Douglas. s8º. 1924
Luna Benamor, suivi de Les Plumes du Cabouré. Tr. p. Mme. R. Lafont. s8º. 1922
The mad virgins, & o. stories. [Tr. H. Wishnieff, J. Padin &c.] s8º. [1926]
Mare nostrum. Auth. tr. by C. B. Jordan. [2nd impr.] s8º. [1923]
The mayflower. Tr. A. Livingston. s8º. [1922]
The mob. Tr. M. J. Lorente. s8º. [1927]
Le prêt de la morte, *see* Œuvres libres, No. 6, 1921.
La révolution mexicaine & la dictature militaire. Tr. L. Fonges. s8º. 1923
Le roi des prairies, nouv., *see* Œuvres libres, No. 36, 1924.
Le roi Lear, imprimeur, nouvelle, *see* Œuvres libres, No. 62, 1926.
Sonnica. Auth. tr. by F. Douglas. s8º. 1919
„ „ [Pop. ed.] s8º. [1924]
The temptress. [Tr.] s8º. [1923]
The torrent. Tr. s8º. [1923]
La tragédie sur le lac. Tr. R. Lafont. s8º. [1921]
La vieille du cinéma. nouvelle, tr. F. Ménétrier, *see* Œuvres libres, No. 19, 1923.
Le vieux de la Promenade des Anglais, *see* Œuvres libres, No. 41, 1924.
Woman triumphant. [Tr. H. Keniston]. s8º. [1921]
References.
see Gascó Contell (E.) B.-I., 1925.
„ Pitollet (C.) V. B.-I., s. novelas y la novela de su vida, 1921.
„ ——— V. B.-I., ses romans & le roman de sa vie, 1921.

Blaser (Fritz). Les Hautt: hist. d'une famille d'imprimeurs &c., 17e & 18e siècles. Thèse, Neuchâtel. 8º. Lucerne. 1925

Blashill (Thomas). Sutton-in-Holderness. The manor, berewic & village community. [*la. paper*]. 4º. 1896

Blasi (Benedetto). Vie—piazze—ville di Roma. Ordin. a diz. alfab. Con pref. di F. Tambroni. s8º. [1923]

Blass (Friedrich W.) Pronunciation of anc. Greek. Tr. f. 3rd German ed. by W. J. Purton. 8º. C. 1890

Blau (Christian Friedrich). De genuina eorum verborum indole quibus Paulus epist. ad Titum scriptam præfatur. s8º. Longosalissæ. 1846

Blaumanis (Rudolfs) [Blaumann]. The builders of new Rome & o. Lettish tales. [By] R. Blaumanis, J. Akuraters, K. Skalbe, J. Poruks. Tr. L. A. Marshall. s8º. 1924
Durch den Sumpf. Übers. vom Aut. u. O. Schönhoff. [Lett. Lit., B9]. 8º. Riga. [1922]
Die Indrans. Drama. Übers. v. Autor. [Lett. Lit., B3]. 8º. Riga. [1921]
Novellen. Übers. v. Autor. [Lett. Lit. B5]. 8º. Riga. [1921]

Blaumüller (Edvard), *1851–1911*.
Agnete og Havmanden. Et Digt. [Efter 4e Oplag]. s8º. 1914

Blavatsky (*Mme.* H. P.), *see* Butt (G. B.) Mme. B., 1926.
see Cleather (A. L.) H. P. B. as I knew her, 1923.
„ ———. H. P. B.: a gt. betrayal, 1922.
„ ———. H. P. B., h. life &c., 1922.

Blavignac (Jean Daniel). Armorial genevois. Essai hist. sur les armoiries, les sceaux &c. 8º. Genève. 1849

Blaxland (Bruce). The struggle w. Puritanism. [Hdbks. of Eng. Ch. Hist.] s8º. [1910]

Blažek (Conrad). Abgestorbene Adel d. preuss. Prov. Schlesien, T1; bearbt. v. C. B., *see* Sibmacher (J.), *ed.* Wappenbuch, B6viii, 1887.
Adel v. oesterr. Schlesien; bearbt. &c. v. B., *see* Sibmacher (J.), *ed.* Wappenbuch, B4xi, 1885.
Preuss. Grafen u. Freiherren; bearbt. &c. C. B., *see* Sibmacher (J.), *ed.* Wappenbuch, B7ii, 1866.

Blazquez (Antonio). Cartas sobre Brasil, 1556–65, *see* Instituto Hist. e Geog. Brazil. Revista, t49, 1886.

Bleackley (Horace William) [*ps.* Tivoli]. The beautiful duchess: Eliz. Gunning, Duchess of Hamilton & Argyll. [Cheap ed.] s8º. [1927]
Casanova in England: acc. of visit to London, 1763–64, told by himself. Ed. H. B. 8º. [1923]
Ladies fair & frail: sketches of the demi-monde dur. 18th cent. [repr.] 8º. [1925]
The monster. s8º. 1920
see Fauntleroy (H.) Trial of H. F. &c.; ed. H. B., 1924.

Blease (Walter Lyon).
Suvorof. Intr. by Maj.-Gen. Sir C. E. Callwell. 8°. 1920

Bleby (Henry). Death struggles of slavery. s8°. 1853

Blechschmid (Christoph). Matæologiam Labadianam, sub moder. J. F. Mayeri, p. p. C. B., 1685. Recusa. [P600]. s4°. Wittenbergae. 1717

Blécourt (A. S. de) & N. Japikse. Klein plakkaatboek van Nederland. Verzameling van ordonnantiën en plakkaten &c. (14e eeuw tot 1749). 8°. Groningen, den Haag. 1919

Bledisloe (Charles Bathurst, *baron*). Potatoes & pigs w. milk as basis of Britain's food supply. [P2563]. 8°. 1921

Bleek (Wilhelm Heinrich Immanuel). Reynard the Fox in South Africa; or, Hottentot fables &c. Tr. W. H. I. B. s8°. 1864

Blegen (Carl W.) Korakou, a prehist. settlement near Corinth. [Amer. School of Class. St. at Athens]. 4°. Boston. 1921

Bleich (Johann Andreas). Dissert., idolum pontif. destructum quem vocant Christophorum. Præses J. A. B., resp. A. C. S. Meyerus. [P2638]. 8°. Vitembergæ. 1688

***Blemish** (The) of govt., shame of relig. &c.: or, a charge agst. drunkards pres. to the Ld. Protector &c. s8°. 1655

Blemmidas (Nicephorus), *see* ALLACCI (L.) Græciæ orthodoxæ scriptores. N. B. &c., 2t, 1652–59.

Blencowe (*Mrs.* **Ann),** *wife of John Blencowe, form. Wallis.* Receipt book, 1694. [Intr. by G. Saintsbury]. 8°. 1925

Blenkinsop (*Maj.-Gen. Sir* **Layton John),** *see* WAR. Hist. of the Gt. War: veterinary services; ed. Sir L. J. B. &c., 1925.

Blennerhassett (W. L.) The red shadow. s8°. [1922]

Bléry (*le Capt.* **Paul).** En mission en Roumanie. Anecdotes de Guerre &c. s8°. 1919

Blessebois (Pierre Corneille), *1646?–1700?*, [BLESSEBOIS (PAUL ALEXIS)], *see* LACHÈVRE (F.) Le Casanova du 17e s.: P.-C. B., suiv. d'un inéd. de B.: les aventures du parc d'Alençon, 1668, 1927.

Bleton (Auguste). Petite hist. pop. de Lyon. 8°. Lyon. 1885

Bleuler (Louis). [Vues pittoresques du Rhin. Publ. & dessiné par L. B. Gravé par Salathé. *no tp.*] obl.4°. [Suisse, *n.d.*]

Blewitt (Jonas), *d. 1805.* Love & war: song [*b. w.* Corelli (A.) Twelve concertos, 1790?] 4°. *Hodsoll.* [1800?]

Bleyswijk (Diderik van). Memorien, 1734–55. Uitg. &c. door T. Jorissen. [Hist. Genoots. Werken, N.S., 45]. 8°. Utrecht. 1887

Blicher (Steen Steensen).
Noveller. Udvalgt &c. af S. Vasegaard. 2B. 8°. 1922
Udvalgte Noveller. Udg. af G. Christensen. 2B. 8°. 1922

Blicq (A. Stanley). Norman Ten Hundred. 1st (Service) Bn. Royal Guernsey Light Infantry. s8°. Guernsey. 1920

Bliemetzrieder (Franz Pl.) Zu den Schr. Ivos von Chartres (†1116), 1917, *see* KAISERL. AKAD. D. WISS. ZU WIEN. Sitzungsber., B182, 1918.
see ANSELMUS, *Laudunensis.* Systemat. Sentenzen; hrsg. &c. v. F. P. B., T1, 1919.

Bligh (N. M.) The evolution & development of the quantum theory. Foreword by M. Planck. 8°. 1926

Bligh (Stanley M.) The direction of desire. Applic. of psychology to everyday life. 4th imp. s8°. [1919]

Bligh (*Admiral* **William).** Narr. of the mutiny of the Bounty. [P2703]. la8°. 1838
see MARRIOTT (C. B.) Capt. B.'s second voyage to the South Sea, 1920.

Blight (Isaac), *see* PATCH (R.) Trial of R. P. for murder of I. B., 1806.

Blin (A.) Dict. français-tamoul & tamoul-français. [*lithogr.*] obl.s8°. 1831

***Blind** fiddler (The). s8°. E. *n.d.*

Blinders (Belinda), *ps.*, *see* COKE (D.)

Blin de Sainmore (Adrien Michel Hyacinthe). Hist. de Russie, représ. par figures, gravées par F. A. David, d'ap. les dessins de Monnet. Le discours par B. de S. 3t. [*in* 1v.] la8°. 1797–1806

Blinkenberg (Christian Sørensen).
Works in KONG. DAN. VID. SELSK. Hist.-fil. Medd.
Fibules grecques & orientales, 1925. [13.]
Hades's munding, 1918–19. [2.]
L'image d'Athana Lindia, 1917–18. [1.]
Lindiaka, 2–5, 1925–26. [11, 12.]
Le temple de Paphos, 1924–25. [9.]
see CORPUS vasorum ant.: Danemark, par C. B. &c., 1924.

Blinkinsop (Vicesimus), *ps.*, *see* HOOK (T. E.)

Blinov (Ivan Andreevich) & A. I. Bukovetsky, *edd.*
Финансовая энциклопедия. la8°. Москва. [1924]

Bliss (Frank E.), *see* LEGROS (A.) Cat. of paintings &c. by A. L., f. coll. of F. E. B., 1922.

Bliss (George), *ps.*, *see* WHITE (G. M.)

Blizard (John). The economic use of coal for steam-raising & house heating. [Canada: Dept. of Mines: Bull. 28. P2413]. 8°. Ottawa. 1919
The prepar., transport. & combustion of powdered coal. [Canada: Dept. of Mines, No. 564. P2624]. 8°. Ottawa. 1921
—— & E. S. Malloch. Gas producer trials w. Alberta coals. [Canada. Geolog. Survey. P2713]. 8°. Ottawa. 1921

Bloch (Camille). Bibliog. méthod. de l'hist. écon. & soc. de la France pend. la Guerre. [C. E. for Internat. Peace]. la8°. [1925]
see FRANCE: ASSEMBLÉE NAT. CONSTIT. Procès-verbaux du Comité des Finances de l'Assemblée Constit., 1922.
„ LEBLANC (H.) La Grande Guerre: iconographie &c., t6, Répertoire méthod. de la presse quotid. franç. par C. B., t1, 1914, 1919.

Bloch (Ernst). Thomas Münzer als Theologe d. Revolution. 8°. München. [1921]

Bloch (Gustave).
L'empire romain. Évolution & décadence. s8°. 1922

Bloch (Hermann), *see* STRASSBURG. Regesten d. Bischöfe, B1, Die elsäss. Annalen v. Stauferzeit: Einl. v. H. B., 1908.

Bloch (Jean Richard).
Sur un cargo. [Les doc. bleus, 10]. 4e éd. s8°. 1924

Bloch (Jules).
La formation de la langue marathe. [H. E., 215]. 8°. 1919

Bloch (Marc). Les rois thaumaturges: ét. sur le caractère surnaturel attrib. à la puissance royale partic. en France & en Angleterre. [Univ. de Strasbourg]. 8°. Str. 1924

Bloch (*Dr.* **Oscar),** *see* RINDOM (E.) Minder fra Studenterdagene [*by* O. B. &c.], 1924.

Bloch (Oscar), *prof. au Lycée Buffon.* La pénétration du français dans les parlers des Vosges mérid. [H. E. 232]. 8°. 1921

Blochet (Edgard). Les enluminures des mss. orient. turcs, arabes, persans de la Bibl. Nat. 4°. 1926
Notes sur des peintures hindoues de la Bibl. Nat., *see* Soc. FRANÇ. de Reprod. de MSS. &c. Bull., Ann. 10, 1926.
Notices sur les mss. persans & arabes de la coll. Marteau, *see* BIBLIOTHÈQUE NAT. Notices, t41, 1923.
Les peintures des mss. orientaux de la Bibl. Nat. [Soc. Franç. de Reprod. de MSS. &c.] sfol. 1914–20
Peintures des mss. persans de la Coll. Marteau à la Bibl. Nat., *see* ACAD. DES INSCR. FOND. PIOT. Mons. &c., t23, 1918–19.

Bloem (J. C.) Het verlangen. la8°. A. 1921

Bloemers, *see* BLÖMERS.

Blok (Aleksandr Aleksandrovich).
Возмездие. 8°. П. 1922
Двѣнадцать [1918]. Съ пред. П. Сувчинскаго. 8°. Софія. *n.d.*
За гранью прошлых дней. Стихотворения. s8°. П. 1920
О современном состоянии русск. символизма. s8°. П. 1921
Об Александре Блоке. Статьи Н. Анциферова, Ю. Верховского [*& others*]. s8°. П. 1921
Отроческіе стихи. Автобіографія. 4°. Москва. 1922
Песня судьбы. Драм. поэма. s8°. П. 1919
Последние дни императ. власти, по неизд. док. 8°. П. 1921
Письма. s8°. Ленинград. 1925
Письма к родным. С предисл. М. А. Бекетовой. s8°. Ленинград. 1927
Скифы-Двѣнадцать, *see* IVANOV-RAZUMNIK (R. V.) Испытаніе, 1920.
Собрание сочинений. т9. s8°. Берлин. 1923
9, Статьи, кн. 3, о театре, 1907–21.
Стихотворенія. 3кн. s8°. [Берлинъ]. 1922
Сѣдое утро: стихотворения. s8°. П. 1920
Театръ. s8°. [Berlin]. 1922
Ямбы, стихи (1907–14). s8°. П. 1919
TRANSLATIONS.
The twelve. [*Poems*]. Tr. w. intr. & notes by C. E. Bechhofer. 4°. 1920
REFERENCES.
see BEKETOVA (M. A.) А. Блок, 1922.
„ CHUKOVSKY (K.) Книга объ А. Б., 1922.
„ KNYAJNIN (V. N.) А. А. Б., 1922.
„ MEDVEDEV (P.) Драмы &c. А. Б., 1928.
„ TSINGOVATOV (A. YA.) А. А. Б.: жизнь и творчество, 1926.
„ VOLKOV (N.) А. Б. и театр, 1926.

——, A. F. Koni *& others.*
Пушкин. [*By A. B., A. F. K. &c.*]—Достоевский. [*By A. G. Gornfeld & A. M. Remizov. Essays*]. s8°. Петербург изд. дома литератовъ. 1921

Blok (G.) Рождение поэта. Повесть о молодости Фета. s8°. Ленинград. 1924

Blok (Petrus Joh.) Gesch. d. Niederlande. Verdeutscht d. O. G. Houtrouw. [Gesch. d. europ. Staaten]. B6, bis 1795. 8°. Gotha. 1918
Gesch. van het Nederl. volk. 8d. 8°. Leiden. 1892–1908
Willem de Eerste, Prins van Oranje. [Nederl. Hist. Bibl., 11 & 12]. 2d. la8°. 1919–20
see MOLHUYSEN (P. C.) & P. J. B. Nieuw nederl. biograf. woordenboek, d5–7, 1921–27.
Blom (Eric). Stepchildren of music. s8°. [1925]
Blom (Frans), *see* TULANE UNIV. Tribes & temples: exped. to Middle Amer., 1925; by B. & La Farge, 2v, 1926–27.
Blöm (Walter).
Dreiklang des Krieges. Szenen aus d. Zeit. s8°. L. [1918]
Blome (Richard). A descr. of the island of Jamaica, w. o. isles &c. in America. [*Imperfect, title & 3 maps wanting*]. s8°. 1672
The gentlemans recreation. In 2p. The 1st being an encycl. of arts & sci.; the 2nd treats of horsemanship, hawking &c. fol. 1686
2p in 1v, each w. sep. tp. & pagin.
The present state of H.M. Isles &c. in America, w. new maps, astronom. tables from 1686–1700 &c. s8°. 1687
Blomefield (Francis).
Suppl. to B.'s Norfolk. [*By var. a.*] p1–4. sfol. [1926–27]
Blomefield (Leonard), *see* JENYNS (L.)
Blömers (Kurt). W. T. Mulvany (1806–85): e Beitr. z. Gesch. d. rhein.-westfäl. Grossindustrie u. d. deut.-engl. Wirtschaftsbezieh. im 19J. [Veröffentl. d. Archivs f. Rhein.-Westfäl. Wirtschaftsgesch., 8]. la8°. Essen. 1922
Blomfield (Charles James).
Sermons in St. Botolph, Bishopsgate. 8°. 1829
Blomfield (*Sir* Reginald). French archit. & its rel. to mod. pract. Zaharoff lect. [P2872]. 8°. O. 1927
Hist. of French architecture, 1661–1774. 2v. la8°. 1921
The tangled skein: art in Engl., 1800–1920. [Brit. Acad. H. Hertz trust]. [P2432]. 8°. [1920]
„ „ *For a. copy see* Brit. Acad. Proc., v9, 1919–20.
The touchstone of architecture. 8°. O. 1925
Blommaert (Samuel). Brieven aan A. Oxenstierna, 1635–41; Kernkamp, *see* HISTORISCH GENOOTS. Bijdragen, d29, 1908.
Blomquist (F. A.) Helga de La Brache: bidrag till svensk rätts-och samhällshist. s8°. 1877
Blondel (David) [*ps.* FLAVIAN AMAND]. Actes authent. des églises reformées de France, Germanie, Gr. Bret., Pologne, Hongrie, Païs Bas &c. s4°. Amsterdam. 1655
De jure plebis in regimine eccl., *see* GROTIUS (H.) De imperio summ. potestatum &c., 1677.
Extr. de l'examen de la Bulle du pape Innocent X contre la paix conclue à Munster 1648. Fait en Lat. par A. Flavien. [*In French. b. w. h.* Actes authent. des églises ref., 1655]. s4°. *n.p. n.d.* c. 1655
see DESMARETS (S.) Joanna Papissa restituta &c., ad D. Blondelii libr., 1658.
Blondel (Louis Augustin), *1696–c. 1760.* Memorie aneddot. s. corte di Sardegna; ed. V. Promis, *see* REGIA DEP. DI STORIA PATRIA. Misc., t13, 1871.
Blondel (Maurice), *see* PASCAL (B.) Et. sur P.; par M. B., &c., 1923.
Blondus (Flavius). [BIONDO DA FORLI]. Roma ristaurata, & Italia illust. Tr. L. Fauno. s8°. Venetia. 1543
Roma trionfante. Tr. pur hora per L. Fauno. s8°. [Venetia. 1544]
Blonina (Elena). Почему я стала защитницей Советской власти? [P2722]. s8°. Москва. 1919
Bloodgood (Ruth). Federal courts & the delinquent child, 1922, *see* UNITED STATES: LABOUR.
Bloom (James Harvey).
Bygone Balham & Tooting Bec. 8°. 1926
Bygone Streatham. 8°. 1926
Eng. tracts, pamphlets & pr. sheets. Bibliog. v1, 2. 8°. 1922–23
1, Early period (1473–1650) Suffolk.
2, Early period (1473–1650) Leicestershire, Staffordshire, Warwickshire & Worcestershire.
Shakespeare's church, Holy Trinity, Stratford-upon-Avon. 8°. 1902
Bloom (Ursula). Our lady of marble. 2nd ed. s8°. [1926]
Bloomfield (Leonard). Tagalog texts w. gramm. analysis. [Univ. of Illinois. St^s^. in lang. &c., v3ii–iv]. 3p. la8°. [Urbana]. 1917
Bloomfield (Maurice). The Atharvaveda. [Grundr. d. indo-ar. Phil., B2, H1, B]. la8°. Str. 1899
Bloomfield (Meyer). The new labour movement in Gt. Brit. Management & men (1920). [2nd impr.] 8°. *n.d.*
Bloomfield (Samuel Thomas), *see* BIBLE: NEW TEST.: GREEK. The Gk. T., w. Eng. notes by B., 4th ed., 2v, 1841; 5th ed., rev., 2v, 1843.
Blosius (Franciscus Ludovicus). Directeur des âmes relig., *see* BUCHON (J. A. C.) Choix d'ouvr. myst., 1840.
A mirror f. monks (Specul. monach.) Tr. 1676. Rev. & ed. by R. Hudleston, w. intr. [Works, 3]. s8°. 1926
Blossom (Frederick Augustus). La composition de Salammbô d'après la corr. de Flaubert (1857–62). [Elliott Monographs, 3]. 8°. Baltimore. 1914
Blossoms. *The blossoms of morality, 1806, *see* BERQUIN (A.)
***Blot** (The) on Parliament, 1923, *see* ARCANUM, *ps.*
Blot (Claude de Chouvigny [CHAUVIGNY], ***baron* DE),** *1605–55.* Chansons libertines. Préc. d'une notice & suiv. de couplets de s. amis: C. de Besançon, Condé &c. [Le libertinage au 17e s., t6]. la8°. 1919
Bloudoff (D. N.), *see* BLUDOV (*count* D. N.)
Blount (Bertram). Cement. By B., ass. by W. H. Woodcock & H. J. Gillett. 8°. 1920
Blount (Charles), *see* KING (J.) Mr. B.'s Oracles of reason, examined &c., 1698.
Blount (*Mrs.* George), *see* NORMAN (*Mrs.* G.), *ps.*
Blount (Godfrey). Science of symbols. s8°. 1905
Blount (Thomas). *Boscobel: or, hist. of H.M. preservation aft. the battle of Worcester, 1651. repr. s8°. 1832
Blount (*Sir* Thomas Pope), *bart.*
Censura celebr. authorum. fol. 1690
Blow. *Blow (A) at the root: Christ stabbed, 1762, *see* WESLEY (J.)
Bloy (Léon), *1846–1917.* La porte des humbles: pour faire suite Au seuil de l'Apocalypse, 1915–17. 6e éd. s8°. 1920
see MARTINEAU (R.) L. Bloy: souv. d'un ami, 1921.
Blücher (Evelyn, *princess*), *née E. Stapleton-Bretherton.* An English wife in Berlin. Mem. of events &c. in Germany throughout the War &c. 8°. 1920
„ „ ....3rd impr. 8°. 1920
„ „ ....7th impr. 8°. 1920
Bludov (*count* Dimitri Nikolaevich). *Les dern. heures de la vie de Nicolas I. Tr. du Russe. [P2603]. la8°. Vienne. 1855
Blue Guides, *see* MUIRHEAD (F.), *ed.*
Blue (Frederick Omar).
When a state goes dry. s8°. Westerville, Ohio. [1916]
Blum (André). Abraham Bosse & la société fr. au 17e siècle. Préf. de G. Hanotaux. [Archives de l'amateur]. 8°. [1924]
Un ms. inéd. du 13e siècle de la "Bible des pauvres," *see* ACAD. DES INSCRS. Fond. Piot. Mons. & mems., t28, 1925.
Les orig. de la gravure en France. Estampes sur bois & métal—Incunables xylograph. 4°. 1927
Blum (Edgar). La commise féodale. [*Extr. f.* Revue d'hist. du droit, t4]. [P2621]. 8°. Haarlem. 1922
Blum (Léon).
Au théâtre: réflexions crit. s4. s8°. [1911]
Blum (Oscar). Russische Köpfe. la8°. [1923]
Blumberg (Christian Gotthülff). Anti-sincerus evangelicus. Acc. dissert. anti-Bertiana de justitiæ Christi imput. prærogativa. s8°. Chemnitii. 1714
Veritas mysterii tiaræ Romani pontificis &c. Acc. N. Hausmanni & J. G. Dorschei epistolæ. s8°. Cygneæ. [1710]
Blumberg (*Gen. Sir* Herbert Edward). Britain's sea soldiers: record of the Royal Marines dur. the War, 1914–19. 4°. [*maps in case sep.*] Devonport. [1927]
Blume (Clemens), *see* ANALECTA HYMNICA MEDII ÆVI, ed. B., *in prog.*
Blume (Friedrich), *ed., see* COLLATIO. Lex Dei sive Mosaic. & Roman. legum coll., 1833.
Blume (Henricus Julius). De constit. episcop. Germaniæ. [P2587]. s4°. Helmaestadi. 1647
Blümel (Carl). Griech. Bildhauerarbeit. [Deut. Archäeolog. Inst. Jahrbuch, Ergänzungsh., 11]. la8°. 1927
Blumenthal (Hermann Friedrich Thomas). Vorgesch. d. Constanzer Concils bis z. Berufung. [P2725]. 8°. Halle a. S. 1897
Blumhardt (Christian Gottlieb). Hist. gén. de l'établ. du Christianisme. D'apres l'allemand de B. par A. Bost. 4t. 8°. Valence. 1838
Blumhardt (James Fuller), *see* INDIA OFFICE. Cat., v2iv, Suppl. 1906–20, Bengali bks. by J. F. B., 1923.
Blümlein (Carl). Bilder aus d. röm.-german. Kulturleben (nach Funden u. Denkmälern). Hrsg. C. B. la8°. München. 1918

Blumler (Martin Frederick). A hist. of amulets. Englished by S. H. [Coll. Adamantæa, 18]. 2v. [*in* 1]. 8°. *p.p.* E. 1887
Blümml (Emil Carl) & G. Gugitz.
Von Leuten u. Zeiten im alt. Wien. 8°. Wien. 1922
Blümner (Hugo). Fahrendes Volk im Altertum, *see* KÖNIGL. AKAD. D. WISS. ZU MÜNCHEN. Phil. Cl., Sitz., 1918.
Blundell (Herbert Joseph Weld-), *see* WELD-BLUNDELL (H. J.)
Blundell (Joseph Hight). Toddington: annals & people. Intr. by G. H. Fowler. la8°. Toddington, *Beds*. 1925
Blundell (Peter). The city of many waters. 8°. [1923]
Blundell (Peter), *founder of B.'s school, 1520–1601, see* SNELL (F. J.) Blundell's, 1928.
Blunden (Edmund).
Christ's Hospital: a retrospect. 8°. [1923]
On the poems of Henry Vaughan, w. princ. Latin p. tr. into Eng. verse by E. B. 8°. [1927]
[Poems. The Augustan Books of Modern Poetry]. 8°. [1925]
Shelley & Keats as they struck their contemporaries. Ed. E. B. 8°. 1925
The shepherd & o. poems of peace & war. 8°. 1922
see BRIDGES (R.) Dialectal words in E. B. poems, 1921.
Blunt (John Henry). The book of Church law. Pref. by Ld. Phillimore. Revised by G. E. Jones. 11th ed. corr. s8°. 1921
Blunt (Reginald).
By Chelsea Reach: some riverside records. 8°. [1921]
The wonderful village. Famous folk & places by Chelsea Reach. s8°. 1918
see MONTAGU (*Mrs.* E.) Mrs. E., h. letters &c., 1762–1800; ed. R. B., 2v, 1923.
Blunt (Wilfrid Scawen).
Mr. Blunt & the "Times." [P2718]. 8°. 1907
My diaries, 1888–1914. p2, 1900–1914. 8°. 1920
„ „ [repr., w. pref. by Lady Gregory]. 2p. 8°. [1921]
Poetical works. 2v. 8°. 1914
see LYTTON (*Hon.* N. S.) The Eng. country gentleman, *w. chap. on B.*, 1925.
Blüthen. *Blüthen d. Jesuiten-Moral &c., 1873, *see* JESUITS.
Blyth (Alex. Wynter) & M. W. Blyth. Poisons: th. effects & detection. 5th ed., rev., enl. & rewr. 8°. 1920
Blyth (Estelle). When we lived in Jerusalem. 8°. 1927
Blyth (Meredith Wynter), *see* BLYTH (A. W.) & M. W. B. Poisons: th. effects &c., 5th ed., 1920.
Blythe (Samuel George). Cutting it out. s8°. Chicago. 1912
Boaden (James). An inquiry into the authenticity of var. pictures & prints of Shakespeare. 8°. 1824
Boaistuau (Pierre) *called* LAUNAY. [BOISTEAU], *see* FISCHER (R.) Quellen zu Romeo u. Julia, 1922.
Board of Agriculture [MINISTRY OF A. & FISHERIES].
Brit. breeds of live stock. 3rd ed. 8°. 1920
Journal. v25–27. 8°. 1918–21
see LEATHAM (I.) Agric. of the E. Riding of Yorks &c., 1794.
„ RENNIE (G.), R. BROWN &c. Agric. of the W. Riding of Yorks &c., 1794.
„ TUKE (J.) Agric. of the N. Riding of Yorks &c., 1794.
Board of Education. Rep. of the Consultative Comm. on the education of the adolescent. 8°. 1926
see ENGLISH. Teaching of Eng. in England, 1921.
„ SELBY-BIGGE (*Sir* L. A.) B. of E., 1927.
„ WELSH in educ. & life, 1927.
Board of Trade, *see* COMMISSIONERS FOR TRADE & PLANTATIONS. Journal, 1704–22, 1920–25.
Boas (Andreas). Disput. de תרגומים. Resp. T. C. Raumerus. [P431]. s4°. [Francofurti? 1664]
Boas (Franz). Ethnology of the Kwakiutl, based on data coll. by G. Hunt, *see* SMITHSONIAN INSTIT., *Bureau of Ethn.* Rep. 35, 2p, 1921.
Handbook of Amer. Indian languages. p2, w. illust. sk^s. by E. Sapir, L. J. Frachtenberg & W. Bogoras. [S.I. Bureau of Amer. Ethnol., Bull. 40]. 8°. Wash. 1922
Boas (Frederick S.) Shakespeare & the universities & o. st. in Eliz. drama. 8°. O. 1923
see CHRISTMAS PRINCE (THE): acc. of the St. John's Coll. revels, 1607–8; prep. by F. S. B., 1922 [1923].
Boas (Johan Erik Vesti). *Works in* KONG. DAN. VID. SELSK. Biol. Med.
Das Gehörn v. Antilocapra, 1917–19. [1.]
Die verwandtschafts. Stellung d. Gattung *Lithodes*, 1923–25. [4.]
Zur Kenntnis d einsiedlerkrebses Paguropsis, 1926. [5.]
Zur Kenntnis symmetr. Paguriden, 1926. [5.]
Boase (Frederic). Mod. English biography; persons who have died since 1850, w. index.
v6. (Suppl. v3, L–Z). la8°. Truro. 1921

Boatto (Antonio). Le nuove rime con l'amoroso concetto del B. s8°. [Padua?]. 1540
Bobart (Henry Hodgkinson), *see* BASKETMAKERS' Co. Rec. of the B. C.; comp. by H. H. B., 1911.
Bobbio Missal (The): a Gallican mass-book (MS. Paris. Lat. 13246). Text; ed. E. A. Lowe. [Henry Bradshaw Soc., v58]. 8°. 1920
„ „ ......Notes & Studies: By A. Wilmart, E. A. Lowe & H. A. Wilson. [Henry Bradshaw Soc., v61]. 8°. 1924
Bobrovnikov (Aleksei Aleksandrovich). Грамоты вдовы Дармабаловой и Буянту-хана, *see* IMPERAT. RUSS. ARCH. OBSCH. Труды Восточ. отд., ч16, 1872.
Bocage (Pierre François) [TOUZÉ-BOCAGE], *see* GINISTY (P.) B. [Acteurs &c. d'autrefois], 1926.
Boccaccio (Giovanni).
Opere. [Ed. C. Zacclori, *i.e.* L. Ciccarelli]. s8°. Firenze. 1723–24
1, 2, Il Filocopo. 3, La Fiammetta—Il Corbaccio. 4, L'Ameto — Urbano — Orig., vita &c. d. Dante—Lettere. 5, 6, Comento s. la Commedia di Dante. *Each work has sep. tp. & pagin.*
DECAMERON.
Il D. Di nuovo riformato da L. Groto. [Dedic. *by* G. Sega. Vita *by* F. Sansovino]. 8°. Venetia, *Zoppini &c.* 1590
D. Corr. ed illust. con note dal dott. G. Ferrario. 4v. 8°. 1803
Il D. Riscont. co' migl. testi e annot. [Vita *by* F. Villani]. 2v. 8°. Milano. [1893 ?]
Il D. A cura di A. F. Massèra. [Scr. d'Italia, 97, 98] 2t. 8°. Bari. 1927
Libro d. donne illustri, tr. per G. Betussi. Con. una add. d. donne famose fino a i giorni nostri, con la vita del Boccaccio. s8°. Venetia. 1547
Il Philocopo infino a qui falsamente detto Philocolo diligẽtemẽte da Messer Tizzone Gætano di Pofi revisto. s8°. [Venegia. 1538]
TRANSLATIONS.
Contes. Illust. de J. Wagrez. Tr. & notes per F. Reynard. [Ed. artist. illust.] 3t. 8°. [1907]
TRANSLATIONS [*continued*].
The Decameron. Tr. 4v. s8°. 1906
Il Filostrato. Tr. H. Cummings. 8°. Princeton. 1924
Lydgate's Fall of princes. Ed. H. Bergen. [C.I. of Wash.] 4p [*pagin. of p1–3 cont.*] 8°. Wash. 1923–27
„ „ [*E.E.T.S., E.S.*, 121–4]. 4p [*pagin. of p1–3 cont.*] 8°. 1924–27
REFERENCES.
see CRESCINI (V.) Contrib. agli studi sul B. con doc. ined., 1887.
„ CROCE (B.) La novella di Andreuccio da Perugia, 1911.
„ DANTE ALIGHIERI. Lectura D., Fiammetta di G. B.; conf. da V. Crescini, 1913.
„ —— Lectura D.: G. B.: l' uomo e l'artista; conf. da G. Arcoleo, 1913.
„ GUERRI (D.) Il Commento del B. a Dante: sua autenticitá e quest. crit., 1926.
„ NICOLINI (F.) Lettera di G. B. a Fr. de 'Bardi, 1924.
„ *PEARL; ed., w. B.'s Olympia, by I. Gollancz, 1921.
„ RENIER (R.) La Vita nuova e La fiammetta: st. crit., 1879.
„ SCHOLFIELD (W. H.) Source &c. of the 7th novel in the 7th day of the D., 1893.
Boccius (Albertus Benedictus). Principii Aristotelici impossibile est idem simul esse & non esse & Cartesiani Cogito, ergo sum &c. collatio. Sub præs. G. P. Rötenbeccii &c. [P428]. s4°. Altdorffi. [1685]
Boccone (Paolo, *afterwards* **Silvio).** Recherches & obs. naturelles touch. le corail, la pierre étoilée, les pierres de figure de coquilles &c. [Tr.] s8°. Amsterdam. 1674
Bochart (Samuel). Hierozoicon, sive, de animalibus S. Scripturæ. Rec. suis notis adj. E. F. C. Rosenmüller. 3t. s4°. Lipsiæ. 1793–96
Bochorinck (Henricus), *see* BOXHORN (HENDRIK).
Bock (Ernst). Der Schwäbische Bund u. s. Verfassungen (1488–1534). 8°. Breslau. 1927
Bock (Friedrich Samuel).
Hist. Antitrinitariorum maxime Socinianismi & Socinianorum &c. 3t. 8°. Regiomonti. 1774–84
Bock (Hermann) & C. Weitzel. Der hist. Roman als Begleiter d. Weltgesch. s8°. L. [1921]
Böck (Josef). Zincography. Tr. E. Menken. s8°. [1885]
Böckel (Ernst Gottfried Adolf). Die Bekenntnissschr. d. evang.-reformirten Kirche. Hrsg. B. 8°. L. 1847
Bocken (Hendrick Jan). Goden en menschen. 8°. A. 1895
Böckh (H.), Z. Lázár *& others.* Mining & stone industry of Hungary. [P2519]. 8°. Budapest. 1920
Böckler (Albert. Die Regensburg-Prüfeninger Buchmalerei d. 12. u. 13 Jhdts, *see* MÜNCHEN. Miniaturen; hrsg. G. Leidinger, 1924.
Das Stuttgarter Passionale. fol. Augsburg. 1923
Böcklin (Arnold), *see* OSTINI (F., *baron* v.) B., [Knackfuss, 70], 7e A., 1921.
Böcler (Johann Heinrich). De lingua Nov. Test. orig. dissert., *see* OLEARIUS (J.) De stilo &c., 1731.

Bocop (Arent toe) [BOECOP]. Kronijk, *see* CODEX diplomat. Neerland., d5, 1860.

Bod (Peter).
A' Szent Bibliának historiája &c. s8°. Szebenben. 1748
Judiciaria fori eccl. praxis &c. s8°. Cibinii. [1757]

Bodart (Gaston). Losses of life in mod. wars: Austria-Hungary; France, by G. B., & Milit. selection & race deterioration, by V. L. Kellogg. Ed. H. Westergaard. [C. E. for Internat. Peace]. la8°. O. 1916

Bode (Adolph). Verbreitungs-Gränzen d. wicht. Holzgewächse d. Europ. Russlands, *see* BAER (C. E. v.) & GR. v. HELMERSEN. Beitr., B18, 1856.

Bode (Christoph August) [BODIUS]. Diss. inaug., de primæva linguæ Hebrææ antiq. &c. s8°. Halæ Magdeburgicæ. 1747
Evang. sec. Lucam ex vers. Persici interpret. in Lat. tr. &c. [P430]. s4°. Helmstadii. 1751
Evang. sec. Marcum ex vers. Persici interpret. in Lat. tr. &c. [P430]. s4°. Helmstadii. 1751

Bode (Wilhelm v.), *keeper of the Royal Museum, Berlin.*
Adriaen Brouwer, s. Leben u. Werke. la8°. 1924
Italien. Bildhauer d. Renaissance. 8°. 1887

Bode (Wilhelm F.), *Dr. Phil.* Weib u. Sittlichkeit in Goethes Leben u. Denken. s8°. 1916

Bodel (Jean), *poet.* Le jeu de Saint Nicolas. Ed. A. Jeanroy. [Classiques fr. du moyen âge, 48]. s8°. 1925

Bodel Nijenhuis (J. T.), *see* WILLIAMS (*Sir* R.) Memoriën, voorafgegaan door eene verhandeling over hem, door J. T. B. N., 1864.

Bodelsen (C. A.)
Studies in mid-Victorian imperialism. 8°. Kjøbenhavn. 1924

Bodenstedt (Friedrich M.) [*ps.* MIRZA-SCHAFFY].
Die Lieder d. Mirza-Schaffy. 26e A. s8°. 1869

Bodenstein (Andreas) [CAROLSTAD (A. Bo. v.)]
Antwort: geweicht wasser belangend: wider e. bruder Johan. Fritzhans. s4°. Vuittemberg. 1521
De legis litera sive carne, & spiritu A. B. enar. s4°. Wittembergæ. 1521
Dyalogus oder eyn Gesprechbüchlein. Von dem missprauch d. Sacraments J. C. s4°. *n.p.* [c. 1524]
Missive vonn der allerhochste tugent gelassenheyt. s4°. Wittenbergæ. [1520]
Predig oder homilien ü. d. prophetē Malachiam. s4°. Wittemberg [*Nichol. Schyr*]. 1522
Ayn schöner Sermonn v. Spalttung der gůtten v. bössen Engel. gaystern im himel. s4°. Strassburg. [c. 1524 ?]
Ein Sermon vom stand der Christglaubigen Seelen von Abrahams schoss u. Fegfeur der abgeschydnen Seelen. s4°. Wittemberg. [1523]
„ „ *a. ed.* s4°. *n.p.* [1523]
Ursachen das A. Carolstat ain zeyt still geschwigen. s4°. *n.p.* 1524
Von Bepstlicher heylickeit. [*a. c. in* P2539]. s4°. Vuittemberg. [1520]
Von geweychtem wasser u. saltz Doct. A. Carlstadt wider F. Seyler. [*a. c. in* P2539]. s4°. *n.p.* [Leipzig ?] [1520]
Von manigfeltigkeit des eynfeltigen eynigen willen gottes. was sundt sey. A. B. von C. eyn newer Ley. [*Decor. border to tp.* P2539]. s4°. *n.p.* 1523
Welche bucher Biblisch seint. s4°. Vuittembergk. [1520]
see DINCKEL (M.) Carolstadius redivivus, 1597.
„ ECK (J. VON). Disputatio I. E. & A. Carolostadij &c., 1519.
„ ERASMUS (D.) Contenta in hoc libello E.R. epist.—Conclusiões A. Carolostadii &c., 1519 ?.
„ LANGIUS (J.) Oratio: encomium disput. And. Carolstadii &c., 1519.

Boderianus (Guido Fabricius), *see* LE FÈVRE DE LA BODERIE (G.)

Bodham stone inscr. of r. of Trailokyamalla, A.D. 1056, *see* HYDERABAD Arch. Ser., No. 7, 1925.

Bodin (Charles).
Principes de science économique. 8°. 1926

Bodin (Jean), *political writer.*
De republica libri sex. Lat. ab autore redd. fol. Parisiis. 1586
The six bookes of a commonweale. Done into Eng. by R. Knollers. la8°. 1606
see CLUTEN (J.) Fasc. paradox. hist.-polit. ex J. B. lib. de republica coll., 1613.
„ FOURNOL (E.) B., prédécesseur de Montesquieu: ét. s. théories polit. de la République & de l'Esprit des lois, 1896.
„ HEARNSHAW (F. J. C.) B. & the genesis of doctrine of sovereignty, 1924.

Bodin (Richard Pierre-), *see* PIERRE-BODIN (R.)

Bodington (Oliver E.)
The Romance churches of France. 8°. 1925

Bodius (Robertus), *see* BOYD (R.)

Bodkin (Matthias McDonnell), *K.C.* Another considered judgment. 2nd rep. of Judge B. [P2529]. s8°. D. 1921

Bodkin (Thomas). The approach to painting. 8°. 1927
Four Irish landscape painters, G. Barret, J. A. O'Connor, W. F. Osborne, N. Hone. 8°. D. 1920

Bodleian Library. Cat. impress. librorum Bibl. Bodl. Curâ T. Hyde. fol. O. 1674
Exhib. of scient. MSS. &c. [Brit. Assoc. Oxf. meeting]. [P2876]. la8°. O. [1926]
Summary cat. of Western MSS. in the B. Lib. at Oxford, w. ref. to the Or. MSS. & papyri. By F. Madan & H. H. E. Craster. v2i, 6. 8°. O. 1922–24
see BIBLE: PSALMS. 2 E. Anglian Psalters at the B. L., Oxf.: Ormesby Ps., Bromholm Ps., 1926.
„ —— REVELATION. Apocalypse in Lat. & French (Bodleian MS. Douce 180); descr. by M. R. James, 1922.
„ CÆDMON. The C. MS.: Junius XI in B. L., 1927.
„ INDEX gen. libr. prohib.; in usum B. B. design. per T. James, 1627.
„ MADAN (F.) B. L. at Oxford, 1919.
„ —— R. Burton & the Anatomy of Melancholy, B.'s books in B. L. &c., 1926.
„ MARGOLIOUTH (D. S.) Arabic papyri of the B. L., 1893.
„ RUSSELL (C. W.) & J. P. PRENDERGAST. The Carte MSS. in B. Lib., 1871.
„ SHELLEY (P. B.) S. corr. in the B.; ed. R. H. Hill, 1926.

Bodley (R. V. C.) Algeria f. within. 8°. 1927

Bodley (*Sir* Thomas). Letters to Th. James, 1st keeper of the Bodleian Lib. Ed. w. intr. by G. W. Wheeler. la8°. O. 1926
Letters to the Univ. of Oxford, 1598–1611. Ed. G. W. Wheeler. 4°. *p.f.p.c.* O. 1927

Bodø. Bodø-saken: Brit. diplom. corresp. &c., 1926, *see* GATHORNE-HARDY (G. M.)

Bodoni (Giovanni Battista). Pel battesimo di Ludovico principe di Parma, iscrizioni esotiche &c. [P2605]. 4°. [Parma. 1774]
see BERTIERI (R.) L'arte di G. B.: con. notizia biog. a cura di G. Fumagalli, 1924.

Boeckel (Richard). Labor's money. s8°. N.Y. [1923]

Boecop (Arent toe), *see* BOCOP (A. TOE).

Boehm (Anthony William), *see* BÖHME (A. W.)

Boehm (Max Hildebert), *see* BÖHM (M. H.)

Boehme (Jacob), *see* BÖHME (J.)

Boehn (Max von), *see* BÖHN (M. v.)

Boellet (Nicolette), *see* COLETTE, *Saint.*

Boemicae. *Grammatica ling. B. &c., ed. 4a., 1739; ed. 5a, 1753, *see* JANDYT (V.)

Boemicum. *Alphabetum B., 1718, *see* ALPHABETUM.

Boener (Jan). Delineatio hist. Fratrum Minorum prov. Germaniæ Infer., a Geusiis occisorum.—Historische Afbeeldinghe der Minder-Broeders &c. [*Lat. & Dutch.*] s4°. Antverpiæ. 1635

Boer (C. de). Essais de syntaxe franç. mod. 8°. 1923

Boerio (Giuseppe). Diz. del dialetto venez. 2a ed., aum. e corr., agg. l'indice ital. veneto &c. 4°. Venezia. 1856

Boerschmann, *see* BÖRSCHMANN.

Boessière (*le marq.* de la), *see* LA BOESSIERE (*le marq.* DE).

Boethius, *v. Dacien* [BOETIUS *Dacus*], *see* GRABMANN (M.) Neu aufgef. Werke d. B. v. Dacien &c., 1924.

Boethius (Anicius Manlius Torquatus Severinus).
De consolatione philosophiæ libri 5. Quos rec. A. a Forti Scuto. Diss., app. &c. edendum curavit G. D. Smith. 8°. Londini. 1925

TRANSLATIONS.
Summum bonum, or an explic. of the divine goodness [*i.e.* the Consol. of phil.] in the words of B. Tr. by a lover of truth & virtue. s8°. O. 1674
Of the consol. of phil. 5 bks. Eng. by Richard Visct. Preston. s8°. 1695
Consol. of phil. Tr., w. notes by P. Ridpath. 8°. 1785
Consol. de la phil.; tr., *see* BUCHON (J. A. C.) Choix d'ouvr. myst., 1840.

TRANSLATIONS [*continued*].
De consol. phil. Tr. J. Walton. Ed. M. Science. [E.E.T.S., 170]. 8°. 1927
Theological tractates, w. Eng. tr. by H. F. Stewart & E. K. Rand. Consol. of phil., w. Eng. tr. of "I. T." (1609), rev. by H. F. Stewart. [Loeb Class. Lib.] [repr.] s8°. 1926
see BAUR (G.) De A. M. S. Boethio Xtnæ doct. assertore, 1861.
„ KLINGNER (F.) De B. Consol. phil., 1921.
„ THOMAS (A.) Notice sur le ms. lat. cont. une tr. franç. avec comm. par Maître Pierre de Paris, de la Consol. phil. de B., 1923.

Boetticher (Jacob Gottlieb Isaak), *see* BÖTTICHER (J. G. I.)

B-off (A.) *Mém. sur le mouv. communiste en Bulgarie, 1921–22, 1923, *see* BASCHMAKOFF (A.)

Bogan (Zachary), *see* ROUS (F.) Archæologia Atticæ libri 7 &c., w. add. of customes in marriages &c., by Z. B., 1671.

Bogart (Ernest Ludlow). Direct & indirect costs of the Gr. World War. [C. E. f. Internat. Peace]. 2nd (rev.) ed. la8°. N.Y. 1920
War costs & their financing. Intr. by R. C. Leffingwell. 8°. N.Y. 1921
— **& C. M. Thompson.** The industrial state 1870–93. [Cent. hist. of Illinois, v4]. 8°. Springfield. 1920

Bogatzky (Carl Heinrich v.) B.'s Lebenslauf, von ihm selbst beschrieben. 8°. Halle. 1801

Bogdan-Duică (Gheorghe). T. L. Maiorescu, *see* ACADEMIA ROM. Disc., 51, 1921.

Bogdanov (I. M.) Статистика и отчетность в школе. [P2698]. 8°. П. 1921

Bogdanov (Nikolai D.), *see* OLMINSKY (M.) О воспоминаниях Н. Д. Б., 1921.

Bogdanov (V. I.) Учительство и советская власть. [P2723]. 8°. Москва. 1919

Bogdanovich (Aleksandr Viktorovich). Три последних самодержца [1879–1912]. Дневник Б. [*Ed.* E. Vavilov]. 8°. Москва. 1924

Bogdanovich (Ippolit Fedorovich), *1743–1802.* Избранныя сочиненія. Изд. И. Глазунова. 8°. С.-П. 1907

Bogdanovich (Modest Ivanovich). *Исторія царствованія Имп. Александра I и Россіи въ его время. [*App. to each vol. w. sep. pagin.*] 6т. la8°. С.-П. 1869–71

Bogeng (Gustav Adolf Erich). Die grossen Bibliophilen. Gesch. d. Büchersammler u. ihrer Samml. 3B. la8°. L. 1922

Bogenhard (C. F.), *see* STICKEL (J. G.) & C. F. B. De morali primæv. Christ. cond., 1826.

Bogg (Edmund).
A thousand miles in Wharfedale. la8°. Leeds. [1892]

Bøggild (O. B.) On the labradorization of the feldspars, *see* KONG. DAN. VID. SELSK. Math.-fys. Medd., 6, 1924–25.

Boggis (Robert James Edmund).
A hist. of the diocese of Exeter. 8°. Exeter. 1922

Boghazköi. Keilschrifttexte aus Boghazköi. Autographien v. H. H. Figulla &c. [Deut. Orient-Gesell., Wiss. Veröffentl., 30, 36]. H1–6 *in* 2v. [H3 *in* 2 Hälfte]. fol. L. 1916–23

Bogino (Gian Lorenzo), P. Balbo & *conte* **di Perrone.** Lettere a G. Ferrari; pubbl. C. Negroni, *see* REGIA DEP. DI STORIA PATRIA. Misc., t21, 1883.

Bogitshevich (M.) Kriegsursachen, mit spez. Berücksicht. Russlands u. Serbiens. 8°. 1919

Bogler (Wilhelm). Hartmuth v. Kronberg. [Verein f. Ref.-gesch. Schr., Jhrg. 14, Nr. 57]. 8°. Halle. 1897

Bogolepov (A. A.), *see* BOLSCHEWISMUS. Staat, Recht u. Wirtschaft d. B., verfasst v. A. A. B. &c., 1925.

Bogolepov (D. P.) Деньги Советской России. [P2823]. 8°. Ленинград. 1924

Bogoras (Waldemar). Chukchee, *see* BOAS (F.) Hdbk. of Amer. Ind. lang., p2, 1922.

Bogoslovsky (Boris B.) The techn. of controversy. 8°. 1928

Bogoslovsky (Mikhail Mikhailovich). Изъ ист. верховной власти въ Россіи (16 & 17с.) [P2445]. 8°. Москва. 1905

Bogucharsky (Vasily Yakovl.) [*ps.* B. BAZILEVSKY].
Государств. преступленія въ Россіи въ xix в. Сборникъ. Составл. подъ редакціей Б. Б. t1, 2i. s8°. Stuttgart. 1903–4
„ „ t1–3 [*in 1v*]. (1, 1825–76; 2, 3, 1877). 8°. С.-П. 1906–*n.d.*
Литература Партіи Народной Воли (1879–85). s8°. Paris. 1905
„ „ 2B. *in 1v.* 8°. *n.p.* [1907]
Мат. для ист. революц. движенія въ Россіи въ 60хъ гг. [P2447]. 8°. С.-П. *n.d.*
Процессъ 20ти народовольцевъ въ 1882 г. Съ предисловіемъ В. Я. Б. [P2447]. 8°. Ростовъ на Дону. [1906]
Революц. журналистика 70хъ годовъ. [P2447]. 8°. *n.p. n.d.*
„ „ s8°. Paris. 1905

Bohar Library, *see* BÛHÂR LIBRARY.

Bohemen, *see* BÖHMEN.

Bohemi. *Protestatio Bohemorum od. d. aus voll. Prag. Reichs-Versammlung, 1415, an das Concil. nacher Costnitz abgefert. Hussitenbrieff &c. Hrsg. v. J. H. Löder. s4°. L. 1712

Bohemia [BOHEMICA; BÖHMEN; BOIEMIA; BEHEMEN].
*Aller drey evangel. Stãnd d. Cron Böhmen einhellige Glaubensbekantnuss &c. s8°. *n.p.* 1609
Antiqua & constans conf. fidei eccl. Christi in regno B. &c. [*Pref. by* M. Collinus]. s8°. *n.p.* 1574
Briève & fidèle expos. de l'orig. de la doct., des constit. &c. de l'Église de l'Unité des Frères, de Bohème & de Moravie &c. par un auteur impartial. Avec 16 planches. s4°. *n.p.* 1758
Catechismus d. Rechtgleubigen Behemischer Brüder, 1554, *repr.* [18 cent.], *see* CATECHISMUS.
Confessio Bohemica, hoc est, Conf. sanctæ & Christ. fidei, omnium 3 ord. regni B. E Bohem. idiom. Lat. donata. s4°. Francofurti. 1619

Bohemia [*continued*].
Confessio: das ist Bekentnis des Glaubens, dem König Ferdinando. Von d. Herren u. Ritterschafft d. Krō Behem, 1535. Verdeutscht, 1564. s8°. *n.p. n.d.*
Confessio fidei ac religionis baronum ac nobilium regni B. &c. s4°. [Witebergæ, *G. Rhaw.* 1535 ?]
„ „ Adject. quorundam virorum judicium. s8°. *n.p.* 1558
Confessio fidei & relig. Xtnæ quam regi Ferdinando, obtulerūt Viennæ in Austria a. 1535 Barones &c. in regno Bohemiæ &c. [Præf. M. Lutheri]. s8°. Basileæ. 1575
De bono unitatis & ordinis &c. eccl. B., 1660, *see* COMENIUS (J. A.)
Hist. persecutionum eccl. B., 894–1632. [*Pref. signed N. N. N.*] s8°. [Amsterdam]. 1648
Kirchengesänge darinnen die Hauptartickel &c. (Evangel. Kirchen in B. u. Mährern), 1606, *see* KIRCHENGESÄNGE.
*Relatio itineris Jesuitar. ex regnis B. & Ung., 1619, *see* JESUITS.
Topographie d. hist. u. Kunst-Denkmale im Königr. Böhmen v. d. Urzeit b. z. Anf. d. 19. Jhdt.'s Hrsg. v. d. Archæolog. Commiss. b. d. Böhm. Kais.-Franz-Josef-Akad. u. Leit. J. Hlávka. B1–6, 9, 10, 13, 15, 19, 27, 28, 30, 36, 37, 40 *&* Häuptstadt Prag: Hradschin, 2i, ii. la8°. Prag. 1897–1916
The following, with the exception of Prag, are "Polit. Bezirke."
Karolinenthal; Podlaha & Šittler, 1903. [15.]
Kolin; Mádl, 1898. [1.]
Königgrätz; Čechner, 1915. [19.]
Kralowitz; Podlaha, 1916. [37.]
Laun; Matějka, 1897. [2.]
Melnik; Podlaha, 1901. [6.]
Mies; Kamper & Wirth, 1911. [30.]
Mühlhausen; Podlaha & Šittler, 1901. [5.]
Nachod; Wirth, 1911. [36.]
Prag, II, Abt. 1, Domschatz &c.; Podlaha & Šittler, 1903.
Prag, II, Abt. 2, Bibl. d. Metrop. Kapit.; Podlaha, 1904.
Přibram; Podlaha, 1902. [13.]
Raudnitz, [T1]; Matějka, 1900. [4.]
Raudnitz, T2, Schloss; Dvořák & Matějka, 1910. [27.]
Rokytzan; Podlaha, 1901. [9.]
Sankt Joachimsthal; Schmidt, 1913. [40.]
Selčan; Podlaha & Šittler, 1899. [3.]
Weinberge; Podlaha, 1916. [28.]
Wittingau; Mareš & Sedláček, 1904. [10.]

Bohemian. Church constit. [Ratio disciplinæ] of B. & Moravian Brethren, 1864, *see* SEIFFERTH (B.), *ed.*

Bohemus (Eusebius), *see* PAPPUS (J.) Epitome hist. eccl. N.T.; recogn. & contin. studio E. B., 1626.

Boher (Pierre). Art of knowing one's self. Tr. by P. H[anbury]. 2p. *in* 1v. s8°. 1695–96

Bohigas Balaguer (P.) Los textos esp. y gallego-port. de la Demanda del Santo Grial. [Revista de filol. esp., anejo 7]. 8°. 1925

Böhlau (Helene) [*Frau* AL RASCHID BEY].
Das Haus zur Flamm. s8°. St. 1922

Bohlen (Peter von). De Buddhaismi orig. & ætate defin. tentamen. s8°. Regimontii Pruss. [1827]
Symbolæ ad interpret. S. Codicis ex lingua Persica. [P527]. 8°. Lipsiæ. 1822

Böhm (Gottfried v.) Ludwig II. König v. Bayern. Sein Leben u. s. Zeit. 8°. 1922

Böhm (Max Hildebert) [BOEHM]. Europa irredenta: e. Einführung in d. Nationalitätenproblem d. Gegenwart. 8°. 1923

Böhme (Anton Wilhelm) [BOEHM (A. W.)], *1673–1722, see* JACKSON (T.) Lib. of Xtn. biog., v8, A. W. B., by J. J. Rambach, tr. J. C. Jacobi, 1838.
see JACOBI (J. H.) Mem. of life & death of B., 1735.

Böhme (Christian Friedrich). Epistola Pauli ad Romanos Græce ex rec. Griesbachii cum comm. ed. B. 8°. Lipsiæ. 1806

Böhme (Franz Magnus). Altdeut. Liederbuch: Volkslieder aus d. 12.–17. Jhdt. [*w. music*]. 3.A. la8°. L. 1925

Böhme (Jacob).
Alle theosoph. Wercken &c. Nebst einem zweyfachen Register. [16p *in* 9v]. s8°. Amsterdam. 1682
The gen. tp. occurs in v1 only. The parts are not numbered & have titles of var. works.
Works. Intr. by a graduate of Glasgow Univ., v1, Epistles; tr. J. E[llistone]. 8°. Glasgow. 1886
Confessions. Comp. & ed. by W. S. Palmer. Intr. by E. Underhill. s8°. [1920]
De signatura rerum; das ist, Bezeichnung aller Dingen, wie das Innere vom Eusseren bezeichnet wird. 1622. s8°. 1635
Mysterium magnum, or, an expos. of the 1st Bk. of Moses called Genesis. Tr. J. Sparrow. Ed. C. J. B[arker]. 2v. [*pagin. cont.*] 8°. 1924
The way to Christ, 1622. Republ., w. mem. 8°. Canterbury. 1894
see *ALTE u. neue Zeugnisse v. Zustande d. Seelen &c. [*incl.* Boehmens gründl. Eröffnung], *n.d.*
„ CALO (J. A.) Hist. J. B., 1715.
„ —— Vita J. B., 1707.
„ MORE (H.) De J. Boehmio judicium &c., 1709.
„ OKELY (F.) Mem[s]. of Life, &c. & writings of J. B., 1780.
„ WILD (A.) Specimen sist. luem animarum Boehmisticam, 1705.

Böhmen, *see* BOHEMIA.

Böhmer (Georg Ludwig).
Principia juris Canonici. Ed. 6ª emend. s8°. Gottingæ. 1791
Böhmer (Heinrich), *Prof. an d. Univ. Bonn.*
Loyola u. d. deut. Mystik, *see* Kön.-Sächs. Ges. d. Wiss. zu Leipzig. Berichte, Philol.-hist. Cl., B73, 1921.
Luther im Lichte d. neueren Forschung. s8°. L. 1906
" " 5ᵉ verm. A. 8°. 1918
Luthers erste Vorlesung, *see* Königl.-Sächs. Gesell. d. Wiss. zu Leipzig. Berichte, B75, 1924.
see Liebermann (F.) Texte u. Forsch. z. engl. Kulturgesch; Festgabe für F. L. z. 20 Juli 1921, v. H. B., &c., 1921.
Böhmer (Justus Henning). Dissert. juris eccl. antiqui, ad Plinium sec. & Tertullianum &c. s8°. Lipsiæ. 1711
Instit. juris Canonici. 8°. Halæ Magdeb. 1738
Jus eccl. protestantium usum mod. juris canonici iuxta seriem libri 3 decretalium ostendens. s4°. Halæ. 1717
Jus parochiale ad fundamenta genuina revocatum &c. Ed. 3ª. auct. suppl. novo. [*b. w. h.* Jus eccl. protestantium, 1717]. s4°. Halæ Magdeb. 1721
Böhmisch-Mährischen Brüder. Kurze &c. Nachricht v. d. unter d. Namen d. Böhm.-Mähr. Brüder bekanten, Kirche Unitas Fratrum Herkommen &c., mit 16 Vorstellungen erl. s8°. *n.p.* 1757
Bohn (Henry Geo.) Catalogue of books. 8°. 1841
Bohn (John). Cat. of anc. & mod. theol. works in for. lang., on sale by J. B. 8°. 1842
Böhn (Max von).
Carl Spitzweg. [Knackfuss, 110]. la8°. L. 1921
Miniatures & silhouettes. Tr. E. K. Walker. 8°. 1926
Die Mode: Menschen u. Moden im Mittelalter. 8°. München. [1925]
Die Mode: Menschen u. Moden im 18. Jhdt. Nach Bildern &c. ausgewählt v. O. Fischel, Text v. B. 3. verb. Aufl. 8°. München. [1923]
Die Mode: Menschen u. Moden im 19. Jhdt. Nach Bildern &c. ausgewählt v. O. Fischel, Text v. B. 4B [B1, 3. Aufl.; B2, 5. verm. Aufl.; B3, 4. Aufl.] 8°. München. 1919–24
*Modes & manners of the 19th cent. as repr. in pictures &c. of the time. [Sel. by O. Fischel. Text by M. B.] Tr. M. Edwardes, w. intr. G. Rhys. 3v. 8°. 1909
Spanien: Gesch.-Kultur-Kunst. la8°. 1924
Bohomolec (Franciszck), *see* Stender-Petersen (Ad.) Die Schulkomödien d. Paters F. B., 1923.
Bohorizh (Adamus). Arcticæ horulæ succisivæ de Latino-carniolana literatura, ad Lat. ling. analogiam accommodata, unde Moshoviticæ, Rutenicæ, Polonicæ, Boëmicæ & Lusaticæ linguæ, cum Dalmatica & Croatica cognatio, facile deprehenditur. 2p. s8°. Witebergæ. 1584
Bohr (Niels). On the applic. of the quantum theory to atomic structure. Tr. L. F. Curtiss. p1, Fundamental postulates. [Camb. Phil. Soc. Proc. Suppl.] 8°. C. 1924
On the quantum theory of line-spectra, 3p, *see* Kong. Danske Vidensk. Selskab. Skrifter, Række 8, B4, 1918–22.
The theory of spectra & atomic constit. 3 essays. 8°. C. 1922
see Kramers (H. A.) & H. Holst. The atom & the B. theory of its structure; tr., 1923.
Bohun (Edmund). *The doctr. of non-resistance or pass. obedience no way concerned in controv. betw. Williamites & Jacobites. By a lay gentleman &c. [P527]. 8°. 1689
Boiardo (Matteo Maria), *conte di Scandiano.* Orlando innamorato. Comm. di G. Stiavelli. Illust. di L. Edel. fol. 1894
" " Riscontrato sul cod. trivulziano e su le prime stampe da F. Fòffano. [R. Comm. pe'testi di lingua n. Prov. dell' Emilia]. 3v. 8°. Bologna. 1906–7
see Edwards (E. W.) The Orlando Furioso & its predecessor, 1924.
" Panzini (A.) M. M. B., 1918.
" Reichenbach (G.) Un gent. poeta del quattrocento: M. M. B., p1, 1923.
Boiemia, *see* Bohemia.
Boigey (Maurice). The science of colours & the art of the painter. Tr. J. B. Hewitt. 8°. 1925
Boigne (Eléonore Adèle Le Borgne, *ctsse* **de).** Récits d'une tante; mém. [t]5. 8°. 1923
5, Fragm.—Corr. inéd.—Index gén.
Boi-Kot. Бой-Котъ. Пѣсни о четырехъ свободахъ. B1. [P2453]. 8°. 1906
Boileau (Ethel) [*Mrs.* Raymond Boileau].
Hippy Buchan. s8°. [1924]
Boileau (Jacques). *Remarques d'un théologien sur le Traité histor. de l'établ. &c. de l'Église de Rome & de ses évêques, composé par [L.] Maimbourg. s8°. Cologne. 1688
see Du Cerceau (J. A.) *Lettre à M. de L. C. P. D. B. sur Hist. Flagell. [*by J. B.*], *n.d.*
Boileau-Despréaux (Nicolas), *see* Clark (A. F. B.) B. & the French classical critics in England, 1925.
Boilet (Coletta), *see* Colette, *Saint.*
Boillot (Felix).
Impressions sensorielles chez La Fontaine. 8°. 1926
The method. study of literature. 8°. Paris. 1924
Boine (Giovanni), *see* Amoretti (G. V.) G. B. e la lett. ital. contemp., 1922.
Boinet (Amédée). Saint-Quentin. s8°. [1919]
Boinville (*Mrs.* **N. M. Chastel de),** *see* Chastel de Boinville (*Mrs.* N. M.)
Boirac (Emile). The psychology of the future. Tr. & ed. w. introd. by W. de Kerlor. 8°. [1920]
Bois (Henri), *see* Steed (H. W.) *&c.* Les démocraties mod.: par W. S., C. Bouglé, H. B. &c., 1921.
Bois (*Mr.* **Vieux)** *ps.* *Les amours de Mr. Vieux Bois. obl.8°. *n.d.*
Boisgelin de Cucé (*le card.* **Jean de Dieu Raimond de),** *see* Lavaquery (E.) Le Card. de B., 1732–1804, 2t, 1921.
Boislisle (Jean de), *see* Puisieux (R. B., *marq. de Sillery & de*). Les Suisses & le marq. de P.; notice hist. par J. de B., 1906.
Bois-Robert (François Le Metel de), *see* Le Metel de Bois-Robert (F.)
Boissard (Henry).
Discours: Peiresc. [Cour Imp. d'Aix]. 8°. Aix. 1867
Boissard (Maurice) *ps., see* Léautaud (Paul).
Boissardus (Joannes Jacobus). Bibliotheca chalcographica ill. virtute &c. virorum coll. J. J. B., sculptore Jan. Theod. de Bry primum ed., et ab ipsorum obitu hactenus cont. [*by* Seb. Furckius & Clem. Ammonius. 9p. in 1v.] s4°. Francofurti & Heidelbergæ. *n.d. &* 1650–54
p. 6–9 *have tp*ˢ. Continuatio prima[-quarta], 1650–54.
Boissier (Gaston). Nouv. promenades archéol.: Horace & Virgile. 5ᵉ éd. s8°. 1904
Boissonnade (Prosper).
Du nouveau sur la Chanson de Roland. 8°. 1923
Life & work in medieval Europe, 5th–15th cent. Tr., w. intr., by E. Power. 8°. 1927
Le travail dans l'Europe chrét. au moyen âge (5–15ᵉ s.) 8°. 1921
Boissonnas (Fréd.)
see Baud-Bovy (D.) L'Épire berceau des Grecs; 100 héliogr. by F. B., 1915.
" —— Berceau des Serbes; photographies de F. B., 1919.
" —— Cradle of the Servians; photographs of F. B., 1919.
" —— Salonique; héliogr. de F. B., 1919.
Boisteau (Pierre), *see* Boaistuau.
Boito (Camillo). La basilica di San Marco, illust. n. storia e arte da scrittori venez. sotto dir. di C. B. fol. Venezia. 1888–[1893]
Boix (Vicente). Crón. de la prov. de Alicante, 1868, *see* España. Crón. gen., v7, 1865 &c.
Crón. de la prov. de Valencia, 1867, *see* España. Crón. gen., v7, 1865 &c.
Bojani (F. de), *see* Innocent XI, *pope.* I. XI: sa corr. avec ses nonces, t3, 1680–84, p1, 1912–13.
Bojer (Johan).
Le caméléon. Tr. P. G. La Chesnais. s8°. [1921]
God & woman. s8°. [1921]
Life. [Tr. J. Muir]. s8°. 1922
Our Kingdom. s8°. [1920]
Verdens ansigt: roman. 8°. 1917
see Gad (C.) J. B., 1917.
Bojnev (B.) & K. Parchevsky, *edd.* Русская лирика. B1. [P2574]. s8°. Софія. 1920
Bojničič (Ivan v.) Adel v. Kroatien u. Slavonien; v. I. v. B., *see* Sibmacher (J.), *ed.* Wappenbuch, Bxiii, 1899.
Bok (Edward William). Autobiography. With an intr. by Visct. Northcliffe. 8°. [1921]
Bokelmann (Julius Christian) [†Bokelman (J. C.)] Bibl. Agendorum, bestehend aus e. Catalogo derer Kirchen-Ordnungen &c. welche C. J. B. gesammelt. Ausgefertigt v. H. C. König. s4°. Zelle. 1726
Boladeres Ibern (Guillermo de). Enrique Granados: vida y est. crít. s8°. Barcelona. [1921]
Bolas (Bernard D.)
Handbook of laboratory glass-blowing. s8°. 1921
Bolchevik [Bolcheviki] (*see also* Bolsheviki &c). Code b. du mariage, 2ᵉ éd., 1920, *see* Russia: Soviet Republic.
Programme du parti social-démocrate ouvrier de Russie (Bolcheviki). [P2392]. s8°. *n.p. n.d.*
Bolchevisme. Le Bolchevisme & l'Islam. [Revue du monde musulman, t51, 52]. 2[t]. la8°. [1922]
1, Les organis. soviét. de la Russie musul.; par J. Castagné.
2, Hors de Russie [*By var. wr.*]

Bolchéviste. Docs. secrets de la propagande b.; publ. L. S., 1920, *see* SZABÓ (L.)

Bölcke (Wilhelm).
Deutschlands neue Wehrmacht. [P2409]. 8º. [1919]

Bolckow (H. W. F.) Cat. of MSS. by or rel. to Capt. James Cook, the prop. of B. Sold by Sotheby, 21 March 1923. [P2853]. la8º. 1923

Boldrewood (Rolf), *ps.* [*i.e.* TH. ALEX. BROWNE].
Robbery under arms. s8º. 1920
„ „ ....[repr.] s8º. 1922

Boldrin (Gustavo), *ed.* Due scritture sul commercio venez. in Egitto [Giustinian (G. A.) Terminazione per il Cairo—Relazione dei baili e dei cinque savj &c., 1773. Nozze Bisacco-Palazzi, N. 134]. 8º. [Venezia. 1872]

Bolduanus (Paulus). Bibl. theologica sive elenchus script. eccl. &c. usque in a. 1614. s4º. Jenæ. 1614

Boldur (Alexandre). La Bessarabie & les relations russo-roumaines. 8º. 1927

Bolechow, Ber *of*, *see* BER, *of Bolechow.*

Bolin (Iwan). Kemien & prakt. livet. 1, Oorgan. Kemi. 3. Uppl. s8º. [1924]

Bolingbroke (Henry Saint-John, *viscount***),** *see* CLAYTON (R.), *bp.* Vindic. of hist. of O. & N. Test. in ans. to B., 1752.
see HERVEY (J.) Remarks on B.'s Letters on the study &c. of hist., 1752.

Bolitho (William). Murder for profit. 8º. [1926]

Bolivar (Simon), *1783–1830, pres. of the Republic of Colombia.* Cartas de Bolivar, 1823–25. Con un apéndice que cont. cartas, 1801–22. Notas de R. Blanco-Fombona. 8º. 1921
see †O'LEARY (*Gen.* D. F.) B. y la emancip. de Sur-América &c., t1, 2, 1915.

Boll (Franz). Antike Beobacht. farbiger Sterne, mit Beitr. v. C. Bezold, 1916, *see* KÖNIGL. AKAD. D. W. ZU MÜNCHEN, Abhdlgn., B30, 1920.
see ALTERTUM (Vom) zur Gegenwart; Kulturzusammenhänge in d. Hauptepochen &c.; Skizzen v. F. B., U. Curtius &c., 1919.

Bolland (William Craddock). Chief Justice Sir W. Bereford. Lect. Intr. by Sir H. Duke. s8º. C. 1924
The General eyre. Lectures, Univ. of London. Intr. by H. D. Hazeltine. s8º. C. 1922
Manual of year-book studies. 8º. C. 1925
The Year Books. Lect. Intr. by Sir F. Pollock. s8º. C. 1921
see SELDEN SOCIETY. Year Books of Edward II, v16–18 (1313–15); ed. W. C. B., 1920–25.

Bollati di Saint-Pierre (Fed. Emmanuele). *Works in* REGIA DEP. DI STORIA PATRIA. Misc.
Di un ined. doc. sulla Tregua di Dio, 1879. [18.]
Documenti ined. s. casa di Savoia, 1884. [22.]
Frammento (Articuli &c. super substractione Benedicti xiij), 1882. [20.]

Bollea (Luigi Cesare). Assedio di Bricherasio dato da Carlo Eman. duca di Savoia, 1594, *see* REGIA DEPUT. Miscellanea, t43, 1907.

Bolles (Albert S.) Chapters in polit. economy. s8º. N.Y. 1874

Bollettino d'arte del Min. d. P. Istruzione. Notizie d. gallerie, dei musei &c. 1907–20 (Anno 1–14). sfol. 1907–20
Annos 8–14 *have Suppl. w.t.* Cronaca d. belle arti, *sep. pagin.*, *b. w.* Boll. *for same year.*

Bolleville (*le prieur de*) *ps.*, *see* †SIMON (R.) [SIMONVILLE].

Bollig (P. Laurentius). Die Bewohner d. Truk-Inseln. [Anthropos, B3, H1]. 8º. Münster i. W. 1927

Bolman (Theodor). De tumba Servatoris. Præs. J. A. Schmidio. [P432]. s4º. Helmstadii. 1727

Bolney. Parish registers of B., 1541–1812. Ed. E. Huth. [Sussez Rec. Soc., v15]. 8º. 1912

Bologna. Cat. d. biblioteca d. Liceo Music. Comp. da G. Gaspari. Comp. e pubbl. da F. Parisini [*&* L. Torchi]. 3v. la8º. Bologna. 1890–93
Rotuli dei lettori legisti e artisti d. Studio bolognese, 1384–1799; pubbl. dal Dr. U. Dallari. 3v. [*v3 in 2p., b. together, w. sep. tp. & pagin.*] fol. Bologna. 1888–1919
Studi e memorie per la storia dell' Univ. di B. [Comm. per la storia dell' Univ. di B., Bibl. "L'Archiginnasio," s1, v4–7]. v4–7. 8º. Bologna. 1920–22
see MALAGUZZI VALERI (F.) I migliori dipinti d. R. Pinacoteca di B., 1919.

Bolron (Robert). The papists' bloody oath of secrecy &c. for the carrying on of this present plot. [P525]. sfol. 1680

Bölsche (Wilhelm), *see* SCHEFFLER (J.) Cherubin. Wandersmann, mit St. ü. Wert d. Mystik f. uns. Zeit, v. W. B., 1921.

Bolschewismus.
Sammlung v. Quellen z. St. d. B. H1–4 [*b. in* 1v]. 8º. 1919–20
1, Führer durch d. bolsch. u. antibolsch. Literatur.
2, Die Agrargesetzgebung d. Sowetrepublik.
3, Die Organis. d. Volkswirtschaft in Sowetrussland.
4, Die Propaganda-Schulen d. B.; v. H. Fenner.
Der Staat, d. Recht u. d. Wirtschaft d. B. Verfasst v. A. A. Bogolepoff &c. Hrsg. im Auftr. d. Internat. Verein. f. Rechts-u. Wirtschaftsphil. v. F. v. Wiese &c. 8º. 1925

Bolshaya. Б. Совет. энциклоп., 1926 &c., *see* ENCYCLOPÆDIA.

Bolsheviki. Большевики въ Царицынѣ, *see* RUSSIA: SOVIET REP. Особая ком., в3, 1919.

***Bolshevism** in Russia. Extr. f. Reps. to Brit. For. Office. [P2484]. 8º. [1919]

***Bolshevists** (The) of ancient hist. [By "Apionus"]. 8º. [1924]

Bolte (Johannes). Drei Schauspiele vom sterbenden Menschen. Hrsg. J. B. [Lit. V. in St. 269/270]. 8º. L. 1927
Das Münchner Spiel v. 1510; Macropedius, Hecastus, 1539; Naogeorgus, Mercator, 1540.

Bolton (Arthur Thomas).
Archit. & decor. of R. Adam & Sir J. Soane (1758–1837). [P2740]. la8º. 1920
Archit. educ. a cent. ago: office of Sir J. Soane, w. spec. ref. to G. Basevi. [Soane Mus. Publ., No. 12. P2751]. 4º. [1924]
The architecture of Robert & James Adam (1758–94). 2v. fol. 1922
Eng. 18th cent. sculptures in Sir J. Soane's museum. [Soane Mus. Publ., No. 7. P2740]. la8º. *n.d.*
Life & work a cent. ago: Sir J. Soane. [Soane Mus. Publ., No. 11. P2751]. 4º. [1923]
see SOANE (*Sir* J.) Descr. of house & museum, residence of Sir J. S.; ed. f. orig. "Descr." by A. T. B., 10th ed., 1920.
„ —— Works [ed. A. T. B.], 1924.

Bolton (Charles Knowles). The Founders. Portraits of persons born abroad who came to the colonies of N. Amer. before 1701. Intr., biog. outlines &c. by C. K. B. [Boston Athenæum: Billings Fund]. v3. 8º. [Boston, Mass.] 1926
see BOSTON ATHENÆUM. Influence &c. of the B. A., 1807–1907 &c.; [by B. Wendell & C. K. B.], 1907.

Bolton (Edward Richards) & R. G. Pelly. Oils, fats, waxes & resins. Intr. by Sir E. Geddes & J. N. Batty. [Resources of the Empire, v9]. 4º. 1924

Bolton (Herbert Eugene), *Ph.D.* Guide to materials for the hist. of the U.S. in princ. archives of Mexico. [C. I. of Wash. Publ. 163]. la8º. Wash. 1913
The Spanish borderlands. Old Florida & the S.W. [Chron. of Amer. ser., v23]. 8º. New Haven, *Yale.* 1921

—— & T. H. Marshall.
The coloniz. of N. America, 1492–1783. 8º. N.Y. 1920

Bolton (Lyndon). Intr. to the theory of relativity. s8º. [1921]
Time measurement. 8º. 1924

Bolton (Robert), *Puritan Divine.* A cordiall for Christians in affliction, a sermon publ. by I. S. [*b. w. h.* Foure last things &c., 1639]. s4º. 1640
General directions for a comfortable walking w. God. s8º. 1837
Mr. B.'s worke of the Foure last things, death, judgment, hell & heaven w. h. Assise-sermons & notes on Justice Nicoll's his funerall. With life &c. of the a. Added sermon at B.'s funerall by Nic. Estwick. [*w. sep. tp. & pagin.*] 4th ed. s4º. 1639

Bolton (Samuel), *D.D.* The true bounds of Christian freedome. Annexed a disc. of John Cameron's, t. the threefold covenant. s8º. 1645

Bolton (Theodore). Early Amer. portrait painters in miniature. 8º. N.Y. 1921

Bolts (William), *see* HALLWARD (N. L.) W. B., a Dutch adventurer under John Co., 1920.

Boltwood (Lucius M.) Genealogies of Hadley families, *see* JUDD (S.) Hist. of Hadley &c., 1905.

Boltz (August). Beiträge z. Völkerkunde aus Wort u. Lied. 8º. Oppenheim a. Rh. 1868

Bolufer (José Alemany), *see* ALEMANY BOLUFER (J.)

Bolwell (Robert George Whitney). The life & works of John Heywood. [Columbia Univ. St. in Eng. &c. lit.] 8º. N.Y. 1921

Bolza (Giorgio). Turati. Con presentaz. di F. Bonavita & app. di A. G. Bianchi. la8º. Milano. 1919

Bolza (Giovanni Battista).
Vocab. genetico-etimolog. d. lingua ital. la8º. Vienna. 1852

Bolza (Oskar). Gauss u. d. Variationsrechung, *see* GAUSS (C. F.) Werke, B10ii, Abh. 5, 1922.

Bolzano (Bernard). Athanasia, oder Gründe f. d. Unsterblichkeit d. Seele. 2e. A. 8º. Sulzbach. 1838

Bomann (Wilhelm). Bäuerl. Hauswesen u. Tagewerk im alt. Niedersachsen. la8º. Weimar. 1927

Bombaci (*il conte* **Gasparo).** L'araldo, overo dell' arme d. famiglie. 8º. Bologna. 1651

Bombay. The Bombay Code.
4th ed. 5v. [*&* Index, *b. sep.*] la8º. Calcutta. 1924–25
Census, 1921, *see* INDIA: CENSUS.
Hist. of services of gazetted officers in Civil Dept. Corr. up to 1 July 1921. fol. Bombay. 1922
Hist. of services, B. Presidency. Corr. to 1 July 1922–27. *Each year in 7p.* fol. Bombay. 1922–27
ARCHAEOLOGICAL SURVEY OF INDIA.
Progress report of the A. S. of I., W. Circle for year ending 31st March 1919–21. fol. Bombay *&* Calcutta. 1920–22
SELECTIONS FROM THE RECORDS OF THE B. GOVT.
Hist. & o. inform. conn. w. prov. of Oman, Muskat, Bahrein, & o. places in the Persian Gulf. [Prep. by R. Taylor, F. Warden &c.] Comp. & ed. by R. H. Thomas. [N.S. 24]. la8º. Bombay. 1856
Memoirs by Comm. J. F. Jones, *see* JONES (J. F.)
Survey Settlement [Papers rel. to]. N.S., 531, 557i, ii, 558, 559, 561, 562, 564, 566, 567, 569, 570, 573, 575, 577, 593. fol. Bombay. 1916–22
C.=Collectorate. D.=District. T.=Táluka.
Revision Survey Settlement.
Poona C. Sirur T. [558.]
Ratnagiri C., Sangameshwar T. [559.]
2nd Revision Survey Settlement.
Ahmednagar C., Parner T. [567.]
„ „ Nagar T. [575.]
„ „ Shevgaon T. incl. Pathardi Mahal. [569.]
Ahmednagar D., Akola T. [573.]
Belgaum C., Chikodi & Hukeri T. [557.]
„ „ Godak T. [563.]
Bijapur C., Bagalkot T. incl. Bilgi Peta. [564.]
„ „ Hungund T. [566.]
East Kha'ndesh D., Jalgaon T. [593.]
„ „ „ Raver T. [570.]
„ „ „ Yawal T. [562.]
Nasik D., Igatpuri, Dindori, Nasik, Niphad, Sinnar, Chandor, Yeola & Nandgaon T, 3v. [531.]
Poona D., Haveli T. [577.]
„ „ Junnar T. [561.]
„ „ Sirur T. [558.]
see PLAYFAIR (*Sir* R. L.) A hist. of Arabia Felix or Yemen, 1859. [N.S., 49].

Bombinus (Paulus).
Vita & martyrium Edmundi Campiani. s8º. Antverpiæ. 1618
„ „ ....[*a. ed.*] s8º. Mantuæ. 1620

Bomelius (Henricus) [HENDRIK VAN BOMMEL]. Bellum Trajectinum. [Ed. B. J. L. de Geer. Hist. Genoots. Werken, N.S., 28]. 8º. Utrecht. 1878

Bömer (Aloys), *ed., see* GRATIUS (ORTWINUS). Epistolæ obscurorum virorum; [Einl. von A. B.], 1924.

Bömlerus (Marcus), *see* HOLDER (W.) Asinus avis: metamorph. nova qua M. B. in asinum commut. est, 1587.

Bommel (Hendrik van), *see* BOMELIUS (H.)

Bona (*card.* **Joannes).** De sacrificio Missæ tract. asceticus &c., *see* MIGNE (J. P.), *ed.* Theol. cursus, t23, 1860.
Epistolæ selectæ aliæque eruditorum sui temp. virorum ad eumdem scriptæ. Collegit &c. D. R. Sala. [De vita J. B. enarr. a P. I. Tardito. *b. w. h.* Rer. liturg. t3, 1753]. fol. Augustæ Taurin. 1755
Princ. de la vie chrét.; tr., *see* BUCHON (J. A. C.) Choix d'ouvr. myst., 1840.
Rerum liturgic. libri 2. 3t. fol. Augustæ Taurin. 1747–53

Bonade (François) [BONADUS (F.)] Eximii prophet. antistitis regia Davidis oracula per F. B. numeris poëticis exarata. s8º. Parisiis. 1531

Bonafous (Norbert Alexandre).
Etudes sur l'Astrée & sur Honoré d'Urfé. 8º. 1846

Bonamy (Pierre Nicolas). Mém. sur les dern. années de Jacques Coeur, *see* BUCHON (J. A. C.) Choix de chron. &c., 1875.

Bonaparte, *The family of, see* SFORZA (G.) Gli antenati di Napoleone I in Lunigiana, 1915.

Bonaparte (Charles J. L. Lucien), *prince de Canino.*
see WILSON (A.) & C. L. B. Amer. ornithology, 3v, 1832.

Bonar (Andrew Alex.) Memoir & remains of Rev. R. M. M'Cheyne. n. ed. w. app. &c. 8º. E. 1892
—— & R. M. MacCheyne.
Narr. of a mission of inquiry to the Jews f. the Church of Scot. in 1839. s8º. E. 1843

Bonar (Horatius).
Catechisms of the Scot. Reformation. Ed. H. B. s8º. 1866
Hymns of faith & hope. New ed. 8º. 1876

Bonar (James).
Malthus & h. work. [2nd ed.] 8º. [1924]

Bonar (John), *of Perth.* *An analysis of the moral & relig. sentiments cont. in the writings of Sopho & D. Hume. [*wrongly attrib. to G. Anderson. b. w.* Kames (H. H.) Essays &c., 1751]. 8º. E. 1755

Bonati (Teodoro). Piano del Collega Guglielmini int. ai fiumi infer. &c. con riflessioni [*di B.*] [*Ed.* Cerutti. Nozze Baruchello-Turazza. N127]. 8º. Padova. 1866

Bonaventura, *Saint, cardinal, bp. of Albano.*
Opera emendata & aucta. [Cum præf. Constantii card. Sarnani]. 7t [t3 *wanting*]. fol. Romæ. 1588–96
[Auctoritates utriusque Testamenti.] *f1ª*, [P]Recepit dñs Ade dicẽs ex oñi ligno ꝑadisi comedes Gen. ii. &c. *Ends f47ª*. Expliciunt auctorites vtriusq. testamẽti]. sfol. *n.p.* [Strassburg, *Heinr. Eggestein. n.d.* [c. 1472] *48ff. a–d in tens, e1–8. last f. blank.*
B. de preparatione ad missam, *see* AUGUSTINE, *Saint.* Manuale &c., 1506.
Dieta salutis a beato B. ultimate emend. ac parisius noviter impressum. [*Foll. by* Meditatio. de nativitate domini. Tractatus de resurrectione. *b. w.* Anima fidelis, 1501]. s8º. Parisiis [*Pierre Dru.*] 1500 *116 numbered leaves & unnumbered 36.*
Privity of the Passion; tr. &c. G. E. Hodgson, *see* ROLLE (R.) *of Hampole.* Some minor works, 1923.
see ANTONIO MARIA *da Vicenza* & JOANNES *a Rubino.* Lexicon Bonavent., 1880.
„ CLOP (E.) St. B., 1221–74, 1922.
„ DEANESLY (M.) Gospel harmony of John de Caulibus, or S. B., 1922.
„ GILSON (E.) La philos. de St. B., 1924.
„ LUYCKX (B. A.) Erkenntnislehre B.'s, 1923.
„ ROSENMÖLLER (B.) Relig. Erkenntnis nach B., 1925.

Bonaveri (Gian Francesco). Della città di Comachio &c. Ampliata dal dott. P. Proli. fol. Cesena. 1761

Bonbright (James Cummings). Railroad capitalization. [Columbia Univ. Stud. in Hist. &c., 95, i]. 8º. N.Y. 1920

Bonciarius (Marcus Antonius), *the elder* [BONCIARIO]. Lettere scr. a B. [1597–1614. Ed. Conte O. Angaran-Porto. Nozze Nani-Mocenigo—Gradenigo. N124]. 8º. Venezia. 1839

Boncompagni (Carlo).
La chiesa e lo stato in Italia. s8º. Firenze. 1866
see FONTANA (L.) Commem. del Conte C. B.-C., 1882.

Boncour (Joseph Paul-), *see* PAUL-BONCOUR (J.)

Boncquet (Henri), *see* PIERRON (S.) H. B., 1909.

Bond (Frederick Bligh). The company of Avalon: st. of script of Brother Symon, sub-prior of Winchester Abbey. 8º. 1924
The Glastonbury scripts, 2–9. [*b. in* 1v.] 8º. 1923–25
The hill of vision. Forecast of the Gt. War &c. f. automatic writings, 1909–18, of J. Alleyne. 8º. 1919
see LEA (T. S.) & F. B. B. Materials for st. of the apostolic gnosis, p1, 2, 1919–1922.
—— & T. S. Lea, *D.D.* A prelim. investig. of the Cabala cont. in the Coptic Gnostic books & of a similar gematria in the Greek text of the New Test. 8º. O. 1917

Bond (Richard Warwick). Art of narrative-poetry, *see* ROY. SOC. OF LIT. Essays, N.S., v4, 1924.

Bond (Thomas E.), *sen., M.D.* The economy of Methodism illust. &c. 8º. N.Y. 1852

Bond (W. G.) Wanderings of Charles I & h. army in the Midlands, 1642–45. s8º. B'ham. 1927

Bondar (D.) B.'s simplified Russian method. Ass. by A. Calvert. 8º. 1915

Bonde (Christer), *see* LAACHE (R.) Friherre C. B. om Cromwell, 1655–56, 1924.

Bondelmont (Christophe), *see* BUONDELMONTI.

Bondi (Clemente).
Giornata villereccia: poemetto. s8º. Parma. 1794

Bondy (François de). Adalbert orateur, nouvelle, *see* ŒUVRES (Les) libres, 21, 1923.
Framboise Pépin & s. environs. s8º. 1923

Bondy (William). The separation of gov. powers in hist., theory &c. [Columbia Univ. St. in Hist. &c., v5, No. 2]. 8º. N.Y. 1896

Bone (David William). The brassbounder. [2nd impr.] 8º. 1910

Bone (James).
Edinburgh revisited. Drawings by H. Fletcher. 4º. 1911
The London perambulator: w. pictures by Muirhead Bone. la8º. [1925]
The perambulator in Edinburgh. [Enl. ed. of E. revisited]. Pictures by E. S. Lumsden. s4º. [1926]

Bone (Muirhead).
War drawings. [ed. de luxe]. 6p. *in* 1v. lafol. 1917–18

Boner (Charles).
Chamois hunting in the m^s. of Bavaria. 8°. 1853
" " ....n. ed. 8°. 1860

Bonfadius (Jacobus).
[Opere volg. e lat. 2p.] 8°. Brescia. 1746–47
1, Lettere famigl., componimenti e Vita, scr. d. c. G. M. Mazzuchelli.
2, Annalium Genuensium libri 5; cura A. Sambuca.

Bonfils (Henri), *see* Fauchille (P.) Traité de droit internat. public; 8e éd. refondue &c. du Manuel de B., t2, 1921.

Bonfinius (Antonius). Rerum Ungaric. decades quatuor cum dimidia. Acc. J. Sambuci appendices. Tertium rec. &c. per J. Sambucum. fol. Hanoviæ. 1606

Bonghi (Ruggero). Leone XIII e l'Italia. Seg. d. testo d. Tre pastorali, le sue poesie latine &c. s8°. Milano. 1878

Bongi (Salvatore). Bandi lucchesi del sec. 14. tratti d. reg. d. R. Arch. di Stato in Lucca. [Coll. di opere ined. &c., R. Comm. pe' Testi di Lingua &c.] 8°. Bologna. 1863

Bonham (Milledge Louis), *Jr.* Robert R. Livingston, *see* Bemis (S. F.), *ed.* Amer. Secr. of State, v1, 1927.

Bonhoffer (Johann Friedrich). Diss. de genuino conjugiorum prohibit. fundamento. Præs. G. G. Zeltnero. [P428]. s4°. Altorfii Noric. [1717]

Bonhomus (Johannes Franciscus) [Bonomi (G. F.), *bp. of Vercelli*], *see* Colombo (G.) Not. e doc. s. vita di B., 1879.

Boni (Giacomo).
Arse verse. [P2840]. 8°. 1920
The Niger Lapis in the Comitium at Rome. Pref. & tr. by St. C. Baddeley. [Fr. Archæologia, v57. P2508]. 4°. 1900
Santa Maria dei Miracoli in Venezia. [P2836]. 8°. Venezia. 1887
La torre di S. Marco. [*Estr. d.* Atti d. Congr. internaz. di sc. stor., 1903, v. 5. P2840]. 8°. 1904
Trajan's column, 1907, *see* Brit. Acad. Proc., 1907–8.
Vecchie mura. [*Estr. d.* Ateneo Veneto, 1885. P2840]. 8°. Venezia. 1885

—— **& L. Mariani.** Rel. int. al consolid. &c. dell' Arco di M. Aurelio in Tripoli, *see* Italy: Min. delle Colonie. Not. arch., Anno 1, 1915.

Boni (Mauro). *Lettere sui primi libri a stampa dell' Italia superiore. la8°. Venezia. 1794

Boniface VIII, *pope.* Acta inter B. VIII, Benedictum XI, Clementem V et Philippum Pulc. regem. Tractatus de potestate PP. scr. c. 1300. s8°. 1614
see Decretales. Sextus d. liber per B. VIII ed., 1569.
" Del Lungo (I.) I Bianchi e i Neri, 1921.
" Scholz (R.) Die Publizistik z. Zeit Philipps d. Schönen u. B.'s, 1903.

Boniface, *Saint, bp. of Ferento in Etruria, see* Assemanus (J. S.) De B. ac Redempto, diss., 1745.

Boniface, *Saint, abp. of Mainz, apostle of Germany.*
Briefe d heil. B. u. Lullus [*Latin*]. Hrsg. v. M Tangl. [M. G. H. Epist. sel., 1]. 8°. 1916
Vitæ S. Bonifatii [auctore Willibaldo, Otloho &c.] Rec. W. Levison. [Scr. rerum Germ. in usum schol.] 8°. Hannoveræ. 1905
see Guden (H. P.) Diss. de B., 1720.
see Hanisch (G. D.) Diss. de propag. per B. int. Germanos relig. Xtiana, 1770.
" Kurth (G.) St. B. ["Les saints"], 2e éd., 1902.
" Laux (J. J.) Der heilige B., 1922.
" Tangl (M.) Bonifatiusfragen, 1919.

Boniface, *Saint, abp., Apostle of Russia.* *Témoignage d'un contemp. sur St. Vladimir. [*Lat. & Fr.*] Publ. par le pr. A. Galitzin. s8°. 1861

Boniface, *of Savoy, abp. of Canterbury, see* Strickland (J.), *S.J.* Ricerche storiche sopra il B. B. di S., 1207–70, 1895.

Bonilla y San Martin (Adolfo). Las Bacantes o del origen del teatro. la8°. 1921
see Altolaguirre y Duvale (A. de) & A. B. y. San M. Indice gen. de los papeles del Consejo de Indias, 6t, 1923–26.

Bonington (Richard Parkes), *see* Dubuisson (A.) R. P. B.: h. life & work; tr. w. annot. by C. E. Hughes, 1924.
see Stokes (H.) Girton & B., 1922.

Bonis (Josephus de). De oratoriis publicis, *see* Assemanus (J. A.) Comm. de ecclesiis &c., 1766.

Bonjour (Felix). Real democracy in operation: the example of Switzerland. Tr. C. L. Leese. s8°. [1920]

Bonn. Bericht ü. d. 1875 z. B. Unions-Conferenzen; hrsg. v. F. H. Reusch. [P2656]. 8°. Bonn. 1875

Bonn (Moritz Julius).
The crisis of European democracy. 8°. New Haven. 1925
Das Schicksal d. deut. Kapitalismus. 8°. 1926
Die Stabilisierung der Mark. s8°. [1922]

Bonnaffé (Edouard). Dict. étymolog. & hist. des Anglicismes. Pref. de F. Brunot. 8°. 1920

Bonnal (*le gén.* **Henri).**
Les condit. de la guerre moderne. s8°. 1916
Frœschwiller. Récit comm. des événements milit., 15 juil. au 12 août 1870. [*&* Atlas, *in case, sep.*] 8°. 1899
La vie milit. du maréchal Ney. t3. la8°. 1914
see Travaux tactiques publ. par le Journal des sc. milit.; préf. de Gén. H. B., 3s, 1909–13.

Bonnard (Abel). En Chine, 1920–1. [3e éd.] s8°. 1924

Bonnard (Camille).
Costumes des 13e, 14e & 15e siècles. 2t. 4°. 1829–30

Bonnard (Pierre), *see* Fosca (F.) B. (Peintres &c. d'auj.), 1919.

Bonnardot (Alfred), *see* Paris. Reprod. d'anc. plans, notice par A. B., 1908.

Bonneau (Georges).
Albert Samain, poète symboliste. 2e éd. s8°. 1925

Bonnefon (Jean de). Voyage d'explor. en Hongrie inconnue, *see* Œuvres libres, 8, 1922.

Bonnefon (Joseph), *docteur en droit.*
Le régime parlement. sous la Restauration. 8°. 1905

Bonnel de Mézières (A.) Rech. sur l'emplacement de Ghana & sur le site de Tekrour, *see* Acad. des Inscr. Mém. &c., s1, t13i, 1923.

Bonnell (Ernst). Beiträge z. Alterthumskunde Russlands, v. d. ält. Zeiten bis um 400 n. Chr. B1 (Herodot, s. Vorgänger u. e. später Schriftsteller). [*no more publ.?*] la8°. St. Petersb. 1882
Russ.-liwländ. Chronographie v. d. Mitte d. 9. Jhdts. bis z. Jahre 1410. [Kaiserl. Akad. d. Wiss.] 4°. St. Petersburg. 1862

Bønnelycke (Emil). Margrethe Menkel. Roman. s8°. 1921
Spartanerne. Roman. 2en Udg. s8°. 1919
Udvalgte Digte. 8°. 1922

Bonnemaison (F.), *see* Berry (C. F. L. *dsse.* de). Galerie de la Dsse. de B.; école fr.; ouvrage lithogr. sous la dir. de Chev. B., 2t, 1822.

Bonner (Carey). Child songs. [v1, 12th ed.] 2v. la8°. [1914–22]

Bonner (Edmund), *bp. of London.* A profitable & necessarye doctryne. [*Imperf. want. tp. &c.*] s4°. [Londini. In ædibus J. Cawodi. 1555?]
see Gardiner (St.) De vera obedientia, w. pref. [*by B.*], 1553.
" Townsend (G.) *Life & defence &c. of E. B., 1842.

Bonnerot (Jean). Jérôme & Jean Tharaud, leur œuvre. s8°. 1927
Romain Rolland; sa vie, son œuvre. s8°. 1921
Les routes de France. la8°. 1921

Bonnet (Charles), *naturalist.* Conjectures conc. the nature of future happiness. Tr. [P2537]. s8°. 1790

Bonnet (Giisbert).
Orationes duæ. s4°. Trajecti ad Rhenum. 1793

Bonnet (Hans). Die ägypt. Tracht bis z. Ende d. neuen Reiches. la8°. L. 1917
Die Waffen d. Völker d. alt. Orients. 8°. L. 1926

Bonnet (*l'abbé* **J.-Esprit).** *Essai sur l'art de rendre les révolutions utiles. 2t. 8°. 1801

Bonnet (Jules). Aonio Paleario: ét. sur la réforme en Italie. s8°. 1863
Vie d'Olympia Morata: épisode de la Renaissance &c. en Italie. 3e ed. augm. 8°. 1856

Bonneval (*le cte.* **Claude Alex. de),** *aft. Aḥmad Pāshā, see* Vandal (A.) Le Pacha B., 1885.

Bonney (Thomas George). Memories of a long life. 8°. C. 1921
see Europe. Picturesque E., by T. G. B. &c., 5v, 1881–86.

Bonney (William H.) [Billy *the Kid*], *see* Burns (W. N.) Saga of Billy the Kid, 1926.

Bonnier (Gaston).
British flora. Tr. & adapted by E. Mellor. s8°. 1925
Flore complète illust. de France, Suisse & Belgique. 7t. la8°. [1911 &c.]

Bonnin (Alfred). Tutenag & paktong, w. notes on o. alloys in domestic use dur. the 18th cent. s4°. O. 1924

Bonola (Rocco). *Auch eine Enthüll. od. ein alt. Buch geg. d. neu. Irrungen. [Being a tr. of R. B.'s "La lega d. teologia mod. colla filosofia &c., 1787]. Hrsg. v. K. Martin. [P520]. 8°. Mainz. 1871

Bonoli (Girolamo). Storia di Cottignola, terra n. Romagna Inf. 8º. Ravenna. 1734
Storia di Lugo ed annessi, libri 3. s4º. Faenza. 1732
Bonoli (Paolo). Istorie d. città di Forli &c. s4º. Forli. 1661
Bonomi (G. F.), *bp. of Vercelli, see* BONHOMUS (J. F.)
Bonomi (Ivanoe). Dal socialismo al Fascismo. 8º. 1924
Bononio, *St., abbot of Locedio.* La Vita ratbertiana di S. B. nei mss. dell' abbate G. Grandi, *see* ARCHIVIO STOR. ITAL., Anno 83, v1, 1925.
Bonsels (Waldemar).
Die Biene Maja u. i. Abenteuer. 319. bis 349. A. s8º. 1921
Himmelsvolk. Ein Buch v. Blumen, Tieren u. Gott. 186.–225. A. 8º. [1915]
Mario u. d. Tiere. 8º. St. 1928
Bonsor (George). Colonies agricoles pré-romaines de la vallée du Bétis. [Extr. de la Revue arch., t35, 1899]. 8º. 1899
Tartesse. [Hispanic Soc. of Amer.] s8º. N.Y. 1922
Bonstetten (Carl Victor v.) Philos. d. Erfahrung: oder ü. d. Menschen u. s. Vermögen. 2B [in 1v]. s8º. St. 1828
see HERKING (M. L.) C.-V. de B., 1745–1832; sa vie, ses œuvres, 1921.
Bontempelli (Massimo). Maria Melato. la8º. Milano. 1921
Viaggi e scoperte. s8º. Firenze. [1922]
La vita intensa. Romanzo. s8º. Firenze. [1920]
La vita operosa. s8º. Firenze. [1921]
Bonvalot (Gabriel). Marco Polo. s8º. 1924
Bonvicino (Alessandro), *called Il Moretto* [MORETTO DA BRESCIA], *see* NICODEMI (G.) Il Moretto da Brescia, 1921.
see PAPA (U.) Il genio e le opere di A. B., 1898.
Bonwetsch (G. Nathaniel). Texte z. Gesch. d. Montanismus; hrsg. N. B., *see* KLEINE TEXTE, T129, 1914.
Bonwick (James). An octogenarian's remin. s8º. 1902
Boodin (John Elof). A realistic universe. An intr. to metaphysics. 8º. N.Y. 1916
Book.
*Book (The) & its missions. Ed. by L. N. R[anyard]. v1, 2 [in 1v]. 8º. 1856–57
Book of Common order of Ch. of Scot. &c., 1868, *see* CHURCH OF SCOTLAND.
Book of Cupid: anthology f. Eng. poets, 1909, *see* NEWBOLT (*Sir* H. J.)
Book (A) of Danish verse; tr. S. F. Damon &c., 1922, *see* DANISH.
*Book (A) of favourite mod. ballads, 1860, *see* BALLADS.
Book (A) of golden deeds, 1893, *see* YONGE (C. M.)
Book (The) of protection; ed. f. Syriac MSS., w. tr. &c., 1912, *see* GOLLANCZ (H.), *ed.*
Book (The) of saints: a dict. &c., 1921, *see* SAINTS.
Book (The) of the apple, ascr. to Aristotle, *see* ARISTOTLE.
*Book (The) of the chron. of Wm., duke of Cumberland &c., 1746, *see* CUMBERLAND (W. A., *d. of*).
Book (The) of the Himyarites; ed. &c. A. Moberg, 1924, *see* HIMYARITES.
Book (The) of the numerical sayings, p2, 1925, *see* AṄGUTTARA-NIKĀYA.
*Book (The) of the ranks & dignities of Brit. society [1805]. Attr. to C. Lamb. Intr. by C. Shorter. s8º. 1924
Book of the words of glees, madrigals &c., 1880, *see* CITY GLEE CLUB.
*Book (A) w. seven seals. la8º. 1928
Book (The) of the Dead, *see* BRIT. MUSEUM. Bk. of the d., 1920.
see DAVIS (T. M.) Excavations: Biban el Molûk; funeral papyrus of Iouiya, 1908.
Böök (Fredrik).
Artur Hazelius: en levnadsteckning. 8º. [1923]
Esaias Tegnér. d1, till 1814. 4º. [1917]
Essayer och kritiker, 1915–16. 8º. 1917
" " 1917–18. 8º. 1919
" " 1919–20. 8º. 1921
Resa till Konstantinopel genom Mellaneuropa, 1922. 8º. [1922]
Resa till Tyskland och Polen, 1916. 2ª uppl. 8º. [1916]
Den romantiska tidsåldern, *see* SVENSKA litt. hist., d2, 1919.
Svensk vardag. Essayer. 8º. 1922
Sveriges mod. litt., *see* SVENSKA litt. hist., d3, 1921.
Book-auction records. v17–20 (1919–23). 8º. 1920–24
" " Gen. index, 1902–12. By W. Jaggard. 8º. 1924
" " 2nd Gen. index, 1912–23 (v10–20). Ed. K. L. Stevens. 8º. 1928
Bookman (The).
v62–68, 70, 71 (Apr. 1922–March 1927). fol. [1922–27]
Bookman (The): illust. mag. of lit. & life.
v44–59 (Sept. 1916–August 1924). 8º. N.Y. [1917–24]
Book-prices current. Record of prices &c. v34–40. 8º. 1920–26
" " Index, 1907–16. With a suppl. of bibliophiles & bibliopoles. By J. H. Slater. 8º. 1920
Bookseller (The). 1920–27. la8º. 1920–27
Boole (Mary Everest).
The forging of passion into power. 8º. 1910
Lect. on the logic of arithmetic. s8º. O. 1903

Boole (Mary Everest) [*continued*].
Logic taught by love. s8º. 1905
The message of psychic science. 8º. 1908
Boon (Abrahamus). Dissert. de duplici principio, unde in Eccl. emend. exierunt sæc. 16 reformatores. 8º. Groningæ. 1839
Boon (George), *character in fiction, see* WELLS (H. G.) Boon: 1st select. f. lit. remains of G. B., 1920.
Boone (Joannes Baptista), *see* ACTA. De prosec. op. Bollandiani quod Acta Sanct. inscrib. [*signed* J. B. B. *&c.*] 1838.
Boonzaier (D. C.) My caricatures. [Pref. by J. X. Merriman]. 4º. Cape Town. *n.d.*
Boorman (H. G. T.), *see* ASHE (A. W.) & H. G. T. B. Chemicals, 1924.
Booth (Cecily). Cosimo I, Duke of Florence. 8º. C. 1921
Booth (Charles), *bp. of Hereford.* [BOTHE]. The register of C. B., bp. of Hereford, 1516–35. Ed. A. T. Bannister. [Cantilupe Soc.] 8º. Hereford. 1921
Registrum C. B., episcopi Hereford., 1516–35 [*w.* App. cont. abstract of reg. of E. Foxe & E. Bonner]. Ed. A. T. Bannister. [Cant. & York Soc., v28]. 8º. 1921
Booth (Edward Charles). The tree of the garden. s8º. [1922]
Booth (Evangeline) & G. L. Hill. The war romance of the Salvation Army. s8º. Phila. [1919]
Booth (Everard). Dagelijksche aanteekeningen gedur. het verblijf d. Franschen te Utrecht, 1672–73, *see* HISTORISCH GENOOTS. Berigten, d6ii, 1857.
Booth (James), *D.C.L.*
Exam. the province of the state. [P2558]. 8º. 1847
Booth (Meyrick).
Social reconstr. in Germany. [P2405]. 8º. [1919]
Booth (William), *see* BEGBIE (H.) Life of W. B., 2v, 1920.
Boothby (Robert John Graham), J. de V. Loder *& others.*
Industry & the state: a Conservative view. 8º. 1927
Bootius (Arnoldus). Animadv. sacræ ad textum Vet. Test. [*2 pagins.*] s4º. Londini. 1644
Bopp (Franz).
Gramm. crit. ling. Sanscritæ. 2ª emend. ed. s4º. Berolini. 1832
Krit. Gramm. d. Sanskrita-Spr. 8º. 1834
" " 3ᵉ verm. A. 8º. 1861–63
Vergleich. Accentuationssystem, nebst. grammat. Übereinstimmungen d. Sansk. u. Griech. 8º. 1854
Vergleich. Gramm. d. Sanskrit, Ṣend, Armen., Griech., Lat., Litau., Altslav., Goth. u. Deutschen. 2ᵉ gänzl. umgearb. A. 3B [*wanting* B2ii & B3]. 8º. 1857–61
Vocalismus oder sprachvergleich. Kritiken ü. Grimm's deut. Gramm. u. Graff; ahd. Sprachschatz &c. la8º. 1836
Bopp (Léon).
H. F. Amiel: sa pensée &c. d'ap. docˢ. inéd. 8º. 1926
see AMIEL (H. F.) Principes gén. de pédagogie; avec intr. par L. B., 1925.
Boppard (Wilhelm Nikolaus Dörkes-), *see* DÖRKES-BOPPARD.
Boquinus (Petrus). Assertio vet. ac veri Christianismi adv. novum & fictum Jesuitismum seu soc. Jesu [*b. w.* Daneau (L.) Elenchi hæret., 1573]. s8º. *apud Jo. Mareschallum Lugdun.* 1576
Boraston (*Lt.-Col.* John Herbert), *C.B., see* DEWAR (G. A. B.) Sir D. Haig's command; by G. A. B. D., assist. by Lt.-Col. J. H. B., 2v, 1922.
Borba. Въ Борьбѣ. Сборникъ 1–3. [P2453]. 8º. С.-П. 1906
Borba za Rossiyu. Борьба за Россію. La lutte pour la Russie. Noˢ. 1–52. 4º. Paris. 1926–27
Borchardt (Ludwig). Die ältägypt. Zeitmessung. 4º. 1920
Die Annalen u. d. zeitl. Festegung d. alt. Reiches d. ägypt. Gesch. fol. 1917
Das Grabdenkmal d. Königs Nefer-ỉr-kȝ-reᶜ. [Deut. Orient-Gesell., Wiss. Veröffentl., 11]. fol. L. 1909
Das Grabdenkmal d. Königs Ne-user-reᶜ. [Deut. Or.-G., Wiss. V., 7]. fol. L. 1907
Das Grabdenkmal d. Königs S'aȝ ḥu-reᶜ. [Deut. Or.-G., Wiss. V., 14, 26]. 2B. fol. L. 1910–13
1, Der Bau. 2, Die Wandbilder.
Der Porträtkopf d. Königin Teje im Besitz v. J. Simon; [beschr. u. erläut. v. L. B. Deut. Or.-G., Wiss. V., 18]. fol. L. 1911
Borchardt (Rudolf). Schriften. Jugendgedichte. 8º. 1920
Borchling (Conrad). Mittelniederdeut. Hss. in d. Norddeutschl., Rheinlanden &c., *see* KÖNIGL. GESELLS. D. WISS. ZU GÖTTINGEN. Nachrichten, 1898, 1913. Beihefte.
Bord (Gustave). La fin de 2 légendes; L'affaire Léonard—Le Baron de Batz. 8º. 1909

Bordeaux. Archives municip. de B. [t1]. Livres des bouillons. 4º. Bordeaux. 1867
„ „ [t2]. Livre des priviléges. [Publ. &c. par H. Barckhausen]. 4º. Bordeaux. 1878
„ „ Livre des coutumes. Publ. avec des notes &c. par H. Barckhausen. 4º. Bordeaux. 1890

Bordeaux (Henry).
L'amour et le bonheur ou les frères ennemis. [La rançon—Ricochets]. s8º. [1925]
Amours du temps passé. Anne d'Este & J. de Nemours—J. Charles & A. de Lamartine—H. de Dœnniges & F. Lassalle. s8º. [1923]
Le barrage. s8º. [1927]
La bataille devant Souville. s8º. [1920]
Le calvaire de Cimiez. s8º. [1928]
Le carnet d'un stagiaire: scènes de la vie judic. Préf. de Henri-Robert. s8º. [1926]
La Chartreuse du Reposoir. s8º. [1924]
Le cœur & le sang. s8º. [1925]
Le fantôme de la Rue Michel-Ange. s8º. [1922]
Le gén. Maistre. s8º. [1923]
La glorieuse misère des prêtres. [Préf. de Col. Luçon]. s8º. 1923
Le Guignol de Bellerive, *see* ŒUVRES libres, 65, 1926.
Henri Brémond. s8º. [1924]
Les jeux dangereux. s8º. [1926]
Jules Lemaître. s8º. [1920]
La maison morte. s8º. 1922
Le maréchal Fayolle. s8º. 1921
Le marchand de bonheur. Visites soc. s8º. [1927]
Ménages d'après Guerre. s8º. [1921]
Paysages romanesques des Alpes. s8º. 1925
La peur de vivre. s8º. [1925]
Le Plessis-de-Roye, 1914–18. s8º. 1920
Portraits d'hommes. 2t. 8º. [1924] 1, P. Loti—M. Barrès—R. Kipling—E. Faguet—P. Hervieu—F. de Curel—C. Guérin—M. Faucon—P. Gilbert—L. Hémon. 2, J. Lemaitre—J. de Maistre—F. Masson—M. Barrès—P. Bourget—C. Isaure—H. Brémond—S. François de Sales.
Rap & Vaga. s8º. [1927]
Le retour de Barrès à sa terre & à ses morts. s8º. [1924]
Los Roquevillard. Intr. de F. Roz. Tr. R. Mesa y Lopez. s8º. [1912]
St. François de Sales & notre cœur de chair. s8º. [1924]
La vie au théâtre. s5, 1919–21. s8º. 1921
La vie est un sport—Le chemin d'Annibal—La nuit blanche. s8º. [1923]
La vie recommence. La chair et l'esprit. s8º. [1921]
La vie recommence. La résurrection de la chair. s8º. [1920]
Voici l'heure des âmes. 4e éd. s8º. 1921
Voyageurs d'Orient. 2t. s8º. 1926 1, Pèlerins aux Meharistes de Palmyre. 2, Lamartine, Michaud, Barrès.
Le Walter Scott normand: Barbey d'Aurevilly. s8º. [1925]
Yamilé sous les cèdres. s8º. [1923]
see BERTAUT (J.) H. B., s. œuvre, 1924.

Bordeaux (Paule Henry-). Lady Stanhope en Orient. [2t]. (1, La circé du désert. 2, La sorcière de Djoun). s8º. [1924–26]

Borden (Mary), *aft. wife of Brig.-Gen. E. L. Spears.*
Flamingo. s8º. 1927
Four o'clock & o. s. s8º. [1926]
Jane—our stranger. [n. impr.] s8º. [1924]
Jericho sands. s8º. [1925]
The romantic woman. [n. impr.] s8º. [1924]
Three pilgrims & a tinker. s8º. 1924

Borden (*Sir* Robert Laird). Canadian constit. studies. Marfleet Lect., Toronto, 1921. rev. ed. s8º. [1922]

Bordes (J. van Walré de). The Austrian crown, its depreciation &c. Foreword by Sir H. Strakosch. 8º. 1924

Bordes-Pagès, *Family of, see* AGEORGES (J.) Une famille franç. au 19e s.: les Pagès & les B.-P., 1920.

Bordeux (Jeanne).
Eleonora Duse: story of her life. 8º. [1925]

Bordier (Henri Leonard). Les églises & monastères de Paris, pièces, 9–14 siècles. Publ. H. L. B. [Trésor des pièces rares &c.] s8º. 1856
see *CHANSONNIER huguenot du 16e. siècle; [*ed.* H. L. B.], 1870.

Bordone (Paris) [BORDON], *see* BAILO (L.) & G. BISCARO. Della vita e d. opere di P. B., 1900.

Bordoni (Benedetto). Isolario, nel qual si ragiona di tutte l'Isole del mondo con li lor nomi ant. e mod., historie, favole &c. la8º. [Vinegia]. 1547

Bordoni (Faustina), *aft. Hasse, see* HASSE (F.)

Bordoni (Francesco) [†BORDONUS (F.)] Opus posthumum quod consistit in duas app. ad Man. consultorum in causis S. Officii c. hæreticam pravitatem occurr. Subseq. nova reimpr. Tractatus de legatis. Industria F. O. Mancini. fol. Parmæ. 1703
Propugnaculum opinionis probabilis in concursu probabilioris. fol. Lugduni. 1669

Bordonio (Hieronymo) *de Sermoneta.* Incomencia il devoto libro chiamato Recitoria Virginis. 8º. [Neapoli. 1529]

Borel (Emile). Space & time. s8º. 1926

Borel (Pierre). Gustave Courbet & la Col. Vendôme, *see* ŒUVRES libres, 6, 1921.
Le roman de Gustave Courbet. Préf. de C. Mauclair. s8º. 1922
Le visage inconnu de Marie Bashkirtseff, *see* ŒUVRES libres, 42, 1925.

Borel (Tony). L'abbé de Watteville, conseiller au parlement de Dole & sa mission en Suisse. la8º. Bale. 1923

Borenius (Tancred). Four early Italian engravers: A. del Pollaiuolo, A. Mantegna, J. de' Barbari, G. Campagnola. la8º. 1923
The picture gallery of A. Vendramin. [Brit. Sch. at Rome]. la8º. 1923
see ELTON HALL. Cat. of pictures at E. H. in poss. of Col. D. J. Proby, by T. B. &c., 1924.
„ LEE OF FAREHAM (A. H. L., *1st visct.*) Cat. of pictures &c.; coll. by Visct. L. of F.; descr. by T. B., 2v, 1923–26.

Boretius (Alfred). Friedrich d. Grosse in s. Schriften, *see* VIRCHOW (R.) & F. v. HOLTZENDORFF. Vorträge, H114, 1870.

Boretskaya (Mariya).
Как они умирали [P2722]. s8º. Москва. 1919

Boreux (Charles). L'art égyptien. la8º. 1926
Etudes de nautique égypt.: l'art de la navigation en Egypte jusqu' à la fin de l'anc. empire, *see* INSTITUT FRANÇ. D'ARCH. ORIENT. DU CAIRE. Mém., t50, 1925.
La stèle-table d'offrandes de Senpou &c., *see* ACAD. D. INSCR. &C.: FOND. PIOT. Mon. &c., t25, 1921–22.

Borger (Elias Annes).
Disputatio de mysticismo. 8º. Hagæ Com. 1820

Borger (Petrus Abraham). Dissert. de parte epistolæ Pauli ad Romanos parænetica &c. 8º. Lugduni-Batav. 1840

Borgese (Gius. Ant.)
La città sconosciuta. s8º. Milano. [1924]
Risurrezioni. [Il Pascoli minore—L'op. poet. di G. d'Annunzio *& o. e.*] s8º. Firenze. 1922
Rubè. Romanzo. s8º. Milano. 1921
Rubè. Auth. tr. by I. Goldberg. s8º. [1923]
Storia d. crit. romantica in Italia, con una nuova pref. s8º. Milano. 1920
I viva e i morti. Romanzo. s8º. 1923
see AMENDOLA (G.) Il patto di Roma; scr. di G. A., G. A. B. &c., 1919.
„ PALMIERI (E.) B., 1928.

Børgesen (F. H.) Contrib. to the knowl. of vegetation of the Canary Islands, w. app. Lichenes Teneriff. scr. E. A. Wainio, *see* KONG. DAN. VID. SELSKAB. Skr., Række 8, B6, 1920–24.
Marine Algæ f. the Canary Islands, 1–3, *see* KONG. DAN. VID. SELSKAB. Biolog. Medd., 5, 6, 1925–27.

Borgex (Louis).
Vincent d'Indy, sa vie & son œuvre. s8º. 1913

Borghese (Pietro), *see* DELLA FRANCESCA (PIERO).

Borghesi (Diomede).
Rime amorose, con argomenti di C. Perla. s4º. Padova. 1585

Borghetti (E.)
Caporetto e la terza Italia. pl. 8º. Perugia. [1921]

Borghini (Raffaello). Il riposo. Della pittura, e d. scultura &c. s8º. Fiorenza. 1584

Borgia, *The family of, see* PORTIGLIOTTI (G.) I Borgia, 1921; tr. B. Miall, 1928.

Borgia (*il card.* Cesare), *duc de Valentinois.*
see GOBINEAU (*le c.* J. A. DE). La fleur d'or [B. &c.], 1923.
„ LA SIZERANNE (R. DE). C. B. & le duc d'Urbino, 1502–3, 1924.
„ PORTIGLIOTTI (G.) I Borgia: C. &c., 1921; tr. B. Miall, 1928.
„ SABATINI (R.) Banner of the bull: C. B. [*fict.*], 1927.

Borgia (Lucrezia), *consort of Alphonso I, duke of Ferrara, see* PORTIGLIOTTI (G.) I Borgia: L. &c., 1921; tr. B. Miall, 1928.

Borgman (Aleksandr Ivanovich).
Русская исторія. 2ч. 8º. С.-П. 1912–13

Borgno (Girolamo Federico). Dissert. sul carme di U. Foscolo &c., *see* FOSCOLO (N. U.) Ult. lett., 1817.

Borgstroem (Arthur Travers-), *see* TRAVERS-BORGSTROEM (A.)

Boria (Alexander de), *see* CHERUBIN DE SAINT-JOSEPH.

Borino (Giov. Batt.) L'elezione e la depos. di Gregorio VI, *see* REALE SOC. ROM. Archivio, v39, 1916.

Borinski (Carl). Die Antike in Poetik u. Kunsttheorie v. Ausgang d. klass. Altertums bis auf Goethe u. W. v. Humboldt. [Das Erbe d. Alten, H9, 10]. 2[B, B2 hrsg. R. Newald]. la8º. L. 1914–24

Borinski (Carl) [*continued*].
Works in KÖNIGL. AKAD. D. WISS. ZU MÜNCHEN. Phil. Kl. Sitz.
Braun als Trauerfarbe, 1918.
Die Deutung d. Piero di Cosimo zugeschr. Prometheus-Bilder, 1920.
Nochmals d. Farbe Braun, 1920.
Die Weltwiedergeburtsidee i. d. neu. Zeiten, 1, Der Streit um d. Renaissance, 1919.

Boris Fedorovich, *emp. of Russia* [BORIS GODUNOV], *see* PLATONOV (S. F.) Борис Годунов, 1921.

Borisov (I.) Начало конца: крит. моментъ въ жизни Народа и Соц.-Револ. Партіи. [P2390, 2824]. s8°. Женева. 1881

Borja (Francisco de), *duke of Gandia, see* FRANCIS [DE BORJA], *Saint.*

Borja (Juan de), *Count of Mayalde.* Emblemata moralia B. Lat. donata a L. C. C. P. s4°. Berolini. 1697

Borlace (Edmund) [BORLASE]. Latham Spaw in Lancashire; w. a farther acc. [*w. sep. pagin.*] s8°. 1672

Borluut de Noortdonck (—). Cat. des livres &c. formant le cabinet de B. de N. Vente, Avr. [*&* Juillet], 1858. 2t. 8°. Gand. [1858]

Born (Max). The constit. of matter: mod. atomic & electron theories. Tr. f. 2nd rev. ed. by E. W. Blair & T. S. Wheeler. 8°. [1923]
Einstein's theory of relativity. Tr. H. L. Brose. 8°. 1924
Die Relativitätstheorie Einsteins u. i. physikal. Grundlagen. [Naturwiss. Monogr. &c.; hrsg. A. Berliner &c., B3]. 8°. 1920

Bornate (Carlo). La guerra di Pietrasanta (1484–85) sec. doc[ti]. dell' Arch. Genovese, *see* REGIA DEPUT. Miscellanea, t50, 1922.
Hist. vite & gest. per dom. magnum cancellarium (M. Arborio), con note &c., *ed.* C. B., *see* REGIA DEPUT. Miscellanea, t48, 1915.

Bornemann (Johann Alfred). Anselmus & Abaelardus, sive initia scholasticismi. Dissert. 8°. Hauniæ. 1840

Borneo. Views of Brit. North B., w. brief hist., comp. f. offic. records &c. obl. 8°. 1899

Börner (C. G.), *see* JAGD. Samml. v. Kupferstichen &c. d. 16.–19. Jhdts auf d. Jagd; Versteig. durch C. G. B., 1921.

Börner (Christian Friedrich) [BOERNERUS]. Auserlesene Bedenken d. theol. Facultät zu Leipzig. 3T. [*in* 1v. *pagin. contin.*] s4°. Leipzig. 1751
De altera migrat. lit. Græc. e Græcia in Italiam, sæc. 15. Disser. C. F. Boernerus & J. G. Zeiske. [P2744]. s4°. [Lips. 1704]
Dissert. 2[a] de exulibus Græciæ &c. [P2744]. s4°. Lipsiæ. [1705]
Instit. theologicæ symbolicæ. s8°. Lipsiæ. 1751

Börner (Otto). Die Willensfreiheit, Zurechnung u. Strafe. [P2491]. 8°. Freiberg. 1857

Bornhak (Conrad).
Deutsche Gesch. unter Kaiser Wilhelm II. 8°. L. 1921

Bornius (Benedictus). Neueröffnete Schatz-Kammer aller theolog. Wissenschaften &c. Nebst e. Vorrede J. E. Kappens. 4T. s8°. L. 1746–47
1, 1701–10. 2, 1711–20. 3, 1721–30. 4, 1731–40.

Borodin (Aleksandr Porfirevich), *see* ABRAHAM (G. E. H.) B.: the composer & h. music, 1927.

Borodkin (Mikhail Mikhailovich). Finland, its place in the Russ. state. From the Russian. [P2451]. 8°. St. Petersburg. 1911

Borotto (Marco Sartori), *see* SARTORI BOROTTO (M.)

Boroughs (*Sir* **John**), *see* BURROUGHS (*Sir* J.)

Borovka (Gregory O.) Scythian art. Tr. V. G. Childe. 8°. 1928

Borra (Luigi). L'amorose rime di L. B. 8°. [Milano. 1542]

Borradaile (Lancelot Alexander), *see* BRIT. ANTARCTIC EXPED., 1910–13: Zoology, v3, Crustacea, pl–3; by B., 1915–23.

Borrassá (Luis), *see* GUDIOL (J.) El pintor L. B., 1926.

Borren (Charles van den), *see* VAN DEN BORREN (C.)

Borrichius (Andreas).
Vindiciæ Latinitatis purioris &c. s8°. Havniæ. 1706

Borrichius (Olaus). De caussis diversitatis linguarum diss. Cur. J. G. Joch. s8°. Ienæ. 1704

Borrius (Hieronymus), *see* BORRO (GIROLAMO).

Borrmann (Richard). Aufnahmen mittelalterl. Wand-u. Deckenmalereien in Deutschland. Unter Mitwirkung v. H. Kolb [u.] O. Vorlaender. Hrsg. R. B. [2B.] fol. [1897–1914]

Borro (Gasparino). Triumphi: Sonetti: Canzon: & Laude dela Gloriosa madre de dio vergine Maria. 8°. Bressa, *Anzolo Britãnico.* 1498
4 prelim. leaves, a–g in eights, A–D in eights, E10.

Borro (Girolamo) [BORRIUS (HIERONYMUS)]. De peripatetica docendi atque addiscendi methodo. s8°. Florentiæ. 1584

Borromée (*Saint* **Charles**), *see* CHARLES (*Borromeo*), *Saint.*

Borromini (Francesco), *see* HEMPEL (E.) F. B., 1924.
see MUÑOZ (A.) F. B.; 30 riprod. con testo e cat., 1921.

Borrow (George).
Works. Ed. C. Shorter. Norwich ed. 16v. 8°. 1923–24
1, 2, The Bible in Spain.
3, 4, Lavengro.
5, 6, The Romany Rye.
7–9, Songs of Scandinavia & o. p. & ballads.
10, The Zincali: acc. of Gypsies of Spain.
11, Romano Lavo-Lil: word-bk. of the Romany or Eng. Gypsy language
12–14, Wild Wales. 3v. [v3, Welsh bards &c.]
15, 16, Miscellanies.
Ballads of all nations. Tr. G. B. A sel., ed. R. B. Johnson, f. texts of H. Wright. 8°. [1927]
The Bible in Spain. s8°. 1843
" " With biog. intr. [Minerva Lib. Ed. G. T. Bettany]. 5th ed. s8°. 1894
Lavengro. [Everyman's Lib.] [repr.] s8°. [1907]
Wild Wales. 3rd ed. s8°. 1872
" " [7th ed.] s8°. 1907
" " [Intr. by T. Watts-Dunton]. [repr.] s8°. [1920]
see STEPHEN (G. A.) B. House museum &c., w. bibliog., 1927.

Borsa (Mario). La Cascina sul Po. s8°. Milano. 1920
see ANSALDO (G.), C. ARIAGHI, M. B. *& o.* Che cos'è l'Inghilterra, 1924.

Börschmann (Ernst). Picturesque China: archit. & landscape. [Tr. L. Hamilton]. 4°. [1924]

Borschov (Ilya Grigorevich). Мат. для ботан. геогр. Арало-Каспійск. края. [I. Akad. Nauk. Зап., т7]. 8°. С.–П. 1865

Börsenverein d. deut. Buchhändler, *see* KAPP (F.) & J. GOLDFRIEDRICH. Gesch. d. deut. Buchhandels; im Auftr. d. B. d. deut. B. hrsg. v. d. Hist. Komm. dess., 4B, 1886–1913.

Bortolo (Belotti). La vita di B. Colleoni. la8°. [1927]

Borwick (F.), *see* CLIFTON COLLEGE. C. C. annals & reg., 1862–1912; ed. F. B., 1912.

Borzakovsky (Vladimir Stephanovich). Ист. Тверскаго княжества. [*2 pagin.*] 8°. С.–П. 1876

Bos (Lambert), *of Workum: the philologist.* Ellipses Græcæ. Ed. G. H. Schäffer. 8°. Glasguæ. 1813

Bos (Lambert van den), *poet & historian* [L. VAN DEN BOSCH], *see* CAMPBELL (O. J.) Position of the "Roode en Witte Roos" [by L. v. d. B.] in saga of Richard III, [*w. text & tr.*], 1919.

Bos (R. P.) Bos' schoolatlas der geheele aarde. Herzien door J. F. Niermeyer. 27[e] dr. fol. Groningen. 1922

Bosanquet (Bernard).
Croce's æsthetic. [*a. c. in* P2432]. 8°. [1920]
Implication & linear inference. s8°. 1920
The meeting of extremes in contemp. philos. s8°. 1921
The philosoph. theory of the State. [3rd ed.] 8°. 1920
Science & philosophy & o. essays. 8°. 1927
3 chapters on the nature of mind. s8°. 1923
What religion is. 8°. 1920
" " [repr.] 8°. 1920
see BRADLEY (A. C.) B. B., 1848–1923, 1924.
" MUIRHEAD (J. H.) Contemp. Brit. philos.; personal statements by J. B. Baillie, B. B. &c., s1, 1924.

Bosanquet (*Mrs.* **Ellen**), *wife of Robert Carr B.,* **& R. M. Dawkins.** Unpubl. objects from the Palaikastro excav., 1902–6, pl, *see* BRIT. SCHOOL AT ATHENS, Suppl. paper, No. 1, 1923.

Bosanquet (Theodora). Harriet Martineau. 8°. 1927
Henry James at work. 8°. *Hogarth Press.* 1924

Boscan Almogaver (Juan), *see* MENÉNDEZ Y PELAYO (M.) Antología de poetas líricos castell., t14, B. &c., 1916.

Boscawen (William St. Chad). "From under the dust of ages." Lect. on Assyria &c. s8°. 1886

Bosch (Hieronymus) [HIERONYMUS VAN AKEN, *called B.*], *see* FRIEDLÄNDER (M. J.) Die altniederl. Malerei, B5, Geertgen van Haarlem u. H. B., 1927.

Bosch Gimpera (Pedro). La arquelogía prerromana hispánica, *see* SCHULTEN (A.) Hispania; app., 1920.
El problema de la cerámica ibérica. [Junta p. Ampl. de Estud. &c. cient.] la8°. 1915

Boschini (Marco).
L'Archipelago, cont. le isole &c. 8°. Venetia. 1658

Boschmans (Raymond). Les ailes repoussent. Comment l'Allemagne prép. sa revanche. s8°. 1921

Bosco (Giovanni), *founder of the Salesian Soc.* Der Diener Gottes Dominikus Savio, Zögling d. Salesian. Oratoriums in Turin. 2e A. s8°. München. [1925]
see CRISPOLTI (F.) Don B.; bearb. v. F. R. v. Lama, 1922.

***Boscobel:** or, hist. of H.M.'s preservation aft. battle of Worc., 1832, *see* BLOUNT (T.)

Boscovich (Ruggiero Giuseppe). A theory of natural philosophy. Lat.-Eng. ed., f. text of 1st Venetian ed., 1763. [Tr. by J. M. Child]. With a sh. life of B. [by B. Petroniević]. fol. Chicago. 1922

Bose Research Institute, *Calcutta.*
Transactions. v1–4. 8°. Calcutta. 1918–23.
see Bose (*Sir* J. C.) Life movements in plants, 1918–23. [1–4].

Bose (Barada Das). Digest of Ind. law cases &c., 1862–1909.
For subsequent vol. see Webb-Johnson (S.)

Bose (Gottfried Christian). De anathemate comm. philologica, *see* Virorum &c. molimina theolog., 1761.

Bose (*Sir* Jagadis Chunder). Life movements in plants. [Bose Research Inst., Calcutta, Trans., v1–4, 1918–23].
4v. [*pagin. cont. 3, 4 b. in 1v*]. 8°. Calcutta. 1918–23
Nervous mechanism of plants. 8°. 1926
Plant autographs & their revelations. 8°. 1927
see Geddes (P.) Life & work of J. C. B., 1920.

Bose (Thilo v.) Das Marnedrama, 1914. [Schlachten d. Weltkrieges, B22, 23]. 2T. 8°. Oldenburg. 1928

Boselli (Paolo). Commem. d. G. Rossi, *see* Regia Deput. Misc., t48, 1915.
Il ministro Vallesa e l'ambasc. Dalberg nel 1817, *see* Regia Deput. Misc., t30, 1893.

Bosio (*il cav.* Antonio). Due monumenti ined. d. Piemonte illust. (Urna sepolcr. di F. Vagnone &c.), *see* Regia Deput. Misc., t15, 1874.
Not. sui sepolcri di Bianca di Monferrato &c. in Carignano, e sul passaggio in Piemonte di Carlo VIII, *see* Regia Deput. Misc., t10, 1870.
see Danna (C.) Commem. del Teol. Cav. A. B., 1882.

Bosius (Joannes Andreas). Introd. in notitiam script eccl. ed. cura J. G. Meuscheni. Acc. oratio de hist. eccl. colenda. s8°. Koloni. 1704
Introd. in notitiam script. eccl. J. F. Buddei, J. G. Meuscheni & T. Crenii obs. aucta ejusque opuscula hist. & antiq. sacr. [Exercit. critica ad. Flavii Josephi periocham de J. C. &c.] Coll. & ed. cura J. G. Walchii. s8°. Jenæ. 1723

Bosler (J.) Théories mod. du soleil. s8°. 1910

Bosmans (C. J. E.) & M. Visser. Repertoire des traités & des engagements internat. du 20e. s. conc. les Pays-Bas. la8°. La Haye. 1921

Bosquier (Philippe) [Bosquierus (Ph.)] Antiq. Franciscanæ, seu speculum vitæ beati Francisci & sociorum ejus antoribus F. F. Fabiano & Hugelino &c. Castigatore P. B. s8°. Coloniæ Agrippinæ. 1623

Bosschère (Jean de).
Job le pauvre. With Eng. tr. 8°. London. 1922

Bosse (Abraham), *see* Blum (A.) A. B. & la société fr. au 17e siècle, 1924.

Bosse (Heinrich).
Die Ideenwelt d. Bolschewismus. [P2410]. 8°. 1920

Bosseck (Johann Gottlieb). De professoribus extraord. in academiis Judæorum. Diss. [P431]. s4°. [Lipsiæ. 1745]
—— **& H. A. Ibbeken.** Cultum fluminum ad Esa. 57 comm. 6 exponunt B. & I. [P428]. s4°. Lipsiæ. [1740]

Bossert (Gustav). Augustin Bader v. Augsburg &c. nach d. Prozessakten v. 1530, *see* Archiv. f. Reformationsgesch., Jhrg. 10–11, 1913–14.
Das Interim in Württemberg. [Verein f. Ref.-gesch. Schr., Jhrg. 12, Nr. 46/47]. 8°. Halle. 1895
Württemberg u. Janssen. [Verein f. Ref.-gesch. Schr., Jhrg. 2, Nr. 5, 6]. 2T. 8°. Halle. 1884

Bossert (Helmuth Th.) Altkreta, Kunst u. Handwerk in Griechenland, Kreta u. a. d. Kykladen währ. d. Bronzezeit. 2e verm. A. la8°. 1923

Bosshart (Jakob). [Erzählungen]. 6B. s8°. L. 1919–21
1, Im Nebel, 2e bis 5e A.
2, Vor dem Umsturz, 2e bis 7e A.
3, Durch Schmerzen empor, 2e u. 3e A.
4, Früh vollendet, 2e u. 3e A.
5, Erdschollen, 3e bis 6e A.
6, Opfer.

Neben der Heerstrasse. Erzählungen. s8°. Zürich. [1923]

Bossuet (Jacques Bénigne), *bp. of* (*1*) *Condom &* (*2*) *of Meaux.*
Œuvres; revue sur les mss. &c. [*Ed.* N. P. Hemey d'Auberive & abbé Caron]. 43t. 8°. Versailles. 1815–19
t43, Lettres inédites & Table.
Œuvres oratoires. Ed. crit. de l'abbé J. Lebarq. Rev. & augm. par C. Urbain & E. Levesque. t3, 1659–61. 8°. 1916
Correspondance. n. éd. augm. de lettres inéd. & publ. avec notes &c. par C. Urbain & E. Levesque. [G. é. de la F.] t11–15. 8°. 1920–25
11, 1698–9; 12, 1699–1700; 13, 1701–2; 14, 1702–4 & Suppl.; 15, Table alphabét. &c. Chronologie.

Bossuet (Jacques Bénigne) [*continued*].
Défense de la déclar. de l'assemblée du clergé de France de 1682 touch. la puissance éccl. Tr. 3t. 4°. Amsterdam. 1745
Défense de l'Hist. des variations contre la réponse [*cont. in the* " Hist. de la relig. des églises réformées "] de M. Basnage. s8°. 1727
Defensio declar. Conventus cleri Gallicani, 1682. 2t *in* 1v. 4°. Amstelodami. 1745
Hist. des variations des églises protest. 2t. s8°. 1688
Hist. of the variations of the Protestant Churches. 2v. 8°. Antwerp. 1742
Justification des Réflexions [*of P. Quesnel*] sur le Nouv. Test. comp. en 1699, contre le Problême eccl. [*b. w. h.* Defense de la déclar. 1682, t3, 1745]. 4°. Amsterdam. 1745
Lettres inéd. 8°. 1820
Lettres inéd. à Mme. de La Maisonfort, religeuse de St. Cyr, commun. à Fénelon. 8°. 1829
Sermon prononcé à la profession de Mme. de la Valiere. [*b. w.* Le Noble (E.) Esprit de Gerson, 1710]. s8°. 1732
*Super reunione protestantium cum eccl. Catholica tractatus inter B. & Molanum (1691). 4°. Viennæ. 1782
An universal hist. to the empire of Charlemagne. Tr. by J. Elphinston. 2v. s8°. *n.d.*
see Basnage de Beauval (J.) Traité des préjugez, ou réponse aux lettres de B. &c., 1701.
,, Bausset (*le card.* L. F. de). Hist. de B., 2e éd., 4t, 1819.
,, Burchardus (P. A.) Schediasma de communione sub una, contra B., 1688.
,, Fecht (J.) De origine &c. missarum, J. B. B. &c. oppos., 1725.
,, Hardy (G.) Le " De civitate Dei " source princ. du " Disc. sur l'hist. univ.," 1913.
,, Letellier (A.) B. notre plus grand écrivain, 1920.
,, Louis *Dauphin, son of Louis XIV.* Hist. de France d'après les leçons de B., 3t, 1821.
,, Renoult (J. B.) Hist. des variations, lettres à Mr. de Meaux &c., 1703.
,, Sanders (E. K.) J. B. B.: a study, 1921.
,, Vincent *of Lerins, Saint.* Commonitorium adv. hæreses; adnexa J. B. B. Doctr. catholicæ expos., *n.d.*

Bost (Ami). Mém. p. s. à l'hist. du réveil relig. des églises protest. de la Suisse & de la France &c. 3t [in 2v.] 8°. 1854–55
see Blumhardt (C. G.) Hist. gén. de l'établ. du Christianisme; [*tr.*] par A. B., 4t, 1838.

Bost (Pierre). Hercule & Mademoiselle. 3e éd. s8°. [1924]
L'imbécile: comédie. [Répert. du vieux-colombier]. 2e éd. s8°. [1923]
Les viellards, *see* Œuvres libres, 53, 1925.

Bostanai, *Resh Galutha.* מעשה, *see* Maimon (A.) מעשה, 1647?.

Bostock (John Knight). Albertanus Brix. in Germany: acc. of the M. H. G. trs. of h. treatises. s8°. O. 1924

Boston, *Massachusetts.*
Public Library.
Annual report, 71st–75th (1922/23–1926). 8°. Boston. 1923–27
Bulletin. s4, v2–5, [s5, v1, 2], s6, v1, 2. la8°. Boston. 1920–27
s5 *has t.* Bull. of recent bks. added, 1924–25.
s6 *has t.* More books, 1926–27.
Index to the Cat. of books in the Upper Hall of the P. L. of the C. of B. la8°. Boston. 1861
A list of books rel. to housing in P. Lib. of B. [P2415]. la8°. Boston. 1918
Lower Hall. Class list for Eng. prose fiction, includ. trs. & juvenile books &c. 6th ed. la8°. Boston. 1877
The pilgrims: sel. list of wks.; comp. by M. A. Tenney. [P2496]. s8°. Boston. 1920
see Keats (J.) Cat. of loan exhib. comm. anniversary of death of K., 1821–1921, held at P. L., Boston, 1921.

Boston Athenæum. Cat. of the Washington Coll. in the B. A. Compiled &c. by A. P. C. Griffin. With App., Inventory of W.'s bks., w. notes by W. C. Lane. la8°. [Cambridge, U.S.] 1897
Influence & hist. of the B. A. (1807–1907), w. rec. of officers &c. [By B. Wendell & the Librarian]. 8°. [Camb. U.S.A.] 1907
see Bolton (C. K.) The Founders, v3, 1926.

Boston (John) [†Bostonus (Joannes)], *see* James (M. R.) List of libraries prefixed to Cat. of J. B. &c., 1922.

Bosville, *The family of, see* Baverstock (J. H.) Some acc. of Maidstone; added, genealog. tables of B. fam., 1832.

Boswall (*Capt.* James D.), *see* Hoste (P. P.) Treatise on naval tactics; tr. J. D. B., w. add. notes &c., 1834.

Boswell (James).
B.'s note-book (1776–77), Johnson's early life. [Ed. R. W. Chapman. The Oxford Miscellany]. s8°. 1925
Journal of a tour to Corsica; & mem. of P. Paoli. Ed., w. intr. by S. C. Roberts. s8°. C. 1923

Boswell (James) [*continued*].

Journal of a tour to the Hebrides, w. Samuel Johnson &c. 6th ed. rev. &c. 8º. 1813
Journal of a tour to the Hebrides w. S. Johnson, *see* JOHNSON (S.) Journey to West Isl. &c.; ed. R. W. Chapman, 1924.
Letters, 1758–95. Coll. & ed. C. B. Tinker. 2v. 8º. 1924
Life of Johnson.
4v. *la. paper.* la8º. O. 1826
Life of Johnson. Notes &c. by Malone. 4v. 8º. 1826
„ „ & the Journal of h. tour to the Hebrides. Illust. by Sir J. Reynolds. [Sir Joshua Reynolds ed.] 5v. la8º. 1885
„ „ [Everyman's Lib. repr.] 2v. s8º. [1907]
see TINKER (C. B.) Young Boswell: chapters on J. B., 1922.

Boswell (Percy George Hamnall). A suppl. mem. on Brit. resources of sand & rocks used in glass-manufacture &c. Contribs. by W. B. Wright &c. [P2495]. 8º. 1917
Bosworth. *Some partic. of B. Park estate &c., for sale priv. by Knight, Frank & Rutley. fol. *n.d.*
Bosworth (George F.) The manor of Higham Bensted, Walthamstow. [W. Antiq. Soc. Publ. No. 6. P2508]. 4º. Walthamstow. 1919
The manors of Low Hall & Salisbury Hall, Walthamstow. [W. Antiq. Soc. Publ. No. 7. P2508]. 4º. Walthamstow. 1920
Bosworth (Joseph). Anglo-Saxon dict., based on MS. coll. of B. Supplement by T. N. Toller. la8º. O. [1921]
A compendious Anglo-Saxon & Eng. dict. 8º. 1849
The elements of Anglo-Saxon gramm. 8º. 1823
Bosworth (Thomas Owen). Geology of the tertiary & quatern. periods in the N.-W. part of Peru; w. acc. of palæontology by H. Woods, T. W. Vaughan, J. A. Cushman &c. 8º. 1922
Botanical (The) magazine (Curtis's). Ed. O. Stapf. v148–151 (1922–25). 8º. [1922–25]
Botelho (Diogo), *governor of Brazil.* Correspondencia (1602–8), *see* INSTITUTO HIST. &C. BRAZIL. Rev., t73, 1911.
Botelho (J. J. Teixeira), *see* TEIXEIRA BOTELHO (J. J.)
Botero (Giovanni), *see* POLONIA. Respublica P. &c. div. aut. (G. B. &c.), 1627.
Botha (Colin Graham).
The French Refugees at the Cape. 8º. Cape Town. 1919
Records for early hist. of S. Africa. [Helps for students, No. 42. P2573]. s8º. 1921
Botha (*General* Louis), *see* BUXTON (S. C. B., *1st earl*). B., 1924.
Bothe (Charles), *bp. of Hereford, see* BOOTH (C.)
Bothe (Friedrich). Gesch. d. Stadt Frankfurt am Main. 2e umgearb. A. la8º. Frankfurt a. M. 1923
Botho, *Benedictine, see* POTHO.
Bothwell (Francis Stewart, *earl of*), *see* ROUGHEAD (W.) The rebel earl, 1926.
Botrel (Théodore Jean Marie). Songs of Brittany. [Tr.] G. E. Morrison. Foreword by E. Preston. s8º. 1915
Botsford (Jay Barrett). English soc. in 18th cent. as influenced from oversea. 8º. N.Y. 1924
Bott (Alan) [*ps.* "CONTACT"].
Eastern nights—& flights. s8º. 1920
Botta, *The family of, see* ROSSI (B. DE'). Istoria genealog. &c. d. case B. &c., 1719.
Böttcher (Walter).
Port of Hamburg. Guide. s8º. Hamburg. 1921
Bottereau (René). Hadrianus legislator, *see* HOFFMANN (C. G.) Hist. jur. Romano-Justin., v2, 1726.
Böttger (Adolf).
Teut. Kriegslieder. Gesammelt v. A. B. s8º. L. 1841
Böttger (Johann Friedrich), *see* KALKSCHMIDT (E.) Der Goldmacher J. F. B. u. d. Erfindung d. europ. Porzellans, 1926.
Botticelli [†FILIPEPI (ALESSANDRO), *called Botticelli*].
see BERENSON (B.) 3 essays in method; (Neglected altarpiece by B.), 1927.
„ STEINMANN (E.) B.'s Tempelscene, 1895.
„ VENTURI (A.) Il B., interprete di Dante, 1921.
„ —— B.; tr., 1927.
„ YASHIRO (Y.) S. B., 3v, 1925.
Bötticher (Carl G. W.), *see* KÖNIGLICHES MUSEUM, *Berlin.* Erklär. Verzeichniss der Abgüsse antiker Werke v. C. G. W. B., 2e rev. A., 1872.
Bötticher (Carl Heinrich v.), *see* EPPSTEIN (G. *Frhr.* v.) Fürst Bismarcks Entlassung; nach d. Aufzeichn. d. B. &c., 1920.
Bötticher (Jacob Gottlieb Isaak). Statist. tables of all the states of Europe; tr., 1800, *see* GERMANY. Geogr., hist. &c. descr.; tr., 1800.
Botticini (Francesco), *see* KÜHNEL (E.) F. B., 1906.
Bottin-mondain, *see* DIDOT-BOTTIN.

Bottomley (Gordon).
Gruach & Britain's daughter. Two plays. 8º. 1921
King Lear's wife—The crier by night—The riding to Lithend—Midsummer eve—Laodice & Danaë. Plays. 8º. [1920]
„ „ ....[n. ed., w. a new poem]. 8º. [1922]
Poems of 30 years. 8º. 1925
Bottoni (Antonio). Cinque secoli d'Univ. a Ferrara, 1391–1891. 8º. Bologna. 1892
Pomposa al tempo di Guido suo monaco. 8º. Firenze. 1883
Bottoni (Mario Saverio).
Nisida e Pausilippo: serenata. [N125]. 8º. Napoli. 1706
Serenata a 4 voci, per l'arrivo d. D. I. de la Cueva &c. [N125]. 8º. Napoli. 1705
Boüard (Alain de). Le régime polit. & les instit. de Rome, 1252–1347. [Bibl. d. Écoles Franç. d'Athènes & de Rome, 118]. la8º. 1920
Bouasse (Henri). Acoustique gén. Ondes aériennes. la8º. 1926
Boucat (Antoine). Theologia Patrum dogmatica &c. Ed. 2a Veneta accurat. &c. 8t. s4º. Venetiis. 1765–66
t4–8 *have t.* Theol. Patr. scholastico-dogmat.
Bouchardon (Marie Pierre Gilbert). L'assassinat de l'archévêque, souv. inéd., *see* ŒUVRES libres, 56, 1926.
Madame Lacoste, *see* ŒUVRES libres, 73, 1927.
Bouchaud (Pierre de).
Bologne. [Villes d'art célèbres]. la8º. 1909
Boucher (—), *dramatist.* Champagne le coiffeur: comédie, *see* FOURNEL (V.) Contemp. de Molière, t3, 1875.
Roman des oyseaux. s8º. 1661
Boucher (Édouard). Robert de Luzarches. Discours. [Acad. des sciences &c. d'Amiens. P2520]. 8º. Amiens. 1903
Boucher (François), *see* BURNAND (R.) & F. B., *edd.* L'hist. de Napoléon rac. par les gr. écrivains, 1922.
Boucher (François), *painter, see* HIND (A. M.) Watteau, B. & the Fr. engravers, 1911.
Boucher (Philippe). Les harmonies de la croix. s8º. 1851
Boucherie (*le colonel*). Hist. du corps de cavalerie Sordet. Rédigé par le Col. B. 8º. 1923
Bouches-du-Rhône (Les). Encyclopédie départementale. Publ. par le Cons. gén. avec le concours de la ville de Marseille & de la Chambre de Comm. sous la dir. de P. Masson. t2, 3, 6–13. 4º. Marseille. 1913–28
1ère partie. Des origines à 1789.
2, Antiquité & Moyen Âge; par V. L. Bourrilly, R. Busquet &c.
3, Les temps modernes, 1482–1789; par G. A. d'Agnel &c.
2e partie. Le bilan du 19e s.
6, La vie intellectuelle; par A. Combes, B. Durand &c.
7, Le mouvt. écon.: l'agric.; par P. Masson & E. Estrangin.
8, Le mouvt. écon.: l'industrie; par P. Masson, A. Oppermann &c.
9, Le mouvt. écon.: le commerce; par P. Masson, A. Batard-Razelière, F. Denizet.
10, Le mouvt. social; par H. Pellissier-Guys, P. Masson &c.
11, Biographies; par H. Barré.
3e partie. Le sol & les habitants.
12, Le sol. Géog. phys.; par H. Bourget & J. Repelin. Biogéographie; par H. Caillol, E. Decrock & A. Vayssière.
13, La population; par H. Barré, J. Bourrilly & P. Masson.
Bouchet (Jean). Les annales d'Aquitaine. Augm. de pièces recueillies par A. Mounin. [*incl.* Jean de la Haye's Mémoires, 1643, De l'Univ. de Poictiers &c., 1643; *each w. sep. pagin. & tp.*] Ed. dern. & nouv. sfol. Poictiers. 1644
Bouchet (*père* Jean Venant), *see* JESUITS. Travels of several learned missioners [B. &c.], 1714.
Bouchié de Belle (Edmond). La Macédoine & les Macédoniens. Préf. de J. Bainville. s8º. 1922
Bouchier (Edmund Spenser).
Short hist. of Antioch, 300 B.C.–A.D. 1268. s8º. O. 1921
Bouchitté (Henri), *see* ANSELM, *St.* Le rationalisme chrétien &c., 1842.
Bouchor (Jean). Les plaisirs de la vanité &c., roman inéd., *see* ŒUVRES (Les) libres, 16, 1922.
Bouchot (Henri). La toilette à la cour de Napoléon. Chiffons &c. de grandes dames, 1810–15. 8º. [1895]
see DUPLESSIS (G.) & H. B. Dict. d. marques & monogrammes de graveurs, 1886.
Boucicault (Dion) [BOURCICAULT (DION L.)]
London assurance. Comedy. [P2582]. s8º. *Lacy. n.d.*
Old heads & young hearts; a comedy. [P2583]. s8º. *n.d.*
Boucoiran (L.) Dict. analog. & étymolog. des idiomes méridionaux &c. n. éd. la8º. L. 1898
Boudier-Bakker (Ina).
Armoede. 8e dr. s8º. A. *n.d.*
Het Spiegeltje. 6e dr. s8º. A. *n.d.*
Kinderen. 5e dr. s8º. [A.] *n.d.*
De ongeweten Dingen. s8º. A. *n.d.*
De straat. 8º. A. [1924]

Boudin (Louis Eugène), *1824–98, see* Aubry (G. J.) E. B., 1922.

Boudot (Paul), *see* Valens (P.) M. P. B. Burgundi laurus theologica, 1604.

Boué (Ami).
Ueb. d. Nummuliten-Ablagerungen. [P2872]. 8°. [Wien. 1847]

Boufflers (Madeleine Angélique de N. de V., *marquise* **de),** *aft. dsse. de Luxembourg, see* Luxembourg.

Bougainville (*le cte.* **Louis Antoine de).** Voyage de B. autour du monde, 1766–69. Préf. & notes de P. Deslandres. 8°. [1924]

Bougard (R.) The little sea torch: or, True guide for coasting pilots. Tr., w. corr. & add. by J. T. Serres. fol. 1801

Bougaud (Emile), *bp. of Laval.* Revelations of the sacred heart to B. Margaret Mary [Alacoque], & hist. of h. life. [Tr.] by a Visitandine of Baltimore. 2nd ed. 8°. N.Y. [1890]

Bougeant (Guillaume Hyacinthe). Hist. des guerres & des negoc. qui préc. le traité de Westphalie. Compos. sur les mem. du cte. d'Avaux par B. 3t. 4°. 1767
see Hildrop (J.), *D.D.* Free-thoughts upon the brute-creation: exam. of B.'s Philos. amusement, 1742–43.

Bouglé (Camille), *see* Steed (H. W.), C. B. &c. Les démocraties mod.: par W. S., C. B., H. Bois &c., 1921.

Bouhéreau (Elias), *see* White (N. J. D.) 4 good men, E. B. &c., 1927.

Bouhours (Dominique).
*La vie de S. Ignace. s8°. Liége. 1680
,, ,, ...[*a. ed.*] 2v. s8°. Lyon. 1688
Vita S. Francisci Xaverii S. J., Indiarum & Japonicæ apostoli. A P. Python lat. redd. s8°. *n.p.* 1712

Bouilhet (Louis), *see* Letellier (L.) L. B., 1821–69, sa vie & s. œuvres, 1919.

Bouillard (G.) Notes div. sur les cultes en Chine. Les attitudes des Buddhas. 8°. Pékin. 1924

Bouillé (*le marq.* **François Claude Amour de).** Mémoires. Avec notice sur sa vie &c. par F. Barrière. [Bibl. des mém. rel. à l'hist. de Fr. &c., t21]. s8°. 1890

Bouillet (Marie Nicolas), *see* Plotinus. Les Ennéades; tr., accomp. de sommaires, de notes &c., & préc. de la vie de P. avec des frag. de Porphyre &c., par M. N. B., 3t, 1857–61.

Bouillier (Victor).
La renommée de Montaigne en Allemagne. s8°. 1921

Boulainvilliers (Henri), *Count, see* Fénelon (F. de S. de la M.) Réfut. des erreurs de B. de Spinosa par F., le Cte. de B. &c., 1703.

Boulais (Gui). Manuel du code chinois, fasc. 1, *see* Variétés sinolog., No. 55, 1923.

Boulanger (André). Orphée: rapports de l'orphisme & du christianisme. s8°. 1925

Boulanger (Henri). Le doc. confident. du Grand Etat-Major allemand s. l'état de l'indust. dans la France occupée: Die Indust. im besetzten Frankreich, 1916. 4°. 1923

Boulay de La Meurthe (*le cte.* **Alfred).** Hist. de la négociation du Concordat de 1801. la8°. Tours. 1920

Boulé (Georges). La Perse. [P2845]. 8°. Versailles. 1893

Boule (Marcellin). Fossil men: elem. of human palæontology. Tr., w. intr. by J. E. & J. Ritchie. rev. & enl. ed. la8°. E. 1923
Les hommes fossiles. Éléments de paléontologie humaine. 8°. 1921
see Grimaldi. Grottes de G., t1ii–iv, Géologie & paléontologie; par M. B., 1906–10.

Boulenger (Charles L.) Myzostomida, *see* Brit. Antarctic Exped., 1910–13. Zoology, v2, 1914–20.

Boulenger (Edward George), *F.Z.S.*
Animal mysteries. 8°. [1927]
The aquarium book. 8°. [1925]

Boulenger (George Albert). Revision of the lizards of the genus Tachydromus. [*Extr. f.* As. Soc. of Bengal, Mems., v5. P2751]. 4°. Calcutta. 1917
see Brit. Mus. of Nat. Hist.: Zoology. Monogr. of the Lacertidæ, 2v, 1920–21.

Boulenger (Jacques).
. . . Mais l'art est difficile! s1. s8°. [1921]
The 17th cent. [National Hist. of France, ed. Fr. Funck-Brentano]. Tr. 8°. [1920]
Romans de la Table Ronde. [4t]. s8°. [1922–23]
1, L'hist. de Merlin l'enchanteur—Les enfances de Lancelot. Préf. J. Bédier.
2, Les amours de Lancelot du Lac.—Galehault, Sire des Iles Lointaines.
3, Le Chevalier à la charrette—Le château aventureux.
4, Le Saint Graal—La mort d'Artus.

Boulenger (Marcel).
C'est donc sérieux?, *see* Œuvres libres, No. 79, 1928.
Le duc de Morny, créateur de Deauville: souvenirs inéd., *see* Œuvres libres, No. 50, 1925.
Le Duc de Morny. 8°. [1925]
L'enfant prodigue, *see* Œuvres libres, No. 30, 1923.
Marguerite. Roman. s8°. [1921]
Vénerie, choses vues, *see* Œuvres libres, No. 46, 1925.

Boulfroy (*l'abbé*). Quatre années de captivité &c., 1914–18, *see* †Pages actuelles, Nos. 134–5, 1919.

Boulgakov, *see* Bulgakov.

Boulger (George Simonds). Brit. flowering plants. Illust. by Mrs. Henry Perrin. 4v. 4°. 1914
see Owen (*Mrs.* J. A.) & G. S. B. The country month by month, n. ed., 1914.

Boulin (Pierre). L'organis. du travail dans la région envahie de la Fr. [1914–18]. [C. E. for Internat. Peace]. 8°. [1927]

Boulitchov (N. de), *see* Bulichev (N. I.)

Boullainvilliers (Henri de), *Count, see* Boulainvilliers (Henri), *Count.*

Boulnois (Helen Mary). Into Little Thibet. s8°. 1923

Boulnois (Henry Percy). Practical road engineering for the new traffic requirements. [*By var. wr.* Ed. H. P. B.] 4°. [1910]

Boulogne. *Chien (Le) de B., ou l'amant fidelle, 1668, *see* Torche (*l'abbé* de).

Boultbee (Rosamond). Pilgrimages & personalities. 8°. 1924

Boulting (William). Four pilgrims. [Hiuen-Tsiang—Sæwulf—Mohammed ibn Abd Allah—L. Varthema]. 8°. [1920]

Boulton (B. C.)
The manufacture & use of plywood & glue. 8°. 1920

Boulton (Matthew), *see* Westwood (A.) M. B.'s medal on reconq. of Naples, 1799, 1926.

Boulton (Richard), *see* Boyle (R.) Theolog. works, ed. by R. B., 3v (3, Life, by R. B.), 1735.

Boulton (S. B.) The Russian Empire. 2nd ed. s8°. 1883

Bounine (Ivan Alekseevich), *see* Bunin (I. A.)

Bouquet (Alan Coates). The Christian relig. & its competitors to-day: Hulsean lect., 1924–5. s8°. C. 1925

Bouratchinski (Joseph), *see* Burachinsky (J.)

Bourbon, *The house of.*
see Cabanès (A.) Le mal héréditaire, t2, Les B. d'Espagne, 1927.
,, Dumax (V. A.) Album généalog. & biog. des princes de la maison de B., 1873.
,, Pannone (A.) Lo Stato borbonico, v1, 1924.

Bourbon (Charles de), *abp. of Lyons; 1437–88, see* Labande (L. H.) Avignon au 15e siècle: légation de C. de B. & du Card. J. de La Rovère, 1920.

Bourbon (*le prince* **Sixte de).** L'offre de paix séparée de l'Autriche (5 déc. 1916–12 oct. 1917). 12e éd. s8°. [1920]

Bourcart (Jacques). L'Albanie & les Albanais. s8°. 1921

Bourcet (Pierre Joseph de).
Principes de la guerre de montagnes, 1775. la4°. 1888

Bourchier (James David), *see* Grogan (*Lady* E. T.) Life of B., 1926.

Bourcier (Emmanuel). Le crime du train 624, choses vues, *see* Œuvres libres, 22, 1923.
Sous le D. K. V., *see* Œuvres libres, 40, 1924.

Bourde de La Rogerie (H.) Les voyageurs en Bretagne: le voyage de Mignot de Montigny, 1752. [Mém. de la Soc. d'Hist. &c. de Bretagne]. 8°. [1925]

Bourdeau (*le capt.* **Henry).** Pichegru a-t-il trahi à Mannheim? sept. 1795. [Publ. s. dir. de la Sect. Hist. de l'Etat-Maj. de l'Armée]. 8°. 1909

Bourdeau (Jean).
Tolstoï, Lénine & la Révol. Russe. s8°. 1921

Bourdet (Edouard). L'heure du berger: comédie, *see* Revue hebdom. Suppl.: coll. nouv., No. 12, 1922.
La prisonnière: comédie, *see* Œuvres libres, 60, 1926.

Bourdillon (A. F. Claudine). The Order of Minoresses in Eng. Thesis. [Brit. Soc. of Franciscan St., v12]. 8°. M'ter. 1926

Bourdillon (Francis William).
Ailes d'alouette. [*Poems*]. s8°. *H. Daniel*: O. 1890
,, Moth-wings (Ailes d'alouette). s8°. 1913
Gerard & Isabel: romance in form of cantefable. s8°. 1921
Minuscula. Lyrics of nature &c. s8°. 1897

Bourdon (B.) L'intelligence. 8°. 1926

Bourelly (*Gén.* **Jules).** Campagne d'Egypte & de Syrie contre les Turcs (1914–18), *see* Pages actuelles, no. 137, 1919.

Bourgeois (Emile). Manuel hist. de polit. étrang. t4, La polit. mondiale (1878–1919). s8°. 1926

Bourgeois (Emile) & L. André. Les sources de l'hist. de France, 1610–1715. [Sources de l'hist. de Fr. jusqu'n 1815, p3]. [t]3–5. 8º. 1923–26
p3 *is by* L. André *only*.

—— **& G. Pagès.** Les origines & les responsabilités de la Grande Guerre. Preuves & aveux. 8º. 1921

Bourgeois (Jean), *docteur de Sorbonne, abbé de la Merci-Dieu.* Relation de M. B. député de 20 évêques de France vers le S. Siège pour la défense du livre: " De la fréquente Communion," par M. Arnauld, 1645 et 46; avec les lettres des évêques aux papes Urbain VIII & Innocent X &c. [*w. sep. pagin. b. w.* Quesnel (P.) Hist. abr. de M. Arnauld, 1695]. s8º. *n.p.* [1695]

Bourgeois (Léon).
L'œuvre de la Soc. des Nations, 1920–23. 8º. 1923
Le Traité de paix de Versailles. 3e éd. s8º. 1919

Bourgeois (Nicolas). Les théories du droit internat. chez Proudhon. Le fédéralisme & la paix. 8º. 1927

Bourgerel (Gustave).
Fragments d'architecture & de sculpture. fol. 1863

Bourges (Elémir). La nef. la8º. 1922

Bourges (Ernest). Recherches sur Fontainebleau, préc., d'un ms. inéd. de N. De Fer, 1699. [*Ed.* M. Bourges]. la8º. Fontainebleau. 1896

Bourget (Henry), *see* Bouches-du-Rhône; encyclop. départ., t12, Géog. phys., par B., 1914.

Bourget (Paul).
Anomalies. s8º. [1920]
Cœur pensif ne sait où il va. s8º. [1924]
Conflits intimes. s8º. [1925]
Le danseur mondain. s8º. [1926]
Un drame dans le monde. s8º. [1921]
L'écuyère. s8º. [1921]
La geôle. s8º. [1923]
Laurence Albani. s8º. [1922]
Nos actes nous suivent. 2t. s8º. [1927]
Nouv. pages de critique & de doctrine. 2[t]. s8º. [1922]
Le roman des quatre. [Par] P. B., G. d'Houville, H. Duvernois, P. Benoit. 2[t]. s8º. [1923–26]
2, *has t.* Micheline & l'amour.
Stendhal. Discours 28 juin 1920 à l'inaug. du monument, suivi du discours de E. Champion & d'une bibliog. 8º. 1920

Bourgignon d'Herbigny (Pierre François Xavier).
*Revue polit. de l'Europe en 1825. 3e éd. [P2764]. 8º. 1825

Bourgin (Georges), *see* Carrère (J.) & G. B. Manuel des partis polit. en France, 1924.
see Commune. Procès-verbaux de la C. de 1871; éd. G. B. &c., t1, 1924.

Bourg-lès-Valence. Cartul. du prieuré de Saint-Pierre du B.-lès-V. Publ. C. U. J. Chevalier. [Soc. d'Arch. de la Drôme. Coll. de cartul. dauphinois, t6, livr. 1]. 8º. 1875

Bourgogne. Chartes de communes & d'affranchissements en B. Publ. s. les auspices de l'Acad. Imp. des Sciences &c. de Dijon par J. Garnier. 3t. 4º. Dijon. 1867–77
,, ,, ...Introd. de J. Garnier, terminée par E. Champeaux 4º. Dijon. 1918

Bourgogne (A. J. B. F.) Memoirs of Sergeant B. (1812–13). Tr. Intr. by J. W. Fortescue. 8º. 1926

Bourgoing (*baron* Jean François de).
Atlas to the mod. state of Spain. 4º. 1808

—— **& L. A. M. de Musset,** *marq. de Cogners.* *Corresp. d'un jeune militaire, ou Mém. du Marq. de Luzigni & d'Hortense de Saint-Just. 2t *in* 1v. s8º. En Suisse. 1778–79

Bourguignon (Daniel). La Cabale des ministres huguenots intendans. Par un Bourguignon converty &c. s8º. Paris. 1618
Les impiétez & athéismes evidens des hérésiarches huguenots. p1, par le-sieur B. s8º. 1617
Rencontre & conférence verbale entre B. & Du Moulin avec propositions verif. que, par les maximes de la doctrine huguenote, on vient à deshonorer Jesus-Christ &c. s8º. Paris. 1617

Bourignon (Antoinette).
The academy of learned divines. [Tr.] 3p *in* 1v. s8º. 1708
A coll. of letters upon occ. of the persecutions agst. her. Pref. Confess. of Faith. [Tr.] [*b. w. h.* A warning agst. Quakers &c. 1708]. 8º. 1708
The confusion of the builders of Babel. [*b. w. h.* Acad. of learned divines, 1708]. s8º. 1708
La vie de A. B., écrite partie par elle-mème, partie par une personne de sa connoissance [Pierre Poiret] &c. 2v. s8º. Amsterdam. 1683
A warning against the Quakers. [Tr.] 8º. 1708
see Cockburn (J.) Bourignianism detected, 2 narr., 1698.
,, Jäger (J. W.) Exam. theol. nov. Mad. de B. &c., 1708.
,, —— Nova purgatio animæ, excocta in cerebro Mad. B. &c., 1716.

Bourinot (*Sir* John George). Canada. n. & rev. ed. w. add. chap. by W. H. Ingram. s8º. [1922]

Bourke (*Sir* Richard), *1777–1855, see* Australia. Hist. records, s1, Governors' despatches, v16–19, 1923.

Bourmont (*le cte.* Louis Auguste Victor de), *maréchal de France.* [†Chaisne (L. A. V. de), *cte. de Bourmont*; Ghaisne], *see* Gautherot (G.) Un gentilhomme de grand chemin, le maréchal de B., 1926.

Bourne, *Lincs.* Parish reg. of B., 1562–1650. Ed. C. W. Foster. [Lincoln Rec. Soc. Par. Reg. Sect., v7]. la8º. Horncastle. 1921

Bourne (George) [*i.e.* George Sturt]. A farmer's life, w. a mem. of the farmer's sister. 8º. 1922
The wheelwright's shop. 8º. C. 1923
William Smith, potter & farmer, 1790–1858. s8º. 1920

Bourne (Gilbert Charles). A text-book of oarsmanship, w. essay on muscular action in rowing. 8º. O. 1925

Bourne (Vincent). Poematia. [Memoir by J. Mitford. Tr. by W. Cowper]. s8º. 1840

Bournon (Fernand). Paris—atlas illustré. 4º. [1900]

Bournville Works, *see* Cadbury Bros. Ltd.

Bourrienne [†Fauvelet de Bourrienne (Louis Antoine)]. Mém. sur Napoléon &c. 10t. 8º. 1829

Bourrilly (J.), *see* Bouches-du-Rhône; encyclop. départ., t2, 3, 13, par B. &c., 1920–24.

Boursault (Edme). Le médecin volant: comédie (1661)—Le portrait du peintre: comédie (1663), *see* Fournel (V.) Contemp. de Molière, t1, 1863.

Bousfield (Paul). The omnipotent self: st. in self-deception & self-cure. s8º. 1923

Bousquet (*Mrs.*)
Diary, 1765. Ed. Mrs. Tindall. [repr.] la8º. Norwich. [1927]

Bousquet (Joseph Claude François). Hist. du clergé de France dep. l'introd. du christianisme dans les Gaules j. nos jours. 4t [*& Suppl. b. w.* t4, *pagin. contin.*] 8º. 1847–51

Bousquet (P. H. Jacques) & H. Falk. Un ange passa, comédie, *see* Œuvres libres, 39, 1924.

Boussac de Saint-Marc (André). Le loup de Gubbio: pièce, *see* Revue (La) hebdomadaire. Suppl.: coll. nouv. &c., No. 8, 1922.

Boussard (Geoffroy). *De continentia sacerdotum. Sub hac quæstione nova utrum Papa possit cum sacerdote dispensare ut nubat. s4º. Landsshüt *Joannes Weyssenburger.* [c. 1515]

Boussat (Maurice Audubert-), *see* Audubert-Boussat (M.)

Bousset (Hermann).
*Das Spartakus Programm. [P2574]. s8º. [1919]

Bousset (Wilhelm). Apophthegmata: Studien z. Gesch. d. ält. Mönchtums. Aus d. Nachlass hrsg. v. T. Hermann & G. Krüger. la8º. Tübingen. 1923
Kyrios Christos: Gesch. d. Christusglaubens, bis Irenæus. 2e umgearb. A. 8º. Göttingen. 1921
see Gunkel (H.) W. B.: Gedächtnisrede, 1920.
,, Weiss (J.) Die Schriften d. Neuen Test.; neu übers. u. erklärt, 3e A., hrsg. v. W. B. &c., 4B, 1917–18.

Boussingault (Adam). Le théatre de la Moscovie. s8º. 1859

Boutens (Petrus Cornelis).
Beatrys. 16e dr. s8º. Bussum. 1919
Carmina. 8º. A. 1920
Præludiën. 8º. A. 1919
Stemmen. 5. uitg. 8º. A. 1925
Vergeten liedjes. 4e dr. 8º. Bussum. 1918
Verzen. 8º. A. 1920

Boutet (Frédéric). *Works in* Œuvres libres.
Les dames Barigny, nouvelle, 1926. [61.]
Faiseurs d'or—Faiseurs d'hommes—Faiseurs d'églises, choses vues, 1926. [57.]
La fille de Mme. Tranchart, 1923. [29.]
Georgette, roman, 1922. [13.]
Gribiche, nouvelle, 1925. [44.]
Le harem éparpillé, 1924. [39.]
Mages noirs—messes noir, le satanisme mod., 1925. [51.]
Morgane passa, 1923. [22.]

Boutflower (Charles), *vicar of Terling, Essex.* In & around the Book of Daniel. Pref. by T. G. Pinches. 8º. 1923

Boutflower (Douglas Samuel), *see* Durham. Fasti Dunelm.; ed. D. S. B., 1926.

Boutroux (Émile).
The beyond that is within, & o. addresses. Tr. J. Nield. s8º. 1912
De l'idée de loi naturelle dans la sci. & la philos. contemp. n. éd. 8º. 1925
Nouv. études d'hist. de la philos. 8º. 1927
see Curel (*vte.* F. de). Disc. pour la récept. de F. de C. (Rép. de É. B.), 1919.
,, Gaultier (P.) Maîtres de la pensée franç., E. B. &c., 1921.
,, Nolhac (P. de). Disc. pour la récept. de P. de N. [*on* E. B.], 1923.

Bouts (Dietrick), *see* Friedländer (M. J.) Altniederländ. Malerei, B3, 1925.

Bouts (Thiéry), *see* Fierens-Gevaert (H.) L'exposition v. E.-B. &c. 1921.

Bouvet (Charles). L'Opéra : l'Acad. de Musique—le Musée —la bibliothèque. s8º. [1924]

Bouvet (Joachim) [Bovet (Giovanni)]. *Icon regia monarchæ Sinarum nunc regnantis. Ex Gallico versa. [*wanting portrait*]. s8º. 1699

„ „ *for a. ed. see* Sinica. Noviss. Sinica hist. &c., 1699.

Ist. de l'Imperador de la Cina. Tr. F. Cisnocilio. s8º. Padova. 1710

Bouvet de Cressé (Auguste Jean Baptiste). Hist. de la catastrophe de Saint-Domingue, avec corr. des gén. Leclerc, Henry-Christophe &c. Publ. par B. de C. 8º. 1824

Bouvier (Eugène Louis).
Le communisme chez les insectes. s8º. 1926
Habitudes & métamorphoses des insectes. s8º. 1921
The psychic life of insects. Tr. L. O. Howard. 8º. 1922

Bouvier (Jean-Baptiste), *bp. of Le Mans.* Traité dogmat. &c. des indulgences des confréries & du jubilée. 4e éd. 8º. au Mans. 1832

Bouvier (Louis). Flore des Alpes, de la Suisse & de la Savoie. 2e éd., augm. s8º. 1882

Bouwhuys (M. ten), *see* Meulen (A. J. van der). Platenatlas voor de Vaderl. gesch. ; door A. J. van der M. mid medewerk. van M. ten B., 1912.

Bouyer (Raymond). Claude Lorrain : biog. crit. 8º. [1927]

Bove (Emmanuel). Armand. Roman. [16e éd.] s8º. 1927
Le crime d'une nuit, *see* Œuvres libres, 57, 1926.
Un père & sa fille, *see* Œuvres libres, 81, 1928.

Bovet (Giovanni), *see* Bouvet (J.)

Bovet (*Mlle.* Marie Anne de). Cracovie. la8º 1910

Bovet (Pierre). The fighting instinct. Auth. Eng. tr. by J. Y. T. Greig. 8º. [1923]

Bovius (Joannes Carolus), *bp. of Oustuni, abp. of Brindisi, see* Apostolic : Constit. Apost. De Constit. Apost. libri 8 ; Io. C. B. interprete, 1564.

Bovy (Daniel Baud-), *see* Baud-Bovy (D.)

Bow Street Police Court. [Newspaper cuttings of accounts of cases at B. S., 1801–23, w. MS. index]. 4º. [1801–23]

Bowden (Witt). Indust. society in England tow. end of 18th cent. 8º. N.Y. 1925

Bowdler (John), *the younger, Barrister-at-law.*
Select pieces in verse & prose. 2v. 8º. 1817

Bowen (*Sir* Albert E.), *bart.* Illustr. particulars &c. of sale of Colworth [Bedfordshire] by Knight, Frank & Rutley. fol. 1924

Bowen (Francis), *Alford prof. of Moral Philos. at Harvard.*
Amer. polit. economy &c. 8º. N.Y. 1870

Bowen (Frank C.) The sea, its hist. & romance. 4v. 4º. [1925–26]

Bowen (Harold). The life & times of 'Alí ibn 'Isà, " The Good Vizier." 8º. C. 1928

Bowen (Marjorie), *ps.* [*i.e. Mrs.* Gabrielle Margaret Long].
The cheats. s8º. [1920]
Dark Ann & o. s. s8º. 1927
The Glen o' Weeping [*Glencoe*]. pop. ed. s8º. [1923]
The haunted vintage. s8º. [1921]
The Leopard & the Lily. s8º. [1920]
" Luctor et emergo " : essay on state of Eng. at Peace of Ryswyck, 1697. [*a. c. in* P2785]. 8º. Newcastle-upon-Tyne. 1925
Mr. Misfortunate. s8º. [1919]
The Netherlands display'd. 8º [1926]
Stinging nettles. s8º. 1923
Sundry great gentlemen. 8º. [1928]
The viper of Milan. pop. ed. s8º. [1923]

Bowen-Rowlands (Ernest). Judgment of death. 8º. [1924]
Seventy-two years at the bar, a memoir [of H. B. Poland]. 8º. 1924

Bower (Bertha Muzzy), *wife of (1) C. J. Bower ; (2) B. W. Sinclair ; (3) R. E. Cowan.* The uphill climb. s8º. [1923]

Bower (Frederick Orpen). The ferns (Filicales) treated compar. w. a view to th. nat. classific. v1, 2. la8º. C. 1923–26
Plants & man : botany of ordinary life. 8º. 1925
see Evolution. E. in the light of mod. knowledge ; [*by* F. O. B. &c.], 1925.

Bower (H. Syndercombe), *see* Graham (P. A.) Iwerne Minster, w. contrib. by H. S. B. &c., 1923.

Bower (*Sir* John William Nott-), *see* Nott-Bower (*Sir* J. W.)

Bowers (Claude Gernade). Jefferson & Hamilton : the struggle for democracy in America. 8º. 1925

Bowers (R. S.)
Drawing & design for craftsmen. [repr.] 8º. [1919]

Bowes (James Lord). Notes on shippo. A sequel to Japanese enamels. la8º. *p.f.p.c.* Liv'l. 1895

Bowes-Lyon (Muriel) & Winnifred Bowes-Lyon. Woodcote Manor, Bramdean, for sale by J. D. Wood & Co. &c., 11th Oct. 1921. By dir. of Misses B.-L. [P2752]. 4º. [1921]

Bowhay (*Miss* Bertha Louisa). Hector of Welcome's. s8º. [1927]

Bowhay (T. A.) Life & man. 8º. [1926]

Bowlby (*Maj.-Gen. Sir* Anthony Alfred), *see* War. Gen. hist. of the Gt. War : medical services ; surgery, ed. Maj. Gen. Sir W. Macpherson, Sir A. A. B. &c., v1, 2, 1922.

Bowles, *The family of, see* Bowles (W. H.) Records of B. family, 1918.

Bowles (Charles), *of Chatham, see* Bowles (W. H.) Records of the Bowles family : line deriving f. C. B., 1918.

Bowles (E. A.), *F.L.S.* Handbook of crocus & colchicum. 8º. 1924

Bowles (George Frederic Stewart).
The strength of England. 8º. [1926]

Bowles (William Henry). Records of the Bowles family : hist. of a line deriving f. Ch. Bowles of Chatham &c. 4º. *n.p., p.f.p.c.* 1918

Bowles (William Lisle). A Wiltshire parson & h. friends : corr. of W. L. B., w. 4 reviews by Coleridge. Ed. G. Greever. 8º. [1926]

Bowley (Arthur Lyon).
The change in the distrib. of the nat. income, 1880–1913. Lect. [P2395]. 8º. O. 1920
An elem. manual of statistics. 3rd ed. 8º. 1920
„ „ 3rd. ed. rev. 8º. 1923
„ „ Key. 8º. 1923
Elements of statistics. 4th ed. 2p [*pagin. contin.*] 8º. 1920
Official statistics : what they contain & how to use them. s8º. 1921
Prices & wages in the U.K., 1914–20. [C.E. for I.P.] la8º. O. 1921

—— **& M. H. Hogg.** Has poverty diminished ? Sequel to " Livelihood & poverty." 8º. 1925

—— **& *Sir* J. Stamp.**
The national income, 1924. 8º. O. 1927

Bowman (Eric Fisher). Intr. to polit. science. 8º. [1927]

Bowman (Florence L.) & E. J. Roper. Traders in east & west ; trade in 17 & 18 cent. [Texts for students, No. 37]. 8º. 1924

Bowman (Frederick H.)
The structure of the cotton fibre. 8º. M'ter. 1881

Bowman (Isaiah). The Andes of Southern Peru. Geogr. reconnaissance. Publ. for The Amer. Geogr. Soc. of N.Y. la8º. [1920]
The new world : problems in polit. geography. 8º. 1922
„ „ Suppl. 8º. N.Y. 1924

Bowman (T. & A.), *publishers.*
B.'s guide to Richmond & Rokeby. 8º. Richmond. 1836

Bowne (Borden Parker). Personalism. 8º. Boston. 1908
Studies in theism. s8º. N.Y. 1880
Theory of thought & knowledge. 8º. N.Y. 1897

Bowrey (Thomas). Papers, 1669–1713 ; discov. in 1913 by J. Humphreys. P1, Diary of a 6 weeks' Tour in 1698 in Holland & Flanders. P2, Story of the Mary Galley, 1704–10. Ed. Sir R. C. Temple. [Hakluyt Soc., II, 58]. 8º. 1927
see Malay. Grammar of M. tongue ; compiled f. B.'s dict., 1800.

Bowring (*Sir* John). Lang. & lit. of Friesland. [From Westminster Rev., 1829. P2561]. 8º. 1829
Matins & vespers, w. hymns &c. 2nd ed. altered &c. s8º. 1824
Specimens of the Russian poets, w. biog. not. Tr. J. B. 2v. s8º. 1821–3

Bowyer (*Sir* George), *7th bart.* Readings delivered before the Middle Temple in 1850. 8º. 1851

Bowyer (William). Crit. conjectures & obs. on the New Test., coll. f. var. a. By W. B., Bp. Barrington &c. 4th ed., enl. & corr. s4º. 1812
*The origin of printing, in 2 essays : 1, the substance of Middleton's diss., 2, Meerman's acc. of the invention. 8º. 1774

Bowyer (William) *ps., see* Morrell (W.)

Box (George Herbert), *see* Oesterley (W. O. E.) & G. H. B. Sh. survey of the lit. of Rabbinical & med. Judaism, 1920.

—— **& C. Gore.** Divorce in the New Test. A reply to Dr. Charles. s8º. 1921

Box (John), *civil engineer.* Chron. of the castle of Amelroy, or Ammerzode ; w. notices of its anc. barons. 4º. 1870

Box (Pelham H.) Three master builders & another [*i.e.* Lenin, Mussolini, Venizelos, Woodrow Wilson]. Intr. by E. Barker. 8º. 1925

Boxer (Edward Mourrier). An answer to a pamph. by Col. Lefroy. [*b. w. h.* Remarks on ordnance, 1862]. 8º. Woolwich. *p.f.p.c.* 1862

Boxer (Edward Mourrier) [*continued*].
Diagrams ref. to in Treatise on artillery, prep. for R. M. Acad. Sect. 2, 2p. obl.4°. 1853–54
Remarks on permanent forts & moveable floating batteries &c. [*b. w. h.* Remarks on ordnance, 1862]. 8°. 1862
Remarks on system prop. by Royal Comm. for defence. [*b. w. h.* Remarks on ordnance, 1862]. 8°. Woolwich. *p.f.p.c.* 1862
Remarks on the system of ordnance most efficient against iron-clad ships &c. 8°. Woolwich. 1862

Boxhorn (Hendrik) [Bochorinck (H.)], *see* Cuyckius (H.) Panegyricæ orationes 7; add. Parænetica in H. B. Cath. relig. desertorem, 1596.

Boyce (Warren Scott). Econ. & soc. hist. of Chowan Co., N. Carolina, 1880–1915. [Columbia Univ. Sts. in hist. &c., 76]. 8°. N.Y. 1917

Boyce (William Binnington).
The higher criticism & the Bible. s8°. 1881
Introd. to the study of hist., civil, eccl. & lit. la8°. 1884
An Irenicum. [P2506]. 8°. 1886
*Mem. of W. Shaw. Ed. by h. friend. [W. B. B.] s8°. 1874
Six lect. on the higher criticism upon the Old Test. 8°. Sydney, *p.f.p.c.* 1878
*Statistics of Protest. missionary soc., 1872–73. [Comp. by W. B. B.] 8°. 1874

Boyd (Archibald), *Dean of Exeter, see* Ulster. The plea of presbytery, reply to A. B., 1843.

Boyd (*Major* Charles). The Turkish interpreter. 8°. Paris. 1842

Boyd (Ernest Augustus). Guy de Maupassant. 8°. 1926
Ireland's literary renaissance. [n. ed.] la8°. 1923

Boyd (Robert), *of Trochrig.*
In Epist. ad Ephesios prælectiones. fol. Genevæ. 1661

Boyd (Thomas Stirling). The web. Play. s8°. O. 1925

Boyd (William), *lecturer in Univ. of Glasgow.*
The hist. of Western educ. 8°. 1921

Boyd of Kilmarnock, *The family of.* Sel. f. papers of the fam. of B. of K., 1468–1590, *see* Abbotsford Club. Misc., v1, 1837.

Boyé (Pierre). Le roi Stanislas grand-père (1725–66). Recueil de lettres &c. 8°. Nancy. 1922

Boy-Ed (Carl). Verschwörer? Die ersten 17 Kriegsmonate in d. Verein. Staaten. s8°. [1920]

Boyer (Abel). Characters of the virtues & vices of the age &c. Tr. & extr. s8°. 1695

Boyer (Auguste M.), *see* Kharoṣṭhī. K. inscriptions discov. by Sir A. Stein; transcr. & ed. by A. M. B. &c., 2p, 1920–27.

Boyer (Charles). Christianisme & Néo-platonisme dans la formation de St. Augustin. 8°. 1920

Boyer (Clarence Valentine). The villain as hero in Elizabethan tragedy. 8°. [1914]

Boyer (Jean Pierre), *president of the Republic of Hayti, see* Wallez (J. B.) Précis hist. des négoc. entre France & St.-Domingue &c.; suivi d'une notice biog. sur le Gén. B., 1826.

Boyer (Paul), *see* Paris. University. La vie univ. à P.; publ. par P. B. &c., 1918.

Boyer (Pierre Denis). Apologie du St.-Office dans les décisions sur le prêt à interêt—Lettre de l'a. de la Défense de l'Eglise, *see* Migne (J. P.), *ed.* Theol. cursus, t16, 1859.

Boylan (Patrick). Thoth the Hermes of Egypt. la8°. 1922

Boyle: Fashionable court & country guide [Boyle's Court Guide], 1808, 1814, 1829, 1916, 1922. s8°. 1808–1922

Boyle (Constance Nina).
What became of Mr. Desmond. s8°. [1922]

Boyle (*Hon.* Robert), *5th son of 1st earl of Cork.* Experiments & notes abt. the mechan. orig. &c. of electricity [& magnetism], 1675–76. [Ed. R. T. Gunther. Old Ashmolean repr., 7]. s8°. O. 1927
Some consid. t. the style of the H. Scriptures. [*b. w. h.* Some motives &c. 4th ed., 1665]. 3rd ed. s8°. 1668
Some motives &c. to the love of God. 4th ed. corr. s8°. 1665
Theolog. works epitomiz'd. Ed. R. Boulton. [With author's life]. 3v. [v2, *wanting*]. s8°. 1735

Boylesve (René).
Ah! plaisez-moi. . . . s8°. 1922
Le carrosse aux deux lézards verts. s8°. 1921
Le dangereux jeune homme. s8°. [1921]
Les deux romanciers. s8°. [1926]
Elise. s8°. 1921
Feuilles tombées. Intr. de C. Du Bois. 8°. 1927
La fin—enfin!—des leçons d'amour dans un parc: nouvelle, *see* Œuvres libres, 52, 1925.
La leçon d'amour dans un parc. [4e éd.] s8°. [1920]
Nouv. leçons d'amour dans un parc. s8°. [1925]
Tu n'es plus rien. s8°. 1919
see Valéry (P.) Disc. de récep. [*on* R. B.], 1927.
„ —— P. V.; [*by var. a.* R. B. &c.], 1926.

Boynton (Edward C.) Hist. of West Point dur. the Revol., & of the U.S. Milit. Acad. 8°. N.Y. 1863

Boys (John), *dean of Canterbury, 1571–1625.*
Workes [*Engraved tp.*] sfol. 1622
There are 4 other tps. An exposition of all the principall scriptures used in our liturgie, 1622—An exposition of the Dominicall Epistles & Gospels &c., 1622—An exposition of the festivall Epistles and Gospels &c. 1622—Lectures, 1622.

Boys (Thomas Shotter). Orig. views of London as it is, 1842. Re-issue, w. notes & intr. by E. B. Chancellor. 4°. 1926

Boys (William), *F.S.A.* A coll. of shells discov. near Sandwich. Figures drawn by G. Walker. [*b. w.* Maton (W. G.) & T. Rackett. Hist. acc., 1804]. 4°. [1784]

Boyse (Joseph). Remarks on late discourse of William [King], bp. of Derry, conc. the inventions of men &c. s8°. 1694

Boysen (Petrus Adolphus). Diss. de cod. Græco N.T. & consilio quo usus est Lutherus &c. [P430]. s4°. Lipsiæ. 1723

Boysen Jensen (P.) Genet. Zusammenhang zw. d. normal. u. intramolekular. Atmung d. Pflanzen, *see* Kong. Dan. Vid. Selsk. Biol. Medd., 4, 1923–25.

Boyson (V. F.) The Falkland Islands, w. notes on the natural hist. by R. Vallentin. 8°. O. 1924

Boyvin (Jean Gabriel). Philosophia Scoti vindic. &c. 4p *in* 4v. s8°. Bononiæ. 1681–90
Theologia Scoti. 6a. ed. corr. 4p. [p4, 5a. ed. Parisiis, 1682]. s8°. Venetiis. 1682–90

Bozman (John Leeds). Sketch of the hist. of Maryland. Prefixed copious intr. 8°. Baltimore. 1811

Bozzelli (Francesco Paolo), *see* Croce (B.) F. P. B. & Giacinto de Sivo, 1918.

Bozzola (Annibale). Un capitano di guerra &c. Guglielmo VII di Monferrato (1254–92), *see* Regia Deput. Miscellanea, t50, 1922.

Braatz (Kurt Wassiljewitsch von). Fürst A. P. Lieven im Kampfe gegen d. balt. Separatismus, Bolschewismus u. d. Awaloff-Bermondt Affäre. 8°. St. [1926]

Brabant. Chambres des comptes de Flandre & de B.; inventaire &c., 1914, *see* Nelis (H.), *ed.*
Inventaire des chartes &c. des duchés de B. &c., p1, t1–7, 1910–17, *see* Verkooren (A.)
Inventaire gén. des archives ecclés. du B., t2, 3, 1914–22, *see* Hoop (A. d') *ed.*

Brabant (Frederick Gaspard). Berkshire. 2nd ed. s8°. [1919]
Oxfordshire. s8°. 1906
Sussex. 6th ed. s8°. [1920]

Bracci (Pietro), *see* Domarus (K. v.) P. B.: Beitr. z. röm. Kunstgesch. d. 18. Jhdts., 1915.

Bracciolini (Poggio). The Facetiæ of Poggio &c. Tr. E. Storer. Intr. & notes. s8°. 1928
O livro de Nicoláo Veneto [escr. por Pogio], *see* Polo (M.) Livro de M. P., 1922.

Bracco (Roberto). Col permesso del babbo. Versi dialettali—Teatro—Novelle—Scritti var. Pref. di M. Serao. 8°. Palermo. 1926
Teatro. v1–11. [1–3, 11, 3a ed.; 4, 6, 4a ed.; 5, 7, 8, 2a ed.] s8°. Milano. [1907?–25]
see Flaviis (C. de). R. B., 1920.

Bracey (Robert), *O.P.* Eighteenth cent. st. & o. papers. Foreword by Bp. of Clifton. s8°. O. 1925

Brach (Albert). Nicola u. Giov. Pisano u. d. Plastik d. 14. Jhdts. in Siena. la8°. Str. 1904

Brach (Paul). La protégée: roman, *see* Œuvres libres, 60, 1926.

Brache (Helga de la), *see* La Brache (H. de).

Brackel (Ly van). Zuchthäuslerin Nr. 5553. Kriegs-Erlebnisse e. deut. Frau in Frankreich. s8°. [1918]

Brackenbury (*Major.-Gen.* Charles Booth). Defence of villages & street fighting. [P2593]. s8°. Aldershot. 1889
European armaments in 1867. s8°. 1867
Field works. With app. & Plates. [*b. separately.* Milit. Hdbks., v7]. s8°. 1888
The use & abuse of field artillery. [P2602]. s8°. Aldershot. 1888

Brackenbury (Robert Carr). Sacred poems in 3 parts. s8°. 1791
Sacred poetry. s8°. 1800

Brackenhoffer (Elias). Voyage en France, 1643–4. Tr. d'ap. le ms. du Musée hist. de Strasbourg par H. Lehr. Intr. de J. Hatt. 8°. 1925

Brackett (Oliver). Encyclop. of Eng. furniture. Pictorial review, f. Gothic times to mid-nineteenth cent. Ed., w. intr. by O. B. fol. 1927
Thomas Chippendale: h. life, work & influence. 4°. [1924]
see Victoria & Albert Mus. Jones Coll.; p1, Furniture, by O. B., 1922.

Brackley (Thomas Egerton, *viscount***),** *Lord Chancellor* [*baron* ELLESMERE]. Letters (1608–16), *see* ABBOTSFORD CLUB. Misc., v1, 1837.
Brackmann (Albert), *see* KEHR (P. F.) Regesta Pontificum Rom.: Germania pontificia, v1i, ii, Provincia Maguntin. auctore A. B., 1923–27.
Bracton (Henry de), *see* GÜTERBOCK (C.) B. & his relat. to the Rom. law, 1866.
Bradburn (Samuel).
Hymns, among Methodists. [*in MS.*] s8°. 1781
Bradbury (Fred). Flax culture & preparation. 8°. *n.d.*
Bradby (E. D.)
Short hist. of the French Revol., 1789–95. 8°. O. 1926
Bradby (Godfrey Fox).
The chronicles of Dawnhope. s8°. 1921
The eternal past. s8°. 1927
The face in the mirror. s8°. [1923]
The gt. days of Versailles: court in later yrs. of Louis XIV. [2nd impr. of re-issue]. 8°. 1927
The Lady of the Manor. s8°. [1925]
The way. [Poems]. s8°. O. 1921
„ „ ....2nd ed. [P2867]. s8°. Rugby. 1923
Bradby (*Miss* M. K.)
The logic of the unconscious mind. 8°. 1920
Braddell (Roland St. John), *see* MAKEPEACE (W.) & R. ST. J. B., *edd.* 100 yrs. of Singapore, 2v, 1921.
Brade (William Robert Victor). From Plotinus to S. Thomas Aquinas: later phases of the tradition of Greek philos. s8°. [1926]
Bradford Library. Catalogue of books in the B. Lib. & Lit. Soc., w. laws. 8°. Bradford. 1895
Bradford (Alden). Hist. of Mass., 1620–1820. 8°. Boston. 1835
New England chronology, 1497–1800. s8°. Boston [Mass.] 1843
Bradford (*Adm. Sir* Edward Eden), *K.C.B.*
Life of Adm. Sir A. K. Wilson, Bart., V.C. 8°. 1923
Bradford (Ernest Smith). Indust. unemployment: statist. study, *see* UNITED STATES: LAB., Bull., No. 310, 1922.
Bradford (Gamaliel), *Jr.* Union portraits. 8°. Boston [Mass.] 1916
Bradford (Orlando George Charles Bridgeman, *3rd earl of***),** *see* †BOYLE (M. L.) Biog. cat. of portraits at Weston, seat of the Earl of B., 1888.
Bradford (Samuel), *bp of (1) Carlisle, (2) Rochester.* The credibility of the Christian revelation; in 8 sermons, St. Paul's, 1699 &c. With a 9th as an app. s4°. 1700
Each sermon is a distinct publn.: the collect. title has been pr. subsequently to bring the whole into one vol.
Bradford (William), *Governor of New Plymouth.* Hist. "of Plimoth Plantation," f. orig. MS. With rep. on proc. incid. to the return of MS. to Mass. la8°. Boston [Mass.] 1898
„ „ ....[repr.] la8°. Boston [Mass.] 1900
Bradlaugh (Charles). [Theological essays]: Heresy [*& o. p. each w. sep. pagin.*] s8°. *n.d.*
see ROBERTSON (J. M.) C. B., 1920.
Bradley, *Family, ps.* The Bradleys' visit to Thistledown Hall, 1864, *see* BRIERLEY (B.)
Bradley (Andrew Cecil). B. Bosanquet, 1848–1923. [*By* A. C. Bradley & Ld. Haldane. From Proc. of Brit. Acad., v11. P2731]. 8°. [1924]
Shakespearean tragedy. 2nd ed., 16th impr. 8°. 1922
Bradley (Arthur Granville). A book of the Severn. 8°. [1920]
Exmoor memories. 8°. [1926]
Hist. of Canada to the Great War, *see* BUCHAN (J.), *ed.* Nations of to-day, Brit. Amer., 1923.
——, A. C. Champneys & J. W. Baines. Hist. of Marlborough College. Rev. & cont. by J. R. Taylor, H. C. Brentall &c. 8°. 1923
Bradley (Cuthbert) [*ps.* WHIPSTER]. Fox-hunting f. shire to shire. Intr. note by Capt. E. P. Elmhurst. la8°. 1912
Bradley (Edward) [*ps.* CUTHBERT BEDE]. Argyll's Highlands: or MacCailein Mor & the Lords of Lorne, w. tradit. tales &c. Ed. J. Mackay. la8°. Glasgow. 1902
Bradley (Francis Herbert).
Appearance & reality. 2nd ed. rev. [5th impr.] 8°. 1908
Ethical studies. 2nd ed. 8°. O. 1927
The principles of logic. Anastatic repr. of 1883 ed. 8°. N.Y. 1912
Principles of logic. 2nd ed. rev. w. comm. & terminal essays. 2v. 8°. 1922
see RASHDALL (H.) The metaphysic of Mr. F. H. B., 1912.
„ TAYLOR (A. E.) F. H. B., 1926.
Bradley (Harriett). The enclosures in England: econ. reconstruction. [Columbia Univ. St^s. in hist. &c., 80ii]. 8°. N.Y. 1918
Bradley (Henry). The Cædmonian Genesis, *see* ENGLISH Assoc. Essays & studies, v6, 1920.
Coll. papers. Mem. by R. Bridges. 8°. O. 1928
The Goths. [Story of the nations]. 5th ed. s8°. *n.d.*
Numbered sections in old Eng. poetical MSS., 1915, *see* BRIT. ACAD. Proc., 1915–16.
On the relations betw. spoken & wr. lang., w. spec. ref. to English. s8°. O. 1919
—— & R. Bridges. On the terms Briton, British, Britisher—Preposition at end, by H. W. Fowler. [S.P.E. Tract, No. 14]. 8°. 1923
Bradley (Herbert Dennis). The wisdom of the gods. s8°. 1925
Bradley (John William). Illum. MSS. 2nd ed. s8°. [1920]
Bradley (Orlando Charnock).
Hist. of Edinburgh Veterinary College. 8°. E. 1923
Bradley (Richard), *F.R.S.* New improvements of planting & gardening. 3p [2 & 3 *sep. pagin.*] p3, w. the Gentleman & gardener's Kalendar [*sep. tp. & pagin.*] 4th ed., added, tract int. Herefordshire orchards. [*By J. Beale, sep. tp. & pagin.*] 8°. 1724
Bradley (Robert Noël). Racial origins of Eng. character., w. app. on language. s8°. [1926]
Bradner (Leicester). Life & poems of Richard Edwards. [Yale St. in Eng., 74]. 8°. New Haven, *Yale.* 1927
Bradney (Joseph Alfred).
Hist. of Monmouthshire. v3i, ii & Index. fol. 1921–23
Bradshaw (Frederick). A social hist. of Eng. 2nd ed. s8°. 1921
Bradshaw (George), *publisher of the "Railway guide."* Descriptive guide to the G. W. Ry. By E. L. Blanchard. pl. s8°. 1845
Bradshaw (Harold Chalton). Præneste: a st. for its restoration, *see* BRIT. SCH. AT ROME. Papers, v9, 1920.
Bradshaw (Henry), *Benedictine, see* RADEGUNDA, *St.* *The lyfe of Saynt Radegunde: [*attrib. to* B.]; ed. F. Brittain, 1926.
Bradshaw (William), *Puritan Divine.* *Puritanismus Anglicanus. [Tr., *w. pref.* by W. Ames]. Annectitur discept. de circulo pontificio. s8°. Francofurti. 1610
Bradstock (William Burton), *ps., see* HALL (J. R. C.)
Bradwardinus (Thomas), *abp. of Canterbury.* De causa Dei, contra Pelagium, & de virtute causarum, ad suos Mertonenses, libri tres; opera & studio H. Savilii nunc primum ed. fol. Londini. 1618
Bradway (John S.), *see* SMITH (R. H.) & J. S. B. Growth of legal aid work in the U.S., 1926.
Brady (Alexander). Thomas D'A. McGee. [Canadian Statesman, 2]. 8°. Toronto. 1925
Brady (John). Clavis calendaria; or analysis of the Calendar &c. 3rd ed. 2v. 8°. 1815
Brady (Nicholas), *see* BIBLE: PSALMS. New version of the Ps., *var. ed.*
Braekeleer (Henri de), *see* VANZYPE (G.) H. de B., 1923.
Braga (Theophilo). Cancioneiro popular portuguez. [Bibl. das tradições port., 2]. 2ª ed. ampl. [v]1. 8°. 1911
Romanceiro geral portuguez. [Bibl. das tradições port., 3]. 2ª ed. ampl. 3[v]. 8°. 1906–9
1, Romances heroicos, novellescos e de aventuras.
2, Romances de aventuras, hist., lendarios e sacros.
3, Romances com fórma litt. do sec. 15 a 18 *&* Notas.
Bragg (W. B.), *see* MARKET HARBOROUGH. Parish records, to 1837; by J. E. Stocks, assisted by W. B. B., 2v, 1890–1926.
Bragg (*Sir* William Henry).
Conc. the nature of things. 6 lect^s. 8°. 1925
Old trades & new knowledge. 6 lect^s. s8°. 1926
The world of sound. s8°. 1920
—— & W. L. Bragg.
X-rays & crystal structure. 4th ed., rev. & enl. 8°. 1924
Bragg (William Lawrence), *see* BRAGG (*Sir* W. H.) & W. L. B. X-rays & crystal structure, 1924.
Braghirolli (Willelmo), *see* INTRA (G. B.) G. B., cenni biog., 1885.
Braham (Ernest G.)
Problem of the self & immortality. 8°. [1925]
Brahe (Tycho), *see* BECKETT (F.) T. B.'s Uraniborg & Stjerneborg (*Dan. & Eng.*), 1921.
Brahm (Alcanter de).
Curiosités de Carnavalet d'ap. des doc. inéd. 8°. 1920
Brahms (Johannes). Symphonien. Op. 68 (C moll), Op. 73 (D dur), Op. 90 (F dur), Op. 98 (E moll). [4v *in* 2. v3, London]. s8°. *Simrock.* [1901]
see SCHUMANN (C.) & J. B. Briefe, 1853–96, 2B, 1927; tr., 2v, 1927.

Brailsford (Henry Noel). After the Peace. s8⁰. [1920]
A league of nations. 2nd & rev. ed. s8⁰. 1917
The Russian workers' republic. s8⁰. [1921]

Brailsford (Mabel Richmond).
A Quaker f. Cromwell's army: J. Nayler. 8⁰. [1927]

Brain. A journal of neurology. Ed. H. Head. v42–47. la8⁰. 1919–24

Braine (A.) Hist. of Kingswood forest: manors &c. 8⁰. 1891

Brainerd (David), *missionary, 1718–47.*
see EDWARDS (J.) Works, v3, Life &c. of D. B., 1807.
„ —— Life &c. of D. B., 1826.
„ PRATT (J.) The life of D. B., 1856.
„ WESLEY (J.) Extr. of the life of D. B., 3rd ed., 1793; 1825.

Braines (W. W.) *The site of the Globe Playhouse, Southwark. Publ. by arr. w. the London County Council. 2nd ed., rev. & enl. la8⁰. 1924

Brais (Etienne de) [†BRAIS (STEPHANUS DE)]. Epistolæ S. P. ad Romanos analysis paraphrastica &c. [*b. w.* Schmid (S.) Comm. in primam Joannis epist., 1707]. s4⁰. Francofurti & Lipsiæ. 1707

Braithwaite (John), *Wesleyan preacher, see* DICKINSON (R.) The life of J. B., 1825.

Braithwaite (Martha), *see* ALSOP (C. M.) Memorials; comp. by M. B., 1881.

Braithwaite (William Stanley). Anthology of magazine verse, 1926, & Yearbook of Amer. poetry (sesquicent. ed.) [*With* Intr. essays *by var. wr.* Poetry in the U.S.] 8⁰. Boston. 1926

Braithwaite-Batty (*Mrs.* Beatrice).
Mrs. Fauntleroy's nephew. s8⁰. [1923]

Brakelond (Jocelin, *of*) [JOCELINUS, *de Brakelonda, monk of St. Edmundsbury*]. The chronicle of B. Tr. & ed. L. C. Jane. Intr. by Abbot Gasquet. s8⁰. 1907

Brakspear (Harold), *see* STEWART-BROWN (R.) Birkenhead priory, w. chap. on monastic buildings by H. B., 1925.

Bramah (Ernest).
Kai Lung's golden hours. Pref. by H. Belloc. s8⁰. 1922
Max Carrados mysteries. s8⁰. [1927]
The wallet of Kai Lung. 3rd ed. s8⁰. [1923]

Bramante (Donato Lazzari), *see* MALAGUZZI-VALERI (F.) D. B.: 31 riprod., con testo e cat., 1924.

Brame (John Samuel Strafford).
Fuel, solid, liquid & gaseous. 2nd ed., 2nd impr. 8⁰. 1919

Bramhall. New court book of the manor of Bramhall, 1632–57; by H. W. Clemesha, *see* CHETHAM MISC., N.S., v4, 1921.

Bramhall (Frederick Dennison). Democracy the basis for world-order. [Univ. of Chicago. War papers, 3]. [P2509]. 8⁰. Chicago. [1918]

Bramhall (John), *abp. of Armagh.* A defence of true liberty, an answer to T. Hobbs. s8⁰. 1655
see SIMPSON (W. J. R.) Abp. B., 1927.

Bramson (Karen). Le Dictateur: pièce, *see* ŒUVRES libres, 53, 1925.

Bramwell (William), *1759–1818, Wesleyan minister.*
see HARRIS (T.) The Xtn. minister in earnest; W. B., 1846.
„ SIGSTON (J.) Mem. of W. B., 1839.

Brañas (Ricardo Puente y), *see* PUENTE Y BRAÑAS (R.)

Branca (Martino). Contesa per il dominio d. Sardegna tra Pisa e Genova, *see* ARCHIVIO STORICO ITAL. Anno 78, v1, 1920.

Branca (Taddeo del), *see* CIPOLLA (C.) T. del B. e una tradiz. leggend. sull 'Alighieri, 1887.

Brancaccio di Carpino (Francesco). I papi e i 19 sec. del papato. Cenni stor.-cron. v1, 2. la8⁰. Torino. 1897–99

Brancaleone (Niccolò), *Venetian painter* [MARCOREOS], *see* LA RONCIÈRE (C. DE). La découv. de l'Afr. au m. a., t3, 1927.

Branco (Wilhelm) [BRANCA]. Bericht ü. Urteile betreff. "Ziele vulkanolog. Forsch.," *see* KÖN.-PREUSS. AKAD. Abh., Phys.-math. Kl., 1914.
Einige Betracht. ü. d. ält. Säuger d. Trias- u. Liaszeit, *see* KÖN.-PREUSS. AKAD. Abh., Phys.-math. Kl., 1915.

Brancour (René). Hist. des instruments de musique. Préf. de C. M. Widor. la8⁰. 1921

Brand (*Sir* Henry Bouverie William), *see* OSSINGTON (J. E. D., *visct.*) & H. B. W. B. Decisions on points of order &c., 1857–84, [ed.] by E. G. Blackmore, 1892.

Brand (Neville). Narrow seas. s8⁰. [1923]

Brand (Robert Henry). War & nat. finance. 8⁰. 1921

Brand (*Rev.* Thomas), *see* ANNESLEY (S.) Life & fun. sermon of T. B., 1692.

Brandenburg [BRANDEMBURGK].
Catechismus oder Kinder predig. [*b. w.* Brandenburg. Kirchen Ordnung, 1533]. sfol. [Nürnberg, *Joh. Petreius.* 1533]
„ „ wie in B. gepred. [*forming part of* Kirchen Ordnung, 1540]. s4⁰. Berlin. 1540
„ „ [*a. ed. b. w.* Kirchen Ordnūg, 1543]. s8⁰. Nürnberg. 1543
*Kirchen Ordnung im Churfurstenthum d. Marcken zu B., wie man sich beide mit der Leer u. Ceremonien halten sol. [Catechismus *&* Von d. gebrauch d. Sacramenten *have sep. tp*ˢ. *& sig*ˢ., *3p in 1v*]. s4⁰. 1540
*Kirchen Ordnung In m. gned. Herrn der Marggraven zu B. &c. d. Stat Nürmberg Oberkeyt &c., Wie man sich mit d. Leer u Ceremonien halten solle. sfol. *n.p.* [Nürnberg, *Joh. Petreius*]. 1533
„ „ [*another ed.*] s8⁰. [Nürnberg]. 1543
Die Kunstdenkmäler d. Provinz B. Hrsg. v. Brandenburger Provinzialverbande. Bli, ii, Beihefte, 1iii, 3i, 5i, 6vi, 7i, 1, 2. [Bliii *no tp.*] 4⁰. 1907–27
1i, ii, Beihefte, Die vor- u. frühgeschichtl. Denkmäler d. Kreises Westprignitz *&* Ostprignitz. 1iii, Ruppin. 3i, Prenzlau. 5i, Luckau. 6vi, Crössen. 7i, Königsberg, H2, 3.
*Lehrbuch d. B.-Preuss. Gesch. z. Gebrauch in Gymnasien &c. s8⁰. 1825
*Von dem gebrauch der heilig. Sacramenten, Auch v. d. Ceremonien &c. [*b. w.* Kirchen Ordnung &c., 1540]. s4⁰. [1540 ?]

Brandenburg, *House of.*
see FREDERICK II. *Comment on [F.'s] Mems. of House of B., 1751.
„ WOLFF (R.) Politik d. Hauses B., 1486–99, 1919.

Brandenburg (Barbara, *Markgräfin* **von),** *see* BILLER (E.) Markgräfin B. v. B., 1886.

Brandenburg (Erich). From Bismarck to the World War: German for. policy, 1870–1914. Tr. A. E. Adams. 8⁰. 1927
Die Reichsgründung. 2B [*B2, 2. verb. A.*] 8⁰. L. 1916–23
Von Bismarck zum Weltkriege: deut. Politik in d. Jahrzehnten vor dem Kriege. 8⁰. 1924

—— & G. Eberlein.
Vorträge gehalten auf d. 6. Generalversamml. d. Vereins f. Ref.-gesch. am 11. Apr. 1901 in Breslau. [Verein f. Ref.-gesch. Schr., Jhrg. 19, Nr. 70]. 8⁰. Halle. 1901

Brandenburg (Hans).
Fr. Hölderlin, s. Leben u. s. Werk. s8⁰. L. 1924

Brandenburg (Nikolai Efimovich). Азовскій походъ Шеина 1697. [*Extr. f.* Военный Сборникъ, 1868. *b. w.* Dubrovin (N. F.) Походъ Зубова, 1874]. 8⁰. [1868]

Brander (A. A. Dunbar). Wild animals in Cent. India. 8⁰. 1923

Brandes (Georg). Cajus Julius Caesar. [Autor. Übers. v. E. Magnus]. 2B. 8⁰. 1925
Jesus: a myth. Tr. E. Björkman. s8⁰. [1927]
Tragediens anden Del. Fredslutningen. 8⁰. 1919

Brandes (Jan Laurens Andries). Beschrijving van Tjandi Singasari; en de wolkentooneelen van Panataran [*w. sep. pagin.*] Samengesteld door H. L. L. Melville &c., onder leiding van B. Benevens e. herdenking van B. door G. P. Rouffaer. Uitg. door het Kon. Inst. voor de Taal-, Land- en Volkenkunde van Ned.-Indië &c. [Arch. Onderzœk op Java en Madura, 2]. fol. 's-Gravenhage. 1909

Brandes (Johann Christian). Meine Lebensgesch. [Hrsg. v. W. Franke]. 8⁰. München. 1923

Brandi (Salvatore Mª.) Del regio patronato s. chiesa patriarcale di Venezia. 2ª ed. [P2842]. la8⁰. Venezia. 1893

Brandin (Louis), *archiviste-paléographe, see* ASPREMONT. La chanson d'A.: poème du 13ᵉ s.; [ed.] L. B., 1924.

Brandis-Zelion (Emma v.) Die Violinspielerin. Roman. 2ᵉ verb. A. s8⁰. Paderborn. 1890

Brandl (Alois).
Byron im Kampf mit d. engl. Politik &c., *see* DEUTSCHE Reden in schwerer Zeit, 20, 1915.
Shakespeare: Leben, Umwelt, Kunst. Neue A. s8⁰. 1922
Shakespeare & Germany; lect., 1913, *see* BRIT. ACADEMY. Proc., 1913–14.
Thomas Elyot's Verteidigung guter Frauen (1545) u. d. Frauenfrage in Eng. bis Shakespeare &c., *see* DEUT. SHAKESPEARE-GESELLSCHAFT. Jahrbuch, Jhrg. 51, 1915.
Zur Geographie d. altengl. Dialekte, *see* KÖNIGL. PREUSS. AKAD. Abh. (Phil.-hist. Kl.), 1915.

Brandon (Edgar Ewing). A short hist. of the U.S. s8⁰. 1920

Brandon (Samuel). The tragicomœdi of the vertuous Octavia. [*2nd part only, cont. the* missive epistles betw. Octavia & Anthony, *beginning at dedic.* To the honorable &c. Mistresse Mary Thinne. *no tp.*] s8⁰. [1598]

Brandrud (Andreas), *see* STAVANGER (S.) Domkapitels protokol 1571–1630; udg. ved A. B., 1901.

Brandstetter (Renward). Architekton. Sprachverwandtschaft in allen Erdteilen. [P2395]. 8°. *n.p.* 1920
Wir Menschen d. indones. Erde. [p]1–5. [1, *in* P2521, 2, 3, *in* P2718, 4, 5 *in* P2848]. 8°. Luzern. 1921–27

Brandt (Caspar) [BRANTIUS (C.)] Hist. vitæ Jacobi Arminii. Acc. H. Grotii & Dom. Baudii in Arminii obitum epicedia. s8°. Amstelodami. 1724
„ „ ......ed. corr. J. L. Moshemius præf. &c. add. s8°. Brunsvigæ. 1725

—— & A. van Cattenburgh. Hist. van het leven d. Heeren Huig de Groot, beschr. door C. B., en vervolgt tot zyn doodt door A. v. C. Met een Aanhangsel &c. [*w. sep. pagin.*]; [Vervolg *has sep. tp. & pagin.*] 2p *in* 1v. fol. Dordrecht. 1727

Brandt (Christian). De sacramentali corporis &c. J. C. in pane & vino κοινωνία. Præs. J. G. Dorscheo. [P437]. s4°. Argentorati. [1630]

Brandt (Lilian), *see* DEVINE (E. T.) Disabled soldiers & sailors pensions & training, by E. T. D., assisted by L. B., 1919.

Brandt (M. v.) Die Zukunft Ostasiens. [P2714]. 8°. St. 1895

Brandt (Sebastian), *see* POMPEN (A.) Eng. versions of the Ship of Fools, 1925.

Branford (Benchara). Study of mathemat. educ. incl. the teaching of arithmetic. n. ed. enl. & rev. s8°. O. 1921

Branford (Victor V.) Theology, poetry & civics, *see* PAPERS for the present, No. 13, 1920.

Brangwyn (Frank), *see* FURST (H. E. A.) Decorative art of F. B., 1924.
see RODO (L.) Ex-libris & marks; intr. by F. B., 1921.
„ SALAMAN (M. C.) F. B., 1924.

—— & W. Shaw Sparrow. A book of bridges. [2nd ed.] la8°. 1920

Brankovics (György). Az 1848–49-iki szabadságharcz története. [P2394]. s8°. 1906

Brannon (George).
Vectis scenery: beauties of the I. of Wight. 4°. 1855

Branson (Eugene Cunningham). Farm life abroad: field letters f. Germany, Denmark & France. 8°. Chapel Hill, *N. Carolina.* 1924

Brantius (Casparus), *see* BRANDT (CASPAR).

Branzoli (Giuseppe). Ricerche s. studio del liuto. 8°. 1889

Brasca (Herasmo), *see* PÉLISSIER (L. G.) L'alliance milano-allem. à la fin du 15 s.: l'ambass. d'H. B. à Maximilien (1498), 1898.

Brasichellen (Joannes Maria), *see* GUANZELLI (G. M.)

Brassey (Annie, *Lady*). Cat. of the natural hist., ethnolog. specimens &c. coll. by Lady B., dur. voyages of the "Sunbeam," 1876–1883. By B. Wright. [*With* App.] 8°. 1885

Brassey (Thomas Brassey, *1st earl*). *Cat. of works of art &c. at Normanhurst Court, Battle [prop. of Lord B. Comp. by A. Maskell. Add., Objects coll. dur. tour in Shetland Is., 1881, & Cat. of geolog. spec. &c., by B. M. Wright]. 8°. 1878–81
Work & wages illust. 8°. 1872
see HARRISON (F.) Progress of industry; or Mr. B. on work & wages, 1872.

Brassey's naval & shipping annual, *see* NAVAL ANNUAL (THE).

Brassinne (Joseph), *see* HEURES. Deux livres d'heures néerland., 1924?.

Brathwait (Richard) [BRAITHWAITE; *ps*s. CORYMBAEUS; BARNABY HARRINGTON; HESYCHIUS PAMPHILUS]. *Drunken Barnaby's 4 journeys to the North of Eng. [*In Lat. & Eng. metre*]. [n. ed.] s8°. 1805
The English gentleman. 2nd ed. rev., corr. & enl. [*wanting frontispiece*]. s4°. 1633

Bratti (Ricciotti). Vecchie isole Veneziane. 8°. Venezia. 1913
Venezia scomparsa. [*b. w. h.* Vecchie isole Venez., 1913. *a. c. in* P2841]. 8°. Venezia. 1911

Braubach (Max). Max Franz v. Österreich, letzt. Kurfürst v. Köln &c. 8°. Münster i. W. 1925
see SCHULTE (A.), *ed.* Tausend Jahre deut. Gesch. &c. am Rhein, bearb. v. M. B. &c., 1925.

Brauer (August Bernard), *see* WALDEYER (W.) Gedächtnisrede auf A. B., 1918.

Braun (Adolf). Sturmvögel d. Revolution! Aktenstücke z. Vorgesch. d. Revolution. Hrsg. A. B. [P2408]. 8°. 1919

Braun (Felix). Hyazinth u. Ismene. Dramat. Gedicht. la8°. Muenchen. 1919

Braun (Friedrich, *Edler* **von) & H. Dade.** Arbeitsziele d. deut. Landwirtschaft nach d. Kriege. Hrsg. v. F. v. B. & H. D. unter Mitwirk. v. Freier-Hoppenrade & v. Wangenheim-Kl.-Spiegel. 8°. 1918

Braun (Fritz). Die östl. Grenzländer Norddeutschlands. Landeskunde d. Weichsellandes (Kongresspolens). s8°. Bonn. 1921

Braun (Georg), *see* EMPSYCHOVIUS (H.) Demonstratio: refut. totius doct. papist. opposita G. B. rationibus &c., 1617.

Braun (Johann Wilh. Joseph).
De Culdeis comm. [*Progr.*] [P558]. 4°. Bonnæ. 1840

Braun (Joseph). Der christl. Altar in s. geschichl. Entwicklung. 2B. la8°. München. 1924
Liturg. Handlexikon. 2e verm. Aufl. 8°. Regensburg. 1924

Braun (Louis), W. Diez *& others.* Zur Gesch. d. Kostüme. Bogen nach Zeichnungen v. L. B., W. D. &c. fol. München. *n.d.*

Braun (Otto). Geschichtsphilosophie, 1913, *see* GRUNDR. D. GESCHICHTSWISS.; Meister, 1vi, 1913.
O. B. aus nachgelassenen Schriften. Hrsg. J. Vogelstein. s8°. L. 1922
Diary, w. sel. f. h. letters & poems. Ed. J. Vogelstein. Intr. by H. Ellis. Tr. E. Winter & F. W. S. Browne. 8°. 1924

Braun (Placidus Ignatius). *Notitia de libris usque ad a. 1479 [& 1480–1500] impress. in Bibl. monast. SS. Udalricum & Afram Augustæ extant. 2p. s4°. Augustæ Vind. 1788–89

Braun (Robert), *see* PIKLER (B.) & R. B. List of all Hungarian books in trade, 1925.

Braune (Wilhelm), *philologist.*
Gotische Gramm. 2e A. 8°. Halle. 1882

Brauns (C. W. Emma). Japan. Märchen. Gesamm. &c. v. C. W. E. B. 8°. Glogau. [1889]

Brauns (Reinhard). Mineralogie. 6e, verb. A. s8°. 1925

Braunschweig. *Bedencken d. Theologen zu B. v. d. neuen Wittenberg. Catechismo gestellet &c. [*signed* M. Kemnetius; *b. w.* Wittenberg. Christl. Fragstück &c., 1571]. s4°. [Braunschweig?]. 1571
*Bekenntnisse van d. Sacramente d. lives unde blodes Christi, Aller Predicanten tho Brunswig. Dorch M. Luther tho Wittenberge overlesen unde Christlick erkandt. s8°. [Magdeborch. *M. Lotther.* 1534]
Christliches Bedencken auff D. Maiors [*i.e.* Georg Meier's] Repetition, u. endliche Erklerung, Belangend d. Streidt. Ob Gute Werck zur Seligkeit nötig &c. Durch das Ministerium d. Kirchen in B. [P2436]. s4°. [Eisleben. *Andreas Petri*]. 1568
Vom Catechismo etlicher Wittenberg. Der Lerer im Land zu B. Bedencken. s4°. [Braunschweig]. 1571

Braunschweig (Hieronymus), *see* BRUNSCHWIG.

Braunschweig-Lüneburg, *see* BRUNSWICK-LUNEBURG.

Brausewetter (Artur). Die grosse Liebe. 2e A. s8°. L. 1918

Bravo (Charles Delaunay Turner), *see* HALL (*Sir* J. R.) The B. mystery &c., 1923.

Bray (Ruth). Sir Thomas More's house at Chelsea. [Play]. s8°. *Cayme Press,* Kensington. 1926

Braybrooke (Patrick).
Consid. on E. Gosse. Intr. by G. Frankau. 8°. [1925]
G. K. Chesterton. Intr. by A. F. Thorn. 8°. 1922

Braye (Alfred Thomas Townshend Verney-Cave, *5th baron*). Lutterworth lect. on Xty & language. By var. a. [J. Rickaby &c.], w. foreword &c. by Ld. B. 8°. Rugby. 1913

Brazil. Annaes da Confer. Interestadoal de Ensino Prim. [Publ. sob a dir. de J. B. de Mello e Souza]. la8°. Rio de Janeiro. 1922
20th cent. impressions of B. Director-in-Chief R. Lloyd. Edd. W. Feldwick [&] L. T. Delaney. Historian A. Wright. 4°. 1913

Brazza Savorgnan (*conte* **Giuseppe di),** *see* SAVORGNAN (*conte* G. DI B.)

Breadalbane (Gavin Campbell, *1st marq. of*). Partic. of east. portion of estates of Breadalbane, incl. Taymouth Castle &c., auction, Knight, Frank & Rutley, 9 Dec., 1920. By dir. of Marq. of B. fol. 1920

Breadalbane (John Campbell, *1st earl*); *1635–1716, see* SCOTLAND. *Impartial acc. of some trans. in S. conc. the earl of B. &c., 1695.

Bready (J. Wesley). Lord Shaftesbury & social-indust. progress. 8°. [1926]

***Breakfasts,** luncheons & ball suppers. By Major L——. 8°. 1887

Breasted (James Henry).
Ancient times. A hist. of the early world. s8°. Boston [U.S. 1916]
The conq. of civilization. 8°. N.Y. 1926
Hist. of Egypt, to the Persian conq. 2nd ed., rev. la8°. 1921
A hist. of the anc. Egyptians. s8°. 1920

Breasted (James Henry) [*continued*].

Oriental forerunners of Byzantine painting. 1st-cent. wall paintings f. fortress of Dura, Middle Euphrates. [Univ. of Chicago. Or. Inst. Publ., v1]. 4°. Chicago. [1924]

see BRUNTON (*Mrs.* W.) Kings & queens of anc. Egypt; foreword by J. H. B., 1924.

„ CARTER (E. H.), *ed.* The new past & o. essays &c.; by J. H. B. &c., 1925.

——, J. H. Robinson & C. A. Beard.
Outlines of European hist. 2p. 8°. Boston. *n.d.*
p1. Earliest man &c. by J. H. B.—Europe f. break-up of Rom. Emp. to 18c. by J. H. R.
p2. From 17c. to pres. time, by J. H. R. & C. A. B. Rev. to inc. Gt. War.

Brébel (*l'abbé* Eugène).
Essai hist. sur Pleudihen. 8°. Rennes. 1916

Brebner (Percy James). Christopher Quarles. s8°. [1921]

Breccia (Evaristo). Alexandrea ad Ægyptum: guide de la ville anc. & mod. & du Musée Gréco-Rom. s8°. Bergamo. 1914

Brechenmacher (Joannes Caspar).
Notitia Sueviæ antiq. &c. s4°. Jenæ. 1716

Brecht (Bertolt). Baal. [*Play*]. s8°. Potsdam. [1922]
Mann ist Mann. Lustspiel. 8°. [1927]
Trommeln in d. Nacht. 2e A. s8°. [1927]

Breckinridge (Sophonisba Preston). Legal tender: a study in Eng. & Amer. monetary hist. [Chicago Univ. decenn. publ. s2, v7]. 8°. Chicago. 1903
see ABBOTT (E.) & S. P. B. Admin. of the aid-to-mothers law in Illinois, 1921.

Brecknock (Albert).
Byron: st. in light of new discoveries. 8°. [1926]

Brécourt (Guillaume Marcoureau de), *see* MARCOUREAU DE BRÉCOURT.

Bredenburg (Jan), *the elder, see* FÉNELON (F. DE S. DE LA M.) Réfut. des erreurs de B. de Spinosa [*Foll. by* Certamen philos. adv. J. B.], 1703.

Bredius (Abraham). Künstler-Inventare. Urkunden z. Gesch. d. holländ. Kunst, 16.–18. Jhdt. Hrsg. A. B. [Quellenst. z. holländ. Kunstgesch., B13, 14].
T7 (Nachträge) & Register. 8°. Haag. 1921–22
see AMSTERDAM. Cat. des peintures du Musée de l'Etat à A., 3e éd., 1891.

Bredon (Juliet). Peking. Histor. &c. descr. 8°. Shanghai. 1920

—— & I. Mitrophanow.
The moon year: Chinese customs &c. 8°. Shanghai. 1927

Bredow (Gabriel Gottfried), *see* BELL (J.) View of univ. hist., lit. &c., to 1842; tables founded on German of G. G. B. &c., 5th ed., 1842.

Bredt (Ernst Wilhelm). Belgiens Volkscharakter—Belgiens Kunst. 8°. München. [1915]

Bree (Charles Robert). Hist. of the birds of Europe not in the Brit. Isles. 2nd ed., enl. 5v. la8°. 1875–6

Breen (Dan). My fight for Irish freedom. Intr. by J. McGarrity. s8°. D. 1926

Bregendahl (Marie). Jungvolk. Roman. Übertr. v. E. v. Hollander-Lossow. 8°. Braunschweig. [1927]

Bréhier (Louis). L'art byzantin. 8°. [1924]
Les miniatures des "Homélies" du moine Jacques & le théâtre relig. à Byzance, *see* ACAD. DES INSCR. FOND. PIOT. Mon., t24, 1920.
see DESDEVISES DU DEZERT (C.) & L. B. Clermont-Ferrand, 1926.
„ GESTA. G. (Anonymi) Francorum &c.; éd. & tr. par L. B., 1924.

Brehm (Alfred Edmund).
Merveilles de la nature. [Tr.] t6. la8°. *n.d.*
6, Poissons & crustacés, éd. fr. par H. E. Sauvage & J. Künckel d'Herculaïs.
Tierleben. 4e, neubearbt. A., hrsg. v. O. Strassen. [B13]. la8°. L. 1920
13, Säugetiere, v. A. Brehm, B4.
„ „ ......Kleine Ausgabe. 3e A., hrsg. W. Kahle. Neudruck. 4B. la8°. L. 1921–22

Brehm (Otto), *see* STRZYGOWSKI (J.) *ed.* Der Norden in d. bild. Kunst Westeuropas: Heidn. u. Christl. um d. Jahr 1000; unter Mitwirk. v. B. B. &c., 1926.

Breif, *see* BRIEF.

Breiger (Gottlieb Christian). Comm. de difficilioribus Asiæ Herodoteæ. s4°. Gottingæ. [1793]

Breiger (Jacob). Oratio de orthodoxias reductione &c. [P483]. s4°. Rostochii. 1617

Breitfuss (Leonid). Erforsch. d. Polargebietes Russ.-Eurasiens, 1912–24, 1925, *see* PETERMANNS MITT. Ergnzb., 41, 1927.
Internat. Studiengesells. z. Erforsch. d. Arktis mit d. Luftschiff; hrsg. L. B., 1927, *see* PETERMANNS MITT. Ergnzb., 41, 1927.

Breithaupt (Joachim Justus).

Catal. bibl. J. J. B. contin. libros theol. &c. s8°. Halæ Magdeb. [1732]

Epistolæ antipelagianæ, contra disquis. Fechtianam. 2p. [P2631]. s4°. Halæ Magdeb. 1711–14

Instit. hermeneutico-homiletica &c. [*b. w. h.* Instit. theolog., 1694]. s8° Halæ Magdeb. [1694]

Instit. theolog. libri 2, priore credenda, posteriore agenda. [*2 pagins.*] s8°. Halæ. [1694]

Instit. theologic. de credendis & agendis &c. 3t. s4°. Halæ Magdeb. 1716–32

Programmata selecta, de vario argumento. ed. 2a. s8°. Halæ. 1703

Breitinger (Johann Jacob). De antiq. Turicensis Bibl. Græco Psalmorum libro in membr. purpurea &c. epistola. s4°. Turici. 1748

Brémaud (Yvonne).
La brève idylle du Prof. Maindroz. s8°. [1924]

Bremen.
*Antwort d. Diener Göttl. Worts in d. Kirchen &c. zu B. auff J. Andreae unter d. namen der Würtemberg. Theologen Widerlegung d. Verantwortung &c. V. d. Person u. beyden Naturn in Christo u. v. d. heil. Abentmal. [& Kurtzer Innhalt *w. sep. tp. & pagin. b. w.* Bremen. Warhaffte u. Christl. Verantwortung &c., 1581]. s4°. Bremen. 1583
Brem. u. Verdische Bibliothek &c. theol., philol. u. hist. Abhandl. &c. 4B. s8°. Hamburg. 1754–58
*Kurtze anzeigūg &c. d. zugemessenen Artickel u. Puncten, in welchen die Prediger zu Br. irthümb bezichtiget &c. Sampt einverleibter Accusationschrifft &c. [*b. w.* Bremen. Warhaffte u. Christl. Verantwortung &c., 1581]. s4°. Bremen. 1581
Warhaffte christl. &c. Widerlegung d. Entschuldigung d. Prediger zu B. v. d. Person Christi u heyl. Abendtmal. Gestellet durch Theologen. [*b. w.* Kirchner (T.), N. Selneccer & M. Chemnitz. Apologia, 1583]. fol. Heydelberg. 1583
*Warhaffte u. Christl. verantwortung d. Prediger zu Br. &c. 1, Von d. Person Christi. 2, Von d. heyl. Tauff. 3, Von d. H. Abendmahl. 4, Von d. götl. Wahl. 5, Von d. Ceremonien. s4°. [Bremen]. 1581

Bremen (Walter von). Deutscher Kriegshumor, B2, *see* KAISER-WILHELM-DANK. Kriegsschr., H65, 1916.

Bremensis. Bibliotheca B. nova, 1760–67, *see* BIBLIOTHECA.

Bremisches u. Verdisches theolog. Magazin, hrsg. v. J. C. Velthusen. 4B. *in* 2v. s8°. Bremen. 1795–98

Brémond (É.) La Cilicie en 1919–1920. [Extr. de la Revue des études armén., 1921]. 8°. 1921

Brémond (Henri).

Discours de réception à l'Acad. franç. [*on Mgr. Duchesne*]. s8°. 1924

En prière avec Pascal. Sermon. s8°. 1923

Hist. litt. du sentiment relig. en France. t1–6. 8°. 1920–22
1, L'humanisme dévot, 1580–1660. 2, L'invasion mystique, 1590–1620.
3–6, La conquête mystique: 1, L'école franç., 2, L'école de Port-Royal, 3, L'école du Père Lallemant & la tradition mystique dans la Co. de Jésus, 4, Marie de l'Incarnation—Turba magna.

Maurice Barrès. s8°. 1924

La poésie pure, avec Un débat sur la poésie par R. de Souza. s8°. 1926

Pour le romantisme. 8°. 1923

Prière & poésie. [Les cahiers verts, 67]. s8°. 1926

Le roman & l'hist. d'une conversion: U. Guttinguer & Sainte-Beuve, d'après des corr. inéd. s8°. [1925]

see BORDEAUX (H.) H. B., 1924.

„ MARTIN DU GARD (M.) De Ste.-Beuve à Fénelon: H. B., 3e éd., 1927.

Brémond d'Ars (Eusèbe de). Les tilleuls de juin. s8°. 1920

Brenchley (Winifred Elsie).
Weeds on farm land. 8°. 1920

Brendan, *St., abbot of Clonfert, son of Finnloga, see* TUFFRAU (P.) Merveill. voyage de B., renouv. par P. T., 1925.

Brendel (Franz). Gesch. d. Musik in Italien, Deutschland u. Frankreich. 6e verm. A. 8°. L. 1878
Grundzüge der Gesch. d. Musik. 4e verm. A. s8°. L. 1855

Brendel (Georg Christoph), *see* STECHE (C. F.) Explorat. spiritus Brendeliani, 1717.

Brendel (Johann). Des Sendbrieffes an d. Engel d. Gemeine zu Smyrna summar. Erklerung uff Caspar Peucern, bey dess. Begräbnuss. [P2611]. s4°. Zerbst. 1603

Brenet (Michel). Haydn. Tr. C. L. Leese, w. comm. by Sir W. H. Hadow. 8°. 1926

Brennan (M. M.)
The young man from Rathmines. Play. s8°. D. 1923

Brennecke (A.), *see* WESTFALEN. Bau- u. Kunstdenkm., 23, Kreis Tecklenburg, gesch. Einl. v. A. B., 1907.

Brennecke (Ernest), *Jr.* Thomas Hardy's universe: st. of a poet's mind. 8°. [1924]

Brenot (Alice). Les mots & groupes ïambiques réduits dans le théâtre latin, Plaute-Térence. [H. E., 239]. 8°. 1923

Recherches sur l'Ephébie attique & en partic. sur la date de l'institution. [H. E., 229]. 8°. 1920

Brentano (Clemens), J. v. Görres & B. Weber. A. K. Emmerich, M. v. Mörl u. D. Lazzaris. Hrsg. v. e. Curatpriester. [P519]. 8°. Regensburg. 1874

Brentano (Dominik v.) Die heil. Schrift d. N.T. Hrsg. D. v. B. 2T *in* 3B. 8°. Stift Kempten. 1790–91

Das letzte Wort ü. d. Brentanoische Bibelübersetzung. s8°. Freyburg. 1793

Brentano (Franz), *see* KRAUS (O.) F. B., 1919.

Brentano (Lujo).

Die Urheber d. Weltkriegs. la8°. München. 1922

Brent-Dyer (Elinor M.) Jo of the Châlet School. s8°. [1926]

Brentius (Ioannes), *see* BRENTZ (JOHANN), *the Elder.*

Brentz (Johann), *the elder.* [BRENTIUS; BRENTZEN].

Operum tomus primus [—octavus]. 8t. fol. Tubingæ. 1576–90

1–7, Commentarii &c. 8, Polemica scripta contra P. à Soto & sacramentarios.

Argumenta & sacræ Scr. summa, librorum Veteris videlicet N. Test. s8°. [Norimbergæ, *I. Petreius*], 1544

Ein Christliche Predig von erhaltung gemeynes frides. s4°. [Nürmberg, *Joh. Petreius*]. 1535

De majestate J. C. ad dextram Dei Patris & de vera præsentia in coena. Resp. P. Martyri, & H. Bullingero. [*b. w. h.* De person. unione, 1561]. s4°. Francoforti. 1562

De personali unione duarum naturarum in Christo et ascensu Christi &c. s4°. Tubingæ. 1561

In Evangelii quod inscribitur, sec. Lucam, duodecim priora capita [*& 12 posteriora cap.*] homiliæ. [2p *in* 1v. *pagin. cont.*] fol. Francoforti. 1552

Wie sich Prediger u. Leyen halten sollen, so der Türck das Teutschland uberfallen würde. Christl. unterricht ... s4°. Wittemberg [*pr. at* Nürmberg, *Künigund Hergotin*]. 1531

see ANDREÆ (J.) Assertio &c. qua resp. ad prim. partem libri T. Beze. Resp. ad J. B. argumenta &c., 1565.

„ BUCER (M.) Apologia &c. [*agst. J. B.*], 1526.

„ CHÂTEILLON (S.) De hæreticis an sint perseq. Luteri & B. sententiæ, 1554.

„ CHRISTOPH, *Herzog zu Würtemberg.* Confessio, cum apolog. scr. J. B. &c., 2t, 1561.

„ HOSIUS (S.) Confut. prolegomenon B. adv. Petrum à Soto &c., 1561.

„ KÖHLER (W.) Bibliogr. Brentiana, 1904.

„ —— Brentiana u. a. Reformatoria, 1912–14.

„ LUTHER (M.) Catechismus lat. factus per V. Obsopœum; adj. alii quoque gemini Catechismi J. B., 1529.

Brenz (Samuel Friedrich). Theriaca Judaica, ad exam. revocata, sive scripta amoibæa S. F. B. & S. Zevi &c., vers. Lat. & animadv. aucta, studio J. Wülferi. Acc. I. Vivæ Vindex sanguinis, contra J. Geusium. [*w. sep. tp.*] [*3 pagin.* P1015]. s4°. Norimbergæ. 1681

Brequet (Abraham Louis), *see* SALOMONS (*Sir* D. L.) Breguet, 1747–1823, 1921; Suppl., 1921.

Brereton (Austin). A walk down Bond Street. Cent. souvenir of the house of Ashton & Mitchell, 1820–1920. [P2415]. s4°. [1920]

Brescia. La pinacoteca Tosio e Martinengo. 8°. Bologna. [1927]

Brescia (Arnold *of***),** *see* SCHNIZLIN (J. G. C.) Diss. de A. Brixiensi libertatis Xtianæ vindice, 1742.

Bresemann (Friedrich).

Danske Ordsprog og Mundheld. s8°. Kjøbenhavn. 1843

Bresnitz (Philipp Franz) [BRESNITZ V. SYDAČOFF].

Die Wahrheit ü. Habsburgs Ende. 8°. L. 1920

Bresslau (Harry). Die ältere Salzburger Annalistik, *see* KÖN.-PREUSS. AKAD. Abhdln., Phil.-hist. Kl., 1923.

Aus. d. ersten Zeit d. abendländ. Schismas, *see* KÖNIGL. PREUSS. AKAD. D. WISS. Abhdl. (Phil.-hist. Klasse), 1919.

Hdbch. d. Urkundenlehre für Deutschland u. Italien. 2e A. B2i. 8°. L. 1915

see ARCHIVIO STOR. ITAL. Anno 85, v1, Necrologia, 1927.

Brest-Litovsk. Мирные переговоры в Брест-Литовске 1917–18. Полный текст под редак. А. А. Иоффе, с предисловием Л. Д. Троцкого. t1. 8°. Москва. 1920

Die Friedensverhandlungen in B.-L. u. d. Friede mit Russland. [Deut. Geschichtskal., Lief. 44. *a. c. b. w.* Europäische (Der) Krieg in aktenmäss. Darst., B7ii]. 8°. L. [1917]

Die Zusatzverträge z. Frieden v. B.-L. Authent. Berichte. [Deut. Geschichtskal. *b. w.* Europäische (Der) Krieg in aktenmässiger Darstellung, B8i, 1914]. 8°. L. [1918]

Bret (Alexandre), *see* NOUVEL. N. annuaire de France &c., rédigé par A. B., 1836?

Bret (Antoine). *Mém. sur la vie de Mlle. de Lenclos. *For an Eng. tr. of the above, see* †LENCLOS (N. DE). *N. de L.; [tr. &c. f. auth. Fr. sources], 1904.

Bret (Charles) [BRETUS (CAROLUS)]. Ordo perantiq. judiciorum, *see* HOFFMANN (C. G.) Hist. jur. Rom.-Justin., v2, 1726.

Brétagne. Édits, déclar. & lettres patentes du roy, & réglemens conc. le Parl. de B., 1554–1754. Imp. par ordre du Parl. s4°. Rennes. 1754

Liste gén. de nos seigneurs du Parl. de B., 1554–1754. Imp. par ordre du Parl. [*b. w.* Brétagne. Édits &c., 1754]. s4°. Rennes. 1754

Bretaigne, *héraut d'armes* [BRETAGNE; *i.e.* PIERRE CHOQUE]. Récit des funérailles d'Anne de Bretagne. Publ. avec intr. &c. par L. Merlet & M. de Gombert. [Trésor des pièces rares &c.] s8°. 1858

Bretez (Louis). Plan de Paris, 1739, *see* PARIS. Reprod. d'anc. plans, 1908.

Bretherton (Ralph Harold). Two sisters. s8°. [1920]

Bretholz (Bertold).

Gesch. Böhmens u. Mährens. 4B. s8°. Reichenberg. [1921–25]

Latein. Paläographie, 2e A, 1912, *see* GRUNDR. D. GESCHICHTSWISS.; Meister, 1i, 1912.

Neuere Gesch. Böhmens, B1, 1920, *see* GESCH. D. EUROPÄ. STAATEN.

Z. Gesch. d. kais. Akad. d. Wiss. in Wien: e. Gutachten d. Grafen K. v. Sternberg, ü. d. Gründungsplan, 1837, 1914, *see* KAISERL. AKAD. D. WISS. ZU WIEN. Sitzungsber., B176, 1916.

Breton, Cape. *Two letters, conc. some farther advantages & improvements necessary on taking &c. C. B. [P608]. s8°. 1746

Breton (Nicholas).

The passionate shepheard. Ed. F. Ouvry. s4°. *p.p.* 1877

Breton (William Henry), *R.N.* Excursion in N. S. Wales, W. Australia & Van Dieman's Land, 1830–33. 8°. 1833

Bretschneider (Carl Gottlieb). Capita theologiæ Judæorum dogmat. e Flavii Josephi scriptis coll. Diss. [P2654]. s8°. Vitebergæ. [1812]

Bretschneider (E.) Botanicon Sinicum, p3, *see* ROYAL ASIATIC SOC: N. China Br., n.s., v29, 1895.

Brett (George Sidney). A hist. of psychology. v2, 3. 8°. [1921]

Brett (Henry). White wings: 50 years of sail in N. Zealand trade, 1850–1900. v1. [*no more publd.*] la8°. Auckland. 1924

Brett (*Hon.* **Oliver Sylvain Baliol).**

A defence of liberty. 8°. [1920]

Brett (Thomas), *LL.D.*, *see* BROXAP (H.) The later Nonjurors [*w.* acc. of the Brett MSS &c. by S. L. Ollard], 1924.

Brett (William Baliol), *visct. Esher, see* ESHER (W. B. B., *1st visct.*)

Brettell (Thomas). A topog. & hist. guide to the Isle of Wight. s4°. 1840

Brett-James (Norman George).

Life of P. Collinson, F.R.S. 8°. [1925]

Breuck (Jacobus de), *see* DUBROEUCQ (J.)

Breuer (Hermann), *see* CATHERINE, *of Alexandria, St.* Eine gereimte altfranz.-verones. Fassung d. Legende d. hlgn. K.; hrsg. H. B., 1919.

Breugel (Pieter), *the elder* [BRUEGEL], *see* †BERNARD (C.) P. B. l'anc., 1908.

see FRIEDLÄNDER (M. J.) P. Bruegel, 1921.

„ VAN BASTELAER (R.) Les estampes de P. B. l'anc., 1908.

Breuil (Henry), *see* ALCALDE DEL RIO (H.), H. B. & L. SIERRA. Les cavernes de la rég. Cantabrique, 1911.

see CAPITAN (L.), H. B. & D. PEYRONY. La caverne de Font-de-Gaume, 1910.

„ CARTAILHAC (E.) & H. B. La caverne d'Altamira à Santillane, 1906.

——, H. Obermaier & *Col.* W. Verner. La Pileta à Benaojan (Malaga). [Inst. de Paleónt. Humaine: peintures &c. des cavernes paléolith.] fol. Monaco. 1915

Breval (John Durant de). The art of dress, 2nd ed., *see* SCHOOL of Venus, 1739.

Brevern de La Garde (*comtesse*). Un ambassadeur de Suède à la Cour de Catherine II; Feld-Maréchal Cte. de Stedingk, dépêches diplomat. &c., 1790–6. 2[t]. 8°. Stockholm. [1919]

Breviary [BREVIARIUM, *see also* DIURNAL; DIURNUM; OFFICIA].

B. Chaldaicum. 3p. 8°. Lutetiæ Paris. 1886–87

B. Romanum ex sacra Scriptura & probatis sanctorũ historiis nuper confectum [*by card. Quignon*]. 4°. Lugduni, *Baltazard Arnoullet.* 1544

Breviary [*continued*].
B. Rom. ex decreto Conc. Trident.
4p. 8º. Antverpiæ, *Plantin*. 1703
Each part has sev. tp. & pagin.
B. Rom. ex decreto Conc. Trident. [*3 pagin.*]
s8º. Patavii. 1788
B. Rom. ex decreto Conc. Trident. restit. S. Pii V jussu ed. Clementis VIII & Urbani VIII auctor. rec. Cum officiis Sanctorum [*& Preparatio ad missam, w. sep. pagin.*] 4º. Romæ. 1856
B. Rom. Slavonico idiomate jussu Innocentii xi ed.
s4º. Romæ. 1688
Einführung in d. Röm. Brevier v. H. Lietzmann, *see* KLEINE TEXTE, T141, Liturg. Texte, T10, 1917.
Zamakargouthiun (Hours of the Armenian Church &c.), 1889, *see* ARMENIAN.
see AREVALO (F.) Hymnodia Hispanica; acc. app. de Brev. Quignon. fata, 1786.

Brevint (Daniel). Saul & Samuel at Endor &c., & service which temt men to Rome &c. refuted. As also acc. of R. F. his Missale vindicatum, by the same [*sep. tp.*] 8º. O. 1674

Brevis. *Brevis disquis., an & quomodo Evangelici Pontificios refutare queant, 1633, *see* STEGMANN (J.)
Brevis orthod. fidei prof. &c., 1595, *see* PROFESSIO.
*Brevis relat. colloq. author. Wilhelmi Hessiæ landgr., inter theologos Marpurg. & Ritel., Cassellis Jul. [1661], habiti, 1662?, *see* MARBURG.

Brewer (C.) & Co. Rep. of case of C. B. & Co. vs. J. R. v. Pfister. [P2775]. 8º. Honolulu. 1845

Brewer (Ebenezer Cobham).
Dict. of phrase & fable. n. ed. 8º. 1923
Reader's handbook. [rev. ed.] s8º. 1923

Brewer (H. W.) Old London illust., 16th century, w. descr. notes by H. A. Cox. 2nd ed. rev. & enl. fol. 1921

Brewer (John Marks). Mental measurement in educ. & vocat. guidance. [P2769]. 8º. Camb., Mass. 1924

Brewer (John Sherren).
The Athanasian Creed vindicated. s8º. 1871

Brewer (Robert Frederick). Orthometry. Art of versific. &c., w. rhyming dict. n. & rev. ed. s8º. E. 1918

Brewer (Robert W. A.) The art of aviation: hdbk. upon aeroplanes & th. engines. pop. ed. 8º. 1914

Brewster (Adolph Brewster). The hill tribes of Fiji. 8º. 1922

Brewster (Charles W.) Rambles about Portsmouth, ser. 1. 2nd ed. 8º. Portsmouth, N. H. 1873

Brewster (Earl H.) Life of Gotama the Buddha comp. f. the Pali Canon. Intr. note by C. A. F. Rhys Davids. 8º. 1926

Brewster (John). Parochial hist. & antiq. of Stockton-upon-Tees. 2nd ed., w. add. la8º. Stockton-upon-Tees. 1829

Brex (Twells), *see* FYFE (H. H.) T. B., a conqueror of death, 1920.

Breymann (Henriette Juliane Johanna Schrader-). H. S.-B., ihr Leben aus Briefen u. Tagebüchern zusamm. u. erläut. v. M. I. Lyschinska. 2B. 8º. 1922

Breysig (Curt) & F. Wolters. Gesch. d. brandenburg. Finanzen, 1640–97. Darstellung u. Akten. [Urkunden &c. z. Gesch. d. inn. Politik d. Kurf. Fr. Wilhelm v. Brandenburg, T1i, ii]. 2B (B1, v. C. B.; B2, v. F. W.) 8º. L. 1895–1915

Brézé (Jacques de), *Grand Seneschal of Normandy.* *Le livre de la chasse & les Ditz du bon chien Souillard [*by* J. Du Fouilloux]. Publ. J. Pichon. [Trésor des pièces rares &c.] s8º. 1858

Březina (Otakar), *see* SELVER (P.) O. B., st. in Czech lit., 1921.

Briand (Aristide), *see* LAURENT (M.) Nos gouv. de Guerre: B. &c., 1920.

Briand (Auguste).
Le livre de poche du voyageur en France. s8º. [1837]

Briand (Emile). Hist. de sainte Radegonde, reine de France, & des sanctuaires &c. la8º. 1898

Briantchaninov (Aleksandr Nikolaevich), *see* BRYANCHANINOV (A. N.)

Brias (Charles de) [*le père* C. DE L'ASSOMPTION; *ps.* EUPISTINUS (G. P.)] Thomistarum triumphus, *i.e.* S. Augustini & Thomæ summa concordia. Per G. P. E. t1, 2 *in* 1v. s4º. Duaci. 1672–73

Bribiesca (Juan). [Ayuntamiento constit. de México]. Discurso[s] d. S. Camacho, M. S. Macedo &c. y Memoria document. por J. B. la8º. México. 1898

Brickell (Alfred). Few but roses. Poems f. the French. Sel. &c. by A. B. 8º. [1924]

Brickwood (Edwin D.) [*ps.* ARGONAUT]. *The arts of rowing & training, w. laws of boat-racing &c. By "Argonaut." s8º. 1866

Bricon (Etienne). Les 3 salons de 1920. 4º. 1921

***Bridge** (The) of light, 1899, *see* ASTER, *ps.*

Bridge (*Sir* Frederick), *Mus. Doc.* The old cryes of London, w. illust. & musical examples. la8º. 1921
Shakespearean music in the plays & early operas. la8º. 1923

Bridge (James Howard).
Inside hist. of the Carnegie Steel Co. 8º. N.Y. 1903

Bridge (John Seargeant Cyprian). Hist. of France f. the death of Louis XI. v1, 2. 8º. O. 1921–24
1, 1483–93. 2, 1493–98.

Bridgeman (Charles G. O.) Betley Morris dance window, *see* STAFFORDSHIRE. Coll. for hist. of S., 1923, 1924.
Forest pleas in Staffs. Pipe Roll of 13 Hen. II (1166–7), *see* STAFFORDSHIRE. Coll. for hist. of S., 1923, 1924.
Genealog. acc. of the family of Aldersey of Aldersey & Spurstow, Co. Chester. sfol. *p.p.* 1899
Some unidentified Domesday vills, *see* STAFFORDSHIRE. Coll. for hist. of S., 1923, 1924.
The Staffordshire hidation, *see* STAFFORDSHIRE. Coll., N. S., v21, 1920.

Bridges (James Winfred), *see* YERKES (R. M.), J. W. B. &c. Point scale for measuring mental ability, 1915.

Bridges (John), *bp. of Oxford.* A defence of the gov. establ. in the Ch. of Englande for eccl. matters &c. [*tp. wanting*]. s4º. 1587

Bridges (John Henry), *see* LIVEING (S.) A 19th cent. teacher, J. H. B., 1926.

Bridges (Joseph S.) & A. J. Dicks.
Plant study in school, field & garden. s8º. 1908

Bridges (Philippa). The green wave of destiny. s8º. E. 1911
A walk-about in Australia. Foreword by Lt.-Gen. Sir T. Bridges. 8º. [1925]

Bridges (Robert).
Achilles in Scyros. [repr.] s8º. 1892
Coll. essays, papers &c. [v1]. 8º. 1927
1, Infl. of the audience on Shakespeare's drama.
The dialectal words in E. Blunden's poems, *see* MATTHEWS (J. B.) Englishing of French words &c., 1921.
English handwriting. Ed. R. B., w. notes on penmanship by A. Fairbank. [S.P.E. Tract, 28]. 8º. O. 1927
New verse written in 1921 & earlier pieces. s8º. O. 1925
October & o. poems. With verses on the War. s8º. 1920
Pictorial, picturesque &c., *see* FOWLER (H. W.) The split infinitive &c., 1923.
Poetry in schools, *see* FOWLER (H. W.) Subjunctives, 1924.
Reviews & notes (S.P.E. Tract, 22), *see* PAGET (R. A. S.) Nature of human speech, 1925.
Shorter poems. [2nd ed.] s8º. 1891
The Society's work. [S.P.E. Tract, 21]. 8º. 1925
see BRADLEY (H.) Coll. papers; w. mem. by R. B., 1928.
„ —— & R. B. On the terms Briton, British, &c., 1923.
„ WILLIAMS (I. A.) Bibliographies of mod. a., No. 1, R. B., 1921.

Bridges (Roy). Green butterflies. s8º. [1923]
Through another gate. s8º. [1927]

Bridges (Thomas) [COTTON, *Junior, pseud.*] *Homer travestie; burlesque transl. of 10 first bks. of the Iliad. 2v. s8º. 1764.

Bridges (Victor). The girl in black. s8º. [1926]
Greensea Island. s8º. [1922]
The lady from Long Acre. s8º. [1918]

Bridget, *Saint, see* WILLIAMSON (B.) The Bridgettine order, foundress &c., 1922.

Bridgett (R. C.) Dry-fly fishing. 8º. 1922
Loch-fishing. 8º. [1924]

Bridgman (Percy Williams).
The logic of mod. physics. 8º. N.Y. 1927

Bridoul (Toussaint). The school of the Eucharist. Now made Engl. [by W. Clagett]. [P2664]. s4º. 1687

Brief [BREIF; BRIEFE].
*Breif [*sic*] (A) genealog. acc. of the ffamily of McLean, 1872, *see* MACLEAN (A.)
*Brief acc. of many persecutions of Quakers, 1736, *see* BESSE (J.)
*Brief (A) acc. of the Mechitaristican Soc. &c., 1835, *see* AUCHER (P.)
*Brief (A) & full acc. of Tate's & Brady's new version of the Psalms. By a true son of the Ch. of E. [*b. w.* Phillips (J.) Daveidos, 1698]. s8º. 1698
„ „ *see* REMARKS upon a late pamph.: A brief &c. acc., 1699.
*Brief (A) & necessary catechisme or instructiō &c., *n.d.*, *see* DERING (E.), *B.D.*
Briefe (A) & plaine declaration, &c., 1584, *see* CHURCH.
*Brief (A) & true represent. of our affairs, 1745, *see* REPRESENTATION.
*Brief (A) defence of the Reformation of the Ch. of Eng. &c., 1654, *see* CHURCH.
*Brief (A) descr. hist. of Holland, 1826, *see* HOLLAND.
*Brief (A) descr. of the island of Jersey, 1826, *see* JERSEY.
*Brief (A.) descr. of the notor. life of J. Lambe &c., 1628, *see* LAMBE (J.)

Brief [*continued*].
*Brief (A) histor. acc. of the Jesuites &c. for first 25 years of Q. Eliz. reign &c., 1689, *see* JESUITS.
*Brief hist. of the rise &c. of Popery, 1690, *see* POPERY.
*Brief (A.) narr. of rival relig. in Virginia, 3rd ed., 1786, *see* RANKIN (T.)
*Brief rel. of the persecution agst. Catholike Xtns. in Japonia; tr. W. W., 1619, *see* JESUITS.

Briefe. Briefe u. Akten z. Gesch. d. 30 jähr. Krieges. Hrsg. durch d. hist. Komm. bei d. K. Akad. d. Wiss. zu München. [N. F.], T2, B2. 8º. München, 1918
N.F., Die Politik Maximilians I v. Baiern u. s. Verbündeten, 1618–51, T2, B2, 1625; bearbt. v. W. Goetz.

Briegleb (Johann Christian). Gesch. d. Gymnasii Casimiriani Acad. zu Coburg. s8º. Coburg. 1793

Brière (Gaston), *see* LOUVRE. Musée Nat. du L. Cat. des peintures expos., pl, École fr.; par G. B., 1924.

Brierley (Benjamin). The Bradleys' visit to Thistledown Hall. [P2850]. s8º. M'ter. [1864]
A bundle o' fents f. a Lancashire loom. No. 3, 4. [P2850]. s8º. M'ter. [1865–66]
Lancs. wit & humour. [P2867]. s8º. Oldham. [1892?]

Brierley (Jonathan). Studies of the soul. 8º. 1898

Brieux (Eugène). La Française. Comédie. 4e éd. s8º. 1917
La Régence: pièce, *see* ŒUVRES libres, 67, 1926.
Théâtre complet. 7t [*var. ed.*] s8º. 1921–24
1, Ménages d'artistes—Blanchette—Monsieur de Réboval—L'école des belles-mères.
2, Les bienfaiteurs—L'évasion—La robe rouge.
3, Les trois filles de M. Dupont—Résultat des courses.
4, Les remplaçantes—L'engrenage—Maternité.
5, Le berceau—Simone—Suzette.
6, Les avariés—Les hannetons—La petite amie.
7, La femme seule—Le bourgeois aux champs—Les Américains chez nous.

***Briève** & fidèle expos. de l'orig. de la doct. &c. de l'Église de l'Unité des Frères, de Bohème &c., 1758, *see* BOHEMIA.

Brifaut (Charles). Souv. d'un académicien sur la Révolution, le premier Empire & la Restauration. Intr. & notes du Dr. Cabanès. 2[t]. 8º. [1921]

Briffault (Robert). The making of humanity. 8º. [1919]
The mothers: st. of orig. of sentiments & institutions. 3v. la8º. [1927]
Psyche's lamp. A revaluation of psycholog. princ. 8º. [1921]

Brigader (Anna). Sprihditis. Märchen. Übers. E. Eckardt-Skalberg. 8º. Riga. [1922]

Briggs (Charles Augustus). The Bible, the Church &c. 8º. E. 1892

Briggs (Frederick W.) Bishop Asbury. 2nd ed. s8º. 1879
Pentecost, & the founding of the Church. s8º. 1861

Briggs (Geo. Wallace). The Chamārs. s8º. Calcutta. 1920

Briggs (Martin Shaw). The architect in history. 8º. O. 1927
Muhammadan architecture in Egypt & Palestine. 4º. O. 1924
Short hist. of the building crafts. 8º. O. 1925

Briggs (R. A.) Bungalows & country residences. Designs &c. 2nd ed. 4º. 1894

Brigham (Albert Perry).
The U.S. of Amer.: physical, regional &c. geog. 8º. 1927

Bright (Charles), *F.R.S.E.* The life story of Sir C. T. Bright, w. story of the Atlantic cable, & the 1st telegraph to India. rev. & abr. ed. 8º. 1908

Bright (*Sir* Charles Tilston), *see* BRIGHT (C.) Life story of C. T. B., 1908.

Bright (John), *see* REID (W.) The "pract. side" of Amer. educ.: J. B. & the Civil War, 1907.

Bright (William), *canon of Ch. Ch., Oxford.* Ancient collects & o. prayers, sel. f. var. rituals. 6th ed. s8º. O. 1887

Brightman (Thomas). The workes of T. B., viz. a revelation of the Apocalyps [w. tr.] Expos. of the last part [xi. *26 to end of* xi] of Daniel, w. a comm. on the Song of Solomon. [*Sep. tp. of* Revel. 4th ed. *engraved*; *gen. tp. missing*]. s4º. 1644

Brighton. *B. as it is, 1828, *see* WALLIS (E.)

Brignole Sale (Antonio Giulio), *Marquis di Grappoli.*
Novella. [*Ed.* A. Tessier. P2787]. 8º. Venezia. 1854

Brigode (Emilie, *Ctsse.* **de),** *see* CHIMAY (E. L. M. F. P., *pcsse.* DE).

Brilioth (Yngve). The Anglican revival: st. in the Oxford Movt. Pref. by Bp. of Gloucester. [Tr.] 8º. 1925

Brill (Abraham Arden).
Fundamental conceptions of psychoanalysis. 8º. [1922]
Psychoanalysis its theories & pract. applic. 3rd ed. rev. 8º. Phila. 1922

Brillant (Maurice). Les années d'apprentissage de Sylvain Briollet. s8º. 1921

Brinchmann (Chr.), *see* HVEM ER HVEM?; udg. av C. B. &c., 1912.

Brinckmann (Albert Erich). Stadtbaukunst vom M.- a. b. z. Neuzeit. [Hdbch. d. Kunstwiss., Ergzb.] 2. Aufl. 4º. Potsdam. [1925]

Brinckmann (Julius), *see* BEIT (*Sir* O.) Japanese colour-prints &c. in coll. of Sir O. B. [*by* J. B. &c.], 1924.

Brinckmeyer (Hermann).
Hugo Stinnes. 4e A. 8º. München. [1921]
Hugo Stinnes. Tr. A. B. Kuttner. s8º. N.Y. 1921

Brinquier (Octavien), *see* TOURTOULON (C.) & O. B. La langue d'oc et la langue d'oil, 1876.

Brinkley (*Capt.* Frank), *of Tokyo.* Hist. of the Japanese people to end of the Meiji era. 8º. N.Y. [1915]
Japan & China. [Oriental Ser.] Author's ed. 12v. 8º. Boston [Mass.] 1901–2
The above is the half tp., which is undated.
v1–8 *have tp.* Japan, its hist., arts & lit.; v9–12 *have tp.* China, its hist. &c.
——, **F. Nanjo & Y. Iwasaki.**
An unabridged Japanese-Eng. dict. s8º. Tokyo. [1896]

Brinkmann (Carl), *see* GRUNDRISS D. SOZIALÖKONOMIK, Abt. 4, Spezif. Elemente d. mod. kapitalist. Wirtschaft, T1, mit Beitr. v. C. B., 1925.

Brinkmann (Hennig). Gesch. d. latein. Liebesdichtung im M-a. 8º. Halle a. S. 1925

Brinkmann (Theodor), *see* GRUNDRISS DER SOZIALÖKONOMIK, Abt. 7, Land-u. forstwirtschaftl. Produktion &c., bearb. v. T. B. &c., 1922.

Brinsley (John), *the younger.* Two treatises: the one, the doctrine of Christ's mediatorship. The other, of Mystical implantation &c. [With a preface by S. Ashe]. 2p. *in* 1v. s8º. 1651–52

Brinsmade (Peter Allen). Rep. of case of B., v. J. J. Jarves, ed. of the Polynesian, for alledged libelous publ. [P2775]. 8º. Honolulu. 1846

Brinton (Christian), *see* REPIN (I. Y.) The I. R. exhibit.: intr. & cat. of paintings, by C. B., 1921.
see ROERICH (N. K.) The N. R. exhib., w. intr. & cat. of paintings, by C. B., 1920.

Brinton (Jasper Yeates), *see* CANFIELD (G. L.) & G. W. DALZELL. Law of the sea, w. summary of navig. laws of U.S. by J. Y. B., 1921.

Brinton (Selwyn). The golden age of the Medici (Cosimo, Piero, Lorenzo de' Medici), 1434–94. 8º. [1925]
The Gonzaga—Lords of Mantua. 8º. [1927]
Venice past & present. Text by S. Ed. G. Holme. [Studio. Spec. No.] 4º. 1925

Briollay (Sylvain).
Ireland in rebellion. Tr. s8º. D. 1922
L'Irlande insurgée. s8º. [1921]

Brion (John) & Sons, *see* WILKINS (E. P.) Geol., antiq. &c. of I. of Wight; topog. &c. by J. B. & Sons, 1861.

Briquet (Louis Hilaire Alexandre). Hist. de la ville de Niort. Avec une biog. [des Deux-Sèvres, *w. sep. pagin.*] 2t. 8º. Niort. 1832

Brisacier (Jean de), *Jesuit, see* NOUET (J.), F. ANNAT *& others.* Responses aux Lettres Provinciales &c., 1668.

Brisbane (*Gen. Sir* THOMAS MAKDOUGALL).
Reminiscences. 4º. *p.f.p.c.* E. 1860

Briscoe (John Potter). A Nottingham translator of Dante and Homer (I. C. Wright). [Ye Nottingham sette of Odde Vol. Opusc. 15]. [P2421]. s8º. 1901
The tale of Prince Dorus [Ye Nottingham sette of Odde Vol. Opusc. 4]. [P2421]. s8º. 1897

Briscoe (Walter Alwyn). Byron, the poet. Ed. W. A. B. Coll. of addr. & essays, by Vsct. Haldane, Sir A. Quiller-Couch &c. 8º. 1924

Brise (La) au clair de lune: roman chinois; tr. G. Soulié de Morant, 1925, *see* HAOU KEW CHUEN.

Brise (*Sir* Evelyn John Ruggles), *see* RUGGLES-BRISE (*Sir* E. J.)

Brissa (José). Parnaso ecuatoriano. Antologia de las poesías del Ecuador. Col. por J. B. s8º. Barcelona. *n.d.*
Parnaso español contemp.: antologia de los mejores poetas. 8º. Barcelona. 1914

Brissaud (Jean), *late prof., Univ. of Toulouse.* Hist. of French public law. Tr. J. W. Garner. Intr. by H. D. Hazeltine & W. W. Willoughby. la8º. Boston. 1915

Brissenden (Paul Frederick). Employment system of the Lake carriers' assoc., *see* UNITED STATES: LABOUR. Bull., 235, 1918.
The I. W. W. A study of American syndicalism. [Columbia Univ. Stud. in hist. &c., v83]. 8°. N.Y. 1920
,, ,, ...2nd ed. 8°. N.Y. 1920

Brisson (Adolphe). Le théâtre. s2, 3, 5–8. s8°. [1907–13]
For s1, see h. Théâtre & les mœurs.

Brisson (Barnabé), *president of the Parliament of Paris.* Additamentorum ad B. B. opus de verborum quæ ad jus civile pert. signific. vol. Coll. &c. J. Wunderlich. fol. Hamburgi. 1778
De verborum quæ ad jus civile pertinent significatione opus. Prodit opera J. G. Heinecii. Præm. præf. de interpret. gramm. in jure civili fatis &c. J. H. Böhmeri. fol. Halæ Magdeburg. 1743
Supplementi ad B. B. opus de verborum quæ ad jus civile pert. signific., spec. 1. Auct. A. G. Cramer. [*b. w. h.* Additam. &c., 1778]. s4°. Kiliæ. 1813

Bristol. *Apology (An) for the clergy of B., 1712, *see* APOLOGY.
Bristol & its environs. [*By var. wr.*] Publ., Local Comm. of Brit. Assoc. s8°. 1875
Official guide to the city of B. la8°. Bristol. [1927]
*A short hist. of B.'s Little Theatre, 1923–25. 8°. Bristol. 1925

Bristol & Gloucestershire Archæological Society.
Transactions, v42–48 (1920–26). 8°. Bristol. [1921–27]

Bristol (Frederick Augustus Hervey, *4th earl of***),** *5th baron Howard de Walden, bp. of Derry, see* CHILDE-PEMBERTON (W. S.) The Earl Bishop: life of F. H., Bp. of Derry &c., 2v, 1925.

Bristol (George Digby, *2nd earl of***),** *see* TOWNSHEND (D.) G. D., 2nd Earl of B., 1924.

Bristol (Lucius Moody). Social adaptation. Pref. by T. N. Carver. [Harvard Econ. St., v14]. 8°. Camb. [Mass.] 1915

Bristow (Richard), *see* FULKE (W.) A retentive to stay good Christians agst. the motives of R. B., 1580.

Bristow (W.) *The genuine acc. of the trial of Eugene Aram; added, defence. 11th ed. s8°. 1815

Bristowe (Samuel Boteler), *see* BURN (R.) Justice of the Peace &c., 30th ed., v2 by S. B. B., 1869.

Britannica. Gloria B.: acc. of the Royal Navy &c., 1696, *see* GLORIA.
*Justitia B. &c., 1584, *see* BURGHLEY (W. C., *b.*)

Britannicus, *ps.* *Letters of B. on Mr. Grattan's bill for the relief of Roman Catholics &c. Added, App. [*b. w.* Kenyon (G. K., *b.*) Obs., 1810]. 8°. 1813

Britannus (Bonifacius). Pro Evangelist. ac sectarum nostri temp. peste antidotus, *see* COCHLÆUS (J.) Hist. de actis &c. M. Lutheri, 1565.

British.
*Accentuated list of the B. Lepidoptera, 1858, *see* LEPIDOPTERA.
*Biog. of Brit. stage, 1824, *see* BIOGRAPHY.
Book (The) of the ranks & dignities of Brit. soc. 1805, 1924, *see* BOOK.
British (The) Army &c., 1892, *see* STANHOPE (E.)
British (The) constit. triumphant &c., *see* LOYALIST'S (THE) house that Jack built, 1819?
British diplomacy, 1813–15: sel. docs., 1921, *see* WEBSTER (C. K.), *ed.*
British diplomatic instructions, 1689–1789. [Roy. Hist. Soc. Camden ser., v32, 35, 36, 38]. v1–4. 8°. 1922–27
1, Sweden, 1689–1727; J. F. Chance.
2, France, 1689–1721; L. G. W. Legg.
3, Denmark, 1689–1789; J. F. Chance.
4, France, 1721–27; L. G. W. Legg.
Brit. documents on the orig. of the War, 1898–1914. Ed. G. P. Gooch & H. Temperley. v1, 2, 11. la8°. 1926–27
1, End of Brit. isolation. 2, Anglo-Jap. Alliance & the Franco-Brit. Entente.
11, Outbreak of the War: For. off. docs., June 28–Aug. 4, 1914; coll. &c. by J. W. Headlam-Morley.
British Empire (The). A survey. Ed. H. Gunn. [12v]. 8°. [1924]
see BALFOUR (A.) & H. H. SCOTT. Health problems, 1924. [5.]
,, BELCHER (E. A.) & J. A. WILLIAMSON. Migration, 1924. [12.]
,, DOMINIONS (THE) & depend. of the Emp.; [*by* Ld. Morris, Sir G. E. Foster & o.], 1924. [1.]
,, GUNN (H.) Makers, 1924. [8.]
,, KEITH (A. B.) Constit., admin. & laws, 1924. [3.]
,, LAGDEN (*Sir* G. Y.) The native races, 1924. [9.]
,, LEWIN (E.) Resources & th. development, 1924. [4.]
,, LUCAS (*Sir* C. P.) Story, 1924. [2.]
,, MACLEOD (*Sir* C. C.) & A. W. KIRKALDY. Trade, commerce &c., 1924. [7.]
,, MILLS (J. S.) The press & communic., 1924. [6.]

British [*continued*].
see NEWTON (A. P.) The univ. & educ. systems, 1924. [10.]
,, SALMON (E.) Lit. of the Emp.—Art by A. A. Longden, 1924. [11.]
British Empire (The) at war, A pictorial souvenir. [P2422]. obl.8°. *n.d.*
British fairy & folk tales, 1920, *see* GLOVER (W. J.), *ed.*
*British grasses, 1920, *see* MACGILL (J. F.)
*British (The) hero: or, a disc., shewing interest &c. of every Briton to avow his loyalty to King George. s8°. 1715
British home (The). Mod. domestic architecture &c. Ed. W. S. Sparrow. [Art & life lib., no. 1]. 4°. 1904
*British India; by an Indian Mahomedan, 1926, *see* INDIA.
British Jewry: bk. of honour [1914–18], 1922, *see* ADLER (M.), *ed.*
British labour &c., 1921, *see* GRIER (*Miss* L.) *&* *Miss* A. ASHLEY.
British labour delegates in red Petrograd. Speeches &c. [P2466]. 8°. Petrograd. 1920
*British post-armistice policy in Constantinople &c. [P2712]. 8°. *n.p.* 1921
British water-colour painting of to-day, 1921, *see* HOLME (G.), *ed.*
*Cat. of Brit. scientific & technical books &c., 1921, *see* BRITISH SCI. GUILD.
*Examination of the Brit. doctrine wh. subjects to capture a neutral trade, 2nd ed., 1806, *see* MADISON (J.)
Statistics of milit. effort of the Brit. Emp. dur. the Gt. War, 1914–20, 1922, *see* WAR.
Summary of Brit. official rep. on the Metric System, arranged by J. H. T. [P2832]. 8°. *n.p.* [1908]

British Academy [*London*].
Proceedings, 1907/8, 1909/10, 1911/12, 1913/14, 1915/16, 1917/18, 1919/20. la8°. 1908–20
Records of the social & econ. hist. of Eng. & Wales. v3–6. la8°. 1924–27
see CANTERBURY. Register of St. Augustine's Abbey; ed. G. J. Turner &c., p2, 1924. [3.]
,, FLEET, *Lincs.* Terrier of F.; ed. N. Neilson—11th c. Inquisition of St. Augustine's, Canterbury; [ed.] A. Ballard, 1920. [4.]
,, LODGE (E. C.) Account bk. of a Kentish estate, 1616–1704, 1927. [6.]
,, STENTON (F. M.) Docs. illust. of soc. &c. hist. of the Danelaw, 1920. [5.]
Supplemental papers, 4, *see* ROBINSON (J. A.) The Saxon bishops of Wells, 1919. [4.]
PUBLICATIONS.
see ABRAHAMS (I.) Campaigns in Palestine (Schweich lects., 1922), 1927.
,, ALLEN (P. S.) Erasmus' services to learning (Hertz lect. on a master mind), 1925.
,, BARKER (H. G.) From Henry V to Hamlet (Shakespeare lect.), 1925.
,, BLOMFIELD (*Sir* R.) The tangled skein art in Eng., 1800–1920, 1920.
,, BRADLEY (A. C.) B. Bosanquet, 1848–1923 [*by* A. C. B. & Ld. Haldane], 1924.
,, BURNET (J.) Aristotle, 1924.
,, CÆDMON. The C. MS.; intr. by Sir I. Gollancz, 1927.
,, CHAMBERS (E. K.) Disintegrat. of Shakespeare (S. lect.), 1924.
,, CHAMBERS (R. W.) W. P. Ker, 1925.
,, CHARLES (R. H.) Lect. on the Apocalypse, Schweich lects., 1919, 1922.
,, CIPPICO (A.) Poetry of U. Foscolo (Ital. lect.), 1926.
,, CLARK (A. C.) & J. R. HARRIS. F. C. Conybeare, 1926.
,, COURTHOPE (W. J.) A consideration of Macaulay's comp. of Dante & Milton, 1908.
,, COWLEY (A. E.) The Hittites (Schweich lect.), 1920.
,, DE SÉLINCOURT (E.) Keats (Warton lect. 11), 1921.
,, FIRTH (C. H.) Polit. significance of "Gulliver's travels," 1920.
,, FORTESCUE (J. W.) Brit. soldier & the Empire, 1921.
,, GASTER (M.) The Samaritans (Schweich lects., 1923), 1925.
,, GRIERSON (H. J. C.) Ld. Byron: Arnold & Swinburne (Warton lect.), 1920.
,, HILL (G. F.) Ital. portraits of 15th cent. (Ital. lect.), 1925.
,, HODGSON (S. H.) Some cardinal points in knowledge, [1911].
,, HOGARTH (D. G.) Kings of the Hittites (Schweich lect., 1924), 1926.
,, HOLMES (C. J.) Leonardo da Vinci, 1919.
,, JONES (*Sir* J. M.-) Sir John Rhŷs, 1926.
,, LEACH (A. F.) Milton as a schoolboy & schoolmaster, 1908.
,, LEGOUIS (E.) Bacchic elem. in Shakespeare's plays, 1926.
,, LITTLE (A. G.) Some recently disc. Franciscan doc., 1926.
,, MACCALLUM (M. W.) Dram. monol. in Victorian period (Warton lect. 16), 1925.
,, MACDONALD (G.) Silver coinage of Crete, 1919.
,, MACKAIL (J. W.) Bentley's Milton (Warton lect.), 1924.
,, MACLAGAN (E.) The appreciation of sculpture (Hertz lect. on art), 1925.
,, —— A romanesque relief in York Minster, 1923.
,, MARGOLIOUTH (D. S.) Rel. betw. Arabs & Israelites (Schweich lects., 1921), 1924.

British Academy [*London*] [*continued*].
PUBLICATIONS [*continued*].
see MARGOLIOUTH (D. S.) 2 South Arabian inscr., 1925.
,, MILTON (J.) Tercentenary of M.'s birth, 1908.
,, NOTESTEIN (W.) Winning of the initiative by H. of Commons, 1926.
,, PLUMMER (C.) On colophons & marginalia of Irish scribes, 1926.
,, POLLARD (A. W.) The found. of Shakespeare's text (Shakespeare lect.), 1923.
,, POLLOCK (*Rt. Hon. Sir* F.) Sir C. P. Ilbert, 1926.
,, POOLE (R. L.) Beginning of the year in M. A., 1921.
,, —— Early corresp. of John of Salisbury, 1924.
,, POSTGATE (J. P.) On anc. Gk. accentuation, 1925.
,, ROBINSON (J. A.) Somerset hist. essays, 1921.
,, RODD (J. R.) Italian people, 1920.
,, SCOTT (W. R.) Alfred Marshall, 1926.
,, SETH (A.) The philos. of hist. (Hertz lect.), 1924.
,, STOUT (G. F.) Nature of universals & propositions, 1921.
,, TAIT (J.) Study of early munic. hist. in Eng., 1922.
,, TAYLOR (A. E.) F. H. Bradley, 1926.
,, —— Francis Bacon, 1926.
,, THACKERAY (H. ST. J.) The Septuagint & Jewish worship (Schweich lect., 1920), 1921.
,, TOUT (T. F.) Begin. of a mod. capital: London & Westminster in 14 c. (Raleigh lect.), 1923.
,, —— Sir A. W. Ward, 1926.
,, —— Sir J. H. Ramsay, 1926.
,, TOYNBEE (P. J.) The bearing of the cursus on the text of Dante's De vulgari eloquentia, 1923.
,, —— Britain's tribute to Dante in lit. & art, 1921.
,, VILLARI (L.) Develop. of polit. ideas in Italy in 19th cent., 1926.

British & Foreign Anti-slavery Society. Proc. of Gen. Anti-slavery Convention, June 13–20, 1843. By J. F. Johnson. 8º. [1843]

British & Foreign Bible Society.
Cat. of the lib. By G. Bullen. 8º. 1857
Reports 1805–15 [1803–13 repr. *in* 2v. 1814, 15 *b. separately*]. 8º. *n.d.*
St. John iii, 16 in lang. &c. in wh. Soc. has pr. the Scriptures. enl. ed. s8º. 1878
,, ,, [*a. ed. w. t.* The Gospel in many tongues]. s8º. 1925
see BROWNE (G.) Hist. of Brit. & For. Bible Soc., 1804–54, 2v, 1859.
,, DEALTRY (W.) A review of Norris's attack on the B. & F. B. S., 1815.
,, MARSH (H.) Consequences of neglecting to give the Prayer bk. w. the Bible; w. matter rel. to B. & F. B. Soc., 1812.
,, MILNER (I.) Strictures on publ[s]. of Rev. H. Marsh: reply to h. objections agst. the B. & F. B. S., 1813.
,, NORRIS (H. H.) A pract. expos. of tendency & proc. of B. & F. B. S., 1815.

British Antarctic (Terra Nova) Expedition, *1910–13.* 4º. 1914–24
Determinat. of gravity; by C. S. Wright, 1921.
Glaciology; by C. S. Wright & R. E. Priestley, 1922.
Meteorology; by G. C. Simpson, 3v, 1919–23.
Misc. data; compiled by Col. H. G. Lyons, 1924.
Natural hist. reports. Zoology. [Brit. Museum (Nat. Hist.)], v1–3, 1914–23.
1, Vertebrata; 2, Collecting stations, Mollusca, Brachiopoda & worms; 3, Arthropoda.
Adelie penguin; by G. M. Levick, 1915. [1.]
Arachnida; p1; by H. R. Hogg, 1918. [3.]
Brachiopoda; by J. W. Jackson, 1918. [2.]
Cetacea; by D. G. Lillie, 1915. [1.]
Collecting stations: List of; by S. F. Harmer & D. G. Lillie, 1914. [2.]
Crustacea; by L. A. Borradaile, W. T. Calman, R. W. Barney & W. M. Tattersall, p1–7, 1916–23. [3.]
Fishes; by C. T. Regan, 1914. [1.]
,, Larval & post-larval; by C. T. Regan, 1916. [1.]
Hirudinea; by W. A. Harding, 1922. [2.]
Insecta; by G. H. Carpenter & J. Waterston, 1921. [3.]
Mollusca; by E. A. Smith, A. L. Massy & R. H. Burne, p1–4, 1915–20. [2.]
Myzostomida; by C. L. Boulenger, 1916. [2.]
Nemertinea; by H. A. Baylis, 1915. [2.]
Oligochæta; by H. A. Baylis, 1915. [2.]
Parasitic worms; by R. T. Leiper & E. L. Atkinson, 1915. [2.]
Pycnogonida; by W. T. Calman, 1915. [3.]
Observations on the aurora; by C. S. Wright, 1921 [*b. w.* Determ. of gravity, 1921].
Physiography of the Beardmore Glacier Region; by C. S. Wright, 1923. [*b. w.* Physiog. of Ross Arch., 1923].
Physiogr. of the McMurdo Sound & Granite Harbour reg.; by G. Taylor, 1922.
Physiogr. (Robertson Bay & Terra Nova regions); by R. E. Priestley, 1923. [*b. w.* Physiog. of Ross Arch., 1923.]
Physiogr. of the Ross Archipelago; by F. Debenham, 1923.
Report on the maps & surveys; by F. Debenham, 1923.
Terrestrial magnetism; by C. Chree, 1921.

British Apollo (The), or, Curious amusements for the ingenious &c. Perform'd by a Society of Gentlemen. v1–4, No. 20, Mar. 13, 1708–May 11, 1711. [*b. in 3v.*] sfol. 1708–11
British Apollo (The), cont. answers to curious questions &c. 4th ed. v1. s8º. 1740

British Archæological Association.
Journal. New ser., v25–29. 8º. 1919–23
v27 in 2p, p1, Lincoln Congress part.
v29 ,, ,, p1, York Congress part.

British archivist (The). Ed. R. Holworthy. v1 (March 1913–May 1920). [*No more publ.*] sfol. [1921]
After 1920 publ. w. Miscellanea genealogica et heraldica.
,, ,, ...[Suppl.] sfol. [1921]
see DEW, *Fam. of.* Dew wills & admin. in Prerogative Court of Canterbury, 1921.

British Association for the Advancement of Science. Report of 87th, 89th–95th meeting, 1919, 1921–27. 8º. 1920–27
see BRISTOL. B. & its environs; publ., Local Comm. of Brit. Assoc., 1875.
,, HOWARTH (O. J. R.) The Brit. Assoc.: a retrospect, 1831–1921, 1922.

British Dominions Year Book, 1921. Ed. E. Salmon & J. Worsfold. Publ. by Eagle, Star & Brit. Dom. Gen. Insurance Co., Ltd. 8º. 1921

British Gazette, The. Publ. by H.M. Stationery Office. No. 1–8, May 5–13, 1926 [*& Sunday issue* No. 1, May 9, *without title. No more publ. With specimens of o. strike emergency newspapers bound in*]. lafol. 1926

British Institute of International Affairs, *see* ROYAL INST. OF INTERNAT. AFFAIRS.

British (The) journal of psychology.
Ed. C. H. Myers. v10–18, 1919–28. la8º. C. 1920–28
Monograph supplements. [No.] 3, 6, 11, 12. la8º. C. 1915–27
see MAGSON (E. H.) How we judge intelligence, 1926. [11.]
,, STEVANOVIĆ (B. P.) Experimental st. of mental processes involved in judgment, 1927. [12.]
,, WEBB (E.) Character & intelligence, 1915. [3.]
,, WOHLGEMUTH (A.) Pleasure-unpleasure, 1919. [6.]

British Malaya. Hdbk. to Brit. Malaya, 1926, 1927. Comp. by C. L. German. 8º. 1926–27

British Museum.
Cleaning (The) & restor. of m. exhibits, investig. at B.M., 1926, *see* CLEANING.
see BRITISH MUSEUM QUARTERLY, v1, 1927.
ANTIQUITIES &c.
Babylonian legends of the creation & the fight between Bel & the dragon as told by Assyrian Tablets f. Nineveh. [By E. A. W. Budge]. [P2577]. 8º. 1921
Babylonian story of the deluge & the epic of Gilgamish, w. acc. of the Roy. libraries of Nineveh. [By E. A. W. Budge]. [P2577]. 8º. 1920
The book of the dead. [By E. A. Wallis Budge]. la8º. 1920
Carchemish: Rep. on excav. at Jerablus; conducted by C. L. Woolley & T. E. Lawrence. p2, The town defences, by C. L. Woolley. 4º. 1921
English pottery & porcelain; [by R. L. Hobson]. 2nd. ed. 8º. 1910
Engraved gems & cameos, Greek, Etruscan & Roman, in B.M. By H. B. Walters. rev. & enl. ed. 4º. 1926
Exhib. illust. Greek & Roman life. Guide. 2nd ed. 8º. 1920
The fall of Nineveh: newly disc. Babylonian chron., in the B.M. Ed. w. translit., tr., notes &c. by C. J. Gadd. la8º. 1923
Frank Lloyd coll. of Worcester porcelain of the Wall period, pres. in 1921 to Dept. of Ceramics &c. By R. L. Hobson. la8º. 1923
[Franks bequest]. Treasure of the Oxus, w. o. examples of

ANTIQUITIES [*continued*].
early oriental metal-work. By O. M. Dalton. 2nd ed. 4º. 1926
Grecian antiq. Photog. by S. Thompson. 2v. fol. 1872
Greek & Roman lamps in B.M. By H. B. Walters. 8º. 1914
Guide to Anglo-Saxon & for. Teutonic antiq. in Dept. of Brit. & Mediæval Antiq. [By R. A. Smith]. 8º. 1923
Guide to early Xtn. & Byzantine antiq. in Dept. of Antiq. 2nd ed. 8º. 1921
Guide to the Eng. pottery & porcelain in Dept. of Ceramics & Ethnog. 3rd ed. 8º. 1923
Guide to the Maudslay coll. of Maya sculptures f. Cent. Amer. [By T. A. Joyce]. 8º. 1923
Guide to the pottery & porcelain of the Far East in the Dept. of Ceramics & Ethnography. [Sir W. Franks coll. Prep. by R. L. Hobson]. 8º. 1924
Hdbk. to ethnogr. coll. 8º. 1910
*How to observe in archæology: suggestions. s8º. 1920
Silver plate (Greek, Etruscan & Roman) in B.M.; by H. B. Walters. 4º. 1921
see KITCHIN (J. G.) Bible student in the B.M., 1893.
,, READ (*Sir* C. H.) C. H. R.: tribute on h. retirement f. B.M. & record of add. to Dept. of Brit. &c. Antiq., 1896–1921, 1921.
,, UR excav., v1, Al-'Ubaid, 1927.

British Museum [*continued*].
BOOKBINDINGS.
Early stamped b. in B.M.: descr. of bindings of 12th–15th c. in Dept. of MSS. & Pr. Books. Mainly by W. H. J. Weale, completed by L. Taylor. 8°. 1922
see FLETCHER (W. Y.) Eng. bookbindings in B.M.; illust. of 63 examples, w. intr. & descr. by W. Y. F., 1895.
CATALOGUES &C.
Outlines for classific. of a library. 4°. 1825
*Rules for comp. the cat. in Dept. of Pr. Books. 8°. 1920
CERAMICS & ETHNOGRAPHY, *see* ANTIQ. &C. *above*.
COINS & MEDALS.
Coins of the Roman Empire in the B.M.; by H. Mattingly. v1. la8°. 1923
Greek coins of Arabia, Mesopotamia & Persia. By G. F. Hill. 8°. 1922
Guide to the exhib. of medals of the Renaissance in the B.M. By G. F. Hill. 8°. 1923
see HILL (G. F.) Greek coins acquired by B.M., 1917–
INSCRIPTIONS.
Cuneiform texts f. Babylonian tablets &c. p32, 34. sfol. 1912–14
Cuneiform texts f. Cappadocian tablets in the B.M. p1. sfol. 1921
Hieroglyphic texts f. Egyptian stelæ &c. p1, 3, 5. sfol. 1911–14
Hittite texts in the Cuneiform character f. tablets in the B.M. sfol. 1920
see THOMPSON (R. C.) Assyrian medical texts f. originals in B.M., 1923.
LAMPS, *see* ANTIQUITIES *above*.
MANUSCRIPTS [*see also* BOOKBINDINGS *above*].
Add. to MSS. in B.M., 1911–15. la8°. 1925
Armenian MSS.; by F. C. Conybeare. App., Cat. of Georgian MSS., by J. O. Wardrop. 4°. 1913
Harleian MSS., Cat. of ref[s]. to Sussex, by L. F. Salzmann, *see* SUSSEX. Misc. rec., 1905.
Irish MSS. v1, 2. la8°. 1926
1, By S. H. O'Grady. 2, By R. Flower.
MSS. &c. exhib., Nelson centenary. 8°. 1905
MSS. portuguezes &c. de int. para o Brazil; p. O. Lima, *see* INSTITUTO HIST. &C. BRAZIL. Rev., t65, 1902.
Reprod. f. illum. MSS. 3rd ed., s1–3. s4°. 1923–25
Western MSS. in the old Royal & King's Coll[s].; by Sir G. F. Warner & J. P. Gilson. 4v. fol. 1921
1, 2, Royal MSS. 3, King's MSS. & Indexes. 4, Plates.
see BIBLE. ANGLO-SAXON. The Lindisfarne Gospels: plates f. Cotton MS. in B.M., w. intr. by E. G. Millar, 1923.
„ MARCHAM (F.) King's Office of the Revels, 1610–22, doc. in B.M., 1925.
„ REICH (N.) Papyri jurist. Inhalts in hierat. u. demot. Schr. aus d. B.M., T1, 1914.

MANUSCRIPTS [*continued*].
see SERVICE DES ANTIQ. DE L'ÉGYPTE. Temples immergés: doc., t1 [1, B.M.], 1920.
„ VINCI (L. DA). Mss. e disegni, v1, Il cod. Arundel 263, 2p, 1923–26.
MAPS.
see CONTARINI (G. M.) Map of the world by C., engraved by F. Roselli, 1506, 1924.
PAPYRI.
Facsimiles of Egyptian Hieratic p. in B.M., w. descr[s]., summaries of contents &c. by E. A. W. Budge. s2. fol. 1923
see BELL (H. I.) Jews & Xtns. in Egypt; illust. by texts f. Greek papyri in B.M.; ed. H. I. B., 1924.
PRINTED BOOKS [*see also* BOOKBINDINGS *above*].
Bible Exhib., 1911. Guide. 8°. 1911
Books printed in 15th c. [*comp. by* A. W. Pollard, A. J. K. Esdaile & J. V. Scholderer]. p5 (Venice). 4°. 1924
Catalogue: Aristotle. [*a. c. b. w.* Marr (N. Ya.) Сказ. о катол. Петрѣ, 1895]. fol. 1884
Subject index of books rel. to the European War, 1914–18, acquired by B.M., 1914–20. 8°. 1922
Subject index of mod. books acquired by the B.M., 1916–1920, other than those rel. to the European War. 8°. 1922
Subject index of mod. works acquired, 1921–25. la8°. 1927
—— *Special foreign catalogues.*
Arabic books in B.M. Suppl. cat. By A. S. Fulton & A. G. Ellis. 4°. 1926
Books pr. in France & Fr. bks. pr. in other countries, 1470–1600 now in the B.M.; [by H. Thomas &c.] 8°. 1924
Books pr. in Spain & Span. books pr. elsewhere in Europe bef. 1601 in B.M.; by H. Thomas. 8°. 1921
Persian printed books in B.M. By E. Edwards. 4°. 1922
PRINTS, DRAWINGS &C.
Book of drawings form. ascribed to Mantegna pres. to B.M. in 1920 by the Earl of Rosebery. Intr. by C. Dodgson. 4°. 1923
Drawings by Dutch & Flemish artists in B.M.; by A. M. Hind. v1–3. la8°. 1915–26
1, Rembrandt & h. school. 2, Rubens, Van Dyck & o. artists of 17th c. 3, Dutch drawings of the 17th cent. (A–M).
Engraved Brit. portraits in B.M. v5, 6. la8°. 1922–25
5, Groups; by F. M. O'-Donoghue & H. M. Hake. 6, Suppl. & Indexes; by H. M. Hake.
Index of Chinese artists repres. in sub-dept. of Oriental prints &c. in B.M., by A. Waley. 8°. 1922
VASES.
Greek & Etruscan vases in B.M. v1i. la8°. 1925
1i, Prehist. Ægean pottery; by E. J. Forsdyke.
see CORPUS vasorum antiq. Gt. Brit.: Brit. Museum, fasc. 1, 2; by A. H. Smith &c., 1925–26.

British Museum of Natural History.
Cat. of the books, MSS., maps & drawings. v6, Suppl., A–I. 4°. 1922
BOTANY.
Flora of Jamaica. By W. Fawcett & A. B. Rendle. v5, Dicotyledons. 8°. 1926
Handbook of the larger Brit. fungi. By J. Ramsbottom. Based on the Guide to Sowerby's models of Brit. fungi, by W. G. Smith. 8°. 1923
Monogr. of the Brit. lichens, p2; by A. L. Smith. 2nd ed. rev. 8°. 1926
GEOLOGY & PALÆONTOLOGY.
Cainozoic plants in Dept. of G., B.M. (Nat. Hist.) v1. 8°. 1926
1, The Bembridge flora, by E. M. Reid & M. E. J. Chandler, w. sect. on the Charophyta by J. Groves.
Cat. of fossil birds in the B.M.; by R. Lydekker. 8°. 1891
Cat. of the fossil Reptilia & Amphibia; by R. Lydekker. 4p. 8°. 1888–90
Fossil Bryozoa. The Cretaceous Bryozoa. v3, 4, The Cribrimorphs, 2p, by W. D. Lang. 8°. 1921–22
Machæridia; by T. H. Withers. 8°. 1926
MINERAL DEPT.
Cat. of meteorites, w. spec. ref. to those in coll. of B.M. By G. T. Prior. 8°. 1923
ZOOLOGY.
Birds beneficial to agriculture. By F. W. Frohawk. [Econ. Ser., 9]. 8°. 1919
Bombyliidæ of the Ethiopian region, based on material in the B.M. By M. Bezzi. 8°. 1924
Furniture beetles, their life hist. &c. By C. J. Gahan. [P2523]. 8°. 1920
Handbook of British mosquitoes. By W. D. Lang. 8°. 1920
The house-fly; by E. E. Austen. [P2423]. 8°. 1920

ZOOLOGY [*continued*].
Insects of Samoa & o. S. terrestrial arthropoda. p2i, 3i, ii, 7i, & Maps. la8°. 1927
2i, Hemiptera. Fulgoroidea, by F. Muir: Psyllidæ (Chermidæ), by Prof. D. L. Crawford; Coccidæ &c. by F. Laing.
3i, Lepidoptera. Butterflies of Samoa &c. by G. H. E. Hopkins.
3ii, Micro-lepidoptera, by E. Meyrick.
7i, Other orders of insects. Isoptera: fam. Termitidæ, by G. F. Hill; Odonata, by Lt.-Col. F. C. Fraser.
Lepidoptera Phalænæ, subfamily Noctuinæ. New genera & species. 8°. 1926
Marine boring animals; by W. T. Calman. [P2423]. 8°. 1919
Monograph of the Lacertidæ. By G. A. Boulenger. 2v. 8°. 1920–21
Monograph of the Mycetozoa; descr. cat. of the species in B.M. By A. Lister. 3rd ed., rev. by G. Lister. 8°. 1925
Monograph of the sea-snakes (Hydrophiidæ). By M. Smith. 8°. 1926
Monograph of the voles & lemmings (Microtinæ), living & extinct. By M. A. C. Hinton. v1. 8°. 1926
Recent sea-urchins (Echinoidea) in Coll. of B.M. By H. L. Clark. 8°. 1925
Synonymy of Brit. non-marine Mollusca (recent & post-tertiary); by A. S. Kennard & B. B. Woodward. 8°. 1926
Synopsis of families & genera of Nematoda; by H. A. Baylis & R. Daubney. 8°. 1926
Type specimens of Lepidoptera Rhopalocera in B.M. By N. D. Riley & A. G. Gabriel. p1–3. 8°. 1924–27
see BRIT. ANTARCTIC (TERRA NOVA) EXPED., 1910–13. Zoology, v1–3, 1914–23.
„ SHERBORN (C. D.) Index animalium &c., sect. 2, 1922–27.

British Museum (The) quarterly. v1, 1926–7. la8°. 1927
British Numismatic journal, & Proc. of the Brit. Num. Soc. v10–17 (1911–24) [v11–17=s2, v1–7]. la8°. 1914–27
British Photographic Manufacturers Association.
Photographic industry of Gt. Britain. la8°. 1918
British Plate Glass Company. Tariff of the prices of polished plates of glass. s8°. 1807
British Record Society.
Index Library. v50–54. la8°. 1920–25
Canterbury. Index of wills & admin. in Probate Reg. at C., 1396–1558 & 1640–50. Transcr. &c. H. R. [illegible]. [50.]
Canterbury. Index of wills in Prerogative Court of C. Ed. T. M. Blagg & J. S. Moir, v7, 1653–56. [54.]
Dorset. Calendar of wills &c. rel. to D. Ed. G. S. Fry. [53.]
Leicester. Index to wills & admin. &c. in Archdeaconry Court of L., 1660–1750 &c. now in Probate Reg. at L. Transcr. &c. H. Hartopp. [51.]
Lincoln. Calendars of admin. in Consistory Court of L., 1540–1659; ed. C. W. Foster. [52.]
Taunton. Cal. of wills &c. in Court of Archdeacon of T., p3, 4; ed. E. A. Fry. [53.]
British Red Cross Society.
Acc. of Auxil. Hospitals, 1916. s4°. [1917]
Rep. by the Joint War Comm. & Joint W. Finance Comm. of the B. R. C. Soc. & Order of St. John on voluntary aid to Sick &c. at home & abroad, & to Brit. Prisoners of War, 1914–19, w. App. fol. 1921
British School at Athens. Annual of the B. S. at A. No. 23–26, session[s] 1918–19—1924–25. 4°. [1920–26]
No. 25 *cont.* Rep. of excavations at Mycenæ, 1921–23.

British School at Athens [*continued*].
Suppl. paper No. 1., Unpubl. objects f. the Palaikastro excav., 1902–6; descr. by R. C. Bosanquet & R. M. Dawkins. pl. 4°. 1923

British School at Rome. Papers. v9, 10. la8°. 1920–27
Ashby (T.) Antiq. statuæ urbis Romæ [*by* G. B. de' Cavalieri, 1569], 1920. [9.]
—— The Palazzo Odescalchi, 1920. [9.]
Ashmole (B.) Hygieia on Acropolis & Palatine, 1927. [10.]
Bradshaw (H. C.) Præneste: st. for its restoration, 1920. [9.]
Cordingley (R. A.) & I. A. Richmond. The Mausoleum of Augustus, 1927. [10.]
Gardner (R.) The Via Claudia Valeria, 1920. [9.]
Hill (G. F.) Roman medallists of the Renaissance, 1920. [9.]
Mann (H. K.) Portraits of the Popes, 1920. [9.]
Richmond (I. A.) Rel. of the Prætorian Camp to Aurelian's Wall, 1927. [10.]
Sandys (*Sir* J. E.) J. P. Steele, 1836–1917, 1920. [9.]
Strong (*Mrs.* E.) Bronze plaque in Rosenheim coll., 1920. [9.]
—— Note on a copy of the Responsiones of R. Parsons, 1920. [9.]
—— Sepulchral relief of a priest of Bellona, 1920. [9.]
see BORENIUS (T.) Picture gallery of A. Vendramin, 1923.

British School of Archaeology in Egypt &c.
see BIBLE: COPTIC. Gospel of St. John acc. to earliest Coptic MS.; ed. w. tr. by Sir H. Thompson, 1924.
,, BRUNTON (G.) Lahun I, The treasure, 1920.
,, —— & R. ENGELBACH. Gurob, 1927.
,, ENGELBACH (R.) Harageh, 1923.
,, PETRIE (*Sir* W. M. F.) Anc. weights & measures, 1926.
,, —— Buttons & design scarabs, 1925.
,, —— Corpus of prehist. pottery & palettes, 1921.
,, —— Glass stamps & weights, 1926.
,, —— The Hawara portfolio: paintings of the Rom. age, 1913.
,, —— Objects of daily use, 1927.
,, —— Prehist. Egypt, 1920.
,, —— Tombs of the Courtiers & Oxyrhynkhos, 1925.
,, —— & G. BRUNTON. Sedment, 2v, 1924.
,, ——, G. BRUNTON & M. A. MURRAY. Lahun II, 1923.

British School of Archaeology in Jerusalem, *see* TURVILLE-PETRE (F.) Researches in prehist. Galilee, 1925–26, & A report on the Galilee skull by Sir A. Keith, 1927.

British Science Guild. Catalogue of Brit. scient. & techn. books &c. Prep. by committee of the B. Sc. G. 8°. 1921

British Ski year book. Ski Club of Gt. Brit. Ed. A. Lunn. v3, No. 7. 8°. Uxbridge. 1926

British Society of Franciscan Studies.
Publications. v9–12. E. S. v2. 8°. M'ter. 1920–26
see BOURDILLON (A. F. C.) Order of Minoresses in Eng., 1926. [12.]
see COLLECTANEA Franciscana, v2, 1922. [10.]
,, COTTON (C.) Grey Friars of Canterbury, 1224–1538, 1924. [E.S. 2.]
,, FITZMAURICE (E. B.) & A. G. LITTLE. Materials for hist. of Franciscan Prov. of Ireland, 1920. [9.]
,, SETON (W. W.) N. Glassberger & h. works &c., 1923. [11.]

British Somaliland, *see* WAR OFFICE, Military report on B. S., v1, 1925.

British Spa Federation. Spas of Brit. Offic. hdbk. of Brit. Spa Fed. Intr. by R. F. Fox. s8°. [1924]

British Trades Union.
see FEDOROV (M.) La Russie sous le régime communiste: rép. au rapp. de la Délég. des Trades-Unions Britt., 1926.
,, RUSSIA, ANON. WORKS. R.: official rep. of the B. T. U. deleg. 1924, 1925.

British Worker, The. Official strike news bulletin. Publ. by the Gen. Council of the T. U. C. No. 1–10, May 5–15, 1926. fol. 1926
b. w. Brit. Gazette, 1926, *w. specimens of o. strike emergency newspapers.*

British Workers' Delegation.
Soviet Russia to-day. Rep. 8°. 1927

British year book (The) of international law, 1920–1, 1923–27. la8°. [1920–27]

Brito Aragão e Vasconcellos (Antonio Luiz de). Memorias s. o estab. do imperio do Brazil. pl [*no more publ.*] la8°. Rio de Janeiro. [1927?]

Brito Aranha (Pedro Wenceslau de), *see* †PORTUGAL. Le P., géogr., ethn. &c., par B. A. &c., 1900.

Britonio (Girolamo) [BRITTONIO (GEROLAMO)]. Opera volgare, intit. Gelosia del sole. [Sonetti, canzoni &c.] s4°. Napoli. 1519
Del Britonio i cantici, et i ragionamenti; et quelli d. Pontefice in favore d. Sant. Rom. Chiesa. s8°. Vinegia. 1550

Britsch (Amédée). La jeunesse de Philippe-Egalité, 1747–85, d'ap. des docs. inéd. 8°. 1926
Le maréchal Lyautey. s8°. [1921]

Britten (Frederick James). The watch & clock makers' handbook. Dict. & guide. 13th ed. 8°. 1922

Britton (John). Graphical & lit. illust. of Fonthill Abbey, w. heraldical &c. notices of the Beckford family. *large paper copy.* 4°. 1823

Britton (Nathaniel Lord) & J. N. Rose. The Cactaceæ: descr. & illust. of plants of the cactus family. [C.I. of Wash.] 4v. 4°. Wash. 1919–23
Neoabbottia, a new cactus genus f. Hispaniola, *see* SMITHSONIAN INST. Misc. coll., v72, 1922.

Britwell Court, see CHRISTIE-MILLER (S. R.) Cat. of rare works &c., f. lib. form. at B. Ct., 1921–27.

Brix (Hans).
Johannes Ewald: en række krit. undersøgelser. 8°. 1913

Brizio (Edoardo). La necropoli di Novilara, *see* REALE ACCAD. D. LINCEI. Mon. ant., v5, 1895.
Scavi a Marzabotto pr. Bologna, 1888–9, *see* REALE ACCAD. D. LINCEI. Mon. ant., v1, 1890.

Broad (Charles Dunbar).
The mind & its place in nature. 8°. 1925
The philos. of F. Bacon. Address. s8°. C. 1926
Scientific thought. 8°. 1923

Broadbent (Ellinor Lucy). Under the Ital. Alps. With geog. essay by M. I. Newbigin. 8°. [1925]

Broadley (Alexander Meyrick).
Boyhood of a great king, 1841–58. Edward VII. 8°. 1906
Collectanea Napoleonica. Cat. of coll. of autographs, hist. doc. &c. rel. to Nap. &c., 1769–1821, formed by A. M. B. Comp. by W. V. Daniell, w. pref. by A. M. B. &c. 8°. [1905]

Broad-sheets. [*Miscellaneous broad-sheets,* 1670–1800]. Advice to the fair, Affectionate soldier &c. fol. *var. p. var. d.*
[*Miscellaneous broad-sheets*: Declar. of Prince of Orange, 1688, Rome's hunting match for 3 kingdoms, 1680 *& similar pieces*]. fol. *var. d.*

Broadsides, ballads &c. pr. in Massachusetts, 1639–1800, *see* MASSACHUSETTS HIST. SOC. Coll., v75, 1922.

Broadus (Edmund Kemper). The laureateship. The office, w. acc. of the poets. 8°. O. 1921

Brocardo (Antonio). Rime del B. et d'altri authori. [N. Delphino *&* F. M. Molza. *Dedic. signed* A. Pellegrini]. s8°. [Venetia. 1538]

Brocardus, *de Monte Sion* [BURCHARD]. Descr. locorum Terræ Sanctæ, *see* PEUCER (C.) De dimensione terræ &c., 1544.
Palæstina, seu descr. Terræ Sanctæ solertissima. Restitutore P. Bosquiero. s8°. Coloniæ Agripp. 1624

Brocardus, *theologian.* Tract. de conscientia, *see* MIGNE (J. P.), *ed.* Theol. cursus, t11, 1861.

Brocas (Thomas).
Calvinism unmasked. 2p. [*pag. cont.*] s8°. Shrewsbury. 1812
,, ,, 2nd ed. Ann., 2nd p. in ans. to Arminianism dissected. [*w. sep. tp*]. s8°. Shrewsbury. 1812

Brocchi (Virgilio).
L'arcolaio: novelle. s8°. [1924]
La bottega degli scandali. [I romanzi dell' isola sonante]. s8°. Milano. [1920]
Il destino in pugno. Romanzo. s8°. [1923]
Fragilità. s8°. [1922]
L'isola sonante. s8°. Milano. [1920]
Il labirinto. s8°. Milano. [1921]
Il lastrico dell' inferno. [Romanzi dell' Isola sonante]. s8°. *n.d.*
Mitì. Romanzo. s8°. [1920]
Nètty. Romanzo. s8°. Milano. [1924]
Il posto nel mondo. Romanzo. s8°. [1921]
La rocca sull' onda. s8°. Milano. [1926]
Sul caval d. morte—Amor cavalca. s8°. Milano. [1920]

Brocense (El), *see* SANCHEZ (F.), *of Salamanca.*

Brochard (Victor).
Les sceptiques grecs. 8°. 1897
,, ,, ...2e éd. la8°. 1923

Broche (Lucien). Cathédrale de Laon. 8°. 1926

Brochet (André). La soude électrolytique. 8°. [1909]

Brock (A. St. H.)
Pyrotechnics: hist. & art of firework making. la8°. 1922

Brock (*Sir* Isaac), *see* EAYRS (H. S.) Sir I. B., 1924.

Brock (Lynn), *ps.*, *see* WHARTON (A.)

Brockdorff-Rantzau (Ulrich K., *Graf* **v.)**
Dokumente. 8°. Charlottenburg. 1920

Brockelmann (Carl). 'Alī's Qiṣṣa'i Jūsuf, d. älteste Vorläufer d. osman. Lit., *see* KÖNIGL. PREUSS. AKAD. D. WISS. Abhdl. (Phil.-hist. Klasse), 1916.
Grundriss d. vergl. Gramm. d. semit. Sprachen. 2B (1, Laut- u. Formenlehre. 2, Syntax). la8°. 1908–13
Précis de linguistique sémit. Tr. (avec reman. de l'a.) par W. Marçais & M. Cohen. s8°. 1910

Brockhaus, *publishing firm.*
Hdbch. d. Wissens. 4B. la8º. L. 1922–27

Brockhaus (F. A.) Bibl. américaine. Cat. rais. d'une coll. de livres sur l'A., jusqu'à l'an 1700, en vente chez B. Rédigé par P. Trömel. 8º. L. 1861

Brocklebank (Ralph). Cat. of mod. pictures &c., property of R. B. Auction by Christie &c. July 7, 1922. [*Illust.*] 8º. 1922
Pictures & engravings at Haughton Hall, Tarporley, in poss. of R. B. Descr. & biog. notes &c. by R. R. Carter. fol. 1904

Brockway (Archibald Fenner).
India & its gov. [P2563]. 8º. 1921
see HOBHOUSE (S.) & A. F. B., *edd.* Eng. prisons to-day, report &c., 1922.

Brockway (Beman). Fifty years in journalism, w. an auto-biog. 8º. Watertown. N.Y. 1891

Brockwell (David). The Alsatian. s8º. [1926]

Brockwell (Maurice Walter), *see* HUNTINGTON (H. E.) Cat. of paintings in coll. of H. E. H. at San Marino, Cal.; by M. W. B., 1925.

Brod (Max). Rëubēni, Fürst d. Juden: e. Renaissance-roman. s8º. München. 1925
Weiberwirtschaft. s8º. L. 1917

Brodetsky (Selig). Sir Isaac Newton. s8º. [1927]

Brodie (William).
Kelvinside Academy, 1878–1923. 8º. *p.f.a.* G. 1924

Brodrick (Mary), *see* MURRAY'S HANDBOOKS. Syria &c.; ed. M. B., 1903.

Brodsky (Boris).
Эротика въ русс. поэзіи (сборникъ стиховъ). Ред. &c. Б. Б. s8º. Берлинъ. 1922

Brodsky (Nadja Ornstein-), *see* ORNSTEIN-BRODSKY (N.)

Brodsky (Nikolai Leont.), N. M. Mendelson & N. P. Sidorov.
Историко-литерат. хрестоматия. Ч1–3. la8º. Москва. [1922–23]

Broeck (Joannes van den), *1648–1739, see* VONCK (C. H.) Oratio in funere J. van den B., 1739.

Broeder-Gemeente [*see also* BRÜDER-GEM.] Singi-boekoe vo da Evangel. B.-G. na Suriname-Kondre, 1867, *see* *SINGI-BOEKOE.

Broek (J. van den), *1565–1630, see* PALUDANUS (J.)

Broeke (James Ten), *see* TEN BROEKE (J.)

Brøgger (A. W.), *see* OSEBERGFUNDET; utgit av d. Norske Stat under red. av A. W. B. &c., B1–3, 1917–28.

Broglie (Achille Charles Léonce Victor, *5e duc* **de).** Opinion sur le projet de loi rel. à la presse. [Chambre des Pairs]. [P2866]. s8º. 1822
Rapp. rel. à la répression des crimes &c. commis par la voie de la presse &c. [Chambre des Pairs de Fr.] [P2866]. s8º. 1819

Broglie (Emmanuel de). La B. Marie de l'Incarnation, Mme. Acarie, 1566–1618. ["Les saints"]. 5e éd. s8º. 1921

Broglie (Pauline de), *see* PANGE (*Ctsse.* J. DE).

Broglie (Victor François, *duc de*), *maréchal de France.* Corresp. inéd. avec le prince Xavier de Saxe, cte. de Lusace, p. s. à l'hist. de la Guerre de 7 ans (1759–61). Publ. par le duc de Broglie & J. Vernier. 4t. 8º. 1903–5

Brognoligo (Gioachino).
Tommaso Grossi: vita e opere. s8º. Messina. 1916

Brokesby (Francis). Life of H. Dodwell; w. acc. of h. works, abrmt. of them &c.; added. Letter f. Halley cont. abstract of D.'s De cyclis. 2v [*pagin. cont.*] 8º. 1715

Brölemann (Henri Auguste). Cat. of a coll. of illum. MSS. &c. formed by B., sold by order of Mme. E. Mallet by Sotheby, May 1926. [Illust.] la8º. 1926

Brom (Gisbert), *see* BULLARIUM Trajectense; coll. & ed. G. B., 2v, 1891–96.

—— & A. H. L. Hensen, *edd.* Romeinsche Bronnen voor d. kerkelijk-staatkundigen toestand d. Nederlanden in de 16de eeuw. [Rijks Gesch. Publ., 52]. la8º. 's-Gravenhage. 1922

Bromberger (André) & E. Gaujoux.
Aix-en-Provence. 2e éd. 8º. Marseille. 1924

Brome (Alexander), *see* COVENT GARDEN drollery, 1672 [*sometimes attrib. to A. B.*]; ed. G. Thorn-Drury, 1928.

Brome (Richard). The Antipodes (1640); ed. w. crit. essay &c., by G. P. Baker, *see* GAYLEY (C. M.) Repres. Eng. comedies, v3, 1914.

Bromehead (Cyril Edward Nowill). Geology of North London. With contrib. by H. G. Dines & J. Pringle. [Geolog. Survey of Eng. &c. Mem.] 8º. 1925
see DEWEY (HENRY), C. E. N. B. &c. Geol. of country around Dartford, 1924.
„ —— & C. E. N. B. Geol. of country around Windsor &c., 1915.
„ —— & C. E. N. B. Geology of South London, 1921.

Brömel (Christian Heinrich). De cellis sacris vet. Xtn. [P2638]. s4º. Longo-Salissæ. [1710]

Bromfield. The first extent of B. & Yale, 1315. [Ed., w. intr. &c.] by T. P. Ellis. [Cymmrod. Rec. Ser., No. 11]. la8º. 1924

Bromfield (J. C. Coley-), *see* COLEY-BROMFIELD (J. C.)

Bromfield (Louis). The green bay tree. s8º. [1924]

Bromfield (William), *1713–1792, see* PEACHEY (G. C.) W. B., 1915.

Bromholm Psalter, *see* BIBLE: PSALMS. 2 E. Anglian Ps. at Bodl. Lib., Oxf.: B. Ps. &c., 1926.

Bromley, *Kent.* Mon. inscr. in the ch. & churchyard of Bromley, Co. Kent. Transcr. by R. Holworthy. [*Extr. f.* Misc. Genealog.] sfol. 1922

Bromley (Henry), *ps.* [*i.e.* ANTHONY WILSON].
see CATALOGUE. *C. of portraits &c., in order of B.'s Cat., *n.d.*
„ FLINDALL (J. M.) Amateur's pocket companion: books mentioned in wks. of B. &c., 1813.

Bronchorst (Everardus). Diarium, sive adversaria omnium quæ gesta sunt in Acad. Leydensi, 1591–1627. Uitg. door J. C. Van Slee. [Hist. Genoots. Werken., s3, 12]. 8º. 's-Gravenhage. 1898

Brøndsted (J.) Early English ornament. Pref. by R. A. Smith. Tr. A. F. Major. 8º. 1924

Bröndsted (Peter Oluf). Voyages dans la Grèce accomp. de recherches arch. [Tr.] livr. 1, 2 [*no more publ.*] fol. 1826–30

Bronnen (Arnolt). Vatermord. Schauspiel 8º. 1925

Bronstein (Leiba Douvitz), *see* TROTSKY (L.)

Bronsveld (Sigisbert Abraham). Singaleesche Psalmen en Lofzangen &c. [*w. tunes*]. s8º. Colombo. 1768

Brontë (Anne). Complete poems. Ed. C. Shorter, w. biblog. intr. by C. W. Hatfield. 8º. [1920]
The tenant of Wildfell Hall. n. ed. s8º. 1870
see DIMNET (E.) The Brontë sisters; tr., 1927.

Brontë (Charlotte), *aft. Mrs. Nicholls.*
An early essay by C. B. [*on* Millevoye's La chute des feuilles, *in French*]. Intr. by M. H. Spielmann. [Repr. f. Publ. of Bronte Soc., p34]. 8º. 1924
Jane Eyre. n. ed. s8º. 1871
The professor. Added, Poems of C. E. & A. Bell. n. ed. s8º. 1870
Shirley. n. ed. s8º. 1871
Villette. n. ed. s8º. 1871
see DIMNET (E.) The Brontë sisters; tr., 1927.

Brontë (Emily Jane). Wuthering Heights, by E. B. Agnes Grey, by A. Brontë. Pref. & mem. by C. Brontë. Intr. by Mrs. H. Ward. [Works, v5]. 8º. 1920
„ „ s8º. 1922
see DIMNET (E.) The Brontë sisters; tr., 1927.
„ KAVANAGH (C.) The symbolism of "Wuthering Heights," 1920.
„ LAW (A.) E. J. B. & the authorship of "Wuthering Heights," 1925.

Brontë (Patrick).
The cottage in the wood. 2nd ed. s8º. Bradford. 1818

Brontë (Patrick Branwell), *see* LAW (A.) P. B. B., 1924.

Bronzino, Il, *ps., see* ALLORI (A.)

Broodbank (*Sir* **Joseph Guinness).**
Hist. of the Port of London. 2v. 4º. 1921

Brook (Arthur). The buzzard at home. 8º. 1920
see GILBERT (H. A.) & A. B. Secrets of bird life, 1924.
„ —— & —— Secrets of the eagle &c., 1925.

Brooke (Arthur), *translator & poet, see* FISCHER (R.) Quellen zu Romeo u. Julia (*B.'s tr. in Eng. & Germ.*), 1922.

Brooke (Arthur St. Clair Richard).
Slingsby & Slingsby Castle. s8º. 1904

Brooke (Dorothy), *see* ATHENS. Acropolis Museum. Catalogue, v2, Sculpture &c. by S. Casson., w. sect. upon the terra-cottas by D. B., 1921.

Brooke (Edward), *of Fieldhouse, see* LORD (J. H.) Squire B., 1872.

Brooke (Gilbert Edward), *see* MAKEPEACE (W.) & G. E. B. &c., *edd.* 100 yrs. of Singapore, 2v, 1921.

Brooke (Henry). Gustavus Vasa, *see* INCHBALD (*Mrs.* E.) Brit. theatre, v7, 1808.
*The hist. of Henry, earl of Moreland. [*a. ed. of* The fool of quality. *wanting tp.*] 8º. *n.p. n.d.*

Brooke (*Sir* **James),** *rajah of Sarawak, see* FOGGO (G.) Adventures of Sir J. B., 1853.

Brooke (James) & Co. The Fairfield orchids, w. cat. of J. B. & Co., Fairfield, M'ter. 8º. 1872

Brooke (*Sir* **John Arthur).** Cat. of library of Sir J. A. B., sold by Sotheby, May 25th[–June 3rd], 1921. [*Illust.*] la8º. [1921]

Brooke (Margaret, *Lady*), *wife of Sir C. Brooke, Rajah of Sarawak.* Impromptus. s8º. 1923

Brooke (Robert Greville, *2nd baron***)** [BROOK]. A discourse, opening the nature of episcopacie in England. s4°. 1641

Brooke (Rupert). Coll. poems. With a memoir [by E. Marsh]. [4th impr.] 8°. 1918
,, ,, ...[7th impr.] 8°. 1920
Letters f. America. Pref. by H. James. [3rd impr.] 8°. 1916
1914 & o. p. [14th impr.] s8°. 1916

Brooke (Stopford A.)
Christian hymns. Ed. & arr. by S. A. B. s8°. 1881
,, ,, ...s8°. 1891
Naturalism in English poetry. s8°. 1920

Brookes (Edgar H.) Hist. of native policy in South Africa f. 1830. 2nd rev. ed. 8°. Pretoria. 1927

Brookes (Joshua Alfred Rowland).
Murder in fact & fiction. 8°. [1925]

Brookes (Thomas), *Preacher at Fish Street Hill.*
An arke for all God's Noahs. Sermons. s8°. 1662

Brookhouse (Ann). Narr. of the seizure & confinement of A. B. &c., by two hired ruffians, May 7–Aug. 25, 1798, rel. by herself. [*Imperf.*] [P2781]. 8°. [1798 ?]

Brooklyn Institute of Arts & Sciences, *see* EDINBURGH ARCHIT. ASSOC. Illust. cat. of photos. &c. of archit. refinements &c. lent by B. I. of A. & S., 1905.
Museum. Mem. of Art &c. v1i, ii, iv. la8°. N.Y. 1902–4
see GOODYEAR (W. H.) Architect. refinements of St. Mark's at Venice, 1902 [1ii].
,, —— A Renaiss. leaning façade at Genoa, 1902 [1i].
,, —— Vertical curves &c. in Gothic cathedrals &c. of N. France &c., 1904 [1iv].

Brooklyn Library. Catalogue. Authors, titles, subjects & classes. 4°. Brooklyn, N.Y. 1877[–80]

Brooks (Alfred Mansfield).
Architecture & the allied arts. 8°. [1926]
From Holbein to Whistler. Notes on drawing & engraving. la8°. New Haven. *Yale.* 1920

Brooks (Charles), *of Medford, Mass.* Hist. of town of Medford, Middlesex Co., Mass., 1630–1855. Rev., enl. &c. to 1885 by J. M. Usher. 8°. Boston. 1886

Brooks (Charles Ernest Pelham). Climate thr. the ages. 8°. 1926
The evolution of climate. Pref. by G. C. Simpson. 8°. 1922

Brooks (Francis A.) The unlawful &c. conquest of the Filipinos. [P2620]. s8°. Boston [Mass.] 1901

Brooks (Neil Conwell). The sepulchre of Christ in art & liturgy. [Illinois, Univ. of. Studies in lang. &c., v7ii]. la8°. Urbana. 1921

Brooks (Phillips). Sermons. [repr.] s8°. 1888

Brooks (Robert Clarkson).
Govt. & politics of Switzerland. s8°. 1920

Brooks (Sidney). America & Germany, 1918–25. Pref. by G. B. Baker. 8°. N.Y. 1925

Brooks (Thomas), *Preacher at Fish Street Hill, see* BROOKES (T.)

Brooks (Van Wyck). The malady of the ideal: Obermann, Maurice de Guérin, & Amiel. s8°. 1913
The ordeal of Mark Twain. 8°. 1922
The pilgrimage of Henry James. 8°. [1928]

Brooks (William), *alderman, see* BURY (J.) A true narr. of the late design of the papists to charge their horrid plot upon the protest. by endeavouring to corrupt J. Bury & B., 1679.

Brooks-Bryce Foundation.
Brooks-Bryce Anglo-Amer. prize essays, 1925. Intr. by H. van Dyke. s8°. [1925]
,, ,, 1927. Intr. by H. A. Gibbons. s8°. N.Y. [1927]

Broom. An internat. magazine of the arts publ. by Americans in Italy. v1–3 (Nov. 1921–Nov. 1922). fol. Rome. [1921–22]

Broome (Dorothy M.) The ransom of John II, 1360–70, *see* CAMDEN MISC., v14, 1926.

Broomhall (Marshall). Marshal Feng. Foreword by Sir G. K. Scott Moncrieff. 5th ed. s8°. 1924

Broqua (*le cte.* **de).** Le maréchal de Monluc: sa famille & s. temps. 8°. 1924

Broquelet (A.) Nos châteaux. Préf. de H. Robert. s8°. 1924

Brosch (Moritz).
Albizzi u. Medici. [Aus Hist. Vierteljahrschr. P2871]. 8°. L. [1908]
Don Juan d'Austria in d. Niederl. [Abdr. aus d. Mitth. d. Inst. f. österr. Gesch., B21. P2763]. 8°. [Wien]. *n.d.*
Die Ermordung d. Veltliner Protestanten, 1620 [Abdr. aus Z. für Kirchengesch., B32. P2862]. 8°. Gotha. *n.d.*
Machiavelli am Hofe &c. Maximilians I. [*Extr. f.* Mitth. d. Inst. für österr. Gesch., B24. P2835]. 8°. *n.d.*
Paul IV gegen Karl V u. Philipp II. [Aus Inst. f. öst. Gesch., Mitth., B25. P2838]. 8°. [Vienna]. *n.d.*
Zu d. Conflicten Karls V mit Paul III. [Aus Mitth. d. Inst. f. österr. Gesch., B23. P2838]. 8°. [Vienna]. *n.d.*

Brossard de Ruville (—). Hist. de la ville des Andelis &c. 2t. la8°. Les Andelis. 1863–64

Brosses (*Président* **Charles de),** *1709–77.*
Lettres d'Italie. 2[t]. 8°. Dijon. [1927]

Brosset (Marie Félicité). Chronique géorgienne [Vie du Sakarthwelo Karthli]. Tr. M. F. B. [*& Georgian text w. sep. tp. & pagin.*] 8°. 1829–31
Coll. d'historiens armén. Tr. par M. B. 2t. 8°. St. Pétersbourg. 1874–76
Abraham III, *catholicus.* Mon hist. & celui de Nadir, Chah de Perse. [2.]
Arakel, *of Tabriz.* Livre d'histoires. [2.]
Davith-Beg. Hist. choisie de D.-B., 1871. [2.]
Hasan-Chalaliantz (I.) Hist. d'Aghovanie. [2.]
Samuel, *presbyter Aniensis.* Tables chronol. [2.]
Souvenirs d'un officier dans le Caucase, 1835–38. [2.]
Thomas, *Ardzrouni.* Hist. d. Ardzrouni. [1.]
Zacharias, *the deacon.* Cartul. de Iohannou-Vank (6–17c.) [2.]
—— Mém. sur les Sofis. [2.]
Élém. de la langue géorgienne. 8°. 1837
Ruines d'Ani, capitale de l'Armenie. Atlas, 2 livr. [*b. w.* Rostomov (I. P.) Картв. племя, 1896]. obl.4°. St.-Pétersb. 1860–61
see ECHMIADZIN. Cat. de la bibliothèque, publ. B., 1840.
,, MARR (N. YA.) Къ столѣтію дня рожд. Броссе, 1902.

Brosso. Statuti minerari d. valle di B. d. sec. 15, per A. Bertolotti, *see* REGIA DEP. DI STORIA PATRIA. Misc., t11, 1870.

Broster (Dorothy Kathleen).
The flight of the heron. [n. impr.] s8°. 1925
The happy warrior [*i.e.* Ange Achille C. B., cte. de Neuilly. Cayme Press Pamph., No. 1]. 8°. *Cayme Press,* Kensington. 1926
The gleam in the North. s8°. 1927
" Mr. Rowl." s8°. [1924]
The wounded name. s8°. 1922
The yellow poppy. s8°. [1920]

Brouard (Arsène), *F.S.C., see* THÉRIOT (I.) Mexican mosses coll. by B., tr., 1926.

Brough (J. C. S.)
see FURNITURE repairing &c. [ed. J. C. S. B.], 1919.
,, WOOD-TURNING; ed. J. C. S. B., 1921.
,, WOODWORK JOINTS; ed. J. C. S., 2nd ed., 1919.

Brougham (Henry), *1st baron Brougham & Vaux.*
*Lord Brougham: Letter to the Queen on Monarchy. By a friend to the people. [*no tp.* P2552]. 8°. *n.p.* [1838]
Speech in the H. of Lords, Jan. 29, 1838, upon the slave trade, &c. [P2554]. 8°. Lindfield. 1838
Taxes on knowledge. Stamps on newspapers; extr. f. evidence. [P2782]. 8°. 1834
Tracts, mathemat. & phys. s8°. 1860
see ASPINALL (A.) Lord B. & the Whig party, 1927.
,, KNIGHT (C.) The workingman's companion [*in a Germ. tr. attrib. to Lord B.*], 1831.

Broughton (Gladys M.), *aft. wife of Sir Atul Chandra Chatterjee.*
Labour in Indian industries. 8°. 1924
Labour turnover in munition &c. factories; by B. &c., *see* INDUST. FATIGUE RESEARCH BOARD. Rep. 13, 1921.

Broughton (Hugh). Comm. in Danielem. Lat. don. per J. Boreel. s4°. Basileæ. [1599]
*Daniel his Chaldie visions & his Ebrew: both tr. &c. [*tp. imperf.*] s4°. 1597
An epistle to the learned nobilitie of England t. translating the Bible &c. 8°. Middelburgh. 1597

Broughton (Leslie Nathan). The Theocritean element in the works of W. Wordsworth. 8°. Halle (Saale). 8°. 1920
see BALDWIN (D. L.), L. N. B. &c. Concordance to J. Keats, 1917.

Broughton (Richard), *brother of Hugh Broughton, see* DEVEREUX, *Family of.* D. papers, w. R. B.'s memoranda (1575–1601), ed. Malden, 1923.

Broughton (Urban Huttleston Rogers). Dress of the 1st Regt. of Life Guards in 3 cents. 4°. 1925

Broun (Joannes), *see* BROWN (JOHN), *of Wamphray.*

Broun (Robert), *see* BROWN (R.)

Brounrig (Ralph), *bp. of Exeter, see* BROWNRIG (R.)

Brousseau (Georges). Souvs. de la mission Savorgnan de Brazze. Préf. de M. Delafosse. 8°. 1925

Broussillon (*le comte* **Arthur Bertrand de),** *see* BERTRAND DE BROUSSILLON.

Brousson (Jean Jacques).
Anatole France en pantoufles. s8°. 1924
,, ,, ...[repr.] s8°. 1926
Itinéraire de Paris à Buenos-Ayres. s8°. 1927

Brousson (Jean Jacques) [*continued*].
La nuit de prairial, *see* ŒUVRES LIBRES, 76, 1927.
see POLLOCK (J.) Anatole France & Mrs. Grundy, w. passages hitherto unpubl. f. A. F. en pantoufles by J. J. B., 1926.
Brouwer (Adriaan), *see* BODE (W. v.) A. B., Leben u. Werke, 1924.
Brown University, *Providence, Rhode Island.* The Anthony memorial. Cat. of the Harris Coll. of Amer. poetry [pres. to the Lib. of B. Univ. by H. B. Anthony], w. notes by J. C. Stockbridge. la8°. Providence, R.I. 1886
Civil War record of Brown Univ. Compiled by H. S. Burrage. 8°. Providence, R.I. 1920
see JOHN CARTER BROWN LIBRARY. Bibl. Amer.: cat. of J. C. B. Lib., B. Univ., 2v, 1919–22.
Brown (—), *publisher, of Salisbury.* Stranger's hdbk. &c. to Salisbury cathedral. [*Orig. comp. by J. B. Moore*]. s8°. Salisbury. 1884
Brown (A. Samler). Brown's Madeira, Canary Islands, & Azores: a guide. 12th & rev. ed. s8°. 1922
—— **& G. G. Brown.**
The South & East African yearbook & guide. 26th ed. s8°. 1920
" " ....28th ed. s8°. 1922
" " ....29th ed. s8°. 1923
" " ....33rd ed. s8°. 1927
Brown (Alfred Reginald). The Andaman islanders: st. in social anthropology. 8°. C. 1922
Brown (Alice). Homespun & gold. s8°. N.Y. 1920
Brown (Arthur Charles Lewis). Iwain: st. in the origins of Arthurian romance, *see* HARVARD UNIV. St. &c. in philology &c., v8, 1903.
Brown (Ashley). Greece old & new. 8°. [1927]
Sicily, present & past. s8°. [1928]
Brown (Beatrice Daw), *see* JESUS CHRIST. The southern Passion; ed. &c. by B. D. B., 1927.
Brown (C. L. M.) The conquest of the air: hist. survey. s8°. 1927
Brown (Carleton). Register of Middle English relig. & didactic verse. [Bibliog. Soc.] p2. 8°. O. 1920
2, Index of 1st lines & of subjects and titles.
Relig. lyrics of the 14th c. Ed. C. B. s8°. O. 1924
see STONYHURST pageants (The); ed. C. B., 1920.
Brown (Cecil Jermyn). The coins of India. s8°. Calcutta. 1922
see LUCKNOW. Cat. of coins in Provincial Museum, L.; by C. J. B., Coins of the Mughal emperors, 2v, 1920.
Brown (David), *D.D., Chaplain of the East India Co., see* SIMEON (C.) Memor. sketches of D. B. (journals, corresp. & sermons), 1816.
Brown (David), *of Kallara, N.S.W.*
Wealth & wages in N. S. Wales. s8°. Sydney. 1891
Brown (Edward Thomas).
Motors & motoring. [Home Univ. Lib.] s8°. [1927]
Brown (Elmer Ellsworth), *Ph.D.* The making of our middle schools. Acc. of develop. of secondary educ. in U.S. 8°. 1903
Brown (Ford K.) Life of W. Godwin. 8°. 1926
Brown (G. Gordon), *see* BROWN (A. S.) & G. G. B. The South & East African year book & guide, 1914; 1920; 1922; 1923; 1927.
Brown (G. P.) Drainage channel & waterway. 8°. Chicago. 1894
Brown (George Edward).
Ferric & heliographic processes. s8°. [1900]
Brown (Gerard Baldwin). The arts in early England. [v5], The Ruthwell & Bewcastle crosses, The Gospels of Lindisfarne & o. Xtn. mons. of Northumbria. 8°. 1921
The arts in early England. n. ed., recast & enl. [v]2. 8°. 1925
2, Anglo-Saxon architecture.
The fine arts: a manual. 4th ed. rev. 8°. 1916
William Hogarth. s8°. 1905
Brown (H. Darell). Cat. of early Eng. landscapes &c., the property of H. D. B. Sold by Christie, May 23, 1924. [*Illust.* P2748]. 8°. 1924
Brown (Harry Gunnison).
Internat. trade: econ. advantages. s8°. N.Y. 1920
Brown (Horatio Forbes).
Cat. of pr. bks. &c., lib. of H.B. &c. Sold by Sotheby, 21–23 Feb. 1927. [Illust. P2857]. 8°. 1927
Dalmatia. Painted by W. Tyndale. 8°. [1925]
Inglesi e Scozzesi all' Univ. di Padova, 1618–1765. [Estr. da: Contrib. del R. Istit. Veneto alla Celebr. del 7 centen. d. Univ. di Padua]. [P2703]. la8°. Venezia. 1921
Inglesi e Scozzesi all' Univ. di Padova, 1618–1765, *for a copy, see* PADOVA. Monogr. stor. s. Studio di P., 1922.
Pensieri Persi. [Aus Studien aus Kunst u. Gesch. P2843]. la8°. Freiburg im Br. 1906
The Venetians &c. in Constantinople to close of 12th cent. Repr. f. Journal of Hellenic St., v11. [P2516]. la8°. 1920
Brown (Ivor John Carnegie). Eng. polit. theory. s8°. [1920]
H. G. Wells. s8°. [1923]
Lighting-up time. s8°. 1920
Masques & phases. 8°. [1926]
Parties of the play. 8°. 1928
Brown (J. D.) Ballads, founded on Ayrshire traditions; w. minor poems & lyrics. s8°. Kilmarnock. 1850
Brown (J. Tom). Among the Bantu nomads: 40 yrs. am. the Bechuana. 8°. 1926
Brown (James), *a. of "Deeside Guide."* Epitaphs & monument. inscr. in Greyfriars churchyard, Edinb. Coll. w. intr. & notes by J. B. s8°. E. 1867
Brown (James Duff). Manual of library economy. 3rd & memor. ed. rev. & rewr. by W. C. B. Sayers. 8°. 1920
Brown (*Capt.* **John),** *1800–59, see* WILSON (H. P.) J. B., soldier of fortune: critique, 1918.
Brown, (John), *B.A., m. of the Bunyan Church, Bedford.* The Pilgrim Fathers of New England & th. Puritan successors. 4th ed. s8°. 1920
Brown (John), *D.D., minister of Langton.* Vindic. of Presbyterian form of church govt. &c. 2nd ed. s8°. 1812
Brown (John), *D.D., vicar of Newcastle.* Barbarossa, *see* INCHBALD (*Mrs.* E.) Brit. theatre, v15, 1808.
Essays on the Characteristics [of the Earl of Shaftesbury]. [5th ed.] 8°. 1764
The hist. of the rise & progr. of poetry &c. 8°. New Castle. 1764
Brown (John), *M.D., of Edinburgh.* Letters; w. letters f. Ruskin, Thackeray, & others. Ed. by h. son & D. W. Forrest, w. biog. intr. by E. T. M'Laren. (repr.) s8°. [1912]
Rab & h. friends. [Illust.] la8°. E. 1862
see PEDDIE (A.) Recoll. of Dr. J. B., 1893.
Brown (John), *of Gt. Yarmouth.* The hist. gallery of criminal portraitures. 2v. 8°. M'ter. 1823
Brown (John), *minister at Wamphray* [BROUN]. An apologet. rel. of the sufferings of ministers &c. of the Ch. of Scotland, *see* PRESBYTERIAN's armoury, v3, 1843.
*Libertino-Erastianæ Lamberti Velthusii sententiæ de ministerio &c., eccl. confutatio. s8°. *n.p.* 1670
Libri duo, in priori, Wolzogium in lib. 2 de interprete Scr. causam orthod. prodidisse demonstratur. In posteriori L. Velthusii sententia in lib. de idololatria &c. confut. 2p *in* 1v. s8°. Amstelodami. 1670
Brown (John Aq.) The Jew, the master-key of the Apocalypse, in ans. to Mr. Frere's "Gen. structure." 8°. 1827
Brown (John Coggin). The Burma earthquakes of May 1912, *see* INDIA: GEOL. SURVEY. Mem., v42i, 1914.
India's mineral wealth. s8°. 1923
The mines & mineral products of Yunnan &c., *see* INDIA: GEOL. SURVEY. Mem., v47i, 1920.
—— **& A. M. Heron.** Geology & ore deposits of the Tavoy Distr., *see* INDIA: GEOLOG. SURVEY. Memoirs, v44ii, 1923.
Brown (John Macmillan).
Peoples & problems of the Pacific. 2v. la8°. 1927
The riddle of the Pacific. la8°. [1924]
Brown (Joseph), *Q.C.* The Tichborne case comp. w. previous impostures. [P2827]. 8°. 1874
Brown (Joseph Epes), *ed., see* JOHNSON (S.) Crit. opinions, 1926.
Brown (Joseph P.), *see* CARR (D. L.) & J. P. B. Mfantsi gramm., 1868.
Brown (*Mrs.* **Kenneth),** *see* VAKA (D.)
Brown (Lilian Mabel Alice, *Lady*), *wife of Sir M. Richmond B.* Unknown tribes, uncharted seas. [2nd impr.] 8°. [1924]
Brown (M. J.) Hist. ballad poetry of Ireland; arr. by M. J. B., *see* BROWN (S. J.) *for* n. & enl. ed.
Brown (Percy). Germany in dissolution. s8°. 1920
Brown (Peter Hume). Life of Goethe. Pref. note by Visct. Haldane. 2v. 8°. 1920
Brown (Philip Anthony). The French Revol. in English hist. Intr. by G. Murray. [repr.] 8°. [1923]
see BLAND (A. E.), P. A. B. &c., *edd.* Eng. econ. hist.; sel. doc., 1921.
Brown (Philip Marshall).
Internat. society, its nature & interests. s8°. N.Y. 1923
Brown (R. Grant). Burma as I saw it, 1889–1917, w. chap. on recent events. 8°. [1926]
Brown (Richard), *architect.* Domestic architecture. 4°. [1841]
Brown (Robert), *farmer at Markle, see* RENNIE (G.), R. B., & J. SHIRREFF. Gen. view of the agric. of Yorks., 1794.
Brown (Robert Neal Rudmose). A naturalist at the Poles: life, work & voyages of Dr. W. S. Bruce. With 5 chapters by W. G. B. Murdoch. 8°. 1923

Brown (Robert Neal Rudmose) [*continued*].
The Polar regions: phys. & econ. geog. 8º. [1927]
Princ. of econ. geography. 8º. 1920
Brown (Rollo Walter).
The creative spirit: inq. into Amer. life. 8º. N.Y. 1925
The writer's art. By those who have practiced it. Sel. &c. R. W. B. 8º. Camb. [U.S.] 1921
Brown (Samuel Gilman), *see* CHOATE (R.) Works; w. mem. by S. G. B., 2v, 1862.
Brown (Stephen James), *S.J.* Poetry of Irish hist. Ed. S. J. B. n. & enl. ed. *of* Hist. ballad poetry of Ireland, arr. by M. J. Brown. s8º. D. 1927
The world of imagery: metaphor & kindred imagery. 8º. 1927
Brown (Thomas), *prof., Univ. of Edinb., see* WELSH (D.) Acc. of T. B., 1825.
Brown (Thomas), *of Shiffnal, Shropshire.* Amusements, serious & comical, & o. works. Ed. w. notes by A. L. Hayward. la8º. 1927
see SACHEVERELL (W.) An acc. of the I. of Man; added diss. about Mona of Cæsar &c. by T. B., 1702.
Brown (Thomas), *the younger, ps., see* MOORE (THOMAS), *the poet.*
Brown (W. Robertson). The orange: trial of stocks at Peshawar, *see* AGRIC. RES. INST., *Pusa.* Bulletin, 93, 1920.
Brown (William), *D.Sc.*
The essentials of mental measurement. 8º. C. 1911
„ „ ......3rd ed., by W. B. & G. H. Thomson. 8º. C. 1925
Mind & personality. 8º. 1926
Psychology & psychotherapy. Foreword by W. A. Turner. s8º. 1921
Psychology & the sciences. Ed. W. B., w. contrib. by J. S. Haldane, R. R. Marett, F. C. S. Schiller &c. 8º. 1924
Suggestion & mental analysis: theory &c. of mind cure. s8º. 1922
Brown (William), *M.D.* The hist. of the propagation of Christianity among the heathen since the Reformation. 2v. 8º. 1814
„ „ ....3rd ed. 3v. 8º. [1854]
The hist. of missions of the 16–19 c. 3rd ed. enl. 3v. 8º. 1864
Earlier issue had title: Hist. of the propag. of Christianity &c.
Brown (William), *of Montreal.* The lab. question: thoughts on paper currency & lending on interest. s8º. Phila. 1872
Brown (William Adams), *D.D.* The Church in America: st. of pres. condition &c. of Amer. Protestantism. 8º. N.Y. 1922
Brown (William Adams), *Jr.* The groping giant. Revolut. Russia. s8º. New Haven. 1920
Brown (William Lawrence), *D.D., principal of Marischal Coll., Aberdeen.* Dissert., *see* PAP (J.) Disp., 1784.
Brown (William Wells), *fugitive slave.* 3 yrs. in Europe &c., w. mem. by W. Farmer. s8º. 1852
Brownbill (John), *see* ROYDEN (E. B.) 3 Roydon families; [arranged &c. by J. B.], 1924.
Browne (A. E. Wilson), *see* WILSON-BROWNE (A. E.)
Browne (Charles Orde). Armour, & its attack by artillery. [Extr. f. Proc. of R.A. Instit.] 8º. Woolwich. 1887
„ „ Suppl. dealing w. develop. of armour 1887–93, 1893–99. [2p *in* 1v]. 8º. Woolwich. 1893–99
Short notes on field batteries. 2p *in* 1v. s8º. [1871]
Browne (*Capt.* D. G.) The tank in action. 8º. 1920
Browne (Dorothy Margaret Stuart), *see* STUART (D. M.) *ps.*
Browne (*Sir* Edmond) & *Sir* K. Wood.
Law of National Health Insurance, 1911–18. 8º. 1919
Browne (Edith A.) Vegetable oils. s8º. 1924
Browne (Edward Granville).
Arabian medicine. Fitzpatrick Lect. 8º. C. 1921
Cat. & descr. of 27 Bábí MSS. [*From* J. of Roy. Asiatic Soc. &c., 1892]. 8º. [1892]
A hist. of Persian lit. in mod. times (A.D. 1500–1924). 8º. C. 1924
A hist. of Persian lit. under Tartar Dominion, 1265–1502. [*Cont. of h.* Lit. hist. of Persia]. 8º. 1920
The lit. of Persia, *see* PERSIA SOCIETY. Lect., 1912.
A Persian anthology. Tr. E. G. B. Intr. mem. by J. B. Atkins. Ed. E. D. Ross. s8º. [1927]
The Persian constitut. movt., *see* BRIT. ACAD. Proc., 1917–18.
Persian press & P. journalism, 1913, *see* PERSIA SOCIETY. Lect., 1913.
A year amongst the Persians, 1887–8. Mem. by Sir E. D. Ross. [n. ed.] la8º. C. 1926
Browne (F. Balfour-), *see* BALFOUR-BROWNE (F.)
Browne (George), *Independent minister.* Hist. of the Brit. & For. Bible Soc., 1804–54. 2v. 8º. 1859
Browne (George Forrest), *bp. of Bristol.* Continuity of the Holy Cath. Church in Eng. [P2690]. s8º. 1897
Echt-Forbes family charters, 1345–1727—Records of the forest of Birse—Notarial signs, 926–1786. 4º. E. 1923
King Alfred's books. 8º. 1920
On some antiq. in neighbourhood of Dunecht House, Aberdeenshire. 4º. C. 1921
Theodore & Wilfrith. Lectures. s8º. 1897
Browne (George Lathom) & C. G. Stewart.
Reports of trials f. murder by poisoning. 8º. 1883
Browne (*Maj.* Granville St. J. Orde), *O.B.E. (Mil.)*
The vanishing tribes of Kenya. 8º. 1925
Browne (Isaac Hawkins), *the elder.*
*A pipe of tobacco. [*Verse*]. 3rd. ed., w. notes. 8º. 1744
A pipe of tobacco: in imitation of 6 several a. (1736). Ed. H. F. B. Brett-Smith. s8º. O. 1923
Browne (John Ross). Resources of the Pacific Slope, w. sketch of settlement &c. of Lower California, [by A. S. Taylor, *w. sep. pagin.*] 8º. N.Y. 1869
Browne (Kenneth Robert Gordon).
A lady from the south. s8º. [1925]
Browne (Laurence Edward). Early Judaism. 8º. C. 1920
Browne (Lewis). The story of the Jews to pres. day. s8º. [1926]
Browne (Phillis). A year's cookery. 17th thousand. 8º. *n.d.*
Browne (*Sir* Richard), *bart., Resident at the Court of France, see* EVELYN (J.) Mems. &c.; subj., corr. betw. Clarendon & B., 1818.
Browne (Robert Gore-), *see* GORE-BROWNE (R.)
Browne (T. B.), *Ltd., see* ADVERTISER'S A. B. C. (The); standard advert. dir., 1921.
Browne (*Sir* Thomas), *M.D.*
Works. [*4 pagin.*] fol. 1686
„ „ Ed. S. Wilkin. [repr.] 3v. s8º. *Bohn.* 1910–15
Posthumous works. 8º. 1712
1, Repertorium: or, Antiqs. of Cath. Ch. of Norwich. 2, Urnes, found at Brampton. 3, Letters betw. Sir W. Dugdale & Sir T. B. 4, Misc. [4 *pagins.*] Added, Antiq. capellæ D. Johannis Evangel., hodie Scholæ Reg. Norwicensis. Authore J. Burton [*w. sep. tp. & pagin.*]
Hydriotaphia: [Urne-Burial]. Ed. W. Murison. s8º. C. 1922
*Religio medici cum annot. [*Latin tr. by J. Merryweather*]. s8º. Argentorati. 1652
Religio medici. 4th ed., corr. s8º. 1656
Religio medici, Urn burial, Christian morals & o. e. Ed. w. intr. by J. A. Symonds. [Camelot classics]. s8º. 1886
see KEYNES (G. L.) Bibliography of Sir T. B., 1924.
„ TILDESLEY (M. L.) Sir T. B.: h. skull, portraits, & ancestry, 1923.
Browning Society. Index & notes to B. Soc. Papers. [*Comp. by N. Hardy Wallis. Typescript*]. 8º. [1924]
Browning (Carl Hamilton).
Bacteriology. [Home Univ. Lib.] s8º. [1925]
Browning (*Mrs.* E. B.) Aurora Leigh. Vertaald door M. van Walcheren. 8º. Amsterdam. 1885
Poet. works. Oxf. compl. ed. s8º. O. 1904
A selection f. the poetry of E. B. B. 2nd ed. s8º. 1869
see WHITING (L.) The Brownings, th. life & art, 1911.
Browning (Oscar). Memories of later years. 8º. [1923]
see WORTHAM (H. E.) O. B., 1927.
Browning (Robert).
Essay on Shelley, *see* PEACOCK (T. L.) Four ages of poetry, &c.; ed. H. F. B. Brett Smith, 1921.
The ring & the book. n. ed. 8º. 1898
Der Ring u. das Buch. Üb. v. C. Gräfin Keyserlingk. la8º. L. 1927
Sel. f. the poet. works of B. 2s. s8º. 1872–80
see COOK (A. K.) Comm. upon B.'s The ring & the book, 1920.
„ FURNIVALL (F. J.) R. B.'s ancestors, 1890.
„ GEST (J. M.) The Old Yellow Book, source of B.'s Ring & the book; tr. w. notes, 1925.
see HODELL (C. W.) The old Yellow Book, source of B.'s Ring & the book, w. tr. &c. by H., 1911.
„ JONES (H.) B. as a philosoph. & relig. teacher, 1912.
„ SIM (F. M.) R. B., poet & philosopher, 1850–89, 1923.
„ —— R. B., the poet & the man, 1833–46, 1923.
„ SYMONS (A.) Intr. to B., 1916.
„ WHITING (L.) The Brownings, th. life & art, 1911.
Brownlee (William Craig). Letters in the R. C. controversy. 2nd ed. rev. & enl. 8º. N.Y. 1834
Brownlie (John), *D.D.* Hymns of the Russian Church, being tr., centos &c. f. the Greek office books. Intr. by J. B. s8º. 1920
Brownrig (Ralph), *bp. of Exeter, see* GAUDEN (J.) Sermon at the funeral of Dr. B.; w. acc. of h. life, 1660.

Brownrigg (Beatrice). Life & letters of Sir J. Moore. 8º. O. 1923
Brownrigg (*Rear-Adm. Sir* **Douglas Egremont Robert**), *Bart.* Indiscretions of the naval censor. 8º. 1920
Brownrigg (Elizabeth). *Acc. of the life, trial, & execution of E. B. [P2828]. s8º. 1767
Brownson (Orestes Augustus). The Amer. Republic: its constit., tendencies &c. 8º. N.Y. 1866
Broxap (Henry). The later Non-Jurors. [With acc. of the Brett MSS. &c. by S. L. Ollard]. 8º. C. 1924
Brož (Alexander). First year of the Czecho-Slovak Republic. Pref by H. M. Hyndman. [P2523]. 8º. 1920
The rise of the Czecho-Slovak Republic. [P2493]. 8º. [1919]
Brucaeus (Henricus), *of Rostock.* De scorbuto proposit., 1589, *see* EUGALENUS (S.) De scorbuto morbo liber &c., 1624.
Bruce (Alex. Balmain). The chief end of revelation. 8º. 1881
Parabolic teaching of Christ. 3rd ed. w. new pref. 8º. 1889
Bruce (Charles). Twenty years in Borneo. 8º. [1924]
Bruce (*Brig.-Gen. Hon.* **Charles Granville).** The assault on Mount Everest, 1922. By Brig.-Gen. C. G. B. & o. members of the Exped. la8º. 1923
Bruce (Everend Lester). Amisk-Athapapuskow Lake District. [Canada. Geol. Survey]. 8º. Ottawa. 1918
Bruce (Finetta). The mysticism of colour. s8º. 1912
Bruce (Henry). Life of Gen. Oglethorpe. s8º. N.Y. [1890]
Bruce (James Douglas). Evol. of Arthurian romance to 1300. [Hesperia, Ergänzungsreihe, H8]. 2v. 8º. Göttingen. 1923
Bruce (John Collingwood). Hdbk. to the Roman Wall. 8th ed. Ed. R. Blair. s8º. Newcastle. 1925
Bruce (Joseph Percy). Chu Hsi & his masters: intr. to C. H. & the Sung school of Chin. philos. s8º. 1923
see CHU HSI. The philos. of human nature; tr., w. notes by B., 1922.
Bruce (Michael), *poet.* Poet. works. Collated by T. Park. [*b. w.* Smollett (T. G.) Poet. wks., 1807]. s8º. 1807
Bruce (Robert), *king of Scotland, see* PEARSON (K.) King R. the B., skull & portraiture, 1925.
Bruce (*Rt. Hon.* **Stanley Melbourne).**
Financial position of Australia. [P2848]. 8º. 1926
Bruce (William Spiers), *see* BROWN (R. N. R.) Naturalist at the Poles: life, work & voyages of W. S. B., 1923.
Bruck (Robert), *ed.* Die Malereien in d. Hss. d. Königr. Sachsen. la8º. Dresden. 1906
Brücke (Ernst Wilhelm v.) Farbenwechsel d. afrikan. Chamäleons. Hrsg. v. M. v. Frey. 8º. L. 1893
Pflanzenphysiolog. Abhdlgn., 1844–62. Hrsg. v. A. Fischer. 8º. L. 1898
Brückner (Alex.), *1856–*
Gesch. d. poln. Litt. 8º. L. 1901
Gesch. d. poln. Lit. [Literaturen d. Ostens]. 2e. A. 8º. L. [1922]
Gesch. d. russ. Litt. 8º. L. 1905
Gesch. Russlands bis z. Ende d. 18. Jhdts., B1, 2, 1896–1913, *see* GESCH. D. EUROP. STAATEN.
Lit. hist. of Russia. Ed. E. H. Minns; tr. H. Havelock. 8º. 1908
Die poln. Lit., *see* HINNEBERG (P.) Die Kultur d. Gegenwart, T1, Abtlg. 9, 1908.
Der Weltkrieg. u. d. Slawen, *see* DEUTSCHE Reden in schwerer Zeit, 21, 1915.
Brückner (Alfred). Slavisch-Litauisch, *see* GRUNDRISS d. indogerman. Sprach-u. Altertumskunde, Abt. 2, B3, 1917.
Bruckner (Anton), *see* AUER (M.) B., 1923.
Bruckner (Wilhelm).
Hermannstadt in Siebenbürgen. s8º. L. [1909]
Brüder-Gemeinen, *see* *GESANGBUCH z. Gebr. d. evangel. Brüder-Gemeinen, 1850.
Brüder-Gesang. *Etwas v. Liede Mosis &c., d. i.: Alt u. neuer Brüder-Gesang, 1753, *see* ZINZENDORF (N. L., *Graf* v.)
*Hist. Nachricht vom B.-G. d. J. 1778, 1835, *see* HISTORISCHE.
Bruder (Carl Hermann). Ταμιεῖον, sive concordantiæ omnium vocum N. Test. Græci &c. ed. 4a ster. auct. 4º. L. 1888
Bruegel (Pieter), *see* BREUGEL (P.)
Brueys (David Augustin de), *see* AUBERT DE VERSÉ (N.) L'avocat des protestans, contre B., 1686.
Brügel (Ludwig). Soziale Gesetzgebung in Österreich von 1848 bis 1918. Mit Geleitworte d. F. Hanusch. 8º. Wien. 1919
Brugerette (Joseph).
Grégoire VII & la réforme du 11e siecle. s8º. 1908
Bruges. Invent. des archives de Bruges. Publ. sous les auspices de l'admin. communale. sect. 1, 13e au 16e s. 9v. 4º. Bruges. 1871–85
Introduction.
Inventaire des chartes [*texts*; publ.] par L. Gilliodts-Van Severen, t1–6.
Table analyt. par E. Gailliard.
Table des noms & glossaire flamand par E. Gailliard.

Brügge (Roger van), *see* ROGER, *van Brügge.*
Bruggeman (A.)
see SELLIER (H.), A. B. &C. Paris pend. la Guerre, 1926.
„ —— & A. B. Le probl. du logement, 1927.
Bruggen (Carry J. A. van).
De verlatene. Roman van het Joodsche leven. 5e dr. s8º. A. *n.d.*
Das zerstörte Ameisenreich. Phantasie. [Üb. v. E. Hollander]. 8º. Zürich. 1922
Brugmann (Carl). Die Syntax d. einfachen Satzes im Indogerman. [Beiheft z. 43. B. d. Indogerman. Forsch.] 8º. 1925
see GRUNDRISS d. indogerman. Sprach- u. Altertumskunde; hrsg. K. B. &c., 1916–17.
Brühl (Heinrich, *Graf* **v.),** *see* SCHMIDT (O. E.) Minister Graf. B. u. K. H. v. Heinecken: Briefe u. Akten &c., 1733–63, 1921.
Bruinier (Johannes Weygardus).
Das deutsche Volkslied. s8º. L. 1921
Bruining (Hendrik). Disput. de anabaptismo, sub præs. G. Vossii. [P2632]. s4º. Lugd. Batav. 1618
Bruins (G. W. J.) Memorandum, *see* INTERNAT. FINANCIAL CONF. Paper No. 13ii, 1920.
Bruix (Eustache), *admiral, 1759–1805, see* DOUIN (G.) La campagne de B. en Méditerranée, 1923.
Brulard (Henri), *ps., see* BEYLE (M. H.)
Brulart (Roger), *marq. de Sillery & de Puisieux, see* PUISIEUX (R. B., *marq. de S. & de*).
Brulius (Joachimus). Breves resolut. casuum reservatorum apud regulares. s8º. Coloniæ Agrippinæ. 1640
Brum (Baltasar), *president of Republic of Uruguay.*
American solidarity. Conf. [P2435]. s8º. Montevideo. 1920
Brummell (George Bryan) [BEAU BRUMMELL], *see* MELVILLE (L.) B. B.: h. life & letters, 1924.
Brummer (Friedrich). Exercit. de Scabinis. Sub præs. J. Thomasii. [P2671]. s4º. Lipsiæ. [1662]
Brun (A.) Recherches hist. sur l'intr. du Français dans les Prov. du Midi. 8º. 1923
Brun (Charles). Le roman social en France au 19 s. 8º. 1910
Brun (J.), *Jesuit.* Dict. Syriaco-Lat. s8º. Beryti Phœnic. 1895
Brun (Johan Nordahl), *bp. of Bergen, see* WINSNES (A. H.) J. N. B.: en monografi, 1919.
Brun (Rudolf). Das Leben d. Ameisen. 8º. L. 1924
Brune (*l'abbé* **Paul).** Dict. des artistes & ouvriers d'art de la Franche-Comté. la8º. 1912
Bruneau (Alfred). La vie & les œuvres de G. Fauré. s8º. 1925
see HERVEY (A.) A. B., 1907.
Bruneau (Charles). Enquête linguist. s. les patois d'Ardenne. [H. E., 248]. t2, M–Y. 8º. 1926
Brunel (Henri). Avant le Christianisme; ou hist. des doctrines relig. et philosoph. de l'antiquité. 8º. 1852
Brunelleschi (Filippo), *architect, see* VENTURI (A.) F. B.: 32 riprod. con testo e cat., 1923.
Brunengo, *bp. of Asti, see* BRUNINGUS.
Brunet (Émile). German calumnies. "The Anglo-Belgian conventions (1906–12)." [P2415]. s4º. *n.d.*
Brunet (Georges).
Le mysticisme social de Saint-Simon. s8º. 1925
see LEFÈVRE-DEUMIER (J.) Les vespres de l'abbaye du Val; intr. &c. par G. B., 1924.
Brunet (Raymond).
A travers les grands vignobles franç. & étr. la8º. 1913
Brunet (René). La constit. allemande du 11 août 1919. Préf. par Joseph-Barthélemy. 8º. 1921
La Soc. des Nations & la France. s8º. 1921
Brunfels (Otto). Almanach ewig werend, Teütszch u. Christlich Practick, von dem xxvi. Jar an bitz zů endt der welt aller welt. s4º. *n.p.* [1526]
12 leaves, sig A-C in fours.
see HUTTEN (U. v.) U. ab H. cum Erasmo expostul.—O. B. pro U. H. ad Erasmi Spongiam responsio, 1530 ?
Brunhes (Jean). Géographie humaine de la France, v1, 2, *see* HANOTAUX (G.) Hist. de la nation franç., t1, 2, 1920–26.
Human geography. Tr. by T. C. Le Compte. Ed. I. Bowman &c. 8º. [1920]
—— **& C. Vallaux.** La géographie de l'hist. la8º. 1921
Brunhild, *see* LÖWIS OF MENAR (A. v.) Brünhildsage (Die) in Russland, 1923.
Bruni (Domenico).
Novella. [*Ed.* A. Tessier. P2787]. 8º. Venezia. 1854
Bruni (Leonardo), *Aretino, see* ARETINO (L.)
Bruni (Lodovico). Poème adressé à Maximilien après la bataille de Guinegate [*in Latin*] (Louvain, c. 1479), facs. & tr., *see* PICOT (E.) & H. STEIN. Recueil, 1923.

Brunialti (Attilio). Il Friuli orientale. la8°. Torino. 1920

Bruningus, *bp. of Asti, 931–64, see* CIPOLLA (C.) Di Brunengo, vescovo di Asti, e di tre doc. ined., 1890.

Brunner (Balthasar). De scorbuto tractatus duo, 1619, *see* EUGALENUS (S.) De scorbuto morbo liber &c., 1624.

Brunner (Carl), *see* SCHWARZWALD (Der) in Farbenphotogr.; Text v. K. B., 1911.

Brunner (Edmund de Schweinitz), G. S. Hughes & M. Patten. Amer. agricultural villages. 8°. N.Y. [1927]

Brunner (Hugo). Wilhelmstal. 8°. Marburg. [1925]

Bruno, *Saint, founder of Carthusians, see* MADARIAGA (I. DE). Vida d. S. B., 1596.

Bruno, *Magdeburgensis.* De bello Saxon. liber. ed. 2ª rec. W. Wattenbach. [Scr. rerum Germ. in usum schol.] 8°. Hannoveræ. 1880

Bruno, *Saint, bp. of Würzburg* [*Herbipol.*] Psalteriū beati Brunonis a J. Cochleo restitutum & Hebraica veritate adauctum. s4°. Lipsiæ. 1533

Bruno, *The family of.* La famiglia Bruno e le sue alleanze &c. la8°. Milano. 1922

Bruno (Giordano).
Opere ital. [t]1–3. [1, 3, 2ª ed.] 8°. Bari. 1908–23
1, Dialoghi metafisici, nuov. ristampati con note da Giov. Gentile.
2, Dialoghi morali, con note da Giov. Gentile.
3, Candelaio. Commedia. Con intr. &c. a cura di V. Spampanato.
Opera Lat. conscripta. Cur. F. Tocco & H. Vitelli. v1iii, iv, 2ii, iii, 3. la8°. Flor. 1889–91
see ATANASSIEVITCH (X.) Doctrine métaphys. &c. de B. exposée dans s. ouvrage "De triplici minimo," 1923.
,, GENTILE (G.) G. B. e il pensiero del Rinascimento, 1920.
,, SPAMPANATO (V.) Vita di G. B., 2v, 1921.

Brunot (Ferdinand). L'expression des relations & des modalitése n français, *see* KONGELIGT DAN. VID. SELSK. Hist.-fil. Med., B4, 1921–22.
Hist. de la langue franç., des origines à 1900. t4ii [*pagin. contin.*], 7, 9i. 8°. 1924–27.
4ii, La Langue classique, 1660–1715, p2.
7, La propagation du franç. en France jusqu'à la fin de l'anc. régime.
9, La Révol. & l'Empire, p1., Le fr. langue nat.
La pensée & la langue. Méthode &c. d'une théorie nouv. du langage appliquée au français. la8°. 1922

Brunquell (Johann Salomon). Diss. de pictura famosa. Sub præs. J. S. B. exam. subm. C. F. Voit a Berg. [P2746]. s4°. Jenæ. 1733

Bruns (Carl E. Georg).
Fontes juris Romani antiq. 8°. Tubingæ. 1860

Bruns (Friedrich), *see* LÜBECK. Bau- u. Kunstdenkmäler, B3, 4, bearbt. v. F. B. &c., 1920–28.

Bruns (Friedrich), *of Wisconsin Univ.* Mod. thought in German lyric poets, f. Goethe to Dehmel. [Univ. of Wisconsin Studies, No. 13.] 8°. Madison. 1921

Bruns (Paul Jacob). De libello contra B. K. ejusque collat. MSS. Hebraicorum, nuper Gallice ed. epistola ad amicum; ex Anglico vertit suasque ad B. K. litteras adjecit P. J. B. s8°. Romæ. 1772

Brunschvicg (Léon).
Cambronne. Sa vie civile, polit. & milit. 8°. Nantes. 1894
L'expérience humaine & la causalité physique. 8°. 1922
Le génie de Pascal. s8°. 1924
Nature & liberté. s8° [1921]
Progrès de la conscience dans la philos. occident. 2t. 8°. 1927
see PASCAL (B.) Études sur P., par M. Blondel, L. B. &c., 1923.

Brunschwig (Hieronymus) [†BRAUNSCHWEIG]. The Book of cirurgia [Buch d. Cirurgia], Strassburg, J. Gruninger, 1497. [*Facsimile*]. With study on H. B. by H. E. Sigerist. 4°. Milano. 1923

Brunswick, *House of, see* RIMIUS (H.) Memoirs of H. of B., 1750.

Brunswick Clubs. Brunswick meeting on Penenden Heath, Oct. 24, 1828: speeches &c. to freeholders of Kent [*by Mr. Shiel, Marquis of Camden, Lord Teynham, &c.*] [P2782]. 8°. Liv'l. 1828

Brunswick-Luneburg. La discipline eccl. & la conf. de foi des églises reform. de France, pour l'usage des égl. de B.-L., 1711, *see* FRANCE.

Brunswick-Lüneburg (Ernest A. W. A. G. F., *duke of*), *see* CUMBERLAND (E. A. W. A. G. F., *duke of*).

Brunton (George) & D. Haig. Hist. acc. of the senators of the College of Justice fr. its instit in 1532. 8°. 1832

Brunton (Guy). Lahun I, The treasure. [Brit. School of Arch. & Egypt. Res. Acc.] 4°. 1920
see PETRIE (*Sir* W. M. F.) & G. B. Sedment, 2v, 1924.
,, ——, G. B. &c. Lahun II, 1923.

—— & R. Engelbach.
Gurob. [Brit. Sch. of Arch. in Egypt &c.] 4°. 1927

Brunton (John), *of Barclay's Bank.*
Bankers & borrowers. Intr. by E. Sykes. 8°. 1921
Letters on pract. banking. 8°. 1923

Brunton (Mary), *novelist.* Self-control. [2460]. 8°. 1839

Brunton (*Mrs.* Winifred). Kings & queens of anc. Egypt. Portr. by W. B. Hist. by egyptologists [*i.e.* T. Gray, W. & G. Brunton &c.] Foreword by J. H. Breasted. la8°. [1924]

Brunus (Conradus). Adversus novam hist. eccl. [Magdeb. Cent.] quam Matthias [Flacius] Illyricus & ejus collegæ Magdeburgici nuper ediderunt &c. s8°. [Dilingæ]. 1565

Bruschetti (Lodovico), *see* BRYSKETT (L.)

Brusendorff (Aage). The Chaucer tradition. 8°. [1925]

Brusnev (Mikhail Ivanovich). Мат. по делу М. И. Б., *see* BLAGOEV (D.) От группы Б. 1921.

Brusov (Valery Yakovlevich).
В такие дни, стихи 1919–20. 8°. [Москва]. 1921
Дали: стихи 1922 года. s8°. Москва. 1922
Дневники, 1891–1910. Приготов. к печ. И. М. Брюсова. 8°. [Москва]. 1927
Миг. Стихи1920–21. s8°. П. 1922
Последние мечты. Лирика, 1917–19. s8°. Москва. 1920
Полное собраніе сочиненій t15, Театръ, 1904–12. 8°. С.-П. 1914
see JIRMUNSKY (V. M.) В. Б. и наследие Пушкина, 1922.

Brusse (M. J.) Boefje. 14e dr. 8°. Rotterdam. 1920
Landlooperij. 5e dr. 8°. Rotterdam. 1916

Brussels. [BRUXELLES].
MUSÉES DE B.
Donation d'antiq. égypt. aux Musées Roy. de Brux. Descr. &c. par J. Capart. s8°. Brux. [1911]
Musées Royaux des Arts Décor. & indust. Cat. des sculpt. & inscr. ant. par F. Cumont. [P2794]. 8°. Bruxelles. [1889]
see CORPUS vasorum antiq. Belgique, fasc. 1, Brux., fasc. 1; par F. Mayence, 1926.

Brüstlein (Johann). Luther's Einfluss auf d. Volksschulwesen u. d. Religionsunterricht. [Abdr. aus Beitr. d. theol. Wiss., B4]. 8°. Jena. 1852

Brustoloni (Andrea), *1662–1732, see* PERSICINI (P.) Di A. B. scultore bellunese, 1882.

Bruton (Francis Archibald), *see* HALL (J. P.) Caer Llugwy, excav. of the Roman Fort &c. 1st rep. ed. by F. A. B., 1923.
see PETERLOO. 3 acc. of Peterloo, 1921.

Brutus (Stephanus Junius), *ps.* Defence of liberty against tyrants. Tr. w. intr. by H. J. Laski. 8°. 1924
Vindiciæ contra tyrannos, S. J. B. Celta sive, ut putatur, T. Beza auctore. [*also attr. to* H. Languet *& also to* P. de Mornay]. s8°. Amstelodami. 1660

Bruun (L. E.) Cat. of the Bruun coll. of coins. Sold by Sotheby, 18th of May &c., 1925. [*Illust., large paper copy*]. 2p. [*in 1v.*] la8°. [1925]

Bruun (Laurids). Heimwärts. 53–60. A. s8°. [1921]
Kronen. s8°. 1911

Bruyère (Bernard). Fouilles de Deir el Médineh (1922–25), 4p, *see* INSTITUT FR. D'ARCH. OR. DU CAIRE. Fouilles, t1–4, 1924–27.

Bruyère (*Mme.* Jenny), *abbess of Solesmes; 1845–1909, see* HOUTIN (A.) Une gr. mystique, Mme. B., 1845–1909, 1925.

Bruzen de la Martinière (Antoine Augustin).
see PUFENDORFF (S. *Frhr.* v.) Introd. to hist. of states of Europe beg. by S. P., contin. by Mr. de La M., 1764.
,, SCHOLA SALERNITANA. L'art de conserver sa santé; tr. M. B. L. M., 1766.

Bruzza (Luigi). Notizie int. alla patria e ai primi studi del pittore G. A. Bazzi, *see* REGIA DEPUT. DI STORIA ITAL. Misc., t1, 1862.

Bruzzi (Stefano), *1835–1911, see* SAPORI (F.) Maestri, No. 13, 1919.

Bry (Johanne Theodor de). 4ª pars Iconum viros virtute &c. ill. repraesentantium. Natalium notatis adjuncta &c., opera & studio [J. A. Loniceri]. In aere facta &c. per haeredes Th. de Bry. [p. 1–3 *wanting*]. s4°. Francfordii ad Moenum. 1599
see BOISSARDUS (J. J.) Bibliotheca chalcograph., sculptore J. T. de B., *n.d. &* 1650–54.

Bryan (George), *justice of Pennsylvania, see* KONKLE (B. A.) G. B. & the constit. of Penn., 1731–91, 1922.

Bryan (J. Ingram).
The civilization of Japan. [Home Univ. Lib.] s8°. [1927]

Bryan (P. W.), *see* JONES (L. R.) & P. W. B. N. America, 1924.

Bryan (Tom) [BRYAN (THOMAS)], *see* WOOD (H. G.) & A. E. BALL. T. B., 1st Warden of Fircroft: a mem., 1922.

Bryan (Walter Reid). Italic hut urns & hut urn cemeteries: early iron age of Latium & Etruria. [Papers &c. of Amer. Acad. in Rome, v4]. 8°. Rome. 1925

Bryan (William Jennings). The first battle. Story of the campaign of 1896. With coll. of h. speeches & biog. sketch by h. wife. 8°. Chicago. 1896
Speeches. Rev. & arr. by himself; w. biog. intr. by h. wife. 2v. s8°. N.Y. 1913
see UNITED STATES: FOR. AFFAIRS. Treaties for the adv. of peace, negot. by W. J. B.; w. intr. by J. B. Scott, 1920.

Bryanchaninov (Aleksandr Nikolaevich) [BRIANTCHANINOV]. Ideological foundations of Russian Slavonism. Tr. S. de Bellegarde. [P2384]. 8°. 1916

Bryant (Lorinda Munson).
American pictures & their painters. 8°. 1921
What sculpture to see in Europe. s8°. 1920

Bryant (*Mrs.* **Sophie).** Moral & religious educ. s8°. 1920

Bryant (T. Hugh). Suffolk. [County Churches]. 2v. s8°. 1912

Bryant (William Cullen). The Bryant festival at "The Century," Nov. 5, 1864. s8°. N.Y. 1865

Bryce (James), *D.D.* Ten years of the Ch. of Scotland, 1833 to 1843; w. hist. retrospect fr. 1560. 2v. 8°. E. 1850

Bryce (James Bryce, *viscount***).**
The Holy Roman Empire. n. ed., enl. s8°. 1922
Internat. relations. 8 lect. del. in U.S., 1921. [Williams Coll., Williamstown, Mass.] s8°. 1922
Memories of travel. 8°. 1923
Modern democracies. 2v. 8°. 1921
Proposals for the prevention of future wars. By Visc. B. & others. [P2602]. 8°. [1917]
The study of American hist. Lect., Sir G. Watson chair. s8°. C. 1921
World hist., lect., *for a. copy see* BRIT. ACAD. Proc., v9, 1919–20.
see DANTE ALIGHIERI. D.: essays, 1321–1921; [by Visct. B., &c.], 1921.
,, FISHER (H. A. L.) J. B., 2v, 1927.
,, LEAGUE (The) of nations & China: speeches by B. &c., 1919.

Brydges (*Sir* **Samuel Egerton),** *bart.* *Biograph. peerage of Gt. Brit. 3v. s8°. 1808–9
*Biograph. peerage of Ireland &c. s8°. 1817

Bryher (Winifred), *ps.* [*i.e.* ANNIE WINIFRED ELLERMAN].
Amy Lowell: crit. apprec. [P2518]. la8°. 1918
Development. s8°. 1920

Brynildsen (J.)
Norsk-Engelsk Ordbog. Anden omarb. utg. 8°. 1917

Brynjúlfsson (Gísli), *the elder.* [BRYNJULFI FIL.]
Periculum Runologicum. Diss. s8°. Hauniæ. 1823

Bryn Mawr notes & monographs. No. 2–4, 6. s8°. 1921–25
see CARPENTER (R.) Greeks in Spain, 1925. [6.]
,, CHEW (S. C.) Thomas Hardy, poet & novelist, 1921. [3.]
,, KING (G. G.) A citizen of the twilight: J. A. Silva, 1921. [4.]
,, —— Play of the Sibyl Cassandra, 1921. [2.]

Brynmor-Jones (*Sir* **David),** *see* RHYS (*Sir* J.) & D. B.-J. The Welsh people, 6th impr., 1923.

Bryskett (Lodowick) [BRUSCHETTI], *see* PLOMER (H. R.) & T. P. CROSS. Life & corr. of L. B., 1927.

Bryusov (Valery), *see* BRUSOV.

B. S. A., *see* BIRMINGHAM SMALL ARMS CO.

Buat (*gén.* **Edmond).**
L'artillerie de campagne, hist. &c. 3e éd. s8°. 1911
Hindenburg & Ludendorff stratèges. 8°. 1923
Ludendorff. s8°. 1920

Buber (Martin).
Der grosse Maggid u. s. Nachfolge. s8°. Frankfurt a. M. 1922

Buberl (Paul). Die Denkmale d. polit. Bezirkes Hallein. Archiv. Teil v. F. Martin. [Österreich. Kunsttopog., 20]. 4°. Wien. [1927]
Die Miniaturenhandschr. d. Nationalbibl. in Athen, 1917, *see* KAISERL. AKAD. D. WISS. ZU WIEN. DENKSCHR., B60, 1918.

Bucaille (Victor). Denys Cochin, *see* PAGES ACTUELLES, N°. 138, 1922.
G. Goyau. s8°. [1926 ?]

Bucelleni (Giovanni) [†BUCELLENUS (JOANNES)]. Asceticæ consid., in usum eorum, qui per sacras comment. se & alios ad perfectionem animant.
5t *b. in* 2v. [t4 *in* 2p] fol. Viennæ Austriæ. 1666–1671

Bucer (Martin) [BUTZER].
Abusuum eccl. &c. indicatio imp. majestati in comitiis Regespurgi postulanti, exhib. [*b. w. h.* Scripta duo adversaria &c., 1544]. s4°. Argentorati. 1541
Acta colloquii in comitiis Imp. Ratisponæ habiti per M. B. [*b. w. h.* Scripta duo adv., 1544]. s4°. Argentorati. 1541
Alle Handlungen u. Schrifften, zu vergleichung der Religion durch die Churfürsten, Fürsten &c., Auch Päbst. Legaten auff Reichstag zu Regenspurg verhandlet. &c. A. 1541. s4°. [Strassburg, *W. Rihel*], *n.d.* [1541 ?]
Apologia B. qua fidei suæ &c. circa Christi Cœnam. s8°. [Argentorati ?]. 1526
Das ym selbs niemät, sonder anderen leben soll. u. wie der mensch dahyn kummen mög. s4°. [Strassburg ?]. 1523
De vera eccl. in doctrina, ceremoniis &c. reconciliatione &c. Resp. ad calumnias A. Pighii &c. & refut. suggillationis Eccianæ contra Acta Ratispon. s4°. *n.p. n.d.*
Doctrina de prædestinatione—causa peccati—libero arbitrio—excæcatione impiorum. s8°. *n.p.* 1562
Epistola ad Ephesios &c. In eandem Comm. s8°. *n.p. n.d.* [1527 ?]
Gratulatio ad Eccl. Anglic., de relig. Christi restit. Et, Resp. ejusdem ad duas Stephani episcopi Vinton. epistolas de coelibatu sacerdotum &c. s4°. *n.p.* 1548
In sacra quatuor Evangelia enarr. &c. fol. Basileæ. 1536
Metaphrases & enarr. perpetuæ epistol. Pauli. t1, contin. Metaphrasim & enarr. in Epist. ad Romanos, per M.B. [*b. w.* Anselm, In omnes Pauli epist., 1533]. fol. Argentorati. 1536
Noviss. conf. de Cœna Domini excerpta de ipsius enarr. in 4 Evangelia ed. 1553. Præm. Formula Concordiæ Vuitebergæ, 1536. s8°. Lipsiæ. 1562
Præfatio in quartum tomum Postillæ Lutheranæ, cont. summam doctrinæ Christi. Ejusdem Epistola; Epistola M. Lutheri; Resp. ad hanc M. Buceri. s8°. *n.p.* 1527
Scripta duo adversaria D. B. Latomi & M. B. de dispensatione sacramenti &c. Resp. etiam Pighii & Alphonsi atque deputatorum Colon. argumentis. s4°. Argentorati, *W. Rihel.* 1544
see BUGENHAGEN (J.) Psalter door J. B. in Latijn beschreven; door M. B. verduytscht &c., *n.d.*
,, COCHLÆUS (J.) In prim. Musculi Anticoch. repl. J. C.; add., app. in librum B. &c., 1545.
,, COLOGNE. Antididagma &c., Sententia item delectorum &c. de vocatione M. B., 1544.
,, DIEHL (W.) M. B.'s Bedeutung f. d. kirchl. Leben in Hessen, 1904.
,, ECK (J. v.) Apologia pro principibus adv. calumnias B. &c., 1542.
,, —— Replica adv. scripta secunda B., 1543.
,, EELLS (H.) Attitude of B. toward bigamy of Philip of Hesse, 1924.
,, GARDINER (S.) Stephani Winton. ad M. B. de impudenti ejusdem pseudologia, 1545.
,, HUBERTUS (C.) *Hist. de vita, obitu &c. M. B. &c., 1562.
,, RATISBON. Actes of the disput. at Regenspurg; set forth by M. B. &c.; tr., 1542.
,, VERPOORTEN (A. M.) Comm. hist. de M B., 1709.

Bucerus (Gerson). Diss. de gubernatione Eccl., maximeque de presbyterio & episcopatu. s4°. Middelburgi Zelandorum. 1618

Buch (Johann v.), *see* STEFFENHAGEN (E.) Die Entwickl. d. Landrechtsglosse d. Sachsenspiegels, 11, 12, J. v. B. u. d. Accursische [*& kanon.*] Glosse, 1922–23.

Buchan Club, The, *see* GREIG (G.) Last leaves of tradit. ballads, &c., 1925.

Buchan (*Miss* **Anna),** *see* DOUGLAS (O.), *ps.*

Buchan (James Walter), *ed.*
Hist. of Peeblesshire. [*By var. a.*] 3v. 8°. Glasgow. 1925–27

Buchan (John).
The dancing floor. s8°. [1926]
,, ,, [repr.] s8°. [1926]
Francis & Riversdale Grenfell. Memoir. [2nd ed.] 8°. [1920]
Hist. of Eng. lit. [*By var. wr.*] Ed. J. B., w. intr. by Sir H. Newbolt. 8°. 1923
A hist. of the Great War. 4v. 8°. [1921–22]
Hist. of the Royal Scots Fusiliers, 1678–1918. Pref. by the Prince of Wales. 8°. [1925]
The hist. of the S. African forces in France. 8°. [1920]
Homilies & recreations. 8°. [1926]
Huntingtower. s8°. [1922]
,, ...[repr.] s8°. [1925]
John Burnet of Barns. [repr.] s8°. [1926]
John Macnab. [repr.] 8°. [1925]
The last secrets: final mysteries of exploration. s8°. [1923]
Lord Minto: a memoir. 8°. [1924]
Midwinter. s8°. [1923]
,, ...[repr.] s8°. [1927]
The nations of to-day: new hist. of the world. Ed. J. B. 8°. [1923–4]
Baltic & Caucasian States. By T. L. Gilmour &c.
Brit. America. By A. G. Bradley &c.
Bulgaria & Romania. By Lady Grogan &c.
France. By A. Hassall &c.
Great Britain. By R. S. Rait &c., 2v.
India. By Sir V. Lovett &c.
Ireland. By Rev. R. H. Murray & H. Law.
Italy. By J. C. Powell &c.
Japan. By J. H. Longford.
Yugoslavia. By H. L. Lorimer &c.

Buchan (John) [*continued*].

The old & new in lit., *see* ROY. SOC. OF LIT. Essays, N.S., v5, 1925.
Path of the king. s8°. [1921]
Some notes on Sir Walter Scott. [Eng. Assoc., Pamph. 58. P2737]. 8°. 1924
The thirty-nine steps. s8°. 1915
The three hostages. s8°. [1924]
" " [repr.] s8°. [1924]
The watcher by the threshold & o. t. s8°. [1922]
Witch Wood. [repr.] s8°. [1927]
see STEWART (*Lt.-col.* J.) & J. B. The 15th (Scottish) Div., 1914–19, 1926.

Buchan (William), *M.D.* Domestic medicine. 15th ed. 8°. 1797

Buchan (William Comyn, *earl of*). Charter by W. Cumin, to Robert de Warderoba, of 4th part of land of Drumry, in Levenax, ante 1233, *see* MAIDMENT (J.) & R. PITCAIRN. Nugæ derelictæ, 1822.

Buchanan (*Capt.* Angus), *M.C.* Sahara. 8°. 1926
Wild life in Canada. 8°. 1920

Buchanan (Claudius). Christian researches in India. Ed. W. H. Foy. s8°. 1858
Colon. eccl. establishment. 2nd ed. 8°. 1813

Buchanan (David), *historical writer.*
Hist. animæ humanæ. s8°. *n.p.* [Paris ?]. 1636

Buchanan (Dugald), *1716–68.* His confessions & spiritual songs rendered into Eng. verse. With h. letters & life by L. Macbean. s8°. [1919]

Buchanan (Francis), *aft. Hamilton.* Journal; ed. w. notes &c. by V. H. Jackson, 1922, *see* BIHAR & ORISSA RESEARCH SOC. Journal, v8, 1922.

Buchanan (George), *the historian.*

De jure regni apud Scotos dial. s8°. Glasguæ. 1750
De jure regni apud Scotos; tr. into Eng. by R. Macfarlan, *see* PRESBYTERIAN's armoury, v3, 1843.
Paraphrasis Psalmorum Davidis poetica. s8°. Antverpiæ. 1582
" " [*a. ed., w. t. beg.*] Psalmorum &c. Ejusdam tragœdia Jephthes [*w. sep. tp.*] s8°. Londini. 1583
" " Eiusdem Bl. Tragœdiæ 2, Jephthes & Baptistes. s8°. Lugd. Bat. 1621
Poemata quæ extant, ed. postr. s8°. Lugduni Batav. 1628
Rerum Scoticarum hist. sfol. E., *Apud A. Arbuthnetum.* 1582
Sacred dramas; tr. into Eng. verse by A. Brown. s8°. Ed. 1906
see MAHON (*Maj.-Gen.* R. H.) The indictment of Mary Queen of Scots, w. comments on the authorship &c., 1923.
" MEYER-COHN (M.) G. B. als Publizist &c. Maria Stuarts &c., 1913.
" PEARSON (K.) On the skull & portraits of G. B., 1926.

Buchanan (*Sir* George William), *G.C.B.*
My mission to Russia & o. diplomatic mem. 2v. 8°. 1923

Buchanan (James), *D.D., minister of the Free Church, Edin.*
Analogy, consid. as a guide to truth, &c. 8°. E. 1864
The "Essays & reviews" examd. Articles contrib. to "Morning Post," w. pref., intr. &c. s8°. E. 1861

Buchanan (James), *president of the U.S.*
*Mr. Buchanan's admin. on eve of the Revol. 8°. N.Y. 1866

Buchanan (*Miss* Meriel). Recollect. of Imperial Russia. 8°. 1923

Buchannan (John). Albert, poem—Hilda & o. poems. s8°. 1828

Bucharest [BUKAREST].
Der Friede v. Bukarest. Authent. Berichte. 8°. L. [1918]
MUZEUL NAŢIONAL DE ANTICHITĂŢI, *see* TOCILESCU (G. G.) Mon. epigr. şi sculpt. ale Mus. Nat. de Ant. din B., v1, 1902–8.

Buchel (Arnold), *see* BUCHELL (A. VAN).

Bücheler (Franz), *see* ANTHOLOGIA LATINA, pars post., Carmina lat. epigraph., 3, Suppl., 1926.

Buchell (Arend van) [BUCHEL (A.)] Diarium. Uitg. door G. Brom & L. A. van Langeraad. [Hist. Genoots. Werken, s3, 21]. 8°. A. 1907
Trajecti Bat. descr.; medeged. S. Muller, *see* HISTORISCH GENOOTS. Bijdragen, d27, 1906.

Bucher (Samuel Fridericus). Antiq. biblicæ ex N.T. selectæ. s4°. Vitembergæ. 1729

***Bücherschatz** d. deut. Nat. Litt. &c., 1854, *see* HEYSE (C. W. L.)

Buchheim (Carl A.) Balladen u. Romanzen: sel. w. notes & lit. intr. by C. A. B. s8°. 1891
Deutsche Lyrik, sel. &c. s8°. 1892
German poetry for repetition, &c. s8°. 1879

Buchheit (Hans), *see* MÜNCHEN: Das Miniaturenkabinett der M. Resid., Vorwort &c. von H. B. &c., 1921.

Buchhorn (Josef).
Hindenburg, d. Führer in unsere Zukunft. 8°. 1920

Büchi (Albert). Kardinal M. Schiner als Staatsmann u. Kirchenfürst. T1 (bis 1514). la8°. Zürich. 1923
Korresp. u. Akten z. Gesch. d. Kard. M. Schiner; gesammelt u. hrsg. A. B., 2B, 1489–1527, *see* QUELLEN Z. SCHWEIZER GESCH., N. F., Abtlg. 3, B5, 6, 1920–25.

Buchler (Joannes). Sacrarum profanarumque phrasium thesaurus. ed. 18a repurg. &c., add. nonnulla de carmine dramat. ab E. Philippo. s8°. 1679

Buchmann (Otto). Marias Lied. s8°. Hannover. 1919

Buchner (Ernst) & C. Feuchtmayr. Oberdeut. Kunst d. Spätgotik u. Reformationszeit. Hrsg. E. B. u. K. F. [Beitr. z. Gesch. d. deut. Kunst, B1]. 4°. Augsburg. 1924

Büchner (F. C. C. Ludwig).
Aus Natur u. Wissenschaft. 2e. A. 8°. L. 1869
Man in the past, present, & future. Tr. W. S. Dallas. 8°. 1872

Büchner (Georg). Sämtl. poet. Werke, nebst e. Auswahl s. Briefe. Hrsg. &c. v. A. Zweig. 8°. München. 1923
see MARCUSE (L.) G. B. u. s. besten Bühnenwerke: Einführung, 1921.

Büchner (Gottfried). Von. d. zweimal Verstorbenen u. v. d. Ort wo sich deren Selen in d. Zwischenzeit aufgehalten &c. s4°. Jena. 1736

Buchner (Max). Einhards Künstler- u. Gelehrtenleben: ein Kulturbild aus d. Z. Karls d. Gr. u. Ludwigs d. Frommen. s8°. Bonn. 1922

Bucholcerus (Nohas). Carmen de natalibus, vita &c. Flacii, *see* DIASSORINUS (J.) Encomium &c., 1558.

Buchon (Jean Alex. C.) Choix de chroniques &c. la8°. 1875
Bonamy (P. N.) Mém. sur les dern. années de Jacques Cœur, 1409–65.
Du Clercq (J. de) Mémoires, 1448–67.
Le Febvre de Saint-Remy (J.) Mémoires, 1407–35.
Saad Eddin Effendi. Annales de l'Emp. Ottoman. [*Extr.*]
Trasne (Francisco de). Lettre du card. d'Avignon.

Choix de chroniques &c. la8°. 1884
Aubigné (Th. A. d'). Mémoires.
La Place (P. de). Comm. de l'estat de la relig. & république.
Rabutin (F. de). Comm. des dern. guerres en la Gaule Belgique.
Regnier de la Planche (L.) Hist. de l'estat de France.
" " Livres des marchands.

Choix d' ouvrages mystiques, avec notices par B. [Tr.] la8°. 1840
Augustin, Confessions—Méditations. Boèce, Consol. de la phil. Bernard, Traité de la consid. Gersen, Imit. de Jésus Christ. Bona, Princ. de la vie chrét.—Chemin du ciel. Tauler, Institutions. Louis de Blois, Directeur des âmes relig.

Buchot (Auguste) & C. G. Gauthey.
Hist. de P. Vaux. 8°. Louhans. 1889

Buchta (Richard). Der Sudan unter ägypt. Herrschaft. Nebst Anh.: Briefe Dr. Emin-Pascha's u. Lupton-Bey's an W. Junker, 1883–85. Bearbt. & hrsg. v. R. B. 8°. L. 1888

Bucintoro, *ship.* *Ricostruz. d. B., 1900, *see* SUGANA (L.)

Buck (Albert Henry).
The dawn of modern medicine. 8°. New Haven, *Yale*, 1920

Buck (Carl Darling). Intr. to study of the Greek dialects. Grammar, sel. inscr., glossary. 8°. Boston [Mass.] [1910]

Buck (Howard Swazey).
Smollett as poet. 8°. New Haven, *Yale.* 1927

Buck (Katherine M.) The saga of Dietrich of Bern &c., prec. by that of Wayland Smith. [The Wayland-Dietrich saga]. pl, v1–6. 8°. 1924–27

Buck (Percy Carter).
The Oxford song book. Coll. & arr. by P. C. B. la8°. 1919
The scope of music. 8°. O. 1924

Buck (Solon Justus). The Agrarian crusade. The farmer in politics. [Chron. of Amer. ser., v45]. 8°. New Haven. *Yale.* 1920

Buckalew (Charles R.) Speech in Senate, U.S., 1868, upon bill to abolish appell. juris. of sup. court in cases of hab. corp. &c. [*n. tp.*] [P2625]. 8°. *n.d.*

Buckingham, *The family of.* Compota domestica famil. de Bukingham & d'Angouleme, 1443, 52, 63. Annexæ expensæ cujusdam comitis, 1273. [Ed. W. B. D. D. Turnbull. Abbotsford Club]. 4°. E. 1836

Buckingham (Edgar), *see* HUNSAKER (J. C.), E. B. &c. Rep. on wind tunnel experiments in ærodynamics, 1916.

Buckingham (George Villiers, *2nd duke of*). Cat. of coll. of pictures, incl. coll. of Sir P. P. Rubens, w. life of B. by B. Fairfax &c. [*b. w.* Charles I. Cat., 1757]. s4°. 1758

Buckingham & Chandos (Alice Anne, *duchess of*).
War-time ditties. [P2427]. s8°. 1917

Buckinghamshire.
B. parish reg. Marriages. Ed. R. F. Bale. v9. 8°. 1923
*A B. story of 1663, 1875, *see* ROTHSCHILD (C. DE).
Cal. of Pipe Rolls of r. of Rich. I for Bucks. &c., 1189–99; by G. H. Fowler &c., 1923, *see* BEDFORDSHIRE HIST. REC. SOC. Publs., v7, 1923.

Buckinghamshire (John Sheffield, *duke of***).**
Works. 2v [*in* 1v]. s8°. 1726
Works. 2nd ed. corr. 2v. s8°. 1729

Buckland (William Warwick). Textbook of Roman law f. Augustus to Justinian. la8°. C. 1921

Buckle (George Earle), *see* †MONYPENNY (W. F.) Life of B. Disraeli, v5, 6, by B., 1920.

Buckler (Benjamin). *Complete vindic. of the mallard of All-Souls College agst. injurious suggest. of Mr. Pointer. 8°. 1750
„ „ ....2nd ed. [*b. w.* 1st ed., 1750]. 8°. 1751

Buckler (Johann), *called Schinderhannes, see* ELWENSPOEK (C.) Schinderhannes, d. rhein. Rebell, 1925.

Buckler (William Hepburn), *see* RAMSAY (*Sir* W. M.) Anatolian st.; presented to Sir W. M. R.; ed. W. H. B. &c., 1923.

Buckley (Francis).
Hist. of old Eng. glass. Foreword by B. Rackham. 4°. 1925

Buckley (Jessie K.) Joseph Parkes of Birmingham & part wh. he played in Radical Reform movt., 1825–45. s8°. [1926]

Buckridge (John), *see* BURGESS (J.) Lives of mod. painters *wrongly attrib. to J. Buckridge*, 1754.

Buckrose (J. E.), *ps.* [*i.e.* Mrs. FALCONER JAMESON].
The house with golden windows. s8°. [1921]
The single heart. s8°. 1924

Buckstone (John Baldwin).
A rough diamond. Comic drama. [P2582]. s8°. *Lacy. n.d.*

Bucolic Poets. Bucoliques grecs. Texte établi & tr. par P. E. Legrand. [Coll. des univ. de France]. 2t. 8°. 1925–27
1, Théocrite. 2, Pseudo-Théocrite, Moschos, Bion, Divers.
The Greek B. poets; w. Eng. tr. by J. M. Edmonds. [Loeb Class. Lib.] [repr.] s8°. 1919
„ „ ....[repr.] s8°. 1923

Budai-Deleanu (Ioan), *see* NISTOR (I.) Românii & Rutenii in Bucovina [Anexă: Bemerk. de I. B.-D.], 1915.

Buda-Pest. Die Gemäldegalerie d. Museums f. bild. Künste. Vollst. beschr. Kat. Bearb. v. G. v. Térey. 1. Abt., Byzant., ital., span., portug. u. franz Meister. 8°. 1916
*Index rariorum librorum Bibl. Univers. Reg. Budensis. 2p. s8°. Budæ. 1780–81

Buday (Ladislaus de). Dismembered Hungary. s8°. *n.p.* 1922
The economic unity of Hungary. Tr. J. György. [P2519]. 8°. [1920?]

Budde (Conrad), *resp.* De legibus eccl. univ., pariter de Conciliis Oecumen. Præs. J. P. Hebenstreit. [P2646]. s4°. Jenæ. 1699

Buddein (Charlotta Catharina), *aft. wife of J. G. Walch, see* WALCH (C. C.)

Büddemann (Bernhard Heinrich). Ἱστορούμενα de Reformat. Lutheri ministerio instit. Præs. J. W. Rumpæo. [P484]. s4°. Susati. [*i.e.* Soest.] [1717]

Budden (Charles William).
English Gothic churches; th. architecture. s8°. [1927]

Buddenseig (Rudolf). Joh. Wiclif u. s. Zeit. Zum 500.-jahr. Wiclifjubiläum, 1884. [Verein f. Ref.-gesch. Schr., Jhrg. 2, Nr. 8 u. 9]. 8°. Halle. 1885

Buddeus (Joannes Franciscus).
Comm. de criteriis veræ falsæque inspirat. [P2637] s4°. Jenæ. [1715]
Comm. de Pelagianismo in Eccl. Rom. per bullam anti-Quesnellianam triumphante. ed. nova. [P2630]. s4°. Jenæ. 1719
Compendium institut. theologiæ dogmat., cura J. G. Walchii. s8°. Francofurti. 1731
De Conciliis Lateran. rei Xtnæ noxiis. [P2647]. s4°. Jenæ. 1725
De orig. cardinalitiæ dignitatis schediasma hist. s8°. Jenæ. 1693
Delin. comm. de veritate relig. evang. [P1042]. s8°. Jenæ. [1729]
Disquis. de moderamine inculp. tutelæ in certam. theolog. [*b. w.* Pufendorf (S. v.) Jus fec. divin., 1695]. s8°. Jenæ. 1708
Diss. de jure Zelotarum. Resp. G. F. Wille. Emend. recusa. [P431]. s4°. Halæ. 1699
Diss. de orig. & potestate episcop sententiam H. Dodwelli expendens. Præses J. F. B., resp. J. D. Baierus. [P2636]. s4°. Jenæ. [1705]
Diss. theolog. syntagma. Acc. Orationes &c. s4°. Jenæ. 1715
Eccl. Apostolica. s8°. Jenæ. 1779
Eccl. Rom. cum Ruthenica irreconcil. &c. [P436]. s4°. Jenæ. 1719
Hist. eccl. Vet. Test. ab orbe condito usque ad Christum natum. 2t. s4°. Halæ Magdeburg. 1715–19
Introd. ad hist. philos. Ebræorum. Acc. diss. de hæresi Valentiniana. Ed. nova auct. s8°. Halæ Sax. 1720
Isagoge ad theologiam univ. Novis suppl. auctior. 2t *in* 1v. [*pagin. cont.* Suppl. *w. sep. pagin.*] 4°. Lipsiæ. 1730
*Magni theologi Salani Hist. crit. theologiæ. s4°. Francofurti a. M. 1724

Buddeus (Joannes Franciscus) [*continued*].
Meditationes sacræ seu prolus. festarum decas. [*b. w. h.* Diss., 1715]. s4°. Jenæ. 1713
Miscellanea sacra: sive, diss. coll. 3p *in* 2v. s4°. Jenæ. 1727
Oratio de festo Orthodoxiæ in Eccl. Græca celeb. [P2639]. 8°. Jenæ. 1726
see BOSIUS (J. A.) Intr. in notit. scr. J. F. B. &c., 1723.
„ GROSSE (C. F.) Diss. de cultu ingenii; præs. J. F. B., 1699.
„ MOSHEIM (J. L. v.) Vindiciæ antiq. Xtnorum discipl. &c.; præf. præmisit J. F. B., ed. 2a., 1722.

Buddha.
Dialogues [*&* Further d.] of the B., tr., *see* SACRED BOOKS OF THE BUDDHISTS, tr., v4–6, 1921–27.
The Majjhima-Nikāya. 1st 50 discourses f. coll. of medium-length ds. of Gotama. Freely rendered & abr. f. the Pāli by the Bhikkhu Sīlācāra. 2nd ed. 8°. München. 1924
Die Reden Gotamo Buddho's aus d. längeren Sammlung Dīghanikāyo d. Pāli-Kanons. Übers. v. K. E. Neumann. 3B. la8°. München. 1907–18
„ „ aus d. mittl. Sammlung Majjhimanikāyo d. Pāli-Kanons. 2e A. 3B. [B1, 3e A.] s8°. München. 1921–22
Some sayings acc. to the Pāli canon. Tr. F. L. Woodward. s8°. 1925
see AṄGUTTARA-NIKĀYA. Bk. of the numerical sayings, p2; tr. A. D. Jayasundere, 1925.
„ AUFHAUSER (J. B.) B. u. Jesus in i. Paralleltexten, 1926.
„ BREWSTER (E. H.) Life of Gotama the B. comp. f. the Pāli canon, 1926.
„ HACKIN (J.) Scènes figurées de la vie du B. d'ap. des peintures tibet., 1916.
„ KLAPROTH (H. J. VON). Asia polyglotta; [*foll. by* Leben d. B. nach mongol. Nachr.], 1823.
„ STEIN (*Sir* M. A.) The thousand Buddhas, 1921.
„ ZIEGLER (L.) Der ewige B., 1922.

Buddhaghosha, *see* LAW (B. C.) Life & work of B., 1923.

Buddhist. Psalms of the early Buddhists; [tr. &c.] Mrs. Rhys Davids, 2v, 1909–13, *see* THERAGĀTHĀ.

Budé (Guillaume) [G. BUDÆUS; G. BUDEO]. Comm. linguæ græcæ. Recog. & amplius 3a parte aucti. fol. Parisiis. 1548
Quædam de moneta Græca, De moneta Rom. &c., *see* ALCIATUS (A.) De ponderibus &c., 1530.
see PLATTARD (J.) G. B., 1468–1540 & les orig. de l'humanisme franç., 1923.

Büdel (Anton). Transkaukasien: e. techn. Geogr., 1926, *see* PETERMANNS MITT. Ergnzb., 41, 1927.

Budel (Hubert van), *see* UTRECHT. Registers & rekeningen v. Bisdom Utrecht; (Schuldregister &c. v. B.), 2d, 1889–91.

Buder (Christian Gottlieb). Diatriba de juramentis principum eccl. S. I. R. Germanici &c. ed. 2a. [P2646]. s4°. Jenæ. 1737

Budge (*Sir* Ernest A. T. Wallis).
Babylonian life & hist. 2nd ed. rewr. & enl. 8°. [1925]
By Nile & Tigris. Narr. of journeys in Egypt & Mesopotamia on b. of B.M., 1886 *&* 1913. 2v. 8°. 1920
Cleopatra's needles & o. Egypt. obelisks. 8°. 1926
Cook's hdbk. f. Egypt & the Sudan. 2nd ed. s8°. 1906
The dwellers on the Nile. [rewr. & enl.] 8°. 1926
Egypt. [Home Univ Lib.] s8°. [1925]
Egyptian hieroglyphic dict. la8°. 1920
Legends of Our Lady Mary & h. mother Ḥannā. Tr. f. Ethiopic MSS. by B. 8°. 1922
Literature of the anc. Egyptians. 8°. 1914
The mummy: hdbk. of Egyptian funerary archæology. 2nd ed., rev. & enl. la8°. C. 1925
The Nile. Notes. 9th ed. s8°. 1905
One hundred & ten miracles of our Lady Mary. Tr. f. Ethiopic MSS. in B.M. &c. w. extr. f. anc. Europ. versions. 8°. 1923
Rise & progress of Assyriology. 8°. 1925
The teaching of Åmen-em-åpt, son of Kanekht. Egypt. text & Eng. tr., w. tr. of moral &c. teachings of Egypt. kings &c. illust. develop. of relig. philos. &c. 8°. 1924
Tutānkhāmen: Amenism, Atenism & Egyptian monotheism, w. texts, tr. &c. 8°. 1923
see BRITISH MUSEUM: ANTIQ. Babylonian legends of the creation &c., by B., 1921.
„ ——: —— Babylonian story of the deluge & the epic of Gilgamish by B., 1920.
„ ——: —— Book of the dead, by E. A. T. W. B., 1920.
„ ——: PAPYRI. Facs. of Egyptian Hieratic p. in B.M., w. descr. &c. by E. A. T. W. B., s2, 1923.
„ KEBRA NAGAST. The Queen of Sheba & her only son, Menyelek; compl. tr. of K. N., w. intr by E. A. T. W. B., 1922.
„ ME 'ĀRATH GAZZÊ. Bk. of the Cave of treasures; tr. B., 1927.
„ SOANE (*Sir* J.) MUSEUM. An acc. of the sarcophagus of Seti I; by B., 1908.
„ SYNAXARIUM. Bk. of the saints of the Ethiopian Ch.; tr. B., 4v, 1928.

Budgen (Walter), *ed., see* SUSSEX. Abstr. of S. deeds &c., 1924.

Budinic (Siméon) [BUDINEUS (S.)] Ispravnik za erei [tr. by S. B.], 1636, *see* POLANCUS (J.)

Buell (Raymond Leslie). Contemp. French politics. Intr. by C. J. H. Hayes. 8°. N.Y. 1920

Buer (M. C.) Economics for beginners. s8°. 1921
Health, wealth, & population in early days of the indust. revol. 8°. 1926

Buffenoir (Hippolyte). J. J. Rousseau, ami des chiens & des chats. [Extr. de la Rev. du Plateau Cent., 1926. P2847]. 8°. 1927
La maréchale de Luxembourg, 1707–87 : souv., doc. &c. [Et. sur le 18e siècle]. 8°. 1924

Buffon (Georges Louis Le Clerc, *cte.* de). Discours sur le style. Avec vers. lat. de J. A. Nairn. 8°. 1926
see ROULE (L.) B. & la descr. de la nature, 1924.

Bugeaud (*le maréchal*) [†BUGEAUD DE LA PICONNERIE (T. R.), *duc d'Isly*]. Lettres inéd., 1808–49. Coll. & annot. par Cap. Tattet & publ. par Mlle. Féray-Bugeaud d'Isly. 8°. 1922

Bugenhagen (Johann), *Pommer.* [PUGENHAG].
Annot. in decē epistolas Pauli &c. Item concordia Evang. de resurr. &c. Domini. s8°. Norembergæ [*Joh. Petreius*] 1524
Annot. in Deuteronomium, in Samuelem. Ab eodem ex Evangelistis hist. passi Christi &c. s8°. [Argentorati, *I. Knobloch*]. 1524
„ „ s8°. [Norembergæ, *J. Petreius*. 1524]
Annot. in epistolas Pauli ad Galatas, Ephesios, Philippēses, Colossenses, Thessalonicēses, Timotheū, Titum, Philemonem, Hebræos. s8°. [Nurembergæ, *Joh. Petreius*]. 1525
Auslegung der kurtzen Episteln S. Pauls. 2p. s8°. Wittemberg, *J. Klugen*. 1524-25
Contra novum errorem [*of Zwingli*] de sacramento corporis &c. D. N. Iesu Christi epistola. s8°. *n.p.* 1525
„ „ [*a. ed.*] s8°. *n.p.*, *n.d.* [c. 1525]
Epist. de peccato in spiritum sanctū. s4°. Wittembergæ. [1521]
In epist. Pauli ad Rom. interpret. &c. s8°. Haganoæ, *J. Secerus*. 1527
In librum Psalmorum interpret. Denuo recog. &c. s4°. Basileæ, [*Adam Petri*]. 1524
In Regum duos ult. libros annot. s8°. Argentorati, *J. Knoblochus*. 1525
Katechismuspredigten, 1525 u. 1532. Hrsg. G. Buchwald, mit Einl. v. O. Albrecht. 8°. L. 1909
Psalter d. Kon. Proph. Davids. Eertijts door J. B. in Lat. beschr. Daer na door M. Bucerum wt Hebr. Spraken verduytscht &c. la8°. " Ghedr. te Geneve door P. Stephanum v. Gendt." [*probably pr. in Holland*]. *n.d.* [c. 1530]
Ungedruckte Predigten, 1524–29. Veröffentl. v. G. Buchwald. [Quellen &c. aus d. Gesch. d. Reformationsjhdts., B13]. 8°. L. 1910
see DANIA. Ordinatio eccl. regnor. Daniæ &c. [Pia & vere catholica ordinatio (*by J. B.*)], 1537.
„ GEISENHOF (G.) Bibl. Bugenhagiana : Bibliog. d. Druckschr. d. B., 1908.
„ HERING (H.) Dr. Pomeranus, J. B. : e. Lebensbild, 1888.
„ KRAFT (F. C.) Disput. de I. B. in res scholast. emendatas meritis, 1829.
„ LUTHER (M.) Confessiones duæ altera M. L., altera I. B., 1539.
„ ZWINGLI (U.) Antwurt uff d. Epistel J. Pugenhag, 1526.

Bugge (Elseus Sophus).
Bidrag til den aeldste Skaldedigtnings historie. 8°. 1894
Norges indskrifter med de ældre Runer. Udg. S. B. & M. Olsen. [Norske Hist. K.]
Indledning *&* 3B. [1 & 2 *pagin. cont.*] 4°. 1891–1924
B3 *contains* Arkeol. tidsbestemmelser av aeldre Norske Runeindskr. ved. H. Schetelig.
Norges indskrifter med de yngre Runer [2p *in* 1v.] [Norske. Hist. K.] 4°. 1902–6
[1] Hønen-Runerne fra Ringerike. Udg. af S. B.
[2] Runerne paa en Sølring fra Senjen. Udg. af S. B. & M. Olsen.

Bugiel (V.) La Pologne & les Polonais. s8°. 1921

Buglioni (Benedetto), *see* MARQUAND (A.) B. & Santi Buglioni, 1921.

Buglioni (Santi), *see* MARQUAND (A.) Benedetto & S. Buglioni, 1921.

Bugnion (Ed.) The origin of instinct: war betw. ants & termites. Tr. C. K. Ogden. 8°. 1927

Bûhâr Library.
Cat. raisonné of the B. L. [Imperial Library]. v1, 2. la8°. Calcutta. 1921–23
1, Persian MSS.; by Maulavî Qâsim Ḥasîr Raḍavî; rev. &c. by Maulavî Abd-ul-Muqtadir.
2, Arabic MSS.; by Shams-ul-'Ulamā' M. Hidāyat Ḥusain.

Buhle (Johann Gottlieb). De optima ratione: hist. populorum qui ante sæc. 9 terras nunc imp. Russ. subj. inhab. &c. Oratio. s4°. Mosquæ. [1806]

Bühler (Adolf).
Salzburg u. s. Fürsten. 4. A. s8°. Salzburg. 1923

Bühler (Christian). Der Altkatholismus, histor.-krit. dargestellt. 8°. Leiden. 1880

Bühler (Johann Georg). Ind. Paläographie, c. 350 A. Chr.—c. 1300 P. Chr.; m. Tafeln. [Grundr. d. indo-ar. Phil., B1, H11]. la8°. Str. 1896
Ind. paleography. Ed. as app. to Ind. Antiq., v33, by J. F. Fleet. 4°. Bombay. 1904
see GRUNDRISS. G. d. indo-ar. Philol. u. Altertumskunde; begr. v. G. B., 3B, 1896–1920.
„ JOLLY (J.) G. B., 1837–98, 1899.

Bühler (Johannes). Das deut. Geistesleben im M.-a. Nach zeitgenöss. Quellen v. J. B. 8°. L. 1927
Die Germanen in d. Völkerwanderung. 8°. L. 1922
Ordensritter u. Kirchenfürsten. 8°. L. 1927

Builder (The). v118–133 (Jan. 1920–Dec. 1927). fol. 1920–27

Builders of Our Nation, *see* MEN OF 1914, 1915.

Buininck (Goswin Joseph de). Cœlibatus clericorum firmatus. [P2637]. s4°. Dusseldorpii. 1786

Buist (George), *D.D.* The Book of Psalms in metre. s8°. 1784

Buist (George), *LL.D.* Mem. of Sir Alex. Burnes, *see* BURNES (J.) Notes on h. name &c., 1851.

Buitenrust Hettema (Foeke). Friese plaatsnamen, *see* KONINKL. NEDERL. AARDRIJKSKUND. GENOOTSCHAP. Nomina geogr. Neerlandica, d4, 1896–99.

Bujac (*lt.-col.* E.) La Grèce aux côtés des Alliés (1916–18). Préf. du Gén. P. E. Bordeaux. 8°. 1926
Namur: la bataille-la retraite, août 1914. 8°. 1924
La Roumanie. s8°. 1916

Bukharin (Nikolai I.)
Где настоящая свобода? [P2722]. s8°. Москва. 1919
Классовая борьба и революція въ Россіи. [P2397]. 8°. [Москва]. 1917
Программа коммунистовъ (большевиковъ). [P2397]. 8°. Москва. 1918
Работница, к тебе наше слово! [P2722]. s8°. Москва. 1919
Церковь и школа въ Совѣтской Республикѣ. [P2381]. s8°. Москва. 1918
Экономика переходного периода. ч1. 8°. Москва. 1920
TRANSLATIONS.
Anarchismus u. wissensch. Kommunismus. Aus dem Russ. übers. v. W. R. [*Ed.* F. Sturm]. [P2410]. 8°. Hamburg. [1920]
TRANSLATIONS [*continued*].
De la dictature de l'impérialisme à la dictature du prolétariat. [P2396]. 8°. Genève. 1918
Econ. theory of the leisure class. [Tr.] 8°. 1927
Hist. materialism: system of sociology. Auth. tr. f. 3rd Russ. ed. 8°. [1926]
Karl Kautsky u. Sowjetrussland: e. Antwort. s8°. [Wien. 1925]
Das Programm d. Kommunisten. Mit e. Vorworte v. K. Radek. Übers. [P2410]. 8°. Zürich. 1918
Le programme des Communistes [Mai 1918] [P2396]. 8°. *n.p.* [1919 ?]
Soviets or parliament. [P2381]. s8°. [1919]

—— **& E. Preobrajensky.** Das ABC d. Kommunismus. Pop. Erläuterung d. Programms d. Kommun. Partei Russ. (Bolschewik). [2B in 1v]. 8°. Wien. 1920

Bukhsh (S. Khuda). Studies: Indian & Islamic. 8°. 1927
see KREMER (A. *Frhr.* v.) The Orient under the Caliphs; tr. by S. K. B., 1920.

Bukovetsky (Ant. Ios.), *see* BLINOV (I. A.) & A. I. B. Финансовая энциклопедия, 1924.

Bukvar. Букварь славенскій писмены преподобнаго Кирілля &c. напечатанъ. s8°. въ Римѣ. 1783

Bulaeus (Christophorus).
Charitilla, sive phaleucorum promulsis. s8°. Lipsiæ. 1635

Bulard (Marcel). Descr. des revêtements peints à sujets relig., *see* ECOLE FRANÇ. D'ATHÈNES. Explor. archéol. de Délos &c., fasc. 9, 1926.

Bulcock (H). The passing & the permanent in St. Paul. 8°. 1926

Buletinul cărţii. Revistă bilunară de bibliografie scoasă de " Centrala cărţii." Anul 1, 2, 1923–24. [*No more publ.*] la8°. [1923–24]

Bulferetti (Domenico). Giuseppe C. Abba (1838–1910), versi e prose. s8°. Torino. [1924]
Ippolito Nievo (1831–61), versi e prose. s8°. Torino. [1925 ?]

Bulgakov (P.) Жадность (Власть лукавого). 8°. Берлин. 1923

Bulgakov (Sergei Nikolaevich). На пиру Боговъ. Современные діалоги. s8°. Софія. [1921]
Чеховъ какъ мыслитель. 8°. Кіевъ. [1905]
see VEKHI. Вѣхи: сборникъ, 1909.

Bulgakov (Valentin Fedorovich) [BOULGAKOV]. Tolstoï, la tragédie de ses dern. jours, *see* ŒUVRES libres, 35, 1924.
see GUSEV (N. N.) Замолчанное о Толстом, ответ на стат. Б., 1926.

Bulgaria. A hdbk. of B., 1920, *see* ADMIRALTY: NAVAL INTELL. DIV.
Сборникъ за народни умотворения &c.; изд. Българск. Акад. на Наукитѣ, кн. 25–30, 1909–14, *see* SBORNIK.

Bulgarian [BULGARIANS]. *A gramm. of the B. lang. &c., 1859–60, *see* MORSE (C. F.)

Rep. of the Inter-Allied Comm. on the violation of the Hague Convention &c. by the B. in occupied Serbia, 1919, *see* INTER-ALLIED COMMISSION.

*Rep. of the Univ. Committee on B. atrocities &c. in E. Macedonia. [P2484]. 8°. 1919

Bulić (Frano). *Works in* BULLETTINO DI ARCH. &C. DALM.

Melita del naufragio di S. Paolo: notizie bibliog., 1913. [36, Suppl.]

Mučenici Solinski, 1919. [38, Suppl.]

Orgulje, 1919. [38, Suppl.]

Stridone luogo natale di S. Girolamo [*Ital. & Croatian. Extr. f.* Misc. Geronim.], 1919–22. [40–43.]

see BULLETTINO DI ARCH. E STORIA DALMATA; pubbl. F. B. &c., 1911–22.

—— **& J. Bervaldi.** Kron. solinskih biskupa—Kron. spljetskih nadbiskupa, *see* BULLETTINO DI ARCH. &C. DALM., 35, Suppl., 1912.

—— **& P. Skok.** Natpis Petra Crnoga, *see* BULLETTINO DI ARCH. &C. DALM., 38, Suppl., 1919.

Bulichev (N. I.) [BOULITCHOV (N. DE)]. Kourgans & gorodietz. Rech. archéol. sur la ligne de partage des eaux de la Volga & du Dniéper. [*Coloured plates*]. fol. Москва. 1900

Les rives de l'Oka. [*b. w. h.* Kourgans &c., 1900]. fol. Москва. 1900

Bulkeley (John Pearson). Adult educ., Eng. & Wales. [India, Bur. of Ed. Occas. rep. 10]. 8°. Calcutta. 1922

Bulkley (Mildred Emily). Bibliogr. survey of contemp. sources for the econ. & soc. hist. of the War. [C. E. f. Internat. Peace.] la8°. O. 1922

The establ. of legal min. rates in boxmaking indust., *see* TAWNEY (R. H.) St. in min. wages &c., No. 3, by M. E. B., 1915.

Bull, *The family of, see* BULL (J. C.) Misc. notes, pedigrees &c. rel. to surname of B., p1–6, 1911–12 *& n.d.*

Bull (Bertie Paul). God & our soldiers. Foreword by Gen. Sir C. Douglas. n. ed. s8°. [1914]

Bull (E. Bagnall-), *see* BAGNALL-BULL (E.)

Bull (Edv.) Folk og kirke i Middelalderen: st. til norges hist. 8°. 1912

see NORSK. BIOGRAFISK LEKSIKON: redaktion: E. B. &c., B1–3, 1923–26.

Bull (Francis).

Ludvig Holberg som historiker. 8°. 1913

Bull (George), *bp. of St. David's.* Opinion of Catholic Ch. for first 3. cent. on Christ is truly God. Tr. Prefixed, memoir by T. Rankin. 8°. 1825

see NELSON (R.) The life of G. B. &c., 1714.

Bull (John), *ps.* Half-a-crown lost! Exam. extraord. of the Vice R—y of B—d—y Boro! [*A satire on the King*]. [P425]. 8°. 1820

Bull (Joseph Cecil). Misc. notes, pedigrees &c. rel. to persons of the surname of Bull. p1–6 [*forming* v1, *&* p1 *of* v2, *pagin. cont.*] *&* Add. &c. to v1. [*No more publ.*] la8°. *p.f.p.c.* 1911–13 & *n.d.*

Bull (Percival George). Chemistry of to-day. 8°. 1923

Marvels of sound, light & electricity. s8°. [1926]

Bull (Tage), *see* CASANOVA (J.) Corresp. inéd. *&* Le vrai texte des Mém[s]., par T. B., 2t, 1925.

Bullard (Arthur). The A.B.C.'s of disarmament & the Pacific problems. s8°. N.Y. 1921

Bullard (John Vincent). Flamstead: its church & hist. Chap. by Sir E. R. S. Sebright, w. notes by E. F. Cobb. 4°. *p.p.* Flamstead. 1902

Bullarium. Bullarium Romanum novissimum. Tertio nunc ed. a A. M. Cherubino. 4t. fol. Romæ. 1638

„ „ App. *&* App. noviss. (-1659). [*b. w.* Bull., t4, 1638]. fol. Romæ *&* Viterbii. 1638–59

Bullarium Trajectense. Roman. pontif. diplomata, usque ad an. 1378 in vct. episc. Traj. destinata. Coll. & ausp. Soc. Hist. Rheno-Traj. ed. G. Brom. 2v. 4°. Haga-Com. 1891–96

Bulle (Heinrich). Archaisierende griech. Rundplastik, 1918, *see* KÖNIGL. AKAD. D. W. ZU MÜNCHEN, Abhdlgn., B30, 1920.

Bullen (Arthur Henry). Elizabethans. 8°. 1924

Lyrics f. song-books of the Elizabethan age. Ed. B. n. & rev. ed. s8°. 1889

Musa proterva: love-poems of the Restoration. *p.p.* s8°. 1902

Speculum amantis: love-poems of the 17 cent. 8°. *p.p.* 1902

Weeping-Cross & o. rimes. s8°. 1921

Bullen (George), *see* BRITISH & FOREIGN BIBLE SOCIETY. Cat. of lib., by G. B., 1857.

Buller (Charles), *see* WRONG (E. M.) C. B. & responsible govt., *w. repr. of h.* Respons. govt., 1926.

Buller (*Sir* John Yarde). *Sir J. Y. B.'s motion: Letter to John Temple Leader, M.P. By a Whig county member. [P2556]. 8°. 1840

Buller (*Sir* Redvers Henry), *see* MELVILLE (*Col.* C. M.) Life of Sir R. B., 2v, 1923.

Bullet (Pierre). Plan de Paris [1676], rev. & augm. par Jaillot le fils, 1710, *see* PARIS. Reprod. d'anc. plans, 1908.

Bulletin (Le) monténégrin. Publ. par le Com. montén. pour l'Union nat. No. 1 [*no more publ.* P2753]. 8°. Genève. 1917

„ *see* MONTENEGRIN BULLETIN, 1917–18, *for Eng. issue & contin.*

Bulletins of State intelligence. [*Comp. f.* "The London Gazette," *Cont. f.* B. of the Campaign]. 1817. s8°. [1818]

Bulletins of the Campaign. [*Comp. f.* "The London Gazette," *Cont. as* B. of State intelligence]. 1793–1815. [1802 *not issued.* 1814 *wanting*]. s8°. 1794–1816

Bullett (Gerald). Mice & o. p. s8°. C. [1921]

Mr. Godley beside himself. Comedy. s8°. 1926

The panther. s8°. 1926

Bullettino di archeologia e storia dalmata. Pubbl. p. c. di Fr. Bulić &c. Anno 34–45. la8°. Spalato &c. 1911–22

Each vol. has suppl. w. sep. pagin., some w. sep. tp. Années 43–45 *have title* Vjesnik za arheol. i hist. dalm.—Bulletin d'archéol. &c.

Bulley (Margaret H.) Anc. & med. art: short hist. re-issue w. new intr. 8°. [1919]

Art & counterfeit. 4°. [1925]

Büllheim (Stephan von) [BÜLLHEYM]. Ein brůderl. warnung an Mathis Pharherren zů sant Lorentzen im Münster zů Strassburg, sich vor seinen widersächeren zu verhüten &c. [*Verse.* P2539]. s4°. [Lanstal]. *n.d.* [c. 1522]

Bulliat (*Dom* Ambroise Marie). Chartreuse & seigneurie du Val-St-Martin de Sélignac, près de Bourg-en-Bresse. 8°. 1884

Bullingbrooke (Edward). Eccl. law of the Ch. of Ireland, w. a comm. 2v. [*pagin. cont.*] 4°. D. 1770

Bullinger (Heinrich).

Absoluta de Christi & eccl. sacramentis tract. Adj. epistola per J. a Lasco. s8°. Londini. 1551

Antithesis & comp. evangel. & papistic. doct. &c. s8°. *n.p., C. Froschouer.* 1551

Catechesis pro adultioribus scr. &c. s8°. Tiguri, *Frosch.* 1563

Comp. Christianæ relig. 10 libris comprehensum, e German. lingua in Lat. conv. s8°. Tiguri. 1569

De conciliis. s8°. Tiguri. 1561

De orig. erroris libri 2. s4°. Tiguri. 1539

De prophetæ officio &c. oratio. s8°. [Tyguri, *C. Froschouer.* 1532]

De Scripturæ authoritate &c. déq. episc. institutione &c., ad Angliæ regem Heinrychum viii &c. 8°. Tiguri. 1538

De testamento &c. Dei unico &c. brevis expos. s8°. Tiguri, *C. Frosch.* 1534

In Acta Apostol. comm libri 6. s8°. Tiguri, *C. Froschover.* 1533

„ „ [*b. w. h.* In omnes Apostol. Epist. Pauli 14 &c., 1537]. fol. Tiguri. 1535

In Apocalypsim Iesu Christi conciones centum. fol. Basileæ. 1557

In epistolam Ioannis Apostoli &c. canonicam brevis &c. expos. s8°. Tiguri, *C. Froschover.* 1532

In Evang. sec. Joannem comm. libri 10. [*b. w. h.* In Ev. sec. Matth., 1544]. fol. Tiguri. 1548.

For a. ed. see Novi Test. hist. evang. *below.*

In Evang. sec. Lucam comm. libri 9. [*b. w. h.* In Ev. sec. Matth., 1544]. fol. Tiguri. 1548

For a. ed. see Novi Test. hist. evang. *below.*

In Evang. sec. Marcum comm. libri 6. [*b. w. h.* In Ev. sec. Matth. 1544]. fol. Tiguri. 1545

For a. ed. see Novi Test. evang., 1554 *below.*

In Evang. sec. Matthæum comm. libri 12. fol. Tiguri. 1544

For a. ed. see Novi Test. hist. evang., 1554 *above.*

In omnes Apostol. Epist. Pauli 14 & 7 Canonicas comm. Acc. Index; 2 libelli, de Testamento Dei unico &c., de utraq. in Christo natura. 2p *in* 1v [*sep. tp*[s]. *& pagin.*] fol. Tiguri. 1537

In Petri epist. utranque comm. [*b. w. h.* In poster. Pauli ad Corinthios epist. comm., 1535]. s8°. Tiguri. 1533

In poster. Pauli ad Corinthios epist. comm. s8°. Tiguri. 1535

Novi Test. hist. Evangelica [*The comm. on Mark, Luke & John have sep. tps. w. dates* 1554, 1558, 1556 *& sep. pagins. The comm. on the Acts, Epistles &c. are catalogued separately*]. fol. Tiguri. 1554

see BRENTZ (J.) De majestate Dom. nost. J. C. &c., resp. H. Bullingero, 1562.

„ COCHLÆUS (J.) De Sanctorum invocatione &c., adv. H. B., 1544.

„ —— In prim. Musculi Anticochlæum replica J. C.; adj., resp. in Antibolen B., 1545.

„ —— Replica adv. respons. H. B. &c., 1544.

Bullinger (Heinrich) [*continued*].
see SCHULTHESS-RECHBERG (G. v.) H. B., d. Nachfolger Zwinglis, 1904.
,, SIMLER (J.) De æterno Dei Filio Domino &c.; acc. H. B. Præfatio &c., 1582.
see ZÜRICH. Orthodoxa Tigurinæ Eccl. ministrorum Conf. una cum resp. ad M. Lutheri calumnias [*by H. B.*], 1545.

Bullivant (Cecil H.) The unbarred door. s8°. [1927]

Bullmann (Johann Carl). Denkwürdige Zeitperioden d. Univ. Halle &c. s8°. Halle. 1833

Bulloch (John Malcolm).
The ancestry of Sir J. Forbes-Robertson. [P2847]. 8°. Aberdeen. 1926
Bibliog. of the Gordons, *see* ABERDEEN. A. Univ. studies, No. 94, sect. 1, 1924.
For a. c. see Aberdeen Univ. Library. Bull., v4, 5, 1922–25.
Centenary of J. Morison. [P2786]. 8°. Aberdeen. 1925
Centennial bibliog. of George Macdonald. 8°. Aberdeen. 1925
The Earls of Aboyne. [P2844]. s8°. Huntly. 1908
Gay adv. of Sir A. Gordon, knight of Navidale. [P2770]. s8°. *p.p.* Dingwall. 1925
Gordon Highlanders muster roll [1815]. [P2876]. 4°. *p.p.* 1927

Bullock (Christopher). Woman is a riddle; a comedy. s4°. 1717

Bullock (S. S.), *see* LASCELLES (E. C. P.) & S. S. B. Dock labour & decasualisation, 1924.

Bullock-Webster (George Russell), *see* GROVES (J.) & G. R. B.-W. Brit. Charophyta, 2v, 1920–24.

Bullokar (John). *English expositor: teaching interpret. of the hardest words &c. By I. B. s8°. 1641

Bullokar (William), *see* ZACHRISSON (R. E.) Eng. pronunc., 1927.

Bulman (Harrison Francis).
Coal mining & the coal miner. 8°. [1920]

Bulmer (Agnes). Messiah's kingdom. Poem. s8°. 1833

Bulmerincq (Alexander von). Einl. in d. Buch d. Maleachi, *see* DORPAT UNIV. Acta &c., B, v7, 1926.

Bülow (Frieda *Freiin* v.) Im Lande d. Verheissung. Roman. 3. Aufl. 8°. Dresden. 1907

Bülow (Gabriele v.), *wife of H. v. Bülow.* G. v. B. Ein Lebensbild aus d. Familienpapieren W. v. Humboldts u. s. Kinder, 1791–1887. 7e A. 8°. 1896

Bülow (Heinrich Wilhelm). Über Gesch. u. Verfassung d. Corporis Evangelic. 8°. [Regensburg]. 1795

Buloz (François), *1803–77, see* PAILLERON (M. L.) F. B. & s. amis: ecrivains du 2nd Emp., 1924.

Buls (Charles). Croquis congolais. 8°. Brux. 1899

Bulstrode (*Mrs.* Beatrix), *aft. Gull.*
A tour in Mongolia. Intr. by D. Fraser. 8°. [1920]

Bulstrode (Whitelock). Essays &c. s8°. 1724

Bultmann (Rudolf).
Die Gesch. d. synopt. Tradition. 8°. Göttingen. 1921

Bum (Lili Fröhlich-), *see* FRÖHLICH-BUM (L.)

Bumpus (Thomas Francis).
The cathedrals & churches of Italy. la8°. 1926

Bunbury (*Sir* Henry Edward), *7th bart.* Narr. of milit. trans. in the Mediterranean, 1805–10. 8°. *p.p.* 1851
Narr. of passages in the great war. w. France, 1799–1810. Intr. by Hon. Sir J. Fortescue. 8°. 1927

Bunbury (William St. Pierre). Notes on armour & the artillery defence of a coast fortress. 8°. Sydney. 1888
Notes on elementary gunnery. s8°. Sydney. 1888

Bunderius (Joannes). Comp. concertationū in quo hæreses confunduntur &c. s8°. Antverpiæ. 1555

Bundle (A) of ballads, 1891, *see* MORLEY (H.)

Bünemann (Aug. Rudolf Iesaias). De studiosis bacchantibus &c., *see* TREIBER (J. P.) Comm. de excuss. fenest., 1736.

Bungener (L. Louis Félix). Hist. du Concile de Trente. 2e éd. revue. 2t. s8°. 1854
Hist. of the Co. of Trent. Tr. 2nd ed., w. index. s8°. E. 1853

Bunhill Fields. Bunhill mem.: sacred reminˢ. of ministers &c. buried in B. F., 1849, *see* JONES (J. A.) *ed.*

Bunin (Ivan Alekseevich).
Господинъ изъ Санъ-Франциско. s8°. Paris. 1920
Русскіе писатели подъ ред. Н. А. Б. Фонвизинъ, Бригадиръ—Недоросль—Капнистъ, Ябеда—Грибоѣдовъ, Горе отъ ума. s8°. Парижъ. 1921
Сны Чанга, *see* RUSSKII. P. сборникъ, 1920.
Стихотворенія — Черноземъ — Памяти Чехова, *see* SBORNIK, Сб. товар. "знаніе" 1, 3, 1904–5.
Черноземъ. [P2499]. s8°. Москва. 1915
TRANSLATIONS.
Le calice de la vie Tr. par Maurice. s8°. 1923
Fifteen tales. [Auth. tr. by I. F. Hapgood]. 8°. [1924]
The gentleman from San Francisco & o. stories. Tr. by S. S. Koteliansky, [D. H. Lawrence] & L. Woolf. s8°. Richmond. 1922
Le monsieur de San-Francisco [*& o. tales*]. Tr. du russe par Maurice. [2e éd.] s8°. 1922
The village. [Tr. I. Hapgood]. 8°. [1923]
Le village. Roman. Tr. Maurice. s8°. 1922

Bunkim Chandra Chatterjee. The abbey of bliss. Tr. of B. C. C.'s Anandamath by Nares Chandra Sen-Gupta. s8°. Calcutta. *n.d.*

Bunner (Henry Cuyler), E. A. Dithmar, L. Hutton *& others.* A portfolio of players w. a packet of notes thereon. 4°. N.Y. 1888

Bunsen (Hilda Elizabeth de), *aft. wife of Baron A. D. Deichmann, see* DEICHMANN (*Baroness* H. E.)

Bunsen (Victoria de). Old & new in the countryside. 8°. 1920

Bunt (Cyril G. E.), *see* CHURCHILL (S. J. A.) Goldsmiths of Italy; f. papers &c. coll. by S. J. A. C., by C. G. E. B., 1926.

Bunten (Alice Chambers). Life of Alice Barnham (1592–1650), wife of Sir Francis Bacon. Fr. unpubl. docs. 8°. 1919
Sir Thomas Meautys, sec. to Lord Bacon, & h. friends. 8°. 1918

Bunting (Henry). Itin. totius sacræ Scripturæ, or the travels of the patriarchs, &c. Also treat. of the weights & monies &c. done into Eng. by R. B. s4°. 1623
The travels of the patriarchs, prophets, apostles &c. as rel. in the Old & New Test. &c. 4th ed. with add. 8°. 1705

Bunting (J. H.) Is trade unionism sound? [2nd ed.] 8°. 1922

Bunting (Jabez), *see* BUNTING (T. P.) Life of J. B., 2v, 1859–87.

Bunting (Thomas Percival). The life of Jabez Bunting. By h. son, T. P. B., v2 completed by G. S. Rowe. 2v. 8°. 1859–87

Bunting (William Maclardie). Memorials of B.: being sels. f. sermons, letters, &c. Ed. G. S. Rowe; w. biogr. intr. by T. P. Bunting. 8°. 1870

Bunyakovsky (Viktor Yak). Опытъ & Антропобіол. изслѣд [I. Akad. Nauk. Зап., т8, 23]. 8°. C.–П. 1865–73

Bunyan (John).
Holy war, *see* WESLEY (J.) Xtn. lib., v32, 1753.
The pilgrim's progress. 2p *in* 1v. 8°. 1728
,, ,, 26th ed. w. new cuts. s8°. 1743
,, ,, 2p, 31st ed. w. engr. by J. Sturt. 8°. 1766
,, ,, 2nd ed. [*sic*], pref. life of the a. 8°. 1776
,, ,, ...55th ed. s8°. 1776
,, ,, [*Engl. & Tamil*]. 4°. Vepery. 1793
,, ,, Notes by J. Newton, Dr. Hawker, &c. s8°. 1803
,, ,, ...n. ed. s8°. 1838
,, ,, Notes by W. Mason. Life by J Conder. 2nd ed. 8°. [1838]
,, ,, Ed. G. Godwin, w. mem. &c. Illust. &c. by H. C. Selous. obl. 4°. 1844
The pilgrim's progress. s8°. 1845
,, ,, ..8°. *Pickering.* 1849
,, ,, Illust. by C. Bennett. Pref. by C. Kingsley. 8°. *Longman.* 1860
,, ,, facs. reprod. of 1st ed. s8°. 1875
,, ,, Grace abounding & A rel. of h. imprisonment. Ed. w. biog. intr. &c. by E. Venables. 2nd ed., rev. by M. Peacock. [n. impr.] s8°. O. 1925
,, ,, Intr. by C. Whibley. 8°. 1926
TRANSLATIONS.
Il pellegrinaggio del Christiano. Tr. 2ª ed. s8°. Genova. 1855
Die Pilgerreise. [Tr.] 2T [*in* 1v]. s8°. Bremen. [1870]
see MACKAIL (J. W.) The pilgrim's progr.: lect., 1924.
,, SOUTHEY (R.) Sel. lives, 1849.

Bunyard (Edward A.) Handbook of hardy fruits grown in Gt. Brit.: stone & bush fruits, nuts &c. 8°. 1925

Bunzel (Julius). Geldentwertung u. Stabilisierung in ihr. Einfl. auf d. sozial. Entwickl. in Österreich. Hrsg. B. [V. f. Sozialpol., B169]. 8°. München. 1925

Buonaiuti (Ernesto). Gnostic fragments. Ed., w. intr. & notes by E. B. Eng. by E. Cowell. s8°. 1924
Le modernisme catholique. Tr. R. Monnot. s8°. 1927

Buonanni (Filippo) [BONANNI]. Numismata Pontif. Rom. quæ a temp. Martini V. ad 1699 prodiere. 2t. fol. Romæ. 1699
Numismata summ. Pontif. templi Vaticani fabricam indic. &c. Opus secundò impr. cum corr. &c. fol. Romæ. 1696

Buonarroti (Michel Agnolo), *the younger, 1568–1646.* La fiera, commedia e La tancia. Con annot. di P. Fanfani. 2p *in* 1v. [*pagin. cont.*] s8°. Firenze. 1860

Buondelmonti (Cristoforo de') [BONDELMONTIBUS; BONDELMONT]. C. B. librum insularum Archipelagi ed. &c. G. R. L. de Sinner. 8°. Lips. 1824

Buonfigli (*le père* Niccoló Aurifico). De dignitate, vita &c. clericorum &c., *see* WILD (J.) Examen ordinandorum, 1589.

Burachinsky (Joseph), *see* TEMNITSKY (V.) & J. B. Polish atrocities, 1919.

Burana, *see* FRAGMENTA BURANA ; hrsg. v. W. Meyer, 1901.
Burbach (O.), *see* LENZ (H. O.) Gemeinnütz. Naturgesch., 5. A., bearb. v. O. B., B1–3, 1875–84.
Burbery (John), *see* BURBURY (J.)
Burbidge (Frederick William).
Book of the scented garden. 8°. 1905
Burbury (John). *The hist. of Christina Alessandra, queen of Swedland. s8°. 1658
Burcardus (Johannes) *Argentinus, see* BURCHARD (JOHANN).
Burch (Vacher), *see* HARRIS (J. R.) Testimonies; by H. w. assist. of V. B., p2, 1920.
Burchard (Johann) *of Strassburg.* Ordo missæ pro inform. sacerdotum [*b. w.* Cochlæus (J.) Speculum missæ &c., 1572]. s8°. Venetiis. 1572
Burchard (Otto). Chines. Kleinplastik. [Orbis Pictus, 12.] la8°. [1922]
Burchardt (C. B.) Norwegian life & lit. Eng. acc. & views espec. in 19th c. 8°. 1920
Burchardt (Hermann). Aus d. Jemen: H. B.'s letzte Reise durch Südarabien. [*Wr. in Arabic by* Aḥmed b. Muḥammad el-Ǧarādī, 1910.] Bearb. [*w. Germ. tr.*] v. E. Mittwoch. la8°. L. [1926]
Burchardus, *Ursperg.* Chronicon. [Scriptores rer. Germ. in usum schol.] 2e A. hrsg. v. O. Holder-Egger u. B. v. Simson. 8°. Hannover. 1916
Burchardus (Peter Antonius). Schediasma de communione sub una, contra Bossuetum. [P2743]. s4°. Hafniæ. 1688
Burchiello, *ps.* [*i.e.* DOMENICO DI GIOVANNI], *1404–49.* I sonetti del B., et di A. Alamanni, alla Burchiellesca. nuov. ammend. e. corr. & ristamp. s8°. Firenze. 1552
Burci (Serlo de), *see* MAXWELL-LYTE (H. C.) B., &c., 1919.
Burckard (Georg), *Spalatinus, see* SPALATIN (G.)
Burckhardt (Jacob).
Erinnerungen aus Rubens. 3e A. s8°. Basel. 1918
Bürckstümmer (Christian). Gesch. d. Reformation u. Gegenref. in Dinkelsbühl (1524–1648). [Verein f. Ref.-Gesch. Schr., Jhrg. 31, 32 (Nr. 115/16, 119/20)]. 2T. 8°. L. 1914–15
Burdach (Konrad). Reformation, Renaissance, Humanismus, 2 Abhdlgn. 2 A. s8°. 1926
Burdekin (Richard). Mem. of the life of Robert Spence, bookseller: w. notices of h. early introd. of Methodism into York. 2nd ed. enl.8°. York. 1840
Burdett (*Sir* Henry C.), *K.C.B., see* BURDETT's Hospitals & charities, 1920, 1924.
Burdett (Osbert). The Beardsley period. [repr.] 8°. 1925
The idea of Coventry Patmore. s8°. 1921
W. E. Gladstone. 8°. 1927
William Blake. [Eng. men of letters]. 8°. 1926
Burdett-Coutts (*Baroness* Angela Georgina). Cat. of coll. of pictures & drawings, of the late Bar. B.-C. Sold by Christie, May 1922. [*Illust.*] 8°. 1922
Cat. of coll. of porcelain, objects of art & decorative furniture of the late Bar. B.-C.; sold by Christie, May 1922. 8°. 1922
Burdett's Hospitals & charities, 1920, 1924. Year book of philanthropy & the hospital annual. Founded by Sir H. Burdett. 31st, 34th year. s8°. [1920–24]
Burdick (Charles Kellogg). Law of the Amer. constit.: origin & development. With 2 intr. chapters by F. M. Burdick. 8°. N.Y. 1922
Burdick (Francis Marion), *see* BURDICK (C. K.) Law of the Amer. constit., w. 2 intr. chapters by F. M. B., 1922.
Burdinus (Mauritius), *abp. of Braga.* [GREGORY VIII, *antipope*], *see* ERDMANN (C.) M. B., 1927.
Burdon (Katharine Janet). A handbook of St. Kitts-Nevis: Leeward Islands colony. s8°. 1920
Burdon Sanderson (*Sir* John Scott), *see* SANDERSON (*Sir* J. S. B.)
Burdsall (Richard).
Memoirs. 2nd ed., corr. s8°. York. 1811
Bure (Jean Jacques de). Cat. des livres, mss. & impr. de la bibl. de J. J. de B. Vente, déc. 1853. 8°. 1853
Bureau (Paul). L'indiscipline des mœurs. 8°. 1924
Tow. moral bankruptcy. [Tr.] Intr. by M. Scharlieb. 8°. 1925
Bureau Central Statistique de l'Esthonie, *see* EESTI STATISTIKA: recueil mensuel, Nr. 1–13, 1922–23.
Bureau International du Travail, *see* INTERNAT. LABOUR OFFICE.
Buren (E. Douglas van), *see* VAN BUREN (E. D.)
Büren (Ernst Johann), *duke of Courland, see* BIRON (E. J.)
Burevoi (K.) Колчаковщина [P2722]. s8°. Москва. 1919
Burford (James) & J. D. M. Harvey. Some lesser known archit. of London. la8°. 1925
Burg (Johann Friedrich). Chrestomathia patristica Græca, versione Lat. scholiisque adorn. [*b. w. h.* Instit. theol., 1738]. s8°. Vratislaviæ. 1739
Instit. theologicæ theticæ. s8°. Vratislaviæ. 1738
„ „ Ed. altera emend. s8°. Vratislaviæ. 1746
Burg (Margret). Ottonische Plastik. 8°. Bonn. 1922
Burg (Paul), *ps* [*i.e.* P. SCHAUMBURG].
Die schöne Gräfin Königsmarck. s8°. Braunschweig. [1919]
Burge (*Rt. Rev.* Hubert Murray), *bp. of Oxford.* The doctrine of the resurrection of the body: rel. to quest. of heresy agst. Rev. H. D. A. Major. 8°. [1922]
Burge (William). Commentaries on colonial & foreign laws generally. n. ed. under gen. ed. of A. W. Renton & W. A. Bewes. v4, p2. 8°. 1928
Burger (A.) Les mots de la famille de φύω en grec anc. [H. E., 246]. 8°. 1925
Burger (C. P.), *Jr.*
De Poolzee-reizen van 1595–96. 8°. 's-Gravenhage. 1921
see AMSTERDAM. De incunabelen en de Nederland. uitg. tot 1540 in de Bibl. d. Univ. van A., beschr. door C. P. B., 2d, 1919–23.
Burger (Christian Gottlob). Antiquitas liturgiæ Evangelico-Lutheranæ ex Justino M. demonstrata. Præs. C. G. Hofmanno. [P442]. s4°. Vitembergæ. [1755]
„ „ [*a. ed. w. t. beg.* Liturgiam &c. P2637]. s4°. Vitembergæ. 1755
Burger (Fritz). Francesco Laurana: Studie z. ital. quattrocentoskulptur. [Zur Kunstgesch. d. Auslandes, H50]. la8°. Str. 1907
Burger (Konrad). The printers & publishers of the 15. cent., w. lists of their works: index to Suppl. to Hain's Repert., *see* COPINGER (W. A.) Suppl., v2ii, 1902.
Burger (Willy).
Die Malerei in. d. Niederlanden, 1400–1550. 4°. München. 1925
Roger van der Weyden. la8°. L. 1923
Burgerstein (Leo) & A. Netolitzky.
Hdbh. d. Schulhygiene. 8°. L. 1912
Burges (*Sir* James Bland), *aft. Sir J. Bland Lamb, 1st bart.*
Reasons in favour of a new tr. of the Holy Scr. 8°. 1819
see TODD (H. J.) Vindic. of our auth. tr. of the Bible: occ. by objects. by Bellamy & B., 1819.
Burgess (Ernest Watson), *see* PARK (R. E.), E. W. B. &c. The city, 1925.
Burgess (Fred. William).
Chats on old copper & brass. 8°. [1914]
Old pottery & porcelain. 2nd impr. 8°. [1924]
Silver: pewter: Sheffield plate. 8°. 1921
Burgess (James). *The lives of the most emin. mod. painters omitted by M. de Piles. By J. B. [*o. c. in* P554; *& b. w.* Evelyn (J.) Sculptura, 1755.] 8°. 1754
Burgess (John Stewart), *see* GAMBLE (S. D.) Peking: social survey; by G., assisted by J. S. B., 1921.
Burgess (John William).
Recent changes in Amer. constit. theory. s8°. N.Y. 1923
Burgess (Thomas), *bp. of (1) St. David's, (2) Salisbury.* Remarks on gen. tenour of the N. Test., reg. nature &c. of Jesus Christ. 8°. Salisbury. 1831
Burgess (William Penington), *Wesleyan Minister.* Wesleyan hymnology. s8°. 1846
Burgh (Alexander Henry Leith, *7th baron*). Cat. of old pictures &c., prop. of B. &c. Sold by Sotheby, July 1926. [Illustr.] 8°. 1926
Burghausen (Lovisa v.), *1697–1733, see* LEIJONHUFVUD (S.) Två Kvinnoöden, 1907.
Burghclere (Winifred H. C. Gardner, *baroness*), *wife of 1st baron, see* WELLINGTON (A. W., *1st baron*). A gt. man's friendship: letters of W. to Mary, Marchioness of Salisbury, 1850–52; ed. Lady B. &c., 1927.
Burghley (William Cecil, *baron*). *Justitia Brit. &c. sum in Lat. [*Foll. by h.* De summa eorum clementia &c., contra proditores &c. *w. sep. tp. & pagin.*] s8°. Londini. 1584
see ALLEN (W.) *card.* Ad persecutores Anglos pro catholicis contra libellum: Justitia Brit. [by W. C. lord B.], 1589.
„ CAVENDISH (G.) Mem. of Card. Woolsey &c., w. a mem. pres. to Q. Elizabeth by W. C., Ld. B., 1706.
Burgin (George Brown). A gentle despot. s8°. [1919]
Love & the locusts. s8°. [1922]
Memoirs of a clubman. 8°. [1921]
Pilgrims of circumstance. s8°. 1920

Burgmann (Joachim Heinrich). Diss. de hist. Mennoniticæ fontibus & subsidiis quam præs. J. C. Burgmann publ. discut. prop. J. H. B. [P434]. s4°. Rostochii. [1732]

Burgon (John William), *dean of Chichester.*
Lives of 12 good men. n. ed., w. portraits. 8°. 1891

Burgoyne (*Gen. the Rt. Hon.* **John).** The heiress, *see* INCHBALD (*Mrs.* E.) Brit. theatre, v22, 1808.
see STONE (W. L.) Mem. of the centen. celebr. of B.'s surrender, 1877, 1878.

Burgoyne (*Sir* **John Fox),** *bart.* Remarks on maintenance of macadamised roads, *see* LAW (H.) Rudiments, 1861–62.

Burgundesch. *Burgundesch legende, Strasb. 1477 *&* 2e éd. Augsb. 1477, facs. & tr., *see* PICOT (E.) & H. STEIN. Recueil, 1923.

Burgundofara, *Saint, see* FARA, *St.*

Burgundy [BURGUND]. Der dreyen Ständ des Hertzogthumbs Burgund verordneten von der Landschafft, erinnerung &c. an den Künig zu Franckreich das Edictum Pacificationis belangend. [P2436]. s4°. *n.p.* 1563

Burgundy, *The dukes of, see* CARTELLIERI (O.) Am Hofe d. Herzöge v. Burgund, 1926.

Burguy (Georges Frédéric). Gramm. de la langue d'oïl ou gramm. des dialectes français aux 12 & 13 s. suivie d'un glossaire. 3t [t1, 2 2ème éd.] 8°. Berlin. 1856–69

Burgwart (Der). Zeitschr. f. Burgenkunde u. Baukunst. Organ d. Vereinig. z. Erhalt. deut. Burgen. Jhrg. 10–13. 4°. 1909–12

Burian von Rajecz (Stefan, *Graf* **v.)** Austria in dissolution: personal recoll., 1915–18. Tr. B. Lunn. 8°. 1925
Drei Jahre aus d. Zeit m. Amtsführung im Kriege. 8°. 1923

Burius (Guilielmus), *see* BURY (GUILLAUME DE).

Burk (Johann Christian Friedrich).
J. A. Bengel's Leben u. Wirken. 8°. St. 1831
Mem. of the life & writings of John Albert Bengel, prelate in Würtemberg. Tr. R. F. Walker. 8°. 1842

Burke (*Mrs.* **Anna Christian).**
The miniature language of flowers. s8°. *n.d.*

Burke (Ashworth Peter), *see* BURKE (*Sir* J. B.) Geneal. & heraldic hist. of peerage &c., 80th ed., 1921; 82nd ed., 1924.

Burke (*Rt. Hon.* **Edmund).**
Letter to a member of the Nat. Assembly, in ans. to obj. to h. bk. on French affairs. [P2552]. 8°. Paris. 1791
Letter to a noble lord on attacks made upon him & h. pension, in H. of L., by Bedford & Lauderdale. 8°. 1796
Reflect. on the Revol. in France, & on the proc. in certain societies in London &c. 8°. 1790
2 speeches on conciliation w. America & 2 letters on Irish questions. Intr. by H. Morley. 8°. 1886
see BURKE (P.) Public &c. life of Rt. Hon. E. B., 1853.
„ MACCUNN (J.) Polit. philos. of B., 1913.
„ O'BRIEN (W.) E. B. as an Irishman, 1924.
„ REID (W.) Our foremost friend in Gt. Brit.: addr., E. B., 1908.
„ SAMUELS (A. P. I.) Early life, corr. & wr. of B., 1923.

Burke (John), *genealogist.* Burke. [P2503]. s8°. [1921]

Burke (*Sir* **John Bernard).** Burke's hdbk. to the O.B.E., cont. biog. &c. Ed. A. W. Thorpe. la8°. 1921
Genealog. & heraldic hist. of the landed gentry of Gt. Brit. 13th ed. la8°. 1921
Genealog. & heraldic hist. of the peerage & baronetage &c. 80th ed. 8°. 1921
„ „ ....82nd ed. Ed. A. T. Butler. 8°. 1924
Genealog. hist. of the house of Gwysaney [Davies of G.] fol. *p.f.p.c.* 1847
„ „ ....*a. copy w. add. gen. table.* fol. *p.f.p.c.* 1847

Burke (*Mrs.* **L.),** *see* BURKE (*Mrs.* A. C.)

Burke (M.)
Obs. on Queens' Colleges, Ireland. [P2558]. 8°. D. 1849

Burke (Peter).
Public & domestic life of Rt. Hon. E. Burke. s8°. 1853

Burke (Philipp David) [BURKIUS]. Gnomon Psalmorum. 2t *in* 1v [*pagin. cont.*] s4°. Stutgardiæ 1760

Burke (Thomas).
Limehouse nights. Tales of Chinatown. [repr.] s8°. [1923]
The London spy: book of town travels. 8°. [1922]
The sun in splendour. s8°. [1927]
The wind & the rain. [2nd impr.] s8°. [1924]

Burke (William), *murderer.* Burke & Hare. Ed. W. Roughead. [Notable Brit. trials]. 8°. E. [1921]
see LEIGHTON (A.) The court of Cacus, or the story of B. & Hare, 1861.
„ MACGREGOR (G.) Hist. of B. &c., 1884.

Burkers. *The hist. of the London Burkers, 1832, *see* BISHOP (J.), *murderer.*

Burkhard (Johann Daniel). Diss. de 2 codd. MSS. Bibl. publ. Norimberg. [P430]. s4°. Altdorfii. [1769]

Burkhardt (Georg), *Spalatinus, see* SPALATIN (G.)

Burkhardt (Johann Gottlieb) [BURKHARD (J. G.)] Vollständige Gesch. d. Methodisten in Eng. nebst Lebensbeschr. J. Wesley & G. Whitefield. 2T. *in* 1v. s8°. Nürnberg. 1795

Burkhardt (Robert). Gesch. d. Hafens u. d. Stadt Swinemünde. T1, A. [*no more publ.*] 8°. Swinemünde. 1920

Burkitt (Francis Crawford).
Christian beginnings. 8°. 1924.
The earliest sources for the life of Jesus. n. & rev. ed. s8°. [1922]
The early Syriac lectionary system. [From Proc. of Brit. Acad., v11. P2717]. 8°. [1923]
The Gospel hist. & its transmission. 8°. E. [1920]
Relig. of the Manichees. Donnellan Lect., 1924. s8°. C. 1925

Burkitt (Miles Crawford). Our early ancestors. s8°. C. 1926
Prehistory: st. of early cultures in Europe &c. Pref. by l'Abbé H. Breuil. la8°. C. 1921
„ „ ....2nd ed. la8°. C. 1925

Burkitt (William).
Expository notes, &c. on the New Test. 4°. Liv'l. *n.d.*

Burland (E. G.) Trend of econ. restoration since the Dawes repar. settlement, *see* INTERNAT. CONCILIATION, N°. 215, 1925.

Burlington Fine Arts Club.
Anc. Egypt. art. [*Illust.*] la4°. *p.p.* 1922
Blake centenary exhib. [*Illust.*] 4°. *p.p.* 1927
Brit. heraldic art to end of Tudor period. [Intr. by O. Barron. *Illust.*] 4°. 1916
Chinese art. [*Illust.*] 4°. *p.p.* 1915
Early Chinese pottery & porcelain, 1910. [Intr. by R. L. Hobson. *Illust.*] fol. *p.p.* 1911
Early drawings & pictures of London w. some contemp. furniture. [Pref. by P. Norman. *Illust.*] 4°. *p.p.* 1920
Early Eng. earthenware. [*Illust.*] la4°. 1914
Etched work of Rembrandt, w. intr. remarks. 4°. *p.p.* 1877
European enamels to end of 17th c. [*Illust.*] fol. 1897
Faience of Persia & the Nearer East. [*Illust.*] fol. 1908
Florentine painting bef. 1500 [Intr. by R. Fry. *Illust.*] 4°. *p.p.* 1920
French art of the 18th c. [*Illust.*] 4°. *p.p.* 1914
Holford coll. Sel. f. illum. MSS. at Dorchester House & pictures at Westonbirt in Glos. [*Illust.*] 4°. *p.p.* 1924
Ital. art. of the 17th c. [Intr. by O. Sitwell. *Illust.*] 4°. *p.p.* 1925
Late Eliz. art in conjunc. w. tercent. of Bacon. 4°. 1926
„ „ [*Illust.*] 4°. 1926
Persian & Arab art. [*Illust.*] fol. 1885
Pictures by masters of the Netherlandish &c. schools of 15. & early 16. c. [*Illust.*] fol. 1892
Pictures by the brothers Le Nain. [Intr. by R. C. Witt. *Illust.*] 4°. 1910
Pictures of the school of Siena & examples of the minor arts. [*Illust.*] fol. 1904
Portrait min. [*Illust.*] fol. 1889
The Venetian school: pictures by Titian & h. contemp. [*Illust.*] 4°. *p.p.* 1915
see SCHUBRING (P.) Ital. Renaissanceplastik, 1912.

Burlington (The) magazine. v36–51. 4°. 1920–27
MONOGRAPHS. 1, 2. 4°. [1925]–27
see FRY (R. E.) &c. Chinese art, 1925. [1.]
„ TATLOCK (R. R.), R. TYLER, &c. Spanish art, 1927. [2.]

Burluguay (Jean). *Toilette de M. l'archevesque de Sens, ou réponse au Factum [*by A. Varet*] des Filles Ste-Cathérine lés Provins, contre Cordeliers. s8°. *n.p.* 1669

Burma [BURMAH].
*Beautiful B.: 34 views. obl. 8°. Rangoon. *n.d.*
Burma: the Cinderella of the Indian Empire. [P2404]. 8°. 1919
Gazetteer. vA. 8°. Rangoon. 1920
Tharrawaddy.
Hist. of services of gazetted & o. officers in Burma. Corr. up to 1st July 1920–27. 8°. Rangoon. 1920–27
Maps & plans to accomp. Report & Gazetteer of B. By Maj. D. MacNeill. 8°. Simla. 1883
Report on the admin. of B., 1918–19—1925–26. fol. & 8°. Rangoon. 1920–27
Typical photographs of B. obl. 4°. Rangoon. [1922]
ARCHÆOLOGICAL SURVEY.
List of inscr. found in Burma. p1, List of inscr. arr. in order of their dates. Comp. & ed. by Chas. Duroiselle. fol. Rangoon. 1921
Report, year ending March 1920–26. fol. *&* 8°. Rangoon. 1920–26
see EPIGRAPHIA BIRMANICA; ed. C. Duroiselle, v1, 2, 1919–24.

Burma Research Society.
Journal. v1–17 (1911–27). 8°. & la8°. Rangoon. 1911–27

Burman (Frans), *the elder.* Synopsis theologiæ & speciatim œconomiæ fœderum Dei. [Acc. Consilium de studio theol. &c.] 2a ed. emend. 2t *in* 1v. s4°. Genevæ. 1678

Burmania (Reynken van), *see* AARSSENS (F. v.) Verbaal van de ambassade van A., Joachimi & B. naar Engeland, 1625, 1867.

Burmannus (Franciscus), *see* BURMAN (FRANS).

Burmeister (Hermann). Reise durch die La Plata-Staaten, 1857–1860. 2B. 8°. Halle. 1861

Burmeister (Joh. Peter Theodor) [*ps.* J. P. T. LYSER]. Erklärg. d. hogarth. Kupferstiche, 13e. Lfg., 1833.
This forms part of LICHTENBERG (G. C.) Erklärg. d. Hogarth Kupferstiche, 1794–1835, *q.v.*

Burmese, *see also* BARMANI.

Burn (Andrew Ewbank), *dean of Salisbury.* Council of Nicæa. Mem. for 16th centenary. s8°. 1925
The hymn Te Deum & its a. [*i.e.* S. Niceta of Remesiana ?] s8°. 1926
S. Eustathius of Antioch. 8°. [1926]

Burn (Richard), *LL.D.* Justice of the Peace & Parish Officer. Ed., except the vol. " Poor " [*i.e.* 4], by J. B. Maule. 30th ed. 5v. 8°. 1869
1, By T. S. Pritchard. 2, By S. B. Bristowe. 3, By L. W. Cave. 4, By J. E. Davis. 5, By J. B. Maule.

Burn (*Col.* Robert), *R.A.* A naval & milit. technical dict. of the French lang. 2p [in 1v.] Fr.-Eng., & Eng.-Fr. 5th ed. s8°. 1870
Questions & answers on artillery. 2nd ed. rev. & enl. s8°. Woolwich. [1854]

Burnand (Eugène). *Quelques peintres suisses: Hodler, B. &c., 1921, *see* SUISSE.

Burnand (Robert) & F. Boucher, *edd.* L'hist. de Napoléon racontée par les gr. écrivains. Textes rec. par R. B. & F. B. s8°. [1922]

Burne (Richard Higgins), *see* BRIT. ANTARCTIC EXPED., 1910–13: Zoology, v2, Mollusca, p4; by B., 1914–20.

Burne-Jones (*Sir* Edward C.-B.), *see* BELL (M.) Sir E. B.-J., a rec. & review, 1892.

Burnes, *The family of.*
see BURNES (J.) Notes on h. name & fam., 1851.
,, ROGERS (C.) Genealog. mem. of fam. of R. Burns & Scot. house of B., 1877.

Burnes (*Sir* Alex.)
Travels into Bokhara &c. 3v. [*&* Map *b.* sep.] 8°. 1834
see BUIST (G.) Mem. of Sir A. B., 1851.

Burnes (James), *physician-gen. in India.* Notes on h. name & family. [*Foll. by* Mem. of Sir A. Burnes, by G. Buist, & Mem. of J. B., by W. A. Laurie; *each w. sep. pagin*]. 8°. *p.f.p.c.* E. 1851

Burnet (Etienne).
La Porte du Sauveur. s8°. 1926
,, ,, ...8e éd. s8°. 1926

Burnet (Gilbert), *bp. of Salisbury.*
Citation of G. B., for high treason, w. h. answer, & 3 letters to the Earl of Midletoune. 8°. 1687
*An enquiry into the present state of affairs &c. [P2572; 2653]. s4°. 1689
Expos. of the 39 Articles. fol. 1699
Hist. of the Reformation of Ch. of Engl. 2nd ed. corr. 2v. fol. 1681–83
,, ,, p3, a Suppl. fol. 1753
each p. has a Coll. *of records &c. w. sep. pagin.*
The hist. of the rights of princes in the disposing of eccl. benefices &c. Added, A coll. of letters &c. [1681, *w. sep. tp. & pagin.*] s8°. 1682
The letter writ by the last Assembly Gen. of the clergy of France to the Protestants &c. Tr & exam^d^. s8°. 1683
Life & death of Sir M. Hale. [*218 pages*]. s8°. 1682
,, ,, [*a. issue, 128 pages*]. s8°. 1682
Life of W. Bedell, bp. of Kilmore [&* Copies of cert. letters betw. J. Waddesworth & W. B.; *w. sep. tp.*] 8°. 1685
Lives, characters, & address to posterity. Ed., w. intr. &c. by J. Jebb. [*a. c. bound as* Jebb (J.) Works, v12]. 8°. 1833
*Reflect. on His Majesty's reasons f. withdrawing himself fr. Rochester. [P2572]. s4°. 1689
Reflect. on Varillas's Hist. of revolutions in matters of relig. s8°. Amsterdam. 1686
Some remarkable passages in the life & death of the Rt. Hon. John, earl of Rochester. 8°. Chedgrave. [1813]
*Three letters conc. the pres. state of Italy wr. in 1687, being a suppl. to B.'s Letters. [*b. w. h.* Life &c. of Sir M. Hale, 1682]. s8°. *n.d.* 1688
Travels or Letters cont. an acc. of what seemed remarkable in Switzerland, France, Germany & Italy. [3 *pagin^s^. b. w. h.* Life &c. of Sir M. Hale, 1682]. s8°. Amsterdam. 1687
A vindic of the authority, constit., & laws of the Church & State of Scotland. [*Foll^d^. by* Obs. on the 1st & 2nd of the Canons, ascr. to the Apostles

Burnet (Gilbert) [*continued*].
&c. [*w. separ. tp. & pagin. but register cont.*] s8°. Glasgow. 1673
see HICKES (G.) Some disc. upon Dr. B. & Dr. Tillotson, 1695.
see HILL (S.) A vindic. of the prim. Fathers agst. Gilbert, bp. &c., 1695.
,, SALMON (T.) An impartial exam. of B.'s Hist., 2v, 1724.

Burnet (John), *fellow of Merton Coll., Oxford.* Aristotle. Lect. [From Proc. of Brit. Acad., v11, P2769]. 8°. 1924
Early Greek philosophy. 3rd ed. 8°. 1920
Ignorance. [Romanes lect. 1923]. 8°. O. 1923
see LIVINGSTONE (R. W.), *ed.* Legacy of Greece, essays by B. &c., 1921.

Burnet (Thomas), *LL.D., Master of the Charterhouse.* De fide et officiis Christianorum. ed. nova. s8°. Londini. 1729
De statu mortuorum &c. Of the state of the dead &c. Tr. by M. Earbery. 2nd ed. 2v. *in* 1. [*Foll'd by* A re-survey of the Mosaic system of creation. Tr. by Mr. Foxton.] s8°. 1728
The faith & duties of Christians. Tr. Mr. Dennis. s8°. 1733
see MURATORI (L. A.) De Paradiso regnique cœlestis gloria, adv. T. B. librum, 1738.

Burnett (Edmund Cody), *ed.* Letters of members of the Continental Congress. [C. I. of Wash. Publ., 299]. v1–3 (1, Aug. 29, 1774–July 4, 1776; 2, July 5, 1776–Dec. 31, 1777; 3, Jan. 1–Dec. 31, 1778). la8°. Wash. 1921–26

Burnett (*Sir* Edward Napier). Voluntary hospitals in Gt. Brit. (exclud. London). 4th ann. rep., 1922. Intr. note by Sir A. Stanley. [P2750]. la8°. [1923]

Burnett (*Mrs.* Frances Hodgson).
The head of the House of Coombe. s8°. 1922
Robin. s8°. 1922
The secret garden. [n. impr.] 8°. [1925]

Burnett (Frank). Summer isles of Eden. 8°. 1923

Burnett (Gilbert T.) Outlines of botany. 2v. 8°. 1835

Burnett (Isabel). Exper. investig. into repetitive work, *see* INDUST. FATIGUE RES. BD. Rep. 30, 1925.

Burnett (*Sir* William), *K.C.B., see* ROLLESTON (*Sir* H.) Sir W. B., first medical director-gen. of the R. N., 1922.

Burney, *The family of, see* JOHNSON (R. B.), *ed.* Fanny Burney & the Burneys, 1926.

Burney (Charles), *Mus.D.* Dr. C. B.'s continental travels, 1770–72. Comp. f. h. journals &c. by C. H. Glover. 8°. 1927

Burney (Charles Fox).
The Aramaic origin of the 4th Gospel. 8°. O. 1922
The gospel in the Old Test. [Sermons]. 8°. E. 1921
The imprec. Psalms, *see* EMMET (C. W.), C. F. B. &c. Use of the Psalter, 1918.
Notes on the Hebrew text of the Book of Kings, w. intr. & app. by C. F. B. 8°. O. 1903
The poetry of our Lord. Formal elem. of Heb. poetry. 8°. O. 1925

Burney (*Capt.* H.) Burney papers [1822–49. Vajirañāṇa Nat. Lib.] v1–5i. [*in* 15.] la8°. *p.f.p.c.* Bangkok. 1910–14

Burnham (*Maj.* Frederick Russell). Scouting on two continents. Elicited & arr. by M. N. Everett. 8°. 1926

Burnham (Gordon W.) Proc. at the inaug. of the statue of Daniel Webster, erected, 1876, by G. W. B. 4°. N.Y. 1876

Burnham (William Henry).
The normal mind: intr. to mental hygiene &c. 8°. N.Y. 1925

Burning. *Burning of the Solemn League & Covenant, May 29, 1662, *see* MAIDMENT (J.), *ed.* Hist. fragm., p2, 1833.
*Burning spear (The): experiences of Mr. John Lavender in time of war. Recorded by A. R. P—M. s8°. 1919

Burnley (James). Two sides of the Atlantic. s8°. [1880]
Yorkshire stories re-told. s8°. Leeds. [1885]

Burnouf (Eugène). Obs. gramm. sur quelques passages de l'Essai s. le Pali de E. B. & Lassen. 8°. 1827
—— **& Chr. Lassen.** Essai sur le Pali. 8°. 1826

Burnov (A.) Die Hauptmomente in d. Entwickl. d. kommunist. Partei in Russland. s8°. L. 1921

Burns, *The family of, see* BURNES.

Burns (A. R.)
Money & monetary policy in early times. la8°. 1927

Burns (Cecil Delisle).
Contact betw. minds: a metaphys. hypothesis. 8°. 1923
Government & industry. 8°. [1921]
Industry & civilisation. 8°. [1925]
Internat. politics. s8°. [1920]
The philosophy of labour. s8°. [1925]
The principles of revolution. s8°. [1920]
Short hist. of Birkbeck College. Foreword by Visct. Haldane. 8°. 1924
Short hist. of internat. intercourse. s8°. [1924]
Whitehall. [The world of to-day]. s8°. 1921

Burns (E. M.), *B.Sc. (Econ.) Lond.*
Wages & the state. 8º. 1926

Burns (Elinor). Brit. imperialism in China. s8º. 1926

Burns (Emile). Modern finance. s8º. 1920

Burns (James), *bailie of the city of Glasgow.* Memoirs, 1644–61, 1832, *see* MAIDMENT (J.), *ed.* Hist. fragm., pl, 1833.

Burns (Robert), *the poet.*
Works; w. life & crit. Pref. Obs. on Scot. peasantry. [Ed. J. Currie]. 3rd ed. 4v. 8º. 1802
„ w. life & crit., pref. obs. on character &c. of Scot. peasantry. 8th ed., added Reliques of R. B. 5v [*v2 wanting*]. 8º. 1814
„ w. Currie's mem., & essay by Prof. Wilson &c. 2v. la8º. Glasgow. 1843–44
B. holograph MSS. in Kilmarnock Monument Museum. Ed. D. Sneddon. s8º. 1889
Poems, chiefly in the Scot. dialect. 8º. Kilmarnock. 1786 [facs. ed., 1927]
„ „ ....8º. E. 1787
Poet. works. Coll. by T. Park. 2v. s8º. 1807
„ „ [Mem. by Sir H. Nicolas. Aldine ed.] 3v. s8º. *n.d.* [*& 1875*]
see CORRODI (A.) R. B. u. P. Hebel, 1873.
„ DRINKWATER (J.) R. B.: address, 1924.
„ —— Robert Burns; play, 1925.
„ HECHT (H.) R. B., Leben u. Wirken, 1919.
„ MACNAUGHT (D.) Truth about B., 1921.
„ ROGERS (C.) Genealog. mem. of fam. of R. B., 1877.
„ ROSS (J. D.) Who's who in B., 1927.

Burns (Walter Noble).
The saga of Billy the Kid [*i.e.* W. H. Bonney]. 8º. N.Y. 1926

Burr (Jane). The passionate spectator. s8º. [1920]

Burrage (Henry Sweetser), *see* BROWN UNIVERSITY. Civil War record of B. Univ.; comp. by H. S. B., 1920.

Burrage (Walter Lincoln), *see* KELLY (H. A.) & W. L. B. Amer. medical biographies, 1920.

Burrard (W. Dutton).
Chronicles of an eminent fossil. s8º. 1896
A first bear-shoot in Kashmir. [P2602]. 8º. Allahabad. 1892
A great platonic friendship. 3v. s8º. 1887
Out of the depths. Poems. s8º. 1892
A weaver of runes. s8º. 1899

Burrell (Arthur). The piebald horse & o. s. s8º. 1896

Burroughs (Edgar Rice). The god of Mars. s8º. [1920]
Tarzan & the golden lion. s8º. [1924]
Thuvia maid of Mars. s8º. [1921]

Burroughs (Edward Arthur), *dean of Bristol.* Education & religion. Lect. [*by var. a.*] Foreword by Abp. of Canterbury. Ed., w. intr. chapter, by E. A. B. s8º. [1924]
The Latin culture. [P2500]. s8º. [1920]

Burroughs (Jeremiah), *Puritan Divine.*
An expos. of the 8th, 9th & 10th chap[s]. of Hosea. s4º. 1650
Gospel conversation. [Ed. T. Goodwyn &c. *b. w. h.* The rare jewel &c., 1649]. s4º. 1648
Gospel-worship. [Ed. T. Goodwyn &c. *b. w. h.* The rare jewel &c., 1649]. s4º. 1648
Jerusalem's glory breaking forth &c. [Sermons *ed. by* W. Adderley]. s8º. 1675
The rare jewel of Christian contentment [in 11 sermons on Phil. iv, 11. Ed. T. Goodwyn &c.] s4º. 1649

Burroughs (*Sir* John) [BOROUGH; J. BURRHUS].
The soveraignty of the Brit. seas &c. fol. 1686
„ „ ....Ed. w. introd. essay & notes by T. C. Wade. 8º. E. 1920

Burroughs (Stephen). Memoirs. Pref. by Robert Frost. 8º. [1924]

Burrow (Edward John), *F.R.G.S.*
Anc. earthworks & camps of Somerset. 4º. Cheltenham. 1924
Anc. entrenchments & camps of Gloucestershire. 4º. Cheltenham. [1919]
„ „ ......[n. & abr. ed.] obl. s8º. Cheltenham. [1924]
see MAJOR (A. F.) & E. J. B. Mystery of Wansdyke, 1926.

Burrow (Trigant).
The social basis of consciousness. 8º. 1927

Burrowes (Peter). Speeches on the trials of E. Sheridan & T. Kirwan, under the Convention Act &c. [P2557]. 8º. D. 1812

Burrows (Margaret F.)
Robert S. Hawker: h. thought & poetry. 8º. O. 1926

Burrows (Roland), *see* FRASER (*Hon. Sir* H.) Compend. of law of torts; 11th ed. by R. B., 1927.

Burrows (Ronald Montagu). The abdication of King Constantine: articles, *see* ANGLO-HELLENIC LEAGUE. Publ., No. 34, 1917.
see GLASGOW (G.) R. B., 1924.

Burschenschaftliche Historische Kommission, *see* HAUPT (H.) Quellen &c. z. Gesch. d. Burschenschaft u. d. deut. Einheitsbewegung; im Auftrage d. B. H. Komm.; hrsg. H. H., B4–10, 1913–27.

Bursfeld, *monastery of.* Ceremoniale Benedictinum, A PP. congregat. Bursfeld. comp. Prodit ex vet. MS. abbatiæ S. Germani. s8º. Parisiis. 1610

Burt (Cyril). Mental & scholastic tests. Pref. by Sir R. Blair. [L.C.C.] [2nd impr.] la8º. 1922
The young delinquent. 8º. [1925]

Burt (Edward). *Letters f. a gentleman in the N. of Scot. 5th ed. w. app., intr. &c. by R. Jamieson. 2v. 8º. 1822

Burt (*Rt. Hon.* Thomas). Autobiography. With suppl. chapters by A. Watson & foreword by W. Burt. 8º. [1924]

Burtchaell (George Dames). Genealog. mem. of members of Parl. for the city & co. of Kilkenny. 8º. D. 1888
see DUBLIN UNIV.: TRINITY COLL. Alumni Dublin.: reg. of students &c.; ed. G. D. B. &c., 1924.

Burthogge (Richard). Philos. writings [1678–99]. Ed. w. intr. & notes, by M. W. Landes. 8º. Chicago. 1921

Burton Historical Collection Leaflet. [Publ. by] Detroit Public Library. v1–4, Jan. 1922–May 1926. s8º. [Detroit. 1923–26]

Burton (Edward), *D.D.*
see APOSTOLIC. The Apost. Fathers; intr. by B., 2v, 1888–89; 1909.
„ PRIMER. Three primers put forth in r. of Henry VIII, 1834.

Burton (Ernest De Witt), *see* BIBLE. COMPL. TEXTS &C. Internat. Crit. Comm.: Galatians; by E. De W. B., 1921.

Burton (George), *Rector of Elden, Suffolk.* Essay towards reconciling the numbers of Daniel & St. John. 8º. Norwich. 1766

Burton (Henry), *Rector of St. Matthew's, Friday Street, see* DOW (C.) Innovations charged upon Church & State; ans. to H. B. Apologie of an appeale, 1637.

Burton (John), *D.D.* The folly &c. of misplacing our trust &c. Sermon, Oxford, April 9, 1744. [P2434]. 8º. O. 1744
The principles of Xtn. loyalty. Sermon, Oxford, Jan. 31, 1742–43, martyrdom of K. Charles I. [P2434]. 8º. O. [1743]
Sermon bef. Univ. of Oxford, Feb. 4, 1740–1. [P2434]. 8º. O. [1741]

Burton (John), *master of the Free School at Norwich.* Antiq. capellæ D. Johannis Evangel., hodie Scholæ Reg. Norwic. [*w. sep. tp. & pagin.*], 1712, *see* BROWNE (*Sir* T.) Posthumous wks., 1712.

Burton (Richard Francis). Descr. of vol. of Shakespeareana. Sold by Sotheby, March 1920. [*Illust.*] [P2853]. la8º. 1920

Burton (*Sir* Richard Francis) [*ps.* FRANK BAKER, D. O. N. &c.]
A glance at the "Passion-play." s8º. 1881
The Kasîdah of Hâjî Abdû el-Yezdî; tr. &c. by his friend [*i.e.* Sir R. F. B.] [8th ed.] s8º. Portland Maine. 1911
Sel. papers on anthropology, travel &c. Ed. w. intr. &c. by N. M. Penzer. 8º. 1924
see DODGE (W. P.) The real Sir R. B., 1907.
„ PENZER (N. M.) Annot. bibliogr. of Sir R. F. B., 1923.

Burton (Robert), *a. of "Anatomy of melancholy"* [*ps.* DEMOCRITUS, *junior*]. *The anatomy of melancholy. Prefixed, A satyr. pref. 16th ed. 8º. 1840
„ „ Ed. A. R. Shilleto, w. intr. by A. H. Bullen. [repr.] 3v. s8º. *Bohn.* 1896
see MADAN (F.) R. B. & the A. of M., 1926.

Burton (Theodore Elijah), *see* SCHOENRICH (O.) Former Senator B.'s trip to S. Amer., 1915, 1915.

Burton (William), *F.C.S.*
A general history of porcelain. 2v. s4º. 1921
Handbook of marks on pottery & porcelain. s8º. 1919
Josiah Wedgwood & his pottery. la8º. 1922

Burtsev (Vladimir Lvovich). Борьба за свободную Россію. Мои воспоминанія, 1882–1922. т1. 8º. Берлинъ. 1923
Процессъ шестнадцати террористовъ (1880). Подъ редак. В. Б. [P2447]. 8º. С.-П. 1906
Der Zar und die auswärtige Politik [Das geheime Mem. d. Grafen Lambsdorff &c. *Tr.*] [P849]. s8º. Berlin. 1910

Burtt (Edwin Arthur).
Metaphys. found. of mod. phys. science. 8º. 1925.

Burtt (Joseph). The people of Ararat. s8º. 1926

Bury (Arthur), *D.D.* *An histor. vindic. [*Attrib. to J. Le Clerc*] of The naked gospel [*by A. B.*] 8º. 1691

Bury (*Lt.-Col.* C. K. Howard), *see* HOWARD-BURY (*Lt.-Col.* C. K.)

Bury (Guillaume de) [Burius (G.)]. Brevis Roman. Pontificum notitia. Acc. Onomasticon, quo voces obscuriores explicantur. [*w. sep. pagin.*] s8°. Mechliniæ. 1675
Roman. pontificum brevis notitia. Acc. Onomasticon vocum obscur. quæ in Missali &c. cont. s8°. Patavii. 1741

Bury (Herbert), *bp. (1) of Brit. Honduras &c., (2) for N. & C. Europe.* Russia f. within: pers. exper. since 1923. 8°. [1927]

Bury (*Capt.* John). A true narr. of the design of the papists to charge their plot upon the protestants &c. by endeav. to corrupt B. & alderman Brooks &c. [P525]. sfol. 1697

Bury (John Bagnell). The Hellenistic age: aspects of H. civiliz. treated by J. B. B., E. A. Barber, E. Bevan & W. W. Tarn. s8°. C. 1923
Hist. of the Later Roman Empire, 395–565. 2v. 8°. 1923
Hist. of the names Hellas, Hellenes. [Repr. f. Journ. of Hellen. St., v15; P2793]. la8°. 1895
The idea of progress: its origin & growth. 8°. 1920
„ „ ....[repr.] 8°. 1921
The invasion of Europe by the barbarians. 8°. 1928
see Cambridge (The) ancient hist.; ed. J. B. B. &c., 1923–27.
„ Constantine VII, *emp.* Slavonic settlements in Dalmatia &c., ed. J. B. B., 1920.

Bury (Richard de) [Aungervile (Ricardus d'), *bp. of Durham*]. Philobiblion. Tr., intr. & texte latin, par H. Cocheris. [Trésor des pièces rares &c.] s8°. 1856

Bury St. Edmonds. A tryal of witches at B. &c., 1682, *see* Trial.

Busæus (Joannes). 30 paradoxa G. Swencfeldii hæresiarchæ, de toto Christo Deo & Homine. s4°. Moguntiæ. 1595
see Fleck (G.) Refutatio errorum &c. a J. B. opposit. &c., 1592.
„ Gerlach (S.) De persona Christi disput. 2, adv. J. B. &c. 1695.

Busbecq (Ogier Ghiselin, *seigneur* de). A. G. B. quæ extant omnia. Quibus acc. Epitome de moribus Turcarum [*by* B. Georgievits, *w. sep. tp.*] s8°. Londini. 1660
Turkish letters. Tr. f. Elzevir ed., 1633, by E. S. Forster. 8°. O. 1927
see Laurent-Vibert (R.) Routiers &c. aux échelles du Levant [B. &c.], 1923.

Busca (Berengario I, *marchese* di), *see* Berengarius I.

Buscemi (Niccolò). Notizie d. Basilica di San Pietro, detta la Cappella Regia, raccolte ed esposte dal N. B. [Libro primo & Note *w. sep. pagin.*] 4°. Palermo. 1840

Busch (Rudolf). Sammlung R. B., Mainz. Versteigerung, J. Bauer & Co., 3., [4.] Mai 1921. 2T [*in* 1B]. 4°. Frankfurt a. M. [1921]
1, Kupferstiche u. Holzschnitte alt. Meister Dürer, Rembrandt &c.
2. Illum. MSS., Buchminiaturen, Incunabeln, &c.

Buschan (Georg). Illust. Völkerkunde. Hrsg. v. G. B. 2te vollst. umgearb. A. 2B *in* 3 [2i, ii]. 8°. St. 1922–26
1, Amerika—Afrika, v. R. Lasch, W. Krickeberg & A. Haberlandt.
2i, Australien u. Ozeanien—Asien, v. G. B., A. Byhan, W. Volz, A. Haberlandt &c.
2ii, Europa u. s. Randgebiete, v. A. Byhan, A. Haberlandt, M. Haberlandt.
Die Sitten d. Völker. 3B. la8°. St. [1914–16]

Buschmann (P.), *jun., see* Art (L') flamand & Holland. Études &c. publ. sous la dir de P. B., s1, 1904.

Buschor (Ernst).
Greek vase-painting. Pref. by P. Gardner. la8°. 1921

Busco (Pierre). Les cosmogonies mod. & la théorie de la connaissance. 8°. 1924

Busenbaum (Hermann) [Busembaum]. Medulla theologiæ moralis. Acc. proposit. ad hunc usque diem proscriptæ. Ed. 10ª Patavina. [*2 pagin.*] s8°. Patavii. 1729
Theologia moralis nunc aucta à Alphonso de Ligorio. Acc. etiam F. A. Zachariæ diss. proleg. de casuisticæ theologiæ orig., locis atque præstantia. 3t [*in* 1v. *each w. sep. tp. & pagin.*] fol. Romæ. 1757

Bush (Jane). Joseph Bush: a memorial ed. by his wife. W. mem. by A. Hoyle. 8°. [1907]

Bush (Joseph), *editor, 1826–1906.* W. O. Simpson, Methodist minister. Early life, by S. Wray. Mission life by R. Stephenson. s8°. [1886]
see Bush (J.) J. B.: a memorial, 1907.

Bushby (Olive Mary). Studies in the development of the fool in Eliz. drama. Thesis. 8°. 1923

Bushe (Charles Kendal). Rep. of the speeches of B. in the cases of E. Sheridan & T. Kirwan, f. violat. of the Convent. Act. Added the charge of Ld. Chief Justice Downes & the act of Parl. [*4 pagin*ˢ. P2557] 8°. D. 1812

Bushe-Fox (J. P.) Excav. of the late-Celtic urn-field at Swarling, Kent. [Soc. of Antiq. of London]. la8°. O. 1925
Excav. on the site of the Roman town at Wroxeter, 1914, 3rd rep. [Soc. of Antiq. of London]. la8°. O. 1916
First rep. on excav. of the Roman fort at Richborough, Kent. [Soc. of Antiq. of London]. la8°. O. 1926

Bushell (Thomas), *farmer of H.M.'s Mines in Wales; 1594–1674, see* De La Pryme (A.) Mems. of T. B., "the recluse of the Calf," 1878.

Bushell (William Done) *of Harrow.*
Will. D. Bushell of Harrow. [*By var. wr.*] s8°. C. 1919

Bushnell (David Ives), *Jr.* Burials of the Algonquian, Siouan & Caddoan tribes west of the Mississippi. [S.I.: B. of Ethn., Bull. 83]. 8°. Wash. 1927
Native cemeteries & forms of burial east of the Mississippi. [S.I.: B. of Ethn., Bull. 71]. 8°. Wash. 1920
Native villages & village sites east of the Mississippi. [S.I.: B. of Ethn., Bull. 69], 8°. W. 1919
Villages of the Algonquian, Siouan & Caddoan tribes west of the Mississippi. [S.I.: B. of Ethn., Bull. 77]. 8°. Wash. 1922

Bushnell (Horace).
Women's suffrage; the reform against nature. s8°. N.Y. 1869

Bushnell (John), *see* Esdaile (K. A.) J. B., sculptor, 1927.

Busila (V.), *see* Babes (A.) & V. B. Cercetări orig. despre pelagra in România, 1915.

Business directory (The), 1925. Publ. J. S. C. Morris. 4°. [1925]

Busini (Giovanni Battista), *see* Varchi (B.) Opere: agg. le lettere di G. B. B. sopra l'assedio di Firenze, 2v, 1858–59.

Busk (Edward Teshmaker), *see* Busk (*Mrs.* M.) E. T. B., a pioneer in flight &c., 1925.

Busk (Hans Acworth), *Flight-Comm., R.N.A.S., see* Busk (*Mrs.* M.) E. T. Busk, w. sh. mem. of H. A. B., 1925.

Busk (*Mrs.* Mary), *wife of T. T. Busk, form. Acworth.* E. T. Busk, a pioneer in flight, w. sh. mem. of H. A. Busk, Flight-Comm., R.N.A.S. 8°. [1925]

Busken Huet (Coenraad). Oude romans. 4ᵉ dr., met inl. woord v. A. G. van Hamel. 2d [*in* 1v]. s8°. Haarlem. 1904
see Tielrooy (J.) C. B. H. & la litt. franç., 1923.

Busnelli (Manlio D.) Diderot & l'Italie. la8°. 1925

Busquet (Raoul), *see* Bouches-du-Rhône; encyclop. départ., t2, par B. &c., 1924.

Busse (Fedor Fedorovich). Списокъ словъ бытоваго значенія нѣкоторыхъ кочевыхъ народовъ Восточной Сибири. [I.R.G.O. Записки по отдѣл. этнограф., 6ii]. 8°. С.-П. 1880

Busse (Kurt).
Hermann Sudermann, s. Werk u. s. Wesen. 8°. St. 1927

Bussemaker (Carel Hendrik Theodor). De afscheiding d. Waalsche gewesten van de Generale Unie. Uitg. door Teyler's 2ᵉ Genootschap. 2d [dl *wanting*]. 8°. Haarlem. 1896

Busset (Maurice). La technique mod. du bois gravé & les procédés anc. des xylographes du 16s & des grav. jap. la8°. 1925

Bussi (Feliciano). Istoria d. città di Viterbo. fol. Roma. 1742

Busson (Henri). Charles d'Espinay, évêque de Dol, & s. œuvre poét., 1531?–91. [Bibl. litt. de la Renaiss., n.s., t6]. 8°. 1923

Bussy (Honorée de), *see* Magne (E.) Une amie inconnue de Molière [*i.e.* H. de B.] &c., 1922.

Bussy-Rabutin.
Comedie gallante. [*b. w. h.* Hist. amoureuse, 1722]. s8°. 1690
Hist. amoureuse des Gaules. s8°. Cologne. 1722
„ „ Rev. & annot. par P. Boiteau; suiv. des romans hist.-satir. du 17ᵉ s. rec. &c. par C.-L. Livet. [Bibl. Elzev.] 4t. s8°. 1856–76

Bustico (Guido). Vincenzo Monti: vita. s8°. Messina. [1921]

Bustros (Eveline). La main d'Allah. Préf. de Jérome & Jean Tharaud. s8°. 1926

Busuioceanu (Al.) P. Cavallini e la pitt. rom. (13–14c.), *see* Scuola Romena di Roma. Ephemeris Dacorom., v3, 1925.

Butakov (Aleksandr). Словарь морскихъ словъ и реченій съ англ. на франц. и русс. языки. s8°. С.-П 1837

Bute (John Patrick Crichton Stuart, *3rd marq. of*), *see* Goodrich-Freer (A.) & J., *3rd marq. of* B., *edd.* The alleged haunting of B—— House, 1899.

Bute (John Stuart, *3rd earl of*), *see* Stuart-Wortley (*Hon. Mrs.* V.) A prime minister & h. son, f. corresp. of 3rd Earl of B. & Lt.-Gen. Sir C. Stuart, 1925.

Butler (A. S. G.), *F.R.I.B.A.* The substance of architecture. Foreword by Sir E. Lutyens. 8°. 1926

Butler (Alfred Joshua). Islamic pottery. fol. 1926

Butler (Arthur John). The Gioliti & th. press at Venice. [Repr. f. Trans. of Bibliog. Soc.] 8°. 1910

Butler (Charles), *barrister.*
An address to the Protestants of Gt. Brit. & Ireland. [*a. c. b. w.* Kenyon (G. K., *b.*) Obs. 1810]. 2nd ed. 8°. 1813
Conn. ser. of notes on revol. of states wh. comp. the Emp. of Charlemagne, &c. 814–1806; on the House of Habsburgh &c., & Rom., Germ., &c. nobility. la8°. 1807
Hist. mem. of Eng., Irish, & Scottish Catholics since the Reformation. 3rd ed., corr., rev. & augm. 8°. 1822
Horæ biblicæ, notes on text, early versions, & pr. eds. &c. s8°. O. 1799
„ „ ....2v (v1, 4th ed., 2, 2nd ed.) 8°. 1807
A succinct hist. of the revolutions of the Emp. of Germany, 814–1806. 8°. 1812
Vindication of "The Book of the Roman Catholic Church," agst. G. Townsend &c. 2nd ed., enl.8°. 1826
see APPEAL (An) to Protest. of Gt. Brit. &c. on Rom. Cath. q. in reply to B., 1813.
„ PHILLPOTTS (H.) A suppl. letter to C. B. &c., 1826.
„ TOWNSEND (G.) The accusations of hist. agst. the Ch. of R. in remarks on C. B.'s "Book of the R. Cath. Ch.," n. ed., 1845.

Butler (E. M.)
The Saint-Simonian relig. in Germany. 8°. C. 1926

Butler (Edmund), *process server, see* KENNEDY (J.) Report of trials of J. K., J. Ryan &c. for the murder of E. B., at Carrickshock, 14th Dec. 1831, 1832.

Butler (Edward Cuthbert), *abbot of Downside.* Authorship of the Dial. de vita Crysostomi. [P2789]. la8°. Roma. 1908
Benedictine monachism: B. life & rule. 2nd ed. 8°. 1924
Life & times of Bp. Ullathorne, 1806–89. 2v. 8°. 1926
Western mysticism: teaching of SS. Augustine, Gregory & Bernard on contemplation &c. 8°. 1922
„ „ ....2nd ed., w. afterthoughts. 8°. 1927

Butler (Elizabeth, *Lady*), *wife of Sir W. F. Butler.*
An autobiography. 8°. 1922

Butler (Frank Hedges), *F.R.G.S.* Fifty years of travel by land, water & air. [2nd imp.] 8°. [1921]
Round the world. [2nd ed.] 8°. [1925]
Through Lapland w. skis & reindeer. [3rd impr.] 8°. [1919]
Wine & the wine lands of the world, w. acc. of places visited. 8°. [1926]

Butler (*Sir* **Geoffrey Gilbert).** Handbook to the League of Nations, to end of 5th Assembly. Intr. by Visct. Cecil. 2nd ed., rev. & enl. 8°. 1925
Studies in statecraft: chapters, biog. & bibliog., mainly on the 16th c. 8°. C. 1920

Butler (Harold Edgeworth), *see* BUTLER (H. J.) & H. E. B. Black Bk. of Edgeworthstown &c., 1585–1817, 1927.
see VIRGIL. Aeneid. 6; intr. & notes by H. E. B., 1920.

Butler (Harriet Jessie) & H. E. Butler. The Black Book of Edgeworthstown & o. Edgeworth mem., 1585–1817. Ed. H. J. B. & H. E. B. 8°. 1927

Butler (Henry Montagu).
see BUTLER (J. R. M.) H. M. B., a memoir, 1925.
„ GRAHAM (E.) Harrow life of H. M. B., 1920.

Butler (Howard Crosby). Sardis, v1, The excavations, p1, 1910–14, 1922, *see* SARDIS.
Syria, div. 2, Architecture, *see* PRINCETON UNIV. Syria, div. 2, §A, B, by B., 1919–20.

Butler (James Ramsay Montagu). H. M. Butler, Master of Trin. Coll., Cambridge, 1886–1918. 8°. 1925

Butler (Joseph), *bp. of (1) Bristol, (2) Durham.* Analogy of religion. Intr. by R. Bayne. [Everyman's Lib.] [repr.] s8°. [1906]
„ „ Ed. W. E. Gladstone. [World's classics]. s8°. [1907]
see WILKINSON (J.) Analysis of B.'s Analogy, 1853.

Butler (*Mrs.* **Josephine Elizabeth).**
see FAWCETT (M. G.) & E. M. TURNER. J. B.: work &c., 1927.
„ HAY-COOPER (L.) J. B. & h. work for social purity, 1922.
„ STEAD (W. T.) J. B., 1887.

Butler (Kathleen Theresa Blake).
A hist. of French literature. 2v. s8°. 1923.

Butler (*Lieut.-Col.* **Lewis).** The annals of the King's Royal Rifle Corps. v2, 3. 8°. 1923–26

Butler (Nicholas Murray).
Building the Amer. nation. 8°. C. 1923
Development of the internat. mind, *see* INTERNAT. CONCILIATION, No. 192, 1923.
A dinner tendered to B. by Faculties of Columbia Univ. [P2876]. la8°. N.Y. 1927
Les États-Unis d'Amérique: orig., dévelop., unité. [Tr.] 8°. 1925
The faith of a Liberal. Essays &c. on polit. princ. &c. 8°. N.Y. 1924
Is America worth saving? Addresses &c. s8°. N.Y. 1920

Butler (Nicholas Murray) [*continued*].
Nicholas M. B., h. quarter centenary. [P2876]. la8°. N.Y. 1927
The republican party & internat. policy. Address. [P2465]. 8°. *n.p.* 1920
see AMERICAN foreign policy: statements of presids. &c., w. intr. by N. M. B., 2nd ed., 1920.
„ FRANCE-AMERICA SOC. Addresses [by] N. M. B. &c., 1918.

Butler (R. K.), *wife of Thomas Butler.* Missions as I saw them: acc. of visit to centres of United Methodist Miss. Soc. in China & Africa. 8°. 1924

Butler (S.), *of Bristol.* *An essay upon educ. &c., w. a plan of a new method. By a Gent. of Bristol. [P2668]. 8°. [1752]

Butler (Samuel), *bp. of Lichfield & Coventry.*
An atlas of mod. geography. 8°. 1822
A sketch of mod. & ant. geography. 3rd ed. 8°. 1814

Butler (Samuel), *of St. John's Coll., Cambridge.*
Erewhon. 15th impr. s8°. [1922]
Life & habit. [n. ed. repr.] s8°. [1924]
Luck, or cunning, as the main means of organic modification. 2nd ed., w. corr. s8°. 1920
The way of all flesh. 12th impr. of 2nd ed s8°. 1920
„ „ [13th impr. of 2nd ed.] s8°. [1922]
see CAMBRIDGE. ST. JOHN, COLL. OF. S. B. Coll.: cat. & comm. by H. F. Jones &c., 1921.
„ GARNETT (*Mrs.* R. S.) S. B. & h. family relations, 1926.
„ HOPPÉ (A. J.) Bibliog. of S. B., w. letters to F. G. Fleay, now 1st publ., 1925.

Butler (Samuel), *the poet.*
Hudibras. corr. & amended. 3p *in* 1v. s8°. 1709–10
„ Added, annot. w. index. Cuts by Hogarth. s8°. 1739
„ With annot. & pref. by Z. Grey. 2v. 8°. 1799
„ w. notes. Ed. H. G. Bohn. s8°. 1893
Poet. works. Coll. by T. Park. 3v. s8°. 1806
see WARD (E.) Secret hist. of the Calves-Head Club, 5th ed. [*w.*] a vindic. of the Royal Martyr, by B. &c., 1705.

Butler (Samuel), *settler in Australia.*
Hand-book for Australian emigrants. s8°. Glasgow. 1839

Butler (*Rev.* **William),** *D.D.* The land of the Veda: remin. of India; w. incidents of the Sepoy Rebellion &c. la8°. N.Y. 1872

Butler (William F. T.) Gleanings f. Irish history. 8°. 1925

Butt (G. Baseden). Mme. Blavatsky. 8°. [1926]

Butt (George), *D.D.* Isaiah versified. 8°. 1785

Butt (Newbern Isaac), *see* HARRIS (F. S.) & N. I. B. Fruits of Mormonism, 1925.

Buttel-Reepen (H. v.), *see* ROTTER (E.), H. v. B.-R. &c. Die Biene in Ägypten, 1921.

Butter (Archibald Edward). Illust. partic., w. plan &c. of the estates of Faskally, Cluniemore &c., Perthshire, auction by Knight, Frank & Rutley, 15 July, 1910. By instructs. of A. E. B. final ed. fol. 1910

Butter (Oscar) & B. Ruml, *edd.* Tschechoslowak. Republik. Übersicht d. intell., polit. &c. Verhältnisse. 8°. Prag. 1921

Butterworth (Alan). The southlands of Siva: some reminisc. of life in S. India. 8°. [1923]

Butterworth (George). Eccl. buildings of Deerhurst, Gloucs. s8°. Tewkesbury. *n.d.*

Buttet (Marc Claude de). La victoire de Prince Emmanuel Philibert duc de Savoie [*Poem*, 1561], réimpr. avec bibliog. & notes par le chev. d'Arcollières, *see* REGIA DEPUT. Miscellanea, t48, 1915.

Büttinghausen (Carl). Specimen horarum Hebr. ac Arabic. ut et observ. Biblic. s8°. Trajecti ad Rhenum. 1758

Buttingha Wichers (J. van).
Schaatsenrijden. 8°. 's-Gravenhage. 1888

Büttner (Carl).
Die Sprache in F. Burneys Evelina. 8°. Giessen. 1924

Butts (Thomas). Harmonia sacra, or a choice coll. of Psalm &c. tunes, 1744, *see* HARMONIA.

Butt-Thompson (F. W.) Sierra Leone in hist. & tradit. Intr. by Sir A. R. Slater. 8°. 1926

Buturlin (*count* **Dmitry Petrovich)** [BOUTOURLIN].
Hist. milit. de la campagne de Russie. Atlas. fol. *n.d.*

Butzbach (Johannes). Von d. berühmten Malern, 1505. Mit d. Urschr. (*Lat.*) in Nachbildung, hrsg. u. übers. v. O. Pelka. 4°. Heidelberg. 1925

Butzer (Martin), *see* BUCER (M.)

Buxton (Charles Roden).
Exploitation of the coloured man. la8°. [1925]
In a Russian village. s8°. 1922

Buxton (Dorothy Frances).
The war for coal & iron. [P2519]. 8o. [1921]

Buxton (Edward North).
Epping Forest. 9th ed. rev. 8o. 1923

Buxton (Harry John Wilmot). English painters, w. chap. on Amer. painters by S. R. Koehler. s8o. 1883

Buxton (Leland). The black sheep of the Balkans. Introd. by A. Herbert. s8o. [1920]

Buxton (Leonard Halford Dudley). The Eastern road. 8o. 1924
The peoples of Asia. 8o. 1925

Buxton (Patrick Alfred). Animal life in deserts: st. of fauna in rel. to environment. 8o. 1923

Buxton (Sydney Charles Buxton, *1st earl***).** General Botha. 8o. 1924

Buxton (*Sir* **Thomas Fowell),** *1st bart.*
see Binney (T.) Sir T. F. B., Bart.; Lect., 1849.
,, Parl.: H. of Commons. Auth. rep. of debate, June 1825, on Mr. B.'s motion rel. to demolition of Methodist Chapel in Barbadoes &c., 1825.

Buxtorfius (Joannes), *the elder.* Instit. epistolaris Hebraica. Acc. app. var. epist. R. Majemonis &c. quas rec. J. Buxtorfius filius. [*b. w.* Buxtorfius (J.) Florilegium Heb., 1648. *a. copy b. w.* Moses, *ben Joseph Kimchi.* 'Οδοιπορία, 1631]. s8o. Basileæ. 1629
Lexicon Chaldaicum, Talmud. et Rabbin. Nunc. primúm in lúcem ed. á J. Buxtorfio F[ilio]. fol. Basileæ. 1639
Lexicon Hebr. & Chald. s8o. Basileæ. 1631
,, ,, ..acc. lex. breve rabbinico-philos. & index lat. ed. nova. la8o. Glasguæ. 1824

Buxtorfius (Johannes), *the younger.*
Catalecta philologico-theolog. &c. s8o. Basileæ. 1707
Diss. philolog.-theolog. Acc. R. Isaaci Abarbenelis Dissertationes in Lat. versæ. 4o. Basileæ. 1662
Exercitationes ad hist. (1) Arcæ fœderis, (2) Ignis sacri, (3) Urim & Thummim, (4) Mannæ, (5) Petræ in deserto, (6) Serpentis Ænei &c. s4o. Basileæ. 1659
Florilegium Hebraicum cont. sententias, proverbia, &c. s8o. Basileæ. 1648

***By** an Unknown Disciple, 1920, *see* Phillimore (*Mrs.* J. S.)

Byelii, *see* Belii.

Byelinsky (Vissarion Grigorevich). Сочиненія. Изд. К. Солдатенкова и Н. Щепкина. 12ч. *in* 6v. [1, 2 2e изд.] 8o. Москва. 1859–62

Byeloruss (M.), *see* Beloruss (M.)

Byelyaev, *see* Belyaev.

Byfield (Nicholas). Comm. upon the 1st 3 chapters of the 1st Epistle of St. Peter. la8o. 1637
An expos. upon Colossians; sermons. 2nd ed. corr. sfol. 1617

Bygott (John).
Eastern England: geog. w. ref. to econ. signif. s8o. 1923

Byhan (Arthur), *see* Buschan (G.), *ed.* Illust. Völkerkunde, B2i, ii, 1923–26.

Byles (Phoebe G.), *see* Ashby (A. W.) & P. G. B. Rural education, 1923.

Bynaeus (Antonius). De natali Jesu Christi libri 2. Acc. diss. de J. C. circumcisione. 2p *in* 1v. s4o. Amstelædami. 1689

Byne (Arthur) & M. Stapley Byne. Decorated wooden ceilings in Spain. Coll. of photographs & drawings, w. descr. text. [Hisp. Soc. of Amer.] fol. N.Y. 1920
,, ,, (Manual). [Hisp. Soc. of Amer.] s8o. N.Y. 1920
Rejería of the Span. Renaissance. Coll. of photographs & drawings, w. descr. text. [Hisp. Soc. of Amer.] fol. N.Y. 1914
Span. ironwork. [Hisp. Soc. of Amer.] 8o. 1915
see Las Almenas (*cde.* de). Med. & early Renaiss. works of art f. Spain; cat., wr. by M. S. B. & A. B., 1927.

Byne (*Mrs.* **Mildred Stapley).**
Forgotten shrines of Spain. 8o. Phila. 1926
see Byne (A.) *for works wr. in collabor. w. A. Byne.*

Byng (*Adm. the Hon.* **John).** Position of the Eng. & French fleets, 20th May, 1756. Publ. for Adm. B.'s trial, 1757. [*4 sheets.* Maps, 7]. folded fol. 1757

Byng (Lucy).
Roumanian stories [*by var. authors*]. Tr. by L. B. s8o. 1921

Byng (*Lady* **Rachel).** How to make money by Angora rabbit-breeding &c. 8o. Bradford. [1926]
Mr. Jim & the Brownies. s8o. 1922

Bynkershoek (Cornelis van). De dominio maris diss. Reprod. of 2nd ed. (1744), w. tr. by R. van Deman Magoffin, & intr. by J. B. Scott. [C. E. for Internat. Peace]. la8o. N.Y. 1923

Byrd (William), *musician.*
see Fellowes (E. H.) W. B.: sh. acc. of h. life & work, 1923.
,, Glyn (M. H.) About Eliz. virginal music & its composers [W. B. &c.], 1923.
,, Howes (F. S.) W. B., 1928.

Byrne (Donn).
Blind Raftery & his wife, Hilaria. 8o. [1925]
Brother Saul. s8o. [1927]
Hangman's house. s8o. [1926]

Byrne (Muriel St. Clare).
Elizabethan life in town & country. s8o. [1925]
see Topsell (E.) Elizabethan Zoo: [sel. f. P. Holland's tr. of Pliny, 1601, & T.'s "Hist. of foure-footed beastes," 1607 &c.; ed. M. St. C. B.], 1926.
—— & C. H. Mansfield. Somerville College, 1879–1921. With intr. chap. by Mrs. T. H. Green, & pref. by G. Murray. s8o. O. [1921]

Byrnes (Thomas), *Inspector of Police, N.Y.*
Profess. criminals of America. 4o. N.Y. [1882]

Byrom (John), *M.A., fellow of Trin. Coll., Cambridge.*
Misc. poems. 2v. 8o. Leeds. 1814
see Hobhouse (S.) W. Law & 18th cent. Quakerism, incl. letters & fragm. of W. L. & J. B., 1927.

Byron (*Lady***),** *wife of the poet.*
see Fox (J.) *Vindication of Lady B., 1871.
,, Lovelace (M. *countess of*). Portrait mis-named Lady B., 1918.

Byron (*Lord***),** *the poet.*
Works, w. letters & journals, & life by T. Moore. 17v. s8o. 1832–33
Arm. exercises & poetry. s8o. Venice. 1870
Childe Harold's pilgrimage. s8o. 1857
Descr. cat. of exhib. of MSS. & 1st ed. of B., Univ. of Texas, 1924. Comp. &c. by R. H. Griffith & H. M. Jones. la8o. Austin, Texas. 1924
English bards & Scoth [*sic*] reviewers. s8o. Boulogne-sur-Mer. 1822
Letters & journals; w. notices of h. life by T. Moore. 2v. 4o. 1830
Lord B. in h. letters. Sel. [1798–1824], ed. V. H. Collins. 8o. 1927
Lord B.'s corr. chiefly w. Lady Melbourne, Mr. Hobhouse, Hon. D. Kinnaird, & P. B. Shelley. Ed. by J. Murray. 2v. 8o. 1922
Poems on his domestic circumstances. 6th ed. [P2433]. 8o. 1816
,, ,, 7th ed. [*b. w. h.* Engl. bards, 1822]. 8o. 1816
Poetry of B., chosen & arr. by M. Arnold. [repr.] s8o. 1913
The prisoner of Chillon. 2nd ed. [*b. w. h.* Engl. bards, 1822]. 8o. Lausanne. 1822
Sardanapalus—The two Foscari—Cain. 8o. 1821
see Aberdeen. Proc. at present. to A. Gram. Sch. of statue of Ld. B., 1923.
,, Åman-Nilsson (G.) Lord B. och det sekelgamla förtalet, 1915.
,, Beauties of Eng. poets, [B. &c. *Eng. & Armen.*], 1852.
,, Brandl (A.) B. im Kampf mit d. engl. Politik &c., 1915.
,, Brecknock (A.) B. in light of new discoveries, 1926.
,, Briscoe (W. A.), *ed.* B., the poet, 1924.
,, Cantoni (F.) La prima dimora di Ld. B. a Bologna, 1926.
see Chew (S. C.) B. in England, h. fame & after-fame, 1924.
,, De Beer (E. S.) & W. Seton. Byroniana: archives of London Greek Com., 1926.
,, Drinkwater (J.) The pilgrim of eternity: B.—a conflict, 1925.
,, Eng. Goethe Soc. Publs., n. s., v2, Goethe & B.; ed. J. G. Robertson, 1925.
,, Farinelli (A.) Ld. B.: [saggio], 1921.
,, Ferriman (Z. D.) Engl. philhellenes, 8, B., 1920.
,, Fox (*Sir* J. C.) The B. mystery, 1924.
,, Galt (J.) Life of B., 1832.
,, Gamba (P.) B.'s last journey to Greece, 1825.
,, Grierson (H. J. C.) Ld. B.: Arnold & Swinburne, 1920.
,, Henson (H. H.) B., Rede Lect., 1924.
,, Lovelace (R. G. N. M., *2nd earl of*), Astarte; fragm. of truth conc. B., 1921.
,, Magnien (E.) Mortel, ange ou démon: [*play on* Ld. B.], 2t, 1836.
,, Malling (M.) Manden, Hustruen & Lord B., Roman, 1912.
,, Maurois (A.) Quatre études angl., B. & le démon de la tendresse &c., 1927.
,, Mayne (E. C.) B., 2nd ed. rev., 1924.
,, Nicolson (H.) B.: the last journey, Apr. 1823–Apr. 1824, 1924.
,, Rodocanachi (E.) B., 1788–1824, 1924.
,, Roth (G.) La couronne poét. de B.: textes choisis & publ. par G. R., 1924.
,, Spender (H. E.) B. & Greece, 1924.
,, Symon (J. D.) B. in perspective, 1924.
,, Wiel (T.) Versioni da Th. Gray, Ld. B. &c., 1906.
,, Zacchetti (C.) L. B. e l'Italia, 1919.

Byron (Henry James). Aladdin; or, The wonderful scamp. With alterations &c. by J. H. Leslie & E. A. P. Hobday. 8o. Lahore. 1882

Byron (*Vice-admiral the Hon.* **John**). Narr. of B., on coast of Patagonia, 1740–46; w. descr. of St. Jago de Chili; loss of the Wager. s8º. 1785

Byron (*Col.* **Richard**), *see* KING'S ROYAL RIFLE CORPS CHRONICLE; ed. R. B., 5v, 1915–19.

Bysshe (Edward), *gent.* The art of Eng. poetry. Rules, coll. & dict. [*each w. sep. pagin.*] 4th ed. 8º. 1710

Bysshe (*Sir* **Edward**), *Clarenceux King of Arms, see* ESSEX, Visitation of E., 1664–8, by E. B.; ed. J. J. Howard, 1888.

Byström (*Col.* **H.**), *see* HEDIN (S.) S. Tibet; maps, v2, Hypsometrical maps, constr. &c. by H. B., 1922.

Bythner (Victorinus). Lyra prophetica Davidis regis sive analysis Psalmorum &c. Add. Brevis instit. linguæ Heb. & Chald. [*w. sep. tp. & pagin.*] s4º. Londini. 1650

Byvanck (A. W.) Les princ. mss. à peintures de la Bibl. Roy. des Pays-Bas & du Musée Meermanno-Westreenianum à La Haye. [Soc. Fr. de Reprod. de mss. &c.] sm. fol. 1924

—— **& G. J. Hoogewerff.** La miniature holland. dans les mss. des 14e, 15e and 16e siècles. Rec. &c. par A. W. B. & G. J. H. 3v. fol. La Haye. 1922–26

Bywater (Hector C.)
Sea-power in the Pacific: Amer.-Jap. naval problem. 8º. 1921

Bywater (Ingram), *see* CHAPMAN (R. W.) Portrait of a scholar [I. B.], &c., 1920.

Bywaters (Frederick) & E. Thompson. Trial of F. B. & E. T. Ed. F. Young. [Notable Brit. trials]. 8º. E. 1923

Byzantina. Βυζάντινα χρονικά, παράρτημα τοῦ ί τόμου, No. 1. Actes de l'Athos, 1, publ. L. Petit, *see* ATHOS.

Byzantine Research Fund. [In association w. the Brit. Sch. at Athens. Publications]. fol. 1920
see JEWELL (H. H.) & F. W. HASLUCK. The church of Our Lady of the Hundred Gates in Paros, 1920.
„ TRAQUAIR (R.) Frankish archit. in Greece, 1923.
„ WADI SARGA. Coptic & Greek texts f. the excav. by the Byz. Research Acc., 1922.

Byzantinische Zeitschrift. Bergründet v. K. Krumbacher. B23–27, 8º. L. 1920–27

Byzantinisch-neugriechische Jahrbücher. Internat. wissenschaftl. Organ. Hrsg. v. N. A. Bees. B1–5. 8º. 1920–27
„ „ Beiheft: Texte u. Forsch. z. byz.-neugr. Philol. Nr. 1, 4–7. 8º. 1922–27
see ANAGNOSTOPULOS (G. P.) Tsakon. Grammatik, 1926. [5.]
„ BEES (N. A.) Französ-mittelgr. Ritterroman " Imberios u. Margarone," 1924. [4.]
„ —— Die Inschriftenaufzeichn. d. Kodex Sinait. Gr. 508 &c., 1922. [1.]
„ DEMETRIOS (C. M.) 'Οι ἐξωκατακοίλοι ἄρχοντες, 1927. [7.]
„ HADZOPULOS (A.) Die Flüchtlingsfrage in Griechendland, 1927. [6.]

Byzantinologie, Congrès de, *Bucarest.* Méms., *see* ACADEMIA ROMANA. Bull. de la sect. hist., t11, 1924.

Bzovius (Abrahamus), *see* JANSSENIUS (N.) Animadv. &c. in Apolog. nuper ed. de vita &c. J. Duns Scoti adv. A. B., 1622.

C

C. Eltham tragedy, 1871, *see* CROSLAND (N.)

C. (*Feldwebel*). *Diary of a German soldier; [tr.], 1919, *see* SOUVENIRS.

C. (A.), *see* LAUD (W.), *abp.* Rel. of conference betw. L. & Fisher the Jesuit, w. ans. to A. C., 3rd ed., 1673; 1839.

C. (E. D. L. J.), *see* L'ALLOUETTE (E. DE), *juris consulte.*

C. (F. I. F. C. R. S. T. P. A. P.), *see* FRONTO (JOANNES).

C. (G.) *Suomen historia; suomentanut G. C., 1858, *see* SUOMEN.

C. (H.) The Eng. dict., 9th ed., 1650; 10th ed., 1651, *see* COCKERAM (HENRY).

C. (J.) *The rustick rampant &c., 1687, *see* CLEVELAND (J.)

C. (J.) *Sacred hymns, 2nd ed., 1741, *see* CENNICK (JOHN).

C. (J.), *D.D.*, *see* COLLINGES (JOHN), *D.D.*

C. (J.), *O.P.* *Intr. to the celeb. devotion of the Rosary, 1737, *see* ROSARY.

C. (J. V.), *see* CANE (JOHN VINCENT).

C. (M.) Veld-Deuntjens, *see* AMSTERDAM. A. Pegasus, 1627.

C. (*M.* **G. C.**), *see* CLAUDIUS (G. C.)

C. (M. L. D.) Journ. du voyage de Siam, 1685 & 1686, 1687, *see* CHOISY (F. T., *abbé* DE).

C. (R.) Minerva, or, the art of weaving, 1677, *see* MINERVA.

C. (T.) *An admonition to the people of Eng., 1589, *see* COOPER (THOMAS).

C* (V.)** Tableau gén. de la Russie mod., 1807, *see* DELPUECH DE COMEIRAS (V.)

C. (W.) Decimarum &c. tabula, 1676, *see* CRASHAW (W.)

C... de L... (*M.*), *see* CHODERLOS DE LA CLOS (P. A. F.)

Caāb-Ekbaar, *see* KAĀB-AKBAR.

Caadaev, *see* CHAADAEV.

Cabal (C.) La mitologia asturiana: los dioses de la muerte. 8º. 1925

Cabala. Cabala, sive Scrinia sacra: mysteries of state in letters of illust. persons, Hen. VIII–Ch. I. 2p [*in* 1v]. fol. 1663

Cabala [KABALAH; QABBALAH].
see BOND (F. B.) & T. S. LEA. Prelim. investig. of the C. cont. in Coptic Gnostic bks. &c., 1917.
„ GINSBURG (C. D.) The K.; its doctrines &c., 2nd ed., 1920.
see KNORR VON ROSENOTH (C.) Kabbala denudata, 2t, 1677–84.
„ SCHOLEM (G.) Bibliogr. K., 1927.
„ SENNERTUS (A.) Diss. de Cabbala: maxime Ebræorum, 1655.

Cabalistica. Artis C. t1, 1587, *see* PISTORIUS (J.)

Caballero Audaz (El), *ps.*, *see* CARRETERO (J. M.)

Cabanés (Auguste).
Les curiosités de la médecine. 3t. 8º. 1925–26
t2 *has sub-title* Les cinq sens. 3, Les fonctions de la vie.
Dans l'intimité de l'Empéreur. 8º. [1924]
L'enfer de l'histoire. [2s]. s8º. [1925–27]
1, Les réprouvés & les calomnies.
2, Princesses & souverains.
L'hist. éclairée par la clinique. 8º. [1921]
Légendes & curiosités de l'histoire. s4, 5 (s5 *includ.* Table, s1–5). s8º. [1921]
Le mal héréditaire. 2[t]. s8º. [1926–27]
1, Les descendants de Charles V.
2, Les Bourbons d'Espagne.
Mœurs intimes du passé. s5–7. s8º. *n.d.*–1923
La Princesse de Lamballe intime, d'ap. s. médecin [*i.e.* Dr. Saiffert]. 8º. *n.d.*

—— **& L. Nass.** La névrose révol. 2 éd., ref. & augm. 2t. s8º. [1925.]

Cabanyes (Manuel de). Poems. Ed., w. intr., notes & bibliog. by E. A. Peers. [Span. texts & sts.] s8º. M'ter. 1923

Cabasilas (Nicolaus), *the Younger, abp. of Thessalonica; d. c. 1371.* Homélies [*Gr. & Lat.*], *see* MARY, *the Virgin.* Homélies mariales byz.; éd. &c. M. Jugie, p2, 1926.

Cabassutius (Joannes).
Notitia conciliorum sanctæ Eccl. s8º. Venetiis. 1759

Cabell (James Branch).
Beyond life. Dizain des démiurges. 8º. N.Y. 1921
The cords of vanity. s8º. 1909
The cream of the jest [4th printing]. s8º. N.Y. 1921
„ „ Intr. by H. Ward. [repr.] s8º. N.Y. 1922
„ „ [repr.], w. intr. by H. Ward. s8º. 1923
The eagle's shadow. s8º. 1904
Figures of earth. s8º. 1921
Gallantry. Intr. by L. Untermeyer. [rev. ed.] s8º. N.Y. 1922
The high place. s8º. [1923]
Jurgen. Comedy of justice, Illusts. by F. C. Papé. Intr. by H. Walpole. 8º. 1921
„ „ [8th ed.] s8º. N.Y. 1922
The rivet in grandfather's neck. s8º. 1916
„ „ [repr.] s8º. N.Y. 1921
Something about Eve. s8º. [1927]

Cabestanh (Guilhem de), *see* GUILHEM, *de Cabestanh.*

Cable (Boyd), *ps.* [*i.e. Col.* E. A. EWART].
Between the lines. [repr.] s8º. 1918
A double scoop. s8º. [1924]
Labour & profits. s8º. [1925]
The rolling road. s8º. [1923]

Cable (Mildred) & F. French. Thr. Jade Gate & Cent. Asia: journeys in Kansu, Turkestan & the Gobi Desert. Intr. by J. S. Holden. 8º. 1927

Cabos (Alban). Guy Du Faur de Pibrac. la8º. 1922

Cabot (John), *see* BIGGAR (H. P.) Voyages, 1903.

Cabot (Sebastian).
see BIGGAR (H. P.) Voyages, 1903.
„ HELLWALD (F. VON). S. C., Vortrag, 1871.

Cabré Aguiló (Juan). El arte rupestre en España (regiones sept. y orient.) [Junta p. Ampl. de Estud. &c.] la8°. 1915
Las pinturas rupestres de Aldeaquemada. [Junta p. Ampl. de Estud. &c.] la8°. 1917
see HERNANDEZ-PACHECO (E.) & J. C. Pinturas prehist. de Peña Tú, 1914.
—— **& E. Hernández-Pacheco.** Avance al estud. de las pinturas prehist. del extr. sur de España. [Junta p. Ampl. de Estud. &c. cient.] la8°. 1914
Cabrol (Fernand Michael). Dict. d'archéologie chrétienne & de liturgie &c. Publ. F. C. & H. Leclercq. t4i–7ii. (D-Jubilus). la8°. 1920–27
Liturgical prayer, its hist. & spirit. Tr. by a Benedictine of Stanbrook. 8°. 1922
Cacavelas (Jeremiás) [†CACABELAS]. The siege of Vienna by the Turks in 1683. Tr. into Greek f. Ital. work publ. anon [*w. t.* Ragguaglio hist. d. Guerra tra l'Armi Cesaree e Ottomane &c., 1683]. Ed. f. unpubl. MS., 1686, w. intr., text, tr. &c. by F. H. Marshall. 8°. C. 1925
Caccia (Giovanni Agostino), *see* CAZZA (G. A.)
Caccia (Joseph), *see* FERRARI (C.) & J. C. Grand dict. franç.-ital. & ital.-franç., 1885.
Caccini (*fra* Tommaso), *see* RICCI-RICCARDI (A.) Galileo Galilei e fra T. C., 1902.
Cacegas (Luis de). Vida de D. Fr. Bartholomeu dos Martyres, abp. de Braga. Reformada &c. por Fr. L. de Souza. 3t. 8°. Braga. 1890
„ „ ....2ª ed. [Antologia portug. organiz. por A. de Campos]. t1. s8°. Paris. 1921
Cacella (Estevão), *see* WESSELS (C.) Early Jesuit travellers in C. Asia, 1603–1721 [app. letter of C., Oct., 1627 &c.], 1924.
Cachin (Marcel), *see* SOKOLOV (B.) Voyage de C. & de Frossard dans la Russie des Soviets ; tr., 2ᵉ éd., 1921.
Cadafalch (J. Puig y), *see* PUIG Y CADAFALCH (J.)
Cadbury Bros., *Ltd.*
Cocoa : its cultivation. [P2876]. la8°. Bournville. [1927]
Oil fuel, employment by C. B. Ltd. [P2563]. 8°. Bournville. 1921
A works council in being. [P2563]. 8°. Bournville. [1921]
Cadbury (Edward) & G. Shann.
Sweating. [2ⁿᵈ ed.]. s8°. [1908]
Cadbury (George), *the elder ; 1839–1922, see* GARDINER (A. G.) Life of G. C., 1923.
Cadbury (Henry Joel). The making of Luke–Acts. 8°. 1927
Cadby (Carine), *see* CADBY (W.) & C. C. Switzerland in summer, p2, 1923.
Cadby (Will) & C. Cadby.
Switzerland in summer, p2, the Grisons. s8°. [1923]
Cadic (François).
Nouv. contes & légendes de Bretagne. 2s. 8°. 1922–25
Cadière (Marie Catherine). The case of Mrs. M. C. C. agst. the Jesuit J. B. Girard in a mem. to the parl. of Aix. s8°. D. 1731
see GIRARD (J. B.) Defence agst. the accus. of M. C. C., 3p, 1731.
„ —— Recueil de pieces du procez entre le père J. B. G. & C. C. &c., 1732.
Cadorin (Giuseppe). Pareri di 15 architetti e notizie stor. int. al Palazzo ducale di Venezia. 8°. Venezia. 1858
Cadorna (*il gen.* Luigi).
Altre pagine s. Gr. Guerra. 8°. Milano. [1925]
La Guerra alla fronte Ital. (24 Maggio 1915–9 Nov. 1917). 2v. la8°. Milano. 1921
Cadouin, *abbey.* Cartulaire, préc. de notes sur l'hist. écon. du Périgord mérid. à l'époque féodale par J. M. Maubourguet. Thèse. la8°. Cahors. 1926
Cadoux (Cecil John). The early Ch. & the world : Xtn. attitude to pagan society & the state &c. 8°. E. 1925
Cadvalla, *see* CAEDWALLA.
Cædmon. The C. MS. of Anglo-Saxon biblical poetry : Junius XI in Bodl. Lib. Intr. by Sir I. Gollancz. [Brit. Acad.] fol. O. 1927
see BRADLEY (H.) 'Cædmonian' Genesis, 1920.
„ CHRIST. C. & Satan [*attrib. to C.*], 1925.
Cædwalla, *king of Wessex, d. 686 or 705* [CADVALLA], *see* EBNER (J. G.) Diss. de Cadvalla regc Saxonum, 1736.
Caelius (Michael), *see* JONAS (J.) & M. CAELIUS. Vom. christl. abschied &c., 1546.
Caemmerer (*Gen. Lt.* Rudolf v.), *see* CÄMMERER (*Gen. Lt.* R. v.)
Cæremoniale [CEREMONIALE]. C. Benedictinum &c., 1610, *see* BURSFELD, *mon.*
C. cont. ritus electionis Gregorii papæ XV. iussu ed. cui præfiguntur Constit. Pontificiæ & Concil. decreta. s4°. Romæ. 1724

Cæremoniale [CEREMONIALE] [*continued*].
C. episcoporum, Innocentii Papæ X auctor. recog. fol. Matriti. 1779
Cæsar (Caius Julius).
C. quæ exstant, ex emend. I. Scaligeri. s8°. Lugd. Bat., *Elzevir.* 1635
Comm. Rec. &c. R. Du Pontet. 2p. s8°. O. [1900–1]
1, Libri 7 De bello Gallico cum A. Hirte Suppl.
[2], Libri 3 De bello civili cum libris De bello Alexandrino, Africo, Hispan.
De bello civili. Erkl. v. F. Kraner u. F. Hofmann. 11ᵉ umgearb. A. v. H. Meusel. 8°. 1906
De bello Gallico. Erkl. v. F. Kraner u. W. Dittenberger. 17ᵉ umgearb. A. v. H. Meusel. 3t. 8°. 1913–20
TRANSLATIONS.
Commentari, con figure in rame di A. Palladio. Di nuovo corr. &c. s4°. Venetia. 1619
Comm. of h. warres in Gallia & the Civile warres. Tr. w. obs. by C. Edmonds. With life of Cæsar &c. rev., corr. & enl. 4°. 1655

TRANSLATIONS [*continued*].
Guerres des Gaules. Texte établi & tr. par L. A. Constans. [Coll. des univ. de Fr.] 2t. 8°. 1926
see BRANDES (G.) C. J. C. ; Übers., 2B, 1925.
„ COLOMB (G.) L'énigme d' Alésia ; solution proposée d'après le livre 7 des Comm. de C., 1922.
„ FOWLER (W. W.) J. C. & found. of Roman imper. system, 1925.
„ HARDY (E. G.) Some problems in Roman hist. : essays on admin. &c. work of J. C., 1924.
„ HOLMES (T. R. E.) The Roman Rep. & the founder of the Empire [*i.e.* C.], 3v, 1923.
„ MESS (A. v.) C., s. Leben, s. Zeit &c., 1913.

***Cæsarea** legatio ad Portam Ottoman, 1668, *see* TAVERNER (P.)
Caetani (Leone), *principe di Teano, duca di Sermoneta.*
Annali dell' Islam. v9, 10. 4°. Milano. 1926
9, a. 36–37 H. 10, a. 38–40 H.
Chronographia islamica, 1–922 H. [fasc. 1–5]. 4°. Paris. [1912–26]
Caetani (Michelangelo), *duca di Sermoneta.* Carteggio dantesco del Duca di S. con G. Giuliani, C. Witte, A. Torri &c. Con ricordo biog. di A. de Gubernatis. s8°. Milano. 1883
Tre chiose n. Div. Commedia. 2ª ed. 8°. 1876
Caetani Lovatelli (*la ctssa.* Ersilia). Una piccola larva conviviale in bronzo, *see* REALE ACCAD. D. LINCEI. Mon. ant., v5, 1895.
Caetano (Scipione). Rime. s4°. Viterbo. 1612
Caffaro (Albino). L'arte del lanificio in Pinerolo e statuti—Avvisi rig. la guerra in Piemonte &c., 1642 ; pubbl. A. C., *see* REGIA DEP. DI STORIA PATRIA. Misc., t30, 1893.
Caffarus, *de Taschifellone.* Annali genovesi di C. e dei suoi contin. Tr. C. R. Ceccardi & G. Monleone. Pref. di A. Beltrami. 3t. la8°. Genova. 1923–25
1, Caffaro ; tr. Ceccardi & Monleone, 1923.
2, Oberto cancelliere—Ottobono scriba ; tr. Monleone, 1924.
3, Ogerio Pane—Marchisio scriba ; tr. Monleone, 1925.
Caffè (Il), ossia brevi e varj disc. distrib. in foglj periodici dal Giugno 1764 a tutto Maggio 1765. [*By* A. Verri, L. de Baillou &c.] [t1]. 8°. Brescia. 1765
Caffi (Francesco).
Tre novelle ined. [*Ed.* A. Tessier. P2787]. 8°. Venezia. 1855
Caffiéri, *The family of, see* GUIFFREY (J. J.) Les Caffiéri, sculpteurs &c., 17–18 s. 1877.
Caffiéri (Jean Jacques), *1723–92, see* GUIFFREY (J. J.) Les Caffiéri, sculpteurs &c., 17–18 s. 1877.
Caffin (Charles Henry).
How to study pictures. [repr.] 8°. N.Y. 1925
Cafici (Corrado). Stazioni preist. di Tre Fontane e Poggio Rosso (Catania), *see* REALE ACCAD. D. LINCEI. Mon. ant., v23, 1914.
Caggese (Romolo). Firenze d. decadenza di Roma al risorgimento d'Italia. [t] 3. s8°. Firenze. [1921]
see FIORENTINA. Stat. della Repubbl. F. ; ed. a cura del Comune di Firenze da R. C., v1, 2, 1910–21.
Cagliostro [†BALSAMO (GIUSEPPE), *calling himself count Alessandro di C.*]
see MALTHE. *M., Corse &c. [*cont.* *Lettre sur C.], 1797.
„ NATOLI (L.) Il primo sogg. di G. B. a Parigi e un amore di Lorenza, 1925.
Cagna (M. Giocopo). Sommario dell' orig. & nobiltà d'alcune famiglie di Padova. 8°. Padua. 1589
Cagnat (René). En pays romain. 8°. 1927
see TUNISIE. Atlas archéolog. de la T. ; accomp. d'un texte explic. rédigé par E. Babelon, R. C. &c., 1893–1913 ; 2ᵉ sér., livr. 1–3, 1914–26.
—— **& V. Chapot.** Manuel d'archéologie romaine. t2. 8°. 1920

Cahen (Léon) & A. Mathiez.
Les lois franç. de 1815 à nos jours. 2e éd. s8o. 1919
Cahen (Samuel), *see* BIBLE: HEBREW. La B., trad. nouv., notes &c. par S. C., 18t, 1831–39.
Cahiers (Les) de l'anti-France, 6 No., 1922, *see* MAXE (J.)
Cahiers belges (Les). No. 23–32, s8o. Brux. 1918–19
Beyens (*le baron* E.) Le roi Albert, 1919. [28.]
Carton de Wiart (*Mme.* H.) L'enfant belge & la Guerre, 1918. [25.]
Daye (P.) La polit. coloniale de Léopold II, 1918. [26.]
Rotsaert (A.) Hist. du duché de Limbourg dep. la Révol. brabançonne, 1919. [29–31.]
Ryckman de Betz (F. de). Polit. extér. de la Belgique (1830–1914), 1919. [27.]
Sohr (F.) Port d'Anvers, 1919. [32.]
Cahill (J. R.), *see* OVERSEAS TRADE, *Dept. of.* Rep. on econ. condit. in France, rev. to June 1924 by J. R. C., 1924.
Cahuet (Albéric). Les amants du lac. s8o. 1927
Le missel d'amour. Préf. de P. Bourget. s8o. 1923
Moussia, ou la vie & la mort de M. Bashkirtseff. s8o. 1926
Caillard (Alphonse-Auguste). *Caillard, le sextuple assassinat de Nassandres, [1898. *no tp.* P2826]. s8o. [Sceaux]. *n.d.*
Caillard (Gaston). L'Indochine: géogr., hist., mise en valeur. Kouang-tchéou-wan. [Notre Domaine Colon., 8]. la8o. 1922
Caillaux (Joseph). Whither France? whither Europe? Tr. K. M. Armstrong. 8o. [1923]
Caillavet (Gaston Armand de), *see* FLERS (R. *marq.* DE) & G. A. DE C. *for plays wr. in collaboration.*
——, R. de Flers & E. Rey.
La belle aventure. Comédie. s8o. [1920]
Caillol (Henri), *see* BOUCHES-DU-RHÔNE; encyclop. départ., t12, Biogéog., par C. &c., 1914.
Cain (Georges). Tableaux de Paris. s8o. [1920]
Caine (Cæsar). A brief chron. of Methodism in Leyton, Essex. s8o. Leyton. [1896]
Caine (*Sir* T. H. Hall). The master of man. s8o. 1921
The woman of Knockaloe. s8o. 1923
Caine (William). The strangeness of Noel Carton. s8o. 1920
The wife who came alive. s8o. 1919
Cair (Mary). After all. s8o. 1927
Caird (Edward), *see* JONES (H.) & J. H. MUIRHEAD. Life & philos. of E. C., 1921.
Caire (Pietro). Monografie novaresi, Mem. 2a, Sigilli e medaglie, *see* REGIA DEPUT. Misc., t19, 1880.
Cairel (Elias). Der Trobador E. Cairel: krit. Textausgabe mit Uebers. u. Anmerk. v. H. Jaeschke. [Roman. Studien, H20]. 8o. 1921
Cairnes (C. E.) Coquihalla area, British Columbia. [Canada, Geol. Survey. Mem. 139]. la8o. Ottawa. 1924
Cairns (John Arthur Robert). The loom of the law: expers. & reflects. of a Metropolitan magistrate. 8o. [1922]
Sidelights of London. 8o. 1923
Cairo. Cat. gén. des antiq. égypt. du Musée de C. Service des antiq. de l'Egypte.
see EDGAR (C. C.) Zenon papyri, v1, 1925.
,, LEGRAIN (G.) Statues &c. de rois & de particuliers, 3t & Ind., 1906–25.
,, MASPERO (J.) Papyrus grecs d'époque byz., 3t, 1911–16.
Guide to the Cairo Museum. [By G. Maspero]. Tr. J. E. & A. A. Quibell. 4th ed. s8o. Cairo. 1908
Map showing Mohammedan mon. [Survey of Egypt. With numerical index, comp. by K. A. C. Creswell]. atlas folio [folded]. *n.d.*
Cais de Pierlas (*le comte* Eugène).
Works in REGIA DEP. DI STORIA PATRIA. Misc.
I conti di Ventimiglia, il priorato di San Michele ed il principato di Seborga, 1884. [23.]
Le fief de Châteauneuf dans les Alpes Marit. du 11e au 15e siècle, 1892. [29.]
Gli statuti d. gabella di Nizza sotto i conti di Provenza, 1894. [31.]
see MANNO (A.) E. C. di P. [*includ.* Bibliog.], 1904.
,, SAINT-PONS. Chartrier de l'abbaye de St.-P.; publ. &c. C. de P. &c., 1913.
Cajal (Santiago Ramon y). Recuerdos de mi vida. 3a ed. 2p *in* 1v. [*pagin. contin.*] la8o. 1923
Cajetanus (Thomas), *see* VIO (THOMAS DE).
Čakste (Jānis), *see* KURMIS (A.), *ed.* J. C. [*by var. a.*], 1928.
Calabre-Perau (Gabriel Louis), *see* FRANCS-MAÇONS. *Les Francs-Maçons écrasés; suite du livre int. L'ordre des F.-M. trahi [*by* G. L. C.-P.], 1762.
Calabrese (*il cavalier*), *see* PRETI (M.), *called Il Cavalier Calabrese.*
Calamandrei (E. Polidori), *see* POLIDORI CALAMANDREI (E.)
Calamy (Benjamin), *D.D.* Sermons. 2nd ed. corr. s8o. 1690
Calamy (Edmund), *D.D.* A compl. coll. of farewell Sermons, 1663, *see* COLLECTION.
The great danger of Covenant-refusing &c. Sermon. [P2662]. s4o. 1646
see LONG (T.) A rebuke to E. Calamy, 1704.
Calancaitoutz (Moïse de), *see* MOSES *Kalankatouatzi.*
Calas (Jean), *see* VOLTAIRE. Relig. toleration; occas. by exec. of J. C.; tr., 1764.
Calasanzio (Giuseppe), *Saint, see* JOSEPH [*Calasanzio*].
Calbrecht (Jozef). De oorsprong der Sinte Peetersmannen, tot bij d. aanvang d. 16e eeuw. [Univ. de Louvain: Rec. de trav. par membres des conf. d'hist. &c., s2, fasc. 2.] 8o. Leuven. 1922
Calcaterra (Carlo).
Storia d. poesia frugoniana. 8o. Genova. 1920
Gli studi danteschi di Vincenzo Gioberti, *see* REALE ACCAD. D. SCIENZE DI TORINO. Dante e il Piemonte., 1922.
Calcot (John Wall), *see* CALLCOTT (J. W.)
Calcott (Wellins). Candid disq. of the princ. &c. of free &c. masons, 1847, *see* OLIVER (G.) Golden remains &c., v2, 1847.
Calcutta. The Victoria Mem., Calcutta. Illust. cat. of exhibits. 8o. [Calcutta]. 1925
ROYAL BOTANIC GARDEN.
Annals of the R. B. G., C. v12ii [*& Plates, fol.*] 4o. Calcutta. 1918–21
see BECCARI (O.) Asiatic palms—Lepidocaryeæ, p3, 1918–21. [12ii.]
Calcutta Historical Society.
see BENGAL, PAST & PRESENT, v8–30, 1914–25.
,, FIRMINGER (W. K.) The diaries of 3 surgeons of Patna, 1763, 1909.
Calcutta review (The). N.S., 8th year (1920), 3rd ser., v1–25 (Oct. 1921–Dec. 1927). 8o. Calcutta. 1920–27
Calder (Frederick). Mem. of Simon Episcopius. Added acc. of the Synod of Dort. 8o. 1835
Calder (George), *see* STATIUS (P. P.) Togail na Tebe, Thebaid; Irish text ed. w. intr., tr. &c. by G. C., 1922.
Calder (John).
Capital's duty to the wage-earner. s8o. N.Y. 1923
Calder (Robert) [*ps.* CURATE (JACOB)]. *Scotch Presbyterian eloquence display'd &c. [*Signed* Jacob Curate, *i.e.* R. C.?] s8o. 1789
Calderini (Giovanni). Tractatus novus de hæreticis &c. [*b. w.* Albertinus (A.) Tract. de agnosc. assert. &c., 1571]. s4o. Venetiis. 1571
Calderini (Marco). Alberto Pasini, pittore. 50 tavole con intr. di M. C. la8o. Torino. 1916
Vincenzo Vela, scultore. 50 tavole con intr. di M. C. la8o. Torino. 1920
Calderisi (Raffaele). Saggio crit.: A. Sebastiano Minturno, poeta &c. del cinquecento, vita e opere. la8o. Aversa. 1921
Calderon (George) [*ps.* TIHOTI]. Eight one-act plays. 8o. 1922
Tahiti. 8o. 1921
Three plays & a pantomime. 8o. 1922
see LUBBOCK (P.) G. C.: a sketch, 1921.
Calderon de la Barca (*Mme.* Frances Erskine).
Life in Mexico. [Everyman's Lib.] s8o. *n.d.*
Calderon de la Barca (Pedro). C. segun sus obras, sus crit. &c., y crón. del 2o cent. de su muerte. Por J. Alonso del Real. s8o. Barcelona. 1881
La vie est un songe: comédie; tr. A. Arnoux, *see* REVUE (LA) HEBDOMADAIRE. Suppl.: coll. nouv. &c., No. 10, 1922.
see COTARELO Y MORI (E.) Ensayo sobre la vida y obras de P. C. de la B., p1, 1924.
,, MADARIAGA (S. DE). Shelley & Calderon & o. essays, 1920.
Calderwood (David) [*pss.* DIDOCLAVIUS (EDWARDUS) PHILADELPHUS (HIERONYMUS)]. Altare Damascenum, seu politia Eccl. Angl., obstrusa Eccl. Scot. Interserta Confutatio Paræneseos Tileni ad Scotos, & adj. Epist. H. Philadelphi de Regimine Eccl. Scot. & vind. contra calumnias J. Spotsvodi per anon. s4o. *n.p.* 1623
,, ,, ...ed emend. 4o. Lugd. Bat. 1708
The pastor & the prelate, or Reformation & conformity (1628), *see* PRESBYTERIAN'S armoury, v3, 1843.
The true hist. of the Ch. of Scotland, 1560–1625. fol. [Edinb.] 1680
see ADIAPHORA. De adiaphoris Scoti τοῦ τυχόντος aphorismi [*sometimes attrib. to D. C.*], 1622.
Caldwell (Harry R.)
Blue tiger. Intr. by R. C. Andrews. 8o. [1925]

Caldwell (Wallace Everett).
Hellenic conceptions of peace. 8°. N.Y. *Columbia Univ.* 1919
Caldwell-Johnston (John).
The book of the beloved. A mod. epic poem. la8°. 1923
Cantabile. Songs & poems. 8°. [1927]
***Caledonia,** a poem, 1707, *see* DEFOE (D.)
Caledonian Society of London, *see* HEPBURN (D.) & J. DOUGLAS. Chron. of the C. Soc. of L., 2p, 1837–1905, 1923.
Calendar.
*C. of customs, superstitions &c. conn. w. Co. of Somerset, 1920, *see* SOMERSET.
C. of deeds & doc., v1, The Coleman Deeds; comp. by F. Green, 1921, *see* NAT. LIB. OF WALES.
C. of early mayor's court rolls, 1298–1307; ed. A. H. Thomas, 1924, *see* LONDON.
C. of Plea & Memoranda Rolls of London, 1323-64; ed. A. H. Thomas, 1926, *see* LONDON.
New calendar (The) of great men, 1920, *see* HARRISON (F.), *ed.*
Calendar (The) of mod. letters. v1–3 (March 1925–Jan. 1927). 8°. 1925–27
Calendar of State Papers &c. [*see also* STATE PAPERS].
see CHANCERY, *Court of.* C. of Chancery warrants, v1, 1244–1326, 1927.
,, CLOSE ROLLS. C. of C. R.: Henry III [6], 1247–51, 1922.
,, ROME. C. of S. P. rel. to Eng. affairs, in Vatican Archives &c., ed. J. M. Rigg, v2, 1926.
Calendarii. Ant. Cal. d. chiesa di Bergamo, ed. G. Finazzi, 1871, *see* REGIA DEP. DI STORIA PATRIA. Misc., t13, 1871.
Calhoun (John Caldwell), *see* FOSTER (T.) & G. COCHRAN, *edd.* *Eulogies on J. C. &c., 1853.
California. C. & the Oriental. Rep. of State Board of Control, June 1920. Rev. to Jan. 1922. 8°. Sacramento. 1922
UNIVERSITY.
Museum of Vertebrate Zoology, *see* GRINNELL (J.) & T. I. STORER. Animal life in the Yosemite, 1924.
—— Publications. Egypt. arch. (Hearst Exped.), v2, 3. fol. L. 1908–9
see REISNER (G. A.) & A. C. MACE. Early dynastic cemeteries of Naga-ed-Dêr, 2p, 1908–9. [2, 3]
—— Publications in history. v14ii, iii. 8°. Berkeley, *Cal.* 1926
see GUTTRIDGE (G. H.) D. Hartley, M.P., 1774–83, 1926. [14iii.]
,, MORRIS (W. A.) Early Eng. county court, 1926. [14ii, pp. 89–230.]
Calina (Josephine), *see* NICOLL (*Mrs.* ALLARDYCE).
Calinescu (Gh.) Alc. missionari cattol. ital. n. Moldavia (17–18c.), *see* SCUOLA ROMENA DI ROMA. Diplom. Ital., v1, 1925.
Calixtus (Friedrich Ulrich). Dissensus theolog. Jenensium hodiern. a suis majoribus &c. [P440]. s4°. [Jena?]. 1679
Tract. theol. de hæresi, schismate & hæreticorum pœnis &c. s4°. Helmstadi. [c. 1690]
see CAROLUS (A.) Apologeticus Memorabilia eccl. A. C. â criminat. C. vindic., 1699.
,, STRAUCH (Æ.) Consensus repet. fidei vere Lutheran., a calumn. &c. C. vindic., 1668.
Calixtus (Georg).
Apparatus theolog. & fragmenti hist. eccl. occident [*w. sep. pagin.*] ed. 2ª aucta. s4°. Helmstadii. 1661
Colloquium Hemelschenburg. inter G. C. & P. Augustinum Jesuitam habitum 1614. ed. 2ª. [P2647]. s4°. Helmestadi. 1665
Consideratio doct. pontif. juxta ductum Concil. Trident. & reformatæ juxta Confess. Thoruni Boruss., 1645. F. U. Calixtus altera vice ed. s4°. Helmestadii. 1672
De bono perfecte summo &c. liber. s4°. Helmestadi. 1643
De conjugio clericorum liber. Ed. H. P. C. Henke. 2p *in* 1v [*pagin. contin.*] s8°. Helmstadii. 1783
De immortalitate animæ & resurr. carnis. s4°. Helmæstadi. 1635
De transsubstantiatione contra Pontificios exercit., quam sub præs. G. C. sustin. P. C. Dörer. [Exercit. 2a q. sustin. J. A. Quenstedt]. [P2645]. s8°. Helmestadi. 1643
Epitome theologiæ &c. Adj. ejusdem disput. de principio theol. c. pontif. s8° Brunsvigæ. 1634
,, ,, [*a. ed.*] s8°. Brunsvigæ. 1547 [*i.e.* 1647]
,, ,, Acc. quorundam locorum declar. autore G. Titio. [*sep. pagin.*] s8°. Brunsvigæ. 1653
,, ,, n. ed. 8°. Helmestadii. 1661
In Acta Apostolorum; [in Romanos; in Corinthios; in Galatas; in Ephesios; in Philipp.; in Coloss.; in Thessalon.] expos. litt. [8p, *sep. pagin. & tp. b. in 1v*]. s4°. Brunsvigæ. 1652–54
Quatuor Evangelic. script. concordia & locorum difficilium &c. explic. &c. s4°. Halberstadii. 1624
see CALOVIUS (A.) Instit. theolog.; cum exam. nov. theol. C. &c., 1649.
,, DISQUISITIONES theol. de anima sep. a corpore &c. a [G. C. &c.], 2p, 1730.

Calixtus (Georg) [*continued*].
see FASCICULUS rar. & curios. script. de animæ statu, a C. &c., 1692.
,, HULSEMANN (J.) Dialysis apologet. problematis Calixtini: mysterium Trinitatis &c., 1650.
,, LIPSIUS (J.) De Cruce libri 3; acc. G. C. De vera forma Crucis, 1640.
,, NIHUSIUS (B.) Anticriticus de fabrica Crucis incert. G. C. opinionem esse indicans, 1640.
,, SCHARF (J.) Protest. adv. atrocia G. Calixti scandala, 1652.
Call, *The family of, see* ROMANES (C. S.) The Calls of Norfolk & Suffolk, th. Paston connect[s]. &c., 1920.
Callahan (Daniel F.), *see* CLARK (LINDLEY D.) & D. F. C. Decisions of courts &c., 1923.
Callard (Ernest). The manor of Freckenham, an anc. corner of East Anglia, w. app. of early doc. s4°. [1924]
Callaway (John).
Hints on the Cingalese & Eng. lang. s8°. Colombo. 1821
Vocabulary w. useful phrases &c., in Eng., Portuguese & Cingalese lang. 8°. Colombo. 1818
Callcott (John Wall) [CALCOTT].
Gram. of music &c. 11th ed. s8°. *n.d.*
Calle (Pedro Urbano Gonzalez de la), *see* GONZALEZ DE LA CALLE (P. U.)
Calleja y Fernández (Saturnino).
Dicc. biogr. de hombres ilust. s8°. [1920]
Callenberg (Johann Heinrich).
Comm. de scepticismo exegetico. s8°. Lipsiæ. 1730
Vitæ J. D. Herrnschmidii illustr. [*b. w.* Herrnschmid (J. D.) Vita M. Lutheri, 1742]. s8°. Halæ. 1735
Callender (Geoffrey Arthur Romaine).
Naval side of Brit. history. [repr.] 8°. [1925]
Callender (Guy Stevens). Selections f. the econ. hist. of the U.S., 1765–1860, w. intr. essays. 8°. Boston. [1909]
Callender (John), *M.A., of Newport, Rhode Island.* Histor. disc. on the civil & relig. affairs of Rhode Island & Providence plantations, 1638 to end of first cent. s8°. Boston [Mass.] 1739
Callet (Auguste). Les orig. de la Troisième Rép. s8°. 1921
Callias (Suzanne de). Jerry, roman inéd., *see* ŒUVRES libres, 28, 1923.
Callières (François de). Hist. pöetique de la guerre nouv. entre les anciens & les modernes. s8°. Amsterdam. 1688
Calligaris (Giuseppe). Due pretese dominaz. straniere in Sardegna nel sec. 8, *see* REGIA DEP. DI STORIA PATRIA. Misc., t34, 1896.
Callimachus. C. & Lycophron; w. Eng. tr. by A. W. Mair, — Aratus w. tr. by G. R. Mair. [Loeb Class. Lib.] s8°. 1921
Fragmenta nuper reperta ed. R. Pfeiffer, *see* KLEINE TEXTE, T145, 1921.
Hymnes — Épigrammes — Les origines — Hécalé — Iambes — Poèmes lyriques. Texte établi par E. Cahen. [Coll. des univ. de Fr.] 8°. 1922
see WILAMOWITZ-MÖLLENDORFF (U. v.) Hellenist. Dichtung in d. Zeit des K., 2B, 1924.
Callinus, *see* HUDSON-WILLIAMS (T.) Early Greek elegy: fragm. of C. &c., 1926.
Callisthenes [PSEUDO-CALLISTHENES]. Hist. Alexandri Magni. Recensio vet., ed G. Kroll. v1. 8°. Berlin. 1926
see ALEXANDER, *the Gt.* Ἱστόρια Ἀ.: armen. Übers. d. A.-Biog. (Pseudo-C.), 1896.
,, DASHEAN (H.) St[s]. of Pseudo-C.'s Life of Alexander; *in Arm.*, 1895.
Callistus (Nicephorus). Scriptores vere Catholici, eccl. hist. libri 18. Adjecimus: M. A. Cassiodori Tripartitam hist. &c. repurgatam. [*b. w.* Columna (P.) *Galatinus.* De Arcanis Cath. veritatis, 1603]. 2p. [*sep. tp. & pagin.*] fol. Francof. 1588
Serm. in M. Magdalenam, Græce, *see* BANDINI (A. M.) Fasc. rer. Gr. eccles., 1764.
Callixenus, *of Rhodes, see* STUDNICZKA (F.) Das Symposion Ptolemaios II n. d. Beschr. d. K., 1914.
Callot (Jacques). Les misères & les mal-heurs de la guerre, representez par J. C. (1633, *facs.*), *see* FREYTAG (G.) Bilder, B4, 1925.
see FAITHORNE (W.) Art of graveing & etching, 1662.
,, LEVERTIN (O.) Studier öfver J. C., 3e uppl., 1920.
,, PLAN (P. P.) J. C., n. éd. rev. &c., 1914.
,, POLLHAMMER (C.) J. C. als Illustrator, 1925.
Callwell (*Maj.-Gen. Sir* Charles Edward).
The armed strength of Roumania. 8°. 1888
Experiences of a dug-out, 1914–18. 8°. 1920
Field-Marshal Sir H. Wilson: life & diaries. Pref. by Marshal Foch. 2v. 8°. 1927

Callwell (*Maj.-Gen. Sir* **Charles Edward)** [*continued*].
Lessons to be learnt f. small wars since 1870. [P2591]. s8°. 1895
Life of Sir S. Maude, Lt.-Gen., K.C.B. &c. 8°. 1920
Stray recoll. 2v. 8°. 1923
The tactics of to-day. 2nd ed. s8°. 1909
see MacCalmont (*Maj.-Gen. Sir* H.) Memoirs; ed. & compl. by C. E. C., 1924.

Calman (William Thomas). Pynogonida, *see* Brit. Antarctic Exped., 1910–13. Zoology, v3, 1918–23.
see Brit. Antarctic Exped., 1910–13: Zoology, v3, Crustacea, p4; by C., 1915–23.
„ Brit. Museum of Nat. Hist. Marine boring animals; by W. T. C., 1919.

Calmberg (E. Ph. L.) De utilitate ex accur. linguæ Sanscr. cognit. in linguæ Gr. Latinæque etymologiam. s4°. Hamburgi. 1832

Calmet (Augustin). Comment. littéral, hist. &c. sur la règle de saint Benoit. 2t. 4°. 1734
see Chevrier (F. A. de). Mém^s^. p. s. à l'hist. des hommes illust. de Lorraine, avec une réfut. de la Bibl. lorraine de C., 2t, 1754.

Calmette (Joseph). La société féodale. s8°. 1923
see Montpellier. Cartul. de l'Univ. de M., t2, Inventaires de la Fac. de Méd. &c.; intr. par J. C., 1912.
—— **& P. Vidal.** Hist. de Roussillon. 8°. 1923

Calmettes (Pierre). Les joujoux, hist., technique &c. Préf. d'A. France. s8°. 1914

Calmeyn (Maurice). Au Congo belge. Chasses à l'éléphant, les indigènes, l'admin. la8°. Brux. 1912

Calmon-Maison (Jean Joseph Robert).
Le maréchal de Château-Renault, 1637–1716. 8°. 1903

Calo (Johann Adam).
De vita Jacobi Bœhmii. [P595]. s4°. Vitembergæ. 1707
Hist. Jacobi Bœhmii. s4°. Vitembergæ. 1715

Calomnie. *Calomnie (De la) ou instruction du procès entre les Jésuites & leurs adversaires [*by A. Arnauld*], 1716, *see* Jesuits. *Morale pratique &c., 2e éd., t8, 1716.

Calonne (*le vte.* **Albéric de).** La vie agricole sous l'anc. régime dans le nord de la France, *see* Soc. des Antiq. de Picardie. Mém., s4, t9, 1920.

Calonne (Charles Alex. de), *see* Necker (J.) Sur le compte rendu au roi, 1781 [*in ans. to the* "Reponse" *of C.*, 1788], 1788.

Calovius (Abraham) [Kalau]. Cassellana de unione Reformatorum cum Lutheranis consult. Denuo ed. per A. C. [P441]. s4°. Witenbergæ. 1664
Institutionum theologic. τὰ προλεγόμενα. Cum examine nov. theologiæ Calixtinæ &c. s8°. Dantisci. 1649
Systema locorum theolog. 12t. *in* 5v. s4°. Wittebergæ. 1655–77
Theologia positiva per definitiones, &c. s8°. Francof. 1690

Calpurnius (Titus Julius), *Siculus*, *see* Chiavola (C.) Della vita e dell' opera di T. C. S., 1921.

Cals (Jeanne Ramel). Amour en province, nouvelle, *see* Œuvres libres, 51, 1925.

Calthrop (Dion Clayton).
A diary of an 18th-cent. garden. 8°. [1926]
Hyacinth. An excursion. 8°. 1927
Little flower of the street. s8°. 1923
Punch and Judy. With essay. s8°. 1926

Calthrop (E. R.), *see* Mawson (E. O.) Pioneer irrig., w. add. ch. on light railways by E. R. C., 1904.

Calthrop (*Capt.* **Everard Ferguson).** A dict. of milit. terms. Eng.-Jap.—Jap.-Eng. With list of 1200 Chinese characters. s8°. Tokyo. 1907

Calva (Estéban). Instit. de derecho civil segun el código del Distr. Federal &c. de la Baja California. Por E. C. y colab. de F. de P. Segura. 2t. 8°. Mexico. 1874–75

Calverley. The Calverley charters. Transcr. by S. Margerison. Ed. W. P. Baildon & S. M. [Thoresby Soc., 6]. v1. 8°. Leeds. 1904

Calverley, *Family of*, *see* Calverley. The C. charters; ed. W. P. Baildon &c., v1, 1904.

Calverley (Charles Stuart). Fly leaves. 7th thousand. s8°. 1878
Verses & trans. 6th ed. s8°. 1877

Calvert (Albert Frederick).
The Spanish royal tapestries. s8°. 1921

Calvert (Alfred). Shipping office organis. 8°. [1910]

Calvert (C.)
see Henderson (B.) & C. C. Wonder tales of Alsace-Lorraine, 1925.
„ —— & —— Wonder tales of anc. Spain, 1924.

Calvert (E. Roy).
Capital punishment in the 20th cent. 8°. [1927]

Calvert (Edward), *see* Binyon (L.) Followers of W. Blake: E. C. &c., 1925.

Calvert (*Hon. Mrs.* **Frances),** *wife of Nicolson Calvert*, *see* Richardson (E. M.) Next door neighbours [*i.e. Hon. Mrs. C.* &c.], 1926.

Calvert (James), *see* Fiji & the Fijians, v2, Mission hist., by C., 1860.

Calvert (John). Vazeeri Rupi, the silver country of the Vazeers, in Kulu &c. 8°. 1873

Calves-Head Club. Secret (The) hist. of the C.-H. Club, 1705, *see* Ward (E.)

Calvet (J.) L'abbé Gustave Morel. Tr. by E. J. I. Dredge, w. intr. by W. J. Birkbeck. 8°. 1913

Calvi (Felice). Gius. Cossa: commem., *see* Regia Deput. Misc., t25, 1887.

Calvi (Gerolamo). I manoscritti di Leonardo da Vinci, cronol., stor. & biog. 8°. Bologna. 1925

Calvin (Jean).
Catechismus eccl. Genev. [*b. w. h.* Epistolæ duæ &c. 1550]. s8°. Genevæ. 1550
Comm. in Acta Apostolorum &c. fol. Genevæ. 1584
Comm. in Epist. P. ad Romanos. s8°. Argentorati, *W. Rihel.* 1540
Comm. in utranque Pauli epist. ad Timotheum. s8°. Genevæ. 1548
Defensio orthodoxæ fidei de Trinitate, contra prodig. errores Mich. Serveti &c. s8°. [Genevæ]. 1554
De prædestinatione &c. libellus. [*b. w. h.* Epistolæ duæ &c. 1550]. s8°. Genevæ. 1550
Epistolæ duæ, de rebus hoc seculo cognitu necessariis. s8°. Genevæ. 1550
In omnes Pauli epistolas, atque in epist. ad Hebræos, & canonicas comm. [Comm. in epistolas canon., *w. sep. tp. & pagin.*] 8°. Genevæ. 1565
Instit. Christianæ relig. s8°. *n.p.*, *A. Rebulius.* 1561
„ „ ....fol. Genevæ. 1568
„ „ compendium &c. per E. Bunnium. s8°. Antverpiæ. 1582
Interim adultero-Germanum &c. Adj., Vera Xtnæ pacific. &c. ratio. [*Foll. by* Appendix, 1550, *w. sep. signatures*]. s8°. [Geneva ?] 1549
*Rudimenta fidei Xtianæ sive Cat. Adj. Catechismus alius. (*Greek & Lat.*) s8°. [Geneva, *R. Stephanus*]. 1575
Summar. Begriff d. lehr v. Sacramenten, verteuscht auss d. 4ten Buch der Underweisung Christl. Relig. [*b. w.* Heidelberg, Bekanntnuss &c., 1592]. s4°. Newstadt a. d. Hardt. 1592
*Supplex exhortatio ad Carolum V. &c. Spiræ. [*b. w.* Bucer (M.) Scripta duo adversaria, 1544]. s4°. *n.p.*, *Pressa valentior.* 1543
Ultima admonitio ad J. westphalū. s8°. [Genevæ, *apud J. Crispinum*]. 1557

Translations.
An abridgement of the Instit. of Xtn. religion, by W. Lawne. Tr. out of Lat. by C. Fetherstone. s8°. E., *T. Vautrollier.* 1585
„ „ ....s8°. E. 1586
The catechisme cont. the grounds of Christian relig. [Tr.] s8°. E. 1645
Christian theology, sel. & arranged, w. life of a. by S. Dunn. s8°. 1837
Comm. on a harmony of Matthew, Mark & Luke. Tr. W. Pringle. 3v. 8°. E. 1845–46
Comm. on Daniel. Tr. T. Myers. 2v. 8°. E. 1852–53
Comm. on Genesis. Tr. J. King. 2v. 8°. E. 1847–50
Comm. on Isaiah. Tr. W. Pringle. 4v. 8°. E. 1850–54
Comm. on Jeremiah & Lamentations. Tr. & ed. J. Owen. 5v. 8°. E 1850–55
Comm. on Joshua. Tr. H. Beveridge. Prof. Tholuck's dissert. &c. of divines as to the value &c. of C.'s writings. 8°. E 1854
Comm. on Psalms. Tr. J. Anderson. 5v. 8°. E. 1845–49
Comm. on the Catholic Epistles. Tr. J. Owen. 8°. E. 1855
Comm. on the Ep. to the Corinthians. Tr. J. Pringle. 2v. 8°. E. 1848–49
Comm. on the Ep. to the Galatians & Ephesians. Tr. W. Pringle. 8°. E. 1854
Comm. on the Ep. to the Hebrews. Tr. J. Owen. 8°. E. 1853
Comm. on the Ep. to the Philippians, Colossians & Thessalonians. Tr. J. Pringle. 8°. E. 1851
Comm. on the Ep. to the Romans. Tr. J. Owen. 8°. E. 1849
Comm. on the Ep. to Timothy, Titus & Philemon. Tr. W. Pringle. 8°. E. 1856
Comm. on the first 20 chaps. of Ezekiel. Tr. T. Myers. 2v. 8°. E. 1849–50
Comm. on the 4 last books of Moses. Tr. C. W Bingham. 4v. 8°. E. 1852–55
Comm. on the Gospel acc. to John. Tr. W. Pringle. 2v. 8°. E. 1847
Comm. on the twelve minor prophets. Tr. J. Owen. 5v. 8°. E. 1846–49

Calvin (Jean) [*continued*].
TRANSLATIONS [*continued*].
The Comm. upon the Actes of the Apostles. Tr. by C. Fetherstone. 8°. 1585
„ „ Ed. f. tr. of C. Fetherstone by H. Beveridge. 2v. 8°. E. 1844
Foure sermons. With expos. of 87. Psalme. Tr. J. Fielde. [*b. w. h.* Thirteene sermons, 1579]. 8°. 1579
A harmonie upon the three Evangelists Matthew, Mark & Luke w. the comm. of J. C. Tr. by E. P[aget]. Added a comm. upon S. John, by the same author [tr. by C. Fetherstone; *w. sep. pagin.*] 8°. 1584
The instit. of Christ. relig. Tr. by T. Norton. sfol. 1634
„ „ ....s4°. Glasgow. 1762
„ „ ....Tr. H. Beveridge. 3v. 8°. E. 1845–46
Thirteene sermons, entreating of the free election of God in Jacob &c. Tr. J. Fielde. 8°. 1579
Tracts rel. to the Reformation. With h. life by T. Beza. Tr. H. Beveridge. 3v. 8°. E. 1844–51
v2 *has t.*: Tracts cont. treatises on the Sacraments &c. v3, *has t.*: Tracts cont. Antidote to the Council of Trent &c.
REFERENCES.
see ANDREÆ (J.) Solida refutat. compilat. Cingl. & Calvin., 1584.
„ BALDUIN (FRANÇOIS). Responsio ad Calvinum & Bezam, 1564.
„ BAUER (C.) Die Bezieh. C. zu Frankfurt a. M., 1920
„ BEZA (T.) Vie de J. C., n. éd., 1864.
„ CAMERARIUS (B), *Beneventanus.* De gratia & libero arbitrio, cum J. Calvino disput., 1556.
„ COCHLÆUS (J.) De autoritate eccl. & Script. in Calvini errores, 1549.
„ —— De Interim resp. ad librum J. C., 1549.
„ —— De sacris reliquiis contra J. C. calumnias resp., 1549.
„ —— De votis discept. contra impugn. J. C., 1550.
„ CUTHBERTSON (D.) A tragedy of the Reform.: hist. &c. of the "Christianismi restitutio," 1553, w. acc. of controv. betw. M. Servetus & C., 1912.
„ DOUMERGUE (E.) J. C., t5–7, 1917–27.
„ FRONTEAU (J.) Antithesis Augustini & C., 1651.
„ HAUSSHERR (H.) Der Staat in C.'s Gedankenwelt, 1923.
„ HUNNIUS (E.) Calvinus Judaizans &c., 1593.
„ KŬYPER (A.) Disquisitio exhib. J. C. & J. à Lasco de ecclesia sent. &c., 1862.
„ LANG (A.) J. C.: e. Lebensbild zu s. 400. Geburtstag, 1909.
„ ROSSEEUW SAINT HILAIRE (E. F. A.) Etudes (Disc. sur C. &c.), 1863.
„ WERNLE (P.) Der evangel. Glaube nach d. Hauptschr. d. Reformatoren, B3, C., 1919.
„ ZIJNEN (F. P. J. S.) Specimen hist.-dogmat. quo Anselmi & C. placita de redemtione inter se conf., 1852.

Calvinianæ. *Crudelitatis C. exempla duo recentiss. ex Anglia, 1585, *see* CRUDELITAS.
***Calvinischer** Abzug vom Necker u. Rhein, 1628, *see* CHRISTIAN, *von Jerusalem, ps.*
***Calvinism** defended & Arminianism refuted &c., 1780, *see* CALVINISTICUS, *ps.*
Calvinistic Methodists, *see* METHODISTS.
Calvinisticus, *ps.* Calvinism defended, & Arminianism refuted; or remarks on pamphlet by Philalethes ent. Solemn caution agst. ten horns of Calvinism. [P2535]. s8°. Leeds. 1780
Calvisius (Andreas Christoph) [KALLWITZ]. Disput. de causis incrementi literarii post barbara secula. Præs. A. C. C., resp. J. P. Gumprecht. [P444]. s4°. Lipsiæ. 1698
Calwer (Richard). Staatsbankerott. Darstellung s. Ursachen u. Wirkungen. [*Typescript*]. [P2508]. 4°. 1921
Calza (Guido). Pola. Con lettera di C. Ricci. s8°. [1920]
La preminenza dell' "insula" n. edilizia romana, *see* REALE ACCAD. D. LINCEI. Mon. ant., v23, 1914.
Gli scavi recenti nell' abitato di Ostia, *see* REALE ACCAD. D. LINCEI. Mon. ant., v26, 1920.
Calzini (Raffaele). L'amore escluso. s8°. Milano. [1920]
Giorgio Lukomski. la8°. Milano. 1923
Cam (Helen M.) Studies in the hundred rolls; some aspects of 13th cent. admin., 1921, *see* VINOGRADOFF (*Sir* P.) St. in legal &c. hist., v6, 1921.
Cama (Kharshedji Rustamji), *see* EDWARDES (S. M.) K. R. C., 1923.
Camacho (Sebastián). Discurso, *see* BRIBIESCA (J.) Ayuntamiento constit. de México &c., 1898.
Cámara del libro y de la propiedad intelectual. Corporación oficial. [P2415]. s4°. Barcelona. 1919
Camarasa (*Marquis* de). *Causeries brouettiques: notes &c. pour un traité hist. &c. de la brouette. [*Dedic. signed* Le Cte. de Moriana &c.] 4°. [Madrid. 1924?]
Cambert (Robert), *see* POUGIN (A.) Les vrais créateurs de l'opéra franç.: Perrin & C., 1881.
Cambiano (Giulio), *di Ruffia.* Memorabili dal 1542 al 1611; con note illust. di V. Promis, *see* REGIA DEP. DI STORIA PATRIA. Misc., t9, 1870.
Cambolive (Étienne). Hist. de divers événements cont. en abrégé les persécutions en France, les moyens diaboliques &c. s8°. Amsterdam. 1698
Cambon (Joseph), *1756–1820, see* ARNAUD (R.) Le débâcle financ. de la Révol.: Cambon, 1926.
Cambon (Jules). Disc. pour la récept. de J. C. [*on* F. Charmes. Rép. de A. Ribot. Acad. Fr., 20 nov. 1919. P2869]. 4°. 1919
see BERTRAND (L. M. E.) Disc. pour la récept. de L. B. (Rép. de J. C.), 1926.
Cambray, *The family of, see* DUNBAR-DUNBAR (J. A.) Fam. of C. of Gt. Rissington, 1898.
Cambrian Archæological Association.
see WESTWOOD (J. O.) Lapidarium Walliæ, 1876–9.
„ YARDLEY (E.) Menevia sacra, 1927.
Cambridge [UNIVERSITY, TOWN &c.].
Alumni Cantab.: list of students, graduates &c., to 1900, pl, 4v, 1922–27, *see* VENN (J.) & J. A. VENN.
C. Anglo-Norman texts, 1924, *see* ANGLO-NORMAN.
C. bk. of lesser poets, 1927, *see* SQUIRE (J. C.), *ed.*
C. bk. of prose & verse (7–15 c.); 1924, *see* SAMPSON (G.), *ed.*
C. essays on adult education, 1920, *see* PARRY (R. St. J.), *ed.*
C. in the 17th cent., 3p, 1855–71, *see* MAYOR (J. E. B.), *ed.*
C. readings in Spanish lit., 1920, *see* FITZMAURICE-KELLY (J.)
C. readings in the lit. of science, *see* WHETHAM (W. C. D. & M. D.), *edd.*
C. studies in Eng. legal hist. Ed. H. D. Hazeltine.
see BOLLAND (W. C.) Manual of year-book studies, 1925.
„ PLUCKNETT (T. F. T.) Statutes & th. interp. in 1st half of 14th c., 1922.
„ SELDEN (J.) Ad Fletam dissert.; intr. &c. by D. Ogg, 1925.
C. University calendar, 1816, 1819, 1920/21, 1923/24, 1924/25, 1926/27. s8°. C. [1816]–1926
[Carmina Cantab. Ed. K. Strecker]. Die cambridger Lieder &c. [Mon. Germ. Hist.] 8°. 1926
College rhymes, v1–3, 1860–62, *see* COLLEGE.
Demosthenes demobilised. Record of C. Union Soc. debates, Feb. 1919–June 1920. By the 4 Presidents [*i.e.* W. L. McNair, J. W. Morris &c.] Pref. by Rt. Hon. A. Chamberlain. Intr. by J. R. Tanner. 8°. C. 1920
*Guide (A) thr. the University of C. n. ed. s8°. C. 1820
Histor. register of Univ. of C., suppl., 1911–20. 8°. C. 1922
Index to Tripos lists, 1748–1910, cont. in The hist. reg. of Univ. of C. to 1910. Compiled by C. W. Previté-Orton. s8°. C. 1923
Lacrymæ Cantab. in obitum reginæ Mariæ. s4°. Cantabrigiæ. 1694/5
*Querela Cantab. or remonstrance for banished members &c., 1647; 1685, *see* BARWICK (J.)
Student's hdbk. 20th ed., rev. to June 30, 1921. s8°. C. 1921
see SMITH (G. C. M.) College plays performed in Univ. of C., 1923.
CHRIST'S COLLEGE.
Descr. cat. of the Western MSS. in the lib. of C.'s C.; by M. R. James. la8°. C. 1905
Early eds. of Milton's works in C. C. Lib. [Repr. f. C. C. mag. v. 33]. [P2755]. s8°. [1921]
see MILTON (J.) Portraits, prints & writings of M., by G. C. Williamson: exhib. at Ch. Coll., 1908; repr., *large paper copy*, 1908.
CLARE COLLEGE.
Descr. cat. of the Western MSS. in the lib. of C. C.; by M. R. James. la8°. C. 1905
CORPUS CHRISTI COLLEGE.
Early printed bks. in Lib. of C. C. Coll. Hand-list arr. in order of country &c., w. ref. to Proctor's Index &c. Comp. by S. Gaselee. la8°. C. 1921
„ „ ....Add. (1922) [*b. w.* Hand-list]. la8°. C. [1922]
see CORPUS. The C. gloss.; ed. W. M. Lindsay, 1921.
„ MIDDLETON (J. H.) Lewis coll. of gems & rings &c., 1892.
EMMANUEL COLLEGE.
Western MSS. in the lib. of E. C.; descr. cat.; by M. R. James. la8°. C. 1904
FITZWILLIAM MUSEUM.
Cat. of pictures in the Marlay bequest, F. Mus., Camb. Compiled by W. G. Constable. 8°. C. 1927
Cat. of the McClean coll. of Greek coins. By S. W. Grose. v1, 2. la8°. C. 1923–26
1, West. Eur., Magna Græcia, Sicily.
2, Greek Mainland, Ægæan Isls., Crete.
see WACE (A. J. B.) A Cretan statuette in the F. M., 1927.

Cambridge [*continued*].
GIRTON COLLEGE.
Cat. of printed bks. & Semitic & Jewish MSS. in the Mary Frere Hebrew Library at Girton Coll. By H. Loewe. [P2762]. 8°. [C. 1915]
JESUS COLLEGE.
Descr. cat. of the MSS. in the lib. of J. C.; by M. R. James. la8°. 1895
MAGDALENE COLLEGE.
Bibliotheca Pepysiana: a descr. cat. of the lib. of S. Pepys. p3. 8°. 1923
3, Mediæval MSS; by M. R. James.
Descr. cat. of naval MSS. in the Pepysian Lib. at M. C. Ed. J. R. Tanner. [Navy Records Soc., 57]. v4. 8°. 1923
4, Admiralty journal [1673–9].
Descr. cat. of the MSS. in the coll. lib. of M. C.; by M. R. James. la8°. C. 1909
see BIBLE: GOSPELS. The Pepysian Gospel harmony; ed. M. Goates, 1922.
QUEENS' COLLEGE.
Descr. cat. of the Western MSS. in the lib. of Q. C.; by M. R. James. la8°. C. 1905
ST. CATHERINE'S COLLEGE.
Descr. cat. of MSS. in the library; by M. R. James. la8°. C. 1925
ST. JOHN THE EVANGELIST, COLL. OF.
The Samuel Butler Coll. at St. J.'s Coll. Cat. & comm. by H. F. Jones & A. T. Bartholomew. 8°. C. 1921
SIDNEY SUSSEX COLLEGE.
Descr. cat. of MSS. in the lib. of S. S. C.; by M. R. James. la8°. C. 1895
TRINITY COLLEGE.
see ESDAILE (K. A.) Roubiliac's work at T. C., Camb., 1924.
Cambridge (The) Ancient History. Ed. J. B. Bury, S. A. Cook, F. E. Adcock. v1–6 *&* Plates, v1, prep. by C. T. Seltman. 8°. C. 1923–27
1, Egypt & Babylonia to 1580 B.C.
2, Egyptian & Hittite Empires to c. 1000 B.C.
3, Assyrian Empire.
4, Persian Empire & the West.
5, Athens, 478–401 B.C.
6, Macedon, 401–301 B.C.
Cambridge Anglo-Norman Society, *see* ANGLO-NORMAN. Camb. Anglo-Norman texts: Poem on the Assumption; ed. J. P. Strachey &c., 1924.
Cambridge Antiquarian Society.
Communications, v5, 1880–84. 8°. C. 1886
Proceedings (1920–21, 1925–26), w. Communications. v23, 28. 8°. C. 1922–27
Report, 1881. [*b. w.* Camb. Antiq. Soc. Communic., v5, 1880–84.] 8°. C. 1883
PUBLICATIONS.
see CARÖE (W. D.) King's Hostel, Trin. Coll., 1909. [Quarto. N.S. 2]
,, GRAY (A.) Dual origin of the town of Camb., 1908. [Quarto. N.S. 1]
Cambridge Camden Society. [*Aft.* ECCLESIOLOGICAL SOCIETY.]
*Hand-book of Eng. ecclesiology. s8°. 1847
Cambridge historical journal (The). v1, 1923–25. 8°. C. 1925
Cambridge (The) Hist. of British foreign policy, 1783–1919. Ed. by Sir A. W. Ward & G. P. Gooch. 3v. 8°. C. 1922–23
Cambridge (The) Hist. of Eng. lit. Ed. A. W. Ward & A. R. Waller. v15, Gen. index. 8°. C. 1927
,, ,, ...[n. impr. *or* repr.] 14v. 8°. C. 1912–22
,, ,, Suppl.: A hist. of American lit. Ed. W. P. Trent, J. Erskine, S. P. Sherman, C. van Doren. v3, 4. [*pagin. cont.*] 8°. C. 1921
,, ,, ,, *Abridgment w. t.:* A short hist. of Amer. lit. Ed. W. P. T., J. E. &c. Intr. by C. van Doren. 8°. C. 1924
Cambridge (The) Hist. of India. Ed. by E. J. Rapson. v1. 8°. C. 1922
Cambridge Medieval History (The). Planned by J. B. Bury. Ed. H. M. Gwatkin, J. P. Whitney [*& others*]. v3–5 [3, 4 *have* maps *sep.*], la8°. C. 1922–26
3, Germany & the Western Empire.
4, Eastern Roman Empire.
5, Contest of Empire & Papacy.
Cambridge Philos. Society, *see* BOHR (N.) Applic. of quantum theory to atomic structure, p1, 1924.
Cambridgeshire. C. parish reg. Marriages. Gen. ed., T. M. Blagg. v7, 8, ed. E. Young. 8°. 1916–27
Cambronne (Pierre Jacques Étienne), *see* BRUNSCHVICG (L.) C., sa vie &c., 1894.

Camden Miscellany (The).
v13, 14. [R. Hist. Soc., III, 34, 37]. s4°. 1924–26
Cont. the following works, each of wh. has sep. tp. & pagin.
Castilla (J. de). The Eng. conquest of Jamaica, 1655–56; tr. by I. A. Wright, 1923. [13.]
Devereux, *Family of.* D. papers, w. R. Broughton's mem. (1575–1601); ed. H. E. Malden, 1923. [13.]
Durham. Gesta Dunelmensia, A.D. 1300; ed. R. K. Richardson, 1924. [13.]
Embajada española. Tr. & ed. H. J. Chaytor, 1926. [14.]
Fannant (T.) Hist. mirab. parliamenti, 1386; ed. M. McKisack. [14.]
Jackson (*Capt.* W.) Voyages (1642–45); ed. V. T. Harlow, 1923. [13.]
John II, *k. of France.* Ransom of, 1360–70; ed. D. M. Broome, 1926. [14.]
Peter *de Aqua Blanc, bp. of Hereford.* Will of; ed. C. E. Woodruff, 1926. [14.]
Stonor, *Family of.* Suppl. S. letters & papers (1314–1482), by C. L. Kingsford, 1923. [13.]
Wright (I. A.) Span. narratives of Eng. attack on Santo Domingo, 1655; transcr. & tr. by I. A. W., 1926. [14.]
Camden Society. List & index of publ. of the Roy. Hist. Soc., 1871–1924 & of the C. Soc., 1840–97; ed. H. Hall, 1925, *see* ROY. HIST. SOC.
Camden (Theophilus).
The imperial hist. of England &c. 2v *in* 1. fol. 1809–11
Camden (William), *the antiquary.* Anglica, Hibernica, Normannica, Cambrica, a veteribus scr.; ex bibl. G. Camdeni. fol. Francofurti. 1603
Annales rerum Anglic. & Hibernic. regn. Elizabetha. s8°. Lug. Batavorum. 1625
Britannia. Nunc tertio recog. &c. 8°. Londini. 1590
TRANSLATIONS.
Annales, the true & royall history of Elizabeth, &c. [1558–88 being p1–3 of Camden's Annales rerum Anglic. tr. fr. the French version of P. d[e] B[elligent] by A. Darcie]. s4°. 1625
A 2nd vol. (1629) cont. a mem. of affaires of state [1589–1603. Being p4 of Camden's Annales, tr. by T. Browne] is wanting.
Britannia. Tr., w. add. &c. 2nd ed., rev. &c. by E. Gibson. 2v. fol. 1722
The hist. of Elizabeth, 3rd ed. rev. sfol. 1675
Remaines conc. Britaine. rev., corr. &c. s4°. 1614
,, ,, 6th impr. By the care of J. Philipot &c. [*Portrait wanting*]. s4°. 1657
Camera (Matteo). Mem. storico-diplomat. dell' ant. città e ducato di Amalfi. 2v. 4°. Salerno. 1876–81
Camerarius (Bartholomæus), *Beneventanus.* De gratia & libero arbitrio, cum J. Calvino disput. [*b. w. h.* De prædestinatione, 1556]. s4°. Parisiis. 1556
De prædestinatione. s4°. Parisiis. 1556
Camerarius (Joachimus), *the elder.*
Capita pietatis &c. versibus Græcis comprehensa &c. s8°. Lipsiæ. 1545
Commentatiuncula: Non esse ex eventis de consiliis &c. hominum pronuntiandum: de exordio v. Ovidiani: Exitus acta probat. s8°. Lipsiæ. 1572
De Philippi Melanchthonis ortu, totius vitæ curriculo & morte, narr. s8°. Lipsiæ [*E. Vœgelin.* 1566]
,, ,, [*a. ed w. t.* Vita P. M.] s8°. Hagæ-Com. 1655
,, ,, [*a. ed.*] s8°. Lipsiæ. 1696
,, ,, Rec., notas, doc., bibl. libr. M. &c. add. G. T. Strobelius. Præf. est J. A. Nœsselt. 8°. Halæ. 1777
Hist. narr. de fratrum orthodox. eccl. in Bohemia, Moravia, Polonia &c. [Ed. a Ludovico Camerario]. s8°. Heidelbergæ. [1605]
Narr. de Georgio principe Anhaltino & Ascaniæ &c. [*b. w. h.* De P. Melanchthoni ortu &c., 1696]. s8°. Lipsiæ. 1696
Narr. de Helio Eobano Hesso &c. [*b. w. h.* De P. Melanchthoni ortu &c., 1696]. s8°. Lipsiæ. 1696
Notatio figurarum orationis & mutatæ simplicis elocutionis in Apostolicis scr. s8°. Lipsiæ. 1556
,, ,, Acc. & in librum Πράξεων & Ἀποκαλύψεως similes notationes nunc prim. elab. studio J. C. [*b. w. h.* Notatio figur. sermonis &c., 1572]. s4°. Lipsiæ. 1572
Notatio figurarum sermonis in libris 4 Evangeliorum & indicata verborum significatio & orationis sententia, studio J. C. s4°. Lipsiæ. 1572
Symbolorum & emblematum centuriæ 4 coll. [4 *pagin.*] s8°. Moguntiæ. 1688
Vita P. Melanchthonis, *see* De P. M. ortu &c., *above.*
see BIBLE: NEW TEST. [GREEK]. Nov. Test.; acc. J. C. in Nov. Foed. comm., 1642.
,, LINACRE (T.) De emendata structura Lat. sermonis libri 6; acc. Libellus C. de arte gramm. &c., 1573.
,, NICEPHORUS, *Saint.* Chronologia, conversa in serm. Lat. & explic. à J. C.; add., Cl. narr. de Syn. Nicæna, 1573.

Camerata (*ctssa.* **Napoléone Elisa**), *see* FLEISCHMANN (H.) Le Roi de Rome & les femmes: la ctsse. N. C. &c., 1910.
Cameron, *The family of, see* DRUMMOND (J.) Mem. of Sir Ewen C., w. intr. acc. of hist. &c. of family &c., 1842.
Cameron (Alan Grant), *see* DAKYNS (J. H.), C. E. FOX-STRANGWAYS & A. G. C. Geol. of country betw. York & Hull., 1886.
see FOX-STRANGWAYS (C. E.), A. G. C. & G. BARROW. Geol. of country around Northallerton &c., 1886.
Cameron (Allan Gordon).
The wild red deer of Scotland. 8°. E. 1923
Cameron (Annie I.), *see* MARY, *of Lorraine.* Scot. corr. of M. of L.; ed. A. I. C., 1927.
see RAIT (R. S.) & A. I. C., *edd.* King James's secret, 1927.
Cameron (*Mrs.* **Charlotte**).
A cheechako in Alaska & Yukon. 8°. [1920]
Cameron (*Sir* **David Young**). The paintings of D. Y. C. Foreword by A. J. Finberg. [Studio spec. no. *b. w.* Salaman (C.) Charm of the etcher's art, 1920]. obl. 4°. 1920
Cameron (*Sir* **Ewen**), *see* DRUMMOND (J.) *Mem. of Sir E. C. &c., 1842.
Cameron (Hector Charles). The nervous child. s8°. 1919
,, ,, ...3rd. ed. s8°. [1924]
Cameron (Jenny), *see* CUMBERLAND (W. A., *d. of*). *Book of chron.; added, mem. of the life of J. C., 1746 ?.
Cameron (John), *Scottish Divine.* A disc. t. the threefold covenant of God; tr., *see* BOLTON (S.) The true bounds &c., 1645.
Cameron (William Bleasdall). The war trail of Big Bear: connect. of B. B. &c. w. the Canadian N.-W. Rebellion, 1885, &c. s8°. [1926]
Cameron (William Ernest), *see* †ALLERTON (M.), *ps.*
Camilla (Tedisio di), *bp. of Turin* [THEDISIUS], *see* STAGLIENO (M.) Due doc. di Tedicio, vescovo di Torino, 1300–19, 1902.
Camino y Orella (Joaquín Antonio). Hist. de la ciudad de San Sebastián, con var. not. conc. Guipúzcoa. [Bibl. de hist. Vasca, v7]. t1. 8°. 1923
Camisards. *Histoire des Camisards &c. 2t. s8°. Londres. 1744
Cammaerts (Emile). Belgium f. Roman invasion to present day. 8°. [1921]
Poèmes intimes. s8°. Brux. 1922
The treasure house of Belgium: h. land & people, h. art & lit. la8°. 1924
Cämmerer (*Gen. Lt.* **Rudolf v.**) The develop. of strateg. science dur. the 19th c. Auth. tr. by K. v. Donat. 8°. 1905
Camo (Pierre). Les beaux jours. Poèmes. s8°. 1913
see PLÉIADE (LA): [*poems by* Ctsse. de Noailles, C. &c.], 1921.
Camoens (Luis de). Camoens & s. temps. [Cat. d'une expos. en comm. du 4e cent. de C., 1524–1924. Maggs Bros.] [P2770]. s8°. 1925
C. lírico. Redondilhas &c. 3v. s8°. Paris. 1923–25
,, ,, ...2a ed. v1. s8°. Paris. 1925
see BELL (A. F. G.) L. de C., 1923.
,, PRESTAGE (E.) Minor works of C., 1924.
Camp (Charles W.) The artisan in Elizabethan lit. [Columbia Univ.] 8°. N.Y. 1924
Camp (Jean). Jep le Catalan. s8°. 1928
Campagnac (Ernest Trafford). Education in its rel. to the common purposes of humanity. 8°. 1925
Society & solitude. s8°. C. 1922
Campagnes coloniales belges, 1914–18, t1, 1927, *see* BELGIQUE.
Campagnola (Giulio), *painter & engraver, see* BORENIUS (T.) Four early Ital. engravers, 1923.
see KRISTELLER (P.) G. C., Kupferstiche &c.: 22 Tafeln; hrsg. P. K., 1907.
Campan (*Mme.* **Jeanne L. H.**) Méms. sur la vie privée de Marie Antoinette &c. 2t. 8°. Londres. 1823
Campanella (Tommaso).
La cité du soleil, ou idée d'une républ. philos. Tr. Villegardelle. s8°. 1840
City of the sun; tr., *see* MORLEY (H.) Ideal commonw., 1885.
Lettere. A cura di V. Spampanato. [Scr. d'It., 103]. 8°. Bari. 1927
T. C., his advice to the king of Spain for attaining the univ. monarchy of the world. Tr. by E. Chilmead, w. pref. by W. Prynne. 8°. [1660 ?]
see BLANCHET (L.) C., 1920.
,, DENTICE DI ACCADIA (C.) T. C., 1921.
,, GARDNER (E. G.) T. C. & h. poetry, 1923.
Campanus (M.), *poet.* Veld-Deuntjens, *see* AMSTERDAM. A. Pegasus, 1627.

Campbell, *The family of, see* CAMPBELL (F. W.) *Letter cont. acc. of the C. of Barbreck, 1830.
see CAMPBELL (H.) The C. of Duntroon, p2, 1921.
,, CAMPBELL OF BARCALDINE (*Maj. Sir* D. A. D.) Records of Clan C. in milit. service of the Hon. East India Co., 1600–1858, 1925.
Campbell (Agnes). Rep. on publ. baths & wash-houses in the U.K. [Carnegie U.K. Trust]. la8°. E. 1918
Campbell (Alexander), *advocate.* The MS. hist. of Craignish; ed. H. Campbell, *see* SCOTTISH HISTORY SOC. Misc., v4, 1926.
Campbell (Archibald), *bp. of Aberdeen.* *Some primit. doctrines reviv'd: or The intermediate state of departed souls &c. Pref., the judgment of G. Hickes. s8°. 1713
Campbell (Archibald Young).
Horace, a new interpretation. 8°. [1924]
Poems. 8°. C. 1921
Campbell (Charles A. R.)
Bats, mosquitoes & dollars. 8°. Boston, *Mass.* 1925
Campbell (Charles MacFie), *see* PRINCE (M.) Problems of personality: st. pres. to M. P.; ed. C. MacF. C. &c., 1925.
Campbell (Charles William), *C.M.G.* China, *see* FOREIGN OFFICE. Handbooks, No. 67, 1920.
Campbell (*Rev.* **Colin**), *B. A.* Instruction for youth: No. 3. [*Kanarese*]. s8°. Bangalore. 1852
Campbell (Daniel), *of Shawfield.* Provost Drummond's acc. of discussion in Commons upon applic. of D. C. for compens. for losses by riot in Glasgow, 1726, *see* ABBOTSFORD CLUB. Misc., v1, 1837.
Campbell (Donald), *R. A.M.C.*
Arabian medicine & its infl. on the M. A. 2v. 8°. 1926
Campbell (Dugald). In the heart of Bantuland. 8°. 1922
Campbell (Frederick William). *Letter to Mrs. Campbell of Barbreck, cont. acc. of the Campbells of Barbreck. 8°. Ipswich. 1830
Campbell (George), *minister of Eastwood.*
Eastwood: eccles. antiq. 4°. Paisley. 1902
Campbell (George), *prof. of Divinity in Marischal Coll.*
The philosophy of rhetoric. 7th ed. 8°. 1823
see SKINNER (J.), *bp.* Primitive truth &c., w. a def. of episcopacy agst. C. &c., 1803.
Campbell (Herbert). The Campbells of Duntroon. [*Repr. f.* The Genealogist, N.S., v31, 32, 37]. p2. 8°. Exeter. 1921
Campbell (John), *D.D., of London.*
John Angell James: hist. &c. s8°. 1860
The martyr of Erromanga: labours &c. of J. Williams. 2nd ed. 8°. 1842
Mem. of David Nasmith &c. 8°. 1844
Campbell (John), *LL.D.* *The present state of Europe. 3rd ed. 8°. 1752
Campbell (*Sir* **John**), *see* BREADALBANE (J. C., *1st earl*).
Campbell (John Francis). The Celtic dragon myth, w. the geste of Fraoch & the dragon. Tr. w. intr. by G. Henderson. 4°. E. 1911
Campbell (Lewis).
The study of Greek. Inaug. lecture. 8°. E. 1863
Campbell (Lily Bess). Scenes & machines on the Eng. stage dur. the Renaissance. 8°. C. 1923
Campbell (Marius Robison). Guidebook of the West. U.S., by C. & others, pA–D, 1915, *see* UNITED STATES: GEOLOG. SURVEY. Bulletin, No. 611–14, 1915.
Campbell (Norman Robert).
Mod. electrical theory. 2nd ed. 8°. C. 1913
,, ,, ...Suppl. chap. 15, Series spectra. 8°. C. 1921
,, ,, ...Suppl. chap. 16, Relativity. 8°. C. 1923
,, ,, ...Suppl. chap. 17, Structure of the atom. 8°. C. 1923
Physics: the elements. la8°. C. 1920
What is science ? s8°. [1921]
Campbell (*Mrs.* **Olwen Ward**).
Shelley & the unromantics. 8°. [1924]
see WARD (J.) Essays in philos.; w. mem. of a. by C., 1927.
Campbell (Oscar James). The position of the "Roode en Witte Roos" [by L. v. d. Bos] in the saga of King Richard III. [*With text & tr.* Univ. of Wisconsin]. 8°. Madison. 1919
Campbell (*Mrs.* **Patrick**) [BEATRICE STELLA CORNWALLIS-WEST].
My life & some letters. 8°. [1922]
Campbell (Reginald John).
The life of Christ. A short study. 8°. [1921]
Thomas Arnold. 8°. 1927
Campbell (Thomas), *the poet.* Compl. poet. works. Ed. w. notes by J. L. Robertson. [Oxford ed. *Thin*]. s8°. O. 1907

Campbell (Thomas), *LL.D., chancellor of St. Macartin's.* Strictures on eccl. & lit. hist. of Ireland till intr. of Roman ritual: also, Hist. sk. of constit. &c. of I. to 1783. 8°. 1790
Campbell (Thomas Joseph). The Jesuits, 1534–1921. 8°. [1921]
Campbell (W. Graham). "The apostle of Kerry": life of Rev. Ch. Graham. s8°. D. 1868
Campbell (Wilfred).
Poet. works. Ed., w. mem. by W. J. Sykes. 8°. [1922]
Campbell-Bannerman (*Rt. Hon. Sir* **Henry).** Early letters to h. sister Louisa, 1850–51. Chosen by Lord Pentland. 8°. [1925]
see SPENDER (J. A.) Life of Sir H. C.-B., 2v, 1923.
Campbell of Barcaldine (*Maj. Sir* **Duncan Alex. Dundas),** *3rd bart.* Records of Clan Campbell in the milit. service of the Hon. East India Co., 1600–1858. Foreword by Sir R. Temple. 8°. 1925
Campello (*il conte* **Enrico di).** Autobiog.: reasons for leaving Papal Ch. Ed. w. intr. by W. Arthur. s8°. 1881
Camphausen (Walter), *see* ROMANUS, *rhetor.* Περὶ ἀνειμένου; ed. W. C., 1922.
Campion (Arturo). Euskariana. pl, Hist. á través de la leyenda. [Bibl. bascongada, t4]. 8°. [Bilbao]. 1896
Euskariana. p3, Algo de hist. [Bibl. Bascongada, t35]. 8°. Bilbao. 1899
Campion (Edmund) [†CAMPIAN (E.)]
Decem rationes propositæ in causa fidei & opuscula ejus sel. [Narr. divortii Hen. VIII &c.] Auct. ed. [Ed. Sylvester Petra Sancta]. s8°. Antverpiæ. 1631
Opuscula, *see* TURNER (R.) Orationum vol. 1 & 2, 1615.
*A true report of the disput. &c. in the Tower of London w. E. C. 1581. Whereunto a rep. of the other three dayes conferences. [Pref. signed A. Nowell, W. Daije]. s4°. *C. Barker.* 1583
see BOMBINUS (P.) Vita & martyrium E. C., 1618; 1620.
„ DURIE (J.) Confut. Resp. G. Whitakeri ad rationes decem quibus fretus E. C. &c., 1582.
„ VINCENT, *of Lerins, St.* Adv. prophanas hæresewn novat. lib.; item E. C. oblati certaminis in causa fid. rationes decem, 1600.
„ WHITAKER (W.) *D.D.* Responsionis ad decem illas rationes quibus fretus E. C. certamen obtulit &c. def., 1583.
Campion (Samuel S.) Castle Ashby. A histor. sk. [P2601]. 8°. Northampton. 1874
Campion (Thomas). The maske by T. C. (1607), Hatfield Palace, May 1924. [Foreword by K. Talbot]. la8°. *p.p., Cayme Press.* 1924
Obs. in the art of Eng. poesie (1602), *see* DANIEL (S.) A defence of ryme &c., 1925.
Campoamor y Campoosorio (Ramón de).
Poesias. Ed. y notas de C. Rivas Cherif. s8°. 1921
see GONZALEZ-BLANCO (E.) Campoamor, 1911.
Campomanes (Pedro Rodriguez Campomanes y Sorriba, *conde* **de).** Tradato de la Regalia de Amortizacion. [*w.* Elogio por V. Gonzalez Arnao *&* Dictamenes de algunos teólogos]. [Impreso en Madrid. 1765]. s4°. Gerona. 1821
Campon (Pedro).
Le moderne Hippocrate. [Tr. R. Karcer]. 8°. 1927
Campori (Giuseppe). Memorie biograf. degli scultori, architetti, ec., di Carrara & di Massa. Con cenni rel. agli artisti ital. & esteri, & un saggio bibliogr. 8°. Modena. 1873
Campos (Agostinho de).
see ANTOLOGIA portuguesa; organiz. por A. de C., 1920–26.
„ PALADINOS da linguagem; *ed.* C., 3v, 1922–26.
Campos (Ricardo de Mária y), *see* MÁRIA Y CAMPOS (R. DE).
Campredon (*Général Baron* **Jacques David Martin de).** Doc. milit. du Lt.-Gén. de C. La défense du Var & le passage des Alpes. Lettres des Gén. Masséna &c. Annot. & publ. par C. Auriol. s8°. 1889
Camsell (Charles) & W. Malcolm. The Mackenzie river basin. [Canada. Geol. Survey]. 8°. Ottawa. 1919
Camurrini (Eugenio), *see* MACCHIONI (B.) Descr. d. famiglia Cilnia fatta d. E. C., esaminata d. B. M., 1688.
Camus (Armand Gaston). Hist. & procédés du polytypage & de la stéréotypie. s8°. an X.—1802
Camus (Jean Pierre), *bp. of (1) Belley (2) Arras.* Appropinquatio protestant. ad eccl. Cath.-Roman., *see* MIGNE (J. P.) *ed.* Theol. cursus, t5, 1841.
Camus (Jules). Les prem. autographes de la maison de Savoie, *see* REGIA DEPUT. Misc., t42, 1906.
La venue en France de Valentine Visconti, dsse. d'Orléans, & l'invent. de ses joyaux apportés de Lombardie, *see* REGIA DEP. DI STORIA PATRIA. Misc., t36, 1900.

Canaan (T.) Aberglaube u. Volksmedizin im Lande d. Bibel. [Hamburg. Kolonialinst. Abh., B20]. la8°. Hamburg. 1914
Canada.
ANON. & MISC. WORKS.
Canada as a field for Brit. branch ind. la8°. Ottawa. 1922
60 years of C. progress, 1867–1927. 8°. [Ottawa. 1927]
Government Publications.
Annual departmental reports, 1924–25, 7v, 1925–26, v1. la8°. Ottawa. 1927
For earlier reports, see CANADA: PARLIAMENT. Sessional papers.
7th report f. Sel. Comm. of Hse. of Assembly of Upper C. on grievances &c., added, Rep. on petition of W. Forsyth &c. [*sep. pagin.*] 8°. Toronto. 1835
CANADIAN ARCHIVES.
Cat. of pictures, incl. drawings & prints, in the Public Archives of C. Intr. & notes by J. F. Kenney. pl. la8°. Ottawa. [1925]
Doc. rel. to C. currency, exchange &c. dur. the French per. Sel. & ed. by A. Shortt. [*In French & Eng.*] 2v. la8°. Ottawa. 1925
Report of the Public Archives, 1918, 1921, 1923; A. G. Doughty. 8°. Ottawa. 1920–24
For other issues, see CANADA: PARL. Sessional papers, *var. years.*
Publications. No. 11. 8°. Ottawa. 1924
Cartier (J.) Voyages; publ. f. orig. w. tr. &c. by H. P. Biggar, 1924. [11.]
see NORTHCLIFFE (A. C. W. H., *1st baron*). The N. Coll. [papers of Gen. R. Monckton &c.]; pres. to Gov. of C., 1926.
CENSUS.
6th Census of Canada, 1921. v1, 5. la8°. Ottawa. 1924–25
1, Population. 5, Agriculture.
COMMISSION OF CONSERVATION.
see WHITE (A. V.) Water powers of Brit. Columbia, 1919.
GEOLOGICAL SURVEY & DEPT. OF MINES.
Annual report on the mineral prod. of C., 1919, 1920 [by J. McLeish]. 8°. Ottawa. 1920–21
Index to sep. reports, 1906–10 & summary reports, 1905–16. Comp. by F. J. Nicolas. 8°. Ottawa. 1923
Investig. in ceramics & road materials, 1923–25. 8°. Ottawa. 1925–26
Investig. in ore dressing & metallurgy, 1923–25. 8°. Ottawa. 1925–26
Investig. of fuels & fuel testing, 1923–25. 8°. Ottawa. 1924–27
Investig. of mineral resources &c., 1923–25. 8°. Ottawa. 1924–26
Mineral ind. of C. Comp. by A. H. A. Robinson &c. Brit. Emp. Exhib. ed. s8°. [Ottawa]. 1924
The mining laws of C. Digest. [P2786]. 8°. Ottawa. 1924
Museum bulletin. Nos. 22–40 [*in* 2v]. 8°. Ottawa. 1916–25
Nos. 36 *& onwards have title* Victoria Memorial Mus. Bulletin.
Prelim. rep. on the mineral prod. of C., 1918 [P2771]; 1919, 1920 [P2713]. 8°. Ottawa. 1919–21
Production of coal & coke in C. dur. 1918 [P2413]; 1920 [P2713]. 8°. Ottawa. 1919–21
Production of copper, gold, lead, nickel, silver, zinc, & o. metals in C. dur. 1918. [P2413]; 1919 [P2713]. 8°. Ottawa. 1919–20
Production of iron & steel in C. dur. 1918. [P2413]; 1919 [P2713]. 8°. Ottawa. 1920
Rep. of Dept. of Mines, for 1921 [P2771], 1922 [P2713], 1923, 1924 [P2771], 1925, 1926. 8°. Ottawa. 1921–26
Smelter treatment rates. Rep. of Comm. [P2413]. 8°. Ottawa. 1919
Summary rep., 1917 A, 1918 A, 1919 A–G, 1920 A–E, 1921 A–E, 1922 A–D, 1923 A–C2, 1924 A–C, 1925 A–C, 1926 B. 8°. Ottawa 1919–27
Summary rep., Mines branch, 1920–22. 8°. Ottawa. 1922–24
REFERENCES.
see ALCOCK (F. J.) Mt. Albert map-area, 1926.
„ —— The Reed-Wekusko map-area, N. Manitoba, 1920.
„ BLIZARD (J.) Econ. use of coal for steam-raising & house-heating, 1919.
„ —— The prepar., transport. & combustion of powdered coal, 1921.
„ —— & E. S. MALLOCH. Gas producer trials w. Alberta coals, 1921.
„ BRUCE (E. L.) Amisk-Athapapuskow Lake dist., 1918.
„ CAIRNES (C. E.) Coquihalla area, Brit. Columbia, 1924.
„ CAMSELL (C.) & W. MALCOLM. Mackenzie river basin, 1919.
„ COCKFIELD (W. E.) Sixtymile & Ladne Rivers area, Yukon, 1921.
„ —— & A. H. BELL. Whitehorse dist., Yukon, 1926.
„ COLE (L. H.) Sodium sulphate of W. Canada, 1926.
„ COLEMAN (A. P.) North-eastern part of Labrador, & New Quebec, 1921.
„ COLLINS (W. H.) North shore of Lake Huron, 1925.
„ ——, T. T. QUIRKE, & E. THOMSON. Michipicoten iron ranges, 1926.
„ COMBE (F. A.) Central & district heating, 1924.
„ COOKE (H. C.) Geology of Matachewan dist., 1919.
„ —— Kenogami, Round, & Larder Lake areas Timiskaming Distr., Ontario, 1922.
„ DOWLING (D. B.) Geolog. notes to accompany map of Sheep River gas & oil field, Alb., 1914.

Canada [*continued*].
see Dowling (D. B.), S. E. Slipper & F. H. McLearn. Investig. in the gas & oil fields of Alberta &c., 1919.
,, Dresser (J. A.) Prelim. rep. on Serpentine & assoc. rocks of S. Quebec, 1913.
,, Dyer (W. S.) Minto Coal Basin, New Brunswick, 1926.
,, Eardley-Wilmot (V. L.) Abrasives, p1–3, 1927.
,, —— Molybdenum, 1925.
,, Ells (S. C.) Bituminous sands of N. Alberta, 1924; 1926.
,, —— Use of Alberta bituminous sands, 1927.
,, Elworthy (R. T.) Helium in Canada, 1926.
,, Goudge (M. F.) Limestones of Quebec & Ontario, 1927.
,, Haanel (B. F.) Facts about peat, 1924.
,, Hayes (A. O.) Malagash salt deposit, Cumberland county, N.S., 1920.
,, —— & W. A. Bell. South. part of the Sydney coal field, Nova Scotia, 1923.
,, Hume (G. S.) Palæozoic outlier of L. Timiskaming, Ontario & Quebec, 1925.
,, Johnston (W. A.) Geology of Fraser River Delta map-area, 1923.
,, —— Sediment. of the Fraser river delta, 1921.
,, —— Winnipegosis & Upper Whitemouth River areas: pleistocene &c., 1921.
,, —— & W. L. Uglow. Placer & gold vein dep. of Barkerville, 1926.
,, †Kalmus (H. T.) Researches on cobalt &c., p2, 3, 5, by H. T. K. & C. Harper, &c., 1914–16.
,, Keele (J.) Prelim. rep. on clay & shale of Ontario, Ottawa, 1924.
,, —— & L. H. Cole. Struct. materials along the St. Lawrence River, 1922.
,, Lambe (L. M.) Hadrosaur Edmontosaurus f. the Upper Cretaceous of Alberta, 1920.
,, Landt (J. L.) Coke as a household fuel, 1925.
,, MacCann (W. S.) Geology &c. of Bridge River map-area, B.C., 1922.
,, MacConnell (R. G.) Portland canal & Skeena mining div., 1913.
,, MacEvoy (J.) Smoky River Coal Field, 1925.
,, MacKay (B. R.) Beauceville map-area, Quebec, 1921.
,, MacLearn (F. H.) Palæontology of Silurian rocks of Arisaig, Nova Scotia, 1924.
,, MacLennan (J. C.) Some sources of Helium in Brit. Emp., 1920.
,, Mawdsley (J. B.) St. Urbain Area, Charlevoix dist., Quebec, 1927.
,, O'Neill (J. J.) Econ. geol. of Hazelton dist., B.C., 1919.
,, Picher (R. H.) Road materials along the St. Lawrence river, 1920.
,, Reinecke (L.) Mineral deposits betw. Lillooet & Prince George, B.C., 1920.
,, —— Road materials in vicinity of Regina, S., 1919.
,, Robinson (A. H. A.) Titanium, 1922.
,, Saint John (H.) Botan. explor. of N. shore of the Gulf of St. Lawrence, 1922.
,, Schofield (S. J.) Geol. & ore deposits of Ainsworth mining camp, B.C., 1920.
,, —— & G. Hanson. Geology &c. of Salmon River dist., B.C., 1922.
,, Slipper (S. E.) Sheep River gas & oil field, Alberta, 1921.
,, Spence (H. S.) Barium & Strontium in Canada, 1922.
,, —— Bentonite, 1924.
,, —— Graphite. 1920.
,, —— Phosphate in Canada, 1920.
,, —— Talc & soapstone in Canada, 1922.
,, Stewart (J. S.) Geol. of the disturbed belt of S.W. Alberta, 1919.
,, Tanton (T. L.) Harricanaw-Turgeon basin, N. Quebec, 1919.
,, Taverner (P. A.) Birds of E. Canada, 1919.
,, Walker (J. F.) Geol. & min. dep. of Windermere map-area, B. Columbia, 1926.
,, Wilson (A. W. G.) Develop. of chemical &c. indust. in C., 1924.
,, —— Potash recovery at cement plants, 1919.
,, Wilson (M. E.) Arnprior-Quyon & Maniwaki areas, Ontario &c., 1924.
,, —— Geol. & mineral deposits of Amherst township, Quebec, 1919.
,, —— Talc dep. of C., 1926.
,, Wright (J. F.) Brockville-Mallorytown map-area, Ontario, 1923.
,, Wright (W. J.) Geol. of the Moncton map-area, 1922.
,, Young (G. A.) Geol. & econ. minerals of C., 1926.
,, —— & W. L. Uglow. Iron ores of C., v1, B. Columbia & Yukon, 1926.
Interior, Dept. of.
see Patton (M. J.) Nat. resources of Quebec, 1923.
Munition Resources Commission.
Final rep. Nov. 1915–March 1919. 8°. Toronto. 1920
Natural Resources Intelligence Service.
Nat. resources of the Prairie Provinces. [P2771]. 8°. [Ottawa. 1925]

Canada [*continued*].
Parliament.
Journals of the House of Commons. v55–64. 8°. Ottawa. 1920–27
55, 58 *have* 2 App.; 56, 57 *have* 1 App. *each*; 60 *has* App. 1, 2, 3, 5; 61, App. 1, 4, 6; 62, App. 2; 64, App. 1, 2.
Journals of the Senate. v57–64 (1920–27) [58, *wanting*]. la8°. Ottawa. 1920–27
Sessional Papers. v54viii, ix, 56–61 (2nd session of 13th Parl. 1919–4th session of 14th Parl. 1925). la8°. [Ottawa. 1919–25]
v56 *has* 10 vols. *or* "numbers"; v57, 9 no.; v58, 9 no. [7 *wanting*]; v59, 6 no.; v60, 7 no.; v61, no. 1–5.
No. 1 *of each vol.* (*except* 61) *is in* 3v. No. 2 *of each vol.* (*except* 59 & 60) *is in* 2v. No. 9 *of* v56 *is in* 2v *& contains* Canadian Archives.
Public Archives, *see* Canadian Archives *above*.
see United States: Dept. of Interior. Joint rep. upon survey &c. of boundary betw. U.S. & Canada, 1924–25.

Canada Year Book, 1919, 1921, 1922–23, 1924, 1925, 1926. 8°. Ottawa. 1920–27

Canadian.
Canadian annual review of public affairs. By J. C. Hopkins, 1915, 1923. 8°. Toronto. [1916–24]
Canadian progress, 1925–26, 1927. fol. & 4°. 1926–27
Cat. of C. books (English section). Brit. Emp. Exhib., Wembley, 1924. [P2770]. s8°. 1924
Select British doc. of the C. war. of 1812, v1–3i, 1920–26, *see* Wood (W.), *ed.*

Canadian Alpine journal. Publ. by the Alpine Club of Canada. v1–13 (1907–23). 8°. Calgary, Alberta. 1907–23

Canadian Arctic Expedition.
Report of, 1913–18. v11–14. 8°. Ottawa. 1922–25
11, A, Geol. of Arctic coast of C.: west of Kent Pen., by J. J. O'Neill. B, Geogr. notes, by K. G. Chipman & J. R. Cox.
12, [A], The life of the Copper Eskimos, by D. Jenness. B, Physical characteristics, by D. Jenness. C, Osteology, by J. Cameron.
13, Eskimo folk-lore: A, Myths &c. of N. Alaska &c., B, Eskimo string figures; by D. Jenness.
14, Eskimo songs: songs of the Copper Eskimos; by H. H. Roberts & D. Jenness.

Canale (Achille). Canti pop. calabresi. Scelti e rec. in versi ital. per A. C. [*Calabrian & Ital.*] s8°. Reggio. 1859

Canale (Antonio), *called Canaletto, see* Canaletto.

Canale (Michel Gius.) Nuova istoria d. rep. di Genova, d. orig. a. 1797. v1–4. [*no more publd.*] s8°. Firenze. 1858–64

Canaletto [Bellotto (Bernardo), *called C.*]
see Ferrari (G.) Les 2 Canaletto, A. Canal, B. B.; 56 planches avec intr., 1914.
,, Finberg (H. F.) C. in England, 1921–22.

Canals (Salvador).
Spain: monarchy & constit. [P2786]. 8°. Peckham. [1925]

Canano (Joannes Baptista); *1515–78.* Musculorum humani corporis picturata dissectio, 1541? [With drawings by G. da Carpi]. Facs. ed. annot. by H. Cushing & E. C. Streeter. [Mon. medica, 4]. 8°. Florence. 1925

Canary Islands. Jews in the C. I.: cal. of Jewish cases extr. f. records of the Canariote Inquisition; tr. &c., 1926, *see* Wolf (L.), *ed.*

Canaye (Philippe Du Fresne-), *see* Du Fresne-Canaye (Ph.)

Cancellieri (Francesco). Lettera ined.; pubbl. G. Albertotti [Nozze Reymond—Buffa di Perrero. N122]. 8°. Padova. 1908
Osserv. int. alla quest. promossa dal Vannozzi &c., espec. d. G. Giustino di Costanzo, s. l'orig. d. Div. Comm. di Dante, appog. alla storia d. visione d. Monaco Casinese Alberico &c. s8°. 1814

Cancerinus (Nicolaus). Rettung der Augspurg. Confession; wider das fürgeben D. Tossani. 8°. Tübingen. 1579

Cancioneiro. C. geral (1516), n. ed., 5t, 1910–17, *see* Resende (G. de).
C. popular portuguez, 2ª ed. ampl., [v]1, 1911, *see* Braga (T.)

Candale (Henri, *duc* de) [†Nogaret de la Valette & de Foix (H. de)]. Déclaration et conf. de foy, faicte par Msgr. de C. dans le synode des Eglises Reformées des Cevennes &c. en Alez. s8°. Nismes. 1616
see Toulouse. Arrest du Parlement de Thoulouse contre la déclar. &c. de C., 1616.

Candia (Cecilia de), *aft. wife of Godfrey Pearse, see* Pearse (*Mrs.* G.)

Candid (*Captain*), *ps.* *The Limburg manœuvre of Aug. 1914. [P2383; 2564]. 8°. Utrecht. 1919

Candidus (Liberius), *ps., see* Henri de Saint-Ignace.

Candler (Edmund). Abdication. s8°. [1922]
The mantle of the East. s8°. E. 1910
Youth & the East: an unconvent. autobiog. 8°. E. 1924

Candlish (Robert Smith), *D.D.*
The Atonement. 8°. 1861
The Fatherhood of God. [Cunningham lect.] 8°. E. 1865
The 1st Epistle of John expounded. 3rd ed. 8°. E. 1877
Four letters to E. B. Elliott, on the Horæ Apoc. &c. 2nd ed. 8°. 1847
Reason & revelation. 8°. 1860

Candolle (Augustin Pyramus de), *see* LA RIVE (A. DE). A. P. de C., 1851.

Candolle (Casimir de). Begoniaceæ Centrali-Amer. et Ecuador., 1919, *see* S.I. Misc. coll., v69, 1921.
New species of Piper f. Panama, *see* S.I. Misc. coll., v71, 1920.

Candy (Hugh Charles Herbert), *see* MILTON (J.) Some newly discov. stanzas by M. on engr. scenes illust. Ovid's Metamorphoses; [*ed.*] C., 1924.

Cane (John Vincent). *Fiat Lux, or a gen. conduct to a right understanding in the great combustions &c. about relig. in Eng. betw. papist & protestant, presbyterian & independent. By Mr. J. V. C. s8°. [Douai?]. 1661

Cane (Percy S.) Mod. gardens, Brit. & foreign. Ed. C. G. Holme & S. B. Wainwright. [Studio (The). Spec. Winter No., 1926–27]. la8°. [1926]

Canedo (Enrique Diez-), *see* DIEZ-CANEDO (E.)

Canel (Alfred). Recherches sur les jeux d'esprit, les singularités & les bizarreries litt., princ. en France. 2t. 8°. Evreux. 1867

Canevari (Demetrio), *see* HOBSON (G. D.) Maiolo, C. &c., 1926.

Canfield (Dorothy), *aft. wife of John Redwood Fisher.*
The bent twig. s8°. 1922
The brimming cup. s8°. [1921]
Her son's wife. s8°. [1926]
Hillsboro people. With occas. Vermont verses by S. N. Cleghorn. s8°. [1923]
Home fires in France. s8°. 1919
Raw material. s8°. [1924]
Rough-hewn. s8°. [1923]

Canfield (George Lewis) & G. W. Dalzell. The law of the sea: man. of princ. of admiralty law, w. summary of navig. laws of the U.S. by J. Y. Brinton. 8°. N.Y. 1921

Cangardel (Henri). La marine marchande franç. & la Guerre. [C.E.f.I.P.] la8°. 1927

Caniglia (Giuseppe). Genti di Somalia. la8°. München. 1921

Canina (Attilio Garino). La finanza d. Piemonte [1559–80], *see* REGIA DEPUT. Misc., t52, 1924.

Caninius (Angelus). Disquis. in locos aliquot Novi Test. obscur. s8°. Francofurti. 1602

Canisius (Petrus).
Catechisme. s8°. 1686
Catechismus Græco-Lat. s8°. Coloniæ Agripp. 1607
Catechismus imaginibus expressus. [*Ed.* Georg Mayr. *Lat. & Gk., each w. sep. tp. & pagin.*] s8°. Augustæ. 1613
Catechismus Latino-Ungaricus. s8°. Posonii. 1758
Comm. de verbi Dei corruptelis liber primus; de Joannis Baptistæ hist. evangel. &c. 8°. Dilingæ. 1571
„ „ ....s4°. Dilingæ. 1577
Katechismus in 113 Bildern. Geordn. v. G. Morel. s8°. Einsiedeln. 1865
*Summa doctrinæ Christ. Per quæst. tradita & in usum Christ. pueritiæ ed. s8°. [Vienna? 1554?]
see DREWS (P.) P. C., d. erste deut. Jesuit, 1892.
„ KNÖPPEL (A.) Der selige P. C., 2er Apostel Deutschlands, 1897.

Cankar (Ivan). Le valet Barthélemy & s. droit, *see* ŒUVRES libres, 65, 1926.

Cannan (Edwin). The econ. outlook. [Re-issued]. s8°. 1922
An economist's protest [1914–26]. 8°. 1927
London essays in economics: in honour of E. C. Ed. by T. E. Gregory & H. Dalton. Foreword by Sir W. Beveridge. 8°. 1927
Money: its connexion w. rising & falling prices. 4th ed., rev. s8°. Westminster. 1923

Cannan (F. Laura), *see* THOMPSON (N. G.) & F. L. C. Hand-in-hand figure-skating, 1896.
see ——, F. L. C. & *Visc.* DONERAILE. Combined hand-in-hand figure-skating, 1904.

Cannan (Gilbert).
Annette & Bennett. s8°. [1922]
Little brother. s8°. 1912
Pugs & peacocks. s8°. [1921]
The release of the soul. s8°. 1920
Sembal. s8°. [1922]
Seven plays. s8°. 1923

Cannicci (Niccolò), *1846–1906, see* SAPORI (F.) Maestri, No. 24, 1920.

Canning (Elizabeth), *see* MACHEN (A.) Canning wonder [1753], 1925.

Canning (*Rt. Hon.* George), *see* TEMPERLEY (H. W. V.) Foreign policy of C., 1822–27, 1925.

Cannon (T. G.) Old Spode. 8°. [1924]

Cannon (William Austin), *botanist.* Plant habits & habitats in the arid portions of S. Australia. [C.I. of Wash., 308]. la8°. Wash. 1921

Cannons (Harry George Turner). Bibliog. of industr. efficiency & factory management. With indexes of authors & subj. 8°. 1920
Classified guide to 1700 annuals, directories &c. s8°. 1923

Cano (Baldomero Sanin).
Elem. Spanish grammar. [Oxf. Span. Ser.] s8°. O. 1918
Spanish reader. Ed. w. notes & vocab. by C. [Oxf. Span. Ser.] s8°. O. 1920

Cano (Francisco Melchor), *bp. of the Canary Islands.* De locis theologicis, *see* MIGNE (J. P.), *ed.* Theologiæ cursus, t1, 1860.
Locorum theolog. libri 12. [*tp. missing*]. s8°. Coloniæ Agrippinæ. 1583

Canoni. *Canoni indocti Lutherani, 1519, *see* OECOLAMPADIUS (J.)

Canons [CANONES; CANONUM].
Canones concilii prov. Colon. &c., 1537, *see* COLOGNE.
*Canones eccl. ex vet. quâ Hungar., quâ Transilvan., coll. &c. [a S. Katona Gelejinus]. s8°. Claudiopoli. 1768
Canones eccl. in 5 classes distrib. ed. suffragio minist. in Synodo Comjathina congreg. s8°. Pestini. *n.d.*
*Canones eccl., in quinque classes distrib., quibus eccl. Helveticam conf. amplexæ in Comitatibus Mosoniensi, Posoniensi &c. [*Lat. & Hung.*] 2p. [*pagin. contin. Tp. & o. missing leaves supplied in MS.*] s8°. Varadini. 1642
Canons des conciles de Tolede &c., 2p, 1615, *see* TOLEDO.
Συνοδικόν, sive Pandectæ canonum SS. Apost. &c. ab eccl. Gr. recept., 2t, 1672, *see* BEVERIDGE (W.)

Canova (*il march.* Antonio), *1757–1822.*
see SAPORI (D.) Maestri, No. 26, 1921.
„ VERRUA (P.) O. Nelson nel pensiero e nell' arte del Foscolo e del C., 1919.

Canstein (Carl Hildebrand, *Frhr.* von). Das Muster e. rechtschaff. Lehrers in d. erbaul. Lebens-Beschreibung d. P. J. Speners. Mit Anmerk. u. Lebens Lauf d. Barons z. Druck befördert v. J. Langen. s8°. Halle. 1740
see BERTRAM (O.) Gesch. d. Canstein. Bibelanstalt, 1863.

Cantacuzène (*Princess*) [SPÉRANSKY (*Countess*), *née* JULIA DENT GRANT]. Revolutionary days: recoll. of Romanoffs & Bolsheviki. 8°. 1920

Cantagrel (François Jean Felix). Mettray & Ostwald. Et. sur ces 2 colonies agric. [P2654]. 8°. 1842

***Cantata** per fest. il giorno natalizio di S. M. la Regina, 1775, *see* CAROLINE, *queen of Naples.*

Cantemiru (Demetriu), *prince of Moldavia, see* ACADEMIA ROMÂNA. Anal., s2, t37, Secț. lit. (Stilul lui D. C., de D. Protopopescu), 1915.

Canterbury [& CANTERBURY CATHEDRAL]. Calendar of instit. by the Ch. of C. Sede vacante. Ed. C. E. Woodruff, w. add. &c. by I. J. Churchill. [Kent. Arch. Soc. Records Branch, v8]. 8°. [Canterbury]. 1923
Descr. &c. cat. of 2 old Dutch painted &c. windows in Roy. Museum & Free Library at C. Comp. by W. P. Thornton. 8°. Canterbury. 1899
Index of wills &c. in Probate Reg. at C., 1396–1558 & 1640–50; transcr. &c. H. R. Plomer, 1920, *see* BRIT. REC. SOC. Index Lib., v50, 1920.
Index of wills proved in Prerogative Court of C., v7, 1653–56, 1925, *see* BRIT. RECORD SOC. Index Library.
*Notes on painted glass in C. C. Preface by F. W. Farrar. 8°. Aberdeen. 1897
Year Books of Probates; Abstracts of Probate Acts in Prerog. Court of C., v5, 6, 1650–53—Extra vol.: Abstracts of Probates & Sentences, 1620–24; ed. J. Matthews &c., 1910–11, *see* YEAR BOOKS.
MONASTERY OF SAINT AUGUSTINE.
An 11th c. Inquis. of St. Augustine's. C.; [ed. w. intr.] by A. Ballard, *see* FLEET, *Lincs.* Terrier of Fleet; ed. N. Neilson, 1920.
Register of St. Augustine's Abbey, C., commonly called the Black Bk. Ed. G. J. Turner & H. E. Salter. [Brit. Acad. Rec. of social &c. hist. of Eng. &c., v3]. p2 [*pagin. cont.*] la8°. 1924

Canterbury & York Society. [*Publications*]. 8°. 1914–26
see BOOTH (C.) *bp.* Registrum C. B., 1516–35; ed. E. T. Bannister, 1921.
„ GRAVESEND (R. DE). Rotuli R. Gravesend, Dioc. Lincoln.; transcr. &c. F. N. Davis, 1925.

Canterbury & York Society [*continued*].
see HETHE (H.) Registrum H. H., pl, 2, 1914–16.
„ MAYEW (R.) *bp.* Registrum R. M., episc. Hereford., 1504–16 ; ed. A. T. Bannister, 1921.
„ MYLLING (T.) Registrum T. M., 1474–92 ; ed. A. T. Bannister, 1920. [26.]
„ PONTOISE (J. DE) *bp.* Registrum, 1282–1304 ; transcr. &c. C. Deedes, 2v, 1915–24.
„ SALTER (H. E.) *ed.* Chapters of the Augustinian canons, 1922.
„ TREFNANT (J.) *bp.* Registrum, 1389–1404 ; ed. W. W. Capes, 1916.
„ WOLSEY (T.) *card.* Registrum T. W., Eccles. Winton. admin. ; transcr. F. T. Madge &c., 1926.

Canti. Inni della terza armata : racc. di canti milit., 1919, *see* INNI, &c.

Cantica sacra, 1855, *see* HAUBER (J. M.)

Canticos. Canticos é himnos escog. de ant. y mod. poesías esp. para el uso de los Protestantes, *see* COLECCION de poesías esp., pl, 1872.

Cantideva, *see* SANTIDEVA.

Cantilupe Society. [*Publications*].
see BOOTH (C.) *bp.* Register, 1516–35 ; A. T. Bannister, 1921.
„ HEREFORD. Index to registers of Diocese of H., 1273–1535 ; compiled by E. N. Dew, 1925.
„ —— Institutions &c., 1539–1900, 1923.

Cantiques. Recueil de c., 1878, *see* RECUEIL.

Cantón (F. J. Sánchez), *see* SÁNCHEZ CANTÓN (F. J.)

Cantoni (Fulvio). La prima dimora di Ld. Byron a Bologna. la8°. Bologna. 1926

Cantrill (Thomas Crosbee). Iron ores &c. by C. &c., *see* GEOLOG. SURVEY OF ENG. &C. Spec. rep. on min. resources, 9, 1910.
see STRAHAN (*Sir* A.), T. C. C. &c. Geol. of S. Wales coalfield, 1909–21.

Canu (Ferdinand) & R. S. Bassler. Bryozoa of the Canal Zone & related areas. [S.I., U.S. Nat. Mus. Bull., 103]. 8°. Wash. 1918
North Amer. early Tertiary Bryozoa. [S.I., U.S. Nat. Mus. Bull., 106. *Plates b. separately*]. 4°. Wash. 1920
North Amer. later Tertiary & Quaternary Bryozoa. [S.I., U.S. Nat. Mus. Bull., 125]. 4°. Wash. 1923

Canus (Melchior), *bp. of the Canary Islands, see* CANO (F. M.)

Canute, *the Great, k. of Eng. & Denmark.* Cnutonis regis gesta, sive encomium Emmæ reginæ auctore monacho S. Bertini. Rec. fecit G. H. Pertz [Scr. rer. Germ. in us. schol.] 8°. Hannoveræ. 1865

Canz (Israel Gottlieb).
Disciplinæ morales omnes &c. s8°. Lipsiæ. 1739
Philosophiæ Leibnitianæ & Wolfianæ usus in theologia per præcipua fidei capita. Præm. diss. de ratione & revelatione, natura & gratia auct. I. T. Canzio. 2t *in* 1v. s8°. Francofurti. 1739
Überzeug. Beweiss antreff. d. Unsterblichkeit d. Seelen, bes. d. Kinder-Seelen &c. s8°. Tübingen. 1741

Canzius (Israel Theophilus), *see* CANZ (I. G.)

Canzone n. presenti turbationi di Stato [?Venezia]. [P2839]. s8°. *n.p.* 1606

Canzoniere. Poesie scelte da un c. ined. d. sec. 16, 1819, *see* POESIE.

Caoursin (Guielmus). Acc. of the siege of Rhodes in 1480. Tr. J. Kay. Ed. H. W. Fincham. Intr. by E. J. King. 8°. *p.f.p.c.* 1926

Capablanca (José Raúl). Chess fundamentals. [repr.] 8°. 1922

Capaccio (Giulio Cesare) [CAPACIUS (J. C.)]
Delle imprese trattato &c. 8°. Napoli. 1592
Neapolitanæ hist. tomus primus. [*said to have been wr. in Italian by F. Gordiani*]. s4°. Neapoli. 1607

***Capacity** & extent of the human understanding &c., 1745, *see* KIRKBY (J.)

Capart (Jean).
L'art égyptien. Choix de doc. accomp. d'indications bibliograph. [t]1, L'architecture. 8°. Brux. 1922
L'art égyptien : études & hist. t1. 8°. 1924
L'art égypt. & la loi de frontalité, *see* ACAD. DES INSCR. &c. FOND. PIOT. Mon^s. &c., t26, 1923.
Egyptian art : intr. studies. Tr. W. R. Dawson. la8°. [1923]
Notes sur les origines de l'Egypte d'ap. les fouilles récentes. [Extr. de la Revue de l'Univ. de Brux., t4]. 8°. Brux. 1898
Thèbes : la gloire d'un grand passé. Avec collab. de M. Werbrouck. [Fond. égyptol. Reine Élisabeth]. fol. Brux. 1925
The tomb of Tutankhamen. Tr. W. R. Dawson. s8°. [1923]
see BRUSSELS : MUSÉES DE B. Donation d'antiq^s. égypt. ; descr. &c. par J. C., 1911.

Capasso (Bartolommeo).
La casa e la famiglia di Masaniello. s8°. [1919]
Fonti d. storia d. prov. napolitane dal 568 al 1500, con note &c. del Dr. E. O. Mastrojanni. 8°. Napoli. 1902

Capasso (Carlo). Paolo III, 1534–49. v1. 8°. Messina. 1924

Capdevila (J. M.) Poetes i crítics. s8°. Barcelona. 1925

Cape Colony & Cape of Good Hope [KAAP DE GOEDE HOOP]. Bepalingen & instructiën v. het bestuur v. de buitendistr. v. de Kaap de Goede Hoop, 1805. Uitg. G. W. Eybers met inleidung door S. J. Fockema Andreæ &c. [Hist. Genoots. Werken, s3, 45]. 8°. Amsterdam. 1922

Cape Times Weekly Edition, *see* KERR (T. H.) The Golf-House tragedy ; trial of T. H. K. C. T. W. Ed., Feb. 5th, 1908.

Cape (*Lt.-Col.* **Herbert Anderson),** *D.S.O., see* HARVEY (*Col.* J. R.) Hist. of 5th (Royal Irish) Regt. of Dragoons &c., compl. to 1921 by H. A. C., 1923.

Capece, *The family of, see* CAPECE (B.) *Nobilitá &c. d. famiglia C., 1687.

Capece (Bruto) [*ps.* SCIPIONE AMETRANO]. *Nobilitá et antichitá d. famiglia Capece. ristamp. 8°. Napoli. 1687

Capecelatro (*card.* **Alfonso).**
Papa Pio X e la Francia. [P2844]. s8°. 1907

Capecelatro (Giuseppe), *abp. of Taranto, see* PIERI (P.) Taranto, 1799 e Mgr. C., 1924.

Capeille (*l'abbé* **Jean).**
Dict. de biographies roussillonn. 4°. Perpigan. 1914

Čapek (Josef).
see ČAPEK (K.) & J. Č. " And so *ad infinitum* " : the life of insects ; tr., 1923.
„ —— & —— Života hmyzu, 4. vyd., 1924.

Čapek (Karel). The absolute at large. 8°. 1927
Krakatit. Tr. L. Hyde. s8°. [1925]
Letters f. England. Tr. P. Selver. 8°. [1925]
The Macropulos secret. Comedy. Tr. P. Selver. 8°. 1927
R.U.R. (Rossum's Universal Robots). Play. Tr. P. Selver & adapted for the Eng. stage by N. Playfair. 2nd impr. s8°. 1923

—— & J. Čapek. " And so *ad infinitum.*" The life of insects. Entomolog. review in 3 acts. Auth. tr. by P. Selver. s8°. 1923
Ze života hymzu : Komedie. 4. vyd. s8°. Praha. 1924

Capel (Arthur Capel, *baron*), *see* HAMILTON (J. H., *1st d. of*). Sev. speeches of Duke H., A. Ld. C. &c., upon the scaffold, 9 March [1648], 1649.

Capel (Richard), *fell. of Magd. Coll., Oxford.* Tentations : Their nature &c. Add. dispute as restit. in the case of usury. 4p. [*in* 1v. *2 pagin.*] s8°. 1655

Capel (Thomas John). A reply to Gladstone's " Polit. expostulation." [Repr. w. add. f. The Weekly Register &c.] [P2561]. 8°. 1874

Capell (*Lt.-Col.* **Algernon Essex).** The 2nd Rhodesia Regt. in East Africa. Foreword by Maj.-Gen. Sir A. H. M. Edwards. 8°. 1923

Capellen (*baron* **Johan Derk van der),** *Heer tot den Pol.* Brieven van en aan C. Uitg. door W. H. De Beaufort. [Hist. Genoots. Werken, N.S. 27a]. 8°. Utrecht. 1879

Capello (*Generale* **Luigi).** Note di Guerra. 2v. 8°. Milano. 1920
1, Dall' inizio alla presa di Gorizia.
2, Vodice—Bainsizza—Caporetto—La vittoria finale.

Capen (Samuel Paul). Facilities for for. students in Amer. coll. & univ., 1921, *see* UNITED STATES : INTERIOR.

Capetown. The Corporation of the City of C. Minute of the Mayor, for year ending Sept. 1919–26. fol. Cape Town. 1919–27
Three months' visit. by the bp. of C., 1856, *see* GRAY (R.)
see GREY (*Sir* G.) Library of G. [pres. to S. Afr. Publ. Lib.], v1–3i, 1858–62.

Capetti (Vittorio), *see* DANTE ALIGHIERI. Lectura D. : c. 25 dell' Inferno letto da V. C., 1907.

Capilupus (Camillus), *see* CAPILUPUS (L.) Rime, 1585.

Capilupus (Hippolytus), *see* CAPILUPUS (L.) Rime, 1585.

Capilupus (Laelius) [†CAPILUPI (LELIO)]. Rime d. L. e fratelli de Capilupi. Nouamente poste in luce. s8°. Mantoua. 1585

***Capitalist** England—socialist Russia. Publ. by Communist Internat. [P2486]. s8°. *n.p.* [1920]

Capitan (Louis), H. Breuil & D. Peyrony. La caverne de Font-de-Gaume aux Eyzies (Dordogne). [Peintures &c. des cavernes paléolith. publ. s. l. ausp. d'Albert I de Monaco]. fol. Monaco. 1910

Capito (Wolfgang Fabricius).
see HOFFET (J. C.) Esquisse biogr., 1850.
,, LUTHER (M.) Indicium de Erasmo: ad C. epist. &c., 1522 ?
,, ŒCOLAMPADIUS (J.) In prophetam Ezechielem comm. per V. C. æditus, 1534.
Capmany y Montpalau (Antonio de).
Filosofía de la elocuencia. n. ed. s8°. Gerona. 1826
Capon (William). Views of Westminster sketched 1801–15 & drawn by W. C. Reprod. w. Capon's descr., annot. by P. Norman. [London Topog. Soc.] 4°. 1923–24
Caporali (Cesare). Rime piacevoli di C. C. del Mauro & d'altri a. Acc. in questa 4 impr. di molte rime del T. Tasso &c. [*Ed.* V. Baldini]. s8°. Venetia. 1588
Rime. s8°. Venetia. 1656
Cappelius (Johannes), *see* SCHOPPER (J.) Oratio de encomio theol.; altera oratio J. C. De republ. lit., 1594.
Cappelle (Richard), *see* STADE. Gesch. d. Reg.-Bez. Stade, 2, 3, Die Karolingerzeit &c.; v. R. C., 1925–26.
Cappelletti (Giuseppe). Storia dell' isola di S. Lazzaro e d. congreg. de' monaci armeni, unita alla storia d. magistrature Venete, 2ª ed. [*w. sep. tp. & pagin.*] 8°. Venezia. 1877
Cappello (Bernardo). Rime. s4°. Venetia. 1560
Cappello (Jacobus). Disputationes, *see* DU MOULIN (P.) Thesaurus disputat., v1, 1661.
Capper (Henry). South Australia: hist., hints to emigrants &c. 3rd ed., enl., s8°. [1839]
Cappol (Jacomo). Nomenclatura Romanscha & Todischa; informatiun n. noassa Christiana reformata relig. s8°. [Scuol]. 1770
Capponi (Alessandro Gregorio).
Cat. d. libreria Capponi. 4°. 1747
Capponi (*il march.* **Gino A. G. G.),** *see* TOMMASÉO (N.) N.T. e G. C.: carteggio ined., 1833–74; per cura di I. Del Lungo &c., v2–4i, 1914–23.
Caprin (Giulio). Sommario storico d. Guerra univ. (1914–18) s8°. Firenze. 1921
Caprivi (Georg Leo, *Graf* **v.),** *see* ECKARDT (J. W. A. v.) Aus d. Tagen v. Bismarcks Kampf gegen C.: Erinnerungen, 1920.
Capuana (Luigi). La sfinge. Romanzo. s8°. Milano. 1921
***Capuchin's** (The) journal, 1671, *see* CLOUET (F.) *an ex-Capuchin.*
Capus (Alfred).
Années d'aventures. Roman. s8°. 1922
Faux départ. s8°. 1922
Scènes de la vie difficile. Roman. s8°. [1922]
see ESTAUNIÉ (E.) Disc. de récep. (*on* A. C.), 1925.
Caputo (Massimo). A Frassati. la8°. Milano. 1921
Carabella (Ninon). Les noces de Mioara, *see* ŒUVRES libres, 48, 1925.
Carabellese (Francesco). L'Apulia &c. nell' alto medio evo. [Doc. per la storia di Bari. Vol. 7]. la8°. Bari. 1905
La Puglia nel sec. 15 da fonti ined. [Doc. per la storia di Bari. Vol. 3, 8]. 2p. la8°. Bari. 1901–8
Caracciola, *The family of, see* PIETRI (F. DE'). Cronologia d. fam. C., 1605.
Caraccioli (*le marq.* **Louis Antoine de).** The life of Clement XIV. 2nd ed. rev. & comp. w. the 3rd ed. publ. at Paris [App. *w. sep. pag. cont.* Marzoni's Letter on his death, Brief of the abolition of the Order of Jesuits &c.] 8°. 1778
Caracciolo (Enrichetta). Misteri del chiostro napoletano. Mem. di E. C. 5ª ed. s8°. Firenze. 1864
Caracciolo (*Col.* **Mario).** L'intervento d. Grecia n. Guerra mondiale e l'opera d. diplom. alleata. Pref. d. E. Corradini. la8°. [1925]
Caraffe (Armand Charles), *see* MUSÉE NAPOLÉON. Galerie [livr. 1–9 *by* C.], 10t, 1804–15.
Caragiale (Ión L.) Le péché; tr. J. Voilquin, *see* ŒUVRES (Les) libres, 63, 1926.
Caramurú, *The family of, see* SANTA MARIA JABOATAM (A. DE). Cat. gen. das princ. fams. proced. de C. &c., 1889.
Caranza (Bartholome), *see* CARRANZA (B.)
Carapella (Tommaso).
Il genio austriaco, serenata. [N125]. 8°. [Nap. ?] *n.d.* [1717 ?]
Teti, favoletta dram. [Nozze Spinelli-Pignatelli]. [N125]. 8°. Nap. 1714
Caravaggio (Michel Angelo) [AMERIGHI (M. A.)]
see MARANGONI (M.) Il C., 1922.
,, PATRIZI (M. L.) Il C. e la nova critica d' arte, 1921.
,, VENTURI (L.) Il C.; 32 riprod. con testo e cat., 1921.
Caravajal (Baltasar de) [CARVAJAL]. La Bandolera de Flandes. (El hijo de la terra). Comedie Spagnuole, sec. 17; publ. A. Restori. [Roman. Bibl., 9]. s8°. Halle a. S. 1893

Caravia (Alessandro). *Naspo Bizaro con la zonta del lamento che'l fá per haverse pentito de haver sposao Cate Bionda Biriota. [*In verse, Venetian dialect*]. Nov. ristamp. s8°. Trevigi. 1620
Caravita (Andrea). I codici e le arti a Monte Cassino. 3v. s8°. Monte Cassino. 1869–70
Carboneano (Philippus de). De proposit. ab eccl. damnatis, *see* MIGNE (J. P.), *ed.* Theol. cursus, t6, 1862.
Carbone de Costacciaro (Lodovico) [†CARBON (LUDOVICUS) à *Costacciaro*]. Compend. totius summæ theolog. T. Aquinatis. s4°. Coloniæ. 1609
Carcano (Filippo), *see* RIBERA (A.) F. C.: 52 tavole con intr., 1916.
Carcano (Giulio). Dodici novelle. s8°. Firenze. 1853
Carcano (Paolo).
In memoria di P. C. [*By var. a.*] 8°. [1919 ?]
Carco (Francis Carcopino *dit***).**
Au coin des rues. Contes. Ed. défin. s8°. 1922
L'équipe. Roman. s8°. 1919
L'homme traqué. s8°. 1922
Les humoristes. 8°. 1921
La légende & la vie d'Utrillo. s8°. [1928]
Maurice de Vlaminck. Reprod. de peintures &c., préc. d'une ét. crit. s8°. 1920
Maurice Utrillo. Reprod. de peintures &c., préc. d'une ét. crit. s8°. [1921]
Rien qu'une femme. Eaux-fortes de M. Asselin. la8°. 1923
,, ,, : roman, *see* ŒUVRES libres, 4, 1921.
Le roman de François Villon. s8°. [1926]
Carcopino (Jérôme).
La loi de Hiéron & les Romains. la8°. 1914
Virgile & les origines d'Ostie. [Ecoles Franç. d'Athènes & de Rome, fasc. 116]. la8°. 1919
Cardauns (Ludwig). Von Nizza bis Crépy: europ. Politik, 1534–44. [Bibl. des Preuss. Hist. Inst. in Rom., B15]. la8°. 1923
Carden (Percy Theodore). The murder of Edwin Drood: attempted solution based on Dickens' MS. &c. Intr. by B. W. Matz. s8°. [1920]
Cardenal (Peire), *see* CARDINAL (P.)
Cardenas (Bernardino de), *bp. of Paraguay, see* JESUITS. *Morale prat. &c., t5, Hist. de la persécution de C. [*by A. Arnauld*], 2e éd., 1717.
Cárdenas (Cipriano). Hom-idyomo. Proyecto de lengua auxiliar internac. ed. esp. s8°. Viena. 1921
Cardenio. Cinco poesias; [ed. J. M. Hill], *see* REVUE HISPANIQUE, t56, 1922.
Cardi (Lodovico), *called Il Cigoli, see* BATTELLI (G.) L. Cardi, detto Il Cigoli, 1922.
Cardiff Public Libraries.
Handlist of docs. (bef. 1500). [P2847]. 8°. Cardiff. 1926
Cardim (Fernão). Viagem e missão Jesuitica [1582–90], *see* INSTITUTO HIST. &c. BRAZIL. Rev., t65, 1902.
Cardinal (Peire), *du Puy* [CARDENAL], *see* VOSSLER (C.) P. C., 1916.
Cardinall (Allan Wolsey).
A Gold Coast library. [P2733]. 8°. 1924
In Ashanti & beyond. 8°. 1927
The natives of the N. territories of the Gold Coast. 8°. [1920]
Cardonne (C. de). L'emp. Alexandre II, (1855–81). la8°. 1883
Cardonnel (Adam de). Numismata Scotiæ. 4°. E. 1786
Carducci (Giosuè).
Levia gravia. Satana e polem. satan. Con note di A. Saletti. s8°. Bologna. [1910]
Odi barbare. Con note di A. Albertazzi. s8°. Bologna. [1921]
Primavera e fiore d. lirica ital. n. ed. riv. t1. s8°. Firenze. [1911]
,, ,, ed. riv. n. tir. 2t. s8°. Firenze. 1917–18
A selection f. the poems of G. C. Tr. & annot. w. biogr. intr. by E. A. Tribe. 8°. 1921
Il "Torrismondo" di T. Tasso. [*Extr. f.* Nuova antol., v133. P2813]. 8°. 1894
see CHROUST (G.) Saggi di letterat. ital. mod., da G. C. al futurismo, 1921–22.
,, CROCE (B.) G. C.: st. crit., 2e ed., 1927.
,, FERRARI (D.) Comm. d. Odi barbare di C., 3v, 1919–21.
,, MINGHETTI (M.) Alcune lettere ined. di M. M. e di G. C. a E. Masi, 1910.
Carducho (Vincencio). Dialogos de la pintura. Siguēse inform. y pareceres en fabor del' arte, escr. por varones insignes [*i.e.* I. Rodriguez de Leon, Lope de Vega &c. *each w. sep. pagin.*] s4°. 1633
The colophon is dated 1634 & the title-page to the Informaciones "Memorials inform. &c." *is dated 1629.*
Cardwell (John Henry).
Story of a charity school, Soho, 1699–1899. 8°. 1899
see SOHO. 20 yrs. in S., review of work, St. Anne's, 1911.

Carel (*l'abbé* **Ernest**).
Vieira, sa vie & s. œuvres. Thèse. 8°. [1879]
Carelz (Elias), *see* CAIREL (E.)
Carême (Maurice). Hôtel bourgeois. [*Poèmes*]. Préf. de G. Marlow. s8°. Liége. [1926]
Carena (Angelo Paolo Francesco). Consid. sopra una nuova divis. d. provincie e diocesi d. stati di S. M. il Re di Sardegna; [*ed. E. Bollati*], *see* REGIA DEP. DI STORIA PATRIA. Misc., t17, 1878.
Caresinus (Raphainus). Cronaca tr. in volgare Veneziano nel sec. 14. [Ed. R. Fulin]. 8°. Venezia. 1877
Carew (Bampfylde Moore). The surprising adv. of B. M. C., king of beggars. n. ed., corr. s8°. 1812
Carew (Edith May Hallowell), *wife of W. R. H. Carew*. [Crown *v*. Mrs. Carew for murder of her husband. Inquest, Magister. proc^s^., Trial &c., *w. add. paper*, The Carew case: Miss Jacob arrested, *w. sep. pagin. Repr. f. the* "Japan Gazette." *no tp.*] 8°. [1896–97]
Carew (Henry). The vampires of the Andes. s8°. 1925
Carew (John), *see* HARRISON (*Maj.-Gen.* T.) Speeches &c. of late King's judges, *viz.* Maj.-Gen. H., J. C. &c., 1660.
Carew (Thomas).
Poems. 3rd ed. 2p [p1 *wanting*. p2 *no tp.*] s8°. 1651
Poems & masque. With intr. mem. Ed. J. W. Ebsworth. s8°. 1893
Carey (Eustace). Memoir of William Carey. 8°. 1836
Carey (Felix). A gramm. of the Burman lang. Added, list of roots. 8°. Serampore. 1814
Carey (Henry), *dramatic writer* [*ps. Sig.* CARINI]. *The dragon of Wantley. Burlesque opera. Modernized f. the old ballad by Sig. Carini [*i.e.* H. C.] 14th ed., w. add. 8°. 1738
Poems on sev. occasions. [2nd ed.] s8°. 1720
Carey (Henry Charles). The slave trade. 3rd ed. s8°. Phila. 1859
Carey (S. Pearce). William Carey, D.D. [2nd ed.] 8°. 1923
Carey (William), *D.D.*
Dict. of the Mahratta lang. 8°. Serampore. 1810
A gram. of the Bengalee lang. 2nd ed., w. add^s^. 8°. Serampore. 1805
A gram. of the Bengalee lang. 4th ed., w. add^s^. 8°. Serampore. 1818
A gram. of the Kurnata lang. 8°. Serampore. 1817
A gram. of the Mahratta lang. &c. [App. *w. sep. pagin.*] 8°. Serampore. 1805
A gram. of the Punjabee lang. 8°. Serampore. 1812
A gram. of the Sungskrit. lang. [App.] 4°. Serampore. 1806
Gram. of the Telinga lang. 8°. Serampore. 1814
see CAREY (E.) Memoir of W. C., 1836.
„ CAREY (S. P.) W. C., 1923.
Carfort (*cte.* **Henri Le Nepvou de**), *see* LE NEPVOU DE CARFORT.
Cargill (David). Mem. of Margaret Cargill, incl. Xtianity in Tonga & Feejee. s8°. 1841
Cargill (Margaret), *wife of D. Cargill, d. 1840, see* CARGILL (D.) Mem. of M. C., 1841.
Carhart (Margaret S.) Life & work of Joanna Baillie. Diss. [Yale st. in English, 64]. 8°. New Haven, *Yale*. 1923
Carier (Benjamin), *see* HAKEWILL (G.) An answere to the treatise by Dr. C. &c., 1616.
Carini (*Sig.*), *ps.*, *see* CAREY (H.)
Carini (Luigi), *see* BENEDETTI (L. DE-). L. C., 1920.
Carinthia. Monumenta hist. ducatus C. [Im Auftr. d. Geschichtsvereins f. Kärnten; hrsg. v. A. v. Jaksch.] 4B *in* 5 [4i, ii (*pagin. contin.*) *w.* Erg. Heft]. la8°. Klagenfurt. 1896–1915
1, 2, Gurker Geschichtsquellen, 864–1269.
3, 4, Kärntner Geschichtsquellen, 811–1269.
Erg.- Heft zu B1–4, 811–1269.
Cario (Louis) & C. Régismanset. La pensée franç.: anthol. des auteurs de maximes du 16e s. à nos jours. 8°. 1921
Carion (Johann). Chronicorum ab orbe condito libri 3. s8°. Parisiis. 1563
Carl Wilhelm Ludwig, *Prince of Sweden, see* WILLIAM, *prince of Sweden*.
Carlé (Erwin), *see* ROSEN (E.), *ps.*
Carlell (Lodowick).
The passionate lovers, a tragi-comedy. s8°. 1655
Carles (Lancelot de), *bp. of Riez*. Poëme s. la mort d'Anne Boleyn, *see* ASCOLI (G.) La Gr.-Bret. dev. l'opinion fr., 1927.
Carleton (George), *bp. of* (1) *Llandaff*, (2) *Chichester*. Tithes examined & proved to bee due to the clergie. s4°. 1606
Carleton (John Will.) [*ps.* CRAVEN], *see* WALKER (D.) W.'s manly exercises; rev., or wr. by "Craven," 9th ed., 1855.
Carleton (Mary), *see* BERNBAUM (E.) M. C. narratives, 1663–1673; missing chap. in hist. of the Eng. novel, 1914.
Carleton (S.), *ps.* [*i.e.* SUSAN CARLETON JONES].
The La Chance mine mystery. s8°. [1921]
Carletus (Angelus), *see* ANGELUS [CARLETUS], *de Clavasio*.
Carlier de Lantsheere (Antoine). Trésor de l'art dentellier. Préf. de A. Lefébure. 4°. Brux. 1922
Carlill (Harold Flamank). Socrates or the emancipation of mankind. s8°. [1927]
Carlo Emanuele III, *king of Sardinia, see* VESME (A.) Sull' acquisto fatto da C. E. III d. quadreria del Pr. Eugenio di Savoia, 1887.
Carlo Emanuele I, *duke of Savoy, see* FULVIO (V.) Castigo essemplare de' calunniatori, al duca di S., 1618.
see MANFRONI (C.) Ginevra, Berna e C. E. I (1589–92) &c., 1894.
„ VENETIA. *Avviso di Parnaso, la povertà &c. dove è giunta la rep. di V. & il duca di S. [tr.], 1621.
Carlos (*Don*) [CHARLES, *infante of Spain, son of Philip II*], *1545–68, see* MAURENBRECHER (W.) Don Carlos, Vortrag, 1869.
Carlos (*Don*), *b. 1848, see* APARISI Y GUIJARRO (A.) Le roi d'Espagne, 1869.
Carlotti (Regolo). Poesie di alcuni mod. autori corsi. Racc. R. C. Con not. biogr. e due lettere &c. di N. Tommaséo. s8°. Firenze. 1870
Carlstadt (Andreas), *see* BODENSTEIN (ANDREAS).
Carlton (George), *admiral*. *The voyage of adm. G. C., in search of loyalty. A poetic epistle. [*A satire on King George IV*]. [P425]. 8°. 1820
Carlton (H. W.) Spaniels: th. breaking for sport &c. Intr. by W. Arkwright. s8°. [1915]
Carlyle (Alex James), *see* CARLYLE (R. W.) & A. J. C. Hist. of med. polit. theory in the West, v4, by A. J. C., 1922.
Carlyle (Jane Welsh). J. W. Carlyle: letters to h. family, 1839–63. Ed. L. Huxley. 8°. 1924
Carlyle (*Sir* **Robert Warrand**). Claims of Innocent III to authority in temporal matters. [*Extr. f.* Tijdschr. v. Rechtsgesch., d5. P2717]. 8°. Haarlem. 1923
—— **& A. J. Carlyle**. A hist. of mediaeval polit. theory in the West. v4, 5. 8°. 1922–28
4, Theories of the rel. of the Empire & the Papacy, 10–12c.; by A. J. C. 5, Pol. theory of 13c.
Carlyle (Thomas).
Early kings of Norway; also an essay on the portraits of J. Knox. Also Gen. index [to Coll. works. Library ed.] 8°. *Chapman & Hall*. 1882
The French Revol. [Library ed.] 3v. 8°. *Chapman & Hall. n.d.*
Hist. of Friedrich II, the Great. [Library ed.] 10v [v5 *wanting*, 1–4, 6–8 repr.] 8°. *Chapman & Hall. n.d. &* 1888
Letters to J. S. Mill, J. Sterling & R. Browning. Ed. A. Carlyle. 8°. [1923]
Sartor Resartus. [Library ed. repr.] 8°. *Chapman & Hall*. [1887]
„ „ Ed. P. C. Parr. s8°. O. 1913
see GAZEAU (J.) L'impérialisme angl.: C. &c., 1903.
„ HAMILTON (M. A.) T. C., 1926.
„ LEOPOLD (W.) Die religiöse Wurzel v. C.'s literar. Wirksamkeit, darg. an s. State of Germ. lit., 1922.
„ RYE (W.) 2 Cromwellian myths: alleged royal descent of O. C. &c. wh. deceived C., 1925.
„ WILSON (D. A.) C. at his zenith, 1848–53, 1927.
„ —— C. on Cromwell &c., 1837–48, 1925.
„ —— C. till marriage, 1795–1826, 1923.
„ —— C. to "The French Revolution," 1826–37, 1924.
„ YOUNG (N.) C., h. rise & fall, 1927.
Carman (Harry James). The street surface rly. franchises of N.Y. City. 8°. N.Y. *Columbia Univ.* 1919
Carmelitana. Bibliotheca C., 2t, 1752, [repr.], 1927, *see* VILLIERS (C. DE).
***Carmelite (The)**: tragedy, 3rd ed., 1785, *see* CUMBERLAND (R.)
Carmelites [ORDO B. V. M.] Chron. of events, 1623–1733, rel. to settlement of C. in Mesopotamia, 1927, *see* AGATHANGELUS, *of St. Theresa*.
Disput. habita a reuerendis patribus discalceatis: ord. B. V. M. de m. Carmelo, contra Arianos. Lublini in Polonia, 1616. [Assertiones theologicæ, 1616]. s8°. Zamoscii. 1617
Carmen. Carmen de bello Lewensi (1264); ed. &c. C. L. Kingsford, 1890, *see* LEWES.
*Carmen de bello Saxonico. Ex rec. O. Holder-Egger. Acc. Conquestio Henr. IV Imp. [Scr. rerum Germ. in usum schol.] 8°. Hannoveræ. 1889
Carmen Dolores, *ps.* [*i.e.* EMILIA MONCORVO BANDEIRA DE MELLO]. Aunt Zeze's tears, 1924, *see* GOLDBERG (I.), *tr.*
Carmichael (Montgomery). Christopher & Cressida. s8°. 1924
The inscriptions in the old Brit. cemetery of Leghorn. Transcr. by G. Milner-Gibson-Cullum &c. Intr. by M. C. 8°. Leghorn. 1906

Carmichael-Smyth (*Sir* **James),** *1st bart.* Chronolog. epitome of the wars in the Low Countries 1659–1815. 8°. 1825

Carmina.

Carmina Burana, *see* FRAGMENTA Burana, hrsg. W. Meyer, 1901.

„ „ Deut. Lieder d. C. B.; hrsg. F. Lüers, *see* KLEINE TEXTE, 148, 1922.

„ „ Vagantenlieder aus d. lat. Dichtung d. 12. u. 13. Jhdts. Übertr. &c. R. Ulich. Text bearb. M. Manitius. 8°. Jena. 1927

Carmina Cantab., ed. K. Strecker, 1926, *see* CAMBRIDGE.

Carmina quadragesimalia, 2v, 1757, *see* OXFORD: CHRIST CHURCH.

Carnahan (David Hobart), *see* GERSON (J. C. DE). Ad Deum vadit; publ. [w. intr. &c.] by D. H. C., 1917.

Carnarvon (Almina, *Countess of*), *wife of 5th earl.* Cat. of French furniture, Sèvres porcelain &c., bequeathed by A. de Rothschild. Sold by Christie, May 1925. [*Illust.*] 8°. 1925

Cat. of pictures & drawings by o. masters (bequeathed by A. de Rothschild). Also early Eng. portraits, property of Earl of C. Sold by Christie &c. May 1925. [*Illust.*] 8°. 1925

Carnarvon (Elisabeth Catharine, *Countess of*), *wife of 4th earl.* Malaria. Foreword by Sir R. Ross. s8°. [1926]

Carnarvon (George Edward Stanhope Molyneux Herbert, *5th earl of*), *see* CARTER (H.) & A. C. MACE. Tomb of Tut-ankh-Amen, disc. by late E. of C. & H. C., 2v, 1923–27.

Carnarvon (Henry Howard Molyneux Herbert, *4th earl of*), *see* HARDINGE (*Rt. Hon. Sir* A. H.) Life of H. H. M. H., 3v, 1925.

Carnarvon (Henry John George Herbert, *3rd earl of*). *Portugal & Gallicia; social &c. state of Basque provs. 2v. s8°. 1836

***Carnatic** (The) question stated. 8°. 1808

Carnaval des prétieuses, *see* JOURNÉE des madrigaux (1653), 1856.

Carnavalet. Les grands salons litt., 17e & 18e siècles. Conférences du Musée C., 1927. Par L. Batiffol &c. Intr. de L. Gillet. 8°. 1928

Carné (Gaston de), *see* HOZIER (J. F. L. D'). Les chevaliers bretons de St.-Michel, 1469–1665; notices rec. par H.; publ. avec préf. par C., 1884.

Carnegie Endowment for International Peace [DOTATION CARNEGIE]. Year book, 1919–27. la8°. Wash. [1919]–27

DIVISION OF ECONOMICS & HISTORY (*General References*).

see also ECONOMIC & SOC. HIST. OF THE WORLD WAR; JAPANESE MONOGRAPHS; PRELIM. ECON. STUDIES &C. *below.*

see BODART (G.) Losses of life in mod. wars *&* Milit. selection & race deterior., by V. L. Kellogg, 1916.

„ †DRACHMANN (P.) Indust. development &c. of 3 Scandinavian countries, 1915.

„ DUMAS (S.) & K. O. VEDEL-PETERSEN. Losses of life caused by war, 1923.

„ GIRAULT (A.) The colonial tariff policy of France, 1916.

„ GRUNZEL (J. L.) Econ. protectionism, 1916.

„ HECKSCHER (E. F.) The Continental System: econ. interp., 1922.

„ LEITES (K.) Recent econ. develop. in Russia, 1922.

„ MUNRO (D. G.) The 5 rep. of Cent. Amer., 1918.

„ NELSON (E.) Las Bibliotecas en los Estad. Unid., 1927.

„ PORRITT (E.) The fiscal & diplom. freedom of the Brit. oversea dominions, 1922.

„ PRINZING (F.) Epidemics resulting f. wars, 1916.

„ ROBERTSON (W. S.) Hispanic-Amer. rel. w. the U.S., 1923.

„ SUBERCASEAUX (G.) Monetary & banking policy of Chile, 1922.

„ WESTERGAARD (H.) Econ. development in Denmark, 1922.

DIVISION OF INTERCOURSE & EDUCATION.

see AMERICAN foreign policy, w. intr. by N. M. Butler, 2nd ed., 1920.

„ BACON (R.) For better relations w. our Latin Amer. neighbours, 2p, 1916.

„ JONES (G. E.) Hygiene & war, 1917.

„ LANGE (C. L.) Russia, the Revol. & the War, 1917.

„ LICHTENBERGER (H.) Rel. betw. France & Germany, 1923.

„ —— The Ruhr conflict, 1923.

„ MABIE (H. W.) Educat. exchange w. Japan, 1914.

„ RUSSIA. Greetings to the new R.: addr. &c., 1917.

„ SCHOENRICH (O.) Former Senator Burton's trip to S. Amer., 1915, 1915.

DIVISION OF INTERNATIONAL LAW.

see ALVAREZ (A.) Internat. law & rel. subjects f. the point of view of the Amer. Continent, 1922.

„ —— The Monroe doctrine, 1924.

„ BYNKERSHOEK (C. VAN). De dominio maris diss.; reprod. of 2nd ed. (1774), w. tr. &c., 1923.

„ CONSORTIUM (THE): offic. text of the four-power agreement for a loan to China &c., 1921.

Carnegie Endowment for International Peace [*continued*].

DIVISION OF INTERNATIONAL LAW [*continued*].

see CRESSON (W. P.) The Holy Alliance, 1922.

„ DEUTSCH: D. Weissbuch, 1919. German White Book; tr., 1924.

„ FOSTER (J. W.) Limitat. of armament on the Gt. Lakes (1892), 1914.

„ GENTILIS (A.) Hispanicæ advocat. libri 2, 2v, 1921.

„ GERMANY. GOV. PUBL. Prelim. hist. of the Armistice; tr., 1924.

„ HAGUE (THE). Docs. rel. to 1st H. Peace Conf.; tr., 1921.

„ —— Final acts of 1st & 2nd H. Peace Conf. &c., 1915. [Pamph. 10].

„ —— The H. convent. & declar. of 1899 (1 & 4i) & 1907 (1, 2, 6–9, 11–14), 1915. [Pamph. 4, 7, 11, 14–20.]

„ —— The H. convent. & declarat. of 1899 & 1907; ed. J. B. Scott, 3rd ed., 1918.

„ —— The H. Court reports; ed., w. intr., by J. B. Scott, 1916.

„ —— H. Court reps.: Gt. Brit., Spain & France *v.* Portugal: awards rend. Sept. 2 & 4, 1920.

„ —— Instr. to Amer. delegates to H. Peace Conf. &c.; ed., w. intr. by J. B. Scott, 1916.

„ —— Proceedings: Conf. of 1899, 1920.

„ —— Proceedings: Conf. of 1907, 3v, 1920–21.

„ —— Proceedings: Conf. of 1899 & 1907, Index vol., 1921.

„ —— Rep. to H. Conf. 1899 & 1907; ed., w. intr. by J. B. Scott, 1917.

„ —— Signat., ratific. &c. to the convent. &c. of 1st & 2nd Hague Peace Conf., 1914.

„ INSTITUTE OF INTERNAT. LAW. Resolutions dealing w. the law of nations &c.; ed. J. B. Scott, 1916.

„ JAY (W.) War & peace; repr. f. ed. of 1842, 1919.

„ KAUTSKY (C.) Outbreak of the World War: German doc. coll. by K. K. & ed. M. Montgelas &c.; tr., 1924.

„ LADD (W.) An essay on a congress of nations, repr. f. ed. of 1840, w. intr. by J. B. Scott, 1916.

„ LANSING (R.) Notes on sovereignty, 1921.

„ LONDON, DECLAR. OF. D. of L. Coll. of offic. papers &c., 1908–9, 1919.

„ LOUTER (J. DE). Le droit internat. public positif, 2t, 1920.

„ MACMURRAY (J. V. A.) Treaties &c. w. & conc. China, 1894–1919, 2v, 1921.

„ MADISON (J.) The debates in the Federal Convention of 1787 wh. framed the constit. of the U.S., 1920.

„ MANNING (W. R.), *ed.* Arbitration treaties among Amer. nations to 1910, 1924.

„ —— Diplom. corr. of U.S. conc. independ. of Lat.-Amer. nations, v1—3, 1925.

„ NIPPOLD (O.) Development of internat. law after the World War; tr., 1923.

„ OPPENHEIM (L. F. L.) The future of internat. law, 1921.

„ PAN AMERICAN SCIENTIFIC CONGRESS (SECOND). Recomm. on internat. law & offic. comm.; ed. J. B. Scott, 1916.

„ ROOT (E.) The effect of democracy on internat. law: addr., 1917.

„ SCHÜCKING (W.) The internat. union of the Hague Conf., 1918.

„ SCOTT (J. B.) Autonomy & federat. within empire: Brit. self-govern. dominions, 1921.

„ —— Controversy over neutral rights betw. U.S. & France, 1797–1800, 1917.

„ —— Declar. of Independ.—Articles of Confeder. &c., 1917.

„ —— An Internat. Court of Justice, 1916.

„ —— Judicial settlement of controversies betw. States of the Amer Union, 2v, 1918, *&* Analysis, 1919.

„ —— Offic. statements of war aims & peace proposals, Dec. 1916–Nov. 1918, 1921.

„ —— Prize cases in the U.S. Supreme Court, 1789–1918, 3v, 1923.

„ —— The project of a Perman. Court of Internat. Justice &c., 1920.

„ —— The Recommend. of Habana conc. internat. organiz.: addr. & comm. by J. B. S., 1917.

„ —— The status of the Internat. Court of Justice, 1916.

„ —— The U.S. of Amer.: st. in internat. organiz., 1920.

„ UNITED STATES. Treaties for the adv. of peace, betw. the U.S. & o. powers, negot. by the Hon. W. J. Bryan; w. intr. by J. B. Scott, 1920.

„ WAMBURGH (S.) Monograph on plebiscites, 1920.

„ WEHBERG (H.) Limitat. of armaments, 1921.

„ —— Problem of an Internat. Court of Justice; tr. C. G. Fenwick, 1918.

„ WILLOUGHBY (W. W.) Constit. govt. in China, 1922.

ECONOMIC & SOCIAL HIST. OF THE WORLD WAR. J. T. Shotwell, gen. ed. Outline of plan: European ser. la8°. Wash. 1924

——: AMERICAN SERIES.

see LELAND (W. G.) & N. D. MERENESS. Intr. to Amer. offic. sources, 1926.

Carnegie Endowment for International Peace [*continued*].
ECONOMIC & SOCIAL HIST. OF THE WORLD WAR [*continued*].
——: AUSTRIAN & HUNGARIAN SERIES.
see EXNER (F.) Krieg u. Kriminalität in Österreich, 1927.
,, GRATZ (G.) & R. SCHÜLLER. Äussere Wirtschaftspolitik Ö.-U., 1925.
,, HANUSCH (F.) Regelung d. Arbeitsverhält. im Kriege, 1927.
,, HOMANN-HERIMBERG (E.) Kohlenversorgung in Ö., 1925.
,, LÖWENFELD-RUSS (H.) Regelung d. Volksernährung, 1926.
,, PIRQUET (C.), *ed.* Volksgesundheit, 2T, 1926.
,, POPOVICS (A.) Das Geldwesen, 1925.
,, REDLICH (J.) Österreich. Regierung u. Verwaltung, 1925.
——: BELGIAN SERIES.
see HENRY (A.) Ravitaillement de la B., 1924.
,, KERCHOVE DE DENTERGHEM (*cte.* C. DE). L'indust. belge, 1914–18, 1927.
,, MAHAIM (E.) Secours de chomage en B., 1926.
,, PIRENNE (J.) & M. VAUTHIER. Legisl. & admin. allemandes, 1926.
,, VAN LANGENHOVE (F.) L'action du Gouv. belge en matière écon. pend. la Guerre, 1927.
——: BRITISH SERIES.
see BOWLEY (A. L.) Price & wages in U.K., 1914–20, 1921.
,, BULKLEY (M. E.) Bibliogr. survey of contemp. sources f. econ. & soc. hist., 1922.
,, COLE (G. D. H.) Labour in coal-mining ind., 1914–21, 1923.
,, —— Trade unionism & munitions, 1923.
,, —— Workshop organiz., 1923.
,, FAYLE (C. E.) The War & shipping indust., 1927.
,, HALL (H.) Brit. archives & sources, 1925.
,, HENDERSON (H. D.) The Cotton Control Board, 1922.
,, HILL (*Sir* N.) &c. War & insurance, 1927.
,, HIRST (F. W.) & J. E. ALLEN. Brit. War Budgets, 1926.
,, JENKINSON (C. H.) Manual of archive admin. &c., 1922.
,, JONES (D. T.) &c. Rural Scotland, 1926.
,, KEITH (A. B.) War govt. of the Brit. Dom., 1921.
,, LLOYD (E. M. H.) Experiments in State control at the War Office & Ministry of Food, 1924.
,, MIDDLETON (T. H.) Food production, 1923.
,, REDMAYNE (*Sir* R. A. S.) Brit. coal-mining ind., 1923.
,, SALTER (J. A.) Allied shipping control, 1921.
,, SCOTT (W. R.) & J. CUNNISON. Industries of the Clyde Valley dur. the War, 1924.
,, WOLFE (H.) Labour supply & regulation, 1923.
——: FRENCH SERIES.
see AFTALION (A.) Industrie textile en France, 1924.
,, AUGÉ-LARIBÉ (M.) L'agric., 1925.
,, —— Agric. & food supply, by M.A-L. *&* P. Pinot; tr. & abr., 1927.
,, BERNARD (A.) L'Afrique du Nord, 1926.
,, BLANCHARD (R.) Forces hydro-électr., 1924.
,, BLOCH (C.) Bibliog. méthod. de l'hist. écon. & soc. de la France, 1925.
,, BOULIN (P.) L'organis. du travail dans la rég. envahie de la Fr. (1914–18), 1927.
,, CANGARDEL (H.) La marine march. fr., 1927.
,, CHARDON (E. H.) L'organis. de la répub. pour la paix, 1926.
,, CHEVALIER (*le gén.*) Les bois d'œuvre pend. la Guerre, 1927.
,, COURTEAULT (P.) La vie écon. à Bordeaux, 1925.
,, CRÉHANGE (A.) Chomage & placement, 1927.
,, FONTAINE (A.) L'industrie fr., 1924; tr., 1926.
,, FROIS (M.) Santé & travail des femmes, 1926.
,, GIDE (C.) & A. DAUDÉ-BANCEL. La Guerre & la vie soc.: lutte contre la cherté &c., 1926.
,, GIGNOUX (C. J.) Bourges, 1926.
,, HAUSER (H.) Le problème du régionalisme, 1924.
,, HERRIOT (E.) Lyon, 1925.
,, JÈZE (G.) Les dépenses de guerre de la France, 1926.
,, KERVILER (G. DE). Navig. intér. en France, 1926.
,, LEVAINVILLE (J.) Rouen, 1926.
,, LHÉRITIER (M.) Tours &c., 1926.
,, MARCH (L.) Mouvement des prix & des salaires, 1926.
,, MASSON (P.) Marseille, 1926.
,, NOGARO (B.) & L. WEIL. La main-d'œuvre étr. & coloniale, 1926.
,, PESCHAUD (M.-C.) Polit. & fonct. des transports par chemin de fer, 1926.
,, PINOT (P.) Controle du ravitaillement de la population civile, 1925.
,, RENOUVIN (P.) Formes du gouv. de guerre, 1926; tr. & abr., 1927.
,, SELLIER (H.) &c. Paris, 1926.
,, ——, & A. BRUGGEMAN. Probl. du logement (1914–18), 1927.
,, TRUCHY (H.) Les finances de guerre de la France, 1926.
——: GERMAN SERIES.
see AEREBOE (F.) Einfl. d. Krieges auf d. landwirtschaftl. Produktion &c., 1927.
,, BAUMGARTEN (O.) Geistige &c. Wirk. d. Kr. in Deut., 1927.
,, KÖHLER (L. v.) Staatsverwalt. d. besetz. Gebiete, B1, 1927.
,, LOTZ (W.) Deut. Staatsfinanzwirtschaft, 1927.
,, SKALWEIT (A.) Die deut. Kriegsernährungswirtschaft, 1927.
,, UMBREIT (P.) & C. LORENZ. D. Kr. u.d. Arbeitsverh., 1928.

Carnegie Endowment for International Peace [*continued*].
ECONOMIC & SOCIAL HIST. OF THE WORLD WAR [*continued*].
——: ITALIAN SERIES.
see BACHI (R.) L'alimentazione &c., 1926.
,, EINAUDI (L.) La Guerra e il sistema tribut. ital., 1927.
,, MORTARA (G.) La salute pubbl. in Italia &c., 1925.
,, PRATO (G.) Il Piemonte e gli effetti d. Guerra, 1925.
,, STEFANI (A. DE). La legislazione econ., 1926.
——: NETHERLAND SERIES.
see VAN DER FLIER (M. J.) War finances in the N. up to 1918, 1923.
——: SCANDINAVIAN SERIES.
see HECKSCHER (E. F.), *ed.* Sveriges ekon. &c. hist., d1, 1926.
,, KEILHAU (W.) Norge & Verdenskrigen, 1927.
JAPANESE MONOGRAPHS.
see KOBAYASHI (U.) Milit. industries of J., 1922.
,, —— War & armament loans of J., 1922.
,, —— War & armament taxes of Japan, 1923.
,, OGAWA (G.) Conscription system in J., 1921.
,, —— Expend. of the Russo-Jap. War, 1923.
,, ONO (G.) Expend. of the Sino-Jap. War, 1922.
,, —— War & armament expenditures of J., 1922.
PRELIM. ECON. STUDIES OF THE WAR.
see ANDREWS (I. O.) & M. A. HOBBS. Econ. effects upon women & children in Gt. Brit., 2nd (rev.) ed., 1921.
,, BAKER (C. W.) Govern. control & operat. of industry in Gt. Brit. & U.S., 1921.
,, BOGART (E. L.) Direct & indirect costs, 2nd (rev.) ed., 1920.
,, CARVER (T. N.) Govt. control of liquor business &c., 1919.
,, —— War thrift, 1919.
,, COFFEY (D.) Coop. movement in Jugoslavia, Rumania & N. Italy, 1922.
,, CROWELL (J. F.) Govt. war contracts, 1920.
,, DEVINE (E. T.) Disabled soldiers & sailors pensions &c., 1919.
,, DIXON (F. H.) & J. H. PARMELEE. War admin. of the rlys. in the U.S. & Gt. Brit., 2nd ed., 1919.
,, FAIRLIE (J. A.) Brit. War. admin., 1919.
,, GIDE (C.), *ed.* Effects of the War upon French econ. life, 1923.
,, HAMMOND (M. B.) Brit. labor condit. & legisl., 1919.
,, ROWE (L. S.) Early effects of the War upon finance &c. of Peru, 1920.
REFERENCES.
see CARNEGIE (A.) Man. of the public benefact. of A. C., 1919.
,, GERMAN. Official German doc. rel. to World War: tr., v1, 2, 1923.
,, HAGUE. Palace of peace, designs, 1907.
,, INTERNATIONAL CONCILIATION, 1923–.
,, JONES (A. H.) C. E. for I. P.: organiz. & work, 1924.
,, TREATIES. T. of peace, 1919–23, 2v, 1924.

Carnegie Institute, *Pittsburgh.* 24th, 26th–31st celeb. of Founder's day, April 29, 1920, 1922–1927. la8°. Pittsburgh. 1920–27

Carnegie Institution of Washington.
Classified list of publications. [*no tp.*] 8°. Wash. 1923
Year book. No. 20–26, 1921–27. la8°. Wash. 1922–27
see ADAMS (E. D.) Infl. of Grenville on Pitt's for. policy, 1787–98, 1904.
,, ALLISON (W. H.) Inventory of unpubl. mat. for Amer. relig. hist. in Protestant Ch. archives &c., 1910.
,, ANDREWS (C. M.) Guide to mat. for Amer. hist., to 1783, in Publ. Rec. Office of Gt. Brit., 2v, 1912–14.
,, —— & F. G. DAVENPORT. Guide to MS. mat. for hist. of U.S. to 1783, in Brit. Mus., &c., 1908.
,, AYALA (B.) De jure et offic. bellicis et discip. militari libri 3, 2v, 1912.
,, BALDWIN (D. L.), L. N. BROUGHTON &c. Concordance to poems of J. Keats, 1917.
,, BELL (H. C.), D. W. PARKER &c. Guide to Brit. West Ind. archive mat. &c., 1926.
,, BENEDICT (F. G.), W. R. MILES, &c. Human vitality &c. under prolonged restricted diet, 1919.
,, BIDWELL (P. W.) & J. I. FALCONER. Hist. of agric. in Northern U.S., 1620–1860, 1925.
,, BOCCACCIO (G.) Lydgate's Fall of princes, 4p, 1923–27.
,, BOLTON (H. E.) Guide to mat. for hist. of U.S. in princ. archives of Mexico, 1913.
,, BRITTON (N. L.) & J. N. ROSE. The Cactaceæ, 4v, 1919–23.
,, BURNETT (E. C.) *ed.* Letters of members of the Continental Congr., v1–3, 1921–26.
,, CANNON (W. A.) Plant habits & habitats, in S. Australia, 1921.
,, CATTERALL (*Mrs.* H. T.) Judic. cases conc. Amer. slavery & the Negro, v1, 1926.
,, CHURCHILL (W.) Easter Island, 1912.
,, —— Polynesian wanderings, 1911.
,, —— Sissano, 1916.
,, CLARK (V. S.) Hist. of manufactures in U.S., 1607–1860, 1916.
,, CLEMENTS (F. E.) Plant succession, 1916.

Carnegie Institution of Washington [*continued*].
see CLEMENTS (F. E.) & F. L. LONG. Experimental pollination, 1923.
„ COOPER (L.) Concord. to works of Horace, 1916.
„ CORNER (G. W.) Anatom. texts of earlier M. A., 1927.
„ DAVENPORT (C. B.) Body-build & its inheritance, 1923.
„ DAY (A. L.) & E. T. ALLEN. Volcanic activity & hot springs of Lassen Peak, 1925.
„ DICKSON (L. E.) Hist. of theory of numbers, 3v, 1919–23.
„ DORSEY (G. A.) The Pawnee : mythology (pl), 1906.
„ FAUST (A. B.) Guide to mat. for Amer. hist. in Swiss & Austrian archives, 1916.
„ FINLEY (*Lt.-col.* J. P.) & W. CHURCHILL. The Subanu, 1913.
„ FISH (C. R.) Guide to mat. for Amer. hist. in Roman & o. archives, 1911.
„ FRANCISCUS, *a Victoria.* De Indis & De jure belli reflect., 1917.
„ GOLDER (F. A.) Guide to mat. for Amer. hist. in Russian archives, 1917.
„ GULICK (J. T.) Evolution, 1905.
„ HACKETT (C. W.), *ed.* Hist. doc. rel. to New Mexico &c.; coll. by A. F. A. & F. R. Bandelier, v1, 2, 1923–26.
„ HASSE (A. R.) Index to U.S. doc. rel. to foreign affairs, 1828–61, 3p, 1914–21.
„ HAY (O. P.) Pleistocene of N. Amer. &c., 1923.
„ HILL (G. W.) Coll. mathemat. works, 4v, 1905–7.
„ HILL (R. R.) Descr. cat. of docs. rel. to hist. of U.S. in the Papeles Procedentes de Cuba, 1916.
„ HYDE (W. W.) Olympic victor mon. & Gr. athletic art, 1921.
„ IVENS (W. G.) Dict. &c. of lang. of Sa'a & Ulawa, Solomon Isl., 1918.
„ JACKSON (A.) Corr.; ed. J. S. Bassett, v1–3, 1926–28.
„ JAMES (H. G.) Constitut. system of Brazil, 1923.
„ JOCHELSON (W.) Archæol. invest. in Aleutian Isl^s., 1925.
„ JOHNSON (E. R.) &c. Hist. of domestic &c. commerce of the U.S., 2v, 1922.
„ KEY (W. E.) Heredity & social fitness, 1920.
„ LANCASTER (H. C.) P. Du Ryer, 1913.
„ LEARNED (M. D.) Guide to MS. mat. rel. to Amer. hist. in German State archives, 1912.
„ LOTHROP (S. K.) Tulum : east coast of Yucatan, 1924.
„ LOWE (E. A.) & E. K. RAND. A 6th-c. fragment of the Letters of Pliny the Yr. : a st. &c., 1922.
„ MACDOUGAL (D. T.) & F. SHREVE. Growth in trees & massive organs in plants, 1924.
„ MACGILL (C. E.) Hist. of transport. in U.S. bef. 1860, 1917.
„ MACLAUGHLIN (A. C.) Rep. on diplom. archives of Dept. of State, 1789–1840, rev. ed., 1906.
„ ——, W. A. SLADE &c. Writings on Amer. hist., 1903, 1905
„ MATTESON (D. M.) List of MSS. conc. Amer. hist. in Europ. libraries, 1925.
„ MILES (W. R.) Alcohol & human efficiency, 1924.
„ MORLEY (S. G.) Inscr. at Copan, 1920.
„ MÜLLER (W. MAX). Egyptolog. researches, v1, 3, 1906.
„ OSGOOD (C. G.) Concordance to poems of E. Spenser, 1915.
„ PARKER (D. W.) Cal. of papers in Wash. archives rel. to territories of U.S. (to 1873), 1911.
„ —— Guide to mat. for U.S. hist. in Canadian archives, 1913.
„ PAULLIN (C. O.) & F. L. PAXSON. Guide to mat. in London archives for hist. of U.S. since 1783, 1914.
„ PÉREZ (L. M.) Guide to mat. for Amer. hist. in Cuban archives, 1907.
„ PERRET (F. A.) Vesuvius eruption of 1906, 1924.
„ RACHEL (S.) De jure naturæ et gentium diss., 2v, 1916.
„ SARTON (G.) Intr. to hist. of science, v1, 1927.
„ SETCHELL (W. A.) American Samoa, vegetation &c., 1924.
„ SHEPHERD (W. R.) Guide to mat. for hist. of U.S. in Spanish archives, 1907.
„ STOCK (L. F.), *ed.* Proc. & debates of Brit. Parliaments resp. N. Amer., v1, 2, 1924–27.
„ STUART (G. H.) Governmental system of Peru, 1925.
„ TATLOCK (J. S. P.) & A. G. KENNEDY. Concordance to compl. wks. of Chaucer &c., 1927.
„ TEXTOR (J. W.) Synopsis juris gentium (1680), 2v, 1916.
„ VAN DEMAN (E. B.) The Atrium Vestæ, 1909.
„ VAN TYNE (C. H.) & W. G. LELAND. Guide to archives of govt. of U.S. in Washington, 2nd ed., 1907.
„ VATTEL (E. DE). Le droit des gens &c., 3v, 1916.
„ WARD (W. H.) Seal cylinders of W. Asia, 1910.
„ WILLIS (B.), E. BLACKWELDER &c. Research in China, 3v [& atlas], 1906–13.
„ WOODRING (W. P.) Miocene mollusks f. Bowden, Jamaica, 1925.

Carnegie Library, *Keighley.* Unveiling of marble bust of A. Carnegie by F. Harrison, March 14th, 1908. [P2484]. 8°. Keighley. 1908

Carnegie United Kingdom Trust
7th–14th annual rep., 1921–27. la8°. E. 1921–28
County Library Conf., 1924, 1926. Rep. of Proc^s. la8°. East Port, Dunfermline. [1925–27]
The public library system of Gt. Brit. & Ireland, 1921–23: rep. prep. for the C.U.K. Trustees by J. M. Mitchell. Sequel to Rep. prep. in 1915 by W. G. S. Adams. la8°. E. 1924
Some impressions of the public lib. system of the U.S. of Amer. Papers by 6 of the Brit. delegates, 1926. la8°. 1927
see CAMPBELL (A.) Rep. on pub. baths &c., U.K., 1918.

Carnegie (Andrew).
Autobiography. [Pref. signed L. W. Carnegie]. 8°. 1920
Man. of the public benefact. of A. C. Comp. & publ. by the C. E. f. Internat. Peace. 8°. Wash. 1919
The reunion of Britain & America. [P524]. 8°. E. 1898
see CARNEGIE LIB., *Keighley.* Unveiling of bust of A. C., by F. Harrison, 1908.
„ CASTELNUOVO (E.) La filosofia d'un miliardario, 1903.

Carnegie (David). Can Church & industry unite? Foreword by G. N. Barnes. s8°. [1920]
Hist. of munitions supply in Canada, 1914–18. 8°. 1925

Carnesecchi (Pietro), *d. 1567.* Estratto del processo di P. C.; ed. G. Manzoni, see REGIA DEP. DI STORIA PATRIA. Misc., t10, 1870.
see GIBBINGS (R.) Rep. of trial &c. of P. S., 1856.

Carnot (*le cte.* **Lazare Nicolas Marguerite).**
Mémoire adressé au roi, 1814. [*Ed.* E. D.] 8°. 1814
see DOUGLAS (H.) Obs. on fortification, incl. that prop. by M. Carnot, 1859.

Carnot (Marie François Sadi), *president of the French Republic,* see SIMOND (E.) Hist. de la 3e Républ., [t1], 1887–94: présidence de M. C., 1913.

Carnovale (Luigi). How America can prevent wars forever. [P2756]. s8°. Chicago, Ill. [1924]
Only by the abolit. of neutrality can wars be prevented. [5th ed. P2617]. s8°. Chicago. [1922]

Caro (Annibale). I mattaccini: sonetti 10 contra L. Castelvetro. 8°. Parma, 1558. [*repr.* Venice. 1823]
Rime. 8°. Venetia, *Aldo.* 1569

Caro (Elme Marie). Problèmes de morale sociale. 8°. 1876

Caro (Georg). Genua u. d. Mächte am Mittelmeer, 1257–1311. 2B. 8°. Halle a. S. 1895–99

Carocci (Guido). L'illustratore fiorentino: calendario storico, 1911, 1912. [2v. *b. in 1*]. s8°. Firenze. 1910–11

Caro-Delvaille (Henry). Phidias ou le génie grec. 8°. 1922

Caro de Torres (Francisco). Hist. de las ordenes militares de Santiago, Calatrava y Alcantara [*w.* Disc. apolog. en gracia &c. de las ordenes milit. par F. Pizarro y Orellana.] sfol. 1629

Caröe (William Douglas). King's Hostel, Trin. Coll., Camb. [Camb. Antiq. Soc. Quarto publ. N.S. 2]. 4°. C. 1909
see WREN (*Sir* C.) "Tom Tower" Christ Ch., Oxf.: Letters of W. to J. Fell, set forth & annot. by W. D. C., 1923.

Caroline, *queen consort of George IV.*
Report of proc. in the House of Lords agst. the Queen. 3v. 8°. E. 1820
*Royal investig. &c.: acquittal of H. R. H. By a serjeant at law. 4th ed. s8°. 1808
see BARRON (E.) The royal wanderer, or secret memoirs of C., 1820.
„ HONE (W.) *The political Queen that Jack loves [*a satirical poem*], 1820.
see *JACK & the Queen Killers, 1820.
„ *NEW (The) pilgrim's progress &c., 1820.
„ PLAYFAIR (P.) The Queen & h. pawns agst. the King & his pieces, 1820.
„ *QUEEN (The) [C.] & the Mogul [Geo. IV], 1820.
„ QUEEN (The) in the moon, 1820.

Caroline, *queen of Naples.* *Cantata a 3 voci per fest. il giorno natalizio di S. M. la Regina [*on birth of Carlo Tito*]. [P2765]. 8°. Napoli. 1775
see QUINCI (G. B.) Un breve soggiorno di M. C. in Mazara, 1813, 1924.

Caroline Louise, *ps.*
Baruch v. Spinoza. Drama. [P2400]. s8°. 1855

Carols. Book of old c., v1, 1910, see MASSÉ (H. J. L. J.) & C. K. SCOTT, *edd.*

Carolsfeld (Ludwig Schnorr v.), see SCHNORR V. CAROLSFELD (L.)

Carolus (Andreas). Apologeticus Memorabilia eccl. A. C. à criminat. Calixtinis vindic. [*b. w. h.* Mem. eccl., 1697–1702]. s4°. Tubingæ. 1699
Memorabilia eccl. sec. 17 juxta annorum seriem natata &c. 2t *in* 1v. s4°. Tubingæ. 1697–1702
T2 has 2 pagin. & 2 tp., dated 1702 & 1699.

Carolus (Andreas David). De religione Lutherana, disquis. Præs. A. D. C., resp. A. C. Bauer. [P2628]. 8°. Wittenbergæ. 1685
Wirtenberg. Unschuld durch Prüfung dessen, was G. Arnold v. d. Herzogthums W. Regenten, Regierung u. Lehrern, bevorab v. J. Andreæ aufgez. u. s. Kirchen-u. Ketzer-Hist. einverleibt hat. s4°. Ulm. 1708

Caron (Frans). Rel. conc. l'emp. du Japon, [*&* Mémoires, *add. in 1732 ed.*], *see* BERNARD (J. F.), *ed.* Recueil, t3, 1715 ; t4, 1732.

Caron (Pierre). Concordance des calendriers républ. & grégorien, avec notice prélim. [Soc. d'Hist. Mod.] 8º. 1905
see RÉPERTOIRE BIBL. DE L'HIST. DE FRANCE, t1, par P. C. & H. Stein, 1923.

Caron (Raymond) [R. CARONUS]. Apostolatus evangel. missionariorum regul. per univ. mundum expos. s8º. [Antwerp]. 1653
Controversiæ gen. fidei, contra infideles omnes, Iudæos, Mahometanos, paganos &c. s8º. Parisiis. 1682

Caro Sassone (Il) *ps.*, *see* HASSE (J. A.)

Carotti (Giulio). Hist. of art. Tr. J. Ross. v3. s8º. 1923
3, Ital. art in M. A.—Art in Upper & S. Italy.

Caro y Sureda (Pedro, *3rd marq.* **de la Romana),** *see* ROMANA (P. C. Y S., *3rd marq.* DE LA).

Carpasio. Ant. statuti di C. (1433) ; [*ed. V. Poggi*], *see* REGIA DEP. DI STORIA PATRIA. Misc., t40, 1904.

Carpeaux (Charles), *see* DUFOUR (H.) Le Bayon d'Angkor Thom : bas-reliefs publ. d'ap. docs. rec. par la Mission H. D., avec collab. de C. C., 2p, 1910–13.

Carpenter (*Capt.* **Alfred Francis Blakeney).**
The blocking of Zeebrugge. Intr. by Earl Beatty. 8º. 1922
—— **&** *Capt.* **D. Wilson-Barker.**
Nature notes for ocean voyagers. 8º. 1915

Carpenter (Edward), *social reformer, formerly fellow of Trinity Hall, Camb.*
Anthology of friendship (Ioläus). Ed. E. C. [repr.] s8º. 1920
Civilisation : its cause & cure &c. newly enl. & compl. ed. s8º. [1921]
Imperialismo in India &c. Tr. W. W. Strickland ; rived. da G. V. Santa Giustina. [P2486]. s8º. Genova. 1920
An unknown people. [Repr. f. " Reformer "]. [P2862]. 8º. 1897
see ARUNACHALAM (*Sir* P.) Light f. the East ; letters, ed. [*w.* suppl. articles] by E. C., 1927.
„ SWAN (T.) E. C., the man & h. message, 1922.
—— **& G. Barnefield.** The psychology of the poet Shelley. s8º. [1925]

Carpenter (Frederic Ives).
Reference guide to Edmund Spenser. 8º. Chicago. 1923

Carpenter (Geoffrey Douglas Hale).
A naturalist in East Africa. 8º. O. 1925
A naturalist on Lake Victoria, w. acc. of sleeping sickness & the Tse-tse fly. 8º. [1920]

Carpenter (George Herbert). Insect transformation. 8º. [1921]
—— **& J. Waterston.** Insecta, 2p, *see* BRIT. ANTARCTIC EXPED., 1910–13. Zoology, v3, 1915–23.

Carpenter (H. Barrett).
Suggestions for the study of colour. [repr.] 8º. Rochdale. 1923

Carpenter (Joseph Estlin). The first 3 Gospels. 4th ed. s8º. 1906
The Johannine writings. 8º. 1927
Theism in medieval India. Lect[s]., 1919. [Hibbert Lect., s2]. 8º. 1921

Carpenter (Niles). Immigrants & th. children, 1920, *see* UNITED STATES : CENSUS.

Carpenter (Rhys). The esthetic basis of Greek art, 5–4. cent. B.C. [Bryn Mawr notes &c., 1]. s8º. Bryn Mawr. 1921
The Greeks in Spain. [Bryn Mawr notes &c., 6.] s8º. 1925

Carpenter (Richard), *vicar of Poling.* Experience, historie & divinitie. 2p in 1v. [*sep. pagin.*] s8º. 1642

Carpenter (Stephen D.) Logic of history. 500 polit. texts : abolitionism &c. 2nd ed. 8º. Madison, Wis. 1864

Carpenter (William Boyd), *bp. of Ripon.*
Further pages of my life. 8º. 1916
Intr. to the study of the Scriptures. s8º. 1902

Carpi (Girolamo da), *Ferranese artist, see* GRASSI (G.) *da Carpi.*

Carpino (Francesco Brancaccio di), *see* BRANCACCIO DI CARPINO (F.)

Carpov (Jacob).
Revelatum sacro-sanctæ Trinitatis mysterium. s8º. Jenæ. 1735
Theologia revelata dogmatica. 4 Th. *in* 4v. 4º. Francof. & Lipsiæ &c. 1737–65
t4 *has t.* Œconomia salutis Novi Test. *&* *is foll. by h.* Auflösung d. Zweifel, 1766, *&* Erläuterung, *each w. sep. tp. & pagin.*
see CLUG (C. G.) Singularia theol. C. de creatione, 2p, 1738–39

Carpzov (Benedict), *the younger, German Jurisconsulte.* Jurisprudentia eccl. &c. rerum et quæstionum in Electoris Saxon. senatu eccl. &c. ventilatarum & decisarum definitiones exhibens &c. libri 3. [*3 pagin.*] fol. Lipsiæ. 1649

Carpzov (Johann Benedict), *prof. of anc. lit. at Helmstadt, 1720–1803.* De Λόγῳ Philonis non Johanneo, adv. Th. Mangey. Resp. J. F. Moeller. [P445]. s4º. Helmstadii. [1739]
Liber doctrinalis theologiæ purioris &c. s8º. Brunswigæ. 1767
Sacræ exercit. in S. Pauli epist. ad Hebræos ex Philone Alex. Præf. Philoniana. s8º. Helmstadii. 1750

Carpzov (Johann Benedict), *the younger, prof. of oriental lit. at Leipzig, 1639–99.* Disput. acad., philol., exeget., polemicæ &c. Præmissa : præf. S. B. Carpzovi. s4º. Lipsiæ. 1699
Disput. theologi Lips. de jure decid. controversias theol. [*b. w. h.* Disput., 1699]. s4º. Halæ Magdeb. [1701]
Hodegeticum brevibus aphorismis. Ed. noviss. s8º. Lipsiæ. 1689
see RIVINUS (T. A.) Hodegetici Carpzov. explanatio, 1686.

Carpzov (Johann Gottlob.) A defence of the Hebrew Bible in ans. to Mr. Whiston &c. Tr. f. Latin by M. Marcus. 8º. 1729
Introd. ad libros canon. Bibliorum Vet. Test. omnes &c. 3p *in* 1v. [*sep. tp. & pagin.*] s4º. Lipsiæ. 1721–27

Carpzov (Samuel Benedict). Examen novæ praxeos orthod. fidem discernendi &c., à J. Masenio S. J. propos. s8º. Wittebergæ. 1677

Carr (Cecil Thomas). Delegated legisl. 8º. C. 1921

Carr (Daniel L.) & J. P. Brown.
Mfantsi grammar. s8º. Cape Coast. 1868

Carr (Elma B.) Use of cost-of-living figures in wage adjustments, *see* UNITED STATES : Labor. Bull. 369, 1925.

Carr (Herbert R. C.) & G. A. Lister, *edd.* The mountains of Snowdonia. [*by var. wr.*] 8º. [1925]

Carr (Herbert Wildon).
Changing backgrounds in religion & ethics. 8º. 1927
The gen. princ. of relativity. s8º. 1920
The scient. approach to philosophy. 8º. 1924
A theory of monads : outlines of philos. of the princ. of relativity. 8º. 1922
" Time " & " history " in contemp. philos., w. spec. ref. to Bergson & Croce, *see* BRIT. ACADEMY. Proc., 1917–18.

Carrà (Carlo). Ardengo Soffici, avec 32 reprod. s8º. Rome. 1922
Daniele Ranzoni, w. 33 reprod. in phototype. s8º. Rome. 1924

Carracci (Agostino), *see* PEYRE (R.) Les Carraches [Gr. artistes], 1924.

Carracci (Annibale), *see* PEYRE (R.) Les Carraches [Gr. artistes], 1924.

Carracci (Lodovico), *see* PEYRE (R.) Les Carraches [Gr. artistes], 1924.

Carrach (Johann Philipp). Exercit. de jure condendi capellas. [P2636]. s4º. Hallæ Sal. [1750]

Carra de Vaux (*Baron* **Bernard).** Avicenne. 8º. 1900
Gazali. 8º. 1902
Les penseurs de l'Islam. 5t. s8º. 1921–26
1, Les souverains, l'hist. & la philos. polit.
2, Les géographes, les sciences math. & nat.
3, L'exégèse, la tradition & la jurisprudence.
4, La scholastique, la théologie & la mystique, la musique.
5, Les sectes—Le libéralisme mod.
see PHILO, *Byzantius.* Le livre des appareils pneumat. &c. : éd. & tr. par C. de V., 1903.

Carranza (Anjel Justiniano). Campañas navales de la Rep. Argentina. Cuadros hist. 4t. la8º. Buenos Aires. 1914–16

Carranza (Bartholome), *abp. of Toledo.* Summa Conciliorum, usque ad Julium III. J. Sylvii add. aucta. s8º. Duaci. 1679

Carrara, *The family of, see* LAZZARINI (V.) Tratt. tra Venez., Firenze e i C., 1337–99, 1899.

Carrara (Ange François Xavier). *C., l'assassin du garçon de recettes Lamarre, 1897. [*no tp.* P2826]. s8º. [Sceaux]. *n.d.*

Carrard (Henri). Une commune vaudoise au 13 s. : les statuts de Pierre de Savoie & la charte de Moudon, *see* REGIA DEP. DI STORIA PATRIA. Misc., t25, 1887.

Carrasco (José).
Bolivia's case for the League of Nations. s8º. 1920

Carrasco (Tomas).
Carrascon [1633]. 2ª ed. corr. s8º. *n.p.* [1847?]

Carré (Le), *Church of, London, see* FRENCH CHURCH, *Soho Sq.*

Carré (E.), *see* PRESLE (LA). Hist. & cartul. du prieuré de Notre-Dame &c. de la P. ; [publ. &c. par], E. C., 1893.

Carré (*Lt.-Col.* **George Tennant).**
A tour in Bulgaria, 1887. [P2590]. s8º. Lahore. 1888

Carré (Henri). La France sous Louis XV, 1723–74. 8º. [1891]
La noblesse de France & l'opinion publique au 18e s. la8º. 1920
La véritable hist. des taxis de la Marne, 6–8 sept. 1914. Préf. du Gén. Maunoury. s8º. 1921

Carré (Jean Marie). Bibliogr. de Goethe en Angleterre. 8°. 1920
La vie aventureuse de J. A. Rimbaud. s8°. [1926]
La vie de Goethe. 6e éd. s8°. 1927

Carré (Louis). Les poinçons de l'orfèvrerie franç, 14e–19e s. 4°. 1928

Carré Aldao (Eugenio). Influencias de la lit. gallega en la castellana. s8°. [1915]

Carré de Malberg (*Mme.* Caroline Barbe), *née Colchen, 1829–91,* see LAVEILLE (*Mgr.* A.) Madame C. de M., 1917.

Carrer (Antonio), see DOLCETTI (G.) Scuola d. Tira &c. ora gabin. artist. A. C., 1905.

Carrer (Luigi). Anello di sette gemme, o Venezia e la sua storia. 8°. Venezia. 1838
Prose. [Opere scette, v2, 3]. 2v. s8°. Firenze. 1855
1, Elogi, discorsi, relazioni accad., discorsetti, prose morali.
2, Prose estetiche, narrazioni storiche (C. Corner &c.), Vita di U. Foscolo, articoli crit., traduzioni.

Carreras (Luis). Crón. de la prov. de Segovia, 1866, see ESPAÑA. Crón. gen., v10, 1865 &c.

Carrère (Jean). Degeneration in the gt. French masters. Tr. J. McCabe. 8°. 1922
Les mauvais maîtres. Rousseau, Chateaubriand &c. s8°. [1922]

—— & G. Bourgin.
Manuel des partis polit. en France. s8°. 1924

Carretero (José Maria) [*ps.* EL CABALLERO AUDAZ].
Hombre de amor. Novela. s8°. [1922]
Un hombre extraño. Novela. 2a parte de Hombre de amor. s8°. [1922]

Carriazo (Juan de M.), see VALERA (D. DE). Cron. de los Reyes Catol.; ed. y estudio por J. de M. C., 1927.

Carrier (E. H.), see CARRIER (J. B.) Corr. of J.-B. C., 1793–94; coll., tr. &c. by E. H. C., 1920.

Carrier (Jean Baptiste). Corr. of C., people's repres. to the Convention, dur. h. mission in Brittany, 1793–94. Coll., tr. & annot. by E. H. C. 8°. 1920
see MARTIN (G.) C. & sa mission à Nantes, 1924.

Carrière (Auguste).
[The Abgar legend in Moses of Khoren's Hist. Tr. *into Armenian* by G. Menevishean. P2814]. s8°. Vienna. 1897
De psalterio Salomonis: disquis. [P2794]. 8°. Argentorati. 1870
Moïse de Khoren & les généal. patriarcales. [P2801]. s8°. 1891
Nouv. sources de M. de Khoren. [P2801]. s8°. Vienne. 1893
Sur un chap. de Grégoire de Tours rel. à l'hist. de l'Orient, see ÉCOLE PRAT. DES HAUTES ÉTUDES. Sci. hist. &c. Annuaire, 1898, 1897.
see MACLER (F.) Moïse de Khoren & les travaux de A. C., 1902.

Carrière (Eugène), see SÉAILLES (G.) E. C., l'homme & l'artiste, 1901.

Carriere (Moriz). Vom Geist. Schwert- u. Handschlag für F. Baader. [P2483]. 8°. Weilburg. 1841

Carrière (*l'abbé* Victor), see PROVINS. Hist. & cartul. des Templiers de Provins, avec intr. sur les débuts du Temple en France par V. C., 1919.

Carrington (Edith). The ass, h. welfare, wants &c., see TUPPY: autobiog. of a donkey, 1903.

Carrington (Hereward H. L.)
The phys. phenomena of spiritualism. 8°. 1920

Carrington (John Bodman) & G. R. Hughes.
The plate of the Co. of Goldsmiths. 4°. O. 1926

Carrington (Philip). Christian apologetics of the 2nd cent. in their rel. to mod. thought. 8°. 1921

Carro (Jean de).
Carlsbad, ses eaux minérales. s8°. Carlsbad. 1827

Carroll (Charles), *of Carrollton.* Journal, dur. visit to Canada in 1776; w. mem. & notes by B. Mayer. [Maryland Hist. Soc.] 8°. Baltimore. 1876

Carroll (Lewis), *ps.* [*i.e.* C. L. DODGSON].
Feeding the mind. Pref. note by W. H. Draper. 8°. 1907
see COLLINGWOOD (S. D.) Life & letters of L. C., 2nd ed., 1899.

Carr-Saunders (Alexander Morris).
Eugenics. [Home Univ. Lib.] s8°. [1926]
Population. s8°. 1925
The population problem. St. in human evolution. 8°. O. 1922

—— & D. C. Jones. A survey of the soc. structure of Eng. &c., illust. by statistics. 8°. O. 1927

Carrucci (Jacopo), *called Il Pontormo,* see PONTORMO (J. DA).

Carruthers (John).
Scheherazade, or the future of the Eng. novel. s8°. [1927]
The virgin wife. s8°. [1925]

Carruthers (Robert George). *Works in* GEOLOG. SURVEY OF ENG. &C. Spec. rep. on min. resources.
Fluorspar by C. &c., 2nd. ed., 1917. [4.]
Lead & zinc ores of Durham, Yorks &c., 1923 [26.]

Carse (Adam). The hist. of orchestr. 8°. 1925

Carson (Alexander), *A. M.*
The knowledge of Jesus. 2nd ed. s8°. E. 1840

Carson (*Sir* Edward Henry), see BATES (J. V.) Sir E. C., Ulster leader, 1921.

Carson (Hampton Lawrence). The Supreme Court of the U.S.: its hist. by C. &c. 4°. Phila. 1891

Carstairs (John), *d. 1686,* see MEMOIRS of Mrs. W. Veitch, T. Hog, H. Erskine & J. C., 1846.

Carstenn (Edward).
Was die Danziger Strassennamen erzählen. 8°. Danzig. 1922

Carswell (Catherine).
The camomile. An invention. s8°. 1922
Open the door! s8°. [1920]

Carswell (Donald), see TRUE (R.) Trial of R. T.; ed. D. C., 1925.

Cartagena (Alonso de) [ALFONSO], see ALFONSO, *de Cartagena.*

Cartailhac (Emile), see GRIMALDI. Grottes de G., t2ii, Archéologie; par E. C., 1912.

—— & H. Breuil. La caverne d'Altamira à Santillane, près Santander (Espagne). 4°. Monaco. 1906

Cartari (Vincenzo).
Le imagini de i dei de gli antichi. 8°. Venetia. 1571

***Carte** gén. des limites entre les trois Empires &c., 1788, see GEOGRAPHISCHE gen. Karte, 1788.

Carte Papers, see RUSSELL (C. W.) & J. P. PRENDERGAST. The C. MSS. in the Bodl. Lib.: rep. to Master of the Rolls, 1871.

Cartellieri (G. M. Alexander). Philipp II. August, König v. Frankreich. B4i, ii [*pagin. cont.*] 8°. L. 1921–22
4, i. P. A. u. Johann ohne Land, 1199–1206. ii, Bouvines u. d. Ende d. Regierung, 1207.

Cartellieri (Otto). Am Hofe d. Herzöge v. Burgund: kulturhist. Bilder. 8°. Basel. 1926

Cartellieri (Walther). Die röm. Alpenstrassen ü. d. Brenner-, Reschen-Scheideck u. Plöckenpass. [Philologus, Suppl.- Band 18, H1]. 8°. L. 1926

Carter (Albert Thomas).
Elements of the law of contract. 6th ed. s8°. 1925
Hist. of Eng. courts. 5th ed. of A hist. of Eng. legal instit. 8°. 1927

Carter (E. Ellin). Artistic leather work. 2nd ed. s8°. 1921

Carter (Edmund). Hist. of the co. of Cambridge. [1753]. 8°. 1819

Carter (Edward Henry). The new past & o. essays on the development of civilis. By J. H. Breasted, H. J. Fleure, W. J. Perry &c. Ed. E. H. Carter. s8°. O. 1925

Carter (Harry). Autobiog. of a Cornish smuggler, Capt. H. C., of Prussia Cove, 1749–1809. Intr. by J. B. Cornish. s8°. Truro. 1894

Carter (Herbert R.)
The decortication of fibrous plants. 8°. [1921]
Jute & its manufacture. 8°. [1921]

Carter (Howard) & A. C. Mace. The tomb of Tut-ankh-Amen, discov. by the late Earl of Carnarvon & H. C. 2v. la8°. 1923–27
v2 by H. C. only, w. app. by D. E. Derry &c.

Carter (Humphrey Gilbert) [GILBERT-CARTER (H.)] Genera of Brit. plants. Arr. acc. to Engler's Syllabus d. Pflanzenfamilien (7th ed. 1912), w. add. of the characters of the Genera. s8°. C. 1913

Carter (Huntly). The new spirit in the European theatre, 1914–24. la8°. 1925
The new theatre & cinema of Soviet Russia. 8°. 1924
Spiritualism: its meaning. [*By var. wr.*] Ed. H. C. 8°. [1920]

Carter (Jefferson). Madam Constantia: romance of a prisoner of war in the Amer. Revol. Ed. J. C. s8°. 1919

Carter (Matthew). Honor redivivus, or, An analysis of honor & heraldry. s8°. 1660

Carter (Nellie), see WEST (W.) & G. S. WEST. Monogr. of the Brit. Desmidiaceæ, v5, by N. C., 1923.

Carter (Pierson Cathrick). Hist. of the church & parish of St. Alphage, London Wall, w. extrs. f. vestry minutes &c. 4°. *p.p.* 1925

Carter (R. Radcliffe), see BROCKLEBANK (R.) Pictures & engr.; descr. &c. notes &c. by R. R. C., 1904.

Carter (Thomas Francis). Invention of printing in China & its spread westward. 8°. N.Y. 1925

Carter (William Fowler). Notes on Staffordshire families, *see* STAFFORDSHIRE. Colls. 1925, 1927.
see KING EDWARD'S SCHOOL, *Birmingham.* Records, v1, w. intr. by W. F. C., 1924.
,, WARWICK. Abstr. of bailiffs' acc. of monastic &c. estates in W., 1547 ; tr. ; intr. by W. F. C., 1923.

Carteret (Léopold). Le trésor du bibliophile romant. & mod., 1801–75. 3t *&* Tables. la8°. 1924–28
1, 2 Editions orig. 3, Livres illust. du 19e s.

Carteret (Philip), *see* CHIJS (J. A. v. DER). P. C. in Ned.-Indië, 1767–68, 1891.

Cartesius, *see* DESCARTES (R.)

Carthew (George A.) The Hundred of Launditch & Deanery of Brisley, in Co. of Norfolk. Evidences & topog. notes f. Public Records &c. ; coll. by G. A. C. 3p [1, 2 *pagin. cont.* 3, *sep. tp. & pagin.*] 4°. Norwich. 1877–79

Carthill (Al.), *ps.* *False dawn. 8°. E. 1926
The garden of Adonis. 8°. 1927
*The lost dominion [*i.e.* India]. 8°. E. 1924
,, ,, ...[2nd ed.] 8°. E. 1924

Cartier (Jacques). Voyages. Publ. f. orig. w. tr., notes &c. by H. P. Biggar, *see* CANADA. Public Archives. Publ., No. 11, 1924.

Cartilha. *Nova cartilha da doutrina Christaã &c., 1733, *see* NOVA.

Cartland (Barbara). Sawdust. s8°. [1926]

Carton de Wiart (*Mme.* **H.)** L'enfant belge et la Guerre, *see* CAHIERS (LES) BELGES, No. 25, 1918.

Cartulaire [CARTULAIRES ; CARTULARE ; *see also* CHARTES ; CHARTULARIUM]. Catalogue gén. des cartulaires des archives dépt. ; publ. par la Comm. des Archives Dépt. &c., 1847, *see* CATALOGUE.
For sep. cartularies see under the following names in catalogue.

Aoste.	Lérins.	Quimperlé.
Arras.	Longpont.	Ribemont.
Artevelde.	Lyons.	Roc-Amadour, *see* Tulle.
Baigne.	Manosque.	Romans.
Basse-Fontaine.	Metz.	Rouen.
Baugency.	Mirepoix.	Royallieu.
Beauvais.	Molesme.	St-Bertin.
Bourg-lès-Valence.	Monastier.	Ste-Foy-de-Peyrolières.
Compiègne.	Montiéramey.	Ste-Hoïlde.
Dauphiné.	Montier-la-Celle.	Sorde.
Domène.	Mont-Morel.	Térouane.
Fontenay le Marmion.	Montpellier.	Tiron.
Gorze.	Montreuil-sur-Mer.	Tréport (Le).
Guillems de Montpellier.	Nevers.	Tulle.
Hugues de Chalon	Paunat.	Vienne.
La Presle.	Porrois, *see* Port Royal.	Vigeois.
Le Mans.	Prouille.	Vignory.
	Provins.	

Cartulare, *see* CARTULAIRE.

Cartwright (Charles), *M.D.* A faithful narr. of the adv. of C. C. in a voyage to Jamaica. [P607]. s8°. 1741

Cartwright (Christopher). Certamen religiosum : or, a conf. betw. the late King of Eng. & the late Marq. of Worcester. With a vindic. of the Protestant cause. [2p *in* 1v. *sep. pagin.*] s4°. 1652

Cartwright (*Sir* **Fairfax Leighton).** The mystic rose f. the garden of the king. Fragm. of the vision of Sheikh Haji Ibrahim of Kerbela. [*Tr. or rather written*] by F. L. C. s8°. *p.p.* [1899]
,, ,, ...8°. 1925

Cartwright (*Major* **John),** *1740–1824.*
*A memoir of J. C. the reformer. [P2782]. 8°. 1831

Cartwright (Julia) [*Mrs.* H. ADY].
Raphael. [reissued]. 8°. [1914]

Cartwright (Thomas), *Puritan divine.* A directory of Church-govt., drawn up & used by Elizabethan Presbyterians. Repr. in facs. f. 1644. [Intr. by P. L., *i.e.* Peter Lorimer]. 8°. 1872
see PEARSON (A. F. S.) T. C. & Elizabethan Puritanism, 1535–1603, 1925.
,, WHITGIFT (J.) Defense of the Aunswere to the admon. agst. the replie of T. C., 1574.

Carucci (Jacopo), *called Il Pontormo, see* PORTORMO (J. DA).

Carus (Joseph Maria), *ps., see* TOMASI (*card.* G. M.)

Carus (Paul).
Fundamental problems : method of philos. &c. 8°. 1889
Primer of philosophy. rev. ed. 8°. Chicago. 1899
The soul of man. Physiological &c. psychology. 8°. Chicago. 1891

Caruso (Enrico).
see KEY (P. V. R.) E. C. : a biog., 1923.
,, LEDNER (E.) Erinnerungen an Caruso, 1922.

Carutti (Domenico). *Works in* REGIA DEP. DI STORIA PATRIA. Misc.
Il barone Gius. Manuel di S. Giovanni, 1887. [26.]
Il Canonico E. Bérard : cenno commem., 1890. [28.]
Il Conte della Roche d'Allery e il Col. Fresen all' assedio di Verrua (1704–5), 1901. [37.]
Il Conte G. Porro Lambertenghi, 1887. [25.]
Della famiglia di Gaetano Pugnani, 1895. [33.]
In mem. d. Senatore C. Negroni, 1896. [34.]
Mgr. Jacopo Bernardi, 1900. [36.]
L'on. Quintino Sella, 1884. [23.]
Suppl. ai " Regesta comitum Sabaudiæ, ad an. 1253," 1904. [40.]
see SEGRE (A.) D. C. di Cantogno, 1913.

Carvajal (Baltasar de), *see* CARAVAJAL (B. DE).

Carvajal (Valentin Lamas), *see* LAMAS CARVAJAL (V.)

Carvalho (Valentino), *see* JESUITS. Iappon. Imp. admirabilis comm. expos. litt. [*by* V. C.], Lat. fecit Ioh. Hay, 1604.

Carvalho e Vasconcellos (Ernesto Julio de).
Portugal colonial. s8°. Lisboa. *n.d.*

Carver (John). Treatise on the culture of the tobacco plant, &c. 8°. 1779

Carver (Thomas Nixon).
Economy of human energy. s8°. N.Y. 1924
Elementary economics. 8°. Boston. [U.S. 1920]
Govt. control of the liquor business in Gt. Brit. & the U.S. [C. E. for Internat. Peace. Div. of Econ. &c. *b. w. h.* War thrift, 1919]. la8°. N.Y. 1919
War thrift. [C. E. for Internat. Peace. Div. of Econ. &c.] la8°. N.Y. 1919

Carvosso (William). The efficacy of faith : mem. of W. C. wr. by himself, ed. by his son. s8°. *n.d.*

Carwell (Thomas), *see* STILLINGFLEET (E.) Rational acc. of grounds of Prot. relig. vindic. of [Laud's] Rel. of a Conf. &c., f. the ans. of T. C., 1681.

Cary (Arthur Deering Lucius) & S. McCance. Regimental rec. of the Royal Welch Fusiliers (late the 23rd Foot). Compiled by C. & McC. Illust. by G. C. Hudson. 2v. *in* 1. la8°. 1921–23

Cary (D. M.) Some ballad-legends of Somerset. Comp. by D. M. C. [Somerset Folk Ser., No. 14]. s8°. 1924

Cary (Henry Francis). Early French poets. Intr. by T. E. Welby. [Campion reprints]. s8°. 1923
see KING (R. W.) Translator of Dante, 1772–1844, 1925.

Cary (John), *geographer.* Map of England & Wales w. part of Scotland. folded. 8°. 1841
New map of Ireland, exhib. turnpike roads, rivers & canals &c. folded. 8°. 1820
A new map of Yorkshire. folded. s8°. 1825
see FORDHAM (*Sir* H. G.) J. C., a bibliog. w. notes, 1925.
,, —— Work of J. C. & h. successors, 1924.

Caryl (Joseph). Exposition, with pract. obs., upon Job. 2v. lafol. 1676–77
Nature &c. of a sacred Covenant Sermon. [P2662]. s4°. 1643
see BAXTER (R.) Apology &c. w. Crandon's Anatomy for satisfaction of Mr. C., 1654.

Casalis (Alfred), *missionary.*
Croquis du Zambèze. [Préf. de J. Bianquis]. s8°. [1919]

Casalius (Gaspar), *bp. of Leria, see* CAZAL (GASPARDO).

Casalius (Joannes Baptista). De profanis & sacris vet. ritibus. [3p *in* 1v. (p. 3 *sep. pagin.*)]. la8°. Romæ. 1644

Casals (J. Goday y), *see* GODAY Y CASALS (J.)

Casanova (Giuseppe), *see* CERUTI (A.) Commem. dell' avv. G. C., 1889.

Casanova (Jacques).
Corresp. inéd. (1760–72)—Le vrai texte des Méms. de C., par T. Bull—Le ms. des Méms. [*by* R. Vèze]. [Pages Casanov., 3, 4]. [2t]. 8°. 1925
Le duel, ou essai sur la vie de G. C. Vénitien. [Pages Casanov.] 8°. 1925
Lana Caprina : lettre d'un lycanthrope—Corr. inéd.—L'intermédiaire des Casanovistes. [Pages casanov.] 8°. 1926
Méms. Suivis de fragm. des méms. du Pr. de Ligne. n. éd. [*la. paper, extra illust.*] 8t. 8°. *Garnier. n.d.*
Méms. éd. orig. 6t. s8°. [1912]
Méms. Ed. nouv., d'ap. le texte de l'éd. princeps, 1826–38 &c., préfs. & comms. Intr. par [t1] O. Uzanne [2, A. Rava, 3, B. Marr, 4, C. Samaran, 5, H. de Régnier, 6, G. Cucuel, 7, R. Vèze]. t1–7. 8°. 1924–28
,, ,, [*orig. issue of* t1]. 8°. 1922
Le messager de Thalie. 11 feuilletons inéd. de crit. dram. Précis de ma vie &c. [Pages casanov.] 8°. 1925
Nè amori nè donne ovvero La stalla ripulita. Tr. franç. [Intr. par R. Vèze. Pages casanov.] s8°. 1926

Casanova (Jacques) [*continued*].
Soliloque d'un penseur [&] Corr. inéd. 1773–83. [Pages casanov.] s8°. 1926
see BLEACKLEY (H. W.) C. in England: acc. of visit to London, 1763–64, 1923.
„ DOLCETTI (G.) La fuga di G. C. d. piombi di Venezia, 1905.
„ GRELLET (P.) Les aventures de C. en Suisse, 1919.
„ GUGITZ (G.) G. C. u. s. Lebensroman, 1921.
„ LE GRAS (J.) C., adventurer & lover, tr. Steuart, 1923.
see RAVÀ (A.) Contrib. a. bibliogr. di G. C., 1910.
„ —— Il fallimento di un console &c. e una lettera di C., 1910.
„ ROGGENDORFF (*ctss.* C. DE). La dern. amie de C.: corresp. inéd., 1797–98, (Pages casanov.), 1926.
„ SAMARAN (C.) J. C. vénitien, 1914.
„ SCHNITZLER (A.) C.'s Heimfahrt, Novelle, 1919.
„ —— C.'s homecoming [*fiction*]; tr., 1923.

Casanova (Paul). Essai de reconstitut. topogr. de la ville d'al Fousṭâṭ ou Miṣr, t1, see INSTITUT. FRANÇ. D'ARCH. DU CAIRE. Mém., t35, 1919.

Casas (Ramon), see ABRIL (M.) R. C., 1919.

Casati (Giovanni). Diz. d. scrittori d' Italia. v1. la8°. Milano. [1925]

Casaubon (Isaac). De rebus sacris & eccl. exercit. 16 ad Baronii proleg. in Annales & primam p. de Jesu Christi nativ., vita &c. s4°. Genevæ. 1655
Theocritic. lectionum libellus, 1596, see THEOCRITUS, 1603.

Casaubon (Méric). De enthusiasmo precat., see MAYER (J. F.) De pietistis &c., 1716.

Cascales (Francisco), see SORIANO (J. G.) El humanista F. C., vida y obras, 1924.

Çascorbi (Paul), see HEINTZE (A.) Die deut. Familiennamen, 6e, verb. &c. A., hrsg. P. C., 1925.

Case.
*Case (A) of conscience &c., in favour of Jansenism, 1703, see JANSENISM.
*Case (The) of orphans consider'd &c., 1725, see ORPHANS.
Case (The) of the people of Eng. consid.; shewing how far they are, or are not obliged by the oath of allegiance. [P2572]. s4°. 1689
*Case (The) stated betw. the Church of Rome & the Church of Eng., 2p, 1721, see MANNING (R.)

Case (Clarence Marsh).
Non-violent coercion: methods of social pressure. 8°. [1923]

Case (*Miss* Ethel).
see EARLE (*Mrs.* C. W.) & E. C. Gardening, 1912.
„ —— Pot-pourri mixed by two, 1914.

Case (Thomas), *form. Fellow of Brasenose Coll., Oxon.* Materials for the hist. of the Athenian democracy. [P2862]. 8°. O. 1874
Realism in morals. [P2474]. 8°. O. 1877

Casel (Odo). De philosophorum Græc. silentio mystico. [Religionsgesch. Versuche, B16ii]. 8°. Giessen. 1919

Casella (E.) Re Moro: autobiog. di un cavallo. Pref. di F. Z. Salazar. s8°. Torino. 1904

Cases (Antonio). El buque anclado. s8°. *n.d.*

Cash (James) & G. H. Wailes. The Brit. freshwater Rhizopoda & Heliozoa. By C. & W. assisted by J. Hopkinson. [Ray Society]. v5, Heliozoa by G. H. W. 8°. 1921

Cashmore (Adeline). The mount of vision, a bk. of Eng. mystic verse. Introd. by A. Meynell. s8°. [1910]

Casimir (Philippe).
La Turbie et son trophée romain. [P2496]. s8°. Nice. 1914

Casimir-Perier (Jean Paul Pierre), *president of the French Republ.,* see SIMOND (E.) Hist. de la 3e Républ., [t2], 1894–96: présidence de C.-P., 1921.

Casio de' Medici (Girolamo). Libro de fasti giorni sacri de li quali si fa mẽtione ĩ Capitoli 45. Canzoni 7, sonetti 175 & madrigaletti 12. s8°. [Bologna. 1528]

Caskey (John Homer). Life & works of E. Moore. 8°. New Haven, *Yale.* 1927

Caslon (H. W.) & Co., *Ltd.* Two centuries of typefounding. Annals of the Letter Foundry establ. by Will. Caslon in Chiswell St., London, 1720. [Text by J. F. McRae]. 4°. 1920

Caslon (William), see CASLON (H. W.) & Co., LTD. 2 cents. of typefounding &c., 1720, 1920.

Casmannus (Otho). Angelographia, seu Comm. de angelis &c. 2p [*in* 1v. *sep. tps.; pagin. contd.*] s8°. Francofurti. 1597

Casmirius (Franciscus Antonius).
Scotus dilucidatus. s8°. Neapoli. 1607

Caspari (Carl Paul). Alte u. neue Quellen z. Gesch. d. Taufsymbols u. d. Glaubensregel. [Videnskabs.-Selskab., Christiania. *b. w. h.* Ungedr. Quellen &c., B3, 1875]. 8°. Chr. 1879
Gramm. d. arab. Spr. 2e verbess. A. 8°. L. 1859

Caspari (Carl Paul) [*continued*].
Ungedruckte, unbeachtete &c. Quellen z. Gesch. d. Taufsymbols &c., hrsgg. u. erläut. v. C. 3B [*in* 2v.] 8°. Christiania. 1866–75

Caspari (Johann Bucckhard). Not. δαιμονίου sive δαίμονος &c. s4°. Jenæ. [1761]

Cassagnac (P. A. de Granier de), see GRANIER DE CASSAGNAC (P. A. DE).

Cassan (*le général* **Louis Pierre Jean Aphrodise),** see HENNET DE GOUTEL (*baron*). Le Gén. C. & la défense de Pampelune, 1813, 1920.

Cassander (Georgius) *of Bruges.* Opera. Epist. 117 & Colloquia 2 cum Anabaptistis. fol. Parisiis. 1616
Cassander Evangelicus, sive in plærisqʒ assertor Aug. Conf. graviss. Das ist: Die jenige Puncten worinn G. C. die Augspurg. Conf. gebillichet &c. Ausgezogen u. ins Teutsche gebracht, durch J. Saubertum. [*Lat.* & *Germ.*] s4°. Nurnberg. 1631
Comm. de duabus in Christo naturis &c., see VIGILIUS. *Saint, bp. of Trent.* Opera, 555.
Consultatio C. & H. Grotii annot., see GROTIUS (H. DE). Via ad pacem eccl., 1642.

Cassau (Theodor O.) Konsumvereinsbeweg. in Deutschl., see UNTERSUCHUNGEN ü. Konsumvereine, 1924.

Cassel (Gustav).
Fundamental thoughts in economics. s8°. [1925]
Money & foreign exchange after 1914. 8°. 1922
„ „ ....[2nd impr.] 8°. [1923]
Theory of social economy. Tr. J. McCabe. 2v. 8°. [1923]
The world's monetary problems. 2 memoranda. s8°. [1921]
World's monetary problems, see INTERNAT. FINANCIAL CONF. Paper 13iii, 1920.

Cassel (Johann Philipp). Diss. de templo Oniæ Heliopolitano, 1730, see SCHLÄGER (C. J.) Diss. fasc. novus, 1744.
Hist. Nachr. v. d. Märtirer Sanct Hulpe, besonders in Bremen. [P600]. s4°. Bremen. 1765

Cassell, *publisher.* C.'s classified quotations, 1921, see BENHAM (W. G.)
C.'s Doré gallery, 1887 ?, see DORÉ (P. G.)
C.'s Latin dict. (Lat.-Eng., Eng.-Lat.) Rev. by J. R. V. Marchant & J. F. Charles. s8°. 1907
Picturesque Europe, 5v, 1881–86, see EUROPE.

Cassellana de unione Reformat. cum Lutheranis consult., 1664, see CALOVIUS (A.)

Casserly (*Lt.-Col.* Gordon), *F.R.G.S.* Algeria to-day. 8°. [1923]

Cassian (John) [†CASSIANUS (JOANNES), *Eremita*]. Opera omnia, cum comm. Alardi Gazaei &c. fol. Francofurti. 1732
see GUYON (*Mme.* J. M.) Justif. de la doctr. de Mme. G.; avec un examen de la 9e & 10e conf. de C., par Fénelon, 3t, 1790.

Cassidy (William). Memorial of W. C. la8°. Albany. 1874

Cassiodorus (Marcus Aurelius). *Hist. eccl. quam tripartitam vocant libri 12 [ex Sozomeno, Socrate & Theodoreto ab Epiphanio Scholastico versa.] s8°. Parisiis. 1566
„ „ *f. a. ed.,* see CALLISTUS (N.) Scriptores vere Cath. &c., 1588.

Cassirer (Ernst). Das Erkenntnisproblem in d. Philos. &c. d. neu. Zeit. [3e A.] 2B. 8°. 1922
Idee u. Gestalt: Goethe—Schiller—Hölderlin—Kleist. [2e A.] 8°. 1924
Kants Leben u. Lehre. 8°. 1921
Substance & function & Einstein's theory of relativity. Auth. tr. by W. C. & M. C. Swabey. 8°. Chicago. 1923
Zur Einstein'schen Relativitätstheorie. [T1]. 8°. 1921

Cassius (Paul Gottfried). Meditat. de Ianne & Iambre Aegypt. magis. Præs J. G. Michaelis. [P427]. s4°. Halæ Magdeb. [1747]

Casson (Herbert Newton). Ads. & sales. St. of advertising. &c. 8°. *Pitman.* [1913]

Casson (Stanley). Ancient Greece. s8°. 1922
Hellenic studies. s8°. 1922
see Athens. Acropolis Museum. Cat., v2, Sculpture & arch. fragms. &c. by S. C., 1921.

Cassou (Jean). La nuit du 15 mai, nouvelle, see ŒUVRES libres, 69, 1927.

Castagné (Joseph). Les organiss. soviét. de la Russie musulmane, see BOLCHEVISME (LE) & l'Islam, t1, 1922.

Castaing (Edme Samuel). Affaire C.: accus. d'empoisonnement. Rec. des piéces de la procédure &c., préc. de notices sur les frères Ballet &c. 2e éd. 8°. 1823

Castaldi (Giuseppe).
Memorie stor. del comune di Afragola. 8°. Napoli. 1830

Castaldi (Panfilo), *see* MINOTTO (A. S.) Monumenti a V. de' Rambaldoni e P. C. in Feltre, 1869.

Castaldini (Gio. Paolo). Breve poema sopra il senso &c. [*b. w.* Casio de' Medici (G.) Libro, 1528]. s8°. Bologna. 1585
Cento sonetti. [*b. w.* Casio de' Medici (G.) Libro, 1528]. s8°. Bologna. 1585

Castaneda y Alcover (Vicente), *ed.* Rels. geogr., topogr. e hist. d. Reino de Valencia, hechas en el siglo 18 a ruego de T. López. Prov. de Valencia. [2p]. 8°. 1921–22

Castanhoso (Miguel de). Hist. das cousas que C. da Gama fez nos Reynos do Preste João &c., 1564, *see* COLLECÇÃO de opusc. reimpr., t1, 1875.

Castelar (Emilio).
Cartas sobre politica europea. 2s. s8°. 1876
La cuestion de Oriente. 8°. 1876
see MARTINEZ RUIZ (J.) De Granada a C., 1922.

Castelbajac (Léontine, *comtesse* **de),** *see* VILLENEUVE (L. DE).

Castelfranco (Pompeo) & G. Patroni. La stazione palustre di Campo Castellaro pr. il Vhò di Piadena, *see* REALE ACCAD. D. LINCEI. Mon. ant., v24, 1916.

Castell (Edmund) [CASTELLI]. Lexicon heptaglotton Heb., Chaldaicum, Syr., Samarit., Æthiop., Arab. conjunctim; & Persicum, separatim [Lex. orient. heptagl. pars altera: seu Dict. Persico-Lat. opera J. Golii atque C. Castelli concinnatum] cui acc. Gramm. 2t. [*pagin. cont.*] fol. Londoni. 1669
Lex. Syriacum ex ejus heptaglotto. Cur. &c. J. D. Michaelis. 2p. [*in* 1v. *pagin cont.*] s4°. Gettingæ. 1788

Castellan (Antoine Laurent). Lettres sur la Grèce, l'Hellespont & Constantinople, faisant suite aux Lettres sur la Morée. 2p. [*in* 1v]. 8°. 1811

Castellane (*le comte* Boni de). Vingt ans de Paris, *see* ŒUVRES libres, 52, 1925.

Castellani (Carlo). L'orig. tedesca e l'orig. olandese d. invenzione d. stampa. [P2841]. 8°. Venezia. 1889

Castellani (Giacomo), *see* FULVIO (V.), *Savoiano, ps.*

Castellani (Giuseppe) & G. Ceresole. Bibliog. nuziale d. famiglia Papadopoli. [Nozze d'argento Papadopoli-Hellenbach. N123]. la8°. Venezia. 1905

Castellani (Tomaso).
Rime. [*Ed.* B. Castellani]. s8°. Bologna. 1545

Castellano (Giovanni).
Benedetto Croce, il filosofo, &c. s8°. Napoli. 1924
Intr. allo studio d. opere di B. Croce. 8°. Bari. 1920

Castellanos (Juan de), *1522–1607.* Discurso de el capitán Francisco Draque, 1586–87. [Intr. *by* A. Gonzalez Palencia. Inst. de Valencia de D. Juan]. la8°. 1921

Castellar (Giov. Andrea Saluzzo di), *see* SALUZZO DI CASTELLAR (G. A.)

Castelletti (Cristoforo). Il Furbo, comedia. s8°. Vinegia. 1597

Castellion (Sébastien) [†CHÂTEILLON (S.)] Adnot. Bibliorum Sacr. interpret. cum contin. hist. usque ad Christum &c. Acc. Suppl. hist. ad ult. excidium Hierosolym. ex L. Capelli Hist. Denuo emend. I. L. Bünemann. s8°. Lipsiæ. 1738
see BIBLE: LATIN. Biblia, interp. S. C., cum annots., 1551.

Castello (Maria Ricci Paternò), *see* RICCI PATERNÒ CASTELLO (M.)

Castello Branco (Camillo). Amor de perdição. 32a ed., com estudos crit. de M. Pinheiro Chagas &c. s8°. Pôrto. 1920
Amor de salvação. 7a ed. s8°. Pôrto. *n.d.*
see QUEIROZ DA SILVEIRA (J. DE). Memorias, com intr. &c. por C. C.-C., 1868.

Castelnau (de Curières de), *see* GIRAUD (V.) Le Gén. de C., 1921.

Castelnuovo (Enrico).
Commem. di A. Pascolato. [P2841]. 8°. Venezia. 1905
La filosofia d'un miliardario. [A. Carnegie. *Extr. f.* R. Ist. Veneto, Atti, 62ii. P2841]. 8°. Venezia. 1903

Castenbaur (Stephan) [†CASTENBAUER; CASTENPAWR]. *Artickel wider Doctor S. C. eingelegt auch was er darauf geantwort. hat. s4°. *n.p.* 1523

Castéra (Jean Henri), *see* CATHERINE II, *emp. of Russia.* Théâtre de l'Hermitage, *ed.* J. H. C., 2t, 1799.

Casti (Giov. Batt.) Lettere polit. scr. da Vienna 1793; pubbl. E. Greppi, *see* REGIA DEPUT. Misc., t21, 1883.

Castiglione (Saba da), *see* RANIERI (V.) Mem. stor. p. s. alla vita di S. B., 1821.

Castilla (Julian de). The Eng. conquest of Jamaica, 1655–56; tr. by I. A. Wright, 1923, *see* CAMDEN MISCELLANY (THE), v13, 1924.

Castillejo (Christóbal de). Obras. Prólogo &c. de J. Domínguez Bordona. [Clás. Castellanos]. [v]1. s8°. 1926
1, Sermón de amores—Diálogo de mujeres.

Castillo (John). Awd Isaac, & o. poems; w. a gloss. of Yorks. dialect. s8°. Whitby. 1843

Castillo Solorzaño (Alonso de). La Garduña de Sevilla, y Anzùelo de las Bolsas. 4a imp. s8°. 1733
,, ,, ... 8°. Paris. *n.d.*

Castillo y Soriano (José del).
Núñez de Arce: apuntes para su biog. s8°. 1904

Castim (Josephus), *ps., see* PISECIUS (T.)

Castiñeiras (Alejandro).
El alma de Rusia. s8°. Buenos Aires. 1923

Castle (*Mrs.* Agnes) & E. Castle.
Enchanted casements. s8°. [1923]
John Seneschal's Margaret. s8°. 1920
New wine. s8°. [1919]
Pamela Pounce. s8°. [1921]
Wolf-lure. s8°. [1917]

Castlereagh (Robert Stewart, *visct.***),** *2nd marq. of Londonderry, 1769–1822, see* WEBSTER (C. K.) Foreign policy of C., 1815–22, 1925.

Castletown (Bernard Edward Barnaby Fitz-Patrick, *2nd baron***).** "Ego." Random recolls. of sport, service &c. in many lands. 8°. 1923

Caston (M.), *see* SIBREE (J.) & M. C. Independ. in Warwick., 1855.

Castorius, *cosmographer, see* MILLER (K.) Weltkarte d. C., 1888.

Castrén (Gunnar). G. B. Shaw. [P2430]. s8°. Helsingfors. 1906
Stormaktstiden, *see* SVENSKA litt. hist., d1, 1919.

Castrén (Matthias Alexander) [KASTREN].
De affixis personal. ling. Altaicarum, diss. Resp. E. Rudbäck. s4°. Helsingforsiæ. [1850]
De nominum declin. in lingua Syrjaena. 4°. Helsingforsiæ. [1844]
Diss. acad. De affinitate declin. in lingua Fennica, Esthonica & Lapponica. 8°. Helsingforsiæ. 1839
Elementa gramm. Syrjaenae. s8°. Helsingforsiæ. 1844
Gramm. der samojed. Sprachen. Hrsg. A. Schiefner. [Kais. Akad. d. Wiss.] la8°. St. Petersburg. 1854
Опытъ перевода остяцской грамматики съ краткимъ словаремъ. [P2399]. 8°. Тобольскъ. 1902

Castries (*le cte.* Henry de). Les sources inéd. de l'hist. du Maroc. la8°. 1920–27
Sér. 1, Dynastie Saadienne: Archives &c. Angleterre, t1, 2. Espagne, t1. France: bibliog. & index. Pays-Bas, t5, 6
Sér. 2, Dynastie Filalienne: Archives &c. de France, t1–3.

Castrioto (João Fernandes Vieira), *see* VIEIRA CASTRIOTO (J. F.)

Castro (Agnes de). *Agnes de Castro: tragedy, 1696, *see* COCKBURN (C.)

Castro (Alonso de). Adversus omnes hæreses libri 14. Ab auctore recog. & auct. s8°. Venetiis. 1546

Castro (Alvaro Gomez de), *see* GOMEZ DE CASTRO (A.)

Castro (Américo). El pensamiento de Cervantes. [Rev. de filol. esp., 6]. 8°. 1925

Castro (Guillem de) [CASTRO Y BELLVIS (G. DE)]. Obras. [R. Acad. Esp.: Bibl. sel. de clas. esp.] 2t. 8°. 1925–26

Castro (J. Paul de), *see* DE CASTRO (J. P.)

Castro (José Villa-Amil y), *see* VILLA-AMIL Y CASTRO (J.)

Castro (Joseph de S. Pedro de Alcántara), *d. 1792.* Apologia de la theología escholástica. 6t. s4°. Segovia. 1796

Castro (Luis de Salazar y), *see* SALAZAR Y CASTRO (L. DE).

Castro (Roque Leal de), *see* LEAL DE CASTRO (R.)

Castro e Almeida (Eduardo de). Inventario dos doc. rel. ao Brasil, t6, *see* RIO DE JANEIRO: BIBL. NAC., Annaes., v39, 1921.

Castro y Bellvis (Guillén de), *see* CASTRO (G. DE).

Castro y Lopez (José), *see* VEGA INCLAN (M. DE LA), J. DE C. Y L. &C. Rel. hist. de la últ. campaña de Marq. del Duero, 1874.

Casual Club papers, 1907–20, *see* ALLPORT (H. R.)

Casuistical morning exercise, v4, 1690, *see* ANNESLEY (S.), *ed.*

Casuistry. *Chapters on C., 1868, *see* JONES (D.), *Jesuit.*

Casus. *Casus quibus Cristifideles ab Eucharistie Sacramento abstinere debeāt, a Plebanis publicandi. s4°. [Oppenheym. 1514]

Catá (Alfonso Hernandez), *see* HERNANDEZ CATÁ (A.)

Catafago (Joseph).
An Engl. & Arabic dict. in 2 parts. 2nd ed. 8°. 1873

Catalán (M. Jiménez), *see* JIMÉNEZ CATALÁN (M.)

Catalani (Giuseppe).
see PATRICIUS PICCOLOMINEUS (A.) Sacrarum cæremon. libri 3, auctore J. C., 1750.
„ RITUALE. Rituale Romanum Benedicti XIV jussu ed., comm. exorn., auctore J. C., 2v, 1757.

Cataldus, *Saint, bp. of Taranto, see* SOLITO (D.) Notizie del glor. S. C., 1850.

Catalogo. *C. dell' inventori d. cose &c.; comp. da M. Anonymo, cittadino di Utopia, *see* LANDI (O.)
C. d. oggetti del Risorgimento ital., 1894, *see* RISORGIMENTO.
C. gen. d. libreria ital. dall' anno 1847 a tutto il 1899. Comp. A. Pagliaini. Ind. per materie. [v3], Q–Z. la8°. Milano. 1922
„ „ Suppl. 2, 1911–20. [v1], A–K. la8°. Milano. 1925

Catalogue.
C. de monnaies franç. de Hugues Capet à Charles VIII (pl). Vente, 22–26 nov. 1927, L. Ciani. [*Illust.*] la8°. [1927]
C. des mss. alchim. grecs, 1924–27, *see* UNION ACAD. INT.
C. d'œuvre d'art conserv. à Rome à l'ép. imp., 1906, *see* NICOLE (J.).
C. gén. des cartul. des archives dépt. Publ. par la Comm. des Archives Dépt. & Communales. 4°. 1847
C. of all graduats, 1772, *see* OXFORD UNIVERSITY.
*C. of an important assemblage of jewellery, 18th cent., part of Russian State jewels. Sold by Christie. [P2849]. 8°. 1927
*C. of books on angling, 1811, *see* ELLIS (*Sir* HENRY).
C. of Brit. scient. & techn. books &c., prep. by comm. of the Brit. Sci. Guild, 1921, *see* BRITISH SCI. GUILD.
C. of coll. of Eng. portraits by a collector [*Sir W. Musgrave*]; sold by Mr. Richardson, 1800, *see* MUSGRAVE (*Sir* W.).
C. of coll. of engr. portraits on sale by E. Evans [1836 ?], *see* EVANS (E.).
C. of decorative furniture, pictures, porcelain &c., sold by Knight, Frank & Rutley, June 29–30, 1922. [*Illust.*] 8°. 1922
*C. of fine armour of a Russian prince (16 c.), sold by Christie &c. [*Illust.* P2849]. 8°. 1926
*C. of fine old chased &c. plate &c. [*prop. of Mrs. Clarke &c.*], sold by Farebrother, 1821, *see* CLARKE (*Mrs.*)
C. of French furniture &c.; property of a lady [*Miss A. de Rothschild*], sold by Christie &c., Nov. 23, 1922, *see* ROTHSCHILD (*Miss* A. de).
C. of maps publ. by the Geogr. Sect., General Staff, 1920, *see* WAR OFFICE.
*C. of portraits, &c, in order of Bromley's Cat. [*no tp.*] 8°. *n.p.*, *n.d.*
*C. of the Chancellors of Eng. &c., 1636, *see* PHILIPOT (J.)
C. of the choice coll. of Chinese porcelain, sold by Christie &c., July 4, 1923. [*Illust.*] la8°. 1923
*C. of valuable pr. books, MSS. &c., *var. owners*, sold by Sotheby 14 Apr. 1924, 29 Mar. 1926, 14–16 June 1926, 26–28 July 1926, 15–18 Nov. 1926. [Illust. *in* 1v]. la8°. 1924–26
Descr. cat. of Latin MSS. in John Rylands Lib., by M. R. James, 2v, 1921, *see* JOHN RYLANDS LIBRARY, *M'ter.*
A true & exact cat. of all plays &c. pr. in Eng., to Apr. 1732. s8°. *for W. Feales.* 1732

Catalogus. C. dissert. & orat. juridic., 1600–1866, 1867, *see* MULLER (F.)
*C. testium veritatis &c., 1556, *see* FLACIUS (M.)

Cataluccio (Matteo di), *da Orvieto.* Ricordi (1422–58), *see* MURATORI (L. A.) Rerum Ital. scr., t15v, 1920.

Catechesis. *C. cont. explic. simplicem &c. contextam ex Corp. doct. Xtnæ &c., 1571; 1572, *see* MELANCHTHON (P.)
C. eccl. quæ in regno Poloniæ &c., 1609; 1651; 1659, *see* RACOVIAN CATECHISM.
C. Racoviensis, *see* RACOVIAN CATECHISM.
C. relig. Christ., quæ trad. in eccl. &c. Palatinatus, 1563; *Gr. & Lat.*, 1614, *see* HEIDELBERG CAT.
*Incerti monachi Weissenburg. C. Theotisca sec. 9 conscr. Ed. &c. I. G. Eccardus [*b. w.* Eckhart (J. G. v.) Hist. studii etym., 1711]. s8°. Hanoveræ. 1713

Catechisem. Catechisem in il quæl las controversias &c. da quaist temp mis gio in Rumaunsch d'Engiadina Zura. [*Foll. by* La confessiun ù descr. dall' intêra relig. & cretta reformæda. *w. sep. tp. & pagins.*] s8°. Coira. 1720

Catechism. C. oder informat. da la vaira relig. Christ., 1724, *see* PORTA (N. DA).
*C. on the corn laws, 14th ed.; by a member of the Univ. of Camb., 1830; 16th ed., 1832, *see* THOMPSON (T. P.)
The Racovian C., by J. Crell &c.; tr. by T. Rees, 1818, *see* RACOVIAN.
The Russian C., publ. by order of the Czar [Peter I. Tr. by J. T. Philipps]. Annex'd a short acc. of the church-govt. of the Muscovites [by the translator]. 2nd ed. s8°. 1725

Catéchisme. C. à l'usage de toutes les églises de l'Emp. français. [Mandement de M. de Belloy]. s8°. 1806

Catéchisme [*continued*].
*C. (Le) des Jesuites &c., 1602, *see* PASQUIER (E.)
C. du diocése de Montpellier impr. par order de C. J. Colbert. [*b. w.* Catéchisme. Instructions gén., t4, 1704]. s8°. Brusselle. 1704
C. du diocèse de Nice &c., 1839, *see* NICE.
*C. hist. & dogmat. &c., 5t, 1750–68, *see* FOURQUEVAUX (J. B. R. DE P. DE) & L. TROYA D'ASSIGNY.
Instructions gén. en forme de C. Impr. par ordre de C. J. Colbert évèque de Montpellier. 4t. *b. in* 3. s8°. Brusselle. 1704

Catechismo.
C. de' Gesuite. ult. ed. 8°. Lipsia. 1820
C. ord. &c. per uno studio regolare &c. d. religione. Con una dissert. [*2 pagin.*] s8°. Modena. 1874
Vom Catechismo etl. Wittenberg., 1571, *see* BRAUNSCHWEIG.

Catechisms of Scot. Reformation, 1866, *see* BONAR (H.), *ed.*

Catechismus. Ausführl. u. gründl. Wiederlegung d. deut. Arian. C., Rackaw, 1608; durch d. theolog. Facultet zu Wittenberg, 1619; Lat., 1620, *see* BALDUIN (F.)
C. Crypto-Calviniano-Saxon. jussu Nicolai Crellii ed., 1590, *see* SALMUTH (H.)
*C. d. evang. Kirchen in Franckreich. [*Tr.*] [*b. w.* *Ordnung d. evang. Kirchen in Fr., 1563]. s8°. Heydelberg. 1563
C. d. Gemeine d. Leute im Königreich Poln &c., 1608, *see* RACOVIAN CATECHISM.
C. d. Rechtgleubigen Behem. Brüder. Verdeutscht durch F. Gyrck, 1554. [*Reprint*]. s8°. *n.p.*, *n.d.* [18th cent.]
C. ex decreto Conc. Tridentini, 1567; *& o. eds.*, *see* TRENT, *Council of.*
*C. oder kinder Predig &c., 1533; 1540; 1543, *see* BRANDENBURG.
C. pro iis qui volunt suscip. bapt., *Lat. & Tonkin.*, 1651, *see* RHODES (A. DE).
*Rudimenta fidei Xtianæ sive C.; adj. C. alius, 1575, *see* CALVIN (J.)

Catena. A chronol. c. of anc. Fathers & councils, w. teaching of reformers on doct. of spiritual regener. in holy baptism. 8°. 1850

Catergian (Joseph) [KATHERDZEAN (HOVSEPH)], *see* JOHN, *the evangelist.* Eccl. Ephes. de obitu J. narr.; ex vers. arm. Lat. prod. curavit J. C., 1877.

Cathedral [CATHEDRALS].
*Notes on the Cathedrals. v1–5. s8°. 1902–4

Cathelineau (Jacques), *see* GENOUDE (A. E.) *Vie de C., 1821.

Cather (Willa Sibert). April twilights & o. poems. 8°. 1924
A lost lady. s8°. 1924
My Antonia. s8°. 1919

Catherine, *of Alexandria, Saint.* Eine gereimte altfranz.-verones. Fassung d. Legende d. hlgn. K.; hrsg. H. Breuer, *see* THIERRY *de Vaucouleur.* Johanneslegende &c., 1919.

Catherine [*de Bourbon*], *duchesse de Bar, sister of Henry IV.* Lettres & poésies (1570–1603). Publ. R. Ritter. 8°. 1927

Catherine [DE' MEDICI], *q. c. of Henry II, of France, see* MARIÉJOL (J. H.) C. de M., 1519–89, 1920.
see ROMIER (L.) Le royaume de C. de M., 2t, 1922.
„ VAN DYKE (P.) C. de M., 2v, 1923.

Catherine [*Parr*], *q. c. of Henry VIII, see* ROSE TROUP (F.) 2 book bills of K. P., 1911.

Catherine I, *empress of Russia* [EKATERINA ALEKSEEVNA], *see* SEMEVSKY (M. I.) Царица К. А., Анна и В. Монсъ, 1692–1724, 1884.

Catherine II, *empress of Russia.* *Дворъ Екатерины II, ея сотрудники &c. 189 силуетовъ. [La cour de C. II: silhouettes]. 2t. la8°. С.-П. 1899
Lettres au Prince de Ligne, 1780–96. Publ. avec notes par la Psse C. de Ligne. 8°. Brux. 1924
Memoirs. Tr. K. Anthony. 8°. 1927
Théâtre de l'Hermitage de C. II. [*By C. & var. as. Ed.* J. H. Castéra ?]. 2t. 8°. an 7. [1799]
see ANTHONY (K.) C. the Great, 1926.
„ BILBASOV (V. A.) Исторія Е. II, 2т, 1900.
„ BREVERN DE LA GARDE (*ctsse.*) Un ambassadeur de Suède à la Cour de C. II: Cte. de Stedingk, 1790–6, 2t, 1919.
„ FALCONET (E. M.) Corr. de F. avec Cath. II, 1767–78, 1921.
„ KIRCHEISEN (G.) K. II, 1919.
„ MURAT (*psse.* L.) Vie amoureuse de la Grande C., 1927.
„ PEKARSKY (P. P.) Журн. &c. дѣят. Е. II, 1863.
„ STEPANOV (A. V.) Е. II, 1897.

Catherine, *Grand Duchess of Russia, aft. Queen of Würtemberg, 1788–1819, see* ALEXANDER I, *emp. of Russia.* Corresp. de l'emp. A. I avec sa sœur C., 1805–18, 1910.

Catherine, *of Siena, Saint.*
see FAWTIER (R.) Ste. C. de Sienne: essai de critique des sources, t1, Sources hagiograph., 1921.
,, JOERGENSEN (J.) Ste. C. de S., 1920.
,, POLLIO LAPPOLI (G.) Opera d. C. da S.: in rima &c., 1505.

Catherine [*of Spain*], *consort of Charles Emanuel I, d. of Savoy.* Relaz. dell' ingresso d. Infanta C. d' Austria in Torino, 10 agosto 1585 [*by* G. A. Silva]; pubbl. da A. Angelucci, *see* REGIA DEP. DI STORIA PATRIA. Misc., t15, 1874.

Catherine [*de Vigri*], *Saint of Bologna.*
see MERLANI (A.) S. C., 1912.
,, NUNEZ (L. M.) Cenni storici; ricordo del 20 centen. d. canonizz. di S. C., 1912.

Catherine Alexeevna, *empress of Russia, see* CATHERINE I.

Catholic. Appeal (An) to Protest. of Gt. Brit. &c. on R.C. q., 1813, *see* APPEAL.

Catholic directory (The) for 1912. 8°. [1911]

Catholic Encyclopedia (The). Ed. E. A. Pace [*& others*]. v17, Suppl. 1. la8°. N.Y. [1923]

Catholic Record Society. Publ[s]. v22–26. 8°. *p.p.* 1921–26
Miscellanea, XII, XIII, 1921–26. [22, 26].
see DOMINICANA. Card. Howard's letters, Eng. Dominican friars &c., 1925. [25.]
,, FRANCISCANS. Eng. Franciscan nuns, 1619–1821 & the Friars Minor, 1618–1761; ed. R. Trappes-Lomax, 1922. [24.]
,, LANCASHIRE registers; ed. J P. Smith, v4, 1922. [23.]

Catholic Who's who & yearbook, 1921. s8°. [1920]

Catholics [CATHOLIKES]. *The supplic. of certaine Masse-priests falsely called C., 1604, *see* SUPPLICATION.

Catholicum. Catholicum hymnologium German. &c., 1584, *see* LEISENTRITT (J.)

Catlin (George Edward Gordon).
The science & method of politics. 8°. 1927

Cato (Marcus Portius), *see* AGRONOMES (Les) latins: Caton, &c. (*Lat. & Fr.*); Nisard, 1877.

Caton (Richard), *see* LUNN (*Sir* H. S.), *ed.* Ægean civilizations: lect[s]. by Dr. C. &c., 1925.

Catrou (François).
Hist. des Anabaptistes. s8°. Amsterdam. 1699

Cattadori (*Mme.* Pietro). The Cattadori coll.: Ital. &c. textiles &c. [Sale, Jan. 28 & 29, 1927. Amer. Art Assoc. *Illust.*] la8°. [N.Y. 1927]

Cattaneo (Cajetan), *Jesuit, see* MURATORI (L. A.) Rel. of the missions to Paraguay; added letters of C. C. on h. voy. f. Cadiz to Paraguay, 1754.

Cattenburgh (Adrian van). Bibl. script. Remonstrantium; subj., Spec. controv. inter Remonstrantes & Socinum &c. [*2 pagin[s].*] s8°. Amstelædami. 1728
Spicilegium theologiæ Xtnæ Ph. a Limborch &c. fol. Amstelædami. 1726
see BRANDT (C.) & A. VAN C. Hist. van Huig de Groot, 2p, 1727.

Catterall (*Mrs.* Helen Tunnicliff), *wife of R. C. H. Catterall.* Judicial cases conc. Amer. slavery & the Negro. Ed. H. T. C. [C.I. of Wash.] v1. 8°. Wash. 1926

Cattois (François), *see* VERDIER (A.) & F. C. Architecture civile &c., 2t, 1858.

Catullus (Caius Valerius).
C., Tibullus, Propertius. s8°. Parisiis, *apud S. Colinæum.* 1529
C., Tibulli & Propertii opera. 4°. B'hamiæ, *Baskerville.* 1772
,, ,, [*a. ed.*] s8°. B'hamiæ, *Baskerville.* 1772
C. Hrsg. u. erkl. v. W. Kroll. 8°. 1923
TRANSLATIONS.
Catullus; [w. Eng. tr. by F. W. Cornish]—Tibullus; [w. Eng. tr. by J. P. Postgate]—Pervigilium Veneris; [w. tr. by J. W. Mackail. Loeb Class. Lib.] [repr.] s8°. 1919
Catullus. Tr. Sir W. Marris, w. Lat. text. s8°. O. 1924
Poems. Done into Eng. verse by H. Macnaghten [w. text]. s8°. C. 1925
Poésies. Texte établi & tr. par G. Lafaye. [Coll. des univ[s]. de Fr.] s8°. 1922
Some poems. Tr. w. intr. by J. F. Symons-Jeune. 8°. 1923
Translations f. C. Intr. R. K. Davis. s8°. 1913

Caucasus [*see also* ZAKAVKAZ].
Сборникъ матеріаловъ для описанія мѣстностей и племенъ Кавказа, в1–39, 1881–1908, *see* SBORNIK.
Сборникъ свѣдѣній о кавказскихъ горцахъ. Изд. при Кавк. горскомъ управленіи, в3. [*var. pagin[s].*] la8°. Тифлисъ. 1870

Cauche (François). Voyage to Madagascar &c., *see* STEVENS (J.) New coll. of voyages &c., v2, 1711.

Cauchie (Maurice). Doc[s]. pour servir à l'hist. litt. du 17e siècle. la8°. 1924

Caudel (Maurice), *see* VIALLATE (A.) La vie polit. dans les deux mondes; publ. sous la dir. de A. V. & M. C., 9, La Grande Guerre, 1922.

Cauer (Paul). Grundfragen d. Homerkritik. 3e umgearb. u. erweit. A. 2 Hälfte. 8°. L. 1921–23

Caulaincourt (Armand Augustin Louis de), *duke of Vicenza, see* VICENZA.

Caulfeild (Vivian). How to ski &c. 8°. 1911

Caulfield (James). Calcographiana: printsellers chron. &c. to engr. Brit. portraits. 8°. 1814
Portraits, mems. &c. of remark. persons f. Ed. III to the Revol. v1. la8°. 1794

Caulibus (Joannes de), *see* JOANNES, *de Caulibus.*

Caulincourt, *see* CAULAINCOURT.

Caullery (Maurice).
see HANOTAUX (G.) Hist. de la nation franç., t15, Hist. des sci[s]., v2, sci[s]. biolog.; par M. C. &c., 1924.
,, PARIS. UNIVERSITY. La vie univ. à P.; publ. par P. Boyer, M. C. &c., 1918.

Caumont (Joseph de Seytres, *marq.* **de),** *see* FAVART (C. S.) & LARGILLIÈRES. Polichinelle, comte de Paonfier; suivi des Champs Elysées de MM. de C. & Destouches [1714], 1924.

Caumont de La Force (Charlotte Rose de), *see* LA FORCE.

Causa. Causa episcopatus &c. or a confut. of J. S.'s vindication &c., 1706, *see* FORRESTER (T.)

Causæ. *Causæ cur electores, &c. August. Confess. ad Conc. à Pio IIII Tridenti indict. non accedant, 1564; 1664, *see* AUGSBURG CONFESSION.
Causæ quare synod. indict. a Paulo III recus. principes &c., 1537, *see* SCHMALKALD, *League of.*

***Cause.** Cause (The) of the world unrest. With intr. by the Editor of the Morning Post, 1920, *see* GWYNNE (H. A.), *ed.*

***Causeries** brouettiques, 1924, *see* CAMARASA (*Marquis* DE).

Causes.
Causes célèbres &c., n. éd. augm., 20t, 1739–59, *see* PITAVAL (F. G. DE).
Causes célèbres de tous les peuples, 1858–74, *see* FOUQUIER (A.)
*Causes criminelles célèbres du 19e siècle, réd. par une Société d'avocats. 4t. 8°. 1827–28
*Causes (The) of the decay of Xtn. piety. By the a. of " The whole duty of man " [? R. Allestree]. [*b.w.* Gentleman's calling, 1672]. s8°. 1672

Causse (A.) Les " pauvres " d'Israël (Prophètes, Psalmistes, Messianistes). 8°. Str. 1922
Les plus vieux chants de la Bible. la8°. Str. 1926

Causse (Johann Isaac Ludwig). Disq. de clerico cum capsa monachis Fuldens. donato. [P440]. s4°. Francofurti a. V. [1770]

Cautley (*Sir* Proby Thomas). Ganges Canal. Disq. on heads of the G. & Jumna Canals, in reply to Sir A. Cotton. 8°. 1864
Notes &c. on E. Jumna, or Doab Canal & on the water courses in the Deyra Doon [*w. sep. pagin.*] 8°. Roorkee. 1862
Report on the central Doab canal. [*Each section & app. has sep. pagin.*] fol. [1840]
Rep. on the Ganges Canal Works, until 1854, 2v, 1860.

Cauwenbergh (Etienne van), *see* VAN CAUWENBERGH (E.)

Cavaignac (Eugene). Popul. & capital dans le monde méditerranéen antique. [Publ[s]. de l'Univ. de Strasbourg, fasc. 18]. la8°. Str. 1923

Cavalcante, *The family of, see* SANTA MARIA JABOATAM (A. DE). Cat. gen. das princ. fam[s]. proced. de C. &c., 1889.

Cavalcanti (Andrea), *see* RUSPOLI (F.) Sonetti; col. comm. di A. C., 1876.

Cavalier & Puritan ballads &c., 1640–60, 1923, *see* ROLLINS (H. E.), *ed.*

Cavalieri (Giovanni Battista), *see* ASHBY (T.) Antiq. statuæ urbis Romæ [*by* G. B. C., 1569], 1920.

Cavallari (F. Saverio), *see* ORSI (P.) & F. S. C. Megara Hyblæa, 1890.

Cavallera (Ferdinand). Saint Jérôme, s. vie & s. œuvre. p1, 2t. la8°. Louvain. 1922

Cavalli (Francesco), *1602–76, see* WIEL (T.) F. C., 1912.

Cavalli (Giovanni Battista), *see* SOMMI-PICENARDI (G.) Tentativo fatto dai Francesi per impadronirsi del Castello di Cremona nel 1537, 1885.

Cavallier (Jean) [CAVALIER]. Mem. of the wars of the Cevennes under C. By C. Tr. 2nd ed. [*Dublin ed. 1726, w. new tp.*] s8°. 1727

Cavallini (Pietro), *see* BUSUIOCEANU (AL.) P. C. e la pitt. rom. (13–14c.), 1925.

Cavallino (Bernardo), *see* RINALDIS (A. DE). B. C.; 26 riprod. con testo e cat., 1921.

Cavallotti (Felice). Versi. 8°. Sesto S. Giovanni. 1911
Cavaré (L.) L'occup. pacifique: ét. partic. de l'occup. de Haute-Silésie. Extr. de la Revue gén. de droit internat. publ. la8°. 1924
Cave of treasures (Book of the); tr. Sir E. A. W. Budge, 1927, *see* ME'ÂRATH GAZZÊ.
Cave (Alfred). The Script. doctrine of sacrifice. 8°. E. 1877
Cave (Charles John Philip).
Cloud & weather phenomena. s8°. C. 1926
Cave (Estella, *countess*). Memories of old Richmond, w. sidelights on Eng. hist. 8°. 1922
Cave (Henry W.), *M. A.* Picturesque Ceylon: Colombo & the Kelani Valley. 4°. 1893
Cave (*Sir* **Lewis William),** *Judge of the High Court of Justice, see* BURN (R.) Justice of the Peace &c., 30th ed., v3 by L. W. Cave, 1869.
Cave (Thomas). John Baskervile, 1706–75, the printer, h. ancestry—R. Baxter, 1615–91, & Kidderminster parish ch. [*sep. pagins.*] la8°. Kidderminster. 1923
Caveat Emptor, *gent., see* STEPHEN (*Sir* G.)
Caveler (William). Archit. illusts. of Warmington Church, Northants. lafol. O. 1850
Cavelier de La Salle (R. R.), *see* HENNEPIN (L.) New discovery &c. in Amer., w. contin. giving acc. of attempts of the Sieur De La S. upon the mines of St. Barbe &c., 1698.
Caven (Robert Martin).
Gas & gases. [Home Univ. Lib.] s8°. [1926]
Cavendish Society, *see* HENRY (W. C.) Mems. of life of J. Dalton, 1854.
Cavendish (*Lady* **Frederick),** *née Lucy Caroline Lyttelton.*
Diary. Ed. J. Bailey. 2v. 8°. [1927]
Cavendish (George). Life & death of T. Wolsey (wr. 1557). [Ed. F. S. Ellis, *added,* Churchyard's Tragedy of Wolsey. Temple Classics]. s8°. 1899
The mem. of Card. Woolsey w. remarks upon h. rise & fall &c. With a mem. pres. to Queen Elizabeth by W. Cecil, Lord Burleigh. s8°. 1706
Cavendish (*Hon.* **Henry).** Scientific papers. 2v. la8°. 1921
1, Electrical researches; ed. J. C. Maxwell, rev. by Sir J. Larmor.
2, Chemical & dynamical; ed. Sir E. Thorpe, w. contribs. by C. Chree, Sir F. W. Dyson, Sir A. Geikie, Sir J. Larmor.
Cavia (Mariano de) [CAVIA Y LAC]. Cháchara. Prólogo de J. Ortega Munilla. [Obras compl.] s8°. [1923]
Limpia y fija. [Obras compl.] s8°. [1922]
Caviglia (Alberto). Claudio de Seyssel (1450–1520), *see* REGIA DEPUT. Misc., t54, 1928.
Cavour [†BENSO DI CAVOUR (*il conte* CAMILLO)].
Il carteggio Cavour-Nigra, 1858–61. A cura d. R. Comm. Editrice. v1, 2. 8°. Bologna. [1926]
see LUZIO (A.) Garibaldi, C. &c., 1924.
,, MATTER (P.) C. & l'unité ital., 3v, 1922–27.
see PALÉOLOGUE (G. M.) C.; tr., 1927.
,, PRATO (G.) Fatti e dottr. econ. &c.: l'Assoc. agraria subalp. e C. C., 1921.
,, WHYTE (A. J.) Early life & letters of C., 1810–48, 1925.
Cavoye, *Family of, see* HUGUET (A.) Le Marquis de C., 1920.
Cavoye (Louis, *marq.* **de),** *1640–1716* [OGIER DE CAVOYE], *see* HUGUET (A.) Le Marquis de Cavoye, 1920.
Cavriolo (Helia), *see* †CAPREOLUS (ELIAS).
Cavrois (Louis), *see* ARRAS. Cartul. de Notre-Dame-des-Ardents à A.; [publ.] par L. C., 1876.
Caw (James Lewis). Scottish painting, 1620–1908. la8°. E. 1908
Caxias (Luis Alves de Lima y Silva, *duque* **de).** Campanha do Paraguai: diarios do exercito em operações sob o comm. do Marechal C., *see* INST. HIST. &C. BRAZIL. Revista, t91, 1926.
Caxton (William), *see* AURNER (N. S.) C., mirrour of 15th-cent. letters: st. of lit. of the 1st Eng. press, 1926.
see BLADES (W.) Biog. & typography of C., 2nd ed., 1882.
,, LULLY (R.) Book of the ordre of chyvalry; tr. & pr. [c. 1483], by W. C.; ed. A. T. P. Byles, 1926.
,, PLOMER (H. R.) W. C., (1424–91), 1925.
Cayenne. Mission de C. &c., 1857, *see* JESUITS. Voyages &c. des missionnaires de la C. de Jésus, t1, 1857.
Cayet (P. V. Palma), *see* PALMA CAYET (P. V.)
Cayley (Cornelius). Tour thr. Holland, Flanders, & part of France. n. ed. [P2486]. s8°. Leeds. 1815
Cayot Délandre (François Marie).
Le Morbihan. Album. 4°. Vannes. [1847]
Cayrou (Gaston). Le Français classique. Lexique de la langue du 17e s. s8°. 1923
Caza (Francesco). Tract. vulg. de canto figurato, Mailand 1492. In facs. mit Übers. hrsg. v. J. Wolf. [Veröffentl. d. Musik Bibl. v. P. Hirsch, 1]. s8°. 1922
Cazal (Edmond). Sainte Thérèse. 4e éd. s8°. 1921
Cazal (Gaspardo), *bp. of Seria* [CASALIUS]. De quadripertita justitia libri tres, in quibus orthodoxa de justificatione nostra fides asseritur & Lutheri, Calvini, Buceri, Bullingeri aliorumque a T. R. Eccles. dissidentium opiniones eliduntur. fol. Venetiis. 1563
Cazalet (Edward). Bimetallism & its conn. w. commerce. [*a. c. in* P2829]. 8°. 1879
Cazals (F. A.) & G. Le Rouge. Les derniers jours de P. Verlaine. Préf. de M. Barrès. n. éd. rev. & compl. 8°. 1923
Cazamian (Louis). L'évolution psycholog. & la litt. en Angleterre (1660–1914). s8°. 1920
see LEGOUIS (E.) & L. C. Hist. de la litt. angl., 1924; tr., 2v, 1926–27.
Cazamian (Madeleine L.) Le roman & les idées en Angleterre. [t]1. la8°. Str. 1923
1, L'infl. de la science, 1860–90.
Cazenove (Quirin Jules Raoul de). Le peintre Van der Kabel & ses contemp. avec cat. de s. œuvre 1631–1705. 8°. 1888
Cazin (Paul). Décadi ou la pieuse enfance. s8°. [1921]
L'hôtellerie du Bacchus sans tête. s8°. [1925]
Cazza (Giovanni Agostino) [CACCIA]. Rime date in luce la 2a volta da G. Albetti. 8°. Torino. 1770
Cazzago (*il conte* **Francesco Bettoni-),** *see* BETTONI-CAZZAGO.
Ce. Ce que veut le parti de Spartacus, 1919, *see* SPARTACUS.
*Ce qui se passe au Concile, 1870, *see* VATICAN COUNCIL.
Cé (Camille), *see* GAUMENT (J.) & C. C. La grand'route des hommes, 1923.
Céard (Henry), *see* DEFFOUX (L.) & E. ZAVIE. Le groupe de Médan: H. C., 1920.
Ceawlin, *king of Wessex, see* GODSAL (*Maj.* P. T.) Conquests of C., the 2nd Bretwalda, 1924.
Cebes [CEBETE]. Parafrasis arabe de la Tabla de Cebes. Tr. en Castellano e illust. con notas por D. Pablo Lozana y Casela. s4°. Madrid. 1793
see EPICTETUS. Life & philos. of E., w. Embleme of humane life, by C., 1670.
Cecchetti (Bartolomeo).
Di alcune fonti d. storia veneta al sec. 13. [P2852]. 8°. Venezia. 1867
La Rep. di Venezia e la corte di Roma nei rapporti d. religione. [2v, v2, Documenti]. 8°. Venezia. 1874
Le scritture occulte n. diplom. veneziana. [Estr. d. R. Istit. Veneto, Atti, v14, Ser. 3. P2836]. 8°. [Venezia. 1869]
La vita dei Veneziani fino al 1200. 8°. Venezia. 1870
La vita dei Veneziani fino al sec. 13. [*Extr. f.* Archivio veneto, t2i, 1871. *b. w. h.* La vita fino al 1200, 1870]. 8°. [Venezia. 1871]
see VENEZIA. Documenti per la storia di San Marco in V., d. 9. sec. s. a. 18., *pref. by C.*, 1886.
Cecchi (Domenico) [IL CORTONA], *see* RAVAGLI (F.) Il Cortona (D. C.), 1896.
Cecchi (Emilio). L'osteria d. cattivo tempo. 8°. Milano. 1927
Les peintres siennois. (Trecentisti senesi). Tr. J. Chuzeville. la8°. 1928
Pesci rossi. s8°. Firenze. [1920]
Pittura ital. dell' ottocento. Testo di E. C. con 200 illust. 8°. [1926]
Cecchi (Giovanni Maria), *1517–87.* L'Assivolo. [*b. w.* Grasso (N.) Eutychia, 1524]. s8°. Vinegia. 1550
Cecconi (Eugenio). Storia del Conc. ecumenico Vaticano scr. sui doc. orig. Parte prima, Antecedenti. 2v *in* 4 [v2 *in* 2 sezioni & contn.] la8°. Roma. 1873–79
Ceccucci (Egisto). Storia dei conc. ecumenici fino a Pio IX &c. 8°. Venezia. 1869
Cecelidze, *see* KEKELIDZE.
Cechner (Anton). Topogr. d. hist. u. Kunstdenkm., Polit. Bez. Königgrätz, *see* BÖHMEN. Topographie d. hist. u. Kunstdenkmale &c., B19, 1915.
Cecil, *The family of, see* HIST. MSS. COMM. Salisbury, *m. of.* Cal. of MSS., p 13, 14, 1915–23.
Cecil (Algernon), *M. A., barrister.* Brit. Foreign Secretaries, 1807–1916. 8°. 1927
The world we live in. s8°. [1925]
Cecil (Edgar Algernon Robert Cecil, *1st visct.*), *of Chelwood.*
The new outlook. [P2405]. 8°. [1919]
Cecil (*Lt.-Col. Lord* **Edward Herbert).**
The leisure of an Egyptian official. 8°. [1921]
Cecil (*Lady* **Gwendolen).**
Life of Robert Marquis of Salisbury. v1, 2. 8°. 1921

Cecil (*Lord* **Hugh Richard Heathcote**), *see* ROYAL FLYING CORPS. Work & training of the R.F.C. [*Intr. by* Lord H. C.], *n.d.*

Cecil (*Sir* **Robert**), *aft. 1st earl of Salisbury, son of W. Cecil, Lord Burghley.* *An answere to certaine scandalous papers, scattered under colour of Catholicke admon. [P2669 ; *a. c. b. w.* Garnet (H.) True &c. rel. of proc. agst. G. &c., 1606]. s4º. 1606

Cecil (Thomas), *fl. 1630, engraver, see* WOODBURN (S.) W.'s gallery of portraits, plates by C. &c., 2v, 1816.

Cecilia [*Vasa*], *princess, 1540–1627, see* BELL (J.) Q. Eliz. & a Swedish princess, 1565 ; ed. E. Seaton, 1926.

Cedar of Lebanon, *ps.*
Syria reborn. An appeal. [P2424]. 8º. Alexandria. 1919

Cederbaum (Julius), *see* MARTOV (L.), *ps.*

Cedillo (Jerónimo Lopez de Ayala Alvarez, *conde* **de).** El card. Cisneros. [Real Acad. de la Hist.] 8º. 1921

Cei (Francesco). Opera gentile et amorosa in laude di Clitia. [*tp. wanting*]. s8º. [Milano. 1520]

Cejador y Franca (Julio). El cantar de Mio Cid y la epopeya castell., *see* REVUE HISPAN., t49, 1920.
Hist. de la lengua y lit. castellana. t9–14. 8º. 1918–22
9, Epoca realista, p2, 1870–87.
10–12, Epoca regional y modernista, 1888–1907, 3p.
13–14, Epoca contemp., 1908–20, 2p.
Tesoro de la lengua castellana. [El lenguaje, t10, 11]. Silbantes, p3, 4. 8º. 1912–13

Celarié (Henriette).
Madame de Sévigné, sa famille & s. amis. 8º. 1925

Celebrated. *Celeb. trials of all countries, 1835, *see* SMITH (J. J.)

Celestial [COELESTIAL] **atlas (The)** ; or A new ephemeris for 1800–8. By R. White. [*b. w.* Gentleman's diary, 1800–8]. s8º. 1800–8

Celestina. Interlude of Calisto & Melebea, c. 1530, *see* ROJAS (F. DE). Celestina ; tr. J. Mabbe &c. ; ed. H. W. Allen, 1923.

Cell (Erhard) [CELLIUS (ERHARDUS)]. Oratio funebris : de vita & morte Annæ Mariæ quondam Christophori ducis Wirtembergici conjugis 1589 mortuæ. s4º. Tubingæ. 1592

Cellarius (Christophorus), *the elder.*
Chaldaismus : gramm. s4º. Cizæ. 1685
Collectanea hist. Samaritanæ. [*b. w. h.* Horæ Sam., 1682]. s4º. Cizæ. 1688
Curæ posteriores de barbarismis & idiotismis sermonis Lat. 4. recogn. s8º. Jenæ. 1709
„ „ App. s8º. Jenæ. 1708
De Latinitate mediæ & infimæ æt. liber, sive Antibarbarus. recogn. 4. [*b. w. h.* Curæ poster., 1708]. s8º. Jenæ. 1710
Discussio app. Danicæ ad Curas suas posteriores iterum auctior ed. [*b. w. h.* Curæ poster., 1708]. s8º. Jenæ. 1712
Diss. acad. varii argumenti. Red. cura J. G. Walchii, diss. de auct. vita &c. s8º. Lipsiæ. 1712
Hist. universalis. ed. 8ª. emend. [3p *in* 1v]. s8º. Jenæ. 1730–32
Each p. has sep. tp. Hist. antiqua, Hist. medii ævi, Hist. nova.
Horæ Samaritanæ, excerpta Pentateuchi S. vers. cum Lat. interpret. &c. : etiam gramm. & gloss. s4º. Cizæ. 1682
Inauguratio Acad. Fridericianæ &c., 1694. sfol. Halæ Magdeburg. 1798
Isagoge in ling. Arabicam. [*b. w. h.* Horæ Samarit., 1682]. s4º. Cizæ. 1686
Notitiæ orbis ant. alt. ed. auxit L. I. C. Schwartz. 2t. s4º. Lipsiæ. 1731–32
Orthographia Latina ex vetustis mon. &c. Ed. 2ª Patavina. s8º. Patavii. 1739
Programmata varii argumenti, & orationes. Add. indices. s8º. Lipsiæ. 1689

Cellier (*Mrs.* **Elizabeth).** The tryal & sentence of E. C. for writing &c. a scandalous libel called Malice defeated. [P525]. sfol. 1680
see DANGERFIELD (T.) Ans. to a pamph. entitled Malice Defeated, or the deliv. of E. C., 1680.
„ PRANCE (M.) Ans. to Mrs. C.'s libel &c., 1680.

Cellini (Benvenuto).
Memoirs ; wr. by himself. [Everyman's lib.] s8º. *n.d.*
Vita. Per cura di B. Bianchi. s8º. Firenze. 1852
see KAISERL.-KÖNIGL. MÜNZ-U. ANTIK. KABIN. ZU WIEN. Die Cinque-Cento Cameen u. Arb. d. B. C. &c. im K.-K. M.-u. A.-Cab. z. W., 1858.

Cellius (Erhardus), *see* CELL (E.)

Celsius (Anders). Abhandl. ü. Thermometrie v. Fahrenheit, C. &c., 1894, *see* ÖTTINGEN (A. J. v.), *ed.*

Celsus, *the philosopher.* 'Αληθὴς λόγος, excuss. &c. O. Glöckner, *see* KLEINE TEXTE, 151, 1924.
see ORIGEN. Contra Celsum libri 8, 1605.

Celsus (Aurelius Cornelius). Quæ supersunt ; rec. F. Marx, *see* CORPUS medic. Lat., v1, 1915.

Celsus (Minus) *ps.* [*i.e.* LÆLIUS SOCINUS?]. In haereticis coercendis quatenus progredi liceat disput. [Aequis &c. lectoribus, typographi nom. S. I. F. D. M. D.] s8º. Christlingæ. 1577

Celtes (Conrad) [CELTIS ; PICKEL (KONRAD)], *see* WERMINGHOFF (A.) C. C. u. s. Buch ü. Nürnberg, 1921.

Cena (Giovanni). In Umbra : versi. 8º. Torino. 1899

Cenacchi (Oreste). Vecchia Bologna : echi e memorie. Con pref. di G. de Frenzi. s8º. Bologna. [1926]

Cenci (Beatrice), *see* RICCI (C.) B. C., 2v, 1923 ; 1925 ; tr. M. Bishop &c., 2v, 1926 ; tr. M. Hélys, 1926.

Cendrars (Blaise). L'or, la merveilleuse hist. du Gén. Johann August Suter. s8º. 1925

Cenni sull' origine &c. d. stampa n. provincie venete, 1887, *see* BERNARDI (J.)

Cennick (John). *Sacred hymns for children of God. By J. C. 2nd. ed. s8º. 1741
Sacred hymns for religious Societies. 3p. *w. sep. tps. & pag.* s8º. Bristol & London. 1743–44

***Censure** de quelques propos. des P. P. Le Comte & Le Gobien &c., 1700, *see* LECOMTE (L.)

Centaur. *Centaur (The) not fabulous &c., 1755, *see* YOUNG (E.), *the poet.*

Centlivre (*Mrs.*) Bold stroke for a wife, *see* INCHBALD (E.) Brit. th., v11, 1808.
Busy body, *see* INCHBALD (E.) Brit. th., v11, 1808.
The wonder. 6th ed. [P2865]. s8º. 1766
„ „ ....[Dolby's Brit. th.] s8º. 1823
„ „ *For a. ed., see* INCHBALD (E.) Brit. th., v11, 1808.

Centorio (Ascanio) [†CENTORIO DEGLI HORTENSII].
Le amorose rime. s8º. [Venetia]. 1553

Central Asian Society. Journal. v1–14 (1914–27). 8º. [1914–27]
see CHINESE. Some problems of the C. Republic, 1927.

Central Association Volunteer Regiments. The Vol. Force & the V. Training Corps dur. the Great War. s8º. 1920

Central Committee for the Protection of Churches. The prot. of our Eng. churches. Rep. for 1923 of the Cent. Comm., &c. 2nd rep., 1924–25. 8º. 1923–25

Central Executive Campaign Committee, *see* HANDBOOK for the democracy, 1864.

Central London Railway (The). Repr. f. The Engineer, 1898. 4º. 1898

Central Provinces [India]. Hist. of services of gazetted & o. officers. Corr. to 1st July 1920[–1927]. 8º. Nagpur. 1920–27
Rep. on [Review of] admin. of the C. P. & Behar, 1919/20–1925/26. 8º. Nagpur. 1921–27

Centralblatt für Bibliothekswesen. Jhrg. 37–44. 8º. L. 1920–27
Generalregister z. 21.–40. Jahrgange (1904–23). Begonnen v. G. Leyh, fortgeführt v. P. Gehring. 8º. L. 1925

Centro Oficial de Estudios Amer.
see ARCHIVO GEN. DE ESTUDIOS. Amer. Cat. de legajos, 1919–22.
„ ARCHIVO GEN. DE INDIAS. Cat. : cuadro gen. de la doc., 1918.
„ LATORRE (G.) Rel. geogr. de Indias, [2t], 1919–20.
„ QUIROGA (P. DE). Libro intit. Coloquios de la verdad, 1922.
„ SANTA CRUZ (A. DE). Libro de las longitud. &c., 1921.

Centurion, *ps.* *The man who didn't win the War : exposure of Lloyd Georgism, 1923, *see* LLOYD-GEORGE (*Rt. Hon.* D.)

***Centurions** of a century, 1922, *see* GARDINER (C. H.)

Century Association, *see* BRYANT (W. C.) The Bryant festival at " The Century," Nov. 1864, 1865.

Century (The) illustrated monthly magazine.
v99–115 (Nov. 1919–Apr. 1928). 8º. 1919–28

Centz (P. C.) The Republic of republics ; or, American federal liberty. 4th ed. 8º. Boston. 1881

Cepari (Virgilio) [CEPARY]. The life of St. Aloysius Gonzaga. s8º. Derby. 1844
Vita I. Berchmanni Flandro-Belgæ religiosi. Lat. redd. a P. H. Hugone. s8º. Antverpiæ. 1630

Cerasoli (Francesco), C. Cipolla &c., *edd.* Clemente VI e Casa Savoia : doc. vaticani & App., Nuovi doc., *see* REGIA DEPUT. Misc., t36, 1900.
Innocenzo VI e Casa Savoia : doc. dell' Arch. Vaticano, *see* REGIA DEPUT. Misc., t38, 1902.

Ceratinus (Jacobus), *see* BEZA (T.) De vera pronunt. Gr. & Lat. linguæ &c. (J. C. de sono literarum Græcarum), 1587.

Cercamon, *Gascon troubadour, 12 c.* Les poésies de C. Ed. par A. Jeanroy. [Class. fr. du M. A.] s8º. 1922

Cereceda (Juan Dantin), *see* DANTIN CERECEDA (J.)

Ceremoniale, *see* CÆREMONIALE.

Ceresole (G.), *see* CASTELLANI (G.) & G. C. Saggio di una bibliog. nuz. della fam. Papadopoli, 1905.
Cerinthus, *see* PAULUS (H. E. G.) Historia C., 2p, 1795.
Cernuschi (Henri).
Monetary Conf. Questions. [P2829]. 8°. 1881
Monetary diplomacy in 1878. [P2829]. 8°. 1878
Carracchini (Luca Giuseppe). Fasti teologali. Notizie ist. d. Coll. de' Teologi d. sacra Univ. fiorentina. s4°. Firenze. 1738
Cerretesi (Giuseppe). A S.E. il Princ. di Francavilla per la festa data n. occas. d. nasc. d. Real Infante. [*Carlo Tito. Verses.* P2765]. s8°. [Napoli ? 1775]
Cerri (Urbano). Acc. of state of Rom. Cath. relig. Tr. Added: A disc. conc. state of relig. in Eng., now tr. By Sir R. Steele [*or rather* Bishop Hoadly]. 2nd ed. s8°. 1715
Ceruti (Antonio). *Works in* Regia Dep. di St. Patria. Misc.
Ant. mura milan. di Massimiano, 1869. [7.]
Commem. dell' avv. G. Casanova, 1889. [27.]
Statuta Soc. S. Iohannis Bapt. Augustæ Taurin., 1389, ed. A. C., 1870. [11.]
Rime di poeti ital. del sec. 16. [Ed. A. C. Scelta di curiosità lett. ined. &c.] s8°. Bologna. 1873
Cervantes [†CERVANTES SAAVEDA (MIGUEL DE)].
Don Quixote. n. ed. 4t. s8°. Madrid. 1778–82
Don Quixote. 4t *in* 2. s8°. en Burdeos. 1815
Don Quijote. ed. econ. ilust. s8°. 1902
Don Quijote de la Mancha. n. ed., corr. &c. [Anglo-Span. Soc.] s8°. 1928
Don Quijote. Dibujos de G. Doré. 8°. Barcelona. *n.d.*
Algunos juicios acerca de la ed. crít. del "Quijote" anot. por F. R. Marin. n. ed. [P2420]. s8°. 1919
Exhib. of books rel. to C. Tercent., April–May, 1916. [Hisp. Soc. of Amer.] la8°. N.Y. 1916
La Galatea, div. en seys libros. pl. s8°. Valladolid. 1617
Novelas y teatro. Sel. por J. Sela. s8°. 1922
Teatro. [Bibl. econ. de clás. castell.] s8°. Paris. *n.d.*
TRANSLATIONS.
Don Quixote. Tr. C. Jarvis. 4th ed. 4v. s8°. 1766
Don Quixote. [Tr.] T. Smollett. Mem. by T. Roscoe. Illust. by G. Cruikshank. 3v. s8°. 1833
Don Quichote. Tr. Théry. 2t. 8°. 1888
see CASTRO (A.) El pensamiento de C., 1925.
„ GAYTON (E.) Pleasant notes upon Don Quixot, 1654.
„ GRIERSON (H. J. C.) Don Quixote: war-time refl. on its character & infl., 1921.
„ SERÍS (H.) La coleccion Cervantina de la Soc. Hisp. de Amér.: ed^s^. de Don Quijote, 1918.
„ UNAMUNO (M. DE). Life of Don Quixote & Sancho acc. to C. expounded w. comm. by U., tr., 1927.
Cesare (Giuseppe di).
Esame d. D. C. di Dante in 3 disc. div. 8°. [? Naples]. 1807
Cesareo (Giovanni Alfredo). Le origini d. poesia lirica, e la poesia siciliana sotto gli Svevi. 2ª ed. accresc. s8°. Milano. 1924
Cesari (Antonio). Bellezze d. Commedia di Dante Alighieri. Dialoghi. [4v]. 8°. Verona. 1824–26
Cesari (Cesare de). Romilda: tragedia. s8°. [Venetia. 1551]
Cesarotti (Melchoirre). Diss. resp. controv. on authenticity of Ossian's poems; tr., *see* OSSIAN. Poems in orig. Gaelic &c., v3, 1807.
Cesbron (C. Leroux), *see* LEROUX-CESBRON (C.)
Cescinsky (Herbert). Chinese furniture. Examples f. coll. in France. Intr. by H. C. 4°. 1922
The old-world house, its furniture & decoration. 2v. la8°. 1924
—— & E. R. Gribble.
Early Eng. furniture & woodwork. 2v. fol. 1922
Česka Akademie, *see* ZÍBRT (Č.) Bibl. České hist., 1900–12.
Československý Ústav Bibliografický. Bibliogr. kat. časopisectva republiky českoslov., 1920. 8°. Praha. 1921
Cessi (Benvenuto). Le fraglie dei barcaioli in Padova dur. la dom. d. rep. Veneta. [Estr. d. Ateneo Veneto, a. 25, fasc. 3. P2836]. 8°. Venezia. 1902
Cessi (Roberto). Un falso eroe d. rivolta di Famagosta (1473). [P. G. Davila. *Extr. f.* R. Istit. Veneto, Atti, t70ii. P2836]. 8°. Venezia. 1911
"Maone" medioevali, *see* ARCHIVIO STORICO ITAL. Anno 77, v1, 1919.
Venezia ducale. [v] 1, Le orig. 8°. Padova. 1927
Venezia e i regni di Napoli e Sicilia, sec XIV. [Estr. d. Arch. stor. p. la Sicilia or., anno 8. P2835]. 8°. Catania, *n.d.*
see ALBERTI (A.) & R. C. Polit. mineraria d. Repubbl. Veneta, 1927.
***Ceux** qui nous mènent: L. Barthou, L. Bérard, H. Bérenger &c. Par * * *. s8°. [1922]
„ „ Tr. W. Katzin. *w. title* As they are. By * * *. s8°. 1924
Cevennees. *A compleat history of the Cevennees [*sic*]. By a doctor of the Civil Laws. s8°. 1703
Ceylon. The C. directory; cal. &c. for 1875. Comp. by A. M. & J. Ferguson. 8°. Colombo. 1875
Return of architect. & archæolog. remains &c. exist. in C., 1887. sfol. Colombo. 1890
ARCHÆOLOGICAL SURVEY.
Memoirs. Ed. A. M. Hocart. v1. 4°. Colombo. 1924
Cézanne (Paul).
see BELL (C.) Since C., 1922.
„ FRY (R. E.) C.: h. development, 1927.
„ GASQUET (J.) C., 1921.
„ LECLERE (T.) C.; tr. J. B. Manson, 1925.
„ MEIER-GRÄFE (J.) C.; tr., 1927.
„ VOLLARD (A.) P. C.; tr., 1924.
Chaadaev (Petr Yakovlevich) [TSCHAADAJEW (PETER)].
Schriften u. Briefe. Übers. &c. v. E. Hurwicz. s8°. München. 1921
see WINKLER (M.) P. J. C.: russ. Geistesgesch. d. 19. Jhdts., 1927.
Chabaneau (Camille), *see* MANOSQUE. Livre des privilèges de M., suivi de Remarques philol. sur le texte provençal, par C. C., 1894.
Chabaneix (Philippe). Écrit des feuillantines suivi de Couleur du temps perdu. s8°. 1925
Chaboseau (A.) Hist. de la Bretagne avant le 13e siècle. 8°. 1926
Chabot (E.), *of Constance.* Des Königs Geige, eine Weihnachtsgesch. s8°. Konstanz. [1890]
Chabot (Georges). Les plateaux du Jura central. Et. morphogénique. [Univ. de Strasbourg. Publ., 41]. la8°. 1927
Chabot (J. B.) Choix d'inscr^s^. de Palmyre, tr. & comm. par J. B. C. 4°. 1922
Chabot (Rohan-), *see* ROHAN-CHABOT (—).
Chabrillan (*la comtesse* de) [*ps.* CELESTE MOGADOR].
Mémoires de C. Mogador. 4t. s8°. 1858
Chabrol (Guillaume Michel), *see* DU MOULIN (C.) Coutumes de la prov. d'Auvergne; préc. de 2 diss. par C., 4t, 1784–86.
Chack (Paul). The Entente upon the seas. Tr. L. B. Denman. s8°. Liége. 1928
On se bat sur mer. s8°. 1926
Chaderton (Laurence). An excellent &c. sermon, preached at Paules Crosse, 26 Oct. 1578. s8°. *Barker.* 1580
Chadourne (Louis). L'inquiète adolescence. Roman. s8°. [1920]
Chadsey (Charles Ernest). The struggle betw. Pres. Johnson & Congress over reconstruction. 8°. N.Y., *Columbia Univ.* 1896
Chadwick (D.)
Social life in the days of Piers Plowman. 8°. C. 1922
Chadwick (*Sir* Edwin), *see* MARSTON (M.) Sir E. C. (1800–90), 1925.
Chadwick (Herbert C.), *see* JOHNSTONE (J.), A. SCOTT & H. C. C. The marine plankton, 1924.
Chadwick (Luie M.) Fashion drawing & design. la8°. [1926]
Chaffers (Alexander). *The Twiss libel case. [P2827]. 8°. [1872 ?]
Chaffers (William). Hall marks on gold & silver plate &c. 10th ed., enl. &c. Ed. C. A. Markham. la8°. 1922
The Keramic gallery. 3rd ed., enl., rev. & ed. H. M. Cundall. 2v. la8°. 1926
This ed. has t. The new Keramic gallery.
Marks & monograms on pottery & porcelain. 4th ed. rev. & augm. 8°. 1874
Chaikovsky (Petr Ilich), *see* PROSHLOE. Прошлое русс. музыки. Матеріалы &c., 1, П. И. Чайковскій, 1920.
Chaine (M.) La chronologie des temps chrét. de l'Egypte & de l'Ethiopie. la8°. 1925
Chaine (Pierre). Les scrupules de Mons. Bonneval. s8°. 1921
Chaisne (Louis Auguste Victor), *cte. de Bourmont* [GHAISNE], *see* BOURMONT.
Chaitanya, *founder of a sect of Vaishnavas; 1485–1527.*
see KENNEDY (M. T.) The Chaitanya movt., 1925.
„ KRISHNADAS KAVIRAJ. C.'s pilgrimages & teachings; fr. contemp. Bengali biog.; tr. J. Sarkar, 1913.
„ SEN (D. C.) C. & h. companions, 1917.
Chakhrukhadze [TCHAKHROUKHADZÉ]. Пѣвецъ Тамары (Georgian text &c.), *see* MARR (N. YA.) Древнегруз. одописцы (12в.), 1902.
Chalaliantz (Isaiah Hasan-), *see* HASAN-CHALALIANTZ.
Chalandon (Ferdinand).
Hist. de la 1re Croisade j. Geoffroi de Bouillon. 8°. 1925
Chalcraft (William), *see* CHENNELL (G.) & W. C. Trial of G. C. & W. C. for murder of G. Chennell, Sen., &c., 1818.
Chaldaicum. *Alphabetum Chald., 1636, *see* ALPHABETUM.
Chaldeæ.
*Chaldeæ, seu Æthiopicæ linguaæ instit. s8°. Romæ. 1630
Chaliapin (Fedor Ivanovich) [Шаляпин], *see* TELYAKOVSKY (V. A.) **Мой сослуживец Ш., 1927.**

Challant (Bianca Maria di), *see* VACCARONE (L.) B. M. di C. e il suo corredo, 1898.
Challaye (Felicien). Le Japon illustré. 4°. *Larousse.* [1915]
Challenger, *H.M.S.*
Report of the scientific results of the voyage of the C., 1873–76, under Capt. G. S. Nares & Capt. F. T. Thomson. 4°. 1885–89
Narrative. v1i.
Physics & chemistry. v2.
Zoology. v17, 19, 20, 21 text, 21 plates, 23, 24 text, 24 plates, 25–28, 29i, 29ii, 29 plates, 30 text, 30 plates, 31, 32.
Challoner (Luke), *Fellow of Trin. Coll., Dublin, 1592, see* WHITE (N. J. D.) Four good men, L. C. &c., 1927.
Challoner (Richard), *bp. of Debra.*
Grounds of the old religion. 4th ed. s8°. 1781
Mems. of missionary priests & o. Catholics that suffered death in Eng. 1577–1684. 2v. s8°. Derby. 1844
„ „ ....n. ed., rev. & corr. by J. H. Pollen. 8°. 1924
Chalmers (Dalzell) & C. Asquith. Outlines of constit. law. With notes on legal hist. 8°. 1922
—— & L. H. Barnes.
Student's guide to Roman law (Justinian & Gaius). 8°. 1907
Chalmers (James), *M.R.C.V.S.* Export of meat. [U. of S. Afr., Dept. of Agric. Bull. 3. P2820]. 8°. Pretoria. 1921
Chalmers (Robert Chalmers, *1st baron***).** Richard Crashaw: "poet & saint," *see* WARD (*Sir* A. W.) In memoriam, 1924.
Chalmers (Thomas), *D.D., see* ANGUS (J.) The voluntary system: reply to Lect. of C. on Ch. establishments, 1839.
Chalon (Hugues de), *see* HUGUES *de Chalon.*
Chalybäus (Heinr. Moritz). Hist. development of speculative philos., f. Kant to Hegel. [Tr.] A. Edersheim. 8°. E. 1854
Chamaillard (Edmond). Pascal, mondain & amoureux. s8°. 1923
Chamard (François), *see* DENIAU (F.) Hist. de la guerre de la Vendée; t5, 6, par D., C. &c., 1911–12.
Chambardel (Louis Dubreuil-), *see* DUBREUIL-CHAMBARDEL (L.)
Chambeau (*le père*), *see* HAVRET (H.), C. &c. Mélanges s. la chron. chin., 1920.
Chamberlain (Basil Hall).
Things Japanese. 4th ed. rev. & enl. 8°. 1902
Chamberlain (Houston Stewart), *see* FÖRSTER (FR. W.) England in C.'s Beleuchtung, 1917.
Chamberlain (John), *commissioner of the repair of St. Paul's, see* STATHAM (E. P.) A Jacobean letter writer: life & times of J. C., 1920.
Chamberlain (*Rt. Hon.* **Joseph),** *M.P., see* ROBERTSON (*Rt. Hon.* J. M.) Collapse of "Tariff Reform": Mr. C.'s case exposed, 1911.
Chamberlain (Joshua Laurence). Universities & their sons. Hist., infl. &c. of Amer. univs. Ed.-in-chief J. L. C. Spec. eds., Harvard, W. R. Thayer; Yale, C. H. Smith; Princeton, J. De Witt & J. L. Williams; Columbia, J. H. van Amringe. Biog. ed. C. E. L. Wingate &c. Intr. by W. T. Harris. 5v. 4°. Boston. 1898–1900
Chamberlain (*Col.* **Weston P.),** *U.S. Army, see* UNITED STATES: ARMY. Med. Dept. in the World War, v6, Sanitation; by W. P. C., 1926.
Chamberlayne (Edward). M. Britanniæ Notitia; or, the pres. state of Gt. Brit. By J. Chamberlayne. 2p *in* 1v. [*p2 conts. also*: Gen. list of all officers].
22nd ed. of Eng., 1st of Scot. 8°. 1708
„ „ ......24th ed. of Eng., 3rd of Scot. s8°. 1716
„ „ ......26th ed. of Eng., 5th of Scot. s8°. 1723
Chamberlayne (John), *F.R.S.* Oratio Dominica in div. linguas versa. Cum diss. de ling. orig. [*w. sep. tp. & pagin.*] Ed. J. C. s4°. Amstelædami. 1715
see CHAMBERLAYNE (E.) M. Brit. Notitia &c., 24th [*&c.*] ed., by J. C., 1716; 26th [*&c.*] ed., by J. C., 1723.
Chamberlayne (Peregrin Clifford). Compendium geogr.: or, more exact &c. intr. to all geography &c. s8°. 1682
Chamberlayne (Tankerville James). Lacrimæ Nicossienses. Rec. d'inscripts. funéraires dans l'Ile de Chypre.
t1. [*no more publ.*] 4°. 1894
Chamberlin (Frederick). The Balearics & th. peoples. 8°. [1927]
The private character of Q. Elizabeth. 8°. 1921
Sayings of Q. Elizabeth. 8°. [1923]
Chamberlin (Thomas Chrowder). Certain phases of megatectonic geol. [Repr. f. Journ. of Geol., v34. P2818]. 8°. 1926
The genesis of planets. [C.I. of Wash. Extr. P2818]. la8°. *n.p.* 1924
The origin of the earth. [3rd impr.] s8°. Chicago, Ill. 1916
—— & R. D. Salisbury.
Geology (shorter course). [repr.] 8°. 1921

Chambers, *publishing firm.* Encyclopædia. n. ed., ed. D. Patrick & W. Geddie. 10v. la8°. 1923–27
Mathematical tables. Ed. J. Pryde. n. ed. 8°. [1921]
Chambers (Charles Haddon).
The tyranny of tears. Comedy. [repr.] s8°. [1921]
Chambers (*Sir* **Edmund Kerchever).** Arthur of Britain. s8°. 1927
The disintegr. of Shakespeare. [Brit. Acad., Ann. Shakespeare lect., 1924. P2753, 2769]. 8°. 1924
The Elizabethan stage. 4v. 8°. O. 1923
Shakespeare: a survey. 8°. 1925
Sir T. Malory. [Eng. Assoc., Pamph. 51. P2683]. 8°. 1922
Chambers (George), *1803–40, see* WATKINS (J.) Life &c. of G. C., 1841.
Chambers (George Frederick).
A handbook for East-bourne, &c. 8th ed. s8°. 1876
Story of eclipses. s8°. 1899
Story of the weather. s8°. 1900
Chambers (John), *M.D., of East Dereham, Norfolk.*
A pocket herbal. s8°. *pr. for the a.* Bury. 1800
Chambers (John David).
Lauda Syon. Anc. Latin hymns. Tr. pl. s8°. 1857
Chambers (Raymond Wilson).
Beowulf: an introd. to the poem w. a discuss. of the stories of Offa & Finn. 8°. C. 1921
Conc. certain gt. teachers of Eng. lang. Inaug. lect. [P2733]. 8°. 1923
England bef. the Norman conquest. Foreword on Rom. Brit. by M. Cary. 8°. 1926
Long Will, Dante, & the righteous heathen, *see* ENGLISH ASSOC. Essays &c., v9, 1924.
The teaching of English in the univs. of Eng. With note by J. Bailey. [Eng. Assoc., Pamph. 53. P2683]. 8°. 1922
W. P. Ker, 1855–1923. [From Procs. of Brit. Acad., v11. P2821]. 8°. [1925]
see UNIVERSITY COLL., *London.* Centenary addresses; pref. by R. W. C., 1927.
Chambers (Robert), *publisher.* The book of days; pop. antiqs. in conn. w. the calendar; ed. R. C. 2v. la8°. [1869]
The picture of Scotland. 3rd ed. 2v. s8°. E. 1834
Traditions of Edinburgh. n. ed. 8°. 1869
Chambers (Robert William).
The flaming jewel. s8°. [1922]
The girl in golden rags. s8°. [1925]
The man they hanged. s8°. 1926
Marie Halkett. [2nd impr.] s8°. [1925]
The moonlit way. s8°. N.Y. 1920
The mystery lady. s8°. [1926]
The talkers. [2nd impr.] s8°. [1925]
„ „ [5th impr.] s8°. [1925]
Chambers (William), *LL.D.*
Hist. sketch of St. Giles' Cath. 8°. E. [1905 ?]
Chambers (William), *publisher.*
The book of Scotland. 8°. E. 1830
France, its hist. & revolutions. s8°. E. 1871
Chambord (*le cte.* **de),** *d.* 1883 [*styled* "HENRI V" *by h. adherents*; †HENRY C. F. M. DIEUDONNÉ, *duc de Bordeaux*].
see HAUTPOUL (*le marq.* A. D'). Souvs.: 4 mois à la cour de Prague: l'éduc. du Duc de Bordeaux, 1833–34, 1902.
„ JORISSEN (TH.) Hist. Karakters, 2, De Traditiën van De Ch., 1912.
Chambrun (Clara Longworth de). Giovanni Florio, un apôtre de la Renaissance en Angleterre à l'époque de Shakespeare. 8°. 1921
Shakespeare actor-poet. [Tr.] 8°. N.Y. 1927
Chambrun (Jacques Pineton de) [*ps.* I. MELANCHTHON], *see* THOU (J. A. DE). Posteritati J. A. T. poem. in quo argutias criticorum refellit; opera I.M., 1722.
Chambure (A. de).
A travers la presse. Préf. de A. Brisson. [3e éd.] 8°. 1914
Chamchean (Miqael), *see* TCHAMTCHEAN (M.)
Chamier (Daniel). Panstratiæ catholicæ: seu controv. de relig. adv. pontif. corpus. [Ed. A. Chamier].
5t [t1, 2 *wanting*, 3–5 *in* 1v.] fol. Genevæ. 1626–30
5, Suppl. t4, De sacramentis & t5, De ecclesia; studio J. H. Alstedii.
Chamier (Frederick). Ben Brace. 3rd ed., rev. & corr. s8°. 1840
Chamonard (Joseph). Le Quartier du Théâtre: ét. sur l'habitation délienne, *see* ECOLE FRANÇ. D'ATHÈNES. Explor. arch. de Délos, fasc. 8i, ii, 1922–24.
Champagne.
La bataille de Champagne 1915. [P2422]. 4°. *n.d.*
*Champagne (Die). Herbstschlacht, 1915, 1916, *see* SANTEN (*Hauptmann* VON).
Champagne & Brie, *The Counts of, see* PITHOU (P.) Prem. livre des méms. des comtes heredit. de C. & B., 1572.
Champaigne (Philippe de), *1602–74, see* ROUJON (H.) P. de C., 1912 ?

Champeval (J. B.), *ed.*, *see* TULLE. Cartul. de T. &c., 1903.

Champfleury, *ps.* [*i.e.* JULES FLEURY]. Chansons pop. des prov. de Fr.: notices par C., *see* DUMERSAN (T. M.) Chants & chansons pop. de la Fr., t4, 1890 ?.

The faïence violin. Tr. H. B. Dole. s8°. [1895]

Le violon de faïence. [Les enfants du prof. Turck. Les trouvailles de M. Bretoncel]. s8°. *n.d.*

Champignelles (Adélaïde Marie de), *marquise de Douhault, see* DOUHAULT (A. M. DE C., *marquise de*).

Champion (Edouard). Cat. gén. de la librairie franç., cont. de l'ouvrage d'O. Lorenz &c., *see* LORENZ (O.) Cat. gén. &c., t28, 29, 1924–27.

Hommage à Stendhal. [P2488]. s8°. [Abbeville. 1920]

Le livre aux Etats-Unis. Extr. de la Rev. des 2 Mondes. [P2870]. 8°. 1927

Champion (Pierre).

Françoise au Calvaire. [Cahiers verts, 44]. s8°. 1924

Hist. poétique du 15e s. [Bibl. du 15e s., t27, 28]. 2t. la8°. 1923

Louis XI. 2t. la8°. 1927
1, Le Dauphin. 2, Le Roi.

Marcel Schwob & son temps. 8°. 1927

La plus anc. ed. de F. Villon, *see* VILLON. Le grant testament (*facs.* 1489), 1924.

Rabat & Marrakech. [Villes d'art célèb.] la8°. 1926

Ronsard & son temps. la8°. 1925

Tanger, Fès & Meknès. [Villes d'art célèb.] la8°. 1924

see ARC (J. D') Procès de condamn. de Jeanne d'Arc: texte, tr. & notes [par] P. C., 2t, 1920–21.

Champion de Cicé (Jérôme Marie), *abp. of Bordeaux; 1735–1810, see* LÉVY-SCHNEIDER (L.) L'applic. du Concordat par un prélat d'anc. régime, Mgr. C. de C., 1802–10, 1921.

Champlain Society. Publications. v13–15 & n.s. (*not numbered*). 8°. Toronto. 1920–27

see CHAMPLAIN (S. DE). Works; repr., tr. &c. under ed. of H. P. Biggar, v1, 2, 1922–25. [n.s.]

,, LAVERENDRYE (P. G. DE V. DE). Journals & letters; ed. &c. L. J. Burpee, 1927. [n.s.]

,, WOOD (W.) Sel. Brit. docs. of the Canadian war of 1812; ed. w. intr. by W., v1–3i, 1920–26. [13–15.]

Champlain (Samuel de). Works. Repr., tr. & annot. under ed. of H. P. Biggar. [Champlain Soc.] v1, 2 [& Maps *in case*]. 8°. Toronto. 1922–25
1, 1599–1607, tr. & ed. H. H. Langton &c. 2, 1608–13, tr. J. Squair, Fr. texts collated by J. H. Cameron.

see FLENLEY (R.) S. de C., 1924.

Champlý (Henry). Celle qu'on tue, *see* ŒUVRES libres, 47, 1925.

L'étranger dans l'alcove. s8°. 1921

La Juive errante. s8°. 1921

Champmeslé (Marie de), *wife of Charles Chevillet, sieur de Champmeslé, née Desmares, see* MAS (E.) La Champmeslé, 1927.

Champneys (Arthur Charles), *see* BRADLEY (A. G.), A. C. C. &c. Hist. of Marlborough College, rev. &c., 1923.

Champollion (Jean François). [" C. LE JEUNE "]

Dict. égypt. Publ. J. J. Champollion-Figeac. livr. 1–3 *in* 1v. fol. 1841–43

Gramm. égypt. [*Ed. w. pref. by* J. J. Champollion-Figeac]. pl. fol. 1836

Lettre à M. Dacier rel. à l'alphabet des hiéroglyphes, 1822, *see* ACAD. DES INSCR.: FOND. PIOT. Mons. &c., t25, 1921–22.

Rec. d'études égyptolog. dédiées à la mém. de C. [H. E. 234]. 8°. 1922

Champsaur (Félicien).

Les crassiers. [L'empereur des pauvres]. s8°. 1921

Floréal. [L'empereur des pauvres]. s8°. 1922

Les hommes de la route. [Cahiers verts, n.s., 5]. s8°. 1927

Nuit de fête. s8°. [1926]

Chamson (André).

Roux le bandit. [Cahiers verts, 59]. s8°. 1925

Chānakya, *see* KAUTILYA.

Chance (Edgar). The cuckoo's secret. 8°. 1922

Chance (Henry). Crown & sheet glass, *see* POWELL (H. J.) Princ. of glass-making, 1883.

Chance (James Frederick). The alliance of Hanover: Brit. for. policy in last years of George I. 8°. 1923

see BRITISH. Brit. diplomatic instr., 1689–1789, v1, 3, ed. J. F. C., 1922–26.

Chancellor (Edwin Beresford).

Col. Charteris & the Duke of Wharton. [Lives of the Rakes, v3]. 8°. 1925

Disappearing London. 4°. *Studio*. 1927

The 18th century in London, its social life & arts. la8°. [1920]

The hist. & antiq. of Richmond, Kew, Petersham, Ham, &c. 4°. Richmond. 1894

Chancellor (Edwin Beresford) [*continued*].

Life in Regency & early Victorian times, 1800–50. la8°. [1927]

The London of C. Dickens. 8°. 1924

The London of Thackeray. 8°. 1923

Lost London. Descr. of landmarks wh. have disappeared pictured by J. Crowther c. 1879–87, & descr. by E. B. C. la8°. *Chiswick Press*. 1926

Mem. of St. James's Str. w. the annals of Almack's. 8°. 1922

Pleasure haunts of London dur. 4 cents. 8°. 1925

The private palaces of London, past & present. s4°. 1908

Wanderings in Marylebone: squares & streets &c. 8°. 1926

The West End of yesterday & to-day. la8°. 1926

see BOYS (T. S.) Orig. views of London, 1842; re-issue, w. notes & intr. by E. B. C., 1926.

Chancellor (Richard), *see* ADAMS (C.) C.'s voyage to Muscovy (1630) &c., 1886.

Chancerel (Léon). Jean Julien Lemordant. s8°. [1920]

Chancerel (Lucien). Flore forestière du globe. la8°. 1920

Chancery, *Court of*. Calendar of Chancery warrants pres. in the Public Record Office. [Cal. of State Papers]. [v1], 1244–1326. la8°. 1927

Index of C. procs. (ser. 1), James I, v1, A-K: [Lists & Indexes, 47], 1922, *see* RECORD OFFICE (PUBLIC).

Index of persons named in early Ch. procs., Richard II (1385) to Edward IV (1467), preserved in Publ. Rec. Office. Ed. C. A. Walmisley. [Harleian Soc., 78]. [p1, A-J]. la8°. 1927

*Reports of cases in equity, argued &c. in Courts of C. &c. chiefly in r. of George I, 1734, *see* GILBERT (*Sir* G.)

Chancy (Isaac), *see* CHAUNCY (I.)

Chand (Gyan), *M.A.* The financial system of India. Foreword by E. H. Young. 8°. 1926

Chanda (Ramaprasad), *see* RAMAPRASAD CHANDA.

Chandler (Edward), *bp. of (1) Lichfield, (2) Durham*. A sermon preached to the Soc. for Reform. of Manners, Jan. 4, 1724. [*w.* 30th acc. of progress made in London &c. by the Soc., *w. sep. pagin.*] [P2669]. s8°. 1724

Chandler (Frank Wadleigh).

Aspects of modern drama. [repr.] 8°. N.Y. [1922]

Chandler (John E.), *see* COX (H.) & J. E. C. House of Longman, 1724–1924, 1925.

Chandler (Julian Alvin Carroll). Genesis & birth of the Federal constit. Addresses &c. Coll. of William & Mary. [*By var. a*s.] Ed. J. A. C. C. 8°. N.Y. 1924

Chandler (Marjorie Eliz. Jane), *see* BRIT. MUS. OF NAT. HIST.: GEOLOGY. Cainozoic plants in Dept. of G., v1, Bembridge flora; by E. M. Reid & M. E. J. C., 1926.

Chandler (*Mrs.* Mary). The descr. of Bath. A poem. Added, several poems. 3rd ed. 8°. 1736

Chandler (Samuel), *D.D.* The hist. of persecution, to r. of George II. n. ed. Added Dr. Buchanan's Inquis. at Goa. App. of persecutions in Brit. Emp. &c., by C. Atmore. 8°. Hull. 1813

Chandos, *the herald, see* LONDON UNIVERSITY. Cat. of MSS. &c. in the U. libr., w. descr. of MS. life of Edward, the Black Prince, by C., 1921.

Chandrasekhara Ayyar (S. N.), *see* MADRAS: CENTRAL MUS. Cat. of exhibits in Econ. Products Sect., by S. N. C. A., 1921.

Chaney (Lucian West). Accidents &c. in machine building, *see* UNITED STATES: LABOR, Bull. 256, 1920.

Statistics of indust. accidents in the U.S., *see* UNITED STATES: LABOR, Bull. 339, 1923.

Chang Chih-tung [TCHANG TCHE-TONG]. K'iuen-hio p'ien: exhortations à l'etude; n. éd. enrichie du texte chin. par J. Tobar, *see* VARIÉTÉS sinolog., No. 26, 1909.

***Changed** life (The), 2nd ed., 1891, *see* DRUMMOND (H.)

Channel pilot, 3p & Suppls. 2, 4, 5, 1917–22, *see* ADMIRALTY.

Channel Tunnel (The). Prelim. report on passengers & goods traffic likely to pass thr. the tunnel, & on estim. revenue, expenditure &c. [P2508]. sfol. 1907

Channing (Alice). Child labor on Maryland truck farms, *see* UNITED STATES: LABOR. Children's bureau. Publ. 123, 1923.

Channing (C. G. Fairfax). Siberia's untouched treasure, its future rôle in the world. 8°. N.Y. 1923

Channing (Edward).

Hist. of the U.S. v5, 6. 8°. N.Y. 1921–25
5, 1815–48. 6, War for Southern independence.

Channing (William Ellery). Slavery. s8°. Boston. 1835

Chanson (La) de Roland. La C. de R. Tr. nouv. d'ap. les textes orig. s8°. Londres. [1910]
„ „ Texte annoté [par] E. Aubé. s8°. 1924
„ „ Publ. d'ap le ms. d'Oxford & tr. par J. Bédier. s8°. [1924]
„ „ Comm. par J. Bédier. s8°. [1927]
see BOISSONNADE (P.) Du nouveau sur la C. de R., 1923.

Chanson (André). Ecrits. Par A. C., A. Malraux, J. Grenier, H. Petit. Suivis de 3 poèmes par J. P. Jouve. [Les cahiers verts, 70]. s8°. 1927

Chansonnier. *Chansonnier huguenot du 16e siècle. [*Ed.* H. L. Bordier]. s8°. 1870

Chansons. Chansons pop. de la France, 1891, *see* CRANE (T.F.), *ed.*
Chansons pop. des prov. de Fr.: notices par Champfleury, 1890 ?, *see* CHAMPFLEURY.
Chansons satiriques &c. du 13e s., 1921, *see* JEANROY (A.) & A. LÅNGFORS, *edd.*

Chantavoine (Jean). Munich. [Villes d'art célèbres]. la8°. 1908
Ver Meer de Delft: biog. crit. 8°. 1926

Chantemesse (Robert).
Le roman inconnu de la duchesse d'Abrantès. 8°. 1927

Chantepie de La Saussaye (P. D.) Lehrbuch d. Religionsgesch. Begrundet v. C. de La S. 4e, neubearbt. A., in Verb. mit B. Ankermann, A. Brückner &c. hrsg. A. Bertholet u. E. Lehmann. 2B. la8°. Tübingen. 1925
see HUBERT (H.) Introd. à la tr. fr. du Manuel d'hist. relig. de C., 1904.

Chantepleure (Guy), *ps.* L'inconnue bien-aimée. s8°. [1925]
Le magicien. [14e éd.] s8°. [1927]

Chantilly.
MUSÉE CONDÉ.
Le cabinet des livres. Imprimés antérieurs au milieu du 16e s. [Inst. de Fr.] 4°. 1905
„ „ Mss. [Inst. de Fr.] 3t. 4°. 1900–11
1, Théologie—Jurisprudence—Scis. & arts. 2, Belles-lettres. 3, Histoire.
Crayons franç. du 16e s. Cat., préc. d'une intr. par E. Moreau-Nélation. [Inst. de Fr.] 4°. 1910
see CLERMONTOIS. Chartes du C., au Musée C., 1904.

Chanting. *On chanting; its claims & princs. By compilers of Congr. Ch. music &c. [P2684]. s8°. 1854

Chantrey (*Sir* Francis), *see* ARMITAGE (H.) F. C.; donkey boy & sculptor, 1915.

Chantry. Chantry certificates & Edwardian inventories for Oxfordshire, 1919; 1920, *see* GRAHAM (R.), *ed.*

Chants. Chants & chansons pop. de la France, 4t, 1890?, *see* DUMERSAN (T. M.)
Chants hist. & pop. (1408–72), 1857, *see* LE ROUX DE LINCY (A. J. V.), *ed.*

Chapel Royal. Registres des eglises de la C. R. de St. James, 1700–56 & de Swallow Street, 1690–1709. Ed. W. & S. Minet. [Huguenot Soc. of London, v28]. 4°. 1924

Chapin (Harold). Comedies. [The new morality—Art & opportunity—Elaine—The marriage of Columbine]. Intr. by J. M. Barrie. 8°. 1921

Chaplin (*Hon.* Edith), *aft. wife of 7th marq. of Londonderry, see* LONDONDERRY (E., *marchioness of*).

Chaplin (Frank Knight). Effects of the Reformation on ideals of life & conduct. 8°. C. 1927

Chaplin (*Rt. Hon.* Henry Chaplin, *1st visc.*) Bimetallism. Speech in H. of C. [P2829]. 8°. M'ter. 1889
Bimetallism & agric. Addr. [P2829]. 8°. M'ter. 1888
see LONDONDERRY (E., *marchioness of*). H. C.: memoir, 1926.

Chapman (Abel).
The borders & beyond: Arctic—Cheviot—Tropic. 8°. 1924
Savage Sudan, its wild tribes, big-game &c. 8°. 1921

Chapman (Arthur Thomas), *see* BIBLE: COMPL. TEXTS &c. Camb. Bible: Leviticus; by A. T. C. &c., 1914.

Chapman (Carlton T.) American & Engl. naval & marine prints, models &c. Sold, Anderson Gall. [Illust.] [P2854]. la8°. N.Y. 1924

Chapman (Cecil Maurice). The poor man's court of justice: 25 yrs. as a Metropolitan magistrate. 8°. 1925

Chapman (Charles Edward). A hist. of Spain. Founded on the Hist. de España &c. of R. Altamira. [repr.] 8°. N.Y. 1925

Chapman (Conrad). Michel Paléologue, restaurateur de l'emp. byzantin, 1261–82. 8°. 1926

Chapman (Daniel). The great principles involved in the pres. act of papal aggression &c. [P524]. 8°. 1851
see GROSE (*Rev.* J.) Mem. of D. C.; also, C.'s Sermon on death of Rev. J. Beaumont, 1857.

Chapman (Ervin S.)
Particeps criminis. California rabbit drive. 8°. N.Y. [1910]

Chapman (Frank Michler). Distribution of bird-life in Ecuador. [Amer. Mus. of Nat. Hist., Bull., v55]. 8°. N.Y. 1926
Distrib. of bird life in Urubamba valley of Peru: rep. on birds coll. by Yale Univ. Nat. Geogr. Soc. expeds. [S.I., U.S. Nat. Mus., Bull. 117]. 8°. Wash. 1921

Chapman (Frederick).
The Foraminifera: intr. to st. of the Protozoa. 8°. 1902
—— **& W. Howchin.** Foraminifera of the permo-carbonif. limestones of N.S.W. [N.S.W.: Geolog. Survey. Palæontology, No. 14]. 4°. Sydney. 1905

Chapman (George), *the poet.* Works. Plays, ed. w. notes by R. H. Shepherd. n. impr. s8°. 1911
see CHARLEMAGNE. Charlemagne (The distracted emperor): drame élisabéth. anon. [*sometimes attrib. to* G. C.]; ed. crit. avec intr. &c. par F. L. Schoell, 1920.
„ SPENS (J.) C.'s ethical thought, 1925.

Chapman (James), *Methodist Minister.*
Jesus Christ & the present age. 25th Fernley lect. 8°. 1895

Chapman (*Dom* John), *O.S.B.*
*L'auteur du Canon muratorien. [*Extr.* P2790]. la8°. *n.p.n.d.*

Chapman (John), *publisher.*
An analytical cat. of Mr. C.'s publ. [P2777]. s8°. 1852

Chapman (Robert William). The portrait of a scholar [I. Bywater] & o. essays wr. in Macedonia, 1916–18. 8°. O. 1920
Proposals for a new ed. of Johnson's letters, *see* ENG. ASSOC. Essays, v12, 1926.

Chapman (*Mrs.* Susanna), *form. Dingley, wife of Dr. W. Chapman; c. 1705–58, see* YOUNG (R.) Mrs. C.'s portrait, a beauty of Bath of the 18th cent., 1926.

Chapman-Huston (*Maj.* Desmond). Sir J. Reckitt. 8°. [1927]
—— **& *Maj.* O. Rutter.** Gen. Sir J. Cowans: the Q.-M.-Gen. of the Gt. War. Intr. by Sir W. Robertson. 2v. 8°. 1924

Chapot (Victor).
see CAGNAT (R.) & V. C. Manuel d'archéologie rom., t2, 1920.
„ HELLÉNISATION. L'h. du monde ant.; leçons faites à l'Ec. des H. Et. Soc. par V. C. &c., 1914.

Chappe d'Auteroche (Jean). A journey into Siberia. Tr. 4°. 1770

Chappell (George Shepard), *see* TRAPROCK (W. E.), *ps.*

Chappell (Henry).
The Day & o. poems. Intr. by Sir H. Warren. s8°. 1918

Chappell (William), *F.S.A.*
Popular music of the olden time. 2v. la8°. [1855–59]

Chapple (William Allan). Fiji—problems & resources. s8°. 1921

Chappuzeau (Samuel) [CHAPUZEAU]. L'académie des femmes (1661), *see* FOURNEL (V.) Contemp. de Molière, t3, 1875.
La dame d'intrigue (1663), *see* FOURNEL (V.) Contemp. de Molière, t1, 1863.

Chapuis (Alfred) & E. Gélis. Le monde des automates. Préf. de E. Haraucourt. 2t. 4°. 1928

***Character** (The) of the Parl. commonly called the Rump, begun Nov. 1640, 1721, *see* PARLIAMENT.

Characters. *C. of Geo. I, Q. Caroline, Sir R. Walpole, &c. reviewed, 1777, *see* DAVIES (T.)

Charagan, *see* SHARAKAN.

Charaka-Samhitā. Tr. into Eng. Publ. by Avinash Chandra Kaviratna. [p38–68 publ. by h. son Pareshnath Sarma]. p1–68. [*pagin. contin.*] 8°. Calcutta. 1892–1925

Charasch (A.)
Lenin. Vorwort v. P. Axelrod. [P2464]. 8°. Zürich. 1920

Charaya (P. G.) Объ отношенiи абхазск. языка къ яфетич., *see* MARR (N. YA.) Мат. по яфет. яз., 4, 1912.

Charbonneaux (Jean). Trois armes d'apparat du Palais de Mallia, Crète, *see* ACAD. DES INSCRS. FOND. PIOT. Mons. & Méms., t28, 1925–26.

Charbonnel (J. Roger).
La pensée ital. au 16e s. & le courant libertin. la8°. 1919

Charbonnier (—), *Oberbürgermeister, see* LIEGNITZ. Die Stadt L.; hrsg. C. &c., 1927.

Chardin (Jean).
Travels in Persia. Intr. by Sir P. Sykes. la8°. 1927
see HARMER (T.) Obs. on passages of Scripture &c., w. new obs. f. papers of J. C., 4v, 1776–87.

Chardon (Charles). Hist. des sacrements, *see* MIGNE (J. P.), *ed.* Theol. cursus, t20, 1860.

Chardon (E. Henri), *maître des requêtes au Conseil d'État.* L'organis. de la répub. pour la paix. [C. E. for Int. Peace]. 8°. [1926]

Chardonne (Jacques). Le chant du bienheureux. s8°. 1927
L'épithalame. 2[t]. s8°. 1922

Charette de la Contrie (François Athanase), *see* LENÔTRE (G.), *ps.* Monsieur de C., 1924.

***Charitativi** pontif. in Polonia colloquii consilia secretiora, 1644, *see* POLONIA.

Charity Commission. War Charities Act, 1916. Index of Charities reg. under the Act. [*Typewritten*]. fol. [1919]

Charity Organisation Society, *see* LOCH (*Sir* C. S.) A gt. ideal &c.: papers & addrs. [C. O. S.], 1923.

Charity-schools. *Account (An) of charity-schools in England, &c. [*b. w.* Kennett (W.) Charity of schools &c., 1706]. 8o. 1706

Charkov, *see* KHARKOV.

Charlemagne [†CHARLES I, *emperor of the West*].

Anon. fragm. de bello C. contra Saracenos: ed. J. G. Scherzius, *see* SCHILTER (J.) Thes. antiq., t2, 1727.

Augusta Concilii Nicæni II. censura; Caroli M. de impio imaginum cultu libri 4. Præm. primi ed. [J. Tilii] præf. Rec. &c. C. A. Heumannus. s8o. Hanoveræ. 1731

Charlemagne (The distracted emperor). Drame élisabéthain anon. [*sometimes attrib. to* G. Chapman]. Ed. crit. avec. intr. & notes par F. L. Schoell. 8o. [Princeton]. 1920

Libri C. sive C. M. Capit. de imaginibus; rec. H. Bastgen, *see* MONUMENTA GERM. HIST. Legum sect. III, Concilia, t2, Suppl., 1924.

Le pèlerinage de C. Publ. avec glossaire par A. J. Cooper. Intr. de F. Klein. la8o. 1925

see BALDAUF (R.) Der Mönch v. St. Gallen, 1903.

„ EGINHARD. Early lives of C. by E. & the Monk of St. Gall; tr. & ed. A. J. Grant, 1922.

„ —— Eginhartus vita C. M.; cur. J. H. Schminckio, 1711.

„ —— Vie de C.; éd. & tr. par L. Halphen, 1923.

„ FRANCE. Gr. chrons. de Fr.; publ. par J. Viard, t3, C., 1923.

„ GESTA C. M ad Carcassonam & Narbonam; ed. &c. S. Ciampi, 1823.

„ HALPHEN (L.) Ets. crit. sur l'hist. de C., 1921.

„ KETTERER (J. A.) Karl. d. Grosse u. d. Kirche, 1898.

Charles, *archduke of Austria, son of Leopold II, see* JOHN (W.) Erzherzog Karl u. s. Armee, 1913.

Charles II, *archduke of Austria, see* LOSERTH (J.) Acten u. Corresp. z. Gesch. d. Gegenreformation in Innerösterr. unter K. II; gesamm. &c. v. J. Loserth, 1898.

Charles, *emperor of Austria, see* WERKMANN (*Baron* C. v.) Tragedy of C. of Habsburg, 1924.

Charles [*Borromeo*], *Saint, cardinal, abp. of Milan.* Monita ad confessores, *see* MIGNE (J. P.) Theol. cursus, t22, 1860.

see CONCINA (D.) De spectaculis theatralibus &c.; S. C. B. Opusc. de choreis &c. adj., 1754.

„ DAON (R.) Conduite des confesseurs selon les instructions de C. B., 1760.

Charles, *duke of Burgundy, called the Bold, see* LA MARCHE (O. DE). Le Chevalier delibéré [1483], facs., 1923.

Charles [*de France*], *duc de Guienne, see* STEIN (H.) C. de France, 1919.

Charles V, *king of France.*

see FRANCE. Les Grandes chron. de F.: Chron. des règnes de Jean II & C. V; publ. R. Delachenal, t3, 4, 1920.

„ PISAN (C. DE). Hist. (c. 1400), 1743.

Charles VIII, *king of France.*

see BOSIO (A.) Not. sul passaggio in Piemonte di C. VIII, 1870.

„ BRIDGE (J. S. C.) Hist. of France &c., v1, 2, Reign of C. VIII, 1921–24.

„ SANUTO (M.), *the younger.* La spediz. di C. VIII in Italia, 1873.

Charles IX, *king of France.* La chasse royale. Nouv. éd., préc. d'une introd. par H. Chevreul. s8o. 1858

see GALLIA. Ad Regis Galliæ [*i.e.* C. IX] consiliarios exhortatio, 1561.

„ MÉRIMÉE (P.) Chron. du règne de C. IX, 1912.

„ ROMIER (L.) Catholiques & Huguenots à cour de C. IX, 1924.

Charles X, *king of France; 1757–1836* [*Comte* D'ARTOIS].

see LUCAS-DUBRETON (J.) Le Cte. d'Artois, C. X, 1927.

„ ROBERT (C.) 1795: Expéd. des émigrés à Quiberon: le comte d'A. à l'île d'Yeu, 1899.

Charles IV, *emperor of Germany.* Aurea bulla, *see* CHARLES V, *emp.* Abschiedt &c., 1548–49.

see PORTA (J.) Liber de coronatione K. IV, 1913.

Charles V, *emperor of Germany.*

Abschiedt d. Röm. Key. M. u. gemeyner Stend uff dem Reichsstag zu Augspurg uffgericht, A.D. 1548 [30 June] Resolution &c. d. Röm. Key. M. wie es d. Religion halben biss nach endung dess. Concilii gehalten werden soll, inn Latein. u. Teütscher Sprach.—Key. M. Reformation, den Geystl. Standt betreffendt. —Landtfriden d. Key. Maie. u. dess Reichs, uff gemeltem Reichsstag erklert.—Cammergerichts Ordnung, sampt d.

Charles V [*continued*].

Güldin Bull, inn Lat. mit ettl. a. Constit.—Reformation &c. guter Pollicey im heyligen Reich, zu befürderung des gemeynen Nutzen uffgericht. [8p]. fol. Meyntz. *Durch Iuonem Schöffer.* 1548–49

Each p. has sep. tp., except the first; all have sep. pagins. & registers.

Antwort [*18 Oct. 1542 to the Brief of Pope Paul III of 26 Aug. 1542*], *see* PAUL III, *Pope.* Ein Sendbrieff &c., 1543.

Artickel das fürgenumen Concilium betreffend. Von Karolo V. u. Babst Clemente, Hertzog Hannsen Friderich v. Sachsen Churfürsten, newlich überschickt. Antwort Hertzog H. F. 1533 & Dess Churfürsten v. Sachsen &c. Antwort. s4o. *n.p.* [1533]

Artickel des Frides zw. Kay. M. u. könig Franciscen zu Franckreich in Madrill in Castily &c. s4o. *n.p.* 1526

Ausschreiben an alle Stende des Reichs. Die beschwerung des Kayserl. Cammergerichts belangende. s4o. [Wittemberg, *Georg. Rhaw*]. 1538

Das Ausschreiben K. Maiestat, auff den tag zu Speier, 1540, darauff antwort u. entschuldigung. s4o. [Augsburg ?] 1540

Cammergerichts Ordnung, *see* Abschiedt &c., 1548–49 *above.*

Formula Reformationis per Cæsaream Statibus Eccl. in comitiis Augustanis ad delib. proposita, & ab eisdem, ut paci publicæ consulerent &c., probata &c. s8o. Lovanii, *M. Rotarius.* 1548

„ „ ....s4o. Augustæ Vindel, *P. Ulhardus.* [1548 ?]

„ „ ....*For a. ed., see* Abschiedt *above.*

Keyserl. Mayestat fürhalten den Stenden des Reychs gethan, mit anzeyge etlicher Artickel zům Abschid dienlich.—Der Ausgpurger Conf. verwanten Stende antwort &c.—Keyserl. M. declaration auff etliche Artickel des Regenspurg. Abschids 1542. [P2439]. s4o. *n.p.* 1542

Ordenung u. Mandat Keiser Caroli V vernewert im April a. 1550. Zu aussrotten u. zu vertilgen, die Secten u. spaltung &c. Item ein Register d. verbottenen Büchern, Vermanung d. Rectors d. Univ. zu Louen, &c. [*Pref. by M. Flacius Illyr.*] s4o. *n.p. n.d.* [1550 ?]

L'ordonnance & edict &c., 1550, *see* LOUVAIN, *Acad. Lovan.*

Peinlich Gerichts Ordnung auff d. Reichsstägen zu Augspurg u. Regenspurg im Jaren 30 u. 32 gehalten. [*b.w.* Charles V. Abschiedt, 1548–49]. fol. Meyntz, *J. Schöffer. n.d.*

Pro divo Carolo, ejus nominis quinto Roman. Imper. in satisfactionē quidem eorū quæ in illum scripta &c. fuere. Apologetici libri duo nuper ex Hispaniis allaticum &c. [Privilegium C.—Clementis VII literæ—Responsio[nes] Caroli &c.]. s4o. [Moguntiæ, *J. Schœffer.* 1527]

Der röm. Kaiserl. M. erclärung, wie es der Religion halben im hailig. Reich biss zu ausstrag des gemainen Concili gehalten werden soll auff dem Reichstag zu Augspurg 1548 &c. s4o. [Augspurg, *P. Ulhart.* 1548]

„ „ *For. a. ed., see* Abschiedt *above.*

Röm. keyserl. M. Caroli des V. Antwort auff Bapst Pauli des III jüngstes aussschreiben, ein Gemeyn Concilium, so zů Trient solt gehalten werden, belangend. Ausz d. Latin verteütscht, 1543. Item der Keysz. Maye. obgemelt Antwort auff des Künigs v. Frankreichs Schreiben &c. [P2439]. s4o. *n.p.* [1543]

Röm. Kayserl. M. Einreytten, gen Boloniga &c. s4o. [Augsburg ?] 1529

Röm. kayserl. M. mandat, den Fridl. anstand des Glaubens &c. halben, des heyligen Reichs Deutscher nation belangend, 1532 [Aug. 3]. s4o. *n.p.* [1532]

Röm. Kayserl. M. u. des Bapsts geschickten werbung, an Hertzog Iohans Fridrichen zu Sachssen &c. Von wegen des kunfftigen Concilii &c. Antwort. s4o. [Wittemberg, *Georg Rhaw*]. 1533

Röm. Kayserl. M. u. gemeiner Stende des heil. Reichs Ordnūgē, auff jungst zu Augsspurg u. Regensspurg gehaltnenn Reichsstägen gemacht, wie es in sachen vnsern heyligen Christl. glauben &c. betreffen &c. [*Pref. &c. by V. Teutleben*]. s4o. [Colnn, *Peter Quentel*]. 1538

Sacræ Cæsareæ M. Declaratio quomodo in negocio religionis per Imperium usq. ad definit. Concilii gen. vivendum sit, in Comitiis Augustanis, 15 Maii, 1548. In Lat. versa. [P2440]. s4o. Francophordiæ ad Oderam, *Nicolaus Vuolrab.* 1548

„ „ *For a. ed., see* Abschiedt *above.*

*Von Kayserl. M. einreytten, auff den Reychstag gen Augspurg, Beschehen am 15. Junii, 1530. s4o. *n.p.* [1530]

see ARTOEPUS (J. C.) Disput. de abdicat. C. V., 1676.

„ BACMEISTER (L.) De morte Caroli V, 1719.

„ BARTENSTEIN (J. C.) Diss. de bello C. V a Mauritio Saxon. elect. illato, 1709.

„ BAUMGARTEN (H.) K. V u. d. deut. Reformation, 1889.

„ BROSCH (M.) Paul IV gegen K. V &c., *n.d.*

„ —— Zu d. Confl. K. V mit Paul III, *n.d.*

„ CABANÈS (A.) Le mal héréditaire, t1, Les descendants de C. V, 1926.

„ FLECKEISEN (C. F.) August. Confess. C. V exhib. hist., 1731.

„ KORTE (A.) Konzilspolitik K. V, 1538–43, 1905.

„ LUTHER (M.) Auff das Vermeint Keiserl. Edict &c., 1531.

„ MAYER (J. F.) De morte C. V evangelica, 1682.

„ —— Eccl. papæa &c.; acc. oratio de morte C. V, 1698.

„ —— Triga diss., 3, De morte C. V, 1707.

„ MEIER (G.) Ewiger Göttl. &c. Declaration, wider Carl u. Bapst Paulum III, c. 1546.

Charles V [*continued*].
see MERRIMAN (R. B.) Rise of the Spanish Empire, v3, The Emperor, 1925.
,, ROSENBERG (W.) Der Kaiser u. d. Protestanten, 1537–39, 1903.
,, SANTA CRUZ (A. DE). Crón. del Emp. C. V ; publ. R. Beltrán y Rózpide &c., 5t, 1920–25.
,, SCHOPPE (C.) Classicum belli sacri, ad C. V suasoria, 1619.
,, SCHRADIN (J.) Expostul. das ist Klag u. Verwiss &c., 1546.

Charles VI, *emp. of Germany, calling himself* CHARLES III, *k. of Spain.* Manifesto shewing right of C. III to Span. monarchy, *see* MONTHLY REGISTER, v1, Dec. Suppl., 1703.

Charles I, *king of Gt. Brit.*
*Ans. to A letter conc. the Kings going f. Holdenby to the Army, 1647, *repr.*, *see* HARTSHORNE (E. S.) Mem. of Holdenby, 1868.
Cat. & descr. of King C.'s coll. of pictures, bronzes &c. Publ. f. MS. in Ashmolean Musæum ; transcr. &c. by Mr. Vertue. s4°. 1757
His M. ans. to a pr. book, entit., A remonstrance of the Lords & Commons in Parl. May 26, 1642. In ans. to a declar. under H. M. name, conc. the businesse of Hull. [P2571]. s4°. 1642
His M.'s ans. to the petition of the Lords & Commons, at York, June 17, 1642. [P2571]. s8°. 1642
His M. finall answer conc. episcopacie. Deliv. 1st Nov. 1648. [*pagin. beg. 15.* P2662]. repr. s4°. 1660
His M.'s message to both Houses, Apr. 28, 1642, conc. h. refusall to passe the bill for the militia. [P2571]. s8°. 1642
His M. reason why he cannot &c. abolish episcopal gov. Deliv. at Newport 2nd Oct. 1648. With answ. 1648. [P2662]. s4°. 1660
His M.'s resolution conc. establ. of religion &c., also, H.M.'s speech to the gentry of York, May 1642, annexed, Declar. of both Houses of Parl. &c. [P2571]. 8°. 1642
Humble petition of the gentry &c. of Co. of York, 5th April, 1642, w. H.M.'s speech &c. [P2571]. 8°. 1642
*King C. h. Royall welcome, 1647, repr., *see* HARTSHORNE (E. S.) Mem. of Holdenby, 1868.
The King's M. answer to the paper conc. Church govt. (6 Oct., 1648). [P2662]. repr. s4°. 1660
see BAYLY (T.) Certamen relig. : conf. betw. C. & Henry, marq. of Worcester, conc. religion, 1646, 1649.
,, BIRCH (T.), *D.D.* *Inq. into the share wh. Ch. I had in the transactions of the E. of Glamorgan &c., 1645–46, 1747.
,, BOND (W. G.) Wanderings of Charles I & h. army in the Midlands, 1642–45, 1927.
,, BUNTEN (A. C.) Sir Thomas Meautys, & h. friends, 1918.
,, CARTWRIGHT (C.) Certamen relig. or conf. betw. the late K. of E. & the late Lo. Marq. of Worcester &c., 1652.
,, CLARENDON (E. H., *1st e. of*). Mems. of C. I. & the loyalists &c., 1795.
,, CROUCH (N.) Wars in Eng., Scot. & Ir. dur. r. of C. I, w. his tryal, 10th ed., 1737.
,, DIVINES. An humble ans. to 2nd paper by H.M., Oct. 6, 1648, about episc. govt., 1660.
,, EVELYN (J.) Mems. &c. ; subj., private corr. betw. C. I & Sir E. Nicholas &c., 1818.
,, HARRISON (*Maj.-Gen.* T.) Speeches & prayers of late King's judges &c., 1660.
,, HERBERT (*Sir* T.) Mems. ; added, acc. of funeral of C., 4th ed., 1839.
,, HOLLINGWORTH (R.) H.'s defence of Εἰκὼν Βασιλική, 1692.
,, LAYARD (G. S.) The headless horseman, P. Lombart's engraving : C. or Cromwell ? 1922.
,, LUDLOW (E.) Imprisonment & death of C. &c., 1882.
,, MILTON (J.) Εἰκονοκλαστης &c., 1690.
,, NALSON (J.) True copy of journal of High Court of Justice for tryal of C., w. introd., 1684.
,, PARLIAMENT. Declar. in Parl. in ans. to the King's [*i.e.* C. I] declar. conc. Hull, 1642.
,, —— New declar. sent to the Kings Majesty upon h. removall f. Huntington to York, 1641, 1642.
,, —— Petition to H.M. conc. h. intended going to Ireland, 1642.
,, ROSEDALE (H. G.) Spanish match, 1908.
,, SALMASIUS (C.) *Defensio regia, pro C. I, 1649.
,, STEVENSON (G. S.) C. I in captivity, 1927.
,, VINES (R.) H.M. concessions to Bill of abolition of abps. & bps. &c., 1660.
,, WAGSTAFFE (I.) *Defence (A) of the Vindic. of C., 1699.
,, WISHART (G.) *I. G. : De rebus auspic. C. &c., sub imp. J. Montisros. Marchionis &c. gestis, comm., 1647.

Charles II, *king of Gt. Brit.*
An act f. renouncing &c. disanull. the title of Charles Stuart, *see* *FURTHER (A) narr. of these times, 1658.
Instructs. to Alex, Earl of Balcarres [*& Passeport du Roy en faveur de B.*], 1654, *see* MAIDMENT (J.), *ed.* Hist. fragms., p3, 1833.
see BLOUNT (T.) Boscobel : hist. of H.M.'s preservation aft. Worc., repr., 1832.
,, COOKE (E.) Memorabilia : speeches by the King &c. (1660–80), 1681.
,, DRINKWATER (J.) Mr. C., k. of Eng., 1926.
,, HALIFAX (G. S., *1st marq. of*). Character of C. II &c., 1750.

Charles II [*continued*].
see HAMILTON (C.) His M. the King, *fict.*, 1926.
,, OGILBY (J.) Entertainment of C. II, h. coronation &c., 1662.
,, PEPYS (S.) Acc. of C.'s escape, dictated by the King, n.d.
,, SALVETTI ANTELMINELLI (G.) Banchetto fatto dal Re [1661], 1896.
,, SCOTLAND. Declar. of Comm. of Estates of S. agst. the forces of C. II &c., 1649.

Charles I, *landgrave of Hesse-Cassel.* Edict wieder d. heut. Quacker, neuen Freygeister &c. publ. zu Cassel, 1702. Beygefüget ein Extr. aus d. Reichs-Abschieden wieder Quäcker &c. [*& Caroli XI d. Schweden Königs Edicta &c. w. sep. tp. & pagin.*] [P2632]. s4°. *n.p.* 1703

Charles [*de Lorraine*], *cardinal, abp. & duke of Rheims, see* GUISE (C. DE), *cardinal.*

Charles I, *king of Naples & Sicily* [*count of Anjou*]. Actes & lettres de C. I, conc. la France (1257–84). Extr. des Registres Angevins de Naples ; publ. A. de Boüard. [École Fr. de Rome]. la8°. 1926

Charles, *prince of Poland, see* CHARLES [*de Saxe*], *duke of Courland.*

Charles [*de Saxe*], *duke of Courland.* [*C., pr. of Poland*], *1733–96.* C. de S., Duc de Courlande ; sa vie, sa corresp. &c. : publ. B. Lopacinski. 8°. 1870

Charles II, *king of Spain.* *Gli applausi d. virtú, per le nozze di C. II e Maria Luisa, celeb. d. nobiltá napolitana. [N125]. 8°. Napoli. 1680
see MAURA GAMAZO (G.) C. II y su corte, t2, 1915.

Charles III, *king of Spain, form. k. of the 2 Sicilies.* Capitoli, patti &c. conced. l'affitto dell' arrendamento d. diritto proib. d. tabacco al D. A. Gomes Figueiro, 1748–51. [P2766]. 8°. Napoli [1748?]
Constit. de la real orden españ. de C. III, instit. 19 Sept. 1771. [P2767]. 8°. [1771]
*La gara d. virtù né trionfi di Carlo. Compon. dramm. [poesia di P. T. pastore arcade. P2766]. 8°. Napoli. 1745
see NAPLES, *University.* In Regis C. Borboni & Amaliæ Saxon. nuptis, 1738.
,, SERGIO (G. A.) Orazione alla M. Carlo Borbone, 1747.
,, VIENNA. Tratado de paz, 1738, con la access. de el Rey [Carlos] al Tratado, 1739, 1739.

Charles IV, *k. of Spain, see* INDEX. Indice ultimo de los libros prohibidos &c. para todos los reynos del rey C. IV, 1747–89, 1790.

Charles XI, *k. of Sweden, see* CHARLES I, *landgr. of Hesse-Cassel.* Edict wieder d. heut. Quacker (*& C. XI d. Schweden* Königs Edicta &c.), 1703.

Charles XII, *king of Sweden, see* AMIRA (A.) Storia d. soggiorno di C. in Turchia, 1905.

Charles XIV, John [*Bernadotte*], *king of Sweden & Norway.*
see BARTON (*Sir* D. P.) Bernadotte & Nap., 1763–1810, 1921.
,, —— B., prince & king, 1810–44, 1925.

Charles Albert, *king of Sardinia.*
Lettere al Cav. L. B. di Barbania ; [ed.] A. Luzio, *see* REGIA DEP. S. GLI ST. DI STORIA PATRIA &c. Bibl., v12, 1926.
see DEGLI ALBERTI (M.) Politica estera del Piemonte sotto C. A. &c., 3t, 1913–19.
,, LUZIO (A.) Carlo Alberto e Mazzini, 1923.
,, —— Dalle Riforme a. statuto di C. A., 1926.
,, —— Inizi del regno, nuovi docs., 1923.
,, —— Ult. giorni di C. A., 1924.
,, SALUZZO (A. DI). C. A. dalla restaur. all' avvenimento al trono n. mem. ined. di A. di S. ; [ed.] M. Zucchi, 1926.
,, SOLARO DELLA MARGHERITA (*il conte* C.) Mem. stor. polit. per gli affari esteri del Re C. A., 1835–47, 1851.
,, VIDAL (C.) C.–A. & le Risorg. (1831–48), 1927.

Charles Edward [*Stuart*], *prince, the Young Pretender.* Some acc. of the Young Pretender in Scotland after h. defeat near Inverness. Part wr. by himself, tr. f. the French of 2 letters found near Arisaig &c. [*Advert. signed Robert Douglass of Straithbogie*]. [P2781]. 8°. [1746]
see CORDARA (G. C.) Comm. on exped. to Scotland by C. E. S. ; tr., 1926.
,, FARQUHAR (H.) Some portrait medals struck, 1745–52, for Pr. C. E., 1927.
,, GRIFFITHS (R.) *Ascanius, or the young adventurer [*i.e. C. E.*], 1802.
,, SCOTLAND. Letter f. a gentleman at Edinb., w. copy of the Pr—d—r's declaration, 1745.

Charles Eugene, *duke of Würtemberg, see* LORCK (J.) Bibl. Biblica Würtemberg. ducis olim Lorckiana, 1787.

Charles Louis, *elector palatine of the Rhine, see* AUSSARESSES (F.) & H. GAUTHIER-VILLARS. La vie privée d'un prince allemand au 17e s., 1926.

Charles Titus, *prince of the 2 Sicilies.*
see CAROLINE, *queen of Naples.* *Cantata per fest. il giorno natalizio di S. M. la Regina [*on birth of C. T.*], 1775.
,, FONSECA PIMENTEL (E.) La nascita di Orfeo (C. T.), 1775.

Charles (C. H.) Love letters of gt. men & women f. 18th cent. to pres. day. 8°. [1924]

Charles (*Mrs.* Elizabeth) [*Mrs.* RUNDLE CHARLES].
Chron. of the Schönberg-Cotta family. s8°. 1885

Charles (*Gen.* Hipólito), *see* MEXICO. Informe que el Gen. H. C., comandante en jefe del Cuerpo "Gendarmeria Fiscal" pres. al Secr. de Hacienda &c., 1886–7, 1888.

Charles (J. Ernest-), *see* ERNEST-CHARLES (J.)

Charles (*Mme.* J. F.), *see* BORDEAUX (H.) Amours du temps passé: J. C. & A. de Lamartine, 1923.

Charles (Robert Henry).
Comm. on the Revelation of St. John; w. intr. &c., Gr. text & Eng. tr., 2v, *see* BIBLE: COMPL. TEXTS &c. Internat. Crit. Comm.
The Decalogue. Warburton Lect^s^., 1919–23. 8°. E. 1923
Lect. on the Apocalypse. Schweich lect^s^., 1919. [Brit. Academy]. la8°. 1922
Relig. development betw. Old & New Test. [Home Univ. Lib.] [repr.] s8°. [1921]
The teaching of the New Test. on divorce. s8°. 1921
see BOX (G. H.) & C. GORE. Divorce in the New Test.: reply to Dr. C., 1921.

Charles-Roux (François). Autour d'une route. L'Angleterre, l'Isthme de Suez & l'Egypte au 18e siècle. 8°. 1922
L'expéd. des Dardanelles au jour le jour. 8°. 1920

Charles-Roux (J.), *ancien député, 1841–1918.* Le costume en Provence. Avec un sonnet de F. Mistral. [Souvs. du passé]. 2[t]. 4°. 1907

Charlesworth (Martin Percival).
Trade-routes & commerce of the Roman Emp. s8°. C. 1924

Charléty (Sébastien), *see* LAVISSE (E.) Hist. de la France contemp., t4, 5, par S. C., 1921.

Charlevoix (Pierre François Xavier de).
Hist. du Japon. n. éd. rev. &c. 6t. s8°. 1754
Hist. of Paraguay. Tr. 2v. 8°. D. 1769

Charlier (Guillaume), *see* PIERRON (S.) G. C., 1913.

Charlotte, *princess* [†CHARLOTTE CAROLINE AUGUSTA, *of Wales, consort of Leopold, duke of Saxe-Coburg*]. *Address to the people on the death of Princess C.; by The hermit of Marlow (1817), 1883, *see* SHELLEY (P. B.)

Charlotte, *de Belgique, see* CHARLOTTE, *empress of Mexico.*

Charlotte, *queen of Cyprus; 1436–87* [CHARLOTTA v. LUSIGNAN], *see* HERQUET (C.) C. v. L. u. Caterina Cornaro, 1870.

Charlotte, *empress of Mexico, wife of Maximilian of Mexico* [CHARLOTTE DE BELGIQUE; MARIE CHARLOTTE].
see CORTI (E. C.) Maximilian u. C. v. M., 2B, 1924; tr., 2v, 1928; [Fr.] tr., 2t, 1927.
,, REINACH FOUSSEMAGNE (*Ctsse* H. DE). C. de Belgique, Impératrice du M., 1925.

Charlotte Elizabeth, *duchesse d'Orléans, 1652–1722* [*princesse palatine; "Madame"*]. Briefe, 1707–15. Hrsg. W. L. Holland. [Litt. V. in St., 107]. 8°. [Tübingen]. 1871
Corr. de Madame, dsse. d'Orléans. Publ. L. W. Holland. Tr. & notes par E. Jaeglé. 2e éd., rev. & augm. 3t. 8°. 1890
Letters of Madame, 1661–1722. Tr. & ed. by G. S. Stevenson. 2v. 8°. 1924–25
see PALATINATE. Electa juris publici hist. Palat. illustr. [In causa ducissæ Aurelianæ contra &c.], 1700.
,, WILLE (J.) E. C., Herzogin v. O., 3e erweit. A., 1921.

Charlton (Richard).
Exposure of villany &c. of R. C., in case of h. imputation on character of G. Pelly. [P2776]. 8°. [1844]
see ABERDEEN (G. H.-G., *4th earl of*). Award upon meaning of Ld. A.'s letter, R. C. claiming lands in Honolulu, 1844.
,, FRENCH (W.) In Chancery: estate of W. F. &c., vs. R. C. &c., 1844.
see HAWAII. Corr. on R. C.'s claim to land, 1845.
,, —— Investig. by King &c. of H. Isl^s^. in vindic. of course pursued by H.M., impugned by W. Miller who took poss. of land claimed by R. C. &c., 1846.
,, PELLY (G.) Trial, G. P. vs. R. C., action for trespass &c., 1844.

Charma (Antoine).
Saint Anselme: notice biogr., littér. & philos. 8°. 1853

Charmeil (Pierre).
Les gouverneurs gén. des colonies franç. 8°. 1922

Charmes (Francis), *see* CAMBON (J.) Disc. pour la récept. de J. C. [*on* F. C.], 1919.

Charmes (Thomas ex), *see* THOMAS [*Thomas*] *ex Charmes.*

Charmy (Roland). Nordia, nouvelle, *see* ŒUVRES libres, 49, 1925.

Charnock (Robert). The tryals & condemnation of R. C., E. King, & T. Keyes for the conspiracy to assassinate H.M. King William. [*a.c. in* P2606]. fol. 1696

Charnwood (Godfrey Rathbone Benson, *1st baron*).
According to St. John. 8°. [1926]
Theodore Roosevelt. 8°. 1923
Tracks in the snow. [re-issued]. s8°. 1927
Walt Whitman & America, *see* ROY. SOC. OF LIT. Essays: Trans., N.S., v1, 1921.

Charpentier (Gustave), *see* HIMONET (A.) Louise de G. C., etude-analyse musicale, 1922.

Charras (Jean Baptiste Adolphe). Hist. de la campagne de 1815: Waterloo. [*&* Atlas spécial, par Vandermaelen]. 2t [*in 1*]. s8°. Brux. 1858
,, ,, ...3e éd. [in 1v.; Atlas *b. sep.*] s8°. Leipzig. 1858

Charron (Pierre).
De la sagesse trois livres. s8°. Amsterdam, *Elzevier.* 1662

Chart (David Alfred). An econ. hist. of Ireland. s8°. D. 1920

Charterhouse [*incl.* CHARTERHOUSE SCHOOL].
Charterhouse prize exercises, 1814–32. s8°. 1833
[List of scholars w. prize compos., 1816–25 *in* 1v.] 8°. 1816–25

Charteris (*Hon.* Evan). John Sargent. 8°. [1927]
William Augustus, Duke of Cumberland, & the Seven Years' War. 8°. [1925]

Charteris (*Col.* Francis) [CHARTRES], *see* CHANCELLOR (E. B.) Col. C. &c. [Lives of the Rakes], 1925.

Charters. C. & docs. rel. to the Burgh of Peebles, w. extr. f. rec^s^., 1165–1710, 1872, *see* PEEBLES.
Transcripts of c. rel. to the Gilbertine houses of Sixle, Ormsby &c., 1922, *see* STENTON (F. M.), *ed.*

Chartes [CHARTRIER].
C. de Beauvoir; [publ. &c.] par l'abbé Lalore, 1878, *see* BEAUVOIR.
C. de communes &c. en Bourgogne, 3t, 1867–77, *see* BOURGOGNE.
C. de l'abbaye de St.-Etienne de Dijon, 1907–14, *see* DIJON.
C. de N.-D. de Bertaud, diocèse de Gap, 1888, *see* BERTAUD.
C. de St.-Maurice de Vienne &c., 1912, *see* VIENNE.
C. du Clermontois, 1068–1352, 1904, *see* CLERMONTOIS.
C. du prieuré de St.-Nicholas de Royan, 1891, *see* ROYAN.
C. & diplômes rel. à l'hist. de France. Publ. par les soins de l'Acad. des Inscr^s^. &c. [t5, 6, 7ii, 8]. 4°. 1916–26
[5], Rec. des actes des rois de Provence, 855–928; publ. sous la dir. de M. Prou par R. Poupardin.
[6], Rec. des actes de Philippe Auguste, roi de France; publ. sous la dir. de E. Berger par H. F. Delaborde. t1, 1179–94
[7ii], Rec. des actes de Henri II, roi d'Angleterre & duc de Normandie, conc. les provinces franç. & les affaires de France. Œ. posthume de L. Delisle; rev. & publ. par E. Berger. t2 [Textes, *cont.*]
[8], Rec. des actes de Pépin I & de Pépin II, rois d'Aquitaine, 814–48; publ. sous la dir. de M. Prou par L. Levillain. [8.]
C. servant de pièces justif. à la géogr. du Perche &c., 1890–1902, *see* ROMANET (*le vte.* DE).
Chartrier de l'abbaye de Saint-Pons, 1913, *see* SAINT-PONS.
Rec. des c. de l'abbaye de St.-Benoît-sur-Loire, t1, 2i, 1900–12, *see* SAINT-BENOÎT-SUR-LOIRE.
Rec. des c. de l'abbaye royale de Montmartre, 1883, *see* MONTMARTRE.

Chartier (Alain). Le curial. Texte franç. du 15e s. avec l'orig. lat. Publ. par F. Heuckenkamp. 8°. Halle s. S. 1899
Le quadrilogue invectif. Ed. E. Droz. [Classiques fr. du moyen âge]. s8°. 1923

Chartier (E.) [*ps.* ALAIN]. 81 chapitres s. l'esprit & les passions. Par l'a. des propos d'A. 8°. 1921

Chartraire (Eugène). La cathédrale de Sens. s8°. [1921]
Le trésor de la Cath. de Sens. [Coll^s^. publ. de France]. s8°. [1924 ?]

Chartres. Cathédrale de C. [*plates, w. notes*], 13t, *n.d.*–1926, *see* HOUVET (E.), *ed.*

Chartres (*Mrs.* Annie Vivanti), *see* VIVANTI (A.)

Chartres (*Col.* Francis), *see* CHARTERIS (*Col.* F.)

Chartreux. *Maisons de l'Ordre des C. Vues & notices. 4t. fol. Montreuil-sur-Mer. 1913–19

Chartrier, *see* CHARTES.

Chartularium [CHARTULARY; *see also* CARTULAIRE]. C. abbatiæ Sti. Vincentii Cenoman., 1886, *see* LE MANS.

Chasdai Ben Abraham Crescas, *see* WAXMAN (M.) Philos. of Don Hasdai C., 1920.

Chase (Frederic Henry), *bp. of Ely, see* GLAZEBROOK (M. G.) The letter & the spirit: reply to Bp. of Ely's crit^s^. on The faith of a mod. churchman, 1920.

Chase (George Henry). Greek & Roman sculpture in Amer. collections. 8°. Cambridge, *Mass.* 1924

Chasles (Pierre). Le bolchévisme expliqué par l'état social de la Russie. la8°. [1921]

Chasoslov. Часословъ и Млітвы повседнівный. По предáнїю Цркóвному въ кратцо изббранный. s8°. в. Мон. Кіево Печéрск. 1679

Chasseloup-Laubat (*le marq.* **Louis de).** Les chaudières marines. [Extr. des Mém^{s}. de la Soc. des Ingénieurs Civils de France, 1897]. 8°. 1897
Les grands paquebots. Conférence. [Soc. d'Encour. pour l'Indust. Nat. Extr. du Bull. d'août 1898. *b. w. h.* Marines de guerre, 1903]. 4°. 1898
Les marines de guerre modernes. 4°. 1903
see EXHIBITIONS: CHICAGO. Rapports: Congrès tenus à C. en 1893 [Rapport de C.-L.], 1894.

Chassériau (Théodore), *1819–57, see* MARCEL (H.) C.; 48 planches; notices par J. Laran, 1911.

Chassinat (Emile). A propos d'une tête en grès rouge du roi Didoufrî (4e dynastie), *see* ACAD. D. INSCR.: FOND. PIOT. Mon^{s}., t25, 1921–22.
Fouilles à Baouît, t1i, *see* INSTITUT FRANÇ. D'ARCH. ORIENT. DU CAIRE. Mém., t13i, 1911.
Le Temple d'Edfou, *see* †MISSION ARCH. FR. AU CAIRE, t10, 11, 20, 1897–1928.

Chastel de Boinville (*Mrs.* **N. M.)** The lad. s8°. [1923]
O'Reilly of the glen. s8°. 1918

Chastellux (Georgine de), *see* LA BÉDOYÈRE (G., *ctsse.* DE).

Chastenet (J. L.)
The banker's republic. Tr. C. H. Douglas. s8°. [1926]

Château Malet, *see* MALET, *Château.*

Chateaubriand (Armand Louis Marie de), *see* HERPIN (E.) Hero of Brittany: A. de C. &c.; tr. 1914.

Chateaubriand (*le vte.* **François René de).**
Les aventures du dernier Abencerage. Ed. P. Hazard & M. J. Durry. [Bibl. de la Revue de litt. comp., t27]. 8°. 1926
Congrès de Vérone. Guerre d'Espagne. Négoc.: Colonie esp. Suivie de la Vie de Rancé. la8°. *n.d.*
Corr. gén. Publ. L. Thomas. t5. la8°. 1924
De Buonaparte, des Bourbons, &c. [*&* Réflex. de M. Bergasse sur l'acte constit. du Sénat]. 2e éd. 8°. 1814
*Du système adopté pour arriver au ministère, en réponse à C. [P2553]. 8°. 1818
Du système polit. suivi par le ministère. [P2553]. 8°. 1817
Mémoires d'outre-tombe. 6t.la8°. *Penaud & Krabbe.* [1856]
*Un mot sur la philippique [Du système polit.] de C. [P2553]. 8°. 1818
Proposition faite à la Chambre des Pairs &c. 8°. 1816
Remarques sur les affaires du moment. 8°. 1818
see ANCELOT (J. A. P. F.) Vie de C., 1856.
„ AUBERT DE VITRY (F. J. P.) Obs. sur "Du système polit." par C., 1818.
„ FAURE (G.) Pélerinages passionnés, s2, Ames &c. (C. &c.), 1922.
„ GIRAUD (V.) Passions & romans d'autrefois, 1925.
„ LEVAILLANT (M.) Splendeurs &c. de C., 1922.
„ MAURRAS (C.) Romantisme &c., éd. déf., C. &c., 1922.
„ MILLER (M. H.) C. & Eng. lit., 1925.
„ PALÉOLOGUE (G. M.) Romantic diplomat, C. &c., 1926.
„ —— Talleyrand, Metternich, C., 1924.
„ VILLENEUVE (L. DE). Le roman de l'Occitanienne, avec 70 lettres de C., 1925.

Châteaubriant (Alphonse de).
La brière. Roman. s8°. [1923]

Chateaumorand (Jean de), *c. 1355–1429, see* SCHLUMBERGER (G. L.) J. de C., un des princ. héros franç. des arrière-croisades en Orient, 1919; [*& in h.* Byzance & Croisades, 1927].

Château-Renault (*le comte* **de)** [CHÂTEAU-RENAULT (FRANÇOIS LOUIS DE ROUSSELET, *marq.* DE)], *see* CALMON-MAISON (J. J. R.) Le maréchal de C.-R., 1637–1716, 1903.

***Châteaux (Les)** de la Loire; dir. M. Monmarché, 6e éd., 1919; 7e éd., 1923, *see* LOIRE.

Châteillon (Sebastien) [*ps.* BELLIUS (MARTINUS)]. De hæreticis an sint persequendi &c. Luteri & Brentii &c. sententiæ. s8°. Magdeburgi. 1554

Chatelain (Émile), *see* QUICHERAT (L.) Dict. fr.-lat., rev. &c. par E. C., 45e éd., *n.d.*

***Châtelaine (La)** de Vergy. Conte du 13e siècle. Publ. & tr. par J. Bédier. [6e éd.] s8°. [1927]

Chater (Daniel), *see* GALLEY (W.) Full &c. hist. of the murders of W. G. & D. C., 1749.

Chater (James).
A gram. of the Cingalese lang. 8°. Colombo. 1815
Hist. catechism for children & youth. Tr. into Singhalese by J. C. pl. s8°. Colombo. 1819
Intr. to reading in Singhalese & Eng. pl. s8°. Colombo. 1818

Chatfield-Taylor (Hobart Chatfield).
An American peeress. s8°. Chicago. 1894

Chatham (William Pitt, *1st earl*). Love-letters [to Lady H. Grenville, 1754, *w. replies*]. Ed. E. A. Edwards. 8°. 1926

Chatillon (Gaspard de Coligny, *Seigneur* **de),** *see* COLIGNY (G. II. DE).

Chatillon (Walter de), *see* GAUTIER (P.)

Chatinières (Paul). Dans le grand Atlas marocain, 1912–16. Intr. du Gén. Lyautey. s8°. [1919]

Chatterjee (B. C.)
Gandhi or Aurobindo? [P2500]. s8°. [Calcutta]. [1921]

Chatterjee (Gladys M., *Lady*), *wife of Sir Atul Chandra Chatterjee, see* BROUGHTON (G. M.)

Chatterton (Edward Keble).
The Auxiliary Patrol. 8°. 1923
The brotherhood of the sea. 8°. 1927
Captain John Smith. 8°. [1927]
Chats on naval prints. 8°. [1926]
The mercantile marine. 8°. [1923]
Q-ships & their story. 8°. 1922
The romance of piracy. s8°. 1914
Romance of the sea rovers. 8°. 1924
Ship-models. Ed. by G. Holme. [Publ. by The Studio]. 4°. 1923
Steamship models. 4°. 1924

Chatterton (Eyre), *bp. of Nagpur.*
Hist. of the Ch. of England in India. 8°. 1924

Chatterton (F. J. S.) Canaries: & how to keep them. s8°. [1924]
Ducks & geese: & how to keep them. s8°. [1924]

Chatterton (G. G.) The mistake. s8°. [1923]

Chatterton (Thomas). Godred Crovan: poem (1768); ed. &c. W. Harrison, *see* MANX SOC. Manx misc., v2, 1880.
Poems supposed to have been wr. by T. Rowley & others. Added, Pref., intr. acc. &c. 8°. 1777

Chatwin (Charles Panzetta), *see* DEWEY (HENRY) &c. Geol. of country around Dartford, 1924.

Chatwood (Arthur Brunel), *see* JOHNSON (R.) & A. B. C. Photography, 1895.

Chaucer Society. *Publications for 1908–15.* 4°. & 8°. 1914–22
Root (R. K.) MSS. of Troilus w. facs. of var. handwritings. 4°. 1914 [I, 98]
—— Textual trad. of Troilus, &c. 8°. 1916 [I, 99]
Spurgeon (C. F. E.) 500 yrs. of Chaucer crit. & allusion, 1357–1900. 5p. 8°. 1914–22 [II, 48–50, 52–54]
1–3, Text, 1357–1900. 4, App. A. 5, App^{s}. B. & C., French & Germ. allusions.
For Suppl., *not issued by Soc., see* SPURGEON (C. F. E.)
Tatlock (J. S. P.) Scene of the Franklin's tale visited. 8°. 1914 [II, 51]

Chaucer (Geoffrey).
[Workes. Ed. T. Speght. *Imperfect*]. fol. 1602
Compl. works. Ed. W. W. Skeat. 8°. O. 1920
Poet. works. Ed. R. Morris, w. mem. by Sir H. Nicolas. [Aldine ed.] 6v. s8°. 1886–8
The book of Troilus & Criseyde. Ed. R. K. Root. 8°. Princeton, *N.J.* 1926
Prologue, Knightes T.—Nonne Prestes T. Rev. text ed. R. Morris. s8°. O. 1885
The riches of C. &c., w. notes & n. mem. by C. C. Clarke. 2v [*b. in 1*]. s8°. 1835–39
see BRUSENDORFF (A.) The C. tradition, 1925.
„ JACK (A. A.) Poetry of C. & Spenser, 1920.
„ KITTREDGE (G. L.) The authorship of the Eng. Roumaunt of the Rose, 1892.
see MANLY (J. M.) Obs^{s}. on lang. of C.'s Legend of good women, 1893.
„ NEILSON (W. A.) Origins &c. of the Court of love [*wrongly ascribed to C.*], 1899.
„ ORD (H.) C. & the rival poet in Shakespeare's sonnets, 1921.
„ SKEAT (W. W.) Evol. of the Canterbury tales, 1907.
„ SMYTH (E. C.) Essay on C., 1924.
„ SPURGEON (C. F. E.) 500 yrs. of C. crit. & allusion, 1357–1900, 5p, 1914–22; Suppl., 1920.
„ SWEET (H.) Second Middle Engl. primer: extr. f. C., 2nd ed., 1905.
„ TATLOCK (J. S. F.) & A. G. KENNEDY. Concordance to compl. wks. of C. &c., 1927.

Chaucer (Thomas), *son of Geoffrey Chaucer; c. 1364–1434, see* RUUD (M. B.) T. C., 1926.

Chauchard (*Capt.*), *see* GERMANY. Geogr., hist. &c. descr. of G. &c.; comp. &c. f. German [*w.* C.'s maps], 1800.

Chauffepié (Jacques Georges de). Life of Servetus; article of h. Hist. dict., v4. Tr. J. Yair. 8°. 1771

Chauffier (Louis Martin-), *see* MARTIN-CHAUFFIER (L.)

Chaulieu (*l'abbé* **de)** [†ANFRIE DE CHAULIEU (GUILLAUME)], *1636–1720, see* LACHÈVRE (F.) Dern. libertins, 1924.

Chaulne (Claude de), *c. 1595–1675, see* LACHÈVRE (F.) Dern. libertins, 1924.

Chaume (*l'abbé* **M.)** Les orig^{s}. du duché de Bourgogne. [Acad. des Sc. &c. de Dijon]. pl, 2i. 8°. Dijon. 1925–27

Chauncy, *The family of, see* TUCKER (S. I.) Pedigree of fam. of C., 1884.

Chauncy (Isaac) [CHANCY], *see* WILLIAMS (D.) A defence of Gospel truth, reply to C.'s First part, 1693.

Chauncy (Maurice) [†CHANCÆUS (M.)] *Hist. aliquot nostri sæculi martyrum. s4°. [Maguntiæ]. 1550

Chausson (Ernest), *see* REVUE MUSICALE, déc. 1925, No. spéc., 1925.

Chauvet (Stephen). Coutances & ses environs. s8°. 1921

Chauvière (Claude). Crimes: roman, *see* ŒUVRES libres, 60, 1926.

La femme de personne, roman, *see* ŒUVRES libres, 11, 1922.

Un homme s'est jeté . . ., nouvelle, *see* ŒUVRES libres, 51, 1925.

Chauvigny (Claude de), *baron de Blot l'Eglise; 1605–55, see* BLOT (C. DE C., *baron* DE).

Chauvin (Victor). Hist. des lycées & collèges de Paris. s8°. 1866

Chavagnac (*le cte.* **X. de),** *see* GROLLIER (C. DE). Manuel de l'amateur de porcelaines, manufact. europ., 1914.

Chavannes (Edouard). Contes & légendes du bouddhisme chinois. Tr. E. C. Préf. & vocab. de S. Lévi. 8°. 1921

L'expression des vœux dans l'art pop. chinois. 8°. 1922

Le jet des dragons, *see* ACAD. DES INSCRs. &c. Mém. conc. l'Asie Or., t3, 1919.

Mission archéol. dans la Chine septentr. [Ecole Franç. d'Extr.-Or.] t1, p2, La sculpture bouddhique. [*no more publ.*] 8°. 1915

Six mons. de la sculpture chin. [Ars Asiatica, 2]. fol. Brux. 1914

see GUIMET: Bull. arch. du Musée G., fasc. 1, Salle E. C. &c., 1921.

,, TRIPITAKA. Cinq cents contes &c., extrs. du T. chinois, tr. E. C., 3t, 1910–11.

Chavigny (*Dr.* **Paul Maurice Victor).**

Psychologie de l'hygiène. s8°. 1921

Chayanova (Olga Em.) Театр Маддокса в Москве. 1776–1805. 8°. Москва. 1927

Chayim, *ben Benjamin Zeeb Bochner.* Tabulæ vitæ [*Heb. & Lat.*], *see* WAGENSEIL (J. C.) Exercit., 1687; 1719.

Chaytor (Henry John). Dramatic theory in Spain: extr. f. lit. Ed. H. J. C. 8°. C. 1925

The troubadours & England. s8°. C. 1923

Cheal (Henry). The story of Shoreham. 8°. Hove. 1921

Cheape (Maude), *aft. Mrs. Ellis, see* ELLIS (*Mrs.* M.)

Cheape (*Mrs.* **Maude Mary),** *wife of Lt.-Col. G. C. Cheape, form. Hemming, see* ELLIS (*Mrs.* M.) The squire of Bentley (Mrs. C.): a gt. sportswoman, 1926.

***Cheats** (The) of Scapin: farce, 1792, *see* OTWAY (T.)

Cheesman (*Maj.* **R. E.)** In unknown Arabia. Foreword by Maj.-Gen. Sir P. Z. Cox. 8°. 1926

Cheesman (T. F.) Illusts. of New Zealand flora. Ed. T. F. C., w. assist. of W. B. Hemsley. Plates by M. Smith. 2v. 4°. Wellington, N.Z. 1914

Cheeswright (R. J.) Hist. essay on the livery companies of London, w. a short hist. of the W. Co. of Cutlers. 8°. [Croydon]. 1881

Cheetham (*Miss* **L.),** *see* ADAMS (D.) Skating; w. ch. for ladies, by L. C., 1890.

Cheever (George Barrell).

God agst. slavery &c. s8°. Cincinnati. *n.d.*

Cheevers (Sarah), *see* EVANS (C.) & S. C. A brief hist. of voyage to Malta &c., 1715.

Cheffins (Charles Frederick). Map of the Eng. & Scotch railways. *folded* 8°. 1848

Maps & sections of the railway communic. f. London to the North. folded 8°. [1850?]

Chefs-d'œuvre. Chefs-d'œuvre des poètes galantes, 1921, see LÉLY (G.), *ed.*

Che-Ka. Че-ка. Материалы по деятельности чрезвычайных комиссий. [*By var. as. Intr. by V. Chernov*]. s8°. Берлин. 1922

,, ,, Tr. (Tche-ka) par E. Pierremont. s8°. 1922

Chekhov (Anton) [TCHEKHOFF].

Вишневый садъ, *see* SBORNIK, Сб. товар. "Знаніе," 2, 1904.

Записные книжки А. П. Ч. Пригот. к печати Е. Н. Коншина. Ред. Л. П. Гроссмана. [Госуд. Акад. Худож. Наук.] 8°. Москва. 1927

Новые письма. под редакц. Б. Л. Модзалевского. s8°. П. 1922

Полное собраніе сочиненій. изд. 2oe. 16t. *b. in 4* (1–12, Разсказы; 13, 14, Пьесы; 15, 16, Островъ Сахалинъ). 8°. С.-П. 1903

Письма к О. Л. Книппер-Чеховой. 8°. Берлин. 1924

Чеховскій юбилейный сборникъ, 1860–1910. 8°. [Москва. 1910]

TRANSLATIONS.

The bishop & o. s. [Tr.] C. Garnett. [Tales, v7]. [repr.] s8°. 1922

Le bourbier, *see* ŒUVRES libres, 73, 1927.

The cherry orchard & o. plays. [Tr.] C. Garnett. s8°. 1923

The cherry orchard—The 3 sisters—Uncle Vanya, *see* SAYLER (O. M.) Moscow Art Theatre ser. of Russ. plays; tr., 1923.

Le choc: nouvelle, *see* ŒUVRES libres, 64, 1926.

The chorus girl & o. s. [Tr.] C. Garnett. [Tales, v12]. [repr.] s8°. 1922

The cook's wedding & o. s. [Tr.] C. Garnett. [Tales, v12]. s8°. 1922

The darling & o. s. [Tr.] C. Garnett w. intr. by E. Garnett. [Tales, v1]. [repr.] s8°. 1925

Une demande en mariage: comédie; tr. A. Chaboseau, *see* REVUE HEBDOMADAIRE. Suppl.: coll. nouv. &c., No. 11, 1922.

The duel & o. s. [Tr.] C. Garnett. [Tales, v2]. [repr.] s8°. 1922

The horse-stealers & o. s. [Tr.] C. Garnett. [Tales, v10]. s8°. 1921

Ivanoff [tr. M. Fell], *see* SAYLER (O. M.) Moscow Art Theatre ser. of Russ. plays, s2, 1924.

Le jour de fête. Tr. D. Roche. [5e éd.] s8°. [1926]

The lady with the dog & o. s. [Tr.] C. Garnett. [Tales, v3]. [repr.] s8°. [1922]

Letters to his family & friends. Tr. by C. Garnett. 8°. 1920

Letters to Olga L. Knipper. Tr. C. Garnett. 8°. 1926

Life & letters of A. Tchekhov. [*By var. wrs.*] Tr. & ed. S. S. Koteliansky & P. Tomlinson. 8°. [1925]

Literary & theatrical remin. [*By var. as.; w.* C.'s Unpubl. works]. Tr. & ed. S. S. Koteliansky. 8°. 1927

Love & o. s. [Tr.] C. Garnett. [Tales, v13]. s8°. 1922

Ma femme. Tr. D. Roche. s8°. [1924]

My life & o. s. Tr. S. S. Koteliansky & G. Cannan. s8°. 1920

Note-books; w. remin. of Tchekhov, by M. Gorky. Tr. S. S. Koteliansky & L. Wolf. s8°. 1921

The party & o. s. [Tr.] C. Garnett. [Tales, v4]. [repr.] s8°. [1925]

Plays. Uncle Vanya—Ivanoff—The sea-gull—The swan song. Tr., w. intr. by M. Fell. [repr.] s8°. 1920

The schoolmaster & o. s. [Tr.] C. Garnett. [Tales, v11]. s8°. 1921

The schoolmistress & o. stories. [Tr.] C. Garnett. [Tales, v9]. s8°. 1920

Sel. tales. Tr. C. Garnett. s8°. [1927]

The shooting party. Tr. A. E. Chamot. s8°. [1926]

Three sisters & o. plays. [Tr.] C. Garnett. s8°. 1923

The wife & o. s. [Tr.] C. Garnett. [Tales, v5]. [2nd impr.] s8°. 1921

The witch & o. s. [Tr.] C. Garnett. [Tales, v6]. [2nd impr.] s8°. 1921

The wood demon. Comedy. Tr. S. S. Koteliansky. s8°. 1926

see BULGAKOV (S. N.) Чеховъ &c., 1905.

,, BUNIN (I.) Памяти Чехова, 1905.

,, GERHARDI (W.) A. C.: a crit. study, 1923.

,, KUPRIN (A.) Памяти Чехова, 1905.

,, NEMIROVICH - DANCHENKO (V. I.) На кладбищахъ, 1921.

,, SKITALETS (—) Памяти Чехова, 1905.

Chekrezi (Constantine Anastasi). Albania past & present. Intr. C. D. Hazen. s8°. N.Y. 1919

Chélard (Raoul). Les armées françaises jugées par les habitants de l'Autriche, 1797–1800–1809. s8°. 1893

Chelbatz (P.), *see* GENET (J.) & P. C. Hist. des Mayas-Quichés, 1927.

Chelli (Maurice). Le drame de Massinger. la8°. Lyon. 1923

Et. sur la collab. de Massinger avec Fletcher & s. groupe. [Univ. de Paris. Bibl. de la Fac. des Lettres, s2, 6]. la8°. 1926

Cheloukhine (Serge). L'Ukraine, la Pologne & la Russie & le droit de libre disposition des peuples. [P2402]. la8°. [1919]

Chelsea. Acts of 30 & 43 Geo. III rel. to district in C. called Hans Town, 1807, *see* HANS TOWN.

Papers illust. of the origin & early hist. of the Royal Hospital at C. Comp. in Sec. Office at that Instit. Ed. G. Hutt]. la8°. 1872

Cheltenham.

*A new guide to C. & its environs. s8°. Cheltenham. [1834 ?]

Chemical Society of London.

List of the officers & fellows, 1920, 1921. 8°. 1920–21

Cheminant (Keith le), *see* LE CHEMINANT (K.)

Chemis (Annie), *see* CHEMIS (L.) Publ. petitions &c., 1892.

Chemis (Louis). [Public petitions A to L Comm. Rep. on petition of Annie Chemis on behalf of her husband, L. C. *b. w.* Chemis (L.) Regina *v.* L. C., 1889]. fol. [Wellington. 1892]

Regina *v.* L. C.: papers rel. to the case of. [Trial for murder, Supreme Court, Wellington. *no tp.*] fol. [Wellington. 1889]

Chemistry in the 20th cent.; [by var. wrs.], 1924, *see* ARMSTRONG (E. F.), *ed.*

Chemnitius (Christian), *see* EBART (J.) Enchiridion in Compend. L. H. cum præf. C. C., 1665.

Chemnitius (Martinus), *see* CHEMNITZ (MARTIN).

Chemnitz (Bogislav Philipp von) [*ps.* HIPPOLITHUS A LAPIDE]. Diss. de ratione status in Imp. nostro Romano-German. s8°. Freistadii. 1647

Chemnitz (Martin) [Kemnicius], *Lutheran Divine.*
De duabus naturis in Christo, &c. Jam denuō recogn. &c. Cum præf. N. Selneccerì. s4°. Lipsiæ. 1580
Examen decret. Conc. Tridentini. [4p. 2p, *n.d.*; p3, 4 Francofurti]. s8°. *n.p.* & Francofurti ad M. 1566–73
„ „ 3p [*p3 has sep. pagin.*] fol. Francofurti ad Moenum. 1707
see Anhalt. Das die 42 Anhalt. Argument wider der Ubiquisten Trewme noch fest stehen, Verantw. uff C. &c., 1584.
„ Braunschweig. *Bedencken d. Theologen zu B. &c. [*signed* M. Kemnitius], 1571.
„ Daneau (L.) Examen libri de duabus in Christo naturis &c. a M. K. conscr., 1581.
„ Gesner (S.) Disput. 1[–17] pro exam. Conc. Trident. conscr. à M. C. & pro 2a parte. disput. 1[–21], 1602–3.
„ Kirchner (T.), N. Selneccer & M. C. Apologia &c. d. christl. Concordien Buchs, 1583.
„ Morlin (J.) Themata de imag. Dei in homine; brevis tract. M.K., 1570.
„ Paiva de Andrade (D. de). De soc. Jesu orig. lib. cont. Kemnicii petulantē audaciā, 1566.
„ Peters (F.) Pro libello M. Ch. &c., 1585.
„ Wigand (J.), M. C. &c. De peccato orig. scripta &c., 1571.

Ch'en (Eugene).
Chinese affairs. [Cent. Asian Soc. P2784]. 8°. [1913]

Chen (Shao-Kwan). The system of taxation in China in the Tsing dynasty, 1644–1911. 8°. N.Y., *Columbia Univ.* 1914

Chen (Ta). Chin. migrations, *see* United States: Labor. Bull. 340, 1923.

Chenevière (Jacques). Jouvence ou la chimère. s8°. 1922

Chénier (Marie André). Œuvres en prose. Préc. d'une notice sur le procès d'A. C. &c. n. éd., annot. &c. par. L. Moland. s8°. *n.d.*
see Estève (E.) Ét. de litt. préromant.: Le sens de la vie dans l'œuvre d'A. C., 1923.

Chennechot (L. E.) Hist. de la vie polit., milit. & privée de Nap. Bonaparte &c., *see* Napoleon I. Recueil de pièces authent., t12, 1825.

Chennell (George) & W. Chalcraft. Trial of G. C. & W. C. for murder of G. Chennell, Sen., & Eliz. Wilson. 8°. Guildford. 1818

Chennevière (Daniel).
Claude Debussy, & son œuvre. s8°. [1918 ?]

Chennevière (Georges). Poèmes, 1911–18. s8°. 1920

Chénon (Émile). Hist. gén. du droit fr. publ. & priv. des orig. à 1815. t1, 8°. 1926
see Batiffol (P.) P. Monceaux, E. C. &c. L'église & le droit de guerre, 2e éd., 1920.

Chenu (Charles Maurice).
Thea, ou le chant de l'alouette. s8°. [1927]

Chéradame (André). La mystific. des peuples alliés. s8°. 1922
The mystific. of the Allied peoples. Tr. J. A. Fitzgerald. s8°. [1923]

Chérau (Gaston).
Le flambeau des Riffault, *see* Œuvres libres, 29, 1923.
Monseigneur voyage. Roman. s8°. 1927
Picolo, *see* Œuvres libres, 56, 1926.
Le vent du destin. s8°. [1926]

Cherbonneau (Auguste). Dict. arabe-franç. (Langue écrite). 2t. [*pagin. cont.*] s8°. 1876
Leçons de lecture arabe. s8°. 1852

Cherchel. Musée de C.: Suppl., par M. Durry, *see* Algérie. Musées, 1924.

Chéréf (Moustapha), *see* Mustapha Chéréf.

Cherel (Albert). La famille française: pages choisies. Le m-â. & 16s. 8°. [1924]

Chérémétef (Boris Pétrovich), *see* Sheremetev.

Cherevanin (—). Организац. вопросъ. Съ пред. Л. Мартова. Изд. Р. Соц. Р. Партіи. [P2715]. s8°. Женева. 1904
Пролетаріатъ въ революціи, *see* Gorn (Vl.), V. Mech. & C. Борьба обществ. силъ, в2, 1907.

Cherfils (*le gén.* **Pierre Joseph Maxime).**
La Guerre de la délivrance. 3t. 8°. 1920–22

Cherikover (V.), *see* Tscherikower (V.)

Cherington (Paul Terry).
Advertising as a business force. 8°. *Pitman.* [1913]

Cherkinsky (M.) [Tcherkinsky]. The Landschaften & th. mortgage credit operat. in Germany (1770–1920). [Internat. Inst. of Agric. P2682]. 8°. Rome. 1922

Chernilo (Capel), *ps.* Queer stories from Russia. s8°. [1892]

Chernishevsky (Nikolai Gerasimovich).
Прологъ пролога. Романъ. 8°. Лейпцигъ. *n.d.*
Что дѣлать? романъ. изд. 3e. 8°. С.–П. 1906
„ „ .... новое изд. 8°. Лейпцигъ. *n.d.*

Chernov (J.) [Tchernoff]. La polit. des nationalités d'ap. la tradition républ. [P2464]. 8°. 1918

Chernov (Viktor) [Tschernow].
Записки социалиста революционера. кн. 1. s8°. Берлин. 1922
Meine Schicksale in Sowjet-Russland; übers. v. E. Hurwicz. 8°. 1921
Mes tribulations en Russie Soviét. Tr. par V. O. s8°. 1921
see Che-Ka. Че-ка: мат. по деятельности грезвычайных комиссий; [*by var. a*[s]*.; intr. by V. C.*], 1922; tr. (Tche-ka) par E. Pierremont, 1922.

Cherrie (George Kruck). Contrib. to ornithology of San Domingo, *see* Field Columbian Mus. Ornith. ser., v1i, 1896.

Cherrington (Ernest Hurst).
Hist. of the Anti-Saloon League. 8°. Westerville, Ohio. 1913

Cherry-Garrard (Apsley). The worst journey in the world: Antarctic, 1910–13. 2v. 8°. [1922]

Chertkov (Vladimir). Наша Революція. Съ послѣсловіемъ Л. Н. Толстого. изд. 2[e]. [P849]. s8°. Москва. 1907
Уход Толстого. 8°. Москва. 1922
Last days of Tolstoy. Tr. N. A. Duddington. s8°. 1922
Letter to Brit. working men. [P2466]. 8°. *n.p.* [1919]
Save Russia. With an appeal to humanity by Paul Birukoff. [P2419]. s8°. 1919
see Gusev (N. N.) & V. C. Толстой и о Толстом, сб. 1–3, 1924–27.

Cherubin de Saint-Joseph [†Cherubinus, *a Sancto Joseph;* Alexander de Boria]. *Bibl. crit. sacræ circa omnes fere Sacrorum librorum difficultates. Opus collect. ab uno ord. Carmel.Discalceat. religioso. 4t. fol.Lovanii, Bruxellis. 1704–6
T3 & 4 bear imprint; Bruxellis. *T2, 3, 4 have a second tp.:* Apparatus Biblicus in tres libros distrib. &c. *Only 4 vols. were printed.*

Cherubinus (Angelus Maria), *ed., see* Bullarium Romanum nov., 4t, 1638.

Chervin (Arthur).
Anthropologie bolivienne. [Mission scient. G. de Créqui Montfort &c.] 3t. la8°. 1907–08
1, Ethnologie, demographie, photographie métrique. 2, Anthropométrie. 3, Craniologie.

Cheshire. Cal. of persons commem. in monument. inscr[s]. &c., 1922, *see* Lancashire.

Chesney (Alexander). The journal of A. C., a S. Carolina loyalist. Ed. E. A. Jones. Intr. by W. H. Siebert. [Ohio State Univ., Bull. 26, iv.] 8°. [Columbus. 1921]

Chesney (*Gen.* **Francis Rawdon),** *1789–1872.* Exped. for survey of Euphrates & Tigris, 1835–37. [*la. paper*]. v1, 2. [*no more publ.*] 4°. 1850
„ „ ....Maps. fol. 1850
[Report of the navig. of the Euphrates, submitted to Gov. by F. R. C.] [*no tp.*] fol. [1833]
The Russo-Turkish campaigns of 1828–9 &c. 3rd ed. s8°. 1854

Chesney (*Sir* **George Tomkyns).**
*The Battle of Dorking. Remin. [P2584]. s8°. 1871

Chess. *An easy intr. to the game of c., incl. Philidor's analysis; added: Caissa, by Sir W. Jones, Morals of c. by Dr. Franklin &c. n. ed. rev. s8°. 1820

Chester. Calendar of Co. Court, City Court & Eyre Rolls of C., 1259–97, w. inquest of milit. service, 1288. Ed., w. intr. by R. Stewart-Brown. [Chetham Soc., N.S., v84]. 8°. 1925
Index to wills & administrations (incl. "Infra" wills), in Probate Registry, C., 1811–20. Ed. W. A. Tonge. [Record Soc. for Lancs. & Cheshire, 78]. p1, A–L. 8°. 1928
Marriage licences gr. within the Archdeaconry of C. Ed. W. F. Irvine. [Record Soc. for Lancs. & C., v77]. v8, 1691–1700. 8°. 1924
*The stranger's companion in C. Incl. a descr. of Eaton Hall. [*w. sep. tp. & pagin.*] 5th ed. s8°. *n.d.*

Chester (Samuel Beach). Life of Venizelos. 8°. 1921

Chesterfield (Philip Dormer Stanhope, *4th earl of***).** Characters of eminent personages of h. own time. 2nd ed. s8°. 1777
Letters to Ld. Huntingdon. Intr. by A. F. Steuart. 8°. 1923
Letters; w. the Characters. Ed., w. intr. &c. by J. Bradshaw. [repr.] 3v. 8°. [1926]
Lettres à son fils P. Stanhope. Tr., rev., corr. &c. par A. Renée. 2t. s8°. 1842
see Coxon (R.) C. & h. critics, 1925.
„ Davies (T.) Char. of George I &c. [*by C.*] reviewed, 1777.
„ Jorissen (Th.) Hist. studiën, v5, Lord C. en de Rep. d. Nederlanden, 1912.

Chesterton (*Mrs.* **Cecil).**
In darkest London. [n. & rev. ed.] s8°. [1926]

Chesterton (George Laval).
Revelations of prison life. 3rd ed. rev. s8°. 1857

Chesterton (Gilbert Keith).
The ballad of St. Barbara & o. verses. 8°. [1922]
The defendant. [repr.] s8°. [1918]
The everlasting man. 8°. 1925
„ „ ....[4th ed.] 8°. [1926]
Eugenics & other evils. 8°. 1922
The incredulity of Father Brown. s8°. [1926]
Magic. Fantastic comedy. [New Adelphi Lib.] s8°. 1926
The man who knew too much & o. s. [repr.] s8°. [1922]
The new Jerusalem. 8°. [1920]
The outline of sanity. s8°. [1926]
The return of Don Quixote. s8°. [1927]
R. L. Stevenson. s8°. [1927]
St. Francis of Assisi. s8°. [1923]
The secret of Father Brown. s8°. [1927]
The superstition of divorce. s8°. 1920
The Victorian age in lit. [Home Univ. lib.] s8°. [1920]
What I saw in America. 8°. 1922
„ „ ....[repr.] 8°. 1923
William Cobbett. s8°. [1925]
„ „ [essay], *see* ROY. SOC. OF LIT. Essays, N.S., v3, 1923.
see BRAYBROOK (P.) C., 1922.
„ PEACE WITH IRELAND COUNCIL. Leaflets, by G. K. C., &c., 1920–21.

Chestov (Léon), *see* SHESTOV (L.)

Chetham Library, *Manchester.* Bibliotheca Ch., notitia, 3 indic. comprehensa. [*3 pagin*[s].] 8°. Mancunii. 1826

Chetham miscellanies.
new ser., v4. [Chetham Soc., N.S., 80]. s4°. [M'ter.] 1921
4, Dunkenhalgh deeds, c. 1200–1600; ed. G. A. Stocks & J. Tait. Extracts f. Manchester churchwardens' acc[s]., 1664–1710; ed. E. Broxap. New court bk. of Manor of Bramhall, 1632–57; ed. H. W. Clemesha. Latin verses &c. by scholars of Manchester Grammar Sch., 1640 & 1750–1800; ed. A. A. Mumford. Records of some Salford portmoots in 16th c.; ed. J. Tait.

Chetham Society. Remains hist. & lit. conn. w. the Palatine Co. of Lancaster & Chester. N. Ser. v79–86. 8°. M'ter. 1920–27
see CHESTER. Cal. of Co. Court, City Court & Eyre Rolls, 1259–97; ed. R. Stewart-Brown, 1925. [N.S., 84.]
„ CHETHAM MISCELLANIES. New ser., v4, 1921. [80.]
„ EKWALL (E.) Place-names of Lancashire, 1922. [N.S., 81.]
„ SAINT WERBURGH, *abbey of.* Chartulary of Abbey of St. W.; ed. &c. J. Tait, p1, 1920. [N.S., 79, 82.]
see SALFORD. Taxation in S. Hundred, 1524–1802; ed. &c. J. Tait, 1924. [N.S., 83.]
„ TRAPPES-LOMAX (R.) Hist. of Clayton-le-Moors, 1926. [N.S., 85.]
„ TUPLING (G. H.) Econ. hist. of Rossendale, 1927. [N.S., 86.]

Chettle (Henry). Kind-hartes dreame, 1592—Will. Kemp, Nine daies wonder, 1600. [Bodley Head 4tos; ed. G. B. Harrison]. s8°. [1923]

Chevalier (*le gén.*) Les bois d'œuvre pend. la Guerre. [La Guerre & l'indust. fr. C.E. for Internat. Peace]. 8°. [1927]

Chevalier (Cyr Ulysse Joseph). Repertorium hymnolog. Cat des chants &c. en usage dans l'Eglise lat. dep. les orig. [Extr. des Analecta Bolland.] t4–6. 8°. Louvain & Brux. 1912–21
4, Suppl. 2[a]. (34828–42060). 5, Addenda & corrigenda. 6, Préface—Tables.
see ALBANÈS (J. H.) Gallia christ. noviss., complétée &c. par U. C., t1–7, 1899–1920.
„ BAYEUX. Ordinaire & coutumier de l'église de B. (13e s.); publ. C., 1902.
„ BOURG-LÈS-VALENCE. Cartul. du prieuré de St.-Pierre; publ. C., 1875.
„ DAUPHINÉ. Choix de doc[s].; publ. &c. C., 1874.
„ MONASTIER. Cartul. de l'abbaye de St.-Chaffre du M.; publ. C., 1884.
„ VIENNE. Chartes de St.-Maurice de V., de l'abbaye de Léoncel &c.; suppl. aux recueils impr. publ. par C., 1912.

Chevalier (J.), *comedian.* La désolation des filoux (1661)—Les amours de Calotin, *see* FOURNEL (V.) Contemp[s]. de Molière, t3, 1875.

Chevalier (Jacques). Essai sur la formation de la nationalité & les réveils relig. au pays de Galles à la fin du 6e s. 8°. Lyon. 1923
Pascal. [7e éd.] 8°. [1923]

Chevalier (Julien). L'inversion sexuelle. Préf. du dr. A. Lacassagne. s8°. Lyon. 1893

Chevalier (Marcel). Andorra. la8°. Chambéry. 1925

Chevalley (Abel).
Le roman anglais de notre temps. s8°. Londres. 1921
Thomas Deloney. Le roman des métiers au temps de Shakespeare. 2e éd. s8°. 1926

Chevalley (Heinrich). Arthur Nikisch, Leben u. Wirken. In Beitr. v. F. Pfohl &c. Hrsg. H. C. 8°. 1922

Chevallier (*le chanoine* **Gustave**). Mgr. Sonnois, Archevêque de Cambrai. Sa vie—s. œuvre. [Lettre-préf. de Mgr. Chollet]. 8°. Cambrai. 1920

Chevillet (Charles), *called* "*Champmeslé.*" Les grisettes: comédie (1671), *see* FOURNEL (V.) Contemp[s]. de Molière, t2, 1866.

Chevreul (Michel Eugene). Des couleurs & de leurs applic. aux arts indust. à l'aide des cercles chromat. la4°. 1864

Chevrier (François Antoine de). Mém[s]. pour servir à l'hist. des hommes illust. de Lorraine, avec une réfut. de la Bibl. lorraine de Dom Calmet. 2t. s8°. Brux. 1754

Chevrillon (André). Disc. pour la récept. de A. C. [*on* E. Lamy. Rép. de P. de la Gorce. Acad. Fr., 21 avr. 1921. P2869]. 4°. 1921
Marrakech dans les palmes. s8°. [1919]
Trois études de litt. angl. La poésie de R. Kipling—J. Galsworthy—Shakespeare et l'âme anglaise. s8°. [1921]
3 studies in Eng. lit. Kipling, Galsworthy, Shakespeare. Tr. F. Simmonds. s8°. [1923]

Chew (Beverly).
Library. Sold, Dec. 1924, Anderson Gall. pl. 8°. N.Y. 1924

Chew (Samuel Claggett). Byron in England, h. fame & after-fame. [With bibliog.] 8°. 1924
Thomas Hardy, poet & novelist. s8°. Bryn Mawr, *Penn.* 1921

Cheylud (Emile). Les anc. corporations médecins, chirurgiens & apothicaires de Murat, 1630–1776, d'ap. des doc[s]. authent. 8°. 1896

Cheyne (George). An essay of health & long life. s8°. 1724

Cheyne (*Sir* **William Watson).**
Lister & h. achievement. [Lister mem. lect.] 8°. 1925

Cheynel (Francis), *see* HAMMOND (H.) *A copy of some papers past at Oxford betw. [H.] & Mr. Ch., 1647.

Cheyney (Edward Potts). A hist. of England f. the defeat of the Armada to death of Eliz. v2. 8°. 1926

Chezy (Antoine Léonard de), *see* VALMĪKI. Yajnadattabada, ou la mort d'Yadjnadatta &c.; *ed.* A. L. de C. *Sanskr., Fr. & Lat.*, 1826.

Chhatrapati, *see* KOLHAPUR (*Shri* S. C., *Mah. of*).

Chiabrera (Gabriello). Poemetti. 8°. Fiorenza. 1598
see NERI (F.) C. e. la Pleiade franç., 1920.

Chiappelli (Alberto). Maestri e scuole in Pistoia fino al sec. 14, *see* ARCHIVIO STORICO ITAL. Anno 78, v1, 1920.

Chiappelli (Alessandro), *see* DANTE ALIGHIERI. Lectura D.: c. 31 del Paradiso letto da A. C., 1904.

Chiappelli (Luigi). L'età longobardo e Pistoia, *see* ARCHIVIO STOR. ITAL. Anno 79, v1, 1921.
La formaz. storica d. comune cittadino in Italia (Territorio Lombardo-Tosco), p2, *see* ARCHIVIO STOR. ITAL., Anno 85, v1, 1927.
Una lettera mercantile del 1330, e la crisi d. commercio ital., *see* ARCHIVIO STOR. ITAL. Anno 82, v1, 1924.

Chiapusso (Felice). Di uno statuto concesso dal duca Ludovico di Savoia a. Susa 1462, *see* REGIA DEP. DI STORIA PATRIA. Misc., t19, 1880.
Relaz. ant. d. stato di Piemonte e Savoia (frammenti), 1571; *ed.* F. C., *see* REGIA DEP. Misc., t28, 1890.

Chiara (Stanislao de). La mia Calabria. 8°. Milano. 1920

Chiavola (Clementina). Della vita e dell' opera di Tito Calpurnio Siculo. s8°. Ragusa. 1921

Chicago. UNIVERSITY OF C.
Decennial Publications. s2. v7. 8°. Chicago. 1903
see BRECKINRIDGE (S. P.) Legal tender, Eng. & Amer. monetary hist., 1903. [sII, 7.]
Manly anniv. studies, 1923, *see* MANLY (J. M.)
Oriental Institute Publications. v1, 2. 4°. Chicago. 1924
see BREASTED (J. H.) Oriental forerunners of Byzantine painting, 1924. [1.]
„ LUCKENBILL (D. D.) Annals of Sennacherib, 1924. [2.]
War papers. 1–4, 6, 7. 8°. Chicago. 1918
see BRAMHALL (F. D.) Democracy &c., 1918. [3.]
„ JUDD (C. H.) Democracy & Amer. schools, 1918. [7.]
„ JUDSON (H. P.) Threat of German world-politics, 1918. [1.]
„ MACLAUGHLIN (A. C.) 16 causes of war, 1918. [4.]
„ READ (C.) Eng. & Amer., 1918. [6.]
„ SMALL (A. W.) Americans & the world-crisis, 1918. [2.]

Chicago Commission of Race Relations. The negro in Chicago: st. of race rel[s]. & a race riot. 8°. Chicago. [1922]

Chicago Daily news (The) almanac & year-book, 1926. Ed. J. Langland. 42nd year. s8°. [Chicago. 1926]

Chicherin (Boris Nikolaevich). Опыты по ист. русс. права. Изд. К. Солдатенкова и Н. Щепкина. 8°. Москва. 1858

Chicherin (Georgy V.) [TSCHITSCHERIN].
Der Friede v. Versailles. [P2408]. 8°. Hamburg. [1919]
Die internat. Politik zweier Internat. [Hrsg. v. Westeurop. Sekret. d. Kommun. Internationale. P2521]. 8°. Hamburg. [1920]

Chicherin (Georgy V.) [TSCHITSCHERIN] [*continued*].
Rede auf der Konf. in Genua, am 10. Apr. 1922, *see* KAMPF (DER) in Genua, 1922.
Zwei Jahre auswärt. Polit. Sowjet-Russ. 8°. 1920
see RUSSIA: *Soviet Rep.* R. plan of the League of nations, peace proposals sent by C. to Pres. Wilson, 1918.

Chichester-Constable (*Lt.-Col.* Raleigh). Cat. of early Eng. portraits &c. prop. of C.-C. &c. Sold by Christie &c. July 8, 1927. [Illust. P2873]. 8°. 1927

*__Chien (Le)__ de Boulogne, ou l'amant fidelle, 1668, *see* TORCHE (*l'abbé* DE).

Chiera (Edward). Lists of personal names f. the Temple school of Nippur. [Univ. of Penn., Univ. Mus., Babylon. sect., v11iii]. [v3]. la8°. Phila. 1919
3, Lists of Sumerian personal names.

Chiesa (La). *La C. ducale di S. Marco, 2t, 1753, *see* MESCHINELLO (G.)

Chiesa (Francesco). Poesie e prose. s8°. Zurigo. [1920]
Tempo di marzo. Romanzo. s8°. Milano. 1925

Chiesa (*il conte* Ludovico della). Dell' hist. di Piemonte, libri 3, sin' all' anno 1585, con la orig. d. casa di Savoia &c. 8°. Torino. 1608

Chifflet (Philippe), *see* TRENT, *Council of.* Canones & decreta; P. C. præf., 1677.

Chiggiato (Giovanni).
All' amata, tre canzoni. [N. 134]. 8°. Bologna. 1902
La dolce stagione. [*Poems*]. s8°. Torino. 1901

Chigi (*card.* Flairo) [CHISI], *see* DUPEYRAT (G.) Traitté de l'orig. des cardinaux; avec 2 Traittez curieux des legats [*Card. C. &c.*], 1665.

Chigi-Albani (*il princ.* Agostino), *1771–1855, see* CUGNONI (G.) Notizia d. vita, 1893.

Chignell (Arthur Kent).
An outpost in Papua. Pref. by Abp. of Brisbane. 8°. 1911

Chijs (Jacob Anne van der) [CHYS]. Gesch. d. stichting v. de Vereen. O. I. Compagnie. 2e verm. dr. 8°. Leyden. 1857
Kapitein Jonker, 1630?–1689, *see* TIJDSCHRIFT VOOR IND. TAAL &c., d28, 30, 1883–85.
Philip Carteret in Ned.-Indië, 1767–68, *see* TIJDSCHRIFT VOOR IND. TAAL &c., d34, 1891.

Chikamatsu Monzaémon, *ps.* [*i.e.* SUGINOMORI NOBUMORI].
Masterpieces of Chikamatsu, the Jap. Shakespeare. Tr. w. intr. by Asataro Miyamori. Rev. by R. Nichols. la8°. 1926

Chilcot (William). A pract. treatise conc. evil thoughts. s8°. Exon. 1698

Chilcott (Catherine M.), *see* STREETER (B. H.) Adventure; by B. H. S., C. M. C. &c., 1927.

Chilcott (J.), *printer.* Chilcott's strangers' guide to Bristol, Clifton, & the Hotwells. s8°. Bristol. [c. 1840]

*__Child__ (The) of time &c., 1925, *see* JACKSON (W. S.)

Child (Charles Manning).
Individuality in organisms. s8°. Chicago. [1915]

Child (Harold).
Hugh the Drover. Ballad opera. [P2785]. 8°. *n.d.*

Child (James Mark), *see* LEIBNITZ (G. W., *Frhr.* v.) Early mathemat. MSS. of L.; tr., w. notes by J. M. C., 1920.

Child (Richard Washburn).
A diplomat looks at Europe. 8°. [1926]

Childe (Charles Plumley).
The control of a scourge; or how cancer is curable. 8°. [1907]

Childe (V. Gordon). The Aryans: st. of Indo-Europ. origins. [Hist. of civiliz.] 8°. 1926
The dawn of European civilization. [Hist. of Civiliz.] 8°. 1925
How labour governs: st. of workers' represent. in Australia. 8°. 1923

Childe-Pemberton (William S.) The Earl Bishop: life of F. Hervey, Bp. of Derry, Earl of Bristol. 2v. 8°. [1925]

Childers (Erskine). Military rule in Ireland. [Repr. f. The Daily News]. [P2487]. s8°. D. 1920

Childers (Hugh). Romantic trials of 3 centuries. 8°. 1913

Childs (James Bennett). Sixteenth-cent. books: bibliog. of lit. descr. bks. pr. 1501–1601. [*Extr. f.* Bibliog. Soc. of Amer. Papers, v17]. 8°. Chicago, Ill. [1925]

Chilesotti (Oscar). I nostri maestri del passato. Note biog. sui più gr. musicisti ital. da Palestrina a Bellini. 8°. Milano. 1882
see BASSANO. Matricola d. congreg. di M. V. d. Pace &c. in B., 1450; ed. O. C., 1887.

Chilhaud de La Rigaudie (Pierre). Opinion s. le projet de loi rel. à la restit. aux Emigrés de leurs biens. [Chambre des députés, 25 oct. 1814]. [P2772]. [*no tp.*] 8°. *n.d.*

Chillingworth (Rudolf). Cat. de la Coll. C. Tableaux anc., 13e–17e s., vente, 5 sept. 1922. 4°. Lucerne. [1922]

Chillingworth (William). Mr. C.'s bk. called The relig. of Protestants a safe way to salvation, made more gen. useful &c. [*by* J. Patrick]. w. add. of pieces never bef. pr. [*w. sep. tp.*] s4°. 1687

Chimay (Emilie L. M. F. Pellapra, *pcsse.* de), *ctsse. de Brigode, 1808–71.* A daughter of Napoleon: mems. of E. de P. Intr. by Pcss. Bibesco. Pref. by F. Masson. Tr. K. Miller. s8°. N.Y. 1922
Une fille de Napoléon: mémoires de E. de P. Publ. avec intr. par la pcsse. Bibesco. Préf. par F. Masson. 8°. 1921

Chimirri (B.) & A. Frangipane.
Mattia Preti, detto Il Cavalier Calabrese. 8°. Milano. 1914

China.
China Sea pilot, 5v & Suppls. 6, 7, 1912–22, *see* ADMIRALTY.
*China's position in internat. finance. [P2385; 2419]. s8°. [1919]
Consortium (The): offic. text of the four-power agreement for a loan to C. & rel. docs., 1921, *see* CONSORTIUM.
Treaties &c. w. & conc. C. 1894–1919, 2v, 1921, *see* MACMURRAY (J. V. A.)

China Medical Board. Report, 1919, *see* ROCKEFELLER FOUNDATION.

China Year Book (The), 1921–22, 1923, 1924–25, 1926–27. Ed. H. G. W. Woodhead. 8°. [1921–26]

Chine. *Etat actuel de l'art & de la science militaire à la Chine; tiré des livres milit. des Chinois. [*By* St. Maurice de St.-Leu & marq. J. F. M. Chastenet de Puységur, *rev. by* cte. F. F. d'Espie]. s8°. Londres. 1773
*Hist. des deux conquerans tartares qui ont subjugué la C. &c., par le R. P. J. D. . . ., 1690, *see* ORLÉANS (*le père* P. J. D').

Chinensis. *Regni Chin. descr. ex variis auct., 1639, *see* TRIGAULT (N.)

Chinese.
Ch. furniture: examples f. coll. in France, 1922, *see* CESCINSKY (H.)
*Ch. manifesto on the Shantung question. [P2487]. s8°. [1920]
*Ch. manual. Recueil de phrases chin. [Ed. w. Eng. tr. by H. baron Stanley]. fol. 1854
Ch. sculpture, 4v, 1925, *see* SIRÉN (O.)
Gems of Ch. verse, 1919, *see* FLETCHER (W. J. B.)
Mod. Ch. hist.: sel. readings, 1923, *see* MACNAIR (H. F.), *ed.*
*Remin. of a Ch. official, 1922, *see* REMINISCENCES.
Some problems of the Ch. Republic. Papers, repr. f. "Journal of C. As. Soc." [by var. a.] 8°. [1927]
*The world peace & Ch. tariff autonomy, 1919, *see* WORLD.

Chinese & Japanese Repository (The), of facts &c. rel. to East. Asia. Ed. J. Summers. July 1863–Dec. 1865. 3v [in 2.] 8°. 1863–5

Chinese Eastern Railway, *see* MANCHURIA. North M. & the Chin. East. Railway, 1924.

Chinesische Schattenspiele; üb. W. Grube, 1915, *see* LAUFER (B.), *ed.*

Ching-Wai (Wong), *see* WONG CHING-WAI.

Chini (Giuseppe). Il Palazzo Munic. di Rovereto. [Nozze Piscel-Sant' Ambrogio. N124]. 8°. Rovereto. 1897

Chinois [CHINOISE; CHINOISES]. Chrestomathie ch., 1833, *see* SOCIÉTÉ ASIATIQUE.
*Lettre à M.** touch. les honneurs que les Ch. rendent au philos. Confucius & à leurs ancêtres. [P2559]. s8°. *n.p.* 1700
Sentiment d'un jurisconsulte sur la contest. d'entre les miss. étr. & les P. P. Jésuites touch. les cérémonies ch., 1700, *see* JESUITS.

Chiocchetti (O. F. M.)
La filosofia di Giovanni Gentile. s8°. Milano. 1922

Chion (—), *ministre, see* DESMARETS (D.) Tableau des papes de Rome; *publ.* C., 1714.

Chipman, *Family of, see* MORSE (W. I.), *ed.* Genealogiæ or data, 1925.

Chipman (Kenneth G.), *see* CANADIAN ARCTIC EXPED. Rep., v11, B, Geogr. notes, by K. G. C. &c., 1924.

Chippendale (Thomas), *of St. Martin's Lane.*
The gentleman & cabinet-maker's directory. 3rd ed. fol. 1762
see BLAKE (J. P.) &c. Little bks. on old furniture, v3, C. & h. school, 1919.
,, BRACKETT (O.) T. C., 1924.
,, LAYTON (E. J.) T. C.: rev. of h. life & origin, 1928.

Chippenham. Records of C., 1554–1889. [*Ed.*] by F. H. Goldney. la8°. [*f.p.c.*] 1889

Chipperfield (Robert Orr), *ps., see* OSTRANDER (I. E.)

Chiquito de Cambo, *ps.* [*i.e.* B. J. APESTEGUY], **G. Bénac & E. Vogt.** La pelote basque. [P2756]. s8°. [1924]
Chirico (Giorgio de), *see* TERNOVETZ (B.) G. De C., 1928.
Chirikov (Evgeny Nikolaevich). На порукахъ-Иванъ Мироны чъ, *see* SBORNIK. Сб. товар. "Знанiе" 2, 5, 1904–5.
Русскiй народъ подъ судомъ Максима Горькаго. [P2398]. 8°. [Москва]. 1917
Chirol (*Sir* Valentine).
The Egyptian problem. [repr.] 8°. 1921
Fifty years in a changing world. 8°. [1927]
India. [The mod. world]. 8°. 1926
" " ....[2nd impr.] 8°. 1926
" " ....[3rd impr.] 8°. 1926
India old & new. 8°. 1921
The Occident & the Orient. Lect[s]., Harris Found., 1924. s8°. Chicago. [1924]
see EVERSLEY (G. J. S.-L.) & *Sir* V. C. Turkish Emp., 1914–22, 1923; 1914–24, 1924.
Chisenhale (Edward). Catholike history. Occas. by a book by T. Vane intit. The lost sheep returned home. s8°. 1653
Chisholm (Archibald). Labour's Magna Charta. St. of the labour clauses of the Peace Treaty &c. 8°. 1921
Chisholm (George Goudie). Hdbk. of commercial geography, n. ed., w. maps & diagrams. 8°. 1922
Chishull (Edmund). A charge of heresy, agst. Mr. Dodwel's late disc. conc. the mortality of the soul. 8°. 1706
Chisi (*card.* **Flavio),** *see* CHIGI (*card.* F.)
***Chit chat**: farce, 1792, *see* WALWYN (B.)
Chiti (Alfredo). T. Baldinotti poeta pistoiese. Vita e rime. la8°. Pistoia. 1898
Chitor. *Chitor & the Mewar family, 1881, *see* STRATTON (J. P.)
Chittenden (Frederick James). The garden doctor. Plants in health & disease. s8°. 1920
Chittenden (Lucius Eugene).
Recoll. of Pres. Lincoln & h. admin. 8°. N.Y. [1891]
Chittick (V. L. O.)
T. C. Haliburton ("Sam Slick"). 8°. N.Y. 1924
Chiuso (Tomaso). Saggio di ant. doc. dell' Archivio Arcivesc. di Torino; pubbl. T. C., *see* REGIA DEP. DI STORIA PATRIA. Misc., t18, 1879.
Chkonia (Ilia). Грузинскiй глоссарiй [*in Georgian*], *see* MARR (N. YA.), *ed.* Матерiалы по яфет. яз., 1, 1910.
Chladenius (Martinus) [CHLADNI (M.)] Instit. theol. moralis. Cum præf. G. Wernsdorfii. Ed. altera. s8°. Vitebergæ. 1789
Jubilæa [Luther]. [P484]. s4°. [Vitebergæ. 1718]
Chlebik (Franx). Die Philos. d. Bewussten u. d. Wahrheit d. Unbewussten nach Hegel u. C. L. Michelet. [*b. w.* Fechner (G. T.) Tagesansicht &c., 1879]. 8°. 1870
Chłędowski (Kasimierz). Siena. 2B [*in 1v.*] la8°. 1918
Chmel (Josef). Latein.-Böhm.-Deutsches Wörterbuch nach I. J. G. Schellers etym. Grundlage. Verm. & hrsg. v. J. C. 8°. Königingräz. 1830
Choate (Joseph Hodges), *see* MARTIN (E. S.) Life of J. H. C., chiefly f. h. letters, incl. h. own story of h. boyhood &c., 2v, 1920.
Choate (Rufus). Works. With mem. by S. G. Brown. 2v. 8°. Boston [Mass.] 1862
Chocarne (Bernard). Inner life of Lacordaire. Tr.; pref. by [J. D.] Aylward. s8°. 1883
Choderlos de La Clos (P. A. F.)
*Les liaisons dangereuses. s8°. [1894]
" " ....s8°. [1923]
see PALACHE (J. G.) Four novelists &c.; Crébillon, L. &c., 1926.
Chodowiecki (Daniel M.), *see* FREYTAG (G.) Bilder, B5 (Kupferstiche a. d. "Göttinger Taschen Cal. 1778–83," *& o. repr.*), 1925.
Chodzko (Jacob Leonard), *see* MALTE-BRUN (C.) Tableau de la Pologne; augm. &c. par L. C., 1830.
Choeroboscus (Georgius), *see* THEODOSIUS, *of Alexandria.* Canones, G. Ch. Scholia &c., rec. A. Hilgard, 1894.
***Choice (A)** coll. of hymns, 1776, *see* HULL (C.)
Choisy (*l'abbé* **François Timoleon de).** *Journal du voyage de Siam fait en 1685 & 1686 par M. L. D. C. [*a. c. wanting tp., b. w. a. c. of* Tachard (G.) Voyage de Siam, 1688]. s8°. [Amsterdam. 1687]
Le livre du boudoir. Mém. de l'abbé de C., avec notice & bibliog. par le Chev. de Percefleur. s8°. 1920
Choisy (Gaston). La revanche d'Adam. s8°. 1922
Choisy (Louis Frédéric).
Sainte Beuve: l'homme et le poète. s8°. 1921
Choler (Adolphe), *see* SIRAUDIN (P.), A. DELACOUR & A. C. Après le bal, 1864.
Cholet (Paul François Etienne), *see* BAIGNE. Cartul. de l'abbaye de St.-Etienne de B.; [publ. &c.] par C., 1867.
Cholmeley (Robert F.) Canned literature. [P2493]. 8°. [1906]
Cholmondeley (*Miss* Mary).
The romance of his life & other romances. s8°. 1921
Cholnoky (Eugen v.) Resultate d. wiss. Erforschung. d. Balatonsee, B1, T2, Hydrographie v. E. v. C., 1920, *see* BALATON, *lake.*
Chong Su See, *see* SEE (C. S.)
Chope (R. Pearse). New light on Sir R. Grenville. [Repr. f. Devon Assoc. Trans., 1917]. [2p *in* 1v.] 8°. Plymouth. 1917
Chopin (Frédéric François).
see POURTALÈS (G. DE). C., 1927.
,, STRACHEY (M.) The nightingale (A life of C.), [*fiction*], 1925.
Choque (Pierre), *ps.*, *see* BRETAIGNE, *héraut d'Armes.*
Chorley (Herbert). Cleeves End. s8°. [1908]
Chosen, *see* COREA.
Chosrow, *see* KHOSROV.
Chossat (Edouard de). Classific. des caractères cunéiformes. [*Lithogr. b. w. h.* Répertoire, 1879]. 4°. Lyon. 1878
Répertoire assyrien. Trad. & lecture. 4°. Lyon. 1879
Chotkowski (Władysław). Ueber d. russ. Jubiläumsfeier d. Vernichtung d. griech.-unirten Kirche in Lithauen u. Weissruthenien, 1839. [*Extr. f.* Histor.-polit. Blätter, B104, 1887]. 8°. [München. 1887]
Chotzner (Joseph), *Ph.D.* Hebrew satire. s8°. 1911
Choulant (*Dr.* Ludwig). Graph. Incunabeln f. Naturgesch. u. Medicin. Nebst Nachtr. zu d. Verfassers Gesch. u. Bibl. d. anat. Abbildung, 1852. [*repr. of Leipzig 1858 ed.*] 8°. München. 1924
Choulguine (Alexandre).
Les problèmes de l'Ukraine. [P2401]. 8°. 1919
Chounavel (C.) A grammar of the Sinhalese Lang. 8°. Colombo. 1886
Chouvigny (Claude de), *baron de Blot l'Eglise; 1605–55* [CHAUVIGNY], *see* BLOT (C. DE C., *baron* DE).
Chowanetz (Joseph). Das Leben u. Wirken d. grossen heil. Väter, Lehrer u. Schriftsteller &c. s8°. Neisse. 1855
Chree (Charles). Terrestrial magnetism, *see* BRIT. ANTARCTIC EXPED., 1910–13, 1919–23.
see CAVENDISH (*Hon.* H.) Sci. papers, v2, w. contrib[s]. by C. C. &c., 1921.
Chrestomathie chinoise; publ. aux frais de la Soc. asiat., *see* SOCIÉTÉ ASIATIQUE, 1833.
Chrismann (Philippus Nerius). Regula fidei catholicæ & coll. dogmatum credendorum, *see* MIGNE (J. P.), *ed.* Theol. cursus, t6, 1862.
Christ. [*For biograph. works &c. see* JESUS CHRIST]. Christ & Satan: old Eng. poem. Ed. w. intr., notes &c., by M. D. Clubb. [Yale St. in Eng., 70]. 8°. New Haven. 1925
Medit. on the life & passion of C., from Brit. Mus. Add. MS. 11307. [Ed.] C. D'Evelyn. [E.E.T.S., 158]. 8°. 1921
A stanzaic life of C. Comp. f. Higden's Polychronicon & the Legenda Aurea. Ed. F. A. Foster. [E.E.T.S., 166]. 8°. 1926
Christaã. *Nova cartilha da doutrina C. &c., 1733, *see* NOVA.
Christenius (Johannes), *see* DAMCKE (B.) & J. C. Leben d. J. F. Gronovii, 1723.
Christenliche, *see* CHRISTLICHE.
Christensen (Arthur).
Works in KONGELIGT DAN. VID. SELSK. Hist.-fil. Med.
Contes persans en langue pop., publ. avec tr. & notes, 1917–18. [1.]
Le règne du roi Kawādh I & le communisme mazdakite, 1924–25. [9.]
Smeden Kāvāh og det gamle persiske rigsbanner, 1918–19. [2.]
Textes ossètes, rec. par A. C., 1921–22. [6.]
Xavāṣṣ-i-āyāt: ms. persan trait. la magie des versets du Coran [*by* 'Abd Ullāh ibn Muḥammed ibn Husan], 1920–21. [3.]
see BENEDICTSEN (A. M.) & A. C. Dialectes d'Awromān &c., 1921.
Christensen (Carl). Monogr. of the genus Dryopteris, p2, *see* KONG. DANSKE VIDENSK. SELSKAB. Skrifter, Række 8, B6, 1920.
Christensen (L. P.) Grænsebogen. [*By var. wr[s].*] Red. af L. P. C. s8°. Flensborg. 1923
Christian.
*C. doctrine (*in Georgian*), 1741; 2nd ed. 1797, *see* TLUKAANTI (D.)
C. (A) library, 50v, 1749–55, *see* WESLEY (J.)

Christian [*continued*].
*C. moderator, 4th ed., 1652, *see* AUSTIN (J.)
*C.'s (The) memorandum-book or, family instructor. By a clergyman of London. s8°. 1755
*Of C. communion, 3p, 1693, *see* KETTLEWELL (J.)
Christian, The, *newspaper.* *The Christian portrait gallery. With biographic sketches. 4°. [1889]
Christian Evidence Society, *see* NOLLOTH (C. F.) The Xtn. faith, 1922.
Christian, *margrave of Brandenburg, 1581–1655, see* ELLROD (J. M.) De C. marchione B., 1694.
Christian V, *king of Denmark, see* PREBENSEN (N.) & HJ. SMITH. Forarb. til C. V norske Lov af 15 Apr. 1687, 1887.
Christian VII, *king of Denmark & Norway, see* NORS (P.) The court of C. VII, 1928.
Christian VIII, *king of Denmark.* Dagbok, fra h. ophold i Norge i 1814. Utg. som tillæg til "Riksforsaml. Forhandlinger" efter d. franske orig.-hs. av A. Olafsen og oversat til Norsk av J. Raabe. la8°. 1914
see GIESSING (H. P.) Kong C.'s Regjeringshist., 1852.
Christian IX, *king of Denmark.*
see BARFOD (H. P. B.) H.M. Kong C., 2B, 1888–1906.
,, CHRISTIAN X, *of Denmark.* Kong C. IX's Forældre, 1918.
,, THORSØE (A.) Fra Kong K.'s yngre dage, 1913.
,, —— Kong C. IX, 1906.
Christian X, *of Denmark.* H.M. Kong Christian IX's Forældre Hertug Vilhelm af Glyksborg og Louise, født Prinsesse af Hessen. Udg. paa 100 aarsdagen for Kong C. IX's Fødsel. 8°. 1918
Christian, *von Jerusalem, ps.* *Calvin. Abzug vom Necker u. Rhein, nach den Niderlandt. [P2438]. s4°. *n.p.* 1628
Christian, *abp. of Mainz, 1167–83, see* TORELLI (P.) Patti d. liberaz. dell' arciv. C. di Magonza prigione dei marchesi di Monferrato, 1909.
Christian Frederick, *king of Denmark, see* CHRISTIAN VIII.
Christian (Edmund B. V.) Herbert R. Allport & h. Casual Club papers. 8°. 1924
Christian (P.), *see* HOFFMANN (E. T. W.) Contes fantast., tr. nouv. préc. de souv. s. la vie de l'a. par P. C., 1843.
Christianismus. *Christianismi restit., 1553, *see* SERVETUS (M.)
Christianity. The beginnings of C., pl, v1–3, 1920–26, *see* FOAKES-JACKSON (F. J.) & K. LAKE, *edd.*
Future (The) of C.; [*by var. wr.*], 1927, *see* MARCHANT (*Sir* J.), *ed.*
*A plain acc. of genuine C., 1761, *see* WESLEY (J.)
Christiano-Ernestina Bibliotheca, *see* WERNIGERODE.
Christie, *The firm of, see* MARILLIER (H. C.) "Christie's," 1766–1925, 1926.
Christie (Mrs. Agatha). The Big Four. s8°. [1927]
The murder of Roger Ackroyd. [2nd impr.] s8°. [1927]
The secret adversary. s8°. 1922
The secret of Chimneys. s8°. [1925]
Christie (Archibald H.) Tradit. methods of pattern designing. 8°. O. 1910
Christie (Mrs. Archibald H.)
Embroidery & tapestry weaving. 4th ed. s8°. [1920]
Samplers & stitches. la8°. [1921]
Christie (Ella R.), *F.R.G.S.*
Through Khiva to golden Samarkand. 8°. 1925
Christie (John).
Lairds & lands of Loch Tayside. 8°. Aberfeldy. 1892
Christie (Mrs. Mabel E.), *F.R.Hist.S., form. Seebohm.*
The evolution of the Eng. farm. 8°. [1927]
Henry VI. [Kings & Queens of England; ed. by R. S. Rait &c.] 8°. 1922
Christie (Octavius Francis).
The transition f. aristocracy, 1832–67. 8°. 1927
Christie-Miller (Sydney Richardson).
Cat. of a further portion of the lib. of C.-M. comp. early Eng. works on the arts & sciences. Sold by Sotheby, Mar.–Apr. 1925. [*Illust. & w.* Prices & buyers' names. *b. w.* Cat. of a further sel., 1925]. la8°. 1925
Catalogue of a series of books f. the lib. of J. A. de Thou, 1553–1617, w. o. fine bindings. Sold by Sotheby, May 1920. [Illust. *b. w. h.* Cat. of rare works &c., 1921–24]. la8°. [1920]
Cat. of early Eng. & Scot. works on law & hist. f. Britwell Court, Bucks. Property of S. R. C.-M. Sold by Sotheby, 22nd &c. March 1926. [*Illust.*] la8°. 1926
Cat. of early Eng. tales &c. Sold by Sotheby, June 1920. [*Illust.*] la8°. 1920
Cat. of rare &c. books in all branches of lit. Sold by Sotheby, Apr. 1924. [Illust. *b. w. h.* Cat., June 1920]. la8°. 1924
Catalogue of rare &c. works in early Eng. poetry & o. lit. f. lib.

Christie-Miller (Sydney Richardson) [*continued*].
form. at Britwell Court. Sold by Sotheby, Mar. 1921, Feb. 1922, Mar. 1923, Mar.–Apr. 1924, Mar. 1925 & Mar. 1926. [Illust. *& w.* Prices & buyers' names *except for* 1922 *&* 1926. 6p *in* 4v]. la8°. [1921–26]
Cat. of the final portion of the library form. at Britwell Court, Bucks. Property of S. R. C.-M. Sold by Sotheby, 28th March–8th April 1927. [*Illust.*] la8°. 1927
Catalogue of valuable early Eng. & Scot. works on theology &c. Sold by Sotheby, May 1920 & Jan.-Feb. 1921. [Illust. 2p, *b. w. h.* Cat. of rare works &c., 1921–24]. la8°. [1920–21]
Christifideles [CRISTIFIDELES]. *Casus quibus C. ab Eucharistie Sacramento abstinere debeāt, a Plebanis publicandi, 1514, *see* CASUS.
Christina, *duchess of Savoy; 1603–63* [MARIA CHRISTINA].
see MAGGIOROTTI (M.) In Piemonte, 1637–42: contrasti n. reggenza di M. C. e l'opera dei nunzi papali, 1923.
Christina, *queen consort of Alfonso XII, of Spain* [MARIA CHRISTINA].
see MARTIN ALONSO (A.) Diez y seis años de regencia (M. C. de Hapsburgo-Lorena, 1885–1902), 1914.
,, MAURA GAMAZO (G.) Hist. crit. del reinado de Alfonso XIII dur. la regencia de M. C., 2t, 1919–25.
Christina, *queen of Sweden.*
*The hist. of the intrigues & gallantries of C. & h. court, whilst at Rome. Render'd into Eng. [*by* P. Hollingworth, 1697]. [repr.] la8°. 1927
see BURBURY (J.) *Hist. of C. Alessandra, queen of Swedland, 1658.
,, FRIIS (H. E.) König. C. v. S., 1626–89; autor. Übers., 1899.
,, GRAUERT (W. H.) C. v. Schweden, 2B, 1837–42.
,, MOHNIKE (G. C. F.) Zur Gesch. d. ung. Fluchformulars; Anhg. betreff. d. Uebertritt d. Kön. C., 1823.
Christlich [CHRISTENLICHER; CHRISTLICHE, -ES, -ER; CRISTLICH].
Ander Theil (Das) Christl. Cathol. Gesengen &c., 1584, *see* LEISENTRIT (J.)
Christenl. betrachtung (Ain) in der Mess. s4°. *n.p.* [1524]
Christenl. Ratschlag (Eyn) &c., Reichstag zu Speyer, 1526 &c. s4°. *n.p.* [1526]
Christl. Bedencken auff D. Maiors Repetition &c., 1568, *see* BRAUNSCHWEIG.
Christl. Fragstück v. d. unterschied d. zweyen Artickel d. Apost. Glaubens &c., 1571, *see* WITTENBERG.
Christl. Gesangbuch, 1873, *see* GESANGBUCH.
Christl. Glaubens-Bekentnus, 1664, *see* MENNONISTEN.
Christl. Lutheraner (Der) stellet vor d. Kirchen-Historien vom J. 1370 &c., 1717, *see* LUTHERANER.
Christl. u. allein auf Gottes wort gegründete Glaubensbekäntnus &c., 1610, *see* GLAUBENSBEKANTNUS.
Christl. u. Cathol. gegenberichtung eyns erwirdigen Dhomcapitels zu Cöllen wider das Buch d. gnanter Reformatioñ &c. des Ertzstiffs Cöllen &c. vorgehalten &c. [*b. w.* Hermann V. Einfältigs Bedenken, 1543]. fol. Coloniæ. 1544
Christl. vnderricht (Ein) ob u. uss welcher ursach, auch zu wem, was u. waruff d. ware Christen mensch betten soll &c. s4°. *n.p. n.d.* [16 *cent.*]
Cristl. unterrichtung eins Pfarhern auff viertzig Artickel &c. gestelt, was eins Evangel. Pfarhern &c., Predigen u lere sein soll &c. • [*Imperf.*] s4°. *n.p.* 1526
Dialogus: e. Christl. spacier gesprech &c., 1553, *see* DIALOGUS.
Kurtze C. u. Einfeltige widerholung d. Bekentnis, der Kirchen Gottes, In d. Churfursten zu Sachsen Landen, 1571, *see* SACHSEN.
Christlieb (Theodor). The Indo-British opium trade & its effect. Tr. D. B. Croom. s8°. 1879
Christmas prince (The). [Acc. of the St. John's College revels, held at Oxford, 1607–8, f. MS. in the College Library. Prep. by F. S. Boas in collab. w. W. W. Greg. Malone Soc.] s4°. [O.] 1922 [1923]
Christodoulos (Constantin), *see* SVORONOS (J. N.) Synopsis de 1000 coins faux du faussaire C. C., 1922.
Christoffel (Ulrich).
Augsburg. [Berühmte Kunststätten, 79]. s8°. L. 1927
Han Holbein D. J. [Die führenden Meister]. la8°. [1926]
Christoph, *Herzog zu Württemberg* [†CHRISTOPHER, *duke*].
Confessio piæ doct., *see* CONFESSIONES fidei Christ., 1553.
Confessio piæ doct. C. Ducis Wirtemberg. & Teccensis a. 1552 congregationi Trid. Conc. proposita. s8°. Tubingæ. *U. Morhard. n.d.* [1553?]
Confessio C. una cum apologeticis scriptis, quorum autores sunt, J. Brentius, J. Beurlinus, J. Heerbrandus, J. Isenmannus, T. Snepffius. [Refutatio Sotici scr.] 2t *in* 1v. [t2 *has* 5 *tp. pag. contin.*] fol. Francofurti. 1561
Confessio, *see* BRENTZ (J.) Op., t8, 1590.
Confession des Herrn C. Herzogen zu Wirtemberg u. zu Teckh an. 1552 dem Concilio zu Trient überantwort. s8°. [Laugingen, *S. Mayer*]. *n.d.* [1553 ?]

Christophe (Henri) [†HENRY (CHRISTOPHE) I, *king of Hayti*], *see* BOUVET DE CRESSÉ (A. J. B.) Hist. de la catastrophe de St.-Domingue, avec corr. des gén. Leclerc, H. C. &c., 1824.

Christopher III, *king of Denmark; (I of Sweden), 1418–48.* Maanlaki, Herra Martin Suomeksi kääntämä. i. Tukholman codex B96. Julkaisseet E. N. Setälä & M. Nyholm. [Mon. ling. Fennicæ, 2]. la8°. Helsingissä. 1905

Christopher, *Saint.*
see BLEICH (J. A.) Dissert. idolum pontif. destruct. quem vocant C., 1688.
„ RYPINS (S.), *ed.* Three old Eng. prose texts (Life of St. C. [*O. Eng. & Lat.*]), 1924.
„ TEZA (E.) Le geste di S. C. n. trad. armena, 1895.

Christopher (Joseph Patrick), *see* AUGUSTINE, *Saint.* De catechiz. rudibus liber; tr., intr. & comm. by J. P. C., 1926.

Christus (Petrus) [*or* CHRISTI; PETRUS CHRISTOPHORI; PIETRO CRISTA], *see* FRIEDLÄNDER (M. J.) Altniederländ. Malerei, B1, P. C. &c., 1924.

Chronica [CHRONICÆ; CRONACA; CRONICA].
Breves chron. Bergomenses [Manfredi Zenunonis, Petri Assonica &c., 1117–1512]; nunc. primum ed. cura I. Finazzi, *see* REGIA DEP. DI STORIA PATRIA. Misc., t5, 1868.
Chronica breviora aliaque mon. faventina, v1, 1905–21, *see* AZZURRINIO (B.)
Chronica de Mailros, 1835, *see* MELROSE ABBEY.
*Chronica di Milano dal 948 al 1487; ed. G. Porro Lambertenghi, 1869, *see* MILANO.
Chronica do condestabre de Portugal Dom Nuno Alvarez Pereira (1526), 1911, *see* ALVAREZ PEREIRA (N.)
Chronica Regia Colon., 1880, *see* COLONIENSIS.
Cronaca d'Orvieto, 1342–63, 1845, *see* ORVIETO.
Cronaca modenese (1588–1636), 1911, *see* SPACCINI (G. B.)
Crónica gen. de Esp., ó sea hist. ilust. y descr. de sus prov[s]., 1865–71, *see* ESPAÑA.
Cronica rimada. Reprod. in facs. f. MS. in Bibl. Nat. by A. M. Huntington. [Hispanic Soc. of Amer.] fol. N.Y. 1904

Chronicle. *Chronicle (The) of Abomilech, king of the Isles, 1820, *see* WILLIAM, *of Salisbury.*

Chronicles. Chronicles of America series. Abr. Lincoln ed. v12, 13, 15, 17, 21–24, 31, 33, 35, 37, 38, 40–42, 45, 47, 48, 49. 8°. New Haven, *Yale.* 1919–21
see BOLTON (H. E.) The Spanish borderlands: Old Florida & the S.W., 1921. [23.]
„ BUCK (S. J.) Agrarian crusade, 1920. [45.]
„ FARRAND (M.) The Fathers of the Constit., 1921. [13.]
„ HOWLAND (H. J.) Theodore Roosevelt & h. times, 1921. [47.]
„ HULBERT (A. B.) Paths of inland commerce; trail, road & waterway, 1920. [21.]
„ JOHNSON (A.) Jefferson & h. colleagues, 1921. [15.]
„ MOODY (J.) Masters of capital, 1919. [41.]
„ —— Railroad builders, 1919. [38.]
„ ORTH (S. P.) Armies of labor, 1919. [40.]
„ —— Our foreigners, 1920. [35.]
„ PAINE (R. D.) Fight for a free sea, 1920. [17.]
„ SEYMOUR (C.) Woodrow Wilson & the World War, 1921. [48.]
„ SKELTON (O. D.) Canadian Dominion, 1919. [49.]
„ SKINNER (C. L.) Adventurers of Oregon, 1920. [22.]
„ SLOSSON (E. E.) The Amer. spirit in education, 1921. [33.]
„ STEPHENSON (N. W.) Texas & the Mexican War, 1921. [24.]
„ THOMPSON (H.) The age of invention, 1921. [37.]
„ —— New South; soc. & indust. evolution, 1919. [42.]
„ WOOD (W.) Captains of the Civil War, 1921. [31.]
„ WRONG (G. M.) Washington & h. comrades in arms, 1921. [12.]
The new historians; a booklet about the authors of the Chron. of A. [P2502]. 8°. N.Y. [1920]

Chronicon.
C. Hierosolymitanum, i.e. de bello sacro hist., espos. libris 12 & ed. opera R. Reineccii. Quæ operis subjecti est pars prima. Brevibus scholiis &c. illust. [Chronologia in Chron. Hierosol. *by* H. Meibomius]. s4°. Helmæstadii. 1584
C. Hollandiæ (–1459); med. door H. Obreen, *see* HISTORISCH GENOOTS. Bijd., d46, 1925.
C. marchiæ Tarvisinæ et Lombardiæ, 1207–70; a cura di L. A. Botteghi, *see* MURATORI (L. A.) Rerum Ital. scr., t8iii, 1916.
C. Novaliciense, 1846, *see* NOVALESE, *Abbey.*
C. Saxonicum; ed. & Lat. fecit E. Gibson, 1692, *see* ANGLO-SAXON CHRONICLE.
C. Spinozanum, 3t, 1921–23, *see* SPINOZA (B. de).

Chronijken van Braband en Vlanderen, 1863, *see* CODEX. C. diplomat. neerland., d6, 1863.

Chronika [Хроника]. Хроника соціалист. движенія въ Россіи, 1878–87, 1906, *see* RUSSIA.

Chronique. *C. (La) de Messire B. Du Guesclin, Connétable de France; texte établi &c. par G. Richou, 1879, *see* DU GUESCLIN (B.)
*C. des tribunaux, 3t, 1835–36, *see* TRIBUNAUX.
C. du mouvement socialiste en Russie 1878–87. Réd. sous la dir. de l'adjoint du Min. de l'Intérieur lt.-gén Schébéko. 8°. [St. Petersbourg. 1890]
C. géorgienne, 1829–31, *see* BROSSET (M. F.)

Chronique (La) des arts & de la curiosité: suppl. à la Gazette des beaux arts. année 1920–22 [*no more publ.*] la8°. 1920–22

Chronique des lettres françaises. J. Place, directeur. t1–5, 1923–27. 8°. 1923–27

Chronological (A) catena of anc. Fathers &c., 1850, *see* CATENA.
*C. couplets. 8°. 1819
*C. (A) series of engravers, 1770, *see* MARTYN (T.)

Chronologie. *C. des princ. événements en Ukráine, 1917–19, 1919, *see* UKRAINE.

Chronology. C. of the War. Issued under the Ministry of Information. v3, 1918–1919. 8°. 1920

Chrosner (Alexius) [†CROSNER], *see* CLEMEN (O.) A. C., Hofprediger, 1907.

Chroust (Giovanna). Saggi di letteratura ital. mod. Da G. Carducci al futurismo. Con note biogr., bibliogr. &c. 3 Abt. [*in 1v. pagin. contin.*] 8°. Würzburg. 1921–22

Chrussachi (Matthew G.), *see* MILLS (J. S.) & M. G. C. The question of Thrace, Greeks &c., 1919.

Chrysander (Friedrich).
G. F. Händel. B1–3i [*no more publ.*] 8°. L. 1858–67

Chrysander (Wilhelm Christian Justus). Diptycha professorum theologiæ qui in Acad. Julia docuerunt. s4°. Wolfenbüttelæ. 1748

Chrysanthos, *metropolitan of Neopatras, see* CONTARINI (C.)

Chrysippus, *presbyter, of Jerusalem.* Homélies [*Grec & Lat.*], *see* MARY, *the Virgin.* Homélies mariales byz.; ed. &c. M. Jugie, p2, 1926.

Chrysostom, *Saint.*
Αἱ θεῖαι λειτουργίαι Ἰωάννου τοῦ Χρυσοστόμου, Βασιλείου &c. s4°. Ἐνετίῃσι. 1760
[Comm. on Isaiah. *In Armenian*]. 8°. Venetik. 1880
[Comm. on the Acts of the Apostles compiled from the works of C. & Ephraim. *In Armenian*]. 8°. i Venetik. 1839
[Comm. on the Epistles of Paul. *In Armenian*]. 2v. 8°. i Venetik. 1862
[Comm. on the Gospel of John. *In Armenian*]. s4°. i Kostantnoupolis. [1717]
De sacerdotio libri 6. Acc. Diss. de dignitate sacerdotali, item S.C. vita e Cavii Hist. lit. desumpta &c. s8°. Cantabrigiæ. 1710
Homilia in ramos palmarum. Slovenice, Lat. & Gr. cum not. &c. ed. F. Miklosich. [P2807]. 8°. Vindobonæ. 1845
[Homiliæ super Mattheum. *Tr. by G. Trapezuntius. Beg.* fol. 1a: Intrante autem jhesu. In capharnaū advenit ei centurio deprecans eum &c. *Ends:* Rubrica ptiēs ad principiū libri. Traductio libroꝝ Sancti Johannis crisostomi Super matheum e greco ī latinū edita a Georgio trapezonico directaqꝫ Santissimo presuli Nicholao pape V]. fol. [Strassburg? J. Mentelin? 1466?]
252 leaves, of which 128 & 130b *are blank, the former being cut away, while the latter is preceded by the note* "Hic nll's est deffect. Sequit. text?" *Capitals, initial-strokes, paragraph-marks & underlines in red. The rubricator has written the title at the head of 1a:* Traductio libroꝝ sancti iohannis crisostomi &c. *Without pagin. or signatures; 39 lines to a full page.*
[Homilies on Matthew, *in Armenian*]. 8°. i Venetik. 1826
Ἰωάννου τοῦ Χ. τῶν εὑρισκομένων τομος 1[–8]. fol. Etonæ. 1612
τομος 1 *has add. engraved tp.* Opera Græce, 1613.
In Ninivitarum pœnitentiam homilia. Anastasii Sinaitæ sermo III de hominis creatione. Acc. Formula abjur. Athinganorum, S. Gregori Naz. Epigrammata &c. cura A. M. Bandini. [Gr. Eccl. vet. mon. ex Bibl. Medicea]. 8°. Florentiæ. 1764
Missa græcolatina. Erasmo interprete. s8°. Parisiis. 1537
Of the priesthood. Tr. by J. Bunce. s8°. 1759
[Panegyrics of Gregory the Illuminator, by C. & Gregory the Archdeacon; *in Armenian*] (Soferq Hayk., v4). s8°. i Venetik. 1853
Tres homiliæ; per P. Nannium in ling. Lat. tr. [P2544]. s8°. Antverpiæ. 1542
see BUTLER (E. C.) Authorship of Dial. de vita C., 1908.
„ LITURGY. L. of Eastern Orthodox Ch. [*incl.* Lit. of C.], 1916.
„ PALLADIUS, *bp. of Helenopolis.* Dialogus de vita C., 1928; tr., 1921.
„ VOLLANDUS (C. G.) Vindiciæ C. contra J. Harduinum, 1714.

Chrystal (*Maj.* R. A.) [*ps.* C. TROUT]. Angling theories & methods. Intr. by Sir H. Maxwell. 8°. [1927]

Chrystall (Thomas), *abbot of Kinloss, see* CRYSTALL (T.)

Chtets. Чтецъ декламаторъ: сборникъ русской поэзіи. 8°. Берлинъ. 1922

Chuang Tzŭ. Musings of a Chinese mystic. Sel. f. the philos. of Ch. T. Introd. by L. Giles. s8º. 1906
Chubb (Charles). The birds of Brit. Guiana, based on the coll. of F. V. McConnell. Pref. by Mrs. F. V. McConnell. 2v. la8º. 1916–21
Chubb (Thomas), *of Map Room, Brit. Mus.* Printed maps in atlases of Gt. Brit. & Ireland. Bibliog. (1579–1870). Intr. by F. P. Sprent. Biog. notes on map makers &c. by T. C., J. W. Skells &c. 4º. [1927]
Chubinov (David) [Tchoubinof (D.)]
Dict. géorgien-russe-franç. 4º. C.–П. 1840
Chudleigh (Thomas), *Eng. envoy at the Hague, see* Plott (T.) & T. Chudleigh. Dispatches, 1681–85 ; ed. F. A. Middlebush, 1926.
Chudoba (František). Short survey of Czech. lit. s8º. 1924
Chu Hsi, *1130–1200.* The philos. of human nature. Tr., w. notes, by J. P. Bruce. s8º. 1922
see Bruce (J. P.) C. H. & his masters, 1923.
Chukovsky (Kornei). Жена поэта (Авдотья Я. Панаева). 8º. П. 1922
Книга об Александре Блоке. 8º. П. 1922
Некрасов, как художник. 8º. П. 1922
Поэт и палач (Некрасов и Муравьев). 8º. П. 1922
Chulkov (Georgy). Стихотворения. s8º. Москва. 1922
Chumnos (Georgios). Old. Test. legends f. a Greek poem on Genesis & Exodus. Ed. w. intr., metr. tr., notes &c. by F. H. Marshall. 8º. C. 1925
Chung (Henry). The case of Korea. Foreword by S. P. Spencer. 8º. N.Y. [1921]
***Chung-Yung (The)** ; tr. L. A. Lyall &c., 1927, *see* Tzu-ssu.
Churberg (Waldemar) [*ps.* Gammalfennoman]. The situation of Finland. [Tr.] [P2451]. 8º. St. Petersburg. 1911
Church [& Church of England ; English Church].
*Apologia ad. Verantworttungsschrifft d. Evangel. reform. Kirchen in Eng. &c., 1589, *see* Apologia.
*Brief (A) defence of the Reformation of the Ch. of E. by King Edward & Q. Elizabeth. s8º. 1654
Briefe (A) & plaine declaration, conc. the desires of ministers that seeke for the discipline & reformation of the Ch. of E. &c. s8º. 1584
Church hymns, w. tunes. Ed. A. Sullivan. s8º. 1874
*Church (The) of E. vindic. f. the charge of Arminianism ; by a presbyter of the Ch. of E., 1769, *see* Toplady (A. M.)
*Church (The) of St. Bartholomew the Gt., West Smithfield, 7th ed., 1912, *see* Saint Bartholomew the Gt.
Church (The) of the Fathers, 1840, *see* Newman (J. H.)
Coll. of articles, &c. of Ch. of E., 1661 ?, *see* Sparrow (A.)
*Coll. (A) of articles, canons &c. w. sev. acts of Parl. conc. eccl. matters. s8º. 1699
*Coll. of cases &c. wr. to recover Dissenters to the Ch. of E., 2nd ed., 1694, *see* Dissenters.
*Directory (A) for ch.-govt. &c., 1690, *see* Directory.
Doc. rel. to the settlement of the Ch. of E. by the Act of Uniformity of 1662. W. hist. introd. [Eng. Puritanism by Peter Bayne]. 8º. 1862
Future (The) of the Ch. of E. : essays, 1926, *see* Marchant (*Sir* J.), *ed.*
*Independent (The) power of the Ch. not Romish, 1716, *see* Independent.
Official Year-Book of the Ch. of E., 1921 [*includ.* 13th rev. of missions overseas ; ed. by H. U. W. Stanton, *w. sep. tp. & pagin.*] 8º. 1921
*Resolution (The) of this case of conscience, Ch. of E.'s symbolizing w. Ch. of Rome, 1683, *see* Fowler (E.)
*Synodus Anglicana : or, constit. &c. of an Eng. convocation, 1702, *see* Gibson (E.)
Church Assembly, *see* National Assembly of C. of E.
Church Congress. Official report[s], 1882–1921 [1885, 1895, 1899, 1900, 1907–9, 1911–12, 1914–20 *wanting*]. 8º. 1882–1922
Church Historical Society.
[Publications]. Nos. 8, 33. s8º. 1897–98
see Browne (G. F.) Continuity of the Holy Cath. Ch. in Eng. 1897. [8.]
,, Lacey (T. A.) Gregory IX & Greek ordinations, 1898. [33.]
Church League for Women's Suffrage.
Monthly paper. Jan.–Dec. 1912. 4º. 1912
Church of Scotland.
Acts & proc. of the general assemblies of the Kirk of S. from 1560 [–1618]. 3p [*pagin. contin.*] & App. (1597–1603) [Maitland Club, 49]. 4º. Edinburgh. 1839–45
The App. *has pagin.* 931–1161.
Book (The) of Common order of the Ch. of S. known as J. Knox's Liturgy & Directory for public worship. W. hist. introd. & notes by G. W. Sprott & T. Leishman. s8º. E. 1868
Booke (The) of the Universall Kirck of S. Ed. A. Peterkin. la8º. E. 1839
Causes of the Lord's wrath agst. S. &c. agreed upon by the Gen. Assembly, 1651, *see* Presbyterian's armoury, v3, 1843.

Church of Scotland [*continued*].
Coll. (A) of confessions of faith, catechisms, &c. of public authority in the Ch. of S. &c. 2v. s8º. E. 1719–22
Compendium of the laws of the Ch. of S. 2p. s8º. E. 1830–31
Each part has 2nd tp. as under :
1, Coll. & obs. conc. worship &c. of Ch. of S. ; by W Steuart, 4th ed.
2, Abridgement of the Acts of the Gen. Assembly, 1560–1830.
Confessions (The) of faith, Catechisms, Directories, form of ch. government &c. in the Ch. of S., also a coll. of Acts &c. s8º. E. 1725
,, ,, ... s8º. E. 1739
*Directory (A) for ch.-govt. & ordin. of ministers, 1690, *see* Directory.
*Govt. & order of Ch. of S., 1690, *see* Henderson (A.)
Principall (The) Acts of the Gen. Assembly of the Kirk of S., 1638–1863, *b. in* 17v [1650–89, 91 *wanting*]. smfol. E. 1639–1863
1692 *is a reprint* 1852.
Psalms (The) of David in metre : allowed by Kirk of S., 1812, *see* Bible : Psalms.
Records of Kirk of S., v1 (1638–54), 1838, *see* Peterkin (A.)
True (A) copy of the pr. acts of the Gen. Assemblies of the Ch. of S., 1638–49. By a welwisher of the Ch. of S. s8º. *n.p.* 1682
see Bible : Psalms. Ps. of David in metre, approv. by Ch. of S., 1850.
Church quarterly review (The).
v89–105 (Oct. 1919–Jan. 1928). 8º. 1920–28
Church (Alfred John) & A. Gilman.
Carthage. [Story of the Nations]. 5th ed. 8º. 1890
Church (*Maj.* Archibald George).
East Africa : a new dominion. 8º. 1927
Church (Arthur Henry). Intr. to plant-life of the Oxford district. 3[p] *in* 1v. 8º. 1922–25
On the interpretation of phenomena of phyllotaxis. [P2418]. 8º. 1920
Church (Arthur Herbert), *F.R.S.*
Colour : elem. manual. s8º. 1901
Church (Richard). Philip & o. poems. s8º. O. 1923
Church (Richard William), *dean of St. Paul's.*
Dante & o. essays. [repr.] s8º. 1906
Churches. Lectures on foreign churches, s1, 2, 1845–46, *see* Lectures.
Churchill (*Major* Arthur Benjamin Norton). The command of the sea ; What is it ? [P2592]. 8º. [1911]
Churchill (Charles), *the poet.*
Epistle to William Hogarth, re-versified w. notes. 4º. 1763
Poet. works. Coll. by T. Park. 3v. s8º. 1807
see Forster (J.) D. De Foe & C. C., 1855.
,, Williams (I. A.) 7 18th cent. bibliog., C. C. &c., 1924.
Churchill (Irene Josephine), *see* Kent. East Kent records : cal. of unpubl. deeds &c. ; ed I. J. C., 1922.
Churchill (Sidney J. A.) The goldsmiths of Italy : th. guilds, statutes & work. Comp. f. papers, notes &c. coll. by S. J. A. C., by C. G. E. Bunt. 4º. 1926
Churchill (William), *Consul general of U.S.* Easter Island. The Rapanui speech & the peopling of Southeast Polynesia. [C.I. of Wash.] la8º. Wash. 1912
The Polynesian wanderings. Tracts of the migration deduced f. exam. of the Proto-Samoan content of Efaté &c. [C.I. of Wash.] la8º. Wash. 1911
Sissano. Movements of migration within & thr. Melanesia. [C.I. of Wash.] la8º. Wash. 1916
see Finley (*Lt.-col.* J. P.) & W. C. The Subanu, 1913.
Churchill (*Rt. Hon.* Winston L. Spencer), *b. 1874 ; eldest son of Ld. R. Churchill.* The world crisis, 1911–14. 8º. [1923]
The world crisis, 1915. 8º. [1923]
The world crisis, 1916–18. 2p. 8º. [1927]
see Keynes (J. M.) The econ. conseq. of Mr. C., 1925.
Churchman (Theophilus), *ps., see* Heylyn (Peter).
Churchward (Albert). The arcana of freemasonry. 8º. [1915]
The origin & evolution of freemasonry conn. w. the origin &c. of the human race. 8º. [1920]
Origin & evolution of the human race. la8º. [1921]
Churchyard (Thomas). Misery of Flanders &c., 1579. repr. [*in facs.* Ed. H. W. Adnitt]. s4º. Shrewsbury. 1876
The tragedy of Card. Wolsey (1587), *see* Cavendish (G.) Life &c. of Wolsey, 1899.
Churiolandus (Jonas Fulevius), *see* Fulevius (J.)
Churton (Edward), *publisher.*
Railroad book of England &c. la8º. [1851]
Chute (Charles Lionel). Probation in children's courts, 1921, *see* United States : Labor.

Chwolson (Orest Danilovich). Die Physik u. i. Bedeutung für d. Menschheit. Übers. G. Kluge. 8°. Braunschweig. 1924

Chys (Jacob Anne van der), see CHIJS (J. A. v. D.)

Chytræus (David), *the elder.*

Catechesis. Ab. ipso auctore recog. & aucta. s8°. Francoforti. 1583

„ ....postremo recog. [*b. w. h.* Oratio, 1580]. s8°. Witebergæ. 1588

De morte & vita æterna. 2p *in* 1v [*pagin. cont. Foll. by* Imagines mortis ill. epigrammatis G. Æmilii, *w. sep. tp. no pagin.*] s8°. Vitebergæ. 1583

Onomasticon theolog. postrem. recog. s8°. Witebergæ. 1585

Oratio de statu eccl. hoc temp. in Græcia, Asia, Africa, Ungaria, Boëmia &c. Cui epistolae aliquot Patriarchæ Byzantini & aliorum, ex Oriente rec. scr. &c. access. [*b. w. h.* Oratio de st. theol., 1580]. s8°. Francofurti. 1580

„ „ Quibus in hac ed. epistolae Gr. & Lat., De Russorum & Tartarorum relig. & alia access. s8°. Francofurti. 1583

Oratio de studio theologiæ. s8°. Witebergæ. 1580

Præcepta rhetoricæ inventionis. [*Added*: Oratio in funere Henrici ducis Megapol., Oratio de Johanne Luccano &c.] [*b. w. h.* Oratio 1580]. s8°. Witebergæ. 1576

see SCHÜTZ (O. F.) De vita d. Chytraei, 2v, 1720–22.

Chytræus (Nathan). Supplicium Jesu Christi Servatoris. [*Verse*]. 8°. Rostochii. 1570

Ciampi (Sebastiano), *see* PISTOIA. Statuti dell' Opera di S. Jacopo di Pistoja &c., publ. da S. C., 1923.

Ciampini (Giovanni Giustino). Ad. Jo. C. opera de vet. mon. & de sacris ædificiis Constantini Magni Additamentum &c. fol. Romæ. 1748

Cianetti (Enea). Il Campo di Siena e il Palazzo Pubblico. s8°. Firenze. 1921

Ciaran, *St., abbot of Clonmacnois, 515–c. 549* [KIARAN], *see* MACALISTER (R. A. S.) Lat. & Irish lives of C.; [ed. w. intr. &c.] by R. A. S. M., 1921.

Ciarlanti (Gio. Vincenzo). Mem. hist. del Sannio, prov. del regno di Napoli. fol. Isernia. 1644

Cibber (Caius Gabriel), *see* FABER (H.) C. G. C., 1630–1700, h. life & work, 1926.

Cibber (Colley).

Careless husband, *see* INCHBALD (E.) Brit. th., v9, 1808.

Love makes a man, *see* INCHBALD (E.) Brit. th., v9, 1808.

She wou'd & she wou'd not, *see* INCHBALD (E.) Brit. th., v9, 1808.

see NICHOLSON (W.) A. Aston; appended A.'s Brief suppl. to C.'s Lives, 1920.

„ VANBRUGH (*Sir* J.) & C. C. Provoked husband, 1808.

„ ——: —— The provoked husband, 1823.

Cibber (*Mrs.* Susanna Maria).

The oracle. Comedy. [P2783]. 8°. 1752

Cibot (Pierre Martial), *Jesuit.* *Lettre de Pekin sur le génie de langue chinoise. Par un père de la Comp. de Jésus. [*b. w. h.* Lettre sur les caractères chin., 1773]. s4°. Brux. 1773

*Lettre sur les caractères chinois, par le Rev. Père ****. s4°. Brux. 1773

Ciccarelli (Alfonso), *fl. 1570.* De orig., antiq. &c. illust. domus Sanctacruciæ; ed. G. B. Adriani, *see* REGIA DEP. DI STORIA PATRIA. Misc., t5, 1868.

Cicé (Jérôme Marie Champion de), *abp. of Bordeaux, see* CHAMPION DE CICÉ.

Cice (Louis de), *bp. of Sabula.* *Lettere ad un' abate di qualità int. alla Lettera di L. di C., s. idolatrie &c. d. Cina. [*b. w.* Montecatini (B.) Discrepanze, 1700]. s8°. Colonia. 1701

Cicero (Marcus Tullius).

WORKS.

Opera, cum optimis exempl. collata. [10t, 9 *&* 10 *wanting*]. s8°. Lugd. Bat., *Elzevir.* 1642

Only t1 *has gen. tp.* t2–4, Orat., 5, Epist. ad fam. 6, Epist. ad Atticum. 7, 8, Philosoph.

Opera omnia; ex rec. J. A. Ernesti, cum ejusdem notis, & Clave Ciceron. 5t [*in 8v.* 2–4, *each in 2p*]. 8°. Londini. 1819

ORATIONS (COMPLETE EDS. &c.)

Orationes: Divinatio in Q. Caecilium—In C. Verrem. Rec. &c. G. Peterson. 2a ed., rec. & emend. s8°. O. [1917]

Orationes: Pro Milone—Pro Marcello—Pro Ligario—Pro Rege Deiotaro—Philippicae i–xiv. Rec. &c. A. C. Clark. 2a. ed. s8°. O. [1918]

Orationes: Pro P. Quinctio—Pro Q. Roscio Comoedo—Pro A. Caecina—De lege agraria &c.—Pro C. Rabirio &c.—Pro L. Flacco—In L. Pisonem—Pro C. Rabirio postumo. Rec. &c. A. C. Clark. s8°. O. [1909]

Orationes: Pro Sex. Roscio—De Imp. Cn. Pompei—Pro Cluentio—In Catilinam—Pro Murena—Pro Caelio. Rec. &c. A. C. Clark. [2a impr.] s8°. O. [1908]

Cicero (Marcus Tullius) [*continued*].

WORKS (TWO OR MORE).

Cato major seu de senectute, cum Græca tr. T. Gazae. Eiusdem: Laelius, seu de amicitia, Paradoxa & Somnium Scipionis Græcolatinum. s8°. Ingolstadii. 1596

De officiis lib. 3, cum Viti Amerbachii comm., annot. Erasmi, P. Melanch. &c. Ejusdem, De senectute, De amicitia, Paradoxa, Somnium Scipionis [*all w. sep. tps. & pagins.*] s4°. Parisiis. 1556

„ „ ....[*a. ed.*] s8°. Francofurti. 1569

De divinatione liber primus [—secundus]. Ed. A. S. Pease. [Univ. of Illinois. St. in lang. &c., v6ii, iii, 8ii, iii]. [4p]. la8°. [Urbana]. 1920–23

FINIBUS (DE) BONORUM & MALORUM.

De f. b. Lib. 1, 2. Ed. J. S. Reid. 8°. C. 1925

LETTERS.

Epistol. famil. libri 16. Cum scholiis & annotat. P. Manutii. s8°. Argentorati. 1560

Select letters. Notes &c. by A. Watson. 3rd. ed. 8°. O. 1881

„ „ With hist. intr., notes &c. New ed. based upon that of Watson. Rev. & annot. by W. W. How. Crit. intr. by A. C. Clark. 2v. s8°. O. 1925–26

OFFICIIS (DE).

M. T. C. Arpinatis Ad M. T. C. filium suum Officiorum liber. 8°. [Argentini, *H. Eggesteyn.* 1472]

92 printed leaves; without tp., pagin. or register; 27 lines to a full page.

Officia C. rursus accurat. recog. per Erasmum. Acc. Somnium Scipionis & Græca tr. T. Gazae in Senectutem & Somnium. [Gaza's tr. *wanting*]. 4°. [Louanii. 1519]

ORATORE (DE). De o. libri 3. Ejusdem de perf. oratore ad M. Brutum liber &c. Cum Ph. Melancthonis castig. &c. s8°. Coloniæ. 1564

PHILIPPICAE.

Second Philippic. W. intr. & notes tr. f. K. Halm; ed. w. add. by J. E. B. Mayor. Rev. ed. s8°. 1921

REPUBLICA (DE).

De republica. Rec. &c. F. Steinackerus. 8°. Lips. 1823

TRANSLATIONS.

Brutus. Texte établi & tr. par J. Martha. [Coll. des univ. de Fr.] s8°. 1923

Cato & Laelius; tr. by Melmoth. s8°. 1812

De finibus. [Tr.] by S. Parker; rev. by J. Collier. n. ed. 8°. 1812

Discours. Texte établi & tr. par H. De La Ville de Mirmont &c. [Coll. des univ. de Fr.] t1–5. 8°. 1921–27

Divisions de l'art oratoire. Topiques. Texte établi & tr. par H. Bornecque. [Coll. des univ. de France]. 8°. 1924

Letters to h. friends. [Text], w. Eng. tr. by W. G. Williams. [Loeb Class. Lib.] v1. s8°. 1927

[Officiis (De)]. M. T. C., h. 3 bks. of duties to Marcus h. sonne, Eng. by N. Grimald. Lat. adjoyned. [*Imperf.*] s8°. [1600 ?]

Les offices. Tr. avec notes &c. par M. Du Bois. dern. éd., rev. & corr. s8°. 1714

„ „ Tr., w. notes &c., by W. M'Cartney. 8°. E. 1798

Three books of Offices &c. Lit. tr. w. notes by C. R. Edmonds. s8°. *Bohn.* 1856

L'orateur. Du meilleur genre d'orateurs. Texte établi par H. Bornecque. [Coll. des univs. de Fr.] 8°. 1921

„ „ Livre 1. Texte établi & tr. par E. Courbaud. [Coll. des univ. de France]. 8°. 1922

Pensées. Tr. par l'abbé d'Olivet. 11e éd., rev. & corr. s8°. 1805

Philippics. With Eng. tr. by W. C. A. Ker. [Loeb Class. Lib.] s8°. 1926

Political works: Republic & Laws. Tr., w. diss. & notes, by F. Barham. 2v. 8°. 1841–42

[Senectute (De) &c.] Two essays of old-age & of friendship w. h. stoical paradoxes & Scipio's dream. Eng. by S. Parker. 3rd ed. corr. & rev. s8°. 1736

On old age. Tr. into Eng. verse by Sir R. Allison. s8°. 1916

Senectute (De), De amicitia, De divinatione. [Text], w. Eng. tr. by W. A. Falconer. [Loeb Class. Lib.] s8°. 1923

Two essays on old age & friendship. Tr. E. S. Shuckburgh. [repr.] s8°. 1927

Speeches. Pro Archia poeta—Post reditum in Senatu—Post reditum ad quirites—De domo sua—De haruspicum responsis—Pro Plancio. With Eng. tr. by N. H. Watts. [Loeb Class. Lib.] s8°. 1923

Speeches. Pro lege Manilia—Pro Caecina—Pro Cluentio—Pro Rabirio—[Text], w. Eng. tr. by H. G. Hodge. [Loeb Class. Lib.] s8°. 1927

Tusculan disputations. n. ed. rev. & corr. by W. H. Main. 8°. 1824

„ „ [Text], w. Eng. tr. by J. E. King. [Loeb Class. Lib.] s8°. 1927

REFERENCES.

see ASCONIUS PEDIANUS (Q.) Commentarii, 1920.

„ —— Orationum C. 5 enarr.; rec. &c. A. C. Clark, 1907.

„ CONSTANS (L. A.) Un correspondant de C.: Ap. Claudius Pulcher, 1921.

„ DATI (A.) Super Tullianis eleganciis &c. in sua Rethorica libellus, c. 1479, 1905.

„ GOLDBACHER (A.) Z. Kritik v. C.'s De officiis, 1, 2, 1921–22.

„ HAVET (L.) Notes crit. sur le texte de l'Orateur &c., 1927.

„ HORNE (G.) *The theol. & philos. in C.'s Somnium Scipionis explained &c., 1751.

Cicero (Marcus Tullius) [*continued*].
REFERENCES [*continued*].
see OLIVET (*l'abbé* D'). Delectus comm. in M. T. C. opera omnia, ad ed. J. A. Ernesti accomod., 3t, 1819.
„ SALLUST. Des hochberompten Latin. historischreibers S. hist.; auch d. Oration d. C. &c., 1515.
„ SJÖGREN (H.) Ad C. Ep. ad Atticum adnot., 1927.
„ STRIGELIUS (V.) In P. Melanchthonis lib. de anima notae; item V. S. in primam Tuscul. quaest. C. comm., 1590.
„ WYTTENBACH (D. A.) Oratio de philosophia, auctore C., 1779.

Cichorius (Conrad). Röm. Studien: Hist., Epigraph., Literargesch. aus 4 Jhdten Roms. 8°. 1922

Cichowski (Mikołaj) [CICHOVIUS (N.)] Centuria argumentorum cæsa. [*b. w.* Apostle's Creed. Confessio &c., 2a ed., 1651]. s8°. *n.p.* 1652
Confessionis Xtnæ. ad rogum damnatæ & combustæ manium a N. C., sui vindices [*by* J. Szlichting]. [*b. w.* Apostle's Creed. Conf. &c., 2a ed., 1651]. s8°. *n.p.* 1652

Cicogna (Michele). Fiamme d'amor divino. s8°. Venetia. 1683

Cicognani (Bruno).
Il figurinaio e le figurine. s8°. Firenze. [1920]
La velia. s8°. Milano. 1923

Cid, El. Contrib. to restor. of text of the Poema del C., by H. R. Lang, *w. text, see* REVUE HISPAN., t66, 1926.
Poem of the Cid. Repr. f. MS. at Madrid by A. M. Huntington. [Hisp. Soc. of Amer. Hisp. notes &c.] 3v. s8°. *n.p.* [1921]
Übers. u. Glossar d. altspan. Poema del C., v. J. Adam, *see* ROMAN. FORSCH., B32, 1913.
see CEJADOR Y FRAUCA (J.) El cantar de Mio Cid y la epopeya castell., 1920.

Ciervo (Joaquin).
Pintores de España, 1480–1874. la8°. Barcelona. 1925

Cieza de León (Pedro de). The war of Las Salinas. Tr., w. intr. by Sir C. Markham. [Hakluyt Soc., s2, v54]. 8°. 1923

Cigogna (Emmanuele Antonio).
Saggio di bibliografia veneziana. la8°. Venezia. 1847
see MOSCHINI (G. A.) & E. A. C. Trasporto d. osse di P. Sarpi, 1828.
„ NEUMANN RIZZI (I.) *Di alcuni scritti pubbl. da E. A. C., 1807–50, 1850.
„ SORANZO (G.) Bibl. venez., in agg. d. Saggio di C., 1885.

Cigoli (Il), *see* CARDI (L.)

Cihac (A. de). Dict. d'étymologie daco-romane. Elém. lat. comp. avec a. langues romanes. 8°. Francfort s/M. 1870
Dict. d'étymologie daco-romane. Eléments slaves, magyars, turcs &c. 8°. Francfort s/M. 1879

Cilibrizzi (Saverio). Storia parl. polit. e diplom. d'Italia. v1, 2 (1, 1848–70. 2, 1870–96). la8°. Milano. 1923–25

Cilicius (Christianus) *Cimber, ps., see* RANZOVIUS (H.)

Cilnea, *The Family of* [CILNIA], *see* MACCHIONI (B.) Descr. d. fam. C. d. E. Camurrini, esamin. &c. d. B. M., 1688.

Ciminelli (Serafino de'), *see* AQUILANO (S.)

Cimino (Serafino), *see* AQUILANO (S.)

Cingis Han, *see* JENGHIS KHAN, *Great Khan of the Moguls.*

Ciobanu (Ștefan). Orig. & moart. Dosofteiu, *see* ACADEMIA ROM. Disc., 50, 1920.

Ciocci (Raffaele). Narr. of iniquities &c. pract. at Rome in 19th cent. [Tr.] 5th ed. s8°. 1845

Cionini (Natale). Teatro e arti in Sassuolo. la8°. Modena. 1902

Cip, *ps., see* GIACHETTI (C.)

Cipolla (Carlo), *1854–1916.*
Works in REGIA DEP. DI STORIA. PATRIA. Misc.
A. M. Bandini a Verona [1778], 1913. [47.]
Commem. del prof. C. Merkel, 1900. [36.]
Di Audace, vescovo di Asti, e di due doc. ined., 1889. [27.]
Di Brunengo, vescovo di Asti &c., 1890. [28.]
Inventari trascr. das pergamene Bobbiesi dei sec. 13–14, 1909. [44.]
Un Italiano n. Polonia e n. Svezia, 16 e 17 sec. [*A. Guagninus*], 1887. [26.]
Nuovo doc. rig. Aless. Guagnini, 1904. [40.]
La pergamena orig. del trattato conchiuso nel 1188 tra Berengario I, Marchese di Busca, e il comune di Asti, 1900. [36.]
La pergamena rappres. le ant. pitture d. Basilica di S. Eusebio in Vercelli, 1901. [37.]
Quattro doc. astesi conserv. n. Bibl. di Sua Maestà in Torino (955–1078); ed. C. C., 1887. [25.]
Taddeo del Branca e una tradiz. leggend. sull' Alighieri, 1887. [25.]
see ARCHIVIO STOR. ITAL., Anno 76, v2 (Necrologia), 1918.

Cippico (Antonio).
An all-embracing genius: Leonardo da Vinci, *see* ROY. SOC. OF LIT. Essays &c.: Trans., N.S., v1, 1921.
Carme umanistico. 4°. *Asphodel Press.* 1923
Italy, the central problem of the Mediter. [Williams Coll., Mass.] 8°. New Haven. 1926
The poetry of U. Foscolo. [Brit. Acad. P2821]. 8°. [1926]
see DANTE ALGHIERI. D.: essays in commem., 1321–1921; [ed. by A. C. &c.], 1921.

Cipriani (Francesco Maria). Poesie calabre. s8°. Napoli. 1859

Cirbied (Jacques Chahan de). Gramm. de la langue arm. 8°. 1823

Cirencester (Richard, *of*) [RICARDUS, *Corinensis*]. De situ Brit libri 2, *see* BERTRAM (C. J.)

Cironius (Innocentius). Obs. juris canon. Rec. &c. J. S. Brunnquell. [P2741]. s4°. Jenæ. 1726

Císař (Jar.) The Czechoslovak Rep., its resources. Coll. under dir. of J. C. by F. Pokorný & P. Selver. [Ed. of Soc. l'Effort de la Tchécoslov.] [*a. c. in* P2526]. 8°. Prague. 1920

Cisneros (José Maria de Valdenebro y), *see* VALDENEBRO Y CISNEROS (J. M. DE).

Cisterni (*le vcte.*), *ps., see* MICARD (E. J. P. N.)

Citador. *Citador; *tr. f. MS. in Lat., n.d., see* THEOPHRASTUS REDIVIVUS, *ps.*

Citanna (Giuseppe).
La poesia di U. Foscolo. Saggio crit. 8°. Bari. 1920

Citizen. *C.'s (The) companion: or the tradesman's mirrour. [*add. engr. tp.*] s8°. 1673

Citoyen (Un) de la Corse, *ps.* *La vérité sur les Cent Jours, 1825, *see* DELFICO (M.)

Citroën (André), *see* HAARDT (G. M.) & L. AUDOUIN-DUBREUIL. Le raid C.: la prem. traversée du Sahara en automobile, 1923.

Cittadella (Luigi Napoleone). Istrumento di divis., 12 sett. 1493, tra Angela ed Ippolita Sforza Visconti di Milano; pubbl. con note da C., *see* REGIA DEP. DI STORIA PATRIA. Misc., t4, 1863.
Notizie rel. a Ferrara, ric. da doc. la8°. Ferrara. 1864

Citters (Aarnout van), *the Elder, ambassador of the Unit. Prov. in England, see* WASSENAAR-DUIVENVOORDE (J. VAN). Verbaal van de buitengewone ambassade van J. van W.-D., A. van C. &c. naar Engeland in 1685, 1863.

***City** of lilies (The); by a. of "Jenny Essenden" & R. W. Weekes, 1923, *see* WEEKES (A. R.) & R. W. W.

City Glee Club. Book of the words of glees, madrigals &c. [Pref. *signed* H. S.] s8°. 1880

City of Dublin Steam Packet Company. Comp. view of inland navig. of Eng. & Irel. [*map.*] *folded* s8°. 1833

City of London Churches Commission, *see* LONDON, CITY OF, CHURCHES COMM.

Civic Arts Association. [*Publications*], *see* RICARDO (H.) The perfect citizen, 1920.

Civics Institute of Ireland. Publications. v1, 2. 4°. Liv'l. 1922–25
see ABERCROMBIE (P.), S. KELLY & A. KELLY. Dublin of the future, 1922. [1]
„ DUBLIN. D. Civic Survey: Report; prep. by H. T. O'Rourke &c., 1925. [2]

Civil. Development (The) of the C. Service. Lect. [*by var. a.*], Soc. of Civil Servants, 1920–21. Pref. by Visct. Haldane. s8°. 1922

Civilization. C. in U.S., 1922, *see* STEARNS (H. E.), *ed.*
Intr. to contemp. civiliz.: a syllabus, 5th ed., 1925, *see* COLUMBIA UNIVERSITY.

Civiltà (La) cattolica. Anno 1–24, 26–33. [Ser. 1–11 *in* 131v. s1, v1, 6a ed.] 8°. [s1–7 Roma; s8–11 Firenze]. 1850–82
s2, v4, s7, v4, 6, 12, s8, v1, 3, 6, 9–11, s11, v2iii, 5i–ii *wanting.*

Civinini (Guelfo).
La stella confidente. Novelle. s8°. Milano. [1919]

Civis, *ps.* A history of Albany. [P2516]. la8°. [1920]

C. K. S.: an autobiog., 1927, *see* SHORTER (C. K.)

Clagett (Nicholas), *M.A., of Magdalen Hall, Oxford.*
The abuse of God's grace. s4°. O. 1659

Clagett (William), *D.D.* *A disc. conc. the worship of the Virgin &c. [P2664]. s4°. 1686
*Queries offered by T. W. [*i.e.* Thomas Ward] to the Protestants conc. the Engl. Reformation repr. & answ. [P2652]. s4°. 1688
*A reply to the Mischief of impositions [*by* V. Alsop]; wh. pretends to answer the Dean of St Paul's Mischief of separation [*by* E. Stillingfleet]. [P2653]. s4°. 1681

Claim. The claim of antiquity, w. annot. list of bks. &c., 1922, *see* ANTIQUITY.

Clairevoie (Georges de). Hinter d. Coulissen. Erlebnisse e. Ex-Cisterzienser Mönches. 2e A. [P2691]. 8°. Zürich. 1869

Clairon (*Mlle.*) Mémoires. n. éd. 8°. 1822

Claius (Johannes), *Hertzbergensis* [CLAJ]. Gramm. Germanicæ linguæ ex Bibliis Lutheri German. & aliis eius libris coll. s8°. 1578

Clan Donnachaidh Society, *see* ROBERTSON (D.) Brief acc. of the Clan Donnachaidh, 1894.

Clap (Thomas), *president of Yale College, see* YALE UNIVERSITY. Catalogue of books, 1755.

Claparède (Edouard). Psychologie de l'enfant &c. 8e éd. augm. 8°. Genève. 1920

Clapham. Clapham & the Clapham Sect. [*By var. wr.* R. de M. Rudolf &c. Clapham Antiq. Soc.] 8°. 1927

*Clapham w. its common &c. & a list of inhabitants to 1841. s8°. Clapham. *D. Batten.* 1841

Clapham (Alfred W.), *see* LONDON. Survey of L., v9, Parish of St. Helen, Bishopsgate, p1; by M. Reddan & A. W. C., 1924.

Clapham (John Harold). The economic develop. of France & Germany, 1815–1914. 8°. C. 1921

An econ. hist. of mod. Britain. The early railway age, 1820–50. la8°. C. 1926

Clapham (Richard).

The book of the otter. Intr. by W. Thompson. 8°. [1922]

Sport on fell, beck & tarn. Foreword by Sir T. Cook. 8°. 1924

Clapp (Frederick Mortimer). Jacopo Carucci da Pontormo, h. life & work. Foreword by F. J. Mather. la8°. New Haven, Yale. 1916

Clapperton (Hugh). Journal of a second exped. into the interior of Africa. Added, journal of R. Lander from Kano to the sea-coast &c. 4°. 1829

see DENHAM (D.), H. C. &c. Travels in N. & C. Africa (1822–24), 1826.

Clará (José), *see* FRANCÉS (J.) J. C., 1920.

Claraz (Jules). Le confessionnal. s8°. [1913]

Clare (de), *The family of, see* DE CLARE.

Clare [*Scefi*], *St., of Assisi.*

see MAUCLAIR (C.) Vie de S. Claire, 8e éd., 1924.

,, RICARD (*mgr.* A.) Sainte C. d'Assise, 1895.

Clare (John), *poet.* Poems, chiefly from MS. [Sel. & ed. by E. Blunden & A. Porter]. 8°. [1920]

Clare (John Fitzgibbon, *1st earl of*), *1749–1801.* Speech in the H. of Lords of Ireland, Feb. 10, 1800. [P524]. 8°. D. 1886

Clare (John Holles, *1st earl of*), *1564?–1637, see* HIST. MSS. COMM. Portland MSS., R., v9, Letter-bk. of Sir J. H. &c., 1923.

Claremont (Claude A.)

A review of Montessori literature. [P2430]. 8°. 1919

Clarendon (Edward Hyde, *1st earl of*). Hist. of the Rebellion & Civil Wars in Eng., 1641–60. 3v. fol. 1707

,, ,, ...n. ed. *la. paper.* 3v *in* 6. la8°. 1807

Mem. of Charles I & the loyalists who suffered in h. cause. Chiefly extr. f. C.'s Hist. Portraits f. Vandyke &c. s8°. 1795

see EVELYN (J.) Mems. &c.; subj., corr. betw. C. & Sir R. Browne, 1818.

Claretie (Jules). Cat. de la bibl. de C. [Vente jan. *&* mars 1918]. 2p *in* 1v. la8°. 1918

Souv. du Diner Bixio. s8°. 1924. [1923]

see JOFFRE (*mar.* J. J. C.) Disc. de récep. (*on* J. C.), 1919.

Claretta (*il barone* **Gaudenzio).**

Works in REGIA DEP. DI STORIA PATRIA. Misc.

Commem. del conte A. Franchi-Verney, 1883. [21.]

Lettere scelte di illust. personaggi, per cura di C., 1862. [1.]

I reali di Savoia, munifici fautori d. arti, sec. 18, 1893. [90.]

see MANNO (A.) Il lavoro quadragen. del B. G. C., *&* Bibliog., 1900.

Clari (Robert de), *see* ROBERT, *de C.*

Claridge (G. Cyril).

Wild bush tribes of trop. Africa. 8°. 1922

Claris, *see* KLOSE (M.) Der Roman v. C. u. Laris, 1916.

Clark University, *see* BLAKESLEE (G. H.), *ed.* Mexico & the Caribbean; C. Univ. addr., 1920.

Clark (A. F. B.) Boileau & the French class. critics in England (1660–1830). 8°. Paris. 1925

Clark (Albert Curtis) & J. R. Harris.

F. C. Conybeare. [Brit. Acad. P2821]. la8°. [1926]

Clark (Andrew), *fellow of Lincoln College, Oxford, see* FELSTED SCHOOL. Foundation deeds &c.; intr. notes by A. C., 1916.

Clark (Austin Hobart). Echinoderms as aberrant arthropods, *see* SMITHSONIAN INST. Misc. coll., v72, 1921.

Monograph of the existing crinoids, v1, The Comatulids, p2. [S.I., U.S. Nat. Mus. Bull. 82]. 4°. Wash. 1921

Sea-lilies & feather-stars, *see* SMITHSONIAN INST. Misc. coll., v72, 1922.

Clark (Barrett Harper). Great short novels of the world. Chosen by B. H. C. 8°. 1927

A study of the mod. drama. 8°. N.Y. 1925

—— & M. Lieber.

Great short stories of the world. Chosen by B. H. C. &c. [n. impr.] 8°. [1926]

Clark (Davis Wasgatt). Life & times of Rev. Elijah Hedding. W. introd. by E. S. Janes. 8°. N.Y. 1855

Clark (Donald).

Australian mining & metallurgy. 8°. Melbourne. 1904

Clark (Edwin Charles). Engl. academ. costume (mediæval). [*Repr. fr.* Archaeolog. Journal, v1]. [P2592]. 8°. Exeter. 1894

Clark (G. N.) Unifying the world. s8°. 1920

Clark (G. W.)

Reynard, the case agst. the fox. [P2690]. s8°. Lode. [1923]

Clark (Gavin Brown).

The Transvaal & Bechuanaland. [P2832]. 8°. [1883]

Clark (George Norman). The Dutch alliance & the war agst. French trade, 1688–97. 8°. 1923

Clark (Hartley).

Bokhara, Turkoman & Afghan rugs. 4°. 1922

Clark (Hubert Lyman), *see* BRIT. MUSEUM OF NAT. HIST.: ZOOLOGY. Recent sea-urchins (Echinoidea) in coll. of B.M.; by H. L. C., 1925.

Clark (J. M.) The Abbey of St. Gall as a centre of literature & art. 8°. C. 1926

Clark (J. O. A.), *ed., see* WESLEY (J.) W. memorial vol., 1881.

Clark (John J.) The housing problem: hist., growth, legislation &c. Intr. by Brig.-Gen. G. Kyffin-Taylor. 8°. 1920

Clark (John Maurice).

Studies in the economics of overhead costs. 8°. Chicago. 1923

Clark (John Spencer). The life &c. of John Fiske. 8°. N.Y. [1917]

Clark (John Willis). On the library of S. Mark, Venice. [Fr. Camb. Ant. Soc. Commun., v15. P2872]. 8°. C. 1911

Clark (Lindley Daniel). Compar. of Workmen's compensation laws of U.S., *see* UNITED STATES: LABOR. Bull. 379, 1925.

Workmen's compensation legisl. of the U.S. & Canada, 1920–22, *see* U.S.: LABOR. Bull. 332, 1923.

—— & D. F. Callahan. Decisions of courts &c. affect. labor, 1922, *see* U.S.: LABOR. Bull. 344, 1923.

—— & M. C. Fricke. Workmen's compensation legisl. of the U.S. & Canada, *see* U.S.: LABOR. Bull. 272, 1921.

—— & S. J. Tracy. Decisions of courts affect. labor, 1923–24, *see* U.S.: LABOR. Bull. 391, 1925.

Laws rel. to payment of wages, *see* U.S.: LABOR. Bull. 408, 1926.

Clark (Richard). An exam. into the derivation, etymology, & defin. of the word "madrigale." s8°. 1852

Clark (Ruth).

Anthony Hamilton: h. life & works & h. family. 8°. 1921

Clark (Samuel), *see* CLARKE (S.), *minister of St. Bennet Fink.*

Clark (Victor Selden). Hist. of manufactures in the U.S., 1607–1860. [C.I. of Wash.] la8°. Wash. 1916.

Clark (William Andrews), *junior.* Library of W. A. C. The Kelmscott & Doves Presses. Coll. & comp. by R. E. Cowan &c. Introd. by A. W. Pollard. 2p *in* 1v. 4°. San Francisco. 1921

The library of W. A. C.: Wilde & Wildeiana, coll. & comp. by R. E. Cowan & W. A. C. v3. la8°. San Francisco. 1924

Clark (William George), *fellow of Trin. Coll., Cambridge.*

Gazpacho: summer months in Spain. 2nd ed., rev. s8°. 1851

Clark (William Robinson).

Savonarola, h. life & times. 8°. Chicago. 1896

Clarke (*Mrs.*) *Cat. of fine old chased & modern plate &c. [*prop. of Mrs. C. &c.*] which will be sold by auction by Farebrother, 31 Jan. 1821. 8°. [1821]

Clarke (A. H. F.) To Kiel in the German raider Wolf—& after. 2nd ed. s8°. Colombo. 1920

Clarke (Adam), *LL.D.*

An acc. of the life of A. C. By one who was acquainted w. him [*i.e. A. C. himself*]. Ed. J. B. B. Clarke. 3v [v2, 3, by a member of h. family (M. A. Smith)]. 8°. 1833

A diss. on the use & abuse of tobacco. 4th ed. [P2511]. 8°. 1814

Mem. of Mrs. Mary Cooper. 6th ed. s8°. 1828

Misc. works. 13v. s8°. 1836–41

Clarke (Adam), *LL.D.* [*continued*].
Succinct acc. of the princ. ed. of the Greek Test., 1514–1797 &c. [P2757]. s8°. M'ter. 1804
see ETHERIDGE (J. W.) Life of A. C., 1859.
„ JONES (W.) Mem. of the life of A. C., 1834.

Clarke (Amy Key). 3 one-act plays. Persephone by A. K. C. —Cloudbreak, by A. O. Roberts—Wind o' the Moors, by L. du G. Peach. s8°. O. 1925

Clarke (Austin). The fires of Baäl. [*Poem*]. s8°. D. 1921

Clarke (Benjamin), *F.R.C.S.* *Glimpses of anc. Hackney & Stoke Newington. Repr. of articles in the Hackney Mercury, Apr. 1892–Nov. 1893, w. an App. &c. By F. R. C. S. la8°. [1894]

Clarke (Charles Cowden), *see* CHAUCER (G.) Riches of C. &c., w. notes & n. mem. by C. C. C., 2v, 1835–39.

Clarke (D. E. Martin), *see* EDDA: POETIC E. The Hávamál &c.; ed. & tr. by C., 1923.

Clarke (Edward), *of Chipley, barrister, 1651–1710, see* LOCKE (J.) Corresp. of J. L. & E. C.; ed. &c. B. Rand, 1927.

Clarke (Edward Daniel), *see* OTTER (W.) Life & remains of E. D. C., 1824.

Clarke (*Rt. Hon. Sir* **Edward George).**
Benjamin Disraeli, 1804-1881. 8°. 1926

Clarke (Edwin Leavitt).
Amer. men of letters: their nature & nurture. 8°. N.Y. *Columbia Univ.* 1916

Clarke (*Sir* **Ernest).** The family letters of O. Goldsmith. Bibliogr. Soc., 1917. [Repr.] 8°. 1920

Clarke (Francis Coningsby Hannam).
Statistics & geography of Russian Turkestan. [P2604]. fol.1879
see WAR OFFICE, Staff duties; prep. by F. C. H. W. rev. &c. by J. S. Rothwell, 1890.

Clarke (Frederick).
Recht über alles. German verses. [P2484]. *n.p.* [1918]

Clarke (Geoffrey). The post office of India & its story. 8°. 1921

Clarke (George Aubourne). Clouds: descr. guide-book to obs. & classific. of clouds. Pref. by Sir N. Shaw. 8°. 1920

Clarke (George Herbert), *M.A.*, **& C. J. Murray.**
Grammar of the German lang. s8°. C. 1906

Clarke (Henry Wilberforce). The Persian manual. s8°. 1878

Clarke (Isabel Constance). Carina. s8°. [1923]
The Castle of San Salvo. s8°. [1926]
Viola Hudson. s8°. [1923]

Clarke (John), *lect. at the Univ. of Aberdeen.*
Short studies in educ. in Scotland. s8°. 1904

Clarke (John Henry), *M.D.*
The call of the sword. [P2520]. 8°. 1917
Constitut. medicine, w. spec. ref. to The 3 constitutions of Dr. v. Grauvogl. s8°. 1926
*England under the heel of the Jew. By the a. of The call of the sword [*i.e.* J. H. C.] 8°. 1918
*England under the heel of the Jew. Ed. J. H. G. 2nd ed. 8°. 1921
Hahnemann & Paracelsus. [P2688]. 8°. 1923
William Blake on the Lord's Prayer. s8°. 1927

Clarke (John Joseph). Local govt. of the U.K. Foreword by Sir H. Crawford. s8°. 1922
Outlines of local govt. of the U.K. incl. Educ. Act, 1921 &c. 5th ed., rev. & enl. s8°. 1922
Social administr. incl. the poor laws. s8°. 1922
—— & J. E. Pratt.
Outlines of indust. & soc. economics. s8°. 1919

Clarke (John Mason). L'Ile Percée, the finial of the St. Lawrence, or Gaspé flaneries. 8°. New Haven. 1923

Clarke (Joseph Butterworth Bulmer), *ed., see* CLARKE (A.) Life of A. C., 3v, 1833.

Clarke (*Mrs.* **Mary Cowden).**
Life & labours of V. Novello, by h. daughter. 8°. [1864]

Clarke (Maude Violet). The medieval city state. s8°. [1926]

Clarke (Samuel), *minister of St. Bennet Fink.* The lives of sundry emin. persons chiefly extr. f. C., *see* WESLEY (J.) Xtn. lib., v26, 27, 1753.
The marrow of eccl. hist. cont. in the lives of the Fathers, divines &c. 2p *in* 1v. [p2 in 2 bks. *sep. pagin.*] s4°. 1650
The saint's nosegay. Coll. &c. S. C. Repr., w. mem. by G. T. C. C[lark]. s8°. *p.p.* 1881
Suppl. to Fox's Acts & mon.; extr. f. C.'s gen. martyrology, *see* WESLEY (J.) Xtn. lib., v6, 1751.

Clarke (Samuel), *D.D., rector of St. James's, Westminster.* A letter to Mr. Dodwell; w. a defense of an argument in the letter to prove the immateriality &c. of the soul. In 4

Clarke (Samuel), *D.D.* [*continued*].
letters to the a. [A. Collin] of Some remarks &c. Added reflections on part of book [by J. Toland.] called Amyntor &c. 5th ed. 8°. 1718
see LEIBNITZ (G. W., *Frhr.* v.) Epistolarum pentas una cum respons. S. C., 1740.

Clarke (Samuel C.), *see* VAN DOREN (L. O.) Fishes of East Atlantic coast, incl. Fishes of East coast of Florida by S. C. C., 1884.

Clarke (Somers).
The unrest in Egypt. [P2488]. s8°. [Cairo. 1919]

Clarke (Thomas). *Hist. of the Church, parish & manor of Howden. 8°. Howden. 1850

Clarke (Thomas J.) Glimpses of an Irish felon's prison life. Intr. by P. S. O'Hegarty. s8°. D. 1922

Clarke (W.), *1800–38.* *Three courses & a dessert. Illust. by G. Cruikshank. 5th ed. s8°. 1852

Clarke (William George), *F.G.S.*
Our homeland prehist. antiq. s8°. [1922]

Clarke (William Kemp Lowther).
*The New Prayer Book explained. [P2878]. s8°. [1927]

Clarkson (Christopher).
*Hist. of Richmond in the co. of York. s8°. Richmond. 1814

Clarkson (David). A disc. conc. liturgies. s8°. 1689
*The pract. divinity of the Papists destructive of Christianity &c. s4°. 1676
Primitive episcopacy &c. [*b. w. h.* Disc. con. liturgies, 1689]. s8°. 1688

Clasen (Daniel). Exercit. sacræ ad Passionem Dominicam. s4°. Magdeburgi. 1657
Noturfftiger Bericht: Jubelfest, nebst Erzehl. d. Reformation &c. [P2647]. s4°. Magdeburg. 1655
Theologia gentilis. s8°. Francofurti. 1684

Clason (A. W.) Seven conventions. 8°. N.Y. 1888

Class (Heinrich). Einhart, 1914–19, Sonderdruck aus "Einhart, Deutsche Gesch." 8. Auflage. 8°. L. 1920
Zum deut. Kriegsziel. [P2689]. 8°. München. 1917
see ZWANZIG Jahre alldeut. Arbeit &c.; hrsg. v. d. Hauptleitung d. Alldeut. Verbandes [Vorwort v. H. C.], 1910.

Classen (Ernest).
Outlines of the hist. of the Eng. lang. s8°. 1919

Classen (Walther). Das Werden d. deut. Volkes. 2e durchgearb. A. 3B. 8°. [1926]

Classical. Class. collector's vade mecum, 1822, *see* POOLE (—).
*Class. dict. of the vulgar tongue, 1785, *repr.*, *see* GROSE (F.)

Classical Association. Proceedings. 1920–26 (v17–23); w. rules & list of members. 8°. 1920–26
Year's work in class. studies, 1918–19, 1921–27. Ed. for the Class Assoc. 8°. Bristol. 1920–27
see ANTIQUITY. Claim of ant., w. annot. list of bks., 1922.

Classical quarterly. v14–21. la8°. 1920–27

Classical review (The). v34–41. la8°. 1920–27

Clauberg (K. W.) & W. Dubislay.
Systemat. Wörterbuch d. Philosophie. s8°. L. 1923

Claude, *le Lorrain.*
see BOUYER (R.) C. L., 1927.
„ HIND (A. M.) C. L. & mod. art, 1926.
„ —— Drawings of C. L., 1925.
„ MANWARING (E. W.) Ital. landscape in 18th c. England: infl. of C. L. &c., 1925.

Claude (Jean), *1618–87.* The Catholick doctrine of the Eucharist in ans. to M. Arnaud. Added an acc. [*w. sep. tp.*] of the Book of the body & blood of our Lord by Bertram [*i.e.* Ratramnus] & of the authority of J. Scot or Erigenus. 6 bks. [Tr. by J. R. R.] 2p *in* 1v. [p1 *has 2nd engr. tp., dated* 1683. p2 *has sep. pagin. but no tp.*] fol. 1683–84
*La défense de la Réform. contre le livre [*by* Barthélemi *pseud. i.e.* P. Nicole] intitulé Préjugez légitimes contre les Calvinistes. s4°. *Se vend à Quevilly.* 1673
„ „ ....s8°. Amsterdam. 1683
A defence of the Reform.: tr. by T. B. Prefixed a sk. of the author's life &c. by J. Townsend. 2v. 8°. 1815
see BOSSUET (J. B.) Œuvres, t23, Conf. avec M. C. sur la matière de l'église—Réflex. sur un écrit de M. C., 1816.
„ JACKSON (T.) Lib. of Xtn. biog., v10, 1839.
„ NICOLE (P.) Les pretendus reformez &c., réponse à Considérations &c. [*by J. C.*], 1684.

Claudel (C.) Les vilains: nouvelle, *see* ŒUVRES libres, 54, 1925.

Claudel (Paul).

The city. Play. Tr. J. S. Newberry. 8°. New Haven. 1920
Corona benignitatis anni Dei. [*Poems*]. 7e éd. s8°. 1920
Deux farces lyriques, Protée—L'ours & la lune. 4e éd. s8°. 1927
Feuilles de saints. 5e éd. s8°. [1925]
Morceaux choisis. 5e éd. s8°. [1925]
Le père humilié. Drame. 7e éd. s8°. 1920
Poëmes de guerre, 1914–16. 3e éd. s8°. 1922
Le soulier de satin, 1er journée, *see* ROSEAU (LE) D'OR. Chron., 1, 1925.
see ÆSCHYLUS. Les Choéphores d'E. [tr. & essai par P. C.], 1920.
„ —— Les Euménides d'Eschyle [tr., *w.* Note *by* P. C.], 1920.
„ RIVIÈRE (J.) & P. C. Corr., 1907–14, 1926.
„ SAINTE-MARIE PERRIN (E.) Intr. à l'œuvre de P. C., avec textes, 1926.
„ TRUC (G.) P. C., 1925.

Claudianus (Claudius). Claudian. With Eng. tr. by M. Platnauer. [Loeb Class. Lib.] 2v. s8°. 1922

Claudius, *King of Ethiopia.* Conf. fidei [*Ethiop.*] cum vers. Lat. notis & præf. Iobi Ludolfi. revisa &c., cura I. H. Michaelis. s4°. Halæ. 1702

Claudius I, *emperor of Rome, see* SENECA (L. A.) D. Claudii apotheosis; ed. O. Rossbach, 1926.

Claudius (Gottfried Christoph). Das entdeckte Heiligthum d. Schwärmer, d. ist gründl. Untersuchung der Conventiculorum &c. s8°. Zittau. 1736
Hist. Fratrum Sportulantium, exercit. ad Cæcil. Cypriani lib 1. epist. 9. s8°. Francofurti. 1724

Claudius (Matthias) [*ps.* ASMUS; *and* DER WANDSBECKER BOTE]. Sämmtl. Werke. 1. u. 2. Theil [*in* 1v]. s8°. Breslau. [1774]

Claudius Pulcher (Appius), *brother of P. Clodius, see* CONSTANS (L. A.) Un correspondant de Cicéron: A. C. P., 1921.

Clausen (George). George Clausen. [Plates, w. descr. &c. signed D. H.] la8°. 1923

Clauser (Christoph), *d. 1552, see* WEHRLI (G. A.) Der zürcher Stadtarzt Dr. C. C. u. s. Stellung z. Reform. d. Heilkunde im 16. J. [*w.* Faksimiledr. d. Harnschrift Clausers, 1531], 1924.

Clausewitz (Carl v.) Vom Kriege. Mit e. Einführ. v. Graf v. Schliessen. Sach- u. Namenregister v. P. Creuzinger. 9e verb. A. 8°. 1915
War according to C. [*Tr. of v1 of h.* Vom Kriege]. Ed., w. commentary by Maj.-Gen. T. D. Pilcher. 8°. 1918
see MURRAY (*maj.* S. L.) Reality of war; intr. to C., 1909.

Clauss (Hermann). Die Schwabacher Kirchenbibliothek [*&* Bücherverzeichnis]. la8°. München. 1921

Clauswitz (Benedict Gottlob). Syntagma doct. de fide in Iesum Christum disput. [*each w. sep. tp. & pagin.*] s4°. Halæ. 1748

Clavasio (Angelus de), *see* ANGELUS [CARLETUS], *de Clavasio.*

Claverhouse (Jean Graham), *viscountess of Dundee, aft. wife of Will. Livingston, visct. Kilsyth, form. Lady Jean Cochrane, see* PARKER (*Mrs.* K.) "My Ladie Dundie," 1926.

Claverie (Joseph). La jeunesse d'Hoelderlin jusqu'au roman d'Hypérion. 8°. 1921

Clavijo (Jose de Viera y), *see* VIERA Y CLAVIGO.

Clawson (John L.) Elizabethan & early Stuart lib. of J. L. C. Auction, May 1926, Anderson Gall. 2p *in* 1v. 8°. N.Y. [1925]

Clay (Albert Tobias). The empire of the Amorites. [Yale Or. ser., v6]. la8°. New Haven [U.S.] 1919
see MURASHÛ, *Sons, of Nippur.* Business doc. of M. S.; [ed., w. pref.] by A. T. C., 1912.

Clay (Henry). Economics: an intr. [repr.] s8°. 1920
see FOSTER (T.) & G. COCHRAN, *edd.* *Eulogies on H. C. &c., 1853.

Clay (John William), *see* HAMERTON (L.) Olde Eland, w. chapters on the antiqs. of E. by J. W. C., 1901.

Clay (Richard Challoner Cobbe), *see* CRAWFORD (O. G. S.) & A. KEILLER. Wessex f. the air; w. contrib. by C. &c., 1928.

Clayton (C. H. J.) Land drainage. From field to sea. Pref. by Sir A. Fellowes. s8°. 1919

Clayton (Henry Helm). *Works in* S.I. Misc. coll.
Solar activity & long per. weather changes, 1926. [78.]
Solar radiation & weather, 1925. [77.]
Variation in solar radiation & the weather, 1920. [71.]
World weather records; coll. f. sources by Dr. F. Exner, Sir G. Walker &c.; arr. by H. H. C., 1927. [79.]
see HUNTINGTON (E.) Earth & sun, w. chapter by C., 1923.

Clayton (John), *physician, of Virginia, see* GRONOVIUS (J. F.), *the younger.* Flora Virginica exhib. plantas quas J. C. in Virginia observavit, &c. J. F. G., 1762.

Clayton (Joseph). The rise & decline of socialism in Gt. Brit., 1884–1924. 8°. 1926

Clayton (Robert), *bp. of Clogher.* A vindic. of the histories of the Old & New Test. In answ. to Lord Bolingbroke. repr. s8°. [1752]

Clayton (William). Margarine. 8°. 1920

Cleaning (The) and restor. of museum exhibits. 3rd rep. of investig. at B. M. [Dept. of Sci. & Indust. Research]. 8°. 1926

***Cleanness:** an allit. tripartite poem on the deluge, the destruction of Sodom & the death of Belshazzar, by the poet of "Pearl." [Sel. early Eng. poems; ed. by Sir I. Gollancz, 7]. 8°. 1921
see PEARL. Pearl, Cleanness &c.; reprod. in facs.; intr. by Sir I. Gollancz, 1923.

Cleather (Alice Leighton).
H. P. Blavatsky: a gt. betrayal. 8°. Calcutta. 1922
H. P. Blavatsky as I knew her, w. add. by B. Crump. 8°. Calcutta. 1923
H. P. Blavatsky, h. life & work for humanity. 8°. Calcutta. 1922

Cleaveland (John), *poet, see* CLEVELAND (J.)

Cleberus (Eusebius), *see* POUCHEN (A.) Theses oppositæ blasphemæ disput. tertiæ E. C. &c., 1585.

Clédat (Jean). Le monastère & la nécropole de Baouît, t2i, *see* INSTITUT FRANÇ. D'ARCH. ORIENT. DU CAIRE. Mém., t39i, 1916.

Clédat (Léon). Dict. étymolog. de la langue franç. 10e éd., rev. & augm. d'un index lat. 8°. [1925]
Gramm. raisonnée de la langue franç. Avec préface de G. Paris. 2me éd. s8°. 1894
Manuel de phonétique & de morphologie hist. du Français. 8°. 1917
Manuel de phonétique & de la morphologie romanes. 8°. 1925

Cleemann (Christian Gottfried) *& others.*
Vitæ eremiticæ origines. [P433]. s4°. Dresdæ. 1733

Clef (La) des songes. Facs. &c. par M. Hélin, 1925, *see* DANIEL, *the prophet, ps.*

Clegg (Arthur Henry), *1858–1886, see* PAWLYN (J. S.) Fallen on the field: mem. of A. H. C., 1889.

Clegg (John Trafford) ["TH' OWD WEIGHVER"]. Works [v2]. Stories &c. in the Rochdale dialect. 8°. Rochdale. 1898
Cotton: a play. [P2867]. s8°. Rochdale. 1894
Reaund bi th' Derby &c. [P2867]. s8°. M'ter. 1890

Cleghorn (Hugh), *of Stravithie; 1751–1834.* Cleghorn papers. Diary, 1795–96. Ed. W. Neil. Foreword by Sir A. Sprot. 8°. 1927

Cleinow (Franz). Bürger, Arbeiter rettet Europa!. Erlebnisse im sterbenden Russland. [P2456]. 8°. 1920

Cleinow (Georg). Der grosse Jahrmarkt v. Nishnij-Nowgorod. la8°. Erfurt. 1925

Cleland (Mary). The sure traveller. s8°. [1923]

Clemangiis (Nicolaus de) [N. DE CLAMENGIS; N. CLAMENGIUS].
De diebus festis & sabbato c. 1412 scr. s8°. Helmstadii. 1703
Opera omnia, quæ descr. &c. & ed. J. M. Lydius. Acc. ejusdem Glossarium Latinobarbarum [*w. sep. pagin.*] s4°. Lugd. Batav. 1613

Clemen (Carl). Die griech. u. latein. Nachrichten ü. d. pers. Religion. 8°. Giessen. 1920
see STETTINGER (G.) Gesch. d. Johann. Abschiedsreden; gegen K. C., 1919.

Clemen (Otto). Alexius Chrosner, Herzog Georgs v. Sachsen evangel. Hofprediger. 8°. L. 1907
Studien zu Melanchthons Reden u. Gedichten. 8°. L. 1913

Clemen (Paul). Kunstschutz im Kriege. Berichte ü d. Zustand d. Kunstdenkmäler auf d. verschied. Kriegsschauplätzen &c. In Verb. mit G. Bersu, H. Braune &c. hrsg. v. P. C. 2B. (1, Die Westfront. 2, Italien, Osten u. Südosten). fol. L. 1919

—— **& C. Gurlitt.** Die Klosterbauten d. Cistercienser in Belgien. Im Auft. d. kaiserl. deut. Generalgouv. in B. hrsg. v. P. C. & C. G. fol. 1916

Clemenceau (Georges Eugène Benjamin).

Au pied du Sinaï. s8°. 1920
Au soir de la pensée. 2 [t]. 8°. [1927]
Démosthène. 8°. [1926]
The strongest. [Tr.] s8°. [1919]
see JUDET (E.) Le véritable C., 1920.
see LANSING (R.) The Big Four, 1922.
„ LAURENT (M.) Nos gouvernements de Guerre: C. &c., 1920.
„ TERRAIL (G.) Le combat des trois: la Confér. de la paix, 1922.

Clemens, *Alexandrinus* [†Clemens (Titus Flavius)].

Opera quæ extant. Recog. & illust. per J. Potterum. [*Gr. & Lat.*] 2t [*pagin. contin.*] fol. Oxonii. 1715

Operum C. A. suppl. Coll. & cum præf. ed. T. Ittigius. [*b. w.* Ittig (T.) Bibl. Patr. Apostol. Gr.-Lat., 1699]. s8°. Lipsiæ. 1700

see Chapman (J.), *O.S.B.* L'auteur du Canon murator., *n.d.*

,, Hering (J.) Et. sur la doct. de la chute & de la préexistence des âmes chez C., 1923.

,, Kaye (J.) Writings &c. of C., 1890.

Clemens, *Romanus* [†Clement I, *Saint, pope*].

Αἱ δύο πρὸς Κορινθίους ἐπιστολάι. 8°. Ἐν Κωνσταντινουπόλει. 1875

The Epistle of C. to the Corinthians. With introd. & notes. Tr. B. H. Cowper. [*b. w.* Tischendorf. When were Gospels wr. ?, 1867]. s8°. [1867]

see Apostolic. The A. Fathers ; [tr.], v1, 1888 ; 1909.

,, Cotelerius (J. B.), *ed.* SS. patrum C. &c. ; una cum Cis actis &c., 2v, 1724.

,, Harnack (C. G. A.) Neue St. z. lat. Übers. d. 1. Clemensbriefs, 1894.

see Ittig (T.) Bibl. Patrum Apost. Gr.-Lat., 1699.

,, Lietzmann (H.) Hdbh. z. N.T. : Ergänzungsband, 1, Die 2 Clemensbriefe, erkl. v. R. Knopf, 1920.

,, Lutterbeck (J. A. B.) Die Clementinen u. ihr Verhältn. z. Unfehlbarkeitsdogma, 1872.

,, Mark, *St.* Div. liturgia S. M. ; Clem. P. R. De ritu missæ, 1583.

Clemens August, *elector of Cologne ; 1700–61, see* Renard (E.) C. A., Kurfürst v. K., 1927.

Clemens (Andreas). Walach. Sprachlehre für Deutsche, nebst e. kleinen Walach.-Deutsch u. Deutsch.-Walach. Wbche. [*w. sep. tp. & pagin.*] s8°. Hermannstadt. 1823

Clemens (Benjamin Gottlieb). Isagoge crit.-dogmat. gen. in theolog. univ. acroamaticam &c. s4°. Rostochii. 1753

Clement IV, *pope.* Registres de C. IV. Publ. E. Jordan. [Ecoles Franç. d'Athènes & de Rome]. t1, (1265–66). 4°. 1893–1912

Clement V, *pope, see* Boniface VIII, *pope.* Acta inter B. VIII, C. V & Phil. regem, 1614.

see Eitel (A.) Kirchenstaat unter C. V, 1907.

Clement VI, *pope* [Pierre Roger]. C. VI e Casa Savoia : doc. vaticani & App., Nuovi doc., *see* Regia Dep. di Storia Patria. Misc., t36, 1900.

Lettres (1342–1352). Textes &c. rec. & éd. P. Van Isacker ; publ. par U. Berlière. [Analecta Vaticano-Belg., v6]. t1, 1342–46. 8°. Rome. 1924

Clement VII, *pope* [Giulio de' Medici].

see Charles V, *Emp. of Germany.* Pro divo Carolo &c. apologetici libri duo (C. VII literæ &c.), 1527.

,, Rungius (D.) Bericht &c. : C. Bull v. Jubeljahr, 1601.

Clement VIII, *pope* [Ippolito Aldobrandini].

see Lemos (T. de). Acta omnia Congregat. ac Disput. coram C. VIII &c., 1702.

,, Meyer (A. O.) C. VIII u. Jakob I v. Eng., 1904.

Clement XI, *pope* [Giovanni Francesco Albani].

C. XI damnatio quamplurium propositionum excerpt. ex libro Gallico idiomate impr. (*Bull* Unigenitus). [P2659]. s8°. Romæ. 1713

Homiliæ in Evangelia. fol. Romæ. 1722

Opera omnia &c. Accedit vita C. XI à Præsule quondam Romano perscr. 4p [1, 2 & 4, *b. together*]. fol. Francofurti & Romæ. 1729

Orationes consistoriales. fol. Romæ. 1722

see Gordon (J.) The famous bull Unigenitus put forth by C. XI &c., 1731.

,, N. (*abbas*). *Epistolæ. abbatis N. ad episcopum N. ; æquitas Constit. Unigenitus [*of C. XI &c. w. text of bull*], 1716.

,, Quesnel (P.) Errores &c. P. Q. ; constit. C. XI &c., 1717.

,, Viva (D.) Quesnellianæ theses a C. XI confixæ, 1724.

Clément XIII, *pope, see* La Croix de Ravignan (G. F. X. de). C. XIII & C. XIV, 1854.

see La Croix de Ravignan (G. F. X. de). C. XIII & XIV, vol. suppl., 1854.

Clement XIV, *pope.*

Breve del papa C. XIV col quale è soppressa la Comp. di Gesú, 21 Luglio 1773. [P520]. 8°. 1873

Epistolæ et brevia &c. Ed. A. Theiner. 8°. Parisiis. 1852

Letters. Pref. anecdotes of his life. Tr. 2v *in* 1. [v1, 4th ed.] 1777–1804

Lettres intéress. Tr. n. éd. t1. s8°. 1777

see Caraccioli (*marq.* L. A. de). Life of C. XIV, 1778.

,, La Croix de Ravignan (G. F. X. de). C. XIII & C. XIV, 1854.

,, —— C. XIII & C. XIV, vol. suppl., 1854.

,, Theiner (A.) Hist. du Pontificat de C. XIV ; tr., 2t, 1852.

Clement (Charles). Michelangelo. [Tr.] s8°. 1885

Clement (*Mrs.* **Clara Erskine**), *aft. Mrs. Waters.* Hdbk. of Xtn. symbols & stories of the Saints as illust. in art. Ed. K. E. Conway. [*repr.*] 8°. Boston [U.S.] *n.d.*

Clément (François), *see* Art (L') de vérifier les dates. 3e éd. [*cont. & publ.*] par [F. C.], 3t, 1783–87.

Clement (John) [Clements], *d. 1572, see* Wenkebach (E.) J. C., 1925.

Clement (John), *surgeon, of Weymouth, see* Hooper (J.) Advantages of early piety in a mem. of J. C., 1813.

Clementi (*Mrs.* **Marie Penelope Rose**), *wife of Cecil C. ; form. Eyres.* Through Brit. Guiana to the summit of Roraima. s8°. [1920]

Clementia. De summa eorum clementia qui habendis quæstionibus prefuerant, contra proditores quosdam, 1584, *see* Burghley (W. C. *b.*) Justitia Brit., 1584.

Clements (Frederic Edward). Plant succession. Analysis of the develop. of vegetation. [C.I. of Wash.] la8°. Wash. 1916

—— **& F. L. Long.** Experimental pollination : outline of ecology of flowers & insects. [C.I. of Wash.] la8°. Wash. 1923

Clements (J. Morgan). China : automotive condit. & good roads movement, 1922, *see* United States : Commerce.

Gold placer area in Mongolia, China, 1922, *see* United States : Commerce.

Clements (John), *d. 1572, see* Clement (J.)

Clements (Paul Henry).

The Boxer rebellion. 8°. N.Y. *Columbia Univ.* 1915

Clements (William Lawrence), *see* Michigan. Univ. The W. L. C. Library of Americana at Univ. of M., 1923.

Clemmensen (Mogens), *see* Dugas (C.), J. Berchmans & M. C. Le sanctuaire d'Aléa Athéna à Tégée, 1924.

—— **& V. Lorenzen.** Kallundborg Kirke. [Selskab til Udg. af Danske Mindesmærker. *Dan. & Eng.*] fol. 1922

Clemow (Frank G.) The geography of disease. s8°. C. 1903

Cleopatra, *queen of Egypt.*

see Bethell (A. J.) C. to Christ, 4v, 1921.

,, Ferval (C.) La vie & la mort de C., *fiction,* 1922.

,, Harry (M.) La vie amoureuse de C., 1926.

,, Weigall (A. E. P.) Life & times of C., n. & rev. ed., 1923.

Clerc (Henri) & L. Landry. Le tentateur, *see* Œuvres libres, 82, 1928.

Clerc (Michel). Massalia : hist. de Marseille dans l'antiquité. t1. la8°. Marseille. 1927

Clercq (René de). Toortsen. s8°. A. 1909

Clergerie (*le gén*) **& L. Delahaye d'Anglemont.** La Bataille de la Marne. Le rôle du gouvt. milit. de Paris, 1–12 sept., 1914. s8°. 1920

Clergue (Helen). Phases of France on the eve of the Revolution. s8°. [1922]

Clergyman, *of London, ps.* *The Christian's memorandum-book, 1755, *see* Christian.

Clergyman (A) of the Church of Eng., *ps.* *An exam. of Dr. Rutherforth's argument : clergy to subscribe to an establ. confess. &c., 1766, *see* Dawson (D.)

Clergyman of the country, *ps.* *Devotional poems, 1699, *see* Devotional.

Clerical Library. *Bibliotheca Clericalis. Catalogue of the C. Lib. [By J. Darling]. 8°. 1843

Clerical, Medical & General Life Assurance Society, *see* Besant (A. D.) Our centenary : hist. of 1st 100 yrs. of C. &c. Life Assur. Soc., 1924.

Clericus (Joannes), *theologian, see* Le Clerc (J.)

Clericus a Belliberone (Nicolaus Franciscus), *see* Le Clerc de Beauberon (N. F.)

Clerk (*Sir* **Dugald**). Discovery & invention. [Repr. f. J. of R. Soc. of Arts]. [P2484]. 8°. [1917]

Eng. & German methods contrasted. [Repr. f. Journal of Royal Soc. of Arts]. [P2484]. 8°. [1915]

——, **A. Smithells, & J. W. Cobb.** Rep. on the coal-gas & electrical supply indust. of U.K., to the pres. of Inst. of Gas Engineers. [P2687]. fol. [1919]

Clerk (John), *of Eldin, see* Douglas (H.) Naval evolutions ; review &c. of J. C.'s claims in relat. to the manœuvre of 12 April, 1782, 1832.

Clerk-Maxwell (James). Matter & motion. s8°. 1876

see Lorentz (H. A.) C. M.'s electromagn. theory, 1923.

Clermont (Émile).

Le passage de l'Aisne. [Les cahiers verts, 5]. s8°. 1921

Clermont-Ganneau (Ch.)

Recueil d'archéologie orientale. t8. 8°. 1924

,, ,, *a. c. of* t8, livr. 1–9 (1907) *b. sep.*

Clermontois. Les chartes du C. du Musée Condè, à Chantilly, 1069–1352. [Publ. avec intr. &c. par] A. Lesort. 8°. 1904
Clermont-Tonnerre (*duchesse* **Elisabeth de**), *née Gramont*.
Robert de Montesquiou et Marcel Proust. s8°. [1925]
Mémoires. [Cahiers verts (2e sér.), 9]. [t1]. s8°. [1928]
Clerval (*l'abbé* **A.**)
Guide chartrain: Chartres. s8°. Chartres. [1896]
Clery (*Sir* **Cornelius Francis**).
Minor tactics. 12th ed., rev. s8°. 1893
Cleugh (Sophia). Matilda. s8°. [1925]
Cleve (Sibylla von), *see* SIBYLLA [*von Cleve*].
Cleveland (John), *poet* [CLEAVELAND]. Revived poems, orations &c. [*incl.* *The rustick rampant &c. in the insurrect. of Wat Tyler, *w. sep. tp.*] s8°. 1687
Cleveland (S. Grover), *president of U.S.*, *see* MACELROY (R. M.) G. C., auth. biog., 2v, 1923.
Cleveland (*corporal* **W.**) Extr. f. journal kept on board "Madagascar" on passage f. Calcutta to Eng. cont. acc. of Sikh Exped. &c. [P2846]. 8°. Deal. [1847]
Cliff (A. B.) Imperial taxation: tax-system of U.K., w. tables, Jan. 1921. 8°. [1921]
Clifford, *Family of*, *see* CLIFFORD (I. G. C.) Descent of Charlotte Compton, Baroness Ferrers de Chartley &c., 1892.
Clifford (*Lady* **Anne**), *wife of (1) R. Sackville, earl of Dorset, & (2) P. Herbert, earl of Pembroke & Montgomery.*
Diary. Intr. by V. Sackville-West. s8°. 1923
Clifford (*Sir* **Hugh**). The downfall of the gods. s8°. 1911
The Gold Coast Regiment in the E. Afr. Campaign. 8°. 1920
Clifford (Isabella Georgiana Camilla). The descent of Charlotte Compton, Baroness Ferrers de Chartley &c. 8°. 1892
Clifford (Mary), *1842–1919*, *see* WILLIAMS (G. M.) M. C., 1920.
Clifford (W. G.) The ex-soldier by himself. s8°. 1916
Clifton College. C. C. annals & register, 1862–1912. Ed. F. Borwick. Intr. by J. E. King. 8°. Bristol. 1912
*Clifton College 40 yrs. ago, 1927, *see* NEWBOLT (*Sir* F. G.)
Clifton (C. Ebenezer). Manual of conversation. English-Portuguese. By M. C. s8°. Paris. [1887]
Clifton (*Mrs* **Talbot**), *see* CLIFTON (*Mrs.* V. M.)
Clifton (*Mrs.* **Violet Mary**), *wife of J. Talbot Clifton, form. Beauclerk.* Islands of Queen Wilhelmina. Intr. by Lord Dunsany. 8°. 1927
Pilgrims to the isles of penance: orchid gathering in the East. 8°. [1911]
Clifton of Rathmore (Edward, *Lord*), *see* DARNLEY (E., *5th earl*).
Climent (Manuel). Crón. de la prov. de Huelva, 1866, *see* ESPAÑA. Crón. gen., v5, 1865 &c.
Clinch (George). English coast defences f. Roman times to early 19th c. 8°. 1915
Clisson (Olivier de), *1336–1407*, *see* LEFRANC (*l'abbé* A.) O. de C., connétable de France, 1898.
Clive (Robert Clive, *1st baron*), *see* DODWELL (H.) Dupleix & C., 1920.
Clockmakers' Company, *London*, *see* ATKINS (S. E.) & W. H. OVERALL. Some acc. of the W. Co. of C., 1881.
Clodd (Edward). Magic in names & in o. things. 8°. 1920
Memories. 8°. 1926
The story of the alphabet. s8°. 1900
Clodius (Christian Conrad). De nummorum Ebraic. inscr. Samaritanis. Præs. C. D. Koch. [P431]. s4°. Helmstadii. [1712]
Cloker (Henry), *see* LAKE (C.) Notes on the will of H. C. 1573 &c., 1924.
Clop (Eusèbe). Saint Bonaventure, 1221–74. s8°. 1922
Cloria. *The princesse Cloria: or, The royal romance, 2nd ed., 1665, *see* PRINCESSE.
Cloriston (Henry), *ps.* [*i.e.* WILL. HART]. Sonnets & semblances, relat. to the War. v1. s8°. 1921
Close Rolls. Calendar of Close Rolls. [C. of State Papers]. la8°. 1922–27
Henry III [6], 1247–1251, [7], 1251–53.
Henry IV, v1, 1399–1402.
Richard II, v2–6, 1381–99.
Close (Albert). The naval war in the North Sea. [*folded chart*]. 8°. [1921]
Close (Etta), *F.R.G.S.* A woman alone in Kenya, Uganda & the Belgian Congo. s8°. 1924
Close (Upton), *ps.*, *see* HALL (J. W.)
Closson (Ernest).
André-Modeste Grétry. s8°. Turnhout. 1920
Roland de Lassus. s8°. Turnhout. 1919
Clouard (Henri). La poésie franç. mod., des romantiques à nos jours. 8°. [1924]
Cloud (D. C.)
Monopolies & the people. 8°. Davenport, Iowa. 1873
Clouet (François), *an ex-Capuchin.* *The Capucin's journal, *see* DU MOULIN (P.) The monk's hood pull'd off &c., 1671.
Clough (Arthur Hugh).
Poems: w. a memoir [*by F. T. Palgrave*]. s8°. 1862
see HUDSON (W. H.) Studies in interpretation; Keats–C. &c., 1896.
Clough (Benjamin).
Compendious Pali grammar, w. vocab. 8°. Colombo. 1824
A dict. of the Eng. & Singhalese & Singh. & Eng. langs. 2t [t1, Eng. & Singh. *wanting*]. 8°. Colombo. 1821–30
see PRAYER BOOK. Prayers sel. & tr. into Singhalese by B. C., 1819.
Clough (Charles Thomas), *F.G.S.* Geology of the Cheviot Hills. [Geolog. Survey]. 8°. 1888
Geology of Plashetts & Kielder. [Geolog. Survey]. 8°. 1889
see GUNN (W.) & C. T. C. Geol. of part of Northumberland, 1895.
Clouston (Joseph Storer).
Carrington's cases. s8°. E. 1920
The lunatic at large again. s8°. [1922]
The lunatic in charge. s8°. [1926]
The lunatic *still* at large. s8°. 1923
Mr. Essington in love. s8°. [1927]
Simon. s8°. E. 1919
Clouzot (Henri) & R.-H. Valensi. Le Paris de la Comédie humaine. (Balzac & ses fournisseurs). 8°. 1926
Clowes (William), *Primitive methodist, 1780–1851*, *see* DAVISON (J.) Life of W. C., 1854.
Cloz (Paris), *Count*, *see* KOPITAV (B.) Glagolita Clozianus &c., 1836.
Club (The). The Club. [List of members &c. P2600]. 8°. 1883
Club Cubano de Bellas Artes. Biblioteca. El arte y la lit. en Cuba. [1a ser. de Conferencias]. t1. La Habana. 1925
Club Men of New York, 1901–2. 4th issue. 8°. N.Y. 1901
Club (The) of Odd Volumes, *Boston, U.S.*, *see* ODD VOLUMES, THE CLUB OF.
Clubb (Merrel Dare), *ed.*, *see* CHRIST. C. & Satan: old Eng. poem, 1925.
Clug (Christian Gottlieb) [CLUGIUS]. De baptismo Adami comm. &c. [P2634]. s4°. Vitembergæ. 1747
Singularia theol. Carpovianæ in loco de creatione. Interseruntur Sententiæ philos. Wolfianæ. 2p *in* 1v. s4°. Vitembergæ. 1738–39
Cluny (Richard of), *see* RICHARD, *of Cluny*.
Clusius (Carolus), *see* L'ESCLUSE (C. DE).
Cluten (Joachim). Fasc. paradoxorum hist.-polit. ex J. Bodini lib. de republica coll. [P2743]. s4°. Basileæ. 1513 [*i.e.* 1613]
Clutton-Brock (Arthur).
Essays on books. s8°. [1920]
„ „ ..2nd ed. s8°. [1921]
Essays on life. Intr. by J. L. Hammond. s8°. [1925]
Essays on religion. Intr. by B. H. Streeter. s8°. [1926]
More essays on books. s8°. [1921]
The necessity of art. By A. C.-B., P. Dearmer, A. S. Duncan-Jones, J. M. Murry, A. W. Pollard & M. Spencer. [Ed. P. Dearmer]. 8°. 1924
Shakespeare's "Hamlet." s8°. [1922]
Shelley, the man & the poet. 2nd & rev. ed. s8°. [1923]
The ultimate belief. 5th impr. s8°. [1920]
see B. (E.), H. W. FOWLER & A. C.-B. Metaphor, 1922.
Clyde (James). Romaic & mod. Greek compared w. one another & w. anc. Gr. 8°. E. 1855
Clyde (Paul Hibbert). Internat. rivalries in Manchuria, 1689–1922. [Ohio State Univ.] la8°. Columbus. 1926
Cnapius (Gregorius), *see* KNAPSKI (GRZEGORZ).
Coaker (*Sir* **William Ford**), *Chairman of the Fisherman's Protective Union*, *see* SMALLWOOD (J. R.) C. of Newfoundland, 1927.
Coal. Coal & power: rep. of enquiry p. over by D. Lloyd George, 1924, *see* LLOYD GEORGE (D.)
The Coal crisis. Statement by Scot. c. owners, 12 Mar. 1912. [P2763]. 8°. 1912
*Coal mines, the dangers of nationalisation. [P2600]. 8°. *n.d.*
Coalfleet (Pierre). Hare & tortoise. s8°. N.Y. 1925
***Coastwise** trade of the U.K. [*Intr. by* A. Read]. 8°. 1925
Coate (*Miss* **Mary**). Social life in Stuart England. s8°. [1924]
Coates (*Sir* **Edward Feetham**), *1st bart.* Cat. of the Towneley Mysteries & the York missal. Sold by Sotheby, Feb. 1922. [Illust. P2853]. la8°. 1922

Coates (Harper Havelock), *see* Shunjō Hōin. Honen the Buddhist saint; tr., intr. &c. by H. H. C. &c., 1925.

Coates (Henry). Charlie Macintosh, post-runner, naturalist &c. [abr. ed.] s8°. [1924]

Coates (James). Photographing the invisible: pract. sts. &c. n. & rev. ed. s8°. [1921]

Coates (Zelda Kahan-), *see* Kahan-Coates (Z.)

Coatman (J.), *see* India: Anon. Works &c. India in 1925–26, 1926–27: statement prep. for Parl. by J. C., 1926–28.

Coats (A. H. Glen-), *see* Glen-Coats (A. H.)

Coats (Robert Hay).
John Galsworthy as a dramatic artist. 8°. [1926]

Cobb (Cyril Stephen), *see* Rationale. R. (The) of ceremonial, 1540–43; notes &c. & essay on regul. by C. S. C., 1910.

Cobb (Irvin Shrewsbury).
A laugh a day keeps the doctor away. Stories. 8° [1923]

Cobb (James), *dramatist.* Ramah Droog, *see* †Inchbald (*Mrs.* E.) Mod. theatre, v6, 1811.
The wife of two husbands, *see* †Inchbald (*Mrs.* E.) Mod. theatre, v6, 1811.

Cobb (John William), *see* Clerk (*Sir* D.), A. Smithells, & J. W. C. Rep. on coal-gas & electr. supply indust. of U.K., 1919.

Cobb (William Frederick). Hymns for men & women. Comp. by W. F. C. [f. priv. use]. s8°. 1915

Cobbett (William), *M.P.*
Advice to young men. s8°. 1829
Cottage economy. n. ed. s8°. 1823
The emigrant's guide; in 10 letters to the tax-payers of Eng. n. ed. s8°. 1830
The English gardener. s8°. 1829
A French grammar. s8°. 1824
A grammar of the Eng. lang. 4th ed. s8°. 1820
„ „ ....[a. ed.] s8°. 1831
Hist. of last 100 days of Eng. freedom; w. intr. & biog. index &c. by J. L. Hammond. 8°. 1921
Hist. of the Protestant Reform. in Eng. & Ireland. 2p. s8°. 1824–27
„ „ ....ster. ed. s8°. 1847
The political Proteus. A view of the public character &c. of R. B. Sheridan. 8°. [1804]
Rural rides. s8°. 1830
Rural rides, 1821–32. n. ed., w. notes by P. Cobbett. 2v. 8°. 1886
Tour in Scotland & in the 4 northern counties of Eng. s8°. 1833
Twelve sermons. s8°. 1823
A year's residence in the U.S. of Amer. 3rd ed. 3p [*in* 1v.] s8°. 1828
see Chesterton (G. K.) W. C., 1923.
„ —— W. C., 1925.
„ Cole (G. D. H.) Life of W. C., w. ch. on Rural rides by F. E. Green, 1924; 1925.

Cobbett (William Pitt). Leading cases on internat. law, w. notes &c. 4th ed., by H. H. L. Bellot. 2v. 8°. 1922–24

Cobbin (Ingram). The French preacher; or sermons tr. f. French Divines &c. Pref., an hist. view of the Reformed Ch. of France. 8°. 1816
*Some acc. of the Reformed ch. of France [1514–1815]. s8°. 1819

Cobden (Richard).
1793 & 1853, in three letters. [P505]. s8°. [1853]
see Holtzendorff (F. v.) R. C.; Vortrag, 1866.

Cobden-Sanderson (Thomas James). Cat. of pr. books &c. publs. of Doves Press, prop. of T. J. C.-S., bindings, the prop. of Earl of Haddington &c. Sold by Sotheby, Mar. 1923. [Illust.] la8°. 1923

Cobenzl (Joh. Ludwig Joseph *Graf* v.), *1753–1809.* Joseph II u. C.; ihr Briefwechsel, 2B, *see* Fontes rerum Austriac., B53, 54, 1901.
see Fournier (A.) Gentz u. C.: Gesch. d. österr. Diplomatie, 1801–5, 1880.

Cobern (Camden McCormack). The new archeolog. discov. & th. bearing upon the New Test. &c. Intr. by E. Naville. 3rd ed. 8°. N.Y. [1918]

Cobham (*Sir* Alan). Australia & back. 8°. 1926
Skyways. 8°. [1925]

Cobham (Claude Delaval). Arnalda, sive captiva victrix [1570]. Incerti scriptoris fabella. Ed. C. D. C. [P2862]. 8°. 1910
The churches & saints of Cyprus. [P2862]. s8°. 1910

Cobham (Richard Temple, *visct.*), *4th bart. of Stowe; 1669?–1749, see* Stowe. Descr. of the gardens of Lord Visct. C. at Stowe, 6th ed., 1749.

Cobham (Thomas de), *bp. of Worcester; d. 1327, see* Pearce (E. H.) T. de C., bp. of W., 1317–27: sts. f. h. register w. acc. of h. life, 1923.

Coblentz (William Weber). Instruments & methods used in radiometry, p1–3, 1907–18, *see* United States: Commerce, Dept. of.

Coccejus (Joannes), *1603–69* [Coch; Koch (J.)] Opera omnia theologica, &c. 8t. fol. Amstelodami. 1673–75
Index *in* t1. Lexicon sermonis Hebr. *in* t8. *Each work has sep. pagin. in var. vols.*
Opera ἀνέκδοτα theologica et philologica. 2t [*in* 1v.] fol. Amstelodami. 1706
see Flier (A. v. d.) Specimen hist.-theolog. de J. C., 1859.
„ Mishnah. Duo tituli thalmudici Sanhedrin & Maccoth; annot. a J. C., 1629.

Coccinius (Michael) [Köchlin]. Opusculum M. C. De imperii a Grȩcis ad Germanos translatione. Qui Galliæ populi spectent ad jus et ditionem imperii. Item de Francorum origine &c. Apologiæ duæ ejusdē C. s4°. Argeñ. *Ioannes Grüninger.* [1506]

Coccoluto-Ferrigni (Pietro) [*ps.* Yorick].
Uomini e fatti d'Italia. s8°. Firenze [1921]

Coch (Joannes), *see* Coccejus (Joannes).

Cochem (Martin v.), *1634–1712* [Martin Linius], *see* Kosch (W.) P. M. v. C. d. Apostel Deutschlands, 1921.

Cochet (Louis) [Cochetus (Ludovicus)]. Diss. orthodoxorum, Remonstrantium & Socin. deducta exhibens, præs. A. Ruchat. [P2631]. s4°. Bernæ. 1736

Cochin (Augustin), *see* France: Convention Nationale. Actes du gouvt. révol.: rec. de docs. publ. pour Soc. d'Hist. Contemp. par A. C. &c., t1, 1920.

Cochin (Denys), *1851–1921.*
see Bucaille (V.) D. C., 1922.
„ Goyau (G.) Séance de l'Acad. Franç.: disc. de récept. de G. G., éloge de D. C., 1923.

Cochinchine. Mission de la C. &c., 1858, *see* Jesuits. Voyages & travaux, t2, 1858.

Cochlaeus (Joannes) [†Dobneck (Johann)].
Adv. cucullatum Minotaurum Wittenberg. de sacram. gratia (1523); hrsg. J. Schweizer, *see* Corpus Catholic., H3, 1920.
Adv. latrocinantes & raptorias cohortes Rusticorum. Mar. Lutherus. Responsio I. C.—Cathalogus tumultuum &c. in superiori Germania nuper gestorum—132 articuli, excerpti, ex libro M. Lutheri contra eccl. Responsio brevis I. C. ad singulos. In Lat. tr. [*The* 132 articuli &c. *wanting*]. [P2540]. s4°. *n.p.* [1525?]
Articuli CCCCC. Martini Lutheri. Ex sermonibus ejus 36, quibus singulatim responsum est a I. C. s4° [Cologne?] 1526
Comm. de actis & scr. M. Lutheri chronographice, ex ordine ab a. 1517 ad 1546 incl. conscripta. Adjunctis 2 indicibus & Edicto Vuormaciensi. fol. Moguntiae. 1549
De animarum purgatorio igne epitome. s8°. Ingolstadii. 1544
De autoritate eccl. et Scripturae in Calvini errores &c. s8°. [apud S. Victorem prope Moguntiam]. 1549
De autoritate &c. Gen. Concilii. Testimonia 30. [*b. w. h.* De votis, 1550]. s8°. [Moguntiæ. 1546]
De Interim brevis resp. ad librum J. Calvini. [*b. w. h.* De votis, 1550] s8°. [Moguntiæ]. 1549
De novis ex Hebraeo translationibus S. Scr. disceptatio. [*a. c. in* P2544]. s8°. Ingolstadii. 1544
De sacris reliquiis Christi & sanctorum ejus, brevis contra J. Calvini calumnias resp. [*b. w. h.* De votis, 1550]. s8°. [Moguntiæ]. 1549
De Sanctorum invocatione &c., deq; imaginibus &c. piè colendis, adv. H. Bullingerum. [P2540]. s4°. Ingolstadii. 1544
De votis brevis disceptatio contra impugnationes J. Calvini. s8°. [Moguntiae]. 1550
Ex compendio actorum M. Lutheri caput ult., & ex epistola quadam Mansfeldensi hist. narr. &c. de Lutheri ult. actis & vitæ exitu. [*b. w. h.* De votis, 1550]. s8°. [*Mentz*]. 1548
Hist. de actis & scriptis M. Lutheri, 1517–46, cum edicto Vuormac. Adjecimus Antidotum contra veneficium sectarum hujus temp. B. Britann auctore [*w. sep. tp. & pagin.*] s8°. Parisiis. 1565
Hist. Hussitarum lib. xii. [*a. c. b. w.* Vigerius (J.) Instit. ad Christ. theolog., 1565]. fol. prope Moguntium. 1549
In primum Musculi Anticochlaeum replica J. C. pro sacerdotii &c. assertione. Adj., resp. in Antibolen Bullingeri. Add., app. in librum Buceri &c. s4°. [Ingolstadii]. 1545
Pia exhortatio Romæ ad Germaniam, suam in fide Christi filiam. s8° Tubingæ. 1525
Quadruplex concordiae ratio &c. super Conf. August. &c. 1. Brevis ad singula puncta Conf. responsio, Augustae scripta. a. 30.—2. Compendiosa explic. actorum Augustae a. 40.—3. Septem viæ praepar. ad ineundam per Colloquium concordiam, Vuormaciae a. 40.—4. Discussio Conf. & Apol. articul. &c. a. 41. s8°. [Ingolstadii]. 1544
Quatuor excusationum Lutheran. confut. una pro Concilio gen. ad Mantuam indicto. s8°. Lipsiae, *N. Wolrub.* 1537
Replica adv. prolixam respons. H. Bullingeri De Script. & Eccl. authoritate. [P2540]. s4°. Ingolstadii. 1544
Sacerdotii ac sacrificii novae legis defensio adv. W. Musculi Arrosiones. [P2540]. s4°. Ingolstadii. 1544
*Ein Sendbrieffe an e. fürnemen Thumbherren des Stiffts Eychstat

Cochlaeus (Joannes) [†DOBNECK (JOHANN)] [*continued*].
von D. J. Cochles auszgangner Schrifft an Kayserl. M. wider P. Melanthonem. [*Signed N. N.*] [P2439]. s4°. *n.p.* 1544
Speculum missae ex antiq. Patribus [Amalarius episc. quondam Treverensis *& others*] à J. C. coll.; nunc à Nicolao Aurifico recogn. &c. s8°. Venetiis. 1572
Wie verkerlich widder Georgen, Hertzogen zu Sachssen etc. Martin Luther den sibenden Psalm verdewtzscht, u. gemissbraucht. s4°. *n.p.* [Dresden ?] 1529
see ALESIUS (A.) Responsio ad Cochlei calumnias, 1535 (?).
,, BRUNO, *Saint, bp. of Würzburg.* Psalteriū a J. C. restit. &c., 1533.

Cochran (Charles Blake). The secrets of a showman. 8°. [1925]

Cochran (George), *see* FOSTER (T.) & G. C. *Eulogies on J. C. Calhoun &c.; comp. f. offic. sources, 1853.

Cochrane (Alex. Dundas R. W. Baillie), *1st baron Lamington.*
In the days of the dandies. s8°. E. 1890

Cochrane (Charles Norris).
David Thompson, explorer. s8°. Toronto. 1924

Cochrane (*Lady* Jean), *see* CLAVERHOUSE (J. G.), *vtess. Dundee.*

Cochrane (*Sir* John). Rels. of particulars in negoc. since coming to Hamburgh, 1649, *see* MAIDMENT (J.), *ed.* Hist. fragms., p2, 1833.

Cochrane (John), *of the Inner Temple.* Treatise on the game of chess; fr. the Traité des Amateurs &c. 8°. 1822

Cochrane (John Dundas). Pedestrian journey through Russia & Tartary to Kamtchatka. 2nd ed. 2v. 8°. 1824

Cockayne (Leonard). The cultiv. of N. Zealand plants. [N.Z. pract. hdbks.] s8°. Auckland. [1923]
New Zealand plants & their story. 2nd ed. 8°. Wellington, N.Z. 1919

Cockayne (William), *see* FRIIS (A.) Alderman C.'s project & the cloth trade, 1927.

Cockburn (Catherine), *wife of P. Cockburn, form. Trotter.*
*Agnes de Castro. Tragedy. 8°. 1696
*Remarks upon the princ. &c. of Dr. Rutherforth's Essay on virtue. Publ. by Warburton. [*b. w.* Warburton (W.) Alliance betw. Ch. & State, 1736]. s8°. 1747

Cockburn (*Gen. Sir* George). Six letters on subjects important to England. [P2566]. 8°. 1831

Cockburn (*Maj.-Gen.* James Pattison).
Swiss scenery f. drawings. la8°. 1820
Views to illust. the route of Mont Cenis. fol. 1822
Views to illust. the route of the Simplon. [*Gen. tp. missing*]. fol. [1822 ?]

Cockburn (John), *D.D.* Bourignianism detected: or the delusions &c. of Antonia Bourignon & h. sect. 2 Narr. [P2652]. s4°. 1698

Cockeram (Henry).
*The English dict. By H. C. 9th ed., rev. & enl. s8°. 1650
,, ,, ... 10th ed., rev. & enl. s8°. 1651

Cockerell (Sydney Carlyle), *see* BIBLE: PSALMS. Two E. Anglian Psalters: the Ormesby P., descr. by S. C. C., 1926.

Cockerham (Kirby Lee), *see* HAND (T. E.) & K. L. C. The sweet potato, 1921.

Cockfield (William Egbert). Sixtymile & Ladne Rivers area, Yukon. [Canada. Geol. Survey. P2512]. 8°. Ottawa. 1921
—— **& A. H. Bell.** Whitehorse district, Yukon. [Canada. Geol. Survey.] 8°. Ottawa. 1926

Cocks (F. Seymour). Russia & the Allies. Repr. f. The Herald. [P2381]. s8°. [1919]

Cocteau (Jean).
Antigone—Les mariés de la Tour Eiffel. 5e éd. s8°. [1928]
A call to order. Tr. R. H. Myers. 8°. 1926
Le grand écart. s8°. 1923
Les mariés de la Tour Eiffel, spectacle, *see* ŒUVRES (Les) libres, 21, 1923.
Orphée. Tragédie. s8°. 1927
Le Potomak, 1913–14, préc. d'un Prospectus 1916. s8°. 1924
Le rappel à l'ordre, 1918–26. [n. éd.] 8°. 1926
Thomas l'imposteur. 5e éd. s8°. [1923]

Codagnello (Johannes). Annales Placentini. Rec. O. Holder-Egger. [Scr. rerum Germ. in usum schol.] 8°. Hannoveræ. 1901

Codasch, *see* CUDESCH.

Code. Code bolchevik du mariage 2e éd., 1920, *see* RUSSIA: SOVIET REPUBLIC.
Code hittite prov. de l'Asie min., pl, 1922, *see* HROZNÝ (F.)

Codera y Zaidin (Francisco).
Estudios crit. de hist. árabe española. s2. [2t.] s8°. 1917

Codex.
Codex Bezae; ed. &c. T. Kipling, 1793, *see* BIBLE: NEW TEST. (GREEK).
,, ,, Gospels & Acts [*Gr. & Lat.*], 1864, *see* BIBLE: GOSPELS

Codex [*continued*].
Codex Claromontanus, sive Epist. Pauli &c., 1852, *see* BIBLE: PAUL.
Codex diplomaticus Austr.-Frising.; hrsg. v. J. Zahn, 3B, *see* FONTES RERUM AUSTRIAC., B31, 35, 36, 1870–71.
Codex diplomaticus neerlandicus. Verzameling v. oorkonden, betrekk. de vaderlandsche gesch. [Hist. Genootschap te Utrecht]. Ser. 2, Afd. 1–6 [Afd. 1–4 *have* 2d *each*; 1ii, 2i *wanting*]. 8°. Utrecht. 1852–63
d5 *has 2nd tp.* Kronijk van Arent toe Bocop.
d6, Chronijken van Braband en Vlanderen.
Codex doc. sac. indulgent. Neerland. (1300–1600), 1922, *see* FREDERICQ (P.)
Codex Fuldensis, N.T. Lat., 1868, *see* BIBLE: NEW TEST.
Codex juris canonici, *see* KÖSTLER (R.) Wörterbuch, Lief. 1, 1927.
Codex Theodosianus, rec. P. Krueger. fasc. 1, 2, Liber 1–8. la8°. Berolini. 1923–26

Codicele. Doua manuscripte vechi Cod. Todorescu & Cod. Martian, 1914, *see* DRAGANU (N.)

Codinus (Georgius), *Curopalata.* De officialibus Palatii Constantinop. & officiis magnæ Eccl. F. Iunius in Lat. tr. &c. [*Greek & Lat.*] s8°. *n.p.* 1596
De officiis et officialibus magnæ Eccl. et Aulæ Constantinop. Studio J. Gretseri Lat. versus. [*Gr. & Lat.*] Adj. tribus comm. &c. libris. Acc. Diss. de imaginibus non manufactis. [*by* J. Gretser. *w. sep. tp.*] fol. Parisiis. 1625

Codogno (Ottavio), *see* COTOGNO (O.)

Codrington (Humphrey William). Ceylon coins & currency. [Colombo Museum.] 4°. Colombo. 1924

Codrington (K. de B.) Ancient India f. earliest times to the Guptas, w. notes on architecture &c. of mediæval period. Pref. essay on Ind. sculpture by W. Rothenstein. fol. 1926

Codrington (Thomas), *M.Inst.C.E., F.G.S.*
Roman roads in Britain. repr. of 3rd ed. s8°. 1919

Codronchi Argeli (Eugenia), *see* SFINGE, *ps.*

Coeck (Peter) *of Aelst* [†ALST (PETER COECKE VAN); KOECK]. The Turks in 1533. Drawings made at Constantinople, publ. f. woodcuts, Antwerp, 1553. Reprod., w. intr. by Sir W. Stirling Maxwell. oblong atlas fol. *p.p.* 1873

Coedes (George). A propos d'une stèle sculptée d'Angkor-Vat, *see* ACAD. DES INSCR. &C. Mém. conc. l'Asie Or., t2, 1916.

Co-education. Advance in co-educ.: articles by var. as., 1919, *see* WOODS (A.), *ed.*

Coeffeteau (Nicolas). Response à l'advertissement adressé par le roy, Jacques I à tous les princes &c. de la Chrestienté. dern. éd., rev. s8°. 1615

Coelestial atlas, 1800–08, *see* CELESTIAL ATLAS.

Coelestinus (Georgius). Hist. comitiorum 1530 Augustæ celeb. 4t. *in* 1v. fol. Francofurti ad Oderam. 1597

Coelestinus (Johann Friedrich), *see* WIGAND (J.), T. HESHUSIUS & T. KIRCHNER. Erinn. v. C. Büchlin v. d. Erbsünde, 1572.

Coelho (Trindade). Os meus amores. Contos e balladas. 5a ed. s8°. Paris. 1922

Coen (Achille), *1844–1921.* Necrologia, *see* ARCHIVIO STOR. ITAL. Anno 79, v2, 1923.

Coen (Jan Pietersz.), *see* COLLENBRANDER (H. T.) J. P. C.: bescheiden omtren zijn bedrijf in Indië, 3d, 1919–21.

Coen-Cagli (Enrico), *see* ITALY: MIN. DEI LAVORI PUBBL. Porti marit. [Not. racc. da E. C.-C. e O. Bernardini], 1905.

Coeranides, *see* KOERANIDES.

Coesveldt (Anna Maria Helena), *aft. wife of Comte de Noailles, see* NOAILLES (A. M. H., *ctsse.* DE).

Cœur (Jacques).
see BONAMY (P. N.) Mém. sur les dern. années de J. C., 1875.
,, KERR (A. B.) J. C., merchant prince, 1927.

Coffey (Diarmid) [O COBHTHAIGH (D.)] Co-operative movement in Jugoslavia, Rumania & N. Italy dur. & after the World War. [C.E. f. Internat. Peace]. la8° N.Y. 1922

Coffin (Levi), *1798–1877.* Remin., being a brief hist. of labors in beh. of the slave. 2nd ed. w. app. 8°. Cincinnati. 1880

Coffin (Richard), *of Portledge, Bideford, see* LAPTHORNE (R.) The P. papers: letters to R. C., 1687–97, 1928.

Cogelerus (Johannes), *see* COGLER (J.)

Coghlan (T. A.)
Picturesque N.S. Wales. [repr.] la8°. Sydney. [1903]

Cogler (Johann) [COGELERUS]. Imagines elegant., ad intellig. doct. Xtnæ. locos coll., ex prælect. P. Melanthonis &c. Cum præf. G. Maioris. s8°. Vitebergæ. 1558

Cohen (Abraham), *Ph.D.* The teachings of Maimonides. 8°. 1927

Cohen (Arthur). Besteuerung u. Geldentwertung. [V. f. Sozialpol., B168ii]. 8°. München. 1924

Cohen (Gustave). Ecrivains franç. en Hollande dans le prem. moitié du 17e s. la8o. 1920
Cohen (Herman). The spirit of our laws. s8o. C. 1922
Cohen (Joseph L.) Insurance agst. unemployment. 8o. 1921
Social insurance unified & o. essays. 8o. 1924
Cohen (Louis). Napoleonic anecdotes. 8o. 1925
Cohen (Marcel), *see* LANGUES (Les) du monde; sous la dir. de M. C. &c., 1924.
Cohn (Marie Meyer-), *see* MEYER-COHN (M.)
Cohn (William).
Ind. Plastik. [Kunst d. Ostens, B2]. la8o. 1922
Die Kunst d. Ostens. Hrsg. W. C. B1–11. la8o. 1921–25
see COHN (W.) Ind. Plastik, 1922. [2.]
,, GLÜCK (H.) Die christl. Kunst d. Ostens, 1923. [8.]
,, FECHHEIMER (H.) Kleinplastik d. Ägypter, 1921. [3.]
,, —— Plastik d. Ägypter, 1923. [1.]
,, GLASER (C.) Ostasiat. Plastik, 1925. [11.]
,, GROSSE (E.) Die ostasiat. Tuschmalerei, 1922. [6.]
,, KÜHNEL (E.) Maurische Kunst, 1924. [9.]
,, —— Miniaturmalerei im islam. Orient, 1922. [7.]
,, KÜMMEL (O.) Die Kunst Ostasiens, 1921. [4.]
,, —— Ostasiat. Gerät, 1925. [10.]
,, SARRE (F.) Die Kunst d. alt. Persien, 1922. [5.]
Versuch e. Aufhebung d. "Ich" bei e. neu. Philosophen. Diss. [P2477]. 8o. 1904
Cohn (Willy). Die Gesch. d. sizil. Flotte unter d. Regierung Konrads IV & Manfreds (1250–66). 8o. 1920
Cohnstädt (Wilhelm).
Die Deutschen an der Saar. [P2733]. 8o. Frankfurt. 1922
Cohorn (Thomas de). Une lettre inéd. à Peiresc. Publ. Ph. Tamizey de Larroque. [Extr. du Journal du Comtat. P2844]. s8o. Carpentras. 1897
Cohrs (Ferdinand). Philipp Melanchthon. [Verein f. Ref.-gesch. Schr., Jhrg. 14, Nr. 55]. 8o. Halle. 1897
Cohu (John Rougier). The Bible & modern thought. 8o. 1920
Evolution of the Xtian ministry. s8o. 1918
Cõic conara fugill: 5 Wege z. Urteil, altir. Rechtstext; hrsg., übers. &c. v. R. Thurneysen, *see* KÖN.-PREUSS. AKAD. Abhdln., Phil.-hist. Kl., 1925.
Coignard (Pierre), *adventurer; c. 1774–1834* [*ps.* SAINTE-HÉLÈNE DE PONTIS (*comte* DE)], *see* MASSARD (E.) & G. DALLIER. P. C. ou Le Forçat-Colonel, *n.d.*
Coignet (*le capt.* **Jean Roch).**
Cahiers, 1799–1815. Publ. par L. Larchey. s8o. 1883
Coigny (*ctsse.* **Aimée de),** *aft. wife of A. H. M. L. de R. de R., duc. de Fleury, see* ARRIGON (L.-J.) La jeune captive: A. de C., dsse. de Fleury, 1921.
see GIRAUD (V.) Passions & romans d'autrefois, 1925.
Coimbra, *see* COLLEGIUM CONIMBRIC. SOC. JESU.
Coimbra (Leonardo). La alegría, el dolor y la gracia. Tr. V. de Pedro. 8o. [1921]
***Coin** (Le) du voile levé s. l'affaire Fualdès, 1819, *see* MANSON (M. F. C.)
Coindet (François), *see* ROUSSEAU (J. J.) Corresp. avec F. C., 1756–68, 1922.
Cokayne (George Edward). *Compl. peerage of England, Scotl., Ireland, Gt. Brit. & the U.K. n. ed. rev. & enl., ed. Hon. V. Gibbs & H. A. Doubleday. v5, 6, Eardley of Spalding to Hurstpierpont. 4o. 1926
Coke (Desmond F. T.) Half-way. s8o. 1927
The nouveau poor. By Belinda Blinders. s8o. 1921
Pamela herself. s8o. 1922
Coke (*Sir* **Edward),** *lord chief justice, see* PARSONS (R.), *the Jesuit.* An answer to the fifth part of Reportes by Sir E. Cooke &c., 1606.
Institutes of the lawes of Eng. p2–4 *in* 2v. fol. 1642–44
see EUDÆMON-JOANNES (A.) Ad actionem proditoriam E. C., apologia pro H. Garneto, 1610.
Coke (Richard). The heart of the Middle East. 8o. [1925]
Coke (Thomas), *LL.D., 1747–1814.*
A comm. on the New Test. 2v. 4o. 1803
Extr. of C.'s journal f. Gravesend to Antigua in letter to J. Wesley. [P2535]. s8o. 1787
Sermon preached at Baltimore at the ordin. of the Rev. F. Asbury, 27th Dec. 1784. [P2536]. s8o. 1785
Statement of the receipts &c. for the support of missions establ. by the Methodist Soc. for conversion of Negroes in W. Indies. 8o. 1794
The substance of a sermon on the Godhead of Christ, preached at Baltimore, Dec. 1784. [P2535; *a. c. b. w.* Taylor (T.) Redeeming grace &c., 1785]. s8o. 1785
see CROWTHER (J.) The life of T. C., 1815.
,, DREW (S.) Life of T. C., 1817.
,, ETHERIDGE (J. W.) Life of T. C., 1861.
,, ROGERS (*Mrs.* H. A.) Experience & spiritual letters, w. sermon on her death by T. C., 1840.

Coke (Thomas) & Francis Asbury. The doctrines &c. of the Methodist Episc. Ch. in America. With notes. 10th ed. s8o. Phila. 1798
Colagrosso (Francesco). Un' usanza lett. in gran voga nel settecento. s8o. Firenze. 1908
Colamonico (Carmelo).
La geografia d. Puglia. 2a ed. riv. 8o. Bari. 1926
Colaneri (Giustino). Bibliografia araldica &c. d'Italia. Con intr. del Cte. F. Pasini-Frassoni. 8o. 1904
Colasanti (Arduino). L. Laurana. 24 riprod. con testo e cat. a cura di A. C. [Bibl. d'arte illust. s2. fasc. 13. Architetti dal 15 al 18 sec.] 8o. 1922
Colbeck (Alfred). When the earth swung over. 8o. [1926]
Colberg (Johann). Analysis problematis de syncretismo fugiendo. [P441]. s4o. Lipsiae. 1652
Colbert (Charles Joachim), *bp. of Montpellier, see* CATECHISME. Instructions gén. en forme de Cat. &c., 4t, 1704.
Colbert (*card.* **Jacques Nicolas),** *abp. of Rouen, see* BASNAGE DE BEAUVAL (J.) Traité des préjugez, ou réponse aux lettres de C. &c., 1701.
Colbert (Jean Baptiste), *minister of Louis XIV; 1619–85, see* MIMS (S. L.) Colbert's West India policy, 1912.
Colby (*Maj.-Gen.* **Thomas),** *see* MUDGE (*Col.* W.) Acc. of operations for accompl. trigonom. survey of Eng. &c., v3, 1800–9, by M. & T. C., 1811.
Colchester. Court rolls. Tr. & epitomized by I. H. Jeayes. Intr. &c. by W. G. Benham. v1 (1310–52). 4o. 1921
Colchester Castle Society.
Cat. of the Library, 1856 [P2847]. 8o. Colchester. [1856]
Colchester (Walter Edmund). Hampshire church bells: th. founders & inscr. Foreword by W. A. Fearon. 8o. Winchester. 1920
Colchester (William de), *abbot of Westminster; c. 1338–1420, see* PEARCE (E. H.) W. de C., 1915.
Colden (Cadwallader). Letters & papers, v3–7, 1743–75, *see* NEW YORK HIST. SOC. Coll., Publ. Fund Ser., v52–56, 1921–23.
Cole, *The family of, see* ARDEN (*Miss* J.) Cole, 200–1920 A.D., 1920.
Cole (*Maj.* **Brian Lytton).** Rajputana classes. 8o. Simla. 1922
Cole (Francis Joseph). Hist. of anatom. injections, *see* SINGER (C.) St. in hist. &c. of sci., v2, 1921.
Cole (Frank R.), *see* VAN DUZEE (M. G.), F. R. C. & J. M. ALDRICH. The dipterous genus Dolichopus &c., 1921.
Cole (George Douglas Howard).
The Brooklyn murders. s8o. [1923]
Chaos & order in industry. s8o. [1920]
The future of local gov. s8o. 1921
Guild socialism re-stated. s8o. [1920]
Labour in the coal-mining industry, 1914–21. [C. E. for Internat. Peace]. la8o. O. 1923
Life of W. Cobbett, w. chapter on Rural rides by F. E. Green. 8o. [1924]
,, ,, [2nd impr.] 8o. [1925]
National guilds & the Coal Commission. Evidence submitted to the Comm. [P2405]. 8o. [1919]
Organised labour: an intr. to trade unionism. 8o. 1924
Out of work. Intr. to st. of unemployment. s8o. [1923]
Robert Owen. 8o. 1925
Short hist. of the Brit. working class movt., 1789–1927. 3v. 8o. [1925–27]
Social theory. s8o. 1920
Trade unionism & munitions. [C. E. for Internat. Peace]. la8o. O. 1923
Workers control series. Nos. 1–5 *in* 1v. s8o. 1921
1, Mining industry. 2, Distributive industry. 3, Railwaymen. 4, Engineering & shipbuilding. 5, Textile industries.
Workshop organiz. [C. E. for Internat. Peace]. la8o. O. 1923
The world of labour. Pres. & future of trade unionism. 4th ed. s8o. 1920
—— **& M. I. Cole.** The death of a millionaire. s8o. [1925]
Rents, rings & houses. s8o. 1923
Cole (George Watson), *see* HUNTINGTON (H. E.) Check-list or brief cat. of lib. of H.: Eng. lit. to 1640; comp. G. W. C., 1919–20.
Cole (Grenville Arthur James).
Common stones: essays in geology. s8o. [1921]
Memoir & map of localities of minerals of econ. import. &c. in Ireland. [Mem. of Geolog. Survey of Ireland]. 8o. D. 1922
——, **A. M. Davies, J. W. Evans &c.** The British Isles. [Hdbch. d. regionalen Geologie, 3i]. la8o. [Heidelberg. 1917]
Cole (Herbert). Heraldry & floral forms as used in decoration. la8o. 1922
Cole (Humphrey), *see* GUNTHER (R. W. T.) The gt. astrolabe & o. sci. instruments of H. C., 1927.
Cole (John), *of Scarborough.* *Histrionic topography. 8o. [1818]

Cole (John Harding). Church & parish records of Cork, Cloyne, & Ross f. 1863 to pres. time. 8°. Cork. 1903

Cole (Lionel Heber). Silica in Canada. [Canada: Dept. of Mines]. p1, Eastern C. 8°. Ottawa. 1923

Sodium sulphate of W. Canada. [Canada: Dept. of Mines]. 8°. Ottawa. 1926

see KEELE (J.) & L. H. C. Rep. on struct. materials along the St. Lawrence River, 1922.

Cole (Margaret Isabel).

The control of industry. [P2563]. 8°. 1921

see COLE (G. D. H.) & M. I. C. Death of a millionaire, 1925.

„ —— & —— Rents, rings & houses, 1923.

Cole (Reginald Sorré). Treatise on photographic optics. s8°. 1899

Cole (Rex Vicat). Perspective: practice & theory &c. 8°. 1921

Cole (Robert Eden George). Glossary of words used in S.-W. Lincolnshire (Wapentake of Graffoe). [Eng. Dialect Soc., 52.] 8°. 1886

see LINCOLN. Chapter acts of Cathedral &c., 1547–59; ed. R. E. G. C., 1920.

Cole (Sophie).

The cypress tree. s8°. [1920]
The devil's chapel. s8°. 1919
Linda Trust. s8°. [1926]
The other gate. s8°. [1921]
Passing footsteps. s8°. [1922]
Paying the piper. s8°. [1927]
The speaking silence. s8°. [1921]

Colebrook (Leonard), *see* WRIGHT (*Sir* A. E.) & L. C. Technique of the teat & capillary glass tube, 1921.

Colebrooke (Henry Thomas). A gram. of the Sanscrit lang. v1. [*No more publ.*] fol. Calcutta. 1805

Colección. C. de doc. inéd. para la hist. de Ibero-Amér. Recop. por S. Montoto. [Comp. I.-A. de Publ.] t1, 2. (1, Doc.; 2, Nobiliario d. s. 16, por S. Montoto). la8°. 1927–[28]

C. de documentos inéd. rel. al descubr., conquista &c. de las ant. posesiones esp. de Ultramar. Publ. por la Real Acad. de la Hist. s2, t1–19. 8°. 1885–1926

1, 4, 6, Isla de Cuba. 2, 3, De Filipinas. 5, 9, 10, Docs. legislativos. 7, 8, Pleitos de Colón. 11, 13, Rels. de Yucatán. 12, Vaticinios de la pérdida las Indias. 14–19, Consejo de Indias.

C. de documentos para el estudio de la hist. de Aragon. t8–12. 8°. Zaragoza. 1912–21

8 & 11, Memorias de la Univ. de Huesca, por R. del Arco.
9, Doc. corresp. al reinado de Sancio Ramírez., v2, 1063–94: Docs. proced. de San Juan de la Peña; transcr., prol. y notas de E. Ibarra y Rodriguez.
10, Carta de población de la ciudad de Santa Maria de Albarracin: estudio y transcr. de C. Riba y Garcia.
12, El libro de la Cadena del Concejo de Jaca: docs. reales, episcop. y municip. de los siglos 10–14; transcr. y notas de D. Sangorrin.

C. de obras arábigas de hist. y geografía, 1867, *see* REAL ACAD. DE LA HIST.

C. de poesías españolas antig. y mod. escoj. para uso de los Protestantes. 4p. s8°. Londres. (1, 2, *Dalton*; 3 & 4, *Hatchards*). 1872–79

1, Canticos é himnos; 2, poesías morales; 3, Poesías escript. con app. a la 2ª p. (*w. sep. pagin.*); 4, Los Salmos.

C. de var. doc. para la hist. de la Florida &c., 1857, *see* SMITH (T. B.)

Coleman (Algernon). Flaubert's literary development in light of h. Mém. d'un fou, Novembre & Education sentimentale (vers. of 1845). [Elliott Mon., 1]. 8°. Baltimore. 1914

see FAY (P. B.) & A. C. Sources &c. of Flaubert's Salammbô, 1914.

Coleman (Arthur Mainwaring). The Biblical text of Lucifer of Cagliari (Acts). [P2872]. 8°. Welwyn. 1927

Coleman (Arthur Philemon).

Ice ages, recent & ancient. 8°. 1926

Northeastern part of Labrador, & New Quebec. [Canada. Geolog. Survey. P2624]. 8°. Ottawa. 1921

Coleman (Christopher Bush). Constantine the Great & Xtianity. 8°. N.Y., *Columbia Univ.* 1914

Coleman (J. Bernard) & F. T. Addyman.

Pract. agric. chemistry. n. impr. s8°. 1913

Coleman (James), *see* NATIONAL LIB. OF WALES. Calendar of deeds &c., v1, C. deeds, 1921.

Colenbrander (H. T.) Gedenkstukken d. algemeene geschiedenis van Nederland, 1795–1840. Uitg. d. H. T. C. [Rijks Gesch. &c., 46, 50]. d10iv, v. 4°. 's-Gravenhage. 1921–22

10iv, v. Regeering v. Willem 1, 1830–40.

Inlijving en opstand. [Nederl. Hist. Bibl., 7]. la8°. Amsterdam. 1913

Jan Pietersz. Coen. Bescheiden omtrent zijn bedrijf in Indië, verzam. door H. T. C. 3d. la8°. 's-Gravenhage. 1919–21

Colenbrander (H. T.) [*continued*].

Koloniale gesch. 3d. 8°. 's-Gravenhage. 1926

Schimmelpenninck en Koning Lodewijk. [Nederl. Hist. Bibl., 5]. la8°. Amsterdam. 1911

Colenso (John William), *bp. of Natal.*

First steps in Zulu-Kafir. s8°. Ekukanyeni. 1859

Coler (Christoph Martin). Exercitatio polit. divisionem majestatis in personalem et realem excutiens &c. Præs C. M. Colerus, resp. S. Kripnero. [P2587]. s4°. Jenæ. 1686

Coler (Jean), *see* COLERUS (JOANNES).

Coler (Johann Christoph) [COLERUS (J. C.)], *ed.*, *see* *ACTA historico-eccl., 1734–58.

Coleraine (Henry Hare, *3rd baron*). Hist. & antiqs. of the town & church of Tottenham, *see* DYSON (R. R.) Hist. &c. of Tottenham, 2nd ed., 1792.

Coleridge (Arthur Duke). Remin. Ed. J. A. Fuller-Maitland: w. add. by F. Warre Cornish, Sir W. R. Adkins & L. S. Holland. 8°. 1921

Coleridge (Bernard John Seymour Coleridge, *2nd baron*).

This for remembrance. 8°. [1925]

Coleridge (*Hon.* **Gilbert James Duke).**

Pan's people, the lure of little beasts. 8°. [1923]

Coleridge (Henry James). Reviews of famous books, 1, The Provincial Letters. [Extr. f. The Month, v14]. 8°. [1871]

Coleridge (John Duke Coleridge, *1st baron*), *see* HURLBERT (W. H.) Eng. under coercion; letter to Ld. C., 1893.

Coleridge (*Miss* **Mary Elizabeth)** [*ps.* ANODOS].

*Fancy's guerdon. s8°. 1897

Coleridge (Samuel Taylor).

Aids to reflection. Added, his essays on Faith & the Book of Common Prayer. [*Repr. mainly fr. 4th ed. & also fr. Remains*]. s8°. *Bohn.* 1890

Biographia literaria; or sketches of my lit. life & opinions; & two lay sermons. [Reprint of orig. ed., 1816–17]. s8°. *Bohn.* 1889

Biographia lit.; chap. 1–4, 14–22. Wordsworth, Pref. & Essays on poetry, 1800–15. Ed. G. Sampson, w. introd. essay by Sir A. Quiller-Couch. 8°. C. 1920

Dram. works. Ed. D. Coleridge. s8°. *Moxon.* 1852

The Friend: essays. [*Reprint of 1818 ed.*] s8°. *Bohn.* 1890

„ „ ......s8°. *Bohn.* 1899

Lect. & notes on Shakespere &c. Coll. by T. Ashe. s8°. *Bohn.* 1902

Poems. Ed. D. & S. Coleridge. s8°. *Moxon.* 1852

Rime of the ancient mariner. Illustr. 8°. 1857

Table talk & Omniana. Ed. T. Ashe. s8°. *Bohn.* 1896

Treatise on method. [Gen. intr. to Encycl. Metrop.] 5th ed. [P2777]. s8°. *n.d.*

see BOWLES (W. L.) A Wiltshire parson, w. 4 reviews by C., 1926.

„ COTTLE (J.) Second pref. to "Early recoll. of S. T. C.", 1839.

„ LOWES (J. L.) The road to Xanadu, 1927.

„ LYRICAL ballads &c. [*by* C. & Wordsworth], 1798; [Noel Douglas Replicas], 1926.

„ WATSON (L. E.) C. at Highgate, 1925.

„ WISE (T. J.) Coleridgeiana: Suppl. to The bibliog. of C., 1919.

Coleridge (*Hon.* **Stephen W. B.)** Letters to my grandson on the glory of English prose. 2nd ed. enl. 8°. 1922

Letters to my grandson on the happy life. s8°. [1922]

Colerus (Jacobus). Hist. disput. inter J. C. & M. Flacium Illyr., de peccato orig. habitae in arce Langenaw Siles. 1574. s4°. Berlini. 1585

Colerus (Joannes) [†COLER (JEAN)]. Schediasma de Jesuitissis, s. Jesuiter-Nonnen. Resp. J. T. Gleich. Acc. bulla papali. [P2631]. s4°. *n.p.* 1701

La verité de la résurr. de Jésus Christ def. contre B. de Spinosa, &c. [*b. w. h.* Vie de Spinosa, 1706]. s8°. La Haye. 1706

La vie de B. de Spinosa, &c. s8°. La Haye. 1706

see FÉNÉLON (F. DE S. DE LA M.) Réfut. des erreurs de B. de Spinosa; avec la vie de S. par J. C., 1703.

Coles (William), *botanist.* Adam in Eden or nature's paradise. The hist. of plants, fruits, herbs &c. with obs. on the seasons of planting & gathering our Eng. simples &c. sfol. 1657

Coles-Finch (William). In Kentish pilgrim land. 8°. [1925]

Colet (H.), *see* DUMERSAN (T. M.) Chants &c. pop. de la France; notices par D.; accompagnement par H. C., 4t, 1890?

Colet (*Mme.* **Louise)** [†RÉVOIL (L.) *aft. Colet.*], *see* ENFIELD (D. E.) A lady of the Salons: story of L. C., 1922.

Colette, *Saint* [†COLETTA BOILET], *Saint*; [NICOLETTA BOELLET].

see SAINTE-MARIE-PERRIN (E.) La belle vie de St. C., 1921.

„ ——. St. C. & h. reform; tr., 1923.

Coletti (Luigi). Treviso. [Ital. art. 90]. la8°. Bergamo. [1926]

Colevelt (J. J.) Cupidoos Dartelheydt, *see* AMSTERDAM. A. Pegasus, 1627.

Coley-Bromfield (J. C.)
A short hist. of the Military Knights of Windsor. s8°. 1916

Colfe (Isaac). A comfortable treatise conc. the temptations of Christ. [*b. w.* Chaderton (L.) Excell. &c. sermon, 1580]. s8°. *A. I. for R. Watkins.* 1592

Coligny, *Ain, see* RHYS (*Sir* J.) The C. Calendar, 1910.

Coligny (Gaspard II de) *admiral of France, d. 1572* [CHATILLON]. *see* PARIS. Vero, Il, successo occorso n. Parigi contro l'Armiraglio &c., 1572.
,, SERRES (J. DE). The three partes of comm. &c., w. add. of murther of Adm. C., 1574.

Colijn (H.) Neerlands Indië: land & volk, gesch. & bestuur, bedrijf & samenleving. Onder leiding v. H. C. Voorwoord van J. B. Van Heutsz. 2d. 4°. Amsterdam. 1913

Colin (Gaston). Rome & la Grèce de 200 à 146 av. J.-C. [Ecoles Franç. d'Athènes & de Rome, 94]. 8°. 1905

Colin (Jean Lambert Alphonse).
L'éducation milit. de Napoléon. 8°. 1900
The transformations of war. Tr. L. H. R. Pope-Hennessy. 8°. 1912
see HANOTAUX (G.) Hist. de la nation franç., t7, v1, Hist. milit. & navale, par J. C. &c., 1925.

Colin (Paul). Van Gogh. 8°. 1925

Colini-Baldeschi (Elia). Bologna n. opere di Dante. [P2524]. s8°. Bologna. [1921]

Colisée, *Paris.* Livret de l'expos. du C. (1776). Préc. d'une hist. du C. &c. par J. J. Guiffrey. Complément des livrets de l'Acad. Royale & de l'Acad. de Saint-Luc. s8°. 1875

Collado (Casimiro del). Poesías. 2ª ed., corr. y aument. 8°. 1880

Collado (Diego).
Ars gramm. Japonicae ling. &c. 8°. Romæ. 1632
Niffou no cotōbani yô conf. &c. Modus confitendi &c. pœnitentem Japonensem, formula suamet. lingua Japonica. [*Jap. & Lat.*] s4°. Romæ. 1632

Collalto (Collatino di), *conte di Trevigi.* Rime, *see* STAMPA (G.) Rime &c., 1738.

Collalto (*il conte* **Vinciguerra II di).** Rime, *see* STAMPA (G.) Rime &c., 1738.

Collan (Fabian). De Reformationis in Fennia initiis. Diss. [P2654]. 8°. Helsingforsiæ. 1843

Collas (Émile). La belle-fille de Louis XIV. [Marie Anne Christine Victoire]. 8°. *n.d.*

Collatio. Lex Dei sive Mosaic. & Roman. legum coll. [*attrib. to* Licinius Rufinus]. Ed. F. B. 8°. Bonnæ. 1833
Mosaycarum & Roman. legum coll. &c. Ex bibl. P. Pithoei. s8°. Heidelbergæ. 1654

Colle (*le r. p.*), *missionaire des Pères Blancs d'Afrique.* Les Baluba (Congo Belge). Préf. de C. Van Overbergh. [Coll. de mongr^s. ethnogr., t10, 11]. 2t. 8°. Brux. 1913

Colle (Charles). Le partie de chasse de Henri IV, *see* THÉÂTRE choisi du 18e s., t2, 1914.

Collecçao. C. chronol. dos assentos das casas da supplic. &c., 1791, *see* PORTUGAL. Coll. da legisl. &c. do reino de P. &c.
C. da legislaçaõ ant. e mod. do reino de Portugal, 2p *in* 13t, 1790–95, *see* PORTUGAL.
C. de opusc. reimpr. rel. á hist. d. navegações &c. dos Portuguezes. [Acad. Real. das Sci. de Lisboa]. t1. 8°. 1875
1, Rel. verdad. d. trabalhos q̃ ho gov. dõ F. de Souto &c. passarom no descob. da prov. da Frolida [*sic*], 1557.
2, Hist. das cousas que Dom C. da Gama fez nos Reynos do Preste João, por M. de Castanhoso, 1564.
3, Hist. da prov. Santa Cruz, a que vulg. chamamos Brasil, feita por Pero de Magalhães de Gandavo, [1576].
4, Breve rel. da embaixada que D. João Bermudez trouxe do imp. da Ethiopia &c., 1565.

Collectanea. C. Alexandrina, 1925, *see* POWELL (J. U.)
C. de rebus Albanicis, 1847, *see* IONA CLUB.
C. de rebus Hibernicis, 6v, 1770–1804, *see* VALLANCEY (C.)
C. Franciscana. [v]2. Ed. C. L. Kingsford. [Brit. Soc. of Franciscan St^s., 10]. 8°. 1922
Cotton (C.) Notes on doc^s. in Cathedral Lib. at Canterbury rel. to Grey Friars. [2.]
Deanesly (M.) Gospel harmony of John de Caulibus &c. [2.]
Gilson (J. P.) Friar Alexander & h. hist. interp. of the Apocalypse. [2.]
James (M. R.) List of libraries pref. to Cat. of J. Boston &c. [2.]
Kingsford (C. L.) Add. material for hist. of Grey Friars, London. [2.]
Little (A. G.) Friar Henry of Wodstone & the Jews. [2.]
C. Friburgensia, N.S., Fasc. 11, 12, *see* AMOROS (B.) Canzon. provenzale, 2v, 1911.

Collectio. C. constit. Imper., 4t, 1713, *see* GOLDAST (M.)
C. judic. de novis error., 3t, 1728–36, *see* DU PLESSIS D'ARGENTRÉ (C.)

Collection.
C. de cartul. dauphinois, *see* CARTULAIRE.
C. de doc. hist. publ. par ordre de Pr. Albert I de Monaco, *see* ALBERT I, *prince of Monaco.*
C. de doc. inédits sur l'hist. écononm. de la Révolution Franç., *see* FRANCE: MINISTÈRE DE L'INTÉRIEUR.
C. de doc. publ. avec le concours de la Comm. des Antiq^s. de la Côte-d'Or, *see* COMMISSION DES ANTIQUITÉS &c.
C. de textes rel. au droit &c. de la Bourgogne, 1907–14, *see* DIJON.
C. des princ. cartul. du diocèse de Troyes; [ed. C. Lalore]. t3, 6, 7. 8°. 1878–90
see BASSE-FONTAINE. Cartul. de l'abbaye de B.-F.—Chartes de Beauvoir, 1878. [3.]
,, MONTIÉRAMEY. Cartul. de l'abbaye de M., 1890. [7.]
,, MONTIER-LA-CELLE. Cartul. de M.-la-C., 1882. [6.]
C. of all such statutes as rel. to the Admiralty, Navy &c., 1742, *see* ADMIRALTY.
*C. (A) of articles &c. conc. eccles. matters, 1699, *see* CHURCH.
*C. of cases &c. wr. to recover Dissenters to the Ch. of Eng., 2nd ed., 1694, *see* DISSENTERS.
C. (A) of confess. of faith, catechisms, &c. in Ch. of Scot. &c., 2v, 1719–22, *see* CHURCH OF SCOTLAND.
*C. of epitaphs &c. chiefly in Scotland, 1834, *see* SCOTLAND.
*C. (A) of epitaphs: pref., An essay on epitaphs by Dr. Johnson. 2v *in* 1. s8°. 1806
C. of hymns, *for anon. coll^s. w. title* Collection, New Collection &c., *see* HYMNS.
C. (A) of letters &c. rel. to Popish plot &c., 1681, *see* POPISH.
C. of moral &c. poems, 3v, 1744, *see* WESLEY (J.), *ed.*
*C. (A) of papers, all wr. dur. the late rebellion, 1748, *see* GORDON (T.)
C. (A) of papers rel. to pres. juncture of affairs, 1688, *see* ENGLAND.
*C. of psalms & hymns; Charles-Town, 1737, *n.d.*, *see* WESLEY (J.)
*C. (A new) of voyages & travels into several parts of the world &c., 1711, *see* STEVENS (*capt.* J.), *ed.*
A compleat c. of farewell Sermons by Mr. Calamy, Dr. Manton [*& o. evicted ministers*]. With Mr. Lye's Rehearsal &c. Rev. & corr. s8°. 1663
*Exact c. (An) or cat. of our Eng. wr. on the old & New Test., 1663, *see* CROWE (W.)
Sel. c. of views &c. in Rome &c., 1810, *see* ROME.

Collections. *C. by a private hand at Edinburgh, 1650–61, *see* MAIDMENT (J.), *ed.* Hist. fragm. rel. to Scot. affairs, p2, 1833.
C. d'histor. armén.; tr., 1874–76, *see* BROSSET (M. F.)

College. College rhymes, contrib. by Members of Univ. of Oxf. & Camb. v1–3. s8°. 1860–62

College of William & Mary, *Williamsburg, Va., see* CHANDLER (J. A. C.), *ed.* Genesis &c. of the Federal constit.: addresses &c., 1924.

Collegio de gli Spetiali. Ordini et capitoli d. C. di Venezia (1565), 1891, *see* VENEZIA.

Collegium Conimbricense Soc. Jesu, *see* ARISTOTLE *for* Commentarii *on various books of A.*, 1599–1607.

Collegno (Luigi Provana di), *see* PROVANA DI COLLEGNO (L.)

Cöllen, *see* KÖLN.

Collen (*Lt.-Gen. Sir* **Edwin Henry Ethelbert).** Defence of India. [*Extr. fr.* Roy. Geogr. Soc. Journal. [P2589]. 8°. 1906

Collenuccio (Pandolfo). Hist. Neapolitanae ad Herculem I Ducem libri 6. Ex Ital. in Lat. conversa. J. N. Stupano, interpr. s4°. Basileæ. 1572

Colleoni (Bartolomeo) [COLEONI; COLEUS (B.)], *1400–75, see* BORTOLO (B.) Vita di B. C., 1927.

Coller (Frank Herbert). A state trading adventure. 8°. 1925

Colles (Henry Cope).
The growth of music. 3p. s8°. O. 1919–20
,, ,, ...3p [*in* 1v]. s8°. O. 1923

Colles (Ramsay). In castle & court house: remin. of 30 yrs. in Ireland. 8°. [1911]

Collet (Léon W.), *D.Sc.*
Les lacs: éléments d'hydro-géologie. la8°. Paris. 1925
The structure of the Alps. 8°. 1927

Collet (Octave J. A.)
Terres & peuples de Sumatra. 4°. Amsterdam. 1925

Collet (Pierre). *Works in* MIGNE (J. P.), *ed.* Theol. cursus.
De censuris—De irregularitatibus, 1860. [17.]
De purgatorio—De indulgentiis—De jubilæis, 1862. [18.]
Tract. de poenitentia, 1860. [22.]
see TOURNÉLY (H.) & P. C. De subjecto sacramentorum, 1841.

Colletet (Guillaume). Notices sur les trois Marot. Publ. G. Guiffrey. 8°. 1871
P. de Ronsard, *see* RONSARD (P. DE). Œ. inéd., 1855.

Collett (Anthony). The changing face of England. 8°. [1926]

Collett (Henry).
Little Gidding & its founder, N. Ferrar. s8°. 1925
Collibus (Hippolytus a). Incrementa urbium sive de caussis magnitudinis urbium. [*App.* Ausonii De claris urbibus & Scaligeri Urbes. *b. w.* Polanus (A.) De æterna Dei prædestin., 1600]. s8°. Hanoviæ. 1600
Collier (*le card.*), *see* ROHAN (*le card. pr.* L. R. E. DE).
Collier (Arthur). Clavis universalis [1713]. Ed. w. intr. & notes by E. Bowman. s8°. Chicago. 1909
Clavis universalis, or a new enquiry after truth (1713). repr. 8°. E. 1836
Collier (Jeremy), *the Nonjuror.* An eccl. hist. of Gt. Brit.; w. acc. of relig. in Irel. [Coll. of records *in* t2 *has sep. pagin.*] 2t. fol. 1708–14
Essays upon moral subjects. 3rd ed. 2p *in* 1v. 8°. 1698
A short view of the immorality &c. of the Eng. stage. 4th ed. s8°. 1699
see CONGREVE (W.) Amendments of Mr. C.'s citations f. The old batchelour &c., 1698.
Collier (*Hon.* **John),** *2nd son of 1st baron Monkswell.*
The relig. of an artist. s8°. 1926
Collier (John Payne). *A few odds & ends for cheerful friends. A Christmas gift. 8°. *p.f.p.c.* 1870
Five old plays illust. early progress of Eng. drama. Ed. J. P. C. [Roxburghe Club]. 4°. 1851
The conflict of conscience, by N. Woodes, 1581.
The rare triumphes of love & fortune, 1589.
The three ladies of London, 1584.
The three lords & three ladies of London, 1590.
A knack to know a knave, 1594.
*Punch & Judy, w. illust. by Cruikshank &c., dialogue of the puppet-show, acc. of its origin &c. 6th ed. s8°. 1881
Collier (Thomas). *Brief answer to objections agst. Jews &c. [*b. w. h.* The pulpit-guard routed, 1652]. s4°. 1656
*A conf. of the faith of several churches of Christ in Somerset &c. [*imperf. b. w. h.* The pulpit-guard routed, 1652]. s4°. 1656
The font-guard routed; ans. to T. Hall, The font guarded &c.; w. ans. to R. Sander's Balm to heal relig. wounds. [*w. sep. pagin. b. w. h.* The pulpit-guard routed, 1652]. s4°. 1652
The pulpit-guard routed; ans. to T. Hall, The pulpit guarded &c. 2nd ed. corr. s4°. 1652
A word in season; or, some grounds tending to unity &c. [*b. w. h.* The pulpit-guard routed, 1652]. s4°. 1655
Collignon (Maxime). L'emplacement du Cécropion à l'Acropole d'Athènes, *see* ACAD. DES INSCR. Mém. de l'Inst., t41, 1920.
Collin de Plancy (Jacques A. S.) Petit dict. class. d'hist. naturelle, par B. de St. Pierre, Buffon &c. [*Ed. C. de P.*] 2t. s8°. 1827
Collin d'Harleville (Jean François). Les châteaux en Espagne. Comédie. (1789). Préf. par P. Guitet-Vauquelin]. 8°. *n.d.*
Le vieux célibataire, *see* THÉÂTRE choisi du 18e s., t2, 1914.
Colling (Alfred). Un mauvais lieu à la mode, choses vues, *see* ŒUVRES libres, 61, 1926.
Colling (James Kellaway). Examples of Eng. mediæval foliage & coloured decoration, 12th–15th cs. 4°. 1874
Collinge (Walter E.) The food of some Brit. wild birds. 2nd rev. & enl. ed. la8°. York. 1924–27
see HOME (G. C.) Roman York: w. co-op. of W. E. C., 1924.
Collinges (John), *D.D.* *A reasonable acc. why some nonconform. ministers in Eng. judge it sinful to perform minist. acts in publick, &c. s8°. *n.p.* 1679
„ „ ....Suppl. [*b. w. above*]. s8°. 1680
*The weaver's pocket-book: or, weaving spiritualized. By J. C., *D.D.* s8°. 1675
see MARTIN (J.), S. PETTO &c. The preacher sent: in ans. to Vindiciæ minist. evang., by J. C., 1658.
Collings (*Rt. Hon.* **Jesse).**
Land reform. n. & pop. ed. 8°. 1908
Life of Rt. Hon. J. C. Intr. by Rt. Hon. A. Chamberlain. 2p [in 1v]. 8°. 1920
p1, [Before entering Parl.], by J. C.
p2, [Mr. C. & land reform], by Sir J. L. Green.
Collingwood (Robin George), *F.S.A.*
Roman Britain. s8°. 1923
Speculum mentis or the map of knowledge. 8°. O. 1924
see MARVIN (F. S.), *ed.* England & the world: essays [by W. J. Perry, R. G. C. &c.], 1925.
Collingwood (Stuart Dodgson).
Life & letters of Lewis Carroll. [2nd ed.] 8°. 1899
Collingwood (William Gershom). Northumbrian crosses of the pre-Norman age. 4°. 1927
Collino (Giovanni). Sui cartolari d. prevostura d'Oulx, *see* REGIA DEP. DI STORIA PATRIA. Misc., t40, 1904.
Collins (A. S.)
Authorship in the days of Johnson, 1726–80. 8°. 1927
Collins (Anthony), *see* THORSCHMID (U. G.) Crit. Lebensgesch. A. C., 1755.
Collins (Caspar Wever), *see* SPRING (A. W.) C. C., 1844–65, 1927.
Collins (Dale). Ordeal. s8°. [1924]
The sentimentalists. s8°. [1927]
Collins (Frederick Howard).
Authors' & printers' dict. 5th ed. (6th impr.) rev. s8°. 1921
Collins (Greenvile), *hydrographer.* Great-Britain's coasting pilot: sea-coast of Eng. & Scot. 2p *in* 1v. lafol. 1762
Collins (H. P.) Mod. poetry. s8°. [1925]
Collins (John), *accomptant, F.R.S.*
An intr. to merchants-accompts. &c. fol. 1675
Collins (Joseph).
Italy re-visited. My Italian year 1917–1918. 8°. [1918]
Collins (Michael).
Arguments for the treaty. [P2580]. 8°. D. [1921]
Michael Collins' own story. Told by H. Talbot. s8°. [1923]
see BEASLEY (P.) M. C. & making of a new Ireland, 2v, 1926.
Collins (V. H.) Ghosts & marvels. Sel. of uncanny tales f. Defoe to Blackwood. Intr. by M. R. James. s8°. [1924]
„ „ ....[repr. [s8°. [1925]
Collins (Varnum Lancing).
President Witherspoon: a biog. 2v. 8°. Princeton. 1925
Collins (W. H.) North shore of Lake Huron. [Canada, Geolog. Survey.]. 8°. Ottawa. 1925
——, **T. T. Quirke & Ellis Thomson.** Michipicoten iron ranges. [Canada, Geolog. Survey.] 8°. Ottawa. 1926
Collins (Wilkie). The moonstone. s8°. 1920
The woman in white. s8°. 1920
see PHILLIPS (W. C.) Dickens, Reade, & C., sensation novelists, 1919.
Collins (William), *poet.*
Odes on sev. descr. & allegoric subjects, 1747. 8°. [1926]
Persian eclogues, 1742. [facs. repr.] 8°. [O. 1925]
Poet. works. Coll. by T. Park. s8°. 1805
Poet. works. [Ed.W.M.Thomas. Aldine ed.] s8°. [1858]
see MACKAIL (J. W.) C., & the Eng. lyric in the 18th c., 1921.
„ WILLIAMS (I. A.) 7 18th cent. bibliog., W. C. &c., 1924.
Collins (William Edward), *bp. of Gibraltar.* The beginnings of Eng. Xty., St. Augustine. s8°. 1898
Lects. on Abp. Laud, w. bibliog. of L. lit. & the L. Exhib. cat. &c. Ed. W. E. C. [Abp. L. commem.] 8°. 1895
Collins (*Sir* **William Job).** The life & work of Sir S. Romilly. Repr. f. Trans. of the Huguenot Soc. [P2786]. 8°. *n.p.* 1908
Some notes on Sir S. Romilly & E. Dumont. Repr. f. Proc. of the Huguenot Soc. of London, v12. [P2786]. 8°. 1924
Collins-Baker (Charles Henry), *see* BAKER (C. H. C.)
Collinson (Peter), *see* BRETT-JAMES (N. G.) Life of P. C., 1925.
Collinus (Matthaeus) *Gurimenus.* De summa Christianæ relig. brevia axiomata, olim ab H. Noppo trad. & nunc versibus illig. a M. C. G. Cum praef. P. Melanchthonis. [*b. w.* Brentz (J.) Argumenta &c., 1544]. s8°. [Norimbergae. I. *Petreius*]. 1543
Collis (J. S.) Shaw. 8°. [1925]
Collison-Morley (Lacy). Naples thr. the cent. 8°. 1916
Shakespeare in Italy. 8°. Stratford-on-Avon. 1916
Collitz (Hermann), *ed.* Sammlung d. griech. Dialekt-Inschriften. B4. H1–4 [*in* 1v]. 8°. Göttingen. 1886–1915
4i, Wortregister z. 1ten B., v. R. Meister.
ii, Wortregister z. 2ten B., v. J. Baunack, H. Meyer u. C. Wendel.
iii, Gramm. u. Wortreg. z. 1ten Hälfte d. 3ten B., v. O. Hoffmann.
iv, Gramm. u. Wortreg. z. 2ten Hälfte d. 3ten B., Abt. 1, v. O. Hoffmann, Abt. 2, v. P. Gärtchen u. O. Hoffmann, Abt. 3, v. E. Fraenkel u. K. H. Meyer.
Collomp (Paul). Recherches sur la chancellerie & la diplomatique des Lagides. 8°. Str. 1926
Collon (A.) Etude sur la cryptographie, s. emploi à la guerre &c. [Extr. de la Revue de l'armée belge]. t2. s8°. Brux. [1902 ?]
Colloquial (The) who's who, 2v, 1924, *see* ABBATT (W.)
Collum, *ps.*
*The dance of Çiva. Life's unity & rhythm. s8°. [1927]

Collyer (Doric). Ann of the House of Barlow. s8°. [1926]
Collyer (Robert) & J. H. Turner. Ilkley: anc. & med. With chapters by J. W. Davis, F. A. Lees &c. 8°. Otley. 1885
Colman (Frederick Selincourt). Hist. of parish of Barwick-in-Elmet, in Co. of York. [Thoresby Soc., 17]. 8°. Leeds. 1908
Colman (George), *the elder.* The English merchant, *see* †INCHBALD (E.) Mod. th., v9, 1811.
Jealous wife, *see* INCHBALD (E.) Brit. th., v16, 1808.
*Polly Honeycombe, dram. novel of 1 act. s8°. 1760
—— **& D. Garrick.** Clandestine marriage, *see* INCHBALD (E.) Brit. th., v16, 1808.
Colman (George), *the younger.*
Works in INCHBALD (*Mrs.* E.) Brit. theatre, 1808.

Battle of Hexham.	[20.]	John Bull.	[21.]
Heir at law.	[21.]	The mountaineers.	[21.]
Inkle & Yarico.	[20.]	Poor gentleman.	[21.]
Iron chest.	[21.]	Surrender of Calais.	[20.]

The rodiad. Repr., w. pref. by Y. Nicolas. 8°. *Cayme Press.* 1927
Who wants a guinea? *see* INCHBALD (E.) Mod. th., v3, 1811.
Colmenares (Diego de). Hist. de Segovia y compendio de las hist. de Castilla (1637). Ilust. con. notas &c. y otras de T. Baeza y Gonzalez. Rev. &c. por G. M. Vergara. 8°. Segovia. 1921
Cologne. *For anon. works in German see* KÖLN.
Antididagma, seu Christianae &c. relig. per Canonicos Metropol. Eccl. Colonieñ. propugnatio, adv. librum quendam [*by* Hermann V, *Abp. of C.*] titulo Reformationis exhib. &c. fol. Coloniæ. 1544
Canones concilii provinc. Colon. celebrati anno 1536 quibus, adjectum est Enchiridion Christianae instit. [*wanting tp. & all after* MMM4. *Foll. by:* Formula ad quam visitatio intra Diocoesim Colon. exigetur, *w. sep. pagin.*; *wanting fol. 1 & all after* fol. 10]. fol. [Coloniae. 1537]
„ „ .... fol. Coloniae. 1538
Chronica Regia Colon. (Annales maximi Colon.), cum cont. in Monast. S. Pantaleonis scr. aliisque hist. Colon. mon. [*includ.* Chron. rhythm. C. fragm.—Dial. clerici & laici—Oliveri relatio—Gosvini de expugn. Salaciæ carmen—Martini Contin. Colon.] Rec. G. Waitz. [Scr. rerum Germ. in usum schol.] 8°. Hannoveræ. 1880
Condemnatio libr. M. Lutheri per quosdam magistros Lovanieñ & Colon., 1520, *see* LOUVAIN.
Coloma (Luis), *S. J.*
Jeromín. Estud. hist. sobre el siglo 16. 5ª ed. 8°. Bilbao. 1921
Colomb (G.) L'énigme d'Alésia. Solution proposée d'après le livre 7 des Comm. de César. s8°. 1922
Colomb (George Hatton) [*ps.* LOVELACE (RICHARD)]. The miller of Wandsworth (poem), 1648. With notes [or rather written] by R. L. 2nd ed. [P2590]. s8°. 1879
The Miss Crusoes. s8°. [1888]
A regicide's career. Pseudo St. Peter, or the Prince of Army Chaplains [*i.e.* Hugh Peters]. 8°. [1899]
For King & Kent (1648). 3v. s8°. 1882
Colomb (Philip Howard), *see* GREAT. Gt. war of 189–; aut. Übers. v. E. A. Witte, 2e A., 1894.
Colombe (Marie Catherine) [M. C. RIGGIERI], *see* STERN (J.) Mdlles. C. de la Comédie-Ital., 1751–1841, 1923.
Colombe (Marie Madeleine, dit Adeline) [M. M. RIGGIERI], *see* STERN (J.) Mdlles. C. de la Comédie-Ital., 1751–1841, 1923.
Colombe (Thérèse Théodore) [T. T. RIGGIERI], *see* STERN (J.) Mdlles. C. de la Comédie-Ital., 1751–1841, 1923.
Colombey (Émile), *ps.* [ÉMILE LAURENT], *see* JOURNÉE (La) des madrigaux (1653); intr. &c. par E. C., 1856.
Colombino (Emilio).
Tre mesi n. Russia dei Soviet. s8°. Milano. 1921
Colombo Museum.
1st rep. on exhib. coins. [*no tp.*] [P2786]. 8°. *n.p.* [1889]
see CODRINGTON (H. W.) Ceylon coins & currency, 1924.
Colombo (Elia). Iolanda, dssa. di Savoia (1465–78), *see* REGIA DEP. DI STORIA PATRIA. Misc., t31, 1894.
Colombo (Giuseppe), *of Moncalieri, 1838–84.* Doc. notizie int. gli artisti vercellesi. Pubbl. G. C. 8°. Vercelli. 1883
Notizie e doc. s. vita di G. F. Bonomi, vescovo di Vercelli, *see* REGIA DEP. DI STORIA PATRIA. Misc., t18, 1879.
see PROMIS (V.) Brevi sceni s. vita e s. scritti del p. G. C., Barnabita, 1884.
Colomiès (Paul) [COLOMESIUS (P.)]. Gallia orientalis sive Gallorum qui linguam Heb. &c. excoluerunt vitæ. s4°. Hagæ-Com. 1665
Italia & Hispania orient., sive Italorum & Hispan. qui ling. Hebr. &c. excol. vitae. s4°. Hamburgi. 1730
Colonia (Dominique de).
Antiq. de la ville de Lyon &c. s8°. à Lyon. 1701
*Dict. des livres Jansénistes &c. [Nouv. éd. augm. par Louis Patouillet]. 4t. s8°. Anvers. 1755

Colonial Office List, 1918–1923. 8°. 1918–23
Coloniensis, *see* COLOGNE.
Colonization. C. of waste-lands in Assam, 1899, *see* ASSAM.
Colonna (Francesco), *Dominican, 1449–1527* [*ps.* POLIPHILO]. The Dream of Poliphilus. Fac-similes of woodcuts, Venice, 1499. With not. & descr. by J. W. Appell. 4°. 1888
see HÜLSEN (C.) Le illust. d. Hypnerotomachia Polifili [*by* F. C.], 1910.
„ POPPELREUTER (J.) Der anonyme Meister d. Poliphilo: St. z. ital. Buchillust. &c., 1904.
Colonna (Francesco Maria Pompeo) [*ps.* CROSSET DE LA HAUMERIE]. *Les secrets les plus cachés de la philos. des anciens. s8°. 1722
Colonna (Gustavo Brigante).
Roma papale: storie e leggende. 8°. Firenze. 1925
Colonna (Marco Antonio), *Viceroy of Sicily, see* GUGLIELMOTTI (A.) St. d. marina pontif., v6, M. C. alla Battaglia di Lepanto, 1570–3, 1887.
Colonna (Stefano). *Sonetti, canzoni e i trionfi di M. Laura in risposta di M. F. Petrarca [*really by S. C.*] s8°. Venezia. 1740
Colonna (Vittoria), *aft. V. d'Avalos, march. di Pescara.* Rime, di nuovo ristamp., agg. le sue stanze, e corr. s8°. *n.p.* [Parma?]. 1539
Rime spirituali. 8°. Vinegia. 1546
Tre lettere ined. [*Ed.* P. D. Pasolini. Nozze Rasponi-Corsini. N119]. fol. 1901
Colonne (François Marie Pompée), *see* COLONNA (F. M. P.)
Colquhoun (Archibald Ross) & H. S. Hallett. Report on the railway connexion of Burmah & China, w. acc. of explor.-survey by H. S. H. fol. [1885]
Colquhoun (*Mrs.* Ethel), *wife of Arch. Colquhoun, aft. wife of J. T. Jollie.* The real Rhodesia. 8°. 1924
Colson (Albert), *see* HANOTAUX (G.) Hist. de la nation franç., t14, Hist. des sciences, v1, Chimie par A. C., 1924.
Colson (Francis Henry).
The week: orig. & develop. of 7-day cycle. 8°. C. 1926
Colston (Edward), *see* WILKINS (H. J.) E. C., 1636–1721, suppl., 1925.
Colton (Joseph H.), *publ.*
Plans of U.S. harbors. [No. 5]. folded. 8°. N.Y. 1862
Colum (Padraic). Dramatic legends & o. p. 8°. 1922
The road round Ireland. 8°. N.Y. 1926
Columba, *Saint, called Columkille, see* SIMPSON (W. D.) The historical St. C., 1927.
Columban, *Saint.*
see JONAS *Elnon.* Vitae SS. C., Vedastis &c.; rec. B. Krusch, 1905.
„ MARTIN (E.) St. C., 2e éd., 1905.
Columbia [*British Columbia*]. Annual report of the Min. of Mines, 1919. la8°. Victoria, B.C. 1920
Archives of B.C. Memoir No. 5. 8°. Victoria, B.C. 1923
see MENZIES (A.) Journal of Vancouver's voyage, 1792; ed. &c. C. F. Newcombe, 1923. [5.]
B.C. pilot, 2v, suppl. 6, *&* Not. to mariners, 1913–22, *see* ADMIRALTY.
Rep. on oriental activities. [P2876]. la8°. Victoria, B.C. 1927
Water powers, Brit. C. la8°. [Victoria, B.C. 1925]
Columbia University [NEW YORK].
Intr. to contemp. civilization. A syllabus. 5th ed. 8°. N.Y. 1925
BIOLOGICAL SER. [v]4. 8°. N.Y. 1919
see WILSON (E. B.) The cell in develop. &c., 1919. [4.]
GERMANIC STUDIES.
see LIPTZIN (S.) Shelley in Germany, 1924.
INDO-IRANIAN SERIES. v10, 11. 8°. N.Y. 1923–26
see HARDṢADEVA. Priyadarśikā: Sanskrit drama; tr. G. K. Nariman &c., w. intr. &c., 1923. [10.]
„ PAVRY (J. D. C.) Zoroastrian doct. of a future life, 1926. [11.]
ORIENTAL STUDIES. v15, 17, 23. 8°. N.Y. 1920–25
see ABŪ-MANṢŪR 'ABD-AL-KĀHIR IBN-ṬĀHIR, *al Baghdādī.* Moslem schisms & sects; tr. by K. C. Seelye, p1, 1920. [15.]
„ NEWMAN (L. I.) Jewish infl. on Xtn. reform movts., 1925. [23.]
„ WAXMAN (M.) Philos. of Don Hasdai Crescas, 1920. [17.]
SLAVONIC STUDIES. v1. 8°. N.Y. 1922
see STANOYEVICH (M. S.) Early Jugoslav lit. (1000–1800), 1922. [1.]
STUDIES IN CLASSICAL PHILOLOGY.
see WILSON (P. C.) Wagner's dramas & Greek tragedy, 1919.
STUDIES IN ENG. & COMPARATIVE LIT.
see AMOS (F. R.) Early theories of transl., 1920.
„ BABENROTH (A. C.) Eng. childhood: Wordsworth's treatment &c., 1922.

Columbia University [NEW YORK] [*continued*].
STUDIES IN ENG. & COMPARATIVE LIT. [*continued*].
see BEATY (J. O.) J. E. Cooke, Virginian, 1922.
,, BOLWELL (R. G. W.) Life & works of J. Heywood, 1921.
,, CAMP (C. W.) The artisan in Elizabethan lit., 1924.
,, GAINES (F. P.) The Southern plantation, 1924.
,, HEROLD (A. L.) J. K. Paulding, 1926.
,, LYON (J. H. H.) A st. of The newe metamorphosis, wr. by J. M., Gent, 1600, 1919.
,, PATTERSON (W. M.) Rhythm of prose, 1917.
,, PHILLIPS (W. C.) Dickens, Reade, & Collins, sensation novelists, 1919.
,, REED (A. L.) Background of Gray's Elegy, 1924.
,, YARBOROUGH (M. C.) J. Horne Tooke, 1926.
STUDIES IN HIST., ECONOMICS & PUBLIC LAW.
vliii, 5ii, 9i, 46iii, 52iii, 65ii, 68, 74i, 75ii, 76i, ii, 77, 79ii, 80ii, 83, 91i, ii, 92, 94i, iii, 95i, ii, 100i, ii, 101i, ii, 103i, 104ii, 107ii, 115i, 276, 281. 8º. N.Y. 1891–1926
see AHMAD IBN YAHYĀ, *al Balādurī*. Origins of the Islamic state; tr., w. notes by F. C. Murgotten, p2, 1924. [68.]
,, ALZONA (E.) Some Fr. contemp. opinions of Russ. Revol. 1905, 1921. [100ii.]
,, AYUSAWA (I. F.) Internat. labour legisl., 1920. [91ii.]
,, BLACK (G. A.) Hist. of municipal ownership of land on Manhattan Isl., to 1844, 1891. [liii.]
,, BONBRIGHT (J. C.) Railroad capitaliz., 1920. [95i.]
,, BONDY (W.) Separ. of gov. powers in hist. &c., 1896. [5ii.]
,, BOYCE (W. S.) Econ. & soc. hist. of Chowan Co., N. Carolina, 1880–1915, 1917. [76i.]
,, BRADLEY (H.) Enclosures in England, 1918. [80ii.]
,, BRISSENDEN (P. F.) The I. W. W.: Amer. syndicalism, 1920. [83.]
,, COMSTOCK (A.) State taxation of personal incomes, 1921. [101i.]
,, CURTIS (E. N.) French Assembly of 1848 &c., 1918. [79ii.]
,, DOUGLAS (P. H.) Amer. apprenticeship & indust. educ., 1921. [95ii.]
,, DRURY (H. B.) Sci. managem., a hist. & crit., 1915. [65ii.]
,, DUNAWAY (W. F.) Hist. of the James River & Kanawha Co., 1922. [104ii.]
,, EDWARDS (W. G.) New York as an 18th cent. municipality, 1731–76, 1917. [75ii]
,, GILLESPIE (J. E.) Infl. of oversea expansion on Eng. to 1700, 1920. [91i.]
,, HINKHOUSE (F. J.) Prelim. of the Amer. Revol., 1763–75, 1926. [276.]
,, LAWSON (L. A.) Rel. of Brit. policy to the declar. of the Monroe doct., 1922. [103i.]
,, LEVINE (L.) Syndicalism in France, 2nd ed., 1914. [46iii.]
,, MALTBIE (M. R.) Eng. local govt. of to-day, 1897. [9i.]
,, MINER (C. E.) Ratif. of the Fed. constit. by the state of N.Y, 1921. [94iii.]
,, MÜLLER (H. R.) Whig party in Pa., 1922. [101ii.]
,, NEWCOMER (M.) Separ. of state & local revenues in the U.S., 1917. [76ii.]
,, OAKLEY (T. P.) Eng. penitential discipline & Anglo-Saxon law &c., 1923. [107ii.]
,, PRINCE (S. H.) Catastrophe & soc. change, Halifax disaster, 1920. [94i.]
,, RAYMOND (D. N.) Brit. policy &c. dur. Franco-Prussian War, 1921. [100i.]
,, RIDDELL (W. A.) Rise of eccl. control in Quebec, 1916. [74i.]
,, STEWART (I.) Consular privileges &c., 1926. [281.]
,, WATERMAN (W. R.) F. Wright, 1924. [115i.]
,, WOOD (F. A.) Finances of Vermont, 1913. [52iii.]
,, WOOD (G. A.) W. Shirley, gov. of Massachusetts, 1741–56, v1, 1920. [92.]
,, ZOLLMANN (C.) Amer. civil church law, 1917. [77.]
STUDIES IN ROMANCE, PHILOLOGY & LITERATURE.
see ATKINSON (G.) The extraord. voyage in French lit. bef. 1700, 1920.
,, BEARDSLEY (W. A.) Infinitive constructions in Old Spanish, 1921.
,, CUSHING (M. G.) Pierre Le Tourneur, 1908.
,, RUSSO (J. L.) Lorenzo da Ponte, 1922.
,, VAETH (J. A.) Tirant lo Blanch: st. of authorship &c., 1918.
see BUTLER (N. M.) Dinner tendered to B., 1927.

Columbus (Bartholomew).
see JANE (C.) The admin. of the Colons in Española, 1924.

Columbus (Christopher).
Journal of h. first voyage to America. [Intr. by Van Wyck Brooks]. 8º. [1925]
Nuevas autografos de C. Colon, y rel. de ultramar. Publ. la duquesa de Berwick y de Alba. la8º. 1902
Los restos de Colon. Informe de la Real Acad. de la Hist. sobre el supuesto hallazgo en la catedral de Santo Domingo. s8º. 1879
Eyn schön hübsch lesen von etlichen insslen (1497, *facs.*), *see* FREYTAG (G.) Bilder, B3, T1, 1924.
see ANDRÉ (M.) Das wahre Abenteuer d. C. C.; Übertr., 1927.
see COLECCIÓN de docs. inéd. de Ultramar, s2, t7, 8, De los pleitos de Colón, 1892–4.
,, JANE (C.) The admin. of the Colons in Española, 1924.
,, JENSEN (J. V.) C. C., 1921.
see LA RONCIÈRE (C. B. DE). Découv. de l'Afr. au m. â., t3, 1927.
,, RIBEIRO (P.) Nacionalidade portug. de C. C. [*w. Eng. tr.*], 1927.
,, VIGNAUD (H.) The Columbian trad. on the discov. of Amer. & part played by Toscanelli &c., 1920.

Columbus (Diego) [COLON], *admiral, 1474–1526.* Memoriale, con nota s. bolla di Aless. VI d. 4 maggio 1493, di V. Promis, *see* REGIA DEP. DI STORIA PATRIA. Misc., t9, 1870.
see COLECCIÓN de docs. ined. de Ultramar, s2, t7, 8, De los pleitos de Colón, 1892–94.

Columella (Lucius Junius Moderatus). De re rustica; übers. durch H. Österreicher. Hrsg. K. Löffler. [Lit. V. in St. 263, 264]. 8º. Tübingen. 1914
see AGRONOMES (Les) latins: Caton, C. &c. (*Lat. & Fr.*); Nisard, 1877.

Columna (Petrus) *Galatinus.* De arcanis Catholicae veritatis libri 12. Item. I. Reuchlini, De Cabala, dialogus. [*a. c. b. w.* Habermann (J.) Liber radicum seu lexicon, 1589]. Postrema ed. expurg. fol. *n.p.* 1603

Colver, *The family of, see* ROSENBERGER (J. L.) Thr. 3 cent. (1620–1922), 1922.

Colvile (K. N.)
Fame's twilight: st. of 9 men of letters. 8º. 1923
see MISCELLANY. Misc. (A.) of the wits: intr. by C., 1920.

Colville (Charles Frederick). Notes on organiz. of Army and Militia reserves. [P2831]. 8º. Plymouth. [1878]

Colville (Henry Charles Asgill).
T. W. Harvey, prophet & priest. s8º. Bristol. 1918

Colvin (Ian Duncan). Life of Jameson. 2v. 8º. 1922

Colvin (*Sir* Sidney).
John Keats: h. life, poetry &c. [2nd ed.] 8º. 1918
Memories & notes of persons & places, 1852–1912. 8º. 1921
,, ,, ... 2nd impr. 8º. 1921

Colvinus (Alexander). Disputationes, *see* DU MOULIN (P.) Thesaurus disput., v2, 1661.

Colvinus (Ludiomæus), *ps., see* DU MOULIN (L.)

Colwell (Stephen). Ways & means of payment: analysis of credit system. 8º. Phila. 1859

Colyer (William Thomas). Americanism: a world menace. Pref. by T. Mann. s8º. 1922

Comandini (Alfredo). L'Italia nei cento anni del sec. 19, 1801–1900. Giorno per giorno illust. [v1–3]. s8º. Milano. 1900–18

Comazzi (*il conte* Giovanni Battista), *see* BAZZONI (A.) Uno storiografo cesareo del sec. 18 arrestato nei pressi di Vienna [*G. B. C.*], 1895.

Combarieu (Jules). Hist. de la musique. t2, 3. 8º. 1913–19

Combe (F. A.) Central & district heating; possibilities of applic. in Canada. [P2771]. 8º. [Ottawa. 1924]

Combe (George Alexander), *see* SHERAP (P.) A Tibetan on Tibet, w. introd. chap. &c. by G. A. C., 1926.

Combe (William) [*ps.* VALERIUS].
*The Diabo-lady: a poem. [P2597]. 8º. 1777
The Diaboliad, a poem. n. ed. [P2597]. 8º. 1777
*Hist. of the Abbey Church of St. Peter's, Westminster. 2v. 4º. *Ackermann.* 1812

Comber (Thomas), *D.D., dean of Durham.*
Friendly &c. advice to the Roman Catholics of England. 4th ed. enl. s8º. 1685
The occas. offices of matrimony &c., s8º. 1679
*The plausible arguments of a Romish priest from Antiquity answered. [P2103]. s8º. 1735
The right of tythes asserted &c. W. a vindic. f. the cavils of T. Elwood. s8º. 1677
Roman forgeries in the councils &c. 4p *in* 1v [p3 & 4 *have title*: The Church hist. clear'd f. Rom. forg. *2 pagin.*] s4º. 1689–95
A scholastical hist. of the use of liturgies. 2p *in* 1v. s8º. 1690

Comberbach, *The family of, see* MARSHALL (G. W.) Coll. for genealog. acc. of family of C., 1866.

Combes (Adrien), *see* BOUCHES-DU-RHÔNE; encyclop. départ. t6, Vie intellect., par C. &c., 1914.

Combés (Francisco). Hist. de Mindanao y Joló. Publ. en 1667, y que con collab. d. P. Pastells, saca nuev. á luz W. E. Retana. fol. 1897

Combetti (Celestino), *see* DANNA (C.) Biografia doc. di C. C., archivista &c., 1882.

Comboulot (Gautheret-), *see* GAUTHERET-COMBOULOT (—).

Comedies. Restoration comedies, 1921, *see* SUMMERS (M.), *ed.*

Comeiras (Victor Delpuech de), *see* DELPUECH DE COMEIRAS (V.)

Comenius (J. A.) [†Komensky (Jan Amos)].
De bono unitatis & ordinis &c. in eccl. rectè constit. eccl. Bohemicae ad Anglic. paraenesis. Cum praem. ordinis &c. in eccl. F. F. Boh. usit. descr. [*3 pagins.*] s8°. Amsterdami. 1660
De irenico irenicorum, hoc est condit. pacis à Socini secta oblatis. s8°. Amsterodami. 1660
De rerum human. emend. consultatio catholica. [*b. w. h.* Hist. Fratrum Bohem., 1702]. s4°. Halae. 1702
Hist. Fratrum Bohemorum, eorum ordo & disciplina eccl., cum Eccl. Bohem. ad Anglic. paraenesi &c. Praef. J. F. Buddei de instaur. discipl. eccl. [*2 pagins.*] s4°. Halæ. 1702
Janua linguarum trilinguis, ab authore recog. &c.: adj. metaphrasi Gr. & Angl. vers. s8°. Londini. 1662
Sapientiae primae usus triertium Catholicum appellandus. [Publ. J. V. Klima. Epilogue *in Eng. & Fr.*] s4°. Lugd. Batav. 1681 [*facs. repr.* Prague. 1920]
see Kvačala (J.) Komenský, 1914.
,, Turnbull (G. H.) S. Hartlib: sketch of h. life & h. rels. to J. A. C., 1920.
,, Zwicker (D.) Irenicomastix perpetuo [& iteratò] victus, 1661–62.

Comic muse (The): anthology of humorous verse, 1925, *see* Squire (J. C.), *ed.*

***Comicall** hist. of Alphonsus, King of Aragon, 1599, 1926, *see* Greene (R.)

Comicorum. C. Attic. frag., 3v, 1880–88, *see* Kock (T.), *ed.*

Comines (Philippe de), *seigneur d'Argenton.* Mémoires. Ed. J. Calmette &c. [Class. de l'hist. de Fr. au m. â.] 3t. 1464–98. s8°. 1924–25

Coming renaissance (The); [*by var. wr.*], 1923, *see* Marchant (*Sir* J.), *ed.*

Comino (Felice). Il conte L. Montagnini, *see* Regia Deput. Misc., t24, 1885.

Comisión Nacional del Homenaje al General Urquiza, *see* Urquiza (J. J. de).

Comité d'Experts, *see* Reparation Comm. Rep. of 1st C. of E. [*Fr. & Eng.*], 1924.

Comité Français Catholique pour la céléb. du 6e cent. de la mort de Dante Alighieri. Bull. du jubilé, Jan. 1921–Jan. 1922. No. 1–5. 8°. [1921–22]

***Commedia** di dieci vergine [*w.* Nota. Op. ined. &c. pubbl. d. Libr. Dante in Firenze, 1]. 8°. [Firenze. 1882]

Commemorative wreath (The): in celeb. of extinction of negro slavery in Brit. dominions. [*Poems by var. a.*] s8°. 1835

Commendone (Giovanni Francesco), *cardinal.* Lettere n. nunziatura di Germania; [*ed. G. Finazzi*], *see* Regia Dep. di Storia Patria. Misc., t6, 1865.

Comment. *C. (A) upon the Memoirs of the Hse. of Brandenburg, 1751, *see* Frederick II, *king of Prussia.*

Commentaria. *C. de statu relig. & reipublicæ in regno Galliæ, 4p, 1572–75, *see* Serres (J. de).

***Commentario** d. più notabili &c. cose d'Italia &c., 1548, *see* Landi (O.)

Commentationes theologicae, 6v, 1794–99, *see* Velthusen (J. C.), C. T. Kuinoel &c., *edd.*

Comminges (Jean de Lescun, *comte* **de),** *see* Lescun (J. de).

Comminges (Odet d'Aydie, *comte* **de),** *see* Aydie (O. d').

Comminges (Roger de), *sieur de Saubole*, *see* Derblay (C.) R. de C., Gouv. de Metz, 1533–1615, 1927.

Commission. Rep. of Comm. apptd. by Govt. of Palestine to inq. into affairs of Orthodox Patriarchate of Jerusalem, 1921, *see* Bertram (*Sir* A.) & H. C. Luke.

Commission Archéologique de l'Indochine, *see* Dufour (H.) Le Bayon d'Angkor Thom: bas-reliefs publ. par les soins de la Comm. Arch. de l'I., 2p, 1910–13.

Commission d'Enquête sur les Violations des Règles du Droit des Gens &c., *see* Belgique. Rapports & doc. d'enquête, 4v, 1921–23.

Commission des Antiquités de la Côte-d'Or. Coll. de doc. publ. avec le concours de la Comm. des Antiq. &c. [t]1. 4°. 1907–11
see Molesme. Cartul. de l'abbaye de M., 916–1250; publ. &c. J. Laurent, 2t, 1907–11. [1.]

Commission des Réparations, *see* Reparation Commission.

Commission for Relief in Belgium. Review of oper., 1914–19 [1925], *see* Gay (G. I.)

Commission Internat. de l'Eclairage [*form. de Photométrie*]. Rec. des travaux & compte rendu des séances. 5e session (1921), 6e session, 1924. 8°. C. 1923–26.

Commission of Inquiry into the Resources & Indust. of Ireland. Memoir on the coalfields of Ireland. 2v. (1, Text. 2, Maps). 8°. D. 1921

Commission Royale d'Histoire de Belgique.
Bulletin. [Acad. Roy. de Belg.] t84–90. 8°. Brux. 1920–26

Commission Royale d'Histoire de Belgique [*continued*].
Publications. 4°. 1920–27
see Artevelde, *The family of.* Cartul. hist. & généalog. des A.; [*ed.*] par N. de Pauw, 1920.
,, Dotrenge (B. J.) Corr., 1781–94; publ. E. Hubert, 1926.
,, Espinas (G.) & H. Pirenne, *edd.* Rec. de doc. rel. à l'hist. de l'industrie drapière en Flandre, pl, t3, 4, 1920–24.
,, France. Corr. des ministres de F. accréd. à Brux., 1780–90; publ. E. Hubert, 2t, 1920–24.
,, Hemricourt (J. de) Œuvres, t2, 1925.
,, Hocsem (J. de). Chron.; n. éd. publ. G. Kurth, 1927.
,, Laenen (J.) Archives de l'état à Vienne &c., 1924.
,, Liége. Invent. des chartes de la Collég. de Ste. Croix á L.; par E. Poncelet, t2, 1921.
,, —— Invent. des chartes de la Colléq. de St. Jean l'Evang. á L.; par L. Lahaye, t1, 1921.
,, Lonchay (H.) & J. Cuvelier. Corr. de la cour d'Espagne sur les aff. des Pays-Bas au 17e s., t1, 2, 1923–27.
,, Louvain. Actes ou procès-verbaux des séances, l'Univ. de L., t2, 1917.
,, Luxembourg. Dénombrements des feux des duché de L. & comté de Chiny, t1, 1921.

Commissione Provinciale di Archeologia e Storia Patria.
Documenti e monografie. v3, 5, 7, 8. la8°. Bari. 1901–8
see Carabellese (F.) L'Apulia ed il suo comune, 1905. [7.]
,, —— La Puglia nel sec. 15, 1901–8. [3, 8.]
,, Massa (T.) Le consuetudini d. citta di Bari, 1903. [5.]

Commissioners. C. of Inq. into State of Educ. in Wales, 1848, *see* Wales.

Commissioners for Trade & Plantations.
Journal. Preserved in the P. Rec. O. [v1–4]. la8°. 1920–25
1, Apr. 1704–Feb. 1708–09. 2, Feb. 1708–09–Mar. 1714–15. 3, Mar. 1714–15–Oct. 1718. 4, Nov. 1718–Dec. 1722.

Committee for State police. [Report &c.] [P2509]. 8°. N.Y. 1920

Committee of Experts, *see* Reparation Comm.

Committee of Imperial Defence. Hist. of the Great War; comp. by Hist. Sect. of C. of I. D., 1921–27, *see* War.
see Russo-Japanese War. Official hist., v3, 1920.

Committee on Alleged German Outrages. Evidence & docs. laid before the Comm. (App. to the Rep.) 8°. 1915
For the Report, *which was publ. as a Parl. paper, see special cat.*

Committee on Venereal Disease. Prevention of v. d. Rep. &c. [Nat. Co. of Public Morals]. 8°. 1921

Common Cause, The. The organ of the women's movement for reform. [Nat. Union of Women's Suffrage Societies]. Ed. Mrs. F. T. Swanwick. v2, 3. (Apr. 14, 1910–Apr. 4, 1912) [*b. in* 3v.] 4°. 1910–12

Common (Thomas), *see* Nietzsche (F. W.) N. as critic, philosopher, &c., sel. f. his works, comp. by T. C., 1901.

***Commoner,** The, a poem [*by* Incognito]. [P2868]. s8°. 1710

Commons (John Rogers). Industrial gov.; by J. R. C., W. Wisler *& others* [of] Univ. of Wisconsin. s8°. N.Y. 1921

——, **D. L. Saposs** *& others.* Hist. of labour in the U.S. Intr. note by H. W. Farnam. 2v. 8°. N.Y. 1918

Commonwealth. *Further (A) narr. of these times in the C.-w. of Eng., 1658, *see* Further.

Commune. Procès-verbaux de la Commune de 1871. Ed. crit. par G. Bourgin & G. Henriot. [Bibl. de l'Inst. d'Hist. &c. de Paris]. t1 (Mars–Avril, 1871). la8°. 1924

Communion. Order (The) for the admin. of the Holy C., *see* Prayer-Book.

Communist. *C. (The) exper. in Hungary, 1919, *see* Hungary.
*New (The) communist manifesto of the Third Internat. Pref. by W. Paul. [P2487]. s8°. Glasgow. [1919]

Communist International (The). No. 1, 2. fol. Moscow. 1919

Comnenus (Andronicus), *see* Andronicus [*Comnenus*].

Comoediae. Novae comoediae fragm. in papyris reperta &c., 1915, *see* Kleine Texte, T135, 1915.

***Compagnia (La) del Mantellaccio.** Componimento del sec. 15. [*sometimes attrib. to Lorenzo de' Medici*]. Ripr. a facs. d. prima stampa [of 1489], con cat. d. ediz. 8°. Firenze. [1861]

Compagnoni (Giuseppe). Les veillées du Tasse [*or rather C.*] Ms. inéd., mis au jour par C., & tr. de l'Ital. par J. F. Mimaut. 8°. [an] 8. [1800]

Compañía Ibero-Américana de Publ., *see* Colección de doc. inéd. para la hist. de I.-Amér., 1927 &c.

Company of Scotland Trading to Africa &c., *see* Darien Company.

Comparative education; by H. W. Foght, A. H. Hope &c., 1927, *see* Sandiford (P.), *ed.*

Comparetti (Domenico). Nuovi framm. d'iscriz. arcaiche trov. nel Pythion, *see* Reale Accad. d. Lincei. Mon. ant., v1, 1890.

Compendiolum. Compendiolum regnorum Slavoniae, Croatiae, Dalmatiae &c. geograph. [*Compiled f. J. Severin's ed. of J. Tomka Szaszky's* Introd. *b. w.* Bel (M.) Comp. Hung. geog., 1792]. s8°. Posonii. 1792

Compendious. *C. (A) olde treatyse shewynge howe that we ought to have the Scripture in Englysshe, *see* Roy (W.) & J. Barlow. "Rede me & be nott wrothe" &c., 1871.

Compendium.
C. doctr. Christ. quam omnes pastores &c. in Ungaria &c. docent, 1655, *see* Hungaria.
*C. hist. eccl. decreto Ernesti Saxon. &c. ducis in usum gymnasii Gothani libr. 2. [Lib. tertius decreto Friderici II, ducis Saxo-Gothani]. 3p [*in* 1v, *sep. tps. & pagins.*] s8°. Gothae. 1723
C. privileg. &c. Soc. Jesu, 1535; 1584, *see* Jesuits.
C. privileg. & grat. Soc. Jesu, 1703, *see* Jesuits.
C. relig. Christ.; tschanta & miss in nos ling. tras H. Robar, 1693, *see* Robar (H.)

Competition: st. in human motive. Wr. for the "Collegium" by J. Harvey, J. St. G. C. Heath &c. s8°. 1919

Compiègne. Cartul. de l'abbaye de Saint-Corneille de Compiègne. Publ. par le chanoine Morel. [Soc. Hist. de C.] t1, 877–1216. 4°. Montdidier. 1904
Musée Vivenel.
see Corpus vasorum antiq.; France, fasc. 3, Musée de C. (Musée V.); par M. Flot, 1924.

***Complaint** (The): or, Night thoughts, 1742–43; 1756, *see* Young (E.), *poet.*

Complete [Compleat].
Compleat acc. (A) of the Portugueze lang., 1701, *see* Portugueze.
Compleat (A) coll. of farewell Sermons pr. by Mr. Calamy, &c., 1663, *see* Collection.
*Compleat (A) hist. of the Cevennees [*sic*], 1703, *see* Cevennees.
*Compleat mem. of the life of that impostor W. Morrell &c., 1694, *see* Settle (E.)
Complete aeronautics; [*by var. a.*], v1, 1920, *see* Winchester (C.), *ed.*
*Complete angler (The), 1760, *see* Walton (I.)
*Complete grammar (The) of anarchy. [P2488, 2529]. s8°. D. 1918
*Complete grazier (The), 1805, *see* Horne (T. H.)
Complete guide (A) to all who have trade &c. w. London, 7th ed., 1758, *see* London.
*Complete vindic. (A) of the mallard of All-Souls Coll., 1750; 2nd ed., 1751, *see* Buckler (B.)

Complot (Le) germano-bolchéviste. 70 doc. sur les rel. des chefs bolch. avec l'armée &c. allem. Publ. par Comité d'Inf. Publ. d. Etats-Unis. Tr. fr. d'ap. l'éd. allem. s8°. 1920

Compositions. *Joint compositions, 1840?, *see* Lushington (F. & H.)

Compota domestica familiarum de Bukingham &c., 1443 &c., 1836, *see* Buckingham, *The fam. of.*

Compston (Herbert Fuller Bright). The Magdalen Hospital: story of a great charity. Foreword by the Abp. of Canterbury. 8°. 1917

Comptes. Comptes-faits, ou tarif gén. des monnoies, n. éd., 1774, *see* Barrême (F.)

Compton (Charlotte, *Baroness*), *Baroness Ferrers de Chartley*, *see* Clifford (I. G. C.) Descent of C. C., Baroness F. de C. &c., 1892.

Compton (E. Harrison), *see* Farrer (R. J.) The Dolomites; painted by E. H. C., 1913.

Comrie (John Dixon).
Hist. of Scottish medicine to 1860. 8°. 1927

Comstock (Alzada). State taxation of personal incomes. [Columbia Univ., St., 101i]. 8°. N.Y. 1921

Comstock (Harriet Theresa), *wife of Philip Comstock.*
The shield of silence. s8°. [1921]

Comte (Charles François Louis). Du nouv. projet de loi sur la presse. [P2772]. 8°. 1817

Comte (I. Auguste M. F. X.)
Catechisme positiviste. 2e éd. s8°. 1874
see Gould (F. J.) A. C., 1920.
„ Harrison (F.), *ed.* The new calendar of great men; biog. of the 559 worthies in the Positivist Cal. of C., 1920.
see Maurras (C.) Romantisme &c., éd. déf., A. C. &c., 1922.
„ Rouvre (C. de) L'amoureuse hist. d'A. C. & de C. de Vaux, 1920.

Comte (Louis Charles François), *see* Comte (C. F. L.)

Comyn-Platt (*Sir* Thomas). By mail & messenger. 8°. 1925

Conacher (H. M.), *see* Jones (D. T.) &c. Rural Scotland dur. the War; by D. T. J., H. M. C. &c., 1926.

Conant (*Mrs.* Frances Ann), *wife of J. H. C., née Crowell.* Biog. of C., the world's medium. [Comp. by J. W. Day]. 8°. Boston. 1873

Conard (Pierre). Napoléon & la Catalogne, 1808–14. [t]1, La captivité de Barcelone, 1808–10. 8°. 1910

***Concerning** solicitors; by one of them, 1920, *see* Solicitors.

***Concerto** per mus. a 3 voci. [N125]. 8°. Napoli. 1718

Concha (Manuel Gutierrez de la), *Marq. del Duero*, *see* Duero, M. G. de la C. (*Marq.* del).

Concile, 1869–70, *see* Vatican Council, 1869–70.

Concilia. Sacra concilia eccl. Rom.-Cath. in regno Hungariæ, 2p, 1741–42, *see* Péterfi (K.)

Concina (Daniele). De spectaculis theatralibus vetitis diss. 2. Acc. diss. 3a De Presbyteris personatis. & S. C. Borromei Opusc. de choreis &c. ed. 2a. 2p *in* 1v. s4°. Romæ. 1754
De vita &c. T. M. Ferrarii cardinalis libri 3. [*b. w. h.* De spectaculis, 1754]. s4°. Venetiis. 1757

Concise dictionary (The), *see* Dict. of nat. biog. C. dict., 1920.

Conclavi.
C. de' pontefici romani. [*attrib. to* G. Leti]. s8°. *n.p.* 1668

***Concordantiæ** majores sacræ Bibliæ, 1540, *see* Bible: Concordances.

Concordia [Concordiæ].
Apologeticus contra R. Bellarmini judic. pro s. & orthod. C. lib., 1605, *see* Höe (M.)
C. Christl. widerholete &c. Bekentnüs nachbenanter Churfürsten, Fürsten u. Stende Augspurg. Conf. &c., 1581 &c., *see* Augsburg Confession.
C. Germanico-Latina, 1735, *see* Reineccius (C.)
C. pio & unanimi consensu repetita conf. &c., 1705, *see* Augsburg Confession.
*C.; seu sacræ cœnae theoria sacra. Auctore P. D. K. S. T. P. 8°. Londini. 1776
De libro C. admon. à theologis in ditione Joh. Casimiri, 1581, *see* John Casimir, *Count Palatinate of the Rhine.*
Justa def. orthod. verit. in Lib. C. &c., 1622, *see* Osiander (L.)

Condé, *The House of*, *see* Aumale (H., *duc* d'). Hist. of princes de C., 16th & 17th c.; tr., 2v, 1872.

Condé (Charlotte Marguerite de Montmorency, *princesse* **de),** *1594–1650.*
see Noailles (A. M. R. A., *vte.* de). La mère du Gr. Condé, C. M. de M., psse. de C., 1924.
„ Virey (C. E.) L'enlèvement innocent, retraite de Msgr. le Prince avec la Psse. [*i.e.* C. M.], 1609–10, 1859.

Condé (Henry I, *prince de*) [Henry I [*de Bourbon*], *prince de Condé*], *see* Sixtus V, *pope.* Brutum fulmen adv. Hen., regem Navarrę & Hen. Borbonium, 1585.

Condé (Henry II, *prince de*) [Henry II [*de Bourbon*], *prince de Condé*], *see* Virey (C. E.) L'enlèvement innocent, retraite de Msgr. le Prince [*i.e.* C.] avec la Psse., 1608–10, 1859.

Condé (Louis II, *prince* **de),** *the "great Condé"; 1621–86.*
see Godley (*Hon.* E. C.) The gt. Condé: life of L. II, 1915.
„ Magne (E.) Le Grand C. & le Duc d'Enghien: lettres inéd., 1660–67; publ. &c. par E. M., 1920.

Condé (Louis Joseph, *prince* **de).** Journal d'émigration, 1789–95. Publ. par le cte. de Ribes. 4°. 1924

Condeminas Mascaró (F.)
La marina española. 8°. Barcelona. 1923

Conder (Claude Reignier) & H. H., *visc.* **Kitchener.** Map of W. Palestine, f. surveys by C. & K. Spec. ed., illust. nat. drainage & mtn. ranges, by T. Saunders. [Pal. Expl. F.; *b. w.* Warren (Sir C.) Plans &c., *n.d.*] lafol. 1882

Conder (Josiah). The lit. hist. of the New Test. 8°. 1850
On protestant nonconformity. 2v [*b. in I.*] 8°. 1818
The poet of the sanctuary. Cent. comm. of I. Watts. s8°. 1851

Condliffe (John Bell).
Short hist. of New Zealand. s8°. Christchurch. 1925

Condorcet (*le marq.* de). Esquisse d'un tableau hist. des progrès de l'esprit humain. 8°. 1795

Conestaggio (Girolamo). Dell' unione del regno di Portogallo alla Corona di Castiglia. 8°. Genova. 1589

Conference. C. de Moscou pour la limit. des armements (1922), 1923, *see* Moscou.
Report of the C. on new ideals in education, held at Stratford-on-Avon, Aug. 1915. 8°. 1915

Conférence Financière Internationale, *see* International Financial Conf., Brussels, 1920.

Conference on Christian Politics, Economics &c. Treatment of crime. Report pres. to Conf., Birmingham, Apr. 1924. [C.O.P.E.C. Comm. Rep., v6]. s8°. 1924
see Rural life; rep. prep. by Copec Contin. Comm., 1927.

Conferencia Interestadoal de Ensino Primario, *see* Brazil: Govt. Publications.

Confessio.
Antiqua & constans c. fidei eccl. Christi in regno Boiemiae &c. 1574, *see* Bohemia.
C. Bohemica: conf. sanctae & Christ. fidei &c. 1619, *see* Bohemia.
C. Cath. fidei Xtiana a patribus factae in synodo provinc. Petrikoviae, 1551, 1557, *see* Petricovia.
C. Christ. fidei &c., 1577, *see* Beza (T.)

Confessio [*continued*].
C. Christ. fidei &c. 1645, *see* LUCAR (C.)
C. : das ist Bekentnis d. Glaubens, 1564, *see* BOHEMIA.
C. doct. Saxon. eccl. 1551, 1552, *see* SAXONY.
C. eccl. reformat. in Belgio &c., 1618, *see* HOMMIUS (F.) Spec. controv. Belg., 1618.
*C. & apol. pastorum &c. eccl. Magdeburg, 1550, *see* MAGDEBURG.
C. & expositio fidei Chr. (1566), 1755, *see* HELVETIA.
C. fidei ac religionis baron. & nobil. B., 1535 ; 1558, *see* BOHEMIA.
*C. fidei Chr. &c., 1642 ; 1651, *see* APOSTLES' CREED.
*C. fidei Chr. sec. Unitarios in Transylvania &c. [*by J. Kermötzi*], 1782, *see* TRANSYLVANIA.
C. fidei communi eccl. quae sparsae sunt in Gallia. Cum praef. quae cont. Apologiam &c. s8°. *n.p.* 1559
C. fidei de eucharistiae sacramento in qua ministri eccl. Saxoniae &c., 1557, *see* SAXONY.
C. fidei & relig. quam regi Ferdinando, obtulerũt barones Bohemiae &c., 1575, *see* BOHEMIA.
C. fidei in conventu theol. author. Parl. Angl., 1656, *see* WESTMINSTER CONFESSION.
C. Helvetica posterior, 1825, *see* HELVETIA.
C. ministrorum J. C. in eccl. Antverp. &c., 1567, *see* ANTWERP.
C. piæ doct. Christophori Ducis Wirtembergensis &c., 1553, *see* CHRISTOPH *Herzog zu Würtemberg.*
C. relig. Chr., 1530, per legatos Argentorati &c., 1531, *see* STRASSBURG.
*C. sive declar. sentent. pastorum, qui Belgio Remonstrantes vocantur, 1622, *see* BELGIUM.
Orthodoxa C. Cathol. & Apostol. Eccl. Orient. Interprete L. Norrmanno. [*Gr. & Lat.*] s8°. Lipsiae. 1695
Orthodoxa Tigurinae eccl. ministr. c. &c., 1545, *see* ZÜRICH.

Confession.
C. de foy, faicte &c. par les fideles qui conversent és pays bas. s8°. 1561. [*repr.* Genève. 1855]
C. des Christoff Herzogen zu Wirtemberg &c., 1553 ? *see* CHRISTOPH, *Herzog zu Würtemberg.*
C. gén. de la vraye foy & religion Chrest., signée par le roy &c. [*Foll. by* Extr. de la resp. du Roy aux Eglises refugiées]. s8°. Londres. 1603
*C. oder Bekañtnuss des Glaubens der evangel. Kirchen in Franckreich &c. Item Eine kurtze C. T. Beze. Tr. s8°. Heydelberg. 1553
,, ,, ...s4°. [Haidelberg. 1557]
,, ,, Item. Eine kurtze C. T. Beze. Verdeutscht. [*b. w.* *Ordnung d. evangel. Kirchen in Fr., 1563]. s8°. [Heydelberg. 1563]
C. (The) of faith & the larger & shorter catechisme &c., 1649 ; 1658 ?, *see* WESTMINSTER CONFESSION.
*C. of faith by elders &c. of Xtns. baptized upon profession, 1677, *see* BAPTISTS.
C. (The) of faith of those called Arminians or a declaration of the opinions &c. of Remonstrants &c. Tr. s8°. 1684
C. (A) of the faith of sev. churches of Christ in Somerset &c., 1656, *see* COLLIER (T.)
C. u. Bekentnis d. Glaubens d. Fürsten Joh. Frid. &c., 1550, *see* JOHN FREDERICK II, *duke of Saxony.*
La discipline eccl. & la c. de foi des égl. reform. de France, 1711, *see* FRANCE.

Confessions [CONFESSIONES].
Coll. of c. of faith, catechisms, &c. in Ch. of Scot. &c., 2v, 1719–22, *see* CHURCH OF SCOTLAND.
C. duae &c., 1539, *see* LUTHER (M.)
C. fidei Christ. tres diversis quidem temporibus editae, sed cum verae & Catholicae Eccl. sententia incorrupta congruentes. 1, Carolo V in Comiciijs Augustae a XXX. 2. Eccl. Saxonic. (1541). 3. Christophori, ducis Vuirtebergensis a 1552. [3p *in 1v, sep. tps. & signatures*]. s4°. Francoforti. 1553
C. of faith, Catechisms &c., 1725 ; 1739, *see* CHURCH OF SCOTLAND.
*Corpus & syntagma c. fidei, 1654, *see* CORPUS.
*Extractum ex harmonia c. oblatum eccl. reform., 1671, *see* DURY (J.)
*Harmonia c. fidei orthodoxarum & reformat. eccl. &c. Add., Brev. obs. [*w. sep. tp. & sign.*] s4°. Genevæ. 1581
*Harmony (An) of the c. of the faith of the Christian & reformed churches of Europe. Tr. [*by Salnar*]. Added the C. of the Ch. of Scot. [*w. sep. pagin.*] s8°. C., *T. Thomas.* 1586
,, ,, n. ed. rev. & enl. by P. Hall. 8°. 1842
Sylloge c. sub tempus reform. eccl. ed. Subj. Catechismus Heidelberg. & Canones Synodi Dordrechtanae. 8°. Oxonii. 1804

Confessiun (La) ù descr. dall' intêra relig. &c., *see* CATECHISEM in il quael las controv. &c., 1720.

Conformitez. *Les c. des cérémonies mod. avec anc., 1667, *see* MUSSARD (P.)

Confortus, *de Custodia* [CONFORTO *da Costoza*]. Frammenti di storia vicentina, 1371–87 ; a cura di C. Steiner, *see* MURATORI (L. A.) Rerum Ital. Scr., t13i, 1915.

Confraternita. Nuove regole per la real C. de' Bianchi col titolo d. S. Croce. [P2767]. 8°. Napoli. [1768]

Confucius.
C. Sinarum philosophus sive scientia Sinensis Lat. exposita. Studio &c. P. Intorcetta &c. Adjecta, Tabula chronol. Sinicae monarchiae [auctore P. Couplet, 1686. *w. sep. tp. & pagin.*] fol. Parisiis. 1687
Tchoung young, ou l'invariable milieu, 2e livre de C. [*en Chinois*], lithogr. par M. Levasseur. s8°. Paris. [1833]
Works cont. the orig. text w. a tr. Pref. a dissert. on the Chinese lang. & character by J. Marshman. v1 [*Lun-yu. No more publ.*] 4°. Serampore. 1809
see CHINOIS. *Lettre à M.** touch. les honneurs que les Chinois rendent au philos. C. &c., 1700.
see COUCHOUD (P. L.) Japan. impressions, w. note on C. ; tr., 1921.
,, LA VICOMTERIE DE SAINT-SAMSON (L.) Le code de la nature, poëme de C. ; tr. & comm. [*or rather wr.*] par le Père Parennin [*i.e.* La V. de St. S.], 1788.
,, TZU-SSU. The Chung-Yung : [wr. to record teachings of C.] ; tr., 1927.
,, WATTERS (T.) Guide to tablets in a temple of C., 1879.
,, WU TING-FANG. C. & Mencius, address, 1901.

Confutatio. *C. determinationis doctor. Parrhisiensium contra M. L. &c., 1523, *see* PARIS.
*C. Lutheranorum confessatorum articulorũ fidei, per egregios papistas conglũtinata & Augustae in presentia Caroli V &c. producta &c. [*in MS.*] s4°. *n.p., n.d.* [*16 cent.*]

***Confutation (A)** of the Earle of Newcastles reasons for taking under h. command &c. Popish recusants, 1643, *see* NEWCASTLE (W. C., *1st duke of*).

Congdon (Charles Taber). Tribune articles : leading a. contrib. to New York Tribune, 1857–63. Intr. by H. Greeley. s8°. N.Y. 1869

Congo. *The Congo treaty. Surrender of Brit. govt. to Portugal. [P2832]. 8°. 1884
A manual of Belgian C., 1920, *see* ADMIRALTY : NAVAL INTELL. DIV.

Congratulations (The) of sev. kings &c. of Europe to James II on the birth of the Pr. of Wales, 1688, 1701, *see* JAMES EDWARD [STUART].

Congregatio (Sacra) de Propaganda Fide. *For Alphabetum Arabicum & o. alphabets publ. by the C. de P. F., see* ALPHABETUM.
Acta S. Congreg. pro Terra Sancta, pl, 2, 1622–1847 ; ed. L. Lemmens &c., *see* GOLUBOVICH (G.) Bibl. bio-bibliog. &c., n.s., t1, 2, 1921–22.
Constit. apostolicae, brevia, decreta &c. pro missionibus Sinarum, Tunquini &c. [*6 pagins.*] s8°. Parisiis. 1576
see GRAMATICA INDOSTANA, 1778.

Congregational. *Declar. (A) of the faith & order owned &c. in the C. Churches in Eng., 1688, *see* DECLARATION.
New C. hymn book, *n.d.*, *see* HYMN.

Congrès International des Etudiants (3e). Guide des étudiants, Budapest, Sept. 1902. [P848]. s8°. [Budapest.] 1902

Congress of Archæological Societies. Rep. of Com. on ancient earthworks &c. 1903, 1904, 1906, 1919–23 [*in* 2v]. 8°. [1903]–26
1918 *is covered by* 1919 Rep. The Rep. for 1921 *forms part of* The year's work in archæology, No. 1.
Rep. of Cong. & of the Earthworks Com. for 1924–26. 8°. 1925–27
Scheme for recording anc. defensive earthworks &c. [*b. w.* Rep., 1919–23 &c.] rev. 8°. 1910
The year's work in archæology, 1921. 8°. 1922

Congressional globe, 1835–73, *see* UNITED STATES : CONGRESS.

Congressional record, 1873–97, *see* UNITED STATES : CONGRESS.

Congreve (William).
*Amendments of Mr. Colliers citations f. the Old batcheleour, Double dealer, Love for love, Mourning bride. By the a. of those plays. s8°. 1698
Compl. works. Ed. M. Summers. 4v. la8°. Soho, *Nonesuch Press.* 1923
Incognita : or, Love & duty reconcil'd. Ed. H. F. B. Brett-Smith. [Percy Reprints, 5]. s8°. O. 1922
Love for love, *see* INCHBALD (E.) Brit. th., v13, 1808.
Mourning bride, *see* INCHBALD (E.) Brit. th., v13, 1808.
Mourning muse of Alexis, *see* ADDISON (J.) Letter f. Italy, 1709.
Poems upon sev. occasions. s8°. Glasgow. 1752
W. C. : a sheaf of poet. scraps, w. A satyr agst. love, prose misc. & letters. Ed. D. Protopopesco. 2nd ed. enl. 8°. [1925]
see GOSSE (*Sir* E.) Life of W. C., 2nd impr., rev. & enl., 1924.

Coningham (Arthur). *Secret hist. of the Coningham case. [Petition for divorce. Rev. D. F. O'Haran, co-respondent]. By "Zero." 8°. Sydney. 1901

***Conjecturae** hist.-crit. Sadducæorum, 1779, *see* SCHULTZE (B.)

*****Conjugal** duty set forth in a coll. of wedding-sermons. [*By var. a.*] 2p [in 1v]. s8°. [1732–34]

Conklin (Edward Grant).
The direction of human evol. 8°. [1921]
Heredity & environment in the development of men. [N. W. Harris lect., 1914]. 5th ed. rev. s8°. Princeton. 1922

Conley (Carey Herbert). The first Eng. translators of the classics. 8°. New Haven, *Yale*. 1927

Connaught; [*by var. wr.* Prov. of Ireland], 1922, *see* FLETCHER (G.), *ed.*

Connell (Norreys), *ps., see* O'RIORDAN (C.)

Connes (G. A.) Dict. of characters & scenes in the novels &c. of H. G. Wells. la8°. Dijon. 1926

Connes (Georges). Le mystère shakespearien. s8°. [1926]

Connington (J. J.) Death at Swaythling Court. s8°. 1926

Connoisseur (The): an illust. magazine for collectors. Ed. J. T. H. Baily &c. v55–78. [Sept. 1919–Aug. 1927]. 4°. 1919–27
„ „ Christmas annual, 1914. Ed. J. T. H. Baily. fol. [1914]
„ „ Compl. index, Sept. 1901 to Aug. 1905. 4°. 1906
„ „ „ „ Sept. 1905 to Aug. 1909. 4°. 1911
see ROBERTS (W.) Cries of London, 1924.

Connolly (James), *see* Ryan (D.) J. C., 1924.

Connolly (Louise). Tibet, the country, climate &c. [P2564]. 8°. Newark, N.J. 1921

Connor (Bernard).
Hist. of Poland. Publ. &c. [J.] Savage. 2v. s8°. 1698

Connor (Ralph), *ps.* [*i.e.* CHARLES W. GORDON].
The friendly four & o. s. s8°. [1926]

Conny-catcher (Cuthbert), *ps.* *The defence of conny-catching (1592), *see* GREENE (R.) The blacke bookes messenger, 1924.

Conolly (Matthew Forster). Fifiana: or, mem. of the East of Fife. la8°. Glasgow. 1859

Conon *de Béthune, see* QUÈNES *de Béthune.*

*****Conqueror (The),** a dramatic phantasy. *p.p.* 8°. [E.] 1906

Conquest (Joan). Forbidden. s8°. [1927]
Zarah the Cruel. s8°. [1923]

Conrad II, *emp. of Germany, called "the Salic," see* WIPPO. Weerk (*Lat.*, Gesta C. &c.); hrsg. H. Bresslau, 1915.

Conrad, *von Helmsdorf.* Der Spiegel des menschl. Heils. Hrsg. v. A. Lindquist. [Deut. Texte d. M.-a., hrsg. v. d. Preuss. Akad. d. Wiss., 31]. 8°. 1924

Conrad, *of Lichtenberg, bp. of Strassburg, see* KREBS (M.) K. III v. L., Bischof v. S. (1273–99), 1926.

Conrad, *v. Würzburg.* Kleinere Dichtungen. Hrsg. E. Schröder. 3[T *in* 1v]. 8°. 1924–26
Die Legenden. Hrsg. P. Gereke. [Altdeut. Textbibl., 19, 20]. [2T *in* 1v]. s8°. Halle/Saale. 1925–26
see KÖNIGL. GESELLS., GÖTTINGEN. Nachrichten, 1912 & 1917 *for* Schröder's Studien, 1912–18.

Conrad (Jessie), *wife of Joseph Conrad.*
Joseph Conrad as I knew him. n. impr. s8°. [1926]

Conrad (Joseph), *ps.*
Almayer's Folly. 3rd impr. s8°. [1914]
„ „ 8th impr. s8°. [1920]
„ „ & Tales of unrest. [Uniform ed.] 8°. 1923
The arrow of gold. Story between 2 notes. 8°. [1919]
„ „ [Uniform ed.] 8°. 1924
Chance. 15th ed. s8°. [1920]
„ [Uniform ed]. 8°. 1923
J. C.: life & letters. By G. Jean-Aubry. 2v. 8°. 1927
Last essays. 8°. 1926
Lord Jim. [repr.] s8°. [1917]
„ „ ....[repr.] s8°. [1920]
„ „ [Uniform ed.] 8°. 1923
The mirror of the sea: mem. &c. [Uniform ed.] 8°. 1923
„ „ ....12th ed. s8°. 1924
The Nigger of the Narcissus. [Acme Lib.] s8°. 1921
„ „ & Typhoon [& Amy Foster — Falk — To-morrow]. [Uniform ed.] 8°. 1923
Nostromo. [Uniform ed.] 8°. 1923
Notes on life & letters. 8°. 1921
„ „ [Uniform ed.] 8°. 1924
An outcast of the islands. [5th impr.] s8°. *Unwin*. [1923]
„ „ [Uniform ed.] 8°. 1923
A personal record. s8°. [1919] *A re-issue of* "Some reminiscences."
„ „ [*b. w. h.* Mirror of the sea, 1923]. [Uniform ed.] 8°. 1923
The rescue. s8°. [1920]
„ „ [Uniform ed.] 8°. 1924
The rover. 8°. [1923]
„ „ [2nd impr.] 8°. [1923]
„ „ [4th impr.] 8°. [1924]
The secret agent. [Uniform ed.] 8°. 1923
A set of six. [Uniform ed.] 8°. 1923
The shadow-line. [Uniform ed.] 8°. 1923
Suspense. Intr. by R. Curle. s8°. 1925
„ Intr. by R. Curle. [Uniform ed.] 8°. 1927

Conrad (Joseph) [*continued*].
Tales of hearsay. Pref. by R. B. Cunninghame Graham. 8°. [1925]
„ „ & Last essays. [Uniform ed.] 8°. 1928
Tales of unrest. s8°. 1922
„ [4th impr.] s8°. *Unwin*. [1923]
see also Almayer's folly.
Twixt land & sea. Tales: A smile of fortune—The secret sharer—Freya. s8° 1918
„ „ ....[repr.] s8°. 1920
„ „ [Uniform ed.] 8°. 1923
Typhoon & o. stories, *see also* Nigger of the "Narcissus," &c., *above*.
Under Western eyes. [Uniform ed.] 8°. 1923
Victory. [Uniform ed.] 8°. 1923
Within the tides. [*b. w. h.* Shadow-line, 1923. Uniform ed.] 8°. 1923
Youth, & 2 o. s. [Heart of darkness—End of the tether]. s8°. N.Y. 1903
„ „ ....[repr.] s8°. [1918]
„ „ [Uniform ed.] 8°. 1923
see BENDZ (E.) J. C.: an apprec., 1923.
„ CONRAD (JESSIE). J. C. as I knew him, 1926.
„ HUEFFER (F. H. M.) J. C., 1924.
„ MÉGROZ (R. L.) A talk w. J. C. & crit. of h. mind & method, 1926.
„ NOUVELLE REVUE FRANÇAISE, déc., 1924 [cont. apprec. of C.], 1924.
„ SCOTT-MONCRIEFF (C. K.), *ed.* Marcel Proust: an Eng. tribute; by J. C. &c., 1923.
„ STAWELL (F. M.) C., 1920.
„ SYMON (A.) Notes on J. C., w. unpubl. letters, 1925.
„ WISE (T. J.) Bibliogr. of wr. of J. C., 1895–1920, 1920.
„ —— A Conrad library: cat. of pr. bks., MSS. & letters by C.; coll. by T. J. W., 1928.

—— & F. M. Hueffer.
The inheritors. [Works. Uniform ed.] 8°. 1923
The nature of a crime. s8°. [1924]
Romance. [Works. Uniform ed.] 8°. 1923

Conrad (Martin). Disput. de dignitate & officio magistratus. Moderat. J. G. Volckmaro, resp. P. Sthenio. [P522]. s4°. Witebergae. 1595
see KNOGLER (C.) Disput. de habit. morum laudab. & vitiosis; propos. à M. C., 1595.

Conradi (Ludolph Carl). Hist. sec. 4. fabulis var. maculat. in rebus Constantini. Praes. J. A. Schmidio. [P432]. s4°. Helmstadii. [1712]

Conradi (Maurice), *see* AUBERT (T.) L'affaire C.: plaidoirie, 14 & 15 nov. 1923, 1924.

Conradus, *Schirensis* [†C. *Philosophus*]. Chronicon Schirense, saec. 13 conscr., a P. F. Stephano addit., notisque auctum. Joannis Aventini Chron. Schirense, nova hac ed. accur. G. C. Joannis. [*b. w.* Freher (M.) Orig. Palat., 1686]. s4°. Argentorati. 1716

Conrad v. Hötzendorf (*Feldmarschall* **Franz**). Aus meiner Dienstzeit 1906–18. B1–5 [Anlagen u. Karten *to* B4 *b. separately*]. 8°. Wien. 1921–25
see PASTOR (L. v.) C. v. H., ein Lebensbild, 1916.

Conrady (A. E.), *see* PHOTOGRAPHY as a sci. implement; by A. E. C., &c., 1924.

Conringius (Hermannus), *see* WITZEL (G.) Via regia; acc. varia; H. C. redegit &c., 1650.

Cons (Louis). L'auteur de la farce de Pathelin [? Guillaume Alecis]. [Elliott Monogr., 17]. la8°. Princeton. 1926

Consalvi (*il card.* **Ercole**) **&** *card.* **B. Pacca.** Corr. ined. dei card. C. e P. nel tempo del Congr. di Vienna, 1814–15. Corr. di sommarii e note, prec. da una st. stor. sugli stati d'Europa &c. [*by*] I. Rinieri. 8°. Torino. 1903

Consalvus Montanus (Reginaldus), *see* GONSALVIUS MONTANUS (R.)

Conscience. *The advocate of c. liberty, 1673, see ADVOCATE.

Conscience (Hendrik), *1812–83.* Der Löwe v. Flandern. [Bearb. besorg. K. L. Walter van d. Bleek]. s8°. 1916
Hoe men schilder wordt. Avec remarques & tr. des mots difficiles par E. T. [P2430]. s8°. Brussel. *n.d.*

Conselheiro (Antonio) [MACIEL (ANT. VICENTE MENDES)], c. *1842–97*, *see* GRAHAM (R. B. C.) A Brazilian mystic: life & miracles of A. C., 1920.

*****Consensus** orthod. Sacrae Script & Vet. Eccl. de sententia & veritate verborum Coenae &c. 1578, *see* HARDESHEIM (C.)

Consentius (Ernst), *see* DIETZ (J.) Meister J. D. &c.; nach d. alt. Handschr. gegeben v. E. C., *n.d.*

Conservateur (Le) litt., 1819–21. [*Contrib. by* V. Hugo &c.] éd. crit. publ. par J. Marsan. [Soc. d. Textes Fr. Mod.] t1, pl. s8°. 1922

*****Conservative** (The) mind. By A gentleman with a duster. 8°. [1924]

Conservative (A) Whig, *ps.* *A letter to Visc. Melbourne &c. on admin. of Earl Mulgrave, in rel. to applic. of the law &c., 1836, *see* WALLACE (T.)
*Three letters &c. on pres. state of parties &c., 1835, *see* WALLACE (T.)

Consett (*Rear-Adm.* **Montagu Will. Warcop P.**) The triumph of unarmed forces, 1914–18; trans. by wh. Germany was able to obtain supplies &c. By C. ass. by Capt. O. H. Daniel. 8°. 1923

Considerations [CONSIDÉRATIONS].
*C. of present use conc. the danger resulting f. change of church govt., 1644, *see* HAMMOND (H.)
*C. on divorce a vinculo matrimonii, 1857, *see* BADELEY (E.)
C. s. les dern. révol. de l'Europe, 1824, *see* SALVO (*le marq.* C. DE).
*C. sur l'état prés. de la colonie franç. de St.-Domingue, 2t, 1776, *see* HILLIARD d'AUBERTEUIL (M. R.)
*Farther c. upon a reduct. of the land-tax, 1751, *see* NUGENT (R. C.-N., *earl*).

Consilia. Thesauri consiliorum, &c., 3v, 1671, *see* DEDEKENNUS (G.)

Consolatio. Incerti Consol. ad Liviam, *see* BÄHRENS (E.) Poetæ Lat. minores, v2ii, 1923.

Consortium (The): offic. text of the four-power agreement for a loan to China & rel. docs. [C. E. f. Int. Peace]. la8°. Wash. 1921

Conspiracy (The) agst. the Brit. Empire. Rep. of meeting, H. of Commons, 1st March 1921. [P2509]. 8°. 1921

Constable (John) [*ps.* ALETHES (CLEROPHILUS)]. Spec. of amendments prop. to the compiler [H. Tootell] of The Church-hist. of Eng., 1500–1688. s8°. 1741
see TOOTELL (H.) *Apology for the Ch. hist. of Eng., 1500–1688 pr. in 1737; reply to a libel under name C. Alethes, 1742.

Constable (John), *R.A.*, *see* HOLMES (*Sir* C. J.) C., Gainsborough & Lucas: early drawings by C., 1921.

Constable (*Lt.-Col.* **Raleigh Chichester-**), *see* CHICHESTER-CONSTABLE.

Constable (W. G.) John Flaxman, 1755–1826. 8°. 1927
see CAMBRIDGE. FITZWILLIAM MUSEUM. Cat. of pictures in the Marlay bequest; comp. by W. G. C., 1927.
„ ROYAL ACADEMY. Exhib. of Brit. primitive paintings; [intr. by W. G. S.], 1924.

Constance, Council of. [CONCILIUM CONSTANT.] Acta C. C. Hrsg. in Verbind. mit J. Hollnsteiner &c. v. H. Finke. B1–3. 8°. Münster i. W. 1896–1926
1, Vorgesch. (1410–14). 2, Konzilstagebücher, Sermones, Reform-u.- Verfassungsakten. 3, Die 3 Päpste u. d. Konzil —Schr. z. Papstwahl.
C. C., 1414–18. [*Facsimile of drawings illust. Reichental's Chron.*] Изд. И.Р.А.О. [*ed. Prince* G. Gagarin *& others*]. fol. С.-П. 1874
*De legatis acad. Lips. ad C. C. [P2646]. s4°. [Lipsiæ. 1785]

Constance (*M.*), *prime minister of the King of Siam, see* PHAULKON (C.)

Constans (Léopold Albert). Arles antique. 8°. 1921
Un correspondant de Cicéron: Ap. Claudius Pulcher. 8°.1921

Constans (Lucius Antistus), *ps.* *De jure ecclesiasticorum, liber singularis. [*attrib. to Spinoza & to P. de la Court*]. s8°. Alethopoli. [Amsterdam]. 1665

Constant (Benjamin).
Adolphe. Éd. hist. & crit. par G. Rudler. s8°. M'ter. 1919
Annales de la Session de 1817 à 1818. [P2553]. 8°. 1817
Comm. sur l'ouvr. de Filangieri. 8°. 1822
Mém. sur les Cent Jours. n. éd., augm. d'une intr. [2p *in* 1v]. 8°. 1829
see POURTALÈS (G. DE). De Hamlet à Swann, ét. sur B. C. &c., 1924.
see SCHERMERHORN (E. W.) B. C., h. private life & contrib. to liberal govt. in France, 1767–1830, 1924.
„ WOŁOWSKI (L. F. M. R.) Mém. sur le Cours de polit. constit. de B. C., 1862.

——, **C. Ganilh & D. D. de Pradt.** Mélanges polit. & hist. rel. aux évènements contemp., par C., G., de P. et autres publicistes célèb. 3t. 8°. 1829
For a 4th vol. in which above tp. has been inserted, see PRADT (D. D. DE). Des progrès du gouvt. &c., 1817.

Constant (G.) Concession à l'Allemagne de la Communion sous les 2 espèces: la réforme cath. en Allem., 1548–1621. [Ecoles Franç. d'Athènes &c., 128]. 2t. la8°. 1923
La légation du card. Morone près. l'Empereur & le Concile de Trente, 1563. [H. E. 233]. 8°. 1922

Constant (Louis Alphonse) [*ps.* ELIPHAS LÉVI]. The hist. of magic. Tr., w. pref. & notes by A. E. Waite. 2nd ed. 8°. 1922
Transcendental magic, its doctrine & ritual. Tr., annot. & intr. by A. E. Waite. n. & rev. ed. 8°. 1923

Constantin (Antoine), *d. 1616, see* LEGRÉ (L.) La botanique en Provence au 16e s.: L. Anguillara &c., 1901.

Constantine V, *emp. of the East, surnamed Copronymus.*
see LEO III, *emp. of the East.* Manual of later Rom. law; founded upon Ecloga of L. III & C. V &c., tr., 1927.
„ —— Manual of Roman law; publ. by L. III & C. V; tr., 1926.
„ —— Rev. manual; tr., 1927.

Constantine VII, *emp. of the East, surnamed Porphyrogenitus.* Early hist. of the Slavonic settlements in Dalmatia, Croatia, & Serbia. De admin. Imp. chaps. 29–36 [*in Greek*]. Ed. J. B. Bury. [P2488]. s8°. 1920
see VASILEV (A. A.) Византія и Арабы: К. VII &c., 867–959, 1902.

Constantine *of Erzenga, see* KOSTANTIN ERZNKATZI.

Constantine I, *king of the Greeks.*
see BURROWS (R. M.) The abdic. of K. C., 1917.
„ HIBBEN (P.) C. I & the Greek people, 1920.
„ MÉLAS (G. M.) Ex-king C. & the War, 1920.

Constantine I, *emperor of Rome, "the Great."*
see ALTUS (H.) Donatio C. facta (ut ajunt) Sylvestro, 1703.
„ COLEMAN (C. B.) C. & Xtianity, 1914.
„ CONRADI (L. C.) Hist. sec. 4. fabul. macul. in rebus C., 1712.
„ EUSEBIUS. Hist. of the Church & life of C., 1709.
„ HOFMANN (C. F.) & G. E. HEBENSTREIT. Disput. de C. M. sepulcro, 1759.
see KIST (N. C.) Disput. inaug. de commut., C. m. auctore &c., 1818.
„ MAURICE (J.) C. le Grand, 1926.
„ POLE (*card.* R.) De concilio *&* de baptismo C., 1562.
„ VALLA (L.) Treatise on Donation of C.; text & tr. Coleman, 1922.

Constantine Constantinovich, *grand duke, son of pr. C. Nikolaevich* [*ps.* K. R.] *Царь Іудейскій; драма. изд. 2ое. 8°. С.-П. 1914

Constantinian Order. *Ant. notizie nec. per i sign. cavalieri d. ord. costantiniano di S. Giorgio. [*no tp.* P2767]. 8°. *n.p.* [1769]

Constantinople. C. to-day, or The Pathfinder Survey of C., 1922, *see* JOHNSON (C. R.), *ed.*
Константинополь и Проливы, 2т. 1925–26, *see* ADAMOV (E. A.), *ed.*

Constantius (Franciscus). Biblia L. Salmuths, wie er u. seine Calvin. Rotte d. heilige Biblia M. Lutheri glossiret u. verfelchet haben. s4°. *n.p.* 1592

Constantius (Jiří) [KONSTANTIUS], *see* JANDYT (V.) *Gramm. ling. Boem.; insert. sunt regulae orthogr. K., ed 5a, 1753.

Consten (Hermann). Weideplätze d. Mongolen im Reiche d. Chalcha. 2B. 8°. 1919–20

***Constituciones** artis gemetriæ secundum Euclydem. Facs. of early poem on freemasonry, f. orig. MS. now in B. M. [*Ed.* H. J. Whymper]. s8°. 1889

Constitution de la Répub. de Pologne du 17 mars, 1921, 1921, *see* POLOGNE.

Constitutiones. Aliquot constit. et decreta apostolica &c. [1567–1699]. ed. 4a s8°. Leodii. 1700
Coll. constit. Imper., 4t, 1713, *see* GOLDAST (M.)
C. apost., brevia, &c. pro missionibus, 1576, *see* CONGREGATIO DE PROPAGANDA FIDE.
C. facte in div. sessionibus sacri gen. concilii pisani, 1512, *see* PISA.

Constitutionnel (Un) salarié *ps.* *Le ministère vengé, 1818, *see* THIERY (A.)

Constitutions. The C. & canons eccl. & 39 articles of the Ch. of Eng. n. ed. [*b. w.* Homilies. Certain sermons &c., 1846]. 8°. [1846]
C. of freemasonry &c., 1858, *see* FREEMASONRY.
Sel. c. of the world. Prep. for pres. to Dáil Eireann, 1922. 8°. D. [1922]

Consul (Stipan), *Istrian, see* TRUBER (P.) Hauptartickel christl. Lehre, in d. Crobat. verdolm. *by S. C. &c.*, 1562.

***Consultation** (A) about religion: or, What relig. is best to be chosen. w. App. s8°. 1693

Contarenus (Caspar), *see* CONTARINI (*card.* G.)

Contarini (Chrysanthos), *metropolitan of Neopatras.*
О странахъ Средней Азіи 1790. Издалъ В. В. Григорьевъ. [P2399]. la8°. Москва. 1861

Contarini (Francesco). A propos. dell' Acquedotto. Lettera [1540. *Ed.* L. C. Borghi. Nozze Jachia-Sacerdote. N. 134]. 8°. Venezia. 1879

Contarini (*il card.* **Gasparo**) [CONTARENUS].
Opera. [Ed. L. Contarini. G. Contareni vita, a J. Casa conscr. fol. Parisiis. 1571
see ECK (J. v.) Apologia adv. calumnias Buceri &c., apologia pro G. C., 1542.

Contarini (*il card.* **Gasparo)** [*continued*].
see ECK (J. v.) Apologia pro principibus &c.; Apologia pro G. C., 1542.
„ PAUL III, *Pope*. Concilium delect. card. &c. de emendanda eccl. &c. [*signed C. C. &c.*], 1538.
Contarini (Giovanni Matteo). Map of the world designed by C., engraved by F. Roselli, 1506. [Intr. by J. A. J. de Villiers. Brit. Mus. Dept. of Maps]. sfol. 1924
Contarini (Giovanni Pietro). Hist. d. guerra mossa da Selim Ottomano a' Venetiani &c., rid. a. luce da G. B. Combi. la8°. Venetia. 1645
Contarini (Paolo). Diario d. viaggio da Venezia a Costantinopoli, 1580. [Nozze Grimani-Fracanzani. N132]. 8°. Venezia. 1856
Conte (Edouard). Ribera. s8°. [1924]
Contell (Emilio Gascó), *see* GASCÓ CONTELL (E.)
Contelorio (Felice). Mathildis comitissæ genealogia. s4°. Interamnæ. 1567 [*i.e.* 1657]
Contemporaneo (Il): giornale quotid. [Comp. da una soc. di letterati in Roma]. a. 2, No. 65 (3 Giug. 1848)–a. 3, No. 141 (14 Lugl. 1849). lafol. 1848–49
Contemporary Brit. philos.: personal statements, s1, 2, 1924–25, *see* MUIRHEAD (J. H.), *ed.*
Contemporary review (The).
v117–133 (Jan. 1920–June 1928). la8°. 1920–28
***Contempt** (The) of the clergy, 1739, *see* HILDROP (J.)
Contenau (Georges).
L'art de l'Asie occident. ancienne. la8°. 1928
La civilis. assyro-babylon. s8°. 1922
La civilis. phénicienne. s8°. 1926
Eléments de bibliog. hittite. 8°. 1922
La glyptique syro-hittite. [Haut-Comm. de la Républ. Fr. en Syrie &c.] la8°. 1922
Manuel d'archéologie orientale. [t]1. 8°. 1927
Mission archéolog. à Sidon (1914). [Extr. de Syria, t1]. 4°. 1921
Contention. The contention of the bards. Ed. w. tr., notes, gloss^s. &c. by L. M'Kenna. [Irish Texts Soc., v20, 21]. 2p [*pagin. cont.*] 8°. 1918
Contes. Cinq cents contes &c., extr. du Tripiṭaka chinois, tr. E. Chavannes, 3t, 1910–11, *see* TRIPIṬAKA.
Contes & légendes du bouddhisme chinois; tr., 1921, *see* CHAVANNES (E.)
Contessa (Carlo). Decadenza d. diplomazia ital. nel sec. 17: aned. di relazioni veneto-sabaude, *see* REGIA DEPUT. Misc., t42, 1906.
Progetti econ. d. 2ª Madama Reale di Savoia [Maria Giovanna Battista] fond. sopra un contratto nuziale, 1678–82, *see* REGIA DEPUT. Misc., t48, 1915.
Conti, *Family of*, *see* NAUD (J.) Château d'Issy & s. hôtes; les C. &c., 1926.
Conti (Antonio), *see* SALZA (ABD-EL-KADER). L'Ab. A. C. e le sue tragedie, 1898.
Conti (Armand de Bourbon, *prince* **de).** Traité de la comédie, & des spectacles selon la trad. de l'Eglise. s8°. 1669
Conti (Cosimo). Ricerche stor. sull' arte d. arazzi in Firenze. s8°. Firenze. 1875
Conti (François Louis de Bourbon, *prince* **de),** *1664–1709*, *see* LA FORCE (B. N. DE C., *duc* DE). Le grand Conti, 1922.
Conti (Giuseppe). Firenze dopo i Medici. la8°. Firenze. 1921
Conti (Louise Marguerite, *princesse* **de),** *see* LA FORCE (C. R. DE C. DE). Jeux d'esprit, ou la promenade de la Psse. de C. à Eu, 1862.
Conti (Niccolò de'). O livro de Nicolao Veneto [escr. p. Pogio], *see* POLO (M.) Livro de M. P., 1922.
Conti (Pietro de'), *see* CALEPIO (PIETRO DE' CONTI, *cte.* DA).
Continental Congress, *see* UNITED STATES: CONGRESS.
Continental echo & Protestant witness. 2v. 8°. 1845–46
***Continentia** (De) sacerdotum, c. 1515, *see* BOUSSARD (G.)
***Continuation** de la Nouv. défense de la tr. du Nouv. Test. impr. à Mons, 1682, *see* ARNAULD (A.)
***Contra** Amaurianos (13c.), *see* GARNERIUS, *de Rochefort*.
Contrasty (*l'abbé* **Jean),** *see* SAINTE-FOY-DE-PEYROLIÈRES. Cartul. de Ste.-Foy-de-P.; [intr. &c.] par J. C., 1919.
Contreras (Alonso de). The life of Capt. A. de C., wr. by himself (1582–1633). Tr. C. A. Phillips. Intr. by D. Hannay. 8°. 1926
Contri (Cosimo Giorgieri).
Le orme del satiro. Romanzo. s8°. Milano. [1920]
Control (The) of parenthood; by J. A. Thomson &c., 1920, *see* MARCHANT (J.), *ed.*
***Controversia** de sabbatho Christian. decisa a J. M. D. s4°. Lipsiæ. 1704

Contugi, *The family of*, *see* LE PAULMIER (C. S.) L'Orviétan: hist. d'une famille de charlatans du Pont-Neuf [*i.e.* C.] aux 17ᵉ & 18ᵉ siècles, 1893.
Contzen (Adam) [CONZEN], *see* LEYSER (P.) Examen 10 doc. A. C. Jesuitae Moguntin. &c., 1618.
Convention conc. la créat. d'une Union internat. pour la protect. des œuvres litt. & artist., 9 sept. 1886. [P2877.] 8°. Berne. 1900
Conversations. C. (The) at Malines, 1921–25, 1927, *see* MALINES.
*C. on harmony. By the a. of "Conversations on botany." 8°. 1855
Convicts. *Sel. acc. of the lives of the most remark. convicts, 2nd ed., 1745, *see* SELECT.
Conway, *The family of*, *see* MACCARTHY (S. T.) Three Kerry families, 1925.
Conway (Moncure Daniel). Testimonies conc. slavery. 8°. 1864
Conway (Robert Seymour). The making of Latin; intr. to Latin, Greek & Eng. etymology. s8°. 1923
New studies of a gt. inheritance. Lect. on mod. worth of some anc. wr. s8°. 1921
Conway (*Sir* **William Martin).**
Art treasures in Soviet Russia. 8°. 1925
Mountain mem. Pilgrimage of romance. la8°. 1920
Palestine & Morocco. 8°. 1923
The Van Eycks & their followers. 4°. 1921
Conwell (Eugène Alfred). Discovery of the tomb of Ollamh Fodhla (Olläv Fōla). 8°. D. 1873
Conybeare (Frances Annie).
Dingle Bank, the home of the Croppers. s8°. C. 1925
Conybeare (Frederick Cornwallis).
The age of the old Armenian vers. of Irenaeus. [Sonderabdr. aus Huschardzan. P2805]. 4°. Wien. 1911
The Armenian version of Revelation, & Cyril of Alexandria's Scholia on the Incarnation & Epistle on Easter. [Text & Trans. Soc.] 8°. 1907
[Exam. of writings of David the Invincible, tr. of Aristotle. Tr. of C.'s Proleg. to h. "Collation w. anc. Arm. versions &c." *into Armenian*. App. Aristotle De Deo *in Arm. a c. in* P2801]. 8°. Vienna. 1893
On the codex Pamphili & date of Euthalius. [From Journ. of Philol., v23. P2810]. 8°. [1895]
[*Photographic facsimiles of Armenian MSS.*] 8°. *n.d.*
Russian dissenters. [Harvard Theol. St. 10]. 8°. Camb. [U.S.] 1921
Survival of animal sacrifices. [*Extr. f.* Amer. journ. of theol., *w. corr^s. & typed adds. by the a.*] 8°. *n.p. n.d.*
see AḤIḲAR. The story of A. [*ed.*] C. &c., 2nd ed., 1913.
„ ARCHIERATIKON. Georgian version of the Liturgy of St. James; *tr.* F. C. C. &c., 1915.
„ BRIT. MUSEUM: MSS. Armenian MSS.; by F. C. C., 1913.
„ CLARK (A. C.) & J. R. HARRIS. *F. C. C., 1856–1924, 1926.
Conybeare (John), *bp. of Bristol.*
A defence of reveal'd religion. 8°. 1732
Conybeare (William John) & J. S. Howson.
Life & epistles of St. Paul. n. ed. 2v. 8°. 1877
Conyers (*Mrs.* **Dorothea).**
The adventures of Gerry. s8°. [1924]
Grey brother & others. s8°. [1927]
Irish stew. s8°. [1920]
Sporting remin. 8°. [1920]
Tiranogue. s8°. [1919]
The toll of the black lake. s8°. [1922]
Treasury notes. s8°. [1926]
The waiting of Moya. s8°. [1921]
Conyngton (Mary K.) Effect of workmen's compensation laws in diminishing indust. employment of women & children, *see* UNITED STATES: LABOR. Bull., 217, 1918.
Conzen (Adam), *see* CONTZEN (A.)
Cooch Behar, *Maharani of.* [SUNITY DEVEE, *Maharani of Cooch Behar*]. Autobiogr. of an Indian princess. 8°. 1921
Cook (Albert Stanburrough), *see* CYNEWULF. Old Eng. Elene, Phoenix, & Physiologus; ed. A. S. C., 1919.
Cook (Alfred Marshall).
A Latin anthology. [Golden Treasury Ser. repr.] s8°. 1912
Cook (Arthur Bernard). Zeus: study in anc. relig., v2 *in* 2p. (1, Text & notes. 2, App. & Index). 8°. C. 1925
Cook (Arthur Kemble).
A comm. upon Browning's The ring & the book. s8°. 1920
Cook (E. M.) Jamaica. Pref. by Visc. Burnham. s8°. [1924]
Cook (*Sir* **Edward),** *see* COKE (*Sir* E.)
Cook (*Sir* **Edward Tyas).** Life of Florence Nightingale. [repr.] 2v. 8°. 1914
„ „ ....Abridged & rev. by R. Nash. 8°. 1925
More literary recreations. s8°. 1919

Cook (*Mrs.* **Elsie Thornton**).
Her Majesty: queens of Eng., 1066–1910. 8º. 1926
Cook (Emile Francis), *1829–74, see* FARJAT (E.) E. F. C.: souvenirs, 1877.
Cook (Ernest Thomas).
Gardening for beginners. 4th ed. 8º. [1905]
Cook (*Sir* **Francis**), *Bart.*
see COOK (H. W.) Cat. of coll. of Greek &c. antiq. &c., portion of coll. of Sir F. C., sold by Christie, July 14, 1925.
„ —— Cat. of coll. of objects of art, prop. of H. W. C., portion of coll. formed by Sir F. C., sold 1925.
Cook (George), *D.D.* Gen. & hist. view of Xty. 3v. 8º. E. 1822
Cook (George Cram).
see GLASPELL (S.) Road to the temple, 1926.
„ —— Trifles, & 6 o. plays (2 wr. in collab. w. G. C. C.), 1926.
Cook (Henry Caldwell).
The play way: essay in educat. method. 3rd ed. 8º. [1920]
Cook (Humphrey W.) Cat. of coll. of Greek, Roman &c. antiq. & antique &c. gems, property of H. W. C., portion of coll. of Sir F. Cook, sold by Christie, July 14, 1925. 8º. [1925]
Cat. of coll. of objects of art of the Middle Ages &c., prop. of H. W. C., portion of coll. formed by Sir F. Cook. Sold by Christie, July 7, 1925. 8º. 1925
Cook (James), *the circumnavigator.* Voyage to the Pacific, 1776–80. 2nd ed. 3v. [v1, 2 by C. v3, by Capt. King]. 4º. 1785
Voyages of discovery. [Everyman's lib. 2nd ed.] s8º. [1906]
see BOLCKOW (H. W. F.) Cat. of MSS., by or to J. C., 1923.
„ DOUGLAS (J.) Introd. to 3rd voyage [*in h.* Sel. Works, 1820].
„ YOUNG (G.) Life & voyages of Capt. J. C., 1836.
Cook (Joseph). Heredity. [Boston Monday Lect.] s8º. 1879
Cook (Stanley Arthur). A Pre-Massoretic biblical papyrus. [Repr. f. Proc. of Soc. of Bibl. Arch.; P2791]. 8º. 1903
see PEAKE (A. S.), *ed.* The People & the Bk., essays by C. &c., 1925.
Cook (*Sir* **Theodore Andrea**).
Leonardo da Vinci, sculptor. Illust. essay on the Albrizzi Madonna. 8º. 1923
Old Provence. 2nd impr. 2v. s8º. 1914
Old Touraine. 4th ed., rev. 2v. s8º. 1903
„ „ 7th ed. 2v. s8º. 1920
Rowing at Henley, 8º. 1919
The sunlit hours: record of sport & life. 8º. [1925]
Cook (Thomas) & Son. Hdbk. to Norway & Denmark, w. Iceland & Spitsbergen. 7th ed., rev. & enl. s8º. 1910
Traveller's hdbk. for Belgium & the Ardennes. s8º. 1914
see BUDGE (*Sir* E. A. T. W.) C.'s hdbk. to Egypt & the Sudan, 1906.
„ ELSTON (R.) Traveller's hdbk. for Constantinople, Gallipoli & Asia Minor, 1923.
Cook (W. B.) The Murrays of Touchadam & Polmaise. Genealog. chart. *folded.* fol. 1907
Cook (William), *chess player.*
Chess players' compend. 4th ed. la8º. 1907
Cook (William Victor). The story of Sussex. 8º. 1920
Cooke (*Comm.* **A. P.**), *U.S. Navy.* Text-book of naval ordnance & gunnery for use at U.S. Naval Acad. 8º. N.Y. 1875
Cooke (Alexander), *vicar of Leeds.* Worke, more worke &c. for a masse-priest. With an epistle of an unknown priest, w. the authours answere. [*b. w.* Sutcliffe (M.) The unmasking of a massemonger, 1626]. s4º. 1628
Cooke (Alfred Hands). Early Hist. of Mapledurham. [Oxf. Rec. Soc., v7]. 8º. O. 1925
Cooke (*Mrs.* **Bella**), *b. 1821, formerly Beeton.* Rifted clouds or the life story of B. C. wr. by herself. s8º. 1886
Cooke (Conrad William). Automata old & new. [Sette of Odd Volumes, Opusc., No. 29]. s8º. *p.p.* 1893
Cooke (Edward), *of the Middle Temple, temp. Jac. II.* Memorabilia, or passages & counsels coll. out of the declar. & speeches by the King &c., 1660–80. Of the protest. relig. —Of popery.—Of liberty & property &c.—Of parliaments. [P529]. fol. 1681
Cooke (Edward Alexander). Diocesan hist. of Killaloe, Kilfenora, Clonfert & Kilmacduagh. s8º. D. 1886
Cooke (Edward William). 65 plates of shipping & craft, drawn & etched. 4º. 1829
Cooke (George Alexander). Topograph. & statist. descr. of Essex. s8º. *n.d.* [c. 1825]
Topograph. library, or Brit. traveller's pocket co. dir. Cornwall. [n. ed.] s8º. *n.d.*
Cooke (Harold Caswell). Gabbros of E. Sooke & Rocky Point, *see* CANADA: GEOLOG. SURVEY. Museum bull., No. 30, 1919.
Geology of Matachewan district, N. Ontario. [Canada. Geolog. Survey. P2512]. 8º. Ottawa. 1919
Kenogami, Round, & Larder Lake areas, Timiskaming Distr., Ontario. [Canada: Geolog. Survey. P2624]. 8º. Ottawa. 1922
Cooke (J. Herbert). The velvet & corduroy industry. [Pitman's common commodities]. s8º. [1922]
Cooke (*Capt.* **John**). Memoirs of the late war: personal narr. of Capt. C.; Hist. of campaign of 1809 in Portugal, by the Earl of Munster; & a narr. of the camp. of 1814 in Holland, by T. W. D. Moodie. 2v. s8º. 1831
Cooke (John Esten), *see* BEATY (J. O.) J. E. C., Virginian, 1922.
Cooke (Joseph), *dissenting minister at Rochdale.* Methodism condemned; vindic. of 2 sermons on justification by faith &c. s8º. Rochdale. 1807
Cooke (Robert), *Clarenceux King of Arms, see* KENT. Visitations, 1574 & 1592, by R. C. &c.; ed. W. B. Bannerman, 2p, 1923–24.
Cooke (S. W.), *see* LONDON. New plan of L. &c.; engraved by S. W. C., 1823.
Cooke (Sidney Russell), *see* DAVENPORT (E. H.) & S. R. C. Oil trusts & Anglo-Amer. rel., 1923.
Cooke (Thomas Lalor). Early hist. of town of Birr, or Parsonstown &c. 8º. D. 1875
Coke (William), *rector of Oldbury & Didmarton.* The medallic hist. of Imp. Rome; w. intr. cont. Gen. hist. of Roman medals. 2v. 4º. 1781
Cooke (William Bernard). *A new picture of the Isle of Wight. Plates by W. C. Pref., introd. acc. &c. [*signed* J. E.] 8º. 1808
see HOFLAND (*Mrs.* B.) Richmond &c.; engr. by C., 1832.
Cookery [COOKERY-BOOKS]. *Cookery & domestic economy, by the mistress of a family. s8º. E. 1845
*Little bk. of Jewish cookery. s8º. *n.d.*
Cooks, Company of, London, *see* PHILLIPS (C. M.) Short acc. of the silver plate &c. belong. to Worshipful Co. of C., 1909.
Coolidge (Asenath Carver). The independence Day horror at Killsbury. 8º. Watertown, N.Y. 1905
Coolidge (Julian Lowell).
Intr. to mathemat. probability. 8º. O. 1925
Coolidge (Thomas Jefferson), *the elder.* T. J. C., 1831–1920, an autobiog. [Mass. Hist. Soc.] la8º. [Camb., Mass.] 1923
Coolidge (Thomas Jefferson), *jun., see* JEFFERSON (T.) T. J., architect; orig. designs in the coll. of C., 1916.
Coolus (Romain) Les vacances de Paques, comédie, *see* ŒUVRES libres, No. 75, 1927.
Coomaraswamy (Ananda Kentish), *see* RODIN (A.), A. C. &c. Sculptures çivaïtes, 1921.
Cooper (C. S.) The outdoor monuments of London. la8º. [1928]
Cooper (Clayton Sedgwick). The Brazilians &c. la8º. 1919
Understanding Italy. 8º. 1923
Understanding South America. 8º. N.Y. 1918
Cooper (Elizabeth). *The hist. & poet. medley: or Muses library. 8º. 1738
Cooper (James), *of Compton, Surrey.* The trial of J. & Mary C. for murder of Joseph Hollis. 8º. Guildford. [1809]
Cooper (James Fenimore). Corr. Ed. by h. grandson J. F Cooper. 2v. 8º. New Haven. 1922
The last of the Mohicans. [repr.] s8º. [1923]
Cooper (L. Hay-), *see* HAY-COOPER (L.)
Cooper (Lane). A concordance to the Latin, Greek & Ital. poems of John Milton. 8º. Halle (Saale). 1923
A concordance to the works of Horace. [C.I. of Wash., Publ., 202]. la8º. Wash. 1916
Cooper (Mary), *1786–1812, wife of John Cooper, see* CLARKE (A.) Mem. of M. C., 1828.
see COOPER (J.) Trial of J. & M. C. for murder, 1809.
Cooper (Merian C.)
Grass. Foreword by W. Beebe. 8º. N.Y. 1925
Cooper (Thomas), *bp. of (1) Lincoln, (2) Winchester.* *An admonition to the people of England, wherein are answered the slaunderous untruethes uttered by Martin [Marprelate], the libeller &c. By T. C. [*wanting tp.*] s8º. 1589
Cooper (Thomas), *of Manchester.* Lects. on the elem. of polit. econ. 2nd ed. 8º. Columbia, S.C. 1831
Cooper (*Sir* **William Earnshaw**), *C.I.E.*
Spiritual science: here & hereafter. 8º. 1911
Cooper (William Henry Hewlett).
Old Keston. [P2596]. s8º. Bromley. 1879

Coopers' Company, *London, see* LAKE (C.) Notes on the will of H. Cloker, 1573, & St. Magnus the Martyr & th. conn. w. the Co. of C., 1924.

Coopland (G. W.) An unpubl. work of John of Legnano: the Somnium of 1372. [Estr. d. Nuovi studi med., v2. P2834]. 8°. Aquila. 1925

Coorg. Report on admin. of C., 1919–20—1925–26. fol. Mercara & Bangalore. 1920–26

Coote (*Sir* Charles), *bart., of Donnybrooke.* Statist. survey of county of Armagh, 1802–3, under dir. of the Dublin Soc. 8°. Dublin. 1804

Coote (Colin Reith). Ital. town & country life. 8°. [1925]

Coote (*Lieut.-Gen. Sir* Eyre), *K.B., see* WYLLY (*Col.* H. C.) Life of Lt.-Gen. Sir E. C., 1922.

Cope (Alan) [COPUS (ALANUS)], *see* HARPSFIELD (N.) Dialogi sex contra Pontificatus oppugnatores &c. ab A. C. ed., 1566.

Cope (*Capt.* William), *see* MAUGRIDGE (J.) Life &c. of J. M., executed for murder of Capt. C., 1708.

Cope (*Sir* William Henry), *12th bart.* Position of officers as adjutants of Volunteers. [P2831]. 8°. 1879

Copeau (Jacques). La maison natale. Drame. 5e éd. s8°. [1923]

—— **& J. Croue.** Les frères Karamazov: drame. D'apres Dostoievsky. s8°. [1921]

C.O.P.E.C., *see* CONFERENCE ON CHRISTIAN POLITICS &C.

Copeland (Alfred James).
Bridewell Royal Hospital, past & present. s8°. 1888

Copeland (Edwin Bingham). The coco-nut. 2nd ed., rev. 8°. 1921

Copeland (Melvin Thomas). The cotton manufacturing industry of the U.S. [Harvard Econ. St., v8]. 8°. Camb., Mass. 1912

Copenhagen. Cat. librorum Sansk., quos bibl. Univ. Havn. vel dedit vel paravit N. Wallich. Scr. E. Nyerup. s8°. Hafniae. 1821

Vases grecs réc. acquis par la Glyptothèque de Ny-Carlsberg; par F. Poulsen, *see* KONG. DAN. VID. SELSK. Hist.-fil. Med., B5, 1921–22.

*Zeytung, Von der eroberung C. &c., 1536, *see* ZEITUNG.

see CORPUS vasorum antiq.: Danemark: C., Musée Nat.; par C. Blinkenberg &c., 1924.

„ PHONETIC transcription &c.: proposals of C. Conf., Apr. 1925, 1926.

Copernicus (Nicolaus). *N. C. martire d. scienza. [*Ed.* G. M. Piazza. Nozze Baruchello-Turazza. N127]. 8°. Padova. 1866

Copho. Anatomia Porci [Rev. Lat. text, *w. tr.*], *see* CORNER (G. W.) Anatom. texts, 1927.

Copia. Copia di scrittura informativa conc. le pres. vertenze di Portogallo con li PP. Gesuiti, sec. notizie trasm. in Roma da Monsignor Nungio [*Portug. & Fr.*] &c., *see* PORTUGAL. Recueil de decrets apostol. &c., pl, 1758.

Copinger (Harold Bernard). The Elzevir Press. Handlist, w. refs. to Willems & o. bibliographers. 8°. 1927

Copland (Douglas Berry). Wheat production in New Zealand: w. chap. by F. W. Hilgendorf. Intr. by J. Hight. s8°. Auckland. [1920]

Copleston (Edward), *bp. of Llandaff.* Advice to a young reviewer, 1807, *see* GORDON (G.), *ed.* Three Oxf. ironies, 1927.

An enq. into doct. of necessity & predestination. App. on the 17th article of the Ch. of Eng. 2nd ed. 8°. 1821

Copley (Frank Barkley). Frederick W. Taylor, father of sci. management. 2v. 8°. N.Y. 1923

The impeachment of President Israels. s8°. N.Y. 1913

Coppard (Alfred Edgar). The black dog & o. s. s8°. [1923]

Coppée (François). Le luthier de Crémone. 6e éd. 8°. 1878

„ „ .... Notes by A. Mariette. s8°. 1882

see HALL (J. N. VAN). De viool van Cremona, naar F. C. &c., 1882.

Coppen, *The family of, see* COPPYN.

Coppen (John Maurice).
*The Coppyns of Kent, 1300–1800. la8°. *p.p.* 1900

Coppin, *The family of, see* COPPYN.

Copplestone (Bennet) *ps.* [*i.e.* F. HARCOURT KITCHIN].
The last of the Grenvilles. s8°. 1919
Madame Gilbert's cannibal. s8°. [1920]
Moberly Bell & h. times. 8°. 1925
The treasure of Golden Cap. s8°. 1922

Coppyn, *The family of, see* COPPEN (J. M.) *The C. of Kent, 1300–1800, 1900.

Coptae. *Rudimenta ling. C. sive Ægyptiacae, 1778, *see* TUKI (R.)

Coptic. [*Coptic grammars, in MS.* (*Coptic & Arabic*)]. 4°. *n.d.*
[Coptic-Arabic dictionary, *in MS.*] 4°. *n.d.*
Two C. homilies &c., 1923, *see* WORRELL (W. H.)

Coptica; consilio & impensis Inst. Rask-Oerstediani ed. [v] 2, 3. 8°. Hauniae. 1922–25

see PISTIS SOPHIA. P. S., neu hrsg. v. C. Schmidt, 1925. [2.]
„ WADI SARGA. Coptic & Greek texts f. the excavs. by the Byz. Research Asc., 1922. [3.]

***Copy** (A) of some papers past at Oxford betwixt the a. of the Pract. Catechisme & Mr. Ch., 1647, *see* HAMMOND (H.)

Coquiot (Gustave).
Degas. Avec 24 reprod. 8°. [1924]
Les indépendants, 1884–1920. 3e éd. 8°. [1920]
Lautrec ou 15 ans de mœurs paris. 1885–1900. s8°. 1921
Monticelli. 8°. [1925]
Seurat. 8°. [1924]
Vincent van Gogh. 8°. 1923

Coquus (Edouardus), *see* COKE (*Sir* E.)

Corbach (Otto). Moskau als Erzieher: Erlebnisse &c. aus Sowjet-Russ. [Entschiedene Schulreform; hrsg. v. P. Oestreich, H17]. s8°. L. [1924]

Corbacho (George M.) South American hist. docs., f. the coll. of G. M. C., exhib. at the Hispanic Soc. of Amer. s8°. N.Y. 1919

Corbet (John), *bp. of Chichester.* Self-imployment in secret. With pref. epistle of J. Howe. 3rd ed., corr. s8°. 1691

Corbet (John), *Nonconformist divine.*
The kingdom of God among men. s8°. 1679
*The point of church-unity & schism discussed &c. [*b. w. h.* Kingdom of God &c., 1679]. s8°. 1679

Corbet (Richard), *bp. of (1) Oxford, (2) Norwich, see* CROFTS (J. E. V.) Life of Bp. C., 1582–1635, 1924.

Corbett (*Sir* Julian Stafford).
Monk. [Eng. men of action]. s8°. 1908
Naval operations, *see* WAR. Hist. of the Gt. War based on off. doc. Nav. op., v1–3, 1920–23.

Corbett-Smith (*Maj.* Arthur). National opera hdbks. 1–6 [*in* 1v]. s8°. 1922
1, Parsifal (Wagner). 2, The Master-singers. 3, Tristan & Isolda. 4, The Ring of the Nibelungs. 5, The magic flute (Mozart). 6, The marriage of Figaro (Mozart).

Corbin (*Maj.-Gen.* Henry Clark), *see* UNITED STATES: ARMY. Legisl. hist. of Gen. Staff, 1775–1901; 1901.

Corbin (Thomas W.)
The romance of lighthouses & lifeboats. 8°. 1926
The romance of modern railways. 8°. 1922

Corbinianus, *episc. Frisingensis, see* CYRINUS [ARBEO], *episc. Frising.* Vitae SS. Haimhrammi & C., 1920.

Corbridge (Thomas *of*), *abp. of York.* Register of Thomas of Corbridge, Ld. Abp. of York, 1300–04. [Surtees Soc., v138]. pl. 8°. Durham. 1925

Corcoran (Bryan). Guide to St. Olave's, Hart St., London. Rev. ed. 8°. 1908

Corcyra. *Primordia Corcyrae. Post ed. Lyciensem anni 1725 ab auctore rec. & adaucta. 4°. Brixiae. 1738

Cordara (Giulio Cesare). Comm. on exped. to Scotland by Charles Edward Stuart; [Eng. tr. by Collison-Morley]; ed. Sir B. Seton, *see* SCOTTISH HISTORY SOC. Misc., v4, 1926.

Cordatus Evangelicus, *ps., see* DASSOV (T.) Justa animadv. in C. E. inanem loquac., 1716.

Corday (Charlotte) [†CORDAY D'ARMANS (MARIE ANNE C.)], *see* JORISSEN (TH.) Hist. Karakters, 1, C. de. C., 1912.

Cordemoy (*l'abbé* Louis Géraud de), *see* SAGITTARIUS (C.) Diss. pro doct. Lutheri de missa; confut. calumniae ab abbate [de C.] &c., 1684.

Corder (William). The trial of W. C. for the murder of Maria Martin. 8°. Bury St. Edmund's. [1828]

see CURTIS (J.) Authentic &c. hist. of murder of Maria Marten; added, trial of W. C. &c., 1834.

Corderius (Balthasar), *see* CORDIER (B.)

Cordero di Pamparato (Stanislao). Doc. per la storia del Piemonte (1265–1300), *see* REGIA DEP. DI STORIA PATRIA. Misc., t40, 1904.

Corderoy (Jeremy). A short dialogue, that no man can be saved without good workes. ed. 2. s8°. O. 1604

Cordery (Marian Hadfield), *aft. Phillpotts, see* PHILLPOTTS (M. H.)

Cordès (Claude). Les feux sur le Liban. s8°. [1924]

Cordes (Gottlieb). Psych. Analyse d. Thatsache d. Selbsterziehung. Inaug. Diss. Würzburg. [P2479]. 8°. 1898

Cordes (Simon de), *see* WIEDER (F. C.) De reis v. Mahu & de C., 1598–1600, 3d, 1923–25.

Cordier (Balthasar) [CORDERIUS]. Catena patrum Graec. in S. Joannem. [*Gr. & Lat.*] fol. Antverpiæ. 1630

Cordier (Balthasar) [CORDERIUS] [*continued*].
Catena 65 Graec. patrum in S. Lucam. Annotat. ill. à B. C. fol. Antverpiæ. 1628
Expos. Patrum Græc. in Psalmos [*w. text*] a B. C. in paraphrasin, comm. & catenam digesta Lat. don. & annot. illust. [*Gr. & Lat.*] 3t. fol. Antverpiæ. 1643–46
—— **& P. Possinus.** Symbolarum in Matthæum tom. prior [& alter] [collatae a B. C. & P. P.] 2t. fol. Tolosæ. 1546–47
1, exhib. Catenam Graec. patrum 21 ; P. Possinus eruit, Lat. interp. illust. &c.
2, Catena patrum Græc. 30, coll. Niceta, episc. Serrarum : interp. B. Corderio.
Cordier (Henri).
Annales de l'Hôtel de Nesle, *see* ACAD. DES INSCR. Mém. de l'Inst., t41, 1920.
Bibliog. des œuvres de G. Maspero. s8°. 1922
Bibliotheca Sinica. Dict. bibliogr. des ouvrages rel. à l'Empire chin. 2e. éd. Suppl. & ind. fasc. 1, 2. la8°. 1922–23
Hist. gén. de la Chine & de ses rel. avec les pays étrangères j. la chute de la dyn. Mandchoue. 4[t]. 8°. 1920
Mélanges d'hist. & de géographie or. 4t. la8°. 1914–23
Orig. de deux établ. franç. dans l'Extrême-Orient, Chang-haï—Ning-po. Docs. inéd. la8°. 1896
Ser Marco Polo. Notes & addenda to Sir H. Yule's ed., cont. the results of recent research &c. 8°. 1920
see ODORICUS [*Matthuissi*]. Voyages en Asie au 14e siècle ; publ. avec intr. & notes par H. C., 1891.
Cordingley (R. A.) & I. A. Richmond. The Mausoleum of Augustus, *see* BRIT. SCHOOL AT ROME. Papers, v10. 1927.
Cordova (Rudolf de), *see* DE CORDOVA (R.)
Corea [KOREA ; CHOSEN].
Admin. reforms in Korea. Articles repr. f. the "Seoul Press." [P2395]. 8°. Seoul. [1919]
Ann. report on reforms &c. in Chosen (Korea), 1910–11, 1917–18, 1918–21. Comp. by Govt.-gen. of Chosen. la8°. Keijo (Seoul). 1911–21
[Antiquities of S .Corea. Rep. of Service of Antiq., v2, 4, 5. *In Corean*]. la8°. [Chosen. 1925–27]
v4 has Eng. t.: Archæolog. researches on anc. Lolang Distr. By T. Sekino, S. Yatsui &c. *&* Plates, 2v. fol.
v5 has Plates, *b. sep.* fol.
East coasts of Korea & Siberia & Sea of Okhotsk pilot, *&* Suppl. 7, 1913–22, *see* ADMIRALTY.
Economic hist. of Chosen. Comp. in commem. of the decennial of the Bank of C. [by T. Hoshino. Foreword *by* S. Minobe]. s8°. Seoul. 1920
Econ. hist. of Manchuria ; comp. in commem. of decennial of the Bank of C., 1920, *see* MANCHURIA.
[Korean-Japanese dict. Publ. by the Japanese Govt. Office in Korea. *In Japanese.*] la8°. [1920 ?]
The new admin. in Chosen. Comp. by Govt.-gen. of Chosen. [P2620]. 8°. *n.p.* [1921]
Corelli (Arcangelo), *1653–1713.* The score of twelve concertos for 2 violins &c. Rev. by Dr. Pepusch. Engr. by T. Cross. v2. fol. *B. Cooke.* [1732]
v1, *wanting, has title.* The score of the four setts of sonatas.
Twelve concertos, adapted for organ, harpsichord or pianoforte by T. Billington. Op. 9. 4°. [1790 ?]
Corelli (Marie).
Open confession : to a man f. a woman. s8°. [1925]
Corelli (Pietro). La stella d'Italia o 9 secoli di Casa Savoia. 5v. la8°. Milano. 1863
Coret (Jacques).
*L'ange conducteur dans la dévotion chrét. s8°. Liége. 1780
Corfe Castle. *Topogr. & hist. guide to Corfe Castle, Dorset. [Pref. signed L. C. B. P2711]. s8°. *n.d.*
Corfe (Charles John), *bp. in Corea, see* MONTGOMERY (H. H.) C. J. C., naval chaplain-bishop, 1927.
Coriat (Isador Henry). Repressed emotions. 8°. N.Y. [1920]
Corinna, *the poetess.*
see DIEHL (E.) Suppl. lyricum, 3e A. 1917.
,, LYRA Græca ; ed. & tr. J. M. Edmonds, v3, 1927.
Corinth (Louis) [CORINTH (FRANZ HEINRICH LOUIS)].
Selbstbiog. la8°. L. 1926
see BIERMANN (G.) L. C., 2e A., 1922.
Cork. *Who burnt Cork city ? [P2530]. 8°. D. 1921
Cork Historical & Archaeological Society.
Journal. s2, v25–31. 1919–26. la8°. [Cork. 1919–26]
see WHITE (*Col.* J. G.) Hist. & topog. notes &c. on Buttevant &c. : [*suppl. to* Journal of C. H. & A. S.], v3, 4, 1913–25.
Cork and Orrery (John Boyle, *5th earl of*), *d. 1762.* Letters f. Italy, 1754–55. With explan. notes by J. Duncombe. s8°. 1773

Corkery (Daniel).
The hidden Ireland : Gaelic Munster in 18th cent. 8°. D. 1925
The hounds of Banba. s8°. D. 1920
The labour leader. Play. s8°. D. 1920
The threshold of quiet. s8°. 1917
,, ,, ...[repr.] s8°. D. 1919
Corlette (Hubert Christian). Cathedral Ch. of Chichester, w. acc. of diocese. [Bell's Cath. Ser.] [3rd ed. repr.] s8°. 1922
Cormack (Alexander A.) Poor relief in Scotland : Poor Laws f. M. A. to pres. day. 8°. Aberdeen. 1923
Cormack (*Mrs* **Annie),** *wife of J. G. Cormack.*
Chinese birthday, wedding &c. customs. 3rd ed. s8°. Peking. [1927]
Cormon (Pierre Étienne Piestre), *dit* **Eugène, & E. Grange.**
Le violon du père Dimanche. Pièce. la8°. 1854
Corn [*incl.* CORN-LAWS &C.] *Catechism on the c. laws, 14th ed. ; by a member of the Univ. of Camb., 1830 ; 16th ed., 1832, *see* THOMPSON (T. P.)
Cornaby (W. Arthur). A necklace of peach-stones. "A string of Chinese peach-stones," rewr., w. App. 8°. Shanghai. 1925
Cornara (Elena Lucrezia) [PISCOPIA (HELENA L. CORNELIA)].
Opera [ed. B. Bacchino]. s8°. Parmæ. 1688
see ACCADEMICI INFECONDI, *Rome.* Le pompe funebri celeb. da signori A. I. per la morte d. E. L. C., 1686.
,, LUPIS (A.) L'Eroina Veneta, overo la vita di E. L. C. P., 1689.
Cornaro (Caterina) [CORNER (C.)], *1454–1510.*
see CARRER (L.) Prose, v2 (C. Corner &c.), 1855.
,, HERQUET (C.) Charlotta v. Lusignan u. C. C., 1870.
Cornaro (Luigi). Treatise of the benefits of a sober life ; Eng. by T. S[mith], *see* LESSIO (L.) Hygiasticon ; tr., 1742.
see MOLMENTI (P. G.) Curiosità di storia Veneziana [L. C. e la vita sobria, &c.], 1920.
Corneille (Pierre).
see CROCE (B.) Ariosto, Shakespeare e C., 1920 ; tr., 1920.
,, PHILIPS (K.) Poems : Added C.'s Pompey & Horace &c., tr., 1669.
—— **& T. Corneille.**
Théâtre. Avec notes & comm. 2t. s8°. *n.d.*
Corneille (Thomas), *see* CORNEILLE (P.) & T. C. Théâtre, 2t, *n.d.*
—— **& J. D. de Visé.** La devineresse, *see* FOURNEL (V.) Contemp. de Molière, t3, 1875.
Cornell University. Cat. of the Dante Coll. presented by W. Fiske. Additions, 1898–1920. Comp. by M. Fowler. la8°. Ithaca, N.Y. 1921
Cat. of the Icelandic Coll. bequeathed by W. Fiske. Additions, 1913–26. Comp. by H. Hermannsson. 4°. Ithaca. 1927
Corner (Caterina), *see* CORNARO (C.)
Corner (George Washington). Anatomical texts of the earlier M. A., w. rev. Lat. text of Anatomia Cophonis & tr. of 4 texts. [C.I. of Wash.] la8°. Wash. 1927
Corner-stone (A) of reconstruction : working for social purity &c., 1919, *see* ALLEN (B. W.) &c.
Cornerus (Christophorus). Cantica sel. Vet. Novique Test. : cum hymnis & collectis &c. [*b. w. h.* Psalterium Lat., 1575]. s8°. Lipsiæ. [*A. Schneider.* 1575]
Psalterium Davidis, cum expos. scr. à C. C. s8°. [Lipsiæ. *A. Schneider.* 1575]
Cornet (A), *in E. India Co.'s service, ps., see* PETTIGREW (T. L.)
Cornet (Enrico). Le guerre dei Veneti nell' Asia, 1470–74. Doc. 8°. Vienna. 1856
Cornford (Francis Macdonald). Greek relig. thought f. Homer to age of Alexander. 8°. 1923
Cornford (Leslie Cope). Designers of our buildings. Foreword by W. J. Locke. [R.I.B.A.] 8°. 1921
English composition. s8°. 1900
The paravane adventure. s8°. [1919]
Cornford (M. E.) & E. B. Miller. Calendar of MSS. in Will. Salt Library, Stafford, see STAFFORDSHIRE. Colls. for hist. &c., 1921.
Cornhill magazine (The).
New ser., v48–64 (Jan. 1920–June 1928). 8°. 1920–28
Cornicelius (Georg), *see* SIEBERT (C.) Verzeichnis d. Werke d. Malers G. C., 1914.
Cornides (Daniel). Comm. de relig. vet. Hungarorum. Ed., de orig. Hungaricae gentis diss. adj. C. Engel. s8°. Viennæ. 1791
Cornillier (P. E.) La survivance de l'âme & son évol. ap. la mort. 2e éd. 8°. 1921

Cornish (Vaughan). The geogr. position of the Brit. Emp. [Repr. f. Brit. Assoc. Rep., 1923. P2754]. 8o. [1923]
A geog. of Imperial defence. 8o. 1922
The great capitals. 8o. [1923]
Strategic geog. of the Gt. Powers. s8o. 1918

Cornuaud (Isaac). Méms. sur Genève & la Révol., 1770–95. Publ. avec not. biog., notes &c. par E. Cherbuliez. 8o. Genève. 1912

Cornulier-Lucinière (*gén.* **de)**, *see* HETHAY (J.), *ps.*

Cornutus (Lucius Annaeus). De natura deorum, *see* ÆSOP, 1505.

Cornwall. *Account of the remark. revival in C.: in extr. of sev. letters. [P2674]. s8o. D. 1814
C. parish registers. Marriages. Gen. ed., T. M. Blagg. v24, 25, ed. T. Taylor. 8o. 1915–17

Cornwallis (*Miss* **Caroline Frances).** *Philos. theories & phil. experience. By a pariah. 2nd ed. s8o. 1845

Cornwallis (*Sir* **Charles),** *kt., treasurer of the household to Henry, p. of Wales.* A disc. of the most illust. Prince Henry, late P. of Wales. Wr. 1626. s8o. 1641
see WINWOOD (*Sir* R.) Mems. of aff. of state, negotiations of C. &c., 3v, 1725.

Cornwallis (Charles Cornwallis, *2nd earl, aft. 1st marq.*), *see* FORREST (*Sir* G. W.) Sel. f. State Papers of Gov.-Gen. of India, v3, 4, 1926.

Cornwallis (Jane, *Lady*), *aft. Lady Bacon, see* BUNTEN (A. C.) Sir Thomas Meautys, & h. friends, 1918.

Cornwallis (*Adm. Sir* **William),** *1744–1819, see* CORNWALLIS-WEST (G. F. M.) Life & letters of Adm. C., 1927.

Cornwallis-West (Beatrice Stella), *see* CAMPBELL (*Mrs.* PATRICK).

Cornwallis-West (*Maj.* **George F. M.)**
Life & letters of Adm. Cornwallis. 8o. 1927

Coromandel. *Genuine (A) acc. of some trans. in the E.I., on coast of C., since July 1749, 1753, *see* EAST INDIES.

Coronado (Martin). Literatura americana: trozos en prosa y verso. Sel. hecha por M. C. n. ed. s8o. Buenos Aires. 1903

Coronation.
*C. celebrations in Ceylon. 4o. [1911]
*C. Durbar at Delhi, 1903; 1911, *see* DELHI.
The form & order of the service &c. in c. of King George V & Queen Mary, 22 June, 1911, w. music. Ed. Sir F. Bridge. la8o. 1911

Coronedi Berti (Carolina).
Vocabolario bolognese ital. 2v. la8o. Bologna. 1869–72

Coronelli (Vincenzo Maria). Atlante veneto, descr. degl' imperj, regni &c. dell' universo. 2t *in* 3 (t2i, ii, Isolario). [*some plates missing*]. lafol. [Venetia]. 1692–97

Coroner's inquest & post mortem exam. on the Inquisition. s8o. Glasgow. 1851

Corot (J. B. Camille), *see* LAFARGUE (M.) C., 1925.

Corp (Harriet). An antidote to the miseries of human life in the hist. of the widow Placid & h. daughter Rachel. 8th ed. (v2, 4th ed.) 2v *in* 1. s8o. 1814

Corpechot (Lucien). Mem. of Queen Amélie of Portugal. [Tr. M. H. M. Capes]. 8o. 1915

Corpus.
Corpus Catholicorum. Werke kathol. Schriftsteller im Zeitalter d. Glaubensspaltung. Hrsg. J. Metzler. H1–3. la8o. Munster in Westfalen. 1919–21
Cochlaeus (J.) Adv. cucullatum Minotaurum Wittenberg. (1523), 1920. [3.]
Eck (Johannes). Def. contra A. Bodenstein invectiones (1518), 1919. [1.]
„ „ Epistola de ratione Studiorum suorum (1538), 1921. [2.]
Wolph (Erasmus). De obitu Ioan. Eckii adv. calumniam Viti Theodorici (1543), 1921. [2.]
Corpus d. griech. Urkunden d. Ma. u. d. neu. Zeit. Hrsg. v. d. Akad. d. Wiss. in München u. Wien. 4o. München. 1924–25
Reihe A: Regesten.
Abt. 1: Reg. d. Kaiserurkunden d. oströmischen Reiches, 565–1453; bearb. v. F. Dölger, T1, 2, 565–1204.
*Corpus & syntagma confessionum fidei. Annectitur, Catholicus consensus ex sententiis veterum desumptus [*by* G. Laurentius]. Ed. nov. [4p *in* 1v]. s4o. Genevae. 1654
Each p. has sep. tp. & pagin. 1, Confessio & expos. simplex &c. 2, Syntagmatis conf. fidei pars illa. 3, Articuli conf. Basil. &c. 4, Catholicus veterum.
Corpus glossar. Lat. A G. Loewe incohatum auspiciis Acad. Litt. Saxonicae, rec. G. Goetz. v1. la8o. L. 1923
1, De glossar. Lat. orig. et fatis. Scripsit G. Goetz., 1923.

Corpus [*continued*].
The Corpus glossary. Ed. W. M. Lindsay, w. Anglo-Saxon index by H. McM. Buckhurst. 8o. C. 1921
Corpus hippiatricorum Graec. Ed. E. Oder & C. Hoppe. 2v. s8o. Lipsiæ, *Teubner.* 1924–27
1, Hippiatrica Berolin. 2, Hippiatrica Paris., Cantab., Lond., Lugd.—App.
Corpus inscr. Indic. [Pr. for Govt. of India]. n. ed. fol. O. 1925
1, Inscr. of Asoka; by E. Hultzsch.
Corpus inscriptionum Latinarum. Consilio &c. Acad. Litt. R. Borussicae editum. fol. Berolini. 1862–1926
1, Tabulæ lithographae: Priscae Lat. mon. epigraphica; ed. F. Ritschelius, 1862.
6, I. urbis Romae Lat. vi, Indices; ed. M. Bang, fasc. 1.
11, I. Aemiliae, Etruriae, Umbriae; ed. E. Borman. ii, fasc. 2, Addenda ad partes priores & ind.
13, I. trium Galliarum & Germaniarum Latinae. p4, Addenda ad partes 1 & 2.
Corpus juris canonici, emend. &c. Greg. XIII jussu ed.; Lib. vii Decretalium; J. P. Lancelotti Institut. adauctum. Acc. Loci communes et indices.
ed. purgata &c. 2t *in* 1v. 8o. Coloniæ Munationæ. 1717
Corpus juris civilis. 2t. s8o. Amstelaedami. 1663–64
*Corpus juris Evangelic. eccl., oder Sammlung evangel.-Luther. u. reform. Kirchen-Ordnungen. Mit e. Vorrede J. J. Mosers. 2T. s4o. Züllichau. 1737–38
Corpus medic. Graec. Ausp. Acad. Assoc. ed. Acad. Berolin. v1i, 2, 4, 5iv, 2, 5ix, 1, 2, 6i, 1, 6iii, 9i, ii, 10i, 1, 11ii, 1. la8o. Lips. 1914–28
1i, Hippocratis: ed. I. L. Heiberg. 2, Aretaeus; ed. C. Hude.
4, Soranus. Gynaeciorum libri 4—De signis fracturarum—De fasciis—Vita Hippocratis; ed. J. Ilberg.
5iv, 2, Galen. De sanitate tuenda—De alimentorum facultatibus—De bonis malisque sucis—De victu attenuante—De ptisana.
5ix, 1, Galen. In Hippocratis de natura hominis—In Hippocratis de victu acutorum—De diaeta Hippocratis in morbis acutis; ed. J. Mewaldt, G. Helmreich &c.
5ix, 2, Galen. In Hippocratis Prorrheticum I—De comate secundum Hippocratem—In Hippocratis Prognosticum: ed. H. Diels &c.
6i, 1, Oribasius. Coll. medic. reliq., v1, libri 1–8; ed. J. Raeder.
6iii, —— Synopsis ad Eustathium—Libri ad Eunapium; ed. J. Raeder.
9i, ii, Paulus Aegineta, libri 1–7, 2p; ed. I. L. Heiberg.
10i, 1, Philumenus. De venenatis animalibus eorumque remediis; ed. M. Wellmann.
11ii, 1, Galen. Pseudo Galeni in Hippocratis de septimanis comm. ab Hunaino q. f. Arabice versum; ed. G. Bergstraesser.
Corpus medic. Latin. Ed. consilio &c. Instit. Puschmanniani Lips. v1, 2iii, 4, 5. 8o. Lipsiae. 1915–27
1, A. Cornelii Celsi quae supersunt; rec. F. Marx.
2iii, Quinti Sereni Liber medicinalis; ed. F. Vollmer.
4, A. Musae de herba vettonica liber—Pseudoapulei herbarius—Anon. de taxone liber—Sexti Placiti liber medicinae ex animalibus &c. Ed. E. Howald & H. E. Sigerist.
5, Marcellus. De medicamentis liber; rec. M. Niedermann.
Corpus Reformat., B91, 95, 96, *see* ZWINGLI (U.) Sämtl. Werke, B4, 8, 9, 1914–27.
Corpus script. eccl. Latin. Ed. consilio &c. Acad. Litt. Caesareae Vindobonensis. v45, 49, 56, 61, 63, 65. 8o. Vindobonae. 1904–26
see AUGUSTINE, *St.* Opera; rec. P. Knöll, sect. 1, pars 3, 1922. [63.]
„ HILARY, *St.* Opera, p4, rec. &c. A. Feder, 1916. [65.]
„ JEROME, *St.* Opera, sect. liii, rec. I. Hilberg, 1918. [56.]
„ PRUDENTIUS CLEMENS (A.) Carmina; rec. &c. I. Bergman, 1926. [61.]
„ SCRIPTORES eccl. minores s. 4–6, fasc. 1; rec. E. Bratke, 1904. [45.]
„ VICTORINUS, *St.* Opera; rec. &c. J. Haussleiter, 1916. [49.]
Corpus vasorum antiquorum. [Union Acad. Internat.] 4o. 1922–[28]
Belgique, fasc. 1: Bruxelles, Musées Royaux du Cinquantenaire, fasc. 1; par F. Mayence.
Danemark, fasc. 1, 2: Copenhague, Musée Nat., fasc. 1, 2; par C. Blinkenberg & K. Friis Johansen.
France, fasc. 1–7.
Bibl. Nat., fasc. 1; par M. Flot. [7.]
Musée du Louvre, fasc. 1–4; par E. Pottier. [1, 2, 4, 5.]
Musée de Compiègne (Musée Vivenel); par M. Flot. [3.]
Coll. Mouret (Fouilles d'Ensérune); par F. Mouret. [6.]
Great Brit., fasc. 1–3.
Brit. Museum, fasc. 1, 2; by A. H. Smith & F. N. Pryce. [1, 2.]
Oxford, fasc. 1, Ashmolean Museum; by J. D. Beazley. [3.]

Corpus [*continued*].
Corpus vasorum ant. [*continued*].
Italia, fasc. 1–3.
Museo Naz. di Villa Giulia in Roma, fasc. 1–3; a cura di G. Q. Giglioli.
Pays Bas, fasc. 1.
Musée Scheurleer (La Haye); par C. W. L. Scheurleer, fasc. 1.
United States, fasc. 1.
Hoppin & Gallatin colls.; by J. C. Hoppin & A. Gallatin.
„ „ Organisation (1919–21). [P2686]. 8º. 1921
see UNION ACAD. INTERNAT. Classif. des céramiques antiq.; par C. Dugas [*& o. wr.*], 12p, 1921–27.
Corra (Bruno), *see* ROST (P.) B. C., 1921.
Corra (Emile). Les devoirs naturels de l'homme. s8º. 1905
La morale sociale. s8º. 1905
Corradi (Alfonso), *see* MAGENTA (C.) A. C.: commem., 1893.
Corradus (Pyrrhus). Praxis dispensationum apostol., *see* MIGNE (J. P.), *ed.* Theol. cursus., t19, 1859.
Corraro (Angelo). Rel. of the state of the court of Rome &c., tr. by J. B., 1664, *see* ROME exactly descr., 1664.
Corre (Amand). L'ancien corps de la Marine. 8º. [1900]
Correa (E. Solar), *see* SOLAR CORREA (E.)
Corrêa (Gaspar), *see* BELL (A. F. G.) G. C., 1924.
Corrêa d'Oliveira (Antonio). Verbo ser e Verbo amar. [Poema relig.] 2ª ed. 8º. Paris. [1926]
Corréard (Alexandre), *see* SAVIGNY (J. B. H.) & A. C. Narr. of voyage to Senegal in 1816 &c., 2nd ed., 1818.
Corredor La Torre (Jorge).
L'Église rom. dans l'Amér. latine. s8º. 1910
Correggio [CORRÈGE; †ALLEGRI (ANTONIO), *called* "*Correggio*"], *see* ROI (P.) Il C., 1921.
Correnti (Cesare). Scritti scelti in parte ined. &c. Ed. postuma per cura di T. Massarani. 3v. 8º. 1891–93
Correspondance. *C. d'un jeune militaire, ou Mém. du Marq. de Luzigni & d'Hortense de Saint-Just, 2t, 1778–79, *see* BOURGOING (*b.* J. F.) & L. A. M. DE MUSSET.
C. fraternelle de l'Église Angl. avec les églises réformées &c., 1705, *see* GROSTESTE (C.)
*C. p. s. de suite à l'Hist. secrette de la cour de Berlin, 1789, *see* MIRABEAU (H. G. R., *cte.* DE).
Correvon (Henry). Les plantes alpines & de rocailles. s8º. 1895
Corrie, *The family of*, *see* CORRIE (J. E.) Records of the C. family, 2p, 1899.
Corrie (Jessie Elizabeth).
Records of the Corrie family, 802–1899. 2p. 4º. 1899
Corrie (Joan). A B C of Jung's psychology. s8º. 1927
Corrigeen, *ps.*, *see* ADAMS (J.)
Corrodi (August). R. Burns u. P. Hebel, *see* VIRCHOW (R.) & F. v. HOLTZENDORFF. Sammlung, H182, 1873.
Corrozet (Gilles). Le Comte du Rossignol [*&* Fables du très anc. Esope en rithme fr.] Réimpr. de l'éd. de J. de Tournes (1547), avec intr. par F. Gohin. s8º. 1924
Corse. *Malthe, Corse, Minorque &c., 1797, *see* MALTHE.
Corsetti (Bartolomeo). Novissima &c. praxis sacr. rituum ac cæremoniarum. s8º. Bruxellis. 1656
Corsica. *The impossible island: C., its people & its sport, 1923, *see* SNAFFLE, *ps.*
Corsini (Andrea). Il costume d. medico n. pitture fiorentine del Rinascimento. 8º. Firenze. 1912
Medici ciarlatani e ciarlatani medici. 8º. Bologna [1922]
Corso (Antonio Giacomo). Le rime. s8º. [Vinegia. 1550]
Corso (Renaldo), *see* SANSOVINO (F.), *ed.* Osserv. d. lingua volg., 1562.
Corson (Hiram). Intr. to the prose & poet. works of J. Milton. Autobiog. passages in h. wks. &c., Comus, Lycidas & Samson Agonistes. With notes &c. by H. C. [repr.] s8º. N.Y. 1914
Cortambert (*Mme.* **Louise**) [*ps.* CHARLOTTE DE LA TOUR].
Le langage des fleurs. 2ᵉ éd. s8º. *n.d.*
„ „ ....11ᵉ éd. augm. s8º. *n.d.*
Corte (Cornelius de) [CURTIUS (C.)] D. Thomas de Villanova. [*Foll. by:* D. T. de V. carmen heroicum a Joanne Rivio. [P2510]. s8º. Antverpiæ. 1658
Virorum illust. ex ordine Eremitarum D. Augustini elogia cum iconibus. s4º. Antverpiæ. 1636
Corte (Matteo della), *see* DELLA CORTE (M.)
Corte-Real (Gaspar), *see* BIGGAR (H. P.) Voyages, 1903.
Cortes de los antiguos reinos de Aragon &c., 25, 26. Cortes de Cataluña, 1473–79. 4º. 1919–22
Cortes (Hernando), *see* SEDGWICK (H. D.) C. the conqueror, 1927.
Cortés (Narciso Alonso). Representaciones populares: [textes]; publ. N. A. C., *see* REVUE HISPANIQUE, t60, 1924.
Zorrilla, su vida y sus obras. t2, 3. 8º. Valladolid. 1918–1920
Corthis (André), *ps.* [*i.e. Mlle.* ANDRÉE HUSSON].
Belle-Ombre, *see* ŒUVRES libres, 78, 1927.
L'entraîneuse. s8º. [1923]
Pour moi seule. Roman. s8º. 1919
Le vent dans les oliviers, *see* ŒUVRES libres, 67, 1926.
Victime expiatoire, *see* ŒUVRES libres, 35, 1924.
Corti (*conte* **Egon Caesar).** Alexander v. Battenberg, s. Kampf mit d. Zaren u. Bismarck. 8º. Wien. 1920
Der Aufstieg d. Hauses Rothschild, 1770–1830. 8º. L. 1927
Leopold I of Belgium: secret pages. Tr. J. McCabe. 8º. [1923]
Maximilian u. Charlotte v. Mexiko. 2B. la8º. Zürich. [1924]
„ „ Tr. C. A. Phillips. 2v. 8º. 1928
„ „ Tr. J. Vernay. 2[t. t1, 4ᵉ éd.] 8º. [1927]
The rise of the House of Rothschild. Tr. B. & B. Lunn. 8º. 1928
Corticelli (Salvadore). Regole ed osserv. d. lingua toscana. Accresciute di corr. &c. p. c. di P. dal Rio. s8º. Firenze. 1845
Cortie (A. L.), *S.J.* Sir Norman Lockyer, 1836–1920. [Repr. f. Astrophys. Journal, v53]. [P2525]. 8º. 1921
Cortigiane. Lettere di cortigiane del sec. 16; *ed.* L. A. Ferrai, 1884, *see* LETTERE.
Cortina (José Manuel).
Cuba's internat. ideal. [P2784]. 8º. Paris. 1925
Cortissoz (Royal).
The life of Whitelaw Reid. 2v. la8º. [1921]
Cortona, *see* ACCADEMIA ETRUSCA, *Cortona.*
Cortona, Il, *ps.*, *see* CECCHI (D.)
Cortona (Pietro da), *see* BERRETTINI (P.)
Cortrejus (Adam). *Excerpta hist. & jurid. de natura successionis in monarchiam Hispaniæ. [*&* Contin. 1, 2]. [P444]. s4º. *n.p.* 1700–1
Cortsen (S. P.) Die etrusk. Standes- u. Beamtentitel, durch d. Inschr. beleuchtet, *see* KONG. DANSKE VIDENSK. SELSKAB. Hist.-filol. Medd., B11, 1925.
Cortuso (Giacomo Antonio), *see* TONI (G. B. DE). Spigolature Aldrovandiane, 19, il botan. padov. G. A. C. &c., 1922.
Corvalan (Juan Loperraez), *see* LOPERRAEZ CORVALAN (J.)
Corvey, *abbey of*, *see* LEHMANN (P.) Corveyer Studien, 1919.
Corvinus (Antonius). Colloquia theologica quibus jam tertius liber acc. 2p *in* 1v. s8º. Argen. *apud Vv. Cœpha.* 1540
see TSCHACKERT (P.) Analecta Corvin.: Quellen z. Gesch. d. niedersächs. Reformators A. C., 1910.
„ UHLHORN (J. G. W.) A. C., e. Martyrer d. evangel.-luth. Bekenntnisses, 1892.
Corvinus (Arnoldus), *a Belderen*, *see* CORVINUS VAN BELDERN.
Corvinus (Joannes Arnoldus) [RAVENS]. Posthumus Pacianus, seu definitiones juris utriusque viri cl. Julii Pacii, posthumae. Ed. altera recog. &c. ab A. Corvino. s8º. Amstelædami. 1659
Corvinus van Beldern (Arnold).
Jus Canonicum per aphorismos. s8º. Amstelodami. 1663
Corvisart (*le col.*) Règlement du 14 oct. 1907 sur le service en campagne dans l'armée japonaise &c. Tr. & annoté par col. C. s8º. 1909
Cory (Charles Barney).
Works in Field Columbian Museum. Ornith. ser.
Birds of Leeward Isl., Caribbean Sea, 1909. [1v.]
Descr. of appar. new S. Amer. birds, w. notes, 1916. [lx.]
Descr. of new birds f. S. Amer. & adj. Isl., 1915. [lviii.]
Descr. of 28 new species &c. of neotropical birds, 1913. [lvii.]
Notes on S. Amer. birds, w. descrs., 1915. [lix.]
„ —— Zoolog. ser.
Cat. of birds of the Americas, p2–5, 1918–27. [13ii–v.]
Cory (*Sir* **Geo. Edward).**
The rise of South Africa. v4. [1838–46]. 8º. 1926
Cory (*Miss* **Vivian)** [*psˢ.* VICTORIA CROSS; VICTORIA CROSSE].
Over life's edge. s8º. [1921]
Cory (William) [†JOHNSON (WILLIAM), *aft. Cory*].
see DRINKWATER (J.) W. C., 1924.
„ ESHER (R. B. B., *2nd visct.*) Ionicus: [sel. of letters &c. of W. C.], 1923.
Cosack (Carl Johann). Literarum asceticarum quae reperiuntur inter evangel. Germanos hist. brevis adumbratio. [P2651]. 8º. Regèmonti Boruss. 1862
Coşbuc (Gheorghe), *see* GOGA (O.) Coşbuc, 1923.
Cosby (Pole), *of Stradbally.* Autobiog., 1703–41, *see* KILDARE (Co.) ARCH. SOC., Journal, v5, 1908.
Cosin (—), *sec. to Comm. for Forfeited Estates.* *Names of Roman Catholics, Nonjurors &c. who refus'd to take oaths to K. George, w. th. titles &c. [P2780]. 8º. 1745

Cosin (John), *bp. of Durham.*
Hist. transubstant. papalis &c. s8°. Londini. 1675
*The hist. of transubstantiation. [Tr.] by L. B. [*i.e.* Luke de Beaulieu]. s8°. 1687
see WATSON (R.) The Rt. Rev. J. C. his opinion for communicating w. Geneva, 1684.
Cosmas, *Pragensis.* Chronik d. Böhmen [*Latin*]. Unter Mitarbeit v. W. Weinberger hrsg. v. B. Bretholz. [M. G. H.: Scr. rer. Germ., n.s. 2]. 8°. 1923
Cosmo [*de' Medici*], *1389–1464, see* BRINTON (S.) Golden age of the M. (C. &c.), 1434–94, 1925.
Cosmo I [*de' Medici*], *grand duke of Tuscany; 1519–74.*
see AMIATI (A.) Cosimo I e i frati di S. Marco, 1925.
„ BOOTH (C.) C. I, duke of Florence, 1921.
Cosmo III [*de' Medici*], *grand duke of Tuscany; d. 1723.*
De 2 reizen van C. door de Nederlanden, 1667–69. Journalen & doc. [*Italian &c.*] Uitg. door G. J. Hoogewerff. [Hist. Genoots. Werken., s3, 41]. 8°. A. 1919
***Cosmos:** a scheme for indust. co-oper. betw. cap. & lab. By an employer of labour. Ed., w. intr., by D. Sladen. [P2488]. s8°. [1920]
Cosquin (Emmanuel). Etudes folkloriques. Rech. s. les migrat. des contes pop. la8°. 1922
Cosri. Liber c., 1660, *see* JUDAH *ben Samuel, the Levite.*
Coss (Mekhithar), *see* MEKHITHAR, *Gosh.*
Cossa (Giuseppe), *see* CALVI (F.) G. C.: commem., 1887.
Cossa (Pietro). Cecilia. [Teatro in versi]. s8°. Torino. 1885
Cossio (Manuel B.) El Greco. [Hispanic Soc.] s8°. Barcelona. *n.d.*
Lo que se sabe de la vida del Greco. s8°. 1914
Cossmann (*Oberleutnant*), *see* SACHSSE (*Kapitän*) & *Oberleut.* C. Kriegsgefangen in Skipton, 1920.
Costa (Afonso). Parnaso brasileiro: cem poetas contemp. s8°. Barcelona. *n.d.*
Costa (Claudio Manoel da), *1729–89.* Commem. do centenario de C. M. da C., *see* INSTITUTO HIST. E GEOG. Revista, t53, 1890.
Costa (Eduardo Maria Vilarrasa y), *see* VILARRASA Y COSTA.
Costa (Estanisláo de). *Vida do padre E. de C. [*Latin*, 1765, *w. Portug. tr. by* T. Alencar Araripe], *see* INSTITUTO HIST. E GEOG. BRAZIL. Revista, t52, 1889.
Costa (Izaak da). De mensch en de dichter W. Bilderdijk [*b. as* d19 *of h.* Dichtwerken]. s8°. Haarlem. 1859
Costa (Joaquin). Instituciones econ. para obreros: habitaciones de alquiler barato en la Expos. Univ. de Paris en 1867. s8°. 1918
Costa (Alberto de Sousa), *see* SOUSA COSTA (A. DE).
Costa (Uriel da), *see* ACOSTA (U.)
Costa Lobo (A. de Sousa Silva). Hist. da sociedade em Portugal no sec. 15. secção 1. 8°. 1903
Costantini (Antonio). Lodi de gli ill. ss. Ferrante Gonzaga & Isabella G. di Novellara ne lor nozze. [*By A. C. & o. wr.*] [*b. w.* Arrivabene (L.) Della orig. de' cavagl. d. Tosoni, 1589]. 8°. Mantova. 1594
Costantiniano, Ordine, *see* CONSTANTINIAN ORDER.
Costa-Rica.
*Coup d'œil rapide s. C. R. Par F. M. [P2830]. 8°. 1849
Costa y Llobera (Miquel).
Líriques. Tria de J. Estelrich &c. s8°. Barcelona. 1923
Coste (Guillaume de), *see* AUDIGUIER (V. D'). *Tragi-comicall hist. of our times [*sometimes attrib. to G. de C.*; tr.], 1627.
Coste (Hilarion de), *see* BIE (J. DE). Vrais portraits des rois de France, 2e éd., augm. &c. par H. de C., 1637.
Coste d'Arnobat (Charles Pierre). Lettres sur le voyage d'Espagne (1756); réimpr. par C. Vernier, *see* REVUE HISPANIQUE, t56, 1922.
Coster (Charles de). The legend of Ulenspiegel & Lamme Goedzak &c. Tr. F. M. Atkinson. 2v. 8°. 1922
see DES OMBIAUX (M.) Prem. romanciers nationaux de Belgique, C. &c., 1919.
Coster (Dirk). Marginalia. 3e dr. s8°. Arnhem. 1921
Coster (Franciscus), *Jesuit.* De vita & laudibus Mariae Virginis meditationes 50. s8°. Ingolstadii. 1597
see OSIANDER (L.) Enchiridion controv. relig. &c., p1, 1615.
Coster (Geraldine), *see* MACMUNN (N. E.) & G. C. Europe, 1922.
Coster (Lourens Janszoon), *see* ZEDLER (G.) Von C. zu Gutenberg: holländ. Frühdruck u. d. Erfindung d. Buchdrucks, 1921.
Costes (René). Antonio de Guevara, sa vie [& son œuvre]. 2p *in* 1v. la8°. Bordeaux. 1925–26

Costo (Tommaso). Ist. dell' orig. del sagr. luogo di Montevergine, vita di S. Guglielmo, di S. Amato, e di S. Donato, con vite de gli abati &c. 8°. Vinezia. 1591
***Costume** (The) of Yorkshire illust. by 40 engravings &c., 1885, *see* YORKSHIRE.
Cotarelo y Mori (Emilio). Bibliog. de las controv. s. la licitud del teatro en España. la8°. 1904
Ensayo sobre la vida y obras de P. Calderon de la Barca. pl. 8°. 1924
Cotelerius (Joannes Bapt.) [J. B. COTELIER].
Ecclesiæ Græcæ mon. 4t. 4°. Lutetia Paris. 1677–92
a. c. of t4 *has t.* Analecta Græca hactenus non edita &c. Ex Mss. eruerunt, Lat. verterunt &c. Monachi Bened. Congreg. S. Mauri.
SS. Patrum qui temp. Apostolicis floruerunt, Barnabæ, Hermæ, Clementis, Ignatii, Polycarpi, opera. Unà cum Clementis, Ignatii, Polycarpi actis &c. Acc. notæ aliorum. Rec. &c. J. Clericus. ed. 2a, 2v. lafol. Amstelædami. 1724
Cotelle (H.) Le langage arabe ordinaire, ou dialogues arabes. 4e éd. sm. obl. 8°. Alger. [1850]
Cotes (*Sir* Merton Russell-), *see* RUSSELL-COTES (*Sir* M.)
Cotes (Rosemary A.) Dante's garden &c. s8°. 1898
Cotman (John Sell). Archit. antiq. of Normandy; accomp. by hist. &c. notices by D. Turner. 2v. lafol. 1822
Letters f. Normandy, 1817–20; ed. H. I. Kay, *see* WALPOLE Soc. Vol. 14, 15, 1926–27.
see CUNDALL (H. M.) The Norwich school [w. reprod. after] J. Crome, J. S. C. &c., 1920.
„ OPPÉ (A. P.) Water-colour drawings of J. S. C., w. comm., 1923.
„ SMITH (S. C. K.) C., 1926.
Cotogno (Ottavio) [CODOGNO; COTTOGNO]. Compendio d. poste: dichiarat. dell' orig. & carico d. Maestri Gen. d. Poste &c. [*5 lib. in 1v; lib. 4 & 5 have sep. tp., pagin. cont.*] s8°. Milano. 1623
Cotossichin (G. C.), *see* KOTOSHIKHIN (G.)
Cotovicus (Joannes). Itinerarium Hierosolymitanum & Syriacum. Acc. Synopsis Reipublicae Venetę. [*a. ed.*] s4°. Antverpiæ. *H. Verdussius.* 1619
Cotta (Giovanni Battista). Dio: sonetti ed inni. 3v. [v3 *wanting*]. s8°. Venezia. 1820
Cotta (Joannes), *poet, see* MISTRUZZI (V.) G. C., 1924.
Cotta (Joannes Franciscus), *ps., see* PIRCKHEIMER (WILIBALD).
Cotta (Johann Friedrich), *prof. of theology at Tübingen.* Comm. de fallibili pontificis auctoritate M. Petit-Didierio oppos. s8°. Lugd. Batav. 1732
Exerc. de relig. Muhammedica. Disput. subjicient F. T. Bühler &c. [P431]. s4°. Tubingae. [1761]
Cottalambergius (Joannes Franciscus) *pseud., see* PIRCKHEIMER (WILIBALD).
Cotte (Jules). Sponge culture. Tr. [Fr. Bull. of Bur. of Fisheries, v28, 1908]. [P2702]. la8°. Wash. 1910
Cotter (Christoph), *see* KOTTER (C.)
Cotter (Gerald de Purcell). Alkaline lakes & soda industry of Sind, *see* INDIA: GEOL. SURVEY. Mem., v47ii, 1923.
Cottle (Joseph). Hymns & sacred lyrics. s8°. 1828
A new version of the Psalms of David. [*Verse*]. s8°. 1801
Second pref. to "Early recoll. of S. T. Coleridge." [*no tp.*] [P2777]. s8°. [1839]
Cottogno (Ottavio), *see* COTOGNO (O.)
Cotton. Crisis in the cotton industry. Report of proc. of Provisional Emergency Cotton Comm., Sept. 27, 1922, to May 17, 1923. 2v. 8°. M'ter. 1923
Cotton Control Board, *see* HENDERSON (H. D.) The C. C. B., 1922.
Cotton, *Junior, pseud., see* BRIDGES (T.)
Cotton (*Sir* Arthur T.), *see* COUTLEY (*Sir* P. T.) Ganges Canal: in reply to strictures by Sir A. C., 1864.
Cotton (Charles), *F.R.C.P.* The Grey Friars of Canterbury, 1224–1538. With chap. on remains of the Friary, by R. H. Goodsall. [Brit. Soc. of Franciscan St., Extra ser., v2]. 8°. M'ter. 1924
Notes on doc. in Cathedral Lib. at Canterbury rel. to the Grey Friars, *see* COLLECTANEA Franciscana, v2, 1922.
Cotton (Charles), *poet.*
Poems. Ed., w. intr. & notes by J. Beresford. 8°. [1923]
Poems f. the works of C. C. Decor. by C. L. Fraser. 8°. [1922]
Poems on several occasions. s8°. 1689
*Scarronides: or Le Virgile travesty. s8°. 1664
see GIRARD (G.) *Life of the Duke of Espernon, Engl. by C. C., 1670.
„ WALTON (I.) The complete angler, [p2, *by* C. C., prefixed, Some acc. of life &c. of C. C. *by* W. Oldys], 1760.

Cotton (Harry Evan August). Calcutta old & new: hist. & descr. hdbk. s8°. Calcutta. 1907
The century in India, 1800–1900. Repr. f. "Englishman," Jan. 1901. s8°. *n.p.* [1901]
Cotton (Henry). Editions of the Bible & parts thereof in Eng. 1505–1850, &c. 2nd ed. 8°. O. 1852
Cotton (John). Some Midland musings & o. verses. s8°. 1910
Cotton (John), *of Boston, U.S.A.* A brief expos. of the book of Canticles. s8°. 1642
Singing of Psalmes a Gospel-ordinance. [*Imperfect*]. 8°. 1647
The way of congregational churches cleared: in two treatises. From aspersions of Mr. R. Baylie, f. contradictions of Vindicae Clavium, & misconstructions of Mr. Rutherford. s4°. 1648
The way of the churches of Christ in New England &c. measured by the golden reed of the sanctuary. s4°. 1645
Cotton (Nathaniel). Poet. works. Coll. by T. Park. s8°. 1806
Cotton (*Sir* Robert Bruce), *bart.* Cottoni posthuma: divers pieces of C. [*gen. tp. wanting*]. s8°. 1672
Cotton (Walter Aidan). The race problem in S. Africa. Pref. by E. W. Smith. s8°. 1926
Cotton (William), *F.S.A.* Graphic & hist. sketch of Bodyam Castle in Sussex. [P2460]. 8°. [1831]
Cottret (*Abbé*), *see* BILIOTTI (E.) & C. L'île de Rhodes, 1881.
Couchoud (Paul Louis). The enigma of Jesus. Tr. W. Whale. Intr. by Sir J. Frazer. s8°. 1924
Japanese impressions, w. a note on Confucius. Tr. F. Rumsey, w. pref. by A. France. 8°. 1921
see MYTHOLOGIE asiat. illust.; avant-propos par P. L. C., 1928.
Coudenhove (Hans). My African neighbours: man, bird & beast in Nyasaland. 8°. [1925]
Couderc (Camille). Enluminures des mss. du m. â. (6e–15e s.) de la Bibl. Nat. 4°. 1927
Couderc de Saint-Chamant (Henri).
Napoléon, s. dern. armées. 8°. [1902]
Coudreau (Henri).
Chez nos Indiens, la Guyane franç. (1887–1891). la8°. 1895
Coué (Emile). *Is Coué a foe to Xty.? By Another gentleman with a duster. s8°. N.Y. 1923
La maîtrise de soi-même par l'autosuggestion consciente. n. éd. s8°. [1922]
Couissin (Paul). Les armes romaines. Essai s. l'orig. &c. des armes du légionnaire. Avant-propos par S. Reinach. la8°. 1926
Statuette de femme acrobate du Musée de Rennes, *see* ACAD. DES INSCR. Fond. Piot. Mons. &c., t28, 1925–26.
***Could** a man be secure, 1790?, *see* GOODWIN (S.)
Couling (Samuel), *see* LANNING (G.) & S. C. Hist. of Shanghai, p1, 1921.
Coull (Thomas). Hist. & traditions of St. Pancras. 8°. 1861
Coulon (Auguste), *see* JOHN XXII, *pope*. J. XXII, 1316–34: lettres secrètes &c. rel. à la France, extr. des reg. du Vatican par A. C., t1, 1906.
Coulon (Marcel).
Le problème de Rimbaud, poète maudit. s8°. 1923
Raoul Ponchon. Préf. de C. Maurras. 8°. 1927
Coulson (John E.) The peasant preacher: mem. of Charles Richardson. 3rd ed. s8°. 1867
Coulter (John Merle) & M. C. Coulter.
Where evolution & relig. meet. s8°. N.Y. 1924
Coulter (Merle C.), *see* COULTER (J. M.) & M. C. C. Where evolution & relig. meet, 1924.
Coulton (George Gordon).
Five centuries of religion. v1, 2. 8°. C. 1923–27
1, St. Bernard, h. predecessors &c., 1000–1200.
2, The friars & the dead weight of tradition, 1200–1400.
A mediæval garner. Sel., tr. &c., by G. G. C.
" " [2nd ed., re-arr. & enl. *w. t.*] Life in the Middle Ages. v1. s8°. C. 1928
Mediæval studies. [*Articles repr. f. reviews &c.*]
No. 12–14 *in* 1v, 15–17 [14, 2nd ed., rev.] 8°. 1915–24
12, Med. graffiti, espec. in the E. Counties.
13, Plain man's relig. in the Middle Ages.
14, Roman Catholic Church & the Bible.
15, More Roman Catholic history.
16, Infant perdition in the Middle Ages.
17, Roman Catholic truth: discussion betw. G. G. C. & L. J. Walker.
The mediæval village. 8°. C. 1925
Social life in Britain f. the Conquest to the Reformation. Comp. by G. G. C. [repr., *w.* index]. 8°. C. 1919
A Victorian schoolmaster: Henry Hart of Sedbergh. 8°. 1923
Workers & War. [P2849]. 8°. 1914
see THURSTON (H.) Some inexactitudes of Mr. G. G. C., 1927.

Councilman (William Thomas).
Disease & its causes. [Home Univ. Lib.] s8°. N.Y. [1913]
***Country (The)** & "Labour." [w. app., Lab. & the "Capitalist" press, by E. T. Good]. [P2484]. 8°. [1920]
Country heart (The). [Quarterly mag., w. wh. is incorp. The vineyard]. Jan. 1920–Dec. 1922. [v1]. 8°. [1922]
Country Justice of the Peace, *ps.*, *see* *SERIOUS thoughts in regard to the publick disorders, 1750.
County chronicle (The) & Weekly advertiser for Essex, Herts, Kent &c. Aug. 19, 1794–Jan. 16, 1798. Nos. 316–500. [*in* 1v.] lafol. 1794–98
County (The) Gentleman, *see* LAND & WATER.
County Kerry Society, *see* DENNY (H. L. L.) Hdbk. of Co. K. fam. hist. &c., 1923.
County Kildare Archaeological Society, *see* KILDARE (Co.) ARCH. SOC.
County Library Conf., 1924, 1926, rep., *see* CARNEGIE UNITED KINGDOM TRUST.
Coup d'Etat. *C. d'Etat (Le) anecdotique, 2 déc. 1851, avec lettres & docs. inéd. 8°. [1873]
Secret of the C. d'Etat: unpubl. corr. of Pr. Louis Napoleon &c., 1848–52, *see* LANSDOWNE (H. W. E. P.-F., *6th marq. of*), *ed.*
Coup d'oeil. *Coup d'oeil rapide s. Costa Rica; par F. M., 1849, *see* COSTA-RICA.
*Coup d'oeil s. l'état polit. de Pologne, 1815–30, *see* HOFFMANN (C. A.)
Couperin, *The family of*, *see* TIERSOT (J.) Les C., 1926.
Couperus (Louis).
Het heilige weten. 2d. 8°. A. *n.d.*
Het late leven. 2d. 8°. A. *n.d.*
Xerxes of de hoogmoed. 8°. Rotterdam. 1919
Zielenschemering. 2d. 8°. A. *n.d.*
TRANSLATIONS.
The comedians. Tr. J. M. Wilson. s8°. [1926]
Dr. Adriaan. Tr. A. Teixeira de Mattos. s8°. [1918]
Eastward. Tr. J. Menzies-Wilson & C. C. Crispin. 8°. 1924
The hidden force. Tr. A. Teixeira de Mattos. s8°. [1922]
The later life. Tr. A. Teixeira de Mattos. 8°. [1915]
The law inevitable. Tr. A. Teixeira de Mattos. s8°. [1921]
The tour. Story of anc. Egypt. Tr. A. Teixeira de Mattos. s8°. [1920]
The twilight of the souls. Tr. A. Teixeira de Mattos. s8°. [1917]
Coupin (Henri Eugène Victor) & J. Lea.
Romance of animal arts & crafts. 8°. 1913
Coupland (Reginald). The Quebec Act (1774). 8°. O. 1925
Raffles, 1781–1826. 8°. 1926
The study of the Brit. Commonwealth. [P2580]. 8°. O. 1921
Wilberforce: a narrative. 8°. O. 1923
Coupland (Sidney), *see* STURGES (O.) & S. C. Natural hist. of pneumonia, 1890.
Couplet (Philippe), *Jesuit.* Tabula chronolog. Monarchiae Sinicae, *see* CONFUCIUS. C. Sinarum philos. &c., 1687.
Courajod (Louis C. L.), *see* MARIGNAN (A.) Un historien de l'art franç.: L. C., t1, 1899.
Courant (Maurice). L'Asie Centrale aux 17 & 18 s.: empire kalmouk ou emp. mantchou? [Annales de l'Univ. de Lyon]. la8°. Lyon. 1912
Bibliographie coréene j. 1890. [Ecole des Langues Or. Vivantes, s3, 18–21]. 3t *&* Suppl. (–1899). la8°. 1894–1901
La Sibérie, colonie russe j. la construct. du Transsibérien. 8°. 1920
Courbet (Gustave) [COURBET (JEAN DÉSIRÉ G.)].
see BOREL (P.) Roman de G. C., 1922.
" DURET (T.) C., 1918.
" MEIER-GRÄFE (J.) C., 1924.
Courboin (Eugène), *see* QUATRELLES, *ps.* Légende de la Vierge de Münster; illust. par E. C., 1881.
Courboin (François). L'estampe française. [1], Graveurs & marchands. [Bibl. de l'art du 18e s.] la8°. Brux. 1914
La gravure en France, des origines à 1900. 4°. 1923
Hist. illust. de la gravure en France. 3p [*&* Planches *in case*. lafol.] sfol. 1923–26
1, Des orig. à 1660. 2, De 1660 à 1800. 3, 19e siècle.
Courbon (Anne Marie, *ctsse. de*), *see* MORAS (A. M.)
Courby (Fernand). Les vases grecs à reliefs. [Ecoles Franç. d'Athènes & de Rome, fasc. 125]. la8°. 1922
see ECOLE FRANÇ. D'ATHÈNES. Fouilles de Delphes, t2, La terrasse du Temple, par F. C., 1927.
Courcelles (—), *French ambassador at the Court of Scotland.* Extract f. despatches of C., 1586–87. [Bannatyne Club]. 4°. E. 1828
Courcelles (Etienne de) [CURCELLAEUS (S.), *see* DESMARETS (S.) Joanna Papissa &c. add. Brevis refut. praef. quam præfixit S. C., 1658.

Courchetet d'Esnans (Luc). *Hist. des négociations, & du traité de paix des Pyrénées. 2t. s8°. Amsterdam. 1750

Courier (Paul Louis).
see HALL (*Sir* J.) Four famous mysteries: murder of C. &c., 1922.
,, LELARGE (A.) P. L. C., Parisien, 1925.

Courières (Ed. des), *see* DES COURIÈRES (E.)

Courland (Charles de Saxe, *duke of*), *see* CHARLES [*de Saxe*], *d. of C.*

Cournos (John). Sport of gods. Play. s8°. 1925
see O'BRIEN (E. J.) & J. C., *ed.* Best short stories of 1924[-25], 1925-26.

Cournot (Antoine Augustin). Essai s. les fondements de nos connaissances &c. n. éd. 8°. 1912

Couronnement (Le) de Louis. Chanson de geste. Ed. E. Langlois. [Class. fr. du m. â.] s8°. 1920

Cours élém. de langue flamande par A. D. T., pl, 1895, *see* FLAMANDE.

Court. *Court (The) of sapience. Spät-mittelengl. allegor.-didakt. Visionsgedicht. [*Sometimes attrib. to J. Lydgate*]. Krit. Textausgabe &c. v. R. Spindler. [Beitr. z. engl. Philol.; hrsg. M. Förster, H6]. 8°. L. 1927
*Court-secret (The): a melancholy truth. Tr. f. Arabic. By an adept in the oriental tongues. [*Satire*]. [P2783]. 8°. 1741
Origins &c. of The Court of love [*form. attrib. to Chaucer*], 1899, *see* NEILSON (W. A.)

Court of Common Council, *London, see* LONDON: CIVIC INSTIT.

Court of King's Bench. Curia Regis rolls of the reigns of Richard I & John preserved in the Public Record Office. Pr. under superint. of the Deputy Keeper. [1], Richard I-2 John. [2] 3-5 John. [3] 5-7 John. la8°. 1922-26

Courteault (Paul). La Place Royale de Bordeaux, *see* SOCIÉTÉ DE L'HIST. DE L'ART FRANÇ. Archives, nouv. pér., t12, 1922.
La vie écon. à Bordeaux pend. la Guerre. [C.E. of Int. Peace]. la8°. [1925]

Courteille (Abel Jean Baptiste Pavet de), *see* PAVET DE COURTEILLE.

Courteline (Georges) *ps.* [*i.e.* G. MOINAUX].
Boubouroche. s8°. [1924]
Théâtre. [t]1. s8°. [1925]
1, Boubouroche—Un client sérieux—Les Boulingrin—M. Badin—La cruche—La peur des coups—La paix chez soi—Le commissaire est bon enfant.
see TURPIN (F.) G. C., s. œuvre, 1925.

Courten (Maria Luisa Giartosio de).
Percy Bysshe Shelley e l'Italia. s8°. Milano. 1923

Courthion (Pierre). La vie de Delacroix. s8°. 1927

Courthope (William John). The connexion betw. anc. & mod. romance; Warton lect., 1911, *see* BRIT. ACAD. Proc., 1911-12.
A consid. of Macaulay's comparison of Dante & Milton. [From Brit. Acad. Proc., v3. P2411]. 8°. 1908
The country town & o. p. With a memoir by A. O. Prickard. s8°. 1920
Hist. of Eng. poetry. 6v [v2-6, repr.] 8°. 1895-1920

Courtilz de Sandras (Gatien de).
Mems. of d'Artagnan. Tr. R. Nevill. 3p. 8°. [1925]
see WOODBRIDGE (B. M.) Gatien de C., 1925.

Courtney (*Mrs.* Janet Elizabeth).
Freethinkers of the 19th century. 8°. 1920
Recollected in tranquillity. 8°. 1926

Courtney (William Leonard). Is it a new world? Articles &c. contrib. to "Daily Telegraph," Aug.-Sept., 1920. Foreword by W. L. C. s8°. [1920]

Courtney of Penwith (Leonard Henry Courtney, *1st baron*), *see* GOOCH (G. P.) Life of Lord C., 1920.

Courtois (Louis J.) Chronolog. crit. de vie & œuvres de J.-J. Rousseau, *see* SOCIÉTÉ JEAN-JACQUES ROUSSEAU. Annales, t15, 1923.

Courtot (*la baronne* Cecile de), *see* KAISENBERG (M. v.) Mem. d. Baronesse C. de C., 2e A., 1899.

Cousens (Henry). Architect. antiqs. of West. India. la8°. 1926
The Chālukyan architecture of the Kanarese districts. [Arch. Survey of India, v42]. la4°. Calcutta. 1926

Cousins (James H.)
The new Japan: impress. &c. s8°. Madras. 1923

Coustet (Ernest). L'électricité. s8°. [1923]

Cousturier (Lucie). Seurat. la8°. [1921]

Coutanche (A. M.), *see* ANSPACH (L. E. F.) & A. M. C. Dict. of Anglo-Belg. law, 2p, 1897-1919.

Coutet (Alex.)
Toulouse. Préf. de P. Neveux. la8°. Toulouse. 1926

Couthon (Georges). Opinion s. le jugement de Louis XVI; préc. de réflex. par A. Havard & d'une lettre secrète de Louis XVI. [P2774]. 8°. 1833

Couto (Diogo de), *see* BELL (A. F. G.) D. do C., 1924.

Coutts (Francis). Sel. poems. s8°. [1923]

Coutts (William Strachan), *see* BIHAR & Orissa local statutory rules & orders, 1917; comp. by W. S. C., 3v, 1918-19.

Coutumier. *Grand (Le) coutumier de France, n. éd. par E. Laboulaye &c., 1868, *see* FRANCE.

Couturier (*le père* Abel). Cours de liturgie grecque-melkite. Fasc. 2, Office divin. s8°. Jérusalem. 1914

Couturier (Paul Vaillant-), *see* VAILLANT-COUTURIER (P.)

Couvreur (André). *Works in* ŒUVRES libres.
L'androgyne, 1922. [7.]
Le biocole, 1927. [72.]
Les mém^s. d'un immortel, 1924. [42.]
Le valseur phosphorescent, 1923. [30.]

Covarrubias (Jose Diaz), *see* DIAZ COVARRUBIAS (J.)

Covenant. *The National C. [1638] & Solemn League & C., w. Acknowledgement of sins &c., as renewed at Douglas, 1712, &c. With introd. pref. [*w. sep. pagin. last leaf wanting*]. s8°. *n.p.* [E.] 1712

Covenanters. *Minute bk. kept by the War comm. of the C., Kirkcudbright, 1640-41, 1804, *see* KIRKCUDBRIGHT.

Covens (Jan). [4 plans of fortified towns, Mayence, Siége du Quesnoy (1712), Luxembourg (1744) &c. Maps, 7]. folded fol. *Covens & Mortier*, Amsterdam. *n.d.*
Hambourg, par J. C. & C. Mortier. [Plan & view]. folded fol. [? Amsterdam. c. 1730]

Covent Garden. Covent Garden drollery: a miscellany of 1672. [Coll. by A. B. *Sometimes attrib. to A. Brome*]. Ed. G. Thorn-Drury. s8°. 1928
*Tom K——g's, w. humours of C. G., 1738, *see* KING (TOM).

Coventry Plays. Ludus Coventriæ, or, the plaie called Corpus Christi. [Ed.] by K. S. Block. [E.E.T.S., E.S., 120]. 8°. 1922

Coventry (Bernard Okes). Wild flowers of Kashmir. s2. s8°. 1927

Coventry (Walter Bulkeley).
Technics of the hand camera. 8°. 1901

Coventry (*Sir* William), *1628-86.* The character of a trimmer. His opinion of laws & gov. &c. 2nd ed. [P2653]. s4°. 1689

Coverdale (Miles), *bp. of Exeter.* Memorials, w. matter rel. to promulg. of the Bible in r. of H. VIII. 8°. 1838
see FRY (F.) The Bible by C. 1535, 1867.

Coville (Alfred). Les états de Normandie, leurs orig. &c. au 14e s. la8°. 1894

Cowan (Andrew Reid). Guide to world-history. 8°. 1923

Cowan (Bertha Sinclair), *wife of R. E. Cowan, see* BOWER (B. M.)

Cowan (James).
Fairy folk tales of the Maori. s8°. Auckland, N.Z. 1925

Cowan (P. C.) Rep. on Dublin housing. [P2597]. 8°. D. 1918

Cowan (Robert Ernest).
see CLARK (W. A.) *jr.* Lib. of W. A. C., coll. &c. by R. E. C. &c., v3, 1924.
,, —— Library of C.: Kelmscott & Doves Presses; collated &c. by R. E. C. &c., 1921.

Cowans (*Gen. Sir* John Steven), *see* CHAPMAN-HUSTON (*Maj.* D.) & *Maj.* O. RUTTER. Gen. Sir J. C.: the quarter-master-gen. of the Gt. War, 2v, 1924.

Coward (Henry). Choral technique & interpret. 8°. [1914]

Coward (Noel). Easy virtue. [2nd impr.] s8°. 1926
The Marquise, a comedy. s8°. 1927
The queen was in the parlour. s8°. 1926

Coward (Thomas Alfred), *F.Z.S.* Bird life at home & abroad w. o. nature obs. 8°. [1927]
The birds of the Brit. Isles & their eggs. ser. 2, 3. s8°. 1920-26
s3, Migration & habits.
—— & C. Oldham. The birds of Cheshire. 8°. M'ter. 1900

Cowell (Edward Byles), *see* VARARUCHI. Pràkrita-Prakáśá; text, w. notes & Eng. tr. &c. by E. B. C., 1854.

Cowell (John), *gardener.* The curious & profitable gardener. Added, descr. of the gt. Amer. aloe [*w. sep. pagin.*] 8°. 1730

Cowfold, *Sussex.* Parish register, 1558-1812. Ed. P. S. Godman. [Sussex Rec. Soc., v22]. 8°. 1916

Cowley (The) carol book, rev. ed., 1912, *see* WOODWARD (G. R.), *ed.*

Cowley (Abraham). Poemata Latina. s8°. Londini. 1668
Poem on the late Civil War. s8°. 1679
Sel. poems. s8°. E. 1773
Works. 12th ed. 3v [3, 10th ed.] s8°. 1721

Cowley (Arthur Ernest). Aramaic papyri of the 5th cent. B.C. Ed., w. tr. & notes by A. C. 8°. O. 1923
The Hittites. [Brit. Acad. Schweich Lects., 1918]. 8°. 1920
see SAMARITAN (THE) liturgy; ed. A. E. C., 2v, 1909.

Cowley (Hannah).
The belle's stratagem. [Dolby's Brit. th.] s8°. 1823
Belle's stratagem, *see* INCHBALD (E.) Brit. th., v19, 1808.
Bold stroke for a husband, *see* INCHBALD (E.) Brit. th., v19, 1808.
Which is the man ?, *see* †INCHBALD (E.) Mod. th., v10, 1811.

Cowling (George Herbert). The Felon Sew: mock-heroic poem of 15th c. [1st transcr. by R. Rokeby, 1565, *w. text*], *see* ENGLISH ASSOC. Essays &c., v8, 1922.

Cowper (Emily, *Countess*), *aft. Visctess. Palmerston, see* PALMERSTON (E., *Visctess.*)

Cowper (Frank). Cruising sails & yachting tales. v1. 8°. 1921

Cowper (Joseph Meadows). Our parish books &c.: Holy Cross, Westgate, Canterbury. 2v. s8°. Canterbury. [1884–]85

Cowper (Mary Cowper, *countess*), *wife of 1st earl, see* IMBERT-TERRY (*Sir* H. M.) Reminisc. of a Chancellor & h. wife, 1927.

Cowper (William), *bp. of Galloway.*
Heaven opened. 3d ed. s4°. 1613

Cowper (William), *the poet.*
Mem. of the early life of C., wr. by himself: w. app. cont. letters &c. s8°. 1816
Poems. 6th ed. 2v. s8°. 1794–5
Unpubl. & uncoll. letters. Ed. T. Wright. 8°. 1925
see GREATHEED (S.) Pract. improv. of the Divine counsel &c., sermon occas. by death of W. C., 1800.
see HAYLEY (W.) Life & letters of C., 1835.
„ HURDIS (J.) Letters of J. H. to W. C., 1791–94, 1927.
„ WRIGHT (TH.) Life of C., 2nd ed., 1921.

Cowper (William Cowper, *1st earl*), *Lord Chancellor, see* IMBERT-TERRY (*Sir* H. M.) Reminisc. of a Chancellor [*i.e.* C.] & h. wife, 1927.

Cox (Catherine Morris). Early mental traits of 300 geniuses, *see* TERMAN (L. M.) Genetic st. of genius, v2, 1926.

Cox (David). A treatise on landscape painting in water colours (1813). Foreword by A. L. Baldry. Ed. G. Holme. [Studio. Spec. No.] [repr.] la8°. 1922

Cox (Euan H. M.) Farrer's last journey, Upper Burma, 1919–20. With list of rhododendrons coll. by F., & h. field notes compiled by H. T. Maxwell. 8°. 1926
Rhododendrons for amateurs. 8°. 1924
see GOSSE (*Sir* E.) The library of E. G.: cat. comp. by E. H. M. C., 1924.

Cox (Frances Elizabeth).
Sacred hymns f. the German; tr. by F. E. C. s8°. 1841

Cox (Francis Augustus), *D.D.* History of the Baptist Miss. Soc., 1792–1842. 2v. s8°. 1842
—— **& J. Hoby.** Religion in America. Narr. of the deputation f. the Baptist Union in Eng. to the U.S.A. & Canada. 3rd ed. rev. 8°. 1837

Cox (George James). Pottery, for artists, craftsmen & teachers. 8°. N.Y. 1914

Cox (*Sir* **George William),** *bart., see* MALLARMÉ (S.) Les dieux antiq.: nouv. mythologie d'ap. G. W. C. &c., 1925.

Cox (Harold).
The coal industry; dangers of nationalis. [P2484]. 8°. 1919
Economic liberty. s8°. 1920
The failure of State railways. [P2773, 2785]. 8°. 1924
Problem of population. s8°. [1922]
—— **& J. E. Chandler.** The House of Longman, w. record of th. bicentenary celebrations, 1724–1924. 8°. *p.f.p.c.* 1925

Cox (Herbert A.), *see* BREWER (H. W.) Old London illust., w. descr. notes by H. A. C., 1921.

Cox (*Capt.* **Hiram).** Burmha game of chess comp. w. the Indian &c., *see* AUNGERVYLE SOC. Reprints, s2, 1883.

Cox (John), *F.R.S.C.* Mechanics. [repr.] 8°. C. 1919

Cox (John Charles), *rector of Barton-le-Street.*
Cornwall. [Co. Churches]. s8°. 1912
Cumberland & Westmorland. [Co. Churches]. s8°. 1913
English church fittings, furniture &c. Intr. by A. Vallance. 8°. [1923]
Kent. [Little guides, 2nd ed.] s8°. [1915]
Mem. of old Surrey. Ed. J. C. C. 8°. 1911
Surrey. [Little guides]. 4th ed. s8°. [1921]

Cox (John R.), *see* CANADIAN ARCTIC EXPED. Rep., v11, B, Geogr. notes, by K. G. Chipman & J. R. C., 1924.

Cox (Montagu H.), *see* LONDON. Survey, v10, Parish of St. Margaret, Westminster, p1; ed., w. hist. notes by M. H. C., 1926.

Cox (R. Hippisley).
The green roads of England. 2nd ed., rev. & enl. 8°. [1923]

Cox (Samuel). An expositor's note-book. 7th ed. 8°. 1889

Cox (William), *felon.* *Acc. of the life, robberies, trial, & execution of W. C. [P2828]. s8°. 1773

Cox (William Lang Paige), *archdeacon of Chester, see* ANGLICAN essays; by Abp. of Armagh, Archd. of Chester &c., 1923.

Coxon (Roger). Chesterfield & h. critics. 8°. 1925

Coxwell (Charles Fillingham). A kingdom of hate. A romantic satire [*in verse*]. s8°. [1925]
Pharaoh & o. poems. s8°. 1927
Siberian & o. folk-tales. Coll. & tr., w. intr. & notes by C. F. C. 8°. [1925]

Coxworthy (Franklin). Electrical cond.: how & where our earth was created. Ed. &c. by J. Coxworthy. 8°. [1925]

Coyzevox (Antoine) [COYSEVOX], *see* JOUIN (H.) A. C., sa vie, s. œuvre &c., 1883.

Cozza (A.) Scavi nel territ. falisco (Narce &c.), *see* REALE ACCAD. D. LINCEI. Mon. ant., v4, 1894.
—— **& V. Mariani.** Nuovi scavi d. stadio palatino, *see* REALE ACCAD. D. LINCEI. Mon. ant., v5, 1895.

Cozza (*card.* **Lorenzo).** Atti d. P. L. C., custode di Terra Santa, 1709–15; racc. dal p. E. Castellani, 2t, *see* GOLUBOVICH (G.) Bibl. bio-bibl., n.s., t4, 5, 1924.
Vita e diarii del Card L. C., 1654–1729; a cura d. p. L. Oliger, *see* GOLUBOVICH (G.) Bibl. bio-bibl., n.s., t3, 1925.

Craan (W. B.) Plan du champ de bataille de Waterloo & Notice hist. *folded* 8°. Brux. 1816

Crabb (George), *M.A.* Extracts f. the best German authors, w. dict. 3rd ed. s8°. 1821

Crabbe (George), *the poet.* The borough: a poem. 8°. 1810
Poems, *see* †CHAMBERS. Misc., v6, 1872.
Poet. works., w. life of the a. [by W. R.] s8°. [1858]
„ „ Ed. A. J. & R. M. Carlyle. Oxf. ed. s8°. O. 1908

Crabtree (John). Concise hist. of parish &c. of Halifax. 8°. Halifax. 1836

Crabtree (John Henry). Richard Arkwright. s8°. 1923
Wonders of insect life. Habits &c. of insects. s8°. [1919]

Crace (Frederick), *see* VICTORIA & ALBERT MUSEUM. Maps, plans, & views of London &c., coll. by F. C., lent by J. G. Crace, 1879.

Cradock (*Mrs.* **Anna Francesca).** La vie française à la veille de la Révol., 1783–86. Journal inéd. Tr. Mme. Odelphin Balleyguier. s8°. 1911

Cradock (Joseph). The Czar, tragedy. [P2863]. 8°. 1824

Cradock (Samuel). The harmony of the 4 Evangelists & their text methodiz'd &c. 4°. 1668

Craen (A.) Pastorellen, ofte Bosch-Gezangen, *see* AMSTERDAM. A. Pegasus, 1627.

Craft (Ellen), *see* CRAFT (W.) & E. C. Running a 1000 miles for freedom, 1860.

Craft (William) & E. Craft. Running a 1000 miles for freedom; or, escape of W. & E. C. f. slavery. s8°. 1860

Cragg (*Mrs.* **Edith),** *form. Webb.* Cat. of old French & Eng. furniture &c., prop. of Mrs. C., coll. by J. Webb. Sold by Christie, June 1925. [*Illust.*] 8°. 1925

Cragg (Rowland). Anvil & loom. 8°. 1926

Craggs, *The family of, see* ELIOT, *The family of.* Genealog. mem. rel. to families of E. of Port Eliot & C. of Wyserley, 1868.

Craig (*Sir* **Algernon Tudor Tudor-),** *see* TUDOR-CRAIG (*Sir* A. T.)

Craig (Edward Gordon). Books & theatres. 8°. 1925
The theatre advancing. 8°. 1921

Craig (Edward Hubert Cunningham).
Oil-finding: geolog. study of petroleum. 2nd ed. 8°. 1920
see BARROW (G.), J. S. G. WILSON & E. H. C. C. Geol. of co. round Blair Atholl &c., 1905.

Craig (Edwin Stewart), *see* OXFORD. Oxford Univ. Roll of Service; ed. E. S. C. & W. M. Gibson, 1920.

Craig (J. D.), *Lecturer in Humanity in the Univ. of St. Andrews.* Jovialis & the Callopian text of Terence. [St. Andrews Univ. Publ., 22]. 8°. O. 1927

Craig (John), *Scottish reformer.* A shorte summe of the whole catechisme; repr. in facs. f. orig. ed. of 1581. w. mem. of a. by T. G. Law. s8°. E. 1883

Craigie (William Alexander). The Icelandic sagas. s8°. C. 1913
see Gosse (*Sir* E.) & W. A. C. Oxf. bk. of Scand. verse, 1925.
Craignilder. *Battle (The) of C.: anc. Gallov. ballad, 1832, *see* Battle.
Craignish, *The family of, see* Campbell (A.) MS. hist. of C.; ed. H. Campbell, 1926.
Craik (*Mrs.* **Dinah Maria**) [Mulock (D. M.), *aft. Craik*], *see* Reade (A. L.) The Mellards &c., w. mem. of D. M. M. &c., 1915.
Craik (George Lillie). English of Shakespeare illust. in philol. comm. on h. Julius Cæsar. 5th ed., rev. s8°. 1875
Craik (Henry). English prose selections, w. crit. intr. &c. [repr.] v5, 19th c. s8°. 1917
Craik (W. W.) A short hist. of the mod. Brit. working-class movement. 3rd ed. s8°. 1919
Crake (Ernest Edward), *see* Scarthoe. Par. reg. of S. Giles' (1562–1837), w. hist. notes by E. E. C., 1926.
Cram (Eloise B.) Bird parasites of the Nematode suborders Strongylata, Ascaridata &c. [S.I., U.S. Nat. Mus., Bull. 140]. 8°. Wash. 1927
Cram (Ralph Adams).
see Princeton University. Holder Tower & the new dining-halls of P.U.; w. apprec. by C., 1918.
,, Soule (W.) Spanish farm houses, w. intr. by R. A. C., 1924.
Cramer (A. G.), *see* Brisson (B.) Suppl. ad B.B. opus de verb. signific., spec. 1; auct. A. G. C., 1813.
Cramer (Andreas Wilhelm). De verborum signific. tituli Pandectarum & Codicis &c. s8°. Kiliae. 1811
Cramer (Daniel). Oratio, qualenam animal sit papa Romanus, ex cap. 9 Apoc.: oppos. Bellarmino. [*Extr.* P1042]. s8°. [Francofurti. 1595]
see Volckmar (J. G.) De eccl. triumphante in coelis disput. duae, altera De Sanct. cultu quam D. C. def., 1595.
Cramer (Ludwig Dankegott). De bibliologia in sacris N. Test. libris proposita tract. pl. 4°. Lipsiae. *n.d.*
Crammer (Anton). Magnifica sanctitatis gloria in episc. Boicis resplendens &c. s8°. Frisingæ. 1775
Crammond (Edgar). Cantor lectures on effect of the War on econ. cond. &c. [Roy. Soc. of Arts. P2739]. la8°. 1918
Cramon (*Gen.* **August v.**) Quatre ans au G. Q. G. Austro-Hongrois pend. la Guerre mondiale. Tr. Capt. Koeltz. 8°. 1922
Cramp (J. M.) *The council of Trent. s8°. 1839
Cramp (K. R.) Australian winners of the Victoria Cross, 1914–19. [P2423]. 8°. Sydney. 1919
Cramp (W. B.) Narr. of a voyage to India; of a shipwreck & a descr. of N.S.W. [*&* Recoll. of Sicily, by Count de Forbin]. 8°. 1823
Cranach (Lucas) [†Sunder (Lucas), *called Cranach, the elder*]. L. Cranach's Stammbuch. Nebst kurzen biogr. Nachrichten &c. Hrsg. v. C. Mechel. fol. 1814
see Bible: German. Dath nyge Test. tho dude [*w. 21 full-page woodcuts by L. C.*], 1528.
,, Glaser (C.) L. C. (Deut. Meister), 1921.
,, Passional Christi u. Antichristi, 1521, facs., 1924.
Cranage (David Herbert Somerset). The home of the monk: Eng. monastic life & bldgs. in Middle Ages. s8°. C. 1926
Cranat, *Saint, see* Plummer (C.) Misc. hagiogr. Hibern., 1925.
Cranbrook (Gathorne Gathorne-Hardy, *3rd earl*). Illust. partic. of the estate of Hemsted, nr. Cranbrook, sale, 25 & 26 June 1912, by Knight, Frank & Rutley. By dir. of the Earl of C. fol. 1912
Crandon (John), *see* Baxter (R.) Apology, w. C.'s Anatomy for satisfact. of Mr. Caryl &c., 1654.
Crandon (*Mrs.* **L. R. G.**), *see* Margery, *psychic medium.*
Crane (*Mrs.* **Louise**). China in sign & symbol. Decor. by K. Crane. [Pref. by E. Morgan]. 4°. Shanghai. 1926
Crane (Ronald Salmon) & F. B. Kaye. Census of Brit. newspapers & periodicals, 1629–1800. With ass. of M. E. Prior. 8°. Chapel Hill, N. Carolina. 1927
Crane (Stephen), *see* Beer (T.) S. C.: st. in Amer. letters, 1924.
Crane (Thomas Frederick). Chansons pop. de la France. Sel., ed. &c. by T. F. C. s8°. N.Y. [1891]
Italian social customs of 16th c.: influences on the lit. of Europe. la8°. 1920
Crane (Verner Winslow). The promotion literature of Georgia. Repr. f. Bibliogr. essays, tribute to W. Eames. [P2784]. 8°. Cambridge [Mass.] 1925
Crane (W. J. E.) Bookbinding for amateurs. [*repr.*] s8°. [c. 1893]

Crane (Walter).
Cat. of exhib. of paintings &c. [P2421]. s8°. 1920
Queen Summer. la8°. 1891
see Massé (G. C. E.) Bibliog. of 1st ed. of bks. illust. by W. C., 1923.
Cranke (James), *1746–1826.* *Memoir of J. C., artist. [P2428]. 8°. Warrington. 1883
Crankshaw (W. P.) Weaving. 8°. 1924
Cranmer (Thomas), *abp. of Canterbury.*
Answer unto a crafty &c. cavillation devised by S. Gardiner agaynst the trewe & godly doctrine of the Sacrament. Also answered places of the booke of R. Smyth. sfol. 1551
Assertio veræ et cath. doctrinæ de Sacramento corporis &c. J. C. s8°. Lichæ. 1601
see Gilpin (W.) Life of C., 1784.
,, Jackson (T.) Lib. of Xtn. biog., v5, T. C., by W. Gilpin, 1838.
see Sargant (J. A.) Life of C., 1829.
,, Smyth (C. H. E.) C. & the Reformation under Edward VI, 1926.
,, Strype (J.) Abridg. of life of C., 1725.
,, —— Memorials of C., 1694.
,, Todd (H. J.) Vindication of C. &c., 1826.
Craon (Maurice de). Zwei altdeut. Rittermaeren. Moriz v. Craon—Peter v. Staufenberg [*by Egenolt. Texts*]. Neu hrsg. E. Schröder. 3e A. s8°. 1920
Crashaw (Richard). Eng. poems. Ed., w. intr. & notes by E. Hutton. s8°. 1901
Poems, Eng., Lat. & Greek. Ed. L. C. Martin. 8°. O. 1927
Steps to the Temple, w. The delights of the muses [*w. sep. tp. & pagin.*] 2nd ed. s8°. 1648
see Chalmers (R. C., *1st b.*) R. C.; "poet & saint," 1924.
Crashaw (William). *Decimarum &c. tabula. A tithing table. Comp. by W. C. [P2653]. s4°. 1676
Craster (Herbert Henry Edmund), *see* Bodleian Library. Summary cat. of Western MSS. in the B. L., w. ref. to the Oriental MSS. &c.; by F. Madan & C., v2i, 6, 1922–24.
Cratippus, *the historian.* C[1]. Hellenicorum fragm. Oxyrhynchia ed. J. H. Lipsius, *see* Kleine Texte, T138, 1916.
see Hellenica Oxyrhynchia cum C. fragm., 1909.
Crato ab Erffa (Joh. Fridericus). De annulo Gygis. [Diss.] s4°. *n.p.* [c. 1745]
Crauford (Alexander H. G.)
The religion of H. G. Wells & o. essays. s8°. 1909
Craufurd (James). The history of the house of Esté, until the death of Alphonsus. s8°. 1681
Craven, *ps., see* Carleton (John William).
Crawford (Charles). The Marlowe concordance, [p2, 3], 1912–13, *see* Bang (W.) Materialien, B34ii, iii, 1912–13.
Crawford (F. Marion).
Mr. Isaacs: a tale of mod. India. s8°. 1883
Paul Patoff. [n. ed.] s8°. 1890
Crawford (Henry S.) Hdbk. of carved ornament f. Irish mon. of Xtn. period. Pref. by R. A. S. Macalister. la8°. D. 1926
Crawford (Isabella Valancy), *see* Hale (K.) I. V. C. [biog. sk., anthology &c.], 1923.
Crawford (Osbert Guy Stanhope). Air survey & archaeology. [O. Survey Prof. Papers, N.S., No. 7]. 4°. 1924
Long barrows of the Cotswolds, area cov. by Sheet 8 of ½-inch O. Survey. la8°. Gloucester. 1925
Man & h. past. 8°. 1921
—— & **A. Keiller.** Wessex f. the air. With contrib. by R. C. C. Clay [&] E. Gardner. 4°. O. 1928
Crawford (Samuel John), *see* Bible: Anglo-Saxon. The Old Eng. version of the Heptateuch, Aelfric's Treatise on the Old & New Test. &c.; ed. w. intr. &c. by S. J. C., 1922.
Crawford & Balcarres (David Alexander Edward Lindsay, *27th/10th earl of*). Donatello. [reissue]. 8°. [1911]
Crawford & Balcarres (James Ludovic Lindsay, *26th/9th earl of*). Cat. of coll. of autograph letters & hist. doc. illust. hist. of Fr. Revol. & Napoleon, formed by Earl C., sold by Sotheby, Dec. 1924 *&* Apr. 1925. [2p *b. in* 1v.] 8°. 1924–25
see Bibliotheca. Bibl. Lindesiana, v7, Cat. of the philatelic library of the Earl of C.; by E. D. Bacon, re-issue, 1911; Suppl., 1926.
Crawfurd Papers, *see* Crawfurd (J.)
Crawfurd (George), *Scottish historian.* *A genealog. hist. of the royal &c. family of the Stewarts, 1034–1710. Prefixed, Gen. descr. of Renfrew &c. [*w. sep. pagin.*] sfol. E. 1710
Crawfurd (John), *F.R.S.* Crawfurd papers: offic. rec. rel. to the mission of J. C. to Siam, 1821. [Vajirañāṇa Nat. Lib]. la8°. Bangkok. 1915
The newspaper stamp & postage. [P2782]. 8°. 1836
Taxes on knowledge. [P2782]. 8°. 1836

Crawfurd (Oswald J. F.) Lyrical verse f. Eliz. to Victoria. Sel. &c. O. C., w. notes. s8°. 1896
Lyrical verse. Sel. & ed. C. [repr.] 2v. s8°. [1910]
Crawley (Alfred Ernest). The mystic rose, a study of prim. marriage &c. n. ed. rev. &c. by T. Besterman. 2v. 8°. 1927
Crawshay-Williams (*Lt.-Col.* **Eliot).**
5 Grand Guignol plays. s8°. 1924
Creagh (*Gen. Sir* **O'Moore).**
Autobiography. Intr. &c. by Sir C. E. Callwell. 8°. [1924]
Cream (Thomas Neill). The trial of T. N. C. Ed. W. T. Shore. [Notable Brit. trials]. 8°. [1923]
Crébillon *fils*. [†Jolyot de Crébillon (Claude Prosper)]. The sofa, a moral tale. Tr. w. introd. by B. Dobrée. [Broadway Lib. of 18th cent. Fr. lit.] 8°. [1927]
Le sylphe. s8°. 1873
see Palache (J. G.) Four novelists &c.; C. &c., 1926.
Creccelius (Joannes). Descr. & refut. ceremoniarum, gesticulationumque pontificiae missae. s8°. Magdeburgi. 1603
Credito Italiano, *see* Italy. Econ. resources of I., 1895–1920; publ. by the C.I., 2v, 1920.
Creedy (F.) Human nature in business. 8°. [1927]
Creevy (Thomas), *M.P.* Creevy papers: sel. f. corr. & diaries of T. C. Ed. Sir H. Maxwell. [repr.] 8°. 1923
Créhange (André). Chomage & placement. [C.E. for Internat. Peace]. 8°. 1927
Creide (Hartmann) [†Creidius], *1606–56*. Meditationes apostolico-epistolicae [*b. w.* Dorschaeus (J. G.) T. Aquinas, 1656]. s4°. Francofurti. 1665
Creighton (James). *Appeal to the candid &c. members of Establ. Church conc. irreg. preaching. [P2537]. s8°. *n.p.* 1786
Creighton (*Mrs.* **Louise),** *wife of bp. Creighton* [*ps.* Lois Hume].
The bloom off the peach. 2v. s8°. 1882
G. A. Selwyn, D.D., Bp. of New Zealand & Lichfield. s8°. 1923
The social disease & how to fight it. s8°. 1914
see Creighton (O.) Letters, 1883–1918; ed. L. C., 1920.
Creighton (Mandell), *bp. of (1) Peterborough, (2) London.*
The age of Elizabeth. 22nd impr. s8°. 1925
Creighton (Oswin).
Letters, 1883–1918. Ed. L. Creighton. 8°. 1920
Crell (Fortunatus), *see* Valentia (G. de). Redargutio inscitiarum & fraudum qui nonnulli theologici subsid. F. C. &c., 1590.
Crell (Heinrich Christian). Missae ad Indos sacrae legationis orig. & progr. 8°. L. [1727]
Crell (Johann) [Crellius].
see Musaeus (J.) Collegium controversiarum Becano, C. oppos., 1701.
,, Racovian Catechism. Catechesis Eccl. Polon. a J. C. recog., 1659; tr., 1818.
Crellius (Nicolaus), *see* Krell (N.)
Crellius (Samuel), *see* Zöllner (D.) Strict. libelli Cogit. nov. de primo & sec. Adamo [*by C.*], 1702.
Cremer, *Benedictine monk, see* Cremerus
Cremer (Bernhard Sebastian). Naziraeus sive comm. in legem Naziraeorum ad Num. Cap. 4. 1. &c. Acc. diss. in loc. Matth. 2. 23. de Jesu Nazoraeo. [*b. w. h.* Typologia, 1727]. s4°. Amstelædami. 1727
Summa theologiae supranat. s4°. Harderovici. 1722
Theologia naturalis. Ed. 2ª. auctior. s8°. Amstelædami. 1729
Typologia. In V. & N. Test. loca illust. [2p *in* 1v. pl *has add. tp.*: Prodromus typicus; p2 *has tp.*: Prophetico-typ. exercit. tetras, 1723]. s4°. Amstelædami. 1727
Cremer (Hermann). Biblico-theolog. lexicon of N. Test. Greek. 3rd Engl. ed. w. Suppl. Tr. by W. Urwick. 4°. E. 1886
Cremerus, *Benedictine monk, abbot of Westminster.* Testament, *see* Hermetic museum, v2, 1893.
Cremieux (Benjamin).
Panorama de la litt. ital. contemp. 4e éd. s8°. [1928]
Le premier de la classe. Roman. s8°. 1921
20e siècle. 9e éd. sl. s8°. [1924]
Crenius (Thomas), *ps., see* Crusius (T. T.)
Crépin (*Mr.*), *ps.*
*Hist. véritable de Mr. Crépin &c. [*no tp.*] obl. 8°. *n.d.*
Crepin (Pierre). Mahé de La Bourdonnais, Gouv. Gén. des Iles de France &c., 1699–1753. 8°. [1922]
Créqui Montfort (G. de) & E. Sénéchal de la Grange. Mission scient. en Amér. du Sud, *see* Chervin (A.) Anthropologie bolivienne, 3t, 1907–8.
Cresci (Migliore). Storia ital. [1524–46]; comm. U. G. Oxilia, *see* Regia Deput. Miscellanea, t43, 1907.
Crescini (Vincenzo). Contributo agli studi sul Boccaccio con doc. ined. 8°. Torino. 1887
see Dante Alighieri. Lectura D., Fiammetta di G. Boccaccio; conf. letta da V. C., 1913.
,, Floire et Blanchefleur. Il cantare di F. e B., 1889–99.
Crespi (Angelo). Contemp. thought of Italy. 8°. 1926
Crespi (Giuseppe Marie), *called Lo Spagnuolo, see* Voss (H.) G. M. C.; 29 riprod. con testo e cat., 1921.
Crespigny (*Lady* **Mary Champion De).** Letters of advice f. a mother to her son. 8°. 1803
Crespin (Jean) [Crispinus (J.)] *Acta martyrum eorum videlicet qui hoc sec. in Gallia, Germania, Anglia, Flandria, Italia constans dederunt nomen Evangelio &c. [*Tr. f. the French of J. C. by C. Baduellus*]. s8°. [Genevae]. 1556
Cressé (Auguste Jean Baptiste Bouvet de), *see* Bouvet de Cressè (A. J. B.)
Cressener (Drue), *D.D.* A demonstr. of the first princ. of the Protestant applic. of the Apocalypse &c. s4°. 1690
Cressini (Carlo), *see* Arano (A.) C. C., 1924 ?.
Cresson (William Penn). Diplomatic portraits. Europe & the Monroe Doct. 100 years ago. 8°. Boston. 1923
The Holy Alliance: the Europ. background of the Monroe Doct. [C.E. f. Int. Peace]. la8°. N.Y. 1922
Cresswell (Beatrix F.) Rambles in old Exeter. s8°. Exeter. 1927
Cresswell (Nicholas).
Journal, 1774–77. [Foreword by S. Thornely]. 8°. [1925]
Cressy (Edward). Outline of indust. hist. [repr.] s8°. 1925
Creswell (K. A. C.) The evolution of the minaret. [Repr. f. Burlington Mag. P2861]. 4°. 1926
see Cairo. Map, comp. by K. A. C. C., *n.d.*
Crétet (P. de Crousaz-), *see* Crousaz-Crétet (P. de).
Creutziger (Caspar) [Cruciger]. De judiciis piarum synodorum sententia, initio enarr. Symboli Niceni expos. s8°. Witebergæ. 1548
In epistolam Pauli ad Timotheum priorem Comm. &c. s8°. Argentorati. 1540
In Evang. Johannis enarr. s8°. Argentorati. 1546
Crèvecoeur (M. G. J. de), *calling himself Saint John de Crèvecoeur.* Sketches of 18 cent. America: more "Letters f. an Amer. farmer." Ed. H. L. Bourdin, R. H. Gabriel, S. T. Williams. 8°. New Haven. 1925
Crévélier (Jacques). La conscience de Sophie, *see* Œuvres libres, 74, 1927.
Crevenna (Pietro Antonio). Cat. raisonné de la coll. de livres de C. 6v. 4°. [Amsterdam]. 1776
Crew (Albert). Conduct of & procedure at public & company meetings. 6th ed., rev. & enl. s8°. 1920
Crew (F. A. E.) Animal genetics. 8°. 1925
Crewdson, *The family of, see* Foster (S. B.) Pedigrees of C. of Crook &c., 1890.
Crewe (Robert O. A. Crewe-Milnes, *1st marq. of*). The Roy. Soc. of Lit.: an outline, *see* Roy. Soc. of Lit. Essays &c., n.s., v6, 1926.
Criado y Domínguez (Juan P.)
Literatas españolas del siglo 19. Apuntes bibliog. 8°. 1889
Crichton-Browne (*Sir* **James).**
Stray leaves f. a physician's portfolio. 8°. [1927]
Victorian jottings f. an old commonplace book. 8°. [1926]
Crichton-Miller (Hugh), *see* Miller (H. C.)
Crignis-Mentelberg (Anna de). Herzogin Renata, die Mutter Maximilians des Gr. v. Bayern. s8°. Freiburg i. B. [1912]
Crimean. *Etude diplomat. sur la Guerre de Crimée, 1852–56, 2t, 1878, *see* Jomini (A. de).
Россія и Европа въ эпоху Кр. Войны (*tr. f.* Et diplom., 1886, *see* Jomini (Alex. de).
Criminal [Criminals]. *C. (The) recorder, or biog. sketches. By a student of the Inner Temple. 4v. s8°. 1804–09
*Lives of the most remarkable c., 3v, 1735, *see* Lives.
Cripps (Ernest C.) Plough Court: story of a notable pharmacy [*i.e.* Allen & Hanburys, Ltd.], 1715–1927. 8°. 1927
Cripps (Henry William). Pract. treatise on the law rel. to the Church & clergy. 7th ed., by A. T. Lawrence & Hon. R. S. Cripps. la8°. 1921
Cripps-Day (Francis Henry). On armour preserved in Eng. churches. With gen. bibliog. sfol. *p.p.* 1922
Crisianio (Giorgio), *see* Krijanich (Y. G.)
Crisp (Francis E. Fitzjohn). Essentials of the figure art. With mem. by E. Hutton. 8°. 1916
Crisp (*Sir* **Frank),** *Bart.* Mediæval gardens. Ed. C. C. Paterson, w. illust. f. orig. sources. 2v. 4°. [1924]

Crisp (Frederick Arthur). Memorial rings, Ch. II to William IV, in poss. of F. A. C. fol. *p.p.* 1908
see HOWARD (J. J.) & F. A. C., *edd.* Visitation of Engl. &c., Notes, v5 ; ed. F. A. C., 1903.
„ —— & —— Visit. of Engl. &c., v21, 1921.
Crisp (Tobias), *D.D. ; 1600–42.* Christ alone exalted, being Compl. works of T. C., cont. 52 sermons &c. Added, notes w. mem. by Dr. Gill. 4th ed., corr. 2v. 8°. 1791
Crispi (Francesco).
see PALAMENGHI-CRISPI (T.) F. C.: polit. interna, 1924.
„ SALVEMINI (G.) La politica estera di F. C., 1919.
Crispien (Arthur), *see* RADEK (C.) Masken sind gefallen, Antwort an C. &c., 1920.
Crispinus (Joannes), *see* CRESPIN (J.)
Crispolti (Crispolto) & G. Aureli. La politica di Leone XIII, da L. Galimberti a M. Rampolla su doc. ined. 8°. 1912
Crispolti (Filippo). Don Bosco, Leben u. Werk. Nach F. C. bearb. v. F. R. v. Lama. s8°. Freiburg i. B. 1922
Crista (Pietro), *see* CHRISTUS (P.)
Criste (Oskar), *see* JOHN (W.) Erzherzog Karl u. s. Armee ; mit Beiträgen v. O. C. &c., 1913.
Cristiani (Federico Nicoli), *see* NICOLI CRISTIANI (F.)
Cristiano (Giuseppe).
Egloghe pescatorie. [P2765]. 8°. Napoli. 1728
Cristifideles, *see* CHRISTIFIDELES.
Cristliche, *see* CHRISTLICHE.
Criterion, The. A quarterly review.
v1–6 (Oct. 1922–Dec. 1927). 8°. 1922–27
v4 *has title* The New Criterion.
v5, 6 *have title* The Monthly Criterion.
Critica (La). Rivista di letteratura, storia e filosofia. Diretta da B. Croce. v13–25 (1915–27). 8°. Napoli. [1915–27]
Critici. Critici sacri sive clar. virorum annotationes &c., 9t, 1695–1701 ; 1698, *see* PEARSON (J.)
Critopolus (Metrophanes), *see* KRITOPOULOS (M.)
Crittonius (Georgius). Augurium Romæ visum pro aede D. Ludovici, Nov. 1600. Ejusdem interpret. s4°. Parisiis. 1601
Cathedrae regiae Camerac. Querela [*b. w. h.* Augurium, 1601]. s4°. Parisiis. 1600
Crivelli (Carlo), *see* DREY (F.) C. C. u. h. Schule, 1927.
Crivelli (Gustavo Balsamo-), *see* BALSAMO-CRIVELLI (G.)
Croce, *The family of, see* CROCE (B.) Montenerodòmo ; storia di un comune e di due famiglie [C. &c.], 1919.
Croce (Benedetto).
Ariosto, Shakespeare e Corneille. [Scr. di storia lett. e polit.,14]. 8°. Bari. 1920
Il caso Gentile e la disonestà n. vita universit. ital. 8°. Bari. 1909
Cultura e vita morale. Intermezzi polemici. [Scr. varii, 2]. 2ª ed. 8°. Bari. 1926
F. P. Bozzelli & Giacinto de Sivo. [Estr. d. Atti dell' Accad. Pontan., v48. P2516]. la8°. Napoli. 1918
Una famiglia di patrioti [i Poerio] ed altri saggi storici &c. 8°. Bari. 1919
Le fonti della gnoseologia Vichiana. [Estr. d. Atti dell' Accad. Pontan., v42. P2516]. la8°. Napoli. 1912
Frammenti di etica. [Saggi fil., 6]. 8°. Bari. 1922
Giosuè Carducci. Studio crit. 2ª ed. 8°. Bari. 1927
Giov. Pascoli. Studio crit. n. ed., con aggiunte. 8°. Bari. 1920
Leonardo filosofo, *see* VINCI (L. DA). L. da V.: conf. fior., 1910.
La letteratura d. nuova Italia. [Scr. di storia lett. &c., 6]. 8°. Bari. 1915
Maria Cristina di Savoia, regina d. 2 Sicilie. s8°. Napoli. 1924
Montenerodòmo. Storia di un comune e di due famiglie. [P2423]. 8°. Bari. 1919
La novella di Andreuccio da Perugia. Conf. [Estr. dall' Arch.st.perleprov.napol.,v36] 8°. Bari. 1911
Nuovi saggi di estetica. [Saggi filos., 5]. 8°. Bari. 1920
Pagine sparse. Racc. da G. Castellano. Ser. 3. Mem., schizzi biog. &c. s8°. Napoli. 1920
Pescasseroli. 8°. Bari. 1922
La poesia di Dante. [Scr. di storia lett. &c., 17]. 8°. Bari. 1921
Poesia e non poesia. Note s. lett. europea del sec. 19. [Scr. di storia lett., 18]. 8°. Bari. 1923
Primi saggi. [Scr. varii, 1]. 8°. Bari. 1919
Ricerche e doc. Desanctisiani. [Estr. d. Atti d. Accad. Pontan., v45, 47]. [p]9, 10. la8°. Napoli. 1915–17
9, Dal carteggio ined. di A. C. de Meis.
10, Il centenario di F. de Sanctis.
Gli scritti di F. de Sanctis e la loro varia fortuna : saggio bibliog. &c. 8°. Bari. 1917
Storia del regno di Napoli. [Scr. di st. lett. &c., 19]. 8°. Bari. 1925
Storia d'Italia, 1871-1915. 2ª ed. 8°. Bari. 1928
Storia d. storiografia ital. nel sec. 19. [Scr. di st. lett. &c., 15, 16]. 2v. 8°. Bari. 1921
Sulla filosofia teologizzante &c. [Estr. d. Atti d. Accad. Pontan., v49. P2516]. la8°. Napoli. 1919
Teoria e storia d. storiografia. [Filos. come sci. d. spirito, 4]. 2ª ed. riv. 8°. Bari. 1920
Uomini e cose d. vecchia Italia. [Scr. di st. lett. &c., 20, 21]. 2s. 8°. Bari. 1927

Croce (Benedetto) [*continued*].
TRANSLATIONS.
Æsthetic as science of expression & gen. linguistic. Tr. by D. Ainslie. 2nd. ed. 8°. 1922
Ariosto, Shakespeare & Corneille. Tr. D. Ainslie. 8°. [1920]
Autobiography. Tr. R. G. Collingwood. Pref. by J. A. Smith. 8°. O. 1927
The conduct of life. Tr. A. Livingston. 8°. [1925]
The essence of æsthetic. Tr. D. Ainslie. s8°. 1921
European lit. in the 19th cent. [*f.* Poesia e non p.] Tr. w. intr. by D. Ainslie. 8°. 1924
Goethe. [Tr.] Intr. by D. Ainslie. 8°. [1923]
Grundlagen d. Politik. Übertr. H. Feist. 8°. München. 1924
The poetry of Dante. Tr. D. Ainslie. s8°. 1922
Theory & hist. of historiography. Tr. by D. Ainslie. 8°. [1921]
see CARR (H. W.) "Time" & "history" in contemp. philos., w. spec. ref. to C. &c., 1918.
„ CASTELLANO (G.) B. C., il filosofo, il critico, lo storico, con app. bibliog., 1924.
„ —— Introd. allo studio d. opere di B. C., note bibliog. e crit., 1919.
„ CRITICA (LA) ; rivista di lett., stor. e filos. ; dir. da B. C., 1915–.
„ DANTE ALIGHIERI. D.: essays in commem., 1321–1921 ; [by B. C. &c.], 1921.
„ PICCOLI (R.) B. C.: intr. to h. philosophy, 1922.
„ POWELL (A. E.) Romant. theory of poetry, in light of C.'s Æsthetic, 1926.
„ STRUCKMEYER (O. K.) C. & lit. criticism, 1921.
Croce (Ireneo della), *see* DELLA CROCE (I.)
Croce (Vincenzo Alsario dalla), *see* ALSARIO DALLA CROCE (V.)
Crockett (Samuel Rutherford). Rogues' island. s8°. [1926]
Crockett (William Shillinglaw). Berwickshire & Roxburghshire. [Camb. Co. Geog.] s8°. C. 1926
Crockford's Clerical Directory, 1921–22, 1924. la8°. 1921–24
Crocus (Cornelius). De vera Christi eccl. libelli duo, quorum alter a C. C. ed. ; alter a Jacobo Latomo conscr., libello P. Melanchthonis De eccl. respondet, &c. s8°. *n.p. n.d.* [c. 1545]
Ecclesia, ad confirmandam fidem catholic. dogmatum. [P2544]. s8°. Antverpiæ. 1536
Croese (Gerard). Hist. Quakeriana, usque ad recens natum schisma libri 3. Ed. 2ª. s8°. Amstelodami. 1696
Croft (George).
Gen. observat. conc. education. [P2668]. 8°. Hull. 1775
A plan of educ. delineated & vindic. &c. [P2668]. 8°. Wolverhampton. 1784
Croft (John), *F.S.A.* *Excerpta antiqua: or, a coll. of orig. MSS. 8°. York. 1797
Crofton (Morgan W.) & E. Kensington. Tracts on mechanics: Theory of work—Graph. solution of statical problems, by M. W. C.—Artillery machines, by E. Kensington. 2nd ed. 8°. 1881
Crofton (Zachary). 'Ανάληψις ἀνελήφθη, The fastning of St. Peter's fetters &c. or the efficacy &c. of the Solemn League & Covenant. [P2662]. s4°. 1660
Crofts (Freeman Wills).
Inspector French & the Cheyne mystery. s8°. [1926]
Inspector French's greatest case. s8°. [1924]
The Ponson case. s8°. [1921]
Crofts (J. E. V.) Life of Bp. Corbett, 1582–1635, *see* ENG. Assoc. Essays &c., v10, 1924.
Cröger (Carl). Gesch. Liv-, Ehst- u. Kurlands, 1159–1561. 2T. [*in 1v*]. 8°. St. Petersburg. 1867–70
Crohn-Wolfgang (Hermann Felix). Lettlands Bedeutung f. d. östl. Frage. [P2739]. 8°. 1923
Croiset (Alfred) & M. Croiset. Hist. de la litt. grecque. 3ᵉ éd., rev. & corr. t4, 5 [t5, 2ᵉ éd.] 8°. 1901–21
Croiset (Jean). *Spiritual (A) retreat for one day in every month. By a priest of the Soc. of Jesus. Tr. s8°. *n.p.* 1698
Croiset (Maurice), *see* CROISET (A.) & M. C. Hist. de la litt. grecque, t4, 5, 1901–21.
Croisset (Francis de), *ps.* [*i.e.* FRANZ WIENER].
Théâtre. Ed. E. Flammarion. 4[t]. s8°. [1919–22]
see FLERS (R., *marq.* DE) & F. DE C. Les nouveaux messieurs, 1926.
„ —— & —— Les vignes du Seigneur, 1927.
Croke (Richard), *D.D., 1489–1558, see* SHEPPARD (J. T.) R. C., 1919.
Croker, *The family of, see* FOSTER (J.) Rev. acc. of fam. desc. f. Francis Fox, app. pedigree of the Crokers, of Lineham &c., 1872.
Croker (*Mrs.* B. M.), *wife of Lt.-Col. John Croker.*
Some one else. n. impr. s8°. 1919
The Spanish necklace. s8°. Liv'l. *n.d.*
Croker (*Rt. Hon.* John Wilson). *The battles of Talavera. Poem. 8th ed. [*b. w.* Scott (G. E.) Waterloo, 1820]. 8°. 1810

Crollalanza (G. B. di). Diz. storico-blasonico d. famiglie nobili &c. ital. &c. 3v[in 1]. la8°. Pisa. 1886–90
Crollalanza (Goffredo di). Enciclopedia araldico-cavalleresca. Prontuario nobiliare. la8°. Pisa. 1876–77
Crollius (Georg Christian).
Originum Bipontinarum pars 1 [& 2]. s4°. Biponti. 1761–69
2, Hist. Comitum Geminipontis, v1.
Croly (David).
An index to the Tracts of the times; w. a. diss. 8°. O. 1842
Croly (David Goodman). Seymour & Blair: their lives & services. App. cont. a hist. of reconstruction. s8°. N.Y. 1868
Croly (George). *Paris in 1815. [*Poem, w. notes, b. w.* Scott (G. E.) Waterloo, 1820]. 8°. 1817
Croly (Herbert). Willard Straight. 8°. N.Y. 1924
Cromartie, *The earldom of, see* FRASER (*Sir* W.) The Earls of C., th. kindred, country &c., 2v, 1876.
Cromartie (George Mackenzie, *3rd earl of***),** *see* KILMARNOCK (W. B., *4th e. of*). Trials of K., C. &c. f. high treason, 1746, 1746.
Cromb (James).
The Highland Brigade: battles & heroes. 2nd ed. 8°. 1886
Crome (John).
see BAKER (C. H. C.) Crome, 1921.
,, CUNDALL (H. M.) The Norwich school [w. reprod. after] J. C. &c., 1920.
,, SMITH (S. C. K.) C., w. note on Norwich school, 1923.
Cromek (Robert Hartley), *see* MILLER (F.) A. Cunningham's contrib. to C.'s Rem. of Nithsdale & Galloway song, 1920.
Cromer (Evelyn Baring, *1st earl of***),** *see* TSCHISCHWITZ (W. v.) Rules for the conduct of the war-game: comp. &c. by E. B., 1872.
Cromer (Martin), *bp. of Ermeland, d. 1589.* De conjugio & coelibatu sacerdotum comm., ad S. Orechovium. s8°. Coloniæ. 1564
Oratio in synodo Cracov. nuper habita. [Ed. J. Cochlæus]. [P2544]. s8°. Moguntiæ. 1550
see POLONIA. Respublica Poloniæ &c., div. aut. (M. C. &c.), 1627.
Crommelynck (Fernand). Le cocu magnifique. Farce. s8°. 1921
Crompton (Iwan). Crompton "U 41" d. 2. "Baralong" Fall. Selbsterzählt. s8°. [1917]
Crompton (Richmal). Leadon Hill. s8°. [1927]
Crompton (Samuel), *inventor of the spinning mule, see* DANIELS (G. W.) Early Eng. cotton industry, w. some unpubl. letters of S. C., 1920.
Crompton (William), *the younger.*
*A remedy agst. superstition. s8°. 1667
Cromwell (Oliver).
Letters & speeches, w. elucid. By T. Carlyle. [Library ed. repr.], 5v [2 *wanting*]. 8°. *Chapman & Hall.* [1887–88]
see ALLPORT (H. R.) O. C. &c., 1922.
,, BETHELL (S.) *World's mistake in O. C., 1668.
,, DOUGLAS (W. S.) C.'s Scotch campaigns, 1650–51, 1899.
,, DRINKWATER (J.) C.: character st., 1927.
,, —— O. C.: play, 1921.
,, EXHIBITION of anc. female court costume worn at court of C. 1654, 1835.
,, FIRTH (*Sir* C. H.) O. C. & the rule of the Puritans, n. ed., 1923.
,, HASSEN (M.) & J. G. ULBRECHT. Characteres tyranni in O. C., 1712.
see LAACHE (R.) C. Bonde om C., 1924.
,, —— C. og Puritanerne i samtidens folk. satire, 1920.
,, —— C.'s regiment, 1925.
,, LAYARD (G. S.) The headless horseman, P. Lombart's engraving: Charles or C.?, 1922.
,, OSMASTON (F. P. B.) Cromwell: drama, 1906.
,, ROSEBERY (A. P. P., *5th e. of*). O. C.; eulogy & apprec., 1900.
,, RYE (W.) 2 Cromwellian myths: royal descent of O. C. &c., 1925.
,, SOUTHEY (R.) Sel. lives of C. &c., n. ed., 1849.
,, TAYLOR (G. R. S.) O. C., 1928.
,, WILSON (D. A.) Carlyle on C. &c., 1837–48, 1925.
Cromwell (Richard), *Lord Protector.* A Coll. of sev. passages in the addresses pres. to R. C., 1658, *see* JAMES EDWARD [STUART]. Congrat. &c., 1701.
Cromwell (Robert G. W. Bewicke-Copley, *baron***).** Cat. of library. Sold by Messrs Sotheby, Nov. 1925. [Illust. P2857]. 8°. 1925
Cronaca, *see* CHRONICA.
Cronaca delle belle arti, *see* BOLLETTINO D'ARTE: Suppl.
Cronberg (Hartmuth v.) [KRONBERG].
see BOGLER (W.) H. v. K.: e. Charakterstudie, 1897.
,, SICKINGEN (F. VON). Eyn Sendbrieff—Missive H. v. C. an F. v. S., 1522.

Crone (G. C. E.) Nederl. jachten, binnenschepen, visschersvaartuigen en daarmee verwante kleine zeeschepen, 1650–1900. Met e. verkorte vertaling in het Engelsch. [*w. sep. tp. & pagin.*] 4°. 1926
Cronenberg (Wilhelm). Half-tone on the American basis. Tr. W. Gamble. s8°. Bradford. 1896
Cronica, *see* CHRONICA.
Cronin (Patrick Henry), *see* HUNT (H. M.) Crime of the cent.; assassin. of P. H. C., 1889.
Cronshaw (H. B.) Oil shales. 8°. 1921
Silver ores. 8°. 1921
see IMPERIAL INSTITUTE. Petroleum; prep. jointly w. H.M. Petroleum Dept., w. co-op. of H. B. C., 1921.
Cronwright-Schreiner (Samuel Cron).
The life of Olive Schreiner. 8°. [1924]
Croocq (*l'abbé* **Ch. de).** Bergues aux 17 & 18 s. 8°. Bergues. 1924
Crook (James Walter).
German wage theories. 8°. N.Y., *Columbia Univ.* 1898
Crook (Thomas). Economic mineralogy: a pract. guide. 8°. 1921
Crook (William), *the younger.* Ireland & the cent. of American Methodism. s8°. 1866
James B. Gillman. s8°. Belfast. 1889
Crooke (William), *C.I.E.* Fight at the Gauna of Queen Bela. [*Text. & tr.* Repr. f. Ind. Antiquary, v54. P2851]. 4°. Bombay. 1925
Religion & folklore of N. India. Prep. f. press by R. E. Enthoven. 8°. O. 1926
Crookes (*Sir* **William).**
Dyeing & tissue-printing. s8°. 1882
The wheat problem. Rev., w. ans. to critics. 3rd ed., w. ch. on future wheat supplies by Sir R. H. Rew. s8°. 1917
see FOURNIER D'ALBE (E. E.) Life of Sir W. C., 1923.
Crooks (George Richard). The life of bp. Matthew Simpson of the Methodist Episcopal Church. 8°. N.Y. 1890
,, ,, ...8°. 1891
Crookshank (Charles H.) Hist. of Methodism in Ireland. 3v. 8°. Belfast. 1885–88
Crookshank (Francis Graham), *M.D.* The Mongol in our midst: st. of man & h. 3 faces. s8°. 1924
Crookshank (William). The hist. of state &c. of the Ch. of Scotland, f. the Restor. to Revol. 2nd ed. 2v. s8°. E. 1751
Crool (Peter). Poitiers, hist. & guide. s8°. Poitiers. [1920]
Croon (Theodorus van der). Acta quaedam eccles. Ultrajectinae, exhib. in def. archiepisc. &c. adv. scr. archiep. Mechlin. 4°. Hagæ-Comitum. 1737
Croonendael (Paul de), *seigneur de Vlieringhe.* Cronicque cont. l'estat anc. & mod. du pays & conté de Namur. Publ. par le Comte de Limminghe. 2p [*pagin. contin.*] 4°. Brux. 1879
Cropper, *The family of, see* CONYBEARE (F. A.) Dingle Bank, the home of the Croppers, 1925.
Cropper (L. Cuthbert). Book-keeping & accounts: text-book. 12th ed. rev. s8°. 1922
Crosbie (Andrew), *advocate, see* MILLER (F.) A. C.: reputed orig. of Paulus Pleydell in Guy Mannering, 1919; 2nd ed., 1925.
Crosby (Emily A.) Une romancière oubliée, Mme. Riccoboni: sa vie, s. œuvres &c. 8°. 1924
Crosby (*Sir* **John),** *see* THOMPSON (E.) Conc. Sir J. C. & h. hall, 1927.
Crosby (Josiah), *C.I.E.* Siam, *see* FOREIGN OFFICE. Handbooks, No. 74, 1920.
Crosby (Margaret).
A violin obligato & o. s. s8°. Boston. [U.S.] 1891
Crosfield (*Sir* **Arthur Henry).** Remin. of Kenwood & the northern heights. 8°. 1925
The settlement of the Near East, *see* ANGLO-HELLENIC LEAGUE, Publ. No. 45, 1922.
Crosfield (Helen G.)
Margaret Fox of Swarthmoor Hall. 8°. [1913]
Crosland (Newton). Apparitions: an essay. s8°. 1873
*The Eltham tragedy reviewed, by C. [*i.e.* N. C. P2827]. 8°. 1871
Crosland (Thomas William Hodgson).
The lord of creation. 8°. [1904]
Cross. *Masculine cross: hist. of anc. & mod. crosses, 1904, *see* MASCULINE.
Cross (Tom Peete). List of books &c. introd. to the bibliog. & methods of Eng. lit. hist. s8°. Chicago. [1919]
see PLOMER (H. R.) & T. P. C. Life &c. of L. Bryskett, 1927.

Cross (Trueman). Milit. laws of the U.S., prefixed The constit. of the U.S. [U.S., War Dept.] 8º. Wash. 1825
„ „ ....2nd ed. 8º. Wash. 1838
„ „ 3rd ed., under supervision of Capt. A. R. Hetzel. 8º. Wash. 1846
Cross (Wilbur Lucius).
Life & times of Sterne. n. ed. 2v. 8º. New Haven. 1925
Cross (William), *missionary, 1797–1842, see* HUNT (J.) Mem. of W. C. &c., 1846 ; 1861.
Crosse (Gordon). The religious drama. s8º. [1913]
Crosset de la Haumerie (—), *ps., see* COLONNA (F. M. P.)
Crossley (Frederick H.)
Eng. church monuments, 1150–1550. la8º. 1921
Crosswood Estate, *Co. Cardigan.* The Crosswood deeds, *see* NAT. LIB. OF WALES. Cal. of deeds &c. ; comp. by F. Green, v2, 1927.
Croston (James).
Hist. sites of Lancs. & Cheshire. la8º. M'ter. 1883
Nooks & corners of Lancs. & Cheshire. la8º. M'ter. 1882
Crosweller (William Thomas). The Gardeners' Company: hist., 1605–1907. 8º. *p.p.* 1908
Crotch (W. Walter), *see* FARROW (T.) & W. W. C. How to win the War, 1916.
Crottet (Alexandre). Hist. des églises réformées de Pons, Gemozac & Mortagne en Saintonge. 8º. Bordeaux. [1841]
Crouch (Nathaniel) [*ps.* RICHARD BURTON, ROBERT BURTON].
Hist. remarques, & obs. of London & Westminster. s8º. 1681
The wars in Eng., Scot. & Ireland dur. r. of Charles I, w. h. tryal &c. 10th ed. s8º. 1737
Croue (Jean), *see* COPEAU (J.) & J. C. Les frères Karamazov : drame, 1921.
Crousaz-Crétet (P. de).
Paris sous Louis XIV. 2t. 8º. [1922–23]
Crowder (*Mrs.* **Mary E.**), *form. M. E. Palgrave.* Blind Jem & h. fiddle. By the a. of " Wee Hunchie " &c. s8º. 1884
Crowder (Tom). Bardney Abbey. 8º. Horncastle. 1925
Crowder (William). Dwellers of the sea & shore. 8º. [1925]
Crowdy (W. M.) Burgundy & Morvan. Illust. by P. F. Gethin. With note on P. F. G. by C. Dodgson. 4º. [1925]
Crowe (Henry). Zoophilos ; moral treatment of animals. 2nd ed., enl. s8º. Bath. 1820
Crowe (Henry Stuart Wheatly-), *see* WHEATLY-CROWE (H. S.)
Crowe (John Henry Verinder).
Military history notes. [P2589]. 8º. Woolwich. 1907
see HOPPENSTEDT (J.) Problems in manœuvre tactics, after the German of J. H. by C., 1905.
Crowe (William), *schoolmaster at Croydon* [CROWAEUS (G.)] Elenchus scriptorum in S. Scr. tam Graec. quam Lat. &c. s8º. Londini. 1672
*An exact coll. or cat. of our Eng. writers on the Old & New Test. s8º. 1663
Crowell (Frances Ann), *see* CONANT (*Mrs.* F. A.)
Crowell (John Franklin). Govt. war contracts. [C.E. f. Int. Peace.] la8º. N.Y. 1920
Crowne (John). Dramatic works, w. mem. & notes. [D. o. t. R. *la. paper*]. 4v. s8º. E. 1873–74
Sir Courtly Nice : or, It cannot be (1685), *see* SUMMERS (M.), *ed.* Restoration comedies, 1921.
Crowther (D. Stoner). Cat. of mod. pictures &c., property of D. S. C., Capt. J. A. Harvey &c., sold by Christie, May 2, 1924. [*Illust.*] 8º. 1924
Crowther (J.), *see* CHANCELLOR (E. B.) Lost London : landmarks wh. have disappeared pictured by J. C. c. 1879–87, & descr. by E. B. C., 1926.
Crowther (Jonathan).
*The life of T. Coke. 8º. Leeds. 1815
A portraiture of Methodism. 8º. 1811
„ „ ....2nd ed. 8º. 1815
Crowther (Samuel).
see FORD (H.) My life & work, by H. F. in collab. w. S. C., 1922 ; 24.
„ —— Today & tomorrow ; by H. F. in collab. w. S. C., 1926.
Crowthers (Thomas). Rare ship models &c. sold, 1924, *see* HOWE (R. G. P. C., *4th e.*)
Croxall (Samuel), *see* ÆSOP. Fables : w. applic. by S. C., 1825.
Croxton (Frederick E.) Unemployment in Columbus, Ohio, 1921–25, *see* UNITED STATES : LABOR. Bull. 409, 1926.
Croydon.
*The C. railway & its adjacent scenery. [P2586]. s8º. [1839]

Crozet-Fourneyron (Marcel).
Invention de la turbine. Préf. de G. Kœnigs. la8º. [1927]
Crozier (William Armstrong). Crozier's general armory : reg. of Amer. families entitled to coat armor. 8º. N.Y. 1904
Cruciger (Caspar), *see* CREUTZIGER (C.)
Crucius (Vincentius Alsarius), *see* ALSARIO DALLA CROCE.
Crudelitas. Crudelitatis Calvin. exempla duo recentiss. ex Anglia. Cont. editum contra Catholicos ; mortem comitis Northumbriae. s8º. [Cologne ?] 1585
Cruden (Alex.)
A complete concordance to the O. & N. Test. 2p [*in* 1v.] 4º. 1734
Concordance to the N.T. s8º. 1833
Cruden William). Hymns. s8º. Aberdeen. 1761
Crüger (Theodor). Obs. ad hist. censurae eccl. &c. 4 diss. (1, Praes. J. G. Jano, prop. Th. C. ; 2–4, Praeses Th. C., resp. J. Spärcke &c.) [P426]. s4º. Vitembergæ. [1718]
Cruickshank (Alfred Hamilton). Massinger & 'The two noble kinsmen.' Lect. [P2683]. 8º. O. 1922
Philip Massinger. 8º. O. 1920
Thomas Parnell : or what was wrong w. the 18th cent., *see* ENGLISH ASSOC. Essays &c., v7, 1921.
Cruikshank (*Col.* **Ernest Alexander).** Document. hist. of the campaign upon the Niagara frontier, 1812[–14]. Coll. & ed. f. the Lundy's Lane Hist. Soc. by E. C. 9p. 8º. Welland. [1896–1908]
Cruikshank (George). Bachelor's own book, progress of Mr. Lambkin. [P2861]. 4º. Glasgow. [1883]
The bands in the parks. Picked up & publ. by G. C. [P2701]. 4º. *n.d.*
Cruikshank (Percy), *see* PIERCE (WILLIAM). *Full rep. of gt. gold robbery [trial of W. P. *&c.*], illust. by P. C., 1859.
Crull (Cornelius). Orationes jubilares duae, de heroica electorum Saxoniae constantia in relig. evang. 2p. *in* 1v. s4º. Witebergae. 1630
Crum (John Macleod Campbell). The original Jerusalem Gospel, essays on document Q. 8º. 1927
Crum (Walter Ewing). A Coptic palimpsest. [Repr. f. Proc. of Soc. of Bibl. Arch. P2794]. 8º. 1897
Eusebius & Coptic Church hist. [*Repr. f.* Soc. of Bibl. Archaeol. P2791]. 8º. 1902
Der Papyruscodex saec. 6–7 d. Phillippsbibl. in Cheltenham Kopt. theolog. Schriften. Hrsg. u. übers. v. W. E. C Beitr. v. A. Ehrhard. [Schr. d. Wiss. Gesells. in Str., H18] la8º. Str. 1915
see WADI SARGA. Coptic & Greek texts f. the excav^{s}. by the Byz. Research Acc., 1922.
Crump (Charles George) & E. F. Jacob. The legacy of the Middle Ages. [*By var. wr^{s}.*] Ed. C. G. C. & E. F. J. 8º. O. 1926
Crump (Lucy), *see* MORNAY (C. DE). A Huguenot family in the 16 cent. : mems. of P. de Mornay ; tr. L. C., w. intr. 1926.
Crump (M. Marjorie). The growth of the Æneid. s8º. O. 1920
Crus (Luis Felis). Manifesto das ostillidades, 1651. Publ E. Prestage. 8º. Coimbra. 1919
Cruse (Amy). The shaping of Eng. lit. 8º. [1927]
Crusius (Artur Baumgarten-), *see* BAUMGARTEN-CRUSIUS (A.)
Crusius (Christian August). Abh. v. d. Ueberbleibseln d Heidenthums in d. Meynungen v. Tode. Übers. [P1041]. s8º. L. 1765
Hypomnemata ad theologiam propheticam. 3p *in* 3t. s8º. Lipsiae. 1764–78
Crusius (Jacob Andreas). Witikindus, sive de Witikind vita &c. fol. Mindae. 1679
Crusius (Martinus), *prof. of Greek at Tübingen.* Turcogræcia libri octo. A M. C. Gr. & Lat. ed. fol. Basileae. [1584
Crusius (Otto), *see* HERODAS. Mimiamben d. H. : Deut. mi Einl. &c. [v.] O. C., 2^{e} A., 1926.
—— **& R. Herzog.** Der Traum d. Herondas. [aus Philologus, B79, H4]. 8º. L. 1924
Crusius (Thomas Theodor) [*ps.* CRENIUS (THOMAS)]. Fasc dissertationum histor.-critico-philolog. &c. Coll. a T. C. s8º. Rotterdami. 1691
Fascis [1–5] exercitationum philol.-historic., coll., rec., emend &c. a T. Crénio. 5t. s8º. Lugduni in Batavis. 1687–1701
see BOSIUS (J. A.) Intr. in notit. scr. J. F. Buddei, J. G Meuscheni, & T. C. &c., 1723.
Crutius (G.)
Monita Calvinistarum. s8º. Coloniae Agrippinæ. 161?
Cruttwell (*Miss* **Maud).** The princess des Ursins. 8º. [1927
Cruz (F. A. D'), *see* D'CRUZ (F. A.)

Cruz (Ramon de la). 5 sainetes inéd., con otra a él atrib.; publ. C. E. Kany, *see* REVUE HISPANIQUE, t60, 1924.

Crystall (Thomas), *abbot of Kinloss; d. 1535, see* FERRERIUS (J.) Hist. Abbatium de Kynlos: una vita T. C. Abbatis, 1839.

Csáky (*count* **Stephen).** Responsibility of Hungarian nation in the War. [P2567]. s8°. 1921

Csergheö (Géza v.) Adel v. Ungarn sammt d. Nebenländern d. St. Stephans-Krone; bearbt. G. v. C. & Suppl., *see* SIBMACHER (J.), *ed.* Wappenbuch, B4xv, 1893–94.

Csipkes (György) [*ps.* THYSANODES (GEORGIUS NICOLAI)]. Molimen Sisyphium. Frustaneitas conatus istius G. B[arsony] E. V. P. S. S. C. R. M. C. C. reformatos in Ungaria, non esse Confess. Helveticae, probare. s4°. Theopoli Hypozygiodae. 1672

Csoma (Sándor), *Körösi* [ALEX. CSOMA DE KÖRÖS].
A dict.; Tibetan & Engl. 4°. 1834
Gram. of the Tibetan lang. in Eng. 4°. Calcutta. 1834

Ctesias [KTESIAS]. Anc. India as descr. by K.; a tr. of the abridg. of h. Indika by Phôtios &c., by J. W. McCrindle, 1882, *see* MACCRINDLE (J. W.)

Cuba. Col. de docs. inéd. de Ultramar, s2, t1, 4, 6, Isla de C., 1885–91, *see* COLECCIÓN.

Cubberley (Ellwood Patterson). The history of educ. 8°. [1920]
Readings in hist. of educ.: sources &c. 8°. Boston. [1920]

Cube (Johann v.) [WONNECKE (JOHANN)]. [Hortus sanitatis. *In German. Also called* Ein Gart d. Gesuntheit & Herbarius. *Pr.* P. Schöffer, Mainz, 1485. *Facs., w.* Nachtrag *ent.* Die Kräuterbücher d. 15. u. 16. Jhdts., *by* W. L. Schreiber. *no tp.*] la8°. [München. 1924]

Cubitt (George), *Wesleyan minister.* Obs. on Dr. S. Warren's pamph. agst. the Wesleyan Instit. In a letter to Rev. J. Taylor. [P449]. 8°. 1834

Cubí y Soler (Mariano). La frenolojía. Lecciones &c. 8°. Barcelona. 1853

Cuchullin, *see* GRUAIDH GHRIANSHOLUS. Pursuit of G. G. [*C. legend*]; ed. & tr. C. O'Rahilly, 1924.

Cuckfield, *Sussex.* Parish registers of C., 1598–1699. Ed. W. C. Renshaw. [Sussex Rec. Soc., v13]. 8°. 1911

Cuckson (John). A brief hist. of the First Church in Plymouth, 1606–1901. s8°. Boston. [Mass.] 1902

Cudesch [CODASCH; CUDASCHET]. *Codasch da liger per la sagonda classa d. scolas elementaras Rumanschas an dialect de Surmeir. Tr. antras ena soc. scolastica. s8°. Coira. 1857
*Cudesch da scoula. Compost e publ. per uorden del lodevol Cussagl. d'educ. cantonal. s8°. Coira. 1856
Seguond cudaschet per las scoulas dell' Engiadin' ota. s8°. Coira. 1860

Cudmore (P.) Civil govt. of the States, & the constit. hist. of the U.S. 8°. N.Y. 1875

Cudsemius (Petrus) [CUTSEMIUS]. Saxonia Catholica. [*b. w.* Stalenus (J.) Papissa monstrosa, 1639]. s8°. Coloniae Agrippinae. 1621

Cudworth (Ralph). The true intellectual system of the universe, w. a disc. conc. the Lord's Supper. 2nd ed., w. Acc. of life &c. of the a. by T. Birch. 2p *in* 1v. 4°. 1743

Cudworth (William), *of Bradford.* Hist. of Bolton & Bowling (townships of Bradford). 8°. Bradford. 1891

Cuenca (Carlos Luis de). Juan el Tonto. s8°. [1923]

Cuénot (Lucien). L'adaptation. s8°. 1925
La genèse des espèces animales. 2e éd., ent. refondue. 8°. 1921

Cuervo (Rufino José). Dicc. de construccion y regimen de la lengua castellana. t1, 2 (A–D). [*no more publ.*] la8°. Paris. 1886–93

Cues (*card.* **Nicolas de),** *see* CUSA (*card.* N. DE).

Cueto (Leopoldo Augusto de), *aft. Marqués de Valmer.* Hist. crit. de la poesía castellana en el siglo 18. 3a ed. corr. y aum. 3t. s8°. 1893

Cueva (Alphonso de la), *marq. de Bedmar, cardinal, see* VENETA. Squitinio d. liberta v., [*attr. to C.*], 1612.

Cueva (Gutierre de la), *bp. of Palencia, d. 1469, see* HISP. SOC. OF AMER. Tombs, 1927.

Cueva (Juan de la). Comedia de la muerte d. Rey don Sancho &c., *see* LOMBA Y PEDRAJA (J. R.) Teatro ant. a L. de Vega, 1924.
Comedias y tragedias. [Est. biog. &c. por F. A. de Icaza. Soc. de Bibliofilos Esp., 40]. 2[t]. 8°. 1917

Cuevas (Julian Zarco), *see* ZARCO CUEVAS (J.)

Cuevas (Luis Gonzaga), *see* GONZAGA CUEVAS (L.)

Cugnoni (Giuseppe). Notizia d. vita &c. d. princ. A. Chigi Albani. [Nozze Chigi-Aldobrandini. N123]. la8°. 1893

Cuisinier (Jeanne). Jules Laforgue. 8°. 1925

Cujas (Jacques) [†CUJACIUS]. Opera ad Paris. Fabrot. ed. auct. & emend. 2p [*in*] 11t. [t11, Index]. fol. Venetiis [&] Mutinae. 1758–83
[*p1, i.e. t1–3, Venet. 1758; p2, t4–11, Mutinae, 1777–83*]

Culley (George). Obs. on live stock. 4th ed., w. app. 8°. 1807

Cullum (Gery Milner-Gibson-), *see* MILNER-GIBSON-CULLUM (G.)

Culloden Papers. More C. P., 1626–1745. Ed. D. Warrand. 3v. la8°. Inverness. 1923–27

Cullum (Ridgwell). The candy man. s8°. [1926]

Culpeper (Nicholas). Complete herbal: annex. h. Eng. physician enl. & Key to physic &c. s4°. 1815

Culpin (Millais). Spiritualism & the new psychology. Explan. of phenomena &c. Intr. by L. Hill. s8°. 1920

Cultrera (Giuseppe). Vasi dipinti d. Museo di Villa Giulia, *see* REALE ACCAD. D. LINCEI. Mon. ant., v24, 1916.

Cumberland, *County.* Feet of fines, C. [1547–1603]. Extr. f. publ. rec. by J. P. Steel. 8°. *p.f.p.c. n.d.*
Feet of fines, C. dur. the r. of Henry VIII. Extr. f. the publ. recs. by J. P. Steel. [P2433]. 8°. *f.p.c.* [1913]

Cumberland (Ernest Augustus William Adolphus George Fred., *3rd duke of), duke of Brunswick-Lüneburg.*
Cat. of a coll. of miniatures, the property of Duke of C., comp. by Dr. Williamson. 4°. *p.p.* 1914
Cat. of tapestries f. coll. of Duke of B.-L., old French furniture, the property of a lady &c., sold by Christie, April 3, 1924. [*Illust.*] la8°. [1924]

Cumberland (George Clifford, *3rd earl of***),** *see* WILLIAMSON (G. C.) George, 3rd earl of C., 1558–1605, life & voyages, 1920.

Cumberland (Gerald), *ps.* [*i.e.* C. F. KENYON].
The poisoner. s8°. 1921
Tales of a cruel country. s8°. 1919

Cumberland (Richard), *LL.D., dramatist.*
The Battle of Hastings. Tragedy. 8°. 1778
The box-lobby challenge, *see* INCHBALD (*Mrs.* E.) Mod. theatre, v5, 1811.
Brothers, *see* INCHBALD (*Mrs.* E.) Brit. theatre, v18, 1808.
Calvary; a poem. s8°. D. 1794
The Carmelite. 3rd ed. 8°. 1785
" " *f. a. c., see* †INCHBALD (E.) Mod. th., v5, 1811.
False impressions, *see* †INCHBALD (E.) Mod. th., v5, 1811.
*The fashionable lover. 8°. 1772
First love, *see* INCHBALD (E.) Brit. th., v18, 1808.
The impostors, *see* †INCHBALD (E.) Mod. th., v6, 1811.
The Jew, *see* INCHBALD (E.) Brit. th., v18, 1808.
Mems., wr. by himself. 4°. 1806
" " Suppl. [*b. w.* Mems.] 4°. 1807
The mysterious husband, *see* †INCHBALD (E.) Mod. th., v5, 1811.
The natural son, *see* †INCHBALD (E.) Mod. th., v5, 1811.
*The note of hand; or, trip to Newmarket. 8°. 1774
*The summer's tale, a mus. comedy. 8°. 1765
West Indian, *see* INCHBALD (E.) Brit. th., v18, 1808.
Wheel of fortune, *see* INCHBALD (E.) Brit. th., v18, 1808.

Cumberland (William Augustus, *duke of***),** *1721–65.* *The book of the chronicles of W., d. of C.: rise & progress of late rebellion &c. Added, an abstract of the life of the earl of Kilmarnock; concl. w. mem. of life of Jenny Cameron. [P536]. s8°. [1746 ?]
see CHARTERIS (*Hon.* E.) W. A., Duke of C. & the Seven Years' War, 1925.

Cumin (William), *see* BUCHAN (W. C., *earl of*).

Cuming (E. D.), *see* SURTEES (R. S.) R. S. S., 1803–64; by himself & E. D. C., 1924.

Cumming (Caroline King) & W. W. Pettit, *edd.* Russ.-Amer. relations, 1917–20. Doc. &c. 8°. N.Y. 1920

Cumming (Constance Frederica Gordon). The inventor of the numeral-type for China [*i.e.* W. H. Murray]. n. ed. s8°. 1899

Cumming (Hanway Robert). A brigadier in France, 1917–18. Intrs. by W. Robertson & D. Campbell. s8°. [1922]

Cumming (*Sir* **John Ghest).** Bibliography rel. to India (1900–26). la8°. *n.p.* [1927]
A contrib. tow. a bibliography dealing w. crime. 2nd ed. [*rev. in MS. to Feb. 1927*]. 8°. Calcutta. 1916

Cummings (Homer), *see* DEMOCRATIC NAT. COMMITTEE. Democr. doctrine; keynote speech [of H. C.] &c., 1920.

Cummings (J. P.) Argument of C. C. Whittelsey, 1865, on appeal of J. P. C. [*no tp.*]. [P2625]. 8°. *n.d.*

Cummins (Thomas J.), *see* DUNPHY (T.) & T. J. C. Remark. trials, 1870.

Cummy, *ps., see* CUNNINGHAM (ALISON).

Cumont (Franz). After life in Roman paganism. Lect., Yale. 8°. New Haven, *Yale.* 1922
Les mystères de Mithra. 3e éd. rev. 8°. 1913

Cumont (Franz) [*continued*].
La plus anc. géog. astrolog. [Sonderdr. aus Klio, B9. P2789]. la8°. Leipzig. 1909
Works in ACAD. DES INSCR.: FOND. PIOT. Mon.
L' "Aphrodite à la tortue" de Doura-Europos, 1924. [27.]
Le Culte égypt. & le mysticisme de Plotin, 1921–22. [25.]
"Le sacrifice du tribun romain Terentius" & les Palmyréniens à Doura, 1923. [26.]
see BRUSSELS. Musées Roy. des Arts Décor. &c. Cat. des sculpt. &c. par F. C., 1898.
„ UNION ACAD. INTERNAT. Cat. des mss. alchim. grecs, 1924–27.

Cumston (Charles Greene). Intr. to the hist. of medicine, to end of 18th cent. With essay on the rel. of hist. & philos. to m. by F. G. Crookshank. 8°. 1926

Cunaeus (Joan), *see* SPEELMAN (C.) Journaal der reis van den gezant der O. I. Compagnie J. C. naar Perzië, 1651–52; uitg. door A. Hotz, 1908.

Cunæus (Petrus).
De republica Hebræorum libri 3. s8°. Lugduni Batav. 1617
„ „ ....ed. nova. s4°. Lugduni Batav. 1732
Of the common-wealth of the Hebrews. Tr. by C[lement] B[arksdale]. s8°. 1653

Cunard Steamship Company, *see* HURD (A. S.) A merchant fleet at war [C. S. Co., 1914–18], 1920.

Cundall, Downes & Co., *see* WELLS CATHEDRAL. Archit. details &c.: photogr. by C., D. & Co., 1865.

Cundall (Frank).
The Darien venture. [Hisp. Soc. of Amer.] s8°. N.Y. 1926
Jamaica's part in the Great War, 1914–18. la8°. 1925
see JAMAICA. J. in 1924: hdbk. &c.; by F. C., 1924.

Cundall (Herbert Minton). Bygone Richmond. la8°. 1925
Masters of water-colour painting. With intr. by C. Ed. G. Holme. [Studio Winter No. 1922–23]. 4°. 1922–23
The Norwich school [w. reprod. after] J. Crome, J. S. Cotman &c. Ed. G. Holme. [Studio: Spec. No.] la8°. 1920
Sudbrook & its occupants. 8°. 1912

Cundall (J. W.) "Pipes & tobacco." 8°. [1901]

Cundall (L. B.) & T. Landman. Wales, an econ. geog. 8°. 1925

Cundill (John Ponsonby). A dict. of explosives. Re-arr. &c. by J. H. Thomson. 2nd ed. 8°. 1895

Cuneo. Cronache ant. al sec. 17 conc. la storia di C. &c. [Chron. Cunei (1120–1484) libri 3—Cronaca dal 1484 al 1570 di Grasso Dalmazzo—De gestis Antonii Torresani brevis narr.], ed. D. Promis, *see* REGIA DEP. DI STORIA PATRIA. Misc., t12, 1871.

Cunha (Luis da). Carta ao Card. Acciaioli para sahir da Corte de Lisboa. Lettre &c. [*Port. & Fr.*], *see* PORTUGAL. Recueil de decrets &c., Suite, 1760.

Cunha (Simon A.) [*form.* OU LI YU-CHAN], *1631–1718*, *see* TCHANG (M.) & P. DE PRUNELÉ. Le père S. A. C., 1914.

Cuningham (Thomas), *of Campvere.* Journal, 1640–54, w. h. Thrissels-banner & explic. thereof. Ed. E. J. Courthope. [Scot. Hist. Soc., s3, v11]. 8°. E. 1928

Cuninghame (John), *of Craigends.*
Diary. Ed. J. Durham. 8°. C. 1919

Cunliffe (E. F.) Verses at sunset. 8°. 1899

Cunliffe (John William), *see* BACOURT (P. DE) & J. W. C. French lit. dur. last half-cent., 1923.

Cunliffe (Richard John).
A lexicon of the Homeric dialect. 8°. 1924

Cunliffe-Owen (*Lady* Marguerite), *wife of Fred. Philip Lewis Cunliffe-Owen.* *The martyrdom of an Empress. [2nd ed.] 8°. 1899

Cunningham (*Major-Gen. Sir* Alex.) Anc. geog. of India. Ed., w. intr. & notes by S. M. Sastri. 8°. Calcutta. 1924

Cunningham (Alison). Cummy's diary. Diary kept by R. L. Stevenson's nurse, A. C., dur. 1863. Pref. & notes by R. T. Skinner. la8°. 1926

Cunningham (Allan), *botanist, see* MARRIOTT (*Mrs.* C. B.) Early explorers in Australia, Diary of A. C., 1817–18, 1925.

Cunningham (Allan), *poet.* The songs of Scotland, anc. & mod.; w. intr. & notes. 4v. 8°. 1825
see MILLER (F.) A. C.'s contrib. to Cromek's Rem. of Nithsdale & Galloway song, 1920.

Cunningham (Ebenezer). Relativity, the electron theory & gravit. 2nd ed. 8°. 1921

Cunningham (George H.)
London: hist., buildings &c. in alphab. order. 8°. 1927

Cunningham (Gustavus Watts). Problems of philosophy. Foreword by Visct. Haldane. 8°. [1925]

Cunningham (John). Poet. works. Coll. by T. Park. s8°. 1805

Cunningham (John), "*sorcerer,*" *see* FIAN (*Dr.*)

Cunningham (Joseph Thomas). Hormones & heredity. 8°. 1921

Cunningham (Peter), *F.S.A.* Hdbk. of London, past & pres. n. ed., rev. & corr. [*With MS. addit. & cuttings by C. A. Ward*]. *b. in* 8v. 4°. 1850

Cunningham (William), *D.D., principal of F.C. Coll. of Edinburgh.*
Discussion on Church principles: Popish, Erastian, & Presbyterian. 8°. E. 1863
Historical theology. 2v. 8°. E. 1863
The Reformers; & the theology of the Reformation. 8°. E. 1862

Cunningham (William), *D.Sc., D.D., Trin. Coll., Cam., 1849–1919.*
Mon. of Eng. municipal life. Ed. D. H. S. Cranage. s8°. 1920
The story of Cambridgeshire. 6 lects. s8°. C. 1920
see BRIT. ACAD. Proc., v9, Obit. not., by W. R. Scott, 1919–20.

Cunnington (B. Howard). Annals of the borough of Devizes: extr. f. Corp. Records, 1555–1791. la8°. Devizes. 1925

Cunnington (M. E.), *wife of B. H. Cunnington.* Early iron age inhabited site at All Cannings Cross Farm, Wilts. Descr. of excav. &c. by Mr. & Mrs. B. H. C., 1911–22. 4°. Devizes. 1923

Cunnison (J.), *see* SCOTT (W. R.) & J. C. Industries of the Clyde Valley dur. the War, 1924.

Cuno (Rudolf). Der Kampf um d. Ruhr. 8°. L. 1923

Cunow (Heinrich). Die Marxsche Gesch.-Gesells.-u. Staatstheorie. Grundzüge d. M.-Soziologie. 2B. 8°. 1920–21

Cuntz (Otto), *see* PTOLEMY, *geographer.* Die Geogr. d. P. Hss., Text u. Unters. v. O. C., 1923.

Cuoco (Vincenzo). Platone in Italia. A cura di F. Nicolini. v2. 8°. Bari. 1924
Scritti vari. A cura di N. Cortese e F. Nicolini. 2p. 8°. Bari. 1924

Cupar. Eccl. records: sels. f. minutes of presbyteries of St. Andrews & Cupar, 1641–98, 1837, *see* SAINT ANDREWS.

Cupar-Angus. Rental book of the Cistercian Abbey of Cupar-Angus, w. the breviary of the register. Ed. C. Rogers [Grampian Club]. 2v. 8°. 1879–80

Cupid. Book of C.: anthology f. Eng. poets, 1909, *see* NEWBOLT (*Sir* H. J.)

Cuq (Edouard). Les nouv. fragments du code de Ḫammourabi sur le prêt à intérêt & les sociétés, *see* ACAD. DES INSCR. Mém. de l'Inst., t41, 1920.

Curaçao. Naam-lyst van de Heeren d. Regeeringe &c. op 't Eyland C. &c. [P2614]. s8°. A. 178-

Curaçao, *Steamship, see* NOUHUYS (J. W. VAN), *ed.* De eerste Nederl. Transatlant. stoomvaart in 1827 van Z. M. Stoompakket Curaçao, d1, 1927.

Curate (Jacob), *ps., see* CALDER (ROBERT).

Curcellæus (Stephanus), *see* COURCELLES (ETIENNE DE).

Curci (Carlo Maria), *see* SAVARESE (G. B.) La civiltà mod difesa contro la rip. al lib. La nuova Italia [*by C.*], 1881.

*__Cure__ (The) of evil-speaking: sermon on Matt. xviii, 15–17 1777, *see* WESLEY (J.)

Curé (Le) de S. Sulpice, *ps., see* HAMON (A. J. M.)

Curel (*le vte.* François de).
La comédie du génie. s8°. 1921
Disc. pour la récept. de F. de C. [*on* P. Hervieu. Rép. de E. Boutroux. Acad. Fr., 8 mai 1919. P2869]. 4°. 1919
L'envers d'une sainte. Comédie. ed. déf. s8°. 1921
L'ivresse du sage. Comédie. 8°. 1921
Terre inhumaine. Drame. la8°. 1923
Théâtre complet. 6t. s8°. 1920–24
1, La danse devant le miroir—La figurante.
2, L'envers d'une sainte—Les fossiles.
3, l'invitée — La nouv idole.
4, Le repas du lion—La fille sauvage.
5, Le coup d'aile—L'âme en folie.
6, La comédie du génie—L'ivresse du sage.
see BLANCHART (P.) F. de C. s. œuvre, 1924.

Cureus (Joachimus), *see* *EXEGESIS perspicua &c. de sacr coena [*by J. C.?*], 1574.

Curia Regis, *see* COURT OF KING'S BENCH.

Curiander (Abel). Vitae operumque J. Drusii editorum de lineatio &c. [*b. w.* Andres (J. F.) Vida de S. Orencio 1648]. s4°. Franekerae. 161-

Curie (Pierre), *see* CURIE (*Mme.* S.) P. C., 1924.

Curie (*Mme.* Sklodowska), *wife of Pierre Curie.*
Pierre Curie. s8°. 192-

Curières de Castelnau (de), *see* CASTELNAU (DE C. DE).

Curieuse [CURIEUSER]. Curieuse, u. mit 800 Bildern erleut 252 Bibl. Kern-Sprüche, 1687, *see* BILDER-BIBEL.

*Curieuser Geschichts-Calender M. Lutheri &c., 1698, *see* LUTHER (M.)

Curiis (Joannes de), *Dantiscus, bp. of Ermeland, see* LISKE (J.) Viajes de extranjeros por España y Portugal en los siglos 15, 16 & 17: J. D. (1519–31) &c., 1878.

Curio (Coelius Secundus) [*ps.* MONTFORDIUS (B.)]. Dalle epistole di C. S. C. [1543–53], *see* PALADINO (G.) Opusc. &c. di Riform. ital., v2, 1927.

Pasquillus ecstaticus, unà cum aliis dialogis. Adj.: quaestiones Pasquilli, in futuro concilio a Paulo III indicto, disputandae &c. [*2nd ed.? 304 numbered pages*]. s8°. *n.p., n.d.* [c. 1550]

see CHÂTEILLON (S.) De haereticis an sint perseq. &c. (Basilii Montfordii refut.), 1554.

Curle (Alexander Ormiston). The treasure of Traprain: a Scottish hoard of Roman silver plate. 4°. Glasgow. 1923

Curle (James Herbert). This world of ours. s8°. [1921]

To-day & to-morrow: the testing period of the White Race. 8°. 1926

Curle (Richard Henry Parnell). Into the East. Notes on Burma & Malaya. Pref. by J. Conrad. 8°. 1923

Wanderings. A bk. of travel & remin. 8°. 1920

Curll (Edmund), *see* STRAUS (R.) The unspeakable C.: added, list of h. bks., 1927.

Curran (*Rt. Hon.* **John Philpot**), *Master of the Rolls in Ireland, see* PHILLIPS (C.) C. & h. contemps., 4th ed., 1851.

Currency. *Elem. proposit. illust. of the princ. of c., 1819, *see* DRUMMOND (H.)

Currie (Jessie Monteath). The hour of splendour. s8°. [1922]

Curry (H. Ida). Public child-caring work, Minnesota, N. Car. & N.Y., *see* UNITED STATES: LAB. Children's Bur., No. 173, 1927.

Curry (*Rev.* **John**). Catholicity, liberty, allegiance: disq. on Gladstone's Expostul. 2nd ed. [P2622]. 8°. 1875

Cursius (Petrus), *civis Romanus.* Ad humani generis Servatorem in urbis Romæ excidio deploratio. s8°. Parisiis. 1528

Curthose (Robert), *duke of Normandy, see* ROBERT.

Curti (Leopoldo). *Mém. justif. de l'a. [*i.e.* L. C.] des Mém. hist. &c. sur la républ. de Vénise. s8°. Lyon. 1796

*Méms. hist. & polit. sur la républ. de Venise, 1792. [Tr.] 2p [*in 1v*]. s8°. [Lyon]. 1795

Curtin (Philip). Noted murder mysteries. 8°. [1914]

Curtis's Botanical magazine, *see* BOTANICAL MAGAZINE.

Curtis (A. C.) The small garden beautiful. n. & rev. ed. 8°. 1909

Curtis (Charles B.) Journal of travels thr. Russia to Constantinople, & in Asia Minor, 1815–16. [*MS.*] 2v. s4°. *n.d.*

Curtis (Edmund).

Hist. of mediaeval Ireland, 1110–1513. 8°. 1923

Richard II in Ireland, 1394–95 &c. 8°. O. 1927

Curtis (Edward E.) The organiz. of the Brit. army in the Amer. Revol. 8°. New Haven, *Yale.* 1926

Curtis (Eugene Newton). The French Assembly of 1848 & Amer. constit. doctrines. [Columbia Univ.] 8°. N.Y. 1918

Curtis (J.), *shorthand writer.* Authentic &c. hist. of the murder of Maria Marten in the Red Barn. Added, the trial of W. Corder &c. 8°. 1834

Curtis (James), *surgeon to the Embassy to Morocco.* Journal of travels in Barbary, 1801, w. obs. on the gum trade of Senegal. s8°. 1803

Curtis (Lionel). Papers rel. to applic. of the princ. of dyarchy to Govt. of India. App. Rep. of Joint Sel. Comm. & Govt. of India Act, 1919. Intr. by L. C. 8°. O. 1920

see KERR (P.) & L. C. Prevention of war, 1923.

Curtis (William Eleroy).

Turkestan: "The heart of Asia." 8°. 1921

Curtis (Winterton Conway). Science & human affairs, f. viewpoint of biology. 8°. [1922]

Curtius (Cornelius), *see* CORTE (CORNELIUS DE).

Curtius (Ernst). Beiträge zur Gesch. u. Topogr. Kleinasiens. [Aus d. Abh. d. Königl. Preuss. Akad. d. Wiss. zu B.] 4°. 1872

Curtius (Ernst Robert). Die lit. Wegbereiter d. neu. Frankreich. [2e A.] 8°. Potsdam. 1920

Curtius (Friedrich).

Deut. Briefe u. Elsäss. Erinnerungen. 8°. Frauenfeld. 1920

Curtius (Otto). Demokratie und Rätesystem. [P2410]. 8°. 1919

Curtius (Valentinus), *see* GERCKEN (J. H.) Diss. de formula consensus Lubecensi, 1560 [*subscr. by C. &c.*], 1755.

Curtius Rufus (Quintus).

De rebus gestis Alex. Magni hist. Aucta &c. s8°. Lugduni. 1548

„ „ Cum comm. S. Pitisci. Acc. Mottevayeri de Curtio dissert.; Freinshemii suppl.; Alexandri genealogia &c. [*2 pagin.*] 8°. Ultrajecti. 1685

Curtler (W. H. R.)

The enclosure & redistrib. of our land. 8°. O. 1920

Curtz (Albert), *see* BIBLE: PSALMS. Harpffen Davids mit Teut. Saiten bespannet [*Lat. & Germ. by A. C.*], 1659.

Curwen (John). Acc. of the Tonic Sol-fa method. [*b. w. h.* Gram. of vocal music, *n.d.*] 8°. 1855

A gram. of vocal music &c. 7th ed. 8°. *n.d.*

Curwen (John Christian), *see* WINDHAM (*Rt. Hon.* W.) Speech on C.'s Bill, "for better secur. the independ. & purity of Parl. &c.," 1810.

Curwood (James Oliver). The flaming forest. s8°. [1922]

God's country: the trail of happiness. s8°. [1921]

Curzon (G.) The violinist of the Quartier Latin. 3v. s8°. 1884

Curzon (Henri de). Ernest Reyer, 1823–1909. s8°. 1924

Rossini. 8°. 1920

Curzon (Louis Henry), *ps., see* BERTRAM (J. G.)

Curzon (Richard George Penn), *4th earl Howe, see* HOWE.

Curzon (*Hon.* **Robert**), *aft. 14th baron Zouche.*

Visits to monasteries in the Levant. 6th ed. s8°. 1881

„ „ Intr. by D. G. Hogarth. s8°. 1916

Curzon of Kedleston (George Nathaniel Curzon, *1st marquess*).

Bodiam Castle, Sussex: hist. & descr. survey. 4°. 1926

British gov. in India: story of the viceroys & Govt. Houses. 2v. 4°. [1925]

Cat. of early Eng. portraits, prop. of late Marq. C. of K. &c., sold by Christie, Dec. 22, 1927. [P2876]. 8°. 1927

Kedleston Church: account, hist., descr. &c. 4°. *p. f. p. c.* 1922

Leaves f. a Viceroy's note-book & o. papers. [Ed. F. W. Pember &c.] 8°. 1926

Persian autonomy, 1911, *see* PERSIA SOCIETY. Lect., 1911.

The personal hist. of Walmer Castle & its Lords Warden. Ed. S. Gwynn. 8°. 1927

Tales of travel. 8°. 1923

see HOGARTH (D. G.) G. N. C., 1926.

„ REMARKS. *Remarks on Ld. C.'s speech on May 5, 1921 on ratific. of Hungarian Peace treaty of the Trianon, 1921.

„ RONALDSHAY (L. J. L. D., *e. of*). The life of Ld. C., v1, 2, 1928.

Cusa (*card.* **Nicolaus de**) [N. CUSANUS; N. DE CUES; †KHRYPFFS (N.) DE CUSA], *see* VANSTEENBERGHE (E.) Le Card. N. de C., 1401–64, 1920.

Cusa (Salvatore). I diplomi greci ed arabi di Sicilia. Pubbl. nel testo orig., tr. &c. da S. C. [Doc. d. Archivi Sicil.] v1. 4°. Palermo. 1868

Cushing (Harvey). Life of Sir W. Osler. 2v. 8°. O. 1925

Cushing (Mary Gertrude).

Pierre Le Tourneur. [Columbia Univ.] s8°. N.Y. 1908

Cushing (Sumner W.), *see* HUNTINGTON (E.) & S. W. C. Princ. of human geogr., 1921.

Cushman (Joseph Augustine).

Works in Smithsonian Inst.: U.S. Nat. Mus. Bull.

Foraminifera of the Atlantic Ocean, p1–5, 1918–24. [104.]

Foraminifera of the Philippine & adjacent seas, 1921. [100.]

Larger fossil Foraminifera of the Panama Canal Zone, 1918. [103.]

Smaller fossil Foraminifera of the Panama Canal Zone, 1918 [103.]

Introd. to morphology & classific. of Foraminifera, 1925, *see* SMITHSONIAN INST. Misc. colls., v77, 1926.

see BOSWORTH (T. O.) Geology of tertiary &c. periods in N. W Peru: w. acc. of palæontology by J. A. C. &c., 1922.

Cust, *The family of, see* CUST (L.) Rec. of the C. f., s3, Sir J. C. (1718–70), 1927.

Cust (*Lady* **Elizabeth**) **& E. G. Pelham.** Edward, 5th Earl of Darnley & Emma Parnell, h. wife: story told in th. letters &c. Ed. &c. Lady E. C. & E. G. P. 8°. Leeds. 1913

Cust (*Sir* **John**), *bart., 1718–70, see* CUST (L.) Rec. of the Cust fam., s3, Sir J. C., 1927.

Cust (Lionel) [CUST (LIONEL HENRY)]. Arden of Feversham. [Repr. f. "Arch. Cant.", v34, P2489]. 8°. 1920

La collection de M. R. H. Benson. [Les Arts, Oct. 1907]. fol. 1907

The portraits of Sir Walter Ralegh. [Extr. f. Walpole Soc. Publ. v8]. [P2508]. 4°. [1920]

Records of the Cust family. s3, Sir John Cust, bart. [Mem. & Corres.] 4°. *p.p.* 1927

For ser. 1 & 2, see †CUST (*Lady* E.)

Cust (*Lieut.* **Lionel George Archer**). From Ploegsteert to Graudenz: story of a prisoner-of-war. 8°. *p.p.* 1919

Cust (*Sir* **Reginald John**). Early poems. s8°. 1892

Custance (*Sir* **Reginald Neville**). A study of war. 8°. 1924

Custine (*le marq.* **Astolphe de**). Lettres inéd. au Marq. de la Grange [1818–24]. Publ. par le Cte. de Luppé. s8°. [1925]

Custodi (*barone* **Pietro**), *see* VERRI (P.) Storia di Milano, cont. fino al 1792 da P. C., 2v, 1890.

Custodie Franciscaine de Terre Sainte, *see* ORFALI (G.) Capharnaüm & ses ruines: d'ap. les fouilles par la C. F. de T. S., 1922.

Customs & privileges of the manors of Stepney & Hackney, 1736, *see* STEPNEY.

Custos (Dominicus), *see* FUGGER, *Fam. of.* Fuggerorum et Fuggerarum imagines; D. C. desin. & sc., 1618.

Cuthbert (*Fr.*), *O.S.F.C.* The romanticism of St. Francis & o. st. in the genius of the Franciscans. n. ed. 8°. 1924

Cuthbertson (David). Edinb. Univ. Lib.: its origin, rarer books & MSS. &c. la8°. E. 1910

A tragedy of the Reformation. Hist. &c. of "Christianismi restitutio," 1553, w. acc. of the controv. betw. M. Servetus, its author, & Calvin. 8°. E. 1912

Cuthell (*Mrs.* Edith E.) The Scot. friend of Frederick the Gt., the last Earl Marischall [*i.e.* George, Baron Keith]. 2v. 8°. [1915]

Cutlack (F. M.) The Australian Flying Corps in the War, 1914–18. [Offic. hist. of A. in the War, v8]. 8°. Sydney. 1923

Cutler (Richard). Orig. notes of Dorchester & the Durotriges. s8°. Dorchester. 1865

Cutlers, *Company of.*

see CHEESWRIGHT (R. J.) Hist. essay on the livery cos., w. sh. hist. of the W.C. of C., 1881.

,, WELCH (C.) Hist. of Cutlers' Co., v2, 1923.

Cutsemius (Petrus), *see* CUDSEMIUS (P.)

Cutting (A. K.)

Caso del Americano, A. K. C. Nuevas notas entre los Est. Unid. y la Rep. Mexicana. [P2721]. 8°. México. 1888

Case of the American, A. K. C. Latest notes betw. the U.S. & the Rep. of Mexico. [P2721]. 8°. Wash. 1888

Cuvelier (Joseph).

see BELGIQUE. Archives de l'Etat en Belg. pend. la Guerre, 1914–18.

,, LONCHAY (H.) & J. C. Corr. de la cour d'Espagne sur les affaires des Pays-Bas au 17e s., t1, 2, 1923–27.

Cuvier (*le baron* Georges L. C. F. D. de). Éloges hist. Préc. de l'éloge de l'auteur par M. Flourens. 8°. *n.d.*

Iconographie du règne animal de Mr. le Bon. C. [*coloured plates*], par F. E. Guérin. [*Text & many plates wanting*]. 4°. 1829–44

see BAER (C. E. v.) Lebensgesch. C.'s, 1896.

Cuvillier-Fleury (Alfred Auguste), *see* VALLERY-RADOT (R.) Le duc d'Aumale, d'ap. sa corres. avec C.-F., [t1], 1840–71, 1922.

Cuyás y Sampere (Antonio). Apuntes hist. sobre la prov. de Entre Rios en la Rep. Argentina. la8°. Mataró. 1888

Cuyckius (Henricus), *bp. of Ruremonde.* Panegyricae orationes septem. Add.: Paraenetica in H. Bochorinck. s8°. Lovanii. 1596

Cuyper (Cornelius de). Diss. de Cemarim, ad illust. locorum 2 Reg. 23, 5 &c. Praes. C. Ikenio. [P427]. s4°. Bremæ. [1729]

Cuzacq (Pierre). La naissance, le mariage & le décès. Sud-ouest de la France. s8°. 1902

Cybo (Maria Teresa), *dssa di Massa, see* MASSA (M. T. CYBO, *dssa* DI).

Cyclos, *ps., see* ANDERSON (G.)

Cylchgrawn Cymdeithas Alawon Cymru: Journal of the Welsh Folk Song Soc., *see* WELSH FOLK SONG SOCIETY.

Cymmrodorion or Metropolitan Cambrian Institution.

Y Cymmrodor. v30–38. 8°. 1920–27

v30 *cont.* Giraldus Cambrensis: De invectionibus; [ed. w. intr.] by W. S. Davies.

v33 *cont.* Segontium & the Roman occupation of Wales; by R. E. M. Wheeler.

v34 *cont.* Taliesin: or the critic criticised; by J. G. Evans.

v37 *cont.* The Roman fort near Brecon; by R. E. M. Wheeler.

Cymmrodorion Record Series. 9, 11. 8°. 1923–24

see BROMFIELD. The first extent of B. & Yale, 1315; [ed. &c.], by T. P. Ellis, 1924. [11.]

,, MAP (W.) De nugis curialium; tr. M. R. James, 1923. [9.]

Transactions. Session 1918–19—1926–27. 8°. 1920–28

vol. for 1925–26 *has* Suppl. *w. sep. tp. & pagin.*: Richards (T.) The relig. census of 1676, 1927.

,, ,, Suppl. vol. Goronwy Owen & h. bicentenary [*By var. wr.*] 8°. 1924

Cynewulf. The old English Elene, Phoenix, & Physiologus. Ed. A. S. Cook. 8°. New Haven. 1919

Cynn (Hugh Hueng-Wo). The rebirth of Korea. s8°. 1920

Cyon (Elie de) [Ціонъ].

Какъ установить въ Россіи правовой государств. строй. [Wie soll Russland ein Rechtsstaat werden. P2446]. 8°. Paris. 1905

Cyprian, *Saint, bp. of Carthage.*

Opera. 2t *in* 1v. s8°. Lugduni. 1550

Cyprian, *Saint, bp. of Carthage* [*continued*].

Corr. Texte établi & tr. par le chanoine Bayard. [Coll. des univ. de France]. t1, 2. 8°. 1925

De idolor. vanitate, *see* MINUCIUS FELIX (M.) Octavius, 1643.

Epistolae. [*Prec. by 2 leaves cont.* Tabula super epistolas Cipriani. *Text begins on leaf 3.* Incipiunt epistolę C. C. ad Cornelium Papam. Et prima de confessione feliciter. *Ends*: Loquitur lector ad Vindelinum spirensem Artificem qui Epistolas Beati Cipriani reddit in lucem 1471]. fol. [Venice, *Wendelin.* 1471]

[*Without tp., pagin. or signatures. 182 leaves, of which 10 are duplicates in place of 10 missing leaves.*]

TRANSLATIONS. The genuine works of St. C. w. h. life by Deacon Pontius. Done into Eng., w. notes &c. by N. Marshall, LL.B. fol. 1717

Sel. epistles treating of the episcopate after the tr. of N. Marshall. Ed. w. intro. & notes by T. A. Lacey. [Trans. of Xtn. lit., s2]. s8°. [1922]

Serm. sopra l'elemosina; *tr.* A. Caro, *see* GREGORY, *Nazianzen.* Due orationi, 1569.

see CLAUDIUS (G. C.) Hist. Fratrum Sportulantium, exercit. ad C. C. lib. 1. epist. 9 &c., 1724.

,, MONCEAUX (P.) St. C., 1914.

,, POOLE (G. A.) The life & times of C., 1840.

Cyprian (Ernst Salomo).

Allgem. Anmerck. ü. G. Arnolds Kirchen-u. Ketzer-Historie. s4°. Helmstädt. 1700

Bibliotheca Cyprianica, sive Cat. librorum historico-theolog. quos E. S. C. conquisivit. ed. auctior. Acc. Indices. &c. s8°. Lipsiæ. 1733

De omophorio episcop. Græc. Praes. J. A. Schmidt. [P433]. s4°. Helmestadi. [1698]

Diss. publ. habitae, coll. & praef. adjecit E. R. Fischer. s4°. Coburgi. 1755

Mon. aliquot minora maxime hist. In publ. emissa a A. L. Ballstaedt. s8°. Gothae. 1749

Überzeugende Belehrung v. Urspr. u. Wachsthum d. Pabstthums, nebst e. Schutz-Schr. vor die Reformation &c. s8°. Gotha. 1721

see JACOBI (J.) Hist. eccl. Arminianae a E. S. C. adv. J. Clerici object. def., 1726.

Cyprius (Philippus), *see* PHILIP *of Cyprus.*

Cyprus. The handbook of C. Ed. by H. C. Luke & D. J. Jardine. s8°. 1920

Cyrano de Bergerac (Savinien). Œuvres libertines de C. de B. préc. d'une notice biog. par F. Lachèvre. [Le libertinage au XVIIe siècle, 8]. 2t. 8°. 1921

Le pédant joué: comédie, *see* FOURNEL (V.) Contemps. de Molière, t3, 1875.

Voyages to the moon & the sun. Tr. R. Aldington; w. intr. & notes. [Broadway trans.] s8°. 1923

see LEFÈVRE (L. R.) Vie de C. de B., 1927.

Cyriaque, *of Gandsak, see* KIRAKOS.

Cyriax (Edgar Ferdinand).

The elements of Kellgren's Manual treatment. la8°. 1903

Cyril, *Saint, patriarch of Alexandria.* Contra impium Julianum, *see* JULIAN, *emp. of Rome.* Opera, 1696.

Five tomes agst. Nestorius—Scholia on the Incarnation—Christ is one—Frags. agst. Diodore of Tarsus, Theodore of Mopsuestia, the Synousiasts. 8°. O. 1881

In XII Prophetas. A J. Pontano Graecè et Lat. ed. Cum notis, et indice. fol. Ingolstadii. 1607

see CONYBEARE (F. C.) The Armenian version of Revelation, & C. of A.'s Scholia on the Incarnation & Epistle on Easter: ed. &c. F. C. C., 1907.

,, EPHESUS, *1st synod.* Synodus Ephesina &c., ex Cyrillo &c., 1581.

Cyril, *Saint, bp. of Jerusalem* [C. HIEROSOLYMITANUS]. Opera quæ supersunt omnia. Ed. &c. T. Miller. fol. Oxoniæ. 1703

see EUCHOLOGION. Anaphora of St. Basil, St. C. &c. *Copt. & Arab.*, 1736.

,, VOLLENHOVEN (J. J. v.) Spec. theol. de C. catech., 1837.

Cyril, *Saint, of Thessalonica.*

see HILFERDING (A. F.) Собраніе соч., т1, К. и Меѳодій, 1868.

,, MINNS (E. H.) St C. knew Hebrew, 1925.

,, STREDOWSKY (J. G.) Sacra Moraviae hist., sive vita C. &c., 1710.

Cyril (Victor). L'amour avait raison. s8°. [1921]

Mayotte, *see* ŒUVRES libres, 46, 1925.

Cyrinus [ARBEO], *episc. Frisingensis.* Vitae SS. Haimhrammi & Corbiniani. Rec. B. Krusch. [Scr. rerum Germ. in usum schol.] 8°. Hannoverae. 1920

Cyrion, *patriarch of Georgia, see* AKINEAN (N.) C. (574–610), *in Armenian*, 1910.

Cyrus, *king of Persia, " the Great,"* *see* PRÁŠEK (J. V.) Kyros d. Grosse, 1912.

Czambel (Samu). Rukovät spisovnej reči slovenskej. 2e vydanie. s8°. Turčiansky Sv. Martin. 1915

A cseh-tót nemzetegység multja, jelene, ës jövöje. [P2392]. s8°. 1902

Czarnowski (Stefan). Le culte des héros & s. condit. sociales. St. Patrick, héros nat. de l'Irlande. Préf. de H. Hubert. [Trav. de l'Année sociolog.] 8°. 1919

Czech. Mod. Cz. poetry, 1920, *see* SELVER (P.)

Czechoslovak Bibliographical Institute, *Prague, see* ČESKOSLOVENSKÝ ÚSTAV BIBLIOGRAFICKÝ.

Czechoslovakia. C.: econ. & soc. conditions; tr., 1924, *see* GRUBER (J.), *ed.*

Czedik (Alois, *Frhr.* **v.)** Zur Gesch. d. k. k. österreich. Ministerien, 1861–1916. Nach d. Erinnerungen v. A. C. B3, 4. la8°. Teschen. 1920

Czepanski (Laurentius). Instructio compendiosa examinandorum pro ordinibus &c. s8°. Varsaviae. 1697

Czermak (Wilhelm), *see* JUNKER (H.) & W. CZERMAK. Kordofân-Texte im Dialekt v. Gebel Dair, 1913.

Cziapinskis (M.) Lithuania under the heel of Germany. [P2382]. 8°. Glasgow. [1919]

Czwalina (Arthur).
Archimedes. [Math.-phys. Bibl., 64]. s8°. L. *Teubner.* 1925

D

D*.** *An abstract of what is nec. to be known conc. the Constit. Unigenitus; tr., 1724, *see* UNIGENITUS.

D. (B.) *Voyage à la Louisiane, 1794–98, 1802, *see* BAUDRY DE LOZIÈRES (*Gen.* L. N.)

D. (F. A.) Early connexion of the Roy. Soc. w. Oxford, 1912, *see* DIXEY (F. A.)

D. (H.) *Heliodora & o. poems. s8°. [1924]

D. (H.), *M.A.* *A sober &c. disc. conc. interest of words in prayer &c., 1661, *see* SOBER.

D. (J.) *Poems, 1633, *see* DONNE (J.)

D. (J.) *True &c. narr.; or sundry &c. injuries &c. wh. the Hollanders have exercised agst. the English &c., 1665, *see* DARELL (J.)

D. (J.) Vence, ses mons., s. saints, &c., 1914, *see* VENCE.

D. (J.), *of Kidwelly.* *Epictetus Junior, 1670, *see* DAVIES (J.)

D. (J.), *Phil-Alethius.* *Velitationes polemicæ, 1652, *see* DOUGHTY (J.)

D . . . (*R.P.* **J.)** *Hist. des deux conquerans tartares qui ont subjugué la Chine &c., 1690, *see* ORLÉANS (*le père* P. J. D').

D. (J. M.) *Controversia de sabbatho Christian., 1704, *see* CONTROVERSIA.

D. (M. H.) *Consids. sur l'état prés. de Saint-Domingue, 2t, 1776, *see* HILLIARD D'AUBERTEUIL (M. R.)

D. (P.) Procès du parricide Ravaillac; publ. P. D. [*i.e.* P. Deschamps], 1858, *see* RAVAILLAC (F.)

D. (R.) *A little more nonsense, 1923, *see* DAVIES (R.)

*A lyttel booke of nonsense, n. ed., 1925, *see* DAVIES (R.)

D. (S. A. C.) *A case of conscience &c., in favour of Jansenism [*pref. signed* S. A. C. D.], 1703, *see* JANSENISM.

D. (W.) Nil dictum quod non dictum prius, 1681, *see* DISNEY (W.)

D. (W.) *Richborough, 3rd ed., 1919, *see* RICHBOROUGH.

D. (W.) *Tragi-comicall hist. of our times; tr. W. D., 1627, *see* AUDIGUIER (V. D').

Daae (Ludvig). Matrikler over Nordiske studerende ved fremmede Universiteter. Saml. &c. af. L. D. [Norske Hist. K.] 8°. 1885

D'Abernon (Edgar Vincent, *1st baron*), *see* VINCENT (*Sir* EDGAR).

Dabot (Victor Hallays-), *see* HALLAYS-DABOT (V.)

Dacca, *see* BENGAL: RECORDS OF GOVT. Proc. of the Comm. of Circuit at Krishnagar, D. &c., 1772, v4, 1926.

Dachian (Jacobus), *see* DASHEAN (H.)

Dachs (Friedrich Bernhardt), *see* TALMUD. Talmudis Babylon. cod. Succa, sive de tabernac. festo &c.; Lat. don. &c. F. B. D., 1726.

Dacier (Emile). Expos. des Saint-Aubin organ. par la Soc. Artist. des Amateurs: Cat. raisonné par E. D. avec collab. de E. Girod de l'Ain, 7–29 avril, 1925. s8°. [1925]

La gravure de genre & de mœurs. [La grav. en France au 18e siècle]. 4°. 1925

Da Costa (Izaak), *see* COSTA (I. DA).

Da Costa (Uriel), *see* ACOSTA (U.)

Dacre (Barbarina, *Lady*).
see SULLIVAN (A. J.) *Recoll. of a chaperon; ed. Lady D., n. ed., 3v, 1833.
„ —— *Tales of the peerage & the peasantry; ed. Lady D., 1849.

Dactus (Augustinus), *see* DATI (A.)

Dade (Heinrich), *see* BRAUN (*F. Edler* v.) & H. D. Arbeitsziele d. deut. Landwirtschaft nach d. Kriege, 1918.

Dadean (Nikolai). Исторія Грузіи [1788–1823]. *Georgian & Russian*; Е. С. Такайшвили, *see* SBORNIK. Сборникъ матер. для опис. Кавказа, 31, 1902.

Daffner (Hugo).
Salome: i. Gestalt in Gesch. u. Kunst. la8°. München. 1912

Dafforne (James). Pictures by J. Phillip, R.A.; w. descr. & biog. sketch. fol. [1877]

Da Gama (Christovão), *see* CASTANHOSO (M. DE). Hist. das cousas que Dom C. de G. &c. fez nos Reynos do Preste João, 1564, 1875.

Dageförde (Carl), *see* TECKLENBURG (A.) & C. D. Gesch. d. Prov. Hannover, 1921.

Daglish (E. Fitch). Marvels of plant life. 8°. [1924]

Woodcuts of Brit. birds, w. descr. 4°. 1925

Dagmar, *princess, daughter of Christian IX, k. of Denmark* [MARIE SOPHIA FREDERIKA DAGMAR], *see* MARIE, *empress, consort of Alexander III, emp. of Russia.*

Dahl (André). Le sucrier Empire, nouvelle, *see* ŒUVRES libres, 42, 1924.

Dahl (Knut). In savage Australia: acc. of hunting &c. exped. Foreword by F. Nansen. 8°. 1926

Dahl (Michael), *c. 1659–1743, see* NISSER (W.) M. D. & the contemp. school of painting in Eng., 1927.

Dahlerup (Verner). Ordbog over det danske sprog. Grundlagt af V. D. B3–9. la8°. 1921–27

Dahlgren (Erik Wilhelm). Les débuts de la cartographie du Japon. [P2526]. 8°. Upsal. 1911

Louis de Geer, 1587–1652: hans lif & verk, på uppdrag af Friherre L. de Geer till Leufsta. 2d. 4°. Uppsala. 1923

see GEER, *Family of.* Ätten de Geer &c. [intr. by D.], 1920.

Dahn (Felix). Gesamm. Werke. neue wohlfeile Gesamtausg. 2e Serie (Erzähl. u. poet. Schr.) 8B. s8°. L. [1912]

1, Julian der Abtrünnige.
2, Vom Chiemgau—Ebroin—Kämpfende Herzen.
3, Bis zum Tode getreu—Weltuntergang—Was ist die Liebe—Skirnir.
4, Sind Götter?—Odhins Trost—Die Kreuzfahrer.
5, Am Hof Herrn Karls—Herzog Ernst v. Schwaben—Meine welschen Ahnen.—Odhins Rache—Friggas Ja—Die Finnin—Der Vater u. d. Söhne.
6–7, Gedichte.
8, Kaiser Karl u. s. Paladine.

Bis zum Tode getreu. 8e A. s8°. L. 1889

Die Könige der Germanen. B8vi, 11, 12, *&* Gesamt-Register, zusamm. v. Friedel Dahn. 8°. L. 1900–11

Dähnert (Johann Carl). Platt-Deutsches Wörter-Buch nach d. alten u. neuen Pommerschen u. Rügischen Mundart. s4°. Stralsund. 1781

Dail Eireann, *see* IRELAND: PARLIAMENT.

Daillé (Jean) [J. DALLÆUS]. Apologia pro 2 eccl. in Gallia protestantium synodis nat., altera Alensone a. 1637, altera verò Carentone a. 1645, hab. Adv. F. Spanhemii exercit. de gratia univ. 2t *in* 1v. [*sep. tps., pagin. contd.*] s8°. Amstelædami. 1655

De jejuniis & quadragesima liber. s8°. Daventriæ. 1654

De usu Patrum ad ea definienda relig. capita quæ sunt hodie controversa libri 2. Lat. è Gallico à I. Mettayero redd. s4°. Genevæ. 1656

„ „ ....s4°. Genevæ. 1686

An expos. of the Epistle of St. Paul to the Philippians. Tr. J. Sherman. la8°. 1841

Daille (M.) La bataille de Montdidier. 8°. 1922

Daily Courant, The. Nos. 85 (July 27, 1702), 354 (June 5, 1703) [& subsequent odd nos. to June 11, 1720. *b. w.* Post Man, 1704–20]. fol. 1702–20

Daily extracts from the foreign press, 1 June 1915–6 Aug. 1919 [Jan. 17 & Mar. 28, 1918 & Nos. 1, 2, 13, 18, 27, 29, 40, 42, 69 & 83 of 1919 *wanting*]. [War Office]. fol. 1915–19
No. for Mar. 20–22, 1916 *called* Daily digest, *after which the title was changed to* Daily review of the foreign press, *q. v.*, Jan. 1917–1919 *are divided into series* 2–10.
„ „ Index, July–Dec. 1916, Jan.–June 1917. fol. 1917

Daily Journal, The. No. 673 (Mar. 20, 1722/3) [*b. w.* Post Man, 1720–24]. fol. 1723

Daily Review of the Foreign Press.
Allied Press Supplement. vols. 1–6, Nov. 1916–July 1919. [*Incomplete*]. fol. 1916–19
Blockade & Supply Suppl. v1–6, March 1917–July 1919. [*wanting a few Nos.*] fol. 1917–19
Economic Supplement. v1–7, Nov. 1916–Aug. 1919. [*Incomplete*]. *The 1st issue has t.* German Econ. Summary. fol. 1916–19
„ „ Ind. to Ec. & Reconstr. Suppl. May–Nov. 1918. fol. 1918
Enemy Press Supplement. vols. 1–6, Nov. 1916–July 1919. [*wanting* v2, No. 19 ; v3, No. 22 ; v4, No. 9 ; v5, No. 3]. fol. 1916–19
Food Supplement. vols. 2–7, June 1917–Aug. 1919. [*wanting a few Nos.*] fol. 1917–19
Neutral Press Supplement. vols. 1–6, Nov. 1916–Aug. 1919. [*wanting a few Nos.*] fol. 1916–19
Press & Propaganda Supp. Aug. 1917. [*b. w.* Daily Rev. of F. P. ; Short Guide, 1916]. fol. 1917
Press Extracts. Index. Vols. 1–4. fol. 1916–17
Reconstruction Supplement. v1–4, Sept. 1917–July 1919. [*wanting* v2, Nos. 2, 6 ; v3, No. 5]. fol. 1917–19
„ „ Ind. to Econ. & Reconstr. Suppl. May-Nov. 1918. fol. 1918
Review of situation in enemy countries, May–Sept. 1918. [*b. w.* Daily Rev. of F. P. ; Short Guide, 1916]. fol. 1918
Short Guide, June–July 1916. fol. 1916
Short Press Guide. Sept. 1917. [*b. w.* Daily Rev. of F. P. ; Short Guide, 1916]. fol. 1917
Summary of comment in European Press on Peace Treaty. May 1919. [*b. w.* Daily Rev. of F. P. ; Short Guide, 1916]. fol. 1919
Weekly Supplement. July–Nov. 1916. [*wanting* Sept. 8, 1916 ; *b. w.* Daily Review of F. P. ; Short Guide, 1916]. fol. 1916

Daily Telegraph, *see* COURTNEY (W. L.) Is it a new world ? : articles &c. contrib. to D. T., Aug.–Sept., 1920.

Daimler Company, *see* FROST (G. H.) Munitions of war : work of the B.S.A. & D. Co., 1914–18, 1921.

Dianelli (Giotto). Studi sul glaciale [*w.* Tavole], *&* Le condiz. fis. attuali, *see* FILIPPI (F. DE). Rel. sci. d. Spediz. Ital. de F. n. Himàlaia &c., s2, v3, 4, 1923–28.
I tipi umani; [*by*] R. Biasutti e G. D., *see* FILIPPI (F. DE). Rel. sci. d. Spediz. Ital. de F. n. Himàlaia &c., s2, v9, 1925.

Daireaux (Max). La Clota, *see* ŒUVRES libres, 54, 1925.
Le poète & l'infidèle, *see* ŒUVRES libres, 15, 1922.

Dakin (William John). Elements of gen. zoology. 8º. 1927

Dakyns (John Roche), *see* GREEN (A. H.), C. LE N. FOSTER & J. R. D. Geol. of the carbonif. limestone &c. of N. Derbyshire, 1887.

—— & C. E. Fox-Strangways.
Geol. of Bridlington Bay. [Mems. of G.S.] 8º. 1885
Geol. of the co. around Driffield. [Mems. of G.S.] 8º. 1886

——, —— *& others.* Geol. of the co. betw. Bradford & Skipton. [Mems. of G.S.] 8º. 1879

——, —— **& A. G. Cameron.** Geol. of the co. betw. York & Hull. [Mems. of G.S.] 8º. 1886

——, **R. H. Tiddeman** *& others.* Geol. of the co. around Ingleborough. [Mems. of G.S.] 8º. 1890
Geol. of the co. around Mallerstang &c. [Mems. of G.S.] 8º. 1891

——, —— **& J. G. Goodchild.** Geol. of co. betw. Appleby, Ullswater & Haweswater. [Mems. of G.S.] 8º. 1897

Dal (Vladimir Ivanovich). Сочиненія. Новое полное изд. 8t [*b. in* 6]. s8º. С.–П. 1861
see SHEIN (P. V.) Дополненія &c. къ Словарю Д., 1873.

Dalberg (Emmerick Joseph Franck, *duc* **de),** *see* BOSELLI (P.) Il ministro Vallesa e l'ambasc. D. nel 1817, 1893.

Dalberg (Nils), *see* STENHAMMAR (C.) Äminnelse-Tal öfver N. D., 1822.

Dalbono (Eduardo), *see* MORELLI (D.) & E. D. La scuola napoletana di pittura nel sec. 19 &c., 1915.

Dalby (Isaac), *see* MUDGE (*Col.* W.) Acc. of operations for accompl. trigonom. survey of Eng. &c., v1, 1784–96, by M. & I. D., 1799.

Dalcho (Frederick). Orations [on freemasonry]. Repr. *engr. tp.* 8º. D. 1808

Dalcroze (Emile Jaques). Rhythm, music & education. Tr. H. F. Rubinstein. Intr. by Sir W. H. Hadow. 8º. 1921

Dale (*Capt.* **Andrew Murray),** *see* SMITH (E. W.) & A. M. D. The Ila-speaking peoples of N. Rhodesia, 2v, 1920.

Dale (Hylton B.) The Fellowship of Woodmongers. [*Repr. f.* Coal Merchant & Shipper]. s8º. [1923]
Landmarks in Armenian hist. [P2564]. 8º. Enfield. 1921

Dale (Johan Hendrik van). Groot woordenboek d. Nederl. taal. 5e opn. bewerkte uitg. [*ed.* P. J. v. Malssen, jr.] 8º. 's-Gravenhagen. 1914

Dale (Robert William).
Christian doctrine. Discourses. 8º. 1894
The Epist. to the Ephesians. 5th ed. 8º. 1890
Nonconformity in 1662 & in 1862 : lect. 2nd ed. [P2770]. s8º. [1862]
see JAMES (J. A.) Life &c. of J. A. J., 1861.

Dale (Thomas Cyril). Our Clapham forefathers. Pref. by R. de M. Rudolf. s8º. [1921]

Dalgado (Sebastiao Rodolfo). Glossário luso-asiático. [Acad. das Sci. de Lisboa]. v2. la8º. Coimbra. 1921

Dalhousie (James Andrew B. Ramsay, *10th earl, aft. marq. of***),** *see* GRANT (A.) Physician & friend : A. G., autobiog. & letters f. marq. of Dalhousie ; ed. G. Smith, 1902.

Dalin (D.) Послѣ войнъ и революцій. 8º. Берлинъ. 1922

Dalin (Olof), *1708–63*, *see* WARBURG (C. J.) O. D., hans lif och gerning, 1884.

Dall (William Healy). Summary of the marine shellbearing mollusks of the N.W. coast of America [*&* Adds.] [S.I. U.S. Nat. Mus.] 8º. Wash. 1921

Dall' Acqua Giusti (Ant.)
La loggia d. Doge Ziani. [P2835]. 8º. Venezia. 1880
I quattro cavalli s. facciata di San Marco. [P2842]. la8º. Venezia. 1894

Dalla Croce (Vincenzo Alsario), *see* ALSARIO DALLA CROCE (V.)

Dallæus (Joannes), *see* DAILLÉ (JEAN).

Dalla Quercia (Jacopo), *see* DELLA QUERCIA (J.)

Dallari (Umberto). L'occupaz. francese di Reggio (1702–06), *see* REGIA DEP. DI STORIA PATRIA. Misc., t40, 1904.
see BOLOGNA. Rotuli dei lettori, 1384–1799 ; pubbl. dal Dr. U. D., 3v, 1888–1919.

Dallas, *The family of*, *see* DALLAS (J.) Hist. of the family of D., f. 12c., 1921.

Dallas (Helen Alex.) Mors janua vitae ? Discuss. of communic. f. F. W. H. Myers. Introd. by W. F. Barrett. s8º. 1910

Dallas (James). Hist. of the family of Dallas, f. 12th cent. 4º. *p.p.* E. 1921

Dalla Santa (Giuseppe). Le appellazioni d. rep. de Venezia d. scomuniche di Sistó IV e Giulio II. [P2840]. 8º. Venezia. 1899
Di un patrizio mercante veneziano d. quattrocento & di F. Filelfo. [Estr. d. N. Arch. Veneto, N.S., v11ii]. [P2841]. 8º. Venezia. 1906
Una pagina stor. di due paeselli friulani (Sequals e Solimbergo). [Estr. d. Pagine Friulane. P2839]. s8º. Udine. 1900
Il vero testo d. appellaz. di Venezia d. scomunica di Giulio II. [Estr. d. Nuovo Arch. Ven., t19. P2836]. 8º. Venezia. 1900

Dalla Torre (Carl Wilhelm von). Atlas der Alpenflora. Gemalt v. A. Hartinger, Text v. C. W. v. D. T. 4B. 8º. Wien. 1884

—— & L., *Graf* **v. Sarnthein.** Flora d. Grafsch. Tirol, d. Landes Vorarlberg u. d. Fürstenth. Liechtenstein. 6B [*in* 9v, B6 *in* 4T, B3 *has* Nachtrag, *b. sep.*] 8º. Innsbruck. 1900–26
1, Litt. d. Flora. 2, Die Algen. 3, Die Pilze (Fungi) ; unter Beistand v. K. W. v. D. T., bearbt. v. P. Magnus, *w.* Nachtrag v. P. M., *b. sep.* 4, Die Flechten. 5, Die Moose (Bryophyta). 6, Die Farn- u. Blütenpflanzen (Pteridophyta & Siphonogama), 4T.

Dallier (Gustave), *see* MASSARD (E.) & G. D. P. Coignard, *n.d.*

Dallimore (W.) & A. B. Jackson.
Handbook of Coniferæ incl. Ginkgoaceæ. 8º. 1923

Dallinger (William H.) The Creator & what we may know of the method of creation. Fernley Lect., 1887. 8º. 1888

Dallington (*Sir* **Robert).** A method for travell. Shewed by taking the view of France, 1598. s4º. [1606 ?]

Dalman (Gustaf Herman). Aram.-neuhebr. Hdwbch. zu Targum, Talmud u. Midrasch. 2e verb. A., mit Lex. d. Abbrev. v. G. H. Händler, u. e. Verzeichnis d. Mischna-Abschnitte, beides bearb. v. J. Kahan. [*w. sep. tp. & pagin.*] 8º. Frankfurt. 1922
Orte u. Wege Jesu. 8º. Güterslch. 1919

Dalmasso (Luigi). I Piemontesi alla guerra di Candia, 1644–69, *see* REGIA DEPUT. Misc., t44, 1909.
Dalmatia [DALMATIEN]. Bau-u Kunstdenkmale in D., 2e A., 6B, 1927, *see* IVEKOVIĆ (C. M.), *ed.*
Izvješće o djelatnosti Pokrajinskog Konservatorskoga Ureda za Dalmaciju &c., 1920–22, *see* BULLETTINO DI ARCH. &C. DALM., 43–45, Suppl., 1920–22.
Dalmedico (Angelo). Proverbi veneziani &c. 8º. Venezia. 1857
Dal Piaz (Giorgio), *see* PARONA (C. F.) Trattato di geologia; collab. per la geol. stor., prof. G. D. P. &c., 1924.
Dal Pozzo (Cassiano), *see* LUMBROSO (G.) Notizie s. vita di C. Dal P., con ricordi e lettere, 1874.
Dalrymple (*Gen. Sir* **Hew Whiteford).** Memoir by D., of h. proc. &c. & commencement of the Peninsular War. 8º. 1830
Dalrymple (*Sir* **James**), *bart., Baron of the Exchequer in Scotland.* A vindic. of the eccl. part of Sir J. D.'s Hist. coll.: in ans. to a late pamph. [by J. Gillane]: The life of the Rev. J. Sage &c. s8º. E. 1714
see GILLANE (J.) *Some remarks upon Sir J. D.'s Hist. coll., 1714.
Dalton (Hugh).
The capital levy explained. [2nd impr.] s8º. 1923
Principles of public finance. s8º. 1923
Some aspects of the inequality of incomes in mod. communities. 8º. 1920
D'Alton (John), *barrister.* Illusts., hist. & genealog., of K. James's Irish Army List, 1689. 8º. D. 1855
Dalton (John), *D.D.* Two epistles: the 1st, to a young nobleman f. h. preceptor, the 2nd, to the Countess of Hartford. [*In verse*]. 4º. 1745
Dalton (John), *F.R.S.*
see HENRY (W. C.) Mem. of life & sci. researches of J. D., 1854.
,, NEVILLE-POLLEY (L. J.) J. D., 1920.
Dalton (John Patrick).
Rudiments of relativity. la8º. Witwatersrand. 1921
Dalton (Leonard V.) Venezuela. [3rd impr.] 8º. [1918]
Dalton (Moray). The sword of love. s8º. [1920]
Dalton (Ormonde Maddock).
East Xtn. art: survey of the monuments. 4º. O. 1925
see BRIT. MUSEUM: ANTIQ. Franks bequest: Treasure of the Oxus, w. o. examples of early oriental metal-work; by O. M. D., 2nd ed., 1926.
,, GREGORY, *of Tours.* Hist. of Franks; tr. w. intr. by O. M. D., 2v, 1927.
,, MORGAN (J. P.) Byzantine enamels in P. M.'s coll.; by O. M. D., 1912.
Dalton (W.)
Inferences at bridge. Repr. f. "Sat. Review." s8º. 1908
The laws of bridge (rev. 1904). Ed. W. D. s8º. 1907
"Saturday" bridge. Reprod. w. rev. f. the "Saturday Review." s8º. 1906
Dalton (William Herbert), *F.G.S.* Geol. of the co. around Aldborough, Framlingham, Orford & Woodbridge. Ed., w. adds. by W. Whitaker. [Mems. of G.S.] 8º. 1886
Geol. of the neighb. of Colchester. [Mems. of G.S.] 8º. 1880
see WHITAKER (W.) & W. H. D. Geol. of co. around Halesworth & Harleston, 1887.
Daly (Charles P.) Gulian C. Verplanck. [P2621]. 8º. N.Y. 1870
Daly (Reginald Aldworth). Igneous rocks & th. origin. 1st ed., 4th impr. 8º. N.Y. 1914
Our mobile earth. 8º. N.Y. 1926
Dalzell (George Walton), *see* CANFIELD (G. L.) & G. W. D. Law of the sea, 1921.
Damas, *see* DAMASCUS.
Damas (Ange Hyacinthe Maxence, *baron* **de).** Mémoires, 1785–1862. Publ. par le comte de Damas. 2t. 8º. [1922–23]
Damascius, *the Syrian.* Problèmes & solutions touch. les premiers principes, avec le tableau sommaire des doct. des Chaldéens de Michel Psellus. Tr. & accomp. de comm. &c. par A. E. Chaignet. 3t. 8º. 1898
Damascus [DAMAS]. *Les trophées de Damas: controverse jud.-chrét. du 7e siècle; texte grec & tr. par G. Bardy, *see* GRAFFIN (R.) & F. NAU. Patr. orient., t15, 1927.
Damas-Hinard (Jean Jos. Stanislas Alb.), *see* NAPOLEON I. Dict.-Napoléon; intr. & notes par D. H., 2e éd., 1854.
Damasus, *St., pope.* Opera quae extant & vita ex codd. MSS. cum notis M. M. Sarazanii. s8º. Parisiis. 1672
see ANTHOLOGIA LATINA. Anthol. lat. suppl.; rec. M. Ihm, v1, Damasi Epigrammata &c., 1895.

Damcke (Bernard) & Joh. Christenius. Leben d. J. F. Gronovii &c. [*b. w.* Canstein (C. H. v.) Das Muster: Lebens-Beschr. Speners, 1740]. s8º. Hamburg. 1723
Dames (Thomas Longworth). Views in the Crimea. obl. fol. 1856
Dameto (Juan) & Vicente Mut. *The anc. & mod. hist. of the Balearick Islands. Tr. f. the Span. [by C. Campbell]. s8º. 1716
Dami (Luigi).
see OJETTI (U.) & L. D. Atlante di storia dell' arte ital., t1, 1924?.
,, PITTI, *Palace.* La pittura ital. alla mostra di Palazzo P.; [*by*] U. Ojetti, L. D. &c., 1924.
—— **& B. Barbadoro.** Firenze di Dante: città, storia, vita, Dante. 8º. Firenze. 1921
Damiani (Joannes).
Justa relig. coactio. ed. altera. s8º. Budæ. 1763
Damiani (Wilhelm Friedrich), *see* LUTHER (M.) *Defensio vit. &c. M. L. contra imput. calumnias a G. F. D., 1755.
Damien (*Father*), *see* STEVENSON (R. L.) Father D., 1911.
Damm (Christian Tobias). Novum lexicon Græcum etym. & reale, concord. &c. Homericæ. Cura J. M. Duncan. 2v. 8º. Glasguæ. 1824
Damon (Samuel Foster). Bk. of Dan. verse; tr. S. F. D. &c., 1922, *see* DANISH.
William Blake, h. philosophy & symbols. la8º. 1924
Dampier (E. M. Smith-), *see* SMITH-DAMPIER (E. M.)
Dampier (William). New voyage round the world. [Ed. N. M. Penzer]. Intr. by Sir A. Gray. la8º. 1927
Dampier-Whetham (William Cecil), *see* WHETHAM (W. C. D.)
Dana (Richard Henry), *son of R. H. D., the younger, b. 1851.* Hospitable England in the seventies. Diary of a young American, 1875–76. 8º. 1921
Dana (Richard Henry), *the younger, 1815–82.* Two years before the mast: narr. of life at sea. Intr. by Sir W. Grenfell. [repr.] s8º. N.Y. 1921
see LAWRENCE (W. B.) W. B. L. *vs.* R. H. D. &c. [3p], 1868.
Danæus (Lambertus), *see* DANEAU (L.)
Dance (The) of Çiva, 1927, *see* COLLUM, *ps.*
Dance of Death. Coll. of S. Minns. Books, prints &c. illust. of "The dance of death." Sold, May 1922, Amer. Art Gall. 8º. N.Y. 1922
Dance (Charles), *dramatic writer.*
A wonderful woman. Comic drama. [P2582]. s8º. *Lacy. n.d.*
Dancing Master. [The D.M., 16th ed., 1718], *see* PLAYFORD (J.)
Dancourt (F. C.) [†CARTON DANCOURT (FLORENT)]. Le chevalier à la mode, *see* THÉÂTRE choisi du 18e s., t1, 1914.
Dandelot (A.)
Francis Planté. Une belle vie d'artiste. s8º. [1920]
Dandolo (Andrea), *see* LAZZARINI (V.) Il testamento d. A. D. (1354), 1904.
Dandolo (Milly).
Il vento n. foresta. Romanzo. s8º. Milano. 1922
Dane (Clemence), *ps.* [*i.e. Miss* WINIFRED ASHTON].
A bill of divorcement. Play. s8º. 1921
Legend. s8º. 1919
Wandering stars together w. The lover. s8º. [1924]
Will Shakespeare. An invention in 4 acts. [repr.] s8º. 1922
Dane (Edmund). Common sense of econ. science. 8º. [1922]
Wages & labour costs. s8º. 1927
Daneau (Lambert) [DANAEUS (L.)].
Ad novas G. Genebrardi calumnias quibus de Trinitate doct. traducit, V. Gentilis errorem tuetur &c., L. Danaei responsio. s8º. Genevae. 1578
Christianae isagoges ad Christ. theologorum locos communes libri 2 [*&* p2–4]. Cum præf. T. Bezæ. p1–4 *in* 1v [*pagin. of p2, 3 contin.*] s8º. Genevæ. 1583–86
The tp. of p2 & 4 read Isagoges Christianæ p2a. [*&* 4a.]
Elenchi hæreticorum &c. s8º. Genevæ. 1573
Examen libri de duabus in Christo naturis, de earum hypostatica unione, & varia, à M. Kemnitio conscr. &c. s8º. Genevæ. 1581
In Petri Lombardi librum primum sententiarum qui est de vero Deo comm. triplex &c. s8º. Genevæ. 1580
Orationis Dominicæ explic. &c. ed. 2a. s8º. Genevæ. 1583
Paratitla in D. A. Augustini tomos duos &c. s8º. Genevæ. 1578
Politices Christ. libri 7. [*b. w. h.* Examen libri à M. Kemnitio conscr., 1581]. s8º. [Genevæ]. 1596
Symboli apostolici explic. quatuor thesibus. s8º. Genevæ. 1587
Tractatus de Antichristo recens ed. [*b. w. h.* Elenchi hæret., 1573]. s8º. Genevæ. 1576
see ABUSIGER (H.) Epistola Terentiana ad L. D., 1581.
,, FRISCHLIN (N.) Breve responsum adv. contumelias quas L. D. scripsit, 1581.

Daneau (Lambert) [DANAEUS (L.)] [*continued*].
see GERLACH (S.) Hyperaspistes Antidanæi &c., 1581.
,, PETERS (F.) Pro libello M. Chemnitii, ad examen a L. D. conscr. resp., 1585.
Danemark [DÄNEMARK]. *Histor. &c. Untersuchung d. Uhrsachen (*sic*) durch welche d. zw. D. u. Schweden vorgefall. Streitigkeiten &c., 1715, *see* AMTHOR (C. H.)
Danes (Petrus Ludovicus). Tractatus de fide, spe &c. s8°. Lovanii. 1735
Danese (Orlando). Mussolini. [P2707]. 8°. Mantova. [1922]
Danewsky (Vsevolod). La Russie & l'Angl. dans l'Asie Centrale. Obs. sur " La Russie &c.," par F. Martens. [P2714]. 8°. 1881
Danger. *D. (The) of enthusiasm discov., in an epistle to the Quakers, 1674, *see* ALLEN (W.)
Dangerfield (Thomas). Ans. to a pamph. entitled Malice defeated, or the deliverance of Eliz. Cellier. [P525]. sfol. 1680
Information deliv. at bar of H. of Commons, 20 Oct. 1680 [*rel. to Popish Plot.* P525]. sfol. 1680
Dangerous [DAUNGEROUS]. *Daungerous positions & proceedings &c., 1593, *see* BANCROFT (R.)
Dangibeaud (M.) Saintes au 16 s. Annot. de M. de la Morinerie. [P2515]. 8°. Evreux. 1863
Dangin (François Thureau-), *see* THUREAU-DANGIN (F.)
Danguy (R.) Les grands vins de Bourgogne (La Côte-d'Or). Par R. D. avec collab. de C. Aubertin. 8°. Dijon. [1892]
see VERMOREL (V.) & R. D. Les vins du Beaujolais, du Mâconnais &c., 1893.
Dania. *Ordinatio eccl. regnorum Daniæ & Norwegiæ & Ducatuum Sleswicensis Holsatiæ &c., 1537. [Pia & vere catholica &c. ordinatio cæremoniarum pro canonicis & monasteriis (by J. Bugenhagen)]. s8°. [Haffnie, *J. Vinitoris Stutgardioni*]. 1537
Danibegov (Rafail). Путешествіе въ Индію грузинск. дворянина. Переводъ съ Грузинскаго. s8°. Москва. 1815
Danici. Annales D. medii ævi; ed. novam cur. E. Jørgensen, 1920, *see* ANNALES.
Daniel [*see also* BIBLE: DANIEL]. Die 7. Vision Daniels. Arm. Text m. deut. Übers. v. G. Kalemkiar. [Apokr. bei d. Arm., 3. Sep.-abdr. a. d. Wiener Zeitschr. f. d. Kunde d. Morgenl., 6.] [P2792]. 8°. Wien. 1892
Daniel *à Jesu, ps., see* FLOYD (JOHN).
Daniel, *the prophet, ps.* La clef des songes. Facs., notes &c. des éd. incun. [*of the* Interp. seu somnia D. &c. *Ed.* M. Hélin]. 8°. 1925
*Das Traumbuch d. Proph. D. nach d. cod. Vat. Palat. gr. 319; [ed. F. Drexl], *see* BYZANT. ZEITSCHR., B26, 1926.
Daniel, *Stylites, Saint, see* DELEHAYE (H.) Saints stylites, 1923.
Daniel (Charles Henry Olive). The Daniel Press. Mem. of C. H. O. D. [*by var. wr.*], w. bibliog. of the Press, 1845–1919, by F. Madan. Ed. C. H. Wilkinson. 8°. O. 1921
Daniel (Florence). Are women monkey-minded? s8°. 1921
Daniel (Francesco Salvador) [SALVADOR-DANIEL (F.)]. Music & musical instruments of the Arab. [Tr.], ed. w. notes, mem. &c. by H. G. Farmer. s8°. [1914]
Daniel (Gabriel). Litterae ad R. P. Alexandrum Dominicanum in q. Thomistarum doctrina cum doct. theologorum Soc. Jesu comparatur. s8°. Augustæ Vindelic. 1700
Daniel (George), *of Canonbury.*
Recoll. of Charles Lamb. s8°. 1927
Daniel (João). Thesouro descub. no maximo rio Amazonas, p2, 6, *see* INSTITUTO HIST. E GEOG. BRAZIL. Rev., t2, 3, 41, 1840–78.
Daniel (*Capt.* **Octavius Harold),** *R.N., see* CONSETT (*Rear-Adm.* M. W. W. P.) Triumph of unarmed forces, 1914–18; by C. ass. by O. H. D., 1923.
Daniel (R. J.) Animal life in the sea. 8°. Liv'l. 1925
Daniel (Samuel), *poet & historian.* The collection of the hist. of Eng. w. contin. unto the r. of Henry VII, by J. Trussel. sfol. 1685
A defence of ryme against Obs. in the art of Eng. poesie, 1603—T. Campion: Obs. in the art of Eng. poesie, 1602 [*w. sep. pagin.* Ed. G. B. Harrison. Bodley Head Quartos]. s8°. [1925]
Daniel (Walter), *see* POWICKE (F. M.) Ailred of Rievaulx & h. biog. W. D., 1922.
Daniell (Alfred Ernest).
London City churches. 8°. Westminster. 1895
Daniell (*Mrs.* **E. H.),** *see* YOUNG (E. H.)
Daniell (Walter V.), *see* BROADLEY (A. M.) Coll. Napoleonica; cat. of coll. of A. M. B.; comp. by W. V. D., 1905.

Daniels (George William). The early Eng. cotton industry, w. some unpubl. letters of S. Crompton. Intr. chap. by G. Unwin. s8°. M'ter. 1920
Daniels (H. G.) The rise of the German Republic. 8°. [1927]
Daniels (William H.), *of Chicago.*
D. L. Moody & his work. s8°. 1875
Danielson (Henry).
Bibliographies of mod. authors. 8°. 1921
,, ,, ...*For* Ser. 2, 1925, *see* STONEHILL (C. A.) &c.
G. Moore: bibliogr., *see* FREEMAN (J.) Portrait of G. M., 1922.
Danielson (J. Rich.) Соединеніе Финляндіи съ Россійскою державою. Переводъ. 8°. Гельсингфорсъ. 1890
Danielsson (Olof Aug.) Zu d. lyd. Inschr., *see* KUNG. HUM. VET.-SAMF. I UPPSALA. Skr., B20, 1917.
Danilevsky (M). Нѣкоторыя выписки изъ бумагъ М. Д. [*b. w.* Trubetskoi (S. P.) Записки, 1874]. 3e изд. s8°. Лейпцигъ. *n.d.*
Danilov (*Gen.* **Jury Nikiforovich).** Россія въ Міровой Войнѣ, 1914–15. 8°. Берлинъ. 1924
Russland im Weltkriege, 1914–15. Übers. v. R. v. Campenhausen. 8°. Jena. 1925
Dänische. Kurtzgefassete Nachr. v. d. gegenwärt. Zustande d. hier z. Tranckenbar angericht Königl. D. Mission, 1754, 67, 70–73, 77, 1780, 81, 86, 1755–87, *see* TRANQUEBAR.
Dänische Missionarien. Der Königl. Dän. Miss. aus Ost-Indien eingesandter ausführl. Berichten. 108p. 1–9 Teil [*b. in* 15v]. 8°. Halle. 1735–70
continued as:—
Neuere Gesch. d. Evangel. Missions Anstalten zur Bekehrung d. Heiden in Ost.-Indien. 95 p. 8t [*b. in* 11v]. 8°. Halle. 1776–1848
continued as:—
Missionsnachrichten d. Ostind. Missionsanstalt zu Halle in vierteljährl. Heften; hrsg. v. H. A. Niemeyer. Jhrg. 1–17 [*in* 3v], 19–26 [*in* 2v], 30–32. 8°. Halle. 1849–80
see ZIEGENBALG (B.) & H. PLÜTSCHO. Merckwürdige Nachricht &c., 1708–17.
Danish. Book of Danish verse. Tr. S. F. Damon & R. S. Hillyer. Sel. & annot. by O. Friis. s8°. N.Y. 1922
34 conf. betw. D. missionaries &c., 1719, *see* PHILIPPS (J. T.)
Danish ballads; tr., 1920, *see* SMITH-DAMPIER (E. M.)
Dánkovszky (Gergely) [GREGORIUS D.] Hungaræ gentis avitum cognomen, origo sedesque priscae. 8°. Posonii. 1825
Hungariae constit. origines, gentis incunabula &c. 8°. Posonii. 1826
Magyaricae linguae lex. [*Lat. & Hung.*] 8°. Posonii. 1833
Dankovszky (Gregorius), *see* DÁNKOVSZKY (GERGELY).
Danloux (Henry Pierre), *see* PORTALIS (*le baron* R.) H. P. D., peintre de portraits, & s. journal dur. l'émigration, 1753–1809, 1910.
Danmark. Danmark-Norges traktater, 1523–1750, med dertil hørende aktstykker. Udg. af L. Laursen. B1–7, 1523–1682. la8°. 1905–26
Danna (Casimiro). Biografia doc. di C. Combetti, *see* REGIA DEP. DI STORIA PATRIA. Misc., t20, 1882.
Commem. del Teol. Cav. A. Bosio, *see* REGIA DEP. DI STORIA PATRIA. Misc., t20, 1882.
see DIONISOTTI (C.) Commem. del Comm. C. D., 1885.
Danne (Ferdinand). Das altfranz. Ebrulfusleben: e. Dichtung aus d. 12. Jhdt., *see* ROMAN. FORSCH., B32, 1913.
Danneberg (Robert).
Kampf gegen die Wohnungsnot! [P2564]. 8°. Wien. 1921
Dannemann (Friedrich). Die Naturwissenschaften in i. Entwicklung &c. 2e A. 4B. 8°. L. 1920–23
Dannhauer (Johann Conrad).
Diss. instituta ad collat. Carthagin. inter Catholicos & Donatistas. Cui adj. Sigalion Croesiaden Hyperaspisten. [*w. sep. tp.*] s4°. Argentorati. 1658
Hodomoria spiritus Calviniani. 2p [*pagin. cont.*] s8°. Argentorati. 1654
Liber conscientiae apertus, sive theologiae conscient. tomus primus. Editore J. C. D. 2p *in* 1v. s4°. Argentorati. 1662
T. posterior publ. 1667 *by Baltasar Bebel, after the author's death, is wanting.*
Mysterium syncretismi detecti &c. [P2646]. s4°. Argentorati. 1648
Nuncius nuncio-Britannico J. Duraeo a J. C. D. cui accessit: Hypomnema apologet. B. Bebelii. [*a. c. b. w.* Dury (J.) Irenic. tract. prodromus, 1662]. s8°. [Argentorati ?]. 1664
Ὁδοσοφία Christiana, seu theologia positiva &c. ed. 4a. auct. s4°. Argentorati. 1713
see DURY (J.) Consultat. irenic. Προδιόρθωσις, inter J. C. D., &c. & J. D., 1664.
,, VEIEL (E.) Exercit. de Eccl. Græcanica, sub præs. J. C. D., 1666.

Danovius (Ernst Jacob). Theologiae dogmaticae instit. 2 lib. *in* 1v. [*pagin. cont*]. s4º. Jenæ. 1772–76

Dans (Adolphus van). Poemata. Acc. vita reginae Elisabethae. Ed. J. à Dans. s8º. Lugduni Batav. 1636

Dansaert (G.) Anciennes faiences de Bruxelles. Préf. de G. des Marez. 4º. Brux. 1922

Danske. Danske folkeviser i udvalg, Saml. 1, 1918, *see* Olrik (A.)

Danske Sprog-og Litteraturselskab, *see* Dahlerup (V.) Ordbog over det danske sprog, B3–8, udg. af D. S. L., 1921–26.

Danson (Thomas), *see* Sherlock (W.) An answer to A friendly debate &c., by T. D., 1677.

Dante Alighieri, *Society.*
see Stringher (B.) Relaz. al XVI congresso d. " D. A.," 1905.
,, Villari (P.) La " D. Alighieri " a Siena, 1902.

Dante Society, *Cambridge, Mass.* Annual report[s] 37th–41st [*w.*] accompanying papers. 8º. Boston. 1920–24
see Dante. Lyrics of the Vita nuova ; tr. H. Johnson, 1924. [39–41.]
,, Goggio (E.) Longfellow & Dante, 1924. [39–41.]
,, Grandgent (C. H.) The choice of a theme. [37.]
,, Toynbee (P. J.) Dante in Eng. art. [38.]
,, Wilkins (E. H.) Il chi e il quale. [37.]

Dante Alighieri.

Dante e la Lunigiana. Nel sesto cent., 1306–1906. [*By var. wr.*] 8º. Milano. 1909

Dante. Essays in commem., 1321–1921. [By Visct. Bryce, B. Croce *&* *others.* Ed. by A. Cippico &c.] 8º. 1921

Dante. Mélanges de crit. & d'érudition franç. publ. à l'occ. du 6e cent. de la mort du poète. 4º. 1921

Laude ined. in onore di Nostra Donna, con disc. d. A. Bonucci. [P2787]. 8º. Bologna. 1854

Lectura Dantis. 8º. Firenze. [1899–1923]
D. e Lucano. Conf. (V. Ussani).
La D. C. n. comm. d. scienziati ital. ; conf. (A. Garbasso).
Fiammetta, di G. Boccaccio ; conf. (V. Crescini).
G. Boccaccio : l'uomo e l'artista, Conf. (G. Arcoleo).
Inferno. Canto 2 (I. Della Giovanna), c. 4 (L. Valli), c. 5 (C. Ricci), c. 7 (G. Rosadi), c. 8 (E. Romagnoli), c. 11 (O. Bacci), c. 13 (A. Medin), c. 18 (R. Fornaciari), c. 20 (G. M. Donati), c. 25 (V. Capetti), c. 28 (G. Ferretti), c. 29 (N. Zingarelli), c. 31 (A. Ghignoni), c. 32 (A. Messeri), c. 34 (P. Papa).
Paradiso. Canto 2 (E. G. Parodi), c. 15 (E. Donadoni), c. 16 (L. Rocca), c. 20 (G. Albini), c. 21 (F. P. Luiso), c. 24 (G. Giovannozzi), c. 28 (G. Vandelli), c. 29 (V. Ferrari), c. 31 (A. Chiapelli), c. 33 (E. Pistelli), n. ed., c. 33 (I. Del Lungo).
Purgatorio. Canto 7 (P. Giacosa), c. 8 (E. Donadoni), c. 9 (G. Lesca), c. 14 (E. Pistelli), n. ed., c. 17 (P. Rajna), c. 30 (S. Monte).
Sensi terreni n. Paradiso di D. ; lett. (G. Bertacchi).

Works.
Opera omnia. 2v. s8º. L. *Insel-Verlag.* 1921
Opere. Testo critico d. Soc. Dantesca Ital. ; a cura di M. Barbi &c., con indice &c. s8º. Firenze. 1921

Single Works.
De Monarchia.
De M. libri 3. Rec. L. Bertalot. 8º. Gebennae. 1920

De Vulgari Eloquentia.
De v. e. libri 2. Rec. Bertalot. s8º. Gebennae. 1920

Divina Commedia.
Le terze rime di D. [Inferno, Purgatorio & Paradiso]. s8º. [Venetiis *in aedib. Aldi.* 1502]
[L'Onferno, él Purgatorio, él Paradiso]. s8º. [Vinegia. *Aldo.* 1515]
La D. C. 2t. s8º. Londra. 1778
D. C. Corr. &c. dal P. B. Lombardi nel 1791. Nuov. emend. di annot. e di un vol. arricchita. 4t. la8º. 1815–17
1, Inferno. 2, Purgatorio. 3, Paradiso. 4, Le princ. cose appart. alla D. C. &c. [*This tome has spec. tp. & is divided into 3 parts, each w. sep. pagin.*]
La D. C. di mano del Boccaccio. [*Ed.* A. Fantoni]. la8º. Roveta. 1820
La D. C. giusta la lez. del cod. Bartoliniano. 3v *in* 4 [3i, ii ; 3ii *cont.* Dizionario, da Q. Viviani, Indici &c.] 8º. Udine. 1823–28
,, ,, ...[*la. paper*].
v1, 2. la8º. Udine. 1823
D. C. ; con note di P. Costa. 8º. Monza. 1837
La D. C. espos. in prosa dal conte F. Trissino, col testo. 3v. 8º. Milano. 1864
C. ; col. comm. di J. di G. dalla Lana. [*Ed.*] L. Scarabelli. fol. Milano. [1865]
Codice framm. d. D. C., Bibl. dell' Univ. di Bologna. Ed. L. Scarabelli. la8º. Bologna. 1869
Commedia. Prec. d. vita &c. comm. da A. Lubin. 8º. Padova. 1881
La D. C. Con comm. sec. la scolastica d. P. G. Berthier. [*Illust.*] v1 [Inferno]. fol. Friburgo. 1892
D. C. Con note dei celeb. comm., racc. G. B. Francesia. 12a. ed. 3v [*b. in 1*]. s8º. Torino. 1897
La D. C., illust. nei luoghi e n. persone. A cura di C. Ricci. [3v]. sfol. Milano. [1921]

Dante Alighieri [*continued*].

Divina Commedia [*continued*].
La D. C. N. figuraz. artist. e nel secolare comm. a cura di G. Biagi. [v1, Inferno]. fol. [1924]

Inferno.
Prolusioni alle tre cantiche e comm. all' " Inferno." Per I. Del Lungo. 8º. Firenze. 1921

Letters.
Epistolae. Emended text, w. introd., trans., notes &c. by P. Toynbee. 8º. O. 1920

Translations.
Inferno.
The Inferno. [Text, & Eng. tr. by P. H. Wicksteed ; notes by P. H. W. & H. Oelsner. Temple Classics]. [3rd ed.] s8º. [1902]

Paradiso.
The Paradiso. [Text, & Eng. tr. by P. H. Wicksteed; notes &c. by P. H. W. & H. Oelsner. Temple Classics]. [4th ed.] s8º. [1903]
,, ,, [*repr.*] s8º. 1919

Purgatorio.
The Purgatorio. [Text, & Eng. tr. by P. H. Wicksteed ; notes by P. H. W. & H. Oelsner. Temple Classics]. s8º. 1900
,, ,, [2nd ed.] s8º. [1902]

References.
see Asin Palacios (M.) Islam & the D. C. ; tr. &c., 1926.
,, Bambagiuoli (G. de') Il comm. piú ant. e la piú ant. vers. lat. d. Inferno, 1892.
,, Barbi (M.) Studi D., v1–12, 1920–27.
,, —— Studi sul Canzoniere di D., 1915,
,, Barrès (M.) D., Pascal &c., 1923.
,, Caetani (M.) Carteggio dantesco del Duca di Sermoneta, con G. Giuliani &c., 1883.
,, —— Tre chiose n. D. C., 1876.
,, Cancellieri (F.) Osserv. int. alla quest. promossa dal Vannozzi &c. sopra l'originalità d. D. C. &c., 1814.
,, Cesare (G. di) Esame d. D. C., 1807.
,, Cesari (A.) Bellezze d. C. di D. A., 4v, 1824–26.
,, Chambers (R. W.) Long Will, D., & the righteous heathen, 1924.
,, Church (R. W.) D. &c., 1906.
,, Cipolla (C.) Taddeo del Branca e una tradiz. leggend. sull' Alighieri, 1887.
,, Colini-Baldeschi (E.) Bologna n. opere di D., 1921.
,, Comité Français Catholique pour la célébr. du 6e cent. de D., Bull., Jan., 1921–Jan. 1922.
,, Cornell University. Cat. of the D. Coll. pr. by W. Fiske, Additions, 1898–1920, 1921.
,, Cotes (R. A.) D.'s garden &c., 1898.
,, Courthope (W. J.) Macaulay's comparison of D. & Milton, 1908.
,, Croce (B.) La poesia di D., 1921.
,, —— The poetry of D. ; tr. D. Ainslie, 1922.

References [*continued*].
see Dami (L.) & B. Barbadoro. Firenze di D., 1921.
,, Dante Soc., *Camb., Mass.* Ann. rep. *w.* papers, 1920–.
,, De La Fontaine (H. C.) D. & war, *& essays on* De Monarchia & Convito, 1915.
,, Del Lungo (I.) I Bianchi e i Neri, 1921.
,, —— Il " giusto giudicio " imprecato da D., 1921.
,, Falorsi (G.) Le concordanze D., 1920.
,, Farinelli (A.) D. in Spagna, Fr., Ingh., Germ. &c., 1922.
,, Fletcher (J. B.) Dante, 1916.
,, —— Symbolism of the D. C., 1921.
,, Foligno (C.) D., 1920.
,, Foscolo (N. U.) Sec. di D., 2t, 1830.
,, Galimberti (A.) D. nel pensiero inglese, 1921.
,, Giornale stor. d. lett. ital. Suppl. 19–21, Misc. D., 1921.
,, Göschel (C. F.) D.'s Unterweisung ü. Weltschöpfung u. Weltordnung, 1842.
,, Grandgent (C. H.) Discourses on D., 1924.
,, Guerri (D.) Il Commento del Boccaccio a D., 1926.
,, Hatzfeld (H.) D., seine Weltanschauung, 1921.
,, Hefele (H.) Dante, 1921.
,, Jakubczyk (C.) D., s. Leben u. s. Werke, 1921.
,, Labusquette (R. de). Autour de Dante : les Béatrices, 1921.
,, Levi (C.) D. " dramatis persona," 1921.
,, Maggini (F.) La mostra dantesca alla Laurenziana di Firenze, 1921.
,, Majenza (M.) La natura e l'amore n. D. C., 1922.
,, Marcolini (C.) Degli ordinamenti ond' ebbe informata D. la prima cantica d. D. C. investig. di F. Lanci, 1855, 1856.
,, Mather (F. J.) Portraits of D. &c., 1921.
,, Mazzoni (G.) Il nome di D. e le 2 società ital. intit. da lui, 1921.
,, Minocchi (S.) L'ombra di D., 1921.
,, Moore (E.) The " DXV " prophecy in the D. C. (Purg. 33, 37–45), 1901.
,, Oxford Dante Society.
,, Panella (A.) Firenze e il sec. crit. d. fortuna di D., 1921.
,, Passerini (G. L.) Il ritratto di D., 1921.
,, Picchioni (L.) La D. C. illust. da A. Kopisch, G. Picci e M. G. Ponta : cenni crit. di L. P., 1846.
,, Ponta (M. G.) Nuovo esperimento s. princ. allegoria d. D. C., 2a ed., 1845.
,, —— Saggio di critica ai nuovi studi sopra D. del Sig. G. P., 1845.
,, Ramsey (R. W.) D. & St. Louis, 1924.
,, Reale Accademia d. Scienze di Torino. Dante e il Piemonte, 1922.
,, Rébora (P.) Immortal in D., 1922.

Dante Alighieri [*continued*].

REFERENCES [*continued*].
see RENIER (R.) La Vita nuova e La fiammetta: st. crit., 1879.
„ REVELLI (P.) L'Italia n. D. C., 1922.
„ RICCI (C.) L'ultimo rifugio di D., 1921.
„ —— Ore ed ombre dantesche., 1921.
„ RIO DE JANEIRO: Bibl. Nac. Cat. de expos. bibl.-icon. (Dante bibliog.), 1925.
„ SANTAYANA (G.) 3 philos. poets: Lucretius, D. &c., 3rd impr., 1922.
„ SAPORI (A.) Rassegna crit.: pubbl. dantesche ital. del cent., 1921.
„ SOLMI (A.) Stato e chiesa nel D., 1921.
„ TIEPOLO (G.) Sopra D. A.: discorso, 1864.
„ TORRACA (F.) Nuovi studi Danteschi, 1921.

REFERENCES [*continued*].
see TOYNBEE (P. J.) The bearing of the cursus on the text of D.'s De vulgari eloquentia, 1923.
„ —— Britain's tribute to D. in lit. & art, 1921.
„ —— D. studies, 1921.
„ —— The Oxford Dante, 1926.
„ TRÖLTSCH (E.) Der Berg d. Läuterung, Rede, Todestag D., 1921.
„ TURRI (V.) D., 1265–1321, 1907.
„ VENTURI (A.) Il Botticelli interprete di D., 1921.
„ —— L. Signorelli interprete di D., 1921.
„ VOSSLER (C.) D. als relig. Dichter, 1921.
„ WICKSTEED (P. H.) Fr. Vita Nuova to Paradiso, 1922.

Dantin Cereceda (Juan). Exploradores y conquistadores de Indias, relatos geogr. Seleccion, notas y mapas (1492–1540). s8°. 1922

Dantiscus (Joannes), *see* CURIIS (J. DE).

Danton (Georges Jacques).
see BELLOC (H.) D., *n.d.*
„ LECOMTE (G.) La vie amoureuse de D., 1927.
„ MADELIN (L.) Danton; tr., 1921.
see MATHIEZ (A.) Autour de D., 1926.
„ —— D. & la paix, 1919.
„ ROBINET (J. F. E.) D. émigré, 1887.

Dantscher von Kollesberg (Theodor *Ritter*). Der staatsrechtl. Charakter d. Delegationen. 8°. Wien. 1903

Danube. Strategic geography: theatres of war of the Rhine & D., 1891, *see* RHINE.

D'Anvers (Alicia), *? ps.* *Academia: or, The humours of the Univ. of Oxford. In burlesque verse. s8°. 1716

Danvers (Henry), *see* BAXTER (R.) More proofs of infants' church-membership &c.; of forgeries of H. D. &c., 1675.

Danz (Johann Andreas) [DANZIUS]. Divina inter co-aequales de primo homine condendo deliberatio. [P2634]. s4°. Jenæ. [1715 ?]
Inauguratio Christi ad doc. haud obscurior Mosaica, e spectaculis circa bapt. Christi. s4°. Jenæ. 1717

Danz (Johann Traugott Lebrecht). Epistolae P. Melanchthonis ad J. Stigelium &c. [P2672]. 4°. Jenæ. 1824
Epistolae P. Melanchthonis ad Nic. Medlerum &c. [P2672]. 4°. Jenæ. 1825

Danzig [*see also* GDANSK]. *The Free city of D.'s legal & polit. status. [P2844]. s8°. [1923]
Polit. Hdbh. d. Freien Stadt D. Im amtl. Auftrage v. Gross. s8°. Danzig. 1924
Theolog. Berichte v. neuen Büchern &c. v. e Gesells. zu D., 1764–73, *see* THEOLOGISCHE BERICHTE.

Daon (Roger). Conduite des confesseurs dans le tribunal de la pénitence, selon les instructions de Saint Charles Borromée &c. 5e éd. revûe &c. s8°. 1760

Darboux (Gaston), *1842–1917.* Leçons s. la théorie gén. des surfaces. 4p. [p1, 2, 2e éd., p4, n. tir.] la8°. 1894–1925

Darby (Charles). The Bk. of Psalms in Eng. metre. s8°. 1704

Darcie (Abraham), *see* CAMDEN (W.) Annales, true hist. of Eliz. [tr. f. the Fr. vers. of P. de Belligent by A. D.], 1625.

D'Arcy (Charles F.), *D.D., bp. of Down, aft. Abp. of Dublin, aft. Abp. of Armagh, see* ANGLICAN essays; by Abp. of Armagh &c., 1923.

Dardanelles. *Uncensored letters f. the D. Wr. to his Eng. wife by a French medical officer. s8°. 1916

Dárday (D.) The solution of the Fiume q. [P2567]. s8°. 1920

Dardis (Patrick G.) The occup. of land in Ireland in 1st half of the 19th c. Pref. by T. A. Finlay. [Thesis]. s8°. D. 1920

Darell (John), *merchant.* *True &c. narr.; or (2nd part of Amboyna) of sundry &c. injuries &c. agst. the English in the East Indies, & partic. of plundering &c. of the Dragon & Katherine. By J. D. [*i.e.* Darell]. 8°. 1665

Daremberg (Charles V) & E. Saglio, *edd.* Dict. des antiquités grecques & rom. Ouvrage fondé par C. D., & réd. par une soc. d'écr. spéc., sous la dir. de E. S., avec concours de E. Pottier &c. t5, T–Z. *&* Table. 4°. [1919]

Dares, *Phrygius.* De excidio Troiae, *see* DICTYS *Cretensis.* De bello Trojano &c., 1630.

Daressy (Georges). Une représent. égypt. du pèsement des actions, *see* ACAD. D. INSCR.: FOND. PIOT. Mon., t25, 1921–22.

Dargan (Edwin Preston), *see* NITZE (W. A.) & E. P. D. Hist. of French lit., 1923.

Dargomijsky (Aleksandr Sergeevich), *see* RIESEMANN (O. v.) Monographien z. russ. Musik, B1, 1923.

Darien, *Scots colony.* *Defence (A) of the Scots settlement at D., 1699, *see* FLETCHER (A.)
*An enquiry into the causes of the miscarriage of the Scots colony at Darien or an ans. to A defence of the Scots abdicating D. [*b. w.* Fletcher (A.) A defence, 1699]. s8°. Glasgow. 1700
*A just & modest vindic. of the Scots design for a colony at D. [*attrib. to R. Ferguson*]. [*b. w.* Fletcher (A.) A defence, 1699]. s8°. [E.] 1699
see DARIEN COMPANY. Original papers & letters *&* Supplement, 1700.

Darien Company [COMPANY OF SCOTLAND TRADING TO AFRICA &C.] *The original papers & letters rel. to the Scots Company trading to Africa & the Indies. [*&* A supplement, *w. sep. tp. & pagin. b. w.* Darien. A defence, 1699]. s8°. [E.] 1700
Papers rel. to the ships & voyages of Co. of Scotland trading to Afr. & the Indies, 1696–1707. Ed. G. P. Insh. [Scot. Hist. Soc., s3, v6]. 8°. E. 1924

Daries (Joachim Georg), *see* MÜLLER (J. S.) Intr. in theol. revelat. usu philos. D. adornata, 1770.

Dario (Rubén).
Obras compl. Prólogo de A. Ghiraldo. 22v. [2, 4, 7 *wanting*]. s8°. "*Mundo Latino.*" 1917–25

1, La caravana pasa.
3, Tierras solares.
5, Parisiana.
6, Los raros.
8, Letras.
9, Canto a la Argentina &c.
10, Rimas y abrojos.
11, Poema del otoño &c.
12, Peregrinaciones.
13, Prosa polit. (Republ. Amer.)
14, Cuentos y crónicas.
15, Autobiografía.
16, El canto errante.
17, El viaje a Nicaragua.
18, Todo al vuelo.
19, España contemp.
20, Prosa dispersa.
21, Lira póstuma.
22, Cabezas.

Baladas y canciones. Pról. de A. González-Blanco. s8°. "*Ruben Dario.*" [1924]
Eleven poems. Tr. by T. Walsh & S. de la Selva. Intr. by P. H. Ureña. [Hisp. Soc. of Amer.] s8°. N.Y. 1916
Epistolario. 1. Prol. de A. Ghiraldo. Ap., Cartas de M. de Unamuno *&* de J. Santos Zelaya. 8°. "*Ruben Dario.*" 1926

***Dark** deeds, 1849, *see* NEALE (E.)

Dark (Sidney).
How to enjoy life: everyday philos. s8°. [1924]
Mainly about other people. 8°. [1925]
The outline of H. G. Wells. s8°. [1922]
—— & R. Grey.
W. S. Gilbert, h. life & letters. 8°. [1923]

Darkest Russia: a weekly record &c. New ser., v1, 2 (Jan. 1912–July 1913). [*no more publ. No.* 1–4 *wanting*]. sfol. 1912–13

Darley (Mary). Cameos of a Chinese city. 8°. 1917

Darling (Charles John, *1st baron*).
A pensioner's garden. 8°. [1926]
*Seria ludo. By a dilettante. 8°. 1903

Darling (James), *see* CLERICAL LIBRARY. Bibliotheca clericalis, 1843.

Darling (Malcolm Lyall). The Punjab peasant in prosperity & debt. Foreword by Sir E. Maclagan. 8°. O. 1925

Darling (Samuel Taylor), M. A. Barber & H. P. Hacker. Hookworm & malaria research in Malaya, Java, & the Fiji Islands. Rep. of Uncinariasis Comm. to the Orient, 1915–17. s8°. N.Y. 1920

Darlington (William Aubrey). Through the fourth wall. 8°. 1922

Darlow (Thomas Herbert).
William R. Nicoll: life & letters. [2nd impr.] 8°. [1925]

Darmesteter (Arsène). Cours de grammaire hist. de la langue fr. Publ. L. Sudre. 4p *in* 2v. [1, 5e; 2, 3, 4, 4e éd.] s8°. [1902–5]
La vie des mots. s8°. 1887
The life of words as symbols of ideas. [Tr.] s8°. 1886

Darmesteter (*Mme.* James) [†ROBINSON (AGNES MARY FRANCES), *aft. Darmesteter, aft. Duclaux*].
The life of Racine. 8°. [1925]
Portrait of Pascal. 8°. 1927
20th c. French writers. Reviews & remin. s8°. [1919]
Victor Hugo. 8°. 1921

Darmon (J. E.) Dict. des peintres miniaturistes sur vélin, parchemin &c. 8°. [1927]
—— **& Granger.** Dict. des gravures en couleurs &c. du 18e s., avec leur prix. 8°. 1920
Darmstadt. *D. in d. Tagen d. Weltkriegs. H.1–12 [in 1v]. 8°. [Darmstadt. 1914–16]
H.1 *has t.* D. in d. Tagen d. Mobilmachung. H.8–12 *have t.* Hessische Kriegshefte.
see SCHMIDT (A.) Bucheinbände, 14–19 Jhdt. in d. Landesbibl. zu D., 1921.
Darmstaeder (Ernst).
Georg Agricola, 1494–1555. 8°. München. 1926
Darney (William).
A coll. of hymns. p4. [P2551]. s8°. Leedes. 1751
Darnley (Edward, *5th earl***),** *see* CUST (*Lady* E.) & E. G. PELHAM. E., 5th Earl of D., & Emma Parnell, h. wife: story told in th. letters &c., 1913.
Darnley (Emma Jane, *ctss. of*), *form. Parnell, wife of 5th earl Darnley, see* CUST (*Lady* E.) & E. G. PELHAM. Edward, 5th Earl of D., & E. Parnell, h. wife: story told in th. letters &c., 1913.
Darnley (Ivo Francis Walter Bligh, *8th earl***).** Cat. of pictures by old masters, property of Earl of D., Cobham Hall, Kent, sold by Christie &c., May 1, 1925. [*Illust.*] 8°. [1925]
Darpe (Franz), *see* WESTFALEN. Bau- u. Kunstdenkm., 25, 29, 31, 32, 34, 35, gesch. Einl. v. F. D., 1907–10.
Darroch (G. R. S.) Deeds of a great railway: L. & N.-W. R. Co. dur. the Gt. War. Pref. by L. J. Maxse. 8°. 1920
Darton (Frederick Joseph Harvey).
The marches of Wessex. 8°. [1922]
Vincent Crummles, h. theatre & h. times. Arr. by D., w. intr. note & app. f. Nicholas Nickleby by C. Dickens. la8°. [1926]
see SAWYER (C. J.) & F. J. H. D. Eng. bks., 1475–1900, 2v, 1927.
Darusmont (Frances), *see* WRIGHT (F.), *aft. Mme. d'Arusmont.*
Darwin (Bernard), *see* DUNCAN (G.) & B. D. Present-day golf, 1921.
Darwin (Charles Galton). Recent developments in atomic theory. Boyle Lect., 1926. 8°. O. 1927
Darwin (Charles Robert). Expression of emotions in man & animals. Ed. F. Darwin. 11th thousand. 8°. 1892
see PAULIN (G.) No struggle for existence &c.: exam. of D. theory, 1908.
,, PEARSON (K.) C. D., 1809–82, 1923.
Darwin (Florence Henrietta, *Lady*), *wife of Sir F. Darwin, née Fisher.* 6 plays. [Lovers' tasks—Bushes & briars—My man John—Princess Royal—The seeds of love—The New Year]. Intr. by C. Sharp. 8°. C. 1921
Darwin (*Sir* **Francis Sacheverell),** *1786–1859.* Travels in Spain & the East, 1808–10. [Ed. F. D. S. Darwin]. s8°. C. 1927
Darwin (Leonard).
The need for eugenic reform. 8°. 1926
Organic evolution: difficulties &c. 8°. C. 1921
Das (Rajani Kanta).
Factory labour in India. 8°. Berlin. 1923
Hindustani workers on the Pacific coast. 8°. Berlin. 1923
Das (Taraknath).
The Anglo-Jap. alliance & America. [P2620]. 8°. Wash. 1921
Das (Tulsi), *see* TULSI DÁS.
Dasent (Arthur Irwin). Nell Gwynne, 1650–87, w. acc. of Whitehall &c. in reign of Charles II. 8°. 1924
Piccadilly in 3 cent. w. acc. of Berkeley Sq. & the Haymarket. 8°. 1920
Story of Stafford House, now the London Museum. s8°. 1921
Dasgupta (Surendranath).
A hist. of Indian philosophy. v1. 8°. C. 1922
Dashean (Hakobos) [DACHIAN; TASHEAN]. [Doct. of the Apostles, Apoc. book of canons—Letter of James to Codrat—& Canons of Thaddaeus. Comm. & text. *In Armenian.*] s8°. Vienna. 1896
[Short bibliog. studies &c. *In Armenian*]. 2v. [1, *b. w.* Vetter (P.) Arm. studies, 1895; 2 *in* P2814]. s8°. Vienna. 1895–1901
1, Nemesius, Proclus, Khosrov, Epiphanius & Secundus.
2, Ahikar, Agapetus, Abgar & George of Pisidia.
[Study of Pseudo-Callisthenes' Life of Alexander. *In Armenian. b. w.* Vetter (P.) Arm. studies, 1895]. s8°. Vienna. 1892
see MEKHITARISTS. Cat. d. arm. Hss. in d. M. Bibl., Wien, v. J. Dashian, 1895.
,, VETTER (P.) Armenian st.; tr. &c. H. D., 1895.

Dashwood (*Mrs.* **Elizabeth M.),** *wife of Arthur Paul D., see* DELAFIELD (E. M.), *ps.*
Dassigny (Fifield). Serious &c. enquiry into pres. decay of free-masonry in Ireland (1744); repr., 1913, *see* HUGHAN (W. J.) Memorials &c., 1913.
Dassov (Theodor) [DASSOVIUS]. Ad titulum Celim, nonnulla ex Hebr. magistris. Praes. T. Dassovius, resp. Th. Battus. [P2666]. s4°. Vitembergæ. 1714
Avem, ungue sectam, inque sacrificium oblatam, prop. T. D., resp. J. C. Kirstenius. [P2666]. s4°. Vitembergæ. [1697]
Comam Hebræorum lic. & interdict., præs. Th. D., collat. sistit C. Alten-Eck. [P2744]. s4°. Vittenbergæ. 1695
Justa animadv. in Cordati Evangelici inanem loquacitatem. [P2631]. s4°. Hamburgi. 1716
Dasypodius (Petrus).
Dict. Latinogerman. et Germanicolat. s4°. Argentorati. 1537
Dathe (Johann August) [DATHIUS (I. A.)] Opuscula ad crisin & interpret. Vet. Test. spect. Coll. & ed. E. F. C. Rosenmüller. 8°. Lipsiæ. 1796
—— **& S. F. N. Morus.** Disput. in Aquilae reliquias interpret. Hoseae, quam def. J. A. D. & S. A. D. Morus. [P430]. s4°. Lipsiæ. 1757
Dathenus (Petrus). *Kurtze u. warhafftige erzelung, welcher massen den Frantz. u. Niderländ. Christen in Franckfurt im 54 &c. jar die öffentl. predig &c. verbotten worden ist &c. Item etliche tractetlein [Purgation v. J. v. Lasko—Antidotus V. Pollani—Kirchen Ordnung &c. zu Franckfurt. *Ed.* M. Fronberger]. s4°. Heydelberg. 1598
Dati (Agostino) [DACTUS (AUG.)] Super Tullianis eleganciis &c. in sua Rethorica libellus. Pr. at St. Albans, c. 1479. [Facs., ed. F. Jenkinson]. la8°. C. 1905
Daubeny (Ulric).
Ancient Cotswold churches. la8°. Cheltenham. [1921]
Orchestral wind instruments, anc. & mod. 8°. [1920]
Däubler (Theodor). Das Nordlicht. 2B. s8°. L. 1921
Daubney (H.) A sober &c. discourse conc. interest of words in prayer, by H. D. M. A. [*attrib. to H. D.*], 1661, *see* SOBER.
Daubney (R.), *see* BRITISH MUSEUM OF NAT. HIST.: ZOOLOGY. Synopsis of families &c. of Nematoda, by H. A. Baylis & R. D., 1926.
Daucher (Adolf) [DAUHER; DAWHR], *see* HALM (P. M.) A. D. u. d. Fuggerkapelle bei St. Anna in Augsburg, 1921.
Daudé-Bancel (A.), *see* GIDE (C.) & A. D.-B. De la lutte contre la cherté &c., 1926.
Daudet (Alphonse).
Contes du lundi. n. éd. s8°. 1922
Lettres de mon moulin. Intr. par C. Sarolea. s8°. *Nelson.* [1910]
Lettres de mon moulin. éd. définit. s8°. 1920
Sapho. Illust. de L. Montégut. la8°. [1885 ?]
TRANSLATIONS.
Tartarin of Tarascon & Tartarin on the Alps. [Tr.] s8°. [1910]
Daudet (Ernest).
L'avant-dernier Romanoff, Alexandre III. s8°. 1920
Un drame d'amour à la cour de Suède, 1784–95. [Baron d'Armfelt & M. de Rudenschold]. s8°. 1913
Daudet (Léon A.)
La Chambre Nat. du 16 nov., portraits, *see* ŒUVRES libres, 25, 1923.
Le drame des Jardies (1877–82). 8°. [1924]
L'hécatombe. Récits & souv. polit., 1914–18. s8°. 1923
L'homme & le poison, *see* ŒUVRES libres, 41, 1924.
Le rêve éveillé: ét sur la profondeur de l'esprit. s8°. 1926
Souv. des milieux litt., polit. &c., 1880–[1914]. s5, 6. s8°. 1920–21
Le stupide 19e siècle: insanités meurtrières, France, 1789–1919. s8°. [1922]
Sylla et son destin. s8°. [1922]
Daugars (Guillaume Gustave), *see* LEAKEY (J. S.) In Chancery; betw. G. G. D., plaintiff, & A. H. Rivaz, &c., def., 1858 ?.
Dauher (Adolf), *see* DAUCHER (A.)
Daulier Deslandes (André).
The beauties of Persia, 1673. Tr. A. T. Wilson. 8°. 1926
Daumet (Georges), *see* BENEDICT XII, *pope.* B. XII, 1334–42: lettres closes &c. se rapp. à la France; [publ.] par G. D., 1920.
Daumier (Honoré).
see ESCHOLIER (R.) D., 1913.
,, KLOSSOWSKI (E.) H. D., 2e A., 1923.
,, RÜMANN (A.) H. D., s. Holzschnittwerk: Text u. Katalog, 1914.
Daun (Berthold). V. Stoss u. s. Schule in Deutschland, Polen u. Ungarn &c. 2e erweit. A. la8°. L. 1916
Daungerous, *see* DANGEROUS.

Daunou (Pierre Claude François). *Papal (The) power: or, essay on the temporal power of the popes. Tr. [by R. T. H.] 2v. 8°. D. 1825
see DUMOURIEZ (*gén.* C. F.) Mem., p. s. à l'hist. de la Convention Nat. par D., 1886.
„ —— Suite des Mém. du Gén. D. &c. & Mém. &c. par D., 1886.

Dauphiné. Choix de doc. hist. inéd. sur le D. Publ. &c. par C. U. J. Chevalier. [Coll. de cartul. dauph., t7. Extr. du Bull. de la Soc. de Stat. de l'Isère, s3, t6.] la8°. Lyon. 1874

Dauthendey (Max).
Gesamm. Werke. 6B. s8°. München. [1925]
1, Autobiographisches. 2, Aus fernen Ländern. 3, Novellen u. Romane. 4, Lyrik u. kl. Versdicht. 5, Gross. Versdicht. 6, Dramen.

D'Auvergne (Edmund B.) The merciful darkness. s8°. [1924]

Daux (Camille). Le pèlerinage à Compostelle & la Confrérie des pèlerins de Mgr. Saint-Jacques de Moissac. 8°. 1898

Dauzat (Albert).
Les noms de personnes: orig. & évol. s8°. 1925
La Suisse ill. 4°. *Larousse.* [1913]
La Suisse mod. s8°. 1910

Dávalos (Juan Carlos).
Salta. Prólogo de M. Gálvez. s8°. Buenos Aires. 1918

Daveluy (*contre-amiral* René). L'action maritime pendant la guerre anti-german. 2t. 8°. 1920

Davenant (Charles), *see* †WHITWORTH (*Sir* C.) Tracts on trade & commerce, suppl. to D.'s works, 1778.

Davenant (John), *bp. of Salisbury* [DURAEUS]. De pacis eccl. rationibus inter Evangelicos usurpandis &c. in colloquio Lips. inito J. D., T. Mortoni, J. Halli sententiae J. Duraeo ab ipsis trad. s4°. *n.p.* 1635
An exhortation to brotherly communion betw. the Protestant churches. [2p *in* 1v. p2 *has sep. pagin. & tp.* An exhort. to the restoring of b. c. &c.] s8°. 1641
see MORTON (T.), *bp. of Chester.* De pace inter Evangel. procuranda, a T. Dunelm., Jo. Sarisb. &c., 1638.

Davenport (Charles Benedict). Body-build & its inheritance. [C.I. of Wash.] la8°. Wash. 1923
see UNITED STATES: ARMY. Medical Dept. in the World War, v15, p1, Army anthropology; by C. B. D. &c., 1921.

Davenport (Christopher), *called Franciscus a Sancta Clara.*
Deus, natura, gratia, sive Tractatus, De praedestinatione &c. 8°. Lugd. 1634
Operum omnium scholastic. & hist. ed. nov. 2t. fol. Duaci. 1665–67
1, Systema Fidei—De Schismate—Hist. minor provinciae Angliae [& Suppl., 1671]—Manuale missionar. *each w. sep. tp. & pagin.*
2, Apologia episcop.—Liber dialogorum—Problemata scholast. —De medio statu animarum—Paralipomena philos.—Religio philosophi—Epist. adv. judiciarium astrologiam *each w. sep. tp. & pagin.*

Davenport (Cyril James H.)
Byways among Eng. books. s8°. 1927
Cameo book-stamps figured & described. la8°. 1911

Davenport (E. H.) & S. R. Cooke.
Oil trusts & Anglo-Amer. relations. s8°. 1923

Davenport (Salusbury Fynes). Immanence & Incarnation. Foreword by F. R. Tennant. 8°. C. 1925

Davey (E. C.) Notable catholics who lived & died at Bath, 1678–1823. 8°. *n.d.*

Davey (Norman).
Desiderium, 1915–18. [*Poems.*] s8°. C. 1920
Good hunting. s8°. 1923
Guinea girl. s8°. 1921
The pilgrim of a smile. s8°. [1921]

David, *Armenian philosopher* [DAVID, *the Invincible*; DAVITH, *Anyalth*]. Girq Sahmanatz. [Book of definitions. *In Armenian*]. s8°. K.-polis. *n.d.* [1731?]
see CONYBEARE (F. C.) Exam. of the wr. of D., *in Armenian,* 1893.
„ MANANDIAN (Y.) Davith Anyalthi khndire [*in Armen.*], 1904.

David III, *king of Georgia, d. 1125* [DAVID *Stroitel, or Restorer*].
see SHAVTEL. Пѣвецъ Д. (12c. Georgian text &c.); изд. Н. Марръ, 1902.

David, *King of Israel.*
see DREXEL (H.) D. regius Psaltes, 1652.
„ SMITH (G.) Life &c. of D., 1867.

David *ben Joseph Kimchi.* Comm. on the prophecies of Zechariah. Tr. w. not. &c. by A. McCaul. 8°. 1837
Joel & Malachias cum comm. rabi David Kimhi. [*b. w.* Bible: Psalms. Ps. Hebr., 1533]. s8°. Basileæ. 1530
Radicum liber sive Hebraeum Bibliorum lexicon. Ed. J. H. R. Biesenthal & F. Lebrecht. [*Foll. by* Breves notae de vitis &c. auctorum qui in K. citantur.] 4°. Berolini. 1847
see GENEBRARD (G.) R. J. Albonis, R. D. Kimhi &c., argumenta &c., 1566.

David, *Saint, abp. of Wales, see* RICEMARCH, *the Wise.* Life of St. D. (11c.); [tr., w. sel. f. o. lives &c.] by A. W. Wade-Evans, 1923.

David (André). L'escalier de velours. [Le roman du désir]. Préf. de Rachilde. s8°. [1922]
Rachilde, homme de lettres, s. œuvre. s8°. 1924

David (Charles Wendell). Robert Curthose, duke of Normandy. [Harvard hist. studies, v25]. 8°. C. 1920

David (Ferencz [FRANCISCUS]**).** De non invoc. Jesu Christo in prec. sacr.: Theses F. D., propos. Fausto Socino. [*No tp.*] s8°. [Racov. 1595?]

David (François Anne), *see* BLIN DE SAINMORE (A. M. H.) Hist. de Russie, représ. par figures, gravées par F. A. D., 3t, 1797–1806.

David (Jacques Louis), *see* ROBESPIERRE (F. M. J. I.) Rapp. s. les idées relig. [*foll. by* Plan de la fête à l'Être Suprême, proposé par D.], 1794.

David (Joseph), *Syrian abp. of Damascus.* Antiqua Eccl. Syro-Chaldaicae traditio circa Petri Apostoli & successorum primatum. Acc. duae append. &c. [*&* Textus Syrochaldaici vel Arabici &c.] 8°. Romæ. 1870

David-Beg, *see* DAVITH-BEG.

Davids (Caroline Augusta Foley Rhys), *wife of T. W. R. Davids.* Buddhist psychology.
2nd ed. [*w.* Suppl^y. chapters]. s8°. 1924
see THERAGĀTHĀ. Psalms of the early Buddhists; [tr. &c.] Mrs. R. D., 2v, 1909–13.

Davids (T. W.), *Dissenting Minister.* Annals of Evangel. nonconformity in Essex, f. Wycliffe to Restor., w. mem. of Essex ministers ejected, 1660–62. 8°. 1863

Davids (Thomas William Rhys).
Buddhist India. 5th impr. s8°. [1917]
Cosmic law in anc. thought, *see* BRIT. ACAD. Proc., 1917–18.

Davidsohn (Paul). Sammlung P. D. Kupferstiche alt. Meister. Versteigerung, Mai & Nov. 1920, Apr. 1921, durch C. G. Boerner, Leipzig. 3T. [*w. plates*]. 4°. L. 1920–21

Davidsohn (Robert). Gesch. d. Florenz. B4, 3T [*&* Anmerk. *to each T.*]. la8°. 1925–27
4i–iii, Frühzeit d. flor. Kultur.
Vorstellungen v. alten Reich i. ihrer Einwirk. auf d. neuere deut. Gesch., *see* KÖNIGL. AKAD. D. WISS. ZU MÜNCHEN. Phil. Cl., Sitz., 1917.
Wirtschaftskrieg im M-a., *see* KÖNIGL. AKAD. D. WISS. ZU MÜNCHEN. Phil. Classe, Sitz., 1915.

Davidson (A. B.)
Outlines of Heb. accentuation. [P2496]. s8°. 1861

Davidson (Charles R.), *see* PHOTOGRAPHY as a sci. implement; by A. E. Conrady & C. R. D. &c., 1924.

Davidson (D.) & H. Aldersmith.
The Great Pyramid, its divine message. v1. la8°. 1924

Davidson (George). Methods & results: voyages of discovery &c. on N.W. coast of Amer., 1539–1603, 1887, *see* UNITED STATES: COAST SURVEY.

Davidson (John), *poet, see* STONEHILL (C. A.) &c. Bibliog. of mod. a., s2, 1925.

Davidson (Norman James). Modern travel: record of explor. &c. 8°. 1921. [1920]

Davidson (Peter Wylie).
Decorative leatherwork. Pref. by A. Macbeth. 8°. 1923

Davidson (Randall Thomas), *abp. of Canterbury.* The Prayer Book measure. Sp. by Abps. of Canterbury & York, 1927. [P2871]. 8°. [1927]

Davidson (Samuel), *D.D.* The eccl. polity of the New Test. unfolded. 8°. 1848

Davidson (Thomas), *misc. writer.* The philosophy of Goethe's Faust. Ed. C. M. Bakewell. 8°. Boston. [1906]

Davidson (V. M.) By dead reckoning. s8°. [1924]

Davie (Maurice Rea), *see* SUMNER (W. G.), A. G. KELLER & M. R. D. Sci. of society, 4v, 1927.

Davies, *The family of, see* BURKE (J. B.) Geneal. hist. of the house of Gwysaney, 1847.

Davies (Albert Emil). The case for nationalization. s8°. [1920]

Davies (Alfred Mervyn). The influence of George III on the development of the constit. s8°. O. 1921
Davies (Arthur Llewelyn), *see* ABRAHAM (M. E.) & A. L. D. Law rel. to factories & workshops, 3rd ed., 1901.
Davies (Arthur Morley). Buckinghamshire. s8°. C. 1912
Intr. to palaeontology. s8°. 1920
see COLE (G. A. J.), A. M. D. &c. The Brit. Isles, 1917.
Davies (D. T.) The barber & the cow. s8°. O. 1926
Davies (Emily), *LL.D.* [DAVIES (SARAH EMILY)], *see* STEPHEN (B., *Lady*). E. D. & Girton College, 1927.
Davies (F. S.) Cochin, British & Indian. s8°. [1923]
Davies (G.) Early hist. of the Coldstream Guards. la8°. O. 1924
Davies (Gerald Stanley).
Charterhouse in London: monastery &c. 8°. 1921
Davies (Hubert Henry).
Plays. Intr. by H. Walpole. 2v. 8°. 1921
Davies (John) *of Hereford, see* HEIDRICH (H.) J. D. of H. u. s. Bild v. Shakespeare's Umgebung, 1924.
Davies (John), *of Kidwelly.* *Epictetus Junior, or Maximes of mod. morality. Coll. by J. D. s8°. 1670
Davies (*Sir* **John**), *attorney general for Ireland.* *A discoverie of the true causes why Ireland was never subdued &c. (1612). s8°. 1747
Hist. relations: or, Discovery of causes why Ireland was never entirely subdued &c., 1704, *see* WARE (*Sir* J.) Annals &c., 1704–05.
Letter to Earl of Salisbury (1606) [cont. acc. of the Ld. Deputy's proc[s]. in Ulster], *see* VALLANCEY (C.) Coll. de rebus Hibern., v1, 1774.
Orchestra, or a poem of dauncing. (1596). [Ed. R. S. Lambert]. repr. la8°. 1922
Sir Martin Mar-People, his coller of Esses. (1590). Offered to sale by J. D. [*Probably not by J. Davies*]. 8°. [repr. 1923]
Davies (John Humphreys). Cat. of MSS., by J. H. D., v1, 1921, *see* NATIONAL LIBRARY OF WALES.
Davies (Mary), *aft. wife of Sir T. Grosvenor, Bt., 1665–1730, see* GATTY (C. T.) M. D. & the Manor of Ebury, 2v, 1921.
Davies (Nina de Garis).
see GARDINER (A. H.) The tomb of Amenemhēt; copied by N. de G. D., 1915.
,, —— The tomb of Ḥuy; copied by N. de G. D., 1926.
Davies (Norman de Garis). The tomb of Antefoḳer, vizier of Sesostris I, & of h. wife, Senet. With ch. by A. H. Gardiner. [Egypt. Explor. Soc. Theban Tombs Ser., 2nd mem.] 4°. 1920
The tomb of Puyemrê at Thebes. [Metrop. Mus. of Art. Egypt. Exped. R. de P. Tytus Mem. Ser., v2, 3]. 2v. atlas fol. N.Y. 1922–23
The tomb of 2 sculptors at Thebes. [Metrop. Mus. of Art: Egyptian Exped. Ed. A. M. Lythgoe. R. de P. Tytus Mem. Ser., v4]. lafol. N.Y. 1925
Tombs of 2 officials of Tuthmosis the Fourth. [Egypt. Explor. Soc. Theban Tombs Ser. 3rd Mem.] 4°. 1923
Two Ramesside tombs at Thebes. [Metrop. Mus. of Art. Egypt. Exped. Ed. A. M. Lythgoe. R. de P. Tytus Mem. Ser., v5]. lafol. N.Y. 1927
Davies (R. Trevor). Docs. illust. hist. of civiliz. in med. Eng., 1066–1500. 8°. [1926]
Sketch of hist. of civilis. in med. Eng., 1066–1500. s8°. 1924
Davies (Randall), *F.S.A.*
Chats on old Eng. drawings. 8°. [1923]
*A little more nonsense. [*By*] R.D. [*Verse, the cuts f. W. Dodd's Specimens of early wood engraving &c.*, 1862]. 8°. Kensington, *Cayme Press.* 1923
*A lyttel booke of nonsense. [*By*] R. D. [Verse, illust. by reprod. of old woodcuts &c.] [n. ed.] 8°. Kensington, *Cayme Press.* 1925
Notes upon some of Shakespeare's sonnets. 8°. *Cayme Press.* 1927
Six cent. of painting. s4°. [1914]
Davies (Samuel), *President of the College of New Jersey.*
Sermons. 5th ed. 4v. 8°. 1804–06
Davies (Sarah Emily), *see* DAVIES (EMILY).
Davies (Thomas), *bookseller.* *The characters of George I, Queen Caroline, Sir Robert Walpole &c. reviewed & sk. of Lord Chesterfield's character. s8°. 1777
Davies (William Henry).
The autobiography of a super-tramp. Pref. by B. Shaw. 5th ed., w. note by a. & 5 poems. s8°. 1920
,, ,, ...[repr.] s8°. [1924]
Forty new poems. s8°. 1918
The hour of magic & o. poems. 8°. [1922]
Later days. 8°. [1925]
A poet's pilgrimage. s8°. 1918
Sel. poems. 8°. [1923]
A song of life & o. p. s8°. 1920
Davies (William S.), *see* GIRALDUS, *Cambrensis.* De invectionibus; [ed. w. intr.] by W. S. D., 1920.
Davies (William Watkin).
Wales. [Home Univ. Lib.] s8°. [1924]
Davignon (Henri). Aimée Collinet. Roman. s8°. [1922]
Davila (Enrico Caterino), *see* STEPHENS (E.) *A disc. conc. the Powder-Plot &c., coll. out of Davila &c. 1674.
Davila (Pietro Giacomo), *see* CESSI (R.) Falso eroe d. rivolta d. Famagosta (1473), P. G. D., 1911.
Dávila (Sancho) [AVILA (SANCHEZ DE); †DAVILA Y DAZA (S.)] *see* MIRAFLORES (*el marq.* DE). Vida del general esp. S. D. y D., el Rayo de la Guerra, 1857.
Dávila y Daza (Sancho), *see* DÁVILA (S.)
Davis (Charles Oliver B.) Coll. of laments &c., *see* GREY (*Sir* G.) Maori mementos, 1855.
Davis (Cyril Frederick Lan-), *see* LAN-DAVIS (C. F.)
Davis (Deltena J.), *see* TREFETHEN (J. A.) & W. H. SMITH. Trial of T. & S. for murder of D. J. D., 1895.
Davis (Eliza Jeffries). The transformation of London, *see* POLLARD (A. F.) Tudor studies, 1924.
Davis (Elmer Holmes).
Hist. of the N.Y. Times, 1851–1921. 8°. N.Y. 1921
Times have changed. s8°. [1923]
Davis (Frederick Hadland).
Jalálu 'd-Dín Rúmí. [repr.] s8°. 1920
Jámí. [repr.] s8°. 1918
Myths & legends of Japan. [repr.] 8°. [1919]
Davis (George Lynn Lachlan). The day-star of Amer. freedom; birth &c. of toleration in Maryland: w. sk. of colonizat. upon the Chesapeake &c. s8°. N.Y. 1855
Davis (Henry William Carless).
Eng. under the Normans & Angevins, 1066–1272. [Hist. of Eng., ed. C. W. C. Oman, v11]. 6th ed. 8°. [1919]
The great game in Asia, 1800–44. [Brit. Acad.] 8°. [1927]
Medieval Europe. [Home Univ. Lib.] repr. s8°. [1919]
,, ,, ...repr. s8°. [1922]
The study of history. Inaug. lect. 8°. O. 1925
see BARNARD (F. P.) Mediæval Eng.; n. ed. of Compan. to Eng. hist., ed. D., 1924.
Davis (James Edward), *see* BURN (R.) Justice of the Peace &c., 30th ed., v4 by J. E. D., 1869.
Davis (*Hon.* **James John**). Humanity in gov., *see* UNITED STATES: LAB. Bull. No. 346, 1923.
Davis (James Richard Ainsworth-), *see* AINSWORTH-DAVIS (J. R.)
Davis (Jefferson), *pres. of the Confederate States, see* ROWLAND (D.) J. D.'s place in hist., 1923.
Davis (*Col.* **John**), *of the 2nd Royal Surrey Militia.* Hist. of the Queen's Royal Regt. v7 [1903–23]. Comp. by Col. H. C. Wylly. [*w.* Maps *in case, sep.*] 8°. Aldershot. [1925]
Davis (Nicholas Darnell).
Chiefs, & th. wars, in W. Africa. [P2846]. *f.p.c.* 8°. *n.p.* 1876
Davis (R. A.) Citrus growing in S. Africa. [Union of S.A. P2820]. 8°. Pretoria. 1919
Davis (Richard), *minister at Rothwell.* Faith the grand evidence of our interest in Christ, John vi. 40. s8°. 1704
Hymns. 7th ed. w. pref. by J. Gill. s8°. 1748
Davis (Theodore M.) Excav.: Biban el Molûk. The funeral papyrus of Iouiya. Introd. by E. Naville. 4°. 1908
Excav.: Bibân el Molûk. The tomb of Iouiya & Touiyou. 4°. 1907
Finding of the tomb, by D.—Notes on Iouiya & Touiyou, by G. Maspero.—Descr. of objects found in tomb, by P. E. Newberry.
Davis (W. J.), *of Mosely, Birmingham,* **& A. W. Waters.**
Tickets & passes of Gt. Brit. & Ireland. la8°. *p.p.* Leamington Spa. 1922
Davis (William Brownlee). Experiences &c. of an Amer. consular officer dur. rec. Mexican revol. s8°. Los Angeles. 1920
Davis (William J.), *missionary.* A dict. of the Kaffir lang., includ. Xosa & Zulu dialects. [2p]. 1, Kaffir-Eng.; 2, Engl.-K. 8°. & s8°. 1872–77
A gram. of the Kaffir lang. 8°. 1872
Davis (William Morris). Physical geography. By W. M. D. ass. by W. H. Snyder. s8°. Boston. [1898]
Davis (William Stearns). The beauty of the purple. Romance of Constantinople 12 cent. ago. s8°. [1925]
Europe since Waterloo: hist., 1815–1919. 8°. [1927]
Life on a mediæval barony: a feudal community in the 13th cent. 8°. N.Y. 1923
A short hist. of the Near East, 330–1922. 8°. 1923

Davis (William T.) The New England states, th. constit., judicial, educ., commercial &c. hist. [*By var. a.* W. T. D. ed.] 4v. 4°. Boston. 1897
see SUFFOLK COUNTY, *Mass.* Professional & indust. hist., v1, Bench & bar, by W. T. D., 1894.

Davis (William Thomas).
Naval dict., Ital.-Eng. & Eng.-Ital. s8°. 1921

Davison (Charles).
The founders of seismology. 8°. C. 1927
A hist. of Brit. earthquakes. 8°. C. 1924
Manual of seismology. 8°. C. 1921

Davison (G. M.) *The fashionable tour: a guide to travellers. 4th ed. enl. s8°. Saratoga Springs. 1830

Davison (John), *Primitive methodist.*
Life of William Clowes. s8°. 1854

Davison (Lawrence H.), *ps., see* LAWRENCE (D. H.)

Davith-Beg, *melik of Karabagh.* *Hist. choisie de D.-B. [1722]; publ. avec add. par Abgar, fils de S. Goulamiriants, 1871, *see* BROSSET (M. F.) Coll. d'histor. arm., t2, 1876.

Davout (*le maréchal* **Louis Nicolas**), *duc d'Auerstädt, prince d'Eckmühl.*
see MONTÉGUT (E.) Le maréchal D., s. caractère &c., 1882.
„ VIGIER (*cte.*) D., (1770–1823), 1898.

Davrigny (Giles), *see* AURIGNY (G. D').

Davy (Charles H.), *master printer.* List of words, names &c., early 15th cent. spelling. s8°. *Dryden Press.* 1909

Davy (G.)
see MORET (A.) & G. D. Des clans aux empires, 1923.
„ —— & —— From tribe to empire; tr., 1926.

Davy (*Sir* **Humphry**), *Bart., see* MAYHEW (H.) Wonders of science, or young H. D., *n.d.*

Davy (John), *1763–1824.* Just like love is yonder rose: rondo. [*b. w.* Corelli (A.) Twelve concertos, 1790 ?]. 4°. *n.d.*

Davy du Perron (*le card.* **J.**), *see* DU PERRON.

Dawbarn (Climenson Yelverton Charles). Uncrowned: a story of Queen Elizabeth & the early life of Francis "Bacon." Suppl. notes. s8°. 1923

Dawes (C. R.) The Marquis de Sade, h. life & works. 8°. 1927

Dawes (Charles Gates), *see* REPARATION COMM. Rep. of 1st Com. of Experts; letter f. chairman [C. G. D.], 1924.

Dawhr (Adolf), *see* DAUCHER (A.)

Dawkins (Richard McGillivray), *M.A., see* BOSANQUET (*Mrs.* R. C.) & R. M. D. Unpubl. objects from the Palaikastro excav., p1, 1923.

Dawkins (William Boyd). The anc. sources of the endowments of the Church of Eng. [P2489]. 8°. 1912

Dawlish (Hope), *ps., see* PIGGOTT (*Sir* F. T.)

Dawson (Alec John). Britain's life-boats: century of heroic service. Intr. by the Prince of Wales, & foreword by J. Conrad. 8°. 1923
Everybody's dog book. 8°. 1922

Dawson (Benjamin), *rector of Burgh, Suffolk.* *An exam. of Dr. Rutherforth's argument resp. right of Protest. churches to require the clergy to subscribe to an establ. confess. &c. By a Clergyman of the Ch. of Eng. [P490]. 8°. 1766

Dawson (Bertrand Dawson, *1st baron*), *of Penn.* Love—marriage—birth control. Speech. [repr.] 8°. [1922]

Dawson (Charles Frederick). Elementary design. 8°. 1903

Dawson (Coningsby).
It might have happened to you. Foreword by Ld. Weardale. s8°. 1921
The kingdom round the corner. s8°. 1921
The little house. s8°. 1920
Old youth. s8°. 1925
Slaves of freedom. [re-issued]. s8°. [1920]

Dawson (Lawrence H.)
Introductions to London, 1926. Ed. L. H. D. la8°. [1926]

Dawson (Nelson). The maritime coll. of N. D. Sold Anderson gall. [1924–25]. [*Illust.* P2854]. 2p. la8°. N.Y. [1924]

Dawson (*Sir* **Philip**). Germany's indust. revival. 8°. 1926

Dawson (Robert MacGregor). The princ. of official independence, w. partic. ref. to polit. hist. of Canada. Intr. by G. Wallas. 8°. 1922

Dawson (Thomas), *barrister-at-law.*
The law of the press. 8°. 1927

Dawson (Warren Royal), *see* SMITH (G. E.) & W. R. D. Egyptian mummies, 1924.

Dawson (Warrington). Adventure in the night. s8°. [1924]

Dawson (William), *Wesleyan, 1773–1841.*
Sel. fr. the corr. of W. D. s8°. 1842

Dawson (William Harbutt).
The evol. of mod. Germany. [5th impr.] 8°. [1914]
Hist. of Skipton. 8°. 1882
South Africa: people, places & problems. 8°. 1925

Dawson-Scott (Catharine Amy), *see* RHYS (E.) & C. A. D.-S.

Dawtrey (John). The Falstaff saga. Capt. N. Dawtrey, immortalized by Shakespeare as Falstaff. 8°. 1927

Dawtrey (*Capt.* **Nicolàs**), *seneschal of Claneboye, see* DAWTREY (J.) The Falstaff saga: N. D., immortalized by Shakespeare as Falstaff, 1927.

Dax. Le Livre noir & les Etablissements de Dax. Publ. Soc. des Arch. Hist. de la Gironde &c. [*Ed. w. intr. &c. by*] F. Abbadie. 4°. Bordeaux. 1902

Day (Arthur Louis) & E. T. Allen. Volcanic activity & hot springs of Lassen Peak. [C.I. of Wash.] 4°. Wash. 1925

Day (Clive).
A hist. of commerce. rev. &c. 8°. N.Y. 1925
Hist. of commerce of the U.S. 8°. N.Y. 1925

Day (Francis), *F.L.S.* The land of the Permauls, or Cochin, its past & its present. 8°. Madras. 1863

Day (John W.), *see* CONANT (*Mrs.* J. H.) Biog. of J. H. C. [comp. by J. W. D.], 1873.

Day (Lewis Foreman). Ornament & its applic. 8°. 1904

Day (Mabel), *ed., see* WHEATLEY MANUSCRIPT; coll. of Eng. verse &c., 1921.

Day (Thomas). Sandford & Merton. 11th ed. s8°. 1802

Day (William), *trainer.*
The horse, how to breed & rear him. 2nd ed. 8°. 1890

Dayal (Har). Forty-four months in Germany & Turkey, Feb. 1915–Oct. 1918. s8°. 1920

Daye (Pierre). L'empire colonial belge. s8°. Brux. 1923
La politique colon. de Léopold II, *see* CAHIERS BELGES, No. 26, 1918.

Daye (Stephen), *printer, d. 1668.* *S. D. & h. successors: Univ. Press, Camb., Mass., 1639–1921. 8°. Camb., *Mass.* 1921

Dayot (Armand).
Grands & petits maîtres hollandais. fol. [1912]

Dazil (Claude). Madiette. Roman. s8°. [1922]

Dchalaliants (Esai Hasan-), *see* HASAN-CHALALIANTZ.

D'Cruz (F. A.) St. Thomas in India. 8°. Madras. 1922

De.
*De adiaphoris Scoti τοῦ τυχόντος aphorismi, 1622, *see* ADIAPHORA.
*De arte illuminandi (14 c.) [MS. in Bibl. Naz., Naples], *see* ART D'ENLUMINURE, 1886; tr. 1927.
*De arte peregrinandi lib. 2, 1591, *see* PYRCKMAIR (H.)
*De continentia sacerdotum, c. 1515, *see* BOUSSARD (G.)
*De controv. inter Catholicos agitatis, circa auctorit. summi pontif. [*signed* N.], *see* MIGNE (J. P.), *ed.* Theol. cursus, t5, 1841.
*De Deo invisibili, 1790–91, *see* HEMPEL (—).
*De fide. [*A sermon in MS. on Gal. II, 16, & III, 2*]. [P2539]. s4°. *n.p. n.d.* [c. 1522]
*De haeresi abjuranda quid statuat eccl. Rom.-Cath., 1721, *see* WALD (S. G.)
De inclito &c. actu eccl. Aug. celebrato 1518, 1518, *see* MENNEL (J.)
*De jure ecclesiasticorum, 1665, *see* CONSTANS (L. A.), *ps.*
*De justa reipub. Xtnae. in reges impios &c. authoritate, 1590, *see* RAINOLDS (W.)
*De l'amour, *n.d., see* BEYLE (M. H.)
*De mysterio Incarnat. Verbi et unionis hypostaticae, 1577, *see* FRANCUS (T. A.)
*De persecutione Anglic. comm. [*or* libellus. 2 *eds.*], 1582, *see* PARSONS (R.)
*De pontificia infall. qualis in Conc. Vatic. defin. proponitur, 1870, *see* PONTIFICIA.
*De primis scientiarum elementis seu theologia nat. &c., 1734, *see* THEOLOGIA.
*De summa eorum clementia qui habendis quaestionibus prefuerant, contra proditores quosdam, 1584, *see* BURGHLEY (W. C., *b.*) Justitia Brit., 1584.
*De summi pontificis infall. personali, 1870, *see* PONTIFEX.
*De suprema Romani Pontif. autoritate hodierna eccl. Gallic. doctrina, 1747, *see* SUARDI (V. A.)
*De tribus impostoribus, 1598, *see* PRESSER (J.) Das Buch "De tribus impostoribus," 1926.
*De unione personali duarum in una persona Domini nostri naturarum &c., 1587, *see* HASSIA.

De (M. N.) How to improve silk-reeling in Bengal, *& o. p., see* AGRIC. RES. INST., Pusa. Bulletin 44, 48, 74, 1915–17.

Deacon (J. L.), *of Rye.*
Ancient Rye: hist. hdbk. 5th ed. s8°. Rye. 1927

Deacon's court guide, gazetteer &c.: reg. &c. of Yorkshire. 8°. [1883]

De Agostini (Alberto M.), *see* AGOSTINI (A. M. DE).

Deák (Ferencz), *1803–76*.
Adalék a magyar Közjoghoz. [P2393]. 8°. Pest. 1865
Deák F. beszédei. 2[ik] kiadás. 6k. (1829–68). 8°. 1903
see GAAL (MÓZES). D. F., 1900.
„ PULSZKY (F.) D. F., 1904.
Deakin (Alfred). Musical bibliography, 15–18c., chronologically arr. la8°. B'ham. 1892
Deakin (Alfred), *premier of the Australian Commonwealth, see* MURDOCH (W.) A. D.: a sketch, 1923.
Deakin (Frank B.) Spain to-day. s8°. 1924
Dealtry (William), *B.D.* A review of Mr. Norris's attack on the Brit. & For. Bible Soc. [*b. w.* Norris (H. H.) A pract. expos. &c., 2nd ed., 1814. 8°. 1815
Dean (Bashford), *Ph.D.* Helmets & body armor in mod. warfare. [Metrop. Mus. of Art]. la8°. New Haven, *Yale*. 1920
Deane (Charles) *of Cambridge, Mass.* A bibliogr. essay on Governor Hutchinson's hist. publ. 8°. Boston [Mass.] 1857
Deane (Edmund). Spadacrene Anglica: or the Eng. Spa fountain (1626). Repr. w. intr. [*& facs. tp.*] by J. Rutherford, & biog. notes by A. Butler. s8°. Bristol. 1922
Deane (Edward James), *ed., see* ROSSALL REGISTER, 1844–1905, 1905.
Deane (Samuel), *minister of Portland, U.S., see* SMITH (T.) Journals of T. S. & S. D. &c., 1849.
Deane (Samuel), *topog. writer.*
Hist. of Scituate, Mass. 8°. Boston. 1831
Deanesly (Margaret). The Gospel harmony of John de Caulibus, or S. Bonaventura, *see* COLLECTANEA Franciscana, v2, 1922.
Hist. of the medieval church, 590–1500. 8°. 1925
The Lollard Bible & o. medieval biblical versions. 8°. C. 1920
Dean-Pitt (*Capt.* **Douglas Charles).** Rep. of long distance rides in India, 1886–87. [P2591]. 8°. Bombay. 1887
Dearborn Independent (The), *see* JEW. Internat. Jew (The): repr. of articles in The D. I., May-Oct. 1920, 1920.
Dearborn (Ned). Cat. of coll. of birds f. Guatemala, [*& f.* Brit. E. Africa], *see* FIELD COLUMBIAN MUS. Ornith. ser., v1iii, iv, 1907–9.
Dearden (Harold). The science of happiness. 8°. 1925
Deardorff (Neva R.) Child dependency &c. in 7 Penn. counties, *see* UNITED STATES: LAB. Children's Bur., No. 176, 1927.
Dearing (Christopher), *see* PROBST (A.) Trial of A. P., for murder of C. D., 1866.
Dearmer (Percy).
The cathedral church of Wells. [3rd ed.] 8°. 1903
Illust. of the Liturgy. 13 drawings of celeb. of Holy Communion by C. O. Skilbeck. Notes & intr. by P. D. [Alcuin Club, 19]. la8°. [1912]
The ornaments of the ministers. [n. ed.] 8°. [1920]
see CLUTTON-BROCK (A.) Necessity of art; by A. C. B., P. D. &c., 1924.
Deas (Lizzie).
Flower favourites, legends, symbolism &c. s8°. 1898
De Bathe (Emily Charlotte, *lady*), *see* LANGTRY (L.), *aft. Lady de Bathe.*
De Beer (E. S.) & W. Seton. Byroniana: archives of the London Greek Com. [Repr. f. Nineteenth Cent., Sept. 1926. P2834]. 8°. [1926]
De-Benedetti (Leonardo), *see* BENEDETTI (L. DE-).
Debenedetti (Santorre). Il "Sollazzo." Contrib. alla storia d. novella, d. poesia musicale e del costume nel trecento. la8°. Torino. 1922
Debenham (Frank). The physiography of the Ross Archipelago, 1923, *see* BRIT. ANTARCTIC EXPED., 1910–13.
Report on the maps & surveys, 1923, *see* BRIT. ANTARCTIC EXPED., 1910–13.
Deberly (Henri).
Un homme & un autre. 6e éd. s8°. [1928]
Le supplice de Phèdre. 19e éd. s8°. [1926]
Debidour (Antonin). Hist. diplomat. de l'Europe depuis le Congrès de Berlin. Préf. de L. Bourgeois.
3e éd. rev. 2p (1, 1878–1904. 2, 1904–1916). 8°. 1919–20
Debrett (John). House of Commons & the Judicial Bench, 1921, 1926. Ed. A. G. M. Hesilrige.
55th, 60th ann. ed. 8°. 1921–26
Peerage of Gt. Brit. & Ireland. 14th ed. 2v. s8°. 1822
De Britaine (Wm.) [†BRITAINE (W. DE), *ps.*] *Humane prudence. 7th ed. corr. & enl. s8°. 1697
De Bunsen (Victoria), *see* BUNSEN (V. DE).
De Burgh (William George).
The legacy of the ancient world. 8°. 1924

Debussy (Claude Achille).
see CHENNEVIÈRE (D.) C. D. & son œuvre, [1918 ?].
„ REVUE MUSICALE, déc. 1920, mai 1926, nos. spéc., 1920–26.
Decaen (*gén. cte.* **Charles Mathieu Isidore)** [†CAEN (C. M. I. DE), *count*]. Mém. & journaux, 1793[-1803]. Publ. avec intr., notes &c. par E. Picard & V. Paulier. [Publ. sous la dir de la Sect. Hist. de l'Etat de l'Armée]. 2t. 8°. 1910–11
„ „ ....2e éd. 2t. 8°. 1910–11
Decameron. The new D. [Tales by var. a.], 1920–27, *see* NEW.
Decamps (Jules). Les changes étrangers; exposé général &c., 1914–21. Préf. de A. Liesse. 8°. 1922
De Castro (J. Paul). The Gordon riots. 8°. 1926
Law & practice of hall-marking gold & silver wares. 8°. 1926
Dechamps (*card.* **Victor Auguste Isidore)**, *abp. of Malines.*
Drei Briefe ü. d. Unfehlbark. d. Papstes an Pater Gratry. Uebers. [P2691]. 8°. Mainz. 1870
*Lettre à Mgr. Dechamps sur sa 2e réponse à l'évêque d'Orléans. [P2692]. 8°. Naples. 1870
see DUPANLOUP (F. A. P.) Réponse à Mgr. D., 1870.
Déchelette (Joseph). Manuel d'archéol. préhist., celt. & gallo-romaine. 2e éd. augm. d'un index. [t]2, 3. 8°. 1924–27
De Chirico (Giorgio), *see* CHIRICO (G. DE).
***Decimarum** &c. tabula: a tithing table, 1676, *see* CRASHAW (W.)
Decimator (Henricus). Erklerung d. Passion u. Triumphs Jesu Christi. s8°. [Leipzig]. 1589
Décisions du Conseil suprême sur la Galicie or.; Docs. avec intr. par M. L., 1919, *see* LOZYNSKY (M.)
Deck (Norris). Hand-book to Cambridge. 8°. C. 1862
Deck (Suzanne). La ville d'Eu, s. hist., s. instit., 1151–1475. [H.E., 243]. 8°. 1924
***Declaratio** vanitatis &c. libelli, Colloquium inter theologos Acad. Rostoch. &c. expon., De controv. Coenae Dominicae, 1587, *see* ROSTOCK.
Declaration [DECLARATIOUN].
*D. (A) f. nobility of Scotland &c., 1647, *see* SCOTLAND.
*D. (A) of the faith & order owned &c. in the Congregat. Churches in England agreed upon &c. s8°. 1688
*D. of the inhabitants of the hill countreys of Scotland, 1653, *see* MAIDMENT (J.), *ed.* Hist. fragm., p3, 1833.
D. (Ane) of the just &c. causis, moving us of the nobillitie of Scotland &c., 1582; repr., 1822, *see* SCOTLAND.
De Clare, *The family of, see* LAMBERT (U.) Blechingley: w. acc. of the fam. of De C., 2v, 1921.
Declareuil (Joseph). Hist. gén. du droit franç. à 1789. 8°. 1925
Rome & l'organisation du droit. 8°. 1924
Rome the law-giver. [Tr. E. A. Parker. Hist. of civilization; ed. C. K. Ogden]. 8°. 1927
***Declension.** By A gentleman with a duster. 8°. [1925]
Décor (Le) de la vie sous le Second Empire, 1922, *see* MUSÉE DES ARTS DÉCORATIFS.
Decorde (Jean Eugène). Dict. du patois du pays de Bray. [*b. w.* Tarbé (P.) Rech. s. lang. de Champagne, 1851]. 8°. 1852
De Cordova (Rudolf). Royalties of the world. Portraits, w. monographs. fol. [1901]
***Découvertes** sur le cavalier, 1837, *see* JÄNISCH (C. F.)
De Crespigny (*Lady* **Mary Champion)**, *see* CRESPIGNY (*Lady* M. C. DE).
De Crespigny (*Mrs.* **Philip Champion).**
The mind of a woman. s8°. 1922
The missing piece. s8°. [1927]
Decretales. Epistolæ decretales summ. pontificorum a Gregorio IX coll. s8°. Parisiis. 1570
Sextus decretalium liber per Bonifacium VIII in Conc. Lugdun. ed. jam recens emend. [*b. w.* Epistolae decret., 1570]. s8°. Antverpiæ. 1569
Decrock (Élie), *see* BOUCHES-DU-RHÔNE; encyclop. départ., t12, Biogéog., 1914.
Decsey (Ernst). Johann Strauss: ein Wiener Buch. 8°. St. 1922
Decurtins (Caspar). Rätoroman. Chrestomathie, B10–12 & Ergzgsband 1, *see* ROMANISCHE FORSCH., B33, 35–38, 1913–19.
Dedalo. Rassegna d'arte. Diretta da U. Ojetti.
Anno 4–7 (1923–27). la8°. Milano. [1923–27]
Each Anno *is in* 3v, *bound together, pagin. cont.*
Dedekennus (Georg). Thesauri consiliorum &c. vol. primum [—tertium & App. nova]. Das ist: Vornehmer Universitüten &c. Rath, Bedencken, &c. In Druck gegeben durch J. E. Gerhardum. [App. nova in Druck geg. durch M. C. Grübelium]. 3v *in* 2t. fol. Hamburg. 1671

Dedieu (Joseph). Le rôle polit. des protestants français, 1685–1715. s8º. 1920

Dee (John). List of MSS. form. owned by Dr. J. D., w. pref. &c. by M. R. James. [Bibliog. Soc. Trans. Suppl., No. 1. *b. w.* Library (The), s4, v1, 1921]. 8º. 1921
see HORT (G. M.) Dr. J. D., 1922.

Deedes (Cecil), *M.A.*, see LEICESTER. Old Town Hall Library; cat. &c. comp. by C. D. &c., 1919.

Deeming (Frederick Bailey). *Biog. of F. B. D.; a romance of crime. [*b. w.* Deeming (F. B.) Hist. of the Windsor &c. tragedies, 1892]. 8º. [Melbourne. *n.d.*]
*Hist. of the Windsor & Rainhill tragedies: the career of F. B. D. 8º. Adelaide. 1892
*The life & adventures of F. B. D. [*b. w.* Deeming (F. B.) Hist. of the Windsor & Rainhill tragedies, 1892]. 8º. Melbourne. 1892
*The Windsor & Rainhill murders. [*b. w.* Deeming (F. B.) Hist. of the Windsor &c. tragedies, 1892]. s8º. Melbourne. 1892

Deeping (Warwick).
Doomsday. [2nd impr.] s8º. [1927]
Kitty. s8º. [1927]
Lantern Lane. s8º. [1921]
Second youth. s8º. 1919
The secret sanctuary, or The saving of John Stretton. s8º. [1923]
Sorrell & son. [2nd impr.] s8º. [1925]
,, ,, [4th impr.] s8º. [1925]
Three rooms. s8º. [1924]

Deering (*Sir* **Edward),** see DERING (*Sir* E.)

Defence.
D. (The) of conny-catching (1592), see GREENE (R.) The blacke bookes messenger, 1924.
*D. (A) of freemasonry (1765), see SADLER (H.) Masonic repr^s^. &c., 1898.
*D. (A) of the first head of the charge agst. the bp. of Bangor [*i.e.* B. Hoadly], 1718, see STEBBING (H.)
*D. (A) of pluralities, 1692, see WHARTON (H.)
*D. (A) of the Scots settlement at Darien, 1699, see FLETCHER (A.)
*D. (A) of the Vindication of Charles, 1699, see WAGSTAFFE (T.)

Défense. *La d. de la Réformation, 1673, see CLAUDE (J.)

***Defensio** regia, pro Carolo I, 1649, see SALMASIUS (C.)

Deffontaines (Pierre), see HANOTAUX (G.) Hist. de la nation franç., t2, Géogr. humaine de la France, v2, Géogr. polit. &c. par J. Brunhes & P. D., 1926.

Deffoux (Léon) & E. Zavie. Le groupe de Médan. E. Zola; G. de Maupassant; J.-K. Huysmans &c. Suivi de deux essais sur le naturalisme. s8º. 1920

Defoe (Daniel). Works. With the a.'s preface[s], & intr.[s] by G. H. Maynadier. 16v. 8º. Boston [U.S. 1903]
1–3, Robinson Crusoe [*&* Vision of the angelic world *in* v3].
4, Mr. Duncan Campbell [*&* Passage of an apparition *&* The friendly demon].
5, Memoirs of a cavalier.
6, Capt. Singleton.
7, 8, Moll Flanders [*&* An appeal to honour & justice *in* v8].
9, Journal of the Plague year.
10, 11, Col. Jacque [*&* The true-born Englishman *&* The shortest way w. Dissenters *in* v11].
12, 13, The fortunate mistress, Lady Roxana.
14, A new voyage round the world &c.
15, Due preparations for the Plague [*&* The dumb philosopher *&* The apparition of Mrs. Veal *&* The destruction of the Isle of St. Vincent].
16, The king of pirates: acc. of Capt. Avery, w. lives of o. pirates & robbers.
*Caledonia, a poem. 8º. 1707
Earlier life & chief earlier works [1661–1706]. Ed. H. Morley. 8º. 1889
*An elegy on the a. of the True-born-Engl.-man &c. [P2868]. s8º. 1708
*Hannibal at the gates: or, the progress of Jacobitism &c. s8º. 1712
Journal of the plague year, 1665. Intr. by H. Morley. 2nd ed. s8º. 1886
Novels & misc. works. [repr.] 7v. s8º. *Bohn.* 1893–1900
*The polit. hist. of the devil. [*Imperf.*] 4th ed. s8º. 1739
Robinson Crusoe. rev. for young. n. ed. s8º. 1818
,, ,, With engr. f. designs by T. Stothard. 2v. la8º. 1820
*A system of magick; or a hist. of the black art. s8º. 1728
*Tour through the whole island of Gt. Brit. By a gentleman. 3rd ed. 4v. s8º. 1742
,, ,, ...Intr. by G. D. H. Cole. 2v. 8º. 1927
see DOTTIN (P.) D. De F. & s. romans, 3t, 1924.
,, FORSTER (J.) D. De F. &c., 1855.
,, HORTEN (F.) Studien ü. die Sprache D.'s, 1914.

Defoe (Daniel) [*continued*].
see HUTCHINS (H. C.) Robinson Crusoe & its printing, 1719–31, 1925.
,, LANNERT (G. L.) An investig. into the lang. of Robinson Crusoe, 1910.
,, NICHOLSON (W.) Hist. sources of D.'s Journal of the plague year, 1919.
,, SCHMIDT (R.) Der Volkswille als realer Faktor d. Verfassungslebens u. D. D., 1924.
,, SECORD (A. W.) St^s^. in the narrative method of D., 1924.
,, SMEEKS (H.) Dutch source for Robinson Crusoe: narr. of the El-Ho "Sjouke Gabbes" &c. by H. S., 1708; tr. & compared w. R. C. by L. L. Hubbard, 1921.

Defrasse (Alphonse), see LECHAT (H.) Epidaure: sanctuaire d'Asclépios; relevés & restaur. par A. D., 1895.

Degani (Ernesto). I signori di Ragogna, di Toppo e di Pinzano [P2709]. 8º. Udine. 1894

Degarre. Sire Degarre: metrical romance of 13th c., 1849, see DEGORE.

Degas (Edgar Hilaire Germain). Expos. Degas, au profit de la Ligue Franco-Anglo-Amér. contre le cancer. la8º. 1924
see COQUIOT (G.) D., avec 24 reprod., 1924.
,, HERTZ (H.) D. [Art & esthétique], 1920.
,, VOLLARD (A.) D., 4e éd., 1924.

Degen (Johann Georg). Romae urbem direptam, papam Clementem captum &c., 1527. Praes. J. P. M. Roesero. [P444]. Baruthi. [1691]

Degli Alberti (Mario). La politica estera del Piemonte sotto Carlo Alberto, 1835–46, 3t, see REGIA DEP. S. GLI STUDI DI STORIA PATRIA &c. Bibl., v5–7, 1913–19.

Degli Almieri (Ginevra), see VELLETTI (A.) Storia di G. d. A. che fu sepolta viva in Firenze, 1863.

Degli Alvari, *The family of*, see ERVARI.

Degli Obizzi (*il march.* **Pio Enea).**
see BETUSSI (G.) Descr. d. Cataio, luogo d. march. P. E. d. O., 1669.
,, —— Ragionamento sopra il Cathaio, luogo d. ill. S. P. E. O., 1673.

Degner (Jacob). Diss. de rosario. Sub moderamine J. F. Mayeri 1708. [P437]. s4º. Gryphiswaldæ. 1720

Degore [DEGARRE]. Sire Degarre. Metrical romance of end of 13th c. [Abbotsford Club]. 4º. E. 1849

Degrandpré (L.), see GRANDPRÉ (L. M. J. *conte* O'HIER DE).

De Groot (Johann Jacob M.) [†GROOT (J. J. M. DE)]. Chines. Urkunden z. Gesch. Asiens. Übers. u. erl. 2T. 4º. 1921–26
1, Die Hunnen d. vorchr. Zeit.
2, Die Westlande Chinas in vorchr. Zeit; hrsg. v. O. Franke.
Sinolog. Seminare u. Bibliotheken, see KÖN.-PREUSS. AKAD. Abhdln., Phil.-hist. Kl., 1913.
Der Thūpa, d. heil. Heiligtum d. Buddhismus in China, see KÖNIGL. PREUSS. AKAD. D. WISS. Abhdl. (Phil.-hist. Klasse), 1919.

Deguileville (Guillaume). Die Pilgerfahrt d. träumenden Mönchs. Nach d. Kölner Hs. hrsg. v. A. Meijboom. [Rhein. Beitr. &c. z. germ. Philol., B10]. 8º. Bonn. 1926

Deguise (*lt.-gén.* **V.)** La défense de la position fortifiée d'Anvers en 1914 (20 août–10 oct.) la8º. Brux. 1921

De Haas (Rudolf). An Lagerfeuern d. Sahara. la8º. 1923

Dehan (Richard), *ps.* [*i.e. Miss* CLOTILDE GRAVES].
The just steward. s8º. 1922
The sower of the wind. s8º. [1927]
The villa of the peacock & o. stories. s8º. 1921

De Heere (Gerrit), *Governor of Ceylon, 1697–1702.* Diary of tour of G. de H. f. Colombo to Jaffna, July 9 to Sept. 3, 1697. Tr. S. Anthonisz. Intr. &c. by the Govt. Archivist. [Mem. &c. of Dutch Governors &c.] 8º. Colombo. 1914

Dehio (Georg).
Gesch. d. deut. Kunst. B1–3 [*in* 6T, B2, 2^e^ A.] la8º. 1919–26
Text, B1–3. Abbildungen, B1–3.
Das Strassburger Münster. la8º. München. 1922

Dehmel (Richard).
Bekenntnisse. [Gesamm. Werke]. s8º. 1926
Gesamm. Werke. 3B. s8º. 1920
Die Menschenfreunde. Drama. verbess. A. s8º. 1918
see LUDWIG (E.) R. D., 1913.

Dehn (—) *of Rostock.* Deutschlands Städtebau: Rostock [*by* D. &c.], 1922, see ROSTOCK.

Dehn (*Mme.* **Lili).** The real Tsaritsa. 8º. [1922]

Dehner (Sebastian). Hadriani Reliquiae. p1. Diss. philologica. 8º. Bonnae. 1883

Deichmann (*Baroness* **Hilda Elizabeth**), *wife of Baron A. D. Deichmann, form. De Bunsen.*
Impressions & memories. 8°. 1926
Deichmann (Johann Georg), *see* TEICHMANN (J. G.)
Dei Franceschi (Pietro di Benedetto), *see* DELLA FRANCESCA (P.)
Deissmann (G. Adolf). Licht vom Osten: das Neue Test. u. d. neuentdeckten Texte d. hellenist.-röm. Welt. 4e neubearb. A. la8°. Tübingen. 1923
Light f. the anc. East. Tr. L. R. M. Strachan. n. & rev. ed. 8°. [1927]
Paul. Study in soc. & relig. hist. Tr. W. E. Wilson. 2nd ed., rev. & enl. 8°. 1926
Paulus: e. kultur-u. religionsgesch. Skizze. 2. neubearb. &c. A. 8°. Tübingen. 1925
The religion of Jesus & the faith of Paul. Selly Oak Lects., 1923. Tr. W. E. Wilson. 8°. 1923
Deists. *A short & easie method w. the Deists, 4th ed., 1711, *see* LESLIE (C.)
Deitsch (Leo), *see* DEUTSCH (L.)
Dejeans (Elizabeth). The winning game. s8°. [1925]
Dejerine (Joseph Jules) & E. Gauckler. The psychoneuroses & their treatment by psychotherapy. Tr. S. E. Jelliffe. 2nd Eng. ed. 8°. Phila. [1915]
De Jonge (C. H.) Holländ. Möbel u. Raumkunst, 1650–1780. Hrsg. C. H. de J. Eingel. v. W. Vogelsang. 4°. S-Gravenhage. 1922
Dekabristi. Поэты-декабристы; ред. Ю. Н. Верховского, 1926, *see* VERKHOVSKY (YU. N.)
Deken (Aagje), *see* WOLFF (E.) & A. D. Hist. van Sara Burgerhart, 2d, 1915.
De Keyser's Royal Hotel, *Ltd.*, *see* SCOTT (L. F.) & A. HILDESLEY. The case of requisition; De K.'s Roy. Hotel Ltd. *v.* The King, 1920.
Dekker (Eduard Douwes) [*ps.* MULTATULI]. Max Havelaar. Tr. by W. Siebenhaar. Intr. by D. H. Lawrence. 8°. N.Y. 1927
Verzamelde werken van Multatuli. Voorafgeg. door Studien over M. door C. Vosmaer. 4e druk. 10d. s8°. A. 1916–18
1, Max Havelaar & Studiën door C. Vosmaer. 2, Minnebrieven—Over vryen-arbeid in Ned. Ind.—Indrukken v. d. dag. 3–9, Ideen. 10, Verspreide stukken—Een en ander over Pruisen en Ned.—De bruid daar boven—Divag. over zeker soort liberalismus.
Dekker (Thomas) [DECKAR; DECKER (T.)]
Dram. works; w. notes & mem. 4v. s8°. 1873
Foure birds of Noahs Arke (1609). Ed. F. P. Wilson. s8°. O. 1924
Plague pamphlets. Ed. F. P. Wilson. s8°. O. 1925
The wonderfull yeare—Newes f. Graves-end—Meeting of gallants—Rod for run-awayes—London look backe—Blacke Rod & White Rod.
The seven deadly sinnes of London (1606). Ed. H. F. B. Brett-Smith. [Percy Repr. No. 4]. 8°. O. 1922
The shomakers holiday (1600); ed., w. crit. essay &c., by A. F. Lange, *see* GAYLEY (C. M.) Repres. Eng. comedies, v3, 1914.
The wonderfull yeare, 1603. [Bodley Head Quartos: ed. G. B. Harrison]. s8°. [1924]
Dekobra (Maurice).
Flammes de velours. s8°. [1927]
La gondole aux chimères. s8°. [1926]
La Madone des Sleepings. s8°. [1927]
De Kruif (Paul). Microbe hunters. 8°. [1927]
Delabrousse (Lucien).
Joseph Magnin & s. temps, 1824–1910. 2t. 8°. [1924]
1, Le Corps législatif—Le siège de Paris.
2, Le siège de Paris—Le Min. des Finances—Le gouvt. de la banque de France.
Delachénaye (B.), *see* LA CHÉNAYE (B. DE).
Delacour (A.), *ps.* [*i.e.* ALFRED CHARLEMAGNE LARTIGUE], *see* SIRAUDIN (P.), A. D. & A. CHOLER. Après le bal, 1864.
De La Court (Pieter Cornelius), *see* CONSTANS (L. A.), *ps.* De jure eccles. [*attrib. to Spinoza & to P. de la C.*], 1665.
Delacroix (F. V. Eugène). Œuvres litt. 2[t]. s8°. [1923]
see COURTHION (P.) La vie de D., 1927.
Delacroix (Henri). Analyse psycholog. de la fonction linguist. Zaharoff lect. [P2847]. 8°. O. 1926
Le langage & la pensée. 8°. 1924
La religion & la foi. 8°. 1922
De Lacy, *Family of*, *see* SYNNOTT (N. J.) Notes on fam. of De L., 1919.
De Laet (Joannes). Hist. ou annaes dos feitos da Companhia Privil. das Indias Occident. (-1636). Tr. J. H. Duarte Pereira e P. Souto Maior. 2v. la8°. Rio de Janeiro. 1916–25
„ *for a. issue, see* RIO DE JANEIRO: BIBL. NAC. Annaes, v30, 33, 38, 41, 42, 1912–25.

Delafield (E. M.), *ps.* [*i.e.* ELIZABETH M. DASHWOOD, *wife of Arthur Paul Dashwood.*]
The chip & the block. s8°. [1925]
The entertainment. 3rd ed. s8°. [1927]
The heel of Achilles. s8°. [1921]
Humbug. s8°. [1922]
Jill. s8°. [1926]
Messalina of the suburbs. s8°. [1924]
Mrs. Harter. s8°. [1924]
The optimist. s8°. [1922]
A reversion to type. s8°. [1923]
Tension. s8°. [1920]
De La Fontaine (Henry Cart). Dante & war. [*& essays on the* De Monarchia & Convito.] 8°. 1915
Delafosse (Maurice). Les noirs de l'Afrique. s8°. 1922
Delage (Yves). Le rêve: ét. psycholog. &c. 8°. [1919]
De Laguna (Grace Andrus). Speech. 8°. New Haven. 1927
Delahache (Georges). Strasbourg. la8°. 1923
Delahaye (Ernest). Rimbaud: l'artiste & l'être moral. 8°. 1923
Verlaine. 8°. 1919
Delahaye d'Anglemont (*capitaine* **Lucien**), *see* CLERGERIE (*gén.*) & L. D. d'A. La Bataille de la Marne: le rôle du gouvt. milit. de Paris, 1–12 sept. 1914, 1920.
Delaine (Walter) [DELOENUS (GALTERUS)], *see* BIBLE: N. TEST. [LAT.] Novum Test. Lat., ad antiq. Gr. exempl. castig. & tr. per B. Galterum Deloenum [*i.e.* D.], 1540.
Delaire (Alexis).
St. Jean-Bapt. de la Salle, 1659–1719. 7e éd. s8°. 1923
Delaisi (Francis). Polit. myths & economic realities. 8°. [1925]
Delamare (*l'abbé* **R.**) Le calendrier de l'église d'Evreux. Et. liturg. & hagiogr. 8°. 1919
De la Mare (Walter).
Broomsticks & o. t. 8°. 1925
Christina Rossetti, *see* ROY. SOC. OF LIT. Essays &c., n.s., v6, 1926.
Come hither: coll. of rhymes & poems for the young &c., made by W. De la M. 8°. 1923
Ding dong bell. 8°. 1924
Henry Brocken. [repr.] s8°. [1924]
Memoirs of a midget. s8°. [1921]
Poems, 1901–18. [2v]. s8°. [1920]
Poems, 1901–18. [3rd impr. 2v]. s8°. [1922]
The return. [rev. ed.] s8°. [1922]
The riddle & o. s. s8°. [1923]
Songs of childhood. n. impr. s8°. 1922
Thus her tale. Poem. 8°. E. 1923
The veil & o. p. s8°. [1921]
see MÉGROZ (R. L.) W. de la M.: biog. & crit. st., 1924.
„ SAINT ANDREWS: 2 poems by W. De la M. &c., 1926.
Deland (*Mrs.* **Margaret**). The Kays. s8°. [1926]
Delaney (L. T.), *see* BRAZIL. 20th cent. impressions of B.; edd. W. Feldwick [&] D., 1913.
Delano (Edith Barnard). The way of all earth. s8°. [1925]
Delany (Mary Cecilia). The hist. geog. of the Wealden iron industry. 8°. 1921
Delany (Patrick). An essay tow. evidencing the divine orig. of tythes &c. [P2669]. s8°. D. 1748
*Revelation exam. with candour. 2nd ed. corr. 3v. 8°. 1732–63
Delaporte (Louis). Mesopotamia: the Babylon. & Assyr. civiliz. [Tr. V. G. Childe. Hist. of civiliz.] 8°. 1925
La Mésopotamie: les civiliz. babylon. & assyr. [L'évol. de l'humanité: synthèse coll.] 8°. 1923
Delaporte (*l'abbé* **Y.**) Les vitraux de la cathédrale de Chartres: hist. & descr. par Y. D., 1926, *see* HOUVET (E.) Cath. de Chartres, *n.d.*–1926.
De La Pryme (Abraham). Mems. of T. Bushell; intr. &c. by W. Harrison, 1878, *see* MANX SOC. Manx misc., v2, 1880.
Delaquys (Georges). Ma femme, comédie, *see* ŒUVRES libres, 62, 1926.
Delaram (Francis), *d. 1627, engraver, see* WOODBURN (S.) W.'s gallery of portraits, plates by Cecil, D. &c., 2v, 1816.
Del Arco (Ricardo). Mem. de la Univ. de Huesca, *see* COLECCION de docs. para el estudio de la hist. de Aragon, t8, 11, 1912–16.
Delarue-Mardrus (Lucie), *wife of Dr. Mardrus.* A côté de l'amour, roman, *see* ŒUVRES libres, 12, 1922.
L'ex-voto. s8°. 1922
Hortensia dégénéré, *see* ŒUVRES libres, 50, 1925.
M'sieu Gustave, nouv., *see* ŒUVRES libres, 4, 1921.
Delattre (Floris). Dickens & la France; interaction litt. anglo-française. 8°. 1927
Delaunay (Paul). Le monde médical parisien au 18e s. 2e éd. rev. & augm. la8°. 1906
De Laune (Thomas). A plea for the non-conformists &c. in a letter to Dr. B. Calamy upon h. sermon Scrupulous conscience. [*Foll. by* Two letters upon h. imprisonment, *w. sep. pagin.*] s4°. 1684
„ „ W. a pref. [by Defoe]. 8°. Nottingham. 1817
Delavigne (Casimir Jean François). Œuvres compl. la8°. 1836
Delavrancea (Barbu), *see* DENSUSIANU (O.) D. B., 1919.
Delayen (Gaston). L'affaire du courrier de Lyon: les procès Lesurques &c. s8°. 1905

Delbrück (Hans).

Gesch. d. Kriegskunst im Rahmen d. polit. Gesch. T4. (Neuzeit). 8°. 1920
„ „ 3e A., T1, 2 (1, Altertum. 2, Germanen). 8°. 1920–21
Kautsky u. Harden. [P2410]. 8°. 1920
Das Leben d. Feldmar. Graf. N. v. Gneisenau. 4e A., 2B *in* 1v. 8°. 1920
Ludendorff, Tirpitz, Falkenhayn. 8°. 1920
Ludendorffs Selbstporträt m. e. Widerleg. d. Försterschen Gegenschrift. 8°. 1922
see GERMANY: REICHSTAG. Ursachen d. Zusammenbruchs: Enstehung d. Offensive v. 1918; Gutachten D. &c., 1923.
„ KAUTSKY (C.) D. u. Wilhelm II, 1920.

Delbrück (Richard). Antike Porträts. Bearb. v. R. D. [Tabulae in usum schol.; ed. J. Lietzmann, 6]. la8°. Bonn. 1912
Die Consulardiptychen u. verwandte Denkmäler. Lfg. 1. [St. z. spätant. Kunstgesch., 2]. lafol. 1926

Del Collado (Casimiro), *see* COLLADO (C. DEL).

Delcourt (Joseph). Essai sur la langue de Sir T. More d'ap. s. œuvres angl. 8°. 1914

Delden-Laerne (C. F. van), *see* LAERNE (C. F. v. D.)

Delécluze (Etienne Jean). Souvs. de 60 années. s8°. 1862

Deledda (Grazia), *aft. Madesani.*

Annalena Bilsini. s8°. Milano. 1927
La danza della collana: romanzo, seguito dal bozzetto drammatico A sinistra. s8°. Milano. 1924
Il Dio dei viventi. Romanzo. s8°. Milano. 1922
L'edera. s8°. Milano. 1921
Il flauto nel bosco. s8°. Milano. 1923
La fuga in Egitto. s8°. Milano. 1926
I giuochi della vita. [repr.] s8°. [1920]
La madre. Romanzo. s8°. Milano. 1920
Naufraghi in porto. Romanzo. s8°. Milano. 1920
Il sigillo d'amore. s8°. Milano. 1926

—— **& C. Antona-Traversi.** Le lierre: drame, *see* ŒUVRES libres, 81, 1928.

Délégation en Perse. Mémoires. [Min. de l'Instruction Publ. &c.] t15–18. 4°. 1914–27
t15 *onwards h. title* Méms. [*or* Publs.] de la Mission arch. de P.
15, Mission à Bender-Bouchir: docs. arch. & épigraph.; par M. Pézard.
16, Mission en Susiane: empreintes de cachets élamites; par L. Legrain.
17, „ „ : Textes de comptabilité protoélamites, nouv. sér.; par V. Scheil.
18, „ „ : Autres textes sumér. & accad.; par G. Dossin.

Délégation Nationale Armenienne.
Mém. sur la question armén. [P2521]. 8°. [1919?]

Delehaye (Hippolyte). Contrib. bibliog. alla quest. dei martiri Salonitani, *see* BULLETTINO DI ARCH. &C. DALM., 35, Suppl., 45, Suppl., 1912–22.
L'œuvre des Bollandistes, 1615–1915. s8°. Brux. 1920
Les passions des martyrs & les genres litt. 8°. Brux. 1921
Les saints stylites. [Soc. des Bollandistes: Subsid. Hagiogr., 14]. la8°. Brux. 1923
The work of the Bollandists, 1615–1915. [*Tr.*] s8°. Princeton. 1922

Deléphine (*l'abbé* G.) Recherches sur le calcaire carbonifère de la Belgique. la8°. 1911

Delfico (Melchiorre). *La vérité sur les Cent Jours, princ. par rapp. à la renaiss. projetée de l'Emp. rom. Par Un citoyen de la Corse [M. D., L. Corvetto &c.]. 8°. Brux. 1825

Delfino (Niccolò) [DELPHINO]. Rime, *see* BROCARDO (A.) Rime, 1538.

Delfino (Pietro), *general of the order of Camaldolese monks* [†DELPHINUS (PETRUS)], *see* SCHNITZER (J.) P. D., Gen. d. Camaldulenserordens, 1444–1525, 1926.

Delgado (Francisco Martinez y), *see* MARTINEZ Y DELGADO (F.)

Del Grosso (Remigio). Poesie; prec. da una breve not., da L. Settembrini. s8°. Napoli. 1877

Delhi. *Coronation Durbar at D. [1903. Bengal camp guide]. Notes &c. for use of guests. s4°. *n.p.* [1902]
Coron. Durbar, D., 1911. Official directory &c. s8°. Calcutta. 1911
Recs. of the D. resid. & agency [1807–57], *see* PUNJAB. P. govt. records, v1, 1911.

De l'Hôpital (Winefride), *see* L'HÔPITAL (W. DE).

D'Elia (Pascal M.), *see* ELIA (P. M. D').

Delicado (Francisco).
La Lozana Andaluza. s8°. Paris. *n.d.*
„ „ (La gentille Andalouse) 16e siècle. [Tr.] Introd., essai bibliogr. par G. Apollinaire. 8°. 1912

Delilah. *A strange D., 1921, *see* STRANGE.

Delille (Jacques). Œuvres compl. Avec les notes de MM. Parseval-Grandmaison, de Féletz, de Choiseul-Gouffier, &c. 5e éd. la8°. 1863

Delior (Paul), *ps.*, *see* ESCOUBE (P.)

Delisle (Arthur L.), *see* KELLNER (L.), P. ARNOLD & A. L. D. Austria of the Austrians &c., 1914.

Delisle (Guillaume), *see* L'ISLE (C. DE).

Delisle (Leopold Victor). Mélanges de paléographie & de bibliog. [Atlas, *no tp.*] fol. 1880
see CHARTES & diplômes rel. à l'hist. de France, t7ii, Rec. des actes de Henry II, roi d'Angleterre, conc. les provinces franç.; œ. posthume de L. D.; rev. &c. E. Berger, t2, 1920.
„ POOLE (R. L.) L. D., 1826–1910, 1911.

De L'Isle & Dudley (Algernon Sidney, *4th baron*), *see* HIST. MSS. COMM. Rep. on MSS. at Penshurst Place, v1, 1925.

De L'Isle & Dudley (Philip Sydney, *2nd baron*), *see* ROBERTSBRIDGE. Cal. of charters &c. rel. to Abbey am. muniments of Lord D., 1873.

***Delitti** (Dei) e delle pene, 1807, *see* BECCARIA (C.)

Delitzsch (Franz).
Complutens. Varianten z. altтest. Texte. 4°. L. 1878
TRANSLATIONS.
Comm. on Isaiah. Tr. f. 4th ed. Introd. by S. R. Driver. 2v. 8°. E. 1890
Comm. on Job. Tr. F. Bolton. 2v. 8°. E. 1866
Comm. on the Psalms. Tr. D. Eaton. 3v. 8°. 1887–89
Iris: st. in colour & talks about flowers. Tr. A. Cusin. 8°. E. 1889
see KEIL (C. F.) & F. D. Comm. on Bks. of Samuel; tr., 1891.
„ —— & —— Joshua, Judges, Ruth; tr., 1865.
„ —— & —— The Pentateuch, 3v, 1864–65.

Delitzsch (Friedrich). Die grosse Täuschung. Krit. Betracht. zu d. altтest. Berichten. 2T. 8°. St. 1920–21
1, Israels Eindringen in Kanaan &c. 2, Prophetenschriften u. Psalmen.
Die Lese-u. Schreibfehler im Alt. Test. 8°. 1920
Sumer.-akkad.-hett. Vokabularfragm., *see* KÖN.-PREUSS. AKAD. Abhdln., Phil.-hist. Kl., 1914.

Delius (Frederick), *see* HESELTINE (P.) F. D., 1923.

Delius (Nicolaus). Radices Pracriticae. Ed. & illust. N. D. Suppl. ad Lassenii Instit. 8°. Bonnae ad Rhenum. 1839

Delius (Rudolf von). Der chines. Garten. 8°. St. [1923]

Dell (Anthony). Llamaland, E. & W. of the Andes in Peru. 4°. [1927]

Dell (Ethel M.), *wife of Lt.-Col. G. T. Savage.*

The black knight. s8°. [1926]
By request. [2nd impr.] s8°. [1927]
Charles Rex. s8°. [1922]
The hundredth chance. [repr.] s8°. *n.d.*
A man under authority. s8°. [1925]
The obstacle race. s8°. [1921]
The rocks of Valpré. [31st impr.] s8°. [1926]
The top of the world. s8°. [1920]
The unknown quantity. 8°. [1924]

Dell (Floyd). Janet March. 8°. [1924]
Moon-calf. s8°. 1922

Dell (Robert). My second Country (France). s8°. 1920

Dell (William). Works. 2v. [v1 *wanting; v2 has 4 pagins.*] 8°. 1817

Della Casa (Giovanni), *abp. of Benevento* [†CASA (G. DELLA)]. Carmina & orationes plæræque Thucydidis in Lat. serm. conversae. 8°. Helmæstadi. 1610
Galateo of manners & behaviours. [*Tr. R. Peterson*, 1576]. Intr. by J. E. Spingarn. [Humanist's Lib., 8]. 8°. Boston, *Merrymount Press.* [1914]

Della Corte (Andrea). L'opera comica ital. nel '700: studi ed appunti. 2v. 8°. Bari. 1923
Paisiello, con una tavola tematica. L'estetica mus. di P. Metastasio. [Settecento ital.] s8°. Torino. 1922

Della Corte (Matteo).

Case e abitanti a Pompei. la8°. Pompei. 1926
Dipinti pompeiani. [Estr. da Ausonia, a. 10. P2861]. 4°. *n.p.* 1921
Due dipinti murali d. agro Pompeiano. [Estr. d. Symbolae litt. in hon. J. de Pétra. P2852]. la8°. [Napoli. 1911]
Ercole e l'ara massima in un dipinto pompeiano. [Estr. d. Mem. d. R. Accad. di Arch. &c., v1. P2861]. 4°. Napoli. 1909
Fullones. [Estr. d. vol. in onore di G. A. Galante. P2861]. fol. Napoli. 1920
Groma, *see* REALE ACCAD. D. LINCEI. Mon. ant., v28, 1922.
„ Riassunto. [Estr. d. L'Eco d. ingegneri &c., a. 30. P2852]. la8°. Pescia. 1924

Della Corte (Matteo) [*continued*].
Juventus. Un nuovo aspetto d. vita pubbl. di Pompei. la8°. Arpino. 1924
Leggende del ciclo tebano in pitture d. Pompei. [Estr. d. Revista Indo-Graeco-Ital., anno 1. P2852]. la8°. Napoli. 1917
Librae Pompeianae, *see* REALE ACCAD. D. LINCEI. Mon. ant., v21, 1912.
Novacula. [Estr. da Ausonia, a. 9. P2861]. 4°. *n.p.* 1914
Nuovi scavi (case &c.). 8°. Napoli. 1924
Il "pagus Urbulanus" &c., Pompei. [Estr. d. Revista Indo-Graeco-Ital., a.5. P2852]. la8°. Napoli. [1921]
Il pomerium di Pompei. [Estr. d. R. Accad. dei Lincei, Rendiconti, v22. P2852]. la8°. 1913
Pompei: scavi e scoperte. [Estr. d. Notizie d. scavi, 1911–19 *in* 1v]. 4°. 1911–19
Pompeji, the new excav. (houses & inhabitants). 8°. Valle di Pompei. 1925
Sui mon. scoperti fuori la Porta d. Vesuvio. [Estr. d. Mem. d. R. Accad. di Arch. &c., v2]. [P2861]. 4°. Napoli. 1912

Dell' Acqua (Carlo). Im memoria del Prof. C. Magenta, *see* REGIA DEP. DI STORIA PATRIA. Misc., t33, 1895.

Della Croce (Ireneo). Hist. d. città di Trieste. fol. Venetia. 1698

Della Francesca (Piero) [DEI FRANCESCHI (PIETRO DI BENEDETTO); PIERO BORGHESE].
see GRABER (H.) P. della F.: 68 Tafeln mit Text, 1922.
„ LONGHI (R.) P. della F.; tr., 1927.
„ VENTURI (A.) P. della F., 1922.

Della Giovanna (Ildebrando), *see* DANTE ALIGHIERI. Lectura D., Il c. 2 dell' Inferno, 1905.

Dell' Agostino (Erminia). Cenni s. poesia patriottica popolare &c. nel Lombardo-Veneto (1847–66). la8°. [1921?]

Della Lega (Alberto Bacchi), *see* BACCHI DELLA LEGA (A.)

Della Marra, *House of, see* DELLA MARRA (F.) Disc. d. famiglie; C. Tutini, 1641.

Della Marra (Ferrante), *duca della Guardia.* Discorsi d. famiglie estinte &c. comprese ne' Seggi di Napoli, imparentate c. Casa della Marra. Dati in luce da C. Tutini. fol. Napoli. 1641

Della Porta (Giov. Batt.)
La Trappolaria: comedia. s8°. Bergamo. 1596

Della Quercia (Jacopo), *see* SUPINO (I. B.) J. dalla Q., 1926.

Della Robbia (Giovanni) [†ROBBIA (GIOV. DELLA)], *see* MARQUAND (A.) G. della R., 1920.

Della Robbia (Luca), *1400?–1482, see* MARQUAND (A.) L. della R., 1914.

Della Scala, *The family of* [*Scaliger*].
see BIADEGO (G.) Tre doc. scaligeri rig. Spinetta Malaspina, 1915.
„ SCALIGER (J. J.) Epist. de vetustate &c. gentis S. 1594.

Della Scala (Paolo), *Marquis of Verona* [SCALIGER (PAULUS)]. Loci communes theologici, sive pro Eccl. Rhom., adv. vesaniam Neopistorum, oratio. s4°. Coloniæ. 1571

Della Seta (Alesandro). Italia antica, d. caverna preist. al palazzo Imp. la8°. Bergamo. 1922
Vasi di Campagnano, *see* REALE ACCAD. D. LINCEI. Mon. ant., v23, 1914.

Dellenbaugh (Frederick Samuel). The romance of the Colorado River, w. ref. to voyages of Powell thro' the Gt. Canyons. 8°. N.Y. 1902

Dellmensingen (*Gen.* **Krafft von),** *see* KRAFFT VON DELLMENSINGEN.

Del Lungo (Isidoro).
I Bianchi e i Neri, pagine di storia fiorentina da Bonifazio viii ad Arrigo vii per la vita di Dante. 2ª ed. 8°. Milano. 1921
La donna fiorentina del buon tempo antico. 2ª ed. 8°. Firenze. [1926]
Il "giusto giudicio" imprecato da Dante, *see* ARCHIVIO STOR. ITAL. Anno 79, v1, 1921.
Leonardo scrittore, *see* VINCI (L. DA). L. da V.: conf., 1910.
Le vicende d'un' impostura erudita (Salvino degli Armati), *see* ARCHIVIO STORICO ITAL. Anno 78, v1, 1920.
see DANTE ALIGHIERI. Inferno. Prolus. alle tre cantiche e comm. all' "Inferno" per I. Del L., 1921.
„ —— Lectura D.: c. 33 del Paradiso, 1913.

Del Mar (Frances). A year among the Maoris: their arts & customs. Foreword by Sir W. Dunstan. 8°. 1924

Deloche (Maximin). Les Richelieu. Le père du Cardinal: F. du Plessis. Docs. inéd. 8°. 1923

Deloenus (Galterus), *see* DELAINE (W.)

De Lolme (Jean Louis). Constit. of Eng. 8°. 1775

Deloncle (Charles).
Capital & travail. Vers des temps nouv. s8°. 1921

Deloney (Thomas), *see* CHEVALLEY (A.) T. D.: le roman des métiers au temps de Shakespeare, 1926.

Delorme (*abbé,* **M. J. F. E. C.)** De Immaculata, seu de ratione congruentiæ pro Immac. Conceptione, *see* MIGNE (J. P.), *ed.* Theol. cursus, t26, 1859.

Delorme (Marion) [MARIE DE LORME], *see* PELADAN (J.) Hist. & lég. de M. de L., 1927.

Delorme (Philibert) [†L'ORME (P. DE)]. L'œuvre de P. D. comp. t1 de l'Architecture & Les nouv. inventions p. bien bastir &c. (1567). Reprod. en facs. Publ. C. Nizet. fol. 1894
see ROY (M.) P. de L. à Paris (1546–59), 1924.

Délos. Explor. archéol. de D. faite par l'Ecole Fr. d'Athènes, 1909–26, *see* ECOLE FRANÇ. D'ATHÈNES.
Inscriptions de D.: comptes des Hiéropes, 1926, *see* DURRBACH (F.), *ed.*

De Louter (J.), *see* LOUTER (J. DE).

Delpech (François Seraphin), *see* VERNET (C.) Les cris de Paris; lithog. de F. D., *n.d.*

Delpech (Joseph). La démocratie & le régime représentatif. [P2488]. s8°. 1910
see MOREAU (F.) & J. D. Les règlements des assemblées législat.; éd. & tr. par M. & D., 2t, 1906–7.

Delphes. Fouilles de D., *see* ECOLE FR. D'ATHÈNES.

Delphino (Niccolo), *see* DELFINO.

Delphinus (Petrus), *see* DELFINO (P.)

Delphius (Joannes). Quæst. proponendæ ordinandis in maioribus. [*b. w.* Fulevius (J.) Diss. jurid., 1627]. s8°. Coloniæ. 1581

Del Ponte, *the family of, see* GIROLAMO MARIA, *di Sant' Anna.* Della stor. geneal., p1, 1708.

Delpuech de Comeiras (Victor).
*Tableau gén. de la Russie mod. n. éd. 2t. 8°. 1807

Delsart (H. M.), *ps.* [*i.e. Mme.* MONNIER]. Une fondatrice d'abbaye au 7e s.: Ste. Fare, sa vie & s. culte. s8°. 1911

Del Sella (*conde* **de la Vega),** *see* VEGA DEL SELLA (*conde* DE LA).

Del Techo (Nicolaus), *see* TECHO (N. DEL).

Delteil (Joseph). Jeanne d'Arc. [Cahiers Verts, 53]. s8°. 1925
Sur le fleuve Amour. s8°. [1925]

Delteil (Loys). Man. de l'amateur d'estampes des 19e & 20e s. (1801–1924). 2t [*pagin. cont.*] la8°. 1925
„ „ ....Compl., 700 reprods. 2p. la8°. [1926]
—— **& H. J. L. Wright.** Cat. raisonné of etchings of C. Meryon by L. D., w. add., ed. H. J. L. W. [*w.* Addenda & errata, 1925]. sm. fol. N.Y. 1924

Delvaille (Henry Caro-), *see* CARO-DELVAILLE (H.)

Delvig (*baron* **Anton Antonovich).**
Сочиненія. Состав. В. В. Майковымъ. 8°. С.-П. 1893
Неизданные стихотворения. Под редакцией М. Л. Гофмана. s8°. П. 1922
see VERKHOVSKY (YU. N.) Баронъ Д., 1922.

Del Vita (Alessandro). Castiglion Fiorentino. [Il Piccolo Cicerone Mod. Nr. 19]. s8°. [1920]

De Maar (Harko G.)
Hist. of mod. Eng. romanticism. v1. 8°. 1924

Deman (Esther Boise van), *see* VAN DEMAN (E. B.)

Demangel (Robert). Un nouvel alabastre du peintre Pasiadès, *see* ACAD. DES INSCR. &C. FOND. PIOT. Mons. &c., t26, 1923.

Demangeon (Albert). Le déclin de l'Europe. s8°. 1920
L'Empire brit.: ét. de géogr. colon. s8°. 1923

De Mareschal de Luciane (F. C.), *see* MARESCHAL DE LUCIANE (F. C. DE).

Demarest (David D.) Hist. & characteristics of the Ref. Protest. Dutch Church. s8°. N.Y. 1856

Demaria (Giacinto). La guerra di Castro e la spediz. de' presidii (1639–49), *see* REGIA DEP. DI STORIA PATRIA. Misc., t35, 1898.

Demarteau (Gilles), *see* NEUVILLE (A. DE). G. D. [Les grands Belges], 1920.

De Meester (Johan), *see* MEESTER (J. DE).

Demel (Hans). Die Tonware [Kloster am Isisberg], *see* JUNKER (H.) Bericht ü. d. Grabungen, El-Kubanieh-Nord, T3, 1924.

Demelitsch (Fedor v.) Actenstücke z. Gesch. d. Coalition v. 1814, *see* FONTES RERUM AUSTRIAC., B49ii, 1899.

Demelius (Christoph Friedrich). Diss. de emendatione Eccl. Rom. per nov. concil. Lateran. haud sperandae. Praes. J. G. Walchio. [P436]. s4°. Jenæ. [1726]

Demetrescu (Mihail). Izvoade, 1880–90. s8°. Bucuresci. 1891

Demetriadi (*Sir* **Stephen).**
Inside a Govt. Office. [repr.] 8º. [1921]
A reform for the Civil Service. 8º. 1921
The Springett family of Kent & Sussex. [Genealog. table. *no tp.*] folded. 8º. 1924

Demetrios (Chrusostomos M.) Οἱ ἐξωκατακοίλοι ἄρχοντες τῆς ἐν. Κων/πόλει Μεγ. Ἐκκλησίας. [Texte u. Forsch. z. byzant.-neugr. Phil., Nr. 7]. 8º. Athen. 1927

Demetrius, *Cydonius.* De contemnenda morte oratio, *Gr. & Lat.*, 1559, *see* THEOLOGI. Theol. aliquot Græc. libri, 1560.
Orat. ined. [*Greek; ed.* G. Cammelli], *see* BYZANTINISCH-NEUGRIECH. JHRBR., B3, 1922.

Demetrius, *Phalereus.*
De elocutione. [*Greek.*] s8º. Florentiae. 1552
On style, w. tr. by W. R. Roberts [Loeb Class. Lib.], 1927, *see* ARISTOTLE, Poetics, 1927.

Demetrius, *Saint, Metropol. of Rostov, see* RUSSIAN. Lives of emin. R. prelates, 1854.

Demetrius, *called "The Imposter," Tsar of Russia.*
see MASSA (I.) La légende de D.; tr., 1606 [*in h.* Hist. des guerres &c., 1866].
,, RUSSELL (W.) *Récit du sanglant &c. massacre &c. du dern. duc D., 1606; tr. prince Galitzin, 1869.

Demeure Historique (La). Expos. d'art anc. espagnol, organisée par la "D. H.," en l'Hôtel Jean Charpentier. [*Pref. by* J. Carvallo]. s8º. 1925

Demidov (Mathilde L. W., *ctss.*), *see* LA FAYE (J. DE) La Pesse. M., 1820–1904, 1928.

Demmin (Auguste).
Guide de l'amateur de faïences &c. 2p. s8º. 1867

***Democracy**: an Amer. novel, 1882, *see* ADAMS (H.)

Democrates, *the Pythagorean, see* DEMOPHILUS. Des D. pythagor. Vergleichungen &c., wie auch des D. Sprüche [*Gr. & Germ.*], 1827.

Democratic National Committee. The Democratic doctrine. The keynote speech [of H. Cummings] &c. [P2465]. 8º. [1920]

Democritus, *of Abdera.*
see LÖWENHEIM (L.) Die Wissenschaft D., 1914.
,, WELLMANN (M.) Georgika d. D., 1921.

Demolder (Eugène). Albions Todeskampf. [Hrsg. v. S. Strizek. 2e A.] s8º. München. 1915
Constantin Meunier. la8º. Brux. 1901
see RAMAEKERS (G.) E. D. [Les grands Belges], 1920.

***Demonologia**; or, natural knowledge revealed, 1827; 1831, *see* FORSYTH (J. S.)

***Demonstratio** hist.-diplom. ducat. & judic. provinc. Franconiae &c., 1758, *see* DRÜMEL (J. H.)

De Montgomery (B. G.), *see* MONTGOMERY (B. G. DE).

De Montmorency (Hervey). From Kant to Einstein. 8º. C. 1926

De Montmorency (James Edward Geoffrey). Francis Will. Fox: a biog. Pref. note by G. P. Gooch. s8º. 1923
John Gorell Barnes, 1st Ld. Gorell, 1848–1913. Intr. by Ronald, 3rd Ld. Gorell. 8º. 1920
Poor students & new halls, *see* WARD (*Sir* A. W.) In memoriam, 1924.

Demonts (Louis), *see* LOUVRE. Musée Nat. du L. Cat. des peintures expos., p3, Écoles flam. &c.; par L. D., 1922.

Demophilus. Des D. pythagor. Vergleichungen nebst dessen pythagor. Sittensprüchen, wie auch d. Demokrates gold. Sprüche. Uib. [*sic*] v. J. M. Fleischer. [*Gr. & Germ.*] s8º. Nürnberg. 1827

De Morgan (Augustus).
Elements of arithmetic. [5th ed., repr.] s8º. 1853
First notions of logic. s8º. 1839
,, ,, ...2nd ed. [P2434]. 8º. 1840

De Morgan (Mary), *sister of W. De M., see* DODSON (W.), *ps.*

De Morgan (Mary Evelyn), *wife of W. De M., formerly Pickering.*
see STIRLING (*Mrs.* A. M. W.) W. de M. & h. wife, 1922.

De Morgan (William). The old man's youth. s8º. 1921
see STIRLING (*Mrs.* A. M. W.) W. de M. & h. wife, 1922.

De' Mori (Ascanio). Giuoco piacevole. Stamp. la 3a v., corr.; con giunta d'alc. sue rime, d'un Ragion. in lode d. donne & d'alc. lettere [1569–89]. 4p [*w. sep. tps. & pagin.*] 8º. Mantova. 1590
Novelle, *see* †RACCOLTA di novellieri ital., 1853.

Demosthenes. Δημοσθένους λόγοι, καὶ προοίμια δημηγορικὰ, καὶ ἐπιστολαὶ, σὺν ταῖς ἐξηγήσεσιν &c. Διὰ ἐπιμελείας Γ. Μορελίου. Προετέθη βίος Δ. fol. Lutetiae. 1570
Orationes. Rec. &c. S. H. Butcher. t1, 2i. s8º. O. [1903–07]

Demosthenes [*continued*].
TRANSLATIONS.
De corona & De falsa legatione. [Text] w. Eng. tr. by C. A. & J. H. Vince. [Loeb Class. Lib.] s8º. 1926
Harangues. Texte établi & tr. par M. Croiset. [Coll. des univs. de Fr.] 2t. 8º. 1924–25
Olynthiac & o. publ. orations. Tr. C. R. Kennedy. 8º. *Bell.* 1881
Orations agst. Leptines, Midias, Androtion, Aristocrates; tr. w. notes &c. by C. R. Kennedy. s8º. *Bohn.* 1856
O. on the Crown, & on the Embassy. Tr. C. R. Kennedy. s8º. *Bohn.* 1865
see CLEMENCEAU (G.) D., 1926.
,, DOBSON (W. S.), *ed.* Oratores Attici, t5–8. D., 9, 10, Animadv. & Scholia, 11, Dobree Adversaria & ind., 15, 16, D. &c. interpret. Lat., 1828.
,, DRERUP (E.) D. im Urteile d. Altertums, bis Tzetzes, 1923.

Dempster (*Miss* **Charlotte Louisa Hawkins).**
The manners of my time. 8º. 1920

De Napoli (Giuseppe), *see* NAPOLI (G. DE).

Denarié (Emmanuel). La chapelle des morts. Préf. de H. Bordeaux. s8º. [1928]

Denbigh.
*The castle & borough of D. [P2421]. s8º. Denbigh. 1881

Dendy (Arthur). Biolog. found. of society. 8º. 1924
Problems of mod. science. Lects. [*by var. as.*], King's Coll., London. Ed. A. D. 8º. [1922]

Dendy (Frederick Walter), *ed., see* ENGLAND. Visitations, p2, 1921.

Dendy (Ralph). Relation of form to matter in literature. Haileybury Coll. prize essay. [P2709]. 8º. M'ter. 1911

Denham (Dixon), H. Clapperton & W. Oudney. Travels &c. in N. & C. Africa, 1822–24. 2p *in* 1v. 4º. 1826

Denham (*Sir* **John),** *the poet.*
Poet. works. Collated by T. Park. s8º. 1807
A version of the Psalms of David. 8º. 1714
see DOBRÉE (B.) Sir J. D.: a conversation, 1927.
,, WARD (E.) Secret hist. of the Calves-Head Club. 5th ed. [w.] character of a Presbyterian by D., 1707.

Deniau (Félix). Hist. de la guerre de la Vendée. t5, 6, par le chanoine D., Dom Chamard, & l'abbé Uzureau. la8º. Angers. [1911 ?–1912]

Denifle (Heinrich), *see* ARCHIV. F. LITT.-U. KIRCHENGESCH. D. MITTEL ALTERS; hrsg. v. H. D. u. F. Ehrle, B1–7, 1885–1900.

De Nijse (Nicolai), *see* DENYSE (N.)

Deniker (Joseph). Bibliog. des travaux sci. publ. par les soc. savantes de la France j. 1888. t1, 2, livr. 1. (t2, livr. 1 par R. Descharmes). 4º. 1916–22

Denikin (*gen.* **Anton Ivanovich).** Очерки русской смуты. t1–5 [1i, ii]. 8º. & la8º. Paris [3, Berlin]. 1921–22
The Russian turmoil. Mem.: military, soc. & polit. 8º. [1922]
see BECHHOFER-ROBERTS (C. E.) In D.'s Russia &c., 1921.
,, KING (J.) Three bloody men: D. &c., 1919.
,, SOKOLOV (K. N.) Правленіе Д., 1921.

Denina (Carlo G. M.) Delle rivol. d'Italia. Contin., 1713–92. s8º. Venezia. 1792

Denis (Alberta Johnston). Spanish Alta California. 8º. N.Y. 1927

Denis (J. N. C. Michael). Suffragium pro J. de Spira primo Venetiarum typographo. [P2688]. 8º. Viennae. 1794

Denis (Léon).
La vérité sur Jeanne d'Arc. [J. d'A. médium]. 8º. 1910

Denis (Louis J.), *see* LE MANS. Cartul. du Chapitre Royal de l'église collég. de St.-Pierre-de-la-Cour &c.; [publ.] par le vte. M. d'Elbenne & L. J. D., *& Introd.* Le Chap. Royal, 1903–10.

Denis (Maurice), *1870–.* A. Maillol. 4º. 1925
Théories, 1890–1910, du symbolisme & de Gauguin vers un nouvel ordre class. 4e éd. 8º. 1920
see FOSCA (F.) M.D., 1924.

Denis (Pierre). La Rép. Argentine. La mise en valeur du pays. 8º. 1920
,, ,, ...Tr. J. McCabe. 8º. 1922

Denison (John), *D.D.* The heavenly banquet; or the doctrine of the Lord's Supper in 7 sermons &c. s8º. 1619

Denison (Merrill). The unheroic North. 4 Canadian plays. [Brothers in arms—The weather breeder—From their own place—Marsh Hay]. 8º. Toronto. [1923]

Denizet (Frédéric), *see* BOUCHES-DU-RHÔNE: encyclop. départ., t9, par F. D., 1922.

Denjean (François).
Le commerce russe & la Révolution. s8°. 1920
Denkmalschutz-Kommando, *see* WISSENSCHAFTLICHE VERÖFFENTLICHUNGEN d. deut.-türk. D.-K., H1–3, 1920–21.
Denmylne MSS. Extracts f. coll. in Advocates' Lib., *see* HIGHLAND papers, v3, 1920.
Dennemeyer (Camille).
Im Höllenrachen d. Bolschewismus. s8°. Luxemburg. 1920
Dennie (Joseph) [*ps.* OLIVER OLDSCHOOL], *see* PORTFOLIO (THE). By O. O. n. ser., v1, 2, 1806–7.
Denning (J. Renton-), *see* RENTON-DENNING (J.)
Dennis (Alfred Louis Pinneo).
Foreign policies of Soviet Russia. 8°. 1924
Dennis (Geoffrey).
Harvest in Poland. [*Fiction*]. s8°. [1925]
Mary Lee. s8°. 1922
Dennis (Thomas).
A new vers. of the Psalms in blank verse. s8°. 1808
Denniston (John Dewar). Greek lit. criticism. [Lib. of Greek thought; ed. E. Barker]. 8°. 1924
Denny (Henry Lyttelton Lyster). Hdbk. of County Kerry family hist., biog. &c. [Co. Kerry Soc.] 8°. 1923
The manor of Hawkesbury & its owners. 4°. Gloucester. 1920
Dens (Petrus). Theologia moralis &c. Ed. nov., acc. epitome ex operibus Benedicti XIV &c. [*forming* t8]. 8t *in* 4v. s8°. Dublinii. 1832
Tract. de quatuor novissimis, *see* MIGNE. Theol. cursus, t7, 1861.
Densmore (Frances). Handbook of coll. of musical instruments. [S.I., U.S. Nat. Mus., Bull. 136]. 8°. Wash. 1927
Mandan & Hidatsa music. [S.I., B. of Amer. Ethnol., Bull. 80]. 8°. Wash. 1923
Music of the Tule Indians of Panama, *see* SMITHSONIAN INST. Misc. colls., v77, 1926.
Northern Ute music. [S.I., B. of Amer. Ethnol., Bull. 75]. 8°. Wash. 1922
Densusianu (Ovid). Barbu Delavrancea, *see* ACADEMIA ROM. Disc., 45, 1919.
Dent (Arthur). The plaine-mans path-way to heaven: w. 3 prayers &c. [*Foll. by* *The ark & *Some medit^s. on Exodus, in meeter, *each w. sep. pagin.*] 20th ed. s8°. 1629
The ruine of Rome: expos. upon Revelation. s8°. 1603
Dent (Edward Joseph).
Terpander: music & the future. s8°. [1926]
Dent (Guy). Emperor of the If. s8°. [1926]
Denterghem (*cte.* **Charles de Kerchove de**), *see* KERCHOVE DE DENTERGHEM.
Dentice di Accadia (C.)
Tommaso Campanella. 8°. Firenze. [1921]
Denton (Francis Medforth).
Einstein theory explained. [P2704]. la8°. [1919]
Denton (V. L.) The Far West coast. 8°. Toronto. 1924
Denton (William), *M.D.* *Horae subsecivae: or treat. showing grounds &c. necess. our sanguinary laws agst. the papists. By D. W. Esq. s4°. 1664
Denyse (Nicolaus) [NIJSE (N. DE)]. De observantia in 4 libros sententiarum, opus, Resolutio theologorum inscr. s8°. Venetiis. 1568
Denzinger (Heinrich J. D.) Enchiridion symbolorum &c. de rebus fidei & morum. Ed. H. D. Ed. 4ª aucta. s8°. Wirceburgi. 1865
Deodata (Maria), *ps.* [*Sister* SCHOLASTIKA]. Frauenkloster Lichtental: Gesch., Kirchen u. Altertümer. 8°. Lichtental. 1915
Deonna (Waldemar).
L'archéologie, s. domaine, s. but. s8°. 1922
Trois têtes antiq. du Musée d'Art &c. à Genève, *see* ACAD. DES INSCR.: FOND. PIOT. Mon., t27, 1924.
see RIDDER (A. DE) & W. D. L'art en Grèce, 1924; tr., 1927.
Deor, *bard of the Heodenings, see* BEOWULF. Widsith—Beowulf—Deor &c.; Eng. by C. Scott Moncrieff, 1921.
Depew (Chauncey Mitchell).
My mem. of 80 years. 8°. N.Y. 1922
Depoli (Guido). Fiume e la Liburnia: schizzo antropogeogr. 8°. Bari. 1919
De Quincey (Thomas). Letters on self-education, w. hints on style & dialogues on polit. econ. s8°. [1861]
Suspiria de profundis: sequel to Confessions & o. misc. wr. [Works: Author's ed.] s8°. E. 1871
see FOWLER (J. H.) De Q. as literary critic, 1922.

Der Aa (Pieter van), *bookseller.* Les royaumes d'Espagne & de Portugal, represés. en tailles-douces &c. obl. 8°. Leide. *n.d.*
De Raaf (K. H.), *see* RAAF (K. H. DE).
De Rance (Charles E.), *F.G.S.* Geol. of the country around Blackpool, Poulton & Fleetwood. [Mems. of G.S.] 8°. 1875
Superficial geol. of the co. adj. the coasts of S.-W. Lancashire. Lists of fossils rev. by R. Etheridge. [Mems. of G.S.] 8°. 1877
Derblay (Claude). Roger de Comminges, Sieur de Saubole, Gouv. de Metz, 1553–1615. 8°. 1927
Derby. *A plain &c. acc. of the conduct & proc^s. of the rebels at D., 4th–6th Dec., 1745. [*b. w.* Broad-sheets. Misc. b.-s., *var. d.*] fol. Derby. [1745 ?]
Derbyshire. D. parish reg. Marriages. Ed. T. M. Blagg & L. L. Simpson. v14, 15. 8°. 1917–22
*Old halls, manors, & families of D., v1, 2, 1892–93, *see* TILLEY (J.)
Derbyshire Archaeological & Natural History Society.
Journal. v42–45, N.S. v1, 2 (1920–26). 8°. [1920–26]
Derème (Tristan).
La verdure dorée. Poèmes. Préf. de P. Huc. s8°. 1922
Derennes (Charles).
L'agneau, nouvelle, *see* ŒUVRES (Les) libres, 22, 1923.
Bellurot, roman, *see* ŒUVRES libres, 32, 1924.
La chauve-souris. s8°. [1922]
The life of the bat. Tr. Mrs. L. C. Wilcox. 8°. [1925]
Mouti, fils de Mouti, roman, *see* ŒUVRES libres, 69, 1927.
Le pou, nouvelle, *see* ŒUVRES libres, 4, 1921.
Dérieux (Henry). La belle & la bête, *see* ŒUVRES libres, t71, 1927.
Dering (Edward), *B.D.* *A briefe & necessary catechisme. With prayers. [*b. w.* Two godly sermons, *n.d.*] newly impr. s8°. *n.d.* [c. 1590]
Certaine godly &c. letters full of Christ. consolation. [*imperf. b. w. h.* Two godly sermons, *n.d.*] newly impr. s8°. *n.d.* c. 1590
27 lectures or readings upon parte of the Epistle to the Hebrues. s8°. *for T. Woodcoke.* 1583
„ „ newly impr. [*b. w. h.* Two godly sermons, *n.d.*] s8°. [c. 1590 ?]
Two godly sermons [*half-title reads* Maister Derings Workes]. newly impr. s8°. *n.d.* [c. 1590]
Dering (*Sir* Edward), *1st Bart.* A coll. of speeches in matter of relig. [*With portrait*]. 8°. 1642
Derjavin (Nikolai Sevast.) Болгарскія колоніи въ Россіи, *see* SBORNIK. Сборникъ за нар. умотвор., кн. 29, 1914.
Der Linden (Fritz van), *see* VAN DER LINDEN (F.)
Der Meer (Jan van) [J. VERMEER].
see CHANTAVOINE (J.) Ver M. de Delft: biog. crit., 1926.
„ HAUSENSTEIN (W.) Das Bild, B10, Vermeer; Nachwort v. B. Reiffenberg, 1924.
„ LUCAS (E. V.) Vermeer of Delft, 1922.
„ VANZYPE (G.) Vermeer de Delft, n. éd., rev. &c., 1925.
Der Meer (Marten Jan van). Hist. Gramm. d. niederl. Sprache. [German. Bibl.; hrsg. W. Streitberg]. B1. 8°. Heidelberg. 1927
Dermott (Lawrence). The constit. of free-masonry. Added, Sel. of masonic songs &c. Rev., &c. w. add^s. by T. Harper. 8°. 1801
see FREEMASONRY. *Defence of f. &c., cont. refut. of D.'s Acc. &c., 1765.
„ SADLER (H.) Masonic repr^s., Defence of L. D. & the Antients &c., 1898.
Dernburg (Bernhard).
Der Weg z. Wirtschaftsfrieden. [P2383]. 8°. 1919
see REPPLIER (A.) & J. W. WHITE. Germany & democracy: reply to D., 1914.
Dernière. *D. (La) heure des Turcs; tr., 1920, *see* SEVELINGES (C. L. DE).
*D. (La) heure du Concile, 1870, *see* VATICAN COUNCIL.
Dernschwam (Hans). Tagebuch e. Reise nach Konstantinopel u. Kleinasien, 1553–55; hrsg. &c. F. Babinger, *see* JANSEN (M.) & J. STRIEDER. St. z. Fugger-Gesch., H7, 1923.
Derosne (Judith Bernard), *see* JUDITH (*Mme.*)
Derossi (Johannes Bernardus), *see* ROSSI (GIOVANNI BERNARDO DE).
Der Osten (H. H. von), *see* VON DER OSTEN (H. H.)
Déroulède (Paul), *see* THARAUD (J.) & J. T. Vie & mort de D., 1925.
Der Pyl (Roelof van).
Pract. gram. of Dutch language. 8°. Rotterdam. 1819
Derry almanac (The), North-West directory &c., 1919. s8°. Londonderry. [1919]

Dertinger (Christoph Friedrich). Solani tuberosi esculenti jura quaedam. Praes. G. D. Hoffmann. [P447]. s4°. Tubingæ. [1774]
De Ruyter (*Adm.* **Michiel [Adriaanszoon]),** *see* WASSENAER-OBDAM (*Adm.* J. VAN). Journalen van de admiralen Van W.-O., 1658–59 & De R., 1659–60; uitg. door G. L. Grove, 1907.
Derviches. Les saints des D. tourneurs; récits tr. du Persan &c. par C. Huart, 2t, 1918–22, *see* HUART (C.)
Dervishian (Seraphin). Armeniaca I. Das altarm. P. Anhang: Altarm.-baktr. Etymologien. [P2799]. la8°. Wien. 1877
Der Vlugt (W. van).
La question des îles d'Aland. [P2519]. 8°. Leyde. 1921
Desaivre (Léo). La dime royale à Niort et à La Rochelle en 1718. la8°. Niort. 1880
De Salis (Rachel).
Hillingdon thr. 11 centuries. la8°. Uxbridge. [1926]
Desanctis (Luigi). Il papa non è successore di San Pietro. [*b. w. h.* Il papa, 1864]. s8°. Firenze. 1866
Il papa: osservaz. dottr. e stor. s8°. Firenze. 1864
De Sanctis (Sante), *see* SANCTIS (S. DE).
Désaugiers (Marc Antoine Madeleine). L'hôtel garni. Comédie (1814). [Préf. par P. Guitet-Vauquelin]. 8°. [1920]
Des Bancels (J. Larguier), *see* LARGUIER DES BANCELS (J.)
Desbordes-Valmore (Marceline).
Poésies. Intr. par F. Gohin. s8°. 1925
Descamps (*baron* **Edouard E. F. J.)** Le génie des religions. Les orig. avec un essai sur la vérité & la civilis. la8°. 1923
Descartes (René).
Corr. of D. & C. Huygens, 1635–47. Ed. L. Roth. 4°. O. 1926
Discours de la méthode. Texte, & comm. by E. Gilson. 8°. 1925
Discourse on method. [*Foll. by* The Meditations. Tr., *sep. tp. & pagin.*] 2nd ed. s8°. E. 1853
The geometry of R. D. Tr. f. Fr. & Lat. by D. E. Smith & M. L. Latham. 8°. Chicago. 1925
see ANCILLON (L. F.) Judicium de judiciis circa argum. Cartes. pro existentia Dei, 1792.
,, DIMIER (L.) Vie raisonnable de D., 1926.
see KOYRÉ (A.) Essai sur l'idée de Dieu &c. chez D., 1922.
,, MARITAIN (J.) 3 réformateurs: Luther, D. &c., 1925.
,, MILHAUD (G.) Descartes savant, 1921.
,, MORE (H.), *D.D.* Enchiridion ethicum; acc. epist., apolog. pro Cartesio, 1679.
,, PÉGUY (C. P.) Œuvres compl., t9, Note conjointe sur M. D. &c., 1924.
,, ROTH (L.) Spinoza, D. & Maimonides, 1924.
,, SPINOZA (B. DE). Opera, v1, R. D. Princip. philos., 1925.
Descepeaux (J. Duchemin), *see* DUCHEMIN DESCEPEAUX (J.)
Desch (Cecil Henry). Metallography. 3rd ed. s8°. 1922
Deschamps (Émile). Un manifeste du romantisme: la Préf. des études franç. &c. d'E. D. Publ. avec intr. &c. par H. Girard. s8°. [1923]
see GIRARD (H.) E. D. dilettante, 2t, 1921.
,, THÉRET (A.) Littérat. du Berry, avec H. de Latouche & E. D., 1902.
Deschamps (John). Scenery & remin. of Ceylon: f. orig. drawings & notes. fol. 1845
Deschamps (Paul). La légende arturienne à la cath. de Modène, *see* ACAD. DES INSCRS. FOND. PIOT. Mons. & méms., t28, 1925–26.
Deschamps (Pierre), *see* RAVAILLAC (F.) Procès du F. R.; publ. P. D., 1858.
Deschanel (Paul). Disc. de récept. [*on* E. Hervé]. Rép. de Sully Prudhomme [Acad. Fr., 1 fév. 1900]. 8°. 1900
Gambetta. 8°. 1920
see JONNART (C. C. A.) Disc. pour la récept. de C. J. [*on* P. D.], 1925.
,, SONOLET (L.) La vie & l'œuvre de P. D., 1926.
Descharmes (René). Le centenaire de Flaubert. Autour de Bouvard & Pécuchet, études document. & crit. s4°. 1921
see DENIKER (J.) Bibliog. des travaux sci. publ. par les soc. sav. de la Fr., t2, livr. 1, par R. D., 1922.
—— & R. Dumesnil.
Autour de Flaubert: ét^{s}. hist. &c. suiv. d'une biog. chron., d'un essai bibliog. &c. 2v. s8°. 1912
Desclot (Bernardo). Rel. hist. de la famosa invasion del exercito y armada de Francia en Cataluña en 1285 &c. s4°. 1793
Descombaz (Samuel).
Hist. des missions évangél. 2e éd. 2[v]. s8°. 1860
Descorches de Sainte-Croix (Marie Louis Henri, *marquis*), *see* MARCÈRE (E. L. G. H. DE). Une ambass. à Constantinople [de D. de S.-C.], 2t, 1927.
Descour (L.) Pasteur & his work. Tr. by A. F. & B. H. Wedd. [2nd ed.] 8°. [1922]
Des Courières (Ed.) Van Dongen. la8°. 1925
Descripción. *D. de parte del Japón, *see* MAGELLAN (F.) Descr. de los reinos, &c., 1920.
Description. *D. (A) of the machine for fireworks, exhib. in St. James's Park, on acc. of the gen. peace. [*tp. supplied in MS.*] s8°. [1749]
D. of Millenium Hall, 1762, *see* MONTAGU (*Lady* B.) & *Mrs.* S. SCOTT.
Desdevises du Dézert (G.) & L. Bréhier. Clermont-Ferrand: Royat & Puy de Dôme. [Villes d'art célèb.] la8°. 1926
De Selincourt (Basil).
The English secret & o. essays. 8°. 1923
Rhyme in Eng. poetry, *see* ENGLISH ASSOC. Essays &c., v7, 1921.
De Sélincourt (Ernest). Keats [Warton Lect. 11. From Proc. of Brit. Acad., v10. P2498]. 8°. 1921
,, ,, *f. a. ed.*, *see* KEATS HOUSE COMMITTEE. John Keats Mem. vol., 1921.
De Selincourt (Hugh).
Women & children. Novel. s8°. [1921]
Young 'un. s8°. [1927]
Desenfans (Noel). A plan to preserve among us portraits of distinguished characters. [*b. w.* Hogarth (W.) *Explan. &c., 1800]. 8°. 1799
Deseoso. *Desiderius, or the orig. pilgrim. Render'd into English [*f. the Spanish of* "El Deseoso"] & expl. w. notes by L. Howel. s8°. 1717
Des Freux (*le père* **André),** *see* FRUSIUS (ANDREAS), *Jesuit.*
Des Gachons (Jacques). Ma tante Anna. s8°. [1922]
Deshairs (Léon). Aix-en-Provence: archit. & décor. aux 17e & 18e siècles. fol. *n.d.*
Des Houlières (*Mme*), *1637–94*, *see* LACHÈVRE (F.) Dern. libertins, 1924.
Desika (*Sri* **Vedanta)** [VENKATANÁTHA]. Sankalpa-Sûryôdaya, or, The dawn of the divine will. With Eng. tr. by K. Narayanacharya &c. v1, acts 1–5. s8°. Srirangam. 1917
Desimoni (Cornelio). Commem. di M. Remondini, *see* REGIA DEP. DI STORIA PATRIA. Misc., t27, 1889.
Desjardins (Paul), *see* STEWART (H. F.) & P. D. French patriotism, 1814–33, 1923.
Desjardins (Raoul). Contre sa joue, *see* ŒUVRES libres, 2, 1921.
Deslandes (André Daulier), *see* DAULIER DESLANDES (A.)
Deslinières (Lucien). Délivrons-nous du Marxisme. 8°. 1923
Des Longrais (Frédéric Joüon), *see* JOÜON DES LONGRAIS (F.)
Desmares (Marie), *see* CHAMPMESLÉ (M. DE), *née Desmares.*
Desmarets (Daniel). *Tableau des papes de Rome. Pour bien juger de la Constit. de Clément XI du 8 sept. 1713 contre les Réflex. mor. sur le Nouv. Test. par Quesnel. Avec une lettre prelim. [Publ. par Chion]. s8°. Cologne. 1714
Desmarets (Samuel) [MARESIUS (S.)] Disputationes, *see* DU MOULIN (P.) Thesaurus disputat., v2, 1661.
Joanna Papissa restituta: sive animadv. &c. ad D. Blondellii librum. Add.: Brevis refut. præf. apolog. quam præfixit S. Curcellæus & Dissert. pro Trinitate eidem Curcellæo oppos. [*w. sep. pagin.*] s4°. Groningæ Frisiorum. 1658
Refut. fabulae praeadamiticae; cum praef. apologet. pro αὐθεντίᾳ Script. ed 2^{a}. s8°. Groningae. 1656
Theologiae elenchticæ nova synopsis; sive index controv. fidei ex Script. à J. Tirino concinnatus &c., emend. &c. per S. M. 2t. [t2 *wanting*?]. s4°. Groningae. 1646–48
Desmond, *the earls of*, *see* FLYNN (P. F.) Book of the Galtees &c., 1926.
Desmond (Shaw).
Labour. The giant w. feet of clay. 8°. [1921]
Ragnarok. s8°. [1926]
De Sola (David Aaron), *see* TEPHILOTH. Forms of prayer acc. to custom of Span. &c. Jews, w. Eng. tr. &c. by D. A. De S., 3v, 1836–37.
***Desolation** (The) of France demonstrated, 1697, *see* SOULIGNÉ (— DE).
Des Ombiaux (Maurice). Les premiers romanciers nat. de Belgique. [C. de Coster, C. Lemonnier &c.] s8°. 1919
Victor Rousseau. la8°. Brux. 1908
Despard (Edward Marcus).
*Mems. of the life of Col. E. M. D. 3rd ed. [P2828]. s8°. [1803]
The trial of Col. E. M. D. &c. on a charge of high treason, Southwark, Feb. 1803. [P2825]. s8°. York. [1803]
see OMAN (*Sir* C. W. C.) The unfort. Col. D. &c., 1922.
Despaux (Albert). L'inflation dans l'hist. s8°. [1922]

Despériers (Jean Bonaventure) [DESPÉRRIERS].
Cymbalum Mundi. Avec une lettre crit. &c. par P. Marchand. n. éd., rév. &c. & augm. de notes. s8°. Amsterdam. 1732
„ „ Texte de l'éd. de 1537, avec notice, comm. &c. par F. Frank. s8°. 1873
see BECKER (P. A.) B. des P. als Dichter u. Erzähler, 1924.
„ SAINÉAN (L.) Probl. litt. du 16e s., Joyeux devis &c., 1927.

Despiau (Charles), *see* ROGER-MARX (C.) C. D., 1922.

Despierres (*Mme* Gérasime). Hist. du point d'Alençon [*&* Dict. des marchands &c.] 8°. 1886

Desplanques (Charles).
Barbiers, perruquiers, coiffeurs. s8°. 1927

Despréaux (E.), *see* LETTONIE. *La L. histor.; éd. E. D., 1921.

Despréaux (*le col.* Frignet). Le maréchal Mortier, duc de Trévise. t3. 1804–7. la8°. Nancy. 1920

Desroches (Jean Jacques). *Hist. du Mont Saint-Michel & de l'anc. diocèse d'Avranches. Atlas. obl.4°. Caen. 1839

Dessaignes (G. Ribemont-), *see* RIBEMONT-DESSAIGNES (G.)

Dessau (Hermann).
Gesch. d. röm. Kaiserzeit. B1, 2i. 8°. 1924–26
Inscr. Latinae selectae. v3ii [*pagin. cont.*] 8°. Berolini. 1916

Desselius (V. A.), *see* ANDREAS (VALERIUS), *Desselius.*

Dessoir (Max).
Lehrbuch d. Philos. Hrsg. M. D. [2B.] la8°. [1925]
1, Gesch. d. Philos.; dargestellt v. E. v. Aster, E. Cassirer &c.
2, Philos. in i. Einzelgebieten; dargestellt v. E. Becher, K. Koffka &c.

Dessy (Mario). Petrolini. [Uomini del giorno, N. 43 *for* 45]. la8°. Milano. 1921

De Stacpoole (George, *duke*). Irish & o. memories. 8°. 1922

Destez (Robert). Monsieur Papanoix, *see* ŒUVRES libres, No. 63, 1926.

Destouches (Jacques), *see* DUPONT (E.) Le véritable Chevalier D., 1924.

Destouches (Philippe Néricault) [†NERICAULT DESTOUCHES (P.)] The conceited count; tr., *see* ALDINGTON (R.) Fr. comedies of 18th c., 1923.
Le philosophe marié—Le glorieux, *see* THÉÂTRE choisi du 18e s., t1, 1914.
see FAVART (C. S.) & LARGILLIÈRES. Polichinelle; parodie inéd. du Glorieux de D. (1732), 1924.

Destrée (Joseph). Hugo van der Goes. 4°. Brux. 1914
—— & P. Bautier. Les Heures dites da Costa: ms. du 16e siècle. Etude & descr. 8°. Brux. 1924

Destrée (Jules). En Italie avant la Guerre, 1914–15. Préf. de M. Maeterlinck. s8°. 1915
Les fondeurs de neige. Révol. Bolchévique à Petrograd, 1917–18. s8°. Brux. 1920

Des Ursins (*la princesse*), *see* CRUTTWELL (*Miss* M.) The p. des U., 1927.
see SAINT-RENE TAILLANDIER (*Mme*). La p. des Ursins, 1926.

Des Vignoles (Alphonse), *see* KOHLREIFF (G.) Def. restit. antiq. temp.; acc. def. c. Des V., 1728.

Desyatovsky (A. P. Zablotsky-), *see* ZABLOTSKY-DESYATOVSKY.

Des Yveteaux (Nicolas Vauquelin, *seigneur*), *see* VAUQUELIN (N.)

Dethlevi (Johann). Silentium sacrum, sive de occultatione mysteriorum apud vet. Xtnos. dissert. Præs. C. Kortholt. [P2635]. s4°. Kiloni. 1689

Detlefsen (Detlef). Die Anordnung d. geograph. Bücher d. Plinius u. i. Quellen. 8°. 1909
see PLINY, *the elder.* Geog. Bücher d. Nat. Hist.; hrsg. D. D., 1904.

De Toldo (Vittorio), *see* TOLDO (V. DE).

Detroit Public Library, *see* BURTON HIST. COLL. LEAFLET, v1–4, 1923–26.

De Tunzelmann (G. W.) [TUNZELMANN (GEORGE WILLIAM VON)]. God & the universe. Physical basis for religion & ethics. s8°. 1912

Detweiler (Frederick G.) The negro press in the United States. 8°. Chicago. [1922]

Detzner (Hermann). Vier Jahre unter Kannibalen, im Innern v. Neuguinea. 8°. 1921

Deumer (Robert). Der private Kriegskredit u. s. Organ., *see* STAATS-U. SOZIALWISS. FORSCH., H186, 1916.

Deurwerders (Franciscus). Militia angelica Thomae Aquinatis. s8°. Lovanii. 1659

Deussen (Paul). Allg. Gesch. d. Philosophie mit bes. Berücks. d. Religionen. B2, Abtlg. 2ii, 3 [Abt. 3, 2e A.] 8°. L. 1915–20
2, Abt. 2ii, Die Philos. d. M.-a.
2, Abt. 3, Die neuere Philos. v. Descartes bis Schopenhauer.
Les éléments de la métaphysique. Tr. E. Nyssens. s8°. 1899
Die Philosophie d. Mittelalters. 8°. L. 1915

Deutsch [DEUTSCHE; DEUTSCHEN; DEUTSCHES].
Deutsch- russ. (Das) Handelsabkommen, 1921, 1921, *see* RABINOWITSCH (J. M.)
*Deutsche (Die) Kriegführung u. d. Völkerrecht. Beiträge z. Schuldfrage. Hrsg. im Auftrage d. Kriegsministeriums &c. [P2384, 2407]. 8°. 1919
Deutsche Lyrik seit Liliencron, 1921, *see* BETHGE (H.), *ed.*
Deutsche Reden in schwerer Zeit. H20–33. 8°. 1915
Baumgarten (O.) Der Krieg u. d. Bergpredigt. [24.]
Brandl (A.) Byron im Kampf mit d. engl. Politik &c. [20.]
Brückner (A.) Der Weltkrieg u. d. Slawen. [21.]
Gruber (M. v.) Krieg, Frieden u. Biologie. [30.]
Kahl (W.) Dreibund-Treubund. [26.]
Lehmann-Haupt (C. F.) Der Krieg u. d. Deutschtum im Auslande. [28.]
Luschan (F. v.) Rassen u. Völker. [33.]
Meinecke (F.) Deut. Kultur u. Machtpolitik im engl. Urteil. [29.]
Penck (A.) Was wir im Kriege gewonnen u. was wir verloren haben. [23.]
Schmid (H. A.) Deutschtum u. bild. Kunst. [25.]
Schmidt (F. J.) Das heilige Vermächtnis uns. gefallenen Helden. [31.]
Stammler (R.) Die Gerechtigkeit in d. Gesch. [22.]
Tröltsch (E.) Der Kulturkrieg. [27.]
Waldeyer (W.) Die im Weltkriege stehenden Völker in anthrop. Betrachtung. [32.]
Deutsche (Die) Reichsverfassung v. 11. August 1919. [Deut. Geschichtskal. Europ. Krieg. Ergzb.] 4H *in* 1v. 8°. L. 1919
Deutsche (Die) Revolution. Hrsg. F. Purlitz. H5, 6, März–Apr. 1919. [Deut. Geschichtskal]. 8°. L. [1919–23]
Deutsche Sagversdichtungen d. 9–11 Jhdts., 1924, *see* SIEVERS (E.)
Deutsche Texte d. Mittelalters; hrsg. Preuss. Akad., 1920 &c., *see* KÖN.-PREUSS. AKAD. D. WISS. ZU BERLIN.
Deutsche (Das) Weissbuch.
The German army in Belgium. The White Bk. of May 1915. Tr. E. N. Bennett, w. foreword on milit. reprisals in Belgium & Ireland. 8°. 1921
German White Book conc. responsibility of authors of the War. Tr. [C. E. for Intern. Peace]. la8°. N.Y. 1924
see BERNSTEIN (E.) Dokumente z. Weltkrieg 1914, H1, 1919.
„ DEUTSCHLAND schuldig? D. Weissbuch ü. d. Verantwortl. d. Urheber d. Krieges, 1919.
„ VERSAILLES, *Treaty of.* Materialien, T6, 1919.
Deutschen (Die) Dokumente z. Kriegsausbruch; Vollständige Sammlung, 4B, 1919; (*Fr.*) tr. C. Jordan, 4t, 1922; (*Eng.*) tr., 1924, *see* KAUTSKY (C.)
Deutsches biograph. Jahrbuch. Hrsg. v. Verbande d. deut. Akademien. Überleitungsband 1, 1914–16. 8°. 1925
Contin. of Biograph. Jahrbuch, *q.v.*
Deutsches Bücherverzeichnis: e. Zusammenstellung d. im deut. Buchhandel erschien. Bücher &c. B2–11. (2, 3, 1911–14. 4–6, 1915–20. 7–11, 1921–25). la8°. L. 1916–27
2, L–Z. 3, Stich- u. Schlagwortregister. 4, 5, A–Z. 6, Stich- u. Schlagwortregister. 7–9, A–Z. 10, 11, Stich- u. Schlagwortreg.
Deutsches evangel. Kirchen- Gesangbuch, 1855, *see* GESANGBUCH.
Entwurf zur Staats-Verfassung der Deut. Repub., 1919, *see* HORST (H.)
Gegenvorschläge d. deut. Regierung zu d. Friedensbedingungen, 1919, *see* GEGENVORSCHLÄGE.
Hdbch. f. d. D. Reich, 1922, 1926, 1922–26, *see* HANDBUCH.
*Kein Vertrauen zur deut. Regierung, 1920, *see* KEIN.
Ursachen (Die) d. deut. Zusammenbruchs im Jahre 1918; hrsg. A. Philipp, B1–3, 1925, *see* GERMANY: REICHSTAG & NATIONALVERSAMMLUNG.
Verfassung (Die) d. Deutschen Reichs v. 11. Aug. 1919. Mit. Sachregister u. e. Einl. v. W. v. Massow. [P2384]. 8°. 1919
„ „ Kurz erläut. &c. v. G. Zöphel. s8°. 1920
„ „ Taschenausgabe. Erläut. v. F. Giese. 2e. verb. A. s8°. 1920
„ „ *for a. ed.*, 1920, *see* SÄNGER (*Dr.* K.)
Wappen u. Flaggen d. Deut. Reiches nach d. neu. Verordnungen. [P2502]. 8°. L. [1920]

Deutsch (Babette) & A. Yarmolinsky. Mod. Russian poetry: an anthology. Chosen & tr. by B. D. & A. Y. 8°. [1923]

Deutsch (Emanuel Oscar Menahem). Le Talmud; tr. T. Baudaunas [*ps., i.e.* Alphonse Thibaudeau]. 8°. Londres. 1868

Deutsch (Leo) [DEITSCH]. Въ Сибирь и обратно. Воспоминанія (1884–91). B1. [P2715]. s8°. Женева. 1903

Deutsch (Léon). Le coup de vent, roman, *see* ŒUVRES libres, 31, 1924.

Deutsche Landesgeschichten. Hrsg. A. Tille. [Allg. Staatengesch., Abt. 3]. Werk 6ii, 11–13. 8°. Gotha. 1920–27
see BAASCH (E.) Gesch. Hamburgs, 1814–1918, 2B, 1924–25. [13.]
„ PIRCHEGGER (H.) Gesch. d. Steiermark, B1, bis 1283, 1920. [12.]
„ VANCSA (M.) Gesch. Nieder- u. Oberösterreichs, B2, 1927. [6ii.]
„ VITENSE (O.) Gesch. v. Mecklenburg, 1920. [11.]

Deutsche Morgenländische Gesellschaft. Zeitschrift d. D. M. G. Hrsg. v. d. Geschäftsführen, unter d. Redaction d. Prof. Brockhaus [*& others*]. B68–81 (76–81=N.F. B1–6). 8°. L. 1914–27

Deutsche (Die) Nationalversammlung, *see* GERMANY: REICHSTAG & NATIONALVERSAMMLUNG.

Deutsche Orient-Gesellschaft. Wissenschaftl. Veröffentlichungen d. D. O.-G. B1–33, 34i–v, 35i, 36, 37 [1–6 *in 1v.*; 9, 21 *in 1v.*; 11–13 *in 1v.*; 16 & 37 *in 1v.*] fol. L. 1900–23
3, 6, 7, 8, 11, 14, 26 *have 2nd tp*ˢ.: Ausgrabungen in Abusir, 1902–4, T1–7.
27, *has 2nd tp.*: Augsgrab. auf d. Gräberfeld v. Abusir el-Meleq, T2.
10, 16, 23, 24, 28, 35 *have 2nd tp*ˢ.: Ausgrabungen in Assur, A, T1–3, E, T1–3.
15, 32 *have 2nd tp*ˢ.: Ausgrabungen in Babylon, T1, 2.
18, 23 *have 2nd tp*ˢ.: Ausgrabungen in Tell el-Amarna, T1, 2.
see ANDRAE (W.) Der Anu-Adad-Tempel in Assur, 1909. [10.]
„ —— Die Festungswerke v. Assur, 2B, 1913. [23.]
„ —— Hatra: Assur-Exped. d. Deut. Or.-Gesell., 2T, 1908–12. [9, 21.]
„ —— Die Stelenreihen in Assur, 1913. [24.]
„ BACHMANN (W.) Kirchen u. Moscheen in Armenien u. Kurdistan, 1913. [25.]
„ BOGHAZKÖI. Keilschrifttexte aus B.; Autographien v. H. H. Figulla &c., 1916–23. [30, 36.]
„ BORCHARDT (L.) Das Grabdenkmal d. Königs Nefer-ir-keꜣ-reᶜ, 1909. [11.]
„ —— Das Grabdenkmal d. Königs Ne-user-reᶜ, 1907. [7.]
„ —— Das Grabdenkmal d. Königs Sꜣaꜣ ḥu-reᶜ, 2B, 1910–13. [14, 26.]
„ —— Der Porträtkopf d. Königin Teje im Besitz v. J. Simon, 1911. [18.]
„ EBELING (E.) Keilschrifttexte aus Assur relig. Inhalts, B1, 2, 1919–23. [28, 34.]
„ HÖLSCHER (U.) Das Hohe Tor v. Medinet Habu, 1910. [12.]
„ KOHL (H.) Kasr Firaun in Petra, 1910. [13.]
„ —— & C. WATZINGER. Ant. Synagogen in Galilaea, 1916. [29.]
„ KOLDEWEY (R.) Die hettit. Inschrift gefunden in d. Königsburg v. Babylon &c., 1900. [1.]
„ —— Das Ischtar-Tor in Babylon, 1918. [32.]
„ —— Die Pflastersteine v. Aiburschabu in Babylon, 1901. [2.]
„ —— Die Tempel v. Babylon u. Borsippa, 1911. [15.]
„ MESSERSCHMIDT (L.) & O. SCHRÖDER. Keilschrifttexte aus Assur hist. Inhalts, 2H, 1911–22. [16, 37.]
„ MÜLLER (F. W.) Die anthropolog. Ergebnisse d. vorgeschichtl. Gräberfeldes v. Abusir el-Meleq, 1915. [27.]
„ PREUSSER (C.) Nordmesopotam. Baudenkmäler, 1911. [17.]
„ PUCHSTEIN (O.) Boghasköi: d. Bauwerke, 1912. [19.]
„ REUTHER (O.) Ocheïder: Babyl.-Exped. d. Deut. Or.-Ges., 1912. [20.]
„ SCHÄFER (H.) Priestergräber &c. vom Totentempel des Ne-user-reᶜ, 1908. [8.]
„ SCHRÖDER (O.) Keilschrifttexte aus Assur verschied. Inhalts, 1920. [35i.]
„ SELLIN (E.) & C. WATZINGER. Jericho, 1913. [22.]
„ TIMME (P.) Tell el-Amarna vor d. deut. Ausgrabung im J. 1911, 1917. [31.]
„ TIMOTHEOS *of Miletus*. Der Timotheos-Papyrus gefund. bei Abusir &c., 1903. [3.]
„ WATZINGER (C.) Griech. Holzsarkophage aus d. Zeit Alex. d. Gr., 1905. [6.]
„ WEISSBACH (F. H.) Babylon. Miscellen, 1903. [4.]
„ —— Die Inschr. Nebukadnezars II im Wâdī Brîsā &c., 1906. [5.]
„ WETZEL (F.) Islam. Grabbauten in Indien, 1320–1540, 1918. [33.]

Deutsche Philosophische Gesellschaft, *see* BEITRÄGE Z. PHILOSOPHIE D. DEUT. IDEALISMUS.

Deutsche Revue. Jhrg. 45–47. [*no more publ.*] la8°. St. 1920–22

Deutsche Rundschau.
B182–214. (Jan. 1920–März 1928). la8°. [1920–28]

Deutsche Shakespeare-Gesellschaft. Jahrbuch d. D. S.-G. [Sh.-Jahrbuch]. Jhrg. 51–63. 8°. 1915–27
Shakespeare's Quellen. B2. s8°. Bonn. 1922
see FISCHER (R.) Quellen zu Romeo u. Julia, 1922 [2].

Deutsche Spielmann (Der); hrsg. E. Weber. Gespenster. 2ᵉ A. 8°. München. 1925

Deutscher Alpenverein, *see* DEUTSCHER U. ÖSTERREICH. ALPENVEREIN.

Deutscher Geschichtskalendar.
see BREST-LITOWSK. Die Zusatzverträge z. Frieden v. B.-L.: authent. Berichte, 1918.
„ BUCHAREST. Der Friede v. Bukarest: authent. Berichte, 1918.
„ DEUTSCH. Deut. (Die) Reichsverfassung v. 11. Aug. 1919, 1919.
„ —— Deut. (Die) Revol.; hrsg. F. Purlitz, H5, 1919.
„ DIPLOMATISCHE Enthüllungen, 2H, 1919.
„ EUROPÄISCHE Krieg; hrsg. F. Purlitz, B2–9, 1915–19.
„ SKAGERRAK. Die Seeschlacht am S., 1916.
„ VERSAILLES, *Treaty of*. Der Friede v. Versailles: authent. Berichte, 1919.
„ WAFFENSTILLSTAND. Vom W. z. Frieden v. Versailles, Oct. 1918–Juni 1919, 1919; Zwischen Waffenstillstand u. Frieden, Juni 1919–Jan. 1920, 1920.

Deutscher Herold (Der). Monatsschrift für Heraldik &c. Organ des Vereins für Siegel- u. Wappenkunde zu Berlin. Hrsg. A. M. Hildebrandt-Mieste &c. Jhrg. 1–10 [*in 3v*]. 4°. 1870–79

Deutscher Literatur-Kalendar. 1917, 1922, 1924–26, 1928. s8°. [1917–28]
With t. Kürschners Deutscher Lit.-Kal.; hrsg. H. Klenz, G. Lüdtke &c.

Deutscher Literatur-Katalog, 1927. Bearb., hrsg. &c. v. Koehler & Volckmar A.-G. & Co. la8°. L. [1927]
„ „ Schlagwort- u. Stichwortreg. la8°. L. [1927]

Deutscher Palaestina Verein.
Zeitschrift. B8, 25. 8°. L. 1885–1902

Deutscher und Österreichischer Alpenverein [*form.* DEUTSCHER ALPENVEREIN]. Mittheilungen. Redigirt v. Th. Petersen [*& others*]. B1–36. 1875–1911. 8° & 4° (1–10, 8°; 11–36, 4°.) *var. p.* Frankfurt, Salzburg, München, Wien &c. 1875–1911.
B11–36 *are also called* N.F., B1–27.
Zeitschrift. Redigirt v. Th. Trautwein [*& others*].
B1–44. 1869–1913. 8° & la8° (1–25, 8°; 26–35, 44, la8°.) *var. p.* München, Berlin, Wien &c. 1870–1913.
B1, 2 *have t.* Zeitschrift d. Deutschen Alpenverein.

Deutscher Werkbund. Handwerkl. Kunst in alt. u. neu. Zeit. Hrsg. v. D. W. [*Text by C. Gross & o.*] 4°. 1922

Deutsches Archäologisches Institut, *see* KAISERLICH DEUT. ARCHÄOLOG. INST.

Deutschland [DEUTSCHLANDS].
*Bestrebungen (Die) für e. wirtschaftl. Annäherung D. u. Oesterr.-Ungarns, 1916, *see* BESTREBUNGEN.
D. schuldig? Deutsches Weissbuch ü. d. Verantwortlichkeit d. Urheber d. Krieges. Hrsg. mit Genehm. d. Auswärt. Amtes. 8°. 1919
D. u. Armenien, 1914–18: Sammlung diplomat. Atkenstücke, 1919, *see* LEPSIUS (J.), *ed.*
Deutschlands Städtebau. [6p *in* 3v]. 4°. 1921–26
Freiberg i Sa. (Die Bergstadt) u. i. Umgebung; bearb. v. O. E. Schmidt.
Hildersheim; bearb. v. A. Knoch.
Kulmbach; hrsg. v. Stadtrat Kulmbach.
Lübeck; bearb. F. W. Virck.
Nordhausen; bearb. v. Stadtbaurat Geissler.
Paderborn; bearb. v. Stadtbaurat Michels.
Gesch. d. niederen Volkes in D., 2B, 1907, *see* ECCARDUS, *ps.*
Verfassung (Die) d. Deutschen Reiches v. 11. Aug. 1919, *var. ed*ˢ., *see* DEUTSCH.
Was kann D. leisten? D. wirtschaftl. Lage angesichts der Forderungen d. Entente. 8°. 1920

Deutschmann (Johann), *see* LUTHER (M.) Christ-L. Unterr. üb. J. D.'s Tractat, 1699.

Deutschösterreich, *see* ÖSTERREICH.

Deutsch-Österreich. Archäolog. Institut, *see* HEBERDEY (R.) Altatt. Porosskulptur, 1919.

Deutsch-Türkisches Denkmal-Schutz-Kommando.
Wiss. Veröff.; hrsg. T. Wiegand. H6. fol. 1922
see WEISSBACH (F. H.) Denkmäler u. Inschr. an d. Münd. d. Nahr el-Kelb, 1922. [6.]

Deval (Jacques). Beauté: comédie, *see* ŒUVRES libres, 32, 1924.
Dans sa candeur naive, comédie, *see* ŒUVRES libres, 58, 1926.

De Valera (Eamonn).
Ireland's case against conscription. [P2487]. s8°. D. 1918
see IRELAND. I.'s request to Govt. of U.S. for recog. as a sov. indep. state [pref. by E. de V.], 1920.

Devanny (Jean). The butcher shop. [2nd impr.] s8°. [1926]

Devarius (Matthaeus) [DEVARIS (M.)] Liber de Graecae ling. particulis. [*b. w.* Vigerus (F.) De praecip. Gr. dict. idiot., 1647]. s8°. [Londini.] 1657

Devay (Mátyás Biro), *see* BIRO (M.), *Dévay.*
Devee (Sunity), *Maharani of Cooch Behar, see* COOCH BEHAR, *Maharani of.*
Development. D. (The) of Civil Service, 1922, *see* CIVIL.
Deventer (Marinus Lodewijk van). Gesch. der Nederlanders op Java. 2d. 8°. Haarlem. 1886–7
De Vere (Stephen Edward). Is the hierarchy an aggression? [P2554]. 8°. 1851
Devereux, *The family of.* D. papers, w. R. Broughton's memoranda (1575–1601); ed. H. E. Malden, 1923, *see* CAMDEN MISCELLANY (THE), v13, 1924.
Devereux (Roy). Poland reborn. 8°. 1922
Devie (Alexandre Raymond), *bp. of Belley.* Litteræ monitoriæ circa quoddam opus de mutuo, *see* MIGNE (J. P.) Theol. cursus, t16, 1859.
Devigne (Marguerite).
Constantin Meunier. s8°. Turnhout. 1919
Thomas Vinçotte. s8°. Turnhout. 1919
Dévigne (Roger). Un continent disparu: l'Atlantide. s8°. 1924
Devil. *Devil (The) in disguise: or, Rome run a roving, 1710, *see* AUBIN (N.)
*Political hist. (The) of the d., 4th ed., 1739, *see* DEFOE (D.)
De Villamil (*Lt.-Col.* Richard).
War balloons. [P2591]. s8°. D. 1891
Deville (J.) Les vins du Rhône: crus princ. du Beaujolais & du Lyonnais. obl.4°. Lyon. 1914
Deville (J. Achille). Essai sur l'église & l'abbaye de Saint-Georges de Bocherville, près Rouen. 4°. Rouen. 1827
Hist. du Château Gaillard &c. [*a. c. b. w. h.* Essai sur Saint Georges de Bocherville, 1827]. 4°. Rouen. 1829
De Villiers (Henry John de Villiers, *1st baron*), *see* WALKER (E. A.) Ld. de V. & h. times: S. Africa, 1842–1914, 1925.
De Villiers (Melius).
The numeral-words, th. origin &c. s8°. 1923
Devine (Alex.) Off the map; the suppression of Montenegro. [P2562]. 8°. 1921
Devine (Edward Thomas). Disabled soldiers & sailors pensions & training. By D., ass. by L. Brandt. [C.E. f. Internat. Peace]. la8°. N.Y. 1919
Devine (Minos). The story of Job. s8°. 1921
Devises. *Devises & emblèmes anc. & mod. oder: Emblemat. Gemüths-Vergnügung bey Betrachtung v. 715 Sinnbildern mit Deutsch, Latein., Franz. u. Ital. Beyschrifften. 3te Aussfert. s4°. Augspurg. 1697
De-Vit (Vincenzo). Memorie dell' ant. castello di Matarella &c., *see* REGIA DEP. DI STORIA PATRIA. Misc., t28, 1890.
Devon & Exeter Institution, *see* DRAKE (F. M.) 100 years w. the D. & E. I., 1913.
Devonian year book, 1926. Ed. R. P. Chope. [London Devonian Assoc.] 8°. [1926]
Devonshire. Abstracts of the exist. transcripts of the lost parish-regs. of Devon, 1596–1644 &c. By R. Granville & W. E. Mugford. v1, A-Bra. 8°. Exeter. 1908
Devonshire Assoc. for the advancement of science, literature & art. Report [& Transactions] of the D.A., 1862–80. v1–12 [v1 (1862–66) *has 5p, each w. sep. tp. & pagin.*] 8°. 1863–80
" " ....v52–57. 8°. Plymouth. 1920–26
Devonshire (Georgina Cavendish, *duchess of*).
*Sylph (The). A novel. 3rd ed. 2v. s8°. 1783
Devonshire (*Mrs.* R. L.) Quatre-vingts mosquées & autres mon. musulmans du Caire. [Soc. Roy. de Géog. d'Egypte]. la8°. [Caire]. 1925
Rambles in Cairo. 8°. 1920
Some Cairo mosques & th. founders. 8°. 1921
Devonshire (Victor Christian William Cavendish, *9th duke of*). Designs by I. Jones for masques & plays at Court: cat. of drawings &c. mainly in coll. of the Duke of D., *see* WALPOLE Soc., v12, 1924.
Devoti (Giovanni), *bp. of Anagni, aft. abp. of Carthage.*
De hierarchia eccl., *see* MIGNE (J. P.), *ed.* Theol. cursus, t5, 1841.
***Devotional** poems. By a clergy-man of the country. s8°. 1699
***Devotions;** 1st part: in the ant. way of offices, 1685, *see* AUSTIN (W.)
Devrient (Ernst). Thüringische Gesch. 2e, verb. A. s8°. 1921
Dew, *The family of.* Dew wills & admin. in Prerog. Court of Canterbury. Abstr. by R. Holworthy. [*b. w.* Brit. archivist, v1, 1921]. sfol. [1921]
Dew (Edward Napleton), *see* HEREFORD. Index to reg. of Diocese of H., 1273–1535; comp. by E. N. D., 1925.
Dew (Roderick). Hist. of the parish & church of Kilkhampton. Intr. by Bp. of Truro. s8°. 1926
Dewar (*Capt.* Alfred C.), *R.N.* & *Capt.* **K. G. B. Dewar.**
*Narrative of the Battle of Jutland. 8°. 1924
Dewar (Douglas). Bygone days in India. 8°. 1922
Himalayan & Kashmiri birds. 8°. [1923]
Dewar (Duncan), *student of St. Andrew's.* Accounts [1819–27]. Comm. by Sir P. R. S. Lang. Intr. by Lord Sands. 8°. Glasgow. 1926
Dewar (George Albemarle Bertie).
Nature: the supreme problem. s8°. 1925
Sir D. Haig's command, Dec. 1915–Nov. 1918. By D., assist. by Lt.-Col. J. H. Boraston. 2v. 8°. 1922
" " ....3rd impr. 2v. 8°. 1922
A younger son. His recolls. & opinions in middle age. 8°. 1920
Dewar (*Sir* James). Cat. of contents of 1 Scroope Terrace, Cambridge, prop. of Sir J. D. Auction by Puttick &c., May 1924. [*Illust.* P2747]. 8°. [1924]
see ARMSTRONG (H. E.) J. D., 1842–1923, 1924.
Dewar (John Michael), *M.D.* The bird as a diver. 8°. 1924
Dewar (Katherine C.) The girl. With a chapter on "welfare work," by G. H. Dick. s8°. 1921
Dewar (*Capt.* Kenneth G. B.), *R.N., see* DEWAR (*Capt.* A. C.) & K. G. B. D. Narr. of Battle of Jutland, 1924.
De Watteville (*Lt.-Col.* Herman Gaston). Waziristan, 1919–20. [Campaigns & th. lessons]. 8°. 1925
D'Ewes (*Sir* Symonds), *bart.* Journal, f. begin. of Long Parl. to trial of Earl of Strafford. Ed. W. Notestein. [Yale Hist. Publs. MSS. &c., 7]. la8°. New Haven, *Yale.* 1923
Dewey (Evelyn). New schools for old. The regener. of the Porter school. [Mrs. M. T. Harvey]. s8°. New York. 1920
Dewey (Henry), *F.G.S.*
Works in GEOLOG. SURVEY OF ENG. &C. Spec. reports.
Arsenic & antimony ores, by H. D. &c., 1920. [15.]
Copper ores of Cornwall & Devon, 1923. [27.]
Copper ores of the Midlands &c.; by H. D. &c., 1925. [30.]
see REID (C.), G. BARROW & H. D. Geol. of co. around Padstow & Camelford, 1910.
—— **& C. E. N. Bromehead.** Geol. of co. around Windsor & Chertsey. [Mems. of G.S.] 8°. 1915
Geol. of South London. [Mems. of G.S.] 8°. 1921
——, **C. E. N. Bromehead, C. P. Chatwin & H. G. Dines.** Geol. of co. around Dartford. [Mem. of G.S.: explan. of sheet 271]. 8°. 1924
—— **& H. G. Dines.** Tungsten & Manganese ores, *see* GEOLOG. SURVEY. Spec. rep. on min. resources, 3rd ed., v1, 1923.
Dewey (John). Human nature & conduct: intr. to social psychology. 8°. 1922
De Windt (Harry). My note-book at home & abroad. 8°. 1923
De Wit (Augusta), *see* WIT (A. DE).
De Witt (John), *see* CHAMBERLAIN (J. L.) Universities & th. sons; spec. eds., Princeton, J. De W. & J. L. Williams, &c., 5v, 1898–1900.
De Witt (Norman Wentworth).
Virgil's Biographia litteraria. 8°. Toronto. 1923
Dexter (T. F. G.) Cornish names. s8°. 1926
Dey (*Sri* Mukul Chandra). My pilgrimages to Ajanta & Bagh. Intr. by L. Binyon. 8°. [1925]
Deyling (Christian Erdmann) & J. A. Egenolf. Aeliæ Capitolinae orig. & hist. [P2649]. s4°. Lipsiae. 1743
Deyling (Salomo). Instit. prudentiae pastoralis. ed. 3a. auct. per C. W. Küstnerum. s8°. Lipsiae. 1768
Obs. misc. var. argumenti ex theol., hist. & antiq. s4°. Lipsiae. 1736
Obs. sacr. pars prima &c. App. oratio de ingenio Israelitarum Ægyptiacorum. [*w. sep. tp.*] [*b. w.* Majus (J. H.) Repet. exam. &c., 1708]. s4°. Lips. 1708
" " pars 1a [2a, 3a]. ed. 3a emend. &c. 3p *in* 1v. s4°. Lipsiae. 1735–39
Dez (Jean), *Jesuit, 1643–1712.* La réunion des protestans de Strasbourg à l'Egl. rom. nécessaire &c. s8°. Str. 1687
see FECHT (J.) De origine &c. missarum, J. D. &c. oppos., 1725.
Deza (Massimiliano).
Istoria d. famiglia Spinola. fol. Piacenza. 1694
Dhalla (Maneckji Nusservanji).
Zoroastrian civiliz., to 651 A.D. 8°. N.Y. 1922
Dhammapāla, *see* THERAGĀTHĀ. Psalms of the early Buddhists; tr. &c. by Mrs. Rhys Davids; [w. chron. f. Comm. of D.], 2v, 1909–13.

Dhaṇavāla [DHANAPĀLA]. Bhavisatta Kaha: e. Jaina Legende in Apabhraṃśa; hrsg. H. Jacobi, 1918, *see* KÖNIGL. AKAD. D. W. ZU MÜNCHEN. Abhdlgn., B29, 1918.

Dharma (Vijaya), *see* VIJAYA DHARMA SURI.

Dhātumañjūsā, *see* DHĀTUPĀTHA.

Dhātupātha. The Pāli Dhātupātha & the Dhātumañjūsā, ed. D. Andersen & H. Smith, *see* KONGELIGT DAN. VID. SELSK., Hist.-fil. Med., B4, 1921–22.

D'Hisca (*Madama* Charlotta), *see* AMOMO, *ps.*

Dhont de Waepenaert (Ed.) Quartiers généalog. des familles flamandes. fol. Bruges. 1871

***Diabo-lady** (The): a poem, 1777, *see* COMBE (W.)

***Diaboliad**, a poem, 1777, *see* COMBE (W.)

Diack (Francis C.) The Newton Stone & o. Pictish inscript. [P2710]. s8°. Paisley. 1922

Diadochus (Marcus), *bp. of Zigris.* Sermo contra Arianos, ex MS. erutus a J. R. Wettstein, *see* ORIGEN. De oratione, 1694.

Dial (The). v68, 70–75. 8°. N.Y. 1920–23

Dialogue.

*Dialogue (A) betw. the pulpit & reading desk. By a member of the Ch. of Eng. [*Attrib. to* Wm. Green of Rotherham, Rev. Ch. Perronet *&* Ed. Smyth. P2537]. s8°. *n.p.* 1786

" " ....[*a.ed.* P221]. s8°. York. 1795

*D. (A) bytwene the commune secretary & jalowsye, t. the unstableness of harlottes. [*Facs. reprint by J. P. Collier.* P2433]. 8°. [1844]

*Proper d. (A.) betw. a gentillman & a husbandman &c., 1871, *see* ROY (W.) & J. BARLOW. "Rede me & be nott wrothe" &c., 1871.

Dialogues.

[**D. in Tamil betw. a Christian & an idolator, in Tamil*]. s8°. [Tranquebar?. 1719?]

*D. rustiques d'un prestre de village, d'un berger, le censier & sa femme. Par I. D. M. 8°. Quevilly. 1616

Dialogus.

D. de statu turbulento eccl. hujus sec., 1591, *see* FABRICUS (F.)

Ein Christlich spacier gesprech, zweyer guten freund, v. etlich verderbl. missbreuchen, auch recht u. gutem brauch der Gaben Gottes. . . . [P2442]. s4°. Nürnberg, *J. Daubman.* 1553

Diamantopulo (Hercule). Le réveil de la Turquie. Etudes &c. 8°. Alexandrie. [1909]

Dian (Girolamo). Cenni storici s. farmacia veneta. 4p *in* 1v. 8°. Venezia. 1900–1904

Dianese (Olindo). Per lo ingresso al gonfalonierato di giustizia d. A. Gozzadini, egloga. [N125]. 8°. Bologna. [1713]

Diario.

D. d. guerra d'Italia, racc. dei Bullettini uffic., ser. 1–64, 1915–23, *see* ITALIA.

*D. dell' assedio di Torino del 1640 di anon. contemp.; pubbl. A. Manno, *see* REGIA DEP. DI STORIA PATRIA. Misc., t24, 1885.

*D. [Veneto], 1763, con la serie de' piu distinti principi &c. di Europa &c. s8°. Venezia. [1763]

Diary.

D. (The) of a German soldier: by Feldwebel C., [tr.], 1919, *see* SOUVENIRS.

*D. of a nursing sister on the W. Front, 1914–15. s8°. 1915

*D. of a young lady of fashion, 1764–65, 1925, *see* KING-HALL (*Miss* M.)

*D. (A) of roy. movements &c. of Victoria, v1, 1883, *see* VICTORIA, *q. of Gt. Brit.*

Dias (Antonio Gonçalves), *see* GONÇALVES DIAS (A.)

Dias (Demetrio Lossada), *see* LOSSADA DIAS (D.)

Diassorinus (Jacobus). Encomium M. Flacii Illyrici scr. Græcis versibus à J. D. Item carmen de natalibus &c. eiusdem Flacii, autore N. Bucholcero. s4°. *n.p.* 1558

Diaz (Juan), *Spanish reformer, see* SENARCTAEUS (C.) Hist. vera de morte J. D. [*&* Christ. relig. summa, I. D. auctore], 1546.

Diaz (Porfirio), *pres. of the Republic of Mexico.* Discurso[s], 1884–92 [*no tp.*, pages 153–172, 209–230, 295–518]. [P2720]. 8°. [Mexico ?. *n.d.*]

Informe, acerca de los actos de su admin. [1877–80], 1888–92, 1896–1900, 1900–1904.
4v. [1877–80 *&* 1888–92 *in* P2720]. 8°. Mexico. 1880–1904

Opiniones acerca d. gen. P. D. y de su reeleccion para presid. de la Republica. 3t. 4°. Guanajuato. 1901

Visita a la ciudad de Monterrey, Díc. 1898. 4°. Monterrey. 1899

see MEXICO. President's message, Sept. 1882, 1882.

Diaz Covarrubias (Jose).

La instruccion publica en Mexico. 8°. Mexico. 1875

Diaz del Castillo (Bernal).

La conquista de Nueva España. 4[t]. s8°. Paris. *n.d.*

Discovery & conq. of Mexico, 1517–21. Ed. G. Garcia. Tr. w. intr. &c. by A. P. Maudslay. [Broadway Travellers]. 8°. 1928

Diaz de Luco (Juan Bernardo), *bp. of Calahorra.* Practica criminalis canonica, Omnia propemodum, quae à clerico committi possunt flagitia, una cum poenis eorundem &c. complectens. s8°. Venetiis. 1581

Díaz Mercado (Hector), *see* PALLARES (J.) Legisl. federal compl. del derecho civil mexicano: col. formada por J. Vazquez Tagle, H. D. M. &c., 1897; App., 1898.

Dibble (Roy Floyd). Strenuous Americans. 8°. 1925

Dibblee (George Binney).

The psycholog. theory of value. 8°. 1924

Dibdin (Charles). Sea songs & ballads. By D. & others. s8°. 1865

Dibdin (Thomas Frognall). Bibliograph. &c. tour in France & Germany. 2nd ed. 3v. 8°. 1829

Intr. to knowl. of ed. of the Classics, incl. acc. of polyglot Bibles &c. 3rd ed. 2v. s8°. 1808

Dibdin (Thomas John). Of age to-morrow. [P2863]. 8°. 1828

The school for prejudice, *see* †INCHBALD (E.) Mod. th., v4, 1811.

Dibelius (Martin). *Works in* LIETZMANN (H.), *ed.* Hdbh. z. N.T., 1911–23.

Die Briefe d. Paulus, An Timotheus I, II, An Titus, 1913. [3ii, 3.]

Die Briefe d. Paulus, II, An d. Kolosser, Epheser, An Philemon, 1912. [3iii.]

Die Briefe d. Paulus, II, An d. Thessalonicher I, II, An d. Philipper, 1911. [3ii, 2.]

Der Hirt d. Hermas, 1923. [Ergzb. 4.]

Dibelius (Wilhelm). Charles Dickens. 8°. Leipzig. 1916

England. 2 Halbb. 8°. St. 1923

Dicey (Albert Venn). Intr. to the study of the law of the constit. 8th ed. 8°. 1924

see RAIT (R. S.) Mem. of A. V. D., 1925.

—— **& A. B. Keith.** A digest of the laws of England w. ref. to conflict of laws. 3rd ed. 8°. 1922

" " ....4th ed. 8°. 1927

—— **& R. S. Rait.** Thoughts on the Union betw. England & Scotland. 8°. 1920

Dick (Andrew Coventry).

Diss. on Church polity. 2nd ed. s8°. 1850

Dick (Charles Hill).

Highways & byways in Galloway & Carrick. 8°. 1916

Dick (Gladys H.), *see* DEWAR (K. C.) The girl: w. chap. on "welfare work," by G. H. D., 1921.

Dickens Fellowship, *see* DICKENSIAN, THE: offic. record of the D.F., v16–23, 1920–27.

Dickens (Charles).

[Works. Library ed. Illust.] 24v. 8°. *Chapman & Hall, n.d.*—1870

Barnaby Rudge [*&* Hard times], *n.d.* [9, 10.]

Bleak House, *n.d.*—1867. [18, 19.]

Christmas books, 1868. [22.]

David Copperfield, 1870. [15, 16.]

Dombey & Son, 1868. [13, 14.]

Great expectations, 1866. [24.]

Little Dorrit, 1867–69. [20, 21.]

Martin Chuzzlewit, 1869. [5, 6.]

Nicholas Nickleby, *n.d.* [3, 4.]

The old curiosity shop, *n.d.* [7, 8.]

Oliver Twist, 1866. [12.]

Pickwick papers, *n.d.* [1, 2.]

Picts. f. Italy & Amer. notes, *n.d.* [17.]

Sketches by Boz, *n.d.* [11.]

Tale of 2 cities, *n.d.* [23.]

David Copperfield. repr. s8°. 1916

" " ......repr. s8°. 1920

Great expectations. [repr.] s8°. [1920]

The mystery of Edwin Drood. Illust. S. L. Fildes w. intr. &c. by C. D., the younger. s8°. 1923

Mystery of Edwin Drood completed by A loyal Dickensian. 8°. 1927

Our mutual friend. Illust. by M. Stone. 2v. 8°. *Chapman & Hall.* 1866

" " Illust. by M. Stone. Repr. of ed. corr. by a. in 1869, w. intr. biog. & bibliog. by C. D., the younger. s8°. 1908

*Sketches by Boz. Illust. by G. Cruikshank. n. ed. 8°. 1877

Unpubl. letters to Mark Lemon. Ed. W. Dexter. la8°. 1927

TRANSLATION.

Возвращенный преступникъ. Разсказъ [Tr.] [P846]. s8°. Москва. 1886

see CARDEN (P. T.) The murder of Edwin Drood: solution based on Dickens' MS. &c., 1920.

" CHANCELLOR (E. B.) The London of C. D., 1924.

" DARTON (F. J. H.) Vincent Crummles, h. theatre &c.; arr. by D., w. intr. note & app. f. Nicholas Nickleby, 1926.

Dickens (Charles) [*continued*].
see DELATTRE (F.) D. & la France; interaction litt. anglo-française, 1927.
,, DIBELIUS (W.) Charles Dickens, 1916.
,, DICKENSIAN, THE, v16–23, 1920–27.
,, DÖRNENBURG (E.) & W. FEHSE. Raabe u. D., 1921.
,, ECKEL (J. C.) 1st eds. of wrs. of C. D. & th. values, 1913.
,, GISSING (G. R.) The immortal D., 1925.
,, HAYWARD (A. L.) D. encyclop., 1924.
,, MATZ (B. W.) Inns & taverns of "Pickwick," 1921.
see MAUROIS (A.) Essai sur D., 1927.
,, —— Etudes angl., D. &c., 1927.
,, NICOLL (*Sir* W. R.) D.'s own story, 1923.
,, PHILLIPS (W. C.) D., Reade & Collins, sensation novelists, 1919.
,, QUICKENS (Q.), *ps.* English notes, a reply to C. D.'s Amer. notes, 1920.
,, QUILLER-COUCH (A.) C. D. & o. Victorians, 1925.
,, WILKINS (W. G.) D. coll., 1922.

Dickensian, The. Quarterly mag. for Dickens lovers & the offic. record of the Dickens Fellowship. Ed. B. W. Matz. v16–20, 22, 23. 8°. 1920–27

Dickenson (Mary), *wife of John Dickenson, see* HAMILTON (M.)

Dickins (Guy).
Hellenistic sculpture. Pref. by P. Gardner. s4°. O. 1920

Dickinson Bros., *publishers, see* EXHIBITIONS: LONDON, 1851. Dickinsons' pictures of the gt. E. of 1851, 2v, 1854.

Dickinson (Emily), *see* BIANCHI (M. D.) Life & letters of E. D., 1924.

Dickinson (Francis Henry). *A list of pr. service books acc. to uses of Angl. Ch. 8°. 1850

Dickinson (Goldsworthy Lowes).
Causes of internat. war. s8°. 1920
The internat. anarchy, 1904–14. 8°. [1926]
The magic flute. A fantasia. s8°. [1920]
Revolution & reaction in mod. France. [2nd ed.] s8°. [1927]
War: its nature, cause & cure. [repr.] s8°. [1923]

Dickinson (Peard), *1758–1802, see* JACKSON (T.) Lib. of Xtn. biog., v2, P. D., by J. Benson, 1837.

Dickinson (Robert). The life of John Braithwaite. With a short mem. of Mrs. Mary B. 8°. 1825

Dickinson (Thomas Herbert).
The contemp. drama of England. 8°. 1920

Dickinson (William), *genealogist.*
see LITTA (*il c.* P.) Armory of celeb. Ital. families; blazoned by W. D., w. Suppl., *n.d.*
,, SAINT JOHN OF JERUSALEM, ORDER OF. Arms of Grand Masters to 1799; comp. by W. D., *n.d.*
,, TETTONI (L.) & F. SALADINI. Dict. of heraldic terms—Ital. armory; comp. f. T. & S.'s "Teatro araldico" by W. D., *n.d.*

Dicks (Arthur J.), *see* BRIDGES (J. S.) & A. J. D. Plant study, 1908.

Dicksee (Lawrence Robert).
Bookkeeping for accountant students. 8th ed. 8°. 1921

Dickson (David), *prof. of divinity, Edinburgh.* A brief explic. of the first fifty [last fifty & o. fifty] Psalms. [3p *in* 1v. (First & o. fifty, 2nd ed. corr.)] s8°. 1654–55
*The new Jerusalem: a hymn, sometimes attrib. to D. D., 1852, *see* JERUSALEM.

Dickson (Leonard Eugene). Hist. of the theory of numbers. [C.I. of Wash. Publ., 256]. 3v. 4°. Wash. 1919–23

Dickson (Thomas George), *see* VINCENT (*Sir* E.) & T. G. D. Hdbk. to mod. Greek, 2nd ed., 1893.

Dickson (*Brig.-Gen.* **William Edmund Ritchie).** East Persia, a backwater of the Great War. 8°. 1924

Dickstein (Szymon). Кто чѣмъ живетъ. изд. 3e. [P2716]. s8°. Женева. 1901

Dictionarium. *Dict. Lat.—Armen. compos. per D. N. E. T., 1695, *see* NIERSZESOVICZ (D.)
*Dict. theolog. portatile &c., ed. alt., 1762, *see* ALLETZ (P. A.)

Dictionary.
D. of mod. music & musicians, 1924, *see* HULL (A. E.), *ed.*
D. of national biography.
The concise d., to 1911; Epitome of main work & its suppl.; added, an epitome of the suppl., 1901–11. Ed. Sir S. Lee. 8°. [1920]
D. of n. b., 1912–21. Ed. H. W. C. Davis & J. R. H. Weaver. With index, 1901–21. 8°. O. 1927
D. of the Irish language, fasc. 1, 1913, *see* ROYAL IRISH ACAD.
*New (A) d. of the terms anc. & mod. of the canting crew. By B. E. gent. [repr.] 8°. *n.d.*
*New univ. Eng. & Ital. d., 2p, 1849, *see* ENGLISH.

Dictionnaire.
*D. de la langue romane, ou du vieux lang. fr., 1768, *see* LACOMBE (F.)
D. de théologie cathol., sous la dir. de A. Vacant, cont. sous celle de E. Mangenot. t6–8. la8°. 1920–25
Each tome in 2p, pagin. contd.
*D. des livres Jansénistes &c., 4t, 1755, *see* COLONIA (D. DE).
D. gén. des artistes de l'école franç., 2t, 1882–5, *see* BELLIER DE LA CHAVIGNERIE (E.)
*D. portat. des Conciles &c., 1761, *see* ALLETZ (P. A.)
D. topog. de la France. Publ. par ordre du Min. de l'Instr. [Docs. inéd.] 4°. 1912
Aude, par l'abbé Sabarthès, 1912.
Petit d. class. d'hist. naturelle, par B. de St. Pierre &c., 2t, 1827, *see* COLLIN DE PLANCY (J. A. S.)

Dictys *Cretensis.* De bello Trojano & Dares Phrygius De excidio Troiae. s8°. Amsterodami. 1630

Didache.
see LIETZMANN (H.) Hdbh. z. N.T.: Ergzgsband., 1, Die Lehre d. 12. Apostel, erkl. v. R. Knopf, 1920.
,, ROBINSON (J. A.) Barnabas, Hermas & the D., 1920.

Didascalia Apostolorum. Ethiopic Didascalia; Ethiop. version of the Apost. Const. rec. in the Ch. of Abyssinia. Ed. & tr. T. P. Platt. [O. T. F.] 4°. 1834
The Ethiopic Didascalia. [Tr., w. intr.] by J. M. Harden. [Trans. of Xtn. lit., s4]. s8°. 1920

Diderot (Denis).
Œuvres choisies. Préc. d'une intr. par P. Albert. 6t. s8°. 1878–92
1, Contes & mélanges. 2, Œuvres dramat. 3–5, Corr. avec Mdlle. Volland. 6, Variétés.
Dialogues. Tr. w. intr. by F. Birrell. [Broadway Lib. of 18 c. Fr. lit.] 8°. [1927]
Entretien entre d'Alembert & Diderot. Rève de d'Alembert. Suite de l'Entretien. Intr. & notes de G. Maire. s8°. 1921
see BUSNELLI (M. D.) D. & l'Italie, 1925.
,, LEDIEU (P.) D. & Sophie Volland, 1925.
,, PALACHE (J. G.) Four novelists &c.; Crébillon, Laclos, D. &c., 1926.

Didier (Edouard). La bague d'opale. s8°. 1881

Didoclavius (Edwardus), *ps., see* CALDERWOOD (DAVID).

Didot-Bottin.
Annuaire D.-B., 1921, 1928. Bottin mondain. la8°. 1921–28

Didymus, *Alexandrinus, the theologian, see* HIPPOLYTUS, *St.* Compend. hist. philosoph. ant. &c.; acc. diss. qua ostend. D. A. auctorem non esse, auct. J. C. Wolfio, 1706.

Didymus, *Faventinus, ps., see* MELANCHTHON (P.)

Didymus *Taurinensis, ps., see* VALPERGA DI CALUSO (T.)

Diebolt (Johann), *see* DIEPOLT (J.)

Diecman (Johann). Exercit. de Eccl. Orient. & Lat. de purgatorio dissensione. [P2639]. s4°. [1671]

Diehl (Carl), *Dr. phil. Königsberg.* Die Diktatur d. Proletariats u. d. Rätesystem. 8°. Jena. 1920
Über Sozialismus, Kommunismus u. Anarchismus. 4e verm. A. 8°. Jena. 1922
see WIRTSCHAFTSTHEORIE. Beiträge z. W.; hrsg. K. D., T1, 1926.

Diehl (Charles).
L'art chrétien primitif & l'art byzantin. la8°. 1928
Byzantine portraits. Tr. H. Bell. 8°. N.Y. 1927
Choses & gens de Byzance. s8°. 1926
Constantinople. la8°. 1924
Hist. de l'Empire Byzantin. s8°. 1919
Hist. of the Byzantine Empire. Tr. G. B. Ives. 8°. Princeton. 1925
Jérusalem. s8°. [1921]
Manuel d'art byzantin. 2e éd., rev. & augm. 2t. [*pagin. cont.*] 8°. 1925–26
Sur quelq. étoffes coptes du Musée du Louvre, *see* ACAD. D. INSCR. FOND. PIOT. Mon., t25, 1921–2.

Diehl (Ernst). Anthologia lyrica Graeca. Ed. E. D. [*n. ed. of Bergk*]. 2v. s8°. L., *Teubner.* 1925
1, Poetae elegiaci—Theognis—Carmen aureum—Phocylidea—Iamborum script.—Poetae melici—Monodia.
2, Poetae melici: Chori—Peplus Aristoteleus—Scolia—Carmina pop.–Poetae Alexandrini.
Inscr. Lat. Coll. E. Diehl. [Tabulae in usum schol.; ed. J. Lietzmann, 4]. la8°. Bonnae. 1912
Inscr. Lat. Christianae veteres. v1, 2. 8°. Berolini. 1925–27
Supplementum lyricum: neue Bruchstücke, ausgewählt u. erkl. v. E. D. [Kleine Texte, T33, 34]. 3e A. 8°. Bonn. 1917

Diehl (Wilhelm). M. Bukers Bedeutung f. d. kirchl. Leben in Hessen, *see* EGELHAAF (G.) & W. D. Landgraf Philipp v. Hessen &c., 1904.

Dielitz (J.) Die Wahl-u. Denksprüche, Feldgeschreie, Losungen, Schlacht-u. Volksrufe. &c. 4°. Frankfurt. 1884

Diels (Hermann).
Antike Technik: 7 Vorträge. 3. A. s8°. L. 1924
De Alcæi voto. [P2509]. 8°. Berolini. 1920
Elementum: e. Vorarbeit z. griech. u. lat. Thesaurus. 8°. L. 1899
Die Entdeckung d. Alkohols, *see* KÖN.-PREUSS. AKAD. Abhdln., 1913.
Die Fragm. d. Vorsokratiker. Gr. & Deut. 4A. Abdr. d. 3ten m. Nachtr. 3B [B3, Wortindex v. W. Kranz &c.] 8°. 1922
Über d. v. Prokop beschr. Kunstuhr v. Gaza, *see* KÖNIGL. PREUSS. AKAD. D. WISS. Abhdl., 1917.
Zur Pentemychos d. Pherekydes. [*Extr. f.* K. Preuss. Akad. d. Wiss. Sitz., 1897. P2793]. la8°. 1897
Diepenbrock (*Cardinal* **Melchior v.**), *prince-bishop of Breslau, see* VIGENER (F.) 3 Gestalten aus d. mod. Katholizismus, D. &c., 1926.
Diepolt (Johann) [DIEBOLT (J.)] Ain nützliche Sermon zů allen Crĭstē menschē, von der rechte Evangel. mess, uñ von der beraytung zů dem Tisch gottes &c. [*Border to tp.* P2539]. s4°. [Ulm?]. 1523
Ein nützlicher Sermon von dem wort Gottes &c. Ein anderer Sermon Von dreyerlay büecher &c. [*wanting*]. [*Border to tp.* P2539]. s4°. [Ulm?]. 1522
Dierauer (Johannes). Gesch. d. Schweizer. Eidgenossenschaft, B5, bis 1848, 1917, *see* GESCHICHTE D. EUROP. STAATEN.
Hist. de la Confédér. suisse. Tr. A. Reymond. t5i, ii, 8°. Lausanne. 1918–19
5i, 1798–1913. 5ii, 1814–48.
Dieren (Bernard van), *see* VAN DIEREN (B.)
Diest (Heinrich von).
De ratione studii theologici. s8°. Hardervici. 1634
Dietelmair (Johann Augustin). Hist. dogm. de descensu Christi ad inferos litt. Cum prol. I. B. Bernholdi. s8°. Norimbergae. 1741
Verm. Abhlgn. aus allen Theilen d. Theologie. 2B. s8°. Altdorf. 1764–67
Dieterdt (Joachim). Exerc. de Henotico Zenonis, quod habetur apud Evag. lib. 3, 14 & Niceph. lib. 14, 12. Praes. B. Bebelio. [P433]. s4°. Argentorati. [1673]
Dieterich, *friar, Barfüsser.* Ain practica oder weyssagung eins brůders Barfüsser ordenns mit namen D. beschehen zu Zeng in Granatenn, 1420. s4°. *n.p.* [1523?]
Dieterich (—). Weltkriegsende an d. mazedon. Front. [Schlachten d. Weltkrieges, B11]. 8°. Oldenburg. 1926
Dieterich (Albrecht).
*H. Usener. [*Signed* A. D.; P2791]. 8°. Dresden. 1905
Kleine Schriften. 8°. L. 1911
Dieterich (Cunrad), *Director of the Gymnasium at Ulm.* Epitome catechetic. praeceptorum. Kurtzer Ausszug &c. [*Lat. & Germ.*] ed. 2ª. s8°. Ulm. 1630
Instit. catecheticae, depromptae E. B. Lutheri catechesi &c. Ch. Chemnitii notis illustr. ed. nov. s8°. Lipsiae. 1613
Instit. dialecticae, ex probatiss. Aristotelis & Rami interpretibus conscr. &c. ed. 9ª. rev. & aucta. s8°. Jenae. 1623
Instit. rhetoricae. [*b. w. h.* Instit. dialecticae, 1623]. s8°. Jenae. 1621
see BECHMANN (F.) Ad Instit. catechet. C. D. annot. uberiores, 1707.
Dieterich (Elias Gottlieb). Ἱστορούμενα de actis &c. Gebhardi Truchsessii archiep. Colon. infausti mariti. Moderat. J. D. Koelero. [P484]. s4°. [Altdorf]. [1773]
Dieterich (Jacob Andreas). Disq. de fulmine &c. Sub praes. J. C. Sturmii. [P447]. s4°. Altdorfi. [1696]
Dieterich (Johann), *Pastor in Giessen.* Discursus de actis Colloquii Marpurg. inter Lutherum & Philippum ex unâ: Zuinglium & Oecolampadium ex alterâ parte, 1529. [P2468]. s4°. Marpurgi. 1627
Dieterici (Carl Friedrich Wilhelm), *see* MOREAU DE JONNÈS (A.) La Prusse; suivi d'un exposé écon. &c. tr. de l'allem. de D., 1848.
Dieterici (Friedrich Heinrich). Die Naturanschauung u. Naturphil. d. Araber im 10 Jhdt. 2ᵉ. A. s8°. 1876
Dietlein (Sigismundus). Disput. de natura logices. Praes. Æ. Strauchio. [P522]. s4°. Witebergae. 1607
Dietrich, *of Bern, see* BUCK (K. M.) The saga of D. of Bern & h. companions &c., pl, v1–6, 1924–27.
Dietrich, *v. Freiburg, Dominicaner, see* BIRKENMAJER (A.) Verm. Unters. (Drei neue Hss. d. Werke Meister D.), 1922.
Dietrich (Bruno). Oberschlesien. [P2465]. 8°. Breslau. 1920
Dietrich (Veit) [THEODORICUS (VITUS)], *see* WOLPH (E.) De obitu I. Eckii adv. calumniam Viti Theodorici (1543), 1921.

Dietschy (Charlotte). Die "Dame d'intrigue" in d. franz. Originalkomödie d. 16. u. 17. Jhdts. [Zeitschr. f. rom. Phil., Beih. 64]. 8°. Halle a. S. 1916
Dietz (Alexander). Zur Gesch. der Frankfurter Büchermesse, 1462–1792. [P2682]. 8°. Frankfurt. [1921]
Dietz (Jean). Maurice Barrès. s8°. [1927]
Dietz (Johann), *1665–1738.* Master J. D., surgeon in army of the Gt. Elector &c., f. MS. in R. Lib., Berlin. Tr. B. Miall. 8°. [1923]
Meister J. D. Nach d. alt. Hs. in d. Kön. Bibl. zu Berlin gegeben v. E. Consentius. [Neudruck]. s8°. Ebenhausen. [1921]
Dietzel (Heinrich). Engl. u. preuss. Steuerveranlagung: Einkommensbesteuerung. [V. f. Sozialpol., B157ii]. 8°. München. 1919
Dieu (Lodewijk de). Animadv. in Acta Apostol. s4°. Lugd. Bat. 1634
Animadv. in Epist. Pauli ad Romanos. Acc. Spicilegium in reliquas ejusdem Apostoli epist. s4°. Lugd. Bat. 1646
Animadv. in Vet. Test. libros omnes &c. s4°. Lugd. Bat. 1648
Animadv. sive comm. in 4 Evangelia &c. s4°. Lugd. Bat. 1631
Apocalypsis Joh. Ed. charact. Syro & Ebræo cum vers. Lat. & notis opera L. de D. s4°. Lugd. Batav. 1627
Dieudonné (Adolphe). Les monnaies franç. s8°. 1923
Dieudonné (Robert). Huguette, *see* ŒUVRES (Les) libres, 25, 1923.
Rosette Langlois, *see* ŒUVRES libres, 50, 1925.
Dieulafoy (*Mme.* **Jane).** Isabelle la Grande, Reine de Castille, 1451–1504. la8°. [1920]
Dieulafoy (Marcel). La mosquée d'Hassân, *see* ACAD. D. INSCR. & BELLES-LETTRES. Hist. & mém., t42, 1922.
Diez (Ernst). Churasanische Baudenkmäler. [Kunsthist. Inst. d. K. K. Univ. Wien]. B1, Mit e. Beitr. v. Max van Berchem. fol. 1918
Persien. [B1], Islam. Baukunst in Churasan. 4°. Hagen i. W. 1923
Diez (Friedrich C.) Etymolog. Wbch. d. roman. Sprachen. 3ᵉ verb. u. verm. A. 2T. 8°. Bonn. 1869–70
Gramm. d. roman. Sprachen. 3ᵉ, neu bearb. u. verm. A. 3T. 8°. Bonn. 1870–72
Diez (Johann Wilhelm.) Diss. de praesagiis mortis. Praes. J. F. Mayero. [P428]. s4°. Vitembergae. 1713
Diez (Wilhelm), *see* BRAUN (L.), W. D. *& others.* Zur Gesch. d. Kostüme, *n.d.*
Diez Barroso (Francisco).
El arte en Nueva España. 4°. Mejico. 1921
Diez-Canedo (Enrique). Prosistas mod. Seleccion. s8°. 1922
Difford (*Capt.* **Ivor D.)** The story of the 1st Batt. Cape Corps, 1915–19. Intr. by Rt. Hon. J. X. Merriman. la8°. Cape Town. [1920]
Digeon (Aurélien). Les romans de Fielding. 8°. 1923
Digges (Dudley), *M.A., 3rd son of Sir D. D.* The unlawfulnesse of subjects taking up armes agst. th. soveraigne. 8°. [Oxford?]. 1647
Digges (Leonard), *the elder.* A prognostic. &c. to judge the wether for ever, 1555. [Ed. R. T. Gunther. Old Ashmolean repr.] s8°. [O. 1926]
The theodelitus & topog. instrument of L. D. Descr. by h. son, T. Digges, 1571. Repr. f. Pantometria. [Ed. R. T. Gunther. Old Ashmolean reprˢ., 4]. s8°. O. 1927
Digges (Thomas), *see* DIGGES (L.), *the elder.* The theodelitus & topog. instrument of L. D., descr. by h. son T. D., 1571; repr., 1927.
Dígha Nikâya, *see* SACRED BOOKS OF THE BUDDHISTS, v4, Dialogues of the Buddha, tr. f. Pali of the D.N. by T. W. & C. A. F. Rhys Davids, p3, 1921.
Dighton (B. L.), *see* LAWRENCE (H. W.) & B. L. D. French line engrav., 1910.
Dignat (Paul). Hist. de la médecine & des médecins à travers les âges. s8°. [1888]
***Dignity (The)** of human nature, 1786, *see* WESLEY (J.)
Diguet (*le col.* **E.)** Annam & Indo-Chine franç. 8°. 1908
Dihigo (L. Barrau-), *see* BARRAU-DIHIGO (L.)
Dijkveld (Everard van Weede van).
see MUILENBURG (J.) Embassy of E. van W., Ld. of D., to England in 1687, 1920.
„ WASSENAAR-DUIVENVOORDE (J. VAN). Verbaal van de buitengewone ambassade van J. van W.-D., E. van W. van D. &c. naar Engeland in 1685, 1863.

Dijon. Chartes de l'abbaye de Saint-Etienne de Dijon, 8e s. [-1400]. [Coll. de textes rel. au droit &c. de la Bourgogne]. [19p *in* 6v.] 8°. [1907–14]
8e–11e ss.; par J. Courtois.
1098–1140; par A. Bièvre Poulalier.
1140–1155; par M. Bourrier.
1155–1200; par G. Valat.
1200–1230; par E. Collette.
1230–1250; par A. Ridard.
1250–1260; par G. Bloc.
1260–1270; par L. Berthoumeau.
1270–1276; par P. Toussaint.
1280–1286; par P. Riandey.
1291–1300; par H. Cottin.
1300; par M. Guillemard.
1300–1309; par J. Quesnel.
1309–1320; par P. Parisot.
1320–1330; par J. Fricaudet.
1341–1346; par H. Bonneviot.
1377–1384; par G. Janniaux.
1385–1394; par H. Guigon.
1395–1400; par L. Gally.

Dijon (Hippolyte). Le bourg & l'abbaye de Saint-Antoine, 1562–97. 8°. Grenoble. 1900
L'église abbatiale de Saint-Antoine en Dauphiné: hist. & arch. la8°. Grenoble. 1902

Dikshit (K. N.) Six sculptures f. Mahoba, *see* INDIA: ARCH. SURVEY. Mem., No. 8, 1921.

Dilherr (Johann Michael). Göttliche Liebesflamme: Andachten &c. ü. das Königl. Brautlied Salomonis &c. Zum 3. Mahl aufgelegt &c. s8°. Nürnberg. 1654
Manuductio Aristotelica ad locos inventionis rhetoricæ &c., *see* ARNOLD (C.) Linguae Latinæ ornatus &c., 1668.

Dill (*Sir* Samuel), *prof. of Greek in Queen's Coll., Belfast.*
Roman society in Gaul in the Merovingian age. 8°. 1926
Roman society in the last cent. of the Western Empire. 2nd ed., rev. [repr.] 8°. 1919

Dillen (J. G. van). Bronnen tot de gesch. d. Wisselbanken (Amsterdam, Middelburg, Delft, Rotterdam). Uitg. d. J. G. van D. [Rijks Gesch. Publ., 59, 60]. 2 stuk [*pagin. cont.*] 4°. 's-Gravenhage. 1925

Dillens (Julien), *see* GOFFIN (A.) J. D., 1919.

Dillingham (Francis). A quatron of reasons, comp. by Dr. Hill unquartered, & proved a quatron of follies. [P2660]. s4°. C. 1603

Dillingham (Robert Barclay), *ps.*, *see* FOULKE (W. D.) The Quaker boy: autobiog. of R. B. D., 1910.

Dillistone (George). The planning & planting of little gardens. Notes &c. by L. Weaver. 8°. 1920

Dillmont (Thérèse de). Encyclopedia of needlework. n. ed., rev. & enl. s8°. Mulhouse. *n.d.*

Dillon (Emile Joseph). Mexico on the verge. 8°. [1921]
President Obregón. 8°. 1922

Dillon (Harold Arthur Dillon, *17th visct.*), *see* TOWER OF LONDON. Illust. guide to armouries, by D., 1910.

Dillon (*l'abbé* Henri). *Lettre à M. l'abbé . . . sur le Concordat de 1817. [*sgnd. L'abbé Dillon*]. [P2553]. [n. tp.] 8°. [1817]

Dillwyn (Lewis Weston), *see* TURNER (D.) & L. W. D. Botanist's guide, 2v, 1805.

Dilnot (George).
Story of Scotland Yard. 8°. [1926]
see WEBSTER (J. W.) Trial of J. W. W.; intr. by G. D., 1928.

Dilthey (Wilhelm).
Gesammelte Schriften. B1, 3–7. la8°. L. 1921–27
1, Einltg. in d. Geisteswissenschaften, 2e A., B1.
3, St. z. Gesch. d. deut. Geistes: Leibnitz u. s. Zeitalter—Friedr. d. Gr. u. d. deut. Aufklärung &c.
4, Die Jugendgesch. Hegels u. a. Abhdl. z. Gesch. d. deut. Idealismus.
5, 6, Die geist. Welt: Einl. in d. Philos. d. Lebens, 2H.
7, Der Aufbau d. gesch. Welt in d. Geisteswiss.
see WACH (J.) Typenl. Trendelenburgs u. i. Einfl. auf D., 1926.

Dimier (Louis). Hist. de la peinture de portrait en France au 16e s., acc. d'un cat. de tous les ouvrages &c. [3p]. la8°. 1924–26
„ „ Suppl.: Douze crayons de F. Quesnel. la8°. 1927
Vie raisonnable de Descartes. s8°. [1926]
see ART (L') d'enluminure (14c.); tr. &c. par L. D., 1927.

Dimnet (Ernest). The Brontë sisters. Tr. L. M. Sill. 8°. 1927

Dimpfel (Rudolf). Biograph. Nachschlagewerke. Adelslexika—Wappenbücher. la8°. L. 1922

Dimringer (Peter) *von Staufenberg, see* STAUFENBERG (P. v.)

Dimsdale (Marcus Southwell). Happy days & o. essays. Ed. E. Dimsdale. Mem. by N. Webb. 8°. C. 1921

Dina (Achille). Isabella d'Aragona, Dssa. di Milano e di Bari, 1470–1524. 8°. Milano. 1921

Dinarchus, *see* DOBSON (W. S.), *ed.* Oratores Attici, t4, Isaeus, D. &c., t14, Isocratis, D. &c. interpret. Lat., 1828.

Dinckel (Martin). Carolstadius redivivus, disput. theol. s4°. Witebergæ. 1597

Dindorf (C. Wilhelm). Poetarum scenicorum Graec. Aeschyli Sophoclis Euripidis & Aristophanis fabulae superstites & perdit. fragm. ed. 5a corr. la8°. Lond. 1869

Dindsenchas, *see* GWYNN (E.) The metrical D., p4, 1924.

Dines (Henry George).
see DEWEY (H.) &c. Geol. of co. around Dartford, 1924.
„ —— & H. G. D. Tungsten & Manganese ores, 3rd ed., 1923.
—— **& F. H. Edmunds.** Geol. of the country around Romford. [G.S. of Eng. &c. Mem.] 8°. 1925

Dines (William Henry), *F.R.S.* Characteristics of the free atmosphere. [Meteorolog. Office, Geophys. Mem., no. 13]. [P2417]. 4°. 1919

Dingelshtedt (Nikolai Aleksandrovich). Опытъ изученія ирригаціи Туркестанск. Края. Сыръ-Дарьинская область. т2. ч3. la8°. С.-П. 1895

Dingle (Herbert). Mod. astrophysics. 8°. [1924]

Dingley (Susanna), *aft. wife of Dr. W. Chapman, see* CHAPMAN (*Mrs.* S.)

Dingwall (Kenneth). The derivation of some Kakiemon designs on porcelain. Adapt. f. paper read bef. Or. Ceramic Soc., 23rd Jan. 1924. 4°. *publ. f. restricted c. only.* 1926

Dini (Giuseppe). Diario de la peregrin. apostólica de Pio VI à la Imperial corte de Viena en 1782. Escrito en idioma Latino. Tr. por el abate Bzn. de Mza. s8°. Barcelona. [1783]

Dinnis (Enid). Emily Hickey, poet, essayist &c. A memoir [*w. sel. of* Poems]. s8°. 1927

Dinsmore (William).
Lancs. novelists: Miss Lahee. [P2871]. 8°. *n.d.*

Diocletian, *emp. of Rome, see* ZEILLER (J.) Spalato, le palais de D., 1912.

Diodati (Giovanni). Pious annot. upon the Holy Bible &c. Also analysis. [Tr. R. G.] 2nd ed. corr. & enl. [2p. *p2 w. sep. pagin.*] s4°. 1648
„ „ ....3rd ed. sfol. 1651

Diodorus, *Siculus.* Bibliothecae hist. ex nova recens. L. Dindorfii. Graece & Latine. Perdit. liberor. excerpta &c. C. Müllerus. 2v. la8°. Parisiis, *Didot.* 1855
Hist. library in 15 books. Added, the fragments of D. found in the Bibliotheca of Photius; w. those publ. by H. Valesius, L. Rhodomannus & F. Ursinus. English by G. Booth. fol. 1700

Diogenes, *Laertius.* De vita &c. philosoph. libri 10. [*Tr.* A. Traversarius]. s8°. Lugduni. 1546
Lives of eminent philosophers. [Text], w. Eng. tr. by R. D. Hicks. [Loeb Class. Lib.] 2v. s8°. 1925

Diomedes (Alex. N.), *Greek minister of finance.* Address, King's College, Feb. 1917, *see* ANGLO-HELLENIC LEAGUE. Publ., No. 31, 1917.

Dion (*le cte.* Adolphe de), *see* PORT ROYAL, *abbey of.* Cartul.; [ed. &c. A. de D.], v1, 1204–80, 1903.

Dion Cassius. Hist. Rom. quae sup. Ed. U. P. Boissevain. v4, Index hist.; comp. H. Smilda. 8°. Berolini. 1926
Roman hist. [Text], w. Eng. tr. by E. Cary. [Loeb Class. Lib.] v7–9. s8°. 1924–27

Dionisi (Gian Giacomo). Notizie appart. alla prov. Veronese. [Nozze Dionisi-Bembo. N134.] 8°. Verona. 1875

Dionisotti (Carlo). La Cappella d. Corte d'Appello di Torino, *see* REGIA DEPUT. Misc., t29, 1892.
Commemoraz. del Comm. C. Danna, *see* REGIA DEPUT. Misc., t24, 1885.
see FONTANA (L.) Commem. del Comm. C. D., 1901.

Dionysius, *Carthusianus, see* LEUWIS (D. DE) *de Rickel.*

Dionysius, *Exiguus.* Liber de Paschate, *see* HOFFMANN (B.) Hist. cycli Dionysiani &c., 1718.

Dionysius, *of Halicarnassus.* Antiq. Romanarum quae sup. Ed. C. Jacoby. Suppl. indices cont. s8°. L., *Teubner.* 1925
Romanarum antiq. pars hactenus desiderata ope Cod. Ambrosian. ab A. Maio restituta. [*Gr. & Lat.*] 4°. Mediolani. 1816

Dionysius, *Periegetes.* Geographia emend. &c., add. scil. geogr. hod. Graeco carmine pariter donatae. Ab E. Wells. s8°. Oxonii. 1704
Orbis descr. cum vet. scholiis & Eustathii comm. *Greek.* Acc. Periegesis Prisciani cum notis A. Papii. *Latin.* 8°. Oxoniæ. 1697
see HUDSON (J.), *ed.* Geog. vet. scriptores Gr. min., v4, 1712.

Dionysius, *Saint, called the Areopagite.* Opera omnia, Textus & G. Pachymeræ paraphrasis Gr. & Lat. cum adnot. B. Corderii [*& S. Maximi scholia*]. 2t. fol. Venetiis. 1755–56

Dionysius, *Saint* [*continued*].
De mystica theologia lib. 1. Graece Joan. Sarraceno, Ambrosio Camaldul., Marsilio Ficino interpret. Cum vercelleñ extractione. J. Eckius Comm. adj. pro theologia negativa Ingolstadii. fol. [Augustæ Vindel, *J. Miller.* 1519]
see Ball (H.) Byzantin. Christentum: 3 Heiligenleben [*i.e.* D. &c.], 1923.
„ Hersent (C.) In D. A. de mystica theologia librum apparatus, interpret. &c., 1626.
„ Launoy (J. de). Opera, t2i, Varia de duobus D., 1731.
„ Müller (H. F.) D., Proklos, Plotinos, 1918.

Dionysius, *the Thracian.* Ars grammatica. Ed. G. Uhlig. Praemissa prolegomena, A. Merxii de versione Armen. disput. &c. [Gram. Graeci, p1, v1]. 8°. Lipsiæ. 1883
Д. Θ. и арм. толкователи. [Ars D. gramm. & Armen. in eam scholia Davidis philos., Moysis Qerdoli &c. Rec. & disp. N. Adontz. (*Greek & Arm.*) Bibl. Arm.-Georgica, 4. *a. tp. in Armenian*]. la8°. Петроградъ. 1915
Scholia in D. Artem gramm. Rec. &c. A. Hilgard. [Gram. Graeci, p1, v3]. 8°. Lipsiæ. 1901

Dios de la Rada y Delgado (Juan de). Crón de la prov. de Granada, 1869, *see* España. Crón. gen., v9, 1865 &c.
see Amador de los Rios (J.) & J. de Dios de la R. y D. Hist. de la villa y corte de Madrid, 4t, 1860–64.

Dios Peza (Juan de), *see* Peza (J. de D.)

Diotima, *ps., see* Gontard (Susette), *formerly* Borkenstein.

Diphilos, *see* Pottier (E.) D. & les modeleurs de terres cuites grec., 1909.

Diplomatarium. Dipl. Islandicum: islenzkt fornbréfasafn. [Islenzka Bókmentafélagi]. B10, 11. 8°. Reykjavík. 1911–25
10, 1169–1542. 11, 1310–1550.
Dipl. Italicum: doc. racc. n. archivi ital., v1, 1925, *see* Scuola Romena di Roma.

Diplomatische. Dipl. Akten d. Auswärt. Amtes, 1871–1914, T1–5i, 1923–26, *see* Schwertfeger (B.), *ed.*
Dipl. Aktenstücke z. Gesch. d. Ententepol. d. Vorkriegsjahre, 1921; tr., 1923, *see* Siebeit (B. von), *ed.*
Dipl. Enthüllungen. 2H *in* 1v. [H2 *h. t.* Der Weg z. Zusammenbruch, T1. Deut. Geschichtskal., Lief. 54, 65]. 8°. L. [1919]

Diplomi. I d. greci ed arabi di Sicilia, v1, 1868, *see* Cusa (S.)

Diplovataccio (Tomaso), *1468–1541, see* Besta (E.) T. D. e l'opera sua, 1903.

Diprose (John).
Acc. of parish of St. Clement Danes. 2v. s4°. 1864–76
Book of epitaphs. s8°. *n.d.*

Directorium chori, à I. Guidetto olim ed. nuper ad Rom. Breviarii corr. restitutum &c., 1604, *see* Guidettus (J.)

Directory.
*D. (A) for church-govt. & ordin. of ministers. [*b. w.* Henderson (A.) Govt. &c. of Ch. of Scot., 1690]. s8°. E. 1690
D. for publ. worship, *see* Church of Scotland. Book of Common order of Ch. of Scot., 1868.
D. (A) for the publique worship of God, w. an ordinance of Parl. for the taking away of the Book of C. P. &c. s4°. 1646
D. (Internat.) of booksellers &c., 1927. *With title*: "The Librarian" internat. directory &c. Clegg's successor. Ed. A. J. Philip. 8°. Gravesend. 1927
D. (A) of Ch.-govt., 1872, *see* Cartwright (T.)
View of the new D. &c., 1645, *see* Hammond (H.)

Dirlos, *Count.* Romance del conde D., 1510. Ed. w. intr. by H. Thomas. [Early Span. Ballads in B.M., 1]. 8°. 1927

Dirr (A.) Colloquial Egyptian Arabic grammar. Tr. W. H. Lyall. s8°. 1904

Disbrowe (C. A. A.), *eldest daughter of Sir E. C. Disbrowe.*
*Orig. letters f. Russia, 1825–28. [*By* E. C. Disbrowe *& others.* Ed. C. A. A. D.] 8°. *p.f.p.c.* 1878

Disbrowe (*Sir* Edward Cromwell), *see* Disbrowe (C. A. A.) Orig. letters f. Russia, 1825–28; [*by* E. C. D. &c.], 1878.

Disciple (A), *ps.* *Stories f. the lips of the teacher; retold by a disciple, 5th ed., 1876, *see* Frothingham (O. B.)

***Disciplina** & institutio puerorum. s8°. Coloniæ, *I. Prœl.* 1532

***Discours** s. les princ. éd. des Bibles polyglottes; par l'a. de la Bibl. Sacrae, 1713, *see* Le Long (J.)

Discourse.
*D. (A) about church-unity &c., by a Presbyter of the Ch. of E., 1681, *see* Sherlock (W.)
*D. (A) conc. the illegality of the late Eccl. Comm. &c., 1689, *see* Stillingfleet (E.)
*D. (A) conc. the original of the Powder-Plot &c., 1674, *see* Stephens (E.)
*D. (A) conc. the worship of the Virgin &c., 1686, *see* Clagett (W.)

Discourse [*continued*].
*D. of auxiliary beauty, or artificial hansomenesse in point of conscience. [*By bp. Jeremy Taylor? or rather O. Walker?*] s8°. 1656
*D. (A) proving the divine instit. of water baptism &c., 1697, *see* Leslie (C.)
*D. (A) shewing who are qualify'd to admin. baptism &c., 1698, *see* Leslie (C.)
*D. (A) upon the uniting Scotland w. Eng., 1702, *see* Fairfax (B.)

Discourses. *Five d. by the a. of The snake in the grass &c., 1700, *see* Leslie (C.)

Discovery [Discoverie]. *Discoverie of the true causes why Ireland was never subdued (1612), 1747, *see* Davies (J.)
*Discovery (The), a comedy; wr. by the ed. of Miss Sidney Bidulph, 2nd ed., 1763, *see* Sheridan (*Mrs.* F.)

***Discrepanze,** o' contradiz. int. al fatto tra' mod. impugnatori de' riti cinesi, 1700, *see* Montecatini (B.)

Discursus. *D. de modo peregrinationes bene inchoandi & absolv., publ. redd. per D. P. P. K. [P1035]. 8°. Jenæ. 1670
*D. de successione foeminea in regna & prov. Austriacas occas. Sanctionis Pragmaticae publ. Adj. ipsa Sanctione & Privilegio Friderici I. [P428]. s4°. *n.p.* 1733

***Discusion** del proyecto de decreto sobre el tribunal de la Inquisicion, 1813, *see* Inquisicion.

Discussion amicale &c., 1817, *see* Le Pappe de Trévern (J. F. M.)

Disher (Maurice Willson). Clowns & pantomimes. la8°. 1925

Dishler (P. Ya.) Организация коллективных трудовых хозяйств. 8°. П. 1920

Disney (John), *vicar of St. Mary's, Nottingham.* Essay upon the execution of the laws agst. immorality & profaneness. 2nd ed. enl. s8°. 1710
A view of anc. laws agst. immorality &c., to middle of 11th c. fol. C. 1729

Disney (W.) *Nil dictum quod non dictum prius or a transcript of government &c. Further of the govt. of our own nation & of parliamentary power. By W. D. s8°. 1681

Disorders Inquiry Committee [India], 1919–20. Report. 8°. Calcutta. 1920

***Dispassionate** (A) remonstrance of the nature &c. of the laws for the reduct. of interest, 1751, *see* Remonstrance.

Dispensary (The): a poem, 1699; 3rd ed., 1699, *see* Garth (*Sir* S.)

Disputacion. Disp. (Die) vor den xii orten, 1527, *see* Baden, *Switzerland.*

Disputatio. D. hab. a rev. patribus discalc. ord. B. V. M. de m. Carmelo, contra Arianos, 1617, *see* Carmelites.
*D. de majestate hominis Christi in Acad. Ingols. &c., 1564, *see* Ingolstadt.

Disputationes. Thesaurus disp. theolog. in alma Sedanensi Acad., 2t, 1661, *see* Du Moulin (P.)

***Dispute** (A) agst. the ceremonies obtruded upon the Ch. of Scotland &c., 1660, *see* Gillespie (G.)

Disquisitiones. *Disq. theolog. de anima separata a corpore & aeterna salute a theologiae doctoribus [B. Bebelius, G. Calixtus] &c. Congestae & in 2 coll. distrib. [2p *in* 1v]. s8°. Francofurti. 1730
Two tracts Das Leben d. Seelen im Tode *by* Th. Reincking *&c. have sep. tp. & pagin.*

Dissenters.
Abs. of proceed. of dep. & comm. for support. civil rights of protestant-d. [P1041]. s8°. 1796
*A coll. of cases &c. wr. to recover D. to the communion of the Church of Eng. By some divines of London. 2nd ed. fol. 1694
*D. marriages: debate in H. of Lords, June 12, 1823, w. obs. &c. [P2782]. 8°. 1823
*A sketch of the hist. & proc. of the deputies app. to protect the civil rights of the protestant d., summary of laws, app. of statutes &c. s8°. 1814

***Dissertatio** de admirando prorsus renati Evang. solis ortu cursuque & progr., 1517–1617 &c. [P483]. s4°. *n.p.* 1618

***Dissertations** théologiques &c., 1727, *see* Duguet (J. J.)

Dissertazione. *Diss. dell' estatico int. all' erruzioni [*sic*] del Vesuvio, c. 1753, *see* Vesuvio.
*Diss. epistolare s. letteratura Ravennate, 1749, *see* Ravenna.

Distelmair (Conrad). Ain trewe ermanung, das ain yeder Christ selbs zu seiner seel hail sehe u. das schwert (das ist die hailig geschrifft) auch selbs zu s. handen neme &c. s4°. *n.p.* 1523

***Distinction** (The) betw. the ordin. & extraordin. gifts of the Holy Spirit &c., 1767, *see* Ashdowne (W.)

Distinctiones monast. & morales (13c.), *see* Lehmann (P.) Mittellat. Verse in D., 1922.

Distracted emperor; éd. crit., 1920, *see* Charlemagne.

Ditchfield (Peter Hampson). The city of London. s8°. 1921
London's West End. 8°. [1925]
Old village life. 8°. [1920]
The parson in literature, *see* Roy. Soc. of Lit. Essays &c.: Trans., N.S., v1, 1921.
The parson's pleasance. 8°. [1910]
Dithmar (Edward A.), *see* Bunner (H. C.), E. A. D. &c. Portfolio of players, 1888.
Dithmar (Justus Christoph). Vita Gregorii VII. [*b. w.* Du Moulin (P.) De monarchia temp. pontif. Rom., 1716]. s8°. Francofurti ad Viadrum. 1710
Ditmars (Raymond Lee). Reptiles of the world. 8°. N.Y. 1922
Ditmarus, *bp. of Merseburg.* Chronicon. Post ed. J. M. Lappenbergii rec. F. Kurze. [Scr. rerum Germ. in usum schol.] 8°. Hannoveræ. 1889
Dittenberger (Wilhelm). Sylloge inscript. Graecarum. Nunc tertium ed. v4. 8°. Lipsiæ. 1924
Dittmann (Wilhelm). Die Marine-Justizmorde v. 1917 u. d. Admirals-Rebellion v. 1918. 8°. 1926
Dittmar (Wilhelm Anton Heinrich). De nomine, aetate, studiis ac scriptis Gaii jcti Rom. spec. I. s4°. Lipsiæ. [1820]
Diurnal (Le) du bréviaire rom. [2 *pagin.*] s8°. Paris. 1762
Diurnum Augustin. ad usum Fratrum &c. ord. Eremit. S. Augustini. [*3 pagin.*] s8°. Venetiis. 1756
Divaev (A. A.) Этнограф. матеріалы [*Kirghiz tales &c.*]; собранные А. А. Д., *see* Sir-Daria. Сборникъ, 1892–1902.
Diver (*Mrs.* **Maud).**
But yesterday— s8°. [1927]
Coombe St. Mary's. s8°. E. 1925
The great amulet. 8th impr. s8°. E. 1919
Lonely furrow. s8°. 1923
Strange roads. s8°. 1918
Diverres (P.) Le plus ancien texte des Meddygon Myddveu. [*W. text & Fr. tr.*] la8°. 1913
Divine. *D. (The) companion or David's Harp new tun'd, 1722, *see* Playford (H.)
*D. hymns &c. on sev. occ., 1708, *see* Hymns.
D. office for use of laity, 1763, *see* Officia.
Divines. *Humble (The) answer of the d. to 2nd paper by H. M., Oct. 6, 1648, about episc. govt., deliv. Oct. 17 (1648). [P2662]. s4°. 1660
*Humble (The) proposals of sundry learned &c. d., 1650, *see* Reynolds (E.)
***Divinitas** Jesu Christi &c., 1746, *see* Maran (P.)
***Divisiones** decem nationũ totius christ. s8°. *n.p.* [Romæ ?]. *n.d.* [*15c.*]
„ „ *for a. ed.*, *see* Loreto. Trãslatio miraculosa &c., c. 1500.
Divoire (Fernand). Découvertes sur la danse. 8°. 1924
Divyāvadāna, *see* Zimmer (H.), *ed.* Karman, buddh. Legendenkranz, üb., 1925.
Dix (Arthur).
Polit. Geographie. Weltpolit. Hdbch. la8°. München. 1921
Wirtschaftskrieg u. Kriegswirtschaft: Gesch. d. deut. Zusammenbruchs. 8°. 1920
Dix (Rudolf). Ziele d. deut. Demokratie. Rede, Demokrat. Club, 15. Juli 1919. [P2383]. 8°. 1919
Dixelius (Hildur). Prästdottern. Berättelse. s8°. [1926]
Sonsonen. Forts. av Prästdottern &c. s8°. [1926]
Dixey (Frederick Augustus). *Early connexion of the Royal Soc. w. Wadham Coll. & the Univ. of Oxford. [*Signed* F. A. D.] [P2488]. s8°. O. 1912
Dixon (Charles). Annals of bird life. 8°. 1890
Dixon (Charles George). Sketch of Mairwara; origin & habits of the Mairs &c. 4°. 1850
Dixon (Ernest Edward Leslie), *F.G.S.*
see Strahan (*Sir* A.) Geol. of S. Wales coal-field, p13, Co. around Pembroke &c. by D., 1921.
„ Whitehead (T. H.), E. E. L. D. &c. Country betw. Stafford & Market Drayton, 1927.
——, **J. Maden, F. M. Trotter &c.** Geol. of the Carlisle, Longtown & Silloth district. [Mem. of G.S.] 8°. 1926
Dixon (Frank Haigh) & J. H. Parmelee. War admin. of the rlys. in the U.S. & Gt. Brit. [C.E. f. Int. Peace.] 2nd ed. la8°. N.Y. 1919
Dixon (Hugh Neville). *Works in* S.I. Misc. coll.
The mosses coll. by the Smithsonian Afr. exped. 1909–10, 1918. [69.]
Rep. upon 2 coll. of mosses f. Brit. E. Africa, 1922. [72.]
Uganda mosses coll. by R. Dümmer & others, 1918. [69.]
Dixon (James), *D.D., Wesleyan Minister, 1788–1871.*
Methodism in America. 3rd ed. s8°. 1849
Select writings. Ed. by E. Lightwood. s8°. 1890
see Dixon (R. W.) Life of J. D., 1874.

Dixon (James Main), *see* Grant (W.) & J. M. D. Manual of mod. Scots, 1921.
Dixon (Richard Watson).
The close of the 10th cent. [P524]. 8°. O. 1858
The life of James Dixon, D.D. s8°. 1874
Dixon (Roland Burrage).
The racial hist. of man. 8°. N.Y. 1923
Dixon (William Hepworth), *jun.*
The match industry. s8°. *Pitman.* [1925]
Dixon (William Macneile). Tragedy. 8°. 1924
Dixon (William Scarth). Influence of racing & the thoroughbred horse on light-horse breeding. 8°. [1924]
Dixon (Winifred Hawkridge).
Westward hoboes: frontier motoring. 8°. N.Y. 1924
Dizionario biografico univ. [*Tr. & comp. chiefly f.* Biog. Univ. *by* F. Scifoni]. 5v. la8°. Firenze. 1840–49
Djabarti, El, *see* 'Abd al Raḥmān ibn Ḥasan.
Djanoumova (Hélène). Mes rencontres avec Raspoutine, journal; tr. A. Pierre, *see* Œuvres libres, 24, 1923.
Djarean (Abraham). Patmouthiun Gall iatzvotz. [Hist. of France. *In Armenian*]. 2v. s8°. Venice. 1849
Djelalean (Jacobos). Varg imastasiratz. [Lives of philosophers. *In Armenian*]. s8°. Venice. 1826
Djemal *Pasha*, *see* Aḥmad Djemal *Pasha.*
Djraqal [monthly lit. review. *In Armenian*]. v1, 2. 8°. i Mosqoua. 1859–61
„ „ Suppl., tetrak 1, 2 [*b. w.* v2]. 8°. i Mosqoua. 1858
Dmitrevsky (N. P.), *see* Gurevich (S. A.) & N. P. D. Законы о торговле, т1, 1922.
Dmitriev-Mamonov (A. I.) & A. F. Zdziarski, *editors.* Guide to the Great Siberian Rly. Publ. by the Min. of Ways &c. Engl. tr. by L. Kukol-Yasnopolsky; rev. by J. Marshall. la8°. St. P. 1900
Dobb (Maurice).
Capitalist enterprise & social progress. 8°. 1925
Russian econ. development since the Revol. By M. D. assist. by H. C. Stevens. 8°. 1928
Dob Baer, *of Meseritz*, *see* Buber (M.) Der gr. Maggid u. s. Nachfolge, 1922.
Dobbie (H. B.) New Zealand ferns. 2nd ed. 8°. Auckland. 1921
Dobbs (Arthur Conway). Green-manuring in India, *see* Agric. Res. Inst., *Pusa.* Bulletin 56, 1916.
Dobbs (*maj.-gen.* **Richard Stewart).** Remin. of life in Mysore, S. Africa & Burmah. s8°. D. 1882
Dobell (Percy John).
John Dryden. Bibliog. memoranda. 8°. 1922
Döbeln (Ernst von), *see* Upsala: Kongl. Univ. &c. Matrikel, höst. 1926, av T. Fries & E. v. D., 1927.
Döberl (Michael). Bayern u. d. wirtschaftl. Einigung Deutschlands, 1915, *see* Königl. Akad. d. W. zu München. Abhdlgn., B29, 1918.
Rheinbundverfassung u. bayer. Konstit., *see* Königl. Akad. d. Wiss. zu München. Phil. Kl., Sitz., 1924.
Dobiache-Rojdestvensky (Olga). Le culte de St. Michel & le moyen âge latin. 8°. 1922
Dobler (Friedrich). Geistl. Blumenstrauss aus d. röm. Brevier. s8°. Dillingen. 1847
Döblin (Alfred). Reise in Polen. 8°. 1926
Wallenstein. Roman. 2B. 8°. 1922
Dobneck (Johann), *see* Cochlæus (Joannes).
Dobrée (Bonamy). Essays in biog., 1680–1726. [Etheridge-Vanbrugh-Addison]. 8°. 1925
Restoration comedy, 1660–1720. 8°. O. 1924
Sir John Denham: convers. betw. Bp. Henry King & Edmund Waller, 1699. 8°. *Cayme Press.* 1927
Timotheus: the future of the theatre. s8°. [1925]
Dobrizhoffer (Martin).
Historia de Abiponibus. 2v. 8°. Viennæ. 1784
Dobrolyubov (Nikolai Aleksandrovich). Сочиненія. изд. 3е. 4т. 8°. С.-П. 1876
Dobronravov (N. E.) Разбитіе четырехъ японскихъ броненосцевъ. [P2454]. 8°. Москва. 1904
Dobroudja, *see* Dobrudja.
Dobrov (Leongradt Yakovl.) О важнѣйшихъ событіяхъ нашей внутренней жизни, 1855–80. [P2445]. 8°. С.-П. 1880
Dobrowitz (Alexis), *ps.*, *see* Omessa (Ch.) & H. Omessa. La dernière Tsarine: révélations d'A. D., 1920.
Dobrowsky (Josef).
Gesch. d. Böhmisch. Sprache u. Litt. s8°. Prag. 1792
Instit. ling. Slavicæ dialecti veteris. 8°. Vindobonæ. 1822

Dobrowsky (Josef) [*continued*].
Instit. ling. Slavicæ dialecti veteris. Ed. 2ª. 8º. Vindobonæ. 1852
Slovanka. Zur Kenntniss d. alten u. neuen slaw. Lit., d. Sprachkunde &c. 2 Lief. *in* 1v. s8º. Prag. 1814–15
Dobrudja [DOBROUDJA]. *La Dobroudja Mérid. Le quadrilatére. [P2464]. 8º. 1919
Mem. presented by the representatives of the D., 1917–18. [P2417]. fol. 1918
Dobrynine (V.) La lutte contre le bolchév. dans la Russ. mérid. : particip. des Cosaques du Don (1917–20). Tr. A. G. 8º. Prague. 1920
Dobschütz (Ernst v.) Der Apostel Paulus. 1, Weltgeschichtl. Bedeutung. 8º. Halle. 1926
Dobson (A. Mary R.) Mount Sinai : a mod. pilgrimage. Pref. by R. Harris. 8º. [1925]
Dobson (H. Austin). An anthology of prose & verse. Foreword by E. Gosse. s8º. 1922
Later essays, 1917–20. s8º. 1921
Old-world idylls & o. verses. [7th ed.] s8º. 1887
Dobson (William Stephen). Oratores Attici & quos sic vocant Sophistae. Opera & studio G. S. D. 16t. la8º. Londini. 1828
1, Antiphon & Andocides.
2, Lysias.
3, Isocrates.
4, Isæus Dinarchus &c.
5–11, Demosthenes.
12, Æschines.
13, Antiphontis, Andocidis & Lysiæ interpret. Lat.
14, Isocratis, Isæi Dinarchi, Lycurgi Demadis & Sophistarum interpret. Lat.
15, Demosthenis interpret. Lat.
16, Demosthenis & Æschinis interpret. Lat.
Dock (Lavinia L.) Short hist. of nursing. By L. L. D. in collab. w. I. M. Stewart. 8º. N.Y. 1920
Doctor Williams' Library, *see* WILLIAMS' LIBRARY.
Doctrina. *D. & politia Eccl. Anglicanae &c., 1617, *see* MOCKET (R.)
*D. Xtna. Armenice in Lat. versa à T. Petraeo, 1667, *see* BELLARMINO (*il card.* R. F. R.)
Doctrine. *D. (The) of non-resistance &c. no way conc. in controv. &c., 1689, *see* BOHUN (E.)
*D. of salvation, faith & good works &c., 1748, *see* WESLEY (J.)
***Doctrines** (The) & practises of the Church of Rome, &c., 1686, *see* STILLINGFLEET (E.)
Documentary hist. of campaign upon Niagara frontier, 1812[–14], 1896–1908, *see* CRUIKSHANK (*Col.* E. A.)
Documente. Doc. din vechiul ocol al câmpulungului Moldovenesc, 1915, *see* STEFANELLI (T. V.)
Doc. privitóre la ist. Românilor, cul. de E. de Hurmuzaki, v14–19, 1911–22, *see* HURMUZAKI (E. DE).
Documenti. D. di storia ital. ; pubbl. a cura d. Regia Deput. Toscane. v11, 13. 4º. Firenze. 1899–1916
see AREZZO. Doc. per a storia d. città di A. &c., 2v, 1899–1916.
D. per la storia di S. Marco in Venezia, d. 9. sec. s. a. 18., *see* VENEZIA, 1886.
Documentos. *D. para a hist. da typographia portugueza, sec. 16 & 17. 2v. 8º. 1881–82
Documents.
Coll. de doc. inédits sur l'hist. économ. de la Révolution Franç., *see* FRANCE : MIN. DE L'INTÉRIEUR.
D. allemands relat. à l'orig. de la Guerre ; coll. complète ; tr., 4t, 1922 ; (*Eng.*) tr., 1924, *see* KAUTSKY (C.)
D. hist. rel. à l'hist. de France, tirés des archives de Strasbourg, 1818–19, *see* KENTZINGER (A. DE).
D. illust. hist. of civiliz. in med. Eng., 1066–1500, 1926, *see* DAVIES (R. T.), *ed.*
D. illust. of the hist. of the Church, v1, 2, 1920–23, *see* KIDD (B. J.), *ed.*
D. illust. of soc. &c. hist. of the Danelaw, 1920, *see* STENTON (F. M.), *ed.*
D. inéd. sur la campagne de 1815, 1840, *see* NEY (J. N.), *ed.*
D. on Xtn. unity, 1920–4, 1924, *see* BELL (G. K. A.), *ed.*
D. rel. to settlement of Ch. of Eng. by the Act of Uniformity of 1662, *see* CHURCH OF ENGLAND.
D. sur la prov. du Perche, *see* ROMANET (*le vte.* DE). Géographie du Perche &c., 1890–1902 ; Table, 1901–2.
Official German d. rel. to World War ; tr., v1, 2, 1923, *see* GERMAN.
Dod, *see* POPULAR (The) Dod, 1881.
Dod (Anthony Hurt Wolley-), *see* WOLLEY-DOD (A. H.)
Dod (Charles Roger). Peerage, Baronetage, &c., 1841, *see* DOD'S.
Dodd (Agnes F.) Early English social hist. f. the chronicles. s8º. 1913
Dodd (Catherine). The Farthing spinster. s8º. 1925
Dodd (Francis). Generals of the Brit. army : portraits in colours, w. introd. & biogr. notes. p2. [P2700]. 4º. [1918]
Dodd (John). Journal of a blockaded resident in North Formosa dur. Franco-Chinese War, 1884–85. 8º. *p.f.p.c.* Hongkong. 1888
Dodd (William Clifton). The Tai race. Results of exper., explor. & research. Comp. & ed. by [*Mrs.* D.] 8º. Cedar Rapids, Iowa. 1923
Dodd (William Edward). Woodrow Wilson & his work. 8º. Garden City, N.Y. 1920
see MACLAUGHLIN (A. C.), W. E. D. &c. Source probˢ. in U.S. hist., by M., W. E. D. &c., 1918.
Doddington, *ship, see* †TEMPLE (*Sir* R. C.) Wreck of the "D," 1755, 1902.
Doddridge (Philip).
Hymns. Publ. f. the a.'s MS. by J. Orton. s8º. Salop. 1755
Passages in the life of Col. J. Gardiner. n. ed. s8º. Bungay. 1807
Dodds (Elliott).
The social gospel of liberalism. [P2848]. 8º. [1926]
Dodds (Eric Robertson). Sel. passages illust. Neoplatonism. Tr. [*f.* Plotinus, Porphyry *&* Proclus], w. intr. by E. R. D. s8º. 1923
Dodds (*Mrs.* Eric Robertson), *see* POWELL (A. E.)
Dodds (Isaac), *see* SNELL (S.) Story of railway pioneers : inventions of I. D. &c., 1921.
Dodds (Madeline Hope). The parishes of Ovingham, Stamfordham & Ponteland, *see* NORTHUMBERLAND. Hist. of N., v12, 1926.
Dodds (Thomas Weatherburn), *see* SNELL (S.) Story of railway pioneers : inventions of I. & T. W. D., 1921.
Dodeon (Reinbert), *see* DODOENS (R.)
Döderlein (Johann Christoph). Auserlesene theolog. Bibliothek. [*Contin. of* Kraft's & Ernesti's Neue theolog. Bibl., *q.v.*]. 4B. s8º. L. 1780–92
„ *Continued as* Theolog. Journal ; hrsg. v. J. C. Döderlein. 1B. s8º. Jena & Nürnberg. 1792
„ *For further continuation see :* NEUES THEOLOGISCHES JOURNAL.
Instit. theologi Christ. Ed. 2ª. emend. 2p *in* 1v. 8º. Norimbergæ. 1782
Dodge (Walter Phelps). The real Sir Richard Burton. 8º. 1907
Dodgson (Campbell).
The etchings of Charles Meryon. Ed. by G. Holme. [Studio. *Spec. No.*] la8º. 1921
The etchings of J. McN. Whistler. Ed. G. Holme. [Studio. Spec. No.] 4º. 1922
The etchings of Sir David Wilkie, *see* WALPOLE Soc. 11th ann. vol., 1922–23.
French etching f. Meryon to Lepère. Lect., Print Collectors' Club, June, 1922. [Pr. Coll. Club, Publ. No. 2]. la8º. [1922]
Holzschnitte zu 2 nürnberg. Andachtsbüchern [Evangelia, 1534—Salus anime &c.] aus d. Anfange d. 16. Jhdts. 106 Abbildungen. Hrsg, C. D. [Graph. Gesellschaft. 11]. fol. 1909
Ostendorfer & the Virgin of Regensburg. [Sonderabdr. a. d. Monatsheften f. Kunstwiss.] [P2702]. 4º. L. *n.d.*
see BRIT. MUS. : PRINTS, DRAWINGS &c. Bk. of drawings form. ascr. to Mantegna pres. to B.M. by Earl of Rosebery ; intr. by C. D., 1923.
„ DÜRER (A.) Notes & sketches ; sel. & ed. by C. D., 1911.
—— **& J. Pennell.** The Senefelder Club. s8º. 1922
Dodington (George Bubb). Diary, 1748–1761, w. app. Publ. by H. P. Wyndham. 8º. 1784
Dodoens (Rembert) [DODEON (REINBERT)]. A niewe herball or hist. of plantes. First set forth in Doutche, nowe first tr. out of French by H. Lyte. fol. 1578
Dod's Parliamentary Companion, 1923. s8º. [1923]
—— Peerage, Baronetage, & Knightage. s8º. 1841
Dods (Marcus), *D.D., the younger.*
Erasmus & o. essays. 2ⁿᵈ ed. s8º. 1892
Dodsley (Robert). *Oeconomy of human life ; tr. [*attrib. to D. &c.*], 1798, *see* ECONOMY.
Dodson (William), *ps.* [*i.e.* MARY DE MORGAN].
A choice of chance. 2v. s8º. 1887
Dodwell (Henry), *Curator of Madras Rec. Office.*
Dupleix & Clive. The beginning of Empire. la8º. [1920]
The Nabobs of Madras. 8º. 1926
A sketch of the hist. of India, 1858–1918. 8º. 1925
see MADRAS ; MISC. GOVT. PUBLS. Calendar of Madras despatches, 1744–55, 1920.
Dodwell (Henry), *the elder.* Diss. de Pontificum Roman. primævâ successione usq; ad Annales Cl. Cestriensis Cyprianicos, *see* PEARSON (J.) Opera posthuma, 1688.

Dodwell (Henry) [*continued*].
Explic. of passage in dial. of Justin Martyr w. Tryphon, conc. immortality of humane souls. App. letter to J. Norris, &c. s8°. 1708
A prelim. defence of the Epistolary disc., conc. distinction betw. soul & spirit. 2p *in* 1v. (p2 *has sep. tp. & pag.*) s8°. 1707
Separation of churches f. episcopal gov. as pract. by non-conformists &c. s4°. 1679
see BUDDEUS (J. F.) Diss. de orig. & potest. episcop. sentent. H. D. expendens, 1705.
„ CHISHULL (E.) A charge of heresy agst. Mr. D.'s disc. conc. mortality of the soul, 1706.
„ CLARKE (S.) Letter to D., 1718.
„ WHITBY (D.) Reflections on D., 1707.

Doeberl (Michael), *see* DÖBERL (M.)

Doelschius (Johannes) [†TOLTZ (J.)] Contra doctrinalem Magistrorum damnationem Louan. & Colon. studii J. D. defensio pro M. Luthero. s4°. Vuittenbergæ. *n.d.* [c. 1525]

Doerkes-Boppard (Wilhelm Nikolaus), *see* DÖRKES-BOPPARD.

Does (Franck van der), *see* HOUTMAN (C. DE). De eerste schipvaart d. Nederlanders naar Oost-Indië; Journalen &c., 2, Van der Does (Hs. 1598), 1925.

***Dogi** (I) di Venezia, 1871, *see* VENEZIA.

Doglioni (Giovanni Nicolò).
Hist. Venet., sino all'a. 1597. s4°. Venetia. 1598
L'Ungheria, spiegata da G. N. D. s4°. Venetia. 1595

***Dogs**, birds, & others, Nat. hist. letters f. Spectator, 1921, *see* MASSINGHAM (H. J.)

Doguereau (*General* Jean Pierre). Journal de l'expéd. d'Egypte. Publ. d'ap. le ms. orig., avec intr. &c. par C. de La Jonquière. 8°. 1904

Döhring (Carl). Siam. 2B. 4°. Darmstadt. 1923

Dokumente. D. z. Gesch. d. Europ. Krieges, 1914/16, Abt. 2, B1, 1916, *see* JUNKER (C.)
D. z. Weltkrieg 1914, H1, 1919, *see* BERNSTEIN (E.), *ed.*

Dokumenti. Д. по ист. литературы и обществ., в1, 1922, *see* DOSTOEVSKY (F. M.)
Д. и матерьялы по внѣшней политикѣ Закавказья и Грузіи, 1919, *see* ZAKAVKAZ.

Dolby (Thomas). Dolby's Brit. theatre, w. pref. remarks, stage directions &c. s8°. 1823–24
The plays were issued separately & aft. in vol. The following poss. by the Lib. are b. sep.
Bickerstaffe (I.) The hypocrite.
Centlivre (Mrs.) The wonder.
Cowley (H.) The belle's stratagem.
Farquhar (G.) The inconstant.
Goldsmith (O.) She stoops to conquer.
Holcroft (T.) The road to ruin.
Knowles (J. S.) Caius Gracchus.
—— Virginius.
Kotzebue (A. F. F. v.) Pizarro.
Macklin (C.) The man of the world.
Massinger (P.) A new way to pay old debts.
Moore (E.) The gamester.
Murphy (A.) The way to keep him.
Otway (T.) Venice preserved.
Rowe (N.) Jane Shore.
Shakespeare (W.) As you like it—Cymbeline—Julius Caesar—Henry IV, p1—Henry VIII—King John—King Lear—King Richard III—Macbeth—Much ado about nothing—Othello—Romeo & Juliet—The winter's tale, *b. in* 2v.
Sheridan (R. B. R.) A trip to Scarborough.
Vanburgh (J.) & C. Cibber. The provoked husband.

Dolce (Lodovico). Imprese nobili &c. di div. prencipi &c. [*by B. Pittoni*], con versi di L. D. e d'altri. la8°. Venetia. 1578
„ „ Nov. ristamp. Con stanze sonetti di L. D. la8°. Venetia. 1602

Dolcetti (Giovanni). La fuga di G. Casanova dai piombi di Venezia. [Nozze Magno- Romanello. N. 121]. s8°. Venezia. 1905
La profumeria dei Veneziani. [P2839]. s8°. Venezia. 1898
Scuola dei Tira e Battioro ora gabinetto artist. A. Carrer. [P2839]. s8°. Venezia. 1905

Dolch (Walther), *see* LANGER (E.) Bibliographie d. österr. Drücke; hrsg. E. L., B1, i, bearb. v. W. D., 1913.

Doleschalius (Paullus), *see* DOLEŽAL (PAWEL).

Doležal (Pawel) [DOLESCHALIUS]. Gramm. Slavico-Bohemica. Praef. est M. Belius. [*Lat. & Bohem.*] s8°. Posonii. 1746

Dolfi (Pompeo Scipione). Cronologia d. famiglie nobili di Bologna, con disc. s4°. Bologna. 1670

Dölger (Franz), *ed.*, *see* CORPUS d. griech. Urkunden d. M.-a. &c., 1924.

Dölger (Franz Joseph). Ἰχθῦς. B2-4. la8°. Münster in W. 1922–27
2, 3, D. heil. Fisch in d. ant Relig. u. im Christentum, Textb. & Tafeln.
4, Die Fisch-Denkmäler in d. frühchristl. Plastik, Malerei &c., Tafeln.

Dolgorukov, *Family of*, *see* DOLGORUKOV (*pr.* P. V.) Сказанія о родѣ кн. Д., 1842.

Dolgorukov (*prince* Ivan Mikhailovich). Изборникъ 1764–1823. s8°. Москва. 1919

Dolgorukov (*prince* Petr Vladimirovich) [DOLGOROUKY (PIERRE)]. Сказанія о родѣ князей Долгоруковыхъ. 8°. С.-П. 1842
Notice sur les principales familles de la Russie. n. éd. s8°. Berlin. 1859

Dolgov (N.) А. Н. Островский: жизнь и творчество, 1823–1923. s8°. Москва. 1923

Dolinin (Ark. Sem.), *ps.* [*i.e.* A. S. ISKOZ], *see* DOSTOEVSKY (F. M.) Ф. М. Д.: статьи &c.; под ред. А. С. Д., 1922.

Dolleris (Andreas). De levendes Land: Digtsamling. s8°. 1899

Döllinger (Joh. Jos. Ignaz v.)
Erklärung a. d. Erzbischof v. München-Freising. [P2691]. 8°. München. 1871
*Erwägungen f. d. Bischöfe d. Conc. ü. päpstl. Unfehlbarkeit. [P2691]. 8°. München. [1869]
The first age of Xty., & the Church. Tr. H. N. Oxenham. 2v. 8°. 1866
Heidenthum u. Judenthum. Vorhalle z. Gesch. d. Christenthums. 8°. Regensburg. 1857
Üb. d. Unfehlbarkeitsadresse u. Die neue Geschäftsordnung d. Concils, 1870, *see* KATHOLISCH. Stimmen, B1, 1870.
see HERGENRÖTHER (*card.* J. A. G.) Kritik d. v. D. Erklärung, 1871.
„ HÖTZL (P. DE A.) Ist D. Häretiker? 1870.
„ REINDL (J. N.) Die Altkatholiken od. D.'s Anhang aus Klerus u. Volk, 1872.
„ STÖCKL (A.) Infallibilität u. d. Zustimmungsadressen an D., 1870.
„ VATICAN COUNCIL. Le Conc. du V. & le mouvem. infaillibiliste en Allemagne, p2, L'excomm. du chan. Dr. v. D., 1874.
„ VIGENER (F.) 3 Gestalten aus d. mod. Katholizismus, D. &c., 1926.

—— **& J. Friedrich** [*ps.* JANUS].
see HERGENRÖTHER (*card.* J. A. G.) Anti-Janus: Kritik d. Schr. "Der Papst u. das Concil" v. Janus, 1870.
„ —— Anti-Janus: crit. of "The Pope & the Council" by J.; tr., 1870.

Dollman (Francis T.)
The Priory of St. Mary Overie, Southwark. atl. fol. 1881

Dolman (Alfred). In the footsteps of Livingstone: diaries &c. by A. D. Ed. J. Irving. 8°. [1924]

Dolman (John), *minister of the Gospel.*
Hymns & spiritual songs &c. s8°. 1758

Dolomieu (Déodat), *see* GRATET DE DOLOMIEU (D. G. S. T. DE).

Dolscius (Paulus), *see* GUEINZ (J. C.) De Aug. Confess. P. D. cura Graece reddita, 1730.

Doltz (Joannes). Elementa pietatis in tres dialogos conjecta. [Studium pietasque puerilis ex D. Eras. ac P. Mosel.—Monitoria paedagogica D. Erasmi]. s8°. Wittembergæ. 1530

Dom (A.), *ps.* [*i.e.* ANNA LUISE DOMEIER].
Das Geiger-Evchen. 8°. Breslau. 1889

Domanig (Carl), *see* LÖHR (A. O. v.) K. D., 1915.

Domarus (Kurt von). Pietro Bracci. la8°. Str. 1915

Domaszewski (Alfred v.) Bellum Marsicum, 1924, *see* KAISERL. AKAD. D. WISS. ZU WIEN. Sitzungsber., B20, 1925.

Domat (Jean). Traité des lois, *see* MIGNE (J. P.), *ed.* Theol. cursus, t12, 1861.

Dombog. Norske Herredags-Dombøger (1578–1623), 1893–1911, *see* THOMLE (E. A.), *ed.*

Domeier (Anna Luise), *see* DOM (A.), *ps.*

Domel (Georg). Die Zünfte in Köln am Ausgang d. M.-a. s4°. Köln. 1923

Domelier (Henri). Behind the scenes at German headquarters. Intr. by M. Barrès. 8°. 1920

Domène. Cartulare mon. beatorum Petri & Pauli de Domina, Cluniac. ord. &c. Nunc primun sub ausp. delphinalis Acad. Gratianopoli constit. cura &c. typis mand. 8°. Lugduni. 1859

Doménech (Raphael).
The House of El Greco. [Hispanic Soc.] s8°. Barcelona. *n.d.*

Domenichi (Lodovico). Rime. s8°. Vinegia. 1544
*Rime div. di molti auttori nuov. racc. Libro primo. [*Dedic. signed* L. D.] s8°. Vinetia. 1545

Domenichino [†ZAMPIERI (D.), *called* D.], *see* SERRA (L.) Il D., 1921.

Domenico, *di Giovanni*, *see* BURCHIELLO, *ps.*

Domenico Sardini (Giovanni Battista), *see* SARDINI (G. B. D.)

Domesday [DOM BOC; DOMESDAY BOOK].
D. B. Facs. of the part rel. to Cheshire [& Lancashire, *w. sep. tp., pagin. contin.*] fol. Southampton. 1861
D. B. Facs. of part rel. to Sussex. fol. Southampton. 1862
D. B. Facs. of the part rel. to Yorks. Photo-zincogr. at O.S. Office. fol. Southampton. 1862
Libri censualis vocati D.-B. Indices. lafol. 1811

Domesday [Dom Boc; Domesday Book] [*continued*].
Lincolnshire D. & the Lindsey survey. Tr. & ed. C. W. Foster & T. Longley, w. intr. by F. M. Stenton & App^s. of extinct villages by C. W. Foster. [Lincoln Rec. Soc., v19]. la8°. 1924
Lit. extension & tr. of portion of D. B. rel. to Cheshire & Lanc. &c., w. intr. & notes by W. Beaumont. To accompany the facs. of orig. [publ., 1861]. fol. Chester. 1863
*Notes on the Oxfordshire D., 1892, *see* Mowat (J. L. G.)
see Fowler (G. H.) Beds. in 1086: analysis &c. of D. Bk., 1922.
,, Leicester (*Sir* P.) Hist. antiq.: transcr. of D.-b. conc. Cheshire, 1673.

Domina, *see* Domène.

Domingos *do Rosario, Frei, see* O'Daly (D.)

Domínguez (Juan P. Criado y), *see* Criado y Domínguez (J. P.)

Dominguez (Luis León), *see* León Dominguez (L.)

Dominic [*Manso*], *St., abbot of Silos, see* Berceo (G. de). Prosas [Vida de S. D. de S. &c.], *n.d.*

Dominicains. *Apol. d. D. missionnaires de la Chine, 1699, *see* Alexandre (N.)

Dominicana. Card. Howard's letters, Eng. Dominican friars, nuns, students, papers & mission reg. [Catholic Record Soc., v25]. 8°. *p.p.* 1925

Dominions (The) & dependencies of the Empire. [By Lord Morris, Sir G. E. Foster *& others*]. Foreword by the Duke of Connaught. [Brit. Emp.: survey; ed. H. Gunn, v1]. 8°. [1924]

Dominique (Pierre). *Works in* Œuvres libres.
Le feu du ciel, 1926. [58.]
Joseph vendu par ses frères, 1925. [49.]
Les poux du lion, 1927. [69.]
La proie de Vénus, 1924. [40.]
Notre-Dame de la sagesse. [Cahiers verts, 37]. s8°. 1924
,, ,, ...[18e éd.] s8°. 1924

Dominis (Marco Antonio de), *bp. of Segni, abp. of Spalato.* De republica eccl. libri x. v1, 2. [v3, Francofurti. 1658, *wanting*]. fol. Londini. 1617–20
v2, cum app. in quibus refell. opus Card. Perronii, de Eucharistia. Add. Responsio ad magnam partem Defensionis Fidei P. F. Suarez. v3, cum G. Cassandri tractatu De officio pii viri circa religionis dissidia &c.
The rockes of Christian shipwracke. Wr. in Ital. & tr. s8°. 1618
see Hall (Jos.) Roma irreconcil., atque M. A. de Dominis Consilium, 1706.

Domitian, *emp. of Rome, see* Henderson (B. W.) 5 Roman emperors, 1927.

Domnius, *Saint, bp. of Salona, d. 303, see* Lenzi (F.) San Domnio, 1913.

Doms (Emile), *see* Verstraeten (Fr.) & E. D. Cours de la langue flamande, p1, 1883.

Domville-Fife (Charles W.)
Among wild tribes of the Amazons. 8°. 1924
Savage life in the black Sudan. 8°. 1927

Donadeo (Alfredo).
Tragedia di un popolo. [P2753]. 8°. Bologna. 1921

Donadoni (Eugenio). Il canto 15 del Paradiso, *see* Dante. Lect. D., 1923.
Gaspara Stampa: vita e opere. s8°. Messina. [1919]
see Dante Alighieri. Lectura D.: c. 8 del Purgatorio letto da E. D., 1919.

Donald (*Sir* Robert). A danger spot in Europe & its gov. by the League of Nations. s8°. [1925]

Donaldson (John). Hist. & statist. acc. of the barony of Upper Fews, Co. of Armagh (1838). s8°. Dundalk. 1923

Donaldson (John William), *D.D.*
A complete Latin gramm. 2nd ed. enl. 8°. C. 1860

Donaldson (John William Edward). Milit. hist. appl. to mod. warfare. 2nd ed., rev. & enl. by A. F. Becke. 8°. 1907

Donaldson (Mary E. Muir). Further wanderings—mainly in Argyll. 8°. [1926]
Wanderings in the W. Highlands & Islands. 8°. Paisley. [1920]

Donatello [†Bardi (Donato), *called Donatello*].
see Crawford & Balcarres (D. A. E. L., *27th/10th earl of*). D., 1911.
,, Villari (P.) D. u. s. Werke; übers., 1887.

Donati (Guido Marco), *see* Dante Alighieri. Lectura D.: c. 20 dell' Inferno letto da G. M. D., 1906.

Donato (Francesco), *1744–1815, see* Rigobon (P.) Di N. & F. Donà, 1910.

Donato (Nicolò), *1705–65, see* Rigobon (P.) Di N. & F. Donà, 1910.

Donatus (Ælius). Ars minor. Tr., w. intr. sk. by W. J. Chase, *w. text.* [Univ. of Wisconsin. St., 11]. 8°. Madison. 1926

Donatus (Joannes Christophorus).
Tract. de virginum jure. [P2745]. s4°. Vitembergæ. 1735

Donatus (Ludovicus), *bp. of Bergamo.* Oratio pro gloriosissimi doctoris ecclesie Augustini solennitate in ejusdem ede &c. s4°. *n.p. n.d.* [Rome, *J. Schoemberger.* c. 1482]

Doncaster. D. Regional Planning Scheme. Rep. p. by P. Abercrombie & T. H. Johnson, w. app. on coal subsidence by J. Humble. 4°. 1922

Doncaster (Leonard), *Sc.D.*
An introd. to the study of cytology. 8°. C. 1920

Dondel du Faouëdic (*Mme.* Noémi). Guide de l'excursionniste pour Redon & environs. s8°. Redon. [1905]

Donders (Frans Cornelis). On the anomalies of accommodation & refraction of the eye, w. prelim. essay. Tr. W. D. Moore. [New Sydenham Soc., v22]. 8°. 1864

Dondey (Théophile) [*ps.* Philothée O'Neddy]. Feu & flamme; publ. avec intr., notes par M. Hervier, suivi de la corr. inéd. de T. D. & d'E. Havet. s8°. 1926

Dondi-Orologio (Galeazzo). Relaz., Bergamo, 30 Sett. 1753; con cenni biog. &c. [Nozze Dondi Dall' Orologio—Paulucci Dalle Roncole. N. 124]. 8°. Venezia. 1871

Doneau (Hugues), *see* Donellus (Hugo).

Donellan (John) [Donnellan (J.)] The genuine case of J. D., as wr. by himself. [*b. w.* Donellan (J.) Trial, &c., 1781]. 8°. [1781]
The trial of J. D. for murder of Sir T. Boughton, Bart. 8°. [1781]
see *Theory of presumptive proof; includ. exam. of evid. on trial of J. D., 1815.

Donellus (Hugo) [Doneau (Hugues)], *see* Stintzing (R. v.) H. D. in Altdorf, 1869.

Doneraile (Edward St. Leger, *6th visc.*), *see* Thompson (N. G.), F. L. Cannan & *Visc.* D. Combined hand-in-hand figure-skating, 1904.

Dongen (Kees van), *see* Des Courières (E.) Van D., 1925.

Doni (Antonio Francesco). I Marmi. A cura di E. Chiòrboli. [Scr. d'It., 106, 107]. 2v. 8°. Bari. 1928

Donisthorpe (Horace St. John K.) Brit. ants: life-hist. & classif. 2nd ed., rev. & enl. 8°. 1927

Donizetti (Giuseppe), *1788–1856, see* Bacolla (A.) La musique en Turquie, G. B. &c.; tr., 1911.

Don Juan (*conde V^do.* de Valencia de), *see* Valencia de Don J.

Donkey. *Tuppy: autobiog. of a d., 1903, *see* Tuppy.

Donnachaidh, *The family of, see* Robertson (D.) Brief acc. of the Clan D., 1894.

Donnadieu (*le docteur* A.) La Pompéi de la Provence. Fréjus. Forum Julii. 8°. 1927

Donnay (Maurice).
Autour du Chat Noir. 6e éd. s8°. 1926
La chasse à l'homme. Comédie. s8°. [1920]
Molière. [8e éd.] s8°. [1921]
La reprise, comédie, *see* Œuvres libres, No. 46, 1925.
Sous le sourire d'Elisabeth. s8°. [1924]
Théâtre. t7, 8. s8°. 1919–27
7, Le mariage de Télémaque—Les éclaireuses—L'impromptu du paquetage—Le théâtre aux armées.
8, La chasse à l'homme—Le roi Candaule—Le geste.
see Nolhac (P. de). Disc. pour la récept. de P. de N. (Rép. de M. D.), 1923.

Donne (John).
Βιαθάνατος. A declar., that selfe-homicide is not so naturally sinne &c. s4°. [1644]
Devotions upon emergent occasions. Ed. J. Sparrow, w. biog. note by G. Keynes. 8°. C. 1923
LXXX sermons. fol. 1640
Love poems. With some acc. of h. life taken f. wr. in 1639 of I. Walton. la8°. Soho. 1923
*Poems, by J. D. With elegies on the authors death. [*3 prelim. ll. & pp. 393–406 wanting*]. s4°. 1633
Poet. works, w. a mem. s8°. Boston [U.S.] 1855
A sermon upon Psalm 38, v. 9 [Facs. reprod. of MS.] 8°. 1921
Sermons: sel. passages, w. essay by L. P. Smith. s8°. O. 1920
see Fausset (H. I'A.) J. D.: st. in discord, 1924.
,, Sampson (J.) A contemp. light upon J. D., 1921.
,, Simpson (E. M.) Study of prose works of J. D. (app. Sermon unpubl.), 1924.

Donne (Thomas Edward).
Game animals of New Zealand. 8°. 1924
The Maori, past & present. 8°. 1927

Donneau de Visé (Jean). L'embarras de Godard: comédie (1667), *see* Fournel (V.) Contemp. de Molière, t3, 1875.
see Corneille (T.) & J. D. de V. La devineresse, 1875.

Donnellan (John), *see* Donellan (J.)

Donoghue (Stephen). "Just my story." 8°. [1923]
Donop (Stanley Brenton v.), *see* VON DONOP (S. B.)
Donovan (Edward). Nat. hist. of Brit. shells. v5. 8°. 1803
Donovan (Herbert D. A.) The Barnburners: internal movt. in polit. hist. of New York State, 1830–52. 8°. N.Y. 1925
Donovan (Patrick) [†P. DONOVANUS], *see* THYRAEUS (G.) Discursus panegyrici S. Patricii &c.; ed. P. D., 1617.
Doolittle (Thomas). A plain method of catechizing: w. catechism. s8°. 1698
Doon, *de Laroche.* Doon de la Roche. Chanson de geste. Publ. par P. Meyer & G. Huet. [S. d. a. t. f.] 8°. 1921
Doon, *de Mayence.* Doon de Maience, chanson de geste; publ. A. Pey, *see* GUESSARD (F.) Anc. poëtes, t2, 1859.
Doppia (La) impiccata, o vero espos. d. necessitá all' august. tribunale d. sapienza contro le raggioni d. doppia. s8°. Orbitello. 1667
Dopsch (Alfons). Wirtschaftl. u. soziale Grundlagen d. europä. Kulturentwicklung aus d. Zeit v. Caesar bis auf Karl d. Gr. T2. 8°. Wien. 1920
Die Wirtschaftsentwicklung d. Karolingerzeit, vorn. in Deutschland. 2e. verm. A. T1. 8°. Weimar. 1921
Dorbec (Prosper).
L'Hôtel Carnavalet & la Marquise de Sévigné. 8°. 1916
Dorchain (Auguste).
L'art des vers. n. éd., revue & augm. s8°. [1919]
see RONSARD (P. DE). Chefs-d'œuvre lyriques; choix & notice de A. D., 1920.
Dordrecht, *see* DORT.
Doré (Henri), *S.J.* Recherches sur les superstitions en Chine, 14t, *see* VARIÉTÉS sinolog., 1911–19.
Dore (John Reid). Old Bibles, or an acc. of the var. vers. of the Eng. Bible. s8°. 1876
Doré (P. Gustave). Cassell's D. gallery: w. memoir of D., crit. essay & descr. letterpress by E. Ollier. 4°. [1887 ?]
Doré (Robert). Essai d'une bibliogr. des congrès internat. [P2707]. la8°. 1923
État des inventaires & répertoires des Archives Nat. &c. de la France. [Extr. de la Revue des Bibl.] 8°. 1919
Doreff (Pantcho). A view on the policy of Gt. Brit. in the Near East & C. Europe. [P2563]. 8°. 1921
Doren (Alfred), *see* SCHWERTFEGER (B.) Zur europ. Politik, B3, 4, bearb. v. A. D., 1919.
Doren (Mark van), *see* VAN DOREN (M.)
Dorgelès (Roland).
Le cabaret de la belle femme. éd. augm. s8°. [1922]
Partir. . . . Roman. s8°. [1926]
Le réveil des morts. Roman. s8°. [1923]
Saint Magloire. Roman. s8°. [1922]
Doria (Angiola). Un Giobertiano di Toscana: V. Salvagnoli, *see* ARCHIVIO STOR. ITAL., a. 80, 1922.
Doria (Luis Gastão d' Escragnolle), *see* ESCRAGNOLLE DORIA (L. G. D').
Döring (Christian). Die Bevölkerungsbewegung im Weltkrieg. [2H. P2383]. 8°. Kopenhagen. 1919
Döring (Hans), *see* EHLERS (E.) H. D., e. hess. Maler d. 16. Jhdts., 1919.
Döring (Heinrich), *see* LEHMANN (W.) Kunstgesch. d. alten Peru; unter Mitarb. v. H. D., 1924.
Döring (Herbert).
Die Geldtheorien seit Knapp. 8°. Greifswald. 1922
Döring (Oskar). Goslar u. Hildesheim. s8°. L. 1926
Das Tagebuch König Ludwigs II. [Roman]. s8°. München. 1921
Dorini (Umberto). Le carte d. fam. Arnolfini acq. dal R. Arch. di Stato di Lucca, *see* ARCHIVIO STORICO ITAL., Anno 82, v2, 1924.
Dörkes-Boppard (Wilhelm Nikolaus). Das Ende d. Dreibundes, nach diplomat. Aktenstücken &c. 8°. 1916
Dorling (*Commander* **H. Taprell),** *D.S.O.* [*ps.* TAFFRAIL].
H.M.S. Anonymous. s8°. 1920
Ribbons & medals of the Great War. [3p *each w. sep. tp. & pagin.* p2, 2nd ed.] s8°. 1920
Dorlodot (Henry de). Darwinism & Catholic thought. Tr. E. Messenger. v1. s8°. 1922
Dormer (Ernest W.) Gray of Reading, a 16th cent. controversialist & ballad-writer [*w.* Ballads]. 4°. Reading. 1923
Dorn (Bernard) [DORN (JOH. ALB. D.)] De Psalterio Æthiopico comm. [*a. c. in* P2603]. s4°. Lipsiae. 1825
Отчетъ объ ученомъ путешествіи по Кавказу и южному берегу Каспійск. моря, *see* IMPERAT. RUSS. ARCH. OBSCH. Труды Восточ. отд., ч8, 1864.
Dornan (S. S.) Pygmies & bushmen of the Kalahari. 8°. 1925
Dornau (C. v.), *ps.* [*i.e. Freifrau* CHARLOTTE V. SCHAUROTH].
Die Vetternreise. Humor. Roman. 5e A. s8°. L. *n.d.*
Dornellas (Affonso de) & A. de Gusmão Navarro. Tombo historico genealogico de Portugal. v1, 2. 4°. Lisboa. 1911–14
Dörnenburg (Emil) & W. Fehse.
Raabe u. Dickens. 8°. Magdeburg. 1921
Dornier (Charles). Les demi-mariées. Roman. s8°. 1924
Dornseiffen (I.), *see* KONINKL. NEDERL. AARDRIJKSK. GENOOTSCHAP. Nomina geogr. Neerlandica, onder red. v. I. D. &c., 1885–1901.
Dorogobujinov (—). Костромской крестьянинъ Иванъ Сусанинъ, какъ онъ положилъ жизнь за царя. изд. 3e [P2433]. 8°. Москва. 1882
Dorotheus, *Saint, bp. of Tyre, ps.* The lives of the Prophetes, Apostles & 70 Disciples &c., *see* EUSEBIUS, *Pamphili.* Anc. eccl. hist.; tr. M. Hanmer &c., 1607.
Dorp (*Jonkheer* **Arend van).** Brieven & onuitg. stukken. Uitg. door J. B. J. N. Ridder de van der Schueren. [Hist. Genoots. Werken, N.S., 44, 50]. 2d. 8°. Utrecht. 1887–88
Dorpat University. Acta & commentationes Univ. D. B, Humaniora, [v]5, 7. 8°. Tartu. 1924–26
Dörpfeld (Wilhelm) & E. Reisch. Das griech. Theater. Beitr. z. Gesch. d. Dionysos-Theaters in Athen &c. 4°. Athen. 1896
Dorpius (Heinrich). Warhafftige hist., wie d. Evangelium zu Münster angefangen, u. darnach durch d. Widderteufer verstöret, widder auffgehört hat. s4°. [Wittenberg ?] 1536
Dorrien (*Gen. Sir* **H. L. Smith-),** *see* SMITH-DORRIEN (*Gen. Sir* H. L.)
Dorrington (Theophilus). A familiar guide to receiving the Lord's Supper &c. [P2467]. s8°. 1735
D'Ors (Eugenio), *see* ORS (E. D').
Dorsch (Anton Joseph). De auctoritate S.S. Eccl. Patrum. [P2645]. s4°. Moguntiæ. [1781]
Dorscheus (Joannes Georgius) [DORSCHAEUS], *1597–1659.* Diss. de Satanae obsessione &c. ed. 4a. [P434]. s4°. Rostohii. 1714
Syllogismum de Anti-Christo subm. T. Szirmay. [P2628]. s4°. Gryphiswaldiæ. [1707]
Thomas Aquinas exhibitus confessor veritatis evang. August. Conf. repetitæ, juxta seriem controv. [in] tomis 4 R. Bellarmini exam. s4°. Francofurti. 1656
Dorsenne (Jean). Vie sentimentale de Paul Gauguin. 8°. [1927]
Dorset. Calendar of wills &c. rel. to D.; ed. G. S. Fry, 1922, *see* BRIT. RECORD SOC.: Index Lib.
Memorials of old D., 1907, *see* PERKINS (T.) & H. PENTIN, *edd.*
Dorset County Museum. Guide to the D. C. M. Comp. by J. E. Acland. 13th ed. [P2711]. s8°. [Dorchester]. 1911
Dorset Natural History & Antiquarian Field Club. Proceedings. Ed. J. M. J. Fletcher. v40–43 (May 1918–May 1922). 8°. Dorchester. 1920–23
Dorset, *Earls of, see* SACKVILLE-WEST (V.) Knole & the Sackvilles, 1922.
Dorsey (George Amos). The Pawnee: Mythology (p1). [C.I. of Wash.] la8°. Wash. 1906
Why we behave like human beings. [repr.] 8°. N.Y. [1926]
Dort [DORDRECHT].
Acta & scripta synodalia D. ministr. remonstrantium in foederato Belgio. 2p [in 1v; *3 pagin.*] s4°. Herderwiici. 1620
Acta synodi nat. autoritate D. D. ordinum gen. foederati Belgii provinc. D. habitae a. 1618 & 19. [3 *pagins.*] s4°. Dordrechti. 1620
Judicium Synodi nat. reformatarum eccl. Belg. habitae D. a. 1618 & 1619 [*w. engraved tp.* Synodus. [*Foll. by* Sententia de doct. C. Vorstii—Edictum, ne ullos sep. conventus agant &c.—Decretum adv. nonnullos citatos, *each w. sep. tp.*, Hagae-Com. 1619]. s4°. Dordrechti. 1619
The judgement of the Synode holden at D. conc. the 5 articles: As also their sentence t. C. Vorstius. [Tr.] s4°. 1619
De oudste stadsrekeningen van D., 1284–1424. Uitg. d. C. M. Dozy. [Hist. Genoots. Werken, s3, 2]. 8°. 'sGravenhage. 1891
Rekeningen van de gilden van D., 1438–1600. [Hist. Genoots. Werken., s3, 6]. 8°. 'sGravenhage. 1894
Sententia de divina praedestin. &c. quam Synod. D. verbo Dei consentaneam &c. judicat &c. s4°. *n.p. n.d.* [c. 1619]
Dortsman (Adriaan). Documenten betreff. de ontdekkingstochten v. A. D. beoosten & bezuiden Banda, 1645–46, *see* BIJDRAGEN tot de taal &c. v. Ned. Ind., volg. 6, d2, 1896.
Dósa (György) [DOZSA], *see* ÁLDOR (I.) D. G. &c., 1899.
Dosne (*Mme.* **Sophie Eurydice).** Mémoires de Mme. D., l'Egérie de M. Thiers. Publ. avec intr. &c. par H. Malo. 2t. 8°. [1928]

Dosofteiu, *mitropolitul Moldovei.*
see ACADEMIA ROMANA. Anal., s2, t36, Secţ. lit. (Molitvenicul lui D., de D. Puşchilă), 1915.
,, CIOBANU (S.) Orig. & moart. D., 1920.

Dos Passos (John). Three soldiers. s8°. [1922]

Dos Remedios (Mendes).
Hist. da lit. portuguêsa. 5a ed. 8°. Lumen. 1921

Dos Santos (José), *see* AZEVEDO (*Conde* DE). Cat. da livraria que pert. aos Condes de A. e de Samodães ; red. por J. dos S., 2p, 1921.

Dossin (Georges). Autres textes sumér. & accad., *see* Délégation en Perse, t18, 1927.

Dostoevsky (Aimée). Vie de Dostoïewsky par sa fille. Préf. d'A. Suarès. 8°. 1926

Dostoevsky (Anna Grigorevna). Воспоминания. Под ред. Л. П. Гроссмана. la8°. Москва. 1925
Дневник А. Г. Д. 1867г. 8°. Москва. 1923
Dostoevsky portrayed by h. wife. Diary &c. of Mme. D. Tr. & ed. S. S. Koteliansky. 8°. 1926
see AIKHENVALD (Y. I.) Двѣ жены, Толстая и Д., 1925.
,, DOSTOEVSKY (F. M.) Письма Д. К. женe, 1926.

Dostoevsky (Feodor M.)
Полное собраніе сочиненій [*t1 has* Очеркъ жизни &c., составл. К. К. Случевскимъ]. изд 4ce. 12t [*wanting* t4]. 8°. С.-П. 1891–92
Братья Карамазовы. 2t. s8°. Berlin. 1919
Документы по ист. литературы и обществ. в1, Ф. М. Достоевский, Исповедь Ставрогина — План жития великого грешника. [*a. c. in* P2689]. 8°. Москва. 1922
Из архива Достоевского. Письма русс. писателей. Ред. Н. К. Пиксанова. s8°. Москва. 1923
Исповѣдь Ставрогина. Три ненапечатанныя главы изъ романа Бѣсы. 8°. München. [1922]
Письма Д. к Женe, [1866–80]. Предисл. &c. Н. Ф. Бельчикова. Ред. В. Ф. Переверзева. la8°. Москва. 1926
Униженные и оскорбленные.—Вѣчный мужъ. s8°. Берлинъ. 1921
Ф. М. Достоевскій: статьи и материалы [*By var. authors*]. Под ред. А. С. Долинина. 8°. П. 1922
Четыре статьи 1847 г. С предисловием В. С. Нечаевой. s8°. П. [1922]
TRANSLATIONS.
The brothers Karamazov. Tr. C. Garnett. [Everyman's Lib.] 2v. s8°. [1927]
,, ,, [*dramatic version tr. J. Covan*], *see* SAYLER (O. M.) Moscow Art Theatre ser. of Russ. plays, s2, 1924.
Une fâcheuse histoire, nouvelle, *see* ŒUVRES libres, 45, 1925.
Les frères Karamazov. Tr. &c. par E. Halpérine-Kaminsky & C. Morice. [17e éd.] s8°. [1919]
The friend of the family & a. story [Nyctochka Nyezvanov]. [Tr.] C. Garnett. s8°. [1920]
Les inédits. Tr. & annotés par J. W. Bienstock. s8°. 1923
Le "journal" de Raskolnikov, *see* ŒUVRES libres, 51, 1925.
TRANSLATIONS [*continued*].
Letters f. the underworld. Tr. C. J. Hogarth. s8°. [1913]
Letters to h. family & friends. Tr. E. C. Mayne. 2nd ed. 8°. [1917]
Stavrogin's confession, & the plan of Life of a great sinner. Intr. & notes. Tr. S. S. Koteliansky & V. Woolf. s8°. 1922
see ANTONY, *metropolitan.* Словарь къ твореніямъ Д., 1921.
,, BLOK (A.), A. F. KONI ETC. Пушкин, *by A. B. &c.* Достоевский, *by A. G. Gornfeld & A. M. Remizov*, 1921.
,, COPEAU (J.) & J. CROUE. Les frères Karamazov : drame, d'ap. D., 1921.
,, DOSTOEVSKY (A.) Vie de D. par sa fille, 1926.
,, DOSTOEVSKY (A. G.) Дневник, 1923.
,, —— D. portrayed by h. wife : diary of Mme. D. ; tr. & ed. S. S. Koteliansky, 1926.
,, GIDE (A.) D. : articles & causeries, 1923.
,, GROSSMAN (L. P.) Путь Д., 1924.
,, —— Семинарий по Д., материалы, библиогр. &c., 1922.
,, LAVRIN (J.) D. & h. creation : psycho-crit. st., 1920.
,, MEIER-GRAEFE (J.) D., the man & h. work ; tr., 1928.
,, MEREJKOVSKY (D. S.) Л. Толстой и Д., 2т, 1903.
,, NIKOLSKY (YU.) Тургеневъ и Д., 1921.
,, NÖTZEL (C.) Leben D.'s, 1925.
,, PEREVERZEV (V.) Творчество Д., 1922.
,, PERSKY (S.) La vie & œuvre de D., 1924.
,, ROZANOV (V. V.) Легенда о великом инквизиторе Ф. М. Д., 1924.
,, SHESTOV (L.) Révélations de la mort : D. &c., 1923.
,, THURNEYSEN (E.) D., 1921.

Dotrenge (Barthélemy Joseph), *diplom. agent to the prince-bishop of Liège.* Corr., 1781–94. Publ. par E. Hubert. [Comm. Roy. d'Hist. de Belg.] 4°. Brux. 1926

Dottin (Georges). Les littératures celtiques. s8°. 1924

Dottin (Paul). Daniel De Foe & s. romans. 3t. 8°. 1924

Dottrina christiana tr. in lingua civile giorgiano, 2a ed., 1797, *see* TLUKAANTI (D.)

Doubassoff, *see* DUBASOV.

Doubleday (H. Arthur). Dr. Round's 'Barons' & 'Peers.' A reply. [P2421]. s8°. [1919]

Doublet (Edouard). Gustave Lambert : s. projet de voyage au Pôle—sa mort. [P2733]. 8°. Bourg. 1922
Hist. de l'astronomie. s8°. 1922

Doucet (Roger). Etude s. le gouvt. de François I dans s. rapps. avec le Parlement de Paris. pl, 1515–25. la8°. 1921

Doudan (Ximénès). Des révolutions du goût. Intr. par H. Moncel. s8°. [1924]

Doudeauville (Ambroise de La Rochefoucauld, *1er duc* de), *1765–1841, see* DOUDEAUVILLE (A. DE LA R., *5e duc* DE). Une polit. franç. au 19e s., 1927.

Doudeauville (Armand F. J. M. de La Rochefoucauld, *5e duc* de), *1870–.* Une politique franç. au 19e s. [Ducs de Doudeauville &c.] 8°. 1927

Dougal (Samuel Herbert). Trial of D. Ed. F. T. Jesse. 8°. 1928

Dougall (*Miss* Lily) & C. W. Emmet. The Lord of thought : study of prob. wh. confronted Jesus Christ &c. 8°. 1922

Doughtie (John), *see* DOUGHTY (J.)

Doughty (Charles Montagu). Mansoul, or The riddle of the world. [*Poem*]. [n. & rev. ed.] 8°. 1923
Travels in Arabia Deserta. Intr. by T. E. Lawrence. [2nd ed]. 2v. 8°. 1921
,, ,, ...[n. ed.] 2v. 8°. [1923]
,, ,, ...[n. ed. repr.] 2v. 8°. [1924]
Wanderings in Arabia. Abridgment [*by* E. Garnett] of "Travels in Arabia Deserta." [repr.] 8°. [1926]

Doughty (John), *D.D.* [DOUGHTIE]. *Velitationes polemicæ : polem. sh. discussions &c. By I. D. Phil-Alethius. s8°. 1652

Doughty (Oswald). Eng. lyric in the age of reason. 8°. 1922
—— *see* ROSSETTI (D. G.) Letters to h. publ. ; ed. &c. O.D., 1928.

Doughty Deeds, *ps., see* GRAHAM (ROBT.) *of Gartmore.*

Douglas, *The House of.*
see ADAMS (P. W. L.) Hist. of the D. family of Morton & Fingland &c., 1921.
,, AIRD (G.) *Geneal. of fam. of D. of Mulderg &c., 1895.
,, FRASER (*Sir* W.) The D. book, 4v, 1885.

Douglas (A. Elizabeth). Shadowed blood. s8°. 1925

Douglas (*Maj.* Archibald John Angus) & P. H. Johnson. The South Seas of to-day. Cruise of yacht St. George to S. Pacific. 8°. [1926]

Douglas (Charles Noël). Forty thousand quotations, prose & verse, classified accord. to subject. 8°. 1921

Douglas (*Maj.* Clifford Hugh).
Credit-power & democracy, w. draft scheme for mining industry. With a comm. by A. R. Orage. s8°. 1920
,, ,, ...2nd ed. s8°. 1921
Economic democracy. [2nd ed.] s8°. [1921]
Social credit. 8°. 1924

Douglas (David C.) Soc. structure of medieval E. Anglia, *see* VINOGRADOFF (*Sir* P.) Oxf. st. in soc. &c. hist., v9, 1927.

Douglas (Gawin), *bp. of Dunkeld.* A descr. of winter [modernized] f. G. D. by F. Fawkes. [*w. original*]. s4°. 1754
see MAITLAND (*Sir* R.) Maitland folio MS. cont. poems by Sir R. M., D. &c., v2, 1927.
,, WATT (L. M.) D.'s Æneid, 1920.

Douglas (*Sir* Howard). Naval evolutions ; review &c. of Mr. Clerk's claims in relat. to the manœuvre of 12 April, 1782. 8°. 1832
Obs. on mod. systems of fortification, incl. that prop. by M. Carnot. 8°. 1859
On the defence of Eng. [*b. w.* Malins (W.) Plan, 1848]. 8°. 1860
Postscript on iron defences [*a. c. b. w.* Malins (W.) Plan, 1848]. 2nd ed. w. add. 8°. 1861
Treatise on naval gunnery [*&* Postscript, *sep. tp. & pagin.*] 5th ed. rev. 8°. 1860

Douglas (John), *bp. of* (1) *Carlisle,* (2) *Salisbury.* Select works ; w. biograph. mem. by W. Macdonald. 4°. Salisbury. 1820

Douglas (John), *F.S.A. (Scot.), see* HEPBURN (D.) & J. D. Chron. of the Caledonian Soc. of London, 2p, 1923.

Douglas (John Albert). The relations of the Anglican churches w. the Eastern-Orthodox, esp. in reg. to Anglican Orders. 8°. 1921

Douglas (Katharine Waldo), *see* FEDDEN (*Mrs.* R.)

Douglas (Langton). Fra Angelico. [2nd ed.] la8°. 1902

Douglas (Norman).
Alone. 8°. 1921
London street games. s8°. [1916]
Old Calabria. [n. ed.] 8°. [1920]
South wind. 6th impr. s8°. [1921]
They went. s8°. 1920
Together. 8°. 1923

Douglas (O.), *ps.* [*i.e. Miss* Anna Buchan].
Penny plain. [11th ed.] s8°. [1922]
Pink sugar. s8°. [1924]
The proper place. s8°. [1926]

Douglas (Paul Howard). Amer. apprenticeship & indust. educ. [Columbia Univ.] 8°. N.Y. 1921
Wages & the family. 8°. Chicago. [1925]

Douglas (Robert), *minister at Edinburgh.* Diary, when w. the Scotish army in England, 1644, *see* Maidment (J.), *ed.* Hist. fragm., p1, 1833.
Mem. to be communicat to Mr. R. Johnson [? by R. D.], *see* Maidment (J.), *ed.* Hist. fragm., p2, 1833.

Douglas (*Sir* Robert Kennaway).
Confucianism & Taouism. s8°. 1889

Douglas (William S.)
Cromwell's Scotch campaigns, 1650–51. cheap ed. 8°. 1899

Douglas-Pennant (*Miss* Violet), *see* Ockham (D.) Eng. Dreyfus case, 1922.

Douglass (Robert), *of Strathbogie, see* Charles Edward [Stuart], *prince.* Some acc. of the Young Pretender &c.; [advert. signed R. D.], 1746.

Douhault (Adélaïde Marie de Champignelles, *marquise de*), *see* Lenotre (G.) La femme sans nom, 1922; tr., 1923.

Douin (Georges).
L'attaque du Canal de Suez (3 fév. 1915). la8°. 1922
La campagne de Bruix en Méditerranée, mars-août 1799. la8°. 1923

Doujat (Jean). Praenotionum canonicarum libri 5. Ed. 6a accurat. s4°. Venetiis. 1762

Doulton (*Sir* Henry), *see* Blacker (J. F.) ABC of Eng. salt-glaze stoneware, f. Dwight to D., 1922.

Douma (J.), *see* Hague (The). Bibliog. list of publ. conc. Perm. Court of Internat. Justice; prep. by J. D., 1926.

Doumergue (Emile). J. Calvin. t5–7. 4°. Lausanne. 1917–27
5, La pensée ecclés. & la pensée politique de Calvin.
6, La lutte. 7, Le triomphe.
Moïse & la Genèse d'ap. les trav. de E. Naville. 8°. 1920
see Steed (H. W.) *&c.* Les démocraties mod.: par W. S., C. Bouglé, H. Bois, E. D. &c., 1921.

Doumic (René).
see Flers (R. de). Disc. de récep.; réponse de R. D., 1921.
„ Hachette & Cie. Centenaire; texte de R. D., 1926.

Dourean (Elishe). [Hist. of Armenian lit. *In Armenian.* P2809]. s8°. K. polis. 1885

Doutrepont (Georges). Notice sur le ms. franç.: la croisade projetée par Philippe le Bon c. les Turcs, *see* Bibliothèque Nat. Notices, t41.

Doutrina. *Ordem (A) da salvacaõ ou a doutrina Christaã, 1712, *see* Ordem.

Doutté (Edmond). Merrâkech. [Comité du Maroc]. la8°. 1905

Douvillé (Robert). Sur q. gisements nummulit. de Madagascar. [*Extr. f.* Annales de paléont., t1. P2875]. 4°. [1906]

Douvres. Chartes de la tour de Douvres, 1250–1624. Doc. p. s. à l'hist. du Bas-Bugey &c. Par F. Marchand. 8°. Bourg. 1891

Doves Press, *see* Clark (W. A.), *jr.* Library of W. A. C.: Kelmscott & D. Presses, 1921.

Dovnar-Zapolsky (Mitrofan Viktorovich).
Идеалы декабристовъ. 8°. Москва. 1907

Dow (Alex.), *see* Ferishta. Hist. of Hindostan; tr. D., 3v, 1768–72.

Dow (Christopher). Innov. unjustly charged upon the pres. Church & State. Ans. to passages of a pamphlet by H. Burton, An apologie of an appeale &c. s4°. 1637

Dow (George Francis) & J. H. Edmonds. Pirates of the New Eng. coast, 1630–1730. Intr. by E. H. Pentecost. [Marine Res. Soc. Publ. No. 2]. la8°. Salem, Mass. 1923

Dow (Lorenzo), *1777–1834.*
A coll. of spiritual songs, used at the camp-meetings in the U.S. Sel. by L. D. [P2674]. s8°. D. 1808
Extr. f. orig. letters to Methodist bps., f. their preachers &c. in N. Amer. since 1800; w. sketch of camp meetings. [P2674]. s8°. Liv'l. 1806
Reflections on the love of God &c. [*Imperfect, tp. & all before page 6 wanting.* P2674]. s8°. [D. 1806 ?]
Travels & provid. experience &c. of L. D. [v2, p1. *Tp. wanting*]. s8°. [D. c. 1806]
see Jennings (S. K.) Defence of the camp meetings; added, Thoughts on the signs of the times &c., by L. D., 1806.

Dowd (Jerome). The negro in Amer. life. 8°. [1927]

Dowdall (*Hon.* Mary F. H. Borthwick), *wife of H. C. Dowdall.*
Susie. s8°. [1919]
The tactless man. s8°. [1922]
Three loving ladies. s8°. [1921]

Dowden (Edward). Milton in the 18th c., 1701–50, 1908, *see* Brit. Acad. Proc., 1907–08.
Shakspere. [Lit. primers]. s8°. 1877
——, **R. Garnett & W. M. Rossetti.** Letters about Shelley interchanged by 3 friends—E. D., R. G. & W. M. R. Ed., w. intr. by R. S. Garnett. 8°. 1917

Dowley (Peter), *see* Wells (E.) Controv. treatises [*incl.* Copy of letter by D.], 1716.

Dowling (Donaldson Bogart). Geolog. notes to accompany map of Sheep River gas & oil field, Alberta. [Canada. Geol. Survey. P2512]. 8°. Ottawa. 1914
——, **S. E. Slipper & F. H. MacLearn.** Investig. in the gas & oil fields of Alberta, Saskatchewan & Manitoba. [Canada. Geol. Survey. P2512]. 8°. Ottawa. 1919

Downame (George), *bp. of Derry.* A treatise of justification. fol. 1639

Downes (George), *A.M.* Glossary to the first six Psalms & Chaldee gram., *see* Frey (J. S. C. F.) Heb. gram., 1823.

Downey (Alan). The glamour of Waterford. s8°. D. 1921

Downey (Thomas). Naval poems. Pleasures of naval life & The Battle of Trafalgar. 4°. 1813

Downing Street. *The mirrors of Downing Street. Some polit. reflections. By a gentleman with a duster. 2nd ed. s8°. [1920]
„ „ ....Pop. ed., w. 2 new chs. s8°. [1922]

Downing (Clement). A hist. of the Indian wars. Ed. w. intr. & notes by W. Foster. 8°. O. 1924

Downing (*Sir* George), *3rd bart., see* Beresford (J.) Godfather of D. street, 1925.

Downshire (Arthur W. P. W. B. Trumbull Sandys Hill, *7th m. of*). Report on MSS. of the M. of D., *see* Historical MSS. Comm. Downshire. v1, i, ii, 1924.

Dowson (Ernest Christopher).
Poems & prose. Memoir by A. Symons. s8°. N.Y. [1919]
see Stonehill (C. A.) &c. Bibliogs. of mod. as., s2, 1925.

Dowty (Aglen A.) & S. O. Beeton. *The coming K—— [*i.e.* Edward VII. *Extr. f.* Beeton's Xmas Annual, 13th season]. 8°. *n.d.*
*Jon Duan. By a. of "The coming K—— &c." [*b. w. th.* The coming K——.] 8°. 1874
*The Siliad or the siege of the seats. By a. of "The coming K——." [*Extr. f.* Beeton's Xmas Annual, 14th season. *b. w. th.* The coming K——, *n.d.*] 8°. *n.d.*

Doyle (*Sir* Arthur Conan).
Adventures of Gerard. n. ed. s8°. 1918
The Brit. campaign in France & Flanders, 1914[–18]. v6. 8°. [1920]
Case-book of Sherlock Holmes. s8°. [1927]
The exploits of Brigadier Gerard. [repr.] s8°. 1922
The great shadow. 5th ed. s8°. [1924]
Hist. of spiritualism. 2v. 8°. [1926]
The land of mist. s8°. [1926]
Memories & adventures. 8°. [1924]
The new revelation. 11th ed. s8°. [1925]
Pheneas speaks. s8°. [1927]
Poems. Collected ed. 8°. 1922
Return of Sherlock Holmes. n. impr. s8°. 1918
La rivale, nouvelle, *see* Œuvres libres, t14, 1922.
Sir Nigel. new impr. 8°. 1918
Tales of adventure & medical life. [repr.] s8°. [1925]
Tales of twilight & the unseen. [repr.] s8°. [1924]
The vital message. [repr.] s8°. [1925]
The White Company. 18th ed. s8°. 1897
„ „ [uniform ed., repr.] s8°. [1926]
see Murchison (C.), *ed.* Case for & agst. psychical belief, by Sir A. C. D. &c., 1927.

Doyle (James), *R.C. bp. of Kildare & Leighlin, see* Phillpotts (H.), *bp. of Exeter.* A suppl. letter to C. B. on evidence by Dr. Doyle &c., 1826.

Doyle (John). *A key to the polit. sketches of H. B. [*i.e.* J. D.] No. 501–600. [P2600]. s8°. 1839

Doyle (Kinsley Dryden). Agriculture & irrig. in continental & tropical climates. 8°. 1921

Doyle (Richard). The foreign tour of Messrs. Brown, Jones & Robinson. 4°. 1855

D'Oyly (*Sir* John), *1774–1824.* A sketch of the constit. of the Kandyan Kingdom. [*MS.*] fol. [1818]

Doyon (René Louis), *see* Eberhardt (I.) Mes journaliers; préc. de La vie tragique de la bonne nomade, par D., 1923.

Dozsa, *see* Dósa.

Drabik (Mikuláš) [DRABICIUS (NICOLAUS)].
see GRÜNENBERG (O. F.) De N. D. neopropheta in Hungaria, 1721.
,, KOTTER (C.) Lux in tenebris &c.: subm. de statu eccl. in terris per C. Cotterum, C. Poniatoviam, N. D., 1616–56, 1657.

Drachmann (Anders Björn).
Atheism in pagan antiquity. [Tr.] 8°. 1922
Sagunt u. d. Ebro-Grenze in d. Verhandlungen zw. Rom u. Karthago, 220–18, *see* KONGELIGT DAN. VID. SELSK., Hist.-fil. Med., B3, 1920–21.

Drachmann (Holger).
Poul og Virginie under nord. Bredde. s8°. 1879

Draconites (Johann). Comm. in Danielem ex Ebræo versum cum oratione & indices [*3 pagin.*] s8°. Marpurgi. [1544]
Ioel propheta cum tr. fontis Ebraici &c. & explic. [*b. w. h.* Micheas, 1565]. fol. Vitebergæ. 1565
Micheas propheta cum tr. fontis Ebraici &c. & explic. &c. fol. Vitebergæ. 1565
Zacharias propheta cum tr. fontis Ebraici &c. & explic. [*b. w. h.* Micheas, 1565]. fol. Vitebergæ. 1565
see BIBLE, PSALMS. Psalmi in Lat. conversi per J. D., 1536.

Dracup (John). Hymns. s8°. Bolton. 1787

Draganu (Nicolae). Doua manuscripte vechi Cod. Todorescu & Cod. Martian. Studiu & transcr. [Ed. Acad. Române]. la8°. București. 1914

Drage (Geoffrey). Lithuania: economics, *see* BUCHAN (J.), *ed.* Nations, Baltic &c. States, 1923.
National economy & public assistance. [*Repr. f.* Nineteenth Cent. P2497]. 8°. [1921]

Dragomanov (Mikhailo Petrovich).
see ANTONOVICH (VL.) & M. D. Истор. пѣсни малорусск. народа, t1, 2i, 1874.
,, BAKUNIN (M. A.) М. А. Б.: біограф. очеркъ М. Д. &c., 1906.

***Dragon** (The) of Wantley: burlesque opera, *see* CAREY (H.)

Dragonzino (Giovanni Battista). Marfisa bizarra. Di nuovo ristamp. &c. s8°. Padova. *n.d.*

Drahn (Ernst). Brest-Litowsk; Reden, Aufrufe u. Manifeste d. russ. Volkskommissare Trotzki, Lenin, Joffé, Radek &c. Gesammelt &c. v. E. D. [P2502; P2526]. 8°. 1920
Führer durch d. Schrifttum d. deut. Sozialismus. 2. verm u. verb. A. s8°. [1919]
Lenin, e. Bio-Bibliographie. [P2755]. 8°. 1924
—— **& S. Leonhard.** Unterird. Lit. im Revol. Deut. währ. d. Weltkrieges. 8°. 1920

Drake (Barbara). Women in trade unions. 8°. [1920]

Drake (Durant). Essays in critical realism. By D. D., A. O. Loveday, J. B. Pratt, A. K. Rogers, G. Santayana, R. W. Sellars, C. A. Strong. 8°. 1920
Mind & its place in nature. 8°. N.Y. 1925

Drake (F. Morris). A 100 years w. the Devon & Exeter Instit. [P2751]. obl.8°. Exeter. 1913

Drake (*Sir* Francis).
The world encompassed & analogous contemp. docs. &c. With an apprec. by Sir R. C. Temple. la8°. *Argonaut Press.* 1926
see BENSON (E. F.) Sir F. D., 1927.
,, CASTELLANOS (J. DE). Discurso de el capitan F. D., 1921.
,, HARTE (W. J.) Sir F. D., 1920.
,, JOHNSON (S.) Life of R. Savage; added lives of Sir F. D. &c., 1769.
see LA RONCIÈRE (C. B. DE). Atlas inconnu de la dern. expéd. de D., 1909.
,, RAY (J. A.) D. dans la poésie espagn. (1570–1732), 1906.
,, ROBERTS (H.) A farewell to Sir F. D.; transcr. &c. by E. M. Blackie, 1924.
,, SAUVAGE (J.) Mém. du voiage en Russie en 1586; l'expéd. de Fr. D. en Amér., 1855.
,, WAGNER (H. R.) Sir F. D.'s voyage around the world, 1926.

Drake (Samuel Adams). Old landmarks & hist. fields of Middlesex. [Mass.] 8°. Boston. 1876

Drake (Samuel Gardner). Indian captivities: narr. of captives carried away by Indians. 8°. Auburn. 1853
The old Indian chronicle; a collect. of rare tracts, publ. in the time of King Philip's war &c. Intr. & notes by D. 8°. Boston. 1867
Present state of New-Eng., 1675, *&* Contin. [by E. Rawson], 1676—New & further narr., by N. S., 1676—True acc. of the most considerable occurrences, 1676—Warr in New-Eng. ended [by R. Hutchinson], 1677—News f. N.-E., 1676—Farther brief narr. of the late wars, 1676.

Drake (*Sir* William Richard). Notes of fam. of Mervyn of Pertwood. 4°. *p.p.* 1873

Drakenborch (Arnold). Oratio funebris in obitum H. S. van Alphen. [*Foll. by poems in Lat. & Dutch by var. a.* P2594]. s4°. Trajecti a. R. 1743

***Drama** (Das) v. Mayerling, 1921, *see* MAYERLING.

Dramatic magazine (The). March-Nov. 1829. 8°. [1829]

Drane (Augusta Theodosia). Christian schools & scholars, to the Co. of Trent. n. ed., ed. W. Gumbley. 8°. 1924

Dransfeld (Justus von). Exercitatio [& Exercit. altera] de episcopis. 2p *in* 1v. (2, De juribus episc.) s4°. Helmestadi. 1700

Draper (*Mrs.* Eliza), *see* WRIGHT (A.) & W. L. SCLATER. Sterne's Eliza: acc. of h. life in India, w. letters, 1757–74, 1922.

Draper (John William). Hist. of intell. development of Europe. rev. ed. 2v. s8°. *Bohn.* 1902

Draper (Warwick H.) Chiswick. la8°. 1923

Draper (William Henry), *Master of the Temple, see* FREMANTLE (*Hon. & Rev.* W. H.) Recoll.; ed. by the Master of the Temple, 1921.

Draper's Company, *London, see* JOHNSON (A. H.) Hist. of the Co. of Drapers of London, v3–5, 1922.

Draud (Georg) [DRAUDIUS (G.)] Bibl. librorum Germanic. classica: Verz. Bücher bis 1625 in Teutscher Spraach, in Truck aussgangen &c. s4°. Franckfurt a. M. 1625

Drawings of buildings in area descr. in "The early hist. of Piccadilly &c., by C. L. Kingsford," 1926, *see* LONDON TOPOG. SOC.

Drayson (*Major-Gen.* Alfred Wilks).
The art of practical billiards. s8°. 1901
The art of practical whist. 5th ed. s8°. 1892
Experiences of a Woolwich professor dur. 15 years at the R.M.A. 8°. 1886
From keeper to captain. s8°. 1889
The gentleman cadet: h. career &c. at Roy. Milit. Acad., Woolwich. A tale. s8°. 1875
Intellectual whist. s8°. 1899
Pract. milit. surveying & sketching &c. 4th ed. s8°. 1872
Sporting scenes amongst the Kaffirs of S. Africa. 2nd ed. s8°. 1860
30,000 years of the earth's past history. s8°. 1888
see POLE (W.), A. W. D. &c. Hdbk. of games, enl. ed., v1, 1890.

Drayton (Michael).
The Battaile of Agincourt; The miseries of Queene Margarite; The Moone-Calfe *&* o. p. la8°. 1627
Minor poems. Chosen & ed. by C. Brett. 8°. O. 1907
Nimphidia, the Court of Fayrie. s8°. Stratf. upon Av. 1921
Poems. Newly corr. & augm. [*Engrd. tp.; Idea added, pagin. cont. Imperf.*] s8°. [1630]
Poly-olbion. [*With "Illustrations," or notes by J. Selden. Portrait of Prince Henry wanting*]. sm. fol. [1612]

Drechsler (Johann Alexander). Diss. de studiorum apostatis. Resp. G. E. Lechla. [P2671]. s4°. Lipsiae. [1717]

Drechsler (Wolfgang). Hist. Arabum, *see* ARABIA, 1635.

Drecker (Joseph). Die Theorie d. Sonnenuhren. [Gesch. d. Zeitmessung &c.; hrsg. E. v. Bassermann-Jordan, B1, Lief. E.] 4°. 1925

Dreiser (Theodore). An American tragedy. 2v [*in* 1]. 8°. [1926]
Sister Carrie. [n. ed.] 8°. [1927]
A traveller at forty. 8°. 1914

Drelincourt (Charles), *the elder.* Avertissement sur les disputes & le procedé des missionnaires. [*b. w. h.* Dialogues, 1660]. s8°. 1654
Dialogues familiers sur les princ. objections des miss. 3ème éd. revue & augm. s8°. Genève. 1660
Neuf dialogues contre les miss. sur le service des Eglises Reformées. [*b. w. h.* Dialogues, 1660]. s8°. Genève. 1655

Drerup (Engelbert). Demosthenes im Urteile d. Alt. [St. z. Gesch. u. Kultur d. Alt., B12, H1, 2]. 8°. Würzburg. 1923
Homer. Poetik. Hrsg. E. D. B1, 3. la8°. Würzburg. 1921
1, Drerup (E.) Das Homerproblem.
3, Stürmer (F.) Die Rhapsodien d. Odyssee.

Drescher (Joannes Theophilus Fridericus).
De vet. Xtianorum agapis. [P2651]. s8°. Giessae. 1824

Dresden. Katalog d. Hss. d. Sächs. Landesbibl. (vormals Kgl. Öff. Bibl.) zu Dresden; bearb. L. Schmidt. B4 (Abthlgn. e-n u. App.) 8°. L. 1923
see GRÜNES GEWÖLBE, *Dresden.*

Dresig (Sigismund Friedrich). Comm. de verbis mediis N.T. Ed. cura J. F. Fischeri. Add. L. Kusteri lib. & J. Clerici diss. s8°. Lipsiae. 1755
De meritis Gustavi Adolphi in eccl. Luther., oratio, 1732. [P442]. s4°. Lipsiae. [1732]

Dresler (Gallus). Musicae practicae elementa in usum Scholae Magdeburg. ed. s8°. Magdeburgi. 1575

Dress. Dress worn at H.M.'s court, 1912, *see* TRENDELL (H. A. P.), *ed.*

Dressel (Albert Rudolf Maximilian). Vier Documente a. röm. Archiven. Beitr. z. Gesch. d. Protestantismus. 2e A. 8°. 1872

Dresser (Henry Eccles). A monograph of the Meropidæ, or family of the bee-eaters. fol. 1884–86

Dresser (Horatio Willis).
A book of secrets. Art of self-control. s8°. N.Y. 1906
A hist. of the New Thought movement. s8°. [1920]
Human efficiency. Psycholog. study of mod. problems. s8°. N.Y. 1912
In search of a soul. 2nd ed. 8°. Boston [Mass.] 1898
Man & the divine order. Essays &c. s8°. N.Y. 1903
A message to the well. Art of health. s8°. N.Y. 1910
Methods & problems of spiritual healing. s8°. N.Y. 1899
The perfect whole. 3rd ed. 8°. N.Y. 1899
The philos. of the Spirit. W. essay on the logic of Hegel. 8°. N.Y. 1908
The spirit of the New Thought. Essays & addresses. Ed. H. W. D. s8°. [1917]
Voices of freedom & studies in the philos. of individuality. 3rd impr. s8°. N.Y. 1906

Dresser (John Alexander). Prelim. rep. on the Serpentine & assoc. rocks of S. Quebec. [Canada. Geolog. Survey. P2512]. 8°. Ottawa. 1913

Dresser (Matthaeus). De festis diebus Christ. & Ethnic. liber. s8°. Lipsiae. 1590
De statu eccl., &c. in Æthiopia, sub precioso Joanne, oratio. s8°. Lipsiae. 1584
„ „ ....[a. ed.] s8°. *n.p.*, *n.d.* [1584 ?]

Dreux (*r. p.* **Robert de),** *see* ROBERT DE DREUX.

Drever (James).
Intr. to the psychology of educ. 8°. 1922
The psychology of everyday life. s8°. [1921]
The psychology of industry. s8°. [1921]

Dreves (Guido Maria). Ein Jahrtausend latein. Hymnendichtung. Aus d. Analecta hymnica. Revid. v. C. Blume. 2T. 8°. L. 1909

Dreves (Lebrecht Blücher), *1816–70*, *see* ROSENBACHER (M.) D., 1919.

Drew (D. L.) The allegory of the Æneid. s8°. O. 1927
Culex: sources & problem of authorship. s8°. O. 1925

Drew (Elizabeth A.)
The mod. novel: aspects of contemp. fiction. 8°. [1926]

Drew (*Lt.* **H. T. B.),** *see* NEW ZEALAND. War effort; ed. H. T. B. D., 1923.

Drew (Joan H.) Embroidery & design; w. foreword by M. M. Allan. 8°. [1915]

Drew (*Mrs.* **Mary),** *formerly Gladstone.*
Acton, Gladstone & others. 8°. [1924]
Catherine Gladstone. 8°. [1919]
„ „ ....[repr.] 8°. [1919]

Drew (Samuel).
Life of Thomas Coke, incl. his travels &c. 8°. 1817
Remarks on first p. of "The Age of Reason." 2nd ed. rev. s8°. 1820

Drew (W. S.) Notes on technique of song-interpret. 8°. O. 1926

Drewitt (Frederic George Dawtrey).
Lat. names of common plants. s8°. 1927
The romance of the Apothecaries' Garden at Chelsea. s8°. 1922

Drews (Arthur). Das Ich als Grundproblem d. Metaphysik. 8°. Freiburg i. B. 1897

Drews (Paul). Petrus Canisius, d. erste deut. Jesuit. [Verein f. Ref.-gesch. Schr., Jhrg. 10, Nr. 38]. 8°. Halle. 1892

Drexel (Hieremias) [†DREXELIUS].
Daniel &c. s8°. Antverpiæ. 1651
David regius Psaltes descr. &c. s8°. Antverpiæ. 1652
Iobus divinæ providentiæ theatrum. s8°. Antverpiæ. 1653
Noe architectus arcæ, descr. & morali illust. s8°. Antverpiæ. 1652

Drey (Franz). Carlo Crivelli u. s. Schule. la8°. München. 1927

Dreyer (Aloys). Nürnberg u. d. Nürnberger in d. Karikatur u. Satire i. Zeit. 8°. München. 1920

Dreyer (Johann Carl Heinrich). De usu genuino juris Anglo-Saxonici in explic. jure Cimbrico & Saxonico. [*b. w.* Arpe (P. F.) Themis Cimbrica, 1737]. s4°. Kilonii. 1747

Dreyfus (Carle). Les objets d'art du 18 siècle. Epoque de Louis XV [*& Louis XVI*]. [Doc. d'art. Musée du Louvre]. [2v.] 8°. [1923]

Dreyfus (Robert). Marcel Proust à 17 ans, avec des lettres inéd. s8°. [1926]
Souvs. sur M. Proust, avec lettres inéd. de M. P. [Cahiers verts, 68]. s8°. 1926

Driault (Edouard). La grande idée. Renaissance de l'Hellénisme. Préf. de M. Politis. s8°. 1920
Mohamed Aly & Napoléon, 1807–14. Corr. des consuls de France en Egypte. [Drovetti, St.-Marcel &c.] Rec. & publ. par E. D. [Soc. Roy. de Géog. d'Egypte]. 8°. 1925
Napoléon & l'Europe. Le Grand Empire, 1809–12. 8°. 1924
—— **& M. Lhéritier.** Hist. diplomat. de la Grèce de 1821 à nos jours. t1–5. la8°. 1925–26
1, L'insurrection & l'Indépendance, 1821–30; par E. D.
2, Le règne d'Othon—La grande idée, 1830–62; par E. D.
3, Le règne de Georges I, 1862–78; par M. L.
4, Suite du règne de Georges I, 1878–1908—Hellénisme & Germanisme; par M. L.
5, La Grèce & la Gr. Guerre—De la révol. turque au Traité de Lausanne, 1908–23; par E. D.

Driberg (J. H.) The Lango, a Nilotic tribe of Uganda. Foreword by Sir R. T. Coryndon. la8°. [1923]

Driesch (Hans).
Das Ganze u. die Summe: Rede. s8°. L. 1921
Leib u. Seele. 3e A. 8°. L. 1923
Wirklichkeitslehre. 2e durchges. &c. A. 8°. L. 1922
Wissen u. Denken: Proleg. zu aller Philos. 2e A., mit Ergänz. 8°. L. 1922

Drieu La Rochelle (Pierre).
Mesure de la France. [Cahiers verts, 15]. s8°. 1922

Driffield (Vero Charles), *see* HURTER (F.) & V. C. D. Photographic researches: repr. of publ. papers; ed. W. B. Ferguson, 1920.

Drinkwater (John).
Abraham Lincoln. A play. [13th impr.] s8°. 1921
„ „ *see* PLAYS of to-day, v1, 1925
Авраам Линкольн. С введенiем П. Г. Виноградова. Перевод Л. Смолл. s8°. Лондон. 1921
Bird in hand. Play. s8°. 1927
Coll. plays. 2v. 8°. 1925
Coll. poems, 1908[–22]. 2v. 8°. 1923
Cotswold characters. s8°. New Haven, *Yale*. 1921
Cromwell: character st. s8°. [1927]
From an unknown isle. 8°. 1924
The lyric: an essay. s8°. [1922]
Mary Stuart. Play. s8°. 1921
„ „ [2nd impr.] s8°. 1921
„ „ ....rev. ed. s8°. 1922
Mr. Charles, k. of England. 8°. 1926
Oliver Cromwell. Play. s8°. 1921
„ „ ..4th impr. s8°. 1923
Outline of literature. Ed. J. D. la8°. [1923]
Patriotism in lit. [Home Univ. Lib.] s8°. [1924]
The pilgrim of eternity: Byron—a conflict. 8°. [1925]
The poet & communication. Conway Mem. Lect., 1923. s8°. 1923
Preludes, 1921–22. [*Poems*]. 8°. 1922
R. Burns: addr., Ninety Burns Club of Edinb., 25th Jan. 1924. [P2731]. 8°. E. 1924
Robert Burns. Play. s8°. 1925
Robert E. Lee. Play. s8°. 1923
Seeds of time. s8°. [1921]
Sel. poems. s8°. 1922
William Cory, *see* ROY. SOC. OF LIT. Essays, N.S. v4, 1924.
William Morris. 8°. 1912

Drinkwater (*Col.* **John),** *aft. Bethune.*
Hist. of the siege of Gibraltar, 1779–83. s8°. 1844

Drioton (Etienne). Fouilles de Médamond: les inscr., 2p, *see* INST. FR. D'ARCH. OR. DU CAIRE, Fouilles, t3ii, 4ii, 1926–27.
Un second prophète d'Onouris: statuette du Louvre, *see* ACAD. D. INSCR.: FOND. PIOT, Mon., t25, 1921–22.

Drival (E. van), *see* ARRAS. Cartul. de l'abbaye de St.-Vaast d'A.; réd. au 12e s. par Guimann; publ. &c. Van D., 1875.

Driver (Samuel Rolles).
see BIBLE. COMPL. TEXTS &C. Internat. Crit. Comm.: Job; by S. R. D. &c., 1921.
„ NEUBAUER (A.) 53 chap. of Isaiah, v2, Tr. by S. R. D. &c., 1877.

Droin (Alfred).
M. Paul Valéry & la tradition poét. franç. s8°. [1924]

Dröling (Ursisinus), *see* BADBERGER (M.) & U. D. Tract. theol. de jure, &c., 1720.

Drolsum (A. C.) Sovereign Norway & h. state rights. Repr. f. the Farmand. s8°. [1905]

Dron (Robert Wilson).
Coal-fields of Scotland. rev. & enl. ed. 8°. Glasgow. 1921

Drossbach (Maximilian). Wiedergeburt. [*b. w.* Du Prel (C. *Frhr.*) Planetenbewohner, 1880]. 8°. Olmütz. 1849

Drouet (Joseph), *see* SAINT-PIERRE (*l'abbé* DE). Annales polit. (1658–1740), n. éd. avec intr. &c. par J. D., 1912.

Drouin (René Hyacinthe). De bonitate & licitate matrimonii —De solemnit. ad contractum matr. requistis—De ritibus matr. conf., *see* MIGNE (J. P.) Theol. cursus, t25, 1860.
De sacramentis in genere, *see* MIGNE (J. P.) Theol. cursus, t20, 1860.
Drouot (Paul). Eurydice 2 fois perdue. Préf. de H. de Régnier. Publ. par la Soc. Litt. de France. 8°. 1921
Drouville (Gaspard).
Voy. en Perse, 1812 & 1813. 2e éd. 2t. 8°. 1825
Drovetti (Bernardin), *see* DRIAULT (E.), *ed.* Mohamed Aly & Napoléon, 1807–14: corr. des consuls de France en Egypte [D. &c.], 1925.
Droysen (Johann Gustav). Aktenstücke u. Aufzeichn. z. Gesch. d. Frankfurter Nat.-versammlung aus d. Nachlass v. J. G. D. Hrsg. R. Hübner. [Bayer. Akad. d. Wiss.] 8°. St. 1924
Droz (E.) & G. Thibault.
Poètes & musiciens du 15e siècle. 4°. 1924
Drübel (Eckhart zum), *see* ECKHART ZUM DRÜBEL.
Druce (Christopher). Eccl. entertainers. s8°. [1924]
Druce (George Claridge).
Flora of Buckinghamshire. 8°. Arbroath. 1926
Drucker (J. C. J.) Some corr. conc. a British passport confiscated by H. B. M.'s Minister. [P2425]. 8°. *f.p.c.* [1918]
Druery (Charles T.) Book of Brit. ferns. 8°. [1903]
Drujinin (Nikolai Petrovich). На сходахъ волости особаго устройства. [*Extr. f.* Русская Мысль, 99г. P2813]. 8°. [Moscow. 1899]
Drumann (Wilhelm). Gesch. Roms in s. Übergange v. d. republikan. z. monarch. Verfassung. 2te A. hrsg. v. P. Groebe. B5. 8°. L. 1919
Drümel (Johann Heinrich). *Demonstr. ducatum & judicium provinc. Franconiae pert. ad episc. Wurzburg. s4°. Erfordiæ. 1758
Drummond, *The family of, see* MALCOLM (D.) Genealog. mem. of Hse. of D., 1808.
Drummond (George), *Lord Provost of Edinburgh.* Provost D.'s acc. of discussion in Commons upon applic. of D. Campbell for compensation &c., 1726, *see* ABBOTSFORD CLUB. Misc., v1, 1837.
Drummond (Henry), *F.R.S.E.*
*The changed life. An address. 2nd ed. s8°. 1891
Drummond (Henry), *M.P.* *Elem. proposit. illust. of the princs. of currency. [*b. w.* Thompson (T. P.) Catechism, 1830]. 8°. 1819
Drummond (James L.)
Letters on the study of nature &c. s8°. 1831
Drummond (John), *of Balhaldy.* *Mem. of Sir Ewen Cameron of Locheill, w. intr. acc. of hist. &c. of family &c. [Ed. J. Macknight. Abbotsford Club]. 4°. E. 1842
Drummond (Margaret). The dawn of mind: intr. to child psychology. 2nd impr. s8°. 1919
Five years old or thereabouts: psychology of little children. 3rd impr. s8°. 1925
see MELLONE (S. H.) & M. D. Elements of psychology, 1907.
Drummond (Robert). Illustr. of the gram. parts of the Guzerattee, Mahratta & Engl. lang. fol. Bombay. 1808
Drummond (William), *of Hawthornden.* Ben Jonson's conversations w. W. D. of H. Ed., w. intr. & notes by R. F. Patterson. 8°. 1923
Poems. s8°. 1790
Poet. works. Ed. W. B. Turnbull. s8°. 1890
Drummond (William Hamilton).
The life of M. Servetus. s8°. 1848
Drunkards. *The blemish of govt. &c.: or, a charge agst. d. &c., 1655, *see* BLEMISH.
***Drunken** Barnaby's four journeys &c., n. ed., 1805, *see* BRATHWAIT (R.)
Drury (Charles), *see* SHEFFIELD. Parish Reg.; transcr. & ed. by C. D. &c., p3, 5, 1921–27.
Drury (Francis Edson), *see* JAGGARD (W. R.) & F. E. D. Archit. building construction, v2, p1, 2, 1922–23.
Drury (Francis Keese Wynkoop). Technical & sci. serials in the lib. of Providence, 1920. Ed. F. K. W. D. [P2525]. 8°. Providence, R.I. [1921]
Drury (G. Thorn-), *see* THORN-DRURY (G.)
Drury (Heber).
Hand-book of the Indian flora. 3v. 8°. Madras. 1864–69
Drury (Horace Bookwalter). Sci. management, a hist. &c. [Columbia Univ.] 8°. N.Y. 1915
Drury (William). The significance of transport in the production of wealth. [P2495]. s8°. 1921
Drury (William Price). All the king's men. s8°. 1919
Drusius (Joannes), *the elder* [DRUYS].
Ad loca difficiliora Pentateuchi comm. s4°. Franekeræ Frisiorum. 1617
Ad voces Heb. Novi Test. comm. [*b. w.* Gallia. *Vet. aliq. G. theol. scr., 1586]. 8°. Antverpiae. 1582
Animadv. libri duo in quibus praeter dict. Ebraicam plurima loca Script. explicantur &c. 2p *in* 1v. s8°. Lugduni Batav. 1585
Annot. in Coheleth. [*With Lat. vers.*] s4°. Amstelrodami. 1635
Comm. in Prophetas minores 12. s4°. Amstelredami. 1627
De quæsitis per epistolam. [*b. w. h.* Animadvers., 1585]. s8°. *Aere Autoris.* 1595
Liber Hasmonaeorum, vulgo prior Machabæorum, Græce ex ed. Rom. & Lat. ex interpret. J. D. cum notis. Acc. Disput. A. Gentilis [*wanting*]. s4°. Franekeræ. 1600
Quaest. Ebraic. libri tres. [*b. w. h.* Animadvers., 1585]. Ed. 2a. auct. s8°. *n.p.* 1599
Tetragrammaton. Item Pauli Burg. episc. de nomine t. & I. Drusii scholia. s4°. Amstelodami. 1634
see CURIANDER (A.) Vitae operumque J. Drusii &c., 1616.
Druskowitz (Helene). Wie ist Verantwortung u. Zurechnung ohne Annahme d. Willensfreiheit möglich? [P2476]. 8°. Heidelberg. 1887
Dryburgh. Liber S. Marie de D. Reg. cartarum abbacie premonstrat. [Bannatyne Club]. 4°. E. 1847
Dryden (John).
Alexander's feast, 1697 [facs. repr.] fol. [O. 1925]
All for love, *see* INCHBALD (*Mrs.* E.) Brit. theatre, v6, 1808.
Fables f. Boccaccio & Chaucer. Coll. by T. Park. 2v [v1 *wanting*]. s8°. 1806
MacFlecknoe: a poem. With Spencer's ghost, by J. Oldham. [P2868]. s8°. 1709
Poet. works. Coll. by T. Park. 3v. s8°. 1806
Poetry & prose. With essays by Congreve, Johnson, Scott &c. Intr. & notes by D. N. Smith. s8°. O. 1925
Religio Laici, or A laymans faith. Poem. 8°. 1682
see BAUMGARTNER (M. D.) D.'s rel. to Germany in 18th c., 1914.
„ DOBELL (P. J.) J. D., bibliog. memoranda, 1922.
„ ELIOT (T. S.) Homage to J. D.; 3 essays, 1924.
„ NICOLL (A.) D. as an adapter of Shakespeare, 1922.
„ —— D. & h. poetry, 1923.
„ SAINT-EVREMOND (C. M. DE S.-D., *seigneur* DE). Misc. essays; contin. by D., v1, 1692.
„ VAN DOREN (M.) The poetry of J. D., 1920.
Drysdale (A. H.)
Early Bible songs w. intr. on Heb. song. s8°. 1890
Dschakhdschakhean (Manouel Vardapet). Hochiosi. [Sidonius, *poem, in Armenian*]. 8°. i Venetik. 1830
Dschouansher [TSCHOUANSHER]. [Short hist. of the Iberians. *In Armenian.* P2812]. 8°. Venetik. 1884
Duarenus (Franciscus). De sacris eccl. ministeriis &c. libri 8. Item pro libertate Eccl. Gallicæ adv. Rom. aulam def. Acc. Concordata nationis German., cum notis Jo. Schilteri. [*b. w.* Schilter (J.) Instit. juris canon., 1699]. s8°. *n.p.* [Jena ?] 1699
Dubail (*le gén.* **Augustin Yvon Edmond).** Quatre années de commandement, 1914–18. Journal de campagne. t1–3. la8°. 1920–21
Duban (Claude). Lettre s. le nouv. établ. de la mission dans la Krimée, 1713, [*signed* Duban], *see* BERNARD (J. F.), *ed.* Recueil de voy., t10, 1738.
Dubasov (Irina Fedorovna) [DOUBASSOFF].
Ten months in Bolshevik prisons. 8°. E. 1926
Dubech (Lucien).
Les chefs de file de la jeune génération. s8°. [1925]
Cyclone Niger, *see* ŒUVRES libres, 56, 1926.
Du Bellay (Joachim). Divers jeux rustiques. Ed. crit., publ. H. Chamard. [Soc. des Textes Fr. Mod.] s8°. 1923
Œuvres poét. [Soc. d. Textes Franç. Mod.] t5. s8°. 1923
5, Recueils lyriques [t] 3; éd. crit. publ. H. Chamard.
Duberry (E.), *see* GENEST (E.) & E. D. La maison de Molière, 1922.
Dubislav (Walter), *see* CLAUBERG (K. W.) & W. D. Systemat. Wbch. d. Philos., 1923.
Dublan (Manuel), *see* MEXICO. Informe sobre el empréstito contrat. en Europa &c., 1888.
Du Bled (Victor).
L'envers & l'endroit. Roman. s8°. 1923
La société franç. dep. cent. ans. [2s.] s8°. 1923–24
1, Quelques salons du 2e Empire.
2, Mme. Auberon & s. amis.

Dublin. Calendar of anc. records of D. Ed. Lady Gilbert. v14–18. la8°. D. 1909–22
14–18, [Assembly Rolls, 1787–1831]
D. Civic Survey. Report. Prep. by H. T. O'Rourke & the D. C. S. Comm. [Civics Inst. of I., v2]. 4°. Liv'l. 1925
Six views in D. obl.s8°. [1812 ?]
Standing (The) rules & orders of the commons & of the common co. of D. &c. Pref. list of aldermen &c. s8°. D. 1838
Volume of farces performed at the Theatre Royal, Smoke-Alley, Dublin. Cont.: The spoiled child—The farmer—Animal magnetism—The village lawyer—Modern antiques—Chit chat—Cheats of Scapin—Peeping Tom. [*Each play has sep. tp. & pagin.*] s8°. [D.] 1792
Dublin Castle.
D. C. & the estimates, N°. 1, Indust. schools. 8°. [1901]
*Hist. reminiscences of D. C., 849–1895. s8°. D. 1895
Dublin Parish Register Society [*aft. incorp. w.* IRISH MEMORIALS ASSOC.], *see* ASSOC. FOR THE PRESERVATION OF THE MEMORIALS OF THE DEAD IN IRELAND.
Dublin review (The).
v166–182. (Jan. 1920–April 1928). 8°. 1920–28
Dublin University. Calendar, 1920–21—1927–28 [2v *each year*]. s8°. D. 1920–27
TRINITY COLLEGE.
Alumni Dublin.: reg. of students, graduates, &c. & provosts of T. C. Ed. G. D. Burtchaell & T. U. Sadleir. illust. ed. la8°. 1924
Cat. of Irish MSS. in the library of T. C. D. Comp. by T. K. Abbott & E. J. Gwynn. 8°. D. 1921
Dublin verses by members of Trinity Coll. Ed. H. A. Hinkson. 8°. D. 1895
War list, Feb., 1922. s8°. D. [1922]
see KOTTABOS; ed. R. Y. T. (1869–95), 1873–95.
Dubnow (Semen Markovich). Hist. of the Jews in Russia & Poland. Tr. I. Friedlaender. 3v. s8°. Phila. 1916–20
Duboc (Julius).
Das Ich u. d. Uebrigen. (Für u. wider M. Stirner). 8°. L. 1897
Jenseits vom Wirklichen. [*b. w. h.* Das Ich, 1897]. 8°. Dresden. 1896
Das Leben ohne Gott. [P2461]. s8°. Hannover. 1875
Der Optimismus als Weltanschauung u. s. relig. ethische Bedeutung. 8°. Bonn. 1881
Plaudereien u. Mehr. [*b. w. h.* Der Optimismus, 1881]. 8°. Hamburg. 1884
Dubois (*le général* **A.**) Deux ans de commandement sur le Front de France, 1914–16. 2t. la8°. 1921
Dubois (Henri). Et. sur les princ. travaux exégét. de l'école d'Antioche en partic. sur ceux de T. de Mopsueste. [P2506]. 8°. Genève. 1858
Du Bois (Henri Pène). Four private libraries of New-York. Pref. by O. Uzanne. 1st ser. 8°. N.Y. 1892
Dubois (Jean), *see* BIBLIOTHÈQUE & MUSÉE DE LA GUERRE. Cat. méthod. du fonds allem. de la Bibl.; rédigé par J. D. &c., t1–3, 1921–22.
Du Bois (Nicolas). *Responsio ad Cleri Gallicani de potestate eccl. declarationem ex summ. pontif. doc. &c. excerpta. [*b. w.* Opstraet (J.) Theologus Christ., 1697]. s8°. Coloniæ Agripp. 1683
Dubois (Paul), *prof. à l'Univ. de Berne.* The psychic treatment of nervous disorders. Tr. & ed. by S. E. Jelliffe & W. A. White. 6th ed. rev. 8°. 1909
Self-control. Author. tr. by H. H. Boyd. s8°. 1909
Dubois (Urbain) & E. Bernard. La cuisine classique: ét. prat. &c. de l'école franç. 12e éd. 2t. 4°. 1886
Du Bois (William Edward Burghardt).
The Negro. [Home Univ. Lib.] s8°. N.Y. [1915]
Du Bois-Melly (Charles). Relations de Sardaigne & de Genève, 1754–1773, *see* REGIA DEP. DI STORIA PATRIA. Misc., t28, 1890.
Dubosc (François), *archiviste de la Manche, see* MONT-MOREL. Cartul. de Mt.-M.; publ. par D., 1878.
Duboscq (André). La Chine en face des Puissances. s8°. 1926
Du Boulay (E.) Bembridge. 8°. Ryde. 1911
Text-book on marine motors. 2nd ed. la8°. 1907
Du Boulay (N.) *Vies des papes Alexandre VI & Léon X. Par Monsieur D. B. s8°. Londres. 1751
Du Boulay (*Capt.* **Noel Wilmot Houssemayne).**
An epitome of the Chino-Japanese war, 1894–95. s8°. 1896
Dubourg (Augustus W.), *see* TAYLOR (T.) New men & old acres, 1869.

Dubravius (Janus), *bp. of Olmütz* [DUBRAWSKY (JAN)]. Hist. Bohemica, a T. Jordano, genealog. catalogis ornata &c. Adj. Aeneae Sylvii, de Bohem. orig. &c. [*sep. tp. & pagin.* Ed. J. Crato]. s8°. Francofurti. 1687
Dubreton (J. Lucas-), *see* LUCAS-DUBRETON (J.)
Du Breuil (Alphonse). The sci. & profitable culture of fruit trees. [Tr.], rev. with intr. by G. Glenny. 7th ed. s8°. 1914
Du Breuil (Guillaume). *Stilus supremæ Curiæ Parlamenti Paris. Cum novis annot. C. Molinæi, adds. S. Auffrerii &c. 4°. Parisiis. [*Apud Galeotum a Prato*]. 1551
Dubreuil (Jean). *La perspective pract. Par un Parisien &c. [*i.e.* J. D.] la8°. 1642
*Practical perspective. Tr. by E. Chambers. 7th ed., prefixed, The theory of perspective, by J. Hodgson. 4°. *n.d.*
Dubreuil (Léon). François Rever, 1753–1828. Préf. d'A. Le Braz. [La Bretagne & les pays celt., 19]. 8°. 1924
Dubreuil (Louis Audouin-), *see* AUDOUIN-DUBREUIL (L.)
Dubreuil-Chambardel (Louis). La Touraine préhist. Préf. de C. Jullian. la8°. 1923
Dubroeucq (Jacques), *of Mons; c. 1500–84, see* HEDICKE (R.) J. D. v. Mons, e. niederl. Meister aus d. Frühzeit, 1904.
Dubrovin (Nikolai Fedorovich). Походъ графа В. А. Зубова въ Персію въ 1796 г. [*Extr. fr.* Военный Сборникъ, 1874]. 8°. [1874]
Dubs (Homer H.) Hsüntze. s8°. 1927
Dubuisson (A.) Richard P. Bonington: h. life & work. Tr. w. annot. by C. E. Hughes. 4°. [1924]
Duc (Joseph Auguste), *bp. of Aosta.* A quelle date est mort St. Bernard de Menthon ?, *see* REGIA DEP. DI STORIA PATRIA. Misc., t31, 1894.
Doc. sur l'hist. eccl. du m. âge; publ. J. A. D., *see* REGIA DEP. DI STORIA PATRIA. Misc., t24, 1885.
Du Cambont de Pont Château (Sébastien Joseph). *La morale pratique des Jésuites, 8t (t. 1, 2 *by* Du C. de P. C.; t. 3–8 *by* A. Arnauld), 1649 &c., *see* JESUITS.
Du Cange (C. du F., *seigneur*). Illyricum, sive hist. Dalmatiae, Croatiae, Slavoniae, Bosniae &c. fol. Posonii. 1746
Ducange (Victor Henri Joseph Brahain, *dit*). [†BRAHAIN DUCANGE; *ps.* VICTOR]. L'artiste & le soldat. 5t. s8°. 1828
Ludovica, ou Le testament de Waterloo. 6t. s8°. 1830
Ducarel (Andrew Coltee), *see* LAMBETH. [Testamenta Lambethana, list of wills &c. in the reg. of L., extr. by Dr. D.: *MS. copy of p1*], *n.d.*
Ducati (Pericle).
L'arte classica. la8°. Torino. 1920
Etruria antica. 2v. 8°. Torino. [1925]
Framm. di rilievo in argento del Museo Civico di Bologna, *see* REALE ACCAD. D. LINCEI. Mon. ant., v21, 1912.
Le pietre funerarie felsinee, *see* R.A. D. LINCEI. Mon. ant., v20, 1910.
La Sedia Corsini, *see* R.A. D. LINCEI. Mon. ant., v24, 1916.
Storia dell' arte Etrusca. 2v. la8°. 1927
Duccio, *di Boninsegna, b.c. 1260.*
see MARLE (R. v.) Rech. sur l'iconogr. de Giotto & de D., 1920.
„ WEIGELT (C. H.) D. di B.: St. z. Gesch. d. frühsienes. Tafelmalerei, 1911.
Duccio (Agostino d'Antonio di), *b. 1418, see* POINTNER (A.) Werke d. Bildhauers A. di Duccio, 1909.
Du Cerceau (Jean Antoine), *Jesuit.* *Lettre à M. de L. C. P. D. B. sur le livre Hist. Flagellantium [*by J. Boileau*]. [P2559]. s8°. *n.p.*, *n.d.* [c. 1703]
Duchartre (Pierre Louis). La comédie ital. 4°. [1924]
—— **& R. Saulnier.** L'imagerie populaire. 4°. [1925]
Duchatel (Edmond) & R. Warcollier. Les miracles de la volonté. 8°. [1914]
Duchemin (Paul-Victor). Mdlle. de Sombreuil, l'héroine au verre de sang (1767–1823). 8°. 1925
Duchemin Descepeaux (J.) Lettres sur l'orig. de la Chouannerie &c. du Bas-Maine. 2t. 8°. 1825–27
Duchêne (Albert). G. Malès & la reconstit. financ. de la France après 1789. Préf. de L. Madelin. 8°. [1923]
Duchêne (Ferdinand). Au pas lent des caravanes. [Les Barbaresques]. Roman. s8°. [1922]
Du Chesne (André) [A. QUERCETANUS]. Hist. genealog. de la maison de Montmorency & de Laval. [2p]. fol. 1624
p2 has title Preuves de l'hist. de la maison de M. &c.
see MARRIER (M.) & A. DU C. Bibl. Cluniac. (1614), 1915.
Duchesne (E.), *see* STOGLAV (LE) ou les 100 chapitres; rec. des décisions de l'Assemblée eccl. de Moscou, 1551; tr., avec intr. & comm. par E. D., 1920.

Duchesne (Jean) [Duchesne, *aîné*]. Museum of painting & sculpture: princ. paintings &c. in the gall. of Europe, drawn &c. by Réveil, w. descr. notices by D. [*Eng. & Fr.*] v1–6. s8°. 1828–30

Duchesne (*l'abbé* Louis).
Early hist. of the Xtn. church. Tr. C. Jenkins. v3, The 5th cent. 8°. 1924
L'église au 6e siècle. 8°. 1925
Hist. anc. de l'Eglise. 5e éd. t3. 8°. 1911
see Brémond (H.) Disc. de récept. à l'Acad. franç. [*on D.*], 1924.
„ Lyautey (*gén.* H.) Disc. de récep.; réponse de mgr. D., 1921.

Duchet (Th.), *see* Térouane. Cartul. de l'église de T.; publ. T. D. &c., 1881.

Duckitt (Mabel) & H. Wragg, *edd.*
Sel. Eng. letters (15–19c.) [repr.] s8°. [1916]

Duckworth (Henry Thomas Forbes).
The Church of the Holy Sepulchre. 8°. [1922]

Du Clercq (Jacques), *Sieur de Beauvoir en Ternois.* Mémoires, 1448–67, *see* Buchon (J. A. C.) Choix de chron., 1875.

Du Cleuziou (Alain Raison), *see* Raison du Cleuziou (A.)

Duclos (Charles Pinot). Mém. secrets sur le r. de Louis XIV, la Régence & le r. de Louis XV. s8°. 1891

Ducor (Henri). Aventures d'un marin de la Garde Imp., prisonnier de guerre dans l'Ile de Cabréra. Préf. de E. Cère. s8°. [1895]

Ducray-Duminil (François Guillaume).
Le petit carillonneur. 4t. s8°. 1809

Ducreux (Claire). Le cimetière d'Hotchista, *see* Œuvres libres, 68, 1927.

Ducros (Louis). French society in the 18th cent. Tr. W. de Geijer. Foreword by J. A. Higgs-Walker. 8°. 1926
Jean-Jacques Rousseau. [v2, 3]. 8°. 1917–18
2, De Montmorency au Val de Travers, 1757–65.
3, De l'île de Saint-Pierre à Ermenonville, 1765–78.

Dudan (Alessandro).
La Dalmazia nell' arte ital. 2v. 8°. Milano. 1921–22

Dudding (Reginald Charles). Hist. of the manor & parish of Saleby w. Thoresthorpe in Co. of Lincoln. 8°. [Horncastle]. 1922

Du Deffand (*la marq.* Marie), *1697–1780* [Vichy-Chamrond (M. de)]. Lettres à Voltaire. Intr. & notes de J. Trabucco. s8°. 1922
see Maurois (A.) Quatre études angl., Mme. du D. & H. Walpole, &c., 1927.

Dudeney (*Mrs.* Henry E.)
A baker's dozen. s8°. 1922
Manhood end. s8°. [1920]
Quince Alley. s8°. [1925]
Seed pods. s8°. [1927]
Spade work. s8°. [1919]

Dudeney (Henry Ernest).
Amusements in mathematics. 8°. [1917]

Dudgeon (Gerald Cecil). The agricult. & forest products of Brit. W. Africa. Pref. by W. R. Dunstan. [Imp. Inst. Hdbks.] 2nd ed. 8°. 1922

Dudley (*Rev. Sir* Henry Bate), *bart.* **& M.** *Lady* **Dudley.** *Passages selected &c. on trial of Vortigern & Rowena "whether it be &c. f. pen of Shakspeare." [*Satire*]. v1–3. [*b. in* 1. v1, 6th ed.; 2, 5th ed.; 3, 2nd ed.] s8°. [1796 ?–98]

Dudley (Howard). *Hist. & antiq. of Horsham. By a. of Juvenile researches. s8°. 1836

Dudok (Gerard).
Sir T. More & h. Utopia. la8°. Amsterdam. [1923]

Duero (Manuel Gutierrez de la Concha, *Marq.* **del)** [†Gutierrez de la Concha], *see* Vega Inclan (M. de la), J. de Castro y Lopez &c. Rel. hist. de la últ. campaña de Marq. del D., 1874.

Du Faouëdic (*Mme.* Noemi Dondel), *see* Dondel du Faouëdic (*Mme.* N.)

Du Faur (Gui), *Seigneur de Pibrac, see* Cabos (A.) G. Du F. de P., 1922.

Dufay (Guillaume), *see* Van Den Borren (C.) G. D., évol. de la musique au 15 s., 1925.

Duff (The), *missionary ship.* Particulars of the 2nd voyage, by the miss. ship The Duff; capt. by the Buonaparte privateer, 1800. By W. H. [William Hargrove ?] s8°. Knaresbrough. 1809

Duff, *The family of, see* Baird (W.) Genealog. mem. of D., 1869.

Duff (Alexander), *D.D., 1806–78, see* Duff (W. Pirie). Mem. of A. D., 1890.

Duff (Archibald). Hist. of Old Test. criticism. s8°. 1910
Hist. of the relig. of Judaism 500–200 B.C. s8°. [1927]

Duff (Edward Gordon). Cat. of the library of D. Sold by Sotheby, Mar. 1925. 2 portions *in* 1v (1, Early stamped bindings. 2, Gen. lib.) 8°. 1925

Duff (James), *2nd earl of Fife, 1729–1809, see* Fife (J. D., *2nd earl of*).

Duff (James Cuninghame Grant). Hist. of the Mahrattas. Rev. annot. ed., w. intr. by S. M. Edwardes. 2v. s8°. 1921

Duff (John Wight). Lit. hist. of Rome in the Silver Age, f. Tiberius to Hadrian. 8°. 1927

Duff (*Rt. Hon. Sir* Mountstuart Elphinstone Grant).
Afghanistan & Central Asia: a letter. [P2714]. 8°. 1878

Duff (Ursula Grant), *ed., see* Avebury (J. L., *1st b.*) Life-work of Ld. A., 1834–1913, 1924.

Duff (W. Pirie). Mem. of Alexander Duff. s8°. [1890]

Duffin (Henry Charles).
The quintessence of Bernard Shaw. s8°. [1920]

Duffy (James), *see* Duffy's Hibernian Magazine, 1862–64.

Duffy's Hibernian Magazine, 1862–64. 5v. 8°. D. *n.d.*

Du Fouilloux (Jacques). Les ditz du bon chien Souillard (16c.), *see* Brézé (J. de). Livre de la chasse, 1858.

Dufour (Auguste Henri) & F. Rabut. Renonciat. du Comte Amédée VI de Savoie au mariage arrêté entre lui & la Pcsse. Jeanne de Bourgogne, *see* Regia Dep. di Storia Patria. Misc., t17, 1878.

Dufour (Henri). Le Bayon d'Angkor Thom. Bas-reliefs rec. par la Mission H. D., avec collab. de C. Carpeaux. [Min. de l'Instr. Publ. &c. *b. in* 2v.] fol. 1910–13

Dufour (Philippe Sylvestre) [Sylvestre Dufour]. *Tractatus novi de potu caphe, de Chinensium thé, et de chocolata. s8°. Parisiis. 1685

Dufourcq (Albert). L'avenir du Christianisme. p1, le passé chrétien: vie & pensée. [t]1–7. [1, 7e éd., 2, 4, 5e éd., 3, 5, 6, 3e éd., 7, 4e éd.] s8°. 1909–25

Dufour-Feronce (Albert), *see* Georgi (O. R.) & A. D.-F. Urkunden z. Gesch. d. Suezkanals, 1913.

Dufourt (Jean). Sur la route de lumière. s8°. [1921]

Du Fresne-Canaye (Philippe). Le voyage du Levant (1573). Publ. &c. par M. H. Hauser. [App., texte ital. Rec. de voyages &c. p. s. à l'hist. de la géog., 13–16s. t16]. la8°. 1897

Du Fresny (Charles Rivière) [†Rivière Du Fresny (C.)] Amusements sérieux & comiques. Intr. & notes par J. Vic. s8°. 1921

Du Gard (Maurice Martin), *see* Martin Du Gard (M.)

Du Gard (Roger Martin), *see* Martin Du Gard (R.)

Dugas (Charles). La céramique des Cyclades. [Bibl. des Ecoles Fr. d'Athènes &c., fasc. 129]. la8°. 1925
Greek pottery. Tr. W. A. Thorpe. s8°. 1926
Un plat rhodo-ionien trouvé à Délos, *see* Acad. des Inscrs. Fond. Piot. Mons. & méms., t28, 1925–26.
see Union Acad. Internat. Classif. des céramiques antiq.; par C. D. &c., 12p, 1921–27.

——, J. Berchmans & M. Clemmensen. Le sanctuaire d'Aléa Athéna à Tégée au 4e siècle. [Fouilles de l'Ecole Franç. d'Athènes]. [2t *in* 1v. 1, Texte. 2, Atlas]. fol. 1924

Dugdale Society. Publications. v1–6. la8°. 1921–26
see King Edward's School, *Birmingham.* Records, v1, 1924. [4.]
„ Stratford-upon-Avon. Minutes & acc. of Corpor. of S., 1553–1620, v1–3, 1921–26. [1, 3, 5.]
„ Warwick. Abstr. of bailiffs' accs. of monastic &c. estates, 1547; tr., 1923. [2.]
„ Warwickshire. Lay Subsidy Roll, 1332; ed. W. F. Carter, 1926. [6.]

Dugdale, *Family of, see* Schomberg (A.) D. of Seend, 1924.

Dugdale (Stephen). Information, deliv. at bar of H. of Commons, 1 Nov. 1680 [*rel. to Popish Plot.* P525]. sfol. 1680

Dugdale (*Sir* William).
see Memoirs of the antiquities of Gt. Brittain &c., w. remarks on Stevens' first addit. vol. to D.'s Monastichon &c., 1713.
„ Touchet (G.) Hist. colls., w. add. of passages taken out of Sir W. D., 1686.

Duggan (Stephen Pierce Hayden). The League of Nations. Principle & practice. Ed. S. P. D. 8°. Boston. [U.S. 1919]

Dugmore (Arthur Radclyffe). The vast Sudan. la8°. [1924]

Dugout (Henry). Carte de la prov. du Kiang-sou, feuille 1, *see* Variétés sinolog., No. 54, 1922.

Dugovich (Titus). Az általános választói jog és a felirdék. [P2397]. 8°. 1905
A tót nemzetiségi mozgalmak fejlödésének története. [P2397]. 8°. 1903

Duguay-Trouin (René), *see* Le Nepyou de Carfort (*cte.* H.) Hist. de Du G. T., le corsaire, 1922.

Du Guesclin (Bertrand), *Constable of France.* *Chron. de B. Du G. Texte établi & rapproché du fr. mod. par G. Richou. s8°. 1879

Duguet (Jacques Joseph). *Diss. théolog. & dogmat. 1, Sur les exorcismes. 2, Sur l'Eucharistie. 3, Sur l'usure. [2 *pagin.*] s8°. 1727

Du Guillet (Pernette), *see* AYNARD (J.), *ed.* Les poëtes lyonnais, 1924.

Duguit (Leon).
Law in the modern state. Tr. F. & H. Laski. 8°. [1921]
Traité de droit constit. 2e éd. 5t. 8°. 1921–25
—— **& H. Monnier.** Les constit. & les lois polit. de la France dep. 1789. Ouvrage cont. par L. Duguit. 4e ed. s8°. 1925

Du Halde (Jean Bapt). Descr. de la Chine & de la Tartarie Chin. 4t. fol. 1735

Duhamel (Georges) [*ps.* DENIS THÉVENIN].
Civilisation, 1914–17. 5e éd. s8°. 1916
Compagnons. Poèmes. s8°. [1918]
Confession de minuit. 15e éd. s8°. 1920
Deux hommes. 15e éd. s8°. 1924
Élégies. 3e éd. s8°. 1920
Guerre & litt. 8°. 1920
Les hommes abandonnés. 4e éd. s8°. 1921
Journal de Salavin. 12e éd. s8°. 1927
La journée des aveux, comédie—Quand vous voudrez, comédie. s8°. 1924
Lettres au Patagon. 8e éd. s8°. 1926
La lumière. 2e éd. s8°. 1919
L'œuvre des athlètes, suivie de Lapointe & Ropiteau. Comédie[s]. 4e éd. s8°. 1920
Origine & prospérité des singes, nouv., *see* ŒUVRES libres, 4, 1921.
La pierre d'Horeb. Roman. 11e éd. s8°. 1926
Les plaisirs & les jeux. 2e éd. s8°. 1922
„ „ . . . .4e éd. s8°. 1922
Le Prince Jaffar. 4e éd. s8°. 1924
Le voyage de Moscou. 6e éd. s8°. 1927
see DURTAIN (L.) G. D., 1920.

Duhamel (Maurice). Essai sur la litt. bretonne anc. s8°. 1905

Duhamelet (Geneviève).
La vie & la mort d'Eugénie de Guérin. s8°. [1925]

Du Hausset (*Mme.*) Mém. de Mme. Du H., & extr. des Mém[s]. de Bachaumont, 1762–82. Avec not. &c. par F. Barrière. s8°. [1882]

Duhem (Pierre).
La théorie physique. 2e éd., rev. & augm. 8°. 1914

Duhm (Bernhard). The 12 Prophets. Version in var. poet. measures of orig. wr. Auth. tr. by A. Duff. 8°. 1912

Duhourcau (François).
L'enfant de la victoire. 8°. 1925
Un homme à la mer. Préf. de M. Barrès. s8°. [1923]

Duhr (Bernhard), *S.J.* Gesch. d. Jesuiten in d. Ländern deut. Zunge. B3. (2te Hälfte d. 17 Jhdts.) la8°. München-Regensburg. 1921

Dühring (Eugen). Cursus der Philosophie. 8°. L. 1875
Ersatz d. Relig. durch Vollkommeneres u. d. Ausscheidung alles Judenthums. 8°. Karlsruhe. 1883
Sache, Leben u. Feinde. Als Hauptwerk u. Schlüssel z. s. sämmtl. Schr. 8°. Karlsruhe. 1882
Der Werth d. Lebens. [*b. w. h.* Ersatz d. Relig., 1883]. 4e A. 8°. L. 1891

Duică (Gheorghe Bogdan-), *see* BOGDAN-DUICĂ (G.)

Duigenan (*Rt. Hon.* **Patrick).** Lachrymæ acad.; or, the pres. state of the Coll. of the Holy Trinity of Q. Eliz. nr. Dublin. 8°. D. 1777

Duine (F.) [*ps.* HENRI DE KERBEUZEC].
La Mennais, sa vie, &c. 8°. 1922

Duisburgenses. Symbolae litt. ex Haganis factae D., 2t, 1783–84, *see* SYMBOLAE.

Duivenvoorde (Jacob van Wassenaar), *see* WASSENAAR-DUIVENVOORDE (J. VAN).

Dujardin (Edouard). De Stéphane Mallarmé au prophète Ezéchiel & essai d'une théorie du réalisme symbol. 8°. 1919

Du Jardin (Thomas). De officio sacerdotis, qua judicis &c. in sacramento pœnitentiæ, *see* MIGNE (J. P.), *ed.* Theol. cursus, t22, 1860.

Du Jarric (Pierre). Akbar & the Jesuits: acc. of Jesuit missions to the court of A. by P. Du J. Tr. w. intr. &c. by C. H. Payne. [Broadway Travellers; ed. Sir E. D. Ross &c.] 8°. 1926
Thesaurus rerum Indic. [Nova hist. rerum mem., quae in India orient. &c., in ortu &c. fidei Chr. contig.] A M. Martinez in lat. serm. tr. 3t. s8°. Coloniæ Agrip. 1615

Du Jeu (*Vicomte* **E.)** A Prussian Casanova [Baron F. v. d. Trenck]. Tr. W. Montgomery. 8°. 1924

Du Jon (François), *the elder, see* JUNIUS (F.), *1545–1602.*

Dukas (Jules). Etude sur le Satyricon de J. Barclay. 8°. 1880
Recherches sur l'hist. litt. du 15e siècle: Laurent Maioli—Pic de la Mirandole—Elie del Medigo. 8°. 1876

Dukas (Paul), *see* SAMAZEUILH (G.) P. D., 1913.

Duke (Edward). Prolusiones hist.; or, essays illust. of the Halle of John Halle, of Salisbury. v1 [*no more publ.*] 8°. Salisbury. 1837

Duke (Thomas Samuel). Celebrated criminal cases of America. 8°. San Francisco. 1910

Duke (Winifred).
Lord George Murray & the Forty-Five. 8°. Aberdeen. 1927

Dukelsky (Benedikt). Душа в заветной лире: стихотворения. s8°. Париж. 1927

Duker (Carl Andreas) [DUKERUS (C. A.)]. Opuscula varia de Latinitate jurisconsult. vet. Ed., & animadv. adj. C. A. D. s8°. Lugduni Batav. 1711

Dukes (Ashley). Drama. [Home Univ. Lib.] s8°. [1926]
One more river, comedy. s8°. 1927
The youngest drama: st[s]. of 50 dramatists. 8°. 1923

Dukes (*Sir* **Paul),** *K.B.E.* Red dusk & the morrow: adv[s]. &c. in red Russia. 8°. 1922

Dulac (Benoet), *see* JOLY (A.) Note sur B. du L. ou le théâtre & la Bazoche à Aix à la fin du 16e s., 1862.

Du Lac (F. M. Perrin), *see* PERRIN DU LAC (F. M.)

Dulaurier (Édouard). Bibl. hist. armén.: choix d. princ. historiens arm.; tr. [Orient. Tr. Fund, 70]. 8°. 1858
Chron. de Matthieu d'Édesse (962–1136), avec la contin. de Grégoire le Prêtre j. 1162.
Recherches s. la chronol. armén. t1, Chron. tech. 4°. 1859

***Dulce** domum C.: song & chorus [*Lat. & Eng.*] [*b. w.* Corelli (A.) Twelve concertos, *n.d.*] 4°. *n.d.*

Du Lis (Charles). Opusc. hist. rel. à Jeanne Darc (1610). n. éd. par M. Vallet de Viriville. [Trésor des pièces rares &c.] s8°. 1856

Dullaert (Joannes), *de Janduno, see* TOOLEY (M. J.) The authorship of the Defensor pacis [? J. D. *joint a. w.* Marsilio, *da Padova*], 1926.

Dulong (Gustave). L'abbé de Saint-Réal; étude s. les rapports de l'hist. & du roman au 17e siècle. 2t (t2, Notes & doc[s].) 8°. 1921

Dulsky (Petr). Николай И. Фешин. s4°. Казань. 1921

Du Luc (Charles Gaspard Guillaume de Vintimile), *see* VINTIMILE DU LUC (C. G. G. DE).

Dulwich College. Cat. of pictures in Gallery of Alleyn's Coll. &c. Rev. &c. by Sir E. Cook.
„ „ Dulwich Picture Gallery. 1921 Suppl. to cat.; by E. T. Hall, *b. w. above.* s8°. 1921

Duly (Sidney John). Timber & timber products incl. paper making materials. Intr. by Sir E. Geddes & Ld. Lovat. [Resources of the Empire, v2]. 4°. 1924

Duma. Трудовая группа въ государств. думѣ. Составилъ В. Ш. [P2719]. 8°. [Москва. 1906]
see KLASSON (V. N.), *ed.* Депутаты 1й думы подъ судомъ, 1908.

Dumaine (Alfred). La dern. ambassade de France en Autriche. Notes & souv[s]. 6e éd. s8°. [1921]

Dumas (Alexandre), *fils* [*Dumas Davy de La Pailleterie (A.)*]
Contes & nouvelles: Un paquet de lettres—Le prix de pigeons—Le pendu de la Piroche—Ce que l'on voit tous les jours.—Césarine. s8°. 1853
La dame aux camelias. Préf. de J. Janin. s8°. *Nelson.* [1913]
L'étrangère. Comédie. s8°. 1897
Les Madeleines repenties. Refuge Sainte-Anne. 2e éd. [P2505]. s8°. 1869
see GIRARDIN (E. DE). L'homme & la femme: lettre à D., 9e éd., 1872.
„ GROS (J.) A. D. & M. Duplessis, 1923.
„ HOMME (L'). À Dumas fils: L'homme qui sait, 1872.
„ LESGUILLON (*Madame* H.) L'homme: réponse à D., 1872.

Dumas (Alexandre), *père.*
Le capitaine Paul. n. éd. s8°. 1895
Crimes célèbres. 8t. 8°. 1842–47
Impressions de voyage: Suisse. n. éd. 3v. s8°. 1902–3
Louis XV. & sa cour. 2t. s8°. 1866
Le meneur de loups. n. éd. s8°. 1883
Le trou de l'enfer. n. éd. s8°. 1873
Vicomte de Bragelonne. n. éd. 6t. s8°. 1898–99
Vingt ans après. n. éd. 3t. s8°. 1898
TRANSLATIONS.
The companions of Jehu. 2v. s8°. 1901
The Count of Monte Cristo. [Tr. World's Gt. Novels]. s8°. [1917]
The Count of Monte Cristo. Illust. by F. T. Merrill. 8°. *W. Scott. n.d.*
The three musketeers. [Tr.] [repr.] 8°. [1922]

Dumas (Alexandre), *père* [*continued*].
The three musketeers. Tr. A. Allinson, w. intr. by A. Lang. 8°. *n.d.*
Twenty years after. Illust. [by F. T. Merrill]. 8°. *W. Scott. n.d.*
The two Dianas. 2v. s8°. 1906
see LUCAS-DUBRETON (J.) La vie d'A. D. père, 3e éd., 1928.
„ SIMON (G. M. S. C.) Hist. d'une collabor. : A. D. & A. Maquet, 1919.
Dumas (Charles). Contes & légendes des pays d'Orient. s8°. 1925
Dumas (Georges). Traité de psychologie. Avec la collab. de L. Barat, G. Belot &c. Préf. de T. Ribot. t1. 8°. 1923
Dumas (Samuel) & K. O. Vedel-Petersen. Losses of life caused by war. Ed. H. Westergaard. [C.E. for Internat. Peace. Div. of econ. &c.] la8°. O. 1923
Du Maurier (George L. P. B.)
Eng. soc. at home. From Punch. fol. 1880
Dumax (Victor Alfred). Album généalog. & biog. des princes de Bourbon dep. St.-Louis j. nos jours. fol. [1873]
Dumay (Gabriel). Guy de Pontailler, sire de Talmay, maréchal de Bourgogne, (1364–92). [Extr. des Mém. de la Soc. Bourguign. d'Hist. &c., t23]. 8°. Dijon. 1907
Dumay (*l'abbé* **Joseph Adolphe).** *A new & faithful tr. [*by* W. Stevens] of letters f. Mr. l'abbé *** [*i.e.* D.] to B. Kennicott, w. pref. & App. [*b. w.* Kennicott (B.) 2 diss. &c., 1747]. 8°. 1773
Dumbadze (Vasili D.) The Caucasian Republics. la8°. N.Y. 1925
Dumbeath. Note of letters taken out of the trunk that came to D., w. letters f. Col. Gordon & the Earl of Kinnoul to the Marq. of Montrose, 1649, *see* MAIDMENT (J.), *ed.* Hist. fragms., p2, 1833.
Dum-Dum, *ps., see* KENDALL (J.)
Dumersan (Théophile Marion) [†MARION DUMERSAN (T.)] **& N. Ségur.** Chansons nat. & pop. de France, accomp. de notes hist. &c. [2t]. 8°. 1866
Chants & chansons pop. de la France. Notices par D. Accompagnement par H. Colet. [4t]. la8°. [1890 ?]
t4 *has t.* Chansons populaires des provinces de France: notices par Champfleury, accomp. de piano par J. B. Wekerlin.
Dumesil (René), *see* DESCHARMES (R.) & R. D. Autour de Flaubert, 1912.
Du Mesnil (Edmond Révérend), *see* RÉVÉREND DU MESNIL (E.)
Dumesnil (Jean Baptiste Gardin). Latin synonyms. Tr. by J. M. Gosset. 2nd ed. 8°. 1819
Dumézil (Georges). Le crime des Lemniennes: rites & légendes du monde égéen. la8°. 1924
Le festin d'immortalité: ét. de mythologie comp. indo-europ. [Annales du Musée Guimet. Bibl. d'Etudes, t34]. la8°. 1924
Duminil (François Guillaume Ducray-), *see* DUCRAY-DUMINIL (F. G.)
Dümmler (Ernst L.) Epistolae Merowingici et Karolini aevi. [Mon. Germ. hist.] t4. [*Pref. by E. Perels*]. 4°. Berolini. 1925
t2–4 *have t.* Epist. Kar. aevi.
Dumolard (Henry). Le véritable Julien Sorel [*i.e.* A. Berthet], *see* ŒUVRES libres, 71, 1927.
Dumolin (Maurice). Notes sur les vieux guides de Paris, *see* SOCIÉTÉ DE L'HIST. DE PARIS. Mém., t47, 1924.
see ROCHEGUDE (*Le marq.* F. DE) & M. D. Guide prat. à tr. le vieux Paris, n. éd., 1923.
Du Mont (*le sieur*), *see* DUMONT (JEAN).
Dumont (Jean), *baron de Carlscroon.* New voyage to the Levant; acc. of Germany, France, Italy, Malta & Turkey. [Tr.] 4th ed. 8°. 1705
Dumont (P. Étienne L.), *see* COLLINS (*Sir* W. J.) Notes on Sir S. Romilly & E. D., 1924.
Dumont-Wilden (Louis). Bruges. [Cités d'art]. s8°. [1925]
Dumor (Carl). De scholis & acad. vet. Hebr. diss. [*b. w.* Bode (C. A.) Diss. de prim. ling. Heb. antiq., 1747]. s8°. Wirceburgie. 1782
Du Motey (Henry Jacques François Renault, *vicomte*). Le champion de la Normandie: Robert II de Bellême &c. & s. temps 1056–112 . . . la8°. 1923
Dumoulin (Alain).
Gramm. Latino-Celtica. 8°. Pragae Bohem. 1800
Du Moulin (Charles). Coutumes de la prov. d'Auvergne, avec les notes de C. Du M. &c. Préc. de 2 diss. par M. Chabrol. 4t. 4°. Riom. 1784–86
see DU BREUIL (G.) Stilus Curiae Parl. Paris., 1551.
Du Moulin (Louis) [*ps.* LUDIOMÆUS COLVINUS], *see* BAXTER (R.) Apology &c.; added animadvers. on a late diss. of L. Colvinus, 1654.

Du Moulin (Pierre), *the elder.*
Anatomie de la messe. 2p *in* 1v [p1, 3e éd. rev. & augm; p2, cont. la messe en franç. & en latin]. s8°. Genève. 1640–53
The anatomy of the mass. Tr. Pref. A hist. of the Eucharist, by R. Shanks. s8°. E. 1833
The anatomy of Arminianisme. Tr. s4°. 1626
Apologie pour la Saincte Cène du Seigneur contre la présence corporelle &c. 2e éd. s8°. La Rochelle. 1609
Bouclier de la foy, ou defense de la conf. de foy des églises reformées de France, contre les obj. du sieur Arnoux jésuite. Dern. éd. rev. & augm. s8°. Genève. 1670
The buckler of the faith: or, a defence of the conf. of faith of the reformed churches in France agst. the obj. of M. Arnoux. Tr. 2nd ed. s4°. 1623
De monarchia temporali pontif. Romani liber. Liber regis Jacobi ab adversar. object. vindic. s8°. Londini. 1614
„ ....[*a. ed.*] s8°. Francofurti. 1716
*The monk's hood pull'd off [The Capucin treated] or the Capucin fryar descr. [*Foll. by* The Capucin's journal *by F. Clouet.* 2p, *sep. pagin.*] Tr. s8°. 1671
Thesaurus disputat. theolog. in alma Sedanensi Acad., a P. Molinaeo, J. Cappello, Ab. Ramburtio, S. Maresio, A. Colvino, L. Le Blanc, J. Le Vasseur, J. Alpaeo de S. Maurice. Coll. &c. ac in 2 tomos distrib. &c. 2t. la8°. Genevae. 1661
see BOURGUIGNON (D.) Rencontre &c. entre B. & Du M., 1617.
Dumouriez (*le gén.* **Charles François).** Mém. p. s. à l'hist. de la Convention Nat. par Daunou. Avec notices par F. Barrière. s8°. 1886
Nouv. tableau spéculatif de l'Europe. [P2764]. 8°. *n.p.* 1798
Suite des Mém. du Gén. D., Mém. de Louvet, & Mém. p. s. à l'hist. de la Convention Nat. par Daunou. Avec notice par F. Barrière. s8°. 1886
Dumur (Louis). Le boucher de Verdun. Roman. s8°. [1921]
Les défaitistes. s8°. [1923]
Nach Paris. Roman. s8°. 1920
Dumville (J.) & S. Kershaw.
The worsted industry. s8°. *Pitman.* [1924]
Dunaev (Boris I.) Городъ Устюгъ Великій. изд. 2ое подъ ред. П. Н. Бороздина. [Культурныя Сокровища Россіи, 15]. la8°. 1919
Dunan (Charles). Essais de philos. gén. Cours de philos. 2e éd. rev. 8°. 1902
Dunan (Renée). Asie, nouvelle, *see* ŒUVRES libres, 68, 1927.
Dunaway (Wayland Fuller). Hist. of the James River & Kanawha Co. [Columbia Univ. St. in hist. &c., v104ii]. 8°. N.Y. 1922
Dunbar, *The Family of, see* MASSON (P. A.) *Legends of the D., 1854.
Dunbar (Ianthe). The edge of the desert. la8°. [1923]
Dunbar (William), *the poet, see* MAITLAND (*Sir* R.) Maitland folio MS. cont. poems by Sir R. M., D. &c., v2, 1927.
Dunbar-Dunbar (John Archibald). Family of Cambray of Gt. Rissington & Icomb, Gloucs. 4°. *p.p.* 1898
Duncan (Edmonstoune). Lyrics f. the old song books. Coll. & ed. E. D. s8°. 1927
see REEVES' dict. of musicians; ed. & partly re-wr. by E. D., w. adds., 1926.
Duncan (Francis). Canada: a lecture. [P2602]. 8°. 1871
Canada in 1871. [P2590]. 8°. 1872
Hist. of Royal Regt. of Artillery. 2nd ed. 2v. 8°. 1874
Duncan (George) & B. Darwin. Present-day golf. 8°. [1921]
Duncan (Herbert Spencer) & A. H. Mackenzie. The training of teachers. [Bur. of Ed., India. Occ. Rep., No. 8]. [P2412]. 8°. [Calcutta. 1919]
Duncan (John) & S. G. Starling.
Text book of physics. [repr., w. add. chapter]. s8°. 1919
Duncan (Joseph F.), *see* JONES (D. T.) &c. Rural Scotland dur. the War; by D. T. J., J. F. D. &c., 1926.
Duncan (Peter), *Wesleyan Minister.* A narr. of the Wesleyan mission to Jamaica &c. s8°. 1849
Duncan-Jones (Arthur Stuart). Archbishop Laud. 8°. 1927
see CLUTTON-BROCK (A.) Necessity of art; by A. C. B., P. Dearmer, A. S. D.-J. &c., 1924.
Dundas, *The family of, see* MACLEOD (W.) Royal letters & o. hist. doc. sel. f. family papers of D., 1897.
Dundas (*Hon.* **Charles Cecil Farquharson).**
Kilimanjaro & its people: hist. of the Wachagga &c. 8°. 1924
Dundas (*Field-Marshal Sir* **David).** Principles of military movt., illust. by manœuvres of Prussian troops & by an outline of Brit. campaigns in Germany, 1757. 4°. 1788
Dundas of Dundas (*Adm. Sir* **Charles).**
An admiral's yarns: memories of 50 years. 8°. 1922
Dungern (Otto, *Frhr.* **v.)** Thronfolgerecht d. Blutsverwandtschaft d. deut. Kaiser seit Karl d. Gr. [*b. w.* Roland. Bücher-Kat., 1909]. 8°. 1910

Dunham (*Lt.-Col.* **Edward Kellogg**), *U.S. Army*, *see* UNITED STATES: ARMY. Medical Dept. in World War, v11, Surgery, p2; by E. K. D. &c., 1924.

Dunhill (Alfred). The pipe book. 8°. 1924

Dunk (John L.)
Hyperacoustics. Div. 2, Successive tonality. 8°. 1921

Dunkenhalgh deeds, c. 1200–1600; ed. G. A. Stocks &c., *see* CHETHAM MISC., n. ser., v4, 1921.

Dunkin (Edwin Hadlow Wise).
see SUSSEX. Cal. of S. marriage licences; by E. H. W. D., 6v, 1906–26.
,, —— S. manors, advowsons &c. rec. in Feet of fines, 1509–1833; arr. & ed. by E. H. W. D., 2v, 1914–15.

Dunkin (John). Outlines of the hist. &c. of Bromley, in Kent. Added, Invest. of antiq^s^. of Holwood Hill, Keston, by A. J. Kempe. 8°. Bromley. 1815

Dunlop (*Miss* **Alison Hay**), *see* DUNLOP (J. C.) & A. H. D. Bk. of old Edinburgh, 1886.

Dunlop (John Charles) & A. H. Dunlop.
Book of old Edinburgh. s8°. E. 1886

Dunlop (Madeline A. Wallace). Glass in the old world. 8°. [1883]

Dunlop (Robert), *writer on Irish hist.*
Ireland: fr. the earliest times. 8°. O. 1922

Dunn (George), *of Woolley Hall, Maidenhead, see* JENKINSON (F. J. H.) List of incunabula coll. by G. D. &c., 1923.

Dunn (Waldo Hilary). The life of D. G. Mitchell. 8°. N.Y. 1922

Dunne (John William). An experiment with time. 8°. 1927

Dunning (James Edmund).
The Roman road to Portslade. 8°. 1925

Dunning (William Archibald). Hist. of polit. theories f. Rousseau to Spencer. 8°. N.Y. 1922
see MERRIAM (C. E.) & H. E. BARNES, *edd.* Hist. of polit. theories, recent times; contrib. by students of W. A. D., 1924.

Dunoyer de Segonzag (André), *see* JEAN (R.) A. D. de S., 1922.

Dunphy (Thomas) & Thomas J. Cummins.
Remark. trials of all countries. 8°. N.Y. 1870

Dunraven & Mountearl (Windham Henry W.-Q., *5th e. of*).
Dunraven Castle, Glamorgan. 8°. 1926

Dunraven & Mountearl (Windham T. W.-Q., *4th earl of*).
The crisis in Ireland: federal union, thr. devolution. [P2485, 2490]. 8°. 1920
Past times & pastimes. 2v. 8°. [1922]

Duns (Joannes), *Scotus.* [DOCTOR SUBTILIS].
[Questiones super primo sententiarum. *F. 1, beg.*: Utrum homini pro statu isto sit necc^m^. *Colophon:* Expliciunt questiones Ioannis Scoti. . . . Super primo sētentirarum [*sic*]: Quod opus ab Antonio Tronbeta: theologo patavino . . . diligentia emendatum est: Antonii vero bononiensis phisici ꝯdam Ioannis genuēsis ittidem phisici: iussu & sumptibus venetiis impressum. Anno iesu Christi f. dei & Marie virginis, 1472, xiii Kal. Decenbres. ? x. s. Finis]. fol. [Venetiis. 1472]
245 ff. no pag. foliat. or sign. f. 246 blank. [*Sig. a–z in tens, except m, n, s in twelves; aa1–11.* f. 3 & 8 *wanting. Hain 6423 gives 247ff, & adds:* "Christofori bellapiera Veneti" *to colophon.*]
Theologia D. Subtilis Scoti. In 4 libros sententiarum elucid. per G. Mahler. s8°. Tugii Helvet. 1702
see ANTONIUS, *a Sancta Maria Angelorum.* Scotus Aristotelicus, seu philos. peripatetica juxta mentem J. D. S. concinnata, 2t, 1747–59.
,, BADBERGER (M.) & U. DRÖLING. Tract. theol. de jure &c. cum parergis ex 3 lib. Sentent. juxta mentem J. D. S., 1720.
,, BAUMGARTEN-CRUSIUS (L. F. O.) De theologia S., 1826.
,, BOYVIN (J. G.) Philosophia S. &c., 4p, 1690.
,, —— Theologia S., 6^a^. ed., 1682–90.
,, CASMIRIUS (F. A.) Scotus dilucidatus, 1607.
,, FERCHIUS (M.) Vita J. D. S. & Apologiae, 1622 [*repr.*], 1629.
,, HARRIS (C. R. S.) Duns Scotus, 2v, 1927.
,, HERMANN (A.) Tractatus theol. in primum Sentent. librum de Deo uno et trino; ad mentem J. D. S., 1690.
,, HILLINGER (W.) Memorab. theol. dogmat. tractatus tres de Deo uno, ex univ. theol. J. D. S., 1750.
,, JANSSENIUS (N.) Animadv. & scholia in Apologiam nuper ed. de vita &c. J. D. S., 1622.
,, KRUMP (E.) Quaest. cum parergis in 4 libr. Sentent. J. D. S., 1709.
,, MACEDO (F.) Collationes doctrinae S. Thomae & S., 1680.
,, MAYR (C.) Gemini justitiae actus restitutio &c. juxta mentem J. D. S., 1718.
,, —— Ord. hierarch. descensus &c., cum sel. assert. theolog. ex J. D. S. expos., 1726.
,, MÖHR (A.), B. STAUB &c. Amphib. beatitud. decis. theolog. ad mentem I. D. S. determin. &c., 1663.

Duns (Joannes), *Scotus.* [DOCTOR SUBTILIS] [*continued*].
see MÖHR (A.) & A. STUMPH. Graphis theol. human. ad mentem J. D. S. deducta &c., 1665.
,, RADA (J. DE). Controversiae theolog. inter S. Thomam & S., 1599.
,, STANISLAUS *a Placentia.* Augustini & S. de gratia Xti. consensus, 2v, 1768.

Duns (John). Biblical natural science; an explan. of all references to geology, botany, zoology & phys. geog. 2v. la8°. [1863–68]

Dunsany (Edward John Moreton Drax Plunkett, *18th baron*).

The charwoman's shadow. s8°. [1926]	The gods of Pegāna. [3rd ed.] s8°. 1919
The chronicles of Rodriguez. [2nd ed.] s8°. [1922]	If. Play. [repr.] 8°. [1923]
Fifty-one tales. [3rd ed.] 8°. 1919	Plays of near & far. s8°. [1922]
	Tales of 3 hemispheres. s8°. 1920
	Tales of war. s8°. D. [1918]

Dunstable. Digest of the charters pres. in the Cartulary of the Priory of D.; by G. H. Fowler, *see* BEDFORDSHIRE HIST. REC. SOC. Publ^s^. v10, 1926.

Dunstan, *St., see* ROBINSON (J. A.) Times of St. D., 1923.

Dunstan (Ralph).
A cyclopædic dict. of music. 3rd ed. corr. 8°. [1920]
,, ,, ...4th ed., enl. & rev. 8°. [1925]

Dunster. Doc. & extracts illust. the hist. of the Honour of D. Sel. & ed. Sir H. C. Maxwell-Lyte. [Somerset Rec. Soc., v33]. 8°. 1917–18. [1921]

Dunsterville (*Maj.-Gen.* **Lionel Charles**).
The adventures of Dunsterforce. 8°. 1920
And obey? s8°. 1925

Dunton (John), *bookseller.* *Athenian sport, or 2000 paradoxes to amuse. By a member of the Athenian Soc. [*i.e.* J. Dunton]. 8°. 1707
see WESLEY (S.) *Athenian Oracle [*also attrib. to J. D.*], 1704 &c.

Duntreth, *Lairds of, see* EDMONSTON, *of Duntreth, Fam. of.*

Dupanloup (Félix Antoine Philibert), *bp. of Orleans.* Lettre au clergé de s. dioc. rel. à l'infaillibilité. [P520]. 8°. 1869
Réponse á Mgr. Dechamps. [P520]. 8°. 1870
see GUÉRANGER (P. L. P.) De la défin. de l'infaillibilité papale, 1870.

***Dupe** (The), a comedy; by the a. of The discovery, 1764, *see* SHERIDAN (*Mrs.* F.)

Du Peloux (*vte.* **Charles**). Répertoire gén. des ouvrages mod. rel. au 18 s. franç., 1715–89. la8°. 1926
,, ,, ...Suppl., table méthod. la8°. 1927

Duperon (Albert Pierre A. Grosse-), *see* GROSSE-DUPERON (A. P. A.)

Du Perron (*le card.*) The reply of Card. of P. to the answeare of the King of Gr. Brit. Tr. into Eng. [by E. Cary, viscountess Falkland]. t1. [*No more publ.*] fol. Douay. 1630
see DOMINIS (M. A. DE). De republica eccl. v2, cum app. in quibus refell. opus Card. P., de Eucharistia &c., 1620.
,, JAMES I, *k. of Gt. Brit.* Remonstrance for the right of kings &c. agst. an oration of Card. of P., 1615, 1619.

Dupeyrat (Guillaume). *Traitté de l'orig. des cardinaux du Saint Siége, Avec 2 traittez des Legats [*Card. Chisi &c.*] à Latere & une rel. de leurs receptions &c. [&] le Traitté de Pise. [3p. *sep. pagin.*] s8°. Cologne. 1665

Du Picq (*Col.* **Charles Ardant**), *see* ARDANT DU PICQ.

Dupin (*Baron* **Charles**). *Rép. au disc. de Stanhope, sur l'occup. de la France par l'armée étr. [P2553]. 8°. Londres. 1818

Dupin (Louis Ellies) [†ELLIES-DUPIN (LOUIS)]. Diss. prélim. ou prolégomènes sur la Bible, p. s. de suppl. à la Bibl. des a. eccl. 2t *in* 1v. 4°. 1701
Hist. du Concile de Trente &c. 2t. s8°. Brux. 1721
A new hist. of eccl. writers cont. an acc. of the authors of the Old & New Test.; of the lives &c. of the Primitive Fathers &c. 3v. fol. D. 1723
Nouv. bibl. des auteurs eccl. 19t *in* 8v. [1–3, 3e éd.; 4–6, dern. éd.; 7–19, 2e éd.] 4°. 1693–1715

Duplay (Maurice). L'école des larrons, *see* ŒUVRES libres, 48, 1925.
Robespierre chez les Duplay, *see* ŒUVRES libres, 79, 1928.

Dupleix (Joseph François), *see* DODWELL (H.) D. & Clive, 1920.
see MARTINEAU (A.) D. & l'Inde franç., 2t, 1920–23.

Du Plessis (François), *seigneur de Richelieu; 1548–90, see* RICHELIEU.

Duplessis (Georges) [†GRATET-DUPLESSIS (G.)] **& H. Bouchot.** Dict. des marques & monogrammes de graveurs. s8°. 1886
—— **& G. Riat &c.** Cat. de la coll. des portraits franç. & étrangers conserv. au Dépt. des Estampes de la Bibl. Nat. t6, 7 [*no more publ.*] 8°. 1907–11
t6, *by* G. D. & P. A. Lemoisne. t7, *by* G. D. & J. Laran.
Du Plessis (*le cte.* **J.**) La vie héroique de Jean Du Plessis, commandant du "Dixmude," 1892–1923. 8°. [1924]
Du Plessis (Jean), *see* DU PLESSIS (*le cte.* J.) Vie héroique de J. Du P., 1924.
Duplessis (Marie), *see* GROS (J.) Alex. Dumas & M. D., 1923.
Du Plessis d'Argentré (Charles), *bp. of Tulle.* Coll. judiciorum de novis erroribus, qui ab initio 12 saec. ad a. 1632[–1735] in eccl. proscripti sunt & notati. Censoria &c. 3t. fol. Lutetiae Paris. 1728–36
Du Plessis-Villeneuve (René Le Pays, *sieur*), *see* LE PAYS (R.)
Du Ponceau (Pierre Etienne). A diss. on the Chinese system of writing. Subjoyned a vocab. of the Cochin-Chinese lang. by J. Morrone, w. ref. to plates by M. de la Palun, & a C.-C. & Lat. dict. [Trans. Amer. Phil. Soc., Phila., v2]. 8°. Phila. 1838
Dupont (*Gén.* **Charles Joseph).** Le haut commandement allemand en 1914 (du point de vue allem.) Préf. du Mar. Joffre. 8°. 1922
Du Pont (*Mrs.* **Bessie Gardner).** E. I. du Pont de Nemours & Co.: a hist., 1802–1902. 8°. Boston [U.S.] 1920
Dupont (Etienne). Les pélerinages au Mont S^t. Michel du 8 au 19 s. [P2597]. 8°. [1909?]
Le véritable Chevalier Destouches. Chasseurs & chasseresses du Roi, 1792–1804. 8°. 1924
Dupont (Léon Papin), *see* JANVIER (P. D.) M. Dupont & l'œuvre de la Sainte-Face, 1897.
Dupont (Pierre Samuel) [DUPONT DE NEMOURS]. National educ. in the U.S. Tr. f. Fr. ed. of 1812 & w. intr. by B. G. du Pont. 8°. Newark, Del. 1923
Du Pont de Nemours (E. I.) & Co., *see* DU PONT (B. G.) E. I. du P. de N. & Co., 1802–1902, 1920.
Duportal (Jeanne). La gravure de portraits & de paysages. [La gr. en Fr. au 18e siècle]. 4°. 1926
Dupouy (Edmond). Le moyen âge médical. s8°. 1888
Duppa (Richard). A brief acc. of the subversion of the papal gov., 1798. 3rd ed. la8°. 1807
Dupré (Alexandre), *see* ROYAN. Chartes du prieuré de St.-Nicholas de R.; publ. A. D., 1891.
Duprè (Giovanni), *1817–82, see* SAPORI (F.) Maestri dell' arte, No. 2, 1919.
Duprè (Henri). Un Italien d'Angleterre: D. G. Rossetti. Préf. du Prof. Legouis. 8°. 1921
Dupréel (Eugène). La légende Socratique & les sources de Platon. la8°. Brux. 1922
Du Prel (Carl, *Frhr.*)
Die Entdeckung d. Seele durch d. Geheimwiss. 2B. *in* 1. 8°. L. 1894–95
Entwicklungsgesch. d. Weltalls. 3e verm. A. d. Schr.: Der Kampf ums Dasein am Himmel. 8°. L. 1882
Der gesunde Menschenverstand: J. C. Fischer contra E. v. Hartmann. [P2474]. 8°. 1872
Das hypnot. Verbrechen u. s. Entdeckung. [P2476]. 8°. München. 1889
Intelligenz d. Zufalles u. d. Berechenbarkeit d. Glückes. [P2474]. 8°. München. 1870
Die monistische Seelenlehre. 8°. L. 1888
Die Mystik d. alten Griechen. [*b. w. h.* Planetenbewohner &c., 1880]. 8°. L. 1888
Philos. d. Mystik. [*b. in 2v*]. 8°. L. 1885
Die Planetenbewohner u. d. Nebularhypothese. 8°. L. 1880
Das Rätsel d. Menschen. [*b. w.* Schott (S.) Von menschl. Schwächen, 1865]. s8°. L. [1892]
Der Spiritismus. [*b. w.* Schott (S.) Von menschl. Schwächen, 1865]. s8°. L. [1893]
Studien aus d. Gebiete d. Geheimwiss. 2T [*in* 1v]. 8°. L. 1890–91
Der Tod, d. Jenseits, d. Leben im Jenseits. 2e A. [P2480]. 8°. Jena. 1901
Das Weltliche Kloster. Eine Vision. [*b. w. h.* Planetenbewohner &c., 1880]. 8°. L. 1887
Dupuis (*le commandant* **Victor).** La campagne de 1793 à l'armée du Nord & des Ardennes. [Publ. s. la dir. de l'Etat-Major de l'Armée]. [2t]. la8°. 1906–9
Les opér. milit. sur la Sambre en 1794—Bataille de Fleurus. [Publ. s. la dir. de l'Etat-Major de l'Armée]. la8°. 1907
Du Puitspelu (Nizier), *see* TISSEUR (C.)
Dupuy (Ernest). La jeunesse des romantiques: V. Hugo & A. de Vigny. 8°. 1905
Dupuy (Pierre). Traitez conc. l'hist. de France: sçavoir la condamnation des Templiers &c.: l'hist. du schisme: les papes en Avignon & procez criminels. [*Ed.* J. Dupuy]. s8°. 1700

Dupuyherbault (Gabriel) [PUTHERBÆUS (G.)] Theolimus sive de tollendis &c. malis libris, libri tres. s8°. Parisiis. 1549
Duræus (Johannes), *Jesuit, see* DURIE (JEAN), *Jesuit.*
Duræus (Johannes), *minister, see* DURY (JOHN).
Durand (Bruno), *see* BOUCHES-DU-RHÔNE; encyclop. départ., t6, Vie intellect., par D. &c., 1914.
Durand (*Rt. Hon. Sir* **Henry Mortimer)** [*ps.* JOHN ROY]. The charm of Persia, *see* PERSIA SOCIETY. Lect., 1912.
The 13th Hussars in the Great War. la8°. E. 1921
see SYKES (*Sir* P. M.) Sir M. D., 1926.
Durand (Ralph). The mind healer. s8°. [1921]
Durandi (Jacopo). Diritto pubbl. d. Vercellese e d. Lombardia; comp. da F. Rondolino, *see* REGIA DEP. DI STORIA PATRIA. Misc., t25, 1887.
Durandus, *de Sancto Porciano, bp. of (1) Puy, (2) Meaux, see* KOCH (J.) D. de S. P.: Forsch. z. Streit um Thomas v. Aquin zu Beg. d. 14. Jhdts., T1, 1927.
Durandus (Gulielmus), *bp. of Mende* [DURANTUS]. Inci. rationale diuinorum officiorū edictū p. Guilielmum durāti &c. la8°. [Veñ. *Georgius Vualch.* 1482]
201 printed leaves; sig. a–y, A–F in eights [a1 *blank missing*]; *double columns, 58 lines to a full col.*
Rationale divinorum officiorum. Acc. aliud Divin. offic. rationale a J. Beletho. la8°. Neapoli. 1859
Durante, *Ser.* Il Fiore, poème italien du 13e s., en 232 sonnets, imité du Roman de la Rose, par D. Texte publ. avec facsimilé, introd. & notes, par F. Castets. [Soc. pour l'Et. des Lang. rom., 9]. 8°. Montpellier. 1881
Durantus (Gulielmus), *see* DURANDUS (G.)
Duranty (L. E. Edmond).
La cause du beau Guillaume. s8°. 1920
D'Urban (*Sir* **Benjamin),** *K.C.B.* Abstract of proc. of the Board of Relief for the destitute, app. in Graham's Town by Sir B. D. [P2434]. s8°. Cape Town. 1836
Report of oper. of allied army under Sir W. C. Beresford in the Alemtejo &c., 1811, *see* NAPIER (*Gen. Sir* W. F. P.) Strictures &c., 1835.
Durel (Jean). A view of the gov. & publ. worship of God in the reformed churches beyond the seas. Their conformity w. the Ch. of Eng. &c. [App. The liturgy of the Ch. of Eng. asserted in a sermon [*on 1 Cor. xi, 16*]. Tr. by G. B. &c. *w. sep. tp. & pagin.*] s4°. 1662
Durell (Clement V.) Readable relativity. 8°. 1926
Durell (David), *Vice-Chancellor, Oxon., see* WHITEFIELD (G.) Letter to D. occas. by expulsion of 6 students f. Edmund Hall, 1768.
Durelli (Francesco).
Cenno storico di Ferdinando II. 8°. Napoli. 1859
Dürer Society. Notes & sketches by A. D.; ed. Campbell Dodgson [Publ. 12], 1911, *see* DÜRER (A.)
[Portfolios]. Intr. notes by Campbell Dodgson &c. 10 series. atlas fol. 1898–1908
" " Index to portfolios 1–10, by C. Dodgson & S. M. Peartree, w. suppl. notes. [Publ. 11]. la8°. 1911
Report, 1898–1904. 8°. [1905]
Dürer (Albrecht).
Notes & sketches. Sel. & ed. by Campbell Dodgson. [Dürer Soc., 12]. la8°. 1911
Passion (Kleine). In Holz nachgesehn v. C. Deis. [*Tp. in 4 lang.*] la8°. Eichstätt. 1867
The Passion of Jesus Christ, pourtr. by A. D. [*i.e. The little Passion*]. Ed. by H. Cole. s4°. 1844
Records of journeys to Venice & the Low Countries. Ed. R. Fry. 8°. Boston, *Merrymount Press.* 1913
Tagebuch d. Reise in d. Niederlande. s8°. L. *n.d.*
see BEHAM (B.) Kupferstiche u. Holzschnitte v. B. u. H. S. B. u. A. D., 1921.
" DÜRER SOCIETY. [Portfolios]. Intr. notes by C. Dodgson, &c., 10 series, 1898–1908; Index, 1911.
" GRIMM (H.) A. D., 1866.
" MITIUS (O.) D.'s Schlosshofansichten u d. Cadolzburg bei Nürnberg, 1922.
" ROSENTHAL (E.) D.'s Buchmalereien für Pirckheimers Bibl., 1928.
" ZUCKER (M.) A. D., 1900.
Duret (Théodore). Courbet. s4°. 1918
Hist. de E. Manet & de s. œuvre. Avec catal. des peintures & d. pastels. n. éd. s4°. 1919
D'Urfey (Thomas). A commonwealth of women, 1685. Ed. E. Goldsmid. s8°. *p.p.* E. 1886
Durham.
Durham Protestations, or returns made to H. of Commons, 1641/2, for maintenance of Protestant relig. for Co. of D., Berwick-upon-Tweed & Morpeth. [Ed. H. M. Wood. Surtees Soc., 135]. 8°. Durham. 1922
Fasti Dunelm.: rec. of beneficed clergy of the diocese of D. [to 1548. Ed. D. S. Boutflower. Surtees Soc., 139]. 8°. Durham. 1926

Durham [*continued*].
Gesta Dunelm., A.D. 1300. Ed. f. MS. in Treasury of D., by R. K. Richardson, *see* CAMDEN MISCELLANY (THE), v13, 1924.
Liber vitae Eccl. Dunelm. Facs. of orig. MS., w. intr. essays & notes. [Ed. A. H. Thompson. Surtees Soc., 136]. 8°. Durham. 1923
Rituale eccles. Dunelm. The Durham Collectar. New & rev. ed. of Lat. text w. interlinear Anglo-Saxon version. [Ed. U. Lindelöf. Surtees Soc., 140]. 8°. 1927
UNIVERSITY.
Calendar, 1912–13. s8°. Durham. 1912
see also ARMSTRONG COLLEGE, *Newcastle*.
Durham (James). Christ crucify'd. 72 sermons on 53d ch. of Isaiah. 4th ed., corr. sfol. 1723
Durham (*Miss* Mary Edith). The Serajevo crime. 8°. [1925]
Twenty years of Balkan tangle. 8°. [1920]
Durich (Fortunatus). Bibl. Slavica antiq. dialecti. v1 [*no more publ.*] 8°. Vindobonae. 1795
De Slavo-Bohemica sacri cod. versione diss. 8°. Pragae. 1777
Durie (John), *Jesuit, d. 1587* [DURÆUS (JOANNES)]. Confutatio Respons. G. Whitakeri ad rationes decem quibus fretus E. Campianus certamen Eccl. Anglic. ministris obtulit in causa fidei. s8°. Parisiis. 1582
see WHITAKER (W.), *D.D.* Responsionis ad decem rationes &c., defensio contra confut. J. D. &c., 1553.
Durie (John), *minister of the Gospel, 1596–1680*, *see* DURY (J.)
Durieux (Jehan). Requiem, nouv., *see* ŒUVRES libres, 42, 1925.
Durieux (Louis). Le roi vierge [Louis II de Bavière], *see* ŒUVRES libres, N°. 75, 1927.
Durmart, *le Galois*. Li romans de D. le Galois, altfranz. Rittergedicht, hrsg. v. E. Stengel. [Lit. V. in St. 116]. [*repr.*] 8°. [Tübingen]. 1873
Durnford (Hugh George Durnford). The tunnellers of Holzminden (w. a side-issue). 8°. C. 1920
Duroiselle (Charles). List of inscr. found in Burma, p1, *see* BURMAH. ARCH. SURVEY, 1921.
Pageant of King Mindon, 1865; reprod. f. contemp. doc., *see* INDIA: ARCH. SURVEY. Memoirs, No. 27, 1925.
see EPIGRAPHIA Birmanica; ed. C. D., v1, 2, 1919–24.
Durplatz (Conrad) *von Friedberg*. Oeconomia eccl. Ordnung wie man sich im kirchē ampt &c., halten sol. [*b. w.* Heidelberg Catechism. Catechismus, 1595]. s8°. Basel. 1563
Durrand (A.), *F.R.M.S.*, *see* MILLETT (F. W.) Rep. on rec. Foraminifera of Malay Arch., coll. by A. D., 1898–1904.
Durrant (C. S.) A link betw. Flemish mystics & Eng. martyrs. Pref. by Card. Bourne. 8°. 1925
Durrant (Robert Ernest). Liberia. Rep. for the African Internat. Corpor., Ltd. 8°. [1925]
Durrbach (Félix). Inscrs. de Délos. Comptes des Hiéropes (No. 290–371). Publ. F. D. [Acad. des Inscr. &c.] fol. 1926
Durrieu (*cte.* Paul). La légende du roi de Mercie dans un livre d'heures du 15ᵉ s., *see* ACAD. DES INSCR. FOND. PIOT. Mon., t24, 1920.
Livre d'heures peint par J. Foucquet. Le 45ᵉ feuillet de ce ms. retrouvé en Angl. [Soc. Franç. de Reprod. de Mss. à Peintures]. la8°. 1923
La miniature flamande au temps de la cour de Bourgogne, 1415–1530. Ouvrage publ. avec le c. de l'Acad. des Inscr. &c., Fond. Piot. 4°. Brux. 1921
Une " Pitié de Notre-Seigneur," tableau franç. (Louvre), *see* ACAD. DES INSCR. FOND. PIOT. Mon., t23, 1918–19.
Les très belles Heures de Notre-Dame du Duc J. de Berry. [Soc. Fr. de Reprod. de MSS. à Peintures]. 4°. 1922
Durrieux (Alcée). Las belhados de Leytouro: amassadis de caousotos adubados &c. [Les veillées de Lectoure &c. *Gasc. & Fr.*] s8°. Auch. 1889
Durry (Marcel). Murée de Cherchel: suppl., par M. D., *see* ALGÉRIE. Musées, 1924.
Durtain (Luc). L'autre Europe: Moscou. 5ᵉ éd. s8°. [1928]
Douze cent mille. 7ᵉ éd. s8°. 1922
Georges Duhamel. [*b. w.* Duhamel (G.) Guerre & lett., 1920]. 8°. 1920
Lise. 8°. 1918
Le retour des hommes. 2ᵉ éd. s8°. 1920
Du Rusquec (H.) Dict. franç.-breton. la8°. Morlaix. 1886
Dury (John), *minister of the Gospel, 1596–1680*.
Consultationum irenic. Προδιόρθωσις sive Acta tract. de mediis concordiae Evangel. procur. inter J. C. Dannhawerum, B. Boebelium & J. D. [*b. w. h.* Irenic. tract. prodromus, 1662]. s8°. Amstelodami. 1664
*Extr. ex harmonia conf. oblatum eccl. reformatis. s4°. *n.p.* 1671
Irenicorum tractatuum prodromus. s8°. Amstelodami. 1662

Dury (John), *minister of the Gospel, 1596–1680* [*continued*].
Just re-proposals to humble proposals [by E. Reynolds. *b. w.* Reynolds (E.) Humble proposals, 1650]. s4°. 1650
see BENZEL (C. J.) Comm. de J. D. maxime de actis ejus Suecanis, 1744.
,, DANNHAUER (J. C.) Nuncius nuncio-Brit. J. Duraeo missus a J. C. D., 1664.
,, DAVENANT (J.), *bp. of Salisbury*. De pacis eccl. rationibus &c. sententiae J. D. traditae, 1635.
Duryea (Nina Larrey). Mallorca the magnificent. 8°. [1927]
Du Ryer (André), *sieur de Malezair*.
Rudimenta gramm. linguae Turcicæ. s4°. Paris. 1630
see KORAN. The life of Mahomet; w. the Alcoran; tr., 1718.
Du Ryer (Pierre), *see* LANCASTER (H. C.) P. Du R., 1913.
Dusart (Cornelius). *Les héros de la Ligue, ou la procession monacle cond. par Louis XIV, pour la conversion des Protestans. [*24 caricatures, engr. by D., w. satirical verses beneath*]. 4°. [1691]
Du Saussay (André), *bp. of Toul*. Insignis libri de script. eccl. Bellarmini contin., 1500–1600. [*b. w.* Bellarmino (*card.* R.) De script. eccl., 1684]. s4°. Coloniæ. 1684
Dusautoir (*l'abbé* Augustin). Guide dans la basilique Notre-Dame à Saint-Omer. 6ᵉ. éd. 8°. Saint-Omer. *n.d.*
Saint Omer & s. successeurs sur les sièges épisc. de Thérouanne, de St.-Omer & d'Arras. 8°. Saint-Omer. [1924?]
La tour Saint-Bertin. 4ᵉ éd. 8°. Saint-Omer. *n.d.*
Duse (Eleonora) [DUSE-CHECHI].
see BORDEUX (J.) E. D., 1925.
,, LEBLANC (G.) Mes convers. avec La Duse, 1926.
,, SYMONS (A.) E. D., 1926.
Dussaud (René).
Les Arabes en Syrie avant l'Islam. la8°. 1907
La digue du lac de Homs & le " mur égypt." de Strabon, *see* ACAD. D. INSCR.: FOND. PIOT. Mon., t25, 1921–22.
Topog. hist. de la Syrie ant. & méd. [Haut-Comm. de la Rép. Fr. en Syrie &c. Bibl. arch. &c., t4]. la8°. 1927
Dusseldorp (Frans van) [†DUYSSELDORPIUS (FRANCISCUS)]. Uittreksel uit F. D. Annales, 1566–1616. Uitg. door R. Fruin. [Hist. Genoots. Werken, s3, 1]. 8°. s'Gravenhage. 1893
Dussler (Luitpold). Benedetto da Majano, e. florent. Bildhauer d. späten Quattrocento. la8°. München. [1924]
Du Taillis (Jean).
Le nouveau Maroc. Préf. de M. Dariac. la8°. 1923
Dutch. Dutch papers: extr. f. the " Dagh register," 1624–42, 1915, *see* BATAVIA.
Loan exhib. of Dutch masters, 17th cent., 1925, *see* KNOEDLER (M.) & Co.
New pocket dict. of Eng. & D., 1894, *see* POCKET-DICTIONARY.
Dutch Church, *Austin Friars, London*. Kerkeraads-protocollen d. Nederduit. Vluchtelingen-Kerk te Londen, 1560–63. Uitg. A. A. van Schelven. [Hist. Genoots. Werken, s3, 43]. 8°. Amsterdam. 1921
Dutch East Indies. A manual of Netherlands India (D. E. Ind.), 1920, *see* ADMIRALTY: NAVAL INTELL. DIV.
see also NETHERLANDS EAST-INDIES.
Dutens (Louis). Itinéraire des routes &c. ou journal de plus. voyages aux villes princ. de l'Europe, 1768–83. 6ᵉ éd., augm. s8°. Londres. 1793
Dutil (*Cap.* L.) Les chars d'assaut. Leur création et leur rôle pend. la Guerre, 1915–1918. 8°. 1919
Du Tilliot (J. B. L.) [LUCOTTE DU TILLIOT (JEAN BÉNIGNE)]. Mém. p. serv. à l'hist. de la fête des foux. [*a. c. foll. by MS. copy of letters f. G. de Carli, bp. of Rieti &c.*] 4°. Lausanne. 1741
Du Toit (Alex. Logie). Geology of S. Africa. 8°. E. 1926
Dutrait-Crozon (H.), *see* MAURRAS (C.) Enquête s. la monarchie, suiv. de Si le coup de force est possible [par C. M. & H. D.-C.], 1924.
Dutrèb (Mahot) & P. A. de Granier de Cassagnac.
Mangin. s8°. 1920
Dutt (Newton Mohun).
Baroda Library hdbk. 4th ed. [P2818]. 8°. Baroda. 1926
Hdbk. of the Baroda Lib. Dept. [P2562]. 8°. Baroda. 1921
Library system of the Baroda State. 3rd ed. [P2732]. 8°. Baroda. 1924
Dutt (Rajani Palme). The two Internationals. s8°. 1920
Dutt (William Alfred). Guide to the Norfolk Broads. With chap. by A. Patterson. 8°. [1923]
The King's homeland. Sandringham & W. Norfolk. With intr. by H. Rider Haggard. 8°. 1904
Dutto (Agostino). Le relaz. sull' assedio di Cuneo del 1557, con app., *see* REGIA DEPUT. Misc., t41, 1905.

Dutton (*Maj.* **E. A. T.**) The Basuto of Basutoland. 8°. [1923]
Dutton (Henry Post). Factory management. 8°. N.Y. 1924
Dutton (Louie M.), *form.* *Knight, see* KNIGHT (F. A.) & L. M. D. Devonshire, 1910.
Duty (The) & advantage of early rising, 1783; 1786, *see* WESLEY (J.)
Duun (Olav). I stormen. 5e oppl. 8°. 1923
Duval (Frédéric). De la paix de Dieu à la paix de fer. [Gesta pacis. Publ. s. dir. du Vte. J. de Romanet]. 8°. [1922]
Duval (Mathias). Artistic anatomy. Tr. F. E. Fenton. 8°. 1884
Duvale (Angel de Altolaguirre), *see* ALTOLAGUIRRE Y DUVALE (A. DE).
Duvau (Auguste), *see* JORET (C.) A. D., 1771–1831, 1921.
Duvau (Georges). Le testament romantique. Roman. s8°. 1927
Duvernet (*l'abbé* **Theophile Imarigeon).**
Hist. de la Sorbonne. 2t. s8°. 1791
Duvernois (Henri).
La dame de bronze & le monsieur de cristal: comédie, *see* REVUE (LA) HEBDOMADAIRE. Suppl.: coll. nouv. &c., No. 2, 1922.
Morte la bête—La fugue—Un soir de pluie. Bois orig. de G. Dollian. [Le livre de demain, 16]. 8°. 1924
Works in Œuvres libres.
L'eunuque, nouvelle, 1925. [42.]
Works in Œuvres libres [*contin.*]
La fugue, roman, 1922. [8.]
Le journal d'un pauvre homme, 1927. [75.]
Morte la bête, 1921. [1.]
Le revenant, nouv., 1924. [34.]
Servante, roman, 1923. [26.]
Un soir de pluie, roman, 1922. [15.]
see BOURGET (P.) Le roman des quatre; [par] P. B., H. D. &c., 2t, 1923–26.
—— **& M. Maurey.** L'éternel printemps, comédie, *see* ŒUVRES libres, 51, 1925.
Duysseldorpius (Franciscus), *see* DUSSELDORP (F. v.)
Dvořák (Max). Das Rätsel d. Kunst d. Brüder van Eyck, mit e Anhang ü. d. Anfänge d. holl. Malerei. la8°. München. 1925
—— **& B. Matějka.** Topogr. d. hist. u. Kunstdenkm. Polit. Bez. Raudnitz. T2: Raudnitzer Schloss, *see* BOHEMIA. Topographie d. hist. u. Kunstdenkmale &c., B27, 1910.
Dvorniković (Vladimir).
Die beiden Grundtypen d. Philosophierens. 8°. 1918
Wilhelm Wundt i njegovo značenje. [P2503]. s8°. Zagreb. 1920
Dwelly (Edward), *ed.* D.'s parish records.
v8, 9, 11, 12. 8°. Topsham & Fleet &c. 1921–23
8, (Somerset) parish reg., v1, Chipstable, Raddington, Kittisford & Pitcombe; by E. D.
9, Bishops transcripts at Wells, v6, Bath 1768–1802, Durston, Chipstable, Raddington, Northover, Ilchester & Broadway, 1598–1628; by E. D.
11, 12, North Petherton reg., annot. w. the Bishop's transcripts at Wells. Sect. 2, 3, Copied by E. Dwelly.
Dwelshauvers (Georges).
Les mécanismes subconscients. s8°. 1925

Dwight (H. G. O.) Christianity in Turkey. s8°. 1854
see SMITH (E.) & H. G. O. D. Missionary researches in Armenia &c., 1834.
Dwight (John), *see* BLACKER (J. F.) ABC of Eng. salt-glaze stoneware, f. D. to Doulton, 1922.
Dyboski (Roman).
Mod. Polish lit. Lects. 8°. 1924
Outlines of Polish hist. Lects., King's Coll., London. 8°. [1925]
Periods of Polish lit. hist. Ilchester lect., 1923. 8°. [O.] 1923
Poland old & new; 3 lects. s8°. O. 1926
Rise & fall in Shakespeare's dram. art. [Shakespeare Assoc. P2717]. 8°. 1923
Dyce (Alex.) Specimens of Eng. sonnets. Sel. by A. D. s8°. 1833
Dyeing [DYING]. *Whole (The) art of dying, 1705, *see* WHOLE.
Dyer (Elinor M. Brent-), *see* BRENT-DYER (E. M.)
Dyer (George), *A.B., see* WHERRY (G. E.) Cambridge & C. Lamb (4, Dyer & " Dyer's Frend "), 1925.
Dyer (John). Poet. works. Coll. by T. Park. s8°. 1807
Dyer (*Col.* (*Brig.-Gen.*) **Reginald Edward Harry).** The raiders of the Sarhad: camp. of arms &c. agst. brigands of Persian-Baluchi border dur. the Gt. War. 8°. 1921
Dyer (W. S.) Minto Coal Basin, New Brunswick. [Canada: Geol. Survey. P2874]. 8°. Ottawa. 1926
Dyer (William). A believer's golden chain.
n. ed. [P2467]. s8°. Northampton. 1823
Dyhrenfurth (Günter Oskar). Die Fusulinen v. Darwas. [Sep.-Abdr. aus Palaeontographica, B56. P2875]. 4°. St. 1909
Dykes (Oswald). The Royal marriage. King Lemuel's lesson of chastity &c. s8°. 1722
Dykes (William Rickatson). Handbook of garden irises. 8°. 1924
Dykvelt (Everard van Weede van), *see* DIJKVELD.
Dymes (Dorothy M. E.) The orig. lang. of the Ancren riwle, *see* ENGLISH ASSOC. Essays &c., v9, 1924.
Dymmok (Roger). Liber contra 12 errores et hereses Lollard. Ed. H. S. Cronin. [Wyclif Soc.] 8°. [1921]
Dymock (James). *The great sacrifice of the new law. [The Holy Mass &c., tr.] s8°. *n.p.* 1676
Dymond (Jonathan). An inquiry into the accordancy of war with Xtianity &c. 4th ed. 8°. 1843
Dyott (G. M.) Silent highways of the jungle: advent. in the Andes & along the Amazon. 2nd ed. 8°. 1924
Dyson (George). The new music. 8°. 1924
Dyson (Richard Randall). Hist. & antiq. of Tottenham High-Cross, Middlesex, w. app. cont. Acc. of the parish by Henry, Ld. Coleraine [*w. sep. pagin.*] 2nd ed., w. add. & corr. 8°. 1792
Dyssord (Jacques). L'étrange aventure de Nom-d'un-petit-bonhomme: nouvelle, *see* ŒUVRES libres, 60, 1926.
Dziergowski (Mikolaj), *abp. of Gnesen, see* PETRICOVIA. Confess. Cathol. fidei Christiana in synodo prov. P. a. 1551, [*pres. D.*], 1557.

E

E. (B.), *Gent.* *A new dict. of the terms of the canting crew, *n.d., see* DICTIONARY.
E. (G. d'). *Obs. on a journey to Naples, 1691, *see* EMILIANE (G. D').
E. (J.) New picture of the Isle of Wight: plates by W. C.; pref., introd. acc. &c. [*signed* J. E.], 1808, *see* COOKE (W. B.)
E. (J.), *F.R.S.* *Acetaria: a disc. of sallets, 1699, *see* EVELYN (J.)
E. (J. A.) *Unpartheysche Gedanken ü. d. Wort-Streit Weickmanns mit Willenberg v. d. Polygamie.
[P2745]. s4°. Franckfurt. 1716
E. (Johne). *Satire agst. Scotland [*signed* Johne E. (1617)], *see* ABBOTSFORD CLUB. Misc., v1, 1837.
E. (P.), *monk, of the order of St. Benedict, see* ELLIS (P.)
Eadie (John). A new & compl. concordance to the Holy Scr. Intr. by D. King. 16th ed. 8°. 1853
Eadmer *the monk.* Hist. novorum & alia opusc., *see* ANSELM, *St.* Opera, 1721.
Eady (*Maj.* **H. G.),** *see* PARGITER (R. B.) & H. G. E. The army & sea power, 1927.
Eagar (W. McG.) & H. A. Secretan.
Unemployment among boys. 8°. 1925
Eagle (R. L.) New light on the enigmas of Shakespeare's sonnets. s8°. 1916

Eagle (William). Tithes the property of the public &c.
5th ed. [P2503]. s8°. 1863
Eaglefield-Hull (A.), *see* HULL (A. E.)
Eakin (Frank).
Getting acquainted w. the New Testament. 8°. N.Y. 1927
Ealand (Charles Aubrey). Insect life. 8°. [1921]
The romance of the microscope. 8°. 1921
Eames (James Bromley), *see* ODGERS (W. B.) Digest of law of libel &c.; 5th ed. by J. B. E., &c., 1911.
Eandi (Antonio Maria Vassalli), *see* VASSALLI-EANDI (A. M.)
Eannes de Zurara (Gomes), *c. 1410–74.* Crónica da tomada de Ceuta por el rei D. João I. Publ. F. M. Esteves Pereira. [Acad. das Sci. de Lisboa]. fol. [1915]
see LOPES (F.) Chron., w. tr. extr. by E. Prestage, 1928.
Earbery (Matthias), *see* BURNET (T.) De statu mortuorum &c.; tr. M. E. &c., 1728.
Earconwald, *St., bp. of London, d. 693, see* ERKENWALD.
Eardley (*Sir* **Culling Eardley),** *bart.* The imprisonment &c. of Giacinto Achilli, w. acc. of his prev. hist. 8°. 1850
Eardley-Wilmot (*Sir* **Sydney M.)** Our journal in the Pacific. By officers of H.M.S. Zealous. Ed. by Lt. S. E.-W. 8°. 1873
Eardley-Wilmot (V. L.) Abrasives. [Canada: Dept. of Mines]. pl–3. 8°. Ottawa. 1927
Molybdenum. [Canada. Geolog. Survey]. 8°. Ottawa. 1925

Earland (Arthur), *see* HERON-ALLEN (E.) & A. E., *for works on* Foraminifera, 1908–16.

Earle (*Mrs.* Alice Morse).
The Sabbath in Puritan New England. s8°. 1892

Earle (*Mrs.* C. W. [Maria Theresa]) & Ethel Case.
Gardening for the ignorant. s8°. 1912
Pot-pourri mixed by two. 8°. 1914

Earle (Edward Mead). Turkey, the Gt. Powers, & the Bagdad Railway. s8°. 1923

Earle (*Rev.* John). Remarks on the prefaces pref. to 1st & 2nd vol. of the Holy Bible, tr. by Alex. Geddes. s8°. 1799

Early Eng. & Scot. poetry, 1250–1600, 1888, *see* FITZGIBBON (H. M.)

Early English Texts Society.
Original series, 153–173. 8°. 1919–28
„ „ ....rev. ed. &c. 4, 18, 20, 31 [repr.] 8°. 1902–23
Extra Series, 73, 114, 117, 118, 120–24. 8°. 1920–27
see BIBLE: ANGLO-SAXON. The Old Eng. version of the Heptateuch, Aelfric's Treatise on the Old & New Test. &c.; ed. &c. S. J. Crawford, 1922. [160.]
„ BIBLE: GOSPELS. Pepysian Gospel harmony; ed. M. Goates, 1922. [157.]
„ BOCCACCIO (G.) Lydgate's Fall of princes; ed. H. Bergen, 4p, 1924–27. [E. S., 121–4.]
„ BOETHIUS (A. M. T. S.) De consol. philos.; tr. J. Walton; ed. &c. M. Science, 1927. [170.]
„ CHRIST. Medit. on the life &c. of C.; *ed.* C. D'Evelyn, 1921. [158.]
„ —— A stanzaic life of Christ: comp. f. Higden's Polychron. &c., 1926. [166.]
„ COVENTRY PLAYS. Ludus Coventriae; ed. K. S. Block, 1922. [E. S., 120.]
„ FISHER (J.), *bp.* Life of Fisher, transcr. by R. Bayne, 1921. [E. S., 117.]
„ GAWAINE. Sir Gawayne & the Green Knight, 1, Text: ed. R. Morris, 1864; rev. I. Gollancz, 1923. [4.]
„ HAWES (S.) The pastime of pleasure; intr. &c. by W. E. Mead, 1928. [173.]
„ HOCCLEVE (T.) Works, v2, 1925. [E. S., 73.]
„ HOLY. *Hali Meidenhad, 13th c., rev. ed., 1922. [18.]
„ JESUS CHRIST. *The southern Passion; ed. &c. B. D. Brown, 1927. [169.]
„ LICHFIELD. The Gild of St. Mary, L.: ordinances & o. docs.; ed. F. J. Furnivall, 1920. [E. S., 114.]
„ LULLY (R.) Book of the ordre of chyvalry; tr. & pr. by Caxton, 1926. [168.]
„ MANDEVILLE (*Sir* J.) M.'s travels; tr. f. Fr. of J. d'Outremeuse; ed. P. Hamelius, 2v, 1919–23 [153, 154.]
„ MIDDLETON (C.) Famous hist. of Chinon of England, w. The assertion of King Arthure; ed. &c. W. E. Mead, 1925. [165.]
„ MIRKUS (J.) Instructions for parish priests, 1868; repr., 1902. [31.]
„ PEACOCK (R.), *bp.* The donet; ed. &c. E. V. Hitchcock, 1921. [156.]
„ —— The reule of Crysten religioun; ed. W. C. Greet, 1927. [171.]
„ —— The folewer to the Donet; ed. E. V. Hitchcock, 1924. [164.]
„ PEARL. Pearl, Cleanness, Patience & Sir Gawain; reprod. in facs.; intr. by Sir I. Gollancz, 1923. [162.]
„ ROLLE (R.) Eng. prose treatises; ed. G. G. Perry, n. & rev. text &c., 1921; *&* Officium, rev. issue, 1921. [20.]
„ RYPINS (S.), *ed.* Three O.E. prose texts, 1924. [161.]
„ SAINT BARTHOLOMEW, *Smithfield.* Book of the foundation; ed. Sir N. Moore, 1923. [163.]
„ STEELE (R. R.) Earliest arithmetics in English, 1922. [E. S., 118.]
„ TREVISA (J.) Dialogus inter militem & clericum &c., 1925. [167.]
„ TROY. The seege or batayle of Troye ed. M. E. Barnicle, 1927. [172.]
„ *VICES & virtues: Middle Eng. dialogue, p2, Notes &c., 1921. [159.]
„ WHEATLEY MS.; ed. w. intr. &c. by M. Day, 1921. [155.]

***Earthquake** (The) in Bengal & Assam, 1897, *see* BENGAL.

Earthquakes: *A farther acc. of mem. e., to 1756. By a Gentleman of the Univ. of C. 8°. C. 1756

Earthworks Committee, *see* CONGRESS OF ARCH. SOCIETIES.

***East** & west. Confessions of a princess. By —— ? s8°. [1924]

East (David J.) Western Africa; its condition &c. s8°. 1844

East (Edward Murray).
Heredity & human affairs. 8°. N.Y. 1927
Mankind at the crossroads. 8°. N.Y. 1923
„ „ ....8°. N.Y. 1924

Easterbrook (Joseph), *see* MOORE (H.) Sermon preached on death of J. E., 1791.

Eastern. Eastern Archipelago pilot, 3v, Suppl. 1, 5, 6, *&* Not. to mariners, 1911–22, *see* ADMIRALTY.
From an Eastern Embassy; memories of London, Berlin & the East, 1920, *see* FROM.

Eastern Asia. Offic. guide to Eastern Asia, v1–5, 1914–20, *see* ASIA.

Eastern Associated Telegraph Companies. 50 yrs. of "via Eastern." Souv. & record, jubilee of the East. Assoc. Telegraph Co., 1922. la8°. [1922]

Eastern Europe. For the defence of the new Eastern republics. 1st year. Nos. 1–8 (Sept.–Dec. 1919). 8°. Paris. 1919

East-European problems. Nos. 1–24, 26. [P2567]. s8°. 1920–21
Each pamphlet has been catalogued separately under the author's name.

East Grinstead, *Sussex.* Parish register, 1558–1661. Ed. R. P. Crawfurd. [Sussex Rec. Soc., v24]. 8°. 1917

East India Company. A calendar of the court minutes &c. of the E.I. Co. By E. B. Sainsbury, w. intr. & notes by W. Foster. [v6–7]. 8°. O. 1922–25
6, 1660–63. 7, 1664–67.
5th Report f. Sel. Comm. of H. of Commons on affairs of the E.I. Co., 1812. Ed. w. notes & intr. by W. K. Firminger. 3v. 8°. Calcutta. 1917–18
1, Intr. & text of Rep. 2, Intr. & Bengal App. 3, Brit. acquisit. in Presid. of Fort St. George, Madras App., Gloss. &c.
see CAMPBELL OF BARCALDINE (*Maj. Sir* D. A. D.) Records of Clan Campbell in milit. service of E.I.C., 1600–1858, 1925.
„ FOSTER (*Sir* W.) The E.I. House, 1924.
„ —— John Co., 1926.
„ MORSE (H. B.) Chron. of E.I. Co. trading to China, 1635–1834, 4v, 1926.

East Indies. *Genuine (A) account of some trans. in the E.I., occurrences on the coast of Coromandel, since July 1749. s8°. 1753

Eastlake (*Lady*). *Letters f. the shores of the Baltic. [*a. c. b. w.* Southey (R.) Cromwell &c., 1844]. s8°. 1844

Eastlake (Charles Lock), *architect.* Hints on household taste in furniture, upholstery & o. details. 4th ed. rev. 8°. 1878

Eastman (Max).
Leon Trotsky: the portrait of a youth. s8°. 1926
Marx, Lenin & the sci. of revol. s8°. [1926]

Eastwood (Reginald Allen).
The organiz. of a Britannic partnership. s8°. M'ter. 1922
see WILLIAMS (J.) Princ. of law of real property, 24th ed. by R. A. E., 1926.

Eastwood (Tom). Lead & zinc ores of Lake Dist. &c., *see* GEOLOG. SURVEY. Spec. rep. on min. resources, 22, 1921.
see DEWEY (H.) Copper ores of the Midlands &c.; by H. D., T. E. &c., 1925.
„ WHITEHEAD (T. H.) & T. E. Geol. of S. p. of S. Staffs. coalfield, 1927.

——, W. Gibson &c. Geol. of the co. around Coventry, incl. carbonif. rocks of the Warwick. coalfield. [Mems. of G.S.] 8°. 1923

——, T. H. Whitehead & T. Robertson. Geology of the co. around Birmingham. [G.S. of Eng. &c.] 8°. 1925

Eaton (Nathaniel). Guil. Amesi sententia de orig. sabbati & die Dominico. [*b. w.* Ames (W.) Anti-synodalia scr., 1646]. s8°. Franckerae. 1653
„ „ [*a. ed., b. w.* Ames (W.) Medulla theolog., 1650]. s8°. Amstelodami. 1658

Eaton (Ralph M.) Symbolism & truth. Intr. to theory of knowledge. 8°. Camb. [U.S.A.] 1925

Eaves (Lucile). A legacy to wage-earning women, Brattleboro, Vermont, Thomas Thompson Trust. By L. E. & associates. Intr. by R. M. Bradley. 8°. Boston, Mass. 1925

Eayrs (George).
John Wesley, Xtn. philosopher &c. 8°. [1926]

Eayrs (Hugh Sterling).
Sir Isaac Brock. rev. ed. s8°. Toronto. 1924

Ebart (Johann). Enchiridion theolog. supra nonnullas definitiones &c. Compendii theolog. L. Hutteri. Cum præf. Chr. Chemnitii. s8°. Jenæ. 1665

Ebbits (John), *see* FRENCH (W.) In Chancery; estate of W. F. & F. J. Greenway, in liquid. w. estate of J. E., 1846.

Ebbo, *S. Michaelis Monachus* [EBO]. The life of Otto, Apostle of Pomerania, 1060–1139. By Ebo & Herbordus. [Tr. w. intr. &c. by] C. H. Robinson. s8°. 1920

Ebeid (W. Makram), *see* MAKRAM EBEID (W.)

Ebel (Carl), *see* WALBE (H.) Die Kunstdenkmäler d. Kreises Giessen, B2, Kloster Arnsburg mit Altenburg; bearbt. v. H. W.; geschichtl. Teil v. K. E., 1919.

Ebel (Caspar) [EBELIUS (C.)]
Compend. logicae plenius. s8º. Giessæ Hass. 1660

Ebel (Johann Gottfried). Atlas to E.'s travellers guide thr. Switzerland. s8º. [*map folded.* 1819 ?]

Ebeling (Erich). Keilschrifttexte aus Assur religiösen Inhalts. B1, 2, Autographien. v. E. E. [Deut. Or.-Gesell., Wiss. Veröffentl., 28, 34]. fol. L. 1919–23
Liebeszauber im Alten Orient [Mitteil. d. Altor. Gesellschaft, B1i]. 8º. L. 1925

Eber (Paul). Calendarium hist. conscr. a P. E. & recens ab eodem auctum. s8º. Vitebergæ. 1559
Pia & in verbo Dei fundata assertio, &c. de sacr. cœna Domini nostri J. C. s8º. Witebergæ. 1563
see MANSFELD. *Bericht der Prediger der Irrungen halben &c., 1568.

Eberhard, *von Gandersheim.* Die Gandersheimer Reimchronik. Hrsg. L. Wolff. 8º. Halle (Saale). 1927

Eberhardt (Isabelle). Mes journaliers. Préc. de La vie tragique de la bonne nomade, par R.-L. Doyon. s8º. 1923
Pages d'Islam. Publ. avec préf. &c. par V. Barrucand. s8º. 1920
Trimardeur. Roman. Préf. par V. Barrucand. s8º. 1922

Eberhardus, *Alemannus* [EVERARDUS]. Laborintus, *see* FARAL (A.) Les arts poét. du 12 & 13 s., 1924.

Eberhardus, *Bethuniensis. For the* Laborintus *sometimes ascribed to E. B., see* EBERHARDUS, *Alemannus.*

Eberl (Bartholomäus). Die bayer. Ortsnamen als Grund. d. Siedelungsgesch. 2T *in* 1v. [*pagin. cont.*] la8º. München. 1925–26

Eberlein (Gerhard). Die schles. Grenzkirchen im 17. Jhdt., *see* BRANDENBURG (E.) & G. E. Vorträge, 1901.

Eberlein (Harold Donaldson).
see RICHARDSON (A. E.) & H. D. E. The Eng. inn, 1925.
,, —— & —— Smaller Eng. house, 1660–1830, 1925.

Eberlin (Johann), *von Günzberg.* Mich wundert das kein gelt ihm land ist (*facs.* 1524), *see* FREYTAG (G.) Bilder, B3, T2, 1924.

Ebermann (Veit) [ERBERMANNUS (V.)], *see* BAIER (J. W.), *the elder.* Diss. qua dialogi Erbermanniani int. Lutherum & Arium excutiuntur, 1673.

Ebers (Georg). Egypt. Tr. C. Bell. Intr. & notes by S. Birch. 2v. fol. 1887

Ebersolt (Jean).
Les arts somptuaires de Byzance. 4º. 1923
La miniature byzantine. fol. 1926
Mission archéolog. de Constantinople. la8º. 1921
Sanctuaires de Byzance: recherches sur les anc. trésors d. églises de Constantinople. la8º. 1921

Ebert (Friedrich), *see* PAYER (F.) Von Bethmann Hollweg bis E., 1923.

Ebert (Max). Reallexikon d. Vorgeschichte. Hrsg. M. E. B1–11. 8º. 1924–28
Südrussland im Altertum. s8º. Bonn. 1921

Eble, *d'Ussel, see* USSEL. Poésies des 4 troubadours d'U.; publ. d'ap. les MSS. par J. Audiau, 1922.

Ebner (Jodocus Guilielmus).
Diss. de Cadvalla rege Saxonum. s4º. Altorfii. 1736

Ebner-Eschenbach (Marie v.) Sämtl. Werke. 6B. s8º. *n.d.*

Ebo, *S. Michaelis Monachus, see* EBBO.

Ebrard (Joh. H. August). The Gospel hist.: crit. investig. in support of hist. character of the 4 Gospels. Tr. J. Martin. Rev. & ed. A. B. Bruce. 8º. E., *Clarke.* 1863

Ebrulphus, *St., see* EVROUL.

Ebser (Johann), *bp. of Chiemsée, d. 1438.* *Onus eccl. In hoc libro admiranda quædam de septem eccl. statibus, abusibus &c. sfol. Coloniæ. 1531

Ebury (Francis Egerton Grosvenor, *4th baron*). Illust. partic., plan &c. of the estate of Moor Park, for sale by Knight, Frank & Rutley. 11 Sept. 1919. By dir. of Ld. E. 2nd ed. fol. 1919

Ebury (Robert Grosvenor, *1st baron*). Extracts f. the journal of Ld. G.: acc. of h. visit to the Barbary Regencies, 1830. 8º. Chester. [1831]

Eça de Queiroz (—). A corr. de Fradique Mendes: mem. &c. 7a ed. s8º. Porto. 1923
E. de Q. Selecta. [Antol. portuguesa, por A. de Campos]. 2v. s8º. Paris. 1922–23

Eça de Queiroz (—) [*continued*].
Os Maias. Episodios da vida romantica. 2a ed. 2v. s8º. Porto. [1898]
Prosas barbaras. Intr. por J. Batalha Reis. s8º. Porto. 1903

Eccard (Johann Chilian). Diss. de pontif. Rom. qui reformationem eccl. frustra tentarunt. Praes. J. F. Buddeo. s4º. Jenæ. [1718]

Eccardus, *ps.*
Gesch. d. niederen Volkes in Deutschland. 2B. la8º. [1907]

Eccardus (Joannes Georgius), *see* ECKHART (JOHANN GEORG VON).

Eccles (Francis Yvon).
Racine in England. [Taylorian Lect., 1921]. 8º. O. 1922

Eccles (Herbert) & B. Rackham. Analysed spec. of Eng. porcelain. [V. & A. Museum]. s8º. 1922

Ecclesfield. Marriage &c. registers of E. parish church, Yorks., 1558–1619; also Churchwardens' accounts, 1520–46. Annot. by A. S. Gatty. la8º. 1878

Ecclesia [ECCLESIAE]. Eccl. evang. lib. symbol., 1730, *see* PFAFF (C. M.), *ed.*
Eccl. Graecae mon., 4t, 1677–92, *see* COTELERIUS (J. B.)

Ecclesiastical [ECCLESIASTICALL]. *Disc. conc. illegality of the late Eccl. Comm., 1689, *see* STILLINGFLEET (E.)
*Eccl. (The) discipline of the Reformed churches in France, 1642, *see* FRANCE.

Ecclesiasticus [*see also* APOCRYPHA]. A Jesus Sirah könyue Magyar Nyeluen. [*b. w.* Bible: Solomon. A Bölts Kiralnac Könyuei, 1552]. s8º. Colosvarba [*Helthai Gaspar &c.*] 1551
E. Greek text of Codex 248. Ed. w. textual comm. & proleg. by J. H. A. Hart. s8º. C. 1909

Ecclesiology. Hand-book of Eng. e., 1847, *see* CAMBRIDGE CAMDEN SOC.

Ecelini, *House of, see* EZZELINI.

Echagüe (Juan Pablo) [JEAN PAUL].
Un teatro en formación. s8º. Buenos Aires. 1919

Echartus (Henricus), *see* ECKHARD (H.)

Echecs [ESCHECS]. *Le jeu des eschecs, avec s. invent. &c.; tr. d'Espagnol, 1609, *see* JEU.

Echegaray (Carmelo de). Trabajos de un cronista. [Bibl. Bascongada de F. Herrán, t26]. [v1]. 8º. Bilbao. 1898

Echegaray (José), *dramatic writer.* [Obras. *Coll. of plays bound together & lettered on binding* El teatro, 1–9. *Contents as below*]. 9v. 8º. 1876–97

Á la orilla del mar, 1893. [9.]
Algunas veces aquí, 2ª ed., 1880. [2.]
El bandido Lisandro, 1886. [5.]
Bodas trágicas, 2ª ed., 1881. [3.]
La calumnia por castigo, 1897. [9.]
La cantante callejera, 1896. [9.]
Comedia sin desenlace, 1892. [8.]
Cómo empieza y cómo acaba, 5ª ed., 1881. [1.]
El conde Lotario, 1887. [6.]
Conflicto entre dos deberes, 5ª ed., 1883. [4.]
Correr en pos de un ideal, 2ª ed., 1879. [2.]
Un crítico incipiente, 1891. [8.]
De mala raza, 2ª ed., 1892. [5.]
Los dos curiosos impertinentes, 2ª ed., 1882. [4.]
Dos fanatismos, 2ª ed., 1887. [6.]
En el pilar y en la cruz, 3ª ed., 1881. [2.]
En el puño de la espada, 7ª ed., 1882. [1.]
En el seno de la muerte, 6ª ed., 1882. [3.]
La esposa del vengador, 7ª ed., 1882. [1.]
El estigma, 2ª ed., 1896. [9.]
El gladiador de Ravena, 2ª ed., 1881. [3.]
El gran Galeoto, 6ª ed., 1881. [3.]
,, ,, ...16ª ed., 1882. [4.]
Haroldo el Normando, 4ª ed., *n.d.* [4.]
El hijo de Don Juan, 1892. [8.]
El hijo de hierro y el hijo de carne, 1888. [6.]
Irene de Otranto, 1891. [7.]
Iris de paz, 2ª ed., 1881. [3.]
El libro talonario, 4ª ed., 1884. [1.]
Lo que no puede decirse, 4ª ed., *n.d.* [2.]
Manantial que no se agota, 1889. [7.]
Mancha que limpia, 1895. [9.]
Mar sin orillas, 4ª ed., 1883. [3.]
Mariana, 3ª ed., 1893. [8.]
Un milagro en Egipto, 2ª ed., 1883; *&* Notas, 1883. [4.]
Morir por no despertar, 3ª ed., 1883. [2.]
La muerte en los labios, 6ª ed., 1881. [3.]
El número tres, 1876. [5.]
Ó locura ó santidad, 4ª ed., 1881. [2.]
Para tal culpa tal pena, 3ª ed., 1883. [1.]
La peste de Otranto, 4ª ed., 1884. [5.]
Piensa mal . . . y acertarás ?, 1884. [5.]
El primer acto de un drama, 1895. [9.]
El prólogo de un drama, 1891. [7.]
La realidad y el delirio, 2ª ed., 1887. [6.]
Los rígidos, 2ª ed., 1890. [7.]
Semíramis, ó la hija del aire, p2, 1896. [9.]
Sic vos non vobis o la últ. limosna, 1892. [8.]
Siempre en ridículo, 1891. [7.]
Un sol que nace y un sol que muere, 4ª ed., 1883. [1.]
Lo sublime en lo vulgar, 1888. [6.]

Echegaray (José) [*continued*].
Tierra baja, 1896. [9.]
La última noche, 3a ed., 1880. [1.]
Vida alegre y muerte triste, 4a ed., 1885. [5.]

Echeverria (Juan de). Paseos por Granada y sus contornos o descr. de sus antig. &c. Ed. con notas p[or] D[on] J[ulian] M[aria] P[erez]. 2t. s4°. Granada. 1814

Echlin (Gladys). The thief & o. poems. 8°. 1923

Echmiadzin. Cat. de la bibl. d'E. Publ. M. Brosset. [*Fr. & Russ., w.* Notice *on E.* P2799]. la8°. St.-Pétersbourg. 1840
[Cat. of MSS. *In Armenian*]. la8°. i Tiflis. 1863

Echoes of Exmoor, 2nd ser., 1924, *see* EXMOOR.

Eck (Johann von).
Ad Invictiss. Poloniae regem Sigismundum de sacrificio missae contra Lutheranos libri duo. [*a. copy in* P2540]. s8°. *n.p.* [? Cologne]. 1526
Apologia pro principibus Catholicis &c. adv. mucores & calumnias Buceri, super actis Comitiorum Ratisponae. Apologia pro card. G. Contareno. s4°. Ingolstadii Baioriae. 1542
„ „ ....[*a. ed.*] s8°. Antverpiae. 1542
Articulos 404 ad disputationes Lipsicam, Badeñ, & Berneñ attin. &c. J. Eckius offert se disputaturum, Augustae Vindelicorum. s4°. [Ingolstadii. 1530]
Christenl. ausslegung d. Evangelienn. T1, 2 [*in* 1v], D. erste Tail, vom Advent biss Ostern. [Der Ander Tail, vonn Ostern bis auff den Advẽt. T3–5 *wanting*]. fol. Ingelstat. 1530
Christenl. erhaltung der stell der geschrifft, für das Fegfeur, wider Luthers lasterbüchlin. s4°. [Augsburg ?]. 1530
Defensio contra A. Bodenstein invectiones (1518); hrsg. J. Greving, *see* CORPUS CATHOLIC., H1, 1919.
De poenitentia & conf. secreta, contra Lutherum, libri 2. [*b. w. h.* Enchiridion, 1533]. s8°. Venetiis. 1533
De satisfactione &c., contra Lutherum, liber unus. [*b. w. h.* Enchiridion, 1533]. s8°. Venetiis. 1533
Disputatio D. J. E. & P. Martini Luther in studio Lipsensi futura [*A letter of E. to Card. M. Langius*, 1518 [1519], *& one of Luther to A. Bodenstein w. 12 propositions*]. [P2444]. s4°. [Wittemberg ?]. 1519
Disputatio excellentium D. doctorū Johannis Eccij & Andreę Carolostadij q̄ cepta est Lipsię 27 Junij An. 1519. Disp. secunda J. E. & A. C. 15 Julij. Disp. eiusdem J. E. & D. M. Lutheri 4 Julij. [*a. c., without tp. in* P2444]. 4°. [Leipzig. 1519]
„ „ Der authent. Text der Leipz. Disput. [*betw. Eck, Carlstadt & Luther*] (1519). Hrsg. v. O. Seitz. 8°. 1903
D. M. ludders Underricht an Kurfursten von Sachssen. disputation zu Leypszig belangent: u. D. Eckius brive. s4°. *n.p.* [1519]
Enchiridion locorum communium adv. Lutteranos. Ab autore jam tertio recogn. &c. s8°. Landesutæ Baioariæ. 1526
„ „ ....[*a. ed.*] s8°. [Venetiis]. 1533
„ „ ....[*a. ed.*] s8°. Coloniae. 1573
Epistola de ratione studiorum suorum (1538); hrsg. J. Metzler, *see* CORPUS catholicorum, H2, 1921.
Excusatio E. ad ea que falso sibi P. Melanchton Vuittenburgeñ. super theologica disputatione Lipsica adscripsit. [*Printer's device below title & wood-cut on verso of tp.*] [P2444]. s4°. [Lipsiae. 1519]
Des heiligen Concilij tzu Costenitz, der heylgen Christenheit u. hochlöblichen keyszers Sigmunds &c. entschůldigung, das in bruder Martin Luder, mit unwarheit, auffgelegt. s4°. *n.p.* [Leipzig, *M. Landsberg* ?]. 1520
Prima [-secunda] pars operum contra Ludderum. 2p [*in* 1v]. fol. [Augustae Vindel.] 1530–31
Replica adv. scripta secunda Buceri super actis Ratisponae. Expurg. E. à mendaci infamatione, quia adhuc vivit E. [*Foll. by* Vaticinium J. Thauleri &c.] [P2540] s4°. [Ingolstadii. 1543]
„ „ ....[*a. ed.*] s4°. Ingolstadii, *A. Weissenborn*. 1543
Ein Sentbrieve an ein frum Eidgnossschafft, betreffendt die ketzer. disput. Frantz Kolben u. B. Hallers zu Bern. Ein anderer brieve an U. Zwingli. Der drit brieve an C. Rotenacker zu Ulm. s4°. *n.p.* [1528]
Verlegung der disput. zu Bern, mit grund götlicher geschrifft: durch J. E. An die Christenl. ordt der Eydgnosschafft &c. s4°. *n.p.* [Ingolstadt ?]. 1528
see BADEN. Die disputacion vor den xii orten einer lobl. eidtgnoschafft &c., 1527.
„ DIONYSIUS, *Saint, Areopagite*. De mystica theologia lib. 1; J. E. comment. adjecit, 1519.
„ ERASMUS (D.) Contenta in hoc libello E. R. epist. ad Ducẽ Fridericū, Positiones J. E. scholasticae &c., 1519 ?.
„ LANGIUS (J.) Oratio: encomium disput. J. E. &c., 1519.
„ LUTHER (M.) Contra malignum J. E. iudicium &c., 1519 ?.
„ —— Von den newen E. Bullen vnd lugen, 1520.
„ MELANCHTHON (P.) Defensio P. M. contra I. E., 1519.
„ OECOLAMPADIUS (J.) *Canoni indocti Lutherani: Eccio respondent canonici, 1519.
„ —— Die verdeutscht antwort, der, die E. in s. Sendbrieff an d. Bischoff zu Meyssen hat die ungelarten Lutherischen Thumhern genandt, 1520.
„ PIRCKHEIMER (W.) *Eccius dedolatus, 1520 ?.
„ WOLPH (E.) In obitu I. E. epicedion, 1543; 1921.
„ WORMS. Colloq. Wormaciense instit. A.D. 1540 &c., 1542.

Eckard (Heinrich), *see* ECKHARD (H.)

Eckardstein (Hermann, *Frhr.* **v.)** Lebenserinn. u. polit. Denkwürdigkeiten. B3, Die Isolierung Deutschlands. 8°. L. [1921]
Persönl. Erinnerungen an König Eduard. 8°. Dresden. 1927
Ten years at the Court of St. James', 1895–1905. Tr. & ed. G. Young. 8°. [1921]
see HAGEN (M. v.) Deutschlands Bündnispolitik, Betr. z. d. Mem. d. Frhr. v. E., 1922.

Eckardt (Anton).
Alt. Kunstgewerbe in Unterfranken. la8°. Augsburg. 1925

Eckardt (Hans v.) Die Sozialpolitik in d. Union d. Soz. Sovĕtrepubl. 8°. 1925

Eckardt (Julius W. A. v.) Aus d. Tagen v. Bismarcks Kampf gegen Caprivi. Erinnerungen. 8°. L. 1920

Eckel (Edwin Clarence). Coal, iron & war. 8°. [1921]

Eckel (John C.) The 1st editions of the wr. of C. Dickens & th. values. A bibliog. 8°. 1913

Eckenstein (Lina). History of Sinai. s8°. 1921

Eckeren (Gerard van). Het troostend verleden. [De Van Beemsters, 1]. 2e dr. s8°. [1921]
Ida Westerman. 2e dr. s8°. A. *n.d.*
Uitzichten. [De Van Beemsters, 2]. 2e dr. s8°. [1921]

Eckermann (Johann Peter).
see HOUBEN (H. H.) E., s. Leben f. Goethe, 1925.
„ PETERSEN (J.) Entst. d. E. Gespräche &c., 1924; 2e verb. A., 1925.

Eckett (Robert), *1797–1862*, *see* BAXTER (M.) Methodism, w. recoll. of E., 1865.

Eckhard (Heinrich) [ECHARTUS; ECKARD].
Comp. theologiae Patrum, &c. s8°. Schleusingae. 1609
Fasc. controv. theol.; quaestiones de quibus inter Aug. Conf. theologos & Calvinianos disceptatur. 2° ed., auct. &c. s8°. Lipsiae. 1611

Eckhard (Melchior Sylvester). Pastor conscientiosus, quaestiones de casibus &c., ministri personam tang. s8°. Ulmae. 1651

Eckhard (Paul Jacob). Vindiciae Lutheri & Melanchthonis ab infami pictura commendatariorum Jutrebocensium. s4°. Jutreboci. 1738
Wendische Kirchen-Historie &c. [T1. *no more publ.* ?] s8°. Wittenberg. 1739

Eckhard (Tobias). Codices manuscripti Quedlinburg.; acc. variantes lectiones e cod. Sulpitii Severi de vita S. Martini &c. et epistolæ tres Lutheri & Melanchthonis. [P2443]. s4°. Quedlinburgi. 1723
Non-Christianorum de Christo testimonia. ed. auct. s4°. Quedlinburg. 1736

Eckhart (*Meister*). Eine latein. Rechtfertigungsschrift d. Meister Eckhart, mit e. Geleitwort v. C. Baeumker, hrsg. v. A. Daniels. [Beitr. z. Gesch. d. Philos. d. M.-a.'s, B23, H5]. 8°. Münster i. W. 1923
Latein. Schriften &c., v. Denifle, *see* ARCHIV. F. LITT.- U. KIRCHENGESCH. D. M.-A. B2, 1886.
Meister E. [*Works*], *see* PFEIFFER (F.) M. E.; tr., 1924.
see GURK (P.) Meister E. [*fiction*], 1925.

Eckhart, *zum Drübel* [DRÜBEL (ECKHART ZUM)]. Ein demütige ermanung an ein gantze gemeine Christenheit. [*Border to tp.* P2539]. s4°. [Strassburg, *M. Flach*]. *n.d.* [ca. 1522]

Eckhart (Johann Georg von). Animadv. histor. &c. in J. F. Schannati Dioecesin &c. Fuld. &c. fol. Wirceburgi. 1727
De origine German. eorumque vetust. coloniis, migrationibus libri 2. Ed. & praef. est C. L. Scheidius. s4°. Goettingae. 1750
Hist. studii etymol. linguae German.; acc. quaedam de lingua Venedorum in Germania habit. &c. s8°. Hanoverae. 1711
Leges Francorum, Salicae & Ripuariorum, cum add. regum & imperatorum variis. Acc. formulae vet. Alsaticae, Annales Franc. regni &c. fol. Francofurti & Lipsiae. 1720
see CATECHESIS. *Incerti monachi Weissenburg. Cat. Theotisca sec. 9 conscr.; ed. &c. I. G. E., 1713.

Eckstein (Carl). Die Schmetterlinge &c. 8°. Wiesbaden. 1922

Eclaircissements [ECLAIRCISSEMENS]. *Eclaircissemens sur les miracles operez par l'intercession de M. Paris, 2p, 1733, *see* PARIS (F. DE).

Eclectic Library.
Rep. & catalogue for 1808–9. [P2486]. s8°. [1809]

Eclectic review. N.S. [4th], v3, 4. 8°. 1838

Eclectic Society. Eclectic notes; discuss. at meetings of the E. Soc., 1798–1814. 2nd ed. 8°. 1865

Eclipse. *Total (The) e.: a grand polit.-astron. phenomenon &c., 1820, *see* TOTAL.

Ecloga ad procheiron mutata; tr. E. H. Freshfield, 1927, *see* LEO III, *emp. of East.*

Ecole (L') des Chartes. Bibliothèque de l'E. des C. t79–87, 1918–26. 8°. 1918–26

Mémoires et doc. 10. la8°. 1919

see STEIN (H.) Charles de France, 1919. [10.]

École des Hautes Etudes, *see* BIBLIOTHÈQUE DE L'ECOLE DES HAUTES ETUDES.

Ecole des Hautes Etudes Sociales, *see* HELLÉNISATION du monde ant.: leçons, 1914.

Ecole Française d'Athènes. Bulletin de corresp. hellénique. Annee[s] 40–51 (1916–27). la8°. 1916–27

1917–19 *in* 1v, *containing* Obs. s. les prem. habitats de la Macédoine; [par] L. Rey [*w. sep. tp.*]

Explor. archéol. de Délos faite par l'Ec. Fr. d'A. sous les auspices du Ministère de l'Instr. Publ. & aux frais de M. le Duc de Loubat. Publ. sous la dir. de T. Homolle, M. Holleaux &c. [fasc. 6, 7i, 8i, ii, 9]. 4°. 1921–26

Bulard (M.) Descr. des revêtments peints à sujets relig., 1926. [9.]

Chamonard (J.) Le Quartier du Théâtre, 1922–24. [8i, ii.]

Picard (C.) L'établ. des Poseidoniastes de Bérytos, 1921. [6.]

Vallois (R.) Les portiques au Sud du Hièron, p1, 1923. [7i.]

Fouilles de Delphes. Exécutées par ordre du Gouvt. franç. & publ. sous la dir. de T. Homolle. t2, fasc. 1–[6 *&* Relèves & restaurations], t3, fasc. 1, 2, 4, t4, fasc. 1, 2, t5 (Texte par P. Perdrizet), 3 fasc. [*Each fasc. has accomp. plates.* t4, fasc. 2, *plates only*]. 4°. 1904–27

see DUGAS (C.) &c. Le sanctuaire d'Aléa Athéna à Tégée au 4e siècle, 1924.

„ POTTIER (E.) & S. REINACH. La nécropole de Myrina, 2t, 1888.

École Franç. de Rome, *see* CHARLES I, *k. of Naples.* Actes &c. de C. I conc. la Fr. (1257–84); Boüard, 1926.

Ecole Française d'Extrême-Orient. Bulletin. t14–23. la8°. Hanoi. 1914–24

t21 *cont.* L'École Fr. dep. s. orig. j. 1920 *&* Index gén., t1–20, *each w. sep. tp. & pagin.*

[*Publications*], *see* CHAVANNES (E.) Mission arch. dans la Chine septentr., t1ii, 1915.

Ecole Libre des Sciences Polit., *see* RHÉNANIE, LA. La R.: conf., 1922.

Ecole Pratique des Hautes Etudes. Mélanges publ. pour 10e anniv., 1878—Docs. sur l'E. Pratique, 1893—Cinquantenaire: Mélanges, 1921—Célébr. du cinquant., 1922, *see* BIBLIOTHÈQUE DE L'ECOLE DES HAUTES ETUDES.

Section des sciences hist. &c. Annuaire, 1898. 8°. 1897

Ecoles Françaises d'Athènes & de Rome.

PUBLICATIONS:

see ALBERTINI (E.) La compos. dans les ouvrages philos. de Sénèque, 1923.

„ BENEDICT XII, *pope.* B. XII, 1334–42: lettres se rapp. à la France; [publ.] G. Daumat, 1920.

„ BOÜARD (A. DE). Régime polit. & les instit. de Rome, 1252–1347, 1920.

„ CARCOPINO (J.) Virgile & les orig. d'Ostie, 1919.

„ CLEMENT IV, *pope.* Registres; publ. E. Jordan, t1, 1893–1912.

„ COLIN (G.) Rome & la Grèce de 200 à 146 av. J.-C., 1905.

„ CONSTANT (G.) Concession à l'Allem. de la Communion sous 2 espèces, 2t, 1923.

„ COURBY (F.) Les vases grecs à reliefs, 1922.

„ DUGAS (C.) La céramique des Cyclades, 1925.

„ FAWTIER (R.) Sainte Catherine de Sienne, t1, 1921.

„ HATZFELD (J.) Trafiquants ital. dans l'Orient hellén., 1919.

„ HIRSCHAUER (C.) Polit. de St Pie V en France, 1566–72, 1922.

„ HOLLEAUX (M.) Rome, la Grèce & les monarchies hellénist., 1921.

„ —— Στρατηγὸς ὕπατος: ét. sur la tr. en Grec du titre consulaire, 1918.

„ INNOCENT IV, *pope.* Les registres d'I. IV; publ. &c. E. Berger, t4, 1921.

„ JARDÉ (A.) Céréales dans l'ant. grecque, t1, 1925.

„ JOHN XXII, *pope.* J. XXII, 1316–34: lettres communes anal. par G. Mollat, t2–8, 1905–24.

„ —— J. XXII, 1316–34: lettres secrètes &c. rel. à la France, extr. des reg. du Vatican par A. Coulon, t1, 1906.

„ LA BLANCHÈRE (R. DU C. DE). Terracine, 1884.

„ LAURENT (J.) L'Arménie entre Byzance & l'Islam, 1919.

„ PICARD (CH.) Ephèse & Claros, 1922.

„ PIGANIOL (A.) Essai sur les origines de Rome, 1917.

„ ROUSSEL (L.) Gram. descr. du roméique litt., 1922.

„ ROUSSEL (P.) Délos, colonie athén., 1916.

Ecole Spéciale des Langues Orientales Vivantes [*Paris*]. Publications. s3. t18–21. la8°. 1894–1901

see COURANT (M.) Bibl. coréene, 3t, 1894–7; Suppl., 1901. [s3, 18–21.]

Economic. Econ. consequences of the League, 1927, *see* LEAGUE OF NATIONS.

Econ. (The) rel. betw. France & Australia, 1919, *see* FRANCE.

Econ. (The) resources of Italy, 1895–1920, 2v, 1920, *see* ITALY.

*Econ. value of Upper Silesia for Poland & Germany resp., 1920, *see* SILESIA.

Economic journal (The): the journal of the Royal Econ. Soc. v30–37. la8°. 1920–27

Economic review (The) w. wh. is incorp. the Political review, *see* REVIEW OF THE FOREIGN PRESS.

Economist (The), weekly commercial times, bankers' gazette & railway monitor. v90–105 (Jan. 1920–Dec. 1927). fol. 1920–27

Economiste (L') français: journal hebdomadaire. Année 48–55 (1920–27). fol. 1920–27

Economy [OECONOMY]. *Œconomy (The) of human life. Tr. f. an Indian MS. [*Attrib. to R. Dodsley, also to the Earl of Chesterfield*]. s8°. 1798

Ecton (John). A state of the proc. of the Corp. of the Bounty of Q. Anne, 1714–18. 8°. 1719

Ecuador. *Hist. de la república del Ecuador por J. L. R. t1, 2, 1809–77. s8°. Quito-Ecuador. 1920–25

Edda.

POETIC EDDA.

Ethica Odini, pars Eddae Saemundi voc. Haavamaal, cum ejusdem app. appellato Runa Capitule, Islandicè & Lat. prod. per J. P. Resenium. [*b. w.* Edda Island., op. P. J. Resenii, 1665]. s4°. Havniae. 1665

Philosophia antiq. Norv.-Dan. dicta Woluspa, pars Eddae Saemundi, Islandicè & Lat. publ. juris primum facta à P. J. Resenio. [*b. w.* Edda Island., op. P. J. Resenii, 1665]. s4°. Havniae. 1665

„ „ [*a. ed.*] Ex Bibl. P. J. Resenii [*b. w.* 1665 *ed.*] s4°. Haffniae. 1673

Edda. Die Lieder d. Codex Regius &c. Hrsg. G. Neckel. [German. Bibl. Abt. 2, B9]. 2, Komment. Glossar. 8°. Heidelberg. 1927

Die Lieder d. E. Hrsg. B. Sijmons u. H. Gering. [Germ. Hdbibl., 7iii, H1]. B3, H1, 8°. Halle (Saale). 1927

PROSE EDDA.

Edda Islandorum a. Chr. 1215 Islandice conscr. per Snorronem Sturlae, nunc primum Isl., Dan. & Lat. in lucem prodit op. P. J. Resenii. s4°. Havniae. 1665

POETIC EDDA. [*Translations*].

The Hávamál, w. sels. f. o. poems of the E. Ed. & tr. by D. E. M. Clarke 8°. C. 1923

The poetic Edda. Tr. w. intr. & notes by H. A. Bellows. 2v *in* 1 [*pagin. cont.*] s8°. N.Y. 1923

PROSE EDDA. [*Translation*].

The prose Edda by S. Sturluson. Tr. w. intr. by A. C. Brodeur. s8°. N.Y. 1916

REFERENCES.

see FARADAY (W.) The E.: 1, divine mythol. of the North, 1902.

„ HERMANNSSON (H.) Bibliog. of the E., 1920.

„ PHILPOTTS (B. S.) The Elder E. & anc. Scandinavian drama, 1920.

„ SCHLÖZER (A. L. v.), *ed.* Isländ. Litt. u. Gesch., T1, 1773.

Edda. Nordisk tidsskrift for litteraturforskning. Redaktør: G. Gran. Redaktionssekretær, F. Bull. B1–27. la8°. 1914–27

„ „ ....Register, 1914–19, B1–12. la8°. 1921

Eddington (Arthur Stanley).

The internal constit. of the stars. la8°. C. 1926

The mathemat. theory of relativity. la8°. C. 1923

Space, time & gravitation. 8°. C. 1920

„ „ ....[repr.] 8°. C. 1921

Stars & atoms. 8°. O. 1927

The theory of relativity & its infl. on scient. thought. Romanes Lect., 1922. 8°. O. 1922

Eddison (Eric Rucker). Styrbiorn the Strong. 8°. [1926]

The worm Ouroboros. Romance. 8°. [1922]

Eddius, *Stephanus.* Life of Bishop Wilfrid. Text, tr. & notes by B. Colgrave. 8°. C. 1927

Eddy (*Mrs.* Mary Baker Glover).

Xtn. healing—The people's idea of God—Pulpit & press—Xtn. science versus Pantheism—Message[s] to Mother Church, 1900–2. [*each w. sep. tp. & pagin.*] s8°. Boston, U.S. [1895–1914]

The First Ch. of Christ Scientist, & Misc. s8°. Boston, U.S.A. [1913]

Manual, First Ch. of Christ Scientist, Boston, Mass. 89th ed. s8°. Boston, U.S. 1921

Misc. writings, 1883–96. s8°. Boston, U.S.A. *n.d.*

Poems. s8°. Boston, U.S. [1910]

Unity of good—Rudimental divine science—No & yes—Retrospection &c. [*each w. sep. tp. & pagin.*] s8°. Boston, U.S. [1892–1908]

see WILBUR (S.) Life of M. B. E., 1913.

Eddy (William Alfred).
Gulliver's travels: a crit. study. 8°. Princeton. 1923
Eden (Anthony). Places in the sun. Pref. by Rt. Hon. S. Baldwin. s8°. 1926
Eden (*Hon.* Emily).
The semi-attached couple. Intr. by J. Gore. s8°. 1927
Eden (Frederick Sydney).
Anc. stained & painted glass. s8°. C. 1913
Eden (Robert), *canon of Norwich.* The Athanasian Creed; facts &c., incl. a new tr. 2nd ed. [P2622]. 8°. O. 1872
Eder (Georg). Evangel. Inquisition wahrer u. falscher Religion. In Forma e. Christl. Rathschlags. [Erste Thayl: Warhaffte Abcontrafactur &c.] s4°. [Ingolstatt. 1580]
Malleus hæretic. de variis falsorum dogmatum notis atque censuris libri 2 [*pagin. contin.*] s8°. Ingolstadii. 1580
Matæologia hæretic., sive summa hæretic. fabularum. s8°. Ingolstadii. 1581
see Trent, *Council of.* Catechismus cathol. &c., per G. E., 1569.
Eder (Jozef Károly).
see Felmer (M.) Prim. lineae hist. Transsilv.; acc. Observ. &c. opera J. C. E., 1803.
,, Pariz (F.) Dict. Lat.-Hungar. &c. (emend. & auct. opera J. C. E.), 2t, 1801.
,, Schesaeus (C.) Ruinae Pannonicae libri 4; ed. I. C. E., 1797.
,, Simigianus (A.) Hist. rer. Ungar. & Transsilv. &c. [Scr. rer. Transsilvan., adcur. E., t2], 1800.
Edersheim (Alfred). Life & times of Jesus. 6th ed. 2v. 8°. 1891
Edgar (C. C.) Zenon papyri. [Cat. gén. des antiq. égypt. du Musée du Caire.] v1. fol. Le Caire. 1925
Edgar (John). Hist. of S. Africa. 8°. Cape Town. [1923]
Edgar (Matilda, *Lady*). A colonial governor in Maryland. Horatio Sharpe & his times, 1753–1773. 8°. 1912
Edgar (Pelham). Henry James, man & author. 8°. 1927
Edgar (Samuel). The variations of Popery. 2nd ed. rev. 8°. 1838
Edgcumbe (Ernest Augustus), *3rd earl of Mount Edgcumbe, see* Mount Edgcumbe.
Edgell (Beatrice). Mental life: intr. to psychology. 8°. 1926
Theories of memory. s8°. O. 1924
Edgeworth, *The family of, see* Butler (H. J.) & H. E. B. Black Bk. of Edgeworthstown &c., 1585–1817, 1927.
Edgeworth (*Abbé* Henry Essex), *see* Butler (H. J.) & H. E. B. Black Bk. of Edgeworthstown &c., 1927.
Edgeworth (Maria). Stories of Ireland: Castle Rackrent: The Absentee. Intr. by H. Morley. s8°. 1886
Edgeworth (Richard Lovell), *see* Butler (H. J.) & H. E. B. Black Bk. of Edgeworthstown &c., 1927.
—— & M. Edgeworth.
Essay on Irish bulls. 2nd ed. corr. 8°. 1803
,, ,, ...3rd ed. corr. s8°. 1808
Edgington (May). The two desires. s8°. [1927]
Edgren-Leffler (A. Ch.), *see* Leffler (A. C.), *aft. Fru Edgren.*
Edhem (Halil), *see* Berchem (M. van). Mat. pour un Corpus inscr. arab., p3, Asie min., t1, Siwas &c.; par M. v. B. & H. E., 1917.
Edie (Lionel Danforth). The stabiliz. of business. By W. C. Mitchell, I. Fisher &c. Intr. by H. Hoover. Ed. L. D. Edie. 8°. N.Y. 1923
Edinburgh.
*Collections by a private hand at E., 1650–61, *see* Maidment (J.) *ed.* Hist. fragm., p2, 1833.
Extr. f. the records of the Burgh of E., 1403–[1571. Ed. J. D. Marwick. Scottish Burgh Rec. Soc.] 3v. 4°. E. 1869–75
Liber Conventus S. Katherine Senensis prope E. [Ed. J. Maidment. Abbotsford Club]. 4°. E. 1841
New College, E., *see* New College, *Edinburgh.*
Reg. Domus de Soltre, & Eccl. Coll. S. Trin. prope E. &c., 1861, *see* Soltre.
Register of consultations of the ministers of E. &c. Ed. W. Stephen. [Scott. Hist. Soc., s3, v1]. v1, 1652–7. 8°. E. 1921
Register of marriages of city of E., 1751–1800. Ed. F. J. Grant. [Scot. Rec. Soc.] 8°. E. 1922
Edinburgh Architectural Association. Illust. cat. of photographs &c. of architect. refinements in Med. buildings lent by Brooklyn Mus. of Arts &c. Text & obs. by W. H. Goodyear. la8°. E. 1905
see Gillespie (J.) Details of Scottish domestic architect., 16–17c., 1922.
Edinburgh review or critical journal.
v231–247 (Jan. 1920–Apr. 1928). 8°. 1920–28

Edinburgh University. The Old Quadrangle, E. Univ., 1900–5. By 4 graduates. 8°. E. 1907
Student's handbook, 1925–26. s8°. E. 1925
see Cuthbertson (D.) E. Univ. Library, its origin, w. descr. of its rarer bks. & MSS., 1910.
Édits &c. conc. le parl. de Brétagne, 1554–1754, *see* Brétagne.
Edkins (Joseph). A gramm. of the Chinese colloq. lang., the Mandarin dialect. 8°. Shanghai. 1857
***Edles** (Ein) schönes lieplichs Tractätlein v. d. reynen hyml. ewigen wort &c., c. 1524, *see* Marschalck (H.)
Edmestoun (John). Verses & letter to James VI (1607), *see* Abbotsford Club. Misc., v1, 1837.
Edmondes (*Sir* Clement), *see* Caesar (C. J.) Comm. of h. warres in Gallia &c.; tr. w. obs. by C. E., 1655.
Edmonds (Charles Douglas). Greek hist. for schools. 8°. C. 1916
Edmonds (*Brig.-Gen.* James Edward). Military oper., France & Belgium, 1914, *see* War. Hist. of the Gt. War based on offic. doc., Milit. oper. &c., 2v, 1922–25.
Edmonds (John Henry), *see* Dow (G. F.) & J. H. E. Pirates of the New England coast, 1630–1730, 1923.
Edmonds (John Maxwell), *see* Lyra. L. Graeca: [text], newly ed. & tr. by J. M. E., 3v, 1922–27.
Edmondston (Arthur). A view of the anc. & pres. state of the Zetland Islands. 2v. 8°. E. 1809
Edmonston, *of Duntreth, The family of, see* Edmonston, *of Ednem, Fam. of.* Genealogy of the Lairds of Ednem & Duntreth, 1063–1699, repr., 1834.
Edmonston, *of Ednem, The family of.* Genealogy of the [Edmonstons] Lairds of Ednem & Duntreth, 1063–1699. [Facs. of Glasgow ed., 1699]. [repr.] s8°. [E. 1834]
Edmund [Rich], *St., apb. of Cant., see* Newbolt (M.R.) E.R., 1928.
Edmunds (Frederic Harrison).
see Dines (H. G.) & F. H. E. Geol. of country around Romford, 1925.
,, Whitaker (W.) & F. H. E. Water supply of Wilts., 1925.
Edmundson (George), *M.A.*
Hist. of Holland. [Camb. Hist. Ser.] 8°. C. 1922
The voyage of P. Teixeira on the Amazon, 1637–39. [Repr. f. Trans. of R. Hist. Soc. P2490]. 8°. Aberdeen. 1920
Ednam (William Humble Eric Ward, *viscount*), *see* Normanton (S. J. A., *e.*) Cat. of furniture of Earl of N., & of Visct. E., sold, 1925.
Ednem, *Lairds of, see* Edmonston, *of Ednem, Fam. of.*
Edridge-Green (Frederick William). The physiology of vision. Colour blindness. 8°. 1920
Edrisi. Idrisi-Atlas, 336 photograph. Wiedergaben, *see* Miller (K.), *ed.* Mappae Arab., B6, 1927.
Weltkarte v. 1154 [*&* 1192], *see* Miller (K.), *ed.* Mappae Arab., B1, 1926.
Edschmid (Kasimir).
Die doppelköpfige Nymphe. Aufsätze ü. d. Lit. u. d. Gegenwart. s8°. 1920
Frauen. 3e A. 8°. 1923
Die Fürstin. la8°. 1920
Das rasende Leben. 2 Novellen. s8°. L. [1915]
Die sechs Mündungen. Novellen. s8°. L. [1915]
Timur. s8°. L. [1916]
Üb. d. Expressionismus in d. Lit. u. d. neue Dichtung. 8e A. s8°. 1921
Education. Congrès Internat. d'E. Morale. 3e Congrès, Genève, juil.-août 1922. Rapports & mém. 2[t]. s8°. Genève. [1922]
E. & relig.: lect., 1924, *see* Burroughs (E. A.), *ed.*
*Of e., espec. of young gentlemen, 3rd impr., 1677, *see* Walker (O.)
Readings in hist. of e., 1920, *see* Cubberley (E. P.), *ed.*
Educational movts. & methods; [*by var. wr.*], 1924, *see* Adams (J.), *ed.*
Edvi Illés (Aladár) & A. Halász. The economies [*sic*] of Hungary in maps. Ed. J. de Rubinek. [*Fr., Eng. & Hung.*] 4th enl. ed. obl.8°. [Budapest]. 1920
Hungarian state policy w. r. to the promotion of industry. [P2519]. 8°. Budapest. 1920
Hungary in econ.-statist. maps. obl.4°. Budapest. 1926
Edward, *the Black Prince* [†Edward, *prince of Wales, called The Black Prince*], *see* London University. Cat. of MSS. &c., 1921.
Edward, *the Confessor, king of England.* La estoire de Seint Ædward le Rei; reprod. in facs., w. some pages of the MS. of the life of St. Alban [*by M. Paris?*]. Intr. by M. R. James. [Roxburghe Club]. 4°. O. 1920
Edward II, *king of England.*
see Selden Soc. Year Books of E. II, v9, 14i, ii, 16–18 (1311–15), 1920–27.
,, Tout (T. F.) Captivity & death of E. of Carnarvon, 1920

Edward III, *king of England.* Letter for pardon, by E. to Cecil, wife of John de Ridgeway &c., 25th April 1358, *see* MAIDMENT (J.) & R. PITCAIRN. Nugae derelictae, 1822.
see FINE ROLLS. Cal. of Fine Rolls, v6–8, 1347–77, 1921–24.
„ INQUISITIONES. I. Post Mortem. Cal. of I. p. m. &c. in P. R. O., v10, E. III, 1921.
„ LOW (W. M.) Some descents of 2 19th c. sisters f. E. III, 1922.

Edward IV, *king of England.*
see BARNARD (F. P.) E. IV's French exped. of 1475, 1925.
„ SCOFIELD (C. L.) Life & reign of E. IV, 2v, 1923.

Edward V, *king of England, see* MORE (*Sir* T.) Hist. of the life & death of E. V &c., 1641.

Edward VI, *king of England.* *Doctrina & politia Eccl. Anglic., a Ed. VI, Eliz. stabilitae &c., 1617, *see* MOCKET (R.)
Injunctions, 1547 &c., *see* SPARROW (A.) Coll. of articles &c., 1661 ?.
see FORMA. Forma ac ratio tota eccl. ministerii in peregrinorum German. eccl.; instit. Londini per regem E., 1555.
„ PATENT ROLLS. Cal. of P. R., v1–5, 1924–26.
„ SMYTH (C. H. E.) Cranmer & the Reformation under E. VI, 1926.

Edward VII, *king of England.*
see BROADLEY (A. M.) Boyhood of a great king, 1841–58; E. VII, 1906.
„ DOWTY (A. A.) & S. O. BEETON. The coming K——, *n.d.*
„ ECKARDSTEIN (H., *Frhr.* v.) Persönl. Erinnerungen an K. E., 1927.
„ ESHER (R. B. B., *2nd visc.*) Influence of King E. &c., 1915.
see FARRER (J. A.) England under E. VII, 1922.
„ LEE (*Sir* S.) King E. VII: biog., 2v, 1925–27.
„ SCHWERTFEGER (B.) Zur europ. Politik, B2, König E. VII &c., 1919.
„ WILKINS (W. H.) E. the Peacemaker, 2v, 1911.

Edward, *prince of Parma, see* AURELI (A.) Gloria d'amore: spettacolo festivo fatto rappres. dal Duca di Parma per sponsali del Princ. Odoardo, 1690.

Edward, *Prince of Wales* [EDWARD ALBERT CHRISTIAN G. A. P. D.], *see* ELLISON (B. C.) H.R.H. the P. of W.'s sport in India, 1925.

Edwardes (Alice). Runes & o. poems. s8°. *p.p.* [1925]

Edwardes (Edward Tickner). Bee-keeping for all. 8°. 1923
The bee-master of Warrilow. n. & enl. ed. s8°. [1920]
„ „ ....[2nd] & enl. ed. s8°. 1920

Edwardes (*Sir* Herbert Benjamin). Polit. diaries, Lahore, 1847–49, *see* PUNJAB. P. govt. rec., v5, 1911.

Edwardes (*Sir* Stephen Meredyth). Crime in India. 8°. 1924
Kharshedji Rustamji Cama. A mem. 8°. O. 1923

Edwardes (Tickner), *see* EDWARDES (ED. T.)

Edwardes-Ker (*Lt.-Col.* Douglas Rous), *see* AULD (*Lt.-Col.* S. J. M.) & D. R. E.-K. Pract. agric. chemistry, 2nd ed., 1921.

Edward Fry Library of International Law. Catalogue of books &c. in the Library. Comp. &c. by B. M. Headicar. la8°. 1923
„ „ ....1st suppl. la8°. 1925

Edwardian. Chantry certificates & Edw. inventories for Oxfordshire, 1919; 1920, *see* GRAHAM (R.), *ed.*

Edwards (Albert).
Panama: the canal, country & people. 8°. N.Y. 1911

Edwards (Arthur Trystan).
Good & bad manners in architecture. 8°. [1924]
The things which are seen: a revaluation of the visual arts. 8°. 1921

Edwards (Bateman). Classif. of the MSS. of Gui de Cambrai's Vengement Alixandre. [Elliott monogr., 20]. 8°. Princeton. 1926

Edwards (Bryan). Hist. of the Brit. Colonies in the W. Indies. *Maps & Plates.* 4°. *n.d.*
see MÉMOIRES. Mém. hist. & géogr. sur les pays situés entre la Mer Noire &c. [*Extr. f.* B. E. &c.], 3p, 1797.

Edwards (Charman). "Big, strong man!" s8°. [1923]

Edwards (Chilperic). The Hammurabi code: & the Sinaitic legisl. 3rd ed. rev. 8°. 1921

Edwards (D. Miall). The philosophy of relig. s8°. [1924]

Edwards (Edward), *assist. keeper in Dept. of Oriental Printed Bks., Brit. Mus., see* BRITISH MUSEUM: PRINTED BOOKS. Persian printed books; by E. E., 1922.

Edwards (Ernest Wood).
The Orlando Furioso & its predecessor. 8°. C. 1924

Edwards (Frederick George), *see* WELSH (R. E.) & F. G. E. Romance of Psalter & hymnal, 1889.

Edwards (Frederick Laurence). James, 1st Earl of Stanhope, 1673–1721, & Brit. for. policy. s8°. 1925

Edwards (George), *M.P.* From crow-scaring to Westminster: autobiog. Intr. by W. R. Smith. s8°. [1922]

Edwards (George William). New York as an 18th cent. municipality, 1731–76. [Columbia Univ.] 8°. N.Y. 1917

Edwards (J. F.), *see* NELSON (J. F.) & J. F. E. Life & teaching of Tukārāma, 1922.

Edwards (Jonathan), *the elder, president of the College of New Jersey.*
An acc. of the life of D. Brainerd. With B.'s public journal. Added [C.] Beatty's mission to the westw. of the Allegheny mts. [*w. sep. tp. & pagin.*] 8°. E. 1798
Inq. into that freedom of will supposed essential &c. n. ed. w. introd. essay by a. of Nat. hist. of Enthusiasm [*i.e.* I. Taylor]. s8°. 1831
*Life of J. E. [Sel. f. Dr. Hopkins & S. E. Dwight. Xtn. biog. P2758]. s8°. *n.d.*
Life &c. of the Rev. David Brainerd, missionary. s8°. E. 1826
*Remarks on the Essays on the principles of morality &c. [*b. w.* Kames (H. H.) Essays &c., 1751]. 8°. E. 1758
Revivals of religion, their nature. Abrdgd. by J. Wesley. s8°. 1842
Works. [Ed. by E. Williams & E. Parsons. With mem. of his life by S. Hopkins]. 8v. 8°. Leeds. 1806–11
v3, *cont.* Life & diary of D. Brainerd.

Edwards (Jonathan), *D.D., principal of Jesus Coll., Oxford, see* WHITBY (D.) Full ans. to J. E., 1712.

Edwards (Jonathan), *D.D., the younger, pres. of Union Coll., Schenectady.* Obs. on the lang. of the Muhhekaneew Indians, *see* OCCOM (S.) Sermon, 1788.

Edwards (Ness). Hist. of the South Wales miners. s8°. [1926]

Edwards (Ralph), *see* MACQUOID (P.) & R. E. Dict. of Eng. furniture, 3v, 1924–27.

Edwards (Richard), *poet.* The excellent comedie of Damon & Pithias (1571), *see* ADAMS (J. Q.) Chief pre-Shakespearian dramas, 1925.
The paradise of dainty deuices, 1576 [*by E. & others*]. Intr. remarks &c. by Sir E. Brydges [*Extr. f. h. Brit. bibliog.*, v3]. repr. 8°. 1810
see BRADNER (L.) Life & poems of R. E., 1927.

Edwards (Thomas Charles). A comm. on the 1st Ep. to the Corinthians. 2nd ed. 8°. 1885

Edwards (Wilfrid), *see* WHITAKER (W.) & W. E. Wells & springs of Dorset, 1926.

Edwards (William), *headmaster of Middlesbrough High School.*
Early hist. of the North Riding. 4°. 1924
Notes on European hist. v1–3. 8°. 1925–26

Edzardi (Sebastian). Animadv. ad J. Fabricii Consid. controv. cum Reformatis &c. [P596]. s4°. Hamburgi. 1704
Ex confessionibus minister. Saxonic. a. 1546 ed. excerpta anti-syncretistica. [P2643]. s4°. Hamburgi. 1705
Ex philologia Hebraica &c. Resp. D. Kleselius. [P1015]. s4°. Vitembergæ. [1695]

Eeden (Frederik van).
Ellen, een lied van de smart. s8°. A. 1917
De kleine Johannes. 3d. [1, 10e dr.; 2, 11e druk.; 3, 8–9e druk.] 8°. 's-Gravenhage. 1919–21
Der kleine Johannes. Deut. Uebertr. v. E. Otten. 7e A. s8°. 1921
Het lied van schijn en wezen. 3 boeken. s8°. A. 1917–22
Lioba, drama. 6e dr. s8°. A. 1919

Eekhof (A.) De theolog. Faculteit te Leiden in de 17de eeuw. 8°. Utrecht. 1921

Eells (Hastings). The attitude of M. Bucer toward the bigamy of Philip of Hesse. [Yale Hist. Publ. Misc. 12]. 8°. New Haven. 1924

Eerde (J. C. van). De Volken van Nederl. Indië in monographieën. Uitg. van J. C. van E. 2d. 4°. Amsterdam. 1920–21

Eesti, *see* ESTHONIA.

Eesti statistika: kuukiri. Recueil mensuel du Bureau Central Statist. de l'Esthonie. Nr. 1–13 [*in* 1v]. 8°. Tallinn. 1922–3

Efremov (Filipp Sergeevich). Странствованіе въ Бухаріи, Хивѣ, Персіи и Индіи и возвращеніе оттуда чрезъ Англію въ Россію. Новое изд. 8°. С.-П. 1794
„ „ ....3е изд. 8°. Казань. 1811

Efremov (J.)
The Cossacks of the Don. [P2403]. 8°. Paris. 1919

Egan (Pierce). Acc. of trial of J. Thurtell & J. Hunt: w. app. [Recoll. of J. Thurtell, *w. sep. tp. & pagin.*] 8°. 1824
Recolls. of J. Thurtell: also, the condemned sermon &c. [*a. c. b. w.* Egan (P.) Acc. of trial of J. T. &c., 1824]. 8°. 1824

Egbertus, *abbot of Schönau.* [EGBERT]. Adversus pestiferos &c. Cathar. errores &c., Eckberti sermones. Breve ex Augustino de Manichaeis excerptum. [P2544]. s8°. Coloniae. 1530

Egbertus, *abp. of Treves, see* SAUERLAND (H. V.) & A. HASELOFF. Der Psalter Erzbischof E. v. T., 1901.

Egede (Hans), *bp. of Greenland.* Descr. of Greenland: shewing nat. hist., life &c. Tr. s8°. 1745

Egelhaaf (Gottlob). Gustav Adolf in Deutschland, 1630–32. [Verein f. Ref.-gesch. Schr., Jhrg. 18, Nr. 68]. 8°. Halle. 1901
Württemberg. Gesch. (-1919). 8°. St. 1922

—— & W. Diehl.
Landgraf Philipp v. Hessen—M. Butzers Bedeutung f. d. kirchl. Leben in Hessen. Vorträge. [Verein f. Ref.-gesch. Schr., Jhrg. 22, Nr. 83]. 8°. Halle a. S. 1904

Egenholt (*Herr* v.), *see* CRAON (M. DE). 2 altdeut. Rittermaeren: M. v. C.: Peter v. Staufenberg [*by* E.: *text*]; n. hrsg. E. Schröder, 3e A., 1920.

Egenolf (Johann Augustin), *see* DEYLING (C. E.) & J. A. E. Aeliae Capitolinae orig. & hist., 1743.

Egerton (Hakluyt) *ps.* [*i.e.* ARTHUR BOUTWOOD].
The Holy Cath. Church. An Anglican essay. s8°. 1921
The Holy Grail: a mystery play. s8°. Leighton Buzzard. *n.d.*

Egerton (Hugh Edward).
Brit. colonial policy in the 20th c. 8°. [1922]
Causes &c. of the Amer. revol. s8°. O. 1923
Federations & unions within the Brit. Empire. 2nd ed. 8°. O. 1924
see LUCAS (*Sir* C. P.) Hist. geog. of Brit. Dominions, v5, Canada, p2, Hist., 1763–1921, 3rd ed., 1923.

Egerton-Warburton (Rowland Eyles). Hunting songs. [*With* Intr. *cont.* sh. acc. of the Tarporley Hunt]. [5th ed.] s8°. 1873

Egger (A. Émile). Hist. du livre. 3e éd. s8°. [1880 ?]
see BAILLY (A.) Dict. grec-français, réd. avec le concours de E., 10e éd., *n.d.*

Eggers (Anna). Die Urkunde Hadrians IV für Heinrich II v. England ü. die Besetzung Irlands. [Histor. St., H151]. 8°. 1922

Eggers (Olga). Af en ensoms Optegnelser. 8°. 1910
En grim Kvindes Bekendelse. 8°. 1909
Hvorfor—— ? 8°. [1918]

Eggs (Georgius Josephus ab). Pontificium doctum, seu vitae res gestae &c. pontif. Roman. qui doctrina inclaruere. fol. Coloniæ. 1718

Egidio, *frate, di Ascesi, see* GILES, *Franciscan, of Assisi.*

Egils Saga. Egils saga einhenda ok Ásmundar berserkjabana, *see* LYGISǪGUR. Drei l.; hrsg. A. Lagerholm, 1927.

Eginhard [EGINHARDUS; EGINHARTUS; EINHARD], *abbot of Seligenstadt.*
Vita et gesta Karoli Magni. [Hermanni comitis Nuenarii brevis narr. de orig. &c. Francorum. [*tp. & pref. only Ai–iv*]. s4°. [apud Coloniam. 1521]
,, ,, Cum comm. J. F. Besselii & notis J. Bollandi. Acc. M. H. Goldasti animadv. ined. cum variis dissert. curante J. H. Schminckio. s4°. Trajecti ad Rh. 1711
Early lives of Charlemagne by E. & the Monk of St. Gall. Tr. & ed. by A. J. Grant. [Mediaeval Lib. v14]. s8°. 1922
Vie de Charlemagne. Ed. & tr. par L. Halphen. [*Lat. & Fr.*] [Classiques de l'hist. de France &c.] s8°. 1923
see BUCHNER (M.) Einhards Künstler u. Gelehrtenleben, 1922.
,, ESTÈVE (É.) Ét. de litt. préromant.: Le conte d'Emma & É. dans la litt. franç., 1923.
,, FRANCI. Annales regni Franc. (741–829) q. d. Einhardi &c.; Kurze, 1895.

Eglise. Catéchisme hist. & dogmat. sur les contest. qui divisent l'Eglise, 5t, 1750–68, *see* FOURQUEVAUX (J. B. R. DE P. DE) & L. TROYA D'ASSIGNY.
*L'église & la République; avec une préf. par C. Guyho. s8°. Paris. [1877]

Eglinton Castle. *The E. Tournament, 1839. lafol. 1840

Eglises & monastères de Paris, pièces, 9–14 siècles, *see* BORDIER (H. L.), *ed.*

Egloffstein (*Freiherr* v.), *see* ÖRTHEL (L.)

Egloffstein (Lupoldas de), *bp. of Bamberg* [BEBENBURGIUS]. Lupoldus de iuribus & translatione Imperii. [*Ed.* J. Wimpheling]. s4°. Argentoraci [*M. Schürerius*]. 1508
Veterum Germaniae principum in fide & relig. constantia. Sunt et multa quae Gallorum reges præclare &c. fecerunt. s8°. Parisiis. 1540

Egmond of Zee. Annales Egmundani. [*Lat. Ed.* B. J. L. de Geer v. Jutfaas. Hist. Genoots. te Utrecht. Werken. N.S., 1, Bronnen &c.] 8°. Utrecht. 1863

Egmont (John Perceval, *1st earl of*). Diary, 1730–47, 3v, 1920–23, *see* HIST. MSS. COMM.

Egranus (Johann Sylvius) [WILDENAUER (J.), *Egranus*]. Apologetica responsio contra dogmata, que in M. Egranū a calumniator. invulgata sunt. [*Dedic. by* M. Eleutherius, *i.e. Luther*]. s4°. [Wittenburgii. 1518]
Ungedruckte Predigten, 1519–22. Veröffentl. v. G. Buchwald. [Quellen &c. aus d. Gesch. d. Reformationsjhdts., B18]. 8°. L. 1911

Egypt.
*All about postal matters in E. [P2754]. 8°. Florence. 1898
Kings & queens of anc. E., 1924, *see* BRUNTON (*Mrs.* W.)
Milit. hist. of Camp. of 1882 in E. [War Office, Intellig. Branch], 1908, *see* MAURICE (*Sir* J. F.)
*Mining in E. By an Egyptologist. obl.4°. *n.d.*
GOVT. PUBLS.
Min. des Finances. Dépt. de la Statistique Gén. Annuaire statist. de l'Egypte, 1921–22. 14e année. fol. Le Caire. 1923
Rep. on the financial admin. of Egypt, by E. Vincent, Oct. 1884. 4°. Cairo. [1884]
SURVEY DEPT. &C.
see CAIRO. Map showing Mohammedan monuments, *n.d.*
,, HURST (H. E.) The Lake Plateau Basin of the Nile, 1925.
,, LITTLE (O. H.) Geography & geology of Makalla, S. Arabia, 1925.
,, RICHARDS (F. S.) Age of the temple of Ammon at Karnak, 1921.

Egypt Exploration Fund [Society] & Archaeological Survey.
The Theban Tombs Series. Mem. 1–4. 4°. 1920–26
see DAVIES (N. DE G.) Tomb of Antefoḳer, & of h. wife, Senet, 1920. [2.]
,, —— Tombs of 2 officials of Tuthmosis the Fourth, 1923. [3.]
,, GARDINER (A. H.) The tomb of Amenemhēt; copied by N. de G. Davies, 1915. [1.]
,, —— The tomb of Ḥuy; copied by N. de G. Davies, 1926. [4.]
REFERENCES.
see BLACKMAN (A. M.) Rock tombs of Meir, p4, 1924.
,, PEET (T. E.) & C. L. WOOLLEY. The city of Akhenaten, p1, 1923.
,, OXYRHYNCHUS PAPYRI; ed. w. tr. & notes, by B. P. Grenfell & A. S. Hunt, p15–17, 1922–27.
,, WAINWRIGHT (G. A.) Balabish, 1920.

Egyptian. Admonitions of an E. sage, f. a Hieratic papyrus in Leiden. By A. H. Gardiner. 4°. L. 1909
E. (An) post office list in the Egypt. lang. [P2754]. 8°. Cairo. 1898

Egyptian Expeditionary Force. A brief record of the advance of the E.E. Force, under Gen. Allenby, July 1917 to Oct. 1918. [*Ed.* H. Pirie-Gordon]. 2nd ed. 4°. 1919

Egyptian Government Almanac, 1923. s8°. Cairo. [1923]

Ehe-buch (Das). Hrsg. v. H. K., 1925; tr., 1927, *see* KEYSERLING (H., *Graf.* v.)

Eheordnung. Pfaltzgrave Friderichs Christl. Eheordnung, 1565, *see* FREDERICK III, *Elector Palatine.*

Eher. *Eher Türkisch als Päpstisch, 1627, *see* TÜRKISCH.

Ehl (Heinrich). Älteste deut. Malerei. la8°. [1921]
Die Otton. Kölner Buchmalerei. 8°. Bonn. 1922

Ehlers (Ernst). Hans Döring. Ein hessischer Maler d. 16. Jhdts. s4°. Frankfurt a. Main. 1919

Ehrenberg (Friedrich). Der Charakter u. Bestimmung d. Mannes. 10e A. s8°. Elberfeld. 1822
Das Schicksal. s8°. Elberfeld. 1805

Ehrenberg (Hermann K. A.)
Deut. Malerei u. Plastik v. 1350–1450. 8°. Bonn. 1920

Ehrenberg (Richard).
Das Haus Parish in Hamburg. 2. A. 8°. Jena. 1925

Ehrenberg (Victor). Alexander u. Ägypten, *see* ALTE ORIENT, Beih. 7, 1926.
Karthago. [Morgenland, 14]. 8°. L. 1927

Ehrensperger (F.) Die Pariser Börse u. d. franz. Bankinstitute, 1914–1925. 8°. Zürich. [1925]

Ehrenstein (Albert). Gedichte. 8°. L. [1920]

Ehret (Georgius Dionysius), *see* TREW (C. J.) Plantæ sel., quarum imagines &c. pinxit G. D. E. &c., 1750.

Ehret (Joseph). Das Jesuitentheater zu Freiburg in d. Schweiz. T1, Die äuss. Gesch. d. Herbstspiele, 1580–1700 &c. 8°. Freiburg i. B. 1921
La Lituanie, passé, présent, avenir. s8°. Genève. [1919]

Ehrhard (Albert). Beitr. z. Gesch. d. christl. Altertums u. d. Byzantin. Lit. Festgabe A. E. dargebracht. Hrsg. v. A. M. Koeniger. 8°. Bonn. 1922

Ehrle (Franz). Die Ehrentitel d. scholast. Lehrer d. M-a., *see* KÖNIGL. AKAD. D. WISS. ZU MÜNCHEN. Phil. Cl., Sitz., 1919.

Hist. Bibliothecae Roman. Pontif. tum Bonifatianae tum Avenion. t1. [*No more publ.*] 4°. Roma. 1890

Miscellanea F. Ehrle: scritti di storia e paleografia. [*By var. a.*] Pubbl. sotto gli ausp. di Pio XI in occas. d. 80° nat. d. card. F. E. [Studi e testi, 37–42]. 5v. *&* Album. la8°. 1924

1, Per la stor. della teologia e della filosofia.
2, Per la stor. di Roma e dei Papi.
3, Per la stor. eccles. e civile dell' età di mezzo.
4, Paleografia e diplomatica.
5, Biblioteca ed archivio vaticano—biblioteche diverse.

Neue Materialien z. Gesch. Peters v. Luna (Benedicts XIII), *see* ARCHIV. F. LITT.-U. KIRCHENGESCH., B6, 7, 1892–1900.

see ARCHIV. F. LITT.-U. KIRCHENGESCH. D. MITTEL ALTERS; hrsg. v. H. Denifle u. F. E., B1–7, 1885–1900.

—— **& P. Liebaert.** Specimina cod. Lat. Vaticanorum. Coll. F. E. & P. L. [Tab. in usum schol., 3]. ed. 2ª. la8°. Berolini. 1927

Ehrlich (Ludwik). Proc. agst. the crown (1216–1377), 1921, *see* VINOGRADOFF (*Sir* P.) Studies in legal &c. hist., v6, 1921.

Ehrlich (Paul). Studies in immunity; by E. &c. Coll. & tr. by C. Bolduan. 2nd ed., rev. & enl. 8°. N.Y. 1910

see MARQUARDT (M.) P. E. als Mensch u. Arbeiter (1902–15), 1924.

Eichendorff (Carl, *Frhr.* v.) Ein Jahrhundert Eichendorff-Lit., *see* EICHENDORFF (J. C. B. *Frhr.* v.) Sämtl. Werke, B22, 1924.

Eichendorff (Joseph Carl Benedict, *Frhr.* v.) Sämtliche Werke. Histor.-krit. A. In Verbindung mit P. A. Becker, hrsg. v. W. Kosch & A. Sauer. B1i, ii, 22. 8°. Regensburg. [1923–24]

B1, Gedichte, i, Lyrische Ged., ii, Epische Ged.
22, Ein Jahrhundert Eichendorff-Lit.; zusammengestellt v. K., Frhr. v. Eichendorff.

Eichholz (Paul). Das älteste deut. Wohnhaus: e. Steinbau d. 9 Jhdts. la8°. Str. 1907

Eichhorn (Johann Gottfried), *see* ALLGEMEINE BIBL. D. BIBL. LITT.; v. J. G. E., 10B, 1787–1800.

Eichler (Lillian). Customs of mankind. 8°. 1924

Eichler (Wilhelm). Aesthet. Tanzen u. Turnen. 8°. St. 1922

Eichstädt (Heinrich Carl Abraham). Acroasis pro Soc. Latinae Jenensis instauratione. s8°. Ienæ. 1800

Narr. de C. Peucero Melanchthonis genero. Orat. [P558]. 4°. Jenæ. 1841

Eichstätt. Regesten (Die) d. Bischöfe v. E. Hrsg. F. Heidingsfelder. [Veröffentl. d. Gesell. f. Frank. Gesch. R6]. Lief. 1–6 [*in prog.*] 4°. Innsbruck *&* Würzburg. 1915–27

Eichwald (Carl Eduard v.) Reise auf d. Casp. Meere u. in d. Caucasus, 1825–26. 2B *in* 3v. 8°. St. 1834–38

1i, Periplus d. Casp. Meeres. ii, Reise in d. Kaukasus.
2, Alte Geog. d. Kasp. Meeres.

О чудскихъ копяхъ, *see* IMPERAT. RUSS. ARCH. OBSCH. Труды Восточ. отд., ч3, 1858.

Eidsvold 1814. [Jubilæumsverket]. Med bidrag av C. W. Schnitler, R. Tank, H. Koht &c. 4°. 1914

***Eigendliche** Beschreibung was sich mit d. Gen. Wallenstein begeben &c., 1634, *see* WALLENSTEIN.

Eighty Club. The E.C. Year-Book, 1904. s8°. 1904

see MOULTON (J. F. M. *b.*) Government by Cabinet, speeches by M. &c., 1905.

Eijck (P. N. van), *see* EYCK.

E ἰκονοκόσμησις, or the dres sing of images, *see* ENTERTAINMENT. E. for Lady-days, 1925.

Eikonomos (Constantine) [ICONOMOS (C.)]
Etude sur Smyrne. Tr. B. F. Slaars. la8°. Smyrne. 1868

Eilleaux (*la comtesse* **d').** [*ps.* CHARLOTTE DE SOR]. *Recoll. of Caulincourt, duke of Vicenza. [Tr.] 2v. 8°. 1838

Einarsson (Háfdán) [EINARI]. Sciagraphia hist. lit. Islandicae autorum & scriptorum tum edit. tum inedit. indicem exhibens. 8°. Havniæ. 1777

„ „ n.ed. [*w.t.*] Hist. lit. Island. s8°. Havniae. 1786

Einaudi (Luigi). Appunti per la Storia di Dogliani dell' avv. F. Fracchia, racc. &c. da L. E., *see* REGIA DEPUT. DI STORIA PATRIA. Misc., t51, 1924.

La Guerra e il sistema tributario ital. [C.I. for Int. Peace]. 8°. Bari. 1927

***Einhellige** Bekentnis vieler Theologen &c. 1572, *see* MELISSANDER (C.)

Einkommensteurgesetz u. Körperschaftssteuergesetz für d. Deutsche Reich. Textausgabe mit Anmerk. &c., hrsg. v. K. Pannier. 4ᵉ A. [3p. *in* 1v., *each w. sep. tp. & pagin.* P2684]. s8°. L. [1923]

Einleitung in d. Altertumswiss.; hrsg. A. Gercke u. E. Norden; 3ᵉ A. &c., 1914–27, *see* GERCKE (A.) & E. NORDEN.

Einsiedel (Hildebrand Heinrich), *see* ALBERT (F. R.) Briefwechsel H. v. E. mit Luther, Melanchthon, Spalatin &c.; aus Hss. dargestellt, 1908.

Einsiedeln. Le codex 121 de la Bibl d'E. (10–11s); Antiphonale missarum S. Gregorii, 1894, *see* ANTIPHONALE.

see LANCIANI (R.) Itinerario di E. e l'ord. di Benedetto canonico, 1890.

Einstein (Albert).

Äther u. Relativitäts-Theorie. Rede, Leiden. 8°. 1920

Invest. on the theory of the Brownian movement. Ed. w. notes by R. Fürth. Tr. A. D. Cowper. s8°. [1926]

The meaning of relativity. Lectˢ., Princ. Univ. 1921. Tr. E. P. Adams. 8°. [1922]

Relativity: the spec. & the gen. theory. A pop. exposition. Tr. R. W. Lawson. s8°. 1920

Sidelights on relativity. Tr. G. B. Jeffery & W. Perrett. s8°. [1922]

Üb. d. spezielle u. d. allgem. Relativitätstheorie. [Samml. Vieweg]. 13ᵗᵉ A. 8°. Braunschweig. 1921

see ADLER (F.) Ortszeit &c.: Unters. ü. d. Lorentz. u. E. Kinematik, 1920.
„ BEER (F.) Die E. Relativitätstheorie, 1920.
„ BERGSON (H.) Durée & simultanéité à propos de la théorie d'E., 1922.
„ BORN (M.) E.'s th. of relativity; tr. H. L. Brose, 1924.
„ —— Die Relativitätstheorie E. u. i. physikal. Grundlagen, 1920.
„ CASSIRER (E.) Substance & function & E.'s theory of relativity; tr., 1923.
„ —— Zur E. schen Relativitätstheorie, 1921.
„ DE MONTMORENCY (H.) Fr. Kant to E., 1926.
„ DENTON (F. M.) E. theory explained, 1919.
„ FABRE (L.) Les théories d'E., 1921.
see FREUNDLICH (E.) Found. of E.'s theory of gravit.; pref. by A. E., 1920.
„ —— Die Grundlagen d. E. Gravitationstheorie; Vorwort v. A. E., 1920.
„ GOLDZIER (H.) Gegen E.: Erfahrung im Weltall, 1921.
„ HASSE (M.) E.'s Relativitätstheorie, 1920.
„ KOPFF (A.) Die E.sche Relativitätstheorie, 1920.
„ —— Grundzüge d. E.schen Relativitätstheorie, 1921.
„ LAUE (M. v.) Die Relativitätstheorie, B2, 921.
„ LORENTZ (H. A.), A. E. & H. MINKOWSKI. Das Relativitätsprinzip, 1920; 4ᵉ verm. A., 1922.
„ —— Princ. of relativity; tr., 1923.
„ MOSZKOWSKI (A.) E.: Einblicke in s. Gedankenwelt, 1921.
„ —— E. the searcher; tr. by H. L. Brose, 1921.
„ NORDMANN (C.) E. & l'univers, 1921; tr. by J. McCabe, 1922.
„ —— Notre maître le temps &c.: E. ou Bergson?, 1924.
„ READE (W. H. V.) A crit. of E. & h. problem, 1922.
„ SCHMIDT (H.) Relativity & the universe: intr. to E.'s theory of space & time; tr., 1921.
„ SLOSSON (E. E.) Easy lessons in E., 1920.
„ THIRRING (J. H.) The ideas of E.'s theory; tr., 1921.

Einstein (Carl). Afrikan. Plastik. la8°. [1922]

Der frühere japan. Holzschnitt. la8°. [1923]

Einstein (Lewis). Tudor ideals. 8°. N.Y. 1921

see VINCI (L. DA). Thoughts on art &c., tr. M. Baring; intr. by L. E., 1906.

Eirspennill. Nóregs Konunga sogur-Magnus goði-Hákon gamli, 1916, *see* JÓNSSON (F.), *ed.*

Eiselin (Michel). Disp. theolog. de fide. Praes. M. E.; resp. W. E. Gruner. [P2607]. s4°. [Ingolstadii]. 1593

Eisen (Matthias J.)
Estnische Mythologie. Übertr. v. Dr. E. Erkes. 8°. L. 1925

Eisengrein (Martin). Concio egregia & catholica, cur tam multi hodié ad Luteranismum deficiant &c. [*Tr.*] F. L. Surius. [*b. w.* Staphylus (F.) Apologia, 1563]. s8°. Coloniae. 1558

Eisengrein (Wilhelm) [EYSENGREIN]. Catalogus testium veritatis omnium orthodoxae matris eccl. doctorum. s8°. Dillingae. 1565

„ „ [*a. copy without printed index but w. index in MS. dated 1770*].

Eisenhart (Johann), *professor at Helmstedt.* Instit. moralis scientiae. [*b. w.* Baier (J. W.) Compend. theol. mor., 1698]. s8°. Helmstadii. 1699

Eisenmann (Louis). La Tchécoslovaquie. 8°. 1921

Eisherz u. Edeljaspis, 1927, *see* HAOU KEW CHUEN.
Eisleben (Johann von), *see* AGRICOLA (JOHANN) *of Eisleben.*
Eisler (Max). Josef Israëls. Ed. G. Holme. [Studio. Spring No.] la8°. 1924
Eisler (Moritz). Vorles. ü. d. jüd. Philosophen d. Ma. 2 Abth. [*in 1v.*] 8°. Wien. 1870–76
Eisler (Robert). Orpheus—the fisher. Comp. st. in Orphic & early Xtn. cult symbolism. la8°. 1921
Orphisch-Dionys. Mysterien-Gedanken in d. christl. Antike. la8°. L. 1925
Eisler (Rudolf). Wörterbuch d. philosoph. Begriffe. 4e neubearb. A. hrsg. u. Mitw. d. Kantgesells. Bl. la8°. 1927
Eisner (Curt). Psychopathia spiritualis. Nietzsche u. d. Apostel d. Zukunft. 8°. Leipzig. [1892]
Die neue Zeit. [Hrsg. B. Merkle]. s8°. München. 1919
Eissler (Gottfried). Katalog d. Bibl. G. E., Goethe-Samml. &c. Versteig., Juni 1925, Gilhofer & Ranschburg. la8°. Wien. 1925
Eitel (Anton). Der Kirchenstaat unter Clemens V. 8°. 1907
Eitel (Ernest John). Feng-shui: or, rudiments of nat. sci. in China. 8°. Hongkong. 1873
Eitrem (Samson). Papyri Osloenses. fasc. 1, Magical papyri; ed. S. E. [Norske Videnskaps-Akad.] la8°. Oslo. 1925
Ejegodnik. Ежегодник петроградских государств. театров; под редакц. А. С. П., 1920, *see* POLYAKOV (A. S.)
Ejenedelnik Sovetskoi Yustitsii. Еженедельник Советской Юстиции. Nos. 1–9. [*b. w.* Izvestiya Tsəntral. Kom. R. K. P., 1920–21]. fol. Москва. 1922
Ekelund (Vilhelm). Valda dikter. s8°. [1913]
Ekholm (Nils), *see* HEDIN (S.) S. Tibet, 1906–8, v6i, meteorolog. Beobacht., bearb. N. E., 1920.
Ekwall (Eilert). Eng. place-names in *-ing.* [Kungl. Human. Vetenskapssamfundet, Skr., 6]. 8°. Lund. 1923
The place-names of Lancs. [Chetham Soc., N.S., v81]. s4°. M'ter. 1922
Place-names of Lancs. [M'ter. Univ. Eng. ser., No. 11]. 8°. M'ter. 1922
Elanak. Elanak Biuzantean. [*Almanac, ed.* L. Indjidjean, 1816]. s8°. i Venetik. 1816
Eland (G.) In Bucks. 2nd & enl. ed. of Old works &c. in rural Bucks. 8°. Aylesbury. 1923
Elasippus [ELEUSIPPUS], *see* ACTA Iberica SS. tergemin. martyrum E. &c.; ed. &c. N. Marr, 1906.
Elbe. *Manuscrit de l'Ile d'E., 1820, *see* MONTHOLON (*gén.* C. J. F. T. DE).
Elbenne (*le vicomte* **Samuel Menjot d'**), *see* MENJOT D'ELBENNE.
Elbert (Johannes). Die Sunda-Exped. des Vereins für Geog. u. Stat. zu Frankfurt. 2B. 4°. Frankfurt am Main. 1911–12
Elchies (Patrick Grant, *Lord*), *Scottish judge; 1690–1754.* Letters. With mem. &c. by H. D. MacWilliam. 8°. Aberdeen. 1927
Elchingen (Joseph Napoléon Ney, *duc* **d')**, *see* NEY (J. N.)
Eldad, *the Danite.*
ספר אלדד הדני. [P468]. s8°. Livorno. [1828]
Elder of the Church of Scotland, *ps.* *Mary Queen of Scots: a narr. & defence, 1889, *see* WALKER (A.)
Elder (David), *see* MURRAY (D.) The D. E. Infirmary, Govan, 1927.
Elder (Marc). Le sang des dieux. s8°. [1921]
Elder (William), *M.D.* Questions of the day: econ. & social. 8°. Phila. 1871
Elderkin (George Wicker). Kantharos: st. in Dionysiac & kindred cult. la8°. Princeton. 1924
Elderkin (John). Brief hist. of the Lotus Club. s8°. N.Y. [1895]
Elderton (William Palin).
Frequency curves & correlation. 8°. [1906]
„ „ ....Addendum & errata. 8°. 1917
—— **& R. C. Fippard.** The construction of mortality & sickness tables. s8°. 1914
Eldridge (Benjamin P.) & W. B. Watts. Our rival the rascal: conflict betw. criminals & the police. 8°. Boston, *Mass.* 1897
Eldridge (*Hon.* **C. A.**) *& others.* Against the employment of the bayonet at the ballot box. Speeches by C. A. E., S. S. Cox &c., in House of Repr., 1871. [P2625]. 8°. W. 1871
Eleanor, *de Poitiers, vicomtesse de Furne* [ALIÉNOR]. Les honneurs de la cour (1484–91), *see* †LACURNE DE STE-PALAYE (J. B. DE). Mém., t2, 1759.
Electorat. Acta publ., d. Neundten E. betreffende. [P2746]. s4°. *n.p.* 1693
Eledus. Le roman d'Eledus & Serene. Ed. f. MS. in Bibl. Nat. by J. R. Reinhard. [Univ. of Texas Studies]. 8°. Austin, Texas. 1923
Elegy. *Elegy (An) on the author of the True-born-Engl.-man, 1708, *see* DEFOE (D.)
*Elegy (An) wr. in a country-church-yard, Lat. redd., 1776, *see* GRAY (T.), *the poet.*
Elementary. *Elem. propos. illust. of the princ. of currency, 1819, *see* DRUMMOND (H.), *M.P.*
Elements. *The interlude of the four elements. Ed. J. O. Halliwell. [Percy Soc., 74. *a. c. b. w.* Gotham. Merry tales &c., 1840]. s8°. 1848
For a. ed., see Farmer (J. S.), *ed.* Early Eng. dramatists: 6 anon. plays, s1, 1905.
Elena Pavlovna, *see* HELEN PAVLOVNA, *grand duchess.*
***Elenchus** motuum nuperorum in Anglia, 1649, *see* BATE (G.)
***Elenco** ufficiale nobiliare Ital. s8°. Torino. 1922
Elers (Andreas). Diss. de præstando categoricè in libros symbolic. juramento. Sub praes. V. Alberti. [P426]. s4°. Lipsiae. 1690
Elets (Yuly Lukyanov). Надо знать своего врага. [P2454]. 8°. С.-П. 1904
Elève (Un) de Félix Neff, *ps.* *Essai sur les classes ou réunions d'expér. chrét. &c., 1851, *see* MÉTHODISTES.
Eley (Charles), *M.A., F.L.S.*
Gardening for the 20th cent. 8°. 1923
Elgar (*Sir* **Edward)**, *see* NEWMAN (E.) E., 2nd ed., 1920.
Elgin & Kincardine (James Bruce, *8th/12th earl of*), *see* MORISON (J. L.) The 8th E. of E., 1928.
Elgin & Kincardine (Mary, *countess of*), *wife of T. B., 7th/11th earl, form. Nisbet.* Letters of M. Nisbet of Dirleton, Ctss. of Elgin. Arr. by Lt.-Col. N. H. Grant. 8°. 1926
Elgood (*Lt.-Col.* **Percival George).** Egypt & the army. 8°. 1924
Elgström (Anna Lenah). Fattigfolk. 3e uppl. s8°. [1919]
Gäster och främlingar. 2a uppl. s8°. [1918]
Stjärnan vars namn är Malört. [Lille Louis—Fjärran—Dödsfjäriln—Då liljorna blomma]. 2a uppl. s8°. [1916]
Elia (Pascal M. d'). Catholic native episcopacy in China, 1300–1926. 8°. Shanghai. 1927
Eliae (Paulus), *see* OLIVARIUS (C.) De vita & scr. P. E., 1741.
Elias, *Aristotelian commentator.* Komm. in Aristotelis Kategorias versio armenica ed. J. Manandean. [Bibl. Armeno-Georgica, 1. *a. tp. in Armenian*]. la8°. Petropoli. 1911
Elias, *Cairel, see* CAIREL (E.)
Elias, *Germanus, see* ELIJAH, *ben Asher, the Levite.*
Elias, *d'Ussel, see* USSEL. Poésies des 4 troubadours d'U.; publ. d'ap. les MSS. par J. Audiau, 1922.
Elias (Johan E.) Het voorspel van den eersten Engelschen Oorlog. 2d. 8°. 's-Gravenhage. 1920
Schetsen uit de gesch. van ons zeewezen. 4 ged. 8°. 's-Gravenhage. 1916–27
1, 1568–1652. 2, 1652. 3, 1652–3. 4, 1652–3.
Eliasberg (Aleksandr) & David Eliasberg, *edd., see* RUSSKII. Русскій парнассъ, 1920.
Eliazarean (Hovakim). [Fourth short compos. in mem. of H. E. *In Armenian.* P2798]. s4°. S.-Petrbourg. 1826
Elie de la Primaudaie (F.), *see* LA PRIMAUDAIE.
Elijah, *ben Asher, the Levite* [ELIAS *Levita*]. Capitula cantici de literis, punctis &c. Aeditum & per S. Munsterum Lat. versum. s8°. Basileæ. 1527
Grammatica Hebraica: nuper per S. Munsterum Lat. donata. [Liber electus compl. Gramm. orationes &c.—Tabula omnium Hebr. conjugationum &c.] [*b. w. h.* Capitula cantici, 1527]. s8°. [Basileæ ?. 1525 ?]
„ „ jam ult. manu scholiis illust. &c. s8°. Basileæ. 1543
Opusculum recens Hebraicum cui titulum fecit Thisbites &c. Per P. Fagium Lat. don. [*Heb. & Lat.*] s4°. Isnæ in Algavia. 1541
Eliot, *The family of.* Genealog. mem. rel. to families of Eliot of Port Eliot & Craggs of Wyserley. Fr. docs. in poss. of Earl of St. Germans. la8°. *p.p.* 1868
Eliot (Charles). Vegetation & scenery in the Metropolitan Reservations of Boston. Forestry report. obl.8°. Boston [Mass.] 1898
Eliot (*Sir* **Charles Norton Edgecumbe)** [*ps.* ODYSSEUS].
Hinduism & Buddhism; hist. sketch. 3v. 8°. 1921
Eliot (Charles William). The 90th birthday of C. W. E. Proc. in Sanders theatre &c., Mar. 20, 1924. [Harvard Univ]. 8°. Camb. [Mass.] 1925
Eliot (Edward Granville), *3rd earl of St. Germans, see* ST. GERMANS (E. G. E., *3rd e.*)

Eliot (George), *ps.* Silas Marner. ster. ed. s8°. E. *n.d.*
see HALDANE (E. S.) G. E. & h. times, 1927.
„ MUDGE (I. G.) & M. E. SEARS. A G. E. dict., 1924.
„ PATERSON (A. H.) G. E.'s fam. life & letters, 1928.
„ POND (E. J.) Les idées morales & relig. de G. E., 1927.
Eliot (John), *apostle of the Indians, see* MATHER (C.) Life &c., 2nd ed., 1691; 1755.
Eliot (Thomas Stearns).
Homage to J. Dryden. 3 essays on poetry of the 17th cent. 8°. 1924
Poems. s8°. N.Y. 1920
Poems, 1909-25. 8°. 1926
The sacred wood. Essays on poetry & criticism. s8°. [1920]
Shakespeare & the stoicism of Seneca. Address, Shakespeare Assoc. 8°. 1927
Eliot (William Granville). A treatise on the defence of Portugal, & events of camp. under Wellington 1808-9. 8°. 1810
„ „ ....2nd ed. 8°. 1811
Elisha, *Vardapet.* [Book of E. Hist. of Vardan. *In Armenian*]. s4°. Kipolis. 1213[=1764]
„ „ [*a. ed. Ed.* Kh. Hovhannisean]. 8°. Moskoua. 1892
[Sermon on the Transfiguration &c. *In Armenian;* Soferq. Hayk., v18]. s8°. i Venetik. 1854
[Works. *In Armenian*]. 8°. i Venetik. 1859
see TEZA (E.) La storia dei Vardaniani di Eliseo, 1893.
Elisio (Giovanni) [†J. ELISIUS]. Opusculum de balneis Puteolorum, Baiarum, et Pithecusarum, a S. Mazzella rec., *see* MAZZELLA (S.) Sito &c. di Pozzuolo, 1606.
Elizabeth, *empress of Austria, 1837-98.*
see CUNLIFFE-OWEN (*Lady* M.) *The martyrdom of an Empress, 2nd ed., 1899.
„ TISSOT (E.) Le livre des reines; Victoria, l'imp. E. &c., 1896.
Elizabeth, *queen of England.*
see ALLEN (*card.* W.) Duo edicta E. contra sacerdotes Soc. Jesu &c., 1583.
„ BARLOW (T.) Brutum fulmen, or the bull of Pius V conc. the damnat. of Q. E. &c., 1681.
„ BELL (J.) Q. Eliz. & a Swedish princess, 1565; ed. E. Seaton, 1926.
„ CAMDEN (W.) Annales, true hist. of E. (1558-88); tr. A. Darcie, 1625.
„ CHAMBERLIN (F.) Private character of Q. E., 1921.
„ —— Sayings of Q. E., 1924.
„ CREIGHTON (M.) Age of E., 22nd impr., 1925.
„ DANS (A. VAN). Poemata: acc. vita E., 1636.
„ DAWBARN (C. Y. C.) Uncrowned: story of Q. E. & Bacon; suppl. notes, 1923.
„ FARQUHAR (H.) J. Rutlinger & the phœnix badge of E., 1923.
„ FUGGER, *Fam. of.* F. Newsletters; ed. V. v. Klarwill, ser. 2, ref. to E. &c.; tr., 1926.
„ GARGÀNO (G. S.) Scapigliatura ital. a Londra sotto E. &c., 1923.
see LETI (G.) Hist. di E., p2, 1683.
„ —— La vie d'E.; tr., 2p, 1694.
„ LODGE (E.) Illust. of Brit. hist. &c.; conts. gt. part of corr. of E. w. G., 6th earl of Shrewsbury, Mary Q. of Scots in custody, 3v, 1791.
„ MEYER (A. O.) England & the Catholic Church under E.; auth. tr., 1916.
„ POLLEN (J. H.) Eng. Catholics in r. of E., 1558-80, 1920.
„ RAIT (R. S.) & A. I. CAMERON, *edd.* King James's secret: negot. betw. E. & J. VI rel. to execut. of Mary Q. of Scots, 1927.
„ READ (C.) Walsingham & the policy of E., 3v, 1925.
„ STATE PAPERS. Cal. of S. P., For. ser. of the r. of E., v18-21i, 1914-27.
„ WILSON (V. A.) Q. E.'s maids of honour, 1922.
„ WINWOOD (*Sir* R.) Mems. of aff. of state in r. of E. &c., 3v, 1725.
Elizabeth, *of Hungary, St.*
see HAWKINS (H.) *The hist. of S. E., 1632.
„ LISZT (F.) Heil. E., Oratorium, 3. A., *n.d.*
Elizabeth, *empress of Russia, d. of Peter the Great, see* STEPANOV (A. V.) E. II., 1892.
Elizabeth Sophia Maria, *of Norway, Duchess of Holstein-Ploen, afterw. consort of Augustus William, duke of Brunswick-Luneburg.* Bibliotheca Biblica; Verzeichnis d. Bibel-Sammlung welche E. S. M. gesammelt hat. s4°. Braunschweig. 1752
Elizabethan. The E. home disc. in 2 dialogues [ed. M. St. C. Byrne], 1925, *see* SAINLIENS (C. DE).
E. lyrics, 1925, *see* AULT (N.), *ed.*
E. Zoo (The): bk. of beasts &c.; [ed. M. St. C. Byrne], 1926, *see* TOPSELL (E.)
Typical E. plays, 1926, see SCHELLING (F. R.), *ed.*
Ellacombe (Henry Nicholson).
In a Gloucestershire garden. 2nd ed. 8°. 1896
Ellenborough (Edward Law, *2nd baron, aft. earl of*). India under Lord E., 1842-44: sel. f. unpubl. papers &c. of E. Ed. w. intr. & append. by Sir A. Law. 8°. 1926
Eller (Irvin). The hist. of Belvoir Castle. la8°. 1841
Ellerman (Annie Winifred), *see* BRYHER (W.), *ps.*
Ellershaw (Wilfrid). Optics of the telescope. s8°. [1908]
Elles (Gertrude Lilian), *D.Sc.*
The study of geolog. maps. la8°. C. 1921
Ellicott (Charles John), *bp. of Gloucester & Bristol.*
Hist. lectures on the life of J. C. [Hulsean Lects. for 1859]. 4th ed. 8°. 1865
St. Paul's E. to the Ephesians: w. comm. & rev. tr. 4th ed. corr. 8°. 1868
St. Paul's E. to the Galatians: w. comm. & rev. tr. 4th ed. corr. 8°. 1867
St. Paul's E. to the Philippians, Colossians & Philemon: w. comm. & rev. tr. 3rd ed. corr. 8°. 1865
St. Paul's E. to the Thessalonians, w. comm. & rev. tr. 4th ed. 8°. 1880
see ATHANASIAN CREED (THE). Rep. of the Comm. of bishops, w. intr. &c. by C. J. [E.], 1872.
„ MALAN (S. C.) E.'s tr. of Athanasian Creed, 1872.
Elliger (Christian). Disput. de beatitudinis in Domino morientium privilegio, ex Apoc. xiv. s4°. Jenæ. [1663]
Ellington (Edward). The reproach of Xt. Sermon occ. by death of Rev. G. Whitefield. [P2690]. s8°. 1771
Elliot (Daniel Giraud). Cat. of coll. of birds obt. by the exped. into Somali-Land, *see* FIELD COLUMBIAN MUS. Ornith. ser., v1ii, 1897.
Elliot (*Sir* **Henry George),** *G.C.B.* Some revolutions & o. diplomatic exper. Ed. by h. daughter. 8°. 1922
Elliot (Hugh S. R.) Human character. s8°. 1922
Modern science & the illusions of Prof. Bergson. Pref. by Sir R. Lankester. 2nd impr. s8°. 1912
Elliot (Margaret M.), *see* HARTLEY (D.) & M. M. E. Life &c. of people of Eng. (15c.), 1925.
Elliot (Richard), *A.B.* Psalms & hymns in 2p. (*p2 has a half tp. w. sep. pag.*) s8°. 1761
Elliot (*Sir* **Walter),** *of Wolfelee, see* SEWELL (R.) W. E., sk. of h. life & extrs. f. h. note books, 1896.
Elliot (Walter Elliot). Toryism & the 20th cent. Pref. by Rt. Hon. S. Baldwin. s8°. [1927]
Elliott Monographs. Ed. E. C. Armstrong. 1-4, 11-12, 15, 16, 17, 19, 20. 8°. Princeton, N.J. 1914-26
see APOLLONIUS, *Tyrius.* Libro de Apolonio; ed. C. C. Marden, p2, 1922. [11-12.]
„ ARMSTRONG (E. C.) A. M. Elliott: a retrospect, 1923. [15.]
„ —— The authorship of Vengement Alixandre & Venjance A., 1926. [19.]
„ BLOSSOM (F. A.) La composition de Salammbô, 1914. [3.]
„ COLEMAN (A.) Flaubert's literary development, 1914. [1.]
„ CONS (L.) L'auteur de la Pathelin, 1926. [17.]
„ EDWARDS (B.) Classif. of MSS. of G. de Cambrai's Vengement Alixandre, 1926. [20.]
„ FAY (P. B.) & A. COLEMAN. Sources &c. of Flaubert's Salammbô, 1914. [2.]
„ GUADALAJARA. Fuero de G. (1219); ed. H. Keniston, 1924. [16.]
„ HAMILTON (A.) Sources of relig. element in Flaubert's Salâmmbô, 1917. [4.]
Elliott (Aaron Marshall), *see* ARMSTRONG (E. C.) E.: a retrospect, 1923.
Elliott (Charles), *D.D.* Delineation of Roman Catholicism. n. ed. w. add. by J. S. Stamp. la8°. 1844
„ „ ......3rd ed., w. pref. by J. Hannah. la8°. 1851
Elliott (Charles Boileau).
Travels in Austria, Russia & Turkey. 2v. 8°. 1838
Elliott (Ebenezer) [THE CORN-LAW RHYMER], *see* WATKINS (J.) Life, poetry, & letters of E. E., 1850.
Elliott (Edward Bishop). Apocalypsis Alfordiana: or 5 letters to Alford in refut. of h. Apocalyptic expos. &c. 8°. 1852
see CANDLISH (R. S.) Four letters to E. on h. Horæ Apocalypticæ, 2nd ed., 1847.
Elliott (John Sherman). Memoir of the life & corr. of Rev. W. Lavers. 2nd ed. s8°. 1848
Ellis, *bookseller, 29 New Bond St.* Coll. of armorial book-bindings. Descr. by G. Smith & F. Benger. s4°. 1927
Ellis (*Mrs.*) [†STICKNEY (SARAH), *aft.* ELLIS].
Madagascar: its soc. & relig. progress. s8°. 1863
Ellis (Abijah), *see* ALLEY (L.) Report of trial of L. A. for murder of A. E., 1875.
Ellis (Alexander George), *see* BRIT. MUSEUM. PRINTED BOOKS. Arabic bks. in B.M.: Suppl. cat.; by A. S. Fulton & A. G. E., 1926.
Ellis (Arthur Erskine). Brit. snails: guide to non-marine Gastropoda. s8°. O. 1926
Ellis (B. Eldred). Gloves & the glove trade. s8°. *Pitman.* 1921

Ellis (Clement). The gentile sinner, or England's brave gentleman, character'd. 3rd ed. s8°. O. 1664
Three disc. on the parable of Dives & Lazarus, the unjust steward, the 10 virgins. s8°. 1705
Ellis (*Mrs.* **Edith O. M.**), *wife of H. Havelock Ellis, form. Lees.* The new horizon in love & life. Pref. by E. Carpenter. Intr. by M. Tracy. 8°. 1921
see GOLDBERG (I.) Havelock Ellis, w. suppl. ch. on Mrs. E. E., 1926.
Ellis (Ernest Tetley), *ed., see* BLACK, *publ.* B.'s gardening dict., 1921.
Ellis (Frederick Startridge), *see* ROSSETTI (D. G.) Letters to E., 1928.
Ellis (George), *F.R.S.* *Memoir of a map of the countries betw. Black Sea & Caspian &c., w. acc. of Caucasian nations. [Map *missing*]. la8°. 1788
Ellis (Henry Havelock).
The dance of life. 8°. 1923
Impressions & comments. s2, 3, 1914–23. 8°. 1921–24
Little essays of love & virtue. s8°. 1922
Man & woman. 3rd ed. s8°. 1899
A study of Brit. genius. n. ed., rev. & enl. 8°. 1927
see GOLDBERG (I.) H. E., 1926.
Ellis (*Sir* **Henry**), *princ. librarian of the British Museum.*
*A cat. of books on angling. 8°. 1811
Ellis (Hubert Dynes). Short descr. of the anc. silver plate, W. Co. of Armourers & Brasiers. 4°. 1892
Ellis (John), *F.R.S.* An essay towards a nat. hist. of the Corallines &c. of Gt. Brit. & Ireland. 4°. 1755
Ellis (Lucy), *see* TURQUAN (J.) & L. E. La belle Pamela (Lady E. Fitz Gerald), 2t, 1923–24.
Ellis (*Mrs.* **Maude**), *form. Cheape.* The Squire of Bentley (Mrs. Cheape), a gt. sportswoman. With chapters by J. Fairfax-Blakeborough &c. 8°. E. 1926
Ellis (Philip) [P. E., *monk*]. The first sermon preach'd before their Majesties in English at Windsor, Oct. 1685. [P2594]. s4°. 1686
Second sermon preach'd bef. the King & Queen &c. at St. James's, Nov. 1685. [P2594]. s4°. 1686
Ellis (Richard), *ed.* An Elizabethan broadside in Welsh being a brief, 1591, to Sion Salisburi. fol. O. 1904
Ellis (Stewart Marsh).
George Meredith, h. life &c. [2nd ed.] 8°. 1920
Mainly Victorian. 8°. [1924]
The solitary horseman, life &c. of G. P. R. James. 8°. 1927
see HARDMAN (*Sir* W.) A mid-Victorian Pepys: letters &c. of Sir W. H.; annot. & ed. S. M. E., 2s, 1923–25.
Ellis (Thomas Peter).
Welsh tribal law & custom in the M.A. 2[v]. 8°. O. 1926
see BROMFIELD. The first extent of B. & Yale, 1315; [ed., w. intr. &c.] by T. P. E., 1924.
Ellis (Tristram James).
Sketching f. nature: hdbk. s8°. 1883
„ „ ....2nd ed., rev. & enl. 8°. 1887
Twelve etchings of views &c. in Cyprus. Artist's proof. obl.fol. 1879
Ellis (William). The hist. of the London Miss. Society. v1 [*no more published*]. 8°. 1844
The martyr church. Xtnty. in Madagascar. 8°. 1870
Polynesian researches. n. ed. enl. & impr. 4v. s8°. 1853
Three visits to Madagascar, 1853–56. 8°. 1859
Ellis (William Patterson), *see* OXFORD. Liber albus civitatis Oxon.: abstracts of wills, &c., by W. P. E., 1909.
Ellis-Fermor (U. M.) Christopher Marlowe. 8°. [1927]
Ellison (Bernard C.) H.R.H. the Prince of Wales's sport in India. Ed. Sir H. Perry Robinson. Intr. by the Earl of Cromer. la8°. 1925
Ellison (*Lt.-Gen. Sir* **Gerald Francis**). Perils of amateur strategy as exemplified by the attack on the Dardanelles, 1915. Pref. note by Visct. Esher. s8°. 1926
Ellison (Grace). An Englishwoman in Angora. 8°. [1923]
Ellrod (Johann Michael). De Christiano marchione Brandenburgico. Praes J. M. E. resp. J. N. Oberländer. [P595]. s4°. Lipsiae. [1694]
Ells (Sidney C.) Bituminous sands of N. Alberta. [Canada: Geolog. Survey]. [P2771]. 8°. Ottawa. 1924
„ „ ....[*a. ed.* Maps *sep.*] 8°. Ottawa. 1926
Use of Alberta bituminous sands for surfacing of highways. [Canada: Geolog. Survey. P2874]. 8°. Ottawa. 1927
Ellwood (George Montague). The art of pen drawing. 8°. [1927]
Ellwood (Thomas).
see COMBER (T.), *D.D.* The right of tythes asserted; w. vindic. f. cavils of T. E., 1677.
Ellwood (Thomas) [*continued*].
see LESLIE (C.) *Satan disrob'd &c.; in reply to T. E.'s Answer to G. Keith's Narr. of proc^{s}. at Turners-Hall; 2nd ed., 1698.
Ellys (Anthony), *D.D., bp. of St. Davids.* Tracts on the liberty spiritual & temporal of Protestants [& of subjects] in England. 2p *in* 1v. 4°. 1763
Elmar, *ps.* Народъ и государств. дума. [P2722]. 8°. С.-П. 1906
El-Masudi [†'ALÍ IBN ḤUSAIN IBN 'ALÍ (ABÚ AL ḤASAN) *al Mas 'údi*]. Maçoudi. Le livre de l'avertissement & de la revision. Tr. B. Carra de Vaux. [Soc. Asiatique]. 8°. 1896
Elmore (C. J.) The diatoms (Bacillarioideae) of Nebraska, *see* NEBRASKA UNIV. Studies, v21, 1922.
Elms (E. F. M.) Our migrant birds. s8°. [1922]
Elmslie (William Jackson), *med. missionary, see* THOMSON (W. B.) A memoir of W. J. E., 1881.
Eloesser (Arthur). Thomas Mann, s. Leben u. s. Werk. 8°. 1925
Elphinstone (*Hon.* **Mountstuart**). Hist. of India, Hindu & Mahometan periods. 7th ed., w. notes & add^{s}. by E. B. Cowell. 8°. 1889
Elpizon, *ps., see* SINTENIS (C. F.)
Elrington (Charles Richard). The life of J. Ussher, w. acc. of h. writings. 8°. Dublin. 1848
Elrington (H.) Kensington past & present. s8°. 1922
Elsden (James Vincent) & J. A. Howe. Stones of London; descr. guide to princ. stones used in London &c. s8°. 1923
Elsner (Eleanor).
Romance of the Basque country & the Pyrenees. 8°. [1927]
Romantic France: the enchanted land of Provence. 8°. 1926
Romantic Spain. 8°. [1924]
Elson (Robert). Maxa. s8°. [1922]
Elssler (Fanny), *see* FLEISCHMANN (H.) Le Roi de Rome & les femmes: F. E. &c., 1910.
Elster (Hanns Martin).
W. von Molo u. s. Schaffen. s8°. München. 1920
see MOLTKE (H. C. B. v.) H. v. M.: Lebensbild; hrsg. v. H. M. E., 1923.
Elster (Kristian), *d. y.*
Illust. Norsk litteraturhist. 2[B]. la8°. 1923–24
Den skjønne ungdom. Roman. 8°. 1923
Elston (Roy). Traveller's hdbk. for Constantinople, Gallipoli & Asia Minor. [Cook's Hdbk.] s8°. 1923
Elswich (Johann Hermann v.) De Formula Concordiae num in Dania sit combusta Recusa. [P484]. s4°. Vitebergae. 1716
Elteste (Friedrich Gottfried). Ausführl. Nachricht v. d. Stadt Zoerbig. s8°. L. 1727
***Eltham** (The) tragedy reviewed, by C., 1871, *see* CROSLAND (N.)
Elton Hall, *Hunts.* Cat. of pictures at E. Hall in poss. of Col. D. J. Proby. By T. Borenius & J. V. Hodgson. Pref. by G. Proby. 4°. 1924
Elton (Godfrey).
Revolutionary idea in France, 1789–1871. 8°. 1923
Elton (Oliver). Reason & enthusiasm in the 18th cent., *see* ENGLISH ASSOC. Essays, v10, 1924.
A sheaf of papers. 8°. 1922
A survey of Eng. lit., 1830–80. 2v. 8°. 1920
——, A. F. G. Bell & J. Fitzmaurice-Kelly. James Fitzmaurice-Kelly. [Extr. de la Revue Hisp., t60. P2784]. 8°. N.Y. 1924
Elton (P. M.) Output in silk-weaving, *see* INDUST. FATIGUE RESEARCH BD. Rep., 9, 17, 1920–22.
Elvas. Lettres pastorales, du chapitre de l'Égl. d'E. &c., *see* PORTUGAL. Rec. de decrets &c., p2, 1759; 2e éd., p2, 1761.
Elwell (Joseph Bowne). Advanced bridge. s8°. 1904
Bridge: principles & rules. s8°. 1907
Elwenspoek (Curt). Schinderhannes [J. Buckler], d. rhein. Rebell. s8°. St. 1925
Elwert (Eduard). De antinomia Io Agricolae Islebii, diss. [P2595]. s8°. Turici. 1836
Elwes (Henry John) & A. Henry. The trees of Gt. Brit. & Ireland. 7v [*pagin. contin.* Index, *w. sep. tp., in* v7]. 4°. *p.p.* E. 1906–13
(Elwes John), *see* TOPHAM (*Maj.* E.) Life of J. E., 6th ed., 1790; 10th ed., 1791.
Elworthy (R. T.) Helium in Canada. [Canada: Geolog. Survey. P2874]. 8°. Ottawa. 1926
Ely. Ely episcopal records. Calendar &c. of episc. rec. in muniment room of the Palace of Ely. Comp. by A. Gibbons. 8°. *p.f.p.c.* Lincoln. 1891
Ely (Richard Theodore). Property & contract in th. rel. to distrib. of wealth. 2v. s8°. 1914
—— & E. W. Morehouse. Elem. of land econ. 8°. N.Y. 1924

Elyot (*Sir* **Thomas**). The book named The governour, 1564.
New ed., by A. T. Eliot. 8º. Newcastle-upon-Tyne. 1834
„ „ Ed. f. the ed. of 1531 by H. H. S. Croft. v1. 8º. 1883
T. E.'s "Verteidigung guter Frauen (1545) u. d. Frauenfrage in Eng. bis Shakespeare: Anhang, E.'s Schutzmittell gegen d. Tod (1545) *Eng. texts*; v. A. Brandl, *see* DEUT. SHAKESPEARE-GESELLSCHAFT. Jahrbuch, Jhrg. 51, 1915.

Elze (Theodor). Paul Wiener, Mitreformator in Krain &c. [Aus d. Jahrbuch d. Gesellsch. für d. Gesch. d. Protest. in Oesterr. P2859]. 8º. Wien. 1882

Elzevir [*incl. the family of E. & the E. presses &c.*; †ELSEVIER].
see BERGHMAN (G. S.) Et. sur la bibliog. elzevir., basées sur l'ouvr. de A. Willems, 1885.
„ COPINGER (H. B.) The E. Press: handlist of productions, w refs. to Willems & o. bibliographers, 1927.
„ PIETERS (C.) Annales de l'imprimerie E. &c., 1851.
„ RAHIR (E.) Cat. d'une coll. de vol. impr. par les E. &c. du 17e siècle; rédige par E. R., 1896.
„ WILLEMS (A.) Les Elzevier; suppl. par G. Berghman, 1897.

Emants (Marcellus). Lilith. Gedicht. s8º. Haarlem. *n.d.*

Emanuel, *king of Portugal, surnamed the Fortunate* [MANOEL].
see GOES (D. DE). Crón. do felic. rei D. Manuel, n. ed., dir. J. M. Teixeira de Carvalho &c., 4p, 1926.

Emanuel Philibert, *duke of Savoy, d. 1587.*
see BUTTET (M. C. DE). La victoire de Pr. E. P. duc de S. [*poem*, 1561], 1915.
„ GRANVELLE (*le card.* DE). Lettere al E. F.; pubbl. da E. Ricotti, 1880.
„ VACCARONE (L.) E. F. alla Corte Cesarea di Carlo V imp. (1545–51), 1900.

Emard (Paul). Toiling thr. the dark. Re-educ. of blinded soldiers. Pref. by E. Brieux. [P2501]. la8º. Baltimore, Md. 1919

***Embajada** española: anon. contemp. Span. guide to diplom. proc. in last quarter of 17 cent.; tr. & ed. H. J. Chaytor, *see* CAMDEN MISC., v14, 1926.

Emberios, *see* PIERRE, *de Provence.*

Emblèmes. *Devises & emblèmes anc. & mod. &c., 1697, *see* DEVISES.

***Emblems** for the entertainment & improvement of youth &c. 8º. [1750?]

Embrun, *see* RECUEIL. R. des historiens de la France, Pouillés, t8, Prov. d'E. &c., 1923.

Emden (Alfred Brotherson). An Oxford hall in med. times: early hist. of St. Edmund Hall. 8º. O 1927

Emden (Cecil Stuart). The civil servant in the law & the constit. 8º. 1923
Princ. of Brit. constit. law. s8º. [1925]

Emerson, *The family of.*
see EMERSON (P. H.) Contin. notes on the E. family of Co. Herts & Essex &c., 1923.
— Penultimate notes on the E. fam. of Herts & Essex, & Massachusetts, 1925.

Emerson (Edward Waldo).
Emerson in Concord. A memoir. 8º. 1889

Emerson (Harrington). Efficiency as a basis for operation & wages. 4th ed. enl. s8º. N.Y. 1919
The 12 principles of efficiency. 4th ed. s8º. N.Y. 1916

Emerson (Herbert William), *B.A.*, *see* PUNJAB: GOVT. PUBL.; Customary law of Multan distr.; [n. ed.] by H. W. E., 1924.

Emerson (*Mrs.* **John**), *see* LOOS (ANITA).

Emerson (Peter Henry). The blood eagle & o. tales. s8º. 1925
Continued [*& Penultimate*] notes on the Emerson *alias* Emberson family of Co. Herts & Essex &c. [3rd & 4th booklet[s]]. 8º. *p.f.p.c.* Eastbourne. 1923–25
English idyls. 3rd ed., rev. &c. s8º. 1924

Emerson (Ralph Waldo).
Compl. works. Riverside ed. 11v. s8º. 1883–84
1, Nature, addresses & lects.
2, 3, Essays, 2s.
4, Represent. men.
5, Eng. traits.
6, Conduct of life.
7, Society & solitude.
8, Letters & soc. aims.
9, Poems.
10, Lects. & biog. sketches.
11, Miscellanies.
Works comp. his essays, lectures, poems & orations. 3v. s8º. *Bohn.* 1888–90
Eng. traits & Representative men. [repr.] s8º. [1923]
Essays. s1, 2. s8º. Boston, *Mass.* 1882
Letters & social aims. s8º. Boston. 1876
May-Day & o. pieces. s8º. Boston. 1881

Emerson (Ralph Waldo) [*continued*].
Miscellanies. n. & rev. ed. s8º. Boston. 1882
Natural hist. of intellect; & o. papers. With a gen. ind. to E.'s Coll. works. s8º. 1894
Poems. Oxford ed. s8º. 1914
Representative men. s8º. Boston. 1882
„ „ ......*For a. issue see* Eng. traits *above.*
Society & solitude. s8º. Boston. 1882
see ALBEE (J.) Remembrances of E., 1903.
„ EMERSON (E. W.) E. in Concord, 1889.
„ PHIFER (C. L.) Posthumous essays: automatic wr. f. spirit R. W. E., 1907.
„ SUTCLIFFE (E. G.) E.'s theories of lit. expressions, 1923.

Emerton (Ephraim). Humanism & tyranny: st. in Ital. Trecento. s8º. Camb., *Mass.* 1925
Mediaeval Europe (814–1300). s8º. [1894]

Emery (George Frederick). Executors & administrators &c.: "how to prove a will." 2nd ed. s8º. 1903

Emery (Henry Crosby). Speculat. on the stock & produce exchanges of the U.S. 8º. N.Y., *Columbia Univ.* 1896

Emigrant, *ps.* *Indian emigration, 1924, *see* INDIAN.

Emigrant Mechanic (An), *ps.* *Settlers & convicts &c., 1847, *see* †HARRIS (ALEX.)

Émile-Bayard (J.), *see* BAYARD (J. ÉMILE).

Emiliane (Gabriel d'). *The frauds of Romish monks & priests. 4th ed. s8º. 1704
*Obs. on a journey to Naples. s8º. [1691]

Emiliani (Jerome), *see* JEROME [*Emiliani*], *St.*

Emiliani-Giudici (Paolo).
*Biografia del comm. P. E.-G. [P601]. 8º. Firenze. 1874
Storia polit. dei muncipj ital. 3p *in* 2v. [*pagin. cont.*] & App. [*sep.* Statuto dell' arte di Calimala &c.] 8º. Firenze. 1851–52

Emin (Ahmed). The develop. of mod. Turkey as measured by its press. 8º. N.Y., *Columbia Univ.* 1914

Émïn (Joseph). Life & adventures of J. E., 1726–1809, by himself. Ed. A. Apcar. 2nd ed. 8º. Calcutta. 1918

Emin (Mkrtitch). [Tales of anc. Armenia. *In Armenian. b. w.* Msereantz (M.) Last hours of Nicholas I, 1855]. 8º. Moskva. 1850

Eminent orientalists, 1922, *see* ORIENTALISTS.

Eminian (Sérapion). Dictionnaire franç.-armén.-turc. [*tp. wanting*]. s8º. Vienne. 1853

Eminskii etnograficheskii sbornik, *see* LAZAREVSKY INST. VOSTOCH. YAZIKOV.

***Emma**, 3v, 1816, *see* AUSTEN (J.)

Emma, *daughter of Charlemagne, see* ESTÈVE (E.) Ét. de litt. préromant.: Le conte d'E. & Eginhard dans la litt. franç., 1923.

Emma [*of Normandy*], *queen consort of* (*1*) *Ethelred II*, (*2*) *Canute, see* CANUTE. C. regis gesta, sive encomium E. reginae; rec. fecit G. H. Pertz, 1865.

Emmel (Felix). Der Tod d. Abendlandes: gegen O. Spengler's skept. Philos. 3e A. [P2492]. 8º. 1920

Emmeram, *Saint, bp. of* (*1*) *Poitiers*, (*2*) *Ratisbon, see* HAIMHRAMMUS.

Emmerich (Anna Katharina), *1774–1824, see* BRENTANO (C.) A. K. E. &c., 1874.

Emmerson (H. C.) & E. C. P. Lascelles.
Guide to the Unemploy. Insur. Acts. 8º. 1926

Emmet (Boris). Labor rels. in Fairmont, W. Va., bitum. coal field, *see* UNITED STATES: LABOR. Bull. 361, 1924.
Profit sharing in the U.S., *see* UNITED STATES: LABOR. Bull. 208, 1917.

Emmet (Cyril William).
see DOUGALL (L.) & C. W. E. Lord of thought, 1922.
„ SANDAY (W.) & C. W. E. The Psalms expl., 1918.

——, **C. F. Burney & W. Sanday.**
The use of the Psalter. s8º. O. 1918

Emmius (Ubbo). Rerum Frisicarum hist. decas quarta: Firmum Concordia vallum. [*b. w.* Ens (G.) Rerum Hung. hist., 1604]. s8º. Groningae Frisiorum. 1604

Emmott (Alfred Emmott, *1st baron*) [EMMOTT OF OLDHAM].
Nationaliz. of industries. A criticism. 8º. 1920

Emmott (Elizabeth Braithwaite). Short hist. of Quakerism (earlier periods). Intr. by R. M. Jones. 8º. [1923]

Emo, *abbot of Werum.* Kronijken van E. en Menko, abten te Wittewierum, met het vervolg van een ongenoemde, op nieuw uitg. door H. O. Feith en G. A. Stratingh. [Hist. Genoots. te Utrecht, Werken, N.S., 4]. 8º. Utrecht. 1866

Emperor [EMPEROR'S.] *Emperor's manifesto; right of house of Austria to crown of Spain, 1701, *see* LEOPOLD I, *emp. of Germany.*

Empire. Resources of the E., 10v, 1924, *see* RESOURSES &c.

Empire Cotton Growing Corporation.
Reports f. experiment stations, 1926–27. 8º. 1928

Empire (The) cotton growing review. Journal of the Empire Cotton Growing Corporation. Ed. J. C. Willis. v1–4 (1924–26). 8º. 1924–27

Empire forestry. Journal of the Empire Forestry Assoc., Imp. Inst., London. v1–5, 1922–26. 8º. 1922–26
v2–5 *have t.* Empire forestry journal.

Empire review (The). v37–46 (Jan. 1923–Dec. 1927). 8º. 1923–27

Empson (R. H. W.) The cult of the Peacock Angel: sh. acc. of Yezîdî tribes of Kurdistân. Comm. by Sir R. C. Temple. 8º. 1928

Empsychovius (Herrmann). Demonstratio Lutherum, idem docuisse quod Apostolica eccl. & orthodoxi patres docuerunt. Cui subjic.: Firma refut. totius doct. papisticæ opposita G. Braunii rationibus &c. Præf. Epistola B. Mentzleri. s8º. Gissæ. 1617

Emptor (Caveat), *gent.*, *see* STEPHEN (*Sir* G.)

Emser (Hieronymus) [*ps.* THOMAS PLACENTINUS].
Annotationes uber Luthers naw Testamēt gebessert u. emēdirt. s8º. Dresde. 1524
„ „ *For a. ed.*, *see* BIBLE: GERMAN. Das New Test., durch E. v̊teutscht, 1529.
De disputatioe Lipsicensi: quantum ad Boemos obiter deflexa est: Epistola H. E. [Saphicum eiusdem de eadem disputatione. P2444]. s4º. [Leipzig? 1519?]
Missæ Christianorum contra Lutheranam missandi formula assertio. s4º. *n.p.* 1524
see MELANCHTHON (P.) Didymi Faventini adv. T. Placentinum [*i.e.* H. E.] oratio 1521.
„ KAWERAU (G.) H. E.: e. Lebensbild aus d. Ref.-gesch., 1898.

***Enchanted** April (The), 1922, *see* ARNIM (*ctss.* v.)

Enchiridion. *Enchiridion oder eyn Handbuchlein, nutzlich zur stetter ubung &c., geystl. gesenge &c. [Nach d. Urdrukke, 1524, zu Erfurt v. J. Jonas u. J. Lange, hrsg. Lithogr. facs., ed. K. Rheinthaler]. s8º. [Erfurt. 1848]

Enciclopedia.
E. mod. illust. 10v. 8º. Milano. 1898–1904
Enciclopedia univ. ilustra da europeo-americana. t21–28, 40–57. [28 in 2p]. la8º. Barcelona. *Espasu-Calpe.* [1920–27]

Encina (Juan del) [†ENZINA (JUAN DE LA)]. Eglogas, *see* LOMBA Y PEDRAJA (J. R.) Teatro ant. a L. de Vega, 1924.
Narr. del viaje, *see* ENRIQUEZ DE RIVERA (F.) Viaje a Jerusalem, 1606.

Encyclopædia [CYCLOPÆDIA].
Большая Советская энциклопедия; под ред. Н. И. Бухарина &c.; главн. ред. О. Ю. Шмидт. т1–10. la8º. Москва. 1926–28
C. of Amer. biog., n. enl. ed., v8, 9, 1918–22, *see* APPLETON (D.) & Co.
C. of Biblical, theolog. & eccl. lit., 12v, 1867–91, *see* MAC-CLINTOCK (J.) & J. STRONG.
C. (The) of home arts, 1899, *see* MARKS (M.)
C. of Methodism &c., 1880, *see* SIMPSON (M.), *ed.*
C. of temperance, prohibition &c. Ed. Deets Pickett &c. 8º. N.Y. [1917]
E. (The) Britannica. The new vol. const., in combination w. the 29 vol. of the 11th ed., the 12th ed. &c. & dealing w. events &c., 1910–21. v30–32, 4º. 1922
„ „ 3 new suppl. vols. const. w. the vols. of latest ed. the 13th ed. 3v. 4º. 1926
see EVENTFUL. These eventful years: 20th cent. in making; [publ. E. B. Co.], 2v, 1924.
E. of Eng. furniture, 1927, *see* BRACKETT (O.), *ed.*
E. of furniture, 1926, *see* SCHMITZ (H.) *ed.*
E. of Indo-Aryan research, *see* GRUNDRISS. d. indo-ar. Philologie u. Altertumskunde.
E. of Islam. Ed. M. T. Houtsma, A. J. Wensinck, T. W. Arnold &c. v2, E–K. la8º. Leyden. 1927
E. of religion & ethics. Ed. J. Hastings, w. assist. of J. A. Selbie & L. H. Gray. v11–12, Sacrifice–Zwingli. 4º. E. 1920–21
„ „ .... Index vol. 4º. E. 1926
Relig. e.; based on Real-E. of Herzog, 3v, 1883–4, *see* SCHAFF (P.), *ed.*

Encyclopædie van Nederl.-Indië. 2e druk. Samengesteld door J. Paulus. d4, Soemb-Z., onder red. v. D. G. Stibbe &c. la8º. 's-Gravenhage. 1921

***End** (An) to controv. betw. Rom. Cath. & Prot. religions, 1654, *see* BAYLY (T.)

Ende (Johann Gottfried am). Comm. tres ad theol. nat., antiq. & philol. pert. s8º. Freibergae. 1782

Endelechius (Severus Sanctus). Carmen de mortibus boum, *see* GALLIA. *Vet. aliq. G. theol. scripta, 1586.

Endemann (Samuel). Instit. theologiæ dogmaticæ. 2t. s8º. Hanoviae. 1777–78

***Endlicher** Bericht u. Erklerung der Theologen beider Univ. Leipzig u. Wittemberg &c., 1570, *see* LEIPZIG.

Endre II, *see* ANDREW II, *k. of Hungary.*

Endres (Franz Carl). Die Türkei, mit 215 Abbildungen. Zgest. &c. v. F. C. E. la8º. München. [1916]

Endres (Johann Nepomuk). Diss. de pactorum Hildesiensium in confirmanda communi catholic. doctr. circa simultaneum efficacia &c. [P2648]. s4º. Bambergae. 1765

Enfield (D. E.)
A lady of the Salons: story of Louise Colet. s8º. [1922]

Enfield (R. R.) The agricult. crisis, 1920–23. 8º. 1924

Enfield (William), *LL.D.* The speaker or misc. pieces f. best Eng. writers. s8º. 1808

Enfrey (L. M.) Sous les gonfanons des Croisés. s8º. 1923

Engberg (Russell C.)
Indust. prosperity & the farmer. 8º. N.Y. 1927

Engel (Carl). Music of the most anc. nations, partic. Assyrians, Egyptians, Hebrews. [repr.] 8º. [1909]

Engel (Christian von), *see* CORNIDES (D.) Comm. de relig. vet. Hungarorum; ed., diss. adj., C. E., 1791.

Engel (Georg). Die Herrin u. i. Knecht. Roman. 16.–18. Taus. s8º. L. *n.d.*
Die Mauer. Roman. [2e A.] s8º. St. [1923]
see WEITZ (H. P.) G. E., s. Werk u. s. Zeit, 1923.

Engel (Moritz). Gedanken ü. d. Denken. 8º. 1922

Engel (Nicolas Friedrich). Diss. de superstitione statui nociva. Resp. J. W. Blaufusius. [P2636]. s4º. Jenae. [1741]

Engel (Sigmund). The elements of child-protection. Tr. E. Paul. 8º. 1912

Engelbach (Reginald). Harageh. Inscr. by B. Gunn. [Brit. Sch. of Arch. in Egypt, 20th year, 1914]. 4º. 1923
Problem of the obelisks, f. a st. of the unfinished obelisk at Aswan. 8º. 1923
see BRUNTON (G.) & R. E. Gurob, 1927.

Engelberti (Ulrich), *of Strassburg, d. 1277.* De pulchro, *see* GRABMANN (M.) U. E. Abhdlg. De pulchro, Untersuch. u. Texte, 1925.

Engelberts (F. J.) Souvenirs de famille. [Tr. M. Bresson]. Suppl. au Monde Nouveau, mars-avril 1922. [no tp.] s8º. 1922

Engelbrecht (Arnold Diederich). Bibliothecas eremitarum vet. perlust. dabit A. D. E. [P2636]. s4º. Helmstadi. [1701]

Engelcken (Christian Heinrich). Hist. N. Crellii, capite plexi, variis aberrationibus liberata &c. s4º. [Rostock. 1727]

Engelgardt (B. M.), *see* GONCHAROV (I. A.) И. А. Г. и И. С. Тургенев; с пред. &c. Б. М. Э., 1923.

Engelhard (Nicolaus), *ed.* Feriae Groninganae exhib. var. varii argumenti diss. philosoph. 2v. [*each in 2p. b. together*]. s8º. Groningae. 1733–39
[*p1 & 2 of v1 have titles* "*Feriae aestivae*" *&* "*Feriae hybernae.*"]

Engelhardt (Moritz v.), *prof. of theology at Dorpat.*
V. E. Löscher, nach s. Leben u. Wirken. 8º. Dorpat. 1853

Engelhorn (J.), *see* *FLAT ornament: pattern bk. of designs [*publ.* E.], *n.d.*

Engelmann (Arthur). Hist. of continental civil procedure. By A. E. & o. Tr. & ed. R. W. Millar. Intr. by W. S. Holdsworth & S. Williston. 8º. Boston, *Mass.* 1927

Engelmann (Wilhelm). New guide to Pompeii. s8º. Leipzig. 1925

Engels (Friedrich).
Grundsätze d. Kommunismus. Aus dessen Nachlass hrsg. v. E. Bernstein. [P2456]. 8º. [1920]
The peasant war in Germany. [Tr. M. J. Olgin]. Intr. by D. Riazanov. [2nd ed.] s8º. [1927]
Schriften d. Frühzeit, 1838–44, *see* MAYER (G.) F. E., Ergzb. z. B1, 1920.
Socialism utopian & scientific. Tr. E. Aveling, w. intr. by the a. 5th ed. s8º. 1920
see KAHAN-COATES (Z.) Life & work of F. E., 1920.
„ MARX (C.) & F. E. Aus. d. lit. Nachlass K. M. u. F. E., 1841–50, 3e A, 3B, 1920.
„ —— & —— K. M. & F. E. ueb. d. Diktatur d. Proletariats &c., 1920.
„ MAYER (G.) F. E., Biog., B1 *&* Ergzb., 1920.

Engelspach-Larivière (A.) De la géognosie considérée d. s. diff. rapports. 8º. Bruxelles. 1830

Engelstoft (Christian Thorning), *bp. of Funen.* De Confutatione Lat., quae Apologiæ concionatorum evangel. in Comitiis Haun. 1530 trad. oppos. est, comm. [P2741]. s4º. Hauniæ. 1847

Engerand (Fernand). La bataille de la frontière (août 1914). Briey. 8o. 1920
Rapport (16 Av. 1919) sur le rôle &c. de la métallurgie, 1919, see FRANCE: STATE DEPTS.: CHAMBRE DES DÉPUTÉS.

Engerd (Johann). Methodus, de liberalibus pueritiae &c., studiis recte ordinandis &c. [*b. w.* Jeremiah, *abp. of Larissa.* Censura Orient. Eccl., 1582]. s8o. Ingolstadii. 1583

Engert (Rolf).
Henrik Ibsen als Verkünder d. dritten Reiches. 8o. L. 1921

Enghien, *Hôpital d'.* Vente du triptyque [*attrib. to V. d. Weyden*] de l'anc. Hôp. d'E. (Belgique) &c. 15 Nov. 1926. [*Illust.* P2851]. 4o. Brux. 1926

Enghien (*le duc* **d'**), *see* MAGNE (E.) Le Grand Condé & le Duc d'E.: lettres inéd. sur la cour de Louis XIV, 1660–67; publ. &c. par E. M., 1920.

Engineering Institute of Canada.
World Power Conference, July 1924. 4o. [1924]

England.
I, ANONYMOUS WORKS.
Account (An) of the progress of the reformation of manners in Eng., Scot. & Ir. &c. Added Her M.'s proclamation. 11th ed. [2 *pagin*s.] s8o. 1703
*Antiquarian & topogr. cabinet; views of objects of curiosity in Gt. Brit., 10v, 1807–11, *see* STORER (J. S.) & J. GREIG.
*Antiquarian itinerary, 7v, 1815–18, *see* ANTIQUARIAN &c.
*Britain & h. colonial dependencies &c., 1844, *see* BANISTER (T.)
*Britain's alarm: or seasonable warning to secure British Protestants &c. By a sincere lover of the Protestant Religion. s8o. 1713
Case (The) of the people of E. consid.; shewing how far they are obliged by the oath of allegiance, 1689, *see* CASE.
*Cat. of Chancellors of E., Lord Keepers of the Gt. Seal & the Lord Treasurers of E., 1636, *see* PHILIPOT (J.)
Coastwise trade of U.K., 1925, *see* COASTWISE.
Coll. (A) of papers rel. to pres. juncture of affairs in Eng., *viz.* The humble petition of Seven Bishops &c. [P2572]. s8o. 1688
Daungerous positions & proc., 1593, *see* BANCROFT (R.)
Declar. (The) of the kingdomes of Eng. & Scot. &c. agst. the Popish &c. party &c. [P2571]. s8o. 1643
*Draft (A) bill entitl. An Act to amend the provision for the govt. of E. &c., *n.d.*, *see* OLIVER (F. S.)
*England. By an overseas Englishman. s8o. 1922
E. & the world: essays [by W. J. Perry &c.], 1925, *see* MARVIN (F. S.), *ed.*
E. on the witness stand. [*By var. a.* Intr. by F. F. Schrader]. [P2735]. 8o. N.Y. 1915
*E. under the heel of the Jew, 1918, *see* CLARKE (J. H.)
*E.'s conversion & reformation compared, 1725, *see* MANNING (R.)
*E.'s green & pleasant land. 8o. 1925
E.'s Helicon. Repr. f. ed. of 1600 w. add. poems f. ed. of 1614. [Intr. by H. Macdonald. The Haslewood Books]. 8o. 1925
*E.'s imminent danger, & only remedy. By an impartial hand. s8o. 1671
*Further (A) narr. of these times in the Commonwealth of E., 1658, *see* FURTHER.
*Journey (A) thr. E., 2v, 1732, *see* MACKY (J.)
*Letter (A) f. the Assembly of divines in E. to the A. in Scotland w. the answer. [P2653]. s4o. 1643
*Liberties (The) of E. asserted, in oppos. to popery, slavery &c. s8o. 1714
Mediæval E.; n. ed. of Barnard's Companion to Eng. hist.; ed. H. W. C. Davis, 1924, *see* BARNARD (F. P.)
*Memoirs of the antiq. of Great Brittain &c., 1713, *see* MEMOIRS.
*Memorial (A) of God's last 29 years wonders in E., for its preserv. &c. f. Popery &c. f. Charles II to abdic. of James II. [P2663]. s4o. 1689
*Modest (A) addr. to the Commons of Gt. Brit. &c. occas. by ill-success of naval war w. France &c., 1756, *see* MODEST.
*On the necessity of a general arming in E. &c. [P2831]. 8o. 1859
*Peace againe in Sion &c., E. & Scotland united &c., 1641, *see* PEACE.
*Present state of E. as to coin & public charges, 1697, *see* HODGES (J.)
*Present state of Gt. Brit. & Ireland, 8th ed., 1738, *see* MIEGE (G.)
Rep. on aircraft supply of Gt. Brit., 1918, *see* SMITHSONIAN INSTIT. Misc. colls., v69, 1921.
Сборникъ донесеній о Большевизмѣ въ Россіи (Англійская "Бѣлая книга" [P2578]. la8o. Новочеркасскъ. 1919
*Succinct (A) & impart. hist. of all regencies &c. of Eng., 1751, *see* SUCCINCT.
*Visible (The) pursuit of a foreign interest in opp. to the int. of E. in a letter to my Lord B—e. [P2780]. 8o. 1745
Visit. of the North: early heraldic v. & pedigrees rel. to N. of E. [Ed. F. W. Dendy. Surtees Soc., 133]. p2. 8o. Durham. 1921
West coast of E. pilot, 6th ed., Suppl. 6, & Not. to mariners, 1910–21, *see* ADMIRALTY.

England [*continued*].
II, LAWS & STATUTES.
Defence of the Realm manual. Ed. A. Pulling. 4th, enl. ed., rev. to May 31, 1917. 8o. 1917
Food control manual, rev. to April 30th, 1918. Ed. A. Pulling. 8o. 1918
Manual of emergency legisl. Suppl. 4, to Aug. 31, 1915. 8o. 1915
Public General Acts. 8/9 George V, 1918–17/18 Geo. V, 1927. la8o. [1919–28]
War material, supplies manual, rev. to Feb. 28, 1918. Ed. A. Pulling. 8o. 1918
see HANS TOWN. Acts of 30 & 43 Geo. III rel. to H. T., 1807.
,, ROBERTSON (A. J.), *ed.* Laws of kings f. Edmund to Henry I, 1925.

III, STATE DEPARTMENTS.
see AIR MINISTRY.
,, HEALTH, MINISTRY OF.
,, MUNITIONS, MINISTRY OF.
,, OVERSEAS TRADE, *Dept. of.*
see SCIENTIFIC & INDUSTRIAL RESEARCH, *Dept. of.*
,, STATISTICS.

IV, TREATIES.
Handbook of commercial treaties &c. betw. Gt. Brit. & For. Powers. 3rd ed. 8o. 1924
List of t. &c. rel. to commerce & navig. betw. Gt. Brit. & For. Powers, 1927. 8o. 1927

Englefield (W. A. D.)
Hist. of the Painter-Stainers Co. of London. 8o. 1923

Engler (Adolph). Beitr. z. Entwicklungsgesch. d. Hochgebirgsfloren Saxifragen, *see* KÖN.-PREUSS. AKAD. Abh., Phys.-math. Klasse, 1916.
see CARTER (H. G.) Genera of British plants: arr. acc. to E.'s Syllabus d. Pflanzenfamilien (7th ed., 1912), 1913.

Englische Studien. Organ für engl. Philologie. B53–61. 8o. L. 1920–27
,, ,, Generalregister zu B26–50; Zusammengestellt v. A. Wagner. 8o. L. 1924

English.
Bibliography of E. lang. & lit., 1921; ed. A. C. Paues, 1922, *see* BIBLIOGRAPHY.
Complete Eng. dict., 1777, *see* WESLEY (J.)
English & Scotch hist. ballads, 1871, *see* MILMAN (A.), *ed.*
English Cat. (The) of books. [Annual vol.], 1919–27. la8o. 1920–28
English Cat. (The) of books. v10, 1916–20; v11, 1921–25. la8o. 1921–26
English chairs, 15th–19th cent. Intr. by H. E. Binstead. 4o. 1923
*English (The) dict., 9th ed., 1650; 10th ed., 1651, *see* COCKERAM (H.)
English econ. hist.: sel. doc., 1921, *see* BLAND (A. E.), P. A. B. &c., *edd.*
*English expositor: interpret. of hardest words, 1641, *see* BULLOKAR (J.)
*English forests & forest trees, historical &c. 8o. 1853
English literary autographs, 1550–1650, p1, 1925, *see* GREG (W. W.), *ed.* &c.
English madrigal verse, 1588–1632, 1920, *see* FELLOWES (E. H.), *ed.*
*English medieval embroidery, 1848, *see* HARTSHORNE (C. H.)
English prose, 5v, 1921–22, *see* PEACOCK (W.), *ed.*
English prose f. Mandeville to Ruskin, 7th impr., 1921, *see* PEACOCK (W.), *ed.*
English prose, narr., descr. &c., 1921, *see* TREBLE (H. A.), *ed.*
English song book, ed. H. Scott, 1925, *see* SCOTT (H.)
*English timber & its econ. conversion, 2nd ed., *n.d.*, *see* ACORN, *ps.*
*Hist. (An) acc. of some things rel. to nature of E. govt. &c., 1690, *see* WHITBY (D.)
Hist. of Eng. lit., 1923, *see* BUCHAN (J.), *ed.*
*Libelle (The) of Englyshe polycye. Poem on the use of sea-power, 1436. Ed. Sir G. Warner. 8o. O. 1926
Mod. Eng. essays [1870–1920], 5v, 1922, *see* RHYS (E.), *ed.*
Mod. (The) Eng. house, 1927, *see* PHILLIPS (R. R.)
New Eng. theatre, v10, 1777, *see* NEW.
*New univ. Eng. & Italian dict. 2p [*pagin. contin.*] la8o. Malta. 1849
Old Eng. ballads, 1553–1625, 1920, *see* ROLLINS (H. E.), *ed.*
Readings in Eng. soc. hist. f. contemp. lit., 5v, 1921–22; 1923, *see* MORGAN (R. B.), *ed.*
Sel. Eng. essays, 1922, *see* PEACOCK (W.), *ed.*
Sel. Eng. letters (15–19c.), 1916, *see* DUCKITT (M.) & H. WRAGG, *edd.*
Sel. Eng. short stories (19 c.), 1921, *see* WALKER (H.), *ed.*
Sel. Eng. speeches f. Burke to Gladstone, 1913, *see* JONES (E. R.), *ed.*
*A short introd. to Eng. grammar, 1787, *see* LOWTH (R.)
The teaching of Eng. in England. Rep. of Dept. Comm. of Board of Educ. s8o. 1921

English (The) Association. Essays & studies by members of the E. A. v6–12. 8o. O. 1920–26
Batho (E. C.) Life of Christ in the ballads. [9.]
Birkhead (E.) Sentiment &c. in the 18th cent. novel. [11.]
Bradley (H.) Cædmonian Genesis. [6.]
Chambers (R. W.) Long Will, Dante, & the righteous heathen. [9.]
Chapman (R. W.) Proposals for a new ed. of Johnson's letters. [12.]

English (The) Association [*continued*[.
Essays &c. [*continued*].
Cowling (G. H.) The Felon Sew. [8.]
Crofts (J. E. V.) Life of Bp. Corbett, 1582–1635. [10.]
Cruickshank (A. H.) Thomas Parnell. [7.]
De Selincourt (B.) Rhyme in Eng. poetry. [7.]
Dymes (D. M. E.) The orig. lang. of the Ancren riwle. [9.]
Elton (O.) Reason & enthusiasm in the 18th cent. [10.]
Fairley (B.) The mod. consciousness in Eng. lit. [9.]
Fox Strangways (A. H.) Words & music in song. [7.]
Garrod (H. W.) Milton's lines on Shakespeare. [12.]
Gordon (G.) The Trojans in Britain. [9.]
Grattan (J. H. G.) On the teaching of case. [9.]
Grundy (G. B.) On meanings of certain terms in Anglo-Saxon charters. [8.]
Herford (C. H.) Romanticism in mod. world. [8.]
Holmes (E.) Milton's use of words. [10.]
Keith (A.) Scot. ballads : authorship &c. [12.]
Ker (W. P.) Hazlitt. [8.]
—— Humanist ideal. [6.]
Mackail (J. W.) Allan Ramsay & the romantic revival. [10.]
MacKerrow (R. B.) Eng. grammar & grammars. [8.]
MacMechan (A.) Canadian lit. : beginnings. [12.]
Martin (L. C.) Forgotten poet of the 17th cent. [N. Wanley]. [11.]
Monkhouse (A. N.) The words & the play. [11.]
Morley (E. J.) J. Warton : compar. of h. Essay on Pope w. h. ed. of P.'s works. [9.]
Neilson (G.) A bundle of ballads. [7.]
Notcutt (H. C.) The Faerie Queene & its critics. [12.]
Routh (H. V.) This world's idea of the next. [11.]
Saintsbury (G. E. B.) Trollope revisited. [6.]
Sampson (G.) On playing the sedulous ape. [6.]
Sampson (J.) A contemp. light upon John Donne. [7.]
Seaton (E.) Marlowe's map. [10.]
Simpson (P.) The 1604 text of Marlowe's Doctor Faustus. [7.]
Smart (J. S.) Tragedy. [8.]
Spens (J.) Chapman's ethical thought. [11.]
Stawell (F. M.) Conrad. [6.]
Thompson (A. H.) Mystical elem. in Eng. poetry. [8.]
Wilson (J. D.) Spellings &c. in 2nd Quarto of Hamlet. [10.]
Wright (H.) Assoc. of T. L. Peacock w. Wales. [12.]
Wyld (H. C. K.) Diction & imagery in Anglo-Sax. poetry. [11.]
—— South-East. & S.E. Midland dialects in Mid. Eng. [6.]
Pamphlets. 47–53, 57–59, 63. 8º. 1921–26
see BINYON (L.) Trad. & reaction in mod. poetry, 1926. [63.]
,, BUCHAN (J.) Some notes on Sir W. Scott, 1924. [58.]
,, CHAMBERS (E. K.) Sir T. Malory, 1922. [51.]
,, CHAMBERS (R. W.) The teaching of English in the univs. of Eng., 1922. [53.]
,, ERNLE (R. E. P., *1st b.*) The light reading of our ancestors, 1921. [50.]
,, FOWLER (J. H.) De Quincey as literary critic, 1922. [52.]
,, GALSWORTHY (J.) On expression, 1924. [59.]
,, GREY (E. G., *1st visct.*) Wordsworth's "Prelude," 1923. [57.]
,, GRIERSON (H. J. C.) Don Quixote : some war-time refl., 1921. [48.]
,, HERFORD (C. H.) Normality of Shakespeare, 1920. [47.]
,, MACKERROW (R. B.) Note on the teaching of "Eng. lang. & lit.," 1921. [49.]
Poems of to-day ; publ. for the Eng. Assoc., repr., 1922 ; s2, 1922, *see* POEMS.
The year's work in Eng. studies, 1919–20—1926. Ed. Sir S. Lee [& F. S. Boas &c.] 8º. 1921–28

English Cart-Horse Society.
Stud book. v1–5 (1880–84). 8º. 1880–84

English Catholic (An), *ps.* *see* BESTE (J. R. D.)

English Covenanter (An), *ps.* *The Scottish mist dispel'd : or, a reply to Ans. of the Commissioners of Scot. upon the proposit. for peace, 1648, *see* SCOTTISH.

English Dialect Society. Publ. 52. 8º. 1886
see COLE (R. E. G.) Glossary of words used in S.-W. Lincs., 1886. [52.]

English Europasian (An), *ps.* *Russia in resurrection, 1928, *see* RUSSIA.

English Goethe Society. Publications. New Ser., v2. 8º. 1925
n.s., v2, *has tp.* Goethe & Byron ; ed. J. G. Robertson, 1925.

English Historical Review. v35–42. la8º. 1920–27
,, ,, Gen. index, v31–40, 1916–25. Ed. R. L. Poole & G. N. Clark. 8º. 1927

English Place-Name Society. v1i, ii–4. 8º. C. 1924–27
see MAWER (A.) Chief elements in Eng. place-names, 1924. [1ii.]
,, —— & F. M. STENTON, *edd.* Intr. to survey of Eng. place-names, p1, 1924. [1i.]
,, —— —— Place-names of Beds. & Hunts., 1926. [3.]
,, —— —— Place-names of Buckinghamshire, 1925. [2.]
,, —— —— Place-names of Worcestershire, 1927. [4.]

English Post, The. Sept. 11, 1704, Aug. 12 & Sept. 12, 1705. [*b. w.* Post Man, 1704–8]. fol. 1704–5

English review (The).
v30–45. (Jan. 1920–Dec. 1927). 8º. [1920–27]

English (Douglas). Photography for naturalists. 8º. 1901

English (Thomas H.)
A mem. of the Yorks. Esk Fishery Assoc. 8º. Whitby. 1925

Englishman. *England, by an overseas E., 1922, *see* ENGLAND.
E.'s (The) guide to the U.S. & Canada, n. ed., 1884, *see* UNITED STATES.

Englishwoman. *From a Russian diary 1917–20 ; by an E., 1921, *see* RUSSIAN.

Engravers. *A chronolog. series of e. &c., 1770, *see* MARTYN (T.)

Engström (Albert). Äventyr och hugskott. s8º. [1916]
En bok. s8º. [1915]
Mitt liv och leverne. s8º. [1915]
Skargardshistorier. s8º. [1919]

Enjalran (Clarisse), *see* MANSON (M. F. C.)

Enlart (Camille). Architecture relig., *see* MANUEL d'archéologie franç., 2e éd., 2p, 1919–20.
Les monuments des Croisés dans le Royaume de Jérusalem. [Haut-Comm. de la Rép. Fr. en Syrie &c. Bibl. arch. &c., t7, 8]. 2t [*&* Atlas, 2t]. 4º. 1925–27
Un tissu persan du 10e s. découv. à St.-Josse, *see* ACAD. DES INSCR. Fond. Piot. Mon., t24, 1920.

Enluminure [ENLUMINURES]. Art (L') d'enl. (14c.) ; tr. &c. L. Dimier, 1927, *see* ART.
Enl. (Les) du fameux almanach des PP. Jesuites &c., 1683, *see* LE MAISTRE DE SACY (I. L.)

Ennius (Quintus). Annals. Ed. E. M. Steuart. 8º. C. 1925

Ennos (F. R.) & A. Scott. Refractory minerals : fireclays, *see* GEOLOGICAL SURVEY OF ENG. &C. Mem., v28, 1924.

Enock (Arthur Guy). The problem of armaments. s8º. 1923

Enock (Charles Reginald). The republics of C. & S. America : resources, industries, &c. 2nd & rev. ed. 8º. [1922]
Spanish America, its romance &c. 2v. 8º. [1920]

Enquête faite par ordre du Parl. d'Angleterre, pour constater les progrès de l'indust. en France, 1825, *see* FRANCE.

Enquiry [INQUIRY].
*Enquiry (An) into the causes of the miscarriage of Scots colony at Darien, 1700, *see* DARIEN.
*Enquiry into the nature of the human soul, 2nd ed., 1737, *see* BAXTER (A.)
*Enquiry (An) into the present state of affairs &c., 1689, *see* BURNET (G.), *bp.*
*Inquiry into the share wh. Ch. I had in the trans. of the E. of Glamorgan &c., 1747, *see* BIRCH (T.)
Inquiry (An) resp. the orig. copies & anc. versions of the N.T., unitarian, 5th ed. Pref. A view of the princ. Eng. tr. of the Sacred wr. 2nd ed. [P2531]. s8º. 1822

Enriquez (Colin Metcalfe Dallas). A Burmese arcady : mountain dwellers of the Burmese Hinterland. 8º. 1923
Malaya : people, flora & fauna. 8º. 1927
The Pathan borderland. 2nd ed. s8º. Calcutta. 1921
see INDIA : MILITARY DEPT. Races of Burmah, 1924.

Enriquez (R. de Zayas), *see* ZAYAS ENRIQUEZ (R. DE).

Enriquez de Rivera (Fadrique), *marq. de Tarifa.* Este libro es de el viaje q̃ hize a Jerusalem &c., 24 Nov. 518–20 Ot. 520. [*With* Narr. del viaje, *in verse, by* J. del Enzina]. 8º. Sevilla. 1606

Enriquez de Toledo (Mencia), *dss. of Alburquerque, see* HISP. SOC. OF AMER. Tombs, 1927.

Ens (Gaspar). Rerum Hungaricarum hist. in qua praeter regionis situm &c. res gestae ad annum 1604 describuntur. s8º. Coloniæ Agrippinæ. 1604

Ensign, *Family of, see* MORSE (W. I.), *ed.* Genealogiae or data, 1925.

Enslin (Barend G. Leopold). The wool industry, Gt. Brit. & the U.S. [P2820]. 8º. Pretoria. 1920

Ensslin (Wilhelm). Zur Geschichtschr. u. Weltanschauung d. Ammianus Marcellinus. [Klio, Beiheft 16]. 8º. L. 1923

Entente. Diplom. Aktenstücke z. Gesch. d. Ententepolitik d. Vorkriegsjahre, 1921 ; tr., 1923, *see* SIEBERT (B. VON).

***Entertainment** (An) for Lady-dayes : Εἰκονοκόπτησις, or the dressing of images. [Cayme Press]. 8º. Kensington. 1925

Entfaltung (Die) : Novellen an d. Zeit, 1921, *see* KRELL (M.), *ed.*

Enthoven (Reginald Edward), *C.I.E.*
Folklore of Bombay. 8º. O. 1924

Enthusiasm. *The danger of e. discov., in an epistle to the Quakers, 1674, *see* ALLEN (W.), *controv. wr.*
*Enthusiasm (The) of Methodists & Papists compar'd, 1749, *see* LAVINGTON (G.)

Entner (Gottfried), *see* NEUSS. N. am Rhein ; hrsg. v. G. E., 1926.

Entomological Society of London.
Transactions, 1919–22. 8°. 1919–23

Entomologist (The) : conducted by E. Newman. v2. 8°. 1864–65

Entrecolles (François Xavier d'). Lettre s. la porcelaine, *see* BERNARD (J. F.), *ed.* Recueil de voy., t10, 1738.

*__Entretien__ d'un docteur de la maison de Sorbonne avec un docteur Ubiquiste qui a signé la decision du cas de conscience touch. Jansenius. [P2659]. s8°. Liège. 1703

Entsiklopediya, *see* ENCYCLOPÆDIA.

Entwicklung (Die) d. Kunst i. d. Schweiz, *see* PUPIKOFER (O.), H. HEIERLI *& o.*

Entwisle (Joseph), *Wesleyan minister, see* ENTWISLE (W.) Mem. of J. E., 1848.

Entwisle (William).
Mem. of Joseph Entwisle. By his son. s8°. Bristol. 1848

Eobanus (Helius), *Hessus.* Psalterium Davidis & Salomonis Ecclesiastes carmine redd. s8°. Argentorati. 1563
see CAMERARIUS (J.) Narr. de H. E. H., 1696.

Eon (*le chev.* **d'**) [†EON DE BEAUMONT (C. G. L. A. A. T. d')], *see* LA FORTELLE (DE). La vie &c. de demoiselle Eon, 1779.

Eötvös (*Báró* **József).** A nemzetiségi Kérdés. [Munkái, 16]. 8°. *n.d.*

Eötvös (Károly). Utazás a Balaton Körül. [Munkái, 1, 2]. 3^{ik} Kiadás. 2k. s8°. [1903]

Epaphroditus. Un nouv. texte des traités d'arpentage & de géom. d'E. & de V. Rufus, *see* TANNERY (P.) Mém. scient., t5, 1922.

Épernon (Jean Louis de Nogaret de la Valette, *duc* **d')** [ESPERNON].
see GIRARD (G.) *Life of the Duke of E., Engl. by C. Cotton, 1670.
,, MARTEL (T.) L'intrigue dans l'amour, le duc d'E., 1925.

Ephemerides.
Ephemerides Urbevetanae (1342–69), 1920, *see* URBEVETANÆ.
*Ephemeridum S. Patrum &c., 1708, *see* PATRES.

Ephemeris Dacoromana, 1923–25, *see* SCUOLA ROMENA DI ROMA.

Ephesian, *ps.* Lord Birkenhead. 8°. [1926]

Ephesus, *1st Synod of, 431.* Neue Aktenstücke z. ephesin. Konzil v. 431; [hrsg.] E. Schwartz, 1920, *see* KÖNIGL. AKAD. D. W. ZU MÜNCHEN. Abhdlgn. B30, 1920.
Synodus Ephesina. Qualis sit vera carnis Christi manducatio &c. : contra Nestorium. Ex Cyrillo & toto orthod. consensu. Adj. Theses H. Pacifici de Coena Domini &c. [*w. sep. tp.*] 8°. Neustadii in Palat. 1581

Ephesus, *2nd Synod of, 449.* Akten d. Ephes. Syn. v. 449; Syrisch mit G. Hoffmanns deut. Übers. u. Anm. hrsg. v. J. Flemming, *see* KÖNIGL. GESELLS. D. WISS., *Göttingen,* Phil.-hist. Kl., B15, 1917.

Ephraim, *Saint, Syrus.*
[Works *in Armenian*]. 4v. 8°. i Venetik. 1836
1, Comm. on Pentateuch—Chronicles. 2, Comm. on Tatian's Diatessaron. 3, Comm. on Epistles of Paul. 4, Sermons and prayers.
[Comm. on the Acts of the Apostles. *In Armenian.* Ed. N. Akinean]. 4°. Vienna. 1921
О диахъ празднов. рождества—Объ основаніи перв. Церквей въ Іерусалимѣ, Арм. текстъ съ сир. отрывками; изс. &c. Н. Марръ. [Тексты &c. по арм.-груз. Филол., 1 (Изд. Фак. Вост. Яз. Имп. С.–П. Унив., N°. 5)]. la8°. С.–П. 1900
Prose refutations of Mani, Marcion, & Bardaisan. Transcr. by C. W. Mitchell &c. [Text & Tr. Soc.] v2. 8°. 1921
2, Disc. called "of Domnus" & 6 o. writings. [Intr. by F. C. Burkitt].
Τὰ 'Ε. τοῦ Σ. πρὸς τὴν 'Ελλάδα μεταβλήθεντα. fol. Οξονίᾳ. [1709]
see CHRYSOSTOM, *Saint.* Comm. on the Acts comp. f. works of C. & E. [*in Armenian*], 1839.
,, KOHL (J. P.) Intr. in hist. &c. Slav.; hist. crit. E. Syri, acc. 2 sermones E., 1729.
,, ME'ÂRATH GAZZÊ. Bk. of Cave of treasures [*wrongly ascr. to E.*], tr., 1927.
,, SIMEON, *bp. in Persia.* [Life of S. & Oration on Eastern martyrs (? by E.), *in Armenian*], 1854.

Epicteta. Il "Testamento d'E.," con testo, tr. &c. di S. Ricci, *see* REALE ACCAD. D. LINCEI. Mon. ant., v2, 1893.

Epictetus.
TRANSLATIONS.
Discourses as rep. by Arrian, the Manual, & fragm. [Text] w. Eng. tr. by W. A. Oldfather. [Loeb Class. Lib.] v1. s8°. 1926
Discourses; with Encheiridion & fragments. Tr. w. notes &c. by G. Long. [repr.] s8°. 1916

Epictetus [*continued*].
TRANSLATIONS [*continued*].
His morals, with Simplicius his comm. Eng. by G. Stanhope. 3rd ed. corr. w. life of E. f. Boileau. s8°. 1704
,, ,, ...4th ed. corr. 8°. 1721
,, ,, ...Eng. by E. Walker. s8°. 1764
The life & philosophy of E. With the Embleme of humane life, by Cebes. Eng. by J. Davies [f. Fr. of G. Boileau]. s8°. 1670

*__Epictetus Junior,__ or Maximes of mod. morality, 1670, *see* DAVIES (J.) *of Kidwelly.*

Epicure's (The) almanac [for 1841], 1842, [2v], 1841–42, *see* HILL (B. E.)

Epicurus. The extant remains. With sh. crit. apparatus, tr. & notes by C. Bailey. 8°. O. 1926
Opere, frammenti, testimonianze sulla s. vita. Tr. con intr. e comm. da E. Bignone. 8°. Bari. 1920

Epigrammata [EPIGRAMMATUM]. *Farrago aliquot epigr. P. Melanchthonis &c., 1528, *see* MELANCHTHON (P.)

Epigraphia Birmanica : lithic & o. inscr. of Burma. Ed. C. Duroiselle. Arch. Survey of Burma. v1, 2. 4°. Rangoon. 1919–24
1, Myazedi inscr.; by C. Duroiselle & C. O. Blagden—Mon. inscr.; by C. O. Blagden.
2, Talaing plaques on the Ananda.

Epigraphia Indica & record of the Arch. Survey of India. Ed. F. W. Thomas &c. Publ. as Suppl. to "Indian antiquary." v14, 17, 1917–24. 4°. Calcutta. 1917–24

Epigraphia Indo-Moslemica. Ed. G. Yazdani. Publ. under authority of the Govt. of India, 1917–18—1923–24. 4°. Calcutta. 1921–27

Epigraphicum. Suppl. epigr. Graecum; adjuv. P. Roussel &c., red. curavit J. J. E. Hondius, v1, 2, 1923–25, *see* SUPPLEMENTUM.

Epiphanius, *catholikos of Georgia, see* MARR (N. YA.) Надпись Е., катол. Грузіи, 1910.

Epiphanius, *Saint, bp. of Constantia in Cyprus.*
Anc. weights & measures, *in Greek & Armenian,* 1821, *see* AUCHER (P.)
Ancoratus u. Panarion. Hrsg. K. Holl. [Die griech. christl. Schriftsteller d. ersten 3 Jhdte.] B2. 8°. L. 1922
2, Panarion haer., 34–64.
Ἔκθεσις πρωτοκλησιῶν πατριαρχῶν τε καὶ μητροπολιτῶν. [*Ed.* F. N. Finck. *Greek & Armenian*]. s8°. Marburg i. H. 1902
see DASHEAN (H.) Short bibliog. st., *in Armenian,* p1, E. &c., 1895.

Epiphanius, *Scholasticus, see* CASSIODORUS (M. A.) *Hist. eccl. quam tripartitam vocant libri 12 [ex Sozomeno &c. ab E. S. versa], 1566.

Episcopius (Simon) [BISSCHOP (S.)], *1583–1643.* *Apologia pro conf. sententiae eorum qui vocantur Remonstrantes, super articulis relig. Xtnae. Contra censuram 4 profess. Leid. s4°. *n.p.* 1629
Opera theologica. ed. 2^{a}. 2v *in* 1. fol. Londini. 1678
v2 *has no tp.* v1 *ed. by* S. Curcellæus; v2 *by* P. van Limborch.
The Popish labyrinth. Added life &c. of the a.; also life &c. of J. Arminius. Publ. in Eng. tongue by J. K. [*3 pagin.*] s8°. 1673
,, ,, The labyrinth or popish circle, a confut. of infallibility. Tr. by R. Watson. [P2531; 2543]. s8°. 1826
see CALDER (F.) Mem. of S. E. &c., 1835.

Epistola [EPISTOLÆ, EPISTULA].
*Anon. epist. de nova secta Quaerentium, vulgo Seekers, in Anglia exorta, 1814, *see* SEEKERS.
[Epistola Apost.] Gespräche Jesu mit s. Jüngern nach d. Auferstehung. Ein Kathol.-apostol. Sendschreiben d. 2 Jhdts. [*a. version of* Le Testament en Galilée]. Nach e. Kopt. Papyrus hrsg., übers. u. untersucht nebst 3 Exkursen v. C. Schmidt. Übers. d. äthiop. Textes v. I. Wajnberg. [Texte u. Unters., B43]. 8°. L. 1919
Epist. Apostol., nach d. äthiop. u. kopt. Texte hrsg. v. Duensing, *see* KLEINE TEXTE, T152, 1925.
Epistolae ab eccl. Helveticae reformatoribus vel ad eos scr.; ed. J. C. Fueslinus, 1742, *see* FÜSSLI (J. C.)
*Epistolæ abbatis N. ad episcopum N.; æquitas Constit. Unigenitus &c., 1716, *see* N. (*abbas*).
Epistolae decretales a Gregorio IX coll., 1570, *see* DECRETALES.
*Epistolae duae ad Eccl. Polonicas scr. à Tigur. eccl. ministris &c., 1561, *see* ZÜRICH.
Epistolae & acta Jesuitarum Transylv. (1571–1613); ed. A. Veress, 2v, 1911–13, *see* JESUITS.
Epistolæ Ho-Elianæ, 1645, *see* HOWELL (J.)

Epistola [EPISTOLÆ, EPISTULA] [*continued*].
Epistolæ virorum clar. ad Jacobum VI—Virorum doct. epist., *see* ABBOTSFORD CLUB. Misc., v1, 1837.
Illust. & clar. virorum epist., sel. super. & hoc seculo scr., 1669, *see* GABBEMA (S. A.)

Epitaphs. Coll. of e. &c., 2v, 1806, *see* COLLECTION.
*Coll. of e. &c. chiefly in Scotland, 1834, *see* SCOTLAND.

Epitome. *Epitome emblematum Acad. Altorf., 1602, *see* HULSIUS (L.)
*Rerum Germanicarum gestarum epitome, 1655, *see* PAPPUS (L.)

Eppens tho Equart (Abel). Kroniek. Uitg. &c. door J. A. Feith & H. Brugmans. [Hist. Genoots. Werken, s3, 27, 28]. 2d. 8º. A. 1911

Eppstein (Georg *Frhr.* von). Fürst Bismarcks Entlassung. Nach d. Aufzeichn. d. K. H. v. Boetticher u. F. J. v. Rottenburg. Hrsg. G. v. E. 8º. [1920]

Epsom. *Acc. of a seminary at E., for the instr. of 12 pupils. [P2668]. 8º. 1783

Epstein (Isidore). The "Responsa" of Rabbi Solomon ben Adreth of Barcelona (1235–1310). 8º. 1925

Epstein (Jacob). Jacob Epstein. [Plates, *w. intr. ent.* The sculpture of J. E. *signed* H. W.] la8º. 1925
see VAN DIEREN (B.) Epstein, 1920.

Epstein (Mordecai) [*ps.* BENAMMI]. *Letters of Benammi. [Repr. f. Jewish chron.] 2s. 8º. [1922]–24
1, Aspects of Jewish life & thought.
2, Essays on Jewish life & thought.

Equart (Abel Eppens tho), *see* EPPENS THO EQUART (A.)

Equicola (Mario). Dell' istoria di Mantova libri 5. Riform. per B. Osanna. 8º. Mantova. 1608

Equitable Assurances, Society for, *see* SOCIETY FOR EQUITABLE ASSURANCES.

Erasmus (Desiderius).
Ausslegung über die wort Christi v. d. wercken der Phariseyer.—Ub. Du bist Petrus—Ub. d. wort S. Joannis v. d. Kriegssleütten—Ub. d. wort S. Pauli v. d. Gesang—Aussleg. d. Alleg. S. Hierõnymi. [*b. w. h.* In gen. consol. de morte, 1517]. s4º. *n.p. n.d.* [1521]
*Bibliotheca Erasmiana : bibliographie des œuvres d'E. [8–10]. s8º. Gand. 1912–15
8, Enchiridion militis Christiani. 9, Ratio verae theologiae. 10, De praeparatione ad mortem.
Colloquiorum famil. opus aureum. s8º. Londini. 1683
Contenta in hoc libello, E. R. epistola ad illust. Pr. ac Ducē Sax. &c. Fridericū. Positiones Jo. Eckii scholasticæ. Positiones Lutheri theol. Cōclusiōes A. Carolostadii theologicae. [*6 leaves, no tp. decor. border to A1*]. s4º. [Wittenbergae ?. 1519 ?]
De conscribendis epist. ed. nova. s8º. Amsterod. 1636
De immensa Dei misericordia, concio.—Virginis & martyris comparatio—Concio de puero Jesu. Ex rec. autoris. s8º. Basileæ, *J. Frobenius.* [1523]
De libero arbitrio διατριβή. s8º. [Antwerp ?] 1524
Enchiridion militis Christ., ejusdem De praepar. ad mortem &c. s8º. Cantab. 1685
Epistolarum opus. fol. Basileæ ex off. Frobeniana. 1538
Opus epistolarum. Denuo recog. & auct. per P. S. & H. M. Allen. t4–6 (1519–27). 8º. O. 1922–26
Evangeliae Epistolae quae diebus sacris in templis leguntur, ex tr. D. E. R. cum eiusdem annotat. singulis evangeliis &c. subjectis. s8º. Coloniae, *J. Gymnicus.* 1531
Farrago nova epistolarum D. E. R. ad alios & aliorum ad hunc: admixtis quibusdā quas scripsit etiā adolescens. fol. Basileae, *Jo. Frobenius.* [1519]
Ein fast nutzlich uslegung des ersten psalmen : Beatus vir &c. [*Deutsch v. Leo Jud. b. w. h.* In gen. consol. de morte, 1517]. s4º. [Basel, *A. Petri.* 1520]
Woodcut below title : David praying].
Hyperaspistes diatribæ adv. Servum arbitrium M. Lutheri ab autore recogn. [sep. ed. of p1]. [*b. w. h.* De libero arbitrio, 1524]. s8º. Basileæ, *I. Frob.* 1526
In genere consolatorio de morte declamatio. s4º. [Nurenberge, *F. Peypus. n.d.* 1517]
Lingua, sive De linguæ usu & abusu liber. [*b. w. h.* Vita &c., 1649]. s8º. Lugd. Batav. 1649
Moriæ encomium, cum quibusdam aliis. [Epistola apolog.—Ludus Senecae De morte Claudii Cęsaris—Synesius Cyren. De laudibus calvitii]. s8º. Basileæ. 1551
Ein new vordeutscht büchlein, darinnē er alle menschē Götliche schrifft, mit vleiss tzu lesenn, Auch tzu gemeynem fridt vormandt u. anraytzt. [*Decor. border to tp.* P2539]. s4º. [Basel. 1522]
Querela pacis undique gentium ejectæ profligatæque. s8º. [Argentinæ, *I. Knoblouchus.* 1522]
Spongia adv. aspergines Hutteni. s8º. Basileæ, *I. Frobenius.* 1523
Ursach, warumb E., in e. schrifft an d. Bepstl. Legaten u. Card.

Erasmus (Desiderius) [*continued*].
Compeium, bedenckt, Das es nicht gut sein sol das Röm K. M., die Luther., u. andere lere mit d. schwerdt dempffe &c. s4º. *n.p. n.d.* [Strassburg ?. 1530 ?]
Verteutschte ausslegung, über diese wort sant Pauls, Ich will lieber in m. gemut funff wort in d. Kirchen reden &c. [1 Cor. 14]. Von Gesang. [*b. w. h.* In gen. consol. de morte, 1517]. s4º. [*n.p.* Mainz, *J. Schöffer.* 1521]
Verteutschte ausslegung uber sant Hieronymus Allegation, was guts die Philosophi in d. heyligen schrifft schaffen &c. Uber "Du bist Petrus" &c. Auch uber wort Joannis, Luce III. [*b. w. h.* In gen. consol. de morte, 1517]. s4º. *n.p.* 1521
Vita, partim ab E., partim ab amicis descr. Acc. epistolae illustres &c. P. Scriverii &c. auspiciis. s8º. Lugd. Batav. 1649
Vormanung das heylige Evangeliū u. d. heyligen zwelfbotē schrifft fleissig zu lesen. In kurtz verdeutscht. [*b. w. h.* In gen. consol. de morte, 1517. *a. c. in* P2539]. s4º. Leypszgk [*sic*], *W. Stöckel.* 1522
TRANSLATIONS.
Against war. [Tr. 1553–4]. Intr. by J. W. Mackail. [Humanist's Lib., 2]. 8º. Boston, *Merrymount Press.* 1907
The complaint of peace. Tr. 8º. 1802
L'éloge de la folie. Tr. Mr. Gueudeville, avec notes de G. Listre, & figures de Holbein. n. éd. s8º. Amsterdam. 1728
L'éloge de la folie. Tr. par M. Geudeville, avec notes de G. Listre. n. éd. rev. s8º. Amsterdam. 1735
Enchiridion militis christ. whiche may be called in englysshe the hansom weapon of a chrysten knyght &c. [*Said to be tr. by W. Tyndale*]. s8º. [*Johan Byddell.* 1538]
Instit. principis christiani. ch. 3–11. Tr. w. intr. by P. E. Corbett. [Grotius Soc. Publ., No. 1]. s8º. 1921
Twenty select colloquies. Tr. Sir R. L'Estrange, 1680. Intr. by C. Whibley. [Abbey classics]. s8º. [1923]
Twenty-two select colloquies. [Tr.] by Sir R. L'Estrange. 3rd impr. corr. s8º. 1699
see ALLEN (P. S.) E.'s services to learning, 1925.
,, BIBLE : NEW TESTAMENT. Novum Instrumentū omne, ab E. recog. &c., 1516.
,, ——: ——Test. Nov. per D. E. recog., 1551.
,, BINNS (L. E.) E. the reformer, 1923.
,, GELDENHAUER (G.) Collectanea [E. annot. in leges de haereticis, Epist. aliquot (1529) &c.]; uitg. door J. Prinsen, 1901.
,, HUIZINGA (J.) E., 1924.
,, HUTTEN (U. v.) U. ab H. cum E. expostul., 1530 ?
,, KALKOFF (P.) E., Luther u. Fried. d. Weise, 1919.
,, —— Vermittlungspolitik d. E., 1904.
,, LOPIS STUNICA (J.) Annot. contra E. in def. tr. N.T., 1520.
,, LUTHER (M.) De servo arbitrio M. L. ad E., 1526.
,, —— Iudicium de E. &c., 1522 ?
,, —— On the bondage of the will., ans. to E. ; tr., 1823.
,, MAJOR (E.) E. v. Rotterdam, 1926 ?
,, MOSELLANUS (P.) Tabulae de schematibus & tropis ; item Libelli E., 1527.
,, MÜLLER (A.) Leben d. E., 1828.
,, RATSCHLAG ains d. v. hertzen begerdt das gnůg beschech d. Römischen stůls wirdigkait, &c. [*attrib. to E.*], 1521.
,, SMITH (PRESERVED). E., life, ideals & place in hist., 1923.
,, TITELMAN (F.) Libri duo de authoritate Apocalypsis adv. eos [*D. E. & others*] &c., 1530.

Erastus (Thomas). Der gründl. Bericht T. Erasti vom rechten verstand d. wort: Das ist mein leib (1562), *see* GLAUBENSBEKANTNUS. Christl. &c. Glaubensbekant., 1610.
The nullity of church-censures: or a dispute wherein is proved that ex-communication & church-senates exercising the same, are a mere humane invention. [Tr.] s8º. 1659
see BEZA (T.) Tractatus de excommunicatione &c., T. E. centum mss. thesibus oppositus, 1590.

Erazo (Salvador L.) Parnaso salvadoreño. Antología esmeradamente sel. por S. L. E. s8º. Barcelona. [1917]

Erbach-Schönberg (*princess* **Marie** *of*) [MARIE, *princess of Battenberg*]. Reminiscences. 8º. [1925]

Erben (Wilhelm). Berthold v. Tuttlingen, Registrator &c., 1923, *see* KAISERL. AKAD. D. WISS. IN WIEN. Denkschr., B66, 1924.
Quellen z. Gesch. d. Stiftes u. d. Herrschaft Mattsee ; hrsg. v. W. E., *see* FONTES RERUM AUSTRIAC., B49i, 1896.

Erbermannus, *see* EBERMANN (VEIT).

Erbert (Konstantin), *ed.*, *see* ISKUSSTVO. Искусство старое и новое, 1, 1921.

Ercilla y Zuñiga (Alonso de).
La Araucana. 2p. s8º. Barcelona. 1827

Erckert (R. von). Der Kaukasus u. s. Völker. 8º. L. 1888
Die Sprachen d. Kaukas. Stammes. Mit Vorwort v. F. Müller. 2T *in* 1v. (1, Wörterverzeichniss. 2, Sprachproben u. gramm. Skizzen). la8º. Wien. 1895

Erconwald, *St.*, *bp. of London, d. 693*, *see* ERKENWALD.

Erdmann (Benno). Berkeley's Philos. im Lichte s. wiss. Tagebuchs, *see* KÖNIGL. PREUSS. AKAD. D. WISS. Abhdl. (Phil.-hist. Klasse), 1919.

Erdmann (Benno) [*continued*].
Die Idee v. Kants Kritik d. reinen Vernunft: hist. Untersuchung, *see* KÖNIGL. PREUSS. AKAD. D. WISS. Abhdl. (Phil.-hist. Klasse), 1917.
Die philosoph. Grundlagen v. Helmholtz' Wahrnehmungstheorie, *see* KÖNIGL.-PREUSS. AKAD. Abhandl., Phil.-hist. Klasse, 1921.
Erdmann (Carl). Mauritius Burdinus (Gregor VIII), *see* QUELLEN U. FORSCH. aus ital. Archiv. &c., B19, 1927.
Erdmann (David). Luther u. s. Bezieh. zu Schlesien, insbes. zu Breslau. [Verein f. Ref.-gesch. Schr., Jhrg. 5, Nr. 19]. 8°. Halle. 1887
Erdmann (Günther).
Upsala. [Nord. Stud., 6]. 8°. Greifswald. 1924
Erdmann (Johann Eduard). Leib und Seele. 8°. Halle. 1837
Erdmann (Nils). A. Strindberg. En kämpande och lidande själs hist. 2v. 8°. [1920]
Erdösi (János), *see* SYLVESTER (J.)
Eremundus (Ernestus), *ps., see* HOTMAN (FRANÇOIS).
Erenburg (Ilya).
Звериное тепло. s8°. Москва. 1923
Жизнь и гибель Николая Курбова. 8°. Берлин. 1923
Кануны (стихи 1915–21). s8°. Берлинъ. 1921
Ликъ войны. 8°. Софія. 1920
Необычайныя похожденія Хуліо Хуренито и его учениковъ &c. 8°. Москва. 1922
Поэзія революц. Москвы. Подъ ред. И. Э. s8°. Берлинъ. 1922
Трест Д. Е. ист. гибели Европы. s8°. Берлин. 1923
Тринадцать трубокъ. s8°. Москва. 1923
Eretz-Israel, *see* KEREN HA-YESOD. The K. ha-Y. book; colonis. problems of E.-I. (Palestine) Found. Fund, 1921.
Erfurdt (Carl Gottlob August). Annot. integrae in Sophoclis tragoedias, 1824, *see* SOPHOCLES. Quae extant omnia, t4, 1824.
Erfurth (Richard).
Gesch. d. Stadt Wittenberg. 2T *in* 1v. 8°. Wittenberg. 1910–27
Erhard (Hermann). La Tour, d. Pastellmaler Ludwigs XV. 89 Nachbildungen &c., mit Einführung &c. v. H. E. 4e A. la8°. München. 1920
Erhard (Thomas Aquinas). Polycrates Gersenensis contra scutum Kempense; apologia pro Joanne Gersene, protoparente libelli de Imit. Christi, contra E. Amort. s8°. Augustae Vindel. 1729
Erhardt (Franz). Der Satz v. Grunde als Prinzip d. Schliessens. [P2471]. 8°. Halle a. S. 1891
Mechanismus u. Teleologie. [*b. w.* Schulze (G. E.) Encykl. d. philos. Wiss., 1823]. 8°. L. 1890
Erhebung (Die). Jahrbuch für neue Dichtung u. Wertung. Hrsg. v. A. Wolfenstein. Buch [1], 2. [Buch 1, 5es–7es Tausend, *n.d.*] 8°. 1920
Erichsen (L. Mylius-), *see* MYLIUS-ERICHSEN (L.)
Ericson (Gurli Hertzman-), *see* HERTZMAN-ERICSON (G.)
Ericus (Johannes Petrus). 'Ανθρωπογλωττογονία, sive humanae ling. genesis. pl, t1. [*No more publ.* ?] s4°. Venetiis. 1697
***Erinnerungsschrifft** etlicher vom Adel u. Städten [*C. v. Hoym & others*] &c., 1597, *see* HOYM (C. VON).
Eriu. Journal of the School of Irish Learning, Dublin. v8, 9. 8°. D. 1916–23
Erizzo (Sebastiano). Le sei giornate. s4°. Venetia. 1567
Erkenwald, *St., bp. of London, d. 693* [EARCONWALD; ERCONWALD]. St. Erkenwald, 675–93. Allit. poem, wr. ab. 1386. [Sel. early Eng. poems; ed. Sir I. Gollancz, 4]. 8°. 1922
St. Erkenwald: Mid. Eng. poem. Ed. w. intr. &c. by H. L. Savage. [Yale St. in Eng., 72]. 8°. New Haven, Yale. 1926
Erkes (Eduard). Chines. Literatur. s8°. Breslau. 1922
***Erklärung** d. Gebräuche u. Ceremonien uns. heil. kathol. Kirche. 12e A. s8°. Eger. 1856
Erlande (Albert). Le trajet de la foudre, roman, *see* ŒUVRES libres, 72, 1927.
La vipère dorée, roman, *see* ŒUVRES libres, 10, 1922.
Erlangen: UNIVERSITÄTS-BIBL., *see* VARNHAGEN (H.) Üb. e. Sammlung alter ital. Drucke, 1892.
Erlanger (E. B. d'). L'âge d'or. Poëmes & sonnets. 4°. [1919]
Erler (Fritz), *see* OSTINI (F. *b.* v.) F. E., 1921.
Erler (Josef). Des Kaisers Geigenmacher in Tirol. Drama. s8°. Innsbruck. 1878
Erman (Adolf), *Egyptologist.*
Die ägypt. Schülerhss., *see* KÖN.-PREUSS. AKAD. Abhdln., Phil.-hist. Kl., 1925.
Aegypten u. aegypt. Leben im Altertum. Neu bearb. v. H. Ranke. la8°. Tübingen. 1923

Erman (Adolf), *Egyptologist* [*continued*].
Ein Fall abgekürzter Justiz in Ägypten, *see* KÖN.-PREUSS. AKAD. Abhdln., Phil.-hist. Kl., 1913
Die Hieroglyphen. Neudruck. s8°. 1917
Die Literatur d. Aegypter: Gedichte, Erzählungen u. Lehrbücher, 2. u. 3. Jhdt. v. Chr. 8°. L. 1923
Lit. of the anc. Egyptians: poems, narr. & manuals of instruction. Tr. A. M. Blackman. 8°. [1927]
Papyrus Lansing; hrsg. u. erkl. v. A. E. u. H. O. Lange, *see* KONG. DAN. VID. SELSK. Hist.-fil. Medd., 10, 1924–55.
Reden, Rufe u. Lieder auf Gräberbildern d. alt. Reiches, 1919, *see* KÖNIGL-PREUSS. AKAD. D. WISS. Abhdl. (Phil.-hist. Klasse), 1918.
Röm. Obelisken, *see* KÖNIGL. PREUSS. AKAD. D. WISS. Abhdl. (Phil.-hist. Klasse), 1917.
Ermolov (Aleksei Sergeevich). Наши неурожаи и продовольств. вопросъ. 2ч *in* 1v. [Приложенія *in* r2 *with sep. pagin.*] la8°. С.-П. 1909
Ern (V.) Г. С. Сковорода: жизнь и ученіе. 8°. Москва. 1912
Ernest, *called the Confessor, duke of Brunswick-Lüneberg, see* WREDE (A.) Ernst d. Bekenner, 1888.
Ernest I, *called the Pious, Duke of Saxe-Gotha.*
see COMPENDIUM. *C. hist. eccles. decreto E. S. &c., 1723.
„ LATHBURY (T.) Mem. of E. the P. &c., 1843.
„ PHILIPPS (J. T.) Hist. of E. of Sax-Gotha &c., 1740.
Ernest Augustus, *1st elector of Hanover, see* HILTEBRANDT (P.) Die kirchl. Reunionsverhandl. d. 17. Jhdts.: E. A. v. H. u. d. kath. Kirche, 1922.
Ernest Augustus, *king of Hanover* [*The Duke of Cumberland*]. Letters of the King of Hanover [*i.e.* E. A.] to Visct. Strangford. Hist. note by E. M. Cox. Intr. by C. Whibley. 8°. 1925
Ernest Frederick, *Margrave of Baden.* Christlichs Bedencken u. Motiven E. F., d. Subscription d. Formulæ Concordiæ. Sambt F. G. Confession u. etliche strittige Artickel. [*Known as*: Staffort-Book]. s4°. Staffort. 1590
Ernest-Charles (Jean). La fureur d'aimer, *see* ŒUVRES libres, 59, 1926.
Le nom de Chalanton, *see* ŒUVRES libres, 38, 1924.
Ernesti (Johann August).
Instit. interpretis N. Test. [*b. w.* Baumgarten (S. J.) Theses theol., 1758]. s8°. Lipsiae. 1761
Neue theolog. Bibl. darinnen v. d. neuesten theol. Büchern u. Schriften Nachricht gegeben wird. 10B. s8°. L. 1760–69
Neueste theolog. Bibl. darinnen v. d. neuesten theol. Büchern u. Schriften Nachricht gegeben wird. 4B. s8°. L. 1771–76
Opuscula philologica, critica &c. emend. & aucta. 8°. Lugd. Bat. 1764
Opuscula theolog. ed. 2a. auct. 8°. Lipsiae. 1792
Theses theol. dogmat. Ed. J. C. G. Ernesti. s8°. Lipsiae. 1783
Ernesti (Johann Christoph).
Diatribe de ant. excommunicationis ritu. Resp. V. J. Herwig. [P2635]. s4°. Wittenbergæ. *n.d.*
Ernle (Rowland Edmund Prothero, *1st baron*).
English farming, past & present. 2nd ed., n. impr. 8°. 1919
„ „ ......3rd ed. 8°. 1922
„ „ ......4th ed. 8°. 1927
The land & its people: chapters in rural life & history. 8°. [1925]
The light reading of our ancestors. [Eng. Assoc., Pamph. 50. P2683]. 8°. 1921
„ „ : chapters in the growth of the Eng. novel. 8°. [1927]
The Psalms in human life. [2nd ed.] 8°. 1904
Ernst (Otto), *ps.* [*i.e.* O. ERNST SCHMIDT].
Semper d. Mann. s8°. L. 1916
Ernst (*Dr.* Otto), *see* FRANCIS JOSEPH I, *emp. of Austria.* F. J. in s. Briefen; hrsg. O. E.. 1924.
Ernst (Sergei). Александръ Бенуа. 8°. П. 1921
В. Заміраіло. s8°. Петербург. 1921
В. А. Сѣровъ. 8°. П. 1921
З. Е. Серебрякова. s8°. П. 1922
К. А. Сомовъ. 8°. С.-П. 1918
Erondelle (Pierre), *see* SAINLIENS (C. DE). The Elizabethan home disc. in 2 dialogues [by C. Hollyband & P. E.], 1925.
Erpenius (Thomas) [T. v. ERPE]. Gramm. Arabica, cum fabulis Locmanni &c. Acc. excerpta anthol. Hamasa Abi Temmam. Ed., conv. & notis ill. ab A. Schultens. Praef. imagin. linguam &c. Judaeorum confutat. s4°. Lugd. Batav. 1748
see KORAN. Hist. Iosephi Patriarchae Arab.; cum vers. Lat. & scholiis E. P., 1617.
Erphesfurtensia. Monumenta Erphesfurt. saec. 12–14, 1899, *see* SANKT PETER, *abbey, Erfurt.*

Errera (Carlo). Congo Belga, *see* QUADERNI geograf., N. 4, 1918.
Italiani e Slavi n. Venezia Giulia, *see* QUADERNI geograf., N. 9, 1919.

Errico (Giuseppe). Chi sente. Novelle. 8°. 1921

Ershov (Matvei Nikolaevich). Пути развитія философіи въ Россіи. [P2598]. 8°. Владивостокъ. 1922

Erskine (Henry), *minister of Chirnside, 1624–96, see* MEMOIRS of Mrs. W. Veitch, T. Hog, H. E. &c., 1846.

Erskine (John). Galahad. s8°. 1926
The private life of Helen of Troy. 3rd impr. s8°. 1926

Erskine (John), *Ph.D., see* CAMB. HIST. OF ENG. LIT. Suppl.: Hist. of Amer. lit.; ed. W. P. Trent, J. E. &c., v3, 4, 1921; Short hist., 1924.

Erskine (Ralph). The Gospel sonnets. Pref. acc. of a.'s life &c. 8°. *n.d.* [1800 ?]
Scripture songs in 2 bks. s8°. E. 1771

Erskine (*Mrs.* Steuart).
Madrid: past & present. s8°. 1922
Vanished cities of Arabia. 8°. [1925]

Erskine (William Hugh). Japanese customs, th. origin & value. Intr. by E. W. Clement, C. T. Paul &c. 8°. Tokyo. [1925]

Értekezések a társadalmi tudományok köréböl, 1909, *see* MAGYAR GAZDASZÖVETSÉG.

Ertz (Susan). Now east, now west. s8°. 1927

Ervari, *The family of.* [ARVARI; DEGLI ALVARI], *see* BIADEGO (G.) Fiorentina fam. E. a Verona, 1915.

Ervine (St. John Greer).
The foolish lovers. s8°. [1920]
Jane Clegg. Play. s8°. 1914
,, ,, *for a. ed., see* PLAYS of to-day, v1, 1925.
John Ferguson. Play. [2nd impr.] s8°. [1919]
The Lady of Belmont. Play. s8°. [1923]
Mary, Mary, quite contrary. Play. s8°. [1923]
Mixed marriage. [repr.] s8°. 1920
The organized theatre: a plea in civics. 8°. [1924]
Parnell. 8°. 1925
,, ,, [pop. ed.] 8°. 1928
The ship. Play. [repr.] s8°. [1925]
Some impressions of my elders. s8°. [1923]

Erwägungen f. d. Bischöfe d. Conc. ü. päpstl. Unfehlbarkeit, 1869, *see* DÖLLINGER (J. J. I.)

Erythræus (Janus Nicius), *ps.* [*i.e.* GIOV. VITTORIO ROSSI]. Eudemiæ libri 10. [*b. w. h.* Opuscula, 1648]. s8°. Coloniæ Ubiorum. 1645
Homiliae. [*b. w. h.* Opuscula, 1648]. s8°. Coloniæ Ubiorum. 1649
Opuscula spiritualia tria. s8°. Coloniæ Ubiorum. 1648
Pinacotheca imaginum illust. doct. &c. laude virorum. ed. nov. 3p [*in* 1v. *pagin. cont.*] s8°. Guelferbuti. 1729

Erythraeus (Valentinus). Augustanae Confessionis, ejusque apologiae tabulis delineatae &c. Pars 1(–3). Add. est e regione conf. eccl. Saxon. & Vvirtemb. &c. Studio V. Erythraei &c. Acc. De coena Dominica. 3p *in* 1v. fol. Argentorati. 1565–67

Erzberger (Matthias). Der Prozess E.-Helfferich. Mit e. Begleitwort v. Dr. Löwenstein. 5. A. [P2685]. 8°. Ulm. 1921
Souvenirs de guerre. Préf. de M. Muret. 8°. 1921
see FRENZEL (H.) E. d. Reichsverderber! 1919.
,, LIEBIG (H. v.) Bethmann-Hollweg, E. &c. (Reichsverderber, T1), 1922.

Erzstätt (Joh. E. Kirnbauer v.), *see* KIRNBAUER V. ERZSTÄTT (J. E.)

E. S., *Meister, see* S. (E.), *Meister.*

Escalante (Amos de). Ave Maris Stella. Con prol. de M. Menendez y. Pelayo. s8°. 1920

Escalera (Evaristo). Crón. d. princ. de Astúrias, 1865, *see* ESPAÑA. Crón. gen., v6, 1865 &c.

Escamilla (Pedro). Amor de madre. Novela. s8°. 1882

Escartin y Carrera (Francisco Antonio). Pintura de la hist. de la iglesia &c. Formada en Francés por. . . . y copiada en Esp. por F. A. de E. [? *Tr. of* Alletz (P. A.) Tableau &c.] 7t. 8°. 1796

Eschavannes (Jouffroy d'), *see* JOUFFROY D'ESCHAVANNES.

Eschecs, *see* ECHECS.

Eschenbach (Christian Ehrenfried).
Scripta medico-biblica. s8°. Rostochii. 1779

Eschenbach (Wolfram v.)
see AMIRA (C. v.) Gr. Bilderhs. v. Willehalm, 1917.
,, RICHEY (M. F.) Gahmuret Anschevin: study of W. v. E., 1923.
,, SINGER (S.) W.'s Stil u. d. Stoff d. Parzival, 1916.
,, TROY. Der Göttweiger Trojanerkrieg; [*attrib. to* W. v. E.]; hrsg. A. Koppitz, 1926.

Eschius (Nicolaus), *see* ESS (NICOLAUS VAN).

Escholier (Raymond).
Cantegril. Roman s8°. [1921]
,, [Livre Mod. Illust.] 8°. 1927
Dansons la trompeuse. . . . s8°. 1919
,, ,, ... [8e éd.] s8°. 1921
Daumier. s8°. [1913]
Le nouv. Paris: la vie artistique &c. éd. rev. & augm. la8°. [1925 ?]
La nuit. Roman. s8°. [1923]
Quand on conspire. Roman. s8°. 1925
Le sel de la terre. Roman. s8°. Amiens. 1924
Vers l'autre rive. [*Poems*]. s8°. 1909

Escoffery (John), *see* PARL.: H. OF COMMONS. Rep. of debate, June 1825, on Dr. Lushington's motion resp. deport. of J. E. &c. f. Jamaica, 1825.

Escoffier (Auguste). Le guide culinaire. Par A. E. avec collab. de P. Gilbert & E. Fetu. 3e éd. 8°. 1912

Escosura (Patricio de la). España artística y mon., vistas y descr. &c. Obra &c. por G. P. de Villa-Amil. Text por P. de la E. [*Span. & French*]. 3t. atlas fol. Paris. 1842–50

Escoube (Paul) [*ps.* PAUL DELIOR].
Remy de Gourmont & s. oeuvre. s8°. [1909]

Escouflaire (R. C.) Ireland an enemy of the Allies ? s8°. 1919

Escragnolle Doria (Luiz Gastão d'). Cousas do passado, *see* INSTITUTO HIST. &c. BRAZIL. Rev., t71, 1909.

Escudero (Antonio Vives y), *see* VIVES Y ESCUDERO (A.)

Escudero (José Maria). Crón. de la prov. de Guadalajara, 1869, *see* ESPAÑA. Crón. gen., v1, 1865 &c.

Escudier (Léon), *see* ESCUDIER (M.) & L. E. Vies &c. des cantatrices céléb., 1856.

Escudier (Marie) & L. Escudier. Vie &c. des cantatrices célèbres, Musiciens de l'Empire & Vie de Paganini. s8°. 1856

Escurial. Cat. de los códices esp. de la bibl. del E. [*Comp. &c. by*] P. Miguélez. [t]1, 2. la8°. 1917–25
Cat. de los códices latinos de la Real Bibl. del E. por el P. G. Antolín. v1, 2. 8°. 1910–11
Cat. de los mss. castellanos de la Real Bibl. de el E. [*By*] J. Zarco Cuevas. 2[v.] la8°. 1924–26
see LIBRO de los Tres Reyes de Oriente; publ. in facs. f. MS. in Lib. of the E. by A. M. Huntington, 1904.

Esdaile (Arundell James Kennedy). Sources of Eng. lit.: guide for students. s8°. C. 1928
see PLOMER (H. R.) Dict. of printers &c. in Eng., Scot. & Ireland, 1668–1725; ed. A. E., 1922.

Esdaile (Katharine Ada), *wife of A. J. K. Esdaile.*
Eng. monumental sculpture since the Renaissance. 8°. [1927]
John Bushnell, sculptor, *see* WALPOLE SOC., v15, 1927.
Roubiliac's work at Trinity Coll., Cambridge. 8°. C. 1924

Esdaile (William). Cat. of coll. of pictures of W. E. Sold by Christie & Manson, 1838. [*MS. prices*]. [P2701]. 4°. [1838]
Cat. of coll. of prints & drawings of W. E. Sold by Christie. [*MS. prices*]. 5p *in* 1v. 8°. [1840]
Cat. of engravings, bks. of prints &c. of W. E. Sold by Christie, March 19th &c., 1838. [*MS. prices. b. w. h.* Cat., 1840]. 8°. 1838

Esenin (Sergei Aleksandrovich).
Пугачов. [*Verse*]. s8°. Берлин. 1922
Собраніе стихов и поэм. т1. s8°. Берлин. 1922
Собрание стихотворений. 4т. [1, изд. 2oe]. s8°. Москва. 1926–27
T4 *has t.* Стихи и проза; сост. И. В. Евдокимов.
Стихи скандалиста. s8°. Берлин. [1923]

Eser (Johann Siegmund).
De statu animarum separatarum &c. s4°. Helmestadi. 1653

Esher (Reginald Baliol Brett, *2nd viscount*).
Cloud-capp'd towers. 8°. 1927
The influence of King Edward, & essays. 8°. 1915
Ionicus. [Sel. of letters &c. of W. Cory]. 8°. 1923
The tragedy of Lord Kitchener. 8°. 1921

Esher (William Baliol Brett, *1st viscount*), *see* WARD (C. H. D.) A romance of the 19th c. comp. f. the letters &c. of B., Visct. E., 1923.

Esme (Jean d'). A travers l'empire de Ménélik. 8°. [1928]

Esmoreit. An ingenious play of E., the king's son of Sicily. Tr. f. Mid. Dutch by H. M. Ayres, w. intr. by A. J. Barnouw. s8°. The Hague. [1923]

Esnans (Luc Courchetet d'), *see* COURCHETET D'ESNANS (L.)

Esnault (Gaston), *see* LE LAÉ (C. M.) Vie & œ. comiques; *ed.* G. E., t1, 1921.

Espagne. *L'E. & la France; du mariage d'Isabelle II, 1843, *see* BILLING (*le b.* S. DE).

Espalargucs (Pere), *painter, see* HISP. SOC. OF AMER. Pere E. in coll. of H. S., 1927.

España. Anuario militar de España, 1917, 1918. [Min. de la Guerre]. 8º. 1917–18
Crónica gen. de Esp., ó sea hist. ilust. y descr. de sus provincias. Red. por conocidos escritores. [*b. in* 12v.] fol. 1865–71
Each prov. is by a diff. a., as below, & has sep. tp. & pagin. The numbering of the vols. is arbitrary.

Alava; Bisso, 1868. [8.]
Albacete; Blanch é Illa, 1866. [11.]
Alicante; Boix, 1868. [7.]
Almeria; Santoyo, 1869. [9.]
Antillas; Pezuela, 1871. [12.]
Astúrias; Escalera, 1865. [6.]
Avila; Fulgosio, 1870. [10.]
Badajoz; Henao y Muñoz, 1870. [11.]
Baleares; Fulgosio, 1870. [12.]
Barcelona; Angelon, 1870. [3.]
Búrgos; Maldonado Macanáz, 1866. [10.]
Cáceres; Guzman, 1870. [11.]
Cádiz; Bisso, 1868. [5.]
Canarias; Gimenez Romera, 1868. [12.]
Castellon de la Plana; Miralles de Imperial, 1867. [7.]
Ciudad-Real; Hosta, 1865. [1.]
Córdoba; Gonzalez Llana, 1867. [5.]
Coruña; Fulgosio, 1865. [2.]
Cuenca; Pruneda, 1869. [1.]
Fernando Poo, Corisco y Annobon; Muñoz y Gaviria, 1871. [12.]
Filipinas; Fulgosio, 1871. [12.]
Gerona; Blanch é Illa, 1865. [3.]
Granada; Dios de la Rada, 1869. [9.]
Guadalajara; Escudero, 1869. [1.]
Guipúzcoa; Fulgosio, 1868. [8.]
Huelva; Climent, 1866. [5.]
Huesca; Gonzalez, 1866. [4.]
Jaén; Lozano Muñoz, 1867. [9.]
León; Garcia de la Foz, 1867. [6.]
Lérida; Blanch, 1868. [3.]
Logroño; Gimenez Romera, 1867. [10.]
Lugo; Villa-Amil, 1866. [2.]
Madrid; Rosell, 1865. [1.]
Málaga; Bisso, 1869. [9.]
Murcia; Bisso, 1870. [11.]
Navarra; Nombela, 1868. [8.]
Orense; Fulgosio, 1866. [2.]
Palencia; Villalva, 1867. [6.]
Pontevedra; Fulgosio, 1867. [2.]
Salamanca; Gonzalez de la Llana, 1869. [6.]
Santander; Assas, 1867. [10.]
Segovia; Carreras, 1866. [10.]
Sevilla; Bisso, 1869. [5.]
Soria; Perez Rioja, 1867. [10.]
Tarragona; Fulgosio, 1870. [3.]
Teruel; Pruneda, 1866. [4.]
Toledo; Mariátegui, 1866. [1.]
Valencia; Boix, 1867. [7.]
Valladolid; Fulgosio, 1869. [6.]
Vizcaya; Rodriguez García, 1865. [8.]
Zamora; Fulgosio, 1869. [6.]
Zaragoza; Gonzalez, 1867. [4.]

*Esp. (La) bajo el poder arbitrario de la Congreg. apostólica, 1820–32. s8º. Paris. 1833
Esp. divida en provincias &c., con un nomenclator ó dicc. de todos los pueblos del reyno. 2t. sfol. 1789
La riqueza y el progreso de Esp. Ed. por el Banco Urquijo de Madrid. obl. s4º. 1924

Español [ESPAÑOLA &c.] *Embajada esp., 17 cent., 1926, *see* EMBAJADA.

Espérandieu (Emile). Recueil gén. des bas-reliefs &c. de la Gaule rom. [Docs. inéd.] t5–8. 4º. 1913–22

Espérey (*le maréchal* **Franchet d'**), *see* FRANCHET D'ESPÉREY (*le maréchal*).

Espernon, *see* ÉPERNON.

Espina (Concha). La esfinge maragata. Novela. 4a ed. s8º. 1925

Espinas (Alfred).
Philos. soc. du 18e siècle & la Révol. 8º. 1898

Espinas (Georges) & H. Pirenne, *edd.* Recueil de doc. rel. à l'hist. de l'industrie drapière en Flandre. [C. R. d'H. de Belg.] pl, t3, 4. 4º. Brux. 1920–4
3, Des origs. à l'époque bourguignonne. 4, Suppl. & tables.

Espinay (Charles d'), *bp. of Dol; 1531?-91, see* BUSSON (H.) C. d'E. & s. œuvre poét., 1923.

Espinay (Gustave Marie d'). Les cartul. angevins. Et. sur le droit de l'Anjou au moyen âge. 8º. Angers. 1864

Esprit. *Esprit (L') de M. Arnaud, 2p, 1684, *see* JURIEU (P.)
*Esprit (De l') des loix, 1757, *see* MONTESQUIEU (C. DE S. *baron* DE).

Esprit (Jacques). *The falsehood of human virtue. A moral essay. Done out of French. s8º. 1691

Esquer (Gabriel). La prise d'Alger, 1830. 8º. Alger. 1923

Ess (Carl v.) *Ueber die Vaness. deut. Bibelübers.: Eine Warnung. [*b. w.* Bible: German. Die heil. Schr. d. N.T.; üb. v. C. u. L. van Ess, 1818]. 8º. Str. 1819

Ess (Leander van).
Pragmat-Krit. Gesch. d. Vulgata. 8º. Tübingen. 1824
see Ess (C. v.) Ueber die Vaness. deut. Bibelübers.: eine Warnung &c. 1819.

Ess (Nicolaus van), *see* TAULER (J.) Exercitia s. vita &c. J. Christi; alia access. autore N. E., 1565; 1572.

Essai. Essai sur l'art de rendre les révol. utiles, 2t, 1801, *see* BONNET (J.-E.)
*Essai s. le commerce de Russie, 1777, *see* MARBAULT.
*Essai sur les classes d'expér. chrét., 1851, *see* MÉTHODISTES.
*Essai sur l'étude de la litt., 1761, *see* †GIBBON (E.)

Essay.
*Essay (An) conc. the divine right of tithes, 1700, *see* LESLIE (C.)
*Essay (An) for a new translation of the Bible, tr., 1702, *see* LE CÈNE (C.).
*Essay (An) for the better regul. &c. of free-thinking, 2nd ed., 1739, *see* HILDROP (J.), *D.D.*
*Essay (An) on honour, 1741, *see* HILDROP (J.)
*Essay (An) on laughter. [Tr.] s8º. 1769
*Essay on psalmody, 1775, *see* ROMAINE (W.)
*Essay (An) on the state of the country in resp. to cond. &c. of husb. labourers, 1831, *see* PLACE (F.)
*Essay (An) upon educ. &c., by a Gent. of Bristol, 1752, *see* BUTLER (S.)
*Historical (An) & polit. essay, discov. the affinity of anc. & mod. govt. &c., 1706, *see* HISTORICAL.

Essays.
*Essays & observ. on trade, husbandry of flax &c.; publ. by a Soc. of gentlemen in Dublin, 1740, *see* ROYAL DUBLIN SOC.
Essays, Catholic & critical, 1926, *see* SELWYN (E. G.) *ed.*
Essays in crit. realism, 1920, *see* DRAKE (D.)
*Essays in verse, 1769, *see* MACLAURIN (J.), *Lord Dreghorn.*
*Essays on Jewish life & thought, *see* EPSTEIN (M.) Letters, s2, 1924.
*Essays on the polit. circumstances of Ireland &c., 1798, *see* KNOX (A.)

Essays & Reviews, *see* BUCHANAN (J.) "E. & R." exam., 1861.

Esselborn (Carl). Hessen-Darmstadt. [*Ed. C. E.*] 8º. L. 1926
see HAUPT (H.) Hess. Biografien; in Verb. mit K. E. &c. hrsg. v. H. H., B1, 2, 1918–27.

Essen (Andreas van). Systematis theologici [dogmatici] p1–3. 3p *in* 1v. s4º. Ultrajecti [2, 3, Amstelædami]. 1659–65
see VOET (J.) Orat. funebr. in obit. A. E., 1677.

Essenwein (August), *see* HAUSBUCH. Mittelalt. Hausbuch: Bilder-Hs. d. 15. Jhdts.; Vorwort v. A. E., 1887.

Essex. Rep. on secondary &c. educ. in E., 1906, *see* SADLER (*Sir* M. E.)
Visitation of Co. of Essex, 1664–68, by Sir E. Bysshe. Ed. J. J. Howard. la8º. 1888

Essex Archaeological Society.
Transactions. N.S., v15–18. 8º. Colchester. 1921–27

Essex review (The): an illust. quarterly record. v29–37. 8º. Colchester. 1920–28

Essex (Adela, *countess of*), *wife of George Devereux, 7th earl of E.* Partic., plans &c. of the Cassiobury Park estate, for sale, 8th June 1922, by Humbert & Flint in conj. w. Knight, Frank & Rutley. By dir. of A., Ctss. of E. fol. 1922

Essex (Frances Howard Devereux, *countess of*), *aft. countess of Somerset, see* ROUGHEAD (W.) The fatal countess [*i.e.* Ctss. of Somerset] &c., 1924.

Essex (Robert Devereux, *2nd earl of*).
see DEVEREUX, *Family of.* D. papers, w. R. Broughton's mem. (1575–1601); ed. H. E. Malden, 1923.
,, WINSTANLEY (L.) Hamlet & the Scot. succession: rel. of the play to Essex conspiracy &c., 1921.

Essex (Robert Devereux, *3rd earl of*), *see* JAMES I. *Truth brought to light, p2, Divorce betw. Lady F. Howard & E. (1613), 1692.

Essington (Robert William). The annals of Shenstone. 8º. 1899

Esslemont (J. E.) Bahā'u'llāh & the new era. 8º. [1923]

Essling (*prince* **d'**). Coll. de monnaies & médailles, Consulat & Emp., Napoléon I, N. III &c., appart. au Pr. d'E. Vente, Juin, 1927. [*& Planches*]. la8º. 1927

Esswein (Hermann), *see* HAUSENSTEIN (W.) Das Bild, B8, 9, Deut. Bild d. 16 J., Auswahl v. H. E. & W. H., 1923.

Estaunié (Edouard), *novelist.*
L'appel de la route. [27e éd.] s8º. 1924
Disc. de réception [*on* A. Capus]. Réponse de R. de Flers. [Acad. Fr., 2 avr. 1925. P2819]. s8º. 1925
L'infirme aux mains de lumière. [Cahiers verts, 24]. s8º. 1923
La labyrinthe. s8º. 1924
Le silence dans la campagne. [Une nuit de noces—L'infirme aux mains de lumière & a. n.] 8º. 1926
Tels qu'ils furent. s8º. 1927

Esté, *family of.*
see CRAUFURD (J.) *The hist. of the house of Esté, 1681.
,, PIGNA (G. B.) Hist. de principi di E., 1572.
,, PLANISCIG (L.) Die Estens. Kunstsamml., 1919.

Este (Alfonso II d'), *duke of Ferrara* [†ALPHONSO II [*d'Este*], *duke of F.*], *see* LAZZARI (A.) I "ricordi di governo" di A. II, 1920.

Este (Anne d'), *1531–1607, see* BORDEAUX (H.) Amours du temps passé: A. d'E. & J. de Nemours, 1923.

Este (Beatrice d'), *duchess of Milan, see* LA SIZERANNE (R. DE). B. d'E. & sa cour, 1920.

Este (Charles), *of Ch.Ch., Oxford, see* OXFORD : CHRIST CHURCH. Carmina quadragesimalia ; [ed. C. E. &c.], 2v, 1757.
Estella (Diego de) [STELLA (DIDACUS)]. Fratris D. Stellae in Evang. Lucam enarrat. 2t [in 1v] [*tp. imperfect*]. fol. Antverpiae. 1599
Esternod (Claude d') [*ps.* FRANCHÈRE (*le sieur de*)]. L'espadon satyrique. D'ap. l'éd. orig. de 1619, avec préf., notes &c. par F. Fleuret & L. Perceau. 8º. 1922
Esteva (Adalberto A.) & J. Pablo Rivas. El parnaso mexicano : antología compl. con notas biogr. 2t. s8º. Barcelona. *n.d.*
Estève (Edmond). Études de litt. préromantique. la8º. 1923
Esthonia [EESTI ; ESTHONIAN ; ESTHONIE ; ESTONIAN].
The case of the new rep. of Esthonia, Latvia, Lithuania & Ukraine pres. at Cong. of the League of Esthonians &c. of Amer., Sept. 1919. [P2383]. 8º. [N.Y. ?] 1919
Constit. of the E. Rep. (15th June 1920). [P2751]. 4º. [1920]
Eesti, Esthonie, Esthonia, Estland. [*In Esthonian, Fr., Eng. & Germ. By H. Vellner, J. G. Granö & others*]. la8º. Tallinn. 1923
Estonian year-book, 1927. Ed. A. Pullerits. 8º. Tallinn. 1927
Lettre de la Délég. esthon. à la Conf. de la Paix, à l'occ. de paix faite par le gouvt. des Soviets. [P2751]. 4º. [1919]
Mémoire sur l'indép. de l'E. prés. à la Conf. de la Paix & Addendum. [P2751]. 4º. 1919
Pour l'E. indépendante. Recueil des doc. diplomat. publ. par la Délég. Esth. [P2707]. la8º. Copenhague. 1918
Traités conclus entre la Lettonie & l'E. en 1923, 1923, *see* LETTONIE.
*Treaty of peace betw. Russia & E., *n.d.*, *see* RUSSIA.
Estienne, *The family of.*
see MAITTAIRE (M.) Stephanorum hist., 1709.
,, RENOUARD (A. A.) Annales des Estienne, 2p, 1837–38.
Estienne (Henri), *1528–98* [H. STEPHANUS ; H. STEPHENS].
De Latinitate falsò suspecta, expost. H. Stephani. Ejusdem de Plauti Latinitate diss. s8º. [Genevae]. *H. Stephanus.* 1576
De Lipsii Latinitate palaestra I. s8º. Francfordii. 1695
*Discours de la vie de Catherine de Medici, 1663, *see* HENRY III, *k. of Fr.* Rec. de div. pièces, 1664.
L'introd. au traité de la conformité des merveilles anc. avec les modernes : ou traité prép. à l'Apologie pour Herodote. s8º. *n.p.* [Paris ?]. 1579
La precellence du langage franç. Acc. d'une ét. &c. par L. Feugère. n. éd. s8º. 1850
see BEZA (T.) De vera pronunt. Gr. & Lat. linguae &c. Apolog. pro vet. ac Germana linguae Gr. pronunt. *by H. E.*, 1587.
Estienne (Robert), *the elder.* Les censures des théologiens de Paris, par lesquelles ils avoyent faulsement condamné les Bibles impr. par R. E. : avec la resp. d'iceluy R. E. Tr. de Lat. 8º. 1552 [réimpr. Genève. 1866]
Thesaurus linguæ Lat. Ed. nova, auctior & emend. [Ed. E. Law, J. Taylor &c.] 4t [*in 3v. 2, 3 in 1*]. fol. Londini. 1734–35
Estimate. *Estimate (An) of the manners of the pres. times, 1782, *see* WESLEY (J.)
*Estimate (An) of the profit & loss of religion &c., 1753, *see* ANDERSON (G.)
Estius (Gulielmus), *chancellor of the Univ. of Douay.* Hist. véritable des martyrs de Gorcom en Hollande, Frères Mineurs, mis à mort 1572. App., le martyre de Guillaume de Gaude. Tr. s8º. Lovain. 1668
see BIBLE : LATIN. Biblia maxima, cum annot. G. E. &c., 19t, 1660.
Estonian, *see* ESTHONIA.
Estor (Johann Georg). Specimen I. de statu & orig. Landgrav. Hassiae mon. ined. inlustr. s4º. Giessae. 1729
Estrada (Genaro). Bibliografia de A. Nervo. 8º. Mexico. 1925
Estrades (*le cte.* **Godefroi d').** Correspond. authentique, 1637–60. Publ. p. la Soc. de l'Hist. de Fr. par A. de Saint-Léger & L. Lemaire. t1. 8º. 1924
Estrangin (Etienne), *see* BOUCHES-DU-RHÔNE : encyclop., t7, Le mouvement écon. : l'agric., par P. Masson & E. E., 1928.
Estrella. La Estrella de Sevilla [*sometimes attrib. to Lope de Vega*] ; publ. R. Foulché-Delbosc, *see* REVUE HISPAN., t48, 1920.
Estrix (Ægidius). Logistica probabilitatum &c., *see* MIGNE (J. P.), *ed.* Theol. cursus, t11, 1861.
Estwick (Nicolas), *see* BOLTON (R.) Foure last things &c., added sermon at B.'s funerall by N. E., 1639.
Etat. *Etat actuel de l'art &c. milit. à la Chine, 1773, *see* CHINE.
Etat (L') de la France, 5t, 1727, *see* FRANCE.
*Etat (L') du siége de Rome &c., 1707, *see* FRESCHOT (C.)
Etchegoyen (*le cte.* **Olivier d').**
The comedy of Poland. Tr. N. Bickley. 8º. [1927]

Etchings. On making &c. etchings, 1920, *see* HUBBARD (E. H.)
Eterei, Gli, *see* ACCADEMICI ETEREI.
Ethelwerd. Chronicorum lib. 4, *see* SAVILE [*Sir* H.] Rerum Angl. scr., 1596 ; 1601.
Etherege (*Sir* **George).**
The comical revenge ; or Love in a tub. [P2864]. s8º. *Tonson.* 1735
Dramatic works. Ed. w. intr. &c. by H. F. B. Brett-Smith. [Percy Repr., 6]. v1, 2. 8º. O. 1927
The man of mode. [P2864]. s8º. *Tonson.* 1735
She wou'd, if she cou'd, comedy. [P2864]. s8º. *Tonson.* 1735
see DOBRÉE (B.) Essays in biog., 1680–1726, 1925.
Etheridge (John Wesley). Life of Rev. A. Clarke. s8º. 1859
The life of the Rev. Thomas Coke. s8º. 1861
Etherton (*Lt.-Col.* **Percy Thomas).** China, the facts. 8º. 1927
In the heart of Asia. 8º. 1925
—— **& H. H. Tiltman.** The Pacific : a forecast. 8º. [1928]
Ethiopian. The bk. of the saints of the E. Church ; tr. by Sir E. A. W. Budge, 4v, 1928, *see* SYNAXARIUM.
***Etlich** Artickel gottes lob und d. heil. Röm. Reichs, 1521, *see* ARTICKEL.
Etna, *see* ÆTNA.
Eton College. The Eton Register. [Old Etonian Assoc.] p7, 1899–1909. s4º. *p.p.* Eton. 1922
*Eton school days ; by An old Etonian, 1865, *see* HEMYNG (S. B.)
Register, 1698–1752. Ed. w. biog. notes by R. A. Austen-Leigh. 8º. Eton. 1927
,, ,, 1753–90. Ed. &c. R. A. Austen-Leigh. 8º. Eton. 1921
***Etrennes** spirit. cont. l'Office lat. & franç., 1755, *see* OFFICIA.
Etrusca (Amarilli), *ps.*, *see* BANDETTINI LANDUCCI (T.)
Ettenhusius (J. B.) Epist. ad L. A. Rechenbergium ; examen J. W. Jaegeri, In B. Pufendorfii Jus divinum feciale. [*b. w.* Jäger (J. W.) Jus Dei, 1698]. s8º. Magdeburgi. 1698
Ettmayer (Carl). Ü. das Wesen d. Dialektbildung. erl. an d. Dialekten Frankr., *see* KAIS. AKAD. D. W. IN WIEN. Denkschr., B66, 1924.
Vorläuf. Ber. ü. Phonogramm-Aufnahmen d. Grödner Mundart, 1920, *see* KAIS. AKAD. D. W. ZU WIEN. Sitzber. B191, 1922.
Vulgärlatein, *see* GRUNDRISS d. indogerman. Spr.-u. Altertumskunde, Abt. 2, B1, 1916.
Ettrick (W.) The second Exodus ; or reflections on the prophecies of the last times. 2v. 8º. Sunderland. 1810
***Etude** diplomat. sur la Guerre de Crimée, 1852–56, 2t, 1878, *see* JOMINI (A. DE).
Etudes. *Etudes (Les) arméniennes en Europe, s. 14–19, 1895, *see* ZARBHANALEAN (K.)
*Études biograph. s. S. François de S., 1860, *see* FRANCIS, *St., de Sales.*
Etudes lexov., 2t, 1915–19, *see* LEXOVIENNES.
***Etwas** v. Liede Mosis, u. d. Liede des Lammes, d. i. : Alt. u. neuer Brüder-Gesang, 1753, *see* ZINZENDORF (N. L., *Graf* v.)
Etymologicum Gudianum, fasc. 2, 1920, *see* STEFANI (E. L. DE).
Eu (Gaston d'Orléans, *comte d'*), *see* ORLÉANS (GASTON D').
Eucharist. *A full view of the doctrines &c. rel. to E., 1688, *see* PATRICK (J.)
Euchel (Isak Abraham), *see* TEPHILOTH. Gebete d. hochdeut. u. poln. Juden ; übers. v. I. A. E., 1815.
Euchologion [EUCOLOGIO ; *see also* OFFICIA]. [The Anaphora of St. Basil, St. Gregory & St. Cyril, preceded by the Prayers of the evening & morning incense, & other prayers. *Ed.* by Raphael Tuki, bp. of Arsinoe. *Copt. & Arab.*] 4º. [Rome. 1736]
Eucologio Romano ; comp. &c. segun el brev. y misal romano por J. Sayol y Echevarria. 7ª ed. s8º. Barcelona. [1877]
Eucken (Rudolf). The problem of human life, f. Plato to pres. time. Tr. W. S. Hough & W. R. B. Gibson. rev. & enl. ed. 8º. 1914
Socialism. Tr. J. McCabe. 8º. [1921]
The spiritual outlook of Europe to-day. [Tr. W. R. V. B[rade]. Ed. Hakluyt Egerton]. s8º. 1922
Euclid. Element. lib. priores 6, item 11 & 12, ex vers. Lat. F. Commandini ; subl. aliis a R. Simson. 4º. Glasgow. 1756
Euclid in Greek. Book 1. With intr. & notes by Sir T. L. Heath. s8º. C. 1920
see THOMAS-STANFORD (C.) Early eds. of E.'s Elements, 1926.
Eucologio, *see* EUCHOLOGION.
Eudæmon-Joannes (Andreas), *Cydonius.* Ad actionem proditoriam E. Coqui, apologia pro H. Garneto. s8º. Coloniae Agrippinae. 1610

Eudocia, *Empress, wife of Valentinian III, see* GITTI (A.) Eudossia e Genserico, 1925.

Eudoxus, *of Cnidos, the mathematician, see* GISINGER (F.) Die Erdbeschreibung d. E. v. K., 1921.

Eugalenus (Severinus). De scorbuto morbo liber &c. ordine meliore in lucem prod. a J. Stubendorfio. s8°. L. 1624

Eugène, *prince of Savoy* [EUGÈNE FRANCIS, *prince &c.*]
see LIGNE (C. J., *pr.* DE). *Mém. de E., écrits par lui-même [*by L. not E.*], 1811 ; tr., 1811.
„ SAUTAI (M.) Une opération milit. d'E. & de Marlborough, 1905.
„ VESME (A.) Sull' acquisto fatto da Carlo Eman. III, re di Sardegna, d. quadreria del Pr. E., 1887.

Eugene, *prince of Saxony, see* REBOUL (F.) Campagne de 1813 : les prélim., t2, Le commandement du Pr. Eugène, 1re période, De Posen à Berlin, 1912.

Eugene Francis, *prince of Savoy, count of Soissons, 1714–34, see* SFORZA (G.) Il pr. E. F. di Savoia e il suo fidanz. con Maria T. Cybo dssa di Massa, 1909.

Eugenics review (The). v2, 11–19. la8°. 1911–28

Eugénie, *empress consort of Napoleon III.* Cat. of Gobelins tapestry &c., prop. of E. &c. Sold by Christie, July 7, 1927. [*Illust.* P2873]. 8°. 1927
Cat. of pictures &c. Sold by Christie, July 1, 1927. [P2873]. 8°. 1927
see BAC (F.) Le mariage de l'Imp. E., 1928.
„ FILON (P. M. A.) Souv. sur l'Imp. E., 5e éd., 1920.
„ FLEURY (*cte.* M.) Mems. of the Emp. E., 2v, 1920.
„ SOISSONS (*Count* DE). True story of E., 1921.

Eugenikos (Markos), *abp. of Ephesus.* [MARK, *of Ephesus*]. Doc. rel. au Concile de Florence : textes éd. & tr. par L. Petit, 1, La quest. du purgatoire à Ferrare, 2, Œuvres anticoncil. de M. d'E., *see* GRAFFIN (R.) & F. NAU. Patr. orient., t15, 17, 1923.

Eugenius III, *pope, see* JOHN, *of Salisbury.* Hist. pontif. quae supersunt, ed. R. L. Poole, 1927.

Eugenius II (III), *bp. of Toledo, see* LORENZANA Y BUITRON (F. A.) SS. PP. Toletan. opera &c., t1, 1782.

Eulalia, *Infanta of Spain.*
Courts & countries after the War. 8°. [1925]

Eule (Rob.), *see* PISTORIUS (F.), *ps.*

Eulenberg (Herbert). Letzte Bilder. 8°. 1920
Schattenbilder. 73.–82. Aufl. s8°. 1923

Eulenburg (Franz). Neue Grundlagen d. Handelspolitik, T1, Deutschland, T2, Ausland. Hrsg. v. F. E. [V. f. Sozialpol., B171i, ii]. 2T. 8°. München. 1925
see UNTERSUCHUNGEN üb. Preisbildung, Abt. C., Kosten d. Lebenshaltung ; hrsg. v. F. E., 1915–20.

Eulenburg-Hertefeld (Philipp, *Fürst* zu). Aus 50 Jahren. Erinnerungen, &c. [Hrsg. J. Haller]. la8°. 1923
see HALLER (J.) Aus d. Leben P. zu E.-H., 1924.

Eulenspiegel (Tyll). Master Tyll Owlglass, h. marvellous adv[s]. &c. Tr. K. R. H. Mackenzie. s8°. [1923]
Der wiedererstandene Eulenspiegel. s8°. St. 1839

Euler (Leonhard). Opera omnia. Sub auspiciis Soc. Scientiarum Nat. Helveticae edenda curaverunt F. Rudio, A. Krazer, P. Stäckel &c. ser. 1, Opera math., v2, 3, 6–8, 12–14, 15, 17, 18. ser. 2, Opera mechanica & astron., v14. ser. 3, Opera physica—Misc.—Epistolae, v1. 4°. L. 1914–27
s1, v2, 3, Comment. arithmeticae ; ed. F. Rudio.
6, Comment. algebraicae ad theoriam aequationum pertin. ; ed. F. Rudio, A. Krazer &c.
7, Comment. algebraicae ad theoriam combin. & probabil. pertin. ; ed. L. G. Du Pasquier.
8, Intr. in analysin infinitorum ; ed. A. Krazer & F. Rudio, t1.
12, 13, Institutiones calculi integralis ; ed. F. Engel & L. Schlesinger, v2, 3.
14, 15, Comment. analyticae ad theoriam serierum infinitarum pertin. ; ed. C. Boehm & G. Faber, v1, 2.
17, 18, Comment. analyticæ ad theoriam integralium pertin. ; ed. A. Gutzmer & A. Liapounoff, 2v.
s2, v14, Neue Grundsätze d. Artillerie aus d. Engl. d. B. Robins ; hrsg. F. R. Scherrer.
s3, v1, Comment. physicae ad physicam gen. & ad theoriam soni pertin. ; ed. E. Bernoulli, F. Rudio &c.
L. E.'s u. J. H. Lamberts Briefwechsel [1758–72] ; hrsg. K. Bopp, *see* KÖN.-PREUSS. AKAD. Abhdln., Phys.-math. Kl., 1924.

***Eulogies** on J. C. Calhoun &c., 1853, *see* FOSTER (T.) & G. COCHRAN, *edd.*

Eulogius, *Saint, of Toledo, see* LORENZANA Y BUITRON (F. A.) SS. PP. Toletan. opera, t2, 1785.

Eumorfopoulos (George). The G. E. coll. Catalogue of the Chinese, Corean & Persian pottery & porcelain. By R. L. Hobson. 6v. fol. [1925–28]
The G. E. coll. Cat. of the Chinese, Corean & Siamese paintings. By L. Binyon. fol. [1928]
„ „ Cat. of the Chinese frescoes. By L. Binyon. fol. [1927]

Eunapius. Βίοι φιλοσόφων καὶ σοφιστῶν [Eunapius de vitis philosoph. & sophist. Gr. & Lat. ed. interprete H. Junio.] [2p *in* 1v.] s8°. Antverpiae. 1568
see PHILOSTRATUS. P. & E. : the lives of the sophists ; [text], w. Eng. tr. by W. C. Wright, 1922.

Euonymus, *Philiatrus, ps., see* GESNER (C.)

Euphemia, *brig, see* HAWAII. In Admiralty ; foreclosure of hypothecation on Brit. brig E., 1845.

Eupistinus (Germanus Philalethes), *ps., see* BRIAS (CHARLES DE).

Eurasia Septentrionalis Antiqua. Réd. au nom de la Soc. Finland. d'Arch. par U. T. Sirelius. &c. [v]2. la8°. Helsinki. 1926
see TALLGREN (A. M.) La Pontide préscyth., 1926. [2.]

Euripides.

Fabulae. Rec. &c. G. Murray. t3. s8°. O. 1913
3, Helena, Phoenissae, Orestes, Bacchae, Iphigenia Aulidensis, Rhesus.
Hecuba, Orestes et Phoenissae cum variis lect. &c. S. Musgravii. 8°. Oxonii. 1809

TRANSLATIONS.
Alcestis. Tr. into Eng. verse, w. notes by G. Murray. [repr.] s8°. [1924]
Bacchanals, *see* ÆSCHYLUS. Agamemnon &c. ; tr. H. H. Milman, 1865.
Bacchae. Tr. into Eng. rhyming verse by G. Murray. 8°. [1904]
Die Bakchen. Übers. U. v. Wilamowitz-Moellendorff. [Griech. Tragödien, 13]. s8°. 1923
E., texte établi & tr. par L. Parmentier & H. Gregoire. [Coll. des univ. de Fr.] t1–4, [t2, tr. L. Meridier]. 8°. 1923–27
1, Le Cyclope—Alceste—Médée—Les Héraclides.
2, Hippolyte—Andromaque—Hécube.
3, Heracles — Les suppliantes—Ion.
4, Les Troyennes—Iphigénie en Tauride — Électre.
Feniciaensche ; verduitscht door J. v. Vondel (1668), *see* VONDEL (J. VAN DEN). Werken, d28, *n.d.*
Hippolytus. Tr. into Eng. rhyming verse by G. Murray. 3rd ed. 8°. [1904]

TRANSLATIONS [*continued*].
Ifigenie in Tauren (1666), *see* VONDEL (J. VAN DEN). Werken, d27, *n.d.*
Tragedies. Lit. tr. w. notes by T. A. Buckley. 2v. s8°. *Bohn.* 1854–58
Tragoediae. Latinè soluta orat. redd. &c. e praelect. Ph. Melanthonis. Cum praef. G. Xylandri. s8°. Basileæ. [1558]

REFERENCES.
see ÆSCHYLUS. Tragoediæ selectæ Æschyli, Sophoclis, E. &c., 1567.
„ APPLETON (R. B.) E. the idealist, 1927.
„ DINDORF (C. W.) Poet. scenic. Graec. fabulae &c., ed. 5[a], 1869.
„ KLOTSCHE (E. H.) Supernatural in tragedies of E., 1918.
„ LAGERCRANTZ (O.) E. Hippolytus, 1922.
„ LESKY (A.) Alkestis, 1925.
„ LUCAS (F. L.) E. & h influence, 1924.
„ MURRAY (G. G. A.) Hamlet & Orestes, 1914.
„ SCHMITT (J.) Freiwilliger Opfertod bei E., 1921.
„ STEIGER (H.) E., s. Dichtung u. s. Persönlichkeit, 1912.
„ TUDEER (L. O. TH.) Remarks on the letters of E., 1921.
„ WILAMOWITZ-MÖLLENDORFF (U. v.) Gr. Tragoedien, B4, Die Bakchen, 1923.

Europa Year Book. 1926–28. Ed. M. Farbman, R. Muir & H. F. Spender. 8°. [1926–28]

Europaisch [EUROPAISCHE]. Europ. (Der) Krieg in aktenmässiger Darstellung. Hrsg. F. Purlitz. [Deutscher Geschichtskalender, 1915–18]. B2–9 [B4–9 *are divided into* 2 Hälften *pagin. contin.*] 8°. L. [1915–19]
Grosse (Die) Politik d. europ. Kabinette, 1871–1924, 1922–26, *see* GROSSE.
Zur europ. Politik, B1–5, 1919, *see* SCHWERTFEGER (B.), *ed.*

Europäische Zentralkomitee d. Indischen Nationalisten, *see* FREIHEITSKAMPF (DER) d. ind. Nat., 1906–17 ; aus brit. Quellen zusammengest. u. hrsg. v. E. Z. d. I. N., 1918.

Europe.
The needs of E. : its economic reconstr. Rep. of Internat. Econ. Conf. called by the Fight the Famine Council, Oct. 1920. Addresses by Lord Parmoor, &c. 8°. 1921
Picturesque E. [*By var. a.* T. G. Bonney &c.] 5v. 4°. *Cassell.* 1881–86
*Present (The) state of E., 1688–1712, *see* PRESENT STATE OF E.
*Present (The) state of E., 3rd ed. 1752, *see* CAMPBELL (J.)
Revue polit. de l'Europe en 1825, 3e éd., 1825, *see* BOURGIGNON D'HERBIGNY (P. F. X.)

Europe (L') nouvelle. 5e année (1922). sfol. 1922

European. *Summary acc. & milit. character of the diff. Europ. armies engaged in the late war &c. Tr. f. the French. 8°. 1803

European magazine (The) &c. List of plates of first 54 v. cont. in v54. 8°. 1808

Eusebius, *Pamphili, bp. of Caesarea in Palestine.*
Werke. [Die griech. christl. Schriftsteller d. ersten 3 Jhdte.] B7ii. la8°. L. 1926
7, Die Chronik d. Hieronymus; hrsg. R. Helm, T2, Lesarten d. Hss. u. quellenkrit. Apparat z. Chronik.
Chronicon bipartitum. Nunc prim. ex Armen. in Lat. conversum, adnot. auct., Graecis frag. exorn. [*With Arm. text*]. Op. J. B. Aucher. 2p. 4°. Venetiis. 1818
Contra Hieroclem & Marcellum lib. Ed. T. Gaisford. [*Gr. & Lat.*] 8°. Oxon. 1852
Eusebii, Ruffini, Socratis, Theodoriti, Sozomeni, Theodori, Evagrii et Dorothei Eccl. hist. Per J. J. Grynæum illust., explicata &c., Chronographia &c. exornata. fol. Basileæ. 1570
Evangelicae praeparationis libr. xv. [*In Greek. Ed.* R. Estienne *the elder*]. fol. Lutetiae. 1544
Thesaurus temporum. Eusebii Chronicorum canonum omnimodae hist. libri 2, interprete Hieronymo. Item auctores continuantes. Eusebii utriusque partis Chronicorum canonum reliquae Graecae, ed. opera &c. J. J. Scaligeri. Ejusdem J. J. S. notae & castigationes & Isagogicorum chronologiae canonum libri 3. [5 *pagin.*] fol. Lugduni Batav. 1606
„ „ ed. altera in qua J. Scaligeri notae emendatæ. [5p in 1v]. fol. Amstelodami. 1658
TRANSLATIONS.
The ancient eccl. hist. of the first 600 yeares wr. by Eusebius, Socrates & Evagrius. Annexed, Dorotheus bishop of Tyrus, of the lives of the Prophets, Apostles &c. Tr. by M. Hanmer. Chronographie by the sayd translator. [*Tp. damaged*]. fol. 1607
The hist. of the Church by E., Socrates & Evagrius. Made Eng. f. ed. of Valesius 1659 &c. [*incl.* Valesius's annot.] Also the life of Constantine by Eusebius; Constantine's oration to the convention of saints & Eusebius's speech in praise of Constantine. 2nd ed. fol. 1709
The eccl. hist. of Eusebius, Socrates, Sozomen & Theodorit. Tr. & abridg. f. originals, w. acc. of lives &c., by Mr. Parker. 3rd ed. rev. 4°. 1729
Added, an abridg[t]. of the Hist. of Evagrius.
[Hist. of the Church. Tr. into Armenian by A. V. Djarean]. 8°. i Venetik. 1877
Eccles. hist. With Eng. tr. by K. Lake. [Loeb Class. Lib.] v1. s8°. 1926
Della prepar. evang. s8°. Venetia. 1550
The proof of the Gospel being the Demonstratio Evang. of E. [Tr., w. intr. & notes] by W. J. Ferrar. 2v. s8°. 1920
The Theophania. Syriac version; ed. S. Lee. [Soc. for the Publ. of Or. Textes]. la8°. 1842
see BAUR (F. C.) Comparatur E. cum Herodoto, 1834.
„ CRUM (W. E.) E. & Coptic Church hist[s]., 1902.
„ HELM (R.) E.'s Chronik u. i. Tabellenform, 1923.
„ KIMMEL (E. J.) De Rufino E. interpret. lib. 2, 1838.
„ STOLTZE (J. G.) Diatribe [& Diatr. altera] de E. P., 1689.

Eustace, *St. & Martyr.* Das altfranz. E. leben (l'Estoire d'E.); [hrsg.] A. C. Ott, *see* ROMAN. FORSCHUNGEN, B32, 1913.
3 versions inéd. de la Vie de St. E. en vers franç.; *ed.* H. Petersen, *see* ROMANIA, t48, 51, 52, 1922–26.

Eustace (John Chetwode). Classical tour thr. Italy, 1802. 3rd ed., rev. & enl. 4v. 8°. 1815

Eustathius, *Saint, bp. of (1) Beroea, (2) Antioch* [E. ANTIOCHENUS].
see BURN (A. E.) S. E. of Antioch, 1926.
„ SELLERS (R. V.) E. of Antioch, 1928.

Eustathius, *abp. of Thessalonica, see* DIONYSIUS, *Periegetes.* Orbis descr. cum scholis & E., 1697.

Eustratiades (Sophronios), *form. abp. of Leontopolis.*
see ATHOS. Cat. of Greek MSS. in lib. of the Laura on Mt. A.; by Spyridon, monk & S. E., 1925.
„ —— Cat. of Greek MSS. in lib. of the monastery of Vatopedi on Mt. A.; by S. E. &c., 1924.

Eustratius, *Presbyter.* De statu animarum post mortem &c.; [tr. L. Allacci], *see* MIGNE (J. P.), *ed.* Theol. cursus, t18, 1862.

Eutaxia. *Eutaxia, or the Presbyterian liturgies. By a minister of the Pr. Ch. s8°. N.Y. 1855

Euthalius, *bp. of Sulca.*
see CONYBEARE (F. C.) On cod. Pamphili & date of E., 1895.
„ MEIER (G.) Vita S. Pauli [*foll[d]. by* Euthalii de temp. praedic. S. Pauli &c. *Gr. & Lat.*], 1556.

Euthymius I, *patriarch of Constantinople, d. 917.* Homélies [*Grec. & Lat.*]; préc. d'une intr. sur la vie &c. de E., & de s. oraison funèbre par Aréthas de Césarée, *see* MARY, *the Virgin.* Homélies mariales byz.; ed. &c. M. Jugie, 1922.
2 homélies sur la conception de Ste. Anne [*Gr. & Lat.*], *see* MARY, *the Virgin.* Homélies mariales byz.; ed. &c. M. Jugie, p2, 1926.

Euthymius, *Zigabenus.* Comm. in Psalmos, *see* THEOPHYLACTUS, *abp. of Achreda.* Opera, t4, 1763.
Ismaeliticæ sectae dogm. elenchus. *Gr. & Lat., see* SYLBURGIUS (F.) Saracenica, 1595.
see WOLF (J. C.) Hist. Bogomilorum, ex Panoplia dogm. E. Z. &c., 1712.

Eutychius, *patriarch of Alexandria* [E. ALEXANDRINUS; SA'ĪD IBN AL-BAṬRĪK], *see* YAḤYA IBN SA'ĪD IBN AL-BAṬRĪK. Hist., cont. de Sa'īd-ibn-Bitriq [*i.e.* E.]; éd. & tr. I. Kratchkovsky &c., 1924.

Eutychius, *Saint & martyr, see* ASSEMANUS (J. S.) De Bonifacio ac Redempto: deque Eutychio, &c., 1745.

Euxine. The E. or Black Sea [Admiralty chart], 1853, *see* ADMIRALTY.

Evagrius, *Monachus.* Altercatio legis inter Simonem Judaeum & Theophilum Christ.; rec. E. Bratke, *see* SCRIPTORES eccl. minores, fasc. 1, 1904.

Evagrius, *Ponticus.* E. P. [*Syriac text & German tr., w Greek tr. of* De octo vitiosis cogitationibus]; v. W. Frankenburg, 1912, *see* KÖNIGL. GESELLS. D. WISS. ZU GÖTT. Abhlgn., N.F. 13, 1914.
[Life & Works. *In Armenian* by P. V. Sarkisean]. 8°. Venetik. 1907
see BOUSSET (W.) Apophthegmata (Euagriosstudien), 1923.
„ †MIGNE (J. P.), *ed.*, Pat. graeca, t49.

Evagrius, *Scholasticus.* Eccl. hist.; tr. M. Hanmer, *see* EUSEBIUS, *Pamphili.* Anc. eccl. histories &c., 1607.
see EUSEBIUS. Eccl. hist. of E. &c.; tr.: added, abridgt. of Hist. of E., 3rd ed. rev., 1729.

***Evangelia.** Quae Dominicis &c. leguntur heroico carmine reddita, 1554, *see* AEMILIUS (G.)

Evangelical Alliance. Jubilee of the E. A. Proc. of 10th Internat. Conf., London, 1896. Ed. A. J. Arnold. 8°. 1897
The relig. cond. of Christendom. Papers, 7th Conf., Basle, 1879. Ed. J. M. Mitchell. 8°. 1880
„ „ 8th conf. in Copenhagen, 1884. Ed. L. B. White. 8°. 1885
7[e] Hauptversammlung d. Evangel. Allianz gehalten in Basel, Aug.–Sept. 1879. Berichte u. Reden. Hrsg. C. J. Riggenbach. B1. 8°. Basel. 1879

Evangelical Free Churches of England. The Free Churches & the Lambeth appeal. Rep. of a comm. [P2707]. la8°. [1921]

Evangelici. *Corpus juris Evangelic. eccl. &c., 2T, 1737–38, *see* CORPUS.

Evangelion. Getrewe, Christenl. u. nützl. warnūg &c. d. Evangelion zu predigenn &c., 1525, *see* GETREWE.

Evangelische. Urkundenbuch d. Evang. Union &c., 1853, *see* NITZSCH (C. I.)

Evangelisches Gesangbuch, 1855, *see* KNAPP (A.)

Evangelisches Missions-Magazin. Neue Folge, 1857–83, *see* MAGAZIN FÜR D. NEUESTE GESCH. D. EVANG. MISSIONS &c., 1816–67.

Evangelistarion. Εὐαγγελιστάριον. [*b. w.* Bible: Gospels. Εὐαγγέλιον, 1588]. la8°. Venetiis. 1588

Evans (A. E.) & Son, *printsellers.* Cat. of engrav. Brit. portraits &c. on sale. v2. 8°. *n.d.*

Evans (*Maj.* Alfred John), *R.A.F.* The escaping club. s8°. 1921

Evans (Arthur Humble). A fauna of the Tweed area. [A verteb. fauna of Scotl., by J. A. Harvie-Brown, v11]. 8°. E. 1911

Evans (*Sir* Arthur John).
The early Nilotic, Libyan & Egypt. rel. w. Minoan Crete. [Huxley Mem. lect. 1925]. la8°. 1925
Essays in Aegean archaeology. [*By var. wr.*] Pres. to Sir A. E. Ed. S. Casson. 8°. O. 1927
The palace of Knossos. Summary rep. of excav., 1900 [–05]. [*6 pagin.* Repr. f. Annual of the Brit. School at Athens, No. 6–11, 1899–1905]. 8°. 1900–[1905]
The palace of Minos &c. at Knosses. 2v *in* 3. la8°. 1921–28
"The ring of Nestor" & gold signet-rings & bead-seals f. Thisbê, Boeotia. [Repr. f. J. of Hellenic St[s]., 1925]. la8°. 1925

Evans (Benjamin Edward).
The story of Milton Malzor. 8°. [1925]

Evans (Caleb). *A letter to J. Wesley occ. by his Calm address to the American colonies. [P2595]. s8°. 1775

Evans (Caradoc). Taffy, a play of Welsh village life. s8°. [1923]

Evans (Catharine) & Sarah Cheevers. A brief hist. of the voyage of C. E. & S. Ch. to Malta. Added a short rel. f. G. Robinson of sufferings in journey to Jerusalem &c. [Ed. T. R.] s8°. 1715

Evans (Charles). Amer. bibliog. Chron. dict. of all bks., pamphlets & period. publ. pr. in U.S., 1639–1820, w. bibliog. & biog. notes. v9, 1793–94. 4º. *p.p.* Chicago. 1925

Evans (Daniel Silvan). Dict. of the Welsh language. Geiriadur Cymraeg. pl–2 [A–B, *in 1v. pagin. cont. no tp.*] la8º. Carmarthen. 1886–88

Evans (E. T.) Records of the 3rd Middlesex Rifle Volunteers & 2nd & 6th M. Admin. Battalions &c., 1794–1884. 8º. 1885

Evans (Edward), *printseller.* Cat. of coll. of engr. portraits on sale by E. E. 8º. [1836 ?]

Evans (*Capt.* **Edward Radcliffe Garth Russell).**
South with Scott. 8º. [1921]

Evans (Elida). The problem of the nervous child. Intr. by C. G. Jung. s8º. N.Y. 1920

Evans (Florence May Greir), *aft. wife of C. S. S. Higham.* The principal Secretary of State, 1558–1680. [Manchester Univ. Hist. ser., No. 43]. 8º. M'ter. 1923

Evans (George). The old snuff house of Fribourg & Treyer, Haymarket, 1720–1920. 8º. *p.p.* [1921]

Evans (*Sir* **George De Lacy).** On the designs of Russia. 8º. 1828

Evans (George Eyre).
Aberystwyth & its Court Leet. 4º. Aberystwyth. 1902

Evans (Howard Heber). St. Paul the author of the Acts & of the 3rd Gospel. 8º. 1884

Evans (Ifor Leslie). Agrarian revol. in Roumania. 8º. C. 1924
Econ. aspects of the Eastern q. Inaug. lect. 8º. [1925]

Evans (Illtyd Buller Pole), Mary R. H. Thomson, &c. Further investig. into wastage in export citrus fruits f. S. Africa. [P2820]. 8º. Cape Town. 1921

Evans (Ivor Hugh Norman).
Among primitive peoples in Borneo. 8º. 1922
Papers on the ethnology & archaeology of the Malay Peninsula. 8º. C. 1927
Studies in religion, folk-lore, & custom in Brit. North Borneo & the Malay Peninsula. 8º. C. 1923

Evans (Joan).
English jewellery, f. the 5th c. to 1800. 4º. [1921]
Life in mediaeval France. 8º. O. 1925
Magical jewels of the M. A. & Renaiss., partic. in Eng. 8º. O. 1922
see STUDER (P.) & J. EVANS. Anglo-Norman lapidaries, 1924.

Evans (John), *a boy, of Plymouth Dock, see* HEATON (J.) Extraordinary affliction &c. of a little boy [*i.e.* J. E.], 2nd ed., 1822.

Evans (John Gwenogvryn). Taliesin: or the critic [*i.e.* Sir J. Morris-Jones] criticised, *see* CYMMRODORION. Y Cymmrodor, v34, 1924.

Evans (John Thomas). The church plate of Gowerland, w. summary of church plate in diocese of St. David's. la8º. Stow-on-the-Wold. 1921

Evans (John William), *see* COLE (G. A. J.), J. W. E. &c. The Brit. Isles, 1917.

Evans (Lewis), *see* SHEPPARD (J. G.) & L. E. Notes on Thucydides, Bks. 1–3, n. ed., 1889.

Evans (Maria Millington, *Lady***).** Lustre pottery. 4º. [1920]

Evans (Powys) [*ps.* QUIZ].
88 cartoons. Pref. by R. Sickert. 4º. *Cayme Press.* 1926

Evans (Rachel). Home scenes: or Tavistock & its vicinity. 2nd ed. rev. & corr. s8º. Tavistock. 1875

Evans (Robert Wilson). A day in the Sanctuary: w. treatise on hymnology. s8º. 1843

Evans (*Mrs.* **Rosalie Caden).** Letters f. Mexico. Arr. w. comments by D. C. Pettus. 8º. [1926]

Evans (Sylvia Hope). The book of Nailsea Court. Foreword by C. E. Evans. s8º. Bristol. 1923

Evans (Walter Jenkin). Allitteratio latina, or, allit. in Lat. verse reduced to rule. 8º. 1921

Evans-Wentz (Walter Yeeling), *see* BARDO THÖDOL: Tibetan Bk. of the Dead, by W. Y. E.-W., 1927.

Evarts (Hal George). The yellow horde. s8º. [1921]

Evarts (William Maxwell). Arguments & speeches. Ed., w. intr. by S. Evarts. 3v. 8º. N.Y. 1919

Evatt (*Capt.* **J.),** *see* INDIA: MILIT. DEPT. Garhwâlis, comp. by J. E., 1924.

Evdokimov (Ivan). Север в истории русск. искусства. la8º. Вологда. 1921

Evelyn (John), *F.R.S.*
*Acetaria: a disc. of sallets. By J. E., F.R.S., a. of the Kalendarium. s8º. 1699
Diary & corr. Ed. W. Bray. n. ed. corr. 4v. s8º. *Bohn.* 1859
The early life & education of E. With comm. by H. M. Smith. [Oxford hist. &c. studies, v11]. 8º. O. 1920

Evelyn (John), *F.R.S.* [*continued*].
John Evelyn in Naples, 1645. Ed. H. M. Smith. s8º. O. 1914
Kalendarium hortense or the gardener's almanac. [*incl.* The garden, a poem, by A. Cowley], 8th ed. w. addits. s8º. 1691
Memories for my grand-son. Transcr. &c. by G. Keynes. s8º. *Nonesuch Pr.* 1926
Memoirs: diary & sel. of letters. Subj., priv. corr. betw. Charles I & Sir E. Nicholas & betw. Clarendon & Sir R. Browne. Ed. W. Bray. 2v. 4º. 1818
Silva: disc. of forest-trees &c. Added, Terra: disc. of earth. Notes by A Hunter, 4th ed., w. mem. 2v. 4º. York. 1812
see CRAIG (E. G.) Bks. & theatres: [J. E. & the theatre in Eng., France & Italy], 1925.

Evenepoel (Henri Jacques Edouard), *see* LAMBOTTE (P.) H. E., 1908.

Evening Post, The. Nº. 175. Sept. 23–26, 1710. [*b. w.* Post Man, 1709–11]. 4º. 1710

Eventful. These eventful years: the 20th cent. in the making as told by many of its makers. [Ed. F. H. Hooper; publ. Encyclop. Britannica Co.] 2v. 8º. [1924]

Everard (Edward Cape). Memoirs of an unfortunate son of Thespis. Wr. by himself. s8º. E. 1818

Everard (*Mrs.* **Frances).** A daughter of the sand. s8º. [1922]

Everatus (Joannes), *see* MOSCHUS (J.)

Everett (Edward), *see* FROTHINGHAM (P. R.) E. E., orator & statesman, 1925.

Everett (Helen), *see* LUBIN (I.) & H. E. Brit. coal dilemma, 1927.

Everett (James), *Wesleyan minister.* The polemic divine: or mem. of the life, writings &c. of Daniel Isaac. s8º. 1839
The test law of '35: 2 letters to F. A. West, w. letters in reply. [P2538]. s8º. 1851
Wesleyan methodism in Manchester & its vicinity. v1. [*No more publ.*] 8º. Manchester. 1827

Everett (Walter Goodnow).
Moral values: st. of the principles of conduct. 8º. 1920

Everett-Green (*Miss* **Evelyn).** Miss Anne Thrope. s8º. [1921]
Mistress of Lydgate priory. s8º. *n.d.*

Everitt (Alfred T.), *see* LILLEY (H. T.) & A. T. E. Portsmouth parish church, 1921.

Everitt (Nicholas).
British Secret Service during the Great War. 8º. [1920]

Evers (Edwin). Feldpostbriefe aus d. Osten; hrsg. E. E., *see* KAISER-WILHELM-DANK. Kriegsschr., H59, 1916.

Eversley (George John Shaw-Lefevre, *1st baron***) &** *Sir* **V. Chirol.** The Turkish Empire, 1288–1914, by Lord E.; & 1914–22, by Sir V. C. [2nd ed.] 8º. [1923]
„ „ 1288–1924. [3rd ed., contin. to 1924 by Sir V. C.] 8º. [1924]

Evertsz (N. J.)
Compendio de la gram. d. papiamento. s8º. Curazao. 1898

Every. Every-day ethics: addresses, Yale Univ., 1909, 1910, *see* YALE UNIVERSITY.
*Every man out of his humour, 1600, 1920, *see* JONSON (BEN).

Everyman. The play of Everyman. Based on old Eng. morality play. New version by H. v. Hofmannsthal. Set to blank verse by G. Sterling, in collab. w. R. Ordynski. s8º. San Francisco. 1917

Evoe, *ps., see* KNOX (E. G. V.)

Evolution. Evolution in the light of mod. knowledge. A collective work [*by* F. O. Bower, J. H. Jeans, H. Jeffreys &c.] 8º. 1925
The evolution of world-peace: essays ed. by F. S. Marvin, 1921, *see* MARVIN (F. S.)

Evrard, *l'Allemand, see* EBERHARDUS, *Alemannus.*

Evreinov (Grigory Aleksandrovich).
Автономія царства Польскаго. [P2450]. 8º. С.–П. 1906
Національные вопросы на инородческихъ окраинахъ Россіи. [P2450]. 8º. С.–П. 1908
Прошлое и настоящее значеніе русск. дворянства. la8º. С.–П. 1898
Реформа высшихъ государств. учрежденій Россіи и народное представительство. [P2446]. 8º. С.–П. 1905
Самобытность или отсталость? [P2446]. 8º. С.–П. 1905
Финляндскій вопросъ послѣ манифеста 14 Марта 1910. [P2451]. 8º. С.–П. 1910

Evreinov (Nikolai Nikoloevich).
La mort joyeuse: arlequinade. Tr. D. Roche. s8º. [1922]
Нестеров. s8º. П. 1922
Самое главное въ 4 дѣйствіяхъ. 8º. Ревель. [1922]

Evropeus (David Petrovich). Объ Угорскомъ народѣ, обитавшемъ въ средней и сѣверной Россіи &c. [P2416]. s4º. С.–П. 1874

Evroul, *St.* [EBRULPHUS]. Das altfranz. Ebrulfusleben: e. Dichtung aus d. 12. Jhdt.; v. F. Danne, *see* ROMAN. FORSCH., B32, 1913.

Ewald (Carl) [*ps.* SILVESTER (J.)]
Historier, gamle og nye. s8°. 1909

Ewald (Friedrich Christian).
Journal of miss. labours in Jerusalem, 1842–44. s8°. 1845

Ewald (Johannes), *Danish poet.* The death of Balder (1773); tr. G. Borrow, 1889, *see* BORROW (G.) Wks., v16, 1924.
see BRIX (H.) J. E.: en række krit. undersøgelser, 1913.

Ewald (Oscar). Nietzsches Lehre in i. Grundbegriffen. 8°. 1903

Ewart (*Col.* **E. A.),** *see* CABLE (BOYD), *ps.*

Ewart (Wilfrid). A journey in Ireland, 1921. Intr. by Earl of Winterton. s8°. 1922
Way of revelation. s8°. [1921]

Ewbank (Robert Benson). Indian co-operative studies. [*By var. a.*] [Univ. of Bombay, Econ. ser. 2]. Ed. R. B. E. Introd. by H. W. Wolff. 8°. O. 1920

Ewen, *The clan of, see* MACEWEN (R. S. T.) Clan E., 1904.

Ewers (Hanns Heinz). Alraune. Die Gesch. e. lebenden Wesens. s8°. München. 1919
Die Besessenen. Seltsame Gesch. s8°. München. 1925

Ewing (Alfred Cecil). Kant's treatment of causality. 8°. 1924

Ewing (Greville). A memorial on education for the ministry of the Gospel. s8°. Glasgow. 1808

Ewing (Guy). Hist. of Cowden. 8°. Tunbridge Wells. [1926]
Westmill: a Herts. parish. 8°. Tunbridge Wells. [1928]

Ewing (*Mrs.* **Juliana Horatia).**
Dandelion clocks & o. t. 8°. [1887]
A great emergency & o. t. 8°. 1892
Jackanapes. 8°. 1884
Melchior's dream & o. t. n. ed. 8°. 1886
We & the world. n. ed. [*b. w. h.* Great emergency, 1892]. 8°. 1890

Exact.
*Exact abridgment (An) of all the trials &c., 1690, *see* TRIALS.
*Exact coll. (An) or cat. of our Eng. wr. on the Old & New Test., 1663, *see* CROWE (W.)
*Exact relat. (An) of the persecut[s]. sustained by the Protest[s]. of Killmare, 1689, *see* ORPEN (R.)

Examen. *Ex. regul. Pilcianarum, &c., *n.d., see* PILCIUS (C.)

***Exameron** anglice, *see* ÆLFRIC, *abbot.*

Examination.
*Exam. of a book pr. by the Quakers, ent. Brief acc. of many persecutions &c., 1741, *see* HAYTER (T.), *bp.*
*Exam. (An) of Dr. Rutherforth's argument: clergy to subscribe to an establ. confess. &c., by a Clergyman of the Ch. of Eng., 1766, *see* DAWSON (B.)
*Exam. of the Brit. doctrine wh. subjects to capture a neutral trade &c., 1808, *see* MADISON (J.)

***Examinatorium** ü. die Dogmatik d. evang. Kirche &c., 1830, *see* GRÄFE (H.)

Examiner. *The free & impartial examiner: enq. into causes of pres. situation &c. [P2780]. 8°. 1745

Excerpta.
*Excerpta antiqua: or, coll. of orig. MSS., 1797, *see* CROFT (J.)
*Excerpta hist. & jurid. de nat. successionis in monarchiam H. 1700–1; *see* CORTREJUS (A.)

Exchequer. *Reports of cases in equity, argued &c. in Courts of Chancery & E. chiefly in r. of George I, 1734, *see* GILBERT (*Sir* G.)
see BARKLY (*Sir* H.) Remarks on the Liber Niger, 1890.

Excluded books of the New Test.; tr. J. B. Lightfoot &c., 1927, *see* APOCRYPHA.

Exegesis perspicua & ferme integra controversiae de Sacra Cœna. [*By J. Cureus? or E. Ruediger?*] 8°. [Genevae]. 1574
„ „ ....another issue. s4°. [Genevae?]. 1574

Exempla. Exempla of the Rabbis, 1924, *see* GASTER (M.)
*Magnum speculum exemplorum &c., 2t, 1605, *see* MAGNUM.

***Exercice** de retraite en faveur des enfans qui se disposent à faire leur première communion. [Prières *have sep. pagin.*] s8°. 1683

Exercitium. Exercit. super Pater Noster, 1908, *see* KRISTELLER (P.)
*Incipit exercitium latinitatis p. composita quorundam verborum in fabulis coll. familiarissimo sermone. [*fol. 1 recto cont[s]. pref. beg.* [C]redimus plerosque &c. b[8] *ends* Finis v̄borum deponentaliū &c.] s4°. *n.p. n.d.* [*15c.*]
16 leaves, viz. a, b in eights.

Exeter. Anglo Norman Custumal of E., w. facs. Ed. J. W. Schopp, w. intr. by J. W. S. & R. C. Easterling. [Hist. of Exeter Research Group, Monogr., No. 2]. la8°. 1925
Ordinale Exon. App. 3, Legenda Exon. Ed. J. N. Dalton. [Henry Bradshaw Soc., v63]. v3. 8°. 1926

Exhibition of anc. female court costume worn at court of Cromwell by Lady Cromwell & her daughters, 1654 &c. [Somerset Gallery]. 3rd ed. [P2590]. s8°. 1835

Exhibitions.
BRUSSELS.
see FIERENS-GEVAERT (H.) L'expos. van Eyck-Bouts à B. en 1920, 1921
CHICAGO.
Rapports publ. sous la dir. de C. Krantz. Congrès tenus à C. en 1893 [Rapport de M. L. de Chasseloup-Laubat. Min. du Commerce &c.] la8°. 1894
GENOVA.
La mostra coloniale di Genova 1914. [Min. d. Col.] 2[a] ed. 8°. 1914
LEIPZIG.
Cat. of Brit. section of Internat. E. of Book Industry & Graphic Arts. 8°. L. 1914
LIVRE ITALIEN, PARIS.
Expos. du livre ital., 1926. Cat. des mss., livres impr. &c. [Bibl. Nat. & Musée des Arts Décor.] 8°. 1926
LONDON [1851].
Dickinsons' pictures of the great E. of 1851. From originals by Nash, Haghe, & Roberts. [2v]. atlas fol. 1854
Royal Comm. for the E. of 1851: outline of its activities past & pres. [P2753]. 8°. 1924
LYON.
see LYON. L'art lyonnais: expos., cat., 1925.
MADRID [1892].
Las joyas de la Expós. Hist.-Europea de Madrid. 20 cuaderno [*in 1v*]. fol. 1893
NEW ZEALAND [1906–7].
see SPIELMANN (*Sir* I.) Brit. Govt. exhibit; comp. by S., 1908.
PARIS [1867].
see COSTA (J.) Instit. econ. para obreros: habit. de alquiler barato en la Expos. Univ. de P. en 1867, 1918.
PARIS [1900].
Amtl.-Katalog d. Ausstell. d. Deut. Reichs. s4°. [1900]
PARIS [1900] [*continued*].
Cat. de los expositores de España. 8°. 1900
Cat. gén. de la sect. russe. 8°. 1900
Section Belge. Cat. offic. &c. 8°. Brux. 1900
Suède. Cat. spéc. rédigé par H. Elmquist. s8°. [1900]
PARIS [1925].
Hist. des courses en France j. 1870: expos. mai, 1925, Hôtel Jean Charpentier. 8°. [1925]
Reports on pres. position &c. of the industrial arts as indic. at the Internat. Exhib. of Mod. Decor. & Indust. Arts, Paris, 1925. With an intr. survey. [Dept. of Overseas Trade]. 4°. [1927]
see also LIVRE ITAL. *above,* ROUMANIAN ART, 1925, *below.*
ROUMANIAN ART.
Expos. de l'art roumain organisée par Musée Nat. du Luxembourg au Musée du Jeu de Paume, à Paris, 1925. [*Intr by H. Focillon*]. 8°. 1925
ROYAL NAVAL EXHIBITION [*Chelsea,* 1891].
Official cat. & guide. 4th ed. s8°. [1891]
SAN FRANCISCO.
see RAYMOND (M. W.) *&c.* The archit. &c. of the Panama-Pacific Int. Expos., 1915.
TURIN.
see RISORGIMENTO. Cat. d. oggetti del R. ital. [p3], Doc., 1894.
VENICE.
see NEBBIA (U.) La 14[a] espos. d'arte a V., 1924, 1924.
WEMBLEY [1924].
see CANADIAN. Cat. of C. bks. (Eng. sect.), Brit. Emp. Exhib., W., 1924, 1924.
WORCESTERSHIRE [1882], *see* WORCESTERSHIRE EXHIB.

Exhortatio. *Supplex Exhortatio ad Carolum V &c., 1543, *see* CALVIN (J.)

***Exhortation** aux princes &c. du Conseil privé du Roy, *for Lat. tr., see* GALLIA. Ad Regis G. consiliarios exhort., 1561.

Eximeno (Antonio). Dell' origine & d. regole d. musica, colla storia del suo progresso &c. 4°. Roma. 1774

Exmoor. Echoes of E. Record of discussions &c. of the Men-of-Exmoor Club. 2nd ser. s8°. 1924

Exner (Felix), *see* CLAYTON (H. H.), *ed.* World weather records; coll. by F. E. &c., 1927.

Exner (Franz). Krieg u. Kriminalität in Österreich. Mit. Beitr. ü. d. Kriminalität d. Militärpersonen, v. G. Lelewer. [C.E. for Internat. Peace]. la8°. Wien. 1927

***Explanation** (An) of several of Mr. Hogarth's prints, 1783; 1785, *see* HOGARTH (W.)

Explîcaçaõ. A explîcaçaõ da doutrina Christaã segundo a ordem do catechismo, pelos Padres Miss. de Trangambar. s8°. Trangambar. 1762

Explication. Explic. hist. des princ. médailles &c., *see* LE CLERC (J.) Hist. des Prov.-Unies des Pays Bas, t1, 1723.

Exploradores. Exploradores y conquistadores de Indias; seleccion, *see* DANTIN CERECEDA (J.), *ed.*

Explosives. The rise & progress of the Brit. expl. industry, 1909, *see* BRITISH.

***Exposé** hist. de l'état de l'église réformée des P.-B., 1855, *see* PAYS-BAS.

Exposición Valdés Leal &c., *see* VALDÉS LEAL (J. DE).

Exposition. *Briève & fidèle expos. de l'orig. de la doct. &c. de l'Eglise de l'Unité des Frères, 1758, *see* BOHEMIA.
*Expos. historique de toutes les hérésies &c. que l'église a condamnées sur les matières de la grace & du libre arbitre. s8°. Amsterdam. 1716
Expos. rétrospect. des maréchaux de Fr., 1922, *see* PALAIS DE LA LÉGION D'HONNEUR.
Exposition des Beaux-Arts. Cat. illust. du Salon, 1882–96, *see* SALON.
Expositor (The). Ser. 8, v19–26; ser. 9, v1–4 (Jan. 1920–Dec. 1925). [*No more publ.*] 8°. 1920–25
Expositor's yearbook (The). Survey of Biblical & theolog. lit. of 1925. Ed. J. Moffatt, w. assist. of G. H. Box, W. Fulton &c. 8°. [1926]
Exquemelin (Alex. Olivier). Buccaneers of America. Tr. of 1684–85. Rev. & ed. by W. S. Stallybrass. Intr. essay by A. Lang. [Broadway Trans.] 8°. [1923]
***Extractum** ex harmonia confess. oblatum eccl. reform., 1671, *see* DURY (J.)
Extractus. Extractus benignarum normalium resolutionum in publico-eccl. ad 1844 editarum, ordine materiarum digestus. [*Lat. & Hungarian*]. ed. 4ª. 8°. Tirnaviae. 1846
*Extractus brevis & verus quo demonstr. a cathol. praedicantium è regno Hung. proscriptio &c., 1721, *see* KELLIO (MIKLOS).
Exul, *ps.*
*Twilight & candle-shades. [*Verses & menus*]. s8°. 1888
Exustio. *Exustionis antichristianorum decretalium acta. [*Marginal design on tp. &c.*] s4°. *n.p. n.d.* [1521]
Eychler (Michael). Warnung u. Trost-Spiegel &c. [*expos. of the parable of the rich man & Lazarus*]. [*b. w.* Schütz (J.) Serpens antiquus, 1580]. s8°. Ursel. 1581
Eyck (Hubert van).
see CONWAY (*Sir* W. M.) The v. E.'s & th. followers, 1921.
„ DVOŘÁK (M.) Rätsel d. Kunst d. Brüder van Eyck, 1925.
„ FIERENS-GEVAERT (H.) L'expos. van E.-Bouts &c., 1921.
„ FRIEDLÄNDER (M. J.) Altniederl. Malerei, B1, Die Van E. &c., 1924.
Eyck (Jan van).
see CONWAY (*Sir* W. M.) The v. E.'s & th. followers, 1921.
„ DVOŘÁK (M.) Rätsel d. Kunst d. Brüder van Eyck, 1925.
„ FIERENS-GEVAERT (H.) L'expos. v. E.-Bouts &c. 1921.
„ FRIEDLÄNDER (M. J.) Altniederl. Malerei, B1, Die Van E. &c., 1924.
Eyck (P. N. van). De getooide doolhof. [Nederl. Bibl. 117]. 2. verm. dr. s8°. [A.] *n.d.*
Inkeer. la8°. [Arnhem]. 1922
Eye-Witness, *ps.* *True & authentick narrative of action, 1745, *see* TRUE.
Eylert (Rulemann Friedrich). The relig. life & opinions of Frederick William III, k. of Prussia. Tr. J. Birch. 8°. 1844
Eyles (Margaret Leonora). Captivity. s8°. 1922
Hidden lives. s8°. 1922
The woman in the little house. Foreword by N. March. s8°. 1922
Women's problems of to-day. s8°. [1926]
Eymerich (Nicolas) [EYMERICUS (NICOLAUS)]. Directorium Inquisitorum, cum scholis F. Pegnae [*w. sep. pagin.*] [*Foll. by* Literae apostol. div. Rom. pontificum pro officio Inquisitionis &c. (*sep. tp.* 1579 *& pagin.*), F. Pegnae Disput. de auctoritate &c. Inquis. contra haereticam pravitatem]. fol. Romae. 1578
Manual de inquisidores. Tr. por J. Marchena. s8°. Mompeller. 1821
see TOLEDO. Les canons des conciles de T.: propos. d'un livre [*by* N. E.], intit. Directorium Inquisit. &c., 1615.
Eyraud (Michel). *L'affaire Gouffé. [*Murder of Gouffé by M. E. & Gabrielle Bompard*, 1890. *no tp.* P2826]. s8°. [Sceaux.] *n.d.*
Eyre. Roll of Justices in Eyre at Bedford, 1202, 1227, 1240; [ed.] G. H. Fowler, *see* BEDFORDSHIRE HIST. REC. SOC. Publ^s., v1, 3, 9, 1913–25.
Eyre (Edward John), *see* †HUME (A. H.) Life of E. J. E., 1867.
Eyre (John).
The true convert. [P2467]. s8°. Northampton. [1823]
Eyre (*Sir* Vincent).
Lays of a knight-errant in many lands. s8°. 1874
Military oper. at Cabul, Jan. 1842 &c. 5th ed. s8°. 1843
Eyre (William) *of Salisbury, see* BAXTER (R.) Apology; added, an admonition of W. E., 1654.
Eyring (Ludwig Salomo). Vita Sebastiani de Rotenhan. Praes. L. S. E., resp. W. L. Graefenhahn. [P598]. s4°. Jenae. [1739]
Eysengrein, *see* EISENGREIN.
Eysinga (W. J. M. van). Evolution du droit fluvial internat., 1815–1919. [P2403]. 8°. Leyde. [1920]
Eznik, *of Kolb* [EZNAK], *bp. of Bagrevand.* [Against the sects, *in Armenian. a. c. b. w.* Gregory IV, *cath. of Arm.* Letters, 1865]. s8°. i Venetik. 1275 [=1826]
Wider d. Sekten. Übers. m. Einl. &c. v. J. M. Schmid. [Bibl. d. alt. arm. Lit., B1. P2811]. 8°. Wien. 1900
see MARIÈS (L.) Le De Deo d'E. de K., "Contre les sectes": ét. de crit., 1924.
Ezquerra del Bayo (Joaquin).
La Duquesa de Alba y Goya. la8°. 1928
see ALBA (J. S. F., *d.* DE). Cat.; por J. E. del B., 1924.
Ezra [*see also* BIBLE: EZRA]. Die Apokalypsen d. Esra u. d. Baruch in deut. gestalt. Hrsg. B. Violet. [Esra-Apok., T2. Griech. Schriftst. d. 1^{en} 3 Jhdte., B32]. 8°. L. 1924
see HOWORTH (H. H.) Unconvent. views, 2, 1901.
Ezzelini, *House of, see* VERCI (G. B.) Storia degli Ecelini, 3v, 1841.

F

F. (J.) *Memoir of T. Green, of Ipswich, 1825, *see* FORD (J.)
F. (J.) *Vindic. of Mr. Wesley's last Minutes &c. [*signed* J. F.], 1771, *see* FLETCHER (J. W.)
F. (J. S.) *Demonologia; or, natural knowledge revealed, 1827; 1831, *see* FORSYTH (J. S.)
F. (*Mr.* L. M. D. L.) *Mém^s. &c. sur les princ. évènemens du r. de Louis XIV, 1716, *see* LA FARE (C. A., *marq.* DE).
F. (R.) *a. of Missale Rom. vindic., see* BREVINT (D.) Saul & Samuel at Endor &c., also a brief acc. of R. F. h. Missale vindic. &c., 1674.
F. (T.) *Reply of T. F. in defence of h. Suppl. to discussion &c., 1614, *see* FITZHERBERT (T.)
Fabbri (Ettore). Ada Negri. [P2585]. s8°. Firenze. [1921 ?]
Alfredo Panzini. [P2600]. s8°. Firenze. *n.d.*
Pirandello. [P2585]. s8°. Firenze. [1921 ?]
Fabeln. Noch fünfzig F. für Kinder, 1837 ?, *see* HEY (W.)
Faber (Basilius), *Soranus.* Christl. &c. vnterrichtungen v. d. letzten hendeln d. Welt. [*Foll^d. by* Tractete lein v. d. Seelen d. verstorbenen &c. *b. w.* Mechler (Æ.) Catechismus &c., 1574]. s8°. L. [1582]
Thesaurus erudit. scholast. Post Buchneri, Cellarii, Graevii, operas & adnot., iterum emend. &c. lab. A. Stübelii. fol. Lipsiae. 1717
see MAGDEBURG CENTURIES. Centuriæ Magd. [*by B. F. & others*], 4v, 1757–65.
Faber (Franciscus), *Silesius, see* KOECKRIZ (F.), *called Faber.*
Faber (George Stanley). Sermons. 2v. 8°. 1816
see LE PAPPE DE TREVERN (J. F. M.) An ans. to C. S.'s Difficulties of Romanism; tr., 1828.
Faber (Harald). Caius G. Cibber, 1630–1700. With acc. of the old Danish Church in London. 4°. O. 1926
Danske og Norske i London og deres Kirker. 4°. København. 1915
Faber (Jacobus), *Stapulensis, see* LE FÈVRE (J.), *d'Étaples.*
Faber (Joannes), *bp. of Vienna* [†FABRI (J.); HEIGERLIN (J.)]
Ad sereniss. princ. Ferdinandum Archiducem Austriæ, Muscovit. juxta mare glaciale religio. s4°. [Basileæ, *Jo. Bebelius*]. 1526
Christenl. beweisung über sechs Artickel, des unchristl. U. Zwinglins zů Zürich über antwurt offentl. in d. pfarrkirchen vor den verordnetē vierer Bischoffen &c. s4°. [Tübingen, *U. Morhart.* 1526]
Ein warlich underrichtung wie es zu Zürch by dē zwinglin uff den 29. Ja. nest verschinē ergangen sey. s4°. [Leipzig ?. 1523 ?]
see KETTNER (C. E.) De Joh. F. vita & scriptis, 1737.
„ VANNIUS (V.) De missa integra hist. &c., adv. librum I. Fabri &c., 2t, 1563.
Faber (Johann Gottlieb). Compendii theolog. dogmat. loci 5 priores. s8°. Stuttg. 1780
De Leone III, pontif. Rom. [P436]. s4°. Tubingae. [1748]

Fabert (*le maréchal* **Abraham de**), *see* BARRE (J.) Vie de F., 2t, 1752.
Fabi (Giuseppe). Pro Honorio & sede apost. contra C. J. de Hefele. [P2691]. 8°. Florentiae. 1870
Fabian Society [*Publications*].
see LASKI (H. J.) Karl Marx, 1921.
,, ROBSON (W. A.) Compulsory voting, 1924.
,, WOOLF (L. S.) Internat. government, 1923.
Fabian (Walter), *see* LENZ (K.) & W. F. Die Friedensbewegung, 1922.
Fables. *Forensic fables, 1926, *see* MATHEW (T.)
Sel. fables, w. cuts by T. & J. Bewick, 1822, *see* BEWICK (T. & J.)
Fabre (Augustin).
The life of J. H. Fabre. Tr. B. Miall. 8°. [1922]
Fabre (Ferdinand). Les Courbezon. 2t. s8°. 1921
Fabre (Jean). Sur la vie & la mort de Mme. Henriette Anne Stuart, dsse. D'Orléans. s8°. 1912
Fabre (Jean Henri).
Le livre des champs. Entretiens de l'oncle Paul. s8°. 1921
Le monde merveilleux des insectes. 4°. 1921
La plante. Causeries s. la botanique. 10e éd. s8°. 1923
Souvenirs entomolog. éd. déf. illust. s2–10. la8°. 1920–23
La terre. Lects. &c. sur la physique du globe. 12e éd. s8°. 1924
TRANSLATIONS.
Animal life in field & garden. Tr. F. C. Constable & K. Murray. 8°. [1926]
Farm friends & foes. Tr. B. Miall. 8°. [1925]
The glow-worm & o. beetles. Tr. A. Teixeira de Mattos. 8°. [1919]
TRANSLATIONS [*continued*].
The heavens. Tr. E. E. Fournier d'Albe. 8°. [1924]
The story book of birds & beasts. 8°. [1919]
The story book of science. 8°. [1919]
This earth of ours. Tr. P. F. Bicknell. 8°. 1923
The wonder book of plant life. Tr. B. Miall. 8°. [1924]
The wonders of instinct. Tr. A. T. de Mattos & B. Miall. 8°. [1920]
see FABRE (A.) Life of J. H. F.; tr., 1922.
,, LEGROS (G. V.) Vie de J. H. F., 2e éd., 1919; suivie du répertoire analyt. des Souvs. entomolog., 1924.
Fabre (Lucien). Connaissance de la déesse. Avant-propos de P. Valery. s8°. 1924
Rabevel ou le mal des ardents. 13e éd. [3t]. s8°. [1923]
Le Tarramagnou. 7e ed. s8°. [1925]
Les théories d'Einstein. Préf. de M. Einstein. s8°. 1921
Fabre-d'Olivet (Antoine), *de Ganges.*
Le langue hébraïque restituée &c. 2e éd. t2. 8°. 1905
Fabre-Luce (Alfred). La crise des alliances. Relations franco-brit., 1919–22. s8°. 1922
Locarno sans rêves. s8°. 1927
Russie 1927. [Cahiers verts, s2, v7]. s8°. [1927]
La victoire. 10e ed. s8°. 1924
Fabri (Adémar), *de la Roche, bp. of Geneva; d. 1388, see* VUIJ (J.) A. F., prince-évêque de Genève, 1889.
Fabri (Felix) [SCHMIDT], *see* HÄBERLIN (F. D.) Diss. sist. vitam &c. F. F., 1742.
Fabri (Girolamo).
Effemeride di Ravenna ant. s4°. Ravenna. 1675
Ravenna ricercata: compend. istor. s8°. Bologna. 1678
Fabri (Joannes), *bp. of Vienna, see* FABER (J.)
Fabri (Thomas), *see* WAGNER (M.), T. F. &c. Examen thesium &c. Zuingl. &c., 1586.
Fabrici (Girolamo), *see* FABRICIUS (HIERONYMUS).
Fabricius (Andreas). Brill auff d. Evangel. Augapffel. Ableynung &c. deren im Augapffel Augsburg. Conf. samptl. gesetzter Articul. s4°. [Cologne ?]. 1629
see MENZEL (J.), H. ROTH &c. Auff d. Verleumbdung Spangenbergs &c., 1573.
Fabricius (Franciscus), *Marcoduranus.* *Dialogus de statu turbulento eccl. hujus seculi.
[P1042]. s8°. *n.p. ex Specula Halcyonia.* [Argentorati]. 1591
Fabricius (Georgius), *Chemnicensis.* Poet. vet. eccl. opera Xtna & operum reliq. & fragm., thesaurus. Coll. & comm. expos. [*sep. tp. & pagin.*] studio G. F. 4°. Basiliae. [1564]
Victoriarum coelestium liber unus. [*b. w.* Loss (L.) Catechismus &c., 1553]. s8°. Lipsiae. 1553
Fabricius (Hieronymus), *ab Aquapendente.* Opera anatomica: De formato foetu, formatione ovi & pulli, locutione & ejus instrumentis, brutorum loquela. [4p *in* 1v]. fol. Patavii. 1625
see FAVARO (G.) L'insegnamento anatom. di G. F., 1922.
Fabricius (Johann), *the younger, prof. of theology at Helmstadt.* Consid. var. controv. cum atheis, gentilibus, Judaeis &c., pontif. & reform. Acc. quaedam ined. C. Dreieri, H. Conringii, J. C. Dürrii & J. Fabricii parentis. s4°. Helmstadii. 1704
Fabricius (Johann), *the younger* [*continued*].
Orationes duae de templis vet. Christianorum. [P432]. s4°. Helmstadii. [1704]
see EDZARDI (S.) Animadv. ad J. F. Consider. controv. cum Reformatis, 1704.
Fabricius (Johann Albert). Centifolium Lutheranum, sive notitia litt. script. omnis gen. de B. D. Luthero, &c. 2p *in* 1v. [*pagin. cont.*] s8°. Hamburgi. 1728–30
Codex apocryphus Novi Test. Ed. 2a emend. t1, 2 [*in 1v. pagin. cont.*] s8°. Hamburgi. 1719
Fabricius (Johann Andreas), *see* UNPARTHEYISCHE Kirchenhist. &c., *by F. & others*, 4v, 1735–54.
Fabricius (Johann Ludwig) [*ps.* JANUS ALEXANDER FERRARIUS]. Opera omnia. Praem. hist. vitae & obitus ejusdem, a. J. H. Heideggero. [*w. sep. pagin.*] s4°. Tiguri. 1698
Fabricius (Johann Philipp), *see* HISTORIA. H. eccl. &c. [*in Tamil; attr. to J. P. F.*], 1799.
Fabricius (Knud). Griffenfeld. 8°. 1910
Fabricius (M. P.)
Le Kremlin de Moscou, esquisses &c. la8°. Moscou. 1883
Fabricius (Michael), *see* BALDUIN (F.) Responsio ad Calvinum et Bezam pro F. B. &c. [With address to reader by M. F.] 1564.
Fabricius (Rudolph Anton). *Mem. R. A. F. phil. prof. prorector &c. Acad. Juliae Carol. commendant. [P596]. s4°. Helmstadii. [1772]
Fabricy (*le père* **Gabriel**). Des titres primitifs de la révélation, ou considér. crit. sur la pureté &c. des livres saints de l'Anc. Test. 2t. 8°. Rome. 1772
Fabris (Antonio Maria). La fenice. [Nozze Veronese-Rensovich. N127]. 8°. Padova. 1868
Fabris (Salvator). Della vera pratica & scienza d'armi libri 2. fol. Padoua. 1624
Fabroni (Giovanni Valentino). *I sacrobaccanali festegg. di Firenze e spec. Fierucolone e Befane. s8°. Firenze. 1808
Fabry (Charles), *see* HANOTAUX (G.) Hist. de la nation franç., t14, Physique par C. F., 1924.
Fabry (*Col.* **Jean**), *see* HANOTAUX (G.) & *Col.* F. Joffre, 1921.
Fábulas. Fábulas y cuentos en verso: seleccion, *see* GOYRI DE MENENDEZ PIDAL (M.), *ed.*
Fabyan (Francis W.) Illust. cat. of Americana f. lib. of F., incl. works of T. & C. Mather. Sold 17 Feb. 1920, Amer. Art. Assoc. [P2854]. la8°. N.Y. 1920
Facchin (Attilio). La parrocchia d. Vescovo. 8°. Venezia. 1904
Facchinetti (Vittorino). San Francesco d'Assisi. 4°. Milano. 1921
Faccioli (Carmelo). Ricerche su' Bruzï. 8°. Napoli. 1839
Fachini (Ginevra Canonici).
Prospetto biog. d. donne Ital. rinomate in lett. 8°. 1824
Fachiri (Alexander Pandelli).
The Permanent Court of Internat. Justice. 8°. O. 1925
Fäckh (Ernst), *ed., see* KIDERLEN-WÄCHTER (A. v.) K.-W. d. Staatsmann &c., 2B, 1924.
Facsimiles of letters of Oxford Welshmen, 1903, *see* OXFORD.
Facts rel. to the state of children employed as climbing boys, 1817, *see* ALEXANDER (A.)
Facundo (Quiroga Juan), *1790–1835, see* SARMIENTO (D. F.) Facundo, 4a ed., 1917.
Faddy (Peter). Essay on the defence & milit. system of Gt. Brit. s8°. 1848
Fadeev (Rostislav Andreevich) [Фадѣевъ].
Вооруженныя силы Россіи. 8°. Москва. 1868
Письма о современномъ состояніи Россіи, 1879–1880. 4e изд. 8°. С.-П. [1882]
Faesi (Robert). Gestalten u. Wandlungen schweiz. Dichtung. 10 Essays. s8°. Zürich. [1922]
Fagan (James Bernard). "And so to bed." [2nd ed.] 8°. [1927]
The wheel. A play. s8°. [1922]
Fagan (Louis Alex.)
Descr. cat. of the engr. works of W. Faithorne. la8°. 1888
Fagan (Margaret M.), *see* GAHAN (A. B.) & M. M. F. Type species of Chalcidoidae, 1923.
Fagan (William).
Life & times of D. O'Connell. 2v. s8°. Cork. 1847–48
Fagaras (Josephus Pap de), *see* PAP (J.)
Fage (André). Anthologie des écrivains de la Guerre. [Coll. Pallas]. s8°. 1919
Fage (John). Speculum ægrotorum. The sick-men's glasse. Annexed, Treatise of the foure humours &c. s8°. 1638
Fagg (Edwin). The naturalistic motive in mod. pictures, *see* ROY. SOC. OF LIT. Essays, N.S., v3, 1923.

Fagius (Paulus).
see HUBERTUS (C.) *Hist. de vita, obitu &c. M. Buceri & P. F., 1562.
,, ONKELOS, Thargum ex Chald. in Lat. versa autore P. Fagio, Pentateuchus, 1546.
Fago (Nicolò), *detto Tarantino.* Serenata a 3 voce in lode di S. Maesta Cesarea. [N125]. 8º. Napoli. 1714
Fago (Vincenzo). Arte araba. s4º. 1909
Faguet (Émile).
Chansons d'un passant. Intr. par J. Ageorges. s8º. [1921]
Hist. de la poésie franç., de la Renaiss. au romantisme. Av.-propos de F. Strowski. 3[t]. s8º. 1923–[27]
Rousseau penseur. s8º. [1912]
Fă-Heen. The travels of Fa-hsein, A.D. 399–414, or Record of the Buddhistic kingdoms. Re-tr. H. A. Giles. s8º. C. 1923
Fahie (J. J.) The scient. works of Galileo, see SINGER (C.), *ed.* Sts. in hist. &c. of sci., v2, 1921.
Fahne (Anton). Der Carneval. s8º. Köln. 1854
Fahrenheit (Gabriel Daniel). Abhandl. u. Thermometrie v. F. &c., see ÖTTINGEN (A. J. v.), *ed.*
Faider (Paul). Etudes sur Sénèque. La gloire de S.—La vie & l'œ. de S.—La Vita S., par Paulus Pompilius. la8º. Gand. 1921
Fain (*le baron* **A. J. F.)** MS. de l'an trois (1794–95) p. s. à l'hist. du cabinet. 8º. 1828
MS. de 1813 p. s. à l'hist. de Napoleón. 2e éd. 2t *in* 1v. 8º. 1825
Fairbairn (Andrew Martin).
Christ in the centuries & o. sermons. s8º. 1893
Fairbairn (Steve). Rowing notes. Ed. A. Eggar. s8º. [1926]
Fairbairn (*Sir* **William),** *1st bart.*, see BAINES (T.) Lancs. & Cheshire, w. acc. of the rise &c. of manufactures &c., by W. F., 2v, 1868–69.
Fairbairns (Arnold). A chronology of Brit. hist. s8º. 1910
Fairbank (Alfred), see BRIDGES (R.), *ed.* Eng. handwriting; w. notes on penmanship by A. F., 1927.
Fairbank (Janet Ayer) [*Mrs.* KELLOGG FAIRBANK].
The Smiths. s8º. Indianapolis. [1925]
Fairbridge (Dorothea). Lady Anne Barnard at the Cape of Good Hope, 1797–1802. 8º. O. 1924
Fairbridge (Kingsley). Autobiog. Pref. by L. S. Amery. Epilogue by Sir A. Lawley. 8º. 1927
Fairburn (John). Acc. of murders in Ratcliff Highway &c., incl. life of J. Williams, supp. murderer, & a sermon. [*4 sep. tps. & pagins.*] s8º. [1811]
Fairchild (E. C.) Labour & the indust. revol. s8º. [1923]
Fairchild (Henry Pratt). Elem. of soc. science. 8º. N.Y. 1924
Fairchild (Herman Le Roy). Hist. of the New York Acad. of Sciences form. Lyceum of Nat. Hist. la8º. N.Y. 1887
Fairfax (Blackerby). *A discourse upon the uniting Scotland w. Eng., w. orig. papers &c. [*Incomplete*]. s8º. 1702
Fairfax (*Hon.* **Bryan),** see BUCKINGHAM (G. V., *2nd d.*) Cat. of coll. of pictures &c., w. life of B. by B. F. &c., 1758.
Fairfax (Thomas Fairfax, *3rd baron*).
see HOLLES (D. H., *1st b.*) Full vindic. & ans. of the 11 accused Members to pamph. int. A partic. charge &c. in name of Sir T. F., 1647.
,, TRUE INFORMER; commun. enterprises &c. of army under Lord F., 1648.
Fairfield (The) orchids, see BROOKE (J.) & Co.
Fairless (Michael), *ps.* [*i.e. Miss* MARGERY DOWSON, *form.* BARBER]. The gathering of Brother Hilarius. [repr.] 8º. 1902
Fairley (Barker). The mod. consciousness in Eng. lit., see ENGLISH ASSOC. Essays &c., v9, 1924.
Fairley (John A.) Lauriston Castle. 8º. E. 1925
Fairlie (John Archibald). Brit. War administr. [C.E. for Internat. Peace]. la8º. N.Y. 1919
Centraliz. of admin. in New York State. 8º. N.Y., *Columbia Univ.* 1898
Fairweather (William). Jesus & the Greeks. 8º. E. 1924
Faith, *St. & martyr*, see FIDES, *of Agen, St.*
*__Faithful (A)__ warning to followers of J. W. &c., 1774, see WESLEY (J.)
Faithorne (William). The art of graveing & etching. Allso the manner & method of Callot, & Mr. Bosse. s8º. 1662
see FAGAN (L. A.) Descr. cat. of the engr. works of W. F., 1888.
Falaise (William de), see MAXWELL-LYTE (H. C.) Burci, F. &c., 1921.
Falbe-Hansen (Ida) *&c., ed.*
Digte for Danske skolebørn. 4e Udg. 8º. 1923
see OLRIK (A.) Danske folkeviser &c.; under medvirk. af I. F.-H., 1918.

Falcão (Cristovam), *1515–77*, see RIBEIRO (B.) & C. F. Obras, n. ed., 2v, 1923.
Falce (Antonio). *Works in* ARCHIVIO STOR. ITAL.
Contrib. alla diplom. dei duchi &c. di Tuscia, 1925. [83i.]
Doc. ined. d. duchi &c. di Tuscia, 1927. [85i, ii.]
La Vita ratbertiana di S. Bononio nei mss. d. G. Grandi, 1925. [83i.]
Falck (Anton Reinhard), see JORISSEN (TH.) Hist. Karakters, 2, A. R. F., 1912.
Falck (Nathanael). Nova Reformatorum Heidelberg. methodus infestandi Lutheranos &c. [P440]. s4º. Vitembergæ. 1720
Falcke (Horst P.)
Le blocus pacif. Tr. A. Contat. 8º. Leipzig. 1919
Falconer (John Ironside), see BIDWELL (P. W.) & J. I. F. Hist. of agric. in North. U.S., 1620–1860, 1925.
Falconer (William), *poet.*
Poet. works. [Life by J. Mitford. Aldine ed.] s8º. 1887
see NORIE (J. W.) F. improved &c.: mariner's new &c. naval dict., 3rd ed., rev. &c. by J. W. N., 1804.
Falconet (Etienne Maurice), *d. 1791.* Corresp. avec Catherine II, 1767–78. Publ. avec intr. & notes par L. Réau. [Bibl. de L'Inst. Franç. de Petrograd t7.] 8º. 1921
see HILDEBRANDT (E.) Leben, Werke &c. d. F., 1908.
,, RÉAU (L.) E. M. F., 2t, 1922.
Falconi (Armando), see VENEZIANI (C.) A. F., 1921.
Falda (Giov. Batt.) Nuova pianta et alzata della città di Roma &c. Disegn. &c. da G. B. F. & date al publ. da G. G. de Rossi in Roma, 1676. Con l'agg. d. nove fabriche. fol. 1705
Faleev (N. I.) Шесть мѣсяцевъ военно-полевой юстиціи (1906–7). [P2447]. [*no tp.*] 8º. *n.p. n.d.*
Faletli (Girolamo). Oraz. d. Nativitá di Cristo, see ATHENAGORAS. Della risurrez. de' morti, 1735.
Falgairolle (Adolphe). La dame de Brocart, see ŒUVRES libres, 75, 1927.
Falguera (Antoni de), see PUIG Y CADAFALCH (J.), A. DE F. &c. L'arquit. romànica a Catalunya, v2, 3, 1911–18.
Falk (Adalbert), see KETTELER (W. E. v.) Anschauungen d. Cultusminist. F. ü. d. kathol. Kirche, 1874.
Falk (Henri), see BOUSQUET (P. H. J.) & H. F. Un ange passa, 1924.
Falkbërget (Johan). Den fjerde nattevakt. 8º. 1923
Falke (Gustav.)
Die Auswahl: Gedichte. s8º. Braunschweig. *n.d.*
Neue Fahrt: Gedichte. 2. A. s8º. Hamburg. 1904
Falke (Otto v.) & H. Schmitz. Deut. Möbel v. M.-a. bis z. Anf. d. 19. Jhdts. Hrsg. F. u. S. 3B. 4º. St. 1923–24
Falkeberg (Johann v.), see JOANNES *de Falkaberga.*
Falkenhayn (*General* **Erich G. A. S. v.)** Der Feldzug d. 9. Armee gegen d. Rumänen u. Russen 1916–17. 2T. 8º. 1921
see DELBRÜCK (H.) Ludendorff, Tirpitz, F., 1920.
,, ZWEHL (*Gen.* H. v.) E. v. Falkenhayn, 1926.
Falkenstjerne (Vagn).
Komm. til Haandbog i Dansk Lit. H1, 2. s8º. 1922–25
Falkland (Lucius Cary, *visc.*), see HAMMOND (H.) A view of some exceptions made by a Romanist to F.'s Disc. &c., 1646.
Falkland (Samuel), *ps.*, see HEIJERMANS (H.)
Falkner (John Meade). The lost Stradivarius. s8º. N.Y. 1896
Falkner (S. A.) Das Papiergeld d. französ. Revol., 1789–97. Übertr. v. F. Schlömer. [V. f. Sozialpol., B165iii]. 8º. München. 1924
Falkner (William), *D.D.* Two treatises. 1, conc. reproaching & censure. 2, an ans. to Mr. Serjeant's Surefooting. Annexed, 3 sermons &c. [Ed. W. Sherlock. 2p *in* 1v. *pagin. cont.*] s4º. 1684
Falletti (Pio Carlo), see †FALLETTI-FOSSATI (C.)
Fallex (Maurice). L'Alsace, la Lorraine & les Trois Evêchés du début du 17e s. à 1789. la8º. 1921
—— **& A. Mairey.** Géographie d'après-guerre. La face nouvelle du monde (moins la France). 8º. 1922
Falls (*Capt.* **Cyril),** see WAR. Hist. of Gt. War based on offic. docs., Military oper., Egypt & Palestine; by Sir G. MacMunn & C. F., v1, 1928.
Fallström (Daniel).
Sorte og røde Hjærter, udvalgte Fortaellinger. s8º. 1912
Falorsi (Guido). Le concordanze Dantesche. Intr. a un comm. sintetico d. Div. Comm. s8º. Firenze. 1920
False dawn, 1926, see CARTHILL (AL.), *ps.*
*__Falsehood__ (The) of human virtue; *tr.*, 1691, see ESPRIT (J.)
Falstaff (*Sir* **John),** see DAWTREY (J.) The F. saga: N. Dawtrey as F., 1927.

Faluschi (Giovacchino).
Breve relaz. d. cose notabili d. Siena &c. s8°. Siena. 1784
*Family feuds: or fragm. of a tale of many cent. [P2552]. 8°. 1832
Famine (The) in Russia. Doc. & statistics pres. to Brussels Conf. on Famine Relief. [Russ. Trade Deleg. P2578]. 8°. [1922]
Famous crimes past & present, *n.d.*, *see* FURNISS (H.), *ed.*
Fanciulli (Giuseppe).
"Lascio ai miei figli." Novelle. s8°. Firenze. [1920]
Fandly (Georgius), *see* PAPANEK (G.) Compendiata hist. gentis Slavae, quam compendiavat G. F., 1793.
Fane (Evelyn). The age of consent. s8°. [1922]
Fane (Richard A. B. Ponsonby), *see* PONSONBY-FANE (R. A. B.)
Fanfani (Pietro).
Vocabolario d. pronunzia toscana. s8°. Firenze. 1879
Fangadi (*principessa* **de'**), *ps.* *Lettere de 2 mandarini conc. la pcssa. de F., 3529, *see* LETTERE.
Fannant (Thomas), *really Favent.* Hist. mirab. parliamenti apud Westmonast. 1386; ed. M. McKisack, *see* CAMDEN Misc., v14, 1926.
Fanning (L. S.)
*New Zealand: an illust. descr. &c. 8°. Wellington, N.Z. 1924
Fanshawe (Maurice). Reconstruction: 5 years of work by the League of Nations. s8°. [1925]
Fanshawe (*Sir* **Richard),** *see* HURTADO DE MENDOZA (A.) Fiestas de Aranjuez; tr. Sir R. F., 1670.
Fantasia (Pasquale). Sui mon. medievale di Gaeta &c. [Annali d. R. Inst. Tecn. Giov. Batt. d. Porta, a. 34 e 35. *b. w.* Lo Parco (F.) T. Acciarini &c., 1920]. 8°. Napoli. 1920
Fantin-Latour (Henri).
see GIBSON (F.) The art of H. F.-L.: h. life & work, 1924.
,, KAHN (G.) F.-L. [Maîtres de l'art mod.], 1926.
,, RUFFER (E.) Cat. of mod. pictures &c., by H. F.-L. &c., sold by Christie &c., May 9, 1924.
Fantis (Antonio de), *see* SERENA (A.) Un insigne Scotista trevig., 1922.
Fantoli (Amilcare).
Piccola guida d. Tripolitania. s8°. Tripoli. 1925
Faouëdic (*Mme.* **N. Dondel du),** *see* DONDEL DU FAOUËDIC.
Fara, *Saint, Abbess of Faremoutiers* [BURGUNDOFARA; FARE; PHARA], *see* DELSART (H. M.) Ste. F., sa vie & s. culte, 1911.
Faraday (W. Barnard). Democracy & capital. s8°. 1921
Faraday (Winifred). The Edda: 1, The divine mythology of the North. [P2586]. s8°. 1902
Faraglia (Nunzio Federigo). Storia d. lotta tra Alfonso V d'Aragona e Renato d'Angiò. 8°. Lanciano. 1908
Storia d. Regina Giovanna II d'Angiò. 8°. Lanciano. 1904
Faral (Edmond). Les arts poét. du 12e & du 13e siècle. [M. de Vendôme, G. de Vinsauf, Evrard l'Allemand, J. de Garlande &c.] [H. E., 238]. 8°. 1924
*Faramond, roman, 4t, 1753, *see* LA CALPRENÈDE (G. DE C., *seigneur* DE).
Färber (Eduard). Die geschtl. Entwicklung d. Chemie. la8°. 1921
Färber (Ernst). Sprache der dem J. Renart zugeschr. Werke "Lai de l'Ombre" &c., *see* ROMANISCHE FORSCH., B33, 1915.
Farbige Franzosen am Rhein: ein Notschrei deut. Frauen. 3e A. [P2522]. 8°. 1921
Farbman (Michael S.)
After Lenin: new phase in Russia. 8°. [1924]
Bolshevism in retreat. 8°. [1923]
see EUROPA YEAR BOOK; ed. M. F. &c., 1926 &c.
Farbridge (Maurice Harry).
Studies in Bibl. & Semitic symbolism. 8°. 1923
Farces. Nouv. recueil de farces franç. des 15e & 16e s., 1880, *see* PICOT (É.) & K. NYROP.
Volume of farces at Theatre Royal, Smoke-Alley, Dublin, 1792, *see* DUBLIN.
Farel (Guillaume), *see* KIRCHHOFER (M.) The life of G. F., tr., 1837.
Farewells. [Vale. *Poems, by var. a.* Ed. P. S., & L. Haberly]. 8°. Long Crendon. 1927
Faria (Francisco de). Information, deliv. at bar of H. of Commons, 1 Nov. 1680 [*rel. to Popish Plot.* P525]. sfol. 1680
Faries (John Culbert). Three years of work for handicapped men. Rep. of Inst. for Crippled &c. Men. [P2435]. s8°. N.Y. 1920
Farigoule (Louis), *see* ROMAINS (J.)
Farina (Giulio). Gramm. araba per la lingua lett., con un' app. sul. dialetto tripolino. [Metodo-Gaspey-Otto-Sauer]. s8°. 1912
Farindon (Anthony). 80 Sermons whereof nine of them not till now publ. 2nd ed. rev. & corr. 2v. [*v2 wanting*]. fol. 1672
30 sermons preached at St. Mary Magdalen, Milkstreet, London. Annexed a sermon at funeral of Sir S. Whitmore. sfol. 1657
Farinelli (Arturo). Dante in Spagna—Francia—Inghilterra—Germania (Dante e Goethe). 8°. Torino. 1922
Guillaume de Humboldt & l'Espagne. Avec une esquisse sur Goethe & l'Espagne. 8°. Torino. 1924 [1923]
Lord Byron. [Saggio.] s8°. Milano. 1921
L'opera di un maestro. 15 lezioni ined. e bibliografia. s8°. Torino. 1920
Viajes por España y Portugal. [Junta para Ampl. de Est. &c.] la8°. 1920
Farington (Joseph). The Farington diary. Ed. J. Greig. v1–7 (1793–1814). [v1. 2nd ed.] 8°. [1922–27]
see RUTTER (F.) Wilson & F. [Brit. artists], 1923.
Farini (Luigi Carlo).
Storia d'Italia dall' anno 1814. 2v [*in 1*]. 8°. Torino. 1854–59
Farjat (Emile). Emile F. Cook. Souvenirs. s8°. 1877
Farjat (François). De L'ésprit et des tendances des Méthodistes. [P2538]. s8°. 1852
Farjeon (Eleanor).
Faithful Jenny Dove & o. tales. s8°. [1925]
Martin Pippin in the apple-orchard. 8°. [1921]
Farjeon (Herbert) & H. Horsnell. Advertizing April. [Brit. Drama League Libr., 4]. [2nd ed.] s8°. O. 1923
Farjeon (J. Jefferson). At the Green Dragon. s8°. [1926]
No. 17. s8°. [1926]
Farkas (Pál). Az oláh Kérdésröl. [P2397]. 8°. 1907
Farley (Frank Edgar). Scand. infl. in the Eng. romantic movt., *see* HARVARD UNIV. Sts. &c. in philol. &c., v9, 1903.
Farley (Hugh).
"The singers" & o. poems. [P2732]. 8°. *pr. for the a.* 1920
Farmani Asman, *see* PHARMANI ASMAN.
*Farmer (The): musical entertainment, 1792, *see* O'KEEFE (J.)
Farmer (E.) A compar. of diff. shift systems in the glass trade, *see* INDUST. FATIGUE RES. BD. Rep., 24, 1924.
Time & motion study—Motion st. in metal polishing, *see* INDUST. FATIGUE RES. BD. Reps., 14, 15, 1921.
Farmer (Henry George). The infl. of music: f. Arabic sources. Lect., 1926. 8°. 1926
The rise & development of milit. music. Intr. by A. Williams. s8°. [1912]
Farmer (Hugh), *see* FELL (J.) Dæmoniacs: hypothesis of F. &c., 1779.
Farmer (Sarah Stock).
Wise to win souls. Memoir of Rev. Z. Job. s8°. 1857
Farmer's Almanac & Calendar (The) for 1841–44 *in* 1v. s8°. 1841–44
Farnell (Ida). Spanish prose & poetry old & new. With tr. specimens. la8°. O. 1920
Farnell (Lewis Richard). The attributes of God. Gifford Lects., 1924–25. 8°. O. 1925
Greek hero cults & ideas of immortality. Gifford Lects., 1920. 8°. O. 1921
Outline-hist. of Greek religion. [2nd ed.] s8°. [1921]
Farnèse, *The Family of*, *see* NAVENNE (F. H. DE). Rome & le palais F. pend. les 3 dern. siècles, 2t, 1923.
Farnese (Alessandro), *duke of Parma, 1545–92*, *see* STRADA (F.) De bello Belgico, decas 2, *var. eds. & tr.*
Farnese (Pietro Luigi), *duke of Piacenza*, *see* AFFO (I.) *Vita di P. L. F., 1821.
Farnham (Dwight T.), J. A. Hall *& others.* Profitable science in industry by D. T. F., J. A. Hall, R. W. King [&] H. E. Howe. 8°. N.Y. 1925
Farnol (Jeffrey). Black Bartlemy's treasure. s8°. [1920]
The high adventure. s8°. [1926]
The Loring mystery. s8°. [1925]
The quest of youth. s8°. [1927]
Sir John Dering. s8°. [1923]
Farnsworth (Sidney).
Illumination & its development. 8°. [1922]
Farquhar (George).
The beaux stratagem. [P2575]. 8°. 1778
,, ,, *for a. ed.*, *see* INCHBALD (E.) Brit. th., v8, 1808.
The constant couple. [*Imperf.* P2575]. 8°. 1777
The constant couple. *for a. ed.*, *see* INCHBALD (E.) Brit. th., v8, 1808.
The inconstant. [*Imperf.* P2575]. 8°. 1777
,, ,, [Dolby's Brit. th.] s8°. [1824]

Farquhar (George) [*continued*].

The inconstant. *for a. ed., see* INCHBALD (E.) Brit. th., v8, 1808.

*The recruiting officer. [P2865]. s8°. 1764

The recruiting officer. [*a. ed.*] [P2575]. 8°. 1778

„ „ *for a. ed., see* INCHBALD (E.) Brit. th., v8, 1808.

Farquhar (Helen). John Rutlinger & the phœnix badge of Q. Elizabeth. [Repr. f. "Num. Chron.," s5, v3. P2733]. 8°. 1923

Portrait plaques struck in Stuart times, called shells or clichés. [Repr. f. Brit. Num. J., v16. P2851]. la8°. 1925

Portraiture of our Stuart monarchs on their coins & medals. [Repr. f. Brit. Num. J., v5–11]. 7p [in 1v.] la8°. 1909–16

Royal charities: angels & touchpieces for the King's Evil. [*Repr. f.* Brit. Num. J.] la8°. 1922

Silver counters of the 17th cent. [Fr. Num. Chron., s5, v5. P2858]. 8°. 1925

Some portrait-medals struck betw. 1745 & 1752 for Pr. Charles Edward. [Repr. f. Brit. Num. Journal, v17]. la8°. 1927

Farquhar (John Nicol).

Mod. relig. movements in India. 8°. N.Y. 1919

An outline of the relig. lit. of India. 8°. 1920

Farquharson (A.), *of Honiton.*

Hist. of Honiton. 8°. Exeter. [1868]

Farra (Alessandro). Tre' discorsi. De' miracoli d'amore. D. divinità dell' huomo. Dell' ufficio d. capitano. [*each w. sep. tp. & pagin.*] s8°. Pavia. 1564

Farrago. *Farrago aliquot epigrammatum P. Melanchthonis & alioru͂, 1528, *see* MELANCHTHON (P.)

Farrand (Max). The fathers of the constit. [Chron. of Amer., v13]. 8°. New Haven, *Yale*. 1921

Farrar (Charles Frederick). Old Bedford. la8°. Bedford. 1926

"Ouse's silent tide." s4°. Bedford. 1921

Farrar (Frederic William).

The Lord's prayer. Sermons. s8°. 1894

Mercy & judgment. 2nd ed. 8°. 1882

see PUSEY (E. B.) What is of faith as to everlasting punishment? reply to F., 1880.

Farrar (John), *of Wesleyan Theolog. Inst., Richmond.*

Eccl. dict. 3rd ed. s8°. 1867

Proper names of the Bible. 2nd ed. s8°. 1844

Farrell (James Patrick). Hist. of Co. of Longford. la8°. D. 1891

Farrell (W. J.) The true-tone violin. s8°. [1921]

Farrer (Edmund).

A list of monum. brasses in Suffolk. 8°. Norwich. 1903

Portraits in Suffolk houses, East. Index to MS. vol. [*b. w. h.* Portraits (West), 1908]. 4°. Boston, *Mass.* 1926

Farrer (James Anson).

England under Edward VII. 8°. [1922]

The war for monarchy, 1793–1815. 8°. 1920

Farrer (Reginald John).

The Dolomites. Painted by E. H. Compton. Descr. by R. F. 8°. 1913

My rock-garden. 8°. 1907

„ „ . . . . 6th impr. 8°. 1920

The rainbow bridge. 8°. 1921

The ways of rebellion. s8°. 1908

see COX (E. H. M.) F.'s last journey, Upper Burma, 1919–20, w. list of rhododendrons coll. by F. & h. field notes, 1926.

Farrer (William). Feudal Cambridgeshire. s4°. C. 1920

Honors & knights' fees. 3v. 8°. 1923–25

Farrer (William Francis). Cat. of the coll. of old plate of W. F. F., at No. 7 St. James's Sq., London. Comp. by E. A. Jones. 4°. 1924

Farrère (Claude), *ps.* [*i.e.* CHARLES BARGONE].

Works in ŒUVRES libres.

L'an 1937, 1924. [32.]

Le choix, pièce, 1921. [4.]

L'île au Grand Puits, 1921. [1.]

L'inaccessible dame, 1928. [82.]

Menaces de sécheresse, 1926. [58.]

Où?, document, 1923. [24.]

San Fermin de Pamplona en Navarre, 1926. [55.]

Turquie ressuscitée, 1922. [18.]

L'autre côté. . . . s8°. [1928]

La bataille. Bois orig. de A. Roubille. 8°. *n.d.*

Bêtes & gens qui s'aimèrent. s8°. [1920]

Cent millions d'or. s8°. [1927]

Les condamnés à mort. s8°. [1921]

Le dernier dieu. s8°. [1926]

Les hommes nouveaux. s8°. [1922]

Une jeune fille voyagea. . . . s8°. [1925]

Mademoiselle Dax jeune fille. s8°. [1920]

see REVON (M.) C. F., 1924.

„ X . . . (*cap. de corvette*) & C. F. Journ. de bord de l'expéd. des Dardanelles, 1923.

Farrow (E. Pickworth). Plant life on East Anglian heaths: vegetation of Breckland. la8°. C. 1925

Farrow (Stephen S.) Faith, fancies & fetich or Yoruba paganism. Foreword by R. R. Marett. 8°. [1926]

Farrow (Thomas) & W. W. Crotch.

How to win the War. s8°. [1916]

Farrugia (Luigi). Melita del naufragia di S. Paolo &c., *see* BULLETTINO DI ARCH. &C. DALM., 36, Suppl., 1913.

Farther, *see* FURTHER.

Farthing (F. Hadfield). Saturday in my garden. 8°. [1911]

Farvacques (Franciscus). Augustiniana actuum human. statera, quam præs. F. F. propugn. A. C. de Pallant. [P2659]. s8°. Lovanii. 1683

Fasch (Johann Augustin) [FASCHIUS]. Diss. de insign. vet. Xtnorum. formulis. Praes. J. A. Schmidt. [P433]. s4°. Helmestadi. [1696]

Fasciculo di medicina [*sometimes attrib. to J. de Ketham*], Venice, 1493. With intr. by C. Singer. [Monumenta medica, v2]. 2p. fol. Florence. 1925

1, Descr. & discussion, Tr. of the Anathomia of Mondino da Luzzi, Acc. of mediaeval anatomy & physiology & Atlas of illust. figures.
2, Facsimile.

Fasciculus. Fasc. dissert. hist.-crit.-philolog. &c.; coll. a T. Crenio, 1691, *see* CRUSIUS (T. T.)

*Fasc. quæstionum controvers. de Tropo in verbis Cœnae—proprietatibus essentialibus—praedicationibus inusitatis ex libris super. extr. [*b. w.* Hassia. De unione personali &c., 1537]. s8°. Hamburgi. 1597

Fasc. rariorum & curios. script. theolog., quaestiones de animae post solut. a corpore statu &c. a theologis &c. ut Bebelio, Calixto &c. *Foll*[d]. *by* Reinckings u. Francisci Vom Leben d. Seelen im Tode, *w. sep. tp. & pagin.*] [2p, *w. tp*[s]. *as below*]. s8°. Francofurti a. M. 1692

1, Tractatus curiosus, 1691. 2, Tractatus curiosus theolog., 1692.

Fashionable. *F. (The) lover: comedy, 1772, *see* CUMBERLAND (R.)

*F. (The) tour: a guide to travellers &c., 1830, *see* DAVISON (G. M.)

Fasolo (Giovanni). Legge suntuaria Vicentina. [*Ed.* G. F. Nozze Valeri–Curti. N44]. 8°. Vicenza. [1882]

Fasti. *Fasti Dunelm. &c., 1926, *see* DURHAM.

Fasti triumphales populi Rom.; ed. &c. E. Pais, 1920, *see* PAIS (E.)

***Fatal** jealousie (The): tragedy, 1673, *see* PAYNE (N.)

Fath 'Ali Akhundzādah, *Mīrzā.* The Vazir of Lankuran. Play, tr. f. Persian into Urdu & ed. w. notes by Shams-ul-'Ulamā Mawlavī Muhammad Yūsuf Ja 'Farī, K͟hān Bahādur & Lt.-Col. D. C. Phillott [*& Eng. tr., w. sep. tp. & pagin.*] 8°. Calcutta. 1911

„ „ *For a. ed., see* PHILLOTT (*Lt.-Col.* D. C.) Urdu rozmarra, 4th ed., 1920; Eng. tr., 3rd ed., 1919.

Fathers. *Lives of the holy f., *in Armenian*, 2v, 1855, *see* LIVES.

Fatinelli (Giovanni Giacomo), *ed.* *Hist. cultus Sinensium, seu varia scripta de cultibus Sinarum. [Ed. G. G. F.] [2p *in* 1v. *pagin. cont.* p2 *has add. tp.* Causa Sinensis &c.] s8°. Coloniae. 1700

Fatini (Giuseppe). Su la fortuna e l'autenticità d. liriche di L. Ariosto, *see* GIORNALE STORICO D. LETT. ITAL. Suppl., 23, 1924.

Fatio (Edmond), *see* BERCHEM (M. VAN) & E. F. Voyage en Syrie, t2, 1915.

Fatov (N. N.) А. С. Пушкин, очерк. la8°. [МОСКВА.] 1921

Fattorello (Francesco). A. Fogazzaro. s8°. Udine. 1922

Fauche-Borel (Louis), *see* LENOTRE (G.) 2 Royalist spies of the French Revol. [*i.e.* L.F.-B. &c.]; tr., 1924.

Faucher (Jean). Exorcismes divins, ou Propos. chrest. pour chasser les demons &c. s8°. Nismes. 1626

Zacharie, ou De la saincteté du mariage. [*b. w. h.* Exorc. div., 1626]. s8°. Nismes. 1627

Faucheron (L.), *see* BEAUVERIE (J. J.) & L. F. Atlas colorié de la flore alpine, 1906.

Fauchille (Paul). Traité de droit internat. public. 8e éd. refondue &c. du Manuel de M. H. Bonfils. t2, Guerre & neutralité. 8°. 1921

Fauchois (René). La danseuse éperdue, comèdie., *see* ŒUVRES libres, No. 8, 1922.

Mlle. Jockey, comédie, *see* ŒUVRES libres, No. 76, 1927.

Faucigny-Lucinge (A. de) [*née* CHOISEUL-GOUFFIER].

L'archiduc Jean-Salvator (Jean Orth). s8°. 1911

Faulds (Henry). Man. of pract. dactylography. 8°. [1923]

Faulkner (Thomas), *topographer.* Hist. & antiqs. of Kensington. [*tp. &c. & Index wanting*]. 4°. 1820
Faultrier (Joachim). Cat. librorum bibl. J. F. digestus à P. Marchand. 8°. Parisiis. 1709
Fauntleroy (Henry). Trial of H. F. & o. t. for forgery. Ed. H. Bleackley. [Not. Brit. trials]. 8°. E. [1924]
Fauquier (Francis). Essay on ways & means for raising money for the pres. war, &c. (1756). [J. H. Univ. Repr. of econ. tracts. P2619]. 8°. [Baltimore. 1915]
Faure (Elie). L'arbre d'Eden. s8°. 1922
Henri Matisse. Par E. F., J. Romains, C. Vildrac, L. Werth. la8°. [1923]
Hist. de l'art. 4t. [2, 3, n. éd.] 8°. 1921–22
1, L'art antique. 2, L'art médiéval. 3, L'art renaissant. 4, L'art moderne.
Napoléon. [9e éd.] s8°. 1921
Faure (Félix), *president of the French Republic, see* SIMOND (E.) Hist. de la 3e Republ. [t2, 3], 1894–99 : présidence de F. F., 1921.
Faure (Gabriel). La dern. journée de Sappho. s8°. 1922
Heures d'Italie. 3s. s8°. 1919
„ „ ....éd. compl., rev. &c. s8°. 1921
Pélerinages passionnés. s2. Ames & décors romantiques (Chateaubriand &c.) s8°. 1922
La vallée du Rhône. s8°. 1923
Fauré (Gabriel Urbain), *see* BRUNEAU (A.) Vie & œuvres de G. F., 1925.
see REVUE MUSICALE, oct. 1922, N°. spéc. & Suppl., 1922.
Faure (Jean Baptiste), *Jesuit.* *Apparatus brevis ad theol. & jus Canon. Acc. App. de textibus &c. s8°. Romae. 1751
Faure-Biguet (J. N.) M. Barrès. 8°. 1924
Faure-Favier (Louise).
Mademoiselle Loin-du-Ceil. Roman. s8°. [1920]
Fausse-Lendry (*la marquise* de), *see* MÉMOIRES sur les journées de sept. 1792, par F. &c. ; avec notes par F. Barrière, 1881.
Fausset (Hugh I'Anson). John Donne. 8°. [1924]
Keats. s8°. [1922]
Studies in idealism. s8°. 1923
Tennyson. 8°. [1923]
Tolstoy : the inner drama. 8°. [1927]
Faust (Albert Bernhardt), *Ph.D.* Guide to materials for Amer. hist. in Swiss & Austrian archives. [C.I. of Wash.] la8°. Wash. 1916
Faust (August), *see* ZEN : d. lebend. Buddhismus ; übers. S. Ôhasama, hrsg. A. F., 1925.
Faust (*Dr.* Johann). *The hist. of the damnable life &c. of Dr. J. F., 1592, w. The 2nd report of F. contg. his appearances & the deeds of Wagner, 1594. Modernised & ed. by W. Rose, w. intr. [Broadway Trans.] 8°. [1925]
see RYDBERG (A. V.) F. och Fauststudier, 1921.
Faustus, *of Byzantium.* Gesch. Armeniens. Aus d. Armen. übers. u. mit e. Abh. ü. d. Geog. Armeniens v. M. Lauer. 8°. Köln. 1879
[Hist. of Armenia. *In Armenian*]. [2nd ed.] 8°. Venetik. 1889
Faustus, *Regius, see* FAUSTUS, *St., bp. of Riez.*
Faustus, *St., bp. of Riez.* De ratione fidei &c. [*& o.* Epist.], *see* GALLIA. *Vet. aliq. G. theol. scripta, 1586.
Fauvelle (René). Les étudiants en médecine de Paris sous le grand roi. la8°. 1899
Fava (Domenico). La Biblioteca Estense, con. cat. d. Mostra Permanente. 8°. Modena. 1925
Favaro (Antonio). Monografie stor. s. Studio di Padova [by F. &c.], 1922, *see* PADOVA.
Saggio di bibliog. d. Studio di Padova [1500–1920]. [Estr. d. Misc. di storia ven. d. R. Dep. di Storia Patria, s3, v16, 17]. 2p. la8°. Venezia. 1922
Favaro (Giuseppe). L'insegnamento anatom. di G. Fabrici, *see* PADOVA. Monogr. s. Studio di P., 1922.
Favart (Charles Simon). Les trois sultanes, *see* THÉÂTRE choisi du 18e s., t2, 1914.
—— & Largillières. Polichinelle, comte de Paonfier ; parodie inéd. du Glorieux de Destouches (1732), suivi des Champs Elysées de MM. de Caumont & Destouches [1714]. [P2770]. s8°. 1924
Favent (Thomas), *see* FANNANT (T.)
Favier (Louis Faure-), *see* FAURE-FAVIER (L.)
Favre (Pierre-François). Lettres édifiantes &c. sur la visite apostolique de M. de La Baume à la Cochinchine en 1740, la conduite des miss. Jésuites, p. s. de contin. aux " Mém. hist. du R. P. Norbert." s4°. Venise. 1746
„ „ [*a. ed.*] 3t *in* 1v. [t3 *has title* Premier mém. apolog.] s8°. Venise *&* Avignon. 1753
Favretto (Giacomo), *1849–87, see* OREFFICE (P.) G. F., 1899.

Fawcett (Benjamin), *see* MORRIS (M. C. F.) B. F., colour printer & engraver, 1925.
Fawcett (Charles Bungay). Provinces of England. 8°. 1919
Fawcett (Edward Douglas). Divine imagining. 8°. 1921
Fawcett (Harold W.) & G. W. W. Hooper. The fighting at Jutland. Personal exper. of 45 officers & men of Brit. Fleet. Ed. F. & H. abridged ed. la8°. 1921
Fawcett (Hugh A.), *see* GOFF (A.) & H. A. F. Macedonia, 1921.
Fawcett (*Miss* J.) *Angel's (An) message. 8°. 1858
Fawcett (*Mrs.* Millicent Garrett). What I remember. 8°. [1924]
Women's suffrage : hist. s8°. [1912]
—— & E. M. Turner.
Josephine Butler : h. work & principles. s8°. 1927
Fawcett (William). The banana. Intr. by Sir D. Morris. 2nd & enl. ed. 8°. [1921]
see BRIT. MUSEUM OF NAT. HIST. : BOTANY. Flora of Jamaica ; by W. F. &c., v5, 1926.
Fawtier (Robert). La Bible historiée toute figurée de la John Rylands Lib. Reprod., étude par R. F. [*Repr. f.* Soc. Fr. de Reprod. de Mss. à Peintures. Bull., 1923]. 4°. 1924
Sainte Catherine de Sienne : crit. des sources. [Bibl. des Ecoles Franç. d'Athénes & de Rome, fasc., 121]. [t]1. 8°. 1921
Faxardo (Diego de Saavedra), *see* SAAVEDRA FAJARDO (D. DE).
Faÿ (Bernard). Bibliog. crit. des ouvr. fr. rel. aux États-Unis (1770–1800). la8°. 1925
L'esprit révolut. en France & aux Etats-Unis à la fin du 18e s. [Bibl. de la Revue de litt. comp., t7]. la8°. 1925
Panorama de la litt. contemp. s8°. [1925]
Fay (Charles Ryle). Copartnership in industry. s8°. C. 1913
Life & labour in the 19c. 8°. C. 1920
Fay (*Mrs.* Eliza). Original letters f. India (1779–1815). Intr. & notes by E. M. Forster. 8°. 1925
Fay (Percival Bradshaw) & A. Coleman. Sources & structure of Flaubert's Salammbô. [Elliott Monographs, 2]. 8°. Baltimore. 1914
Fayard (Jean). *Works in* ŒUVRES libres.
Dialogues sur Oxford, 1924. [39.]
Journal d'un colonel, 1925. [45.]
Le monde où l'on s'abuse, choses vues, 1924. [34.]
Plaidoyer pro domo, 1927. [78.]
Oxford & Margaret. s8°. 1924
Faye (Eugène de). Esquisse de la pensée d'Origène : confér. à Upsala. s8°. 1925
Et. s. les origs. des églises de l'âge apostol. [H. E. : Sci. relig., 23]. 8°. 1909
Gnostiques & gnosticisme. 2e éd. augm. la8°. 1925
Origène : sa vie, s. œuvre &c. v1 (Biog. & écrits). [H. E. : Sci. relig., 37]. la8°. 1923
Origen & h. work. Tr. F. Rothwell. s8°. [1926]
Fayle (Charles Ernest). Seaborne trade, 3v, *see* WAR. Hist. of the Gt. War : Seaborne tr., 1920–24.
The War & the shipping industry. [C.E. for Internat. Peace]. la8°. O. 1927
see WRIGHT (C.) & C. E. F. A hist. of Lloyd's, 1928.
Fayolle (François Joseph Marie). *Acanthologie, ou dict. epigrammatique. s8°. 1817
Fayolle (*le maréchal* Marie Emile), *see* BORDEAUX (H.) Le maréchal F., 1921.
Faytinelli (Pietro de'), *called Mugnone.* Rime. Publ., con not. da L. del Prete. s8°. Bologna. 1874
Fayus (Antonius), *see* LA FAYE (A. DE).
Fazande (José Vieira), *see* VIEIRA FAZANDA (J.)
Fazl-i-Ali, *Maulwi* [MAULAVI].
Dict. of the Eng. & Persian langs. la8°. Bombay. 1882
Dict. of the Persian & Eng. langs. la8°. Bombay. 1885
Fè (Giulio). Odolimpia : le trè vie d. perfettione purgativa &c. s4°. Milano. 1607
Fea (Allan). Recollections of 60 years. 8°. 1927
Feales (W.), *see* CATALOGUE. A true & exact cat. of all plays &c. prod. in Eng., to Apr. 1732, *for W. F.*, 1732.
Febres (Gonzalo Picon-), *see* PICON-FEBRES (G.)
Febronius (Justinus), *ps.* [*i.e.* J. N. v. HONTHEIM, *bp. of Myriophitos &c.*] *Hist. Trevir. diplomat. & pragmat., 417–1745. 3t. fol. Augustae Vind. 1750
see BALLERINI (PIETRO). De potestate eccl. summ. pontif., contra opus J. F. &c., 1770.
„ ZACCARIA (F. A.) Antifebronius vindic. seu suprema rom. pontif. potestas &c., 1843.
Febvre (Lucien). Geograph. intr. to history. By L. F. in collab. w. L. Bataillon. la8°. 1925
La terre & l'évol. humaine : intr. géog. à l'hist. Par L. F., avec le concours de L. Bataillon. 8°. 1922

Fechheimer (Hedwig). Kleinplastik d. Ägypter. [Kunst d. Ostens; hrsg. W. Cohn, B3]. la8°. 1921
Die Plastik d. Ägypter. [Kunst d. Ostens; hrsg. W. Cohn, B1]. la8°. 1923
La sculpture égypt. Tr. de C. Marchand. 4°. [1922 ?]
Fechner (E.) Die Vernichtung d. Westmächte durch d. erwachten Orient. [P2685]. 8°. Naumburg. 1922
Fechner (Gustav Theodor) [*ps. Dr.* MISES].
Die drei Motive u. Gründe d. Glaubens. s8°. L. 1863
Die Tagesansicht gegenüber d. Nachtansicht. 8°. L. 1879
Üeber das höchste Gut. [*b. w. h.* Tagesansicht &c., 1879]. 8°. L. 1846
Ueber d. Seelenfrage. [*b. w. h.* 3 Motive &c., 1863]. s8°. L. 1861
Vom Leben nach d. Tode. 2e A. [*b. w. h.* 3 Motive &c., 1863]. s8°. L. 1866
see LASSWITZ (K.) G. T. F., 1896.
,, WIESER (J. E.) Spiritismus &c.: mit e. Beilage ü. F.'s "Tagesansicht," 1881.
Fechnerus (Joannes). Sabothus Montium Silesiae amoenissimus [*verse*], *see* KOECKRIZ (F.) Primitiae Silesiacae, 1715.
Fecht (Johann).
Comp. univers. theologiam, theticam & polemican complexum. Cum vita autoris &c. cura J. Hoxa. s8°. Servestae. 1740
De orig. & superstit. missarum tractatio J. B. Bossueto, J. Dezio & J. Grancolasio oppos.: Acc. app.: De sacrificio missae repraesentativo &c. Ed. G. F. Fechtius, fil. 2p *in* 1v. [*pagin. contin.*] s8°. Rostochi. 1725
De statu damnatorum. s8°. Rostochii. 1708
Diss. de suggestionibus Satanae. Praes. J. Fechtio, resp. J. H. Lochnero. s4°. Rostochi. [1706]
Diss. de versione Lutheri Germ. Præs. J. F., exam. subm. Z. Grapius. [P2742]. s4°. Wittebergae. 1709
Hist. Colloquii Emmending., inter pontificios & lutheranos, 1590. Subjic. protocoll. & conclusio J. Pappus a calumniis J. Pistorii vindic. &c. [2 *pagin.*] s8°. Rostochii. 1694
Kurtze Nachricht v. d. Kirchen-Bann. [*b. w. h.* Noctes Xtnae, 1735]. s8°. Rostock. 1713
Lectiones theolog. in sel. controv. syllogen &c. Rec. G. F. Fecht. Acc. S. Lintrupii, ad edit. epist. ed. 2a, corr. s8°. Rostochii. 1722
Noctes Christianae, seu exercit. varii argumenti liber ed. noviss. &c. s8°. Lipsiae. 1735
Philocalia sacra, *i.e.* variarum doctrinarum farrago. ed. 4a. s8°. Rostochi. 1729
see BREITHAUPT (J. J.) Epist. antipelag., contra disquis. F., 2p, 1711–14.
Fechter (Paul).
Frank Wedekind, d. Mensch u. d. Werk. 8°. Jena. 1920
Gerhart Hauptmann. [3e A.] 8°. Dresden. [1922]
Die Kletterstange. Roman. s8°. St. 1925
Fedden (*Mrs.* **Romilly**) [KATHARINE WALDO DOUGLAS].
The sign. s8°. 1912
Fedele (Pietro), *see* PARIBENI (R.), P. F. &c. Ambasciate &c. a Roma, 1927.
Feder (Alfred Leonhard), *S.J.* Studien zu Hilarius v. Poitiers, 3, 1912, *see* KAIS. AKAD. D. W. ZU W. Sitzb., B169, 1913.
Federal. The debates in the Fed. Convent. of 1787 wh. framed the constit. of the U.S., 1920, *see* MADISON (J.)
Federated Institution of Mining Engineers, *see* INSTITUTION OF MINING ENGINEERS.
Federation of British Industries, *see* RESOURCES OF THE EMPIRE: survey prep. by Fed. of Brit. Ind., 10v, 1924.
Federer (Heinrich). Berge u. Menschen. Roman. s8°. 1925
Lachweiler Geschichten. s8°. 1924
Federici (Federico), *senator de Genova.* Della famiglia Fiesca trattato. [*engr. tp.*] fol. [Genova. 1650 ?]
Federn (Carl). Mazarin. la8°. München. 1922
Federn (Etta). Friedrich Hebbel. 8°. München. [1920]
Federn-Kohlhaas (Etta).
W. Rathenau. 2e A. 8°. Dresden. 1928
Federov (Mikhail), *see* FEDOROV (M.)
Federzoni (Luigi).
Il trattato di Rapallo, con app. di doc. s8°. Bologna. [1921]
see VEO (E.) L'on. F., 1919.
Fedin (Konst). Города и годы: роман. 2oe изд. 8°. Москва. 1926
Fedorov (A. M.) Жатва. Разсказы. 8°. [Москва. c. 1909]
Fedorov (Evg.) [FEODOROFF]. Подготовка Финляндской революціи 1889–1905. [P2451]. 8°. С.-П. 1907
The Finnish revol. in prepar., 1889–1905. Tr. G. Dobson. [*o. c. in* P1320; 2451]. 8°. St. Petersbourg. 1911
Fedorov (F. A.) Финляндія въ нынѣшнемъ ея состояніи. s8°. С.-П. 1855
Fedorov (Mikhail). La Russie sous le régime communiste. Rép. au rapp. de la Délég. des Trades-Unions Britt. [Publ. sous la dir. de M. F.] Préf. de H. Bourgin. 8°. 1926
Fedorov (Yakov). Старые и новые деньги, денежная реформа 1924. [P2845]. 8°. Москва. [1924]
Fedorovich (I. I.) Пособіе при изученіи русскихъ глаголовъ. 8°. С.-П. 1890
Fedorovich (S.) Какъ собираются и на что расходуются народныя деньги. [P848]. s8°. С.-П. 1905
Fè d'Ostiani (Luigi Francesco). Commem. del Conte Fr. Bettoni, *see* REGIA DEP. DI STORIA PATRIA. Misc., t37, 1901.
Feeling (*Lord*), *ps.*, *see* FONTANEY (A.)
***Feet** (The) of the young men, 1928, *see* JANITOR, *ps.*
Fegdal (Charles Mascaux). Coins curieux de Paris. 8°. [1924]
Feguernekinus (Isaacus L.) Enchiridii locorum commun. theolog. ex Aug. Marlorati Thesauro & Chr. Obenhenii Promptuario ab I. F. coll. ed. 2a. Acc. Gemmula partitionum theolog. auct. A. Polano. s8°. Basileae. [1596]
Fehlavius (Georgius), *see* ANGELOS (C.) Status & ritus eccl. Graecae. Lat. conv. à G. F. cum ejusdem annot. &c., 1655.
Fehmel (Amandus Gotthold). Diss. theolog. de criteriis errorum circa relig. communibus. s4°. Lipsiæ. 1713
Fehr (Hans). Das Recht im Bilde. 4°. Erlenbach-Zürich. [1923]
Fehr (Otto). Die Märzoffensive 1918 an d. Westfront, Strategie oder Taktik? 8°. L. 1921
Fehrle (Eugen). Deut. Feste u. Volksbräuche. 2e A. s8°. [1920]
Fehse (Wilhelm). Wilhelm Raabes Erwachen zum Dichter (1849–53). 2te A. s8°. Magdeburg. 1921
see DÖRNENBURG (E.) & W. F. Raabe u. Dickens, 1921.
Feiling (Keith). England under the Tudors & Stuarts. [Home Univ. Lib.] s8°. [1927]
Hist. of the Tory party, 1640–1714. 8°. O. 1924
Feininger (Lyonel), *see* WOLFRADT (W.) L. F., 1924.
Feist (Sigmund). Etymolog. Wörterbuch d. gotischen Sprache. 2e, neubearb. A. 8°. Halle. 1923
Feith (J. A.), *see* MULLER (S.) J. A. F. &c. Handleiding, 1920.
Fejér (György).
Diss. in res Hungariae vet. hist.-crit. 8°. Budae. 1837
Regni per Hungaros in Europa stabiliti rationes. Introd. in hist. regni H. 8°. Budae. 1845
Relig. & eccl. Christianae apud Hungaros initia. 4°. Budae. 1846
Felbinger (Jeremias). Ad Christianos &c. epistola: in qua Socini &c. errores, refutantur. s4°. Amstelodami. 1672
Feldegg (Ferdinand *Ritter* **v.)** Das Gefühl als Fundament d. Weltordnung. [P2471]. 8°. Wien. 1890
Feldkeller (Paul). Graf Keyserlings Erkenntnisweg zum Übersinnlichen. s8°. Darmstadt. 1922
Feldman (Asher). Parables & similes of the Rabbis, agric. & pastoral. 8°. C. 1924
Feldmann (Joseph). Ortsnamen. s8°. Halle (Saale). 1925
Feldpostbriefe aus d. Osten, 1916, *see* EVERS (E.), *ed.*
Feldwick (W.), *see* BRAZIL. 20th cent. impressions of B.; edd. W. F. &c., 1913.
Félice (Roger de). French furniture under Louis XIV. Tr. F. M. Atkinson. s8°. 1922
French furniture under Louis XV. Tr. F. Simmonds. s8°. 1920
Felicianus, *Dominican friar.* Divina providentia. [*Ends:* Explicit tractatulus fratris Feliciani ordinis predicatoꝝ de divina predestinatione intitulatus &c.] s4°. [Mēming, *Albert Kunne.* 1486]
[*12 leaves without pagin. sig. a–b in sixes; 36 lines to a full page.*]
Felix *Pratensis, of the hermits of St. Augustine, see* BIBLE: PSALMS. Psalterium ex hebreo tralatū, f. F. interp., 1522.
Felker (Andreas). Res literaria Hungariae. s8°. Cassoviae. [1735]
Fell (Alfred). Colonist's voyage to New Zealand under sail. Foreword by Sir A. Fell. s8°. Exeter. [1927]
Fell (E. F. B.) Wealth & you & I. s8°. [1921]
Fell (John), *Independent minister of Cockermouth.* Dæmoniacs. Hypothesis of Farmer & others. 8°. 1779
Fell (John), *bp. of Oxford, see* WREN (*Sir* C.) 'Tom Tower' Christ Ch., Oxf.: letters of W. to J. F., set forth & annot. by W. D. Caröe, 1923.
Fell (*Mrs.* **Margaret**), *aft. wife of G. Fox the founder of the Soc. of Friends, see* CROSFIELD (H. G.) M. F., 1913.
Fell (Roland Arthur Lonsdale). Etruria & Rome. Thirlwall prize essay, 1923. s8°. C. 1924
Fell (Sarah) *of Swarthmoor Hall.* Household acc. book of S. F. Ed. by N. Penney. 8°. C. 1920
Feller (Joachim). Cygni, *h. e.* clari aliquot Cygnei quorum in chronico Cygneo nulla facta est mentio &c. [P595]. s4°. Lipsiae. [1686]
Media orthodoxæ relig. inter excessum & defectum via. [P2638]. s4°. [Lips.] 1671
Feller (Joachim Friedrich), *see* LEIBNITZ (G. W. v.) Otium Hanoveranum &c. ex ore & schedis L. cum rebus ad hist. Brunsvic. pertin. op. navaret J. F. F., 1718.

Fellom (James). The rider of the Mohave. s8°. [1926]
Fellowes (Edmund Horace).
The Eng. madrigal. s8°. 1925
The Eng. madrigal composers. 8°. O. 1921
Eng. madrigal verse 1588–1632. Ed. E. H. F. 8°. O. 1920
The music of Westminster, *see* TANNER (L. E.) W. Abbey, 1927.
Orlando Gibbons. 8°. O. 1925
Will. Byrd. s8°. O. 1923
Fellows (John), *Baptist teacher.* Hymns on believers baptism. [*b. w. h.* Six views, 1774]. s8°. B'ham. 1773
Six views of believers baptism. s8°. B'ham. 1774
Felmer (Márton). Primae lineae hist. Transsilv. Acc. Observ. &c. opera J. C. Eder [*w. sep. tp. & pagin.*] s8°. Cibinii. [1803]
***Felon Sew** (The): a mock-heroic poem of the 15th c. [1st transcr. by R. Rokeby, 1565]; *ed.* G. H. Cowling, *see* ENGLISH ASSOC. Essays &c., v8, 1922.
Fels (Florent). Die altfranzös. Bildteppiche. [Übertr. v. F. A. Angermayer]. 8°. [1923]
Felsius (Joannes Henricus). Diss. de varia Confess. Tetrapolitanae fortuna in civ. Lindav. [P2643]. s4°. Gottingae. [1755]
Felstead (Sidney Theodore). Sir R. Muir: mem. of a Public Prosecutor. Ed. Lady Muir. 8°. 1927
The underworld of London. s8°. 1923
Felsted School. Alumni Felsted.: list of boys entered at F. Sch., 1852–1921. Issued by the Old Felstedian Soc. & ed R. J. Beevor. s8°. Felsted. 1921
Foundation deeds of F. S. & charities. Intr. notes by A. Clark. 8°. *p.p.* O. 1916
Feltham (Owen). Resolves: a duple [*sic*] century. [Second cent., *w. sep. tp.*] 4th ed. s8°. 1631
,, ,, 5th ed. [*tp. of* Second cent. *dated* 1633]. 8°. 1634
Felton (Samuel). On the portraits of Eng. authors on gardening, w. biog. notices. 2nd ed., w. add. 8°. 1830
Felton (Sibille), *aft. wife of Sir T. Morley, aft. abbess of Barking; 1359–1419, see* BARKING. Ordinale &c. of Benedictine nuns of B. Abbey; [wr. at instance of S. F.]; ed. J. B. Tolhurst, v1, 1927.
Feltre (Vittorino da) [†RAMBALDONI (V. DE')], *see* MINOTTO (A. S.) Monumenti a V. de' R. &c. in Feltre, 1869.
Feltria. Statuta civitatis F. 4°. Venetiis. 1551
Fenaroli (Stefano). Diz. d. artisti bresciani. 8°. Brescia. 1877
Fenayrou (Gabrielle). *G. F. [*Murder of L. Aubert by G. F. no tp.* P2826]. s8°. [Sceaux]. *n.d.*
Fenchel (Ludwig).
Die deut. Schiffahrtsgesellschaften. 8°. Hamburg. 1920
Fénelon (François de Salignac de la Mothe), *abp. of Cambrai.*
Les avantures de Telemaque. n. éd. s8°. Amsterdam. 1725
,, ,, ...n. éd. s8°. Londres. 1732
,, ,, n. éd., publ. avec intr. &c. par A. Cahen. [G. E. de la F.] 2t. 8°. 1920
Lettre à M. l'Evêque d'Arras sur la lecture de l'Ecr. sainte en langue vulg. [P2505]. s8°. Vienne. 1815
*Lettre de quelques ecclés. du Brabant à l'archévêque au sujet de son mandement &c. Pour la réception de la Constit. Unigenitus &c. [P2659]. s8°. Ville-Dieu. 1715
Réfutation des erreurs de B. de Spinosa par F., le P. Lami, & le Cte. de Boullainvilliers. Avec la vie de Spinosa par J. Colerus, augm. de particularités tirées d'une vie par un de ses amis[-Lucas]. [*Foll. by* Certamen philos. adv. J. Bredenburg, meditab. I. Orobio]. [*Coll. & ed. by* N. Lenglet du Fresnoy]. s8°. Bruxelles [Amstelaedami]. 1703
Traité de l'existence de Dieu, préc. d'un essai par M. Villemain. Notes par M. Danton. 6e éd. s8°. 1880
TRANSLATIONS.
The characters &c. of true charity display'd. Tr. 8°. 1737
Directions for the conscience of a King. Subjoined 2 supplements. *Tr.* [*b. w. h.* The characters &c., 1737] 8°. 1751
Telemachus. Tr. Dr. Hawkesworth. s8°. 1807
see BOSSUET (J. B.) Œuvres, t28, Sommaire de la doctrine du livre. Explic. des maximes des saints &c. [*by* F.], 1817.
,, GUYON (*Mme.* J. M.) Justif. de la doctr. de Mme. G.; avec un examen de la 9e & 10e conf. de Cassien, par F., 3t, 1790.
,, JÄGER (J. W.) Examen theolog., in quo F. de Salignac placita revocantur, 1709.
,, VERAX (*Mons.*) Difficultez sur l'ordonnance de l'archév. de C., 1705.
Feng Hua Huang, *see* HUANG (F. H.)
Feng Yu-hsiang (*Field-Marshal*), *of the Chinese army, see* BROOMHALL (M.) Marshal F., 5th ed., 1924.
Fenn (Amor). Design & tradition. 8°. 1920
Fenn (George Manville). Mem. of B. F. Stevens. s8°. 1903
Fennebresque (Juste). La petite Venise [Versailles]. Hist. d'une corporation nautique. 8°. 1899
Fennel (John). A tribute to the memory of Miss Eliza Mann &c. [P2467]. s8°. Bradford. 1819
Fenner (Heinz). Die Propaganda-Schulen d. Bolschewisten, *see* BOLSCHEWISMUS. Sammlung v. Quellen z. St. d. B., H4, 1920.
Die rote Armee. 8°. 1920
Fenning (Elizabeth), *see* WATKINS (J.) Import. results of investig. into case of E. F., includ. report of h. trial, w. 30 letters wr. in prison, 1815.
Fenwick, *The family of, see* FENWICK (E.) Fate of the F.: letters, 1798–1828, 1927.
Fenwick (Eliza), *wife of John Fenwick, friend of Charles Lamb.* The fate of the Fenwicks: letters to M. Hays, 1798–1828. Ed. A. F. Wedd. 8°. 1927
Fenwick (John), *see* WHITE (T.) Last speeches of the 5 traitors: J. F. &c., 1679.
Feodor Alekseevich, *emperor of Russia, see* BERKH (V.) Царствованіе Θ. А. &c., 2ч., 1834–35.
Feodoroff (Evg.), *see* FEDOROV (E.)
Fer (Nicholas de). Relation, Fontainebleau, (1169–1697; ms. inéd.), *see* BOURGES (E.) Recherches, 1896.
Ferber (Edna). Buttered side down. s8°. [1926]
The girls. s8°. 1922
Mother knows best & o. s. s8°. [1927]
So Big. s8°. [1924]
Ferber (Johann Jacob). Exercit. 2a de fanaticis, G. Arnoldi Kirchen-Hist. oppos., barbara malitia J. Langii &c. Præs. J. J. F., resp. J. P. Aver. [P2631]. s4°. Vitembergae. [1711]
Ferchius (Matthæus). Vita Joannis Dunsii Scoti & Apologiæ. 2p. s8°. Bononiae. 1622. [*repr.*] Neapoli. 1629
Ferdinand I, *emperor of Germany.*
see PASSAU. Abdruck d. Passaw. Vortrags &c. [*beg.* Wir F. &c.], 1552.
,, SUPPLICATIONES, Erklärungen &c., d. Churf. Fürsten &c. item F. Declaration, wie es mit der geistl. eigenen Ritterschaft &c., 1679.
,, TÖKÖLY (I.) Austriaca Austeritas &c., 1671.
Ferdinand IV, *King of Naples.* Orig. & hist. of St. Leucio; tr., *see* CLARKE (A.) Misc. wks., v11, 1837.
Reglamento para la nueva planta en que manda S. M. se extabl. los regimientos de su exercito. [P2766]. 8°. [Nap.] 1765
Ferdinand I, *king of Portugal.*
see LOPES (F.) Chron. de el-Rei F., 3v, 1895–96.
,, —— Cron. de D. Pedro e D. F., 3v, 1921–22.
Ferdinand V, *king of Spain, surnamed the Catholic.*
see ANTONIO, *de Lebrixa.* Rerum a F. et Elis. &c. gestarum decades 2, 1579.
,, VALLA (L.) De rebus a F. Aragoniæ rege gestis libri 3, 1579.
Ferdinand VII, *king of Spain, see* VILLA-URRUTIA (W. R., *marq.* DE). F. VII rey constit.; hist. diplom., 1820–23, 1922.
Ferdinand II, *king of the Two Sicilies.*
see DURELLI (F.) Cenno storico di F., 1859.
,, PAGANO (G.) Storia di F. (1830–1850), 1853.
Ferdinand-Lop (S.) L'Indochine, aperçu économ. s8°. 1923
La Tunisie & ses richesses. Préf. de M. Soulier. 8°. 1921
Ferenczi (Sandor). Psycho-analysis & the war neuroses. By S. F., K. Abraham, E. Simmel & E. Jones. 8°. 1921
Féret (Charles Théophile). Les chauffeurs, nouvelle, *see* ŒUVRES libres, 42, 1924.
Feret (Édouard). Bergerac & ses vins. s8°. 1903
Ferguson (A. M.), *the elder, see* CEYLON. The C. directory, 1875; comp. by A. M. & J. Ferguson, 1875.
Ferguson (Andrew), *captain of Gen. Macdonald's regiment.* Genuine acc. of all the persons of note in Scotland, now engaged in the service of the Chevalier. [P2779]. 8°. [1745 ?]
Ferguson (John), *assistant ed. of the "Ceylon Observer," see* CEYLON. The C. directory, 1875; comp. by A. M. & J. Ferguson, 1875.
Ferguson (John Calvin), *see* MYTHOLOGY of all races, v8, Chinese, by F., 1928.
Ferguson (R. W.)
Educ. in the factory: Bournville Works. [P2719]. 8°. 1924
Ferguson (Robert), *Nonconformist Divine, see* DARIEN, *Scots colony.* *Just &c. vindic. of the Scots design for a colony at D. [*attrib. to F.*], 1699.
Ferguson (Victor).
A dict. of Russian milit. & naval terms. s8°. [1906]
Ferguson (William Bates), *K.C., see* HURTER (F.) & V. C. DRIFFIELD. Photographic researches; ed. W. B. F., 1920.

Fergusson (David). 940 Scottish proverbs, gathered by D. F., &c. s8°. 1675
Scot. proverbs, f. orig. print of 1641, w. MS. coll. Ed. E. Beveridge. [Scot. Text Soc., N.S., 15]. 8°. E. 1924
Fergusson (*Sir* William), *Bart.*
A system of pract. surgery. 2nd ed. s8°. 1846
Feriae Groninganae, 2v, 1733–39, *see* ENGELHARD (N.), *ed.*
Feria y Morales (Bartholemé Sanchez de), *see* SANCHEZ DE FERIA Y MORALES (B.)
Ferishta. Hist. of Hindostan, to the death of Akbar. Tr. w. a diss. conc. the Brahmins [& App. cont. hist. to pres. time. By A. Dow]. [3v.] 4°. 1768–72
Fermat (Pierre de), *see* NIELSEN (N.) Recherches s. l'équation de F., 1922.
Ferme (Charles). Logical anal. of the E. to the Romans. Tr. W. Skae. And a comm. by A. Melville in Lat. Ed., w. life of F. by W. L. Alexander. [Wodrow Soc., 12]. 8°. E. 1850
Fermor (U. M. Ellis-), *see* ELLIS-FERMOR (U. M.)
Fernald (Chester Bailey). To-morrow. Play. 8°. 1928
Fernandes (J. F. St. Antonio), *see* MELLO (*Cap.* F. DE) &c. Révision des champignons appart. au genre Nocardia, 1919.
Fernandes (Pedro), *see* HERNANDES (P.)
Fernandes Valdez (João). Novissimo dicc. inglez-portuguez. 4ª ed. s8°. Rio de Janeiro. 1888
Portuguese & Eng. pronouncing dict. 4th ed. s8°. Rio de Janeiro. 1888
Fernandes Vieira (João), *see* VIEIRA CASTRIOTO (J. F.)
Fernandez (—). La Republica del Salvador. [*So lettered on binding. tp. wanting & otherwise imperf.*] s8°. *n.p. n.d.*
Fernandez (Bartholomeu), *see* BARTHOLOMEU [FERNANDEZ], *dos Martyres.*
Fernández (Francisco Román), *publisher.*
Granada: 24 vistas en fototipia. obl.8°. Granada. *n.d.*
Fernández (Ildefonso Rodríguez y), *see* RODRIGUEZ Y FERNANDEZ (I.)
Hist. relatio de apostolicis miss. patrum Soc. Jesu apud Chiquitos Paraguariae populos. In ling. Lat. tr. s4°. Augustae Vindel. 1733
Fernandez (Ramon). Messages. s1, 2e éd. s8°. [1926]
Fernández Ardavín (Luis).
La eterna inquietud. Versos. s8°. 1922
Fernandez de Béthencourt (Francisco). Hist. genealog. y heráld. de la monarquía esp., casa real y grandes de España. t10. 4°. 1920
Fernandez de La Puente y Acevedo (José), *see* PIFERRER (F.) Nobiliario de los reinos &c. de España; con un dicc. de heraldica por J. F. de La P. y A., 6t, 1855–60.
Fernandez de Navarrete (Martin).
Biblioteca marítima española. 2t. la8°. 1851
Fernandez de Piedrahita (Lucas), *bp. of (1) Santa Marta, (2) Panama.* Hist. gen. de las conquistas del Nuevo Reyno de Granada. [pl *engraved tp. no more publd.*] sfol. Amberes. [1688]
Fernandez Moreno (Francisco), *see* ALCOCER MARTINEZ (M.) Anales universit.: Univ. de Valladolid, t1, estatutos en Latin tr. por F. F. M., 1918.
Fernandez Piedrahita (Lucas de), *see* FERNANDEZ DE PIEDRAHITA (L.)
Fernandez Trancoso (Gonçalo). Histórias de proveito e exemplo. [Antologia portug.; organiz. por A. de Campos]. 2ª ed. s8°. Paris. 1923
Fernández y Ávila (Gaspar). La infancia de Jesu-Christo. Zehn span. Weihnachtsspiele; hrsg. M. L. Wagner. [Z. f. roman. Phil. Beiheft, 72]. 8°. Halle. 1922
Fernand-Laurent (Camille Jean). J.-S. Bailly, prem. maire de Paris. la8°. 1927
Fernan-Núñez (C. J. Gutierrez de Los Rios, *conde* de).
see MOUSSET (A.) Un témoin ignoré de la Révol.: le Cte. de F. N., ambass. d'Esp. à Paris, 1787–91, 1924.
Fernie (John).
Hist. of the town &c. of Dunfermline. 8°. Dunfermline. 1815
Fernley (John), *J.P., of Clairville, Southport, see* POPE (W. B.) Memoir of J. F., 1874.
Feronce (Albert Dufour-), *see* DUFOUR-FERONCE (A.)
Ferrai (Luigi Alberto). Lettere di cortigiane del sec. 16; *ed.* L. A. F., 1884, *see* LETTERE.
Ferrajoli (Alessandro). La congiura dei cardinali contro Leone X. [Reale Soc. Rom. di Storia Patria. Misc. No. 7]. 8°. 1919

Ferrand (—), *médecin du Kan des Tartars.* Rel. t. la Krimée, les Tartares Nogaïs &c.—Voy. de Krimée en Circassie, 1702, *see* BERNARD (J. F.), *ed.* Recueil, t4, 1718; 1732; t10, 1738.
Ferrand (Gabriel).
L'empire sumatranais de Çrīvijaya. 8°. 1922
Instructs. nautiques & routiers arabes & portugais des 15e & 16e siècles. Reprod., tr. &c. par G. F. t1, 2. 8°. 1921–25
1, Le pilote des mers de l'Inde, de la Chine & de l'Indonésie; par Šihāb Ad-Dīn Aḥmad bin Mājid, texte arabe.
2, Par Sulaymān al-Mahri & Bin Mājid, texte arabe.
Les poids, mesures & monnaies des mers du Sud aux 16e & 17e s. [Extr. du Journal Asiat., 1920]. 8°. 1921
Ferrand (Henri). Grenoble & thereabouts. 8°. [1923]
La route des Alpes françaises. 8°. Grenoble. [1925]
Ferrand (Louis), *see* AUBERT DE VERSÉ (N.) L'avocat des protestans, contre F., 1686.
Ferranti (Giuseppe Manini), *see* MANINI FERRANTI (G.)
Ferrar (John), *Deputy Governor of the Virginia Co.* Nicholas Ferrar, *see* MAYOR (J. E. B.) Camb. in 17th cent., p1, 1855.
Ferrar (Nicholas).
see COLLETT (H.) Little Gidding & its founder, N. F., 1925.
„ FERRAR (J.) N. F., 1855.
„ JEBB (*Dr.*) N. F., 1855.
„ PECKARD (P.) Mem. of life of N. F., 1790.
Ferrar (William John). The saints of Cornwall. s8°. 1920
Ferrara. Indice dei mss. d. Civica Bibl. di F.; d. can. G. Antonelli. p1 [*no more publ.*] la8°. Ferrara. 1884
Ferrara, *Council of, see* FLORENCE, *Co. of, 1438–45.*
Ferrara (Mario). Due sonetti contro il Savonarola, *see* ARCHIVIO STOR. ITAL., a. 80, 1922.
Ferraresi. *Rime scelte de' poeti F., 1713, *see* RIME.
Ferrari (*Card.* Andrea Carlo), *see* PASTORI (G.) Il Card. F., 1919.
Ferrari (Constanzo) & J. Caccia.
Grand dict. franç.-ital. & ital.-franç. la8°. 1885
Ferrari (Demetrio). Commento d. Odi barbare di G. Carducci. 3v. s8°. Bologna. [1919–21]
Ferrari (Enrique de Olavarria y), *see* OLAVARRIA Y FERRARI (E. DE).
Ferrari (Francesco Bernardino), *see* BASSI (M.) Dispareri in materia d'archit.; annot. da F., 1771.
Ferrari (Girolamo), *Franciscan monk, see* FORTUNATO, *da Brescia.*
Ferrari (Giulio), *directeur du Musée d'Art Indust. de Rome.* Les deux Canaletto, A. Canal, B. Bellotto, peintres. 56 planches avec intr. par G. F. la8°. Turin. 1914
Il ferro nell' arte ital. 2ª ed. sfol. Milano. [1923 ?]
Ferrari (Giuseppe), *polit. writer* [FERRARI (JOSEPH)].
Hist. de la raison d'état. 8°. 1860
Ferrari (Luigi). Traduzioni ital. d. teatro tragico franc. nei sec. 17° & 18°. Saggio bibliog. 8°. Paris. 1925
Ferrari (Vittorio). Il canto 29 del Paradiso, *see* DANTE ALIGHIERI. Lect. Dantis, 1924.
Ferraria. Ignoti monachi Cisterc. S. Mariae de Ferraria Chronica & Ryccardi de S. Germano Chron. priora. Ed. A. Gaudenzi, adj. Ryccardi Chron. post. ex ed. G. Pertzii. [Soc. Napol. di St. Patria, ser. 1]. sfol. Neapoli. 1888
Ferrari da Grado (Giov. Matteo), *see* FERRARI DA GRADO (H. M.) Une chaire de médecine au 15e s.: un prof. à l'Univ. de Pavie, 1432–72 [*i.e.* G. M. F. da G.], 1899.
Ferrari da Grado (Henri Maxime). Une chaire de médecine au 15e s.: un prof. à l'Univ. de Pavie, 1432–72 [*i.e.* G. M. Ferrari da Grado]. 8°. 1899
Ferrarius (Octavius). De re vestiaria libri septem. 3ª ed., access. Analecta de re vestiaria & diss. de vet. lucernis sepulchral.
[4p in 1v. *each w. sep. pagin. & tp.*] s4°. Patavii. 1685
Ferrarius (*card.* Thomas Maria), *1647–1716, see* CONCINA (D.) De vita & rebus gestis T. M. F. card. libri tres, 1757.
Ferrata (*card.* Domenico), *see* STUTZ (U.) Päpstl. Diplom. unter Leo XIII, nach d. Denkwürd. d. Kard. D. F., 1925.
Ferrazzi (Giuseppe Jacopo).
Di Bassano e dei Bassanesi illustri. la8°. Bassano. 1847
Ferreira (Antonio). A Castro. [*Tragedia*]. Conforme a ed. de 1598, com prologo por Mendes dos Remedios. s8°. Coimbra. 1915
Ferreira (João Sousa), *see* SOUSA FERREIRA (J.)
Ferreira d'Almeida (João). Differença da Christandade. Tr. de Castelhano em Port. pelo P. J. F. A. d'A. s8°. Trangambar. 1728
Livro dos Psalmos de David rev. sobre a trad. do J. F. A. D'A. s8°. Lisboa. 1868

Ferreira de Vasconcellos (Jorge). Comédia Eufrosina. Conforme a impr. de 1561, publ. por A. F. G. Bell. [Acad. das Sci. de Lisboa]. 8°. 1918
Ferrer (Francisco) [FERRER Y GUARDIA], *see* RAMUS (P.) F. F., s. Leben u. s. Werk, 1921.
Ferrer (Vincent), *Saint, see* VINCENT [FERRER], *Saint.*
Ferreres (Jean Baptiste), *see* GURY (J. P.) Casus conscientiae &c., opera J. B. F., ed. 3ª hisp., corr. &c., 2t, 1914.
Ferrerius (Joannes), *Pedemontanus.* Hist. Abbatum de Kynlos: una cum vita Th. Chrystalli Abbatis. [Ed. W. D. Wilson, w. pref. by J. P. Muirhead. Bannatyne Club]. 4°. E. 1839
Ferrero (Ermanno), *1855–1906.* V. Promis e i suoi studii numismatici, *see* REGIA DEP. DI STORIA PATRIA. Misc., t29, 1892.
see MANNO (A.) E. F. commem., 1909.
Ferrero (Guglielmo).
Four years of Fascism. Tr. fr. "Da Fiume a Roma" by E. W. Dickes. 8°. 1924
Memorie e confessioni di un sovrano deposto. [Storia del sec. 19]. s8°. Milano. 1920
La rivolta del figlio. Romanzo. s8°. Milano. 1927
La ruine de la civilisation antique. s8°. [1921]
The ruin of anc. civiliz. & triumph of Xty. &c. Tr. Lady Whitehead. 8°. N.Y. 1921
La tragedia d. pace: da Versailles alla Ruhr. s8°. Milano. 1923
see SERRA (R.) Scritti ined. (Int. alla Grandezza &c. di Roma di G. F.), 1923.
—— **& C. Barbagallo.** Roma antica. 3v. s8°. Firenze. 1921–22
Ferrers (Edmund).
*Illust^s. of Hogarth f. authors he never read &c. 8°. 1816
Ferrers de Chartley (Charlotte Compton, *baroness*), *see* COMPTON (CHARLOTTE).
Ferretti (Giovanni), *see* DANTE ALIGHIERI. Lectura D.: c. 28 dell' Inferno letto da G. F., 1917.
Ferretti (Luigi). Centoventi sonetti in dial. romanesco. Pref. e note di L. Morandi. s8°. Firenze. 1879
Ferretus, *Vicentinus.* Indice sistem. d. Hist. rerum in Italia gest. (Muratori, R. I. S., IX) di F., comp. da G. Filippi &c., *see* REGIA DEP. DI STORIA PATRIA. Misc., t23, App., 1884.
Ferri (Armando). Alessandro Magnasco. 40 riprod. con testi e cat.; a cura di A. F. 8°. [1922]
Ferri (Enrico), *see* AMICI (F. N.) E. F., 1920.
Ferri (Silvio). Alcune iscrizioni di Cirene, *see* KÖN.-PREUSS. AKAD. Abhdln., Phil.-hist. Kl., 1925.
Ferrier (J. Kenneth). Crooks & crime. 8°. 1928
Ferrier (James Frederick).
Philos. works. n. ed. 3v. s8°. E. 1883–88
Ferrier (Paul). Nichtjes román naar P. F., *see* HALL (J. N. VAN). De viool van Cremona &c., 1882.
Ferrier (Vincent), *Saint, see* VINCENT [FERRER], *Saint.*
Ferrières (Guillaume de), *called Le Vidame de Chartres.* Chansons & saluts d'amour (13c.) Notice par L. Lacour. [Trésor des pièces rares &c.] s8°. 1856
Ferrigni (Pietro Coccoluto-), *see* COCCOLUTO-FERRIGNI (P.)
Ferriman (Z. Duckett). Greece & to-morrow, 2nd ed., *see* ANGLO-HELLENIC LEAGUE. Publ^s., No. 23, 1917.
Some Engl. philhellenes, 8, Lord Byron. 8°. 1920
Ferrin (Augustin William). Chinese currency & finance, 1919, *see* UNITED STATES: COMMERCE.
Ferriol (Antoine de), *count de Pont de Veyle, see* PONT-DE-VEYLE (A. DE F., *comte* DE).
Ferri-Pisani (—). Trois couleurs, trois aristocraties, *see* ŒUVRES libres, 72, 1927.
Ferris (John Alexander). Financial economy of the U.S. s8°. San Francisco. 1867
Ferriz (Blas Antonio Nassarre y), *see* NASSARRE Y FERRIZ (B. A.)
Ferro (Antonio) [FERRUS (A.)] Apparato d. statue nuov. trov. n. distrutta Cuma, 1606, *see* MAZZELLA (S.) Sito &c., di Pozzuolo, 1606.
Ferro (Giov. Francesco). Istoria dell' antica cittá di Comacchio. Libri 4. la8°. Ferrara. 1701
Ferruccio Guerrieri (Fr.), *see* GUERRIERI (F. F.)
Ferruggia (Gemma). Il sole nascosto. s8°. Firenze. 1920
Ferry (Abel). La Guerre vue d'en bas & d'en haut. s8°. 1920
Ferry (John Farwell). Cat. of coll. of birds f. Costa Rica, *see* FIELD COLUMBIAN MUS. Ornith. ser., v1vi, 1910.
Ferry (Paul), *see* BOSSUET (J. B.) Œuvres, t23, Réfut. du Catéchisme du Sieur P. F., 1816.
Fersen (*Grefve* **Hans Axel v.**), *see* HEIDENSTAM (O. G. DE). Letters of Marie Antoinette, F. &c.; tr., 1926.
Ferus (Joannes), *see* WILD (JOHANN).

Ferval (Claude), *ps.* [*i.e. la baronne* A. H. DE PIERREBOURG]. The martyr of love: life of L. de La Vallière. Intr. by J. Richepin. Tr. S. Dark. 8°. [1914]
La vie & la mort de Cléopâtre. s8°. 1922
Feshin (Nikolai Ivanovich), *see* DULSKY (P.) Н. И. Фешин, 1921.
Fessler (Joseph), *Bishop of* (1) *Nyssa, &* (2) *Saint Polten.* Das letzte u. d. nächste allgem. Concil. 8°. Freiburg im Br. 1869
True & false infallibility of the popes; reply to Dr. Schulte. Tr. A. St. John. 8°. 1875
Fester (Richard). Das Selbstbestimmungsrecht u. d. deut. Einheitsstaat. [Deut. Rundschau; Sonderheft. P2769]. 8°. 1919
see BADEN. Regesten d. Markgrafen, 1050–1515, B1, bearb. v. R. F., 1900.
Festing (Gabrielle). From the land of princes. Pref. by Sir G. Birdwood. 8°. 1904
Fest-Kalendar. F.-K. in Bildern u. Liedern, 1835–36, *see* POCCI (F., *Graf.* v.)
Festskrift. Festskrift tilegnet A. Kjaer av Venner, 26. Sept. 1924, *see* KJAER (A.)
Fet (Afanasii Afanasevich). Мои воспоминанія, 1848–89. 2ч. la8°. Москва. 1890
see BLOK (G.) Рожденіе поэта, о молодости Ф., 1924.
Feti (Domenici), *see* OLDENBOURG (R.) D. F., 25 riprod. con testo e cat., 1921.
Fétis (François Joseph). Biog. notice of N. Paganini, w. anal. of h. compos. [Tr.] 2nd ed. 8°. [1876]
The hist. of music; or how to understand & enjoy. Tr. s8°. 1846
Notice of A. Stradivari. Prec. by researches on bow instruments; & remarks on F. Tourte. Tr. J. Bishop. s8°. 1864
Fett (Harry). Norges kirker i Middelalderen. 4°. [1909]
Feuchtmayr (Carl), *see* BUCHNER (E.) Oberdeut. Kunst. d. Spätgotik u. Reformationszeit, 1924.
Feuchtwanger (Lion). 3 angelsächs. Stücke. [Die Petroleuminseln—Kalkutta, 4. Mai—Wird Hill amnestiert?]. s8°. 1927
Die hassl. Herzogin Margarete Maultasch. s8°. 1926
Jud Süss. Roman. s8°. München. [1926]
" " ....51.–56. Tausend. s8°. München. [1927]
" " Tr. W. & E. Muir. 6th ed. 8°. 1927
" " " " ....11th ed. 8°. 1927
The ugly duchess. [Tr. W. & E. Muir]. s8°. [1927]
Vasantasena. Schauspiel. s8°. Potsdam. 1927
Feudal. Inquisitions &c. rel. to F. Aids; w. o. doc. in the P. R. O., 1284–1431, v6. [Cal. of State Papers]. la8°. 1920
6, York & additions.
Feuerlein (Jacob Wilhelm) [FEUERLINUS].
Bibl. symbolica evang. lutherana &c. Acc. app^s. 2. s8°. Gottingae. 1752
" " Aucta &c. Ed. J. B. Riederer. 2p *in* 1v. s8°. Norimbergae. 1768
Obs. in August. Conf. articulos cum præf. de Wilhelmi Lindani concordia discorde &c. s4°. Gottingae. [1742]
Feuerlein (Johann Conrad), *see* MÖRL (G. P.) Vindic. doct. Lutheran. de gratia praedest. quam F. propugn., 1702.
Feuerlein (Johann Jacob). Diss. de Christianorum migratione in Pellam. Praes. J. G. Baiero, 1694. Recusa. [P432]. s4°. Jenae. 1712
Feuerzeug. *Fewrzeug Christl. Andacht &c. [*b. w.* Luther (M.) Enchiridion &c., 1566]. s8°. L. [1565]
Feugère (Anatole). L'abbé Raynal, 1713–96. Doc^s. inéd. [Un précurseur de la Révol.] 8°. Angoulême. 1922
Feuillet (Octave). Le village. Comédie. n. éd. s8°. 1864
Feurtado (W. Alexander). Official & o. personages of Jamaica, 1655–1790 &c. 8°. Jamaica. 1896
Feustking (Friedrich Christian). Diss. qua Godof. Arnoldum anistoresias in re sacra convictum, praes. P. L. Hannekenio, 1699, submisit F. ed. 2ª. [P595]. s4°. Wittenbergae. 1719
Feustking (Johann Heinrich). Hist. Colloquii Ieverensis inter Lutheranos & Reformatos a. 1576, acta &c. s4°. Servestae. 1707
Féval (Paul H. C.), *père.* La fille du Juif-errant. n. éd. s8°. 1895
Fèvre (Henry). Galafieu. Roman. s8°. 1923
Février (James G.) Date, compos. & sources de la lettre d'Aristée à Philocrate. [H. E., 242]. 8°. 1924
Few. *Few (A) odds & ends for cheerful friends, 1870, *see* COLLIER (J. P.)
*Few (A) plain reasons why a Protestant &c. sh. not turn R. Catholick, 1688, *see* BARLOW (T.)

Fewkes (Jesse Walter).
Works in SMITHSONIAN INST. BUREAU OF ETHNOLOGY. Rep.
Designs on prehistoric Hopi pottery, 1919. [33.]
Prehist. island culture area of Amer., 1922. [34.]
Prehist. villages, castles &c. of S.-W. Colorado, 1919. [70.]
Works in SMITHSONIAN INST. Misc. Coll[s].
Add. designs on prehist. Mimbres pottery, 1924. [76.]
Archeol. coll. f. Young's Canyon, nr. Flagstaff, Arizona, 1926. [77.]
Designs on prehist. pottery f. the Mimbres valley, New Mexico, 1923. [74.]
Prelim. archeolog. explor. at Weeden Is., Florida, 1924. [76.]
Fewrzeug, *see* FEUERZEUG.
Fewster (Ernest P.) My garden dreams. 8°. Ottawa. 1926
Feyler (*Col.* **Fernand).** Le problème de la Guerre. 8°. 1918
F. F. F. R. D. G., *see* FORTIN (F.)
Ffranck (W.), *ps., see* SHEPPARD (J. W. FFRANCK).
Fhelavius (Georgius), *see* FEHLAVIUS (G.)
Fiamma (Gabriello), *bp. of Chioggia.*
Rime spirituali. s8°. Vinegia. 1570
Fiammazzo (Antonio), *see* BAMBAGIUOLI (G. DE'). Comm. più ant. &c. d. Inferno ; p. c. d. A. F., 1892.
Fian (*Dr.***),** *alias* JOHN CUNNINGHAM, *see* NEWS. Newes f. Scotland : life & death of Dr. F., a notable sorcerer (1591), 1924.
***Fiat** Lux, or a gen. conduct to a right understanding in the great combustions &c. about relig. in Eng. &c., 1661, *see* CANE (J. V.)
Fibiger (Johannes And. Grib). Investig. on the Spiroptera Cancer, 3–6, *see* KONG. DAN. VID. SELSK. Biol. Med., B1, 1917–19.
—— **& P. Møller.** Immunisation agst. metastasis formation in experimental cancer, *see* KONG. DAN. VID. SELSK. Biolog. Med., B6, 1927.
Fichert (Luigi). Scienza e fede, [ode. Nozze Sacchetto-Ragazzini. N127]. 8°. Padova. 1866
Fichet (Guillaume). Poème comp. en l'honneur du card. Phil. de Lévis [*in Lat.*], Rome, 1473, facs., *see* PICOT (E.) & H. STEIN. Recueil, 1923.
Fichot (Charles). Statistique mon. du départ. de l'Aube. t1, 2, Arrondiss. de Troyes. la8°. Troyes. 1884–88
Fichte (Immanuel Hermann). Grundzüge zum Systeme d. Philosophie. [*b. w. h.* Gegensatz, &c. heut. Philos., 1832]. 2T [*in* 1*v*]. 8°. Heidelberg. 1833–36
Die speculat. Theologie. [Syst. d. Philos., Abt. 3]. 8°. Heidelberg. 1846
Über Gegensatz, Wendepunkt u. Ziel heutiger Philos. 8°. Heidelberg. 1832
Fichte (Johann Gottlieb). Addresses to the German nation (1807–08). Tr. R. F. Jones & G. H. Turnbull. 8°. Chicago. 1922
Briefwechsel. Krit. Gesamtausg. Hrsg. H. Schulz. 2B. 8°. L. 1925
Über d. Unterschied d. Geistes u. d. Buchstabens in d. Philos. Hrsg. v. S. Berger. 8°. L. 1924
Ficino (Marsiglio). Comm. s. i 10 dialoghi di Platone del giusto ; tr. Spontone, *see* SPONTONE (C.) Corona d. princ., 1590.
Expos. Prisciani & Marsilii in Theophrastam de sensu &c., *see* IAMBLICHUS *of Chalcis.* De mysteriis &c., 1497.
Liber de voluptate, *see* IAMBLICHUS *of Chalcis.* De mysteriis &c., 1497.
Fick (Rudolf). Einiges ü. Vererbungsfragen, *see* KÖN.-PREUSS. AKAD. Abhdln., Phys.-math. Kl., 1924.
Üb. d. Entst. d. Gelenkformen mit Tierversuchen, *see* KÖN.-PREUSS. AKAD. Abh., Phys.-math. Klasse, 1921.
Fickeler (Paul). Der Altai, *see* PETERMANNS MITT. Ergnzb. 40, 1925.
Fickendey (Ernst). Der Ölbaum in Kleinasien. la8°. L. 1922
Ficker (Johannes). Luther, 1517 : Rede. [Verein f. Ref.-gesch. Schr., Jhrg. 36 (N[r]. 130)]. 8°. L. 1918
Ficker (Julius). Vom Reichsfürstenstande, 12. u. 13. Jhdt. B2 [*in* 3T], hrsg. u. bearbt. v. P. Puntschart. 8°. Innsbruck, Graz & L. 1911–23
Fickler (Johann Baptist) [FIKLERUS]. Spongia contra praedicantium Wirtenberg. aspergines, illorum, qui Patriarchae Constantinop. judicium super cap. Aug. Conf. temere expet. s8°. Ingolstadii. 1585
Ficoroni (Francesco de'). Gemmæ ant. litteratæ &c. Acc. vetera monumenta &c. Omnia coll., adnot. &c. illustr. a N. Galeotti. s4°. Romæ. 1757

Fiddes (*Sir* **George Vandeleur).**
The Dominions & Colonial Offices. 8°. [1926]
Fide. *De fide, 1522, *see* DE.
Fidel (Camille). La réfut. d'accus. contre les troupes franç. de couleur en territoires Rhénans occupés. [P2708]. 8°. 1922
Fidelis, *ps.* *Vier Wochen in Wien, 1827, *see* WIEN.
Fides, *of Agen, Saint.* La chanson de Ste. Foy. [Ed.] E. Hoepffner & P. Alfaric [Univ. de Strasbourg]. 2t. la8°. 1926
1, Facs. du ms. & texte crit. Intr. & comm. philol. ; par E. Hoepffner.
2, Tr. franç. & sources lat. Intr. & comm. hist. ; par P. Alfaric.
La chanson de Ste. Foi d'Agen : poème provençal du 11e s. Ed. A. Thomas. [Class. fr. du m-â., 45]. s8°. 1925
Fidler (Matthias). Woher kommen u. was sind unsere Gedanken ? Übers. v. F. Feilgenhauer. [P2480]. 8°. L. 1896
Fiebig (Paul), *see* TOSEFTA. Der Tosephtatraktat roš haššena, mit. Bemerkungen v. P. F., 1914.
Fiebiger (Otto) & L. Schmidt. Inschriftensammlung z. Gesch. d. Ostgermanen, 1917, *see* KAIS. AKAD. D. WISS. ZU WIEN. Denkschr., B60, 1918.
Fiedler (Hermann Georg). Das Oxforder Buch deut. Dichtung, 12.–20. Jhdt. Hrsg. H. G. F. Mit Geleitworte v. G. Hauptmann. [neu. A.] s8°. O. 1927
Fiedler (Joseph), *ed.*
Relationen Venetian. Botschafter ü. Deutschl. u. Österr. im 16. Jhdt., *see* FONTES RERUM AUSTRIAC., B30, 1870.
„ „ im 17. Jhdt., 2B, *see* FONTES RERUM AUSTRIAC., B26, 27, 1866–67.
see JOSEPH II, *emp.* Joseph II u. Graf Cobenzl ; ihr Briefwechsel, 2B, 1901.
Field [*newspaper*], *see* HASELTINE (H.) Exhib. of sculp., under auspices of the F., 1925.
Field Columbian Museum.
Anthropological series. v16. 8°. Chicago. 1923
Gunsaulus (H. C.) Jap. sword-mounts in F. Mus., 1923. [16.]
Anthropology design series. No. 1. 4°. Chicago. 1924
see LEWIS (A. B.) Block prints f. India for textiles, 1924. [1.]
Botanical ser. v5, 6. 8°. Chicago. 1923–27
MacNair (J. B.) Citrus products, 2 p, 1926–27. [6i.]
Millspaugh (C. F.) & L. W. Nuttall. Flora of Santa Catalina Island, 1923. [5.]
Ornithological series. v1. la8°. Chicago. 1896–1916
Cherrie (G. K.) Contrib. to ornith. of San Domingo, 1896. [1i.]
Cory (C. B.) Birds of the Leeward Isl[s]., Caribbean Sea, 1909. [1v.]
—— Descr[s]. of appar. new S. Amer. birds &c., 1916. [1x.]
—— Descr[s]. of new birds f. S. Amer. &c., 1915. [1viii.]
—— Descr[s]. of 28 new species &c. of neotropical birds, 1913. [1vii.]
—— Notes on S. Amer. birds, w. descrs. &c., 1915. [1ix.]
Dearborn (N.) Cat. of coll. of birds f. Brit. E. Africa, 1909. [1iv.]
—— Cat. of coll. of birds f. Guatemala, 1907. [1iii.]
Elliot (D. G.) Cat. of coll. birds obt. by the Exped. into Somaliland, 1897. [1ii.]
Ferry (J. F.) Cat. of coll. of birds f. Costa Rica, 1910. [1vi.]
Report series. v5, 6 (1915–25). 8°. Chicago. 1915–25
Zoological series. v10, 13, 15, 16, 19. 8°. Chicago. 1909–26
Ayer (E. E.) Cat. of the E. E. A. ornitholog. library ; by J. T. Zimmer, 2p, 1926. [16.]
Cory (C. B.) Cat. of birds of the Americas &c., p2–5, 1918–27. [13ii–v.]
Meek (S. E.) Annot. list. of fishes in Fresh waters of Costa Rica, 1914. [10x.]
—— New species of fishes f. Costa Rica, 1912. [10vii.]
—— & S. F. Hildebrand. Descr. of new fishes f. Panama, 1912. [10vi.]
—— & —— Fishes of fresh waters of Panama, 1916. [10xv.]
—— & —— Marine fishes of Panama, 2p, 1923–25. [15.]
—— & —— New species of fishes f. Panama, 1913. [10viii.]
Osgood (W. H.) Diagnoses of new E. African mammals, 1910. [19ii.]
—— Four new mammals f. Venezuela, 1914. [10xi.]
—— Further new mammals f. B. E. Africa, 1910. [10iii.]
—— Mammals f. coast & islands of N. South America, 1910. [10iv.]
—— Mammals f. W. Venezuela & E. Colombia, 1912. [10v.]
—— Mammals of an exped. across N. Peru, 1914. [10xii.]
—— Mammals of Collins Day S. Amer. exped., 1916. [10xiv.]
—— New mammals f. Brazil & Peru, 1915. [10xiii.]
—— New Peruvian mammals, 1913. [10ix.]
—— A peculiar bear from Alaska, 1909. [10i.]
Zimmer (J. T.) Cat. of the Edward E. Ayer ornitholog. library, 2p, 1926. [16.]

Field Columbian Museum *continued*].
REFERENCES.
see GUNSAULUS (H. C.) Japanese costume, 1923.
,, —— Jap. New Year's festival, games &c., 1923.
,, LANGDON (S.) Excav[s]. at Kish: the H. Weld & Field Museum Exped. to Mesopotamia, v1, 1924.

Field (*Adm. Sir* **Arthur Mostyn**), *see* WHARTON (*Sir* W. J. L.) Hydrograph. surveying, 4th ed., rev. & enl. by F., 1920.

Field (*Col.* **Cyril**), *R.M.L.I.* Britain's sea-soldiers: hist. of the Royal Marines &c. Foreword by Earl Beatty. 2v. 4°. L'pool. 1924

Field (Eugene), *see* THOMPSON (S.) Life of E. F., 1927.

Field (Guy Cromwell).
Guild socialism: a crit. exam. s8°. [1920]
Moral theory. Intro. to ethics. 8°. [1921]

Field (James Hermann) & W. A. Harwood. The free atmosphere in India, *see* INDIA: METEOROLOG. DEPT. Memoirs, v24, 1926.

Field (John), *minister of Wandsworth* [FIELDE], *see* OLEVIANUS (C.) Expos. of the Symbole of the Apostles &c., tr. by J. F., 1582.

Field (John Edward).
The Eng. liturgies of 1549 & 1661. 8°. N.Y. 1920

Field (Robert), *portrait painter, see* PIERS (H.) R. F., 1927.

Field (William).
Ireland & imperial expenditure. [P2706]. 8°. D. [1906]

Field (William), *minister of the Gospel in High Street, Warwick.*
Letter in ans. to charges ag. Dissenters, by the Rev. Mr. Miller. 2nd ed. [P2781]. 8°. B'ham. 1791
Second letter in reply to remarks upon the first l. &c. by the vicar & curate of St. Nicholas. [P2781]. 8°. B'ham. 1791

Fielding (A.) The Charteris mystery. s8°. [1925]

Fielding (Cecil Henry).
The records of Rochester. s8°. Dartford. 1910

Fielding (*Sir* **Charles William).**
Food. Foreword by Visc. Milner. 8°. 1923

Fielding (Henry).
Works. With essay by A. Murphy. n. ed. 10v. 8°. 1821
Cat. of books of H. F., sold by S. Baker, Feb. 10th &c. [1755]. [*Typed copy f. unique copy in B.M., w. prices*]. la8°. [1922]
Don Quixote in Eng. Opera. [P2575]. 8°. 1777
The hist. of the adv. of Joseph Andrews &c. [Pref. to David Simple.—Pref. to the Familiar letters]. s8°. 1776
,, ,, ...Illust. by G. Cruikshank. s8°. 1832
see BLANCHARD (F. T.) F., the novelist: st. in hist. crit., 1926.
,, DIGEON (A.) Romans de F., 1923.

Fiellström (Peter). Gramm. Lapponica &c. s8°. Holmiae. 1738

Fiennes (Gerard) & L. G. Pilkington. Getting our living: intr. to econ. of daily life. s8°. 1924

Fierabras [FERUMBRAS]. Fierabras, chanson de geste; publ. A. Kroeber & G. Servois, *see* GUESSARD (F.) Anc. poëtes, t4, 1860.
*The romaunce of the Sowdone of Babylone & of Ferumbras his sone who conquerede Rome. [Roxburghe Club]. 4°. 1854

Fierbertus (Nicolaus), *see* FITZ-HERBERT (NICOLAS).

Fierens-Gevaert (Hippolyte).
Albert Baertsoen. la8°. Brux. 1910
Antoine Wiertz. s8°. Turnhout. 1920
L'expos. van Eyck-Bouts à Bruxelles en 1920. Retables de l'agneau mystique & du St.-Sacrement. 4°. Brux. 1921
La peinture à Bruges. Guide. 4°. Brux. 1922

Fiesco, *Family of* [FIESCA], *see* FEDERICI (F.) Della fam. F. trattato, 1650.

Fieux (Charles de), *chevalier de Mouhy, see* MOUHY (C. DE F., *chev.* DE).

Fiévée (Joseph). Corresp. polit. & admin. p9. [P2553]. 8°. 1818

Fife, *Synod of.* Eccl. records: sels. f. the minutes of the S. of F., 1611–87. [Ed. G. R. Kinloch. Abbotsford Club]. 4°. E. 1837

Fife (James Duff, *2nd earl*). Lord Fife & h. factor [*i.e.* Will. Rose]: corr. of J., 2nd Ld. Fife, 1729–1809. Ed. A. & H. Tayler. 8°. 1925

Fife (Louise V. A. Dagmar, *duchess of*), *see* LOUISE VICTORIA ALEX. DAGMAR, *princess royal.*

Fifty reasons or motives why the R.C. religion ought to be preferred &c., 1715, *see* ANTHONY ULRIC, *d. of Brunswick.*

Figaro (*Newspaper*), *see* MAURRAS (C.) Enquête s. la monarchie, suiv. de Une campagne royaliste au F. (1901–02), 1924.

Figgis (Darrell) [*ps.* MICHAEL IRELAND].
The econ. case for Irish independence. s8°. D. 1920
The paintings of Will. Blake. 4°. 1925
Recoll. of the Irish War. 8°. 1927
The return of the hero. s8°. 1923

Figgis (John Neville). The polit. aspects of S. Augustine's "City of God." [Pringle-Stewart Lect[s]., 1918]. 8°. 1921
Studies of polit. thought f. Gerson to Grotius, 1414–1625. 2nd ed. s8°. C. 1916

Fight the Famine Council, *see* EUROPE. Needs of E.; rep., 1921.

Figliucci (Flavio). Di una mascherata pastorale fatta in Siena, 1582. [*a. ed.* P2758]. s8°. Firenze. 1882

Figueiredo (Antero de). A. de F. [Antol. portuguesa organiz. por A. de Campos]. s8°. Paris. 1923
Don Sebastião, rei de Portugal (1554–78). 6[a] ed. rev. s8°. Paris. 1925

Figueiredo (Fidelino de).
O pensamento polit. do exercito. s8°. [1926]

Figueroa (Garcia de Silva y), *see* SILVA Y FIGUEROA (G. DE).

Figueroa (Vicente Velasquez de), *see* VELASQUEZ DE FIGUEROA.

Figulla (Hugo Heinrich), *see* BOGHAZKÖI. Keilschrifttexte aus B.; Autographien v. H. H. F. &c., 1916–23.

Fiji & the Fijians; ed. G. S. Rowe. 1, Is. & inhabitants; by T. Williams. 2, Mission hist.; by J. Calvert. 2nd ed. rev. 2v. s8°. 1860

Fiklerus (Joannis Baptista), *see* FICKLER (J. B.)

Filangieri (*cav.* **Gaetano**), *see* CONSTANT (B.) Comm. sur l'ouvr. de F., 1822.

Filareti (*il generale*). In margine del Fascismo. 8°. Milano. 1925

Filelfo (Francesco), *1398–1481, see* DALLA SANTA (G.) Patriz. merc. Venez. & F. F., 1906.

Filhol (*Mme.*), *see* MUSÉE ROYAL DE FRANCE. M. R. de F., ou coll. gravée des chefs-d'œ.; publ. Mme. F., 1827.

Filhol (Antoine Michel), *see* MUSÉE NAPOLÉON. Galerie, publ. F. &c., 10t, 1804–15.

Filiasi (*il conte* **Giacomo**). Mem. stor. de' Veneti &c. 8t *in* 9 [6i, ii]. 8°. Venezia. 1796–98

Filicaja (Vincenzo da). Poesie. 2t. s8°. Londra. 1781

Filipinas. Col. de docs. inéd. de Ultramar, s2, t2, 3, 1886–87, *see* COLECCIÓN.

Filippi (*Cav.* **Filippo de**). Italy's protection of art treasures dur. the War, *see* BRIT. ACADEMY. Proc[s]., 1917–18.
Rel. scientif. d. Sped. Ital. de Filippi, nell' Himàlaia, Caracorùm e Turchestàn Cinese, 1913–14. s1, v1, s2, v3, 4, 6, 8, 9. 4°. Bologna. [1923–28]
s1, Geodesia e geofisica.
1, Astronomia geodetica, geodesia e topog.; [*by*] G. Abetti, A. Alessio &c.
s2, Resultati geolog. e geogr.
3, Studi sul glaciale; [*by*] G. Dainelli. [*Tavole b. sep.*]
4, Le condizioni fis. att.; [*by*] G. Dainelli e O. Marinelli.
6, Fossili d. secondario e d. terziario; [*by*] E. Fossa Mancini C. F. Parona & G. Stefanini.
8, Le condizioni delle genti; [by] G. Dainelli.
9, I tipi umani; [*by*] R. Biasutti e G. Dainelli.
Storia d. sped. scient. Ital. nel Himàlaia Caracorùm e Turchestàn Cinese (1913–14); con capit. agg. di G. Dainelli & J. A. Spranger. 4°. Bologna. [1924]

Filippi (Giovanni). Il comune di Firenze ed il ritorno d. S. Sede in Roma, 1367, *see* REGIA DEP. DI STORIA PATRIA. Misc., t26, 1887.

Filippi (Silvio Spaventa), *see* SPAVENTA FILIPPI (S.)

Filippini (Francesco). Nota sugli scultori del sarcofago di S. Domenico. [P2621]. 8°. Bologna. 1914

Filitti (Ioan C.) Domniile române sub Regulamentul Organic 1834–48. Ed. Acad. Române. la8°. Bucuresti. 1915

***Fille** (La) du comte de Pontieu: conte en prose; vers. du 13e & du 15e s.; publ. C. Brunel, 1923; 1926, *see* PONTIEU.

Filleau (Henri). Dict. des familles de l'anc. Poitou. Publ. par H. Beauchet-Filleau & Ch. de Chergé. 2t. 8°. Poitiers. 1840–54

Filon (P. M. Augustin) [*ps.* SANDRIE (PIERRE)].
Hist. d'Angleterre. Préf. de A. Rébelliau. s8°. [1923]
Souv[s]. sur L'Impératrice Eugénie. Préf. de E. Lavisse. [5e éd.] s8°. [1920]

Filosofov (D. V.) Notre évasion; tr. par Maurice, *see* MEREJKOVSKY (D. S.) Le règne de l'Antéchrist, 1921.
see MEREJKOVSKY (D. S.), D. V. F. &c. Царство Антихриста, 1921.

Filosseno (Marcello) [PHILOXENUS]. Rime. s8°. Treviso. 1823
Sylve de M. Philoxeno Tarvisino. 2p *in* 1v. [*no pagin. p1 has 199 pr. leaves, fol. 200, blank, missing, p2 has 184*

Filosseno (Marcello) [PHILOXENUS] [*continued*].
p2 has tp.—: Sylve de M. P. &c. Capitoli Iuuenili—Capit. Senili — Stramotti Senili — Disperatte — Sonetti Senili—Satyre. *Colophon of p1 has date*, 1507, primo iunio; *col. of p2 has* v. agosto. 1507]. s8°. [Venetia, *Nic. Brenta.* 1507]
see LIZIER (A.) M. F., poeta trivigiano, 1893.

Filow (Bogdan D.) Early Bulgarian art. sfol. Berne. 1919

Filzi (Mario). Contrib. alla sintassi dei dialetti ital., *see* MONACI (E.) Studj romanzi, v11, 1914.

Fimmen (Diedrich). Die kret.-myken. Kultur. la8°. L. 1921

Fimmen (Edo). Labour's alternative: the united states of Europe or Europe limited. Pref. by A. A. Purcell. Tr. E. & C. Paul. s8°. 1924

Financial Conf. (Internat.), *see* INTERNAT. FINANCIAL CONF.

Finazzi (Giovanni). Di alcuni mss. conc. la storia del Conc. di Trento racc. dal P. A. Mazzoleni, *see* REGIA DEP. DI STORIA PATRIA. Misc., t6, 1865.
see BERGAMO. Breves chronicae B. [1117–1512]; nunc primum ed. cura F., 1868.

Finberg (Alexander Joseph). Chron. list of portraits by Corn. Johnson or Jonson, *see* WALPOLE Soc., v10, 1922.

Finberg (Hilda Felicité), *wife of A. J. F.* Canaletto in England, *see* WALPOLE Soc., v9, 10, 1921–22.

Fincati (Luigi). La battaglia navale del Zonchio (1499). [P2835]. 8°. 1883

Finch, *The family of*, *see* HIST. MSS. COMM., Finch, A. G., v2, 1922.

Finch (George Augustus). Dawes rep. on German repar. payments—London Conf. on applic. of Dawes plan, *see* INTERNAT. CONCILIATION, N°. 204, 1924.

Finch (Henry), *Alderman of Londonderry.*
Law, a discourse, in 4 books. s8°. 1671

Finch (*Sir* John), *see* ABBOTT (G. F.) Under the Turk in Constantinople: Sir J. F.'s embassy, 1674–81, 1920.

Finch (M. B.) & E. A. Peers.
Origins of French romanticism. 8°. 1920

Finch (William Coles-), *see* COLES-FINCH (W.)

Finck (Franz Nikolaus). Kleinere mittelarmen. Texte; hrsg. &c. v. F., *see* ZEITSCHRIFT F. ARM. PHILOL., B1, 2, 1903–4.
Lehrbuch d. neuostarmen. Litteraturspr. Unter Mitwirk. v. S. Kanajeanz bearb. v. F. N. F. 8°. Vagarschapat. 1902
see TÜBINGEN, *university.* Hauptkat. d. Universitätsbibl. Verzeichnis d. arm. Hss. v. F. N. F. &c., 1907.

Finck von Finckenstein, *family of*, *see* JOACHIM (E.) & M. KLINKENBORG. Familien-Gesch., 1920–21.

Finckh (Ludwig). Der Rosendoktor. 80.–84. A. s8°. St. [1920]

Finckler (Georg Ernst). Sacra Sodalitas B. Mariae V. in Monte ad Vetus Brandenburgum. Praes. J. D. Koelero. [P2742]. s4°. Altorfii Noric. 1745

Findel (Jos. Gabr.) *Spir. u. d. Bedeutung s. Philos. für. d. Gegenwart. [P2482]. 8°. L. 1881

Finden (Edward) & W. Finden. The royal gallery of Brit. art. [*Dedic. signed* E. & W. Finden & J. Hogarth]. atlas fol. [1851?]

Finder (Ernst). Die Vierlande: Gesch. &c. Niedersachsens. [Veröff. d. Ver. f. Hamburg. Gesch., B3]. 2T *in* 1v. 8°. Hamburg. 1922

Findlay (Adam Fyfe), *D.D.* Byways in early Xtn. lit.: uncanon. Gospels & Acts. Kerr Lects., 1920–21. 8°. E. 1923

Findlay (Alexander).
Chemistry in the service of man. n. imp. 8°. 1920
„ „ ....3rd ed. rev. & enl. s8°. 1925

Findlay (Frederick Roderick Noble). Big game shooting & travel in S.-E. Africa. With ch. by O. Schreiner &c. 8°. 1903

Findlay (George Gillanders), *D.D.* Christian doctrine & morals. Fernley Lect. 8°. 1894

Findlay (Joseph John). The children of England: contrib. to social hist. &c. s8°. [1923]
The foundations of educ.: princs. & projects. 2v. 8°. 1925–27
History & its place in educ. s8°. 1923
An Introd. to sociology. For social workers &c. s8°. M'ter. 1920

Findlay (Robert), *D.D.* *A persuasive to the enlargement of psalmody &c. By a minister of the Ch. of Scotland [*i.e.* R. F.] 8°. Glasgow. 1763

Fine Art Society.
see ALLEN (G.) Tidal Thames; exhib. at F.A.S., 1884.
„ GOSSE (E.) Pictures &c. of A. W. Hunt, exhib. at F.A.S., 1884.

Fine Rolls. Calendar of the Fine Rolls. [Cal. of State Papers]. v6–9. la8°. 1921–26
6, Edward III, 1347–56. 7, Edward III, 1356–68. 8, Ed. III, 1368–77. 9, 1377–83.

Finer (Herman). Represent. govt. & a parliament of industry: German Federal Econ. Council. 8°. 1923

Fines. Abstract of Feet of F. rel. to Sussex; comp. by L. F. Salzmann, v3, 1916, *see* SUSSEX.
Cal. of Feet of F. for Beds., 1192–1272; ed. G. H. Fowler, *see* BEDFORDSHIRE HIST. REC. SOC. Publs., v6, 1919.
Feet of F. for Yorkshire, 1218–46; ed. J. Parker, 2v, 1921–25, *see* YORKSHIRE.
Sussex manors &c. rec. in Feet of F., 1509–1833; ed. E. H. W. Dunkin, 2v, 1914–15, *see* SUSSEX.

Finetti (Bonifacio). Tratt. d. lingua ebraica e sue affini. Agg. una difesa d. capo 2 di San Matteo. [*w. sep. pagin.*] s8°. Venezia. 1756

Finibus. *Finibus (De) virtutis Christianæ. The ends of Christian religion, 1673, *see* SHARROCK (R.)

Finke (Heinrich).
Bilder v. Konstanzer Konzil. [P2727]. 8°. Heidelberg. 1903
see CONSTANCE, COUNCIL OF. Acta Concilii C.; hrsg. in Verbind. mit. J. Hollnsteiner &c. v. H. F., B1–3, 1896–1926.
„ JAMES II, *k. of Aragon.* Acta Aragonensia: Quellen aus d. diplom. Korresp. J. II (1291–1327); hrsg. H. Finke, B3, 1922.

Finland. ANON. WORKS &c.
Finland. [Abstracts f. "Finland, the country, its people &c." *By var. as.*] [6p *in* 1v]. la8°. Helsinki. 1927
Pétition de la diète de Finlande de 1910 conc. le maintien des lois fondementales de la F. (Trad.) [P2451]. 8°. 1910
Trade & industry of Finland. [Ed. F. Tiderman *& others.* Intr. K. Järvinen. Tr. M. Stenbäck]. 4°. Helsingfors. [1922]
*Главнѣйшія событія и мѣропріятія правительства въ Ф., 1905–9. [P2451]. 8°. С.–П. 1910
*Матеріалы по вопросу о порядкѣ изданія касающ. Ф. законовъ &c. la8°. С.–П. 1910
*О положеніи мѣстныхъ школъ въ Ф. [P2451]. 8°. С.–П. 1910
Ф. Обзоръ періодич. печати.
вып. 13–16 (1907–9). [P2451]. 8°. С.–П. 1909–10

Finlands statskalender, 1919–21. s8°. Helsingfors. 1919–20

Finley (James B.) Sketches of Western Methodism. Ed. W. P. Strickland. s8°. Cincinnati. 1855

Finley (*Lieut.-Col.* John Park) & W. Churchill. The Subanu, a sub-Visayan mountain folk of Mindanao. Land & people, by J. P. F.—Ling. material, by W. C.—Vocabularies. [C.I. of Wash. Publ., 184]. la8°. Wash. 1913

Finn, *see* WILLIAMS (R. A.) The F. episode in Beowulf, 1924.

Finn (Frank). Familiar London birds. s8°. [1923]

—— & E. K. Robinson.
Birds of our country. 2v. 4°. *Hutchinson.* [1922–23]

Finn (James). The orphan colony of Jews in China. s8°. 1872

Finnboga. Finnboga saga hins Ramma. Hrsg. H. Gering. 8°. Halle a S. 1879

Finnemore (Emily Pearson), *see* FINNEMORE (J.) & E. P. F. From a Welsh hillside, 1923.

Finnemore (John) & E. P. Finnemore.
From a Welsh hillside. s8°. 1923

Finnsburg. *For edd. of Beowulf wh. also contain this poem, see* BEOWULF.

Finnsson (Jon), *Bp. of Skalholt, see* ARI, *Froði.* Islands Landnamabok (*Latin tr.* by J. F.), 1774.

Finot (Jean).
The philosophy of long life. Tr. H. Roberts. 8°. 1909

Finot (Louis). Recherches sur la litt. laotienne, *see* ECOLE FRANÇ. D'EXTR.-OR. Bull., t17, 1917.

Finot (Louis Jean). La chaste infidèle. s8°. 1927

Fiocca (Lorenzo). Perugia, sua orig. &c. 8°. Perugia. 1926

Fiocco (Giuseppe).
L'arte di Andrea Mantegna. 4°. Bologna. 1927
Bernardo Strozzi. 8°. 1921
Francesco Guardi. la8°. Firenze. [1923]

Fior da fiore, prose e poesie, 1921, *see* PASCOLI (G.), *ed.*

Fiorani (P. L.) Appunti stor. sul territorio &c. di Mombrione (San Colombano), *see* REGIA DEPUT. Miscellanea, t46, 1912.

Fiore (Giovanni), *da Cropani.* Della Calabria illust., opera var. hist. [Ed. G. da Castelvetere]. t1. fol. Nap. 1691

Fiorentina. Consigli d. Rep. F. Per c. di B. Barbadoro. Con prem. di I. del Lundo. [R. Accad. dei Lincei. Atti d. assemblee costit. ital., s3, sez. 4]. la8°. Bologna. 1921

Fiorentina [*continued*].
Statuti della Rep. F. Ed. a cura del Comune di Firenze da R. Caggese. v1, 2. la8°. Firenze. 1910–21
1, Statuto del Capitano del Popolo, 1322-25.
2, Statuto del Podestà, 1325.

Fiorenzo, *di Lorenzo, see* WEBER (S.) F. di L., e. kunsthist. Studie, 1904.

Fiorilli (Carlo). I dipintori a Firenze nell' arte dei medici spez. e merciai, *see* ARCHIVIO STOR. ITAL. Anno 78, v2, 1920.

Fiorini (Vittorio), *see* ARCHIVIO STOR. ITAL., a. 84i, Necrologia, 1926.
—— **& F. Lemmi.** Periodo Napoleonico, 1799–1814. [Storia polit. d'Italia scr. da una soc. di professori ; publ. Vallardi]. la8°. Milano. *n.d.*

Fiorio. F. e Biancifiore, *var. ed., see* FLOIRE ET BLANCHEFLEUR.

Fiorioli Della-Lena (G. B.) Della spiritualità. [Nozze Macola-Gaudio. N127]. 8°. Padova. 1865

Fippard (Richard C.), *see* ELDERTON (W. P.) & R. C. F. Construct. of mortality &c. tables, 1914.

Firdausī. Sháhnáma of F. Eng. by A. G. Warner & E. Warner. v8, 9. 8°. 1923–25
see BANKIPORE. Reprods. of illusts. f. 3 Persian MSS. [Shah Nâmah by F. &c.], in Publ. Libr. at B., 1920.

Firenze. *I sacrobaccanali festegg. di F., 1808, *see* FABRONI (G. V.)

Firenzuola (Agnolo). Prose [*i.e.* Discorsi d. animali—Dialogo d. bellezze d. donne, *w. sep. tp.*] s8°. Fiorenza. 1548
Ragionamenti [*&* Novella 1–8—Discacciamento d. nuove lettere &c. *b. w. h.* Prose, 1548]. s8°. Fiorenza. 1548

Firkovich (Abraam Samuilovich). Археол. развѣдки на Кавказѣ, *see* IMPERAT. RUSS. ARCH. OBSCH. Труды Восточ. отд., ч3, 1858.

Firlalemean (Levon), *Tosbetzi, see* ARMENIA. Notarq Hayotz 1393–1467 ; coll. &c. L. F., 1892.

Firle (Rudolph), *see* KRIEG (Der) zur See, 1914–18, Der Krieg in d. Ostsee ; bearbt. v. R. F., B1, 1921.

Firmian (Leopold Anton, *Graf* **v.),** *abp. of Salzburg, 1679–1744.*
see ARNOLD (C. F.) Ausrottung d. Protestant. in Salzburg unter Erzbischof F., 2H, 1900–01.

Firmicus Maternus (Julius). De errore profan. religionum. Ed. F. Münter. 8°. Havniae. 1826
see MARTIN (E. J.) The Biblical text of F. M., 1923.

Firmin, *Saint, the Confessor, bp. of Amiens.*
see L'ETOILE (P. DE). *L'ombre de M. Thiers, ou rép. à la diss. de M. Lestocq s. la transl. de S. Firmin &c., 1712.
,, —— *Remarques s. le livre de M. Lestocq, Justific. de la transl. de S. F., 1714.

Firminger (Walter Kelly).
Diaries of 3 surgeons [Anderson, Campbell & Fullarton] of Patna, 1763. Ed. W. K. F. [Calcutta Hist. Soc.] 4°. [Calcutta]. 1909
Epistles to the Colossians & to Philemon, w. intr. & notes. [Indian Ch. comms.] s8°. 1921
Hist. intr. to the Bengal portion of "The 5th report." 8°. Calcutta. 1917
see BENGAL. Procs. of Controlling Co. of Revenue at Murshidabad, 1770–72 ; ed. w. intr. &c. by W. K. F., 12v, 1919–24.
see BENGAL DISTRICT RECORDS ; ed. W. K. F., 1920–21.
,, EAST INDIA COMPANY. 5th Rep. of Sel. Comm. of H. of Commons of affairs of E.I. Co., 1812 ; ed. w. notes &c. by W. K. F., 3v, 1917–18.
,, SYLHET. S. District records ; ed. W. K. F., v4, 1788–92, 1919.

Firnhaber (Wolfgang). Disput. Biblica de 15. capite Geneseos. Sub præs. S. Gesneri. [P2640]. s4°. Witebergae. 1598

Firsov (N. N.)
Чтения по ист. Сибири. 2в *in* 1v. [в1, 2ое изд.] 8°. Москва. 1920–21

First Edition Club. Bibliogr. cat. of 1st loan exhib. of bks. & MSS. held by 1st Ed. Club, 1922. 8°. *p.p.* [1922]
see TOMKINSON (G. S.) Sel. bibliog., presses, 1928.

Firth (Charles Harding).
Modern hist. in Oxford, 1841–1918. 8°. O. 1920
Oliver Cromwell & the rule of the Puritans. [Heroes of the Nations]. [n. ed.] s8°. [1923]
The polit. significance of "Gulliver's travels." [P2463]. 8°. 1920
,, ,, *For a. copy see* BRIT. ACAD. Proc., v9, 1919–20.
Sir W. Raleigh's Hist. of the world, *see* BRIT. ACAD. Procs., 1917–18.

Firth (John B.) Highways & byways in Leicestershire. 8°. 1926

Firth (Violet M.) The machinery of the mind. Foreword by A. G. Tansley. s8°. 1922

Fischart (Johannes). Das alte u. d. neue System : d. polit. Köpfe Deutschlands. 8°. 1919

Fischel (Oskar). Chronisten d. Mode. Mensch u. Kleid in Bildern aus 3 Jahrtausenden. 4°. Potsdam. 1923
see BÖHN (M. v.) Die Mode, 18. Jhdt., ausgewählt v. F., 1923.
,, —— Die Mode, 19. Jhdt., ausgewählt v. F., 1919–24.
,, —— Modes & manners of the 19th cent. as repr. in pictures &c. of the time : [sel. by O. F.] ; tr., 3v, 1909.

Fischer (Alex.), *see* FISCHER (M.) & A. F. L'amant de la petite Dubois, 1920.

Fischer (Carl Philipp). Die Unwahrheit d. Sensualismus u. Materialismus. [P2470]. 8°. Erlangen. 1853

Fischer (Christoph).
Instit. hermeneuticae N. Test. 8°. Pragae. 1788

Fischer (Erdmann Rudolph). De Θεοδρόμοις vet. eccl. legatis, in S. Ignatii epist. ad Polycarpum comm. Praef. add. E. S. Cyprianus. [*b. w. h.* Vita I. Gerhardi, 1723]. s8°. Coburgi. 1718
Vita I. Gerhardi. Acc. 43 G. &c. epistolae. s8°. Lipsiae. 1723

Fischer (Ernst). Aus d. Tagen uns. Ahnen. Urkundensamml. 8°. Freiburg im Br. 1928

Fischer (Eugen). Begriff, Abgrenzung u. Gesch. d. Anthropologie, *see* HINNEBERG (P.) Die Kultur d. Gegenwart, T3v, 1923.
Holstein's grosses Nein : d. deut.-eng. Bündnisverhandl., 1898–1901. 8°. 1925
Rassenlehre, *see* HINNEBERG (P.) Die Kultur d. Gegenwart, T3v, 1923.
—— **& T. Mollison.** Allgem. Anthropologie, *see* HINNEBERG (P.) Die Kultur d. Gegenwart, T3v, 1923.

Fischer (Heinrich). Die Vergessenen : 100 deut. Gedichte d. 17. u. 18. Jhdts. Ausgewählt v. H. F. 8°. 1926

Fischer (Hermann).
Die heilige Hildegard v. Bingen. 8°. München. 1927
Üb. d. Entstehung d. Nibelungenliedes, *see* KÖNIGL. AKAD. D. W. ZU MÜNCHEN. Phil. Kl., Sitz., 1914.
Üb. Gottfried v. Strassburg, *see* KÖNIGL. AKAD. D. W. ZU MÜNCHEN. Phil. Kl., Sitz., 1916.

Fischer (J. C.), *philosophical writer, see* DU PREL (C., *Frhr.*) Der gesunde Menschenverstand : J. C. F. contra E. v. Hartmann, 1872.

Fischer (Johann Eberhard). Сибирская исторія, сочиненная на нѣмецкомъ языкѣ. 4°. С.-П. 1774

Fischer (Johann Friedrich). De Phaedro prolusio. Praes. J. F. Christio. [P2649]. s4°. Lipsiae. [1746]

Fischer (Josef Ludwig). Ulm. s8°. L. 1912

Fischer (Louis). Oil imperialism. s8°. [1927]

Fischer (Max) & A. Fischer.
L'amant de la petite Dubois. Roman. s8°. [1921]

Fischer (Paul), *of Halle.* Comm. de Origenis theologia & cosmologia. 8°. Halis. 1848

Fischer (Paul), *of Stuttgart.*
Goethes Altersweisheit. 8°. Tübingen. 1921

Fischer (Rudolf). Quellen zu Romeo u. Julia. Masuccio-Da Porto-Bandello-Boisteau-Brooke [*in Eng. & Germ.*] Hrsg. v. R. F. [Deut. Shakespeare-Gesell., S.'s Quellen, B2]. s8°. Bonn. 1922

Fischer-Benzon (R. v.) Altdeutsche Gartenflora : Unters. ü. d. Nutzpflanzen d. deut. Ma. la8°. Kiel. 1894

Fischlin (Ludwig Melchior). Memoria theolog. Wirtemberg. resuscitata, h. e. biog. praecip. virorum qui in ducatu Wirtemb. verbum Domini docuerunt. 2p *&* Suppl. *in* 1v. s8°. Ulmae. 1709–10

Fiscowich (Eduardo Verdegay y), *see* VERDEGAY Y FISCOWICH (E.)

Fish (Carl Russell). Guide to the mat. for Amer. hist. in Roman & o. Ital. archives. [C.I. of Wash. Publ., 128]. la8°. Wash. 1911

Fish (Henry Clay). Hdbk. of revivals. s8°. [1873]

Fish (Miles), *see* SINDERCOMB (M.)

Fishenden (Margaret White). The coal fire. [Fuel Research Board, Spec. rep. 3]. la8°. 1920

Fisher (A.), *of Newcastle, ps.* [*i.e. Mrs.* SLACK]. The pleasing instructor, sel. essays f. eminent Eng. authors &c. 8°. 1806

Fisher (Alan G. B.), *Ph.D.* Some probl. of wages & th. regul. in Gt. Brit. since 1918. 8°. 1926

Fisher (Clarence Stanley), *see* REISNER (G. A.), C. S. F. &c. Harvard excav. at Samaria, 1908–10, 2v, 1924.

Fisher (*Mrs.* **Dorothea Frances),** *see* CANFIELD (DOROTHY), *aft. wife of John Redwood Fisher.*

Fisher (Ethel Lucie). Clipston. 8°. Kettering. 1926

Fisher (Fred Bohn). India's silent revolution. By F. w. collab. of G. M. Williams. s8°. N.Y. 1919
Fisher (*Lt.-Gen.* **Garret**), *see* LIGHTHALL (W. D.) G. F.: a forgotten loyalist, 1922.
Fisher (George Park). Hist. of the Xtn. church. 8°. 1890
Fisher (H. H.) The famine in Soviet Russia: operations of the Amer. Relief Admin. 8°. N.Y. 1927
Fisher (H. J.) Economics [Bulgaria], *see* BUCHAN (J.), *ed.* Nations of to-day, B. & Romània, 1924.
Fisher (*Rt. Hon.* **Herbert Albert Laurens).**
The common weal. 8°. O. 1924
James Bryce (Visc. Bryce of Dechmont). 2v. 8°. 1927
Napoleon. [Library ed.] 8°. 1924
The pacific. of Europe. Basil Hicks Lect., 1925. [P2785]. 8°. Sheffield. 1925
Paul Valéry. Taylorian Lect. 8°. O. 1927
Paul Vinogradoff, a memoir. 8°. O. 1927
Fisher (*Mrs.* **Herbert Albert Laurens**), *see* FISHER (LETTICE).
Fisher (Irving). Elementary princ. of economics. [repr.] 8°. N.Y. 1923
Fisher (John), *jesuit, 1569–1641.*
see LAUD (W.), *abp.* Rel. of conference betw. L. & F., 3rd ed., 1673.
„ WHITE (F.) Replie to Jesuit Fishers answere to questions by King James, 1624.
Fisher (*card.* **John),** *bp. of Rochester.* Assertionis Lutheranae confutatio. Æd. ult. locupl. s4°. [Coloniæ]. 1525
Confutatio secundae disceptationis per J. Fabrum Stapulensem habitę in qua tribus fæminis partiri molitur quæ consuetudo unicę tribuit Magdalenæ. s4°. [Parisiis, *J. Badius*]. 1519
Defensio Regie assertōis [*of Henry VIII, king of Eng.*] cōtra Babylonicam captivitatē [*of M. Luther*] per Joh. Roffensem Episcop. In qua respondet pro rege Henrico viii ad maledicentissimum M. Lutheri libellū. s4°. Coloniæ, *P. Quentel.* 1525
*The life of F. Transcr. f. MS. Harleian 6382 by R. Bayne. Suppl. to Eng. works of J. F. [E. E. T. S., 117]. 8°. 1921
Sacri sacerdotii defensio cōtra Lutherum per Johannem Roffeñ. Cum tabula & repertorio tractatorum. s8°. Colonie, *P. Quentel.* 1525
This treatyse concernynge the fruytfull sayinges of Davyd in the seven penytencyall psalmes. Devided in 7 sermons &c. s8°. *T. Marshe.* 1555
Fisher (*Adm.* **John Fisher,** *1st visct.*) Lord Fisher on the Navy. Repr. f. "The Times," Sept. 1919. [P2418]. 8°. [1919]
Fisher (John Lionel). The deanery of Harlow. Hist. of the Church in Essex. s8°. Colchester. 1922
Fisher (Lettice), *wife of Rt. Hon. H. A. L. Fisher.*
Econ. position of the married woman. Stansfeld Trust lect. [P2736]. 8°. O. 1924
Getting & spending. Intr. to economics. Intr. by Sir W. Ashley. s8°. 1922
Then & now: econ. problems after the war a 100 yrs. ago. Intr. by D. Lloyd George. 8°. 1925
Fisher (*Mrs.* **Margaret),** *wife of A. O. Fisher, see* PETERSON (M.)
Fisher (Robert Howie), *D.D.*
Relig. experience. Baird Lect., 1924. s8°. 1924
Fisher (Samuel), *1605–65.* Christianismus redivivus, Christndom both un-christ'ned & new christ'ned. fol. 1655
Fisher (W. G.) Somerset worthies. [pl]. s8°. 1927
Fisher (Walter Kenrick). Biology of the Philippine Archipel. &c. Starfishes. [S.I.: U.S. Nat. Mus.; Bull. 100iii]. 8°. Wash. 1919
Fisher (Willard James). Brightness of lunar eclipses, 1860–1922, 1924, *see* SMITHSONIAN INST. Misc. Coll., v76, 1925.
Fishmongers' Company, *London.* Short account of portraits, pictures, plate &c. By J. W. Towse. la8°. 1907
Fisk (George Mygatt) & P. S. Peirce. Internat. commercial policies, w. spec. ref. to the U.S. 8°. N.Y. 1923
Fisk (Harvey Edward). English public finance f. 1688, w. ch. on the Bank of England. 8°. 1921
Fisk (Willbur), *D.D., see* HOLDICH (J.) Life of W. F., 1842.
Fiske (Daniel Willard), *see* FISKE (W.)
Fiske (John), *assistant librarian at Harvard, 1842–1901* [*form.* GREEN (EDMUND FISK)]. The crit. period of Amer. hist., 1783–89. 6th ed. 8°. N.Y. 1890
see CLARK (J. S.) Life & letters of J. F., 1920.
Fiske (Willard) [DANIEL WILLARD FISKE]. Memorials. Coll. by H. S. White. 3[v]. 8°. Boston [U.S.] 1920–22
Willard Fiske Memorial. Papers by H. S. White &c. [Extr. f. Papers of Bibliogr. Soc. of Amer., v12]. 8°. Chicago. [1919]

Fiske (Willard) [DANIEL WILLARD FISKE] [*continued*].
see CORNELL UNIV. Cat. of Icelandic Coll. bequeathed by W. F.; adds. 1913–26, 1927.
„ WHITE (H. S.) Sketch of life & labors of W. F., 1918.
„ —— W. F., life & corr., 1925.
Fitch (Robert F.)
Hangchow itineraries. 2nd rev. ed. s8°. Shanghai. 1922
Fitch (Walter Hood) & W. G. Smith. Illusts. of Brit. flora. Drawn by F. & S. [Companion to Bentham's Hdbk. &c.] s8°. 1880
Fite (Emerson David) & A. Freeman, *edd.* Book of old maps delineat. Amer. hist., to close of Revol. War. fol. Cambridge, *Harvard.* 1926
Fite (Warner). Individualism. 8°. 1911
Fitschen (Jost), *see* SCHMEIL (O.) & J. F. Flora v. Deutschland, 1922.
Fitting (Hans), *see* STRASBURGER (E.) Text-bk. of botany; re-wr. by H. F. &c.; tr., 5th ed., 1921.
Fitton (James). Sketches of the establ. of the Church in New Eng. s8°. Boston. 1872
Fitzgerald (Adolphus L.)
The 30 years' war on silver. s8°. Chicago. 1903
Fitzgerald (Anne Caroline Stéphanie, *dit* **Pamela),** *wife of Lord Edward Fitzgerald, see* FITZGERALD (PAMELA).
Fitzgerald (*Adm.* **Charles Cooper Penrose).** From sail to steam: naval recolls., 1878–1905. 8°. 1916
Fitzgerald (Desmond). Paintings by the impressionists. Coll. of D. F. [Sale by Amer. Art Assoc., Apr. 1927]. la8°. N.Y. 1927
Fitzgerald (Edward).
Letters to B. Quaritch, 1853–83. Ed. C. Q. Wrentmore. 8°. 1926
Polonius: wise saws & mod. instances. [Ed. S. S. Allen]. s8°. 1907
Some new letters. Ed. F. R. Barton, w. foreword by Visct. Grey of Fallodon. 8°. 1923
Fitzgerald (Eileen). Judith Kersley, spinster. s8°. [1922]
Fitz-Gerald (Gerald), *D.D.* Originality &c. of Bibl. Hebrew &c. 8°. D. 1796
Fitzgerald (James Edward). Vancouver's Island. The new Colony. [P2554]. 8°. 1845
Vancouver's Island, the Hudson's Bay Co. & the Govt. [P2554]. 8°. 1848
Fitzgerald (Marion), *see* SIMON (E. D.) & M. F. The smokeless city, 1922.
Fitzgerald (Maurice), *see* MACNAMARA (J.) Sev. informs. of J. M., M. F. &c., rel. to horrid popish plot in Ireland, 1680.
Fitzgerald (Pamela), *wife of Lord Edward Fitzgerald, 5th son of 1st d. of Leinster, see* TURQUAN (J.) & L. ELLIS. La belle Pamela, 1773–1831, 2t, 1923–24.
Fitzgerald (Patrick). Indust. combination in England. 8°. 1927
Fitzgerald (S.), *see* HOWARD (A. L.) Man. of timbers of the world: app., an acc. by S. F. of the artificial seasoning of timber, 1920.
Fitzgerald (Walter), *F.R.Met.Soc.* The hist. geog. of early Ireland. 8°. [1926]
Fitzgerald (William), *bp. of (1) Cork, (2) Cloyne & Ross, (3) Killaloe, see* JACKSON (T.) Aids to truth &c.: letter to W. F., 1862.
Fitzgibbon (Henry Macaulay). Early Eng. & Scot. poetry, 1250–1600. Sel. & ed. w. crit. intr. &c. by H. M. F. 8°. 1888
FitzHarris (Edward), *see* HAWLES (*Sir* J.) Remarks upon the tryals of E. H. &c., 1689.
Fitz-Herbert (Nicolas) [FIERBERTUS (N.); FIZEBERTUS (N.)] De antiq. & contin. Catholicæ relig. in Anglia & De Alani Cardinalis vita libellus. s8°. Romae. 1608
Oxon. in Anglia Acad. descr. s8°. Romae. 1602
Fitzherbert (Thomas). *Reply of T. F. in def. of 1st 2 chap. of h. Suppl. to the discussion &c. impugned by R. Widdrington in Disput. de juramento fidel. &c. s4°. 1614
Fitzhugh (Francis), *ps., see* MACKAY (FRANCIS ALEXANDER).
Fitzinger (Leopold Joseph). Versuch e. Gesch. d. Menagerien d. Österr.-Kaiserl. Hofes. 8°. Wien. 1853
FitzJames (Edouard, *duc* **de).** Opinion sur le projet de loi rel. aux journaux, 1817. [P2866]. s8°. 1818
Fitzjohn (G. J. Monson-), *see* MONSON-FITZJOHN.
Fitzmaurice (E. B.), *O.F.M.* **& A. G. Little.** Materials for the hist. of the Franciscan Province of Ireland, 1230–1450. [Brit. Soc. of Fr. Sts., 9]. 8°. M'ter. 1920

Fitzmaurice-Kelly (James).
Cambridge readings in Span. lit. Ed. J. F.-K. 8º. C. 1920
Fray Luis de Leon. [Hisp. Soc. of Amer.] s8º. 1921
New hist. of Span. lit. 8º. 1926
Some masters of Span. verse. [Hisp. Soc. of Amer.] s8º. 1924
Span. bibliography. [Hisp. Soc. of Amer.] s8º. 1925
see ELTON (O.), A. F. G. BELL &c. J. F.-K., 1924.
,, REVUE HISPANIQUE, t60 (obituary & bibliog.), 1924.

Fitzmaurice-Kelly (Julia).
Antonio Perez. [Hisp. Soc. of Amer.] s8º. O. 1922
El Inca Garcilasso de la Vega. [Hisp. Soc. of Amer.] s8º. O. 1921
see ELTON (O.), J. F.-K. &c. James F.-K., 1924.

Fitzpatrick (John C.), *see* UNITED STATES: LIB. OF CONG. Fitzpatrick (J. C.) List of Washington MSS., 1592–1775, 1919.

Fitzpatrick (Kathleen). Lady Henry Somerset. 8º. [1923]

Fitzralph (Richard), *abp. of Armagh.* Defensio curatorum, *see* TREVISA (J.) Dialogus &c.; tr. by J. T.; intr. by A. J. Perry, 1925.

Fitzrandolph (Helen E.) & M. D. Hay. Rural industries of Eng. & Wales; survey on behalf of the Agric. Econ. Res. Inst., Oxf. 4v. [v4, Wales, by A. M. Jones]. 8º. O. 1926–27

Fitzroy (*Sir* Almeric William), *K.C.B.*
Henry Duke of Grafton, 1663–90. 8º. [1921]
Hist. of the Travellers' Club. 8º. [1927]
Memoirs. 2v. 8º. [1925]

Fitz Roy (*Sir* Charles Augustus), *1796–1858, see* AUSTRALIA. Hist. records, v25, 26 (1846–48), 1925.

Fitzroy (Henry), *1st duke of Grafton, see* GRAFTON.

Fitz-Simon (Henry). Britannomachia ministrorum, in fidei fundamentis &c. dissidentium. s4º. Duaci. 1614

Fitzsimons (Frederick William).
The nat. hist. of S. Africa: Birds. 2v. 8º. 1923
,, ,, Mammals. v3, 4. 8º. 1920

Fiume. Atti e comunicati dell' Ufficio Rel. Estere, Nov. 1919–Mag. 1920. [P2493]. 8º. Fiume. 1920
La Reggenza Ital. del Carnaro. Disegno di un nuovo ordinamento d. Stato libero di Fiume. [Comando di F. d'Italia. Boll. uffic., No. 31. P2501]. la8º. Fiume. 1920
,, ,, ...*a. ed.* sfol. 1920

Five of Clubs, *ps., see* PROCTER (R. A.)

Fizebertus (Nicolaus), *see* FITZ-HERBERT (N.)

Flacchio (Engelbert). Généalogie de la maison de La Tour. [Eloges de princes & seigneurs *&* Pièces autent. & justific. *in* t3 *have sep. pagin*[s]*.*] 3t. lafol. Brux. 1709

Flach (Jacques). Les orig. de l'anc. France. 10e & 11e s. t4. 8º. 1917
4, Les nationalités régionales, leurs rapp. avec la couronne de Fr.

Flach-Francowitz (Matthias), *1520–75, see* FLACIUS (M.), *Illyricus.*

Flacius (Matthias), *Illyricus* [*ps.* AESQUILLUS (PUBLIUS)].
Apologia ad Scholam Vitebergensem in Adiaphororum causa. Ejusdem epist. ad P. Melantho &c. s8º. [Magdeburgi]. 1549
*Cat. testium veritatis qui ante nostram aetatem reclamarunt Papae. Cum praef. M. Flacii Illyr. s8º. Basileæ, *J. Oporinus.* [1556]
,, ,, [*a. ed.* App., Basileae, 1562 *has sep. pagin.*] 4º. Argentinae. 1562
Christiana admonitio de vitando impii Adiaphoristarum fermenti contagio &c. s8º. [Magdeburgi]. 1550
Contra quaedam Interimistica & Adiaphoristica scripta quæ à multis G. Huberino tribuuntur. Item locus Brentii. s8º. [Magdeburgi. 1550 ?]
Das alle verfolger d. Kirchen Christi zu Magdeburgk, Christi d. Herrn selbs verfolger sindt &c. [P2468]. s4º. [Magdeburgk, *M. Lotther.* 1551]
De essentia originalis justitiæ &c. [De peccato orig.] s8º. Basileæ. 1568
Defensio sanae doctr. de orig. justitia, &c. s8º. Basileae. 1570
Defensio verae, piae ac Lutheranae de originali peccato sententiae ac refut. sophismatum opposita colloquio &c. a D. J. Andræa nuper æditus [*sic*]. s4º. *n.p.* 1575
Eine entschůldigung M. F. I. an e. Pfarherr. Item desselben was da sey die Kirchen verlassen &c. Item zween Trewme Philippi [*i.e.* Melanchthon]. [P2440]. s4º. *n.p.* 1549
Entschůldigung M. F. I., geschriebē an die Univ. zu Wittemberg, der Mittelding halben. Item sein brieff an Ph. Melanthonem, &c. Verdeutscht. [P2440]. s4º. [Magdeburg, *C. Rödinger*]. 1549
Epistola apologetica ad quendam pastorem. Item duo somnia Philippi [Melanchthonis; *rel. to the Adiaphoristic controv.*] s8º. *n.p. n.d.* [Magdeburg ?. 1549 ?]
Epistola de morte Pauli III, *see* ROSARIUS (S.) Antithesis Christi &c., 1578.

Flacius (Matthias), *Illyricus* [*ps.* AESQUILLUS (PUBLIUS)] [*contd.*]
Fidelis admonitio de sacrosancto Jesu Christi testamento in corrupto &c. s4º. *n.p.* 1562
Kurtze antwort M. F. I. auff des Larven Bischoffs v. Sydon [M. Helding] Holhiplerey, Damit er s. Antichrist. Catechismum vertedingen wil &c. s4º. *n.p.* [1550 ?]
Kurtze u. klare erzelung d. argument Osiandri v. d. gerechtigkeit d. glaubens. [*no tp.* P2743]. s4º. [Magdeburg. 1552]
Orthodoxa conf. de originali peccato. Disput. Witt. a. 1571 Jan. 20. s8º. [Argentorati ?]. 1571
Quod hoc tempore nulla penitus mutatio in religione sit in gratiam impiorum facienda. Contra scr. in quo suadetur mutatio piarum cæremoniarum in Papisticas per H. Primatem. s8º. *n.p.* 1549
Quod locus Lucae vii. Dico tibi remissa sunt ei peccata multa, nihil Pharisaicæ justiciæ patrocinetur. s8º. Magadaburgi. 1549
Responsio ad epistolam P. Melanthonis. s8º. [Magdeburgæ. 1549]
Vom offentl. Zeugnis M. F. Bericht etl. Prediger &c. [P2665]. s4º. Eisleben. 1573
Widderlegung des Catechismi des Larven-Bischoffes von Sidon [M. Helding]. [*Tr. f. the Latin*]. [P2440]. s4º. Magdeburg. 1550
Widderlegung d. Predigten v. d. allerheiligsten Antichrist. Missa d. frembden Bischoffs v. Sydon [M. Helding]. [P2440]. s4º. [Magdeburg, *C. Rödinger*]. 1550
see AGRICOLA (T.) Kurtze antwurt auff das Büchlein, M. F. wider C. Schwenckfeldt, 1556.
,, BRUNUS (C.) Adv. novam hist. eccl. quam M. [F.] I. &c. ediderunt, 1565.
,, COLERUS (J.) Hist. disput. inter J. C. & M. F. Ill. de peccato orig., 1585.
,, GALLUS (N.) & M. F. Antwort auff den brief etl. Prediger in Meissen &c., 1550 ?; Responsio &c., 1550 ?.
,, HEIMBURG (E. A. H.) Oratio de M. F. I., 1839.
,, HESHUSIUS (T.) Antidotum contra dogma M. F. Quod peccatum orig. sit substantia, 1572.
,, —— Epistola ad M. F. Illyr., 1570.
,, —— Gründl. Beweïsung &c., samt Widerlegung d. Schr. M. F. I. v. d. Erbsünde, 1574.
,, LEIPZIG. Endlicher Bericht &c.; mit angehengter Erinnerung von den streittigen Artickeln so F. M. Illyr. &c., 1570.
,, MAGDEBURG CENTURIES. Centuriae Magdeb. [*by M. F. & others*], 4v, 1757–65.
,, MELANCHTHON (P.) Epistola in qua respondetur F. I., 1549.
,, PAUL III, *pope.* Bulla Antichristi de retrahendo populo &c. [pref. *by* F.], 1549.
,, RITTER (J. B.) Beschr. d. Lebens M. F. I., 1723.
,, TRENT, *Council of.* Recusatio Trident. Synodi a. 1546 &c. Rationes item [M. F. Illyr.] initio compendio recitantur &c., 1550 ?.
,, †ULENBERG (C.) Gesch. d. luther. Reformatoren, B2, 1837.
,, —— Hist. de vita &c. Melanchthonis, F. &c., 1622.
,, WESTPHAL (J.) Confut. sophistici Adiaphor. scripti Lyps. cum 2 praefat. Illyr., c. 1551.
,, —— Verlegung des gründl. Berichts d. Adiaphoristen; mit e. Praef. Illy.: [*i.e.* M. F.] &c., 1551.

Flad (Johann Martin). 60 Jahre in d. Mission unter d. Falaschas in Abessinien. Selbstbiogr. Mit Einl. u. Schlussw. v. F. Flad. s8º. Giessen. 1922

***Flagellum** parliamentarium: sarcastic notices of Members, 1661–78, 1881, *see* MARVELL (A.)

Flagg (Wilson).
Woods & by-ways of New England. 8º. Boston [Mass.] 1872

Flamande. Cours élém. de langue fl. par A. D. T. 4e éd. pl. s8º. Liège. 1895

Flament (Albert). La captive, *see* ŒUVRES libres, 8, 1922.
Une étoile en 1830. La Malibran. s8º. [1928]

Flamini (Francesco). Comp. di storia d. lett. ital. 2[a] ed. s8º. Livorno. 1901
see TANSILLO (L.) L'egloga &c.; intr. e note di F. F., 1893.

Flaminio (Marco Antonio) [FLAMINIUS]. In librum Psalmorum brevis explanatio. s8º. Venetiis [*apud Aldi filios*]. 1545

Flamma (Gualvaneus de la). Chron. extravagans et Chron. maius; ab A. Ceruti ed., *see* REGIA DEP. DI STORIA PATRIA. Misc., t7, 1869.

Flammarion (Camille). Death & its mystery bef. death. Tr. E. S. Brooks. 8º. 1922
Dreams of an astronomer. Tr. E. E. Fournier d'Albe. 8º. [1923]
Les maisons hantées en marge de la mort & s. mystère. s8º. [1923]
La mort et son mystère. [3t]. s8º. [1920–22]

Flanagan (Thomas), *prof. at St. Mary's Coll., Oscott.*
Manual of Brit. & Irish hist. 8º. 1851

Flandern. Unter engl. Feuer; Zerstör. in F. &c., 1918, *see* UNTER.

Flandin (Etienne).
Instit. polit. de l'Europe contemp. t5. s8º. 1914
5, Espagne—Val d'Andorre.

Flandre. Chambres des comptes de F. &c.: inventaire des comptes en rouleaux, 1914, *see* NELIS (H.), *ed.*

Flandre (Juliette Lermina-), *see* LERMINA-FLANDRE (J.)

Flaquer (Concepción Gimeno de), *see* GIMENO DE FLAQUER (C.)

Flasdieck (Hermann M.) Mittelengl. Originalurkunden, 1405–30. Mit Einl. &c. hrsg. H. M. F. s8º. Heidelberg. 1926

Flat. *Flat ornament. A pattern book of designs of textiles, embroideries &c. 4º. Stuttg., *Engelhorn. n.d.*

Flatau (Dorota). Seven journeys. s8º. [1920]

Flattely (Frederic William) & C. L. Walton.
Biology of the sea-shore. Intr. by J. A. Thomson. 8º. 1922

Flaubert (Gustave).
Madame Bovary. Préf. par A. Gondry. s8º. Vienne. [1920]
,, ,, éd. définit., suiv. du procès, 1857. s8º. 1922
,, ,, ...[repr.] s8º. 1928
Premières œuvres. t4, 1848–49. s8º. 1920
4, La tentation de Saint Antoine—Une nuit de Don Juan.
La tentation de Saint-Antoine. Intr. par E. Faguet. [Coll. Nelson]. s8º. [1913]
Trois contes. Un cœur simple—La légende de Saint Julien l'Hospitalier—Hérodias. [Coll. Nelson]. s8º. [1911]
see BERTRAND (L. M. E.) F. à Paris ou le mort vivant, 1921.
,, BLOSSOM (F. A.) La composition de Salammbô &c., 1914.
see COLEMAN (A.) F.'s lit. development, 1914.
,, DESCHARMES (R.) Le centen. de F.; autour de Bouvard & Pécuchet, 1921.
,, —— & R. DUMESNIL. Autour de F., 1912.
,, FAY (P. B.) & A. COLEMAN. Sources & structure of F.'s Salammbô, 1914.
,, HAMILTON (A.) Sources of relig. elem. in F.'s Salammbô, 1917.
,, RIDDELL (A. R.) F. & Maupassant: literary relationship, 1920.
,, SAND (G.) The G. S.–G. F. letters; tr. A. L. McKenzie, w. intr. by S. P. Sherman, 1922.
,, THIBAUDET (A.) G. F., 1821–80: s. vie—s. romans—s. style, 1922.

Flaux (Armand de). La régence de Tunis au 19e siècle. 8º. 1865

Flavell (John) [FLAVEL].
Whole works. 2v. [*v. 2 has var. pagin.*] fol. 1701
Divine conduct; or, the mystery of Providence. s8º. [1677 repr.] 1836
Extract f. works, *see* WESLEY (J.) Xtn. lib., v43, 44, 1755.
Pneumatologia. Treatise of the soul of man &c. n. ed. corr. 8º. 1789
A saint indeed. Prov. iv. 23. s8º. *n.d.*
Worth of the soul; or a treatise of the soul of man. 8º. Burslem. *n.d.*

Flavelle (*Sir* Joseph Wesley), *Bt.* Canada & its relations to the Brit. Empire. [P2426]. 8º. [1917]

Flavien (Amand), *ps.*, *see* BLONDEL (DAVID).

Flaviis (Carlo de). Roberto Bracco. [Uomini d. giorno, N. 39. *a. c. in* P2517]. la8º. Milano. 1920

Flawes (William). Journal dep. la Nouv. Zemble j.'en Angl. (1676), *see* BERNARD (J. F.), *ed.* Recueil, t2, 1715; 1732.

Flaxman (John). Classical compos.: Iliad & Odyssey of Homer & tragedies of Æschylus, engraved by Piroli & Theogony &c. of Hesiod, engr. by W. Blake. lafol. 1870
see CONSTABLE (W. G.) J. F., 1755–1826, 1927.

Flayder (Friedrich Hermann). Ausgewählte Werke. Hrsg. u. eingeleitet v. G. Bebermeyer. [Literar. Verein in Stuttgart, 267/8]. 8º. L. 1925

Fleck (Georg). Refut. errorum, absurditatum, &c., a J. Busæo oppositarum S. Gerlachii Disput. 1. de persona Christi. s4º. Tubingae. 1592

Fleckeisen (Christian Friedrich). August. Confess. Carolo V, exhib. hist. Praes. C. Beyero. [P2642]. s4º. Lipsiae. 1731

Flecker (James Elroy). Coll. poems. Ed., w. intr. by J. C. Squire. 7th impr. 8º. [1922]
,, ,, ...10th impr. 8º. [1924]
Coll. prose. s8º. 1920
Don Juan. Play. Pref. by H. Flecker. 8º. 1925
Hassan. Play. [n. impr.] s8º. 1922
see HODGSON (G.) Life of J. E. F., 1925.

Fleet, *Lincolnshire.* A terrier of Fleet, Lincs. Ed. N. Neilson—An 11th c. Inquisition of St. Augustine's, Canterbury. [Ed. w. intr. by] A. Ballard. [Brit. Acad. Rec. of social &c. hist. of Eng. &c., v4]. la8º. 1920

Fleischer (Heinrich Leberecht). Gramm. d. pers. Spr. Nach Mirza Mohammed Ibrahim's Gramm. Neu bearb. v. H. L. F. 2e A. 8º. L. 1875

Fleischer (Victor).
Frau Monica u. i. Töchter. Roman. s8º. L. 1919

Fleischmann (Georg Wilhelm). Diss. de tumultibus rusticanis sec. 16 motis. Praes. J. H. Boeclero. [P484]. s4º. Argentorati. [1712]

Fleischmann (Hector). Le Roi de Rome & les femmes. La Ctsse. Napoleone Camerata, La danseuse F. Elssler &c. 8º. 1910

Fleischmann (Max), *see* STENGEL (C., *Frhr.* v.) Wbch. d. deut. Staats- u. Verwaltungsrechts; begründet v. S., 2e A. hrsg. v. M. F., B3, 1914.

Fleissner v. Wostrowitz (Eduard B.)
Handbuch d. Kryptographie. 8º. Wien. 1881

Flémalle (*Meister* von).
see FRIEDLÄNDER (M. J.) Altniederl. Malerei, B2, 1924.
,, MAETERLINCK (L.) Namur Martins ou Le Maître de F.: nouv. docs., 1913.
,, WINKLER (F.) Der M. v. F. u. R. van der Weyden, 1913.

Fleming, *family of, see* MAGRATH (J. R.) The Flemings in Oxford, v3, 1691–1700, 1924.

Fleming (*Sir* Daniel), *of Rydal, see* MAGRATH (J. R.) The Fs. in Oxford, v3, 1691–1700, 1924.

Fleming (*Dame* Elizabeth). Inventar of gudis & geir, 1578, *see* MAIDMENT (J.) & R. PITCAIRN. Nugae, 1822.

Fleming (John Ambroise).
Fifty years of electricity: mem. la8º. [1921]

Fleming (Rachel Mary). Round the world in folk tales: 16 stories. Ed. F. 8º. [1924]

Fleming (Robert), *the elder.* *The fulfilling of the Scripture &c. 2nd ed. corr. s8º. [Amsterdam?]. 1671

Fleming (Robert), *the younger.*
Discourses, first publ. in 1701. 8º. Stirling. *n.d.*

Flemming (Ernst). Textile Künste. 8º. [1924]

Flemming (Jessie Hatch). England under the Lancastrians. Pref. by A. F. Pollard. 8º. 1921

Flemming (Johannes), *see* EPHESUS, *2nd Synod of.* Akten d. Ephesin. Synode v. 449; hrsg. J. F., 1917.

Flemming (Louis Andrew).
Putnam's word book. 2nd ed., rev. & enl. s8º. N.Y. 1919

Flemming (Siegbert). Willenslehre als Erkenntnisweg. [Bibl. f. Philos., B14]. 8º. 1917

Flenley (Ralph). S. de Champlain. s8º. Toronto. 1924

Flensburg (Wilhelm). Om Guds Allestädesnärvarelse. [P2654]. s8º. Lund. 1847

Flerovsky (N.) Три политич. системы: Николай I, Александръ II и Александръ III. Воспоминанія Н. Ф. s8º. *n.p.* 1897

Flers (Robert, *marq.* de). Disc. de réception [*on the* Marq. de Ségur]. Réponse de R. Doumic. [Acad. Fr., 16 juin 1921. P2819]. s8º. 1921
see CAILLAVET (G. A. DE), R. DE F. &C. La belle aventure, 1920.
,, ESTAUNIÉ (E.) Disc. de récep.; réponse de R. de F., 1925.

—— & F. de Croisset. Les nouveaux messieurs. [La Petite Illustr., mai 1926]. la8º. 1926
Les vignes du Seigneur Comédie. s8º. [1927]

—— & G. A. de Caillavet.
L'âne de Buridan. 5e [8e] éd. s8º. *n.d.*
Le cœur a ses raisons. s8º. 1904
L'éventail. [3e éd.] s8º. *n.d.*
Miquette & sa mère. 5e éd. s8º. 1922
Papa. [5e éd.] s8º. *n.d.*
Les sentiers de la vertu. [3e éd.] s8º. *n.d.*
La vendetta, d'ap. une nouv. de Loriot-Lecaudey. s8º. 1911

Fleta, *see* SELDEN (J.) Ad Fletam dissert., f. 1647 ed., w. tr. &c. by D. Ogg, 1925.

Fletcher (Andrew), *of Saltoun.* *A defence of the Scots settlement at Darien. With an ans. to the Span. memo. agst. it. s8º. E. 1699
Polit. works. s8º. Glasgow. 1749

Fletcher (*Sir* Banister Flight).
Hist. of architecture. 6th ed., rewr. & enl. 8º. 1921
,, ,, ...8th ed. rev. & enl. la8º. 1928

Fletcher (Charles Brunsdon).
The Murray Valley: a 3000 mile run. s8º. Sydney. 1926
Stevenson's Germany: case agst. Germany in the Pacific. 8º. 1920

Fletcher (Charles Robert Leslie).
Edmond Warre, D.D., Headmaster &c. of Eton. 8º. 1922
The Great War, 1914–18. A brief sketch. s8º. 1920
Introd. hist of England. [v5]. 8º. [1923]
5, Fr. Waterloo to 1880.
,, ,, ...[2nd ed.] v1. 8º. 1905

Fletcher (George), *ed.* Prov. of Ireland. [*each vol. by var. a*[s].] s8°. C. 1921–22
Connaught, 1922. Ireland, 1922. Leinster, 1922. Munster, 1921. Ulster, 1921.

Fletcher (George), *M.D.*
Life & career of Dr. W. Palmer of Rugeley. 8°. [1925]

Fletcher (Giles), *the elder.* О государствѣ Русскомъ (1591). [*Tr. of* Of the Russe common wealth; *Ed.* K. M. Obolensky]. [P2398]. 8°. 1867

Fletcher (Giles), *the younger.* Christ's victory & triumph & o. poems of the 17th c. Ed. w. intr. [by W. T. Brooke]. 8°. 1888

Fletcher (Hanslip). Changing London. Sketches by H. F., w. apprec. by F. Rutter. fol. [1924]
,, ,, ...s2, w. intr. by A. E. Richardson. fol. 1925

Fletcher (J. S.) [Joseph Smith Fletcher; *ps.* A son of the soil].
The Cartwright Gardens murder. s8°. [1924]
Exterior to the evidence. s8°. [1920]
False scent. s8°. 1924
The great Brighton mystery. s8°. [1925]
Green ink & o. s. s8°. 1926
The green rope. s8°. 1927
Harrogate & Knaresborough. s8°. 1920
Life & work of St. Wilfrid of Ripon. 8°. Chichester. 1925
The Markenmore mystery. s8°. 1922
The Massingham butterfly & o. s. s8°. 1926
The middle of things. s8°. 1922
The mill of many windows. s8°. [1925]
The million-dollar diamond. s8°. 1923
The murder in the Pallant. s8°. [1927]
The passenger to Folkestone. s8°. [1927]
Picturesque hist. of Yorkshire. 3v. la8°. 1900–01
The Reformation in N. England. 6 lects. 8°. [1925]
The safety pin. s8°. 1924
The secret of the Barbican & o. s. s8°. [1924]
Short life of Card. Newman. s8°. 1890
Yorkshiremen of the Restoration. 8°. [1921]

Fletcher (James), *of Trinity Coll., Cambridge.* Hist. of Poland, w. narr. of recent events &c. 8°. 1831

Fletcher (Jefferson Butler). Dante. s8°. 1916
Symbolism of the Divine Comedy. s8°. N.Y. 1921

Fletcher (John), *dramatist.* Rule a wife & have a wife (1640); ed. w. crit. essay &c., by G. Saintsbury, *see* Gayley (C. M.) Repres. Eng. comedies, v3, 1914.
see Chelli (M.) Et. sur la collab. de Massinger avec F. &c., 1926.

Fletcher (John Gould). Amer. & Brit. verse; w. foreword by J. G. F., 1920, *see* Yale Review.

Fletcher (John William), *vicar of Madeley, 1729–85* [†La Fléchère (Jean Guillaume de)].
Works. 9v. [v9, Suppl.] 8°. 1806–08
*The Bible & the Sword: gen. fast vindicated. [P2533]. s8°. 1776
Christian theology. Sel. & arr., w. a life of the a., by S. Dunn. 8°. 1838
Five checks to Antinomianism. s8°. 1889
Posthumous pieces. By Melvill Horne. s8°. Madeley. 1791
*Vindication of Mr. Wesley's last Minutes occas. by letter inviting clergy &c. to oppose them &c. In 5 letters. By a lover of quietness &c. [*signed* J. F., *i.e.* J. W. Fletcher. P2533]. [*tp. missing*]. s8°. [Bristol. 1771]
see †Benson (J.) Life of La Fléchère, 10th ed., 1835; *a. c. in* Works, v1, *above.*
,, Manners (N.) A full confutation of J. F.'s Appeal &c., 1789.
,, Tyerman (L.) Wesley's successor: life, letters &c. of F., 1882.
,, †Wesley (J.) *Review of doctrines taught by J. W.; cont. answ. to "2nd check to Antinomianism" by [J. G. de La F.], 2nd ed., 1772.

Fletcher (Joseph), *D.D.* Posthumous sermons &c. Ed. Jos. Fletcher, Jr. [Sel. wks., v3]. 8°. 1846

Fletcher (Joseph Smith), *see* Fletcher (J. S.)

Fletcher (Mary), *1739–1815, wife of Rev. John Fletcher, see* Moore (H.) The life of M. F. &c., 3rd ed., 1818; 11th ed., 1844.

Fletcher (Phineas). Venus & Anchises (Brittain's Ida) & o. poems. Ed. E. Seaton. Pref. by F. S. Boas. 8°. 1926

Fletcher (T. Bainbrigge).
Works in Agric. Res. Inst., *Pusa.* Bulletin.
Borers in sugarcane, rice &c., by T. B. F. & C. C. Ghosh, 1921–22. [102, 134.]
Hints on collecting & preserving insects, 1921. [113.]
Indian crop-pests, 1921. [100.]
Notes on Indian insects, 1916–19. [59, 89.]
Stored grain pests, 1921. [111.]

Fletcher (W. J. B.) Gems of Chinese verse. Tr. into Eng. verse. 8°. Shanghai. 1919
More gems of Chin. poetry. Tr. into Eng. verse, &c. 2nd ed. 8°. Shanghai. 1923

Fletcher (William Younger). Eng. bookbindings in the Brit. Museum. Illusts. of 63 examples, w. intr. & descrs. by W. Y. F. fol. 1895

Flett (John Smith), *see* Barrow (G.), J. S. G. Wilson &c. Geol. of co. round Blair Atholl &c.; w. petrolog. ch. &c. by F., 1905.
see Reid (C.) & J. S. F. Geol. of the Land's End dist., 1907.
—— **& J. B. Hill.** Geol. of the Lizard & Meneage. [Mems. of G.S.] 8°. 1912

Fleurange [*or*, Fleuranges; Florange; *ps.* "Le jeune adventureux." †La Marck (Robert de), *seigneur de Fleurange*]. Mémoires, 1505–25. Publ. R. Goubaux & P. A. Lemoisne. [Soc. de l'Hist. de Fr.] 2t. 8°. 1913–24

Fleure (Herbert John).
Geograph. factors. [P2573]. s8°. 1921
The peoples of Europe. s8°. 1922
The races of England & Wales, a survey of recent research. s8°. 1923
see Carter (E. H.), *ed.* The new past & o. essays; by J. H. Breasted, H. J. F. &c., 1925.
see Peake (H.) & H. J. F. Apes & men, 1927.
,, —— & —— Hunters & artists, 1927.
,, —— & —— Peasants & potters, 1927.
,, —— & —— Priests & Kings, 1927.

Fleurieu (*le cte.* **Ch. P. Claret de**), *see* †Claret de Fleurieu.

Fleuriot (*Mlle.* **Zénaide M. A.**) Une année de la vie d'une femme. 5e éd. s8°. 1875

Fleuron (Svend). Kittens. A family chronicle. [Tr. D. Pritchard]. s8°. [1920]

Fleury (*le card.* **André Hercule de**).
see Hardy (G.) Le Card. de F. & le mouvt. Janséniste, 1925.
,, Vaucher (P.) Walpole & la polit. de F. (1731–42), 1924.

Fleury (Anne F. A. de F. de Coigny, *duchesse de*), *see* Maurras (C.) Romantisme &c., éd. déf., Mdlle. Monk [*i.e. duchesse de F.*], 1922.

Fleury (Claude). Manners of the ant. Israelites. [Tr.] w. acc. of the Samaritans. Enl. by A. Clarke. 4th ed., w. adds. 8°. 1820
,, ,, tr., 5th ed., *see* Clarke (A.) Misc. wks., v9, 1837.
Les moeurs des Chrétiens. s8°. La Haye. 1682
,, ,, [*b. w. h.* Les mœurs des Isrélites, 1700]. s8°. Brux. 1700
Les mœurs des Israélites. 5e éd. corr. & augm. s8°. Brux. 1700
Neuviéme discours sur les libertez de l'Eglise Gallicane. [*no tp. b. w.* Le Noble (E.) Esprit de Gerson, 1710]. s8°. *n.p. n.d.*

Fleury (Élie), *see* La Tour (M. Q. de). Cat. de la coll. M. Q. de la T., par E. F., 1919.

Fleury (Jean). Le mouvement litt. en Russie. [*Extr. f.* Revue internat., t28. P643]. 8°. *n.d.*

Fleury (*cte.* **Maurice**). Mems. of the Empress Eugenie. Comp. f. priv. docs., letters &c. of the Empress &c. by Cte. F. 2v. 8°. N.Y. 1920
—— **& L. Sonolet.**
La société du second Empire. t4. 1867–70. 8°. *n.d.*

Fleury de Chaboulon (*le baron* **P. A. E.**) Mém. p. s. à l'hist. de Napoléon en 1815, avec annot. mss. de N., publ. L. Cornet. 3p. 8°. 1901
p1 *includes* Catalogue of the library of N. sold by Sotheby, 1823.
,, ,, *For another ed., see* Napoleon I. Rec. de pièces authent. &c., t6, 7, 1822.

Flexner (Bernard) & R. Oppenheimer. Legal aspect of the juvenile court, 1922, *see* United States: Labour.

Fliche (Augustin). Études sur la polémique relig. à l'époque de Grégoire VII. Les Prégrégoriens. s8°. 1916
La réforme grégorienne. 2t. (1, Formation des idées grégor. 2, Grégoire VII). [Spicilegium sacrum Lovan. fasc. 6, 9]. la8°. Louvain. 1924–25

Flier (Albertus van der). Specimen de J. Coccejo antischolastico. 8°. Trajecti ad Rhenum. 1859

Flindall (John Morris). The amateur's pocket companion; or a descr. of engr. Brit. portraits; also of books mentioned in works of Granger, Bromley, Noble &c. [*w. sep. tp.*] s8°. 1813

Flitner (Wilhelm), *see* Baumgarten (O.) Geistige &c. Wirk. d. Krieges in Deut. v. O. B., W. F. &c., 1927.

Flodden Field. *Batayle of Floddon-felde [*w.* App. cont. Notes & illustr., *sep. pagin.*], *see* MAIDMENT (J.) & R. PITCAIRN. Nugae derelictae, 1822.

Flögel (Carl Friedrich). Gesch. d. Grotesk-Komischen. [Nach d. A. v. 1788, neu bearb. u. hrsg. v. M. Baur. 2B]. 8°. München. 1914

Floire et Blanchefleur [†FIORIO; FLORIO]. Il cantare di F. e B. Ed. &c. V. Crescini. 2v. s8°. Bologna. 1889–99

F. & B. Middle-Eng. romance. Ed. f. Trentham & Auchinleck MSS. by A. B. Taylor. 8°. O. 1927

see NOREEN (E.) Studier rör. Eufemiavis., 1, 1923.

„ RICKERT (E.) Early Eng. romances in verse, 1908.

Flom (George Tobias). The language of the Konungs Skuggsjá (Speculum regale). [Univ. of Illinois. St. in lang. &c., v7iii, 8iv]. 2p. la8°. [Urbana]. 1921–24

The phonology of the dialect of Aurland, Norway. [Univ. of Illinois. St. in lang. &c., v1i, ii]. 8°. [Urbana. 1915]

Flood (J. M.) Dublin in Irish legend. [P2428]. 8°. D. 1919

Flood (*Chevalier* William Henry Grattan). Early Tudor composers: biog. sketches of 32 musicians &c., 1485–1555. Pref. by Sir W. H. Hadow. s8°. 1925

Flook (Elizabeth). *A short acc. of E. F., of Kingswood. [P2675]. s8°. Bristol. *n.d.*

Floovant. Chanson de geste, *see* GUESSARD (F.) Anc. poëtes, t1, 1859.

Floqit (Krist. V.)

Fe e kombësi. Dramë kombëtare. s8°. Sofje. 1914

Flora. *The toilet of Flora, n. ed., 1784, *see* TOILET.

Flora (Federico). La politica econ. e finanz. del Fascismo, 1922–23. 8°. Milano. 1923

Flora (Francesco). D'Annunzio. 8°. Napoli. 1926

Floran (Mary), *ps.* [*i.e. Mme.* MARIE LECLERCQ].

Maman Cendrillon. s8°. *n.d.*

S'il avait su! s8°. 1923

Floranes (Rafael de) [FLORANES Y ENCINAS]. Memorias y privilegios de Vitoria, 1775. 8°. 1922

La supresion del obispado de Alaba y s. derivac. en la hist. del Pais Vasco. Intr. &c. por S. de Ispizúa. 2t. 8°. 1919–20

t2 *cont.* Carta sobre la vida de San Prudencio Armentiense & Mem. que tiene la prov. de Guipúzcoa en obras inéd. de L. García de Salazar &c.

Florange, *see* FLEURANGE.

Florange (Ch.) Etude sur les messageries et les postes, préc. d'un essai numismat. sur les ponts et les chaussées. la8°. 1925

Flore, *le roi.* *Le roi Flore & la belle Jeanne—Amis & Amiles. Contes du 13e s. adaptés par G. Michaut. [Poèmes & récits de la vieille France, 2]. s8°. 1923

Florence, *Council of.* Acta generalis octavę Synodi Ferrarię incepte Florentię e Greco in Lat. tr. interp. B. Abramo—Magni Basilii contra Eunomium de Spiritu Sancto liber III, interp. G. Trapezuntio—Bessarionis Card. Oratio ad Grecos Bessarione interp.—Ejusdem epist. de successu ipsius Synodi &c. sfol. [Rome. 1526]

Docs. rel. au Concile de Florence: textes éd. & tr. par L. Petit, p1, 2, *see* GRAFFIN (R.) & F. NAU. Patr. orient., t15, 17, 1923–27.

Florence, *of Worcester, see* HOWORTH (*Sir* H. H.) Chron. of John of Worcester prev. assigned to F. of W., 1916.

Florence (Philip Sargant). Econ. of fatigue &c. & the efficiency of labour in Eng. & Amer. industry. 8°. [1924]

Use of factory statist. in investig. of indust. fatigue. 8°. N.Y., *Columbia Univ.* 1918

Florencourt (Franz von). Ueber d. Stellung d. Staatsregierung gegenüber d. Ultramontanismus. [P2656]. 8°. Bonn. 1872

Florens V, *count of Holland, 1254–96* [FLORENTIUS]. Het oude register v. Graaf F., *see* HISTORISCH GENOOTS., Bijdragen, d22, 1901.

Florenz (Carl Adolf). Die hist. Quellen d. Shinto-Religion. Aus d. Altjapan. u. Chin. übers. u. erkl. v. K. P. la8°. Göttingen. 1919

Flóres saga konungs ok sona hans, *see* LYGISǪGUR. Drei l.; hrsg. A. Lagerholm, 1927.

Flores (Manuel M.) Paginas locas. s8°. Puebla. 1878

Florian [CLARIS DE FLORIAN (JEAN PIERRE)]. Gonsalvo of Cordova. Pref. Hist. of the Moors in Spain. Tr. Heron. 3v *in* 1. s8°. Perth. 1792

Novelas nuevas; tr. G. Zavala y Zamora. s8°. 1799

Flöricke (Kurt). Austerbende Tiere. 5e A. 8°. St. 1927

Gesch. d. Bulgaren. [Nachtrag, *w. sep. pagin.*] la8°. St. 1913

Florida. Coleccion de var. doc. para la hist. de la F. &c., 1857, *see* SMITH (T. B.)

Florilegio di canti toscani: folk songs of the Tuscan hills, w. Eng. renderings, 1914, *see* WARRACK (G.)

***Florilegium** hist.-crit. librorum rar., 1763, *see* GERDES (D.)

Florimo (Francesco), *see* BELLINI (V.) Mem. e lettere [& Biog.], a cura di F. F., 1882.

Florio (Francesco). Le mani morte, ossia lettera all' a. del Ragionamento int. ai beni poss. d. chiese [*i.e.* A. Montagnacco]. [P2767]. 8°. Venezia. 1765

Florio (John) [FLORIO (GIOVANNI)].

see ACHESON (A.) Shakespeare's lost years in London 1586–92; J. F. as Falstaff &c., 1920.

„ CHAMBRUN (C. L. DE). G. F., un apôtre de la Renaissance en Angl. &c., 1921.

Floris & Blancheflour, *middle-Eng. romance, see* FLOIRE ET BLANCHEFLEUR.

Florit y Arizcun (J. M.), *see* INST. DE VALENCIA DE DON JUAN. Cat. de las armas d. I. de V. de D. J., 1927.

Florus (Lucius Annaeus). L. A. Florus. Cl. Salmasius add. Lucium Ampelium, e cod. Ms. nunquam antehac ed. s8°. Lugd. Batav., *Elzevir.* 1638

Rerum Romanarum libri IV. Annotationibus illust. auct. J. Minellio. Additus L. Ampelius ex Bibl. Salmasii. s8°. Londini. 1583

see LIVY. Rerum gest. pop. Romani libri 30; L. F. epitome &c., 1525.

„ SALLUST. C. C. S. & L. A. F., 1773.

Flot (*Mme.* Marcelle), *aft. Mme. S. Lambrino, see* CORPUS vasorum antiq.; France, fasc. 3, Musée de Compiègne (Musée Vivenel), fasc. 7, Bibl. Nat.; par M. F., 1924–28.

Flötner (Peter), *see* BANGE (E. F.) P. F. [Meister d. Graphik], 1926.

Flotte (Joseph de), *1734–92, see* MOULIN (S.) Carrière d'un marin au 18s, 1922.

Flottes (Pierre). Baudelaire l'homme & le poète. s8°. 1922

Flourens (M. J. Pierre). Éloge hist. de G. Cuvier, *see* CUVIER (G. L. C. F. D. DE). Éloges, préc. de l'éloge de l'a. par M. F., *n.d.*

Flournoy (Francis Rosebro). Parliament & war. 8°. 1927

Flournoy (Théodore). Des Indes à la planète Mars: ét. sur un cas de somnambulisme. 4e éd. 8°. Genève. [1910]

Flower. Ye flower-lover's booke: anthology, 1911, *see* NUTTALL (G. C.), *ed.*

Flower (Cyril Thomas). Public works in mediaeval law; ed. C. T. F., v2, 1923, *see* SELDEN SOC.

Flower (Newman).

G. F. Handel, h. personality & h. times. 8°. 1923

? (What shall the title be?) [Infants Hospital, Westminster]. 8°. [1925]

see SULLIVAN (H.) & N. F. Sir A. Sullivan, 1927.

Flower (Robin). Love's bitter-sweet: tr. f. Irish poets of the 16th & 17th cent. 8°. D., *Cuala Press.* 1925

see BRIT. MUSEUM: MSS. Irish MSS., v2, by R. F., 1926.

Flower (William), *Norroy King of Arms.* Heraldic visit. of Yorks, 1563–64—Heraldic pedigrees of Yorks. &c., 1567, *see* ENGLAND. Visitations of the North, p2, 1921.

Flowers.

*Language (The) & sentiment of flowers. Comp. &c. by L. V. s8°. 1866

*Language (The) of flowers: alphabet of floral emblems. s8°. 1857

*Language (The) of flowers. Illust. by K. Greenaway. s8°. [1884]

*Language (The) of flowers: w. illust. poetry. s8°. E. 1851

*Language of flowers, w. illust. poetry. Added, Calendar of flowers. 6th ed., rev. s8°. 1838

Floyd (John) [*ps.* DANIEL *à Jesu*]. Apologia S. Sedis apostol., circa regimen catholic. Angliae temp. persecut.; cum defensione relig. status &c. Ed. alt. emend. [2 pagins.] s8°. Audomaropoli. 1631

Floyd (Juanita Helm). Women in the life of Balzac. 8°. N.Y. 1921

Fluegge (Christian Wilhelm), *see* FLÜGGE (C. W.)

Flügel (Felix). Flügel—Schmidt—Tanger. Dict. of Eng. & German lang. Ed. I. Schmidt & G. Tanger. [*2nd tp. in Germ.*] 7th ed. la8°. 2p. Brunswick. 1903–6

„ „ ....8th ed. la8°. 2p. Brunswick. 1913–14

1, Eng.-Germ. 2, Germ.-Eng.

Flügel (Otto). Die Probleme d. Philos. u. i. Lösungen. 2e A. 8°. Cöthen. 1888

Flügge (Christian Wilhelm) [†FLUEGGE (C. W.)]. Gesch. d. Glaubens an Unsterblichkeit, Auferstehung, Gericht &c. 3T [*in 4v.* 3i, ii]. 8°. L. 1794–1800

T3 has 2nd tp., Gesch. d. Lehre v. Zustande d. Menschen nach d. Tode in d. chr. Kirche.

Flugi (Conradin de).
Alchünas rimas romaunschas rev. &c. s8°. Coira. 1861

Flying Post, The. Nos. 407, 410, 419, 458, 461, 464, 466–69, 486, 523, 622, 667, 725–780, 782–976, 978–1051, 1075, 1078, 1081, 1084, 1087, 1090, 1117, 1290, 1293, 1296, 1299, 1302, 1305, 1308, 1311, 1314, 1317, 1320, 1323, 1326, 1329, 1332, 1333, 1338 (Dec. 18, 1697–Dec. 2, 1703). fol. 1697–1703
Subsequent odd numbers are b. w. The Post Man, 1704–15.

Flynn (John Stephen). The influence of Puritanism on polit. & relig. thought of the English. 8°. 1920

Flynn (Paul F.) The book of the Galtees & the Golden Vein. Border hist. of Tipperary, Limerick & Cork. 8°. D. 1926

Flynn (William J.) The Oireachtas companion &c. for 1928: O. Éireann, 1922–27 (Dáil & Seanad). s8°. D. 1928

Foakes-Jackson (Frederick John).
Intr. to hist. of Xty., A.D. 590–1314. 8°. 1921
Life of Saint Paul. 8°. [1927]
Rise of Gentile Xtianity. s8°. [1927]
Studies in the life of the early Church. 8°. [1924]
—— **& K. Lake.** The beginnings of Xty. Ed. F. J. F.-J. & K. L. pl, v1–3. 8°. 1920–26
pl, The Acts of the Apostles. v1, Prolegomena 1, The Jewish, Gentile & Xtn. backgrounds. v2, Prolegomena 2—Criticism. v3, The text of Acts; by J. H. Ropie.

***Focaloir** Gaoidhilge-Sax-Bhéarla or Irish-Eng. dict., 1768, *see* O'Brien (J.), *R.C. bp. of Cloyne.*

Foch (*le maréchal* Ferdinand).
La bataille de Laon, Mars, 1814. [P2564]. 8°. 1921
Disc. de réception [*on* Vogüé]. Réponse de R. Poincaré. [Acad. Fr., 5 fév. 1920. P2819]. s8°. 1920
The 2 battles of the Marne, by F. &c., 1927, *see* Joffre (*le mar.* J. J. C.)
see Lacroix (*gén.* de). Le Maréchal F., 1921.
,, Madelin (L.) Le maréchal F., 1925.
see Maricourt (*le baron* A. de). F., une lignée—une tradition &c., 1920.
,, Recouly (R.) Bataille de F., 1920.
,, —— F., h. character & leadership, 1920.
,, Schwertfeger (B.) Der Irrtum d. Marschalls F., 3. A., 1920.
,, Terrail (G.) Le commandement unique, pl, F. & les armées d'Occident, 1920.

Focillon (Henri), *see* Exhibitions: Roumanian Art. Expos. de l'art r.; intr. *by* H. F., 1925.

Fodor (Ferenc). Econ.-geogr. map. of Hungary. In collab. w. P. Teleki & E. Cholnoky. [P2578]. 8°. Budapest. 1920
The geogr. impossibility of the Czech State. [P2567]. s8°. 1920
see Yearbook of Eastern-Europe, 1923/24, 1923.

Foerer (Lorenz), *see* Forer (L.)

Foerster, *see* Förster.

Foertsch (Paul Jacob), *see* Förtsch (P. J.)

Foffano (Francesco). Il poema cavalleresco. 8°. Milano. [1904]

Fogazzaro (Antonio).
Albo veneziano. [Nozze Clementi-Marchesini. *a. c. in* N127]. 8°. Vicenza. 1865
Malombra. 18 ed. s8°. Milano. 1901
Piccolo mondo antico. s8°. Milano. 1899
see Fattorello (F.) A. F., 1922.
,, Gallarati-Scotti (T. G.) Vita di A. F., 1920; tr. M. P. Agnetti, 1922.
,, Gennari (L.) Ritratto di un poeta: A. F., 1921.

Fogg Art Museum, *Harvard University, see* Harvard University.

Foggo (George).
Adventures of Sir J. Brooke, rajah of Sarawak. 8°. 1853

Foght (Harold Waldstein), *see* Sandiford (P.), *ed.* Compar. education; by H. W. F. &c., 1927.

Foglietta (Uberto) [Folieta]. Clarorum Ligurum elogia [W. pref. by C. Manuzio]. s8°. Romae. 1577
The sieges of Nicosia & Famagusta in Cyprus. Tr. C. D. Cobham. 8°. 1903

Fogolari (Gino). Giovanni Bellini. [Testo ital., fr., eng.] s8°. Firenze. 1921
see Illustrazione Italiana, Suppl., Settecento Veneziano; [by G. F. &c.], 1925.

Foi, *Sainte, see* Fides, *of Agen, St.*

Foigny (Gabriel de) [*ps.* N. Sadeur]. La terre Australe connue, 1676, *see* Lachèvre (F.) Les successeurs de Cyrano de Bergerac, 1922.

Foix (Gaston de), *duc de Nemours, 1489–1512, see* Nemours (Gaston de Foix, *duc* de).

Földes (Béla). A socialismus. [M. Tud. Akad.] 2k. s8°. 1910

Foletier (François de Vaux de), *see* Vaux de Foletier (F. de).

Foleÿ (Charles). Une folle jeunesse. s8°. [1921]
Poison, roman, *see* Œuvres (Les) libres, No. 19, 1923.

Folgore, *da San Gimignano.* I sonetti. Intr. e note di F. Neri. s8°. Torino. [1921]

Folieta (Uberto), *see* Foglietta (U.)

Foligno (Cesare). Di alcuni doc. Viscontei in bibl. inglesi. [Estr. d. Arch. stor. Lombardo, a. 32. P2841]. 8°. Milano. 1905
Dante. la8°. Bergamo. [1920]
Epochs of Italian lit. s8°. O. 1920
see Bailey (C.), *ed.* Legacy of Rome: essays by C. F. &c., 1923.
,, Lovato de' Lovati. Epist.; ed. C. F., 1906.

Foligno (Marco da), *see* Rosiglia (M.)

Foljambe (Cecil George Savile), *baron Hawkesbury, see* Liverpool (C. G. S. F., *1st e. of*).

Folk-lore. v31–37. 8°. 1920–26

Folk-Song Society. Journal, v6, 7 (1918–26). 8°. 1922–26

Follett (Helen Thomas) & W. Follett.
Some mod. novelists. Appreciations &c. s8°. 1919

Follett (Mary Parker). Creative experience. 8°. N.Y. 1924
The new state: group organiz. the solution of pop. govt. 3rd impr., w. intr. by Ld. Haldane. 8°. N.Y. 1920

Follett (Wilson), *see* Follett (H. T.) & W. F. Some mod. novelists, 1919.

Folliott-Stokes (A. G.) The Cornish coast & moors. 8°. [1924]

Fombona (A. Zéréga-), *see* Zéréga-Fombona (A.)

Fondi (Giulia Gonzaga, *ctss.* **di),** *see* Gonzaga (G.)

***Fons** philosophiae: poème inéd. du 12e siècle; publ. &c. A. Charma, *see* †Soc. des Antiq. de Normandie. Mém., s3, v7, 1869.

Fonseca Pimentel (Eleonora). La nascita di Orfeo. Cantata per nasc. di Prencipe ered. d. Due Sicilie. [P2765]. 8°. Napoli. 1775

Fonsegrive (George Lespinasse). François Bacon. s8°. 1893

Fontainas (André) & L. Vauxcelles. Hist. gén. de l'art franç., de la Révol. à nos jours. La peinture—La gravure—Le dessin. 4°. [1922]

Fontaine (Arthur). French industry dur. the War. [C.E. for Int. Peace]. la8°. New Haven, *Yale.* 1926
L'industrie fr. pend. la Guerre. [C.E. for Int. Peace]. la8°. [1924]

Fontaines (Marie Louise Charlotte de Pelard de Givry, *ctsse.* **de).** Hist. de la Comtesse de Savoie. n. éd., publ. avec comm. [*includ.* Le comte Odon], par C. Buet. 8°. Moutiers. 1889

Fontana (Gianjacopo).
La piazza S. Marco di Venezia. 8°. Venezia. 1867

Fontana (Leone), *1836–1905.* Commem. d. Comm. C. Dionisotti, *see* Regia Dep. di Storia Patria. Misc., t37, 1901.
Commem. d. Conte C. Bon-Compagni, *see* Regia Dep. di Storia Patria. Misc., t20, 1882.
see Manno (A.) L. F., ricordi, 1909.

Fontane (Theodor). Fünf Schlösser. Altes u. Neues aus Mark Brandenburg. 5e u. 6e A. 8°. St. 1920
Vor dem Sturm. Roman. s8°. St. 1912
see Hayens (K.) T. F.: a crit. study, 1920.

Fontanellenses, *see* Fontenelle.

Fontaney (Antoine Etienne) [*ps.* Lord Feeling], *1803–37.*
Journal intime. Intr. &c. par R. Jasinski. s8°. 1925
see Asse (E.) Les petits romantiques: A. F. &c., 1900.

Fontaney (Jean de), *Jesuit.* Rel. de ce qui s'est passé à la Chine en 1697–99, 1700, *see* Jesuits.

Fontanini (Giusto), *abp. of Ancyra.* Discus argenteus votivus vet. Christ. Perusiae repertus ex Mus. Albano depromptus &c. s4°. Romae. 1727
Diss. de corona ferrea Langobardorum. s8°. 1719
Hist. lit. Aquilej. libri 5 [Rufinus &c.]. Acc. diss. de anno emortuali S. Athanasii. 4°. Romae. 1742

Fontán Palomo (José). El Somatenista español. Prólogo del Ex. M. Primo de Rivera. 8°. Barcelona. 1924

Fontenay le Marmion. Cartul. de la seigneurie de Fontenay le Marmion. Publ. par G. Saige. 4°. Monaco. 1895

Fontenelle, *Benedictine abbey.* Gesta abbatum Fontanell. Rec. S. Loewenfeld. [Scr. rerum Germ. in usum schol.] 8°. Hannoverae. 1886

Fontenelle (B. Le B. de) [†Le Bovier de Fontenelle], *see* Baltus (J. F.) Réponse à l'Hist. des Oracles de Mr. de F. &c. [& Suite de la Réponse &c.], 1709.

Fontenius (Matth.) Diss. de S. Henrico Fennorum apostolo. Praes. A. A. Scarin. [P2742]. s4°. Aboæ. [1737]

Fontes. Fontes Hispaniae antiquae. Auspiciis &c. Univ. Litt. Barcinon.; ed. A. Schulten & P. Bosch. fasc. 1. 8°. Barcinone. 1922
see Avienus (R. F.) Ora maritima; ed. A. S., 1922. [1.]
Fontes hist. relig. Aegypt., 5p, 1922–25, *see* Hopfner (T.)

Fontes Rerum Austriacarum: österreich. Geschichtsquellen. Hrsg. v. d. Hist. Comm. d. K. Akad. d. Wiss. in Wien. Abtheilung 2, Diplomataria & Acta. B24–57, 61, 62 [*in 2v*]. 8°. Wien. 1865–1909

Bachmann (A.) *ed.* Briefe u. Acten z. Österr.-deut. Gesch. im Zeit. K. Friedrich III, 1885. [44.]

—— Urkunden &c. z. Österr. Gesch. im Zeit. Friedrich III u. Georgs v. Böhmen (1440-71), 1879. [42.]

—— Urkundl. Nachträge z. Österr.-deut. Gesch. im Zeit. K. Friedrich III, 1892. [46.]

Bärwald (H.) *ed.* Das Baumgartenberger Formelbuch; e. Quelle z. Gesch. d. XIII. Jhdt. vornehml. d. Zeiten Rudolfs v. Habsburg, 1866. [25.]

Beck (J.) *ed.* Die Geschichts-Bücher d. Wiedertäufer in Oesterr.-Ungarn, 1526–1785, 1883. [43.]

Beelen-Bertholff (*baron* de). Die Berichte d. ersten Agenten Österr. in d. V. S. v. Amerika Baron de Beelen-Bertholff an d. Regierung d. Österreich. Niederlande in Brüssel, 1784–89; hrsg. v. H. Schlitter, 1891. [45ii.]

Demelitsch (F. v.) Actenstücke a. Gesch. d. Coalition v. Jahre 1814, 1899. [49ii.]

Fiedler (J.) *ed.* Relationen Venetian. Botschafter ü. Deutschl. u. Österr. im 16. Jhdt.; 1870. [30.]

—— im 17 Jhdt., 2B, 1866–67. [26, 27.]

Goldenkron. Urkundenbuch d. Cisterc.-stiftes G. in Böhmen; mit Nachtrage u. Karte; bearbt. v. M. Pangerl. [37.]

Göttweig. Urkunden &c. z. Gesch. d. Benedictinerstiftes Göttweig; vorbereitet v. A. Dungel; bearbt. v. A. F. Fuchs, 3T, 1901–2. [51, 52, 55.]

Höfler (C. A. C. v.) *ed.* Der Congress v. Soissons; nach d. Instruct. d. Kaiserl. Cabinetes u. d. Berichten d. K. Botschafters S. Kinsky, 2B, 1871–76. [32, 38.]

Joseph II, *emp.* J. II u. Graf Ludwig Cobenzl: ihr Briefwechsel; hrsg. v. A. Beer & J. Fiedler, 2B, 1901. [53, 54.]

Klosterneuburg. Urkundenbuch d. Stiftes K. bis z. Ende d. 14. Jhdt.; bearbt. H. J. Zeibig, T2, 1868. [28.]

†Leopold I, *emp. of Germany.* Privatbriefe K. L. I. an d. Grafen F. E. Pötting, 1662–73; hrsg. A. F. Pribram &c., 2T, 1903–4. [B56, 57.]

Lilienfeld. Das Todtenbuch d. Cisterc.-Stiftes L. in Österr.; mitgetheilt v. H. v. Zeissberg, 1879. [41i.]

Loserth (J.) *ed.* Acten u. Corresp. z. Gesch. d. Gegenreformation unter Erzherzog Karl II (1578–90), 1898. [50.]

Mary Christine, *archduchess of Austria.* Briefe an Leopold II; nebst e. Einl. z. Gesch. d. französ. Politik L. II; hrsg. v. H. Schlitter, 1896. [48i.]

Mattsee. Quellen z. Gesch. d. Stiftes u. d. Herrschaft M.; hrsg. &c. v. W. Erben, 1896. [49i.]

Maximilian II, *emp.* Die Registratur Erzherzog M., 1547–51; hrsg. v. J. Loserth, 1896. [48ii.]

Meinhard II. Urbare d. Grafschaft Tirol; v. O. v. Zingerle, 1890. [45i.]

Neustift. Urkundenbuch d. Augustiner Chorherren-Stiftes N. in Tirol; hrsg. v. T. Mairhofer, 1871. [34.]

†Pius II, *pope.* Briefswechsel; hrsg. v. R. Wolkan, B1, 2, 1909. [61, 62.]

St. Lambrecht. Die beiden ält. Todtenbücher d. Benedictinerstiftes St. L. in Obersteier; mitgetheilt v. M. Pangerl, 1869. [29.]

St. Paul. Urkundenbuch d. Benedictiner-Stiftes St. P. in Kärnten; hrsg. v. B. Schroll, 1876. [39.]

Schlitter (H.) Pius VI. u. Josef II, 1782–84, 1894. [47ii.]

—— Die Reise d. Papstes Pius VI nach Wien &c. Beziehungen Josefs II z. röm. Curie, 1892. [47i.]

Seitenstetten. Urkundenbuch d. Benedictiner-Stiftes S.; v. I. Raab, 1870. [33.]

Valentinelli (J.) *ed.* Diplomatarium Portusnaonense (1276–1514), 1865. [24.]

Waldstein (A. v.) Briefe an Karl v. Harrach (1625–7). Hrsg. v. F. Tadra, 1879. [41ii.]

Zahn (J. v.) *ed.* Austro-Friulana: Actenstücken z. Gesch. d. Conflictes Herzog Rudolfs IV v. Österreich mit d. Patriarchate v. Aquileja, 1358–65, 1877. [40.]

—— Codex diplom. Austriaco-Frising., 3B, 1870–71. [31, 35, 36.]

Fontes rerum Hungaricarum. t1–3. la8°. Budapest. 1915–18

see BATHORY (I.), *king of Poland.* Rationes curiae (1576–86); ed. A. Veress, 1918. [3.]

,, HUNGARI. Matricula &c. Hung. in Ital. stud.; ed. A. Veress, 2v, 1915–17. [1, 2.]

Fontes rerum Transylvanicarum. v1–4. la8°. Budapest. 1911–14

see JESUITS. Epist. & acta Jesuitarum Transylvaniae (1571–1613); ed. A. Veress, 2v, 1911–13. [1, 2.]

,, POSSEVINO (A.) Transilvania (1584); A. Veress, 1913. [3.]

,, VERESS (A.) Acta & epist. Transyl. Hungariaeque &c., v1, 1914. [4.]

Fonvizin (Denis Ivanovich), *1745–1792.* Бригадиръ-Недоросль, *see* BUNIN (I. A.) Русскіе писатели, 1921.

see VYAZEMSKY (*pr.* P. A.) Ф.-В., 1848; [*& in h.* Полн. соб. соч., т5, 1880].

Food news notes for public libraries. v1 (Oct. 1917–Sept. 1918) & Oct. 1918. 8°. Wash. [1917–18]

Foord (Edward).

Gloucester, Tewkesbury & dist. s8°. 1925

The last age of Roman Britain. 8°. [1925]

see HOME (G. C.) & E. F. Bristol, Bath &c., 1925.

Foord (J.) Decorative flower studies. fol. 1901

Foote (James Stephen). Circulatory system in bone, *see* SMITHSONIAN INST. Misc. coll., v72, 1922.

Foote (Samuel). [The commissary—The lame lover—Taste—Edgar & Emmeline—The author. Minor theatre (The), v4. *Each play has sep. tp. & pagin.*] s8°. 1794

The minor. Comedy. [P2575]. 8°. 1778

The orators. Comedy. [P2575]. 8°. 1777

Forain (Jean Louis), *see* SALAMAN (M. C.) J. L. F., 1925.

Forbes, *The family of.*

see BROWNE (G. F.), *bp.* Echt-Forbes family charters, 1345–1727 &c., 1923.

,, CULLODEN PAPERS. More C.P., 1626–1745, 3v, 1923–27.

Forbes (Alex. Kinloch). Râs Mâlâ: Hindoo annals of Goozerat. Ed. w. hist. notes & app. by H. G. Rawlinson. 2v. s8°. 1924

Forbes (Allan). Towns of New Eng. & Old Eng., &c. Connecting links &c. Pr. to commem. the tercent. of the landing of the Pilgrims. 2p. la8°. N.Y. 1921

Forbes (*Lady* Angela Selina Bianca).

Memories & base details. 8°. [1921]

Forbes (Bertie Charles).

Men who are making the West. 8°. N.Y. [1923]

Forbes (Duncan), *prof. at King's College.*

Bengālī reader, w. tr. & vocab. n. ed. rev. 8°. 1862

Forbes (Edward), *prof. at King's Coll., London.* On the tertiary fluvio-marine form. of I. of Wight. [Mems. of G.S.] 8°. 1856

Forbes (George), *F.R.S.*

David Gill, man & astronomer: memoirs. 8°. 1916

Forbes (George Hay). Doctrinal errors & pract. scandals of the Eng. Prayer Bk. 8°. Burntisland. 1863

Forbes (Joan Rosita), *see* FORBES (ROSITA).

Forbes (John), *of Corse, 1593–1648* [FORBESIUS (J.)]

Opera omnia. [Ed. G. Garden]. 2t. [T1 *has engr. tp. prec. gen. one; t2, ed. nova, has tp.*: Instructiones hist.-theolog. &c.] fol. Amstelaedami. 1703–2

1st Bk. of the Irenicum. Contrib. to theology of re-union. Tr. & ed. w. intr. &c. by E. G. Selwyn. 8°. C. 1923

Instructiones de doct. Christiana. fol. Amstelodami. 1645

Forbes (Rosita), *aft. Mrs. Arthur T. MacGrath.* El Raisuni, the sultan of the mountains: h. life story. 8°. [1924]

From Red Sea to Blue Nile. Abyssinian adv[s]. la8°. [1925]

The secret of the Sahara: Kufara. 8°. 1921

Forbes (*Hon. Mrs.* Walter). His alien enemy. s8°. 1918

Forbesius (Joannes) *of Corse, see* FORBES (JOHN).

Forbes-Robertson (Frances), *aft. Mrs. Harrod.*

The triumphant rider. s8°. 1925

Forbes-Robertson (*Sir* Johnston).

A player under 3 reigns. 8°. [1925]

see BULLOCH (J. M.) Ancestry of F.-R., 1926.

Forbin (Louis Nicolas Phil. Aug., *cte.* de). Recoll. of Sicily, *see* CRAMP (W. B.) Narr. of voy. to India &c., 1823.

Forcellini (Egidio). Totius Latin. Lexicon. Ampliss. auctum &c. cura V. De-Vit. 6t. *b. in 3.* 4°. Prati. 1858–75

Ford (Charles Lawrence). Lyra Christi. rev. ed. s8°. 1892

Ford (Ford Madox), *see* HUEFFER (F. H. M.)

Ford (Guy Stanton). Stein & the era of reform in Prussia, 1807–15. 8°. Princeton. 1922

Ford (Henry).

My life & work. In collab. w. S. Crowther. 8°. 1922

" " ....[n. ed.] 8°. 1924

" " ....[n. impr.] 8°. 1924

Today & tomorrow. By H. F. in collab. w. S. Crowther. 8°. 1926

Ford (Henry Jones). Timothy Pickering, *see* BEMIS (S. F.), *ed.* Amer. Secr. of State, v2, 1927.

Ford (Horace A.) Archery. 8°. 1856

Ford (James). *Mem. of Th. Green, w. crit. on h. writings & acc. of h. family. [*Pref. signed* J. F., *i.e.* Ford]. 4°. *p.p.* Ipswich. 1825

Ford (James), *Ph.D.* Soc. problems & soc. policy. [*By var. wr.*] Ed. w. intr. by J. F. 8°. Boston. [1924]

Ford (Jeremiah Denis Mathias).

Main currents of Spanish lit. 8°. 1921

Ford (John), *dramatist, see* MASSINGER (P.) Dram. works of M. & F., intr. by H. Coleridge, n. ed., 1848.

Ford (*Col.* Joseph H.), *U.S. Army.*
see UNITED STATES: ARMY. Med. Dept. of U.S. Army in the World War, v2, Admin., v8, Field oper., by Col. J. H. F. &c., 1925–27.

Ford (Richard) *of Heavitree.* Gatherings f. Spain. [Ed. T. Okey. Everyman's lib.] s8°. [1906]

Ford (Robert). Vagabond songs & ballads of Scotland. Ed., w. notes, by R. F. s4°. Paisley. 1899

Ford (Worthington Chauncey), *ed.*
see ADAMS, *Fam. of.* A cycle of Adams letters, 1861–65, 2v, 1921.
,, UNITED STATES: CONGRESS. Journals of the Continental Congress; ed. W. C. F., v1–25, 1904–22.

Forde (Hugh). Sketches of olden days in Northern Ireland. s8°. Belfast. 1923

Fordham (*Sir* Herbert George).

Address on "Evol. of the maps of the Brit. Isles." [P2753]. 8°. M'ter. 1923
Barley. [From Trans. of E. Herts Arch. Soc., v7. P2786]. 8°. 1925
La cartographie des routes de France au 18e s. [Extr. du Bull. de la Sect. de Géog., 1925. P2833]. la8°. 1926
Cat. des guides-routiers & des itinéraires franç., 1552–1850. [Extr. du Bull. de la Sect. de Géog., 1919]. 8°. 1920
,, ,, Illust. supplément. [2p; pl *b. w.* Catalogue, 1920]. 8°. Camb. 1921–26
The earliest tables of the highways of Eng. & Wales, 1541–61. [*Repr. f.* The Library]. 8°. 1927
The early hist. of Central Midwives Board &c. [P2618]. 8°. C. 1922
Les guides-routiers &c. de l'Europe 1500–1850. Conf. la8°. Lille. 1926
John Cary, engraver &c., 1754–1835. A bibliog. w. notes. 8°. C. 1925
John Ogilby (1600–76) & Brit. itineraries of 18th c. [Repr. f. Trans. Bibl. Soc.] 8°. 1925
The Listes gén. des postes de France, 1708–79 & the Jaillots. [P2709]. 8°. 1922
Note sur la liaison entre la cartobibliog. & l'hist. [P2709]. 8°. Brux. 1923
Notes on itineraries &c. of France. [P2847]. 8°. Southampton. 1926
"Paterson's Roads": maps &c., 1738–1825. [Repr. f. The Library]. 8°. O. 1925
Une piraterie litt. au 18e s.: Les contrefaçons de la Liste gén. des postes de France des Jaillot, 1708–79. [P2709]. 8°. Camb. 1922
Road-books & itineraries of Gt. Brit., 1570–1850. Cat., w. intr. &c. 8°. C. 1924
Road-books &c. of Ireland, 1647–1850. [P2706]. 8°. D. 1923
The roads of Eng. & Wales & the turnpike system. [Repr. f. Hist. Teachers' Misc., v5. P2872]. 8°. Linton. 1927
Roads on Eng. & French maps at end of 17c. [P2847]. 8°. Southampton. 1926
Valuation & rating reform. [P2618]. 8°. 1922
The work of John Cary & h. successors. [P2753]. 8°. [1924]

Fordham (Montague Edward).
Rebuilding of rural England. 8°. [1924]
—— **& J. R. Fordham.**
The Eng. agricult. labourer, 1300–1925. s8°. [1925]

Fords [PHORDS], *review in Armenian.* v4, N°. 10. [P2793]. la8°. Tiflis. 1880

Foreign affairs: an American quarterly review. v1–6 (Sept. 1922–July 1928). 8°. N.Y. 1922–28
,, ,, Gen. index, v1–5. 8°. N.Y. 1928

Foreign Office.
Cat. of pr. books in the lib. of the F.O. la8°. 1926
Handbooks prep. under the dir. of the Hist. Sect. of the Foreign Office. [Ed. G. W. Prothero]. No. 1–162. [Nos. 24, 32, 49 & 75 *cancelled*]. 8°. 1920

Abyssinia. [129.]
Aegean, Islands of the N. & E. A. [64.]
Africa, Brit. West. [90.]
Africa, French Equatorial. [108.]
Africa, French West. [100.]
Africa, Germ. East, *see* Tanganyika.
Africa, Partition of. [89.]
Africa, South-West. [112.]
Åland Islands. [48.]
Albania. [17.]
Alsace-Lorraine. [30.]
Anatolia. [59.]
Angola (incl. Cabinda). [120.]
Arabia. [61.]
Armenia & Kurdistan. [62.]
Austria - Hungary: foreign policy. [1.]
Austrian Littoral, The. [10.]
Azores & Madeira. [116.]
Bavarian Palatinate. [37.]
Belgium. [26.]
Belgium, Neutrality of. [29.]
Berlin, Congress of, 1878; by E. L. Woodward. [154.]
Bessarabia. [51.]
Bohemia & Moravia. [2.]
Borneo, Dutch. [84.]
Bosnia & Herzegovina. [12.]
Bukovina. [5.]
Bulgaria. [22.]
Cameroon. [111.]
Canary Islands. [123.]
Cape Verde Islands. [117.]
Carniola, Carinthia & Styria. [9.]
Caucasia. [54.]
Celebes. [85.]
China; by C. W. Campbell. [67.]
Congo, Belgian. [99.]
Courland, Livonia & Esthonia. [50.]

Foreign Office [*continued*].

Croatia-Slavonia & Fiume. [8.]
Cyprus. [65.]
Dalmatia. [11.]
Dahomey. [105.]
Don (The) & Volga Basins. [53.]
Eastern Question, Hist. of the. [15.]
Eritrea. [126.]
European Coalitions, Alliances & Ententes since 1792; by F. J. C. Hearnshaw. [152.]
Falkland Islands: Kerguelen. [138.]
Finland. [47.]
France & the Levant. [66.]
Freedom of the Seas, hist. treated; by Sir F. T. Piggott. [148.]
Galapagos & Juan Fernández Islands. [140 & 143.]
Gambia. [91.]
German colonization. [42.]
German Colonies, Treatment of natives in. [114.]
German opinion on national policy prior to 1914, 2p. [155, 156.]
German opinion on national policy since July 1914. [157.]
Gold Coast. [93.]
Greece w. the Cyclades & North. Sporades. [18.]
Greenland. [132.]
Guiana Colonies, Intr. to the. [134.]
Guiana, British. [135.]
Guiana, Dutch. [136.]
Guiana, French. [137.]
Guinea, French. [103.]
Guinea, Portuguese. [118.]
Guinea, Spanish. [125.]
Holland. [25.]
Honduras, British. [133.]
Indemnities of war: subsidies & loans. [158.]
India, French possessions. [77.]
India, Portuguese possessions. [79.]
Indo-China, French. [78.]
International canals; by E. A. Whittuck. [150.]
International congresses; by Sir E. Satow. [151.]
International rivers; by G. Kaeckenbeeck. [149.]
Ivory Coast. [104.]
Japan; by J. H. Gubbins. [73.]
Java & Madura. [82.]
Juan Fernández Islands, *see* Galápagos.
Jugo-Slav movement. [14.]
Kenya, Uganda & Zanzibar. [96.]
Kiaochow & Weihaiwei. [71, 72.]
Kiel Canal & Heligoland. [41.]
Liberia. [130.]
Libya, Italian. [127.]
Lorraine & Saar minefields. [31.]
Luxemburg & Limburg. [27.]
Macao. [81.]
Macedonia. [21.]
Malpelo, Cocos, & Easter Islands. [141 & 142.]
Manchuria. [69.]
Mauretania. [106.]
Mesopotamia. [63.]
Mohammedan history. [57.]
Mongolia. [68.]
Molucca Islands, *see* New Guinea (Dutch).
Montenegro. [19.]
Morocco, French. [101.]
Morocco, Spanish. [122.]
Mozambique. [121.]
New Guinea, Brit. (Papua). [88.]
New Guinea, Dutch & the Molucca Islands. [87.]
New Hebrides. [147.]
Nigeria. [94.]
Nyasaland. [95.]
Oceania, Brit. possessions in. [144.]
Oceania, Former German possessions in. [146.]
Oceania, French possessions in. [145.]
Pacific, Discovs. & acquisitions in. [139.]
Persian Gulf. [76.]
Poland, Gen. sk. of hist., 1569–1815. [43.]
Poland, Austrian. [46.]
Poland, Prussian. [45.]
Poland, Russian, Lithuania & White Russia. [44.]
Portuguese Colonial Empire, Formation of. [115.]
Prussia, East & West. [39.]
Prussia, Rhenish. [38.]
Rumania. [23.]
Ruthenia, Hungarian. [7.]
Sahara, Spanish. [124.]
Saint-Pierre & Miquelon. [131.]
Sakhalin. [56.]
San Thomé & Principe. [119.]
Schelt, Question of the. [28.]
Schemes for gen. peace; by Ld. Phillimore. [160.]
Schleswig-Holstein. [35.]
Senegal. [102.]
Senegal, Upper & Niger. [107.]
Serbia. [20.]
Siam; by J. Crosby. [74.]
Siberia, Eastern. [55.]
Sierra Leone. [92.]
Silesia, Austrian. [4.]
Silesia, Upper. [40.]
Slovakia. [3.]
Slovenes, The. [13.]
Somaliland, British, & Sokotra. [97.]
Somaliland French. [109.]
Somaliland, Italian. [128.]
Spain. [34.]
Spitzbergen. [36.]
Sudan, Anglo-Egyptian. [98.]
Sumatra. [83.]
Syria & Palestine. [60.]
Tanganyika (German East Africa). [113.]
Tibet. [70.]
Timor, Dutch & the lesser Sunda Islands. [86.]
Timor, Portuguese. [80.]
Togoland. [110.]
Transylvania & the Banat. [6.]
Trentino & Alto Adige. [33.]
Turkey in Asia. [58.]
Turkey in Europe. [16.]
Ukraine, The. [52.]
Vienna, The Congress of, 1814–15. [153.]
Wilson (*Pres.*) Pres. W.'s policy. [161.]
Zionism. [162.]

see BRITISH. Brit. docs. on orig. of the War, 1898–1914, v11, Outbreak: F.O. docs., June 28–Aug. 4, 1914, 1926.

Foreign Office List, 1920–1925. 8°. [1920–25]

Foreign Post, The. N°. 51 (Sept. 15–17, 1697). [*b. w.* Daily Courant, N°. 85 &c., 1702–03]. fol. 1697

Forel (Auguste).
Assez détruit, rebâtissons! [P2734]. s8°. Lausanne. 1916
The social world of the ants. Tr. C. K. Ogden. 2v. 8°. [1928]

Forel (François-Alphonse). Le Léman: monograph. limnologique. 3t. la8°. Lausanne. 1892–1904

***Forensic** fables; by O., 1926, *see* MATHEW (T.)

Forer (Lorenz), *Jesuit* [†FOERER (L.)] Alter u. newer Luther. Katzenkrieg v. d. Ubiquitet. Ins Teutsch. s8°. Dillingen. 1628
Bellum ubiquisticum vet. & nov. inter ipsos Lutheranos. s8°. Dilingae. 1627
Manuale Lutheranorum, seu vindiciae Symboli Lutherani cum Symbolo Apost. collati, adv. M. Nicolai Symbolum L. &c. s8°. Dillingae. [1628]
Septem characteres reformatoris Germaniæ M. Lutheri. Resp. X. Vischero. Præs. & prom. L. F. [*Dedic. epistle by X. Vischer*]. s8°. Dillingæ. 1626

Forest. *English forests & f. trees, 1853, *see* ENGLISH.

Forester (C. S.)
Louis XIV, King of France & Navarre. 8°. [1928]
A pawn among kings. s8°. [1924]
Payment deferred. s8°. [1926]
Victor Emmanuel II & the union of Italy. 8°. [1927]

Foresti (Arnaldo). Viaggi di F. Petrarca dall' Italia ad Avignone, *see* ARCHIVIO STORICO ITAL. Anno 78, v1, 1920.

Forestier-Walker (*Maj.-Gen.* George Townsend). Umpiring. [Aldershot Milit. Soc.] [P2591]. s8°. 1911

Forfarshire Regiment. Muster roll, 1745–46, 1914, *see* MACKINTOSH (A.)

Forget me not. Forget me not, a Xmas & New Year's present for 1826. s8°. *Ackermann.* 1826

Foris (Franciscus), *Otrokocsi.*
Antiqua Hungar. religio &c. s8°. Tyrnaviae. 1706
Examen Reformationis Lutheri & sociorum ejus ab a. 1517 factae &c. s8°. Tyrnaviae. 1696
Laetum ad lugentes Sion nuncium. [*b. w. h.* Roma civitas Dei, 1698]. s8°. Tyrnaviae. 1696
Origines Hungaricae ; seu liber quô vera nationis Hungaricae origo & antiquitas &c. panduntur. 2p *in* 1v. s8°. Franequerae. 1693
Restitutio Israel futura, ex Hoseae III, 4, 5, ostenditur. s8°. Viennae. 1712
Roma civitas Dei sancta. s8°. Tyrnaviae. 1698
see WOODROFFE (B.) Examinis &c. examen, 1700.

Forkel (Johann Nicolaus). J. S. Bach, h. life, art & work. Tr., w. notes &c. by C. S. Terry. 8°. 1920

Forli (Biondo da), *see* BLONDUS (F.)

Form [FORME]. Form (The) of prayers acc. to Span. &c. Jews ; tr. D. Levi, 1789, *see* TEPHILOTH.
Forme (The) of prayers &c. used in the Eng. congreg. at Geneva, 1643, *see* PRAYERS.

Forma. Forma ac ratio tota eccl. ministerii in peregrinorum, potissimum verò German. eccl. ; instituta Londini, Angliae per regem Eduardum. Cum brevi calumniarum quarundam refut. &c. s8°. *n.p.* 1555
*Forma inquisitionis Hispan. &c., 1550, *see* INQUISITIO.

Forman (Harry Buxton). The Library of F. Sale, Mar. & Apr. 1920, Anderson Galleries. 2p *in* 1v. 8°. N.Y. 1920

Forman (Maurice Buxton). A bibliog. of the wr. in prose & verse of George Meredith. [Bibliog. Soc.] 8°. E. 1922
Meredithiana. Suppl. to the bibliog. of Meredith. [Bibliog. Soc.] 8°. E. 1924

Forman (Samuel Eagle). Hist. of the Amer. people. 8°. [1922]

Former ages never heard of &c. : or, brief review of Parl. transact. beg. Nov. 3, 1640, 1656, *see* PARLIAMENT.

Formey (Jean Henri Samuel).
A concise hist. of philosophy &c. Tr. s8°. 1766

Formicola (Gennaro). Poesie liriche. 2ª ed. 8°. Napoli. 1875

Formigé (J. C.) & Jules Formigé. Les arènes de Lutèce, *see* PARIS. COMM. MUNICIPALE DU VIEUX PARIS. Procès-verbaux, 1918.

Formigé (Jules). Le prétendu cirque romain d'Orange, & Remarques s. les théâtres rom., d'Arles & d'Orange, *see* ACAD. DES INSCR. &C. Mém. &c., s1, t13i, 1923.
see FORMIGÉ (J. C.) & J. F. Les arènes de Lutèce, 1918.

Formont (Maxime).
Le bien-aimé. Roman. [2ᵉ éd.] s8°. 1920
La sirène : roman, *see* ŒUVRES libres, 37, 1924.
Les trompeuses. s8°. 1927
Le visage de l'amour. s8°. 1922

Formosa [FORMOSE]. Souv. de F. & des Iles Pescadores. Phototypie K. Ogawa. fol. Tokio. 1896

Formoy (Beryl E. R.) The Dominican order in Eng. bef. the Reformation. s8°. [1925]

Formula. F. Reformationis per Caesaream Maiest. Statibus Eccl. in comitiis August. propos. &c., 1548, *see* CHARLES V, *emp. of Germany.*

Formula Concordiae. *Augenscheinl. Erweisung, dass die F. C. v. allen Ständen u. Nationen unterschrieben sey. Sampt Kurtzer Erinnerung &c. [*The latter wanting*]. s4°. Ingolstadt. 1603

Formula Concordiae [*continued*].
*Kurtzer Ausszug u. einfeltige entwerffung d. F. C. &c. s4°. *n.p.* 1589
see BREMEN. Warhaffte christl. Widerlegung &c., 1583.
,, IRENAEUS (CHR.) *Refutatio I., 1583.
,, KIRCHNER (T.), N. SELNECCAR & M. CHEMNITZ. Apologia, 1583.

Fornaciari (Raffaello).
Disegno stor. d. lett. ital. 7ª ed. s8°. Firenze. 1905
see DANTE ALIGHIERI. Lectura D. : c. 18 dell' Inferno letto da R. F., 1902.

Fornasini (Carlo). Ind. d. Frondicularie fossili d'Italia. [P2875]. 4°. Bologna. 1897

Fornasini (Luigi). Versi. [Nozze Cicogna-Benedetti. N127]. s8°. Brescia. 1840

Forneau (Justa de), *formerly* URIENDT, *see* WANNEMAKERUS (P.) Funus J. U. uxoris J. de Forneau &c., 1614.

Forrer (Emil), *see* BOGHAZKÖI. Keilschrifttexte aus B., H4, Autographien, v. E. F., 1920.

Forrer (Leonard).
Biograph. dict. of medallists. v7. [Suppl., A–L]. 8°. 1923
see WEBER (*Sir* H.) The W. Coll., v1, 2, Greek coins ; by L. F., 1922–24.

Forrer (Ludwig), *see* RUSTEM *Pasha.* Osman. Chronik ; [Übers. &c. v. L. F.], 1923.

Forrer (Robert). Das Mithra-Heiligtum v. Königshofen bei Strassburg. la8°. St. 1915

Forrest (Archibald Stevenson). Tour thr. old Provence. 8°. [1911]

Forrest (C.) Hist. & antiq^{s}. of Knottingley ; w. notices of neighb. villages. s8°. 1871

Forrest (Charles). " All fools together." s8°. [1925]

Forrest (George Topham).
see LONDON. Survey, v8, Parish of St. Leonard, Shoreditch ; drawings &c. by G. T. F., 1922.
,, —— .... v10, Parish of St. Margaret, Westminster, p1 ; drawings &c. by G. T. F., 1926.

Forrest (*Sir* George Wm.) The admin. of the Marq. of Lansdowne as Viceroy &c. of India, 1888–94. la8°. Calcutta. 1894
Selections f. the State Papers of the Governors-Gen. of India. Ed. G. W. F. [v3, 4]. 8°. O. 1926
3, Lord Cornwallis : intr. 4, Lord Cornwallis : docs.

Forrest (H. Edward), *F.L.S.*
Old houses of Stratford-upon-Avon. 8°. [1925]

Forrest (*Capt.* Thomas). Voyage to New Guinea & the Moluccas f. Balambangan, 1774–76. Added, Vocab. of Magindano tongue. 8°. D. 1779

Forrester (R. B.), *M.A., M.Com.* The cotton industry in France. Report to electors of Gartside scholarships. Intr. by D. H. Macgregor. [M'ter Univ. Publ. Econ. Ser., No. 15.] 8°. M'ter. 1921

Forrester (Thomas). *A review &c. of 2 late pamphlets. 1. Queries to the Presbyterians of Scot. 2. A querie turn'd into an argument in fav. of episcopacy. Annexed : Counter Queries &c. [*Dedic. signed Alex. Henderson*]. s4°. E. 1706
*Causa episcopatus hierarchici lucifuga : or a confut. of J. S.'s Vindic. of the principles of the Cyprianic age. [*b. w. h.* Review &c., 1706]. s4°. E. 1706

Fors (Isabella de), *see* ISABELLA, *de Fortibus, ctss. of Albemarle &c.*

Forschungen. F. z. islam. Kunst ; hrsg. v. F. Sarre. 1, 2i–iii. 4°. 1911–27
see HERZFELD (E.) Die Malereien v. Samarra, 1927. [2iii.]
,, —— Der Wandschmuck d. Bauten v. Samarra u. s. Ornamentik, 1923. [2i.]
,, SARRE (F.) Die Keramik v. Samarra, 1925. [2ii.]
,, —— & E. HERZFELD. Archäolog. Reise im Euphrat- u. Tigris-Gebiet, 4B, 1911–20. [1.]

Forsdyke (E. J.), *see* BRIT. MUSEUM : VASES. Greek & Etruscan vases in B.M., v1i, Prehist. Ægean pottery ; by E. J. F., 1925.

Forsh (Olga). Современники : роман. изд. 2ᵒᵉ. 8°. Москва. 1927

Forshaw (Charles Frederick). Poets of Keighley, Bingley, Haworth &c. : biog. & poems. Ed. C. F. F. s8°. Bradford. 1891

Forskål (Per.), *1736–63,* *see* LEGRÉ (L.) La botanique en Provence au 18ᵉ s. : P. F. & le Florula Estac., 1900.

Forssell (Gösta). Üb. d. Beziehung d. Röntgenbilder d. menschl. Magens zu s. anatom. Bau. sfol. Hamburg. 1913

Forst-Battaglia (Otto). Genealogie, 1913, *see* GRUNDR. D. GESCHICHTSWISS. ; Meister, 1iva, 1913.

Förstemann (Carl Eduard). Urkundenbuch zu d. Gesch. d. Reichstages zu Augsburg, 1530. 2B. 8°. Halle. 1833–35

Förstemann (Ernst Wilhelm). Altdeutsches Namenbuch. 3e, völlig neu bearbt. A.; hrsg. v. H. Jellinghaus. B2ii. 4°. Bonn. 1916
2, Orts- u. sonstige geograph. Namen, Hälfte 2, L-Z u. Register.

Forster (Charles de), *of Warsaw, see* FORSTER (KAROL).

Forster (Edward Morgan).
Alexandria: hist. & guide. s8°. Alexandria. 1922
Anonymity. s8°. 1925
Aspects of the novel. 8°. 1927
The celestial omnibus & o. s. [5th impr.] s8°. 1924
The eternal moment & o. s. s8°. 1928
Howards End. [repr., uniform ed.] s8°. [1924]
Longest journey. [repr., uniform ed.] s8°. 1924
A passage to India. s8°. 1924
„ „ 2nd impr. s8°. 1924
Pharos & Pharillon. 8°. Richmond. 1923
A room with a view. [repr., uniform ed.] s8°. 1924
Where angels fear to tread. [repr.] s8°. [1924]

Förster (Erich), *see* BAUMGARTEN (O.) Geistige &c. Wirk. d. Krieges in Deut., von O. B., E. F. &c., 1927.

Förster (Friedrich W.) England in H. St. Chamberlains Beleuchtung. Ein Protest. [P2408]. 8°. München. 1917

Förster (Johann) *the younger.* Gretserus calumniator: oratio pro Luthero. [P2628]. 8°. Witebergæ. 1611
Vindiciae Lutheri, i.e. orationes 2. [P2628]. s4°. Wittebergæ. 1609

Förster (Johann Christian). Übersicht d. Gesch. d. Univ. zu Halle in ihrem ersten Jhdte. 8°. Halle. 1799

Forster (John), *barrister, of the Inner Temple.* Daniel Defoe & C. Churchill. [*each w. sep. tp. & pagin.* Repr. f. Edin. Rev., 1845]. s8°. 1855

Forster (Karol), *of Warsaw.* Du Royaume à l'Empire, 1848–52: Suite à Quinze ans à Paris. 8°. 1854

Forster (M. C.) Karlsbad's 500 jährige Jubiläums-Feier. s8°. Prag. 1858

Förster (Max). Die Beowulf-Handschrift, *see* KÖNIGL.-SÄCHS. GESELLS. D. WISS. Berichte, phil.-hist. Kl, B71, 1919.
see VERCELLI CODEX. Il Codice V. &c.; a cura d. Bibl. Vat. con intr. del Prof. M. F., 1913.

Forster (R. H.) War poems of a Northumbrian. [P2561]. 8°. Newcastle-on-Tyne. 1914

Förster (Wendelin), *see* JEAN. Mervelles de Rigomer, hrsg. v. W. F., 2B, 1908–15.

Forster (Westgarth). Treatise on a sect. of the strata f. Newcastle to Cross Fell &c. 2nd ed. enl. 8°. Alston, Cumb. 1821

Förster (Wilhelm), *astronomer.* Johann Kepler, *see* VIRCHOW (R.) & F. v. HOLTZENDORFF. Vorträge, H146, 1872.

Förster (Wolfgang). Graf Schlieffen u. d. Weltkrieg. 3T in 1B [*sep. tp. & pagin.*] 8°. 1921
see DELBRÜCK (H.) Ludendorffs Selbstporträt m. e. Widerleg. d. F. Gegenschr., 1922.

Förster-Nietzsche (*Frau* Elis.)
The lonely Nietzsche. Tr. P. V. Cohn. la8°. [1915]

Forstner (Christoph). Hypomnematum politic. centuria. [*b. w.* Pareus (D.) Hist. Palatina, 1623]. s8°. Argentorati. 1623
see PACHOM (G. A.) Syn. logomachiarum &c. acc. C. F. De dissid. theol. epist. [1660–61], 1726.

Forsyth (Andrew Russell).
Calculus of variations. la8°. C. 1927
Theory of functions of a complex variable. 3rd ed. la8°. C. 1918

Forsyth (Cecil), *see* STANFORD (C. V.) & C. F. Hist. of music, 1918.

Forsyth (J. S.) *Demonologia; or, natural knowledge revealed. By J. S. F. [*i.e.* Forsyth]. s8°. 1827
„ „ ....s8°. 1831

Forsyth (Peter Taylor). The principle of authority in rel. to certainty, sanctity & society. Lect. 8°. [1921]

Forsyth (Phil). The man who feared. s8°. [1926]

Forsyth (William), *of Kensington.*
A treatise on the culture &c. of fruit-trees. 7th ed. 8°. 1824

Forsyth (William), *proprietor of the Niagara Falls Pavilion, see* CANADA: GOVT. PUBL. 7th rep. on grievances &c., added, Rep. on petition of W. F., 1835.

Fort (J. A.)
The 2 dated sonnets of Shakespeare. 8°. 1924

Fort (Paul).
Ballades françaises. s12–16, 25, 27, 28, 30–34. s8°. 1911–26
12, L'aventure éternelle, livre 1, suivie de En Gatinais.
13, Montlhéry-la-Bataille, suivi de L'aventure éternelle, livre 2. 3e éd.
14, Vivre en Dieu, suivi de Naissance du printemps à la Ferté-Milon & de L'aventure éternelle, livre 3. 2e éd.
15, Chansons pour me consoler d'être heureux. 2e éd.

Fort (Paul) [*continued*].
Ballades françaises [*continued*].
16, Les nocturnes. 2e éd.
[25], Chansons à la Gauloise.
[27], Hélène en fleur & Charlemagne, 4e éd.
[28], Au pays des moulins, le voyage de Hollande, suivi de Comme une solennelle musique.
[30], Louis XI, curieux homme. Préf. A. Antoine.
[31], Les compères du roi Louis (Louis XI, homme considérable).
[32], Ysabeau: chron. en 5 actes.
[33], Fantômes de chaque jour.
[34], Le Camp du Drap d'Or: chron. en 5 actes.
„ „ ....éd. défin. [s,] 1–5. s8°. [1922–26]
1, La ronde autour du monde. Préf. de P. Louys.
2, L'amour et l'aventure. Avant-propos de F. Mistral.
3, Le marchand d'images. Avant-propos de R. de Flers.
4, La Tourangelle. Avant-propos de C. Mauclair.
5, Les fleurs de lys. Avant-propos de M. Renard.
Fantômes en guirlande, ballades franç. inéd., *see* ŒUVRES (Les) libres, 23, 1923.
see MASSON (G. A.) P. F., s. œuvre &c., 1922.

Forteguerri (Niccolò), *bp. of Ancyra.* Ricciardetto, poema. [*Engr. by Lapi &c.*] 3t. s8°. Londra. 1780

Fortescue (Adrian), *Ph.D., D.D.*
The early Papacy to the Synod of Chalcedon in 451. 8°. 1920
The Uniate Eastern Churches: Byzantine rite in Italy, Sicily, Syria & Egypt. Ed. G. D. Smith. 8°. 1923
see VANCE (J. G.) & J. W. FORTESCUE. A. F.: a mem., 1924.

Fortescue (*Lady* Eleanor).
Hymns fr. German. s8°. Exeter. 1843

Fortescue (J. F.) Introd. to theosophy &c. [*sometimes attrib. to F.*], v1, 1855, *see* WALTON (C.)

Fortescue (*Sir* John), *chief justice of the King's Bench.* The difference betw. an absolute & limited monarchy, as partic. reg. the Eng. constit. With remarks by J. Fortescue-Aland. 8°. 1714

Fortescue (*Hon. Sir* John William).
Brit. campaigns in Flanders 1690–1794. Extr. f. Hist. of the Brit. army. 8°. 1918
The Brit. soldier & the Empire. [P2463]. 8°. 1921
„ „ *For a. copy see* BRIT. ACAD. Proc., v9, 1919–20.
A gallant company: deeds of duty &c. f. the st. of the Brit. army. 8°. 1927
Hist. of the Brit. Army. v9–12, 1813–52. 8°. 1920–27
Hist. of the Brit. Army. Maps & plans illust. v9–12 [9, 10 *in 1v*]. 8°. 1920–27
Wellington. 8°. 1925
The writing of history. 8°. 1926
see GEORGE III, *k. of Gt. Brit.* Corr., 1760–83; arr. & ed. by Sir J. F., v1–6, 1927–28.
„ —— Sel. f. papers, 1781–83; ed. J. F., 2v, 1927.
„ VANCE (J. G.) & J. W. F. Adrian Fortescue, 1924.

Fortescue (*Hon. Sir* Seymour John). Looking back. 8°. 1920

Fortgesetzte Sammlung v. alt. u. neu. theolog. Sachen, 1720–50, *see* UNSCHULDIGE NACHRICHTEN V. ALT. U. NEU. THEOLOG. SACHEN.

Fortibus (Isabella de), *see* ISABELLA, *de F., ctss. of Albemarle &c.*

Fortin (François) [F. F. F. R. D. G.] *Les ruses innocentes; comment on prend les oyseaux &c. Avec secrets de la pêche &c. par F[rère] F. F. R[eligieux] d[e] G[rammont]. 4°. Paris. 1688

Fortis (Alberto). Saggio d'osserv. sopra l'Isola di Cherso ed Osero. 8°. Venezia. 1771

Fortnightly review (The).
v113–129 (Jan. 1920–June 1928). 8°. 1920–28

Fortolis (Ludovic). Les Anglais en France: Des cachots de la Terreur aux geôles de l'Empire. s8°. 1923

Forton (Jacques), *sieur de Saint-Ange, see* SAINT-ANGE (J. F., *sieur* DE).

Förtsch (Paul Jacob). De conjungendo cum theologia philos. studio oratio. [*b. w.* Nahmmacher (C.) Diss., 1755]. s4°. Goettingae. 1756

Fortunato, *da Brescia* [*i.e.* GIROLAMO FERRARI]. De oratoriis domesticis, *see* ASSEMANUS (J. A.) Comm. de ecclesiis &c., 1766.

Fortunatus a Sospitello (*frater*), *see* GUBERNATIS (D. DE). Antiq. Franciscana ex t2 Orbis Seraphici &c. coll. a F. F., 1685.

Fortunio (Giov. Francesco), *see* SANSOVINO (F.) *ed.* Osserv. d. lingua volg., 1562.

Forty-five (The): narr. of last Jacobite rising, by contemp. hands, 1922, *see* TERRY (C. S.) *ed.*

Forward (Charles W.) "The fruit of the tree": man's primitive &c. diet. s8°. [1922]

Forwood (*Sir* **William Bower).** Remin. of a Liverpool ship-owner, 1850–1920. 8º. Liv'l. 1920

Forzano (Giovacchino).
Il conte di Bréchard. Dramma. s8º. Firenze. 1924

Fosbroke (Thomas Dudley). The Wye tour, or Gilpin on the Wye, w. add. 3rd ed. s8º. Ross. 1826

Fosbrooke (T. H.), *F.S.A.* **& S. H. Skillington.** The Old Town Hall, Leicester. With note on the stained glass by A. B. McDonald. 8º. Leicester. 1925

Fosca (François).
Bonnard. s8º. [1919]
Liotard. 8º. 1928
La Mal Mariée, nouvelle, *see* ŒUVRES libres, 62, 1926.
Maurice Denis. s8º. 1924
Monsieur Quatorze. s8º. 1923
Renoir. 8º. 1923
Renoir. Tr. H. Wellington. 8º. [1925]

Foscari, *family of, see* LAZZARINI (V.) I F. conti e signori feudali, 1895.

Foscari (Ferigo). Relaz. s. marina russa, 1784, *see* MALAGOLA (C.) L'instituz. d. rappres. diplom. di Venezia, Pietroburgo, 1906.

Foscolo (Andrea). Relaz. d. patria d. Friuli, 1525. [Ed. C. Foucard. Nozze Bergamo-Venanzio. N124]. 8º. Venezia. 1856

Foscolo (N. Ugo).
Prose. A cura di V. Cian. [Scrittori d'Italia, 87]. v3. 8º. Bari. 1920
Il secolo di Dante. 2t. s8º. Firenze. 1830
Ultime lettere di J. Ortis, aggiunt. I sepocri e poesie di U. F. Ed. 5ª compl. s8º. Milano. 1817
see ANTONA-TRAVERSI (A.) & A. OTTOLINI. U. F., v1–4, 1927–28.
,, CARRER (L.) Prose, v2, Vita di U. F., 1855.
see CIPPICO (A.) Poetry of U. F., 1926.
,, CITANNA (G.) La poesia di U. F., 1920.
,, MANACORDA (G.) Studi Foscoliani, 1921.
,, PECCHIO (*il conte* G.) Vita di U. F., 1915.
,, VERRUA (P.) O. Nelson nell pensiero e nell' arte del F., 1919.
,, VIGLIONE (F.) U. F. in Inghilterra, 1910.

Fosdick (Harry Emerson).
The mod. use of the Bible. [2nd ed.] s8º. 1924
A pilgrimage to Palestine. s8º. 1928

Fosdick (Raymond Blaine). Crime in America & the police. [P2503]. s8º. N.Y. [1920]
see LEAGUE OF NATIONS. The L. of N. starts; by its organisers [R. B. F. *& others*], 1920.

Foss (Edward). Tabulae curiales; or tables of courts of Westminster Hall, judges f. 1066 to 1864. Pref. an alphab. list. 8º. 1865

Foss (Hubert J.) The heritage of music. Essays, by R. R. Terry, W. G. Whittaker &c. Coll. & ed. by F. 8º. O. 1927

Foss (Max W. L.) Enthüllungen über d. Zusammenbruch. 8º. Halle (Salle). 8º. 1919

Fossa (Evangelista?), *see* MACCHERONEE di 5 poeti ital. del sec. 15: F. &c., 1864.

Fossa Mancini (Enrico). Fossili, *see* FILIPPI (F. DE). Rel. sci. d. Spediz. It. n. Himàlaia &c., s2, v6, 1928.

Fóstbrœðra saga. Fóstbrœðra saga. Udg. ved B. K. Þórólfsson. [Samfund t. u. a. g. n. l., 49]. 1925–27

Foster (Birket). Pictures of Eng landscape; engr. by the brothers Dalziel, words by T. Taylor. la8º. 1863
see MAYHEW (H.) Lower Rhine; illust. by B. F., 1860.
,, —— Upper Rhine; illust. by B. F., 1860.

Foster (*Capt.* **Cecil P. T.)** 1700 miles in open boats: loss of the s.s. Trevessa in Ind. Ocean &c. 8º. 1924

Foster (Charles Wilmer). Hist. of the villages of Aisthorpe & Thorpe in the Fallows. 8º. Lincoln. 1927
see LINCOLN. State of church in reigns of Eliz. &c. as illust. by docs. rel. to diocese of L.; ed. C. W. F., 1926.
,, LINCOLNSHIRE. Final concords of Co. of L., v2, 1244–72 &c.; ed. C. W. F., 1920.

Foster (*Sir* **Clement Le Neve),** *see* GREEN (A. H.), C. LE N. F. & J. R. DAKYNS. Geol. of the carboniferous limestone &c. of N. Derbyshire, 1887.

Foster (Foster). The old grammar schools. s8º. C. 1916

Foster (Fred W.) A bibliog. of lawn tennis, 1874–1897. [P2770]. s8º. Richmond. 1897
A bibliog. of skating. s8º. *p.p.* 1898

Foster (George Burman). Christianity in its mod. expression. Ed. D. C. Macintosh. 8º. N.Y. 1921

Foster (*Rt. Hon. Sir* **George Eulas),** *see* DOMINIONS (THE) & depend. of the Emp.; [*by Ld. Morris, F. &c.*], 1924.

Foster (James), *D.D.* Acc. of behaviour of the Earl of Kilmarnock, after h. sentence &c., w. sev. papers. [P2781]. 8º. 1746

Foster (John Watson). Limitation of armament on the Gt. Lakes. [Rep. of F. to the Pres. of the U.S., Dec. 7, 1892]. [C.E. for Int. Peace. P2676]. la8º. Wash. 1914

Foster (Joseph), *of Bishopwearmouth.* Descendants of J. Backhouse, yeoman, of Moss Side, Lancs. 4º. *p.p. Chiswick Pr.* 1894
Revised genealog. acc. of families desc. f. Francis Fox of St. Germans, Cornwall. App. pedigree of the Crokers. 4º. *p.p.* 1872
The royal lineage of our noble and gentle families, w. their paternal ancestry. 2[v]. 4º. *p.p.* 1883–84
,, ,, Lib. ed. 2v. 4º. 1885–[87?]

Foster (Joshua James). Dict. of painters of miniatures, 1525–1850, w. acc. of exhib., coll. &c. Ed. E. M. Foster. la8º. 1926
see NORTHUMBERLAND (A. I. P., *d. of*). Cat. of miniatures, prop. of the D. of N., comp. by J. J. F., 1921.

Foster (Robert Frederick). Bridge tactics. s8º. 1903
Complete bridge. s8º. 1906
Whist manual. s8º. 1890

Foster (Sandys Birket). Pedigrees of Crewdson of Crook, Whitwell of Kendal, Pease of Hutton & Low Cross. 4º. *p.f.p.c.* 1890
Pedigrees of Wilson of High Wray & Kendal. 4º. *p.f.p.c.* 1890

Foster (Thomas), *publisher,* **& G. Cochran.** Eulogies deliv. in Senate of U.S. on J. C. Calhoun, H. Clay & D. Webster. 8º. Wash. 1853

Foster (Warren Dunham), *see* ADAMS (E. C.) & W. D. F. Heroines of mod. progress, 1921.

Foster (*Sir* **William).**
Early travels in India, 1583–1619. Ed. W. F. s8º. 1921
The East India House, its hist. & assoc[s]. 8º. [1924]
English factories in India. [v10–13]. 8º. O. 1921–27
10, 1655–60. 11, 1661–64. 12, 1665–67. 13, 1668–69.
John Company. 8º. [1926]

Foster (William Eaton). The point of view in hist. [Repr. f. Proc. of Amer. Antiq. Soc.] [P2465]. 8º. Worcester, [Mass.] 1906

Foster-Melliar (Andrew). The book of the rose. 3rd ed. 8º. 1905

Fothergill (*Miss* **Jessie).** Kith & kin. pop. ed. s8º. 1882

Fotheringham (John Knight).
Hist. eclipses. Halley lect. [P2562]. 8º. O. 1921

Foucart (George). Le vaisseau d'or d'Amon-Râ, *see* ACAD. D. INSCR.: FOND. PIOT. Mon., t25, 1921–22.
see INST. FRANÇ. D'ARCH. ORIENT. DU CAIRE. Fouilles (1921–24), sous la dir. de G. F.; t1–4, 1924–27.

Foucart (Paul), *chef de bataillon d'infanterie hors cadre.*
Campagne de Pologne, 1806–7. 2t. s8º. 1882

Foucart (Paul François). Le culte des héros chez les Grecs—Un décret athén. rel. aux combattants de Phylé, *see* ACAD. D. INSCR. &c. Hist. & mém., t42, 1922.

Foucauld (*le père* **Charles Eugène,** *vicomte* **de).** Ecrits spirituels de C. de F., ermite au Sahara. Préf. de R. Bazin. s8º. 1923
see BAZIN (R.) C. de F., explorateur du Maroc &c., 1921.
,, —— C. de F., hermit & explorer; tr., 1923.

Foucault (André). *Works in* ŒUVRES libres.
D'Alger au Sersou, 1927. [78.]
Calmons l'Alsace, 1928. [85.]
Une colère du Gén. Pétain (1917), 1924. [41.]
La leçon d'Alsace, 1926. [59.]
Un tour au Maroc, 1925. [50.]

Foucaux (Philippe Edouard).
Gramm. de la langue tibét. 8º. 1858

Fouché (Joseph), *duc d'Otrante.* Lettre au Duc de Wellington, avec obs. par M. de Villeneuve. [P2553]. 8º. 1817
,, ,, 2e ed. [*b. w. h.* Mém., 2e éd., 1818]. 8º. Londres. 1818
Mém. de la vie publ. de F. cont. sa corr. &c. 2e éd. 8º. Londres. 1818
see HAUTERIVE (E. D'). La police secr. du prem. Empire: bull. adr. par F. à l'Empereur; publ. E. d'H., t3, 1922.
,, PROUDHON (P. J.) Comm. sur les Méms. de F. &c., 3e éd., 1900.

Fouché (Maurice). Le ciel. s8º. [1921]

Foucher (Alfred). Les bas-reliefs du stûpa de Sikri (Gandhâra). [Extr. du Journ. Asiat. P2791]. 8º. 1903
La Madone bouddhique. [Extr. des Mon. &c. publ. par l'Acad. d. Inscr. Fond. Piot., t17]. fol. 1910
Les représentations de Jâtaka dans l'art bouddhique, *see* ACAD. DES INSCR[s]. &c. Mém. conc. l'Asie Or., t3, 1919.

Foucher (Paul). Rêchain, avare. s8º. 1893

Foucquet (Jean), *see* DURRIEU (*le c.* P.) Livre d'heures peint par J. F., 45e feuillet, 1923.

Foudras (*le marq.* **Théodore Louis Auguste de).**
Un capitaine de Beauvoisis. 2v. 8°. 1925
Les gentilshommes chasseurs. 8°. 1922
Le Père la Trompette. 8°. 1923
Fougasses (Thomas de). Generall hist. of the state of Venice. Coll. out of all a. Eng. by W. Shute. [*2v in 1. v2, no tp., sep. pagin.*] fol. 1612
Fougères (Gustave). Athènes. 4e éd., rev. & corr. la8°. 1923
T. Homolle, 1848–1925, *see* ACAD. DES INSCRS. FOND. PIOT., Mons. & méms., t28, 1925–26.
Foulché-Delbosc (Raymond). Bibliogr. hispano-franç., p3, 1661–1700, *see* HISPANIC SOC. OF AMER. Bibliog. hisp., 1914.
Mme. d'Aulnoy & l'Espagne, *see* REVUE HISPAN., t67, 1926.
—— **& L. Barrau-Dihigo.** Manuel de l'Hispanisant. [Hisp. Soc. of Amer.] 2t. 8°. N.Y. 1920–25
Foulis (James) & N. Thounis. Protocol books of J. F. (1546–53), & N. T. (1559–64), & Intr. & Indexes. Ed. J. Beveridge & J. Russell. [Scot. Rec. Soc.] 8°. E. 1927
Foulke (Wm. Dudley).
A Hoosier autobiography. 8°. N.Y. [1922]
Is our civilization really declining. [P2871]. 8°. 1923
Lyrics of war & peace. s8°. 1916
Maya : drama. s8°. N.Y. 1911
Maya : a story of Yucatan. 2nd ed. s8°. 1901
*The Quaker boy. Autobiog. of R. B. Dillingham. s8°. N.Y. 1910
Roosevelt & the spoilsmen. 8°. [1925]
To-day & yesterday : sonnets & o. v. s8°. 1920
see PETRARCH. Some love sonnets of P. ; tr. w. biog. intr. by W. D. F., 1915.
Fouqué. [†LA MOTTE FOUQUÉ (FRIEDRICH HEINR. CARL DE), *baron*]. Undine. 3. A. s8°. 1820
„ „ Tr. T. Tracy. [P2460]. 8°. *n.d.*
Fouque (Octave). Les révolutionnaires de la musique : Le Sueur—Berlioz—R. Wagner—La musique russe. s8°. 1882
Fouquier (Armand). Causes célèbres de tous les peuples. éd. illust. [*each p. has sep. pagin.*] 10t. 4°. [1858]–74
Fourcaud (Louis de). Richard Wagner : sa vie, sa pensée & s. art. la8°. 1923
Fourest (Georges).
La négresse blonde. [Préf. *by* Willy]. s8°. 1920
Fourgeaud (Alexandre). Les violons de Dalayrac. 8°. 1856
Fourier (*le baron* **J. B. J.),** *see* HOBSON (E. W.) The theory of functions of a real variable theory of Fourier's series, 2v, 1921–26.
Fourmann (Jakob). Üb. d. Spr. d. Mystère de S. Bernard de Menthon &c., *see* ROMAN. FORSCH., B32, 1913.
Fourmont (Hyacinthe D. de).
Hist. de la Chambre des Comptes de Bretagne. 8°. 1854
Fournel (Victor). Contemp. de Molière. Rec. de comédies, 1650–80, avec l'hist. de chaque théâtre, notes &c. par V. F. 3t. 8°. 1863–75
Le théâtre au 17e siècle : la comédie. 8°. 1892
Fourneyron (Marcel Crozet-), *see* CROZET-FOURNEYRON (M.)
Fournier (August). Gentz u. Cobenzl. Gesch. d. österr. Diplomatie, 1801–05. 8°. Wien. 1880
Napoleon I : a biog. ; [w. bibliog.] Tr. A. E. Adams, w. intr. by H. A. L. Fisher. 2nd ed. v1. 8°. 1912
Wie wir zu Bosnien kamen. 8°. Wien. 1909
Zur Textkritik d. Korrespondenz Napoleons I. [Aus d. Archiv f. österr. Gesch., B93]. 8°. Wien. 1903
Fournier (Auguste). La verrerie de Portieux. [P2515]. 8°. 1886
Fournier (Edouard), *misc. writer.*
Chron. & légendes des rues de Paris. s8°. 1864
Enigmes des rues de Paris. s8°. 1860
L'esprit des autres recueilli &c. 4e éd., rev. & augm. s8°. 1861
see PATHELIN (P.) Le farce de P., avec tr. en vers mod., & prologue, par E. F., 1872.
Fournier (Joseph), *see* SAINT-YVES (G.) & J. F. Le département des Bouches-du Rhône, 1800–10, 1899.
Fournier (Paul). Les collections canon. rom. de l'époque de Grégoire VII, *see* ACAD. DES INSCR. Mém. de l'Inst., t41, 1920.
Fournier d'Albe (Edmund Edward). Life of Sir Will. Crookes. Foreword by Sir O. Lodge. 8°. [1923]
Hephæstus, or the soul of the machine. s8°. [1925]
Two new worlds. 1, The infra-world. 2, The supra-world. 8°. N.Y. 1907
Fournival (Richard de). La vieille, ou les dern. amours d'Ovide. Tr. du Lat. de R. de F. par J. L. Publ. H. Cocheris. [Trésor des pièces rares &c.] s8°. 1861
Fournol (E.) Bodin, prédécesseur de Montesquieu. Thèse. 8°. 1896
Fourquevaux (Jean Baptiste Raymond de Pavie de) & L. Troya d'Assigny. *Catéchisme hist. & dogmat. s. les contestations qui divisent l'Église. [Suite du Catéchisme.] n. éd. 5t. s8°. Nancy. 1750–68
Fourreau (Armand). Berthe Morisot. 8°. 1925
Fourth dimension (The) simply explained : coll. of essays &c., 1921, *see* MANNING (H. P.), *ed.*
Foussemagne (*Ctsse.* **H. de Reinach),** *see* REINACH FOUSSEMAGNE (*Ctsse.* H. DE).
Foville (Jean de). L'ennemie de l'amour. s8°. [1921]
Fowke (Gerard). Archeolog. investig. Cave explor. &c. [S.I. Bur. of Amer. Ethnol., Bull. 76]. 8°. Wash. 1922
Fowle (Frederick Eugene). The atmospheric scattering of light, 1918, *see* SMITHSONIAN INST. Misc. coll., v69, 1921.
Smithsonian phys. tables, 7th rev. ed., 1920, *see* S.I. Misc. coll., v71i, 1920.
see S.I. Annals of Astrophys. Obs. of the S.I. ; v4, by F. E. F. &c., 1922.
„ —— Distrib. of energy in spectra of sun & stars, 1923.
Fowler (A.) Geology of Berwick-on-Tweed, Norham & Scremerston. [Mem. of G.S. of Eng.] 8°. 1926
Fowler (Edward), *bp. of Gloucester.* *The resolution of this case of conscience, the Ch. of Engl.'s symbolizing w. the Ch. of Rome &c. [P2653]. s4°. 1683
Fowler (Ellen Thorneycroft), *aft. Hon. Mrs. Alfred Felkin.*
Beauty & bands. s8°. 1920
The lower pool. s8°. [1923]
Signs & wonders. s8°. [1926]
Fowler (F. G.)
see FOWLER (H. W.) & F. G. F. Concise Oxf. dict., 1911.
„ †KINGS. The King's English ; [*pref. signed* H. W. F[*owler*] & F. G. F., 1906 ; 2nd ed., 1908.
Fowler (George Herbert), *C.B.E.* Bedfordshire in 1086 : anal. &c. of Domesday Book. [Beds. Hist. Rec. Soc. Quarto mem., v1]. fol. Aspley Guise. 1922
On the outside edge : hist. of skating. s8°. 1897
Fowler (Harold North).
Hist. of anc. Greek lit. n. & rev. ed. 8°. N.Y. 1923
Hist. of Roman lit. 8°. N.Y. 1923
Fowler (Henry Watson).
Dict. of mod. English usage. s8°. O. 1926
Note on "As to," *see* BARNES (M.) What is pure French, 1922.
On grammat. inversions. [S.P.E. Tract No. 10]. 8°. 1922
On hyphens & shall & will, should & would &c. Corresp. &c. [S.P.E. Tract No. 6]. 8°. 1921
On "ing," *see* AIKIN (W. A.) Eng. vowel-sounds &c., 1927.
On the use of italic &c., *see* PAGET (*Sir* R. A. S.) Nature of human speech, 1925.
Preposition at end, *see* BRADLEY (H.) & R. BRIDGES. On the terms Briton, British &c., 1923.
The split infinitive &c.—Pictorial, picturesque, by R. Bridges. [S.P.E. Tract No. 15]. 8°. 1923
Subjunctives — Poetry in schools, by R. Bridges—Open court on "alright," misc. notes &c. [S.P.E. Tract No. 18]. 8°. 1924
see B. (E.), H. W. F. & A. CLUTTON-BROCK. Metaphor, 1922.
„ †KINGS. *The King's English ; [*pref. signed* H. W. F. &c.], 1906 ; 2nd ed., 1908.
—— **& F. G. Fowler.** Concise Oxford dict. Adapted by H. W. F. &c. f. the Oxf. Dict. 8°. O. 1911
Fowler (John A.) Cotton-goods markets of the Netherlands E. Indies, 1922, *see* UNITED STATES : COMMERCE.
Fowler (John Henry). De Quincey as lit. critic. [Eng. Assoc., Pamph. 52. P2683]. 8°. 1922
The life & letters of E. L. Hicks, Bishop of Lincoln, 1910–19. Ed. J. H. F. 8°. [1922]
Manual of essay-writing. 3rd ed. s8°. 1914
Fowler (Mary), *see* CORNELL UNIV. Cat. of the Dante Coll., Adds., 1898–1920 ; comp. by M. F., 1921.
Fowler (William Chauncey). The sectional controv. ; polit. hist. of the U.S. 8°. N.Y. 1862
Fowler (William Warde). Æneas at the site of Rome : obs. on the 8th bk. of the Æneid. 2nd ed. rev. s8°. O. 1918
Essays in brief for war-time. 2nd ed. s8°. O. 1917
Julius Caesar & found. of the Roman imperial system. [n. ed.] 8°. [1925]
Rome. [Home Univ. Lib.] [repr.] s8°. [1923]
Tales of the birds. 2nd ed. 8°. 1891
*A year w. the birds. By an Oxford Tutor. 2nd ed., enl. 8°. O. 1886
Fox, *The family of, see* FOSTER (J.) Rev. genealog. acc. of fam. descended f. Francis F., of St. Germans, Cornwall &c., 1872.

Fox (Augustus Henry Lane), *aft. Fox-Pitt-Rivers, see* PITT-RIVERS (*Lt.-Gen.*)
Fox (C. E.), *Litt.D.* The threshold of the Pacific: San Cristoval in the Solomon Islands. Pref. by G. Elliot Smith. 8°. 1924
Fox (Charles). Educat. psychology. 8°. [1925]
Fox (*Rt. Hon.* **Charles James)**, *see* TREVELYAN (G. O.) Early hist. of C. J. F., *n.d.*
Fox (Cyril Fred).
Archaeology of the Cambridge region. la8°. C. 1923
Fox (Dixon Ryan). The decline of aristocracy in the politics of N.Y. 8°. N.Y., *Columbia Univ.* 1918
Herbert Levi Osgood. s8°. N.Y. 1924
Fox (Francis), *of St. Germans, Cornwall; d. 1670, see* FOSTER (J.) Rev. genealog. acc. of fam. descended f. F. F. &c., 1872.
Fox (*Sir* **Francis).** Sixty-three yrs. of engineering, sci. & social work. 8°. 1924
Fox (Francis William), *see* DE MONTMORENCY (J. E. G.) F. W. F.: a biog., 1923.
Fox (*Sir* **Frank).** The English, 1909–22. 8°. 1923
*G.H.Q. (Montreuil-sur-Mer). By "G. S. O." 8°. 1920
Fox (George), *founder of the Society of Friends.* New appreciations of G. F. Tercent. coll. of st. Foreword by J. R. Harris. 8°. [1925]
Short journal & itinerary journals. Publ. for Friends' Hist. Assoc., Phila. Ed. N. Penney, w. intr. by T. E. Harvey. 8°. C. 1925
Fox (George), *of Pontefract.*
Hist. of Pontefract. 8°. Pontefract. 1827
Fox (*Hon.* **Henry Edward)**, *aft. 4th Ld. Holland, see* HOLLAND (H. E. F., *4th baron*).
Fox (Henry Elliott). Xtn. inscr. in anc. Rome: their message for today. Pref. by H. Wace. 8°. 1920
Fox (John), *1800–80.* *Vindication of Lady Byron. 8°. 1871
Fox (John), *the martyrologist.* Acts & monuments. Added life of the author in Lat. & Eng. [By S. Fox]. 3v [v1. 9th ed.] fol. 1684
v2 *has 2 pagin.* v3, *includes* Contin. of the Hist. of foreign martyrs, 1684. *pag. contin.*
Acts & mon. of the Christian martyrs; extr. f. F. *&* Suppl. extr. f. Clark, *see* WESLEY (J.) Xtn. lib., v2–6, 1751.
Comm. rerum in eccl. gestarum, maximarumque persecutionum, à Vuiclevi temp. descr. Lib. primus. Acc. Aphorismi J. Vuiclevi, cum collectaneis quibusdam R. Pecoki. Item, Ὀπιστογραφία ad Oxonienses. 8°. Argentorati, *V. Rihelius.* 1554
Rerum in eccl. gestarum, &c. comm. 2p. fol. Basileae. [1559]–63
p2 *h. t.* Martyrum hist., authore H. Pantaleone.
see RICHARDSON (J.) Popery unmasked; ans. to T. Baddeley's Sure way &c.; J. F. defended, 1825.
Fox (John), *minister of the Gospel.* Time & the end of time, in 2 disc. s8°. 1671
„ „ ....[a. ed.] s8°. [1680?]
Fox (*Sir* **John Charles)**, *a Master of the Supreme Court.*
The Byron mystery. 8°. 1924
Hist. of contempt of court. 8°. O. 1927
Fox (Marion I. D.) The luck of the town. 8°. 1922
Fox (*Mrs.* **Rachel J.)** Unexpected tidings of the War &c. Pref. by Countess of Portsmouth. [*Ed.* R. J. F.] s8°. 1915
Fox (Ralph). People of the Steppes. 8°. [1925]
Fox (W. H.) A company-secretary's duties. 8°. 1921
Fox (William), *missionary.* Brief hist. of Wesleyan missions on W. coast of Africa. 8°. 1851
The western coast of Africa: slave-trade, Wesleyan missions &c. 8°. 1851
Fox (William Johnson), *see* WALLAS (G.) W. J. F. (1786–1864), 1924.
Fox-Davies (Arthur Charles). Book of public arms: royal, municipal &c. n. ed. la8°. 1915
Heraldry explained. s8°. [1907]
Fox Strangways (A. H.) Words in music & song, *see* ENGLISH Assoc. Essays &c., v7, 1921.
Fox-Strangways (Charles Edward), *F.G.S.*
The works below are all Mem. of Geol. S.
Geol. of the co. betw. Atherstone & Charnwood Forest, w. notes by W. W. Watts. 8°. 1900
Geol. of the co. betw. Derby &c. & Loughborough, w. chap. on Charnwood Forest by W. W. Watts. 8°. 1905
Geol. of the co. near Leicester. 8°. 1903
Geol. of the co. N. & E. of Harrogate. 2nd ed. 8°. 1908

Fox-Strangways (Charles Edward) [*continued*].
Geol. of the co. N.-E. of York & S. of Malton. 8°. 1884
Geol. of the Leicestershire & S. Derbyshire coalfield. With notes by A. R. Horwood. 8°. 1907
Geol. of the oolitic & cretaceous rocks S. of Scarborough. 2nd ed. 8°. 1904
Geol. of the oolitic & liassic rocks to N. & W. of Malton. Lists of fossils rev. by R. Etheridge. 8°. 1881
The water-supply (f. underground sources) of the E.R. of Yorks. &c. Contrib. by H. R. Mill. 8°. 1906
see DAKYNS (J. R.) & C. E. F.-S. Geol. of Bridlington Bay, 1885.
„ —— & —— Geol. of co. around Driffield, 1886.
„ —— & —— Geol. of co. betw. Bradford & Skipton, 1879.
„ ——, —— & A. G. CAMERON. Geol. of co. betw. York & Hull, 1886.
——, A. G. Cameron & G. Barrow. Geol. of the co. around Northallerton & Thirsk. 8°. 1886
—— & G. Barrow. Geol. of the country betw. Whitby & Scarborough; w. chap. on local jurassic rocks by S. S. Buckman. 2nd ed. 8°. 1915
——, C. Reid, & G. Barrow.
Geol. of Eskdale, Rosedale &c. 8°. 1885
—— & H. B. Woodward. Jurassic rocks of Britain. 5v [1, 2, by F.-S.; 3–5, by W.] 8°. 1892–95
1 & 2, Yorkshire, by C. F.-S. 3, Lias of Eng. & Wales. 4, Lower oolitic rocks of Eng. 5, Middle & upper oolitic rocks of Eng.
Foy (*le gén.* **Maximilien Sébastien).** Hist. de la guerre de la Péninsule. Publ. par la ctsse. Foy. 2e éd. 4t *in* 2v. 8°. 1827
Foy de la Neuville (—). An account of Muscovy as it was in 1689. s8°. 1699
Foye (Martin Wilson). Tracts for the people. Lect. on coincidence of doctrines of the Tractarians w. those of the Ch. of Rome. s8°. 1842
Foz (José Garcia de la), *see* GARCIA DE LA FOZ (J.)
Fracassini (Cesare), *1838–68, see* SAPORI (F.) Maestri, No. 21, 1920.
Fracassini (Tomaso).
Gabriele d'Annunzio convittore. s8°. Firenze. 1916
Fracastoro (Girolamo). Naugerius, sive de poetica dialogus. With Eng. tr. by R. Kelso & intr. by M. W. Bundy [Illinois: Univ. of. St. in lang. &c., v9iii]. la8°. Urbana. 1924
Fraccaroli (Arnaldo). Allegretto. s8°. Milano. [1920]
La vita di G. Puccini. 8°. Milano. 1925
Fracchia (Francesco). Appunti per la Storia di Dogliani, racc. &c. da L. Einaudi, *see* REGIA DEPUT. DI STORIA PATRIA. Misc., t51, 1924.
Fracchia (Umberto). Angela. Romanzo. s8°. [1923]
Frachtenberg (Leo Joachim). Alsea texts & myths. [S.I. Bur. of Ethn. Bull. 67]. 8°. W. 1920
Coos—Siuslawan, *see* BOAS (F.) Hbk. of Amer. Ind. lang., p2, 1922.
Fradeletto (Antonio). Venezia, antica e nuova. 8°. Torino. 1921
Fragmenta. Fr. Burana. Hrsg. v. W. Meyer. [Sonderabdr. aus d. Festschr. d. K. Akad. d. Wiss. zu Göttingen]. 4°. 1901
Fr. histor. Graecorum, *see* JACOBY (F.) Fragm. d. griech. Hist., T1, 2, 1923–27.
Fragmente. Fr. (Die) d. griech. Hist. (F. Gr. Hist.), T1, 2, 1923–27, *see* JACOBY (F.)
Fragonard (Jean Honoré), *see* HIND (A. M.) F., Moreau le jeune & Fr. engravers &c., 1913.
Frähn (Christian Martin). Ibn Foszlan's u. anderer Araber Berichte &c., 1823, *see* AHMAD IBN FUDHLĀN.
Frame (James). Original sin. 2nd ed. 8°. [1871]
***Frammenti** su Venezia, 1864, *see* VENEZIA.
Frampton (John), *merchant, see* MONARDES (N.) Joyfull newes out of the newe founde worlde; Eng. by J. F., 1577, 2v, 1925.
Français [FRANÇAISE; FRANÇOIS]. Anthologie de la nouv. poésie fr., éd. rev. &c., 1926, *see* ANTHOLOGIE.
Essais hist. sur les mœurs des François, ou tr. abr. des chroniques &c. dep. Clovis jusqu'à St. Louis, 5t, 1785–92, *see* BILLARDON DE SAUVIGNY (L. E.)
*Lettres d'un François, 1734, *see* PARIS (F. DE).
Francatelli (Charles Elmé).
The royal Eng. & foreign confectioner. s8°. 1862
France.
Anon Works &c.
Almanach national: annuaire de la Rép. Fr., 1915–19, *see* ALMANACH.
*Amours des grands hommes de F., p1, 2, 1676, *see* AMOURS.
Annuaire généalog. de la noblesse de F., 1914, *see* REX.

France [*continued*].

Anon Works &c. [*continued*].

Atlas départ. Larousse : texte par G. Treffel, 1914, *see* LAROUSSE, *publ. firm.*

Atlas monumental, *see* ROUSSEL (J.) La Normandie : 5 cartes, *n.d.*

Constitution de la Républ. Française. s8°. Londres. 1796

Corr. des ministres de F. accréd. à Bruxelles, 1780–90. Dépêches inéd. Publ. par E. Hubert. [Acad. Roy. des Sci. &c. de Belg. Comm. Roy. d'Hist.] [2t]. 4°. Brux. 1920–24

*Desolation (The) of F. demonstrated, 1697, *see* SOULIGNÉ (— DE).

Discipline (La) eccl. & la conf. de foi des églises reform. de F. pour l'usage des églises de Brounsvic-Lunebourg &c. [*Fr. & Germ.*] s4°. Heidelberg. 1711

*Eccl. (The) discipline of the Reformed Ch. in F. Tr. s4°. 1642

*Economic (The) rel. betw. F. & Australia. Rep. of French mission. [P2592]. 8°. 1919

Enquête faite par ordre du Parl. d'Angleterre, pour constater les progrès de l'industrie en F. [Ed. & tr. R. B. Maiseau. *b. w.* Angleterre. Etat au comm. de 1822, 1822]. 8°. 1825

Etat (L') de la F., cont. les princes, le clergé &c. [Ed. N. Besongne, *w. add. & corr. by* Simplicien, Relig. Augustin Déchaussé]. 5t. s8°. 1727

*France & Germany. The future of reparations &c. [Repr. f. Round Table, March 1923]. [P2689]. 8°. 1923

France (La) maritime, 4t, 1837–42, *see* GRÉHAN (A.)

Grand (Le) coutumier de F. [*Comp. by* Jacques d'Ableiges]. n. éd. par E. Laboulaye & R. Dareste. 8°. 1868

Grandes (Les) chron. de F. Chron. des règnes de Jean II & de Charles V [*sometimes attrib. to* P. d'Orgemont]. Publ. par R. Delachenal. [S. de l'H. de F.] t3, 4. 8°. 1920

Grandes (Les) chroniques de F. Publ. par J. Viard. [S. de l'H. de F.] t1–4. 8°. 1920–27

1, Des origines à Clotaire II.
2, De Clotaire II à Pépin le Bref.
3, Charlemagne.
4, Louis le Débonnaire à Louis V.

*Hist. apologet., ou déf. des libertéz des égl. réform. de F., 1688, *see* GAUTIER (F. DE).

Hist. des derniers troubles de F., 1613, *see* MATTHIEU (P.)

*Hist. véritable des guerres entre les 2 maisons de F. & d'Esp., 1606, *see* MATTHIEU (P.)

*Interesting consider. on affairs of F. prior to the Revol. &c. Tr. f. the French. 8°. 1791

*Itinéraire complet du royaume de F. 5e éd. refaite. 2v [6 *pagin.*] 8°. 1824

Medieval France: companion to F. st., *by var. a.*, 1922, *see* TILLEY (A.) *ed.*

*Memoirs of the court of F. & of Paris. Tr. f. the French. 2p *in* 1v. s8°. 1702

Modern France: companion to French studies, 1922, *see* TILLEY (A.) *ed.*

*Note s. l'état des forces nav. de la F., 1844, *see* JOINVILLE (*le p.* DE).

Nouvel annuaire de F. ; rédigé par A. Bret [1836 ?], *see* NOUVEL.

Opportunities for higher educ. in F. Issued by Inst. of Internat. Educ., N.Y. [P2732]. 8°. N.Y. 1920

Pays (Le) de F., 3t, 1925, *see* MONMARCHÉ (M.) & L. TILLION, *edd.*

Rep. on the econ. condit. in F., rev. to June 1924 by J. R. Cahill, 1924, *see* OVERSEAS TRADE, *Dept. of.*

Sketch of defences of F. agst. invasion f. Germany. [P2579]. 8°. 1887

*Some acc. of Reformed Ch. of F. [1514–1815], 1819, *see* COBBIN (I.)

*Status eccl. Gall. : or the eccl. hist. of F. ; by the a. of the late Hist. of the Ch. of Gt. Brit., 1676, *see* GEEVES (G.)

*Ten learned personages lately converted (in F.) f. papistrie to the Churches reformed &c. Tr. out of Fr. by W. B. 8°. 1601

*Veterum aliq. Galliae theol. scripta, 1586, *see* GALLIA.

The war devastation of N. F. Repr. f. "Engineering," May–June 1921. [P2701]. 4°. 1921

Documents inédits sur l'histoire de France.

see DICTIONNAIRE topog. de la F., Aude, 1912.

„ ESPÉRANDIEU (E.) Rec. gén. des bas-reliefs &c. de la Gaule romaine, t5–8, 1913–22.

see FRANCE. Convention Nationale. Recueil des Actes du Comité de Salut Public, t22–26, 1795, 1912–23.

„ MÂCON. Cartul. de St.-Victor de M., 1864.

„ ROLAND (*Mme.*) Lettres, n. sér., t1, 2, 1913–15.

State Departments & Publications.

ASSEMBLÉE NATIONALE CONSTITUANTE, 1789–91.

Procès-verbaux du Comité des Finances de l'A. C. ; publ. par C. Bloch. [Coll. de doc. inéd. sur l'hist. économ. de la Rév. Fr. ; publ. par le Min. de l'Instr. Publ.] la8°. 1922

ASSEMBLÉE NATIONALE [1848–51].

see BEUGNOT (*le cte.* A. A.) Rapport sur l'instruction publ., 1849.

France [*continued*].

State Departments & Publications [*continued*].

ASSEMBLÉE NATIONALE [1871 &C.]

Enquête parlement. sur les actes du Gouvt. de la Défense Nat. [18t.] 4°. Versailles. 1872–75

Dépêches télégraph. offic. 2t & Annexe [*in* 2v].
Depositions des témoins &c. 5t, Annexe au t5, Note de la Comm. d'Enquête & Table des matières [*in* 6v].
Rapport[s] fait[s] au nom de la Comm. d'Enquête [*by var. a*[s].] *in* 10v [9, 10, Algérie, par M. de la Sicotière].

CHAMBRE DES DÉPUTÉS.

Compte rendu. Comité secret, 16 Juin 1916 [*f.* Journal officiel, 24th Oct. 1919]. fol. [1919]

Procès-verb. sur le rôle &c. de la métallurgie en F. (Aluminium) réunis par M. Viollette. [*b. w.* Rapport (16 Av. 1919)]. 8°. 1919

Rapport (16 Avril 1919) sur le rôle &c. de la métallurgie en F. (Question de Briey &c.), par F. Engerand. [No. 6026]. 2p ; [*with*] Procès-verb., réunis par M. Viollette. 4p [*in* 1v.] 4°. 1919

Rapport (22 Juillet 1919) sur le rôle &c. de la métallurgie en F. (Plomb & Zinc), par le duc de la Trémoille ; [*with*] Procès-verb. réunis par M. Viollette. [*b. w.* Rapport (16 Av. 1919)]. 4°. 1919

COMMISSION DES ARCHIVES DÉPARTEMENTALES & COMMUNALES.

see CATALOGUE gén. des cartul. des archives dépt. ; publ. par la Comm. des Archives &c., 1847.

CONVENTION NATIONALE [1792–95].

Les actes du gouvt. révolut., 23 août 1793—27 juil. 1794. Rec. de doc. publ. pour Soc. d'Hist. Contemp. par A. Cochin & C. Charpentier. t1, 23 août—3 déc. 1793. 8°. 1920

Recueil des Actes du Comité de Salut Public avec corr. offic. Publ. F. A. Aulard. [Doc. inéd.] t22–26 (12 avr.—29 août 1795). la8°. 1912–23

Representants du peuple en mission &c., 1793–94, 5t, 1889–90, *see* WALLON (H. A.)

ETAT-MAJOR DE L'ARMÉE.

Les armées fr. dans la gr. Guerre. [E.-M. de l'A.] t10i, ii. 4°. 1923–24

10, Ordres de bataille des gr. unités.

see BOURDEAU (H.) Pichegru a-t-il trahi à Mannheim?, 1909.

„ DUPUIS (*comm.* V.) La campagne de 1793 à l'armée du Nord & des Ardennes, 2t, 1906–9.

„ —— Les opér. milit. sur la Sambre en 1794, 1907.

„ GRASSET (*le comm.* A.) La guerre d'Espagne, 1807–13, t2, 1925.

„ HENNEQUIN (L.) Campagne de 1794 entre Rhin & Moselle, 1909.

„ LA JONQUIÈRE (C. DE). La bataille de Jemappes, 1902.

„ REBOUL (F.) Campagne de 1813: les prélim., t1, 2, 1910–12.

„ SAUTAÏ (M.) La bataille de Malplaquet, 1904.

„ †—— Les débuts de la Guerre de la Succession d'Autriche, t1, 1909.

„ —— Les prélim. de la Guerre de la Succ. d'Autriche, 1907.

LAWS.

French Transportation Act of 1921 ; tr. Huntington, 1922, *see* UNITED STATES : COMMERCE.

MINISTÈRE DE LA GUERRE.

Not. sur le chemin de fer de Bagdad, les lignes d'Asie Mineure et les régions traversées. [P2711]. s8°. 1916

MINISTÈRE DE L'INSTRUCTION PUBLIQUE.

Comm. arch. de l'Asie occid. *see* CONTENAU (G.) Mission à Sidon, 1921.

see DUFOUR (H.) Le Bayon d'Angkor Thom: Bas-reliefs publ. par la Comm. Arch. de l'Indochine &c., 2p, 1910–13.

„ LÈRINS, *abbey of.* Cartul. ; publ. Min. de l'Instr. Publ., p1, 1883.

„ MONUMENTS DE L'ART BYZANTIN.

„ POINCARÉ (H.) Œuvres, t1, 2, 1916–28.

„ ROHAN-CHABOT (—). Angola & Rhodesia: mission R.-C., 1923–25.

„ TUNISIE. Atlas archéolog. de la T. ; accomp. d'un texte explic. rédigé par E. Babelon &c., 1893–1913 ; 2e sér., livr. 1–3, 1914–26.

MINISTÈRE DE L'INTÉRIEUR.

Corr. du Ministre de l'Intér. rel. au commerce (16 avril—14 oct. 1792) ; publ. & annot. par A. Tuetey. [Coll. de Doc. Inéd. sur l'Hist. Econ. de la Rév. Fr.] la8°. 1917

France [*continued*].
State Departments & Publications [*continued*].
MINISTÈRE DES AFFAIRES ETRANGÈRES.
Doc. diplomat. Doc. rel. aux négoc. conc. les garanties de sécurité c. une agression de l'Allemagne, 10 jan. 1919—7 déc. 1923. fol. 1924
Les orig. diplom. de la Guerre de 1870–71, t11–13, 1920–22, *see* FRANCO-GERMAN.
Traités & conventions entre la France & les puissances étr. Recueil prép. par J. Basdevant. t3, 4. [*no more publ.*] la8°. 1920–22
3, Japon-Venezuéla. 4, Traités conclus entre plusieurs états (1871–1914).
MINISTÈRE DU COMMERCE, DE L'INDUSTRIE, DES POSTES & DES TÉLÉGRAPHES, *see* EXHIBITIONS: CHICAGO. Rapports publ. sous la dir. de C. Krantz, 1894.
SERVICE DES ANTIQUITÉS & DES BEAUX-ARTS, Syrie & Liban, *see* SYRIA.
France-America Society, *New York.* Addresses [by N. M. Butler &c.] delivd. at a dinner tendered by the F.-A. Soc., to M. R. Vesnitch, Feb. 2, 1918. [P2435]. 8°. N.Y. [1918]
France (La) & l'Islam, *Comité.* Recueil de discours en faveur de l'Islam &c., 1921, *see* LE COCONNIER (L.) *& others.*
France (Anatole), *ps.*
Œuvres compl. illust. t1, (1, A. de Vigny: étude—Poésies). la8°. 1925
Balthasar. [61e éd.] s8°. [1921]
Le crime de Sylvestre Bonnard. s8°. [1921]
Hist. contemp. [2], Le mannequin d'osier. éd. rev. & corr. par l'a. s8°. 1924
Le jardin d'Epicure. [142e éd.] s8°. [1924]
Le lys rouge. [repr.] s8°. [1920]
,, ,, [525e éd.] s8°. [1926]
Les noces corinthiennes. Poème dramatique. 8°. 1923
Poésies. Les poèms dorés—Idylles & légendes—Les noces corinthiennes. 3e éd. s8°. 1924
La rôtisserie de la reine Pédauque. éd. rev. & corr. par l'a. s8°. 1924
La vie en fleur. s8°. 1922
,, ,, [159e éd.] s8°. 1924
TRANSLATIONS.
At the sign of the Reine Pédauque. Tr. by Mrs. W. Jackson. Illusts. by F. C. Papé. Intr. by W. J. Locke. 8°. 1922
The bloom of life. Tr. J. L. May. 8°. [1923]
Clio & The Château de Vaux-le-Vicomte. Tr. W. Stephens. 8°. [1923]
The Gods are athirst. Tr. Mrs. W. Jackson. 8°. N.Y. 1914
Life of Joan of Arc. Tr. W. Stephens. [repr.] 2v. 8°. 1923
Monsieur Bergeret in Paris. Tr. B. Drillien. 8°. 1921
On life & letters. Tr. by D. B. Stewart [*& B. Miall*]. s3, 4. 8°. 1922–[24]
Penguin Island. Tr. A. W. Evans. s8°. 1919
The revolt of the angels. Tr. Mrs. W. Jackson. s8°. [1923]
see BROUSSON (J. J.) A. F. en pantoufles, 1924; repr., 1926.
,, GIRARD (G.) La jeunesse d'A. F., 1844–76, 4e éd., 1925.
,, GSELL (P.) A. F. & h. circle: table-talk coll. & rec. by P. G.; tr., 1922.
,, —— Les matinées de la Villa Saïd: àpropos d'A. F., 2e éd., 1921.
,, JOHANNET (R.) A. F., est-il un grand écrivain?, 1925.
,, KÉMERI (S.) Promenades d'A. F., 1927.
,, LE GOFF (M.) A. F. à La Béchellerie, 1914–24, 1924.
,, MAURRAS (C.) A. F., politique & poète, 1924.
,, MAY (J. L.) A. F., the man & h. work, 1924.
,, MICHAUT (G. M. A.) A. F.: ét. psycholog., 5e éd., 1922.
,, POLLOCK (J.) A. F. & Mrs. Grundy, w. passages f. A. F. en pantoufles by J. J. Brousson, 1926.
,, POUQUET (J. M.) Le salon de Mme. Arman de Caillavet: s. amis, A. F. &c., 1926.
,, SÉGUR (N.) Conversations avec A. F., 1925.
Francé (Raoul H.)
Das Leben im Ackerboden. 12e A. 8°. St. [1922]
Francen (Victor). Une bourgeoise, *see* ŒUVRES libres, 79, 1928.
Francés (José).
Dos hombres y dos mujeres. s8°. 1923
Eduardo Rosales. 8°. [1920]
Federico Beltran Masses. 8°. [1920]
Gustavo de Maeztu. 8°. [1920]
José Clará. 8°. [1920]
José M. Lopez Mezquita. 8°. [1920]
Manuel Benedito. 8°. [1920]
El misterio del Kursaal. 2a ed. s8°. 1923
Francesca (Piero della), *see* DELLA FRANCESCA (P.)
Franceschi (Enrico Luigi). In città e in campagna. Dialoghi. 7a ed. illust. s8°. Torino. 1888
Franceschi (Piero dei), *see* DELLA FRANCESCA (P.)
Franceschini (*il conte* Guido), *original of character in Browning's Ring & the book, see* GEST (J. M.) The old Yellow Book; tr. w. notes, 1925.
see HODELL (C. W.) The old Yellow book, [1911].
Francesco [*Voersio*], *da Cherasco, Carmelite.* Hist. compend. di Cherasco posto in Piemonte. 8°. Mondovi. 1618
Francesconi (Pier Emilio), *see* NOZZE. F.-Bariola; Ronda-album, 1885.
Franchère (*sieur de*), *ps., see* ESTERNOD (C. D').
Franchet (Louis). Céramique primitive: intr. à l'ét. de la technologie. 8°. 1911
Franchet-d'Espérey (*le maréchal* **Louis Félix Marie**).
see GRASSET (*le comm.* A.) F. d'E., 1920.
,, HANOTAUX (G.) Hist. de la nation franç., t8, Hist. milit. & navale, par F. d'E. &c., 1927.
Franchi de' Cavalieri (Pio).
Note agiografiche. [Studi e testi, 33]. fasc. 6. la8°. 1920
—— **& J. Lietzmann.** Specimina codicum Graec. Vatican. Coll. P. F. de' C. & J. L. [Tabulae in usum schol.; ed. J. Lietzmann, 1]. la8°. Bonnae. 1910
Franchi-Verney (*il conte* **Alessandro**), *d. 1880, see* CLARETTA (*il barone* G.) Commem. del conte A. F.-V., 1883.
Franci. Annales regni Francorum (741–829), qui dic. Ann. Laurissenses majores & Einhardi. Post ed. G. H. Pertzii rec. F. Kurze. [Script. rer. Germ. in usum schol.] 8°. Hannoverae. 1895
Francia [RAIBOLINI (FRANCESCO), *called Il Francia*].
see JAMES (E. E. C.) Gli autoritratti di F. R., 1922.
,, —— Una pittura d. F. &c., Dresda, 1927.
,, PIAZZI (G.) Opere di F. R. &c., 1925.
Francia (J. G. de), *dictator of Paraguay, see* WHITE (E. L.) El Supremo: romance of the gt. dictator [*i.e.* F. *Fiction*], 1923.
Francis, *St., of Assisi.*
I fioretti. [Impresso n. Chelsea per opera &c. di St. John Hornby n. sua Officina privata di Ashendene]. 8°. [1922]
Regula, *see* JOANNES FRANCISCUS *Brixianus.* Habes isto vol. 4 regulas &c., 1510.
see BOSQUIER (P.) Antiq. Franciscanae, spec. vitae F., 1623.
,, CHESTERTON (G. K.) St. F. of A., 1923.
,, CUTHBERT (*Fr.*) Romanticism of St. F., 1924.
,, FACCHINETTI (V.) San F. d'A., n. storia &c., 1921.
,, GOAD (H. E.) Franciscan Italy, 1926.
see HOUSMAN (L.) Little plays of St. F.: dram. cycle f. life of F., 1922; repr., 1923.
,, KLEINSCHMIDT (B.) Die Basilika San F. in Assisi, 2B, 1915–26.
,, LITTLE (A. G.) Some disc. Franciscan doc., 1926.
,, NICHOLSON (D. H. S.) Mysticism of St. F., 1923.
,, SCHMARSOW (A.) Franciscusfenster in Königsfelden u. d. Freskenzyklus in Assisi, 1919.
,, SCHNEIDER (E.) Sur les traces de St.-F., 1926.
Francis [*de Borja*], *Saint, duke of Gandia, 1510–72, see* KARRER (O.) Der heil. F. v. B., 1921.
Francis I, *king of France* [1515–47], *see* CHARLES V, *emp. of Germany.* Artickel des Fridẽs, 1526.
see DOUCET (R.) Et. s. le gouvt. de F. I dans s. rapp. avec le Parl. de Paris, pl, 1515–25, 1921.
,, VALLET (F.) Rel. inéd. des obsèques de F. I, 1924.
Francis II, *king of France, see* ROMIER (L.) La Conjur. d'Amboise: le règne &c. de F. II &c., 1923.
Francis II, *emperor of Germany* [*Francis I, of Austria*], *see* BIBL (V.) Kaiser F. u. s. Erbe, 1922.
Francis, *Saint, de Sales.*
Œuvres. Ed. compl. Publ. par les religieuses d'Annecy. t21, 22. la8°. Lyon. 1923–25
21, Lettres, v11. 22, Opuscules, v1.
*Études biograph. sur Saint F. de S. s8°. Chambery. 1860
Intr. à la vie dévote. Intr. par H. Bordeaux. s8°. [1910]
Philothea; or, an introd. to a devout life, f. the French of St. F. of S. s8°. Dublin. 1834
see BORDEAUX (H.) St. F. de S. & notre cœur de chair, 1924.
,, STROWSKI (F.) St. F. de S., n. éd., 1928.
Francis Joseph I, *emp. of Austria, b. 1830.* Franz Joseph I in s. Briefen. Hrsg. v. O. Ernst. 8°. Wien. 1924
see BAGGER (E. S.) F. J., 1927.
,, GOPCEVIĆ (S.) Österreichs Untergang—die Folge von F. Josefs Missregierung, 1920.
,, MARGUTTI (A., *Frhr.* v.) Emp. F. J. &c., 1921.
,, —— Vom alt. Kaiser: personl. Erinnerungen an F. J. I, 1921.
Francis (Francis), *jun.* The free trade fall. s8°. 1926
Our ruling class. s8°. 1922
Sunny trails. s8°. 1924
Francis (Grant R.), *F.S.A.* Old Eng. drinking glasses, th. chronology &c. 4°. 1926
Francis (M. E.), *ps.* [*i.e. Mrs.* FRANCIS BLUNDELL].
Beck of Beckford. s8°. 1920
The runaway. s8°. [1923]

Francis (*Sir* **Philip**). Letter missive to Ld. Holland. 8°. 1816

Franciscan. A Span. Franciscan's narr. of a journey to the Holy Land; tr. &c. H. C. Luke, 1927, *see* SPANISH.

Eng. Fr. nuns, 1619–1821 & the Friars Minor, 1618–1761. Ed. R. Trappes-Lomax. [Cath. Rec. Soc., 24]. 8°. 1922

Francisci (Adam). Margarita theologica. In usum scholarum Islandiæ. s8°. *n.p.* 1620

Σύνοψσις primi cap. Johannis Evang. ad disputandum. [P2612]. s4°. Tubingae. 1591

Theses de ascensione Christi in coelum &c. Adj. aliae theses, per E. Hunn. [P2612]. s4°. Tubingae. 1589

Francisci (Erasmus). Vom Leben d. Seelen im Tode, *see* FASCICULUS rar. & curios. scr. &c., 1692.

Francisco, *de los Santos.* Descr. breve del mon. de S. Lorenzo el real del Escorial. fol. 1657

Descr. del real mon. de S. Lorenzo del Escorial. sfol. 1681

Descr. of the royal palace & mon. of St. Laurence, called the Escurial: & of the chapel royal of the Pantheon [*w. sep. tp. & pagin.*] Tr. G. Thompson. 4°. 1760

Francisco, *dos Prazeres Maranhão* [FERNANDES PEREIRA]. Poranduba Maranhense ou rel. hist. da prov. do Maranhão [1826], *see* INSTITUTO HIST. E GEOG. BRAZIL. Revista, t54, 1891.

Franciscus *a Sancta Clara, see* DAVENPORT (CHR.)

Franciscus, *a Victoria.* De Indis & De jure belli reflectiones. Ed. E. Nys. [With tr. by J. P. Bate]. la8°. Wash. 1917

Francis-Williams (Benjamin) & G. Pitt-Lewis. The Coal Mines Regulation Acts, 1887–1896, w. intr. &c. 8°. 1896

Franck (César A. J. G. H.), *see* RUDDER (M. DE). C. F., 1920.

Franck (Christian Friedrich). Imaginem ingenii morumque Lutheri in emend. Sacrorum conspic. exprimit C. F. F. [P2627]. s4°. Vitembergae. 1789

Franck (Harry Alverson).

East of Siam: ramblings in French Indo-China. 8°. 1926

Glimpses of Japan & Formosa. 8°. [1924]

Roaming thr. the W. Indies. 8°. 1921

Roving thr. S. China. 8°. 1926

Wandering in China. 8°. 1924

Working north f. Patagonia. 8°. 1921

Franck (Henri). Lettres à quelques amis. Préf. de A. Spire. [Les cahiers verts, 62]. s8°. 1926

Franck (Johannes), *Privatdocent at the Univ. of Bonn, see* HANSEN (J.) Quellen &c. z. Gesch. d. Hexenwahns &c.: mit Untersuch. d. Gesch. d. Wortes Hexe v. J. F., 1901.

Franck (Sebastian) [FRANCUS], *see* WALD (S. G.) De vita, scriptis & syst. mystico S. F., 1793.

Francke (A. Hermann). Antiq. of Indian Tibet. Ed. &c. F. W. Thomas. [India. Arch. Survey]. p2. 4°. Calcutta. 1926

2, Chron. of Ladakh & minor chron. Texts & tr. w. notes &c.

Francke (August Hermann).

Betrachtungen: Wie ein Mensch sein Leben bessern soll; aus d. Ital. übers. v. A. H. F. [*b. w. h.* Manuductio, 1700]. s8°. Halle. 1699

Comm. de scopo librorum Vet. & Nov. Test. s8°. Halae Magdeb. 1724

Definitio methodi studii theolog. &c. s8°. Halae. 1763

Einleit. z. Lesung d. H. Schrift, N. Test. [*b. w. h.* Manuductio, 1700]. 3e Ed. s8°. Halle. 1699

A guide to the reading & study of the Holy Scr. Tr. W. Jacques. 8°. 1813

Idea studiosi theologiae, & monita pastoralia. In Lat. versa. s8°. Halae Magdeburg. 1723

Kurtze Anleitung z. Christenthum, &c. [*b. w. h.* Manuductio, 1700]. s8°. Halle. 1699

Kurtzer Auszug aus d. Einl. z. Lesung d. H. Schr. [*b. w. h.* Manuductio, 1700]. s8°. Halle. 1699

Manuductio ad lect. Script. S. ed. 2a, auct. s8°. Halae Sax. 1700

Methodus studii theolog. rev. & ed. [*b. w. h.* Definitio, 1763]. s8°. Halae. 1723

Nicodemus: or, the fear of man. Abridg'd J. Wesley. [P2551]. s8°. 1740

Pietas Hallensis: Orphan House &c. at Glaucha, nr. Hall. [Tr.], w. pref. &c. s8°. 1705

Schrifftmässige Lebens-Reglen &c. [*b. w. h.* Manuductio, 1700]. s8°. L. 1695

see BECK (M.) Versio Lutheri à M. A. H. F. Obs. vindicata, 1696–8.

,, GUERICKE (H. E. F.) Life of A. H. F.; tr., 1837.

,, HALLE. Beschr. des H. Waisenhauses u. d. übr. Frank. Stiftungen, 1799.

Francke (Daniel) [FRANCUS (D.)]. Disquis. de Papistarum indicibus libr. prohib. &c. Praem. C. Arnoldi ad aut. epist. s4°. Lipsiae. 1684

Francke (Ernst), *see* SINZHEIMER (L.), E. F. &c. Geist. Arbeiter, T2, 1922.

Francke (Gotthilf August). Denkmal dem weiland Herrn G. A. Francken, gesammelt u. hrsg. v. J. G. Knapp. s4°. Halle. 1770

Francke (Kuno). German after-war problems. [2nd impr.] 8°. Camb. [*U.S.*] 1927

Die Kulturwerte d. deut. Lit. in i. geschichtl. Entwicklung. B2. 8°. 1923

2, Die Kulturwerte d. deut. Lit. v. d. Reform. bis z. Aufklärung.

Francken (Christian), *see* SOCINUS (F.) Disput. inter F. Socinum & C. F. de ador. Christi, 1618.

Franckford, *see* FRANKFORT.

Francklin (Thomas), *D.D., Rector of Brasted, Surrey, 1721–84.*

*Matilda: tragedy, *see* †INCHBALD (*Mrs.* E.) Mod. theatre, v8, 1811.

see LA HARPE (J. F. DE). Earl of Warwick, [*tr.*] T. F., 1808.

Franckreich, *see* FRANKREICH.

Franc-Nohain, *ps.* [*i.e.* MAURICE LE GRAND]. La marche nuptiale, *see* ŒUVRES libres, 29, 1923.

Vingt fables nouv., *see* ŒUVRES libres, No. 18, 1922.

Franco (Niccolo), *1515–70.* De le lettere [1531–38], scr. à prencipi, signori &c., lib. 3. Di nuovo ristamp. &c. s8°. Vicenza. 1604

Dialoghi piacevolissimi. Espurgati da G. Gioannini. s8°. Vinegia. 1590

Franco-German. Les origines diplomat. de la Guerre de 1870–71. Recueil de doc. publ. par le Min. des Affaires Etr. t11–13. 8°. 1920–22

11, 11 juil. 1866–6 août 1866. 12, 7 août 1866–15 Oct. 1866. 13, 18 oct. 1866–31 déc. 1866.

François, *see* FRANÇAIS.

François (Alexis), *see* ROUSSEAU (J. J.) Mat. pour le corr. de J. J. R.; publ. A. F., 1923.

François (*Gen.* **Hermann v.**) Gorlice 1915: d. Karpathendurchbruch u. d. Befreiung v. Galizien. 8°. L. 1922

Marneschlacht u. Tannenberg. 8°. [1920]

Tannenberg, das Cannae des Weltkrieges. 8°. 1926

François (Hugo v.) Nama u. Damara: Deut.-Süd-West-Afrika. la8°. Magdeburg. [1896]

Francs-Maçons. *Les Francs-Macons écrasés; suite du livre intitulé L'ordre des Francs-Macons trahi [*by* G. L. Calabre-Perau]. Tr. du Lat. [? *or rather wr. by* l'abbé Larudan]. s8°. Amsterdam. 1762

Francus (Daniel), *see* FRANCKE (DANIEL).

Francus (Sebastian), *see* FRANCK (S.)

Francus (Theophilus Alymantius). *De mysterio Incarnat. Verbi et unionis hypostaticæ, contra ubiquitatem &c., assertio cathol. 8°. *n.p.* 1577

Frangipane (A.), *see* CHIMIRRI (B.) & A. F. Mattia Preti, 1914.

Frangoudis (G. S.) L'Hellénisme en lutte c. l'Orient & l'Occ. 8°. Athènes. 1925

Frangulis (A. F.) La Grèce & la crise mondiale. t1. 8°. 1926

Franiel (Vinzi), *see* MAULER (*Frau* M. v.) Meine Leiden in russ. Gefangenschaft, 1917.

Frank (Bruno). Tage d. Königs. [21–29. A.] 8°. 1925

Frank (Carl). Die altelam. Steininschriften. [P2717]. 8°. 1923

Frank (Erich).

Plato u. d. sogenannten Pythagoreer. 8°. Halle (Saale). 1923

Frank (Leonhard). Die Räuberbande. Roman. s8°. L. 1922

Frank (Othmar). Chrestomathia Sanskrita, quam ex cod. mss. adhuc ined., ed. O. F. 2p [p2 *wanting*]. s4°. Monachii. 1820–21

Gramm. Sanskrita. s4°. Wirceburgi. 1823

Frank (Reinhard), *see* PITAVAL (DER) d. Gegenwart; hrsg. v. R. F. &c. *in progress* 1904 &c.

Frank (Tenney).

Econ. hist. of Rome. 2nd ed., rev. 8°. 1927

Hist. of Rome. 8°. [1923]

Roman imperialism. 8°. N.Y. 1921

Storia econ. di Roma alla fine d. Repubblica. Tr. B. Lavagnini. 8°. Firenze. [1924]

Vergil. A biography. 8°. N.Y. 1922

Frank (Waldo). The new America. s8°. [1922]

Virgin Spain. 8°. [1926]

Frankau (Gilbert).

Gerald Cranston's Lady. s8°. 1924

,, ,, ...3rd ed. s8°. 1924

Life—and Erica. s8°. [1925]

The love-story of Aliette Brunton. s8°. [1922]

Masterson. s8°. [1926]

Men, maids & Mustard-pot. Coll. of tales. s8°. 1923

Peter Jackson, cigar merchant. s8°. 1920

Peter Jackson, cigar merchant. 2nd ed. s8°. 1920

The seeds of enchantment. s8°. [1921]

So much good. s8°. [1928]

"Tid'apa" (What does it matter?). [*Repr. f.* Eng. Rev.] 8°. 1915

The woman of the horizon. 5th impr. s8°. [1920]

Franke (Arno). Die Wahrheit über Russland. [P2509]. 8°. 1920
Franke (August Hermann), *see* FRANCKE (A. H.)
Franke (Carl Christian Lebrecht). De diei Dominici apud vet. Christianos celebr. s8°. Halae. 1826
Fränkel (Eduard). Plautinisches im Plautus, 1922, *see* KIESSLING (A.) & U. v. WILAMOWITZ-MÖLLENDORFF. Philol. Unters., H28, 1922.
Frankel (Zacharias). Introd. in Talmud Hierosolymit. [*In Heb.*] 8°. Vratislaviae. 1870
Frankenstein (Kuno). Bevölkerung u. Hausindustrie im Kreise Schmalkalden seit Anfang dieses Jhdts. [Neumann (F. J.) Beiträge, B2]. 8°. Tübingen. 1887
Frankfort (H.) St. in early pottery of the Near East. [Roy. Anthrop. Inst. Occas. papers, No. 6, 8]. 2[p]. la8°. 1924–27
Frankfort on the Main. Aktenstücke &c. z. Gesch. d. F. Nationalversammlung, 1924, *see* DROYSEN (J. G.)
*Brieff (A) discours off the troubles at Franckford 1554 abowte the Booke off off [*sic*] common prayer & Ceremonies & cont. by the Englishe men theyre to thende off Q. Maries Raigne &c. [by W. Whittingham ?]. s4°. [Geneva ? *or* Zurich ?]. 1575
„ „ ....Repr. f. ed. 1575. 8°. 1846
Frankfurter Urkundenbuch z. Frühgesch. d. Buchdrucks. Aus d. Akten d. Frankfürter Stadtarchivs hrsg. v. W. K. Zülch u. G. Mori. 8°. Fr. am Main. 1920
Kirchen Ordnung &c. in d. reform. ausslend. Kirchen, 1555, *see* DATHENUS (P.) Kurtze u. warhafft. erzelung &c., 1598.
Ministerii (Des) zu F. &c. judicia v. d. Ehe mit d. Weibes Schwester [1708], *n.d.*, *see* KETTNER (F. E.)
Frankfurt, *see* FRANKFORT-ON-THE-MAIN.
Frankfurter Verein für Geographie und Statistik, *see* ELBERT (J.) Die Sunda-Expedition des V. für G. &c., 2B., 1911–12.
Frankfurter (Salomon), *see* KUBITSCHEK (J. W.) & S. F. Führer durch Carnuntum, 6. A., 1923.
Frankl (Paul). Die Glasmalerei d. 15. Jhdt. in Bayern u. Schwaben. la8°. Str. 1912
Meinungen ü. Herkunft u. Wesen d. Gotik, *see* TIMMLING (W.) Kunstgesch. &c., 1923.
Frankl (Vilmos). A nádori és országbírói hivatal eredete és hatáskörének történeti kifejlödése. [P2393]. 8°. Pesten. 1863
Frankland (Benjamin). Intuitionalism: insufficiency of "pure reason." s8°. 1861
Frankland (Charles Colville). Narr. of visit to the courts of Russia & Sweden, 1830–31. 2v. 8°. 1832
Frankland (Mary C.), *baroness Zouche of Haryngworth, see* ZOUCHE OF HARYNGWORTH.
Frank Lateur (Petrus Franciscus Marie), *see* STREUVELS (STIJN), *ps.*
Franklin (Alfred). Étude hist. & topogr. sur le plan de Paris de 1540, dit Plan de tapisserie. 8°. 1869
Paris & les Parisiens au 16e s. 8°. 1921
Recherches sur la Bibl. de la Faculté de Médecine de Paris. 8°. 1864
Franklin (Benjamin), *LL.D.* Life, wr. by himself. Ed. f. orig. MSS. &c. by J. Bigelow. 2nd ed. rev. 3v [*v1 wanting*]. s8°. 1881
The way to wealth. [P2434]. s8°. 1822
see BERNARDY (A. A.) La missione di B. F. a Parigi &c., 1776–86.
„ RUSSELL (P.) B. F., 1927.
Franklin (Charles A. H.) The bearing of coat-armour by ladies: guide to the bearing of arms &c. Pref. by Marcia, Ctss. of Yarborough. 8°. 1923
Franklin (Fabian).
What prohibition has done to America. s8°. N.Y. [1922]
Franklin (Jane, *Lady*). The life, diaries & corresp. of J., Lady F., 1792–1875. Ed. W. F. Rawnsley. 8°. 1923
Franklin (Thomas), *1721–84, see* FRANCKLIN (T.)
Franklyn (Henry Mortimer).
A glance at Australia in 1880. 8°. Melbourne. 1881
Franko-Russkii. Мат. по ист. франко-русских отношений за 1910–14, 1922, *see* RUSSIA.
Frankreich [FRANCKREICH]. *Catechismus d. evang. Kirchen in F., 1563, *see* CATECHISMUS.
*Confession oder Bekañtnuss d. Glaubens d. evang. Kirchen in F. &c. 1553; 1557; 1563, *see* CONFESSION.
Frankreichs Saarpolitik: Saar Interpell. im bay. Landtag, Feb. 1922, 1922, *see* BAIERN.
Die Indust. im besetzten F., 1916, *see* BOULANGER (H.) Doc. confident. du Grand Etat-Major allem., 1923.

Frankreich [FRANCKREICH] [*continued*].
Kirchen-Ordnung u. Glaubens-Bekäntniss &c., *see* FRANCE. La discipline eccl., 1711.
Ordnung d. evang. Kirchen in F., 1563, *see* ORDNUNG.
Franks (*Sir* Augustus Wollaston).
see BRIT. MUS. ANTIQ. Franks bequest: Treasure of the Oxus w. o. oriental metal-work; by O. M. Dalton, 2nd ed., 1926.
„ —— Guide to pottery & porcelain of the Far East in Dept. of Ceramics &c. [Sir W. F. coll.], 1924.
Franks (James Clarke). On the Apostol. preaching & vindic. of the Gospel. [Hulsean Lect.] 8°. C. 1823
On the evidences of Christianity in discourses of our Lord. [Hulsean Lect.] 8°. C. 1821
Frans Hals Gallery, *see* HAARLEM.
Frantz (Constantin). Schelling's positive Philosophie. 3T *in* 1v. 8°. Göthen. 1879–80
Frantz (Gunther). Russ. auf d. Wege z. Katastrophe: Tagebücher d. Grossfürst. Andrej u. d. Kriegsmin. Poliwanow; Briefe d. Grossf. an d. Zaren. In deut. Bearbt. &c. hrsg. v. G. F. la8°. 1926
Russlands Eintritt in d. Weltkrieg. la8°. 1924
Frantze (Wolfgang) [FRANZIUS (W.)]. Disput. de persona Jesu Christi. Praes. W. F., resp. Æ. Strauchio. [P2612]. s4°. Wittebergae. 1605
Comm. in Leviticum. [*b. w.* Gerhard (J.) Comm. super Genesin, 1693]. s4°. Lipsiae. 1696
Franz Joseph, *Prinz v. Hohenzollern, see* HOHENZOLLERN (F. J., *Prinz* v.)
Franze (Bruno). Die Niederschlagsverhältnisse in Südamerika, 1927, *see* PETERMANNS MITT. Ergnzb., 42, 1927.
Franzen (Adam Wilhelm). Gedanken ü. d. Falschheit im menschlich. Leben. s8°. L. 1754
Franzen (Frans Michael), *bp. of Hernösand.* Julie de St. Julien, eller frihetsbilden. 8°. Örebro. 1925
Franzius (Wolfgangus), *see* FRANTZE (W.)
Franzosen. Farbige Fr. am Rhein, 3e A., 1921, *see* FARBIGE.
Fraoch. Geste of F. &c.; tr. w. intr. by J. F. Campbell, *see* CAMPBELL (J. F.) Celtic dragon myth, 1911.
Frapié (Léon E.) Les amis de Juliette. s8°. [1926]
Fraser (Alex. Campbell). Archbp. Whately & the restor. of the st. of logic. Lect. s8°. 1864
Fraser (Charles), *see* SMITH (A. R. H.) & D. E. H. SMITH. C. F., 1924.
Fraser (Donald), *D.D.* Autobiog. of an African, D. Mtusu. Retold by D. F. 8°. 1925
Fraser (Edward), *see* JOURDAIN (*Lt.-Col.* H. F. N.) & E. F. The Connaught Rangers, 3v, 1924–28.
—— **& J. Gibbons.** Soldier & sailor words & phrases. 8°. 1925
Fraser (George M.)
Dunnideer & its triple fortresses. 8°. Aberdeen. 1927
Fraser (*Sir* Hugh), *LL.D.* Amid the high hills. 8°. 1923
Compendium of the law of torts. 11th ed. by R. Burrows. s8°. 1927
The Represent. of the People Acts, 1918–21, w. explan. notes. 2nd ed. la8°. 1922
Fraser (John), *M.A.* Hist. & etymology. [P2683]. 8°. O. 1923
Fraser (Lovat). Iron & steel in India: ch. f. the life of Jamshedji N. Tata. la8°. Bombay. 1919
Fraser (Lovat Claud), *see* MACFALL (C. H. C.) The book of L. C. F., 1923.
Fraser (Sami Bej). Sqiperia. [P2684]. s8°. Sofje. 1907
Fraser (*Sir* William), *K.C.B.*
The Annandale family book of the Johnstones, Earls & Marquises of A. 2v. 4°. E. 1894
The Douglas bk. 4v. 4°. E. 1885
The Earls of Cromartie, th. kindred &c. 2v. 4°. E. 1876
The Lennox. 2v. 4°. E. 1874
Mem. of the Earls of Haddington. 2v. 4°. E. 1889
Mem. of the Maxwells of Pollok. 2v. 4°. E. 1863
Mem. of the family of Wemyss of Wemyss. 3v. 4°. E. 1888
Papers f. the coll. of Sir W. F. Ed. J. R. N. Macphail. [Scott. Hist. Soc., s3, v5]. 8°. E. 1924
The red book of Menteith. 2v. s4°. E. 1880
The Sutherland book. 3v. 4°. E. 1892
Fraser-Mackintosh (Charles). Antiquarian notes: papers reg. families &c. in the Highlands. 8°. Inverness. 1865
Frassati (Alfredo), *see* CAPUTO (M.) A. F., 1921.
Frati (Carlo). L. Scarabelli, P. Giordani e. i "Paralipomeni di storia piemontese," *see* ARCHIVIO STORICO ITAL. Anno 77, v1, 1919.
Ricordi di prigionia, mem. autobiog., e frammenti poetici, di G. Rasori, *see* REGIA DEPUT. &c. Bibl., v9, 1921.

Frati (Lodovico). La prigionia del re Enzo a Bologna. Con app. di doc. [Bibl. stor. Bolognese, N. 6]. 8°. Bologna. 1902
La vita privata di Bologna dal sec 13 al 17, con app. di doc. ined. 8°. Bologna. 1900

Fratta (Giovanni). La Malteide: poema. 8°. Venetia. 1596

Frattini (Angelo). Ada Negri. la8°. Milano. 1919
E. L. Morselli. la8°. Milano. 1920
Trilussa. la8°. Milano. 1920

Frauenstädt (Julius). Freiheit d. Menschen u. d. Persönlich. Gottes. Nebst e. Briefe d. G. A. Gabler. s8°. 1838

Frazer (James George, *Lady*), *see* Grove (*Mrs.* L.)

Frazer (*Sir* James George).
Adonis: ét. de religions orient. Tr. Lady Fraser. [Guimet. Bibl. d'ét., t29]. 8°. 1921
Belief in immortality & the worship of the dead. v2, 3. 8°. 1922–24
2, Polynesians.
3, Micronesians.
Folk-lore in the Old Test. abr. ed. 8°. 1923
The golden bough: study in magic & relig. abr. ed. [repr.] 8°. 1923
„ „ abr. ed. [repr.]. 8°. 1925
The Gorgon's head & o. lit. pieces. Pref. by A. France. 8°. 1927
Man, God & immortality. Passages f. wr. of F. Rev. & ed. 8°. 1927
Les origines de la famille & du clan. Tr. par la Ctsse. J. de Pange. [Guimet. Bibl. d'ét., t30]. 8°. 1922
Sur Ernest Renan. s8°. 1923
The worship of nature. v1. 8°. 1926

Frazer (John William). The untried civiliz. s8°. N.Y. [1921]

F.R.C.S. *Glimpses of anc. Hackney & Stoke Newington, 1894, *see* Clarke (B.)

Frederic (Henrica). The enchanted violin. Comedy. s8°. 1879

Frederick I, *Grand Duke of Baden; 1826–1907, see* Oncken (H.) F. I. v. Baden u. d. deut. Politik v. 1854–71, 2B, 1927.

Frederick IV, *king of Denmark & Norway.* S. Königl. Maj. zu D. &c. Edict wider die privat &c. Zusammenkünffte d. Pietisten. s4°. [Copenhagen]. 1708

Frederick VIII, *king of Denmark, see* Liljefalk (A.) Kong F. VIII, 1912.

Frederick I, *emperor of Germany, called Barbarossa.* Gesta F. I in Lombardia auct. cive Mediolan. (Annales M. maiores) Rec. O. Holder-Egger. Acced. Gesta F. in exped. sacra. [Scr. rerum Germ. in usum schol.] 8°. Hannoverae. 1892
see Below (G. v.) Ital. Kaiserpolitik &c. mit bes. Hinblick auf d. Politik Fr., 1927.
„ Godefridus, *Viterb.* Gesta F.; rec. G. H. Pertz, 1870.
„ Otto, *bp. of Frisingen.* O. & Rahewini Gesta F. I, 1884.

Frederick II, *emperor of Germany.*
see Kantorowicz (E.) Kaiser F. II, 1927.
„ Knebel (J. W.) F. & Honorius III (1220–27), 1905.

Frederick III, *German emperor, b. 1831, d. 1888* [Frederick William Nicholas Chas.] The emperor's diary of Austro-German War, 1866, & Franco-German War, 1870–71; added, Bismarck's rejoinder. Ed. H. W. Lucy. s8°. 1888
Kriegstagebuch, 1870–71. Hrsg. H. O. Meisner. 8°. 1926
War diary, 1870–71. Tr. & ed. A. R. Allinson. 8°. 1927
see Ponsonby (M. E., *Lady*). Mem., letters &c., 1927.

Frederick, *da Montefeltro, duke of Urbino, see* La Sizeranne (R. de). Le vertueux Condottière, F. de M., 1422–82, 1927.

Frederick, *duke of Normandy, see* Noreen (E.) Studier rör. Eufemiavis., 2, Hertig F. Textkritik, 1927.

Frederick I, *elector Palatine, "the Victorious."*
see Klüber (J. L.) Eheliche Abstammung d. Hauses Löwenstein-Wertheim v. d. Kurfürsten F.; hrsg. v. J. Mülhens, 1837.
„ Tritheim (J.) Res gestae F. &c., 1602.

Frederick III, *Elector Palatine, d. 1576.*
Form wie das heilig Nachtmal in d. Kirchen zu Heidelberg &c. gehalten wirdt. [*b. w. h.* Kirchenordnung, 1569]. s4°. Heidelberg. 1564
Kirchenordnung, wie es mit d. Christl. Lehre, heiligen Sacramenten &c. in Herrn Friderichs &c. Churfürstenthumb bey Rhein gehalten wirdt. s4°. Heidelberg. 1569
Pfaltzgrave F. auffgerichte Christl. Almussenordnung. [*b. w. h.* Kirchenordnung, 1569]. s4°. [Heidelberg ?]. 1574
Pfaltzgrave F. auffgerichte Christl. Policey Ordnung. [*b. w. h.* Kirchenordnung, 1569]. s4°. [Heidelberg ?]. 1565
Pfaltzgrave F. auffgerichte Christl. Eheordnung. [*b. w. h.* Kirchenordnung &c. 1569]. s4°. [Heidelberg ?]. 1565
see Maulbronn. Epitome colloquii inter F. & C. Ducis, de majestate Christi &c., 1564.

Frederick IV, *Elector Palatine.* Assertio propriae gubernationis F. IV, 2 orationibus a conciliario quodam Palatino habitis. Adj. Sigismundi Imp. Aug. Bulla integra. Acc. poemata &c. [*b. w.* Freher (M.) Orig. Palatin., 1599]. ed. 2ª. s4°. Heidelbergae. 1593

Frederick I, *king of Prussia* [Frederick III, *elector of Brandenburg*], *see* Cellarius (C.) Inaug. Acad. Frideric. &c., 1694, 1798.

Frederick II, *king of Prussia "the Great"* [*ps.* Volkna (J.)]
*Anti-Volkna ou nottes d'un publiciste sur le systeme polit.-milit. prussien. s8°. Londres. 1762
Briefe an s. vormaligen Kammerdiener Fredersdorf. Hrsg. &c. J. Richter. 8°. [1926]
Briefwechsel. Nachträge Fr. d. Gr. mit Maupertuis u. Voltaire. Hrsg. H. Droysen &c. [Publ. aus d. K. Preuss. Staatsarch., B90]. 8°. L. 1917
Briefwechsel m. Grumbkow & Maupertuis (1731–59). Hrsg. v. R. Koser. [K. Preuss. Staatsarch., B72]. la8°. L. 1898
Briefwechsel mit s. Bruder, Pr. August Wilhelm. Hrsg. &c. G. B. Volz. Deut. v. F. v. Oppeln-Bronikowski. 8°. L. [1927]
*Comment (A) upon the Mem. of the House of Brandenburg [*by F. II*] &c. [P2783]. 8°. 1751
Dict. polit. ou glossaire alphabét. Tr. s8°. Londres. 1762
Die Kriege F. des Gr. Hrsg. v. grossen Generalstabe. T3, Die siebenjähr. Krieg, 1756–63, B13, Torgau. la8°. 1914
*Poésies diverses. 4°. Berlin. 1760
Politische Correspondenz. B36–40 [B40, bearb. G. B. Volz]. 8°. 1914–28
„ Ergänzungsb., Die polit. Testamente F. d. Gr. Redig. v. G. B. Volz. 8°. 1920
see Boretius (A.) F. d. Grosse in s. Schr., 1870.
„ Carlyle (T.) Hist. of F. II, 10v, *n.d.* & 1888.
„ Cuthell (*Mrs.* E. E.) The Scottish friend of F. the Gt., the last Earl Marischall, 2v, 1915.
„ Dilthey (W.) Gesammelte Schr., B3, Fr. d. Gr. u. s. deut. Aufklärung &c., 1927.
„ Koser (R.) Gesch. F. d. Gr., 6. u. 7. A., 4B, 1914–25.
„ Kugler (F. T.) Gesch. F.'s, 1840.
„ Menzel (A. F. E.) Illust. des œuvres de F. le Grand, 2t, 1882.
„ Voltaire. Letters of V. & F. the Great, 1927.
„ Wiegand (W.) F. d. G., 2e verb. A., 1909.

Frederick II, *Duke of Saxe-Gotha, see* Compendium. *C. hist. eccl. &c. [lib. tertius decreto F.], 1723.

Frederick II, *elector of Saxony, called the "Wise," see* Adrian VI, *pope.* Breve ad F. Saxoniae. ducem adv. Lutherum, 1523?
see Kalkoff (P.) Erasmus, Luther & F. d. Weise, 1919.
„ Kirn (P.) F. d. Weise u. d. Kirche, 1926.
„ Luther (M.) Zwo predigt ü. d. leiche d. Chürf. F., 1525.
„ Melanchthon (P.) Oratio dicta in funere F. &c., 1525.

Frederick, *duke of Würtemberg, see* Andreae (J.) *called Schmidtlein.* Acta colloquii Montis Belligartensis &c.; praes F., *w. pref.*, 1594.

Frederick Augustus I, *elector of Saxony & k. of Poland, 1670–1733, see* Augustus II, *King of Poland, der Starke.*

Frederick William, *elector of Brandenburg.* Urkunden u. Aktenstücke z. Gesch. d. inn. Politik d. Kürfursten F. W. v. B. T1i, ii. la8°. 1895–1915
see Breysig (C.) & F. Wolters. Gesch. d. brandenburg. Finanzen, 1640–97, 2B, 1895–1915. [1i, ii.]
„ Hötzsch (O. E. G.) Stände u. Verwaltung v. Cleve u. Mark, 1666–97, 1908. [2.]
see Kirchen-Ordnung. Kirchen-Ordnungen &c., u. Neben-Recessen &c. zw. F. W. v. B., u. Phil. Wilh., Pf. bey Rhein, 1666–73, 1754.

Frederick William III, *king of Prussia, see* Eylert (R. F.) The relig. life & opinions of F. W. III; tr., 1844.

Frederick William IV, *king of Prussia, see* Andreas (W.) Russ. Diplomatie u. Politik Fr. W., 1927.

Frederick William Ludwig, *Grand Duke of Baden, see* Frederick I, *Grand Duke of Baden.*

Fredericq (Paul), *ed.* Codex doc. sac. indulgent. Neerland. Verzamel. v. stukken betreff. de pauselijke aflaten in de Nederl. (1300–1600). [Rijks Gesch. Publ., Kl. ser., 21]. 4°. s'-Gravenhage. 1922

Fredersdorf (Michael Gabriel), *see* Frederick II, *king of Prussia.* Briefe an s. vormaligen Kammerdiener F., 1926.

Freducci (Conte de Ottomanno). Portolan atlas, 1537. Facs. Intr. by E. L. Stevenson. [Hisp. Soc. of Amer.] atlas fol. N.Y. 1915

Free. *Free & impartial examiner: enquiry into causes of pres. situation, 1745, *see* Examiner.
Free (The) Churches & the Lambeth appeal, 1921, *see* Evangelical Free Ch. of Eng.

Free Church of Scotland. Acts of the Gen. Assembly of the Free Ch. of S. [*with* Rep. on Public Acc. 1–20], 1843–65, 1874. *b. in 6v.* fol. E. 1843–74
Free Church hymn book. Harmonies rev. by E. J. Hopkins. Publ. by Gen. Assembly of Free Ch. of S. s8°. Paisley. 1882
Proceedings [& debates] of the Gen. Assembly, 1843–85. [*wanting* 1867 & 1883]. 8°. E. 1853–85

Free Russia. The organ of the Society of Friends of Russian Freedom. v1–17 (June 1890–Oct. 1910) *in* 9v. 4°. 1890–1910
Jan. 1892–July 1894 of the American ed. *are bound w.* v4, 5.

Freeborough (E.), *ed.* Chess endings. 8°. 1891

Freedom. *Where f. falters, 1927, *see* LYON (L.)

Freedom Association, *see* TEMPERANCE. Hdbk. for speakers &c., 1920.

Free-holder (The), or political essays. [*By* J. Addison]. No. 1–55 (Dec. 23, 1715–June 29, 1716). s8°. 1716

Freeman (The).
v6–8 (Sept. 1922–March 1924). fol. N.Y. [1922–24]

Freeman Library, *see* MANCHESTER: UNIV. Cat. of F.L., 1894.

Freeman (Alexander Martin), *ed., see* VANHOMRIGH (*Miss* H.) Vanessa & h. corresp. w. J. Swift, 1921.

Freeman (Archibald), *F.R.G.S., see* FITE (E. D.) & A. F. Bk. of old maps delineat. Amer. hist., 1926.

Freeman (Benson). The yeomanry of Devon, 1794–1927. Ed. Earl Fortescue. 8°. 1927

Freeman (C. R. Boyd). Towards the answer. s8°. Ripley. [1926]

Freeman (Edward Augustus), *see* MANCHESTER: UNIV. Cat. of F. Lib., 1894.

Freeman (Frank Nugent). Experimental educ. s8°. [1916]
Psychology of the common branches. 8°. [1916]

Freeman (James), *D.D.* *Liturgy for the use of the Episc. Ch. in Boston, 1785, *see* LITURGY.

Freeman (John).
Eng. portraits & essays. 8°. 1924
Herman Melville. [Eng. Men of Letters]. s8°. 1926
Music, lyrical & narrative poems. s8°. 1921
Poems new & old. 8°. 1920
A portrait of George Moore in a study of h. wk. [*Added,* G. M.: a bibliogr. by H. Danielson, *pagin. cont.*] 8°. 1922
Prince Absalom. [Play]. 8°. 1925

Freeman (John Joseph), *C.B.E.* Diversions of Shepperton. [v]4, Language. 8°. *p.f.p.c.* 1923

Freeman (Joseph John) & D. Johns. A narr. of the persecution of the Christians in Madagascar. s8°. 1840

Freeman (Kathleen). The work & life of Solon, w. tr. of h. poems. 8°. Cardiff. 1926

Freeman (Kenneth John). Schools of Hellas: essay on Greek educ., 600–300 B.C. Ed. M. J. Rendall; w. pref. by A. W. Verrall. 3rd ed. 8°. 1922

Freeman (Lewis Ransome).
A certain Dr. Thorndyke. s8°. [1927]
The Colorado river yesterday, to-day & to-morrow. 8°. 1923
Down the Columbia. 8°. 1922
Hell's hatches. s8°. 1921
In the tracks of the trades; yachting cruise to the Hawaiis, Marquesas, Societies, Samoas, &c. 8°. 1921
On the roof of the Rockies: the great Columbia icefield. 8°. 1926

Freeman (Prince Arthur), *see* ROBINSON (S. J.) Trial of S. J. R. for murder of P. A. F., 1888.

Freeman (*Sir* Ralph). *Imperiale, a tragedy. s8°. 1655

Freeman (Richard Austin).
The cat's eye. s8°. [1923]
The D'Arblay mystery. s8°. [1926]
The magic casket. s8°. [1927]
The mystery of Angelina Frood. s8°. [1924]
The puzzle lock. s8°. [1925]
The shadow of the wolf. s8°. [1926]
Social decay & regener. Intr. by H. Ellis. 8°. 1921

Freeman (Samuel), *dean of Peterborough.* *A plain &c. discourse &c. conc. the Catholick Ch. By a divine &c. [P2664]. s4°. 1687

Freemasonry.
*Constit. artis gemetriæ secundum euclydem: facs. of early poem on f., 1898, *see* CONSTITUCIONES.
Constit. of f. &c.; rev. &c., w. add., 1801, *see* DERMOTT (L.) *ed.*
*The constit. of f.; or, Ahiman Rezon. Added, Lect. &c. Publ. by Grand Lodge of Ireland. 8°. D. 1858
*Defence (A) of f. &c. cont. refut. of Dermott's Acc. &c. [*repr. tp.* (1765) *& sep. pagin.*], *see* SADLER (H.) Masonic repr[s]. &c., 1898.
Masonic reprints &c., 1898, *see* SADLER (H.)
*View of the origin &c. of f. by the W. Substitute master of St. David's lodge, Edinburgh. [P2433]. 8°. E. 1830

Freemasons.
Constit. of the ant. fraternity of Free & Accepted Masons, Eng. 8°. 1922
,, ,, ...[rev. ed.] 8°. 1926
List of Regular Lodges Masonic, corr. to April 1920, 1921, 1924. 8°. Bloomington, Illinois. 1920–24
Masonic roll of honour. Names of brethren who fell dur. the Great War, 1914–18. 8°. 1921
Proc. of the 126th annual comm. of the Grand Lodge of Virginia. 8°. Richmond. 1904
see MASONIC YEAR BOOK.

Freemasons' magazine, 1797, *see* SCIENTIFIC MAGAZINE, & FREEMASONS' REPOSITORY.

Freer (Arthur Savile Beresford). The early Franciscans & Jesuits. s8°. 1922

Freer (Charles Lang).
see BIBLE: PROPH. BKS. Facs. of Wash. MS. of Minor P. in F. coll., 1927.
,, SANDERS (H. A.) & C. SCHMIDT. The Minor Prophets in F. coll. &c., 1927.
,, WORRELL (W. H.) 2 Coptic homilies & a magical text in the F. Coll., 1923.

Fregoso (Antonio). Opera nova ītitulata Cerva biācha. s8°. [Venetia, *A. de Bindoni.* 1518]
Opera nova. Lamento d'amore mendicante. Dialogo de musica. Pergoletti de le laudi d'amore. Disc. cottidiani nō volgari. De l'instinto naturale. De la probità. Dei tre peregrini. s8°. [Vinegia, *N. Zoppino.* 1528]
Opera nova: laqual tratta de doi philosophi: cioe Democrito & Heraclyto &c. s8°. [Venetia, *A. & B. di Bindoni.* 1520]

Freher (Marquard). Originum Palatinarum comm. Acc. De legitima electoris aetate disput. & app. H. Thomae comm. &c. s4°. Heidelbergae. 1599

Freiberg. Die Bergstadt F. i. Sa. u. i. Umgebung; bearb. O. E. Schmidt, *see* DEUTSCHLAND. Deutschlands Städtebau, 1926.

Freiesleben (Johann). Sylva quedam testimoniorum ex propriis Papistarum & S. Patrum &c. libris coll. Sola fiducia gratię justif. [*b. w.* Melanchthon (P.) Explic. Proverb., 1551]. s8°. Calae cis Salam, *N. Faber.* 1539

Freigius (Joannes Thomas), *see* VIVES (J. L.) Colloquia &c. J. T. F. notis illust. &c. 1582.

Freiheitskampf (Der) d. indischen Nationalisten, 1906–17. Aus brit. Quellen zusammengestellt u. hrsg. v. Europ. Zentralkomitee d. ind. Nat. 8°. 1918

Freimuth (*Dr.* Philalethes), *ps.* Die kathol. Kirche u. d. mod. Staatsmänner. Ein ultramont. Vergissmeinnicht. 8°. Luxemburg. 1874

Freinat (O. G.) Правда о дѣлѣ Мясоѣдова и др. 8°. Вильна. 1918

Freinsheim (Johann), *see* CURTIUS RUFUS (Q.) De rebus Alexandri Magni; acc. Freinshemii suppl. &c., 1685.

Freire (Francisco José). *Gesch. d. ersten portug. Entdeckungen unter Infant Heinrich, d. Seefahrer. [*Adapted f.* F.'s Vida do infante D. Henrique?]. s8°. Halle. 1783

Freire dos Reis (Pascoal José de Mello), *see* MELLO FREIRE DOS REIS.

Freke, *The family of.* A pedigree of the family of the F. Begun by R. Freke, augm. by J. Freke, reduced to this form by W. Freke, 1707. 4°. 1825

Freke (*Mrs.* Elizabeth), *wife of Percy Freke; 1641–1714.* Mrs. Eliz. Freke, her diary, 1671–1714. Ed. M. Carbery. la8°. Cork. 1913

Fremantle (*Lt.-Col.* Francis Edward). The housing of the nation. Foreword by Rt. Hon. N. Chamberlain. 8°. [1927]

Fremantle (*Hon.* Thomas Francis), *see* HUMPHREY (A. P.) & T. F. F. Hist. of Nat. Rifle Assoc., 1859–1909, 1914.

Fremantle (*Hon. & Rev.* William Henry), *dean of Ripon, 2nd son of 1st baron Cottesloe.* Recolls., chiefly by himself. Ed. by the Master of the Temple [W. H. Draper]. 8°. 1921

Frémont (*Gen.* John Charles), *see* BASHFORD (H.) & H. WAGNER. A man unafraid: J. C. F., 1927.

French (The) preacher, 1816, *see* COBBIN (I.)

French Church, *Berwick Street, see* FRENCH CHURCH, *Soho Square.*

French Church, *Savoy, London.* Livres des conversions &c. faites à l'Eglise Franç. de la Savoye, 1684–1702. Transcr. & ed. W. & S. Minet. [Huguenot Soc., 22]. 4°. 1914
Registres des églises de la Savoye, de Spring Gardens & des Grecs, 1684–1900. Ed. W. & S. Minet. [Huguenot Soc., 26]. 4°. M'ter. 1922

French Church, *Soho Square* [CHURCH OF LE CARRÉ], *aft. moved to Berwick St.* Registers of the Church of le Carré & Berwick Street, 1690–1788. Ed. W. & S. Minet. [Huguenot Soc., 25]. 4°. Reading. 1921

French Church, *Spring Gardens, see* FRENCH CHURCH, *Savoy.* Registres des églises de la Savoye, de Spring Gardens &c., 1684–1900, 1922.

French Church, *Swallow Street, see* CHAPEL ROYAL. Registres des églises de la Chapelle Royale, 1700–56 & de Swallow Street, 1690–1709; ed. W. Minet, 1924.

French Church, *Threadneedle St., London.* Registers of the F.C., Threadneedle St. Ed. T. C. Colyer-Fergusson. [Huguenot Soc., 23]. v4 [1707–1840]. 4°. 1916

French East India Company, *see* PONDICHERY. Corr. du Conseil Supér. de P. & de la Comp.; publ. A. Martineau, t1, 2, 1920.

French Revolution. Royal mem. on the Fr. Revol. Cont^s. Narr. of journey of Louis XVI &c. to Varennes, by Duchess of Angouleme, Narr. of journey to Bruxelles &c., by Louis XVIII, Private mem. of what passed in the Temple, by Duchess of A. With hist. &c. illust. by the tr. 8°. 1823

French (Alfred J.) Life, light & love. A disc. 9th Fernley lect. 8°. 1879

French (Donald Graham), *see* LOGAN (J. D.) & D. G. F. Highways of Canad. lit., 1924.

French (Francesca), *see* CABLE (M.) & F. F. Thr. Jade Gate & Cent. Asia, 1927.

French (*Field-Marshal* **John Denton Pinkstone French,** *1st visc.*) Despatches: Mons, The Marne, The Aisne, Flanders. s8°. 1914

French (William). In Chancery. Estate of W. F. & F. J. Greenway, in liquid. w. Hawaiian Treasury Board. [P2776]. 8°. Honolulu. 1845

In Chancery. Estate of W. F. & F. J. Greenway, repr. by J. Ricord, vs. R. Charlton & H. Skinner. [P2776]. 8°. Honolulu. 1844

In Chancery [Hawaii]. Estate of W. F. & F. J. Greenway, in liquid. w. S. Reynolds, [*w.* A. Simpson & w. estate of J. Ebbits, 3p]. [P2775]. 8°. Honolulu. 1845–46

2nd semi-annual report of Liquidating Agent in matter of estate of W. F. & F. J. Greenway to the Chancellor of Oahu. [P2775]. 8°. Honolulu. 1846

French (William Percy). Prose, poems & parodies. Ed. Mrs. De Burgh Daly, w. foreword by A. P. Graves. s8°. Dublin. 1925

Frencl (Innocenz), *see* SCHAMM (J.) *Liturgik oder Erklärung d. gottesdienstl. Handlungen d. Kathol. Kirche &c. [Umarb. I. F.], 1857.

Frenkel (Z. G.) Петроград пер. войны и революции. Санит. условия и коммунал. благоустройство. la8°. [П.] 1923

Frenken (Goswin). Die Exempla d. Jacob v. Vitry. [Quellen &c. z. latein. Philol. d. M-A., B5i. *b. w.* Lehmann (P.) Vom M-A., 1914]. 8°. München. 1914

Frensdorff (Ferdinand). Beitr. z. Gesch. &c. d. deut. Rechtsbücher, p2–6, *see* KÖNIGL. GESELLS. D. W. ZU GÖTT. Nachr., 1894, 1921, 23, 24, 26.

Frenssen (Gustav).

Briefe aus Amerika. 8°. 1923
Die Brüder. s8°. 1922
Lütte Witt. s8°. 1924
Otto Babendiek. Roman. 8°. 1926
Der Pastor von Poggsee. s8°. 1921
,, ,, ...s8°. 1923
see ALBERTS (W.) G. F., e. Dichter uns. Zeit, 1922.

Frentz (Emmerich Raitz v.), *see* RAITZ V. FRENTZ (E.)

Frenzel (Heinrich). Erzberger der Reichsverderber! Eine Anklageschrift. [P2408]. 8°. L. 1919

Frere (*Rt. Hon. Sir* **H. Bartle E.),** *1st bart.* Afghanistan & S. Africa. A letter to W. E. Gladstone. With o. papers. 3rd ed. [P2429]. 8°. 1881

Corr. rel. to recall of Sir B. F. [P2832]. 8°. 1880

see WORSFOLD (W. B.) Sir B. F., 1923.

Frere (James Hatley), *see* BROWN (J. AQ.) The Jew, the master-key of the Apocalypse in ans. to F.'s gen. structure &c., 1827.

Frere (*Rt. Hon.* **John Hookham)** [*ps.* WILLIAM & R. WHISTLECRAFT]. The monks & the giants. Ed. w. notes & intr. by R. D. Waller. [Univ. of Manchester, Eng. ser., 14]. 8°. M'ter. 1926

Works in verse & prose. 2nd ed., rev. w. add. 3v. 8°. 1874
1, Mem. by Sir B. Frere. 2, Orig. works & minor tr.; ed. W. E. Frere. 3, Tr. f. Aristophanes & Theognis; ed. W. E. Frere.

Frere (Walter Howard), *D.D., bp. of Truro.* Eng. Church ways descr. to Russian friends. s8°. 1914

Expos. de la Messe f. La legende dorée of J. de Vignay, w. illum. repr. f. Fitzwilliam Mus. MS. 22. Ed. W. H. F. [Alcuin Club Coll., 2]. lafol. 1899

Pontifical services illust. f. miniatures of 15th & 16th cent. Descr. notes & liturg. intr. by W. H. F. [Alcuin Club Coll^s., 3, 4]. 2v. lafol. 1901

Frerichs (Johann Heinr. Friedrich). Comm. de P. Abaelardi doct. dogm. & morali. [P2741]. s4°. Jenae. 1827

Freschot (Casimir). *L'état du siége de Rome dès le commenc. du siècle passé j. présent. 3t [*in 1v. t3 has tp.* Idée gén. de la forme du gouv. &c.] s8°. Cologne. 1707

see UTRECHT. *Actes, mém. & autres pièces authent. concern. la paix d'U., *attrib. to F.*, 6t, 1714–15.

Fresen (*il colonnello*) [DE FRESSE], *see* CARUTTI (D.) Il Conte d. Roche d'Allery e il Col. F. all' assedio di Verrua (1704–5), 1901.

Fresen (Wilhelm). De computo Gregoriano diss. Sub præs. Æ. Strauchii. [P446]. s4°. Wittebergae. 1672

Freshfield (Douglas William).

Below the snow line. 8°. [1923]

The life of Horace Benedict de Saussure. By F., w. collab. of H. F. Montagnier. 8°. 1920

Freshfield (Edwin Hanson).

see LEO III, *emp. of East.* Manual of Rom. law (& later R. law): Ecloga; tr. E. H. F. [2v], 1926–27.

,, —— Rev. man.; tr. F., 1927.

Freshfield (James William), *see* NORRIS (*Rev.* H. H.) A pract. expos. of tendency &c. of the Brit. & For. Bible Soc. in a corr. betw. H. H. N. & J. W. F. &c., 1814.

Freshman (C.), *D.D.*

The Jews & the Israelites. 8°. Toronto. 1870

Fresnel (Fulgence), *see* PILLET (M. L.) L'expéd. scient. & artist. de Mésopotamie & de Médie, 1851–55 [*under the dir. of F. F.*], 1922.

Frétat (Amable de), *see* JOVY (E.) Pascal & le p. de F., 1919.

Freud (Sigmund).

Jenseits des Lustprinzips. [Beih. d. Intern. Zeitschr. f. Psychoanalyse, N^r. 2]. 2. durchges. A. la8°. L. 1921

Massenpsychologie u. Ich-Analyse. 8°. L. 1921

Die Traumdeutung. Beitr. v. O. Rank. 7e A. 8°. L. 1922

Vorlesungen z. Einführung in d. Psychoanalyse. Taschenausg. 3T [*in* 1v. *pagin. cont.*] s8°. L. [1922]
Die Fehlleistungen—Der Traum—Allgem. Neurosenlehre.

TRANSLATIONS.

Beyond the pleasure principle. Auth. tr. by C. J. M. Hubback. 8°. 1922

Coll. papers. Auth. tr. by J. Riviere. v1–3. la8°. N.Y. 1924–25
3, tr. by A. & J. Strachey.

Delusion & dream, an interpret. in the light of pyscho-analysis of Gradiva, a novel, by W. Jensen, here tr. by H. M. Downey. Intr. by G. S. Hall. 8°. 1921

The ego & the id. Auth. tr. by J. Riviere. 8°. 1927

TRANSLATIONS [*continued*].

A gen. introd. to psychoanalysis. Auth. tr. w. pref. by G. S. Hall. 8°. N.Y. [1920]

Group psychology & the analysis of the ego. Auth. tr. by J. Strachey. 8°. 1922

The interpret. of dreams. Auth. tr. of 3rd ed., w. intr. by A. A. Brill. [repr.] 8°. [1921]

Intr. lect. on psycho-analysis. Auth. Eng. tr. by J. Riviere, w. pref. by E. Jones. 8°. [1922]

On dreams. Tr. M. D. Eder. Introd. by W. L. Mackenzie. s8°. [1914]

Psychopathology of everyday life. Auth. Eng. ed., w. intr. by A. A. Brill. [6th impr.] 8°. [1920]

see LOW (B.) Psycho-analysis, Freudian theory, 1920.

,, VAN DER HOOP (J. H.) Character & the unconscious: crit. expos. of psych. of F. &c.; tr., 1923.

,, WITTELS (F.) S. F., h. personality, teaching & school; tr., 1924.

Freudenthal (Jacob). Spinoza: Leben u. Lehre. Hrsg. &c. C. Gebhardt. [Bibl. Spinoz., 5. Soc. Spinoz.] 2T *in* 1v. [T1, 2^e A]. 8°. Heidelberg. 1927

Freund (Fritz). Der Österreich. Nationalrat. Ein biog.-statist. Hdbch, 1920–22. s8°. Wien. [1921]

Freund (Wilhelm). Lat.-Eng. lex. W. add. by E. A. Andrews. la8°. N.Y. 1862

Freundlich (Erwin). Die Grundlagen d. Einsteinschen Gravitationstheorie. Mit Vorwort v. A. Einstein. 4^e, verb. A. 8°. 1920

The foundations of Einstein's theory of gravitation. Tr. by H. L. Brose. Pref. by A. Einstein. Intr. by H. H. Turner. 8°. C. 1920

Freundlich (Herbert).

New conceptions in colloidal chemistry. [Tr.] 8°. [1926]

Frey (Alex. Moritz).

Solneman der Unsichtbare. Roman. 8°. München. 1920

Frey (Andreas). *A true & authentic acc. of A. Frey; &c. Tr. f. the German. [*b. w.* Rimius (H.) Cand. narr., 2nd ed., 1753]. 8°. 1753

Frey (Carroll). *The Independence Square neighborhood, Philadelphia. 8°. Phila. 1926

Frey (Dagobert). Denkmale d. polit. Bezirkes Baden. Bearb. D. F. mit Beitr. v. G. Kyrle & F. Eichler. [Österr. Kunsttopog., 18]. 4°. Wien. 1924

Frey (Dagobert) [*continued*].
Die Denkmale d. polit. Bezirkes Schärding. Bearb. D. F. Archiv. Teil v. R. Guby u. E. Strassmayr. [Österr. Kunsttopog., 21]. 4°. Wien. 1927
Denkmale d. Stiftes Heiligenkreuz. Bearb. D. F., unter Mitwirk. v. K. Grossmann. [Österr. Kunsttopog., 19]. 4°. Wien. 1926
Michelangelo Buonarroti. 29 riprod. con testo e cat. [Bibl. d'arte illust., s2, fasc. 19]. 8°. 1923
Frey (Johann Ludwig). Meletematum de officio doctoris Christiani. 4p. [*Each p. has a different resp.*] [P2639]. s4°. Basileae. [1711–15]
Frey (Joseph Samuel C. F.)
Hebrew grammar in the Eng. lang. 8°. [1813]
„ „ n. & enl. ed. Added a glossary to the first 6 Psalms & Chaldee gram., by G. Downes. 8°. 1823
Hebrew, Latin, & Eng. dict. 2v. la8°. 1815
Frey (Max v.) Abhandl. ü. d. Speichel v. C. Ludwig, E. Becher u. C. Rahn (1851), hrsg. v. F. 8°. L. 1890
Freyberg (Pankraz v.), *1508–65, see* PREGER (C.) P. v. F. auf Hohenaschau, 1893.
Freylinghausen (Gottlieb Anastasius), *ed., see* NEGRI (S.) Memoria N. &c., 1764.
Freylinghausen (Johann Anastasius). Geistreiches Gesangbuch. Hrsg. v. J. A. F. 12e A. s8°. Halle. 1721
Via salutis, Arabice expos. a J. H. Callenbergio. s8°. Halae. 1737
see FRITZSCHE (C. F.) Narr. de turbis a pietista quodam [*i.e.* J. A. F.] Vitebergae concitatis, 1844.
Freysinger (Johann Friedrich). De Formula Concordiae Naumburg. anni 1561. Diss. [P2643]. s4°. Tubingae. [1798]
Freytag (Friedrich Benedict). Hagenstolziatus ex antiq. illust. [P2649]. s4°. Lipsiae, 1786
Freytag (Friedrich Gotthilf). Narr. Max. Planudae de insigni Aesopi deformitate. [P2744]. s4°. Lipsiæ. 1717
Freytag (Gustav), *1816–95.* Bilder aus d. deut. Vergangenheit. 5B *in* 6v. [3i, ii]. la8°. L. [1924–25]
1, Aus d. Mittelalter. 2, Vom M.-a z. Neuzeit. 3, Aus d. Jhdt. d. Reformation. 4, Aus d. Jhdt. d. grossen Krieges, 1600–1700. 5, Aus neuer Zeit, 1700–1848.
Soll u. Haben. 24e A. 2B. s8°. L. 1879
Freytag (Gustav), *cartographer.* Karte d. neuen Staaten auf d. Boden d. ehemal. Österreich-Ungarn. [P2409]. 8°. Wien. [1919]
Freytag-Loringhoven (Axel, *Frhr.* **v.)**
Die Gesetzgebung d. russ. Revol. 8°. Halle a. S. 1920
Freytag-Loringhoven (Hugo, *Frhr.* **v.)**
Feldherrngrösse. Vom Denken u. Handeln Heerführer. 8°. 1922
Heerführung im Weltkriege. 2B. 8°. 1920–21
Menschen u. Dinge wie ich sie in meinem Leben sah. 8°. 1923
Die Psyche d. Heere. 8°. 1923
Was danken wir unserem Offizierkorps? 2 Jhdte. s. Gesch. 8°. 1919
Frezza dalle Grotte (Gioseppe). Il cantore eccl. s4°. Padova. 1698
Fribourg & Treyer, *Haymarket, see* EVANS (G.) The old snuff house of F. & T., 1720–1920, 1921.
Fribourg (André). Les semeurs de haine en Allem., av. & dep. la Guerre. s8°. 1922
Friburgenses. *Amoenitates lit. Friburg., 3 fasc., 1775–76, *see* RIEGGER (J. A. S. v.)
Fricasse (*le sergent* **Jacques).** *Journal de marche d'un volontaire [*i.e.* F.] de 1792. Publ. par L. Larchey. s8°. *n.d.*
Friche (V. M.) [Фриче].
Мировой красный празник. [P2455]. s8°. Киев. 1919
Социализм. изд. 2ое исправл. [P2723]. 8°. Москва. 1919
Frick (Johann). Britannia rectius de Lutheranis edocta. [P2647]. s4°. Ulmae. 1709
Meletemata varia theol. crit. hist. argumenti. Coll., rec., vitae descr. [*w. sep. pagin.*] &c. A. Frick. s4°. Ulmae. 1756
Frick (Johann Georg). De Druidis philosophis. Praes. J. G. F., resp. J. F. Hartlieb. [P428]. s4°. Ulmae. 1731
Fricke (Wilhelm), *of Wiesbaden.* Tabellen z. Gesch. d. deut. Litt. u. Kunst. [P2507]. 8°. L. 1870
Frickenhaus (August). Die Hera v. Tiryns, *see* KAISERL. DEUT. ARCH. INST. ATHEN. ABT. Tiryns, B1, 1912.
Fridlander (Ernest D.) Matthew Maris. la8°. 1921
Fridman (M. I.), *see* FRIEDMAN (M. I.)
Fried (Alfred Herm.)
Mein Kriegs-Tagebuch. B3, 4. s8°. Zürich. 1919–20
Der Weltprotest gegen d. Versailler Frieden. Hrsg. A. H. F. [P2415]. s4°. L. 1920

Friedberg (Emil) [FRIEDBERG (EMIL ALBERT)]. Die preuss. Gesetzentwürfe ü. d. Stell. d. Kirche z. Staat. Brief an W. E. Frhrn. v. Ketteler. [P2696]. 8°. 1873
Sammlung d. Aktenstücke z. 1. Vatican. Concil, mit e. Grundrisse d. Gesch. 8°. Tübingen. 1872
*Der Staat u. d. allgem. Concil. [P2695]. 8°. L. 1873
Friedeburg (Friedrich v.) Karpathen- u. Dnjester-Schlacht 1915. 2. A. 8°. Oldenburg. 1925
Friedel (Jean). Personnalité biologique de l'homme. s8°. 1921
Friedensbedingungen (Die) d. Alliierten u. Assoz. Regierungen, 1919, *see* VERSAILLES, *Treaty of.*
Friedensburg (Ferdinand). Deut. Münzgesch., 2e A., 1912, *see* GRUNDR. D. GESCHICHTSWISS.; Meister, 1iv, 1912.
Münzkunde u. Geldgesch. d. Einzelstaaten. [Hdbch. d. m.-a. Gesch., Abt. 4]. la8°. München. 1926
Friedensburg (Walter). Fortschritte in Kenntnis &c. d. Reformationsgesch. [Verein f. Ref.-Gesch. Schr. Jhrg. 27 (Nr. 100)]. 8°. L. 1910
see WITTENBERG UNIV. Urkundenbuch, T1, 2, bearb. v. W. F., 1926–27.
Friedensfrage (Die) in d. Sitzung d. deut. Reichstags v. 9 Dez. 1915. [P2409]. 8°. [1915]
Friedensverhandlungen. Materialien betreff. d. F. 1919, 1919–21, *see* VERSAILLES, *Treaty of.*
Friederici (Georg), *see* GESCH. D. AUSSEREUROP. STAATEN. America: Charakter d. Entdeck. &c., v. G. F., B1, 1925.
Friedjung (Heinrich). Das Zeitalter d. Imperialismus, 1884–1914. B2, 3. 8°. 1922
Friedlaender (V. H.) Mainspring. s8°. [1922]
Friedland (Albrecht v. Waldstein, *Duke of*), *see* WALDSTEIN (A. v.), *d. of F.*
Friedlander (Gerald).
Shakespeare & the Jew. Intr. by M. Moscovich. s8°. 1921
Friedländer (Max J.) Albrecht Altdorfer. 4°. [1924]
A. Altdorfers Landschafts Radierungen. Hrsg. M. J. F. [Graph. Gesells. Veröff. 3]. fol. [1906]
Die altniederländ. Malerei. B1–5. 4°. 1924–27
1, Die Van Eyck—Petrus Christus.
2, Rogier Van der Weyden u. d. Meister v. Flémalle.
3, Dierick Bouts u. Joos van Gent.
4, Hugo van der Goes. 5, Geertgen van Haarlem u. H. Bosch.
Pieter Bruegel. la8°. 1921
Friedländer (Paul). Der grosse Alcibiades: ein Weg zu Plato. 2T *in* 1v. s8°. Bonn. 1921–23
Friedleben (Theodor). Portative Tafeln z. Vergleich. d. übl. hist. Zeitangaben. s8°. Frankfurt a. M. 1841
Friedman (Mikhail Isidorovich) [FRIDMAN].
Наше государств. хозяйство. [P2446]. s8°. [С.-П.] 1906
Friedrich (Johann). Johann Hus: e. Lebensbild. 2 Abtlg. [P2728]. 8°. Fr. am Main. 1864
Das päpstl. gewährleistete Recht d. deut. Nat. nicht a. d. Unfehlbarkeit z. glauben, 1870, *see* KATHOLISCH. Stimmen aus d. K. Kirche, B2, 1870.
Vortr. ü. d. Wesen d. Altkatholicismus. [P2694]. 8°. Carlsruhe. 1873
see VATICAN COUNCIL. Le concile du V. et le mouv. anti-infaillibiliste en Allem.: l'excommun. de J. F. &c., 1871.
Friedrich (Johann Christoph), *see* WENCESLAUS, *of Liegnitz.* Statuta synod. (1410); ed. J. C. F., 1827.
Friedrich (Johannes), *orientalist.* Aus d. hethit. Schrifttum: Übers. v. Keilschr. aus d. Archiv. v. Boghazköi, 2H, *see* ALTE ORIENT, B24, 25, 1925–26.
Friedrich (Johannes), *wr. on finance.* Das internat. Schuldenproblem. [Probl. d. Geld-u. Finanzwesens, 7]. 8°. L. 1928
Friend of the people (The). No. 1–2. [P2568]. sfol. 1783
Friendly. *Short (A) survey of A friendly conf. betw. a countrie-man & h. nephew, 1711 ?, *see* MACMILLAN (*Rev.* J.)
*Friendly (A) conf. conc. the new oath of allegiance to K. William &c., 1689, *see* WILLIAM III.
Friends' Historical Association, *Pennsylvania, see* FOX (G.) Short journal &c.; publ. for F.H.A., 1925.
Friends' Historical Society.
Journal. v16–24 [1919–27]. 8°. [1919–27]
„ Suppl. No. 13. 8°. 1923
see JENKINS (C. F.) Tortola: Quaker exper. in the tropics, 1923.
Friends of Russian Freedom, *see* FREE RUSSIA, 1890–1910.
Friendship. Anthology of f., repr., 1920, *see* CARPENTER (E.), *ed.*
Fries (Theodor Magnus), *see* JACKSON (B. D.) Linnæus: story of h. life f. Swedish of T. M. F. &c., 1923.

Fries (Thorald Christian Elias), *see* UPSALA: KONGL. UNIV. &c. Matrikel, höst. 1926, av. T. F. &c., 1927.

Friesen (Otto v.) Om d. svaga preteritum i germ. språk, *see* KUNG. HUM. VET.-SAMF. I UPPSALA. Skr., B22, 1925.

Om lasningen av codices gotici Ambrosiani, *see* KUNG. HUM. VET.-SAMF. I UPPSALA. Skr., B24, 1927.

Friesz (Achille Emile Othon), *see* SALMON (A.) E. O. F.: reprod. de peintures, préc. d'une ét. crit., 1920.

Friis (Aage), *see* BERNSTORFF, *The family of.* Bernstorffske papirer, 1732–1835; udg. A. F., 3B, 1907–13.

Friis (Astrid). Alderman Cockayne's project & the cloth trade: commercial policy of Eng. &c., 1603–25. la8°. Copenhagen. 1927

Friis (H. E.) Königin Christine v. Schweden, 1626–89: Lebensbild. Autor. Übers. v. P. Klaiber. 8°. L. 1899

Friis (Oluf). Bk. of Dan. verse; tr. S. F. Damon &c.; sel. &c. O. F., 1922, *see* DANISH.

Friis-Møller (Kai). Indskrifter: udvalgte vers 1910–20. 8°. 1920

Friling (Hermann).

Mod. Flachornamente. 2e A. Ser. 1. lafol. [1897?]

Frimmel (Franz v.), *see* HROZNY (F.) Das Getreide im alt. Babylon; mit Beitr. v. F. v. F., 1914.

Frimmel (Theodor v.) Lexikon d. Wiener Gemäldesamml. Buchstabe A–F, G–L. [*no more publ.*] 8°. München. 1913–14

Frincke (Martin Carl), *see* CLARK (L. D.) & M. C. F. Workmen's compens. legisl. of U.S. & Canada, 1921.

Frings (Theodor).

see AUBIN (H.) Gesch. d. Rheinlandes; v. H. A., Th. F. &c., 2B, 1922.

„ RHEINISCHE Beitr. &c. zur german Philol. u. Volkskunde; hrsg. T. F. &c., 1922–26.

„ ROTHER, *König.* K. R.; hrsg. v. T. F. & J. Kuhnt, 1922.

Fripp (Edgar Innes). Master Richard Quyny, friend of Shakespeare. s8°. O. 1924

Shakespeare's Stratford. s8°. 1928

see STRATFORD-UPON-AVON. Minutes &c. of the Corpor. of S. &c., 1553–1620; intr. by E. I. F., v1–3, 1921–26.

Frisch (Johann). Hist.-theol. disquis. de Waldensibus. Sub præs. Æ. Strauchii. ed. 3a. s4°. *n.p.* 1675

Frisch (Johann Leonhard). Hist. ling. Sclavon. [*Foll. by* Hist. ling. Sclavon. contin. 2a, 3a & 4a (*the last in MS.*) *b. w. h.* Origo charact. Sclavon., 1727]. s4°. [Berolini. 1727–34]

Origo characteris Sclavon. vulgo dicti Cirulici. s4°. [Berlin. 1727]

Frischlin (Nicodemus). Breve resp. N. F. adv. contumelias, quas L. Danæus scripsit. [*b. w.* Gerlach (S.) Hyperaspistes, 1581]. s4°. Tubingae. 1581

Frischmuth (Johann). De rege eligendo et deponendo disc., ex Deut. xvii &c. [*b. w.* Buxtorfius (J.) Exercit., 1659]. s4°. Jenae. 1553 [*for* 1653]

Frisi (Antonio Francesco). Mem. stor. d. città di Monza, cont. da G. Marimonti. 8°. Monza. 1841

Frisoni (Gaetano). Diz. commerciale in 6 lingue. Ital., Tedesco, Franc., Ingl., Spagn., Portoghese. 8°. Milano. 1907

Frith (Francis), *photographer.* Lower Egypt, Thebes & the pyramids. [*b. w. h.* Upper Egypt &c., 1862]. fol. [1862?]

Upper Egypt & Ethiopia. fol. [1862?]

Frith (John), *Reformer.* Works, *see* TYNDALE (W.) The works of the Engl. reformers: W. T. & J. F., v3, 1831.

Fritsch (Ahasuerus). Bonus pastor. s8°. Noribergae. 1688

Fritsch (J.) Fabrication de la fécule & de l'amidon. 2e éd. 8°. 1906

Fritsch (K. E. O.), *ed.*

Denkmaeler deut. Renaissance. 4B. fol. 1891

Fritz (Johann Friedrich). Oriental. u. occidental. Sprachmeister: 100 Alphabete, das Gebet d. Herrn in 200 Spr. &c. [*w. commend. letter by B. Schultze*]. 2p *in* 1v. s8°. L. 1748

Fritz (*Father* Samuel). Journal of the travels & labours of F. in the river of the Amazons betw. 1686 & 1723. Tr. f. Evora MS. & ed. by Rev. G. Edmundson. [Hakluyt Soc., s2, 51]. 8°. 1922

Fritze (C. E.) Katalog över flyglitteratur, 1910–23, med anledning av Internat. Luftfarts Utställningen, Göteborg 1923, utg. av A.-B. C. E. Fritzes Hofbokhandel. la8°. 1923

Fritzhans (Hans), *see* BODENSTEIN (A.) Antwort: geweicht wasser belangend: wider e. bruder Johan. F. genant. holtzuger Ordens, 1521.

Fritzsch (Sigismund). Disput. eccl. ministrum a patrono solo minime ab officio removendum. [P2636]. s4°. Vitembergae. [1739]

Fritzsche (Christian Friedrich). De revelatione notione Biblica comm. 8°. Lipsiae. 1828

Narr. de turbis a pietista quodam Vitebergae concitatis. [*i.e.* J. A. Freylinghausen]. [P2655]. 4°. Halis. 1844

Fritzsche (Otto Fridolin), *see* HELVETIA &c. Confess. Helvet. posterior; recogn. & ed. O. F. F., 1839.

Friulano. Parlamento Friulano; p. c. di P. S. Leicht. v1 (1228–1429), p1. [R. Accad. dei Lincei. Atti d. assemblee costit. ital., s1, sez. 6]. la8°. Bologna. 1917

Frizzi (Ernst). Beitr. z. Ethnologie v. Bougainville u. Buka, mit spez. Berücks. d. Nasoi. [Baessler-Archiv, Beih. 6]. [P2417]. fol. L. 1914

Frobenius (Herman). Abriss d. Militärgeogr. Europas, T1, Die Halbinseln d. Mittelmeers, *see* PETERMANNS MITT. Ergnzb, 40, 1925.

Der erste Weltkrieg. [31 Lief. in 1v]. la8°. Hannover. 1917

Frobenius (Leo).

Das sterbende Afrika. 4°. München. [1923]

Das unbekannte Afrika. Aufhellung d. Schicksale eines Erdteils. 4°. München. 1923

Fröbing (Johann Christoph) [FROEBINGIUS]. Lutherus; seu hist. Reformationis breviter comprehensa. s8°. Lipsiae. 1811

Frobisher (*Sir* Martin), *see* BERNARD (J. F.) Recueil de voyages, t1 (3 navig. de M. F., 1576–78), 1731.

Fröding (Gustaf). Samlade skrifter. 10d. s8°. [1920–22]
1, Ungdomsdikter. 2, Gitarr och dragharmonika.
3, Nya dikter. 4, Stänk och flikar.
5, Nytt och gammalt—Gralstänk—Översättningar.
6, Räggler à paschaser. 7, Efterskörd.
8, Reconvalescentia. 9, 10, Prosa.

Froes (Luis). Nova relatio hist. de statu rei Christ. in Japonia &c., 1595, 1598, *see* JESUITS.

see JESUITS. Epist. Indicae [*by F. &c.*], 1566; 3a ed., 1570.

„ —— Literae annuae Iapon. a. 1591 & 92 a L. F., 1596.

Froger (François). Rel. du prem. voyage des François à la Chine, 1698–1700, sur "l'Amphitrite." Hrsg. v. E. A. Voretzsch. la8°. L. 1926

Frohawk (Frederick William). Birds beneficial to agriculture, 1919, *see* BRIT. MUSEUM OF NAT. HIST.

Natural hist. of Brit. butterflies. 2v. fol. [1924]

Fröhlich (Rudolph), *see* RICHTER (A. D.) & A. J. BALLMANN. Illyr.-deut. &c. Handwörterbuch, T2, Deutsch-Illyr., bearb. v. R. F., 1840.

Fröhlich-Bum (Lili).

Parmigianino u. d. Manierismus. 4°. Wien. 1921

Frohschammer (Jakob). Monaden u. Weltphantasie. [*b. w.* Payot (J.) L'éduc. de la volonté, 1895]. 8°. München. 1879

Ueber d. relig. u. kirchenpolit. Fragen d. Gegenwart. 8°. Elberfeld. 1875

Frois (Marcel). La santé & le travail des femmes pend. la Guerre. [C.E. of Int. Peace]. 8°. [1926]

Froissart (Jean). [Chronicle. *Plates reprod. f. MS.* J. Harris sculp. *no tp.*] s4°. *n.d.*

TRANSLATIONS.

Chronicles. Tr. T. Johnes. 2v. la8°. 1839

Chronicles of Eng., France & Spain. [Condensed. Everyman's lib.] repr. s8°. [1908]

Frolov (Mikhail Mikhyeevich). Défense de Sébastopol: exposé de la guerre souterraine, 1854–55, *see* TOTLEBEN (E. I., *cte.* DE). Défense de Sébastopol, 1863–74.

From.

*From a Russian diary 1917–20; by an Englishwoman, 1921, *see* RUSSIAN.

*From an Eastern Embassy. Memories of London, Berlin & the East. 8°. 1920

*From behind the vail [*sic*]; story of Hung. bolshevism. [P2492]. 8°. Budapest. 1920

*From Sedan to Saarbruck, 1870, *see* KNOLLYS (H.)

*From Sepoy to Subadar: life & adv. of a native officer of the Bengal Army; tr. 3rd ed., 1911, *see* SITARAMA, *Subahdar.*

Fromentin (Eugène). Dominique (1862). 8°. Lyon. 1920

see GONSE (L.) F., peintre & écrivain; augm. d'un voyage en Egypte &c. inéd. de F., 1881.

„ THIBAUDET (A.) Intérieurs; Baudelaire, F. &c., 1924.

Frommann (Erhard Andreas). Diss. qua philosophemata quaed. R. Mosis Maimonidis cum rec. quorund. sententiis collata. Resp. F. F. Ulmer. [P431]. s4°. Altorfii Noric. [1745]

*Museum Casimirianum. Particula 1, diss. histor. complexa. Instr. &c. E. A. F. [*no more publ.* ?] s8°. Coburgi. 1771

Frommann (Johann Heinrich). Stricturae de statu scient. & artium in Imperio Russico. Def. J. H. F., resp. J. F. Woelffing. [P427]. s4°. Tubingae. [1766]

Frondaie (Pierre). L'homme à l'Hispano. s8°. 1925

Fronleichnamsspiel. Das Künzelsauer F., 1479; hrsg. A. Schumann, 1926, *see* KÜNZELSAUER.

Fronmüller (Conrad). De div. sententiis Rabbin. &c. Acc. C. Arnoldi Epist. commend. [P1015]. s4°. Altdorfi. 1679

Frontaura (Carlos).
Doce maridos. 2ª ed., corr. y aument. s8°. 1873

Fronteau (Jean) [FRONTO (Jo.)] Antithesis Augustini & Calvini. Authore F. I. F. C. R. S. T. P. A. P. C. [*i.e.* Fratre Joanne Frontone Canon. Regulari Sacrae Theol. Prof. Acad. Paris.] s8°. Parisiis. 1651
Epistolae & diss. eccl., Calendarium Roman. notis illust., S. Ivonis episcopi vita &c. s8°. Hamburgi. 1720
„ „ Acc. var. lect. & emendat. Calendarii, per card. Thomasium. 8°. Veronae. 1733

Frontinus (Sextus Julius). The Stratagems & the Aqueducts of Rome. [Texts], w. Eng. tr. by C. E. Bennett, the tr. of the Aqueducts a rev. of that of C. Herschel. Ed. &c. M. B. McElwain. [Loeb Class. Lib.] s8°. 1925

Fronto (Joannes), *see* FRONTEAU (JEAN).

Fronto (Marcus Cornelius). Corr. w. Marcus Aurelius Antoninus &c. Ed. & tr. by C. R. Haines. [Loeb Class. Lib.] [v]2. s8°. 1920

Froschauer, *Family of, see* RUDOLPHI (E. C.) Die Buchdrucker-Familie F. in Zürich, 1521–95, 1869.

Fröschel (Sebastian). Catechismus wie der in d. Kirchen zu Witteberg nu viel Jar, auch bey leben M. Lutheri ist gepredigt worden durch S. F. s8°. [Wittemberg.] 1562

Frossard (Ludovic Oscar), *see* SOKOLOV (B.) Voyage de Cachin & de F. dans la Russie des Soviets; tr., 2e éd., 1921.

Frost (George H.) Munitions of war. Record of work of the B.S.A. & Daimler Co., 1914–18. Comp. by G. H. F. 4°. B'ham. [1921]

Frost (James), *M.R.I.A.* Co. of Clare Irish local names explained. s8°. Limerick. 1906

Frost (Ludwig).
Ungarn nach d. Bolschewismus. [P2456]. 8°. München. 1920

Frost (William Alfred).
Bulwer Lytton. Errors of his biographers. s8°. 1913

Frothingham (Octavius Brooks).
A child's bk. of relig. Comp. by O. B. F. n. ed., rev. s8°. N.Y. 1876
The cradle of the Xt.: a study in primit. Xtny. 8°. N.Y. 1877
G. Ripley. s8°. Boston. 1882
Gerrit Smith. 8°. N.Y. 1878
*Stories f. the lips of the teacher. Retold by a disciple. 5th ed. s8°. N.Y. 1876
Stories of the Patriarchs. s8°. N.Y. 1876

Frothingham (Paul Revere).
Edward Everett, orator &c. 8°. Boston. 1925

Frothingham (Richard).
The rise of the Rep. of the U.S. 8°. Boston. 1872

Frothingham (Thomas Goddard). Naval hist. of the World War. [3v]. 8°. Camb., Mass. 1924–26
1, Offensive operations, 1914–15.
2, Stress of sea power, 1915–16.
3, U.S. in the War, 1917–18.
True acc. of the Battle of Jutland, May 31, 1916. 8°. Camb., Mass. 1920

Froude (James Anthony). The cat's pilgrimage. Illust. by J. B. la8°. E. 1870

Froumundus. Die Tegernseer Briefsammlung (Froumund) [Latin]. Hrsg. v. K. Strecker. [Mon. Germ. hist.: Epist. sel., t3]. 8°. 1925

***Frown** (A) from the Crown, or the Hydra destroyed. [*A satire upon the King*]. [P425]. 8°. 1820

F. R. S., *ps.* *Calculus made easy, 1910, *see* THOMPSON (S. P.)

Frugoli (Antonio). Pratica e scalcaria intit. Pianta di delicati frutti &c. con tratt. dell' inventori d. vivande &c. tr. d. ling. Armenia. s4°. 1631

Frugoni (Carlo Innocenzo) [*ps.* COMANTE EGINETICO].
Canzonette anacreontiche. s8°. Milano. 1757
see CALCATERRA (C.) Storia d. poesia frugon., 1920.

Frühaufgelesene Früchte d. theolog. Sammlung v. Alten u. Neuen &c. Auf d. Jahr 1735[–41] [6 Beyträge *to each year. b. in 3v.*] s8°. L. 1735–41

Fruin (R.), *see* MULLER (S.), J. A. FEITH & R. F. Handleiding &c., archieven, 1920.

Frusius (Andreas), *Jesuit* [DES FREUX (*le père* ANDRÉ)]. Epigrammata in haereticos. Corr. & aucta. s8°. Coloniae. 1600

Frutolf, *Benedictine monk of St. Michel, Bamberg* [FRUTOLPHE]. Breviarium de musica & Tonarius; veröff. v. C. Vivell, 1916, *see* KAISERL. AKAD. D. WISS. ZU WIEN. Sitz., B188, 1919.

Fry (A. Ruth). A Quaker adventure: 9 years of relief & reconstr. Intr. by Visct. Cecil of Chelwood. 8°. [1926]

Fry (Agnes). A mem. of Sir E. Fry, 1827–1918. Comp. f. autobiog. &c. 8°. O. 1921

Fry (Charles Burgess). Key-book of the League of Nations. With ch. on disarmament q. by Prince Ranjitsinhji. 8°. [1923]

Fry (Edmund). Pantographia; copies of all known alphabets. 8°. 1799

Fry (*Rt. Hon. Sir* **Edward),** *lord justice of the Court of Appeal. see* EDWARD FRY LIBRARY OF INTERNATIONAL LAW.
„ FRY (A.) Memoir of E. F., 1827–1918; compiled f. autobiog., 1921.
„ SELDEN (J.) Table talk; w. acc. of S. by Sir E. F., 1927.

Fry (Edward Alexander). Almanacks for students of Eng. hist.: Easter old style & new style, regnal years &c. 8°. 1915
see GENTLEMAN'S MAGAZINE. Index to marriages in the G. M., 1731–68; by E. A. F., 1922.

Fry (*Mrs.* **Elizabeth),** *see* MATHESON (A.) A plain friend [*i.e.* E. F.], 1920.

Fry (Francis). The Bible by Coverdale, 1535. 8°. 1867

Fry (*Sir* **Frederick Morris),** *see* MERCHANT-TAYLORS-HALL. Hist. cat. of the pictures &c. at M.-T.-H., by F., 1907.

Fry (George Samuel), *C.B.E.* Abstracts of wills rel. to Walthamstow, Co. Essex (1335–1559). [Walthamstow Antiq. Soc. Publs. No. 9]. [P2605]. fol. Walthamstow. 1921

Fry (Katharine). Hist. of the parishes of East & West Ham. Ed. & rev. by G. Pagenstecher. 4°. *p.f.p.c.* 1888

Fry (*Mrs.* **Penrose),** *see* KAYE-SMITH (SHEILA).

Fry (Roger Eliot).
Cézanne: st. of h. development. la8°. N.Y. 1927
Chinese art: intr. review of painting, ceramics, &c. By R. F., L. Binyon, A. F. Kendrick &c. [Burlington Mag.] 4°. [1925]
Flemish art: crit. survey. la8°. 1927
Transformations: crit. & speculative essays on art. 4°. 1926
Vision & design. 4°. 1920
—— **& E. A. Lane.** Eng. handwriting, w. 34 facs. plates &c. [S.P.E. Tract 33]. 8°. 1926

Frye (Prosser Hall). Racine, *see* NEBRASKA UNIV. Studies, v19, 1919.

Fryer (Alfred C.) Wooden monumental effigies in England & Wales. la8°. 1924

Fryer (Percival John). Insect pests & fungus diseases of fruit & hops. 8°. C. 1920

Fuad (R. M.), *bey.* *La Turquie, les massacres &c. Appel. [P2712]. 8°. *n.p. n.d.*

Fualdès (Antoine Bernardin). *Les assassins de F. [*no tp.* P2826]. s8°. [Sceaux]. *n.d.*
Hist. & procès compl. des assassins de F. par le stenographe paris. [*i.e.* H. de Latouche]. Procéd. d'Albi. 2t. 8°. 1818
see *CAUSES crimin. célèb. du 19e siècle, t1, F., 1827.
„ MANSON (M. F. C.) Coin du voile levé s. l'affaire F.; confess. de Mme. M., 1819.
„ PRAVIEL (A.) L'assassinat de M. F., 1922.

Fuchs (Adalbert Franz). Urkunden &c. z. Gesch. d. Benedictinerstiftes Göttweig; bearbt. v. A. F. F., 3T, *see* FONTES RERUM AUSTRIAC., B51, 52, 55, 1901–2.

Fuchs (Eduard). Dachreiter u. verwandte chin. Keramik d. 15.–18. Jhdts. 4°. München. [1924]
Die Juden in d. Karikatur. la8°. München. [1921]
Tang-Plastik: chin. Grabkeramik d. 7.–10. Jhdts. 4°. München. [1924]
Der Weltkrieg in d. Karikatur. B1, Bis z. Vorabend d. Weltkrieges. 4°. München. [1916]
—— **& P. Heiland.**
Die deut. Fayence-Kultur. 4°. München. 192[illegible]

Fuchs (Emil). The work of E. F.: paintings, sculpture medals & studies. la8°. N.Y. 192[illegible]

Fuchs (Leonhard), *M.D.* De hist. stirpium comm. insignes Acc. vocum difficilium &c. explic. &c. s8°. Lugduni. 154[illegible]

Fuchs (Marcus), *see* MASSA (S.) Chron. Fuchsio—Lupino—Oltardinum &c., 2p, 1847–48.

Fucini (Renato) [*ps.* NERI TANFUCIO]. Acqua passata: stor e aneddoti d. mia vita. Ed. postuma, a cura e con pref. d G. Biagi. 8°. Firenze. [1921

Fuḍālī [MUHAMMAD IBN EŠ-ŠĀFI 'I]. Muhammedan. Glaubenslehre: d. Katechismen d. F. u. d. Sanusi; übers. u. erl. v M. Horten, *see* KLEINE TEXTE, T139, 1916.

Fuel Research Board. Special report 3. la8°. 192[illegible]
see FISHENDEN (M. W.) The coal fire, 1920. [3

Fuensalida (Gutierre Gomez de). Corr. de F., embajador em Alemania, Flandes e Inglaterra (1496–1509). Publ. por el duque de Berwick y de Alba. la8º. 1907

Fueslinus (J. C.), *see* FÜSSLI (J. C.)

Fugger, *the family of ; Barons of Kirchberg & Weissenhorn.* The Fugger News-letters: sel. f. corresp. of Hse. of F., 1568–1605. Ed. V. v. Klarwill. Tr. by P. de Chary. Foreword by H. G. Selfridge. 8º. [1924]
„ „ ....[repr.] 8º. [1925]
„ „ ser. 2, spec. ref. to Queen Elizabeth. Tr. L. S. R. Byrne. 8º. [1926]
Fuggerorum et Fuggerarum quæ in familia natæ, quæve in familiam transierunt, quot extant ære expressæ imagines. D. Custodis desin. & sc. [L. & W. Kiliani ampl. &c.] fol. [Augustæ Vindel. 1618]
Fugger-Zeitungen: Ungedr. Briefe an d. Haus Fugger, 1568–1605. Hrsg. V. Klarwill. 8º. Wien. 1923
see JANSEN (M.), H. GRAUERT & J. STRIEDER. St. z. Fugger-Gesch ; H5–7, hrsg. J. S., 1915–23.

Fugger (Johann Jakob).
see HARTIG (O.) Gründung d. Münchener Hofbibl. durch Albrecht V. u. J. J. F., 1917, 1917.
„ MAASEN (W.) H. J. F., 1922.

Fugger-Glött (Hermann Joseph, *Graf.* **v.)** Die Staatsgefährlichkeit d. röm.-kathol. Kirche. [P2696]. 8º. Regensburg. 1875

Fuhrmann (Ernst).
Das Tier in d. Religion. 4º. München. 1922
Reich d. Inka. 4º. Hagen i. W. 1922
—— **& B. Melchers.** China. Das Land d. Mitte, v. E. F.; Der Tempelbau, v. B. M. 2B. 4º. Hagen i. W. 1921

Fujisawa (Rikitaro). The recent aims & polit. devel. of Japan. 8º. New Haven. 1923

Fujiwara (Murasaki), *see* MURASAKI (*Lady*).

Fulbert, *Saint, bp. of Chartres.* Opera varia. Cum notis &c. per M. C. de Villiers. s8º. Parisiis. 1608

Fulcheri (Bartolomeo). I monti frumentari d. Sardegna, *see* REGIA DEPUT. Miscellanea, t41, 1905.

Fulda. Annales F. Acc. annales F. antiq. Rec. F. Kurze. [Scr. rer. Germ. in usum schol.] 8º. Hannoverae. 1891

Fulevius (Jonas), *Churiolandus.* Diss. juridica de sacra Scr. Coll. J. F. C. &c. s8º. Augusta Trebocorum. [1628]

Fulfilling (The) of the Scripture &c., 1671, *see* FLEMING (R.)

Fulgosio (Fernando). Crón. gen. de España, *for provinces by F. F., see* ESPAÑA. Crón. gen., 1865–71 *in vol. numbered as below :*

Avila.	[10.]	Orense.	[2.]
Baleares.	[12.]	Pontevedra	[2.]
Coruña.	[2.]	Tarragona.	[3.]
Filipinas.	[12.]	Valladolid.	[6.]
Guipuzcoa.	[8.]	Zamora.	[6.]

Fuligatti (Jacopo). Vita Roberti Bellarmini: a Silvestro Petra Sancta Lat. redd. &c. 2ª ed. s8º. Antverpiae. 1631

Fulin (Rinaldo). Dell' attitudine di Venezia dinanzi ai viaggi marittimi d. sec. xv. [P2852]. 8º. Venezia. 1881

Fulke (William). A confut. of a treatise by William Allen in defence of the usurped power of popish priesthood to remit sinnes, &c. s8º. C., *Thomas Thomas.* [c. 1586]
A retentive to stay good Christians, in true faith &c. agst. the motives of R. Bristow. Also, A discovery of the dangerous rocke of the Popish Church commended by N. Sander. s8º. *T. Vautroullier.* 1580
The text of the New Test., tr. out of Latine by the Papists at Rhemes. Added, tr. out of the Greeke. With a confut. &c. fol. 1601
Two treatises wr. agst. the papistes. 1, ans. of the Christ. protestant to Popish Catholicke [W. Allen, abp. of Mechlin]. 2, a confut. of the Popish churches doctrine t. purgatory & prayers for the dead. 2p *in* 1v. [*sep. pagin. Imperf.*] s8º. 1577

Full. *Full & exact rel. of the duel betw. James, duke of Hamilton & Lord Mohun, 1713, *see* HAMILTON (J. H., *4th duke of*).
*Full (A) & genuine hist. of the murders of W. Galley &c., 1749, *see* GALLEY (W.)
*Full (A) view of the doctrines &c. rel. to Eucharist &c., 1688, *see* PATRICK (J.)

Fullana Mira (Lluis), *O.F.M.* Vocab. ortográfic Valenciá-Castellá. s8º. Valencia. 1921

Fülleborn (Friedrich). Das deutsche Njassa- u. Ruwuma-Gebiet, Land u. Leute, nebst Bemerk. ü. d. Schire-Länder. la8º. [atlas fol.] 1906

Fuller (Andrew), *1754–1815.* Complete works; w. mem. by A. G. Fuller. la8º. 1841
The complete works of A. F., w. life by A. G. Fuller. la8º. 1846
The gospel its own witness. n. ed. w. life of a. s8º. [c. 1825]
Mem. of Samuel Pearce. s8º. N.Y. *n.d.*
see MORRIS (J. W.) Mem. of A. F., 1826.

Fuller (Benjamin Apthorp Gould). Hist. of Greek phil., Thales to Democritus. 8º. [1923]

Fuller (*Sir* Francis Charles).
A vanished dynasty. Ashanti. 8º. 1921

Fuller (Henry Corbin).
The story of drugs: orig., preparation &c. 8º. [1922]

Fuller (*Col.* John Frederic Charles), *D.S.O.*
Brit. Light Infantry in the 18th cent. 8º. [1925]
Found. of the sci. of war. 8º. [1926]
The reformation of war. 8º. 1923

Fuller (*Sir* Joseph Bampfylde).
Causes & consequences. 8º. 1923
The law within. 8º. 1926
The science of ourselves. Sequel to the "Descent of man." 8º. 1921

Fuller (Joseph Vincent). Bismarck's diplomacy at its zenith. [Harvard Hist. St., v26]. 8º. Cambridge [*Mass.*] 1922

Fuller (Margaret). Love letters, 1845–46. Intr. by J. W. Howe. Added, Remin. of R. W. Emerson, H. Greeley & C. T. Congdon. 8º. 1903
see ANTHONY (K.) M. F.: a psycholog. biog., 1922.

Fuller (Thomas), *D.D., Prebendary of Salisbury.*
Andronicus, or the unfortunate politician. s8º. 1646
The appeal of injured innocence. Controv. betw. P. Heylyn & T. F. [*b. w. h.* Church hist., 1655]. 3p. fol. 1659
The cause & cure of a wounded conscience. s8º. 1647
The Church hist. of Britain, until 1648. Ed. J. S. Brewer. n. ed. 6v. 8º. O. 1845
Hist. of the Holy Warre. sfol. C. 1639
Hist. of the Univ. of Cambridge to 1634 [1643]. Ed. w. notes by M. Prickett & T. Wright. 8º. C. 1840
Hist. of the worthies of Eng. fol. 1662
A Pisgah-sight of Palestine &c., w. the hist. of the O. & N. Test. [2 tp., the first engraved. *2 pagin.*] fol. 1650
Wise words & quaint counsels. Sel. & arr., w. sk. of a.'s life by A. Jessopp. s8º. O. 1892

Fuller (Thomas), *M.D.* Pharmacopœia extemporanea: or a body of medicines, cont. select prescripts. 8º. 1740

Fuller-Maitland (John Alex.)
The "48," Bach's Wohltemperirtes Clavier. Bk. 1, 2 [*in* 1v]. s8º. 1925
Keyboard suites of J. S. Bach. s8º. 1925
Schumann. n. ed. s8º. [1923]
The spell of music. 8º. [1926]
see COLERIDGE (A. D.) Remin.; ed. J. A. F.-M. &c., 1921.

Fullerton (William Young).
The romance of Pitcairn Island. s8º. 1923

Fullwood (Francis). *Agreement betw. the present & former govt.: or, a disc. of this monarchy, whether elective or hereditary? By a divine of the Ch. of Engl. [*? F. F. or D. Whitby*]. [P2663]. s4º. 1689
see JEANES (H.) Want of ch. govt. no warrant for omission of Lord's Supper: added, Reply unto Mr. F., 1653.

Fülöp-Miller (René).
Der heilige Teufel: Rasputin u. d. Frauen. la8º. L. [1927]
Lenin & Gandhi. Tr. F. S. Flint & D. F. Tait. 8º. [1927]
The mind & face of Bolshevism: exam. of cultural life in Soviet Russia. Tr. F. S. Flint & D. F. Tait. 8º. [1927]

Fulton (Alexander S.), *see* BRIT. MUSEUM. PRINTED BOOKS. Arabic bks. in B.M.: Suppl. cat.; by A. S. F. &c., 1926.

Fulton (M.) Blight. s8º. 1919

Fulvio (Valerio), *Savoiano, ps.* [*i.e.* GIACOMO CASTELLANI]. Castigo essemplare de' calunniatori. Avviso di Parnaso. Al seren. Carlo Emanuel, duca di Savoia. [*b. w.* Veneta. Squit. d. lib., 1612]. 8º. *n.p.* "in Antopoli." 1618
see PIÓ (M.) Alleg. per confirmare . . . annot. all' Avviso di Parnaso, 1621.
„ VENETIA. *Avviso di Parnaso, con annot. per V. F. S., 1621.

Fumagalli (Giuseppe). Chi l'ha detto? Tesoro di citazioni ital. e straniere di orig. lett. e storica. Indicate &c. G. F. 5ª ed., riv. s8º. Milano. 1909
see BANDINI (A. M.) Vita di A. Vespucci—bibliogr. d. opere conc. P. Toscanelli & A. V. per G. Fumagalli, 1898.

Funck (Johann Nicolaus).
De imminenti Lat. linguae senectute tract. s4º. Marburgi Catt. 1736
De lect. auctor. class. ad comparandam Lat. linguae facultatem necessaria liber. 2um auct. & emend. ed. 2p *in* 1v. [*tp. of p2 dated* 1763]. s4º. Lemgoviae. 1745

Funck (Johann Nicolaus) [*continued*].
De literarum studio &c. consultationes scholast. s8°. Marburgi. 1742
De scriptura veterum comm. &c. [*b. w. h.* De lit. studio, 1742]. s8°. Marburgi. 1743
De stilo Latino exercit. rhetor. Acc. Epistol. & orat. sel. ideae [*w. sep. pagin.*] ed. alt. auct. s8°. Marburgi. 1737
Dissertationes academ. 8°. Lemgoviae. 1746
Leges 12 tabularum, obs. illust. s4°. Rintelii. 1744
Pro Phaedro ejusque fabulis apologia. [*b. w. h.* De lit. studio, 1742]. s8°. Lipsiae. 1747
Selectae orationes academ. s8°. Lemgoviae. 1748

Funck-Brentano (Frantz).
L'Ancien Régime. [27e éd.] 8°. [1926]
The earliest times. Tr. E. F. Buckley. 8°. 1927]
Les lettres de cachet. s8°. [1926]
The Middle Ages. Tr. E. O'Neill. 8°. [1922]
Le Moyen Age. 8°. 1922

***Funeral** hymns, 3rd ed., 1747, *see* WESLEY (J.) & C. WESLEY.

Funk (Gottfried Benedict). Symbolae ad interpret. S. Codicis. 2p *in* 1v. [*pagin. cont.* P1042]. s8°. Hafniae. 1768–69

Funk (Isaac Kaufman). The psychic riddle. s8°. N.Y. 1907
The widow's mite & o. psychic phenomena. 8°. N.Y. 1904

Funk (Salomon), *see* MONUMENTA Hebr.–monum. Talmud., B1, Bibel u. Babel, v. S. F., 1913–14.

Funk (Wilhelm). Alt Rothenburg, 6 Steinzeichnungen. [P2707]. 8°. Nürnberg. 1922

***Funus** linguae Hellenist., 1643, *see* SALMASIUS (CL.)

Furchheim (Federigo). Bibliogr. d. Insel Capri u. d. Sorrentiner Halbinsel sowie v. Amalfi, Salerno u. Paestum. 2e. umgearb. u. verm. A. 8°. L. 1916

Fürck (Sebastian) [FURCKIUS (S.)], *see* BOISSARDUS (J. J.) Bibl. chalcograph.; cont. *by* S. F., 1650–54.

Furet (L.) Lettres à M. L. de Rosny s. l'Archipel Japonais et la Tartarie or. Intr. par E. Cortambe. Suivi d'un traité de philos. jap. & de vocabs. 2e éd. s8°. 1860

Furetière (Antoine), *see* LEUSCHNER (K.) A. F. u. s. Streit mit d. französ. Akad., 1915.

Furlani (Giuseppe). 6 scritti Antitriteistici in lingua siriaca; [ed. & tr.] per G. F., *see* GRAFFIN (R.) & F. NAU. Pat. Or., t14, 1920.

Furley (John Sampson). City govt. of Winchester f. records of the 14 & 15 c. 8°. O. 1923
see WINCHESTER. Anc. usages of the City of W.; fr. Anglo-Fr. vers. by J. S. F., 1927.

Furmanov (Dm.) Мятеж. [Соб. соч., т2]. 3е изд. 8°. Москва. 1926

Furne (Aliénor de Poitiers, *vtss. de*), *see* ELEANOR, *de Poitiers*.

Furneaux (William S.) Human physiology. 20th impr. 8°. 1918

Furness (Horace Howard), *the elder.* Letters. Ed. H. H. F. J[ayne]. 2v. 8°. Boston [U.S.] 1922

Furniss (Harold).
Famous crimes past & present. Ed. H. F. Police Budget ed. v1–8 (N. 1–104) *in* 2v. 4°. *n.d.* *Suppl. have sep. pagin.*
How & why I illustrated Thackeray. [P2847]. 8°. 1912
My Bohemian days. 8°. [1919]
Paradise in Piccadilly: story of the Albany. 8°. [1925]
Some Victorian women. 8°. 1923
The Two Pins Club. 8°. 1925

Furniture. Encyclopaedia of f., 1926, *see* SCHMITZ (H.), *ed.*
Furniture & its story. [Woodworker Ser.] s8°. [1920]
Furniture repairing &c. [Ed. J. C. S. Brough]. s8°. [1919]

Furnivall (Frederick James). Robert Browning's ancestors. [*Extr. f.* Browning Soc. Papers. P2862]. 8°. 1890
see VILES (E.) & F. J. F., *edd.* Rogues & vagabonds of Shakespeare's youth: Awdeley &c., 1907.

Furse (George Armand).
Information in war: its acquis. & transmission. 8°. 1895

Fürst (Artur). Die Welt auf Schienen. la8°. München. [1918]

Furst (Herbert Ernest Augustus). The decorative art of F. Brangwyn. A st. of the problems of decoration. 4°. [1924]
The mod. woodcut: st. of evolution of the craft. With ch. on xylography by W. T. Smith. 4°. [1924]
Portrait painting. 4°. [1927]

Fürst (Julius). Gesch. d. Karäerthums v. 900–1575 & 1575–1865. [Inst. z. Förd. d. israel. Lit., 10 & 14 J.] 8°. L. 1865–69

Fürstner (Wolfgang), *see* BEUMELBURG (W.) Loretto; dargestellt v. W. B., auf Grund e. hist. Studie v. W. F., 1927.

Further [FARTHER]. *Farther (A) acc. of mem. earthquakes, to 1756, 1756, *see* EARTHQUAKES.
*Farther consid. upon a reduct. of the land-tax, *see* NUGENT (R. C.-N., *earl*).
*Further forensic fables, by O., 1928, *see* MATHEW (T.)
*Further (A) narr. of the passages of these times in the Commonwealth of Eng. An act f. renouncing the title of Charls Stuart.—The triall of Miles Sundercombe &c. [*wanting all after page* 54]. s4°. [1658]

Füssli (Johann Conrad) [FUESLINUS (J. C.)] Epistolae ab eccl. Helvet. reformatoribus vel ad eos scr. Centuria prima. Ed. J. C. Fueslinus. s8°. Tiguri. 1742

Fust (*Sir* Herbert Jenner-), *see* JENNER-FUST (*Sir* H.)

Fustel de Coulanges (Numa Denis). The ancient city: st. of relig., laws &c. of Greece & Rome. Tr. W. Small. 12th ed. 8°. Boston [Mass.] [1901]

Futabatei Shimei, *ps.* [*i.e.* HASEGAWA TATSUNOSUKE]; *1864–1909*. Mediocrity. Tr. G. W. Shaw. s8°. Tokyo. [1927]

Füter (Eduard). Gesch. d. europä. Staatensystems v. 1492–1559. [Hdbch. d. m.-a. &c. Gesch.; hrsg. Below &c., Abt. 2]. la8°. München. 1919
World history, 1815–1920. Tr. S. B. Fay. 8°. [1923]

Future. Future (The) of Xty. [*by var. wr.*], 1927, *see* MARCHANT (*Sir* J.), *ed.*
Future (The) of the Ch. of England, 1926, *see* MARCHANT (*Sir* J.), *ed.*

Fyfe (Henry Hamilton).
The making of an optimist. 8°. [1921]
The religion of an optimist. 8°. [1927]
Twells Brex, a conqueror of death. [repr.] s8°. 1920

Fynne (Robert John).
Montessori & h. inspirers. s8°. 1924

Fyson (Philip Furley). Some experiments in hybridising of Indian cottons. [Mem. of Dept. of Agric. in India: Botan. ser., v2, No. 6. P2750]. la8°. Calcutta. 1908

Fyvie (John). Noble dames & notable men of the Georgian era. 8°. 1910

G

G. (A. S.) *Surrendered: naval War secrets, 1927, *see* GRIFF, *ps.*

G. (C.) *Simple skating club figures; [*intr. signed* C. G.], 1893, *see* SKATING.

G. (C. M.) Northern numbers; sel. f. Scot. poets; [foreword *signed* C. M. G.], 1920, *see* NORTHERN.

G. (D.) *Mem. p. s. à l'hist. de Pierre III, emp. de Russie &c.; publ. par Mr. D. G., 1763, *see* GOUDAR (A. DE).

G. (F.) *Sciocche &c. imposture, 1770, *see* GRISELINI (F.)

G. (F. F. R. D.), *see* FORTIN (FRANÇOIS).

G. (I.) *I. G.: De rebus auspic. Caroli Regis &c., sub. imp. J. Montisros. March. &c. gestis, comm.; interp. A. S., 1647, *see* WISHART (G.)

G. (J.) *The Agreement &c. of brethren, 1679, *see* GOODWIN (JOHN).

G. (R.) *The comicall hist. of Alphonsus, King of Aragon, 1599, 1926, *see* GREENE (R.)

G. (T.) Ant. &c. hist. of York, 1730, *see* GENT (THOMAS).

***G.H.Q.** (Montreuil-sur-Mer), 1920, *see* FOX (*Sir* F.)

"G. S. O.", *ps.* *G.H.Q. (Montreuil-sur-Mer), 1920, *see* FOX (*Sir* F.)

Gaal (Georg v.), *see* STIER (G.) Ungar. Volksmärchen: nach d. aus G. G.'s Nachlass hrsg. Urschrift übers. G. S., 1857.

Gaal (Mózes).
Berzsenyi Dániel élete és költészete. [P2394]. s8°. Pozsony. [1898]
Deák Ferencz élet-és jellemrajz. [P2394]. s8°. 1900
Kazinczy Ferencz élete és költészete. [P2394]. s8°. Pozsony. [1898]
Kölcsey Ferencz élete és költészete. [P2394]. s8°. Pozsony. [1898]
Maria Terézia története. [P2394]. s8°. 1900
II. Endre Magyar király. 2íd kiadás. [P2394]. s8°. 1903
Petőfi Sándor élete és költészete. 2íd kiadás. [P2394]. s8°. *n.d.*
Széchenyi István vagy Magyarország újjászületése. [P2394]. s8°. 1899

Gabalis (*le comte* **de**), *ps.* *Le comte de G. &c. (1670), 1921, *see* VILLARS (*l'abbé* DE).

Gabbema (Simon Abbes). Illust. & clar. virorum epistolae &c. Coll. & ed. G. Ed. altera, aucta. s8°. Harlingae Fris. 1669

Gabelentz (Hans Conon v. der) [CONON DE LA GABELENTZ]. Elem. de la grammaire mandchoue. 8°. Altenbourg. 1832

Gabet (Joseph), *1808–53*, *see* HUC (E. R.) H. & G., travels in Tartary &c., 1844–46; tr., ed. P. Pelliot, 2v, 1928.

Gabianus (Joannes Dominicus), *Jesuit.* Incrementa Sinicæ eccl. a Tartaris oppugnatæ &c. s4°. Viennæ Austriæ. 1673
Gable (Jacob Henry), *jr.* Learned & scient. publ. of the Univ. of Nebraska, 1871–1926. [N. Univ. Bibliog. contrib. 6]. 8°. Lincoln, Neb. 1926
Gabler (Johann Philipp), *see* JOURNAL FÜR AUSERLESENE THEOLOG. LIT.; hrsg. v. J. P. G., 6B, 1804–11.
Gaboriau (Emile). L'affaire Lerouge. 17e éd. s8°. 1876
Le crime d'Orcival. [repr.] s8°. *n.d.*
TRANSLATIONS.
The Lerouge case. [New tr.] s8°. [1921]
The Widow Lerouge. Tr. s8°. 1901
Gabory (Émile). Les Bourbons et la Vendée. 8°. 1923
Napoléon & la Vendée. 8°. 1914
Gabory (Georges). André Gide, s. œuvre. s8°. 1924
Essai s. M. Proust. 8°. 1926
Gabotto (Ferdinando).
Works in REGIA DEP. DI STORIA PATRIA. Misc.
Doc. ined. s. storia del Piemonte (1383–1418), 1896. [34.]
L'età del Conte Verde in Piemonte (1350–83), 1895. [33.]
Invent. e regesto dell' Archivio comunale di Moncalieri, 1418, 1900. [36.]
—— & D. Orsi. Le laudi del Piemonte. Racc. e pubbl. F. G. & D. O. v1. [*no more publ.*] s8°. Bologna. 1891
Gàbrici (Ettore). *Works in* REALE ACCAD. D. LINCEI. Mon. ant.
Bolsena: scavi nel sacellum d. dea Nortia sul Pozzarello, 1906. [16.]
Cuma [& Tavole], 1913. [22.]
Necropoli di età ellenistica a Teano dei Sidicini, 1910. [20.]
Ruderi rom. scop. alla Piazza d. Vittorio in Palermo, 1921. [27.]
Vaso campano à pittura policroma rappr. Sileno e le ninfe, *see* ACAD. DES INSCR.: FOND. PIOT. Mon., t24, 1920.
Gabriel, *Sionita, see* ARABIA. Arabia seu Arabum leges &c. [*by G. S. & others*], 1635.
Gabriel (A. G.), *see* BRITISH MUSEUM: ZOOLOGY. Cat. of type specimens of Lepidoptera Rhopalocera in B.M., p1–3, 1924–27.
Gabriel (Albert).
La cité de Rhodes, 1310–1522. [2t]. fol. 1921–23
Gabriel (Ralph Henry).
The evolution of Long Island. 8°. New Haven, *Yale.* 1921
Gabriele (Giacomo) [GABRIELLO], *see* SANSOVINO (F.), *ed.* Osserv. d. lingua volg., 1563.
Gabriel y Galán (José Maria).
Obras completas. 5a ed. 2t. s8°. [1921]
1, Castellanas—Nuevas Castellanas—Extremenas. 2, Religiosas—Campesinas—Fragmentos.
see REVILLA MARCOS (A.) J. M. G. y G.: vida y obras, 1923.
Gache (Alberto I.) La Argentina en marcha. 8°. [1921?]
Gachon (Paul). Hist. de Languedoc. [5e éd.] 8°. 1921
Gachot (Edouard). Hist. milit. de Massena. La campagne d'Helvétie, 1799. 8°. 1904
Gad (Carl). Johan Bojer. En studie. s8°. 1917
Gadd (Cyril John).
The early dynasties of Sumer & Akkad. s8°. 1921
Sumerian reading-book. s8°. O. 1924
see BRIT. MUSEUM: ANTIQ. The fall of Nineveh: newly disc. Babylonian chron.; ed. w. translit., tr. &c. by G., 1923.
„ UR excavations, 1919 &c., v1, w. chap. by G., 1927.
Gadgil (D. R.)
The industrial evol. of India in recent times. s8°. 1924
Gadsby (John). Memoirs of hymn-writers &c. of the 17th & 18th cent. 2nd ed. s8°. 1855
Gadsby (Margaret). Trade agreement in the silk-ribbon industry of N.Y. city, *see* UNITED STATES: LABOR, Bull. 341, 1923.
Gaetano (Tizzone), *see* BOCCACCIO (G.) Il Philocopo da T. G. di Pofi revisto, 1538.
Gagarin (*prince* **Grigory Grigorevich**) [GAGARINE]. Le Caucase pittoresque dessiné par G.; avec intr. & texte par le comte E. Stackelberg. atlas fol. 1847
Gagern (Friedrich von). Die Wundmale. Roman. 2B. s8°. L. *n.d.*
Gaget (J.) Les abeilles & le miel. s8°. [1920]
Gagini (Carlos). Dicc. de Costarriqueñismos. 2a ed. 4°. San Jose de Costa Rica. 1919
Gagliardi (Ernst). Gesch. d. Schweiz. 3B *in* 2v [1, 2 *b. together*]. 8°. Zürich. 1920–27
Gagnaeus (Joannes), *see* BIBLE: LATIN. Biblia maxima, cum annot. J. G. &c., 19t, 1660.
Gagner (Laurentius Petr.) De colonia Vermelandia diss. quam exhib. L. P. Gagner & J. M. Malmstedt. [P2647]. s4°. Upsaliae. [1819]
Gagneur (*capitaine* **Maurice),** *see* GINISTY (P.) & M. G. Hist. de la Guerre par les combattants, t3, Verdun, 1921.
Gahan (Arthur Burton) & M. M. Fagan. Type species of the genera of Chalcidoidea. [S.I., U.S. Nat. Mus., Bull. 124]. 8°. Wash. 1923
Gahan (Charles Joseph), *see* BRIT. MUSEUM OF NAT. HIST. Furniture beetles, th. life hist. &c.; by C. J. G., 1920.
Gaheis (Alexander). Gaukler in Altertum. s8°. München. [1927]
Gahmuret, *hero of romance, see* RICHEY (M. F.) Gahmuret Anschevin: contrib. to study of W. v. Eschenbach, 1923.
Gaibrois de Ballesteros (Mercedes). Hist. del r. de Sancho IV de Castilla. t1. la8°. 1922
Gaiffe (Félix). L'envers du grand siècle. s8°. [1924]
Gaillard (Claude). Recherches sur les poissons repr. dans quelques tombeaux égypt. de l'anc. emp.; par C. G. avec collab. de V. Loret &c., *see* INST. FRANÇ. D'ARCH. ORIENT. DU CAIRE, t51, 1923.
Gaillard (Emile). Un peintre siennois au 15e siècle: Sano di Pietro, 1406–81. la8°. [1923]
Gaillard (Gaston). The Turks & Europe. [Tr.] s8°. 1921
Gailliard (Corneille). Le blason des armes &c. (1557). Publ., annoté & préc. d'un essai crit. par J. van Malderghem, & d'une notice biog. par L. van Hollebeke. [2p., *w. facs. tp. & sep. pagin.*] 8°. Brux. 1866
p2 has t.: L'anc. noblesse de la contée de Flandres.
Gailliard (Edward), *see* BRUGES. Invent. des archives de B.: Table analyt. & Table des noms &c. & glossaire flamand; par E. G., 2v, 1879–85.
Gailliard (Jean Jacques). Inscr. funéraires & mon. de la Flandre occid. avec des données hist. & généalog. t1, Bruges. [*in* 3p. *no more publ.*] fol. Bruges. 1861–66
Gaimar (Geoffroi), *see* HAVELOK, *the Dane.* Le lai d'H. & G.'s Haveloc episode; ed. A. Bell, 1925.
Gaines (Francis Pendleton).
The Southern plantation. [Columbia Univ.] 8°. N.Y. 1924
Gainsborough. Parish registers of G. v1, 1564–1640. Ed. C. W. Foster. [Lincoln Record Soc. Par. Reg. Sect., v6]. la8°. Horncastle. 1920
Gainsborough (Thomas). Bicent. memorial exhib. of T. G. Under auspices of Council of Borough of Ipswich, 1927. [Cat., illust.] la8°. Ipswich. 1927
see GOWER (*Ld.* R. C. S.-L.-) T. G., 1903.
„ HARVEY (F.) [G.: MS. records of pictures &c.], *n.d.*
„ HOLMES (*Sir* C. J.) Constable, G. & Lucas &c., 1921.
„ STOKES (H.) T. G., 1925.
Gaisford (Thomas), *dean of Christ Church.* Poetæ minores Graeci. Praec. lect. var. &c. instr. T. G. v1, 2 [*? no more publ.*] 8°. Oxonii. 1814–16
Gait (*Sir* **Edward Albert).**
Hist. of Assam. 2nd ed., rev. 8°. Calcutta. 1926
Gaius, *the jurist, see* DITTMAR (W. A. H.) De nomine aetate studiis ac scr. Gaii, 1820.
Gaius (Bartholomæus). Epitome gestorum Patriarcharum, ducum, &c. populi Hebræici ab Adam ad Agrippam usque jun., iconibus illust. fol. Romae. 1751
Galahad, *Sir, ps.*
Idiotenführer durch d. russ. Lit. 8°. München. 1925
Galano (Clemente). Conciliationis eccl. Armenæ cum Rom. ex ipsis Armen. patrum & doctorum testimoniis pars prima [& altera]. [*in Armenian & Lat.*] 2p *in* 3v. [2ii *wanting*]. fol. Romae. 1658–90
„ „ [*a. ed. in Armenian only*]. p1. s8°. Romae. 1690
Gramm. & logicae instit. ling. Armen. Armenis traditae. Add. vocab. Armeno-Lat. dict. s4°. Romae. 1645
Galante (Andrea). La teoria d. relaz. fra lo Stato e la Chiesa sec. R. Hooker (1554–1600). [P2841]. 8°. Faenza. 1908
I tesori artistici d. via d. Brènnero. [*Extr. f.* Archivio per l'Alto Adige, a. 7. P2835]. 8°. Trento. 1912
Galanterie. *Loix (Les) de la g. (1644), 1855, *see* LOIX.
Galatinus (Petrus), *see* COLUMNA (P.)
Galbraith (*Mrs.* **Georgina Rosalie).** Constit. of the Dominican Order, 1216–1360. [M'ter Univ. Hist. Ser., No. 44]. 8°. M'ter. 1925
Galbreath (D. L.) & H. de Vevey. Manuel d'héraldique. Préf. de J. de Pury. s8°. [1922]
Galehault, *Sire des Iles Lointaines, see* BOULENGER (J.) Les amours de Lancelot.-G., sire d. I. L., 1923.
Galemqearean, *see* KALEMKEAREAN.
Galen. *Works in* Corpus medic. Graec.
De sanitate tuenda—De alimentorum facult.—De bonis malisque sucis—De victu attenuante—De ptisana, 1923, *se* CORPUS medicorum Graec., v5iv, 2, 1923. [5iv, 2.]

Galen [*continued*].
Works in Corpus medic. Graec. [*continued*].
In Hippocratis de natura hominis—In H. de victu acutorum—De diaeta H. in morbis acutis ; ed. J. Mewaldt &c., 1914. [5ix, 1.]
In Hippocratis Prorrheticum I—De comate secundum H.—In H. Prognosticum ; ed. H. Diels &c., 1915. [5ix, 2.]
Pseudogaleni in Hippocratis de septimanis comm. ab Hunaino q. f. Arabice versum ; ed. G. Bergstraesser, 1914. [11ii, 1.]
De simplicium medicament. facultatibus lib. 11. T. Gerardo interp. s8º. Parisiis. 1543
see WENKEBACH (E.) Das Proömium d. Komm. G. zu d. Epidemien d. Hippokrates, 1918.
„ —— Pseudogalen. Komm. zu d. Epidemien d. Hippokrates, 1917.
„ —— Unters. ü. G. Komm. z. d. Epid. d. Hippokrates, 1925.
Galerie du Musée Napoléon ; publ. Filhol &c., 10t, 1804–15, *see* MUSÉE NAPOLÉON.
Galés (Pedro), fl. 1593 [GALESIUS], *see* MOREL-FATIO (A.) Etudes sur l'Esp., s4, L'humaniste hétérodoxe catalan P. G., 1925.
Gales (R. L.) Old-world essays. s8º. 1921
Galiani (Ferdinando), *see* NICOLINI (F.) La famiglia del Ab. G., 1918.
Galicia. Eastern G. [West Ukrainian Press.] No. 1–4. [No. 3 publ. by Nat. Counc. of E. Galicia]. [P2569]. 8º. *n.p.* [1920 ?]
Galicia, *Spain* [GALLICIA]. *Portugal & G., 2v, 1836, *see* CARNARVON (H. J. G. H., *3rd earl of*).
Galiffe (Jacques Augustin). Notices généalog. s. les familles genev. 2e éd., rev. &c. t2. 8º. Genève. 1892
Galileo. Consid. al Tasso [*ed. f. MS. of* P. A. Serassi] e disc. di G. Iseo sopra il poema di T. &c. s8º. Venezia. 1793
Memorie e lettere ined. &c. Ord. &c. con annot. dal cav. G. Venturi. 2p. la8º. Modena. 1818–21
see FAHIE (J. J.) Sci. wks. of G., 1564–1642, w. acc. of h. life & trial, 1921.
„ RICCI-RICCARDI (A.) G. G. e fra T. Caccini, processo &c., 1902.
Galimberti (Alice).
Dante nel pensiero inglese. s8º. Firenze. [1921]
Galindo (Beatriz), *see* PALENCIA (I. O. DE).
Galindus (Fortunius). A disc. of the reasons why the Jesuits are hated, *see* JARRIGE (P.) A further discovery &c.: No. 4, 1658.
Galiot de Genouillac (Jacques), *seigneur d'Acier* [GALLIOT DE GENOUILLAC], *see* VAUX DE FOLETIER (F. DE). G. de G., maître de l'artillerie de France, 1465–1546, 1925.
Galitzin (*prince* **Alexander),** *see* PINKERTON (R.) Extr. of letters ; w. letter f. pr. A. G. to Lord Teignmouth, 1817.
Galitzin (*prince* **Emmanuel Mikhailovich).** La Russie du 17e s., 1855, *see* POTEMKIN (P. I.)
Gallais (Jean Pierre). Hist. de la Révol. du 20 mars 1815, ou 5e & dern. partie de l'Hist. du 18 Brumaire &c. 8º. 1815
Hist. du dix-huit Brumaire & de Buonaparte [suivie de pièces justif.] 2e éd., rev., corr. &c. 2p [*in* 1v.] 8º. 1814
Galland (René). George Meredith : les 50 premières années, 1828–78. 8º. 1923
Gallandius (Andreas) [GALLAND (ANDRÉ)]. Bibliotheca vet. patrum antiquorumque script. eccl. Cura &c. A. G. [App. complect. vet. script. mon. nova, *w. sep. pagin.*] 14t. lafol. Venetiis. 1765–81
„ „ ......Index alphab. s8º. Bononiae. 1863
***Gallant** news for London, 1647, repr., 1868, *see* LONDON.
Gallarati-Scotti (Tommaso Gius.) La vita di Ant. Fogazzaro. s8º. Milano. 1920
The life of Ant. Fogazzaro. Tr. M. P. Agnetti. 8º. [1922]
Gallardo (Bartolomé José), *see* SÁINZ Y RODRÍGUEZ (P.) B. J. G. y la crit. lit. de su tiempo, 1921.
Gallatin (Albert). Consid. on the currency & banking system of the U.S. [P448]. 8º. Phila. 1831
Gallatin (Albert Eugene), *see* CORPUS vasorum antiq.: U.S. fasc. 1 : Hoppin & Gallatin colls. ; by J. C. Hoppin & A. G., 1926.
Gallavresi (Giuseppe), *see* MANZONI (A.) Manzoni intimo, v3, a cura di G. G., 1923.
—— **& V. Sallier de La Tour de Cordon.** Le Maréchal Sallier de La Tour : mém. & lettres, p1, *see* REGIA DEP. S. GLI STUDI DI STORIA PATRIA &C. Bibl. di storia ital. rec., v8, 1917.
Galle (A.) Üb. d. geodät. Arbeiten v. Gauss, *see* GAUSS (C. F.) Werke BIIii, Abh. 1, 1924.

Gallée (Johan Hendrick), *see* KONINGL. NEDERL. AARDRIJKSK. GENOOTSCHAP. Nomina geogr. Neerlandica, onder red. v. I. Dornseiffen, J. H. G. &c., 1885–1901.
Gallego (Pedro), *see* PELZER (A.) Un traducteur inconnu : P. G. (1250–67), 1924.
Galleria dei lett. ed artisti più illust. d. prov. veneziane nel sec. 18., 2v, 1824, *see* GAMBA (B.), *ed.*
Gallet (Georges). Cat. des monnaies, grec. & rom., médailles, franç. &c., vente, 28 mai 1924. [*Illust.*] la8º. 1924
Galletti (Alfredo). Alessandro Manzoni. 2v. s8º. Milano. 1927
Galletti (Pietro Luigi), *bp. of Cyrene.* Del primicero d. Santa Sede Apostolica e di altri uffiziali maggiori del Sacro Palagio Lateranese. la8º. 1776
Galley (William). *Full & genuine hist. of the inhuman &c. murders of W. G. & D. Chater, w. acc. of trials of the 7 criminals &c. Wr. by a Gentleman at Chichester. s8º. 1749
Galli (Edoardo). *Works in* REALE ACCAD. D. LINCEI. Mon. ant.
Avanzi di mura e vestigia di ant. mon. sacri sull'Acropoli di Fiesole, 1910. [20.]
Fidia in Etruria, 1921. [27.]
Sarcofago etrusco di Torre S. Severo con 4 scene d. ciclo Trojano, 1916. [24.]
Il sepolcreto visentino d. " Bucacce," 1912. [21.]
Perugia. Il museo funerario del Palazzone. All' Ipogeo dei Volumni. s8º. Firenze. 1921
Galli (Luigi), *see* HERMANIN (F.) L. G. : 42 tavole con intr., 1924.
Galli (Roberto), *see* SIMONSFELD (H.) Sulle scoperte d. R. G. n. Cronaca Altinate, 1888.
Gallia. *Ad Regis Galliae consiliarios, exhortatio. Quo pacto obviam iri possit seditionibus &c. Ex Gallico tr. [S. P. P. faciebat]. s8º. *n.p.* 1561
*Comm. de statu relig. & reipublicae in regno Galliæ, 4p, 1572–75, *see* SERRES (J. DE).
Confessio fidei communi eccl., quae sparsae sunt in G., 1559, *see* CONFESSIO.
Gallia christ. noviss, t1–7, 1899–1922, *see* ALBANÈS (J. H.)
*Veterum aliquot G. theologorum scr. 8º. Parisiis. 1586
Gallicciolli (Giambattista). Delle memorie Venete ant. profane ed eccles. libri 3. 8t. 8º. Venezia. 1795
t8, Indice gen. & Risposta all' errata corr. d. Ab. Tentori, *w. sep. pagin.*
Gallichan (Walter M.) [*ps.* GEOFFREY MORTIMER].
Fishing & travel in Spain. s8º. 1904
The story of Seville ; w. 3 ch. on the artists of S. by C. G. Hartley. [repr.] s8º. 1925
Gallicia, *see* GALICIA.
Galliéni (*Gén.* **Joseph Simon).** Mém. du Gén. G. : défense de Paris, 25 août-11 sept. 1914. 8º. 1920
see GHEUSI (P. B.) G., 1849–1916, 1922.
„ PERCIN (A.) Deux hommes de Guerre : Sarrail & G., 1919.
Gallifet (Joseph de), *Jesuit.* L'excellence & la pratique de la dévotion à la Ste Vierge. s8º. Liége. 1766
Gallinari (Giovanni Battista).
Sonetti, con parafrasi in versi lat. 8º. 1841
Galling (Kurt). Der Altar in d. Kulturen d. alt. Orients. Mit 2 Abschnitten v. P. Lohmann u. e. Vorwort v. H. Gressmann. fol. 1925
Gallinger (August). Gegenrechnung. Die Verbrechen an kriegsgefang. Deutschen. 2e A. 8º. L. 1921
Gallio (Joannes), *see* GALLO (J.)
Galliot de Genouillac (Jacques), *see* GALIOT DE GENOUILLAC (J.)
Gallizioli (Giovanni Battista). Dell' origine d. stampa di Bergamo. [*No tp.*] s8º. *n.p.* [Bergamo. 1786]
Gallo (Eduardo L.), *ed.* Hombres ilust. mexicanos. [*By var. wr.*] 4t. 8º. Mexico. 1873–74
Gallo (Joannes) [GALLIO]. De laudibus Thomae Aquinatis. Oratio ad sacros. Synod. Trident. s4º. Brixiae. 1563
Gallois (Lucien), *see* VIDAL DE LA BLACHE (P.) & L. G. Le bassin de la Sarre, 1919.
Gallouédec (René Louis Marie). La Bretagne. Préf. de M. Faure. 4e éd. 8º. 1923
Le Maine. 8º. 1925
Galloway. Register of the Synod of G., Oct. 1664–Apr. 1671. [Wr. by A. Symson. With an App.] 8º. Kirkcudbright. 1856
Galloway (*Sir* **James).** Sir J. Galloway, h. prophesy, 1649, *see* MAIDMENT (J.) & R. PITCAIRN. Nugae derelictae, 1822.
Gallus (Nicolaus). Disput. de adiaphoris &c. Cum praef. s8º. [Magdeburgi. c. 1550]
Kurtzer Bericht v. Artickeln d. Lehre &c. [P2436]. s4º. [Regenspurg, *H. Geipler*]. 1562

Gallus (Nicolaus) & M. Flacius, *Illyricus.* Antwort auff d. brieff etl. Prediger in Meissen, v. d. frage, Ob sie lieber weichen, denn den Chorrock anzihen sollen. s8°. [Magdeburg, *C. Rödinger*]. *n.d.* [1550?]
„ „ *Lat. ed.* Responsio &c. s8°. [Magdeburg, *C. Rödinger*]. *n.d.* [1550?]

Galmot (Jean). Un mort vivait parmi nous. Roman. s8°. 1922

Galpin (*Lieut.* **W. S.**), *R.N.* From public school to navy; special entry scheme. Ed. W. S. G., w. pref. by Comm. Visct. Curzon. la8°. Plymouth. [1919]

Galpine (John). A synopt. compend of Brit. botany, arr. after the Linnean system. 2nd ed. s8°. 1820

Galsworthy (John) [*ps.* SINJOHN (J.)]
Awakening. la8°. [1922]
Captures. s8°. 1923
Caravan. The assembled tales. s8°. 1925
The forest Drama. s8°. [1924]
The Forsyte saga. [repr.] s8°. 1923
„ „ ...... [repr.] s8°. 1924
„ „ ...... [repr.] s8°. 1925
In Chancery. s8°. 1920
*J. G., an appreciation, w. bibliogr. [P2850]. s8°. 1926
Loyalties. Drama. 8°. 1922
The man of property. s8°. 1921
Old English: play. s8°. [1924]
On expression. [Eng. Assoc., Pamph. 59. P2769]. 8°. 1924
Plays.
[n. impr.] s2–6. s8°. [1920–25]
2, The eldest son—The little dream—Justice.
3, The fugitive—The pigeon—The mob.
4, A bit o' love—The foundations—The skin game.
5, A family man—Loyalties—Windows.
Plays [*continued*].
6, The forest—Old English—The show.
Saint's progress. s8°. 1919
The silver spoon. s8°. [1926]
Six short plays. [The first & the last—The little man—Hall-marked — Defeat — The sun—Punch & go]. s8°. [1921]
The skin-game. A tragi-comedy. s8°. [1920]
Tatterdemalion. s8°. 1920
„ „ [n. impr.] s8°. 1920
To let. s8°. 1921
Two Forsyte interludes. A silent wooing—Passers by. s8°. 1927
Verses new & old. s8°. 1926
The white monkey. s8°. [1924]
„ „ [n. impr.] s8°. [1924]
Windows: comedy. s8°. [1922]
see CHEVRILLON (A.) 3 ét. de litt. angl., J. G. &c., 1921; tr., 1923.
„ COATS (R. H.) J. G. as a dramatic artist, 1926.

Galt (John) [*ps. Rev.* M. BALWHIDDER].
Life of Lord Byron. 4th ed. s8°. 1832

Galton (*Sir* **Francis**). Art of travel. 8th ed. s8°. 1893
see PEARSON (K.) F. G., 1822–1922, 1922.
„ —— Life, letters &c. of F. G., v2, Researches of middle life, 1924.

Galuppi (Baldassare), *see* WOTQUENNE (A.) B. G., 1706–85: ét bibliog. sur s. œ. dramat., 1902.

Galvani (Luigi) [ALOYSIUS GALVANUS]. Abh. ü. d. Kräfte d. Electricität bei d. Muskel bewegung (1791). Hrsg. A. J. v. Oettingen. 8°. L. 1894

Galway, *see* UNIVERSITY COLLEGE, *Galway.*

Galzy (Jeanne). Sainte Thérèse d'Avila. 8°. 1927

Gamargo (Juan Gonzalez), *see* GONZALEZ GAMARGO (J.)

Gamba (Bartolommeo). Galleria dei letterati ed artisti più illust. d. provincie austro-venete [veneziane] nel sec. 18. 2v. [v1 *w. 2 tp.*] 8°. Venezia. 1824

Gamba (Carlo). Il Pontormo. s8°. Firenze. 1921

Gamba (Enrico), *1831–83, see* SAPORI (F.) Maestri, No. 22, 1920.

Gamba (*count* **Pietro**). A narr. of Lord Byron's last journey to Greece extr. f. journal of P. G. s8°. Paris. 1825

Gambara (Lattanzio), *see* NICOLI CRISTIANI (F.) Della vita e d. pitture di L. G., 1807.

Gambara (Laurentius).
Caprarola. [*b. w. h.* Venetiae, 1581]. s8°. Romae. 1581
Expositi. [*Tr. f.* Longus]. s8°. Romae. 1581
Venetiae. s8°. Romae. 1581

Gambara (Veronica). Rime e lettere. Racc. da F. Rizzardi. [Prefixed, Vita di V. G. *by* B. C. Zamboni]. 8°. Brescia. 1759
see RUSCELLI (G.) Rime di div. autori bresciani: V. G. &c., 1553.

Gambetta (Léon).
see DESCHANEL (P.) G., 1920.
„ STANNARD (H. M.) G. & the found. of the 3rd Republ., 1921.

Gambier, *The family of, see* HEATH (S. C. G.) Story of the G., 1924.

Gambier (Sarah Caroline Gore), *aft. wife of Cuthbert E. Heath, see* HEATH (*Mrs.* S. C. G.)

Gamble (James Sykes).
Flora of Madras. p4–7 [*pagin. cont.*] s8°. 1921–25

Gamble (John). Sketches of hist., politics, & manners in Dublin & the N. of Ireland, in 1810. n. ed. 8°. 1826

Gamble (Sidney David). Peking: social survey. By G., assisted by J. S. Burgess. Foreword by G. S. Eddy & R. A. Woods. 8°. [1921]

Gamble (William). Photography & its applic. s8°. [1920]
see MARTIN (L. C.) Colour &c., w. ch. on colour printing & photography by W. G., 1923.

Gamboa (José). Leyes constit. de Mexico dur. el s. 19. Disc. [*& apendice of acts &c.*] 8°. México. 1901

Gambold (John).
Works. Annexed, the life of the a. s8°. Bath. 1789

Gamillscheg (Ernst). Olten. Mundarten, *see* KAISERL. AKAD. D. W. ZU WIEN. Sitzungsber., B190, 1919.

Gamle. 100 " Gamle Bunde-regler " &c. (17–18c.), 1914, *see* KOLSRUD (O.)

Gammalfennoman, *ps., see* CHURBERG (WALDEMAR).

***Gammer** Gurtons nedle. By Mr. S[tevenson], Mr. of Art. Ed. H. F. B. Brett-Smith. s8°. O. 1920
„ „ *G. G.'s needle (1575) [by Wm. Stevenson], *see* ADAMS (J. Q.) Chief pre-Shakespearian dramas, 1925.

Ganander (Henricus).
Grammatica Lapponica. s8°. Holmiae. 1743

Ganay (Ernest de). Cœurs, concerts, couronnes. 8°. [1924]

Ganconagh, *ps., see* YEATS (W. B.)

Gandavo (Pedro de Magalhaens), *see* MAGALHAENS GANDAVO (P. DE).

Gandhi (Mohandas Karamchand). Speeches & writings. Intr. by C. F. Andrews, & biog. sketch. 3rd ed. s8°. Madras. [1922]
see CHATTERJEE (B. C.) Gandhi or Aurobindo?, 1921.
„ FÜLÖP-MILLER (R.) Lenin & G.; tr., 1927.
„ GRAY (R. M.) & M. C. PAREKH. Mahatma G.: essay in apprec., 1924.
„ NAIR (*Sir* C. S.) G. & anarchy, 1922.
„ ROLLAND (R.) Mahatma G., 1924; tr., 1924.

Gandolfo, *Persiano.* Libro del G. P. d. medesine de falconi. Publ. dal G. Ferraro. s8°. Bologna. 1877

Gandusio (Antonio), *see* VENEZIANI (C.) A. G., 1919.

Gandz (Salomon), *see* MONUMENTA Hebr. &c., B2, Recht; v. S. G., 1913–14.

Gane (Douglas M.) Tristan da Cunha. [Repr. f. the Empire Review]. [P2707]. la8°. [1923]

Gangaram, *Brahmin.* Trial of G. & Sew Prasad. (The shoes murder). Ed. A. Page, assisted by B. M. Sen. 8°. Calcutta. 1927

Ganghofer (Ludwig Albert). Almer u. Jägerleut. Neue Hochlandsgesch. 8e A. s8°. St. 1920
Der Dorfapostel. Hochlandsroman. 17.–18. A. s8°. St. 1913
Der hohe Schein. Roman. 58.–71. A. 2B. s8°. St. 1923
Oberland. Hochlandsgeschichten. 7e A. s8°. St. 1920

Ganilh (Charles). De la contre-révol. en France, *see* CONSTANT (B.) &c. Mél. polit. &c., t3, 1829.

Gann (Thomas William Francis). Anc. cities & mod. tribes: explor. &c. in Maya lands. 8°. [1926]
Maya cities. 8°. 1927
Mystery cities: explor. & adv. in Lubaantun. 8°. [1925]

Ganoe (*Maj.* **William Addleman**), *U.S. Army.*
Hist. of the U.S. army. 8°. N.Y. 1924

Ganpat, *ps., see* GOMPERTZ (M. L. A.)

Ganthois (Arnoldus de), *see* STAPLETON (T.) Tres Thomae &c.; adj. oratio funebris in laudem A. de G., 1588.

Ganz (Paul). La peinture suisse avant la Renaissance. Tr. P. Budry. fol. 1925

Ganzenmüller (Constanze), *née Hofmeister, see* GÖBEL (C. v.) Wilh. Hofmeister: work & life; w. biog. suppl. by Prof. G.; tr., 1926.

Gapon (Georgy). Ко всему крестьянскому люду. Воззваніе. [P2390]. s8°. [1905]
see GORKY (M.) 9ое января, *n.d.*

Gara. *La g. d. virtù ne'trionfi di Carlo, 1745, *see* CHARLES III, *of Spain* [*k. of Naples & Sicily*].

Garagashean, *see* KARAKASHEAN.

Garahan (Melbourne). Ship ahoy! s8°. 1922

Garaud (Marcel). L'abbaye Ste.-Croix de Talmond en Bas-Poitou, c. 1049–1250, d'après le cartul. Et. d'hist. écon. &c. du Poitou au m.-â. la8°. Poitiers. 1914

Garbarini (Giuseppe). Cenni stor. int. al borgo di Albisola Marina. 8°. Genova. 1886

Garbasso (Antonio). La Divina Commedia n. comm. d. scienziati ital., *see* DANTE: Lectura Dantis, 1915.

Garbe (Richard K.) Sāmkhya u. Yoga. [Grundr. d. indo-ar. Phil., B3, H4. *no tp.*] la8°. Str. 1896

Garbett (Edward).
The divine plan of revelation. Boyle Lect. 8º. 1864
García (Francisco Rodriguez), *see* RODRIGUEZ GARCÍA (F.)
Garcia (M. F. P. Viardot), *see* VIARDOT (*Mme.* PAULINE).
Garcia (Rodolpho). Dicc. de brasileirismos (pecul. pernambucanas), *see* INSTITUTO HIST. &C. BRAZIL. Rev., t76i, 1915.
Garcia (Zacharias). Bibl. patrum Latin. Hispan., nach d. Aufzeichnungen R. Beers bearbt. u. hrsg. v. G., 2i, 1915, *see* KAIS. AKAD. D. WISS. ZU W. Sitzb., B169, 1913.
García Carraffa (Alberto) & Arturo García Carraffa. Enciclopedia heraldica y genealogica Hispano-Americana. t1–31. 4º. [1919–28]
1, Dicc. de los términos del blasón, métodos &c.
2, 3, 5–31, Dicc. heráldico &c., 1–29.
4, Ciencia heráldica.
Lerroux. [Españoles ilust.] s8º. 1918
Garcia de la Foz (José). Crón. de la prov. de León, 1867, *see* ESPAÑA. Crón. gen., v6, 1865 &c.
García de Salazar (Lope). De las mem. que tiene la prov. de Guipúzcoa en obras inéd. de G. de S. &c., *see* FLORANES (R. DE). Supresion del obispado de Alaba &c., t2, 1920.
Garcia Icazbalceta (Joaquin). Cat. de la col. de mss. rel. a la hist. de America form. por J. G. I. Anot. y adic. por F. Gomez de Orozco. 8º. Mexico. 1927
Garcia Mercadal (J.)
España vista por los extranjeros. [v]2. s8º. [1919]
2, Rel. de viajeros y embajadores, s. 16.
Garcia Soriano (Justo). El humanista Francisco Cascales: vida y obras. [Real Acad. Esp.] la8º. 1924
Garcia Villada (Zacarias), *see* VILLADA (Z. G.)
García y Cubas (Antonio). Cuadro geogr. &c. de los Estados Unidos Mexicanos. 8º. México. 1885
Garcilaso de La Vega, *the Inca.* Comm. Reales, orígen de los Incas &c. Nueva ed. 2p *in* 4t. s8º. Madrid. 1829
see FITZMAURICE-KELLY (J.) El Inca G. de la V., 1921.
Garcilaso de La Vega, *the poet.* Works. Crit. text w. a bibliog. Ed. H. Keniston. [Hispanic Soc. of Amer.] s8º. N.Y. 1925
Las églogas, con las anot. de Herrera. s8º. Paris. [1913]
see KENISTON (R. H.) G. de la V.: crit. st. of h. life & works, 1922.
,, MENÉNDEZ Y PELAYO (M.) Antología de poetas líricos castellanos, t14, Boscán y G., con estudio crít. por J. Rogerio Sánchez, 1916.
Garczyński (Stefan).
Poezye. [Bibl. pisarzy polsk., t1]. s8º. Lipsk. 1863
Gardane (*le cte.* **Alfred de).** Mission du gén. Gardane en Perse. Doc. publ. par s. fils, A. de G. 8º. 1865
Gardane (*le cte.* **Claude Matthieu de).**
see GARDANE (*le cte.* A. DE). Miss. du gén. G. en Perse; publ. par s. fils, 1865.
,, TANCOIGNE (J. M.) Narr. of a journey into Persia [*under G.*]; f. the Fr., 1820.
Gardeners, Company of, *London, see* WELCH (C.) Hist. of Co. of Gardeners, 2nd ed., 1900.
Gardenin (Yu.) Юбилей Николая послѣдняго (1894–1904). [P810]. s8º. *n.p. n.d.*
Gardening. Pictorial guide to g. By the ed. of "Garden Life." [2nd ed.] s8º. *n.d.*
Studies in g.: articles repr. f. the Times, 1908, *see* STUDIES.
Gardes d'honneur. Régiments de gardes d'honneur, 1813–14: notes & doc., 1894, *see* RÉGIMENTS.
Gardiner (Alan Henderson).
Egyptian grammar: intr. to st. of hieroglyphs. 4º. O. 1927
The tomb of Amenemhēt. Copied by N. de G. Davies, w. explan. text by A. H. G. [Egypt. Explor. Fund. Theban Tombs Ser., Mem. 1]. 4º. 1915
The tomb of Ḥuy, Viceroy of Nubia in reign of Tut'Ankhamūn. Copied by N. de G. Davies, w. explan. text by A. H. G. [Egypt. Explor. Fund. Theban Tombs Ser., Mem. 4]. 4º. 1926.
see EGYPTIAN. Admonitions of an Egypt. sage, f. Hieratic papyrus in Leiden; [ed.] A. H. G., 1909.
Gardiner (Alfred George) [*ps.* ALPHA OF THE PLOUGH].
Certain people of importance. 8º. [1926]
John Benn & the progressive movement. 8º. 1925
Life of George Cadbury. 8º. 1923
Life of Sir W. Harcourt, 1827–1904. 2v. 8º. 1923
The War lords. s8º. [1915]
Gardiner (C. H.) *Centurions of a century, am. wh. are many who soldiered in the 12th, or Suffolk Regt. of Foot, 1743–1902. 8º. [1911]
Gardiner (Dorothy). Canterbury. s8º. [1923]
Gardiner (Edward Norman).
Olympia, its hist. & remains. la8º. O. 1925
Gardiner (Frederic John). Hist. of Wisbech & neighbourhood, 1848–98. la8º. Wisbech. 1898
Gardiner (*Col.* **James),** *see* DODDRIDGE (P.) Passages in life of G., n. ed., 1807.
see JACKSON (T.) Lib. of Xtn. biog., v6, J. G., by P. Doddridge, 1838.
Gardiner (Linda), *see* HUDSON (W. H.) Rare, vanishing &c. Brit. birds; comp. f. notes of H. by L. G., 1923.
Gardiner (Ralph), *of Chirton.* Englands grievance in rel. to the coal trade. 8º. Newcastle. 1796
Gardiner (*Sir* **Robert William).**
Is England a military nation or not? 2nd ed. 8º. 1857
National defence. 2nd ed. 8º. 1860
Polit. & legislative consider. on nat. defence. [*b. w.* Malins (W.) Plan, 1848]. 8º. 1860
The position of the R.A. of the Brit. Army; added, obs. on legisl. milit. econ. &c. 2nd ed. 8º. 1858
Gardiner (Samuel Rawson).
The first two Stuarts &c., 1603–60. s8º. 1876
Gardiner (Stephen), *bp. of Winchester.* De vera obedientia. An oration made in Latine by Stephā., bp. of W. With the pref. of E. Bonner t. true obedience. 8º. Rome [*or rather* London, *H. Singleton*]. 1553
Stephani Winton. ad M. Bucerum de impudenti eiusdem pseudologia conquestio. s4º. Coloniae, *Melchior Novesian.* 1545
see BUCER (M.) Gratulatio ad Eccl. Angl. de relig. Christi restit.; et Responsio ejusdem ad duas S. epistolas, 1548.
,, CRANMER (T.) Answer unto a cavillation devised by S. G. &c., 1551.
,, JOYE (G.) G. J. confuteth Winchester; false articles, 1543.
,, MULLER (H. A.) S. G. & the Tudor reaction, 1926.
Gardiner (William), *A.L.S.* The flora of Forfarshire. 8º. 1848
Gardiner (William), *murderer.* The Peasenhall murder. [Trial of W. G.] Repr. f. "Eastern Morning Gazette." 4º. [Norwich]. 1902
The Peasenhall murder case. Re-trial of W. G. at Suffolk Assizes, Jan. 1903. Repr. f. "The Eastern Daily Press." [*b. w.* Gardiner (W.) The Peasenhall murder, 1902]. la8º. [Norwich]. 1903
Gardner (Alice). Hist. of sacrament in rel. to thought & progress. s8º. 1921
Short hist. of Newnham Coll., Camb. s8º. C. 1921
Gardner (Charles). William Blake, the man. 8º. 1919
Gardner (Daniel), *see* WILLIAMSON (G. C.) D. G., painter in pastel &c.: h. life & works, 1920.
Gardner (Edmund Garratt).
The national idea in Italian lit. s8º. M'ter. 1921
Tommaso Campanella & h. poetry. [P2717]. 8º. O. 1923
Gardner (Eric), *see* CRAWFORD (O. G. S.) & A. KEILLER. Wessex f. the air; w. contrib. by G. &c., 1928.
Gardner (Ernest Arthur). The art of Greece. 8º. 1925
Gardner (George Lawrence Harter), *archdeacon of Cheltenham,* **& S. H. Nicholson.** Manual of Eng. church music. [*By var. wr.*] Ed. G. & N. 8º. 1923
Gardner (Helen).
Art through the ages: hist. & significance. 8º. 1927
Gardner (James).
The faiths of the world; a dict. &c. la8º. [1858–60]
Gardner (John Starkie). Ironwork. p3. s8º. 1922
3, Artistic working of iron in Gt. Brit. f. earliest times.
Gardner (Monica M.)
Kościuszko: a biography. s8º. [1920]
The patriot novelist of Poland, H. Sienkiewicz. 8º. 1926
Gardner (Percy).
Modernism in the English Ch. s8º. [1926]
New chapters in Greek art. 8º. O. 1926
Pract. basis of Xtn. belief. 8º. 1923
Gardner (Robert). The Via Claudia Valeria, *see* BRIT. SCHOOL AT ROME. Papers, v9, 1920.
Gardner (Samuel).
A guide to Eng. Gothic architecture. 4º. C. 1922
Gardner-Smith (Percival).
The narratives of the Resurrection. s8º. [1926]
Gardthausen (Victor). Das alte Monogramm. 4º. L. 1924
Handbuch d. wiss. Bibliothekskunde. 2B. 8º. L. 1920
Gareth (Benedetto), *called Il Chariteo.* Tutte le opere volg. di Chariteo. Sonetti, canzoni &c. 8º. [Napoli, *S. Mayr.* 1509]
Garfield (James Abram), *president of the U.S., see* SMITH (T. C.) Life & letters of J. A. G., 2v, 1925.

Garforth. The register of the parish church of G., Co. York, 1631-1812. Transcr. by G. D. Lumb. [Yorks. Parish Reg. Soc., 46]. 8º. *p.p.* [Leeds]. 1913

Gargàno (Giuseppe S.) Scapigliatura ital. a Londra sotta Elisabetta e Giacomo I. s8º. Firenze. 1923

Gargiulo (Raffaelle), *see* MUSEO NAZIONALE. Racc. de' monumenti, publ. da R. G., 1825.

Gariazzo (Pier Antonio), *see* BARTLETT (J. R.) P. A. G. & his works, 1926.

Garibaldi (*gen.* Giuseppe).
see LUZIO (A.) G., Cavour &c., 1924.
,, SMITH (G. B.) Heroes of the 19th c.: Wellington, G. &c., 1899.
,, TREVELYAN (G. M.) G. & the making of Italy, 6th impr., 1919.

Garibay y Zamálloa (Estevan de). Compendio hist. de las chronicas &c. de todos los reynos d'España. [lib. 11-20]. sfol. Anvers. 1571

Garin (N.), *ps.* [*i.e.* NIK. GEORG. MIKHAILOVSKY]. Деревенская драма, *see* SBORNIK. Сб. товар. "Знаніе," 1, 1904.

Garkavi (Abraham Elijah), *see* HARKAVY (A. E.)

Garland (A) of old hist. ballads, 1600-1752: Marie Hamilton—Rob Oig—Willy & Mary, *see* AUNGERVYLE SOC. Reprints, s1, 1881.

Garland (Hamlin). A son of the middle border. s8º. [1917]

Garland (John). Morale scolarium. Ed., w. intr. &c. by L. J. Paetow. fol. Berkeley, *Cal.* 1927

Garland (Richard). *Tour (A) in Teesdale incl. Rokeby &c. 4th ed. s8º. Barnard Castle. 1828

Garland (Robert), *see* WINKLES (H.) & B. WINKLES. Architect. &c. illust. of cathedral churches of Eng. & Wales: drawings f. sketches by R. G., 3v, 1836-42.

Garle (Hubert). A driving tour in the Isle of Wight. Ed. P. Fairclough. 8º. Newport. 1905

Garlick (Phyllis L.) Uganda contrasts. s8º. 1927

Garneau (François Xavier). Hist. du Canada. 5e éd., rev., annot. &c. par H. Garneau. Préf. de G. Hanotaux. t2. 8º. 1920

Garner (James Wilford).
Internat. law & the World War. 2v. 8º. 1920
Prize law dur. the World War, 1914-24. 8º. N.Y. 1927

Garnerius, *de Rochefort, bp. of Langres* [GARNIER]. *Contra Amaurianos [*attr. to G.*] Neu hrsg. v. C. Bäumker. [Beitr. z. Gesch. d. Phil. d. Ma., 24]. 8º. Münster. 1926

Garnet (Henry). A true & perfect rel. of the whole proc. agst. the traitors, G. & h. confederats. And G.'s execution. s4º. 1606
see EUDÆMON-JOANNES (A.) Ad actionem proditoriam E. Coqui, apologia pro H. Garneto, 1610.
,, RULE (W. H.) Celebr. Jesuits, v1, 1852.

Garnet (William), *c. 1390-1465, sergeant at law, see* BEAMONT (W.) Notes on Eng. judges, Nº. 1, 1883.

Garnett (A. Campbell). Instinct & personality. 8º. 1928

Garnett (David). Go she must! s8º. 1927
Lady into fox. Illust. w. wood engravings by R. A. Garnett. [3rd impr.] s8º. 1923
A man in the Zoo. [2nd impr.] s8º. 1924
The sailor's return. s8º. 1925

Garnett (Edward).
Friday nights: lit. crit. & apprec. s1. s8º. [1922]

Garnett (James Clerk Maxwell). Education & world citizenship: essay tow. a sci. of educ. la8º. C. 1921

Garnett (John), *bp. of (1) Leighlin & Ferns, (2) Clogher.* A diss. on Job. Added: Four sermons &c. 4º. 1749

Garnett (*Mrs.* R. S.), *form. Martha Roscoe.*
Samuel Butler & h. family relations. 8º. 1926

Garnett (Richard), *of the Brit. Mus., the younger.*
The age of Dryden. [repr.] s8º. [1927]
The twilight of the gods & o. t. [n. & augm. ed., 3rd impr.] s8º. 1911
,, ,, ...[n. & augm. ed., 4th impr.] s8º. [1924]
see DOWDEN (E.), R. G. &c. Letters about Shelley, 1917.

Garnett (William). A little book on water supply. 8º. C. 1922

Garnier, *de Pont Sainte-Maxence* [GUERNES DE P. STE. M. †GUERNES DEL PUNT]. La vie de Saint Thomas le Martyr. Poème hist. du 12 s. (1172-74). Publ. E. Walberg. [Kungl. Human. Vetenskapssamf. i Lund, Skr. 5]. la8º. Lund. 1922

Garnier, *de Rochefort, see* GARNERIUS.

Garnier (Athanase). *Mém. sur la cour de Louis Napoleon & sur la Hollande. ["Mémoires contemp." pl. *sometimes attrib. to Louis Garnier*]. 8º. 1828

Garnier (Joseph), *archiviste de la ville de Dijon, ed., see* BOURGOGNE. Chartes de communes &c. en B., 3t, 1867-77; Intr. de J. G. &c., 1918.

Garnier (Louis). *Mém. sur la cour de Louis Nap. &c. *sometimes attrib. to L. G.*, 1828, *see* GARNIER (ATHANASE).

Garnier (Paul Louis). Lydia, de Tunis. Roman. s8º. 1919

Garnier (Robert). Œuvres compl., théâtre & poésies, avec notice &c. par L. Pinvert. 2t. s8º. 1923

Garnier (Russell M.) Land agency. 8º. 1891

Garofoli (Gabriello), *see* SORDINI (G.) Il sepolcro di G. da Spoleto, 1895.

Garran (*Hon.* Andrew). Picturesque atlas of Australasia. [*By var. a.*] Ed. A. G. 3v. lafol. Sydney. 1886

Garrard (Apsley Cherry-), *see* CHERRY-GARRARD (A.)

Garrett (A. E.), *B.Sc.* Advance of photography. 8º. 1911

Garrett (Agnes), *see* GARRETT (R.) & A. G. Suggestions for house decor., 6th ed., 1879.

Garrett (Garet).
Ouroboros or the mechanical extension of mankind. s8º. [1927]

Garrett (João Baptista da Silva Leitão, *visc.* **de Almeida).** Frei Luís de Sousa—Um auto de Gil Vicente. [*Plays*]. Ed. 2º, com. pref. de T. Braga. s8º. Porto. *n.d.*
Romanceiro. [Obras compl., t4, 14, 15]. 3v (1, 5a ed.; 2, 3, 3a ed.) s8º. Lisboa. 1900-01
Viagens na minha terra. s8º. *n.d.*
Brother Luiz de Sousa. Eng. by E. Prestage. s8º. 1909

Garrett (Rhoda) & Agnes Garrett.
Suggestions for house decor. 6th ed. s8º. 1879

Garrett (Walter), *vicar of Titchfield &c.*
A disc. conc. Antichrist &c. s8º. 1680

Garrettson (Freeborn), *1752-1827, see* JACKSON (T.) Lib. of Xtn. biog., v. 7 & 8, F. G., by N. Bangs, 1838.

Garrick Club. Rules &c. of the Garrick Club. With list of members. s8º. 1917

Garrick (David). Country girl, *see* INCHBALD (*Mrs.* E.) Brit. theatre, v16, 1808.
The lying valet—A peep behind the curtain—Bon Ton. 3 farces. Ed., w. intr. by L. B. Osborn. s8º. New Haven, *Yale.* 1925
see COLMAN (G.) & D. G. Clandestine marriage, 1808.
,, REYNOLDS (*Sir* J.) Johnson & G.: 2 dialogues, 1927.

Garrido (Antonio). Floresta Española. 4a ed. s8º. Londres. 1827

Garrison (Fielding Hudson). Intr. to the hist. of medicine. 3rd ed., rev. & enl. 8º. Phila. 1922
see WOOD (C. A.) & F. H. G. A physician's anthology &c., 1920.

Garrod (*Sir* Archibald Edward). The debt of science to medicine. [Harveian oration, 1924]. 8º. O. 1924

Garrod (D. A. E.)
The upper palaeolithic age in Britain. 8º. O. 1926

Garrod (Heathcote Wm.) Keats. 8º. O. 1926
Milton's lines on Shakespeare, *see* ENG. ASSOC. Essays, v12, 1926.
Wordsworth: lects. & essays. s8º. O. 1923
,, ,, ...2nd ed. enl. s8º. O. 1927

Garrold (Richard Philip), *S.J., see* MARTINDALE (C. C.) R. P. G., Memoir, 1921.

Garshin (Vsevolod Mikhailovich). Избранные разсказы. [What never happened—The meeting—The signal—Four days]. s8º. O. [1920]

Garside (Joshua T.) Old Eng. furniture: from Tudor times to the Regency. Div. 1 (1, Oak period, 1500-1630). 8º. [1924]

Garstang (Walter). Songs of the birds. Illust. by J. A. Shepherd. s8º. 1922

Garstin (Crosbie). The ballad of the "Royal Ann." s8º. 1922
The Owls' House. s8º. 1923
The West wind. s8º. [1926]

Gart (Ein) d. Gesuntheit (1485); facs., 1924, *see* CUBE (J. v.)

Garth (*Sir* Samuel). *The dispensary; a poem. 8º. 1699
,, ,, ...3rd ed. 8º. 1699
Poet. works. Coll. by T. Park. s8º. 1808

Gartlan (P. M. E.) An hist. sketch of the Irish state prosecution. [P2554]. 8º. D. 1844

Gartner (Theodor). Ladinische Wörter aus d. Dolomitentälern, zusammengest. u. durch e. Samml. v. Hermes Fezzi verm. [Zeitschr. f. roman. Philol., Beiheft 73]. 8º. Halle (Saale). 1923

Garufi (Carlo Alberto). Contrib. alla storia dell' Inquis. di Sicilia nei sec. 16 e 17, *see* SOCIETÀ SICILIANA. Archivio, N.S., 43, 1921.

Garvin (*Mrs.* J. L.) [*ps.* " V "]. As you see it. s8°. [1922]

Garvin (*Mrs.* John W.), *see* HALE (K.)

Gascó Contell (Emilio). Blasco Ibáñez. 8°. Paris. [1925]

Gascoigne (George). A hundreth sundrie flowres. Fr. orig. ed. (1572). [Intr. by B. M. Ward. The Haslewood Bks.] 8°. 1926

Supposes: comedie by Ariosto; Engl. by G. (1566), *see* ADAMS (J. Q.) Chief pre-Shakespearian dramas, 1925.

see WHETSTONE (G.) Metrical life of G. (1577), repr., 1815.

Gascoin (Eugène). Au seuil de la vie secrète, choses vues, *see* ŒUVRES libres, 70, 1927.

Gascón y Guimbao (Domingo).

Rel. de escrit. de la provincia de Teruel. 8°. Zaragoza. 1908

Gaselee (Stephen).

An anthology of medieval Latin. s8°. 1925

The early Spanish printing press. Lect. [P2768]. la8°. 1924

List of early printed bks. in poss. of S. G. [*w. Ms. note of addit. to 1924.* P2768]. la8°. C. 1920

The Oxford book of medieval Latin verse. s8°. O. 1928

The Spanish books in the library of Samuel Pepys. [Suppl. to Bibl Soc.'s Trans., No. 2]. 8°. O. 1921

Stories f. the Xtn. East. 8°. 1918

The Uniats & th. rites. [Alcuin Club Tracts, 16]. 8°. [1925]

see CAMBRIDGE: CORPUS CHRISTI COLL. Early pr. bks. in Lib. of C.C. Coll.: hand-list &c.; comp. by S. G., 1921.

Gaskell (*Mrs.* Eliz. Cleghorn).

Works. [Knutsford ed.] With intr. by A. W. Ward. [repr.] v1, 2, 8. s8°. 1919–20

1, Mary Barton & o. tales.

2, Cranford & o. tales.

8, Wives & daughters.

Life of C. Brontë. s8°. 1871

" ,, Intr. & notes by T. Scott & B. W. Willett. 8°. 1901

Mary Barton. n. ed. s8°. 1882

Ruth. n. ed. s8°. 1880

Sylvia's lovers. n. ed. s8°. 1883

Gaskell (G. A.) Dict. of the sacred language of all scriptures & myths. 8°. [1923]

Egyptian scriptures interpreted through the lang. of symbolism. s8°. [1926]

Genesis interpreted thr. lang. of symbolism. Chap. 1–9. s8°. [1925]

Gaskell (*Lt.-col.* James B.) Cat. of pictures &c., prop. of J. B. G., sold by Christie. [Illust. P2849]. 8°. 1926

Gaskell (N. Kynaston). The romantic career of a great criminal: Charles Peace. [*b. w.* Berry (J.) My exper., 1891]. s8°. 1906

Gaspari (Gaetano), *see* BOLOGNA: LICEO MUSIC. Cat. d. bibl. d. L.M.; comp. da G. G., 1890–93.

Gasparin (*le cte.* Agénor de).

Luther & la Réforme au xvie siècle. s8°. 1873

Gasparotto (Luigi), *see* GIORDANO (O.) L'on. L. G., 1919.

Gasquet (Amédée).

Essai sur le culte & les mystères de Mithra. 8°. 1899

Gasquet (*card.* Francis Aidan). Card. Pole & h. early friends [*i.e.* N. Leonico Tomeo &c.] s8°. 1927

Eng. monastic life. 2nd ed. rev. 8°. 1904

The mission of St. Augustine & o. addresses. s8°. 1924

Monastic life in the Middle Ages, w. note on Gt. Brit. & the Holy See, 1792–1806. s8°. 1922

Relig. life of Henry VI. s8°. 1923

Gasquet (Joachim). Cézanne. la4°. 1921

see PLÉIADE (LA): [*poems by* Ctsse. de Noailles, J. G., &c.], 1921.

Gass (W.) Gennadius u. Pletho, Aristotelismus u. Platonismus in d. griech. Kirche &c. 2 Abt. [*in* 1v]. 8°. Breslau. 1844

Gassen (Kurt). Sibylle Schwarz, eine pommersche Dichterin, 1621–38. 8°. Greifswald. 1921

Gassenko (Georges de). Feuille à ajouter au dict. " Larousse " au mot Ukraine. [P2419]. s8°. [1919]

Gasset (José Ortega y), *see* ORTEGA Y GASSET (J.)

Gassies des Brulies (G.) Anthologie du théâtre fr. au m. âge. Arr. en fr. mod. par G. G. s8°. 1925

Gaster (Moses). Exempla of the Rabbis: coll. of e., apologues &c. f. Hebrew MSS. &c. [*& text w. sep. tp. & pagin.*] 8°. 1924

The Ketubah. 8°. Berlin. 1923

The Samaritans: hist., doctrines & lit. [Brit. Acad.: Schweich lect., 1923]. 8°. 1925

Yiddish lit. of the M.A., *see* ROY. SOC. OF LIT. Essays, N.S., v7, 1927.

see ASATIR. Samaritan bk. of the "Secrets of Moses" &c.; intr., tr. &c., by M. G., 1927.

,, PATRIARCHS. Hebr. text of 1 of the Test. of the 12 patr., by M. G., 1894.

Gaston *de Foix, duc de Nemours, 1489–1512, see* NEMOURS (GASTON DE FOIX, *duc* DE).

Gaston-Dreyfus (Philippe). Cat. raisonné de l'œuvre de N. B. Lépicié, *see* SOC. DE L'HIST. DE L'ART FRANÇ. Bull., 1922.

Gastoué (Amédée).

Les primitifs de la musique franç. s8°. [1922]

Gastrell (Francis), *bp. of Chester.* *Lettre d'un évesque anglois à Mgr. le card. de Noailles. [*no tp.* P2659]. s8°. *n.p. n.d.* [c. 1718]

Gataker (Thomas), *B.D.*, *see* RYSSEN (L. VAN). Veritas de lusu aleae, ab impugnationibus T. G. vindic., 1660.

Gatari (Andrea), *see* GATARI (G.) & B. G. Cronaca carrarese; confront. con la red. di A. C., 1920.

Gatari (Bartolomeo), *see* GATARI (G.) & B. G. Cronaca carrarese, 1920.

Gatari (Galeazzo) & Bart. Gatari. Cronaca carrarese, confront. con la redaz. di A. Gatari, 1318–1407; a cura di A. Medin e G. Tolomei, v1, *see* MURATORI (L. A.) Rerum Ital. scr., t17i, 1920.

Gatell (José Ildefonso), *see* VILARRASA Y COSTA (E. M.) & J. I. G. Hist. de la Revol. de Setiembre, t1, 1875.

Gates (Barrington). The Mulligatawny Medallion & 4 o. sh. plays. s8°. 1926

Gates (Frederick Taylor). The truth about Mr. Rockefeller & the Merritts. [P2619]. 8°. [1912]

Gates (Reginald Ruggles).

A botanist in the Amazon valley. 8°. 1927

Heredity & eugenics. 8°. 1923

Gathorne-Hardy (Geoffrey Malcolm). Bodø-saken. Brit. diplom. corresp. extr. f. Pub. Rec. Off. records. [Kjeldeskriftfondet]. 8°. Oslo. 1926

The Norse discoverers of America: the Wineland sagas, tr. & discussed. 8°. O. 1921

Norway. 8°. 1925

Om 'eykt'-peilingen på Leifs Vinlandsreise. [Særtryk av Maal og minne, 1924. P2769]. 8°. 1924

Gatinais, *see* SOCIÉTÉ HIST. & ARCH. DU G.

Gätschenberger (Stephan), *see* KULLMANN (E. F. L.) Prozess K., v. S. G., 1874.

Gattaker (Thomas), *B.D.*, *see* GATAKER (T.)

Gatteyrias (Joseph André).

L'Arménie & les Arméniens. [P2806]. s8°. 1882

Gatti (Giuseppe). Ogetti scop. n. scavi d. Stadio Palatino, *see* REALE ACCAD. D. LINCEI. Mon. ant., v5, 1895.

see ROMA. Statuti dei mercanti di R.; pubbl. da G. G., 1885.

Gattinara (*Card.* Mercurino Arborio, *conte* di), *see* ARBORIO (*Card.* M.)

Gattinoni (Gregorio). El campaniel de Sa' Marco. [P2839]. s8°. Venezia. 1902

Gatty (*Mrs.* Alfred). Parables from nature. [repr.] s8°. [1911]

Gatty (Alfred Scott), *see* ECCLESFIELD. Marriage &c. reg. of E. parish church, Yorks., 1558–1619; annot. by A. S. G., 1878.

Gatty (Charles T.)

Mary Davies & the Manor of Ebury. 2v. 8°. 1921

Gatty (Ivor). Edgar. s8°. 1923

Gauchez (Maurice), *ps.* [*i.e.* MAURICE GILLES]. Hist. des lettres franç de Belgique, des orig. à nos jours. 2e éd. la8°. Brux. 1922

Romantiques d'aujourd'hui: essais. 8°. Brux. 1924

Gauckler (E.), *see* DEJERINE (J.) & E. G. The psychoneuroses & their treatment; tr., 2nd Eng. ed., 1915.

Gauckler (Paul). Nécropoles puniques de Carthage. Intr. par D. Anziani. 2p [*pagin. cont.*] la8°. 1915

Gaud (Fernand) & C. van Overbergh. Les Mandja (Congo français). Sociologie descriptive. 8°. Brux. 1911

Gaudart (Edmond), *see* PONDICHÉRY. Cat. des mss. des anc. archives de l'Inde franç., t2, publ. avec. intr. par E. G., 1924.

Gaudefroy-Demombynes (Maurice). Le pèlerinage à la Mekke; ét. d'hist. relig. [Annales du Mus. Guimet, Bibl. d'ét., 33]. 8°. 1923

La Syrie à l'époque des Mamelouks [*i.e.* El' Omari, Qalqachandi &c.] Descr. géogr., écon. &c. préc. d'une intr. [Haut-Comm. de la Républ. Fr. en Syrie &c. Services des Antiq. &c. Bibl. arch. &c., t3]. la8°. 1923

Gauden (John), *bp. of (1) Exeter, (2) Worcester.* Ἀνάλυσις. The loosing of St. Peter's bands; sense &c. of the Covenant &c. so far as it relates to episcopacy. [P2662]. s4°. 1660

Gauden (John) [*continued*].
A sermon at the funeral of Dr. Brounrig. W. an acc. of h. life &c. [*w. sep. tp., reading:* The memorials &c. of Dr. B., *pagin. cont.*] s8º. 1660
see CROFTON (Z.) 'Ανάληψις ἀνελήφθη, fastning of St. Peter's fetters &c., 1660.
Gaudenzio (Paganino) [GAUDENTIUS]. De errore sectariorum hujus temp.—Conatus in Genesin.—De philosoph. opinion. vet. eccl. patrum. Opusc. 3. [*b. w. h.* De philos., 1643]. s4º. Pisis. 1644
De philosophiae apud Romanos initio & progressu. s4º. Pisis. 1643
Gaudin (Martin M. C.), *duc de Gaëte.* Mém., souvs., opinions &c. Réimpr. de la prem. éd. de 1826. 3t. 8º. 1926
t3, Suppl. aux Mém., réimpr. de la prem. éd. de 1834.
Gaudioso (Teresita). Il giornalismo lett. in Toscana, 1848–59. la8º. Firenze. 1922
Gaufrey, *le Vaillant.* Gaufrey, chanson de geste, *see* GUESSARD (F.) Anc. poëtes, t3, 1859.
Gaufridi (Jean François de), *baron de Tretz.*
Hist. de Provence. 2t [*pagin. cont.*] fol. Aix. 1694
Gaufridus, *de Vino Salvo, see* GEOFFROY, *de Vinsauf.*
Gauger (Nicolas). Fires improv'd: new method of building chimneys to prevent smoaking &c. Eng. by J. T. Desaguliers. s8º. 1713
Gauguin (Paul).
Avant & après. 8º. 1923
Lettres à G. D. de Monfreid. Préc. d'un hommage par V. Segalen. s8º. 1920
Noa noa. [Voyage de Tahiti]. éd. défin. 8º. 1924
see DORSENNE (J.) Vie sentimentale de P. G., 1927.
,, REY (R.) G., 1923: tr., 1924.
Gaujoux (Émile), *see* BROMBERGER (A.) & E. G. Aix-en-Provence, 1924.
Gaulis (Berthe Georges-), *see* GEORGES-GAULIS (B.)
Gaulot (Paul). Le Foyer de la Comédie Française, 1870–1900: souv. &c. 8º. [1926]
Gaultier (Paul). Les maîtres de la pensée franç. P. Hervieu —E. Boutroux—H. Bergson—M. Barrès. s8º. 1921
Gaument (Jean) & Camille Cé.
La grand'route des hommes. s8º. 1923
Gaunt (Mary), *ps.* [*i.e. Mrs.* H. LINDSAY MILLER].
The surrender & other happenings. s8º. [1920]
Where the twain meet. 8º. 1922
Gaunt (William). Eng. rural life in the 18th cent. Foreword by C. R. Grundy. [The Connoisseur series]. 4º. 1925
Rome past & present. Text by W. G. Ed. G. Holme. [Studio. Spec. Spring No.] la8º. 1926
Gausbert, *de Puycibot, see* JAUSBERT.
Gauss (Carl). Reformationsversuche in d. Basler Bischofsstadt Pruntrut. [Verein f. Ref.-Gesch. Schr., Jhrg. 31 (Nr. 114)]. 8º. L. 1913
Gauss (Carl Friedrich). Werke. Hrsg. v. d. Königl. Gesellschaft d. Wiss. zu Göttingen. B1–11ii. [1–5, 2er Abdr. 10, 11 *have* 2 Abt.] 4º. Göttingen. 1870–1927
Abt. 2 *of* B10 & 11 *cont.* Materialien f. e. wiss. Biog. v. Gauss [*by var. a^s. sep. pagin^s.*]
Gaussen (S. R. Louis). The canon of the Holy Scr. [Tr.] 2nd ed. 8º. 1863
Gautheret-Comboulot (—). Les auteurs beaunois du 16e au 19e s. 2e éd. 8º. Beaune. 1893
Gautherot (Gustave).
La France en Syrie & en Cilicie. s8º. 1920
Un gentilhomme de grand chemin: le maréchal de Bourmont (1773–1846). 8º. 1926
see BUCHOT (A.) & C. G. G. Hist. de P. Vaux, 1889.
Gauthier (Henri). Le Livre des rois d'Egypte; rec. par H. G., t3–5, *see* INSTITUT FRANÇ. D'ARCH. OR. DU CAIRE. Mém., t19–21, 1914–17.
Sur une tombe réc. découv. à Athribis du Delta, *see* ACAD. D. INSCR.: FOND. PIOT. Mon, t25, 1921–22.
Le temple d'Amada. [Les temples immergés de la Nubie. Service des Antiq. de l'Egypte]. fol. Le Caire. 1913
Gauthier (Jules), *see* HUGUES *de Chalon.* Cartulaire (1220–1319); introd. par J. G., 1904.
Gauthier-Villars (Henry) [*ps.* WILLY].
Ça finit par un mariage. s8º. [1923]
see AUSSARESSES (F.) & H. G.-V. La vie privée d'un prince allemand; l'électeur palat. Charles-Louis, 1926.
Gauthiez (Pierre). Milan. [Les villes d'art]. la8º. 1909
Gautier (Charles). L'Angleterre & nous. s8º. 1922
Gautier (E. F.) L'Algérie & la Métropole. s8º. 1920
L'Islamisation de l'Afrique du Nord: les siècles obscurs du Maghreb. 8º. 1927
Gautier (Edmond), *registrar at Loches.*
Hist. du donjon de Loches. 8º. Chateauroux. 1881
Gautier (François de), *sieur de Saint Blancard.* *Hist. apologet., ou défense des libertez des églises réformées de France. [Epitre *signed* S. B., *i.e.* St.-Blancard]. 2t *in* 1v. s8º. Amsterdam. 1688
Gautier (Joseph). De hæresibus—De conciliis—De summis pontif.—De S. Patribus, *see* MIGNE (J. P.), *ed.* Theol. cursus, t5, 1841.
Gautier (Judith). Les parfums de la pagode. 2e mille. s8º. 1919
Gautier (P.) [†GUALTERUS (PHILIPPUS) *de Castellione, also called Walther v. Lille*]. Gedichte Walters v. Chatillon. Hrsg. &c. v. K. Strecker. [Bd.] 1, Die Lieder d. Hs. 351 v. St. Omer. 8º. 1925
Libelli 3 contra Judaeos. [P2684]. s8º. Lugd. Batav. 1692
Gautier (Paul). Anthologie de l'Académie Franç. Un siècle de Discours académ., 1820–1920. [Coll. Pallas]. 2t. s8º. 1921
Gautier (Théophile), *the elder.*
Mlle. de Maupin. n. éd. s8º. 1888
,, ,, ...n. éd. s8º. 1922
Les roués innocents. s8º. 1855
Voyage en Espagne (Tra los montes). n. éd. rev. & corr. s8º. 1914
Voyage en Russie. s8º. 1884
Gauvain (Auguste).
L'Europe au jour le jour [1908–20]. 14t. la8º. 1917–23
see LAVISSE (E.) Hist. de France contemp., t9, La Gr. Guerre; par H. Bidou, A. G. &c., 1922.
Gavan (John) [GAWEN], *see* WHITE (T.) Last speeches of the 5 traitors: J. G. &c., 1679.
Gavin (Antonio).
A master-key to popery. 2nd ed. 2v. s8º. 1725–26
Gavin (Frank I. B.)
The Jewish antecedents of the Xtn. sacraments. s8º. 1928
Gaviria (José Muñoz y), *see* MUÑOZ Y GAVIRIA (J.)
Gavrilin (I. A.) Почему некоторые крестьяне идут против советской власти &c. [P2723]. 8º. Москва. 1919
Gaw (Frances). Performance tests of intelligence, *see* INDUST. FATIGUE RES. BD. Rep. 31, 1925.
Gawaine. Sir Gawain & the Green Knight. Ed. J. R. R. Tolkien & E. V. Gordon. 8º. O. 1925
Sir Gawayne & the Green Knight. 1, Text. Re-ed. R. Morris. Rev. by I. Gollancz. [E. E. T. S., 4]. 8º. 1864 (1923)
see PEARL. Pearl, Cleanness, Patience & Sir Gawain; reprod. in facs.: intr. by Sir I. Gollancz, 1923.
Gawler (*Col.* George). Pres. state of moral princ. in supreme govt. of Brit. Colonial Emp. [P2832]. 8º. 1850
Gawthrop (Hugh). The Mersey & the ferries. s8º. Liv'l. 1853
Gay (Ernest). Paris héroïque: la Grande Guerre. Discours-préf. par M. Poincaré. 8º. 1920
Gay (George I.) Commission for Relief in Belgium. Statist. review, Nov. 1914–Aug. 1919. [Foreword by H. C. Hoover]. 4º. Stanford. [1925]
Gay (João Pedro). Hist. do Paraguay, *see* INSTITUTO HIST. E GEOG. BRAZIL. Revista, t26, 1863.
Gay (John), *the poet.*
The beggar's opera. [repr.] s8º. 1920
,, ,, 2nd ed.: added, ouverture in score [*w. sep. pagin.*] 8º. 1728
,, ,, *for an. ed., see* INCHBALD (*Mrs.* E.) Brit. theatre, v12, 1808.
Fables. [2p in 1v]. s8º. 1750
,, ,, ...2v [in 1]. 8º. 1757
,, ,, ...s8º. 1769
,, ,, Mem. by A. Dobson. s8º. 1882
Poems on sev. occasions. 2v. [v2 *wanting*]. s8º. 1753
Poet. works. Coll. by T. Park. 3v. s8º. 1806
,, ,, Incl. "Polly," "The beggar's opera" & sels. f. o. dram. wks. Ed. G. C. Faber. [The Oxford poets]. 8º. 1926
[Polly, an opera. Music added in lithograph]. [*W. sep. pagin.; tp. missing*]. 4º. [1729 ?]
,, ,, [*Music added in lithogr., w. sep. pagin.; no tp.*] s8º. 1729
Polly, an opera. Second part of the Beggar's opera. Foreword by O. Doughty. s8º. 1922
The Shepherd's week. Ed. H. F. B. Brett-Smith. s8º. O. 1924
*To a lady on her passion for old china (1725). [repr.] 8º. O. [1925]
Trivia: or, the art of walking the streets of London. Intr. & notes by W. H. Williams. la8º. 1922
24 portraits of orig. cast of The beggar's opera, produced at Lyric Theatre, Hammersmith, 5 June 1920. 8º. Hammersmith. [1920]
see KIDSON (F.) The Beggar's opera, its predecessors & successors, 1922.
,, MELVILLE (L.) Life & letters of G., 1921.

Gay (Joseph). The hoop-petticoat, 4th ed., *see* SCHOOL of Venus, 1739.
Gay (Jules), *membre de l'Ecole Franç. de Rome.*
Les papes du 11e siècle & la chrétienté. s8o. 1926
Gay (*Mme.* **Sophie)** [MARIE FRANÇOISE SOPHIE NICHAULT DE LAVALLETTE], *see* MALO (H.) Une muse & sa mère [Mme. S. G.]: D. Gay de Girardin, 1924.
Gayangos (Pascual de).
see PRESCOTT (W. H.) Letters to G. (1838–60), 1927.
„ TICKNOR (G.) Letters to P. de G., 1927.
Gayda (Virginio). Il crollo russo. Dallo zarismo al bolscevismo. s8o. Torino. 1920
Gaydon. Gaydon, chanson de geste, *see* GUESSARD (F.) Anc. poëtes, t7, 1862.
Gaydon (Harry A.) Art & science of the gramophone. s8o. 1926
Gayferos, *Don.* Romance de don G., c. 1515. With intr. & var. readings, ed. H. Thomas. [Early Span. ballads in B.M., 3]. 8o. 1927
Gayley (Charles Mills), *ed.* Representative Eng. comedies. With intr. essays &c. v3, Later contemp. of Shakespeare: Fletcher & o. s8o. N.Y. 1914
Gayton (Edmund). Pleasant notes upon Don Quixot. sfol. 1654
Gaza (Theodorus). Grammaticae instit. liber primus, sic trãslatus per Erasmum. Idem Graece, Colloquiorum familiarium incerto autore libellus Graece & Latine nunq̄ȝ antehac typis excusus. 3p. s4o. Basileae, *J. Frobenius.* 1516
Gazeau (Jacques). L'impérialisme anglais: Carlyle—Seeley—Chamberlain. la8o. 1903
Gazette (La) de tendre, *see* JOURNÉE des madrigaux (1653), 1856.
Gazette de France. Répert. hist. & biog. de la Gaz. de F., 1631–1790, 4t, 1902–06, *see* GRANGES DE SURGÈRES.
Gazette des beaux-arts. 5e pér., t1–17. la8o. 1920–28
see HYMANS (H.) Œuvres, v3. Un quart siècle de vie artist. en Belg.: 26 années de corresp. à la "Gaz. des Beaux-Arts," 1886–1912, 1920.
„ REINACH (S.) Monuments nouv. (Courriers de l'art ant. de la Gazette), t1, 2, 1924–25.
Gazette illustrée des amateurs de jardins. [*Publ. by* Soc. des Amateurs de Jardins]. 1913–14, 1920–27. [*No parts appeared 1915–19*]. la fol. 1913–27
Gazier (Augustin).
Hist. gén. du mouvement janséniste. 2t. s8o. 1922
Gdańsk [*see also* DANTZIG].
Gdańsk & East Prussia. [P2464]. 8o. Paris. 1919
Geary (Frank). Land tenure & unemployment. Pref. by A. S. Comyns Carr. 8o. [1925]
Gebauer (Johannes Heinrich).
Gesch. d. Stadt Hildesheim. 2B. 8o. Hildesheim. 1922–24
Gebet. Ein Gebet-Büchlein &c. z. Gebrauch d. Königl. Deut. Luther. Hof-Capelle zu St. James &c. s8o. London. 1757
Gebete d. hochdeutschen u. poln. Juden, 1815, *see* TEPHILOTH.
Gebhardi (Vitus Christianus). De chiliasmo ex Apocalypsi Joh. disq., studio V. C. G. s4o. Brunsvigae. 1691
Gebhardt [TRUCHSESS VON WALDBURG], *elector & abp. of Cologne, see* DIETERICH (E. G.) Ἱστορούμενα de actis &c. G., 1733.
Gebhardt (Albert). Polit. Gespräche. 1, Die Schuld am Weltkrieg. Nr. 5–8. [P2574]. s8o. [1921]
Gebhardt (Carl), *see* FREUDENTHAL (J.) Spinoza; hrsg. &c. C. G., 2T, 1927.
Gebhart (Emile). Mystics & heretics in Italy at end of the Middle ages. Tr., w. intr. by E. M. Hulme. 8o. [1922]
Gebrauch. *Von dem gebrauch der heilig. hochwirdig. Sacramenten &c., 1540, *see* BRANDENBURG.
Gebsattel (Ludwig *Frhr.* **v.)** Von Nancy bis z. Camp des Romains, 1914. [Schlachten d. Weltkrieges, B6]. 2. A. 8o. Oldenburg. 1924
Gechauf (Thomas), *surnamed Venatorius, see* SPALATIN (G.) Tröstung inn tods nöten, d. mehrern teils aus T. Venatorii Büchlin, c. 1530.
Gedde (John) [GEDDY], *see* MYLNE (R.) Mem. of J. G., 1837.
Geddes (Alexander) [*ps.* AN UPPER GRADUATE]. A modest apology for the Roman Catholics of Gt. Brit. 8o. 1800
A new tr. of the Book of Psalms. W. var. readings & notes. 8o. 1807
see EARLE (J.) Remarks on prefaces pref. to v1 & 2 of the Holy Bible, tr. by A. G., 1799.
Geddes (Alex. Ebenezer McLean).
Meteorology: intr. treatise. 8o. 1921
Geddes (John). Life of St. Margaret of Scotland, w. acc. of h. husband, Malcolm III &c. 8o. Aberdeen. 1794
Geddes (Michael). The church-hist. of Ethiopia. Add.: epitome of the Dominican hist. of that ch. & acc. of the practises of Maria of the Annunciation. 8o. 1696
The hist. of the Ch. of Malabar, f. 1501. With the Synod of Diamper celeb. in 1599. Done out of Portug. into Eng. by M. G. 8o. 1694
Misc. tracts. 2nd ed. 3v. s8o. 1714
Geddes (Patrick). Beginnings of a Survey of Edinburgh. [Repr. f. Scot. Geogr. Mag., v35. Soc. Review Suppl. 1. P2411]. 8o. 1919
The life & work of Sir Jagadis C. Bose. 8o. 1920
Public health in the indust. age, *see* PAPERS for the present, No. 6, 1919.
see SANDEMAN (G.) A gardener of paradise [*i.e.* P. G.], 1920 ?.
—— **& J. A. Thomson.** Biology [Home Univ. Lib.]. s8o. [1925]
Geddie (William), *M.A.*, *see* CHAMBERS, *publ. firm.* Encyclopaedia, n. ed., 1923–27.
Geddy (John), *see* GEDDE (J.)
Geden (Alfred Shenington). Sel. passages illustr. Mithraism. Tr., w. intr. by A. S. G. [Trans. of early doc.] s8o. 1925
Geden (John Dury). The doctrine of a future life as cont. in the Old Test. scr., 1874. 2nd ed. 8o. 1877
Gedik (Simon) [GEDICCUS (S.)] Von Bildern u. Altarn in d. Evangel. Kirchen Augspurg. Conf. Bericht, sampt Kurtzer Wiederlegung des Zerbest. Buchs &c. s4o. Magdeburgk. 1597
Gee (Edward). The divine right & original of the civill magistrate from God. s8o. 1658
A treatise of prayer & of divine providence &c. s8o. 1653
see PARSONS (R.) Jesuit's memorial, w. intr. &c. by E. G., 1690.
Gee (N. Gist), L. I. Moffett & G. D. Wilder. A tentative list of Chinese birds. [Peking Soc. of Nat. Hist., Bull., v1]. la8o. [Peking]. 1926
Geer, *The family of.* Ätten de Geer. Stamtaflor öfver samtliga dess grenar från äldsta till närvarande tid. [Intr. by E. W. Dahlgren]. 4o. Uppsala. 1920
Geer (*baron* **Lodewijk de),** *1587–1652.* Brieven, 1618–52 & Varia betreff. L. de G.; Kemkamp, *see* HISTORISCH GENOOTS. Bijdragen, d. 29, 1908.
see DAHLGREN (E. W.) L. de G., h. lif & verk, 2d, 1923.
Geer (William Chauncey). The reign of rubber. 8o. [1922]
Geeraert, *van Leyden, see* GERARDUS, *van Harlem.*
Geering (Thomas). Our Sussex parish [Hailsham]. Intr. by A. Beckett. [repr.] 8o. [1925]
1st publ. in 1884 w. title: Our parish, a medley; By one who has never been out of it. *Title page bore initials* T. G. H. [*i.e.* T. Geering, Hailsham].
Geertgen, *tot Sint Jans, see* GERARDUS, *van Harlem.*
Geertruydenberg Negociation. *Secret hist. of the G. Negoc. w. sev. orig. papers. Prefix'd 2 letters to R. Harley &c. Done out of French. 8o. 1712
Geeves (George). *Status eccl. Gallicanae: or the eccl. hist. of France. By the a. of the late Hist. of the Church of Gt. Brit. [2p *in* 1v]. s4o. 1676
Geffcken (Johannes). Das Christentum im Kampf u. Ausgleich mit d. griech.-röm. Welt. 3e. umgearb. A. s8o. L. 1920
Kaiser Julianus. la8o. L. 1914
Geffroy (Gustave).
Cécile Pommier. 2p. s8o. 1923
Charles Meryon. la8o. 1926
Claude Monet, sa vie, s. temps, s. œuvre. s4o. 1922
La comédie bourgeoise. s8o. 1922
Constantin Guys, l'hist. du Second Emp. s4o. 1920
L'enfermé [*i.e.* L. A. Blanqui]. 2t. 8o. 1926
Images du jour & de la nuit. 8o. 1924
Les musées d'Europe: la Belgique. 4o. [1905]
Les musées d'Europe: le palais du Louvre. Archit., mobilier, objets. 4o. 1909
Les musées d'Europe: les Gobelins. la8o. [1923]
Sisley. la8o. 1923
see †GRANDE GUERRE (LA) par les artistes; préf. de G. G., 1914–16.
Geffroy (Mathieu Auguste).
Ét. s. les pamphlets de Milton. 8o. 1848
Gegenberichtung. Christl. u. Cathol. g. &c., 1544, *see* CHRISTLICHE.
Gegenvorschläge (Die) d. deut. Regierung zu d. Friedensbedingungen. Amtl. Textausgabe. [P2522]. 8o. 1919
Gehe (Heinrich Christian). Sylloge comment. philologici & theologici argumenti. 8o. Lipsiae. 1792
Gehle (Hendrik).
Disput. de Bedae vita & scriptis. 8o. Lugd. Batav. 1838
Geier (Ivan Ivanovich), *see* SIR-DARIA. Сборникъ матеріаловъ; подъ ред. И. И. Г. &c., t2–10, 1892–1902.

Geier (Martin). Comm. in Proverbia et Ecclesiasten, nec non in Danielem. Acc. opusc. varia philolog. [*w. sep. pagin.* Op. t2]. fol. Amstelodami. 1696
Comm. in Psalmos. ed. nov. fol. Amstelodami. 1695
Geiger (Bernhard). Die Aməša Spəntas, 1916, *see* KAISERL. AKAD. D. WISS. ZU WIEN. Sitzungsber., B176, 1916.
Geiger (Ludwig).
Goethe, s. Leben u. Schaffen. 8°. 1913
Geiger (Magdalene).
see GEIGER (W.) & M. G. Pāli Dhamma, 1921.
,, —— & —— Die 2. Dekade d. Rasavāhinī, 1918.
Geiger (Raymond).
Hist. juives. Rec. par R. G. 73e éd. s8°. 1924
Geiger (Wilhelm). Lit. u. Sprache d. Singhalesen. [Grundr. d. indo-ar. Phil., B1, H10]. la8°. Str. 1900
Pāli Lit. u. Sprache. [Grundr. d. indo-ar. Phil., B1, H7]. la8°. Strassburg. 1916
—— & M. Geiger. Pāli Dhamma, vornehml. in d. kanon. Lit., 1921, *see* KÖN. AKAD. D. W. ZU MÜNCHEN Abhdlgn. B31, 1922.
Die 2. Dekade d. Rasavāhinī, *see* KÖN. AKAD. D. WISS. ZU MÜNCHEN. Phil. Kl., Sitz., 1918.
Geigy (Charles).
Handbook of facs. of famous personages. fol. Basle. 1925
Geijer (Eric Gustaf) & A. A. Afzelius. Musik-bilagor till de af G. och A. utg. Svenska folkvisor. s8°. 1846
Geijerstam (Joh. Gustaf af). The book about little brother. Tr. w. intr. by E. Björkman. s8°. N.Y. 1921
Geikie (*Sir* Archibald). Elem. lessons in physical geography. [3rd ed., rev. &c., repr.] s8°. 1919
A long life's work: an autobiog. 8°. 1924
Geisberg (Max), *see* S. (*Meister* E.) Kupferstiche d. Meisters E. S.; hrsg. M. G., 1924.
Geiselmord. Die Prozesse d. G. im Luitpold-Gymn. in München vor d. Volksgericht, 1920, *see* PROZESSE.
Geisenhof (Georg). Bibl. Bugenhagiana. Bibliog. d. Druckschr. d. J. B. v. G. Geisenhof. [Quellen &c. aus d. Gesch. d. Reformationsjhdts., B6]. 8°. L. 1908
Geisler (*Dr.* Georg), *see* GLEIWITZ; hrsg. v. G. &c., 1925.
Geissler (—), *Stadtbaurat.* Nordhausen, *see* DEUTSCHLAND. D.'s Städtebau, 1921.
Geissler (Paul). Chronologie d. altatt. Komödie, *see* KIESSLING (A.) &c. Philolog. Unters., H30, 1925.
Geistliche [GEISTLICHES]. Geistl. Lieder, derer etliche v. alters her in d. Christl. Kirchen eintrechtiglich gebraucht &c., *see* KIRCHENGESÄNGE. Kirchengeseng &c., 1566; 1606.
*Geistl. Lieder, mit e. n. Vorrede v. M. L. &c. 1560, *see* LUTHER (M.)
*Geistl. Reglement auf Befehl Petri I &c., 1724, *see* PETER I, *emp. of Russia, the Great.*
*Geistl. Urtheil v. Lotterie-Wesen &c. [P447]. s4°. *n.p.* 1723
Geldart (Ernest), *rector of Little Braxted.*
The art of garnishing churches. 2nd ed. la8°. 1884
Geldart (William Martin). The Osborne judgment & after. [Repr. f. M'ter Guardian]. [P2708]. 8°. M'ter. *n.d.*
see JENKS (E.), *ed.* Digeste de droit civil anglais; par E. J., W. M. G. &c.; tr., 2e éd., 2t, 1923.
Geldenhauer (Gerardus), *Noviomagus.* Collectanea, gevolgd door den herdruk van eenige zijner werken [Satyrae octo—Erasmi annot^s^., Epist. aliquot de re evangelica et haereticorum poenis—Vita Philippi a Burgundia &c.] Uitg. door J. Prinsen. [Hist. Genoots. Werken, s3, 16]. 8°. A. 1901
Geldings Close. Map drawn in 1585 to illust. lawsuit conc. G.C., 1925, *see* LONDON.
Geldorpius (Henricus) [*ps.* GRATIANUS VERUS], *1522–85.*
*D. Ruardi Tappart Haeretica pravitatis primi & postremi per Belgium inquisitoris apotheosis. [*A satire* by H. Geldorp]. s8°. Franekerae. 1643
Geley (Gustave). Clairvoyance & materialisation. Tr. S. de Brath. la8°. 1927
From the unconscious to the conscious. Tr. S. de Brath. 8°. [1920]
Les preuves du transformisme & les enseignements de la doctrine évolut. 8°. 1901
Gélis (Edouard), *see* CHAPUIS (A.) & E. G. Le monde des automates, 2t, 1928.
Gell (*Hon. Mrs.* Edith Mary), *wife of Philip Lyttelton Gell.*
Under 3 reigns, 1860–1920. 8°. 1927
Gell (John), *chaplain of St. Mark's, Malew.* Journal dur. early seafaring life, 1789, *see* MANX SOC. Manx misc., v2, 1880.

Gellert (Christian Fürchtegott).
Sämmtl. Schriften. n. rechtmässige A. 10T [*in* 4v]. s8°. 1867
Tagebuch aus d. Jahre 1761. s8°. L. 1862
Gellert (Wilhelm). Vor gross. Katastrophen. Der deut. Aufstieg u. die german. Zeit. 8°. Naumburg a. d. S. 1921
Gellius (Aulus) [AGELLIUS; AULU-GELLE]. The Attic nights. [Text] w. Eng. tr. by J. C. Rolfe. [Loeb Class. Lib.] v1–3. s8°. 1927–28
Geloofsbelijdenis. De nederl. Geloofsbelijdenis, 1864, *see* NEDERLANDSCHE.
Geltentwertung &c. in ihr Einfl. auf d. sozial. Entwickl. in Österreich, 1925, *see* BUNZEL (J.), *ed.*
Gelzer (Heinrich), *1847–1906.* Die Genesis d. byzant. Themenverfassung. [K. Sächs. Gesell. d. Wiss. Phil.-hist. Cl. Abhdlgn., B18v]. la8°. L. 1899
Gelzer (Heinrich), *jun., of Jena, see* YDER. Der altfranzös. Yderroman; hrsg. H. G., 1913.
Gelzer (Jay). The street of a thousand delights. s8°. [1922]
Gemelli (*Fr.* Agostino), *see* VICO (G. B.) G. B. V.; a cura d. A. G., 1926.
Gémier (Firmin), *see* GSELL (P.) F. G., biog.-crit., 1921.
Gemito (Vincenzo).
see GIACOMO (S. DI). V. G., 1923.
,, RICCIUTI (V.) V. G., 1920.
Gemmill (Paul Fleming). Collective bargaining by actors, *see* UNITED STATES: LABOR. Bull. 402, 1926.
Génard (Pierre).
Anvers à travers les âges. [2t]. 4°. Brux. [1888]
Genaro-Perez de Villa-Amil, *see* VILLA-AMIL.
Genast (Ernst Merian-), *see* MERIAN-GENAST (E.)
Genderen Stort (R. van). Hélène Marveil. 2d [*in* 1v]. 8°. A. 1917
Genealogical.
*Geneal. (A) hist. of the royal &c. family of the Stewarts, 1710, *see* CRAWFURD (G.)
*Geneal. mem. rel. to fam. of Sotheron, &c., 1871–73, *see* SOTHERAN (C.)
Genealogical Research Society, *see* I'ANSON (B.) Hist. of the I'A. fam., *n.d.*
Genealogist (The).
N.S., v36–38. [*no more publ.*] 8°. Exeter. 1920–22
SUPPLEMENTS.
see GENTLEMAN'S MAGAZINE. Index to marriages &c., 1731–68, 1922.
,, HAMPTON COURT. Hampton Court &c. wills &c., 1919–22.
Genebrard (Gilbert), *abp. of Aix.* De S. Trinitate libri tres contra hujus ævi Trinitarios, Antitrinitarios & Autotheanos &c. s8°. Parisiis. 1569
R. Josephi Albonis, R. Davidis Kimhi &c. argumenta quibus nonnullos fidei christ. articulos oppugnant. G. G. interprete. Ejusdem responsa. s8°. Parisiis. 1566
see DANEAU (L.) Ad novas G. G. calumnias, responsio, 1578.
General Missionary Conf. held in Allahabad, 1872–73, 1873, *see* MISSIONARY CONFERENCE.
General Assembly. Acts of the Gen. A. of Free Ch. of Scot., *see* FREE CHURCH OF SCOTLAND.
Acts of the Gen. A. of Kirk of Scot., *see* CHURCH OF SCOTLAND.
General Officer (A), *ps.* Our artillery, 1875, *see* ARTILLERY.
General's.
*G. (A) letters to h. son on minor tactics, 1918, *see* PILCHER (*Maj.-Gen.* T. D.)
*G. (A) letters to h. son on obt. h. commission, 1917, *see* PILCHER (*Maj.-Gen.* T. D.)
General Society of Mechanics & Tradesmen of New York. Classif. & numbering system, 3rd ed., 1926, *see* PARKER (H. W.)
Genest (Émile). Où est-ce donc? Dict. de phrases &c. Préf. de H. Berthélemy. s1. s8°. [1925]
—— & E. Duberry. La maison de Molière, connue & inconnue. Préf. de A. Rivoire. 8°. 1922
Génestal (R.) Le privilegium fori en France. [H.E., Sci. relig., v35, 39]. 2t. la8°. 1921–24
Geneste (Maximilian). The parallel histories of Judah & Israel, with notes. 2v. la8°. 1843
Genet (J.) & P. Chelbatz.
Hist. des peuples Mayas-Quichés. 8°. 1927
Genetz (Arvid Oscar Gustaf) [GENETS]. Грамм. Финскаго языка. Переводъ В. Майнова и А. Іернефельда. s8°. Гельсингфорсъ. 1884
Geneva. The forme of prayers &c. used in the Engl. congreg. at G. &c., 1643, *see* PRAYERS.
L'ordre du Collège de G. [1559. *Foll^d^. by* Leges Acad. G. *w. sep. tp.*] 4°. Genève. [1859]

Geneva [*continued*].
see ARIANA, *Musée de l'.*
,, DEONNA (W.) Trois têtes ant. du Musée d'Art &c. à G., 1924.
Geneva Institute of Internat. Relations. The problems of peace. Lect. deliv. at the G.I. of I.R., Aug. 1926. 8º. O. 1927
Genevoix (Maurice). Les Eparges. s8º. [1923]
Euthymos, vainqueur olympique: roman. s8º. 1924
Les mains vides. s8º. 1928
Raboliot. s8º. 1925
Gengenbach (Pamphilus). *Wie der Hailig vater Bapst Adrianus eingeriten ist zů Rom Auff den 28. Tag des Monats Aug. 1522. Darbey ain gesprech von dreyen personen. [*4 leaves. Sig. A. Decor. border to tp.* P2539]. s4º. *n.p. n.d.* [Strassburg?. 1522]
Genghis Khan, *see* JENGHIS KHAN.
Géniaux (Charles). France & Italie en Tunisie, *see* ŒUVRES libres, 65, 1926.
L'idole Batéké, nouvelle, *see* ŒUVRES libres, 39, 1924.
Géniaux (Claire). Le sort le plus beau! Roman. s8º. [1921]
Genlis (*Mme.* **de).** Théâtre à l'usage des jeunes personnes. t1–3. s8º. Londres. 1797
Gennadius, *patriarch of Constantinople in the 15th c.* [GENNADIUS SCHOLARIUS; GEORGE SCHOLARIUS].
Διδασκαλία εὐσύνοπτος. Ἐπιμελείᾳ Σεργίου τοῦ Μακραίου. [*w. pref. notice by D. Petras*]. s4º. [Constantinople]. 1806
G. de praedestin.; Lat. donatus & comm. illust. a C. Libertino. [*Gr. & Lat. 2 pagin.*] s4º. Wratislaviae. [1681]
Homélie [*Gr. & Lat.*], *see* MARY, *the Virgin.* Homélies mariales byz.; éd. M. Jugie, pl, 2, 1922–26.
Gennadius, *Massiliensis presbyter.* De scriptor. eccl., *see* LE MIRE (A.) Bibl. eccl., 1639.
Gennadius (John). The pronunc. & the teaching of Greek. [Repr. f. "Univ. Review," July 1905]. [P2463]. 8º. [1905]
The retirement of M. G.: speeches, Nov. 1918, *see* ANGLO-HELLENIC LEAGUE, No. 38, 1919.
Gennarelli (Achille). Il governo pontificio e lo Stato Romano: doc. prec. da una espos. & racc. d. A. G. 2p. la8º. Prato. 1860
Gennari (Luciano).
Ritratto di un poeta: A. Fogazzaro. s8º. Bergamo. 1921
Gennaro (Giuseppe Aurelio di).
Della famiglia Montalto libri 3. 4º. Bologna. 1735
Gennep (Arnold van).
L'état actuel du problème totémique. la8º. 1920
Gennrich (Friedrich). Rondeaux, Virelais u. Balladen, 12.–14. Jhdt., mit d. überlief. Melodien. Hrsg. F. G. [Gesells. f. roman. Lit. 43, 47]. 2B. 8º. Dresden. 1921–27
Genolini (Angelo).
Maioliche ital.: marche e monogrammi. 4º. Milano. 1881
***Genotigter** u. fremdt eingetragener schrifft &c., 1526, *see* SUABIA.
Genoude (Antoine Eugène) [GENOUD]. *Vie de Jacques Cathelineau. [*b. w.* Duchemin Descepeau (J.) Lettres sur la Chouannerie, t1, 1825]. 2e éd. 8º. 1821
Genouillac (Henri de). Fouilles franç. d'El-'Akhymer. Prem. recherches archéolog. à Kich. Mission d'H. de G., 1911–12. Rapport &c. 2t. 4º. 1924–25
Genouillac (Jacques Galiot de), *see* GALIOT DE GENOUILLAC (J.)
Genova. Capitoli d. consortia d. forestieri d. chiesa d. Servi in G., 1393; ed. G. Rossi, *see* REGIA DEP. DI STORIA PATRIA. Misc., t11, 1870.
Gensel (Walther), *see* KNACKFUSS (H.) & M. G. ZIMMERMAN. Allgem. Kunstgesch., B3, Kunstgesch. d. Barock &c. u. d. Neuzeit, v. M. G. Z. & W. G., 1910.
Genseric, *king of the Vandals, see* GITTI (A.) Eudossia e G., 1925.
Gent (Jan van), *see* JOOS, *van Gent.*
Gent (Thomas), *of York.*
Ancient & mod. hist. of Rippon. 8º. York. 1733
*The antient & mod. hist. of the city of York. Added, descr. of towns in Yorkshire. Coll. by T. G. s8º. York. 1730
Gentile (Giovanni).
Bernardino Telesio, con app. bibliog. 8º. Bari. 1911
Bertrando Spaventa. 8º. Firenze. [1924]
Il carattere storico d. filosofia ital. 8º. Bari. 1918
Che cosa è il fascismo. s8º. Firenze. [1925]
Disc. di religione. 2a ed. riv. 8º. Firenze. [1924]
Dopo la vittoria: nuovi framm. polit. s8º. 1920
I fondamenti d. filosofia del diritto ed altri scr. [St. filos., 1]. 2a ed. riv. 8º. 1923

Gentile (Giovanni) [*continued*].
Giordano Bruno e il pensiero del Rinascimento. s8º. Firenze. 1920
Il modernismo e i rappi. tra relig. e filos. [Scr. filos., 3]. 2a ed. accresc. 8º. Bari. 1921
Le origini d. filosofia contemp. in Italia. [St. filos., 7–9]. v1–3i, ii. 8º. Messina. 1917–23
I problemi d. scolastica e il pensiero ital. 8º. Bari. 1913
La riforma dell' educ. 8º. Bari. 1920
Saggi critici. s1. s8º. Napoli. 1921
Sistema di logica come teoria del conoscere. [Scr. filos., 4i, ii]. 2a ed. 2v. 8º. Bari. 1922–23
Sommario di didattica. [Pedagogia, v2]. 8º. Bari. 1914
Sommario di pedagogia gen. [Pedagogia, v1. Scr. filos., 2]. 2a ed. riv. 8º. Bari. 1920
Studi sul Rinascimento. 8º. Firenze. [1923]
Teoria gen. dello spirito come atto puro. [Scr. filos., 1]. 3a ed. riv. 8º. Bari. 1920
TRANSLATIONS.
The reform of education. Auth. tr. by D. Bigongiari. Intr. by B. Croce. s8º. 1923
The theory of mind as pure act. Tr. f. 3rd ed. w. intr. by H. W. Carr. 8º. 1922
see CHIOCCHETTI (O. F. M.) La filosofia di G. G., 1922.
,, CROCE (B.) Il caso G. e la disonestà n. vita univ. ital., 1909.

Gentile (Panfilo).
Sommario d'una filos. d. religione. s8º. Bari. 1923
Gentili (A. F.), *prof. of mod. language, see* VERRI (A.) Life of Erostratus &c.; pref., Epitome of Ital. grammar by A. G., 1842.
Gentilis (Albericus) [A. GENTILI]. Hispanicae advocationis libri duo. [C.E. for Int. Peace]. 2v. 4º. N.Y. 1921
1, Reprod. of ed. of 1661, w. intr. by F. F. Abbott. 2, Tr. by F. F. Abbott.
Gentilis (Joannes Valentinus), *see* DANEAU (L.) Ad G. Genebrardi calumnias, quibus V. G. errorem tuetur, responsio, 1578.
Gentillet (Innocent). Examen Conc. Trident. s8º. Genevae. 1586
Gentizon (Paul). L'armée allemande depuis la défaite. Préf. du Gén. de Lacroix. s8º. 1920
La résurrection géorgianne. Préf. de F. de Jessen. 8º. 1921
***Gentleman** (The) instr. in conduct of a virtuous &c. life, 1732–33, *see* HICKES (G.)
Gentleman (A) of Bristol, *ps.* *An essay upon educat. &c., 1752, *see* BUTLER (S.)
Gentleman of the North of Ireland, *ps.* *Essays on the polit. circumstances of Ireland &c., 1798, *see* KNOX (A.)
Gentleman (A) of the Univ. of Camb., *ps.* *A further acc. of earthquakes, 1756, *see* EARTHQUAKES.
Gentleman (A) with a duster, *ps.*
*The Conservative mind, 1924, *see* CONSERVATIVE.
*Declension, 1925, *see* DECLENSION.
*The glass of fashion, social reflect., 1921, *see* GLASS.
*The great world, 2nd ed., 1925, *see* GREAT.
*The howling mob, 1927, *see* HOWLING.
*Julius Levine: novel, 3rd ed., 1927, *see* JULIUS.
*The mirrors of Downing Street: polit. reflect., 2nd ed., 1920; pop. ed., 1922, *see* DOWNING STREET.
*The other door: novel, 1926, *see* OTHER.
*Painted windows: st. in relig. personality, 1922, *see* PAINTED.
*Pomps & vanities, 1927, *see* POMPS.
*Seven ages: narr. of the pilgrimage of the human mind &c., 1923, *see* SEVEN.
Gentleman's. *G.'s (The) calling. [By the a. of "The whole duty of man"]. s8º. 1672
G.'s (The) recreation, 1686, *see* BLOME (R.)
Gentleman's diary (The), or The mathematical repository. Almanack, 1800–08. [1804 *wanting*]. s8º. 1800–08
Gentleman's magazine. Index to marriages in the G.M., 1731–68. By E. A. Fry. [Suppl. to The Genealogist, N.S., v34–38, 1917–22]. 8º. Exeter. 1922
Gentz (Friedrich v.) D'Ulm à Iéna, Corr. inéd. du Chevalier de Gentz avec F. J. Jackson, Ministre de la Grande-Bretagne à Berlin, 1804–6. 8º. 1921
see FOURNIER (A.) G. u. Cobenzl: Gesch. d. österr. Diplomatie, 1801–5, 1880.
Genua. Der Kampf in G., 1922, *see* KAMPF.
Genuardi (Luigi), *see* SICILIANO. Parlamento sicil.; p. c. di L. G., v1, p1, 1034–1282, 1924.
***Genuine** (A) acc. of some trans. in the E. Indies, 1753, *see* EAST INDIES.
Geoffrey, *knight, see* JAUFRE.
Geoffroy, *de Vinsauf.* Liber (Carmen) de statu Curie Romane (13c.), *form. attrib. to G., see* HENRICUS (*Mag.*)
Geoffroy de Grandmaison (C. Alex.) La croix-rouge franç., *see* PAGES ACTUELLES, no. 140–41, 1921.
L'Espagne & Napoléon. [t]2, 1809–11. 8º. 1925
Géographe bibliophile (Un), *ps., see* AVEZAC (M. P. D').

Geographical hist. &c. descr. of Germany &c., 1800, *see* GERMANY.

Geographical magazine (The). Ed. C. R. Markham. v1–5. la8°. 1874–78
Contin. of Ocean highways, 1874, *q.v.*

Geographical review, 1874, *see* OCEAN HIGHWAYS: geogr. rev.; ed. C. R. Markham, n.s. v1, 1874.

Geographical Teacher, The. Suppl. 1. 8°. [1926]
see FITZGERALD (W.) Hist. geog. of early Ireland, 1926.

***Geographische** Gen. Karte d. Gränzen zw d. 3 Kaiserthümern &c. v. J. 1718 bis heut. Tags, verschiedene partikulär Karten &c. beigefügt. 2ᵉ A. *folded.* 4°. Wien. 1788

Geographisches Jahrbuch.
B38–41 (1915–26). 8°. Gotha. 1920–26

Geological Magazine (The). v57–64. 8°. 1920–27

Geological Society of London. Geolog. lit. added to the library, 1894–1904. [11p *in* 3v]. 8°. 1895–1905
List of the G. S., 1864, 1893–96, 1898–1903, 1926. 8°. 1864–1926

Geological Survey of Eng. & Wales &c. Mems. of the G.S. of G.B. & of the Museum of Pract. Geology. v2. 2p. v3. 8°. 1848–81
3, Geol. of N. Wales, by A. C. Ramsay, w. app. on fossils, by J. W. Salter, 2nd ed.

Memoirs. Palæontology. v1, 2. 4°. 1908–25
Kidston (R.) Fossil plants of the carbonif. rocks of Gt. Brit., sect. 1, 1923–25. [2iv.]
Lee (G. W.) Brit. carbonif. Trepostomata, 1912. [1iii.]
Peach (B. N.) Higher Crustacea on the carbonif. rocks of Scotland, 1908. [1i.]
Thomas (I.) Brit. carbonif. Orthotetinae, 1910. [2ii.]
—— Brit. carbonif. Producti, 1, Genera Pustula &c., 1914. [1iv.]

Special reports on the mineral resources of Great Britain. [Mems. of Geolog. Survey]. v1–30 [11 & 17, Geol. Survey of Scot.] 8°. 1917–25
1, Tungsten & Manganese ores, by H. Dewey & H. G. Dines &c., 3rd ed., 1923.
2, Barytes & Witherite, by G. V. Wilson, T. Eastwood &c., 3rd ed., 1922.
3, Gypsum & Anhydrite, by R. L. Sherlock & B. Smith. Celestine & Strontianite, by R. L. Sherlock, 2nd ed., 1918.
4, Fluorspar, by R. G. Carruthers, R. W. Pocock & D. A. Wray, 2nd ed., 1917.
5, Potash-felspar, Phosphate of lime, Alum shales, Plumbago, Molybdenite, Chromite, Talc & Steatite, Diatomite, by Sir A. Strahan, J. S. Flett & C. H. Dinham &c., 2nd ed., 1917.
6, Refractory materials: Ganister & silica rock, Sand for open-hearth steel furnaces, Dolomite, 2nd ed., 1920.
7, Mineral Oil, Kimmeridge oil-shale, Lignites, Jets, Cannel coals, Natural gas, by Sir A. Strahan &c., 2nd ed., 1920.
8, Iron ores: Haematites of West Cumberland, Lancashire & Lake District, by B. Smith, 1919.
9, Iron ores: sundry unbedded ores of Durham, East Cumberland, N. Wales, Derbyshire, Isle of Man, Bristol distr. & Somerset, Devon & Cornwall, by T. C. Cantrill, R. L. Sherlock & H. Dewey, 1919.
10, Iron ores: the Haematites of the Forest of Dean & South Wales, by T. F. Sibly, 1919.
11, Iron ores: The iron ores of Scotland, by M. Macgregor, G. W. Lee & G. V. Wilson &c., 1920.
12, Iron ores: bedded ores of the Lias, Oolites & later formations in Eng., by G. W. Lamplugh, C. B. Wedd & J. Pringle, 1920.
13, Iron ores: Pre-carboniferous & carboniferous bedded ores of Engl. & Wales, by Sir A. Strahan, W. Gibson, T. C. Cantrill, R. L. Sherlock & H. Dewey, 1920.
14, Refractory materials: Fireclays, 1920.
15, Arsenic & Antimony ores, by H. Dewey &c., 1920.
16, Refractory materials: Ganister &c. Petrography & chemistry, by H. H. Thomas, A. F. Hallimond & E. G. Radley, 1920.
17, Lead, zinc, copper, & nickel ores of Scotland, by G. V. Wilson, w. contrib. f. J. S. Flett, 1921.
18, Rock-salt & brine, by R. L. Sherlock, 1921.
19, Lead & zinc ores in the carboniferous rocks of N. Wales, by B. Smith, 1921.
20, Lead & zinc: mining district of N. Cardiganshire & W. Montgomeryshire, by O. T. Jones, 1922.
21, Lead, silver-lead & zinc ores of Cornwall, Devon & Somerset, by H. Dewey, 1921.
22, Lead & zinc ores of the Lake District, by T. Eastwood, 1921.
23, Lead & zinc ores in the pre-carboniferous rocks of West Shropshire, by B. Smith, & North Wales, by H. Dewey & B. Smith, 1922.
24, Cannel coals, lignite & mineral oil in Scotland, by W. Gibson, 1922.
25, Lead & zinc ores of Northumberland & Alston Moor, by S. Smith, w. contribs. by R. G. Carruthers, 1923.

Geological Survey of Eng. and Wales &c. [*continued*].
26, Lead & zinc ores of Durham, Yorks. & Derbyshire; by R. G. Carruthers & Sir A. Strahan, 1923.
27, Copper ores of Cornwall & Devon; by H. Dewey, 1923.
28, Refractory materials: fireclays, analyses & physical tests; by F. R. Ennos & A. Scott, 1924.
29, Iron ores: bedded ores of Eng. &c.: petrography & chemistry, by A. F. Hallimond; app. by F. R. Ennos & R. Sutcliffe, 1925.
30, Copper ores of the Midlands, Wales, Lake Distr. & Isle of Man, by H. Dewey & T. Eastwood, w. contribs. by B. Smith & R. G. Carruthers, 1925.

For other Memoirs, *see under the following authors:—*

Aveline (W. T.)	Fox-Strangways (C. E.)	Pocock (T. I.)
Barrow (G.)		Ramsay (*Sir* A. C.)
Bennett (F. J.)	Gibson (W.)	Reid (C.)
Blake (J. H.)	Green (A. H.)	Rutley (F.)
Bromehead (C. E. N.)	Greenly (E. H.)	Sherlock (R. L.)
Clough (C. T.)	Gunn (W.)	Skertchly (S. B. J.)
Dakyns (J. R.)	Hill (J. B.)	Strahan (*Sir* A.)
Dalton (W. H.)	Holmes (T. V.)	Tiddeman (R. H.)
De Rance (C. E.)	Howell (H. H.)	Ussher (W. A. E.)
Dewey (H.)	Hull (E.)	Ward (J. C.)
Dines (H. G.)	Jukes-Browne (A. J.)	Wedd (C. B.)
Dixon (E. E. L.)	Lamplugh (G. W.)	Whitaker (W.)
Eastwood (T.)	Miller (H.)	White (H. J. O.)
Flett (J. S.)	Newton (E. T.)	Whitehead (T. H.)
Forbes (E.)	Penning (W. H.)	Woodward (H. B.)
Fowler (A.)	Pocock (R. W.)	Wright (W. B.)

Geological Survey of Ireland, *see* COLE (G. A. J.) Mem. & map of localities of minerals of econ. import. in Ireland, 1922.

Geological Survey of Scotland. Memoirs. Tertiary & post-tertiary geol. of Mull, Loch Aline & Oban. By E. B. Bailey, C. T. Clough &c.; w. Petrology by H. H. Thomas & E. B. B., & Palæobotany by A. C. Seward & R. E. Holttum. la8°. E. 1924
see BARROW (G.), J. S. G. WILSON &c. Geol. of co. round Blair Atholl &c., 1905.
,, GEOLOG. SURVEY OF ENG. & WALES &c. Spec. rep. on min. resources, 11 & 17, 1920–21.
,, RICHEY (J. E.) &c. Econ. geol. of Ayrshire coalfields, 2v, 1925.

***Geonomia** Armena, 1881, *see* ALISHANIAN (L.)

Geoponica.
Γεωπονικά. [*Old Armenian tr.*] 8°. Venetik. 1877

Georg (Joseph), *see* SCHEFFLER (J.) & J. G. Heilige Seelen-Lust, 1668.

George III, *prince of Anhalt, 1507–53, see* CAMERARIUS (J.) Narr. de G., 1696.
see WESTPHAL (F.) Zur Erinnerung an Fürst G. zu A., 1907.

George I, *king of Gt. Britain & Ireland.*
see *BRITISH (THE) hero: the interest of every Briton to avow h. loyalty to G., 1715.
,, CHANCE (J. F.) Alliance of Hanover: Brit. for. policy in last yrs. of G. I, 1923.
,, IMBERT-TERRY (H. M.) A constit. king, George I, 1927.

George III, *king of Gt. Brit. & Ireland.* Corresp., 1760–83. Pr. f. papers at Windsor Castle. Arr. & ed. by Sir J. Fortescue. 6v. 8°. 1927–28
Sel. f. the papers of George III pres. in archives at Windsor Castle, Nov. 1781–Dec. 1783. Ed. J. Fortescue. [Roxburghe Club]. 2v. 4°. C. 1927
see DAVIES (A. M.) Influence of G. III on constit., 1921.
,, LONDON: CIVIC INSTIT. Addr. f. the Court of Common Co. to the king, 1760–70 [*&* 1769–78], 1778.
,, MUMBY (F. A.) G. III & Amer. Revol., 1924.

George IV, *king of Gt. Brit.*
see ASHTON (J.) Florizel's folly, 1899.
,, BULL (J.), *ps.* Half-a-crown lost!, 1820.
,, HALL (*Sir* J. R.) Bravo mystery &c. [*incl.* G. IV & Jockey Club], 1923.
,, HUDIBRAS, *the younger, ps.* Sultan Sham, & h. 7 wives, 1820.
,, LESLIE (S.) G. the Fourth, 1926.
see LOST. The lost mutton found, 1820?.
,, MUDIE (R.) *Hist. acc. of H.M.'s visit to Scotland, 1822.
,, NERO, *ps.* *Nero vanquished, 1820.
,, OLD. *The old black cock &c. in jeopardy, 1820.
,, PHILOI-D'OR, *ps.* The King the avowed enemy of the Queen, 1820.

George V, *king of Gt. Brit.* The King at the front; official photographs. Publ. by the Daily Mail. [P2422]. obl.8°. *n.d.*
*T.R.H. the Prince & Princess of Wales. 8°. [1902]
see CORONATION. C. celebrations in Ceylon, 1911.
,, —— Form &c. of service, 1911.

George, *of Pisidia.* Vetzoreayq ['Ἑξαήμερον. *In Armenian & Gr. Ed. &c.* A. Tirouyean]. 8°. Venetik. 1900
see DASHEAN (H.) Sh. bibliog. sts. &c., *in Armenian*, v2, 1901.
„ TEZA (E.) Dell' " Essaemero " di G. P., vers. arm., 1893.
George [*of Podiebrad*], *king of Bohemia.*
see BACHMANN (A.) Böhmen &c. unter G. v. P., 1458–61, &c., 1878.
„ JORDAN (M.) Das Königthum G.'s v. P., 1861.
„ KAPRAS (J.) Peace league of Geo. Poděbrad, 1919.
George, *Saint.*
see BALDER (J.) Conflictus de G. martyre, adv. C. C. Sandium, 1685.
„ HEYLYN (P.) Hist. of St. G. of Cappadocia &c., 1631.
„ ROOSVAL (J. A. E.) Nya St. Gorans studier, 1924.
George, *duke of Saxony, 1471–1539.* Welcher gestalt wir G. Hertzog zu Sachssen, von M. Luther des getichten Bündtnus halben ynn schrifften unerfindlich angegeben. Und Antwort. s4°. [Leiptzig, *M. Lotther.* 1528]
see COCHLAEUS (J.) Wie verkerlich widder G. &c. M. Luther d. 7en Psalm verdewtzscht &c., 1529.
„ HENRY VIII, *king of England.* Seren. regis Angliae de coercenda Lutherana factione &c. epistola; item Georgii rescriptio, 1523.
„ LUTHER (M.) Die kleine antwort auff H.[erzog] G. nehestes buch, 1533.
George (Glen). Future of the coal trade & the alternatives to nationalisation. 8°. [1925]
George (Hereford Brooke). Hist. geography of the Brit. Empire. Rev. to 1919 by R. W. Jeffery. 6th ed. s8°. [1920]
Relations of geogr. & hist. 5th ed., ed. O. J. R. Howarth, w. add. chapter by C. B. Fawcett. s8°. O. 1924
George (*Mrs.* M. Dorothy), *wife of Eric George.*
London life in the 18th cent. 8°. 1925
George (Nancy).
L'envouté, *see* ŒUVRES libres, 81, 1928.
La fille des gobes, *see* ŒUVRES libres, 55, 1926.
George (Stefan).
Die Bücher d. Hirten- u. Preisgedichte &c. 7e A. 8°. 1921
Der siebente Ring. 5e A. 8°. 1920
Der Stern des Bundes. 5e A. 8°. 1922
see GUNDOLF (F.) G., 2e A., 1921.
George (Walter Lionel).
Caliban. s8°. [1920]
Children of the morning. s8°. 1926
The confession of Ursula Trent. s8°. 1921
Engines of social progress. s8°. 1907
Gifts of Sheba. 5th ed. s8°. 1926
Hail, Columbia! 8°. 1923
One of the guilty. 4th impr. s8°. 1923
The ordeal of Monica Mary. s8°. [1927]
The stiff lip. s8°. 1922
„ „ 3rd impr. s8°. 1922
The triumph of Gallio. s8°. 1924
George a Green, *called the Pinder of Wakefield.* A pleasant conceyted comedie of George a Greene (1599), *see* ADAMS (J. Q.) Chief pre-Shakespearian dramas, 1925.
Georgel (J. Alcide). Armorial des familles de Lorraine titrées &c. au 19e siècle. fol. Elbeuf. 1882
Georgel (Jean François), *see* MUNIER-JOLAIN (J.) Le card. Collier & M.-Antoinette; préc. d'une vie de l'abbé G. & s. mém., 1927.
Georges (Carl Ernst). Gnomologia sive veterum Latin. sententiae. Collegit C. E. G. s8°. Lipsiae. 1863
George-Samné (*Dr.*), *see* SAMNÉ (G.)
Georges-Gaulis (Berthe). La France au Maroc. (L'œuvre du gén. Lyautey). 8°. 1919
La nouv. Turquie. s8°. 1924
Georges-Michel (Michel). Ballets russes, choses vues, *see* ŒUVRES libres, 13, 1922.
Georgi (Christian Siegmund). Diss. de Chaldaeo Syrismis &c. dictioni Novi Foederis immerito affictis. s4°. Wittebergae. [1726]
Hierocriticus N. Test. sive de stylo N.T. libri 3. [*b. w. h.* Vindic. N.T., 1732]. 2p *in* 1v. s4°. Wittebergae. 1733
Vindiciarum N. Test. ab Ebraismis libri 3. s4°. Francofurti. 1732
Georgi (Otto Robert) & A. Dufour-Feronce. Urkunden z. Gesch. d. Suezkanals veröffentl. v. G. & A. D.-F. 8°. L. 1913
Georgia, *Asiatic.* Chronique géorgienne, 1829–31, *see* BROSSET (M. F.)
Constit. de la G. [P2682]. 8°. 1922
*La G. sous la domin. des armées bolchevistes. [P2585]. s8°. 1921

Georgian. Georgian poetry, 1911–12. [Anthology; ed. E. Marsh]. [5th ed.] 8°. [1913]
Georgian poetry, 1920–22. [Anthology; ed. E. Marsh]. s8°. 1922
Georgian stories, 1922. s8°. 1922
Georgianum. *Alphabetum Ibericum, sive Georgianum, 1629, *see* ALPHABETUM.
Georgievits (Bartholomæus). De Turcarum moribus epitome, 1660 [*w. sep. tp.*], *see* BUSBECQ (O. G., *seigneur* DE). B. quae extant omnia &c., 1660.
Georgievitz-Weitzer (Demeter), *see* SURYA (G. W.)
Georgievsky (Aleksandr Ivanovich). Мат. по университ. вопросу. Извлеченія изъ книги А. И. Г. "Краткій очеркъ правительств. мѣръ &c. Съ предисловіемъ П. Струве. Bl. [P2445]. 8°. Stuttgart. 1902
Georgii (Jacob Friedrich). Imperatorum &c. gravamina adv. sedem Rom. &c.; praes. J. F. Buddeo. s4°. Jenae. [1719]
Georgius (Antonius Augustinus), *see* GIORGI.
Georgius (Christianus Siegmundus), *see* GEORGI (C. S.)
Gepp (Edward). A contrib. to an Essex dialect dict. 8°. [1920]
Géraldy (Paul).
Aimer. Pièce. 24e éd. [P2750]. la8°. 1922
„ „ [73e éd.] s8°. [1927]
„ „ *for a. ed., see* REVUE (LA) HEBDOMADAIRE. Suppl.: coll. nouv. &c., No. 3, 1922.
Les petites âmes. n. éd. s8°. 1923
Robert et Marianne. Comédie. [8e éd.] s8°. [1925]
Toi et moi. 247e éd. s8°. [1925]
Gérando (*le baron* Auguste de).
Essai sur l'origine des Hongrois. 8°. 1844
Gérard (Conrad Alexandre), *see* ORMESSON (W. D'). La 1e. mission offic. de la Fr. aux États-Unis: C.-A. G., 1778–79, 1924.
Gerard (Gilbert).
Institutes of Biblical criticism. 2nd ed. 8°. E. 1808
Gérard (Rosemonde), *aft. wife of Ed. Rostand.*
Les pipeaux. s8°. 1923
Gerard (William). The king of Thulê. A phantasy. s8°. 1921
Gérard de Nerval. Aurélia. Intr. de J. Giraudoux. 8°. 1927
Petits chateaux de Bohême—La Bohême galante, &c. [Œ. compl.] 8°. 1926
see AUDIAT (P.) L'Aurélia de G. de N., 1926.
„ MARIE (A.) Bibliog. des œuvres de G. de N. (Œ. compl.), 1926.
Gérardin (Édouard). Hist. de Lorraine: duchés—comtés—évêchés, j. 1766. 8°. 1925
Gerards (Emile). Un captage de la nappe de l'argile plast., Rue Berton, à Passy, au 17e s., *see* PARIS. COMM. MUNIC. DU VIEUX P. Procès-verb., Année 1923, 1926.
Gerardus, *van Harlem* [GEERAERT VAN LEYDEN; GEERTGEN, *tot S. Jans;* GÉRARD, *de Harlem;* GÉRARD, *de Leyde*].
see BALET (L.) Der Frühholländer G. tot S. J., 1910.
„ FRIEDLÄNDER (M. J.) Die altniederl. Malerei, B5, G. van H. &c., 1927.
Gerardus, *Zutphaniensis* [ZERBOLT (G.)], *1367–98, see* KONING (W. A.) Spec. de G. Z. vita &c., 1858.
Gerardus (Andreas), *Hyperius, see* HYPERIUS (A.)
Gerasimov (*Major Gen.* —) [GUÉRASSIMOFF]. Esquisse de l'hist. des Cosaques du Don. [P2403]. 8°. 1919
La lutte des Cosaques du Don contre les Bolcheviks. [P2403]. 8°. 1919
Gerbaix di Sonnaz (Carlo Alberto de). Relazioni fra Savoia & Portogallo: Italiani in Lusitania 1146–1849, *see* REGIA DEPUT. Miscellanea, t45, 1910.
Ult. anni di regno di Vittorio Amedeo III re di Sardegna (1789–96), *see* REGIA DEPUT. Miscellanea, t49, 1918.
Gerbaldo (Giovanni Giovenale). Mem. d. guerra, carestia e peste del Piemonte, 1629–31; [*ed. D. C. Promis*], *see* REGIA DEP. DI STORIA PATRIA. Misc., t5, 1868.
Gerbeau (*l'abbé* J. B.) Essai hist. sur la baronnie de Pujols en Agenais. la8°. Agen. 1891
Gerber (Christian). Theolog. Bedencken: Ob die Seele e. Gläubigen alsobald zu Christo kom̃e &c.? Dabei e. Anon. Schr. v. d. mittl. Zustande d. Seelen, u. d. D. Peucero gehalt. Leichen-Predigt &c. [*3 pagin.*] s8°. Dressden. 1730
Gerber (Johann). De Latinitate Lutheri oratio. [P2627]. s4°. Jenae. 1754
Gerberon (Gabriel), *see* BAY (M. DE). Opera, cum bullis pontif. &c., studio A. P. [*i.e.* G. G.], 1696.
Gerbert *de Montreuil, see* GIBERT *de Montreuil*.

Gerbert (Martin), *baron v. Hornau.* Demonstratio verae relig. veraeque eccl. contra quasvis falsas. s8°. Typis San-Blasianis. 1760
Eccl. militans, regnum Christi in terris in suis fatis repræsentata. 2t. 8°. Typis San-Blasianis. 1789
Principia theologiae dogmat. s8°. Monast. S. Blasii. 1758
Principia theologiae exeget. Praem. proleg. &c. s8°. Monast. S. Blasii. 1757
Scriptores eccl. de musica sacra potissimum. Ex variis codicibus coll. &c. a M. G. 3t. 4°. Typis San-Blasianis. 1784

Gerbidon (Marcel).
see ARMONT (P.) & M. G. Alain, sa mère &c., comédie, 1922.
,, —— & —— Une petite sans importance, 1927.

Gercke (Alfred) & E. Norden. Einleitung in d. Altertumswiss. Unter Mitwirk. v. J. Beloch &c. hrsg. G. & N. 3e A. 3B [B3 2e A.] la8°. L. 1914–27

Gercken (Johann Hermann). Diss. de formula consensus Lubecensi pro conserv. puriori Evangelii doct., 1560, [*subscribed by V. Curtius &c.* P2643]. s4°. Gottingae. 1755

Gerdes (Daniel) [GERDESIUS].
Exercit. acad. libri tres, ad hist. patriarch., ad antiq. Jud. &c. Acc. orationum biga. s4°. Amstelodami. 1738
*Florilegium hist.-crit. librorum rar. Ed. 3a auct. s8°. Groningae. 1763
Hist. motuum eccl. in civ. Bremensi, 1547–61, temp. A. Hardenbergii suscitat. s4°. Groningae. 1756
Meletemata sacra, sive, isagoge & exegesis in cap. 15 Epist. I ad Corinthios. s4°. Groningae. 1759
see MISCELLANEA DUISBURGENSIA, edita, inedita, &c., 2t, 1732–35.
,, MISCELLANEA GRONINGANA, 1736–45; Scrinium antiq. sive Misc. G. nova, 1748–51.

Gerdil (*card.* **Giacinto Sigismondo).** De adoranda humanite Christi—De cultu Sacri Cordis Jesu, *see* MIGNE (J. P.), *ed.* Theol. cursus, t9, 1841.

Gere (Vladimir Ivanovich) [GUERRIER]. Второе раскрѣпощеніе. Общія пренія по указу 9 ноября 1906 въ думѣ &c. Съ текстомъ Указа 1906 и Закона 1910. 8°. Москва. 1911

Geret (Johann Georg). Naevi medicorum theologici. [P447]. s4°. Weissenburgi Noric. 1728

Gerhaert (Niclaus), *von Leiden, see* MAIER (A. R.) N. G. v. L., e. niederl. Plastiker d. 15 J., 1910.

Gerhard (Andreas), *see* HYPERIUS (A.)

Gerhard (Ephraim). Tract. de judicio duellico. [P2746]. s4°. Francof. 1732

Gerhard (Johann).
Adnotat. in Apocalypsin Johannis. ed. 3a. s4°. Lipsiæ. 1712
Annot. posthumae in Acta Apost. auctae analectis J. E. Gerhardi. s4°. Jenae. 1674
Comm. super Genesin. s4°. Lipsiae. 1693
Comm. super priorem [*& post.*] Petri Epistolam. [2t *in* 1v]. s4°. Jenae. 1641
Conf. catholicae, in qua doctrina catholica & evang. quam Eccl. Augustanae Conf. addictae profitentur &c. partes 4. [4v]. s4°. Ienæ. 1634–37 pl *has engr. tp.*, Noribergæ.
Isagoge Locorum theologic., operâ &c. J. E. Gerhardi. s4°. Jenae. 1658
Loci theologici per theses explic. Ed., praef. de vita auct. adj. J. F. Cotta. 20v *in* 8t. 4°. Tubingae. 1762–80
Tract. de legitima Scr. Sacrae interpret. s4°. Jenae. 1663
see FISCHER (E. R.) Vita I. G., acc. G. epistolae, 1723.
,, THOLUCK (F. A. G.) Spicilegium ex commercio epist. J. Gerhardi, 1864.

Gerhardi (William).
Anton Chehov: a crit. study. s8°. [1923]
Futility. Novel on Russian themes. s8°. [1922]
Perfectly scandalous, or "The immorality lady." Comedy. [2nd impr.] s8°. 1927
The polyglots. A novel. [2nd impr.] s8°. [1925]
Pretty creatures. s8°. 1927
The vanity-bag. s8°. 1927

Gerhardt (Carl Immanuel), *see* LEIBNITZ (G. W., *Frhr.* v.) Early math. MSS. of L.; tr. &c. by J. M. Child [& 2 essays by G.], 1920.

Gerhardt (Paul).
Geistliche Lieder. n. A. s8°. St. 1855
Geistreiche Andachten in 120 Liedern. Nebst Anhang Gebete v. J. G. Ebeling. s8°. Nürnberg. 1683
see BECKER (C.) P. G., c. 1853.
see JACOBI (J. C.) Mem. of A. W. Boehm; ann. 3 hymns [*by P. G.*], 1735.
,, KAWERAU (G.) P. G.: e. Erinnerungsblatt, 1907.
,, KOCHS (E.) P. G., 1926.

Gericke (J. F. C.) Eerste gronden der Javaansche Taal, benevens Jav. leer-en leesboek, met woordenlijst. 3p *in* 1v. 4°. Batavia. 1831

Gering (Hugo). Komm. zu d. Liedern d. Edda, *see* EDDA. Lieder; hrsg. B. Sijmons &c., B3, H1, 1927.

Geringer (Vladimir August) & E. P. Herman. Commerce & finance in Czechoslovakia, 1922, *see* UNITED STATES: COMMERCE.

Gerkan (Armin von). Griech. Städteanlagen. la8°. 1924
Das Theater v. Priene &c. u. s. Bedeutung f. d. hellenist. Bühnenwesen. 4°. Muenchen. 1921

Gerlac, *canon regular of the Order of St. Augustine, see* PETERSEN (G.)

Gerlach (Otto v.) Comm. on the Pentateuch. Tr. H. Downing. 8°. E., *Clark.* 1860

Gerlach (Stephan), *the elder.* Assertio doctrinae de div. majestate Christi hominis. Cum praef. J. Andreæ. [P2504; *a. c. b. w.* Andreae (J.) Confutatio, 1584]. s4°. Tubingæ. 1585
De persona Christi disput. 2, adv. apolog. J. Busaei &c. [*b. w.* Fleck (G.) Refut. errorum &c., 1592]. s4°. Tubingae. 1595
Hyperaspistes Antidanæi: 1. De condemn. errorum. 2. De S. Domini coena. 3. De majestate Christi. s4°. Tubingae. 1581

Gerlacher (Theobald) *von Billican.* [BELLICAN (THEOPALD v.)] An die Christelich kirch versamlung ainem Ersamen Radt d. Stat Weyl. s4°. *n.p.* 1522
Apologia ad excusatoriam epist. L. Marstalleri. De libero arbitrio quædam. Epist. M. [*2 pagins. b. w.* Erasmus (D.) De libero arbitrio, 1524]. s8°. *n.p.* 1524

Gerle (Thorsten), *see* HEURGREN (P. G.) La poste dans les temps anc. & mod.; avec le concours de T. G. &c., 1924.

Gerling (Georg Friedrich). De pietate ministri eccl. [*tp. wanting.* P2634]. 8°. [1740]

Gerlo (Ada). Herinneringen van een onafhankelijke vrouw. 7e dr. s8°. A. 1917

Gerloff (Wilhelm). Steuerbelastung u. Wiedergutmachung. [V. f. Sozialpol., B168i]. 8°. München. 1924

Germain (Alexandre Charles), *see* GUILLEMS, *Seigneurs de Montpellier.* Liber instrument. memorialium &c.; [*ed. w.* Intr. hist. par A. G.], 1884–86.

Germain (Alphonse).
Les Néerlandais en Bourgogne. 8°. Brux. 1909

Germain (André). De Proust à Dada. s8°. [1924]

Germain (Auguste).
Mme. Brazyers antiquaire. Roman. s8°. 1922

Germain (José), *ps.* [*i.e.* J. GERMAIN-DROUILLY]. Le roi des coqs, roman, *see* ŒUVRES libres, 40, 1924.

Germain (Léon).
Mélanges hist. sur la Lorraine. 8°. Nancy. 1889

Germains (Victor Wallace).
The truth about Kitchener. s8°. [1925]

German.
Drill regul. of the G. Field Artillery 1899, 1901, *see* WAR OFFICE.
Evidence & docs. laid before the Comm. on G. Outrages, 1915, *see* COMM. ON ALLEGED GERM. OUTRAGES.
G. (The) army in Belgium: the White Bk. of May 1915; tr. E. N. Bennett, 1921, *see* DEUTSCH. D. Wessbuch II &c.
G. Constitution. (ed. without notes). [P2682]. 8°. 1919
G. legisl. for Belgium, 17s. & Ind., 1915–19, *see* HUBERICH (C. H.) & A. NICOL-SPEYER (A.), *edd.*
G. West-Prussia; reprod. f. docs., 1926, *see* KAUFMANN (C. J.), *ed.*
G. White Book conc. respons. of authors of the War (1919); tr., 1924, *see* DEUTSCH. D. Weissbuch.
[Masterpieces of modern German art. *no tp.*] 2v. fol. *n.p. n.d.* [c. 1885]
Official German doc. rel. to the World War. Tr. under supervision of the C.E. for Internat. Peace. v1, 2. la8°. N.Y. 1923

German East Africa. A hdbk. of German E. Afr., 1920; Suppl., 1923, *see* ADMIRALTY: NAVAL INTELL. DIV.

German (*Capt.* **R. L.),** *Malayan Civil Service, see* BRITISH MALAYA. Hdbk. to B.M.; comp. by R. L. G., 1926.

Germania. Germania Romana: ein Bilder-Atlas hrsg. v. d. Röm.-Germ. Komm. d. Deut. Arch. Instit. fol. Bamberg. 1922

Germanica [GERMANICAE]. Lamentationes Germanicæ Nationis, 1526 ?, *see* LAMENTATIONES.
*Psalmodia Germanica; tr., 1765, *see* PSALMODIA.

Germanicus, *ps.*, Kein Vertrauen zur deutschen Regierung, 1920, *see* KEIN.

Germanische Bibliothek. Abt. 1, Sammlung german. Elem.- u. Hdbücher; hrsg. v. W. Streitberg, *see* SAMMLUNG.
Abt. 2, Untersuchungen u. Texte, B9, 16, 17, 20. 8°. Heidelberg. 1914–27
see EDDA. Edda: Lieder d. Codex Regius &c.; hrsg. G. Neckel. 2B, 1914–27. [9.]
,, HOOPS (J.) Probleme d. engl. Spr. u. Kultur, 1925. [20.]

Germanische Bibliothek [*continued*].
see SCHRÖDER (F. R.) Germanentum u. Hellenismus, 1924. [17.]
,, SIEVERS (E.), *ed.* Deut. Sagversdichtungen d. 9.–11. Jhdts., 1924. [16.]
Germanisches Nationalmuseum, *Nürnberg*. Kunst- u. Kulturgesch. Denkmale. Zusammengest. v. A. Essenwein. 4°. L. [1877]
Germanisch-romanische Monatsschrift. In Verbindung mit F. Holthausen &c., hrsg. v. H. Schröder. Jhrg. VI, VII, 1914–19. 8°. Heidelberg. 1914–19
Germann (Wilhelm). Die Kirche der Thomaschriften. Ein Beitr. z. Gesch. d. Oriental. Kirchen. 8°. Gütersloh. 1877
Germano-bolchéviste. Le Complot g.-b., 1920, *see* COMPLOT.
Germano-Polonaise. Actes & doc. de la Conf. G.-P., à Vienne du 30 avr.-30 août 1924, 1925, *see* ACTES.
Germany.
*Geogr., hist. &c. descr. of Germany, Holland &c., w. Gazetteer. Comp. & tr. f. German [*w.* Chauchard's maps]. Added, Statist. tables of Europe, tr. f. J. G. Boetticher &c. [*sep. tp. & pagin.*] 4°. 1800
*Germany in Europe, 1927, *see* POLIAKOFF (V.)
*Germany's econ. & financ. situation: after-effects of World War. [P2740]. la8°. Berlin. 1923
*Present state of H.M.'s dominions in G., 1737, *see* MIEGE (G.) Pres. state of Gt. Brit. &c., 8th ed., 1738.
*Sk. of defences of France agst. invasion f. G., 1887, *see* FRANCE.
*Sk. of the defences of the W. & Swiss frontiers of Germany. [P2579]. 8°. 1888
GOVERNMENT PUBLICATIONS.
Bestimmungen f. d. Schiedrichterdienst bei Truppenübungen. [P2824]. s8°. 1924
Bismarck u. d. Nordschlesw. Frage, 1864–79, 1925, *see* BISMARCK (O., *Fürst* v.)
Handbuch d. Ostküste Südamerikas [Reichs-Marine-Amt], 2T, & Ergänzung &c., 1911–21, *see* SÜDAMERIKA.
Handbuch für d. West- u. Nordkuste Norwegens [Reichs-Marine-Amt &c.], 3e A., 2T, 1919-21, *see* NORWEGEN.
Prelim. hist. of the Armistice. Doc. publ. by German Chancellery. Tr. [C.E. for Int. Peace]. la8°. N.Y. 1924
see AUSBILDUNGSVORSCHRIFT. A. für d. Nachrichtentruppe, H1–4, 1924–5.
LAWS.
Einkommensteurgesetz u. Körperschaftssteurgestz f. d. Deutsche Reich, 4e A., 1923, *see* EINKOMMENSTEURGESETZ.
REICHSARCHIV.
Weltkrieg (Der), 1914–18; bearbt. im Reichsarchiv, B1–4, 1925–26, *see* WELTKRIEG.
REICHSTAG & NATIONALVERSAMMLUNG.
Deutsche (Die) Nationalversammlung. 15. Ausschuss. Bericht d. 2en Unterausschusses d. Untersuchungsaussch. ü. d. Friedensaktion Wilsons 1916/7. 8°. [1920]
,, ,, Stenograph. Berichte ü. d. öffentl. Verhandlungen d. Untersuchungsausschusses. 15. Ausschuss. 7H *in* 1v [*pagin. cont.*] 8°. 1919
,, ,, Beilage 1, 4, 6, Aktenstücke z. Friedensaktion Wilsons 1916/17. T1, 5, 8. 8°. 1919–20
Ursachen des Zusammenbruchs: Entst. &c. d. Offensive v. 1918. Gutachten d. Obersten Schwertfeger, d. Gen. v. Kuhl, u. d. Prof. H. Delbrück. [Reichstag—12. Ausschuss, Beilage]. 8°. 1923
Verhandlungen. B283–295 (18 März, 1912–20 Mai, 1914), 327–333 (13 März, 1919–21 Mai, 1920). 4°. 1912–20
,, ,, [Vorläufiges Register & Sprechregister, 7 Feb., 1912–22 Mai, 1912. *No tp.*] 2B. 4°. *n.d.*
B327 & subsequent have title: Verh. d. verfassunggeb. Deut. Nationalversammlung.
Werk (Das) d. Untersuchungsausschusses d. Deut. Verfassunggeb. Nationalversamml. u. d. Deut. Reichstages, 1919–26. Unter Mitwirk. v. E. Fischer, W. Bloch &c. hrsg. W. Schücking, P. Spahn &c. Reihe 4., B1–3, 8. la8°. 1925–26
4, Die Ursachen d. deut. Zusammenbruchs, 1918; hrsg. A. Philipp, B1–3, 8.
Germiny (Marc de). Les brigandages maritimes de l'Angleterre. 3[t.] s8°. 1925
Germond de Lavigne (Alfred). Les pamphlets de la fin de l'Empire &c. Cat. raisonné &c., 1814–17. s8°. 1879
Germonius (Anastasius). Lettere, pubbl. da F. Comino, *see* REGIA DEP. DI STORIA PATRIA. Misc., t10, 1870.
Gernet (Mikhail Nikolaevich). Преступный мир Москвы. Сборник статей А. М. Аронович &c. Под ред. М. Н. Г. 8°. Москва. 1924
Gerngross (Vsevol. Nikolaevich Vsevolodsky-), *see* VSEVOLODSKY-GERNGROSS (V. N.)
Gerola (Giuseppe). I monumenti medioev. d. tredici Sporadi. Estr. dall' Annuario d. R. Scuola Arch. di Atene &c., v1, 2]. 2p *in* 1v. sfol. Bergamo. 1914–15
Pezzi erratici Rodiesi. [P2621]. 8°. Venezia. 1919
Gerolamo (Biscaro). Inquisitori ed eretici lombardi (1292–1318), *see* REGIA DEPUT. Miscellanea, t50, 1922.
Gérold (Théodore). Schubert. 8°. 1923
Gerritszoon (Hessel) [GERRITSZ]. Beschryvinghe van der Samoyeden Landt & Hist. du pays nommé Spitsberghe. Uitg. door S. P. L'Honoré Naber. [Linschoten-Ver. Werken, 23]. 8°. 's-Gravenhage. 1924
Gerschuni (G.)
Die Konzessionspolitik Sowjetrusslands. 8°. 1927
Gersen (Joannes), *abbot of Vercelli, see* ERHARD (T. A.) Polycrates G. contra scutum Kempense, 1729.
Gershenzon (Mikhail Osipovich).
Декабристъ Кривцовъ. изд. 2oe. s8°. Москва. 1923
Гольфстрем. 8°. Москва. 1922
Грибоѣдовская Москва. изд. 2oe. s8°. Москва. 1922
Историч. записки (И. В. Киреевский, Ю. Ф. Самарин, Н. В. Гоголь). изд. 2oe. s8°. Берлин. 1923
Ключ веры. s8°. П. 1922
Мечта и мысль И. С. Тургенева. 8°. Москва. 1919
Мудрость Пушкина. 8°. в Москве. [1919]
Русскiе пропилеи. t2. la8°. Москва. 1916
Судьбы еврейского народа. s8°. П. [1922]
see IVANOV (V.) & M. O. G. Переписка, 1921.
Gerson (J. Charlier de) [J. CHARLERUS GERSONIUS].
Opera omnia. Quibus acc. Henrici de Hassia, P. de Alliaco, J. Brevicoxae, J. de Varenis, J. Almaini, et J. Majoris tractatus; necnon monª. omnia ad causam J. Parvi pert. Opera L. Ellies du Pin. ed. 2ª. 5t[*in* 2v]. fol. Hagae Comitum. 1728
Ad Deum vadit. Publ. [*in French*, w. intr., gloss &c.] by D. H. Carnahan. [Univ. of Illinois. Sts. in lang. &c., v3i]. la8°. [Urbana]. 1917
[C]Ollectoriū sup magnificat particulas habet expositas non semp eodē ordine quo sūt in cantico &c. sfol. [Esslingen, *Conrad Fyner*. 1473]
167 printed leaves, 1 blank after leaf 9; without tp., pagin., register or catchwords. 38 lines to a full page. Wanting prelim. 2 leaves cont. Rubricae & Registrum.
Incipit donatus Venerabilis magistri Iohannis Gerson Cancellarij Parisiensis. [*Ends on fol. 14b*: Explicit. donat? egregii doctoris mgři johannis Gerson]. 4°. [Basel, *Martin Flach*.] *n.d.*
14 leaves, 24 lines to a full page, formerly ascribed to M. Flach, Strassburg & dated 1475.
Monotrias G. 1, De defect. clericorum. 2, De flagellat. spontanea. 3, De perfect. relig. Xtnae. &c. Ed. à J. Webero. [*b. w.* Torsellino (O.) De vita Xaveri, 1610]. s8°. [Erfurti. 1616]
see BELLARMINO (*il card.* R. F. R.) Responsio ad libellum: Tract. &c., circa valorem excommunicationum J. G., 1606.
,, LE NOBLE (E.) L'esprit de G., touch. le Saint Siége, 1710.
,, RICHER (E.) Apologia pro J. Gersonio &c., 1676.
,, SARPI (P.) Apologia adv. oppos. factas ab card. Bellarmino ad Tractatus &c. J. G. &c., 1606.
Gerstenberg (Kurt). Hans Multscher. la8°. L. 1928
Gerster (Franz Carl), *see* SCHMIDKUNZ (H.) Psycholog. d. Suggestion: mit ärztlich-psycholog. Ergänzung. v. F. C. G., 1892.
Gerstfeldt (Olga von), *see* STEINMANN (O.)
Gerstinger (Hans). Bruchstücke e. ant. Komm. z Archäologie d. Thukydides im Papyr. gr. Vindob. 29247, *see* KAISERL. AKAD. D. WISS. IN WIEN. Denkschr., 67, 1926.
Gertz (M. Cl.), *see* VITAE sanct. Danorum; nov. ed. crit. cur. M. C. G., 1908–12.
Gerullis (Georg). Die altpreuss. Ortsnamen. 8°. 1922
Gervaisais (*le marq.* de la), *see* LA GERVAISAIS (*le marq.* DE).
Gervinus (Georg Gottfried). The mission of the German catholics. Tr. [Cath. ser.] [P2777]. s8°. 1846
Gesamtkatalog d. Wiegendrucke. Hrsg. v. d. Kommission f. d. Gesamtkatalog d. Wiegendr. B1, 2. 4°. L. 1925–26
Gesangbuch.
Christl. G. für öffentl. Gottesdienst. s8°. Trogen. 1873
Deutsches evang. Kirchen-G. In 150 Kernliedern. s8°. St. 1855
G. f. d. deutschen Wesleyan. Meth., 1878, *see* ZIONSHARFE.
G. für die evang. Kirche in Württemberg. s8°. St. 1854
G. für Schulen, hrsg. v. Lehrervereine zu Köln. 2H *in* 1v [H1, 5e A.; 2, 4e A.] s8°. Köln. 1853–55
*G. z. Gebr. d. evangel. Brüder-Gemeinen. s8°. Gnadau. 1850
*Neue (Das) vermehrte Deutsche u. Wendische G., M. Lutheri &c. Z. Gebr. d. evang. Ober-Lausitz. Kirchen. s8°. Budissin. 1719
Geschichte.
*G. (Die) d. Berggeist Gnome auf d. Schles. Sudetengebirge, *n.d.*, *see* SCHLESISCHE.
*G. (Die) d. Berliner Fünftageregierung, 1920, *see* SPECTATOR, *ps.*
*G. d. ersten portugies. Entdeckungen, 1783, *see* FREIRE (F. J.)
*G. d. evang. Kirche in Ungarn &c., 1854, *see* UNGARN.
*G. d. Generalsynoden beider evang. Conf. in Ungarn v. 1791 von CLVI, 1858, *see* UNGARN.
*G. d. Menschen in s. Zwischenzustande, 1762, *see* VENZKY (G.)
G. d. niederen Volkes in Deutschland, 2B, 1907, *see* ECCARDUS, *ps*
*G. v. Württemberg; hrsg. v. d. Calwer Verlagsverein, 3e A., 1865 *see* GUNDERT (H.)

Geschichte d. aussereuropäischen Staaten. Hrsg. v. K. Lamprecht & H. Oncken. 8°. St. 1915–25
America. Charakter d. Entdeck. u. Eroberung A. durch d. Europäer, v. G. Friederici, B1, 1925.
America. Kampf Westeuropas um Nordamer. im 15.–16. Jhdt. v. A. Rein., 1925.

Geschichte der europäischen Staaten. Hrsg. v. A. H. L. Heeren, F. A. Ukert [*& others*]. 8°. Gotha. 1915–25
Böhmen. Neuere Gesch.; v. B. Bretholz, B1.
Finnlands polit. Gesch., 1809–1919; v. M. G. Schybergson.
Italien im Mittelalter; v. L. M. Hartmann, B4i.
4i, Die Ottonische Herrschaft.
Niederlande; v. P. J. Blok, B6, bis 1795. Verdeutscht durch O. G. Houtrouw.
Österreich, Gesch.; v. O. Redlich, B6.
Polen. Neuere Gesch.; v. E. Zwier, B1 (1506–72).
Schweizerische Eidgenossenschaft; v. J. Dierauer, B5, bis 1848.
Serben; v. C. Jireček, B2i (1371–1537).
Steiermark; v. H. Pirchegger, B1, bis 1283.
Venedig; v. H. Kretschmayr, B2, Die Blüte.

Geschichtschreiber (Die) d. deutschen Vorzeit. Hrsg. v. Pertz, Grimm &c. 2te Gesammtausgabe. B95. s8°. L. 1923
Innocenz III. Register ü. d. Reichsfrage, 1198–1209; nach d. Ausg. v. Baluze, Epist. Innoc. III, t1, in Auswahl üb. & erl. v. G. Tangl, 1923. [95.]

***Geschiedenis** v. d. Kolonie v. Suriname, 1791, *see* SURINAM.

Geschillen. De geschillen over de afdanking van 't krijgsvolk in de Vereenigde Nederlanden, 1649–50, *see* WIJNNE (J. A.)

Gesellschaft für Musikforschung, *see* AGRICOLA (M.) Musica instrumentalis deudsch, 1528 u. 1545, 1896.

Gesellschaft f. rheinische Geschichtskunde.
see AUBIN (H.) &c. Gesch. d. Rheinlandes, 2B, 1922.
,, HAGEN (J.) Römerstrassen d. Rheinprovinz, 1923.
,, KUSKE (B.) Quellen z. Gesch. d. kölner Handels u. Verkehrs im M.-a., 3B, 1917–23.
,, VOULLIÈME (E.) Der Buchdruck Kölns bis z. Ende d. 15. Jhdts., 1903.

Gesellschaft für romanische Literatur. B1, 19, 31, 39, 43, 45–47. 8°. Dresden. 1903–27
see GENNRICH (F.), *ed.* Rondeaux, Virelais u. Balladen, 12–14 Jhdt., 2B, 1921–27. [43, 47.]
,, HERVIS *de Metz.* Hervis von Metz, Vorgedicht d. Lothringer Geste; hrsg. v. E. Stengel, B1, 1903. [1.]
,, HUE, *de Rotelande.* Protheselaus: altfr. Abenteuerroman; hrsg. F. Kluckow, B1, 1924. [45.]
,, JAUFRE: altprov. Abenteuerroman; hrsg. v. H. Breuer, 1925. [46.]
,, JEAN. Mervelles de Rigomer; hrsg. W. Foerster, 2B, 1908–15. [19, 39.]
,, YDER. Der altfranz. Yderroman; hrsg. H. Gelzer, 1913. [31.]

Gesellschaft Schweizerischer Zeichenlehrer, *see* PUPIKOFER (O.), H. HEIERLI & o. Die Entwickl. d. Kunst i. d. Schweiz, im Auftrag d. G. S. Z., 1914.

Gesenius (F. H. Wilhelm). Ausführl. gramm.-krit. Lehrgebäude d. hebr. Sprache. 8°. L. 1817
Hebrew lex. to the O. Test., incl. geogr. names & Chaldaic words &c. Tr. C. Leo. 2p. [*pagin. cont.*] 4°. C. 1825–28
Thesaurus philolog. crit. linguae Hebraeae & Chaldaeae. Vet. Test. ed. 2ª auct. & emend. 3t [*pagin. cont.*] *&* Ind. *in 1v.* 4°. Lipsiae. 1829–58
t3 perfecit Æ. Roediger. Ind. ed. Æ. Roediger.
Versuch über die maltes. Sprache. s8°. L. 1810

Gesenius (Friedrich) [*ps.* VIGIL (CHRISTIANUS)], *see* LYSER (J.) Disc. inter polygamum & monogamum &c.; cum praef. &c. C. Vigilis, 1673.

Gesner (Abraham).
Indust. resources of Nova Scotia. 8°. Halifax, N.S. 1849
New Brunswick. 8°. 1847

Gesner (Conrad). The newe Jewell of health . . . secretes of phisicke &c. [*Tr. f. Euonymi Philiatri* [*i.e.* C. G.] *Thesaurus de remediis secretis, 1554 &c.*] Corr. & publ. in Englishe by G. Baker. [*tp. & 3 prelim. leaves cont. dedication & Baker's pref. wanting, some leaves mutilated; tp. supplied in facs.*] s4°. [*H. Denham.* 1576]
Mithridates. De differentiis linguarum &c. s8°. Tiguri. 1555
,, ,, ed. 2ª. C. Waserus rec. & comm. illust. s8°. Tiguri. 1610

Gesner (Johann Matthias). Memoria H. Eilhardi Schroederi, cur. J. M. G. [P600]. s4°. Gottingae. 1753
see MOSHEIM (J. L.) & J. M. G. Epistolae; ed. C. A. Klotz, 1770.

Gesner (Salomon), *Prof. in Wittenberg.* Comm. in Psalmos in Acad. Witeberg. publice praelectae. fol. Witebergae. 1605
Disput. 1[–17]. Pro examine Conc. Trident. conscr. à M. Chemnicio. Sub praes. S. G. *&* Pro secunda parte exam. Conc. Trident. Disput. 1[–21]. [*each w. diff. respondent, sep. tp. & pagin. b. in 1v.*] 8°. Witebergae. 1602–03
Orthodoxa conf. de persona & officio Jesu Christi, extructa ex Dei verbo, & Lutheri &c. testimoniis. s8°. Witebergae. 1604
Papismi Calvinianarum 25 dogmatici: disput. de reliquiis, trabibus & plumulis S. Matris eccl. Romanae, quas Calviniani venerantur. s4°. Witebergae. 1597

Gespenster, 2ᵉ A., 1925, *see* DEUTSCHE SPIELMANN (DER).

Gespensterbuch (Das), 1920, *see* SCHLÖMP (F.), *ed.*

Gespräche Jesu mit s. Jüngern nach d. Auferstehung, 1919, *see* EPISTOLA Apost.

Gess (Wolfgang Friederich). Merkwürdigk. aus d. Leben u. d. Schr. Hincmars, Erzb. v. Rheims. Mit e. Vorrede v. G. J. Planck. 8°. Göttingen. 1806

Gessen (G. V.), *see* ARKHIV RUSSKOI REVOLYUTSII. Архивъ р. р.; изд. Г. В. Г., 1920–.

Gessner (Ludwig). De jure uxoris legati & legatae. [P2601]. 8°. Halis Sax. 1851

Gessner (Salomon).
Œuvre de S. G. [*plates only*]. 2t. fol. *n.p. n.d.*
Schriften. B1–2. [*in* 1v]. 4°. Zürich. 1777–78
Works. Tr., w. some acc. of h. life & wr. 3v. s8°. Liv'l. 1802

Gest (John Marshall). The Old Yellow Book, source of Browning's Ring & the book. New tr., w. notes &c. 8°. Boston. 1925

Gesta.
G. abbatum Fontanell., 1886, *see* FONTENELLE.
G. (Anonymi) Francorum &c. Hierosolymitanorum. Ed. B. A. Lees. 8°. O. 1924
,, ,, Hist. anonyme de la prem. Croisade. Ed. & tr. par L. Bréhier. [Class. de l'hist. de Fr. au m. â.] s8°. 1924
*G. Caroli Magni ad Carcassonam & Narbonam &c. Ed. ex Cod. Laurent. & obs. illust. a S. Ciampi. 8°. Florentiae. 1823

Gesta Romanorum. G. Romanorum. Tr. C. Swan. Pref. by E. A. Baker. [Broadway Trans.] 8°. [1924]

Gestoso y Pérez (José). Seville. [Art in Spain, 7. Hispanic Soc.] s8°. Barcelona. *n.d.*

Gestrich (Jonas Samuel). Jura sacra Scanensium [*Swedish & Lat.*] 5p. [*Each p. w. diff. joint author*]. [P2648]. s4°. Lundae. [1802–03]

Gesualdo (Carlo), *Prince of Venosa, c. 1560–1613, see* GRAY (C.) & P. HESELTINE. C. G., musician &c., 1926.

Gethin (Percy Francis), *see* CROWDY (W. M.) Burgundy & Morvan; illust. by P. F. G., w. note on G. by C. Dodgson, 1925.

Getrewe Christenliche u. nützl. warnūg etl. obrigkait, die das Evangelion zu predigenn zulassen u. befelhen &c. s4°. *n.p.* 1525

Geuder (Anton Daniel). Vita J. Staupitii, diss. [P600]. s4°. Gottingae. [1837]

Geusius (Jacobus), *see* BRENZ (S. F.) Theriaca Judaica; acc. I. Vivae Vindex sanguinis contra J. G., 1681.

Gevaert (Emile). L'héraldique, s. esprit, s. langage & s. applic. 4°. Brux. [1923]

Gevaert (H. Fierens), *see* FIERENS-GEVAERT.

Gevaerts (Jean Gaspard) [†GEVARTIUS (JOANNES CASPARUS)], *see* HOC (M.) Et. sur J. G. G., philologue & poète, 1593–1666, 1922.

Geyer (Frank P.) The Holmes-Pitezel case. 8°. [Phila.? 1896]

Geyer (Rudolf), *see* MAIMUN IBN KAIS. Zwei Ged. v. Al-'Asâ; hrsg., übers. &c. v. R. G., 1921.

Geyl (Pieter).
De agent Wolters over de woelingen, 1747–48 (*Eng. letters*) medegedeeld d. P. G. [P2600]. 8°. [1922]
,, ,, *for a. issue, see* HISTORISCH GENOOTS. Bijd., d43, 1922.
Holland & Belgium. 3 lectˢ. [P2465]. 8°. Leiden. [1920]
Inaug. lecture, Univ. Coll., London. [*On Dutch studies.* P2423]. 8°. 1919

Gezelle (Guido), *1830–99.* Dichtwerken. 3d. 8°. A. *n.d.*
see RUDDER (M. DE). G. G., 1919.

Ghailan [ABU'L ABBĀS AḤMAD EL-KHADIR BEN 'ALĪ GHAILAN], *see* PÉRETIÉ (A.) Le rais El-Khadir G., 1912.

Ghaisne (Louis Auguste Victor de), *cte. de Bourmont, see* BOURMONT.

Ghalib Kemaly. Le martyr d'un peuple : les Turcs. 3e éd. [P2712]. la8o. Rome. 1919

Gheeraerts (André), *see* HYPERIUS (A.)

Ghent. Annals of the English Benedictines of G. Now at St. Mary's Abbey, Oulton. la8o. *p.f.p.c.* [1894]

Ghent, Justus of, *see* JOOS, *van Gent.*

Ghéon (Henri). The comedian. Tr. A. Bland. 8o. [1927]

La débat de Nicolazic &c., *see* REVUE (LA) HEBDOM. Suppl. : coll. nouv., No. 4, 1922.

Le pauvre sous l'escalier : 3 épisodes d'ap. la Vie de S. Alexis. [Rép. du Vieux-Colombier]. 4e éd. s8o. [1925]

Gherardini (Giovanni), *painter, of Bologna, 1658–1723, see* GUALANDI (M. A.) Lettera di M. G. e risposta di A. Tessier intorno G. G. &c., 1855.

Gherardo delle Notti, *see* HONTHORST (G. J.)

Gheri (Maurice). Inquiries in Anatolia ; rep. of M. G. &c. (1919–22), 1922, *see* ANATOLIA.

Gheusi (P. B.) Gallieni, 1849–1916. s8o. 1922

Ghibu (Onisifor). Din istoria lit. didactice românești, *see* ACADEMIA ROMÂNA. Anal., s2, t38, Secț. lit., 1916.

Ghignoni (Alessandro), *see* DANTE ALIGHIERI. Lectura D. : c. 31 dell' Inferno letto da A. G., 1900.

Ghiotti (Candido). Dialoghi ital.-francesi. 8o. Torino. [1895]

Ghiraldo (Alberto). La Argentina : estado social. s8o. [1922]

Ghirardini (Gherardo). Scavi d. palazzo di Teodorico a Ravenna, *see* REALE ACCAD. D. LINCEI. Mon. ant., v24, 1916.

La situla italica prim., spec. in Este, *see* REALE ACCAD. D. LINCEI. Mon. ant., v2, 7, 10, 1893–1901.

Ghislanzoni (Ettore). Notizie archeolog. s. Cirenaica. [Min. d. Colonie.] 8o. 1915

f. a. issue, see ITALY : MIN. DELLE COLONIE. Not. arch., Anno 1, 1915.

Ghose (Aurobindo), *see* AUROBINDO GHOSE.

Ghosh (C. C.) Bee-keeping, *see* AGRIC. RES. INST., *Pusa.* Bulletin 46, 1915.

Ghoshal (U.) Hist. of Hindu polit. theories to 17th c. 8o. 1923

Ghosts & marvels : sel. of uncanny tales, 1924 ; repr., 1925, *see* COLLINS (V. H.), *ed.*

G͟hulām Ḥusain Salīm. The Riyazu-s-Salāṭīn, hist. of Bengal. Tr. f. Persian by Maulavi Abdus Salam. 8o. Calcutta. 1902

Ghulam Yazdani, *see* YAZDANI (GHULAM).

Giacchetti (Valentino), *ed.* *Delle accoglienze usate dai Viniziani ai principi esteri. Diss. ined. di Dotto Patrizio Veneto. [P2852]. la8o. Venezia. 1840

Giachetti (Cipriano) [*ps.* CIP].

Fascismo liberatore. 8o. Firenze. [1922]

Giacomelli (Antonietta). Vigilie (1914–18). s8o. Firenze. [1919]

Giacomo, *da Carrara, see* MUSSATUS (A.) Princip. di G. da C., 1891.

Giacomo (Salvatore di). Da Capua a Caserta. [Italia artistica, 87]. la8o. Bergamo. *n.d.*

Vincenzo Gemito. [Rassegna d'arte. Dir. da C. Ricci. Monogr. 1]. 4o. 1923

Giacosa (Giuseppe). Tristi amori. Ed. R. Altrocchi & B. M. Woodbridge. Intr. by S. A. Smith. s8o. Chicago. [1920]

Giacosa (Piero). Il canto 7 del Purgatorio, *see* DANTE. Lect. D., 1922.

Un inventario di un castello piemont. (1511), *see* REGIA DEP. DI STORIA PATRIA. Misc., t28, 1890.

Giafferri (Paul Louis de). L'hist. du costume féminin franç. 10 fasc. [*in 1v. no tp. issued*]. fol. [1922]

Hist. du costume masculin franç., [420–1870]. fol. [1927]

Giambullari (Bernardo) [†GIAMBULARI]. Canzone carnescialesche, *see* BIAGI (G.) Biblioteca umanistica, s1, 1–2, 1925.

Gianani (Felice). I comuni, 1000–1300. [St. polit. d'Italia]. la8o. Milano. [1909]

Gianfrancesco (*p.*), *da Venezia* Cenni Storici int. l'ant. chiesa e convento di S. Bonaventura dei Minori Riformati in Venezia. [P2838]. 8o. Venezia. 1874

Giannone (Pietro). The Civil hist. of the Kingdom of Naples. Tr. J. Ogilvie. 2v. fol. 1729–31

see GUARDIONE (F.) Di P. G. e d. " St. civile del Regno di Napoli," 1921.

,, NICOLINI (F.) L' " Istoria civile " di G. ed i suoi crit. rec., 1907.

Giartosio de Courten (Maria Luisa), *see* COURTEN (M. L. G. DE).

Gibass (Carl). Sittenbüchlein, &c. für Kinder. 8o. St. 1855

Gibb (Elias John Wilkinson). E. J. W. G. Memorial. [Publications]. 11ii. N.S. v4. la8o. Leiden. 1921–26

see JALĀL-AL-DĪN, *Rūmī, Maulānā.* The Mathnawī ; ed., w. crit. notes, tr. &c. by R. A. Nicholson, v1, 2, 1925–26. [N.S., 4.]

,, NIẒĀMĪ-I-'ARŪḌĪ, *of Samarqand.* Chahár Maqála ; rev. tr. &c. by E. G. Browne, 1921. [11ii.]

Gibb (H. A. R.) The Arab conquests in Cent. Asia. [Roy. As. Soc., J. G. Forlong Fund, v2]. 8o. 1923

Arabic lit. : an introd. s8o. 1926

Gibbings (Richard), *ed.* Rep. of the trial & martyrdom of P. Carnesecchi, sec. to Clement VII. Transcr. fr. MS. & ed. w. Engl. tr. &c. by R. G. 8o. D. 1856

Roman forgeries & falsific. &c. pl. [*no more publ.*] 8o. D. 1842

see INDEX. An exact reprint of the Roman I. Expurgatorius ; ed. w. pref. by R. G., 1837.

Gibbon (Edward), *the historian.* Hist. of the decline & fall of the Roman Empire. Notes by Milman & Guizot. Ed. w. add. notes by W. Smith. 8v. 8o. 1862

,, ,, ...[World's Classics repr.] 7v. s8o. 1904–[25]

,, ,, ...4th ed. v7. s8o. [1920]

*Obs. on the 3 last vol. of the Roman hist. by E. G. [*Attrib. to* H. J. Pye *in note on tp.*] [P2494]. s8o. 1788

see BLACK (J. B.) Art of hist., 1926.

,, HARRISON (F.) Address, Nov. 1894, G. centenary commem., 1894.

Gibbon (Frederick P.)

The 42nd (East Lancs.) Division, 1914–18. 8o. [1920]

Gibbon (John Murray). Drums afar. s8o. 1920

Gibbons (Alfred W.), *see* ELY. Ely episcopal records : calendar &c. comp. by A. G., 1891.

Gibbons (Herbert Adams). Intr. to world politics. 8o. [1922]

Ports of France. 8o. [1927]

Gibbons (J. S.) Public debt of the U.S. 8o. N.Y. 1867

Gibbons (John), *see* FRASER (E.) & J. G. Soldier & sailor words & phrases, 1925.

Gibbons (Orlando), *see* FELLOWES (E. H.) O. G. : sh. acc. of h. life & work, 1925.

Gibbons (Philip Arnold), *see* GODDARD (E. H.) & P. A. G. Civilis. or civilisations, 1926.

Gibbons (Stanley), *Ltd.* Priced cat. of stamps, pl, Brit. Empire. 27th ed. s8o. 1917

Gibbons (*Lt.-Col.* T.)

With the 1/5th Essex in the East. 8o. Colchester. 1921

Gibbons (Thomas), *D.D.* Hymns. s8o. 1769

Hymns adapted to divine worship. s8o. 1769

Hymns. s8o. 1784

Gibbs, *The family of, see* GIBBS (J. A.) Hist. of Ant. & D. Gibbs &c., 1922.

Gibbs (Anthony), *son of Sir Philip Gibbs.*

The elder brother. s8o. [1926]

High endeavour. s8o. [1927]

Little Peter Vacuum. 3rd ed. s8o. [1925]

Gibbs (Antony), *see* GIBBS (J. A.) Hist. of A. & Dorothea G. &c., 1922.

Gibbs (Arthur Hamilton). Labels. s8o. [1926]

Soundings. 6th ed. s8o. [1925]

Gibbs (Dorothea Barnetta), *wife of Ant. Gibbs, form. Hucks, see* GIBBS (J. A.) Hist. of Ant. & D. G. &c., 1922.

Gibbs (John Arthur). Hist. of Antony & Dorothea Gibbs & th. contemp. relations, incl. hist. of the house of Ant. Gibbs & Sons. [*w.* Add. & Ind., 1927]. la8o. 1922

Gibbs (*Sir* Philip).

Adventures in journalism. 8o. [1924]

Back to life. s8o. 1920

Facts & ideas. s8o. 1905

Heirs apparent. s8o. [1923]

The hope of Europe. 8o. 1921

The middle of the road. Novel. s8o. [1923]

Oliver's kind women. s8o. 1911

Out of the ruins & o. little novels. 3rd ed. s8o. [1927]

Realities of war. 8o. 1920

,, ,, [n. impr.] 8o. 1920

The reckless lady. s8o. [1924]

Ten years after : a reminder. 8o. 1924

Unchanging quest. 2nd ed. s8o. [1925]

,, ,, ...s8o. N.Y. [1926]

Young anarchy. s8o. [1926]

Gibert *de Montreuil.* Gerbert de M. La cont. de Perceval. Éd. M. Williams. [Les classiques franç. du m.-â.] t1, 2. s8o. 1922–25

Gibert (Honoré), *see* AIX-EN-PROVENCE. Musée d'Aix ; pl, Mon. archéol. &c., par H. G., 1882.

Gibert (J. H.) Arles : orig., hist., mons. &c. 8o. Avignon. 1926

Gibieuf (*le père* **Guillaume).** De libertate Dei & creaturae libri duo. s4o. Parisiis. 1630

Gibon (Fénelon). La crise de la natalité & la croisade pour la repop. Préf. de L. Duval-Arnould. 8°. [1923]

Gibson (A. H.), *F.I.B.* Mem. on the world's monetary problems. 4°. 1922

Gibson (A. M.) A political crime: hist. of the great fraud [*i.e.* the election of President Hayes]. 8°. N.Y. 1885

Gibson (Arnold Hartley). Brit. finance dur. & after the War, 1914–21. Ed. by A. W. Kirkaldy. 8°. 1921

Gibson (Charles Dana). Other people. obl.4°. N.Y. 1911

Gibson (Charles Robert). Romance of mod. photography. 8°. 1919

Gibson (Edmund), *bp. of (1) Lincoln, (2) London.* A sermon preached to the Soc. for Reform. of Manners, Jan. 6, 1723. [*W.* 29th acc. of progress made in London &c. by the Soc. *w. sep. pagin.*] 4th ed. [P2669]. s8°. 1725

*Synodus Anglicana: or, the constit. &c. of an Eng. convocation. App., 3 registers, 1562, 1640, 1661 & Journals, 1586 & 1588. [*2 pagin.*] 8°. 1702

see Sykes (N.) E. G., Bp. of London, 1669–1748, 1926.

Gibson (Francis), *of Whitby.* Poet. remains, w. o. detached pieces. s8°. Whitby. 1807

Streanshall Abbey: or The Danish invasion. Play. 8°. Whitby. 1800

Gibson (Frank). The art of H. Fantin-Latour: h. life & work. la8°. [1924]

Six French artists of the 19th cent. [Delacroix, Corot, Millet, Cazin, Rousseau, Puvis-de-Chavannes]. 4°. 1925

Gibson (J. S.), *of Edinburgh.* The wood-carver. Designs & instructions. n. ed. lafol. E. 1896

Gibson (John Campbell), *D.D.* Mission problems & mission methods in S. China. 8°. E. 1901

Gibson (Robert John Harvey-), *see* Harvey-Gibson (R. J.)

Gibson (Walcot).

Cannel coals, lignite & mineral oil in Scotland, *see* Geolog. Survey of Eng. &c. Spec. rep. on min. resources, v24, 1922.

Coal in Gt. Britain. 8°. 1920

The concealed coal-field of Yorks. & Notts. [Mems. of G.S.] 8°. 1913

Geol. of the co. around Stoke-upon-Trent. W. contrib. by C. B. Wedd & A. Scott. [Mems. of G.S.] 3rd ed. 8°. 1925

Geol. of the N. Staffs. coalfields. With contrib. by G. Barrow & C. B. Wedd & palaeont. acc. by J. Ward. [Mems. of G.S.] 8°. 1905

see Barrow (G.), W. G. &c. Geol. of co. around Lichfield &c., 1919.

,, Eastwood (T.), W. G. &c. Geol. of co. around Coventry &c., 1923.

,, Lamplugh (G. W.) & W. G. Geol. of co. around Nottingham, 1910.

,, —— & —— Geol. of co. betw. Newark & Nottingham, 1908.

,, —— & —— Geol. of the Melton Mowbray district &c., 1909.

——, **T. I. Pocock & others.** Geol. of the S. part of the Derbyshire & Notts. coalfield, w. notes by C. Fox-Strangways. [Mems. of G.S.] 8°. 1908

—— **& C. B. Wedd.** Geol. of the N. part of the Derbyshire coalfield &c. With contrib. by G. W. Lamplugh &c., & app. by L. Moysey. [Mems. of G.S.] 8°. 1913

Gibson (Wilfrid Wilson). Battle. [*Poems*]. s8°. 1915

Coll. poems, 1905–25. 8°. 1926

I heard a sailor. [Poems]. 8°. 1925

Kestrel Edge & o. plays. s8°. [1924]

Gibson (William), *Prof. of Christian ethics &c.* The year of grace, Ulster revival of 1859. s8°. E. 1860

Gibson (*Rev.* William), *B. A., of Paris.* Paris dur. the Commune, w. a character sketch by his wife. s8°. 1895

Gibson (William Ralph). Hist. of Dore. s8°. Sheffield. 1927

Gide (André).

Amyntas: Mopsus — Feuilles de route — De Biskra à Touggourt &c. n. éd. s8°. [1927]

Corydon. n. éd. s8°. [1924]

Dostoïevsky: articles & causeries. s8°. [1923]

Les faux-monnayeurs. Roman. 13e éd. s8°. [1925]

,, ,, ...43e éd. s8°. [1925]

L'immoraliste. 25e éd. s8°. 1923

Numquid et tu? ... [Écr. intimes]. 8°. 1926

O. Wilde: In memoriam (souv.) —Le "De Profundis." 12e éd. s8°. 1925

Paludes. 2e éd. s8°. 1920

Le retour du Tchad: suite du Voyage au Congo. 3e éd. s8°. [1928]

Si le grain ne meurt. n. éd. 3t. s8°. 1924

Souvenirs de la Cour d'Assises. 3e éd. s8°. 1913

La symphonie pastorale. 8e éd. s8°. 1919

Voyage au Congo. Carnets de route. 16e éd. s8°. [1927]

see Gabory (G.) A. G., s. œuvre, 1924.

,, Souday (P.) A G., 3e éd., 1927.

Gide (Charles).

Consumers' co-operative societies. Tr. 8°. 1921

Cours d'économie polit. 2t [1, 8e éd., 2, 7e éd.] 8°. 1923

Effects of the War upon French econ. life. Coll. of 5 monogr. [*by* H. Mazel, A. Aftalion &c.] Ed. C. G. [C.E. for Int. Peace]. la8°. O. 1923

Les instit. de progrès social. 5e éd. revue. s8°. 1920

Konsumgenossenschaftsbewegung in Frankreich, *see* Untersuchungen ü. Konsumvereine, 1924.

Notes on financial situation, *see* Internat. Financial Conf. Paper 13v, 1920.

Principles of polit. economy. Auth. tr. f. 23rd French ed. by E. F. Row. 8°. [1924]

La Russie soviét. s8°. La Flèche. 1924

—— **& A. Daudé-Bancel.** De la lutte contre la cherté par les organis. priv. [Dot. C.: Hist. écon. &c. de la Guerre mond. (sér. fr.).] la8°. [1926]

—— **& C. Rist.** Hist. des doctrines écon. 4e éd., corr. 8°. 1922

A hist. of econ. doctrines. Auth. tr. f. 2nd ed. under dir. of W. Smart by R. Richards. 8°. 1917

Gidvani (M. M.) Shah Abdul Latif. Foreword by Sir T. Arnold. [India Soc.] 8°. 1922

Giehrl (Hermann von). Tannenberg. 8°. 1923

Giese (Friedrich), *see* Deutsch. Verfassung d. Deut. Reiches v. 11. Aug. 1919; erläut. v. F. G., 1920.

Giese (Gottlieb Christian). Hist. Nachr. v. d. deut. Bibelausgabe, 1462 z. Mayntz gedruckt. s8°. Görlitz. [1765]

Hist. Nachricht v. d. Bibelübersetzung M. Luthers. Hrsg. &c. v. J. B. Riederer. [Anh. 1, Von d. ersten Ausgabe Zachariä. 2, Nachricht v. d. Wormser Bibel 1529, bey P. Schöffer, u. 2 Strasburger Bibeln v. 1530–32 u. 1537–38 bey W. Köppheln]. 8°. Altdorf. 1771

Giesecke (Albert). Studien ü. Giov. Batt. Piranesi (1720–78), Kap. 1, 2. Diss. [P2701]. 4°. 1911

Giesecke (*Dr.* Walter).

Münzwesen Hierons II v. Syrakus. [P2769]. 8°. 1920

Münzwesen Roms bis z. J. 268 v. Chr. [P2769]. 8°. L. *n.d.*

Sicilia numismatica: Grundlagen d. griech. Münzwesens auf Sicilien. 4°. L. 1923

Gieseler (Johann Carl Ludwig). De Rainerii Sachoni Summa de Catharis & Leonistis comm. crit. [*Progr.* P2648]. s4°. Gottingae. [1834]

Symbolae ad hist. monast. Lacensis ex codd. Bonn. depromptae. [P2655]. 4°. Bonnae. 1826

Giessing (Hans Peter). Kong Christian den Ottendes Regjeringshist. 8°. Kjobenhavn. 1852

Gifford (Thomas), *of Busta.* Hist. descr. of the Zetland Islands in 1773, w. app. of doc. Repr. f. ed. publ. in 1786. 8°. E. 1879

Gigante (Silvino). Venezia e gli Uscocchi, 1570–1620. 8°. Fiume. 1904

Gigli (Giuseppe). Balzac in Italia. s8°. Milano. 1920

Franco Sacchetti: vita e opere. s8°. Messina. [1918]

Giglioli (Enrico Hillyer). Avifauna Italica. Elenco d. specie di uccelli stazionarie o di passaggio in Italia. [Min. di Agric. &c.] 8°. Firenze. 1886

Giglioli (Giulio Quirino), *see* Corpus vasorum antiq. Italia: Museo Naz. di Villa Giulia in Roma; a cura di G. Q. G., fasc. 1–3, 1925–28.

Giglioli (Odoardo H.) Fra Filippo Lippi. s8°. Firenze. 1921

Gignoux (C. J.)

Bourges pend. la Guerre. [C.E. for Int. Peace]. 8°. [1926]

La vie du Baron Louis. 5e éd. s8°. 1928

Gignoux (Régis), *see* Savoir (A.) & R. G. Vertu . . . Vertu!: comédie, 1925.

Gihr (Nikolaus). The Holy Sacrifice of the Mass; dogmat., liturg. &c. expl. Tr. f. 6th German ed. 5th ed. 8°. St. Louis, Mo. 1921

Giichi Ono, *see* Ono (Giichi).

Gikish (Carl) [Hiekisch]. Die Tungusen. Ethnolog. Monographie. 8°. St. Petersburg. 1879

Gil (Augusto). Prosa e verso. s8°. Paris. 1923

Gilbart (James William). Elements of banking. s8°. 1852

Gilbert, *The family of, see* Thompson (S. P.) Fam. & arms of G. of Colchester, 1904.

Gilbert (Bartholomew). Rel. des voyages de G. &c. à la Virginie, 1602–3, *see* Bernard (J. F.), *ed.* Recueil, t3, 1732.

Gilbert (Bernard). Farming lays. s8°. [1914]

The rural scene. s8°. [1923]

Gilbert (Chester G.) Sources of nitrogen compounds in U.S. [S. Inst. P2737]. 8°. 1916

——, **J. E. Pogue & S. S. Wyer.** The mineral indust. of the U.S. [S. Inst.: U.S. Nat. Mus.; Bull. 102]. 8p. 8°. Wash. 1917–23

Gilbert (Claude), *see* LACHÈVRE (F.) Les successeurs de Cyrano de Bergerac [C. G. &c.], 1922.
Gilbert (Gabriel). Les intrigues amoureuses : comédie (1666), *see* FOURNEL (V.) Contemp. de Molière, t2, 1866.
Gilbert (*Rt. Hon. Sir* **Geoffrey),** *Lord Chief Baron of the Exchequer.* *Reports of cases in equity, argued &c. in the C. of Chancery & Exchequer in r. of George I. sfol. 1734
Gilbert (H. A.) & A. Brook. Secrets of bird life. 8°. [1924]
The secrets of the eagle & o. rare birds. 8°. [1925]
Gilbert (*Sir* **Humphrey),** *see* SAMSON (H.) Sir H. G., 1921.
Gilbert (J.) Fragm. tow. the hist. of stained glass &c. of the M. Ages. la8°. *n.d.*
Gilbert (J. A.), *see* JOMINI (A. H. DE). Expos. of Ist. princ. of grand milit. combinations &c., with remarks by J. A. G., 1825.
Gilbert (Joseph), *minister of the Independent Church, Friar Lane, Nottingham.* The Christian atonement. 8°. 1836
Gilbert (Leo), *ps., see* SILBERSTEIN (L.)
Gilbert (Marion). Le joug. s8°. [1925]
Gilbert (Mary), *of Antigua.* An extract of journal. With acc. of Lady E. Hastings &c. [P2535]. s8°. 1769
Gilbert (O. P.) The Prince de Ligne. Tr. J. McCabe. 8°. [1923]
Gilbert (Robert Otto). Diss., Xtianae catecheseos hist. pl. [P2651]. 8°. Lipsiae. [1836]
Gilbert (Rodney). What's wrong w. China. 8°. [1926]
Gilbert (*Maj.* **Vivian).** Romance of the last crusade : with Allenby to Jerusalem. s8°. N.Y. 1924
Gilbert (William), *M.D.* [GILBERD ; G. GILBERTUS].
see THOMPSON (S. P.) Family & arms of G. of Colchester, 1904.
„ WHITE (*Sir* W. HALE-). Bacon, G. & Harvey, 1927.
Gilbert (*Sir* **William Schwenck).** The Savoy operas. Text of Gilbert & Sullivan operas as produced, 1875–96. [repr.] s8°. 1926
see DARK (S.) & R. GREY. W. S. G., h. life & letters, 1923.
Gilbert-Carter (Humphrey), *see* CARTER (H. G.)
Gilbert de Voisins (A.) Écrit en Chine. [*&* Souv. de Segalen. Voyages]. 2t. s8°. 1923
L'enfant qui prit peur. [11ᵉ éd.] s8°. *n.d.*
L'esprit impur. [5ᵉ éd.] s8°. 1919
Les miens. s8°. 1926
Gilbertine. Gilbertine Rite (The). Ed. R. M. Woolley. [Henry Bradshaw Soc., 59, 60]. 2v. 8°. 1921–22
1, Ordinal—Office of St. Gilbert.
2, The Kalendar—The Missal.
Transcripts of charters rel. to the G. houses of Sixle, Ormsby &c., 1922, *see* STENTON (F. M.), *ed.*
Gilbey (*Sir* **Walter),** *1st bart.*
Animal painters of Eng. f. 1600. v3. la8°. 1911
Gilbreth (Frank Bunker) & L. E. M. Gilbreth. Fatigue study : 1st step in motion study. [rev. ed.] s8°. 1919
Gilbreth (Lilian Evelyn Moller), *wife of F. B. G., see* GILBRETH (F. B.) & L. E. M. G. Fatigue study, 1919.
Gilchenko (Nikolai Vasilevich). Матеріалы для антропологіи Кавказа. 1, Осетины. 8°. С.-П. 1890
Gilchrist (John Borthwick). Hindee-Roman orthoepigraph. ultimatum : exempl. in Hindoostanee story-teller. 2nd ed. 8°. 1820
The oriental fabulist or polyglot tr. of Esop's & o. anc. fables into Hindoostanee, Persian &c. 8°. Calcutta. 1803
The strangers Indian guide to the Hindoostanee. 2nd ed. 8°. 1808
Gilchrist (Robert Murray). A Peakland faggot. Coll. sh. stories. Pref. by E. Phillpotts. s8°. [1926]
Gilchrist (Robert Niven).
Principles of political sci. s8°. Bombay. 1921
Gildas. De excidio Britanniae, *see* BERTRAM (C. J.) Brit. gentium ant. scr. : G. &c., 1757.
Gilder (Jeannette Leonard), *see* LATHROP (G. P.) Represent. poems ; pref. by J. L. G., 1886.
Gildon (Charles), *see* BETTERTON (T.) Life of T. B. [by C. G.], &c., 1710.
Giles, *Franciscan, of Assisi, d. 1262, see* BELCARI (F.) Prose, t2, Vita di Frate Egidio ; pubbl. O. Gigli, 1843.
Giles (Herbert Allen). Chaos in China. s8°. C. 1924
Civiliz. of China. [Home Univ. Lib.] [repr.] s8°. [1919]
Gems of Chinese lit. rev. & enl. 4°. Shanghai. 1922
„ „ ....2ⁿᵈ ed. rev. & enl. 2[v]. 8°. 1926
Quips f. a Chinese jest-book. Tr. H. A. Giles. 8°. Shanghai. 1925
Giles (John). The tryal of John Giles for attempt to assassinate &c. J. Arnold. [P525]. sfol. 1681
Giles (William), *a Protestant footman.* A defence of Dr. Sherlock's Preservative agst. Popery. 2ⁿᵈ ed. [P2661]. s4°. 1688
Gilét alla Greca. Norme e regole d. giuoco G. alla G. [P2839]. s8°. Venezia. 1901
Gilferding (Aleksandr F.), *see* HILFERDING (A. F.)
Gilfillan (George). A third gallery of lit. portraits. s8°. E. 1854
Gilfillan (James). The Sabbath viewed in light of reason, &c. 2ⁿᵈ ed. s8°. E. 1862
Gilgamesh. The epic of G. New tr. f. collation of cuneiform tablets in Brit. Mus. into Eng. hexameters by R. C. Thompson. 4°. 1928
see BRITISH MUSEUM : ANTIQ. Babylonian story of deluge & the epic of G. [by E. A. W. Budge], 1920.
Gilhofer & Ranschburg, *booksellers, Vienna.* Catalogue of books &c. Nᵒˢ. 157, 168, 170, 172 [*in 1v*], 180. 8°. & la8°. Vienna. [1923–25]
Early newspapers. Catalogue 183. 8°. 1925
Incunabula & 16. cent. books. [Cat. 190, 192, 195]. la8°. Wien. [1926–27]
Gilhofer (H.) and (H.) Ranschburg, *Lucerne.* Eaux-fortes, lithographies &c. des gr. maitres fr. du 19ᵉ s. Vente aux enchères. la8°. Lucerne. 1926
Kat. e. Privatsamml. v. Kupferstichen, &c. d. 15. bis 18. Jhdts. Versteig. Juni 1926 *&* Nov. 1926. la8°. Luzern. 1926
Kat. e. Samml. v. Kupferst. &c. 15–19. Jhdts., Versteig. d. G. & R. la8°. Luzern. 1925
Orig. etchings & engravings. Cat. Nᵒˢ. 1, 4, 6–8. la8°. Lucerne. [1924–27]
Sammlung v. Kupferstichen alt. Meister d. 15. bis 19. Jhdts., Versteig. 18.–20. Nov. 1924. 4°. Luzern. [1924]
Gilino (Corradino). De morbo Gall. (Ferrara), 1497, *facs., see* SUDHOFF (C.) Earliest pr. lit. on syphilis, 1925.
Gill (C. Lovett), *see* RICHARDSON (A. E.) & C. L. G. Regional architecture in W. of England, 1924.
Gill (Charles Clifford). What happened at Jutland : tactics of the battle. 8°. N.Y. [1921]
Gill (Conrad). Government & people : intr. to st. of citizenship. By C. G. w. collab. of C. W. Valentine. s8°. [1921]
The rise of the Irish linen industry. 8°. O. 1925
Gill (*Sir* **David),** *see* FORBES (G.) D. G., man & astronomer &c., 1916.
Gill (*Capt.* **N. J.)** The flyer's guide. Elem. hdbk. 8°. 1916
Gill (Thomas).
Hist. & topog. of Glen Osmond. 8°. Adelaide. 1905
Gill (*Capt.* **William J.),** *see* YULE (*Sir* H.) Essay introd. to G.'s "River of golden sand," 1880.
Gill (Wilson Lindsley). A new citizenship. Democracy systemat. for moral & civic training. Intr. by P. Du Bois. s8°. [1913]
Gillane (John). *Life of J. Sage. s8°. 1714
*Some remarks upon Sir James Dalrymple's Historical coll. With ans. to the Vindication of eccles. part. s8°. E. 1714
see DALRYMPLE (*Sir* J.) A vindic., in ans. to a pamphl. [by J. G.], 1714.
Gillard (Marcel). La Roumanie nouvelle. s8°. 1922
Gille (Pernette). Un amour. Roman. s8°. [1921]
Gille (Philippe), *see* GONDINET (E.) & P. G. Lakmé, 1885.
Gillen (Francis James), *see* SPENCER (*Sir* B.) & F. J. G. The Arunta, 2v, 1927.
Gillen (John Lewis). Poverty & dependency, th. relief & prevention. 8°. N.Y. 1922
Gilles (Maurice), *see* GAUCHEZ (MAURICE), *ps.*
Gillespie (George), *minister at Edinburgh.* *An assertion of the govt. of the Ch. of Scot. &c. With a postscript in ans to a treatise agst. Presbyteriall govt. [*w. sep. pagin.*] s4°. E. 1644
*A dispute agst. the English-Popish ceremonies obtruded upon the Ch. of Scot. &c. s4°. [Edinburgh ?]. 1660
Works, w. mem. by W. M. Hetherington, *see* PRESBYTERIAN'S armoury, v1, 2, 1844–46.
Gillespie (James), *architect.* Details of Scottish domestic architecture, 16–17 c. Intr. & descr. text by J. G. [Edinb Arch. Assoc.] fol. E. 192[illegible]
Gillespie (James Edward). The influence of oversea expansion on England to 1700. [Columbia Univ., St. in hist. &c. 91] 8°. N.Y. 192[illegible]
Gillespie (*Sir* **Robert Rollo),** *see* THORNTON (L. H.) Campaigners, 1925.

Gillet (*Capitaine*), *see* JOUVIN (G.) & *Capt.* G. Marches & chansons des soldats de France, 1919.
Gillet (Louis). La bataille de Verdun. s8°. 1921
see CARNAVALET. Les gr. salons litt., 17e & 18e siècles; intr. par L. G., 1928.
,, HANOTAUX (G.), *ed.* Hist. de la nation franç., t11, Hist. des arts; par L. G., 1922.
Gillet (Ransom H.) Democracy in the U.S. s8°. N.Y. 1868
Gillet de La Tessonerie (—). Le campagnard: comédie (1657), *see* FOURNEL (V.) Contemps. de Molière, t3, 1875.
Gillett (Henry J.), *see* BLOUNT (B.) Cement; by B., ass. by W. H. Woodcock & H. J. G., 1920.
Gilliard (Pierre). 13 years at the Russian court: last yrs. &c. of Nicholas II &c. Tr. F. A. Holt. 8°. [1921]
Le tragique destin de Nicolas II et de sa famille. 8°. 1921
Gilliat-Smith (Ernest).
St. Anthony of Padua, accord. to h. contemp. s8°. 1926
Some notes conc. the Sacred Constantinian Order. [P2618]. 8°. 1922
Gillies (John), *D.D., minister of the College Church, Glasgow.* Hist. coll. rel. to remark. periods of the success of the Gospel. 2v. 8°. Glasgow. 1754
Gillies (Patrick H.) Netherlorn, Argyllshire, &c. 4°. 1909
Gillin (John Lewis). Criminology & penology. 8°. [1927]
Gillings (James). The Psalms of David metric. arr. in Tamil. s8°. Madras. 1891
Gillingwater (Edmund). Hist. & descr. acc. of St. Edmund's Bury. s8°. St. Edmund's Bury. 1804
Gilliodts van Severen (Louis), *see* BRUGES. Invent. des archives de B.; [publ. par L. G.-van S.], sect. 1, 9v, 1871–85.
Gillman (Frederick John). Evol. of the Eng. hymn. Foreword by Sir H. W. Davies. 8°. 1927
Gillman (James Benjamin), *see* CROOK (W.) J. B. G., 1889.
Gillman (Lucy Eleanor), *see* WATSON (*Mrs.* L. E.)
Gillouin (René). Esquisses litt. & morales. s8°. 1926
Gillpatrick (Wallace) ["THE MAN WHO LIKES MEXICO."]
Wanderings in Mexico. 8°. 1912
Gilman (Arthur).
see CHURCH (A. J.) & A. G. Carthage, 5th ed., 1890.
,, LANE-POOLE (S.) The Moors in Spain; by L.-P., w. collab. of G., 1890.
Gilman (Nicholas Paine). Profit sharing. s8°. Boston. 1917
Gilmore (Charles Whitney). Contrib. to vertebr. palæontology, *see* CANADA: GEOL. SURVEY. Museum bull. 38, 1924.
Fossil footprints f. the Grand Canyon, *see* SMITHSONIAN INST. Misc. colls., v77, 1926.
New Sauropod dinosaur, *see* SMITHSONIAN INST. Misc. coll., v72, 1922.
Osteology of the carnivorous Dinosauria in the U.S. Nat. Mus., w. spec. ref. to the genera Antrodemus & Ceratosaurus. [S.I. U.S. Nat. Mus.; Bull. 110]. 4°. Wash. 1920
Gilmore (Melvin Randolph). Uses of plants by the Indians of the Missouri River Region, *see* SMITHSONIAN INST.: B. OF ETHN. Rep. 33, 1919.
Gilmour (James), *see* NAIRNE (W. P.) G. of the Mongols, 1924.
Gilmour (T. L.) Finland, *see* BUCHAN (J.), *ed.* Nations of to-day, Baltic & Caucasian States, 1923.
Gilpin (Bernard), *rector of Houghton, see* GILPIN (W.) The life of B. G., 1753.
Gilpin (William), *Governor of Colorado.*
Mission of the N. Amer. people. 8°. Phila. 1873
Gilpin (William), *prebendary of Salisbury.* Forest scenery. Ed., w. notes & intr. by F. G. Heath. 8°. 1879
Earlier eds. h. t. Remarks on forest scenery, *q.v.*
The life of Bernard Gilpin. 2nd ed. 8°. 1753
Life of Cranmer. 8°. 1784
The lives of J. Wicliff; & of his disciples: Lord Cobham, J. Huss, Jerome of Prague, & Zisca. 8°. 1765
see FOSBROKE (T. D.) The Wye tour, or G. on the Wye, 3rd ed., 1826.
Gilson (Etienne).
Études de philos. médiévale. la8°. Strasbourg. 1921
La philos. au Moyen Age. s8°. 1925
La philos. de St. Bonaventure. la8°. 1924
The philosophy of St. Thomas Aquinas. Auth. tr. f. 3rd rev. ed. of "Le Thomisme." Tr. E. Bullough. Ed. G. A. Elrington. s8°. C. 1924
St. Thomas d'Aquin. [Moralistes chrét.] 3e éd. s8°. 1925
see DESCARTES (R.) Discours de la méthode: texte, & comm. par E. G., 1925.
Gilson (Julius Parnell). Friar Alexander & h. hist. interpret. of the Apocalypse, *see* COLLECTANEA Franciscana, v2, 1922.

Gilson (Julius Parnell) [*continued*].
see BRIT. MUSEUM: MSS. Cat. of Western MSS. in the old Royal & King's Coll.; by Sir G. F. Warner & J. P. Gilson, 4v, 1921.
,, GREG (W. W.) Eng. lit. autographs, 1550–1650: sel. &c. W. W. G. in collab. w. J. P. G. &c., pl, 1925.
Gimenez Romera (Waldo). Crón. de la prov. de Logroño, 1867, *see* ESPAÑA. Crón. gen., v10, 1865 &c.
Crón. de las Islas Canarias, 1868, *see* ESPAÑA. Crón. gen., v12, 1865 &c.
Gimeno de Flaquer (Concepción).
Suplicio de una coqueta. Novela. s8°. Mexico. 1885
Gimlette (Thomas), *D.D.* Hist. of the Huguenot settlers in Ireland & o. lit. remains [*incl.* The settlement in Waterford, The Synods of Cashel, Feuds of the Bps. of Waterford & Lismore, Annals of Danish Ch. of St. Olaf's, *each w. sep. pagin.*] la8°. *p.f.p.c.* [1888]
Gimpera (Pedro Bosch), *see* BOSCH GIMPERA (P.)
Ginisty (Paul).
Les anc. boulevards. s8°. [1925]
Bocage. 8°. 1926
La comédienne & les 3 inconnus, *see* ŒUVRES libres, 65, 1926.
Mademoiselle Gogo, Mlle. Beauménard de la Comédie-Fr., 1730–99. s8°. 1913
La Terreur. s8°. 1920
—— & M. Gagneur. Hist. de la Guerre par les combattants. [t]3, Verdun. s8°. [1921]
Ginsberg (Morris). The psychology of society. s8°. [1921]
Ginsburg (Christian David). The Kabbalah; its doctrines, development & lit. 2nd ed. s8°. 1920
see MASSORAH. The M. comp. f. MSS. alphab. & lex. arranged by C. D. G., 4v, 1880–1905.
Ginters (Waldemar). Das Schwert d. Skythen u. Sarmaten in Südrussland. [Vorgesch. Forsch.; hrsg. M. Ebert, B2ii]. la8°. 1928
Ginza. G., der Schatz, oder d. grosse Buch d. Mandäer. Übers. u. erkl. v. M. Lidzbarski. la8°. Göttingen. 1925
Ginzel (Friedrich Carl). Histor. Sonnenfinsternisse &c., *see* KÖN.-PREUSS. AKAD. Abh., Phys.-math. Klasse, 1918.
Gioberti (Vincenzo). Meditazioni filosof. ined. Pubbl. E. Solmi. s8°. 1909
see ANZILOTTI (A.) V. G. e il fallimento d. guerre federale, 1920.
,, CALCATERRA (C.) Gli studi danteschi di V. G., 1922.
,, DORIA (A.) Un Giobertiano di Toscana: V. Salvagnoli n. suoi rapp. con V. G., 1922.
,, RUBERTIS (A. DE). V. G. e la Costit. di G. Montanelli, 1923.
,, —— V. G. e la vertenza tosco-piemont. d. Lunigiana, 1927.
—— & G. Massari. Gioberti-Massari, carteggio, 1838–52. Pubbl. e annot. da G. Balsamo-Crivelli. s8°. Torino. 1920
Giogalli (Simone). Scr. ined. int. la decadenza d. commercio di Venezia. [*Ed.* E. Cicogna] [Nozze Reali-Beretta. N123]. la8°. Venezia. 1856
Gioliti de' Ferrari, *Family of, printers, see* BUTLER (A. J.) The G. & th. press at Venice, 1910.
Giolitti (Giovanni). Mem. d. mia vita. Con studio di O. Malagodi. 3° migl. 2v. 8°. Milano. 1922
Mem. of my life. Tr. E. Storer. Intr. by O. Malagodi. 8°. [1923]
Giolla Meidhre (Brian), *see* MERRIMAN (B.)
Giordani (Pietro), *see* FRATI (C.) L. Scarabelli, P. G. e i "Paralipomeni di st. piemontese," 1919.
Giordano (Nicola). Il diritto marittimo sicil. d. orig. al s. 14, *see* SOCIETÀ SICILIANA. Archivio, N.S., 43, 44, 1921–22.
Giordano (Oreste). L'on. L. Gasparotto. la8°. Milano. 1919
Giorgi (Antonio Agostino) [GEORGIUS (A. A.)] Alphabetum Tibetanum &c. 2p. [*pagin. contin.*] 4°. Romae. 1762
Giorgi (Carlo). *Della storia del padre Girolamo Savonarola libri quattro. [*attrib. to V. Bassanti*]. s4°. Livorno. 1782
Giorgini-Manzoni (Vittoria), *formerly* V. MANZONI. V. e M. Manzoni: memorie di V. G.-M., *see* MANZONI (A.) M. intimo, v1, 1923.
Giornale critico della filosofia italiana. Diretto da G. Gentile. v3–8 (1922–27). 8°. Messina. [1922–27]
Giornale storico d. letteratura italiana. Diretto da V. Cian. v74–90. 8°. Torino. 1919–27
,, ,, Suppl. 19–21, Misc. Dantesca. 8°. Torino. 1921
,, ,, Suppl. 22–23. 8°. Torino. 1924
Fatini (G.) Su la fortuna e l'autenticità delle liriche di L. Ariosto, 1924. [23.]
Mistruzzi (V.) Giov. Cotta, 1924. [22.]

Giotto.
see MARLE (R. v.) Rech. sur l'iconogr. de G. &c., 1920.
„ ROSENTHAL (E.) G. in d. mittelalterl. Geistesentwicklung, 1924.
„ SUPINO (I. B.) Giotto, 2v, 1920.
Giovagnoli (Enrico). Città di Castello. Monog. storico-art. 8°. Città di Castello. 1921
Giovagnoli (Raffaello). Risorgimento ital., 1815–48. [Storia polit. d'Italia scr. da una soc. di professori ; *publ.* Vallardi]. la8°. Milano. *n.d.*
Giovanna II, *d' Angiò, see* JOANNA II, *q. of Naples.*
Giovanni [GIULIANO], *da Lucca, dominican.* Relation des Tartares &c., *see* BERNARD (J. F.), *ed.* Recueil de voy., t7, 1725.
Giovannini (Luigi).
Notizie sul Giuoco del Ponte di Pisa. 8°. Firenze. 1906
Giovannozzi (Giovanni), *see* DANTE ALIGHIERI. Lectura D.: c. 24 del Paradiso letto da G. G., 1912.
Gippius (Zinaida Nikolaevna).
Стихи, дневникъ, 1911–21. s8°. [Берлинъ]. 1922
The green ring. A play. Auth. tr. by S. S. Koteliansky. s8°. 1920
Mon journal sous la Terreur; tr. par H. Mongault, *see* MEREJKOVSKY (D. S.) Le règne de l'Antéchrist., 1921.
see MEREJKOVSKY (D. S.), Z. N. G. &c. Царство Антихриста, 1921.
Gipps (G.) The fighting in N. China. 8°. 1901
Gipps (*Sir* **George),** *1791–1847, see* AUSTRALIA. Hist. records, v19–25 (1837–46), 1923–25.
Giraldi Cinthio (Giov. Batt.) Le fiamme. s8°. Vinegia. 1547
Giraldus, *Cambrensis.* De invectionibus; [ed. w. intr.] by W. S. Davies, *see* CYMMRODORION. Y Cymmrodor, v30, 1920.
Giraldus (Lilius Gregorius).
De re nautica libellus. s8°. Basileæ. 1540
Girard (Georges).
La jeunesse d'Anatole France, 1844–76. 4e éd. s8°. 1925
Vie de L. Hoche. 11e éd. 8°. 1926
Girard (Guillaume). *The hist. of the life of the Duke of Espernon. Engl. by C. Cotton. In 3p. fol. 1670
Girard (Henri). Émile Deschamps, 1791–1871. [Un bourgeois dilettante]. 2t. la8°. 1921
t2 *has t.* E. Deschamps dilettante.
—— & H. Moncel. Bibliogr. des œuvres de E. Renan. [Soc. E. Renan. Publ., v1]. 8°. 1923
Girard (Jean Baptiste), *Jesuit.* A defence of G. agst. the accus. of M. C. Cadière. [*b. w.* Cadière (M. C.) Case against J. B. G.] 3p *in* 1v. s8°. D. 1731
Recueil de toutes les pièces du procez entre le père J. B. Girard & Catherine Cadière &c. 5t. 8°. Amsterdam. 1732
see CADIÈRE (M. C.) Case of M. C. C. against J. B. G., 1731.
Girard (Joseph).
Avignon: hist. sommaire, guide. 8°. Avignon. 1923
Girardin (Emile de). L'homme & la femme: lettre à Dumas fils. 9e éd. s8°. 1872
Girardin (*Mme.* **Emile de)** [† GAY (DELPHINE), *aft. Girardin*].
Marguerite ou deux amours. s8°. 1856
Nouvelles. [Le lorgnon, La canne de M. de Balzac, Il ne faut pas jouer avec la douleur. *b. w. h.* Marguerite, 1856]. s8°. 1856
see MALO (H.) La gloire du Vicomte de Launay, Delphine Gay de G., 1925.
„ —— Une muse & sa mère, 1924.
Giraud (—). *Consider. resp. marriage of the D. of Montpensier, w. ref. to the Treaty of Utrecht. 8°. 1847
Giraud (Charles Joseph Barthélemy). Les bronzes d'Osuna: fragm. nouv. découv. de la loi coloniale de Genetiva Julia. la8°. 1874
Les bronzes d'Osuna. Remarques nouv. [*b. w. h.* Bronzes d'Osuna, 1874]. la8°. 1875
Les nouv. bronzes d'Osuna. n. éd., rev. &c. [*b. w. h.* Bronzes d'Osuna, 1874]. la8°. 1877
Giraud (Edoardo). Le mie memorie [*&* Qui-pro-quo & I duu ors]. Con pref. di R. Simoni. 8°. Milano. 1911
Giraud (Eugène), *see* LEMOISNE (P. A.) Les soirées de Louvre: aquarelles d'E. G., 1920.
Giraud (Victor).
Passions & romans d'autrefois; [Aimée de Coigny, Chateaubriand]. 8°. 1925
Le Gén. de Castelnau. s8°. 1921
Georges Goyau, l'homme & l'œuvre. [2e éd.] s8°. 1922
Les maîtres de l'heure. M. Barrès. s8°. 1922
La vie héroïque de B. Pascal. s8°. [1923]

Giraudet (Eugène). Traité de la danse. t2. 8°. 1900
Giraudoux (Jean).
Adorable Clio. s8°. 1920
Bella. [Les cahiers verts, 61]. s8°. 1926
Eglantine. s8°. 1927
Elpénor. s8°. 1926
Juliette au pays des hommes. s8°. 1924
Siegfried & le limousin. s8°. 1922
Simon le pathétique. s8°. 1918
Suzanne & le Pacifique. s8°. 1921
Girault (Arthur). The colonial tariff policy of France. Ed. C. Gide. [C.E. for Internat. Peace &c.] la8°. O. 1916
Girdle. Girdle (The) of Aphrodite; tr. by F. A. Wright, w. intr., 1923, *see* ANTHOLOGIA GRAECA.
Girdlestone, *The family of, see* GIRDLESTONE (R. B.) Genealog. notes on G. family, 1904.
Girdlestone (Robert Baker). Genealogical notes on the Girdlestone family. [*With many MS. notes by var. hands*]. 4°. *p.p.* 1904
Girke (Georg). Die Tracht d. Germanen in d. vor- u. frühgesch. Zeit. 2B. 8°. L. 1922
Girolamo Maria, *di Sant' Anna, Carmelite.* Della storia geneal. d. famiglia del Ponte. pl. fol. in Napoli. 1708
Giron (Alexandro), *ps., see* AFAN DE RIBERA (F.) La virtud al uso &c.; asunto y tema A. G. instruy. á su hijo, 1820.
Gironci (Maria). Recipes of Ital. cookery. Tr. & arr. by M. G. s8°. [1892]
Gironi (Robustiano).
Raccolta di lirici ital., sino al sec. 18. 8°. Milano. 1808
Girq thlthotz: [Book of letters of the patriarchs, *in Armenian*], 1901, *see* LETTERS.
Girtin (Thomas), *see* STOKES (H.) G. & Bonington, 1922.
Girty (George Herbert), *paleontologist.* Report on upper paleozoic fossils coll. in China 1903–04, *see* WILLIS (B.), E. BLACKWELDER &c. Research in C., v3, 1913.
Gisalberti (Andreas) [SANTE BALLARINI], *see* PETHERICK (H.) J. Guarnerius, h. work & h. master [*i.e.* A. G.], 1906.
Gisbert (Miguel de Toro y), *see* TORO Y GISBERT (M. DE).
Gisborne (Thomas), *the elder, prebendary of Durham.* An enquiry into the duties of men in the higher middle classes of society in Gt. Brit. &c. 7th ed. 2v. 8°. 1824
Enquiry into the duties of the female sex. 9th ed., corr. s8°. 1813
Gisborne (Thomas), *the younger, M.P.* On pres. crisis. Addr. to electors of N. Derbyshire. [P2782]. 8°. 1834
Giselinus (Victor). In A. Prudentii Clementis opera comm., *see* PRUDENTIUS CLEMENS (A.), 1564.
Gisinger (Friedrich).
Die Erdbeschreibung d. Eudoxos v. Knidos. 8°. L. 1921
Gislebert, *of Mons* [GISLEBERTUS *Montensis*]. Chronicon Hanoniense ex rec. W. Arndt. Rec. fecit G. H. Pertz. [Scr. rerum Germ. in usum schol.] 8°. Hannoverae. 1869
Gissing (Algernon), *see* GISSING (G. R.) Letters; coll. &c. by A. G. &c., 1927.
Gissing (George R.)
The immortal Dickens. [Intr. signed B. W. M.] 8°. [1925]
Letters. Coll. &c. by A. & E. Gissing. Pref. by h. son [A. C. Gissing]. 8°. 1927
Odd women. [repr.] s8°. 1915
A victim of circumstances & o. s. s8°. 1927
see SWINNERTON (F. A.) G. G.: a crit. study, n. ed., 1924.
„ YATES (M.) G. G.: an apprec., 1922.
Gitti (Alberto). Eudossia e Genserico, *see* ARCHIVIO STOR. ITAL., a. 83ii, 1925.
Giuliani (Giovanni Battista), *see* CAETANI (M.) Carteggio dantesco del Duca di Sermoneta con G. G. &c., 1883.
Giuliani (Vincenzo). Mem. storiche, polit., eccl. d. città di Vieste. 8°. Napoli. 1768
Giuliano, *da Sangallo, see* HÜLSEN (C.) Escurialensis u. Sangallo, 1910.
Giulietta, *contessa di Sciacca, daughter of Count Roger I of Sicily* [JULLITA], *see* SCATURRO (I.) La Contessa normanna G. de S., 1921.
Giuliotti (Domenico) & G. Papini.
Diz. dell' omó salvatico. v1. 8°. Firenze. [1923]
Giunta [JUNTA], *The family of, see* BAUDRIER (H. L.) Bibliog. lyonnaise, s6, 1904.
Giuseppi (M. S.) A guide to the MSS. in the Public Record Office. 2v. 8°. 1923–24
Naturaliz. of foreign Protestants in the Amer. & West Indian colonies. Ed. M. S. G. [Huguenot Soc. of London, 24]. 4°. M'ter. 1921
Giusti (Ant. Dall' Acqua), *see* DALL' ACQUA GIUSTI (A.)
Giusti (Giuseppe). Scritti ed. e ined. Con intr. &c., a cura di F. Martini. s8°. Firenze. 1924
Giusti (Vincenzo). Irene, tragedia. s8°. Venetia. 1579

Giustinian (Antonio), *see* SALTINI (G. E.) A. G. &c., 1877.
Giustinian (Girolamo Ascanio), *1721–91.* Terminazione per il Cairo, *see* BOLDRIN (G.), *ed.* Due scritture &c., 1872.
Giustiniani (Andreolo). Relaz. dell' attacco e difesa di Scio nel 1431; [*poem*] ed. G. Porro-Lambertenghi, *see* REGIA DEP. DI STORIA PATRIA. Misc., t6, 1865.
Giustiniani (Bernardo), *procurator of St. Marks* [GIUSTINIANO].
Hist. d. orig. di Venetia. Tr. da L. Domenichi. s8°. Venetia. 1608
Giustiniani (Giannettino), *see* MAZARIN (*le card.*) Lettere a G. G., patrizio di Genova; ed. V. Ricci, 1863.
Giustiniano (Benedetto), *jesuit* [JUSTINIANUS]. In omnes Catholicas epist. explanat. [2p. *w. sep. pagin.*] fol. Lugduni. 1621
In omnes Pauli epistolas explan. 2t. fol. Lugduni. 1612–13
Giustiniano (Orsatto). Rime, *see* MAGNO (C.) Rime, 1600.
Giustiniano (Pietro).
Dell' historie venetiane, sino all. 1575. s4°. Venetia. 1671
Giuvo (Nicoló). Eco e Narciso: serenata. [N125]. 8°. Nap. 1708
Given (John James), *Ph.D.*
The truth of Scr. in conn. w. revelation, &c. 8°. E. 1881
Givry (Marie Louise Charlotte de Pelard de), *ctsse. de Fontaines, see* FONTAINES.
Gjandschezian (Levon), *see* TÜBINGEN, *university.* Hauptkat. d. Universitätsbibl.; Verzeichnis d. arm. Hss., v. F. N. Finck & L. G., 1907.
Gjerset (Knut). Hist. of Iceland. 8°. [1922]
Hist. of the Norwegian people. 2v. 8°. N.Y. 1915
Gjorgi (Ignaziu). Vulgatae Psalmorum ed. &c. Illyrica metaphrasis, sive Saltjer Slovinki Spjevan po I. G. 4°. Venetiis. 1729
Gladden (*Rev.* Washington).
Working people & th. employers. 8°. Boston [U.S.] 1876
Gladkov (Fedor). Цемент: роман. [Соб. соч., т2]. 2ое изд. 8°. Москва. 1926
Gladstone (*Mrs.* Catherine), *wife of Rt. Hon. W. E. Gladstone, see* DREW (*Mrs.* M.) C. G., 1919.
Gladstone (Cecil Ernest).
Biluchi hand-book. By C. E. G. &c. sfol. Lahore. 1874
Gladstone (*Miss* Florence M.) Aubrey House, Kensington, 1698–1920. Comp. by F. M. G. 8°. 1922
Notting Hill in bygone days. 8°. 1924
Gladstone (*Rt. Hon.* William Ewart).
*Apology for the life of W. E. G. 8°. 1885
The Church of Eng. & ritualism. Repr. fr. Contemp. Rev. & revis. 8°. [1875]
*Pax. The Vatican Decrees & Catholic allegiance. Reply to G.'s polit. expost. By A Monk of St. Augustine's, Ramsgate. [P2576]. 8°. 1874
see BIGELOW (J.) Lest we forget: G., Morley & the Confed. Loan of 1863, 1905.
,, BURDETT (O.) W. E. G., 1927.
,, CAPEL (T. J.) Reply to W. E. G.'s "Polit. expostul.", 1874.
see CURRY (*Rev.* J.) Catholicity, liberty, allegiance: on G.'s Expostulation, 1875.
,, DREW (*Mrs.* M.) Acton, G. &c., 1924.
,, HARRISON (F.) Mr. G.!—or anarchy, *n.d.*
,, SOMERVELL (D. C.) Disraeli & G., 1925.
,, TEUFELSDRÖCKH, *Jun.* Gladstone govt., 1885.
,, ULTRAMONTANE. An U.'s reply to Mr. G.'s Expost., 1874.
,, UMBRA OXONIENSIS. Results of the "Expostulation of W. E. G." &c., 1875.
Gladwin (Francis). The hist. of Hindostan &c. v1 (Jehángír). [No more publ.] 4°. Calcutta. 1788
Glagol (Sergei). М. В. Нестеровъ: жизнь и творчество. [Grabar (I.) Русс. художники, 5]. 4°. Москва. [1914?]
see TRETYAKOV GALLERY. Москов. Городская Худож. Галлерея П. и С. М. Третьяковыхъ: текстъ И. С. Остроухова и С. Г., 2t, 1909.
Glagolita Clozianus, 1836, *see* KOPITAR (B.), *ed.*
Glanius (—). A new voyage to the East-Indies; acc. of Bantam &c. [Tr.] 2nd ed. corr. &c. s8°. 1682
Glanvill (*Sir* John) [GLANVILLE]. Reports of certain cases determined by the Commons in Parl. [1623–24]. Coll. by J. G. 8°. 1775
Glanville, *The House of, see* GLANVILLE-RICHARDS (W. U. S.) Records of Anglo-Norman House of G., 1050–1880, 1882.
Glanville (Bartholomew de), *see* PERDRIZET (P.) La plus anc. descr. de la Lorraine [*f. B. de G.*], 1909.
Glanville-Richards (Wm. Urmston Searle). Records of the Anglo-Norman House of Glanville, 1050–1880. 4°. 1882
Glascock (William Nugent). *Naval sketch-book; or, the Service afloat & ashore. By an officer of rank [*i.e.* W. N. G.] 2v. 8°. 1826
*Sailors & saints. 3v. 8°. 1829

Gläsener (Justus Martin) [J. M. GLAESENERUS]. Comm. de gemino Judaeorum Messia. [*b. w.* Mosheim (J. L.) Hist. Tartar. eccl., 1791]. s4°. Helmstadii. 1739
Glaser (Curt). Die Graphik d. Neuzeit. la8°. 1922
Die Kunst Ostasiens: d. Umkreis ihr. Denkens &c. 2e A. 8°. L. 1920
Lukas Cranach. la8°. L. 1921
Ostasiat. Plastik. [Kunst d. Ostens; hrsg. W. Cohn, B11]. la8°. 1925
Glaser (Eduard). Die Abessinier in Arabien u. Afrika. 8°. München. 1895
Glasgow.
Account of the grand masonic procession, at laying the foundation-stone of the 1st building in London Street. 8°. Glasgow. 1824
The burgesses & guild-Brethren of G., 1573–1750. Ed. J. R. Anderson. [Scot. Rec. Soc.] 8°. E. 1923–25
Charters & o. doc. rel. to G., 1175–[1707]. Ed. Sir J. D. Marwick [*&* R. Renwick. Scott. Burgh Rec. Soc.] 2v [*in* 3, v1 *in* 2p]. la8°. Glasgow. 1894–1906
The City of G., its origin, growth &c., w. maps &c. [*By var. wr.*] M. I. Newbigin, ed. [Roy. Scott. Geogr. Soc. *Extr. f.* Scott. Geogr. Mag., v37]. la8°. E. 1921
Extracts f. the records of the burgh of G., 1573–[1833]. [Ed. Sir J. D. Marwick & R. Renwick. v1–4, Scott. Burgh Rec. Soc. 5–11, pr. for the Corpor. of Glasgow]. [11v]. la8°. Glasgow. 1876–1916
*G. delineated, or a descr. &c. s8°. Glasgow. 1824
Post Office directory, 1917–18, *see* POST OFFICE DIRECTORIES.
PUBLIC LIBRARIES.
G. Corpor. Public Lib. Bull. of add., classified &c. No. 3. 8°. Glasgow. 1925
UNIVERSITY OF GLASGOW.
Dept. of Italian Studies, *see* QUIGLEY (H.) Italy & the rise of a new school of crit. in 18th c., 1921.
Glasgow (The) courant, *aft.* "THE WEST-COUNTRY INTELLIGENCE," *see* STEWART (W.) The first Glasgow newspaper: "The G. c." [1715], 1924.
Glasgow looking glass. v1, No. 1–18, New ser., v1, No. 1, 2 (June 1825–June 1826). [*Bound in* 1v]. fol. [Glasgow. 1825–26]
After the 1st 6 No. of v1 the title is changed to Northern looking glass.
Glasgow (Ellen).
Barren ground. s8°. [1925]
,, ,, ...s8°. N.Y. 1925
The battle-ground. s8°. Westminster. 1902
Glasgow (George). From Dawes to Locarno. Achievement in Europ. diplomacy, 1924–25. 8°. 1925
MacDonald as diplomatist; foreign policy. Foreword by G. P. Gooch. 8°. [1924]
The Minoans. 8°. [1923]
Ronald Burrows: a memoir. Foreword by E. K. Veniselos. 8°. [1924]
Glasier (John Bruce). William Morris & the early days of the Socialist movement. With letters addr. by M. to the a. Pref. by M. Morris. s8°. 1921
Glaspell (Susan), *wife of G. C. Cook.*
Bernice. Play. [*b. w. h.* The verge, 1924]. 8°. 1924
Fidelity. [5th impr.] s8°. 1924
,, ...[6th impr.] s8°. 1925
The glory of the conquered. s8°. 1925
Inheritors. Play. [*b. w. h.* The verge, 1924]. 8°. 1924
The road to the temple. [Life of G. C. Cook. 2nd impr.] 8°. 1926
Trifles, & 6 o. short plays (2 wr. in collab. w. G. C. Cook). 8°. 1926
The verge. Play. 8°. 1924
***Glass** (The) of fashion. Some social reflect. By a gentleman with a duster. s8°. [1921]
Glass Sellers Company. Essays on the glass trade in England. Publ. by the Co. of G.S. 8°. 1883
see YOUNG (S.) Hist. of the Co. of G.S., 1913.
Glass (Andrew). Tales & traditions of Ayrshire & Galloway. s8°. Glasgow. 1873
Glass (Frederick J.)
Drawing, design, & craft-work. 8°. [1920]
The industrial arts. 8°. 1927
Pewter craft. 8°. 1927
Glass (J. G. H.) Rep. on concessions of Pekin Syndicate in Prov. of Shansi & Honan. fol. *n.p.* 1899
Glass (Salomon). Evangelic. & epistolic. textuum, qui dominicis & festis diebus in eccl. tractari solent, exegesis. 4p. s4°. Gotae. 1647–49
Opuscula. Christologia Mosaica—Christologia Davidica—'Ονοματολογία Messiae prophetica &c. T. Crenius conlegit, rec. &c. Acc. M. Waltheri Threnologia &c. s4°. Lugd. Batav. 1700
Glassberger (Nicolaus). Major cronica Boemorum mod., 1200–1310, *see* SETON (W. W.) N. G. & h. works, 1923.

Glasse (*Mrs.* **Hannah**). The complete confectioner. 8°. [1770 ?]

Glasshouse Street Tabernacle, *see* LEICESTER FIELDS.

Glasspool (Alfred John). The Corpor. of the City of London: its ceremonies &c. s8°. 1924

Glaubensbekantnus [*see also* BEKENNTNISS]. *Christl. u. allein auf Gottes wort gegründete G.—Item Sumarische Erzehlung d. Hist., v. d. Menschen Erschaffung, &c.—Item Der gründl. Bericht T. Erasti vom rechten verstand der wort: Das ist mein leib (1562). [*3 tp. & pagin.*] s8°. Herborn. 1610

Glazebrook (Michael George), *canon of Ely.* The letter & the spirit. Reply to Bp. of Ely's criticisms on The faith of a mod. churchman. s8°. 1920

Glazebrook (*Sir* **Richard Tetley**). A dict. of applied physics. [*By var. wr.*] Ed. Sir R. G. 5v. 8°. 1922–23

Glazier (Richard). Historic textile fabrics. Tradition & develop. of pattern in woven & printed stuffs. la8°. [1923]

Glazunov (Ivan Ilich). Древне-русс. повѣсти и романы. Изд. I. Г. 8°. С.-П. 1895

Gleason (Arthur). What the workers want. St. of Brit. labor. 8°. [1920]

Glebov (N.) Le rôle des Syndicats ouvriers dans la révolution russe. [P2396]. 8°. *n.p.* [1919]

Glee Club, *see* HOBLER (J. P.) Words of the favourite pieces, as performed at the G.C., 1794.

Gleich (*Gen-major* **Gerold v.**)
Die alte Armee u. ihre Verirrungen. 2e A. 8°. L. 1919
Vom Balkan nach Bagdad. Milit.-polit. Erinn. an d. Orient. 8°. 1921

Gleich (Joannes Andreas). Diss. de liturgiis oriental. in doctrina de S. Eucharistia antiq. verit. Evang. contra nov. pontif. errores &c. suffrag. [P427]. s4°. Wittenbergae. [1724]

Gleichen (*Maj.-Gen. Lord* **Albert Edward Wilfrid**).
London's open-air statuary. 8°. 1928
see BUCHAN (J.), *ed.* Nations of to-day; [prep. under care of Ld. G.], 1923.
—— **& John H. Reynolds.** Alphabets of for. lang. transcr. into Eng. acc. to R.G.S. II. system. [R.G.S. Techn. Ser., No. 2]. 8°. 1921

Gleichen-Russwurm (Alexander von). Elegantiae. Gesch. der vornehmen Welt im klass. Alt. [Gesch. der Europ. Gesell. B1]. 8es Tausend. [*1st issue*, 1912]. 8°. St. *n.d.*

Gleig (George Robert).
Life of Wellington. people's ed., rev. w. add. s8°. 1873
*The subaltern. s8°. E. 1825

Gleiwitz. G., e. oberschles. Stadt. Hrsg. v. Dr. Geisler, Schabik &c. [Monogr. deut. Städte, hrsg. E. Stein, B12]. 4°. 1925

Glemby (Harry). Early Eng. lit., mod. first ed. &c. coll. by H. G. To be sold, Nov., Anderson Galleries. [*Illust.*] la8°. N.Y. [1926]

Glen-Coats (A. H.), *see* BEATTIE (W.) Cat. of mod. pictures &c. the properties of W. B., A. H. G.-C. &c., 1924.

Glenconner (Pamela, *Lady*), *formerly Tennant, aft. wife of Visc. Grey.* Shepherd's crowns: essays. 8°. O. 1923
The white wallet. Filled by P. G. 8°. 1912

Glendon (Richard A.) & R. J. Glendon.
Rowing. 8°. Phila. 1923

Glendon (Richard J.), *see* GLENDON (R. A.) & R. J. G. Rowing, 1923.

Glenie (James). The antecedental calculus. [*b. w. h.* Doct. of univ. comparison, 1789]. 4°. 1793
The doctrine of universal comparison, or general proportion. la8°. 1789
*Obs. on the Duke of Richmond's plans of fortific. 8°. 1794

Glenn (Garrard). The army & the law. s8°. N.Y. 1918

Gliddon (George R.)
Ancient Egypt. 13th ed. rev. & corr. la8°. Phila. [1848]

Glimpses. *Glimpses of anc. Hackney &c.; by F. R. C. S., 1894, *see* CLARKE (B.)

Glinka (Mikhail Ivanovich), *see* RIESEMANN (O. v.) Monographien z. russ. Musik, B1, 1923.

Glitsch (Heinrich). Der alamann. Zentenar u. s. Gericht, *see* KÖNIGL. SÄCHS. GESELLS. Berichte, B69, 1917.

Gloag (John) & L. Mansfield.
The house we ought to live in. 8°. [1923]

Globe, *brig, see* HAWAII. Rules &c. adopted by Admiralty Court, 1844.

Globe (Le), *see* TRAHARD (P.) Le romantisme défini par "Le Globe" [1824–31], 1925.

Globe Playhouse, *Southwark.* *Site of the Globe Playhouse, 2nd ed., 1924, *see* BRAINES (W. W.)

Gloria. *Gloria Britannica: or the boast of the Brit. seas. Acc. of Royal Navy of Eng. shewing where each ship was built &c. With every man's pay. Coll. &c. by a true lover of the seamen. [*Pref. signed* A. B.] s4°. 1696
*Gloria Patri &c.: hymns to the Trinity, 2nd ed. 1749; 4th ed. 1764, *see* WESLEY (C.)

Gloria (Andrea). Doc. rel. alla storia padovana. [Nozze Emo-Venier. N. 122]. 8°. Padova. 1867
Pontedibrenta e la Villa Breda. [Nozze Belgrado-Breda. N127]. s8°. Padova. 1866

Glorie. Glorie (Le) de gli Incogniti, 1647, *see* ACCAD. DEGL' INCOGNITI.
Glorie (Le) di Maria madre di Dio, 1780, *see* MARY, *the Virgin.*

Glorieux (*l'abbé* **P.**)
La litt. quodlibétique, 1260–1320. la8°. Kain. 1925

***Glorious** (The) & miraculous battel at York, 1644, *see* MAIDMENT (J.), *ed.* Hist. fragm., p1, 1833.

Glory (The) of the world; or, table of Paradise, *see* HERMETIC MUSEUM, v1, 1893.

Glostrup (Nils Simonsen), *bp., d. 1639.* Visitatser i Oslo og Hamar Stifter 1617–37. Udg. ved L. Daae & H. J. Huitfeldt-Kaas. [Norske Hist. K.] 8°. 1895

Glotz (Gustave).
La civilisation égéenne. 8°. 1923
Le droit des gens dans l'antiq. grecque, *see* ACAD. DES INSCR. &c. Mém., s1, t13i, 1923.
Le travail dans la Grèce ancienne. 8°. 1920
TRANSLATIONS.
The Ægean civilisation. [Tr. M. R. Dobie & E. M. Riley]. 8°. 1925
Ancient Greece at work. [Tr. M. R. Dobie]. 8°. 1926

Glover (Cedric Howard), *see* BURNEY (C.) C. B.'s continent. travels, 1770–72; comp. &c. by G., 1927.

Glover (Halcott), *see* RUBINSTEIN (H. F.) & H. G. Exodus: dram. sequence, 1923.

Glover (James), *see* JONES (E.) Social aspects of psycho-analysis: lect. by E. J., J. G. &c., 1924.

Glover (John).
The Plimsoll sensation. 2nd ed. [P2845]. 8°. 1873

Glover (*Sir* **John Hawley**). The voyage of the Dayspring: journal of Sir J. H. G., w. acc. of exped. up the Niger in 1857, by A. C. G. Hastings. Intr. by Lady Glover. 8°. [1926]

Glover (Richard), *a. of Leonidas.*
Poet. works. Coll. by T. Park. 2v. s8°. 1806

Glover (Samuel T.) Argument of C. C. Whittelsey, 1866, on appeal of S. T. G. [*n. t. p.*] [P2625]. 8°. *n.d.*

Glover (Terrot Reaveley).
The conflict of religions in early Rom. empire. 11th ed. 8°. [1927]
Democracy in the anc. world. 8°. C. 1927
Herodotus. [Sather Class. lects., v3]. 8°. Berkeley, Cal. 1924
Jesus in the experience of men. s8°. 1921
The Jesus of history. Foreword by the Abp. of Canterbury. [11th ed.] s8°. 1919
Paul of Tarsus. 8°. 1925
" " ....[2nd ed.] 8°. 1925
The pilgrim. Essays on religion. s8°. 1921
Progress in religion to the Xtn. era. 8°. 1922

Glover (W. J.) British fairy & folk tales. s8°. 1920

Glubokomudraya. Глубокомудрая чуга: монгол. текстъ и русс. переводъ, съ прим. Г. Гомбоева, *see* IMPERAT. RUSS. ARCH. OBSCH. Труды Восточ. отд., ч8, 1864.

Gluck (Christoph Willibald v.), *see* AREND (M. A.) G. 1921.

Glück (Heinrich). Die christl. Kunst d. Ostens. [Kunst d. Ostens; hrsg. W. Cohn, B8]. la8°. 1923
see STRZYGOWSKI (J.) Stud. z. Kunst d. Ostens: J. St. z. 60sten Geburtstage [hrsg. H. G.], 1923.

Glückselig & Wärndorfer, *Firma. For Catalogues of collections of paintings, furniture &c. sold by Messrs. G. & W. see under the names of owners* KOLISCH (R.), POLITZER (A.), REEGER (F. v.) *&c. & under* KATALOG *&* VERSTEIGERUNG *for anonymous coll*s.

Glud (Søren) [GLUDIUS (SEVERINUS PETRI)]. Lacus Asphaltites. Praes. S. P. Gludio. [P2671]. s4°. Hafniae. 1683

Glyn (*Mrs.* **Elinor**). The great moment. s8°. [1923]
Letters f. Spain. s8°. [1924]
Man & maid (Renaissance). s8°. [1922]
Six days. s8°. [1924]

Glyn (Margaret H.) About Elizabethan virginal music & its composers [W. Byrd & others]. s8°. [1923]

Glynde, *Sussex.* Par. register, 1558–1812. Ed. L. F. Salzman. [Sussex Rec. Soc., 30]. 8°. C. 1924

Glynn (Richard), *see* BLAIR (R.) Poet. works of B., G., &c.; coll. by T. Park, 1807.

Gmelin (Julius).
Deutschlands Niedergang. [P2496]. s8°. Winnenden. 1920

Gnecchi (Francesco). I medaglioni romani. 3v. 4°. Milano. 1912

Gneisenau (*Feldmar. Graf* **v.**) [NEIDHARDT V. GNEISENAU], *see* DELBRÜCK (H.) Das Leben d. Feldm. v. G., 4e A., 2B, 1920.

Gnirs (Anton). Istria praeromana. 8o. Karlsbad. 1925

Gnitz (Juliet v. Lepel-), *see* LEPEL-GNITZ (J. v.)

Gnoli (Umberto). Pietro Perugino. sfol. Spoleto. [1923]

Gnostic fragments, 1924, *see* BUONAIUTI (E.), *ed.*

Goad (Charles E.) Conflagrations dur. last 10 years. 8o. 1899

Goad (Harold Elsdale). Franciscan Italy. 8o. [1926]
The kingdom. s8o. 1913

Göbel (Carl), *prof. at Munich.* Wilhelm Hofmeister: work & life. With biog. suppl. by Prof. Ganzenmüller. Tr. H. M. Bower. Ed. F. O. Bower. [Ray. Soc., 111]. 8o. 1926

Göbel (Heinrich). Wandteppiche. T1, Die Niederlande. B1, 2. la8o. L. 1923

Göbel (Wilhelm Adam). Tempus pascha Christi ultimi, disput., præs. J. H. Maio. [P2634]. s4o. Gissae Hass. 1712

Gobelin, *Family of, see* MIROT (L.) Une proprieté rurale de la famille G.: la Cour-Roland, 1924.

Gobii (Joannes). [Scala celi. *Fol. 2a*: Incipit prologus in Scala celi. *Fol. 168b. ends* Liber iste vocat? Scala celi . . . . Explicit feliciter]. fol. [Ulme, *Joh. Zainer.* 1480]
Without tp., pagin., signatures or catchwords. [a–x in eights]. 168 leaves, 40 lines to a full page. Initials in red filled in by hand. Fol. b1 is taken up by the register. Orig. binding with chain.

Gobineau (*le comte* **Joseph Arthur de).**
L'Abbaye de Typhaines. 11e éd. s8o. [1923]
La fleur d'or. [Savonarole —César Borgia—Jules II — Léon X — Michel - Ange. Cahiers verts, 27]. s8o. 1923
Le prisonnier chanceux ou les aventures de Jean de la Tour-Miracle. [Cahiers verts, 47]. s8o. 1924
„ „ . . . .[*a. ed.*] s8o. 1924
Les religions & les philos. dans l'Asie centrale. [4e éd.] 2t. s8o. [1923]
Souvenirs de voyage. Le mouchoir rouge — Akrivie Phrangopoulo—La chasse au caribou. s8o. 1922
Trois ans en Asie (1855–58). 2t. s8o. 1923
TRANSLATIONS.
The lucky prisoner. Tr. F. M. Atkinson. s8o. 1926
see LANGE (M.) Le cte. A. de G., ét. biog. & crit., 1924.
„ SCHEMANN (C. L.) Quellen &c. z. Leben G.'s, B2, 1919.

Goblet d'Alviella (*le cte.* **Eugène).**
Ce que l'Inde doit à la Grèce. n. éd. la8o. 1926

Goblet d'Alviella (*le cte.* **Félix).**
Hist. des bois & forêts de Belgique. 3[t]. la8o. 1927

Goch (Mekhithar), *see* MEKHITHAR, *Gosh.*

Göckingh (H. v.) [GOECKINGK]. Abgestorbene Nassau Adel, *see* SIBMACHER (J.), *ed.* Wappenbuch, B6vii, 1882.

Goclenius (Rudolphus), *the elder, see* GRETSER (J.) Panegyricus Iudic. super discept. R. G. & Bavium [Libavium] alchymistam, 1606.

God. *God's arraignement of hypocrites &c., 1615, *see* YATES (J.)
*God's love to mankinde, 1658, *see* HOARD (S.)
*Van den olden eñ nieuwen God geloove ende leere, 1556, *see* VAN.

Goday y Casals (J.), *see* PUIG Y CADAFALCH (J.), A. DE FALGUERA & J. G. Y C. L'arquitectura romànica a Catalunya v2, 3, 1911–18.

Godchot (*Col.* **Simon).** En Danemark: les Espagnols du Marq. de la Romana (1807–08). la8o. 1924

Goddard (Edward Hungerford) & P. A. Gibbons. Civilisation or civilisations: Spengler. philos. of hist. Intr. by F. C. S. Schiller. 8o. 1926

Goddard (Pliny Earle). Indians of the Northwest coast. [Amer. Mus. of Nat. Hist.] s8o. N.Y. 1924
Indians of the Southwest. [Amer. Mus. of Nat. Hist.] 2nd ed. s8o. N.Y. 1921

Goddard (Robert Hutchings). A method of reaching extreme altitudes, *see* SMITHSONIAN INSTIT. Misc. Collˢ., v71, 1919.

Goddard (Thomas Neilson).
The handbook of Sierra Leone. 8o. 1925

Goddard (William). A neaste of waspes latelie found &c. (1615). [Repr., w. bibliog. note by C. H. Wilkinson]. s8o. [1921]

Godden (Gertrude M.)
Mussolini: the birth of the new democracy. s8o. 1923

Godden (Thomas), *see* WHITBY (D.) A disc. conc. the idolatry of the Ch. of Rome: refut. [by T. G.] of Stillingfleet's Disc. &c. answered, 1674. 1674

Godée Molsbergen (E. C.), *see* MOLSBERGEN (E. C. G.)

Godefridus, *Viterbiensis.* Gesta Friderici I et Heinrici VI. Rec. G. H. Pertz. [Scr. rerum Ger. in usum schol.] 8o. Hannoverae. 1870

Godefroy (Denis). Auctores Lat. ling. in unum redacti corpus: M. Terentius Varro de lingua Lat. &c. Notae D. Gothofredi &c. 4o. [Geneva]. 1585

Godet (Frédéric).
Studies on the Epistles. Tr. A. H. Holmden. s8o. 1889

Godet (Marcel), *see* LEAGUE OF NATIONS. COMM. ON INTELL. CO-OP. Index bibliog., ed. M. G., 1925.

Godfrey (*Sir* **Edmund Berry)** [*often as one word Edmondberry*]. *see* HALL (*Sir* J.) Four famous mysteries: murder of G. &c., 1922.
„ LLOYD (W.) Sermon at funeral of Sir E. B. G., 1678.

Godfrey (John T.) Notes on the churches of Nottinghamshire. Hundred of Bingham. 8o. 1897

Godfrey (Walter H.), *architect.*
see BATSFORD (H.) Engl. mural mon. &c.: sel. by H. B., intr. by G., 1916.
„ LONDON. Survey of L., v7, 11, Parish of Chelsea, p3, 4, by W. H. G., 1921–27.

Godin (A.) Hist. de la ville & du canton de Guîtres. Rev. & compl. par J. Hovyn de Tranchère. [Pièces justific. *have sep. pagin*]. la8o. Bordeaux. 1888

Godin (Annette). L'erreur de Nedjma. s8o. 1923

Godinez (Miguel). Praxis theologiae myst. Hisp. primum ed. nunc Lat. reddit. a P. E. I. de la Reguera. 2t. fol. Romae. 1740–45

Godkin (James). The relig. hist. of Ireland, primit., papal & protest. 8o. 1873

Godlee (*Sir* **Rickman John),** *Bt.*
A village on the Thames: Whitchurch. 8o. [1926]
see LISTER (J. L.) Six papers: w. short biog. &c. by R. J. G., 1921.

Godley (Alfred Denis).
Reliquiae. Ed. C. R. L. Fletcher. 2v. 8o. 1926
see KIPLING (R.) & C. GRAVES. Q. Horati Flacci Carminum librum quintum; ed. A. D. G., 1920.

Godley (*Hon.* **Eveline Charlotte).** The great Condé: life of Louis II de Bourbon, Pr. of Condé. 8o. 1915

Godlonton (R.) *Introd. remarks to a Narr. of the irruption of the Kafir hordes into the Cape of Good Hope, 1834–35. By the ed. of the "Graham's Town journal." pl. 8o. Graham's Town. 1835

Godofredi (Eucharius). Berlin. Reformation: das ist ein gesprech v. d. zu Berlin vorgenomm. Reform. [*b. w.* Altenrath (G.) Catechismus, 1614]. s8o. Franckfurt. 1614

Godolphin (*Sir* **William),** *see* HISPANIA. Hispania illust., 1667–78, in letters f. Sir W. G. also a treat. [*by the same*] about the woolls of Spain, 1703.

Godsal (*Maj.* **P. T.)**
The conquests of Ceawlin, the 2nd Bretwalda. 8o. 1924

Godwin (*Mrs.* **Mary Wollstonecraft),** *wife of W. Godwin; 1759–97, see* GODWIN (W.) Mem. of M. W., 1927.

Godwin (Thomas) [GODWYN], *rector of Brightwell.* Moses & Aaron. Civil & eccl. rites used by Hebrewes &c. 4th ed. [*b. w. h.* Rom. hist. anthol., 1631]. s4o. 1631
„ „ . . . . .10th ed. s4o. 1671
*Romanae hist. anthologia: an Eng. expos. of the Roman antiq. Newly rev. s4o. O. 1631
„ „ Newly rev. [*b. w. h.* Moses & Aaron, 10th ed., 1671]. s4o. 1661
„ „ . . . . .14th ed. s4o. 1685

Godwin (William), *the elder.*
Caleb Williams. [P2460]. 8o. E. 1839
Mem. of M. Wollstonecraft. Ed. w. pref., suppl., &c. by W. C. Durant. 8o. 1927
see BROWN (F. K.) Life of W. G., 1926.

Goebel (Dorothy Burne).
William H. Harrison. 8o. Indianapolis. 1926

Goeckingk (H. v.), *see* GÖCKINGK (H. v.)

Goedhart (G. J. W. C.) Konsumvereine in Holland, *see* UNTERSUCHUNGEN ü. Konsumvereine, 1923.

Goeje (Michiel Johannes de). Mém. sur la conquête de la Syrie. [Mém., No. 2]. 2e éd. s8o. Leide. 1900

Goeje (Petrus de). Comm.: Exponantur praecepta Corani, de officiis hominum. 4o. [Groningen. 1818]

Goens (Rijklof Michael Cuninghame van). Brieven [*mostly in French*] aan G. & onuitg. stukken [*incl.* Mem. of my life]. [Hist. Genoots. Werken, N.S., 38, 43, 56]. 3d. 8o. Utrecht. 1884–90

Goering, *see* GÖRING.

Goes (Adriaen van der), *see* GOES (W. VAN DER) & A. VAN DER G. Briefwisseling, 1659–73; uitg. door C. J. Gonnet, 2d, 1899–1909.

Goes (Damian de). Cronica do rei D. Manuel [1495–1521, *publ.* 1566–67]. n. ed., anot. e pref., dir. J. M. Teixeira de Carvalho e D. Lopes. [Scr. rerum Lusitan., ser. A]. 4p. la8°. Coimbra. 1926

Fides, religio, moresque Æthiopum sub imperio Pretiosi Joannis degentium. Aliquot item epistolae D. a G. ac P. Jovio interpretibus. Deploratio Lapponiae gentis &c. 8°. Lovanii. 1540

Hispania D. a Goes, *see* HISPANICA. Rer. Hisp. scr., t2, 1579.

Goes (Hugo van der), *d. 1482.*
see DESTRÉE (J.) H. van der G., 1914.
,, FRIEDLÄNDER (M. J.) Die altnederl. Malerei, B4, H. van der G., 1926.
,, PFISTER (K.) H. van der G., 1923.

Goes (Willem van der) & A. van der Goes. Briefwisseling t. de gebroeders van der Goes, 1659–73. Uitg. door C. J. Gonnet. [Hist. Genoots. Werken, s3, 10, 11]. 2d. 8°. Amsterdam. 1899–1909

Goessler, *see* GÖSSLER.

Goethals (Arnold).
Chronica mon. S. Andreae juxta Brugas. 4°. Gandavi. 1844

Goethals (Henricus), *de Gand, archdeacon of Tournay.* De scriptor. eccl., *see* LE MIRE (A.) Bibl. eccl., 1639.

Goethe (Johann Wolfgang v.)

WORKS. (*Two or more, selections or misc. wks.*)

Alles um Liebe: G.'s Br. aus d. ersten Hälfte s. Lebens. Hrsg. E. Hartung. s8°. Ebenhausen. 1924

Dramat. Meisterwerke. [Götz v. Berlichingen, Egmont, Iphigenie auf Tauris, Torquato Tasso, *each w. sep. tp. & pagin.*] s8°. L. *n.d.*

Goethes Rheinreise mit Lavater u. Basedow in Sommer 1774. Dok. hrsg. v. A. Bach. 8°. Zürich. 1923

*Götz v. Berlichingen mit d. eisernen Hand: ein Schauspiel. s8°. *n.p.* 1773

Reineke Fuchs, mit Zeichnungen v. W. v. Kaulbach. la4°. München. 1846

BRIEFE, BRIEFWECHSEL &c.

Briefw. mit e. Kinde [Bettina v. Arnim]. 3T *in* 1. s8°. 1920
3, Tagebuch; hrsg. M. Friedländer [*w. sep. tp. & pagin.*]

FAUST.

Faust. Hrsg. mit Anm. v. G. v. Loeper. [Werke, 12, 13]. 2T [*in* 1v]. s8°. *n.d.*

Faust. Part 1, w. Eng. notes &c. by A. M. Selss. 8°. 1880

G. üb. s. Faust. [*Ed.* H. H. Borcherdt]. s8°. L. *n.d.*

GEDIDITE.

Gedichte. s8°. *n.d.*

Gedichte in zeitl. Folge 2B. s8°. L. [1925]

Goethe ü. s. Dichtungen: Samml. v. H. G. Graf. 3T [*in* 9B]. 8°. Frankfurt a. M. 1904–14

HERMANN U. DOROTHEA.

H. u. D. Volksausgabe. s8°. L. [1907]

IPHIGENIE AUF TAURIS.

I. auf T. Annot. by E. A. Oppen. s8°. London. 1868

WERTHER.

Die Leiden d. jungen Werthers. s8°. St. 1874

TRANSLATIONS. [*Two or more works, selections &c.*]

Dram. works. Tr. Sir W. Scott, E. A. Bowring &c. [repr.] s8°. *Bohn.* 1896

Literary essays: a select. in Eng., arr. by J. E. Spingarn. Foreword by Visc. Haldane. s8°. O. 1921

TRANSLATIONS [*continued*].

Misc. travels: Letters f. Switz., Camp. in France, 1792, Siege of Mainz & A tour on the Rhine &c., 1814–15. Ed. L. D. Schmitz. s8°. *Bohn.* 1884

Novels & tales. Tr. s8°. *Bohn.* 1901

Poems. Tr. in orig. metre by E. A. Bowring. [repr.] s8°. *Bohn.* 1900

DICHTUNG U. WAHRHEIT.

Autobiog., w. h. Annals. Tr. J. Oxenford. [repr.] 2v. s8°. *Bohn.* 1897

FAUST.

Faust. Faust. Tr. Lewis Filmore. [*wanting tp.* P2432]. 8°. [1841]

Faust, 2p. Tr. A. Swanwick. [repr.] s8°. *Bohn.* 1902

Faust; översatt av V. Rydberg, *see* RYDBERG (A. V.) Faust &c., 9e uppl., 1921.

Faust. Done into Eng. verse, w. comm. & notes by W. H. Van der Smissen. Intr. by Sir R. Falconer. 8°. 1926

GESPRÄCHE &c.

Conversations of G. w. Eckermann & Soret. Tr. J. Oxenford. n. ed. s8°. 1874

ITALIENISCHE REISE.

Travels in Italy, w. h. 2nd resid. in Rome & Fragm. on Italy. Tr. by A. J. W. Morrison & C. Nisbet. s8°. *Bohn.* 1892

LETTERS.

Early & misc. letters. Notes &c. by E. Bell. s8°. *Bohn.* 1889

Letters to Zelter, w. extr. f. those of Z. to G. Sel., tr. & annot. by A. D. Coleridge. s8°. *Bohn.* 1892

WILHELM MEISTER.

La vocation théâtrale de Wilhelm Meister. Prem. version de W. M. écrite par G. dans sa jeunesse. Tr. F. Halévy. Intr. de M. Arnault. [Cahiers verts, 42]. s8°. 1924

Wilhelm Meister's apprenticeship. Tr. R. D. Boylan. [repr.] s8°. *Bohn.* 1901

Wilhelm Meister's travels. Tr.; ed. E. Bell. [repr.] s8°. *Bohn.* 1902

Goethe (Johann Wolfgang v.) [*continued*].

REFERENCES.

see ARNIM (B. v.) Bettinas Briefwechsel mit G., 1922.
,, BAPP (C.) Aus. G.'s griech. Gedankenwelt: G. u. Heraklit &c., 1921.
,, BODE (W. F.) Weib u. Sittlichkeit in G. Leben u. Denken, 1916.
,, BROWN (P. H.) Life of G., 2v, 1920.
,, CARRÉ (J. M.) Bibliog. de G. en Angleterre, 1920.
,, —— Vie de G., 6e éd., 1927.
,, CASSIRER (E.) Idee u. Gestalt: G. &c., 2. A., 1924.
,, CROCE (B.) G.; tr., 1923.
,, DAVIDSON (T.) Philos. of G.'s Faust, 1906.
,, EISSLER (G.) Kat. d. Bibl. G. E., Goethe-Samml. &c., 1925.
,, ENG. GOETHE SOC. Publs., n.s., v2, G. & Byron; ed. J. G. Robertson, 1925.
,, FARINELLI (A.) G. de Humboldt & l'Espagne, avec une esquisse sur G. & l'Esp., 1924.
,, —— Dante in Spagna, Germ. &c. (Dante e G.), 1922.
,, FISCHER (P.) G.'s Altersweisheit, 1921.
,, GEIGER (L.) G., s. Leben u. Schaffen, 1913.
,, GUNDOLF (F.) G., 9e A., 1920.
,, HOUBEN (H. H.) J. P. Eckermann: s. Leben für G., 1925.
,, KÖRNER (J.) Romantiker u. Klassiker: d. Brüder Schlegel in i. Bezieh. zu Schiller u. G., 1924.

REFERENCES [*continued*].

see LEWES (G. H.) Life, 3rd ed., 1875.
,, LUDWIG (E.) G.: Gesch. e. Menschen, 3B, 1920.
,, MARTIN (E.) G. in Strassburg, 1871.
,, MINOR (J.) G.'s Fragmente v. Ewigen Juden &c., 1904.
,, OBENAUER (C. J.) G. in s. Verhältnis z. Religion, 1921.
,, PAULSEN (F.) Schopenhauer - Hamlet - Mephistopheles: Aufsätze z. Naturgesch. d. Pessimismus, 1926.
,, PETERSEN (J.) Entst. d. Eckermann. Gespräche &c., 1924; 2e verb. A., 1925.
,, PICK (B.) G.'s Münzbelustigungen, 1920.
,, PNIOWER (O.) G.'s Faust: Zeugnisse &c., 1899.
,, SANTAYANA (G.) 3 philos. poets: Lucretius, Dante, G., 3rd impr., 1922.
,, SARAUW (C.) Entstehungsgesch. d. G. Faust, 1917.
,, —— G.'s Augen, 1919.
,, —— G.'s Faust i aar. 1788–89, 1919.
,, —— Zur Faustchronol., 1925.
,, SCHNITZER (M.) G.'s Josephbilder—G.'s Josephdichtung, 1921.
,, SIMMONS (L. VAN T.) G.'s lyric poems in Eng. tr. prior to 1860, 1919.
,, STEINER (R.) G. as founder of a new sci. of aesthetics; tr., 1922.

Goethe (Ottilie v.) Erlebnisse u. Geständnisse, 1832–57. Hrsg. v. H. H. Houben. 8°. L. 1923

Goette (Rudolf), *see* GÖTTE (R.)

Goetzius (Georgius Henr.), *see* GÖTZE (G. H.)

Goeze, *see* GÖZE.

Goezius (Georgius Henricus), *see* GÖTZE (G. H.)

Goff (Alexander) & H. A. Fawcett.
Macedonia. A plea for the primitive. 8°. 1921

Goffe (Thomas) [GOFF (T.)] Three excellent tragedies. The raging Turk—The courageous Turk—The trag. of Orestes. 2nd ed. s8°. 1656

Goffin (Arnold). Julien Dillens. s8°. Turnhout. 1919

Gofman (Viktor Vikt.), *1884–1911* [Гофманъ]. [Сочиненія]. Вступит. статьи В. Брюсова и А. Г. Левенсона. 2t. 8°. Берлинъ. 1923

Goga (Octavian). Coşbuc, *see* ACADEMIA ROM. Disc., 54, 1923.

Gogarty (Oliver).
An offering of swans. [*Poems*]. 8°. D., *Cuala Press.* 1923

Gogel (Sergius). Die Ursachen d. russ. Revol., 1917. [Osteur.-Inst. in Breslau]. 8°. 1926

Goggio (Emilio). Longfellow & Dante, *see* DANTE SOC., *Camb., Mass.* Ann. rep., 1924.

Gogh (Vincent van).
see COLIN (P.) Van G., 1925.
,, COQUIOT (G.) V. v. G., 1923.
,, MEIER-GRÄFE (J.) V. van G.: biog. st.; tr. J. H. Reece, 2v, 1922.
,, —— Vincent, 2B, 1921.
,, PIÉRARD (L.) Life of V. Van Gogh; tr., 1925.

Gogh-Kaulbach (Anna van). Moeder. 6e dr. s8°. [1921]

Gogol (Nikolai Vasilevich).

Полное собраніе сочиненій. 10t. s8°. [Берлинъ]. 1921
,, ,, 4oe изд. его наслѣдниковъ. t1–4. 8°. Москва. 1880

Ревизоръ, комедія. Съ десятью группами фототипій. [Имп. Москов. Малый Театръ]. fol. Москва. 1885

TRANSLATIONS.

Dead souls. [Tr.] 8°. 1893
,, ,, Poem. [Tr.] C. Garnett. 2v. s8°. 1922

Evenings on a farm near Dikanka. [*Tr.*] C. Garnett. [Works, v4]. s8°. 1926

Gogol (Nikolai Vasilevich) [*continued*].

TRANSLATIONS [*continued*].
The government inspector & o. plays [*i.e.* Marriage, The gamblers &c.] [Tr.] C. Garnett. [Works, 6]. 8°. 1926
The inspector. Comedy. Tr. T. Hart-Davies. s8°. Calcutta. 1890
The overcoat & o. stories. [Tr.] C. Garnett. s8°. 1923

TRANSLATIONS [*continued*].
Taras Bulba: also St. John's eve & o. s. s8°. [1887]
see GERSHENSON (M. O.) Историч. записки (Н. В. Гоголь &c.), 1923.
,, KOTLYAREVSKY (N. A.) Н. В. Гоголь, 1829–42, 4ое изд., 1915.
,, LAVRIN (J.) G., 1925.

Goguel (Maurice). L'eucharistie, j. Justin Martyr. la8°. 1910
L'Evangile de Marc & s. rapp. avec ceux de Mathieu & de Luc. [H. E.: Sci. relig., 22]. 8°. 1909

Goichon (Alexandre). Ernest Psichari d'ap. des doc. inéd. Préf. par J. Maritain. s8°. [1921]

Goicoechea (Estanislao Jaime de Labayru y), *see* LABAYRU Y GOICOECHEA (E. J. DE).

Going (Charles Buxton).
David Wilmot, free-soiler. 8°. N.Y. 1924
Star-glow & song. 8°. N.Y. 1909

Góis (Damião de), *see* GOES (D. DE).

Golburne (John), *see* ACTES. Acts of the dispute & conf., Paris, 1566; tr. J. G., 1602.

Gold & Silver Wyre-Drawers, *Company of, see* STEWART (H.) Hist. of the W. Co. of G. & S. W.-D., 1891.

Gold (Ludwig). Die Tragödie v. Verdun, 1916. [Schlachten d. Weltkrieges &c., B13]. T1. 8°. Oldenburg. 1926

Goldast (Melchior), *Haiminsfeldius.*
Coll. constitutionum Imperialium; hoc est Imperatorum, Cæsarum &c. recessus, ordinationes &c. 4t [*in 2v*]. fol. Francofurti ad M. 1713
t2–4 *have title* Imperatorum, Cæsarum &c. recessus &c., t4 *has 3 pagin.*
Comm. de pari, vel dispari forma Boemiae & Austriae, opin. Goldasti &c., *see* BERGER (F. L. v.) Opusc. misc., 1725.
Imperialia decreta de cultu imaginum. Coll. &c. à M. H. G. s8°. Francofurti. 1608
Politica Imperialia: sive discursus, acta publ. &c. de Imp. &c. Rom., Pontif. Rom. &c. juribus, privilegiis &c. fol. Francofurti. 1614
Suevicarum rerum scr. aliquot veteres. Ex bibl. & rec. G. s4°. Francoforti. [1606]
see EGINHARD. Eginhartus vita Caroli Magni; acc. G. animadv. ined. &c., 1711.
,, OTTENTHAL (E.) Die gefälschten Magdeburg. Diplome u. M. G., 1919.

Goldbacher (Alois). Krit. Beitr. z. 41, 42 u. 43 Buche d. T. Livius, 1919, *see* KAIS. AKAD. D. WISS. ZU WIEN. Sitzber., B193, 1922.
Z. Kritik v. Ciceros Schr. De officiis. 1, 2, 1921–22, *see* KAIS. AKAD. D. WISS. Z. WIEN. Sitzber., B196, 1922.

Goldberg (Isaac).
Brazilian lit. Foreword by J. D. M. Ford. 8°. N.Y. 1922
Brazilian tales. [By J. M. Machado de Assis *& others*]. Tr. I. G. s8°. [1924]
Havelock Ellis. Suppl. ch. on Mrs. Edith Ellis. 8°. [1926]
Studies in Spanish-Amer. lit. Intr. by J. D. M. Ford. 8°. N.Y. [1920]

Golden. Golden (The) archer. A book of sonnets by A. B. s8°. [1920]
Golden (The) book: legends of saints &c.; tr. f. med. sources by Mrs. F. Alexander, 1905, *see* LIBRO. L. d'oro (Il).
Golden (The) guide to London, 4th ed. rev., 1879, *see* LONDON.
Golden remains of the early masonic writers, 5v, 1847–49, *see* OLIVER (G.)
Golden tract (The), conc. the stone of the philosophers; by an anon. German philosopher, *n.d.*, *see* HERMETIC MUSEUM, v1, 1893.
Golden treasury (A) of Irish verse, 1925, *see* ROBINSON (L.), *ed.*

Golden hind, The: a quarterly magazine of art & lit. Ed. C. Bax & A. O. Spare. v1. fol. 1922–23

Goldenkron: Urkundenbuch d. Cistercienserstiftes G.; bearbt. v. M. Pangerl, *see* FONTES RERUM AUSTRIAC., B37, 1872.

Goldenveizer (A. B.) Вблизи Толстаго. 2t. 8°. Москва. 1922–23
Talks w. Tolstoi. Tr. S. S. Koteliansky & V. Woolf. s8°. 1923

Goldenweiser (Alexander A.)
Early civiliz. Intr. to anthropology. 8°. [1923]

Goldenweiser (Emanuel Alex.), *see* UNITED STATES: CENSUS. Farm tenancy, by G., &c. 1924.

Golder (Frank Alfred). Guide to mat. for American hist. in Russian Archives. [C.I. of Wash. Publ. 239]. la8°. Wash. 1917

Goldfriedrich (Johann), *see* KAPP (F.) & J. G. Gesch. d. deut. Buchhandels, 4B (B2–4, von J. G.), 1886–1913.

Goldhagen (Hermann), *Jesuit.*
*Instit. stili Latini. ed. 2a. s8°. Augustae Vindel. 1779
Meletema de relig. Hebr. sub lege naturali, *see* MIGNE (J. P.), *ed.* Theol. cursus, t15, 1861.

Goldhorn (David Joh. Heinrich). De summis principiis theol. Abælardeæ. s8°. Lipsiae. 1836

Goldie (John Haviland Dashwood), *see* TREHERNE (G. G. T.) & J. H. D. G. Rec. of the Univ. Boat Race, 1829–80, 1883.

Golding (Louis). Day of Atonement. s8°. 1925
,, ,, ...[2nd impr.] s8°. 1925
Seacoast of Bohemia. s8°. [1923]
Sunward. 8°. 1924

Goldman (Edward Alphonso). Mammals of Panama, 1920, *see* SMITHSONIAN INSTIT. Misc. coll., v69, 1921.

Goldman (Edwin E.) Vitalfärbung am Zentralnervensystem, *see* KÖN.-PREUSS. AKAD. Abhdln., Phys.-math. Cl., 1913.

Goldman (Emma). My disillusionment in Russia. Intr. by R. West. 8°. [1925]

Goldney (Frederick Hastings), *see* CHIPPENHAM. Records, 1554–1889; [*ed.*] by F. H. G., 1889.

Goldoni (Carlo) [*ps.* POLISSENO FEGEJO].
Commedie scelte. s8°. Leipz. 1876
The liar. Comedy. Tr. G. L. Fraser. Intr. by E. G. Craig. 8°. [1922]
Memoirs of C. G., wr. by himself. Tr. J. Black; ed. w. intr. by A. W. Drake. 8°. 1926
Memorie di G. Tr. rivista sull' orig. 3t [*in 1v*]. s8°. Prato. 1822
Mirandolina: a comedy. Tr. & adapted f. La locandiera of G. by Lady Gregory. 8°. [1924]
The mistress of the inn [tr. M. Pierson], *see* SAYLER (O. M.) Moscow Art Theatre ser. of Russ. plays, s2, 1924.
The servant of two masters. Tr. w. intr. by E. J. Dent. s8°. C. 1928
see KENNARD (J. S.) G. & the Venice of his time, 1920.

Goldring (Douglas). Margot's progress. s8°. [1924]
Nobody knows. s8°. 1923
Reputations: essays in criticism. s8°. 1920

Goldschmidt (Adolph).
Got. Madonnenstatuen in Deutschland. 4°. Augsburg. 1923

Goldschmidt (Alfons).
Moskau 1920. Tagebuchblätter. 8°. 1920
Die Wirtschaftsorganis. Sowjet-Russlands. 8°. 1920

Goldschmidt (E. P.) & Co. Rare &c. books &c. Catalogue 6–8 [*in 1v.*] 8°. [1925–26]

Goldschmidt (Ernst Philip). Gothic & Renaissance bookbindings. Exempl. & illust. f. a.'s coll. 2v [1, Text. 2, Plates]. 4°. 1928

Goldschmidt (Fritz). Deutschlands Weinbauorte u. Weinbergslagen. 2e A. 8°. Mainz. 1920
Die italien. Bronzen d. Renaissance u. d. Barock. [Kön. Mus. zu Berlin. Bildwerke d. christl. Epochen, B2]. 3e A. T1. 4°. 1914

Goldschmidt (Meyer Adolph), *1819–87* [MEÏR GOLDSCHMIDT].
Avrohmche Nattergal & andre Fortaellinger. s8°. 1914

Goldsmid (Edmund). Chron. table of princ. dram. works perf. in France, p1, 1200–1599, *see* AUNGERVYLE SOC. Reprints, s2, 1883.

Goldsmith (Oliver), *the poet.*
The deserted village. [1770, Noel Douglas replicas]. la8°. [1927]
Goodnatured man, *see* INCHBALD (*Mrs.* E.) Brit. theatre, v17, 1808.
Misc. works, cont. all h. essays & poems. s8°. 1789
,, ,, Pref., Some acc. of h. life & wr. n. ed. 4v. 8°. 1821
,, ,, Biog. intr. by Prof. Masson. [Globe ed.] 8°. 1899
New essays. Coll. & ed. w. intr. &c. by R. S. Crane. s8°. Chicago. 1927
Poems & plays. Pref., life of the a. s8°. D. 1777
*Poetical dict., or, The beauties of the Eng. poets. 4v. s8°. 1761
Poet. works. Coll. by T. Park. s8°. 1805
Poet. works. w. life by J. Mitford. [Aldine ed.] s8°. 1884
She stoops to conquer. [Dolby's Brit. theatre]. s8°. 1823
,, ,, Ed. w. intr. & notes by G. A. F. M. Chatwin. s8°. O. 1912
,, ,, [*for a. ed.*], *see* INCHBALD (E.) Brit. th., v17, 1808.
The vicar of Wakefield. s8°. 1813
see BALDERSTON (K. C.) Hist. & sources of Percy's Memoir of G., 1926.
,, CLARKE (*Sir* E.) The family letters of O. G., 1920.
,, WILLIAMS (I. A.) 7 18th cent. bibliog., O. G. &c., 1924.

Goldsmiths' Company, *see* CARRINGTON (J. B.) & G. R. HUGHES. Plate of the Co. of G., 1926.

Goldwitzer (Franz Wenzel).
Bibliogr. dogmatica. 8°. Solisbaci. 1831
Bibliogr. d. Kirchenväter u. Kirchenlehrer, 1.–13. Jhdt. 8°. Landshut. 1828
Compend. dogmatum christ.-cath. system. 8°. Solisbaci. 1824
Patrologie verbunden m. Patristik. 2B. (1, 1.–4. Jhdt. 2, 5.–9. Jhdt.) 8°. Nürnberg. 1834

Goldzier (Hans) [*ps.* Th. Newest]. Gegen Einstein: d. Erfahrung im Weltall. Einige Weltprobleme. s8°. Wien. 1921

Goldziher (Ignaz).
Le dogme & la loi de l'Islam. Tr. F. Arin. la8°. 1920
Stellung d'alt. islam. Orthodoxie zu d. ant. Wissenschaften, *see* Königl. Preuss. Akad. d. Wiss. Abhdl. (Phil.-hist. Klasse), 1915.

Golescu, *The family of, see* Bengescu (G.) Despre activit. lit. ai fam. G., 1923.

*__Goliath__ slain, 1768, *see* Hill (*Sir* R.)

Golitsuin (*prince* Aleksandr), *see* Galitzin (*pr.* A.)

Golius (Jacobus), *see* Castell (E.) Lexicon heptaglotton. [Dict. Persico-Lat. opera J. G. &c.], 1669.

Gollancz (*Sir* Hermann). The book of protection: a coll. of charms. Ed. f. Syriac MSS., w. tr., intr. & notes by H. G. 8°. 1912
see Agathangelus, *of St. Theresa.* Chron. of events, 1623–1733, rel. to settlement of Carmelites &c.; ed. &c. Sir H. G., 1927.

Gollancz (*Sir* Israel).
Select Early Eng. Poems. [v] 1–4. 8°. 1913–22
see Erkenwald, *St.* Allit. poem. [4.]
„ Parlement of the thre ages, 1915. [2.]
„ Patience, 1913. [1.]
„ Winner & Waster, 1920. [3.]
The sources of Hamlet. s8°. 1926
see Caedmon. The C. MS.; intr. by Sir I. G., 1927.
see *Cleanness, 1921.
„ *Pearl; ed. w. mod. rendering &c. by I. G., 1921.
„ Shakespeare Assoc. St. in the First Folio, 1925.
„ Stationers' Company. In commem. of 1st folio tercent., w. cat. of Shakespeariana & intr. by Sir I. G., 1923.

Göller (Emil). König Sigismunds Kirchenpolitik, 1404–13. [*a. c. in* P2726]. 8°. Freiburg im Br. 1902

Goller (Engelbert).
Jakob Henot, Postmeister v. Cöln. 8°. Bonn. 1910

Gollerbakh (E. F.) Портретная живопись в России 18 век. 8°. Москва. 1923
see Lerner (N. O.) Царское Село в поэзии; со статьей Э. Ф. Г, 1922.
„ Rozanov (V. V.) Solitaria, w. abr. acc. of a.'s life by E. G., 1927.

Gollob (Hedwig).
Der Wiener Holzschnitt, 1490–1550. la8°. Wien. 1926

Gollomb (Joseph). Scotland Yard. 8°. [1926]

Golovachev (Aleksei Adrian.) Десять лѣтъ реформъ, 1861–71. 8°. С.-П. 1872
„ „ ......Изд. "Вѣстника Европы." la8°. С.-П. 1872

Golovatsky (Yak. Fedorovich). Библіограф. находки во Львовѣ. [I. Akad. Nauk. Записки, т22]. 8°. С.-П. 1873
О народной одеждѣ &c. Русиновъ или Русскихъ въ Галичинѣ и Венгріи [I. R.G.O. Зап. по этнографіи, т7]. 8°. С.-П. 1877

Golovin (Ivan). The Caucasus. 8°. 1854

Golovin (Konstantin Fedorovich) [Orlovsky]. Внѣ партій. Опытъ политич. психологіи. s8°. С.-П. 1905
Наше мѣстное управленіе и мѣст. представительство. 8°. С.-П. 1884
Русскій романъ и русское общество. 8°. С.-П. 1897

Golovin (Nikolai Nikolaevich). The problem of the Pacific in the 20th century. By G. in collab. w. Adm. A. D. Bubnov. Tr. C. Nabokoff. Intr. by H. Williams. 8°. 1922

Golovinsky (M.) New Eng.-Russ. & Russ.-Eng. dict. 2p [*in* 1v.] s8°. Paris. *n.d.*

Golstunsky (Konstantin Fedorovich). Крит. замѣчанія на изд. Юльга: "Die Märchen d. Siddhi-Kûr." [I. Akad. Nauk. Записки, т11]. 8°. С.-П. 1867
Монголо-ойратскіе законы 1640 г. дополнит. указы Галданъ-Хунъ-Тайджія и законы, составл. для волжскихъ Калмыковъ. Калмыцкій текстъ съ переводомъ &c. 8°. С.-П. 1880

Golther (Wolfgang). Parzival u. d. Gral in d. Dichtung d. Ma. u. d. Neuzeit. 8°. St. 1925

Goltz (Bogumil). Die Bildung u. d. Gebildeten. [*b. w. h.* Weltklugheit &c., 1869]. 2e A. 2T [*in* 1v.] s8°. 1867
Das Menschen-Dasein in s. weltewigen Zügen &c. 2e A. 2B [in 1v.] s8°. 1868
Die Weltklugheit u. Lebens-Weisheit &c. 2B [in 1v.] s8°. 1869

Goltz (Colmar, *Frhr.* v. der).
see Kiesling (*Oberstleut.* H. v.) Mit Von d. G. in Mesopotamien u. Persien, 1922.
„ Schmiterlöw (B. v.) Aus d. Leben d. Generalfeldm. v. d. G. nach Briefen, 1926.

Goltz (*Gen. Graf* Rüdiger von der).
Meine Sendung in Finnland u. im Baltikum. 8°. L. 1920

Golubev (Vasily Semen.) Крестьяне въ государств. думѣ. [P2722]. 8°. Ростовъ на Дону. [1905]

Golubev (Viktor).
see Ars Asiatica; publ. sous la dir. de V. G., t1–4, 1914–22.
„ Rodin (A.), A. Coomaraswamy, E. B. Havell & V. G. Sculptures çivaites, 1921.

Golubovich (Girolamo). Biblioteca bio-bibliog. d. Terra Santa e dell' Oriente Francescano. t3–5. (3, 1300–32. 4, 1333–45. 5, 1346–1400). la8°. Firenze. 1919–27
„ „ ....n.s., Doc., t1–5. la8°. Quadracchi presso Firenze. 1921–25
1, 2, Acta S. Congreg. de Propag. Fide pro Terra Sancta; ed. L. Lemmens, p1, 2, 1622–1847.
3, Vita e diarii del Card. L. Cozza, custode di Terra Santa &c., 1654–1729; a cura del p. L. Oliger.
4, 5, Atti del Padre L. Cozza, custode di Terra Santa (1709–15); racc. dal p. E. Castellani, 2t.

Golubtsov (Nikolai). Амурскій календарь 1901 [4 *pagin.*] 8°. Благовѣщенскъ, 1901

Gomarus (Franciscus) [Gomar (François)]. Opera theologica omnia. 2is curis emend. fol. Amstelodami. 1664
The Disputationes theolog. *w.* Davidis Lyra *have sep. pagin.*

Gombauld (Jean Ogier de).
Les épigrammes div. en 3 livres. s8°. 1657

Gomboev (Galsan), *lama.* Глубокомудрая чуга, *see* Imperat. Russ. Arch. Obsch. Труды Восточ. отд., ч8, 1864.
О древнихъ монгол. обычаяхъ &c. описан. у Плано-Карпини, *see* Imp. Russ. Arch. Obsch. Труды Восточ. отд.. ч4, 1859.

Gomboust (Jacques). Plan mon. de Paris, 1652, *see* Paris. Reprod. d'anc. plans de P., 1908.

Gomecius (Alvarus), *see* Gomez de Castro (A.)

Gomes Figueiro (Antonio), *see* Charles III, *k. of Spain.* Capitoli, patti &c. conced. l'affitto dell' arrendamento d. diritto proib. d. tabacco al D. A. G. F., 1748–51, 1748.

Gomez (Alfonso), *see* Hisp. Soc. of Amer. Manuscripts: A. G., 1482, MS. B3, 1927.

Gómez (*Gen.* Juan Vicente), *president of Venezuela, see* Lossada Dias (D.) Gen. J. V. G., Präsident v. V. &c., 1924.

Gomez (Pedro), *see* Jesuits. *Rec. de ampliss. regno Chinae; item narr. rerum in Japonia gest., a P. G., a. 1598, 1601.

Gomez de Castro (Alvaro). De rebus gestis a Fr. Ximenio Cisnerio, libri 8, *see* Hispanica. Rer. Hisp. script., t3, 1581.

Gomez de Fuensalida (Gutierre), *see* Fuensalida (Gutierre Gomez de).

Gomez de la Serna (Ramón). El Doctor Inverosimil. s8°. [1921]
Gustave l'incongru. Tr. J. Cassou & A. Wurmser. 6e éd. s8°. [1927]

Gomez de Orozco (Federico), *see* Garcia Icazbalceta (J.) Cat. de mss. rel. a la hist. de America; anot. &c. por F. G. de O., 1927.

Gómez-Moreno (Manuel). The Alhambra. [Art in Spain, 5. Hispanic Soc.] s8°. Barcelona. *n.d.*
Iglesias mozárabes. Arte esp. de los s. 9 a 11. [Láminas, *sep. tp., bound sep.*] 4°. 1919

Gomez Ranera (Alejandro). Col. de trozos escogidos de los mejores hablistas castell. en prosa y verso. 8a ed., corr. y aument. 2p [*in 1v*]. s8°. 1876

Go-Mizuno-In, *emperor of Japan; 1596–1680.* Kocho. Tr. A. L. Sadler, in collab. w. H. Hoshino & M. Nagai. Pref. by G. Kato. [Meiji Japan Soc.] 8°. Tokyo. 1922

Gomme (A. W.) Mr. Wells as historian. Inq. into those parts of W.'s Outline of hist. wh. deal w. Greece & Rome. [P2562]. 8°. Glasgow. 1921

Gompers (Samuel). American labor & the War. 8°. N.Y. [1919]
Seventy years of life & labour. 2v. 8°. [1925]

Gompertz (Martin Louis Alan) [*ps.* Ganpat].
High snow. s8°. [1927]
Magic Ladakh. 8°. 1928
The road to Lamaland. 8°. [1926]
*Stella Nash. 2nd impr. s8°. E. 1924
The voice of Dashin. s8°. [1926]

Gonçalves Dias (Antonio). Cantos. Coll. de poesias. [Coll. de aut. portug., t1, 2]. 5a ed. 2t *in* 1v. 8°. Leipzig. 1877

Goncharov (Ivan Aleksandrovich). Полное собраніе сочиненій. t1–10 *in* 6v. [11, 12 *wanting*]. s8°. С.-П. 1899

И. А. Г. и И. С. Тургенев по неизд. мат. Пушкинск. Дома. С предисл. &c. Б. М. Энгельгардта 8°. П. 1923

see LYATSKY (E. A.) Г.: жизнь, личность &c., 1920.

Goncourt (Edmond de). Chérie. Postface de J. H. Rosny aîné. éd. déf. s8°. [1921]

La fille Elisa. Postface de J. Ajalbert. éd. déf. s8°. [1921]

La Guimard. Postface de J. H. Rosny jeune. éd. déf. s8°. [1922]

see ROSNY (J. H.) Mem^{s}. de la vie litt.: l'Acad. G., 1927.

—— **& Jules de Goncourt.**

La femme au 18e s. n. éd., rev. & augm. s8°. 1918

La femme au 18e s. Postface de J. H. Rosny, jeune. éd. déf. 2[t]. s8°. [1923]

Germinie Lacerteux. Postface de G. Geffroy. éd. déf. s8°. [1921]

Objets d'art japon. & chin. &c. comp. la coll. des G., vente, mars 1897. [*Pref. by* S. Bing. *Illust.*] 4°. 1897

Portraits intimes du 18e s.: études nouv. s8°. 1878

„ „ Postface de J. Ajalbert. éd. déf. 2[t]. s8°. [1924]

Sœur Philomène. Postface de L. Descaves. éd. déf. s8°. [1922]

Sophie Arnould d'ap. sa corr. & s. méms. inéd. Postface de E. Bergerat. éd. déf. s8°. [1922]

see SABATIER (P.) L'esthétique des G., 1920.

Gondi, *the family of, see* TAMBOUR (E.) Les G. & le château de Noisy, 1568–1732, 1925.

Gondinet (Edmond) & Ph. Gille.
Lakmé. Opéra. [P2420]. s8°. 1885

Gondomar (Diego Sarmiento de Acuña *conde* **de),** *see* PASTOR (A.) Un embajador de España, 1925.

***Gone** native: tale of the South Seas, 1924, *see* ASTERISK, *ps.*

Góngora y Argote (Luis de). Obras poéticas. [Ed. R. Foulché-Delbosc. Hispanic Soc. of Amer., Bibl. Hisp.] 3t. 8°. N.Y. 1921

see ARTIGAS (M.) Don L. de G. y A.: biog. y est. crit., 1925.

„ HISP. SOC. OF AMER. G. in the lib. of H.S.A., 1927.

„ REYES (A.) Cuestiones G., 1927.

Gonnard (René). Hist. des doctrines écon. [t] 1, 2 [t2, 2e éd. rev. & corr.] 8°. 1921–27

Gonsalvius Montanus (Reginaldus). De Inquisitione Hispanica oratiunculæ septem, ex narr. R. C. M. coll. s8°. Haidelbergae. 1603

Sanctæ Inquisitionis Hisp. artes aliquot detectæ, ac palam traductæ &c. s8°. Heidelbergæ. 1567

Gonse (Louis). E. Fromentin. Augm. d'un voyage en Egypte &c. (inéd.) de F. 4°. 1881

Gontard (Susette), *formerly Borkenstein, wife of J. F. Gontard* [*ps.* DIOTIMA]. Die Briefe der Diotima [*to J. C. F. Hölderlin*]. Veröff. v. F. Arnold. Hrsg. v. C. Viëtor. 8°. L. 1922

Gonzaga, *The family of, see* BRINTON (S.) The G.—Lords of Mantua, 1927.

Gonzaga (Aloysius) [LOUIS (*Gonzaga*) *Saint*], *see* CEPARY (V.) Life of St. A. G., 1844.

Gonzaga (Curtio), *c. 1536–99.* Il Fidamante: poema eroico. Ricorr. &c., agg. gli argomenti d. M. Campiglia. 8°. Venetia. 1591

see BELLONI (A.) C. G., rimatore d. sec. 16, 1891.

Gonzaga (*card.* **Ercole),** *bp. of Mantua, 1505–63, see* SEGRE (A.) Un registro di lettere d. card. E. G. (1535–36), con app. di doc. ined. (1520–48), 1913.

Gonzaga (Ferrante I), *cte. di Molfetta & Guastalla, 1507–57, see* COSTANTINI (A.) Lodi, 1594.

Gonzaga (Francesco), *bp. of Mantua.* Relatio pretiosæ mortis C. T. Maillard de Tournon &c. [*&* Acta &c. in causa rituum sinensium]. s4°. Venetiis. 1712

Gonzaga (Giulia), *ctss. di Fondi; 1531–66.*
see AMANTE (B.) G. G., 1896.

„ BENRATH (C.) J. G.: e. Lebensbild, 1900.

Gonzaga (Mary), *see* MARY [*Gonzaga*], *queen consort of Vladislaus IV, of Poland.*

Gonzaga Cuevas (Luis). Porvenir de México, ó juicio sobre su estado polít. en 1821 y 1851. [3 libros, *b. sep., pagin. cont.*] la8°. Mexico. 1851–57

Gonzaghi (Bonaventura). Ragionamenti sopra i sette peccati mortali & s. i sette Salmi penit. rid. in 7 canzoni, & parafrast. s4°. Vinegia. 1567

Gonzales (François), *de Saint Pierre, see* GONZALEZ DE SAN PEDRO.

González (Bartolomé) [GONZÁLEZ LEBRACO (B.)], *see* HISP. SOC. OF AMER. G. in coll. of H.S., 1927.

González (Estebanillo). E. González, hombre de buen humor; vida y hechos. s8°. Paris. *n.d.*

Gonzalez (Ines), *widow of A. Martinez de Las Casas Pintadas, see* HISP. SOC. OF AMER. Manuscripts: I. G., 1408, MS. B11, 1927.

Gonzalez (José Fernando). Crón. de la prov. de Huesca, 1866, *see* ESPAÑA. Crón. gen., v4, 1865 &c.

Crón. de la prov. de Zaragoza, 1867, *see* ESPAÑA. Crón. gen., v4, 1865 &c.

Gonzalez (Thyrsus). De recto usu opinionum probabilium, *see* MIGNE (J. P.), *ed.* Theol. cursus, t11, 1861.

Gonzalez-Blanco (Edmundo).
Campoamor: biog. y estudio crít. 8°. 1911

Gonzalez de la Calle (Pedro Urbano). Ensayo biog.: vida profesional y acad. de F. Sanchez de las Brozas. 8°. 1922

Gonzalez de la Llana (Manuel), *see* GONZALEZ LLANA (M.)

Gonzalez de Mendoza (Juan). Rerum morumque in regno Chinensi hist. Ex Hispan. ling. in Lat. tr. F. J. Brulius. [*2p in 1v.*] s4°. Antverpiae. 1655

Gonzalez de San Pedro (Francisco). Rel. abregée de la nouv. persécution de la Chine, tirée de la rel. compose'e à Macao par les miss. de l'Ordre de St. Dominique &c. [*Foll. by* Extraits des lettres, au mois de Sept. 1711, *w. sep. pagin.*] Tr. s8°. *n.d.*

Gonzalez Gamargo (Juan), *see* PARNASO venezolano: sel. compos. Poét. col. por C. B. A., 2a ed. aum. por J. G. G., 2t, 1918.

Gonzalez Llana (Manuel). Crón. de la prov. de Córdoba, 1867, *see* ESPAÑA. Crón. gen., v5, 1865 &c.

Crón. de la prov. de Salamanca, 1869, *see* ESPAÑA. Crón. gen., v6, 1865 &c.

González Palencia (Angel).
Hist. de la España musulmana. s8°. Barcelona. 1925

see CASTELLANOS (J. DE). Disc. de el capitan Fr. Draque, 1921.

Gooch (George Peabody).

Eng. democratic ideas in the 17th c. With suppl. notes &c. by H. J. Laski. 2nd ed. 8°. C. 1927

Franco-German relations, 1871–1914. 8°. 1923

Frederic Mackarness. A brief memoir. s8°. *p.p.* 1922

The French Revolution. [Helps for stud., No. 29]. s8°. 1920

Germany. Intr. by H. A. L. Fisher. 8°. 1925

Hist. of mod. Europe, 1878–1919. 8°. 1923

Life of Lord Courtney. 8°. 1920

Nationalism. s8°. 1920

Recent revelat. of European diplomacy. 8°. 1927

„ „ 3rd impr., w. suppl. ch. on revel. of 1927. 8°. 1928

Recent revelat. on European diplomacy. [Repr. f. Journ. of Brit. Inst. of Internat. Aff., Jan. 1923]. 8°. [1923]

see BRITISH. Brit. docs. on orig. of the War, 1898–1914; ed. G. P. G. &c., v1, 2, 11, 1926–27.

„ CAMBRIDGE (THE) HIST. OF BRIT. FOREIGN POLICY 1783–1919; ed. A. W. Ward & G. P. G., 3v, 1922–23.

„ RUSSELL (*Lord* J.) Later corresp., 1840–78; ed. G. P. G., 2v, 1925.

Good (Daniel). *Apprehension & exam. of D. G., murderer, [*in* Trials, Newspaper cuttings &c., v1]. 8°. 1842

Good (E. T.), *see* *COUNTRY (THE) & "Labour," w. app., Lab. & the "Capitalist" press, by G., 1920.

Good (James Winder). Irish Unionism. s8°. D. 1920

Goodall (Walter). An introd. to the hist. & antiq. of Scotland. Tr. s8°. E. 1773

Goodchild (John George), *F.G.S., see* DAKYNS (J. R.), R. H. TIDDEMAN & J. G. G. Geol. of co. betw. Appleby, Ullswater, & Haweswater, 1897.

Goode (Francis). The better covenant consid. f. Hebr. viii, 6–12, &c. 8°. 1833

Goode (W. A. M.) With Sampson thr. the war: naval oper. of N. Atlantic Squadron dur. Span.-Amer. War of 1898. With ch. by Rear-Adm. Sampson &c. 8°. N.Y. 1899

Goode (William), *rector of St. Luke's, Chelsea.* An entire new vers. of the Book of Psalms. 3rd ed. s8°. 1816

Goodenough (Erwin R.)
The theology of Justin Martyr. 8°. Jena. 1923

Goodhart (Arthur Lehmann).
Poland & the minority races. 8°. [1920]

Goodman (Arthur Worthington).
A little hist. of S. Botolph's, Camb. s8°. C. 1922

see WINCHESTER. Chartulary of W. Cathedral; ed. in Eng. by A. W. G., 1927.

Goodman (Godfrey), *bp. of Gloucester.* The fall of man, or, the corruption of nature. 8°. 1616

Goodman (John), *D.D.* The penitent pardoned: parable of the prodigal son. With an add. sermon. [*w. sep. tp.* (*1681*) *& pagin.*] s4°. 1683

Goodnow (Frank Johnson).
Comparative admin. law. 2v. 8°. N.Y. 1897
Goodrich (Andrew T.) *Picture (The) of New York, & strangers guide. s8°. N.Y. [1828]
Goodrich (Carter Lyman). The frontier control. Brit. workshop politics. Foreword by R. H. Tawney. s8°. 1920
Goodrich (Edwin Stephen).
Living organisms: th. origin & evol. s8°. O. 1924
Goodrich (James Putnam). The evolution of Soviet Russia, *see* INTERNAT. CONCILIATION, N°. 185, 1923.
Goodrich-Freer (A.) [*Mrs.* H. H. SPOER; *ps. Miss* X].
Arabs in tent & town. 8°. 1924
—— **& John,** *3rd marq. of* **Bute,** *edd.* The alleged haunting of B—— House; includ. a journal kept dur. the tenancy of Col. L. Taylor. 8°. 1899
Goodridge (Charles Medyett). Narr. of a voyage to the South Seas & the shipwreck of the Pcss. of Wales cutter &c. 4th ed. s8°. Exeter. 1841
Goodwin (Gwendoline). Anthol. of mod. Indian poetry. [Tr.] Ed. G. G. s8°. [1927]
Goodwin (Harvey), *bp. of Carlisle.*
Mem. of bp. Mackenzie. 2nd ed. s8°. C. 1865
Goodwin (Henry K.) Offic. rep. of trial of G. for murder of A. D. Swan. 8°. Boston [Mass.] 1887
Goodwin (John), *vicar of St. Stephen's, Coleman St.*
Ἀπολύτρωσις ἀπολυτρώσεως or Redemption redeemed &c. fol. 1671
Xtn. theology. Sel. &c., w. life of the a. by S. Dunn. s8°. 1836
The divine authority of the Scr. s4°. 1648
The pagans debt & dowry. Also: Agreement & distance of brethren: election & reprobation, &c. [*sep. tp. & pagin.*] s8°. 1679
see JACKSON (T.) Life of J. G., 1822.
,, WESLEY (J.) Treatise on justific., extr. f. J. G., 1836.
Goodwin (John Cuthbert). Insanity & the criminal. 8°. 1923
Sidelights on criminal matters. Foreword by Sir B. Thomson. 8°. 1923
The soul of a criminal. 8°. [1924]
Goodwin (Maud Wilder). Historic New York. 1st [& 2nd] ser. of Half Moon Papers. [*By var. wr.*] Ed. M. W. G., A. C. Royce &c. [2v]. 8°. N.Y. 1899
Goodwin (Philip).
Religio domestica rediviva. [*wanting all after p. 542*]. s8°. 1655
Goodwin (Starling). *Could a man be secure: duett [*b. w.* Corelli (A.) Twelve concertos, 1790 ?]. 4°. *Walker.* [1790 ?]
Goodwin (Thomas), *D.D., 1600–79.* Christ set forth. Together w. treat. on the heart of Xt. in heaven &c. s8°. [1841]
Extracts f. works, *see* WESLEY (J.) Xtn. lib., v11-12, 1751.
The returne of prayers &c. s8°. 1638
,, ,, ...s8°. O. 1839
The vanity of thoughts discovered. s8°. 1850
Goodyear (Anson Conger). Amer. & Eng. autograph coll. Sold, Feb. [1927], Anderson Gall. [*Illust.*] la8°. [1927]
Goodyear (William Henry). Amiens Cathedral & Mr. Bilson's rejoinder. [Fr. J. of Roy. Inst. of B. Architects, s3, v16. P2860]. 4°. 1909
The architect. refinements of St. Marks at Venice. [Brooklyn Inst. Mem. of Art &c., v1ii]. la8°. N.Y. 1902
A Renaissance leaning façade at Genoa. [Brooklyn Inst., Mem. vol. 1i]. la8°. N.Y. 1902
Vertical curves & o. architect. refinements in Gothic cathedrals &c. of N. France & Byzantine churches at Constantinople. [Brooklyn Inst., Mem., v1iv.] la8°. N.Y. 1904
see EDINBURGH ARCHIT. ASSOC. Illust. cat. of photographs &c. of archit. refinements; text &c. by W. H. G., 1905.
Goodyer (John), *see* GUNTHER (R. T.) Early Brit. botanists &c., based on G., 1922.
Googe (Barnaby). Eglogs, epytaphes, & sonettes, 1563. [Ed. E. Arber. Eng. repr. *b. w.* Roy (W.) &c. "Rede me" &c., 1871]. s8°. 1871
Goold (William). Portland in the past, w. hist. notes of old Falmouth. 8°. Portland, Maine. 1886
Goosev, *see* GUSEV.
Goossens (Eugene), *Jr., see* PROPERT (W. A.) The Russian ballet, 1909–20, w. ch. on the music by E. G., 1921.
Goovaerts (Alfons). Hist. & bibliog. de la typogr. musicale dans les Pays-Bas. 8°. Anvers. 1880
Gööz (József). Budapest története. 4[ik] Kiadás. 8°. 1896

Gopčevič (Spiridion).
Oberalbanien u. s. Liga. 8°. Leipzig. 1881
Österreichs Untergang—die Folge v. Franz Josefs Missregierung. 8°. 1920
Gopinatha Rao (T. A.) Talamana or iconometry: measurements of Hindu images &c., *see* INDIA. ARCH. SURVEY. Mem[s]., No. 3, 1920.
Gorbunov (L.) Пѣсни борьбы. [P2453]. 8°. Москва. 1906
Gorce (Matthieu Maxime).
Saint Vincent Ferrier (1350–1419). 8°. 1924
Gorceix (Septime), *see* IORGA (N.) & S. G. Anthol. de la litt. roumaine, 1920.
Gordon, *The family of.*
see BULLOCH (J. M.) Bibliog. of the G., sect. 1, 1924.
,, MACMATH (W.) The G. of Craichlaw; ed. T. Fraser, 1924.
Gordon (*Sir* **Alexander),** *of Navidale, see* BULLOCH (J.) Gay adv. of Sir A. G., 1925.
Gordon (Alex. Reid).
The prophets of the old Test. [2nd ed.] s8°. [1919]
Gordon (*Maj.-Gen.* **Charles George).** *Life of Gen. Gordon. By the authors of "Our Queen" &c. s8°. 1885
see MACDONALD (A.) *Why G. perished, 1896.
,, SMITH (G. B.) Heroes of the 19th c.: G. &c., 1899.
,, STRACHEY (L.) Eminent Victorians, 1920.
,, WILSON (A.) The "ever victorious army": Chin. camp. under G., 1868.
Gordon (*Mrs.* **Cora Josephine),** *see* GORDON (J.) & C. J. G. *for works wr. in collab.*
Gordon (*Sir* **David John).** The central state. S. Australia: hist., progress &c. 8°. Adelaide. 1903
The "Nile" of Australia: plea for utiliz. of the Murray. 8°. Adelaide. 1906
Gordon (E. V.) Intr. to Old Norse. s8°. O. 1927
Gordon (*Mrs.* **E. Hamilton),** *see* MOORE (E. HAMILTON).
Gordon (*Hon. Mrs.* **Elisabeth Ann),** *wife of Hon. John Ed. Gordon.* Asian Cristology & the Mahāyāna. Repr. of the cent.-old Indian Ch. hist., by T. Yeates, &c. 8°. Tokyo. 1921
The lotus gospel; or, Mahayana Buddhism & its symbolic teachings &c. 8°. Tokyo. [1911]
Messiah, the ancestral hope of the ages. la8°. Tokyo. [1909]
Gordon (Ernest). Russian prohibition. [P2427]. s8°. Westerville, *Ohio.* 1916
Gordon (G. F. C.) Clockmaking, incorp. portions of "Clocks, watches" &c. by Ld. Grimthorpe. 8°. 1925
Gordon (George Stuart), *prof. of Eng. lit.*
Companionable books. sl. 8°. 1927
The discipline of letters. [P2717]. 8°. O. 1923
Medium aevum & the middle age. [S.P.E. Tract, No. 19, w. notes & rep.] 8°. O. 1925
Mons & the Retreat. Pref. by Ld. French. s8°. 1918
Shakespeare's English. [S.P.E. Tract, 29]. 8°. O. 1928
Shelley & the oppressors of mankind. [Warton lect. From Proc. of Brit. Acad., v10. P2717]. 8°. [1922]
Three Oxford ironies. Copleston's Advice to a young reviewer—Mansel's Phrontisterion, & the Oxford Ars poetica. Ed. G. G. s8°. 1927
The Trojans in Britain, *see* ENGLISH ASSOC. Essays, v9, 1924.
Gordon (H. K.) Prem: a tale of mod. India. Foreword by Sir M. O'Dwyer. s8°. 1926
Gordon (Helen Cameron).
Love's Island [Cyprus]. 8°. Cyprus. 1925
Gordon (*Sir* **Home).** Cricket form at a glance in this century. Intr. by Lord Hawke. la8°. 1924
Gordon (*Col.* **J.)** Note of letters taken out of trunk that came to Dumbeath, w. letters f. Col. G. &c. to Marq. of Montrose, 1649, *see* MAIDMENT (J.), *ed.* Hist. fragm. rel. to Scot. affairs, p2, 1833.
Gordon (James), *minister of Banchory.* *The reformed bishop or 19 articles tendered by Φιλαρχαῖος a well-wisher of the pres. govern. of the Ch. of Scot. s8°. 1680
Gordon (Jan). Mod. French painters. la8°. [1923]
—— **&** *Mrs.* **C. J. Gordon.**
Misadventures w. a donkey in Spain. 8°. 1924
Two vagabonds in Languedoc. 8°. [1925]
Two vagabonds in Sweden & Lapland. la8°. [1926]
Gordon (John), *of Glencat.* The famous bull Unigenitus by Pope Clement XI, agst. Quesnelle's tr. of the N. Test. &c.; added, a refut. of the Rom. Ch. &c. 2nd ed. s8°. [1731]
Gordon (John William), *K.C.*
The judicial crisis in the Transvaal. [P2564]. 8°. 1898
Mary, Queen of Scots & h. execution. [*Fr.* London & Middl. Arch. Soc., N. S., v5]. 8°. Kendal. 1927

Gordon (Lina Duff), *see* WATERFIELD (*Mrs.* L. D.)

Gordon (Lockhart), *see* GORDON (L. H.) Apology for Gordons, &c., 1804.

Gordon (Loudon Harcourt). An apology for the conduct of the Gordons; corr. &c. w. Mrs. Lee; exam. at Bow St. & trial at Oxford. 4th ed. s8°. 1804

Gordon (Mary), *L.R.C.P.* Penal discipline. 8°. 1922

Gordon (*gen.* Patrick), *1635–1699* [GORDON (PETR IVANOVICH)]. Записки, *see* SAKHAROV (I. P.) Записки &c., 1841.

Gordon (*Col.* Philip James). Hdbk. of topography, 1911–26, *see* INDIA: SURVEY.

Gordon (Ronald Gray). Personality. 8°. 1926

Gordon (Seton P.) Amid snowy wastes: wild life on the Spitsbergen Archipelago. 8°. 1922
The Cairngorm Hills of Scotland. la8°. [1925]
Days w. the golden eagle. By S. G. in collab. w. h. wife. 8°. 1927
Hebridean memories. 8°. 1923
Wanderings of a naturalist. 8°. 1921

Gordon (Thomas), *of Kirkcudbright.* *A coll. of papers, all wr. dur. the late rebellion. By the a. of the Independent Whig. s8°. D. 1748

Gordon (William) [*ps.* PARTHENOPÆUS, *Hereticus*]. *Popery agst. Christianity &c. With app., cont. the lives & canoniz. of the last 4 saints &c. s8°. 1719

Gordon (William John).
Our country's flowers. Intr. by G. Henslow. 8°. *n.d.*

Gore (Charles), *bp. of (1) Worcester, (2) Birmingham, (3) Oxford.*
Belief in Christ. s8°. 1922
Belief in God. s8°. 1921
,, ,, ...[repr.] s8°. 1922
Christian moral principles. 7 sermons. n. impr. s8°. [1922]
The creed of the Xtian. 8°. 1895
The Epistles of St. John. s8°. 1920
The Holy Spirit & the Church. s8°. 1924
The religion of the Church as pres. in the C. of Eng. 4th impr. s8°. [1916]
see BOX (G. H.) & C. G. Divorce in the New Test.: reply to Dr. Charles, 1921.

Gore (Hugh), *bp. of Waterford & Lismore; 1613–91, see* GIMLETTE (T.) Life, charities &c. of H. G., 1888.

Gore (*Capt.* John). The evolutions of a field battery &c. s8°. Woolwich. 1846

Gore-Browne (Robert). The crater. s8°. [1925]

Gorell (*Rt. Hon. Sir* John Gorell Barnes, *1st baron*) [OF BRAMPTON], *see* DE MONTMORENCY (J. E. G.) J. G. B., 1st Ld. G.; a mem., 1920.

Gorell (Ronald Gorell Barnes, *3rd baron*).
Education & the army. 8°. 1921
Plush: a romance of the House of Lords. 8°. [1924]

Gorgeous gallery of gallant inventions (1578); ed. H. E. Rollins, 1926, *see* PROCTER (T.)

Gorges (*Sir* Arthur), *d. 1625.* The Olympian catastrophe. Intr. by R. Davies. [Cayme Press]. la8°. Kensington. 1925

Gorges (Mary). Killarney. 8°. 1912

Gorgias *of Leontium* [G. LEONTINUS]. G. de laudibus Helenae [*in Greek*], *see* ORATORES. Orationes horum rhetorum &c., p3, 1513.
Helena. Rec. & interp. est O. Immisch, *see* KLEINE TEXTE, 158, 1927.

Gorgolini (Pietro). Le Fascisme. Préf. de B. Mussolini. Tr. E. Marsan, avec préf. de J. Bainville. s8°. 1923
Il Fascismo n. vita ital. Pref. B. Mussolini. 8°. Torini. 1922
The Fascist movt. in Ital. life. Pref. by B. Mussolini. Tr. & ed. w. intr. by M. D. Petre. 8°. [1923]
La rivoluzione fascista. Pref. di M. Bianchi. Disc. polit. di B. Mussolini. s8°. Torino. 1923

Gorham (*Maj.* Charles Alfred).
A text book of military law. 4th ed. 8°. 1880

Gori (Gino). Il teatro contemp. e le sue correnti caratterist. di pensiero &c. n. varie nazioni. 8°. Torino. 1924

Gori (Pietro). Le feste fiorentine attr. i sec.: le feste per S. Giovanni. 8°. [1926]

Goriainov (Sergius), *see* GORYAINOV (S. M.)

Gorin de Saint Amour (Louis), *see* SAINT AMOUR (L. G. DE).

Göring (August). M. Lutherus quae classica Graec. Latinorumque scripta scholis commendavit tractanda, &c. Progr. s4°. Lubecae. [1817]

Goring (Charles). The English convict: a statist. study. Abr. ed., w. intr. by K. Pearson. 8°. 1919

Gorini (Jean Marie Sauveur). Déf. de l'église contre les erreurs de Guizot, Thierry, Michelet, Ampère &c. 11e éd., préc. d'une notice biog. [*by* C. Hébrard]. 4t. 8°. 1906–07

Goris (J. A.) Les colonies marchandes mérid. (Portugais, Esp., Ital.) à Anvers, 1488–1567. Diss. la8°. Louvain. 1925

Goriun, *the admirable, bp. of Georgia* [KORIUN]. Goriun's Lebensbeschr. d. hl. Mesrop. a. d. armen. Urtext übers. & erläut. v. B. Welte. [P2672]. 4°. Tübingen. [1841]
[Life of St. Mesrob. *In Armenian.* Soferq Hayk., v11]. s8°. i Venetik. 1854

Gorizia. *Sunto storico d. principate contee di Gorizia e Gradisca. la8°. Gorizia. 1853

Gorky (Maksim).
Весельчакъ. Воспоминанія. 8°. Berlin. *n.d.*
Въ Америкѣ. Очерки. s8°. Berlin. *n.d.*
Въ людяхъ. 8°. Berlin. *n.d.*
Въ степи—Дружки. [P2392]. s8°. Москва. 1916
9oe Января. Очеркъ. [*a. c. b. w. h.* Революція и культура, *n.d.*] s8°. Berlin. *n.d.*
Дѣти. [*a. c. b. w. h.* Жалобы, *n.d.*] s8°. Berlin. *n.d.*
Дѣти солнца. Драма. 8°. St. 1905
Дѣтство. [Meine Kindheit]. 8°. Berlin. *n.d.*
Жизнь ненужнаго человѣка. [Leben e. nutzlosen Menschen]. 8°. Berlin. *n.d.*
Заметки из дневника. Воспоминания. 8°. Berlin. 1924
Запрещенное. О писателѣ, который зазнался &c. [P848]. s8°. Берлинъ. 1902
Зыковы. Сцены. 8°. Berlin. *n.d.*
Мать. Романъ. 8°. Berlin. *n.d.*
Мои университеты. 8°. Berlin. 1923
Протестъ противъ общества—Толстой, Письма по поводу Кишинева—Короленко, Домъ No. 13. [P2389]. s8°. Берлинъ. *n.d.*
Рассказы, 1922–24. 8°. Berlin. 1925
Революція и культура. Статы за 1917 г. 8°. Berlin. *n.d.*
Русскія сказки. [*a. c. b. w. h.* Весельчакъ, *n.d.*] 8°. Berlin. *n.d.*
Сказки. 8°. Berlin. *n.d.*
A fuller edition than that of 1908.
Случай изъ жизни Макара—Рожденіе человѣка. Два разсказа. [*b. w. h.* Весельчакъ, *n.d.*] 8°. Berlin. *n.d.*
Солдаты. Очерки. [*a. c. b. w. h.* Весельчакъ, *n.d.*] 8°. Berlin. *n.d.*
Старикъ. Пьеса. [*b. w. h.* Весельчакъ, *n.d.*] 8°. Berlin. *n.d.*
Страсти-мордасти. Воспоминанія. 8°. Berlin. *n.d.*
Три дня. Разсказъ. s8°. Berlin. *n.d.*
Человѣкъ—Дачники—Тюрма—Разсказъ Филиппа Васильевича, *see* SBORNIK. Сб. товар. "Знаніе" 1, 3, 4, 1904–05.
Чудаки; комедія. [*a. c. b. w. h.* Весельчакъ, *n.d.*] 8°. Berlin. *n.d.*

TRANSLATIONS.
L'angoisse (une page de la vie d'un meunier) & autres nouvelles. 3e éd. s8°. 1902
Ein Jahr russ. Revolution. Nachw. v. P. N. Cossmann. [P2689]. la8°. L. 1918
Lénine et le paysan russe. Tr. M. D. de Gramont. s8°. [1924]
The lower depths, *see* SAYLER (O. M.) Moscow Art Theatre ser. of Russ. plays; tr., 1923.
Mother. Foreword by C E. Russell. s8°. N.Y. 1927
Un premier amour. Tr. Dumesnil de Gramont. s8°. [1924]
Remin. of L. N. Tolstoi. Auth. tr. by S. S. Koteliansky & L. Woolf. s8°. 1920
Reminiscences of my youth. Tr. V. Dewey. 8°. 1924
Souv. de ma vie litt. Tr. [*f.* Мои университеты] par M. Dumesnil de Gramont. s8°. [1923]
Strasti - Mordasti: nouvelle inéd., *see* ŒUVRES libres, t28, 1923.
La vie en bleu; tr. D. de Gramont, *see* ŒUVRES libres, 68, 1927.
V. I. Lénine. Préf. de A. Pierre. [P2722]. s8°. 1920
see CHEKHOV (A.) Note-books; w. remin. of Tchekhov, by M. G., 1921.
,, CHIRIKOV (E. N.) Русскій народъ подъ судомъ М. Г., 1917.
,, OBOLENSKY (L. E.) М. Г., 1903.

Gorman (Herbert S.) James Joyce, h. first 40 yrs. s8°. [1926]

Gormanston. Cal. of the G. register. Ed. J. Mills & M. J. McEnery. [Roy. Soc. of Ant. of I., Extra vol.] la8°. D. 1916

Gorn (Vl.), V. Mech & Cherevanin.
Борьба обществ. силъ въ русской революціи. 4B. *in* 1v. 8°. Москва. 1907
1, Mech (V.) Силы реакціи.
2, Cheravanin. Пролетаріатъ въ революціи.
3, Savarensky (N.) Эконом. движеніе крестьянства—Marev (P.) Полит. борьба крестьянства.—Gorn (Vl.) Роль крестьянства въ революціи.
4, Mech (V.) Либеральная &c. буржуазія.

Gornfeld (Arkady Georgevich), *see* BLOK (A.), A. F. KONI &c. Пушкин—Достоевский [*by A. G. G. &c.*], 1921.

Gorostiza (Manuel Eduardo de), *see* PEÑA Y REYES (A. DE LA). G. y la cuestion de Texas, 1924.

Gorra (Egidio). Lingue neolatine. s8°. Milano. 1894

Görres-Gesellschaft. Studien z. Gesch. u. Kultur d. Altertums. Im Auftr. &c. d. G.-G. hrsg. v. E. Drerup, &c. B12, H1/2. 8°. Würzburg. 1923
see DRERUP (E.) Demosthenes, 1923. [12i, ii.]

Görres (Johann Joseph von), *see* BRENTANO (C.), J. v. G., & B. WEBER. A. K. Emmerich, M. v. Mörl u. D. Lazzaris, 1874.

Gorrie (John).
Illust. of martial law in Jamaica. 8°. 1867
Görs (Gustav Friedrich Aug.)
Thurn- u. Taxissches Postwesen. 8°. Rostock. 1907
Gorter (Herman). Mei, een gedicht. 6e dr. 8°. A. 1921
Goryainov (Sergei Mikhailovich). Босфоръ и Дарданеллы. 8°. С.-П. 1907
Le Bosphore & les Dardanelles. Et. d'ap. la corr. diplomat. déposée aux Archives centr. de St.-Pétersb. &c. Préf. de G. Hanotaux. 8°. 1910
Gorze, *abbey.* Cartul. de l'abbaye de G.; publ. A. d'Herbomez, *see* SOC. NAT. DES ANTIQ. DE FR. Mettensia, t2, 1898–1901.
see MARICHAL (P.) Remarques sur la Cartul. de G., 1902.
Gos (François). Rambles in High Savoy. Pref. by G. W. Young, & intr. by F. Regaut. Tr. F. Kemp. 8°. 1927
Zermatt & its valley. Tr. F. F. Roget. la8°. 1926
Gosche (Hermann Richard Adolf). De Ariana ling. gentisque Armen. indole. [P2812]. 8°. Berolini. 1847
Göschel (Carl Friedrich). Dante Alighieri's Unterweisung ü. Weltschöpfung &c. [P2472]. 8°. 1842
Der Mensch nach Leib, Seele u. Geist. [P2472]. 8°. L. 1856
Spekulat. Philos. v. Gott u. d. Menschen &c. [P2472]. 8°. 1838
Zur Lehre v. d. letzten Dingen. [P2472]. 8°. 1850
Göschen (Otto). Doct. de matrimonio ex ordin. Eccl. Evang. saec. 16. [P558]. 4°. Halis. 1848
Goselini (Giuliano) [GOSELLINI]. Compendio stor. d. guerra di Parma e del Piemonte, 1548–53; [*ed. A. Ceruti*], *see* REGIA DEP. DI ST. PATRIA. Misc., t17, 1878.
Gosh (Mekhithar), *see* MEKHITHAR, *Gosh.*
Goslar (Hans). Jüdische Weltherrschaft? Phantasiegebilde oder Wirklichkeit. 3e, umgearb. A. [P2456]. 8°. 1920
Gosnold (Bartholomew). Rel. des voyages de G. &c. à la Virginie en 1602 & 1603, *see* BERNARD (J. F.), *ed.* Recueil, t3, 1732.
Gospel. *An histor. vindic. of The naked g. [*by A. Bury*], 1691, *see* BURY (A.)
Goss (*Sir* John). Intr. to harmony & thorough-bass, w. examples &c. 3rd ed. 4°. [1852]
Goss (L. Allan). The story of Wé-than-da-ya, Buddhist legend. Sk. f. Burmese vers. of Pali text. 8°. Rangoon. 1886
Gossart (Jan), *see* MABUSE (JEAN).
Gosse (*Sir* Edmund), *C.B.*
Aspects & impressions. 8°. 1922
Books on the table. s8°. [1921]
Crit. essay on the life & works of G. Tinworth, w. descr. cat. obl.4°. 1883
The earliest Charles Lamb dinner, *see* WHERRY (G. E.), *ed.* Cambridge & C. Lamb, 1925.
Far och son. En studie över 2 temperaments. Övers. B. Cronstedt. s8°. [1924]
Leaves & fruit. 8°. 1927
The library of E. G.: descr. & bibliogr. cat. of a portion of h. coll. Comp. by E. H. M. Cox, w. intr. essay by G. 8°. 1924
Life of Wm. Congreve. [2nd impr., rev. & enl.] s8°. 1924
More books on the table. s8°. [1923]
Notes on the pictures &c. of A. W. Hunt, exhib. at Fine Art Soc. [P2404]. 8°. 1884
Restoration plays from Dryden to Farquhar. Intr. by G. [Everyman's Lib.] [repr.] s8°. [1925]
Short hist. of mod. Eng. lit. [10th impr.] 8°. [1923]
Silhouettes. 8°. 1925
Swinburne. Essay wr. in 1875 & now first pr. 8°. *p.f.p.c.* 1925
Tallemant des Réaux or the Art of miniature biog. 8°. O. 1925
see BRAYBROOKE (P.) Consid. on E. G., 1925.
„ MARVELL (A.) A. M., 1621–78, tercentenary tributes, by E. G. &c., 1922.
—— **& W. A. Craigie.** The Oxford bk. of Scandinavian verse, 17th–20th cent. Chosen by Sir E. G. & W. A. C. s8°. O. 1925
Gosse (Philip).
Bibliog. of works of Capt. Charles Johnson. 8°. 1927
My pirate library. Intr. note by Sir E. Gosse. 8°. 1926
The pirates' who's who. 8°. 1924
Gosse (Philip Henry). Introd. to zoology. 2v. s8°. [1857]
see GOSSE (E.) *Father & son, 1907; övers., 1924.
Gosselin (Alfred). Monogr. du village de Querrieu, *see* SOC. DES ANTIQ. DE PICARDIE. Mém., s4, t8, 1916.
Gosses (I. H.) & N. Japikse. Handboek tot de staatkundige gesch. van Nederland. 8°. 's-Gravenhage. 1920
Gosset (Alphonse).
Basilique de Saint-Remi de Reims. 8°. Reims. 1911
Gossler (Conrad von).
Erinnerungen an d. grossen Krieg. 8°. Breslau. 1919
Gössler (Peter). Leukas-Ithaka. Die Heimat des Odysseus. la8°. St. 1904

Gosudarstvenii Institut Istorii Iskusstv. Музыка и музыкал. быт старой России. т1. [Сборник работ О. Т. И. М. *by* B. V. Asafev &c.] 8°. Ленинград. 1927
Gosudarstvennaya Akademiya Khudojestvennikh Nauk, *see* CHEKHOV (A.) Записные книжки, 1927.
Gosudarstvennoe Russkoe Geograf. Obschestvo, *see* IMPERATORSKOE R.G.O.
Goswinus [GOSVINUS; GOZWINUS]. De expugnatione Salaciae carmen, *see* COLONIENSIS. Chron. Regia Colon. &c.; rec. G. Waitz, 1880.
Got (Ambroise). Henry Becque, sa vie &c. 8°. 1920
La terreur en Bavière. s8°. 1922
Gotch (John Alfred). Compl. acc. of bldgs. erected in Northants. by Sir T. Tresham, 1575–1605, w. partic. conc. Tresham family & th. home at Rushton. fol. Northampton. 1883
Inigo Jones: a mod. view, *see* ROY. SOC. OF LIT. Essays, N.S., v7, 1927.
Old English houses. 8°. [1925]
Gote (Yury Vladimirovich). Смутное время, 17 ст. 8°. [Москва]. 1921
Gothaischer genealogischer Hofkalender nebst diplom.- statist. Jahrbuch, 1827, 1874, 1882, 1917, 1921, 1922. s8°. Gotha. [1827–1921]
Gothaisches genealogisches Taschenbuch d. adeligen Häuser. Alter Adel u. Briefadel. Jhrg. 15 (1922). s8°. Gotha. [1920]
„ „ Deut. Uradel. Jhrg. 22, 24, 26 (1921, 23, 26). s8°. Gotha. [1920–26]
Gothaisches genealogisches Taschenbuch d. freiherrl. Häuser. Jhrg. 24, 67, 71–73, 76 (1874, 1917, 1921–23, 1926). s8°. Gotha. [1873–1926]
Gothaisches genealogisches Taschenbuch d. gräfl. Häuser. Jhrg. 47, 90, 94–96, 99 (1917, 1921–23, 1926). s8°. Gotha. [1873–1926]
„ „ Historisch-herald. Hdbch. z. genealog. Taschenbuch. s8°. Gotha. 1855
Gotham. The merry tales of the Wise Men of G. Ed. J. O. Halliwell. s8°. 1840
Gothein (Eberhard). Ignatius v. Loyala. [Verein f. Ref.-gesch. Schr., Jhrg. 3, Nr. 11]. 8°. Halle. 1885
Das Ruhrgebiet. [P2735]. 8°. 1923
see KÖLN. Die Stadt Cöln im ersten Jhdt. unter preuss. Herrschaft, 1815–1915, Bli, v. E. G., 1916.
Gother (John). Instructions &c. for conf. & communion, *see* *KEY of heaven &c., 1831.
see STILLINGFLEET (E.) *The doctrines &c. of the Ch. of Rome &c. in ans. to A papist misrepresented &c. [by J. G.], 1686.
Gothica. Missa Gothica, 1770, *see* MOZARABICA.
Gothofredus (Dionysius), *see* GODEFROY (D.)
Gotschalk, *see* GOTTESCHALCUS.
Gotta (Salvator).
Alba di nozze. Dramma.—La nostra ricchezza. s8°. Milano. 1921
L'amante provinciale. Romanzo. 2a ed. s8°. Milano. 1920
La bufera infernal. Romanzo. s8°. Milano. 1925
La donna mia. Romanzo. s8°. Milano. 1924
Pia. Romanzo. 3a ed. s8°. Milano. 1921
La plus belle femme du monde. Tr. Marie Croci. s8°. [1925]
Il primo re. Romanzo. s8°. Milano. 1922
Quelle che preferisco. (Ragnatele—La porta del cielo). n. ed. s8°. Milano. 1920
Tre mondi. Romanzo. s8°. Milano. 1921
see LAZARILLO (—) S. G. 1919.
Götte (Rudolf). Kulturgesch. d. Urzeit Germaniens, d. Frankenreiches u. Deutschlands im frühen M.- a. 8°. Bonn. 1920
Gottes Wort in eiserner Zeit, Folge 3, Lief. 2–6, 1916–18, *see* MEYER (W.)
Gotteschalcus [GOTSCHALK], *called Fulgentius*; *monk of Orbais, see* USSHER (J.) Gotteschalci & praedestinatianae controv. hist. cum ejusdem confess., 1631.
Gottfried, *von Strassburg, see* FISCHER (H.) Üb. G. v. S., 1916
Gottfried (Johann Ludwig), *ps.* [*i.e.* J. PHILIPP ABELIN], *see* MERIAN (M.) View of London: [engr. by M. f. "Neuwe archont. cosmica," durch J. L. G., 1638], 1922.
Gotthardus (Georgius), *see* HEERBRAND (J.) Refut. errorum calumniarum &c. quae G. G. contra J. H. effutivit, 1589.
Gotthelf (Jeremias), *ps.* [*i.e.* ALBERT BITZIUS]. Sämtliche Werke. Hrsg. v. R. Hunziker u. H. Bloesch.
B1–6, 8–15, 19, 21, 22. 8°. München [& Zürich]. 1916–2
1, Der Bauern-Spiegel: Lebensgesch. d. J. G., v. ihm selbst; E. Müller.
2, 3, Leiden u. Freuden e. Schulmeisters; E. Bähler, 2T.

Gotthelf (Jeremias), [*continued*].
Sämtliche Werke. B1–6, 8–15, 19, 21, 22 [*continued*].
4, Wie Uli d. Knecht glücklich wird ; R. Hunziker.
5, 6, Wie Anne Bäbi Jowäger haushaltet u. wie es ihm mit d. Doktern geht ; A. Jneichen, 2T.
8, Der Geldstag ; R. Hunziker & E. Bähler.
9, Jacobs Wanderungen durch d. Schweiz ; R. Hunziker.
10, Käthi d. Grossmutter ; G. Bohnenblust.
11, Uli d. Pächter ; H. Bloesch.
12, Die Käserei in d. Vehfreude ; H. Bloesch.
13, Zeitgeist u. Bernergeist ; H. Bloesch.
14, Erlebnisse e. Schuldenbauers ; R. Hunziker & E. Bähler.
15, Die Wassernot im Emmental—Die Armennot — Eines Schweizers Wort ; R. Hunziker.
19, 21, 22, Kleinere Erzählungen, T4, 6, 7 ; H. Bloesch, R. Hunziker.
„ „ ....Ergzb. 1, 2. 8°. Zürich. 1922
1, 2, Der Herr Esau, 2T.

Göttingen. Arch. Inst. d. Univ. G.
see JACOBSTHAL (P.) Göttinger Vasen, 1912.
„ KÖRTE (G.) Göttinger Bronzen, 1917.

***Göttinger** (Der) Student. Oder Bemerk. &c. ü. Göttingen &c. 8°. Göttingen. 1813

Göttingische gelehrte Anzeigen. Unter d. Aufsicht d. Königl. Gesellschaft d. Wissenschaften. 183.–189. Jahrgang. 8°. 1921–27

***Göttlichen** (Die) Schr. vor d. Zeiten des Messie Jesus &c., T1, 1735, *see* SCHMIDT (J. L.)

Gottlieb (Theodor), *see* ÖSTERREICH. Mittelalt. Bibliotheks-kat. O's, B1, Niederösterr. ; bearb. v. T. G., 1915.

Gottsched (Johann Christoph). *Die vernünftigen Tadlerinnen. 1. Stück, 3 Jenner 1725 [ed. J. C. G.] (*facs.*), *see* FREYTAG (G.) Bilder, B5, 1925.
*Vita, fata & scripta C. Wolfii. [*b. w.* Canstein (C. H. v.) Das Muster : Lebens-Beschr. Speners, 1740]. s8°. Lipsiae. 1739
see MÜLLER (G. F.) О началѣ &c. Козаковъ [tr. f. G.'s Das Neueste], 1760.

Göttweig. Urkunden &c. z. Gesch. d. Benedictinerstiftes G. ; bearbt. v. A. F. Fuchs, 3T, *see* FONTES RERUM AUSTRIAC., B51, 52, 55, 1901–2.

***Götz** v. Berlichingen mit d. eisernen Hand, 1773, *see* GOETHE (J. W. v.)

Götz (Georg). De glossariorum Latinorum orig. et fatis, *see* CORPUS gloss. Lat., v1, 1923.

Götz (Walter Wilhelm) *see* BRIEFE u. Akten zur Gesch. d. 30 jähr. Krieges, N.F., T2, B2, bearbt. v. W. G., 1918.

Götze (Albrecht). Ausgew. hethit. Texte hist. u. jurist. Inhalts ; transkr. v. A. G., *see* KLEINE TEXTE, T153, 1926.
Kleinasien zur Hethiterzeit. 8°. Heidelberg. 1924

Götze (Alfred). Proben hoch- u. niederdeut. Mundarten, *see* KLEINE TEXTE, T146, 1922.

Götze (Georg Heinrich) [GOEZIUS].
De domesticis Lutheri singularia, propos. H. A. Rosenfelden. [P442]. s4°. Lubecae. 1707]
De literis butyricis, Butterbrieffen &c. [P437]. s4°. Lubecae. [1706]
De odio pontificiorum in hymnos eccl. Lutheranae comm. s4°. Lipsiae. 1703
De reliquiis Lutheri. [P442]. s4°. Lipsiae. 1703
Diss. de Lutheranismo Beghinarum, propugn. J. P. Bruhns. [P2631]. s4°. Lubecæ. 1719
Diss. de Macedonianis quam publ. exam. sistit G. H. G., resp. G. Vogelio. [P434]. s4°. Wittebergae. [1688]
Diss. : Luthers Schuhe sind nicht allen Dorf-Priestern gerecht. Acc. diss. de lit. sacr. cultoribus. ed. nov. [P2628]. s4°. Francofurti. 1750
see HÖFER (A. C.) Orat. funebr. im mem. G. H. G., 1728.

Götzinger (Ernst). Joachim Vadian. [Verein f. Ref.- gesch. Schr., Jhrg. 13, Nr. 50]. 8°. Halle. 1895

Goudar (Ange de). *Mem. pour servir à l'hist. de Pierre III, emp. de Russie &c. Publ. par Mr. D. G. [*i.e.* Goudar. *Foll. by* Suppl. *w. sep. tp. & pagin.*]. s8°. Francfort. 1763

Goudge (Henry Leighton). Second Epistle to the Corinthians. Intr. & notes by G. [Westminster Comm.] 8°. [1927]

Goudge (M. F.) Prelim. rep. on the limestones of Quebec & Ontario. [Canada : Dept. of Mines. P2874]. 8°. Ottawa. 1927

Goudy (Henry). Address on law reform. [P2465]. 8°. 1919

Gouffé (Toussaint-Augustin), *see* EYRAUD (M.) *L'affaire G. (1890), *n.d.*

Gouge (Thomas). Christian directions. 8°. 1831
The principles of Christ. religion. [The heads of the foregoing catechism.—The Christ. householder.—A morning prayer for a family &c. *w. sep. pagin.*] s8°. 1679

Gouge (William). Comm. on the Epistle to the Hebrewes. [4 *pagin*s.] 2v. sfol. 1655
The whole-armor of God. 2nd ed. *enl.* Added, a Treatise of the sinne agst. the Holy Ghost. s4°. 1619
see BIBLE : COMPL. TEXTS &c. Annot. upon the O. & N.T. : by [J. Ley, W. G. &c.], 2nd ed., 2v, 1651.

Gouge (William M.) A short hist. of paper money & banking in the U.S. &c. 2p *in* 1v. s8°. Phila. 1833

Gouger (Robert). S. Australia in 1837 : letters, w. postscript as to 1838. s8°. 1838

Gouges (Olympe de), *see* LACOUR (L.) 3 femmes de la Révol., 1900.

Gough (George W.) Wealth & work. s8°. [1920]

Gough (Henry). The N.T. quotations collated w. the Scr. of the O.T. &c. 8°. 1855

Gough (Lewis), *see* ROTTER (E.), L. G. &c. Die Biene in Ägypten, 1921.

Gough (Thomas), *see* GOFFE (T.)

Gouin (Henry). Abbaye de Royaumont, hist. & guide. [P2561]. 8°. Limoges. 1917

Goujon (A.), *chemist, see* MARCHADIER (A.-L.) & A. G. Les poisons méconnus, 1921.

Goujon (Alexandre). Bulletins offic. de la Grande Armée, dictés par Napoléon ; rec. par A. G., 2t, *see* NAPOLEON I. Rec. de pièces authent., t8, 9, 1822.

Gouland (Henry Godfrey). Plan of a proposed new colony to be called Britannia. [P2845]. 8°. Lyttelton [N.Z.] 1851

Goulburn (Edward Meyrick), *dean of Norwich, see* RUGBY SCHOOL. Bk. of R.S. ; [ed. w. pref. by E. M. G.], 1856.

Gould (*Mrs.* Emily Bliss), *1822–75, see* BACON (L. W.) Mem. of E. B. G., 1879.

Gould (F. H. Carruthers), *see* POLEY (A. P.) Hist., law &c. of the Stock Exchange ; by P., asst. by G., 3rd ed. rev., 1920.

Gould (*Sir* Francis Carruthers). The Westminster cartoons, 1895–1903. [Repr. f. The Westminster Gazette]. No. 1–8 [in 1v]. fol. 1895–1904
N°. 1 *has title :* Cartoons of the Campaign.

Gould (Frederick J.) Auguste Comte. s8°. 1920
Is religion growing or decaying ? [P2493]. 8°. 1917
Thomas Paine (1737–1809). s8°. [1925]

Gould (Gerald). The coming revol. in Gt. Brit. Pref. by G. Lansbury. s8°. [1920]
The Eng. novel of to-day. s8°. 1924
The lesson of Black Friday : trade union structure. [P2584, 2585]. s8°. 1921
Lyrics. 2nd ed. s8°. 1906

Gould (*Lt.-Comm.* Rupert T.) The hist. of the chronometer. [Repr. f. Geogr. Journ., Apr. 1920. P2525]. 8°. 1921
Jeremiah Horrox, astronomer. [Sette of Odd Volumes]. s8°. *p.p.* 1923
The marine chronometer, its hist. &c. Foreword by Sir F. W. Dyson. 8°. 1923
The sea-serpent. [Sette of Odd Vols. Opusc. 80]. s8°. *p.p.* 1926

Goulding (Richard W.) Wriothesley portraits, *see* WALPOLE Soc., v8, 1920.

Gouldsbury (Charles Elphinstone).
Remin. of a stowaway. 8°. 1920

Gouldsbury (Cullen). An African year. s8°. 1912

Goulven (Joseph). Les Mellahs de Rabat-Salé. Préf. de G. Hardy. 8°. 1927

Goumy (Edouard). Etude sur la vie & les écrits de l'abbé de Saint-Pierre. 8°. 1859

Gourd (Jean Jacques), *1850–1909, see* TRIAL (J. E. L.) J.-J. G., 1914.

Gourdon (Pierre). Qui-rit le paludier. s8°. [1921]

Gourgaud (*le baron* Gaspard). Napoléon & la grande armée en Russie, ou exam. de l'ouvr. de P. de Segur. 3e éd. 8°. 1826
see NAPOLEON I. Méms. &c. écr. à St. Hélène par les généraux qui ont partagé sa captivité [G. G. &c.], 1823.

Gourmont (Remy de).
Couleurs : contes nouv., suiv. de choses anc. 8e éd. s8°. *n.d.*
Lettre à l'Amazone. 6e éd. s8°. 1927
Lettres à Sixtine. s8°. 1921
Promenades littéraires. s6, 7. s8°. 1926–27
„ „ 10e éd. [s1]. s8°. 1919
Le puits de la vérité. s8°. 1922
Théâtre. Théodat—Le vieux roi. Ed. décorée par P. Guillemat. 8°. 1925
Le vase magique. [Les Quatorze, N°. 1]. 8°. 1923
see ESCOUBE (P.) R. de G. & s. œuvre, 1909.
„ ROUVEYRE (A.) Souv. de mon commerce : G., Apollinaire &c., 1921.

Gournay, *The family of, see* GURNEY (D.) Rec. of House of Gournay, 1848–58.

Gourraigne (Louis Gontran), *see* ROTHSCHILD (H. DE) & L. G. G. La Grande Guerre d'ap. la presse paris., t3, 1920.

Goury (Georges). Orig. & évol. de l'homme. 8°. [1927]

Gousset (Jacques). Consider. sur le projet d'une nouv. version franç. de la Bible, publié 1696 sous le nom de C. Le Cene. s8°. Amsterdam. 1698

Gouvea (Antonio de), *bp. of Cyrene.* Hist. orientale des grans progrès de l'Eglise cathol. en la reduction des anc. chrétiens dits de S. Thomas à l'union de la vraye église. Par les bons devoirs du S[r]. Don A. de Meneses &c. Tournée en Fr. par J. B. de Glen. s8°. Anvers. 1609

Gouvion Saint-Cyr (*le maréchal* **L.**) Atlas des cartes & plans rel. aux campagnes du G. St. C. aux armées du Rhin &c., 1792–97. [Planches 1 & 8 *wanting*]. lafol. 1828

Govea (Antonio), *see* GOUVEA (A. DE), *bp. of Cyrene.*

Gover (Clement Edward John).
Place names of Middlesex. s8°. 1922

Gover (Wm.) A guide to the anc. ch. of St. Mary, Puddletown &c. [P2706]. 8°. Dorchester. 1908

Government. *G. (The) & order of Ch. of Scot., 1690, *see* HENDERSON (A.)

Govoni (Corrado).
Poesie scelte (1903–18). n. ed. riv. 8°. Ferrara. [1920]

Gow (James). Companion to school classics. [repr.] s8°. 1924

Gowan (Walter Edward). Alphab. index to Marvin's works, 1883, *see* MARVIN (C.)

Gower (Richard Hall). Treatise on seamanship, w. a system of naval signals. 3rd ed., corr. & enl. 8°. 1808

Gower (*Rt. Hon. Lord* **Ronald C. Sutherland-Leveson-),** *4th son of 2nd duke of Sutherland.*
Thomas Gainsborough. 8°. 1903

Gowland (W.) Metals & metal-working in old Japan. [Repr. f. Trans. of Jap. Soc. of London, v13]. 8°. [1915]

Goya (F.) [†GOYA Y LUCIENTES (FRANCISCO JOSÉ)].
see EZQUERRA DEL BAYO (J.) La Duquesa de Alba y G., 1928.
,, SALCEDO Y RUIZ (A.) La época de Goya, 1924.
,, TILD (J.) G., 1921.
,, YOUNG (B.) The Proverbs of G.: acc. of "Los proverbios," exam. & expl. &c., 1923.

Goyau (Georges) [*ps.* LÉON GRÉGOIRE].
Une épopée mystique : origines relig. du Canada. s8°. 1924
Orientations catholiques. s8°. 1925
Saint Bernard. 8°. [1927]
Sainte Mélanie (383–439). 10e éd. s8°. 1921
Saint Pierre. s8°. [1923]
Séance de l'Acad. Franç. du 15 fév. 1923. Disc. de réception de G. G., Éloge de D. Cochin, Réponse de A. Ribot, lue par J. Bédier. s8°. 1923
La vie, des livres, & des âmes. s8°. 1923
see BUCAILLE (V.) G. G., 1926.
,, GIRAUD (V.) G. G., l'homme & l'œuvre, 1922.
,, HANOTAUX (G.), *ed.* Hist. de la nation franç., t6, Hist. religieuse : par G. G., 1922.

Goyri de Menendez Pidal (Maria). Fábulas y cuentos en verso. Seleccion. s8°. 1922

Göz (Johann Adam). Gesch.- literar. Überblick ü. Luthers Vorschule, Meisterschaft &c. in d. Dolmetschung d. heil. Schrift &c. 8°. Nürnberg. 1824

Göze (Johann Melchior) [GOEZE; †GŒTZE].
Ausführl. Vertheid. d. Complutens. griech. Neuen Test. &c. Zur Widerleg. d. D. Semlers. [*&* Fortsetz. &c.] [2v]. s8°. Hamburg. 1766–69
Beweis dass d. Bahrdt. Verdeutschung d. N. Test. keine Übers., sondern e. Verfälschung d. Worte Gottes sey, &c. s8°. Hamburg. 1773
Vergleichung d. Orig.-Ausgaben d. Uebers. d. heil. Schrift v. Luther, 1517–45 &c. 2 St. *in* 1v. 4°. Hamburg. 1777–9
Versuch e. Hist. d. gedr. niedersächs. Bibeln v. 1470 bis 1621. 4°. Halle. 1775
Vertheid. d. Complutens. Bibel, insonderheit d. neuen Test. geg. d. Wetsten. u. Semler. Beschuldigungen. Nebst Anhange &c. s8°. Hamburg. 1765
Verzeichnis s. Samlung selt. u. merkw. Bibeln. 4°. Halle. 1777

Gozwinus, *see* GOSWINUS.

Gozzadini (*il conte* **Giovanni).** Delle torri gentilizie di Bologna e d. famiglie alle qu. prima appart. 8°. Bologna. 1875
Note illustr. di due fusti di Carrozze del sec. 16. [*Ed.* P. A. di Serego-Alighieri. P2843]. 4°. Venezia. [1906]

Gozzi (*il conte* **Carlo).** Le fiabe. [Pref. di D. Ciàmpoli]. 2v. s8°. Lanciano. [1912]
see ZICCARDI (G.) Le fiabe de C. G., 1924.

Gozzi (Gaspare), *ed.* [Lazaro Mocenigo. *With extr. f.* Crasso (L.) Elogi di capitani. Nozze Mocenigo—Cais di Pierlas. N. 129]. la8°. [Venezia. 1884]

Gozzi (*il conte* **Gasparo),** *see* ZARDO (A.) G. G. n. lett. del s. tempo in Venezia, 1923.

Graae (Paul). Daenemark. [Polit. Parteien; Hrsg. Dr. Stricker, H1. P2749]. 8°. Münster i. W. [1923]

Grabar (Igor). Русскіе художники.
вып. 4, 5. 4°. Москва. [1913–14 ?]
see GLAGOL (S.) М. В. Нестеровъ, 1914 ?. [5.]
,, ROSTISLAVOV (A.) А. П. Рябушкинъ, 1913 ?. [4.]

Grabau (Amadeus William).
A textbook of geology. 2v. 8°. [1920–21]

Grabe (Joseph) [*ps.* ANTONIUS ARIMATHÆENSIS]. Isagoge monstrans usum &c. verae doct. de invoc. Dei & Filii Dei. Ad analysim thesium E. Hunii. [Praef. J. Nebeltavii]. s4°. Neustadii in Palatinatu. 1586

Grabein (Paul).
Im Auto durch Feindesland. s8°. 1916

Graber (Georg). Der Eintritt d. Herz. v. Kärnten am Fürstenstein z. Karnburg, 1919, *see* KAIS. AKAD. D. WISS. ZU WIEN. Sitz., B190, 1920.

Graber (Hans). Piero della Francesca. 68 Tafeln mit Text v. H. G. 4°. Basel. 1922

Grabmann (Martin). Die echten Schr. d. Thomas v. Aquin. [Beitr. z. Gesch. d. Philos. d. Ma., 22i, ii]. 8°. Münster. 1920
Neuaufgefund. Quaest. Sigers v. Brabant zu Aristoteles, hrsg. M. G., *see* EHRLE (F.) Miscell., v1, 1924.
Works in KÖNIGL. AKAD. D. WISS. ZU MÜNCHEN. Phil. Kl., Sitz.
Neu aufgefund. lat. Werke deut. Mystiker, 1921.
Neu aufgef. Werke d. Siger v. Brabant u. Boetius v. Dacien 1924.
Studien zu Johannes Quidort v. Paris, O. Pr., 1922.
Des Ulrich Engelberti Abhdlg. De pulchro : Untersuch. u Texte, 1925.

Gräbner (Fritz). Ethnologie, *see* HINNEBERG (P.) Die Kultur d. Gegenwart, T3 v, 1923.

Grabowsky (Norbert).
Die Bestimmung d. Menschen. [P2476]. 8°. 188

Grace, *The family of.*
see MASON (W. S.) Descr. & arch. sketch of the Grace Mausoleum in the Queen's Co., 1819.
,, —— Survey of Tullaroan, or Grace's Parish in the Co of Kilkenny, 1819.

Grace (Harvey). The complete organist. Intr. by P. C Buck. s8°. 192
The organ works of Bach. Intr. by E. Newman. 8°. [1922

Grace (Sheffield).
see MASON (W. S.) Sketch of Grace-Mausoleum in Queen's Co.; ed. S. G., 1819.
,, —— Survey of Tullaroan, or G.'s Parish in Kilkenny ed. S. G., 1819.

Graces. *Graces before meat, 1762 ?; 1775 ?, *see* WESLEY (J.) & C. WESLEY.

Gracey (*Mrs.* **J. T.**) Medical work of the Woman's For Miss. Soc. Meth. Episc. Church. [*b. w.* Hart (I.) Hist sketches, 1879]. s8°. Dansville, N.Y. 188

Gracian (Baltasar).
The compleat gentleman. Tr. T. Saldkeld. 2nd ed. 8°. 173
The courtier's oracle : or, the art of prudence. [Tr.] s8°. 169
Hand-Orakel u. Kunst d. Weltklugheit. Übers. A. Schopenhauer. 3e A. s8°. L. 187
L'homme de cour. Maximes tr. sur l'éd. orig. de 1647 pa A. de La Houssaie & préc. d'une intr. par A. Rouveyre. s8°. 192
see BELL (A. F. G.) B. G., 1921.

Gradenigo (Giuseppe). Lettere ined. di illust. Italiani de sec. 18 e 19 al nob. G. G., con note. [*Ed.* A. Tessier P2787]. 8°. Venezia. 185

Gradenwitz (Otto).
Bismarcks letzter Kampf, 1888–98. 8°. [1924
see VOCABULARIUM jurisprud. Rom.; jussu Inst. Savignian compos. O. G. &c., 1903 &c.

Gradisca. *Sunto storico d. princ. contee di Gorizia e G 1853, *see* GORIZIA.

Gradovsky (Aleksandr Dmitrievich). Ист. мѣстнаго управлені въ Россіи. t1 [приложеніе *w. sep. pagin.*] 8°. С.–П. 186

Gradovsky (Grigory Konstantinovich). М. Д. Скобелевъ. Этюд s8°. С.–П. 188

Graduale [GRADUEL]. Le Répons-Graduel Justus ut palma reprod. en fac-sim. d'ap. plus de 200 antiphonaires ms d'orig. div. du 9e au 17e siècle. [Paléogr. Musicale, 2, 3]. 2p. 4°. Solesmes. 1891–9

***Graduated** scale for a property tax. By the a. of "The reply to the 'State of the Nation,'" 1822. [P2782]. 8º. 1833

Graeca. Hagiographica Graeca ined.; ed. B. Latishev, 1914, *see* LATISHEV (V. V.)

Lyra Graeca: remains of all Gr. lyric poets except. Pindar; ed. & tr. by J. M. Edmonds, 3v, 1922–27, *see* LYRA.

Graeci. Mathematici Graeci minores; ed. J. L. Heiberg, *see* KONG. DAN. VID. SELSK. Hist.-fil. Medd., B13, 1927.

Theologorum aliquot Graec. vet. orthodox. libri Gr. & iidem Lat. donati &c., 6p, 1560, *see* THEOLOGI.

Graetz (Leo), *see* GRÄTZ (L.)

Graf (Alfred). Gedichte. s8º. Nürnberg. 1922

Von. d. Minne Überlast. s8º. Nürnberg. 1922

Graf (Arturo). Miti, leggende e superstiz. d. medio evo. la8º. Torino. 1925

Poesie. s8º. Torino. 1922

Prometeo n. poesia. 8º. Torino. 1920

Studii drammatici. 8º. Torino. 1878

Graf (Carl Heinrich). Essai sur la vie & les écrits de J. Le Fèvre d'Étaples. Thèse. 8º. Str. 1842

see MÖLLER (W.) Hist.-krit. Bedenken gegen d. Graf-Wellhausen. Hypothese, 1899.

Graf (Hans Gerhardt), *see* GOETHE (J. G.) Goethe ü. s. Dichtungen, Samml. v. H. G. G., 3T (*in* 9B), 1904–14.

Graf (Theodor). Cat. of the Graf coll. of anc. Greek portraits. [P2700]. 8º. [Plates, 4º]. *n.d.*

Graf (Urs), *see* JESUS CHRIST. *Passio Domini nostri I. C. &c., add. figuris [*attrib. to* U. G.], 1507.

Gräfe (Heinrich). *Examinatorium ü. d. Dogmatik d. evangel. Kirche &c. 8º. Quedlinburg. 1830

Grafenauer (Ivan). Kratka zgodovina slovenskega slovstva. 2ª izd. s8º. Ljubljana. 1920

Graff (Eberhard Gottlieb), *see* BOPP (F.) Vocalismus oder Krit. ü. Graff's ahd. Sprachschatz &c., 1836.

Graff (F. W. Up de), *see* UP DE GRAFF (F. W.)

Graff (Johann). Vocabula exotica Lat.-barbara. Coll. &c. 1746 a J. G. Ed. H. J. Jaeck. fol. Bambergae. 1833

Graffin (Roger) & F. Nau, *edd.*

Patrologia orientalis. t14–19. la8º. Paris. 1920–27

[Bible: Job.] Le livre de Job; version copte bohaïrique; publ. & tr. E. Porcher, 1924. [18.]

Florence, *Council of.* Doc. rel. au Concile de F.: textes éd. & tr. par L. Petit, p1, 2, 1923–27. [15, 17.]

1, La quest. du purgatoire à Ferrare.

2, Œuvres anticoncil. de Marc d'Ephèse.

Furlani (G.) 6 scritti Antitriteistici in lingua siriaca; [ed. & tr.] per G. F., 1920. [14.]

Israel, *Ter.* Synaxaire arménien; publ. & tr. par G. Bayan, p3–6, 1922–27. [15, 16, 18.]

Jesus Christ. Logia & agrapha Domini Jesu apud Moslem. script. usitata; coll., vertit &c. M. Asin & Palacios, fasc. 2, 1926. [19.]

—— Les miracles de Jésus; texte éthiopien publ. & tr. par S. Grébaut, p2, 3, 1920–23. [14, 17.]

John, *of Ephesus.* Lives of the Eastern saints: Syriac text, ed. & tr. E. W. Brooks, p1–3, 1923–26. [17–19.]

John Khamé, *Abba.* Life of Abba J. K.; Coptic text ed. & tr. by M. H. Davis, 1920. [14.]

Mary, *the Virgin.* Homélies mariales byz.: textes grecs éd. & tr. en Lat. par M. Jugie, 2p, 1922–26. [16, 19.]

1, Abraham d'Ephèse—Abbé Théognoste—S. Euthyme—M. Psellos—Néophyte le reclus—Manuel II Paléologue—G. Scholarios.

2, Théodote d'Ancyre—Chrysippe, prêtre de Jérusalem—S. Jean, archevèque de Thessalonique—S. Euthyme, patr. de Constantinople—Nicolas Cabasilas—Georges Scholarios.

Mufazzal ibn Abū al-Fazail. Hist. des sultans mamlouks; texte arabe publ. & tr. par E. Blochet, p2, 1920. [14.]

Philoxenes. De Uno e S. Trinitate incorp. & passo; Syriac. ed. Lat. vertit M. Brière, 1927. [15.]

Severus, *patr. of Antioch.* Coll. of letters of S. f. Syr. MSS.; ed. & tr. par E. W. Brooks, p2, 1920. [14.]

—— Homiliae cathédrales de S.: Homélie 77; texte grec éd. & tr. franç. &c., par M. A. Kugener &c., 1922. [16.]

Synaxaire (Le) arabe jacobite (rédaction copte); texte arabe, publ., tr. & annoté par R. Basset, p4, 5, 1922–23. [16, 17.]

4, Les mois de Barmahat (févr.-mars), Barmoudah (mars-avr.) & Bachons (avr.-mai). 5, Les mois de Baounah, Abib, Mesoré & jours complément.

Synaxaire (Le) éthopien: les mois Taḥschasch, Ṭer & Yakatit; publ. & tr. S. Grébaut, p4, 1927. [15.]

Synaxaire (Le) géorgien; publ. &c. N. Marr, 1926. [19.]

*Trophées (Les) de Damas: controverse jud.-chrét.; texte grec & tr. par G. Bardy, 1927. [15.]

Wessely (C.) Les plus anc. mon. du christianisme écrits sur papyrus; textes éd., tr. & annotés par W., [p] 2, 1924. [18.]

Graffin (Roger) & F. Nau, *edd.* [*continued*].

Yaḥya ibn Sa'īd ibn al-Baṭrīk. Hist., cont. de Sa'īd-ibn-Bitriq; éd. & tr. I. Kratchkovsky &c., 1924. [18.]

Yūḥannā ibn Abū Zakarīyā, *ibn Sabā.* Le perle précieuse: texte arabe, publ. & tr. par J. Périer, 1922. [16.]

Grafton (Henry Fitzroy, *1st duke of*), *see* FITZROY (A. W.) H. duke of G., 1663–90, 1921.

Graham (A. W.), *see* GRAHAM (WALTER ARMSTRONG).

Graham (Alan). The voyage home. s8º. E. 1921

Graham (Charles), *of the Little Newtoun, Waterford, see* CAMPBELL (W. G.) "The apostle of Kerry": life of C. G., 1868.

Graham (Edward), *Assist. master in Harrow School.* The Harrow life of H. Montagu Butler. With intr. ch. by Sir G. O. Trevelyan. 8º. 1920

Graham (Gabriela Cunninghame).

Santa Teresa. Vers. castell. por I. Alonso. la8º. 1927

Graham (George), *see* BARR (J.) The city of Auckland, prec. by Maori hist. of Auckland Isthmus, by G. G., 1922.

Graham (Henry Davenport). Antiq. of Iona. 4º. 1850

Graham (Henry Grey). Social life of Scotland in 18th c. [2nd ed., repr.] 8º. 1909

Graham (Hugh). Early Irish monastic schools. s8º. D. 1923

Graham (James).

see HOOPER (F.) & J. G. The home trade, 1918.

,, —— The import & export trade, 1920.

Graham (John). A century of Welsh music. s8º. 1923

Graham (John William).

Conscription & conscience. A hist., 1916–19. 8º. [1922]

The divinity in man. 8º. [1927]

The faith of a quaker. 8º. C. 1920

The harvest of Ruskin. s8º. [1920]

Graham (Patrick). Essay on authenticity of poems of Ossian; obj. of M. Laing refuted &c. Added, essay on mythology of O.'s poems by prof. Richardson. 8º. E. 1807

Graham (Peter Anderson).

Highways & byways in Northumbria. 8º. 1920

Iwerne Minster before, dur. & after the Gt. War. Ed. by P. A. G., w. contrib. by H. S. Bower, E. Acton &c. 4º. *p.f.p.c., n.p.* [1923]

Lindisfarne: or Holy Island, 635–1920. fol. 1920

Graham (R. P. Howgrave-), *see* HOWGRAVE-GRAHAM (R. P.)

Graham (Richard Percival Devereux), *see* POITEVIN (E.) & R. P. D. G. Mineralogy of Black Lake area, Quebec, 1918.

Graham (Robert), *of Gartmore; 1735–97* [*known as* "DOUGHTY DEEDS"], *see* GRAHAM (R. B. C.) Doughty deeds: life of R. G., f. h. letter-bks. &c., 1925.

Graham (Robert Bontine Cunninghame).

A Brazilian mystic: life & miracles of Antonio Conselheiro. 8º. 1920

Cartagena & the banks of the Sinú. la8º. 1920

The conq. of New Granada: life of G. Jimenez de Quesada. 8º. 1922

Conq. of the River Plate. [8º. 1924]

Doughty deeds: life of R. Graham of Gartmore. 8º. 1925

Pedro de Valdivia, conqueror of Chile. 8º. 1926

Redeemed & o. sketches. 8º. [1927]

Graham (Rose). The chantry certificates; ed. & tr. by R. G. & the Edwardian invent.; ed. R. G. f. transcripts by T. Craib. [Oxf. Rec. Soc. Rec. ser. 1]. 8º. O. 1919

,, ,, [*another issue.* Alcuin Club coll., 23]. la8º. 1920

Graham (Stephen).

Children of the slaves. 8º. 1920

Europe—Whither bound? Letters of travel, 1921. 8º. 1921

London nights. 8º. [1925]

Midsummer music. s8º. [1926]

Russia in division. 8º. 1925

Under-London. s8º. 1923

Graham (Walter). Beginnings of Eng. lit. periodicals, 1665–1715. 8º. N.Y. 1926

Graham (Walter Armstrong).

Siam: hdbk. of information. s8º. 1912

,, ,, ...[3rd ed.] 2v. 8º. 1924

Graham (William). The wages of labour. s8º. 1921

Graham (Winifred), *aft. Mrs. Theodore Cory.*

"And it was so." 2nd ed. s8º. [1923]

Falling waters. s8º. [1919]

In fear of a woman. s8º. [1925]

Grahame (James), *poetical writer.*

The birds of Scotland, w. o. poems. s8º. E. 1806

The Sabbath & o. poems. 8º. 1857

Grahamstown [GRAHAM'S TOWN]. Abstract of proc. of the Board of Relief for the destitute in G.T., 1836, *see* D'URBAN (*Sir* B.)

Views of Grahamstown. Publ. by D. Knight & Cº. obl.8º. Grahamstown. 1892

Grail [†GRAAL; GREEAL; SAINT-GRAAL &c]. The high hist. of the Holy G. Tr. f. the French by S. Evans. 8°. 1903
La queste del S. G. Roman du 13e s. [? *by* W. Map]. Ed. A. Pauphilet. [Class. fr. du m. â.] s8°. 1923
Span. Grail fragments. El libro de Josep Abarimatia—Le estoria de Merlin—Lançarote. Ed. K. Pietsch. 2v. (1, Texts. 2, Comm.) 8°. Chicago. [1924–25]
see BOHIGAS BALAGUER (P.) Textos esp. y gallego-port. de la Demanda del Santo Grial, 1925.
„ BOULENGER (J.) Romans de la Table Ronde, t4, Le S. G. &c., 1923.
„ NUTT (A.) Legends of the Holy G., 1902.
Grainge (William). Hist. & topog. of Little Timble, Great Timble & the hamlet of Snowden. s8°. Otley. 1895
Nidderdale. s8°. Pately Bridge. 1863
Gram (J. P.) Tafeln für die Riemannsche Zetafunktion; hrsg. v. N. E. Nörlund, *see* KONG. DAN. VID. SELSK. Skrifter, Række 8, B10, 1925–26.
Gramatica. *Gramatica Indostana. [Sagr. Congreg. de Propag. Fide]. s8°. Roma. 1778
Gramatica (Emma), *see* MANZINI (A.) E. G., 1920.
Gramberg (Eugen). Pilze d. Heimat. 2B. 8°. L. 1921
Grambs (Johann Georg). Diss. de electione imperatoris Romano-Germ. [P2641]. s4°. Argentorati. 1676
Grammaire. *Gr. générale & raisonnée [par le sieur D. T.], n. éd., 1676, *see* LANCELOT (C.)
*Gr. turque ou méthode, &c. 1730, *see* HOLDERMANN (J. B.)
Grammar (A) of the Malabar Lang., 1789, *see* MALABAR.
Grammatica [GRAMMATICAE; GRAMMATICI]. *Gr. d. ling. armena lett. con app. [P2801]. s8°. 1879
*Gr. ling. Boemicae, ed. 4a, 1739; ed. 5a., 1753, *see* JANDYT (V.)
Grammaticae Lat. auctores antiq., 1605, *see* PUTSCHIUS (H.)
Grammatici Graeci. Rec. et apparatu crit. instructi. p1, v1, 3; p2, v1i, ii, 2, 3; p3, v1, 2; p4, v1, 2. 8°. L., *Teubner*. 1867–1910
see APOLLONIUS, *Alexandrinus*. A. quae supersunt; rec. &c. R. Schneider &c., v1i, ii, 2, 3, 1878–1910. [p2, v1–3.]
„ DIONYSIUS, *Thracian*. Ars gramm; ed. G. Uhlig, 1883. [p1, v1.]
„ —— Scholia in D. Artem gramm.; rec. A. Hilgard, 1901. [p1, v3.]
„ †HERODIANUS (Æ.) Reliquiae; coll. &c. A. Lenz, 2t, 1867–70. [p3, v1, 2.]
„ THEODOSIUS, *of Alexandria*. Canones, G. Choerobosci Scholia, Sophronii excerpta; rec. &c. A. Hilgard, 1894. [p4, v1, 2.]
***Grammatik** d. slav. Spr. in Krain, Kärnten &c., 1808, *see* KOPITAR (B.)
Grammont (Maurice). Le vers franç., s. moyens d'expression, s. harmonie. 3e éd., rev. & augm. la8°. 1923
Gramont (Antoine, *duc* de), *marshal of France, 1604–78*. Corr. inéd. de G. & de H. de Lionne, sept.–déc. 1650; *ed.* H. Courteault, *see* SOC. DE L'HIST. DE FR. Ann.-Bull., 1925.
Grampian Club.
see CUPAR-ANGUS. Rental Bk. of Cistercian Abbey of C.-A.; ed. C. Rogers, 2v, 1879–80.
„ ROGERS (C.) Bk. of Wallace, 2v, 1889.
Gran (Gerhard). Henrik Ibsen: liv og verker. 2B. s8°. 1918
see NORSK BIOGRAFISK LEKSIKON: redaktion: E. Bull, G. G. &c., B1-3, 1923–26.
Granados Campiña (Enrique), *see* BOLADERES IBERN (G. DE). E. G.: vida y est. crít., 1921.
Granberg (Josefine Lippert von), *see* LIPPERT VON GRANBERG (J.)
Grancolas (Jean), *see* FECHT (J.) De origine &c. missarum, J. G. &c. oppos., 1725.
Grand. *Grand (Le) coutumier de France, n. éd. par E. Laboulaye &c., 1868, *see* FRANCE.
Grand (Sarah), *ps.* [*i.e. Mrs.* M'FALL]. Variety. s8°. 1922
Grande (*Mrs.* Constance), *wife of Julian Grande, form. Barnicoat, see* GRANDE (J.) C. G., war corresp. &c., 1925.
—— & J. Grande.
Geneva, its place in the world. s8°. Geneva. 1920
Grande (Julian). Constance Grande, war correspondent—traveller—Alpinist &c. 8°. 1925
see GRANDE (*Mrs.* C.) & J. G. Geneva, its place in the world, 1920.
Granderath (Theodor). Hist. du Concile du Vatican jusqu'à sa prorogation. Ed. C. Kirch & tr. App. & doc. 8°. Brux. 1914
Grandet (*abbé* Joseph). Hist. du Séminaire d'Angers, 1659–95. 2v. la8°. Angers. 1893

Grandgent (Charles Hall).
Disc. on Dante. 8°. Cambridge, *Mass.* 1924
see DANTE SOCIETY, *Cambridge, Mass.*, Report 37, 1920.
Grandjean (Frank). Une révol. dans la philosophie. La doctrine de H. Bergson. 2e éd., rev., augm. & suivie d'une réponse à J. Benda. s8°. Genève. 1916
Grandmaison (*le col.* Louis Loiseau de). 2 conférences: la notion de sureté & l'engagement des grandes unités. 8°. 1912
Grandpré (Louis Marie Joseph, *conte* O'Hier de).
Voyage dans l'Inde & au Bengale, 1789–90. 2t. 8°. 1801
Granet (Marcel). Danses & légendes de la Chine anc. 2t. 8°. 1926
La religion des Chinois. 8°. 1922
Granfelt (Helge). Das Dreibundsystem, 1879–1916. Bl. 8°. 1925
Grange (Eugène), *ps.* [*i.e.* EUGÈNE PIERRE BASTE], *see* CORMON (P. E. F.) & E. G. Le violon du père Dimanche, 1854.
Granger (—), *see* DARMON (J. E.) & G. Dict. des gravures en couleurs &c. du 18e s., 1920.
Granger (James), *vicar of Shiplake*. Cat. of Richardson's coll. of Eng. portraits &c. as descr. in G.'s Biogr. Hist. of Eng. la8°. *n.p. n.d.*
see FLINDALL (J. M.) Amateur's pocket companion: books mentioned in wks. of G. &c., 1813.
„ TOWNELEY (J.) Cat. of coll. of Brit. portraits, illust. of G.; formed by J. T., 1828.
„ WILKINSON (R.) Cat. of engr. Brit. portraits illust. of wks. of G. &c., 1806.
Granges de Surgères (*le marq. de*). Répertoire hist. & biog de la Gazette de France, 1631–1790. 4t. 4°. 1902–0[illegible]
Grangié (Eugène) [E. DE SURGÈS]. Une anc. capitale de Province: Cahors-en-Quercy. Préf. H. Defert. s8°. Nancy. [1922
Granier de Cassagnac (P. A. de), *see* DUTRÈB (M.) & P. A. D[illegible] G. DE C. Mangin, 1920.
Granström (Hanna), *see* SWAN (C. G.) & H. G. English & Finnish dict., 1904.
Grant (*Sir* Alex.), *of Dalvey, 10th bart.* The Ethics of Aristotle illust. w. essays & notes. v1. 8°. 185[illegible]
Grant (Alex.), *F.R.C.S., 1817–1900*. Physician & friend A. G. h. autobiog. & letters f. the Marquis of Dalhousie Ed. G. Smith. 8°. 190[illegible]
Grant (Arthur James). The French monarchy (1483–1789). [repr.] 2v. s8°. C. 191[illegible]
—— & H. W. V. Temperley.
Europe in the 19th cent. (1789–1914). 8°. 192[illegible]
Grant (Asahel), *see* LAURIE (T.) Dr. G. & the Mountai[n] Nestorians, 1853.
Grant (Bartle), *see* RAPER (E.) Receipt book & portion o[f] cipher journal; ed. B. G., 1924.
Grant (Cyril Fletcher).
Studies in N. Africa. [n. ed., rev.] s8°. [1921
1st ed. had title, "Twixt sand & sea."
Grant (Elihu). The Orient in Bible times. 8°. Phila. 192[illegible]
Grant (Francis James). Zetland family histories. Comp. b[y] F. J. G. s4°. Lerwick. 190[illegible]
Grant (Frederick Clifton), *D.D.*
Econ. background of the Gospels. 8°. 192[illegible]
Grant (I. F.) Every-day life on an old Highland farm, 1769–1782. Pref. by W. R. Scott. 8°. 192[illegible]
Grant (James), *advocate*. Thoughts on orig. & descent of th[e] Gael, w. acc. of Picts, Caledonians & Scots, & obs. rel. t[o] poems of Ossian. 8°. E. 181[illegible]
Grant (James), *LL.B.*, *see* BANFF. Records of the co. of B 1600–1760; comp. by J. G., 1922.
Grant (John P.) Cardiff Castle. 8°. Cardiff. 192[illegible]
Grant (*Col.* Maurice Harold). Chronolog. hist. of the o[il] Eng. landscape painters (in oil), 16th to 19th cent. 2v. fol. [192[illegible]
Grant (Patrick), *aft. Ld. Elchies, see* ELCHIES (P. G., *Ld.*)
Grant (Ulysses Simpson), *see* SMITH (G. B.) Heroes of th[e] 19th c.: G. &c., 1899.
Grant (William), *M.A., Aberdeen,* **& J. M. Dixon.**
Manual of mod. Scots. 8°. C. 19[illegible]
Grant (William Alex.) The topography of Stane Street crit. review of "The Stane Street" of H. Belloc. 8°. 19[illegible]
Grantham (A. E.) Hills of blue: picture-roll of Chinese his[tory] to 1799. 8°. [192[illegible]
Grants. Coll. of misc. grants, crests &c. in MSS. preserved [in] Brit. Mus., Ashmolean Lib. &c. Ed. W. A. Littledal[e] [Harleian Soc., 76, 77]. 2v. la8°. 1925–[illegible]

Granvelle (*le card.* **de**) [PERRENOT DE GRANVELLE (*card.* ANTOINE)]. Lettere al duca di Savoia, Emanuele Filiberto; pubbl. da E. Ricotti, *see* REGIA DEP. DI STORIA PATRIA. Misc., t19, 1880.

Granville (George), *aft. baron Lansdowne.*
*Poems upon sev. occasions. 2nd ed. s8°. 1716

Granville (Roger), *see* DEVONSHIRE. Abstr. of the exist. transcr. of the lost parish-reg. of D., 1596–1644; by R. G. &c., v1, A–Bra, 1908.

Granville-Barker (Harley), *see* BARKER (H. G.)

Granville-Barker (Helen), *see* BARKER (H. G.)

Granvilliers (Jean de). Le prix de l'homme, 1914–16. [Roman]. [7e éd.] s8°. [1919]

Graphic (The). A souvenir. The coming of age of the G. (1869–1890). s8°. 1890

Graphische Gesellschaft. Veröffentlichung, 3, 5–11. fol. 1909.
see DODGSON (C.) Holzschnitte zu 2 nürnberg. Andachtsbüchern aus d. 16. Jhdts., 1909. [11.]
,, FRIEDLÄNDER (M. J.) A. Altdorfer Landschafts Radierungen, 1906. [3.]
,, KRISTELLER (P.) Exercit. super Pater Noster, 1908. [6.]
,, —— Florentin. Zierstücke in Kupferstich aus d. 15. Jhdt., 1909. [10.]
see KRISTELLER (P.) Eine Folge venezian. Holzschnitte aus d. 15. Jhdt., 1909. [9.]
,, —— G. Campagnola, Kupferstiche &c., 1907. [5.]
,, LEHRS (M.) Holzschnitte d. 15. Jhdts. im K. Kupferstichkabinett zu Berlin, 1908. [7.]
,, PAULI (G.) Inkunabeln d. deut. u. niederl. Radierung, 1908. [8.]

Grapius (Zacharias), *the younger* [GRAPE]. Systema noviss. controversiarum. Cum praef. A. J. de Krakevitz. Ed. auct. 4t *in* 1v. s4°. Rostochii. 1738
see AHMAD IBN 'ABDALLAH. Epist. theol. de libero arbitrio; ed. &c. Z. G., annexae dissert^{s}., *n.d.*
,, FECHT (J.) Diss. de versione Lutheri Germ., exam. subm. Z. G., 1709.

Grapow (Hermann). Üb. d. Wortbildungen mit e. Präfix m— im Ägypt., *see* KÖN.-PREUSS. AKAD. Abhdln., Phil.-hist. Kl., 1914.
Vergleiche u. a. bildl. Ausdrücke im Ägypt., *see* ALTE ORIENT (DER), Jhrg. 21, 1920.

Grasilier (Léonce). Rétif de La Bretonne inconnu. s8°. [1927]

Grass (C. A., *Frhr.* **v.)** Adel in Baden, *see* SIEBMACHER (J.), *ed.* Wappenbuch, B2vi, 1878.

Grässe (Johann Georg Theodor). Geschlechts-, Namen- u. Wappensagen d. Adels deut. Nation. 8°. Dresden. 1876
Orbis Latinus o. Verzeichnis d. wichtigsten latein. Orts- u. Ländernamen. 3e A. neu bearb. v. F. Benedict. 8°. 1922
see GRÜNES GEWÖLBE, *Dresden.* Descr. du Trésor Royal Saxon dit G. G., par G., 1872.
—— **& E. Jännicke.** Führer für Sammler v. Porzellan u. Fayence &c. Vollständig umgearb. &c. v. E. Zimmermann. 15e A. 8°. 1919

Grasset (*le comm.* **Alphonse Louis).**
La guerre d'Espagne, 1807–13. t2. 8°. 1925
La guerre en action. Neufchâteau. Préf. du gén. Buat. 8°. 1923
Le maréchal Franchet d'Espérey. [5e éd.] s8°. [1920]

Grassetti (Gaetano). Dell' aria Ravennate. 8°. Ravenna. 1809

Grassi (Girolamo), *da Carpi; 1501–56, see* CANANO (J. B.) Musculorum humani corporis picturata dissectio, 1541?: [w. drawings by G. da C.], facs. ed., 1925.

Grasso (Dalmazzo). Cronaca, 1484–1570, ed. D. Promis, *see* REGIA DEP. DI STORIA PATRIA. Misc., t12, 1871.

Grasso (Nicola). Eutychia. Comedia. s8°. [1524]

Grassot (Joseph Antoine), *see* LLORENTE (J. A.) Disc. sobre una constit. relig.; [*folld. by notes signed J. A. G.*], 1820.

Gratarolus (Gulielmus) [GRATAROLI]. De regimine iter agentium, *see* PYRCKMAIR (H.) De arte peregrin., 1591.

Gräter (Friedrich David). Ueb. d. Alter &c. d. teut. Königstitels. [P2739]. la8°. Hall. [1808]

Gratet de Dolomieu (Déodat G. S. T. de), *see* LACROIX (A.) D. D., 1750–1801: sa vie &c., 2t, 1921.

Gratianus, *the Canonist* [GRATIEN; GRATIAN]. Decretum aureū divi Gratiani: cuius titulus talis est. Incipit cōcordatia discordantiū canonū. [Fol. 1 *missing. Ends on fol. 582:* In nomine sancte & individue trinitatis tripartitū decreti aurei opus . . . finem accepit in alma Parisiensi Achademia expensis & opera Joh. Petit & Th. Kerner &c. *Then follow 6 leaves* (*sig. A 1–6*). Decretum abbreviatum in oratione soluta—Decretum abbreviat. in versibus—Materia XXVI causarum, *36 leaves* (*sig. A–C in eights, D–E in sixes*). Tabula capitulorum decreti — Glosarum decreti medulle *& 3 leaves without signatures.* Canones penitentiales—Gratiani vita]. s4°. Parisiis. 1508

Gratianus [*continued*].
see GÉNESTAL (R.) Le privilegium fori en France, du décret de G. à la fin du XIVe s., 2t, 1921–24.
,, VENTURI (A.) La miniatura ferrarese n. sec. 15 e il Decretum G., 1900.

Gratius (Ortwinus) [ORTVINUS DEVENTRIENSIS; ORTVINUS v. DEVENTER]. *Briefe von Dunkelmännern (Epist. obsc. vir.) [*To O. G.*] Übers. v. W. Binder. [P2756]. s8°. Gera. 1898
*Epistolae obscur. virorum [ad O. G. Lat. Text, Einl. von A. Bömer. Stachelschriften; hrsg. G. A. E. Bogeng, ält. Reihe, I, 2]. 2B. la8°. Heidelberg. 1924

Gratry (Aug. Jos. Alph.) Les sources. 19e éd. s8°. 1923

Grattan (*Rt. Hon.* **Henry).** Speech on the re-agitation on tithes, in H. of Commons, Apr. 11, 1788.[P2557]. 8°. D. 1788
Speeches in the Irish Parl. in 1780 & 1782. [P2555]. 8°. 1821
see BRITANNICUS, *ps.* *Letters of B. on G.'s bill for relief of Rom. Catholics &c., 1813.

Grattan (Henry), *the younger.* Speech at the Drogheda election, June 28th, 1818. [P2557]. 8°. D. 1818

Grattan (J. H. G.) On the teaching of case, *see* ENGLISH ASSOC. Essays &c., v9, 1924.

Gratz (Gustav) & R. Schüller. Die äussere Wirtschaftspolitik Österreich-Ungarns: Mitteleurop. Pläne. [C.E. for Internat. Peace]. la8°. Wien. 1925

Grätz (Leo). Recent developments in atomic theory. Tr. G. Barr. 8°. [1923]

Gratzl (Emil). Drei armen. Miniaturen Hss., *see* MÜNCHEN. Miniaturen; hrsg. G. Leidinger, H4, 1913.

Grauert (Hermann). Magister Heinrich d. Poet in Würzburg u. d. römische Kurie, *see* KÖN. AKAD. D. WISS. ZU MÜNCHEN, Abhandl. d. Phil. Kl., B27, 1912.
see JANSEN (M.), H. G. &c. St. z. Fugger-Gesch., H5, hrsg. H. G., 1915.

Grauert (Wilhelm Heinrich). Christina, Königinn v. Schweden &c. 2B. 8°. Bonn. 1837–42
see SRBIK (H. *Ritt.* v.) Ein Schüler Niebuhrs: W. H. G., 1916.

Grautoff (Otto). Nicolas Poussin, s. Werk u. s. Leben. 2B. la8°. München. 1914

Grauvogl (*Dr.* **von),** *see* CLARKE (J. H.) Constitutional medicine, w. spec. ref. to The 3 constit. of Dr. v. G., 1926.

Graux (Lucien).
Les fausses nouvelles de la Grande Guerre. 7t. 8°. 1918–20
Hist. des violations du Traité de Paix. 28 juin 1919–[déc. 1926]. 4t. s8°. [1921–27]

Grauzinis (Casimir). La question de Vilna. 8°. 1927

Grave (B. B.) Буржуазия накануне Февральской Револ. Подгот. к печати Б. Б. Г. [Центрархив]. la8°. Москва. 1927

Gräven (Hans). Leibnizens Bildnisse; hrsg. v. C. Schuchhardt, *see* KÖNIGL. PREUSS. AKAD. D. WISS. Abhdl. (Phil.-hist. Klasse), 1916.

Gravenberg (Wirnt v.) Wigalois, d. Ritter mit d. Rade. Hrsg. J. M. N. Kapteyn. B1. 8°. Bonn. 1926

Gravenweert (Jan van's).
Essai sur l'hist. de la litt. néerland. 8°. A. 1830

Graver (Albert), *see* GRAWER (A.)

Graves (Alfred Perceval).
Irish Doric in song & story. 8°. [1926]
Irish poems: Countryside songs—Songs & ballads. 2nd ed. s8°. 1908

Graves (Algernon).
Art sales f. 18th to 20th c. 3v. 4°. 1918–21

Graves (Charles Larcom).
Hubert Parry, h. life & works. 2v. 8°. 1926
Mr. Punch's hist. of mod. England, 1841–1914. 4v. 8°. 1921–22
see KIPLING (R.) & C. G. Q. Horati Flacci Carminum librum quintum a R. K. & C. G. angl. redditum &c., 1920.

Graves (F. M.), *see* ORLÉANS, *The House of.* 2 invent. de la Maison d'O., 1389 & 1408; publ., & préc. d'une intr. [*by*] F. M. G., 1926.

Graves (Frank Pierrepont). Peter Ramus & the educ. reform. of the 16th cent. 8°. N.Y. 1912

Graves (Philip). Palestine, the land of three faiths. Intr. by D. G. Hogarth. 8°. [1923]

Graves (Richard), *a. of "The spiritual Quixote."* *Recoll. of some particulars in the life of W. Shenstone. In a ser. of letters f. an intimate friend of his [*i.e.* R. G.] to . . . Esq., *F.R.S.* [*i.e.* W. Seward]. s8°. 1788

Graves (Richard), *a. of "The spiritual Quixote"* [*continued*].
The spiritual Quixote: or, the summer's ramble of Mr. Geoffry Wildgoose. Comic romance. Intr. by C. Whibley. 2v. 8°. 1926
The triflers: added, The rout & The farmer's son. s8°. 1806
Graves (*Col.* **Richard)** [GREVES], *see* BATES (F. A.) Graves memoirs of the Civil War; compiled f. 17th cent. records by F. A. B., 1927.
Graves (Robert).
Contemp. techniques of poetry. 8°. 1925
Country sentiment. s8°. [1920]
The English ballad. 8°. 1927
John Kemp's wager. Ballad opera. s8°. O. 1925
Lars Porsena: fut. of swearing &c. 2nd ed. s8°. [1927]
Lawrence & the Arabs. 8°. [1927]
Mock Beggar Hall. la8°. *Hogarth Press.* 1924
On English poetry. 8°. 1922
Over the brazier. [repr.] 8°. [1920]
The pier-glass. [*Poems*]. s8°. [1921]
Poems, 1914–26. 8°. 1927
Poetic unreason & o. studies. 8°. [1925]
Whipperginny. s8°. [1923]
see LINDSAY (J.) Loving mad Tom, 1927.
,, RIDING (L.) & R. G. Survey of modernist poetry, 1927.
Gravesend (Richard de), *bp. of Lincoln; d. 1279.* Rotuli R. G., Dioc. Lincoln. [1259–79]. Transcr., ed. &c. by F. N. Davis, w. add. by C. W. Foster &c., & intr. by A. H. Thompson. [Cant. & York Soc., v31]. 8°. 1925
Graveson (I. H. Amat de), *see* AMAT DE GRAVESON (I. H.)
Gravigny (Jean).
Montmartre en 1925. Éd. déf. augm. 8°. [1925]
Gravina (Vincenzo Palizzolo), *barone di Ramione, see* PALIZZOLO GRAVINA (V.)
Gravius (Henricus), *see* JEROME, *Saint.* Opera omnia; acc. H. G. annot. in Epistolas &c., 4t, 1609.
Gravure Company of America, *see* WHITE HOUSE. The W. H. gallery of offic. portraits of the presidents, 1906.
Grawer (Albert) [†GRAVER]. Colloquium A. G. & W. Amlingi, Schochwitz, 1604. s4°. Magdeburgi. 1604
Gray. *Hist. abrégée des merveilles opérées dans la sainte chapelle de Notre-Dame de G. s8°. Gray. [1755?]
Gray, *the family of, see* GRAY (*Mrs.* A.) Papers &c. of a York fam., 1764–1839, 1927.
Gray (A. Herbert), *see* ALLEN (B. W.), A. H. G. &c. Corner-stone of reconstruction, 1919.
Gray (*Mrs.* **Almira),** *wife of Edwin Gray, formerly Vickers.* Papers & diaries of a York family [Gray], 1764–1839. 8°. 1927
Gray (Andrew), *Engineer.* Explan. of the engravings of implements of husbandry used in Scotland, f. drawings prep. for Board of Agric., by Mr. A. G. 4°. E. 1814
Gray (Andrew), *M.A., F.R.S.* A treatise on gyrostatics & rotat. motion. la8°. 1918
Gray (Arthur).
Cambridge Univ.: episodical hist. [n. ed.] la8°. C. 1926
1st ed., 1912, *had t.* Cambridge & its story.
A chapter in the early life of Shakespeare: Polesworth in Arden. s8°. C. 1926
The dual origin of town of Cambridge. [Camb. Antiq. Soc. Quarto publ. N.S. 1]. 4°. C. 1908
The town of Cambridge: a hist. la8°. C. 1925
Gray (Asa). Memorial of A. G. [Amer. Acad. of Arts &c. P2763]. 8°. Camb. [U.S.A.] 1888
Gray (Cecil). The hist. of music. 8°. 1928
Survey of contemp. music. 8°. 1924
—— **& P. Heseltine.**
Carlo Gesualdo, musician & murderer. 8°. 1926
Gray (Edith S.) Indust. accidents to employed minors in Wisconsin, Mass. & N.J., *see* UNITED STATES: LAB. Children's Bur., 152, 1926.
Gray (*Mrs.* **Edwin),** *see* GRAY (*Mrs.* ALMIRA).
Gray (Faith), *wife of William Gray, 1751–1826, see* GRAY (*Mrs.* A.) Papers &c. of a York fam., 1764–1839 [Diary of F. G. &c.], 1927.
Gray (Francis Calley), *see* HARVARD UNIVERSITY. Cat. of coll. of engravings bequeathed to H. Coll. by F. C. G.; by L. Thies, 1869.
Gray (George Buchanan). Sacrifice in the Old Test. 8°. O. 1925
see BIBLE. COMPL. TEXTS &c. Internat. Crit. Comm.: Job; by S. R. Driver & G. B. G., 1921.
Gray (Harold St. George). Interim [& 2nd & 3rd int.] report[s] on excav. at Maumbury Rings, Dorchester, 1908 [–10. *Fr.* Proc. Dorset Nat. Hist. &c. Club, v29–31]. [*b. in 1v.*] 8°. Dorchester. 1908–10
Gray (Henry). Anatomy descript. & applied. 23rd ed. ed. R. Howden. Notes on appl. a. rev. by J. Clay & J. D. Lickley. la8°. 1926

Gray (James), *American citizen.* Report of case of J. G., plaintiff in appeal, vs. the Hawaiian Govt. [P2775]. 8°. Honolulu. 1845
Gray (*Rev.* **John).** The long road. [*Poems*]. 8°. O. 1926
Gray (John Chipman). The nature & sources of the law. 2nd ed., fr. notes, by R. Gray. 8°. N.Y. 1924
Gray (John Milner). Biograph. notes on the mayors of Cambridge. [repr.] la8°. C. 1922
A hist. of the Perse School, Cambridge. 8°. C. 1921
Gray (Kenneth). Home repairs. s8°. [1923]
Gray (Lewis Cecil). Intr. to agric. economics. s8°. N.Y. 1924
Gray (Louis Herbert). Mythology of all races; ed. L. H. G. &c., v11, 1920, *see* MYTHOLOGY.
Gray (R. M.) & M. C. Parekh. Mahatma Gandhi. s8°. 1924
Gray (Robert), *bp. of Capetown.* Three months' visitation (1855), w. acc. of voyage to Tristan d'Acunha (1856). s8°. 1856
Gray (Thomas), *the poet.*
*An elegy wr. in a country-churchyard. Elegia &c. Lat. redd. auctore Coll. Cant. alumno. [*Eng. & Lat.*] [P519]. 8°. 1776
Eng. poems, orig. & tr. f. the Norse & Welsh. Ed. D. C. Tovey. [repr.] s8°. C. 1914
Poems. s8°. 1768
,, ...n. ed. s8°. 1776
Poet. works. Collated by T. Park. [*b. w.* Collins (W.) Poet. works, 1805]. s8°. 1805
Poet. works. Life by J. Mitford. [Aldine ed.] s8°. 1885
Poetry & prose. With essays by Johnson, Goldsmith & o. Intr. & notes by J. Crofts. s8°. O. 1926
see BLAKE (W.) Designs for G.'s poems; intr. by H. J. C. Grierson, 1922.
,, REED (A. L.) Background of G.'s Elegy: taste for melancholy poetry, 1700–51, 1924.
,, TEMPERLEY (H. W. V.) 2 legends conn. w. T. G.: h. depart. f. Peterhouse—Wolfe & G.'s Elegy, 1924.
,, WIEL (T.) Versioni da T. G. &c., 1906.
Gray (William), *of Reading, see* DORMER (E. W.) Gray of Reading, a 16th cent. controversialist & ballad-writer [*w.* Ballads], 1923.
Grayson (William J.)
James Louis Petigru: a biog. sketch. s8°. N.Y. 1866
Grazebrook (Henry Sydney). Coll. for a genealogy of the noble families of Henzey, Tyttery, & Tyzack. 8°. Stourbridge. 1877
Family of Shenstone the poet. 4°. [*p.p.* 1890 ?]
Great.
*The Great Bastard, 1689, *see* LOUIS XIV, *king of Fr.*
G. (The) delusion: aircraft in peace & war, 1927, *see* NEON, *ps.*
*G. (The) fight; by a. of "Cashel Byron's profession," 1921, *see* Shaw (G. B.)
G. (The) kinship; anthol. of humanit. poetry, 1921, *see* LLOYD (B.), *ed.*
*G. (The) sacrifice of the new law, 1676, *see* DYMOCK (J.)
[*G. (The) War of 189–]. Der grosse Krieg v. 189–: e. Zukunftsbild. Von. Adm. P. Colomb, Oberst J. F. Maurice &c. Übers. v. E. A. Witte. Vorrede v. Gen.-Lt. H. v. Below. 2e A. 8°. 1894
*G. (The) world. By a gentleman w. a duster. 2nd ed. s8°. [1925]
Great Northern Railway. G.N.R. [Map]. *folded* 8°. [1848]
Great Western Railway Co. Cathedrals. [*Postface sgd.* G. E. B.] [2nd ed.] la8°. [1925]
G.W. Ports. Produced &c. by H. N. Appleby, by arrangement w. G.W.Ry. Co. la8°. 1928
see MACDERMOT (E. T.) Hist. of the Gt. West. Railway, v1, 1833–63, 1927.
,, SOUTH WALES PORTS, 2nd annual no., 1924.
,, WYLD (J.) G.W.R. map, 1840.
Greatheed (Samuel). A pract. improvement of the Divine Counsel &c., sermon occas. by death of W. Cowper. 8°. Newport-Pagnel. [1800]
Greaves, *family of, see* SHEFFIELD. Mat. for hist. of Wincobank &c., w. geneals. of fam. of G.; comp. by T. W. Hall, 1922.
Greaves (James Pierrepont). Letters & extr. f. MS. wr. of J. P. G. v1. 8°. Ham Common. 1843
New theosophic revelations. 8°. 1847
Grebenschikov (Aleksandr Vasilevich). Къ ист. русско-маньчжурскихъ отношенiй. 1, посольство Н. Г. Спафари въ Китай. [P2527]. 4°. Владивостокъ. 1912
Greco (El), *see* THEOTOCOPULI (D.), *called El Greco.*
Grécourt (Jean Bapt. Joseph Willart de) [†WILLART DE GRÉCOURT]. Œuvres compl. n. éd. 4t. 8°. 1796
Grecu (Vasile). Darstell. altheidn. Denker &c. in d. Kirchenmalerei, *see* ACAD. ROM. Bull. de la sect. hist., t11, 1924.
Gredt (Joseph). Elem. philosophiae Aristotelico-Thomisticae. ed. 3a. auct. & emend. 2v. 8°. Friburgi Brisg. 1921–22

Greece. A hdbk. of G., v1, 1920, *see* ADMIRALTY: NAVAL INTELL. DIV.
A hdbk. of Serbia, Montenegro & adj. parts of G., 1920, *see* ADMIRALTY: NAVAL INTELL. DIV.

Greek.
G. atrocities in the vilayet of Smyrna, 1919. sl. [P2712]. 8°. Lausanne. 1919
G. (The) Bucolic poets; w. Eng. tr. by J. M. Edmonds, repr. 1919, 1923, *see* BUCOLIC POETS.
G. civiliz. & character: [*extracts*], tr., 1924, *see* TOYNBEE (A. J.) *ed.*
G. economics: [*extr*^s.]; tr., 1923, *see* LAISTNER (M. L. W.) *ed.*
G. hist. thought f. Homer to age of Heraclius: [*extr.*], 1924, *see* TOYNBEE (A. J.), *ed.*
G. Patriarchate. "Persec. of the Greeks in Turkey," 1914–18. 8°. Constantinople. 1919
*G. (A) primer, 2nd ed., 1871, *see* WORDSWORTH (C.).
Sheaf (A) of G. folk songs. Gleaned by an old Philhellene, w. intr. note by Ctss. E. Martinengo Cesaresco. s8°. O. 1922

Greek Church. Eccl. Graecae mon., 4t, 1677–92, *see* COTELERIUS (J. B.)
Tomus primus qua eccl. orient. dogmata &c. contin.; tomus 2 in quo contin. August. Conf., 2t, 1758, *see* JEREMIAH, *abp. & patr.*

Greeley (Horace). Essays designed to elucidate the sci. of polit. econ. &c. s8°. Boston. 1870

Greely (*Maj.-Gen.* Adolphus Washington), *U.S. Army.*
Hdbk. of Alaska, resources, products &c. in 1924. 3rd ed., w. new ch. 8°. N.Y. 1925

Green, *The family of, see* FORD (J.) *Mem. of T. Green, of Ipswich, & acc. of h. family, 1825.

Green (Alexander Henry), *F.G.S.* Geol. of the co. round Banbury, Woodstock, Bicester & Buckingham. [Mems. of G.S.] 8°. 1864
Geol. of the neighb. of Barnsley. [Mems. of G.S.] 8°. 1878
see HULL (E.) & A. H. G. Geol. of co. round Stockport &c., 1866.

——, C. Le N. Foster & J. R. Dakyns. Geol. of the carbonif. limestone, Yoredale rocks & millstone grit of N. Derbyshire. 2nd ed., w. add. by A. H. G. & A. Strahan. [Mems. of G.S.] 8°. 1887

——, R. Russell *& others.* Geol. of the Yorks. coalfield. [Mems. of G.S.] 8°. 1878

Green (Alexander Little Page), *1806–1874, see* GREEN (W. M.) Life & papers of A. L. P. G., 1877.

Green (Arthur Frank Umfreville).
Landscape sketching for military purposes. 8°. 1908

Green (*Major* Arthur Octavius).
A coll. of modern Arabic stories &c. s8°. 1893
A pract. Arabic grammar. 3rd ed. 2p. s8°. O. 1893

Green (Arthur Robert).
Sundials: incised dials or Mass-clocks. 8°. 1926

Green (E. M.) The child of the caravan. 8°. [1889]

Green (Edmund Fisk), *see* FISKE (J.)

Green (Edmund Tyrrell-).
Baptismal fonts. [Hist. mon. of Eng.] 8°. [1928]
Parish church architecture. 8°. [1924]

Green (Eric). Hockey. s8°. [1920]

Green (Francis), *see* NATIONAL LIB. OF WALES. Calendar of deeds &c., v1, Coleman deeds, v2, Crosswood deeds; comp. by F. G., 1921–27.

Green (Frederick Ernest).
Hist. of the agricult. labourer (1870–1920). 8°. 1920
" " ....Cheap ed. 8°. 1927
A new agricult. policy. s8°. [1921]
see COLE (G. D. H.) Life of Cobbett, w. ch. on Rural rides by F. E. G., 1924; 1925.

Green (Georg), *prof. of History at Wittenberg.* Diss. [& Diss. post.] de Sibyllis. Præses G. G., resp. C. Kratz. [P1035]. s4°. Wittebergæ. [1661]

Green (George), *see* WORTH (C.) Yacht cruising, by C. W., w. collab. of G. G. &c., 1910.

Green (Henry), *M.A.*
Knutsford, traditions & hist. 8°. 1859

Green (*Sir* John Little), *ed. of " The rural world" &c., see* COLLINGS (*Rt. Hon.* J.) Life, p2, Mr. C. & land reform, by J. L. G., 1920.

Green (John Richard). Stray studies f. England & Italy. [2nd ed. *repr.*] s8°. 1904

Green (*Mrs.* John Richard) [†GREEN (ALICE STOPFORD)].
The govt. of Ireland. Foreword by G. Russell. [P2530]. 8°. 1921
Hist. of the Irish state to 1014. 8°. 1925
Irish nationality. [Home Univ. Lib.] [repr.] s8°. [1919]
Loyalty & disloyalty. [P2529]. s8°. D. [1918]

Green (Joseph Frederick). Nicholas Tchaykovsky, 1850–1926. [P2877]. 8°. [1926]

Green (Julien). Adrienne Mesurat. s8°. [1927]

Green (Matthew).
Poet. works. Collated by T. Park. s8°. 1808
The spleen & o. poems. 8°. *Cayme Press.* 1925

Green (Peter). The problem of evil. s8°. 1920

Green (Richard).
The mission of Methodism. 20th Fernley Lect. 8°. 1890

Green (Samuel Gosnell). Handbook to Old Test. Hebrew, cont. elem. grammar &c. 3rd ed., rev. by A. L. Williams. 8°. 1921
Handbook to the grammar of the Greek Testament. n. impr., rev. 8°. 1912

Green (Thomas), *of Ipswich, see* FORD (J.) *Mem. of T. G., w. crit. on h. writings & acc. of h. family, 1825.

Green (William), *of Rotherham, see* *DIALOGUE (A.) betw. the pulpit & reading desk: *sometime attrib. to* W. G.] &c., 1786; 1795.

Green (William M.) Life & papers of A. L. P. Green. Ed. T. O. Summers. s8°. Nashville, Tenn. 1877

Greenacre (James). *The trial & life of G., w. h. confess. of the murder of Hannah Brown. [P2828]. s8°. [1837 ?]

Greenaway (Kate).
see FLOWERS. Language of f.: illust. by K. G., 1884.
" MEACHAM (M. I.) The K. G. coll., 1921.

Greenbie (Sydney). Japan real & imaginary. 8°. N.Y. [1920]
The Pacific triangle. 8°. [1921]

Greene (Dominick Sarsfield). [Views in India, f. drawings taken dur. the Mutiny by D. S. G.] [8 *plates. Letterpress wanting*]. obl.fol. 1859

Greene (George Washington). Nathanael Greene. Exam. of statements conc. N. G., in v9 of Bancroft's Hist. of U.S. [P2623]. 8°. Boston. 1866

Greene (Harry Plunket). Where the bright waters meet. 8°. 1924

Greene (Ireland), *daughter of Isaac G., aft. Mrs. Blackburne, see* STEWART-BROWN (R.) Isaac Greene &c., w. diary of I. G., 1748–49, 1921.

Greene (Isaac), *see* STEWART-BROWN (R.) I. G., Lancashire lawyer of 18th c., 1921.

Greene (Nathanael), *maj.-gen. in U.S. army, see* GREENE (G. W.) N. G., 1866.

Greene (Robert), *the poet.*
The blacke bookes messenger (1592) *&* "Cuthbert Conny-catcher," The defence of conny-catching (1592). [*W. sep. pagin.* Bodley Head quartos; ed. G. B. Harrison]. s8°. [1924]
[*The comicall historie of] Alphonsus, King of Aragon [made by R. G.], 1599. [Prep. under dir. of W. W. Greg. Malone Soc.] s4°. [O.] 1926
Friar Bacon & Friar Bungay, 1594. [Prep. under dir. of W. W. Greg. Malone Soc.] s4°. [O.] 1926
Greenes Newes both f. Heaven & Hell [by B. R., *i.e.* B. Rich ?], 1593, & Greenes Funeralls [by R. B. *i.e.* R. Barnfield ?], 1594. Repr. w. notes &c. by R. B. McKerrow. 8°. Stratford-upon-Avon. [1922]
A notable discovery of coosnage, 1591; The second part of conny-catching, 1592. [Bodley Head Quartos, ed. G. B. Harrison]. s8°. 1923
*The Scottish hist. of James IV, 1598. [*w. fac. tp.* Prep. by A. E. H. Swaen, w. asst. of gen. ed. W. W. Greg. Malone Soc.] s4°. [O.] 1921
The 3rd & last part of Conny-catching &c. (1592) *&* A disput. betw. a Hee Conny-catcher & a Shee Conny-catcher (1592, *w. sep. pagin.*) [Bodley Head quartos; ed. G. B. Harrison]. s8°. [1923]
see GREG (W. W.) 2 Elizabethan stage abridgements: Orlando Furioso &c., 1922.
" HARVEY (G.) Foure letters & certeine sonnets: touching R. G., 1592, 1922.

Greene (Thomas), *bp. of (1) Norwich, (2) Ely.* A sermon preached to the Soc. for Reform. of Manners, Jan. 16, 1726. [*W.* 32nd acc. of progress. P2669]. s8°. 1727

Greene (William Chase). The achievement of Greece: a ch. in human experience. 8°. Cambridge, *Mass.* 1923

Greener (William Wellington). Mod. shot guns. 8°. [1888]

Greenfield (William), *philologist.* A defence of the Serampore Mahratta version of the New Test. 8°. 1830

Greenhalgh (J. H. Stobart).
Some notes on Studland, Dorset. [P2734]. s8°. [1924]

Greenhalgh (John). Mem. of Capt. J. G., Gov. of the Isle of Man, 1640–51, by W. Harrison, *see* MANX SOC. Manx misc., v2, 1880.

Greenham (Richard). Workes. 4th ed.; added, sixe treatises of the same a. never before publ., by H[enry] H[olland]. [*dedic. epist. by E. Holland*]. fol. 1605

Greenhill (William).
An expos. upon Ezekiel [5v.; v1, 2nd ed]. s4º. 1649–62
Greenland (George). The guilty innocent. s8º. [1923]
Greenly (Edward Howorth).
The geology of Anglesey. [Mems. of G.S.] 2v. la8º. 1919
Greenstreet (W. J.), *ed., see* NEWTON (*Sir* I.) I. N.: mem. vol., 1927.
Greenup (Albert William), *see* TALMUD. Tr. of the treatise Taanith, by A. W. G., 1918.
Greenway (Francis John). *For pamphlets on the liquidation of the estate of Wm. French & F. J. G., Hawaii, 1844–46, see* FRENCH (W.)
Greenwell (*Miss* Dora).
Poems. Sel., w. biog. intr. by W. Dorling. s8º. 1889
Greenwell (William). The Greenwell deeds preserved in Publ. Lib., Newcastle-upon-Tyne: [coll. of W. G.]; calendared by J. Walton, *see* SOC. OF ANTIQS. OF NEWCASTLE. Arch. Aeliana, s4, v3, 1927.
Greenwich. Gr. parish reg., 1615—1636–37, *see* GREENWICH & LEWISHAM ANTIQ. SOC., Trans. v2, 1920.
Greenwich & Lewisham Antiquarian Society.
Transactions, v2, Greenwich parish registers, 1615—1636–37. 8º. Blackheath. 1920
Greenwood (Alice Drayton).
Hist. of the people of England. 2v. 8º. 1921–23
Greenwood (Arthur).
The educ. of the citizen. [P2423]. 8º. [1920]
Greenwood (Frederick).
Imagination in dreams & their study. 8º. 1894
Greenwood (*Sir* Granville George).
Ben Jonson & Shakespeare. s8º. 1921
The faith of an agnostic; or, 1st essays in rationalism. 2nd & rev. ed. s8º. 1919
Shakespeare's law. s8º. [1920]
Shakspere's handwriting. 8º. 1920
The Shakspere signatures & "Sir Thomas More." s8º. [1924]
Greenwood (James) [*ps.* "THE AMATEUR CASUAL"].
Curiosities of savage life. 8º. 1863
Greenwood (Major) & H. M. Woods. Incidence of indust. accidents upon individuals &c., *see* INDUST. FATIGUE RES. BD., Rep. 4, 1919.
Greenwood (W.), *a. of The Vale of Apperley.*
*Mem. of the life &c. of G. Sykes. s8º. Malton. 1827
Greetings to the new Russia: addr., Hudson Theater, N.Y., Apr. 23, 1917, *see* RUSSIA.
Greever (Garland), *see* BOWLES (W. L.) A Wiltshire parson: corr. of W. L. B.; ed. G. G., 1926.
Grefius (Nicolaus). Lutherus reformator. Præs. J. Scharfio. [P2628]. s4º. *n.p. typis M. Wendt.* [1650]
Greg (Walter Wilson). Eng. literary autographs, 1500–1650. Sel. for reprod. & ed. by W. W. G. in collab. w. J. P. Gilson, H. Jenkinson &c. pl. fol. 1925
1, Dramatists.
Two Elizabethan stage abridgements: the Battle of Alcazar & Orlando Furioso. [Malone Soc., extra vol.] s4º. 1922 [1923]
see POLLARD (A. W.) Shakespeare's hand in the play of Sir T. More: papers by A. W. P., W. W. G. &c., 1923.
Grégoire (Camille Gustave).
Hist. du canton de Montmaraud. 8º. Moulins. 1906
Gregoras (Nicephorus). Epistulae 90; *ed.* St. Bezdeki, *see* SCUOLA ROMENA DI ROMA. Ephem. Dacorom., v2, 1924.
see GUILLAND (R.) Essai sur N. G.: l'homme & l'œuvre, 1926.
Gregorio, *de Valentia, see* VALENTIA (G. DE).
Gregorius (Publius), *Tifernus* [GREGORIO, *Tifernate*], *see* MANCINI (G.) G. T., 1925.
Gregory, *catholicos of Althamar, see* KOSTANEANTS (K.) "Роза и соловей" по стихотв. Г. А., 1913.
Gregory, *of Cyprus, Patriarch of Constantinople. For work ent.* Descr. orbis Romani, *sometimes attrib. to G., see* †GEORGIUS, *of Cyprus, geographer.*
Gregory, *Magistros, Pahlavouni, d. 1058.* [Lettres, 11e s. Texte armén. publ. K. Kostanianz]. 8º. Aleksandrapol. 1910
[Poems. *In Armenian*]. s8º. i Venetik. 1868
Gregory, *a monk of 17. century.* Epistola Constantinopoli missa e Graeco in Lat. tr., 1633, *see* SCHOPPE (C.)
Gregory, *monk, of Narek, 951–1003.*
[Works. *In Armenian*]. 8º. i Venetik. 1840

Gregory, *Nazianzen* [G. NAZANZENUS; G. NAZIANZENUS; G THEOLOGUS; †GREGORY, *of Nazianzus, Saint, patriarch of Constantinople*].
Opera [*Gr. & Lat.*] J. Billius Prunæus emend. & interpretatus est, una cum Nicetae Serronii, Pselli, Nonii & Eliæ Cret. comm. Aucta G. epistolis ed. ex interpret. F. Morelli. 2t. fol. Coloniae. 1690
Due orationi; & Il primo sermone di S. Cecilio Cipriano sopra l'elemosina. [*Tr.*] A. Caro. [*b. w.* Caro (A.) Rime, 1569]. 8º. Venetia, *Aldo.* 1569
Γρηγορίου τοῦ Ν. ἅπαντα τὰ μέχρι νῦν μὲν εὑρισκόμενα. Τοῦ αὐτοῦ Βίος, συγγραφεὶς ὑπὸ Σουίδα, Σωφρονίου, καὶ Γρηγορίου τοῦ πρεσβυτέρου. 2p. [*sep. pagin.*] Ἐν Βασιλείᾳ. fol. 1550
Oratio in novam Dominicam [*Greek*], illustr. introd. &c. F. M. A. Haensel. s8º. Lipsiae. 1836
see AMPHILOCHIUS, *Saint, bp. of Iconium,* Epistola ad Seleucum, &c.; add. G. N. Carm. 33 de libr. bibl., 1740.
,, EUCHOLOGION. Anaphora of St. Basil, St. G. &c. *Copt. & Arab.*, 1736.
,, MAXIMUS, *St.* Scholia in G. theologum, 1681.
,, NONNUS, *of Panopolis.* Scholien z. Reden d. G. v. N. (*in Arm.*), 1903.
Gregory *of Nyssa.* Opera. Nunc denuo correctius ed. [*Gr. & Lat.*] 3t. fol. Parisiis. 1638
see HEYNS (S. P.) Disp. de G., 1835.
Gregory I, *pope* [GREGORY I, *St., surnamed "the Great," pope*].
see BUTLER (E. C.) Western mysticism: teaching of SS. Augustine, G. &c. on contemplation &c., 1922; 2nd ed., 1927.
,, ROQUES (M.) Sur 2 particularités métriques de la Vie de St. Grégoire en anc. Français, 1921; 1922.
Gregory II, *pope.* Libri 10 Explan. Ecclesiastae. Gr. cum Lat. interpret. & comm. Praepos. Vita a Leontio monacho. [S. A. Morelli, Praef.] fol. Venetiis. 1791
Gregory VI, *pope.*
see BORINO (G. B.) L'elezione e la deposizione di G. VI, 1916.
,, POOLE (R. L.) Benedict IX & G. VI, 1917.
Gregory VII, *pope.*
Register G. VII [1073–83]. Hrsg. E. Caspar. [Mon. Germ. hist.: Epist. sel., t2i, ii]. 2[B] [*pagin. cont.*] 8º. 1920–23
see BRUGERETTE (J.) G. VII, & la réforme du 11 s., 1908.
,, DITHMAR (J. C.) Vita G. VII, 1710.
see FLICHE (A.) Études sur la polémique relig. à l'époque de G. VII, 1916.
,, —— La réforme grégor., 2t, 1924–25.
,, FOURNIER (P.) Les coll. canon. rom. de l'époque de G. VII, 1920.
,, GRETSER (J.) Apologia pro G. VII, 1609?
Gregory VIII [*pope*], *antipope, see* BURDINUS (M.)
Gregory IX, *pope.*
see DECRETALES. Epistolae decret. a G. IX coll., 1570.
,, LACEY (T. A.) G. IX & Greek ordinations, 1898.
Gregory XIII, *pope.*
see PARSONS (R.) De persecutione Angl. comm.; add. litt. G. XIII hortatoriis, 1582.
,, PASTOR (L. v.) Gesch. d. Päpste, B9, G. XIII, 1572–85, 1923.
Gregory XV, *pope, see* CÆREMONIALE &c., 1724.
Gregory, *Saint, the Illuminator, of Armenia* [G. *Lousavoritch*]. [Homilies & prayer, *attrib. to G. In Armenian*]. 8º. i Venetik. 1838
,, ,, *Ed.* A. Ter Miqelean. 8º. Tparan. 1894
[*Praise of the sons &c. of the Illuminator. *In Armenian.* Soferq Hayk., v10]. s8º. i Venetik. 1854
see CHRYSOSTOM, *St.* [Panegyrics of G., by C. &c., *in Armenian*], 1853.
,, JOHN, *the Deacon.* [Panegyrics of G., by J., Vardan &c., *in Armenian*], 1853.
,, MARR (N. YA.) Крещеніе Армянъ &c. св. Г., араб. версія, 1905.
Gregory, *Skevratzi, 13th cent.* [Panegyric of St. Nerses Lambronatzi. *In Armenian.* Soferq Hayk., v15]. s8º. i Venetik. 1854
Gregory, *archdeacon of Smyrna, see* CHRYSOSTOM, *St.* [Panegyrics of Gregory the Illuminator, by C. & G., *in Armenian*], 1853.
Gregory, *Thaumaturgus, bp. of Neocæsarea.* Address to Origen. [Tr., w. intr.] by W. Metcalfe. reissue. s8º. 1920
Panegyricus ad Origenem Gr. & Lat. Rec. opera J. A. Bengelii. s8º. Stutgardiae. 1722
Panegyricus in Origenem (*Gr. & Lat.*), *see* ORIGEN. Contra Celsum libri 8, 1605.
see WEICKHMANN (J. S.) De schola Origenis sacra ex G. T. inform., 1744.

Gregory IV, *Tlay, i.e. Child, catholicus of Armenia, 1173–93.* [Letters *in Armenian. Folld. by* Orations, letters & sermons *of* Nerses of Lambron.] s8o. i Venetik. 1865

Gregory, *of Tours* [†GREGORY, *Saint, bp. of Tours*]. De gloria martyrum & confess. libri 3. Emend. &c. labore J. B[alesdens]. [Op. piorum p. 1]. s8o. Parisiis. 1640
Hist. eccl. des Francs. Suivie d'un sommaire de s. autres ouvrages & préc. de sa vie écr. au 10e s. par Odon, abbé de Cluni. Tr. nouv. par H. Bordier. 2t. s8o. 1859–61
Hist. of the Franks. Tr. w. intr. by O. M. Dalton. 2v. 8o. O. 1927
see BILLARDON DE SAUVIGNY (L. E.) Essais hist. sur les mœurs des François, &c., t1–3 (Vie & œuvres de G.), 1785–92.
„ CARRIÈRE (A.) Sur un chap. de G. rel. à l'hist. de l'orient, 1897.

Gregory (Augusta, *Lady*), *wife of Rt. Hon. Sir W. H. Gregory.*
The bogie men. s8o. *n.d.*
Book of saints & wonders acc. to old writings & memory of the people of Ireland. [repr.] 8o. 1920
Damer's gold. Comedy. [*b. w.* The bogie men, *n.d.*] s8o. *n.d.*
The full moon. [*b. w.* The bogie men, *n.d.*] s8o. *n.d.*
The golden apple. Play for Kiltartan children. 8o. 1916
Hugh Lane's life & achievement, w. some acc. of the Dublin Galleries. 8o. 1921
The image & o. p. 8o. [1922]
The image. Play. [repr.] s8o. *n.d.*
The Kiltartan wonder book. 8o. [1910]
McDonough's wife. [*b. w.* The bogie men, *n.d.*] s8o. *n.d.*
Three wonder plays. s8o. [1923]
Visions & beliefs in the W. of Ireland. Coll. & arr. by Lady G., w. 2 essays & notes by W. B. Yeats. 2 ser. 8o. N.Y. 1920
see GOLDONI (C.) Mirandolina: comedy; tr. & adapted f. La locandiera of G. by Lady G. 1924.
„ YEATS (W. B.) Plays in prose & verse; wr. w. help of a friend [Lady G.]. 1922.

Gregory (Benjamin). Consecrated culture: mem. of B. A. Gregory. 2nd ed. 8o. 1888
A handbook of scriptural church princ. & of Wesleyan-Methodist polity & hist. 2p [*in* 1v.] 8o. 1888
The Holy Catholic Church, the communion of saints. Fernley Lect. of 1873. 2nd ed. 8o. 1885
Side lights on the conflicts of Methodism, 1827–52. 8o. 1898

Gregory (Benjamin Alfred), *see* GREGORY (B.) Consecrated culture: mem. of B. A. G., 1888.

Gregory (C. J.), *see* GREGORY (J. W.) & C. J. G. To the Alps of Chinese Tibet, 1923.

Gregory (Dickson).
Australian steamships, past & pres. la8o. [1928]

Gregory (Donald). Hist. of the W. Highlands & Isles of Scotland, 1493–1625, &c. 8o. E. 1836

Gregory (Edward William). Art & craft of home-making, w. app. of household recipes. 2nd ed., w. add. ch., rev. &c. 8o. [1925]

Gregory (Eleanor C.)
Intr. to Xtn. mysticism, w. pref. letter by A. Whyte. s8o. 1901
A little book of heavenly wisdom. Sel. f. Eng. mystics. Ed. E. C. G. s8o. 1904

Gregory (John), *Chaplain of Christ Church, Oxford* [GREGORIE]. Works in 2p. [*sep. tps. & pagins.*] 1, Notes &c. upon passages in Scripture. 2, Posthuma. 4th ed. corr. s4o. 1684

Gregory (John Walter). Evol. of the Essex rivers & of the lower Thames. [P2618]. 8o. Colchester. [1922]
The menace of colour. 8o. 1925
The rift valleys & geology of East Africa. 8o. 1921
—— **& C. J. Gregory.** To the Alps of Chinese Tibet. 8o. 1923

Gregory (Joshua C.) The nature of laughter. 8o. 1924

Gregory (Mary Anne, *Lady*), *wife of Sir C. H. Gregory, see* STIRLING (FANNY).

Gregory (*Sir* Richard Arman). The vault of heaven: intr. to mod. astronomy. 2nd ed., rewr. s8o. [1923]
see HUXLEY (T. H.) Physiography; rev. & partly re-wr. by R. A. G., 1919.

Gregory (S. M.) The land of Ararat: Armenia, h. hist. & h. church. s8o. 1920

Gregory (Theodor Emanuel Gugenheim). Foreign exchange, bef., dur., & after the War. s8o. 1921
The return to gold. s8o. 1925
see CANNAN (E.) London essays in economics; ed. T. E. G. &c., 1927.

Gregory (W.), *of Bath.* The Beckford family. Remin. of Fonthill Abbey & Lansdown Tower. 2nd ed., rev. & enl. s8o. 1898

Gréhan (Amédée).
La France maritime. 4t. [2 & 4 *wanting*]. la8o. 1837–42

Greig (Gavin). Last leaves of tradit. ballads & ballad airs; coll. in Aberdeenshire by G. G.; ed. A. Keith. [Buchan Club]. 4o. Aberdeen. 1925

Greig (John), *see* STORER (J. S.) & J. G. *Antiq. & topogr. cabinet, 10v, 1807–11.

Greig (P. W.)
Annals of a Shetland parish: Delting. 8o. Lerwick. 1892

Grein (J. T.) The new world of the theatre, 1923–24. Pref. by G. K. Chesterton. 8o. 1924

Greiner (Otto), *1869–1916, see* VOGEL (J.) O. G., 1925.

Greins (Zacharias).
Disput. de Regno Christi, &c. [P2436]. s4o. Tubingæ. 1574

Greinz (Rudolf). Allerseelen: e. tiroler Roman. s8o. L. 1924

Grellet (Pierre). Les aventures de Casanova en Suisse: la vie & les mœurs au 18e s. d'ap. des doc. nouv. s4o. Lausanne. 1919

Grenfell (Bernard P.), *see* OXYRYNCHUS PAPYRI; ed. w. tr. by B. P. G. &c., p15, 16, 1922–24.

Grenfell (Francis Octavius), *see* BUCHAN (J.) F. & Riversdale G., 2nd ed., 1920.

Grenfell (*Field-Marshal Lord* Francis Wallace).
Memoirs. Pref. by Sir R. Lane. 8o. [1925]

Grenfell (George), *see* HEMMENS (H. L.) G. G., pioneer in Congo, 1927.

Grenfell (Riversdale Nonus), *see* BUCHAN (J.) Francis & R. G., 2nd ed., 1920.

Grenfell (Wilfred Thomason). Labrador days: tales of the sea toilers. Empire ed. s8o. [1921]
A Labrador doctor. Autobiog. 8o. [1920]

Grenier (Albert). Le génie romain dans la relig., la pensée & l'art. [L'Evol. de l'Humanité]. 8o. 1925

Grenier (Jean), *see* CHANSON (A.) Ecrits; par A. C., J. G. &c., 1927.

Grenier (Nicole). Le bouclier de la foy, extr. de la Saincte Escriture &c. Avec une apologie contre un clabaut Lutherique. s8o. 1580

Grente (*l'abbé* Georges). Jean Bertaut, abbé d'Aunay &c., 1552–1611. la8o. 1903

Grentzing (C.), *see* GRENZING (C.)

Grenville Papers (The), *see* HIST. MSS. COMM., Fortescue MSS., v8–10, 1912–27.

Grenville, *The family of, see* NEWBOLT (*Sir* H. J.) Bk. of the Grenvilles, 1921.

Grenville (Charlotte), *aft. wife of Sir W. W. Wynn; 1754–1832, see* WILLIAMS WYNN (C., *Lady*).

Grenville (*Sir* Richard), *captain of the "Revenge."* The last fight of the Revenge [1591] descr. by Sir W. Raleigh &c. Ed. E. Arber. [Eng. repr. *a. c. b. w.* Roy (W.) &c. "Rede me" &c., 1871]. s8o. 1871
see CHOPE (R. P.) New light on Sir R. G., 1917.

Grenville (William W. Grenville, *baron*).
see ADAMS (E. D.) Infl. of G. on Pitt's for. policy, 1787–98, 1904.
„ SAYERS (J.) Hints to J. Nollekens on h. modelling a bust of Lord G., 1808.

Grenzing (Christophe) [GRENTZING]. Disp. theolog. de baptismo et confirmatione. [P2607]. s4o. Ingolstadii. 1595

***Grenzschlachten** im Westen, *see* WELTKRIEG (DER), 1914 bis 1918, B1, 1925.

Gresham (*Sir* Thomas), *see* WHITE (J. G.) Hist. of 3 R. Exchanges, G. Lects., & G. Almshouses, 1896.

Greslon (Adrien). Hist. de Chine sous la domin. des Tartares, 1651–69. s8o. 1671

Gresset (Jean Baptiste Louis). Œuvres choisies. s8o. [1793]
Le méchant, *see* THÉÂTRE choisi du 18e s., t2, 1914.

Gressmann (Hugo). Die hellenist. Gestirnrelig., *see* ALTE ORIENT, Beih. 5, 1925.
Vom reichen Mann u. armen Lazarus: e. literargesch. Studie, mit ägypt. Beitr. v. G. Möller, *see* KÖNIGL. PREUSS. AKAD. D. WISS. Abhdl. (Phil.-hist. Klasse), 1918.

Greswell (William H. Parr), *M.A., Oxon.* Dumnonia & the valley of the Parret. 8o. Taunton. 1922

Grétry (André Ernest Modeste), *see* CLOSSON (E.) A. M. G., 1920.

Gretschel (Carl Christian Carus).
Kirchl. Zustände Leipzigs vor u. währ. 1539. s8o. L. 1839
Die Universität Leipzig. s8o. Dresden. 1830

Gretser (Jacob), *Jesuit.*
Admonitio ad exteros de bibliis Tigurinis. [P2645]. s4°. Ingolstadii. 1615
Apologia pro Gregorio VII. Acc. de vita &c. d. Gregorii ex libro 4° Onuphrii Panvini &c. [*b. w. h.* Controv. R. Bellarmini def., t2, 1609]. fol. [Ingolstadii. 1609 ?]
Controversiarum R. Bellarmini defensio adv. Witackerum &c. [Sutlivium &c.] aliosque sectarios. 2t. fol. Ingolstadii. 1607–9
De jure & more prohibendi &c., libros haereticos &c., adv. F. Junium Calvinistam & J. Pappum, aliosque Lutheranos. Examen libelli M. Lutheri &c. s4°. Ingolstadii. 1603
Disp. de variis coelis, Lutheranis, Zwinglianis, Ubiquetariis, Calvinianis &c. s4°. Ingolstadii. [1621]
Disp. theolog. de materia &c. Eucharistiae. Praes. J. G.; resp. J. Beringer. [P2607]. s4°. Ingolstadii. 1593
1, Panegyricus Misenicus [*ans. to C. S. Lithus's* "*Gretserus Triumphatus*"]. 2, Stigma frontis Misenicæ. 3, Honorarium Polycarpicum Lauserianum. 4, Demonstratio quorund. fidei dogmat. 5, Iudic. super discept. inter Rud. Goclenium & Bavium [Libavium] alchymistam. 6, Paracletus Lutheranus. s8°. Ingolstadii. 1606
Syntagma de imaginibus manu non factis, *see* CODINUS (G.) De officiis &c., 1625.
see FÖRSTER (J.) G. calumniator, 1611.
,, HULDRICH (J. J.) Vindiciae pro Bibl. tr. Tigur., adv. J. G. Admon., 1616.
,, JAMES (T.) A treatise of the corruption of Scr. by the Ch. of Rome, w. ans. unto J. G. &c., 1611.

Gretton (May Sturge), *see* HENDERSON (M. S.)

Gretton (Richard Henry). The Burford records. A st. in minor town govt. 8°. O. 1920

Greve (Peter) [GREVIUS (PETRUS)].
Exercitationes sacrae. s8°. Flensburgi. 1784

Grevenkop (Albert). Monotheletarum hæresis. Diss. sub praes. A. Strauchii. [P427]. s4°. Wittebergae. 1665

Greves, *see* GRAVES.

Greville (*Hon.* **C. F.),** *see* SPILSBURY (J.) Coll. of 50 prints f. ant. gems in coll. of Earl Percy, C. F. G. &c.; engr. by J. S., 1785.

Greville (Charles Cavendish Fulke). The G. diary, incl. passages hitherto withheld f. publ. Ed. P. W. Wilson. 2v. 8°. 1927
The Greville Mem.: [p1], Journal of r. of Geo. IV & Will. IV. Ed. H. Reeve. 5th ed. 3v. 8°. 1875
Letters of C. G. & H. Reeve, 1836–65. Ed. A. H. Johnson. 8°. [1924]

Greville (Fulke), *1st baron Brooke.*
Certaine learned & elegant workes. [*2 pagins.*] la8°. 1633

Gréville (Henry), *ps.* [*i.e. Mme.* ALICE DURAND].
Un violon russe. 2t *in* 1v. s8°. 1880

Grevinchoven (Nicolaas) [GREVINCHOVIUS].
see AMES (W.) Rescriptio ad N. G. responsum &c., 1615; 1645.
,, SMOUT (A.) N. G., Heautontimorumenos, 1617.

Grevius (Petrus), *see* GREVE (PETER).

Grevs (Ivan Mikhailovich). История одной любви: И. С. Тургенев и Полина Виардо. s8°. Москва. 1927

Grew (*Mrs.* **Marion Ethel),** *form. Tuckwell.* William Bentinck & William III (Pr. of Orange): life of Bentinck, Earl of Portland f. the Welbeck corresp. 8°. 1924

Grew (Sydney). Book of Eng. prosody. 8°. 1924

Grew (W. F.) The cycle industry. s8°. 1921

Grey (Arthur Grey, *14th b.***),** *of Wilton, 1536–93, see* JONES (H. S. V.) Spenser's defence of Ld. G., 1919.

Grey (Edward Grey, *1st visct.***)** [GREY OF FALLODON].
The charm of birds. [2nd impr.] 8°. 1927
Fallodon papers. 8°. 1926
,, ,, ...[repr.] 8°. [1926]
The pleasure of reading, *see* ROY. SOC. OF LIT. Essays, N.S., v5, 1925.
Recreation. [Addr.] s8°. 1920
Twenty-five years, 1892–1916. 2v. 8°. 1925
Wordsworth's "Prelude." [Eng. Assoc., Pamph. 57. P2731]. 8°. 1923
see LUTZ (H.) Lord G. u. d. Weltkrieg, 1927; tr., 1928.

Grey (*Sir* **George),** *K.C.B., 1812–98.* Ko nga whakapepeha &c. Proverb. &c., sayings of the ancestors of the New Zealand race. 8°. Cape Town. 1857
The library of Sir G. G. Philology. [Africa, Australia, Polynesia. Comp. by W. H. I. Bleek, Sir G. Grey, &c. Presented to S. African Public Library]. v1–3i [*in* 1v.] 8°. 1858–62
Maori mementos: addr. pres. to Sir G. G. With remarks, coll. of laments &c. by C. O. B. Davis. 8°. Auckland. 1855

Grey (Henry), *sec. to Stockwell Proprietary School.*
A key to all the Waverley novels. [P2598]. la8°. 1882

Grey (Henry M.) Lloyd's: yesterday & to-day. 8°. 1922

Grey (Pamela, *lady***),** *wife of 1st visct. Grey, see* GLENCONNER (P. *lady*).

Grey (Richard), *D.D.* Liber Iobi in vers. metrice divisus, cum vers. Lat. A. Schultens. Ed. & annotat. adj. R. G. Acc. Canticum Moysis, Deut. 32 cum notis var. [*Heb. & Lat.*] s8°. Londini. 1742

Grey (Rowland), *ps.* [*i.e. Miss* LILIAN ROWLAND BROWN], *see* DARK (S.) & R. GREY. W. S. Gilbert, h. life & letters, 1923.

Grey (Zane).
The call of the canyon. s8°. [1924]
The mysterious rider. s8°. [1921]
To the last man. s8°. [1922]
The vanishing Indian. s8°. [1926]
The young pitcher. 3rd ed. s8°. [1924]

Gribble (Ernest R.), *see* CESCINSKY (H.) & E. R. G. Early Eng. furniture & woodwork, 2v, 1922.

Gribble (Francis H.), *see* POWELL (J.) & F. H. G. The hist. of Ruhleben, 1919.

Gribble (George Dunning).
The masque of Venice. An entertainment. s8°. 1924
The scene that was to write itself. Tragi-comedy. s8°. 1924

Gribble (James Dunning Baker). Hist. of the Deccan. Ed. & finished by Mrs. M. Pendlebury. v2. 8°. 1924

Gribble (Mary), *see* PENDLEBURY (*Mrs.* M.)

Griboyedov (Aleksandr Sergeevich). Горе отъ ума. Редакція полнаго текста &с. составл. И. Д. Гарусовымъ. s8°. С.–П. 1875
,, ,, *see* BUNIN (I. A.) Русскіе писатели, 1921.
The mischief of being clever. Tr. Sir B. Pares. Intr. by Pr. D. S. Mirsky. 8°. [1925]

Grieben's Reise-Bibliothek. B 29. Der Rhein. Prakt. Wegweiser. 13e A. neu bearbt. v. H. T. Luks. s8°. 1882

Griechische. Griechischen (Die) christl. Schriftsteller d. ersten 3. Jhdte. Hrsg. v. d. Kirchenväter-Comm. d. Preuss. Akad. d. Wiss. la8°. L. 1905–26
see EPIPHANIUS, *St.* Ancoratus u. Panarion; hrsg. K. Holl, B2, 1922.
,, EUSEBIUS, *Pamphili.* Werke, B7ii, hrsg. R. Helm, 1926.
,, EZRA. Die Apokalypse d. Esra &c., hrsg. B. Violet, 1924.
,, ORIGEN. Origenes Werke, B6–8, 1920–25.
,, †SCHMIDT (C.) Kopt.-Gnost. Schriften, B1, 1905.
Gr. Tragoedien; übers. v. Wilamowitz-Möllendorff, B4, 1923, *see* WILAMOWITZ-MÖLLENDORFF (U. v.).

Grier (*Miss* **Lynda) &** *Miss* **A. Ashley.** Brit. labour repl. & conciliation, 1914–21. p1, by G. & A. p2, ed. by A. W. Kirkaldy. 8°. 1921

Grier (Richard). An answer to Ward's errata of the Protestant Bible. 4°. 1812

Grier (Sydney C.) Berringer of Bandeir. s8°. 1919
The princess's tragedy. s8°. E. 1918

Grierson (Francis). The invincible alliance & o. essays. s8°. 1913

Grierson (Francis D.) The Zoo murder. s8°. [1926]

Grierson (*Sir* **George Abraham),** *O.M.* The Ōrmurī or Bargistā language. [As. Soc. of Bengal, Mem., v7, No. 1]. 4°. Calcutta. 1918
see HĀTIM TILAWÔN[U]. H.'s tales &c.; recorded by Sir A. Stein; ed. w. tr. &c. by Sir G. A. G., 1923.
,, INDIA: LINGUISTIC SURVEY, v1i, Introd., by G., v10, Eranian fam., v11, Gipsy langs., comp. & ed. by G., 1921–27.
,, —— —— Index of language-names, 1920.

Grierson (Herbert John Clifford).
Background of Eng. lit. & o. e. 8°. 1925
Classical & romantic, 1923. s8°. C. 1923
Don Quixote: war-time refl. [Eng. Assoc., Pamph. 48. P2683]. 8°. 1921
Lord Byron: Arnold & Swinburne. [P2737]. 8°. [1920]
,, ,, *For a. copy, see* BRIT. ACAD. Proc., v9, 1919–20.
Metaphys. lyrics & poems of the 17th c. Donne to Butler. Sel. & ed. w. an essay by G. s8°. O. 1921
see ABERDEEN. Proc. at present. to A. Gram. Sch. of statue of Ld. Byron; [addr. by G.], 1923.

Grierson (*Lt.-Gen. Sir* **James Moncrieff).** The armed strength of Japan. Comp. by J. M. G. [War Office]. 8°. 1886
The armed strength of the German Empire. Ed. C. W. B. Bell. [War Office]. 2nd ed. 2p *in* 1v. 8°. 1888
see MACDIARMID (D. S.) Life of Lt.-Gen. Sir J. M. G., 1923.

Griesbach (Johann Jacob). Diss. locos theol. coll. ex Leone Magno pontif. Rom. sistens. Sub mod. J. S. Semleri. [P437]. s4°. Halae Magdeb. [1768]
Opuscula academ. Ed. J. P. Gabler. 2v. 8°. Jenae. 1824–5
Synopsis Evang. Matthaei, Marci & Lucae, una cum Joannis pericopis &c. Textum rec. &c. J. J. G. ed. 2a, emend. & auct. 8°. Halae Saxon. 1797

Grieve (Alexander), *D.Phil.* Willibrord, miss. in the Netherlands, 691–739 ; incl. tr. of the Vita Willibrordi by Alcuin of York. s8º. 1923

Grieve (Alexander James), *D.D., see* PEAKE (A. S.) Comm. on the Bible : ed. P., w. assist. of G., 1920.

Grieve (Symington). Notes on the I. of Dominica. s8º. 1906

Griff, *ps.* [A. S. G.] *Surrendered : some naval War secrets. By " Griff " (A. S. G.) la8º. *publ. by the a.* Twickenham. [1927]

Griffenfeld (Peder, *Graf* **v.),** *form. Schumacher ; 1635–99, see* FABRICIUS (K.) Griffenfeld, 1910.

Griffet (Henri).
*Hist. des hosties miraculeuses &c. s8º. Brux. 1820

Griffin (Appleton Prentiss Clark), *see* BOSTON ATHENÆUM. Cat. of the Washington Coll. ; comp. &c. by A. P. C. G., 1897.

Griffin (Charles) & Co., *Ltd.* Centenary vol. of C. G. & Co., publishers, 1820–1920. Foreword by Ld. Moulton. [*Contrib. by var. wr.*] 8º. 1920

Griffin (Grace Gardner). Writings on Amer. history, 1917. Comp. by G. G. G. 8º. New Haven, *Yale.* 1919

Griffith (Arthur).
Arguments for the treaty. [P2580]. 8º. D. [1921]
see LYONS (G. A.) Some recoll. of G. & h. times, 1923.

Griffith (Ernest Stacey). Mod. development of city govt. in the U.K. & U.S. 2v. 8º. 1927

Griffith (Francis Llewellyn). The Nubian texts of the Xtn. per. ; ed. G., *see* KÖN.-PREUSS. AKAD. Abhdln., Phil.-hist. Kl., 1913.
Study of Egyptology. [P2769]. 8º. O. 1901

Griffith (Grosvenor Talbot).
Population problems of the age of Malthus. 8º. C. 1926

Griffith (Hubert). The tender passion. s8º. O. 1926

Griffith (Reginald Harvey). Alexander Pope : a bibliog. [Univ. of Texas. St. in Eng.] v1, 2p, P.'s wr., 1709–51. 8º. Austin, *Texas.* 1922–27
The great torch race. Addr. at dedic. of the Wrenn Library. [P2501]. la8º. Austin, *Texas.* [1920]
see BYRON (*Ld.*) Descr. cat. of exhib. of MSS. & 1st ed. of B., Univ. of Texas ; comp. &c. by R. H. G. &c., 1924.

Griffith (William), *barrister.*
*The Sabbath. An essay. [P2658]. 8º. *n.d.* [c. 1882]

Griffiths (Arthur Bower). Biographies of scientific men. 8º. 1912

Griffiths (*Major* **Arthur G. F.)** Mysteries of police & crime. spec. ed. 3v. 8º. *n.d.*

Griffiths (E. T.), *see* LANCELOT. Li chantiri di L. ; ed. w. intr. &c. by E. T. G., 1924.

Griffiths (Frederick Augustus).
The artillerist's manual. s8º. Woolwich. 1839
,, ,, ...Rev. & re-wr. Ed. L. Griffiths & F. Duncan. 11th ed. s8º. 1873
Notes on milit. law ; proceed. of courts martial &c. s8º. Woolwich. 1841

Griffiths (Gertrude) [*Mrs.* PERCIVAL GRIFFITHS].
The secret of the shadow. s8º. [1922]

Griffiths (John William).
Treatise on marine & naval archit. 4th ed. 4º. N.Y. 1854

Griffiths (*Mrs.* **Percival),** *see* GRIFFITHS (G.)

Griffiths (Ralph). *Ascanius, or the Young adventurer [*i.e.* Charles Edw.] ; impartial hist. of the Rebellion, 1745–46. s8º. E. 1802

Griffiths (Roger), *water bailiff.* Essay to prove that the jurisdiction & conservacy of the Thames is committed to the Lord Mayor & City of London &c. Added descr. of fish &c. 8º. 1746

Griffitts (Charles H.)
Fundamentals of vocational psychology. 8º. N.Y. 1924

Grigg (Joseph).
Hymns. [*b. w.* Harrison (E.) Misc., 1756]. 8º. 1806
The voice of danger the voice of God. Sermon. [*b. w.* Harrison (E.) Misc., 1756]. 8º. 1756

Grigg-Smith (Thomas). The child's knowledge of God : helps & hindrances. s8º. 1920

Grignan (*Mme.* **de),** *see* CELARIÉ (H.) Mme. de Sévigné, sa famille &c., 1925.

Grigorean, *Vardapet of Smyrna.* Hrahang Qristonéakan havatoz. [Doct. of Christian faith of the Ch. of Armenia, *in Armenian*]. 8º. Moscow. 1850

Grigorev (Vasily Vasilevich). Имп. С. Петербургскій университетъ въ теченіе первыхъ пятидесяти лѣтъ его существованія. [3 *pagins.*] la8º. С.–П. 1870

Grigorev (Vasily Vasilevich) [*continued*].
Нов. вид. &c. Джучидск. монетъ, *see* IMPERAT. RUSS. ARCH. OBSCH. Труды Восточ. отд., ч8, 1864.
Объ арабскомъ путешественникѣ 10 вѣка Абу-Долефѣ и странствованіи его по Средней Азіи. [P2386]. 8º. С.–П. 1872
О скиѳскомъ народѣ Сакахъ, *see* IMPERAT. RUSS. ARCH. OBSCH. Труды Восточ. отд., ч16, 1872.
Повѣрья и обряды Казанскихъ Татаръ. [I.R.G.O. Записки по отдѣл. этнограф., 6i]. 8º. С.–П. 1880
Разборъ сочиненія П. И. Небольсина : очерки торговли Россіи съ Среднею Азіею. 8º. *n.p.* [c. 1856]
Россія и Азія. Сборникъ статей по исторіи, этнографіи &c. 8º. С.–П. 1876
see CONTARINI (CH.) О странахъ Средней Азіи 1790 ; изд. Г., 1861.

Grigorovich (Dmitry Vasilevich). Мать и дочь. Разсказъ. изд 5е. [P846]. С.–П. 1885

Grill (Julius). Untersuch. ü. d. Entstehung d. vierten Evangeliums. T2. la8º. Tübingen. 1923

Grille (François Joseph). Intr. aux mém. sur la Révol. Franç. &c. 2t. 8º. 1825

Grillet (Jean), *see* JESUITS. Voyages &c., t1, Mission de Cayenne &c. [J. G. &c.], 1857.

Grillo (Angelo). Rime. Nuovamente date in luce [*by* G. B. Licino *&* C. Corbelli]. 2p [*in 1v*]. la8º. Bergamo. 1589

Grillo (Ernesto).
Early Ital. literature. With intr. by G. 2v. 8º. 1920

Grillparzer (Franz). Sämtl. Werke. Im Auftrage d. Bundeshauptstadt Wien, hrsg. v. A. Sauer. [Abt. 1], B2, 4, 6, 7, 14, 16. Abt. 2, B3–6, 8–11. Abt. 3, B2, 6. 8º. Wien. 1913–27
Abt. 1, B2, Das goldene Vliess. B4, Melusine—Szene a. e. unvoll. Trauerspiele—D. Meeres u. d. Liebe Wellen. B6, Libussa—Ein Bruderzwist in Habsburg. B7, Die Jüdin v. Toledo—Esther. B14, Prosaschr. II, Aufsätze. B16, Prosaschr. IV [Erinn., Selbstbiog. &c.]
Abt. 2, B3–6, Jugendwerke, T3–6. B8–11, Tagebücher u. lit. Skizzenhefte, T2–5, 1822–56.
Abt. 3, B2, Briefe u. Dok., T2 [1827–44]. B6, Aktenstücke, 1813–56.
Die Ahnfrau. Trauerspiel. s8º. L. *n.d.*

Grim (Egbert), *see* STALENUS (J.) Papissa monstrosa ; oppos. calumniis E. G., 1639.

Grimald (Nicholas) [GRIMOALDUS]. Life & poems. By L. R. Merrill. [Yale St. in Eng., 69]. 8º. New Haven. 1925

Grimaldi. Les grottes de Grimaldi (Baoussé-Roussé). 2t[*t1 in 4 fasc. t2 in 2 fasc. Each fasc. has sep. tp. except 1iv, pagin. cont.*] fol. Monaco. 1906–12
1i, Hist. & descr., par L. de Villeneuve. 1ii–iv, Géologie & paléontol., par M. Boule. 2i, Anthropologie, par R. Verneau. 2ii, Archéologie, par E. Cartailhac.

Grimaldi, *The family of, see* ROSSI (G.) I G. in Ventimiglia, 1900.

Grimaldi (Giulio), *see* LAUDARIO. Il Laudario dei Disciplinati di S. Croce di Urbino ; [ed.] G. G., 1915.

Grimault (A.) Fouilles effect. pour la constr. du chemin de fer Métrop. Nº. 7, *see* PARIS. COMM. MUNIC. DU VIEUX P. Procès-verb., année 1923, 1925.

Grimaux (Georges). Rais. s8º. 1927

Grime's Graves. Rep. on excav. at G.'s G., Weeting, Norfolk, 1914–1915, *see* PREHISTORIC SOC. OF E. ANGLIA.

Grimm (Carl Ludw. Wilibald). De J. Staupitii in sacr. Xtn. instaur. meritis. Oratio. [P2759]. s8º. Jenae. [1835]

Grimm (Herman). Albrecht Dürer, *see* VIRCHOW (R.) & F. v. HOLTZENDORFF. Sammlung, H16, 1866.

Grimm (Jacob L. C.), *see* BOPP (F.) Vocalismus oder Krit. ü. G.'s deut. Gramm., 1836.

—— & Wilh. Grimm. Anmerkungen zu d. Kinder- u. Hausmärchen. Neu bearb. v. J. Bolte u. G. Polívka. B2, 3. 8º. L. 1915–18
Briefwechsel (1819–47), mit K. Lachmann. Im Auftr. &c. d. Preuss. Akad. d. Wiss. hrsg. A. Leitzmann. Einl. v. K. Burdach. 2[*v. pagin. cont.*] la8º. Jena. 1927
Deut. Wörterbuch. B13, bearbt. v. K. v. Bahder unter Mitwirk. v. H. Sickel. 8º. L. 1922
TRANSLATIONS.
Household tales. Tr. & ed. M. Hunt, w. intr. by A. Lang. [repr.] 2v. s8º. *Bohn.* 1901
Popular stories. Illust. by G. Cruikshank. Repr. of 1st Eng. ed. 8º. 1915

Grimm (Wilhelm C.) *For works by W. G. & J. G. in collab. & for ref. to works upon the two brothers, see* GRIMM (J. L. C.) & W. G.

Grimmelshausen (Hans Jacob Kristoffel v.) *Der erste Beernhäuter sampt Simplicissimi Gauckeltasche (1670, *facs.*), *see* FREYTAG (G.) Bilder, B4, 1925.
Simplicissimus the vagabond. Tr. A. T. S. Goodrick. Intr. by W. Rose. [Broadway Trans.] 8°. [1924]

Grimpret (Berthe) & G. Vair.
Étudiantes. [4e éd.] s8°. 1921

Grimshaw, *Family of*, *see* SKEET, *Family of.* Hist. of the families of S. &c., 1906.

Grimshaw (Beatrice). The little red speck & o. South Sea stories. s8°. [1921]
The terrible island. s8°. 1920

Grimston (*Hon.* Charlotte). Hist. of Gorhambury. [*Lithographed, w. portrait of a. inserted*]. *p.p.* fol. *n.p.* [1821]

Grindal (Edmund), *bp. of London, abp. of (1) York, (2) Canterbury*, *see* STRYPE (J.) Hist. of G., 1710.

Grindrod (Edmund). A compendium of the laws &c. of Wesleyan Methodism. s8°. 1842

Grindrod (Ralph Barnes). Bacchus: nature, causes, &c. of intemperance. 2nd ed., rev. & enl. 8°. 1848

Grinevich (V.), *ps.* Профессіональное движеніе рабочихъ въ Россіи. [*b. w.* Svyatlovsky (V.) Проф. движ., 1907]. 8°. С.-П. 1908

Grinfield (Edward Wm.)
Nature & extent of the Xtn. dispensation &c. 8°. 1827
see BIBLE: NEW TEST.: GREEK. G. (E. W.) Scholia Hellen. in N.T. Philone et Josepho, &c., 2t, 1848.

Grinling (Charles H.), T. A. Ingram *& others, edd.* A survey & record of Woolwich & W. Kent. Commem. of Cong. of S.E. Union of Sci. Socs. 8°. Woolwich. 1909

Grinnell (George Bird). Cheyenne Indians, th. hist. & ways of life. 2v. 8°. New Haven, *Yale.* 1923

Grinnell (Joseph) & T. I. Storer.
Animal life in the Yosemite. la8°. Berkeley, *Cal.* 1924

Grinnell-Milne (*Capt.* Duncan). An escaper's log. s8°. [1926]

Grinstead, East, *see* EAST GRINSTEAD.

Gripenberg (Oskar Kaz.) Изнанка "операціи охвата лѣваго фланга расположенія арміи Оку" въ Янв. 1905. la8°. С.-П. 1908

Grisar (Hartmann), *see* KAWERAU (G.) Luther in kath. Beleuchtung: Glossen zu H. G.'s L., 1911.

Grisebach (Eduard), *see* LICHTENBERG (G. C.) Gedanken u. Max.; mit biogr. Einleit. v. E. G., 1871.

Griselini (Francesco). *Le sciocche &c. imposture per denigrare l'illust. mem. di Paolo Servita reprod. da P. M. D. M. [P2839]. s8°. Venezia. 1770

Griss (J. J.), *see* RAAF (K. H. DE) & J. J. G. Zeven eeuwen: spiegel d. nederl. letteren, 4d, 1918–20.

Gristwood (A. D.) The Somme; includ. The Coward. Pref. by H. G. Wells. s8°. [1927]

Griswold (Hervey de Witt). The relig. of the Rigveda. 8°. O. 1923

Gritti (Francesco). Le giozze d'oro. s8°. Venezia. 1867

Gritzner (A. Maximilian F.), *see* SIBMACHER (J.), *ed.* J. S.'s gr. &c. Wappenbuch, B1–7, 1856–1912, *list of contents for var. parts* "bearbt. v. A. M. F. G."

Gritzner (Erich). Heraldik, 2e A., 1912, *see* GRUNDR. D. GESCHICHTSWISS.; Meister, 1iv, 1912.

***Groan** (A) from the throne. [*A satirical poem on King George IV*]. [P425]. 8°. 1820

Grob (Jacques), *see* LUXEMBOURG. Dénombrements des feux des duché de L. & comté de Chiny; réunis par J. G., t1, 1921.

Gröber (Carl).
Oberpfälz. Burgen u. Schlösser. la8°. Augsburg. 1925
Die Plastik in d. Oberpfalz. la8°. Augsburg. 1924
Unterfränk. Burgen. la8°. Augsburg. 1924

Grocers' Company, *London.* *Grocers' (The) Company, 1345–1920. [P2497]. 8°. [1920]

Groddeck (Gabriel). Caeremonia palmarum in festo Tabernaculorum. 2p. [P1015]. s4°. Lipsiae. [1694–95]

Grodekov (Nikolai Ivanovich). Война въ Туркменіи. Походъ Скобелева, 1880–81. 4t. 8°. С.-П. 1883–84
Чрезъ Афганистанъ. Путевыя записки. s8°. С.-П. 1880
G.'s ride f. Samarcand to Herat. Tr. C. Marvin. Alphab. index by W. E. Gowan. 8°. *n.p.* [1883]

Groen van Prinsterer (Gulielmus). Le parti anti-révolut. &c. dans l'Église réformée des Pays-Bas. 2e éd. 8°. Amsterdam. 1860
Reis naar Parijs & Besançon, 1836; med. W. H. de Savornin Lohman, *see* HISTORISCH GENOOTS. Bijd., d. 42, 1921.
Schriftelijke nalatenschap. Uitg. C. Gerretson & A. Goslinga. [Rijks Gesch. Publ., 58]. d2. la8°. 'sGravenhage. 1925
2, Briefwisseling, d1, 1808–33, bewerkt door C. Gerretson.

Groener (Wilhelm), *see* GRÖNER (W.)

Groenewoud (Jacobus Cornelius Swyghuisen). Oratio de adhibenda ad doc. literas orient. popularitate Socratica. 4°. Leovardiae. 1818

Grogan (Ellinor Theophila, *Lady*). Hist. [of Bulgaria], to Gt. War, *see* BUCHAN (J.), *ed.* Nations of to-day, B. & Romania, 1924.
Life of J. D. Bourchier. [*w. contrib. by var. wr.*] 8°. [1926]

Gröger (Otto). 36. Mitt. d. Phonogramm-Archivs-Komm.: Schweizer Mundarten, 1914, *see* KAIS. AKAD. D. W. ZU WIEN. Sitz., B176, 1916.

Grohmann (Adolf). Æthiop. Marienhymnen. Hrsg., üb. u. erlaut. v. A. G. [Sächs. Akad. d. Wiss., B33iv]. la8°. L. 1919
see NIELSEN (D.), *ed.* Hdbch. d. altarab. Alt., B1, 1927.

Grolier Club, *New York.*
Transactions, 1884–85. pl. s4°. N.Y. 1885
see KEYNES (G. L.) Bibliog. of W. Blake, 1921.
„ WARREN (A.) The Charles Whittinghams, printers, 1896.

Grollier (*le marq.* **de),** *see* GROLLIER (C. DE). Manuel de l'amateur de porcelaines, manufact. europ., d'ap. notes du m. de G., 1914.

Grollier (Charles de). Manuel de l'amateur de porcelaines, manufact. europ. (France exceptée). Suivi du rép. des marques connues d'ap. notes du marq. de G. & du cte. de Chavagnac. [*w. sep. tp. & pagin.*] [2v]. la8°. 1914
„ „ manufact. fr., suivi du Rép. des marques connues, 1914. la8°. 1922

Groman (Vl. G.)
Хозяйств. положение С.С.С.Р. [P2823]. 8°. Москва. 1924
see RUSSIA. Иточи и перспективы: сборникъ статей Вл. Г. &c., 1906.

Gromort (Georges).
Ital. Renaissance architecture. Tr. G. F. Waters. 8°. 1922
Jardins d'Espagne. 2v. fol. 1926

Grøndahl (Illit) & O. Raknes.
Chapters in Norwegian lit. 8°. 1923

Grondijs (Ludovic H.) La Guerre en Russie & en Sibérie. Avant-propos de M. Paléologue. Préf. de E. Haumant. 8°. 1922

Grondona (L. St. Clare). The kangaroo keeps on talking. Intr. by S. Baldwin. 8°. 1924

Gröner (Wilhelm) [GROENER].
Der Weltkrieg u. s. Probleme. 8°. 1920

Groninganae. Feriae Gr., 2v, 1733–39, *see* ENGELHARD (N.), *ed.*

Groningen [*Groninghe*]. Quedam narracio de G., de Thrente, &c., 1888, *see* TRAJECTENSES.
Rekeningen der stad G. uit de 16de eeuw. Uitg. door P. J. Blok. [Hist. Genoots. Werken., s3, 9]. 8°. s'Gravenhage. 1896

Groningen (B. A. van).
Le gymnasiarque des métropoles de l'Egypte rom. 8°. 1924

Gronovius (Abrahamus). Varia geogr. J. F. Gronovii diss. de Gothorum sede orig. adv. P. Cluverium; Lib. provinc. Roman. &c., cum notis A. Schotti, & L. T. Gronovii; ejusdemque animadv. in Vibium Sequestrem. J. C. Hagenbuchii exercit. Acc. animadv. in Strabonis Γεωγραφικῶν libros 9. [Ed. A. G.] 8°. Lugd. Batav. 1739

Gronovius (Joannes Fridericus), *the elder.* Diss. de Gothorum sede origin. adv. P. Cluverium, *see* GRONOVIUS (A.) Varia geogr., 1739.
see DAMCKE (B.) & J. CHRISTENIUS. Leben d. J. F. G., 1723.

Gronovius (Joannes Fridericus), *the younger.* Flora Virginica exhib. plantas quas J. Claytonus in Virginia obs., coll. &c. J. F. G. &c. [*b. w.* Plumier (C.) Nova plant. Amer. genera, 1703]. 4°. Lugd. Bat. 1762

Gronovius (Laurentius Theodorus), *the elder.* Lib. prov. Roman. & civit. prov. Gallic., c. notis A. Schotti & L. T. G. ejusdemque animadv. in Vibium Sequestrem, *see* GRONOVIUS (A.) Varia geogr., 1739.

Grønvold, *Family of*, *see* GRØNVOLD (F.) Slægts-Krøniker, 1500–1800, 1924.

Grønvold (Fr.) Slægts-Krøniker, 1500–1800. la8°. 1924

Groom. *The guide to service: the groom, 1840, *see* STEPHEN (*Sir* G.)

Groom (G. Laurence). The ship of destiny. [*Poems*]. Pref. by G. K. Chesterton. s8°. Leeds. 1926

Groos (*Korvettenkapitän* O.), *see* KRIEG (Der) zur See, 1914–18, Der Krieg in d. Nordsee; bearb. v. O. G., B1–5, 1920–25.

Groot (Hugo de), *see* GROTIUS (H. DE).

Groot (Pieter de). Lettres à A. de Wicquefort, 1668–74. Publ. &c. F. J. L. Krämer. [Hist. Genoots. Werken, s3, 5]. 8°. La Haye. 1894

Groote (Gerard), *see* HYMA (A.) The Xtn. Renaissance: hist. of the "Devotio Moderna," 1925.
Gröpper (Johann). Actes of the disputacio in cowncell of Empyre holden at Regenspurg [*supposed to have been drawn up by J. G. &c.*]; tr., 1542, *see* RATISBON.
Gros (C.), *see* LAVOISNE (C. V.) & C. G. A new geneal. hist. & chron. atlas, &c., 1809.
Gros (Etienne). Philippe Quinault, sa vie & s. œuvre. 8°. 1926
Gros (Johannès). Alex. Dumas & M. Duplessis. 8°. 1923
Grosclaude (Etienne). Un Parisien à Madagascar: aventures &c. 2e éd. la8°. 1898
Gros de Besplas (Joseph Marie). An essay on the eloquence of the pulpit. Tr. by M. Martindale. s8°. 1819
Grosdidier de Matons (Marcel). Le Comté de Bar des orig. au Traité de Bruges, vers 950–1301. 8°. 1922
Grose (Francis). The antiquarian repertory. [Comp. by G. &c.] v4 [*no tp.*] 4°. [1784]
Classical dict. of the vulgar tongue. s8°. 1785 [*repr.*] *n.d.*
see *ADVICE to officers of Brit. Army [*attrib. to* F. G. &c.], 1783.
Grose (*Rev.* James). Mem. of the Rev. D. Chapman. Also, Chapman's Sermon on the death of the Rev. J. Beaumont, M.D. [P601]. 8°. Boston. 1857
Grose (Sidney William), *see* CAMBRIDGE: FITZWILLIAM MUSEUM. Cat. of the McClean coll. of Greek coins by S. W. G., v1, 2, 1923–26.
Grose (Thomas Hodge).
*T. H. G., a memory. [*By C. S. G.* P2763]. 8°. O. 1907
Grosley (Pierre Jean). *Mém. hist. & crit. pour l'hist. de Troyes. Augm. d'une not. par M. Simon. 2t. 8°. 1774–1812
Groslier (George). Recherches sur les Cambodgiens, d'après les textes & les mon. dep. les prem. s. de notre ère. sfol. 1921
La sculpture khmère ancienne. la8°. 1925
Gross (—), *ed.*, *see* DANZIG. Polit. Hdbch. d. Fr. Stadt D., 1924.
Gross (Carl), *see* DEUTSCHER WERKBUND. Handwerkl. Kunst &c. [*by C. G. & o.*], 1922.
Gross (Johann). Biograph.-literar. Lex. d. deut. Dichter &c., 9.–20. Jhdt. la8°. L. 1922
Gross (Johann Georg) [GROSSIUS (J. G.)].
De methodo concionandi. s8°. Basileae. 1629
Gross (Lothar), *see* HAPSBURG. Regesta Habsburgica &c., Abt. 3, bearb. v. L. G., 1924.
Grosse. *Grosse (Der) Krieg v. 189–: e. Zukunftsbild; v. P. Colomb &c.; Übers. v. E. A. Witte, 2e A., 1894, *see* GREAT.
Grosse (Die) Politik d. europ. Kabinette 1871–1914. Sammlung d. diplomat. Akten d. Auswärtigen Amtes. Im Auftr. d. Ausw. Amtes hrsg. v. J. Lepsius, A. Mendelssohn Bartholdy, F. Thimme. 40B *in* 54v. [12, 14, 18, 19, 20, 21, 23, 25, 26, 27, 30, 34, 36, 37 *are in 2 parts*]. la8°. 1922–27
1, Der Frankfurter Friede u. s. Nachwirkungen, 1871–77.
2, Der Berliner Kongress u. s. Vorgesch. [1871–78].
3, Das Bismarck'sche Bündnissystem [1879–85].
4, Die Dreibundmächte u. England [1879–89].
5, Neue Verwickelungen im Osten [1885–88].
6, Kriegsgefahr in Ost u. West. Ausklang d. Bismarckzeit [1887–90].
7, Die Anfänge d. neuen Kurses, 1, Der russ. Draht [1890–94].
8, " " " " 2, Die Stellung Englands zw. d. Mächten [1890–95].
9, Der nahe u. d. ferne Osten [1890–95].
10, Das türk. Problem, 1895.
11, Die Krügerdepesche u. d. europ. Bündnissystem, 1896.
12, Alte u. neue Balkanhändel, 1896–99, 2H.
13, Die europ. Mächte untereinander, 1897–99.
14, Weltpolit. Rivalitäten [1895–99], 2H.
15, Rings um d. Erste Haager Friedenskonferenz [1898–1900].
16, Die Chinawirren u. d. Mächte, 1900–02.
17, Die Wendung im deut.- eng. Verhältnis [1901–04].
18, Zweibund u. Dreibund, 1900–04, 2H.
19, Der Russ.-Jap. Krieg [1902–5], 2H.
20, Entente Cordiale u. erste Marokkokrise, 1904–5, 2H.
21, Die Konferenz v. Algeciras u. i. Auswirkung [1905–7], 2H.
22, Die Österreich.-Russ. Entente u. d. Balkan, 1904–7.
23, Die 2e Haager Friedenskonferenz Nordsee- u. Ostsee-Abkommen [1904–8], 2H.
24, Deutschland u. d. Westmächte, 1907–8.
25, Die Engl.-Russ. Entente u. d. Osten. [1905–8], 2H.
26, Die Bosnische Krise, 1908–9, 2H.
27, Zwischen d. Balkankrisen, 1909–11, 2H.
28, England u. d. deut. Flotte, 1908–11.
29, Die zweite Marokkokrise, 1911.
30, Der italienisch-türk. Krieg, 1911–12, 2H.
31, Das Scheitern d. Haldane-Mission u. i. Rückwirkung auf d. Tripelentente, 1911–12.
32, Die Mächte u. Ostasien, 1909–14.
33, Der erste Balkankrieg, 1912.
34, Die Londoner Botschafterreunion u. d. 2e Balkankrieg, 1912–13, 2H.

Grosse. Grosse (Die) Politik d. europ. Kabinette &c. [*continued*].
35, Der dritte Balkankrieg, 1913.
36, Die Liquidierung d. Balkankriege, 1913–14, 2H.
37, Entspannungen unter d. Mächten, 1912–13, 2H.
38, Neue Gefahrenzonen im Orient, 1913–14.
39, Das Nahen d. Weltkrieges, 1912–14.
40, Namenregister zu B26–39.
see SCHWERTFEGER (B.) Diplomat. Akten d. Auswärtigen Amtes 1871–1914, Wegweiser, 5T, 1923–27.
Grosse (Casimir Friedrich). Diss. de cultu ingenii. Praes. J. F. Buddeo. s4°. Halæ Magdeb. 1699
Grosse (Emil). Estudio geológ. del terciario carbonífero de Antioquia en la Cordillera Cent. de Colombia. Ejecutado, 1920–23. [*German & Ital.*] fol. 1926
Grosse (Ernst). Die ostasiat. Tuschmalerei. [Die Kunst d. Ostens; hrsg. W. Cohn, B6]. la8°. 1922
Grosse (Robert). Röm. Militärgesch. v. Gallienus bis z. Beginn d. byzant. Themenverfassung. 8°. 1920
Grosse-Duperon (Albert Pierre Auguste).
Doc. sur la ville de Mayenne. la8°. Mayenne. 1906
Grosser Generalstab, *see* SCHLACHTEN u. Gefechte d. Grossen Krieges, 1914–18; Quellenwerk v. G. G., 1919.
Grössere (Das) Deutschland: Wochenschrift f. Deutsche Welt- u. Kolonialpolitik. Jahr. 5 (Heft 27–45, Juli–Nov. 1918). [*No more publ.*] 8°. 1918
Grosseteste (Robert), *bp. of Lincoln.* Compotus, *see* BACON (R.) Op. ined., fasc. 6; acced. Comp. R. G., 1926.
Rotuli R. G., Episc. Lincoln., 1235–53, & Rotulus H. de Lexington, Episc. Lincoln., 1254–59. Ed. F. N. Davis. [Lincoln Rec. Soc., v11]. la8°. Horncastle. 1914
see LOSERTH (J.) J. von Wiclif u. R. G., 1918.
" PATRIARCHS. The testaments of the 12 patriarchs; tr. by G., now Englished, 1638; 1666.
Grossgebauer (Johann Caspar). Disput. inaug. de decimis, sub præs. C. Carpzovii. [P2638]. s4°. Wittebergæ. 1629
Grossi (Tommaso), *see* BROGNOLIGO (G.) T. G., vita &c., 1916.
Grossius (Joannes Georgius), *see* GROSS (J. G.)
Grossman (Leonid P.) Путь Достоевского. s8°. Ленинград. 1924
Семинарий по Достоевскому. Материалы, библиогр. 8°. Москва. 1922
Grossmann (Christian Gottlob Leberecht). De collegio Pharisæorum comm. [*Progr.*] 4°. Lipsiae. 1851
Quaest. Philon. 2p. [p1, resp. F. A. Heinichen]. [P558]. 4°. Lipsiae. [1829]
Grossmann (Rudolf). Katalan. Lyrik d. Gegenwart. Deut. Auslese, mit Einführ. 8°. Hamburg. 1923
Grossmith (George) & W. W. Grossmith.
The diary of a nobody. [repr.] s8°. [1924]
Grossmith (Walter Weedon), *see* GROSSMITH (G.) & W. W. G. Diary of a nobody, repr., 1924.
Grosso (Orlando). Decoratori genovesi. 8°. 1921
Genova. la8°. Bergamo. [1926]
Grosso (Remigio del), *see* DEL GROSSO (R.)
Grosteste (Claude), *Sieur de la Mothe.* Corr. fraternelle de l'Église Angl. avec les autres églises réformées &c. publié par C. G. de la M. s8°. La Haye. 1705
Grosvenor Gallery. Cat. of the works of Sir Joshua Reynolds exhib. at the G.G., 1883–84. [Notes by F. G. Stephens]. Illust. 4°. 1884
Grosvenor (Caroline) & *Lord* Stuart of Wortley.
The 1st Lady Wharncliffe & h. family (1779–1856). 2v. 8°. 1927
Grosvenor (Mary, *Lady*), *wife of Sir T. Grosvenor, Bt., form. Davies, see* DAVIES (M.)
Grosvenor (*Lady* Theodora).
Motcombe, past & present. 2nd ed. s8°. Shaftesbury. 1868
Grosvenor (W. M.) Does protection protect? Effect of tariff upon Amer. industry. 8°. N.Y. 1871
Grot (Yakov Karlovich). Литературная жизнь Крылова. [I. Akad. Nauk. Зап., t14]. 8°. С.-П. 1868
Мат. для ист. Пугачевскаго бунта. [I. Akad. Nauk. Зап., t1, 3]. 8°. С.-П. 1862–63
Перѣѣзды по Финляндіи отъ Ладожскаго озера до рѣки Торнео. 8°. С.-П. 1847
Письма Ломоносова и Сумарокова къ И. И. Шувалову. [I. Akad. Nauk. Зап., t1]. 8°. С.-П. 1862
Русское правописаніе. Руководство. 3e изд. 8°. С.-П. 1885
Grote (George). Plato & o. companions of Sokrates. 2nd ed. 3v. 8°. 1867
Grote (*Dr.* H.) Geschlechts- u. Wappenbuch d. Königreichs Hannover u. d. Herzogthums Braunschweig. [*Coloured plates*]. Hrsg. v. H. G. 4°. Hannover. 1843
Grotefend (Hermann). Abriss d. Chronologie d. deut. M.-a. u. d. Neuzeit, 2e A, 1912, *see* GRUNDR. D. GESCHICHTSWISS., 1iii, 1912.

Grote-Hasenbalg (Werner). Masterpieces of oriental rugs. [Tr. G. B. Gifford]. 3v[1, Text. 2, 3, Plates]. s8°. Berlin. [1922]

Groteste (Claude), *see* GROSTESTE (C.)

Grotewold (Christian), *see* SCHMIDT-KLUGKIST (W.) & C. G. Argentinien &c., 2e A., 1919.

Groth (P.) A Norwegian grammar. 2d ed. s8°. Christiania. 1914

Grothe (A. L. Hugo).
Bulgarien. Beitr. z. Landeskunde. 8°. Wien. 1921

Grotius Society. Transactions. v5–11. 8°. 1920–26
5–11, Problems of peace & war: papers read before the Soc. in 1919–25.

PUBLICATIONS.
Nos. 2–4. 8°. 1924–25
see BISSCHOP (W. R.) The Saar controversy, 1924. [2.]
,, KNIGHT (W. S. M.) Life & works of Grotius, 1925. [4.]
,, NATHAN (M.) The renascence of internat. law, 1925. [3.]

TEXTS FOR STUDENTS.
Nos. 1, 2, 4, 6, 8. 8°. 1921–27
see BELLOT (H. H. L.) Texts illust. constit. of Supreme Court of U.S. &c.; intr. by E., 1921. [8.]
,, BENTHAM (J.) Plan for univ. & perpet. peace, 1927. [6.]
,, ERASMUS (D.) Instit. principis christ.; tr., 1921. [1.]
,, QUAKERS & peace [*sel. f. var. a.*], 1927. [4.]
,, SULLY (M. DE B., *duc* DE). Grand design of Henry IV; tr., 1921. [2.]

Grotius (Hugo) [†GROOT (HUGO DE)].
Annot. in Vet. & Nov. Test. Præf. a S. Moody. 2v [v2 *wants tp.*] s4°. Londini. 1727
De imperio summ. potestatum circa sacra. Acc. D. Blondellus De jure plebis in regimine eccl. & De officio magistratus Christ. alius authoris opusc. ed. noviss. s8°. Amstelodami. 1677
De jure belli ac pacis libri tres. 4°. Parisiis. 1625
De Novi Test. auctor. liber ab E. Pocock in linguam arab. tr. s8°. Halæ. 1733
Defensio fidei cathol. de satisfactione Christi. Præm. auctoris vita &c. Elenchum Antidippelianum, cum oratione, subj. J. Lange. s4°. Lipsiae. 1730
H. G.: essays on h. life & works. Sel. for tercent. of h. "De jure belli ac pacis," 1625–1925; by A. Lysen. Pref. by J. Ter Meulen. [*By var. wr. in var. lang.*] 8°. Leyden. 1925
Instit. juris nat. & gentium ex H. G. De jure belli &c. [*by* J. Klenckius]. ed. 2a. s8°. Cantab. 1703
Testament of hooftpunten getrocken wt sijn jongste antwoort aen D. Rivet (1645), *see* VONDEL (J. VAN DEN). Werken, d10, *n.d.*
Verhooren en andere bescheiden betreff. het rechtsgeding. Uitg. door R. Fruin. [Hist. Genoots. Werken, N.S., 14]. 8°. Utrecht. 1871
Via ad pacem eccl.: Conf. fidei sec. Conc. Trid.; Conf. fidei Augustana; Consult. Cassandri. Annot. H. Grotii in Consult. Cassandri; H. Grotii Poema de baptismate, Poema de Eucharistia, Disq. Pelagiana. [3 *pagin.*] s8°. *n.p.* 1642
Votum pro pace eccl. contra examen A. Riveti &c. [*b. w. h.* Via ad pacem eccl., 1642]. s8°. *n.p.* 1642

TRANSLATIONS.
The jurisprudence of Holland. Text, tr. w. notes & comm. by R. W. Lee. v1. 8°. O. 1926

REFERENCES.
see BRANDT (C.) & A. VAN CATTENBURGH. Hist., 2p, 1727.
,, HAMMOND (H.) A contin. of the defence of H. G., 1657.
,, —— 2nd defence of H. G., 1655.
,, KNIGHT (W. S. M.) Life & works of G., 1925.
,, MAJOR (J. T.) De orat. pro defunctis, diss. H. G. &c. oppos., 1649; 1659.
,, NIETZSCHE (F. A. L.) Epist. Petri poster. contra G. vindicata, 1785.
,, REINER (J.) H. G. u. d. Weltschiedsgericht, 1922.
,, SALMASIUS (CL.) De transsubstantiatione lib.; ad J. Pacium contra H. G., 1646.
,, VATABLUS (F.) Annot. in Psalmos, subjunct. H. G. notis &c., 1767.
,, VOGEL (W.) H. G. u. d. Freiheit d. Meere, 1918.

Groto (Luigi), *called* "*Il cieco d'Adria.*"
La Calisto. Nova favola pastorale. s8°. Venetia. 1583
La Dalida, tragedia nova. s8°. Venetia. 1572
La Hadriana: tragedia. s8°. Venetia. 1599
Orazioni volgari. s4°. Venetia. 1604
Rime. p1 [*incl.* Carmina Lat.] s8°. Venetia, *Zopini.* 1577

Grotte (Gioseppe Frezza dalle), *see* FREZZA DALLE GROTTE (G.)

Grottes. G. (Les) de Grimaldi, 2t, 1906–12, *see* GRIMALDI.
*G. (Les) de Yun-Kang, 1924, *see* YUN-KANG.

Grottger (Artur), *see* POTOCKI (A.) Grottger, 1907.

Grotto degli Erri (L. J.), *see* PADOVA. Cenni storici s. famiglie de Padova &c., premesso un trattato sull' arte araldica [*by* G. d. E.], 1842.

Groussac (Pablo). El viaje intelectual: impresiones de naturaleza y arte. s2. 8°. Buenos Aires. 1920

Grousset (Paschal) [*ps.* PHILIPPE DARYL; ANDRÉ LAURIE]. Ireland's disease. [Tr.] 8°. 1888

Grouwels (Mathias). Hist. crit. sacræ indulgentiæ. B. Mariæ Angelorum vulgo de Portiuncula. s8°. Antverpiæ. 1726

Grove (Agnes Geraldine, *Lady*), *wife of 2nd bart.*
The human woman. 2nd imp. 8°. 1908

Grove (*Sir* George). Dict. of music & musicians, v6, Amer. Suppl. W. S. Pratt, ed. 8°. N.Y. 1920
,, ,, ...3rd ed. Ed. H. C. Colles. 5v. 8°. 1927–28

Grove (*Mrs.* Lilly), *aft. wife of Sir J. G. Frazer.*
First aid to the servantless. 8°. 1913

Groves (James), *F.L.S.*, *see* BRIT. MUS. OF NAT. HIST.: GEOL. Cainozoic plants, v1, w. sect. on Charophyta by J. G., 1926.

—— & G. R. Bullock-Webster.
The British Charophyta. [Ray Soc.] 2v. 8°. 1920–24

Groves (John Percy). The Royal Guernsey Militia, 800–1895. s4°. Guernsey. 1895

Grqoyk, nouagaran. Manual of canticles, *in Armenian*, 1794, *see* ARMENIA.

Gruaidh Ghriansholus. The pursuit of Gruaidh Ghriansholus. [*Cúchulainn legend*]. Ed. & tr. C. O'Rahilly. [Irish Texts Soc., v24]. 8°. [1922]. 1924

Grubauer (Albert).
Celebes. Ethnolog. Streifzüge. 4°. Hagen i. W. 1923

Grubb (Edward). The evangel. movement & its impact on the Soc. of Friends. Address. [P2755]. 8°. Leominster. 1924

Grube (Wilhelm), *see* LAUFER (B.), *ed.* Chines. Schattenspiele; üb. W. G., 1915.

Grüber (*Ritter* von).
Die Superphosphatfabrikation. [P2740]. la8°. Halle. 1907

Gruber (Ferdinand Ernst). Adam Müller-Guttenbrunn, der Erzschwab. s8°. L. 1921

Gruber (Franz). Die Kirchenmusik u. ihre Hebung. [*b. w.* Brendel (F.) Grundzüge, 4e A., 1855]. s8°. [Salzburg. 1855]

Gruber (Gabriel), *jesuit general in Russia, see* RULE (W. H.) Celebr. Jesuits, v2, 1853.

Gruber (Josef). Czechoslovakia: econ. & soc. conditions. [*by var. wr.*] Ed. J. G. Tr. by A. Brož, S. V. Klíma &c. 8°. N.Y. 1924

Gruber (Max v.) Krieg, Frieden u. Biologie, *see* DEUTSCHE Reden in schwerer Zeit, 30, 1915.

Gruberus (Daniel), *see* †HENTZNER (P.) Itin.: acc. monita peregrinatoria [*of G. &c.*], 1629.

Grull (Werner).
Die Kontrolle in gewerbl. Unternehmungen. 8°. 1921

Grumbach (Argula von) [GRUNBACH], *née von Stauff* [STAUFFIN]. Argula Stauffiñ. Christl. ermanungenn &c. s4°. Steynburg. 1524

Grumbkow (Friedrich Wilhelm v.), *see* FREDERICK II, *king of Prussia.* Briefwechsel m. G. &c., 1731–59, hrsg. R. Koser, 1898.

Grunbach (Argula v.), *see* GRUMBACH (A. v.)

Grünbeck (Joseph), *see* GRÜNPECK.

Grundler (Johann Ernst).
see MATHER (C.) India Christiana; [*includ. Letter f. J. E. G. in Lat. & Eng.*], 1721.
,, SCHULTZE (B.) Sermam o dia da sepultura do J. E. G., 1720.

Gründlicher [GRÜNDTLICHER]. *Gründl. Bericht auss heyl. göttl. Schrifft v. d. fürnembsten Articuln Christl. Lehr. Auff Befelch des Graffen v. Hohenloe &c. s4°. Franckfurt a. M. 1605
Gründtlicher bericht u. warhafftige erklerungh warumb die Chur u. Fürsten &c. d. Augsp. Conf. &c., 1564, *see* AUGSBURG CONFESSION.

Grundmayr (Franz). Lex. der römischkathol. Kirchengebräuche. s8°. Augsburg. 1801

Grundriss.
Grundriss d. deut. Literaturgesch. B1, 2. 8°. 1920–22
see UNWERTH (W. v.) & T. SIEBS. Gesch. der. deut. Lit., bis z. 11. Jhdt., 1920. [1.]
,, VOGT (F.) Gesch. d. mittelhochdeut. Lit., T1, 1922. [2.]
Grundriss d. Geschichtswissenschaft. Zur Einführung in d. Stud. d. deut. Gesch. d. M.-a. u. d. Neuzeit. In Verbind. mit O. Braun, B. Bretholz, J. Freisen, u. a. hrsg. v. Aloys Meister. 2te A. Reihe 1, Abt. 1, 2, 2a, 3, 4, 4a, 6, 7; Reihe 2, Abt. 1–6, 8 [1iia, 2v, viii, *1st ed.*, 2ii, 3e A.] la8°. L. 1912–22
Braun (O.) Geschichtsphilosophie, 1913. [1vi.]
Bretholz (B.) Latein. Paläographie, 1912. [1i.]
Forst-Battaglia (O.) Genealogie, 1913. [1iva.]
Friedensburg (F.) Deut. Münzgesch., 1912. [1iv.]
Gritzner (E.) Heraldik, 1912. [1iv.]

Grundriss [*continued*].
Grotefend (H.) Abriss d. Chronologie d deut. M.- a. u. d. Neuzeit, 1912. [1iii.]
Hartung (F.) Deut. Verfassungsgesch. v. 15. Jhdt. b. z. Gegenwart, 1922. [2iv.]
Heuberger (R.) Allgem. Urkundenlehre f. Deutschland u. Italien, 1921. [1iia.]
Ilgen (Th.) Sphragistik, 1912. [1iv.]
Jansen (M.) & Schmitz-Kallenberg. Historiographie u. Quellen d. deut. Gesch. bis 1500, 1914. [1vii.]
Kötzschke (R.) Grundzüge d. deut. Wirtschaftsgesch. bis z. 17. Jhdt., 1921. [2i.]
Meister (A.) Deut. Verfassungesch. v. d. Anfängen b. ins 14te Jhdt., 1913. [2iii.]
—— Grundzüge d. hist. Methode, 1913. [1vi.]
Schmitz-Kallenberg (L.) Urkundenlehre, T2, Papsturkunden, 1913. [1ii.]
Schwerin (C. v.) Deut. Rechtsgesch., 1912. [2v.]
Sehling (E.) Gesch. d. protest. Kirchenverfass., 1913. [2viii.]
Sieveking (H.) Grundzüge d. neu. Wirtschaftsgesch. v. 17. Jhdt. bis z. Gegenwart, 3te A., 1921. [2ii.]
Thommen (R.) Urkundenlehre, T1, Grundbegriffe Königs- u. Kaiserurkunden, 1913. [1ii.]
Werminghoff (A.) Verfassungsgesch. d. deut. Kirche im M.- a., 1913. [2vi.]

Grundriss d. indo-arischen Philol. u. Altertumskunde; begr. v. G. Bühler; hrsg. v. J. Wackernagel u. H. Lüders. 3B (1, iA, B (2T), iiiB, iv, vi–viii, x, xi. 2, iB, iiD, iiiB, v, viii. 3, iA, B, ii, iv, vi, viii–x). la8°. Str. *&* Berlin. 1896–1920
B2, H3B & 5 & B3, H8 *have series title in Eng.* Encyclopaedia of Indo-Aryan research.
see Baines (*Sir* J. A.) Ethnography, 1912. [B2v.]
,, Bhandarkar (R. G.) Vaiṣṇavism, Śaivism &c., 1913 [B3vi.]
,, Bloomfield (M.) The Atharvaveda, 1899. [B2i, B.]
,, Bühler (J. G.) Ind. Paläographie (*c.* 350 b.c.–*c.* a.d. 1300), 1896. [B1xi.]
,, Garbe (R.) Sāṃkhya u. Yoga, 1896. [B3iv.]
,, Geiger (W.) Lit. u. Sprache d. Singhalesen, 1900. [B1x.]
,, —— Pāli Lit. u. Sprache, 1916. [B1vii.]
,, Hillebrandt (A.) Ritual-Litt., ved. Opfer u. Zauber, 1897. [B3ii.]
,, Hopkins (E. W.) Epic mythology, 1915. [B3i, B.]
,, Jolly (J.) G. Bühler, 1899. [B1i, A.]
,, —— Medicin, 1901. [B3x.]
,, —— Recht u. Sitte, 1895. [B2viii.]
,, †Kern (J. H. C.) Man. of Indian Buddhism, 1896. [B3viii.]
,, Konow (S.) Das ind. Drama, 1920. [B2, H2, D.]
,, Macdonell (A. A.) Vedic grammar, 1910. [B1iv.]
,, †—— Vedic mythol., 1897. [B3i, A.]
,, Pischel (R.) Gramm. d. Prakrit-Sprachen, 1900. [B1viii.]
,, †Rapson (E. J.) Indian coins, 1897. [B2iii, B.]
,, Speyer (J. S.) Ved. u. Sanskrit-Syntax, 1896. [B1vi.]
,, Thibaut (G. F. W.) Astronomie, Astrol. u. Mathematik, 1899. [B3ix.]
,, Windisch (W. O. E.) Gesch. d. Sanskrit-Philol. u. ind. Altertumskunde, 1917–20. [B1i, B.]
,, Zachariae (T.) Die ind. Wörterbücher (Kośa), 1897. [B1iii, B.]

Grundriss d. indogerm. Sprach- u. Altertumskunde; hrsg. v. K. Brugmann u. C. Bartholomae.
Abt. 2. B1, 2i, 3, 4ii. 8°. Str. 1916–27
II, Die Erforsch. d. indogerm. Sprachen; unter Mitwirk. v. A. Brückner &c. hrsg. v. W. Streitberg.
1, Griech., v. A. Thumb; Ital., v. A. Walde; Vulgärlat., v. K. v. Ettmayer; Kelt. Sprach., v. H. Hartmann.
2i, Germanisch, v. W. Streitberg u. V. Michels.
3, Slav.-Litau. v. A. Brückner; Alban. v. N. Jokl.
4ii, Iranisch, v. H. Reichelt; u. Armenisch, v. H. Zeller.

Grundriss d. slav. Philologie u. Kulturgesch., hrsg. v. R. Trautmann u. M. Vasmer. B[1], 2. la8°. 1925–26
see Karsky (E.) Gesch. d. weissruss. Volksdicht. &c., 1926. [2.]
,, Lorentz (F.) Gesch. d. pomoran. Sprache, 1925. [1.]

Grundriss der Sozialökonomik. Bearb. v. S. Altmann, Th. Brinkmann &c. Abt. 3, 4, 7, 9i, ii. la8°. Tübingen. 1922–27
3, Wirtschaft u. Gesellschaft, bearb. v. M. Weber.
4, Spezif. Elemente d. mod. kapitalist. Wirtschaft, T1, mit Beitr. v. C. Brinkmann &c.
7, Land- u. forstwirtschaftl. Produktion — Versicherungswesen, bearb. v. T. Brinkmann &c.
9, Das soziale System d. Kapitalismus, 2T, mit Beitr. v. G. Albrecht, Th. Brauer &c.

Gründtlicher, *see* Gründlicher.

Grundy (George Beardoe).
Hist. of the Greek & Roman world. 8°. 1926
On the meanings of certain terms in the Anglo-Saxon charters, *see* English Assoc. Essays &c., v8, 1922.

Grundy (Mabel Barnes-), *see* Barnes-Grundy (M.)

Grünenberg (Otto Friedrich). De N. Drabicio neopropheta in Hungaria. Præs. J. D. Koelero, disp. O. F. G. [P2742]. s4°. Altorfii. 1721

Grunert (Joseph). Meine Verhandl. mit d. Bischofe v. Ermland, P. Krementz ü. d. päpstl. Unfehlbarkeit. [P2691]. 8°. Insterburg. 1872

Grünes Gewölbe, *Dresden*. Descr. raisonnée du Trésor Royal Saxon dit " Grüne Gewölbe." Par J. G. T. Graesse. s8°. Dresde. 1872

Grünpeck (Joseph) [†Gruenbeck]. Tract. de pestilentia scorra, 1496, *&* Hübscher Tractat (Augsburg), 1496, *facs.*, *see* Sudhoff (C.) Earliest pr. lit. on syphilis, 1925.

Grunstein (Leo). Minnelieder aus Österreich. Dichtungen d. 12. bis 14. Jhdts. Mit Anhang d. mittelhochdeut. Texte. Ausgewählt u. übertr. v. L. G. 8°. Wien. 1921

Grünwedel (Albert). Alt-Kutscha: archäolog. u. religionsgesch. Forsch. an Tempera-Gemälden aus Buddhist. Höhlen. [Veröffentl. d. Preuss. Turfan-Exped.] fol. 1920
Tusca. 1, Die Agramer Mumienbinden. 2, Die Inschrift d. Cippus v. Perugia. 3, Die Pulena-Rolle. 4, Das Bleitäfelchen v. Magliano. 5, Die Leber v. Piacenza. 6, Golini-Grab. 7, Die Inschrift v. Capua. Übers. v. A. G. Add. Gloss. Tusco-Lat. la4°. L. 1922
see Sambhala. Der Weg nach S.: aus d. tibet. Orig. übers. u. mit d. Texte hrsg. v. A. G., 1915.

Grunzel (Josef L.) [Gruntzel]. Economic protectionism. Ed. E. v. Philippovich. [C.E. for Int. Peace]. la8°. O. 1916

Grupp (Georg). Kulturgesch. d. röm. Kaiserzeit. 2T [T1, 2e u. 3e, verbess. &c. A.] 8°. Regensburg *&* München. 1904–21

Gruppe (Paul Otto), *Dr. Phil., b. 1851.* Gesch. d. klass. Mythologie u. Religionsgesch., 1921, *see* Roscher (W. H.) Ausführl. Lexicon d. griech. &c. Mythologie: Suppl., 1921.

Grützmacher (Georg). Hieronymus: Biogr. Studie &c. [St. z. Gesch. d. Theol. u. d. Kirche; Bonwetsch u. Seeberg, 10]. B2, 3, 385–420. 8°. 1906–08

Grützmacher (Rich. Heinrich), *see* Heim (C.) & R. H. G. O. Spengler u. d. Christentum, 1921.

Gruyer (Paul). Huit jours à Versailles. s8°. [1920]
Saint Germain, Poissy, Maisons, Marly-le-Roi. 8°. 1922
Les saints bretons. s8°. [1923]

Grüzmacher (—). Die waldens. Bibel. [*No tp.; from* Jbch. f. rom. u. eng. Lit., 1862]. 8°. [L. 1862]

Gry (Léon). Israélites en Assyrie, Juifs en Babylonie. [Extr. de " Le Muséon, t35, 36]. la8°. 1923

Gryaduschaya Rossiya. Грядущая Россія. [La Russie future]. Ежемѣсячный журналъ. Подъ ред. Н. В. Чайковскаго &c. кн. 1, 2. Январь 1920. 8°. Парижъ. 1920

Grynaeus (Johann Jacob).
Charac. Christianorum. Theses, 1578—praeside J. J. Grynaeo. [*Foll.* by De certa elect. salute, theses, 1575 *&* De sacramentis, theses, 1574]. s8°. Basileae. [1578]
De Eucharistica controversia &c. s4°. Heidelbergae. 1584
Disp. theol. quae habitae sunt in Basil. Acad. 2p [*in* 1v]. la8°. Genev., Basil. 1584–6
Hypomnemata in Habacuci librum de providentia Dei erga Eccl. &c. [*b. w. h.* Synopsis &c., 1579]. s8°. Basileæ. 1582
Orationes duae. [*b. w. h.* Theol. theorem. &c., 1598]. s4°. Heydelbergae. 1584
Synopsis hist. hominis seu de prima hominis origine &c. theses ducentae &c. Acc. Theses analyt. Symboli Apostolici. s8°. Basileae. 1579
Theologica theoremata &c. de quibus in Basiliensi Acad. Συζητήσεις institutae fuerunt. Ed. J. J. G. 2p *in* 1v. 4°. Basileae. [1589.]
see Andreae (J.) Confutatio disput. J. J. Grynei de Coena &c., 1584.
,, Holder (W.) *of Stuttgart.* Cuculus Calvinisticus advers. blasphemam I. I. G. apologiam commonefactio, 1585.

Gryphius (Christian). Apparatus de script. historiam sec. xvii illustr. s8°. Lipsiae. 1710

Gryphius (Sebastien), *printer, of Lyons, 1493–1556, see* Baudrier (H. L.) Bibliog. lyonnaise, s8, 1910.

Gryse (Nicolaus). Spegel d. Antichrist. Pawestdoms u. Luttherischen Christendoms, na Ordennung d. 5 Hövetstücke unsers H. Catechismi underscheiden &c. s4°. Rostock. 1593

Gschwind (Carl). Die Niederfahrt Christi in d. Unterwelt. 8°. Munster i. W. 1911

Gsell (Martin). Eisen, Kupfer u. Bronze bei d. alten Ägyptern. 8°. Karlsruhe. [1910]

Gsell (Paul). Anatole France & h. circle: being h. table-talk coll. & rec. by P. G. Auth. tr. by F. Lees. 8°. 1922
Firmin Gémier. Biog.-crit. s8°. [1921]
Les matinées de la Villa Saïd: Propos d'Anatole France, rec. par P. Gsell. 2e éd. s8°. 1921

Gsell (Stephane).
Hist. anc. de l'Afrique du Nord. t5, 6. 8°. 1927
5, 6, Les royaumes indigènes.
Promenades archéolog. aux environs d'Alger. 8°. 1926
see ALGÉRIE. Inscr. lat. de l'A. rec. & publ. S. G., 1922.
——, G. Marçais & G. Yver. Hist. d'Algérie. 8°. 1927
Guadalajara. Fuero de G. (1219). [*Facs. & transcr.*] Ed. H. Keniston. [Elliot Monogr.; ed. E. C. Armstrong, 16]. 8°. Princeton, N.J. 1924
Guadet (Joseph). Esquisses hist. & polit. sur Pie VII, suiv. d'une not. s. l'élection de Léon XII, *see* CONSTANT (B.) &c. Mél. polit. &c., t2, 1829.
Guagninus (Alexander), *1548–1674.* Sarmatiæ Europeæ descr. Suppl. loco ea quæ gestá sunt superiori anno inter regem Poloniæ & magnum ducem Moschoviæ adjecta sunt; item genealogia regum Polonorum. fol. Spiræ. 1581
see CIPOLLA (C.), *ed.* Nuovo doc. rig. A. G., 1904.
„ —— Un Italiano n. Polonia e n. Svezia tra il 16 e 17 sec. [*A. G.*], 1887.
„ MOSCOVIA. Respublica M. [*taken f. A. G. & others*], 1630.
„ POLONIA. Respublica, P. &c. div. aut. (A. G. &c.), 1627.
Gualandi (Michel Angelo). Lettera di M. G. e risposta di A. Tessier int. a. G. Gherardini, U. da Carpi e F. Marcolini. [P2787]. 8°. Venezia. 1855
Gualdo, *Monachus Corbeiensis, see* REMBERT, *St.* S. Anscharii vita, altera metr. per G., 1677.
Gualdo Priorato (*il conte* Galeazzo). Hist. of the managements of Card. Mazarine. Tr. t1, pl. s8°. 1671
Gualtherus (Rodolphus), *see* WALTHER (R.), *the Elder.*
Gualtieri (Guido). Relationi d. venuta d. ambasciatori giaponesi a Roma sino alla partita di Lisboa. Racc. da G. G., 1586. fol. Schio. 1895
Gualtieri (Luigi). Mem. di Ugo Bassi, apostolo del Vangelo, martire dell' indipend. ital. 8°. Bologna. 1861
Guanzelli (Giovanni Maria). Indicis lib. expurg. t1 per F. I. M. B. [*i.e.* G.], 1607, *see* INDEX.
Guardi (Andrea), *see* SCHUBRING (P.) Urbano da Cortona &c., nebst e. Anhang: A. G., 1903.
Guardi (Francesco), *1712–93.*
see FIOCCO (G.) F. G., 1923.
„ SIMONSON (G. A.) F. G., 1910.
Guardia (Ferrante della Marra, *duca della*), *see* DELLA MARRA (F.)
Guardian (The) newspaper. v75–[81]. (1920–27). fol. 1920–27
Guardione (Francesco). Di P. Giannone e della "St. civile del Regno di Napoli." Con. App. di alt. scritti &c. 8°. Torino. [1921]
Guards' Brigade. Offic. rec. of the G.B. in S. Africa. [Pref. by H. G. Ruggles-Brise]. 8°. 1904
Guarini (Filippo).
I terremoti a Forlì in varie epoche. s8°. Forlì. 1880
Guarini (Giovanni Battista).
Il pastor fido. [*Engr. by Lapi*]. s8°. Londra. 1778
Guarino, *of Verona* [GUARINUS, *Veronensis*], *see* BERTONI (G.) G. da V. fra letterati e cortigiani a Ferrara (1429–60), 1921.
Guarna (Andreas). *Bellum grammaticale. [*Abridged &c. f. earlier editions publ. w. author's name*]. s8°. Witebergae. 1580
Guarnerius (Joseph) [GUARNERI (GIUSEPPE ANTONIO)], *see* PETHERICK (H.) J. G., h. work & h. master, 1906.
Guarracino (Beatrice). The book of meals; catering, recipes, &c. [5th impr.] 8°. [1924]
Guasco (*le cte.* Octavien de), *see* KANTEMIR (A. D.) Satyres, tr. avec l'hist. de sa vie [*by O. de G.*], 1750.
Guattani (Giuseppe Antonio), *see* MONUMENTI ANTICHI, o. Not. s. antichità &c. per 1787 [*by* G. A. G.], 1787.
Guazzo (Stefano). Dialoghi piacevoli. 8°. Venetia. 1586
La civil conversatione. Di nuovo ristamp. e corr. s8°. Vinegia. 1577
„ „ ....Nuov. corr. & ampl. s8°. Venetia. 1607
Civile conversation. 1st 3 bks. tr. by G. Pettie, 1581, & 4th by B. Young, 1586. Intr. by Sir E. Sullivan. [Tudor Trans., s2]. 2v. 8°. 1925
Gubbins (John Harington). Japan, *see* FOREIGN OFFICE. Handbooks, No. 73, 1920.
The making of modern Japan. 8°. 1922
Gubernatis (Dominicus de), *da Gospello.* Antiquioritas Franciscana ad libram histor. veritatis exam. Opusculum ex tII Orbis Seraphici &c. coll. a F. Fortunato. [*B. w. h.* Orbis Seraph. t2]. fol. Lugduni. 1685
Orbis Seraphicus hist. de tribus ordin. a S. Francisco instit. 4t [*t4 has 2 pagin.*] fol. (1, 3, 4, Romae. 2, Lugduni). 1682–85
Orbis Seraphicus &c. De missionibus inter infideles. t1. fol. Romae. 1689

Guby (Rudolf). Die niederbayr. Donauklöster Niederaltaich &c. s8°. Wien. [1921]
Guddas (Adolf). Michael Styfel (1487–1567), Luthers intimer Freund &c. [P2688]. 8°. Königsberg. 1922
Gude (Gottlob Friedrich) [GUDIUS]. Bibl. disputat. & observ. de sel. hist. eccl. capitibus specimen. s4°. Lipsiae. 1743
De eccl. Ephesinae statu inprimis ævo Apostolico comm. Acc. vita S. Pauli per G. Majorem. s8°. L. 1732
Patres Concilii Constant. veritatis evangel. testes &c. [P2646]. s4°. Laubae. 1737
Gudeman (Alfred). Gesch. d. altchristl. lat. Lit. v. 2.–6. Jhdt. s8°. 1925
Guden (Heinrich Philipp) [†GUDENIUS (H. P.)] Diss. de Bonifacio German. apostolo. Praes. J. C. Böhmer. s4°. Helmstadii. 1720
Gudianum. Etymologicum G., fasc. 2, 1920, *see* STEFANI (E. L. DE), *ed.*
Gudiol (José). El pintor Luis Borrassá. la8°. [Barcelona. 1926]
Els Trescentistes, p2, *see* SANPERE Y MIQUEL (S.) La pintura mig-eval catalana, v2, p2, *n.d.*
Gudius (G. F.), *see* GUDE (G. F.)
Guðmundsson (Jón), *1574–1658, see* HERMANNSSON (H.) J. G. & h. Nat. hist. of Iceland, 1924.
Gudrun [KUDRUN], *see* KÖNIGL. GESELLS. D. W. ZU GÖTTINGEN. Nachr., phil.-hist. Kl., 1917–20. (Überlief. u. Textkritik d. K., v. E. Schröder).
Guébriant (Renée du Bec-Crespin, *maréchale* **de),** *d. 1659, see* LE LABOUREUR (J.) Hist. &c. du voyage de la royne de Pologne & du retour de Mme. de G., &c., 1648.
Guedalla (Philip).
Conquistador: Amer. fantasia. 8°. [1927]
A gallery. 8°. 1924
Independence day: a sketch-book. 8°. 1926
Masters & men. Essays. s8°. 1923
Napoleon & Palestine. [A. Davis Mem. lect.] Foreword by I. Zangwill, afterword by D. Lloyd George. s8°. 1925
Palmerston. 8°. [1926]
„ „ [2nd impr.] 8°. [1926]
The Second Empire. Bonapartism — The prince — The president—The emperor. 8°. 1922
Supers & supermen. St. in politics, hist. & letters. 8°. [1920]
Guéguen (Pierre-Julien).
Quelques vers franç. & bretons. 8°. Quimper. 1894
Guéhenno (Jean). L'évangile éternel: ét. sur Michelet. [Cahiers verts, s2, t4]. s8°. 1927
Gueinz (Johann Christian). De Aug. Confess. P. Dolscii cura Graece reddita. [P484]. s4°. Halis Sax. [1730]
Guelph, *the family of.* Mon. Welforum antiqua. Ed. L. Weiland. Rec. fecit G. H. Pertz. [Scr. rerum Germ. in usum schol.] 8°. Hannoverae. 1869
Guénin (G.) & J. Nouaillac. L'Ancien Régime & la Révol. 1715–1800. Préf. de G. Pagès. 8°. 1921
Guénon (René). Le théosophisme. 8°. 1921
Guépin (Ange). Hist. de Nantes. 2e éd. la8°. Nantes. 1839
Guéranger (Prosper Louis Paschal).
De la défin. de l'infaillibilité papale. [P2691]. 8°. 1870
Rép. aux dern. objections contre la Défin. de l'infaillibilité du pontif. rom. [P2691]. 8°. 1870
Guérard (Albert Léon).
French civiliz. to close of the middle ages. 8°. [1920]
Reflections on the Napoleonic legend. 8°. [1924]
Short hist. of the internat. language movement. 8°. [1922]
Guérassimoff (*Gén. major*), *see* GERASIMOV (*Major Gen.*)
Guerber (Hélène Adeline).
Myths of Greece & Rome. [repr.] 8°. [1921]
Guericke (Heinr. Ernst Ferd.) [†GUERIKE (H. E. F.)] Life of A. H. Franké. Tr. S. Jackson. Intr. pref. by E. Bickersteth. [App. cont. extracts f. wr. of F.] s8°. 1837
Guérin (Armande C. C. E.) [A. BÉJART, *aft. wife of Molière, aft. Mme. Guérin*], *see* LYONNET (H.) Mlle. Molière, 1925.
Guérin (Charles), *poet.* Premiers & derniers vers. s8°. 1923
Guérin (Eugénie de), *see* DUHAMELET (G.) Vie & mort d'É. de G., 1925.
Guérin (F. E.), *see* GUÉRIN-MÉNEVILLE (FÉLIX ÉDOUARD).
Guérin (G. Maurice de). Le cahier vert. Journal intime, 1832–35. éd. rev. sur les mss. de G. S. Trébutien & publ. avec notes &c. par A. Van Bever. s8°. 1921
see BROOKS (VAN W.) Malady of the ideal: Obermann, M. de G., & Amiel, 1913.
Guérin (Paul), *Camérier de Léon XIII.* Concile œcumén. du Vatican; s. hist., s. décisions en lat. & en franç. 2e éd. 8°. Bar-le-Duc. 1871

Guérin-Méneville (Félix Édouard), *see* CUVIER (*le b.* G. L. C. F. D. DE). Iconographie du règne animal de C., par F. E. G., 1829–44.
Guerin Meschino, *see* RISTORI (R. J.) Pozza, e il G. M., 1920.
Guerlin (Henri). L'art enseigné par les maîtres. Choix de textes préc. d'une ét. [t3]. 8º. [1920]
3, La composition.
Les châteaux de Touraine, Luynes, Langeais, Ussé, Azay. 8º. [1922]
Guernes de Pont-Sainte-Maxence, *see* GARNIER, *de Pont Sainte-Maxence.*
Guernsey (Samuel J.), *see* KIDDER (A. V.) & S. J. G. Archeolog. explor. in N.-E. Arizona, 1919.
Guéroult (Constant). Le luthier de Rotterdam [*& o. s.*] s8º. 1884
Guerra Junqueiro (Abilio Manuel). Verso e prosa. [Antologia portug.; organiz. por A. de Campos]. 2ª ed. s8º. Paris. 1921
Guerrazzi (Francesco Domenico). Lettere famigliari, con ricordi d. ult. anni suoi di G. F. G. 8º. Milano. 1924
Guerrero (Maria), *see* OLMET (L. A. DEL) & J. DE T. B. Los grandes españoles: M. G., 1920.
Guerrero (Teodoro) & R. Sepúlveda. Pleito del matrimonio entre T. G. y R. S., entend. en él como jueces &c. disting. escr. 4ᵉ ed. aument. con la 2a parte. s8º. 1880
Guerri (Domenico). Il Commento del Boccaccio a Dante: sua autenticitá e quest. crit. [App. all' ed. Scr. d'Italia, 96]. 8º. Bari. 1926
Guerrier (Edith). The Federal executive depts. as sources of inform. for libraries, 1919, *see* UNITED STATES: EDUCAT.
Guerrieri (Fr. Ferruccio). Per la storia di Terra d'Otranto. Notizia di doc. 8º. Lecce. 1896
Guerrini (Olindo) [*ps.* LORENZO STECCHETTI]. Postuma. Canzoniere di L. Stecchetti. 27ª ed. s8º. Bologna. 1909
Guessard (François). Les anc. poëtes de la France. Publ. sous la dir. de F. G. 10t. s8º. 1859–70

Aliscans.	[10.]	Gui de Bourgogne.	[1.]
Aye d'Avignon.	[6.]	Gui de Nanteuil.	[6.]
Doon de Maience.	[2.]	Hugues Capet.	[8.]
Fierabras.	[4.]	Huon de Bordeaux.	[5.]
Floovant.	[1.]	Macaire.	[9.]
Gaufrey.	[3.]	Otinel.	[1.]
Gaydon.	[7.]	Parise la duchesse.	[4.]

Guest (Carmel Haden). Children of the fog. s8º. [1927]
Guest (Flora Dodge), *wife of the Hon. L. G. W. Guest.* Laughter & tears. s8º. [1926]
Guest (Leslie Haden). The new Russia. 8º. [1926]
Stricken Russia. Health & disease in Soviet R. Repr. f. The Lancet, 1920. [P2516]. la8º. [1920]
The struggle for power in Europe, 1917–21. Econ. & polit. survey of Central St. & Russia. 8º. [1921]
Where is Labour going? s8º. [1927]
Guest (*Hon. Mrs.* Lionel), *see* GUEST (F. D.)
Guesviller (Gustave). Oreilles fendues. s8º. 1891
Guettée (*l'abbé* François René), *aft. Vladimir Guettée.* Hist. de l'Eglise de France. 12t. la8º. 1847–56
La Papauté schismatique, ou Rome dans ses rapports avec l'Église Or. 8º. 1863
Güettel (Caspar), *see* GÜTTEL (CASPAR).
Gueulette (Thomas Simon), *1683–1766.* Chinese tales; adv. of the Mandarin Fum-Hoam. Tr. T. Stackhouse. 2v *in* 1. [*pagin. contin.*] s8º. *Cooke. n.d.*
Guevara (Antonio de), *bp. of Guadix, & of Montenedo.* Aviso de privados ó Despertador de cortesanos. s8º. Paris. *n.d.*
see COSTES (R.) A. de G., vie & œuvre, 2p, 1925–26.
Gugitz (Gustav).
Giacomo Casanova u. s. Lebensroman. la8º. Wien. [1921]
Der weiland Kasperl (Johann La Roche). Beitrag z. Theater- u. Sittengesch. Alt-Wiens. s8º. Wien. 1920
see BLÜMML (E. C.) & G. G. Von Leuten u. Zeiten im alt. Wien, 1922.
Guglielminetti (Amalia), *see* PITIGRILLI. A. G., 2ª ed., 1922.
Guglielmo, *di Tiro, see* GUILLAUME, *de Tyr.*
Guglielmo, *de Vercelli, St., see* WILLIAM, *St., of Monte-Vergine.*
Guglielmotti (Alberto). Squadra ausiliaria d. marina romana, 1644–99. s8º. 1883
For another ed., see Storia d. marina pontif., v8, *below.*
Storia della marina pontificia. 10v. la8º. 1886–93
1, 2, Medio evo, 728–1499. 3, 4, Guerra dei pirati, 1500–60. 5, Le fortificazioni n. spiaggia rom., 1560–70. 6, Marcantonio Colonna, 1570–73. 7, Squadra permanente, 1573–1644. 8, Squadra ausiliaria, 1644–99. 9, Ult. fatti d. squadra rom. da Corfú all' Egitto, 1700–1807. 10, Atlante d. 100 tavole &c., 1458–1570.
Vocab. marino e milit. la8º. 1889

Guhl (Ernst) & W. Koner. La vie antique. Tr. F. Trawinski. p2, Rome. Tr. revue &c. par O. Riemann. Intr. par A. Dumont. 8º. 1885
Gui, *de Bourgogne, of the court of Charlemagne.* Gui de B., chanson de geste, *see* GUESSARD (F.) Anc. poëtes, t1, 1859.
Gui, *de Cambrai.*
see ARMSTRONG (E. C.) Authorship of Vengement Alixandre &c., 1926.
„ EDWARDS (B.) Classif. of MSS. of G. de C.'s Vengement Alixandre, 1926.
Gui, *de Nanteuil.* Gui de Nanteuil, chanson de geste; publ. P. Meyer, *see* GUESSARD (F.) Anc. poëtes, t6, 1861.
Guiard (Amédée). La fonction du poète; étude sur Victor Hugo. s8º. 1910
Guibal-Roland (—).
La vie polonaise. Obs. d'un commerçant. s8º. [1921]
Guibert (Joseph). Les dessins du Cabinet Peiresc au Cabinet des Estampes de la Bibl. Nat. Antiq.—M.-Age—Renaiss. fol. 1910
Guibert (Philibert). Medici officiosi opera. Nunc prim. Lat. reddita [*by* G. Sauvageon]. s8º. Parisiis. 1649
Guibertus, *abbas Novigentinus.* Autobiography. Tr. C. C. S. Bland. Intr. by G. G. Coulton. [Broadway Trans.] s8º. [1925]
Guibourg (Achille). *Relation de l'arrest. de Mme., duchesse de Berry. [P2772]. 8º. Nantes. 1832
Guicciardini (Francesco).
Counsels & reflections. Tr. N. H. Thomson. s8º. 1890
L'historia d'Italia. [*b. in* 2v]. s8º. Firenze. 1561
Il Sacco di Roma [*for this work, wrongly ascribed to F. G.*], *see* GUICCIARDINI (L.)
Guicciardini (Lodovico). Descr. de la cité d'Anvers. Tr. de F. de Belleforest, suiv. l'éd. plantin. de 1582, avec préf. de M. Sabbe & notice de L. Strauss. 4º. Anvers. 1920
Il Sacco di Roma descr. in 2 libri da Francesco [*or rather* L.] G. s8º. Colonia. 1758
Guidalotti (Diomede) [GUIDALOTTO]. *Potentia d'amore. Sonetti &c. [*b. w.* Casio dé Medici (G.) Libro, 1528]. s8º. Bologna. 1528
Tyrocinio de le cose vulgari de D. G.: Sonetti, Canzoni &c. 8º. [Bologna, *Caligula di Bazaleri.* 1504]
Guidarelli (Guidarello), *see* RICCI (C.) La statua di G. G., 1897.
Guide. *Guide des étrangers dans La Haye, 1837, *see* HAGUE (THE).
*Guide to current statistics, v1–5, 1924–27, *see* STATISTICS.
*Guide (The) to service: the groom, 1840, *see* STEPHEN (*Sir* G.)
Guides. *Hist. records of the services of the Queen's Own Corps of G. fol. Lahore. 1886
Guides Bleus, *see* MONMARCHÉ (M.) Vallée du Rhône &c., 1923.
Guides Diamant. Pyrénées. s8º. 1920
Guides Plumon, *see* PLUMON (E.)
Guidettus (Joannes). Directorium chori, a I. G. olim ed., restit. &c. a I. F. Massano. Acc. quamplures Hymnorum & Antiphonarum toni &c. s4º. Romae. 1604
Guidi, *The family of, see* AMMIRATO (S.) Albero e ist. d. fam. de Conti G., 1640.
Guidi (Ignazio). L'Arabie antéislam. s8º. 1921
Guidicini (Giuseppe). I riformatori d. stato di libertà d. città di Bologna, 1394–1797. Pubbl. dal figlio Ferdinando. [3v]. la8º. Bologna. 1876–77
Guido, *Aretinus.*
see BOTTONI (A.) Pomposa al tempo di G., 1883.
„ VIVELL (C.) Comm. anon. in Micrologum G. A., 1917.
Guidobaldo I, *da Montefeltro, duke of Urbino, see* LA SIZERANNE (R. DE). César Borgia & le duc d'U., 1502–3, 1924.
Guidobaldo II, *duke of Urbino, see* PACCIOTTO (F.) Lettere a G. II, ed. C. Promis, 1871.
Guiffrey (Jean). L'œuvre de P. P. Prud'hon, *see* SOC. DE L'HIST. DE L'ART FRANÇ. Archives, nouv. pér., t13, 1924.
Guiffrey (Jules Joseph).
André Le Nostre. Et. crit. 8º. [1912]
Les Caffiéri sculpteurs & fondeurs-ciseleurs, 17ᵉ–18ᵉ siècle. 8º. 1877
Les dessins de l'Hist. des rois de France par N. Houel. [Soc. de l'Hist. de l'Art Fr.] 4º. 1920
see COLISÉE, *Paris.* Livret de l'expos. du Colisée, préc. d'une hist., par J. J. G., 1875.
Guignebert (Charles).
Le Christianisme antique. s8º. 1921
Le Christianisme méd. & mod. s8º. 1922
L'évolution des dogmes. s8º. 1920
Le problème de Jésus. s8º. [1914]

Guigue (Marie Claude). Cartul. lyonnais: doc. inéd. p. serv. à l'hist. des anc. prov. de Lyonnais &c., 2t, 1885–93, *see* LYONS.

Guilbeaux (Henri).
Le portrait authent. de V. I. Lénine. 8°. 1924
W. I. Lenin. Übertr. unter Mitwirkung v. R. Leonhard. 8°. 1923

Guilbert de Pixérécourt (René Charles). Observ. sur les théâtres & la Révolution *& o. p.*, *see* ESTÈVE (E.) Ét. de litt. préromant., 1923.

Guild (William), *D.D., principal of King's College, Aberdeen.* The sealed book opened; explic. of Revelation. s8°. 1656

Guildford. *History of G. &c. 8°. Guildford, *Russell.* 1801

Guildford (Nicholas). Pageant of mediaeval England. s8°. 1923

Guildhall, *London, see* BADDELEY (J. J.) The G. &c., 3rd ed., 1905.

Guildhall Library. Cat. of London antiq. in the G. museum. Under dir. of Library Comm. 2nd ed. 8°. 1908
Cat. of the Lib. of the Corp. of the C. of L. 2v. la8°. 1887–9
Classif. of London lit. based upon coll. in the G. Lib. Pr. under dir. of the Lib. Comm. 8°. 1926
see ROSE (J. A.) Coll. of engraved portraits; cat. & exhib. at opening of the new library &c. of Corp. of London, 1872, 1874; further sel., 2v, 1894.

Guilford (Everard Leaver). Nottingham. s8°. 1920
Travellers & travelling in the M.A. 8°. 1924

Guilhem, *de Cabestanh* [CABESTAING; CABESTANY]. Chansons. Ed. A. Långfors. [Classiques fr. du m-â.] s8°. 1924

Guilland (R.) Essai sur Nicéphore Grégoras: l'homme & l'œuvre. la8°. 1926

Guillard de Beaurieu (Gaspard), *see* BEAURIEU (G. G. DE).

Guillaume, *de Cabestaing* [CABESTANY], *see* GUILHEM, *de Cabestanh.*

Guillaume, *de Dole, see* FÄRBER (E.) Sprache der dem J. Renart zugeschr. Werke "Lai de l'Ombre" &c., 1915.

Guillaume, *de la Tour, troubadour, 13c., see* TORRACA (F.) Le donne ital.—Su la "Treva" di G. de la Tor, 1901.

Guillaume I, *Longue-Epée, see* WILLIAM I, *duke of Normandy.*

Guillaume, *d'Orange.*
Larchanz (La chançon de Willelme). 8°. Freiburg i. Br. 1908
see ESCHENBACH (W. v.) Willehalm, *var. ed.*
,, MONIAGE GUILLAUME.
,, TUFFRAU (P.) La légende de G. d'O.; renouvelée par P. T., 1920.

Guillaume, *de S. Grégori, troubadour, see* BERTONI (G.) La "sestina" di G. de S. G., 1917.

Guillaume, *de Tyr.* Hist. d. guerra sacra di Gierusalemme. Tr. G. Horologgi. 8°. Venetia. 1610

Guillaume (Alfred). The traditions of Islam: intr. to st. of the hadith lit. 8°. O. 1924

Guillaume (James). Karl Marx, Pangermaniste & L'Association Internat. des Travailleurs de 1864 à 1870. s8°. 1915

Guillaume (Paul), *archiviste des Hautes Alpes, see* BERTAUD. Chartes de N.-D. de B., diocèse de Gap; publ. &c. par P. G., 1888.

Guillaumin (Emile). The life of a simple man. Tr. by M. Holden. Foreword by E. Garnett. s8°. 1919

Guillebaud (Charles William). The Works Council: German exper. in indust. democracy. 8°. C. 1928

Guillebert, *de Metz.* Descr. de la ville de Paris au 15e siècle. Publ. Le Roux de Lincy. [Trésor des pièces rares &c.] s8°. 1855

Guillemin (Jean Jacques). Le cardinal de Lorraine, s. influence polit. & relig. au 16e s. 8°. 1847

Guillems, *Seigneurs de Montpellier.* Liber instrument. memorialium. Cartul. des G. de M. Publ. par Soc. Arch. de Montpellier. [*Ed. w.* Intr. hist. par A. Germain]. 4°. Montpellier. 1884–86

Guillermit (*l'abbé* **A.**) Le Folgoat. s8°. Morlaix. 1922

Guillermus *Parisiensis, see* GULIELMUS, *Parisiensis, a dominican.*

Guillié (Sébastien). *Hist. du cabinet des Tuileries dep. le 20 mars 1815 & de la conspiration qui a ramené Buonaparte en France. [*Attrib. to* S. G. *& also to* J. Lingay]. 8°. 1815

Guillim (John). A display of heraldry. [*Added*] Reg. of all Knights of the Garter &c. by F. Nower. [4th ed. *incomplete, tp. wanting*]. la8°. [1660]

Guillim (John), *murderer, see* ASCHAM (A.) Process &c. in court of Spain upon death of A. A. &c. killed by J. G. &c., tr., 1651.

Guillon (Edouard), *rédacteur du "Reveil du Dauphiné,"* &c. Napoléon & la Suisse, 1803–15, d'ap. les doc. inéd. des Aff. Etrangères. s8°. 1910

Guilloteaux (Erique). La Réunion & l'Ile Maurice, Nossi-Bé & les Comores. s8°. 1920

Guilmeth (Alexandre Auguste).
Hist. d'Elbeuf. 2e éd. 8°. Rouen. 1842
Hist. du Havre. 2e éd. 8°. Rouen. 1842
Hist. d'Yvetot. 2e éd. 8°. Rouen. 1842
Hist. de Lillebinne, suiv. de not. sur St.-Valery-en-Caux. 2e éd. [*b. w. h.* Hist. du Havre, 1842]. 8°. Rouen. 1842
Notices hist. sur localités de l'arrond. de Dieppe. 8°. *n.d.*
Notices hist. sur quelques cantons du Havre & d'Yvetot, & de Neufchatel-en-Bray. p3, Neufchâtel. 8°. 1838

Guimannus, *Benedictine of the Abbey of St. Vaast, Arras, see* ARRAS. Cartul. de l'abbaye de St.-Vaast d'A.; réd. au 12e s. par G.; publ. &c. M. Van Drival, 1875.

Guimard (Marie Madeleine), *aft. Mme. Despréaux, see* GONCOURT (E. DE). La G., 1922.

Guimenius (Amadeus), *ps., see* MOYA (M. DE).

Guimerá (Angel). La pecadora (Daniela). Play. Tr. W. Gillpatrick. [Hispanic Soc. of Amer.] s8°. N.Y. 1916

Guimet. Guide-cat. du Musée Guimet. Les coll. bouddhiques (exposé hist. & iconogr.) Inde Cent. & Gandhâra, Turkestan, Chine sept., Tibet; par J. Hackin. 8°. 1923

ANNALES DU MUSÉE GUIMET.
BIBLIOTHÈQUE D'ART. t4, 5. 4°. 1910–12
see GUIMET (E.) Les portraits d'Antinoé au Musée G., 1912. [5.]
,, TCHANG YI-TCHOU & J. HACKIN. La peinture chinoise au Mus. G., 1910. [4.]
BIBLIOTHÈQUE D'ETUDES. t4, 28–34, 36. la8°. 1894–1926
see DUMÉZIL (G.) Le festin d'immortalité, 1924. [34.]
,, FRAZER (*Sir* J. G.) Adonis; tr., 1921. [29.]
,, —— Orig. de la famille & du clan; tr., 1922. [30.]
,, GAUDEFROY-DEMOMBYNES (M.) Le pèlerinage à la Mekke, 1923. [33.]
,, MACLER (F.) Le texte armén. de l'Évang. d'après Matthieu & Marc, 1919. [28.]
,, †MINAEV (I. P.) Rech. sur le Bouddhisme; tr., 1894. [4.]
,, OLTRAMARE (P.) L'hist. des idées théosoph. dans l'Inde, t2, 1923. [31.]
,, PRYZLUSKI (J.) Légende de l'emp. Açoka dans les textes ind. & chin., 1923. [32.]
,, SCHERBATSKY (T.) La théorie de la connaissance &c. chez les Bouddhistes taradifs; tr., 1926. [36.]
BIBLIOTHÈQUE DE VULGARISATION. t44. s8°. 1925
see MEILLET (A.) 3 confér. sur les Gâthâ de l'Avesta, 1925. [44.]
BULLETIN ARCHÉOLOGIQUE. fasc. 1, 2. 4°. 1921
1, Salle Édouard Chavannes. Missions E. C. (1907), V. Segalen, G. de Voisins & J. Lartigue (1914), V. Segalen (1917), 1921.
2, Asie centrale & Tibet. Missions Pelliot & Bacot. (docs. exp. au G.), 1921.

Guimet (Emile). Les portraits d'Antinoé au Musée Guimet. [Annales du Guimet. Bibl. d'art, t5]. 4°. 1912

Guiney (Louise Imogen).
see TENISON (E. M.) L. I. G.: apprec., 1921.
,, —— L. I. G., h. life & works, 1923.

Guiot, *de Provins.* Œuvres. Ed. J. Orr. 8°. M'ter. 1915

Guiraud (Jean). L'Albigéisme languedoc. aux 12e & 13e s., *see* PROUILLE. Cartul. de Notre-Dame de P., t1, 1907.

Guiraud (Jules). Dict. anglais-franç. 8°. 1926

Guisborough (John). A mirage of Sheba. s8°. [1923]
A song of Araby. s8°. [1921]

Guise (Anselm Verner Lee). Six years in Bolivia: adv. of a mining engineer. 8°. [1922]

Guise (Charles de), *cardinal* [CHARLES DE LORRAINE], *see* GUILLEMIN (J. J.) Le cardinal de Lorraine, s. infl. polit. &c. au 16e s., 1847.

Guiteras (Pedro Jose). Hist. de la isla de Cuba. Intr. por F. Ortiz. 2a ed. t1–3. 8°. Habana. 1927–28

Guitet-Vauquelin (Pierre). La passion aragonaise, nouv. inéd., *see* ŒUVRES libres, 28, 1923.

Guitry (Lucien).
Choses entendues, *see* ŒUVRES libres, 1, 1921.
Mlle. Carrière, de l'Odéon, *see* ŒUVRES libres, 9, 1922.
Souvenirs, *see* ŒUVRES (Les) libres, 24, 1923.

Guitry (Sacha). L'amour masqué. Comédie. s8°. 1923
Deburau. Comedy. s8°. 1921
Works in ŒUVRES libres.
Le grand-duc: pièce inéd., 1921. [1.]
L'illusionniste, comédie, 1922. [13.]
Le lion & la poule, 1924. [37.]
Le mari, la femme & l'amant, 1921. [3.]
La pèlerine écossaise, 1922. [7.]
Un type dans le genre de Napoléon, 1923. [20.]

Guizot (François P. G.), *see* POUTHAS (C. H.) G. pendant la Restauration, 1814–30, 1923.

Gukovsky (Grigory).
Русская поэзия 18 века. 8°. Ленинград. 1927

Gulat-Wellenburg (W. v.), C. v. Klinckowström & H. Rosenbusch. Physikal. Mediumismus. la8°. 1925

Gulick (John Thomas). Evolution, racial & habitudinal. [C.I. of Wash., Publ. 25]. la8°. Wash. 1905

Gulielmus, *Arvernus, bp. of Paris* [GUILLAUME *d'Auvergne*]. Guillermus paris. de septem sacramentis [*printer's device* E. I. G. de Marnef *on tp.*] s8°. [*Paris. for De Manef.* c. 1490–1500]
88 leaves (83 numbered); sig. a–l in eights.

Gulielmus, *Parisiensis, a dominican, prof. of theology.* Postilla guillermi super Epistolas et Evangelia de tempore et sanctis. Et pro defunctis. [*Sometimes erroneously attributed to Gulielmus Avernus, bp. of Paris*]. [2p *in* 1v. 1, Super Evangelia. 2, Super Epistolas]. 8°. [Auguste, *Joh. Schensperger.* 1494]
a–m *in eights*; nl–6, n6 *blank & missing; foll. by* a–f *in eights*; g & h *in sixes*, h6 *blank. Coloured woodcuts.* p2, a *has arms of C. Raitt,* 1505 *engraved on recto.*
„ „ [*a. ed. tp. wanting*]. 8°. [Lugduni, *F. Fradin.* 1508]

Gulielmus, *Procurator Egmond.* Chronicon. Uitg. door C. Pijnacker Hordijk. [Hist. Genoots. Werken, s3, 20]. 8°. A. 1904

Gulizia (Nino).
Caltagirone. [Cento città, 83. P2860]. 4°. Milano. *n.d.*

Gull (*Mrs.* Beatrix), *see* BULSTRODE (*Mrs.* B.)

Gullan (M. A.) Theory & practice of nursing. 8°. 1920

Gullett (H. S.) Australian Imp. Force in Sinai & Palestine, 1914–18. [Offic. hist. of Australia in the War, v7]. 8°. Sydney. 1923
see BEAN (C. E. W.) & H. S. G. Photogr. rec. of the War: by Australian offic. photogr.: annot. by C. E. W. B. & H. S. G., 1923.
—— **& C. Barrett,** *edd.* Australia in Palestine. 4°. Sydney. 1919

Gullmann (Benedict). Ex hist. Augustana de S. Ulrico. Præs. G. Ludovici. [P599]. s4°. Lipsiae. [1693]

Gulson (John Reynolds). Philosophy of proof in its rel. to the Eng. law of judicial evidence. 2nd ed. 8°. 1923

Gulston (*Miss* Josepha Heath), *see* †GWYNNE (TALBOT), *ps.*

Gumbel (Emil Julius). Vier Jahre polit. Mord. 8°. 1922

Gumilev (Nikolai Stepanovich).
Дитя Аллаха. Арабская сказка. s8°. Берлинъ. 1922
К синей звезде: неизд. стихи 1918. s8°. [Берлин]. 1923
Колчан: 4-я книга стихов. изд. 2oe. s8°. П. 1923
Костер. Стихи. 2oe изд. s8°. П. 1922
Мик: африкан. поэма. s8°. Петроград. 1921
Огненный столп. s8°. П. 1921
Письма о русской поэзии. s8°. П. 1923
Французские народные песни. s8°. П. 1923
Шатеръ: стихи. s8°. Ревель. [1921]

Gummer (George), *J.P.*
Remin. of Rotherham. 8°. Rotherham. 1927

Gummere (Francis Barton).
Germanic origins. St. in prim. culture. 8°. 1892
Old Eng. ballads. Sel. & ed. by G. s8°. Boston, U.S. 1894

Gummere (Richard Mott).
Seneca the philosopher & his mod. message. 8°. [1922]

Gun (William Tounsend Jackson).
Studies in hereditary ability. 8°. [1928]

Gundert (Hermann). *Gesch. v. Württemberg. Hrsg. v. d. Calwer Verlagsverein. 3e A. s8°. Calw. 1865

Gundisalvi (Dominicus) [GONDISALVI; GONDISSALINUS].
"Von d. Hervorgange d. Welt" (De processione mundi). Hrsg. v. G. Bülow. [Beitr. z. Gesch. d. Philos. d. M.-a.'s, B24iii]. 8°. Münster i. W. 1925

Gundlach (O.) Bibliotheca familiarum nobilium. Repertorium gedr. Familien-Gesch. &c. 3eA. 2T. Neustrelitz. 1897

Gundling (Jacob Paul von). Teutsches Staats-Recht z. d. mittl. u. absonderl. Käysers Conrads III Zeiten. [*b. w.* Berger (F. L. v.) Opuscula, 1725]. s8°. Franckfurt. 1740

Gundling (Wolfgang). Annotat. in Concilii Gangrensis canones 20. s8°. Altdorfi. 1695

Gundolf (Friedrich). George. 2e unveränd. A. 8°. 1921
Goethe. [9e A.] la8°. 1920
Shakespeare u. d. deut. Geist. [5e A.] 8°. 1920

Gunkel (Hermann).
Ein Vorläufer Jesu. [*Isaiah* 53]. s8°. Bern. 1921
Wilhelm Bousset. Gedächtnisrede. [*w. bibliog.* P2498]. 8°. Tübingen. 1920

Gunn (Battiscombe G.), *see* ENGELBACH (R.) Harageh: inscr. by B. G., 1923.

Gunn (Hugh). Makers of the Empire. Ed. &c. H. G. [Brit. Emp., 8]. 8°. [1924]

Gunn (John Alexander).
Bergson & h. philosophy. Intr. by A. Mair. s8°. [1920]
Modern French philosophy: develop. since Comte. Foreword by H. Bergson. 8°. [1922]

Gunn (William), *F.G.S.* Geol. of Belford, Holy Island, & the Farne Islands, Northumberland. [Mems. of G.S.] 8°. 1900
Geol. of the coast south of Berwick-on-Tweed. [Mems. of G.S.] 8°. 1897
Geol. of the co. betw. Norham & Tweedmouth in Northumb. [Mems. of G.S.] 8°. 1897
—— **& C. T. Clough.** Geol. of part of Northumberland; w. petrolog. notes by W. W. Watts. [Mems. of G.S.] 8°. 1895

Gunnarsson (Gunnar). The sworn brothers. Tale of e. days of Iceland. s8°. [1920]

Gunnell (Doris). Sutton Sharpe & s. amis français. Avec des lettres inéd. la8°. 1925

Gunsaulus (Helen C.) Japanese costume. [Field Museum, Leaflet 12. P2736]. 8°. Chicago. 1923
Japanese New Year's festival, games &c. [Field Museum, Leaflet 11. P2736]. 8°. Chicago. 1923
Japanese sword-mounts in colls. of Field Museum, *see* FIELD COLUMBIAN MUSEUM. Anthrop. ser. v16, 1923.

Günter (Heinrich). Die röm. Krönungseide d. deut. Kaiser, *see* KLEINE TEXTE, T132, 1915.

Gunther, *Saint, a hermit, see* RÖNICK (J. T.) De G. eremita reform. sacr. necess. teste, 1759.

Günther (Adolf). Lebenshaltung d. Mittelstandes, *see* UNTERSUCHUNGEN ü. Preisbildung, Abt. C., 1920.

Günther (Albrecht C. L. G.), *see* PLAYFAIR (*Sir* R. L.) & A. C. L. G. G. Fishes of Zanzibar, 1866.

Günther (Friedrich). Der Harz. 2e A. la8°. Bielefeld. 1910
„ „ 3. A. bearb. v. E. Ambrosius. la8°. Bielefeld. 1924

Günther (Hans F. K.)
Rassenkunde d. deut. Volkes. 11e A. 8°. München. 1927
Rassenkunde Europas. 2e verb. A. 8°. München. 1926

Günther (Johann), *of Leipzig.* De religione Quietistarum. [P2630]. s4°. Lipsiæ. [1687]

Gunther (Robert William Theodore). Early Brit. botanists & their gardens, based on unpubl. wr. of Goodyer, Tradescant & others. la8°. O. 1922
Early science in Oxford. 4v. 8°. O. 1923–25
1, Chemistry, mathematics, physics & surveying. 2, Astronomy. 3, The biolog. sciences—The biolog. colls. 4, The Philosophical Soc. [Trans., 1683–90].
„ „ *a. ed.* [Oxford Hist. Soc., 77, 78]. 2v. 8°. O. 1923
The gt. astrolabe & o. sci. instruments of H. Cole, *see* SOC. OF ANTIQ. OF LONDON. Arch., v76, 1927.
see APULEIUS, *Barbarus.* Herbal of A. B. f. early 12th cent. MS.; descr. by R. T. G., 1926.

Günther (Siegmund). Lehren d. Revolution. Zur Frage Reform oder Revol. [P2456]. 8°. München. 1920

Günther Thiele (Johann Carl). Philos. d. Selbstbewusstseins u. d. Glaube an Gott, Freiheit, &c. la8°. 1895

Güntter (Otto v.) F. Schiller: Leben u. Dichtungen. Abbildungen. sm. fol. L. [1925]

Guppy (Henry). Brief sketch of hist. of transmission of Bible down to the rev. Eng. version of 1881–95. 8°. M'ter. 1926
Reconstr. of the library of the Univ. of Louvain: Gt. Brit.'s contrib., 1914–25. [Repr. f. Bull. of John Rylands Lib., v10. P2818]. 8°. M'ter. 1926
see JOHN RYLANDS LIBRARY. Cat. of exhib. illust. hist. of transmission of the Bible, w. intr. sk. by H. G., 1925.
„ —— The J. R. Libr., 1899–1924: record; by H. G., 1924.

Guppy (Henry Brougham). Plant-distribution f. the standpoint of an idealist [*extr. f.* Linnean Soc. Journal, v44. P2416]. la8°. 1918

Gupta (S. N.), *see* LAHORE. Cat. of paintings in the Cent. Museum, L.; by G., 1922.

Gupte (Balkrishna Atmaram). Select. f. the hist. records of the hered. minister of Baroda. Coll. by B. A. G. 8°. Calcutta. 1922

Gurevich (S. A.) & N. P. Dmitrevsky. Законы о торговле. Сборник &c. под ред. А. М. Винавера &c. [т1]. la8°. Москва. 1922

Gurimenus (Matthæus Collinus), *see* COLLINUS (M.), *Gurimenus.*

Gurk (Paul). Meister Eckehart. [*fiction*]. s8°. Trier. 1925

Gurker Geschichtsquellen, 864–1269; hrsg. v. A. v. Jaksch, *see* CARINTHIA. Mon. hist. duc. Car., B1, 2, 1896–98.

Gurlitt (Cornelius). August d. Starke: e. Fürstenleben aus d. Zeit d. deut. Barock. 2B. 8°. Dresden. 1924
Kunst u. Künstler am Vorabend d. Reformation. [Verein f. Ref.-gesch. Schr., Jhrg. 7, Nr. 29]. 8°. Halle. 1890
see CLEMEN (P.) & C. G. Klosterbauten d. Cistercien. in Belgien, 1916.

Gurner (Ronald). The day-boy. s8°. 1924

Gurney, *The family of.*
see GURNEY (D.) Rec. of House of Gournay, 1848–58.
„ LUBBOCK (P.) Earlham: [*Gurneys of E.*], 1922.

Gurney (Daniel). Record of the House of Gournay. 1v & suppl. [*p.p.*] 4°. 1848–58

Gurney (John Henry).
Early annals of ornithology. 8°. 1921
The gannet. 8°. 1913

Gurov (P. Ya.) Состояние сельского хозяйства С.С.С.Р. &c. [P2823]. 8°. Москва. 1924

Gurowski (*Count* **Adam G.**) America & Europe. s8°. N.Y. 1857

Gurtis (F.)
Stimmen aus e. andern Welt. Hrsg. F. G. 8°. Radebeul. 1921
Voices f. another world. Ed. F. G. Auth. tr. by L. A. Clare. 8°. [1923]

Gürtler (M. Jos.) Die Bildnisse d. Erzbischöfe u. Kurfürsten v. Köln. la8°. Str. 1912

Gürtler (Nicolaus).
Historia Templariorum. ed. 2ª. s8°. Amstelædami. 1703

Gury (Joannes Petrus). Casus conscientiae. 8°. Ratisbonae. 1865
Casus conscientiae. Novis casibus aucti &c., opera J. B. Ferreres. ed. 3ª Hisp., corr. &c. 2t. 8°. Barcinone. 1914

Gusev (Aleksandr Fedorovich). Любовь къ людямъ въ ученіи Л. Толстого &c. [P643]. 8°. Казань. 1892

Gusev (Nikolai Nikolaevich). Жизнь Л. Н. Толстого: молодой Т., 1828–62. [Труды Толстовск. Музея]. la8°. Москва. 1927
"Замолчанное о Толстом" Ответ на стат. В. Ф. Булгакова. [P2850]. s8°. Москва. 1926
—— **& V. Chertkov.** Толстой и о Толстом. Новые материалы, ред. Н. Н. Г. [Толстовский Музей]. Сборник 1–3, [2, 3 ред. В. Г. Черткова & Н. Н. Г.] 8°. Москва. 1924–27

Gusev (Sergei Ivanovich) [GUSEV-ORENBURGSKY].
Въ приходѣ—Страна отцовъ, *see* SBORNIK. Сб. товар. "Знаніе" 1, 4, 1904–05.
Die Lehren d. Bürgerkrieges. 8°. Hamburg. 1921

Gusmão Navarro (A. de), *see* DORNELLAS (A. DE) & A. DE G.-N. Tombo hist. geneal. de Portugal, v1, 2, 1911–14.

Gussago (Germano Jacopo). Biblioteca Clarense: notizie ist.-crit. int. agli scrittori e lett. di Chiari. 2v. 8°. Chiari. 1820–22

Gustarelli (Andrea).
Le mie peccatrici. Novelle. s8°. Milano. 1919
V. Alfieri. [v] 1, Vita. s8°. Messina. [1917]

Gustavus III, *king of Sweden.*
see LEVERTIN (O.) Från G. III:s dagar, 4ᵉ uppl., 1916.
„ —— G. III som dramat. författare, 4ᵉ uppl., 1920.
„ —— Teater och drama under G. III, 1920.
„ TEGNÉR (E.) G. M. Armfelt, B1, A. och G. III, 1883.

Gustavus Adolphus, *king of Sweden.*
see ABELIN (J. G.) Arma Suecica: descr. belli quod G. A. contra Ferd. II exercitum gessit, 1631; Contin., 1632.
„ DRESIG (S. F.) De meritis G. A. in eccl. Luther., oratio, 1732.
„ EGELHAAF (G.) G. A. in Deutschland, 1630–32, 1901.
„ FREYTAG (G.) Bilder, B4 (Wehklage, *facs.*, 1632), 1925.
„ HART (B. H. L.) Gt. captains unveiled, 1927.
„ OSSIANNILSSON (K. G.) G. A. Magnus: Roman, 2d, 1916.
„ WITTROCK (G.) G. A.'s krigföring i Tyskland, 1632, 1927.

Gustavus Vasa, *king of Sweden, see* ROMER (R. C. H.) Spec. de G. I rerum sacr. instauratore, 1840.

Gusti (Dimitrie). Fiinţa şi menirea academiilor, *see* ACADEMIA ROM. Disc., 57, 1923.

Gutbirius (Ægidius). Lexicon Syriacum: omnes N.T. dict. &c. complect. Ed. &c. E. Henderson. [*b. w.* Bible: Syriac. Syr. N.T., 1836]. s8°. Londini. *n.d.*
see BIBLE: SYRIAC. Nov. Test. Syr., ed. accur. A. G., 1664.

Gutenberg Jahrbuch, 1927. Hrsg. A. Ruppel. la8°. Mainz. 1927

Gutenberg (Johann). Gedenkblaetter z. G.- feier am 50. Jahrestage d. Erricht. d. G.-denkmals zu Mainz. [*By var. a^s.*] Hrsg. v. d. verein. Mainzer Buchdruckern &c. [*var. pagin.*] 4°. [Mainz]. 1887
The Gutenberg Bible. The Melk copy. Descr. by S. de Ricci. Sold, Anderson Gall. [Illust. P2853]. la8°. 1926

Gutenberg (Johann) [*continued*].
Gutenbergs erster Druck, Facsimile d. ersten Seite. Hrsg. v. O. F. Wehrhan. fol. *n.p.* [1855 ?]
see ZEDLER (G.) Von Coster zu G.: holländ. Frühdruck u. d. Erfindung d. Buchdrucks, 1921.

Güterbock (Carl). Bracton & his relat. to the Rom. law. Tr. B. Coxe. 8°. Phila. 1866

Güterbock (Ferdinand).
Mussolini u. d. Fascismus. 8°. München. 1923

Güthel (Caspar). Von Evangelischer allerbestendigsten Warheyt d. Antichristischen klugen hauffen erschröcklich. s4°. Zwickaw. [*Iörg Gastel desz Schönspergers diener von Augspurg*]. 1523

Guthrie (Charles John Guthrie, *Lord*).
Robert Louis Stevenson: personal remin. 8°. E. 1920
see ORR (R. L.) Ld. G., 1923.

Guthrie (James), *Minister, of Stirling, see* HENDERSON (A.) Lives of A. H. & J. G., 1846.

Guthrie-Smith (H.) Bird life on island & shore. 8°. E. 1925

Gutierrez de la Concha (Manuel), *Marq. del Duero, see* DUERO (M. G. DE LA C., *Marq.* DEL).

Gutkind (Erich). Siderische Geburt. Seraph. Wanderung vom Tode d. Welt zur Taufe d. Tat. la8°. [1914]

Gutman (Johannes), *see* JESUITS. Der Jesuiten Latein &c., 1608.

Gutsmann (Oswald).
Windische Sprachlehre. s8°. Klagenfurt. 1777

Guttinguer (Ulric).
Arthur (1836). Intr. de H. Bremond. s8°. [1925]
see BRÉMOND (H.) Le roman &c. d'une conversion: U. G. & Sainte-Beuve, corr. inéd., 1925.

Guttknecht (Georg Christian). De servorum Hebraeorum acquis. &c. disput. [P2666]. s4°. Lipsiae. [1704]

Guttmann (Jacob). Die Scholastik d. 13ten Jhdts. in i. Bezieh. z. Judenthum u. z. jüd. Lit. 8°. Breslau. 1902

Guttridge (George Herbert). Colonial policy of William III in Amer. & the W. Indies. 8°. C. 1922
David Hartley, M.P. [Univ. of Cal. Publ. in hist., v14iii], 1774–83. 8°. Berkeley, Cal. [1926]

Gutzkow (Carl F.)
Uriel Acosta. Trauerspiel. 11ᵉ A. s8°. Jena. 1882

Gützlaff (Carl F. A.) [CHARLES GUTSLAFF]. Remarks on the Siamese lang. [*Extr. f.* R. As. Soc. Trans. P2604]. 4°. 1831

Guy, *d'Ussel, see* USSEL. Poésies des 4 troubadours d'U.; publ. d'ap. les MSS. par J. Audiau, 1922.

Guy, *earl of Warwick, hero of romance.* Guy of Warwick. Nach Coplands Druck, hrsg. v. G. Schleich. [Palaestra 139]. 8°. L. 1923

Guy (Henry), *of Univ. of Toulouse.* Hist. de la poésie fr. au 16ᵉ s. t2, Marot & s. école. la8°. 1926

Guyard (Marie), *aft. Martin, see* MARIE, *de l'Incarnation.*

Guyard de Berville (——).
Hist. de Bayard. n. éd. s8°. Lyon. 1809

Guyau (Jean Marie). L'irréligion de l'avenir. 21ᵉ éd. 8°. 1921

Guyer (Samuel). Rusāfah, *see* SARRE (F.) & E. HERZFELD. Archäolog. Reise im Euphrat- u. Tigris-Gebiet, B2, 1920.
see SPANNER (H.) & S. G. Ruṣâfa, 1926.

Guyho (Corentin), *see* EGLISE. *L'église & la République; avec. préf. par C. G., [1877].

Guynemer (Paul), *see* ROYALLIEU. Cartul.; [*ed. w.* Intr.] par P. G., 1911.

Guyon (*abbé* **Claude-Marie),** *1699–1771.* Bibliothèque eccl., par forme d'instructions dogmatiques & morales sur toute la religion. 8t. s8°. 1780

Guyon (*Mme.* **Jeanne Marie)** [GUION; GYON].
L'ame amante de son Dieu dans les emblèmes de H. Hugo & dans ceux d'O. Vænius sur l'amour divin. Figures nouv. accomp. de vers. Nouv. éd. augm. s8°. 1790
Discours chrétiens &c. n. éd. 2t. s8°. 1790
Justific. de la doct. de Mme. Guion écr. par elle-même. Avec un examen de la 9 & 10 conf. de Cassien s. l'état fixé de l'oraison contin. par Mr. de Fénelon. 3t. s8°. 1790
Poésies & cantiques spirituelles. 4t. s8°. 1790
La Sainte Bible avec des explications &c. 20t *in* 11v. s8°. 1790
Tractatus myst., cum animadv J. W. Jägeri. [P443]. s4°. Tubingae. 1715
Vie de Mme. G. par elle-même. 3p *in* 1v. s8°. Cologne. 1720
see SONNTAG (C.) Gyonismus confutatus, 1717.
„ WESLEY (J.) An extr. of the life of Madam Guion, 1776

Guyot (Charles). La légende de la ville d'Ys. 5ᵉ éd. s8°. [1926

Guyot (Edouard). H. G. Wells. s8°. 192[illegible]

Guyot (Yves). Political obstacles to the econ. future of the Continent. Addr., Nat. Lib. Club. [*Fr. & Eng.*] [P2493]. 8°. [1920]
Politique parlementaire & politique atavique. s8°. 1924
Guy's Cork almanac & directory, 1919. 8°. Cork. [1919]
Guys (Constantin), *see* GEFFROY (G.) C. G., l'historien du Second Emp., 1920.
Guys (Henri Pellissier-), *see* PELLISSIER-GUYS (H.)
Guzman (Juan P. de). Crón. de la prov. de Cáceres, 1870, *see* ESPAÑA. Crón. gen., v11, 1865 &c.
Gwalior. Admin. of the G. State dur. 1919–20. (1st July–30th June). fol. Lashkar. 1921
Gwatkin-Williams (Rupert Stanley) [*ps.* STANLEY (RUPERT)].
Under the black ensign. 8°. [1922]
Gwilt (Joseph). Rudiments of a gram. of the Anglo-Saxon tongue. 8°. 1829
Gwyer (Maurice Linford), *see* ANSON (*Sir* W. R.) Princ. of law of contract; 16th ed. by M. L. G., 1923.
Gwyn (Nell) [GWYNN], *see* DASENT (A. I.) N. G., 1650–87, 1924.
Gwynn (Aubrey Osborn).
Roman educ. f. Cicero to Quintilian. 8°. O. 1926
Gwynn (Denis).
The "Action Française" condemnation. 8°. [1928]
The catholic reaction in France. 8°. N.Y. 1924
Gwynn (Edward John). The metrical Dindshenchas. [Text, tr. & comm. by E. G.] [R.I. Acad.: Todd Lect. Ser., 11]. p4. 8°. D. 1924
see DUBLIN UNIV.: TRIN. COLL. Cat. of Irish MSS.; comp. by T. K. Abbott & E. J. G., 1921.
Gwynn (J. T.)
Indian politics: a survey. Intr. by Ld. Meston. 8°. [1924]

Gwynn (Stephen Lucius).
The case for Home Rule. Intr. by J. E. Redmond. 8°. 1911
Experiences of a literary man. 8°. [1926]
Hist. of Ireland. 8°. 1923
In praise of France. 8°. [1927]
Ireland. Intr. by H. A. L. Fisher. 8°. 1924
Irish books & Irish people. s8°. D. [1919]
The Irish situation. s8°. [1921]
John Redmond's last years. 8°. 1919
Student's hist. of Ireland. s8°. 1925
Gwynne (H. A.) The cause of the world unrest. With Intr. by the Editor of The Morning Post [*i.e.* H. A. G.] 8°. 1920
Gwynne (Walker), *D.D.* Divorce in Amer. under state & church. Intr. by Bp. of N.Y. 8°. N.Y. 1925
Gwynne-Vaughan (*Dame* **Helen Charlotte Isabella) & B. Barnes.**
Structure & development of the fungi. 8°. C. 1927
Gyarmathi (Samuel). Affinitas ling. Hungar. cum ling. Fennicae orig. Nec non vocab. dialect. Tataric. & Slavic. cum Hung. comp. 8°. Gottingae. 1799
Gyles (Henry), *glass-painter; c. 1640–1709, see* KNOWLES (J. A.) H. G., glass-painter of York, 1923.
Gyllenband (Woldemar *Graf* **Uxkull-),** *see* UXKULL-GYLLENBAND (W., *Graf*).
Gyon (*Mme.* **Jeanne Marie),** *see* GUYON.
Gyp, *ps.* [*i.e. la ctesse.* S. G. M. A. DE MARTEL DE JANVILLE].
Mon ami Pierrot. Conte bleu. s8°. [1925]
Souv. d'une petite fille. [23e éd.] [t]1. s8°. [1927]
Gypsy Lore Society. Journal. N.S., v8, 9 (1914–16), 3rd ser., v1–6 (1922–27). la8°. *p.p.* E. 1915–27
see MACALISTER (*Sir* D.) Rom. versions, 1928. [Monogr. 5].
Gyurkovechky (Victor v.) Warum Tolstoy Liebe verachtet u. Aerzte hasst? [P643]. 8°. Wien. 1892

H

H. (C.) *A choice coll. of hymns, 1776, *see* HULL (C.)
H. (C.) *How we fared in Algeria, 1875, *see* ALGERIA.
H. (D.) G. Clausen: [descr. &c. signed D. H.], 1923, *see* CLAUSEN (G.)
H. (H. M.) Indian policy & Eng. justice, 1875, *see* INDIAN.
H. (J.) Epistolæ Ho-Elianæ, 1645, *see* HOWELL (J.)
H. (J.) *Hermes: or, philos. inq. conc. lang. &c., 1751, *see* HARRIS (JAMES).
H. (J.) *Hist. of the life &c. of Sir T. More, 1662, *see* HODDESDON (J.)
H. (J.) Manuscript writing & lettering [foreword signed J. H.], 1918, *see* HOGG (J.), *publ.*
H. (J.) *Orig. poems in the moral, &c. styles, 14th ed., 1833, *see* HUGMAN (J.)
H. (J.) *The Passion sermon, Paules Crosse, Apr. 14, 1609, by I. H., *see* HALL (J.), *bp.*
*Pharisaisme & Xtianitie compared &c. in a sermon at Paules Crosse, May 1, 1608, by I. H., *see* HALL (J.), *bp.*
H. (J.) *Present state of Eng. as to coin & public charges, 1697, *see* HODGES (J.)
H. (J. G.), *see* HERING (JOHANN GOTTFRIED).
H. (K.) *Bücherschatz d. deut. Nat.-Litt. &c., 1854, *see* HEYSE (C. W. L.)
H. (L.) *The sacrifice of Spring, 1927, *see* HABERLY (LOYD).
*When Cupid wins none lose, 1927, *see* HABERLY (LOYD).
H. (N.) Amanda, a sacrifice to an unknown goddesse (1653), 1923, *see* HOOKES (N.)
H. (O.), *M.A.* Baptismal bonds, 1687, *see* HEYWOOD (O.)
H. (R.) The plant of renown, *n.d.*, *see* HAWKER (R.)
H. (R.) A treatise of the church &c., *see* PEEL (A.) Brownists in Norwich &c., about 1580, w. A treatise &c., by R. H. [*i.e.* Robert Harrison?], 1920.
H. (R.) *The war in New-England, 1677, *see* HUTCHINSON (RICHARD).
H. (R. F.) *Two right profitable &c. concordances, 1622, *see* HERREY (ROBERT F.)
H. (S. H. A.) *Hervey, bp. of Ely, & some others, 1050–1500, f. Domesday &c., 1923, *see* HERVEY (S. H. A.)
H. (T.), *of Malmesbury, see* HOBBES (THOMAS).
H. (T. G.) *Our parish, a medley, 1884, repr., 1925, *see* GEERING (T.)
H. (W.) *Catholic naked truth, 1676, *see* HUBERT (W.)
H. (W.) Some interest. partic. of the 2nd voyage of the Duff, by W. H. [W. Hargrove?], 1809, *see* DUFF, *missionary ship.*

Haagen (Carl Ernst Casimir). Diss. de Saxo-Vinar. Vigilantiae ordine. Praes. C. E. C. H., resp. J. W. Labes. [P428]. s4°. *n.p.* [1734]
Haagner (Alwin). South African mammals. 8°. 1920
Haanel (B. F.) Facts about peat. [Canada. Geol. Survey. P2753]. 8°. Ottawa. 1924
Haardt (Georges Marie) & L. Audouin-Dubreuil. Le raid Citroën. La prem. trav. du Sahara en automobile. Intr. de A. Citroën. 8°. [1923]
Haarhoff (Theodore). Schools of Gaul: st. of pagan & Xtn. educ. in last cent. of Western Empire. 8°. 1920
Haarlem. Cat. of pictures &c. in Frans Hals Gallery. s8°. [Haarlem]. 1914
Haarlem (Geertgen van), *see* GERARDUS, *van Harlem.*
Haas (Arthur).
The new physics. Auth. tr. by R. W. Lawson. s8°. [1923]
Haas (Paul) & T. G. Hill. Intr. to the chemistry of plant products. v2, Metabolic processes. 8°. 1922
Haas (Rudolf de), *see* DE HAAS (R.)
Haase (Felix). Die relig. Psyche d. russ. Volkes. 8°. L. 1921
Russ. Kirche u. Sozialismus. [P2600]. 8°. L. 1922
Haass (Ludwig Ernst Heinrich). Das hessische Postwesen bis z. Anf. d. 18. Jhdts. 8°. Marburg. 1910
Habana, Recommendations of, 1917, *see* AMERICAN INST. OF INTERNAT. LAW.
Habbels Kriegschronik, 1914–18, *see* ASPERN (C.) Illust. Gesch., 1914–19.
Haberdashers' Company. A manual for the use of the court of assistants of the H. C°. Comp. by J. F. Vandercom *& others.* s8°. 1828
Haberditzl (Franz Martin), *see* VIENNA. Die Einblattdrucke d. 15. Jhdts. in d. Kupferstichsammlung d. Hofbibliothek zu Wien; hrsg. F. M. H., 2B, 1920.
Haberkern (Eugen). Der Kampf um Sizilien, 1302–37. 8°. 1921
Haberkorn (John), *see* PSALMODIA Germanica; ed. J. H., tr., 1765.
Haberlandt (Arthur), *see* BUSCHAN (G.), *ed.* Illust. Völkerkunde, B2i, ii, 1923–26.
Haberlandt (Gottlieb). Gedächtnisrede auf S. Schwendener, *see* KÖN.-PREUSS. AKAD. Abh., Phys.-math. Klasse, 1919.
Haberlandt (Michael), *see* BUSCHAN (G.), *ed.* Illust. Völkerkunde, B2i, ii, 1923–26.

Häberlin (Franz Dominicus). Diss. sist. vitam, itinera & scr. Felicis Fabri &c. [P596]. s4o. Goettingae. [1742]
Elogium J. de Trocznova cognomento Zisskae. Moderat. J. D. Koelero. [P599]. s4o. Goettingae. [1742]
Haberly (Loyd). *The sacrifice of Spring : a masque of queens. la8o. Long Crendon. 1927
*When Cupid wins none lose. By L. H. la8o. Long Crendon. 1927
Habermann (Johann), *of Eger* [AVENARIUS (JOH.)] Liber radicum seu lex. Ebraicum. Denuo auct. &c. fol. Witebergae. 1589
Habermann (Max). Die Sozialisierung d. Kohle. [P2487]. s8o. Hamburg. 1920
Habershon (William G.) Records of old London, w. letter-press by H. fol. [1888]
Habert (Louis). Compend. theologiae dogmat. & moral. ad usum Semin. Catalaun. s8o. Venetiis. 1741
——, **J. Lemeur** *& others.* Consultation. [*on bull* Unigenitus. *Signed* Habert *& others.* P2659]. s8o. [Chaalons. 1717]
Ḥabīb ibn Aus (Abū Tammām), *al-Tai, see* ERPENIUS (T.) Gramm. Arab.; acc. excerpta anthologiae, quae inscrib. H. A. Temmam, 1748.
Habich (Georg). Üb. 2 Prometheus-Bilder angebl. v. Piero di Cosimo, *see* KÖNIGL. AKAD. D. WISS. ZU MÜNCHEN. Phil. Kl., Sitz., 1920.
Häbler (Konrad). Die deut. Buchdrucker d. 15. Jhdts. im Ausland. fol. München. 1924
Gesch. d. span. Frühdruckes in Stammbäumen. fol. L. 1923
Handbuch d. Inkunabelkunde. 8o. L. 1925
Maria Josefa Amalia, Königin v. Spanien. 8o. Dresden. 1892
Die wirtschaftl. Blüte Spaniens im 16. Jhrh. u. ihr Verfall. 8o. 1888
Habsburg, *see* HAPSBURG.
Hachberg. Regesten d. Markgr. v. Baden u. H. 1050–1515; hrsg. v. d. Bad. Hist. Commiss., Bl, 3, 4, 1892–1915, *see* BADEN.
Hachette & Cie. Centenaire de la lib. H., 1826–1926. Texte de R. Doumic. 4o. 1926
Häckel (Ernst H. P. A.) Das Leben in d. grössten Meerestiefen, *see* VIRCHOW (R.) & F. v. HOLTZENDORFF. Vorträge, H110, 1870.
Hacker (H. P.), *see* DARLING (S. T.), M. A. BARBER & H. P. H. Hookworm & malaria research in Malaya &c., 1920.
Hackett (Charles Wilson). Hist. doc. rel. to New Mexico, Nueva Vizcaya &c., to 1773. Coll. by A. F. A. & F. R. Bandelier. Span. texts & Eng. trs. Ed., w. intrs. &c. by C. W. H. [C.I. of Wash.] vl, 2. la8o. Wash. 1923–26
Hackett (James T.)
My commonplace book. 2nd Eng. ed. 8o. [1920]
Hackin (J.) Les scènes figurées de la vie du Buddha d'ap. des peintures tibét., *see* ACAD. DES INSCR. &c. Mém. conc. l'Asie Or., t2, 1916.
Sculptures gréco-bouddhiques du Kapiśa, *see* ACAD. DES INSCR. FOND. PIOT. Mons. & méms., t28, 1925–26.
see GUIMET. Guide-cat. du Musée G.: les coll. bouddhiques, par J. H., 1923.
,, TCHANG YI-TCHOU. La peinture chinoise au Musée Guimet, par T. Yi-T. & J. H., 1910.
Hackländer (Friedrich Wilhelm).
Das Geheimniss d. Stadt. 3B *in* 1v. s8o. St. 1868
Hackman (*Rev.* James). *Love & madness; the hist. & corresp. of Rev. J. H. & Martha Ray. [P2828]. s8o. [1805]
Hackmann (Hans). Die Wiedergeburt der Tanz- u. Gesangskunst aus d. Geiste der Natur. 8o. Jena. 1918
Hackney. Customs &c. of the manors of Stepney & H., 1736, *see* STEPNEY.
Hackney (Louise Wallace). Guide-posts to Chinese painting. Ed. P. Pelliot. la8o. Boston [Mass.] 1927
Hackspan (Theodorich).
Fides & leges Mohammædis &c. s4o. Altdorfi. 1646
Manuale theolog. Ex Msto Durriano. Add. prologo J. B. Bernholdi. Ed. noviss. s8o. Altorphii. 1742
Quadriga disput. de locutionibus sacris. ed. 2a auct. s4o. Altdorphi. 1649
Hackwood (Frederick William). Odd chap. in the hist. of Wednesbury. Repr. f. " W. Borough News," 1919–20. sm. fol. Wednesbury. 1920
Haco IV [HAKÓNARSON], *King of Norway* [*called the Old*], *see* JÓNSSON (F.), *ed.* Eirspennill, Hákon gamli &c., 1916.
Hacobian, *see also* HAGOPIAN.
Hacobian (A. P.) L'Arménie & la Guerre. Préf. du Vicomte Bryce. s8o. 1918
Haddington, *Earldom of, see* FRASER (*Sir* W.) Mem., 2v, 1889.
Haddington (Thomas Hamilton, *1st earl*), *form. Th. Ld. Binning, form. Earl of Melrose; 1563–1637.* Instrument of resignatioun of ye Temple-lands, Scotland, 5 Oct. 1614, *see* MAIDMENT (J.) & R. PITCAIRN. Nugae, 1822.
Haddon (Alfred Cort). The pract. value of ethnology. [*a. c. in* P2586]. s8o. 1921
The races of man & th. distrib. n. ed. s8o. C. 1924
Haddon (Archibald). Green room gossip. Foreword by R. D. B[lumenfeld]. s8o. [1922]
Haddon (Walter), *see* OSORIO DA FONSECA (J.), *bp. of Silves.* H. O. in G. H. libri tres, 1567; ed. 3a, 1576.
Haddow (J. G.) Amber. 8o. Liv'l. 1892
Haden (Francis Seymour). The rel. claims of etching & engraving to rank as fine arts. [P2589]. 8o. 1883
Hadfield (Emma).
Among the natives of Loyalty Group. 8o. 1920
Hadfield (James Arthur).
Psychology & morals: analysis of character. 8o. [1923]
,, ,, ...5th ed. 8o. [1925]
Hadfield (*Sir* Robert A.), *F.R.S.* Metallurgy & its influence on modern progress. la8o. 1925
Presid. address deliv. to the Soc. of Brit. Gas Industries. 8o. 1918
Work & position of the metallurg. chemist, also ref. to Sheffield. Address. la8o. 1921
Hadley (Arthur Twining).
The educ. of the American citizen. 8o. N.Y. 1901
Hadley (*Capt.* George).
Gramm. remarks on jargon of Hindostan. s8o. *n.p.* 1790
Hadley (H. E.) Magnetism & electricity. [repr.] s8o. 1920
Hadow (*Sir* William Henry).
Beethoven, *see* BRIT. ACADEMY. Proc., 1917–18.
Citizenship. s8o. O. 1923
A comparison of poetry and music. s8o. C. 1926
Hymn tunes. [Church Music Soc. Occas. papers, No. 5. P2871]. 8o. [1914]
Music. [Home Univ. Lib.] s8o. [1924]
Hadrian, *emperor of Rome.*
see DEHNER (S.) H. Reliquiae, 1; diss. philol., 1883.
,, HENDERSON (B. W.) Life & principate of the emp. H., A.D. 76–138, 1923.
,, HITZIG (H. F.) Stellung Kaiser H. in d. röm. Rechtsgesch., 1892.
see KORNEMANN (E.) Kaiser H., 1905.
,, MOTHERSOLE (J.) H.'s Wall, 1922.
,, PLEW (J.) Quellenuntersuch., 1890.
,, SCHURZ (G.) De mutationibus in Imp. Rom. ordin. ab Imp. H. factis, pl, 1883.
Hadzopulos (Angelos). Die Flüchtlingsfrage in Griechenland. [Texte u. Forsch. z. byzant.-neugr. Philol., Nr. 6]. la8o. Athen. 1927
Haecxs (Hendrik). Dagboek, Brazilië, 1645–54; med. door S. P. L'Honoré Naber, *see* HISTORISCH GENOOTS. Bijd., d 46, 1925.
Haedo (*fray* Diego de). Topografía e hist. gen. de Argel. [Soc. de Bibl. Esp.] [t]1. 8o. 1927
Haeger, *see* HÄGER.
Hægstad (Marius) & A. Torp.
Gamalnorsk Ordbok med nynorsk tyding. 8o. [1909]
Haemmerlein (Jean). Hist. du réveil relig. à Genève. Thèse, Strassbourg. 8o. Colmar. 1856
Haentzschelius (Joannes Godofredus), *see* HÄNTZSCHEL (J. G.)
Haeresiologica. Bibl. hist. h. sel. doct. virorum diss., 1723–29, *see* VOGT (J.)
Haeresis. *De h. abjuranda quid statuat eccl. Rom.-Cath., 1721, *see* WALD (S. G.)
Haering (Th.), *see* HÄRING (T. v.)
Haex (David).
Dict. Malaico-Lat. & Lat.-Malaic. 2p *in* 1v. s4o. Romae. 1631
Hafenreffer (Matthias). Doctrinæ Christ. summa ex M. H. locis communibus contracta à J. V. Andreae. [*MS. copy of 1614 ed.*] s8o. Tubingæ. 1614
Loci theolog. ed. 3a. s8o. Witebergae. 1602
,, ,, ...3a cura recog. s8o. Tubingae. 1606
Templum Ezechielis. fol. Tubingae. 1613
Haferung (Johann Caspar), *see* NEUMEISTER (E.) Articulus de justific. a corruptelis H. assertus, 1732.
Haffner (H. J.) Norsk bokfortegnelse, 1911–20. 8o. 1923–24
Haffner (Melchior), *see* XAVIER (F.) Vita S. F. X. iconibus illust., M. H. sc., 1691 ?.

Haffner (Vilhelm). Stortinget 1919–21, med 128 billeder. s8°. Kristiania. [1919]

Hafiz, *Shīrāzī,*
Memories of Hafiz. [Tr.] by R. Obbard. 8°. Lahore. 1921
Sel. f. the Rubaīyât & Odes of H. Coll. &c. & rendered into Eng. verse by a member of the Persia Soc. of London, w. acc. of Sûfi mysticism. la8°. 1920

Hafner (Philipp), *1735–64, see* ALKER (E.) P. H., e. altwiener Kömödiendichter, 1923.

Hagana [HAGANAE]. Bibliotheca H., 1768–77, *see* BIBLIOTHECA.
Symbolae litt. H., 1777–81, *see* SYMBOLAE.

Hagemann (Johann Georg). Nachr. v. d. fürnehm. Übersetz. d. Heil. Schr. in a. Sprachen &c. 2e verb. A. s8°. Braunschweig. 1750

Hagen (Ernst August). Norika, nürnberg. Novellen aus alt. Zeit. Mit Einl. neu hrsgn. v. P. Sonnekalb. s8°. L. [1910]

Hagen (Friedrich Caspar). Poetarum δημοπαθείαν, ed. F. C. H., commilit. J. G. Dieterico. [P445]. s4°. Vitembergae. [1703]

Hagen (Josef). Römerstrassen d. Rheinprovinz. [Gesells. f. Rhein. Gesch., 12, Erläut. z. gesch. Atlas d. Rheinprov., B8. *Maps &c. b. separately*]. 8°. (Maps, la. fol.) Bonn. 1923

Hagen (Maximilian v.) Deutschlands Bündnispolitik. Betracht. zu d. Mem. d. Frhr. v. Eckardstein. [P2578]. 8°. 1922

Hagenbach (Carl Rudolph). Entst. u. Schicksale d. erst. Baslerkonfession &c. 8°. Basel. 1827

Hagenbuch (Johann Caspar). Exercit., Ostiones, Galliae Celticae Osismios esse conjic., &c., *see* GRONOVIUS (A.) Varia geographica &c., 1739.

Hagendahl (Harald). Die Perfektformen auf-ere u.-erunt, spätlat. Kunstprosa, *see* KUNG. HUM. VET.-SAMF. I UPPSALA. Skr., B22, 1923.

Häger (August Friedr. Christian) [HAEGER]. Lotzes Kritik d. Herbart. Metaphysik u. Psych. [P2434]. s8°. Greifswald. [1891]

Hager (Joseph). De Vár Hunnorum pariter atque Hungar. disq. 4°. Londini. 1800

Hager (Michael). Antichristus sive oratio, adv. calumniam hæretic. nostrae aetatis &c. s8°. Friburgi Brisgoiae. 1583

Hägerström (Axel). Der röm. Obligationsbegriff, B1, *see* KUNG. HUM. VET.-SAMF. I UPPSALA. Skr., B23, 1927.

Haggard (*Lt.-Col.* Andrew Charles Parker).
Madame de Staël: her trials & triumphs. 8°. [1922]
Victor Hugo: h. work & love. 8°. [1923]

Haggard (*Sir* H. Rider).
Allan & the ice-gods. s8°. [1927]
Allan Quatermain. [repr.] s8°. [1926]
The ancient Allan. s8°. [1920]
Child of storm (Mameena). [pop. ed.] s8°. [1925]
The days of my life. Ed. C. J. Longman. 2v. 8°. 1926
Heu-Heu, or the Monster. s8°. [1923]
King Solomon's mines. s8°. 1887
Queen of the dawn. s8°. [1925]
Rural Denmark & its lessons. new impr. 8°. 1917
She. s8°. 1922
She & Allan. 2nd ed. s8°. [1921]
The treasure of the lake. s8°. [1926]
The virgin of the sun. s8°. [1922]
When the world shook. s8°. [1919]
Wisdom's daughter. s8°. [1923]

Hagiensis. Scripta adversaria collat. H. habitae a. 1611 inter quosdam pastores de divina praedestin. &c. Lat. fecit P. Bertius. [*2 pagin.*] s4°. Lugduni Batav. 1615

Hagiographica Graeca ined.; ed. B. Latishev, 1914, *see* LATISHEV (V. V.)

Hagius (Georgius). Disput. ex art. 2°. August. Conf. de blasphemia in Spiritum Sanctum. Sub præs. L. Hutteri. [P2640]. s4°. Witebergae. 1597

Hagopian (V. H.) [HAKOPEAN].
Dict. Eng.—Armenian. s8°. Cple. 1907

Hague (The) [HAAG, LA HAYE].
Bibl. du Palais de la Paix. Catalogue. Par P. C. Molhuysen & E. R. Oppenheim. la8°. Leyde. 1916
*Guide des étrangers dans La H. & environs. s8°. La Haye. 1837
Musée Royal de La H. (Mauritshuis). Cat. rais. des tableaux & des sculptures. [*Illust.*] 8°. La Haye. 1895
,, ,, ...2e éd. s8°. La Haye. 1914
Palace (The) of Peace at the Hague. [Internat. competition]. 6 premiated & 40 other designs. [76 plates]. atlas fol. 1907
HAGUE CONFERENCE.
Docs. rel. to the program of the 1st H. Peace Conf. Tr. [C.E. f. Int. Peace]. la8°. O. 1921
Final acts of the 1st & 2nd H. Peace Conf., w. draft convent. on a judic. arbitrat. court. [C.E. f. Int. Peace. P2676]. la8°. Wash. 1915
H. (The) convent. & declarat. of 1899 & 1907, accomp. by tables of signat. &c. Ed. J. B. Scott. [C.E. f. Int. Peace]. 3rd ed. la8°. N.Y. 1918

Hague (The) [HAAG, LA HAYE] [*continued*].
Instr. to the Amer. delegates to the H. Peace Conf. & their offic. reps. Ed., w. intr. by J. B. Scott. [C.E. f. Int. Peace]. la8°. N.Y. 1916
Proceedings: Conf. of 1899. Prep. under dir. of J. B. Scott. [C.E. f. Int. Peace. *2nd tp. dated* 1907]. la8°. N.Y. 1920
Proceedings: Conf. of 1907. Prep. under dir. of J. B. Scott. [C.E. f. Int. Peace]. 3v. la8°. N.Y. 1920–21
Each vol. has 2nd tp. dated 1907.
Proceedings: Conf. of 1899 & 1907. Index vol. [C.E. f. Int. Peace]. la8°. N.Y. 1921
Reports to the Hague Conf. 1899 & 1907. Ed., w. intr. by J. B. Scott. [C.E. for Int. Peace]. la8°. O. 1917
Signatures, ratific. &c. to the convent. & declar. of the 1st & 2nd Hague Peace Conf. [C.E. f. Int. Peace. Pamph. No. 3. P2676; 2750]. 8°. Wash. 1914
PERMANENT COURTS.
Bibliograph. list of publ. conc. the P.C. of Int. Justice. Prep. by J. Douma. Pref. by J. ter Meulen. [Lib. of the Palace of Peace]. 8°. The Hague. 1926
H. (The) Court reports. Awards &c., 1899–1907. Ed., w. intr. by J. B. Scott. [C.E. f. Int. Peace]. la8°. N.Y. 1916
H. (The) Court reports: Gt. Brit., Spain & France *v* Portugal, in the matter of relig. properties in Portugal. Awards rend. Sept. 2 & 4, 1920. Eng. tr. by the C.E. f. Int. Peace. la8°. Wash. 1921
N. Atlantic Coast Fisheries Tribunal of arbitr. const. under agreement, Jan. 1909, between U.S. & Gt. Brit. 4°. The Hague. 1910
see SCOTT (J. B.) An Internat. Court of Justice (1914), 1916.
,, —— The project of a P.C. of Int. Justice & Resolut. of the Advis. Comm. of jurists, 1920.
,, —— The status of the Int. C. of Justice, 1916.

Hague (William), *D.D.* Life notes, or, 50 years outlook. s8°. Boston [U.S.] 1888

Hahn (Hermann Joachim). *Das betrübte Dressden, Als Pred. H. J. H. von F. Laublern 1726 ermordet worden, Wobey gefüget e. Klag- u. Trost Ode [by Bellamintes, *ps.*] &c. [P596]. s4°. Franckfurt. 1726
De iis quae circa receptam de Sabbatho doct. a non-nemine nuper in dubium vocata sunt, dissert. Præs. G. F. Seligmann. s4°. Lipsiae. [1703]

Hahn (Johann Gottfried). Diss. de medicina Germanorum vet. [P1035]. s4°. Lipsiae [1717]

Hahn (Ludwig). Das Kaisertum. la8°. L. 1913

Hahn (Wilhelm).
Streifzüge durch Sowjetrussland. 8°. Wien. 1921

Hahnemann (Samuel Christian Friedrich), *see* CLARKE (J. H.) H. & Paracelsus, 1923.

Hahn-Hahn (Ida M. L. S. F. G. *Gräfin*).
Das Jahr d. Kirche. s8°. Mainz. 1854

Hahr (August).
Die Architektenfamilie Pahr. la8°. Str. 1908
Skandinav. adelsborgar, *see* KUNG. HUM. VET.-SAMF. I UPPSALA. Skr., B24, 1927.

Haïasdan, Le: organe de l'Assoc. patriot. armén. [*aft.* Assoc. anglo-armén. *in French & Armenian*]. Nov. 1888–Avr. 1892 [*in* 1v. Jan. 1889 *wanting*]. fol. Londres. 1888–92

Haid (Johann Jacob), *see* TREW (C. J.) Plantae sel., quarum imagines &c. in aes incidit & vivis coloribus repraes. J. J. H., 1750.

Haig (Axel Herman), *see* HOOD (R. H.) Ill. cat. of etchings by H., 1919.

Haig (David), *see* BRUNTON (G.) & D. H. Hist. acc. of the senators of the College of Justice, 1832.

Haig (*Field-Marshal* **Douglas Haig,** *1st earl*), *see* DEWAR (G. A. B.) Sir D. H.'s command, Dec. 1915–Nov. 1918, 2v, 1922.

Haig (Elizabeth).
The floral symbolism of the great masters. s8°. 1913

Haime (John), *see* WESLEY (J.) *Short acc. of God's dealings w. J. H., 1785.

Haimhrammus [HEMMERAMMUS], *episc. Ratisbon, see* CYRINUS [ARBEO], *episc. Frising.* Vitae SS. H. &c., 1920.

Hain (Ludwig). Repertorium bibliogr., in quo libri omnes usque ad 1500 enumerantur &c. [Helioplandruck]. 2v. 8°. Berlin. 1925

Hainaut [HENEGOUWEN]. Invent. du fonds de la cour des mortemains de H., 1915, *see* VERRIEST (L.)
De Rekeningen d. Graven en Gravinnen uit het Henegouwsche Huis. Uitg. H. J. Smit. [Hist. Genoots. Werken, s3, 46]. dl. 8°. Amsterdam. 1924

Haines (Charles Reginald).
Notes on the birds of Rutland. s8°. 1907

Hainisch (Michael). Wirtschaftl. Verhältnisse Deutsch-Österreichs. Hrsg. v. M. H., mit Beitr. v. L. Joas &c. [V. f. Sozialpol., B158]. 8°. München. 1919

Haitze (Pierre Joseph de) [*ps.* †PIERRE-JOSEPH; MAGNE AGRICOL].
Hist. de la ville d'Aix, Provence. 6t. 8°. Aix. 1880–92

Haji Ibrahim, *Sheikh, of Kerbala, see* CARTWRIGHT (*Sir* F. L.) The mystic rose f. the garden of the king: vision of Haji Ibrahim of Kerbala; [*tr. or rather wr.*] by F. L. C., 1899; 1925.

Hake (Henry M.) Some contemp. records rel. to Francis Place, *see* WALPOLE SOC., v10, 1922.
see BRIT. MUSEUM: PRINTS &c. Engr. Brit. portraits; by F. M. O'Donoghue & H. M. Hake, v5, 6, 1922–25.

Hakewill (George). An answere to the treatise by Dr. Carier, consider. by wh. he was moved to be reconciled to the Ch. of Rome [*&* An ans. to a second letter of Dr. C.'s. *w. sep. pagin.*] s4°. 1616

Hakluyt Society. Publications. 2nd ser. v47–60. 8°. 1921–28
see BARBOSA (D.) Book of D. B.; tr. &c., v2, 1921. [II, 49.]
,, BOWREY (T.) Papers, 1669–1713; ed. Sir R. C. Temple, 1927. [II, 58.]
,, CIEZA DE LEÓN (P. DE). The war of Las Salinas; tr., w. intr. by Sir C. Markham, 1923. [II, 54.]
,, FRITZ (S.) Journal of travels &c. in the river of the Amazons, 1686–1723, 1922. [II, 51.]
,, HARCOURT (R.) Rel. of a voyage to Guiana, 1613; ed. &c. C. A. Harris, 1928. [II, 60.]
,, HARLOW (V. T.) *ed.* Colonising exped. to the W. Indies & Guiana, 1623–67, 1925. [II, 56.]
,, LOCKERBY (W.) Journal, 1808–9, 1925. [II, 52.]
,, MANRIQUE (S.) Travels, 1629–43; tr. &c. C. E. Luard, v1, 1927. [II, 59.]
,, MONTESINOS (F. DE). Memorias antig. hist. del Peru; tr. &c. P. A. Means, 1920. [II, 48.]
,, MORTOFT (F.) F. M.: his book; travels thr. France &c., 1658–59; ed. M. Letts, 1925. [II, 57.]
,, MUNDY (P.) Travels in Europe & Asia, 1608–67; ed. Sir R. C. Temple, v4, 1925. [II, 55.]
,, MUNTANER (R.) Chronicle; tr. Lady Goodenough, 2v, 1920–21. [II, 47, 50.]
,, ÓLAFSSON (J.) Life, wr. by himself; tr. B. S. Phillpotts, v1, 1923. [II, 53.]

Hakluyt (Richard). Princ. navigations. [Intr. by J. Masefield. Everyman's Lib.] 8v [4–8 repr.] s8°. 1907–[26]
see WATSON (F.) R. H., 1924.

Hakopean, *see* HACOBIAN; HAGOPIAN.

Halász (Albert), *see* EDVI ILLÉS (A.) & A. H. Economies [*sic*] of Hungary *& o. wks. wr. in collab.*

Halbach (Kurt). Walther v. d. Vogelweide u. d. Dichter v. Minnesangs Frühling. 8°. St. 1927

Halbfass (Wilhelm). Die Seen d. Erde, *see* PETERMANNS MITT. Ergnzb. 40, 1925.

Halbherr (Federico). Rel. s. scavi del tempio d'Apollo Pythio in Gortyna, *see* REALE ACCAD. D. LINCEI. Mon. ant., v1, 1890.

Haldane (Elizabeth Sanderson).
George Eliot & h. times. 8°. 1927
Mary Eliz. Haldane (1825–1925). Ed. by h. daughter [*i.e.* E. S. H.] s8°. 1926

Haldane (*Lt.-Gen. Sir* **James Aylmer L.)**
A brigade of the old army, 1914. 8°. 1920
The insurrection in Mesopotamia, 1920. 8°. E. 1922

Haldane (John Burdon Sanderson). Callinicus. A defence of chemical warfare. 2nd ed., rev. s8°. 1925
Daedalus, or, science & the future. s8°. 1924
Possible worlds & o. essays. 8°. 1927
—— & J. Huxley. Animal biology. s8°. O. 1927

Haldane (John Scott).
see BROWN (W.), *ed.* Psychology & the sciences; w. contrib. by J. S. H. &c., 1924.
,, HARVEY SOCIETY OF NEW YORK. The Harvey Lect., 1916–17; by J. S. H. &c., 1918.

Haldane (Mary Elizabeth), *wife of Robert Haldane, see* HALDANE (E. S.) M. E. H., 1926.

Haldane (Richard Burdon Haldane, *1st visct.*), *of Cloan.*
The future of democracy. [P2493]. 8°. 1918
Human experience. s8°. 1926
The philosophy of humanism & of o. subjects. 8°. 1922
The problem of nationaliz. Intr. by R. H. Tawney & H. J. Laski. [P2520]. 8°. 1921
The reign of relativity. 8°. 1921
Speech in Parl., Mar. 8, 1906, on the policy of the army. [P2496]. s8°. 1906
2 speeches, 1906, on the policy of the army. s8°. 1906
see BELL (E. P.) War of democracy: Lord H. states Britain's case, *n.d.*

Haldane (Richard Burdon Haldane, *1st visct.*), *of Cloan* [*contd.*]
see BIRKBECK COLLEGE. B.C. centenary lect. [by H. &c.], 1924.
see BRADLEY (A. C.) B. Bosanquet, 1848–1923 [*by A. C. B. & Ld. H.*], 1924.

Haldane (Winifred Agnes).
A chord f. a violin. s8°. Chicago. [1896]

Haldeman-Julius (Emanuel) & *Mrs.* **Marcel H.-J.**
Dust. s8°. [1922]

Hale (Edward Everett). The man without a country & o. tales. s8°. Boston [Mass.] 1882

Hale (George Ellery). Beyond the Milky Way. 8°. N.Y. 1926
The new heavens. s8°. N.Y. 1922

Hale (Katherine) [*Mrs.* JOHN GARVIN]. Isabella V. Crawford. [Biog. sk., anthology, an apprec. &c. Makers of Canadian Lit.] s8°. Toronto. [1923]

Hale (*Sir* **Matthew).**
Contemplations moral &c. [*sep. tp. but pagin. cont.*] 2p. s8°. 1705
Extracts f. works, *see* WESLEY (J.) Xtn. lib., v29, 30, 1753.
see BAXTER (R.) Add. notes on life &c. of H., 1682.
,, BURNET (G.) Life & death of H., 1682.
see JACKSON (T.) Lib. of Xtn. biog., v3, H. by G. Burnet, 1838.
,, TRIAL. A tryal of witches at the assizes bef. Sir M. H., 1682.
,, WILLIAMS (*Sir* J. B.) Mem. of M. H., 1835.

Hale (*Miss* **Susan),** *see* APPLETON (T. G.) Life & letters; prep. by S. H., 1885.

Halem (Gerhard Anton v.) Vie du Comte de Münnich. Tr. de l'allemand [par J. F. de Bourgoing]. 8°. 1807

Halen (Arnoud van). Panpoëticon batavûm, Kabinet waar in de afbeeldingen van voornaame nederl. dichteren &c. En onder uytbreyding &c. door L. Bidloo. la8°. A. 1720

Haleole (S. N.) The Hawaiian romance of Laieikawai; w. intr. & tr. by M. W. Beckwith, *see* SMITHSONIAN INST.: B. OF ETHNOLOGY. Rep., 33, 1919.

Hales (A. G.) Golden Gorse. s8°. [1926]
Where angels fear to tread. s8°. [1918]

Hales (Alexander de), *see* ALEXANDER, *de Ales.*

Hales (John), *Canon of Windsor, "the ever-memorable."*
*Anonymi diss. de pace & concordia eccl. Ed. per I. Philalethen [*ps. i.e.* Samuel Przypkowski]. Ed. 2ª. [*b. w.* Przypkowski (S.) Vita F. Socini, 1651]. s8°. Eleutheropoli. 1630
Golden remains [*engr. tp. by W. Hollar. With h. & Balcanqual's* Letters f. the Synod of Dort, *w. sep. pagin.*] s4°. 1659
,, ,, ...With adds, 3rd impr. s8°. 1688
Hist. Conc. Dordraceni. I. L. Moshemius Lat. vertit, observ. auxit. Acc. ejusdem De auctoritate Conc. Dordr. &c. s8°. Hamburgi. 1724
Sev. tracts, added, letter to Archbp. Laud. s8°. 1716

Hales (William), *D.D.* Origin & purity of the primit. church of the Brit. Isles &c. 8°. 1819
A survey of the mod. state of the Ch. of Rome, w. obs. on the doct. of the Pope's supremacy. 8°. 1789

Halévy (Daniel). Le courrier de M. Thiers. D'après les doc. au Dépt. des MSS. de la Bibl. Nat. 8°. 1921
Vauban. [Cahiers verts, 21]. s8°. 1923
Vauban, builder of fortresses. Tr. w. notes by Maj. C. J. C. Street. 8°. [1924]
Visites aux paysans du Centre. [Cahiers verts, 4]. s8°. 1921

Halévy (Elie). L'Angleterre & son Empire. s8°. 1905
Hist. du peuple anglais au 19e s. [t]1–3 (1, 3e éd.) 8°. 1923
1, L'Angl. en 1815. 2, 1815–30. 3, 1830–41.
,, ,, ...Epilogue [t]1, Les impérialistes au pouvoir, 1895–1905. la8°. 1926
Hist. of the Eng. people. Tr. E. I. Watkin. [3v]. 8°. [1924–27]

Hale-White (*Sir* **William),** *see* WHITE (*Sir* W. HALE-).

Halford (Frederic M.)
Mod. development of the dry fly. [repr.] 8°. [1923]

Halhed (Nathaniel Brassey).
Grammar of the Bengal lang. s4°. Hoogly. 1778

***Hali** meidenhad. [E.E.T.S.,18], rev. ed., 1922, *see* HOLY.

Haliburton (Arthur L. H., *1st baron*) [*form. Sir A. Haliburton*]. Army organization. The Arnold-Forster scheme. [P2495]. 8°. 1905

Haliburton (Thomas), *see* HALYBURTON (T.)

Haliburton (Thomas Chandler) [*ps.* SAM SLICK], *see* CHITTICK (V. L. O.) T. C. H., 1924.

Halifax (George Savile, *1st marq. of***).**
A character of King Charles II &c. 8º. 1750
The lady's new-years-gift, or advice to a daughter. 4º. *Cayme Press*. 1927
Miscellanies. s8º. 1700
„ „ 8º. 1704
Halkett (*Sir* **James).** Tangier—1680: diary, w. intr. &c. by H. M. McCance, *see* SOCIETY OF ARMY HIST. RESEARCH. Journal, v1, spec. No., 1922.
Halkett (Samuel) & J. Laing. Dict. of anon. & pseud. Eng. lit. n. & enl. ed. by J. Kennedy, W. A. Smith & A. F. Johnson. v1–4. la8º. E. 1926–28
Halkin (Joseph) & E. Viaene. Les Ababua (Congo belge). Sociologie descriptive. 8º. Brux. 1911
Halkyard (Edward). The fossil Foraminifera of the Blue Marl of the Côte des Basques Biarritz. Ed. w. add. by E. Heron-Allen & A. Earland. [Repr. f. M'ter Lit. & Philos. Soc., v62, 1917]. 8º. M'ter. 1919
***Hall** marks on gold & silver articles, by D. T. W. la8º. 1925
Hall (A. Wilford). The problem of human life: embracing the " Evolution of sound " & " Evolution evolved." la8º. N.Y. 1883
Hall (*Sir* **Alfred Daniel).**
Agriculture after the War. [repr.] s8º. 1920
Fertilisers & manures. [repr.] s8º. 1920
Hall (Arnold) & F. Heywood. Shipping: guide to routine in conn. w. export. & import. of goods &c. s8º. *Pitman*. [1909]
Hall (Arthur Vine). " Table Mountain ": pictures w. pen &c., being an attempt in verse. 8º. Cape Town [London, pr. 1896]
Hall (Christopher Newman). The land of the Forum & the Vatican: Easter pilgrimage to Rome. s8º. 1854
Hall (Edgar Vine). In full flight. [*Poems*]. s8º. 1921
Hall (*Mrs.* **Edna Clarke).** Draughtsmen: E. C. H., H. Rushbury, R. Schwabe, L. Underwood. [Plates, *w. intr. signed* R. H. W.] la8º. 1924
Hall (Edwin T.) Dulwich, hist. & romance, 967–1922. 2nd & enl. ed. s8º. [1922]
see DULWICH COLLEGE. D. Picture Gallery: 1921 Suppl. to cat.; by E. T. H., 1921.
Hall (Eleanor Frances). Florence Nightingale. s8º. 1920
Hall (Ernest Frederick).
Coop. betw. Infantry & Artillery &c. [P2591]. s8º. 1912
Hall (George), *bp. of Chester*. *The triumphs of Rome over despised Protestancy. s8º. 1667
Hall (Granville Stanley). Jesus, the Christ, in the light of psychology. 2v. 8º. 1921
Life & confessions of a psychologist. 8º. N.Y. 1923
Morale, the supreme standard of life & conduct. 8º. N.Y. 1920
Senescence: the last half of life. 8º. 1922
Hall (H. Duncan).
The British commonwealth of nations. s8º. [1920]
Hall (Harry Reginald Holland). The anc. hist. of the Near East, to the Battle of Salamis. 5th ed. 8º. [1920]
see PEAKE (A. S.), *ed.* The People & the Bk., by H. &c., 1925.
„ UR excavations, v1, Al-'Ubaid: rep., by H. &c., 1927.
Hall (Henry Sinclair) & F. H. Stevens.
A shorter school geometry. 2p. s8º. 1924
Hall (Herbert C.) [JOHNNY HALL].
Barrack & bush in Northern Nigeria. s8º. 1923
Hall (Hubert). Brit. archives & sources f. the hist. of the World War. [C.E.] la8º. 1925
A repertory of Brit. Archives. Comp. for the Royal Hist. Soc. by H. H. p1 (England). 8º. 1920
Hall (J. A.)
The law of naval warfare. 2nd ed., rev. & enl. 8º. 1921
Hall (J. N. van). De viool van Cremona, naar F. Coppée—Nichtjes roman, naar P. Ferrier—Meisjesdroomen, naar E. Pailleron. 8º. Utrecht. 1882
Hall (J. P.) Caer Llugwy. Excav. of the Roman Fort betw. Capel Curig & Bettsw-y-Coed by H. 1st rep. ed. F. A. Bruton. 4º. M'ter. 1923
Hall (James), *murderer*. *A compleat hist. of the life &c. of J. H., executed for murder of J. Penny, Sept. 14, 1741. [P2828]. s8º. [1741]
Hall (James A.), *see* FARNHAM (D. T.), J. A. H. &c. Profitable sci. in industry, 1925.
Hall (John Carey). A decade of reform work in Japan, opening of 8 c. [Repr. f. Trans. of Jap. Soc., v15]. [P2463]. 8º. [1917]
Teijo's family instruction: a Samurai's ethical bequest, 1763. [Repr. f. Trans. of Jap. Soc., v14]. [P2463]. 8º. [1916]
Hall (John George). Hist. of South Cave & o. parishes in East Riding of Co. of York. 8º. Hull. 1892
Hall (*Sir* **John Richard),** *Bt.* The Bravo mystery & o. cases. [*incl.* George IV & the Jockey Club]. 8º. [1923]
Four famous mysteries. [Mystery of Tilsit—Strange story of Mr. Bathurst—Murder of Sir E. B. Godfrey—Murder of P.-L. Courier]. 8º. [1922]
see BARTLETT (A.) Trial; ed. Sir J. H., 1927.
„ THORNTON (A.) Trial; ed. Sir J. H., 1926.
Hall (John Richard Clark) [*ps.* W. B. BRADSTOCK].
Birth-control & self-control. [P2757]. s8º. 1923
Concise Anglo-Saxon dict. 2nd ed., rev. & enl. 8º. C. 1916
Eirenicon for Churchmen: or the crisis in the Church. s8º. 1902
Not at Gribbin's: chron. of talk & letters. s8º. 1911
see STJERNA (K. M.) Essays on questions conn. w. Beowulf; tr. & ed. J. R. C. H., 1912.
Hall (Johnny), *see* HALL (HERBERT C.)
Hall (Josef Washington) [*ps.* UPTON CLOSE].
The revolt of Asia. [repr.] 8º. N.Y. 1927
Hall (Joseph), *bp. of (1) Exeter, (2) Norwich.*
Works. [*Each w. sep. tp. pagin. cont.*] fol. 1647
[Characters of vertues & vices.] [*b. w. h.* Epistles, 1608]. s8º. [1608]
The gen. tp. is wanting, but each bk. has its own engr. tp.
Comparaison du Pharisaisme & Christianisme. Nouv. tirée de l'Angl. par T. Jaquemot. s8º. Geneve. 1628
Epistles. v1, 2 [*in* 1v.] s8º. 1608
Meditations & vows divine & morall, 2 bks. [*& A 3rd century, w. sep. tp. & pagin.*] s8º. 1606
Mundus alter & idem; fragm., tr., *see* MORLEY (H.) Ideal commonwealths, 1885.
*The Passion sermon, Paules Crosse, Apr. 14, 1609. By I. H. [*b. w. h.* Epistles, 1608]. s8º. 1609
*Pharisaisme & Xtianitie compared, in a sermon at Paules Crosse, May 1, 1608. By I. H. Upon Matth. 5. 20. [*b. w. h.* Epistles, 1608]. s8º. 1608
Recoll. of treatises heretofore sev. publ., now rev., corr. &c., w. add. [*Each treatise h. sep. tp. dated* 1614]. la8º. 1615
Roma irreconciliabilis, & Syllabum autorum qui Romam reconciliabilem statuerunt & Marci Antonii de Dominis consilium red. ex Anglia add. J. F. Mayer. [3 *pagin.*] s8º. Gryphiswaldae. 1706
Salomons divine arts, of ethickes, politickes, &c. With paraphrase upon the Song of Songs. [*w. sep. tp. & pagin. b. w. h.* Epistles, 1608]. s8º. 1609
Virgidemiarum: satires in six books. s8º. O. 1753
see ALDINGTON (R.), *ed.* Bk. of " Characters " f. Theophrastus, J. H. &c.; tr. &c., 1924.
„ JONES (J.) Bp. Hall, his life &c., w. some unpubl. wr., 1826.
„ MORTON (T.) De pace inter Evangelicos procur., a J. Exon. &c., 1638.
Hall (Joseph), *M.A.* Sel. f. Early Middle English, 1130–1250. Ed., w. intr. & notes by J. H. 2p. s8º. O. 1920
Hall (*Lady* **King-),** *see* KING-HALL (*Lady*).
Hall (*Lt.-Col.* **L. J.)** Inland water transport in Mesopotamia. Comp. by H. under dir. of R. H. W. Hughes. 8º. 1921
Hall (*Miss* **Magdalen King-),** *see* KING-HALL (*Miss* M.)
Hall (Maud R.) Eng. church needlework: hdbk. for workers &c. 2nd ed. rev. la8º. [1913]
Hall (*Mrs.* **Newman),** *form. Charlotte Gordon.*
Through the Tyrol to Venice. 8º. 1860
Hall (Peter), *see* CONFESSIONS. Harmony of Prot. Conf., n. ed. rev. &c. by P. H., 1842.
Hall (Radclyffe). Adam's breed. s8º. [1926]
„ „ ....[2nd impr.] s8º. [1926]
The forge. s8º. [1924]
Hall (Robert). Speech at the 7th anniv. of the Auxil. Bible Soc. 3rd ed. [P2543]. 8º. 1819
Hall (T. C. F.), *F.G.S.* Lead ores. 8º. 1921
Hall (T. Walter).
see SHEFFIELD. Descr. cat. of charters &c., part of the Wheat coll. at Publ. Ref. Lib., S.; comp. by T. W. H., 1920.
„ —— Descr. cat. of S. manorial records; comp. &c. by T. W. H., 2v, 1926–28.
„ —— Parish Reg.; transcr. & ed. by C. Drury & T. W. H., p3, 5, 1921–27.
„ —— S. & environs, 13–17 c.: descr. cat. of land charters &c.; comp. by T. W. H., 1922.
„ —— S. & Rotherham f. 12th to 18th c.; descr. cat. of misc. charters &c.; comp. by T. W. H., 1916.
Hall (Thomas).
see COLLIER (T.) The font-guard routed; ans. to T. H., 1652.
„ —— The pulpit-guard routed; ans. to T. H., 1652.

Hall (Thomas D.)
Some Transvaal soils. [P2820]. 8°. Pretoria. 1922
Hall (Thornton). Love intrigues of royal courts. 8°. [1912]
Hall (Trowbridge). Illust. cat. of first editions &c. incl. lib. of T. H. &c. [*w.* Baxter coll. of Thackeray letters]. Sold, April 20 &c., Amer. Art Assoc. [*w. typed prices.* P2855]. la8°. N.Y. 1921
Spain in silhouette. 8°. N.Y. 1923
Hall (William), *M.A.* Poems of a riper experience. s8°. [1922]
Hall (William), *stationer, see* WARD (*Col.* B. R.) Mystery of "Mr. W. H.," 1923.
Hall (William Clarke). Children's Courts. s8°. [1926]
Ḥallaj, *Al* [ABU 'ABDALLAH AL ḤUSAIN IBN MANṢOÛR *al Ḥallâj*], *see* MASSIGNON (L.) La passion d'al Hallaj, martyr de l'Islam, exécuté à Bagdad le 26 mars 922, 2t, 1922.
Hallays (André).
Avignon & le Comtat-Venaissin. 3e éd. rev. la8°. 1921
En flânant: A trav. la France: Autour de Paris. s2. s8°. 1921
" " Bourgogne, Bourbonnais, Velay & Auvergne. 8°. 1923
En flânant: de Bretagne en Saintonge. 8°. 1914
" " Touraine, Anjou & Maine. [7e éd.] 8°. 1923
Jean de La Fontaine. s8°. 1922
Madame de Sévigné. s8°. 1921
Les Perrault. s8°. 1926
Hallays-Dabot (Victor).
Hist. de la censure théâtrale en France. s8°. 1862
Hallbauer (Friedrich Andreas). Animadv. in licentiam novas easque German. Sacri cod. versiones condendi quum L. de Zinzendorf suam Novi Foederis interpret. publ. s4°. Jenae. 1741
Christl. Warnung vor d. römisch-päbst. Lehre, &c. s8°. Jena. 1742
Eccl. Lutherana politioris litt. patrona. Praes. F. A. H., resp. F. Horstmann. [P484]. s4°. Jenae. [1717]
Halle. *Beschr. d. Hall. Waisenhauses u. d. übr. Frank. Stiftungen. [*Pref. signed:* Schulze, Knapp & Niemeyer]. 8°. Halle. 1799
*Kurtze Nachricht v. d. Stadt H., u. v. d. Univ. [*b. w.* Leipzig, Kurtze Nachr., 1709]. s8°. [Halle ?]. 1709
Halle (Fannina W.) Alt-russische Kunst. la8°. [1920]
Halle (John), *merchant, of Salisbury, see* DUKE (E.) Prolus. hist.: essays illust. of H., v1, 1837.
Hallé (*Miss* **Marie Antoinette Caroline),** *see* †HAILE (MARTIN), *ps.*
Haller (Albrecht *Baron* **von),** *see* LISSAUER (*Dr.*) A. v. H. u. s. Bedeut. f. d. deut. Cultur, 1873.
Haller (Berthold).
see BERNE. Handlung oder Acta gehaltner Disput. zu B. [*betw. B. H., F. Kolb & o.*], 1528.
" ECK (J. v.) Ein Sentbrieve an ein frum Eidgenosschafft, betreff. die ketzer. disput. F. Kolben u. B. H. zu Bern, 1528.
" RATSCHLAG. R. halltender Disput. zu Bernn [w. Schlussreden *by* F. Kolb & B. H.], 1528.
Haller (Johannes), *historian.* Die Anfänge d. Univ. Tübingen, 1477–1537. Zur Feier d. 450 jähr. Bestehens d. Univ. &c. la8°. St. 1927
Aus d. Leben d. Fürsten Philipp zu Eulenburg-Hertefeld. la8°. 1924
Bismarcks Friedensschlüsse. 2e A. 8°. München. 1917
Die Epochen d. deut. Gesch. 8°. St. 1925
Hallett (Holt S.), *see* COLQUHOUN (A. R.) & H. S. H. Rep. on railway conn. of Burmah & China &c., 1885.
Hallett (Joseph), *see* PIERCE (J.) A paraphr. & notes on the Epistles of Paul, w. paraphr. of 3 last chaps. of Heb., by J. H., 1733.
Halley (Edmund), *see* MASERES (F.) Tracts on resol. of affected algebraic equations, 1800.
Halliburton (William Dobinson).
Handbook of physiology. [16th ed.] 8°. 1923
For earlier ed., see Kirkes (W. S.)
Physiology & national needs. [*By var. wr.*] Ed. W. D. H. 8°. 1919
Halliday (William Reginald).
Folklore studies anc. & mod. 8°. [1924]
Growth of the city state: lect. on Greek & Roman hist. 8°. Liv'l. 1923
Pagan background of early Xty. 8°. Liv'l. 1925
Hallier (François), *bp. of Cavaillon.* De sacris electionibus & ordinat. ex ant. & novo eccl. usu, *see* MIGNE (J. P.), *ed.* Theol. cursus, t24, 1860.
*Théologie morale des Jesuites & nouv. casuistes &c. [? *by* A. Arnauld *or* F. H.], 1666, *see* JESUITS.
Hallimond (Arthur Francis). Iron ores &c., *see* GEOLOG. SURVEY. Spec. rep. on min. res., v29, 1925.

Halliwell-Phillipps (James Orchard). New lamps or old ? A few addit. words. 2nd ed. 8°. Brighton. 1880
Palatine anthology: coll. of anc. poems & ballads rel. to Lancs. & Cheshire. Ed. J. O. H. 4°. *f.p.c.* 1850
see GOTHAM. Merry tales of the Wise Men of G., 1840.
Hallock (William A.) Mem. of Harlan Page. s8°. 1835
Hallström (Per).
Sel. short stories. Tr. F. J. Fielden. s8°. N.Y. 1922
Hallwachs (Johann Michael). Panegyr. de August. Conf. triumphis. [P484]. s4°. Tubingae. [1730]
Hallward (Norman Leslie).
William Bolts, a Dutch adventurer under John Co. 8°. C. 1920
Halm (Philipp Maria). Adolf Daucher u. d. Fuggerkapelle bei St. Anna in Augsburg, *see* JANSEN (M.) &c. St. z. Fugger-Gesch., H6, 1921.
Halmagrand (Charles Nicolas).
Origine de l'univ. [de Paris]. 8°. 1845
Halmi (Josef). Das schwarze Buch über Kecskemét. Vorwort v. A. Gábor. [P2492]. 8°. Wien. 1920
Halper (Benzion). Post-Bibl. Hebrew lit.: an anthology. [v]2, Trans. s8°. Phila. 1921
Halphen (Louis).
Etudes crit. sur l'hist. de Charlemagne. la8°. 1921
Hals (Frans).
see HOFSTEDE DE GROOT (C.) Echt of onecht? Oog of chemie?: beschouwingen van het mansportret door F. H. &c., 1925.
" STALEY (E.) F. H., 1909.
Halsbury (Hardinge Goulburn Giffard, *2nd earl of***).**
1944. s8°. [1926]
Halsbury (Hardinge Stanley Giffard, *1st earl of***).**
The laws of England.
" " Suppl. No. 18, bringing work up to 1927. [*This vol. incorporates & supersedes all prev. Suppl.*] 8°. 1928
Halse (Edward). Cobalt ores. 8°. [1924]
Mercury ores. 8°. [1923]
Halyburton (Thomas), *1674–1712, Prof. of Divinity in University of St. Andrews.* Mem. of H. With introd. essay by D. Young. 8°. Glasgow. [1824]
Mem. of the life of H. With app. [Ed. Janet Watson]. s8°. E. [1848 ?]
Natural religion insufficient &c. Wherein the writings of Lord Herbert are answered; annexed essays upon o. subjects. [2p in 1v, *sep. pagin.*] s4°. E. 1714
see JACKSON (T.) Lib. of Xtn. biog., v1, 1837.
" WESLEY (J.) An extr. of the life &c. of T. H., 5th ed., 1777.
Hamaker (Henricus Gerardus).
see HOLLAND. De rekeningen der Grafelijkheid van H. onder het Henegouwsche Huis; uitg. door H. G. H., 3d, 1875–88.
" ZEELAND. De rekeningen der Grafelijkheid van Z. onder het Henegouwsche Huis; uitg. door H. G. H., 2d, 1879–80.
Hamann (Chr.)
F. Schiller als Mensch u. Dichter. 2e A. s8°. Hamburg. 1903
Hamann (Richard).
Die deut. Malerei im 19. Jhdt. s8°. L. 1914
Hambach (Johann Nicolaus). Diatribe de orig. perverse sentiendi licentiae ex Bibliorum versione M. Lutheri non repetenda. [P2627]. s4°. Guelpherbuti. 1749
Hamberger (Julius Wilhelm Franz). Die Cardinalpunkte d. Franz Baader'schen Philos. [P2483]. 8°. St. 1855
Hambidge (Jay). Dynamic symmetry: the Greek vase. la8°. New Haven [U.S.] 1920
Hamblin (Robert A.) Eyes of innocence. s8°. [1922]
Hambly (Loveday), *c. 1604–82, see* HODGKIN (L. V.) A Quaker saint: L. H., 1927.
Hambly (Wilfrid Dyson).
The hist. of tattooing & its significance. 8°. 1925
Origins of educ. among prim. peoples. Pref. by C. Hose. 8°. 1926
Tribal dancing & soc. development. Pref. by C. Hose. 8°. 1926
—— **& T. Bedford.** Atmospheric condit. in boot &c. factories, *see* INDUST. FATIGUE RES. BD. Rep., 11, 1921.
Hamburg.
Ein Brieff d. Preger zu H. an die Theologen zu Wittembergk, v. Mitteldingen &c. Item, die Hist. v. güldenen Kalbe Aaronis, durch J. Westphal. Verdeudscht. [P2440]. s4°. Magdeburg. 1549

Hamburg [*continued*].
De rebus adiaphoris epist. concionatorum H. ad P. Melanchton &c., 1550, *see* MELANCHTHON (P.)
Epistola concionatorum H. eccl. ad theologos Witenberg. de adiaphoris &c. Item Responsio. [P2528]. s8°. [Magdeburgi. 1549]
*Hamburg. 36 Ansichten. obl.8°. Frankfurt a. M. [1912 ?]
Responsio ministrorum eccl. Christi, quae est H. & Luneburgi, ad conf. A. Osiandri, de mediatore Jesu Christo &c. s4°. [Magdeburgi. 1553]
STAATS- U. UNIVERSITÄTSBIBLIOTHEK.
Die deut. Bibel v. 15. bis 18. Jhdt. Ausstellung. 2e durchges. A. [P2686]. 8°. Hamburg. 1922
Mitteilungen. Neue Folge. B1. la8°. Hamburg. 1925
see LEMCKE (J.) V. Placcius, 1925. [1.]
Hamburgischer.
*H. Passquillanten-Putzer, Stuck 1–3. [P2594]. s4°. *n.p.* 1722
*H. Pfaffen-Putzer. 1es Stuck. [P2594]. s4°. [Hamburg ?]. 1722
Hamburgisches Kolonialinstitut.
Abhandlungen. B20. la8°. Hamburg. 1914
see CANAAN (T.) Aberglaube u. Volksmedizin im Lande d. Bibel, 1914. [20.]
Hamel (Hendrik). Rel. du naufrage d'un vaisseau holland. s. l'isle de Quelpaerts: avec descr. de Corée, *see* BERNARD (J. F.), *ed.* Recueil, t4, 1718 ; 1732.
Verhaal van het vergaan van het jacht De Sperwer en van het wedervaren d. schipbreukelingen op het Eiland Quelpaert en het vasteland van Korea, 1653–66 &c. Uitg. door B. Hoetink. [Linschoten-Ver., 18]. 8°. 's Gravenhage. 1920
Hamelius (Paul). Intr. à la litt. franç. & flamande de Belgique. 8°. Brux. 1921
Hamelmann (Herrmann). De impostura, fraudulentia &c. C. Pezelii &c. s4°. Tubingæ. 1592
De traditionibus apostol. & tacitis. [*b. w.* Erythraeus (V.) August. conf., 1565–67]. fol. Basileae. 1568
Hamer (Sam Hield).
A wayfarer in the Dolomites. [2nd ed. rev.] s8°. [1926]
Hamerling (Robert). Aspasia. 12e A. s8°. L. [1914]
see ROSEGGER (P. K.) Persönl. Erinnerungen an R. H., v. P. K. R., 1891.
Hamerton (Lucy). Olde Eland, w. ch. on antiqs. of E. by J. W. Clay. Pref. by E. Winter. s8°. Elland. 1901
Hamet (Ismaël). Hist. du Maghreb. 8°. 1923
Hamilton Palace.
H.P. Collection. Illust. priced catalogue. 4°. 1882
H.P. Collection. Cat. of pictures, works of art &c., sold, Christie, June[–July], 1882. [*Illust.*] 5 portions [*in* 1v, *pagin. cont.*] 8°. 1882
Hamilton (Alexander), *General, U.S.* Works: comprising official reports, The Federalist & Pacificus. 3v. 8°. N.Y. 1810
see BEIN (A.) Die Staatsidee A. H.'s, 1927.
„ BOWERS (C. G.) Jefferson & H.: struggle for democracy in Amer., 1925.
Hamilton (Alice). Indust. poisons used &c. in the manufact. of explosives, *see* UNITED STATES: LABOUR. Bull. 219, 1917.
Women in the lead industries, *see* UNITED STATES: LABOUR. Bull. 253, 1919.
—— **& C. H. Verrill.** Hygiene of the printing trades, *see* UNITED STATES: LABOUR. Bull. 209, 1917.
Hamilton (*Lady* Anne), *eldest d. of 9th duke of H.* Key to "Epics of the T'on"; [*by* J. D. Barnett], *see* AUNGERVYLE Soc. Reprints, s2, 1883.
Secret hist. of the court of Eng., f. access. of George III to death of George IV. 2v. 8°. 1903
Hamilton (*Count* Anthony). Fairy tales & romances. Tr. M. Lewis, H. T. Ryde & C. Kennedy. s8°. *Bohn.* 1849
Mém. du Chevalier de Grammont. Publ. avec intr. &c. par M. de Lescure. s8°. 1876
Mem. of the court of Charles II, by Grammont [tr. Boyer]. s8°. *Bohn.* 1864
see CLARK (R.) A. H.: h. life & works &c., 1921.
Hamilton (Arthur). Sources of the relig. elem. in Flaubert's Salammbô. [Elliott Monogr., 4]. 8°. Baltimore. 1917
Hamilton (Cicely). The old Adam. Comedy. 8°. O. 1926
Theodore Savage. s8°. [1922]
—— **& L. Baylis.** The Old Vic. 8°. [1926]
Hamilton (Cosmo) [C. A. C. HAMILTON, *form. Gibbs*].
Among those sailing. 3rd ed. s8°. [1927]
Another scandal. s8°. [1923]

Hamilton (Cosmo) [C. A. C. HAMILTON, *form. Gibbs*] [*contd*].
His friend & his wife. s8°. [1920]
His Majesty the King [Charles II. *Novel*]. s8°. [1926]
The rustle of silk. s8°. [1922]
Unwritten history. 8°. 1924
Hamilton (Elizabeth), *duchess of Hamilton, aft. duchess of Argyle* [E. GUNNING], *see* BLEACKLEY (H. W.) The beautiful duchess: E. G., 1927.
Hamilton (*Lord* Ernest William), *6th son of 1st duke of Abercorn.*
The Irish Rebellion of 1641. 8°. 1920
40 years on. 8°. [1922]
Old days & new. 8°. [1923]
Tales of the troubles. 8°. [1925]
Hamilton (*Lord* Frederic Spencer), *4th son of 1st duke of Abercorn.* The beginnings of Mr. P. J. Davenant. s8°. 1917
The days before yesterday. 8°. [1920]
Here, there & everywhere. 8°. [1921]
*The vanished pomps of yesterday. Remin. of a Brit. diplomat. 8°. 1919
„ „ ....n. & rev. ed. 8°. [1920]
Hamilton (George), *rector of Killermogh.*
A gen. introd. to the study of the Hebrew Scr. 8°. D. 1813
Obs. on the pres. state of the Roman Cath. Eng. Bible. 8°. D. 1825
Hamilton (*Rt. Hon. Lord* George Francis).
Parliamentary remin. & reflect. [v2], 1886–1906. 8°. 1922
Hamilton (Godfrey Heathcote).
Queen Square; its neighb. & instit. 8°. 1926
Hamilton (Harold Francis). Discovery & revelation: st. in comparative religion. s8°. 1915
Hamilton (Henry), *D.Litt.* Eng. brass & copper industries, to 1800. Intr. by Sir W. Ashley. 8°. 1926
Hamilton (*Gen. Sir* Ian Standish Monteith).
Gallipoli diary. 2v. 8°. 1920
The soul & body of an army. 8°. 1921
Hamilton (Ivie George Joseph). Outline of postal history &c., w. hist. of Post Office of India. 8°. Calcutta. 1910
Hamilton (J. A.) Dict.; explan. of 3500 Ital., French, German, Eng. &c. musical terms &c. With repr. of John Tinctor's "Terminorum mus. diffinitorium." Ed. J. Bishop. [47th ed.] s8°. *n.d.*
Hamilton (James Hamilton, 1st duke of) [*3rd marq. of H.; 2nd earl of Cambridge*]. The several speeches of Duke Hamilton, Henry, Earl of Holland, & Arthur Ld. Capel, upon the scaffold, 9. March [1648] &c. 8°. 1649
Hamilton (James Hamilton, 4th duke of). *A full & exact rel. of the duel fought on Nov. 15, 1712, betw. H. & Lord Mohun. [*&* Pharamond's Edict agst. duels]. [P2622]. s8°. 1713
Hamilton (Louis).
Ursprung d. französ. Bevölkerung Canadas. 8°. 1920
Hamilton (M.), *ps.* [i.e. *Mrs.* CHURCHILL LUCK].
Anne against the world. s8°. [1922]
Hamilton (Mary), *aft. wife of John Dickenson, see* ANSON (E. G.) & F. ANSON, *edd.* M. H. at court &c., f. letters &c., 1756–1816, 1925.
Hamilton (Mary Agnes). Folly's handbook. s8°. [1927]
Full circle. s8°. [1919]
The last fortnight. s8°. [1920]
Thomas Carlyle. s8°. [1926]
Hamilton (Patrick). Craven House. s8°. [1926]
Hamilton (*Hon.* Ralph Gerard Alex.), *Master of Belhaven, see* BELHAVEN.
Hamilton (Richard Winter), *1794–1848.* Horae et vindiciae sabbaticae: on the revealed sabbath. s8°. 1848
Missions. 8°. 1842
Revealed doct. of rewards & punishments. 8°. 1847
see STOWELL (W. H.) Mem. of R. W. H., 1850.
Hamilton (Vereker Monteith). Things that happened. 8°. 1925
Hamilton (Walton Hale) & S. May.
Control of wages. s8°. N.Y. [1923]
Hamilton (William) *of Bangour.*
Poet. works. Collated by T. Park. 2v. s8°. 1805
Hamilton (William) *of Fanet, Donegal.*
Letters conc. the northern coast of Antrim. 8°. 1786
Hamilton (*Sir* William), *9th bart., prof. of Logic.*
Lectures on metaphysics & logic. 3rd ed. rev. v1, 2, Metaphysics. 8°. E. 1865
Hamilton (*Sir* William Stirling), *10th bart.*
The army of Gt. Britain. la8°. E. 1871
Hamlet, *prince of Denmark, see* MALONE (K.) Literary hist. of H., v1, 1923.

Hamley (*Sir* **Edward Bruce**).
A chapter on outposts. 2nd ed. [P2602]. 8°. E. 1875
National defence: articles &c. 8°. 1901
The position on the Alma. In 7 sketches. obl. s8°. 1855
The war in the Crimea. 3rd ed. s8°. 1891

Hamlin (Alfred Dwight Foster).
A hist. of ornament. Renaissance & mod. 8°. [1923]

Hamline (Leonidas L.), *bp. of Method. Church in U.S.A.*
Works. Ed. F. G. Hibbard. 2v. s8°. Cincinnati. 1871

Hammann (Otto). Der missverstandne Bismarck. 20. Jahre deut. Weltpolitik. 8°. 1921
Der neue Kurs. Erinnerungen. s8°. 1918
The World policy of Germany, 1890–1912. Tr. M. A. Huttman. 8°. [1927]
Zur Vorgesch. d. Weltkrieges. Erinnerungen, 1897–1906. [Der neue Kurs, 2]. s8°. 1919

Hammer (Bertil). Humanistisk psykologi, *see* KUNG. HUM. VET.-SAMF. I UPPSALA. Skr., B24, 1927.

Hammer (Georg Friedrich). Disput. commemorans Crypto-Calvinianos Vitemberg. Praes. J. A. Calo. [P426]. s4°. Vitembergae. [1714]

Hammer (Simon Christian).
Ludvig Holberg & an Oxford student. [P2433]. 8°. O. 1920

Hammerich (Louis L.) Zur deut. Akzentuation, *see* KONGELIGT DAN. VID. SELSK. Hist.-fil. Med. B7, 1921.

Hammersley (Samuel Schofield).
Indust. leadership. Foreword by S. Baldwin. 8°. [1925]

Hammerton (John Alexander).
Memories of books & places. 8°. 1928

Hammond (Barbara).
see HAMMOND (J. L. LE B.) & B. H. *for wks. wr. in collab.*

Hammond (Charles), *Medium.* The pilgrimage of Thomas Paine & others in the spirit world. s8°. Rochester [N.Y.] 1852

Hammond (Charles Edward). Outlines of textual crit. appl. to the New Testament. s8°. O. 1872

Hammond (*Mrs.* **D. B.**)
Stories of scientific discovery. 8°. C. 1923

Hammond (Hans). Den nordiske Missions-hist. i Nordlandene &c. da Lappernes og Finnernes Apostel T. v. Westen. s8°. Kiøbenhavn. 1787

Hammond (Henry), *D.D.*
An answer to the animadv. [*of J. Owen*] on the diss. t. Ignatius's Epistles & Episcopacie [*& of the plurality of elders in Clement's Epistle &c. b. w. h.* Vindic. of the diss., 1654]. s4°. 1654
*Consider. of present use conc. the danger resulting f. change of our church-govt. [*b. w. h.* Of the power of the Keyes, 1647]. s4°. *n.p.* 1644
A contin. of the defence of Hugo Grotius. [*b. w. h.* Vindic. of the dissert., 1654]. s4°. 1657
*A copy of some papers past at Oxford betw. the a. of the Pract. Catechisme [*i.e. H. H.*] & Mr. Ch[eynell]. [*b. w. h.* Of the power of the Keyes, 1647]. s4°. 1647
Δευτέραι Φροντίδες, or, a review of the paraphrase & annot. on the New Test. s8°. 1656
Letter of resolution to six quæres of present use in the Ch. of England. s8°. 1653
*Of resisting the lawfull magistrate &c. [*b. w. h.* Of the power of the Keyes, 1647]. s4°. *n.p.* 1747
Of schisme, a defence of the Ch. of Eng. s8°. 1654
*Of the power of the Keyes: or, of binding & loosing. s4°. 1647
A practical catechism. 8th ed., added, The reasonableness of Xtn. relig. [5th ed., *sep. tp., pagin. cont.*] s8°. 1668
A second defence of Hugo Grotius. [*b. w. h.* Vindic. of the diss., 1654]. s4°. 1657
Some profitable directions in 2 sermons. [*b. w. h.* Δευτέραι Φροντίδες, 1656]. s8°. 1657
*A view of some exceptions made by a Romanist to Falkland's Disc. &c. [*b. w. h.* Of the power of the Keyes &c. 1647]. s4°. 1646
A view of the new directory & a vindic. of the anc. liturgy of the Ch. of Eng. &c. s4°. O. 1645
,, ,, 3rd ed. [*b. w. h.* Of the power of the Keyes, 1647]. s4°. O. 1646
A vindic. of the dissert. conc. episcopacie f. the answers by the London ministers &c. s4°. 1654
see JACKSON (T.) Lib. of Xtn. biog., v9, H. H., by J. Fell, 1838.
,, JEANES (H.) Dr. H. H. Ἐκτενέστερον, 1657.
,, —— 2nd part of mixture of scholast. divinity &c., w. reply to Dr. H.'s Vindic. of h. Grounds of uniformity, 1660.

Hammond (James). Poet. works. Coll. by T. Park. [*b. w.* Lyttelton (G., *b.*) Poet. works, 1805]. s8°. 1805

Hammond (John Lawrence Le Breton). The terror in action. [*Repr. f. The Nation.* P2496; 2529]. s8°. [1921]
A tragedy of errors. [*Repr. f. The Nation.* P2496; 2529]. s8°. [1921]
see MASSINGHAM (H. W.) H. W. M., sel. f. writings, w. intr. essays by J. L. H. &c., 1925.
—— **& B. Hammond.** Lord Shaftesbury. 8°. 1923
The rise of mod. industry. 8°. [1925]
,, ,, ... 2nd ed. 8°. [1926]
The village labourer, 1760–1832. n. ed. 8°. 1920

Hammond (Matthew Brown). Brit. labor condit. & legislat. dur. the War. [C.E. for Int. Peace.] 8°. N.Y. 1919

Hammond (Robert), *electrician.*
The electric light in our homes. 8°. [1884]

Hammond (*Col.* **Robert**). Letters betw. H. & the Committee at Derby-House &c. rel. to Charles I, while in Carisbrooke Castle. [*Ed. T. Birch*]. [*a.c.b.w.* Berkeley (J. B., *1st b.*) Memoirs, 1699]. s8°. 1764

Hammond (William), *B.A. of St. John's Coll., Cambridge.*
Psalms, hymns & spiritual songs. s8°. 1745

Hammond (William A.), *surgeon-gen., U.S. Army.*
Physics & physiology of spiritualism. s8°. N.Y. 1871

Ḥammurabi, *king of Babylon.* H.'s Gesetz. Von P. Koschaker, A. Ungnad. B6. la8°. L. 1923
6, Übersetzte Urkunden mit Rechtserläuterungen.
see CUQ (E.) Les nouv. fragments du code de H. sur le prêt à intérêt & les sociétés, 1920.
,, EDWARDS (C.) The H. code & the Sinaitic legisl., 3rd ed., 1921.

Hamon (André Jean Marie) [*ps.* CURÉ DE SAINT-SULPICE].
*Notre-Dame de France ou hist. du culte de la Ste. Vierge en France. 7v. 8°. 1861–66

Hamon (Jean), *1618–1687, see* LE CHARPENTIER (C.) M. Hamon, 1925.

Hamp (Adamus). Quaestiones theol. cur Deus homo disput., praes. F. Schilcher. s8°. Dilingae. [1704]

Hamp (Pierre).
Le cantique des cantiques. 5e ed. 2[t]. s8°. 1922
Gens. 2e tableau. 9e éd. s8°. 1923
Théâtre. [s1, 2; 1, 4e éd., 2, 3e éd.] s8°. [1927–28]
1, La maison—La compagnie. Préc. du Prologue pour une pièce sans cocu.
2, Mons. l'administrateur—Mme la Guerre.
La victoire mécanicienne. 4e éd. s8°. 1920

Hampden (Mary). Bulb gardening. 8°. [1921]

Hampe (Carl). Die Aktenstücke z. Frieden v. S. Germano, 1230. Hrsg. K. H. [M. G. H. Epist. sel., 4]. 8°. 1926
Mittelalterl. Gesch. 8°. Gotha. 1922

Hampel (József). Alterthümer d. frühen Mittelalters in Ungarn. 3B. la8°. Braunschweig. 1905

Hampshire Field Club & Archaeological Society. Papers & proc. v2–8 (1891–1919). 8°. Southampton. 1894–[1921?]
Vol. 6, Suppl., 1913, *b. separately.*

Hampson (*Sir* **George Francis**), *see* BRITISH MUSEUM OF NAT. HIST.: ZOOLOGY. Lepidoptera Phalaenae. New genera &c., 1926.

Hampson (John).
Mem. of John Wesley. 3v. s8°. Sunderland. 1791

Hampstead. *The H. murder; or the prediction [*Murder of Deloraine by J. Tucker*]. 8°. 1845

Hampstead Antiquarian & Historical Society.
Transactions, 1898–1905. la8°. Hampstead. 1899–1907

Hampton Court. Hampton Court, Hampton Wick & Hampton-on-Thames wills &c. Ed. H. T. McEleney. [Suppl. to The Genealogist, N.S., v35–38]. [*no tp.*] 8°. [1919–22]

Hampton (Frank Anthony).
The scent of flowers & leaves. s8°. 1925

Hampton (George). Candid remarks upon Mr. Taylor's disc. The Scripture doct. of atonement exam., in a letter to Mr. T. 8°. *n.d.* [1753?]

Hampton's Scholastic Directory. 28th ed.–33rd ed. 8°. 1920–26

Hamsun (Knut).
Samlede Verker.
[3e saml. Udg.] 12B. 8°. 1921
Æventyrland (I.) [4.]
Aftenrøde. [6.]
Benoni. [5.]
Børn av Tiden. [9.]
Dronning Tamara. [7.]
Kratskog. [3.]
Konerne ved Vandposten. [12.]
Livet i Vold. [6.]
Livets Spil. [6.]
Markens Grøne. [11.]
Munken Vendt. [7.]
Mysterier. [2.]
Ny Jord. [3.]
Pan [1.]
Redaktør Lynge. [4.]
Rosa. [5.]
Segelfoss By. [10.]

Hamsun (Knut) [*continued*].
Samlede Verker [*continued*].
Siesta. [7.]
Siste (Den) Glæde. [9.]
Stridende Liv. [8.]
Sult. [1.]
Sværmere. [3.]
Under Høststjærnen. [8.]
Vandrer (En) Spiller med Sordin. [8.]
Ved Rikets Port. [6.]
Victoria. [1.]
Vilde (Det) Kor. [4.]
Konerne ved Vandposten. Roman. 2[b]. 8°. 1920
Siste Kapitel. Roman. 2[v]. 8°. 1923

TRANSLATIONS.
Growth of the soil. [Tr. by M. Worster]. [2nd ed.] s8°. [1920]
Hunger. Tr. G. Egerton. s8°. 1921
Mothwise. [Tr., w. intr. note by W. Worster]. s8°. [1921]
Pan. [Tr. W. Worster]. s8°. [1920]
Segelfoss Town. [Tr.] 2v. 8°. 1925
Victoria. [Tr. A. G. Chater]. s8°. 1923
Wanderers. ("Autumn" & "With muted strings"). [Tr. W. Worster]. s8°. [1922]
— see LARSEN (H. A.) K. H., 1923.

Hanbury-Williams (*Sir* Charles), *see* WILLIAMS (*Sir* C. H.)
Hanbury-Williams (*Maj.-Gen. Sir* John).
The Emperor Nicholas II as I knew him. 8°. 1922
Hancock (John), *D.D., Rector of St. Margaret's, Lothbury.*
*An answer to some things cont. in Dr. Hicks's Christian priesthood asserted &c. By a presbyter of the Ch. of E. s8°. 1709
Hancock (Samuel). Narrative of S. H., 1845–60. Intr. by A. D. H. Smith. 8°. [1927]
Hancock (W. K.)
Ricasoli & the Risorgimento in Tuscany. 8°. 1926
Hand (Thomas E.) & K. L. Cockerham. The sweet potato. Hdbk. for the practical grower. 8°. N.Y. 1921
Handbok för Svenska Kyrkän. The Swedish rite. A tr. of "Handbok för Sv. Kyrkän" by E. E. Yelverton. s8°. 1921
Handbook.
*H. for speakers & writers on so-called Temperance question, 1920, *see* TEMPERANCE.
H. of ceremonials &c.: rev. ed. of the bk. of cerem. of city of London, 1882, 1906, *see* LONDON: CIVIC &C. INSTIT.
H. of Cyprus; ed. H. C. Luke & D. J. Jardine, 1920, *see* CYPRUS.
*H. of Eng. ecclesiology, 1847, *see* CAMBRIDGE CAMDEN SOC.
*H. (A) of script. church principles & of Wesleyan-Methodist polity &c., 2p, 1888, *see* WESLEYAN-METHODIST.
*H. of the democracy for 1863–4. [Soc. for Diff. of Polit. Knowl.] 8°. [1864]
Handbooks prep. under dir. of the Hist. Sect. of the Foreign Office, No. 1–56, 1920, *see* FOREIGN OFFICE.
Handbuch.
H. d. altarab. Altertumskunde, B1, 1927, *see* NIELSEN (D.), *ed.*
H. d. Auslandpresse, 1918. Bearb. v. d. Auslandstelle d. Kriegspresseamts. 8°. 1918
H. d. mittelalt. u. neu. Gesch. Hrsg. v. G. v. Below u. F. Meinecke. la8°. München. 1926
see FRIEDENSBURG (F.) Münzkunde &c. d. Einzelstaaten, 1926.
,, FÜTER (E.) Gesch. d. europäis. Staatensystems v. 1492–1559, 1919.
H. d. Ostküste Südamerikas, 2e A., 2T, *&* Erganzung &c., 1911–21, *see* SÜDAMERIKA.
H. d. Politik. Hrsg. G. Anschütz, F. Berolzheimer &c. 3e A. 5B. 4°. 1920–26
1, Die Grundlagen d. Politik. 2, Der Weltkrieg. 3, Die polit. Erneuerung. 4, Der wirtschaftl. Wiederaufbau. 5, Der Weg in d. Zukunft. 6, Urkunden z. Politik uns. Zeit.
H. d. regionalen Geol., 3i, *see* COLE (G. A. J.), A. M. DAVIES, &c. British Isles, 1917.
H. d. theolog. Wissenschaften, 3B, 1883–85, *see* ZÖCKLER (O.), *ed.*
H. d. Unfallversicherung, *see* REICHS-VERSICHERUNGSAMT. Gesch. u. Wirkungskreis d. R.-V.: Verm. Sonderdruck aus d. H. d. U., 3. A., B3, 1911.
H. deut. Zeitungen, 1917, *see* MICHEL (O.), *ed.*
H. für d. Deutsche Reich. Hrsg. v. Reichsminist. d. Innern. 2te unveränd. A., 41. Jhrg., 1922, 43. Jhrg., 1926. 8°. 1922–26
H. für d. West- u. Nordküste Norwegens, 3e A., 2T, 1919–21, *see* NORWEGEN.
H. zum Neuen Test., B1–4, 1910–19, *see* LIETZMANN (H.), *ed.*
Hist.-herald. H. z. genealog. Taschenbuch d. gräfl. Häuser, 1855, *see* GOTHAISCHES GENEALOG. TASCHENBUCH.
Händel (Christoph Christian). Diss. de eruditis Germaniae mulieribus. Praes. M. D. Omeisio. [P444]. s4°. [Altdorfi. 1688]
Händel (Georg Friedrich). For unto us (Messiah). [*b. w.* Corelli (A.) Twelve concertos, *n.d.*] 4°. *n.d.*
see CHRYSANDER (F.) G. F. H., B1–3i, 1858–67.
,, FLOWER (N.) G. F. H., h. personality & h. times, 1923.
,, LEICHTENTRITT (H.) H., 1924.
,, MAINWARING (J.) Mem. of the life of H.; added, cat. of h. works, 1760.

Handelspolitik. Neue Grundlage d. H., 2T, 1925, *see* EULENBURG (F.), *ed.*
Handes Amsoreay. [Monatsschrift f. armen. Philol.] 8.–32. tari. 1894–1918. [*b. in* 9v. 1914 *wants* Nos. 7–12]. 4°. Vienna. 1894–1918
Handkerchiefs from Paul: verses, by B. Tompson &c., 1927, *see* MURDOCK (K. B.), *ed.*
Händler (G. H.), *see* DALMAN (G. H.) Aramäisch-neuhebr. Hdwbch., 2e A., mit Lex. d. Abbreviaturen v. G. H. H. &c., 1922.
Handling men: selecting & hiring &c. [*By var. a.*] 8°. Chicago. [1917]
Handlirsch (Anton), *see* ZIMMERMANN (H.), A. H. &c. Die beiden Hofmuseen u. d. Hofbibliothek, 1920.
Handlung.
H. d. versamlung inn Zürich, 1523, *see* ZÜRICH.
H. oder Acta gehaltner Disput. zu Bernn, 1528, *see* BERNE.
Hands (Alfred), *F.R.M.S.* Thunderstorms. [P2871]. 8°. 1900
Handschriften d. Reformationszeit ausgewählt v. G. M., 1912, *see* MENTZ (G.)
Handyside (John). The histor. method in ethics & o. essays. 8°. Liv'l. [1919]
Handzeichnungen alter Meister aus d. Albertina u. aus Privatbesitz, N.F., 1922, *see* MEDER (J.)
Haner (Georg).
Hist. eccl. Transylvanicarum. s8°. Francofurti. 1694
Haner (Georg Jeremias). De scriptoribus rer. Hung. & Transilvan. scriptisque antiquior. 2t. s8°. Viennae [t2, Cibinii]. 1774–98
Haney (Lewis Henry).
Hist. of econ. thought. rev. ed. 8°. N.Y. 1922
Hango (Hermann), *see* VIENNA. Quellen z. Gesch. d. Stadt Wien, Abt. II, B5, i, bearb. v. H. H., 1921.
Hanika (*Hauptmann* Carl), *see* UNGAR (H.) Die Ermord. d. H., 1925.
Hänisch (Erich), *see* HEDIN (S.) South. Tibet: researches, 1906–8, v9iv, Eine chin. Beschr. v. Tibet; hrsg. v. E. H., 1922.
Hanisch (Georg Daniel). Diss. de propagata per Bonifacium inter Germanos relig. Xtiana. Praes. J. S. Semler. [P440]. s4°. Halae Magdeb. [1770]
Hanke (Martin) [HANKIUS]. Mon. pie defunctis olim erecta, nunc in unum coll. vol. a G. Hankio. s4°. Vratislaviae. [1718]
see LETSCHIUS (J. C.) & M. H. Dissert. Nestorianismi hist. compl., 1688.
Hankey (Cyril Patrick), *see* YANICH (V.) & C. P. H. Lives of the Serbian saints, 1921.
Hankey (Donald). The beloved captain: sel. chapters f. "A student in arms." s8°. [1917]
Hankin (Ernest Hanbury). Common sense & its cultiv. Foreword by C. S. Myers. s8°. 1926
The drawing of geometric patterns in Saracenic art, *see* INDIA: ARCH. SURVEY. Memoirs, No. 15, 1925.
Hankin (St. John).
Dramatic works. Intr. by J. Drinkwater. 3v. 8°. 1912
Hanks (Ethel E.), *see* SUMNER (H. L.) & E. E. H. Admin. of child labor laws, 2p, 1915–17.
Hann (Julius), *prof. in Univ. of Vienna.* Hdbch. d. Klimatologie, B1, Allgem. Klimalehre. 3e verm. A. 8°. St. 1908
Hanna, *see* ANNA.
Hanna (Hugh Sisson). Labor laws &c. in the Pacific States, *see* UNITED STATES: LAB. Bull. 211, 1917.
Hannaas (Torleiv), *ed.* Ældre norske sprogminder, 1–3. [Norske Hist. K.] 8°. 1911–15
1, Maallaere og ortøke fraa Vest-Agder, 16-talet; udg. T. H.
2, Ordsamling fraa Robyggjelaget, 16-talet; udg. T. H.
3, Jensøn (C.) Den Norske dict. eller glosebog; udg. T. H.
Hannaford (Charles Frederick), *see* BAGSHAW (J. F. G.) Pract. banking; w. chapt. on princ. of currency by C. F. H., 1920.
Hannah (Ian C.) Christian monasticism. 8°. [1924]
Hannah (John), *D.D.* Mem. of the life, ministry &c. of T. Lessey &c. 8°. 1842
Hannak (Emanuel) & F. Umlauft. Histor. Schulatlas in 30 Karten. [2T in 1v]. 8°. Wien. 1920
Hannan (William Everett). Property exempt f. taxation in the 48 states. 8°. Albany. 1916
Hannay (David). The gt. chartered companies. 8°. 1926
Hannay (James Ballantyne). Kosmos: eternal ebb & flow of matter &c. p.p. for the Relig. Evol. Res. Soc. 8°. [1926]
The rise, decline & fall of the Roman religion. 8°. 1925
Sex symbolism in religion. p.p. for Relig. Evol. Research Soc. [2v]. 8°. 1922

Hannay (James Owen) [*ps.* G. A. BIRMINGHAM].

Bindon Parva.	s8°. [1925]	King Tommy.	s8°. [1923]
Fidgets.	s8°. [1927]	Lady Bountiful.	s8°. [1921]
Good conduct.	s8°. 1920	The lost lawyer.	s8°. [1921]
Goodly pearls.	s8°. [1926]	A public scandal & o. s.	s8°. [1922]
The grand duchess.	8°. [1924]	The seething pot.	pop. ed. s8°. *n.d.*
The great-grandmother.	s8°. [1922]	Spanish gold.	26th ed. s8°. [1920]
The gun-runners.	s8°. [1925]	A wayfarer in Hungary.	8°. [1925]
Inisheeney.	s8°. [1920]		
An Irishman looks at his world.	s8°. [1919]		

Hanneken (Philipp Ludovic) [†HANNEKENIUS].
Catechesis de morali Sabbatico Xtianorum. s4°. Coburgi. 1705
***Hannibal** at the gates: or, the progress of Jacobitism, 1712, *see* DEFOE (D.)
Hannibal, *the Carthaginian.*
see JERSEY (M. E., *dowager ctss. of*) & *Hon.* E. WARD. H.'s tribunal: drama, 1927.
„ TORR (C.) H. crosses the Alps, 1924.
Hannover (Emil). Pottery & porcelain. Handbook for collectors. Tr., ed. w. notes &c. by B. Rackham. 3[v]. la8°. 1925
1, Europe & the Near East, earthenware & stoneware. 2, The Far East. 3, European porcelain.
Hannsen Friedrich, *Hartzog v. Sachsen, see* JOHN FREDERICK, *duke of Saxony.*
Hanotaux (Gabriel).
L'Aisne pendant la Grande Guerre. 2e éd. s8°. 1919
La bataille de la Marne. 2t. 8°. [1922]
Le général Mangin. s8°. [1925]
Hist. de la nation française. t1–4, 6, 7, 8, 10–15. 4°. [1920–27]
1, Intr. gén. [par G. H.]—Géogr. humaine de la France, v1, par J. Brunhes.
2, Géogr. humaine de la France, v2, Géogr. polit. & géogr. du travail par J. Brunhes & P. Deffontaines.
3, 4, Hist. polit., v1, Des origines à 1515, par P. Imbart de la Tour; v2, De 1515 à 1804, par L. Madelin.
6, Hist. relig.; par G. Goyau.
7, Hist. milit. & navale, v1, Des orig. aux Croisades, par J. Colin; Des Croisades à la Révol., par F. Reboul.
8, Hist. milit. & navale, v2, De la Constituante au Directoire, par le gén. Mangin; Du Directoire à la Guerre de 1914, par Franchet d'Esperey; La Guerre de 1914–18, par G. Hanotaux.
10, Hist. écon. & financière; par G. Martin.
11, Hist. des arts; par L. Gillet.
12, 13, Hist. des lettres, v1, Des orig. à Ronsard, par J. Bédier, A. Jeanroy, & F. Picavet; v2, De Ronsard à nos jours, par F. Strowski.
14, 15, Hist. des sciences, v1, Intr. gén. par E. Picard—Mathémat., mécanique, astronomie, physique & chimie par H. Andoyer, C. Fabry, P. Humbert, A. Colson; v2, Hist. des sciences biolog. par M. Caullery, Hist. de la philos. par R. Lote.
Hist. illust. de la Guerre de 1914. t10–17. 4°. 1920–24
Les orig. gaul. de Ronsard & de Musset, *see* MARTELLIÈRE (J.)
P. de Ronsard, préf. de G. H., 1924.
Réponse au disc. de P. Valéry (16 juin, 1927). [Acad. Fr.] 8°. 1927
Sur les chemins de l'hist. 2t. 8°. 1924
—— & *Lt.-Col.* **Fabry.** Joffre. s8°. [1921]
Hanoverana. Monimenta medii aevi; ex Bibl. Regia H., 1757–64, *see* WALCH (C. W. F.)
Hansbrow (George). An improved Hibernian gazetteer. Added, Introd. to hist. of Ireland. 8°. D. 1835
Hansen (Adolph), *see* KERNER (A.) Pflanzenleben; 3e A. neubearb. v. A. H., 2B, 1921–22.
Hansen (Alvin Harvey). Cycles of prosperity & depression in the U.S.A., Gt. Brit. & Germany, 1902–08. 8°. Madison. 1921
Hansen (H. P.) & J. C. Möller. La Guerre Europ. & la question du Slesvig. Tr. & intr. par J. de Coussange. s8°. 1918
Hansen (Ida Falbe), *see* FALBE-HANSEN (I.)
Hansen (Joseph). Quellen &c. z. Gesch. d. Hexenwahns u. d. Hexenverfolgung im M.-a. Mit Unters. d. Gesch. d. Wortes Hexe, v. J. Franck. 8°. Bonn. 1901
see AUBIN (H.) Gesch. d. Rheinlandes; v. H. A., Th. Frings, J. H. &c., 2B, 1922.
Hansischer Geschichtsverein [VEREIN F. HANS. GESCH.], *see* HÄPKE (R.) Niederländ. Akten &c. z. Gesch. d. Hanse u. z. deut. Seegesch., B1, 1913.
Hanska (*Mme.* EVELINE *dite* EVE), *née Rzewuska, aft. wife of H. de Balzac, see* BALZAC (*Mme.* E.)

Hanslian (R.) & F. Bergendorff.
Der chemische Krieg: Gasangriff &c. 8°. 1925
Hanslick (Eduard). The beautiful in music.
7th ed. enl. &c. (1885); tr. G. Cohen. s8°. 1891
Vom Musikalisch-Schönen. 4e A. s8°. L. 1874
Hanslik (Joseph A.)
Gesch. u. Beschr. d. Prager Universitätsbibl. 8°. Prag. 1851
„ „ Zusätze u. Inhalts-Verzeichnisse. Hrsg. I. J. Hanuš. 8°. Prag. 1863
Hanson (G.), *see* SCHOFIELD (S. J.) & G. H. Geol. &c. of Salmon River Distr., B.C., 1922.
Hanson (T. W.) The story of old Halifax. s8°. Halifax. 1920
Hanson (W. G.) The early monastic schools of Ireland. Lectures. s8°. 1927
Hansonius (Petrus), *see* WÜRTEMBERG. Abfertigung u. Widerlegung 2 Lästerschrfften &c. das ander durch P. H. Entdeckung d. grossen Thorheit &c., 1587.
Hanssen (H. P.)
Fra Krigstiden. Dagbogsoptegnelser. [3e Opl.] 2[B]. 8°. 1925
Hanssens (Eug.) Le pouvoir législ. sous l'occup. allem. en Belg. Avec. une nouv. lettre d'un provincial. la8°. Brux. 1919
Hansson (Ola). Samlade Skrifter. 17d. s8°. 1920–22
1, Dikter & notturno. 2, Litterära silhuetter & Materialismen i skön-litt. 3, Sensitiva amorosa & Parias. 4, Ung ofegs visor & Kärlekens trångmål. 5, Tidens kvinnor. 6, Fru Ester Bruce & Före giftermålet. 7, Resan hem. 8, En uppfostrare. 9, Vägen till livet & Kåserier i mystik. 10, Tolkare & siare. 11, Det unga Skandinavien. 12, Ur hävden & livet. 13, Djur-och människohumoresker & Aforismer & aperçuer. 14, Dikter på vers & prosa & Det förlovade landet. 15, Svartkonsten & Nya visor. 16, På hemmets altare & Dagbok i Frankrike. 17, Rustgården.
Fr. Nietzsche, s. Persönlichkeit &c. [P2478]. 8°. L. *n.d.*
Hanstein (Otfrid v.)
The world of the Incas. Tr. A. Barwell. 8°. [1924]
Hans Town. Acts of 30 & 43 Geo. III rel. to district in Chelsea, called H. T. s8°. 1807
Hansy (Theodore de). Etrennes spirituelles cont. l'office lat. & fr., 1755, *see* OFFICIA.
Hantes Amsoreay, *see* HANDES.
Hantos (Elemér).
La monnaie, s. systèmes &c. en Europe Cent. 8°. 1927
Häntzschel (Johann Gottfried) [†HAENTZSCHELIUS]. Meditationes de theopneustia Lutheri. [P2742]. s4°. Lipsiæ. 1732
Hanusch (Ferdinand). Die Regelung d. Arbeitsverhältnisse im Kriege. Von E. Adler, F. Aggermann &c. Unter d. Leit. v. F. H. u. E. Adler. [C.E. for Int. Peace]. la8°. Wien. 1927
Hanway (Jonas). An acc. of the Marine Society &c. [*& List of subscribers, w. sep. pagin*]. 6th ed. 8°. 1759
Hao Kiu tschuan, *see* HAOU KEW CHUEN.
Haou Kew Chuen [†KEW]. La brise au clair de lune. [Fong-yue tchoann *also called* Hau Kiou choan. Roman chinois [*By* Ming-tsiac tchong-jenn, *ps.*] Tr. G. Soulié de Morant. [Cahiers verts, 57]. s8°. 1925
Eisherz u. Edeljaspis, oder Gesch. e. glückl. Gattenwahl. Übertr. v. F. Kuhn. s8°. L. 1927
see †DAVIS (*Sir* J. F.) The fortunate union; tr. f. Chinese, 2v, 1829.
Häpke (Rudolf). Niederländ. Akten u. Urkunden z. Gesch. d. Hanse u. z. deut. Seegesch. Hrsg. v. Verein f. hans. Gesch., bearb. v. R. H. B1 (1531–57). la8°. München. 1913
Happold (Frederick Crossfield), *see* PERSE SCHOOL, *Camb.* 2 plays; intr. on "Dram. teaching in schools," by F. C. H., 1921.
Hapsburg, *The House of.* Regesta Habsburgica. Regesten d. Grafen v. Habsburg u. d. Herzoge v. Österreich aus d. Hause H. Hrsg. v. Inst. f. österr. Geschichtsforschung unter Leitung v. O. Redlich. Abt. 1, 3. 4°. Innsbruck. 1905–24
1, Regesten d. Grafen v. H. bis 1281; bearb. H. Steinacker. 3, Regesten d. Herzoge v. Österreich sowie Friedrichs d. Schönen als deut. Königs, 1314–30; bearb. L. Gross.
see MARGUTTI (A., *Frhr. v.*) La tragédie des H., 1924.
„ STEED (H. W.) The H. monarchy, 3rd ed., 1914.
Harap (Henry), *Ph.D.* The educ. of the consumer. 8°. N.Y. 1924
Harbaugh (Henry). The fathers of the German Reformed Ch. in Europe & America. 2v. s8°. Lancaster [Pa.] 1857
Harboe (Friedrich Carl). Comm. de August. Conf. ad Graecos delata. [P2642]. s4°. Lipsiae. [1739]
Harcourt (Robert). A relation of a voyage to Guiana, 1613. With Purchas's transcr. of rep. made at H.'s instance on the Marrawini dist. Ed. w. intr. &c. by Sir C. A. Harris [Hakluyt Soc., N.S., 60]. 8°. 1928

Harcourt (William) [HARRISON], *see* WHITE (T.) Last speeches of the 5 traitors & Jesuits: W. H. &c., 1679.

Harcourt (*Rt. Hon. Sir* William), *see* GARDINER (A. G.) Life of Sir W. H., 1827–1904, 2v, 1923.

Harden (Arthur), *see* ROSCOE (*Sir* H. E.) & A. H. Inorganic chemistry, 2nd ed., rev., 1920.

Harden (John Mason). Intr. to Ethiopic Xtn. lit. s8°. 1926
see BIBLE: PSALMS. Psalterium juxta Hebr. Hieronymi; ed., w. intr. &c. by J. M. H., 1922.

Harden (Maximilian).
Deutschland, Frankreich, England. 8°. 1923
Köpfe. B4. 8°. 1924
Von Versailles nach Versailles. 8°. Dresden. [1927]
see DELBRÜCK (H.) Kautsky u. H., 1920.

Hardenberg (Albert), *see* GERDES (D.) Hist. motuum eccl. in civit. Bremensi, temp. A. H., 1756.

Hardenbroek (Gijsbert Jan van). Gedenkschriften, 1747[–88]. Uitg. &c. door F. J. L. Krämer [& A. J. van der Meulen]. [Hist. Genoots. Werken, s3, 14, 17, 24, 36, 39, 40]. 6d. 8°. A. 1901–18

Harder (Richard), *see* OCELLUS, *Lucanus.* O. L.; Text u. Komm. v. R. H., 1926.

Hardesheim (Christoph). *Consensus orthod. Sacrae Script. & Vet. Eccl., de sententia &c. verborum Cœnæ Dominicæ &c. fol. Tiguri. 1578

Hardie (Alexander). Evolution: is it philosophical, scientific, or scriptural? 8°. Los Angeles. 1924

Hardie (James Keir), *see* STEWART (W.) J. K. H., biog., 1921.

Hardie (William Ross). Res metrica: intr. to st. of Greek & Roman versific. s8°. O. 1920

Harding (George) [*ps.* MINUTIUS FELIX]. *The essence of Malone, or the "Beauties" extr. f. h. "Some acc. of the life &c. of John Dryden." [*a. c. b. w.* Hogarth (W.) *Explan. &c., 1785]. 8°. 1800

Harding (James Duffield).
Elem. art; or the use of the lead pencil. fol. 1834
Lessons on trees. Ed. & rev. by W. Walker. 14th ed. fol. *n.d.*
Picturesque selections: drawn on stone. atlas fol. [1861]

Harding (Jane). Margaret's Mead. s8°. 1921

Harding (Richard Winboult).
The authority of Jesus. s8°. 1922

Harding (*Mrs.* Stan). The underworld of state. Intr. by B. Russell. s8°. [1925]

Harding (Sylvester), *publ.* Biograph. mirrour, Eng. portraits of eminent &c. persons, w. th. lives &c. 3v. la8°. 1795–1810

Harding (*Col.* T. Walter).
Tales of Madingley. 8°. C. 1912

Harding (Walter Ambrose Heath). Hirudinea, *see* BRIT. ANTARCTIC EXPED., 1910–13. Zoology, v2, 1914–20.

Harding (Warren Gamaliel), *president of the U.S.*, *see* PACHECO (F.) Pres. H.: discurso, 1923.

Hardinge (*Rt. Hon. Sir* Arthur Henry).
A diplomatist in Europe. 8°. [1927]
The life of H. H. M. Herbert, 4th earl of Carnarvon, 1831–90. Ed. Elisabeth, Ctess. of Carnarvon. 3v. 8°. O. 1925

Hardinge (Winifred, *Lady*) [HARDINGE OF PENSHURST], *form. Hon. W. Sturt*, *see* KOOVERBA (M.) Lady Hardinge of Penshurst; a tribute, 1915.

Hardman (Oscar). The ideals of asceticism. 8°. 1924

Hardman (*Col.* Reginald Stanley). Morals & maxims for stable management & horse mastership. [*Extr. fr.* Journal of R.A., 38, 1911. P2589]. n. impr. 8°. 1914

Hardman (*Sir* William), *F.R.G.S.* A mid-Victorian Pepys: letters &c. of Sir W. H. Annot. & ed. S. M. Ellis. 8°. [1923]
,, ,, s2, *w. title* Letters & mem. of Sir W. H., 1863–65. 8°. [1925]

Hardouin (Jean). Opera varia. [*Cont.* Athei detecti—Numismata &c.] fol. Amstelodami. 1733
Ad censuram script. vet. prolegomena. 8°. Londini. 1766
see VOLLANDUS (C. G.) Vind. Chrysostomi contra H., 1714.

Hardt (Anton Julius v. d.) Diss. in jubileum Reformationis Brunsvic. a. 1528 &c. [P440]. s4°. Helmstadii. [1728]

Hardt (Hermann von der). Exegesis loc. difficil. 4 Evang., *see* VIRORUM &c. molimina theolog., 1761.
Hoseas, ant. Chaldaicâ Jonathanis paraphrasi, ut & R. Salomonis Jizchak, R. Abrahami Aben Esræ & R. Davidis

Hardt (Hermann von der) [*continued*].
Kimchi comm. illust. Ex ant. R. Stephani emend. cod. Parisino rec. ab H. s4°. Goettingae. 1775
Oratio de fontium Hebr. interprete Luthero. [P2628]. s4°. Helmestadi. 1690
see BEERMANN (S.) Evang. rei integritas H. in negot. Jonae, 1721.

Hardt (Ricardus von der). *Holmia literata. s4°. Holmiae. 1701

Hardtschmidt (Johann Nicolaus). Exercit. acad. de legione fulminatrice. Praes. U. Obrecht. s4°. Argentorati. 1677

Hardwick (John Charlton).
Religion & science f. Galileo to Bergson. 8°. 1920

Hardwick (Rose S.), *see* YERKES (R. M.), J. W. BRIDGES & R. S. H. Point scale for measuring mental ability, 1915.

Hardy (A. C.) Seaways & sea trade. 8°. 1927

Hardy (Campbell). Sporting adv. in the New World; or, Moose-hunting in the pine forests of Acadia. 2v. s8°. 1855

Hardy (Edouard). Les Français en Italie, 1494–1559. 8°. 1880

Hardy (Ernest George). Some problems in Roman hist. 10 essays on admin. &c. work of Julius Caesar. 8°. O. 1924

Hardy (G. M. Gathorne), *see* GATHORNE-HARDY (G. M.)

Hardy (Georges).
Le Cardinal de Fleury & le mouvt. Janséniste. la8°. 1925
Le "De Civitate Dei" source princ. du "Disc. sur l'hist. univ." [H.E.: Sci. relig., 28]. 8°. 1913

Hardy (Godfrey Harold). Some famous problems of theory of numbers, & in partic. Waring's Problem. [P2433]. 8°. O. 1920

Hardy (*Capt.* J. L.), *D.S.O.* I escape! s8°. [1927]

Hardy (*le gén.* Jean). Archives & corr. De Valmy à Maëstricht, 1792–94. [Publ.] par Gén. Hardÿ de Périni. 8°. 1903

Hardy (Marcel E.) The geography of plants. s8°. O. 1920
Introd. to plant geography. s8°. O. 1913

Hardy (Mary). Grounds for divorce. s8°. [1924]

Hardy (Thomas), *novelist.*
Works. [Mellstock ed.] v15–37. 8°. 1920
15, Wessex tales.
16, 17, A pair of blue eyes.
18, 19, The trumpet major.
20, Two on a tower.
21, The well-beloved.
22, A group of noble dames.
23, 24, Desperate remedies.
25, 26, The hand of Ethelberta.
27, 28, A Laodicean.
29, 30, A changed man & o. tales.
31–33, The dynasts.
34, Wessex poems & o. verses—Poems of the past & the present.
35, Time's laughing-stocks & o. verses.
36, Satires of circumstance, lyrics & reveries.
37, Moments of vision & misc. verses.
Coll. poems. [repr.] s8°. 1920
,, ,, [2nd ed. Poet. wks., v1]. s8°. 1923
The dynasts. [repr.] 8°. 1919
,, ,, ...[repr.] 8°. 1920
,, ,, ...[repr.] 8°. 1923
,, ,, [Poet. wks., v2]. s8°. 1923
The famous tragedy of the queen of Cornwall. 8°. 1923
Far from the madding crowd. [repr.] s8°. 1918
,, ,, ...[repr.] s8°. 1921
A group of noble dames. [repr.] s8°. 1914
Human shows, far phantasies; songs & trifles. 8°. 1925
Jude the obscure. [repr.] s8°. 1918
Late lyrics & earlier w. o. verses. s8°. 1922
The Mayor of Casterbridge. [repr.] s8°. 1919
,, ,, ...[repr.] s8°. 1926
A pair of blue eyes. [repr.] s8°. 1924
The return of the native. [repr.] s8°. [1916]
,, ,, ...[repr.] s8°. [1921]
The well-beloved. s8°. 1919
The woodlanders. s8°. 1920
see ABERCROMBIE (L.) T. H.: a crit. study, n. ed., 1919.
,, BRENNECKE (E.) T. H.'s universe: st. of poet's mind, 1924.
,, CHEW (S. C.) T. H., poet & novelist, 1921.
,, HARPER (C. G.) The Hardy country: lit. landmarks &c., 1904.
,, JOHNSON (L.) The art of T. H., w. bibliog., n. ed., 1923.
,, LEA (H.) T. H.'s Wessex, 1913.
,, WHITFIELD (A. S.) T. H.: lect., 1921.
,, WINDLE (*Sir* B. C. A.) Wessex of T. H., 1912.

Hardy (William Le), *see* HERTFORDSHIRE. H. county records: notes &c. f. Sessions Records, v4, comp. by W. Le H., 1923.

Hare (Augustus John Cuthbert).
Florence. 6th ed., rev. by St. Clair Baddeley. s8°. 1904
Venice. 6th ed., rev. by H. & St. Clair Baddeley. s8°. 1904
,, ,, 8th ed., rev. by A. J. C. H. & St. C. Baddeley. s8°. 1922
Walks in Rome. 3rd ed. 2v. 8°. 1872
,, ,, 21st ed., by St. C. Baddeley. s8°. 1923
Wanderings in Spain. 5th ed. s8°. 1885
,, ,, ...8th ed. s8°. 1904

—— & St. C. Baddeley. Sicily. s8°. 1905

Hare (Edward). A refut. of the charges agst. the Methodists, by Dr. Magee. [P2531]. s8°. 1810
A treatise on the script. doct. of justific. 2nd ed., w. pref. by T. Jackson. s8°. 1839
Hare (Henry), *3rd baron Coleraine, see* COLERAINE (H. H., *3rd b.*)
Hare (Julius Charles), *archdeacon of Lewes,* **& A. W. Hare.**
*Guesses at truth. s8°. 1889
The victory of faith & o. sermons. 8°. [1889]
Hare (Kenneth).
Guide to Bruges & environs. 3rd enl. ed. 8°. [Bruges. 1927]
Hare (*Sir* Lancelot). Currency & prices. s8°. 1920
Hare (Rosalie Hancorn Ambrose), *wife of Comm. Robert L. Hare, form. Lind.* Voyage of the Caroline f. Eng. to Van Diemen's Land & Batavia, 1827–28. With ch. on early hist. of N. Tasmania &c. by I. Lee. 8°. 1927
Hare (William), *murderer.*
see BURKE (W.) Burke & Hare; ed. W. Roughead, 1921.
„ LEIGHTON (A.) The court of Cacus, or the story of Burke & H., 1861.
„ MACGREGOR (G.) Hist. of Burke & H. &c., 1884.
Hare (William Loftus). Mysticism of East & West: st. in mystical & moral philos. Intr. by J. E. Carpenter. 8°. [1923]
see RELIGIONS. R. of the Empire, ed. W. L. H., 1925.
Harford (John Battersby) [HARFORD-BATTERSBY (J.)]. Since Wellhausen: rec. Pentateuchal criticism. 8°. 1926
—— & F. C. MacDonald. Handley Carr Glyn Moule, bp. of Durham. A biography. 8°. [1922]
Hargrave (John). Young Winkle. s8°. [1925]
Hargrave (Mary).
The earlier French musicians, 1632–1834. s8°. 1917
Hargreaves (John R.) Illust. partic. of "Arborfield Hall," Arborfield. For sale by Knight &c., 7th Oct. 1924. [By dir. of J. R. H. P2751]. la8°. 1924
Hargrove (Ely). Hist. of Knaresborough, w. Harrogate. 4th ed. s8°. York. 1789
Hargrove (Ethel C.) Wanderings in the Isle of Wight. s8°. 1913
Hargrove (William), *see* DUFF, *missionary ship.* Some interest. partic. of the 2nd voyage of the Duff, &c. by W. H. [*i.e.* W. Hargrove?], 1809.
Haribhadra Sūri. Sanatkumāracaritam, ein Abschnitt aus Haribhadras Nemināthacaritam: e. Jaina Legende in Apabhramśa, hrsg. H. Jacobi, 1921, *see* KÖNIGL. AKAD. D. W. ZU MÜNCHEN. Abhdlgn., B31, 1922.
Harich (Walther). E. T. A. Hoffmann. Leben. 2B. 8°. [1920]
Jean Paul [Richter]. 8°. L. 1925
Häring (Theodor v.)
Der christl. Glaube (Dogmatik). 8°. Calw. 1906
Haringer (Jakob). Dichtungen. 8°. Potsdam. [1925]
Harington (Edward Charles). Brief notes on the Ch. of Scotland, 1555–1842. 8°. Exeter. 1843
The reformers of the Anglic. Church & Macaulay's Hist. of Eng. 8°. 1849
Harington (*Sir* John), *see* SCHOLA SALERNITANA. The sch. of Salernum, Eng. version by Sir J. H. (1608), 1922.
Harischandra, *king of Ayodhya.* *Arichandra, the martyr of truth: Tamil drama. Tr. [*chiefly f. version ascr. to Ranga-Pillai*]. Mutu Coomàra Swàmy. s8°. 1863
Harkavy (Abraham Elijah). О первоначальномъ обиталищѣ Семитовъ, Индо-европейцевъ и Хамитовъ, *see* IMPERAT. RUSS. ARCH. OBSCH. Труды Восточ. отд., ч16, 1872.
Harker (Alfred). Notes on geolog. map-reading. 8°. C. 1920
Petrology for students. 6th ed., rev. s8°. C. 1923
Harker (Joseph Cunningham). Studio & stage. 8°. [1924]
Harker (*Mrs.* Lizzie Allen). The bridge across. s8°. 1921
Hilda Ware. s8°. [1926]
The really romantic age. s8°. 1922
Harland (Richard). A lineal index to the Wesleyan hymn book & suppl. s8°. 1878
Harleian Miscellany (The): scarce pamphlets &c. in MS. [&] print, found in Earl of Oxford's library. With hist. &c. notes. v4–8. la8°. 1745–46
H.M. (The). An entertaining sel., arr., commented upon & ed. by H. Savage. 8°. [1924]
Harleian Society. v71–78 & Regs. v51–57. la8°. 1923–27
see CHANCERY, *Court of.* Index of persons named in early Ch. proc[s]. (1385–1467); ed. C. A. Walmisley, p1, 1927. [78.]
„ GRANTS. Coll. of misc. g., crests &c.; ed. W. A. Littledale, 2v, 1925–6. [76, 77.]
„ KENT. Visit. of K., 1530–1, by T. Benolte, & 1574 [& 1592], by R. Cooke; ed. W. B. Bannerman, 2p, 1923–24. [74, 75.]

Harleian Society [*continued*].
see MARYLEBONE. Reg. of marriages, 1775–1812; ed. W. B. Bannerman, p3–9, 1921–27. [Reg. 51–57.]
„ RUTLAND. Visit. of R., begun by F. Burghill &c., finished by T. May; ed. W. H. Rylands &c., 1922. [73.]
„ SUDBURY, *Suffolk.* Allegations for marriage licences, 1782–1839, p3, 4; ed. W. B. & G. G. B. Bannerman, 1920–21. [71, 72.]
Harlemius (Joannes). Index Biblicus, 1585, *see* BIBLE: LATIN. Biblia Sacra, t2, 1586.
Harlequin, The. A journal of the drama. [Ed. J. Timbs]. No. 1–6, May 16–June 20, 1829. [*b. w.* Dramatic mag., 1829]. 8°. [1829]
Harless (Gottlieb Christoph), *prof. at Erlangen.* Brevior notitia litt. Romanae. [*Foll. by* Additamenta scripsit C. F. H. Klügling, 1819]. s8°. Lipsiae. 1803–19
Harless (Gottlieb Christoph Adolf von). System of Xtn. ethics. Tr. A. W. Morrison. Rev. by W. Findlay. 8°. E. *Clark.*, 1868
Theolog. Encyklopädie u. Methodologie. 8°. Nürnberg. 1837
Harley (Theodore Rutherford).
see ROGERS (H. L.) & T. R. H. Life of Rome, 1927.
„ —— & —— Roman home life & religion, 1923.
Harlez (Charles de). Lao-tze. [*Extr. fr.* Mém. couronnés, Acad. de Belgique, 37. 1884]. [P2601]. 8°. Brux. 1884
Harlow (C. M.), *see* LINDSAY (H. A. F.) & C. M. H. Report on lac & shellac, 1921.
Harlow (Vincent Todd). Colonising exped. to W. Indies & Guiana, 1623–1667. [Lord Willoughby &c. Hakluyt Soc., II, 56]. 8°. 1925
Hist. of the Barbadoes, 1625–85. 8°. O. 1926
Harman (Edward George). The Birds of Aristophanes consid. in rel. to Athenian politics. 8°. 1920
The Countesse of Pembrokes Arcadia exam. &c. by E. G. H. (With chap. on T. Lodge). 8°. [1924]
Poems. s8°. 1920
see ÆSCHYLUS. Prometheus bound; repr. in Eng. & expl. by E. G. H., 1920.
Harman (Thomas), *see* VILES (E.) & F. J. FURNIVALL, *edd.* Rogues & vagabonds of Shakespeare's youth: H.'s "Caveat" &c., 1907.
Harmer (Ernest George). *The coins & medals of the Allan Library. [Repr. f. London Quarterly Rev., Jan. 1888. P527]. 8°. [1888]
Harmer (H. R.), *auctioneer.* Cat. of sheets of stamps in the Mayfair find. Auction, Nov. 9, 1925. [*Illust.*] 4°. [1925]
Harmer (Sidney Frederic) & D. G. Lillie. List of collecting stations, *see* BRIT. ANTARCTIC EXPED., 1910–13. Zoology, v2, 1914–20.
Harmer (Thomas). Obs. on passages of Scripture. 4v. [v1, 2, 2nd ed. w. new obs. f. papers of Sir J. Chardin. v3, 4, w. a spec. of obs. on the classics, Josephus & Jerome]. 8°. 1776–87
Harmonia.
*Harmonia conf. fidei &c., 1581, *see* CONFESSIONS.
Harmonia sacra, or a choice coll. of Psalm & hymn tunes &c. Publ. by T. Butts. obl.8°. [1744?]
Harmony. *Conversations on h., 1855, *see* CONVERSATIONS.
*H. (An) of the conf. of the faith of the Christ. & reformed churches of Europe, 1586, *see* CONFESSIONS.
H. of Prot. Confessions, 1842, *see* CONFESSIONS.
Harms (Paul).
Vier Jahrzehnte Reichspolitik, 1878–1918. 8°. L. 1924
Harmsworth, *publishing firm.* Harmsworth natural history; compl. survey of the animal kingdom. Contrib. R. Lydekker &c. 3v. 4°. 1910–11
Harmsworth (Cecil Bisshopp).
Dr. Johnson a great Englishman. [P2780]. 8°. 1923
Dr. Johnson's house, Gough Sq. [P2871]. 8°. 1924
Harmsworth (*Sir* Harold Sidney), *aft. Visct. Rothermere, see* ROTHERMERE.
Harmsworth (*Sir* Leicester), *bart., see* NORTHCLIFFE (A. C. W. H., *1st baron*). The N. Collection: pres. to Govt. of Canada by Sir L. H., 1926.
Harnack (C. G. Adolf v.)
Die Briefsamml. d. Apostels Paulus u. d. a. vorkonstantin. chr. Briefsamml. 8°. L. 1926
Erforschtes u. Erlebtes. [Reden u. Aufsätze, N.F., B4]. 8°. Giessen. 1923
Marcion: d. Evangelium v. fremden Gott. 8°. L. 1921
Martin Luther u. d. Grundlegung d. Reform. s8°. 192[8]
Die Mission u. Ausbreitung d. Christentums in d. ersten [3] Jhdten. 4e. durchgearb. A[ufl.] 2B [*pagin. cont.*] 8°. L. 192[4]
Neue Stud. z. lat. Übers. d. [I.] Clemensbriefs. [*Extr. f.* K

Harnack (C. G. Adolf v.) [*continued*].
Preuss. Akad. d. Wiss. Phil.-hist. Cl. Sitz., 1894. P2793]. la8°. 1894
Neue Studien zu Marcion. [Texte u. Unters., B44, H4]. 8°. L. 1923
Die Pfaff'schen Irenäus-Fragmente als Fälschungen Pfaffs nachgewiesen.—Misc. zu d. apostol. Vätern &c. [Texte u. Untersuch. z. Gesch. d. altchr. Lit., N.F., 5iii]. 8°. L. 1900
Der Process d. Christen Apollonius. [*Extr. f.* K. Preuss. Akad. d. Wiss. Phil.-hist. Cl. Sitz., 1893]. [P2793]. la8°. 1893
see MOMMSEN (T.) & H. Zu Apostelgesch. 28, 16 (princeps peregrin.), 1895.
" PORPHYRY, *philosopher*. P., "Gegen d. Christen"; hrsg. A. v. H., 1916.

Harnack (Otto). Das karoling. u. d. byzant. Reich in polit. Bezieh. 8°. Göttingen. 1880

Harness (William).
The state of the Eng. Bible. Repr. f. Edinb. Rev. s8°. 1856
see SHAKESPEARE (W.) Dram. wks.: w. life & notes &c. by W. H., 1830.

Haro, *The house of, see* SALAZAR Y CASTRO (L. DE). Hist. genealóg. de la casa de Haro, t1, 1920.

Harper (Charles George).
The Hardy country: lit. landmarks of the Wessex novels. 8°. 1904
The Kentish coast. 8°. 1914
A literary man's London. 8°. 1926
A Londoner's own London. 8°. [1927]
The Manchester & Glasgow road. [2nd & rev. ed.] [v1], London to M. s8°. [1924]
On the road in Holland: notes &c. 8°. [1922]
Queer things about London. s8°. [1923]
see TEIGNMOUTH (*Comm.* H. N. S., *5th baron*) & C. G. H. The smugglers, 2v, 1923.

Harper (George McLean). Wordsworth's French daughter: the story of h. birth &c. s8°. Princeton [U.S.] 1921

Harper (Ida Husted), *see* HISTORY. Hist. of woman suffrage, v4–6, 1883–1920; ed. I. H. H., 1902–22.

Harper (*Rear-Adm.* John Ernest Troyte).
The truth about Jutland. 8°. [1927]

Harper (Malcolm M'Lachlan). Rambles in Galloway. 8°. E. 1876

Harper (Thomas), *Freemason, see* DERMOTT (L.) Constit. of free-masonry &c.; rev. &c., w. add. by T. H., 1801.

Harper's Monthly Magazine. European ed. v140–156. la8°. 1919–28
Index, v1–50, 1850–75. la8°. N.Y. 1875

Harph (Henricus de), *see* HENRICUS, *de Herph.*

Harpsfield (Nicholas) [HARPESFELD]. *Dialogi sex contra summi Pontificatus appugnatores & pseudo-martyres. Nunc primum ab Alano Copo ed. s4°. Antverpiae. 1566

Harrach (Carl *Graf* **v.),** *see* WALDSTEIN (A. v.) Briefe an C. v. H. (1625–27); hrsg. v. F. Tadra, 1879.

Harraden (*Miss* Beatrice). Patuffa. s8°. [1923]
Rachel. s8°. [1926]
Spring shall plant. s8°. [1920]
Youth calling. s8°. [1924]

Harradine (C.) *Hand guide to Lichfield cathedral. 8th ed. s8°. Lichfield. 1906

Harrau (*l'abbé* de). Hist. polit. & relig. de Bergues-St.-Winoc. 2p. [p2 *ed.* C. de Croocq]. 8°. Dunkerque *&* Bergues. 1906–12

Harries (Frederick James).
The Welsh Elizabethans. 8°. Pontypridd. 1924

Harrington (Barnaby), *ps., see* BRATHWAIT (R.)

Harrington (James). Oceana. Ed. w. notes by S. B. Liljegren. [Skrifter utg. av Vetenskaps-soc. i Lund, 4]. la8°. Heidelberg. 1924

Harris, *islands.* The islands of N.H. & S.H. w. Isl. of Lewis. For sale by Knight &c. fol. [1925]

Harris (Caleb Fiske), *see* BROWN UNIVERSITY. Anthony mem.: cat. of H. Coll. of Amer. poetry, w. notes by J. C. Stockbridge, 1886.

Harris (Carlyle W.) The trial of C. W. H. for poisoning his wife, Helen Potts. 8°. N.Y. 1892

Harris (Charles), *rector of Colwall.* Creeds or no creeds? 8°. 1922

Harris (Charles Edward Smith), *M.B., see* SMITH (C. E.) From the deep of the sea: diary; ed. by h. son, C. E. S. H., 1922.

Harris (Charles Reginald Schiller). Duns Scotus. 2v. 8°. O. 1927

Harris (David Fraser). Life & science. s8°. [1923]

Harris (Ethel Alice C., *Lady*), *wife of Sir H. P. Harris.*
Portrait medals of a generation. Modelled by E. A. C. H. Intr. note by G. F. Hill. la8°. 1928

Harris (F. R.), *of New College, Oxford.*
J. N. Tata: chron. of h. life. 8°. 1925

Harris (Frank).
Contemp. portraits. [s1], 2, 4. 8°. N.Y. 1915–24
Oscar Wilde, h. life & confessions [*w.* mem. of O. W., by G. B. Shaw]. 2v. 8°. 1918

Harris (Franklin Stewart) & N. I. Butt.
The fruits of Mormonism. s8°. N.Y. 1925

Harris (George Montague). Local govt. in many lands. 8°. 1926

Harris (H. G.) Plate glass, *see* POWELL (H. J.) Princ. of glass-making, 1883.

Harris (Henry John). Nat. health insurance in Gt. Brit., *see* UNITED STATES: LAB. Bull. 312, 1923.

Harris (Henry Wilson).
What the League of Nations is. s8°. [1925]

Harris (Howell), *1714–73, see* JACKSON (T.) Lib. of Xtn. biog., v12, 1840.

Harris (James). *Hermes: or, a philosoph. inquiry conc. language & universal grammar. s8°. 1751
Works. Life by h. son. 8°. O. 1841

Harris (James Rendel).
The comb in human hist. [P2876]. la8°. C. 1927
The early colonists of the Mediterranean. [Repr. f. Bull. of John Rylands Lib., v10]. 8°. M'ter. 1926
Eucharistic origins. la8°. C. 1927
The finding of the "Mayflower." 8°. M'ter. 1920
The masque of the apple. 8°. M'ter. 1920
Souvenirs of the "Mayflower" tercent. Ed. J. R. H. [Nos. 1–4 in 1v]. 8°. M'ter. 1920
Testimonies. By R. H. w. assist. of V. Burch. p2. 8°. C. 1920
The twelve apostles. la8°. C. 1927
What was the afikoman? [P2876]. la8°. C. 1927
see AHIKAR. The story of A., [*ed.*] H. &c., 2nd ed., 1913.
" CLARK (A. C.) & J. R. H. F. C. Conybeare, 1926.
" FOX (G.) New appreciations; foreword by J. R. H., 1925.
" TATIAN. Perfection acc. to the Saviour; *tr.*, ed. R. Harris, 1923; 1924.

—— **& S. K. Jones.** The Pilgrim press: bks. pr. at Leyden by Pilgrim Fathers [W. Brewster &c.] With chap. by Dr. Plooij. 8°. C. 1922

Harris (John), *D.D., principal of New Coll., London.*
Britannia: moral claims of seamen. 8°. 1837
The great commission. 8°. 1842

Harris (John), *gent.* Peace & not warre: or the moderator: case of the Common-wealth as to sev. councils &c., 1636–59. s8°. 1659

Harris (John H.)
The chartered millions. Rhodesia &c. 8°. [1920

Harris (Mary Dormer). Unknown Warwickshire. 8°. [1924]

Harris (Murray). Egypt under the Egyptians. 8°. 1925

Harris (Richard), *D.D.* Concordia Anglicana de primatu eccl. regio; adv. Becanum De dissidio Anglicano. s8°. Londini. 1612

Harris (Robert), *D.D.* Works. Rev., corr. & coll. into one vol. w. an addit. of sermons. [*4 pagin.; each work has sep. tp.*, 1653]. fol. 1654

Harris (Thaddeus Mason). Discourses, illust. freemasonry, *see* OLIVER (G.) Golden remains &c., v5, 1850.
The natural hist. of the Bible. 8°. 1824

Harris (Thomas), *F.R.I.B.A.* Hist. & descr. sketch of Marylebone Gardens. [*Illust.*] la8°. *f.p.c., Chiswick Press.* 1887

Harris (Thomas), *Wesleyan minister.* The Christian minister in earnest, mem. of W. Bramwell &c. s8°. 1846

Harris (Walter Burton). France, Spain & the Rif. 8°. 1927
Morocco that was. 8°. E. 1921

Harrison (A. W.) The beginnings of Arminianism, to the Synod of Dort. 8°. 1926

Harrison (Ada M.) & R. S. Austin.
Some Tuscan cities. 8°. [1924]
Some Umbrian cities. 8°. [1925]

Harrison (Austin). Frederic Harrison: thoughts &c. 8°. [1926]
Lifting mist. s8°. [1924]

Harrison (*Mrs.* Burton). An edelweiss of the Sierras, Golden-rod & o. t. s8°. 1892

Harrison (Charles), *F.R.A.I.* Ancient warriors of the North Pacific: the Haidas &c., w. acc. of Queen Charlotte Islands. 8°. 1925

Harrison (Cuthbert Woodville), *see* MALAY. Illust. guide to Fed. M. States; ed. C. W. H., 1920.

Harrison (Elizabeth). Misc. on moral & relig. subjects in prose & verse. 8°. 1756

Harrison (Ernest John). Lithuania past & present. 8°. [1922]

Harrison (Ethel Bertha), *wife of Frederic Harrison.* The freedom of women. Agst. female suffrage. [P2708]. 8º. 1908
see HARRISON (F.) Mem. & essays of E. H., 1917.

Harrison (Fred), *vicar-choral of York Minster.*
York Minster. s8º. [1927]

Harrison (Frederic).
An address, Nov. 1894, Gibbon commem. [P2493]. 8º. [1894]
Address to Souvenir Normand on Bodiam Castle. [P2585]. s8º. Hawkhurst. 1903
An appeal to Liberal Unionists. [Repr. f. "Contemp. Rev."] [P2484]. 8º. 1889
The choice of books & o. lit. pieces. [repr.] s8º. 1887
The city of Bath. [P2564]. 8º. 1921
De senectute: more last words. 8º. [1923]
The decay of Parliament. [P2754]. 8º. *n.d.*
The forger party. [*Extr. f.* Home Rule Union. Journal, No. 13. P2753]. 8º. 1889
Grant Allen, 1848–1899. Addr., Woking, Oct. 27, 1899. [P2488, 2710]. s8º. *p.p.* 1899
In mem. of W. D. Hertz. Address. [P2488]. s8º. 1890
Mem. & essays of Ethelbertha Harrison. [P2617]. s8º. *p.f.p.d.* Bath. 1917
Mr. Gladstone!—or anarchy. [P2484]. 8º. *n.d.*
The new calendar of great men. Biog. of the 559 worthies in the Positivist Cal. of A. Comte. Ed. F. H., S. H. Swinny & F. S. Marvin. n. ed. rev. 8º. 1920
Politics & education. Address. [P2487, 2710]. s8º. 1887
The progress of industry; or, Mr. Brassey on work & wages. [Repr., w. add., f. "Fortnightly Rev."] [P2484]. 8º. 1872
A proposal for a new hist. bibliography. [P2493]. 8º. 1896
A real upper house. [Repr. f. The Eng. Review]. [P2487, 2585, 2710]. s8º. 1910
The religion of duty. [Lect. P2710]. s8º. Phila. 1901
Sociology. [Repr. f. Sociolog. Rev., April 1910]. [P2707]. la8º. [1910]
La tâche du nouveau siècle. [Extr. de la Revue Internat. de Soc.] [P2463]. 8º. 1914
Unveiling of marble bust of A. Carnegie by F. H., 1908, *see* CARNEGIE LIB., *Keighley.*
Veteran's appeal to labour leaders. [Repr. f. "Daily Chron."] [P2484]. 8º. *n.p. n.d.*
see HARRISON (A.) F. H.: thoughts & memories, 1926.

Harrison (George Bagshawe).
Shakespeare's fellows: brief chron. 8º. [1923]
see LAMBORN (E. A. G.) & G. B. H. Shakespeare, the man & h. stage, 1923.

Harrison (George L.) The remains of William Penn: Pennsylvania's plea [*for removal*] &c. 8º. *p.p.* Phila. 1882

Harrison (H. D.) Industrial psychology & the production of wealth. 8º. [1924]

Harrison (Henry), *O.B.E.* The Irish case considered. With pref. by Sir H. Plunkett. [P2405]. 8º. 1920

Harrison (Henry Sydnor). Saint Teresa. Novel. s8º. [1922]

Harrison (Jane Ellen).
Aspects, aorists & the classical tripos. [P2404]. 8º. C. 1919
Epilegomena to the st. of Greek religion. 8º. C. 1921
Prolegomena to the st. of Greek religion. 3rd ed. 8º. C. 1922
Remin. of a student's life. 2nd impr. s8º. 1925
Themis. 2nd ed. rev. w. suppl. notes. 8º. C. 1927
—— **& H. Mirrlees.** The book of the bear. 21 tales tr. f. Russian, w. pref. &c. s8º. *Nonesuch Press.* 1926

Harrison (Paul W.) The Arab at home. 8º. 1925

Harrison (Percival T.) Bungalow residences: handbook in building. 2nd ed. rev. 8º. 1920

Harrison (Percy Neale).
The problem of the Pastoral Epistles. 8º. O. 1921

Harrison (Robert), *see* PEEL (A.) Brownists in Norwich &c. about 1580, w. A treatise of the Church & Kgdm. of Christ by R. H. [R. Harrison ?], 1920.

Harrison (T.) Bookbinding craft & industry. s8º. [1926]

Harrison (*Maj.-Gen.* **Thomas).** Speeches & prayers of the late king's judges, *viz.*, Maj. Gen. H., J. Carew &c.: the times of th. death &c. [*Last leaf imperf.*] s8º. 1660

Harrison (Thomas), *Baptist minister, of Wild Street.* Poems on divine subjects. Add. poem to mem. of B. Stinton. [*w. scp. tp.*] s8º. 1719

Harrison (William), *H.M.'s preacher at Hyton, Lancs.*
The difference of hearers. s8º. 1614

Harrison (William), *member of the House of Keys.* Mem. of Capt. J. Greenhalgh, 1640–51, *see* MANX SOC. Manx. misc., v2, 1880.

Harrison (William Henry), *president of the U.S., see* GOEBEL (D. B.) W. H. H., 1926.

Harro-Harring (Paul). Poland under the dominion of Russia. [Tr.] s8º. Boston [Mass.] 1834

Harrop (Angus John). England & New Zealand, f. Tasman to the Taranaki War. Intr. by Earl Jellicoe. s8º. [1926]

Harrow [& HARROW SCHOOL]. Harrow School register, 1845–1925. Ed. J. H. Stogden. [4th ed.] s2. 2v. 8º. 1925

Harrow (Benjamin). Eminent chemists of our time. 8º. 1921
From Newton to Einstein: changing conceptions of the universe. [3rd impr.] s8º. [1921]

Harry (George Owen). Genealogy of James, king of Gt. Brittayne &c. [*tp. mutilated*]. s8º. [1604]

Harry (Gérard). Léopold II. s8º. Turnhout. 1920
see PELTZER (L. & A.) The P. case; by G. H., 1928.

Harry (Myriam) [*Mme.* PERRAULT-HARRY].
L'île de volupté. Bois orig. de P. Falké. 8º. *n.d.*
La petite fille de Jérusalem. Préf. de J. Lemaitre. s8º. 1914
La sainte folie de Jérusalem, choses vues, *see* ŒUVRES libres, 15, 1922.
Le tendre cantique de Siona. s8º. 1922
„ „ *for a. ed., see* ŒUVRES libres, 4, 1921.
La vie amoureuse de Cléopâtre. s8º. [1926]

Harṣadeva [HARSHA]. Priyadarśikā. Sanskrit drama. Tr. G. K. Nariman, A. V. W. Jackson &c., w. intr. & notes. Text in translit. 8º. N.Y. 1923

Harsha, *see* HARṢADEVA.

Harshberger (John William).
Text-book of mycology & plant pathology. 8º. [1917]

Hart, *family of, see* HART (H. T.) Family hist. of H. of Donegal, 1907.

Hart (*Capt.* **Basil Henry Liddell).** Great captains unveiled. [Jenghiz Khan & Sabutai—Mar. de Saxe—Gustavus Adolphus—Wallenstein—Wolfe]. 8º. E. 1927
A greater than Napoleon: Scipio Africanus. 8º. E. 1926
Paris or the future of war. s8º. 1925

Hart (Bernard). The psychology of insanity. [repr.] s8º. C. 1920
Psychopathology, its development &c. 8º. C. 1927

Hart (Ernest). Lectures on Japanese art work. With cat. of objects exhib. [Soc. of Arts &c.] [P2418]. 8º. 1887

Hart (F. H.)
Hist. of Lee & its neighbourhood. 8º. *p.p.* Lee. 1882

Hart (George). The violin, its famous makers & th. imitators. *la. paper copy.* la8º. 1875

Hart (Hans). Wunderkinder. Roman. s8º. L. 1915

Hart (Heber Leonidas), *K.C.*
The bulwarks of peace. s8º. [1918]
The law of banking, w. app. on law of Stock Exchange. 3rd ed. la8º. 1914

Hart (Henry George), *headmaster of Sedbergh, see* COULTON (G. G.) A Victorian schoolmaster: H. H. of S., 1923.

Hart (Henry Travers).
The family hist. of Hart of Donegal. 8º. 1907

Hart (Horace). Rules for compositors & readers at the Univ Press, Oxford. 26th ed. s8º. [1921

Hart (Isabel). Hist. sketches of womans' miss. societies in America & Eng. Intr. by I. H. s8º. Boston [Mass.] 187

Hart (Ivor Blashka).
Makers of science. Intr. by C. Singer. s8º. 192
Mechanical investig. of L. da Vinci. 8º. 192
—— **& W. Laidler.** Elem. aeronautical science. s8º. O. 192

Hart (John), *Chester Herald, see* RAINOLDS (J.) Summe o the conference between J. R. & J. Hart &c., 1588.

Hart (John), *D.D.* *The Port-Royal of Holy Scr., or a new concordance &c. [Pref. by P. Forbes]. 3rd ed. rev. & enl by J[ohn] H[art]. s8º. 165

Hart (John Henry Arthur), *see* ECCLESIASTICUS. E.: Greek text of Codex 248; ed. w. textual comm. & proleg. by J. H. A. H., 1909.

Hart (Joseph).
Hymns &c. w. suppl. & app. (*pag. cont.*) 9th ed. s8º. 177

Hart (Morris D.) & W. W. Smith.
The princ. of sound signalling. 8º. 192

Hart (Rabie J.) Chronos: comp. chronology, 8000 B.C. to 1700 A.D. 2nd ed. rev. 8º. 192

Hart (Robert Edward). Les volontaires Mauriciens au armées (1914–18). [P2427]. s8º. Ile Maurice. 191

Hart (William), *see* CLORISTON (H.), *ps.*

Harte (Francis Bret).
Compl. poet. works. a.'s copyright ed. s8º. 188
Letters. Assembled & ed. G. B. Harte. 8º. [1926
Sel. works in prose & poetry. Essay by J. M. Bellew. 8º. [1887
That heathen Chinee & o. p. s8º. [187

Harte (Walter James). Sir F. Drake. s8º. 192

Hartenau (Alexander Josef, *Graf* **von)** [*prince* ALEXANDER *of Battenberg, to 1889; and* ALEXANDER I, *prince of Bulgaria, f. 1879 to 1886*], *see* CORTI (E. C.) Alex. v. Battenberg, s. Kampf mit d. Zaren u. Bismarck, 1920.

Hartert (Ernst), *see* WITHERBY (H. F.), *ed.* Pract. hdbk. of Brit. birds, 2v, 1920–24.

Hartgill (John), *see* STOURTON (C., *baron*). The Stourton tragedy, 1557, 1901.

Hartgill (Robert), *see* STOURTON (C., *baron*). The Stourton tragedy, 1557, 1901.

Hartig (Franz de Paula, *Graf* **v.),** *1789–1865, see* METTERNICH (*Fürst*). M.-H.: Briefwechsel, 1848–51; hrsg. F. Hartig, 1923.

Hartig (Michael). Augsburgs Kunst. 4°. St. 1922

Hartig (Otto). C. Schorer v. Memmingen u. s. " Sprachverderber " (1643), *see* KÖNIGL. AKAD. D. WISS. ZU MÜNCHEN. Phil. Cl., Sitz., 1921.

Die Gründung d. Münchener Hofbibl. durch Albrecht V. u. J. J. Fugger, 1917, *see* KÖNIGL. AKAD. D. W. ZU MÜNCHEN. Abhdlgn., B28, 1917.

Hartinger (Anton), *see* DALLA TORRE (C. W. VON). Atlas der Alpenflora; gemalt von A. H., 4B, 1884.

Hartker, *hermit, d. 1011 or 1017.* Antiphonale officii monast. écrit par H., 1900, *see* ANTIPHONALE.

Hartknoch (Christoph). De republ. Polonica libri 2. [*Foll. by* Diss. de Curonorum & Semgallorum republica &c. def. B. J. Niresius. *&* De orig. Pomeranicis. *w. sep. pagin.*] s8°. Lipsiae. 1698

Sel. diss. hist. de variis rebus Prussicis, *see* PETRUS *de Duisburg.* Chron. Prussiae, 1679.

Hartland (Edwin Sidney).

The evolution of kinship. [P2601]. 8°. O. 1922

Primitive law. 8°. [1924]

Primitive society. s8°. [1921]

Hartley (Catherine Gasquoine) [*Mrs.* WALTER GALLICHAN].

Mother & son: character formation in children. 8°. [1923]

Spain revisited. A summer holiday in Galicia. 8°. [1911]

see GALLICHAN (W. M.) Story of Seville; w. 3 ch. on the artists of S. by C. G. H., 1925.

Hartley (David), *M.P., see* GUTTRIDGE (G. H.) D. H., M.P., advoc. of conciliation, 1774–83, 1926.

Hartley (Dorothy) & M. M. Elliot. Life & work of the people of Eng. (15 c.) la8°. 1925

Hartley (George Inness), *see* BEEBE (W. C.), G. I. H. &c. Tropical wild life in Brit. Guiana, v1, 1917.

Hartley (Harold), *see* BIRMINGHAM: MUSEUM & ART GALLERY. Cat. of drawings &c. lent by H. H., 1924.

Hartley (*Mrs.* Jonathan Scott), *see* INNESS (G.) Works by G. I., coll. of J. S. H., sold, 1927.

Hartlib (Samuel), *see* TURNBULL (G. H.) S. H.: sketch of h. life & h. rel. to J. A. Comenius, 1920.

Hartlieb (Johann Friedrich), *see* FRICK (J. G.) De Druidis philos.; resp. J. F. H., 1731.

Hartman (Carl Johan). Handbok i Skandinaviens flora. Utg. af C. Hartman. 2d *in* 1v. (d1, 11e uppl., d2, 10e uppl). 8°. 1871–79

Hartmann (C. R. Eduard v.)

Philosophie d. Unbewussten. 7e A. [2B in 1]. 8°. 1876

The religion of the future. Tr. E. Dare. s8°. 1886

see DU PREL (C. *Frhr.*) Der gesunde Menschenverstand: J. C. Fischer contra E. v. H., 1872.

,, STRIEGEL (J.) " Wozu " dienen Vernunft-Anlagen im Hinblick auf H.'s " Philos. d. Unbewussten " &c. [1896].

Hartmann (Cyril Hughes). La belle Stuart: mem. of court &c. in times of Frances T. Stuart, Duchess of Richmond &c. 8°. 1924

The cavalier spirit & its infl. on the life &c. of R. Lovelace, 1618–58. 8°. 1925

Story of the roads. Intr. by Lt.-Col. A. Hacking. 8°. [1927]

The vagabond duchess: Hortense Mancini, duchesse Mazarin. 8°. 1926

Hartmann (Fernande).

L'agriculture dans l'anc. Egypte. la8°. 1923

Hartmann (Franz), *theosophist.* Die weisse u. schwarze Magie. 8°. L. [1894]

Hartmann (Jul.), *Copenhagen.* Flow of water & mercury in pipes: O. Reynolds' law of similarity, *see* KONG. DAN. VID. SELSK. Skrifter, Række 8, B10, 1925–26.

Hartmann (Julius), *ed.* Aelteste katechet. Denkmale d. evang. Kirche oder die kleinen Katechismen, 1527–29. s8°. St. 1844

Hartmann (Ludo Moritz). Gesch. Italiens im Mittelalter, B4i. Die Ottonische Herrschaft, *see* GESCH. D. EUROP. STAATEN, 1915.

Hartmann (Nicolai). Ethik. 8°. 1926

Hartmann (Richard). Die Welt d. Islams, *see* ALTE ORIENT (DER). Beihefte, H11, 1927.

Hartnaccius (Daniel). Hist. univ. eccl. & civilis &c. juxta ord. P. Laurenbergi Chron. obs. s8°. Hamburgi. 1686

see MICRÆLIUS (J.) Hist. eccl.; ed. cura D. H. & contin., 1699.

Hartnacke (Wilhelm). Das Problem d. Auslese d. Tüchtigen. 2e A. [P2733]. 8°. L. 1916

Hartog (Philip J.) The Owens College. [P2875]. 4°. 1900

Hartopp (Henry), *see* LEICESTER. Register of Freemen, 1196–1770; abstr. & ed. by H. H., 1927.

Hart's Army List, 1851, 1857, 1858, 1859, 1865, 1867. 8°. 1851–67

Hartsen (Frederik Antonius v.)

Grundlegung v. Aesthetik, Moral &c. [P2481]. 8°. Halle. 1869

Grundriss d. Philos. Abt. 1. [P2475]. 8°. Nordhausen. 1875

Grundzüge d. Logik. [P2481]. 8°. 1873

Grundzüge d. Psychologie. 2e A. [P2475]. 8°. Halle. 1877

Grundzüge d. Wissenschaft d. Glücks. [P2481]. s8°. Halle. 1869

Moral d. Pessimismus, nach Veranl. v. Taubert's 'Der Pessimismus u. s. Gegner.' 2e A. [P2475]. 8°. L. [1874]

Unters. ü. Logik. [P2481]. 8°. L. 1869

Unters. ü. Psych.: Anmerk. z. R. Zimmermann's " Philos. Propädeutik " &c. [P2481]. 8°. L. 1869

Verm. philosoph. Abhgn. [P2475]. 8°. Heidelberg. 1876

Hartshorne (Charles Henry). *Eng. medieval embroidery. [Pract. chap. *signed* E. C. P.] s8°. 1848

*Illustrations of Alnwick, Prudhoe & Warkworth [by O. Jewitt, engr. by J. H. LeKeux. 92 plates, w. letterpress by C. H. H.] 4°. *for priv. distrib. n.p.* [1857?]

Hartshorne (Emily Sophia). Memorials of Holdenby. 8°. 1868

Hartson (Hall). Countess of Salisbury, *see* INCHBALD (*Mrs.* E.) Brit. theatre, v16, 1808.

Hartung (Fritz). Deutsche Gesch., 1871–1919. 2e neu bearb. A. 8°. Bonn. 1924

Deut. Verfassungsgesch. v. 15. Jhdt. b. z. Gegenwart, 2e A, 1922, *see* GRUNDR. D. GESCHICHTSWISS.; Meister, 2iv, 1922.

Hartwig (Georg), *ps.* [*i.e.* EMMY KOEPPEL].

Haus Bickenbach. Roman. 5. A. s8°. St. [1914]

Hartzenbusch (Eugenio) [*ps.* MAXIRIARTH]. Unos cuantos seudónimos de escritores españoles. Recog. &c. por Maxiriarth. Prol. d. J. Fernández Bremon. ed. corr. y aum. s8°. 1904

Haruaki, *see* SHUNSHŌ (K.)

Harvard African Studies. v4. 4°. [O.] 1923

see MURRAY (G. W.) Eng.-Nubian comp. dict., 1923. [4.]

Harvard Bibliographies: library series. v2. 8°. Camb. [U.S.A.] 1922

see MYERS (D. P.) Man. of colls. of treaties &c., 1922. [2.]

Harvard Economic Studies. v3, 8, 14, 21, 27, 29. 8°. Camb. [Mass.] 1912–26

see ALBION (R. G.) Forests & sea power, 1926. [29.]

,, BRISTOL (L. M.) Social adaptation, 1915. [14.]

,, COPELAND (M. T.) Cotton manufact. industry of U.S., 1912. [8.]

,, KLEIN (J.) The Mesta, 1273–1836, 1920. [21.]

,, RICH (W. E.) Hist. of U.S. post office, to 1829, 1924. [27.]

Harvard Historical Studies. v18, 20, 23, 25, 26, 28. la8°. Camb. [Mass.] 1920

see DAVID (C. W.) Robert Curthose, 1920. [25.]

,, FULLER (J. V.) Bismarck's diplomacy, 1922. [26.]

,, HEMMEON (M. DE W.) Burgage tenure, 1914. [20.]

,, LEWIS (G. R.) The stannaries, 1924. [3.]

,, LORD (R. H.) Orig. of war of 1870, 1924. [28.]

,, —— The 2nd partition of Poland, 1915. [23.]

,, LYBYER (A. H.) The govt. of the Ottoman Emp., 1913. [18.]

Harvard Oriental Series. v26, 27, 31, 32. la8°. Camb., Mass. 1925–26

see KEITH (*Sir* A. B.) Relig. &c. of Veda & Upanishads, 1925. [31, 32.]

,, VIKRAMĀDITYA. Vikrama's adv.; ed. &c. F. Edgerton, 2p, 1926. [26, 27.]

Harvard Semitic Series.

see REISNER (G. A.), C. S. FISHER & D. G. LYON. Harvard excav. at Samaria, 1908–10, 2v, 1924.

Harvard Studies & notes in philology & lit. v1, 2, 6, 8, 9. 8°. Boston [U.S.] 1892–1903

Brown (A. C. L.) Iwain, 1903. [8.]

Farley (F. E.) Scand. infl. in Eng. rom. movt., 1903. [9.]

Kittredge (G. L.) Arthur & Gorlagon, 1903. [8.]

Harvard Studies & notes in philology & lit. [*continued*].
Kittredge (G. L.) Authorship of the Eng. Romaunt of the Rose, 1892. [1.]
Manly (J. M.) Lok-Sounday, 1892. [1.]
—— Obs. on lang. of Chaucer's Legend of good women, 1893. [2.]
Neilson (W. A.) Origins &c. of the Court of Love, 1899. [6.]
Schofield (W. H.) Source &c. of 7th novel of 7th day in the Decameron, 1893. [2.]
Shelden (E. S.) Orig. of Eng. names of letters of the alphabet—Further notes, 1892–3. [1, 2.]

Harvard Studies in Comparative Lit. v1, 5, 6. 8º. Camb. 1920–22
see LEACH (H. G.) Angevin Brit. & Scandinavia, 1921. [6.]
,, SANTAYANA (G.) 3 philos. poets, 3rd impr., 1922. [1.]
,, SCHOFIELD (W. H.) Mythical bards & life of W. Wallace, 1920. [5.]

Harvard Studies in English. v3. 8º. Cambridge [Mass.] 1925
see BERNBAUM (E.) Drama of sensibility, 1925. [3.]

Harvard Studies in Romance Languages. v4. 8º. Camb. [Mass.] 1920
see WRIGHT (C. H. C.) French classicism, 1920. [4.]

Harvard Theological Studies. [v] 5, 10–12. Cambridge, *Harvard*. 1918–25
see ATHOS. Cat. of Greek MSS. in library of the monastery of Vatopedi on Mt. A.; by S. Eustratiades &c., 1924. [11.]
,, —— Cat. of Greek MSS. in library of the Laura on Mt. A.; by Spyridon, monk &c., 1925. [12.]
,, CONYBEARE (F. C.) Russian dissenters, 1921. [10.]
,, MACARIUS, *of Egypt, St., the elder.* Macarii anecdota: 7 unpubl. homilies; ed. G. L. Marriott, 1918. [5.]

Harvard University [HARVARD COLL.] Cat. Bibl. Harvardianæ Cantab. Nov.-Anglorum. 8º. Bostoniæ. 1790
Cat. of coll. of engravings bequeathed to H. College by F. C. Gray. By L. Thies. 4º. Cambridge [U.S.] 1869
,, ,, [Index of portraits in Gray's coll. MS.] 4º. *n.d.*
Cat. of the library of H.U. 3v [v3, System. index]. 8º. C., Mass. 1830
,, ,, ...First suppl. 8º. C., Mass. 1834
Cat. of the maps & charts in the lib. of H.U. 8º. C., Mass. 1831
Cat. of the officers & stud., 1865–66, 1st term. 2nd ed. s8º. Cambridge. 1866
*Student-life at H., 1876, *see* TRIPP (G. H.)
FOGG ART MUSEUM.
Coll. of mediaeval & Renaissance paintings. la8º. Camb. [U.S.] 1919
see ART STUDIES; ed. by members of Dept. of the Fine Arts at H., v1, 2, 1923–24.
,, ELIOT (C. W.) 90th birthday of C. W. E., 1925.

Harvard (W. M.) A narr. of the establ. &c. of the mission to Ceylon & India, &c. 8º. 1823

Harvey Society of New York. The Harvey Lectures, deliv. under auspices of the H. Soc., 1916–17, 1917–18, 1918–19. By J. B. Haldane &c. ser. 12–14. 8º. Phila. [1918]–20

Harvey (Alexander Gordon Cummins). Memoir. [Mostly wr. by L. Wilcox]. Ed. w. intr. by F. W. Hirst. 8º. [1925]

Harvey (D. C.) The French régime in Prince Edward Island. 8º. New Haven, *Yale*. 1926

Harvey (Eustace John). Law of Property Act, 1922. How will it work? 8º. 1923

Harvey (Francis). [Gainsborough. MS. records of pictures &c. 2v.] fol. *n.d.*
Genealog. table of the families of Sheridan, Lefanu & Knowles. Compiled by F. H. Priv. pr. for J. McHenry. 4º. 1875
[Romney. MS. records of pictures &c. 2v.] fol. *n.d.*

Harvey (Gabriel) [*ps.* RICHARD LICHFIELD]. Foure letters & certeine sonnets: touching R. Greene &c., 1592. [Bodley Head Quartos, ed. G. B. Harrison]. s8º. 1923

Harvey (Godfrey Eric). Hist. of Burmah, to 1824. Pref. by Sir R. C. Temple. 8º. 1925

Harvey (H. W.)
Biological chemistry & physics of sea water. 8º. C. 1928

Harvey (J. D. M.)
see BURFORD (B.) & J. D. M. H. Some lesser known architecture of London, 1925.
,, RAMSEY (S. C.) & J. D. M. H. Small houses of the late Georgian period, v2, 1923.

Harvey (John), *see* COMPETITION: st. in human motive: by J. H. &c., 1919.

Harvey (*Col.* John Robert), *D.S.O.* Hist. of the 5th (Royal Irish) Regt. of Dragoons, 1689–1799, aft. 5th Royal Irish Lancers, 1858–1921. By Col. J. R. H., completed to 1921 by Lt.-Col. H. A. Cape. 4º. *f.p.c.o.* Aldershot. 1923

Harvey (*Mrs.* Marie Turner), *see* DEWEY (E.) New schools for old; regen. of the Porter school [*work of H.*], 1920.

Harvey (Thomas William), *see* COLVILLE (H. C. A.) H., 1918.

Harvey (William), *F.S.A.Scot.*
Picturesque Ayrshire. s8º. Dundee. *n.d.*

Harvey (William), *M.D.*, *see* KEYNES (G. L.) Bibliog., 1928.
see SPENCER (H. R.) W. H., obstetric physician, &c.: Harveian oration, 1921.
,, WHITE (*Sir* W. HALE-). Bacon, Gilbert & H., 1927.

Harvey (William), *travelling student of the Royal Acad. of Arts.*
The preserv. of St. Paul's Cath. & o. buildings. 8º. 1925

Harvey (William Henry) & O. W. Sonder. Flora Capensis: systematic descr. of plants of Cape Colony, Caffraria & Natal. Ed. Sir W. Thiselton-Dyer. v5. ii, iii. 8º. 1913–25

Harvey-Gibson (Robert John).
Brit. plant names & th. derivations. s8º. 1923

Harvie-Brown (John A.)
A verteb. fauna of Scotland. v11. 8º. E. 1911
see EVANS (A. H.) A fauna of the Tweed area, 1911. [11.]

Harwood (*Mrs.* Harold Marsh), *see* JESSE (F. TENNYSON).

Harwood (Henry Cecil). Judgment eve. Stories. s8º. 1924

Harwood (James), *B.D.*
A plea for the Common Prayer Book. s8º. 1657

Harwood (W. A.) The free atmosphere in India, *see* INDIA: METEOROLOG. DEPT. Mem., v24, 1926.

Hasaeus (Theodorus), *see* HASE (THEODOR).

Hasan (Zafar), *see* ZAFAR HASAN (*Khan Sahib Maulvi*).

Hasan-Chalaliantz (Isaiah), *Catholicus of Aghouanik.* Hist. d'Aghovanie, *see* BROSSET (M. F.) Coll. d'histor. arm., t2, 1876.

Hasbach (Wilhelm). Hist. of the Eng. agricult. labourer. Tr. R. Kenyon. 2nd impr. 8º. 1920

Häschen (Eine) u. e. Kätzchengesch., 1872, *see* TANTE AMANDA, *ps.*

Hasdai, *see* CHASDAI.

Hase (*Kapitän* Georg v.) Kiel & Jutland. Tr. A. Chambers & F. A. Holt. 8º. [1920]

Hase (Theodor) [T. HASAEUS]. De Liviathan Jobi, & ceto Jonae disq. [*b. w. h.* Diss. &c., sylloge, 1731]. s8º. Bremae. 1723
Diss. & observ. philolog. sylloge. s8º. Bremae. 1731
Museum historico-philologico-theolog. [*Ed. T. H. & N. Nonnen*]. 2v. [*each in 4p. pagin. cont.*] s8º. Amstelodami. 1728–32
see BIBLIOTHECA HISTORICO-PHILOLOGICO-THEOLOGICA, 8v, 1719–27.

Hasegawa Tatsunosuke, *see* FUTABATEI SHIMEI, *ps.*

Hašek (Jaroslav). Die Abenteuer d. braven Soldaten Schwejk währ. d. Weltkrieges. Übertr. v. G. Reiner. 4B [1, 2, 2e A.] s8º. Prag. 1926–27

Haseloff (Arthur), *see* SAUERLAND (H. V.) & A. H. Der Psalter Erzbischof Egberts v. Trier &c., 1901.

Haseltine (Herbert). Exhib. of equestrian portraits in bronze, 1921. [P2525]. 8º. 1921
Exhib. of sculpture of champion animals, July 8–31st, 1925. (Under auspices of The Field). 8º. 1925.

Hasenbalg (Werner Grote-), *see* GROTE-HASENBALG (W.)

Hasenmüller (Elias).
Jesuiticum jejunium. s8º. Francofurti ad Moenum. 1595

Haskins (Charles Homer).
The Renaissance of the 12th cent. 8º. Camb. [*Mass.*] 1927
St. in the hist. of mediaeval sci. 8º. C., *Mass.* 1924
—— & R. H. Lord.
Some problems of the Peace Conf. 8º. Camb. [U.S.] 1920

Haslehurst (Richard Stafford Tyndale). Penitential discipline of the early church in the first 4 c. 8º. 1921

Haslewood (Francis), *rector of St. Matthew's, Ipswich.*
Mem. of Smarden, Kent. s4º. *p.p.* Ipswich. 1886
The parish of Benenden, Kent, [w.] repr. of This winter's wonders, 1673. 8º. *p.p.* Ipswich. 1889
The parish of Chislet, Kent. la8º. *p.p.* Ipswich. 1887

Hasluck (Frederick William). Athos & its monasteries. 8º. 1924
Letters on relig. & folklore. Annot. by M. M. Hasluck. 8º. 1926
see JEWELL (H. H.) & F. W. H. The church of Our Lady of the Hundred Gates in Paros, 1920.

Haspel (Johann David). De Wilhelmis felicibus. Praes. J. B. Beyschlagio. [P599]. s4º. Wittenbergae. [1694]

Haspels (G. F.) Onder den Brandaris. 3e dr. s8º. A. *n.d.*

Hassall (Arthur).
British hist., chronolog. arranged. 2p [in 1v]. 8º. 1920
European hist., chronolog. arranged, 476–1920. n. ed. s8º. 1920
Hist. [of France] to 1871, *see* BUCHAN (J.), *ed.* Nations of to-day, 1923.
Louis XIV & zenith of Fr. monarchy. [*n. ed. repr.*] s8º. 192-

Hassam (A.) Arabic self-taught (Syrian). Enl. & rev. by N. Odeh. 5th ed. s8°. 1915
Hassanein (Ahmed Mohammed) *Bey, F.R.G.S.* The lost oases. Intr. by Sir R. Rodd. 8°. [1925]
Hassard (John R. G.) Life of John Hughes, 1st abp. of New York, w. extr. f. h. private corr. 8°. N.Y. 1866
Hasse (Adelaide Rosalie). Index to U.S. doc. rel. to for. affairs, 1828–61. [C.I. of Wash., Publ. 185]. 3p. 4°. Wash. 1914–21
Hasse (Carl).
Roger van Brügge, d. Meister v. Flemalle. la8°. Str. 1904
Roger van der Weyden u. Roger van Brügge mit i. Schulen. la8°. Str. 1905
Hasse (Carl Paul). Die deut. Renaissance. 2T. s8°. Meerane i. Sa. 1920–25
Hasse (Faustina) [*born* F. BORDONI], *1693–1783* [*ps.* LA "NUOVA SIRENA"], *see* URBANI (G. M.) La "nuova Sirena" &c., 1890.
Hasse (Johann Adolph), *1699–1783* [*ps.* IL CARO SASSONE], *see* URBANI (G. M.) La "nuova Sirena" &c., 1890.
Hasse (John). The coins &c. of Russia [wr. 1554; pr. in Lat. 1630], Eng. tr. taken f. Hakluyt's Voyages; ed. E. Goldsmid, 1886 [*sep. tp. & pagin.*], *see* ADAMS (C.) Chancellor's voyage to Muscovy &c., 1886.
Hasse (Max). Einsteins Relativitätstheorie. 10e A. [P2490]. 8°. [Magdeburg. 1920]
Hassen (Martin) & J. G. Ulbrecht. Characteres tyranni in Oliverio Cromwello. [P2644]. s4°. Vitembergae. [1712]
Hassia. *De unione personali duarum Domini J. C. naturarum &c. Add. Articulorum symboli apost. &c. expos. [Concordia inter doctores Witeberg. & Imperii &c.] A quibusdam eccl. Hassiae ministris conscr. s8°. Smalcaldiae. 1587
Hassl (Guido). Paul Wilhelm v. Keppler, Rottenburgs gr. Bischof. 8°. St. [1927]
Hastings (A. C. G.), *see* GLOVER (*Sir* J. H.) Voyage of the Dayspring; journal of Sir J. H. G., w. acc. of exped., by H., 1926.
Hastings (Basil Macdonald). Faithful philanderers. s8°. [1923]
The new sin, *see* PLAYS of to-day, v2, 1925.
Hastings (*Lady* Elizabeth), *1682–1739.*
see GILBERT (M.) Extr. of journal; w. acc. of E. H., 1769.
,, JACKSON (T.) Lib. of Xtn. biog., v11, Lady E. H., by T. Barnard, 1839.
Hastings (Hugh J.) Ancient Amer. politics. Ed. & rev. by Hugh Hastings. la8°. N.Y. [1886]
Hastings (James), *D.D.* The Christian doctrine of prayer. Ed. J. H. [Gt. Xtn. doctrines]. [3rd imp.] 8°. E. [1917]
The great texts of the Bible. Ed. J. H. [20v *& Index, bound sep.*] 8°. E. 1910–19
see ENCYCLOPÆDIA of relig. & ethics; ed. J. H., v11, 12, 1920–21; Index vol., 1926.
Hastings (Peter). S. P. Q. R. s8°. 1926
Hastings (*Rt. Hon.* Warren), *Gov.-General of India.*
Letters to Sir J. Macpherson. Ed. H. Dodwell. 8°. [1927]
see PEACEY (H.) W. H. [play], 1928.
Hastings (William Thomson).
Syllabus of Amer. lit. s8°. Chicago. [1923]
Hatch (*Mrs.* Cora L. V.), *aft. (1) Tappan, (2) Richmond.*
Disc. thr. the mediumship of Mrs. T. s8°. 1875
The soul. Given thr. Mrs. C. L. V. Richmond, by her guides. 2nd ed. la8°. Chicago. 1887
Hatch (Frederick Henry). Petrology of igneous rocks. 8th ed., rev. w. assist. of A. K. Wells. 2v. s8°. [1926]
Hatch (William Henry Paine). Idea of faith in Xtn. lit. f. death of St. Paul to close of 2nd cent. Thèse. 8°. Str. 1925
Hatfield House. Cat. of paintings, 1865, *see* SALISBURY (M. C., *march.*)
Hātim Tilawônu**.** Hatim's tales, Kashmiri stories & songs. Recorded w. the assist. of Pandit G. Kaul by Sir A. Stein. Ed. w. tr. &c. by Sir G. A. Grierson, w. note of the folklore by W. Crooke. [Ind. Text. Ser.] 8°. 1923
Hatschek (Julius). Britisches u. röm. Weltreich. Eine sozialwiss. Parallele. 8°. München. 1921
Das preuss. Verfassungsrecht. s8°. 1924
Hattingberg (Hans v.) Der nervöse Mensch. Schriftenreihe. Hrsg. H. v. H. 12B [*in 2v*]. 8°. 1924

Hattingberg (H. v.) Anlage u. Umwelt.	[3.]
—— Ist Nervosität e. Krankheit?	[1.]
—— Seel. Hintergrund d. Nervosität.	[2.]
Heyer (G. R.) Das nervöse Herz.	[6.]
—— Nervöse Magen- u. Darmkrankheiten.	[7.]
Marcinowski (J.) Gefühlszerrissenheit d. neurot. Psyche.	[9.]

Hattingberg (Hans v.) [*continued*].

Marcinowski (J.) Minderwertigkeitsgefühle.	[10.]
—— Probleme &c. d. geschlechtl. Aufklärung.	[8.]
—— Schuldgefühle.	[11.]
Mohr (F.) Nervosität u. organ. Leiden.	[5.]
Schultz (J. H.) Nervosität u. erbl. Belastung.	[4.]
—— Hypnose u. Suggestion.	[12.]

Hatton (Richard G.) Design: making patterns. 8°. 1902
Hatvany (Antonia), *see* KELLOR (F. A.) & A. H. Protocol for settlement of internat. disputes, 1925.
Hatzfeld (Helmut).
Dante, s. Weltanschauung. s8°. München. 1921
Hatzfeld (Jean). Les trafiquants ital. dans l'Orient hellén. [Ecoles Fr. d'Ath. & de Rome, 115]. 8°. 1919
Hatzfeldt (Sophie, *Gräfin* **v.),** *see* LASSALLE (F. J. G.) Nachgelassene Briefe &c., B3, 4, L.'s Briefwechsel mit Gräfin S. v. H., 1922–24.
Hatzidakis (Georgios N.) Ἄγγελος u. Verwandtes, 1913, *see* KAIS. AKAD. D. WISS. z. WIEN. Sitzb., B173, 1914.
Hatzouni (Vardan). [The Mass in the Armenian Church. *In Armenian.* 2nd ed. P2800]. s8°. S. Lazar Venet. 1899
Hauber (Eberhard David). De metempsychosi sive Pythagoræa animarum transmigr. [*b. w.* Pipping (H.) Syntagma diss. &c., 1723]. s8°. Ulmae. 1724
Hauber (Johann Michael). Cantica sacra. Coll. & ed. J. M. H. Cantici chorali accommod. vocem organi C. Ett. s8°. Monachii. 1855
Haubold (Christian Gottlieb). Instit. juris Romani litt. t1. [*No more publ.*] 8°. Lipsiae. 1809
Haubtschalck. *Wid' dē haubtschalck uñ todfeind des menschē gewissen, wie man den stillen soll. s4°. *n.p.* [1524]
Hauch (J. Carsten von). Vilhelm Zabern. s8°. 1911
Hauer (August). Kumbuke. Erlebnisse e. Arztes in Deutsch-Ostafrika. 8°. 1922
Hauer (Erich), *see* HUANG-Ts'ing-K'ai-kuo-fang-lüeh: Gründung d. mandschur. Kaiserreiches; übers. u. erklärt v. E. H., 1926.
Hauer (Jakob Wilhelm). Die Religionen, i. Werden, i. Sinn, i. Wahrheit. B1. 8°. 1923
Hauff (Wilhelm). Lichtenstein. 4e A. la8°. St. [c. 1904]
Märchen. s8°. L. *Reclam. n.d.*
Hauge (Hans Nielsen), *see* BANG (A. C.) H. N. H. og hans samtid, 3e opl., 1910.
Haughton Hall. Pictures & engr. at H. H., Tarporley, 1904, *see* BROCKLEBANK (R.)
Haughton (*Sir* Graves Chamney).
Rudiments of Bengali grammar. 4°. 1821
Haughton (Samuel). Natural philos. s8°. [1867]
Haukeil (Henry A.), *see* TYRRELL (H.) & H. A. H. Hist. of Russia, 3v, 1879–80.
Hauksbee (Francis). The patch, 2nd ed., *see* SCHOOL of Venus, 1739.
Hauksbók, *see* KRISTENSEN (M.) "Nokkur blöð úr Hauksbók" (13 c.) undersøgt &c. 1925.
Haupt (Albrecht). Lissabon u. Cintra. s8°. L. 1913
Haupt (Herman). Hessische Biografien. In Verb. mit K. Esselborn u. G. Lehnert hrsg. v. H. H. [Hist. Komm. f. Hessen]. B1, 2. 8°. Darmstadt. 1918–27
Quellen u. Darstellung z. Gesch. d. Burschenschaft u. d. deut. Einheitsbewegung. Im Auftrage d. Burschenschaftl. Hist. Komm. in Gemeinschaft mit B. Bilger, W. Hopf &c. Hrsg. H. H. B5–10. 8°. Heidelberg. 1920–27
B6, 7, 9, 10 *have* 2nd tp. *as under*:—
6, 10, Gesch. d. deut. Burschenschaft, 2B. 1, v. P. Wentzcke, 2, v. G. Heer. 7, 100 Jahre deut. Burschenschaft; ausgewahlt &c., H. Haupt u. P. Wentzcke. 9, Die deut. Farben &c.; P. Wentzcke.
Haupt (Otto). Windmill Hill. la8°. Bremen. 1922
Hauptartickel [HAUBTARTICKEL]. Die haubt artickel durch welche &c., 1522, *see* AMSDORFF (N.)
Die fürnämpsten H. christl. Lehre &c., 1562, *see* TRUBER (P.)
Hauptmann (Gerhart).
Anna. Liebesgedicht. 8°. 1921
Ausblicke. [Aufzeichnungen—Erzählendes — Gedichte — Dramatisches (Helios — Das Hirtenlied — Kaiser Maxens Brautfahrt—Der Dom—Till Eulenspiegel—Veland). Gesamtausgabe, B12]. 8°. 1924
Dorothes Angermann. Schauspiel. [6. bis 8. A.] 8°. [1927]
Indipohdi. Dram. Gedicht. s8°. 1921
Die Insel d. grossen Mutter oder d. Wunder v. Île des Dames. [26.–50. A.] s8°. 1925
Der Ketzer v. Soana. s8°. 1918
Peter Bauer, Tragikomödie. 8°. 1921
Veland: Tragödie. 8°. 1925

Hauptmann (Gerhart) [*continued*].

Der weisse Heiland. Dramat. Phantasie. s8°. 1920

TRANSLATIONS.

Dramatic works. v8, Poetic dramas. 8°. [1925]

Atlantis. Tr. A. & T. Seltzer. 2nd ed. s8°. *n.d.*

The heretic of Soana. [Auth. tr.] s8°. [1923]

see FECHTER (P.) G. H., 3e A., 1922.

„ SCHLENTHER (P.) G. H., n. A. v. A. Eloesser, 1922.

„ THOMPSON (N. M.) Arno Holz &c.: Naturalism & dream motive in works of G. H., 1920.

Hauptmann (Johann Gottfried). Dass die reine Lehre, den Reussischen Kirchen, durch i. Confessionsschrift versichert worden. [P2742]. s4°. Gera. [1766]

Nachr. v. d. Predigern, welche d. Reuss. Confessionsschrift mit unterschrieben haben. [P2742]. s4°. Gera. [1769]

Hauréau (Jean Barthélemy). Hugues de Saint-Victor. Nouvel examen de ses oe. 8°. 1859

Haurigot (Paul). Acide russique: roman, *see* ŒUVRES libres, t53, 1925.

Hausa. Fārawá letåfin māgána Haŭsa. [*Foll. by* H. primer. *w. sep. pagin.*] s8°. Berlin. 1857

Hausaland. The occup. of Hausaland, 1900–04. Tr. of Arabic letters. Ed. w. intr. by H. F. Backwell. 8°. Lagos. 1927

Hausbuch. Mittelalterl. Hausbuch. Bilder-Hs. d. 15. Jhdts. mit vollständ. Text u. facs. Abbildungen. Vorwort v. A. Essenwein. fol. Frankfurt a. M. 1887

Hauschild (*Col.* **L.**), *détaché du grand état-major ottoman.* Solutions des thèmes tactiques, Acad. de guerre, 1886–1903. Tr. P. Corteys. 8°. 1905

Hausen (Carl Renatus). Pragmat. Gesch. d. Protestanten in Deutschland. T1, mit Beylagen & Urkunden. [*w. sep. pagin. No more publ.*] s8°. Halle. 1767

Hausenstein (Wilhelm). Das Bild: Atlanten z. Kunst. Hrsg. W. H. B1–10 [*in* 7. 3–4, 5–6, 8–9 *in* 1v]. la8°. München. 1922–24

1, Tafelmalerei d. deut. Gotik.
2, Bildnerei d. Etrusker.
3–4, Malerei d. früh. Italiener.
5–6, Roman. Bildnerei.
7, Tafelmalerei d. alten Franzosen.
8–9, Deut. Bild d. 16. Jhdts.; v. H. Esswein u. W. H.
10, Vermeer van Delft; Nachwort v. B. Reiffenberg.

Vom Geist d. Barock. 8°. München. 1920

Hauser (Henri). Le problème du régionalisme. [C.E. for Int. Peace]. la8°. 1924

Travailleurs & marchands dans l'anc. France. 8°. 1920

see TILLEY (A.), *ed.* Mod. France [*by* H. H. &c.], 1922.

Haushofer (Max). Tirol u. Vorarlberg. 3e A. bearb. v. A. Rothpletz. la8°. Bielefeld. 1909

Hausschein (Johannes), *see* OECOLAMPADIUS (J.)

Häusser (Ludwig).

Gesch. d. rhein. Pfalz. 2e A. 2B. 8°. Heidelberg. 1856

Haussherr (Hans). Der Staat in Calvins Gedankenwelt. [Verein f. Ref.-gesch. Schr., Jhrg. 41 (Nr. 136)]. 8°. L. 1923

Haussleiter (Johannes). Aus d. Schule Melanchthons: theolog. Disput. &c. zu Wittenberg, 1546–60. 8°. Greifswald. 1897

see MELANCHTHON (P.) M.-Kompend.: unbekannte Sammlg. eth., polit. u. philos. Lehrsätze M. in Luthers Werken, 1902.

Haussmann (Conrad). Schlaglichter: Reichstagsbriefe &c. Hrsg. U. Zeller. la8°. Frankfurt a. M. 1924

Haussonville (G. P. Othenin de Cléron, *cte.* **d'),** *b. 1843.* Madame de Staël et M. Necker d'après leur corr. inéd. 8°. [1925]

Le visite du Czar Pierre le Grand en 1717. 4°. 1896

Hauteclocque (*le cte.* **Gustave de).** Arras & l'Artois sous le gouv. des archiducs Albert & Isabelle (1598–1633). [Extr. des Mém. de l'Acad. des Sci. &c. d'Arras, s11, t6]. 8°. Arras. 1873

Hautecœur (Louis). L'hist. des châteaux du Louvre & des Tuileries sous le r. de Louis XIV. Préf. de P. de Nolhac. 4°. 1927

see LOUVRE. La peinture, école franç. (19 s., pl), par L. H., 1927.

„ —— La peinture, écoles ital., 13–15 s., par L. H., 1927.

Hauterive (Ernest d').

L'armée sous la Révol., 1789–94. 8°. 1894

La police secrète du premier Empire: bull. par Fouché à l'Emp. Publ. E. d'H. t3. [1806–07]. la8°. 1922

Hautpoul (*le marq.* **Amand d').** [HAUTPOUL-FÉLINES (MARIE CONSTANT FIDÈLE HENRI A. D')]. Souv. 4 mois à la cour de Prague: l'éduc. du Duc de Bordeaux, 1833–34. Publ. avec intr. &c. par le Comte Fleury. 8°. 1902

Souv. s. la Révolution, l'Empire & la Restauration: mém. inéd. publ. par le cte. Fleury. 8°. 1904

Hautt, *The family of, see* BLASER (F.) Les Hautt: hist. d'une fam. d'impr., d'éd. &c. des 17e & 18e s., 1925.

Hautz (Johann Friedrich). Die erste Gelehrtenschule reform. Glaubensbek. in Deutschland, Heidelberg, 1565–77. [*b. w. h.* Lycei H. orig. &c., 1846]. 8°. Heidelberg. 1855

Gesch. d. Neckarschule in Heidelberg. [*b. w. h.* Lycei H. orig. &c., 1846]. 8°. Heidelberg. 1849

Jubelfeier d. 300 jährig. Stiftung d. grossherzogl. Lyceums z. Heidelberg. [*b. w. h.* Lycei H. orig. &c., 1846]. 8°. Heidelberg. 1847

Lycei Heidelberg. origines &c. 8°. Heidelbergae. 1846

Urkundl. Gesch. d. Stipendien u. Stiftungen a. d. Lyceum z. Heidelberg. [*b. w. h.* Lycei H. orig. &c., 1846]. 2H. 8°. Heidelberg. 1856–57

Hauviller (Ernst). F. X. Kraus: e. Lebensbild aus d. Zeit d. Reformkatholizmus. 8°. Colmar i. E. 1904

„ „ ....2e A. 8°. München. 1905

Hávamál, *see* EDDA: POETIC EDDA.

Havannah. *Hist. views of ye last glorious exped. of H.M.'s ships &c. agst. the H. &c., 1762, *see* ORSBRIDGE (P.)

Havard (Henry). Hist. de la peinture holland. n. éd. 8°. [1882]

Havard (Oscar). Hist. de la Révolution dans les ports de guerre. [t]2, Brest-Rochefort. 8°. 1913

Havard (William). King Charles I. Tragedy. [P2575]. 8°. 1779

Hávarðar saga. Hávarðar saga Isfirðings. Udg. ved B. K. Thórólfsson. [S. t. u. af g. n. l., 47]. 8°. 1923

Havell (Ernest Binfield). A hdbk. of Indian art. 8°. 1920

The Himalayas in Indian art. 8°. 1924

A short hist. of India to the pres. day. s8°. 1924

see RODIN (A.), A. COOMARASWAMY, E. B. H. &c. Sculptures çivaïtes, 1921.

Havelok, *the Dane.* Le lai d'Havelok & Gaimar's Haveloc episode. Ed. A. Bell. s8°. M'ter. 1925

Havens (Raymond Dexter).

The influence of Milton on Eng. poetry. la8°. C. [Mass.] 1922

Havensius (Arnoldus).

Speculum hæreticæ crudelitatis. s8°. Coloniae. 1608

Havenstein (Martin). Vornehmheit u. Tüchtigkeit. Dem deut. Volker z. Einkehr. 4e A. 8°. 1920

Haverfield (Francis John), *1860–1919.* The Romaniz. of Roman Britain. 4th ed., rev. by G. Macdonald. 8°. O. 1923

The Roman occup. of Britain. Ford Lect. Rev. by G. Macdonald, w. notice of H.'s life &c. 8°. O. 1924

see BRIT. ACAD. Proc., v9, Obit. not., by G. Macdonald, 1919–20.

Havergal (Francis Tebbs). Records of the parish of Upton Bishop. la8°. Walsall. 1883

Hävernick (Heinr. A. Chr.) Gen. hist.-crit. intr. to the Old Test. Tr. W. L. Alexander. 8°. E., *Clark.* 1852

An hist.-crit. introd. to the Pentateuch. Tr. A. Thompson. 8°. E., *Clark.* 1850

Havet (Ernest), *see* DONDEY (TH.) Feu & flamme; suivi de la corresp. inéd. de T. D. & d'E. H., 1926.

Havet (Louis). Notes crit. sur le texte de l'Orateur & sur Isée & Bibliog. de L. H. [H. E., 252]. 8°. 1927

see PICHARD (L.) Tibulle & les auteurs du Corpus Tibullianum; texte établi, d'ap. la Méthode de crit. verbale de L. H., par L. P., 1924.

Havet (Mireille). Carnaval, roman, *see* ŒUVRES libres, No. 17, 1922.

Havlasa (Jan).

Four Japanese tales. [Tr. P2403]. 8°. Prague. 1919

Havret (Henri), Chambeau & P. Hoang. Mélanges s. la chronologie chin., *see* VARIÉTÉS sinolog., No. 52, 1920.

Hawaii.

Corr. betw. H.H.M.'s Sec. of State for For. Aff. & H.B.M.'s Consul-Gen. on R. Charlton's claim to land. [P2776]. 8°. Honolulu. 1845

„ „ ....subject of Koahipau a native Hawaiian subject. [P2776]. 8°. Honolulu. 1846

Corr. betw. the Secretary of State [Hawaii] & U.S. Comm. in case of J. Wiley, 1844–5, *see* WILEY (J.)

In Admiralty. Average adjustment in case of Am. brigantine Lafayette. [P2775]. 8°. Honolulu. 1844

„ „ Foreclosure of the hypothec. on Brit. brig. Euphemia. [P2776]. 8°. Honolulu. 1845.

Hawaii [*continued*].
In Chancery: estate of W. French &c., in liquid. w. H. Treasury Board, 1845, *see* FRENCH (W.)
Investig. by comm. of King &c. of H. Isl. in vindic. of course pursued by H.M., impugned by W. Miller, who took poss. of land in Honolulu claimed by R. Charlton &c. [& Suppl. P2776]. 8º. Honolulu. 1846
Ministerial reports, read to the H. legislature, August 1846. [P2775]. 8º. Honolulu. 1846
Offic. rep. on registry of vessels in the H. Isl. [P2775]. 8º. Honolulu. 1844
[*Proclamations, treaties &c.*, 1843–46. *b. w.* Polynesian, The, n. s. v1, 2]. fol. [Honolulu. 1843–46]
Rules &c. adopted by Admiralty Court of Oahu, H. Isl., in adjusting gen. average, & applied to case of Am. brig. Globe &c. [P2775]. 8º. Honolulu. 1844
Statute laws of Kamehameha III, king of the H. Isl.; passed by the Houses of Nobles & Represent., 1845–6. v1. 8º. Honolulu. 1846

Hawara (The) portfolio, 1913, *see* PETRIE (*Sir* W. M. F.)

Haward (Edwin). European non-officials in the Ind. Legisl., 1921–25. 8º. Allahabad. 1926

Haweis (Hugh Reginald). Old violins. 8º. E. 1910

Haweis (Thomas). Life of Will. Romaine, Rector of St. Ann's, Blackfryars &c. 8º. 1797

Hawes (Charles Boardman). Whaling. [Ed. D. C. H.] 8º. 1924

Hawes (Stephen), *the poet.* The pastime of pleasure (1517). Intr. &c. by W. E. Mead. [E.E.T.S., 173]. 8º. 1928

Hawker (Robert). *The plant of renown by the author of The brother born for adversity. [P2467]. s8º. *n.d.* [1804 ?]

Hawker (Robert Stephen), *see* BURROWS (M. F.) R. S. H.: h. thought & poetry, 1926.

Hawkes (Arthur John). Lancashire printed books: a bibliog. down to 1800. Based on exhib. in Wigan Lib., May 1925. Comp. &c. A. J. H., w. pref. by the Earl of Crawford & Balcarres. 8º. Wigan. 1925

Hawkes (C. P.)
Mauresques, w. some Basque & Span. cameos. s8º. [1926]

Hawkesbury (Cecil George Savile Foljambe, *baron*], *see* LIVERPOOL (C. G. S. F., *1st earl of*).

Hawkins (Edgar). Medical climatology of Eng. & Wales. 8º. 1923

Hawkins (Edward Lovell).
Concise cyclopaedia of freemasonry. s8º. 1908

Hawkins (Henry), *Jesuit.* *The hist. of S. Elizabeth, daughter of the king of Hungary. By H. A. [*i.e.* H. H.] s8º. [Rome ?]. 1632

Hawkins (Herbert Reader).
Invertebrate palaeontology. s8º. [1920]

Hawkins (*Rear-Adm. Sir* **John),** *see* WILLIAMSON (J. A.) Sir J. H., the time & the man, 1927.

Hawkins (Lætitia Matilda). Gossip about Dr. Johnson & others. Chapters f. Mems. of Miss L. M. H. Ed. F. H. Skrine. 8º. [1926]

Hawkins (Thomas), *F.G.S.* My life & works. v1, Prometheus (2nd ed.) la8º. 1887

Hawkins (William), *professor of poetry in Oxford.*
Poems on var. subjects. s8º. O. 1781

Hawles (*Sir* **John).** Remarks upon the tryals of E. Fitzharris, S. Colledge, Count Coningsmark, Ld. Russel, Col. Sidney, H. Cornish & C. Bateman: also on Earl of Shaftsbury's grand jury &c. fol. 1689

Haworth (Paul Leland). The Hayes-Tilden disputed presidential election of 1876. 8º. Cleveland. 1906
Reconstruction & union, 1865–1912. s8º. 1912
The U.S. in our own times, 1865–1920. s8º. [1920]

Hawthorne (Nathaniel). Tales. 4v. s8º. *Bohn.* 1891–1901
1, Twice told tales, s1 & 2; Snow image & o. t. 2, House w. the 7 gables & The Scarlet letter. 3, Transformation & The Blithedale romance. 4, Mosses f. an old manse.
Transformation; or, the romance of Monte Beni. n. ed. s8º. 1861
see MORRIS (L. R.) The rebellious puritan, 1928.

Hawtrey (*Sir* **Charles H.)**
The truth at last. Ed. W. S. Maugham. 8º. [1924]

Hawtrey (Ralph George). Currency & credit. 2nd ed. 8º. 1923
The economic problem. 8º. 1926
The Exchequer & the control of expenditure. s8º. 1921
The gold standard. s8º. 1927
Monetary reconstruction. 8º. 1923

Haxton (—), *of Rathillet* [HAXTOUN]. Speech &c. of H., who suffered at the Cross of Edinburgh, 29th July 1680, *see* MAIDMENT (J.) & R. PITCAIRN. Nugae, 1822.

Hay (*Sir* **Andrew Leith).**
A narr. of the Peninsular War. 2v. s8º. 1831
„ „ ....4th ed. 8º. 1850

Hay (Edward).
Hist. of the Irish insurrection of 1798. s8º. D. 1847

Hay (Ian), *ps.* [*i.e.* JOHN HAY BEITH].
Getting together. s8º. 1917
Half a sovereign. s8º. [1926]
The lucky number. s8º. [1923]
Paid with thanks. s8º. [1925]
The poor gentleman. s8º. [1928]
The willing horse. s8º. [1921]

Hay (James), *Jr.* No clue! s8º. 1923

Hay (John), *Jesuit, see* JESUITS. Iappon. Imperii admirabilis commutatio, Lat. fecit J. H., 1604.

Hay (*Maj.* **Leith),** *see* HAY (*Sir* A. L.)

Hay (M. Doriel), *see* FITZRANDOLPH (H. E.) & M. D. H. Rural indust. of Eng. & Wales, 3v, 1926–27.

Hay (Oliver Perry). Pleistocene of N. Amer. & its vertebrated animals &c. [C.I. of Wash.] la8º. Wash. 1923

Hay (W. R.) Two years in Kurdistan, 1918–20. 8º. 1921

Hay (William Ferris).
Indust. democracy for miners. [Ed. H.] [P2419]. s8º. [1919]

Hayastan, *see* HAÏASDAN, LE.

Hay-Cooper (L.)
Josephine Butler & h. work for social purity. s8º. 1922

Hayden (Arthur). Bye-paths in curio collecting. 8º. [1919]
Chats on old Sheffield plate. 8º. [1920]

Hayden (Mary), *M.A.*, **& G. A. Moonan.**
A short hist. of the Irish people. 8º. 1921

Hayden (Ralston).
The Senate & treaties, 1789–1817. 8º. N.Y. 1920

Haydn (Franz Joseph).
see BRENET (M.) H.; tr. C. L. Leese, 1926.
„ RAVÀ (A.) H. a Venezia, 1909.
„ SCHNERICH (A.) J. H. u. s. Sendung, 1926.

Haydn (Joseph). Haydn's dict. of dates. 13th ed. 8º. 1871
„ „ ....19th ed., to 1889, by B. Vincent. la8º. 1889

Haydon (Benjamin Robert), *1786–1846.* Autobiog. & mem. Ed. f. Journals by T. Taylor. n. ed. w. intr. by A. Huxley. 2v. 8º. *Davies.* 1926

Hayem (Emile). La Garde au Rhin. la8º. 1910

Hayens (Kenneth). Theodor Fontane: a crit. study. s8º. [1920]

Hayes (Archibald Ormston). The Malagash salt deposit, Cumberland county, N.S. [Canada Geol. Survey. P2512]. 8º. Ottawa. 1920
—— & W. A. Bell. South. part of the Sydney coal field, Nova Scotia. [Canada. Geol. Survey.] 8º. Ottawa. 1923

Hayes (Bernard John) & W. F. Masom.
Tutorial Latin grammar. 10th impr. (4th ed.) s8º. 1912

Hayes (*Sir* **Bertram),** *K.C.M.G.*
Hull down: remin. of wind-jammers, &c. 8º. [1925]

Hayes (Carlton Joseph Huntley).
A brief hist. of the Great War. 8º. N.Y. 1920
Polit. & social hist. of mod. Europe. 2v. 8º. N.Y. 1922

Hayes (James Gordon). Antarctica. la8º. [1928]

Hayes (L. Newton). The Chinese dragon. Intr. by Fong F. Sec. 3rd ed. s8º. Shanghai. 1923

Hayes (Matthew Horace).
Illust. horse-breaking. 3rd ed., rev. & enl. 8º. 1905
„ „ ......4th ed. 8º. *n.d.*
Indian racing remin. s8º. 1883
Points of the horse. 3rd ed. la8º. [1903]
Riding & hunting. n. & rev. ed. 8º. 1910
Soundness & age of horses. s8º. 1887
Training & horse management in India. With Hindustanee vocab. 6th ed. s8º. 1905
see SHAW (V.) & M. H. H. Dogs for hot climates, 1908.

Hayes (Rutherford Birchard), *president of the U.S.*
see GIBSON (A. M.) A political crime [election of H.], 1885.
„ HAWORTH (P. L.) H.-Tilden disputed presid. election of 1876, 1906.

Hayford (Joseph Ephraim Casely).
United West Africa. [P2490]. 8º. 1919

***Haykakan.** Hist. litt. de l'Arménie anc., siècles 4–13, *in Armenian, 2nd ed.*, 1886, *see* ZARBHANALEAN (K.)

Hayley (William). Life & letters of W. Cowper; w. remarks on epistolary writers; & app. n. ed. 8º. 1835
Poems & plays. n. ed. 6v. 8º. 1788
see MILTON (J.) Poet. works; w. life by W. H., 3v, 1794–97.

Haymo, *bp. of Halberstadt.* De Christianarum rerum memoria libri 10. [*b. w. h.* In Esaiam comm., 1531]. s8º. Coloniæ. 1531
De varietate librorum, sive de amore cœlestis patriæ libri 3. [*b. w. h.* In Esaiam comm., 1531]. s8º. Coloniæ. 1531
Haymonis Episc. Halberstatt. in divi Pauli epistolas omneis interpret. s8º. [Coloniæ, *P. Quentel*]. 1529

Haymo, *bp. of Halberstadt* [*continued*].
In Esaiam comm. libri 3. [*Pref. by N. Herborn*]. s8°. Coloniæ. 1531
In XII. prophetarum enarr. Eiusdem in Cantica canticorum comm. s8°. Coloniæ. 1533
Hayne (Thomas), *see* ADAMUS (M.) The life & death of M. Luther &c. [pres. in Eng. dresse by T. H.], 1641.
Haynes (Edmund Sidney Pollock).
The belief in personal immortality. s8°. 1913
„ „ 2nd ed., rev. 8°. 1925
The enemies of liberty. 8°. 1923
Fritto misto. 8°. *Cayme Press, Kensington.* 1924
Lycurgus or the future of law. s8°. [1925]
Much ado about women. 8°. *Cayme Press.* 1927
Haynes (Edwin). Timber technicalities: definitions of terms &c. Comp. &c. by E. H. s8°. [1921]
Haynes (James), *dramatic writer.*
Durazzo. Tragedy. [P2863]. 8°. 1823
Haynes (Roy Asa). Prohibition inside out. 8°. 1924
Hays (Mary), *see* FENWICK (E.) Fate of the F.: letters to M. H., 1798–1828, 1927.
Hayter (A. G. K.), *see* QUIBELL (J. E.) & A. G. K. H. Excav. at Saqqara: Teti Pyramid, N. side, 1927.
Hayter (Thomas), *bp. of* (1) *Norwich,* (2) *London.* *Exam. of a book pr. by the Quakers, ent. Brief acc. of many persecutions &c. [by J. Besse], in defence of clergy of York. [*b. w.* Besse (J.) Brief acc. &c., 1736]. 8°. 1741
see BESSE (J.) Vindic. of Brief acc. of persecutions &c. in ans. to [T. H.], 1737; 1741.
Haythonus, *Prince of Gorigos, see* HETOUM.
Haythornthwaite (John Parker). Parish of King's Langley: anc. church & hist. assoc. la8°. 1924
Romantic life of Edmund de Langley & h. tomb &c. 8°. 1927
Hayward (Arthur L.) The Dickens encyclopaedia. la8°. 1924
Hayward (Charles H.)
Eng. rooms & th. decoration. v1, 1066–1620. 8°. 1925
Hayward (Frank Herbert). The reform of moral & biblical educ. on the lines of Herbartianism &c. s8°. 1902
Hayward (H. Richard). Ulster songs & ballads. Coll. &c. by H. R. H. Intr. by St. J. Ervine. s8°. [1925]
Hayward (*Sir* John). The hist. of William I, William II, & Henry I. [*Tp. supplied in MS.*] s8°. 1618
Hayward (Walter Brownell). Bermuda past & present: descr. & hist. account. s8°. [1923]
Haywood (*Capt.* Austin H. Wightwick).
Eng.-Hausa vocab. 2nd enl. ed. [P2596]. s8°. 1914
Hazard (Paul). L'Italie vivante. s8°. 1923
Vie de Stendhal. 6e éd. s8°. [1927]
Hazart (Cornelius). Kirchen-Gesch. Aus d. Nider in die Hoch-Teutsche übers. 3T [T2, vermehret durch M. Soutermans. T3i, ii, *w. sep. pagin.*] fol. Wienn. 1678–1701
Hazay (Oedön v.) Entwicklung u. Poesie d. Gesanges u. d. wertvollen Lieder d. Gesamt-Musiklit. 2e A. 2B. [*pagin. cont.*] 8°. L. 1915
Hazel (Gladys Mary). The house. [*Poems*]. s8°. O. 1920
Hazelius (Artur Immanuel), *1833–1901, see* BÖÖK (F.) A. H.; en levnadsteckning, 1923.
Hazell (W. Howard). Labour & capital in alliance. Foreword by J. R. Clynes. s8°. [1927]
Hazell's Annual Cyclopaedia [NEW HAZELL ANNUAL & ALMANACK]. By T. A. Ingram. 1921. s8°. 1921
Hazen (Charles Downer).
Fifty years of Europe, 1870–1919. 8°. 1919
Hazlitt, *the family of, see* HAZLITT (W. C.) The Hazlitts, p2, later fortunes, 1912.
Hazlitt (Victoria). Ability: a psycholog. study. 8°. [1926]
Hazlitt (William), *the elder, 1778–1830.*
Characters of Shakespeare's plays. s8°. Boston. 1818
The eloquence of the Brit. Senate: speeches, f. reign of Charles I to pres. 2v. 8°. 1808
Lects. on the Eng. comic writers. n. ed., ed. W. C. Hazlitt. s8°. 1870
Sel. essays. Ed. G. Sampson. [repr.] 8°. C. 1926
Table talk. 1st Amer. ed. 2p [*in 1v*]. 8°. N.Y. 1847
see HOWE (P. P.) Life of W. H., 1922.
„ KER (W. P.) H., 1922.
Hazlitt (William Carew). The Hazlitts, part 2: narr. of the later fortunes of the family &c. 8°. E. 1912
Hazon (Jacques Albert). Notice des hommes de la Faculté de Médecine en l'Univ. de Paris, 1110–1750. Extr. du ms. de T. B. Bertrand, réd. par J. A. H. p. s. de suite à l'Hist. abr. de la Faculté (1773). 4°. 1778
He. *He's much to blame, 1811, *see* HOLCROFT (T.)
Head (*Sir* Francis Bond). Rough notes dur. journeys across the Pampas & among the Andes. s8°. 1826
Head (Henry), *M.D., F.R.S.* Studies in neurology. By H. H. in conj. w. W. H. R. Rivers, J. Sherren &c. 2v. [*pagin. cont.*] la8°. 1920
Head (*Mrs.* R. E.) The lace & embroidery collector. s8°. 1922
Head (*Mrs.* Ruth), *wife of Henry Head.*
Compensation. s8°. [1921]
Headicar (B. M.), *see* EDWARD FRY LIBRARY OF INTERNAT. LAW. Cat.; comp. &c. by B. M. H., 1923.
Headlam (Arthur Cayley), *bp. of Gloucester.*
The Ch. of England. With app. by H. M. Smith. 8°. 1924
The doctrine of the Church & Xtn. reunion. Bampton lect. 1920. 8°. 1920
„ „ [2nd ed., repr.] 8°. 1923
Jesus Christ in hist. & faith. s8°. 1925
The life & teaching of Jesus the Christ. 8°. 1923
Theolog. educ. at the univ. [P2576]. 8°. O. 1921
see MARCHANT (*Sir* J.), *ed.* Future of Xty.; intr. by A. C. H., 1927.
Headlam (Cecil).
Prayers of the saints &c. Comp. by C. H. s8°. 1898
The story of Naples. [Med. towns]. s8°. 1927
see MAGNUS (L.) & C. H. Prayers f. the poets, 1899.
Headlam (*Lt.-Col.* Cuthbert). Hist. of the Guards Div. in the Gt. War, 1915–18. 2v. 8°. [1924]
Headlam (Stewart Duckworth), *see* BETTANY (F. G.) S. H., a biog., 1926.
Headlam-Morley (James Wycliffe), *ed., see* BRITISH. Brit. docs. on orig. of the War, 1898–1914, v11, Outbreak: For. Off. docs., 1926.
Headley (Henry). Poet. works. Coll. by T. Park. [*b. w.* Moore (J. H.) Poet. works, 1808]. s8°. 1808
Sel. beauties of anc. Eng. poetry. 2v [*in 1*]. s8°. 1787
Heald (James), *1796–1873.*
see POPE (W. B.) Mem. of J. H., 1876.
„ WESLEYAN THEOLOG. INSTIT. Cat. of books & MSS. pres. to W.T.I., 1859.
Healey (Edward), *see* YORKSHIRE. Series of views of castles &c. in Y.; f. sketches by E. H., 1885.
Health, Ministry of, *see* NEWSHOLME (*Sir* A.) The Min. of Health, 1925.
Healy (Timothy Michael), *see* O'FLAHERTY (L.) Life of T. H., 1927.
Healy (William). Hist. & antiq. of Kilkenny (County & City). [App. Book of survey &c. *w. s. pag.*] v1. 8°. [Kilkenny. 1893]
Healy (William), *M.D.* Pract. value of scient. st. of juvenile delinquents, 1922, *see* UNITED STATES: LABOR.
Heanley (Robert Marshall). Hist. of Weyhill, Hants & its anc. fair. 8°. Winchester. 1922
Heard (Adrian). The ivory fan. s8°. [1920]
Water & wine. s8°. [1922]
Heard (Franklin Fiske), *see* ALLEY (L.) Report of trial of L. A., for murder of A. Ellis; by F. F. H., 1875.
Heard (Gerald). Narcissus: an anatomy of clothes. s8°. 1924
Hearn (Lafcadio) [HEARN (PATRICIO L. TESSIMA CARLOS)].
Appreciations of poetry. Sel. & ed. w. intr. by J. Erskine. 8°. [1916]
Books & habits. Sel. & ed. w. intr. by J. Erskine. 8°. 1922
Hist. of Eng. lit. Lect. 2v & Suppl. *to* v1. la8°. Tokyo. 1927
Karma & o. stories & essays. s8°. [1921]
Kwaidan: stories &c. s8°. 1905
Life & literature. Sel. & ed. w. intr. by J. Erskine. 8°. [1917]
Miscellanies. Articles & stories coll. by A. Mordell. 2v. 8°. 1924
Occidental gleanings. Coll. by A. Mordell. 2v. 8°. 1925
Pre-Raphaelite & o. poets. Lect., sel. & ed. w. intr. by J. Erskine. s8°. 1923
see TINKER (E. L.) L. H.'s American days, 1925.
Hearne (Thomas). Remarks & collections. Ed. H. E. Salter. [Oxf. Hist. Soc., 72]. v11, 1731–35. 8°. O. 1921
Hearnshaw (Fossey John Cobb).
Bodin & the genesis of the doctrine of sovereignty, *see* POLLARD (A. F.) Tudor studies, 1924.
Democracy & labour. Sequel to "Democracy at the crossways." 8°. 1924
Eccl. polity of Abp. Whitgift, *see* WARD (*Sir* A. W.) In memoriam, 1924.
European coalitions, alliances &c. since 1792, *see* FOREIGN OFFICE. Handbooks, No. 152, 1920.
Mediaeval contrib. to mod. civilis. [*by var. a.*] Ed. F. J. C. H. Pref. by E. Barker. 8°. [1921]
Newcastle-upon-Tyne. s8°. 1924
Polit. princ. of notable prime ministers of the 19th cent. [*By var. a.*] Ed. H. 8°. 1926
Social & polit. ideas of some gt. mediæval thinkers. [*By var. a.*] Ed. H. 8°. [1923]
Social & polit. ideas of some gt. thinkers of the Renaissance

Hearnshaw (Fossey John Cobb) [*continued*].
& Reformation. [*By var. a.*] Ed. H. Pref. by E. Barker. 8°. [1925]
see MACMILLAN, *publ.* Hist. atlas of mod. Europe; ed. F. J. C. H., 1920.
see SOUTHAMPTON. Court Leet records; transcr. & ed. F. J. C. H. &c., v1, 1905–07; Suppl., 1908.
Heath (Charles), *engraver, see* PARIS. P. & environs: engr. under sup. of C. H., 2v, 1831.
Heath (Francis George). Brit. woodland trees. 8°. [1913]
The fern portfolio. 4°. 1885
Nervation of plants. s8°. 1912
Heath (Frank R.) Dorset. s8°. [1905]
Heath (J. St. G. C.), *see* COMPETITION: st. in human motive, 1919.
Heath (Robert Samuel).
Elem. treatise on geometr. optics. 2nd ed. s8°. C. 1897
Heath (*Mrs.* **Sarah Caroline Gore),** *wife of C. E. Heath, form. Gambier.* Story of the Gambiers. 4°. 1924
Heath (*Sir* **Thomas Little).** Archimedes. s8°. 1920
The Copernicus of antiquity: Aristarchus of Samos. s8°. 1920
Hist. of Greek mathematics. 2v. 8°. O. 1921
1, Thales to Euclid. 2, Aristarchus to Diophantus.
The Treasury. s8°. [1927]
Heaton (Aldam). Beauty & art. 8°. 1897
Heaton (Eliza Osborn Putnam), *née Putnam.*
By-paths in Sicily. 8°. N.Y. [1920]
Heaton (James). Farther obs. on demoniac possession &c. [*b. w. h.* Extraord. affliction &c., 1822]. s8°. Frome. 1822
The extraordinary affliction &c. of a boy [*i.e.* J. Evans]. 2nd ed., enl. s8°. Plymouth. 1822
Heaton (John Langdon). The story of a page. 30 yrs. of publ. service &c. in the editorial col^s^. of the New York World. [J. Pulitzer]. 8°. N.Y. 1913
Heawood (Edward). The use of watermarks in dating old maps & doc. [Repr. f. Geogr. Journal, May 1924. P2737]. 8°. 1924
The world map bef. & after Magellan's voyage. [Repr. f. Geogr. Journal, 1921. P2859]. 8°. 1921
Hebbel (C. Friedrich). Sämmtliche Werke. Histor. krit. A. besorgt v. R. M. Werner. Abth. 2, Tagebücher, B4, 1854–63. 8°. [1924]
Three plays. [Gyges & h. ring—Herod & Mariamne. Tr. by L. H. Allen.—Maria Magdalena. Tr. by B. Fairley. Everyman's Lib.] s8°. [1914]
see FEDERN (E.) F. H., 1920.
Hebel (Johann Peter), *see* CORRODI (A.) R. Burns u. P. H., 1873.
Hebenstreit (Christoph Wilhelm) [*ps.* Φιλαλήθης Ἐριδαίρων].
*Obs. ad moralem Libr. Sacr. Scr. Φιλαλήθης Ἐριδαίρων. s8°. Lips. 1796
Hebenstreit (Georg Ernst), *see* HOFMANN (C. F.) & G. E. H. Disput. de Constantini M. sepulcro, 1759.
—— & H. M. Hebenstreit.
De Iamblichi doctrina &c. [P2741]. s4°. [Leipzig. 1764]
Hebenstreit (Johann Baptista) [HEBENSTREITT]. Panegyricon pro jubilæo seculari Lutherano. [P2628]. 8°. Ulmæ. 1617
Hebenstreit (Johann Paul). Diss. de August. Confess. auctoritate. Resp. J. C. Zeumero. [P484]. s4°. Jenae. [1706]
Systema theologicum rev. & obs. auxit J. E. Schubert. 4°. Jenae. 1768
Heber (Adolph Reeve) & K. M. Heber.
In Himalayan Tibet. 8°. 1926
Heber (Kathleen Mary), *wife of A. R. Heber, see* HEBER (A. R.) & K. M. H. In Himalayan Tibet, 1926.
Heber (Reginald), *bp. of Calcutta.*
Hymns, adapted to weekly church service. 8°. 1827
Heberdey (Rudolf). Altattische Porosskulptur. [Deut.-Österr. Arch. Inst.] [Tafeln. obl. fol.] fol. Wien. 1919
Hébert (Marcel), *1851–1916, see* HOUTIN (A.) Un prêtre symboliste: M. H., 1925.
Hébrard (Ernest), *see* ZEILLER (J.) Spalato, le palais de Dioclétien: relevés & restaur. par E. H., 1912.
Hebrew. Misc. of H. lit., 1872, *see* SOC. OF HEB. LIT.
Post-Biblical H. lit.: anthol., tr., v2, 1921, *see* HALPER (B.)
H. E. C. *La Argentina, 10^a^ ed., 1926 ?, *see* ARGENTINA.
Hecatæus, *Abderita* [ECATEO]. Eclogae sive fragm. libri de hist. &c. vet. Ebræorum. Graece & Lat. cum notis J. Scaligeri & comm. P. Zornii. Prolegom. & quoddam ἀποσπασμάτιον Hecatæi Milesii. s8°. Altona. 1730
Hecataeus *Milesius, see* HECATAEUS, *Abderita.* Eclogae; & ἀποσπασμάτιον H. Milesii, 1730.

Hecht (Ben). Erik Dorn. s8°. N.Y. 1921
Gargoyles. s8°. N.Y. [1922]
Hecht (Hans). Daniel Webb, mit Abdr. d. Remarks on the beauties of poetry (1762). 8°. Hamburg. 1920
Robert Burns, Leben u. Wirken. s8°. Heidelberg. 1919
Hecht (John S.) The real wealth of nations. 8°. [1920]
Heck (Carl).
Gesch. v. Kaiserswerth. 2^e^ verm. A. s8°. Düsseldorf. 1925
Hecke (Firmin van). Gedichten. 8°. Antwerpen. 1925
Hecker (Heinrich Cornelius). Petrobruisianos & Henricianos testes veritatis saec. 12. Praes. H. C. H., resp. G. L. Dathe. [P434]. s4°. Lipsiae. 1721
Hecker (Oskar E. W. A.) System. geordneter deut.-russ. Wortschatz. Ins Russ. übertr. v. W. Loewenthal. s8°. 1907
Heckewälder (John Gottlieb Ernest) [HECKEWELDER]. Narrat. of the miss. of the Unit. Brethren among the Delaware & Mohegan Indians, 1740–1808, &c. 8°. Phila. 1820
Heckscher (Eli F.) Bidrag till Sveriges ekon. & soc. hist. [1914–25]. Under medverk. av. K. Bergendal &c. Utgiv. E. F. H. [C.E. for Int. Peace]. d1. la8°. [1926]
The Continental System. Ed. H. Westergaard. [C.E. for Int. Peace.] la8°. O. 1922
Hectorson (John), *ps., see* MACKEACHAN (J.)
Hedberg (Anders). Internat. wholesale co-oper. Foreword by A. W. Golightly. 8°. [M'ter.] 1925
Hedding (Elijah), *bp. of Methodist Episc. Church, 1780–1852, see* CLARK (D. W.) Life of E. H., 1855.
Heddle (John George Flett Moodie) & T. Mainland.
Orkney & Shetland. s8°. C. 1920
Heddon (V.), *see* LAUGHTON (L. G. C.) & V. H. Gt. storms, 1927.
Hedemann-Heespen (Paul v.) Die Herzogtümer Schleswig-Holstein u. d. Neuzeit. 8°. Kiel. 1926
Hedén (Erik). Strindberg. 8°. [1921]
Hedenström (Alfred v.)
Gesch. Russlands, 1878–1918. s8°. 1922
Hedericus (Johannes), *see* HEIDENREICH (JOHANN).
Hedges (Frederick Albert Mitchell).
Battles with giant fish. 8°. 1923
Hedicke (Robert).
Jacques Dubroeucq von Mons. la8°. Str. 1904
Hedin (Sven). Ein Warnungsruf. [P2685]. 8°. L. 1912
My life as an explorer. [*Tr.*] 8°. [1926]
Southern Tibet: discoveries in former times comp. w. my own researches in 1906–08. v4, 6–9 [v6 *in* 2p., *sep. tp. & pagin.* v8 *in* 4p., *pagin. cont.* v9 *in* 5p., 1–3 *pagin. cont.*, 4, 5, *sep. pagin.*] 4°. Stockholm. 1920–22
4, Kara-Korum & Chang Tang.
6i, Die meteorolog. Beobachtungen, bearb. v., N. Ekholm.
ii, Les observations astronom. &c. par K. G. Olsson.
7, Hist. of explor. in the Kara-Korum Mts.
8i, The Ts'ung-Ling Mts., by S. H. & A. Herrmann.
ii, Die Westländer in d. chin. Kartographie, by A. Herrmann.
iii, 2 Osttürk. Manuskriptkarten, unter Mitwirk. v. A. v. Le Coq; hrsg. A. Herrmann.
iv, Chin. Umschreib. v. ält. geogr. Namen, v. A. Herrmann.
9i, Journeys in East. Pamir, by S. H.
ii, Osttürk. Namenliste, v. A. v. Lecoq.
iii, Zur Geologie v. Ost–Pamir, von B. Asklund.
iv, Eine chin. Beschreibung v. Tibet. Vermutlich v. J. Klaproth. Nach Amiot's Übers. bearb. Hrsg. v. E. Hänisch.—Das Goldstromland im chin.-tibet. Grenzgebiete, nach d. gr. Kriegswerk v. 1781, v. E. Hänisch.
v, Gen. index.
„ „ Maps, 2v (2 Hypsometrical maps, constr. &c. by H. Byström). la4°. *n.d.* 1922
see OSSIANNILSSON (K. G.) S. H.-adelsman !, 1917.
Heeg (Joseph). Pseudodemokrit. Studien, *see* KÖN.-PREUSS. AKAD. Abhdln., Phil.-hist. Kl., 1913.
Heelis (F.) Pitman's theory & practice of commerce. Ed. F. H. compl. ed. 8°. [1912]
Heemstede (L. v.) Für Rom. Streit u. Weiheklänge deut. Dichter. [P2505]. s8°. Aachen. 1874
Heep (J.) Juan de Valdeś, s. Relig., s. Werden &c. [Quellen &c. aus d. Gesch. d. Reformationsjhdts., B11]. 8°. L. 1909
Heer (Georg). Gesch. d. deut. Burschenschaft, B2, *see* HAUPT (H.) Quellen &c., B10, 1927.
Marburger Studentenleben, 1527–1927. Festgabe z. 400-jähr. Jubelfeier d. Univ. Marburg. 8°. Marburg. 1927
Heer (Jakob Christoph). An heiligen Wassern. s8°. St. 1920
Laubgewind. s8°. St. 1922
Der Wetterwart. s8°. St. 1916
„ „ ....s8°. St. 1923

Heerbrand (Jacob).
Disp. contra purgatorium. Præs. J. H., E. Schweickhardus resp. [P2626]. s4°. Tubingæ. 1569
Disp. contra Romani pontificis, &c. [P2609]. s4°. Tubingae. 1584
Disp. de clavibus regni cœlorum. Præs. J. H., J. Langius resp. [P2626]. s4°. Tubingæ. 1575
Disp. de erroribus pontificiorum &c. [P2626]. s4°. Tubingæ. 1577
Disp. de fructibus, ex quibus pseudoprophetae cognosc. Præs. J. H., C. Lutz def. [P2743]. s4°. Tubingae. 1575
Disp. de gratia. Præs. J. H., E. Marbachius resp. [P2626]. s4°. Tubingae. 1572
Disp. de miraculis. [P2609]. s4°. Tubingae. 1590
Disp. de necessitate & contingentia. Praes. J. H., E. Hunn resp. [P2436; 2626]. s4°. Tubingæ. 1576
Disp. de polygamia, ex Gen. 2, 16, 20, 29, 30 capitibus. Praes. J. H., def. &c. M. Hockius. [P2640]. s4°. Tubingae. [1586?]
Disp. de sacrificiis Vet. Test. [P2609]. s4°. Tubingae. 1591
Disp. de simplici &c. veritate: contra novatorum sectariorumq. nostri sec. idolomaniam. [P2609]. s4°. [Tubingae]. 1580
Disp. de votis. [P2609]. s4°. [Tubingae]. 1586
Disp. theol. contra abominandum missae pontificiae sacrificium. [P2609]. s4°. Tubingae. 1579
Disp. theolog. in Tubingensi acad. s4°. Tubingæ. 1575
Explic. causarum cur cum Gregorio de Valentia de mortuorum invoc., panis consecrati &c. non sit disputandum. s4°. Tubingæ. 1580
Oratio funebris de vita & obitu I. Andreæ. s4°. Tubingæ. 1590
Ein Predig v. Fasten. [P2613]. s4°. Tübingen. 1584
Refut. crassiss. errorum, calumniarum &c. quae contra J. H. G. Gotthardus effutivit. s4°. Tubingae. 1589
Refut. Sotici scripti, *see* CHRISTOPH, *Herzog zu Würtemberg*. Confessio, 1561.
Refut. tractatus Gregorii de Valentia de prophana &c. missa pontificia. s4°. Tubingæ. 1581
see VALENTIA (G. DE). Apologia de S.S. missae sacrificio adv. cavillationes J. H., 1581.
„ —— Confut. calumniarum quas H. effudit, 1579.
„ —— De sacrosancto missae sacrificio contra disput. Tubingę a J. H. propos., 1580.

Heere (Gerrit de) *see* DE HEERE (G.)
Heerfordt (C. F.) A new Europe. Tr. W. Worster. 8°. [1925]
Heeringa (K.), *see* UTRECHT. Rekeningen van het bisdom U., 1378–1573; uitg. K. H., dl, 2 stuk, 1926.
Heespen (Paul v. Hedemann-), *see* HEDEMANN-HEESPEN (P. v.)
Hefele (Carl Joseph von), *bp. of Rottenburgh.* Causa Honorii papae. [*&* Defensio. P2692]. 8°. Neapoli. 1870
Hist. des Conciles d'ap. les doc. orig. Par C. J. H., cont. par J. Hergenrœther. Tr., augm. de notes par H. Leclercq. t7i, ii, 8i, ii. la8°. 1916–21
see FABI (GIU.) Pro Honorio & sede apostolica contra C. J. de H., 1870.
Hefele (Herman). Dante. 1. bis 3. A. 8°. St. 1921
Hefner (Otto Titan v.) Grund-Saeze d. Wappenkunst. [Sibmacher (J.) Wappenbuch]. 4°. Nürnberg. 1855
Handbuch d. theoret. u. prakt. Heraldik. 2T [*in 1v. pagin. cont.*] 4°. München. 1861–63
see SIBMACHER (J.) J. S.'s gr. &c. Wappenbuch; n. hrsg., mit hist. &c. Notizen v. O. T. v. H., B1–7, 1856–1912.
Hegel (Georg Wilhelm Friedrich).
The philosophy of fine art. Tr. w. notes, by F. P. B. Osmaston. 4v. s8°. 1920
see CHLEBIK (F.) Philos. d. Bewussten &c. nach H. u. C. L. Michelet, 1870.
„ DILTHEY (W.) Gesamm. Schr., B4, Die Jugendgesch. H., 1921.
„ DRESSER (H. W.) Philos. of the Spirit &c. w. essay on logic of H., 1908.
see HOFFMANN (F.) F. v. Baader in s. Verhältniss zu H. u. Schelling, 1850.
„ REYBURN (H. A.) The ethical theory of H., 1921.
„ STACE (W. T.) Philos. of H.: system. exposit., 1924.
„ STURGE (*Miss* M. C.) Opposite things [intr. to philos. of H.], 1927.
Hégelbacher (Marcel). La parfumerie & la savonnerie. s8°. 1924
Hegendorff (Christoph) [HEGENDORPHINUS (C.)] Compendiariae titulorum codicis Iustiniani exegeses. [P2541]. s8°. Haganoæ. 1529
Hegh (E.) Les termites. Partie gén. 8°. *n.p.* 1922
Hegi (Gustav). Illust. Flora v. Mittel-Europa. B4, 5, 6i. s4°. München. [1919–27]
B4, 5 *each in* 3T, *pagin. contin.*
see BEAUVERIE (J. J.) & L. FAUCHERON. Atlas colorié de la flore alpine; d'ap. H. &c., 1906.
Hegler (Alfred). Beitr. z. Gesch. d. Mystik in d. Reformationszeit. Hrsg. mit e. biograph. Einl. v. W. Köhler. [Archiv f. Reformationsgesch. Ergzb. 1]. 8°. 1906
Heiberg (Gunnar). Salt og sukker. s8°. 1924
Heiberg (Johan Ludvig), *Dr. Phil.*
Geisteskrankheiten im klass. Altertum. 8°. 1927
Glossae medicinales; ed. J. L. H., *see* KONG. DAN. VID. SELSK. Hist.-filol. Medd., 9, 1924–25.
Mathematici Graeci minores; ed. J. L. H., *see* KONG. DAN. VID. SELSK. Hist.-fil. Medd., B13, 1927.
Mathematics & phys. sci. in class. antiq. Tr. D. C. Macgregor. 8°. 1922
Heichelheim (Fritz). Die auswärtige Bevölkerung im Ptolemäerreich. [Klio, Beiheft 18]. 8°. L. 1925
Heidegger (Johann Heinrich). In Joh. Apocalypseos prophetiam de Babylone magna diatribae. 2t *in* 1v. s4°. Lugd. Batav. 1687
Medulla medullae theologiae Christ. &c. s8°. Tiguri. 1697
Heidelberg. *Bekanntnuss d. Theologen u. Kirchendiener in d. Stadt Heidelberg &c. s4°. Newstadt a. d. Hardt. 1592
Heidelberg Catechism.
Catechesis relig. Christianae quae trad. in eccl. &c. Palatinatus. s8°. Heydelbergae. 1563
Catechismus &c. Item: Der Univ. Heidelberg Theologen verantwort. wider die ungegründte aufflagen &c. Item. M. Luther's meynung v. Brodtbrechen &c. Item: Antwort auf 6 Fragen v. heilig. Abendmal &c. durch Z. Ursinum. s8°. Newstadt a. d. Hardt. [1595]
Catechesis &c., a F. Sylburgio Graece conv. [*Gr. & Lat.*] s8°. Hanoviae. 1614
Catechismus. [*b. w.* Bible: German. Das newe Test., 1621]. 8°. Herborn. 1616
Catechismus [in de Singaleese tale overgeset door W. Konyn]. 8°. Colombo. 1741
The H. C. s8°. Amsterdam. 1744
Der H. K. in s. ursprüngl. Gestalt, hrsg. &c. v. A. Wolters. s8°. Bonn. 1864
see BASTINGIUS (J.) An expos. upon the C. taught in the Low Countries &c., 1614.
„ LANG (A.) Der H. Kat., 1913.
„ LAURENTIUS (J.) Cat. H. orth. contra censuram &c. J. Andreae, 1625.
Heidelberg University. Heidelberger Professoren aus d. 19. Jhdt.: Festschrift. [*b. var. a.* A. Merx &c. Vorrede *by* F. Schöll]. 2B. la8°. Heidelberg. 1903
Heidenreich (Johann) [HEDERICUS (JOHANNES)]. Confess. Waldensicae, in capitibus ab Augustana discrepantibus, notationes. s8°. Francofurti a. O. 1602
Heidenstam (O. G. de). Letters of Marie Antoinette, Fersen & Barnave. Ed., w. foreword by O. G. de H. Tr. W. Stephens & Mrs. W. Jackson. 8°. [1926]
Heidenstam (Verner v.) [KARL GUSTAF V. v. H.]
Dagar och händelser. 5e uppl. s8°. [1922]
Dikter. 9e uppl. s8°. [1920]
Folkungaträdet. [2d. 1, 7e uppl., 2, 6e uppl.] s8°. [1920]
Hans Alienus. 5e uppl. 3d [*in 2v*]. s8°. [1920]
Stridsskrifter. 3e uppl. s8°. [1920]
Tankar och teckningar. 4e uppl. s8°. [1920]
Heider (Wolfgang). Biga schediasmatum bina dicteria Schul-Fuchss [*by* W. H.] & Kalmeuser [*by* C. W. Schneier] &c., cur. M. F. Vossius. [P444]. s4°. Lubbenae. 1728
Heiderich (Franz).
Länderkunde d. aussereurop. Erdteile. 3e verb. A. s8°. 1912
Länderkunde v. Europa. 3e verb. A. s8°. L. 1910
Heidfeldius (Joannes). Sphinx philosophica, erudita ac arguta ęnigmata. [*b. w.* Polanus (A.) De æterna Dei prædestin., 1600]. s8°. Herbornae Nassov. 1600
Heidingsfelder (Georg). Albert v. Sachsen, s. Lebensgang u. s. Komm. z. Nikomach. Ethik d. Aristoteles. [Beitr. z. Gesch. d. Phil. d. M.-a., B22iii, iv]. 8°. Münster. 1921
Heidrich (Hans). John Davies of Hereford (1565?–1618) u. s. Bild v. Shakespeare's Umgebung. [Palaestra 143]. 8°. L. 1924
Heierli (Jakob), *see* PUPIKOFER (O.), J. H. & o. Die Entwickl. d. Kunst i. d. Schweiz, 1914.
Heifetz (Elias). The slaughter of the Jews in the Ukraine in 1919. s8°. N.Y. 1921
Heigerlin (Johann), *called Faber, see* FABER (J.), *bp. of Vienna.*
Heijermans (Hermann) [*ps.* FALKLAND (HERMAN)].
Diamantstad. [*Roman*]. 3e dr. 2d [*in 1v*]. s8°. 1922
Ghetto—De schoone slaapster. s8°. A. 1911
Het zevende gebod. Komedie. 6e dr. s8°. A. 1920
Op hoop van zegen. Spel-van-de-zee. 7e dr. s8°. A. 1920
Schetsen. 18 bundel. [1, 3e dr.; 2–4, 7–12, 2e dr.; 6, 13 & 14 *wanting*]. s8°. A. 1901–14 *n.d.*
Heike monogatari; tr. A. L. Sadler, *see* ASIATIC SOC. OF JAPAN. Trans., v46ii, 49i, 1918–21.
Heiland (Paul), *see* FUCHS (E.) & P. H. Die deut. Fayence-Kultur, 1925.

Heilbrunner (Jacob) [HEILBRONNER]. Colloquium Neubergense. Bericht v. d. Gespräch 1615 zw. J. H. u. J. Keller. [P2608]. s4°. Ulm. 1616
Sendbrieff an S. Hubern. Was auff d. Reichstag zu Regensburg a. 94 mit Hubern gehandelt &c. [*b. w.* Osiander (L). Gründtl. Bericht, 1596]. s4°. Wittemberg. 1597
see KELLER (J.) Protocoll. d. Colloq. 1615 z. Newburg, zw. J. Keller & J. H., 1615.

Heiler (Friedrich).
Das Gebet. 2. verm. A. 8°. München. 1920
The gospel of Sâdhu Sundar Singh. Abr. tr. by O. Wyon. 8°. [1927]
Der Katholizismus. Neubearb. d. schwed. Vorträge ü. "Das Wesen d. K." 8°. München. 1923
Sâdhu Sundar Singh, ein Apostel des Ostens u. Westens. 2e durchges. &c. A. s8°. Basel. 1924

Heilmann (Johann David). Commentatiuncula de S. Livino. [Festa. P2594]. s4°. Gottingae. [1813]
Opuscula max. partem theolog. argumenti coll. & ed. E. J. Danovius. 2v. s8°. Jenae. 1774–78

Heim (Albert). Geologie d. Schweiz. B2i, ii. [*pagin. cont.*] la8°. L. 1921–22

Heim (Carl) & R. H. Grützmacher. O. Spengler u. d. Christentum. 8°. München. 1921

Heimburg (Ernst August Heinrich). De Matth. Flacio Illyrico oratio. [P2755]. 8°. Jenae. [1839]

Heimburg (Heino v.) U-Boot gegen U-Boot. s8°. [1917]

Heimburg (Wilhelmina), *ps.* [*i.e. Frl.* BERTHA BEHRENS].
Ein armes Mädchen. Roman. 3e A. s8°. L. *n.d.*
Lotte Lore. Roman. 23. A. s8°. St. *n.d.*

Heimsöth (Friedrich). Comm. de diversa diversorum mendorum emend., *&* Comm. altera. [P1814; *a. c. of* Comm., 1866 *in* P2751]. 4°. Bonnae. [1866–67]

Heince (Zacharie), *see* VULSON (M. DE). Portraits des hommes illust. franç., desseignez & gravez par H. &c., 1650.

Heine (Anselma), *ps.*, *see* HEINE (SELMA).

Heine (Heinrich).
Briefwechsel. Hrsg. v. F. Hirth. B2, 3. 8°. München. 1917–20
Buch d. Lieder. 12e A. s8°. Hamburg. 1854
Buch d. Lieder. [Textrev. u. Einl. v. E. Elster]. s8°. *n.d.*
Gedichte. s8°. L. 1925
Gespräche mit Heine, ges. u. hrsg. H. H. Houben. s8°. Frankfurt-a.-M. 1926
Neue Gedichte. 6e A. s8°. Hamburg. 1859
see TURNBULL (M. P.) A short day's work: verses, tr. f. H. &c., 2nd ed., 1902.

Heine (Joannes Esaias Christianus). Diss. de Christi ad Abgarum epistola. Praes. J. S. Semler. [P2671]. s4°. Halae Magdeb. [1759]

Heine (Selma) [*ps.* HEINE (ANSELM); HEINE (ANSELMA)]. Gürtelkämpfer. Roman. s8°. 1922

Heineccius (Joh. Gottlieb) [HEINECKE (J. G.)] Elem. jur. civ. sec. ordin. Institutionum. Limavit L. J. F. Hoepfner. Ed. legit. 5ª. s8°. Gottingae. 1806

Heineccius (Johann Michael) [J. M. HEINECKE]. Diss. de absolutione mortuorum excommunicat. &c. in Eccl. Graeca. Praes. J. A. Schmidio. [P433]. s4°. Helmstadii. 1709

Heinecken (Carl Heinrich v.), *see* SCHMIDT (O. E.) Minister Graf Brühl u. K. H. v. H.: Briefe u. Akten &c., 1733–63, 1921.

Heinemann (Carl). Die trag. Gestalten d. Griech. in d. Weltlit. 2B. 8°. L. 1920

Heinemann (Fritz). Plotin. Forsch. ü. d. p. Frage, Plotins Entw. u. s. System. 8°. L. 1921

Heinemann (Isaac).
Poseidonios' metaphys. Schriften. T1. la8°. Breslau. 1921

Heiner (Franz), *see* KURTSCHEID (B.) Neue Kirchenrecht; Ergz. zu H.'s Kathol. Kirchenrecht, 1921.

Heinig (Kurt). Stinnes u. s. 600,000 Arbeiter. [P2563]. 8°. 1921

Heinrich (*magister*), *der Poet in Würzburg*, *see* HENRICUS (*magister*), *poeta.*

Heinrich, *von Morungen*, *see* MORUNGEN (H. v.)

Heinrich, *von Selbach*, *see* HENRICUS, *Surdus, de Selbach.*

Heinrich, *von Zütphen*, *see* MULLER (H.), *van Zütphen.*

Heinrich (Carl). Revis. of N. Amer. moths of subfam. Eucosminae of fam. Olethreutidae. [S.I., U.S. Nat. Mus., Bull. 123]. 8°. Wash. 1923
Revision of the N. Amer. moths of subfam. Laspeyresiinae & Olethreutinae. [S.I., U.S. Nat. Mus., Bull. 132]. 8°. Wash. 1926

Heinrich (Florin) [HENRICUS (FLORIUS)]. Succincta formula. s8°. Scuol. 1763

Heinrich (Jean). *Arrêt de la cour d'assises du dépt. du Haut-Rhin, Colmar, 9 juil. 1818. [*Trial of H. for patricide.* P2772]. [*n. tp.*] 8°. [Avignon. 1818?]

Heinrich (Johann), *see* WELLESZ (E.) Die Ballet-Suiten v. J. H. u. A. A. Schmelzer, 1914.

Heinrici (Daniel). Articuli visitat. eccl. Xtni de Sacra Coena, persona Christi &c. relig. Zwinglio-Calvinianae [1594] &c. Rec. cum explic. D. Heinrici. s4°. Lipsiae. 1662

Heins (Maurice). Gand, sa vie & ses instit. 3v. 8°. Gand. 1912–23

Heinsch (Hans), *see* REGENSBURG. Rathaus zu R.; [*by var. wr.* H. &c.], 1910.

Heinse (Johann Jacob Wilhelm). Sämmtl. Werke. Hrsg. C. Schüddekopf. B2–10 [B3 *in* 2, B8 *in* 3 Abtlg.] 8°. L. 1903–27
2, Begebenheiten d. Enklop—Die Kirschen—Erzählungen.
3i, Laidion—Kleine Schriften 1. 3ii, Kleine Schriften 2.
4, Ardingbello u. d. Glückseeligen Inseln.
5, Hildegard v. Hohenthal, T1, 2.
6, Hildegard v. Hohenthal, T3—Anastasia u. d. Schachspiel.
7, Tagebücher, 1780–1800.
8, Aphorismen; hrsg. A. Leitzmann, 3 Abtlg.
9, Briefe, B1, Bis z. ital. Reise.
10, Briefe, B2, Von d. ital. Reise bis z. Tode.
see JOLIVET (A.) W. H., sa vie & s. œuvre j. 1787, 1922.

Heinsius (Daniel). Emendationes &c., *see* THEOCRITUS. Eidyllia &c., 1603.

Heinsius (J.), *see* VRIES (M. DE) &c. Woordenboek der Nederl. taal, d8ii, bewerkt door J. H., 1924.

Heinsius (Johann Georg), *see* UNPARTHEYISCHE Kirchenhist. &c., T1, 2 *by H. & others*, 1735.

Heinsius (Wilhelm). Krisen kath. Frömmigkeit u. Konvers. z. Protestantismus. 8°. 1925

Heintze (Albert). Die deut. Familiennamen. 6e, verb. A., hrsg. P. Cascorbi. la8°. Halle (Saale). 1925

Heinz *v. Wolfenbüttel*, *see* HENRY IV, *duke of Brunswick-Wolfenbüttel.*

Heinz (Hans). Gil Blas u. d. zeitgenöss. Leben in Frankreich, *see* ROMANISCHE FORSCH., B35, 1916.

Heinze (Richard). Die lyrischen Verse d. Horaz, *see* KÖNIGL. SÄCHS. GESELLS. Berichte, B70, 1918.
Ovids eleg. Erzählung, *see* KÖNIGL.-SÄCHS. GESELLS. D. WISS. Berichte, phil.-hist. Kl., B71, 1919.

Heise (Michael), *see* LUTHER (M.) De libertate Xtna.; cum notis, sistit M. H., 1706.

Heisenberg (August). Aus d. Gesch. d. Palaiologenzeit, *see* KÖNIGL. AKAD. D. WISS. ZU MÜNCHEN. Phil. Kl., Sitz., 1920.
Ikonograph. Studien auf d. lateran. Sarkophag Nr. 174, *see* KÖNIGL. AKAD. D. WISS. ZU MÜNCHEN. Phil. Kl., Sitz., 1921.
Das Kreuzreliquiar d. Reichenau, *see* KÖNIGL. AKAD. D. W. ZU MÜNCHEN. Philos.-philol. &c. Kl., Sitz., 1926.
Neue Quelle z. Gesch. d. lat. Kaisertums u. d. Kirchenunion, 3T, *see* KÖNIGL. AKAD. D. W. ZU MÜNCHEN. Phil. Kl., Sitz., 1922–23.
Neugriechenland. s8°. L. 1919

Heiss (Wilibaldus), *see* HILLINGER (W.) Memorabilium theolog. dogmat. tract. tres de Deo uno; praes. W. H., def. W. Hillinger, 1750.

Heitharvíga Saga [*i.e.* HEIÐARVÍGA SAGA; *The story of the Heath-slayings*]. Heiðarvígá saga. Udg. ved K. Kålund. [Samfund t. u. a. g. n. 1, 31]. s8°. København. 1904

Heitland (William Emerton).
After many years. s8°. C. 1926
Agricola; study of agricult. in the Graeco-Roman world &c. la8°. C. 1921
Behind & before. 2 essays on rel. of hist., politics & eugenist warnings. 8°. C. 1924
Iterum, or a further disc. of the Roman fate. 8°. C. 1925
The Roman fate. 8°. C. 1922
The Roman Republic. [2nd impr.] 3v. 8°. C. 1923

Heitmüller (Wilhelm).
Taufe u. Abendmahl bei Paulus. 8°. Göttingen. 1903
see WEISS (J.) Die Schr. d. N. Test.; neu übers. u. erklärt, 3e A., hrsg. v. W. Bousset u. W. H., 4B, 1917–18.

Heizo, *see* TEIJO.

Helbig (Wolfgang). Busto coloss. d'Alessandro Magno a Ptolemais, *see* REALE ACCAD. D. LINCEI. Mon. ant., v6, 1895.

Held (Matthias) [HELDUS], *see* SCHOPPE (C.) Classicum belli sacri, sive Heldus redivivus &c., 1619.

Helding (Michael), *bp. of Merseburg* [MICHAEL, *suffragan of Mainz*].
Predig auff den Grienen donnerstag v. d. Heyligisten Eucharistia &c. zu Augspurg gethon. [*b. w. h.* Von d. hailig. Messe, 1548]. s4°. Ingolstat. 1548

Helding (Michael), *bp. of Merseburg* [*continued*].
Sacri Canonis Missæ paraphrastica explicatio, cum declar. ceremoniarum & brevi ad populum exhortat. s4°. Augustae Vindelic. [*Ph. Ulhardus*]. [1545 ?]
Ain Trostliche ermanung wie man das Ampt der Hailigen Messe würdigklich u. hailsam hören, &c. [*b. w. h.* Von d. h. Messe, 1548]. s4°. [Augspurg, *Hans Zimmerman*]. 1549
Von der Hailigisten Messe. Fünffzehen Predige, zu Augspurg, 1547. s4°. Ingolstat, *A. Weissenhorn*. 1548
see FLACIUS (M.) Kurtze antwort auff des Larven Bischoffs v. Sydon Holhiplerey &c., 1550 ?.
,, —— Widderlegung d. Catechismi d. Larven-Bischoffes v. Sidon, 1550.
,, —— Widderlegung d. Predigten v. d. Missa, 1550.

Helen Pavlovna, *grand duchess, wife of Michael Pavlovich, grand duke, brother of Alexander I, see* OBOLENSKY (D. A.) Мои воспоминанія о Е. П., 1909.

Helena Flavia Julia, *Saint & Empress, see* CYNEWULF. Old English Elene, &c.; ed. A. S. Cook, 1919.

Helfferich (Carl).
Das Geld. 5e unveränd. A. la8°. L. 1921
Georg von Siemens. Ein Lebensbild &c. 3B. 8°. 1921–23
Money. Tr. L. Infield. Ed. w. intr. by T. E. Gregory. 2v. la8°. 1927
Die Politik der Erfüllung. [P2620]. s8°. München. 1922
Der Weltkrieg. 3B. 8°. 1919
see ERZBERGER (M.) Der Prozess E.-H., 5e A., 1921.

Helfrich (George).
Prakt. Winke für Kunsteisläufer &c. [P2762]. 8°. 1902

Helgensagaer. AM 623, 4o, H., udg. F. Jónsson, 1927, *see* JÓNSSON (F.)

Heliand, *see* SEHRT (E. H.) Vollst. Wbch. z. H. &c., 1925.

Heligoland. Guide-book. s8°. *n.p. n.d.*

Hélin (Maurice), *see* DANIEL, *the prophet, ps.* La clef des songes. Facs. &c. des éd. incun. par M. H., 1925.

Heling (Moritz), *see* ZELTNER (G. G.) Hist. Noriberg. eccl. notabilior pericope in M. H. vita exhib., 1715.

***Heliodora** & o. poems, 1924, *see* D. (H.)

Heliodorus, *of Emesa.* An Aethiopian romance. Tr. T. Underdowne (1587). Rev. &c. by F. A. Wright. [Broadway trs.] s8°. [1923]

Heliodorus, *philosopher poet.* Carmina 4; ed. G. Goldschmidt. Alchemist. Lehrschr. u. Märchen bei d. Arabern v. R. Reitzenstein. [Religionsgesch. Versuche, B19ii]. 8°. Giessen. 1923

Hell (Joseph). Arab civiliz. Tr. S. Khuda Bukhsh. 8°. C. 1926

Helland-Hansen (Björn) & F. Nansen. Temperature variations in N. Atlantic Ocean & in the atmosphere, *see* SMITHSONIAN INST. Misc. coll., v70, 1920.

Hellenic (The) Travellers' Club.
Proceedings, 1910, 1925. s8°. 1910–25
see LUNN (*Sir* H. S.) Ægean civiliz.: lect. [*fr.* Proc. of the H.T.C., 1910–12], 1925.

Hellenica. Hellenica Oxyrhynchia cum Theopompi & Cratippi fragmentis. Rec. &c. B. P. Grenfell & A. S. Hunt. s8°. O. [1909]
Hellenica Oxyrhynchia. Ed. &c. E. Kalinka. s8°. L., *Teubner*. 1927

***Hellenikon,** sonnets after Herodotus, 1898, *see* MACAN (R. W.)

Hellénisation (L') du monde ant. Leçons faites à l'Ecole des Hautes Et. Soc. par V. Chapot, G. Colin, A. & Th. Reinach &c. [Préf. par A. Reinach]. 8°. 1914

Heilens (Franz). Le fauteuil rouge, *see* ŒUVRES libres, 66, 1926.
Sept voyages d'Annibal, roman, *see* ŒUVRES libres, 42, 1925.

Hellespont, *ps.* *Laws & principles of bridge. 3rd ed. s8°. 1903

Hellinghaus (Otto). Bibl. wertvoller Novellen u. Erzählungen. Hrsg. O. H. 12B [B1, 2e A.] s8°. Freiburg im Br. 1908[–12]

Hellingrath (Norbert von). Hölderlin. 2 Vortr.: H. u. die Deutschen—H.'s Wahnsinn. 2. A. 8°. München. 1922

Hellman (George Sidney). Washington Irving, Esq. 8°. [1925]

Hellmann (Gustav). *Works in* KÖN.-PREUSS. AKAD. Abh., Phys.-math. Klasse.
Beitr. zur Erfindungsgesch. meteorolog. Instrumente. [1920]
Die Entwickl. d. meteorolog. Beobachtungen in Deutschl. [1926]
Die Meteorologie in d. deut. Flugschriften &c. d. 16. Jhdts. [1921]
Versuch e. Gesch. d. Wettervorhersage im 16. Jhdt. [1924]

Hellmann (Siegmund). Das Mittelalter bis z. Ausg. d. Kreuzzüge. 2e erweit. &c. A. 8°. Gotha. 1924

Hello (Ernest).
Du néant à Dieu. Fragm. rec. par J. P. Heuzey. 2v. s8°. 1921

Hellwald (Friedrich von). Seb. Cabot, *see* VIRCHOW (R.) & F. v. HOLTZENDORFF. Vorträge, H124, 1871.
see STRIEGEL (J.) "Wozu" dienen Vernunft-Anlagen im Hinblick auf H.'s "Kulturgesch.," &c., 1896.

Hellyer (S. Stevens). Principles &c. of plumbing. s8°. 1891

Helm (Rudolf). Eusebius' Chronik u. i. Tabellenform, *see* KÖN.-PREUSS. AKAD. Abhdln., Phil.-hist. Kl., 1923.

Helm (William Henry). Homes of the past: domestic buildings & life in England f. the Norman to the Georgian age. 4°. 1921

Helmholtz (Hermann L. F. v.)
Vorträge u. Reden. 4e A. 2B. 8°. Braunschweig. 1896
see ERDMANN (B.) Philos. Grundlagen v. H.' Wahrnehmungstheorie, 1921.
,, KARPINSKI (L. C.) H. v. H., 1921.

Helmoldus [HELMOLD]. Cronica Slavorum. ed. 2a, post J. M. Lappenberg rec. B. Schmeidler. Acc. Versus de vita Vicelini et Sidonis epistola. [Scr. rer. Germ. in usum schol.] 8°. Hannoverae. 1909
Historiarum liber scriptus ante annos penè 400 & ab autore inscriptus Chronica Slavorum. Ed. studio S. Schorckelii. s4°. Francoforti. 1556

Helmolt (Hans Ferdinand). Der Weltkrieg in Bildern u. Dokumenten, nebst e. Kriegstagebuch. Zusamm. v. H. F. H. Folge 2, 3. s8°. L. 1915–16
Kautsky, d. Historiker. Das Grünbuch K.'s "Wie d. Weltkrieg entstand" im Lichte d. K.-Akten. 8°. Charlottenberg. 1920

Helmont (Franciscus Mercurius van) [HELMONT (F. M. AB)].
Quaedam cogit. super 4 priora capita Gen. [*b. w.* CROESE (G.) Hist. Quakeriana, 1696]. s8°. Amstelodami. 1697

Helmont (Jan Baptista van), *see* REDGROVE (H. S.) & I. M. L. REDGROVE. J. B. van H., 1922.

Helmore (Thomas). Manual of plain song; together w. the Canticles & Psalter noted. s8°. 1850
,, ,, ...la8°. 1850
The Psalter noted. la8°. 1849
,, ,, Accompanying harmonies [*b. sep.*] la8°. 1849
For another copy see h. Manual of plain song, 1850.

Helmreich (Georg). Handschriftl. St. zu Meletius, *see* KÖNIGL. PREUSS. AKAD. D. W. Abhdl. (Phil.-hist. Kl.), 1918.

Helmsdorf (Conrad von), *see* CONRAD, *von Helmsdorf.*

Helmstedt. Hist. narr. de introd. Univ. Juliæ &c. Per professores Univ. Juliæ conscr. &c. [*Partly Lat. & partly Germ.*] s8°. Helmstadii. 1579
Progr. de invictis Lutheri ad emend. relig. argumentis. [P484]. s4°. Helmstadii. [1717]

Héloise [ELOISA; †HELOISA], *see* JORISSEN (TH.) Hist. Karakters, 1, Abelard en H., 1912.
see MOORE (G.) H. & Abelard [*fiction*], 2v, 1921; 1925; 2nd impr., 1926.

Helphand (Alexander) [*ps.* PARVUS].
Germany's economic remedy. [P2735]. 8°. Berlin. 1921
Der Klassenkampf d. Proletariats. 8°. 1911
Россія и революція. 8°. С.-П. [1906]

Helps (*Sir* Arthur).
*Thoughts in the cloister & the crowd. s8°. 1835

Helt (Georg). Briefwechsel. Hrsg. v. O. Clemen. [Archiv f. Reformationsgesch. Ergzb. 2]. 8°. L. 1907

Helvetia [HELVETICA].
CONFESSIO HELVETICA [*arranged chronologically*].
*Conf. & expos. simplex orthodoxae fidei &c. concorditer ab eccl. ministris in Helvetia, Tiguri, Bernae, Scaphusii, Sangali, Curiae Rhetorum & apud confoederatos &c. [*b. w.* Aretius (B.) Sermones tres, 1578]. s8°. Tiguri. 1568
*Conf. & expos. simplex orthod. fidei &c. [*a. ed.*] s8°. Tiguri. 1608
Bekañtnuss d. waaren Glaubens: Das ist einfaltige Erleuterung d. rechten allgem. Lehr u. Hauptarticklen &c. s4°. Zürich. 1644
Conf. & expos. simplex orthod. fidei &c. [*a. ed. Foll. by* Formula consensus. *w. sep. tp. & pagin.*] s4°. Bern. 1676
Conf. & expos. fidei Xtnae ab Eccl. Chr. ministris in Helvetia [*of* 1566]. [*Foll. by* Formula consensus. *w. sep. tp. & pagin. Lat. & Hung.*] s8°. Kolosváratt. 1755
Conf. H. posterior. Ed. J. P. Kindler. Praef. est G. B. Winer. 8°. Solisbaci. 1825
Conf. H. posterior. Recogn. & ed. O. F. Fritzsche. 8°. Turici. 1839
see CANONES. *Canones eccl., eccl. Helvet. conf., 1642.
,, MESS (J. J.) Sammlung symbol. Bücher d. reform. Kirche, 1828–46.

Helvétius (Claude Adrien). Œuvres complettes. n. éd. corr. &c. avec vie. 5t. 8º. Londres. 1781
[De l'esprit: or, Essays on the human mind. *tp. missing*]. 8º. *n.d.* [1807 ?]

Helvetius (Johann Friedrich), *of the Hague, Physician to the States General.* Golden calf, *see* HERMETIC MUSEUM, v2, 1893.

Helvicus (Christophorus) [C. HELWICH]. De ratione conficiendi Græca carmina. s8º. Giessæ Hassorum. 1610
Theatrum hist.: sive chronologiæ systema novum &c. [*b. w.* Scotus (A.) In P. C. Taciti Annales comm., 1592]. sfol. Marpurgi Cattorum. 1629

Helwig (Johann Andreas). Diss. de Simone Mago [1693]. Praes. J. A. H., resp. P. Alino. [P432]. s4º. [Wittebergae]. 1711

Hemans (Charles Isidore). Hist. of mediaeval Xty. & sacred art in Italy. 2v. s8º. 1869–72

Hemberger (Andreas). Der europ. Krieg u. d. Weltkrieg. Hist. Darstellung. 5B. 4º. Wien. [1914–18]

Hemingius (Nicolaus), *see* HEMMINGSEN (NIELS).

Hemings (William), *M.A., of Christ Church, Oxford* [HEMMINGE]. Elegy on Randolph's finger (c. 1630). Intr. &c. by G. C. M. Smith. s8º. O. 1923

Hemmens (H. L.) George Grenfell, pioneer in Congo. 8º. 1927

Hemmeon (Morley de Wolf). Burgage tenure in med. Eng. [Harvard Hist. Sts., v20]. 8º. Camb. [U.S.] 1914

Hemming (Maude Mary), *aft. wife of Lt.-Col. G. C. Cheape, see* CHEAPE (*Mrs.* M. M.)

Hemming (Nicholas), *see* HEMMINGSEN (N.)

Hemminge (William), *see* HEMINGS (W.)

Hemmingsen (Niels) [HEMINGIUS (NICOLAUS)].
Comm. in omnes epistolas Apostol. &c. fol. Francofurti ad Moenum. 1579
De lege naturae apodictica methodus. s8º. Wittebergæ. 1562
De methodis libri duo. [*b. w. h.* Enchiridion, 1581]. s8º. Lipsiæ. 1578
Enchiridion theolog. præcipua veræ religionis capita cont. s8º. Vitebergæ. 1568
Enchiridion theolog. præcipua veræ religionis capita cont. [*a. ed.*] s8º. [Lipsiæ]. 1581
Libellus de conjugio, repudio, & divortio. [*b. w. h.* Enchiridion, 1581]. s8º. Lipsiae. [1581]
Pastor sive pastoris optimus vivendi agendique modus [*b. w. h.* Enchiridion, 1581]. s8º. [Lipsiae]. 1585

Hémon (Félix). Cours de litt. à l'usage des examens, 6, Molière. 2e éd. s8º. [1922]

Hémon (Louis).
Battling Malone, pugiliste. [Cahiers verts, 60]. s8º. 1925
La belle que voilà. . . . s8º. 1923
Blind man's buff. Tr. A. Richmond. s8º. 1924
Colin-Maillard. s8º. 1924
Maria Chapdelaine. Récit du Canada Français. [Cahiers verts, 1]. s8º. 1921
Marie Chapdelaine. Tr. W. H. Blake. s8º. 1922

Hempel (Christian Friedrich) [*ps.* C. F. PHLEME]. Leben, Thaten u. Fall d. Grafens B. C. von Münnich. [*b. w.* Moscovia gloriosa, 1741]. s8º. Bremen. 1742
Merkw. Leben d., u. d. Namen d. Grafen v. Biron, weltbek. E. J. Bürens. [*b. w.* Moscovia gloriosa, 1741.] s8º. Bremen. 1742
Merkw. Leben u. Fall Andreae Grafens v. Ostermann. [*b. w.* Moscovia gloriosa, 1741.] s8º. Bremen. 1742

Hempel (Eberhard). Carlo Rainaldi: 25 riprod. con testo e catalogo. 8º. [1921]
Francesco Borromini. [Röm. Forsch. d. Kunsthist. Inst. Graz]. la8º. Wien. 1924

Hempel (Ernst Wilhelm). *De Deo invisibili. [*Attrib. on tp. to H.*] 5p *in* 1v. s4º. [Lipsiae ?]. 1790–91
De vera signific. vocabuli semen, de prole Abrahami & Davidis &c., disput. 3p *in* 1v. s4º. Lipsiae. 1787

Hempel (Heinrich). Nibelungenstudien. [German. Bibl.; hrsg. W. Streitberg, Abt. 2, B22]. [B]1. s8º. Heidelberg. 1926

Hempelmann (Friedrich).
Tierpsychologie v. Standpunkte d. Biologen. 8º. L. 1926

Hemricourt (Jacques de). Œuvres. Publ. par C. de Borman & E. Poncelet. [C. R. d'H. de Belg.] t2. 4º. Brux. 1925
2, Le miroir des nobles de Hesbaye. Cod. diplom.—Tabl. géneal.

Hemsley (William Botting), *see* CHEESMAN (T. F.) Illust. of N.Z. flora; ed. C., w. assist. of H., 2v, 1914.

Hemsterhuis (Franciscus), *see* RÖMER (J. W.) Spec. in doct. F. H. de natura divina, 1839.

Hemyng (S. Bracebridge). *Eton school days. By An old Etonian [*i.e.* S. B. H.] s8º. 1865

Henao (Gabriel de). Averiguaciones de las antigüedades de Cantabria &c.
n. ed., corr. por M. Villalta. 7t. 8º. Tolosa. 1894–95
6, 7 *have t.* Complementos á la obra de Averig. cantab. é ignacianas.

Henao y Muñoz (Manuel). Crón. de la prov. de Badajoz, 1870, *see* ESPAÑA. Crón. gen., v11, 1865 &c.

Hénard (Robert). Rouen. s8º. [1925]

Hénault (Jean de). Œuvres. Préc. d'une not. par F. Lachèvre. [Le libertinage au 17e s., 9]. 8º. 1922

Henckel (Thérèse Pauline Blanche, *Grafin*), *née Lachmann, form. wife of marq. Araujo de Païva, see* PAÏVA (T. P. B., *marquise de*).

Hendel (Charles William).
St. in the philos. of D. Hume. 8º. Princeton. 1925

Henderson (A. Keith), *see* HENDERSON (KEITH).

Henderson (Alexander), *Moderator of Gen. Assembly, 1583–1646.* *The gov. & order of the Ch. of Scotland [1641]. s8º. E. 1690
Lives of A. H. [by T. M'Crie] & James Guthrie, with specimens of their writings [sermons &c.] s8º. 1846
Mem. & letter rel. to A. H., by R. Wodrow, 1723, *see* MAIDMENT (J.), *ed.* Hist. fragm., p3, 1833.

Henderson (Archibald), *see* SHAW (G. B.) Table-talk: conversations betw. B. S. & A. H., 1925.

Henderson (Bernard) & C. Calvert.
Wonder tales of Alsace-Lorraine. 8º. 1925
Wonder tales of anc. Spain. 8º. 1924

Henderson (Bernard Lionel Kinghorn).
Morland & Ibbetson. s8º. [1923]

Henderson (Bernard William). Five Roman emperors: Vespasian, Titus, Domitian, Nerva, Trajan, A.D. 69–117. 8º. C. 1927
The gt. war betw. Athens & Sparta. Companion to Thucydides. 8º. 1927
The life & principate of the emperor Hadrian, A.D. 76–138. 8º. [1923]
The study of Roman history. [P2500]. s8º. [1920]
" " ....[2nd ed.] s8º. [1921]

Henderson (Ebenezer), *D.D., 1784–1858.* An appeal on the Turk. N. Test. pr. at Paris, 1819. Hist., errors &c. 8º. 1824
Biblical researches & travels in Russia, includ. Crimea, Caucasus &c. 8º. 1826
The book of the Prophet Isaiah. 8º. 1840

Henderson (Fred.)
The case for socialism. [n. & rev. ed.] s8º. [1924]

Henderson (George), *see* CAMPBELL (J. F.) Celtic dragon myth &c., w. Geste of Fraoch &c., tr. w. intr. by G. H., 1911.

Henderson (Hubert Douglas).
The Cotton Control Board. [C.E. f. Int. Peace]. la8º. O. 1922
Supply & demand. Intr. by J. M. Keynes. [repr.] s8º. [1924]

Henderson (I. F.) & W. D. Henderson.
A dict. of scient. terms. 8º. E. 1920

Henderson (John Brooks), *jr.* A monograph of the East Amer. Scaphopod mollusks. [S.I., U.S. Nat. Mus. Bull. 111]. 8º. Wash. 1920

Henderson (Keith).
Palm groves & humming birds, Brazil. la8º. 1924
Prehistoric man. 8º. [1927]
see PRESCOTT (W. H.) The conq. of Mexico; illust. by K. H., 1922.

Henderson (Lawrence J.)
Fitness of the environment. s8º. N.Y. 1913

Henderson (May Sturge), *aft. Mrs. R. H. Gretton.*
Burford past & present. s8º. O. 1920
George Meredith. 2nd ed. s8º. 1908
Writings & life of G. Meredith. 8º. 1926

Henderson (P. A. Wright).
Life & times of J. Wilkins. s8º. E. 1910

Henderson (Walter Brooks Drayton), *see* PUNCH. Poems f. P., 1909–1920; w. intr. essay by W. B. D. H., 1922.

Henderson (William Dawson), *see* HENDERSON (I. F.) & W. D. H. Dict. of scientific terms, 1920.

Henderson (William James). Early hist. of singing. s8º. 1921

Henderson-Smith (*Mrs.* Flora), *see* KLICKMANN (F.)

Hendewerk (Carl Ludwig). Principia ethica, a priori reperta, in libris S. V. & N.T. obvia. s8º. Regiomonti Pruss. 1833

Hendley (Thomas Holbein).
Ulwar & its art treasures. fol. 1888
see JACOB (S. S.) & T. H. H. Jeypore enamels, 1886.

Hendrick (Burton Jesse). The Jews in America. s8°. 1923
Life & letters of W. H. Page. 3v. 8°. 1922–25
„ „ ....[repr.] 8°. 1924
see SIMS (*Rear-Adm.* W. S.) The victory at sea; by S. in collab. w. B. J. H., 1920; 1921.

Hendryx (James Beardsley). The gold girl. s8°. N.Y. 1920
Without gloves. s8°. [1924]

Henegan (*Sir* Richard D.) Seven Years' campaigning in the Peninsula & Netherlands, 1808–15. 2v. 8°. 1846

Henegouwen [HENEGOUWSCHE], *see* HAINAUT.

Hengest, *see* AURNER (N. S.) H.: early Eng. hero legend, 1918.

Hengstenberg (Ernst Wilhelm).
Comm. on Ecclesiastes w. o. treatises. Tr. D. W. Simon. 8°. E., *Clark.* 1860
Comm. on the Gospel of St. John. Tr. 2v. 8°. E., *Clark.* 1865
Diss. on the genuineness of the Pentateuch. Tr. by J. E. Ryland. 2v. 8°. E. 1847
Egypt & the Bks. of Moses. Tr. R. D. C. Robbins, w. add. notes by W. Cooke Taylor. 8°. E. 1845
Hist. of the kingdom of God under the Old Test. Tr. 2v [v2 *cont.* Essay on H.] 8°. E., *Clark.* 1871–72
The prophecies of Ezekiel. Tr. A. C. & J. G. Murphy. 8°. E., *Clark.* 1869

Henham (Ernest George), *see* TREVENA (JOHN), *ps.*

Henke (Ernst Ludwig Theodor). J. Hus u. d. Synode v. Constanz, *see* VIRCHOW (R.) & F. v. HOLTZENDORFF. Samml., H81, 1869.

Henke (Heinrich Philipp Conrad). Disquis. num liber Jobi cum Odyssea Homeri comparari possit? sect. 1. s4°. Helmstadii. [1773]

Henkelmann (Carl). Gesch. d. Stadt Bensheim bis z. Ausg. d. 30 jähr. Krieges. la8°. Bensheim. 1920

Henley (John), *see* HENLEY (M.) Mem. of J. H. comp. by his widow, 1856.

Henley (Mary), *wife of Rev. J. Henley.* Mem. of J. Henley, ed. by J. G. Avery. s8°. Weymouth. 1856

Henley (Pauline). Spenser in Ireland. s8°. D. 1928

Henley (Samuel), *F.S.A., Rector of Rendlesham, Suffolk.* Obs. on the fourth Eclogue, the allegory in the third Georgic &c. 8°. 1788

Henley (William Ernest).
Hawthorn & lavender, w. o. verses. [2nd ed.] 8°. 1901
Poems. 8°. 1921

Henne (Henri). Fouilles de Tell Edfou (1921–24), 2p, *see* INSTITUT FR. D'ARCH. OR. DU CAIRE. Fouilles, t1, 2, 1924–25.

Hennenberg (Johann Christian). Diss. de quæst.: an mulier violentum pudicitiæ invasorem possit occidere? Præses J. C. H., resp. J. C. Schaller. [P2633]. s4°. Lipsiæ. [1704]

Hennepin (Louis). Découverte d'un pays situé entre le nouv. Mexique & la Mer glaciale, *see* BERNARD (J. F.), *ed.* Recueil, t9, 1737.
A new discovery of a vast country in Amer. betw. New France & New Mexico, w. a continuation giving acc. of attempts of the Sieur De La Salle upon the mines of St. Barbe &c. 8°. 1698
Continuation *has sep. tp. & pagin.*
Voyage entre la Mer Glaciale & le Nouv. Mexique, *see* BERNARD (J. F.), *ed.* Recueil, t5, 1734.

Hennequin (Joseph François Gabriel). Biographie maritime, ou notices histor. sur la vie &c. des marins célèbres franç. & étrang. 3t. 8°. 1835–37

Hennequin (*capitaine* Marcel Louis). La campagne de 1794 entre Rhin & Moselle. [Publ. sous la dir. de l'Etat-Major de l'Armée]. la8°. 1909

Henner (Jean Jacques), *see* ROUJON (H.) H., 1912.

Hennet de Goutel (*baron*). Le Général Cassan & la défense de Pampelune, 25 juin–31 oct. 1813. s8°. 1920

Hennezel (Henri d'). Lyon. [Villes d'Art Célèb.] la8°. 1927
Le Musée Hist. des Tissus de la Chambre de Comm. de Lyon. s8°. [1922]

Hennicke (Carl R.)
Die Raubvögel Mitteleuropas. 8°. Halle a. S. [1901]

Hennig (Ernst). De rebus Jazygum &c. [P2651]. 8°. Regiomonti. 1812

Hennig (Richard). Deutsch-Südwest im Weltkriege. la8°. 1920

Henning (Georg). Die Reiseberichte ü. Sibirien, von Herberstein bis Ides. [*Extr. fr.* Verein für Erdkunde, 1906]. 8°. [1906]

Henning (Hans).
Der Geruch, ein Handbuch. 2e verm. A. 8°. L. 1924

Henningii (Henningius), *see* HENNINGSEN (HENNING).

Hennings (C. R.) Deutsche in England. 8°. St. 1923

Hennings (Justus Christian).
Die Einigkeit Gottes &c. s8°. Altenburg. 1779

Hennings (Margaret A.) England under Henry III illust. f. contemp. sources. 8°. 1924

Henningsen (Henning) [HENNINGII (HENNINGIUS)]. Muhammedanus precans, i. e. Liber precat. Muhamm. Arabicus MS., Lat. nunc donatus & notis illust. [*Arab. & Lat.*] s8°. Sleswigae. 1666

Hennique (Léon), *see* DEFFOUX (L.) & E. ZAVIE. Le groupe de Médan: L. H. &c., 1920.

Henno (Franciscus) [†HENNUS (C.)] Theologia dogmat. ac scholast. de Deo uno & trino. s8°. Duaci. 1713
Theologia sacramentalis dogmat., moralis & scholastica. 2v. s8°. Duaci. 1711–12

Henop (Jacobus). De lingua Sabina. Præf. est G. F. Grotefend. 8°. Altonae. 1837

Henot (Jakob), *d. 1625, see* GOLLER (E.) J. H., Postmeister v. Cöln, 1910.

***Henoticum** Christianorum, 1662, *see* ZWICKER (D.)

Henrichs (P.) Napoleon III, ses princ. actes &c., 1848–57. [*b. w.* Beslay (F.) Voyage, 1873]. s8°. 1857

Henrici (Emil). Das deut Heldenbuch. Auswahl mit verbind. Erzählung. s8°. St. *n.d.*

Henricus, *de Gandavo, archdeacon of Tournay, see* GOETHALS (HENRICUS), *de Gand.*

Henricus, *de Herph* [HENRICHUS *Harphius*]. Theologiæ mysticæ libri 3 [in Cantica Canticorum], castigati & corr. Add. intr., per P. P. Philippium &c. 8°. Romæ. 1586

Henricus (*magister*), *poeta* [HEINRICUS; HEINRICH *d. Poet in Würzburg*], *13c., see* GRAUERT (H.) M. Heinrich d. Poet u. d. römische Kurie, 1912.

Henricus, *de Rebdorf. For the Chronicle form. attrib. to H. de R., see* HENRICUS, *Surdus, de Selbach.*

Henricus *a Sancto Ignatio, see* HENRI DE SAINT-IGNACE.

Henricus, *de Selbach, see* HENRICUS, *Surdus, de Selbach.*

Henricus, *Surdus, de Selbach* [HEINRICH TAUBE]. Die Chronik Heinrichs Taube [*form. attrib. to Henricus de Rebdorf*], mit d. v. ihm verfassten Biogr. Eichstätter Bischöfe. Hrsg. v. H. Bresslau. [M. G. H.: Scr. rer. Germ., n.s. 1.] 8°. 1922

Henricus *Ymera.* Chronicon Lyvoniae ex rec. W. Arndt. Rec. fecit G. H. Pertz. [Scr. rerum Germ. in usum schol.] 8°. Hannoverae. 1874

Henricus (Florius), *see* HEINRICH (FLORIN).

Henri de Saint-Ignace (Henri d'Aumerie, *en religion le P.*) [†HENRICUS A SANCTO IGNATIO; *ps.*, CANDIDUS (LIBERIUS)]. Tuba altera majorem clangens sonum, ad Clementem XI &c. de necessitate reformandi Soc. Jesu per L. Candidum. s8°. Argentinae. 1715

Henrietta, *duchess of Orleans, 1644–70, see* FABRE (J.) Sur la vie & principalement sur la mort de Mme. H. &c., 1912.

Henrietta Maria, *q. c. of Charles I, k. of Gt. Brit. & Ireland.* Lettres à Christine, dsse. de Savoie [1628–66]; publ. H. Ferrero, *see* REGIA DEP. DI STORIA PATRIA. Misc., t20, 1882.

Henriot (Emile).
Aricie Brun ou les vertus bourgeoises. s8°. [1924]
Aventures de Sylvain Dutour, *see* ŒUVRES libres, 18, 1922.
L'enfant perdu. s8°. [1926]
Livres & portraits. s8°. [1923]

Henriot (Gabriel). La Lorraine. 8°. 1923
see COMMUNE. Procès-verbaux de la C. de 1871; éd. G. H. &c., t1, 1924.
„ WEILL (D.) Coll. D. W.; not. par G. H., 2t, 1926–27.

Henriques (*Mrs.* Rose L.), *see* LOEWE (H.) Mediæval Hebrew minstrelsy: 16 Zemiroth arr. acc. to tradit. harmonies by R. L. H., 1926.

Henriquez Ureña (Pedro). La versificación irreg. en la poesía castellana. 8°. 1920

Henroteau (F.) Les étoiles simples. s8°. 1921

Henry Bradshaw Society. [PUBLICATIONS]. v56–65. 8°. 1920–27
see BARKING. Ordinale &c. of Benedictine nuns of B. Abbey; ed. J. B. L. Tolhurst, v1, 1927. [65.]
„ BOBBIO MISSAL (The): a Gallican mass-book; text, ed. E. A. Lowe, 1920: notes & studies by A. Wilmart, E. A. Lowe &c., 1924. [58, 61.]
„ EXETER. Ordinale Exon.; ed. J. N. Dalton, v3, 1926. [63.]
„ GILBERTINE RITE; ed. R. M. Woolley, 2v, 1921–22. [59, 60.]
„ LEOFRIC COLLECTAR; ed. E. S. Dewick &c., v2, 1921. [56.]
„ LONGLONDE (J.), *bp.* Benedictional; ed. R. M. Woolley, 1927. [64.]
„ PLUMMER (C.), *ed.* Irish litanies: text & tr., 1925. [62.]
„ YELVERTON (E. E.) The Mass in Sweden: develop. f. the Latin rite, 1531–1917, 1920. [57.]

Henry E. Huntington Library, *San Marino, California.* Doc. rel. to New Netherland, 1624–26, in H. E. H. Libr. Tr. & ed. A. J. F. van Laer. [Henry E. Huntington Libr. Americana, Fol. Ser., No. 1]. fol. San Marino, Cal. 1924

Henry IV, *duke of Brunswick-Wolfenbüttel.* *Anderweit schrifft, So Röm. K. M. von Churfürst [Joachim II], Fürsten u. Stenden, der Christenl. Religion jüngst auffm Reichstage zu Regenspurg, gegen Hertzog Heinrichs von Braunschweig, vormeinten Verantwortung d. Mordbrennens halben &c. [P2439]. s4º. *n.p.* 1541

see KOLDEWEY (F.) Heinz v. Wolfenbüttel, 1883.
,, MAURICE, *elector of Saxony.* Warhafft. bericht, Hertzog Heinrichs von B. u. s. sones Carln Ergebunge, 1546.
,, WARHAFFTIGE erzelung d. gesch. Hertzog H. v. B. &c., 1545.

Henry I, *king of England, see* HAYWARD (*Sir* J.) Hist., 1618.

Henry II, *king of England.*
see CHARTES & diplômes rel. à l'hist. de France, t7ii, Rec. des actes de H. II conc. provinces franç. &c., t2, 1920.
,, MICHEL (F.) 2 annèes du règne de H. II, 1841.
,, PIPE ROLLS. Great Roll of the P. for 32–34 H. II, 1185–88, 1914–25.

Henry III, *king of England.*
see CLOSE ROLLS. Calendar of C.R.: H. III [6], 1247–51, 1922.
,, HENNINGS (M. A.) Eng. under H. III illust. f. contemp. sources, 1924.
,, MOORE (O. H.) The Young King, H. Plantagenet, in hist., lit. & tradition, 1925.
,, PIPE ROLLS. Great Roll of the P. for 14th year of H. III, 1230; ed. C. Robinson, 1927.

Henry IV, *king of England, see* CLOSE ROLLS. Cal. of C.R., H. IV, v1, 1399–1402, 1927.

Henry V, *king of England.* *The famous victories of Henry the Fifth (pr. 1598), *see* ADAMS (J. Q.) Chief pre-Shakespearian dramas, 1925.

Henry VI, *k. of Eng.* Actes de la Chancellerie d'H. VI conc. la Normandie sous la domination anglaise, 1422–35. Publ. avec intr. & notes par P. Le Cacheux. [Soc. de l'Hist. de Norm.] t2. la8º. Rouen. 1908

Miracles of King Henry VI. Acc. & tr. of 23 miracles f. MS. in B.M., w. intr. by R. Knox & S. Leslie. [*Lat. & Eng.*] 8º. C. 1923

see CHRISTIE (*Mrs.* M. E.) H. VI, 1922.
,, GASQUET (F. A.) Relig. life of H. VI, 1923.

Henry VII, *king of England.* Will of Henry VII. [With abstr. of indentures of covenant betw. the King & the Abbot &c. of Westminster &c., by H. Wanley. Ed. w. pref. by T. Astle]. 8º. 1775

see SKEEL (C. A. J.) Wales under H. VII, 1924.

Henry VIII, *king of England.*

Assertio septem sacramentorum adv. M. Lutherū, aedita ab Henrico eius nominis octavo. s4º. [Londini, *Rich. Pynson.* 1521]

Misc. writings: incl. Assertion of the 7 Sacraments, Love letters to A. Boleyn, Songs &c. Ed. F. Macnamara. la8º. *Golden Cockerel Press.* 1924

Serenissimi regis Angliæ ad Saxoniæ principes de coercenda &c. Lutherana factione & Luthero ipso Epistola. Item: ducis Georgii rescriptio. s4º. [Cologne ?]. 1523

see CAMPION (E.) Decem rationes &c.: Narr. divortii H. VIII &c., 1631.
,, FISHER (J.) *card.* Defensio Regie assertōis [*H. VIII*] contra Babylonicam captivitatem &c., 1525.
,, JERROLD (W.) Henry VIII & h. wives, 1926.
,, LONDON: CIVIC &c. INSTITUTIONS. The order of the hospitalls of H. VIII & Edw. VI, 1557; repr. c. 1700 ?
,, LUTHER (M.) Antwort auff König H. büch, 1522.
,, —— Auff des konigs zu Eng. lester schr. Titel Antwort, 1527.
,, —— Contra H. regem Angliae, 1522.
,, POLLARD (A. F.) H. VIII, n. impr. 1919.
,, PRIMER. The Primer set furth by [H. VIII, 1545], repr., 1710 ?
,, STATE PAPERS. Calendar of letters & papers, foreign & domestic, of r. of H. VIII [Cal. of State Papers], v1, 1920.

Henry III, *king of France; r. 1574–89 (& King of Poland, 1573–75).*

The Edict &c. set forthe by the Frenche Kinge upon the pacifying of the troubles in France. Tr. by A. Golding. s8º. [1576]

Rec. de diverses pièces serv. à l'hist. de H. s8º. Cologne. 1664
1, Journal par M. S. A. G. A. D. P. [*i.e.* L. Servin. *extr. fr.* Journals *of* P. de L'Estoile].
2, Le divorce satyrique, sous le nom D. R. H. Q. M. [? *by* P. V. Palma Coyet].

Henry III, *king of France* [*continued*].
3, L'Alcandre, par M. L. P. D. G. [*i.e.* Princesse de Conti ?].
4, La confession de M. de Sancy, par L. S. D. S. [*i.e.* T. A. d'Aubigné].
5, Apologie pour Henry IV, par la Duchesse de Rohan.
6, Discours de la vie de Catherine de Medici [par H. Estienne. *sep. tp. & pagin.*]

see MATTHIEU (P.) Hist. des dern. troubles de France, regnes de H. III &c., 1613.

Henry IV, *king of France.*

Heures dites de H. IV. Reprod. des peintures du ms. latin 1171 de la Bibl. Nat. [Bibl. Nat. Dépt. des MSS.] 8º. *n.d.*

Incendium Calvinisticum regis Navarri legatione &c. s8º. *n.p.* 1584

*Recueil des Edicts & Articles pour la réunion de ses sujets. [*b. w.* Matthieu (P.) Hist. des dern. troubles, 1613]. s8º. *n.p.* 1613

see ALLPORT (R. H.) H. of Navarre, 1920.
,, LESCURE (M. F. A. DE). Les amours de H. IV, 1864.
,, PEREFIXE (H. DE). Hist. du roy H. le G., 1662.
,, RAINOLDS (W.) De justa reipub. Xtnae. reges impios &c. authoritate, justissimaque cath. ad H. repellendum confœd., 1590.
,, ROHAN (C. DE). Apologie pour le roy H. IV, 1664.
,, SIXTUS V, *pope.* Brutum fulmen adv. H., 1585.
,, —— Declar. contra H. assert. regem Navarrae, 1585.
,, SULLY (M. DE B., *duc* DE). Grand design of H. IV; tr., 1921.
,, WILLIAMS (H. N.) Last loves of Henri of Navarre, 1925.

Henry, *duke of Friuli, aft. d. of Istria, d. 799, see* SAVORGNAN (*c.* G. DI B.) Enrico, &c., 1903.

Henry II, *emperor of Germany, b. 973, d. 1024.* Das Perikopenbuch Kaiser H. II, *see* MÜNCHEN. Miniaturen; hrsg. G. Leidinger, H5, 1914.

Henry III, *emperor of Germany, see* URKUNDEN d. deut. Könige u. Kaiser, B5i, H. III, 1039–47, 1926.

Henry IV, *emp. of Germany, 1050–1106.* Das Leben Kaiser H. IV. Aus d. Latein. übertr. v. J. Bühler. s8º. L. 1921

Vita H. IV Imp. [*attrib. to Otbert &c.*] ex rec. Wattenbachii. Rec. fecit G. H. Pertz. [Scr. rerum Germ. in usum schol]. 8º. Hannoverae. 1855

see CARMEN de bello Saxonico; acc. Conquestio H. IV Imp., 1889.

Henry VI, *emperor of Germany, see* GODEFRIDUS, *Viterb.* Gesta Friderici I et H.; rec. G. H. Pertz, 1870.

Henry VII, *emp. of Germany, 1269–1313, see* SCHNEIDER (F.) Kaiser H. VII, 2H, 1924–26.

Henry [CHRISTOPHE] **I,** *king of Hayti, see* CHRISTOPHE (H.)

Henry V, *duke of Mecklenburg: 1479–1552* [*H. d. Friedfertige*], *see* SCHNELL (H.) H. V, Herzog v. M., 1503–52, 1902.

Henry, *the Minstrel* [BLIND HARRY], *see* SCHOFIELD (W. H.) Mythical bards & the life of Will. Wallace. [Problem of Blind Harry &c.], 1920.

Henry, *earl of Moreland, see* BROOKE (H.) *The hist. of H. earl of M., *n.d.*

Henry, *prince, the Navigator, see* FREIRE (J. F.) Gesch. d. ersten portugies. Entdeckungen unter Infant H., 1783.

Henry, *king of Sardinia, 1220–72.* [ENZIO; ENZO].
see FRATI (L.) La prigionia del re Enzo a Bologna, 1902.
,, PETRACCHI (C.) Vita di Arrigo di Suevia, 1750.

Henry, *Saint, bp. of Upsala, d. 1157, see* FONTENIUS (M.) Diss. de S. H. Fennorum apostolo, 1737.

Henry, *prince of Wales, son of James I* [FREDERICK HENRY]. The funerals of the high & mighty prince H. &c. s8º. 1613

see CORNWALLIS (*Sir* C.) Disc. of P. H., 1641.

Henry, *friar, of Wodstone, see* LITTLE (A. G.) Friar H. & the Jews, 1922.

Henry (Albert). Le ravitaillement de la Belgique pend. l'occupation allem. [C.E. for Int. Peace]. la8º. 1924

Henry (Augustine), *see* ELWES (H. J.) & A. H. The trees of Gt. Brit. & Ir., 7v, 1906–13.

Henry (David), *printer, see* TILLOTSON (J.) Twenty disc. &c., abrdgd. by D. H., 1743.

Henry (Matthew), *Non-conformist minister.* Select works, acc. of his life & sermon on h. death by W. Tong. lafol. E. 1776

Henry (O.), *ps.* [*i.e.* SYDNEY PORTER]. Letters to Lithopolis f. O. H. to M. Wagnalls. s8º. 1922

Sixes & sevens. s8º. [1925]

Henry (Robert Llewellyn). Contracts in the local courts of medieval England. 8º. 1926

Henry (Stuart). French essays & profiles. 8º. N.Y. [1921]

Henry (William Charles), *M.D.* Mem. of life & scient. researches of John Dalton. [Cavendish Society]. 8º. 1854

Henry-Bordeaux (Paule), *see* BORDEAUX (P. HENRY-).
Henry-Jacques (—).
Jean Costebelle, matelot. Roman. s8°. 1920
Henry-Miller (W.) Fatalism. True & false. s8°. 1902
Henryson (Robert), *see* MAITLAND (*Sir* R.) Maitland folio MS. cont. poems by Sir R. M., H. &c., v2, 1927.
Hensen (A. H. L.), *see* BROM (G.) & A. H. L. H., *edd.* Rom. Bronnen v. d. kerk. staatk. toestand d. Ned. in de 16de eeuw, 1922.
Henshall (Samuel). The Saxon & Eng. languages reciprocally illust. &c. 4°. 1798
Specimens & parts; cont. Hist. of Co. of Kent, Hist. of South Britain &c. 4°. 1798
Henslow (George). The uses of Brit. plants traced f. antiquity to pres. day, w. deriv. of names. s8°. 1905
Henslow (T. Geoffrey W.) Garden construction. 8°. 1923
Garden development. 8°. 1923
Hensman (E. W.) Loughborough dur. the Great Civil War. [P2525]. 8°. Loughborough. [1921]
Henson (Herbert Hensley), *bp. of (1) Hereford, (2) Durham.*
Anglicanism. Lect., Olaus Petrie Found., Upsala, 1920. s8°. 1921
Byron. Rede Lect., 1924. s8°. C. 1924
Discipline & law. Lenten addresses. s8°. 1898
see ANSON (*Rt. Hon. Sir* W. R.) A mem. [*by var. wr.*]; ed. H. H. H., 1920.
Henson (Josiah). Life of J. H., form. a slave. [Mrs. H. B. Stowe's "Uncle Tom"]. Narr. by himself. Pref. by T. Binney. s8°. 1852
Hentsch (*Oberstleutnant*), *see* MÜLLER-LÖBNITZ (W.) Die Sendung d. Oberstleutn. H, 8–10 Sept. 1914, 1922.
Henty (George Alfred). Under Drake's flag. s8°. *n.d.*
Hentzner (Paulus). Journey into England, 1598; tr. of part of h. Itinerary; ed. H. Walpole (1797), *see* AUNGERVYLE Soc. Reprints, s1, 1881.
Henzey, *The family of, see* GRAZEBROOK (H. S.) Coll. for a genealogy of noble families of H. &c., 1877.
Hepburn (David) & J. Douglas. Chron. of the Caledonian Soc. of London. 2p [*in 1v, pagin. contin.*] 8°. Leith. [1923]
1, 1837–90, by D. H. 2, 1891–1905, by J. D.
Hépitès (Antoine Th.)
Dict. franç.-grec. [t2]. 8°. ἐν Ἀθήναις. 1912
Dict. françο-grec. Suppl. 8°. ἐν Ἀθήναις. 1920
[Dict. grec-franç.] Suppl. 8°. ἐν Ἀθήναις. 1920
Heppe (Heinrich L. J.)
Die Bekenntnisschriften d. altprot. Kirche Deutschl. Hrsg. H. 8°. Cassel. 1855
Die confessionelle Entwicklung d. altprot. Kirche Deutschlands &c. 8°. Marburg. 1854
Die Entst. &c. d. Luthertums u. d. kirchl. Bekenntnisschriften, 1548–76. 8°. Cassel. 1863
Gesch. d. deut. Protestantismus, 1555–81. 4B [Beilagen *to each B have sep. pagin.*] 8°. Marburg. 1852–59
Der kirchl. Verkehr Englands mit d. evang. Deutschland im 16 Jhdt. s8°. Marburg. 1859
see MARBURG. Die 15 Marburger Artikel v. 3. Oct. 1529 als Facsimile veröffentl. v. H. H., 1854.
Heraclitus, *a. of Allegoriae Homericae.* De allegoriis apud Homerum, *see* ÆSOP, 1505.
Heraclitus, *of Ephesus.* Fragmente. Gr. u. Deut. [Üb. B. Snell]. s8°. München. 1926
see BAPP (C.) Aus G.'s griech. Gedankenwelt: G. u. H. &c., 1921.
,, LASSALLE (F. J. G.) Gesammelte Reden &c., B7, 8, Die Philos. H. des Dunklen v. E., 1920.
Heraclius, *emperor of the East.*
see SEBEOS, *bp. of the Pakradouni.* Hist. d'H.; tr. &c. F. Macler, 1904.
,, —— Patmouthian i Herakln, 1851; 1879.
***Heraldic** verses, ante 1565, *see* MAIDMENT (J.) & R. PITCAIRN. Nugae derelictae, 1822.
***Herb** (The) of the field, 2nd ed., 1858, *see* YONGE (C. M.)
Herbarius (1485); facs., 1924, *see* CUBE (J. v.)
Herbart (Johann Friedrich).
Allgem. pract. Philosophie. s8°. Göttingen. 1808
see HÄGER (A.) Lotzes Kritik d. H. Metaphysik u. Psychologie, 1891.
,, HAYWARD (F. H.) Reform of moral & biblical educ. on lines of H. &c., 1902.
,, STRÜMPELL (L. H.) H.'s Philos., H1, 1834.

Herben (Jan). Huss & h. followers. Foreword by G. A. F. Knight. 8°. [1926]
President Thomas G. Masaryk. Tr. by E. Havlasa. [P2403]. 8°. Prague. 1919
,, ,, ...Tr. par E. Bestaux. [P2403]. 8°. Prague. 1919
Herberstein (Siegmund, *Frhr.* v.) Rerum Moscoviticarum comm. &c. sfol. Basileae. [1551]
Herbert (Alan Patrick). The house by the river. s8°. [1920]
Misleading cases in the common law. Intr. by Lord Hewart. 2nd ed. s8°. [1927]
,, ,, ...3rd ed. s8°. [1928]
The old flame. s8°. [1925]
The secret battle. s8°. [1919]
Herbert (Alice). Garden oats. s8°. 1914
Heaven & Charing Cross. s8°. 192[?]
Herbert (Anne), *ctss. of Herbert, see* PEMBROKE (A. H.), *ctss of P.*
Herbert (*Col.* Arthur H. C. Kenney) [*ps.* WYVERN].
50 breakfasts. 3rd ed. s8°. *n.d*
50 dinners. 2nd ed. s8°. *n.d*
Vegetarian & simple diet. [Cheap. ed.] 8°. 190[?]
Herbert (Arthur Stanley).
The hot springs of New Zealand. 8°. 192[?]
Herbert (*Hon.* Aubrey Nigel Henry Molyneux), *2nd son of 4th earl of Carnarvon.* Ben Kendim: record of Eastern travel. Ed. D. MacCarthy. 8°. 192[?]
*Mons, Anzac & Kut. By an M.P. 8°. 191[?]
Herbert (George), *the poet.*
Poems; n. ed. w. life by I. Walton. s8°. *n.d*
Poems. 8°. *p.p., Gregynog Press.* 192[?]
A priest to the temple; or the country parson. 3rd impress. w. a n. pref. by B. Oley & a view of the life &c. of th[e] author. s8°. 167[?]
Select parts of Mr. H.'s sacred poems. [*Sel. by Wesley*]. [P2546]. s8°. 177[?]
The temple. Facs. repr. of 1st ed., w. intr. by A. B. Grosart. s8°. 187[?]
The works of George Herbert in prose & verse. 2v. 8°. *Pickering.* 185[?]
Herbert (*Sir* Henry). The dramatic records of Sir H. H master of the revels, 1623–73. Ed. J. Q. Adams. [Cornel Studies in Eng.] 8°. New Haven. 191[?]
Herbert (John Alexander).
see HORAE. Miniatures f. a Fr. Horae, reprod. in hon. o[f] J. A. H., 1927.
,, SHERBORNE MISSAL (The): reprod. f. Missal execute[d] betw. 1396 & 1407; w. intr. by H., 1920.
Herbert (*Lady* Lucy). Several excellent methods of hearin[g] mass &c. 2p *in* 1v. [*sep. pagin.*] s8°. Bruges. 174[?]
Herbert (Lucy). Mrs. Ramsay Macdonald. s8°. [1924]
Herbert (Sydney). The fall of feudalism in France. s8°. [192[?]]
Herbert (*Sir* Thomas), *1st bart.* [*cr. 1660*]. Mems. of the tw[o] last years of r. of Ch. I; added acc. of the funeral of C. 4th ed. 8°. 183[?]
see STEVENSON (G. S.) Charles I in captivity; f. contem[p.] sources [*i.e.* Sir T. H. &c.], 1927.
Herbert (Thomas Ernest). Telegraphy; system of the Bri[t.] post-office. 4th ed., w. add. [repr.] s8°. 192[?]
Herbert (William), *antiquary, 1771–1851.* Hist. & antiqs. [of] the parish & church of St. Michaël, Crooked Lane, Londo[n] [p1–3 (pages 1–240) *in* 1v. *no more publ. No tp., wrappe[r] wanting.*] 8°. [183[?]]
Herbert of Cherbury (Edward Herbert, *1st baron*). Poems, En[g.] & Latin. Ed. G. C. Moore Smith. 8°. O. 19[?]
see BAXTER (R.) More reasons for Xtn. relig., 2, Som[e] animadv. on De veritate, by E. H., Baron of C., 1672.
,, HALYBURTON (T.) Natural religion &c., writings of [E. H.] answered, 1714.
Herbig (Gustav). Die Geheimsprache d. Disciplina Etrusca, *s[ee]* KÖNIGL. AKAD. D. W. ZU MÜNCHEN. Phil. Kl., Sitz., 192[?]
Kleinasiat.-etrusk. Namengleichungen, *see* KÖNIGL. AKAD. W. ZU MÜNCHEN. Phil. Kl., Sitz., 1914.
Herbigny (Pierre François Xavier d'), *see* BOURGIGNON D'HE[R]BIGNY (P. F. X.)
Herbinius (Joannes). Status eccl. invariatae Aug. Conf. Polonia addict., & petitio ad episcopos &c. eccl. Daniae & s4°. Hafniae. 16[?]
Herbordus [HERBORD]. Dialogus de vita Ottonis epi[sc.] Babenberg. Ex rec. R. Köpke; rec. fec. G. H. Pertz. [S[cript.] rerum Germ. in usum schol.] 8°. Hannoverae. 18[?]

Herbordus [HERBORD] [*continued*].
see EBBO *S. Michaelis Monachus.* Life of Otto, Apostle of Pomerania, 1060–1139; by E. & H.; [tr. &c.] C. H. Robinson, 1920.

Herborn [*in Nassau*]. Trewhertzige &c. Warnung an alle Evang. Kirchen Deudscher Nation vor d. zu H. nachgedr. Deudtschen Bibel M. Luthers. Gestelt durch die Theolog. Facultet zu Wittenberg. s4°. Wittenberg. 1598

Herbst (Hermann). Alte deut. Bucheinbände. Vorrede u. Einl. v. H. Schneider. la8°. Braunschweig. 1926

Herclet (Auguste), *see* MONATTE (P.), T. ARGENCE & A. H. Left wing trade-unionism in France, 1922.

Herculano (Alexandre) [†HERCULANO DE CARVALHO E ARAUJO (ALEX.)] H. [t]1. Quadros lit. da hist. med. [Antol. portuguesa, organiz. por A. de Campos]. 2ª ed. s8°. Paris. 1921
Lendas e narrativas. 13ª ed. Ed. definit. &c., dirigida por D. Lopes. 2t. s8°. Paris. *n.d.* & 1920

Herczeg (Ferencz). A Gyurkovics-leányok. s8°. Budapest. *n.d.*
Graf S. Tisza. s8°. Wien. 1926
Ocskay brigadéros. Történelmi színmii. s8°. 1909

Herczegh (Mihály). Magyar jogtörténet. 8°. 1902

Herd (Doctor), *butcher, see* WILKINSON (N.), *Dr.* H. &c. The trial of N. W., Dr. H. &c. for murder of G. Battersby, 1816.

Herder (Johann Gottfried v.)
Vom Geist d. ebrä. Poesie. 2T. 8°. L. 1787
The spirit of Heb. poetry. Tr. J. Marsh. 2v. s8°. 1833
see LUTHER (M.) L.'s Katechismus; [hrsg.] v. J. G. H., 1809.

Herdies (Eugène). Jacques Jordaens. s8°. Turnhout. 1920

Herdman (*Sir* William Abbott).
Founders of oceanography & th. work. 8°. 1923
The future of Brit. fisheries investig. [P2600]. s8°. Liv'l. 1903
see HERON-ALLEN (E.) & A. EARLAND. Foraminifera of W. of Scot.; coll. by W. A. H., 1913, 1916.

Heredia (José Maria de). Odes, *see* BELLO (A.) Odes of B., H. &c.; intr. by E. C. Hills, 1920.
Les trophées. s8°. *n.d.*
see IBROVAC (M.) J.-M. de H.: les sources des Trophées, 1923.
,, —— J.-M. de H., sa vie—son œuvre, 1923.

Hereford. Descr. cat. of MSS. in H. Cathedral Library. Comp. by A. T. Bannister. Intr. by M. R. James. la8°. Hereford. 1927
Diocese of H. Institutions &c., 1539–1900. Comp. by A. T. Bannister [from Registers issued by the Cantilupe Soc.] 8°. Hereford. 1923
Index to the registers of the Diocese of H., 1275–1535. Comp. by E. N. Dew. [Cantilupe Soc.] la8°. Hereford. 1925

***Herefordshire** orchards; by I. B. [*i.e.* J. Beale], 1724, *see* BRADLEY (R.) New improvements, 4th ed., 1724.

Heresbach (Conrad) [HERTZBACH]. Hist. anabaptistica de factione Monast. a. 1534 cum notis ed. opera Th. Strackii. Acc. Tumultuum anabaptistarum liber authore L. Hortensio a. 1548 Basileae ed. [*w. sep. tp. & pagin.*] s8°. Amsterdami. 1636–37

Heresies. Girq herdsouadzotz. [Book of heresies. Ed. Miaban. *In Armenian.* P2792]. 8°. Vagharshapat. 1892

Hereticus (Parthenopæus), *ps., see* GORDON (WM.)

Herford (Charles Harold).
Gabriele d'Annunzio. [*Extr. f.* John Rylands Lib. Bull.] [P2463]. 8°. [1920]
The normality of Shakespeare illust. in his treatment of love & marriage. [Eng. Assoc., Pamph. No. 47]. [P2463]. 8°. 1920
The post-war mind of Germany & o. Europ. studies. 8°. O. 1927
Romanticism in the mod. world, *see* ENGLISH ASSOC. Essays &c., v8, 1922.
Shakespeare's treatment of love & marriage & o. essays. 8°. [1921]
Sketch of recent Shakespearean investig., 1893–1923. 8°. 1923
see JONSON (B.) B. J.; ed. C. H. H. &c., v1–3, 1925–27.

Herford (Robert Travers). The Pharisees. 8°. [1924]

Hergenröther (*card.* Joseph A. G.) Anti-Janus: Kritik d. Schrift "Der Papst u. das Concil" v. Janus. [*b. w. h.* Kathol. Kirche, 1873]. 8°. Freiburg im B. 1870
Anti-Janus: crit. of "The Pope & the Council" by Janus. Tr. by J. B. Robertson, w. introd. by him. s8°. Dublin. 1870
Die "Irrthümer" v. mehr als 400 Bischöfen u. ihr theolog. Censor. [*b. w. h.* Kathol. Kirche, 1873]. 8°. Freiburg im B., 1870
Kathol. Kirche u. christl. Staat. n. A. 8°. Freiburg im B. 1873

Hergenröther (*card.* Joseph A. G.) [*continued*].
Kritik d. v. Döllinger'schen Erklärung v. 28 märz. [*b. w. h.* Kathol. Kirche, 1873]. 8°. Freiburg im B. 1871
see HEFELE (C. J. v.) Hist. des Conciles; tr.; cont. [*after* t7], par J. H., 1921.

Hergesheimer (Joseph).
Balisand. s8°. [1924]
The bright shawl. s8°. [1923]
,, ,, [n. impr.] s8°. [1925]
Cytherea. s8°. 1922
The happy end. s8°. 1920
The lay Anthony. s8°. 1922
Linda Condon. s8°. 1920
Mountain blood. 8°. 1922
San Cristóbal de la Habana. 8°. 1921
Tampico. s8°. [1927]
,, ...n. impr. s8°. [1927]

Hergot (Hans). Von d. newen wandlung eynes Christl. lebens. (1527, *facs.*), *see* FREYTAG (G.) Bilder, B3, T1, 1924.

Héricourt (Pierre). Le 418e.; un régiment—des chefs—des soldats. Préf. Gén. Deligny. s8°. 1922

Herimberg (Emil Homann-), *see* HOMANN-HERIMBERG (E.)

Hering (Daniel Webster). Foibles & fallacies of science. 8°. 1924

Hering (Ewald).
Üb. das Gedächtnis &c. Vortrag. 3. A. 8°. L. 1921

Hering (Hermann). Doktor Pomeranus, J. Bugenhagen. [Verein f. Ref.-gesch. Schr., Jhrg. 6, Nr. 22]. 8°. Halle. 1888

Hering (Jean). Et. sur la doct. de la chute & de la préexistence des âmes chez Clément d'Alexandrie. [H. E.: Sci. relig., 38]. 8°. 1923

Hering (Johann Gottfried). Compendieuses Kirchen- u. Ketzer- Lexicon. Hrsg. v. J. G. H. s8°. Schneeberg. 1744

Heriot (Thomas Hawkins Percy). The manufacture of sugar f. the cane & beet. 8°. 1920

Heritage (The) of music: essays, by R. R. Terry &c., 1927, *see* FOSS (H. J.), *ed.*

Herking (Marie Louise).
C.-V. de Bonstetten, 1745–1832. 8°. Lausanne. 1921

Herklots (Gerhard Andreas), *see* JA'FAR SHARIF. Islam in India, &c.: comp. under dir. of G. A. H., 1921.

Herkner (Heinrich).
Die Arbeiterfrage. 7te erweit. & verb. A. 2B. 8°. 1921
see NEUORDNUNG (DIE) d. deut. Finanzwirtschaft; hrsg. v. H. H., T2, 3, 1918.

Herkomer (*Sir* Hubert von), *see* MILLS (J. S.) Life & letters of Sir H. H., 1923.

Hermae Pastor.
see APOSTOLIC (The) Fathers; [tr.], v1, 1888; 1909.
,, COTELERIUS (J. B.), *ed.* SS. patrum Hae &c. opera, 2v, 1724.
,, LIETZMANN (H.) Hdbh. z. N.T.: Ergzb. 4, Hirt d. H., erkl. v. M. Dibelius, 1923.
,, ROBINSON (J. A.) Barnabas, H. &c., 1920.

Hermal (Georges), *see* OLIVIER (E.), G. H. &c. Manuel de l'amateur de reliures armoriées franç., s1–12, 1924–28.

Herman (Edward P.), *see* GERINGER (V. A.) & E. P. H. Commerce & finance in Czechoslovakia, 1922.

Herman (J. B.), *S.J.* La pédagogie des Jésuites au 16e s., s. sources &c. 8°. Louvain. 1914

Hermanin (Federigo). Assise, la ville de St. François. Tr. M. Formont. la8°. [1927]
Luigi Galli: pittore. 42 tavole con intr. di F. H. la8°. Torino. 1924

Hermann, *The family of, see* MULLER (A.) De Hermannis claris, 1746.

Hermann V [VON WIED], *abp. & elector of Cologne.* Einfaltigs bedenken warauff ein christl. Reformation &c. anzurichten sei. fol. [Boñ. 1543]
A simple & religious consult., by what meanes a Christian reformation may be begon &c. s8°. [*John Daye*]. 1547
Nostra Hi &c. simplex ac pia deliberatio, qua ratione, Christ. & in verbo Dei fundata Reformatio &c. instituenda sit &c. fol. Bonnae. 1545
Warshaffte erzelung der Geschicht &c.: ursachen Fürst Herman &c.; zu dem werck Christl. Reformation &c. fol. Bonn, *L. v. d. Mülen.* 1546
see CHRISTLICHE u. Cathol. gegenberichtung, 1544.
,, COLOGNE. Antididagma &c. adversus librum quendam [*by* H.] titulo Reformationis exhib. & Consultoriæ deliberationis nom. impr., 1544.

Hermann (Amandus). Tractatus theolog. in primum Sententiarum librum de Deo uno et trino. Ad mentem J. Dunsii Scoti. fol. Coloniæ. 1690

Hermann (Carl Heinr.) Gesch. d. deut. Volkes in 15 gr. Bildern dargestellt. [*no tp.* Text v. R. Foss, nebst Vorwort v. J. Stahl *wanting*]. atlas fol. Gotha. 1853

Hermann (Franz). Markgrafen-Büchlein. Gesch. d. Markgrafen Ansbach's u. Bayreuth's u. i. Vorfahren, d. Burggrafen in Nürnberg. s8°. Bayreuth. 1902

Hermann (Georg), *ps., i.e.* BORCHARD (G. H.)
Schnee. Roman. s8°. St. 1922

Hermann (Hermann Julius). *Works in* WICKHOFF (F.), *ed.* Beschr. Verz. d. illum. Hss. in Österreich, B8, 1923–28.
Die deut. roman. Hss. [8ii.]
Die frühmittelalterl. Hss. d. Abendlandes. [8i.]
Die ital. Hss. d. Dugento u. Trecento, 1. [8v.]
Die roman. Hss. d. Abendlandes &c. [8iii.]

Hermann (Jules), *see* PICK (U.) & J. H. Vive l'Empire, 1852.

Hermannsson (Halldór). *Works in* ICELANDICA.
Bibliog. of the Eddas, 1920. [13.]
Eggert Ólafsson, 1925. [16.]
Icelandic bks. of the 17th c. (1601-1700), 1922. [14.]
Jón Guðmundsson & h. Nat. hist. of Iceland, 1924. [15.]
Mod. Icelandic, 1919. [12.]
Sir J. Banks & Iceland, 1928. [18.]
Two cartographers: G. & T. Thorláksson, 1926. [17.]
see CORNELL UNIV. Cat. of Icelandic Coll., add. 1913–26; comp. by H. H., 1927.

Hermant (Abel).
Le bourgeois. [Caractères de ce temps]. s8°. [1924]
Le crépuscule tragique. s8°. 1921
Le cycle de Lord Chelsea. [*var. ed.*] 4[t]. s8°. [1923]
1, Le suborneur. 2, Le loyal serviteur. 3, Dern. & premier amour. 4, Le procès du très honorable lord.
La dame de la Guerre. Roman. s8°. [1923]
Dernier & premier amour, roman, *see* Œ. lib., 20, 1923.
La journée brève. s8°. 1920
Le loyal serviteur, roman, *see* ŒUVRES libres, 12, 1922.
Les noces vénitiennes. Roman. 8°. 1924
Le petit prince—La clef. s8°. [1922]
Le suborneur: roman, *see* ŒUVRES libres, 3, 1921.
Xavier, ou les entretiens s. la gramm. franç. s8°. 1923
see PELTIER (R.) A. H., s. œuvre, 1924.

Hermathena: papers by members of Trin. Coll., Dubl. v18, 19 (1914–22). 8°. D. 1919–22

Hermelink (Heinrich). Der Toleranzgedanke im Reformationszeitalter. [Verein f. Ref.-gesch. Schr., Jhrg. 26, Nr. 98]. 8°. L. 1908

***Hermes:** or, a philosoph. inquiry conc. lang. &c., 1751, *see* HARRIS (JAMES).

Hermes: Zeitschrift für class, Philologie. B49–62. 8°. 1914–27

Hermes, *Trismegistus.* De castigatione animae lib. Ed. O. Bardenhewer. [*Arab. & Lat.; b. w.* Aristotle. Bk. of the apple, 1892]. 8°. Bonnae. 1873
The divine Pymander. Tr. by Dr. Everard [1650]. With intr. & prelim. essay by H. Jennings. 8°. 1884
Hermetica. Anc. Gr. & Lat. writings wh. cont. relig. or philos. teachings ascr. to H. Ed. w. Eng. tr. & notes by W. Scott. v1, 2. 8°. O. 1924–25

Hermes (Georg), *1775–1831, see* NIEDNER (C. W.) Philosoph. H. Bonnensis explic. &c., 1838.

Hermetic museum (The), restored & enl. The philosopher's stone &c. Done into Eng. f. Latin orig., 1678. Cont. 22 chem. tracts. [Ed. A. E. Waite]. 2v. 8°. 1893

Hermias, *the philosopher.* Spec. theolog. quo exhib. Ἑρμείου Διασυρμὸς τῶν ἔξω φιλοσόφων [*Gr. & Lat.*] 8°. Lugduni Batav. 1840

Hermosa (*Marqués* **de Torre**), *see* TORRE HERMOSA (*Marqués* DE).

Herms (Fritz). Lille vergewaltigt? Auf Grund d. Akten d. Generalquartiermeisters &c. 8°. Oldenburg i. O. 1920

Hernaman (Irene). Child mediums. Introd. by G. K. Chesterton. [P2708]. 8°. Ditchling. 1923

Hernandes (Pedro) [FERNANDES (PEDRO)]. Comentarios de A. Nunes Cabeça de Vaca [1555]; tr. T. de Alencar Araripe, *see* INSTITUTO HIST. E GEOG. BRAZIL. Revista, t56, 1893.
see DOMINGUEZ (L. L.), *ed.* Conq. of the River Plate: The comm. of Nuñez Cabeza de Vaca [*by* P. H.]; tr., 1891.

Hernández Catá (Alfonso).
El bebedor de lágrimas. s8°. [1926]
Los frutos ácidos. Novelas. s8°. 1919
Pelayo Gonzalez. s8°. 1922
Una mala mujer. Novelas. s8°. [1922]

Hernández-Pacheco (Eduardo). La caverna de la Peña de Candamo (Asturias). la8°. 1919
Las pinturas prehist. de las cuevas de la Araña (Valencia). la8°. 1924
see CABRÉ (J.) & E. H.-P. Av. al estud. de las pinturas prehist., 1914.

Hernández-Pacheco (Eduardo) & J. Cabré.
Las pinturas prehist. de Peña Tú. la8°. 1914

Herndon (John G.), *jr.* Public employment offices, *see* UNITED STATES: LAB. Bull. 241, 1918.

Herndon (William Henry) & J. W. Weik. Herndon's Lincoln: hist. & personal recoll. of L. 3v [*pagin. cont.*] s8°. Springfield, Ill. *n.d.*

Herne (Samuel). Domus Carthusiana: the Charter-House near Smithfield; w. life of T. Sutton, h. will &c. s8°. 1677

Hero. *British (The) hero: the duty of every Briton, to avow h. loyalty to king George, 1715, *see* BRITISH.

Hero, *of Alexandria.* Belopoiika (Schrift v. Geschützbau); Gr. u. Deut. v. H. Diels u. E. Schramm, *see* KÖNIGL. PREUSS. AKAD. D. WISS. Abhdl. (Phil.-hist. Klasse), 1918.

Herod, *the Great, king of Judaea, see* NOLDIUS (C.) Hist. of H. the Gt., 1754.

Herodas [HERONDAS]. Mimes & fragments. Notes by W. Headlam; ed. A. D. Knox. 8°. C. 1922
Mimiamben Deutsch mit Einl. &c. [v.] O. Crusius. 2e A., gänzl. umgearbt. u. mit griech. Text &c. versehen v. R. Herzog. s8°. L. 1926
see CRUSIUS (O.) & R. HERZOG. Der Traum d. H., 1924.

Herodotus.
Περὶ Ὁμήρου γενέσιος &c. *Gr. & Lat., see* REINOLDIUS (J.) Hist. Gr. & Lat. lit. dissert., 1752.
Herodoti Historiae. Rec. &c. C. Hude. 2a ed. 2t. s8°. O. [1912–20]
TRANSLATIONS.
The Egypt of H., 2nd book of the Hist. in Eng. vers. of G. Rawlinson. Pref. & notes by E. H. Blakeney. [New Aldine Libr. 4]. la8°. 1924
The famous hystory of H. Tr. by B. R., 1584. Intr. by L. Whibley. [Tudor Trans., s2, 6]. 8°. 1924
H. [Hist.], w. Eng. tr. by A. D. Godley. [Loeb Class. Lib.] 4[v]. s8°. 1921–24
Hist. New vers., w. notes &c. by G. Rawlinson. n. ed. 4v. 8°. 1862
TRANSLATIONS [*continued*].
see BAUR (F. C.) Comparatur Eusebius cum H., 1834.
,, BONNELL (E.) Beitr. z. Alterthumskunde Russlands, B1 (H.), 1882.
,, BREIGER (G. C.) Comm. de difficil. Asiae H., 1793.
,, ESTIENNE (H.) L'introd. au traité de la conformité des merveilles anc. avec les mod., prép. à l'Apol. pour H., 1579.
,, GLOVER (T. R.) H., 1924.
,, MACAN (R. W.) *Hellenikon, sonnets after H., 1898.
,, SPIEGELBERG (W.) Credib. of H.'s acc. of Egypt; tr., 1927.
,, WELLS (J.) Studies in H. 1925.

Herold (Amos L.) James K. Paulding. [Columbia Univ St. in Eng. &c.] 8°. N.Y. 1926

Herold (Reinhold). Gesch. d. Reformation in d. Grafschaft Oettingen, 1522–69. [Verein f. Ref.-gesch. Schr., Jhrg 20, Nr. 75]. 8°. Halle. 1902

Herold (Tobias). Abgenöth. Antwort auff eine zu Glaz, 1693 gedr. papist. Schmähschrifft: Neue Mode zu bethen &c. [*b. w.* Fecht (J.) Hist. Coll. Emmending., 1694]. s8°. L. 1693

Heroldt (Johann), *Basilius.* Haereseologia, hoc est opus vet. tam Graec. quam Lat. theologorum. fol. Basileae. 1556
see ORTHODOXOGRAPHIA theologiae sacrosanctae ac syncerioris fidei doctores numero 76 &c. [*ed. by* J. H.], 1555.

Herolt (Joannes), *a Dominican.* Sermones discipuli de tempore & de sanctis: & quadragesimale ejusdem cum casibus papalibus & episc.: & a sacra Communione inhib.: noviter impressi &c. [*Ends:* Finit opus compos. per Joh. Herolt tpe & de sanctis cum promptuario exempl. atque tabulis coll. Discipulus, nuncupatū &c.] 3p [*in 1v.* London, *Julian Notary.* 1510]
p1 & 2 *have sep. foliation,* p3 *is unnumbered.* Double columns p1 *wants sign. Aa & Bb,* p2 *wants* A1.

Heron (A. M.) Geology of N.-E. Rajputana &c., *see* INDIA. GEOL. SURVEY. Mem., v45i, 1917.
Gwalior & Vindhyan systems in S.-E. Rajputana, *see* INDIA. GEOL. SURVEY. Mem., v45ii, 1922.
see BROWN (J. C.) & A. M. H. Geol. &c. of the Tavoy Distr., 1923.

Heron (Denis Caulfield).
Constit. hist. of the Univ. of Dublin. 8°. D. 1847

Heron (James). Short hist. of Puritanism. s8°. E. 1908

Heron-Allen (Edward), *F.R.S.*
Alcide d'Orbigny, h. life & work. App., a st. of Foraminifera in neighb. of La Rochelle. [*From* Journ. R. Micr. Soc., 1917]. 8°. 1917
Codex chiromantiae. Codicillus I, Chirognomy. [Sette of Odd Vol.] s8°. 1883
Contrib. to st. of bionomics &c of Foraminifera. [*From* Philos. Trans. of Royal Soc of London. Ser. B., v206 *b. w. h.* Foramin. of W. of Scot., 1916]. 4°. 1915
Inaug. addr., Sette of Odd Vol. 25th Oct. 1927. s8°. 1927

Heron-Allen (Edward) [*continued*].

Memoranda of memorabilia in corr. of Marq. de Sévigne & h. friends. [Sette of Odd Vol., Opusc. 85]. s8°. O. 1928
Nature & hist. at Selsey Bill. 8°. Selsey Bill. 1911
Violin-making. 8°. 1889
The visitors' map & guide to Selsey & to geol. &c. of the sea-shore. 8°. Selsey. 1912
see HALKYARD (E.) Fossil Foraminifera of the Blue Marl of the Côte des Basques Biarritz, ed. w. add. by E. H.-A., 1919.
,, †OMAR KHAYYAM. Rubâ'iyât of O. K. &c. w. orig. Persian sources, collated f. MSS. & tr. by E. H.-A., 1899.

—— **& A. Earland.** Foraminifera of Clare Island dist., Co. Mayo. [From Proc. of Roy. Ir. Acad., v31]. la8°. D. 1913
Foraminifera of the Kerimba Archipelago (Portug. E. Afr.) [Extr. f. Zoolog. Soc. of London. Trans., v22, 1914–15 &c.] fol. 1914–15
Foraminifera of W. of Scot.; coll. by W. A. Herdman, 1913. [*From* Linnean Soc. Trans., v11]. 4°. 1916
The recent & fossil foraminifera of the shore-sands at Selsey Bill, Sussex. [Repr. f. Journal of Roy. Microscop. Soc. *Added*, Prolegom., chalk foramin. 1894, *w. sep. tp. & pagin.*] 8°. 1908–1911

Héron de Villefosse (Antoine), *see* ALGÉRIE. Musées &c. archéolog. de l'A. &c.: Musée Africain du Louvre; par A. H. de V., 1921.

—— **& H. Thédenat.** Cachets d'oculistes romains. t1 [*no more publ.*] 8°. Tours. 1882

***Héros (Les)** de la Ligue, ou procession monacale conduitte par Louis XIV &c., 1691, *see* DUSART (C.)

Herpin (Eugène). The hero of Brittany: Armand de Chateaubriand, 1768–1809. Tr. by Mrs. C. Grant. 8°. [1914]

Herquet (Carl). Charlotta v. Lusignan u. Caterina Cornaro, Königinnen v. Cypern. 8°. Regensburg. 1870

Herrera (*Card.* José Martin de), *see* MARTIN DE HERRERA (*Card.* J.)

Herreros de Mora (Angelo). La asamblea españ. de 1854 y la cuestion relig. Col. de discursos. 8°. 1855
La iglesia de Jesu-Cristo en España. s8°. Nueva York. *n.d.*

Herrey (Robert F.) *Two right profitable &c. concordances &c. Coll. by R. F. H. [*b. w.* Bible. The Holy Bible, 1625]. s4°. 1622

Herrgott (Marquardi), *see* BENEDICTINES. *Vetus disciplina monastica &c.; prodit opera &c. **Presbyteri [*i.e.* M. H.], 1726.

Herrick (Charles Judson).
Neurological found. of animal behavior. 8°. N.Y. [1924]

Herrick (Robert). Hesperides; works human & divine. Intr. by H. Morley. 8°. 1884

Herring (Richard).
Paper & paper making, anc. & mod. [2nd ed.] 8°. 1856

Herringshaw (Thomas William). H.'s Amer. blue-book, 1915, *see* AMERICAN BLUE-BOOK.

Herriot (Edouard).
Amid the forests of Normandy. Tr. J. H. Lepper. 8°. [1926]
Dans la forêt normande. s8°. [1925]
Lyon pend. la Guerre. [C.E. for Int. Peace]. la8°. 1925
La Russie nouvelle. 8°. [1922]

Herrmann (Albert). Alte Geog. d. unteren Oxusgebiete, 1914, *see* KÖNIGL. GESELLS. D. WISS., *Göttingen*, Phil.-hist. Kl., B15, 1917.
Die alt. Seidenstrassen zw. China u. Syrien. Abt. 1. la8°. 1910
Die Verkehrswege zw. China, Indien u. Rom um 100 nach Chr. Geb. [P2750]. 8°. L. 1922
see HEDIN (S.) South. Tibet: researches, 1906–08, v8, by S. H. & A. H., 1922.

Herrmann (Emanuel). Das Geheimniss d. Macht. 2e A. [*b. w.* Liebmann (O.) Ged. u. Thats., B2ii, 1901]. 8°. 1896

Herrmann (Fritz). Evangel. Regungen zu Mainz. [Verein f. Ref.-Gesch. Schr., Jhrg. 27 (Nr. 100)]. 8°. L. 1910

Herrmann (Johann Friedrich). Disput.: testimonia patrum 5 prim. secul. de Pauli Apost. itin. in Hispaniam. Praes. J. J. Spier. [P432]. s4°. Vitembergae. 1740

Herrmann (Paul). Erläut. zu ersten 9 Bücher d. Dän. Gesch. d. Saxo Grammaticus, 2T, 1901–22, *see* SAXO, *Gramm.*

Herrnbaur (Johann Georg). Diss. de Ottonismo. Præs. J. C. Spener. [P2631]. s4°. Vitembergae. [1726]

Herrnschmid (Johann Daniel). Comm. hist. de vita M. Lutheri. In Lat. conv. &c. & ejusdem auct. De magna praerog. eccl. Evang. add. J. H. Grischovius. Cum praef. J. G. Knappii. s8°. Halae Magdeb. 1742
see ANTON (P.) Programmata; acc. J. D. H. progr., 1735.
,, CALLENBERG (J. H.) Vitae J. D. H. illustr., 1735.

Herrwieg (Christoph). Disput. de jure uxoris in bona mariti. Præs. S. Strykio. [P2745]. s4°. Francofurti. [1686]

Hersart de la Villemarqué (*le vte.*), *see* LA VILLEMARQUÉ.

Herschel (*Sir* John F. W.), *1st bart.*
Popular lect. on scient. subjects. s8°. 1876

Herschell (Ghetal), *aft. wife of Sir J. S. Burdon Sanderson, see* SANDERSON (G., *Lady*).

Hersent (Charles). In Dionysii Areopagitæ de mystica theologia librum apparatus, notæ &c. s8°. Parisiis. 1626

Hershon (Paul Isaac). Genesis w. a Talmudical comm. Tr. by M. Wolkenberg w. introd. essay by H. D. M. Spence. 8°. 1883

Hertel (Johannes).
Das Pañcatantra: s. Gesch. u. s. Verbreitung. la8°. L. 1914

Hertford (Frances Seymour, *countess of*) [*countess of Hertford to 1748; after that date duchess of Somerset; wife of 7th duke*]. Corr. betw. F., C. of H. & H. L., Countess of Pomfret, 1738–41. 2nd ed. 3v[v3 *wanting*]. s8°. 1806
see HULL (T.), *ed.* Sel. letters betw. the Duchess of Somerset, Lady Luxborough &c., 2v, 1778.

Hertford (Francis George Hugo Seymour, *5th marq. of*), *see* BEAUFORT (H. A. W. F. S., *9th d. of*). Cat. of old Eng. lacquer furniture, prop. of B. & old Engl. &c. furniture &c. prop. of H., sold, 1921.

Hertfordshire. H. county records. Notes & extr. f. the Sessions Rec. Comp. by W. Le Hardy. v4. 8°. Hertford. 1923

Hertius (Johannes Nicolaus). Comm. de fide diplomatum Germ. imperat. & regum. Acc. epistola. [P2746]. s4°. *n.p.* 1736

Hertling (Georg, *Graf* von), *1843–1919.*
Erinnerungen. B2 (1882–1902). Hrsg. v. K., Graf v. Hertling. 8°. Kempten. 1920

Hertslet (Lewis). A complete coll. of treaties & conventions &c. betw. Gt. Brit. & Foreign Powers so far as they rel. to Commerce &c., Slavery &c. Comp. &c. by C. S. Nicoll & W. L. Berrow. [H.'s Commercial treaties]. v28–31 (31, Index to v23–30). [*No more publ.*] 8°. 1922–25
Henceforward incorporated with Brit. & For. State papers.

Hertwig (Oscar). Allgemeine Biologie. 5e, verb. u. erweit. A., bearbt. v. O. u. G. Hertwig. la8°. Jena. 1920

Hertz (Friedrich). The polit. & econ. murder of the German-Austrian people. [P2484]. 8°. 1919
Race & civilization. Tr. A. S. Levetus & W. Entz. 8°. 1928
Zahlungsbilanz u. Lebensfähigkeit Österreichs. [V. f. Sozialpol., B167ii]. 8°. München. 1925

Hertz (Henri). Degas. 8°. 1920

Hertz (Joseph Herman), *Chief Rabbi.*
Affirmations of Judaism. 8°. 1927
A book of Jewish thoughts sel. &c. by J. H. H. 2nd impr. s8°. 1921
The first pastoral tour to the Jewish communities of the British overseas dominions. la8°. O. 1924

Hertz (William D.), *1825–90, see* HARRISON (F.) In memory of W. D. H., 1890.

Hertzberg (Raphael), *see* UJFALVY (K. J.) & R. H. Gramm. finnoise, 1876.

Hertzberg (Wilhelm Adolf Boguslaw).
De diis Romanorum patriis. 8°. Halae. 1840

Hertzberger (Anton Otto). Etliche Propheceysprüche D. M. Lutheri, d. dritten Elias. [P2468]. s4°. [Northausen?]. 1552
Von dem frölichen Ablas auff das güldene Jar, des itzigen fünfftzigsten Jars. s4°. [Magdeburg, *C. Rödinger*]. [1550]
,, ,, ...[*a. issue in* P2468]. s4°. [Magdeburg. 1550]

Hertzler (Joyce Oramel). Hist. of Utopian thought. 8°. [1923]

Hertzman-Ericson (Gurli). Resan ut. 2a uppl. s8°. [1925]

Hertzsprung (Ejnar). Effective wavelengths of stars in the Pleiades, *see* KONG. DAN. VIDENSK. SELSKAB. Skr., Række 8, B4, 1918–23.

Hervé (Edouard), *see* DESCHANEL (P.) Disc. de récep. (*on* E. H.), 1900.

Hervey, *The family of, see* HERVEY (S. H. A.) *H., 1st bp. of Ely & others, 1050–1500, 1923.

Hervey, *1st bp. of Ely, d. 1131, see* HERVEY (S. H. A.) *H., 1st bp. of Ely &c., 1050–1500, 1923.

Hervey (Arthur). Alfred Bruneau. s8°. 1907

Hervey (Frederick Augustus), *4th earl of Bristol, see* BRISTOL (F. A., *4th earl of*).

Hervey (Harry). Where strange gods call: pages out of the East. 8°. [1925]

Hervey (James). Eleven letters to J. Wesley cont. an ans. to remarks on Theron & Aspasio [by J. H.] With a pref. [by W. Hervey]. s8°. 1765
Remarks on Lord Bolingbroke's Letters on the study &c. of hist., rel. to hist. of the Old Test. [*b. w.* Clayton (R.) Vindic., 1752]. s8°. 1752
Theron & Aspasio, dial. & letters. 2v. s8°. Glasgow. 1790
see Ryland (J. C.) The character of J. H., *w.* letters f. J. H. (1752–56), 1790.
,, Sandeman (R.) Letters on Theron & Aspasio addr. to the author [J. H.], 1768.

Hervey (Mary Frederica Sophia). The life, corresp. &c. of Thomas Howard, Earl of Arundel. la8°. C. 1921

Hervey (Sydenham Henry Augustus). *Hervey, 1st bp. of Ely & others of the same name, 1050–1500. 8°. Ipswich. 1923

Hervez (Jean), *ps.* [*i.e.* Raoul Vèze], *see* Casanova (J.) Corresp. inéd. *&* Le ms. des Mém. [*by* R. V.], 2t, 1925.

Hervieu (Paul).
see Curel (*vte.* F. de). Disc. pour la récept. de F. de C. [*on* P. H.], 1919.
,, Gaultier (P.) Maîtres de la pensée franç., P. H. &c., 1921.

Hervis *de Metz.* Hervis von Metz, Vorgedicht d. Lothringer Geste. Hrsg. E. Stengel. B1, Text u. Varianten. [Gesells. f. roman. Lit., 1]. 8°. Dresden. 1903

Herwig (Franz). Das Schlachtfeld. Roman. s8°. St. 1920

Herz (H.) Energie u. seel. Richtkräfte. [P2479]. 8°. L. 1909

Herzen (Alexander) [*ps.* Iscander].
"Колоколъ" избранныя статьи А. И. Герцена (1857–69). s8°. Женева. 1887
Михаилъ Бакунинъ и польское дѣло. [P2389]. s8°. Берлинъ. *n.d.*
Translations.
De l'autre rive. Tr. par A. H. fils. 4e éd. 8°. Genève. 1870
Translations [*continued*].
Memoirs, p1, 2. Tr. J. D. Duff. 8°. New Haven, *Yale*. 1923
My past & thoughts : memoirs. Auth. tr. by C. Garnett. 6v. s8°. 1924–27
see Shpet (G.) Философ. міровоззрение Г., 1921.
,, Steklov (Yu.) A. J. H.: e. Biog., 1920.

Herzer (*Prof. Dr.* Jan) & V. Prach. Českoněmecký Slovník ; [za] pomocí četných odborníků sestavili J. H. a V. P. d2, 3. 8°. Prag. [1922]

Herzfeld (Ernst). Die Aufnahme d. sasanid. Denkmals v. Paikūli, *see* Kön.-Preuss. Akad. Abhdln., Phil.-hist. Kl., 1914.
Die Malereien v. Samarra. [Forsch. z. islam. Kunst ; hrsg. F. Sarre, 2, B3]. 4°. 1927
Der Wandschmuck d. Bauten v. Samarra u. s. Ornamentik. [Forsch. z. islam. Kunst ; hrsg. F. Sarre, 2, B1]. 4°. 1923
see Sarre (F.) & E. H. Archäolog. Reise im Euphrat- u. Tigris-Gebiet, 4B, 1911–20.
,, —— & —— Iran. Felsreliefs, 1910.

Herzog (Emil).
Gesch. d. Zwickauer Gymnasiums. 8°. Zwickau. 1869

Herzog (Eugen). Französ. Phonogrammstudien, 1, 1912, *see* Kais. Akad. d. W. zu W. Sitz., B169, 1913.

Herzog (Johann Jakob).
see Schaff (P.), *ed.* Relig. encyclopædia ; based on H., 3v, 1883–84.
,, —— & S. M. Jackson. Encycl. of living divines &c., suppl. to Schaff-Herzog, 1887.

Herzog (Rudolf), *novelist.*
Die Buben d. Frau Opterberg. s8°. St. 1921
Hanseaten. Roman. 71.–80. A. s8°. St. 1915
Wieland d. Schmied. Roman. s8°. St. 1925
Windzeit u. Wolfszeit. Gedichte. s8°. St. 1921
Wir sterben nicht ! Lieder u. Balladen. s8°. St. 1921

Herzog (Rudolf), *prof. of class. philol., see* Crusius (O.) & R. H. Der Traum d. Herondas, 1924.

***Herzogin (Die) von Ahlden,** 1852, *see* Schulenburg-Klosterrode (F. A., *Graf* v. d.)

Hesch (Jacob). Disput. de dicto Pauli, Coloss. 2., in Christo inhabitat omnis plenitudo Divinitatis corporaliter. Præs. J. Andreæ. [P2612]. s4°. Tubingae. 1586

Heseltine (Olive). Conversation. 8°. [1927]

Heseltine (Philip). Frederick Delius. 8°. [1923]
see Gray (C.) & P. H. Carlo Gesualdo, musician &c., 1926.

Heshusius (Tilemannus), *bp. of Samland.*
Antidotum contra dogma M. Flacii Illyr. quo adserit : Quod peccatum originis sit substantia. [*b. w. h.* Gratiarum actio, 1567]. s4°. Ienæ. 1572
Bekandtnus v. d. Formula Concordiæ wieder das gottlos &c. gedicht des falschen Brieffs. s4°. Heinrichstadt. 1578

Heshusius (Tilemannus), *bp. of Samland* [*continued*].
De vera Jesu Christi eccl. eiusq. authoritate libri 2. s8°. Jhenae. 157
Epistola ad M. Flacium Illyr. de controversia. An peccatum orig sit substantia. Item : Anal. argument. quibus Illyricu nititur. [*b. w. h.* Gratiarum actio, 1567]. s4°. Ienæ. 157
Examen d. Pfarherrn, das ist, Hauptartickul Christl. Lehre. s4°. Königssperg. 157
Frage : Ob ein rechtgleubiger Christ, mit Unchristen &c. gemein schafft haben. Antwort. s4°. Königsberg. 157
Gratiarum actio pro conversione Eduardi Thornei Angli. s4°. Laugingæ. 156
Gründl. Beweisung aus Gottes Wort das die Erbsünde nicht se des Menschen Wesen &c. Sampt Widerlegung d. Schrifften M Illyr. u. C. Spangenbergii v. d. Erbsünde. s4°. Königsspergi P. 157
Kurtze &c. Anleitung wie die wahre gegenwertigkeit d. Leibs u Bluts Jhesu Christi im heil. Abentmal zu beweisen sey. s4°. Königsperg. 156
Propositiones de baptismo. Praes. T. H., resp. H. Boethio. [P2673]. s4°. Helmstadii. 158
Sechs Predigten vom Gesetz Gottes. s4°. Laugingen. 156
Sexcenti errores, quos Romana pontificia eccl. contra Dei verbum defendit. [*b. w. h.* De vera J. C. eccl., 1572]. s8°. Francofurti ad Moenum, 157
Trewe Warnung an meine lieben Preussen für der unchristl Gemeinschafft mit den Calvinisten. s4°. Königspergi P. 157
Vier Predigten v. d. Busse u. Bekerung zu Gott. s4°. Königsspergi P. 157
Vom Ampt u. gewalt d. Pfarrherr. Auch wer macht &c. hab Pfar herrn zuberuffen. s8°. Königsberg, P. 157
see Leuckfeld (J. G.) Hist. Heshusiana, Leben u. Schr. T. H &c., 1716.
,, Wigand (J.), T. H. &c. De peccato orig. scripta &c., 1571.
,, ——, —— & T. Kirchner. Erinnerung &c., 1572.

Hesiod [Esiodo ; Hesiodus, *Ascræus*].
see Flaxman (J.) Class. compositions : Theogony &c. of H. engr. by W. Blake, 1870.
,, Meyer (E.) Kl. Schr., B2 (Hesiods Erga u. d. Gedich v. d. 5 Menschengeschlechtern), 1924.
,, Wilamowitz-Möllendorff (U. v.), *ed.* Vitae Homer et H. &c., 1916.

Hesketh-Prichard (*Major* H.), *see* Prichard (*Major* H. H.)

Hesnard (A.) La relativité de la conscience de soi : intr. à la psychol. clinique. Préf. du Prof. G. Dumas. s8°. 192

Hesnard (Oswald). F. T. Vischer. 8°. 192
F. T. Vischer : ét. bibliogr. [*b. w. h.* Vischer, 1921, *above*]. 8°. 192

Hespel d'Hocron, *The family of, see* Hespel d'Hocron (A. C. H. d'). Souvenirs, 1927.

Hespel d'Hocron (Alberic Charles Henri d'), *1778–1857*
Souvenirs (1794–97). Notice s. la famille d'Hespel, publ &c. par H. de Landosle. 8°. 192

Hesperia : Schriften z. german. Philol. ; hrsg. v. H. Collitz
see Sehrt (E. H.) Vollst. Wbch. z. Heliand &c., 1925. [14.

Hess (Emil). Sprechen Sie Chinesisch ? Chin. Phraseologie Dial. v. Canton. 8°. L. 189

Hess (Frank Lee) & Eva Hess. Bibliog. of geol. & mineralogy of tin, *see* Smithsonian Inst. Misc. coll., v58ii, 1912.

Hess (Joannes Dominicus). Synodus oecumenica theologorum Protestantium, versibus heroicis exposita &c. [*Satire*]. s8°. Grætii Styriae. 159

Hess (Johann). Von disen nach geschriben Schlussreden, is gehandelt worden auss Göttlicher geschrifft zu Bresslaw. s4°. *n.p.* 152
see Melanchthon (P.) Declamatiunculæ duæ in Pauli doct. ejusdem epistola ad J. H., 1522.

Hesse (Germaine André), *see* André-Hesse (G.)

Hesse (Hermann).
Der Steppenwolf. [16. bis 25. A.] s8°. [1927

Hesse (Kurt).
Das Marne-Drama, 15 Juli 1918. [P2407]. 8°. 191

Hesse (Louisa Caroline, *pcsse. of*), *see* Christian X, *of Denmark.* C. IX's Forældre, 1918.

Hesse (Raymond). L'âge d'or, nouvelle, *see* Œuvres libres No. 46, 1925.
Riquet à la Houppe & s. compagnons. Préf. de A. France. s8°. 192

Hessel (Alfred), *see* Strassburg. Regesten d. Bischöfe, B2i hrsg. A. H. & M. Krebs, 1924.

Hessel (Eliza), *see* Priestley (J.) True womanhood : mem of E. H., 1859.

Hesselgrave (Ruth Avaline). Lady Miller & the Batheaston literary circle. 8°. New Haven, *Yale*. 192

Hesseling (D. C.) Hist. de la litt. grecque mod. Tr. N. Pernot. 8º. 1924

Hesselman (Bengt Ivar). Språkformen i MB I, 5 Mose böcker på Svenska, 1300-talet, *see* KUNG. HUM. VET.-SAMF. I UPPSALA. Skr., B24, 1927.

Hessels (Joannes), *of Louvain.* Probatio corporalis praesentiae corporis &c. dominici in eucharistia &c. s8º. Lovanii. 1563

Tractatus pro invoc. Sanct. contra J. Monhemium & ejus defensorem H. Artopæum. ed. 3ª. s8º. Lovanii. 1568

Hessen. Jahresbericht d. Denkmalpflege im Grossherzogtum H. Bearbt. u. hrsg. im Auftrag Grossh. Min. d. Innern. B2, [1908–11]. [B]3, [1910–13] *&* Beilage 1. la8º. Darmstadt. 1912–14

Die Kunstdenkmäler im Freistaat H. Hrsg. durch eine v. d. Hess. Regierung bestellte Komm. la8º. Darmstadt. 1919

see KAUTZSCH (R. E. & NEEB. Kunstdenkm. d. Stadt Mainz, 1919.

,, WALBE (H.) Kunstdenkm. d. Kreises Giessen, B2, 1919.

Hesshusius (Tilemannus), *see* HESHUSIUS (T.)

Hessische Kriegshefte, H8–12, 1916, *see* DARMSTADT. *D. in d. Tagen d. Weltkriegs, H8–12, 1916.

Hesterberg (Joachim). Eccl. Waldensium orthod. Lutheranae testis &c. s4º. Argentorati. 1668

Hesychius, *of Alexandria.* H. Glossographi discipulus & ἐπιγλωσσίστης Russus in ipsa Constantinopoli sec. 12–13 e cod. Vindob. ed. B. Kopitar. la8º. Vindobonae. 1839

see ALBERTI (J.) Periculum criticum &c., H. &c., 1727.

Hesychius, *of Jerusalem.* [Expos. of Job. *In Armenian.* Coll. of anc. & mod. Arm. lit. Ed. Q. A. Tchraqean, v5]. s8º. Venetik. 1913

Hesychius, *of Miletus* [ESICHIO *Milesio*], *see* THORSCHMID (J. C.) H. M. loc. inter Xtianos, 1716.

Hethay (J.), *ps.* [*i.e. gén.* DE CORNULIER-LUCINIÈRE]. Le rôle de la cavalerie franç. à l'aile gauche de la prem. bataille de la Marne. s8º. 1919

Hethe (Hamo), *bp. of Rochester.* Registrum H. H. [Canterbury & York Soc.] pl, 2. 8º. 1914–16

Hetherington (A. L.) The early ceramic wares of China. Intr. by R. L. Hobson. 4º. 1922

see HOBSON (R. L.) & A. L. H. Art of Chinese potter, 1923.

Hetherington (Hector James Wright).

Internat. labour legisl. s8º. [1920]

Life & letters of Sir Hy. Jones. 8º. 1924

Hetherington (William Maxwell).

Hist. of the Ch. of Scotland. 2nd ed. 8º. 1842

,, ,, ...7th ed. 2v. 8º. E. 1852

Hethitica. Coll. de travaux rel. à la philol., l'hist. & l'arch. hittites. Publ. sur la dir. de F. Hrozný. t1. 8º. 1922

see HROZNY (F.) Code hittite, pl, 1922. [1.]

Hetoum, *Prince of Gorgios* [HAYTHONUS]. Liber hist. partium Orientis sive Passagium Terrae Sanctae scr. anno MCCC. [*Written in French f. dictation of H., by N. Salconi, & by him tr. into Lat.; ed. M. Moltherus*]. s4º. Haganoæ, *J. Sec*[*erius*]. 1529

Hettema (Foeke Buitenrust), *see* BUITENRUST HETTEMA (FOEKE).

Hettema (H.), *Jr.* Hist. schoolatlas ten gebruike bij het onderwijs in de Vaderl. en algem. gesch. 7e herz. en verm. druk. fol. Zwolle. 1913

Hettner (Alfred). Englands Weltherrschaft u. i. Krisis. 3e umgearb. A. d. Werkes Engl. Welth. u. d. Krieg. 8º. L. 1917

Hetzel (*Capt.* **A. R.**), *see* CROSS (T.) Milit. laws of U.S., 3rd ed. under superv. of A. R. H., 1846.

Heuberger (Richard). Allgem. Urkundenlehre für Deutschl. u. Ital., 1922, *see* GRUNDR. D. GESCHICHTSWISS.; Meister, liia, 1921.

Heuen-Tsang, *see* BOULTING (W.) 4 pilgrims [H.-T. &c.], 1920.

Heumann (Christoph August). Diss. sylloge. t1, pl–4 [*in* 1v. *No more publ.*] s8º. Gottingae. 1743–50

Parerga critica. s8º. Jenae. 1712

Primitiae Gotting. Acad., hoc est, diss. partim theolog. partim hist.-criticae. s4º. Hanoverae. 1738

see CHARLEMAGNE. Augusta Concil. Nic. II: de impio imaginum cultu, cur. &c. C. A. H., 1731.

Heumann von Teutschbrunn (Johann) [HEUMANNUS (JOANNES)]. Apparatus jurisprudentiae lit. 8º. Norimbergae. 1752

Heumannus (Joannes), *Jurist, see* HEUMANN v. TEUTSCHBRUNN (JOHANN).

Heupel (Georg Friedrich) [HEUPELIUS]. De Ulphila, seu vers. 4 Evang. Gothica. Resp. G. G. Kirchmaiero. [P430]. s4º. Wittebergae. [1693]

Heuré (Paul).

Sens & ses environs. 2e éd. revue & corr. s8º. Sens. 1901

Heures.

Heures. [*Beg. f. 1 recto* Philippe Pigouchet *below device. f. 1 verso:* Almanach pour XXI an. *End: f. 92 verso (Sig. l 4)* Ces p̄sentes heures a lusage de Rōme furēt acheuees le. XIX. iour de Auril. Lan M.CCCC. IIII. XX. & XIIII. par Philippe pigochet Libraire de luniuersite de paris]. s8º. Paris, *Pigouchet.* 1494

92 leaves, sig. a–l4 in eights; sig. k2 & 3 wanting.

Deux livres d'heures néerlandais. Reprod. des miniatures &c., Bibl. de l'Univ. de Liège. 8º. Brux. [1924 ?]

H. (Les) dites da Costa (16 c.), 1924; *see* DESTRÉE (J.) & P. BAUTIER.

H. dites de Henri IV, *n.d.*, *see* HENRY IV, *k. of Fr.*

Les très belles H. de Notre-Dame du Duc J. de Berry, 1922, *see* DURRIEU (*cte.* P.)

Heurgren (Paul Gerhard). La poste dans les temps anc. & mod. Avec le concours de T. Gerle, A. Henning &c. Publ. P. G. H. la8º. Stockholm. [1924]

Heurtley (Charles Abel).

The Athanasian Creed. [P2658]. 8º. O. 1872

Heusler (Andreas), *the younger.* Die Anfänge d. isländ. Saga, *see* KÖN.-PREUSS. AKAD. Abhdln., Phil.-hist. Kl., 1913.

Nibelungensage u. Nibelungenlied. Die Stoffgesch. d. deut. Heldenepos. 8º. Dortmund. 1921

Heuss (Johann Philipp). Diss. de civitatum dispari nexu cum S. R. Imperio. Praes. J. P. Ludewig. [P2641]. s4º. Halae Vened. [1710]

Heussen (Hugo Franciscus van). *Batavia sacra, s. res gestæ apostololic. virorum qui fidem Bataviae primi intulerunt. [*a. ed.*] 2p *in* 1v. fol. Bruxellis. 1754

Heuzey (Léon). Hist. du costume antique. Préf. par E. Pottier. la8º. 1922

Le péplos des femmes grec., *see* ACAD. DES INSCR. FOND. PIOT. Mon., t24, 1920.

Héverlé, *House of, see* TROOSTEMBERGH (*Baron* M. DE). Les sires d'H., 1125–1446, n. éd., 1924.

Hevesey (André de). L'agonie d'un empire: l'Autriche-Hongrie. [2e éd.] s8º. 1923

La bibliothèque du roi Matthias Corvin. [Soc. Franç. de Reprod. de MSS. à Peintures]. 4º. 1923

Beethoven: vie intime. [4e éd.] 8º. 1926

Hevesy (G. de). Recherches s. les propriétés du hafnium, *see* KONG. DAN. VID. SELSK. Math.-fys. Medd., 6, 1924–25.

Hewer (William F.) Deliver us from evil. s8º. [1924]

Hewett (*Sir* **John Prescott**).

Rep. for the Army Council on Mesopotamia. fol. 1919

Hewins (William Albert Samuel). Empire restored. 8º. 1927

Trade in the balance. 8º. [1924]

Hewison (James King).

The Isle of Bute in the olden time. 2v. la8º. E. 1893

Hewitt (Charles Gordon).

Conserv. of the wild life of Canada. 8º. N.Y. 1921

Hewitt (Edgar Percy).

Trade unions & the law. Repr. f. Solicitors' Journ. 8º. 1927

Hewitt (Eileen). Donna Juana: novel in verse. 8º. 1925

Hewitt (*Hon.* **Norah**). The rulers of Russia. 8º. 1924

Hewitt (William Henry). Mungo Park. s8º. 1923

Hewlett (J. H.) Offa's dyke. 8º. [1924]

Hewlett (Maurice).

Extemporary essays. s8º. 1922

Flowers in the grass. Wiltshire plainsong. 8º. 1920

In a green shade. s8º. 1920

Last essays. s8º. [1924]

Letters. Added, a Diary in Greece, 1914. Ed. L. Binyon, w. intr. mem. by E. Hewlett. 8º. [1926]

The light heart. s8º. 1920

Mainwaring. s8º. [1920]

The outlaw. s8º. [1919]

The stooping lady. s8º. 1910

Wiltshire essays. [Repr.] s8º. 1923

Hext (Harrington). The thing at their heels. s8º. [1923]

Hey (Wilhelm). *Noch fünfzig Fabeln für Kinder. In Bildern gezeichnet v. O. Speckter. s8º. Hamburg. [1837 ?]

Hey (William), *F.R.S.*, *see* PEARSON (J.), *F.R.S.* The life of H. W. [w. extracts f. h. writings]. 2nd ed. 2v. 1823

Heyck (Eduard), *see* ROSENBERG (C. A.) Gesch. d. Kostüms; Text v. E. H., 5B, *n.d.*

Heyd (Wilhelm). Le colonie commerciali d. Ital. in oriente nel medio evo. Publ. nel Giornale d'econ. polit. di Tubinga, e recate in Ital. d. G. Müller. 2v. s8º. Venezia. 1866–68

Heydemann (Heinrich Gustav Dieudonné).

Dionysos' Geburt u. Kindheit. la8º. Halle. 1885

Heydemann (Kurt). Die Schlacht bei St. Quentin 1914. [Schlachten d. Weltkr., B7a, b]. 2. A. 2T. 8°. Oldenburg. 1924–25

Heydenreich (Carl Heinrich).
Philos. ü. die Leiden d. Menschheit. 3T. s8°. L. 1797–99

Heydenreich (Eduard Carl Heinrich).
Familien-Geschichtl. Quellenkunde. la8°. L. 1909

Heyer (Gustav Richard). Das nervöse Herz, *see* HATTINGBERG (H. v.) Nerv. Mensch., B6, 1924.
Nervöse Magen- u. Darmkrankheiten, *see* HATTINGBERG (H. v.) Nerv. Mensch., B7, 1924.

Heyer v. Rosenfeld (Carl Georg Friedrich). Adel d. Königreichs Dalmatien, *see* SIBMACHER (J.), *ed.* Wappenbuch, B4iii, 1873.
Adel v. Galizien, Lodomerien u. d. Bukowina; v. H. v. R., *see* SIBMACHER (J.), *ed.* Wappenbuch, B4, xiv, 1905.

Heylyn (John). A sermon to the Soc. for Reform. of Manners, Jan. 8, 1728. [*With* 34th acc. of progress. P2669]. s8°. 1729
Theolog. lect. at Westminster Abbey; w. an interpret. of the New Test. p1. The 4 Gospels. Added: Sel. disc. upon reveal'd religion. s4°. 1749

Heylyn (Peter) [*ps.* THEOPHILUS CHURCHMAN].
Aërius redivivus: hist. of the Presbyterians, 1536–1647. fol. O. 1670
*The hist. of episcopacie. 2p *in* 1v. s4°. 1642
The hist. of St. George of Cappadocia. The instit. of the order of St. George, named the Garter. [*wanting the engraved title page*]. s4°. 1631
Theologia vet., or the summe of Xtn. theologie cont. in the Apostles' Creed. 3p [*in* 1v, *pagin. cont.*] fol. 1654
see BARNARD (J.) Theologico-Historicus, or the life of P. H. &c., 1683.
,, FULLER (T.) Appeal of injured innocence; controv. betw. P. H. & T. F., 3p, 1659.

Heymans (Gerard). Einführung in d. Metaphysik auf Grundlage d. Erfahrung. 3e verm. A. 8°. L. 1921
Die Gesetze u. Elem. d. wiss. Denkens. 3e verb. A. 8°. L. 1915
Die Psychologie d. Frauen. 2e verb. A. s8°. Heidelberg. 1924

Heyne (Johann Gottlob). De ethnarcha Aretae Arabum regis Paullo Apost. insidiante. Praes. J. D. Rittero. [*&* Diss. 2a, praeses J. G. H., resp. J. F. Henne. *pagin. cont.* P2666]. s4°. Vitembergae. [1755]

Heyne (Moritz). Kleinere altniederdeut. Denkmäler. Mit Glossar hrsg. M. Heyne. 8°. Paderborn. 1877

Heyns (Stephanus Petrus). Disp. hist.-theolog de Gregorio Nysseno. 4°. Lugd. Batav. 1835

Heyse (Carl Wilhelm Ludwig). *Bücherschatz d. deut. Nat.-Litt. d. 16. u. 17. Jhdts. [Vorwort *signed* K. H.] 8°. 1854

Heyse (Paul).
Meraner Novellen. 5e Sammlung. 6e A. s8°. 1879
see MITCHELL (R. M.) H. & h. predecessors in theory of the Novelle, 1915.

Heyse (Theodor), *ed.*, *see* BIBLE: LAT. Biblia sacra Lat. Hieronymo interp., 1873.

Heywood (Frank), *see* HALL (A.) & F. H. Shipping &c., 1909.

Heywood (John). The foure PP., *see* ADAMS (J. Q.) Chief pre-Shakespearian dramas, 1925.
A mery play betwene Johan Johan, the Husbande &c.; [*attrib. to J. H.*], *see* ADAMS (J. Q.) Chief pre-Shakespearian dramas, 1925.
The play of the wether, *see* ADAMS (J. Q.) Chief pre-Shakespearian dramas, 1925.
see BOLWELL (R. G. W.) Life & works of J. H., 1921.

Heywood (Nathanael), *1633–77*, *see* JACKSON (T.) Lib. of Xtn. biog., v3, 1838.

Heywood (Oliver), *M.A., 1630–1702.* *Baptismal bonds renewed. Medit. on Ps. 50, v. By O. H., M.A. s8°. 1687
The whole works of O. H. w. Mem. of h. life. 5v. 8°. Idle. 1825–27

Heywood (Robert), *of Bolton.* Journey in Russia in 1858. [Ed. M. Haslam]. 8°. *p.p.* [M'ter. 1918]
Journey to America in 1834. [Ed. M. Haslam]. 8°. *p.p.* [C.] 1919
Journey to Italy in 1826. [Ed., w. biog. sk. by M. Haslam]. 8°. *p.p. n.p.* 1919
Journey to the Levant in 1845. [Ed. &c. M. Haslam]. 8°. *p.p.* [C.] 1919

Heywood (Thomas). The Captives; or the Lost recovered. Ed., w. intr. notes & gloss., by A. C. Judson. 8°. New Haven. 1921
A marriage triumphe (1613), *see* AUNGERVYLE SOC. Reprints, s2, 1884.

Heywood (William).
A history of Pisa, 11th & 12th cents. 8°. C. 1921

Hibben (Paxton).
Constantine I & the Greek people. 8°. N.Y. 1920

Hibberd (Shirley). The ivy: hist., uses &c. 8°. 1872

Hibbert Journal (The). v18–25 (Oct. 1919–July 1927). 8°. 1920–27

Hibbert (H. G.)
A playgoer's mem. Pref. note by W. Archer. 8°. 1920

Hibbert-Ware (Samuel). A descr. of the Shetland Isl. repr. 4°. Lerwick. 1891

Hibernia. *Analecta sacra nova & mira de rebus Cath. in H., 3p *in* 2v, 1617–19, *see* ROTH (D.)
Vindic. Cathol. H. lib. duo, Rerum in H. gest., 1641–49, Synops. &c. 1650, *see* BELING (R.)

Hibernia (Petrus de), *see* PETRUS, *de Hibernia.*

Hibernian magazine, *see* DUFFY'S HIBERNIAN MAG., 1862–64.

Hichens (Robert Smythe).
After the verdict. 2nd ed. s8°. [1924]
The bacchante & the nun. s8°. [1927]
Bella donna. pop. ed. s8°. 1925
December love. s8°. [1922]
The God within him. s8°. [1926]
The last time & o. s. s8°. [1923]
Mrs Marden. s8°. [1919]

Hick (John). Cat. of princ. paintings, drawings &c. at Mytton Hall, the residence of J. H. fol. *p.f.p.c.* 1893

Hickcox (John H.) Hist. of the bills of credit or paper money issued by N. York, 1709–89. 4°. Albany, N.Y. 1866

Hickeringill (Edmund), *rector of All Saints', Colchester.*
*The naked truth. p2, 3. [P529]. fol. 1681
p1 *was by* H. Croft, *q.v.*; p2, Inquiries conc. canons &c.; p3, Consid. of concern to ruling clergy of Eng. &c.

Hickes (George), *dean of Worcester.* *The gentleman instructed in the conduct of a virtuous & happy life. Added, A word to the ladies. 10th ed. 3p *in* 1v. [*pagin. cont.*] 8°. 1732–33
*Some disc. upon Dr. Burnet & Dr. Tillotson &c. [P2661]. s4°. 1695
*Speculum Beatae Virginis. A disc. of the due praise &c. of the Virgin Mary. By a true Catholick &c. 2nd ed. [P2664]. s4°. 1686
see AUSTIN (J.) *Devotions; publ. by H., 1712.
,, HANCOCK (J.) *An answer to some things cont. in H.'s Christian priesthood &c., 1709.

Hickey (Emily H.)
see DINNIS (E.) E. H.: a mem., 1927.
,, SYMONDS (J. A.) & E. H. The poetry of R. Noel, 1901.

Hickey (William).
Memoirs. Ed. A. Spencer. v3, 4, 1782–1809. 8°. [1923–25]
" " ....3rd ed. [v1], 1749–75. 8°. 1919
" " ....8th ed. v1, 1749–75. 8°. [1926]

Hickey (William), *Colonel.* The Constit. of the U.S. of Amer. &c. 7th ed. s8°. Phila. 1854

Hicks (Edward Lee), *bp. of Lincoln*, *see* FOWLER (J. H.), *ed.* Life & letters of E. L. H., 1922.

Hicks (Edward Seymour).
Difficulties: an attempt to help. 8°. [1922]

Hicks (John Donald). Constit. of the Northwest States, *see* NEBRASKA UNIV. Studies, v23, 1924.

Hicks (William Mitchinson).
A treatise on the analysis of spectra. la8°. C. 1922

Hicks-Beach (*Mrs.* William). Blackmarston. s8°. 1925
Cousin Georgina. s8°. [1927]

Hickson (James Moore). Heal the sick. 8°. [1924]

Hickson (*Col.* Samuel Arthur Einem).
The prince of poets &c. [Shakespeare—Bacon]. s8°. 1926

Hickson (Sydney John).
Introd. to the study of recent corals. 8°. M'ter. 1924

Hidāyat Ḥusain, *Shams-ul-'Ulamā*, *see* BŪHĀR LIBRARY. Cat. raisonné of the B.L., v2, Arabic MSS.; by H. H., 1923.

Hideyoshi, *acting shogun of Japan* [*Quabacundo*], *see* JESUITS. Nova rel. hist., & de Quabacundoni trucidatione; Froes, 1598.

Hielscher (Curt).
Jugoslavien. Landschaft—Baukunst—Volksleben. 4°. [1926]
Picturesque Spain. 4°. [1922]

Hieron II, *king of Syracuse.*
see CARCOPINO (J.) La loi de H. & les Romains, 1914.
,, GIESECKE (W.) Münzwesen H. II v. S., 1920.

Hieron (Samuel). Sermons &c. 2v *in* 1. sfol. 1624–25
The tp. of v1 Sermons &c. *is missing. The tp. of v2* Workes of S. H. *is placed at beg. of v1.*

Hieronymo, *de San Stefano* [JERONIMO *de Santo Estevam*]. Carta, *see* POLO (M.) Livro de M. P., 1922.

Hierotheus, *St., successively bp. of Athens & of Segovia.* [Jeroteo], *see* Rodríguez y Fernández (I.) San J., Obispo de Segovia, 2ª ed., 1919.

Hiesemann (Martin). How to attract & protect wild birds. Tr. E. S. Buchheim; w. intr. by Duchess of Bedford. 3rd ed. (2nd impr.) 8°. 1917

Higby, *The family of, see* Higby (C. D.) Edward H. & h. descendants, 1927.

Higby (Chester Penn). The relig. policy of the Bavarian govt. dur. the Napoleonic period. 8°. N.Y., *Columbia Univ.* 1918

Higby (Clinton David). Edward Higby & h. descendants. 8°. *p.p.* Erie, Penn. 1927

Higby (Edward), *1616–99, see* Higby (C. D.) E. H. & h. descendants, 1927.

Higden (Ranulphus).
see Christ. A stanzaic life of Christ: comp. f. H.'s Polychronicon &c.; ed. F. A. Foster, 1926.
,, Robinson (J. A.) An unrecognized Westminster chronicler, 1381–94 [*contin. of H.*], 1907.

Higgins (Nathaniel), *see* Bible: Ecclesiastes. Paraphrase; notes &c. by N. H., *n.d.*

Higgins (Sydney Herbert). Hist. of bleaching. 8°. 1924

Higginson (Nesta), *aft. Mrs. Skrine, see* †O'Neill (Moira), *ps.*

Higginson (Thomas Wentworth).
Old Cambridge [Mass.] s8°. N.Y. 1899

Higgons (Bevill). The generous conqueror: or, the timely discovery. Tragedy. 8°. 1702
Short view of Eng. hist., w. reflect., to 1688. 3rd ed., w. add. 8°. 1748

Higgs (Henry). Financial reform. 8°. 1924
see Palgrave (*Sir* R. H. I.) Dict. of polit. econ.; ed. H. H., n. ed., 3v, 1925–26.

Higham (*Sir* Charles Frederick). Advertising, its use & abuse. [Home Univ. Lib.] s8°. [1925]

Higham (Charles Strachan Sanders). The Colonial entry-books. Colonial records in Public Rec. Off. bef. 1696. [P2573]. s8°. 1921
The development of the Leeward Isl., 1660–88. 8°. C. 1921

Higham (Florence M. Grier), *wife of C. S. S. Higham, see* Evans (F. M. G.)

Highland Society of Scotland [*afterwards* Highland & Agricult. Soc. of S.] Report of Comm. of H.S. app. to inquire into authenticity of poems of Ossian. Drawn up by H. Mackenzie. With app. [*w. sep. pagin.*] 8°. E. 1805
Transactions. s5, v31–34, 36, 37. 8°. E. 1919–25

Highmore (Anthony). A succinct view of the hist. of mortmain &c. 2nd ed. 8°. 1809

Hight (George Ainslie).
Richard Wagner: a crit. biog. 2v. 8°. [1925]

Hijlkema (S. H.)
Nederl. handboek voor ijs-sport. s8°. A. [1887]

Hilarion, *Saint, see* James, *St., Bp. of Nisibis.* [*Hist. of St. J. (foll. by H. &c.), *in Armenian*], 1861.

Hilary, *St., bp. of Poitiers.* Opera. [Corpus scr. eccl. Lat., 65]. p4. 8°. Vindobonae. 1916
4, Tractatus mysteriorum—Coll. antiariana parisina, cum app.—Liber ad Constantium Imp.—Hymni &c. Rec. &c. A. Feder.
see Feder (A. L.) St. zu H. v. Poitiers, 3, 1912.

Hildebrand, *ps., see* Beets (N.)

Hildebrand (Arthur Sturges).
Magellan: life & times & adv. 8°. [1925]

Hildebrand (Bruno), *see* Marburg. Urkunden-Sammlung über die Verfass. u. Verwalt. d. Univ. Marburg &c.; hrsg. v. B. H., 1848.

Hildebrand (Emil), *Swedish historian.* Sveriges historia intill tjugonde seklet. Under medverkan af O. Montelius, H. Hildebrand &c. Utg. E. H. 10 Afd. [*in 6v.* 3, 4 *b. sep.*] la8°. 1903–10
,, ,, ...Register. la8°. [1910]

Hildebrand (Hans O. H.) The industrial arts of Scandinavia. [S. Ken. Mus. Art Hdbks.] n. ed. 8°. 1894
see Hildebrand (E.), *ed.* Sveriges hist.; under medverkan af O. Montelius, H. H. &c., 10 Afd., 1903–10.

Hildebrand (Hermann) [Гильдебрандъ]. Отчеты о разысканіяхъ &c. въ Рижскихъ и Ревельскомъ архивахъ по части русской ист. [I. Akad. Nauk. Записки, t29]. 8°. С.–П. 1877

Hildebrand (Joachim).
Antiquitates ex univ. Script. S. selectae. s4°. Helmestadi. 1700
Augusta Caesaris Octaviani Augusti & Augusti ducis Bruns. & Luneb. Cum var. memorabilibus &c. s4°. Helmestadii. 1662
De diebus festis libellus. s4°. Helmestadii. 1706
De nuptiis vet. Christianorum libellus. s4°. Helmestadii. 1661
De priscae & prim. eccl. sacris publ., templis & diebus festis enchir. [P2639]. s4°. Helmestadii. 1652
,, ,, Ed. noviss. s4°. Helmæstadi. 1740
De religiosis eorumque var. ordinibus. [P2636]. s4°. Helmestadi. 1701
Hist. Conciliorum, usq. ad 1745, in eccl. habit. s4°. Helmstadi. 1707
Lib. de haeresibus a n. C. ad sec. 16. s4°. Helmstadii. 1710
Prim. ecclesiæ offertorium pro defunctis. [P2639]. s4°. Helmestadii. 1667
,, ,, s4°. Helmstadii. 1693
Rituale baptismi vet., destinatum a J. A. Schmidt. ed. 2ª. s4°. Helmstadii. 1711
Rituale orantium. s4°. Helmstadi. 1713
Sacra publica vet. eccl. in compend. redactá. s4°. Helmstadii. 1721
Theologiae dogmat. medulla, repet. à L. C. H. Ritmeiero. s4°. Helmstadii. [1703]
Tract. de hierarchis vet. eccl. s4°. Helmestadii. 1708
Vet. eccl., martyrum imprimis ars bene moriendi &c. s4°. Helmestadii. 1661
,, ,, [*a. ed.*] s4°. Helmstdii. *n.d.*
see Keuffel (G. G.) Hist. scholarum; acc. J. H. Oratio de fundat. Acad. Juliae, 1743.

Hildebrand (Samuel Frederick), *see* Meek (S. E.) & S. F. H. *for works on fishes wr. in collab.*

Hildebrand (Tobias).
De prima exped. cruciata. [P444]. s4°. Lipsiae. [1694]

Hildebrandt (Ad. M.) Herald. Musterbuch. 4°. 1872
see Sibmacher (J.), *ed.* J. S.'s gr. Wappenbuch, B1–7, 1856–1912, *list of contents for var. parts* bearbt. v. A. M. H.

Hildebrandt (Alfred). Airships past & present, w. chapters on use of balloons in conn. w. meteorology &c. Tr. W. H. Story. 8°. 1908

Hildebrandt (Edmund). Leben, Werke u. Schr. d. Bildhauers E. M. Falconet, 1716–91. la8°. Str. 1908

Hildegarde, *Saint.* The prophecy of S. H. fulfilled in the Jesuits, *see* Jarrige (P.) A further discov. &c., 1658.
see Fischer (H.) Die hl. H. v. Bingen, d. erste deut. Naturforscherin u. Ärztin, 1927.
,, Riesch (H.) Die hl. H. v. Bingen, 2e u. 3e verb. A., 1920.

Hildersam (Arthur). 108 lectures upon the fourth of John. [Ed. by J. C.] 2nd ed. enlarged. sfol. 1632

Hildesheim. Annales H.; contulit cum Cod. Paris. G. Waitz. [Scr. rerum Germ. in usum schol.] 8°. Hannoverae. 1878
Hildesheim; hrsg. v. Magistrat d. H.; bearb. A. Knoch, *see* Deutschland. D.'s Städtebau, 1921.

Hildesley (Alfred). The press gang. [Sette of Odd Volumes, Opusc. 79]. s8°. 1925
see Scott (L. F.) The case of requisition: *In re* a Petition of right of De Keyser's Roy. Hotel Ltd. &c., 1920.

Hildreth (Richard).
Hist. of the U.S. [2s.] 6v. 8°. N.Y. 1849–52
s1, *h. tp.:* Hist of U.S. to organiz. of govt. under federal constit., 3v.
s2, *h. 2nd tp:* Hist. of U.S. f. adoption of federal constit. to end of 16th congress, 3v.
,, ,, ...rev. ed. [s1]. 3v. 8°. N.Y. 1863

Hildrop (John), *D.D.* [*ps.* Timothy Hooker]. A comm. upon the 2nd Psalm. [*b. w. h.* Essay for regul. of free-thinking, 1739]. s8°. 1742
*The contempt of the clergy. [*b. w. h.* Essay for regul. of free-thinking, 1739]. s8°. 1739
*An essay for the better regulation &c. of free-thinking. 2nd ed. s8°. 1739
*An essay on honour. Pref. by R. Hooker. [*b. w. h.* Essay for regul. of free-thinking, 1739]. s8°. 1741
Free-thoughts upon the brute-creation: or an exam. of Bougeant's Philos. amusement. In 2 letters to a lady. [*b. w. h.* Essay for regul. of free-thinking, 1739]. 2p. s8°. 1742–43

Hiley (Wilfred Edward).
The fungal diseases of the common larch. 8°. O. 1919

Hilferding (Aleksandr Fedorovich) [Гильфердингъ].
Собраніе сочиненій. 4t *in* 2. la8°. С.–П. 1868–74
1, Ист. Сербовъ—Кириллъ и Меѳодій—Обзоръ чешской ист. 2, По вопросамъ Славянск. 3, Боснія, Герцеговина и Старая Сербія. 4, Ист. Балтійскихъ Славянъ.
Онежскія былины записанныя А. Ѳ. Г. la8°. С.–П. 1873

Hilgard (Alfred), *see* Dionysius, *the Thracian.* Scholia in D. Artem gramm.; rec. &c. A. H., 1901.

Hilka (Alfons), *ed.* Altfranz. Mystik u. Beginentum, *see* ZEITSCHRIFT F. ROMAN. PHILOL., B47, 1927.

Hill (Aaron). The tragedy of Zara, *see* NEW Eng. theatre, v10, 1777.

Zara, *see* INCHBALD (E.) Brit. th., v7, 1808.

Hill (Alex.), *D.D.* Practice in the sev. judicatories of the Ch. of Scotland. 6th ed. rev. & enl. s8°. E. 1859

Hill (Alonzo). The Pastor's record: a sermon. [P2623]. 8°. Cambridge, U.S. 1867

Hill (Benson Earle) [*ps. Dean* SNIFT OF BRAZEN-NOSE]. The epicure's almanac [for 1841], 1842. [2v]. s8°. 1841–42

Home Service: or, Scenes & characters f. life at out & head quarters. 2v. s8°. 1839

*A pinch of snuff: anecdotes &c. s8°. 1840

Recoll. of an Artillery officer. 2v. s8°. 1836

Hill (Cecilia). Stone walls. s8°. [1921 ?]

Hill (Charles Edward). James Madison, *see* BEMIS (S. F.), *ed.* Amer. Secr. of State, v3, 1927.

Leading Amer. treaties. 8°. N.Y. 1922

Hill (Constance). Good company in old Westminster & the Temple. Founded on Early recolls. of Anne (Rickman) Lefroy. 8°. [1925]

Mary Russell Mitford & her surroundings. 8°. 1920

Hill (David Jayne). The President's challenge to the Senate. [Repr. f. N. Amer. Rev., June 1919. P2465]. 8°. N.Y. 1919

Hill (George Francis).

Alexander of Bruchsal. Repr. f. "Num. Chron." [P2786]. 8°. 1925

Alex. the Gt. & the Persian lion-gryphon. [Repr. f. Jl. of Hellenic St., v43, 1923. P2740]. la8°. 1923

Anc. coinage of S. Arabia, 1915, *see* BRIT. ACAD. Proc., 1915–16.

Anc. methods of coining. [Repr. f. Num. Chron., s5, v2]. [P2601]. 8°. 1922

Andragora. [Tr. L. Cesano. Ist. Ital. di Num. Estr. d. v3ii d. Atti &c. P2411]. 8°. Roma. 1919

L'art dans les monnaies grecques. la4°. 1927

Attambelos I of Characene. [Amer. Num. Soc., Num. notes &c., no. 14. P2684]. s8°. N.Y. 1922

Becker the counterfeiter. 2p. 8°. 1924–25

L'école des médailleurs de Mantoue, fin du 15e s. [*&* début du 16e s. Extr. d'Aréthuse, 1923–24; P2740]. la8°. [1923–24]

A find of coins of Eadgar, Eadward II & Aethelred II at Chester. [Repr. f. Num. Chron., s4, v20, P2489]. 8°. 1920

Greek coins acquired by the Brit. Mus. [Repr. f. Num. Chron., s4, v19, 20, s5, v1–7]. 1917 *&* 1918 [P2404]; 1919 [P2489]; 1920 [P2562]; 1921 [P2706]; 1922 [P2736]; 1923 [P2762]; 1924 *&* 1925 [P2858]; 1926 [P2877]. 8°. 1919–27

Ital. portraits of the 15th c. [From Proc. of Brit. Acad. P2821]. 8°. [1925]

The medallic portraits of Christ—The false shekels—The thirty pieces of silver. la8°. O. 1920

Medals of N. Orsini. [Repr. f. Num. Chron., s5, v5. *& o. p.* P2858]. 8°. 1926

Medals of Turkish sultans *& o. p.* [Repr. f. Num. Chron., s5, v6. P2858]. 8°. 1926

A mint at Wroxeter? [Repr. f. Num. Chron., s5, v5. P2858]. 8°. 1926

On the early use of Arabic numerals in Europe. [From Archaeologia, 62]. 4°. O. 1910

Roman medallists of the Renaissance &c., *see* BRIT. SCHOOL AT ROME. Papers, v9, 1920.

Sel. Greek coins. Ser. of enlargements illust. & descr. by G. F. H. 4°. Paris. 1927

see BRITISH MUSEUM: COINS &c. Greek coins of Arabia, Mesopotamia &c.; by G. F. H., 1922.

„ —— : —— Medals of the Renaissance; by G. F. H., 1923.

Hill (George William), *astronomer.* Coll. mathemat. works. [C.I. of Wash., Publ. 9]. 4v. 4°. Wash. 1905–07

Hill (Grace Livingston), *see* BOOTH (E.) & G. L. H. War romance of Salvation Army, 1919.

Hill (James Bastian), *F.G.S., see* FLETT (J. S.) & J. B. H. Geol. of the Lizard & Meneage, 1912.

—— & D. A. Macalister. The geol. of Falmouth & Truro & of mining dist. of Camborne & Redruth; w. petrolog. notes by J. S. Flett. [Mem. of G.S. Explan. of sheet 352]. la8°. 1906

Hill (John Arthur). From agnosticism to belief. 8°. [1924]

Hill (Joseph), *B.D.* *The interest of these United Provinces. s4°. Middelburg. 1673

Hill (Leonard). Sunshine & open air, w. spec. ref. to the Alpine climate. 8°. 1924

Hill (*Sir* Norman). War & insurance. By Sir N. H., S. G. Warner, S. Preston & A. E. Sich, Sir A. W. Watson, Sir W. Beveridge, Sir W. Schooling. Intr. by Sir W. Beveridge. [C.E. for Internat. Peace]. la8°. 1927

Hill (*Miss* Octavia). House property & its management. [Intr. by I. G. Gibbon]. s8°. [1921]

see TABOR (M. E.) O. H., 1927.

Hill (Pascoe Grenfell). Fifty days on board a slave-vessel in the Mozambique Channel, 1843. s8°. 1848

Hill (*Sir* Richard), *bart.; 1732–1808.* *Goliath slain; a reply to Dr. Nowell's Answer. [*b. w. h.* Pietas Oxon., 2nd ed., 1768]. 8°. 1768

*Pietas Oxon.: or acc. of the expulsion of six students from St. Edmund Hall, Oxon. By a M.A. 2nd ed. rev. 8°. 1768

see NOWELL (T.) Answer to Pietas Oxon., 1768.

„ OLIVERS (T.) A scourge to calumny, ans. to H.'s Farrago &c., 1774.

„ SIDNEY (E.) Life of Sir R. H., 1839.

Hill (Roscoe R.) Descr. cat. of doc. rel. to hist. of U.S. in the Papeles Procedentes de Cuba depos. in Archivo Gen. de Indias at Seville. [C.I. of Wash., 234]. la8°. Wash. 1916

Hill (Rowland), *minister of Surrey Chapel, Blackfriars.*

A coll. of psalms & hymns. 6th ed. s8°. 1805

Imposture detected &c. Strictures on the false &c. harangue by J. Wesley. [P2667]. s8°. 1777

Journal, thr. the N. of England &c. With remarks on Establ. Ch. of Scot. s8°. 1799

see WESLEY (J.) Some remarks on Mr. [? R.] H.'s Review of all the doctrines taught by W., 1772.

Hill (Samuel), *archdeacon of Wells.* *Solomon & Abiathar: or the case of the deprived bishops &c. discussed &c. [P2661]. s4°. 1692

A vindic. of the primitive Fathers agst. the imputations of Gilbert, bp. of Sarum, in his disc. on the divinity & death of Christ &c. s8°. 1695

Hill (Thomas), *Methodist preacher.* The cause of truth defended: facts conn. w. the 2 trials of H., for defam. of the character of Miss Bell &c. 8°. 1827

Facts conn. w. prosecut. of T. H. on a charge of defaming Jane Bell. [P2825.] s8°. Newcastle-on-Tyne. 1823

Hill (Thomas), *Roman Catholic, see* ABBOT (G.) Reasons wh. Dr. H. has brought for upholding of papistry unmasked. pl, 1604.

Hill (Thomas), *Fellow of Trinity Coll., Cambridge* [HYLL; *ps.* DYDYMUS MOUNTAINE]. The gardeners labyrinth: cont. a disc. of the gardeners life, w. instructions for the choise of seedes &c. Gathered out of the best writers by Dydymus Mountaine. [*Compl. by H. Dethick. Imperf.* 2p *in* 1v.] s4°. *J. Wolfe.* 1586

The profitable arte of gardening. Annexed, 2 treatises entitled, The meruailous gouernment &c. of bees, & The yerely coniectures for husbandmen. Added, a treatise of the arte of graffing &c. trees. [The treatises have separate tp. & pag.] s4°. *E. Allde.* 1593

Hill (Thomas George), *see* HAAS (P.) & T. G. H. Intr. to chemistry of plant products, v2, 1922.

Hill (William), *F.G.S., see* JUKES-BROWNE (A. J.) Cretaceous rocks of Brit. &c. 3v, 1900–4.

Hill (William), *Wesleyan minister, see* WESLEYAN METHODIST. An alphabet. arrangement of W. M. ministers &c., by the late W. H., 1847–1900.

Hillary (Augustus William). A letter to Lord John Russell, plan for adj. of rel. betw. landlord & tenant in Ireland. [P2554]. 8°. 1849

Hillebrandt (Alfred). Der freiwill. Feuertod in Indien u. d. Somaweihe, *see* KÖN. AKAD. D. W. ZU MÜNCHEN. Phil. Cl., Sitz., 1917.

Ritual-Litt., ved. Opfer u. Zauber. [Grundr. d. indo-ar. Phil., B3, H2]. la8°. Str. 1897

Über d. Anfänge d. ind. Dramas, *see* KÖN. AKAD. D. W. ZU MÜNCHEN. Phil. Classe, Sitz., 1914.

Hillemacher (Jacques). Les Germains devant l'hist. Préf. de G. Hervé. 8°. 1920

Hiller (Ferd.)

Aus d. Tonleben uns. Zeit. 2B *&* Folge. s8°. L. 1868–71

Hiller (Matthäus). De orig. gentium Celticarum. Diss. [*b. w.* Jäger (A.) De lingua vet. Europae, 1686]. s4°. Tubingae. 1707

Hiller von Gärtringen (Friedrich W., *Frhr.*) Hist. griech. Epigramme; ausgewählt v. H. v. G., *see* KLEINE TEXTE, T156, 1926.

Hillgarth (Alan). The princess & the perjurer. s8°. 1924

Hilliard d'Auberteuil (Michel René). *Consid. sur l'état prés. de Saint-Domingue. Par Mr. H. Dl. [*i.e.* H. d'A.] [2t]. 8°. 1776

Hilliers (Ashton), *ps.* [*i.e.* HENRY MARRIAGE WALLIS].
The Walbury case. s8°. [1923]
Hillinger (Johann Gottlieb). Memoria Aquilina. Leben C. Aquilae, meistentheils aus S. Liebens Ms., nebst dessen erbaul. Catechismo. [*sep. tp. & pag. b. w.* Fabricius (J. A.) Centifolium, 1728–30]. s8°. Jena. 1731
Hillinger (Walfridus). Memorabilium theolog. dogmatum tractatus tres. Praes. W. Heiss, def. W. Hillinger. s8°. Passavii. [1750]
Hillquit (Morris). Hist. of socialism in the U.S. 8°. N.Y. 1903
Der utop. Sozialismus u. d. kommun. Versuche in d. V. S. Nordamer, *see* VORLÄUFER d. neueren Sozialismus, 2e A., B4, 1922.
Hillyard (*Commander* **George Whiteside**), *R.N.*
40 years of first-class lawn tennis. 8°. 1924
Hillyear (Charles Wells).
Monotheism versus priestcraft. s8°. Watford. 1902
Hilmers (Johann Hermann). Comm. de Ubbone Philippi & Ubbonitis, subj. disquis. de habitu doct. Mennonitarum ad rempubl. Praes. J. C. Burgmann. [P434]. s4°. Rostochii. [1733]
Ḥilmi (*prince* **Ibrāhīm**), *see* IBRĀHĪM ḤILMI, *Prince of Egypt.*
Hilpert (Johann). Disq. de Praeadamitis anonymo exercit. theologici auctore [I. de La Peyrère] opposita. s8°. Ultrajecti. 1656
„ „ [*a. ed. b. w.* Desmarets (S.) Refut. fab., 1656]. s8°. Amstelredami. 1656
Hilpert (Joseph Leonhard). Dict. of the German & Eng. langs. 2v. [*each v. has 2p. w. sep. pagin.*] 4°. *n.d.*
Hilprecht (Herman Volrath). The earliest version of the Babylonian Deluge story & the Temple Library of Nippur. [Univ. of Pa. Babyl. Exped., Ser. D., 5i]. 8°. Phila. 1910
Hiltebrandt (Philipp). Die kirchl. Reunionsverhandl. in d. 2ten Hälfte d. 17. Jhdts.: Ernst August v. Hannover u. d. Kath. Kirche. [Bibl. d. Preuss. Hist. Inst. in Rom, B14]. 8°. Rom. 1922
Hilton (James). The passionate year. s8°. [1923]
Storm passage. s8°. [1922]
Hilton (John).
A study of trade organisations &c. in the U.K. s8°. [1920]
Hilton (Walter). The scale of perfection. With essay by J. B. Dalgairns. n. ed. s8°. 1901
„ „ New ed. w. intr. by E. Underhill. s8°. 1923
Hilton-Simpson (Melville William).
Among the hill-folk of Algeria. 8°. [1921]
Hilzheimer (Max).
Natürl. Rassengesch. d. Haussäugetiere. 8°. 1926
Die Tierknochen aus d. Gruben d. Lossower Ringwalls bei Frankfurt a. O., 1923, *see* KÖN. PREUSS. AKAD. Abhdl. (Phil.-hist. Kl.), 1922.
Hime (Henry William Lovett).
Anharmonic coordinates. 8°. 1910
The Greek materials of Shelley's Adonais &c. [P2595]. s8°. 1888
Stray milit. papers. 8°. 1897
Himmel (Johann) [HIMMELIUS (J.)] Syntagma disput. theolog. methodicum &c. ed. 4a. s4°. Wittebergae. 1650
Himnos. Canticos é h., p1, 1872, *see* COLECCION de poesías esp., p1, 1872.
*Himnos para la congregac. esp., 1842, *see* RULE (W. H.)
Himonet (André). Louise de G. Charpentier. Étude hist. & crit. Analyse musicale. s8°. 1922
Himyarites. The Book of the H. Fragm. of unknown Syriac work. Ed., w. intr. & tr. by A. Moberg. [Kungl. Human. Vetenskapssamfundet i Lund. Skr., 7]. la8°. Lund. 1924
Hincks (C. Malcolm). The iron way. s8°. [1920]
Hincmar, *abp. of Rheims.*
see GESS (W. F.) Merkwürdigk. a. d. Leben u. d. Schr. H., 1806.
„ SAINT BERTIN, *abbey.* Annales Bertin. [p3, auct. H.], 1883.
Hind (Arthur Mayger).
Claude Lorrain & mod. art. s8°. C. 1926
The drawings of C. Lorrain. 4°. 1925
Fragonard, Moreau le jeune, & Fr. engravers &c. of later 18th c. 8°. 1913
G. B. Piranesi. Crit. study, w. list of publ. wks. & cat. of prisons & views of Rome. [reprod. of views of Rome]. [lim. ed.] la8°. 1922
The graphic arts new & old. [P2562]. 8°. O. 1921
Hist. of engraving & etching f. the 15th c. to 1914. 3rd & rev. ed. of "A short hist. of engraving" &c. la8°. 1923

Hind (Arthur Mayger) [*continued*].
Watteau, Boucher & the Fr. engravers &c. of the earlier 18th c. s8°. 1911
Wenceslaus Hollar & his views of London & Windsor in 17 c. 4°. 1922
see BRIT. MUS.: PRINTS, DRAWINGS &c. Cat. of drawings by Dutch & Flemish artists in B.M.; by A. M. H., v1–3, 1915–26.
Hind (Charles Lewis). Authors & I. 8°. 1921
Landscape painting f. Giotto to pres. day. 2v. 8°. 1923–24
More authors & I. s8°. 1922
Naphtali: influences & adv. 8°. [1926]
see BEARDSLEY (A.) Uncoll. work, w. intr. by C. L. H., 1925.
Hindenberg (Ilse).
Benno II, Bischof v. Osnabrück, als Architekt. 8°. Str. 1921
Hindenburg (*Generalfeldmarschall* **Paul v. Beneckendorff**).
Out of my life. Tr. F. A. Holt. 8°. 1920
see BUAT (E.) H. & Ludendorff stratèges, 1923.
„ BUCHHORN (J.) H., d. Führer in unsere Zukunft, 1920.
Hindley (Charles), *of Booksellers Row.* The Brighton murder: murder of Celia Holloway, incl. trial of J. W. Holloway; also trial of A. Kennett. 8°. Brighton. 1875
Hindoglu (Artin). Deutsch-armen. Sprachlehre. [*2nd tp. in Armen.*] 8°. Venedig. 1830
Theor.-prackt. Türk. Sprachlehre. 4°. Wien. 1829
Hindoo [HINDU].
[Coloured drawings of Hindu gods &c.] 8°. *n.d.*
Hindoostanee. *Elements (The) of the H. lang. Comp. for the use of the Vepery Acad. s8°. Madras. 1808
Hindus (Maurice). Broken earth. Intr. by G. Frank. s8°. 1926
Hine (Muriel) [*Mrs.* SIDNEY COXON].
The flight. [repr.] s8°. [1922]
The reluctant imposter. s8°. [1925]
The seven lovers & o. s. s8°. [1927]
The spell of Siris. s8°. [1923]
Youth wins. s8°. [1924]
Hine (Reginald L.) Hist. of Hitchin. v1. la8°. [1927]
Hingham. Hist. of H., Norfolk, & its Ch. of St. Andrew. [Pref. by A. C. Wodehouse Upcher]. s8°. East Dereham. 1921
Hingston (Richard William George), *F.R.G.S.*
A naturalist in Himalaya. 8°. 1920
Nature at the desert's edge: Bagdad oasis. 8°. 1925
Hinkhouse (Fred Junkin). Prelims. of the Amer. Revol. as seen in the Eng. press, 1763–75. 8°. N.Y. 1926
Hinkley (Edyth). Mazzini. 8°. [1924]
Hinks (Arthur Robert).
Astronomy. [Home Univ. Lib.] [repr.] s8°. [1919]
Maps & survey. 8°. C. 1913
„ „ ....2nd ed. 8°. C. 1923
Hinkson (Henry Albert), *see* DUBLIN UNIV.: TRINITY COLL. Dublin verses by members of T. C.; ed. H., 1895.
Hinkson (*Mrs.* **K. T.**) [TYNAN (KATHARINE)].
Denys the dreamer. s8°. [1920]
Memories. 8°. [1924]
The second wife, together w. a July rose. s8°. 1921
The wandering years. 8°. 1922
White ladies. s8°. [1922]
The wild adventure. s8°. 1927
—— & F. Maitland. The book of flowers. 8°. 1909
Hinlopen (Nicolaes). Hist. van de Nederl. Overzettinge des Bybels &c. 8°. Leyden. 1777
Hinneberg (Paul). Die Kultur d. Gegenwart; i. Entwicklung u. i. Ziele. Hrsg. P. H. T3, Abtlg. 5. la8°. L., *Teubner.* 1923
III, 5, Anthropologie; unter Leitung v. G. Schwalbe u. E. Fischer.
Fischer (E.) Begriff, Abgrenzung u. Gesch. d. Anthropologie, 1923. [III, 5.]
—— Rassenlehre, 1923. [III, 5.]
—— & T. Mollison. Allgem. Anthropologie, 1923. [III, 5.]
Gräbner (P.) Ethnologie, 1923. [III, 5.]
Hörnes (M.) Prähist. Archäologie, 1923. [III, 5.]
Mollison (T.) Technik u. Methoden d. phys. Anthropologie, 1923. [III, 5.]
Plötz (A.) Sozialanthropologie, 1923. [III, 5.]
Schwalbe (G.) Abstammung d. Menschen u. d. ält. Menschenformen, 1923. [III, 5.]
Hinschius (Paul). Die preuss. Kirchengesetze d. 1873. Hrsg. mit Einleitung v. P. H. 8°. 1873
Die Stell. d. deut. Staatsregierungen gegenüber d. Beschlüssen d. vatikan. Koncils. [P2695]. 8°. 1871
Hinsdale (Burke Aaron). The American gov., national & state. n. & rev. ed. 8°. Chicago. [1895]
Hinton (A. Horsley).
Pract. pictorial photography. 2p [*in* 1v]. s8°. 1900
Hinton (James), *surgeon.* Philos. & relig. Sel. f. MSS. of J. H. Ed. C. Haddon. s8°. 1881

Hinton (Martin A. C.), see BRIT. MUS. OF NAT. HIST.: ZOOLOGY. Monogr. of the voles & lemmings; by M. A. C. H., v1, 1926.
Hints. *Hints to purchasers of horses. s8°. [1825]
*Hints to the public & the legislature on Ev. preaching, 5p, 1811–12, see SEDGWICK (J.)
Hintze (Otto). Gedächtnisrede auf R. Koser, see KÖN. PREUSS. AKAD. Abhdlgn., Phil.-hist. Klasse, 1915.
Gedächtnisrede auf G. v. Schmoller, see KÖN. PREUSS. AKAD. Abhdl. (Phil.-hist. Klasse), 1918.
Hiorns (Arthur Horseman).
Pract. metallurgy & assaying. 3rd ed. rev. s8°. 1914
Hipkins (Alfred James).
Musical instruments, historic, rare &c. 4°. 1921
Hippias, *of Elis, fl. c. 430 B.C.* [†HIPPIAS, *Eleus*], see PLATO. The H. major, attrib. to P., 1928.
Hippiatrica. Corpus hippiatricorum Graec.; ed. E. Oder & C. Hoppe, 2v, 1924–27, see CORPUS.
Hippisley (*Sir* **John Coxe**), *1st bart.* Catholic question. Speech, 24 Ap. 1812, on penal laws agst. R. Cath. in Ir. With notes &c. [Notes *have sep. pagin.*] 2nd ed. 8°. 1812
Letters to the Earl of Fingall on Cath. claims. With suppl. doc. pl. [*b. w. h.* Cath. q., 2nd ed., 1812]. 8°. 1813
The substance of addit. obs. on Roman Cath. of Ireland, 13 & 14 May 1805; w. notes & app. *w. sep. pagin.* [*b. w. h.* Cath. q., 2nd ed., 1812]. 8°. 1806
Substance of speech, May 11, 1813, on Cath. claims; w. notes [*b. w. h.* Cath. q., 2nd ed., 1812]. 8°. 1815
Substance of speech on motion of H. Grattan to refer the petition of R. Catholics of Ir. to a Ctee of H. of C., 18 May 1810. 2nd ed. w. app. &c. [*3 pagins. b. w.* Plowden (F.) Hist. letter, 1814]. 8°. 1810
see PLOWDEN (F.) An hist. letter, 1814.
,, —— A second hist. letter, 1815.
Hippisley (Richard Lionel). Tables of elliptic functions, see SMITHSONIAN INSTIT. Misc. colls., v74, No. 1, 1922.
Hippius (Zinaida Nikolaevna), see GIPPIUS (Z. N.)
Hippocrates.
Hippocrates. [Text], w. Eng. tr. by W. H. S. Jones [*&*] E. T. Withington. [Loeb Class. Lib.] v1–3. s8°. 1923–27
see CORPUS medicorum Graec., v1i, H. ed. I. L. Heiberg, 1927.
,, GALEN. *Commentaries on Wks. of H.*
,, MOON (R. O.) H. &c. in rel. to the philos. of th. time, 1923.
,, ROSCHER (W. H.) Die hippokrat. Schr. v. d. Siebenzahl &c., 1919.
see SORANUS II, *of Ephesus.* Vita H.; ed. J. Ilberg, 1927.
,, WENKEBACH (E.) Das Proömium d. Komm. Galens zu d. Epidemien H., 1918.
,, —— Pseudogalen. Komm. zu d. Epidemien d. H., 1917.
,, —— Unters. ü. Galens Komm. z. d. Epidemien d. H., 1925.
Hippolytus, *Saint, bp. of the Port of Rome.* Compend. hist. philosoph. ant., sive philosophumena q. s. Origenis nom. circumfer. [*Gr. & Lat.*] Ed. a J. Gronovio. Rec. &c. a J. C. Wolfio: acc. C. Gronovii notae. [*&* Diss. qua ostenditur Didymum Alexandr. hujus scr. auctorem non esse, auct. J. C. Wolfio, *w. sep. tp. & pagin.*] s8°. Hamburgi. 1706
Philosophumena sive omnium haeresium refut. E cod. Paris. ed. E. Miller. 8°. O. 1851
Philosophumena or The refut. of all heresies. Form. attrib. to Origen. Tr. [w. intr.] by F. Legge. 2v. s8°. 1921
Толкованіе Пѣсни пѣсней. Грузинскій текстъ Ю. перев. съ армянск. изсл. &c. Н. Марръ. [Тексты &c. по арм.-груз. филол., 3 (Изд. Фак. Вост. Яз. Имп. С.-П. Унив., No. 5)]. la8°. С.-П. 1901
see BIBLE: DANIEL. D. sec. Septuaginta *&* S. H. interp. in D., 1772.
Hirananda Shastri, see SASTRI (H.)
Hird (Frank). The secret terror. s8°. [1926]
Hirnhaim (Hieronymus), *1635–79,* see BARACH (C. S.) Kleine philos. Schr.: H. H. &c., 1878.
Hiroshige, *1797–1858,* see STRANGE (E. F.) Colour-prints of H., 1925.
Hirsch (Charles Henry). *Works in* ŒUVRES libres.
Un aimable voleur, 1925. [45.]
Les détours de la vie, 1927. [76.]
Eva Tumarche, baronne, 1922. [17.]
Mimi Bigoudis, 1921. [2.]
Les nomades, nouvelle, 1922. [10.]
Voyage de noces, 1924. [34.]
Hirsch (F.), see LÜBECK. Bau- u. Kunstdenkmäler, T2, Petrikirche &c.; bearbt. v. F. H. &c., 1906.
Hirsch (Hans). Die echten u. unechten Stiftungsurkunden d. Abtei Banz, 1919, see KAIS. AKAD. D. WISS. ZU WIEN, Sitz., B189, 1919.
Hirsch (S. A.) The Cabbalists & o. essays. s8°. 1922
Hirschauer (*le gén.* **Auguste Edouard) &** *le gén.* **Klein.** Paris en état de défense. Préf. de M. le mar. Joffre. 8°. 1927
Hirschauer (Charles). Les Etats d'Artois, de leurs orig. à l'occup. franç., 1340–1640. 2t. 8°. 1923
La polit. de St. Pie V en France, 1566–72. [Ecoles Franç. d'Athènes & de Rome, fasc. 120]. la8°. 1922
Hirschfeld (Heinrich Otto). Untersuch. a. d. Gebiet d. roem. Verwaltungsgesch. B1, Kaiserl. Verwaltungsbeamten bis auf Diocletian [*no more publ.*] 8°. 1877
Hirschlaff (Leo). Üb. d. Wesen d. Beobact. u. Selbstbeobachtung. Inaug. Diss. [P2477]. 8°. 1896
Hirst (A. Stanley), see †BRIT. MUS. OF NAT. HIST.: ZOOLOGY. Studies on Acari, No. 1, Genus Demodex, Owen; by S. H., 1919.
Hirst (Francis W.)
Early life & letters of J. Morley. 2v. 8°. 1927
From Adam Smith to Ph. Snowden: hist. of free-trade in Gt. Brit. [2nd impr.] s8°. [1925]
Life & letters of T. Jefferson. 8°. [1926]
Safeguarding & protect. in Gt. Brit. & the U.S. 8°. 1927
Trade, expenditure, taxation & money. Lect., 1923. 8°. Johannesburg. [1923]
see HARVEY (A. G. C.) Memoir; ed. w. intr. by F. W. H., 1925.
—— **& J. E. Allen.** Brit. War budgets. [C.E. for Internat. Peace]. la8°. 1926
Hirt (Johann Friedrich). Comm. philol. formationem &c. pronominum pers. &c. apud Ebraeos demonstr. s4°. Jenae. 1747
Opuscula noviss. [*b. w. h.* Varia sacra, 1776]. s4°. Wittebergae. 1783
Oriental. u. exeget. Bibl. 8T [*in 2v*]. s8°. Jena. 1772–76
Varia sacra in primitiis acad. Witteberg. max. partem exhib. s4°. Wittebergae. 1776
Wittemberg. neue oriental. & exeget. Bibliothek. 4T [*in 1v.*] s8°. Jena. 1776–79
Hirth (Friedrich). Syllabary of Chinese sounds, see WILLIS (B.), E. BLACKWELDER &C. Research in China, v1, p2, 1907.
Hirth (Georg).
Das deut. Zimmer d. Renaiss. 2e A. fol. München. 1882
Kulturgeschichtl. Bilderbuch aus 4 Jhdtn. Neu bearb. u. ergänzt. v. M. v. Boehn. 2B. fol. München. 1923–25
B1 *incl.* Kayser Maximilians Triumph.
Hirtzwig (Heinrich).
Lutherus. Drama. ed. corr. s8°. Francofurti. 1617
Hirzel (Rudolf). Die Person: Begriff u. Name im Altertum, see KÖNIGL. AKAD. D. W. ZU MÜNCHEN. Phil. Classe, Sitz., 1914.
Plutarch. la8°. L. 1912
Hisca (*Madama* **Charlotta d'),** see AMOMO, *ps.* Rime toscanie d'A. per C. d'H., 1535.
Hispania. Hispania illustrata: or, the maxims of the Spanish court, & memor. affairs, 1667–78, in letters f. the Earl of Sandwich, the Earl of Sunderland & Sir W. Godolphin. With papers f. Don John of Austria, the conde de Penaranda &c. also a treat. by Lord Sandwich, & another by Sir W. Godolphin. s8°. 1703
Hispanic anthology, 1920, see WALSH (T.), *ed.*
Hispanic (The) Society of America.
The words " in the coll. *or* lib. of the H.S. " *have been omitted from the titles as given below. Many of the works form part of* Hisp. notes & monogr.
Bibliographie hispanique, 1914. s8°. *n.d.*
1914 *cont.* Foulché-Delbosc (R.) Bibliog. hispano-franç., p3, 1661–1700 [*sep. pagin.*]
Carreño de Miranda. s8°. N.Y. 1928
Castilian wood-carvings of late Gothic period. s8°. N.Y. 1927
Catalogue series. 12v. s8°. N.Y. 1924–6
Irving (W.), 1926.
Morales, 1925.
Paintings, 1925.
Publications, 1924.
Sorolla, 5v, 1926.
Velasquez, 1925.
Wood-carvings, 1925.
Zurbaran, 1925.
Choir-stalls f. Lima, Peru. s8°. N.Y. 1928
Figures of the Madonna of Trapani. s8°. N.Y. 1927
Gongora. Eds. of Todas las obras. s8°. N.Y. 1927
Gonzalez. s8°. N.Y. 1927
El Greco. s8°. N.Y. 1927
Hispano-Moresque ivory box. s8°. N.Y. 1927
Incunabula. [4p *in* 1v]. s8°. N.Y. 1928
Manuscripts. MS. B2, Alfonso Rodriguez; B3, Alfonso Gomez; B5, Juan Perez &c.; B6, Nuns of S. Clara Sevilla &c.; B11, Ines Gonzalez, widow; B12, Juan Perez &c. Ed. A. D. Savage—

Hispanic (The) Society of America [*continued*].
Investiture of Siena, 1604. [7p *in* 2v. *a. c.* of B5, 6, 11 & 12 in P2879]. s8°. N.Y. 1927–28
Moro. [*a. c. in* P2879]. s8°. N.Y. 1927
Pere Espalarguès. s8°. N.Y. 1927
Pereda. s8°. N.Y. 1928
Pompeo Leoni. s8°. N.Y. 1928
Tombs of Don Gutierre de la Cueva & Doña M. Enriquez de Toledo. [*a. c. in* P2879]. s8°. N.Y. 1927
PUBLICATIONS.
see AGUILAR Y CUADRADO (R.) Guadalajara—Alcalá de Henares, *n.d.*
,, †ALVAREZ DE AYLLON (P.) & L. HURTADO. Comedia Tibalda, 1903.
,, BAENA (J. A. DE). Cancionero : reprod. in facs. ; foreword by H. R. Lang, 1926.
,, †BANDELIER (A. F. A.) The Islands of Titicaca & Koati, 1910.
,, BARAHONA (D.) Glosa a la obra de J. Manrique, 1541 [repr. 1902].
,, BARBER (E. A.) Mexican maiolica, 1915.
,, —— Span. glass, 1917.
,, BELL (A. F. G.) B. Arias Montano, 1922.
,, —— B. Gracián, 1921.
,, —— D. do Couto, 1924.
,, —— F. Lopez, 1921.
,, —— Francisco Sanchez, El Brocense, 1925.
,, —— Gaspar Corrêa, 1924.
,, —— Gil Vicente, 1921.
,, —— Juan Ginés de Sepúlveda, 1925.
,, —— Luis de Camões, 1923.
,, —— Portuguese bibliog., 1922.
,, BELLO (A.) Odes of B., Olmedo &c. ; intr. by E. C. Hills, 1920.
,, BERUETE Y MORET (A. DE). Velasquez in the Prado Museum, *n.d.*
,, BONSOR (G.) Tartesse, 1922.
,, BYNE (A.) & M. STAPLEY. Decorated wooden ceilings in Spain, 2v, 1920.
,, —— & —— Rejería of Span. Renaissance, 1914.
,, —— & —— Span. ironwork, 1915.
,, †CASTILLO (F. DEL). Cancionero general : nuevamēte añadído [pr. in facs. f. Toledo ed., 1520], 1904.
,, †CASTRO (M. DE). Vida del soldado español M. de C. &c., 1900.
,, CERVANTES. Exhib. of books rel. to C., Apr.-May, 1916.
,, CHRONICA. Croníca rímada ; reprod. in facs. f. MS. in Bibl. Nat. by A. M. Huntington, 1904.
,, CORBACHO (G. M.) S. Amer. hist. doc., 1919.
,, COSSIO (M. B.) El Greco, *n.d.*
,, CUNDALL (F.) The Darien venture, 1926.
,, DARÍO (R.) 11 poems ; tr., 1916.
,, DOMÉNECH (R.) The house of El Greco, *n.d.*
,, †ENGAÑOS. Libro de los engaños &c., 1904.
,, FITZMAURICE-KELLY (J.) Fray Luis de Leon, 1921.
,, —— Some masters of Span. verse, 1924.
,, —— Span. bibliog., 1925.
,, FITZMAURICE-KELLY (JULIA). A. Perez, 1922.
,, —— Garcilasso de la Vega, 1921.
,, FOULCHÉ-DELBOSC (R.) & L. BARRAU-DIHIGO. Manuel de l'Hispanisant, t1, 2, 1920–25.
,, FREDUCCI (C. DE O.) Portolan atlas, 1537 : facs. ; intr. by E. L. Stevenson, 1915.
,, GARCILASO DE LA VEGA, *the poet.* Works ; ed. H. Keniston, 1925.
,, †GESTOSO Y PÉREZ (J.) Biografia del pintor sevillano J. de Valdés Leal, 1916.
,, —— Seville, *n.d.*
,, GÓMEZ-MORENO (M.) The Alhambra, *n.d.*
,, GÓNGORA Y ARGOTE (L. DE). Obras poét., 3t, 1921.
,, GUIMERÁ (A.) La pecadora : play ; tr., 1916.
,, †HUNTINGTON (A. M.) Initials & miniatures f. the Mozarabic MSS. of Santo Domingo de Silos &c., 1904.
,, IRVING (W.) Diary—Spain, 1828–29 ; ed. f. MS. in Libr. of Soc. by C. L. Penney, 1926.
,, JIMÉNEZ (J. R.) Poesías escojidas, 1899–1917, 1917.
,, KENISTON (R. H.) G. de la Vega, 1922.
,, —— List of works for study of Hisp.-Amer. hist., 1920.
,, KING (G. G.) Brief acc. of military orders in Spain, 1921.
,, —— The way of St. James, 3v, 1920.
,, LAMPÉREZ Y ROMEA (V.) Cathedral of Burgos, *n.d.*
,, LAS NAVAS (*conde* DE). The royal Palace, Madrid, *n.d.*
,, LIBRO de los Tres Reyes de Oriente ; publ. in facs. by A. M. Huntington, 1904.
,, LOPEZ DE AYALA (P.) Poesías, 1920.
,, †MANRIQUE (J.) Coplas por la muerte de su padre &c., *n.d.*
,, MARTINES (J.) Portolan atlas, 1582, facs., 1915.
,, MATOS FRAGOSO (J. DE). El ingr. agradecido ; ed. H. C. Heaton, 1926.
,, MOSES (B.) Intellect. background of Revol. in S. Amer., 1810–24, 1926.
,, MUSEO ARQUEOLÓGICO, *Madrid.* Falcata Iberica, *n.d.*
,, OBERMAIER (H.) Fossil man in Spain, 1924.

Hispanic (The) Society of America [*continued*].
PUBLICATIONS [*continued*].
see †OLIVIER, *de Castille.* Hist. de los nobles cavalleros O. de C. &c. [pr. in facs. f. Burgos ed., 1499], 1902.
,, PARKER (W. B.) Argentines of to-day, 2v, 1920.
,, —— Casual letters f. S. Amer., 1921.
,, —— Cubans of to-day, 1919.
,, —— Paraguayans of to-day, 1921.
,, —— Peruvians of to-day, 1919.
,, —— Uruguayans of to-day, 1921.
,, PARSONS (E. C.) Folk-lore f. the Cape Verde Islands, 2p, 1923.
,, PINEDA (J. DE). Libr' o del passo honroso defend. por Suero de Quiñoes, 1588 [repr. 1902].
,, PINTO DE MORALES (J.) Maravillas del Parnaso &c., 1637 [repr. 1902].
,, PRADO, *Madrid.* Tapestries & carpets f. Palace of the P., loaned for exhib. by Hisp. Soc., 1917.
,, PRESCOTT (W. H.) Letters to Gayangos (1838–60) ; ed. C. L. Penney, 1927.
,, PRESTAGE (E.) D. Francisco Manuel de Mello, 1922.
,, QUEVEDO (F. DE). La vida del Buscon, 1917.
,, RAMÓN MÉLIDA (J.) Escorial, 1, *n.d.*
,, †RESENDE (G. DE). Cancioneiro geral [pr. in facs. f. Lisboa ed., 1516], 1904.
,, †ROJAS (F. DE). Comedia de Calisto & Melibea, reimpr., 1900 ; 1902.
,, †ROMANCERO gen. [pr. in facs. f. Madrid ed., 1600], 1904.
,, †SAN PEDRO (D. DE). Carcel de amor, 1492, 1904.
,, SANTILLANA (I. L. DE M., *marq.* DE). Bias contra Fortũa, 1502 [repr. 1902].
,, SERÍS (H.) La colección Cervantina de la Soc. Hisp. de Amér. : ed. de Don Quijote, 1918.
,, SKINNER (A.) Notes on Iroquois archeology, 1921.
,, STEVENSON (E. L.) Facs. of portolan charts belong. to Hisp. Soc., 1916.
,, —— Terrestrial & celestial globes, 2v, 1921.
,, STREET (G. E.) Unpubl. notes &c., 1916.
,, †TAMARIZ (N.) Cartilla, y luz en la verdadera, &c. ; pr. in facs. f. Sevilla ed., 1696, 1902.
,, TAMAYO Y BAUS (M.) A new drama ; tr., 1915.
,, TICKNOR (G.) Letters to P. de Gayangos, 1927.
,, TORMO Y MONZÓ (E.) The monastery of Guadalupe, *n.d.*
,, TRAPIER (E. DU G.) El Greco, 1925.
,, TREND (J. B.) L. Milan & the Vihuelistas, 1925.
,, —— The music of Span. hist., 1926.
,, VILLUGA (P. J.) Reportorio de todos caminos de España, 1546 [repr. 1902].
,, WALSH (T.), *ed.* Hispanic anthology, 1920.
,, WATSON (F.) L. Vives, 1922.
,, WILLIAMS (L.) Art of J. Sorolla, 1926.
,, †XIMENEZ DE URREA (P. M.) Penitencia de amor, 1514, 1902.

Hispanica [HISPANICARUM]. Liturgia antiq. H. Gothica &c., 2t, 1746, *see* LITURGIA.
Rerum H. scr. aliquot. Ex bibl. R. Beli. [t3 *has tp.* De rebus gest. a F. Ximenio &c. authore A. Gomecio]. 3t [*in* 2.] sm. fol. Francofurti. 1579–81

Histoire.
*H. abrégée de la vie &c. de M. Arnauld, 1695, *see* QUESNEL (P.)
*H. abrégée des merveilles opérées dans la sainte chapelle de N. D. de Gray, 1755, *see* GRAY.
H. anonymi de la prem. Croisade ; éd. & tr. L. Bréhier, 1924, *see* GESTA (Anonyme) Franc. &c. Hiersolymitan.
*H. apologet., ou défense des libertéz des égl. réform. de France, 1688, *see* GAUTIER (F. DE).
*H. de Guzman d'Alfarache ; tr. Lesage, 2t, 1787, *see* ALEMAN (M.)
*H. de la républ. de Venise, par l'abbé L., 12t, 1758–68, *see* LAUGIER (M. A.)
*H. de l'Inquisition & son orig., 1693, *see* MARSOLLIER (J.)
*H. de Napoléon d'ap. MM. de Norvins &c. 1837, *see* NAPOLEON I.
*H. des Camisards &c., 2t, 1744, *see* CAMISARDS.
*H. des derniers troubles de France, 1613, *see* MATTHIEU (P.)
*H. des differens entre les miss. Jesuites & ceux des ordres de St. Dominique & de St. François t. les cultes [des] Chinois &c. [*by A. Arnauld*], *see* JESUITS. *Morale prat., t6, 7, 1716–35.
*H. des hosties miraculeuses &c., 1820, *see* GRIFFET (H.)
*H. des négoc., & du traité de paix des Pyrénées, 2t, 1750, *see* COURCHETET D'ESNANS (L.)
*H. des révol. d'Angleterre sous le r. de Jacques II, 1689, *see* ANGLETERRE.
*H. du cabinet des Tuileries &c., 1815, *see* GUILLIÉ (S.)
*H. du chevalier Bayard, 1616, *see* MAILLES (J. DE).
*H. du ministere du comte-duc, 1673, *see* VERA Y FIGUEROA (J. A. DE), *conde de la Roca.*
H. & cartul. des Templiers de Provins &c., 1919, *see* PROVINS.
H. & cartul. du prieuré de Notre-Dame &c. de la Presle, 1893, *see* PRESLE (LA).
*H. héroïque &c. de la noblesse de Provence, 4t, 1776–1901, *see* ARTEFEUIL (L. V.)
*H. impartiale des Jésuites &c., 1768, *see* LINGUET (S. N. H.)

Histoire [*continued*].
H. litt. de la France. Cont. par des membres de l'Institut. t35, 36, suite du 14e s. 4º. 1921–27
H. poëtique de la guerre nouv. declarée entre les anciens & les modernes, *see* CALLIÈRES (F. DE).
*H. remarq. & vérit. de ce qui s'est passé au siège d'Ostende, 1604, *see* OSTENDE.
*H. véritable de Mr. Crépin, *n.d.*, *see* CRÉPIN (*Mr.*), *ps.*
*H. véritable des guerres entre les 2 maisons de France & d'Esp., 1606, *see* MATTHIEU (P.)

Historia.
*H. aliquot nostri sæculi martyrum, 1550, *see* CHAUNCY (M.)
*H. cultus Sinensium, 1700, *see* FATINELLI (G. G.), *ed.*
*H. de la república del Ecuador, por J. L. R., t1, 2, 1809–77, 1920–25, *see* ECUADOR.
*H. eccl., cui add. Synchronismi hist. exoticae praes. Indicae. [*In Tamil. Attr. to J. P. Fabricius*]. Ed. 2a. 8º. Trangambariæ. 1799
*H. Eccl. Evangel. in Hungaria, 1830, *see* MUNYAY (L.)
H. Eccl. integram eccl. Christ. condit. exponens : per studiosos &c. viros in urbe Magdeburgica congesta ; per L. Lucium rec., 1624, *see* MAGDEBURG CENTURIES.
*H. passion. J. C., Tamulice, 1789, *see* JESUS CHRIST.
H. persecut. eccl. Bohemicae, 894–1632, 1648, *see* BOHEMICA.
*H. S. Petri &c., 1639, *see* XAVIER (H.)
*H. Trevir. diplomat. &c., 3t, 1750, *see* FEBRONIUS (J.), *ps.*
*H. vera de vita M. Buceri & P. Fagii &c., 1562, *see* HUBERTUS (C.), *ed.*
*Magni theol. Salani Hist. crit. theologiae dogmat. &c., 1724, *see* BUDDEUS (J. F.)

Historiae.
H. Augustae scriptores VI.
„ „ *a. ed. w. t.* Scr. hist. Augustae. [Text], w. Eng. tr. by D. Magie. [Loeb Class. Lib.] v1, 2. s8º. 1922–24
„ „ *a. ed. w. t.* Scr. hist. Augustae. Ed. E. Hohl. 2v. s8º. *Teubner*, L. 1927
„ „ *see* BAYNES (N. H.) The Hist. Augusta : date & purpose, 1926.
„ „ „ THÖRNELL (G.) Ad Scr. Hist. A. &c. adnot., 1927.
*H. e Scriptis Sacr. sel. in usum juventutis Tamulicae. [*Lat. & Tamil tp.*] 8º. Trankenbariae. 1801
*H. eccl. quam tripartitam vocant libri 12, 1566, *see* CASSIODORUS (M. A.).

Historic Society of Lancashire & Cheshire. Transactions. New ser., v21, 22 (1905–06). 8º. Liv'l. 1906–07

Historica. Hist. narratio de introd. Univ. Juliæ &c. per professores Univ. J. conscripta &c., 1579, *see* HELMSTEDT.

Historical [*incl.* HISTORIC].
Historic gallery of portraits & paintings w. mem. of celeb. men &c. 4v [v4 *wanting*]. 8º. [1835 ?]
*Hist. acc. of H.M.'s visit to Scotland, 1822, *see* MUDIE (R.)
*Hist. (An) acc. of some things rel. to nature of Eng. govt., 1690, *see* WHITBY (D.)
*Hist. acc. of the pres. troubles in Persia &c., by M. de P*** ; tr., 1756, *see* PEYSSONEL (C. C. DE).
*Hist. (The) & poet. medley : or Muses libr., 1738, *see* COOPER (E.)
*Hist. (An) & polit. essay, discov. the affinity of anc. & mod. governments, in respect to our English Parliaments. s8º. 1706
*Hist. & tradit. tales in prose & verse conn. w. the S. of Scotland, *see* SCOTLAND, 1843.
*Hist. churches of Transylvania & Roumania, 1921, *see* TRANSYLVANIA.
*Hist. coll. conc. Church affairs, 1696, *see* LOWTH (S.)
*Hist. coll. out of sev. grave Protestant historians, conc. the changes of religion, 1686, *see* TOUCHET (G.)
*Hist. (An) disc. of the popes usurped supremacy over princes. [*wanting all before B1, except the tp. from which date is missing. b. w. a. c. of* Tuke (R.) Mem. of Sir E. Godfrey, 1682]. s8º. [1682 ?]
*Hist. diss. conc. the antiq. of the Eng. constit., 1768, *see* STUART (G.)
*Hist. (An) essay upon the loyalty of Presbyterians, 3p, 1713, *see* KIRKPATRICK (J.)
Hist. fragm. rel. to Scotish affairs, 1635–64, 3p, 1833, *see* MAIDMENT (J.), *ed.*
*Hist. (An) narr. of the orig. &c. of the Irish Soc., 1865, *see* REED (*Sir* C.)
Hist. records of Australia, 1919–21, *see* AUSTRALIA.
*Hist. reminisc. of Dublin Castle, 849–1895, 1895, *see* DUBLIN CASTLE.
*Hist. views of ye last glorious exped. of H.M.'s ships &c. agst. the Havannah, 1762, *see* ORSBRIDGE (P.)
*Hist. (An) vindic. of The naked gospel [*by A. Bury*], 1691, *see* BURY (A.)

Historical & political monthly mercury, *see* PRESENT STATE (THE) OF EUROPE, *or* The h. & p. m. m., 1692–1712.

Historical Association. Quarterly journal, N.S. v4–11, 1919–27, *see* HISTORY.
see MAXWELL (C.) A short bibliog. of Irish hist., 1921.
„ STENTON (F. M.) Development of the castle in Eng. & Wales, 1910.

Historical Manuscripts Commission. 8º. 1912–27

Bathurst, *e. of* (1923).	Lords, *House of.* N.S., v6–8 (1912-23) not publ. under the auth. of the H. MSS. C.
Buccleuch & Queensberry, *d. of*, Montagu House, v3 (1926).	Mertoun Hse., *Berwickshire, see* Polwarth.
Cirencester Park, *see* Bathurst, *e. of, above.*	Ormonde, *m. of*: N.S., v8 (1920).
De L'Isle & Dudley, *baron* (1925), v1.	Palk MSS., Rep. (1922).
Downshire, *Marquess of*, v1i, ii, Papers of Sir W. Trumbull (1924).	Penshurst Place, *see* De L'Isle & Dudley, *baron.*
Dropmore, *see* FORTESCUE.	Percival, *vsct.*, *see* Egmont.
Easthampstead Park, Berks, *see* Downshire, *m. of, above.*	Polwarth, Lord : R., v2 (1916).
Edinburgh, *u. of*, *see* LAING.	Portland, *d. of.* R., v9 (1923).
Egmont, *e. of*, Diary, 3v (1920–23).	Salisbury, *m. of.* Calendar of MSS., p13, 14 (Addenda), 1915–23.
Finch, A. G., v2 (1922).	Stuart papers at Windsor Castle, v6, 7 (1916–23).
Fortescue, J. B., v8–10 (1912–27).	Trumbull (*sir* W.), *see* Downshire, v1i, ii.
Laing, D. R., 2v (1914–25).	Windsor, *see* Stuart papers.

see ROBERTS (R. A.) Reports of H.M.C., 1920.

Historical Society of Pennsylvania, *see* MACMASTER (J. B.) & F. D. STONE, *edd.* Pennsylvania & the Federal Constit., 1787–88, 1888.

Historical Society of West Wales, *see* WEST WALES HISTORICAL RECORDS : ann. mag. of the Hist. Soc. of W. W., v1–12, 1910–27, 1912–27.

Historicorum Romanorum reliq., v2, 1906, *see* PETER (H.)

Historicus, *ps.* [6], *a. of* Patent law &c., 1919, *see* HULME (E. W.)

***Historie** (The pleasaunt) of Lazarillo de Tormes, *see* HURTADO DE MENDOZA.

Historisch Genootschap te Utrecht. Bijdragen en mededeelingen. d. 41–47. 8º. Amsterdam. 1920–26
Verslag v. de algem. vergadering, 1920, 1923. 8º. A. 1920–23
Werken. N. Ser., 1–61. Ser. 3, 1–50. 8º. Utrecht. 1863–1926
The volumes omitted in following list are given in the Library's Catalogue, 1913.
see AARSSENS (F. v.) Verbaal van de ambassade van A., Joachimi & Burmania, 1625, 1867. [N.S., 10.]
„ ALBERT I, *duke of Bavaria.* De oorlogen van A. met de Friezen &c. 1869. [N.S., 8.]
„ ALPERTUS, *Monachus.* De diversitate temporum, 1916. [s3, 37.]
„ BENNINGE (S.) Kroniek, 1e & 2e deel (Kroniek van van Lemego), 1887. [N.S., 48.]
„ BLEYSWIJK (D. v.) Memorien, 1734–55, 1887. [N.S., 45.]
„ BOMELIUS (H.) Bellum Trajectinum (1539), 1878. [N.S., 28.]
„ BRONCHORST (E.) Diarium, 1591-1627, 1898. [s3, 12.]
„ BUCHELL (A. VAN) Diarium, 1907. [s3, 21.]
„ CAPE COLONY &c. Bepalingen & instruct. v. het bestuur v. de buitendistr. v. de Kaap de G. H., 1805, 1922. [s3, 45.]
„ CAPELLEN (*b.* J. D. VAN DER). Brieven van en aan C., 1879. [N.S., 27a.]
„ COSMO III [*de Medici*]. De 2 reizen van C. d. Nederlanden, 1667–9, 1919. [s3, 41.]
„ DORP (A. v.) Brieven &c., 1887–8. [N.S., 44, 50.]
„ DORT. De oudste stadsrekeningen van Dordrecht, 1284–1424, 1891. [s3, 2.]
„ — Rekeningen van de gilden van D., 1438–1600, 1894. [s3, 6.]
„ DUSSELDORP (F. v.) Uittreksel uit F. D. Annales, 1566–1616, 1893. [s3, 1.]
„ DUTCH CHURCH, *Austin Friars, London.* Kerkeraads-protocollen, 1560–63, 1921. [s3, 43.]
„ EGMOND OF ZEE. Annales E., 1863. [N.S., 1.]
„ EMO, *abbot of Werum.* Kronijken van E. en Menko, 1866. [N.S., 4.]
„ EPPENS THO EQUART (A.) Kroniek, 2d, 1911. [s3, 27, 28.]
„ GELDENHAUER (G.) Collectanea, 1901. [s3, 16.]
„ GOENS (R. M. C. VAN). Brieven aan G. & onuitg. stukken hem betreff., 3d, 1884–90. [N.S., 38, 43, 56.]
„ GOES (W. VAN DER) & A. VAN DER GOES. Briefwisseling, 1659-73, 2d, 1899–1909. [s3, 10, 11.]
„ GRONINGEN. Rekeningen d. stad G. uit de 16de eeuw, 1896. [s3, 9.]
„ GROOT (P. DE). Lettres à A. de Wicquefort, 1668–74, 1894. [s3, 5.]
„ GROTIUS (H.) Verhooren &c., 1871. [N.S., 14.]
„ GULIELMUS, *Procurator Egmond.* Chronicon, 1904. [s3, 20.]
„ HAINAUT. Rekeningen d. Graven &c. uit het Henegouwsche Huis, 1924. [s3, 46.]
„ HARDENBROEK (G. J. VAN). Gedenkschriften 1747[–88], 6d, 1901–18. [s3, 14, 17, 24, 36, 39, 40.]
„ HOLLAND. Kronijk van Holland, 1867. [N.S., 6.]
„ — Rekeningen der Grafelijkheid van H. onder het Henegouwsche Huis, 3d, 1875–8. [N.S., 21, 24, 26.]

Historisch Genootschap te Utrecht [*continued*].
see HOOFT (C. P.) Memoriën &c., 2d, 1871–1925. [N.S., 16, s3, 48.]
,, HORTENSIUS (L.) H. over de opkomst en den ondergang van Naarden, 1866. [N.S., 5.]
,, HUYGENS (K.), *the younger*. Journaal, 1688–96, 3d, 1876–88. [N.S., 23, 25, 46.]
,, —— Reg. op de Journalen, 1906. [s3, 22.]
,, —— Aanteekeningen &c. op het Register, 1915. [s3, 35.]
,, JANSEN (M. H.) Het leven van een vloothouder, 1925. [s3, 49.]
,, LEYDEN. Stadsrekeningen van L., 1390–1434, 2d, 1913–14. [s3, 32, 34.]
,, LIONELLO (G. B.) Brieven v. L. & Suriano uit Den Haag &c., 1616–18, 1883. [N.S., 37.]
,, MARGARET, *duchess of Parma*. Corr. avec Philippe II, t1, 1925. [s3, 47.]
,, MIDDELBURG. Onderzoek van 's Konings wege ingesteld omtrent de M. beroerten, 1566–67, 1873. [N.S., 18.]
,, NASSAU (L., *count of*). Corr. van & betref. L. v. N. &c., 1887. [N.S., 47.]
,, PHEBENS (E. E.) Kronijk, 1565–94, 1867. [N.S., 7.]
,, POSTHUMUS (N. W.) Bescheiden betref. de prov. organis. d. Holland. lakenbereiders, 1917. [s3, 38.]
,, SPEELMAN (C.) Journaal der reis van J. Cunaeus naar Perzië, 1651–2, 1908. [s3, 26.]
,, STOKE (M.) Rijmkroniek, 2d, 1885. [N.S., 40, 42.]
,, THÜLMEYER (H. G. v.) Dépêches, 1763–88, 1912. [s3, 30.]
,, TRAJECTENSES. Quedam narracio de Groninghe &c., 1888. [N.S., 49.]
,, UTENBOGAERT (J.) Brieven &c., 1584[-1644], 3d [*in* 7p], 1868–75. [N.S., 11, 12, 15, 17, 19, 20, 22.]
,, UTRECHT. Registers &c. van het Bisdom U., 1325–36, 2d, 1889–91. [N.S. 53, 54.]
,, —— Rekeningen van het bisdom U., 1378–1573, d1, 1926. [s3, 50.]
,, —— Resolutiën van de Vroedschap v. U. betref. de Academie, 1900. [N.S., 52.]
,, —— Verslagen van kerkvisitatiën in het bisdom U. uit de 16de eeuw, 1911. [s3, 29.]
,, VOECHT (J. DE). Narratio, 1908. [s3, 13.]
,, VOSBERGEN (G. v.) Verbaal van de ambassade van V. bij d. Koning v. Denemarken &c., 1625, 1867. [N.S., 9.]
,, WASSENAAR-DUIVENOORDE (J. VAN). Verbaal van de buitengewone ambassade van W.-D. naar Eng. in 1685, 1863. [N.S., 2.]
,, WASSENAER-OBDAM (*Adm.* J. VAN). Journalen van Van W.-O. & De Ruyter, 1907. [s3, 23.]
,, WIJNNE (J. A.) Geschillen over de afdanking van 't krijgsvolk in de Vereenidge Nederl., 1649–50, 1885. [N.S., 41.]
,, WILLIAM V, *pr. of Orange*. Brieven aan Baron van Lijnden van Blitterswijk, 1893. [s3, 3.]
,, WILLIAMS (*Sir* R.) Memoriën, 1864. [N.S., 3.]
,, WITT (J. DE). Brieven aan J. de W.: bewerkt d. R. Fruin, 2d, 1919–22. [s3, 42, 44.]
,, —— Brieven; bewerkt d. R. Fruin, 4d, 1906–13. [s3, 18, 25, 31, 33.]
,, ZEELAND. De rekeningen der Grafelijkheid van Z. onder het Henegouwsche Huis, 2d, 1879–80. [N.S., 29, 30.]
REFERENCES.
see BULLARIUM Trajectense; ed. G. Brom, 2v, 1891–96.
,, CODEX. C. diplom. neerlandicus, 1852–63.

***Historische** Nachricht vom Brüder-Gesangbuche d. J. 1778 u. v. dessen Lieder-Verfassern. s8°. Gnadau. 1835

Historische Kommission f. d. Grossherzogtum Hessen, *see* HAUPT (H.), *ed.* Hess. Biografien, B1, 2, 1918–27.

Historische Zeitschrift.
B121–136. [3e Folge. B25–38]. 8°. München. 1920–27
Reg. zu B57–96 (N. Folge 21–50). Bearb. P. Wentzcke. 8°. München. 1906
Reg. zu B97–130 (3e Folge 1–34). Bearb. v. F. Schneider. 8°. München. 1925
Beiheft 7, 9–13. 8°. München. 1926–28
see BEIN (A.) Die Staatsidee A. Hamiltons, 1927. [12.]
,, BELOW (G. v.) Ital. Kaiserpolitik d. deut. Ma., 1927. [10.]
,, HOFFMANN-LINKE (E.) Zw. Nationalismus u. Demokratie, 1927. [9.]
,, LEUSSER (H.) Ein Jahrzehnt deut.-amer. Politik, 1897–1906, 1928. [13.]
,, VIGENER (F.) 3 Gestalten aus d. mod. Katholizismus, 1926. [7.]
,, VOSSLER (O.) Mazzinis polit. Denken &c., 1927. [11.]

Historischer Verein f. Steiermark. Beiträge zur Kunde steiermärk. Geschichtsquellen. Jhrg. 1–35. 8°. Graz. 1864–1906
Jhrg. 33–35 [*Neue Folge, 1e–3e J.*] *have title:* Beiträge z. Erforschung steir. Gesch.

Historischer Verein f. Steiermark [*continued*].
Steirische Zeitschrift f. Gesch. Jhrg. 1–16. 8°. Graz. 1903–18
Jhrg. 4 onwards have title: Zeitschrift d. hist. Vereines f. Steiermark.

Historisches Vierteljahrschrift. Neue Folge d. Deut. Zeitschrift für Geschichtswiss. Jhrg. 17, 18 (Der ganzen Folge, Jhrg. 25, 26). 8°. L. 1916–18

Historisch-heraldisches Handbuch z. genealog. Taschenbuch d. gräfl. Häuser, 1855, *see* GOTHAISCHES GENEALOG. TASCHENBUCH.

Historiske. Hist. Samlingar. Udg. af. Norske Hist. Kildeskriftkom. B1–3. 8°. 1900–1914

History.
*Hist. & antiq. of Horsham, 1836, *see* DUDLEY (H.)
*Hist. & antiq. of Thorne &c., 1829, *see* THORNE.
*Hist. & antiq. of Winchester [*by T. Warton?*], v2, 1773, *see* WINCHESTER.
*Hist. (The), constit. & conf. of faith of the Calvinistic Methodists in Wales, 1834, *see* METHODISTS.
*Hist. of Aldborough & Boroughbridge, 1853, *see* TURNER (T. S.)
Hist. of Eng. lit., 1923, *see* BUCHAN (J.), *ed.*
*Hist. of Guildford, 1801, *see* GUILDFORD.
*Hist. of Kirkstall Abbey, 1847, *see* MULREADY (W.)
*Hist. (The) of monastical conventions & milit. instit. &c., 1686, *see* MONASTICAL.
*Hist. of North America &c., 1757, *see* AMERICA.
*Hist. of Poland to 1795, 1795, *see* JONES (STEPHEN).
*Hist. (The) of Popery; by sev. gentlemen, 2v, 1735–6, *see* POPERY.
*Hist. (The) of printing in Europe, 1713, *see* WATSON (J.), *printer.*
*Hist. of Richmond, 1814, *see* CLARKSON (C.)
*Hist. of Ripon, 1806, *see* RIPON.
*Hist. of sin & heresie, 1698, *see* LESLIE (C.)
*Hist. of the Abbey Church of St. Peter's Westminster, 2v, 1812, *see* COMBE (W.)
*Hist. of the Azores, 1813, *see* ASHE (T.)
*Hist. of the church &c. of Howden, 1850, *see* CLARKE (T.)
Hist. of the Great War: princ. events 1914–18; comp. by Comm. of Imp. Defence, 1922–27, *see* WAR.
*Hist. (The) of the house of Esté &c. 1681, *see* CRAUFURD (J.)
*Hist. of the House of Stanley, 1821, *see* SEACOME (J.)
*Hist. (The) of the life & death of Sir T. More, 1662, *see* HODDESDON (J.)
*Hist. (The) of the London Burkers, 1832, *see* BISHOP (J.), *murderer.*
*Hist. (The) of the Moravians, tr. f. the German, 1754, *see* MORAVIANS.
*Hist. (The) of the popish-sham-plots &c., 1682, *see* POPISH.
*Hist. of the Protest. Church in Hungary, 1854, *see* HUNGARY.
*Hist. (A) of the union betw. Presbyt. & Congregat. ministers &c., 1698, *see* TAYLOR (RICH.)
*Hist. (The) of transubstantiation &c., 1687, *see* COSIN (J.), *bp. of Durham.*
*Hist. (The) of Virginia, 1722, *see* BEVERLEY (R.)
Hist. of woman suffrage. v3–6. la8°. Rochester, N.Y. [1886–1922]
3, 1876–85; ed. E. C. Stanton, S. B. Anthony &c.
4, 1883–1900; ed. S. B. Anthony & I. H. Harper.
3, 6, 1900–20; ed. I. H. Harper.

History. Quarterly journal of the Historical Assoc. Ed. A. F. Pollard. N.S. v4–11. 8°. 1919–27

***Histrionic** topography, 1818, *see* COLE (J.), *of Scarborough.*

Hitchener (Elizabeth). Letters to P. B. Shelley. [Foreword by W. E. Peck]. la8°. [*p.p.*] N.Y. 1926

Hitchens (James). Short acc. of the death of S. Hitchens. 5th ed. [P2586]. s8°. 1747

Hitchens (Samuel), *see* HITCHENS (J.) Sh. acc. of death of S. H., 1747.

Hitchings (Francis Noel Wells).
Apepi & Nefertari. Tragedy. 8°. 1920

Hite (Clarence B.), *see* JAMES (F.) *Trial of F. J.; w. confess. by D. Liddil & C. H., 1898.

Hitopadeṣa. The first book of the H. Sanskrit text w. translit. & Eng. tr. 8°. 1864
H. The Sanskrit text of the first book; w. gramm. analysis. Prep. by F. Johnson. 4°. 1840
The second, third & fourth books of the H. Sanskrit text w. interlinear tr. 8°. 1865
see JONES (*Sir* W.) Works, v6, Hitópadésa of Vishnusarma, 1799.

Hitzig (Hermann Ferdinand). Die Stellung Hadrians in d. röm. Rechtsgesch. [P2466]. 8°. Zürich. 1892

Hjort (Johan). The unity of science. A sketch. s8°. [1921]

Hlávka (Josef), *see* BOHEMIA. Topographie d. hist. u. Kunstdenkmale im Königr. B., hrsg. u. Leit. J. H., 1897–1916.

Hoadly (Benjamin), *bp. of Winchester.*
see CERRI (U.) Acc. of state of Rom. Cath. relig.; tr. &c.; by Sir R. Steele (*or rather* Bp. Hoadly), 1715.

Hoadly (Benjamin), *bp. of Winchester* [*continued*].
see LAW (W.) A reply to B.'s answer &c., 1719.
,, STEBBING (H.) Defence of 1st head of charge of Ctee. of Convoc. agst. Bp. of Bangor [*i.e.* B. H.], 1718.

Hoadly (Benjamin), *M.D., F.R.S.*
The suspicious husband, comedy. [P2865]. s8º. *Tonson.* 1761
,, ,, *for a. ed., see* INCHBALD (E.) Brit. th., v13, 1808.

Hoag (Ernest Bryant), *see* WILLIAMS (E. H.) & E. B. H. Our fear complexes, 1924.

Hoagland (Henry Elmer). Collective bargaining in the lithogr. industry. 8º. N.Y., *Columbia Univ.* 1917

Hoang (Pierre). Cat. des éclipses de soleil & de lune rel. dans doc. chin. &c., *see* VARIÉTÉS sinolog., No. 56, 1925.
Cat. des tremblements de terre signalés en Chine d'ap. les sources chin., 2t (t2, compl. par J. Tobar & H. Gauthier), *see* VARIÉTÉS sinolog., No. 28i, ii, 1909–13.
Concordance des chronologies néoméniques, chin. & europ., *see* VARIÉTÉS sinolog., No. 27, 1910.
see HAVRET (H.), CHAMBEAU & P. H. Mélanges s. la chron. chin., 1920.

Hoard (Samuel), *B.D.* *God's love to mankinde. s8º. 1658

Hoare (Alfred). Ital. dictionary. 2nd ed. 4º. C. 1925
A short Italian dictionary. 2v *in* 1. 8º. C. 1919

Hoare (*Sir* Richard Colt), *2nd bart.* Tour thr. the Island of Elba. Illust. w. views by Sir R. C. H. & J. Smith. 4º. 1814

Hobbes (Thomas) [T. H., *of Malmesbury*]. *Behemoth. The hist. of the Civil wars of England, 1640–60. s8º. 1679
,, ,, ...s8º. 1680
Elements of law. Ed., w. pref. & notes by F. Tönnies; subjoined sel. extracts f. unpr. MSS. of T. H. 8º. C. 1928
A letter about liberty & necessity. With obs. by a prelate [*i.e. B. Laney*]. s8º. 1676
Leviathan. *la. paper.* fol. 1651
,, ,, ...Intr. by H. Morley. 8º. 1885
T. H. vita. [Vitæ Hobbianæ auctarium, *by R. Blackburne.* Vita carmine expressa auctore seipso, *ed. by R. Blackburne*]. s8º. Carolopoli. 1681
see BRAMHALL (J.) Defence of true liberty, ans. to T. H., 1655.
,, PERRONET (V.) Some enquiries, opinions of H. w. reg. to sensation &c., 1740.
,, SPENER (P. J.) Philosophema de conform. creaturae ad Creatorem, T. H. oppos., 1716.
,, TÖNNIES (F.) T. H. Leben u. Lehre, 3e A., 1925.

Hobbs (Edward W.) Sailing ships at a glance. Intr. by L. G. C. Laughton. 8º. 1925

Hobbs (John Berry). My cricket memories. 8º. [1924]

Hobbs (Margarett A.), *see* ANDREWS (I. O.) & M. A. H. Econ. effects of World War upon women & children in Gt. Brit., 2nd (rev.) ed., 1921.

Hobbs (T. G.), *F.R.G.S.* Luton parish church: photograph. studies. [Foreword by C. M. Williams. Intr. by E. C. Lee]. 8º. [Luton. 1924]

Hobbs (William Herbert). Earth evolution &c. 8º. N.Y. 1921
Earth features & th. meaning. 8º. N.Y. 1921

Hobhouse (*Rt. Hon.* Henry), *see* WRIGHT (*Sir* R. S.) & H. H. Outline of local govt. & tax. in Eng. & Wales, 5th ed., 1922.

Hobhouse (Leonard Trelawney). Development & purpose; phil. of evol. n. ed. rev. & re-wr. 8º. 1927
The elements of social justice. 8º. [1922]
The rational good. A study in the logic of practice. 8º. [1921]
Social development. 8º. 1924

Hobhouse (Stephen). William Law & 18th cent. Quakerism, incl. letters & fragm. of W. L. & J. Byrom. 8º. [1927]
—— **& A. F. Brockway.** Eng. prisons to-day: rep. of Prison System Enq. Comm. [Labour Res. Dept.] Ed. S. H. & A. F. B. 8º. 1922

Hobler (J. Paul). The words of the favourite pieces, as performed at the Glee Club. Comp. by J. P. H. s8º. 1794

Hobley (Charles William). Bantu beliefs & magic. Intr. by Sir J. G. Frazer. 8º. 1922

Hoblyn (Richard Dennis). Dict. of terms used in medicine &c. 14th ed., rev., w. add. by J. A. P. Price. s8º. 1909

Hobson (Bernard).
The East Riding of Yorks. (w. York). s8º. C. 1924
The West Riding of Yorks. s8º. C. 1921

Hobson (*Mrs.* Coralie). The revolt of youth. s8º. [1919]

Hobson (Ernest William). The domain of natural science. Gifford Lect., 1921 & 1922. 8º. C. 1923
The theory of functions of a real variable & the theory of Fourier's series. 2nd ed. rev. & enl. 2v. la8º. C. 1921–26

Hobson (Geoffrey Dudley). Maioli, Canevari & others. 4º. 1926

Hobson (John Atkinson).
The economics of unemployment. s8º. [1922]
Free-thought in the soc. sciences 8º. [1926]
Die Furcht vor Deutschland. Einl. v. Earl Loreburn. Übers. [P2735]. 8º. München. 1913
Incentives in the new indust. order. 8º. [1922]
Problems of a new world. s8º. [1921]
The science of wealth. [Home Univ. Lib.] [repr.] s8º. [1919]

Hobson (John Morrison).
Some early & later houses of pity. 8º. 1926

Hobson (Robert Lockhart).
Chinese art. 100 plates in colour, intr. by outline sk. of C. art. 4º. 1927
The later ceramic wares of China. 4º. 1925
Wares of the Ming dynasty. 4º. 1923
see BRIT. MUS.: ANTIQ. English pottery & porcelain; by R. L. H., 1910.
,, —— —— F. Lloyd coll. of Worcester porcelain; by R. L. H., 1923.
see BRIT. MUS.: ANTIQ. Guide to pottery &c. of the Far East in Dept. of Ceramics &c.; [prep. by R. L. H.], 1924.
,, BURTON (W.) & R. L. H. Hdbk. of marks on pottery &c., 1919.
,, EUMORFOPOULOS (G.) The G. E. coll.: cat. of the Chinese, Corean & Persian pottery &c.; by R. L. H., 6v, 1925–28.
—— **& A. L. Hetherington.** Art of the Chinese potter f. the Han dynasty to the end of the Ming. 4º. 1923

Hobson (S. G.) National guilds. Inquiry into the wage system &c. Ed. A. R. Orage. 3rd ed. s8º. 1919

Hobson (Thomas Frederick), *Barrister-at-Law.* Adderbury "Rectoria": building of the chancel, 1408–18: account rolls &c. Transcr. & ed. T. F. H. [Oxf. Rec. Soc. ser., 8]. 8º. [O.] 1926

Hoby (James). Mem. of W. Yates, D.D. With his life of W. H. Pearce. 8º. 1847
see COX (F. A.) & J. H. Relig. in America, 1837.

Hoc (Marcel).
Etude s. J. G. Gevaerts, 1593–1666. 8º. Brux. 1922

Hocart (A. M.) Kingship. 8º. O. 1927
A point of grammar & a study in method. [Repr. f. American Anthropologist, v20. P2498]. 8º. *n.p.* [1918]

Hoccleve (Thomas).
Works. [E.E.T.S., E.S., 73]. [v]2. 8º. 1925
2, Minor poems in Ashburnham MS. addit. 133. Ed. Sir I. Gollancz.

Hoche (*le gén.* **C. Lazare**), *see* GIRARD (G.) Vie de L. H., 11e éd., 1926.

Hochsemius (Joannes), *see* HOCSEM (J. DE).

Hochstaterus (Joh. Georgius). Disput. Biblica de 2. cap. Danielis. [P2640]. s4º. Witebergae. *n.d.*

Hochstetter (Andreas Adam). De recta concionandi &c. ratione comm. Tertium ed. cur. C. F. Sartorio. 8º. Tubingae. 1767

Hochstetter (Franz). Mehr Land. [P2409]. 8º. 1917

Hochstetter (Johann Andreas). Diss. de jure jubilæorum. [P484]. s4º. Tubingae. [1731]

Höcker (Paul Oskar). Die blonde Gefahr. 8º. *n.d.*
see LILLER KRIEGSZEITUNG: Auslese aus No. 1–40; hrsg. P. O. H. &c., 1915.

Hocking (Joseph). Rosemary Carew. s8º. [1925]

Hocking (William Ernest). The meaning of God in human experience. 8º. New Haven [U.S.] 1916

Hockliffe (Ernest), *see* SARGEAUNT (J.) Hist. of Bedford school; ed. & compl. by E. H., 1925.

Hocron (Alberic C. H. d'Hespel d'), *see* HESPEL D'HOCRON.

Hocsem (Jean de) [†HOCHSEMIUS (JOANNES)]. Chronique. [C.R. d'H. de Belg.] n. éd. publ. G. Kurth. 8º. Brux. 1927

Hodder-Williams (Ralph). Princess Patricia's Canadian Light Infantry, 1914–19. Intr. by A. Hamilton Gault. 2v. (1, Narrative; 2, Roll of honour & app.) 8º. 1923

Hoddesdon (John). *The hist. of the life & death of Sir Thomas More. Coll. by J. H., Gent. s8º. 1662

Hodell (Charles Wesley). The Old Yellow Book [*i.e.* Setting-forth of criminal cause agst. G. Franceschini, & h. bravoes, 1698]. Source of Browning's Ring & the book. [Everyman's Lib.] s8º. [1911]

Hodges (Charles Clement). Guide to Priory Ch. of St. Andrew, Hexham, w. acc. of the town of H. 2nd ed. s8º. 1921

Hodges (George), *D.D.* Fountains Abbey: st. of a mediaeval monastery. 8º. 1904

Hodges (Harold Winter) & E. A. Hughes.
Sel. naval doc. Ed. H. W. H. & E. A. H. 8º. C. 1922

Hodges (James), *pamphleteer.* *The present state of England as to coin & public charges. By J. H. s8°. 1697

Hodges (Sydney) [*ps.* STANLEY HOPE].
Geoffrey's wife. 2v. s8°. 1874

Hodges (William), *R.A.* Travels in India, 1780–83. 4°. 1793

Hodgetts (Edward Arthur Brayley).
Moss from a rolling stone. 8°. 1924
Reasonable religion: E. Swedenborg, h. message &c. 8°. 1923

Hodgetts (J. Frederick).
The English in the Middle Ages. 8°. 1885

Hodgkin (Edith), *see* HODGKIN (J. E.) & E. H. Examples of early Eng. pottery, 1891.

Hodgkin (Henry Theodore).
China in the family of nations. s8°. [1923]

Hodgkin (John). Proper terms: explan. of meanings of phrases in "The book of St. Albans," 1486 &c., *see* PHILOL. SOC. Trans., Suppl., 1907–10.

Hodgkin (John Eliot) & E. Hodgkin.
Examples of early English pottery. 4°. 1891

Hodgkin (Lucy Violet), *aft. Mrs. John Holdsworth.*
A Quaker saint of Cornwall: Loveday Hambly. 8°. 1927

Hodgkin (Thomas), *D.C.L.* Hist. of Eng. to the Norman Conquest. [Pol. hist. of Eng. v1]. n. impr. 8°. 1920

Hodgson (Geraldine Emma). English mystics. s8°. [1922]
The life of J. E. Flecker, f. letters &c. 8°. O. 1925

Hodgson (James), *F.R.S.* The theory of perspective, *see* DUBREUIL (J.) *Pract. perspect.; tr., 7th ed., *n.d.*

Hodgson (James Vaughan), *see* ELTON HALL. Cat. of pictures at E.H. in poss. of Col. D. J. Proby, by T. Borenius & J. V. H., 1924.

Hodgson (John E.) Hist. of aeronautics in Gt. Brit. to latter half of the 19th cent. la8°. 1924

Hodgson (John L.) Exam. of the probl. of utilizing the earth's internal heat. Paper, Brit. Assoc., 1927. 2nd impr. 8°. 1927
The "Queen Margaret" statue at Lincoln Cath. [Repr. f. "The Builder," Dec. 5, 1924. P2773]. 8°. [1924]

Hodgson (Leonard). The place of reason in Xtn. apologetic: 4 lect. 8°. O. 1925

Hodgson (Ralph). Poems. [repr.] s8°. 1920

Hodgson (Robert), *dean of Carlisle.* *The life of Dr. Beilby Porteus, bp. of London. By a lay-member of Merton Coll., Oxford. 2nd ed. 8°. 1812

Hodgson (Shadworth Hollway).
Some cardinal points in knowledge. [P2507]. 8°. [1911]
„ „ *f. a. issue, see* BRIT. ACAD. Proc., 1911–12.

Hodivala (Shahpurshah Hormasji).
Studies in Parsi hist. 8°. Bombay. 1920

Hodler (Ferdinand).
see BENDER (E.) Die Kunst F. H., B1, 1923.
„ —— Das Leben F. H., 1921.
„ SUISSE. *Quelques peintres suisses: H. &c., 1921.

Hodoş (Nerva).
see BIANU (J.) & N. H. Bibliogr. român., t2, 1717–1808, 1905–10.
„ HURMUZAKI (E. DE). Doc. priv. la ist. Românilor, v16–18, Coresp. diplom. si rap. consulare franceze, 1603–1851; publ. N. H., 1912–16.

Hodson (Leonard J.)
Udimore, past & present. 8°. Robertsbridge, Sussex. 1920

Hodson (Selwyn) & J. Kendrick. Auction bridge. s8°. [1924]

Hodson (Thomas), *Wesleyan missionary.* An elem. gram. of the Karmada, or Canarese lang. 8°. Bangalore. 1859

Hodson (Vernon Charles Paget). List of officers of the Bengal army, 1758–1834. Arr. &c. w. biog. &c. notices by Maj. V. C. P. H. pl [A–C]. 8°. 1927

Hody (Humphrey) [HODIUS]. Contra hist. Aristeae de LXX interpretibus diss. s8°. O. 1684
see LOWTH (S.) Hist. coll. &c.; added, obs. upon Hody's Case of sees vacant, 1696.

Hoë (Matthias) *von Hoënegg.*
Apologeticus contra R. Bellarmini judicium pro s. & orthod. Concordiae libro. s8°. Francofurti. 1605
Auff die newlichst v. d. Calvinisten aussgesprengte Delineation &c. [P2443]. s4°. L. 1620
Comm. super Pauli ad Galatas epist. &c. s4°. Lipsiae. 1605
Expedita &c. responsio ad appellationem & provoc. S. Huberi. Add. brev. delineatio tot. artic. de Praedestinatione. [*b. w.* Osiander (L.), *the elder.* Gründtlicher Bericht &c. 1596]. s4°. Lipsiae. 1604

Hoë (Matthias) *von Hoënegg* [*continued*].
*Kurtze Erleuterung d. bewegl. Schreibens, welches D. Hoë zu Dressden wegen Ausstreibung d. Luther. Kirchen &c. hat ergehen lassen &c. [P2443]. s4°. *n.p.* 1623
Schreiben wegen plötzlicher, unversehener &c. Kirchensperrung u. Ausstreibung d. Lutherischen Prediger u. Schuldiener. [P2438]. s4°. [Dresden ?]. 1622

Höeg (Carsten). Les Saracatsans, tribu nomade grecque. 2[v]. 8°. 1925–26
1, Étude linguist. 2, Textes (contes & chansons) &c.

Hoek (Henry) & E. C. Richardson. Der Ski u. s. sportl. Benutzung. 2e deut. A. 8°. München. 1907

Hoepffner (Ernest), *see* FIDES, *of Agen, St.* La chanson de Ste. Foy; *ed.* E. H. & P. Alfaric, t1, Facs., texte crit., intr. & comm. philol.; par E. H., 1926.

Hoepli (Ulrico), *publisher.* Cat. chronolog. e alfab. per autori e per materie d. ediz. Hoepli, 1872–1922. Intr. di M. Scherillo. la8°. Milano. 1922
Manoscritti, miniature, incunabuli &c. Vendita, Aprile, 1927. la8°. Milano. 1927

Hoeppner, *see* HÖPPNER.

Hoernle (Edward Selwyn). The problem of the Agamemnon. Crit. of Dr. Verrall's theory of the plot; & reply. [*a. c. in* P2683]. 8°. O. 1921
The recognition scene in the Choephoroe. Exam. of Dr. Verrall's intr. &c. [P2683]. 8°. O. 1922

Hoernlé (Reinhold Friedrich Alfred).
Idealism as a philos. doctrine. s8°. [1924]
Studies in contemp. metaphysics. 8°. 1920

Hofbibliothek, *Wien, see* VIENNA.

Höfer (Adam Christoph). Orat. funebr. in mem. G. H. Goetzii. [P427]. s4°. Vitembergae. [1728]

Hoff (Hinrich Ewald). The duchy of Schleswig, its place in hist. &c. Tr. A. Koelbing. [P2419]. s8°. Kiel. 1919

Hoffbauer (E.) Command of artillery. Tr. S. Wilkinson. [P2762]. 8°. M'ter. 1889

Hoffbauer (Johann Christoph).
Gesch. d. Univ. zu Halle, bis 1805. s8°. Halle. 1805

Høffding (Harald).
Works in KONG. DAN. VID. SELSK. Filos. Med. 1, 1920–24.
Begrebet analogi.
Bemærkninger om d. Platon. Dialog Parmenides.
Platon's Bøger om Staten.
Relation som Kategori.
Bemerkungen ü. d. platon. Dialog Parmenides. [Bibl. f. Phil.; hrsg. v. L. Stein, B21]. 8°. 1921
Der Relationsbegriff. [German tr.] 8°. L. 1922
Sören Kierkegaard als Philosoph. Übers. v. A. Dorner u. C. Schrempf. 3te deut. A. 8°. St. 1922
Spinozas Ethica: Analyse &c. [Bibl. Spinozana, t4]. 8°. Heidelberg. 1924
Der Totalitätsbegriff. 8°. L. 1917

Höffelein (Carl August Heinrich). *Neu. Gesch. d. Reform. Kirche in d. Untern Pfalz. [*& Urkunden-Buch w. sep. pagin.*] s8°. Dessau. 1791

Hoffet (Jean Charles).
Esquisse biogr. s. Capiton. [P2658]. 8°. Str. 1850

Hoffman (Frederick Ludwig).
Works in UNITED STATES: LAB. Bull.
Deaths f. lead poisoning, 1927. [426.]
Health survey of the printing trades, 1922–25, 1927. [427.]
Mortality f. respiratory diseases in dusty trades, 1918. [231.]

Hoffman (Murray). A treatise upon the estate & rights of the corpor. of New York. 8°. N.Y. 1853

Hoffmann (Benjamin). Hist. cycli Dionysiani cum argumentis paschalibus &c. Praes. J. G. Janus. [P446]. s4°. Vitembergae. [1718]

Hoffmann (C. A.) *Coup d'oeil s. l'état polit. de Pologne sous la domin. russe, 1815–30. Par un Polonais [*i.e.* C. A. H.] 8°. 1832

Hoffmann (Christian), *of Jena.* Umbra in luce. 2a ed. [*a. c. b. w.* Andres (J. F.) Vida de S. Orencio, 1648]. s4°. Jena. 1680

Hoffmann (Christian Gottfried). Hist. juris Romano-Justinianei. 2v. [*each w. 2p in 1v*]. s4°. Lipsiae. 1726–34
1i, Orig. jur. Rom., Justiniani vita, jur. Graeci fontes &c.
1ii, Thomasius (C.) Del. hist. jur. civ.—Hotmannus (F.) Anti-Tribon.—Selden (J.) Diss. hist. ad Fletam.—Valsechius (V.) Epist. de vet. Pisanae civitat. constitutis.
2i. Jur. Roman. fontes. 2ii, Bretus (C.) Ordo perantiq. judiciorum.—Bottereau (R.) Hadrianus legislator.

Hoffmann (Conrad), *see* SCHAIRER (R.) & C. H., *edd.* Die Universitätsideale d. Kulturvölker, 1925.

Hoffmann (Conrad Philipp) [†HOFFMANNUS]. Disc. de die & nocte nuptiali. [P2745]. s4°. Regiomonti. 1731

Hoffmann (Daniel), *Prof. of theology at Helmstadt.* Abtruck etl. Schrifften, daraus d. gehoffte Genuinus intellectus Formulae Concordiae &c. erscheinet. Allen denen so S. Hubers, E. Hunnen u. D. Hofmans &c. Schrifften mit Nutz lesen &c. s4°. *n.p.* 1597

Zehen starcke anzeigungen &c., das d. Dichter d. Zerbster Buchs verenderung d. Lehr &c. belangend, v. keinem guten Geiste getrieben sey. [*b. w.* Hoym (C. v.) Erinnerungsschrifft, 1597]. s4°. Hall in Sachsen. 1597

see HUNNIUS (E.) Nohtwend. Verantwortung des Christl. Concordibuchs wider D. H. Beschuldigung &c., 1597.

„ —— Widerlegung d. ungegründten Aufflagen damit D. H. sich unterstanden, 1597.

„ LEYSER (P.) Kurtzer Bericht auff d. unter D. H.'s Namen, ausgesprengte Beschuldigung &c., 1597.

Hoffmann (E. T. Wilhelm) [E. T. AMADEUS HOFFMANN].

Sämtliche Werke. Hist.-krit. Ausg., mit Einl. &c. v. C. G. v. Maassen. B8. 8°. München. 1925

8, Die Serapions-Brüder, B4.

Contes fantastiques. Tr. nouv. préc. de souv. s. la vie de l'auteur par P. Christian. Illust. par Gavarni. la8°. 1843

Contes fantastiques. Tr. X. Marmier. s8°. 1849

see HARICH (W.) E. T. A. H. Leben, 2B, 1920.

„ JOST (W.) Von L. Tieck zu E. T. A. H., 1921.

Hoffmann (Franz), *prof. at Würzburg.* Franz v. Baader als Begründer d. Philos. d. Zukunft. [P2483]. 8°. L. 1856

Franz v. Baader in s. Verhältniss zu Hegel u. Schelling. [P2483]. 8°. L. 1850

Hoffmann (Gottfried). Diss. de fide justificante, contra Arminianos. Sub. præs. G. H., def. G. Widmannus &c. [P2630]. s4°. Tubingae. [1721]

Synopsis theol. purioris dogmaticae. s8°. Tubingae. 1720

Hoffmann (Johannes), *rector in Frankenhausen.* Diss. de libellaticis. Praes. S. Niemanno. [P433]. s4°. Jenae. 1669

Hoffmann (Julius). Alpenflora. 2e A., mit neu. Text, hrsg. K. Giesenhagen. 8°. St. 1914

Alpine flora. Tr. E. S. Barton (Mrs. A. Gepp). n. ed. 8°. 1925

Hoffmann (*Prof.* Louis), *ps.* [*i.e.* ANGELO J. LEWIS], *see* HOYLE (E.) Modern H., rev. w. add. by Prof. H., 1888.

Hoffmann (*Gen.* Max). La Guerre des occasions manquées, suivi de "La vraie bataille de Tannenburg." Tr. H. Simondet. Préf. du Gén. Weygand. 8°. 1927

Der Krieg d. versäumten Gelegenheiten. 8°. München. 1924

Tannenberg, wie es wirklich war. [2e A.] 8°. 1926

Hoffmann (Mór). Magyar-német és Német-magyar zsebszótár. [*2 pagin.*] s8°. [1899]

Hoffmann (Otto), *philologist, see* COLLITZ (H.) Samml. v. griech. Dialekt-Inschr., B4, hrsg. v. H. C. u. O. H., 1886–1915.

Hoffmann (Richard).

Das Marienmünster zu Ettal. 4°. Augsburg. 1927

Michelangelo: d. Decke d. Sixtin. Kapelle. Einl. v. R. H. 4°. Augsburg. 1925

Hoffmann (Walther). Ludwig Richter als Radierer. 4°. 1921

Hoffmann-Linke (Eva). Zwischen Nationalismus u. Demokratie: Gestalten d. franz. Vorrevol. [Hist. Zeitschrift, Beiheft 9]. 8°. München. 1927

Hoffmeyer (Ludwig). Gesch. d. Stadt &c. Osnabrück. 2e erweit. A. 8°. Osnabrück. 1920

Hofland (*Mrs.* Barbara). Pop. descr. of Sir John Soane's house, museum & library. Ed. f. descr. of 1835 by Sir J. Soane, by A. T. Bolton. [P2756]. s8°. 1919

Richmond & its surrounding scenery. Engr. by W. B. Cooke. 4°. 1832

Höfler (Alois). Naturwiss. u. Philosophie, 1, 2, 1920–21, *see* KAIS. AKAD. D. W. z. WIEN. Sitzber., B191, 196, 1922.

Höfler (Carl Adolf Constantin v.) Der Congress v. Soissons &c.; hrsg. v. C. v. H., 2B, *see* FONTES RERUM AUSTRIAC., B32, 38. 1871–76.

Hofman (V.), *see* GOFMAN (V. V.)

Hofmann (Albert v.)

Das deut. Land u. die deut. Gesch. 8°. 1920

Polit. Gesch. d. Deutschen. 5B. 8°. St. 1921–28

„ „ Bilderatlas. 8°. 1928

Die Stadt Konstanz. s8°. St. 1922

Die Stadt Nürnberg. s8°. St. 1924

Die Stadt Regensburg. s8°. St. 1922

Die Stadt Ulm. s8°. St. 1923

Hofmann (Carl Friedrich) & G. E. Hebenstreit. Disput. de Constantini M. sepulcro. [P445]. s4°. Lipsiae. [1759]

Hofmann (Carl Gottlob) [HOFFMANN]. Controv. Nestorianam haud fuisse logomachiam diss. Præs. H. Klausingio. s4°. [Lipsiae. 1725]

De manifesto Herrnhuthianorum syncretismo. [*Progr.* P2632]. s4°. [Wittenberg. 1744]

Hofmann (Daniel), *see* HOFFMANN (D.)

Hofmann (Ernst). Die Raupen d. Schmetterlinge Europas. 2e A. [v. A. Spuler]. 4°. St. [1904]

Hofmann (Harald), *see* SCHULTEN (A.) Panorama v. Numantia; gezeichnet v. H. H., mit Text v. A. S., 1922.

Hofmann (Hedwig). Rübezahl: Märchen u. Sagen. Ausgewählt v. H. H. 8°. Chemnitz. [1920]

Hofmann (Victor). Die Devalv. d. österr. Papiergeldes, 1811. [V. f. Sozialpol., B165i]. 8°. München. 1923

Hofmannsthal (Hugo v.) Die Frau ohne Schatten. s8°. 1919

Gedichte u. klein. Dramen. 8°. L. 1911

Die prosais. Schriften gesammelt. 3B. s8°. 1919–20

Der Rosenkavalier: Komödie f. Musik. [5. u. 6. A.] s8°. 1924

Das Salzburger grosse Welttheater. s8°. L. 1922

Der Schwierige. Lustspiel. s8°. 1921

Der Turm. Trauerspiel. 8°. [1927]

see STRAUSS (R.) Corr. betw. R. S. & H. v. H., 1907–18; tr., 1927.

Hofmayr (Wilhelm). Die Schilluk: Gesch., Relig. u. Leben e. Niloten-Stammes. Nach P. Banholzers u. eigenen Aufzeichnungen dargestellt v. W. H. [Anthropos-Bibl., B2v]. 8°. Mödling bei Wien. 1925

Hofmeister (Constanze), *see* GANZENMÜLLER (C.)

Hofmeister (Wilhelm F. B.), *see* GÖBEL (C. v.) W. M.: work & life; tr., 1926.

Hofstede de Groot (Cornelis). Cat. raisonné of works of Dutch painters of the 17th c. Tr. & ed. E. G. Hawke. v7. la8°. 1923

Echt of onecht? Oog of chemie? Beschouwingen naar aanleiding van het mansportret door F. Hals &c. 8°. 's-Gravenhage. 1925

see QUELLENSTUDIEN z. holländ. Kunstgesch.; hrsg. unter d. Leitung v. C. H. de G., B13, 1921.

Høg (Mogen), *see* TANK (G.), *ed.* Akershusregisteret af 1622, optaget af M. H. &c., 1916.

Hog (Thomas), *1628–92, see* MEMOIRS of Mrs. W. Veitch, T. H. &c., 1846.

Hogan (Albert E.), *LL.D.* The government of the U.K., its colonies &c. 4th ed. rev. s8°. 1920

Hogan (James).

Ireland in the European system, 1500–57. v1. 8°. 1920

Hogan (John). Kilkenny. 8°. Kilkenny. 1884

Hogarth (David George).

Arabia. s8°. O. 1922

G. N. Curzon, marq. C. [From Brit. Acad. Proc., *a. c. in* P2833]. 8°. [1926]

Hittite problems & the excav. of Carchemish, 1911, *see* BRIT. ACAD. Proc., 1911–12.

Hittite seals w. partic. ref. to the Ashmolean Coll. 4°. O. 1920

Kings of the Hittites. [Brit. Acad. Schweich Lect., 1924]. 8°. 1926

The twilight of hist. [*a. c. in* P2848]. 8°. 1926

Hogarth (Joseph), *see* FINDEN (E.) & W. F. Royal gallery of Brit. art. [*Dedic. signed* E. & W. F. & J. H.], 1851.

Hogarth (Richard). *Thesaurarium trilingue publicum: being an introd. to English, Latin & Greek &c., in 2p. s8°. 168[illegible]

Hogarth (William). [*Works. 84 plates (early impressions engraved by the artist & others. Followed by later addition of var. sizes & dates, no tp. Portrait, 1764, being first plat as arranged*]. lafol. [18 cent.

The genuine works of W. H., illust. w. biog. anecdotes, a chron. cat. & comm., 1808, *see* NICHOLS (J.) & G. STEEVENS

The works of W. H. reprod. f. orig. engravings in photographs & newly descr. W. an essay on the genius & character o H. by C. Lamb. [Prec. by "a few words about H." by W. C. M., *i.e.* William Cosmo Monkhouse]. 2v. 4°. 187

Analysis of beauty. [*Plates b. separately*]. obl. fol. 175

*Anecdotes of Mr. H., & explan. descr. of the plates of H restored. Engr. by T. Cook. [*Letterpress only*]. 8°. 180

„ „ w. an explan. descr. of h. works. [*Letterpress only*]. 4°. 181

„ w. an explan. descr. of h. work. [The analysis o beauty &c. *begins a fresh pagin. Letterpress only*]. la8°. 181

*An explan. of several of Mr. H.'s prints. [*Attrib. in M. note on tp. to Mr. Felton. a. c. b. w.* Nichols (J.) Beitr. z W. H.'s Lebensbeschr., 1783]. 8°. 178

Lettres de Mons.** [*i.e.* Rouquet] pour lui expliquer le estampes de H. [*Foll. by* Descr. du tableau de W. H

Hogarth (William) [*continued*].
La marche des gardes, *w. sep. pagin.* *a. c. b. w.* Nichols (J.) Beitr. zu W. H. Lebensbeschr., 1783.] 8°. 1846
[**MS. note book rel. to H.'s prints &c., w. records of sales*]. s8°. *n.d.*
see BROWN (G. B.) W. H. [Makers of Brit. Art], 1905.
„ CHURCHILL (C.) Epistle to W. H., re-versified, 1763.
„ FERRERS (E.) Illust. of H., 1816.
„ LICHTENBERG (G. C.) Erkl. d. Hogarth Kupferstiche [*the last two Liefgn. by* Lyser (*i.e.* Burmeister) & Le Petit *respectively*], 1794–1835.
„ —— W. H.'s Zeichnungen &c., 1873.
„ NICHOLS (J.) *Beitr. zu W. H.'s Lebensbeschreib. &c., 1783.
„ —— *Biog. anecd. of W. H., & cat. &c., 1781 ; 2nd ed., 1782 ; 3rd ed., 1785.
„ TRUSLER (J.) H. moralised, n. ed., 1841.
Hogben (Lancelot T.) The pigmentary effector system: physiol. of colour response. 8°. E. 1924
Hogg (H. R.) Arachnida, pl, *see* BRIT. ANTARCTIC EXPED., 1910–13. Zool., v3, 1915–23.
Hogg (James) [*ps.* THE ETTRICK SHEPHERD]. The private memoirs & confessions of a justified sinner. Intr. by T. E. Welby. [n. ed.] 8°. [1926]
see BATHO (E. C.) The Ettrick Shepherd, 1927.
Hogg (John), *publisher.* *Manuscript writing & lettering. A handbook. By an educat. expert. [Publisher's foreword signed J. H.] 8°. [1918]
Hogg (Margaret H.), *see* BOWLEY (A. L.) & M. H. H. Has poverty diminished ?, 1925.
Hoheisel (Johann David). Exerc. de inefficaci ministerio malorum. Praes. S. Schelguigio. [P437]. s4°. Gedani. [1708]
Hohenlandenberg (Hugo von), *bp. of Constance* [LANDENBERG]. Ernstl. ermanung des Fridens u. Christenl. einigkeit d. Fürsten, Hugonis võ Landenberg &c. [*Imperfect after sig. H.*] s4°. [Constance. 1522 ?]
Hohenlohe-Schillingsfürst (*Prinz* Alexander zu).
Aus meinem Leben. 8°. Frankfurt a. M. 1925
Hohenzollern, *The House of.*
see MÜLLER (V.) Die Lüge vom Hohenzollernsegen, 1920.
„ SALOMON (H.) L'incident H., 1922.
Hohenzollern (Franz Joseph, *Prinz* v.) Emden: my experience. [Tr.] 8°. [1928]
Hohepa Te Rake, *Arawa noble, see* ROUT (E. A.) Maori symbolism ; rep. f. evidence of H. Te R., 1926.
Hohlfeld (Johannes). Deut. Reichsgesch. in Dokumenten, 1849–1926. 2H [*pagin. contin.*] la8°. 1927
Gesch. d. deut. Reiches, 1871–1926. 2ᵉ, ergänzte A. 8°. L. 1926
Höhn (Heinrich).
Nürnberger gotische Plastik. la8°. Nürnberg. 1922
Nürnberger Renaissanceplastik. la8°. Nürnberg. 1924
Hoijer (Olof). La solution pacifique des litiges internat. avant & dep. la Soc. des Nations. la8°. 1925
Hōin (Shunjō), *see* SHUNJŌ, *Hōin.*
Höinghaus (R.) Die neuen Kirchengesetze v. 1875. Mit Anhang. 8°. 1875
Hokkaido Imperial University. Catalog. Abridged Eng. ed. 1921–1922. 8°. Sapporo, Japan. [1922]
Holbein Society, *see* LUTHER (M.) Catechism ; reprod. of ed. pr. at Frankfort, 1553 ; ed. W. H. Rylands, 1892.
Holbein (Hans), *1497–1543.* The dance of death. [*Fr. & Eng.*] Enl. facs. of orig. wood engravings by H. Lützelberger in 1st compl. ed., Lyons, 1547. [Pref. by F. H. Evans]. 8°. *p.p.* 1916
Icones Vet. Test. ; illust. of the O.T., engr. on wood, f. designs by H. H. [Introd. *signed* T. F. D.] s8°. 1830
see BROOKS (A. M.) From H. to Whistler: notes on drawing &c., 1920.
„ CHRISTOFFEL (U.) H. H., 1926.
Holberg (Ludvig, *baron* af).
Samlede Skrifter. udg. af C. S. Petersen. B1–8. 4°. 1913–27
Introd. to univ. hist. Tr. w. notes &c. by G. Sharpe. New ed. rev. corr. & impr. by W. Radcliffe. 8°. 1787
see BULL (F.) L. H. som historiker, 1913.
see HAMMER (S. C.) L. H., the founder of Norwegian lit. &c., 1920.
„ HØST (S.) Om H.'s historiske Skrifter, 1913.
„ NIELSEN (H.) H. i Nutidsbelysning, 1923.
„ OLSVIG (V.) H. og England, 1913.
Holbrooke (Josef Charles), *see* LOWE (G.) J. H. & h. work, 1920.
Holcombe (F. D.) Modern sea angling. 8°. 1921
Holcraft (John Edward). The Gravesend guide &c. Add. Steam-Boat companion. 5th ed. [P519]. 8°. 1830
Holcroft (Thomas).
Deserted daughter, *see* INCHBALD (*Mrs* E.) Brit. theatre, v24, 1808.
Duplicity, *see* †INCHBALD (*Mrs.* E.) Mod. theatre, v4, 1811.
*He's much to blame, *see* †INCHBALD (*Mrs.* E.) Mod. theatre, v4, 1811.
The road to ruin. [Dolby's Brit. theatre]. s8°. [1823]
Road to ruin, *see* INCHBALD (*Mrs.* E.) Brit. theatre, v24, 1808.
The school for arrogance, *see* †INCHBALD (*Mrs.* E.) Mod. theatre, v4, 1811.
Seduction, *see* †INCHBALD (*Mrs.* E.) Mod. theatre, v4, 1811.
Holden (Henry), *D.D.* Divinæ fidei analysis &c.—De schismate in genere, *see* MIGNE (J. P.), *ed.* Theol. cursus, t6, 1862.
Holden (William), James Ashcroft *& others.* Corr. rep. of trial of W. H., J. A. &c. for murder of Margaret Marsden & Hannah Partington &c., at Lancaster Assizes, Sept. 1817. Taken in short-hand by G. Taylor. 8°. M'ter. [1817]
Rep. of trial of W. H. &c. [*a. ed.*] 8°. M'ter. 1817
The trial & convict. of J. A., W. H. &c. for robbery & murder of Margaret Marsden & Hannah Partington: added, Lives of the culprits &c. 8°. [1817]
Holdenby. Memorials of H., 1868, *see* HARTSHORNE (E. S.)
Holder (Wilhelm), *of Stuttgart.* Asinus avis ; metamorphosis nova qua M. Bömlerus, dum in falconem transire voluit, in asinum commutatus est. s4°. Tubingae. 1587
Cuculus Calvinisticus sive de gratitudine & modestia Calviniana adv. blasphemam I. I. Grynæi apologiam commonefactio. [P2504]. s4°. Tubingæ. 1585
Hölderlin (J. C. Friedrich).
Sämtliche Werke. Hist.-krit. A. ; begonnen durch N. v. Hellingrath, fortgeführt durch F. Seebass u. L. v. Pigenot. B2, 3. 8°. 1922–23
2, Gedichte — Hyperion — Briefe, 1794–98.
3, Gedichte — Empedokles — Philos. Fragm. — Briefe, 1798–1800.
see BRANDENBURG (H.) F. H., Leben u. Werk, 1924.
see CASSIRER (E.) Idee u. Gestalt: H. &c., 2. A., 1924.
„ CLAVERIE (J.) La jeunesse d'H., 1921.
„ GONTARD (SUSETTE). Briefe der Diotima [*to H.*], 1922.
„ HELLINGRATH (N. v.) H., 2 Vortr., 1922.
„ MONTGOMERY (M.) F. H. & the German Neo-Hellenic movt., pl, 1923.
„ VIËTOR (C.) Die Lyrik H.'s, 1921.
Holdermann (Jean Baptiste), *Jesuit.* *Gramm. turque ou méthode pour apprendre la langue turque. [*By H. & Ibrahim Effendi*]. s4°. Constantinople. 1730
Holderness (*Sir* Thomas William). Peoples & problems of India. [Home Univ. Lib.] [rev. ed.] s8°. [1920]
Holderus (Wilhelm), *see* ZANCHIUS (H.) Ad partem prodromi V. H., 1586.
Holdich (Benjamin). Essay on the weeds of agriculture &c. Ed. G. Sinclair. 3rd ed. 8°. [1827]
Holdich (Joseph). The life of Willbur Fisk, D.D. 8°. N.Y. 1842
Holdsworth (Edward). The Cambrian patriot ; tr., *see* BELLAMY (D.) Young ladies misc., 1723.
Holdsworth (Ethel). The taming of Nan. s8°. 1920
Holdsworth (*Mrs.* Geoffrey Lisle), *see* STERN (G. B.)
Holdsworth (*Mrs.* John), *see* HODGKIN (L. V.), *aft. Mrs. J. H.*
Holdsworth (William) & W. Aldridge. Natural short-hand. Ann. a short-hand character for expressing musical sounds. 8°. [1768]
Holdsworth (William Searle). Hist. of Eng. law. 9v. [1–3, 3rd ed., rewr.] 8°. [1922–26]
Prof. Sir P. Vinogradoff. [From Brit. Acad. Proc. P2833]. 8°. [1926]
Sources & lit. of English law. 8°. O. 1925
see JENKS (E.), *ed.* Digeste de droit civil anglais ; par E. J., W. S. H. &c. ; tr., 2ᵉ éd., 2t, 1923.
Hole (Charles).
A manual of the Bk. of C. Prayer, its hist. &c. s8°. 1887
Hole (Hugh Marshall). The making of Rhodesia. 8°. 1926
Holford (*Lt.-Col. Sir* George Lindsay). Cat. of final portion of the coll. of pictures of old masters, property of H., sold by Christie, May 17 & 18, 1928. [*Illust.*] 8°. 1928
Cat. of old Ital. furniture &c., prop. of H. Sold by Christie, July 13, 1927. [*Illust.* P2873]. 8°. 1927
Cat. of pictures of Ital. school, 1st portion of coll. of Sir G. L. H., sold by Christie &c., July 15, 1927. [*Illust.*] 8°. 1927
The Holford coll. Cat. of 12 illum. MSS. at Dorchester House & 107 pictures at Westonbirt. 4°. 1924

Holford (*Lt.-Col. Sir* **George Lindsay**) [*continued*].
The Holford coll., Dorchester House. With 200 illust. f. 12th to 19th cent. [Ed. R. Benson]. 2v. 4°. O. 1927
Holford coll.: MSS. & pictures [lent by Lt.-Col. Sir G. Holford], 1924, *see* BURLINGTON F.A.C.
The Holford Library. Sold by Sotheby, July [*&* Dec.] 1927, *&* Mar. [*&* June] 1928. [*Illust.*] pl-4 *in* 2v. (1, Illum. on vellum. 2-4, Books & bindings). 8°. 1927–28

Holford (Robert Stayner), *1808–92.* Holford coll., *see* HOLFORD (*Sir* G. L.)

Holinshed (Raphael) [*or Hollingshead*]. Chronicles: Richard II, 1398–1400, Henry IV & Henry V. [Ed. R. S. Wallace &c. *3 pagin.*] s8°. O. 1923
H.'s Chronicle as used in Shakespeare's plays. [Ed. w. intr. by A. Nicoll & J. N. Everyman's Lib.] s8°. [1927]

Holitscher (Arthur). Drei Monate in Sowjet-Russland. s8°. 1921

Holl (Carl). Augustins innere Entwicklung, 1923, *see* KÖNIGL. PREUSS. AKAD. Abhdl., Phil.-hist. Kl., 1922.
Entst. d. 4 Fastenzeiten in d. griech. Kirche, *see* KÖN.-PREUSS. AKAD. Abhdln., Phil.-hist. Kl., 1923.
Gesch. d. deut. Lustspiels. la8°. L. 1923

Holland.
ANONYMOUS WORKS.
*Brief (A) descr. hist. of H. in letters f. grandfather to Marianne, 1819. s8°. 1826
H. en Utrechts Hoogheemraadschap van den Zeeburg en Diemerdyk. [P2614]. s8°. A. 1784
Kronijk van H. van een ongenoemden gestelijke. [*Sometimes attr. to* Philip of Leyden. *Ed.* Geer v. Jutphaas. Hist. Genoots. te Utrecht. Werken., N.S., 6, Bronnen &c.] 8°. Utrecht. 1867
*Late voyage (A) to H., w. brief rel. of trans. at the Hague &c. Wr. by an Eng. gentleman. s8°. *n.p.* 1691
Naamregister van de gecommitteerde Raden in de Coll. ter Admiraliteit als mede de Bewindhebberen van de Oost- en West-Ind. Co. [P2614]. s8°. A. 1784
Naam-register van de predikanten &c. [P2614]. s8°. A. [1784]
Rekeningen (De) der Grafelijkheid van Holland onder het Henegouwsche Huis. Uitg. door H. G. Hamaker. [Hist. Genoots. Werken, N.S., 21, 24, 26]. 3d. 8°. Utrecht. 1875–8
GOVERNMENT PUBL.
Resolutiën d. Staten-Generaal, 1576–1609. Bewerkt door N. Japikse. [Rijks Gesch. Publ., uitg. in opdracht v. d. Min. v. Onderwijs &c., 47, 51, 55, 57, 62]. d5–9. 4°. 's-Gravenhage. 1921–6
5, 1585–7. 6, 1588–9. 7, 1590–92. 8, 1593–5. 9, 1596–97.
Staatsblad van het Koningrijk d. N., 1813–21, *see* STAATSBLAD.
REFERENCES (RIJKS GESCH. PUBL. &c.)
see BROM (G.) & A. H. L. HENSEN. Rom. Bronnen v. d. kerk.-staatk. toestand d. Ned. in de 16de eeuw, 1922.
,, COLENBRANDER (H. T.) Gedenkstukken d. algem. gesch. van Nederland, 1795–1840, d10iv, v, 1921–22.
,, DILLEN (J. G. VAN). Bronnen tot de gesch. d. Wisselbanken, 2 stuk, 1925.
,, FREDERICQ (P.) Codex doc. sac. indulgentiarum Neerland. (1300–1600), 1922.
,, GROEN VAN PRINSTERER (G.) Schriftel. nalatenschap; uitg. C. Gerretson &c., d2, 1925.
,, MOLHUYSEN (P. C.) Bronnen tot de gesch. der Leidsche Universiteit, d4–7, 1920–24.
,, PLOTT (T.) & T. CHUDLEIGH. Dispatches 1681–5, 1926.
,, POSTHUMUS (N. W.) Bronnen tot de gesch. van de Leidsche textielnijverheid, verzameld door P., d6, 1922.
,, UNGER (W. S.) Bronnen tot de gesch. v. Middelburg, d1, 2 (1217–1574), 1923–26.
,, VIERLINGH (A.) Tractaet van dyckagie; uitg. d. J. de Hullu &c., 1920.
,, WILLIAM III, *k. of Eng.* Corr. v. W. III en v. H. W. Bentinck, ged. 1, d1, 1927.

Holland (*Miss* **Caroline**). *The notebooks of a spinster lady, 1878–1903. 8°. 1919

Holland (Harold). Dad. Play. 8°. 1928

Holland (Henry Edward Fox, *4th baron*).
Journal, 1818–30. Ed. Earl of Ilchester. 8°. [1923]

Holland (Henry Rich, *earl of*), *see* HAMILTON (J. H., *1st d. of*).
Sev. speeches of Duke H., H., Earl of Holland &c., upon the scaffold, 9. March [1648], 1649.

Holland (Henry Scott). The 4th Gospel. Ed. W. J. Richmond. [Pref. by C. Gore]. s8°. 1923
The philosophy of faith & The Fourth Gospel. Ed. W. Richmond. 8°. 1920
see DREW (*Mrs.* M.) Acton, Gladstone &c., 1924.
,, PAGET (S.) H. S. H.: mem. & letters, 1921.

Holland (James), *water-colour painter, see* STOKES (H.) J. H. (1800–70), 1927.

Holland (John), *of Sheffield.* The Psalmists of Britain. Authors who have rendered Psalms into Eng. verse. 2v. 8°. 1843

Holland (Louise Adams). The Faliscans in prehist. times. [Amer. Acad. in Rome, v5]. 8°. Rome. 1925

Holland (Philemon). Regimen sanitatis Salerni &c. rev., corr. &c. by P. H., 1649, *see* SCHOLA SALERNITANA.

Holland (Saba, *Lady*), *wife of Sir H. Holland.* Mem. of Sydney Smith; w. sel. f. h. letters, ed. Mrs. Austin. n. ed. s8°. [1878]

Holland (Sydney), *visct. Knutsford, see* KNUTSFORD (S. H., *2nd visct.*)

Holland (*Sir* **Thomas Erskine**). Letters to "The Times" upon war & neutrality, 1881–1920, w. comm. 3rd ed. 8°. 1921
Proposed changes in naval prize law, 1911, *see* BRIT. ACAD. Procs., 1911–12.

Holland (Vyvyan). The mediæval courts of love. [Sette of Odd Volumes, Opusc. 82]. s8°. *p.p.* [1927]

Hollande (La). Par L. van Keymeulen, Zaborowski, L. Bresson [*& o. authors*]. 4°. *Larousse.* [1909]

Hollander (Bernard). The psychology of misconduct, vice & crime. s8°. [1922]

Holländer (Eugen).
Die Karikatur u. Satire in d. Medizin. 2e A. 4°. St. 1921
Wunder, Wundergeburt u. Wundergestalt in Einblattdrucken d. 15. bis 18. Jhdts. 4°. St. 1921

Holländer (Felix). Das Erwachen des Donald Westhof. Roman. 8°. [1927]

Hollandia. Chronicon Hollandiae (–1459); med. door H. Obreen, *see* HISTORISCH GENOOTS. Bijd., d46, 1925.

Hollandsche. Bescheiden betref. de prov. organis. d. H. lakenbereiders, 1917, *see* POSTHUMUS (N. W.), *ed.*

Hollar (Wenceslaus). Drawings. [London Topog. Soc. *b. w.* London T. Soc. Reprod. of unpubl. drawings &c., 1910]. [*no tp. In fol. case.* 1922]
see HIND (A. M.) W. H. & his views of London &c., 1922.
,, VERTUE (G.) Descr. of the wks. of W. H., w. acc. of h. life, 2nd ed., 1759.

Hollatz (David) [HOLLAZ (D.)], *the elder.* Examen theologicum acromaticum &c. Ed. R. Tellerus. ed. altera. s4°. Lipsiae. 1763

Holleaux (Maurice). Rome, la Grèce & les monarchies hellénist. au 3e s. av. J.-C. [Ecoles Franç. d'Athènes & de Rome, 124]. 8°. 1921
Στρατηγὸς ὕπατος. La traduction en Grec du titre consulaire. [Bibl. des Ecoles Franç. d'Athènes &c., fasc. 113]. 8°. 1918

Holleman (Arnold Frederik). A text-book of organic chemistry. Ed. A. J. Walker, ass. by O. E. Mott. 5th Eng. ed. rev. 8°. N.Y. 1920

Holles (Denzil Holles, *1st baron*). *A full vindic. & ans. of the 11 accused Members, viz. D. H., Sir P. Stapleton &c. to A partic. charge &c. in name of Sir T. Fairfax &c. s8°. 1647

Holles (*Sir* **John**), *see* CLARE (J. H., *1st earl of*).

Hollingworth (E. J.) & M. M. O'Reilly. The Anglo-Saxon cemetery at Girton Coll., Cambridge. Based on MS. notes of excavat. made by F. J. H. Jenkinson. 8°. C. 1925

Hollingworth (Joseph), *1781–1836, see* MILNER (J. T.) Mem. of J. H., 1836.

Hollingworth (Richard), *D.D.* Dr. H.'s defence of K. Charles I book Εἰκὼν Βασιλική; agst. the assaults of Dr. Walker. [P2653]. s4°. 1692

Hollis (Gertrude). The rood & the raven. 8°. [1926]

Hollis (Joseph), *see* COOPER (J.) Trial of J. & M. C. for murder of J. H., 1809.

Hollis (Thomas), *F.R.S., see* BLACKBURNE (F.) Mem. of T. H., 2v, 1780.

Hollister (Ned). East African mammals in the U.S. Nat. Mus. [S.I., U.S. Nat. Mus., Bull. 99]. pl–3. 8°. Wash. 1918–24

Holloway (Celia).
see HINDLEY (C.), *ed.* Brighton murder: hist. of murder of C. H., 1875.
,, HOLLOWAY (J. W.) Authentic &c. hist. of atrocious murder of C. H. &c., 1832.

Holloway (Edward Stratton). Pract. book of learning decoration & furniture. 8°. 1926

Holloway (Emory). Whitman: an interpret. la8°. 1926

Holloway (John William). Authentic &c. hist. of the atrocious murder of Celia Holloway, incl. trial of J. W. H., w. h. life, wr. by himself. 8°. Brighton. 1832
see HINDLEY (C.), *ed.* Brighton murder, incl. trial of J. W. H., 1875.

Holloway (M.), *see* MORRISON (A.) Coll. of engravings formed, 1860–68: annot. cat. & index by M. H., 1868.

Holloway (W. H.)
The story of Naseby. 2nd ed. 8°. Northampton. [1923]

Hollweg (Theobald v. Bethmann), *see* BETHMANN HOLLWEG (T. v.)

Hollyband (Claudius), *see* SAINLIENS (C. DE).

Holm (Anders W.) Det nye Danmark. s8°. 1922

Holm (Frits Vilhelm). My Nestorian adventure in China. Intr. by A. Yohannan. 8°. 1924

Holm (Gustav), *see* THALBITZER (W.), *ed.* The Ammassalik Eskimo, p1, Results of G. H.'s exped., 1883–85 &c., 1914.

Holman (Joseph George). The votary of wealth, *see* †INCHBALD (*Mrs.* E.) Mod. theatre, v3, 1811.

Holmberg (Uno), *see* MYTHOLOGY (The) of all races, v4, Finno-Ugric, Siberian; by U. H., 1927.

Holme (Constance). The splendid fairing. s8°. [1919]
The things which belong— s8°. [1925]
The trumpet in the dust. s8°. [1921]

Holme (Geoffrey).
British water-colour painting of to-day. Ed. G. H. [Studio, Winter No., 1921]. la8°. 1921
see BERUETE Y MORET (A. DE). Spanish painting; ed. G. H., 1921.
,, CUNDALL (H. M.) Masters of water-colour painting; intr. by C.; ed. G. H., 1922–23.
,, —— The Norwich school: articles by H. M. C.; ed. G. H., 1920.
,, DODGSON (C.) Etchings of C. Meryon; ed. G. H., 1921.
,, —— Etchings of J. Mc. N. Whistler; ed. G. H., 1922.
,, KENDRICK (A. F.) Book of old embroidery &c.; ed. by G. H., 1921.
see SALAMAN (M. C.) Brit. bk. illustr., w. comm. by M. C. S.; ed. G. H., 1923.
,, —— Londoners then & now, w. comm. by S.; ed. G. H., 1920.
,, SHERINGHAM (G.) Drawings in pen & pencil &c.; ed. G. H., 1922.
,, —— Figure painting in water-colours by contemp. Brit. artists; ed. G. H., 1923.
,, WHITLEY (W. T.) Art coll. of the nation; articles by W. T. W.; ed. G. H., 1920.

Holme Lacy. *Illust. partic. of the domain, Holme Lacy, auction, Knight, Frank & Rutley, Sept. 19, 1922. fol. 1922

Holmer (Mary R. Norris). Bird study in India. Intr. by Lt.-Col. J. Stephenson. 2nd ed. s8°. 1926

Holmes (Arthur), *of Cortland, N.Y.*
Parties & th. principles, w. App. s8°. N.Y. 1859

Holmes (*Sir* Charles John).
Constable, Gainsborough & Lucas: brief notes on some early drawings by J. Constable. 4°. 1921
Leonardo da Vinci. [P2432]. 8°. [1919]
,, ,, *For a. copy, see* BRIT. ACAD. Proc., v9, 1919–20.
Notes on the science of picture-making. [5th ed.] 8°. 1923
,, ,, illust. ed. [6th ed. rev.] 8°. 1927
Old masters & mod. art: the National Gallery. [v1–3]. 8°. 1923–27
1, Ital. schools. 2, Netherlands, Germany, Spain. 3, France & England.
Sir C. Holmes. [Plates, *w. intr. signed* X. B.] la8°. 1924
see SADLER (M. T. H.) The water-colours of C. J. H., 1920.

—— & C. H. C. Baker. Making of the National Gallery, 1824–1924: hist. sketch. 8°. 1924

Holmes (David), *M.A.* The Wesley offering; or, Wesley & his times. s8°. Phila. 1858

Holmes (Edmond Gore Alexander).
The Albigensian or Catharist heresy. s8°. 1925
All is one. Plea for higher pantheism. s8°. [1921]
Freedom & growth & o. essays. 8°. 1923
Give me the young. s8°. [1921]
In quest of an ideal. Autobiog. s8°. [1920]
What is philosophy? s8°. 1905

Holmes (Elizabeth). Some notes on Milton's use of words, *see* ENGLISH ASSOC. Essays, v10, 1924.

Holmes (F. Ratcliffe). Through wildest Africa. 8°. [1925]

Holmes (Harry H.), *alias of H. W. Mudgett, see* GEYER (F. P.) The Holmes-Pitezel case, 1896.

Holmes (John), *of East Retford.* A descr. cat. of books in the lib. of J. H. w. notices. 8°. Norwich. 1828

Holmes (John Henry). In primitive New Guinea. Intr. by A. C. Haddon. 8°. 1924
Way back in Papua. 8°. [1926]

Holmes (Oliver Wendell), *the elder.* The autocrat of the breakfast-table. Intr. by L. Stephen. s8°. 1903
Poems. n. & enl. ed. s8°. Boston [Mass.] 1849
The poet at the breakfast table. s8°. *n.d.*

Holmes (Robert). Sister Matty & Co. s8°. E. 1918

Holmes (Samuel Jackson). St. in evol. & eugenics. 8°. 1923
The trend of the age. Pres. tendencies in the biol. development of civilised mankind. 8°. 1921

Holmes (Thomas J.)
The Mather literature. 8°. *p.p.* Cleveland. 1927

Holmes (Thomas Rice Edward).
The architect of the Roman Empire. 8°. O. 1928
The Roman Republic & the founder of the Empire. 3v. 8°. O. 1923
Sir Charles Napier. 8°. C. 1925

Holmes (Thomas Vincent), *F.G.S.* Geology of the co. around Carlisle. [Mems. of G.S.] 8°. 1899
see STRAHAN (*Sir* A.), T. V. HOLMES &c. On the thicknesses of strata in the co. of Eng. & Wales &c., 1916.

***Holmia** literata, 5p, 1701, *see* HARDT (R. v. D.)

Holmquist (Hjalmar Fredrik). Die schwed. Reformation, 1523–31. [Verein f. Ref.-Gesch. Schr., Jhrg. 43 (Nr. 139)]. 8°. L. 1925

Holmsen (Gunnar).
Hvordan Norges jord blev til. 8°. Kristiania. 1924

Holmström (Ragnar).
Jonas Ödmarks historia. Berättelse. s8°. [1926]

Holroyd (Edward). Obs. upon the case of A. Thornton, tried for murder of Mary Ashford. 2nd ed. 8°. 1819

Holroyd (James B.) *Methodism unmasked, & the calumnies of H. ans. &c., by the Rev. J. L., 1828, *see* METHODISM.

Hölscher (Georg). Das Buch v. Rhein. 4e A. 4°. Köln. 1925

Hölscher (Uvo). Das Hohe Tor v. Medinet Habu: e. baugeschichtl. Untersuchung. [Deut. Orient-Gesells., Wiss. Veröff., 12. *b. w.* Borchardt (L.) Grabdenkmal d. K. Nefer-ir-ke-re, 1909]. fol. L. 1910

Holst (Helge), *see* KRAMERS (H. A.) & H. H. The atom & the Bohr theory of its structure; tr., 1923.

Holst (Henriette Roland), *see* ROLAND HOLST (H.)

Holstein (Friedrich v.), *see* FISCHER (E.) H.'s grosses Nein, Bündnisverhandl., 1898–1901, 1925.

Holstein (Hugo). Die Reformation im Spiegelbilde d. dramat. Litt. d. 16. Jhdts. [Verein f. Ref.-gesch. Schr., Jhrg. 4, Nr. 14/15]. 8°. Halle. 1886

Holt (Henry).
Sixty years as a publisher, w. o. essays &c. 8°. [1924]

Holt (Lucius Hudson).
Elem. principles of mod. govt. 8°. N.Y. 1923

Holtgreven (Anton).
Das Verhältniss zw. Staat u. Kirche. [P2695]. 8°. 1875

Holthusius (Joannes) [OLTHUSIUS], *see* WILD (J.) Examen ordinandorum, auctoribus J. Fero, J. A. &c., 1589.

Holtius (Adrianus Catharinus). Oratio de liberalitate majorum nostr. academiis instit. &c. cognita. 8°. Trajecti a. R. 1806

Holtom (Daniel Clarence). Polit. philos. of mod. Shintō, 1922, *see* ASIATIC SOCIETY OF JAPAN. Trans., v49ii, 1922.

Holtorf (Johann August). Diss. [*&* Diss. posterior] de controv. theol. inter Græcos & Evangelicos. Sub præs. J. C. Schrammii. [P2644]. s4°. Helmstadii. [1726]

Holtzendorff (Franz v.) Richard Cobden; Vortrag, *see* VIRCHOW (R.) & F. v. HOLTZENDORFF. Sammlung, H17, 1866.

Holworthy (Richard), *see* DEW, *Family of.* Dew wills & admin. in Prerog. Court of Canterbury; abstr. by R. H., 1921.

Holy [HALI]. *Hali Meidenhad, an allit. homily of 13th c. Ed. F. J. Furnivall. [E.E.T.S., Orig. Ser. 18]. rev. ed. by O. Cockayne. 8°. 1922

Holyrood.
Hist. of Holyrood, w. descr. guide &c. s8°. E., *J. Rankin. n.d.*

Holy Trinity, *Knightsbridge.* Register of the Chapel of the Holy Trinity, K., 1658–81. Transcr. by J. H. Bloom. la8°. *n.d.*

Holz (Arno), *see* THOMPSON (N. M.) A. H. & orig. of the new poetry, 1920.

Holzapfel (Rudolf Maria).
Panideal: d. Seelenleben &c. n. A. 2T. la8°. Jena. 1923
see ZBINDEN (H.), *ed.* Ein Künder neuer Lebenswege, 1923.

Holzinger (Carl v.) Die Aristophaneshss. d. Wiener Hofbibl., B2, 1912, *see* KAIS. AKAD. D. W. ZU W. Sitzb., B169, 1913.

Høm (Vilhelm). Solskinsbørn. Fortælling. s8°. 1915

Hóman (Bálint). Magyar pénztörténet, 1000–1325. 8°. 1916

Homann (Hans Joachim), *see* MIELKE (H.) & H. J. H. Der deut. Roman d. 19. u. 20. Jhdts., 5e A., 1920.

Homann-Herimberg (Emil). Die Kohlenversorgung in Österreich währ. d. Krieges. [C.E. for Int. Peace]. la8°. Wien. 1925

Hombres ilust. mexicanos, 4t, 1873–74, *see* GALLO (E. L.), *ed.*

Homburger (L.) Le groupe sud-ouest des langues bantoues, *see* ROHAN-CHABOT (—). Angola &c., 1912–14, t3, fasc. 1, 1925.

*Home defence, 1909, *see* JACKSON (F.)

Home Office, *see* TROUP (*Sir* C. E.) The H.O., 1925.

Home (Charles). A new chronolog. abridgement of the hist. of Eng. 8°. 1791

Home (Daniel Dunglas), *see* HOME (*Mme.* D.) D. D. H., h. life & mission, n. ed., 1921.

Home (*Mme.* Dunglas). D. D. Home, h. life & mission. Ed., w. intr. by Sir A. Conan Doyle. [n. ed.] 8°. 1921

Home (George). Inventory of Arbuthnot titles, 1206–1483, fr. the MS. of G. H., *see* MAIDMENT (J.) & R. PITCAIRN. Nugae derelictae, 1822.

Home (Gordon Cochrane). Canterbury of our grandfathers & of to-day. la8°. [1927]

Mediaeval London. By G. H., in collab. w. E. Foord. 8°. 1927

Roman London, w. chronology by E. Foord. 8°. 1926

Roman York. With co-op. of W. E. Collinge. 8°. 1924

Through Yorkshire. s8°. 1922

Yorkshire vales & wolds painted & descr. 8°. 1908

—— **& E. Foord.** Bristol, Bath & Malmesbury, w. sh. acc. of Bradford-on-Avon. s8°. 1925

Home (John). Douglas, tragedy, *see* NEW Eng. theatre, v10, 1777.

Douglas, *see* INCHBALD (*Mrs.* E.) Brit. theatre, v16, 1808.

Homel. *Правда о гомельскомъ погромѣ. [P2716]. s8°. Лондонъ. 1903

Homélies mariales byzantines: textes grecs éd. & tr. en Lat. par M. Jugie, 2p, 1922–26, *see* MARY, *the Virgin.*

Homén (Theodor).

East Carelia & Kola Lapmark. la8°. Helsingfors. 1921

Homer. Works. [*Editions in order of publication*].

Ἰλίας, Ὀδύσσεια, ὕμνοι. *Ed.* D. Chalcondylas, G. Acciajuoli & D. Ducas]. fol. [Florence, *B. di Libri for B. & N. Nerlius.* 1488]

189 leaves, signatures AAi–EtEtv. *Without tp., pagin., or catchwords; the whole work consists of* 439 leaves; *of which* ff1–250 *or signatures* Ai–Rviii *cont. the Iliad, are wanting.*

Ἰλιὰς καὶ Ὀδύσσεια. [*Ed. by Rt. Hon. T. Grenville, R. Porson & others; w. a collation of the Harl. MS. of the Odyssey by Porson*]. 4v [v4 *wanting*]. 8°. ἐν Ὀξονίᾳ. αω [1800–01]

Opera omnia: ex rec. & cum notis S. Clarkii. Acc. var. lect. cura J. A. Ernesti [*Gr. & Lat.*] 5v. 8°. Glasguæ. 1814

Opera. Recog. D. B. Munro & T. W. Allen. 5t [*in* 1v, t1, 2, ed. 2ª]. 8°. [1909–12]

Carmina. Cum proleg., notis, comm. &c. Ed. J. van Leeuwen. Ilias. 8°. Lugd. Bat. 1912–13

ILIAD [*in order of publication*].

ϝΙλιας, digamma restit. red. &c. T. S. Brandreth. 2v. 8°. Pickering. 1841

I. Notes by D. B. Monro. 4th ed. rev. [p2], bks. xiii–xxiv. s8°. O. 1903

The Homeric cat. of ships. Ed. w. comm. by T. W. Allen. 8°. O. 1921

ODYSSEY.

O. Ex rec. G. Dindorfii. 8°. Oxonii. 1855

TRANSLATIONS.

ILIAD.

I. Tr. Mr. Pope. 6v [*each bk. has sep. pagin. in v1*]. la8°. 1715–20

I. Tr. A. Pope. 6v. 8°. *Rivington.* 1760

I. [*Ital. verse by M. Cesarotti.*] 4t (t1, Ragionamento &c.) s8°. Pisa. 1802

I. Tr. d. cav. V. Monti. 3ª ed. ricorr. 2v. 8°. Milano. 1820

I. Tr. G. Chapman. [Temple classics]. [2nd ed.] 2v [*in 1*]. s8°. [1901]

I. [Text], w. Eng. tr. by A. T. Murray. [Loeb Class. Lib.] 2[v]. s8°. 1924–25

ODYSSEY.

O. Tr. A. Pope. 5v. 8°. *Rivington.* 1760

O. Tr. Bks. 1–7 [*in verse*; by C. Lloyd]. s8°. B. 1810

O. Tr. I. Pindemonte. 2v *in* 1. 8°. Verona. 1824

O. Tr. into the Spenserian stanza by P. S. Worsley. n. ed. 8°. E. 1895

O. Tr. G. Chapman. [Temple classics]. [3rd ed.] 2v [*in 1*]. s8°. [1906]

O. Tr. into Eng., in orig. metre by F. Caulfield. Pref. by A. A. David. s8°. 1921

O. Tr. in metre of the orig. by H. B. Cotterill. Intr. by W. Leaf. 8°. [1924]

L'O. Texte établi & tr. par V. Bérard. [Coll. des univ. de France]. 3t. 8°. 1924

REFERENCES.

see ALLEN (T. W.) H.: origins & transmission, 1924.

„ BÉRARD (V.) Intr. à l'Odyssée, 3t, 1924–25.

„ —— Ithaque & la Grèce des Achéens, 1927.

„ BRIDGES (T.) *Homer travestie, 2v, 1764.

Homer [*continued*].

REFERENCES [*continued*].

see CAUER (P.) Grundfragen d. Homerkritik, 3ᵉ A., 1921–23.

„ CUNLIFFE (R. J.) Lex. of Homeric dialect, 1924.

„ DAMM (C. T.) Nov. lex. Graec. etym. &c., concord. &c. H., 1824.

„ DRERUP (E.) Homer. Poetik; hrsg. E. D., Bl, 3, 1921.

„ FLAXMAN (J.) Class. compositions: Iliad & Odyssey engr. by Piroli, 1870.

„ HERODOTUS. Περὶ Ὁ. γενέσιος &c., 1752.

„ MARGOLIOUTH (D. S.) The H. of Aristotle, 1923.

„ RADERMACHER (L.) Die Erzähl. d. Odyssee, 1915.

„ RODD (*Sir* J. R.) H.'s Ithaca, 1927.

„ ROUTH (H. V.) God, man, & epic poetry, v1, 1927.

„ SCOTT (J. A.) Unity of H., 1921.

„ SHEPPARD (J. T.) Pattern of the Iliad, 1922.

„ SMITH (R.) Res. papers, No. 11, Solution of H. q.: orig. Iliad & expans., 1923.

„ STÜRMER (F.) Die Rhapsodien d. Odyssee, 1921.

„ WECKLEIN (N.) Epikrit. z. Homer. Frage, 1923.

„ —— Die Homer. Hymnen u. d. griech. Tragiker, 1920.

„ —— Textkrit. Stud. z. Ilias, 1917.

„ —— Textkrit. Stud. z. Odyssee, 1915.

„ —— Üb. Zusätze u. Auslassung v. Versen im H. Texte, 1918.

„ WILAMOWITZ-MÖLLENDORFF (U. v.) Heimkehr des Odysseus, 1927.

„ —— Das h. Epos, 1927.

„ —— Vitae H. &c., 1916.

Homilies. Certain sermons or h. appointed to be read in churches in the time of Elizabeth. fol. 1683

„ „ ....fol. 1726

„ „ ....8°. 1846

Homme (L'). *A. M. A. Dumas fils. L'homme qui sait, par une Mère. s8°. 1872

Hommel (Carl Ferdinand).

Litteratura juris. ed. 2ª. s8°. Lipsiae. 1779

Hommel (Fritz). Ethnol. u. Geog. d. alt. Orients. [Müller (I. v.) Hdbch. d. k. A.-W., III, 1, i]. la8°. München. 1926

see NIELSEN (D.), *ed.* Hdbch. d. altarab. Altertumskunde, B1, 1927.

Hommius (Festus). Spec. controv. Belgic. Seu Conf. eccl. reformat. in Belgio &c. Lat. ed. & coll. F. H. Add. Harmonia synod. Belgic. s4°. Lugd. Batav. 1618

Homo (Léon). Prim. Italy & beginnings of Roman imperialism. [Tr. V. G. Childe]. 8°. 1927

Homolle (Théophile), *see* FOUGÈRES (G.) T. H., 1848–1925, 1925.

Homsy (Gaston). Le général Jacob & l'expéd. de Bonaparte en Égypte (1798–1801). 8°. Marseille. 1921

Hön (Maximilian *Ritter* **v.)** [HOEN], *see* JOHN (W.) Erzherzog Karl u. s. Armee, Beitr. v. M. v. Hön. &c., 1913.

Hondius (J. J. E.), *see* SUPPLEMENTUM epigraph. graec.; adi. P. Roussel &c., red. curavit J. J. E. H., v1, 2, 1923–25.

Hone (Nathaniel), *see* BODKIN (T.) 4 Irish landscape painters, N. H. &c., 1920.

Hone (William), *bookseller.* *Plenipo & the devil!; by W. H.? 1820, *see* PLENIPO.

*The political house that Jack built. [*Satires in verse*]. 21st ed. [P2557]. 8°. 1819

*The political Queen that Jack loves. [*i.e.* Queen Caroline. *A satirical poem*]. 5th ed. [P425]. 8°. [1820 ?]

Popular polit. tracts. n. ed. 8°. [1820–22]

House that Jack built, Queen's matrim. ladder, Right div. of Kings to gov. wrong, Polit. showman, Man in the moon, Queen's form of Prayer, & A slap at Slop, *each w. sep. tp. & pagin.*

*The right divine of kings to govern wrong! [*Satire in verse.*] 6th ed. [P2825]. s8°. [1821?]

Hōnen *Shōnin, Buddhist saint, 12th cent., see* SHUNJŌ HŌIN. Hōnen, tr., 1925.

Honest Sailor, An, *ps., see* VERNON (*Adm.* E.)

***Honeycombe (Polly),** dram. novel, 1760, *see* COLMAN (G.), *the elder.*

Hongrie. Mém. aux mandataires des puissances alliées &c. à Budapest au sujet des abus dans les parties de la H. sous l'admin. tchécoslovaque & roumaine. [P2519]. la8°. [Pest. 1919]

Traité de Paix avec la H. Publ. par le Min. des Aff. Etr. la8°. Budapest. 1920

Hönig (Fritz Aug.) 24 hours of Moltke's strategy, expl. &c. f. Gravelotte & St. Privat. Tr. Col. N. L. Walford. 8°. 1895

Höniger (Robert).

Russlands Vorbereitung z. Weltkrieg. 8°. 1919

Honigmann (Ernst). Hist. Topographie v. Nordsyrien im Altertum. [Sonderdr. a. d. Ztschr. d. Deut. Palästina Vereins, B46, 47]. 8°. L. 1923

Honnert (Robert). Henri de Régnier & s. œuvre. s8°. 1923
Honold (Jacob). Sidereus Dei clarigator, d. i. Kurtzer Bericht v. d. neuen Cometen, 1677, &c. [P447]. s4°. Ulm. 1677
Honor (Leo L.) Sennacherib's invasion of Palestine. [Columbia Univ.] 8°. N.Y. 1926
Honoré, *de Sainte-Marie, Carmelite* [*i.e.* BLAISE VAUZELLE]. Animadv. in regulas et usum critices spect. ad hist. eccl. Interpr. e Gallius. 3t *b. in 1.* fol. Venetiis. 1768
Honorius, *Augustodunensis.* De scriptor. eccl., *see* LE MIRE (A.) Bibl. eccl., 1639.
Honorius I, *pope.*
see FABI (GIU.) Pro H. & sede apostol. contra C. J. de Hefele, 1870.
„ HEFELE (C. J. v.) Causa H. papae, 1870.
Honorius III, *pope, see* KNEBEL (J. W.) Friedrich II & H. (1220–27), 1905.
Honorius (Philippus), *ps., see* BELLUS (JULIUS).
Hönsbröch (Paul, *Graf* **v.)** Der Jesuitenorden. Eine Enzyklopädie. 2B. la8°. Bern. 1926–27
Wilhelms II. Abdankung u. Flucht. 16e A. 8°. 1919
Hontheim (Johann Nicolaus v.), *see* FEBRONIUS (J.)
Honthorst (Gerard van) [GHERARDO DELLE NOTTI], *see* HOOGEWERFF (G. J.) G. d. N.: 28 reprod. con testo e cat., 1924.
Hood (Richard H.) Ill. cat. of etchings by A. H. Haig. Sold, Amer. Art. Assoc. [P2859]. la8°. N.Y. 1919
Hood (Robin).
see NEWBOLT (*Sir* H. J.) Peacock, Scott & R. H., 1924.
„ NOYES (A.) Robin Hood (*Play*), 1926.
„ RITSON (J.), *ed.* R. H.: coll. of poems &c. rel. to [R. H.], w. hist. anecd. of h. life, repr., 1820.
„ —— R. H.: a coll. of poems &c. rel. to [R. H.]; pref., hist. anecd. of h. life, 1885.
Hood (Samuel Hood, *1st visct.***),** *1724–1816, see* ROSE (J. H.) Lord H. & the defence of Toulon, 1922.
Hood (Thomas), *the elder, 1799–1845.* Compl. poet. works. Ed., w. notes by W. Jerrold. Oxf. ed. s8°. [O.] 1906
Poems. 18th ed. s8°. 1865
Serious poems. s8°. 1886
Hooft (Cornelis Pieterszoon). Mem. & adviezen. [Hist. Genoots. Werken, N.S., 16, s3, 48]. 2d [d2 uitg. H. A. Enno v. Gelder]. 8°. Utrecht. 1871–1925
Hooft (Pieter Corneliszoon) [†HOOFT (P.)]. Gedichten. Volledige uitgave door F. A. Stoett. 2d. la8°. A. 1899
Hoogeveen (Henricus). Doctrinae particularum linguae Græcæ t. prior [*&* alter]. 2t. 4°. Lugduni Batav. 1769
Hoogewerff (G. J.) Gherardo delle Notti. 28 riprod. con testo e cat. 8°. [1924]
Jan van Scorel, peintre de la renaissance hollandaise. la8°. La Haye. 1923
see BYVÄNCK (A. W.) & G. J. H. La miniature holland. dans les mss. des 14e, 15e & 16e s., 3v, 1922–26.
„ COSMO III [*de Medici*], *grand duke of Tuscany.* De 2 reizen van C. door de Nederlanden, 1667–69: journalen &c.; uitg. door G. J. H., 1919.
Hook (Theodore Edward) [*ps.* VICESIMUS BLINKINSOP]. Tentamen; hist. of Whittington [*a satire on Sir M. Wood*]. s8°. 1820
Hooke (Luke Joseph). De vera religione, 2p, & App. (Valsecchi &c.), *see* MIGNE (J. P.), *ed.* Theologiæ cursus, t2, 3, 1861–62.
Hooke (Robert). Extracts f. H.'s Micrographia, 1st pr. 1665, w. add. obs. [Old Ashm. repr., 6]. s8°. O. 1926
Hooker (Katharine) & M. Hunt. Farmhouses & small prov. buildings in S. Italy. Photographs by M. O. Hooker. 4°. N.Y. [1925]
Hooker (Marian O.), *see* HOOKER (K.) & M. HUNT. Farmhouses &c. in S. Italy; photo. by M. O. H., 1925.
Hooker (Richard). The works in eight books of Eccl. polity. With life [by J. Walton]. [*Ed.* J. Gauden]. fol. 1666
„ „ ....w. o. treatises &c. fol. 1682
see GALANTE (A.) La teoria d. relaz. fra lo Stato e la Chiesa sec. R. Hooker, 1908.
Hooker (W. H.) The handicap of Brit. trade w. reg. to E. Africa. Foreword by C. E. Musgrave. [2nd ed.] s8°. 1924
Hooker (*Sir* William Jackson).
The Brit. Flora. 2nd ed. 8°. 1831
Hookes (Nicholas). Amanda, a sacrifice to an unknown goddesse (1653). s8°. 1923
Hookham (George). Will o' the wisp, or the elusive Shakespeare. 8°. O. 1922
Hookstadt (Carl). Comparison of workmen's compensation laws of U.S. to Dec. 1917; to Jan. 1920, *see* UNITED STATES: LABOR. Bull. 240, 275, 1918–20.
Hoole (Elijah). The lady's Tamil book cont. portions of Bk. of Common Prayer in Romanized Tamil, Eng. vers., w. Gramm. & vocab. 8°. 1859
Madras, Mysore & the South of India: narr. of a miss., 1820–28. 2nd ed. s8°. 1844
Mem. of the Rev. James Townley. [P2531]. s8°. 1835
The year-book of missions. 8°. 1847
Hoop (Alfred d'). Invent. gén. des archives eccl. du Brabant. t2, 3. la8°. Brux. 1914–22
Hooper (Franklin H.), *see* EVENTFUL. These eventful years: 20th cent. in the making; [ed. F. H. H.], 2v, 1924.
Hooper (Fredk.) & J. Graham.
The home trade, or mod. practice. [repr.] 8°. 1918
The import & export trade or mod. practice. [repr.] 8°. 1920
Hooper (Geoffroy W. W.), *see* FAWCETT (H. W.) & G. W. W. H., *edd.* The fighting at Jutland, 1921.
Hooper (George), *of Kensington.*
The Campaign of Sedan, 1870. [repr.] s8°. *Bohn.* 1906
Waterloo: the downfall of the 1st Napoleon. n. impr. s8°. *Bohn.* 1904
Wellington. [repr.] s8°. 1913
Hooper (John), *M.A., of Hoxton.* Advantages of early piety displayed in a mem. of J. Clement, surgeon. Comp. f. h. letters &c. 8°. 1813
Hooper (W. G.) The universe of ether & spirit. 8°. 1913
Hooper (W. H.) & W. C. Phillips. Manual of marks on pottery & porcelain. [repr., w. corr. & add.] s8°. 1919
Hoops (Johannes). Probleme d. engl. Sprache u. Kultur. Festschr. J. H., hrsg. W. Keller. [German. Bibl. II, B20]. 8°. Heidelberg. 1925
Hoornaert (H.) Ce que c'est qu'un béguinage. 4°. Lille. 1921
Hoornbeek (Johannes) [†HOORNBEECK]. De paradoxis, & heterodoxis Weigelianis comm. Ubi et de Swencfeldo, aliisque. s8°. Ultrajecti. 1694
Instit. theologiae. s8°. Lugd. Batav. 1658
Socinianismi confutati. 3t. s4°. Ultrajecti [t2 & 3: Amstelodami], 1650–64
Summa controv. relig., cum infidelibus &c. s8°. Trajecti a. Rh. 1653
Theologiae practicae pars prior [*&* tomus alter]. Acc. ejusdem Irenicum &c. 2t *in* 1v. s4°. Francofurti. 1698
Hoover (Herbert Clark). Principles of mining: copper, gold, lead &c. 1st ed., 7th impr. 8°. N.Y. 1909
see KELLOGG (V. L.) H. H., the man & h. work, 1920.
Hope (Anthony), *ps.* Little Tiger. s8°. [1925]
Lucinda. s8°. [1920]
Hope (Arthur H.), *see* SANDIFORD (P.), *ed.* Compar. educ.; by H. &c., 1927.
Hope (Ascot R.), *ps.* [*i.e.* ROBERT HOPE MONCRIEFF].
Book about schools &c. 8°. 1925
Cap & gown comedy: a schoolmaster's remin. [rev. & enl. ed.] 8°. 1926
Classic myth & legend. 8°. [1912]
Romance & legend of chivalry. 8°. [1912 ?]
Hope (Thomas), *esq.* Costume of the ancients. n. ed. enl. 2v. la8°. 1841
see TILLYARD (E. M. W.) The H. vases, 1923.
Hope (*Sir* William Henry St. John). Cowdray & Easebourne Priory in the Co. of Sussex. fol. 1919
Hist. of the London Charterhouse until the suppr. la8°. 1925
—— & J. Bilson. Architect. descr. of Kirkstall Abbey. [Thoresby Soc., 16]. 8°. *p.p.* Leeds. 1907
Hopfner (Theodor). Fontes hist. relig. Aegyptiacae. Coll. T. H. [Fontes hist. relig. ex auct. Gr. & Lat. coll., fasc. 2i, iv.] 5p *in* 2v. [*pagin. cont.*] 8°. Bonnae. 1922–25
Orient. u. griech. Philos., *see* ALTE ORIENT, Beih. 4, 1925.
Works in KAIS. AKAD. D. W. Z. WIEN. Denkschr.
Der Tierkult d. alt. Ägypter, 1913. [57.]
Üb. d. kopt.-sa'id. Apophthegmata Patrum Aegyptiorum u. verw. griech., lat., kopt.-bohair. u. syr. Sammlungen, 1918. [61.]
Üb. Form u. Gebrauch d. griech. Lehnwörter in d. kopt.-sa'id. Apophthegmenversion, 1918. [62.]
Hopkins (A. E. Reveirs-), *see* REVEIRS-HOPKINS (A. E.)
Hopkins (Annette Brown) & H. S. Hughes. The Eng. novel bef. the 19th cent. Excerpts f. repres. types. Sel. by A. B. H. & H. S. H. 8°. Boston. [1915]
Hopkins (Arthur Innes).
In the isles of King Solomon (1900–25). 8°. 1928

Hopkins (Charles Plomer). "National service" of Brit. merchant seamen, 1914–19. la8º. 1920

Hopkins (Edward Washburn). Epic mythology. [Grundr. d. indo-ar. Phil., B3, H1, B]. la8º. Strassburg. 1915
Origin & evol. of religion. 8º. New Haven. 1924

Hopkins (G. H. E.) Butterflies of Samoa &c., 1927, *see* B. M., NAT. HIST.: ZOOLOGY. Insects of Samoa, p3i, 1927.

Hopkins (John), *the Psalmodist, see* BIBLE: PSALMS. The Booke of Psalmes, coll. into Eng. meeter, *var. eds.*

Hopkins (John Henry), *bp. of the episc. church in Vermont.* View of slavery, f. days of Abraham to the 19 cent. 8º. N.Y. [1864]

Hopkins (Robert Thurston).
Some Eng. mills & inns. 8º. [1927]

Hopkins (Tighe). The dungeons of old Paris. 8º. N.Y. 1897
Romance of escapes: hist. flights. [illust. ed.] 8º. 1920

Hopkinson (Austin). The hope of the workers. s8º. [1923]
Religio militis. 8º. [1927]

Hopkinson (Emilius). A list of the birds of Gambia. [P2404]. 8º. Brighton. 1919

Hopkinson (John), *F.L.S., see* CASH (J.) & G. H. WAILES. Brit. freshwater Rhizopoda &c.; by C. & W., assisted by J. H., v5, 1921.

Hopkinson (Leslie White).
Greek leaders. Ed. W. S. Ferguson. s8º. [1923]

Hoppé (A. J.) Bibliog. of the writings of Samuel Butler ("Erewhon"), & of wr. about him, w. letters f. S. B. to F. G. Fleay. 8º. [1925]

Hoppe (Carl). Corpus hippiatric. Graec; ed. E. Oder & C. H., 2v, 1924–27, *see* CORPUS.

Hoppe (Heinrich).
Syntax u. Stil d. Tertullian. 8º. L. 1903

Hoppenrodt (Andreas). Christl. &c. Antwort auff Spangenbergs Lesterschrifften &c. [P2665]. s4º. Eisleben. 1574

Hoppenstedt (*Oberst* Julius). Problems in manœuvre tactics. After the German of J. H. by J. H. V. Crowe. 8º. 1905

Hoppin (Joseph Clark). Handbook of Attic red-figured vases of 6th & 5th c. B.C. 2v. 8º. Camb. [U.S.] 1919
see CORPUS vasorum antiq.: U.S. fasc. 1: Hoppin & Gallatin colls.; by J. C. H. &c., 1926.

Hoppius (Samuel Joachim). De script. hist. Polonicae schediasma lit.; praes. G. Groddeck. s4º. Dantisci. [1707]

Höppner (*General* Ernst v.)
Deutschlands Krieg in der Luft. 8º. L. 1921

Hopstock (H.) Leonardo as anatomist; tr. E. A. Fleming, *see* SINGER (C.), *ed.* St. in hist. &c. of sci., v2, 1921.

Horace.

WORKS. (*Arranged according to date of publication*).

Opera. Denuo emend. s8º. Amsterdami. 1628
Q. Horatius Flaccus. s8º. Lond., *Pickering.* 1829
Opera Rec. O. Keller & A. Holder. v1, 2. 8º. Lips. (v2, Jenae). 1899–1925

CARMINA [ODAE—ODES] & EPISTOLAE.
Omnia poemata cum ratione carminum &c. N. Perotti libellus de metris odarum &c. sfol. Venetiis *apud haeredes J. M. Bonelli.* 1573
Carmina cum annot. J. Juvencii. 2t *in* 1v. s8º. *n.p.* 1701
Odes & epodes. study in poetic word-order. By H. D. Naylor. 8º. C. 1922

TRANSLATIONS.
Works. Tr. lit. into prose by C. Smart. n. ed., rev. by T. A. Buckley. s8º. *Bohn.* 1858
[Ars poet. *Tr. into Armenian by* A. K. Bagratouni. *b. w.* Virgil. Georgics (Arm.), 1847]. 4º. i Venetik. 1847
On the art of poetry. Lat. text, Eng. prose tr., intr. & notes, w. B. Jonson's Eng. verse rendering. Ed. E. H. Blakeney. la8º. 1928

TRANSLATIONS [*continued*].
CARMINA [ODAE—ODES].
Odes. Sel., tr. &c. by S^r T[hos.] H[awkins]. [*w. text*]. 3rd ed. s8º. 1635
Lierzangen; in het rijmeloos vertaelt door J. v. Vondel (1654), *see* VONDEL (J. VAN DEN). Werken, d16, *n.d.*
[Odes]. Tr. P. Francis. With app. cont. tr. of var. odes by B. Jonson, Cowley, Milton &c. 2v [*in* 1]. s8º. 1831
Odes & Epodes. With Eng. tr. by C. E. Bennett. [Loeb Class. Lib.] [repr.] s8º. 1918
,, ,, ...[repr.] s8º. 1919
Odes. Done into Eng. verse by H. Macnaghten. [*With text*]. s8º. C. 1926

SATIRES.
Satires & Epistles, done into Eng. 2nd ed. corr.; added Art of Poetry. By S. Dunster. s8º. 1712
Satires, Epistles & Ars poetica. With Eng. tr. by H. R. Fairclough. [Loeb Class. Lib.] s8º. 1926

REFERENCES.
see BOISSIER (G.) Nouv. promenades archéol.: H. & Virgile, 5e éd., 1904.

Horace [*continued*].

REFERENCES [*continued*].
see CAMPBELL (A. Y.) H., a new interpret., 1924.
,, COOPER (L.) Concordance to works, 1916.
,, HEINZE (R.) Lyr. Verse d. H., 1918.
,, JENSEN (C.) Neoptolemos u. H., 1919.
,, KIPLING (R.) & C. GRAVES. Q. Horati Flacci Carminum librum quintum [*in imit. of H.*] a R. K. &c. angl. redd. &c., 1920.
,, LUGLI (G.) La Villa Sabina di O., 1926.

REFERENCES [*continued*].
see MAZZONE DI MIGLIONICO (M. A.) Fiori di poesia dich. &c. da l'op. di Virgilio, Ovidio & H., 1593.
,, POPE (A.) Sober advice f. H. to the young gentlemen about town, 1735.
,, STEMPLINGER (E.) H. im Urteil d. Jhdte, 1921.
, TRETERUS (T.) Index in Q. H. F., auctus &c. ab I. Verburgio, 1809.
,, VEEN (O. v.) Emblemata Horat., 1684.

Horae. Horae Eboracenses; Prymer or Hours of the B. V. M. acc. to use of the Ch. of York, &c., 1920, *see* YORK, *abps. & church.*
Miniatures f. a French Horae, B.M. Add. MS. 16997, 15th c. Reprod. in hon. of J. A. Herbert. 8º. *pr. for subscribers.* 1927

Horánszky (Nándor). A quotakérdés. 8º. Budapest. 1898

Horányi (Ferenc Jozsef Elek), [†HORANYI (ALEXIUS)]. Memoria Hungarorum & provinc. scriptis ed. notorum, quam excitat A. H. 3p. 8º. Viennae. [p3: Posoniae.] 1775–77

Horapollo. Hieroglyphica, *see* ÆSOP, 1505.

Horbius (Johann Heinrich).
Hist. Origeniana. s4º. Francofurti. 1670

Horder (William Garrett).
The hymn lover: rise &c. of Eng. hymnody. 8º. [1889]
Hymns: suppl. to exist. colls. Sel. & ed. by W. G. H. s8º. [1894]
Treasury of Amer. sacred song. Sel. & ed. by W. G. H. 8º. 1896

Hordijk (C. Pijnacker), *see* PIJNACKER HORDIJK (C.)

Horicke (Petrus van den). B. virgo Maria a peccato orig. &c. immunis. [P2659]. s8º. Lovanii. 1672

Horigoutchi (Nico-D.) Tankas. Petits poèmes japonais. Tr. franç. de l'a. Préf. de P. Fort. s8º. [1921]

Hörle (Emil) & G. Schwegelbaur. Unser schönes Stuttgart. 5e verm. u. verb. A. 8º. St. [1926 ?]

Hörle (Georg Heinrich). Frühmittelalt. Mönchs- u. Klerikerbildung in Italien, 6–9 Jhdt. 8º. Freiburg i. B. 1914

Horman (William). Vulgaria. Pr. by R. Pynson, 1519. Repr., w. intr. by M. R. James. [*Lat. & Eng.* Roxburghe Club]. sfol. O. 1926

Horn, *King.* King H. nach MS. Laud 108; hrsg. Horstmann, *see* ARCHIV F. D. ST. D. NEU. SPR., B50, 1872.

Horn (Alfred Aloysius), *ps.* The life & works of A. A. H., an old visiter. Ed. E. Lewis. Foreword by J. Galsworthy. [v]1, The Ivory Coast in the earlies. 8º. [1927]

Horn (Conrad) [HORNEIUS (CONRADUS)]. In Epist. ad Hebraeos. [In epist. Jacobi; Petri I & II; Joannis 1, 2, 3, & Judae] expos. litteralis. [*b. w.* Calixtus (G.) In Acta Apostol. &c., 1652–54]. [5p *each w. sep. tp. & pagin.*] s4º. Brunsvigae. 1654–55

Horn (Georg), *1620–70* [†HORNIUS (G.)] [*ps.* REGGIUS (HONORIUS)]. De orig. Americanicis libri 4. s8º. Hemipoli. 1669
De statu eccl. Britann. hodierno. s4º. Dantisci. 1647
Hist. philos. lib. 7. [*b. w.* Vossius (G.) De philos., 1656–57]. s4º. Lugd. Batav. 1655
Rerum Britannic. libri 7: res ab a. 1645 bello gestae. s8º. Lugd. Batav. 1648

Horn (Johann Gottlieb).
De privatorum bibliothecis. s8º. *n.p.* 1719

Horn (*Mrs.* Susan G.) The next world. s8º. 1890

Hornblow (Arthur).
A hist. of the theatre in America. 2v. 8º. Phila. 1919

Hornblower (Florence S.), *see* HOUSTON (M. G.) & F. S. H. Anc. Egyptian &c. costumes &c., 1920.

Hornby (R. P.), *see* MEINERTZHAGEN (D.) & R. P. H. Bird life in an Arctic spring, 1899.

Hornby (*Capt.* W. St. J.) The battle of Jutland. Retold fr. Visc. Jellicoe's "The grand fleet." [Repr. f. "The Dorking Advertiser." P2430]. 8º. 1919

Hornchurch Priory. Kalendar of doc. in poss. of New Coll., Oxford. Intr. &c. by H. F. Westlake. 8º. 1923

Horne (Eric Arthur).
The polit. system of Brit. India. 8º. O. 1922

Horne (G.) & G. Aiston.
Savage life in Cent. Australia. 8°. 1924

Horne (George), *bp. of Norwich.* *The theol. & philos. in Cicero's Somnium Scipionis expl.: Newton. system &c. [P490]. 8°. 1751
see JONES (W.) Memoirs of G. H., 1799.

Horne (Melville). An investig. of the definition of justifying faith &c. held by Dr. Coke &c. s8°. 1809

Horne (Thomas), *M. A.* Χειραγωγία, sive manuductio in aedem Palladis, qua methodus authores bonos legendi indigitatur. s8°. Londini. 1641

Horne (Thomas Hartwell). *The complete grazier. By a Lincolnshire Grazier [*i.e.* T. H. H.] [*b. w.* Culley (G.) Obs., 1807]. 8°. 1805
Remin. personal & bibliograph. With notes by S. A. Cheyne, & intr. by J. B. M'Caul. s8°. 1862

Horne (William Wales).
The new songs of Zion. 8°. Norwich. [1795]

Horneck (Anthony), *1641–97.*
Four tracts. Pref. by Mr. Edwards. s8°. 1697
see JACKSON (T.) Lib. of Xtn. biog., v12, A. H., by R. Kidder, 1840.

Horneius (Conradus), see HORN (C.)

Hörner (Georg). Die Waldvölker, 1927, *see* PETERMANNS MITT. Ergnzb. 42, 1927.

Horner (John). The linen trade of Europe dur. the spinning-wheel period. 8°. Belfast. 1920

Hörnes (Moritz). Prähist. Archäologie, *see* HINNEBERG (P.) Die Kultur d. Gegenwart, T3v, 1923.
Urgesch. d. bildenden Kunst in Europa bis um 500 vor Christi. 3e A. durchges. u. erg. v. O. Menghin. la8°. Wien. 1925

Horne Tooke (John), *see* YARBOROUGH (M. C.) J. H. T., 1926.

Horniman (Benjamin Guy).
Amritsar & our duty to India. s8°. [1920]

Hornius (Georgius), *see* HORN (GEORG).

Hornung (Joseph), *advocate.* Idées sur l'évol. jurid. des nations chrét. &c. 8°. Genève. 1850
Pourquoi les Romains ont-ils été le peuple jurid. ? 8°. Genève. 1847

Horologium. Horologiũ devotiõis, c. 1498, *see* BERTHOLDUS, *Dominican.*

***Horrida** bella: pains & penalties v. truth & justice, 1820, *see* ROSCO, *ps.*

Horrocks (J. W.) A short hist. of mercantilism. 8°. [1925]

Horrocks (Jeremiah) [HORROX (J.); HORROXIUS (J.)], *see* GOULD (*Lt.-Comm.* R. T.) J. H., astronomer, 1923.

***Horse (The)** &c., 1831, *see* YOUATT (W.)

Horsetzky (*General* **Ernst).**
Die 4 letzten Kriegswochen. [P2522]. 8°. Wien. 1920

Horsham, *Sussex.* *Hist. & antiq. of Horsham, 1836, *see* DUDLEY (H.)
Parish register, 1541–1635. Transcr., ed. &c. by R. G. Rice. [Sussex Rec. Soc., v21]. 8°. 1915

Horsley (John William).
How criminals are made & prevented. 8°. [1913]
Place names in Kent. s8°. Maidstone. 1921

Horsley (Samuel), *bp. of (1) St. David's, (2) Rochester, (3) St. Asaph.* The book of the Psalms. Tr. w. notes. 4th ed. 8°. 1845

Horsnell (Horace), *see* FARJEON (H.) & H. H. Advertizing April, 1923.

Horst (Anton Heinrich). Disput. de bonis parochialibus. Præs. J. Henningio. [P2636]. s4°. Halae Magdeb. 1729

Horst (Didericus Gertrudus van der), *see* VAN DER HORST.

Horst (Heinrich). *Entwurf zur Staats-Verfassung der Deut. Republik. Sonderabd. aus H. H., Üb. Staatsformen. [P2384]. 8°. 1919

Hörstel (Wilhelm). Die Oberitalien. Seen. Mit e. geogr.-geolog. Übersicht v. A. Tornquist. la8°. Bielefeld. 1910

Horstmann (Carl). Nachträge zu d. Legenden, [5p], *see* ARCHIV F. D. ST. D. NEU. SPR., B62, 68, 74, 79, 80, 1879–88.

Hort (*Sir* **Arthur Fenton),** *Bart.* Brian P. Lascelles. A mem. [*By var. wr.*] Ed. A. F. H. 8°. O. 1924

Hort (G. M.) Dr. John Dee. s8°. 1922

Horten (Franz). St. ü. die Sprache Defoe's. 8°. Bonn. 1914

Hortense [*de Beauharnais*], *queen.* [†HORTENSIA, *q. c. of Louis, king of Holland*]. Mémoires. Publ. par le pr. Napoléon. Notes par J. Hanoteau. 3t. 8°. [1927]
see TURQUAN (J.) La reine H., 2t, 1927.

Hortensius (Lambertus). H. over de opkomst en den ondergang van Naarden, met vertaling &c. van Prof. Peerlkamp, en nalezingen &c. van A. Perk. [Hist. Genoots. te Utrecht. Werken, N.S., 5]. 8°. Utrecht. 1866
see HERESBACH (C.) Hist. anabaptistica &c. Acc. Tumultuum Anabapt. liber auth. L. H., 1636–37.

Horticultural register (The) & general magazine. [Ed.] J. Paxton &c. v1, 2 (July 1831–Oct. 1833). 8°. [1831–]33

Horton-Smith (Lionel Graham H.) The Declar. of London & Naval Prize Bill. Comp. by H.-S. 9th ed., 1913, [repr.] 8°. 1920

Hortulus. *Hortulus animae. Lustgarten d. Seelen: Mit schönen lieblichen Figuren. s4°. Wittemberg, *G. Rhawen Erben.* 1550

Hortus sanitatis (*in Germ.*, 1485); facs., 1924, *see* CUBE (J. v.)

Horváth (János). A közös ügyek elözményei és fejlödése (1526–1848). [*b. w. h.* Az 1867 évi kiegyezés, 1895]. 8°. 1902
Az 1867 évi kiegyerzés. 8°. 1895

Horváth (Mihály). Huszonöt év magyarország történelméböl 1823–48. 2k. 8°. Genfben. 1864
Magyarország függetlenségi harczának története 1848 és 1849–ben. 3k. 8°. Genfben. 1865
Magyarország történelme. Ujonnan átdolgozta Hatvani M. 6k. [k. 1 & 2, 2ed Kiadás. 3–6, új dolgozat]. s8°. Pesten. 1860–63

Horváth (Peter). Comment. de initiis, ac maioribus Jazygum & Cumanorum eorumque constitut. s8°. Pestini. 1801

Horwein (Johann Theophilus) [HORWEINIUS]. Diss. de vaticiniis & de vaticiniis Lutheri. [P2628]. s4°. Vitembergae. [1755]

Horwill (George).
Proport. represent., its dangers &c. s8°. [1925]

Horwill (Herbert William).
The usages of the American constit. 8°. O. 1925

Horwitz (B.) Chess studies & end-games. Pref. by W. Wayte. 8°. 1884

Horwood (A. R.) Outdoor botanist: manual for st. of Brit. plants. 8°. [1920]

Horwood (R.) Plan of the cities of London & Westminster, Southwark &c., 1792–99 [*w.* facts &c. ab. theatres &c. *Extr. f.* The Mask, Apr. & July 1926]. 8°. 1926

Hose (Charles). Fifty years of romance & research. Pref. by Sir A. Keith. la8°. [1927]
Natural man: a record f. Borneo. Pref. by G. E. Smith. la8°. 1926

Hosemann (Sigismund). Diss. de computo Turcico-Arabico &c. Sub praes. Æ. Strauchii. ed. 2a. s4°. Wittebergae. 1661

Hoshangji Jamaspji Asa [HOSHENGJI JAMASPJI (*Destur*)]. An old Zand-Pahlavi glossary ed. in orig. characters &c. by H.; rev. w. notes & intr. by M. Haug. 8°. Bombay. 1867

Hosie (*Sir* **Alexander).**
Szechwan, its products, industries &c. la8°. Shanghai. 1922

Hosie (Dorothea, *Lady*), *wife of Sir Alex. Hosie, form. Soothill.*
Two gentlemen of China. Intr. by Prof. Soothill. 2nd ed. 8°. 1924

Hosier (John).
The mariner's friend, or a treatise on the stars. 8°. 1809

Hosius (Stanislaus), *bp. of Ermeland.* Confut. prolegomenon Brentii quae primum scripsit adv. Petrum à Soto, deinde verò Petrus Paulus Vergerius apud Polonos temerè defendenda suscepit &c. s8°. Antverpiae. 1561

Hosken (Heath), *see* STANTON (C.) & H. H. The oldest land, 1926.

Hosken (James Dryden).
Phaon & Sappho & Nimrod. s8°. 1892

Hoskier (Hermann C.) MSS. of the Apocalypse, 5p, *see* JOHN RYLANDS LIBRARY. Bull. v7, 8, 1922–24.
The text of Codex Usserianus 2. r_2 (" Garland of Howth "), w. crit. notes to Suppl. &c. [Old Lat. Bibl. Texts]. 8°. 1919

Hoskins (John), *the elder, fellow of New College, Oxford* [HOSKYNS]. Supplicatio ad Regem, *see* ABBOTSFORD CLUB. Misc., v1, 1837.

Hospitals. Mod. practice of the London h., 3rd ed., 1770, *see* LONDON.
The order of the h. of Henry VIII & Edw. VI, 1557; repr. c. 1700 ?, *see* LONDON: CIVIC &C. INSTITUTIONS.

Hossfeld (C.) H.'s Eng.-Dutch & Dutch-Eng. dict. By B. L. Teding v. Berkhout. s8°. *n.d.*

Hossfeld's method for learning the Dutch lang., 2nd ed., n.d., *see* SCHNITZLER (J. M.)

Høst (Sigurd).
Om Holbergs historiske skrifter. 8°. Bergen. 1913
Hosta (José de). Crón. de la prov. de Ciudad-Real, 1865, *see* ESPAÑA. Crón. gen., v1, 1865 &c.
Hoste (P. Paul). A treatise on naval tactics. Tr. J. D. Boswall, w. addit. notes &c. 4°. E. 1834
Hotchkiss (Willard Eugene) & H. R. Seager. Hist. of the Shipbuilding Labor Adjustment Board, 1917–19, *see* UNITED STATES: LAB. Bull. No. 283, 1921.
Hotman (François) [HOTOMAN (FRANCIS); *pss.* EREMUNDUS (ERNESTUS) & PALMERIUS (J.)]
Anti-Tribon., *see* HOFFMANN (C. G.) Hist. jur. Rom.-Justin., v1ii, 1734.
Franco-Gallia: or, an acc. of the anc. free state of France &c. [w. Short life of F. H.] Tr. by a. of Account of Denmark [*i.e.* Robert, *visc.* Molesworth]. s8°. 1711
Origo & hist. Belgic. tumultuum. Acc. Hist. tragica de furoribus Gallicis et caede admiralii &c. responsio Ordin. Foed. Belg. ad legatum Caes. Majestatis. s8°. Amstelodami. 1641
see POUCHEN (A.) Ad I. Palmerii protest. &c. responsio, 1579.
Hotson (J. Leslie).
The death of C. Marlowe. 8°. *Nonesuch Press.* 1925
Hotten (John Camden), *see* LARWOOD (J.) & J. C. H. Hist. of signboards, 1867.
Hottinger (Johann Heinrich), *the elder, 1620–67.* Enneas diss. philol.-theolog. Heidelberg. Acc. ejusdem programmata & carmina &c. [2 *pagin.*] s4°. Tiguri. 1662
Exercit. Anti-Morinianæ de Pentateucho Samaritano. Acc. Epitome omn. capit. Libri Josuae &c. s4°. Tiguri. 1644
Hist. eccl. N. Test. enneas seu pars prima—[t. 9. Praef. hist. vitae & obitus ejusdem, authore J. H. Heideggero]. 5p *in* 9t. s8°. 1–3, Hanoviae; 4–9, Tiguri. 1655–67
Thesaurus philologicus, seu clavis Scripturae, &c. ed. 3ª. auct. & emend. s4°. Tiguri. 1696
see ALLACCI (L.) J. H. H., 1661.
Hottinger (Johann Jacob), *1652–1735.* Fata doctr. de praedestin. & gratia Dei salutari. Acc. Exercit. duae. [2 *pagin^s^.*] s4°. Tiguri. 1727
Hist. d. Reformation in d. Eidgenossenschafft. s4°. Zürich. 1708
Hötzendorf (*Feldmarschall* **Franz Conrad v.),** *see* CONRAD V. HÖTZENDORF (*Fm.* F.)
Hötzl (Petrus de Alcantara). *Dr. A. Westermayer u. P. H.; von e. kathol. Geistlichen, 1870, *see* WESTERMAYER (A.)
Ist Dollinger Häretiker ?, 1870, *see* KATHOLISCH. Stimmen aus d. K. Kirche, B1, 1870.
Hötzsch (Otto E. G.) Stände u. Verwaltung v. Cleve u. Mark, 1666–97. [Urk. &c. z. Gesch. d. inn. Pol. d. Kurf. Fr. Wilhelm v. Brandenburg, T2]. la8°. L. 1908
Houben (Heinrich Hubert).
J. P. Eckermann: s. Leben für Goethe. s8°. L. 1925
Verbotene Lit. 2. Aufl. 8°. Dessau. 1925
see HEINE (H.) Gespräche mit Heine; ges. u. hrsg. H., 1926.
Houbraken (Jacob) & G. Vertue. Heads of illust. persons of Gt. Brit., engr. by H. & V., w. lives &c. by T. Birch. n. ed. fol. 1813
Houdini (Harry). Paper magic: whole art of performing w. paper &c. 8°. N.Y. [1922]
Houël (Nicolas), *see* GUIFFREY (J. J.) Les dessins de l'Hist. des rois de France par N. H., 1920.
Hough (James), *incumbent of Ham.* Exercises in English & Tamul on the Pentateuch. 8°. Madras. 1821
Hough (Walter). Coll. of heating & lighting utensils in U.S. Nat. Mus. [S.I., U.S. Nat. Mus., Bull. 141]. 8°. Wash. 1928
Fire as an agent in human culture. [S.I., U.S. Nat. Mus., Bull. 139]. 8°. Wash. 1926
Houghton (Bernard).
Advance, India ! [P2617]. s8°. Madras. [1921]
Agitate ! [P2617]. s8°. Madras. 1922
The foreign policy of India. [P2617]. s8°. Madras. 1922
The menace from the West. [P2617]. s8°. Madras. 1922
The mind of the Indian govt. [P2617]. s8°. Madras. 1922
Reform in India. [Repr. f. Polit. sci. quarterly, Dec., 1920. P2620]. 8°. N.Y. 1920
Houghton (Frederick Tyrie Sidney), *see* MAWER (A.) & F. M. STENTON. Place-names of Worcestershire; by A. M. & F. M. S. in collab. w. F. T. S. H., 1927.
Houghton (Ralph Edward Cunliffe). Infl. of the classics on the poetry of Matthew Arnold. s8°. O. 1923
Houghton (Richard Monckton Milnes, *1st baron*). Briefe an Varnhagen von Ense (1844–54). Mit Einl. u. Anm. hrsg. v. W. Fischer. [Anglist. Forsch.; hrsg. J. Hoops, 57]. la8°. Heidelberg. 1922
Monographs, personal & social. 2nd ed. s8°. 1873
Houghton (Thomas Hurry-), *see* HURRY-HOUGHTON (T.)
Houghton (William Stanley). Hindle wakes, *see* PLAYS of to-day, v1, 1925.
Hounanean, *see* HOVNANEAN.
Hourticq (Louis). De Poussin à Watteau: ou des orig. de l'école paris. de peinture. 8°. [1921]
Encyclopédie des beaux-arts. 2t. 4°. [1925]
House. The smaller h.: sel. examples of mod. Eng. domestic archit., 1924, *see* SMALLER.
*House (The) in Charles Street. s8°. [1924]
*House (The) made with hands. [repr.] 8°. [1924]
House, The. A monthly for the artistic home. v1–12. fol. & s4°. [1897–1903]
v11, 12 *have t.* The house: journal of home arts & crafts *& are* s4°.
House (C. A.) Canaries. 8°. [1924]
House (Edward Mandell). Intimate papers. Arr. as a narr. by C. Seymour. 2v. 8°. [1926]
—— & Charles Seymour, *edd.* What really happened at Paris: Peace Conf., 1918–19. By American delegates. 8°. 1921
Housing (The) q. as affected by recent legisl. Reasons for repeal of p1 of the Finance (1909–10) Act, 1910. [P2508]. sfol. 1917
Housman (Alfred Edward). Last poems. s8°. 1922
„ „ ....[repr.] s8°. 1922
A Shropshire lad. [repr.] s8°. 1922
Housman (*Mrs.* **H.)** The power & pleasure of the divine life. Publ. &c. by R. Pearsall. [*b. w.* Flavell (J.) Pneumatologia, 1789]. 8°. 1789
Housman (Laurence).
Angels & ministers: 3 plays of Victorian shade. s8°. [1921]
„ „ [3rd impr.] s8°. [1922]
Angels & ministers. 4 plays of Victorian shade. [The Queen: God bless her !—His favourite flower—The comforter—Possession]. [illust. ed.] s8°. [1922]
The comments of Juniper. 6 plays f. life &c. of St. Francis of Assisi. 8°. 1926
The death of Orpheus. s8°. 1921
Dethronements: imag. portraits of polit. characters. s8°. [1922]
False premises. 5 plays. s8°. O. 1922
Followers of St. Francis. 4 plays. [Cure of souls—Lovers meeting—The fool's errand—The last disciple]. s8°. 1923
Ironical tales. s8°. [1926]
Little plays of St. Francis. Dram. cycle. Pref. by H. Granville-Barker. s8°. 1922
„ „ ....[repr.] 8°. 1923
Odd pairs. Bk. of tales. s8°. [1925]
Ploughshare & pruning-hook. 10 lect. on soc. subj. 8°. [1919]
Possession: A peep-show in Paradise. s8°. [1921]
Trimblerigg. 8°. 1924
see AUCASSIN & NICOLETTE. Of A. & N.; tr. in prose & verse, w. Amabel & Amoris, by L. H., 1925.
—— & H. Granville Barker. Prunella, *see* PLAYS of to-day, v2, 1925.
Houssay (Frédéric). Force et cause. s8°. 1920
Nature & sciences nat. s8°. 1922
Houssaye (Arsène).
Le violon de Franjolé [*& o. s.*] 6e éd. s8°. 1859
Houssaye (Henry), *ps.* [*i.e.* H. HOUSSET]. 1815: La prem. Restauration—Le retour de l'Ile d'Elbe—Les Cent Jours. 3e éd. 8°. 1893
1815: Waterloo. 20e éd. s8°. 1899
Iéna & la campagne de 1806. Intr. par L. Madelin. 8°. 1912
see LYAUTEY (*gén.* H.) Disc. de récep. (*on* H. H.), 1921.
Housta (Balduinus de). Conclusiones theolog., quas praes. B. de H., defendent L. Roelants &c. [P2659]. s8°. Lovanii. 1709
Houston (Gertrude Craig). The evolution of hist. drama in Germany dur. 1st half of 19th c. 8°. Belfast. 1920
Houston (Mary G.) & F. S. Hornblower. Anc. Egyptian, Assyrian & Persian costumes & decorations. 8°. 1920
Houston (Robert Alexander). Intermediate light. s8°. 1925
Light & colour. 8°. 1923
A treatise on light. n. ed. 8°. 1921
„ „ ....5th ed. 8°. 1927
Houtin (Albert) [HOUTIN (ALBERT JULES HENRI)].
Courte hist. du Christianisme. s8°. 1924
Une gr. mystique, Mme. Bruyère, Abbesse de Solesmes, 1845–1909. 8°. 1925
Le père Hyacinthe. [3t]. s8°. 1920–24
Un prêtre symboliste: Marcel Hébert (1851–1916). 8°. 1925
Une vie de prêtre: mon exper., 1867–1912. s8°. [1926]

Houtman (Cornelis de). De eerste schipvaart der Nederlanders naar Oost-Indië onder C. de H., 1595–97. Journalen, doc. &c. uitg. door G. P. Rouffaer & J. W. Ijzerman. [Linschoten-Vereeniging, Werken, 25]. [d]2. 8º. 's-Gravenhage. 1925
2, De oudste Journalen der reis: Verhael (1597), Journael (1598), Van der Does (Hs.)

Houvet (Etienne). Cathédrale de Chartres. [*Plates.* Notes *by* E. H. Pref. *by* E. Male. 13t]. 4º. *n.d.*–1926
Architecture [*no tp.*]
Portail nord, 13s., 4t.
Portail occidental ou royal, 12s.
Portail sud, 13s., 2t.
Tour (Le) du chœur, 16–18s.
Vitraux; texte [par] Y. Delaporte; planches, 3t.

Houville (Gérard d'), *ps.* L'heure exacte, *see* ŒUVRES libres, Nº. 72, 1927.
Je crois que je vous aime . . . 7 proverbes. [7e éd.] s8º. [1927]
Tant pis pour toi. s8º. 1921
see BOURGET (P.) Le roman des quatre; [par] P. B., G. d'H. &c., 2t, 1923–26.

Hoveden (Roger of). Annalium pl & 2, *see* SAVILE (*Sir* H.) Rerum Angl. scr., 1596; 1601.

Hovelaque (Emile). China. Tr. Mrs. L. Binyon. 8º. 1923
Les peuples d'Extrême-Orient: la Chine. s8º. 1920

Hovelaque (Henri Léon).
Anthologie de la litt. irlandaise. s8º. 1924
Précis de l'hist. des Etats-Unis d'Amér. s8º. 1919

Höver (Otto). Javan. Schattenspiele. Einleit. Text v. O. H. s4º. L. [1923]

Hovhannes, *the Deacon, see* JOHN.

Hovhannesean (Ashot). [Armeno-Russ. orientation. *In Armenian*]. 8º. Edschmiadzin. 1921

Hovhannesean (Mihran). Grakan hambauner. [Lit. reputations &c. *In Armenian*]. 8º. K. Polis. 1909
Zenob Glak [4c. *In Armenian*]. 8º. K. Polis. 1912

Hovnanean (Leuont) [HOUNANEAN]. [Study of anc. dialect. *In Armenian*]. v1i, ii *in* 1v. 8º. Vienna. 1897

Hovsephean (Garegin) [OWSEPIAN]. Die Entstehungsgesch. d. Monotheletismus. [P2811]. 8º. L. 1897
see KHOSROVIK, *the Translator.* K. T., *ed.* G. H., 1899.

Hovyn de Tranchère (Jules Aug.), *see* GODIN (A.) Hist. de la ville &c. de Guîtres; rev. & compl. par H. de T., 1888.

How.
*How the War began in 1914: diary of Russian For. Office, 1925, *see* RUSSIA.
*How to become a naval officer, & life at Osborne & Dartmouth. rev. ed. 8º. 1907
*How to learn Welsh, *n.d.*, *see* WELSH.
How to observe in archaeology: suggest. for travellers in Near & Middle East, 1920, *see* BRITISH MUSEUM.
*How to write for the magazines. By "£600 a year from it." ["How to" series]. s8º. 1900
*How we fared in Algeria, 1875, *see* ALGERIA.

How (Walter Wybergh), *see* CICERO (M. T.) Sel. letters: w. notes &c.; n. ed., rev. & annot. by W. W. H., 2v, 1925–26.

Howard, *The family of, see* RICHARDSON (E. M.) The lion & the rose: the gt. H. story, Norfolk line, 957–1646, Suffolk line, 1603–1917, 2v, 1923.

Howard (Albert). Soil ventilation, [erosion *&* aeration], *see* AGRIC. RES. INST., *Pusa.* Bull. 52, 53, 61, 1915–16.
—— **& G. L. C. Howard.** Improvement of Indigo in Bihar, *see* AGRIC. RES. INST. Bull. 51, 54, 67, 1915–16.
Improvement of tobacco cultiv. in Bihar, *see* AGRIC. RES. INST. Bull. 50, 1915.

Howard (Albert Andreas) & C. N. Jackson. Index verborum C. Suetoni Tranquilli. 8º. Cantabrigiae, Mass. 1922

Howard (Alexander L.) Manual of the timbers of the world. App., an acc. by S. Fitzgerald of the artif. seasoning of timber. 8º. 1920

Howard (Charles), *of the Cyclists' Touring Club.* The roads of Eng. & Wales: itinerary &c. 5th ed. s8º. 1889

Howard (*Maj.-Gen. Sir* **Francis).** Remin., 1848–90. 8º. 1924

Howard (Francis Morton). "'Orace & Co." s8º. [1923]

Howard (Frank). Colour as a means of art. 8º. 1838

Howard (*Mrs.* **Gabrielle Louise Caroline),** *see* HOWARD (A.) & G. L. C. H. Improv. of Indigo &c., 1915–16.

Howard (Henry), *see* NORTHAMPTON (H. H., *1st e. of*).

Howard (Henry Eliot), *F.Z.S.*
Territory in bird life. 8º. 1920

Howard (John), *the philanthropist.*
State of prisons in Eng. & Wales &c. 4º. Warrington. 1777
„ „ . . . . App., cont. farther acc. of foreign prisons &c. 4º. Warrington. 1784

Howard (Joseph Jackson) & F. A. Crisp, *edd.* List of pedigrees in the "Visitation of Eng. & Wales," &c. [*b. w.* Visitation of Eng., v1]. la8º. *p.p. n.d.*
Visitation of England & Wales. v21. la8º. *p.p.* 1921
v21 ed. by F. A. C. only
„ „ Notes, v5; ed. F. A. Crisp. la8º. *p.p.* 1903

Howard (*card.* **Philip Thomas),** *1629–94, known as Cardinal of Norfolk, see* DOMINICANA. Card. H.'s letters &c., 1925.

Howard (R. Endersby).
Lessons f. great golfers. s8º. [1924]

Howard (*Sir* **Robert).** "The Committee," comedy. Ed. w. intr. & notes by C. N. Thurber. [Illinois, Univ. of. Studies in lang. &c., v7i]. la8º. Urbana. 1921

Howard (Thomas), *2nd earl of Arundel, see* ARUNDEL (THOMAS HOWARD, *earl of*).

Howard-Bury (*Lt.-Col.* **Charles Kenneth).** Mount Everest: the reconnaissance, 1921. By C. K. H.-B. &c. la8º. 1922

Howard de Walden (Frederick Augustus Harvey, *5th baron***),** *see* BRISTOL (F. A. H., *4th earl of*).

Howarth (Osbert John Radcliffe). The Brit. Assoc. for the Adv. of Science: a retrospect, 1831–1921. 8º. 1922

Howchin (Walter), *see* CHAPMAN (F.) Foraminifera of the permo-carbonif. limestone of N.S.W., 1905.

Howd (Cloice R.) Indust. relations in the West Coast lumber industry, *see* UNITED STATES: LAB. Bull. 349, 1924.

Howden. *Hist. of the church &c. of H., 1850, *see* CLARKE (T.)
The registers of the parish of H., Co. York. Ed. G. E. Weddall. [Yorks. Parish Reg. Soc., 32, 48]. [p3, 4, 1659–1770]. 8º. [Leeds &c.] *p.p.* 1909–13
p3 is also numbered v2 (continued), & cont. Index to p2 & 3.

Howe (Frederic Clemson).
Denmark: a co-operative commonwealth. s8º. 1922

Howe (Frederick Arthur), *see* TURBERVILLE (A. S.) & F. A. H. Gt. Brit. in the latest age, 1921.

Howe (Harrison Estell).
Chemistry in the world's work. 8º. 1926
The new stone age. 8º. 1921
see FARNHAM (D. T.), J. A. HALL &c. Profitable sci. in industry, 1925.

Howe (John), *of Magdalen Coll., Oxford.* Christian theology. Sel. & arranged, w. a life of the a., by S. Dunn. s8º. 1836
Extr. f. works; pref. acc. of h. life, *see* WESLEY (J.) Xtn. lib., v48, 1755.
*The reconcileableness of God's prescience of the sins of men &c. In a letter to Hon. R. Boyle. s8º. 1677
The Redeemer's tears wept over lost souls, w. App. [*&* 2 sermons]. s8º. Coventry. 1809
see JACKSON (T.) Lib. of Xtn. biog., v11, J. H., by E. Calamy, 1839.
„ ROGERS (H.) Life & character of J. H., 1862.

Howe (John Allen). Stones & quarries. s8º. *Pitman.* [1920]
see ELSDEN (J. V.) & J. A. H. Stones of London, 1923.
„ MUSEUM OF PRACT. GEOL. Hdbk. to coll. of kaolin, china-clay &c., 1914.

Howe (Mark Anthony De Wolfe).
The Boston Symphony Orchestra. 8º. Boston. 1914
George v. Lengerke Meyer. 8º. N.Y. 1920

Howe (Marshall Avery). On some fossil & rec. Lithothamnieae of the Panama Canal Zone. [S.I., U.S. Nat. Mus., Bull. 103]. 8º. Wash. 1918

Howe (Octavius Thorndike). Argonauts of '49: emigrant companies f. Mass., 1849–50. la8º. Camb. [Mass.] 1923

Howe (Percival Presland).
Life of Will. Hazlitt. 8º. [1922]

Howe (Richard George Penn Curzon, *4th earl***).** Rare ship models &c. Sold, Anderson gall. [Illust.] [P2854]. la8º. [1924]

Howell & Stewart [HOWELL & Co.] Cat. of books rel. to the Church of Rome. On sale by H. & Co. [*b. w. t.* Cat. of Eng. theol., 1827]. 8º. 1829
Cat. of Eng. theol. &c. on sale by H. & S. 8º. 1827

Howell (Gerard Charles Lisle).
Ocean research & the great fisheries. 8º. O. 1921

Howell (Henry Hyatt). Geol. of the Warwickshire coal-field &c. [Mems. of G.S.] 8º. 1859

Howell (James), *historiographer royal to Charles II.* Epistolæ Ho-Elianæ: familiar letters, domestic & forren; divided into 6 sections. [*5 sep. pagin.*] By J. H[owell]. 8°. 1645
Instructions & directions for forren travell. With n. app. for travelling into Turkey &c. s8°. 1650
„ „ ....Ed. E. Arber. [Eng. repr.] s8°. [1868]
*Satire agst. Scotland (1617) [*sometimes ascr. to J. H.*] & Answer, *see* ABBOTSFORD CLUB. Misc., v1, 1837.
12 several treatises of the late revolutions in these 3 kingdomes. s8°. 1661
see PRYNNE (W.) Moderate apology &c. in ans. to passages in The preheminence of Parlement by J. H., 1644.

Howell (Laurence) [HOWEL]. A view of the pontificate, to 1563. s8°. 1712
see DESEOSO. *Desiderius, or the orig. pilgrim: Eng. & expl. by L. H., 1717.

Howells (William Dean). Imaginary interviews. 8°. N.Y. 1910
The vacation of the Kelwyns. 8°. N.Y. [1920]

Howes (Frank Stewart). The borderland of music & psychol. Pref. by Sir H. Allen. 8°. 1926
William Byrd. s8°. 1928

Howes (Paul Griswold), *see* BEEBE (C. W.), G. I. HARTLEY & P. G. H. Trop. wild life in Brit. Guiana, v1, 1917.

Howey (M. Oldfield). The encircled serpent: serpent symbolism. 8°. [1926]

Howgill (Francis) [HOWGIL]. The glory of the true Church, discovered. Also, a manifest. how the apostacy came &c. s8°. 1661
The Rock of Ages exalted. [*b. w. h.* The glory of the true Church, 1661]. s8°. 1662

Howgrave-Graham (R. P.) Peter Lightfoot, monk of Glastonbury & the old clock at Wells. 8°. Glastonbury. 1922

Howie (John). The Scots worthies. Rev. & corr. by James Howie. W. hist. introd. by R. Buchanan. la8°. Glasgow. 1856

Howitt (Anna Mary), *aft. Watts* [HOWITT-WATTS]. The pioneers of the spiritual reform.: J. Kerner (*adapted fr. the Ger.*): W. Howitt. 8°. 1883

Howitt (Samuel). The Brit. Sportsman, cont. 70 plates. 4°. 1812

Howitt (William) [*ps. Dr. Cornelius*], *see* HOWITT (A. M.) Pioneers: W. H. & h. work f. spiritualism &c., 1883.

Howkins (F.) Story of Golders Green & its development. la8°. Golders Green. [1923]

Howland (Harold Jacobs). Theodore Roosevelt & h. times. [Chron. of Amer. Ser., v47]. 8°. New Haven, *Yale.* 1921

***Howling** mob (The), an indict. of democracy. By A gentleman with a duster. s8°. [1927]

Howorth (*Sir* Henry Hoyle). The Chronicle of John of Worcester prev. assigned to Florence of Worcester, *see* *ROYAL ARCH. INST. Arch. Journal, v73, 1916.
Hist. of the Mongols, 9th–19th cent. p4, Suppl. & Indices. la8°. 1927
Saint Augustine of Canterbury. 8°. 1913
Some unconventional views on text of the Bible, 2. [*Repr.* f. Proc. of Soc. of Bibl. Archaeol.; P2791]. 8°. 1901

Howson (John Saul), *dean of Chester*, *see* CONYBEARE (W. J.) & J. S. H. Life & epistles of St. Paul, n. ed., 2v, 1877.

Howth. The text of Codex Usser. 2. r_2 ("Garland of Howth"), w. crit. notes &c., 1919, *see* HOSKIER (H. C.)

Hoxie (Robert Franklin).
Scientific management & labor. 8°. N.Y. 1921

Hoxmark (Guillermo). Solar rad. & weekly weather forecast, Argentine, 1925, *see* SMITHSONIAN INST. Misc. coll., v77, 1926.

Hoy (*Sir* William Wilson). The economic position of S. Africa. [P2878]. s8°. 1926

Hoyau (Germain), *see* TRUSCHET (O.) & G. H. Plan de Paris sous Henri II, reprod., 1908.

Hoyland (Francis). Poet. works. Coll. by T. Park. [*b. w.* Blair (R.) Poet. works, 1807]. s8°. 1808

Hoyland (John S.)
Book of prayers for use in an Indian college. s8°. [1924]

Hoyle (Arthur), *see* BUSH (JANE). Jos. B.; w. mem. by A. H., 1907.

Hoyle (Edmond). The modern Hoyle, w. add. by Prof. Hoffmann. n. rev. ed. s8°. 1888

Hoyle (Joshua). A rejoynder to Master Malone's reply [to J. Usher] conc. Reall Presence. s8°. D. 1641

Hoyle (William). Our national resources, & how they are wasted. 4th ed. 8°. [1871]

Hoym (Christoph von). *Erinnerungsschrifft etlicher vom Adel u. Städten [*signed:* C. von H., J. von Müchel *& others*] an Johann Georgen Fürsten zu Anhalt [*conc. doctrines of the Reformed Ch.*] Verantwortung u. erklarung [*by John George, drawn up by W. Amling*]. Item: Anleytung Wie man das Wittemberg. Buch lesen möge. [*w. sep. pagin.*] s4°. [Zerbst ?]. 1597

Hoynovius (Daniel). Exercit. de causis, quibus impulsus Lutherus salutare Reform. negotium inchoavit. Præs. D. H., resp. J. G. Ossa. [P2628]. 8°. Regiomonti. 1695

Hoyos y Vinent (Antonio de). Le royaume secret; tr. F. de Miomandre, *see* ŒUVRES libres, 60, 1926.

Hoyt (Elizabeth Ellis).
Primitive trade, its psychology & economics. 8°. 1926

Hoyt (Franklin Chase), *presiding justice of the Children's Court, N.Y.* Quicksands of youth. s8°. N.Y. 1921

Hozier (Henry Montague). The Russo-Turkish war: incl. rise & fall of the Ottoman Power & Hist. of the E. Question. Ed. H. M. H. [2v in 5. *pagin. cont.*] 4°. [1877–79]
The Seven Weeks' War. 8°. 1907

Hozier (Jean François Louis d'). Les chevaliers bretons de St.-Michel (1469–1665). Publ. avec préf. &c. par G. de Carné. 8°. Nantes. 1884

Hrdlička (Aleš). The Old Americans. 8°. Baltimore. 1925
The races of Russia, 1919, *see* SMITHSONIAN INSTIT. Misc. coll., v69, 1921.

Hrozny (Friedrich). Code hittite prov. de l'Asie mineure (vers 1350 av J. C.) [Hethitica, t1]. pl. 8°. 1922
Das Getreide im alt. Babylon. T1, Mit Beitr. v. F. v. Frimmel: Ü. einige ant. Samen aus d. Orient, *see* KAIS. AKAD. D. WISS. Z. WIEN. Sitzb., B173, 1914.
see BOGHAZKÖI. Keilschrifttexte aus B., H5, 6, Autographien, v. F. H., 1921.

Hrubý (V.) Vergl. Gramm. d. slav. Sprachen. s8°. Wien. [1909]

Hsia (Ching-Lin).
St. in Chinese diplomatic hist. 8°. Shanghai. 1924

Hsieh (Pao Chao). The govt. of China, 1644–1911. [Johns Hopkins Univ.] 8°. Baltimore. 1925

Hsu (Mongton Chih).
Railway problems in China. 8°. N.Y., *Columbia Univ.* 1915

Hsüan-tsang, *Chinese pilgrim*, *see* STEIN (*Sir* M. A.) Desert crossing of H.-t., 630 A.D., 1921.

Hsüntze, *Chinese philosopher, fl. 3 c. B.C.* [HSUN TZŬ]. Works. Tr., w. notes by H. H. Dubs. 8°. 1928
see DUBS (H. H.) Hs., moulder of anc. Confucianism, 1927.

Huang-Ts'ing-K'ai-kuo-fang-lüeh. Die Gründung d. mandschur. Kaiserreiches. Übers. u. erklärt v. E. Hauer. la8°. 1926

Huang (Feng Hua).
Public debts in China. 8°. N.Y., *Columbia Univ.* 1919

Huard (Georges), *see* LEXOVIENNES. Études lex., t2, par G. H., &c., 1919.

Huart (Clement). Anc. Persia & Iranian civiliz. [Tr. M. R. Dobie. Foreword by H. Berr.] 8°. 1927
Les saints des Derviches tourneurs. Récits tr. du Persan & annotés par C. H. [H. E. Sci. relig., 32, 36]. 2t. 8°. 1918–22
Les Ziyârides, *see* ACAD. D. INSCR. &C. Hist. & mém., t42, 1922.

Hubbard (Arthur John) & G. Hubbard.
Neolithic dew-ponds & cattle-ways. 3rd ed. la8°. 1916

Hubbard (Eric Hesketh). How to distinguish prints. Wr. & illust. by members of the Print Soc. Ed. H. H. 4°. 1926
On making & collecting etchings. Wr. by members of the Print Soc. Ed. &c. E. H. H. [Print Soc.] 8°. 1920

Hubbard (Ernst). The utilisation of wood-waste. Tr. f. 2nd rev. &c. ed. 3rd Eng. rev. & enl. ed. by H. B. Stocks. s8°. 1920

Hubbard (Frank Gaylord), *see* SHAKESPEARE (W.) 1st 4° ed. of Hamlet—Romeo & Juliet; ed. &c. by F. G. H., 2v, 1920–24.

Hubbard (George), *see* HUBBARD (A. J.) & G. H. Neolithic dew-ponds, &c., 1916.

Hubbard (Gilbert Ernest). The day of the crescent: glimpses of old Turkey. 8°. C. 1920
Temples of the Western Hills. s8°. Peking. 1923

Hubbard (Lucius Lee), *see* SMEEKS (H.) Dutch source for Robinson Crusoe; tr. & compared w. R. C. by H., 1921.

Hubbard (Wilfranc). Orvieto dust. Intr. by R. B. Cunninghame Graham. s8°. 1925
Shadows on the Palatine. 8°. 1923
Tanagra figures. 8°. 1927

Hubbard (*Rev.* **William**), *minister of Ipswich, Mass.*, General hist. of New England to 1680, 1815, *see* †MASS. HIST. SOC. Coll., s2, v5, 6, 1815.

Hubbell (Jay Broadus) & J. O. Beaty.
Intr. to poetry. s8°. N.Y 1922

Hübbenet (Anton Christian August v.) Service sanit. des hôpitaux russes, 1854–56, *see* TOTLEBEN (E. I., *cte.* DE). Déf. de Sébastopol, App., 1870.

Hüber (Caspar) [HUBERINUS (G.)], *see* FLACIUS (M.) Contra quaedam scripta quae a multis G. H. tribuuntur, 1550.

Huber (Johannes N.)
Die Idee der Unsterblichkeit. 2e A. s8°. München. 1865
Das Papstthum u. d. Staat. Wider d. Anti-Janus *&* Die Freiheiten d. französ. Kirche, 1870, *see* KATHOLISCH. Stimmen aus d. K. Kirche, B1, 1870.

Huber (Samuel).
Actorum Huberian. pars prior [-posterior]. Zwispalt die Prædestination betr. &c. 2p *in* 1v [1, *in Germ.* 2, *in Lat.*] s4°. Tübingen. 1597
Antibellarminus. 6 Lib. *b. in* 1v. fol. Goslariae. 1607–09
Compend. thesium S. H., de universali redemptione. [P2610]. s4°. Tubingae. 1590
Confutatio libri de controv. inter theologos Witteberg. & S. H., de electione &c. [P2610]. s4°. Mulhusii. 1595
Disput. de fine, ad quem homo conditus. Praes. S. H.; resp. J. Terellio. [P2610]. s4°. Vitebergae. 1593
Disput. 2a [*&* 3a], contra Calvinistas. [P2610]. s4°. Witebergae. [1593]
Theses, Christ. J. mortuum pro peccatis totius gen. hum. &c. Acc. confut. thesium Kimedoncij. [P2610]. s4°. Tubingae. 1592
see HEILBRUNNER (J.) Sendbrieff an S. H. &c., 1597.
,, HOË (M.) Expedita &c. respons. ad appellat. S. H. 1604.
,, HOFFMANN (D.) Abtruck etl. Schr., Genuinus intellectus Formulae Concord: S. H. Schr. &c., 1597.
,, HUNNIUS (E.) Theses H. oppos. &c., 1597.
,, LAUTENBACH (S.) Controv. de regener. & electione, explic. E. H. &c. cum refut. S. H., 1594.
,, OSIANDER (L.) Gründtl. Bericht; auff S. Huber's Lästerschrifft &c., 1596.
,, RICHERTZ (L. D.) Diss. de S. H. vita &c., 1706.
,, WITTENBERG. Bekenntnis v. d. ewigen Gnadenwahl &c., 1597.

Huberich (Charles Henry) & A. Nicol-Speyer, *edd.* German legisl. for the occupied territories of Belgium: official texts. [*German, French, Flemish*]. 17 s. (1914–18). s8°. The Hague. 1915–19
,, ,, ...Index to ser. 1–5, 6–9, 10–13, 14–17. [4v]. s8°. The Hague. 1917–19

Huberinus (Gaspar), *see* HÜBER (CASPAR).

Hubert (Eugène), *ed*, *see* FRANCE. Corr. des ministres de F. accréd. à Brux., 1780–90: dépêches inéd., 2t, 1920–24.

Hubert (Henri), *dicreteur adj., École d. Hautes Ét.* Introd. à la tr. fr. du Manuel d'hist. des relig. de P. D. Chantepie de la Saussaye. [P2790]. la8°. 1904

Hubert (W. E.) Lebensbilder kathol. Erzieher. Hrsg. W. E. H. [B]1–7 [*in* 2v]. s8°. Mainz. 1886–97
1, Joseph Calasanza, Stifter d. frommen Schulen.
2, Joh. Bapt. de la Salle.
3, Angela Merici, Stifterin d. Ursulinerinnen.
4, Hieronymus Aemiliani, Stifter d. Kongr. v. Somasca.
5, B. H. Overberg; bearb. A. Knöppel.
6, Alexia Le Clerc: Leben v. i. selbst &c.
7, Petrus Canisius; bearb. A. Knöppel.

Hubert (William), *see* BAXTER (R.) Naked Popery; or the Catholick naked truth [1676], by W. H., 1677.

Hubertus (Conradus). *Hist. vera de vita M. Buceri & P. Fagii. Item hist. C. Vermiliae &c.; cum oration. &c. [Ed. C. H.] s8°. [Argentinae]. 1562 [*colophon has date 1561*]

Hubin (Nicholas), *see* BELLINGHAM (J.) & N. H. Patent (1679) of J. B. & N. H.; manufacture of glass, 1857.

Hübner (Johann), *the elder.* Genealog. Tabellen z. Erlaüt d. polit. Hist. 4T.obl. 4°. L. 1727–37
,, ,, ...Suppl.-Tafeln. 6T *in* 1v. obl.4°. Kopenhagen. 1822–24

Hübner (Johann Valentin). De triplici Ebræorum Cabbala. Præses J. V. H., resp. S. Jorisch. [P2666]. 8°. Wittebergæ. 1669

Hübner (Martin). De la saisie des bâtimens neutres &c. 2t. s8°. La Haye. 1859

Hübner (Rudolf), *ed.*, *see* DROYSEN (J. G.) Aktenstücke &c. z. Gesch. d. Frankfurter Nationalversamml., 1924.

Hübschmann (Heinrich). Die altarmen. Ortsnamen. [Sonderabdr. a. Indogerm. Forsch., B16. *Map wanting.*] 8°. Str. 1904
Armenische Gramm. T1, Arm. Etymologie. [Bibl. d. indogerm. Gramm., B6]. 2 Abt. [*pagin. contin.*] 8°. L. 1895–97

Huc (Evariste Régis). H. & Gabet. Travels in Tartary, Thibet & China, 1844–46. Tr. W. Hazlitt. Ed. w. intr. by P. Pelliot. [Broadway Tr.] 2v. 8°. [1928]
Souv. d'un voyage dans la Tartarie & le Thibet, 1844–46. n. éd. annot. & illust. par J.-M. Planchet. 2t. 8°. Pékin. 1924
,, ,, n. éd., publ. & préf. par H. d'Ardenne de Tizac. 2[t]. 8°. [1925–26]
Travels in Tartary, Thibet, China, 1844–46. Tr. W. Hazlitt. 2nd ed. 2v. s8°. *n.d.*

Huch (Friedrich).
Geschwister. s8°. 1903
Neue Träume. s8°. Mün. 1914
Peter Michel. Roman. 3e A. s8°. Hamburg. 1902
Träume. s8°. 1904
Wandlungen. Roman. s8°. 1905

Huch (Ricarda), *aft. Frau R. Ceconi.*
Das Leben d. Grafen Federigo Confalonieri. s8°. L. 1910
Michael Bakunin u. d. Anarchie. s8°. L. 1923
Michael Unger. Roman. Des Buches Vita somnium breve. 8e A. s8°. L. 1920
Wallenstein: e. Charakterstudie. s8°. L. 1920

Huch (Rudolf).
Die Familie Hellmann. Roman. s8°. L. [1921]
Die Rübenstedter. s8°. München. 1910

Huchet (Charles Angélique François), *comte de La Bédoyère, see* LA BÉDOYÈRE (C. A. F. H., *c.* DE).

Huchon (René). Hist. de la langue anglaise. t1. 8°. 1923

Huck (A.) Synopse d. drei ersten Evangelien. 6. verbess. A. Anhang: Die Johannesparallelen. 8°. Tübingen. 1922

Huckel (Oliver).
Mental medicine. Intr. by L. F. Barker. 8°. [1909]

Hucks (Dorothea Barnetta), *aft. wife of Ant. Gibbs, see* GIBBS (D. B.)

Huddesford (George).
The Wiccamical chaplet, a sel. of orig. poetry &c. s8°. 1804

Huddleston (Sisley). France. [Mod. World]. 8°. 1926
France & the French. 8°. [1925]
In & about Paris. 8°. [1927]
Poincaré: a biog. portrait. 8°. [1924]

Hude (Carl). Les oraisons funèbres de Lysias & de Platon, *see* KONGELIGT DAN. VID. SELSK. Hist.-fil. Med., B1, 1917–18.

Hudeczek (Carl).
Die Wirtschaftskräfte Österreichs. [P2735]. 8°. Wien. 1920

Hudibras, *the younger, ps.* Sultan Sham, & his seven wives: poem. [*A satire on King George*]. [P425]. 8°. 1820

Hudibrastick. *Hudribrastick [*sic*], The, brewer &c.: a satyr upon the suppos'd a. [*i.e.* E. Ward] of the Republ. procession. [P2868]. s8°. 1714

Hudleston (F. J.) Warriors in undress. 8°. [1925]

Hudleston (William), *vicar of Tirley, or Trinley, Glos.* Divine truths vindic. in the Ch. of Eng. 8°. 1733

Hudribrastick, *see* HUDIBRASTICK.

Hudson (Henry), *the navigator.* Reize onder Nederl. vlag van Amsterdam naar Nova Zembla &c., 1609. Volgens het journaal van R. Juet. Uitg. S. P. L'Honoré Naber. [Linschoten Ver., 19]. 8°. 's-Gravenhage. 1921
see ASHER (G. M.) Sketch of H. H., 1867.
,, GERRITSZOON (H.) Beschryvinghe van der Samoyeden Landt &c. (1612/13); uitg. S. P. L'Honoré Naber, 1924.
,, POWYS (L.) H. H., 1927.

Hudson (Henry Arnold). Mediaeval woodwork of Manchester Cathedral. la8°. M'ter. 1924

Hudson (James William). Hist. of adult. Educ. 8°. 1851

Hudson (John), *ed.* Geographiae vet. scr. Graeci minores, cum interpret. Latina [*of J. H. & others*], diss. (H. Dodwelli), & annot. [Acc. geog. Arab. *in* v3]. Gr. & Lat. 4v. s8°. Oxoniae. 1698–1712

Hudson (Manley Ottmer). Advisory opinions of the Permanent Court of Internat. Justice, *see* INTERNAT. CONCILIATION, No. 214, 1925.

Hudson (Samuel). The essence & unitie of the Church Catholike visible. s4°. 1645

Hudson (Stephen).
Elinor Colhouse. s8°. [1921]
Myrtle. s8°. 1925
Prince Hempseed. s8°. [1923]
Richard Myrtle & I. s8°. 1926
Tony. s8°. 1924

Hudson (Thomas), *F.S.S.* Temperance pioneers of the West. Personal experiences. 2nd ed. 8°. 1888

Hudson (William Cadwalader).
Random recoll. Intr. by St. C. McKelway. s8°. N.Y. 1911

Hudson (William Henry), *1862–1918.*
Short hist. of Eng. lit. in the 19th cent. s8°. 1920
A short hist. of French lit. W. mem. of a. by A. A. Jack. s8°. 1919
St. in interpret. Keats-Clough-Matthew Arnold. 8°. N.Y. 1896

Hudson (William Henry), *F.Z.S., 1841–1922.*
Birds in town & village. 8°. 1919
Birds of La Plata. 2v. la8°. 1920
A crystal age. [4th impr.] s8°. [1919]
Dead Man's Plack—An old thorn—& poems. 8°. 1924
El Ombú. [Re-issue]. s8°. [1920]
Green mansions. [5th impr.] s8°. 1919
„ „ [6th impr.] s8°. [1922]
„ „ [7th impr.] s8°. [1925]
A hind in Richmond Park. 8°. 1922
153 letters. Ed., w. intr. & explan. notes by E. Garnett. la8°. 1923
Idle days in Patagonia. [repr.] 8°. 1923
The Land's End: impressions in W. Cornwall. [n. ed.] 8°. 1923
Letters to Ed. Garnett. s8°. 1925
The purple land: the narr. of R. Lamb's advs. in the Banda Orientál, in S. America. [5th impr.] s8°. [1919]
Rare, vanishing & lost Brit. birds. Comp. f. notes of H. by L. Gardiner. 8°. 1923
A shepherd's life: impress. of the S. Wiltshire Downs. [5th ed.] s8°. [1920]
A traveller in little things. 8°. 1921
[Twelve letters on the birds of Buenos Ayres. *No tp., var. pagin.; extr. f.* Roy. Zool. Soc., Proc., 1870–71. P2749]. 8°. [1870–71]
see ROBERTS (M.) W. H. H.: a portrait, 1924.
„ WILSON (G. F.) Bibliog. of writings of W. H. H., 1922.

Hudson's Bay Company, *see* MACKENZIE (N. M. W. J.) Men of the H.B.C., 1921.
Hudson-Williams (Thomas). Early Greek elegy. Elegiac fragm. of Callinus, Archilochus, Mimnermus &c. Ed. w. intr., text, crit. notes &c. by T. H.-W. 8°. Cardiff. 1926
Hue, *de Rotelande.* Protheselaus. Ein altfranz. Abenteuerroman. Krit. hrsg. v. F. Kluckow. [Gesell. f. rom. Lit., B45]. B1. 8°. Göttingen. 1924

Hueffer (Ford H. Madox) [F. M. FORD].
The heart of the country. s8°. 1906
Joseph Conrad: a personal remembrance. 8°. [1924]
A man could stand up—. s8°. [1926]
The Marsden case. s8°. [1923]
Some do not. . . s8°. [1924]
see CONRAD (J.) & F. H. M. H. The nature of a crime, 1924.
„ —— & —— The inheritors, 1923.
„ —— & —— Romance, 1923.

Huesca. Memorias de la Univ. de H., por R. del Arco, *see* COLECCION de docs. para el estudio de la hist. de Aragon, t8, 11, 1912–16.
Huet (Coenraad Busken), *see* BUSKEN HUET (C.)
Huet (Maurice). Amour & alésage, nouv., *see* ŒUVRES libres, t36, 1924.
Huet (Pierre Daniel), *bp. of Avranches* [HUETIUS]. Tract. de situ paradisii terrestris &c. s8°. Lipsiae. 1694
Huffel (W. C. van).
Willem B. van Rhoon, 1725–47. 8°. 's-Gravenhage. 1923
Hüffell (Ludwig). Katechismus d. Glaubens- u. Sittenlehre uns. evangel.-christl. Kirche. s8°. Giessen. 1824
Hüffer (Hermann). Quellen z. Gesch. d. Zeitalters d. französ. Revolution. Hrsg. v. H. H. &c. T1, 2B. 8°. L. 1900–01
I, Quellen z. Gesch. d. Kriege v. 1799 u. 1800.
Hug (Johann Leonhard v.) Introd. to the New Test. Tr. f. 3rd German ed. by D. Fosdick, jr., w. notes by M. Stuart. 8°. Andover. 1836
Hügel (*Baron* Friedrich v.), *1852–1925.*
Essays &c. on the phil. of religion. 2s. 8°. 1921–26
The life of prayer. [2nd impr.] s8°. 1928
Sel. letters, 1896–1924. Ed. w. mem. by B. Holland. 8°. 1927
Hugh [CAPET], *king of France.* Hugues Capet, chanson de geste; publ. par le Mis de La Grange, *see* GUESSARD (F.) Anc. poëtes, t8, 1864.
Hugh, *bp. of Lincoln, St., d. 1200, see* WOOLLEY (R. M.) St. H. of Lincoln, 1927.
Hugh, *of Wells, bp. of Lincoln; d. 1235.* Rotuli H. de W., Episc. Lincoln., 1209–35. Ed. W. P. W. Phillimore. [Lincoln Rec. Soc., v3, 6, 9]. 3v. la8°. Lincoln. 1912–14
Hughan (Jessie Wallace).
A study of internat. govt. 8°. [1924]
Hughan (William James). Mem. of the Masonic Union, 1813, A list of Lodges &c. Also, repr. of Dassigny's "Serious &c. enquiry." Rev. & augm. ed. by J. T. Thorp. 8°. Leicester. 1913
Orig. of Eng. rite of freemasonry. Ed. J. T. Thorp. n. & rev. ed. 8°. Leicester. 1909
Hughes (Alice). My father & I. 8°. [1923]
Hughes (Charles Evans). Addresses, 1906–16. Intr. by J. G. Gould. 2nd ed. rev., w. new material. s8°. N.Y. 1916
Hughes (Collingwood). Bets & the betting tax. 8°. [1927]
Hughes (E. Talbot), *see* SELIGMAN (G. S.) & E. T. H. Domestic needlework, 1926.
Hughes (Edward Arthur), *see* HODGES (H. W.) & E. A. H., *edd.* Select naval doc., 1922.
Hughes (Edward R.), *see* HUGHES (A.) My father & I, 1923.
Hughes (Elizabeth). Infant mortality, Gary, Ind., 1923, *see* UNITED STATES: LABOR.
—— **& L. Roberts.** Children of preschool age in Gary, Ind., *see* UNITED STATES: LAB. Children's Bur., Publ. 122, 1922.
Hughes (George), *B.D.* Aphorisms of the Scripture, determining the doctrin[e] of the sabbath. [*Ed.* O. Hughes]. s8°. *n.p.* [London]. 1670
Hughes (George Ravensworth), *see* CARRINGTON (J. B.) & G. R. H. Plate of the Co. of Goldsmiths, 1926.
Hughes (Gwendolyn S.), *see* BRUNNER (E. DE S.), G. S. H. &c. Amer. agricult. villages, 1927.
Hughes (Helen Sard), *see* HOPKINS (A. B.) & H. S. H. The Eng. novel bef. the 19th c.: excerpts, 1915.
Hughes (Henry Castree). Some stones of Peterhouse, *see* WARD (*Sir* A. W.) In memoriam, 1924.
Hughes (John), *poet, 1677–1720.* Siege of Damascus, *see* INCHBALD (E.) Brit. th., v10, 1808.
„ „ ....*for a. ed., see* NEW Eng. theatre, v10, 1777.
Hughes (John Cecil).
Geolog. story of the I. of Wight. s8°. 1922
Hughes (John Joseph), *R.C. Archbp. of New York, see* HASSARD (J. R. G.) Life of J. H., w. extr. f. corr., 1866.
Hughes (M. W.) Story of Cumnor. s8°. O. 1927
Hughes (Samuel), *C.E.* Gen. survey of princ. metropol. roads, *see* LAW (H.) Rudiments, 1861–62.
Hughes (Thomas), *a. of "Tom Brown."* *Tom Brown's school days. 8°. 1890
Hughes (Thomas), *of Market Rasen.*
Mental furniture. s8°. 1857
Hughes (Thomas Harold) & E. A. G. Lamborn.
Towns & town-planning. 4°. O. 1923
Hughes (Thomas McKenny). *The following items are repr. f.* Camb. Antiq. Soc.'s Proc. *or* Communic.
Acoustic vases in churches. [P2738]. 8°. 1915
Anc. ditches &c. found in rec. excav. near the Pitt Press. [P2738]. 8°. [1893]
Flints. [P2738]. 8°. 1915
On objects found in King's Ditch. [P2738]. 8°. 1915
The war ditches, near Cherryhinton, Camb. [P2738]. 8°. [1903 ?]
see AVELINE (W. T.) & T. McK. H. Geol. of co. around Kendal &c., 1898.

Hughes (*Rev.* W.) Tour thr. Midland & West. Depts. of France, 1802. 8°. 1803
Hughes (W. J.), *lecturer in English, Normal Coll., Bangor.* Wales & the Welsh in Eng. lit. f. Shakespeare to Scott. 8°. Wrexham. 1924
Hugman (John). *Orig. poems in the moral &c. styles. By a Traveller. [*Each poem signed J. H.*] 14th ed. s8°. Halesworth. 1833
Hugo, *de Sancto Charo, Cardinal.* Sacr. Bibliorum vulgatæ ed. concordantiæ; rec. & emend. à F. Luca, posteà expurg. &c. cura H. Phalesii. ed. nov. sm. fol. Venetiis. 1768
„ „ ....denuo expurg. &c. cura H. Phalesii. fol. Viennae. 1825
Hugo *de Sancto Victore.* Opera omnia. Cum vita. Studio &c. canonicorum regul. abb. S. Victoris Paris. 3t. fol. Rothomagi. 1648
see HAUREAU (J. B.) H. de S. V.: nouvel examen de l'éd. de s. œuvres, 1859.
Hugo (*Mme.* Adèle), *wife of V. Hugo, see* SIMON (G.) La vie d'une femme [Mme. V. H.], 1914.
Hugo (C.), *ps.* [*i.e.* HUGO LINDEMANN]. Der Sozialismus in Frankreich im 17. u. 18. Jhdt., *see* VORLÄUFER d. neueren Soz., 2e A., B4, 1922.
Hugo (Hermannus).
Pia desideria libri 3. Ed. 5a. [*imperf.*] s8°. Antverpiae. 1629
„ „ .....Ed. prorsus nova, accur. J. H. Ursino. s8°. Francofurti. 1657
„ „ ....Quatuor noviss. M. Raderi & J. Niesii. s8°. Coloniae Agripp. 1673
„ „ ....Engl. by E. Arwaker. 3rd ed. s8°. 1702
see GUYON (*Mme.* J. M.) L'ame amante de son Dieu repres. dans les emblèmes de H. H. &c., 1790.

Hugo (*le gén. cte.* **Joseph L. S.**), *see* BARTHOU (L.) Le gén. H., 1773–1828 : lettres & docs. inéd., 1926.

Hugo (Victor).

WORKS [*Two or more, & Théâtre*].
France & Belgique—Alpes & Pyrénées. s8°. *Nelson.* [1912]
Marie Tudor—La Esmeralda——Angelo. s8°. *Nelson.* [1912]
WORKS [*Single*].
L'art d'être grand-père. s8°. *Nelson.* [1912]
Choses vues. s8°. *Nelson.* [1914 ?]
Les contemplations. s8°. *Nelson.* [1912]
„ „ n. éd., publ. avec intr. &c. par J. Vianey. [G. E. de la F.] 3t. 8°. 1922
L'homme qui rit. 2t. s8°. *Nelson.* [1912]
Légende des siècles. n. éd., publ. avec intr., notes &c. par P. Berret. [G. E. de la F.] t1–4. 8°. 1920–25
Odes & ballades. n. éd. s8°. 1884
Le Rhin. Lettres à un ami. 2t. s8°. *Nelson.* [1912]
REFERENCES.
see CONSERVATEUR (LE) LITT., 1819–21 ; [*contrib. by* V. H. &c.], t1, p1, 1922.
REFERENCES [*continued*].
see DARMESTETER (*Mme.* J.) V. H. [Makers of 19th c.], 1921.
„ DUPUY (E.) Jeunesse d. romantiques, V. H. & A. de Vigny, 1905.
„ GUIARD (A.) La fonction du poète : étude sur V. H., 1910.
„ HAGGARD (*Lt.-Col.* A. C. P.) V. H. : h. work & love, 1923.
„ LE BRETON (A.) La jeunesse de V. H., 1928.
„ NORAYR *Biuzantatzi.* Crit. of Noupareah tr. of H.'s Notre Dame (*in Arm.*), 1884.
„ SÉCHÉ (L.) Le cénacle de Joseph Delorme (1, V. H. & les poètes. 2, V. H. & les artistes), 1912.
„ SIMON (G. M. S. C.) Enfance de V. H., avec poésies inéd^s^. &c., 1904.
„ VINET (A. R.) Et. sur la litt. fr. au 19e s., t2, Lamartine & V. H., 1916.

Hugo's Institute.
Spanish simplified. "Standard" ed. 4p *in* 1v. s8°. *n.d.*

Huguenot. *Chansonnier H. du 16e s., 1870, *see* CHANSONNIER.

Huguenot Society of London.
Proceedings. v10–12 (1912–23). 8°. *p.p.* 1914–24
Publications. v22–30. 4°. London, M'ter., Reading. 1914–27
see CHAPEL ROYAL. Reg. des églises de la C.R. de St. James 1700–56 & de Swallow Street, 1690–1709 ; ed. W. & S. Minet, 1924. [28.]
„ FRENCH CHURCH, *Savoy.* Livres des conversions &c. faites à l'Eglise Franc. de la Savoye, 1684–1702, 1914. [22.]
„ —— Reg. des églises de la Savoye, de Spring Gardens &c., 1684–1900, 1922. [26.]
„ FRENCH CHURCH, *Soho Square.* Reg. of the Ch. of le Carré &c., 1690–1788, 1921. [25.]
„ FRENCH CHURCH, *Threadneedle Street.* Registers, v4, 1916. [23.]
„ GIUSEPPI (M. S.), *ed.* Naturaliz. of foreign Protestants in the Amer. & West Ind. colonies, 1921. [24.]
„ LEICESTER FIELDS. Reg. of churches of the Tabernacle Glasshouse St. & L. F., 1688–1783 ; ed. W. & S. Minet, 1926. [29.]
„ RIDER COURT. Reg. of Church of R.C., 1700–38, 1927. [30.]
„ SHAW (W. A.) Letters of deniz. & Acts of naturaliz. for aliens in Eng. & Ireland, 1701–1800, 1923. [27.]

Hugues (Jean Pierre). Hist. de l'église réformée d'Anduze, j. la Révol. franç. 2e éd. 8°. 1864

Hugues Capet, chanson de geste, *see* HUGH [CAPET], *king of France.*

Huguet (Adrien). Un Grand Maréchal des Logis de la Maison du Roi. Le Marquis de Cavoye 1640–1716. la8°. 1920

Huguet (Edmond). Dict. de la langue franç. du 16e s. t1. [*in progr.*] la8°. 1925–27

Huidekoper (Christian). Die Sünden Don Alfonsos d. Weisen. Roman. Vom Verf. aus d. Holländ. übertr. 8°. München. 1923

Huisman (Georges).
De S. Martin des Champs aux Halles. s8°. [1925]
Pour comprendre les mon. de Paris. s8°. 1925

Huisseau (Isaac d'). La discipline des églises refformées de France. n. & dern. éd. s8°. Bionne. 1675
*Reuniting (The) of Christianity &c., *attrib. to d'H.* ; tr., 1673, *see* REUNITING.

Huitfeld (Arrild).
Danmarckis Rigis Krønicke. 2t [*pagin. cont.*] sm. fol. 1652
Den geistlige Hist. offver alt Danmarckis Rige. [*b. w. h.* D. R. Krønicke, t1, 1652]. sm. fol. 1653

Huizinga (Johan).
Erasmus. Intr. by the ed. [E. W. Bok]. s8°. N.Y. 1924
Herfsttij der Middeleeuwen. Levens-en gedachten-vormen d. 14 en 15 eeuw en Frankrijk en de Nederlanden. 2e herz. dr. 8°. Haarlem. 1921
The waning of the Middle Ages : France & Netherlands in 14 & 15 cent. [Tr.] 8°. 1924

Hulbert (Archer Butler). The paths of inland commerce. [Chron. of Amer. ser., v21]. 8°. N.H., *Yale.* 1920

Hulbert (Charles). Candid strictures on passages in "Thoughts on the Protest. ascendancy in Ireland," in a letter to [*its a.*] the Hon. H. G. Bennett. [P449]. 8°. Shrewsbury. [1807]

Huldermann (Bernhard).
Albert Ballin. 8°. Oldenburg i. O. 1922
Albert Ballin. Tr. W. J. Eggers. 8°. 1922

Huldrich (Johann Jacob) [HULDRICUS]. Vindiciae pro Bibliorum tr. Tigurina : adv. J. Gretseri Admon. noviter ad exteros emissam. [P2645]. s4°. Tiguri. 1616

Hull (Arthur Eaglefield). Cyril Scott. 2nd ed. s8°. 1919
Dict. of mod. music & musicians. Ed. Comm., Sir H. Allen, G. Bantock &c. Gen. ed. A. E.-H. 8°. 1924
Music, classical, romantic & modern. 8°. 1927

Hull (C.) *A choice coll. of hymns. Taken f. var. a. by C. H. s8°. Bristol. 1776

Hull (Edith M.) Camping in the Sahara. 8°. [1926]
The desert healer. [2nd impr.] s8°. [1923]
The shadow of the East. [8th impr.] s8°. [1923]
The Sheik. s8°. *Nash. n.d.*
Sons of the Sheik. [2nd imp.] s8°. [1926]

Hull (Edward), *F.R.S.*
Geol. of the co. around Cheltenham. [Mems. of G.S.] 8°. 1857
Geol. of co. around Prescot, Lancs. [Mems. of G.S.] 3rd ed. w. add. by Sir A. Strahan. 8°. 1882
Geol. of co. around Woodstock, Oxfordshire &c. [Mems. of G.S.] 8°. 1859
Geol. of the Leicestershire coal-field. [Mems. of G.S.] 8°. 1860
Triassic & Permian rocks of the Midland co. of Eng. [Mems. of G.S.] 8°. 1869
see RAMSAY (*Sir* A. C.), W. T. AVELINE & E. H. Geol. of parts of Wilts &c., 1858.
—— **& A. H. Green.** Geology of the co. round Stockport, Macclesfield, Congleton & Leek. [Mems. of G.S.] 8°. 1866

Hull (Eleanor).
Folklore of the Brit. Isles. Pref. by R. R. Marett. 8°. [1928]
Hist. of Ireland &c., to close of Tudor period. 8°. [1926]

Hull (Thomas), *actor.* Henry the Second, *see* †INCHBALD (*Mrs.* E.) Mod. theatre, v9, 1811.
Sel. letters betw. Duchess of Somerset, Lady Luxborough, W. Shenstone &c., incl. sk. of manners &c. of Venice &c. Publ. by Mr. H. 2v. 8°. 1778

Hull (William Winstanley).
The disuse of the Athanasian creed advisable. 8°. O. 1831

Hullah (John Pyke). Music in the house. [4th ed.] s8°. 1878

Hulme (Arthur), *see* UNWIN (G.) S. Oldknow & the Arkwrights ; w. chaps. by A. H. &c., 1924.

Hulme (Edward Wyndham). *Patent law & the legal standard of novelty. Repr. f. "The Engineer," Apr. 11, 1919. [P2486]. s8°. 1919

Hulme (Thomas Ernest). Speculations : humanism & the philos. of art. Ed. H. Read, w. foreword by J. Epstein. 8°. 1924

Hulpe, *Saint & martyr* (ULPE ; ULPIUS), *see* CASSEL (J. P.) Hist. Nachricht v. S. H., 1765.

Hulricus, *see* ULRIC, *saint, bp. of Augsburg.*

Hülsemann (Johann). De auxiliis gratiæ. Acc. disput. cum H. Grotio de harmonia S. S. Pauli & Jacobi ex cap. 2 Ep. Jacobi. s4°. Francofurti. 1705
Dialysis apologet. problematis Calixtini : mysterium Trinitatis aut Divinitatis Christi &c. s4°. Lipsiae. 1650
Methodus concionandi, auctior ed. Acc. Methodus studii theol. &c. [*b. w.* Carpzov (J. B.) Hodegeticum, 1689]. ed. 5a. s8°. Wittebergae. 1667

Hülsen (Christian). Escurialensis u. Sangallo. [Aus d. Jahresh. d. Österr. Arch. Inst., B13, 1910]. [P2699]. 4°. [Wien]. [1910]
Le illustr. d. "Hypnerotomachia Polifili" [*by* F. Colonna] e le antichità di Roma. [P2699]. 4°. Firenze. 1910
Eine Samml. röm. Renaissance-Inschr. aus d. Augsburger Koll. K. Peutingers, *see* KÖNIGL. AKAD. D. W. ZU MÜNCHEN. Phil. Kl., Sitz., 1920.

Hulshof (Abraham). Deut. u. latein. Schrift in d. Niederlanden (1350–1650). [Tabulae in Usum Schol., ed. J. Lietzmann, 9]. la8°. Bonn. 1918

Hulsius (Levinus). *Epitome emblematum Acad. Altorf. [*b. w.* Taurellus (N.) Emblemata, 1602]. s8°. Noribergae. 1602

Hulton (Ann). Letters of a Loyalist lady, 1767–76. [Intr. signed H. M. &c.] 8°. Camb., *Harvard.* 1927

Hultzsch (Eugen), *see* CORPUS Inscript. Indicarum, n. ed., v1, Inscr. of Asoka, 1925.

Hulzen (G. van).
De man uit de slop. 2e dr. 8o. Rotterdam. 1903
Maria van Dalen. 2d. 8o. 1907
*__Humane__ prudence, 7th ed., 1697, *see* DE BRITAINE (W.)
Humanitarian League, *see* LITERAE humaniores, an appeal to teachers, 1911.
Humanity, the Positivist review, 1924–25, *see* POSITIVIST RÉV.
Humberstone (Thomas Lloyd). Science & labour. Addresses at Conf., May 1924. Ed. T. L. H. Pref. by Ld. Askwith. 8o. 1924
Univ. reform in London. Intr. by H. G. Wells. 8o. [1926]
Humbert (Charles). Chacun son tour. s8o. 1925
Humbert (Jules).
Hist. de la Colombie & du Vénézuéla. la8o. 1921
Humbert (Pierre), *prof. at Montpellier, see* HANOTAUX (G.) Hist. de la nation franç., t14, Hist. des sci., v1, Mathémat., mécanique &c. par H. Andoyer & P. H., 1924.
Humble.
H. answer (The) of the divines to 2nd paper by H.M., Oct. 6, 1648, about episc. govt., 1660, *see* DIVINES.
*H. motion (An) with submission unto H.M. privie counsell &c., 1590, *see* PENRY (J.)
H. petition (The) of the gentry of Co. of York, pres. to H.M., 1642, *see* CHARLES I, *of Gt. Brit.*
*H. proposals (The) of sundry learned &c. divines, 1650, *see* REYNOLDS (E.)
Humble (Joseph), *see* DONCASTER. D. Regional Planning Scheme, w. app. on coal subsidence by J. H., 1922.
Humboldt (Alexander v.) Physical descr. of the heavens. Tr. under E. Sabine. s8o. 1866
see BERNSTEIN (A.) A. v. H. u. d. Geist 2 Jhdte., 1869.
Humboldt (Wilhelm v.) Berichtig. u. Zusätze z. 1. Abschn. d. 2. B. d. Mithridates [*by* J. C. Adelung] ü. d. Cantabr. od. Bask. Sprache. 8o. 1817
Briefe an eine Freundin. Mit Einl. v. R. Habs. [*repr.*] s8o. L. [1894]
Gesammelte Schriften. Hrsg. v. d. Preuss. Akad. d. Wiss. B13, Nachträge. Unter Mitwirkung v. S. Kähler &c. hrsg. v. A. Leitzmann. la8o. 1920
13, Abtlg. 1, Werke 10.
Lettre à M. Abel-Rémusat sur la nature des formes gramm., & sur le génie de la langue chinoise. 8o. 1827
see BÜLOW (G. v.) G. v. B.: Lebensbild aus d. Familienpap. H., 1791–1887, 1896.
,, FARINELLI (A.) G. de H. & l'Espagne &c., 1924.
Hume, *The family of, see* HUME (D.) De familia Humia Wedderburnensi, 1839.
Hume (David), *of Godscroft.* De familia Humia Wedderburnensi. [Ed. J. Miller. Abbotsford Club]. 4o. E. 1839
Hume (David), *the historian.*
Essays moral, polit. & lit. Ed. T. H. Green & T. H. Grose. n. imp. 2v. 8o. 1898
see BLACK (J. B.) Art. of hist., 1926.
,, HENDEL (C. W.) St. in the philos. of D. H., 1925.
see TAYLOR (A. E.) D. H. & the miraculous, 1927.
,, WITTSTEIN (T.) Streit zw. Glauben u. Wiss. auf Grundl. d. Lehre D. H. &c., 1884.
Hume (Ethel Douglas). Béchamp or Pasteur? Lost chapter in hist. of biology. Founded upon MS. by M. R. Leverson, w. foreword by S. J. Lewis. 8o. Chicago. 1923
Hume (G. S.) Palæozoic outlier of lake Timiskaming, Ontario & Quebec. [Canada, G.S.] 8o. Ottawa. 1925
Hume (Hardrada Harold).
Citrus fruits & their culture. s8o. N.Y. 1915
Hume (James Deacon). Evidence upon the corn law, bef. the comm. of the H. of C. in 1839. [*No tp.; b. w.* Thompson (T. P.) Catechism, 1830]. 8o. *n.d.*
Hume (Lois), *ps., see* CREIGHTON (*Mrs.* L.)
Hume (M.) Psychism. s8o. [1902]
Hume (Martin Andrew Sharp). Spain, its greatness & decay (1479–1788). Rev. by E. Armstrong. 3rd ed. 8o. C. 1925
Hume (Robert Ernest).
The world's living religions. s8o. E. 1924
see UPANISHADS. The 13 princ. U.; tr., w. outline of the philos. of the U. & an annot. bibliogr., by R. E. H., 1921.
Humfrey (John), *M.A.*
De justificatione: a letter. [P2653]. s4o. 1706
Humières (Robert d'). Le livre de la beauté. Préc. d'une étude par C. Mauclair. 2é ed. 8o. 1921
Humiston (Charles E.), *see* RILEY (W.), F. W. PEABODY & C. E. H. Faith, falsity & failure of Xtn. Science, 1926.
Hummel (Bernhard Friedrich). Neue Bibl. v. selt. Büchern u. kl. Schr.; hrsg. v. B. F. H. 3B *in* 2v. s8o. Nürnberg. 1776–82
Hummel (Johann Ludwig). *Sum aller Cronicken biss vff den Brachmonat dess M.D.LII. jars. s4o. Basel. 1552
Hümmerich (Franz). Die erste deut. Handelsfahrt nach Indien, 1505–06. 8o. München. 1922
Quellen u. Untersuch. z. Fahrt d. ersten Deutschen [B. Sprenger &c.] nach d. Portugies. Indien, 1505–06, 1918, *see* KÖNIGL. AKAD. D. W. ZU MÜNCHEN. Abhdgn., B30, 1920.
Humphrey (A. P.) & T. F. Fremantle. Hist. of the Nat. Rifle Assoc., 1859–1909. s8o. C. 1914
Humphrey (Frank Pope). The Queen at Balmoral. 8o. 1893
Humphrey (George). The story of man's mind. 8o. 1925
Humphrey (John). Drugs in commerce. s8o. *Pitman.* [1921]
Humphreys (Arthur L.)
Caversham Bridge, 1231–1926. la8o. Reading. 1926
East Hendred: a Berkshire parish hist. treated. la8o. 1923
Eccentric characters of Berkshire. 8o. Reading. 1926
Elias Ashmole. [Repr. f. Berks, Bucks, & Oxon Archælog. Journ.] [P2785]. 8o. Reading. 1925
Old decorative maps & charts. With illust. & a Cat. of atlases &c. in coll. of H. Stevens. 4o. 1926
Somersetshire parishes: hdbk. of hist. ref. [*b. in* 2v.] la8o. 1905
Streets & street lore of Reading. [A lecture]. 8o. *n.p. p.p.* [1926]
Humphreys (C. B.) The Southern New Hebrides: ethnolog. record. 8o. C. 1926
Humphreys (David), *D.D.* An hist. acc. of the Soc. for the Propagat. of the Gospel. 8o. 1730
Humphreys (Thomas), *see* TINLEY (G. F.), T. H. &C. Colour planning of the garden, 1924.
Humphries (Wilfred R.) Patrolling in Papua. Intr. by J. H. P. Murray. 8o. [1923]
Humphris (Edith M.)
Life of Fred Archer. Ed. Ld. A. Grosvenor. 2nd ed. 8o. 1923
Hundreth (A) sundrie flowres (1572), 1926, *see* GASCOIGNE (G.)
Hundsrücken, *see* HUNSRÜCK.
Huneker (James). Ivory, apes & peacocks. s8o. N.Y. 1921
Hungari [HUNGARORUM]. Matricula & acta Hungar. in univ. Ital. stud. Ed. A. Veress. [Fontes rer. Hung., t1, 2]. 2v. la8o. Budapest. 1915–17
1, Padova (1264–1864).
2, Roma: Coll. Germ. & Hung. (1559–1917).
Hungaria [HUNGARIAE; UNGARIA].
Acta & conclusiones conventus seu synodi certorum inclyti H. regni baronum &c. necnon legatorum &c. August. Conf. 1610. s4o. Solnae. 1708
Annales regum H. ab 997 ad 1564, 5p, 1763–70, *see* PRAY (G.)
Apologia ministrorum evang. H., ad innocentiam suam orbi Christ. declar., oppos. judicio tribunalis Poson. à quo perduellionis crimine contra regiam Majest. accusati &c. s4o. *n.p.* 1677
Articuli juxta quos regitur Eccl. in superior. regni U. partibus. s4o. *n.p.* 1667
Compend. doctrinae Christianae quam omnes pastores &c. eccl. Dei in tota U. &c., docent &c., 1562–3. [*Lat. & Hung.*] s8o. Patakini. 1655
Corpus maxime memorab. Synod. evang. August. conf. in H., 1848, *see* SZEBERINYI (J.)
Extractus articul. & diplomatum super relig. negotio in regno H. conditorum. Auszug d. Artikeln &c. [*Latin & Germ.*] s8o. *n.p.* 1790
*Hist. Eccl. Evang. August. Conf. addict. in H, 1830, *see* MUNYAY (L.)
Leges eccl. regni H. & provinciarum adjac., 3t, 1785–1827, *see* BATTHYAN, (I. DE), *ed.*
*Ratio educationis totiusque rei liter. per regn. H. &c., t1, 1777, *see* SZERDAHÉLYI (G. A. v.)
Sacra concilia eccl. Rom.-Cath. in regno H., 2p, 1741–2, *see* PÉTERFI (K.)
*Status cathol. & evang. relig. in regno H. &c. Opera IMi verit. cult. s8o. *n.p.* 1790
Hungarian.
*From behind the vail; story of H. bolshevism, 1920, *see* FROM.
H. (The) peace negociations, Jan.–March 1920. 4o. Budapest. 1920–21
*H.-Polish (The) frontier q. [P2567]. s8o. 1920
Hungarian Geographical Society, *see* MAGYAR FÖLDRAJZI TÁRSASÁG.
Hungarian Nation, The: a monthly review. v2. 4o. Budapest. 1921
Hungarica [HUNGARICAE &c.] Anomymi Belae Regis notarii, hist. H. de 7 primis ducibus Hungariae. [*Usually entitled:* De gestis Hung. liber]. s8o. Cassoviae. 1772
Fontes rerum Hungar., *see* FONTES R. H.
Hungarus (H. M.), *ps., see* ROTARIDES (JÁNOS).

Hungary.
*Balkaniz. of agric.: study of agrarian reform in H. &c. [P2682]. 8°. Budapest. 1921
*The communist experiment in H. [P2708]. 8°. 1919
Conf. nov. Cath., 1823, see MOHNIKE (G. C. F.) Zur Gesch. des ungar. Fluchformulars &c., 1823.
Ethnogr. map of H.; by order of H. For. Min., 1919; Index, 1919, see BÁTKY (Z.) & K. KOGUTOWICZ.
Extractus benignarum normalium resol. in publico-eccl., ad 1844, ed. [*Lat. & Hung.*], 1846, see EXTRACTUS.
*Hist. of the Protest. Church in H. Introd. by J. H. Merle d'Aubigné. Tr. by J. Craig. 8°. 1854
*H. & the World War. [P2567]. s8°. 1921
H. bef. & after the War in econ.-statist. maps, 1926, see EDVI ILLÉS (A.) & A. HALÁSZ, *edd.*
*The partition of H. [P2719]. 8°. Berne. 1919
Topog. Lexicon of the communities of H. comp. offic. in 1773. [*Title & pref. in Hung., Lat., Fr. & Eng.*] la8°. Budapestini. 1920

Hunger (Carl). Zur Gesch. Papst Johanns XXIII. Diss. [P2725]. 8°. Bonn. 1876

Hunger (F. W. T.) Charles de l'Escluse (Carolus Clusius), Nederland. kruidkundige, 1526–1609. la8°. 's-Gravenhage. 1927

Hunnius (Egidius), *the elder.*
Tomus 1 (2–5) Operum Lat. 5t, t5, cum tribus comoediis. fol. Witebergae (1, 3, 5), Francofurti (2, 4). 1606–9
Calvinus Judaizans, hoc est: Judaicae glossae & corruptelæ &c. Add. est corruptelarum confut. per Æ. H. s8°. Witebergae. 1593
Catechismus od. Kinderlehre v. d. christl. Religion &c. [*Imperf.*] s4°. Franckfurt a. M. 1592
Conf. E. H. cum censura viror. quorundam doctor. Add., Resp. ad argumentum contra ubiquitatem. [*b. w.* Grabe (J.) Isagoge &c., 1586]. s4°. Neostadii Palatin. 1586
De regno Christi propositiones. Præs. Æ. H., def. L. Laelius. [P2612]. s4°. Witebergae. 1597
De unione hypostatica 2 naturarum in Christo disp.; [resp.] J. H. Lohnanus. [P2612]. s4°. Witebergae. 1592
Disp. 1[–15] de August. Conf. &c. Præs. Æ. H. [*var. resp in* 1v]. s4°. Wittebergae. 1593–94
Epistola consolatoria &c. qua solatur amicum Augustanum, lugentem sortem Jesuitarum ob rem ab illis Ratisbonæ gestam. Cum notat. [P2468]. s4°. Witebergae. 1602
Labyrinthus primus papisticus. [P2609]. s4°. Witebergae. 1601
Nohtwendige Verantwortung d. Christl. Concordibuchs. [*b. w.* Hoffmann (D.) Abtruck etl. Schr. &c., 1597]. s4°. Franckfurt a. M. 1597
Eine Predigt aus d. 24. Cap. Josuae. [P2613]. s4°. Wittemberg. 1592
Rel. hist. de habito nuper Ratisbonae Colloquio inter August. Conf. theologos &c. s4°. Witebergae. 1602
Theses Huberianismo oppositæ, de electione &c., præs. Æ. H., def. J. Mehlfuhrerus. [P2638]. s4°. Witebergæ. 1597
Theses, quibus ostenditur Sacramentarios Calvinistas Aug. Conf. socios non esse. Praes. Æ. H., resp. J. Schroderus. [*b. w.* Mylius (G.) Spongia, 1591]. s4°. Witebergae. 1594
Widerlegung d. ungegründten Aufflagen, darmit D. Hoffmann, verdächtig zu machen sich unterstanden. [*b. w.* Hoffmann (D.) Abtruck etl. Schr. &c., 1597]. s4°. Franckfurt a. M. 1597
see FRANCISCI (A.) Theses de ascensione Christi &c.; per E. H., 1589.
„ GRABE (J.) Isagoge de invoc. Dei &c., 1586.
„ LAUTENBACH (S.) Controv. de regener. & electione, explic. E. H. &c., 1594.

Hunnius (Nicolaus). Epitome credend., oder Innhalt d. Christl. Lehre. [*b. w.* Fecht (J.) Compendium, 1740]. s8°. Wittenberg. 1738
Kurtze Anweisung oder Unterricht wie d. Jugend z. Xthum anzuführen sey. [*b. w.* Fecht (J.) Comp., 1740]. s8°. Wittenberg. 1739

Hunsaker (Jerome C.) Dynam. stability of aeroplanes, 1916, see SMITHSONIAN INST. Misc. coll., v62, 1923.

——, E. Buckingham &c. Rep. on wind tunnel experiments in aerodynamics, 1916, see SMITHSONIAN INST. Misc. coll., v62, 1923.

Hunstanton & its neighbourhood, 18th ed., rev. &c. by G. Webster, 1903, see WILSON (P.)

Hunt (Alfred William), *artist, see* GOSSE (*Sir* E.) Notes on pictures of H., 1884.

Hunt (Arthur Surridge), see OXYRHYNCHUS PAPYRI; ed. w. tr. by Grenfell & A. S. H., p15–17, 1922–27.

Hunt (Gaillard). Israel, Elihu & Cadwallader Washburn: chap. in Amer. biog. Comp. by G. H. 8°. N.Y. 1925
see MADISON (J.) Debates in the Fed. Convent. of 1787 &c.; H. & J. B. Scott, eds., 1920.

Hunt (George), see BOAS (F.) Ethnology of Kwakiutl, coll. by G. H., 1921.

Hunt (Henry M.) The crime of the century; or the assassin. of P. H. Cronin. s8°. *n.p.* [1889]

Hunt (James), *Ph.D.*
On the negro's place in nature. [P2755]. 8°. 1863

Hunt (John), *D.D., see* LUTHER (M.) Spiritual songs, f. the German, by J. H., 1853.

Hunt (John), *missionary.* Mem. of W. Cross, Wesleyan miss. to the Friendly or Feejee Islands w. early hist. of the missions. s8°. 1846
„ „ ....3rd ed. s8°. 1861
see ROWE (G. S.) The life of J. H., 1866.

Hunt (Joseph).
see EGAN (P.) Acc. of trial of J. Thurtell & J. H., 1824.
„ THURTELL (J.) & J. H. Trial: ed. E. R. Watson, 1920.
„ WEARE (W.) Compl. hist. of murder of Mr. W. by J. H. &c., 1824.

Hunt (Leigh) [HUNT (JAMES HENRY LEIGH)].
Poetical works. Ed. H. S. Milford. 8°. O. [1923]
Prefaces, mainly to h. periodicals. Ed. R. B. Johnson. 8°. 1927

Hunt (Myron), see HOOKER (K.) & M. H. Farmhouses &c. in S. Italy, 1925.

Hunt (Thornton). Unity of the iron network: break of gauge. [P2845]. 8°. 1846

Hunt (Violet), *aft. Mrs. F. Madox Hueffer.*
The flurried years. 8°. [1926]

Hunt (William) & R. L. Poole, see HODGKIN (T.) Hist. of Eng. to the Norman Conquest, n. impr. 1920.

Hunter Archaeological Society of Sheffield, see SHEFFIELD. Parish Reg.; transcr. & ed. by C. Drury & T. W. Hall, p3, 5, 1921–27.

Hunter, *of Hunterston, The family of.* Some family papers. Ed. for Sir A. Hunter-Weston by M. S. Shaw. [Scot. Rec. Soc.] 8°. E. 1925

Hunter (Frederick William). Coll. of books &c. rel. to Whistler coll. by H. Sold, Jan. 21, 1920, Amer. Art Assoc. [P2859]. la8°. N.Y. 1920

Hunter (George Leland).
Practical book of tapestries. 8°. Phila. 1925

Hunter (J. A.) Wool. rev. ed. s8°. *Pitman.* 1922

Hunter (James), *archdeacon of Cumberland, diocese of Rupert's Land.* A lect. on the gram. construction of the Cree lang. &c. sfol. 1875

Hunter (John), *F.R.S., see* PEACHEY (G. C.) Mem. of William & J. Hunter, 1924.

Hunter (Joseph), *F.S.A.* Alienation & recovery of estates of the Offleys of Norton, 1745 &c. [P2777]. s8°. 1841

Hunter (Leslie Whitaker), see ÆNEAS, *Tacticus.* Æ. on siegecraft; ed. L. W. H., 1927.

Hunter (Robert), *of Noroton, Conn.*
Violence & the labour movement. 8°. N.Y. 1919

Hunter (Robert), *of Whitby.* A brief acc. of a tour thr. some parts of Scotland. s8°. 1839

Hunter (Roger), *ps. ?* A peep into the cottage at Windsor. Poem. [*Satire on George* IV]. [P425]. 8°. 1820

Hunter (William), *M.D., F.R.S., see* PEACHEY (G. C.) Mem. of W. & John Hunter, 1924.

Hunter (*Sir* William Wilson). Brief hist. of the Indian peoples. 20th ed. rev. 8°. O. 1892

Hunter-Blair (*Rt. Rev. Sir* David) [OSWALD, *O.S.B., Abbot*]. A medley of memories. 50 yrs. recoll. of a Benedictine monk. 8°. 1919
A new medley of memories. 8°. 1922

Hunting (Eliza), *wife of Charles Hunting.* Diary & letters. Intr. [by R. Waters. Ed.] by h. husband. s8°. *p.f.p.c.* 1881

Huntingdon (Henry [*archdeacon*] *of*). Histor. lib. 8, *see* SAVILE (*Sir* H.) Rerum Angl. scr., 1596; 1601.

Huntingdon (Selina Hastings, *countess of*), *wife of 9th earl.*
see HYMNS. Coll. of hymns sung in ctss. of H.'s chapels, *n.d.*
„ KNIGHT (H. C.) Lady H. & her friends, 1853.

Huntington (Archer Milton).
see CHRONICA. Cronica rimada; reprod. in facs. f. MS. in Bibl. Nat. by A. M. H., 1904.
„ LIBRO de los Tres Reyes de Oriente; publ. in facs. f. MS. in Escorial by A. M. H. 1904.

Huntington (Arria Sargent). Mem. & letters of F. D. Huntington, 1st bp. of Cent. New York. s8°. Boston. 1906

Huntington (Ellsworth).
The character of races. 8°. N.Y. 1924
Civilization & climate. 8°. New Haven. 1915 [*repr.* 1919]

Huntington (Ellsworth) [*continued*].
Earth & sun: hypothesis of weather & sunspots. With ch. by H. H. Clayton. 8°. New Haven, *Yale.* 1923
West of the Pacific. 8°. N.Y. 1925
—— **& S. W. Cushing.**
Princ. of human geography. 8°. N.Y. 1921
—— **& S. S. Visher.**
Climatic changes. 8°. New Haven, *Yale.* 1922
Huntington (Frederic Dan), *bp. of Cent. New York, see* HUNTINGTON (A. S.) Mem. & letters of F. D. H., 1906.
Huntington (Henry Edward). Cat. of paintings of Brit. school in coll. of H. E. H. at San Marino, California. By M. W. Brockwell. 4°. *p.p.* N.Y. 1925
Check-list of lib. of H. E. H. Eng. lit. to 1640. Comp. under dir. of G. W. Cole. [*&* Additions &c. July 1919–June 1920, *pagin. contin.*] la8°. N.Y. *p.p.* 1919–20
see HENRY E. HUNTINGTON LIBRARY, *San Marino, California.*
Huntley (George), *see* JOHNSON (J.) Case of a rector refusing to preach &c.: being Rev. G. H.'s defence, *n.d.*
Huntly, *marquises of, see* BULLOCH (J. M.) The earls of Aboyne, 1908.
Huntly (Charles Gordon, *11th marq. of***).**
Milestones. 2nd ed. 8°. [1926]
Huon, *de Bordeaux, duc de Guienne.* Huon de Bourdeaux, chanson de Geste, *see* GUESSARD (F.) Anc. poëtes, t5, 1860.
Hupel (August Wilhelm). Ehstnische Sprachlehre f. beide Hauptdialekte, d. revalschen u. d. dörptschen; nebst e. Wbch. 8°. Riga. 1780
Hupfeld (Renatus).
Graf H. Keyserling. Vortrag. 8°. Bonn. 1922
Hupp (Otto), *see* REGENSBURG. Rathaus zu R.; Unter d. Leitung v. O. H., 1910.
Huraut (Alfred).
Étude s. Marsile de Padoue. Thèse. la8°. 1892
Hurd (Archibald Spicer). A merchant fleet at war. [Cunard Steamship Co., 1914–18]. 8°. 1920
The merchant navy, 2v, 1921–24, *see* WAR. Hist. of Gt. War.
State socialism in practice. s8°. [1925]
Hurdis (James). Letters of Rev. J. H. to W. Cowper, 1791–94. Repr. f. "Sussex Co. Mag." 1926–27. la8°. 1927
Hurlbert (William Henry). Eng. under coercion. In a letter to Ld. Coleridge. 8°. Genoa. 1893
Hurlbutt (Frank). Bow porcelain. sm. fol. 1926
Old Derby porcelain & its artist-workmen. 8°. 1925
Hurley (*Capt.* **Frank).** Argonauts of the South: voyagings &c. in the Antarctic w. Sir D. Mawson & Sir E. Shackleton. la8°. N.Y. 1925
Pearls & savages: adv. in New Guinea. la8°. N.Y. 1924
Hurmuzaki (*baron* **Eudoxiu de).** Doc. privitoare la istoria Romanilor, culese de E. de H. [Acad. Romàna]. 4°. 1911–22
14, Documente grecești; publ. &c. de N. Iorga, 2p, i, 1320–1716, ii, 1716–77.
15, Acte și scrisori (Bistrița, Brașov, Sibiiu); publ. de N. Iorga, 2p, i, 1358–1600, ii, 1601–1825.
16, Corespondență diplomatică și rapoarte consulare franceze [*in French*], 1603–1824, publ. de N. Hodos.
17, „ „ 1825–1846.
18, „ „ 1847–1851.
19, Corespondență diplomatică și rapoarte consulare austriace; publ. I. I. Nistor [*in Germ., Ital. & Fr.*], i, 1782–1797.
Hurmuzesco (D.), *see* JONESCU (T.) Les questions roumaines; [*by*] T. J., D. H. &c. 1921.
Hurry, *family of, see* HURRY-HOUGHTON (T.) & M. H.-H. Mems. of the family of H., 1926.
Hurry (Jamieson Boyd).
Imhotep, vizier & physician of King Zoser. 8°. O. 1926
„ „ 2nd rev. ed. 8°. O. 1928
The octocent. of Reading Abbey, 1121–1921. la8°. 1921
Poverty & its vicious circles. 2nd & enl. ed. 8°. 1921
Vicious circles in disease. 3rd & enl. ed. 8°. 1919
TRANSLATIONS.
Les cercles vicieux en pathologie. Tr., rev. & augm. 8°. 1923
Los círculos viciosos en patología. Tr., corr. & augm. la8°. Barcelona. [1924]
La pauvreté et ses cercles vicieux. Rev. & augm. 8°. 1924
Hurry-Houghton (Margaret), *see* HURRY-HOUGHTON (T.) & M. H.-H. Mems. of the family of Hurry, 1926.
Hurry-Houghton (Thomas) & M. Hurry-Houghton.
Mem. of the family of Hurry. la8°. Liv'l. 1926
Hurst (Fannie). Lummox. [2nd impr.] s8°. [1924]
Hurst (George H.) Silk dyeing, printing & finishing. s8°. 1892
Hurst (H. E.) The Lake Plateau Basin of the Nile. [Egypt. Pub. Works. Phys. Dept., Paper No. 21]. la8°. Cairo. 1925
Hurst (John Fletcher).
Hist. of rationalism. rev. & enl. f. 3rd Amer. ed. 8°. 1867
Hurt (Jakob). Setukeste laulud. Pihkva-Eestlaste vanad rahvalaulud &c., valja annud Dr. J. H. [Mon. Estoniae ant., vl, Carmina pop. Suomal. Kirjall. Seuran.] 8°. Helsingis. 1904
Hurtado de Mendoza (Antonio), *Comendador de Zurita.* [Fiestas de Aranjuez: festivals repres. at Aranwhez bef. the king & queen of Spain, 1623. Tr. by Sir R. Fanshawe]. s4°. [1670]
No tp.; extr. f. H. de M.'s "Querer por solo querer," 1671. *A prose summary of the* "Comedia de la gloria de Niquea" *of Villamediana, folld. by* "A descr. in verse of the festival."
Hurtado de Mendoza (Diego). Lazarillo de Tormes [*part 1 by H. de M.; part 2 by H. de Luna*]. El diablo cojuelo [*by* L. Vélez de Guevara]. 8°. Paris. *n.d.*
The pleasaunt hist. of L. de T. Drawen out of Spanish by D. Rouland, 1586. Ed. J. E. V. Crofts. [Percy Repr. No. 7]. s8°. O. 1924
La vida de L. de T. Ed. H. J. Chaytor. [Mod. Lang. Texts, Span. ser.] s8°. M'ter. 1922
Hurtado y J. de la Serna (Juan) & A. G. Palencia. Hist. de la literat. españ. [3p *in* 1v., *pag. cont.*] 8°. 1921–22
„ „ ....2a ed. 8°. 1925
Hürter (Ferdinand) & V. C. Driffield. Photographic researches. Repr. of publ. papers, w. hist. of th. early work. Ed. W. B. Ferguson. [R. Photogr. Soc.: Memorial vol.] s4°. [1920]
Hurwitz (Hyman).
Elements of the Hebrew lang. 4th ed. 8°. 1848
The etymology & syntax of the Hebrew lang. 4th ed. 8°. 1850
Hus (Matthieu), *see* JACOBUS, *de Voragine.* Lég. dorée; [impr.] M. H. & P. Hongre (1483), *facs.*, 1924.
Ḥusain Vā'iz, *Kashifi, see* SADI. The 'Iqd-i Gul: sel. f. the Gulistān [of S.] & the Anwār-i Suhailī [*of* H. Vā'iz]; tr. &c. Adalat Khan, 4th ed., 1900.
Husband (Joseph).
A year in a coal mine. s8°. Boston [U.S. 1911]
Huscher (Herbert), *see* PAGE (J.) Siege of Rouen; krit. Textausg. &c. v. H. H., 1927.
Husenbeth (Frederick Charles). The life of Monsig. Weedall, D.D., includ. the early hist. of Oscott Coll. 8°. 1860
Huss (John).
J. H. & Hieronymi Pragensis confess. Christi hist. & mon. 2t *in* 1v. fol. Noribergae. 1558
see FRIEDRICH (J.) J. H., e. Lebensbild, 2 Abtlg., 1864.
„ GILPIN (W.) Lives of Wicliff, J. H. &c., 1765.
„ HENKE (E. L. T.) J. H. u. d. Synode v. Constanz, 1869.
„ HERBEN (J.) H. & h. followers, 1926.
„ LECHLER (G. V.) J. H.: e. Lebensbild, 1889.
see SEYFRIED (W.) Diss. de J. H. ortu &c., 1729.
„ THEOBALD (Z.) Bellum Hussit., J. H. vita &c., 1621.
„ VAN DER HORST (D. G.) Disp. de H. vita, 1837.
„ WALDENSES. Apologia versae doct.: J. Hussitae doct. &c., 1538.
„ WERNER (J.) J. H. martyr, 1671.
Husserl (Edmund). Logische Untersuch. 2e umgearb. A. B2ii. 8°. Halle a. d. S. 1921
Hussey (Arthur). Chronicles of Wingham. Comp. by A. H. s8°. Canterbury. 1896
Hussey (*Brig.-Gen.* **Arthur Herbert) & D. S. Inman.** The 5th Division in the Great War. 8°. [1921]
Hussey (Christopher). Eton College. [2nd ed.] 4°. [1926]
see TIPPING (H. A.) Eng. homes, Period 4, v2, Work of Sir J. Vanbrugh &c.; by H. A. T. & C. H., 1928.
Hussey (Dyneley). Wolfgang A. Mozart. 8°. 1928
Hussiten-Brief. Protestatio Bohemorum, 1415, od. d. Hussitenbrieff &c., 1712, *see* BOHEMI.
Husson (*Mlle.* **Andrée),** *see* CORTHIS (ANDRÉ), *ps.*
Husson (Camille), *fils, pharmacien.*
L'alimentation animale—La viande. 8°. 1881
Etude sur les épices. [*b. w. h.* L'aliment. animale, 1881]. 8°. 1883
Hustache (Jeanne Ancelet-), *see* ANCELET-HUSTACHE (J.)
Huston (*Maj.* **Desmond Chapman-),** *see* CHAPMAN-HUSTON (*Maj.* D.)
Huston (Robert). Life & labours of the Rev. Fossey Tackaberry; w. notices of Methodism in Ireland. 2nd ed. rev. s8°. 1860
Husung (Max Joseph), *see* LOUBIER (H.) Buch u. Bucheinband: Aufsätze &c. z. 60. Geburtstage v. H. L.; [hrsg. M. J. H.], 1923.

Huszti (Andreas). Origo, incrementum, & facies hodierna 3 in Transilvania illustr. gymnasiorum reformat. 1730, &c. s4°. Francofurti a. V. 1731

Hutchins (Henry Clinton). Robinson Crusoe & its printing, 1719–31. Foreword by A. E. Newton. la8°. N.Y. 1925

Hutchinson & Co., *publishers.* Splendour of the heavens. Ed. T. E. R. Phillips & W. H. Steavenson. 2v. 4°. 1923
see KNIGHT (A. E.) & E. STEP. H.'s pop. botany, 2v, 1912.

Hutchinson (Arthur Stuart Menteth).
The eighth wonder & o. s. s8°. [1923]
The happy warrior. [9th ed.] s8°. 1922
If winter comes. s8°. [1921]
On parle d'Alexandre, nouvelle, *see* ŒUVRES libres, 61, 1926.
One increasing purpose. s8°. [1925]
This freedom. 3rd ed. s8°. 1922

Hutchinson (Claud Mackenzie). Saltpetre: origin & extraction in India, *see* AGRIC. RES. INST., *Pusa*, Bulletin 68, 1917.

Hutchinson (Emilie Josephine).
Women's wages. 8°. N.Y., *Columbia Univ.* 1919

Hutchinson (Horatio Gordon).
The Fortnightly Club. 8°. 1922
Hints on the game of golf. 8th ed. enl. s8°. E. 1893
Portraits of the eighties. 8°. [1920]
Saga of the "Sunbeam." 8°. 1911
see KIRKMAN (F. B. B.) & H. G. H., *edd.* Brit. sporting birds, 1924.

Hutchinson (John), *see* SHARP (T.) Mr. H.'s expos. of Cherubim examined, 1755.

Hutchinson (*Col.* John), *see* HUTCHINSON (*Mrs.* L.) Mems. of life of Col. H., 1806.

Hutchinson (John), *F.L.S.* The families of flowering plants arr. acc. to new system based on th. probable phylogeny. [v]1, Dicotyledons. 8°. 1926

Hutchinson (*Sir* Jonathan).
Hernia & its radical cure. 8°. [1923]
see TREVES (*Sir* F.) & J. H. Student's hdbk. of surgical oper., 4th ed. enl., 1924.

Hutchinson (*Mrs.* Lucy), *wife of Col. J. H.* Mems. of the life of Col. Hutchinson &c. Publ. f. MS. by J. Hutchinson. Pref., Life of Mrs. H., by herself. 4°. 1806

Hutchinson (Richard). *The war in New-Eng. visibly ended [by R. H.], 1677, *see* DRAKE (S. G.) The old Indian chron. &c., 1867.

Hutchinson (Robert W.) Advanced text-book of magnetism & electricity. 2nd ed. 2v. s8°. 1920

Hutchinson (Thomas), *governor of Massachusetts Bay.* Hist. of the colony of Mass.-Bay, 1628 [–1750]. 2nd ed. 2v. 8°. 1760–68
see DEANE (C.) A bibliogr. essay on Gov. H.'s hist. publ., 1857.

Hutchinson (Vera). Great waters. s8°. [1924]

Hutchinson (*General* William Nelson).
The navigable balloon. [P2831]. 8°. [Eastbourne. 1888]

Hutchison (Robert). Alcohol as a medicine, *see* STARLING (E. H.) Action of alcohol, 1923.
Food & the principles of dietetics. 6th ed. 8°. 1927

Huth (Hans).
Künstler u. Werkstatt d. Spätgotik. la8°. Augsburg. 1923

Huth (Henry). The Huth Library. Cat. of bks. unsold or imperf. Sold by Sotheby. [P2853]. la8°. 1922

Huth (Louis). Cat. of mezzotint portraits after Sir J. Reynolds & engr. after G. Morland, sold by Christie &c. [*Priced.* P2849]. 8°. 1905

Hutson (James). Chinese life in the Tibetan foothills. [*Repr. f.* New China Review]. 8°. Shanghai. 1921

Hutt (George), *ed., see* CHELSEA. Papers illust. of origin &c. of Roy. Hospital, 1872.

Hutten (*Baroness* Bettina von). Happy house. s8°. [1919]
Mothers-in-law. [repr.] s8°. [1922]
Pam at fifty. s8°. [1923]

Hutten (Ulrich von) [HUTTENUS].
Aula, dialogus. s4°. [Augsburg, *S. Grimm & M. Vuyrsung.* 1518]
Dialogi: Fortuna; Febris prima; Febris secunda; Trias Romana; Inspicientes. s4°. [Moguntiae, *J. Scheffer.* 1520]
Eyn hüpsch new lyed vom dem von H. (1521, *facs.*), *see* FREYTAG (G.) Bilder, B3i, 1924.
Febris Dialogus &c. [*b. w. h.* Ad. Pirckheymer epist., 1519]. s4°. *n.p.* [Landshut, *J. Weissenburger*?]. 1519
Latein. Schriften u. d. Dunkelmännerbriefe. [Hrsg.] K. Buchholz. s8°. Frankfurt am Main. 1926
Nemo. [*tp. wanting.* Aii *beg.* Vlrichi de Hvtten &c. in Neminem praef.] s4°. [Augustae *in officina Millerana*]. *n.d.* [c. 1518]

Hutten (Ulrich von) [HUTTENUS] [*continued*].
U. ab H. cum Erasmo expostulatio—O. Brunfelsii pro U. H. defuncto ad Erasmi Spongiam responsio. s8°. *n.p. n.d.* [1530 ?]
U. de H. ad Bilibaldū Pirckheymer Epistola vitae suę rationem exponens. s4°. [Augustae Vindelic., *S. Grimm & M. Wyrsung.* 1519]
see ERASMUS (D.) Spongia adv. aspergines H., 1523.

Hutter (Elias). Öffentl. Aussschreiben &c., Welcher massen d. Welt &c. durch e. Harmoniam ling. &c. geholffen werden könne, &c. s8°. Nürnberg. 1602

Hutter (Leonhard).
Compend. locorum theologic. ex Script. sacris & Libro Concordiae. Coll. opera L. H. s8°. Wittebergae. 1619
,, ,, [*a. ed.*] s8°. Wittebergae. 1728
Disput. de sacrificio Romanensium missatico. [P2609]. s4°. Witebergae. 1603
Disput. 16. de baptismo ex art. 9 Conf. August. Praes. L. H., resp. G. Meuselius. [P2673]. s4°. Witebergae. 1598
Gründl. Bericht v. ordentl. &c. Beruff, Ordination &c. d. Luther. Evang. Prediger. s4°. Wittenberg. 1608
Irenicum vere Xtnum., tract. Irenici D. Parei consilia refellens. [*b. w.* Pareus (D.) Irenicum &c., 1614]. s4°. Wittebergae. 1616
Libri Christianae Concordiae: Symboli eccl. γνησίως Lutheran. explic. &c. s8°. Witebergae. 1668
Oratio de vita &c. G. Mylii. [P597]. s4°. Vitebergae. 1607
Πρόδρομος disput. de Conf. August. autore &c. Præs. L. H., resp. C. Zecherus. [*b. w.* Mylius (G.) Spongia, 1591]. s4°. Witebergae. 1597
Sadeel elenchomenos disput. 2. Praes. L. H., propugn. M. Ringerus. [P2612]. s4°. Witebergae. 1601
see EBART (J.) Enchiridion theol. supra Compend. L. H. &c., 1665.

Huttmann (Maude Aline). The establ. of Xtny. & the proscription of paganism. 8°. N.Y., *Columbia Univ.* 1914

Hutton (Charles), *LL.D.* Mathemat. tables. 5th ed. 8°. 1811

Hutton (Edward).
Cities of Lombardy. s8°. [1912]
Cities of Sicily. s8°. [1926]
Cities of Spain. 8th ed. 8°. [1927]
The Franciscans in England, 1224–1538. 8°. [1926]
Highways & byeways in Somerset. [repr.] 8°. 1919
Pietro Aretino, the scourge of princes. 8°. 1922
Rome. 4th ed. s8°. [1922]
The Sienese school in the Nat. Gallery. la8°. 1925
The valley of Arno. 8°. 1927

Hutton (James), *a. of A hundred years ago, see* BENHAM (D.) Memoirs of J. H. &c., w. conn. w. the United Brethren, 1856.

Hutton (John Henry), *C.I.E., M.A.*
The Sema Nagas. With maps &c. by H. Balfour. 8°. 1921

Hutton (Mary) *of Sunderland, see* BENSON (J.) Short acc. of the death of M. H., 1777.

Hutton (Maurice). The Greek point of view. 8°. [1925]
Many minds. 8°. [1927]

Hutton (Richard Holt).
Literary essays. 3rd ed. rev. & enl. s8°. 1888
,, ,, ...[3rd ed. rev., repr.] s8°. 1896
Theological essays. 3rd ed. rev. s8°. 1888
,, ,, ...4th ed. rev. s8°. 1895

Hutton (William Holden), *dean of Winchester.* Age of revolution: hist. of the Church, 1648–1815. s8°. 1908
John Wesley. 8°. 1927
Thomas Becket, abp. of Cant. [n. ed. rev. & enl.] 8°. C. 1926
see MARCHANT (*Sir* J.), *ed.* Future of the Ch. of Eng.: essays by the Dean of W. &c., 1926.

Huxley (Aldous).
Along the road: notes & essays of a tourist. s8°. 1925
Antic hay. s8°. 1923
The burning wheel. s8°. O. 1916
Crome yellow. s8°. 1921
,, ,, [2nd impr.] s8°. 1922
Jesting Pilate: diary of a journey. 8°. 1926
Leda. 8°. 1920
Limbo. [4th impr.] s8°. [1924]
Little Mexican [Uncle Spencer] & o. s. s8°. 1924
,, ,, 2nd impr. s8°. 1924
Mortal coils. s8°. 1922
On the margin: notes & essays. [2nd impr.] s8°. 1928
Proper studies. s8°. 1927
Those barren leaves. s8°. 1925
,, ,, [2nd impr.] s8°. 1925
Two or three Graces & o. stories. s8°. 1926

Huxley (Julian Sorell). Essays in pop. science. 8°. 1926
Essays of a biologist. s8°. 1923
The individual in the animal kingdom. s8°. C. 1912
Religion without revelation. 8°. 1927
The stream of life. s8°. 1926
see HALDANE (J. B. S.) & J. H. Animal biology, 1927.

Huxley (Leonard). Anniversaries [*& o. poems*]. s8°. 1920
*The House of Smith Elder. s8°. *p.f.p.c.* 1923
Progress & the unfit. Conway Mem. Lect. s8°. [1926]

Huxley (Thomas Henry).
Lay sermons, addresses & reviews. 8°. 1891
Man's place in nature & o. essays. s8°. [1908]
Physiography. Rev. & partly re-wr. by R. A. Gregory. [repr.] s8°. 1919

Ḥuy, *Nubian viceroy* [AMENḤOTPE], *see* GARDINER (A. H.) Tomb of Ḥ., viceroy of Nubia in reign of Tut 'Ankhamūn, 1926.

Huydecoper (Theodoor Cornelis Reinier). Comm. de solenni Jesu Christi in urbem Hierosolymorum introitu. 8°. Trajecti a. Rh. 1829

Huygens (Christiaan) *van Zuylichem.* Œuvres compl. Publ. par la Soc. Holland. des Sciences. 14t *in* 15 [13 *in* 2 fasc., *pagin. cont.*] 4°. La Haye. 1888–1920
1–10, Corr., 1638–95.
11, Travaux mathémat., 1645–51.
12, Travaux de mathémat. pures, 1652–56.
13, Dioptrique, 1653–92.
14, Calcul des probabilités, travaux de mathémat. pures, 1655–66.

Huygens (Konstantijn), *Heer van Zuylichem, 1596–1687.* Gedichten; naar zijn Hs. uitg. door J. A. Worp. 9d *in* 5v [d9, Registers]. 8°. Arnheim. *n.d.*
see DESCARTES (R.) Corr. of D. & C. Huygens, 1635–47; ed. L. Roth, 1926.

Huygens (Konstantijn), *the younger, 1629–95.* Journaal, 1688–96. [Hist. Genoots. Werken, N.S., 23, 25, 46]. 3d [d3 *has title* Journalen, 1649–82]. 8°. Utrecht. 1876–88
„ „ Register op de Journalen. [Hist. Genoots. Werken, s3, 22]. 8°. A. 1906
„ „ Aanteekeningen & verbeteringen op het Register op de Journalen; bijeenverzameld door J. H. Hora Siccama. [Hist. Genoots. Werken, s3, 35]. 8°. A. 1915

Huysmans (Joris Karl). En marge. Ets. & préfs. réunies & annot. par L. Descaves. 8°. [1927]
En ménage. [repr.] s8°. 1922
Les sœurs Vatard. s8°. 1907
see BACHELIN (H.) J. K. H., 1926.
„ DEFFOUX (L.) & E. ZAVIE. Le groupe de Médan: J. K. H. &c., 1920.

Huzella (Theodor). Krieg u. Frieden im Lichte d. Medezin: Entwurf e. medizin. Soziologie. 8°. 1923

Hvem er hvem? Udg. av Chr. Brinchmann &c. s8°. Kristiania. 1912

Hyacinthe *(le père)* [*i.e.* CHARLES J. M. LOYSON]. De la réforme catholique. 2e éd. t1 [*no more publ.*] s8°. 1874
see HOUTIN (A.) Le père H., 3t, 1920–24.

Hyamson (Albert Montefiore).
A dict. of English phrases. 8°. 1922

Hyamson (Moses). The Jewish method of slaughtering animals. [P2690]. s8°. 1923

Hyatt (Alfred H.) Book of old-world gardens. [*Extr. f. var. wr.*] Ed. &c. by A. H. H. s8°. 1911

Hyde (Walter Woodburn). Olympic victor monuments & Greek athletic art. [C.I. of Wash.] la8°. Wash. 1921

Hyderabad. H. Archaeological Series. Nos. 1, 3. [P2417], 6, 7. 4°. Calcutta. 1915–25
1, New Asokan edict of Maski.
3, Inscriptions at Palampet & Uparpalli.
6, Kotagiri plates of r. of Rudramamba, A.D. 1273. [Ed. S. Hanumant Rao].
7, Bodhan stone inscr. of r. of Trailokyamalla, A.D. 1056. [Ed. R. Narasimhacharya].
Report of the Archaeol. Dept. of the Nizam's dominions, 1921–24, 1924–25. sm. fol. Calcutta. 1926

Hyderabad Archæological Society.
Journal, 1916. 8°. Bombay. 1916

Hyett (*Sir* **Francis Adams).** Notes on portraits of Sir Ed. Massey. [Repr. f. Trans. of Bristol &c. Arch. soc., v43. P2688]. 8°. [1923]

Hylacomylus (Martinus) [WALDSEEMÜLLER (M.); WALTZEMÜLLER (M. H.); ILACOMILUS], *see* AVEZAC (M. P. D'). M. Hylacomylus Waltzemüller, s. ouvrages & s. collab., 1867.

Hyll (Thomas), *see* HILL (T.), *of Trin. Coll., Camb.*

Hylton (William George Jolliffe, *1st baron*), *see* PETERLOO. Three acc. of P. by eyewitnesses, Lord H. &c., 1921.

Hyma (Albert). The Xtn. Renaissance: hist. of the "Devotio Moderna." 8°. N.Y. 1925

Hymans (Henri). Œuvres. 4v. la8°. 1920–21
1, Études &c. rel. à l'hist. de l'art dans les Pays-Bas: la gravure.
2, Près de 700 biog. d'artistes belges parues dans la Biog. Nat. &c.

Hymans (Henri) [*continued*].
3, Un quart de siècle de vie artist. en Belg.: 26 années de corresp. à la "Gazette des Beaux-Arts," 1886–1912.
4, L'art au 17e & au 19e s. dans les Pays-Bas: notes sur des primitifs.

Hymn.
New Congregational h. book. s8°. *n.d.*
Pocket (A) h. book designed as a constant companion for the pious. Coll. f. var. authors. 6th ed. s8°. York, *pr. for R. Spence.* 1786
*A pocket h.b. for use of Xtns. &c., 1785, *see* WESLEY (J.)

Hymnal.
*H. (The) companion to the Bk. of C. Prayer. s8°. *Sampson Low.* 1874
„ „ w. tunes. Under musical ed. of J. T. Cooper. rev. & enl. ed. s8°. 1879
*H. noted. [By J. M. Neale &c. *b. w.* Helmore (T.) Man. of plain song, 1850]. 2p. s8°. 1851–6
„ „ w. app. [Introits, graduals &c. 4th ed., 1880]. 7th ed. enl. s8°. 1877
*Music of the App. to the H. noted. 8°. *n.d.*

Hymnarium. Blüthen latein. Kirchenpoesie. Mit Vorwort v. C. B. Moll. s8°. Halle. 1861
„ „ 2e mit biog. Notizen verm. A. s8°. Halle. 1868

Hymnen (Die) d. Kath. Kirche, 1853, *see* PACHTLER (G. M.)
see also GESANGBUCH.

Hymnendichtung. Ein Jahrtausend latein. H., 2t, 1909, *see* DREVES (G. M.)

Hymni [HYMNORUM]. *Hymni & collectae, item Evangelia, Epistolae, introitus, gradualia & sequentiae &c. Adj. Formula lenè &c. auspicandi &c. s8°. Coloniae. 1573
Liber hymnorum in metra noviter redactorum, 1501, *see* BEBELITTS (H.)

Hymnologia. H. Damulica, ex Germanico &c. exhib. a B. Schultze. s8°. Tranquebariae. 1723
*H. Tamulica. Coll. miss. Danici. ed. 6a auct. s8°. Trangambariae. 1779

Hymnologium. Catholic. h. German. orthod. eccl. &c. auctum a J. L., 1584, *see* LEISENTRIT (J.)

Hymns.
*Choice (A) coll. of h., 1776, *see* HULL (C.)
Christian h., 1881; 1891, *see* BROOKE (S. A.) *ed.*
Christian h. in Tamil, 1820, *see* TAMIL.
Church h.; ed. A. Sullivan, 1874, *see* CHURCH.
*Coll. (A) of divine h., upon sev. occasions. s8°. *Parkhurst.* 169[illegible]
Coll. (A) of h. & psalms. [*b. w.* Prayer Bk. Bk. of C. P.; Clarke 7th ed., 1823]. 6th ed. enl. s8°. 182[illegible]
Coll. (A) of h. for public &c. worship. [*Comp. for Meth. Episc Ch. by T. O. Summers*]. s8°. Nashville, Tenn. 186[illegible]
*Coll. (A) of h. for societies. s8°. Leedes, *J. Lister.* 174[illegible]
Coll. (A) of h. for the use of Methodists, 1781, *see* WESLEY (J.)
Coll. (A) of h. for those that seek &c. redemption, 1761, *see* ALLEN (J.) & C. BATTY.
*Coll (A) of h. for use of United Brethren. 8°. 178[illegible]
*Coll. (A) of h. of the children of God &c. in 2p for use of Brethren' ch. 2p. s8°. 175[illegible]
*Coll. (The) of h. sung in the Ctess. of Huntingdon's chapels. obl. s8°. Bath. *n.d.*
Coll. (A) of h., w. tr. fr. the hymn bk. of the Moravian Brethren. s8°. *Hutton.* 174[illegible]
„ „ Second (A) coll. never before printed. s8°. *Hutton.* 174[illegible]
*Coll. (A) of psalms &c., 1701, *see* PSALMS.
*Coll. (A) of ps. & h. for Xtn., 1781, *see* PSALMS.
*Divine h. & poems. By sev. eminent hands. s8°. *Clements.* 170[illegible]
H. ancient & mod., under the musical ed. of W. H. Monk. s8°. *Novello. n.d.*
„ „ ....s8°. *Clowes.* [1869]
„ „ ....Appendix. s8°. *Clowes.* [1868]
„ „ ....rev. & enlarg. ed. s8°. *Clowes. n.d.* [c. 187[illegible]
„ „ ....compl. ed. 8°. *Clowes.* [1889]
*H. & songs for mission services &c. With tunes. enl. ed. 8°. *Woolmer.* 188[illegible]
H. composed for the use of the Brethren. By C. Z. [*i.e.* Zinzendorf]. s8°. *n.p.* 174[illegible]
*H. for Ascension-day, 2nd ed., 1747; 1775, *see* WESLEY (J.)
*H. for children & o. of riper years, 2nd ed., 1768; 4th ed., 178[illegible] *see* WESLEY (J.) & C. WESLEY.
*H. for New-Year's Day, 1752; 1761, *see* WESLEY (J.) & C. WESLEY.
*H. for our Lord's Resurrection, 3rd ed., 1748; 5th ed., 1769, *see* WESLEY (J.) & C. WESLEY.
*H. for the nation, 1782, *see* WESLEY (J.) & C. WESLEY.
*H. for the nativity of our Lord, 10th ed., 1750; *a. ed.*, 1768, *see* WESLEY (J.) & C. WESLEY.
*H. for the public Thanksgiving-day, 1746; 1769, *see* WESLEY (J.) & C. WESLEY.
H. for the use of the Methodist Episcopal Church. rev. ed. 8°. N.Y. [184[illegible]
H. for the use of the Univ. of Oxford in St. Mary's Church, 187[illegible] *see* OXFORD.

Hymns [*continued*].
*H. for the watch night, 1746 ?, *see* WESLEY (J.) & C. WESLEY.
*H. for the year 1756 &c., 1756, *see* WESLEY (J.) & C. WESLEY.
*H. for those that seek redemption, 3rd ed., 1749 ; 8th ed., 1768, *see* WESLEY (J.) & C. WESLEY.
*H. occasioned by the earthquake, 2p, 1750 ; 1756 ; *see* WESLEY (J.) & C. WESLEY.
*H. of intercession for all mankind, 1759 ; *n.d.*, *see* WESLEY (J.) & C. WESLEY.
H. of the Greek Church ; tr. G. R. Woodward, 1922, *see* WOODWARD (G. R.)
H. of the Russian Church, 1920, *see* BROWNLIE (J.)
*H. on God's everlasting love, 3rd ed., 1770, *see* WESLEY (J.) & C. WESLEY.
*H. on the expected invasion, 1779, 1779, *see* WESLEY (J.) & C. WESLEY.
*H. on the gt. festivals & o. occ., 2nd ed., 1753, *see* WESLEY (J.)
*H. on the Trinity, 1767, *see* WESLEY (J.) & C. WESLEY.
Hymns : suppl. to exist. colls., ed. W. G. Horder, 1894, *see* HORDER (W. G.)
*H. wr. in the time of the tumults 1780, 1780, *see* WESLEY (J.) & C. WESLEY.
Liturgic h. of the United Brethren ; tr., 1811, *see* LITURGIC.
*New (A) coll. of h. for the Christians of all denom. &c. s8°. Bridlington. 1792
*Orig. sacred h., 1776, *see* THOMSON (*Rev.* G.)
Psalms & h. for public worship, w. tunes. Rev. & ed. by J. Turle. s8°. 1863
*Sacred harmony : choice coll. of psalms & h., 1761 ? ; 1789 ?, *see* WESLEY (J.) & C. WESLEY.
Select h., w. tunes annext, for Methodists, 3rd ed., 1770, *see* WESLEY (J.)
Suppl. (A) to the Coll. of h. for the use of Methodists, 1831, *see* WESLEY (J.)

Hyndman (Henry Mayers). The economics of socialism. Marx made easy. 8°. 1922
The evolution of revolution. 8°. 1920
see HYNDMAN (R. T.) Last years of H. M. H., 1923.

Hyndman (Rosalind Travers), *wife of H. M. Hyndman.*
Last years of H. M. Hyndman. 8°. 1923

Hyne (Charles John Cutliffe Wright).
Admiral Teach. s8°. [1920]

Hypatia, *see* WERNSDORF (J. C.) Diss. 1-4 de H., philosopha Alexandrina, 1747-48.

Hyperides. Orationes & fragmenta. Rec. &c. F. G. Kenyon. s8°. O. [1907]

Hyperius (Andreas) [†GERARDUS (A.); GERHARD (A.); GHEERAERTS].
Comm. in omnes Pauli Epist. Op. J. Mylii ed. [5p *in* 2v]. fol. Tiguri. 1584
2-5 *have sep. tp*[s]. *dated* 1582.
De formandis concionibus sacris libri 2. [*b. w. h.* De theologo, 1562]. s8°. Tremoniae. 1555
De sacrae Scr. lectione ac medit. quotidiana &c. libri 2. s8°. Basileae. [1561]
,, ,, [*a. ed.*] s8°. Basileae. [1581]
De theologo seu de ratione studii theologici libri 4. s8°. Basileae. [1556]
,, ,, [*a. ed.* Cum indice]. s8°. Argentinae. [1562]
Elementa Christ. religionis. s8°. Basileae. 1563
In D. Pauli ad Romanos epist. exegema. s8°. Marpurgi. 1549
In Iesaiæ prophetę Oracula, annot. breves &c. s8°. Basileæ. 1574
Methodi theologiæ, sive præcip. Xtnæ. relig. locorum comm. libri 3. Adj. de Hyperii vita & obitu W. Orthii oratio &c. s8°. Basileæ. 1574
Topica theologica. [*Pref. by* C. Froschauer]. s8°. Wittebergae. 1565

Hypnerotomachia. Poliphili Hypnerotomachia, 1499, repr. 1904, *see* †COLONNA (F.)

Hyslop (*Col.* A. G.)
The defence of our coasts. [P2591]. 8°. Jersey. 1858

Hyslop (Theo. Bulkeley).
The borderland : problems of insanity. la8°. [1924]
The great abnormals. 8°. 1925

I

I awoke ! [Life on the other side]. s8°. 1893

Iachaeus, *see* JACCHAEUS.

Iamblichus, *of Chalcis.* Iamblichus de mysteriis Aegyptiorum, Chaldæorum, Assyriorum. Proclus in Platonicum alcibiadem de anima, atq; dæmone. Proclus de sacrificio & magia. Porphyrius de diuinis atq; dæmonibus. Synesius Platonicus de somniis. Psellus de dæmonibus. Expositio Prisciani & Marsilii in Theophrastū de sensu &c. Alcinoi liber de doctrīa Platonis. Speusippi liber de platonis difinitionibus. Pythagoræ aurea verba. Symbola Pythagori. Xenocratis liber de morte. Marsilii Ficini liber de voluptate. [*all tr. by M. Ficino*]. fol. Venetiis in aedibus Aldi. 1497
Life of Pythagoras &c. Accomp. by fragm. of ethical wr., & coll. of Pythagoric sentences omitted by Gale in h. Opuscula mythologica. Tr. T. Taylor. 8°. 1926
see HEBENSTREIT (G. E.) & H. M. HEBENSTREIT. De I. doct. &c., 1764.
,, LLOYD (W.) Chronolog. acc. of life of Pythagoras &c. w. J.'s Lives of P., 1699.

I'Anson, *The family of, see* I'ANSON (B.) Hist. of the I'A. fam., *n.d.*

I'Anson (Bryan). The hist. of the I'Anson family. [Genealog. Research Soc.] fol. *n.d.*

Ianus (Ioannes Guilelmus), *see* JAN (JOHANN WILHELM).

Iasiadès, *see* PASIADÈS.

Ibach (Johann). Der Kampf d. mod. Staates geg. d. Kirche &c. [P2696]. 8°. Frankfurt a. M. 1873

Ibarra (Francisco de), *Governor of Nueva Vizcaya, 1539 ?-75, see* MECHAM (J. L.) F. de I. & Nueva Vizcaya, 1927.

Ibarra y Rodriguez (Eduardo), *ed., see* COLECCION de docs. para el est. de la hist. de Aragon, t9, Docs. corresp. al reinado de Sancio Ramirez, v2, 1913.

Ibbeken (Hero Anton), *see* BOSSECK (J. G.) & H. A. I. Cultum fluminum expon. B. & I., 1740.

Ibbetson (Julius Caesar), *painter ; 1759-1817, see* HENDERSON (B. L. K.) Morland & I., 1923.

Ibericum. *Alphabetum I., sive Georgianum, 1629, *see* ALPHABETUM.

Ibero-América. Colección de doc. inéd. para la hist. de I.-A. ; recop. por S. M., t1, 2, 1927-28, *see* COLECCIÓN.

Ibis, *see* ROSTAGNI (A.) Ibis, un poemetto greco, 1920.

Ibn Abī Ghuddah, *see* AḤMAD IBN 'ABD ALLĀH, *al-Ḳalḳashandī.*

Ibn Abū Zayd [†'ABD ALLĀH IBN ABĪ ZAID, *al-Ḳairuwānī* ; ABŪ MUḤAMMAD B. ABŪ ZAYD]. First steps in Muslim jurisprud. : excerpts f. Bākūrat-al-Sa'd of Ibn Abū Z. Arabic text, Eng. tr., notes &c. by A. D. Russell & A. Suhrawardy. s8°. 1906

Ibn 'Askar [MUḤAMMAD IBN 'ALI IBN MIṢBĀḤ ; ABU ABD ALLAH &c.] La " Daouhat an-Nâchir " ; tr. de A. Graulle, *see* MISSION SCIENT. DU MAROC. Archives maroc., t19, 1913.

Ibn Baṭūtah [ABU ABDALLAH ; EBN BATUTA ; †MUḤAMMAD IBN 'ABD ALLĀH, *called Ibn Baṭūtah*], *see* BOULTING (W.) 4 pilgrims [M. ibn Abd Allah &c.], 1920.

Ibn et Tefrid, *fictitious author, see* PAYNE (J.) The Quatrains of Ibn et Tefrid, 1921.

Ibn Faḍl Allāh, *al-'Umarī* [†AḤMAD IBN YAḤYA], *1301-49.* Masālik el abṣār fi mamālik el amṣār [ch. 8-15]. 1, L'Afrique, moins l'Égypte. Tr. &c. avec intr. par Gaudefroy-Demombynes. [Bibl. des géog. arabes, t2]. 8°. 1927
Polit. Geog. d. Mamlūkenreichs : Kap. 5 u. 6 d. Staatshandbuchs I. F. ; übers. &c. v. R. Hartmann, *see* DEUT. MORGENL. GESELLS. Zeitschr., B70, 1916.
see GAUDEFROY-DEMOMBYNES (M.) La Syrie à l'époque des Mamelouks d'ap. les a. arabes [*i.e.* El 'Omari &c.], 1923.

Ibn Mājid, *dit " Le lion de la mer."* Le pilote des mers de l'Inde, de la Chine & de l'Indonésie, texte arabe, *see* FERRAND (G.), *ed.* Instruct. nautiques & routiers arabes &c. des 15e & 16e s., t1, 2, 1921-25.

Ibn Manṣoûr, *al-Ḥallâj, see* ḤALLÂJ.

Ibn Sabā, *see* YŪḤANNĀ IBN ABŪ ZAKARĪYĀ, *ibn Sabā.*

Ibragimov (I.) Нѣкоторыя замѣтки о Хивинскихъ, Туркменахъ и Киргизахъ. [*Extr. fr.* Военный Сборникъ, 1874. P2386]. 8°. [1874]

Ibrāhīm Ḥilmi, *Prince of Egypt.* The literature of Egypt & the Soudan to 1885. A bibliography. 2v. 4°. 1886-87

Ibrovac (Miodrag).
J.-M. de Heredia : les sources des Trophées. 8°. 1923
J.-M. de Heredia, sa vie—son œuvre. 8°. 1923

Ibsen (Henrik).
Kejser og Galilæer. [2v]. s8°. 1909
TRANSLATIONS.
Collected works. [Rev. & ed., w. intr^s. by W. Archer]. v3, 4, n. impr. s8°. 1920–24
3, Brand; tr. w. intr. by C. H. Herford.
4, Peer Gynt; tr. W. & A. Archer.
Dramat. Werke. Übers. v. W. Lange. Vorwort v. T. Schäfer. B1–3. s8°. *n.d.*
1, Die Stützen d. Gesells. —Nora—Gespenster.
2, Ein Volksfeind — Die Wildente — Rosmersholm.
3, Die Meerfrau — Hedda Gabler — Baumeister Solness.
TRANSLATIONS [*continued*].
Early plays: Catiline—The warrior's barrow—Olaf Liljekrans. Tr. by A. Orbeck. [Scand. Classics, v17]. s8°. N.Y. 1921
An enemy of the people [tr. E. Marx-Aveling], *see* SAYLER (O. M.) Moscow Art Theatre ser. of Russ. plays, s2, 1924.
see BING (J.) H. I.'s Brand: krit. studie, *n.d.*
„ ENGERT (R.) H. I. als Verkünder d. dritten Reiches, 1921.
„ GRAN (G.) H. I.: liv og verker, 2B, 1918.
„ LAVRIN (J.) I. & h. creation &c., 1921.
„ MEYEN (F.) I.-Bibliog., 1928.

Ibsen (Sigurd). Human quintessence. Auth. tr. M. H. Janson. s8°. [1913]

Ibycus, *fl. c. 540 B.C., see* LYRA. Lyra Graeca; ed. & tr. by J. M. Edmonds, v2, I. &c., 1924.

Icaza (Francisco A. de). La universidad alemana: su idea, su función &c. s8°. 1915

Icazbalceta (Joaquin Garcia), *see* GARCIA ICAZBALCETA (J.)

Iceland. *Sportsman's &c. hdbk. to I., 2nd ed., 1900, *see* SCOT (D. H.)

Iceland Year Book (The), 1926, 1927. Ed. S. Jónsson. s8°. Reykjavik. 1926–27

***Icon** regia monarchæ Sinarum nunc regnantis, 1699, *see* BOUVET (J.)

Iconoclast, *ps.* *The man of to-morrow: J. R. Macdonald, 1923, *see* MACDONALD (J. R.)

Iconomos (Constantin), *see* EIKONOMOS (CONSTANTINE).

Idelsohn (A. Z.) Phonogr. Gesänge u. Aussprachsproben d. Hebr. d. jemen., pers. u. syr. Juden, 1917, *see* KAIS. AKAD. D. W. ZU WIEN. Sitzb., B175, 1916.

Ides (Evert) [EVERARD ISBRANTS IDES]. Voyage de Moscou à la Chine, *see* BERNARD (J. F.), *ed.* Recueil, t8, 1727.

Idris, *the pilgrim, Mai, of Bornu* [IDRIS IBN ALI, *Alooma*], *see* AHMAD IBN FARTUA. Hist. of first 12 years of reign of Mai I. A. (1571–83); tr., 1926.

Iénissei. Inscr. de l'I., 1889, *see* SOCIÉTÉ FINLAND. D'ARCH.

Igglesden (Charles).
Ashford Church. [3rd ed.] s8°. Ashford. 1924
A saunter through Kent with pen & pencil. v1–21 [1–13, 2nd ed. ?]. la8°. 1900–[28]

Iglehart (Ferdinand Cowle).
King alcohol dethroned. s8°. N.Y. [1917]

Ignatev (*gen.* **Pavel Nikolaevich),** *see* ZALESOV (—). Col. I.'s mission to Khiva &c., 1858; tr., 1876.

Ignatius, *bp. of Antioch, Saint.*
[Epistles. *In Armenian. Some pages supplied in MS.*] s8°. K.-polis. [1783]
Epistolæ 12 interp. I. Brunnero, *Gr. & Lat.*, 1559, *see* Theologi. Theolog. aliquot Græc. libri, 1560.
see APOSTOLIC. The Apostolic Fathers; [tr.], v2, 1889; 1909.
„ COTELERIUS (J. B.), *ed.* SS. patrum I. &c. opera, unà cum I. actis &c., 2v, 1724.
„ FISCHER (E. R.) De Θεοδρόμοις vet. eccl. legatis, in S. I. epist. ad Polycarpum brevis comm., 1718.
see HAMMOND (H.) An answer to the animadv. on the diss. t. I.'s Epistles &c., 1654.
„ ITTIG (T.) Bibl. Patrum Apost. Gr.-Lat., 1699.
„ JAMES, *St., bp. of Nisibis.* [*Hist. of St. J. (*foll. by* Hilarion & I.), *in Armenian*], 1861.
„ LIETZMANN (H.) Handbuch z. N.T.: Ergänzungsband, 2, Briefe d. I., erkl. v. W. Bauer, 1920.

Ignatius, *abp. of Nicaea* [IGNATIUS, *diaconus*]. Vita Nicephori [*in Greek*], *see* NICEPHORUS, *St.* Opusc. hist., ed. C. de Boor, 1880.

Ignatius (Carl Emil Ferdinand). Aperçu des notions géograph. sur la Finlande. [Extr. P2736]. 8°. [1880 ?]
Grossfürstenthum Finnland. Statist. Mittheil. Übers. v. E. Hårdh. [P2714]. 8°. Helsingfors. 1876

Igor, *Prince.* Das Igorlied metr. u. sprachl. bearb. v. E. Sievers, *see* KÖN.-SÄCHS. AKAD. Berichte, Phil.-hist. Kl., B78, 1926.

Iguiniz (Juan B.) Bibliog. de novelistas mexicanos. Prec. de un estud. hist. de la novela mex. por F. M. G. Icazbalceta. 8°. Mexico. 1926

Ihm (Maximilian), *see* ANTHOLOGIA LATINA. Anthol. lat. suppl.; rec. M. I., v1, 1895.

Ihre (Johann). J. ab Ihre Scripta versionem Ulphilanam & linguam Mæso-Gothicam illustr. ab auctore aucta. Jam vero collecta & cum aliis scr. similis argumenti [*w. sep. pagin*]. ed. ab A. F. Büsching. 4°. Berolini. 1773
Von d. Upsal. Edda, see SCHLÖZER (A. L. v.), *ed.* Isländ. Litt. &c., T1, 1773.

Ikbal Ali Shah, *Sirdar.* [*Faqir Syed* IKBAL].
Afghanistan of the Afghans. 8°. [1928]

Iken (Conrad). Antiq. Hebraicae. Ed. 4^a. s8°. Bremae. 1764
Diss. philolog.-theol. in div. Sacri Cod. loca. 2v. s4°. Lugd. Batav. [2, Trajecti Batav.] 1749–70
see CUYPER (C. DE). Diss. de Cemarim; praes. C. I., 1729.
„ MISHNAH. Tract. Talmud. de cultu quotid. templi; notis illust. &c. C. I., 1736.

Iken (J. Friedrich). Heinrich v. Zütphen. [Verein f. Ref.-gesch. Schr., Jhrg. 3, Nr. 12]. 8°. Halle. 1886

Ikonnikov (Vladimir Stepanovich). Біограф. словарь профессоровъ &c. Унив. Св. Владиміра (1834–84). la8°. Кіевъ. 1884

Ilberg (Johannes). Die Ärzteschule v. Knidos, *see* KÖNIGL. SÄCHS. AKAD. D. WISS. Ber., B76, 1925.

Ilbert (*Sir* **Courtenay Peregrine),** *see* POLLOCK (*Sir* F.) Sir C. P. I., 1926.
—— **&** *Ld.* **Meston.** The new constit. of India. s8°. 1923

Ilchester (Giles Stephen Holland Fox-Strangways, *6th earl of***).** *see* †CATHERINE II, *emp. of Russia.* Corr. w. Sir C. Hanbury-Williams &c.; ed. & tr. I. &c., 1928.
„ HOLLAND (H. E. F., *b.*) Journal, 1818–30; ed. E. of I., 1923.

Ildephonsus, *Saint, abp. of Toledo.* De scriptor. eccl., *see* LE MIRE (A.) Bibl. eccles., 1639.
see LORENZANA Y BUITRON (F. A.) SS. PP. Toletan. opera, t1, 1782.

Ilg (Albert), *see* VIENNA. Album &c. Goldschmeide- u. Steinschlifftechnik; erläut. Text v. A. I., 1895.

Ilgen (Theodor). Sphragistik, 2e A, 1912, *see* GRUNDR. D. GESCHICHTSWISS.; Meister, 1iv, 1912.

Ilharat de la Chambre (François). Intr. à la théologie, *see* MIGNE (J. P.), *ed.* Theol. cursus, t26, 1859.

Illa (Narciso Blanch é), *see* BLANCH É ILLA (N.)

Illaires (Jacques d'), *sieur de Jouyac.* L'heureuse conversion des Huguenots à la foy cathol. &c. Avec la saincte messe en François. [*w. sep. tp. & pagin.*] s8°. Rouen. 1610

Illés (Aladár Edvi), *see* EDVI ILLÉS (A.)

Illgen (Christian Friedrich). Hist. Collegii Philobiblici Lips. [*Progr.*] 4p *in* 1v. s4°. [Leipzig. 1836–41]
Symbolarum ad vitam & doct. Laelii Socini illust. particula 1 [*& 2 in* 1v]. s4°. Lipsiae. [1826]

Illinois, University of. Studies in lang. & lit. v1–8, 9i, iii, 10iii. la8°. Urbana. 1915–25
Each vol. issued in 4 Nos. Nos. omitted f. foll. list are in Suppl., 1913–20.
see ÆSOP. Ysopet-Avionnet: Lat. & French texts, 1919. [5iv.]
„ AUSTIN (J. C.) The significant name in Terence, 1922. [7iv.]
„ BLOOMFIELD (L.) Tagalog texts w. gramm. analysis, 3p, 1917. [3ii–iv.]
„ BROOKS (N. C.) The sepulchre of Christ in art & liturgy, 1921. [7ii.]
„ CICERO (M. T.) De divinatione, 4p, 1920–23. [6ii, iii, 8ii, iii.]
„ FLOM (G. T.) Lang. of Konungs Skuggsjá (Speculum regale), 1921–24. [7iii, 8iv.]
„ —— Phonology of dialect of Aurland, Norway, 1915. [1i, ii.]
„ FRACASTORO (G.) Naugerius, 1924. [9iii.]
„ GERSON (J. C. DE). Ad Deum vadit, 1917. [3i.]
„ HOWARD (*Sir* R.) "The Committee," 1921. [7i.]
„ JONES (H. S. V.) Spenser's defence of Ld. Grey, 1919. [5iii.]
„ KEISER (A.) Influence of Xty. on the vocab. of old Eng. poetry, p1, 2, 1919. [5i, ii.]
„ LOOMIS (R. S.) Illust. of med. romance on tiles f. Chertsey Abbey, 1916. [2ii.]
„ MEYER (K.) Misc. Hibernica, 1917. [2iv.]
„ MONMOUTH (G. *of*). The Vita Merlini, 1925. [10iii.]
„ ROBINSON (R. P.) De fragm. Suetoniani de gramm. &c., 1922. [6iv.]
„ SECORD (A. W.) St. in narrative method of Defoe, 1924. [9i.]
„ SENECA (L. A.) Index verborum &c. a G. A. Oldfather &c. confectus, p1–3, 1918. [4ii–iv.]
„ SERFS (H.) La col. Cervantina de la Soc. Hisp. de Amér.; ed. de Don Quijote, 1918. [6i.]
„ SUTCLIFFE (E. G.) Emerson's theories of lit. expressions, 1923. [8i.]
„ WHITFORD (R. C.) Mme. de Staël's literary reput. in Eng., 1918. [4i.]

Illinois Centennial Commission.
Publ. v1, 4. 8°. Springfield. 1920
see Alvord (C. W.) The Illinois country, 1673–1818, 1920. [1.]
„ Bogart (E. L.) & C. M. Thompson. The indust. state, 1870–93, 1920. [4.]

Illustrated Australian encyclopaedia, 2v, 1925–26, *see* Australian.

Illustrated London news (The). v122–172. fol. 1903–28

Illustrations. *I. of Alnwick, Prudhoe &c., 1857 ?, *see* Hartshorne (C. H.)
*I. of Hogarth &c., 1816, *see* Ferrers (E.)

Illustratore (L') fiorentino: calendario storico, 1911, 1912, 1910–11, *see* Carocci (G.)

Illustrazione Italiana. Suppl., Maggio, 1925. Settecento Veneziano. [*By* G. Fogolari, R. Calzini, E. Modigliani]. fol. [Milano. 1925]

Illustres. Illust. & clar. virorum epist., sel. super. & hoc seculo scr., 1669, *see* Gabbema (S. A.)

Ilminsky (Nikolai Ivanovich). Замѣчаніе о тамгахъ и ункунахъ, *see* Imperat. Russ. Arch. Obsch. Труды Восточ. отд., ч3, 1858.

Ilyās ibn Yūsuf (Abu Muḥammad), *see* Niẓāmī, *Ganjavī*.

***Imaginations** & reveries; by A. E., 2nd ed., 1921, *see* Russell (G. W.)

Imago primi sæculi Soc. Jesu a Prov. Flandro-Belg. &c., 1640, *see* Jesuits.

Imbart de la Tour (Pierre). Orig. relig. de la France: les paroisses rurales du 4e au 11e s. 8°. 1900
see Hanotaux (G.) Hist. de la nation franç., t3, Hist. polit., v1, Des origines à 1515, par I. de La T., 1920.

Imbelloni (J.) La esfinge indiana: probl. de los orig. americanos. la8°. Buenos Aires. 1926

Imberdis (André). Hist. des guerres relig. en Auvergne pend. les 16e & 17e s. 2t. 8°. Moulins. 1840

Imberios u. Margarone, *version of Pierre & Marguelonne, see* Pierre, *de Provence*.

Imbert-Terry (*Sir* Henry Machu).
A constitutional king, George I. 8°. [1927]
In spacious times. s8°. 1927
The reminisc. of a Chancellor & h. wife, *see* Roy. Soc. of Lit. Essays, N.S., v7, 1927.

Imhof (Jacob Wilhelm) [Imhoff]. Genealogiae 20 illust. in Italia famil. Acc. de geneal. fam. de Mediolano-Vicecom. epist. [*w. sep. pagin.*] fol. Amstelodami. 1710

Imhotep, *Egyptian physician & god of medicine.*
see Hurry (J. B.) I., 1926; 2nd rev. ed., 1928.
„ Sethe (K. H.) I., d. Asklepios d. Aegypter, 1902.

Imison (John). The school of arts: exper. &c. in sci. [*w. sep. pagin.*] 2nd ed. 8°. [1790 ?]

Immanuel (Fritz).
La guerre des Balkans de 1912–13. v4. 8°. 1914
Takt. Aufgaben für Übungen u. Kriegsspiel. 4e, neu bearb. A. 8°. 1914

Immermann (Carl L.) Münchhausen. 2B[in 1v.] s8°. L. *n.d.*

Immortality. By Sir F. Petrie, F. M. Cornford, A. A. Macdonell &c. Intr. by Ld. Ernle. Ed. Sir J. Marchant. 8°. [1924]

Imms (Augustus Daniel).
A general textbook of entomology. la8°. 1925

***Impartial** account (An) of some transactions in Scotland, 1695, *see* Scotland.

Impartial Hand (An), *ps.* England's imminent danger &c., 1671, *see* England.

Imperatorskaya Akademiya Nauk [Rossiiskaya Akad. Nauk].
Записки. т1–29, 75i. [5ii, 6ii, 24, 25ii, 26i, 27, 28, 29ii *wanting*]. 8°. С.–П. 1862–94
т22 *cont. a list of members,* 1725–1873. *Each vol. has several* Приложенія *each w. sep. tp. & pagin. These, with the exception of most of the scientific papers, have been catalogued separately under the following names:—*

Amfilokhy *archimandrite*.
Ber (K. M.)
Borschov (I. G.)
Bunyakovsky (V. Ya.)
Gebel (A. F.)
Gedeonov (S. A.)
Gelmersen (G. P.)
Golovatsky (Ya. Th.)
Golstunsky (K. F.)
Grot (Ya. K.)
Hamel (J.)
Hildebrand (H.)
Katanov (N. F.)
Kutorga (M. S.)
Lamansky (V. I.)
Lavrovsky (P. A.)
Lents (R. E.)
Longinov (M. N.)
Maksimovich (K. I.)
Makushev (V. V.)
Melgunov (G. V.)
Metchnikoff (E.)
Middendorf (A. F.)
Patimokkha-sutra.

Imperatorskaya Akademiya Nauk [*continued*].
Pekarsky (P. P.)
Pogodin (M. P.)
Rovinsky (D. A.)
Ruprecht (F. J.)
Sargis (P. di).
Schiefner (F. A.)
Schleicher (A.)
Schrenck (L.)
Shein (P. V.)
Sreznevsky (I. I.)
Stebnitsky (I. I.)
Stefan (L. E.)
Sukhomlinov (M. I.)
Svenske (C. F.)
Velyaminov-Zernov (V. V.)
Wiedemann (F. J.)
Yushkevich (I. A.)

Записки Коллегии востоковедов при Азиатском Музее Р. Акад. Наук. т1. la8°. Ленинград. 1925
т1 *incorporates the contents of* т26 *of* Записки Вост. Отд. Русск. Арх. Общ.

Извѣстія. Bulletin. s5, t1–11 [2ii, iv, 3v, 8ii *wanting*], t12iii, 20v, 21iii, iv, 24iv, v. s6, t8ii–t20 (Sept. 1914–1926). la8°. П. [Ленинград]. 1894–1926
„ „ Table des matières, t1–10 (1907–16). [Прилож. къ No. 18, 1916]. la8°. П. 1916

Извѣстія отдѣленія русскаго языка и словесности. т19–32 (1914–27). 8°. П. 1915–27

Каталогъ изданій. 1, Изд. на русс. языкѣ. 8°. С.–П. 1902

Mémoires (Записки по истор.-Филол. отд.)
s7, t12ii, s8, t1iv, 8iii, 12ii, 13iv, v. la8°. С.–П. 1868–1918
see Bartold (V. V.) Отчетъ о поѣздкѣ въ Сред. Азію, 1897. [viii, 1iv.]
„ —— Улугдекъ, 1918. [viii, 13v.]
„ Latishev (V. V.) Житія св. епископовъ Херсонскихъ, 1906. [viii, 8iii.]
„ —— Hagiographica Gr. ined., 1914. [viii, 12ii.]
„ Methodius, *patr. of Cple.* Vita S. Theophanis; ed. B. Latyšev, 1918. [viii, 13iv.]
„ Schmid (Fr.) Reisen in Amur-Lande &c.: Botan. Theil., 1868. [vii, 12ii.]

Сборникъ отд. русс. языка и слов. т97. 8°. П. 1921

Publications.
see Adelung (F. v.) Rapports entre la langue sanscrit & la langue russe, 1811.
„ Aḥmad ibn Fudhlān. Ibn F. u. a. Araber Berichte &c., 1823.
„ Beneshevich (V. N.) Обозрѣніе трудовъ по Славяновѣдѣнію, 1912, вып. 1, 1913.
„ Bonnell (E.) Russ.-liwländ. Chronographie, 1862.
„ Butkov (P. G.) Мат. для новой ист. Кавказа, 1722–1803, ч1, 1869.
„ Castren (M. A.) Gramm. d. samojed. Spr., 1854.
„ Jaba (A.) Dict. kurde-français, 1879.
„ Khemnitser (I. I.) Сочиненія и письма, 1873.
„ Kozlov (P. K.) Краткое отчеты экспед. по исследов. Северной Монголии, 1925.
„ Lehrberg (A. Ch.) Изслѣдованія русской ист., 1819.
„ Marr (N. Ya.) *for extracts f.* Извѣстія.
„ Russia. Россія и Италія, т3ii, 4, 1915–27.
„ Schmidt (I. J.) Gramm. d. mongol. Spr., 1831.
„ Sjögren (A. J.) Osset. Sprachlehre, 1844.
„ Sreznevsky (V. I.) Описаніе рукописей и книгъ, собр. для И. А. Н. въ Олонецкомъ краѣ, 1913.
„ Uspensky (P.) Путеш. въ Метеорскіе &c. монаст. въ Θессаліи, 1896.
„ Wiedemann (F. J.) Syrjän.-deut. Wbch., 1880.
„ Yafetichesky Institut.

Imperatorskaya Arkheograficheskaya Kommissiya.
Полное соб. русс. лѣтописей. т7, 12, 16. 4°. С.–П. 1856–1901
see Avraamki letopis, 1889. [16.]
„ Nikonovskaya letopis, 1901. [12.]
„ Voskresenskaya letopis, 1856. [7.]
Publications.
see Lavrentiev Chron. Повѣсть врем. лѣтъ, *facs.*, 1872.
„ Novgorod. Новгород. лѣтописи, 1879.
„ Sibirskiya. Сибирскія лѣтописи, 1907.

Imperatorskaya Arkheologicheskaya Kommissiya, *see* Kulakovsky (Y. A.) Прошлое Тавриды, 1914.

Imperatorskoe Moskovskoe Arkheologicheskoe Obschestvo.
Труды 14, Археологическаго съѣзда. вып. 1. 4°. Москва. 1906
see Kuchuk-Ioannesov (Kh. I.) Стар. армян. надписи, *n.d.*

Imperatorskoe Obschestvo Istorii i Drevn. Rossiiskikh, *see* Lyubavsky (M. K.) Очеркъ исторіи Литовско-русс. государства, 1910.

Imperatorskoe Obschestvo Istorii pri Moskov. Univ.
see Belokurov (A. S.) Ю. Крижаничъ, 1659–77, 1901.
„ Sichevsky (—) Записка о китайской границѣ, 1875.

Imperatorskoe Russkoe Arkheologicheskoe Obschestvo.
Записки Вост. Отд. Р. А. О. т21i. la8°. С.-П. 1912
see IMP. AKAD. NAUK. Записки Колл. восток. при Азіат. Музее, т1, 1925, *for* т26 *& contin.*
„ MARR (N. YA.) *for various reprints &c.*
Труды Восточнаго отдѣленія И. А. О.
ч1, 3, 4, 6, 8, 11, 13, 16. 8°. С.-П. 1855–72
1, Tizengauzen (V. A.) О саманид. монетахъ.—Savelev (P. S.) Дополненія къ опис. саманид. монетъ—Извѣстія о восточ. древностяхъ и монетахъ.
3, Eichwald (C. E. v.) О чудскихъ копяхъ—Firkovich (A. S.) Археол. развѣдки на Кавказѣ—Ilminsky (N. I.) Замѣчаніе о тамгахъ—Savelev (P. S.) Изъ писемъ Д. Банзарова—Savelev (P. S.) Монеты джучидскія &c.
4, Vasilev (V. P.) Исторія и древн. восточной части Средней Азіи, 10–13b.—Gomboev (G.) О древн. монгол. обычаяхъ &c.—Velyaminov-Zernov (V. V.) Памятникъ съ араб.-татар. надписью—Sore (F.) Неизд. восточ монеты—Berezin (I. I.) Арм. и груз. надписи &c.—Еврейскія надписи—Velyaminov-Zernov (V. V.) Монеты бухарскія и хивинскія.
6, Altan Tobchi. Алтанъ Тобчи: монголская лѣтопись &c.
8, Gomboev (G.) Глубокомудрая чуга—Kossovich (K. A.) Четыре статьи изъ Зендавесты—Dorn (B.) Отчетъ объ ученомъ путеш. по Кавказу &c.—Grigorev (V. V.) Джучидск. мон.—Два разсказа Мирзы-Шемса Бухари.—Хожденіе въ Кербелу и Неджефъ.—Berezin (I. I.) Очеркъ внутр. устройства Улуса Джучіева.
11, Velyaminov-Zernov (V. V.) Изслѣдованіе о Касимовскихъ царяхъ &c., ч3.
13, Rashīd-al-Dīn. Исторія Монголовъ. Ист. Чингизъ-хана персидскій текстъ &c.
16, Bobrovnikov (A. A.) Грамоты вдовы Дарма-баловой и Буянту-хана—Grigorev (V. V.) О скиѳскомъ народѣ Сакахъ—Patkanov (K. P.) Нѣсколько словъ о названіяхъ древнихъ армянс. мѣсяцевъ.—Harkavy (A. E.) О первоначальномъ обиталищѣ Семитовъ, Индоевропейцевъ и Хамитовъ.
REFERENCES.
see CONSTANCE, COUNCIL OF. Concilium C., 1874.
„ LATISHEV (V. V.) Inscr. oræ septentr. P. Euxini Graecæ & Lat., 2ª ed., v1, 1916.

Imperatorskoe Russkoe Geograficheskoe Obschestvo [GOSUDARSTVENNOE R. G. O.]
Атласъ къ путешествію на Амуръ [*by R. K. Maak*], совершенному отъ Сибирскаго отдѣла И. Р. Г. О. [*Engraved tp. begins* Альбомъ рисунковъ]. la. fol. С.-П. *n.d.* [1859 ?]
Записки И. Р. Г. О. Книжка 6. 8°. С.-П. 1852
Записки Кавказскаго отдѣла. Книжка 4. 8°. Тифлисъ. 1857
Записки по отдѣленію этнографіи.
t6i, ii, 7, 8, 10–12, 29, 31i, ii, 33i, ii. 8°. С.-П. 1877–1906
see ALENITSIN (V. D.) О путешествіи Дженкинсона въ Хиву, 1880. [6ii.]
„ BUSSE (F. F.) Списокъ словъ бытоваго значенія кочевыхъ народовъ Сибири, 1880. [6ii.]
„ GOLOVATSKY (YAK. F.) О народной одеждѣ &c. Русиновъ въ Галичинѣ и Венгріи, 1877. [7.]
„ GRIGOREV (V. V.) Повѣрья и обряды Казанскихъ Татаръ, 1880. [6i.]
„ KALINSKY (I. P.) Церковно-народный мѣсяцесловъ на Руси, 1877. [7.]
„ KUN (A. A.) Очерки Шагрисебзскаго бекства, 1880. [6i.]
„ MAINOV (V. N.) Результаты антропологич. изслѣдованій среды Мордвы-Эрзй, 1883. [11.]
„ MAKSHEEV (A. I.) Географ. свѣдѣнія о Киргизск. степяхъ &c., 1880. [6ii.]
„ OGORODNIKOV (E. K.) Прибрежья Ледовитаго и бѣлаго морей &c., 1877. [7.]
„ PANTUSOV (N. N.) Фергана, 1880. [6i.]
„ PATKANOV (S. K.) Опытъ геогр. &c. Тунгусскихъ племенъ Сибири, 2ч, 1906. [33i, ii.]
„ RADLOV (V. V.) Средняя Зерафшанская долина, 1880. [6i.]
„ SADOVNIKOV (D. N.) Сказки и преданія Самарскаго края, 1884. [12.]
„ SBORNIK. Сборникъ народныхъ юридическихъ обычаевъ, t1 (3 отд. &c. 4 *pagin.*), 1878. [8.]
„ UNKOVSKY (I.) Посолство, 1722–24, 1887. [10.]
„ USPENSKY (V. M.) О бассейнѣ Лобъ-Нора, 1880. [6i.]
„ —— Страна Кукэ-норъ, 1880. [6ii.]
„ VALIKHANOV (CH. CH.) Сочиненія, 1904. [29.]
Записки приамурскаго отдѣла. 5i, ii. 4° & 8°. Хабаровскъ. 1899
see KOLBASENKO (I. S.) Станица Срѣтенская (Забайкальской области), 1899. [5ii.]
„ LOGINOVSKY K.) Свадебныя пѣсни &c. казаковъ вост. Забайкалья, 1899. [5ii.]
„ MARGARITOV (V.) Камчатка и ея обитатели, 1899. [5i.]

Imperatorskoe Russkoe Geograficheskoe Obschestvo [*contd.*].
Извѣстія. t20 (*imperf.*), 48–58 (1912–26).
8°. С.-П. [1884 ?]. 1912–26
Комитет Севера при Р. Г. О. Очерки по ист. колонизации Севера. в1. la8°. П. 1922
Сказочная комиссия, 1924–25, 1926. Обзор работ под ред. С. Ф. Ольденбурга. la8°. Ленинград. 1926–27
Составъ, 1895. [*b. w.* Semenov (P. P.) Исторія И. Р. Г. О., 1896] la8°. С.-П. 1896
REFERENCES.
see KOZLOV (P. K.) Монголия, 1923.
„ MÜLLER (F.) Unter Tungusen u. Jakuten, 1882.
„ POTANIN (G. N.) Очерки сѣверо-западной Монголіи, в1, 2, 1881.
„ POZDNEEV (A. M.) Монголія &c., t1, 1896.
„ ZOLOTAREV (D. A.) Лопарская экспед., 1927.

Imperial & Asiatic quarterly review (The), & oriental & colonial record. New Ser. [*w. t.* Asiatic q.r.] v16–23. la8°. [1920–27]

Imperial Economic Conference, 1923. Records of proc. & doc. *w.* App. to summary of proc., *see* CANADA: PARL. Sess. papers, v60, No. 7, 1924.

Imperial Education Conference. I.E.C. Convened by Imp. Gen. Staff, June 1919. [P2412]. 8°. 1919
Rep. on the cinematograph in educ. 8°. 1924

Imperial Institute.
Indian Trade Enquiry. Reports on rice. 8°. 1920
MONOGRAPHS.
Petroleum. Prep., w. co-op. of H. B. Cronshaw. 8°. 1921
see CRONSHAW (H. B.) Oil shales, 1921.
„ —— Silver ores, 1921.
„ HALL (T. C. F.) Lead ores, 1921.
„ HALSE (E.) Cobalt ores, 1924.
„ —— Mercury ores, 1923.
see JOHNSTONE (S. J.) Potash, 1922.
„ LUMB (A. D.) The platinum metals, 1920.
„ RASTALL (R. H.) Molybdenum ores, 1922.
„ —— & W. H. WILCOCKSON. Tungsten ores, 1920.
„ RONALDSON (J. G.) Coal, 1920.

Imperial Library, *Calcutta*, *see* BÛHÂR LIB. Cat. raisonné of B.L. [Imp. Lib.], v1, 2, 1921–23.

Imperial Maritime League, *see* HORTON-SMITH (L. G. H.) The Declar. of London & Naval Prize Bill &c.; comp. for I.M.L., 1920.

Imperial Mineral Resources Bureau.
Iron ore. (Summary of information). p7, 8. 8°. 1922
The mineral industry of the Brit. Empire & for. countries.
War period. Copper (1913–19). 8°. 1922
„ „ Gold (1913–19). 8°. 1922
„ „ Lead (1913–19). [*b. w.* Copper, 1922]. 8°. 1922
„ „ Platinum & allied metals (1913–19). [*b. w.* Copper, 1922]. 8°. 1922
„ „ Tin (1913–19). [*b. w.* Copper, 1922]. 8°. 1922

Imperial (Adolfo Miralles de), *see* MIRALLES DE IMPERIAL (A.)

*__Imperiale__, a tragedy, 1655, *see* FREEMAN (*Sir* R.)

Imperiale Regio Istituto del Regno Lombardo-Veneto.
Memorie. 4°. Milano. 1838

Imperiale Regio Istituto Veneto, *see* REALE ISTITUTO VENETO.

*__Importance__ (The) of the port of Reval &c., 1921, *see* REVAL.

*__Important__ consid. wh. ought to move all true &c. Catholicks, 1601, repr., 1688, *see* WATSON (W.)

*__Impossible (The)__ island: Corsica &c., 1923, *see* SNAFFLE, *ps.*

Imray, Lawrie, Norie & Wilson, Ltd.
The story of the blue back chart. [P2518]. la8°. 1921

In. *In the mountains. s8°. 1920
*In the Foreign Legion, 1915, *see* ROSEN (E.)

Inada (Hogitarō), *see* KOOP (A. J.) & H. I. Japanese names & how to read them, pl, 1920; 1923.

Incarnatio. *De mysterio I. Verbi et unionis hypostaticae, 1577, *see* FRANCUS (T. A.)

Ince (R. B.)
Franz Anton Mesmer, h. life & teaching. s8°. 1920

Inchbald (*Mrs.* Elizabeth). *Animal magnetism, *see* DUBLIN.
Vol. of farces, 1792.
British theatre: plays acted at the theatres royal, printed f. the prompt books, w. remarks by Mrs. I. [*Each play has sep. tp. & pagin.*] 25v. s8°. 1808
All for love. (Dryden). [6.]
All in the wrong. (Murphy). [15.]
Antony & Cleopatra. (Shakespeare). [4.]
As you like it. (Shakespeare). [3.]
Barbarossa. (Brown). [15.]
Battle of Hexham. (Colman). [20.]
Beaux strategem. (Farquhar). [8.]

Inchbald (*Mrs.* Elizabeth) [*continued*].
British theatre [*continued*].

Beggars' Opera. (Gay). [12.]
Belle's strategem. (Cowley). [19.]
Bold stroke f. a husband. (Cowley). [19.]
Bold stroke f. a wife. (Centlivre). [11.]
Brothers. (Cumberland). [18.]
Busy Body. (Centlivre). [11.]
Careless husband. (Cibber). [9.]
Castle of Andalusia. (O'Keeffe). [22.]
Cato. (Addison). [8.]
Chances. (Beaumont & Fletcher). [6.]
Clandestine marriage. (Colman & Garrick). [16.]
Comedy of errors. (Shakespeare). [1.]
Conscious lovers. (Steele). [12.]
Constant couple. (Farquhar). [8.]
Coriolanus. (Shakespeare). [5.]
Count of Narbonne. (Jephson). [20.]
Countess of Salisbury. (Hartson). [16.]
Country girl. (Garrick). [16.]
Cure f. the heartache. (Morton). [25.]
Cymbeline. (Shakespeare). [4.]
De Monfort. (Baillie). [24.]
Deserted daughter. (Holcroft). [24.]
Distressed mother. (Philips). [7.]
Douglas. (Home). [16.]
Dramatist. (Reynolds). [20.]
Duenna. (Sheridan). [19.]
Earl of Essex. (Jones). [22.]
Earl of Warwick. (La Harpe) (tr.) [19.]
Edward the Black Prince. (Shirley). [14.]
Every man in h. humour. (Jonson). [5.]
Everyone has h. fault. (Inchbald). [23.]
Fair penitent. (Rowe). [10.]
Fatal curiosity. (Lillo). [11.]
First love. (Cumberland). [18.]
Fontainbleau. (O'Keeffe). [22.]
Foundling. (Moore). [14.]
Gamester. (Moore). [14.]
George Barnwell. (Lillo). [11.]
Goodnatured man. (Goldsmith). [17.]
Grecian daughter. (Murphy). [15.]
Gustavus Vasa. (Brooke). [7.]
Hamlet. (Shakespeare). [1.]
Heir at law. (Colman). [21.]
Heiress. (Burgoyne). [22.]
Honey moon. (Tobin). [25.]
Inconstant. (Farquhar). [8.]
Inkle & Yarico. (Colman). [20.]
Iron chest. (Colman). [21.]
Isabella. (Southerne). [7.]
Jane Shore. (Rowe). [10.]
Jealous wife. (Colman). [16.]
Jew. (Cumberland). [18.]
John Bull. (Colman). [21.]
Julius Caesar. (Shakespeare). [4.]
King Henry IV. (Shakespeare). [2.]
King Henry V. (Shakesp.) [2.]
King Henry VIII. (Shakespeare). [3.]
King John. (Shakespeare). [1.]
King Lear. (Shakespeare). [4.]
King Richard III. (Shakespeare). [1.]
Know your own mind. (Murphy). [15.]
Lady Jane Grey. (Rowe). [10.]
Lionel & Clarissa. (Bickerstaffe). [17.]
Love for love. (Congreve). [13.]
Love in a village. (Bickerstaffe). [17.]
Love makes a man. (Cibber). [9.]
Lovers' vows. (Kotzebue) (tr.) [23.]
Macbeth. (Shakespeare). [4.]
Mahomet. (Voltaire) (tr.) [13.]
Maid of the mill. (Bickerstaffe). [17.]
Man of the world. (Macklin). [14.]
Measure f. measure. (Shakespeare). [3.]
Merchant of Venice. (Shakespeare). [2.]
Merry wives of Windsor. (Shakespeare). [3.]
Mountaineers. (Colman). [21.]
Mourning bride. (Congreve). [13.]
Much ado. (Shakespeare). [2.]
New way to pay old debts. (Massinger). [6.]
Oroonoko. (Southerne). [7.]
Orphan. (Otway). [12.]
Othello. (Shakespeare). [5.]
Point of honour. (Kemble). [24.]
Poor gentleman. (Colman). [21.]
Provoked husband. (Vanbrugh & Cibber). [9.]
Provoked wife. (Vanbrugh). [9.]
Recruiting officer. (Farquhar). [8.]
Revenge. (Young). [12.]
Rival queens. (Lee). [6.]
Rivals. (Sheridan). [19.]
Road to ruin. (Holcroft). [24.]
Roman father. (Whitehead). [14.]
Romeo & Juliet. (Shakespeare). [1.]
Rule a wife &c. (Beaumont & Fletcher). [6.]
School of reform. (Morton). [25.]
She stoops to conquer. (Goldsmith). [17.]
She wou'd & she wou'd not. (Cibber). [9.]
Siege of Damascus. (Hughes). [10.]
Speed the plough. (Morton). [25.]
Stranger. (Thompson). [24.]
Such things are. (Inchbald). [23.]
Surrender of Calais. (Colman). [20.]
Suspicious husband. (Hoadly). [13.]
Tamerlane. (Rowe). [10.]
Tancred & Sigismunda. (Thomson). [13.]
Tempest. (Shakespeare). [5.]
To marry or not to marry. (Inchbald). [23.]
Twelfth night. (Shakesp.) [5.]
Venice preserved. (Otway). [12.]
Way to get married. (Morton). [25.]
Way to keep him. (Murphy). [15.]
West Indian. (Cumberland). [18.]
Wheel of fortune. (Cumberland). [18.]
Wild oats. (O'Keeffe). [22.]
Winter's tale. (Shakespeare). [3.]
Wives as they were. (Inchbald). [23.]
Wonder. (Centlivre). [11.]
Zara. (Hill). [7.]

Every one has his fault. Comedy. s8°. 1926
I'll tell you what, *see* †INCHBALD (*Mrs.* E.) Mod. th., v7, 1811.
Nature & art. [P2460]. 8°. *n.d.*
Next door neighbours, *see* †INCHBALD (*Mrs.* E.) Mod. th., v7, 1811.

Inchofer (Melchior). Annales eccl. regni Hungariae, t1(–1059). [*no more publ.*] fol. Romae. 1644
Hist. sacrae Latinitatis libri 6. s8°. Pragae. 1742

Inclan (Miguel de la Vega), *see* VEGA INCLAN (M. DE LA).

Incognito, *ps.* *Commoner, The, a poem, 1710, *see* COMMONER.

Incorporated Accountants' year book. s8°. 1925

Incorporated Association, *see* ASSOCIATION.

Inculetz (Ion). Spaţiul & timpul in noua lumina ştiinţ., *see* ACADEMIA ROM. Disc., 46, 1920.

***Independence Square** neighborhood, 1926, *see* FREY (C.)

Independent.
*I. (An) parliament &c., 1921, *see* IRISH.
*I. (The) power of the Church not Romish: suppl. to Of the subject of church-power, by S. Lowth. By a presbyter of the Ch. of Eng. s8°. 1716

Independent (The) & The weekly review. v107–111 (Oct. 1921–Dec. 1923) [v108–110 *want tp.*] la8°. N.Y. [1921–23]

Independent Labour Party. The capitalist press. Prep. & publ. by the I.L.P. [P2493]. 8°. [1920]

Index. Index Kewensis plantarum phanerogamarum, nomina & synonyma omnium gen. & spec. ab 1911 ad 1915 compl. Suppl. 5, 6. 4°. O. 1921–26
5, 1911–15; ductu & consilio D. Prain, conf. Herbarii Horti Regii Botanici K. curatores. 6, 1916–1920; ductu &c. A. W. Hill.

*Index rarior. libr. Bibl. Univers. Reg. Budensis, 2p, 1780–81, *see* BUDAPEST.

Index generalis. Annuaire gén. des universités, gr. écoles &c. Publ. s. la dir. de R. de Montessus de Ballore. s8°. 1921

Index librorum prohibitorum (*in chronological order*).
I. l. p., cum regulis confectis per Patres a Trident. Synodo delectos, auct. Pii IV comprobatus. 8°. Romae, *P. Manutius.* 1564
,, ,, ...[*a. ed.*] s8°. Coloniae. 1568
,, ,, [*a. ed. b. w.* Philip II. Edictum, 1570]. s8°. Antverpiae. 1570
*I. expurgat. l. qui hoc sec. prodierunt, vel doctrinae non sanae erroribus inspersis &c. Philippi II iussu &c. a. 1571. 8°. Antverpiae. 1571
I. l. authorumque S. Sedis Apostolicae &c. authoritate prohib. &c. s4°. Monachii. 1582
I. & cat. l. p. mandato Gasparis a Quiroga card. archiep. Toletani editus. s4°. Madriti. 1583
I. l. expurgatorum G. Quiroga jussu ed. [*b. w.* Index & cat. libr. prohib., 1583]. s4°. Madriti. 1584
I. expurgat. l. qui hoc seculo prodierunt &c. s8°. [Lugduni]. 1586
I. l. p., 1589, *see* TRENT, *Council of.*
*I. l. expurgat. G. Quiroga card. & archiep. Tolet. &c. jussu editus. s4°. Salmuri. 1601
I. l. expurgandorum tom. primus per Fr. I. M. Brasichellen [*i.e. Guanzelli*]. s8°. Romae. 1607
I. expurgatorius l. qui hoc sæc. prodierunt &c. [Acc. præterea collatio censurae in glossas juris canonici 1572 ed. Cum iisdem glossis 1580 recognitis, &c.] s8°. Argentorati. 1609
*Indices expurgatorii duo, testes fraudum ac falsationum pontific.: prior jussu Philippi II Regis Hisp. consilio concinnatus, 1571. Posterior ed. jussu G. Quiroga, Card. 1571. Additus, Index Librorum prohib. auctorit. Pii IV primum ed., etc. [*w. sep. tp. & pagin.*] [Ed. F. Du Jon, the Elder]. s8°. Hanoviae. 1611
I. gen. l. p. a pontificiis una cum editionibus expurgatis &c. In usum Bibl. Bodleianae design. per T. James. s8°. Oxoniæ. 1627
I. l. p. Alex. VII jussu ed. 4°. Romae. 1664
I. l. p. Alexandri VII Pontif. Max. iussu ed. [*b. w.* Index libr. prohib.; Sotomaior, 1667]. fol. Romae. 1667
I. l. p. & expurg. novissimus. Pro catholicis Hispan. regnis Philippi IV. A. a Sotomaior jussu &c. recog. fol. Madriti. 1667
I. l. p. Clementis X jussu ed. s8°. Romae. 1670
I. l. p. Benedicti XIV jussu ed. 4°. Romae. 1758
Indice ult. de los libros proh. y mandados expurgar, rey Carlos IV, 1747–89. Formado &c. por mandato del D. A. Rubin de Cevallos. 4°. Madrid. 1790
I. l. p. a Sixto V. Ed. J. Mendham. 4°. Lond. 1835
An exact repr. of the Roman I. Expurgatorius &c. Ed. w. pref. by R. Gibbings. s8°. D. 1837
I. l. p. Gregorii XVI jussu ed. ed. nov. s8°. Neapoli. 1862
I. l. p. gedr. zu Parma 1580; hrsg. u. erl. v. H. Reusch. la8°. Bonn. 1889
see MENDHAM (J.) I. of p. bks. by command of Gregory XVI in 1835, *w. repr. of* Cathalogus, 1554, 1840.

India.

I, Government Publications.

AGRICULTURE.
Production of tea in I., 1919–1921. fol. & 4°. Calcutta. 1921–23
Review of agric. operations in India, 1919–20—1923–24. 8°. Calcutta. 1921–25
Prev. yrs. h. t. Report on progress of agric. in India.

India [*continued*].
I, Government Publications [*continued*].
ARCHAEOLOGICAL SURVEY OF INDIA.
Ann. progress rep. of the Superintendent, Hindu & Buddhist monuments, N. Circle, 1919–1921. sm. fol. Lahore. 1920–22
Annual report, 1914/15–1924/25. 4°. Calcutta. 1920–27
Ann. report, Central Circle, 1919/20–1920/21. fol. Patna. 1920–22
The Central Circle was formerly part of the Eastern Circle.
Ann. report, Eastern Circle, 1920–21. fol. Calcutta. 1922
Annual rep., Frontier Circle, 1919–20, 1920/21. fol. Peshawar. 1920–21
Index to Annual reports of the Director Gen. of Arch. in India (Sir John Marshall), 1902–16. By G. R. Kaye. 4°. Calcutta. 1924
Memoirs. Nos. 1–20, 22, 25–32. 4°. Calcutta, Madras & Simla. 1919–28
1, Dates of votive inscr. on the stupas at Sanchi; R. Chanda.
2, Vishnu image; by R. B. Bidyabinod.
3, Talamana or iconometry; by T. A. Gopinatha Rao.
4, Arch. remains & excav. at Nagari; by D. R. Phandarkar.
5, Arch. & Vaishnava tradition; by R. Chanda.
6, Temples at Palampet; by Ghulam Yazdani.
7, Excav. at Taxila, Stupas & monasteries at Jauliāñ; by Sir J. Marshall.
8, Six sculptures from Mahoba; by K. N. Dikshit.
9, Mosque of Shaikh 'Abdu-n Nabi; by Z. Hasan.
10, Guide to Niẓamu-d Dīn; by Zafar Hasan.
11, Sculptures in Museum, Lucknow; by Shastri Hirananda.
12, Astronom. instruments in the Delhi museum; by G. R. Kaye.
13, Kannada poets ment. in inscr.; by T. T. Sharman.
14, Antiq. of Bhimbar & Rajauri; by R. C. Kak.
15, Geometric patterns in Saracenic art; by E. H. Hankin.
16, Temple of Siva at Bhumara; by R. D. Banerji.
17, Pallava archit.; by A. H. Longhurst, p1.
18, Hindu astronomy; by G. R. Kaye.
19, Jami Masjid at Badaun &c.; by J. F. Blakiston.
20, Origin & cult of Tārā; by H. Shastri.
22, Hist. mem. on the Qutb, Delhi; by J. A. Page.
25, Basreliefs of Badami; by R. D. Banerji.
26, Two statues of Pallava kings &c. at Mahabalipuram; by H. Krishna Sastri.
27, Pageant of King Mindon, 1865; reprod. f. contemp. doc. by C. Duroiselle.
28, Bhasa & authorship of 13 Trivandrum plays; by H. Sastri.
29, Spec. of calligraphy in Delhi Mus. of Arch.; by Khan Zafar Hasan.
30, Beginnings of art in E. India; by R. Chanda.
31, Indus Valley in Vedic per.; by R. Chanda.
32, Fragm. of a Prajnaparamita MS.; by B. B. Bidyabinod.
Progress report of the A.S. of I., Muhammadan & Brit. monuments, N. Circle, for years ending 31st March 1917–21. fol. Allahabad. 1917–22
——: PUBLICATIONS.
see CORPUS inscript. Indicarum, n. ed., v1, 1925.
,, COUSENS (H.) The Chālukyan architect. of Kanarese dist., 1926.
,, EPIGRAPHIA INDICA, v14, 17, 1917–24.
,, EPIGRAPHIA INDO-MOSLEMICA, 1917–18—1923–24, 1921–27.
,, FRANCKE (A. H.) Antiq. of Indian Tibet, p2, 1926.
,, INDIAN. South Ind. inscriptions, v3, p3, 1920.
,, MARSHALL (*Sir* J.) Conservation manual, 1923.
,, SANCHI. Cat. of the Museum of Archaeol., 1922.
,, VOGEL (J. PH.) Antiqs. of Chamba state, p1, 1911.
,, —— Tile-mosaics of the Lahore Fort, 1920.
BOARD OF SCIENTIFIC ADVICE.
Annual rep., 1919/20–1922/23. 8°. Calcutta. 1921–24
CENSUS, 1901.
C. of I., 1901. v3, Andaman & Nicobar Isl.; by Sir R. C. Temple. fol. Calcutta. 1903
CENSUS, 1921.
C. of I., 1921. v1, 8i, ii, 13i–iii. fol. Calcutta *&* Bombay. 1922–24
1, India, 2p; by J. T. Marten. 8, Bombay; by L. J. Sedgwick, 2p. 13, Madras; by G. T. Boag, 3p.
COUNCIL OF STATE.
Council of State debates. (Official report). v1, 1st session, 1921. 8°. Delhi. 1921
EDUCATION.
Conf. of Ind. universities, May 1924, Simla. 8°. Calcutta. 1924
Indian education in 1918/19–1924/25. 8° *&* 4°. Calcutta. 1920–26
Progress of educ. in India, 1917–22; by J. A. Richey. 2v. 8°. Calcutta. 1923–24
Some experiments in Ind. education. 8°. Calcutta. 1927

India [*continued*].
I, Government Publications [*continued*].
EDUCATION: PUBLICATIONS.
see BULKELEY (J. P.) Adult educ., Eng. & W., 1922.
,, DUNCAN (H. S.) & A. H. MACKENZIE. Training of teachers, 1919.
,, MACKENZIE (A. H.) State exams. in Scottish schools, 1921.
,, RICHEY (J. A.) Grants-in-aid to schools in Brit. I., 1923.
,, SAWARKAR (D. S.) Visual instr. in Baroda, 1920.
,, SHARP (H.) Vernacular educ. in Ceylon, 1919.
,, SORABJI (R. K.) Facilities for Indian students, 1920.
,, WATKINS (L. T.) Libraries in I. High schools, 1920.
,, WEST (M.) Bilingualism, 1926.
,, WYATT (H. G.) Methods of school inspection in Eng., 1917
,, —— Rural school teachers in the U.S., 1923.
FINANCE & REVENUE.
Rep. on oper. of the Currency Dept. &c. for 1920–21, by A. C. McWatters. la8°. Calcutta. 1921
Statistics f. Finance & Revenue accounts of Govt. of I. Receipts & disbursements of home & Indian accounts, 1st Apr. 1911 to 31st March 1919, 1912–20. fol. Delhi. 1921–22
FOREIGN DEPT.
Letter to H.M.'s Sec. of State for India [on Russ. occup. of Kizil Arvat]. fol. 1877
FORESTS.
Quinquennial review of forest admin., 1914/15–1918/19. App., Statistics for 1918–19. fol. Simla. 1920
Statistics rel. to forest admin., 1919–26. fol. Calcutta. 1920–27
GEOLOGICAL SURVEY.
Memoirs of the G.S. of I. v44–48. la8°. Calcutta. 1920–25
Mems. of the G.S. of I.: Palaeontologia Indica. la4°. Calcutta. 1901–27
Anthracolithic faunæ of Kashmir, Kanaur & Spiti; by C. Diener. [N.S., v5ii.]
Anthracolithic fossils of the Shan States; by C. Diener. [N.S., v3iv.]
Anthracotheriidae of the Dera Bugti deposits in Baluchistan; by C. F. Cooper. [N.S., v8ii.]
Brachiopoda of the Namyau Beds, North. Shan States, Burma; by S. S. Buckman. [N.S., v3ii.]
Contrib. to palæontology of Assam; by E. Spengler. [N.S., v8i.]
Crétacé (Le) & l'Eocène du Tibet Central; by H. Douvillé. [N.S., v5iii.]
Devonian fossils f. Chitral & the Pamirs; by F. R. C. Reed. [N.S., v6ii.]
Fossil Giraffidæ of India; by G. E. Pilgrim. Plates 1–5. [N.S., 4.]
Fossil Suidæ of India; by G. E. Pilgrim. [N.S., v8iv.]
Himálayan fossils: v3, p2, Trias Brachiopoda & Lamellibranchiata; by A. Bittner; tr. A. H. Foord. Plates 1–12. [15.]
,, ,, v4, Fauna of the Spiti Shales, 5p [*pagin. cont.*, p1 *bound sep.*] 1–3, by V. Uhlig. 4, by K. Holdaus. 5, Add. notes, by P. Steiger. [15.]
,, ,, v7, p1, The Cambrian fossils of Spiti; by F. R. C. Reed. Plates 1–6. [15.]
,, ,, v7, p2, Ordovician & Silurian fossils f. the Cent. Himalayas; by F. R. C. Reed. Plates 1–20. [15.]
Incomplete (An) skull of Dinotherium; by R. W. Palmer. [N.S., v7iv.]
Indian Gondwana plants: a revision; by A. C. Seward & B. Sahni. [N.S., v7i.]
Lamellibranchiata of the Eocene of Burma; by G. de P. Cotter. [N.S., v7ii.]
Lower Gondwana plants f. the Golabgarh Pass, Kashmir; by A. C. Seward. Plates 1–3. [N.S., 4.]
Mesozoic plants f. Afghanistan & Afghan-Turkistan; by A. C. Seward. Plates 1–7. [N.S., 4.]
Mollusca of the Ranikot Series. p1, Cephalopoda & Gastropoda; by M. Cossmann & G. Pissarro, w. intr. note on the Stratigraphy of the Ranikot Ser., by E. W. Vredenburg. [N.S., v3i.]
New Ordovician & Silurian fossils f. Northern Shan States; by F. R. C. Reed. [N.S., v6i.]
On some fish-remains f. the Lameta Beds at Dongargaon, Cent. Prov.; by A. S. Woodward. [N.S., v3iii.]
Ordovician & Silurian fossils f. Yun-nan; by F. R. C. Reed. [N.S., v6iii.]
Perissodactyla of the Eocene of Burma; by G. E. Pilgrim. [N.S., v8iii.]
Review of the Genus Gisortia w. descr. of sev. species; by E. Vredenburg. [N.S., v7iii.]
Sivapithecus palate & o. primate fossils f. India; by G. E. Pilgrim. [N.S., 14.]
Triassic faunæ of Kashmir; by C. Diener. [N.S., v5i.]
Upper carboniferous fossils f. Chitral & the Pamirs. [N.S., v6iv.]
Vertebrate Fauna of the Gaj Series in the Bugti Hills & the Punjab; by G. E. Pilgrim. 30 Plates &c. [N.S., 4.]

India [*continued*].
I, Government Publications [*continued*].
GEOLOGICAL SURVEY [*continued*].
Records of the G.S. of I. v50–59. la8°. Calcutta. 1919–26
see LA TOUCHE (T. H. D.) Bibliog. of Ind. geology, p2–4, 1921–26.
IMPERIAL LIBRARY.
Catalogue. p1, Author-cat. of pr. bks. in Europ. lang. Suppl. 2v. 4°. Calcutta. 1917–18
LEGISLATIVE DEPT., CODES &c.
General rules & orders. 3rd ed. v1–4. la8°. Calcutta. 1926–27
India's Parliament at Delhi: résumé of work, 1922. [P2739]. la8°. 1922
Legisl. Assembly debates. (Official report). v1, 1st session, 1921. [*in* 2p. *pagin. cont.*] 8°. Delhi. 1921
Proc. of the I. Legisl. Co. v55, 1916–1917, 57, 58, 1918–1920. fol. Calcutta. 1917–20
Unrepealed general Acts. v9 (1919–23). la8°. Calcutta. 1924
see AGRA & OUDH, *United Prov. of*. Code, 5th ed., 3v, 1922.
,, WEBB-JOHNSON (S.) Digest of Ind. law cases &c., 1922–25, 1925–27; Index of cases (1910–21), 1925.
LINGUISTIC SURVEY OF INDIA. v1i, 10, 11. fol. Calcutta. 1921–27
1i, Introd., by Sir G. A. Grierson.
1, Suppl. 2, Addenda & corrig. min. [*b. w.* v1].
10, Specimens of lang. of the Eranian family, comp. & ed. by Sir G. A. Grierson.
11, Gipsy lang., comp. & ed. by G. A. Grierson.
Index of language-names. Comp. by Sir G. A. Grierson. obl.8°. Calcutta. 1920
MEDICAL & SANITARY DEPT.
Ann. rep. of the Public Health Commissioner for 1922. 2v. 8°. Simla & Calcutta. 1924
METEOROLOGICAL DEPT.
Memoirs of the Ind. Meteorolog. Dept. v21–24 (1910–25). 4°. Calcutta. 1919–26
MILITARY DEPARTMENT.
Enriquez (C. M. D.) Races of Burma. 8°. Calcutta. 1924
Frontier & overseas exped. f. India. Comp. in Intell. Br., Div. of Chief of Staff, Army Head Quarters. 6v & v1, Suppl. A., v2, Suppl. A. la8°. Simla & Calcutta. 1907–11
1, Tribes North of Kabul River. Suppl. A, Oper. agst. the Mohmands, 1908.
2, N.-W. Frontier tribes betw. Kabul & Gumal Rivers. Suppl. A, Oper. agst. Zakka Khel Afridis, 1908.
3, Baluchistan & First Afghan War.
4, North & N.-E. Frontier tribes. 5, Burma.
6, Exped. overseas.
Garhwális. Comp. by J. Evatt, rev. by K. Henderson. [Hdbk. f. Indian Army]. 8°. Calcutta. 1924
Regul. for the army in India to July 1925. 8°. Calcutta. 1926
see AFGHAN. Third Afghan war, 1919; official acc., 1926.
,, INDIAN ARMY LIST (QUARTERLY).
,, WAZIRISTAN. Oper. in W., 1919–20, 1921.
OFFICERS, SERVICES OF. Engineer & State Railway Revenue Establishments. [Railway Board]. Corr. to 1st July 1920–1927. 8°. Calcutta. 1921–27
Post Office. Corr. to 1st July 1921–27. 8°. Calcutta. 1921–27
Telegraph Branch of Posts & T. Dept. Corr. to 1st July 1920–27. 8°. Calcutta. 1921–27
PRICES & WAGES. Dept. of Statistics. War prices & house rents. fol. Calcutta. 1918
Prices & wages in India, 35th–37th issue[s]. fol. Calcutta. 1920–23
RECORD DEPARTMENT (IMPERIAL).
Calendar of Persian corresp. v4, 1772–75. la8°. Calcutta. 1925
Press-list of "Mutiny papers," 1857: corr. of mutineers, rep. of spies &c. la8°. Calcutta. 1921
see WHEELER (J. T.) Mem. on the records in the For. Dept., 1865.
SURVEYS.
General report, 1918–27. fol. & 8°. Calcutta. [1920–27]
Hdbk. of topography, prep. by Col. Gordon. 11 chaps. [*each w. sep. tp. & pagin. in* 1v. Ch. 1, 4th ed.; 11, 2nd ed.] 8°. Calcutta. 1911–26
S. of I. Map publ. & office work, 1924–25. 8°. Calcutta. 1926
see STEIN (*Sir* M. A.) Mem. on maps of Chinese Turkistan &c., 1923.
TRADE.
Dept. of Statistics. Statist. tables showing for 1901–2 to 1917–18 the value of imports & exports. fol. Calcutta. 1919
Inland trade (Rail & River-borne) of I., 1916–21. fol. Calcutta. 1918–22
Rev. of trade of India, 1919–27. fol. Calcutta. 1921–27

India [*continued*].
I, Government Publications [*continued*].
REFERENCES (*Govt. Publ^s.*)
see COLE (*Maj.* B. L.) Rajputana classes, 1922.
,, DISORDERS INQ. COMM., 1919–20.
,, MARJORIBANKS (N. E.) &c. Rep. on Ind. labour emigr. to Ceylon & Malaya, 1917.
,, SCHORN (W. C.) Alphab. index to names of places &c. in map of Turkestan, 1884.
,, SYLHET. S. District records; ed. W. K. Firminger, v4, 1788–92, 1919.
II, Anonymous Works &c.
Ancient I. as descr. in class. lit.; tr. &c., 1901, *see* MAC-CRINDLE (J. W.), *ed.*
*Brit. I. f. Q. Elizabeth to Ld. Reading. By an Indian Mahomedan. Foreword by Sir T. Morison. 8°. 1926
Early travels in I., 1583–1619, 1921, *see* FOSTER (W.), *ed.*
India in 1920, 1921–22—1926–27. Report[s] for pres. to Parl. by L. F. R. Williams [&] J. Coatman. [7v]. la8°. Calcutta. 1921–28
Indian politics, 1921–22. 8°. Calcutta. 1922
Papers rel. to applic. of princ. of dyarchy to Govt. of I., 1920, *see* CURTIS (L.)
Proc. of the All-I. Conf. of librarians, Lahore, 1918. fol. Simla. 1918
*Reflections on the present state of Brit. I. 8°. 1829
Report on Indian constit. reforms. 8°. 1918
Village educ. in I., Rep. of a Comm. of Inquiry. s8°. 1920
West coast of I. pilot, 6th ed. & Suppl. 2, 1919–22, *see* ADMIRALTY.
India Office.
Cat. of lib. of the I.O. v1, Accessions, 9–13. 8°. 1920–26
,, ,, ...2iv, Suppl. 1906–20. Bengali bks. by J. F. Blumhardt. 8°. 1923
India Office List, 1920–23, 1925. 8°. 1920–25
see SETON (*Sir* M. C. C.) The I.O., 1926.
,, SIAM. Records of rels. betw. S. & for. countries in 17th c., 5v, 1915–21.
Indian.
*I. emigration. By "Emigrant." [India of to-day, v5]. s8°. 1924
*I. policy & Eng. justice. By H. M. H. [*b. w.* Mullick (G. B.), Lord Northbrook &c., 1873]. 8°. 1875
I. politics, 1921-22, 1922, *see* INDIA: *Anon. Wks.*
I. (The) viceroyalty, 1858–1921. [By P. E. Roberts &c. Issued w. the "Times of India"]. fol. [Bombay]. 1922
*I. (The) vocabulary. To which is prefixed the forms of impeachment. s8°. 1788
Scenes & characters f. I. hist., 1925, *see* PAYNE (C. H.), *ed.*
South I. inscr. v3, Misc. inscr. f. Tamil country, p3. Ed. & tr. H. Krishna Sastri. [Arch. Survey of I. New Imp. Ser., v29]. la4°. Madras. 1920
South I. Ocean pilot, orig. comp. by H. A. Moriarty, 3rd ed., Suppl. 6, & Not. to mariners, 1911–22, *see* ADMIRALTY.
Indian Antiquary, *see* BÜHLER (J. G.) Ind. palaeog.; ed. as app. to I. A., v33, 1904.
see EPIGRAPHIA INDICA; publ. as Suppl. to the "I.A.," v14, 17, 1917–24.
,, TEMPLE (*Sir* R. C.) 50 yrs. of "The I.A.," 1921.
Indian army list (Quarterly), July–Oct. 1895, Jan.–Oct. 1896, July–Oct. 1897, Jan.–Apr. 1898, Jan.–Oct. 1899, Jan.–Apr. 1900, Apr. 1906, July 1909, Jan. 1914, July 1915, Jan. 1917, Jan. 1918, Oct. 1919, Jan. 1920. 8°. Calcutta. 1895–1920
Indian Historical Records Commission. Proceedings & meetings. v1–9, 1919–26. la8°. Calcutta. 1920–27
Indian (The) journal of medical research. Ed. by the Director Gen., I. Med. Service. v7–12 (1919–26). 8°. Calcutta. 1920–26
v10 *has* Suppl. No., Cercariæ Indicæ, by R. B. S. Sewell.
Ind. medical research memoirs. Suppl. ser. to Ind. Journal &c. Nos. 1–3. 8°. Calcutta. 1924
1, Rep. of the Ankylostomiasis inq. in Madras; by K. S. Mhaskar.
2, Rel. of rice to beri-beri in India; by R. McCarrison & R. V. Norris.
3, Provis. list &c. of the Anophelini; by S. R. Christophers.
Indian Museum, *Calcutta, see* RAMAPRASAD CHANDA. Begin. of art in E. India, sculpt. in I.M., 1927.
Indian Text Series.
see HĀTIM TILAWÔN^U. H.'s tales, &c., 1923.
,, SĀNTIDEVA. Sikshā-Samuccaya, 1922.
Indias. Indice gen. de los papelas del Consejo de I., 6t, 1923–26, *see* ALTOLAGUIRRE Y DUVALE (A. DE) & A. BONILLA Y SAN MARTIN.
Vaticinios de la pérdida de las I., *see* COLECCION de docs. ined. de Ultramar, s2, t12, 1899.

Indica. *Nova Indica, sive memorabilis virtus Xtianorum 61 in Japonia, a. 1639 pro fide Xtna interfectorum &c. s4°. Ingolstadii. [1644]
Indicarum. Corpus inscriptionum Indicarum, n. ed., v1, 1925, *see* CORPUS.
Indice ultimo de los libros prohibidos &c., 1747–89, 1790, *see* INDEX.
Indices. *Quinque novi i. gen. &c., 1623, *see* AQUINAS (T.)
Indischen. Der Freiheitskampf d. ind. Nationalisten, 1906–17, *see* FREIHEITSKAMPF.
Individualism. *Philos. of i.: bibliog., 1927, *see* PHILOSOPHY.
Indjidjean (Loukas) [INGIGIAN]. [Topog. archaeology of the country of the Armenians. *In Armenian*]. 3v. i Venetik. 1835
see ELANAK. Biuzantean: [Almanack; ed. L. I.], 1816.
Indochine (L') Française. 1, Annam. [Publ. du Govt. Gén. de L'Indochine]. obl.8°. 1919
Indogermanische Bibliothek. Abt. 1, Reihe 1, xv, Reihe 2, iii, Abt. 3vii, Abt. 4ii. 8°. Heidelberg. 1922–27
see KRAHE (H.) Alt. balkanillyr. geog. Namen, 1925. [3vii.]
„ LESKIEN (A.) Hdbch. d. altbulgar. Spr., 1922. [1, I, 15.]
„ LOKOTSCH (C.) Etymolog. Wbch. d. europ. Wörter oriental. Urspr., 1927. [1, II, 3.]
„ SOLMSEN (FELIX). Indogerm. Eigennamen als Spiegel d. Kulturgesch., 1922. [4ii.]
Indogermanische Forschungen: Zeitschrift für indogerman. Sprach- u. Altertumskunde. B35–45. 8°. Str. 1915–27
„ „ Anzeiger für indogerm. Sprach- u. Altertumskunde: Beiblatt zu d. I. F. B35–44: [*b. w.* Zeitschrift *above*]. 8°. Str. 1915–27
see BRUGMANN (C.) Die Syntax d. einfachen Satzes im Indogerman.; Beiheft z. 43. B., 1925.
Indostana. *Gramatica I., 1778, *see* GRAMATICA.
Indulgentiae. Codex doc. sac. indulg. Neerland. (1300–1600), 1922, *see* FREDERICQ (P.)
Indumentaria española, 1881, *see* AZNAR (F.)
Indus. *Recoll. of the 1st camp. west of the Indus &c. under Sir W. Nott. By a Bengal officer. s8°. 1845
Industrial. Indust. democracy for miners, 1919, *see* HAY (W. F.), *ed.*
Reports on pres. position &c. of the indust. arts as indic. at the Internat. Exhib. of Mod. Decor. & I.A., Paris, 1925; w. intr. survey, 1927, *see* EXHIBITIONS: PARIS.
Industrial Fatigue Research Board. [Medical Research Council & Dept. of Sci. & Indust. Research]. Annual report[s], 1–7 [1–3 *in* 1v]. 8°. 1920–27
Reports. 1–48 [*in* 3v]. 8°. 1919–28
Industrial Workers of the World [I.W.W.], *see* BRISSENDEN (P. F.) The I.W.W.: st. of Amer. syndicalism, 1920.
Industry. I. & the state: a Conservative view, 1927, *see* BOOTHBY (R. J. G.) &c.
I. in Sweden, 1927, *see* SWEDEN.
Indy (Vincent d') [INDY (THÉODORE VINCENT D')], *see* BORGEX (L.) V. d'I., 1913.
Infaillibilité (L') expliquée &c.; tr. de l'allem., 1872, *see* SCHLEICH (M.)
Infallible astrologer, The: or Mr. Silvester Partrige's prophesie &c. N°. 1. [*b. w.* Flying post, *after* N°. 851, Oct. 22, 1700]. fol. 1700
Infancy. Latin i. gospels, 1927, *see* APOCRYPHA: James (M. R.), *ed.*
Information, Ministry of, *see* CHRONOLOGY of the War, issued M. of I., v3, 1920.
Ingannati (Gl') degli Accad. Intronati di Siena, *see* †SANESI (I.) Commedie del cinquecento, v1, 1912.
Inge (William Ralph).
The Church in the world: coll. essays. s8°. 1927
England. 8°. 1926
The idea of progress. Romanes lect., 1920. [P2395; 2466]. 8°. O. 1920
The Jews. [*Repr. f.* The Jewish Guardian. P2688]. 8°. [1923]
Lay thoughts of a dean. 8°. N.Y. 1926
Light, life & love. Sel. f. the German mystics of the Middle Ages. [Libr. of devotion]. s8°. 1904
„ „ 2nd ed. s8°. [1919]
Outspoken essays. 2nd impr. 8°. 1919
Outspoken essays [*continued*].
„ „ 3rd impr. 8°. 1919
„ „ ......s2. 8°. 1922
Patriotism. [Repr.f. "Quarterly Review"]. [P2484]. 8°. [1915]
Personal religion & the life of devotion. Intr. by Bp. of London. s8°. 1924
The philosophy of Plotinus. Gifford Lect., 1917–18. 2nd ed., 2v. 8°. 1923
The Platonic tradition in Engl. relig. thought. Hulsean Lect., 1925–26. s8°. 1926
Speculum animae: 4 devotional addresses, (Jan. 14 & 15, 1911). n. imp. s8°. 1920

Inge (William Ralph) [*continued*].
Truth & falsehood in religion. 6 lect., 1906. [repr.] s8°. 1920
The Victorian age. Rede lect., 1922. s8°. C. 1922
„ „ [2nd impr.] s8°. C. 1922
see LIVINGSTONE (R. W.), *ed.* Legacy of Greece, essays by I. &c., 1921.
„ MARCHANT (*Sir* J.) Claims of coming generation; by var. wr. [I. &c.], 1923.
see NEEDHAM (J.), *ed.* Science, religion & reality; [by] Earl Balfour, W. R. I. &c., 1925.
„ WHITEHOUSE (J. H.), *ed.* Ruskin the prophet &c.; by J. Masefield, I., 1920.
Ingelo (Nathaniel), *D.D.*
Bentivolio & Urania, in 6 books. 2nd ed. sm. fol. 1669
Ingenuinus, *Saint, bp. of Siben, see* ROSCHMANN (A.) Disq. epist. Tartarottianæ de S. I. actis, p2, 1751.
Ingersleben (Irmgard von). Das Elisabethan. Ideal d. Ehefrau bei Overbury (1613). 8°. Cöthen. 1921
Ingersoll (Ernest).
Birds in legend, fable & folklore. 8°. 1923
The crest of the continent: summer's ramble in Rocky Mts. &c. 8°. Chicago. 1885
Ingersoll (Lurton Dunham). Hist. of the War Dept. of the U.S., w. biog. sk. of the Secretaries. 8°. Wash. 1880
Ingersoll (*Col.* Robert G.) Orations. s8°. 1881
Ingham (Alfred). Cheshire, its traditions & hist., incl. record of freemasonry. 4°. E. 1920
Ingham (Sarson C. J.) An inner-court worshipper: memorials of Eliz. Maw. s8°. 1888
Ingigian, *see* INDJIDJEAN.
Inglis (Elsie Maud), *see* MACLAREN (E. S.) E. I. 1920.
Inglis (Harry R. G.)
The "contour" road book of England. 3v. s8°. 1898–1900
Inglis (Henry David), *misc. writer.*
Tales of Ardennes. n. ed. [P2460]. 8°. 1841
Inglis (*Rt. Hon.* John), *Lord Justice General.* The hist. study of law: address. [P527]. 8°. 1863
Ingolstadt. *Disput. de majestate hominis Christi in Acad. Ingolst.; per theses explic. adv. impias J. Andreæ Schmidelini theses. s4°. Ingolstadii. 1564
Ingram (Collingwood). Birds of the Riviera. 8°. 1926
Ingram (John H.) Flora symbolica; or, the language &c. of flowers. s8°. [1870]
Ingram (T. A.), *see* GRINLING (C. H.), T. A. I. *& others, edd.* Survey &c. of Woolwich & W. Kent, 1909.
Ingres (Jean Aug. Dominique). Exposition Ingres, mai-juin 1921. [P2752]. fol. 1921
Ingulphus, *abbot of Croyland.* Historiarum lib. i, *see* SAVILE (*Sir* H.) Rerum Angl. scr. 1596; 1601.
Inman (*Major* D. S.), *see* HUSSEY (A. H.) & D. S. I. 5th div. in the Great War, 1921.
Inman (James), *D.D.* Nautical tables. Pref. by A treatise on pract. navig. by H. W. Jeans. 8°. 1873
Inman (Samuel Guy). Problems in Pan Americanism. 8°. [1926]
Inman (Thomas), *M.D.* Anc. pagan & mod. Xtn. symbolism. 2nd ed. rev. & enl., w. essay on Baal worship &c. by J. Newton. 8°. 1875
Innes (Arthur Donald). Eng. under the Tudors. [Hist. of Eng., ed. C. W. C. Oman]. 6th ed. 8°. [1920]
Inness (George). Works by G. I., the coll. of Mrs. J. S. Hartley sold Amer. Art Assoc. la8°. N.Y. 1927
Inni della terza armata, racc. di canti militari., 1915–18. [P2508]. 4°. Milano. 1919
Innocent III, *pope.* Register ü. d. Reichsfrage, 1198–1209, in Auswahl üb. u. erläut. v. G. Tangl, *see* GESCHICHTSCHREIBER (Die) d. deut. Vorzeit, 2te Gesamtausg., B95, 1923.
see CARLYLE (R. W.) Claims of I. III, 1923.
Innocent IV, *pope.* Les registres d'I. IV. Publ. E. Berger. [Ecoles Franç. d'Athènes & de Rome.] t4. 4°. 1921
see MANN (H. K.) Lives, v14, I. IV, 1243–54, 1928.
Innocent VI, *pope* [ETIENNE AUBERT]. I. VI e Casa Savoia: doc. dell' Arch. Vaticano; trascr. da F. Cerasoli &c., *see* REGIA DEP. DI STORIA PATRIA. Misc., t38, 1902.
Innocent VIII, *pope, see* RODOCANACHI (E.) Hist. de Rome: une cour princière au Vatican: I. VIII &c., 1925.
Innocent X, *pope, see* BLONDEL (D.) Extr. de l'examen de la Bulle du pape I. X; tr., 1655.
Innocent XI, *pope.* Decreta duo: de suppressione compl. indulgent. & de suppr. officii Immac. concept. B. M. V. [1678]. Adjung. officium. [P2670]. s4°. Coloniæ. *n.d.*
Decretum contra M. de Molinos & ejus sectam cum propos. damnatis. [*b. w.* Kempis T. a). De Christo imit., 1685]. s8°. Romae. [1687]

Innocent XI, *pope* [*continued*].
I. XI. Erectio & instit. congreg. Benedictino-Bavaricae &c. [P2670]. s4°. Monast. Tegernseensis. [1734]
I. XI. Sa corr. avec des nonces. v3, 1680–84, pl, Affaires polit. [*Ed. &c.* F. de Bojani, *w.* Table, *sep. tp.*] 8°. Roulers. 1912–13
see LIPPI (M. G.) Vita di I. XI, 1889.
„ VIVA (D.) Damnatae theses ab Alex. VII, I. XI &c., 1749.

Innocent XII, *pope.*
see LITH (J. W. v. D.) Diss. de superstit. jubil. pontif., inprimis Bullae noviss. I. XII, oppos., 1700.
„ NEPOTISMUS theol. expensus; Quando n. sub I. XII abolitus fuit, 1692 ?.

Inquiry, *see* ENQUIRY.

Inquisicion. *Discusion del proyecto de decreto sobre el tribunal de la I. 8°. Cadiz. 1813

Inquisitio. *Forma I. Hispanicae instituta in inferiori Germania. s8°. [Magdeburgæ, *M. Lotther.* 1550]

Inquisition. *Authentic mem. of the Portuguese I., 1761, *see* PORTUGUESE.
Coroner's inquest &c. on the Inq., 1851, *see* CORONER.
*Hist. de l'I. & s. origine, 1693, *see* MARSOLLIER (J.)

Inquisitiones.
INQUISITIONES POST MORTEM. Cal. of I. p. m. & o. doc. in P.R.O. [C. of S.P.] v10 (Edward III). la8°. 1921
Notes of p. m. i. taken in Sussex, 1 Hen. VII to 1649 &c.; abstr. &c. by F. W. T. Attree, 1912, *see* SUSSEX.
Sussex Inquisitions; ed. M. S. Holgate, 1927, *see* SUSSEX.

Inquisitions. Inquisitions & assessments rel. to Feudal Aids (1284–1431), 1899 &c., *see* FEUDAL AIDS.

Inscriptiones. I. antiq. oræ septentrion. Ponti Euxini Graecæ & Lat., 2ª ed., v1, 1916, *see* LATISHEV (V. V.), *ed.*

Inscriptiones. [I. Deli]. Cons. et auct. Acad. Litt. Boruss. ed. [Inscr. Graecæ, v11, fasc. 3 tab.] fasc. 3 tabulae adnot. F. Hiller de Gaertringen. fol. Berolini. 1927
I. Lat. Christianae veteres, v1, 2, 1925–27, *see* DIEHL (E.)

Inscriptions. I. cunéiformes urartiques transcr. & tr., 1900, *see* SANDALGIAN (J.)

Insh (George Pratt).
Scottish colonial schemes, 1620–86. 8°. Glasgow. 1922
see DARIEN COMPANY. Papers rel. to ships & voyages, 1696–1707; ed. G. P. I., 1924.

Inside passenger (An), *ps.*, *see* JERDAN (W.)

Institor (Henricus), *see* SPRENGER (J.) & H. I. Der Hexenhammer, 3T, 1923.

Institut Américain de Droit International, *see* AMERICAN INST. OF INTERNAT. LAW.

Institut de France. Annuaire, 1902, 1904, 1924. s8°. 1902–24
see CHANTILLY: MUSÉE CONDÉ.

Institut de Paléontologie Humaine. Fondation Albert I, Pr. de Monaco. Peintures & gravures murales des cavernes paléolithiques, *see* BREUIL (H.) &c. La Pileta à Benaojan, 1915.

Institut d'Estudis Catalans, *see* RUBÍO Y LLUCH (A.) Docs. per l'hist. de la cultura catalana mig-eval, v2, 1921.

Institut Egyptien. Mémoires présentés à l'I. E. Publ. sous les auspices de Hussein Kamel. t9. 4°. Le Caire. 1916
9, Les ports submergés de l'anc. Île de Pharos; par G. Jondet.

Institut Français d'Archéologie Orientale du Caire. Fouilles (1921–26) sous la dir. de G. Foucart. Rapports prélim. t1–4. 4°. Le Caire. 1924–27
Bisson de La Roque (F.) Fouilles d'Abou-Roasch, 2p. [1, 2.]
„ „ Fouilles de Médamoud, 2p. [3, 4.]
Bruyère (B.) Fouilles de Deir el Médineh, 4p. [1–4.]
Drioton (E.) Fouilles de Médamoud: Inscrˢ., 2p. [3, 4.]
Henne (H.) Fouilles de Tell Edfou, 2p. [1, 2.]
Mémoires publ. par les membres de l'I. F. d'A. O. du Caire. t4i, 13i, 19–21, 25i, 29, 35, 36, 38, 39i, 40, 41, 42, 43, 44i, 45i, 46–51, 53i. la4°. Le Caire, 1909–27
Baillet (J.) Inscr. grec. & lat. des tombeaux des rois ou syringes à Thèbes, 1926. [42.]
Berchem (M. v.) Mat. pour un Corpus inscr. arabic., p2, 3, t1, 1909–22. [25i, 29, 43, 44i, 45i.]
p2, Syrie du Nord, par M. Sobernheim, fasc. 1. [25i.]
p2, „ „ Sud, t1, t2, fasc.; t3, fasc. 1, 2. [43, 44i, 45i.]
p3, Asie Mineure, t1, Siwas, Diwrigi; par M. v. B. & H. Edhem. [29.]
—— & E. Fatio. Voyage en Syrie, t2, 1915. [38.]
Boreux (C.) Et. de nautique égypt., 1925. [50.]
Casanova (P.) Essai de reconstitution topogr. de la ville d'al Fousṭâṭ ou Miṣr, t1, 1919. [35.]
Chassinat (E.) Fouilles à Baouît, t1i, 1911. [13i.]

Institut Français d'Archéologie Orientale du Caire [*continued*].
Clédat (J.) Le monastère & la nécropole de Baouît, t2i, 1916. [39i.]
Gaillard (C.) Recherches sur les poissons repr. dans quelques tombeaux égypt. de l'anc. emp., 1923. [51.]
Gauthier (H.) Le Livre des rois d'Egypte; rec. par H. G., t3–5, 1914–17. (3, De la 19ᵉ à la 24ᵉ dynastie. 4, De la 25ᵉ dynastie à la fin des Ptolémées. 5, "Les Empereurs romains"). [19–21.]
Jéquier (G.) Les frises d'objets des sarcophages du Moyen Empire, 1921. [47.]
Lesquier (J.) L'armée romaine d'Egypte, 1918. [41.]
Makrizi. Descr. hist. & topog. de l'Egypte; tr. P. Casanova, p4i, 1920. [4i.]
—— El-Mawâ'iz wa'l-i 'tibâr fî dhikr el-Khiṭat wa'l-Âthâr; éd. G. Wiet, t3, 5i, 1922–27. [46, 49, 53i.]
Mallet (D.) Les rapports des Grecs avec l'Egypte, 1922. [48.]
Maspero (J.) & G. Wiet. Matériaux p. s. à la géogr. de l'Egypte, s1, 1919. [36.]
Prost (C.) Les revêtements céramiques dans les mon. musulmans de l'Egypte, 1916. [40.]
see also SERVICE DES ANTIQUITÉS DE L'EGYPTE.

Institut für österreich. Geschichtsforschung [*Vienna*].
see HAPSBURG. Regesta Habsburgica &c., Abt. 1, 3, 1905–24.
„ WICKHOFF (F.), *ed.* Beschreib. Verzeichnis d. illum. Hss. in Österreich, B1–8, 1905–28.

Institut Intermédiaire International, *La Haye*, *see* TRAITÉS. Répertoire gén. des t. &c., 1895–1920, 1926.

Institut International de Statistique. Bulletin. t20, 21. [*in* 2 livr. *&* Suppl.], 22 [*in* 3 livr.] la8°. La Haye *&* Brux. 1915–26
t20, Suppl., *is* Table des matières, t1–20.
t21, „ „ „ t1–21.
Bulletin mensuel de l'Office permanent. (Mai 1920–1927.) la8°. La Haye. 1920–27

Institut Nobel Norvégien.
Publications. t4. 4°. Kristiania. 1919
see LANGE (C. L.) Hist. de l'internationalisme, t1, 1919.

Institut Yafetidolog. Iziskanii, *see* YAFETICHESKY INSTITUT.

Institut z. Förderung d. israelit. Lit.
Schriften. Jahr. 10, 14. 8°. L. 1865–69
see FÜRST (J.) Gesch. d. Karäerthums v. 900–1575 [*&* 1575–1865], 1865–69 [10, 14].

Institute for Crippled & Disabled Men, *see* FARIES (J. C.) 3 yrs. of work for handicapped men, 1920.

Institute of Archaeology, *Liverpool*, *see* LIVERPOOL UNIVERSITY, *Instit. of Arch.*

Institute of Chemistry of Gt. Brit. & Ireland. Register of fellows &c., corr. to Nov. 1923, w. suppl. reg. to March, 1924. 8°. 1924

Institute of Economics.
see MOULTON (H. G.) & C. LEWIS. French debt problem; by M. &c. w. aid of Co. &c. of I. of E., 1925.
„ PAGE (T. W.) Making the tariff in the U.S.; by P. w. aid of Co. &c. of I. of E., 1924.

Institute of Historical Research.
Bulletin. v1–5. la8°. 1925–28

Institute of International Affairs.
see TEMPERLEY (H. W. V.), *ed.* Hist. of the Peace Conf. of Paris; publ. I. of I. Aff., 6v, 1920–24.

Institute of International Education, *New York.* A bibliog. on the U.S. for for. students. [P2686]. 8°. N.Y. 1922
see FRANCE. Opportunities for higher educ. in France, 1920.

Institute of International Law. Resolutions of the I. of I. L., dealing w. the law of nations; w. hist. intr. &c. Ed. J. B. Scott. [C.E. for Int. Peace.] la8°. N.Y. 1916

Institute of Jamaica. Journal. v1, 2 (1891–99). [*No more publ.; v2, N°. 1 wanting*]. la8°. Kingston. 1894–99

Institution of Electrical Engineers.
Journal. v58–64. 4°. 1920–26
„ „ ....Suppl. to v57. 4°. 1920
[Roll of honour], cont. names of Members of the Inst. of E.E., 1914–19. fol. [1924]

Institution of Gas Engineers, *see* CLERK (*Sir* D.), A. SMITHELLS, & J. W. COBB. Rep. on coal-gas & electr. supply indust. of U.K., 1919.

Institution of Mining Engineers [FEDERATED INSTITUTION].
Transactions. v1–74 (1889–1928).
8°. Newcastle-upon-Tyne [*aft.* London]. 1892–1928
v1–14 *have titles* Trans. of the Federated Instit. &c.

***Institutiones** hominum refutandę sunt. [*MS.*] [P2539]. s4°. *n.p. n.d.* [c. 1522]

Instituto Americano de Derecho Internac., *see* AMERICAN INSTIT. OF INTERNAT. LAW.

Instituto de Valencia de Don Juan, *Madrid.* Cat. de las armas del I. de V. de D. J., por J. M. Florit y Arizcun. Compl. por F. J. Sánchez Cantón. 4º. 1927
Cat. de las pinturas del I. de V. de D. J., por F. J. Sánchez Cantón. 4º. 1923
Instituto Historico e Geographico Brazileiro. Revista trimensal. t1-91 (1839-1922). [t1, 4-15, 17, 2ª ed. t11, 18, trimestre 1, 21, trim. 1, 30, trim. 3, 32, 63, p2, 74, p1, 79, 81-82 *wanting*]. 8º. Rio de Janeiro. 1840-1926
t2-13 *have title,* Revista trimensal de hist. e geog. t27-58 *have* 2p *w. sep. pagin.*] t22 *cont.* Indice, v1-22. t45 *cont.* Indice, v1-44. t51 *cont.* Indice, v1-50. t2, 4, 18 & 19 *have* suppl. *w. sep. pagin.* 51 *has* Suppl. *w. sep. tp.,* Homenagem ao seu quinquagenario, 1888. *b. w.* t15. t68 *cont.* Indice dos vol. 1-67.
" " tomos esp. 8º. Rio de Janeiro. 1925-26
Congresso internac. de hist. da Amer. (1922), v1, 1925.
Contrib. para a biog. de D. Pedro II, p1, 1925.
Nobiliarchia paulistana, hist. e genealog., por P. Taques, v1, 1926.
Traslad. dos restos mortaes de D. Pedro II e de D. Tereza Christina, 1925.
Instruction. *I. gén. pour la teinture des laines & manuf. de laine de toutes couleurs, 1671.
For an Eng. tr. of the above, see *WHOLE art of dying, 1705, repr., *n.d.*
*I. sur les dispositions qu'on doit aporter aux sacremens, 1712, *see* TREUVE (S. M.)
Instructions gén. en forme de Cat. impr. par ordre de C. J. Colbert, 4t, 1704, *see* CATECHISME.
Insúa (Alberto). La mujer que necesita amar. s8º. [1923]
Insurance. *Unemployment i. in Gt. Brit., 1925, *see* UNEMPLOYMENT.
Inter-Allied Commission. Inquiries in Anatolia; rep. &c. (1919-22), 1922, *see* ANATOLIA.
Rep., Eastern Macedonia. p1. [P2416, 2518]. la8º. 1919
Rep. on the violation of the Hague Convention in 1915-18 by the Bulgarians in Serbia. [P2416, 2518]. s4º. 1919
***Intercepted** letters: or, the twopenny post-bag &c., 1813, *see* MOORE (T.)
***Interest** (The) of princes & states, 1680, *see* BETHEL (S.)
***Interesting** consid. on public affairs of France &c.; tr., 1791, *see* FRANCE.
Interim. Ex actis Synodicis & aliis collecta expositio, de libro Augustino qui nominatur Interim, 1559, *see* WITTENBERG.
Bekentnuss u. Erklerung auffs Interim durch der Erborn Stedte, Lübeck, Hamburg &c. Superintendenten &c., 1549, *see* LÜBECK.
Intermédiare (L') des chercheurs et curieux. Année 56-63. 8º. 1920-27
" " Table gén., 1897-1920. la8º. 1925
International. I. index to periodicals, v3, *see* READER'S guide: Suppl., v3, 1924.
I. Jew (The): world's foremost problem, 1920, *see* JEW.
I. problems & rel.; ed. T. T. Shotwell &c., 1926, *see* ACAD. OF POLIT. SCIENCE, N.Y. Proc., v12, No. 1, 1926.
International (The), *see* INTERNATIONALE (L').
International Assoc. of Indust. Accident Boards &c. Proc. of ann. meetings, 1920, 1922-1925, *&* Index to proc., 1914-24; by G. L. Tibbott, *see* UNITED STATES: LABOR. Bull. 281, 333, 359, 385, 395, 405, 1921-26.
International Assoc. of Public Employment Services. Proc. of ann. meetings, 1921-24, *see* UNITED STATES: LAB. Bull. 311, 337, 355, 400, 1922-25.
International Assoc. on Unemployment, *see* BELLERBY (J. R.) Control of credit, 1923.
International Boundary Commission, *U.S.A. & Canada, see* UNITED STATES: INTERIOR, DEPT. OF.
International catalogue of scientific literature. Publ. for Internat. Council by Royal Soc. of London. 8º. 1920
Geology (H. v14), 1920.
Physiology, incl. experimental psychology, pharmacology & experimental pathology (Q. v14), 1921.
Zoology, *for continuation,* 1915–, *see* ZOOLOGICAL SOC. OF LONDON. Zool. record.
International chess magazine (The).
Ed. W. Steinitz. v1, 2 *in* 1. la8º. N.Y. 1885-86
International Committee for Bird Protection.
Bulletin. Brief acc. of formation &c. [P2876]. 8º. N.Y. 1927
International Communication Bill, 1872. Estimate of proposed works at Dover—Rep. of the Bd. of Trade—Proc. bef. Hse. of Commons Comm.—Composition of Comm.—

International Communication Bill, 1872 [*continued*].
Proposed heads of agreement betw. S.E. Railway Co. &c. & the Internat. Communic. Co. [*typewritten*]. la. fol. [1872]
Minutes of evidence bef. Sel. Ctee. of the House of Lords, 1872. [*typewritten*]. fol. [1872]
" " Minutes of proc. (speeches &c.) bef. Sel. Ctee. of the H. of L. [*typewritten*]. fol. [1872]
International Conciliation. [Publ. by Amer. Assoc. for Internat. Co.; Nº. 200 *& onwards by* C.E. for Int. Peace]. Nºs. 182-235.
8º. Greenwich, Conn. [*&* Worcester, Mass.] 1923-27
International Conference. The 2nd & 3rd Internationals & the Vienna Union. Offic. rep. of Conf. betw. the Executives, Berlin, Apr. 1922. 8º. 1922
International Correspondence Schools, Ltd.
Stained glass & mosaic. [*typed tp.*] 8º. *n.d.*
International Economic Conference, *see* EUROPE. Needs of E. Report of I.E.C., 1920, 1921.
International Financial Conference, *Brussels, 1920.* Documents. [*In Fr. & Eng.*] Publ. for League of Nations. v4, 5 [*in 1v*]. 4º. [1920]
4, Statist. mem. on currency, finance & trade [rev. & amplified ed. of Papers 3, 4 & 5].
5, Mem. of economic experts. [Papers 13i-vi & 14].
Paper[s]—Rapport[s]. [*In Fr. & Eng.*] Pr. for League of Nations. Nºs. 3-5, 10-12, 13 (ii-vi), 14. 4º. & fol. [1920]
For another ed. of Papers 3-5 & 13-14, see Documents *above.*
3, Currency statistics. 4, Public finance.
5, Internat. trade.
10, Relief credits & promotion of export.
11, Exchange control.
12, Solutions proposed. 13ii, Mem. by G. W. J. Bruins.
13iii, Mem. on world's monet. problems, by G. Cassel.
13iv, Mem. on credit, currency & exchange fluctuations, by A. C. Pigou.
13v, Notes on fin. & monet. situation, by C. Gide.
13vi, Mem. by M. Panteleoni.
14, Price of silver, by G. F. Shirras.
Proceedings (Comptes rendus). Pr. for League of Nations. [*In French & Eng.*]
v1-3 [in 1v]. 4º. Bruxelles & London. [1920]
The Recommendations & th. application. A review after 2 years.
n. & enl. ed. 2v (1, *Var. countries.* 2, Italy). la8º. 1922
Report of the Advisory Comm. Pr. for League of Nations. [*b. w.* Papers 13 & 14]. fol. 1920
International Health Board. Report, 1919 &c., *see* ROCKEFELLER FOUNDATION.
see DARLING (S. T.) &c. Hookworm & malaria research in Malaya &c., 1920.
" MEYER (E. C.) Infant mortality in N.Y. city, 1885-1910, 1921.
International Institute of Agriculture. Bulletin of the Bureau of Econ. & Soc. Intelligence. Year 11-13, 1920-22.
8º. Rome. 1920-22
see CHERKINSKY (M.) The Landschaften (1770-1920), 1922.
International Inst. of Intellectual Co-operation, *see* LEAGUE OF NATIONS.
International Journal of ethics. v30-37. 8º. 1920-27
International Labour Office [BUREAU INTERNAT. DU TRAVAIL].
Bibliog. of indust. & labour questions in Soviet Russia.
8º. Genève. 1922
Condit. (Les) du travail dans la Russie des Soviets. Quest. méthod. & bibliog. prép. pour une Mission d'Enquête en Russie. 8º. 1920
Factory inspection: hist. development & pres. organis.
8º. Geneva. 1923
Industrial life in Soviet Russia, 1917-23. [St. & rep., ser. B, No. 14]. 8º. Geneva. 1924
Labour condit. in Soviet Russia. Systemat. questionnaire & bibliog. 8º. [1920]
Russia Labour Code. [*Tr.* Legisl. Ser., 1922—Russ. 1].
[P2822]. la8º. [Basle]. 1922
Unemployment in its nat. & internat. aspects. [St. & rep., ser. C, No. 9]. Rep. of confer., London, 1924. 8º. Geneva. 1924
see BEHRENS (E. B.) The Int. Labour Office: survey of problems, 1924.
International Law Association.
Report of the 23rd Conf., 1906, 29-34th. 8º. 1907-27
International Peace Bureau, *Berne, see* PEACE MOVEMENT (THE), 1912-19.
International Research Council. 1st report of the Comm. app. to further the study of solar & terrestrial relationships.
8º. Paris. 1926

International review (The). N.S. v1, 2 (1919). 8°. 1919

International Secretariat of the L. o. N., *see* LEAGUE OF NATIONS.

International Societies.

International &c. is abbreviated to I. Congress and Conference to C.

see AMERICA, C. I. DE HIST. DA A.
,, ARCHÉOLOGIE. C. I. d'Arch. Class., 1909.
see DORÉ (R.) Essai d'une bibliographie des c. i., 1923.
,, EDUCATION. C. I. d'E. Morale.
,, MONETARY C. (I.), 1881.
,, MUSICAL SOC. (I.)
,, PSYCHOLOGY (I. C. OF).
,, TRADE C. (I.)

Internationale (L').
Gründung (Die) d. Dritten I. Erste Konf. d. K. I. in M., März, 1919. [P2456]. 8°. Wien. 1919
Kapitalist (Die) Welt u. d. Kommunist. I. Manifest d. II Kongresses d. K. I. [P2462]. 8°. 1920
Organ d. Exekutivkomitees d. Kommunist. I. No. 12, 14, 15, 2er Jahrgang. 8°. Petrograd. [1920]
New (The) communist manifesto of the Third I., 1919, *see* COMMUNIST.
*3me Internationale, ses principes &c. [P2392]. s8°. 1919
2e (Der) Kongress d. Kommunist. I. [Hrsg. im Auftrage d. Komm. Partei Oesterr.] 8°. Wien. 1920
see ZINOVEV (G.) Bericht d. Exekutivkom. d. K. I., 1920.

Internationale Bibliographie d. Kunstwissenschaft. Hrsg. v. I. Beth. B11-15 (1912-18). 8°. 1915-20

Internationale Kommission für Schleswig, 1920, *see* SCHLESWIG.

Inter-Parliamentary Union.
Offic. report of 14th Conf., London, 1906. la8°. 1906

Interpretationes dictionū indeclinabiliū s[ecundu]m alphabeti ordinem perutiles. s8°. [Ingolstadt. *n.d.*, c. 1492 ?]
[*22 leaves ; sig. a & b in eights ; sig. c in sixes, c6 blank*].

***Interpreters** (The) ; by A. E., 1922, *see* RUSSELL (G. W.)

Inter-racial. Papers on inter-racial problems ; ed. G. Spiller, 1911, *see* RACES CONGRESS (UNIV.)

Interrogatoires des ministres, conseillers &c. de la Cour Imp. Russe par la Comm. Extr. du Gouvt. Prov. de 1917 ; tr., 1927, *see* MAKLAKOV (V. A.), *ed.*

***Intervento** (L') dell' Italia n. doc. seg. dell' Intesa, 2a ed., 1925, *see* ITALIA.

Intimatio Jubilæi Evang. &c., 1617, *see* WITTENBERG *University.*

Intorcetta (Prospero).
see CONFUCIUS. C. Sinarum philosophus ; Lat. expos. studio. P. I. &c., 1687.
,, SCHALL (J. A.) Hist. narr. de initio &c. missionis apud Chin. ; ed. 2a, aucta geogr. regni Chin. &c. [*by* P. I.], 1672.

Intra (Giovanni Battista). Gugl. Braghiroli, *see* REGIA DEP. DI STORIA PATRIA. Misc., t24, 1885.

Introduction. I. to Sally ; by the a. of "Elizabeth & h. German garden," 1926, *see* ARNIM (*countess* V.)
*I. to the art of thinking, 1761, *see* KAMES (H. H., *Lord*).
I. to the celeb. devotion of the Rosary, 1737, *see* ROSARY.
*I. to theosophy, v1, 1855, *see* WALTON (C.)

***Introductory** remarks to a Narr. of the irruption of the Kafir hordes into the Cape of Good Hope, 1834-35, p1, 1835, *see* GODLONTON (R.)

Inveges (Agostino). La Cartagine siciliana : città di Caccabe, hoggi Caccamo &c. 8°. Palermo. 1661

Inverness. Records of I. Ed. W. Mackay & G. S. Laing. [New Spalding Club]. v2. 4°. Aberdeen. 1924
2, Burgh Court Books, 1602-37—Minutes of Town Co., 1637-88.

Inwards (Harry).
Straw hats : hist. & manufacture. s8° [1922]

Inwood (Jethro). Sermons ; in wh. are expl. the virtues of freemasonry, *see* OLIVER (G.) Golden remains, v4, 1849.

Inwood (William). Tables of interest & mortality for estates, annuities, &c. Rev. & extended by Sir W. Schooling. 32nd ed., rev. 8°. 1924

"I. O." *The administration of Ireland, 1920, 1921, *see* IRELAND.

Ioannesov (Khr. I. Kuchuk-), *see* KUCHUK-IOANNESOV.

Iohannou-Vank, *monastery, see* ZACHARIAS, *the deacon.* Cartul. du s. asile de I.-V. (6-17 c.), 1876.

Iolanda, *dssa. di Savoia, see* YOLANDA, *duchess of Savoy.*

Iona Club. Collectanea de rebus Albanicis : orig. papers & docs. rel. to Highlands &c. of Scotland. Ed. Iona Club. [*With* App. *cont.* Trans. of I.C., v1, p1. *No more publ.*] 8°. E. 1847

Ionides (Basil). Colour & interior decoration. la8°. [1926]

Ionides (Constantine Alexander), *see* VICTORIA & ALBERT MUSEUM. C. A. I. coll., v1 ; B. Long, 1925.

Iorga (Nicolæ).
L'art populaire en Roumanie. 4°. 1923
Hist. d. États balcan. j. 1924. 8°. 1925
Hist. des Roumains. 8°. 1920
Hist. [of Romania], by I. &c., *see* BUCHAN (J.), *ed.* Nations of to-day, Bulgaria & R. 1924.
Istoria literaturilor romanice. [Acad. Româna]. 3v. la8°. Bucureşti. 1920
1, Evul mediu. 2, Epoca moderna (pânǎ la 1600). 3, Epoca moderna (1600 pânǎ in zilele noastre).
Istoria poporului frances. [Acad. Româna]. 8°. Bucureşti. 1919
Izvoarele contemp. asupra mişcǎrii lui Tudor Vladimirescu. [Acad. Româna]. la8°. Bucureşti. 1921
Rel. entre l'Orient & l'Occident. 8°. 1923
Scurtǎ istorie a Slavilor Rǎsǎriteni Rusia & Polonia. [Acad. Româna]. 8°. Bucureşti. 1919
Un viaggio da Venezia alla Tana (1404-07). [Estr. d. Nuovo Archivio Veneto, t11i. P2836]. 8°. [Venezia. 1896]
La vie intellect. d. Roumains en 1899. s8°. Bucarest. 1899
see AMIRA (A.) Storia d. soggiorno di Carlo XII in Turchia, 1905.
,, HURMUZAKI (E. DE). Doc. priv. la ist. Romanilor, v14, 15, publ. de N. I., 1911-17.

—— **& S. Gorceix.** Anthol. de la litt. roumaine. Tr. &c. introd. par N. J. & S. G. [Colln. Pallas]. s8°. 1920

Ioteyko (*Dr.* Josefa). La fatigue. s8°. 1920

Iouiya.
see DAVIS (T. M.) Excav. : Biban el Molûk ; funeral papyrus of I., 1908.
,, —— Excav. Bibân el Molûk : tomb of I. & Touiyou, 1907.

Ipswich. Bicentenary mem. exhib. of T. Gainsborough ; Ipswich, 1927 [cat.], *see* GAINSBOROUGH (T.)

Iqbal (Sheikh Muhammad). The secrets of self (Askár-i Khudí). A philos. poem. Tr., w. intr. & notes by R. A. Nicholson. s8°. 1920

'Iqd-i Gul, or The rose-necklace : sel. f. the Gulistān & the Anwār-i Suhailī, tr. w. notes by Adālat Khān, 4th ed., 1900, *see* SADI.

Iraq. 'Iraq in War time. fol. Basrah. *n.d.*

Irby (*Hon.* Charles Leonard), *6th son of 2nd baron Boston,* **& J. Mangles.** Travels in Egypt, Nubia, Syria, & the Holy Land. [*b. w.* Drinkwater (J.) Siege of Gibraltar, 1844]. s8°. 1844

Ireland.

I, Government Publications.
Coimisiun na Gaeltachta. Rep. & Maps. fol. & la8°. D. 1926

LAWS, STATUTES &C.
Index to statutes in force in I., 1310-1838. By A. N. Oulton. 2nd ed. 8°. D. 1839
,, ,, ...1839-44. [Suppl. 4-13 *in* 1v]. 8°. D. 1845

PARLIAMENT.
Report of the debate in the H. of C. of I., 22 & 23 Jan. 1799, on union. [P2555]. 8°. D. 1799

PARLIAMENT (DÁIL EIREANN).
The constructive work of Dáil Eireann. Nos. 1, 2. [P2563, 2706]. 8°. D. 1921
Official corr. rel. to the peace negot., June-Sept., 1921. [P2687]. fol. D. 1921
Parliamentary debates. Official report. v1-7 (1923-24). 8°. D. [1923-24]
see CONSTITUTIONS. Sel. c. of the world ; prep. for pres. to Dáil Eireann, 1922.

II, Anonymous works.
*Acc. (An) of the trans. of the late King James in I., 1690, *see* JAMES II.
*Admin. (The) of I., 1920. By "I. O." 8°. [1921]
*Advertisements for I. (1623) : a descr. of the state of I. in r. of James I, cont. in a MS. in Lib. of Trinity Coll., Dublin. Ed. G. O'Brien. [Roy. Soc. of Antiq. of Ireland. Extra vol.] 8°. D. 1923
Amer. (The) Comm. on conditions in I., 1921, *see* AMERICAN.
*Discoverie (A) of true causes why I. was never subdued &c. (1612), 1747, *see* DAVIES (*sir* J.)
Essays on polit. circumstances of I., 1798, *see* KNOX (A.)
*Extract of letter f. a gent. in I. ; to W. T., 1798, *see* THOMPSON (W.)
Hdbk. of the Ulster question [North E. Boundary Bureau], 1923, *see* ULSTER.
*I. in 1887. Proc. at assizes. Proc. of Nat. League branches. [P2560]. 8°. 1887
I.'s request to the Govt. of the U.S. for recog. as a sov. indep. state. [Pref. by E. de Valera. P2735]. 8°. [Wash. 1920]
Map of I. showing the amalgam. of railways, existing lines &c. those in prog. *folded* 8°. *Arrowsmith.* 1848

Ireland [*continued*].
II, Anonymous works [*continued*].
Memoir on the coalfields of I., 2v, 1921, *see* COMMISSION OF INQ. INTO RESOURCES &c. OF IRELAND.
Parliamentary (The) gazetteer of Ireland. 3v. la8°. D., *Fullarton*. 1845
*Reflections &c. proper for the gentlemen of I., 1738, *see* MADDEN (S.)
Report of the labour comm. to I., 1921, *see* LABOUR COMM. TO IRELAND.
*Situation (The) in I. [*Signed*, G. B.] [P2530]. 8°. [1920]
*Truth about I., 1921, *see* JUNIUS, *junior*, *ps.*
Ireland, Northern. Acc. (An) of certain anc. mon. in the public charge. s8°. Belfast. 1926
Ireland (Alleyne). The new Korea. 8°. N.Y. [1926]
Ireland (*Surgeon Gen.* **Merritte W.**), *U.S. Army*, *see* UNITED STATES: ARMY. Medical Dept. in the World War; prep. under dir. of M. W. I., 1921–27.
Ireland (Michael), *ps.*, *see* FIGGIS (D.)
Ireland (William Henry), *see* DUDLEY (*Rev. Sir* H. B.) & M., *Lady* D. Passages sel. &c. on trial of Vortigern & Rowena [by W. H. I.], v1–3, 1796 ?–98.
Ireland (William Wotherspoon). Through the ivory gate: st. in psychol. & hist. [Swedenborg *& others*]. 8°. E. 1889
Irenaeus, *St., bp. of Lyons.* Armon. Irenaeusfragmente m. deut. Übers. nach W. Lüdtke. Hrsg. &c. v. H. Jordan. [Texte u. Untersuch.; hrsg. Harnack & Schmidt, B36iii]. 8°. L. 1913
The demonstration of Apostolic preaching. Tr. w. intr. & notes by J. A. Robinson. [Tr. of Christian lit.] s8°. 1920
Gegen d. Häretiker. Buch 4 u. 5. In Armen. Vers. entd. v. K. Ter-Mĕkĕrttschian; hrsg. v. E. Ter-Minassintz. 8°. L. 1910
Novum Test. Sancti I.: quotations in Old-Lat. version of the Ἔλεγχος καὶ παρατροπὴ ψευδωνύμου γνώσεως. Ed., w. intr., notes &c. by W. Sanday & C. H. Turner. [Old-Lat. Bibl. Texts, No. 7]. 4°. O. 1923
see CONYBEARE (F. C.) Age of the old Armenian vers. of I., 1911.
„ HARNACK (C. G. A. v.) Die Pfaff'schen I.-Fragm. als Fälschungen Pfaffs nachgewiesen &c., 1900.
Irenaeus (Christoph). Refutatio Irenaei. Grunndl. Bericht auff d. Examen C. I. wider d. ersten Artickel d. Concordi Buchs. Gestellet durch Theologen. [*b. w.* Kirchner (T.) N. Selneccer & M. Chemnitz, Apol. 1583]. fol. Heydelberg. 1583
Irenaeus (Philopater), *ps.*, *see* BELING (RICHARD).
***Irenicomastix.** I. iteratò victus &c., 1662, *see* ZWICKER (D.)
*I. perpetuo convictus &c., 1661, *see* ZWICKER (D.)
***Irenicum** Irenicorum &c., 1658, *see* ZWICKER (D.)
Irhoven (Willem van) [IRHOVIUS (GUIL.)]
Conjectanea in Psalmorum titulos. 8°. Lugd. Batav. 1728
Irish.
Golden treasury (A) of I. verse, 1925, *see* ROBINSON (L.), *ed.*
*Independent (An) I. parliament: the path to peace. By an Irish King's Counsel. s8°. D. 1921
Indexes to I. wills. Gen. ed. T. M. Blagg. [Irish Record Ser.] v5. 8°. 1920
5, Derry & Raphoe; ed. G. Thrift.
I. coast pilot, 7th ed., 1922, *see* ADMIRALTY.
I. litanies: text & tr., 1925, *see* PLUMMER (C.), *ed.*
I. poets of to-day, 1921, *see* WALTERS (L. D'O.)
Letters & papers rel. to I. matters, f. Balfour MSS., *see* ABBOTSFORD CLUB. Misc., v1, 1837.
Irish Dominion League (The), *1919–1921.*
Official report. [P2560]. 8°. 1921
Irish Folk Song Society, London.
Journal. v19, 20 (1922–23) *in* 1v. la8°. 1923–24
Irish Memorials Association, *see* ASSOC. FOR THE PRESERVATION OF MEMORIALS OF THE DEAD IN IRELAND.
Irish Society (The). *Contin. (A) of the hist. narr. [*by Sir C. Reed*] of the I.S., 1864–78, 1878, *see* BECK (J.)
*Hist. (An) narrative of the orig. & constit. of the I.S., 1865, *see* REED (*Sir* C.)
Irish Text Society. *Publications.* v20–24. 8°. 1918–26
see CONTENTION. The c. of the bards; ed. &c. L. McKenna, 2p, 1918. [20, 21.]
„ GRUAIDH GHRIANSHOLUS. Pursuit of G. G.; ed. & tr. C. O'Rahilly, 1924. [24.]
„ Ó HUIGINN (T. DALL). A bhfuil aguinn; ed. &c. E. Knott, 2v, 1922–26. [22, 23.]
Irish who's who, 1923, *see* THOM'S IRISH WHO'S WHO.
Irish (*Col.* **John Powell**). The anti-Japanese agitation in California, *see* SHERRILL (C. H.) Korea & Shantung &c., 1920.

Irland (John) [JOHANNES DE IRLANDIA]. The meroure of wyssdome. Ed. C. Macpherson. [Scott. Text Soc., N.S. 19]. 8°. E. 1926
Irons (William Josiah). Athanasius contra mundum. Letter, app. Greek of the Creeds &c. s8°. [1872]
Ironside (*Maj.-Gen. Sir* **William Edmund**). Tannenberg: the first 30 days in East Prussia. 8°. E. 1925
Irsch (Nikolaus). Die trierer Abteikirche St. Matthias u. d. trier.-lothring. Bautengruppe. la8°. Augsburg. 1927
Irvine (Helen Douglas).
The making of rural Europe. s8°. [1923]
Irvine (William). Later Mughals, 1707–39. Ed. [& augm. w. the hist. of Nadir Shah's invasion], by J. Sarkar. 2v. 8°. Calcutta. 1922
Irving (Edward), *minister of the Caledonian Ch., Regent Sq.* Trial of E. I. bef. Presbytery of Annan, 13 Mar. 1833. s8°. Dumfries. 1833
Irving (*Sir* **Henry Brodribb**), *1838–1905.*
see ODELL (G. C. D.) Shakespeare f. Betterton to I., 2v, 1920.
„ RUSSELL (P.) Sir H. I., 1895.
Irving (Henry Brodribb), *son of Sir H. I., 1870–1919.*
Last studies in criminology. 8°. [1921]
see WAINWRIGHT (H.) & T. G. W. Trial of the Wainwrights; ed. H. B. I., w. apprec. by Sir E. M. Hall, 1920.
Irving (John).
Hist. of Dumbartonshire. p2, 3. 4°. Dumbarton. 1920–24
This work is a rev. ed. of Hist. of Dumbartonshire *by* Jos. Irving.
Irving (*Lt.-Com.* **John**), *R.N.*
Coronel & the Falklands. s8°. [1927]
Irving (Walter). Every man's bk. of the greenhouse. s8°. [1907]
Irving (Washington).
The Alhambra. Intr. by E. R. Pennell. Illust. by J. Pennell. s8°. 1896
Bracebridge Hall. Illust. by R. Caldecott. s8°. 1887
Chron. of the conq. of Granada, f. the MSS. of Fray A. Agapida. Added, Legends of the conq. of Spain. 2v [*in 1, pagin. cont.*] s8°. *Bohn.* 1890–1902
Diary—Spain, 1828–29. Ed. f. MS. in Libr. of [*Hisp.*] Soc. by C. L. Penney. [Hisp. Soc. of Amer.] s8°. N.Y. 1926
Old Christmas: f. the Sketch book. Illust. by R. Caldecott. [5th ed.] 8°. 1886
see HELLMAN (G. S.) W. I., Esq., ambassador, 1925.
Irving (William), *see* TINLEY (G. F.), T. HUMPHREYS & W. I. Colour planning of the garden, 1924.
Irwin (Florence). Auction high-lights. s8°. N.Y. 1913
The fine points of auction bridge. rev. ed. s8°. N.Y. [1913]
Irwin (Will). Youth rides West. s8°. [1925]
Is. Is it a new world?: articles &c. contrib. to "Daily Telegraph," 1920, *see* COURTNEY (W. L.)
Is unemployment inevitable?, 1924, *see* UNEMPLOYMENT.
Isaac, *ben Abraham, of Troki.* Liber chissick emuna (munimen fidei). [*Hebr. & Lat.*], *see* WAGENSEIL (J. C.) Tela ignea Satanae &c., 1681.
Isaac, *ben Judah, Abravanel.* Diss. in Lat. versae à J. Buxtorfio, *see* BUXTORFIUS (J.), *the younger*. Diss., 1662.
Exordium comment. in Leviticum, *see* MAIMONIDES. De sacrificiis lib. &c., 1683.
see SCHNELL (S.) Disput. theol.: quae I. A. &c. scripsit, 1647.
Isaac, *the Great, patriarch of Armenia* [SAHAK]. [Hist. of S. & Mesrop—Vision of S.—Canons—Letters &c. *in Armenian*. Soferq Hayk., v2]. s8°. i Venetik. 1853
see JOHN IV, *of Otzun &c.* *Works* (*in Arm.*), 1833.
Isaac, *the patriarch*, *see* SYMON (A.) Tripatriarchicon [*poem*], 1705.
Isaac (Charles Percival).
The menace of money power. s8°. [1921]
Isaac (Daniel), *see* EVERETT (J.) The polemic divine or mem. of the life &c. of D. I., 1839.
Isaac (Stephanus), *see* ISAAK (S.)
Isaacs (Jorge). Poesías compl. Con estudio prelim. de B. Sanín Cano. s8°. Barcelona. [1921]
Isaak (Stephan) [†ISAAC (STEPHANUS)], *see* ROTSCHEIDT (W.) S. I., e. köln. Pfarrer &c., s. Leben v. ihm selbst erzählt &c. 1910.
Isaaki, *see* RASHI.
***Isabel.** Tale, 1810, *see* LLOYD (C.)
Isabella, *de Fortibus, ctss. of Albemarle &c.*, *see* ROSE-TROUP (F.) The Lady of the Isle, 1236–93, 1905.
Isabella *of Milan, princess of Aragon, wife of G. Galeazzo Sforza*, *see* DINA (A.) I. d'A., 1470–1524, 1921.

Isabella, *Infanta of Spain, consort of Albert, archduke of Austria, 1566–1633.*
see HAUTECLOCQUE (*le cte.* G. DE). Arras &c. s. Albert & I., 1873.
,, LONCHAY (H.) & J. CUVELIER. Corr. de la cour d'Espagne &c., t2, Corr. de Philippe IV avec I., 1621–33, 1927.
Isabella I, *queen of Spain* [ISABEL LA CATÓLICA], *see* DIEULAFOY (*Mme.* J.) I. la Grande, Reine de Castelle, 1451–1504, 1920.
Isabella II, *queen of Spain, see* BILLING (*le b.* S. DE). *L'Espagne & la Fr.; du mariage d'I., 1843.
Isabey (Léon) & E. Leblan. Villas, maisons &c. comp. sur les motifs des habitations de Paris mod. fol. 1864
Isæus [ISÆOS; ISÄUS; ISEO]. Discours. Texte établi & tr. par P. Roussel. 8º. 1922
I. [Text] w. Eng. tr. by E. S. Forster. [Loeb Class. Lib.] s8º. 1927
see DOBSON (W. S.), *ed.* Oratores Attici, t4, I. &c., t14, I. &c. interpret. Lat., 1828.
,, HAVET (L.) Notes crit. sur le texte de l'Orateur & sur I., 1927.
,, JONES (*Sir* W.) Works, v4, Speeches of I. [tr.], w. notes, 1799.
Isaev (Andrei Alekseevich).
Характеръ русской революціи. [P2722]. 8º. С.-П. 1906
Isalguier (Anselme d') [IZALGUIER; YSALGUIER], *of Toulouse, fl. c. 1413, see* LA RONCIÈRE (C. DE). La découv. de l'Afrique au m. â., t3, Un explor. fr. du Niger [*i.e.* A. d'I.], 1927.
Isaverdentz (Hagopos).
Armenia & the Armenians. 2nd ed. s8º. Venice. 1878
Isbrants (Everard), *see* IDES (E.)
Isbyam (I. C.) The self-seeker & h. search. 8º. [1926]
Iselin (Jacob Christoph) [ISELIUS]. Diss. de controv. Eccl. Anglic., ejus episcopatum expedens. Praes. J. C. I., disput. L. Miegus, A. Ubelius &c. s4º. Basileae. [1756]
Isenmann (Joannes), *Lutheran divine.* Refutatio Sotici scripti, *see* CHRISTOPH, *Herzog zu Würtemberg.* Confessio, t2, 1561.
Iseo (Giuseppe). Disc. sopra il poema di T. Tasso, *see* GALILEO. Consid. al Tasso &c., 1793.
Isert (Paul Erdmann). Voyages en Guinée & dans les Iles Caraïbes en Amer. Tr. 8º. 1793
Isidore, *of Pelusium, Saint* [ISIDORUS *Pelusiota*]. De interpret. divinae Scr. epistol. libri 4. Cum Lat. interpret. (lib. 1–3) J. Billii Prunaei, quartus Lat. factus a C. Rittershusio. fol. *ex officina Commeliniana.* 1605
Isidore, *bp. of Seville, St.* De scriptor. eccl., *see* LE MIRE (A.) Bibl. eccl., 1639.
see BEESON (C. H.) Isidor-St., 1913.
Isidorus, *Characenus.* Parthian stations, 1st c. B.C. Greek text, w. tr. & comm. by W. H. Schoff. 8º. Phila. 1914
Isidorus, *Mercator* [PSEUDO-ISIDORUS], *see* THEINER (J. A.) De P.-I. canonum coll., 1827.
Iskoz (Ark. Sem.), *see* DOLININ (A. S.), *ps.*
Iskra. Искра. За два года. Сборникъ статей (1903–06). 2ч. [in 1v. ч1 *wants* pp. 609–624]. 8º. [1905]–06
Iskusstvo. Искусство старое и новое. Сборник под редакц. К. Эрберта. I. s4º. П. 1921
Islandica; an annual rel. to Iceland & the Fiske Icelandic Coll. in Cornell Univ. Lib. v12–18. 8º. Ithaca, N.Y. 1919–28
12, Mod. Icelandic: essay by H. Hermannsson.
13, Bibliog. of the Eddas; by H. Hermannsson.
14, Icelandic bks. of the 17th c.; by H. Hermannsson.
15, Jón Guðmundsson & h. Natural hist. of Iceland; by H. Hermannsson.
16, Eggert Ólafsson: biog. sk.; by H. Hermannsson.
17, 2 cartographers: G. & T. Thorláksson; by H. Hermannsson.
18, Sir J. Banks & Iceland; by H. Hermannsson.
Isländische Litteratur u. Geschichte, T1, 1773, *see* SCHLÖZER (A. L. v.), *ed.*
Islandske Annaler indtil 1578, 1888, *see* STORM (G.), *ed.*
Islip (John), *abbot of Westminster, see* WESTLAKE (H. F.) Westminster Abbey: as shown by the life &c. of Abbot J. I., 1464–1532, 1921.
Ismailia Council. [Rules & regul. of the Shia Imami Ismailia Council. *Gujarati & Eng.*] s8º. [1915]
Ismail Kemal, *Bey.*
Memoirs. Ed. S. Story. Pref. by W. M. Fullerton. 8º. [1920]
Ismet, *pasha.*
Déclarations aux journalistes. [P2712]. 8º. Lausanne [1922]
Isnard (E.), *see* ARNAUD D'AGNEL (G.) & E. I. Monticelli, 1926.

Isnard (Marie Zéphirin), *see* MANOSQUE. Livre des privilèges de M., 1169–1315; publ. M. Z. I., 1894.
Isocrates. Cyprian orations. Evagoras, Ad Nicoclem, Nicocles aut Cyprii. Ed., w. intr. & notes by E. S. Forster. s8º. O. 1912
Orationes [*in Greek*], *see* ORATORES. Orationes horum rhetorum &c., p3, 1513.
Panegyricus. Rec., cum animadv. S. F. N. Mori, ed. F. A. G. Spohn. 8º. Lips. 1817
see DOBSON (W. S.), *ed.* Oratores Attici, t3, I., t14, I. &c. interpret. Lat., 1828.
Israel. The legacy of Israel: essays by Sir G. A. Smith &c., 1927, *see* BEVAN (E. R.) & C. SINGER, *edd.*
Israel, *ben Jehudah.* Sendschreiben an Oliger Paulli betreff. Jesu v. Nazaret d. Mann v. Gott. [P1042]. s8º. *n.p.* 1704
Israel, *Ter, 13th cent.* Synaxaire arménien; publ. & tr. par G. Bayan, p3–6, *see* GRAFFIN (R.) & F. NAU. Patr. orient., t15, 16, 18, 1922–27.
Israëls (Jozef), *artist.* Rembrandt. 8º. [1909]
see EISLER (M.) J. I., 1924.
Issaverdens (James), *see* ISAVERDENTZ (H.)
Istituto Britannico di Firenze, *see* VITA (LA) BRITANNICA, Anno 1, 2, 1918–19.
Istituto di Studii Vinciani in Roma. Pubbl.
see LORENZO (G. DE). L. da Vinci e la geologia, 1920.
,, MALAGUZZI VALERI (F.) L. da Vinci e la scultura, 1922.
Istituto Veneto, *see* REALE ISTITUTO VENETO.
Istoria. Istoria d. stati di Algeri &c.; tr., 1754, *see* ALGERI.
Istrati (Constantin I.) Studiu rel. la o nomenclatură gen. în chimia organică &c. Ed. Acad. Române. la8º. București. 1913
Istrin (Vasily Mikhailovich). Очерк истории древнерусской литературы (11–13 вв.) la8º. П. 1922
Iswolsky, *see* IZVOLSKY.
Italia. *Comm. d. più notabili &c. cose d'I. &c., 1548, *see* LANDI (O.)
Diario d. Guerra d'I.: raccolta dei bullettini ufficiali e altri doc^{t}. [7v *in* 8; 3i, ii]. ser. 1–65 [*only p1 of v7 publ^{d}.*] s8º. Milano. 1915–23
*Intervento (L') dell' I. n. doc. segreti dell' Intesa. [2ª ed.] 8º. 1925
Nuov. guida dei viaggiatori in Italia. 3ª. ed. 8º. Milano. 1834
Italia artistica. Nos. 1, 16, 69, 84–92. la8º. Bergamo. [1922 ?–28]
see BANDINI (C.) Spoleto, 1922 ?. [85.]
,, COLETTI (L.) Treviso, 1926. [90.]
,, †DALGAS (A.) La Versilia, 1928. [92.]
,, GIACOMO (S. DI). Da Capua a Caserta, *n.d.* [87.]
,, GROSSO (O.) Genova. [91.]
,, KAMBO (S.) Grottaferrata e il Monte Cavo, 1924 ?. [86.]
see KAMBO (S.) Il Tuscolo e Frascati, 1920. [84.]
,, †MARIOTTI (C.) Ascoli Piceno, 1913. [69.]
,, RICCI (C.) Ravenna, 5ª ed., 1905. [1.]
,, RUSCONI (A. J.) Assisi, 1927. [89.]
,, SÓRIGA (R.) Pavia, 1926. [88.]
,, SUPINO (I. B.) Pisa, 2ª ed., 1910. [16.]
Italia (L') che scrive. Rassegna per coloro che leggono. Suppl. mensile a tutti i periodici. Anno 2–9 (1919–27). 4º. [1919–27]
Italian. Early I. lit., 2v, 1920, *see* GRILLO (E.), *ed.*
*New univ. Eng. & Ital. dict., 2p, 1849, *see* ENGLISH.
Italiana [ITALIANO &c.] Almanacco ital., 1927, *see* ALMANACCO.
*Elenco ufficiale nobiliare I., 1922, *see* ELENCO.
Risorgimento (Il) ital. in un carteggio di patrioti lombardi, 1821–60, 1924, *see* MALVEZZI (A.), *ed.*
Italienische Forschungen. Hrsg. v. Kunsthist. Institut in Florenz. N.F. B1. 4º. L. 1925
see POSSE (H.) Der röm. Maler A. Sacchi, 1925. [N.F., 1.]
Italy.
Government publications.
CODES &c.
Constitution of I. (1848). Tr. w. intr. by S. M. Lindsay & Leo S. Rowe. [Suppl. to Annals of Amer. Acad. of Polit. &c. Sc. Nov. 1894. P2833]. 8º. Phila. 1894
DIREZIONE GENERALE DELLA STATISTICA, *see* MINISTERO DI AGRICOLTURA &C. *below.*
INCHIESTA PARLAMENTARE sulle condiz. dei contadini n. prov. merid. e n. Sicilia. v6, Sicilia, t1, Relaz. d. G. Lorenzoni. p1–5 *in* 2v. fol. 1910
MINISTERO DEGLI AFFARI ESTERI.
see BÉGUINOT (A.) & A. VACCARI. Contrib. [*& 2º contrib.*] alla flora d. Libia, 1912–13.

Italy [*continued*].
Government publications [*continued*].
MINISTERO DI AGRICOLTURA, INDUSTRIA E COMMERCIO.
Annali del credito e d. previdenza, anno 1911. La legislaz. ital. sul credito agrario, dell' Avv. A. Baccaglini. Leggi &c. 8°. 1911
Movimento d. popolazione sec. gli atti d. stato civile 1917, 1918, 1919–23. la8°. 1921–25
Notizie complementari alle statistiche giudiziarie penali, 1896–1900. la8°. 1909
Statistica d. cause di morte, 1911, 1917, 1918, 1919–23. 8°. 1913–25
Statistica d. emigraz. ital. per l'estero, 1918–20, con not. somm. per 1921–24. 4°. 1925
Statistica industriale. Riassunto d. not. s. condiz. indust. del regno. 3p. la8°. 1905–06
see ANNUARIO STATISTICO ITALIANO, *var. years.*
„ GIGLIOLI (E. H.) Avifauna Italica, 1886.
MINISTERO DELLE COLONIE.
Notiziario archeologico. Anno 1, 2. 4°. 1915–16
Anno 1 *consists of repr. articles, each w. sep. tp. & pagin. as under*:—
R. Decreto, 24 sett., 1914.
Boni (G.) & L. Mariani. Rel. intorno al consolid. &c. dell' Arco di Aurelio in Tripoli.
Aurigemma (S.) Not. arch. s. Tripolitania.
Ghislanzoni (E.) Not. arch. s. Cirenaica.
Aurigemma (S.) Iscriz. con dedica alla Domina Caelestis in Sabrata.
see EXHIBITIONS, *Genova.* La mostra coloniale de G., 1914, 1914.
„ GHISLANZONI (E.) Not. arch. s. Cirenaica, 1915.
MINISTERO DELL' ECONOMIA NAZIONALE.
Censimento d. popolazione, 1 Dic. 1921. [v]1–3. 4°. 1925–26
1, Umbria. 2, Venezia Tridentina. 3, Venezia Giulia.
Elenco dei comuni d. regno, e loro pop. (Censimento 1921). 8°. 1925
MINISTERO DELLE FINANZE.
Pubbl. ed. dallo Stato &c., 1861–1923. Cat. gen. la8°. 1924
MINISTERO DI GRAZIA E GIUSTIZIA E DEI CULTI.
Statistica d. criminalità, 1906, 1910, 1918–19, 1920: not. compl. alla stat. giudiz. penale. 4°. 1909–26
MINISTERO DELLA GUERRA.
see ALBERTI (*gen.* A.) L'Italia e la fine d. Guerra Mondiale, p2, 1924.
„ —— Vittorio Veneto, p1, 1924.
„ VITTORIO VENETO. Royal Italian Army; rep. on battle of V. V., 1918, *n.d.*
MINISTERO DEI LAVORI PUBBLICI.
Porti marittimi [Not. raccolte da E. Coen-Cagli e O. Bernardini]. la8°. Milano. 1905
MINISTERO DELLA MARINA.
Monografia stor. dei porti dell' antichità n. penisola ital. [*By var. a.* Avvert. *by* C. Imperiale]. la8°. 1905
MINISTERO DELLA P. ISTRUZIONE.
see BOLLETTINO d'arte del Min. d. P. Ist., 1907–20.
Anonymous works.
*The economic resources of I., 1895–1920. Publ. by the Credito Italiano. 2v. la8°. Milan. 1920
*Transalpine mem.; or, anecdotes &c. of Italy &c.; by an Eng. Catholic, 1826, *see* BESTE (J. R. D.)

Iter [ITINÉRAIRE]. Itinéraire complet du royaume de France, 2v, 1824, *see* FRANCE.

Itogi. Итоги и перспективы: сборникъ статей, 1906, *see* RUSSIA.

Ittig (Thomas). Bibl. Patrum Apostolic. Graeco-Latina Clementis, Ignatii, Polycarpi. Praem. Diss. de Patribus Apost. aut. T. I. [4 *pagins.*] s8°. Lipsiae. 1699
De bibliothecis & catenis Patrum &c. s8°. Lipsiae. 1707
De Synodi Carenton., 1631, indulg. erga Lutheranos. [*b. w. h.* Hist. synod., 1705; *a. c. b. w.* Feustking (J. H.) Hist. Coll. Jever., 1707]. s4°. Lipsiae. 1705
Hist. synod. nationalium, a Reformatis in Gallia habit. s4°. Lipsiae. 1705
see CLEMENS *Alexandrinus.* Operum Clem. Alex. suppl. Colleg. & cum praef. ed. T. I., 1700.
„ KERN (J. F.) De vita, obitu, scriptisque T. I. diss., 1710.

Ivan IV, *emperor of Russia.*
see KLUCHEVSKY (V. O.) Характеристика И., 1917.
„ PLATONOV (S. F.) Иван Грозный, 1924.
„ VIPPER (R. YU.) Иван Грозный, 1922.

Ivanin (Mikhail Ignatovich).
Описаніе зимняго похода въ Хиву 1839–40. 8°. С.-П. 1874
Походъ въ Хиву въ 1839 г. [*Articles extr. f.* Военный Сборникъ.] 8°. [1863]

Ivanov (Georgy). Сады. Третья книга стихов. s8°. П. 1921

Ivanov (Germog. Ivanovich). Россия: краткий курс геогр. la8°. Москва. 1923

Ivanov (P. M.) О том, что сделало Советское правительство в России. [P2722]. s8°. 1919

Ivanov (Vsevolod).
Возвращение Будды, повесть. 8°. Берлине. 1923
Голубые пески: роман. s8°. [Москва]. *n.d.*
Партизаны: рассказ. 8°. Москва. *n.d.*
Цветные ветра. s8°. П 1922
TRANSLATIONS.
L'enfant, nouv. [tr. par A. Pierre], *see* ŒUVRES libres, 34, 1924.
Le train blindé no. 1469. Tr. Sidersky. 3e éd. s8°. [1927]

Ivanov (Vyacheslov). Прометей: трагедия. 8°. П. 1919
see BELII (A.) Сирин ученого варварства, по В. И. Родное и Вселенское, 1922.
—— & M. O. Gershenzon.
Переписка из двух углов. s8°. П. 1921

Ivanov-Razumnik (Razumnik Vasilevich).
Испытаніе въ грозѣ и бурѣ.—А. Блокъ. Скиѳы, Двѣнадцать. 8°. Берлинъ. [1920]
Ист. русской общественной мысли. 2t. 8°. С.-П. 1907

Ivanovsky (Aleksei Arsenovich) [IWANOVSKI]. Zur Anthropologie d. Mongolen. [*Extr. fr.* Archiv. f. Anthropologie B24]. 4°. [Braunschweig. 1896]

Iveković (Cirillo M.) Bau- u. Kunstdenkmale in Dalmatien. [2e veränd. A.] 6B. fol. Wien. 1927
1, Zara. 2, Sebenico. 3, Trau. 4, Spalato. 5. Ragusa. 6, Die Inseln Arbe, Lesina, Curzola.
Die Entwickl. d. mittelalterl. Baukunst in Dalmatien. la4°. Wien. 1910

Ivens Saga.
see BROWN (A. C. L.) Iwain: st. in orig. of Arthurian romance, 1903.
„ ZENKER (R.) Forsch. z. Artusepik, 1, Ivainstudien, 1921.

Ivens (Walter George). Dict. & grammar of lang. of Sa'a & Ulawa, Solomon Islands. With app. [C.I. of Wash.] la8°. Wash. 1918
Melanesians of the S.-E. Solomon Islands. la8°. 1927

Iverach (James). St. Paul: his life &c. s8°. [1890]

Ivernois (*Sir* Francis d'), *see* KARMIN (O.) Sir F. d'I., 1757–1842; sa vie &c., 1920.

Ives (John). Sel. papers chiefly rel. to Eng. antiq.; publ. f. originals in poss. of J. I. la8°. 1773

Ivet (Robert) [JUET]. The 3rd voyage of Master H. Hudson (1609); wr. by R. I. [*Dutch & Eng.*], *see* HUDSON (H.) Reize onder Nederl. vlag &c.; uitg. S. P. L'Honoré Naber, 1921.

Ivo, *St., bp. of Chartres, see* BLIEMETZRIEDER (F. PL.) Zu d. Schr. I. v. Chartres, 1917.
see FRONTEAU (J.) Epistolae &c., S. Ivonis vita, 1720; 33.

Iwand (Fritz Georg). Bibliographie d. deut. Regiments- u. Bataillons Geschichten, 1905–14. [P2408]. 8°. Biberach. 1919

Iwasaki (Uichi). The working forces in Jap. politics. 8°. N.Y., *Columbia Univ.* 1921

Iwasaki (Y.), *see* BRINKLEY (F.), F. NANJO, & Y. I. An unabr. Jap.-Eng. dict., 1896.

I.W.W., *see* INDUSTRIAL WORKERS OF THE WORLD.

Iyengar (T. R. Sesha). Dravidian India. v1. s8°. Madras. 1925

Iyer (C. S. Ranga).
Father India. Reply to Mother India. [by K. Mayo]. [repr.] 8° [1927

Iyer (K. V.) Indian railways. s8°. 1924

Izalguier, *see* ISALGUIER.

Izgoev (—). Значеніе соц.-демократ. пропаганды. [P2824]. s8°. Genève. 1879

Izgoev (Aleksandr Solomonovich) [LANDE (A. S.)], *b. 1872, see* SMENA VEKH. О Смене вех, А. С. И. &c., 1922.

Izoulet (Jean). De J. J. Russeo utrum misopolis fuerit an philopolis. 8°. Parisiis. 1894

Izvestiya. Известия Центральн. Комитета Р. К. П. Nos. 21–30, 33, 34 [*in* 1v]. fol. Москва. 1920–2
Сборникъ "Извѣстій крестьянск. депутатовъ" &c., 1906, *see* SBORNIK.

Izvolsky (Aleksandr Petrovich). Der diplomat. Schriftwechsel I., 1911–14, aus d. Geheimakten d. russ. Staatsarchive. Deut. Üb.; hrsg. F. Stieve. 4B. & Ergzb. la8°. 1924
1, Vom Beginn d. Botschaftertätigkeit I.'s bis z. Beendigung d. Marokkokrisc.
2, Der Tripoliskrieg u. d. erste Balkankrieg.
3, Der 2. u. 3. Balkankrieg.
4, Vom Ende d. Balkanwirren bis z. Mord v. Sarajewo.
Ergzb., *see* STIEVE (F.) I. u. d. Weltkrieg, 1924.
Iswolski i. Weltkriege: dipl. Schriftwechsel, 1914–17. Neue Dok. a. d. russ. Staatsarchive. Im Auftr. d. Deut. Auswärt. Amtes, nebst Komm. v. F. Stieve. la8°. 1925
Memoirs. Ed. & tr. by C. L. Seeger. 8°. [1920]
see MARCHAND (R.) Un livre noir: diplom. d'avant-guerre, 1910–14, corresp. d'I., 2t, 1922–23.
,, STIEVE (F.) I. & the World War; tr., 1926.
Izvolsky (P. P.) Къ вопросу о соединеніи церквей. [P2685]. 8°. Мюнхенъ. 1922

J

J. (A.) *A compleat acc. of the Portugueze language, 1701, *see* PORTUGUEZE.
J. (A.) *J. A. Alberdingk Thijm: door A. J., 1893, *see* THIJM (J. A. A.)
J. (C. F.) *Découvertes sur le cavalier, 1837, *see* JÄNISCH (C. F.)
J. (E.) *Some acc. of the experience of E. J., 1770?, *see* WESLEY (J.)
J. (F. W. *Fhr.* v. W.), *see* WEDEL-JARLSBERG (*b.* F. W. AF).
J. (J. L.) *Polit. issues of the 19th cent., 1886, *see* POLITICAL.
J. (S.) *Hist. of Poland to 1795 [*pref. signed* S. J.], 1795, *see* JONES (STEPHEN).
J. (W. S.) *The child of time, 1925, *see* JACKSON (W. S.)
Jaba (Auguste). Dict. kurde-français. Publ. F. Justi. [Acad. Imp. des Sci.] 8°. St.-Pétersbourg. 1879
Jaba (Sergei). Петроградское студенчество в Борьбе за свободную Высшую Школу. 8°. Paris. [1924]
Jablonski (Daniel Ernst). Hist. consensus Sendomir., inter Evangel. regni Poloniae & M. D. Lithuaniae, 1570. ad praes. usque tempus deducta. Subj. Consensus &c. s4°. Berolini. 1731
see NEUCHÂTEL. Liturgy used in churches of N., w. a letter f. J. conc. liturgies, 1712.
Jablonski (Friedrich Wilhelm). Diss. de orig. & fundamento Nestorianismi. Praeses P. E. J. s4°. Francofurti. [1728]
Jablonski (Paul Ernst). Exercit. hist. theol. de Nestorianismo. [*b. w.* Vogt (J.) Bibl. hist. hæres., 1723–29]. s8°. Berolini. 1724
Instit. hist. Christianae antiq. s8°. Francofurti ad Viadrum. 1754
Jabneel, *see* JAMNIA.
Jaboatam (Antonio de Santa Maria), *see* SANTA MARIA JABOATAM (A. DE).
Jaca. El libro de la Cadena del Concejo de J. &c., siglos 10–14; transcr. y notas de D. Sangorrin, *see* COLECCION de docs. para el estudio de la hist. de Aragon, t12, 1920.
Jacchaeus (Gilbertus) [IACHÆUS].
Oratio in obitum W. Snellii. [P2744]. s4°. Lugd. Bat. 1626
Jachiades (Joseph) [JACHIIA; JOSEPH BEN DAVID ABEN YACHYA], *d. 1539*. Paraphrasis in Danielem. Cum versione & annot. C. L'Empereur. s4°. Amstelodami. 1633
Jack. *Jack & the Queen Killers. [*A satirical poem*]. [P425]. 8°. 1820
*Loyalist's (The) house that J. built, 1819?, *see* LOYALIST'S.
*Political (The) house that Jack built, 1819, *see* HONE (W.)
Jack (Adolphus Alfred). A comm. on the poetry of Chaucer & Spenser. 8°. Glasgow. 1920
Jack (J. W.) The date of the Exodus. 8°. E. 1925
Jack (Robert Logan).
Northmost Australia: 3 cent. of explor. &c. 2v. la8°. [1921]
Jäckh (Ernst Friedrich Wilhelm).
Der deutsche Krieg. H78. 8°. St. 1916
Raché (P.) Wofür kämpfen die Engländer? 1916. [78.]
Jacks (Lawrence Pearsall).
Alchemy of thought. [repr.] 8°. 1927
The challenge of life. [Hibbert lect., 1924]. 8°. [1924]
Constructive citizenship. 8°. [1927]
The heroes of Smokeover. s8°. [1926]
The legends of Smokeover. 8°. [1921]
A living universe. Hibbert lect., 1923. s8°. [1923]
The lost radiance of the Xtn. religion. s8°. 1921
Realities & shams. s8°. [1923]
Jackson (Abraham Valentine Williams).
Early Persian poetry down to Firdausi. 8°. N.Y. 1920
Jackson (Andrew), *pres. of the U.S.* Corr. Ed. J. S. Bassett. [C.I. of Wash.] v1–3. la8°. Wash. 1926–28
Jackson (Benjamin Daydon). Linnæus: h. life, adapted f. Swedish of T. M. Fries &c., by B. D. J. 8°. 1923
Jackson (Carl Newell), *see* HOWARD (A. A.) & C. N. J. Index verborum C. Suetoni, 1922.
Jackson (*Sir* Charles James). English goldsmiths & their marks. 2nd ed. rev. & enl. 4°. 1921
Jackson (*Mrs.* F. Nevill). A student in Sicily. s8°. [1926]
Jackson (Francis James), *see* GENTZ (F. v.) D'Ulm à Iéna; corr. du Chev. de G. avec F. J. J., 1804–06, 1921.
Jackson (Frank G.) Lessons on decorative design. 8°. 1900
Wood-carving. 8°. 1902
Jackson (Frederick). *Home defence. [P2484]. 8°. [1909]
Jackson (*Sir* Frederick John).
Notes on the game birds of Kenya & Uganda. 8°. 1926
Jackson (George), *B.A.*
The old Methodism & the new. s8°. 1903
Jackson (*Adm.* George Vernon), *1787–1876*. Perilous adv. &c. of a Naval officer, 1801–12. Ed. H. Burrows. 8°. E. 1927
Jackson (Henry), *of Trinity Coll., Cambridge, see* PARRY (R. ST. J.) H. J., O.M.: a mem., 1926.
Jackson (Herbert J.) European hand firearms of the 16th–18th c., w. a treatise on Scottish hand firearms by C. E. Whitelaw. 4°. 1923
Jackson (Holbrook). William Morris. [rev. & enl. ed.] 8°. [1926]
Jackson (J.), *photographer, of Rangoon.*
Some views of Burma, w. notes. obl.8°. Rangoon. *n.d.*
Jackson (J. Wilfred). Brachiopoda, *see* BRIT. ANTARCTIC EXPED., 1910–13. Zoology, v2, 1914–20.
Jackson (John), *of Queen's Coll., Cambridge, Nonconform. minister.* Index Biblicus: concordance. [*b. w.* The Holy Bible, 1668]. s4°. C. 1668
Jackson (John Edward). On the hist. of Chippenham, *see* CHIPPENHAM. Records, 1554–1889, 1889.
Jackson (*Col.* John Richard). What to observe. 3rd ed. rev. & ed. by N. Shaw. s8°. 1861
Jackson (Robert Tracy). Fossil Echini of the Panama Canal Zone & Costa Rica. [S.I.: U.S. Nat. Mus., Bull. 103]. 8°. Wash. 1918
Jackson (Samuel Macaulay), *see* SCHAFF (P.) & S. M. JACKSON. Encyclopedia of living divines, 1887.
Jackson (Thomas).
Aids to truth &c.: letter to bp. W. Fitzgerald being a vindic. of J. & C. Wesley, G. Whitefield &c. 8°. 1862
The Church & the Methodists. The principles &c. of Mr. Wesley. 3rd ed. [P2531]. s8°. 1834
Letter to E. B. Pusey being a vindic. of tenets &c. of Methodists [*b. w.* Pusey (E. B.) Letter to abp. of Canterbury, 1842]. 3rd ed. 8°. 1842
A library of Christian biography. Ed. T. J. 12v. s8°. 1837–40
The life of John Goodwin, vicar of St. Stephen's, Coleman St., London. 8°. 1822
Life of Robert Newton, D.D. s8°. 1855
The lives of early Methodist preachers chiefly wr. by themselves. Ed. w. intr. essay by T. J. 3rd ed. 6v. s8°. 1865–66
Mem. of the life & wr. of R. Watson. 2nd ed. 8°. 1834
Recoll. of my own life & times. Ed. B. Frankland. Introd. &c. by G. Osborn. s8°. 1874
see WATSON (R.) Works, v1, Mem. [by T. J.], 1847.
Jackson (*Sir* Thomas Graham), *Bart.*
Architecture. 8°. 1925
Byzantine & Romanesque architecture. 2nd ed. 2v. la8°. C. 1920
Memories of travel. 8°. C. 1923
The renaissance of Roman architecture. 3p. la8°. C. 1921–23
Jackson (Thomas Jonathan), *see* NASH (E.) J.'s strategy, 1904.
Jackson (Wilfrid Scarborough).
*The child of time &c. [*Poems*]. 8°. [1925]

Jackson (William), *of the Inner Temple, Barrister-at-Law.* The new & complete Newgate calendar; or, Malefactor's univ. register. n. ed. w. add. 8v. [v6 *in* 2p]. 8°. 1818
Jackson (*Capt.* **William).** Voyages (1642–45); ed. V. T. Harlow, 1923, *see* CAMDEN MISCELLANY, v13, 1924.
Jacob, *the patriarch.* Jakob u. s. 12 Söhne: engl. Verslegende [16 c.]; *ed.* J. Zupitza, *see* ARCHIV F. D. ST. D. NEU SPR., B138, 1919.
see SYMON (A.) Tripatriarchicon [*poem*], 1705.
Jacob Judah Aryeh [LEON]. J. J. Leonis de Templo Hierosolymitano libri 4 ex Ebraeo, Lat. rec. a J. Sauberto. s4°. Helmaestadi. 1665
Jacob (*General*) [JACOB YOUHANNA; *Moallem* JACOB], *see* HOMSY (G.) Le gén. J. & l'expéd. de Bonaparte en Egypte (1798–1801), 1921.
Jacob (Alfred), *see* SAINTE-HOÏLDE, *abbey.* Cartul. de l'abbaye de Ste.-H.; publ. par A. J., 1882.
Jacob (Antoine), *called Montfleury.* Les bestes raisonnables (1661)—L'impromptu de l'Hostel de Condé (1663)—L'école des jaloux (1664), *see* FOURNEL (V.) Contemp. de Molière, t1, 1863.
Jacob (Ernest Fraser). Studies in the period of Baronial reform & rebellion, 1258–67, *see* VINOGRADOFF (*Sir* P.), *ed.* Oxford st. in soc. &c. hist., v8, 1925.
see CRUMP (C. G.) & E. F. J., *edd.* Legacy of the Middle Ages, 1926.
Jacob (Georg). Schanfarà-Studien, 2T, *see* KÖNIGL. AKAD. D. WISS. ZU MÜNCHEN. Phil. Classe, Sitz., 1914–15.
Jacob (George Andrew).
The eccl. polity of the New Test. 2nd ed. s8°. 1878
The Lord's Supper hist. considered. s8°. [1884]
Jacob (Gerhard). Das Werk Th. Manns. Bibliographie. 8°. 1926
Jacob (Harold Fenton). Kings of Arabia: rise & set of Turkish dominion. 8°. [1923]
Jacob (John), *C.B., Bombay Artillery, see* †SCINDE IRREGULAR HORSE. *Record book of the S.I.H., *comp. by J. J.*, 2v, 1853–56.
Jacob (Joseph). Hardy bulbs for amateurs. 8°. 1924
Jacob (Mary Esther), *see* CAREW (E. M. H.) Crown *v.* Mrs. C.; Trial, *w. added paper*, The Carew case: Miss Jacob arrested, 1896–97.
Jacob (Max). Filibuth, ou la montre en or. 8e éd. s8°. [1922]
Le roi de Béotie. 2e éd. s8°. 1921
Jacob (*Lt.-Col.* **Samuel Swinton) & T. H. Hendley.**
Jeypore enamels. fol. 1886
Jacob (Violet), *wife of Arthur Jacob.*
Tales of my own country. s8°. 1922
Jacoba, *countess of Hainault & Holland, see* PUTNAM (R.) A mediaeval princess, J., 1401–36, 1904.
Jacobi (Charles Thomas).
Printing: practical treatise. 6th ed., repr. s8°. 1925
Some notes on books & printing. [4th ed.] 8°. 1912
Jacobi (Christian Ferd.) & J. H. Martius. De lotionibus Mohammedanorum exercit. prima. [P2744]. s4°. Lipsiæ. [1706]
Jacobi (Franz). Das Thorner Blutgericht 1724. [Verein f. Ref.-gesch. Schr., Jhrg. 13, Nr. 51/52]. 8°. Halle. 1896
Jacobi (Hermann).
see DHAṆAVĀLA. Bhavisatta Kaha: e. Jaina Legende in Apabhraṃśa; hrsg. H. J., 1918.
„ HARIBHADRA SŪRI. Sanatkumāracaritam; hrsg. H. J., 1921.
Jacobi (Joannes Nicolaus).
De vulneribus Jesu Christi tract. s8°. Lipsiæ. 1686
Jacobi (Johann). Hist. eccl. Arminianae a E. S. Cypriano adv. J. Clerici objectiones defensa. s8°. *n.p.* 1726
Jacobi (Johann Adolph). Eichenlaub auf Luther's Grab gestreut. 3e A. 4°. Erfurt. 1818
Jacobi (Johann Balthasar). Diss. de secta Jacobitarum. Praes. J. B. J., resp. H. Dunte. [P434]. s4°. Lipsiae. [1685]
Jacobi (Johann Christian). Mem. of the life & death of A. W. Boehm. Ann., Three favourite hymns [*by* P. Gerhard, *w. sep. tp. & pagin.*] s8°. 1735
see PSALMODIA Germanica; tr. J. C. J., 1722; 1765.
Jacobi (Johann Friedrich). Abhdln. ü. wicht. Gegenstände d. Relig. 2e verb. A. 4T. *in* 1v. s8°. Hannover. 1776–78
Jacobi (*Mrs.* **Mary Corinna Putnam),** *form. Putnam, wife of Abraham Jacobi, see* PUTNAM (R.) Life & letters of M. P. J., 1925.
Jacobite [JACOBITES]. The Forty-five, narr. by contemp. hands, 1922, *see* TERRY (C. S.), *ed.*
J. (The) & the Union, 1708, 15, 19, by contemp. hands, 1922, *see* TERRY (C. S.), *ed.*
*Some verses upon the insurrect. of the J., 1746, *see* TURNBULL (W.)
Jacobitism. *Hannibal at the gates: or, the progress of J., 1712, *see* DEFOE (D.)
Jacobs (Didericus). Diss. philolog. de adspersionibus Hebraeorum. s4°. Bremæ. 1725
Jacobs (Eduard). Heinrich Winckel u. d. Reformation im süd. Niedersachsen. [Verein f. Ref.-gesch. Schr., Jhrg. 13, Nr. 53]. 8°. Halle. 1896
Jacobs (Katharine), *see* UNITED STATES: LIB. OF CONGR. List of Amer. doct. diss. pr. in 1917, 1918; *prep. by K. J.*, 1921.
Jacobs (William Wymark).
A master of craft. s8°. L., *Tauchnitz.* 1901
Sea whispers. s8°. [1926]
Jacobsen (Emil). Sienes. Meister d. Trecento in d. Gemäldegalerie zu Siena. la8°. Str. 1907
Jacobsen (Jens Peter). Madame Marie Grubbe. Tr. T. Hammar. Pref. d'A. Bellessort. s8°. 1920
see BETHGE (H.) J. P. J.: e. Versuch, 1920.
Jacobsohn (Hermann). Arier u. Ugrofinnen. 8°. Göttingen. 1922
Jacobsthal (Paul). Aus d. Arch. Inst. d. Univ. Göttingen, 1, Vasen, nebst Abh. Συμποσιακά, 1912, *see* KÖNIGL. GESELLS. D. WISS. Z. GÖTT. Abhlgn., N.F., 14, 1913.
Jacobsz (Lucas), *called Lucas van Leyden, see* LUCAS, *van Leyden.*
Jacobus, *Cartusiensis, see* JÜTERBOCK (J. v.) Sermones de sanctis, sermones notabiles &c. per J. C., *n.d.*
Jacobus, *de Clusa, see* JÜTERBOCK (J. v.)
Jacobus, *monk of Kokkenobaphos, see* BRÉHIER (L.) Les miniatures des Homélies du moine Jacques & le théâtre relig. à Byzance, 1920.
Jacobus, *episc. Nisibenus, see* JAMES, *saint, bp. of Nisibis.*
Jacobus, *de Paradyso, see* JÜTERBOCK (J. v.)
Jacobus *Trajecti, see* VOECHT (J. DE).
Jacobus, *de Voragine, abp. of Genoa.* [Sermones. *Beg. fol. 1a*: H]vmane labilis vite de cursus &c. [*line 23*]: Incipiunt sermones dñicales ꝑ totũ annũ c[om]pilati ꝑ fratrem Jacobũ de voragine &c. *Ends*: Explicit magistri Jacobi de voragine liber sermonum &c. fol. *n.p. n.d.* [Strassburg, *C. W. or* Nuremberg, *A. Koberger?* 1473 ?]
336 leaves (prec. by 8 leaves of sim. paper cont. MS. index); without tp., pagin. or sign.; 34 lines to a page; final leaf blank.
The golden legend: lives of the saints. Tr. W. Caxton. Sel. & ed. by G. V. O'Neill. 8°. C. 1914
The golden legend. Eng. by W. Caxton. [repr.] 7v. s8°. [1922]
La légende dorée; M. Husz & P. Hongre, 1483. [Livres à grav. imp. à Lyon au 15s., 1]. 4°. Lyon. [1924]
Sermones dominicales. s8°. Venetiis. 1602
Sermones quadragesimales. [*b. w. h.* S. dominic., 1602]. s8°. Venetiis. 1602
see CHRIST. A stanzaic life of Christ: comp. f. the Legenda aurea &c.; ed. F. A. Foster, 1926.
„ FRERE (W. H.), *ed.* Expos. de la Messe f. La legende dorée, 1899.
Jacoby (Felix). Die Fragmente d. griech. Historiker (F. Gr. Hist.) T1, 2, A, Bi, C. la8°. 1923–27
1, Genealogie u. Mythographie. 2, Zeitgesch.
Jacoby (Ludwig S.)
Gesch. d. Methodismus. 2T [*in* 1v]. s8°. Bremen. 1870
Jacolliot (Louis).
Occult science in India &c. Tr. W. L. Felt. 8°. [1884]
Jacopone, *da Todi* [BENEDETTI (G. DE')]. 2 trattati, volgariz. da F. Belcari, *see* BALCARI (F.) Prose, t3, 1843.
see PACHEU (J.) J. de T., 1228–1306, 1914.
„ STAAF (E. S.) Sur une lauda de J. da T., 1927.
„ UNDERHILL (E.) A Franciscan poet, J. da T., 1926.
Jacoubet (Henri). Le Comte de Tressan & les orig. du genre troubadour. 8°. 1923
Jacovleff (Alexandre), *see* TCHOU-KIA-KIEN. Le théâtre chinois: peintures &c. d'A. J., 1922.
Jacquemart (Albert). Les merveilles de la céramique. 3p. [p1, 2e éd.] s8°. 1868–69
Jacques (Hubert).
L'aventure riffaine & ses dessous polit. 8°. 1927
Jadhava (Khashero). Wake up princes. s8°. Bombay. 1926
Jadrinzew (N.), *see* YADRINTSEV (N. M.)
Jaenicke (Joseph Daniel). Memoirs of J., a fellow labourer of Schwartz at Tanjore. s8°. 183[illegible]

Jaenisch, *see* JÄNISCH.
Jaén Morente (Antonio).
Hist. de la ciudad de Córdoba. s8°. Córdoba. 1921
Ja'far Sharif [JAFFUR SHURREEF]. Islam in India, or the Qānūn-i-Islām. Comp. under dir. of G. A. Herklots, n. ed. rev. &c. by W. Crooke. s8°. 1921
Jagadīsa Ayyar (P. V.) South Indian customs. Foreword by K. S. Rāmaswami Sastry. s8°. Madras. 1925
Jagd. Samml. v. Kupferstichen &c. d. 16.–19. Jhdts. auf d. Jagd. Versteig., Nov. 1921, durch C. G. Boerner. [*Illust.*] 4°. L. 1921
Jagel (Abraham), *see* ABRAHAM, *Jaghel ben Hananiah de' Galicchi.*
Jäger u. Prinzessin: e. neuarab. Märchen aus Jerusalem; [hrsg. E. Littmann], *see* KLEINE TEXTE, 150, 1923.
Jäger (Andreas). De lingua vetust. Europae, Scytho-Celtica & Gothica. s4°. Wittenbergae. [1686]
Jäger (Fritz). Forsch. ü. d. diluviale Klima in Mexico, 1926, *see* PETERMANNS MITT. Ergnzb., 41, 1927.
Jäger (G. F.) Über d. Zeitalter Obadja's. [P2655]. 4°. Tübingen. 1837
Jäger (Gustav), *see* SCHNEIDER (G. H.) J.'s Entdeckung d. Seele, 1879.
Jager (*l'abbé* **Jean Nicolas).** Hist. de Photius, patriarche de Constantinople, auteur du schisme des Grecs. 2e éd. 8°. 1845
Jäger (Joh. Wolfgang).
Compendium theologiae &c. ed. 2a. s8°. Stuttgardiae. 1702
„ „ .... ed. 5a. s8°. Stuttgardiae. 1740
Diss. de Johannae Leadææ vita, visionibus &c. Praes. J. W. J., resp. J. V. Harpprechto &c. [P597]. s4°. Tubingæ. 1712
Epistola ad Poiretum. [*b. w. h.* Exam. theol. myst., 1709]. s8°. Tubingae. 1708
Exam. Quietismi. Praes. J. W. J. [resp.] J. B. Knöbel & J. C. Schüz. Adj. Speneri Judicium. [P443]. s4°. Tubingae. [1715]
Examen theol. mysticae vet. & nov., Fenelonis de Salignac, Card. Petruccii, P. Poireti & M. de Molinos placita &c. [*Add.* Diss. de enthusiasmo, *by* J. W. J. *&* De J. Boehmio judicium H. Mori &c.] s8°. Francofurti. 1709
Examen theol. novae, et maxime Poireti ejusque magistrae Mad. de Bourignon. [*b. w. h.* Exam. theol. myst., 1709]. s8°. Francofurti. 1708
Gallia discors, in causa Pietistico mystica. Exerc. prop. à J. W. J., resp. M. F. Brecht & J. C. Kellero. [P443]. s4°. Tubingae. [1715]
Hist. eccl. cum parallelismo profanae in qua conclavia pontif. aperiuntur & sectae omnes recensentur [1600–1710]. 2t. [*b. in* 1. t2 *in* 2p, *w. sep. pagin.*] fol. Hamburgi. 1709–17
Judicium de 2 adversariis J. Lookio & P. Poireto eorumque pugna de ratione et fide. [*b. w. h.* Exam. theol. myst., 1709]. s8°. Francofurti. 1708
Jus Dei foederale delin., exam. B. Pufendorfii Jus feciale divinum &c. s8°. Tubingae. 1698
Nova purgatio animae post mortem, excocta in cerebro Mad. Bourrignion & P. Poireti &c., rejecta ab J. W. J. Resp. C. C. Osiandro. [P426]. s4°. Tubingae. 1716
Tractatus de Ecclesia. Acc. dilucidatio &c. [*which is wanting*]. s4°. Tubingae. 1711
see ETTENHUSIUS (J. B.) Epist. ad L. A. Rechenbergium, examen J. W. J. In B. Pufendorfii, Jus div. feciale &c., 1698.
Jäger (Walter). Weissruthenien. Land, Bewohner, Gesch. &c. Hrsg. v. W. J. 8°. [1919]
Jäger (Werner Wilhelm). Neue philol. Untersuchungen. Hrsg. v. W. J. H1. 8°. 1926
see OCELLUS, *Lucanus.* Text u. Komm. v. R. Harder, 1926. [1.]
Jager-Schmidt (V. A.) Charly, comédie, *see* ŒUVRES libres, 48, 1925.
Jaggard (Walter Robert) & F. E. Drury. Architectural building construction: text book. v2, pl, 2. 8°. C. 1922–23
Jaggard (William), *see* BOOK-AUCTION RECORDS; gen. index, 1902–12; by W. J., 1924.
Jagić (Vatroslav). Ein Beitr. z. Erforsch. d. altkirchenslav. Evangelientexte (Evang. Bucovinense), 1916, *see* KAIS. AKAD. D. W. ZU WIEN. Sitz., B180, 1917.
Zum altkirchenslaw. Apostolus, 1, Grammat. u. Krit., 2, 3, Lexical., 1919–20, *see* KAIS. AKAD. D. W. ZU WIEN. Sitzb., B191, 193, 197, 1922.
Jago (Francis Horatio), *see* SAMSON (H.) F. H. [J.] & h. 3 companions, 1912.
Jago (Richard). Poet. works. Coll. by T. Park. [*b. w.* Green (M.) Poet. works, 1808]. s8°. 1808
Jahāngīr, *emperor of Hindustan.*
see BANKIPORE. Reprod. of illust. f. 3 Pers. MSS. [Bâdshâh Namah: lives of J. & Shāh Jahān &c.] in Publ. Libr. at B., 1920.
„ GLADWIN (F.) Hist. of Hindostan &c., v1 (J.), 1788.
„ PRASAD (B.) Hist. of J., 1922.

Jahier (Piero). Con me e con gli Alpini. s8°. [1920]
Jahn (Johann). De necessitate studii ling. Biblic. &c., *see* LEE (S.) Sylloge libr. or., 1821.
Elementa Aramaicae linguae, Lat. redd. &c. ab A. Oberleitner. [App. *w. sep. pagin.*] 8°. Viennae. 1820
Jahn (Otto) [IAHN]. W. A. Mozart. Neubearb. &c. v. H. Abert. 6. A. 2T. 8°. L. 1923
Jahrbuch der Bücherpreise. Bearb. v. F. Rupp. 1918–19 (Jhrg. 13–14). s8°. L. 1920
Jahrbuch d. Königlich Preussischen Kunstsammlungen. B40–48. 4°. 1919–27
With Beihefte, *as below.*
Rosenthal (E.) Dürers Buchmalereien, 1928. [49.]
Rumohr (C. F. L. F. v.) Briefe an Bunsen ü. Erwerbungen für d. Berliner Museum; mitgeteilt v. F. Stock. [46.]
Amtliche Berichte aus d. Königl. Kunstsammlungen. Beiblatt z. Jahrbuch &c. Jahrgang 35. 8°. 1913–14
Jahrbuch d. Völkerrechts. In Verbindung mit Staatsminister Asser, Prof. v. Bar [*& others*]. Hrsg. v. T. Niemeyer u. K. Strupp. B6–9. 8°. München. 1919–26
B6, 8 *have 2nd tp.* Die völkerrechtl. Urkunden d. Weltkrieges, B4, 6.
B7 *has 2nd tp.* Völker. Chronologie d. Weltkrieges, 1914–19.
B9 (Sonderband) Friedensverträge &c., 1919–26.
Jahrbuch f. Gesetzgebung, Verwaltung u. Volkswirtschaft im Deutschen Reiche. [Schmollers Jahrbuch]. Jhrg. 44–51. 8°. München. 1920–27
Jahrbücher für Nationalökonomie u. Statistik. 3e Folge. B58–72. 8°. Jena. 1919–27
Jahresberichte üb. d. Veränderungen u. Fortschritte im Militairwesen. Hrsg. v. H. v. Löbell. Jhrg. 1–9 (1874–82). 8°. 1875–83
Jahresernte (Die): Auswahl jüngster deut. Dichtung, Jhrg. 1–5, 1923–27, *see* VESPER (W.)
Jaillot, *The family of*, *see* FORDHAM (*Sir* H. G.) Listes gén. des postes de Fr., 1708–79 & the J., 1922.
Jaillot (Hubert Alexis). Tabula regni Poloniae, ducatus Lithuaniae &c. *folded.* 8°. Amsterdam. [1740 ?]
Jaimini Bharata (The), 1852, *see* LAKSHMĪSA, *Dēvapura.*
Jai Singh II, *maharajah of Jaipur*, *see* KAYE (G. R.) Guide to the old observatories [founded by J. S.] at Delhi, Jaipur &c., 1920.
Jakinth, *see* BICHURIN (J.)
Jakobsen (Jakob). Etymologisk ordbog over det Norrøne sprog på Shetland. la8°. 1921
Jaksch (August v.), *see* CARINTHIA. Mon. hist. duc. Car.; hrsg. v. A. v. J., 4B, 1896–1915.
Jakubczyk (Carl).
Dante, s. Leben u. s. Werke. s8°. Frieburg im Br. 1921
Jakubowski (James), B. Srocki & E. Maliszewski. Poland & Lithuania. The question of Wilna. [L'Est Polonais. P2519]. 8°. Warsaw. 1921
Jakuschkin (J. D.), *see* YAKUSHKIN (I. D.)
Jal (Auguste). Archéologie navale. 2t. 8°. 1840
see MUSÉE ROYAL DE FRANCE. M. R. de F., ou coll. gravée des chefs-d'œ.: texte réd. par A. J., 1827.
Jalāl-al-Dīn, *Rūmī, Maulānā.* The Mathnawí. Ed., w. crit. notes, tr., & comm. by R. A. Nicholson. [E. J. W. Gibb Mem. Series, N.S., 4]. v1, 2. la8°. Leiden. 1925–26
see DAVIS (F. H.) Jalálu'd-Dín Rúmí, 1920.
Jalla (Jean). Hist. des Vaudois des Alpes & de leurs colonies. [rev. ed.] 8°. Pignerol. 1922
Jaloux (Edmond).
L'age d'or. s8°. [1926]
L'alcyone. s8°. [1925]
Au-dessus de la ville. Roman. s8°. [1920]
L'aventure nocturne, *see* ŒUVRES libres, 82, 1928.
La branche morte, roman, *see* ŒUVRES libres, 23, 1923.
Le coin des cypres. s8°. [1925]
Le dernier jour de la création, *see* ŒUVRES libres, 63, 1926.
L'escalier d'or. 8°. [1922]
L'esprit des livres. [t]1. s8°. [1923]
L'éventail de crêpe. s8°. [1923]
Fumées dans la campagne. Roman. s8°. [1920]
O toi que j'eusse aimée. [16e éd.] s8°. [1926]
O toi que j'eusse aimée: nouvelle, *see* ŒUVRES libres, 49, 1925.
Rainer Maria Rilke. s8°. 1927
Sophiana, roman, *see* ŒUVRES libres, 27, 1923.
Jamaica. J. at Brit. Emp. Exhib., Wembley, 1924. [P2749]. 8°. 1924
J. in 1924. Hdbk. for visitors &c. By F. Cundall. 9th year of issue. 8°. Kingston. 1924
Jamaspji (Hoshangji), *see* HOSHANGJI JAMASPJI ASA.
James II, *king of Aragon.* Acta Aragonensia: Quellen aus d. diplomat. Korresp. J. II (1291–1327). Hrsg. H. Finke. B3. 8°. 1922

James I, *King of Gt. Brit. & Ir.* Award by James VI as to succ. to barony of Sanquhar, *see* ABBOTSFORD CLUB. Misc., v1, 1837.
A counterblaste to tobacco, 1604, *see* Essayes of a prentise, 1869, *below.*
Dæmonologie (1597)—Newes from Scotland: life & death of Dr. Fian, a notable sorcerer &c. (1591). [*W. sep. pagin.* Bodley Head quartos; ed. G. B. Harrison]. s8°. [1924]
Epistolæ virorum clar. ad J., *see* ABBOTSFORD CLUB. Misc., v1, 1837.
Essayes of a prentise, in the divine art of poesie, 1585 [*&*] A counterblaste to tobacco, 1604. Ed. E. Arber. [Eng. repr. *b. w.* Howell (J.) Instructions, 1868]. s8°. [1869]
Letters &c. rel. to Gt. Brit. dur. reign of J. I, *see* ABBOTSFORD CLUB. Misc., v1, 1837.
Letters to the Countess Dowager of Angus, *see* ABBOTSFORD CLUB. Misc., v1, 1837.
Meditatio in Cap. 27 S. Matth. v. 27, 28, 29. s8°. Londini. 1620
The Psalmes of David. Tr. K. J. [*Completed by Sir W. Alexander. engr. tp.*] s8°. [O. 1631]
„ „ ....s8°. [1637?]
Psalms in metre, 1712, *see* PRAYER BOOK. B. of C.P. for use of Ch. of Scot., 1712.
Remonstrance for the right of kings &c. agst. an oration of Card. of Perron, Jan. 15, 1615. Tr. R. B. [*b. w.* Fitzherbert (T.) Reply &c., 1614]. s4°. C. 1619
To the right high &c. Prince J. An humble supplication for toleration &c. [P2660]. s4°. 1609
Truth brought to light: or the hist. of the 1st 14 years of J. I. 4p. [*w. sep. pagin. & tps.*] s8°. 1692
1, Happy state of Eng. &c. 2, Divorce betw. Lady F. Howard & R. Earl of Essex; also arraign. of Sir J. Ellis about the murther of Sir T. Overbury. 3, Declar. of H.M.'s revenue. 4, Commissions for burning of 2 hereticks &c.
see BARLOW (W.) The summe &c. of Conf. w. clergy at Hampton Court, 1603, 1604.
„ BELLARMINO (*il card.* R. F. R.) Apologia pro responsione sua ad librum J., 1609.
„ COEFFETEAU (N.) Response à l'advertissement par J. I, 1615.
„ CONFESSION gén. de la vraye foy &c. signée par le roy &c., 1603.
„ DU MOULIN (P.) De monarchia temporali pontif. Romani liber; liber J. vindic., 1614; 1716.
„ GARGÀNO (G. S.) Scapigliatura ital. a Londra sotto G. I &c., 1923.
„ HARRY (G. O.) Genealogy of J. k. of Gt. Britain, 1604.
„ MEYER (A. O.) Clemens VIII u. J. I v. Eng., 1904.
„ RAIT (R. S.) & A. I. CAMERON, *edd.* King J.'s secret: negot. betw. Eliz. & J. rel. to execut. of M., Q. of Scots, 1927.
„ SCHOPPE (C.) Ecclesiasticus auctoritate Jacobi oppositus, 1611.
„ STIRLING (W. A., *earl of*). *Complaint of the muses upon Sir W. A. [*probably by J.*], 1837.
„ *SUPPLICATION (THE) of certaine Masse-priests falsely called Catholikes, 1604.
„ WILSON (A.) Hist. of Gt. Brit. being life & reign of J. I, 1653.
„ WINSTANLEY (L.) Macbeth &c.: rel. of the play to personal hist. of J. I &c., 1922.

James II, *King of Gt. Brit. & Ireland.* *An Account of the trans. of J. in Ireland. Wherein is contain'd the Act of Attainder past at Dublin, 1689. [P2653]. s4°. 1690
Cat. of coll. of pictures belong. to J. II [*signed* W. Chiffinch], added: Cat. of pictures in closet of Q. Caroline [*w. sep. pagin. b. w.* Charles I. Cat., 1757]. s4°. 1758
The congrat. of sev. kings &c. of Europe to J. II on the birth of the P. of Wales, 1688, 1701, *see* JAMES EDWARD [STUART].
H.M. late letter in vindic., St. Germans en Laye, 14 Jan., 1688/9. [*no tp.* P2572]. s4°. [1689]
Papers of devotion. Reprod. of MS. in poss. of B. R. Townley Balfour. Intr. by G. Davies. [Roxburghe Club]. 4°. O. 1925
*A remonstrance & protest. of all good Protestants agst. deposing J. II. [P2572]. s4°. 1689
*Second narr. of the signal victory under Duke of York, agst. fleet of The U.N., 3rd June 1665. s8°. 1665
see ALBERTI (G.) Dispacci al Senato Veneto, 1673, matrimonio di Maria con Giacomo, 1890.
„ ANGLETERRE. *Hist. des révolutions d'A. sous J. II &c., 1689.
„ POPERY. *Brief hist. of the rise &c. of Popery, 1690.

James II, *King of Gt. Brit. & Ireland [continued].*
see SANDFORD (F.) Hist. of the coron. of J. II, 1687.
„ VELLACOTT (P. C.) Struggle of J. II w. the Univ. of Cambridge, 1924.

James, *Saint & Apostle, "the Greater."*
see KING (G. G.) Way of St. J., 3v, 1920.

James, *Saint & Apostle, "the Greater," Order of.*
see RUIZ DE VERGARA Y ALAVA (F.) Regla y establ. nuevos de la Orden &c. del Apostol Santiago &c., 1752.

James, *Saint, "the less."* [*See also* BIBLE: JAMES]. Liturgy of St. J. (Georgian), *var. ed. & tr., see* ARCHIERATIKON.

James, *Saint, bp. of Nisibis* [HAKOB, *Mdzbn*]. [*Hist. of St. J. (*foll. by* Hilarion & Ignatius of Antioch). *In Armenian.* Soferq Hayk., v22]. s8°. i Venetik. 1861
Sermones cum praef. &c., & Diss. de Ascetis. fol. Romae. 1756
see AFRAHAT. Girq Zgon [Book called Wise, *wrongly attrib. to J.*], 1824.

James [*de Savoie*], *duc de Nemours, see* NEMOURS (JACQUES *de Savoie, duc de*).

James IV, *king of Scotland.* *Batayle of Floddon-felde [*w.* App. cont. Notes &c. regard. death &c. of J. IV], *see* MAIDMENT (J.) & R. PITCAIRN. Nugae derelictae, 1822.
see GREENE (R.) *The Scottish hist. of J. IV, *play*, 1598, 1921.

James Edward [Stuart], *prince, the [old] Pretender* [†JAMES EDWARD FRANCIS [STUART], *Prince of Wales &c.*] The congrat. of sev. kings &c. of Europe to James II on the birth of the P. of Wales. W. passages in the addresses pres. to Richard Cromwell, 1658. s8°. 1701
see DEFOE (D.) *Hannibal at the gates; w. the pres. danger of the P., 1712.
„ LOUIS XIV, *king.* *The Great Bastard; tr., 1689.

James (C. H.) & F. R. Yerbury. Mod. Eng. houses & interiors. Ed. C. H. J. & F. R. Y. 4°. 1925
Small houses for the community. Foreword by R. Unwin. 4°. 1924

James (Edith Emily Coulson). Gli autoritratti di F. Raibolini, detto Il Francia. [P2731]. 8°. Bologna. 1922
Una pittura d. Francia, Dresda. [P2876]. la8°. Bologna. 1927

James (Edwin Oliver), *see* SELWYN (E. G.), *ed.* Essays, catholic & crit. [by E. O. J. &c.], 1926.

James (Frank), *bandit.* *Trial of F. J. for murder; w. confess. of D. Liddil & C. Hite, & hist. of the "James gang." s8°. Kansas. [1898]

James (George Payne Rainsford), *see* ELLIS (S. M.) The solitary horseman: life of G. P. R. J., 1927.

James (Henry), *novelist.*
The altar of the dead. s8°. [1916]
Daisy Miller. 2nd imp. s8°. [1919]
A little tour in France. [2nd impr. of n. ed.] 8°. 1922
The Madonna of the future & o. t. n. ed. s8°. 1880
Notes & reviews [1864–66]. Pref. by P. de Chaignon la Rose. 8°. Cambridge, *Mass.* 1921
The portrait of a lady. [n. ed.] 2v. 8°. 1921
Refugees in Chelsea. 4°. *f.p.c., Ashendene Press.* [1920]
The turn of the screw. 4th impr. s8°. [1920]
„ „ 6th impr. s8°. [1925]
see BOSANQUET (T.) H. J. at work, 1924.
„ BROOKS (VAN W.) Pilgrimage of H. J., 1928.
„ EDGAR (P.) H. J., man & author, 1927.

James (Henry), *of New York, 1811–82.*
Lectures & miscellanies. s8°. Redfield. 1852
Moralism & Xty. s8°. N.Y. 1850
Society the redeemed form of man. Letters. 8°. Boston, *Mass.* 1879
The old & new theology, & The Church of Christ not an ecclesiasticism, a letter. s8°. 1861
The secret of Swedenborg: elucid. of h. doctrine. 8°. Boston [*Mass.*] 1869

James (Henry Rosher).
Our Hellenic heritage. 2v. (1, p1, 2; 2, p3, 4). s8°. 1921–24
„ „ ....[*a. issue of* v2, p3 *b. sep.*] s8°. 1922

James (Herman Gerlach).
Constit. system of Brazil. [C.I. of Wash.] la8°. Wash. 1923
Local gov. in the U.S. 8°. N.Y. 1921

James (John Angell), *1785–1859.* The life & letters of J. A. J., incl. autobiog. Ed. R. W. Dale. 8°. 1861
see CAMPBELL (J.) J. A. J., his hist. &c., 1860.

James (Katherine). The city of contrasts. s8°. 1915

James (Montague Rhodes).
Drawings of M. Paris, *see* WALPOLE Soc., vol. 14, 1926.
An Eng. Bible-picture book of the 14th c., *see* WALPOLE Soc., 11th ann. vol., 1922–23.
Eton & King's. Recoll., 1875–1925. 8°. 1926

James (Montague Rhodes) [*continued*].
The list of libraries prefixed to Cat. of J. Boston &c., *see* COLLECTANEA Franciscana, v2, 1922.
Lists of MSS. form. in Peterborough Abbey library. [Bibliograph. Soc. Trans., Suppl. 5]. 8°. O. 1926
The wanderings & homes of MSS. s8°. 1919
A warning to the curious & o. ghost stories. 4th impr. s8°. 1925
see APOCRYPHA. The Apocryphal N.T., w. o. narr. & fragm.; tr. M. R. J., 1924.
,, —— Lat. infancy gospels; ed. M. R. J., 1927.
,, BENSON (A. C.) A. C. B. as seen by friends [*i.e.* M. R. J. &c.], 1925.
,, BIBLE: GENESIS. Illust[s]. of the Bk. of G., MS. Egerton 1894, w. intr. by M. R. J., 1921.
,, ——: PSALMS. Two E. Anglian Psalters: the Bromholm P., 1523, descr. by M. R. J., 1926.
,, ——: REVELATION. Apocalypse in Lat. & French (Bodleian MS. Douce 180); descr. by M. R. J., 1922.
,, CAMBRIDGE: CHRIST'S COLLEGE, CLARE, EMMANUEL, JESUS, MAGDALENE, QUEENS', ST. CATHERINE'S *&* SIDNEY SUSSEX *for catalogues of MSS., by J.*
,, DEE (J.) List of MSS. form. owned by Dr. J. D., w. pref. &c. by M. R. J., 1921.
,, EDWARD, *the Confessor*. La estoire de St. Ædward le Rei &c.; intr. by M. R. J., 1920.
,, JOHN RYLANDS LIB., *M'ter*. Descr. cat. of Latin MSS., by M. R. J., 2v, 1921.
,, PETERBOROUGH PSALTER &c., descr. by M. R. J., 1921.
,, SPECULUM humanæ salvationis; descr. & pref. by M. R. J., 1926.

James (Norman G. Brett-), *see* BRETT-JAMES (N. G.)

James (Richard Lloyd Langford-), *see* LANGFORD-JAMES (R. Ll.)

James (Sydney Rhodes).
Seventy years: random remin. &c. 8°. 1926

James (Thomas), *D.D., Sub-dean of Wells*. Bellum Papale, sive concordia discors Sixti V & Clementis VIII circa Hieronymianam ed. &c. s8°. Londini. 1678
A treatise of the corruption of Scripture &c. With ans. unto J. Gretser & A. Possevine Jesuites &c. 5p. s4°. 1611
see INDEX gen. libr. prohib. &c. in usum Bibl. Bodleianae design. per T. J., 1627.

James (Thomas Horton) [*ps.* RUBIO]. Six months in S. Australia; w. some acc. of Port Philip & Portland Bay &c. s8°. 1838

James (W. A.), *honorary librarian of Southwell Minster*. Acc. of the grammar & song schools of the Collegiate Church of Southwell. 8°. Lincoln. 1927

James (W. P.) The lure of the map. s8°. [1920]

James (Will). Cowboys north & south. 8°. N.Y. 1924

James (William), *prof. at Harvard*.
Coll. essays & reviews. 8°. 1920
Letters. Ed. Henry James. 2v. 8°. 1920
The varieties of relig. experience. [Gifford Lect., 1901–02]. 33rd impr. 8°. 1922
see KNOX (H. V.) Philos. of W. J., 1914.
see PERRY (R. B.) Annot. bibliography of wr. of W. J., 1920.
,, SANTAYANA (G.) Character & opinion in the U.S., w. remin. of W. J. &c., 1920.

James (William Milburne). The Brit. Navy in adversity: st. of War of Amer. Independence. 8°. 1926

James (Winifred). Out of the shadows. 8°. 1924

Jameson (*Mrs.* Anna). Characteristics of women, w. 50 etchings. 2nd ed., corr. & enl. 2v. 8°. 1833
Legends of the Madonna as repres. in the fine arts. [2nd ed., repr.] 8°. 1907
Legends of the monastic orders. n. impr. 1905
Sacred & legendary art. 9th ed. 2v. 8°. 1883

Jameson (John Franklin).
The arrival of the pilgrims. [P2710]. s8°. Providence, R.I. 1920

Jameson (*Rt. Hon. Sir* Leander Starr), *Bart.*, ["*Dr.* JAMESON"], *see* COLVIN (I. D.) Life of J., 2v, 1922.

Jameson (Robert Francis). Notices of the Reformation in the S.-W. Provinces of France. 8°. 1839

Jameson (Storm).
The clash. s8°. 1922
The happy highways. s8°. 1920
Lady Susan & life. s8°. 1923
Modern drama in Europe. 8°. [1920]
The pitiful wife. s8°. [1923]
Three kingdoms. s8°. [1926]

Jameson (William), *prof. of hist. in the Univ. of Glasgow*. Roma Racoviana & Racovia Romana, *i.e.* Papistarum & Socinistarum harmonia. s4°. Edinb. 1702

Jami. Le Béharistan. Tr. H. Massé. 8°. 1925
Salámán & Absál. Tr. E. Fitzgerald. s8°. 1904
see DAVIS (F. H.) Jami, repr., 1918.

Jamieson (John). Hist. acc. of the anc. Culdees of Iona, & of their settlements in Scot., Eng. & Ir. 4°. E. 1811

Jamieson (Thomas). Nature's serious tale as revealed by science &c. 8°. Aberdeen. 1926

Jammes (Francis).
Œuvres. [t2–5]. 8°. 1921–26
2, Quatorze prières—Elégies—Tristesses—Eglogues—Tableau d'automne—Tableau d'hiver—En Dieu—L'église habillée de feuilles.
3, Clara d'Ellébeuse—Almaïde d'Etremont—Pomme d'Anis.
4, Le roman du Lièvre—Des choses—Contes—Notes sur des Oasis & sur Alger—Le 15 août à Laruns—Deux proses—Notes sur J. J. Rousseau & Mme. de Warens—Pensée des jardins.
5, Méditations—L'auberge des doulers—L'auberge sur la route—L'auberge des poètes—Quelques hommes—L'évol. spirituelle de Mme. de Noailles—La brebis égarée.
L'amour, les muses & la chasse. [Mém., 2]. s8°. [1922]
Les caprices du poète. [Mém., 3]. s8°. [1923]
Cloches pour deux mariages. Le mariage basque—Le mariage de raison. 4e éd. s8°. 1923
De l'âge divin à l'âge ingrat. [Mém., 1]. s8°. [1921]
Lavigerie. 8°. [1927]
Le livre de Saint Joseph. s8°. [1921]
Ma France poétique. 3e éd. s8°. 1926
Le premier [Le deuxième *&* Le troisième] livre des quatrains. 8°. 1923–24
Les Robinsons basques. 9e éd. s8°. 1925
Le roman du lièvre. 20e éd. s8°. 1920

Jamot (Paul), *see* LOUVRE. La peinture, école franç., 19 s., p2, par P. J., 1927.

Jan (Johann Wilhelm) [IANUS (I. G.)] De antiq. canonum Apostolic. [P433]. s4°. Vitembergae. 1740

Jancsó (Benedek). A román nemzetiségi törekvések története és jelenlegi állapota. 2K. 8°. 1896–99
Szabadságharczunk és a Dako-Román törekvések. 8°. Budapest. 1895
Hungary & Roumania. [P2567]. s8°. 1921
The Székelys. [P2578]. 8°. Budapest. 1921
see AJTAY (J.), B. J. & A. KOVÁCS. The Transylvanian q., 1921.

Janda (Anna). Die Barschalken: e. Beitr. z. Sozialgesch. d. M.-a. 8°. Wien. 1926

Jandonus (Joannes), *see* DULLAERT (J.), *de Janduno*.

Jandyt (Václav). *Gramm. linguæ Boemicæ. Insertæ, Regulæ orthogr. R. P. Konstantii. ed. 4a. s8°. Pragae. 1739
,, ,, ...ed. 5a. s8°. Pragae. 1753

Jane, *of Austria, consort of Francis, grand duke of Tuscany*, *see* VETTORI (P.) Orazione d. lode d. seren. Giovanna d'Austria, 1566.

Jane II, *queen of Naples*, *see* JOANNA II, *q. of Naples*.

Jane (Frederick T.)
Silhouettes of British fighting ships. s8°. [1914]

Jane (Lionel Cecil). The admin. of the Colons in Española (1493–1500). [21e Congrès Internat. d. Américanistes. P2851]. la8°. [La Haye. 1924]
The govt. of N. de Ovando in Española (1501–09). [*No tp.* P2731]. 8°. [1923]

Janelli (Giovanni Battista).
Dizion. biogr. dei Parmigiani illust. &c. 8°. Geneva. 1877

Janes (Edmund S.), *D.D., bp. of Method. Episcopal Church, see* RIDGAWAY (H. B.) The life of E. S. J., 1882.

Janet (Pierre).
De l'angoisse à l'extase. [t]1. la8°. 1926
La médecine psychol. s8°. 1923
La pensée intérieure & s. troubles. 6 fasc. [*in* 1v. *typescr.*] 8°. 1927
Psychologie pathol. [Extr. du Manuel du baccalauréat, p2]. s8°. 1925
TRANSLATIONS.
Principles of psychotheraphy. Tr. H. M. & E. R. Guthrie. 8°. [1925]
TRANSLATIONS [*continued*].
Psychol. healing. Hist. & clinical study. Tr. E. & C. Paul. 2v. 8°. [1925]
see PSYCHOLOGY (INTERNAT. CONGR. OF). 4e Congr., 1900; Comte rendu des séances &c., publ. P. J., 1901.

Janeway (John), *1633–57*, *see* JACKSON (T.) Lib. of Xtn. biog., v2, J. J., by James Janeway, 1837.
see WESLEY (J.) An extr. of the life of J. J., 1753.

Jani (Johann Hermann). Comm. de Luthero Biblici studii instauratore. [P2628]. s4°. Halae Magd. [1730]

Jänichen (Johann Christian). Caussas a Luthero susceptae Reformationis exhib. J. C. J. [P2628]. s4°. Vitembergae. 1755

Jänicke (Hermann) [JAENICKE]. Die deutsche u. d. brandenb.-preuss. Gesch. 10e verb. A. T2. (1648–1909). 8°. 1910

Jänicke (Jos. Dan.), *see* JAENICKE (J. D.)
Janicki (S.)
Industrial reconstruction in Poland. [P2435]. s8°. 1920
The hist. & pres. conditions of the oil industry in Galicia. [P2520]. 8°. 1921
Janin (Jules Gabriel).
La Normandie. 3e éd., rev. & corr. la8°. 1862
Jänisch (C. F.) *Découvertes sur le cavalier (aux échecs). 8°. St. Pétersbourg. 1837
Janitor, *ps.* The feet of the young men. 8°. 1928
Jannasch (*Fraülein* Lilli). German militarism at work: docs. & notes; ed. L. J. Intr. by F. de Marwicz. Tr. J. Pollock. 8°. *Cayme Press.* 1926
Jannaway (Frank G.) Palestine & the world. 8°. [1922]
Janni (Ettore). Machiavelli. 8°. Milano. 1927
Jännicke (E. [Friedrich]), *see* GRÄSSE (J. G. T.) & E. J. Führer für Sammler v. Porzellan u. Fayence &c., 15e A., 1919.
Janowski (Jan Nepomucen). Les dern. momens de la Révol. de Pologne en 1831, depuis l'attaque de Varsovie &c. s8°. 1833
Jansen (Marin Henri), *1817–93* [JANSSEN]. Het leven van een vloothouder. Gedenkschr. v. M. H. J. Uitg. S. P. L'H. Naber. [Hist. Genoots. Werken, s3, 48]. 8°. Utrecht. 1925
Jansen (Max), H. Grauert & J. Strieder.
Studien z. Fugger-Gesch. H5–7. 8° & 4°. München. 1915–23
5, Die Fugger u. d. schmalkald. Krieg; v. H. J. Kirch.
6, A. Daucher u. d. Fuggerkapelle bei St. Anna in Augsburg; v. P. M. Halm.
7, Hans Dernschwam's Tagebuch e. Reise nach Konstantinopel u. Kleinasien, 1553–5; hrsg. F. Babinger.
—— **& L. Schmitz-Kallenberg.** Historiographie u. Quellen d. deut. Gesch. bis 1500, 2e A, 1914, *see* GRUNDR. D. GESCHICHTSWISS.; Meister, 1vii, 1914.
Jansen (Werner).
Gudrun. Das Buch Liebe. Roman. s8°. Braunschweig. 1920
Jansenism. *A case of conscience, propos'd to, & decided by 40 doctors of the Faculty of Paris, in favour of J. [*Pref. letter signed* S. A. C. D.] s8°. 1703
Jansénistes. *Dict. des livres J., 4t, 1755, *see* COLONIA (D. DE).
Les enluminures du fameux almanach des PP. Jesuites &c., 1683, *see* LE MAISTRE DE SACY (I. L.)
Jansenius (Cornelius), *bp. of Ypres.*
see BENITEZ DE LUGO (C.) Concursus Dei prævius & efficax &c.; à J. &c. erroribus vindic., 5t, 1737.
„ *ENTRETIEN d'un docteur de la maison de Sorbonne &c. touch. le fait de J., 1703.
„ VIVA (D.) Damnatae theses ab Alex. VII, Innocentio XI, & Alex. VIII necnon J. ad theol. trutinam &c., 1749.
J'anson, *The family of, see* I'ANSON.
Janson (Kristofer). The spell-bound fiddler. Tr. A. Forestier. Intr. by R. B. Anderson. 2nd ed. s8°. Chicago. 1892
Jansonius (Robertus). Brevis diss. de visionibus cap. 13 & 17 Apocalypseos. [*b. w.* Vaesarti (A.) Chron. prophet., 1682]. s8°. *n.p. n.d.*
Janssen (Barent) [JANSZOON (B.)] Wijdtloopigh verhael van tgene de 5 schepen, 1598–99, *see* WIEDER (F. C.) De reis v. Mahu &c., d1, 1923.
Janssen (C. Luplau), *see* LUPLAU JANSSEN (C.)
Janssen (Johannes). Hist. of the German people after close of Middle Ages. Index vol. 8°. 1925
see BOSSERT (G.) Württemberg u. J. [*crit. of J.'s Gesch. d. deut. Volkes &c.*], 2T, 1884.
Janssen (Marin Henri), *see* JANSEN (M. H.)
Janssenius (Nicolaus). Animadv. & scholia in Apologiam nuper ed. de vita & morte Joannis Duns Scoti adv. A. Bzovium. s8°. Coloniae Agripp. 1622
Janszoon (Barent), *see* JANSSEN (B.)
Jantzen (Hans). Deut. Bildhauer d. 13ten Jhdts. [Deut. Meister. Hrsg. v. K. Scheffler u. C. Glaser]. la8°. L. 1925
Janvier (Pierre Désiré). M. Dupont & l'œuvre de la Sainte-Face. 9e éd. s8°. Tours. 1897
Japan [*see also* JAPON].
Financial & econ. ann. of J., 1920–27 [20th–27th]. Dept. of Finance. la8°. Tokyo. [1920–28]
The hot springs of J. incl. Chosen, Taiwan, S. Manchuria. Issued by Jap. Govt. Railways. s8°. [Tokyo]. 1922
Japan pilot, 2nd ed., & Suppl. 6, 1914–22, *see* ADMIRALTY.
Japan to-day & to-morrow. [*By var. wr.*] fol. Osaka. [1927]
What J. thinks, 1921, *see* KAWAKAMI (K. K.), *ed.*

"Japan Gazette" (The): peerage of Japan. 1st ed. la8°. Yokohama. 1912
Japan Society, London.
Transactions & Proceedings. v16–24. 8°. 1918–27
Japan year book, 1923; by Y. Takenob. 17th ann. publ. s8°. Tokyo. [1923]
Japanese (The) exped. to Chientao &c. [Articles repr. f. Seoul Press]. [P2524]. s8°. Seoul. 1921
Japhétique. Recueil j., 1922–23, *see* YAFETICHESKY INST.
Japikse (Nicolaas). De verwikkeling t. de Republiek en England van 1660–1665. la8°. 1900
Johan de Witt. [Nederl. Hist. Bibl., 9]. la8°. 1915
see BLÉCOURT (A. S. DE) & N. J. Klein plakkaatboek van Nederland, 1919.
„ GOSSES (I. H.) & N. J. Handb. tot de staatk. Gesch. van Nederland, 1920.
„ HOLLAND: GOVT. PUBL. Resolutiën d. Staten-Gen., 1576–1609; bewerkt door N. J., d5-9, 1921–26.
Japon. Descripción de parte del J., 1920, *see* MAGELLAN (F.) Descr. de los reinos, &c., 1920.
*La vigne florissante du J. Hist. de quelques illustres martyrs, qui ont enduré la mort en J. [*French & Dutch*]. s4°. Anvers. 1620
Japonaise. Règlement du 14 oct. 1907 sur le service en campagne dans l'armée japonaise &c.; tr. & annoté par col. Corvisart, 1909, *see* CORVISART (*col.*)
Japonia. *Theater (The) of I.'s constancy: in which 118 martyrs suffered death for Christ in 1622. Also: A briefe rel. of the miracles by the merits &c. of S. Ignatius at Munebrega in Spayne in 1623. Tr. out of Spanish. s4°. *n.p.* 1624
Jaques-Dalcroze (Emile), *see* DALCROZE (E. J.)
Jarava (Hernando). Lo que en este libro esta traduzido de Latin en lengua Castellana, con vna breve exposicion es lo siguiente. Los siete psalmos penitenciales. Los quinze psalmos del canticum grado. Las lamentaciones de Hieremias. [*Tr. w. brief expos. by*] H. Jarava. s8°. Anvers. 1556
Jarchi (Solomon), *see* RASHI.
Jardé (Auguste). Céréales dans l'antiq. grecque. [Bibl. des Éc. Franç. d'Athènes & de Rome, fasc. 130]. v1. 8°. 1925
La formation du peuple grec. 8°. 1923
The formation of the Greek people. [Tr. M. R. Dobie]. 8°. 1926
Jardine (Douglas James), *O.B.E.* The Mad Mullah of Somaliland. Foreword by Visct. Milner. 8°. 1923
see CYPRUS. Hdbk. of C.; ed. by H. C. Luke & D. J. J., 1920.
Jarintsov (*Mdme.* N.) Nicholas K. Roerich. [P2380]. sfol. 1920
Jarrett (Bede), *O.P.* The English Dominicans. 8°. 1921
Social theories of the Middle Ages, 1200–1500. 8°. 1926
Jarrige (Pierre). *A further discovery of the mystery of Jesuitisme in a coll. of several pieces. [*each w. sep. pagin.*] s8°. 1658
Jesuita in fezali pegmate ob nefanda crim. in prov. Guienna perp., cum jud. gen. de hoc ord. s8°. Lugd. Batav. 1665
Jarro, *ps.* [*i.e.* GIULIO PICCINI].
Vita aneddotica di T. Salvini. 8°. Firenze. [1908]
Jarry (Alfred).
Ubu Roi. Drame. Préf. de J. Saltas. s8°. 1922
see VALLETTE (*Mme.* A.) A. J., 6e éd., 1928.
Jartoux (Pierre). Lettre t. la plante de Ginseng, *see* BERNARD (J. F.), *ed.* Recueil, t4, 1718; 1732.
Jarves (James Jackson), *see* BRINSMADE (P. A.) Rep. of case of B., versus J., for libelous publ., 1846.
Jarvey (*Capt.* William Andrew). Trial of Capt. J. on a charge of poisoning his wife. Supreme Court of N.Z. 8°. [Dunedin. 1865]
Jas (Peter). Disp. acad. de Valdensium secta ab Albigensibus bene disting. [P2527]. 4°. Lugd. Batav. 1834
Jäschke (Hilde), *see* CAIREL (E.) Der Trobador E. Cairel, Textausgabe &c., v. H. J., 1921.
Jastrow (Ignaz). Die Reform d. staatswiss. Studien. [V. f. Sozialpol., B160]. 8°. München. 1920
Textbücher zu Studien ü. Wirtschaft u. Staat. Hrsg. v. J. J. B1–6 [1, 2e A. 2, 3, 5, 6, 3e A. 4, 5e A.] s8°. 1914–23
1, Handelspolitik. 2, Arbeiterschutz. 3, Adam Smith. 4, Geld u. Kredit. 5, Neue Wirtschaft. 6, Finanzen.
Jastrow (Morris). The Book of Job, its origin, growth &c.; w. a new tr. based on a rev. text. 8°. Phila. 1920
Zionism & the future of Palestine. 8°. N.Y. 1919

Jasz-Berenyi (Paulus P.) A new torch to the Latin tongue. [*2 pagin. Foll. by* Instit. gram., 1669, *w. sep. tp. & pagin.*] 4th ed. corr. & enl. s8°. 1670

Jātakas. Buddhist birth-stories (Jataka tales). Comm. intr. ent. Nidāna-Kathā, the story of the lineage. Tr. f. Fausböll's ed. of the Pali text by T. W. Rhys Davids. New & rev. ed. by Mrs. Rhys Davids. [Broadway Trans.] 8°. [1925]
see FOUCHER (A.) Les représent. de J. dans l'art bouddhique, 1919.

Jatta (Michele). Vasi dipinti dell' Italia merid., *see* REALE ACCAD. D. LINCEI. Mon. ant., v16, 1906.

Jatva. Жатва. Книга 1-5 (1912-14), 8 (1916). s4°. Москва. 1912-16

Jaubert (*le cte.* **Pierre Amédée Émilien Probe).** Voy. en Arménie & en Perse, 1805-06. Not. s. le Chilan &c. par le col. Trézel. 8°. 1821

Jaucourt (Arnail-François, *cte.* **de).** Corr. avec le Prince de Talleyrand pend. le Congrès de Vienne. Publ. par son petit-fils. la8°. 1905

Jaud (*l'abbé* **Léon).**
St. Filibert: étude d'hist. monast. au 7e s. 8°. Luçon. 1910

Jaufre: altprov. Abenteuerroman d. 13. Jhdts. Mit Einltg. &c. hrsg. v. H. Breuer. [Gesells. f. roman. Lit., B46]. la8°. Göttingen. 1925

Jauneaud (Marcel). L'évol. de l'aéronautique. s8°. 1923

Jaunsudrabin (I.)
Aija. Erzählung. Übers. O. Grosberg. 8°. Riga. [1922]

Jaurès (Jean). Hist. socialiste de la Révol. Fr. Ed. rev. par A. Mathiez. t1-8. la8°. 1922-24
1, La Constituante. 2, L'œuvre de la Constituante. 3, La Législative. 4, La République. 5, La Révol. en Europe. 6, La Gironde. 7, La Montagne. 8, Le gouvt. révol.
see JUSTIN. Jaurès patriote, idées sur la défense nationale, 1920.
„ LEVY-BRUHL (L.) J. J., 6e éd., 1924.

Jaurgain (Jean de). Deux Comtes de Comminges béarnais au 15e s. J. de Lescun & O. d'Aydie. [Extr. du Bull. de la Soc. Arch. du Gers]. 8°. 1919

Jausbert, *de Puycibot* [AUBERT; GAUSBERT]. Poésies. Ed. W. P. Shepard. [Classiques fr. du m-â.] s8°. 1924

Jaussen (J.-Antonin). Coutumes palestin., 1, Naplouse & s. district. la8°. 1927
see MISSION ARCHÉOLOG. EN ARABIE. II, El-'Ela, d'Hégra à Teima, Harrah de Tebouk, par J. &c., 1914; Suppl., Coutumes des Fuqarâ, par J. &c., 1914; III, Les châteaux arabes de Qeṣeir 'Amra, Ḥarâneh & Tuba, par J. &c., 1922.

Javal (Lily Jean). Le brasier. s8°. [1922]

Javorskius (Stephanus), *see* YAVORSKY (S.)

Jay (John), *gov. of the State of New York.*
see BEMIS (S. F.) Amer. Secr. of State, v1, J. &c., 1927.
„ —— J.'s treaty, 1923.

Jay (Stephen). The tragedies of sin &c. With remarques on the life of Abraham [*w. sep. tp. & pagin.*] s8°. 1689

Jay (William), *Congregational minister.* Mem. of the life &c. of C. Winter. 2nd ed. rev. & corr. s8°. 1809

Jay (William), *of New York.*
Misc. writings on slavery. s8°. Boston. 1853
Slavery in America. Intr. by S. H. Cox. Ed. J. Morison. s8°. 1835
View of action of Federal Govt. in behalf of slavery. s8°. N.Y. 1839
War & peace. Repr. f. ed. of 1842, w. intr. note, by J. B. Scott. [C.E. for Int. Peace.] la8°. N.Y. 1919

Jayasundere (A. D.), *see* AṄGUTTARA-NIKĀYA. Bk. of the numerical sayings, p2; tr. A. D. J., 1925.

Jayne (Walter Addison). Healing gods of anc. civilizations. la8°. New Haven, *Yale.* 1925

Jeaffreson, *The family of, see* JEAFFRESON (M. T.) Pedigree of the J. family w. notes &c., 1922.

Jeaffreson (Marie Thérèse). Pedigree of the Jeaffreson family w. notes & memoirs. la8°. *p.p.* 1922

Jealousy. *The fatal jealousie: tragedy, 1673, *see* PAYNE (N.)

***Jean** danse mieux que Pierre; Pierre danse mieux que Jean &c., p1, 2, 1719, *see* LE NOBLE (P.) *Hist. du père La Chaize &c., 2p, 1719.

Jean, *author of Rigomer* [JEHAN]. Les mervelles de Rigomer: altfr. Artusroman d. 13. Jhdts., nach d. Aumale-Hs. hrsg. v. W. Foerster. [Gesell. f. Roman. Lit., B19, 39]. 2B (2, Anmerk. &c. v. W. F. & H. Breuer). 8°. Dresden. 1908-15

Jean, *de Luca, see* GIOVANNI, *da Lucca.*

Jean, *le Névelon* [JOANNES NEVELONIS], *see* ARMSTRONG (E. C.) Authorship of Vengement Alixandre & of Venjance Alixandre, 1926.

Jean, *de Paris* [QUIDORT], *d. 1206, see* JOANNES, *Paris.*

Jean, *Sarrasin, see* SARRASIN (JEAN), *chamberlain to Louis IX.*

Jean, *le Teinturier, d'Arras* [JEHAN]. Le mariage des sept arts par Jehan le T., suivi d'une vers. anon.: poèmes franç. du 13e s. Ed. A. Långfors. [Class. fr. du m.â.] s8°. 1923

Jean, *d'Ypres, dit le Long, d. 1383, see* LIVRE. *Livre des merveilles, *partly comp. by J.*, 2t, *n.d.*

Jean (Pierre). La psychologie organique. 8°. 1925

Jean (René). A. Dunoyer de Segonzag: reprods. préc. d'une notice par R. J. s8°. 1922
Jean Marchand. Reprod. de peintures &c., préc. d'une ét. crit. s8°. 1920

Jean-Aubry (G.), *see* AUBRY (G. JEAN-).

Jean-Bernard, *ps.* [*i.e.* J. B. PASSERIEW]. La vie de Paris, 1920, 1921. [*1v for each yr.*] s8°. 1921-22

Jeancon (Jean Allard). Excav. in the Chama Valley, New Mexico. [S.I.: Bureau of Amer. Ethnol., Bull. 81]. 8°. Wash. 1923

Jeanes (Henry). Dr. Hammond h. Ἐκτενέστερον: or, A greater ardency in Xt.'s love of God &c. proved irreconcileable &c. [*b. w. h.* Sermons, 1660]. s4°. O. 1657
A 2nd part of the mixture of scholasticall divinity, w. practical, in sev. tractates. [*w. sep. tp.*] Annexed, Letters of a. & J. Taylor, conc. orig. sin, w. a reply unto Dr. Hammonds Vindic. [*sep. tp. & pagin.*] [*b. w. h.* Sermons, 1660]. s4°. O. 1660
Sermons conc. the last & gen. judgement, bef. the judges of Assise, Somerset, 1657-58. s4°. O. 1660
*Treatise conc. the fulnesse of Xt. &c. [*b. w. h.* Sermons, 1660]. s4°. O. 1656
The want of church govt. no warrant for omission of the Lord's Supper. Added, Reply unto Mr. Fullwood. [*w. sep. tp.*] s8°. O. 1653

Jeannarakis (Antonios).
Neugriech. Gramm. 8°. Hannover. 1877

Jeanne, *de France, daughter of Louis XI, see* †GENLIS (*Mme.* DE) Jeanne de France [*novel*], 2t, 1816.

Jeanne, *daughter of Philip II, duke of Burgundy, see* DUFOUR (A. H.) & F. RABUT. Renonciat. du Comte Amédée VI de Savoie au mariage arrêté entre lui & la Pcsse. J. de Bourgogne, 1878.

Jeannerat de Beerski (P.)
Angkor: ruins in Cambodia. 8°. 1923

Jeanneret (Claude), *see* OZENFANT (—) & C. J. La peinture mod., 5e éd., 1925.

Jeanroy (Alfred). Jongleurs & troubadours gascons des 12e & 13e s. Matériaux éd. par A. J. [Class. franç. du m.â.] s8°. 1923
Le théâtre relig. en France du 11e au 13e siècles. Intr. & tr. par A. J. s8°. 1924
see CERCAMON, *Gascon troubadour, 12 c.* Les poésies de C.; éd. A. J., 1922.
„ HANOTAUX (G.) Hist. de la nation franç., t12, Hist. des lettres, v1, par J. Bédier, A. J. &c., 1921.
—— **& A. Långfors.** Chansons satir. & bachiques du 13e s. Ed. A. J. & A. L. s8°. 1921

Jeanroy (V.) Vingt-cinq ans de mission au Congo: hist. de la mission des Falls. s8°. Brux. 1923

Jeans (Henry W.), *see* INMAN (J.) Nautical tables; pref. by A treatise on pract. navig. by J., 1873.

Jeans (James Hopwood). Atomicity & quanta. s8°. C. 1926
Nebular hypothesis & mod. cosmogony. Halley Lect., 1922. [P2705; 2733]. 8°. O. 1923
Rep. on radiation & quantum-theory. [Phys. Soc. of London]. 2nd ed. la8°. 1924

Jeans (*Surgeon Rear-Adm.* **Thomas T.),** *R.N.*
Remin. of a naval surgeon. 8°. [1927]

Jebb (*Dr.*) Nicholas Ferrar, *see* MAYOR (J. E. B.) Camb. in 17th cent., p1, 1855.

Jebb (John), *bp. of Limerick, Ardfert & Aghadoe.*
[Works, *incl. books ed. by him. Copy collected & arranged by C. Forster. The vol. numbers appear only on the bindings*]. 12v. 8°. 1816-34
1, Sermons, speech &c. 1818-34. [*sep. tps.*]
2, Sermons, on subjects chiefly practical. 2nd ed. 1816.
3, Sacred lit. 1820.

Jebb (John) [*continued*].
4, Townson (T.) Practical discourses; [pref. signed J.], not publ. 1828.
5, 6, Practical theology. 2v. 1830.
7, Piety without asceticism; or, the Protestant Kempis.
8, 9, Phelan (W.) Remains, w. biog. mem. by J. 2v. 1832.
10, 11, 30 yrs. corr. betw. J. & A. Knox. 2v. 1834.
12, Burnet (G.) Lives &c. Ed., w. intr., by J. 1833.
see PHELAN (W.) Hist. of policy of Ch. of R. in Ireland, 3rd ed., w. mem. by J. J., 1854.

Jebb (Richard), *M.A.* The Empire in eclipse. 8º. 1926

Jebb (*Sir* Richard Claverhouse). Samson Agonistes & the Hellenic drama, 1908, *see* BRIT. ACAD. Proc., 1907–08.

Jebna, *see* JAMNIA.

Jeboult (Harold A.)
Somerset composers, musicians & music. s8º. 1923

Jechiel, *see* JEHIEL.

Jeffcott (J. M.) Mann, its names &c., 1878, *see* MANX SOC. Manx misc., v2, 1880.

Jefferies (Richard), *see* THOMAS (E.) R. J., h. life & work, 1911.

Jeffers (Le Roy). Call of the mountains: rambles &c., U.S. & Canada. la8º. 1923

Jefferson (Samuel).
Jefferson's guide to Carlisle. n. & rev. ed. s8º. *n.d.*

Jefferson (Thomas), *president of the U.S., 1743–1826.*
Notes on the state of Virginia. 8º. 1787
T. J., architect. Orig. designs in the coll. of T. J. Coolidge, jun. With an essay &c. by F. Kimball. fol. Boston [Mass.] *p.f.p.d.* 1916
Writings. Ed. H. A. Washington. 9v. 8º. W. 1853–54
see BEMIS (S. F.) Amer. Secr. of State &c., v1, T. J., 1927.
see BOWERS (C. G.) J. & Hamilton: democracy in Amer., 1925.
„ HIRST (F. W.) Life & letters of T. J., 1926.
„ JOHNSON (A.) J. & h. colleagues, 1921.
„ RANDALL (H. S.) Life of T. J., 3v, 1858.
„ SEARS (L. M.) J. & the Embargo, 1927.
„ UNITED STATES. Constit. of the U.S.; add. J.'s Manual, 1871.

Jeffery (Clement). The philosophy of nature cure. s8º. [1921]

Jeffery (George Barker).
Relativity, for physics students. 8º. [1924]

Jeffery (George H. Everett). Byzantine timber building in Cyprus. [Extr. f. J. of R. Inst. of B. Architects, s3, v14. P2860]. 4º. 1907
Famagusta. [Extr. f. J. of R. Inst. of B. Architects, s3, v15. P2860]. 4º. 1908
Notes on Cyprus. [Extr. f. J. of R. Inst. of B. Architects, s3, v13. P2860]. 4º. 1906

Jeffery (H. J.), *see* BEVIS (J. F.) & H. J. J. Brit. plants, 2nd ed., 1920.

Jeffery (Joseph A.) Text-book of land drainage. s8º. N.Y. 1921

Jeffery (Reginald Welbury). The manors & advowson of Great Rollright. [Oxf. Rec. Soc., v9]. 8º. 1927

Jefferys (Thomas). Jefferys's itinerary; or companion thr. Eng., Wales, & part of Scotland &c. obl. s8º. 1775

Jeffray (James). An addr. on the present state of farriery. [P2701]. 4º. E. 1786

Jeffrey (Edward Charles). Coal & civilization. 8º. N.Y. 1925

Jeffrey (Percy Shaw). Whitby lore & legend. Coll. & ed. P. S. J. Intr. by Marq. of Normanby. 2nd ed., enl. 8º. Whitby. 1923

Jeffreys (George Jeffreys, *1st baron*), *see* BENT (J.) Life & death of J., 1705.

Jeffreys (Harold). The earth, its origin, hist. & physical constit. la8º. C. 1924

Jégou (Joseph François Bonabe), *cte. du Laz.* Hist. de la fondation de Lorient.: ét. archéol. la8º. Lorient. 1870

Jéhan (Louis François). La Bretagne: esquisses pitt. & archéolog. 8º. Tours. 1863

Jehiel, *ben Joseph.* Disput. R. Jechielis cum quodam Nicolao [*Hebr. & Lat.*], *see* WAGENSEIL (J. C.) Tela ignea Satanae &c., 1681.

Jehlitschka (Henry).
Türk. Konv.-Grammatik. 8º. Heidelberg. 1895
„ „ ....Schlüssel. 8º. Heidelberg. 1897

Jekyll (Gertrude). Old English household life: acc. of cottage objects & country folk. 8º. [1925]

—— & L. Weaver.
Gardens for small country houses. 5th ed. 4º. 1924

Jelić (Luka). Traù, storia e mon., *see* BULLETTINO DI ARCH. &C. DALM., 35, Suppl., 1912.

Jelinger (Christopher), *see* TROUP (F. B.) Biog. sketch of the Rev. C. J., w. bibl. notes, 1900.

Jellicoe (*Adm.* John Rushworth Jellicoe, *1st visct.*), [OF SCAPA].
The crisis of the Naval War. la8º. 1920

Jellinghaus (Hermann Friedrich), *see* WESTFALEN. Bau- u. Kunstdenkm., 26, Kreis Herford, gesch. Einl. v. H. F. J., 1908.

Jelyabov (Andrei Ivanovich), *1849–81.* *А. И. Желябовъ. [P2390]. s8º. Carouge-Genève. 1899

Jelyabujsky (Ivan Afanasevich) [Желябужскій], *1638–1692* (*or 1709?*). Записки, *see* SAKHAROV (I. P.) Записки &c., 1841.

Jemana. Hist. J. sub Hasano Pasha, 1838, *see* 'AMĪR IBN MUḤAMMAD, *al-Ru 'āmī.*

Jena. *Das in dem Jahr 1738 [1743 & 1744–49] blühende Jena; Ursprung d. Stadt, Stiftung d. Univ. &c. besonders d. Leben d. Gelehrten. [Durch M. J. C. Mylius]. [3p *in* 1v]. s8º. Jena. [1738–50 ?]
Jubilæa Acad. Jen. festiv. celebr. orationibus 5 [*by J. Major & others*]. [P483]. s4º. Jenae. 1618

Jenghis Khan, *Great Khan of the Moguls.*
see BICHURIN (J.) Исторія первыхъ четырехъ хановъ изъ дома Чингисова, 1829.
„ HART (B. H. L.) Gt. captains unveiled, 1927.
„ KRAUSE (F. E. A.) Cingis Han, d. Gesch. s. Lebens nach d. chin. Reichsannalen, 1922.
„ LAMB (H.) Genghis Khan, 1928.
„ RASHID-AL-DIN (F. A.) Исторія Монголовъ: ист. Чингизъхана, 2p, 1868.

Jenichen (Gottlob August). Contin. Notitiae auctorum juridic. &c. quam olim evulgavit G. Beyerus. s8º. Lipsiae. 1738

Jenichen (Gottlob Friedrich). Disput. de genesimantia. Praes. G. F. J., resp. Z. Dezius. [P427]. s4º. Lipsiae. [1699]
Hist. & examen bullæ anti-Quesnellianae. [P2630]. s4º. Lipsiae. 1714

Jenkins (Charles Francis). Tortola: a Quaker experiment in the tropics. [Friends Hist. Soc. Journ. Suppl., No. 13]. 8º. 1923

Jenkins (Claude). Card. Morton's register, *see* POLLARD (A. F.) Tudor studies, 1924.
The monastic chronicler & the early school of St. Albans. Lect. s8º. 1922

Jenkins (Ebenezer Evans). Modern atheism. 8º. 1877

Jenkins (Harry), *see* AMSTUTZ (N. S.) Hdbk. of photo-engraving; enl. & rev. of J.'s Manual of p.-engr., 1907.

Jenkins (Herbert), *publisher.*
*Patricia Brent, spinster. By the a. of ? s8º. 1918
*Return (The) of Alfred. By a. of Patricia Brent, spinster. s8º. 1922

Jenkins (J. Edward). A week of passion. s8º. 1897

Jenkins (James Travis).
Fishes of the Brit. Isles. s8º. [1925]
The herring & the herring fisheries. 8º. 1927
A hist. of the whale fisheries. 8º. 1921
The sea fisheries. la8º. 1920
Textbook of oceanography. 8º. 1921

Jenkinson, *Family of*, *see* DENNY (D. L. L.) The manor of Hawkesbury & its owners [*i.e.* J.], 1920.

Jenkinson (Anthony). Voy. pour découv. le chemin du Cathay par la Tartarie, 1558, *see* BERNARD (J. F.), *ed.* Recueil, t4, 1718; 1732.
see ALENITSIN (V. D.) О путешествіи Дж. въ Хиву, 1880.

Jenkinson (Charles Hilary). The later court hands in Eng., 15th–17th cent. [Plates, *b. sep.*] fol. 1927
A manual of archive admin. [C.E. for Int. Peace]. la8º. O. 1922

Jenkinson (E. J.) Unwritten sayings of Jesus. 8º. [1925]

Jenkinson (Francis John Henry). List of incunabula coll. by G. Dunn to illust. the hist. of printing. [Bibl. Soc. Trans. Suppl. No. 3]. 8º. 1923
see HOLLINGWORTH (E. J.) & M. M. O'REILLY. Anglo-Saxon cemetery at Girton Coll., based on MS. notes by J., 1925.
„ STEWART (H. F.) F. J., Fellow of Trin. Coll. Camb. & Univ. Librarian, 1926.

Jenkinson (Wilberforce). The royal & bishops' palaces in old London, w. the Parliament Houses &c. s8º. 1921

Jenks (Benjamin). Submission to the righteousness of God. 2nd ed. w. add. s8º. 1708

Jenks (Edward). The book of Eng. law. 8°. [1928]
A digest of Eng. civil law. Bk. 2, p3 & p3 (cont.) 8°. 1908–10
2iii, Law of quasi-contract & tort, by J. C. Miles.
Digeste de droit civil anglais. [Ed. E. J.] Par E. J., W. M. Geldart, R. W. Lee, W. S. Holdsworth, J. C. Miles. Tr. T. Baumann & P. Goulé. 2e éd. 2t. la8°. 1923
Short hist. of Eng. law. 2nd ed. rev. 8°. [1920]
Treatise on law. [P2500]. s8°. [1920]
Jenks (Jeremiah Whipple). The trust problem. 4th ed. enl. w. collab. of W. E. Clark. 8°. N.Y. 1922
Jenks (Leland Hamilton).
Migration of Brit. capital, to 1875. 8°. N.Y. 1927
Jenkyn (William).
An expos. of Jude. 2p *in* 1v. s4°. 1652–54
An expos. of Jude. [*tp. torn. 2 pagin.*] la8°. 1656
An expos. upon Jude [A.D. 1653]. Rev. & corr. by J. Sherman. la8°. 1839
Jennaro (Pietro Jacopo de), *1436–1508.* Il canzoniere di P. J. de J. Cod. d. 15 sec. pubbl. con pref. &c. da G. Barone. 8°. Napoli. 1883
Jenner (Edward), *M.D., F.R.S.* Inq. into causes & effects of the Variolæ Vaccinæ *& o. tracts, see* †CROOKSHANK (F. M.), *ed.* Hist. &c. of vaccination, v2, 1889.
Jenner-Fust (*Sir* Herbert). Stone altar case. Judgment of Sir H. J. F. Ed. f. the judge's notes by J. E. P. Robertson. [P2845]. 8°. 1845
Jenness (Diamond). Copper Eskimos, *see* CANADIAN ARCTIC EXPED. Rep., v12, 1922–23.
Eskimo folk-lore, *see* CANADIAN ARCTIC EXP. Rep., v13, 1924.
see CANADIAN ARCTIC EXPED. Rep., v14, Songs of the Copper Eskimos; by H. H. Roberts & D. J., 1925.
—— **& A. Ballantyne.** The Northern D'Entrecasteaux. Pref. by R. R. Marett. 8°. O. 1920
Jennings (Arthur Ch.)
A manual of Church history. 2v. s8°. 1888
The mediæval Church & the Papacy. s8°. [1909]
Jennings (David). Jewish antiq. Annexed, diss. on Hebrew. n. ed. 8°. 1825
Jennings (Herbert Spencer). Prometheus, or biology & the advancement of man. s8°. [1925]
Jennings (John), *Nonconformist minister.* Two discourses: of preaching Christ &c. Pref. by I. Watts. 3rd ed. s8°. 1736
Jennings (Samuel Kennedy), *M.D.* A defence of the camp meetings (N. Amer.) Added, Thoughts &c. on signs of the times &c., by L. Dow. [P2674]. s8°. Liv'l. 1806
Jennings (William). Lexicon to the Syriac New Test. Rev. by U. Gantillon. s8°. O. 1926
Jensen (Christian). Neoptolemos u. Horaz, 1919, *see* KÖNIGL. PREUSS. AKAD. D. WISS. Abhdl. (Phil.-hist. Klasse), 1918.
see PHILODEMUS, *of Gadara.* Üb. d. Gedichte, 5tes Buch; Gr. Text mit Übers. u. Erläut. v. C. J., 1923.
Jensen (Hans). Gesch. d. Schrift. 4°. Hannover. 1925
Jensen (Ingeborg Hammer). Die älteste Alchymie, *see* KONGELIGT DAN. VID. SELSK. Hist.-fil. Med., B4, 1921–22.
Jensen (Johannes Vilhelm). Christofer Columbus. s8°. 1921
Cimbrernes Tog. s8°. 1922
The long journey. [Tr. A. G. Chater]. s8°. [1922]
Jensen (P. Boysen), *see* BOYSEN JENSEN (P.)
Jensen (Peter). Texte zur assyr.-babylon. Relig., *see* KEILINSCHRIFTLICHE BIBL. Samml. v. assyr. u. babylon. Texten; hrsg. v. E. Schrader, B6ii, 1915.
Jensen (S. Orla-), *see* ORLA-JENSEN (S.)
Jensen (Wilhelm), *see* FREUD (S.) Delusion & dream, interpret. of Gradiva, by W. J., tr., 1921.
Jenson (Christen). Den Norske dict. eller glosbog, *see* HANNAAS (T.) Ældre norske sprogminder, 3, 1915.
Jenyns (Leonard), *aft. Blomefield.* A naturalist's calendar. Ed. by Sir F. Darwin. 2nd ed. s8°. C. 1922
Jenyns (Soame). Poet. works. Coll. by T. Park. s8°. 1807
A view of the internal evidence of the Xtn. relig. 7th ed. s8°. 1799
Jepa. Frühmittelalt. Glossen d. angebl. J. z. Isagoge d. Porphyrius, 1924, *see* BÄUMKER (C.) & B. S. WALTERSHAUSEN.
Jephson (Robert).
Works in †INCHBALD (*Mrs.* E.) Mod. theatre, 1808–11.
Braganza. [6.] | The law of Lombardy. [6.]
Count of Narbonne. [20.]
Jephtha, *see* NAUMANN (J. G.) Diss. de Jephtigenia &c., 1712.
Jepson (Edgar). Peter intervenes. s8°. 1926
Jepson (Selwyn). The death gong. s8°. [1927]
Snaggletooth. s8°. [1926]
Jéquier (Gustave). Les frises d'objets des sarcophages du Moyen Emp., *see* INST. FRANÇ. D'ARCH. OR. DU CAIRE. Mém., t47, 1921.
Manuel d'archéologie égyptienne. [t]1, Architecture. 8°. 1924
Jerdan (William). *Personal narr. of a journey over-land f. the Bank to Barnes. By an inside passenger. Appended, A model f. a magazine &c. s8°. 1829
Jeremiah, *abp. of Larissa, aft. patriarch of Constantinople* [HIEREMIAS]. Censura Orientalis Eccl. De praecipius nostri sæculi hæreticorum dogmatibus &c. A S. Socolobio in Lat. conversa ac quibusdam annot. illust. s8°. Coloniae. 1582
Tomus primus qua Eccl. Orient. dogmata & mysteria contin., a J. compos., 1576 ad Lutheranos, Tubingae missa, labore Gedeonis Cyprii ed. [Tomus 2 in quo contin. Augustana Confessio, 1, 2 & 3 resp. ad tria D. Jeremiae responsa. ed. 2. *Greek & Lat.*] 2t *in* 1v. s4°. Lipsiae. 1758
see LINDANUS (W. D.) Concordia discors &c.; inserta est Censure J. patr. Constantinop. de Conf. Aug. epitome, 1583.
,, SOKOLOWSKI (S.) Ad Wirtemberg. theolog. invect., quam actis &c. cum H. patr. Const. praef., resp., 1585.
,, WÜRTTEMBERG. Acta & scripta theolog. Wirtemberg. et H., 1576–81, de Aug. Conf., 1584.
Jeremias (Alfred). Babylon. Dichtungen, Epen u. Legenden, *see* ALTE ORIENT (DER), Jhrg. 25, 1926.
Jérémie (—), *officer in the French navy.* Rél. du Détroit & de la Baye de Hudson, *see* BERNARD (J. F.), *ed.* Recueil, t3, 1732.
Jermin (Michael). A comm. upon Ecclesiastes. fol. 1639
Jermy (Isaac), *see* RUSH (J. B.) Intr. narr. & rev. report of trial of R. for murder of I. J. & of h. son, 1849.
Jernegan (Marcus Wilson), *see* MACLAUGHLIN (A. C.), W. E. DODD &C. Source probl. in U.S. hist., 1918.
Jernstedt (Peter), *see* ZERETELI (G. F.), *ed.* Papyri russ. u. georg. Sammlungen, 4, bearb. v. P. J., 1927.
Jerome, *of Prague.*
see GILPIN (W.) Lives of Wicliff, J. of P., &c., 1765.
,, HUSS (J.) J. H. & J. P. hist. & monumenta, 1558.
Jerome, *Saint* [EUSEBIUS HIERONYMUS STRIDONENSIS]. Opera omnia labore M. Victorii emendata &c. Acc. Sophronii Graecam interpret. libri de script. eccl. H. Gravii annot. in Epistolas &c. [*w. sep. tp. & pagin.*] Adj. est vita S. Hieronymi quam idem Victorius primus edidit &c. 4t. [*b. in 3v*]. fol. Parisiis. 1609
t4 *cont.* Opuscula quæ olim inven. inter opera S. H. [*w. sep. tp. & pagin.*]
Opera. [Corpus scr. eccl. Lat., 66]. sect. 1iii. 8°. Vindobonae. 1918
Epistulae. p3, Rec. I. Hilberg.
De scriptor. eccl., *see* LE MIRE (A.) Bibl. eccl., 1639.
Vetustius occident. eccl. martyrologium, Hieronymo trib., 1668, *see* MARTYROLOGIUM.
see BIBLE: PSALMS. Psalterium juxta Hebr. Hieronymi, 1874; ed., w. intr. &c. by J. M. Harden, 1922.
,, BULIC (F.) Stridone luogo natale di S. G., 1919–22.
,, CAVALLERA (F.) St. J., s. vie & s. œuvre, p1, 2t, 1922.
,, ERASMUS (D.) Verteut. ausslegung ub. s. Hieronymus Alleg., was guts die Philosophi in d. heyl. schr. schaffen, 1521.
,, GRÜTZMACHER (G.) Hieronymus: e. biogr. Studie, B2, 3, 385–420, 1906–08.
,, LARGENT (A.) Saint J., 8e éd., 1922.
,, MARGARITA. Liber margarita Davitica nuncupatus ex. Hieronimo: Augustino &c., 1471 ?.
Jerome [*Emiliani*], *St., see* HUBERT (W. E.) Lebensbilder kath. Erzieher, B4, 1895.
Jerome [*Miani*], *St., see* JEROME [*Emiliani*], *St.*
Jerome, *de San Stefano, see* HIERONYMOS, *de San Stefano.*
Jerome (Jerome Klapka). All roads lead to Calvary. s8°. [1919]
Anthony John. s8°. [1923]
My life & times. 8°. [1926]
Jerome (Thomas Spencer).
Aspects of the study of Roman hist. 8°. N.Y. 1923
Jeromski (Stefan). Plus blanc que neige: drame; tr. M Grabowska & P. de St. Wall Pinon, *see* REVUE (LA) HEBDOMADAIRE. Suppl.: coll. nouv. &c., No. 14, 1923.
Jeronimus *Ferrariensis, see* SAVONAROLA (G.)
Jeroteo, *St., see* HIEROTHEUS.

Jerrold (Clare). The story of Dorothy Jordan. 8º. 1914
Jerrold (Douglas). The Royal Naval Division. Intr. by Rt. Hon. Winston S. Churchill. 8º. 1923
Jerrold (Walter). Henry VIII & h. wives. 8º. [1926]
Jersey.
*Brief (A) descr. & hist. notices of island of J. s8º. Jersey. 1826
*Letters from J. s8º. 1830
Jersey (Margaret Elizabeth, *dowager countess of*).
51 years of Victorian life. 8º. 1922
,, ,, ...[3rd impr.] 8º. 1922
—— **&** *Hon.* **E. Ward.**
Hannibal's tribunal. Drama. s8º. [1927]
Jerusalem.
Assize of J., 1842, *see* SMITH (T.)
[Chronolog. hist. of J. Comp. by the Congreg. of St. James &c. *In Armenian*]. 2v *in* 1. 8º. Jerusalem. 1890
Іерусалимскій канонарь 7 вѣка, 1912, *see* KEKELIDZE (K. S.)
Jerusalem, 1920–22. Rec. of the Pro-J. Council dur. 1st two years of civil admin. Ed. C. R. Ashbee. Pref. by Sir R. Storrs. 4º. 1924
*The new Jerusalem. A hymn of olden time. [*Attrib. to* David Dickson. Ed. w. pref. &c. by H. Bonar]. s8º. E. 1852
*New (The) pilgrim's progress, or a journey to J., 1820, *see* NEW.
Rep. of the Comm. apptd. to inquire into affairs of Orthodox Patriarchate of J., 1921, *see* BERTRAM (*Sir* A.) & H. C. LUKE.
Синодикъ Крестнаго монастыря въ Іерусалимѣ. Груз. текстъ изд. Н. Марръ. [Bibl. Arm -Georgica, 3. *2nd tp. in Georgian*]. la8º. С.-П. 1914
Jervis (Eustace), *prison chaplain.* Twenty-five yrs. in six prisons. Foreword by Sir E. Wyld. 8º. [1925]
Jervis (*Lt.-Col.* **Swynfen J.)** The South Staffordshire Regiment. The work of the Care Committee, 1914–19. 8º. 1919
Jespersen (Otto).
Chapters on English. [Repr. f. "Progress in lang."] 8º. 1918
Growth & structure of the Eng. language. 4th ed. rev. s8º. O. 1923
Language, its nature, develop. &c. 8º. [1922]
,, ,, ...[repr.] 8º. [1925]
Logic & grammar—Great & Little Britain by D. MacRitchie & W. H. Stevenson. [S.P.E. Tract No. 16]. 8º. 1924
Mankind, nation & individual f. a ling. point of view. s8º. Oslo. 1925
Mod. Eng. gram. on hist. princ. p2, App. to 1st & 2nd eds. [*pagin. contin., b. w.* p2]; p3, Syntax, v2. 8º. Heidelberg. 1927
Negation in Eng. & o. lang., *see* KONG. DAN. VID. SELSK. Hist.-fil. Med., B1, 1917–18.
Notes on relative clauses by O. J.—Amer. slang by F. N. Scott. [S.P.E. Tract No. 24]. 8º. 1926
On some disputed points in Eng. gram. [S.P.E. Tract 25]. 8º. 1926
The philos. of grammar. 8º. [1924]
De to hovedarter av gramm. forbindelser, *see* KONGELIGT DAN. VID. SELSK. Hist.-fil. Med., B4, 1921–22.
Jesse (Edward).
A summer's day at Windsor, & a visit to Eton. s8º. 1841
Jesse (Fryn Tennyson), *wife of Harold Marsh Harwood.*
Anyhouse. Play. 8º. [1925]
The happy bride. [*Poems*]. la8º. 1920
The milky way. [repr.] s8º. [1916]
Moonraker, or the female pirate &c. s8º. [1927]
Murder & its motives. 8º. 1924
Tom Fool. s8º. [1926]
see DOUGAL (S. H.) Trial of D.; ed. F. T. J., 1928.
Jesse (Wilhelm).
Gesch. d. Stadt Schwerin. 2B. 8º. Schwerin i. M. 1913–20
Quellenbuch z. Münz- u. Geldgesch. d. Mittelalters. la8º. Halle a. S. 1924
Jessen (Arnd). Was will d. Dawes-Bericht? 8º. 1924
Jessen (Franz de). Katja. 8º. København. 1912
Jessen (Knud) & J. Lind. Det danske Markukrudts Hist., *see* KONG. DANSK. VIDENSK. SELSKAB. Skrifter, Raekke 8, B8, 1922–23.
Jessen (Otto). Südwest-Andalusien, *see* PETERMANNS MITT. Ergnzb., 40, 1925.
Jessenius (Johannes), *a Jessen.* Ad regni Boemiæ &c. ordines de restaur. Prag. Acad. exhort., 1619, *facs., see* PICK (F.) J. Jessenius, 1926.
see PICK (F.) J. J., Arzt u. Rektor, 1926.
Jessen-Schardebøl (Erik Johan). Tract. de Finnorum Lapponumque Norvegic. relig. pagana, *see* LEEM (K.) De Lapponibus Finmarchiae &c., 1767.
Jessensky (Johannes), *see* JESSENIUS (J.)
Jessop (Gilbert Laird). A cricketer's log. 8º. [1922]
Jesu (Thomas a), *Spanish Carmelite, see* THOMAS, *a Jesu.*

Jesuitism. *Protestant J., 1836, *see* PROTESTANT.
*A further discov. of the mystery of J. &c., 1658, *see* JARRIGE (P.)
Les provinciales, or, the mystery of Jesuitisme, 2nd ed., 1658, *see* PASCAL (B.)
Jesuits [JESUITEN; JESUITES; JESUITARUM].
Annuae literae Soc. Iesu, 1650. Acc. cat. librorum 1650 a nostris ed. &c. [Ed. J. Nadasi]. s8º. Dilingae. 1658
Annuae literae Soc. Iesu, 1651. Acc. indices Annuarum 1581–1614. [*b. w.* Annuae lit. S.I., 1650, 1658]. s8º. Dilingae. 1658
*Aphorismi doct. J. &c. [P2743]. s4º. *n.p.* 1608
*Arcana Soc. Jesu, 1635, *see* SCHOPPE (C.)
*Blüthen d. Jesuiten-Moral, gesam. v. e. Katholiken. [*Lat. & Germ.*] [P519]. 8º. Celle. 1873
*Brief (A) hist. acc. of the behaviour of the J., 25 years of Q. Eliz. reign. Epistle by W. Watson [*w. sep. tp.* P2663]. s4º. 1689
*Brief rel. of the persec. agst. Catholike Xtns. in Japonia. Taken out of the annuall letters of the Soc. of J. &c. Tr. by W. W., Gent. [*i.e.* W. Wright]. pl [*? no more publ.*] s8º. *n.p.* 1619
Cat. de' Gesuiti, 1820, *see* CATECHISMO.
Compendium privilegiorum &c. Soc. J. s8º. Antverpiae. 1535
,, ,, ...[*a. ed.*] s8º. Romae. 1584
,, ,, ...s8º. Pragae. 1703
Constit. S.J. & examen cum declarationibus. s8º. Antverpiæ. 1535
,, ,, ...s8º. Romæ. 1583
Constit. Soc. Jesu, 1558. Repr. w. App. cont. a tr. &c. [*2 tp. & pagin.*] 8º. 1838
De Christianis apud Japonios triumphis, 1612–20; ex annuis S.J. litt., 1623, *see* TRIGAULT (N.)
Epist. & acta J. Transylvaniae (1571–1613). Coll. & ed. A. Veress. [Erdelyi Jezsuiták &c. Fontes rer. Transylvan., t1, 2]. la8º. Kolozsvár. 1911–13
Epist. Indicae de stupendis &c. reb. qu. div. bonitas in India &c., per Soc. J. operari dignata est [*by* F. Xavier, G. Barzée, A. Quadrus, L. Froes &c. Ed. J. R. Bergensis.] [*Foll. by* De S.J. orig. lib. auth. D. Jac. Payva contra Kemnicii audaciam *&* S.J. defensio adv. obtrectatores, ex test. &c. Pii IV, *w. sep. tp*ˢ. *& pagin.*] s8º. Lovanii. 1566
Epist. Indicae et Japanicae de mult. gentium per Soc. J. conversione: item de Tartarorum moribus, &c. [Epist. Jap., *w. sep. tp. & pagin.*] 3ª ed. auctior. s8º. Lovanii. 1570
*Hist. impart. des J., 1768, *see* LINGUET (S. N. H.)
Hist. narr. de initio & progr. missionis Soc. Jesu apud Chinenses &c., 1665; 1672, *see* SCHALL (J. A.)
Imago primi sæculi Soc. Jesu. A Provincia Flandro-Belgica ejusdem Soc. repræsentata. [*By* J. Tollenarius, G. Henschenius, J. Bollandus & A. Poirtres]. fol. Antverpiæ. 1640
Informationes patrum S.J. seu libellus supplex ad S. Congreg. S. Officii, oblatus à 3 e S.J. deputatis ad inform. de controv. Sinensibus. [*no tp.* P2559]. s8º. *n.p. n.d.*
Institutum Soc. Jesu. Ex decreto Congreg. gen. XIV meliorem in ord. digestum &c. 2v. 4º. Pragae. 1705
Japponiensis Imperii admirabilis commutatio exposita litteris [*by* V. Carvalho] ad C. Aquaviva, Lat. fecit Joh. Hay. s8º. Antverpiae. 1604
Jesuiten (Der) Latein. [*Letter at end signed:* Johannes Gutman]. [P2443]. s4º. Wittemberg. 1608
*Jésuites (Les) & leur doctrine. s8º. Brux. 1825
*Jesuits (The) gospel acc. to Ignatius Loiola. [P529]. fol. 1679
*Jesuits (The) morals; tr., 1670, *see* PERRAULT (N.)
Lettera scr. al sant. p. Clemente XI da pp. d. Co. di Gesù d. Cina, con risp. dell' Imperador s. i riti cin. s8º. *n.p.* 1701
Lettres édifiantes & curieuses conc. l'Asie, l'Afr., & l'Amér., avec rel. nouv. des missions & notes &c. Publ. s. la dir. de L. Aimé-Martin. 4t. la8º. 1838–43
Literae annuae Iaponenses a. 1591 & 92 &c. a L. Frois. s8º. Coloniae Agripp. 1596
Litterae annuae Iaponicae a F. Pasio ad C. Aquavivam a. 1601. A B. Lippio Lat. excusae. s8º. Moguntiaci. 1604
*Litteræ Apostolicæ, quibus instit., confirmatio, & varia privilegia Soc. Jesu cont. s8º. Romæ. 1568
Litterae Soc. Jesu e regno Sinarum 1610 & 11. Auctore N. Trigautio. [*b. w.* Rei Chr. apud Jap., 1615]. s8º. Augustae Vindel. 1615
Messis Paraquariensis a patribus S.J. in Paraquaria coll. 1638–43. Conscr. à p. A. Schirmbeck. s8º. Monachi. 1649
*Morale (La) pratique des Jésuites. 8t [8, 2ᵉ éd., 1716. 1, 8 *have 2 pagin*ˢ.] s8º. *n.p.* (1, Cologne). 1683–1716
,, ,, 2ᵉ [*&* nouv.] éd. 8t. s8º. *n.p.* (3, 6 Nancy). 1682–1735
1, 2, *by* S. J. Du Cambout de Pont-Château. 3–8, *by* A. Arnauld. 4, *has 2nd tp.* *Hist. de dom Jean de Palafox &c., 1718. 5, *has tp.* Hist. de la persécution de 2 saints évêques par les Jésuites: Dom Bernardin de Cardenas *&* Philippe Pardo, 2ᵉ éd., 1717. 6, Hist. des differens entre les missionaires Jésuites & ceux des ordres de St. Dominique & de St. François touch. les cultes [des] Chinois, 2ᵉ éd. 1735. 7, Suite de l'Hist. &c. 8, De la calomnie; ou instruction du procès entre les J. & leurs adversaires, 2ᵉ éd., 1716.
*Mysteria Patrum J. &c., 1633, *see* SCHOPPE (C.)

Jesuits [JESUITEN; JESUITES; JESUITARUM] [*continued*].
Nova relatio histor. de statu rei Christianae in Japonia, & de Quabacundoni trucidatione, binis epist. a F. Frois 1595 datis compreh. Ex Ital. in Lat. tr. s8°. Moguntiae. 1598
Plaidoyé contre les J., 1594, *see* ARNAULD (A.)
*Politique (La) des J., 1688, *see* MONPERSAN (L. DE).
*Principles (The) of the J., 1839, *see* NORRIS (H. H.)
Ratio atq. instit. studiorum. s8°. Romae. 1591
Recentissima de amplissimo regno Chinae [a N. Longobardo, 1598]. Item De statu rei Xtnæ apud magnum regem Mogor [ex litt. H. Xaverii & E. Pigneiri 1598–9]. De morte Taicosamæ [a F. Pasio, 1598, & Brevis narr. rerum in Japonia gest. a P. Gomez, 1598. *Ed.* N. Pimenta]. s8°. Moguntiae. 1601
Recueil de pièces qui n'avoient pas encore paru en France, conc. le procès des Jésuites, *see* PORTUGAL. Rec. des decrets apostol. &c., p2, 1761.
Recueil des decrets apost. &c. du roi de Portugal &c. (conc. le conduite des J. dans le Paraguai &c.), 2t *&* Suite, 1758–61; 2e ed., 1761, *see* PORTUGAL.
Reflexions des Jésuites de Rome sur le Manifeste de Portug. [*Fr. & Ital.*], *see* PORTUGAL. Recueil des decrets apostol. &c., p2, 1759; 2e éd., 1761.
Regulæ S.J., auctor. septimæ Congregationis gen. auctæ. [*b. w.* Constit. &c., 1535]. s8°. Antverpiæ. 1535
Regulae Soc. J. s8°. Lugduni. 1604
Rei Christianae apud Japonios comm. ex litteris annuis Soc. Jesu annorum 1609–12 coll. Auctore N. Trigautio. s8°. Augustae Vindel. 1615
*Relaçaõ abbrev. da republica, que os religiosos Jesuitas das Prov. de Portugal, e Hespanha estab. nos Dominios Ultramarinos &c. Relation abrégée &c. [*by* S. J. de Carvalho e Mello, Marquis de Pombal ? tr. *by* P. O. Pinault. *Port. & Fr.*], *see* PORTUGAL. Rec. des decrets apostol. &c., p1, *n.d.*; 2e éd., p1, 1761.
*Relatio nuperi itineris proscribt. J. ex regnis Bohemiæ & Ungariæ [*w. folding-plate*]. s4°. Pragae. 1619
Relation de ce qui s'est passé à la Chine en 1697–99, à l'occas. d'un établ. que M. l'abbé de Lyonne a fait à Nien-Tcheou. [P2559]. s8°. Liége. 1700
*Relation (A) of voy. to Siam by 6 J.; tr., 1688, *see* TACHARD (G.)
Relations inéd. de la Nouvelle-France (1672–79), 2t, 1861, *see* Voyages & trav. des missionnaires, t3, 4, *below*.
*Relig. (La) des J., 1689, *see* JURIEU (P.)
*Remarques sur la protestation des J. &c., 1709, *see* LE GOBIEN (C.)
*Schwarz-Wildpret-Jagd, oder die neueste Jesuiten-Hetze. V. e. kathol. Geistl. d. Erzdiöcese Freiburg. [P519]. 8°. Mainz. 1872
*Secret (The) policy of the Eng. Soc. of J. discover'd in a ser. of attempts ag. the clergy. 24 letters. s8°. 1715
*Secreta monita S.J., 2nd ed., 1746, *see* ZAOROWSKY (J.)
Secrets (Les) des J.: Monita secreta [*Lat. & Fr.*] 8°. 1901
Sentiment d'un jurisconsulte envoyé à son amy sur la contest. d'entre les miss. étr. & les PP. Jésuites touch. les cérémonies Chin. [P2559]. s8°. *n.p.* 1700
Sereniss. pr. Franciae Delphino Xenia Coll. Rothomag. soc. J., 1639, *see* ROUEN.
*Spongia qua absterg. convitia &c. Equitis Poloni cont. Jesuitas, 1591, *see* LANS (J.)
*Théologie (La) morale des J. & nouv. casuistes. Condamnée &c. par plus. censures, decrets d'univ. &c. [? *By* A. Arnauld *or* F. Hallier]. Div. en 5p, & augm. en cette nouv. éd. d'une Censure faite par la Sorbonne [*w. sep. tp. & pagin.*] s8°. Cologne. 1666
The travels of several learned missioners [*Bouchet & others*] of the Soc. of J. into Archipelago, India, China & America. Tr. f. French. 8°. 1714
*Voyage de Siam des pères Jésuites &c., 1688, *see* †TACHARD (G.)
Voyages & travaux des missionnaires de la Cie de Jésus. Pour servir de complément aux Lettres édifiantes. [4t]. 8°. 1857–61
1, Mission de Cayenne & de la Guyane franç. [P. Pelleprat, J. Grillet, J. Lombard &c.]
2, Mission de la Cochinchine & du Tonkin. [A. de Rhodes &c.]
3, 4, Mission du Canada: relations inéd. de la Nouv. France (1672–79).
see ANNALES DE LA PROPAG. DE LA FOI (1822–83), 1841–83.
,, ANNALS OF THE PROPAGATION OF THE FAITH, 1838–59.

Jesup (Edward). The lives of John Picus, prince of Mirandola; & of M. Pascal. [*w. sep. pag. & tp. dated* 1723]. 3rd ed. s8°. *n.d.*

Jesus Christ.
Gespräche Jesu mit s. Jüngern, 2. Jhdt.; hrsg. &c. v. C. Schmidt, 1919, *see* EPISTOLA Apostolorum.
*Hist. passionis J. C., Tamulice ex 4 Evanglistis conscr. Ed. 4a. s8°. Trangambar. 1789
Liber Toldos Jeschu [*Hebr. & Lat.*], *see* WAGENSEIL (J. C.) Tela ignea Satanae &c., 1681.
Logia & agrapha Domini J. apud Moslemicos scr. usitata; coll., vertit &c. M. Asin et Palacios, fasc. 2, *see* GRAFFIN (R.) & F. NAU. Patr. Or., t19, 1926.
Les miracles de J.; texte éthiopien publ. & tr. par S. Grébaut, p2, 3, *see* GRAFFIN (R.) & F. NAU. Pat. Or., t14, 17, 1920–23.
*Passio Domini I. C., ex evangelistarum textuq̄ȝ accuratissime deprompta additis sanctiss. exquisitiss. qȝ figuris [*attrib. to* U. Graff. [*b. w.* Pinder (U.) Speculum, 1507]. fol. [Argentorati, *I. Knoblouchus.*] 1507

Jesus Christ [*continued*].
The sayings of Jesus of Nazareth. Pref. by J. A. Robertson. s8°. 1920
*The Southern Passion. Ed. f. Pepysian MS. 2344, Magdalene Coll., Camb., w. intr. &c. by B. D. Brown. [E.E.T.S., 169]. 8°. 1927
see ANDREWS (S. J.) Life, 1892.
,, APOCRYPHA: James (M. R.), *ed.* Latin infancy gospels, 1927.
,, AUFHAUSER (J. B.) Buddha u. Jesus in i. Paralleltexten, 1926.
,, BARBUSSE (H.) Jésus, 1927.
,, BARRETT (A.) Xt. in the storm, 1859.
,, BATHO (E. C.) Life of Xt. in the ballads, 1924.
,, BECKER (W.) Die Sage v. d. Höllenfahrt Christi in d. altfranz. Lit., 1923.
,, BELLARMINO (R. F. R.) De septem verbis lib. 2, 1618.
,, BENEDICT XIV, *pope*. De festis J. C. &c., 1859.
,, BERGUER (G.) Some aspects of the life of J.; tr., 1923.
,, BESELIN (L. C.) In periocham Fl. Josephi de J. C. exercit., 1673.
,, BETHELL (A. J.) Cleopatra to Xt., 4v, 1921.
,, BILLUART (C. R.) Tract. de mysteriis Chr. &c., 1860.
,, BRANDES (G.) J., 1927.
,, BRUCE (A. B.) Parabolic teaching of C., 1889.
,, BURGESS (T.) Remarks on gen. tenour of New Test. reg. nature &c. of J. C., 1831.
,, BURKITT (F. C.) Earliest sources for the life of J., n. & rev. ed., 1922.
,, BURNEY (C. F.) The poetry of our Lord &c., 1925.
,, CAMPBELL (R. J.) Life of Xt., 1921.
,, CASAUBON (I.) De rebus sacris &c. exercit. 16, de J. C. nativ., vita &c., 1655.
,, CASSANDER (G.) Comm. de duabus in Christo naturis &c., 1555.
,, CHAPMAN (J.) J. C. & the present age &c., 1895.
,, CHRIST. Medit. on the life of C.; ed. C. D'Evelyn, 1921.
,, —— A stanzaic life of C.; comp. f. Higden's Polychronicon &c.; ed. F. A. Foster, 1926.
,, CONNOR (R.) The friendly four & o. s. [of the life of J.], 1926.
,, COUCHOUD (P. L.) Enigma of J.; tr., 1924.
,, DALMAN (G. H.) Orte u. Wege Jesu, 1919.
,, DANZ (J. A.) Inaug. C. ad doc. haud obscurior Mosaica, e spect. circa bapt. C., 1717.
,, DEISSMANN (G. A.) Relig. of J. & the faith of Paul; tr., 1923.
,, DOUGALL (L.) & C. W. EMMET. Lord of thought, 1922.
,, DÜRER (A.) Passion of our Lord, 1844.
,, EDERSHEIM (A.) Life &c. of J., 6th ed., 2v, 1891.
see ELLICOT (CH. J.) Hist. lect. on life of J. C., 4th ed., 1865.
,, FAIRBAIRN (A. M.) Xt. in the centuries, 1893.
,, FAIRWEATHER (W.) J. & the Greeks, 1924.
,, FRANCISCI (A.) Theses de ascensione C. in coelum &c., 1589.
,, FRANKS (J. C.) Evidences of Xty. in discourses of our Lord, 1821.
,, FRANTZE (W.) Disput. de persona J. C., 1605.
,, GARDNER-SMITH (P.) The narratives of the Resurrection, 1926.
,, GESNER (S.) Orthod. confess. de persona & officio J. C. &c., 1604.
,, GLOVER (T. R.) J. in the experience of men, 1921.
,, GOODWIN (T.) Christ set forth &c., 1841.
,, GSCHWIND (C.) Die Niederfahrt C. in d. Unterwelt, 1911.
,, GUIGNEBERT (C.) Le problème de J., 1914.
,, GUNKEL (H.) Ein Vorläufer Jesu, 1921.
,, HALL (G. S.) J., the Xt., in the light of psychology, 2v, 1921.
,, HAMBURG. Responsio ministr. eccl., quae est Hamburgi &c. ad confess. A. Osiandri, de mediatore J. C., 1553.
,, HARDING (R. W.) Authority of J., 1922.
,, HASSIA. De unione personali duarum in una persona Domini nostri naturarum &c., 1587.
,, HEADLAM (A. C.) J. C. in hist. & faith, 1925.
,, —— Life & teaching of J. the Xt., 1923.
,, HEINE (J. E. C.) Diss. de C. ad Abgarum epist., 1759.
,, HILL (G. F.) The medallic portraits of Xt. &c., 1920.
,, HUYDECOPER (T. C. R.) Comm. de solenni J. C. in urb. Hierosol. introitu, 1829.
,, ISRAEL *ben Jehudah*. Sendschr. betreff. J. d. Mann v. Gott, 1704.
,, JEANES (H.) Dr. Hammond h. Ἐκτενέστερον: or, A greater ardency in Xt.'s love of God &c., 1657.
,, —— *Treatise conc. the fulnesse of Xt., 1656.
,, JENKINSON (E. J.) Unwritten sayings of J., 1925.
,, KENEALY (E. V. H.) Testament of J., 1901.
,, KEYSERLING (H., *Graf* v.) Menschen als Sinnbilder (J. d. Magier), 1926.
,, KIDD (J.) Diss. on eternal sonship of Christ, 1872.
,, KLAUSNER (J.) Jesus of Nazareth, life, times, &c.; tr., 1925.
,, KÖHLER (W.) Wie Luther d. Deutschen d. Leben J. erzählt hat, 1917.
,, LÖBER (G. F.) Obs. ad hist. vitae & mortis J. C., 1767.
,, LOWEY (H.) Die myst. Bezeichnungen J. C. als Siloë, Schiloh u. Piscis, 1888.

Jesus Christ [*continued*].

see LUDWIG (E.) Der Menschensohn, 1928; tr., 1928.
,, LUTHER (M.) Das J. C. eyn geborner Jude sey, 1523.
,, MACLER (F.) Miniatures arméniennes: vies du Christ &c., 1913.
,, MARAN (P.) *Divinitas J. C. &c., 1746.
,, MARCHANT (*Sir* J.), *ed.* Anthology of J., 1926.
,, MARSHMAN (J.) Defence of deity &c. of J. C., 1822.
,, MASCOVIUS (G.) Disput. de majest. divina Christi hominis, 1607.
,, MASEFIELD (J.) Trial of J.: a play, 1925.
,, MATTHEW, *vardapet.* Meditations on the Passion (*in Armenian*), 1759.
,, MAULBRONN. Epitome colloquii, de majestate hominis Chr. &c., 1564.
,, MELLOR (S. A.) Jesus of Nazareth: addr. on the hist. J., 1926.
,, MORE (P. E.) The Christ of the New Test., 1924.
,, —— Christ the Word, 1927.
,, MORIES (A. S.) Christ's secret doctrine &c., 1917.
,, MURRY (J. M.) Life of J., 1926.
,, NICOLAI (M.) Consid. de κενώσει J. C., 1676.
,, OSIANDER (A.) Tractatus de omnipraesentia C., 1587.
,, PAPINI (G.) Hist. du C.; tr. de P. H. Michel, 1922.
,, —— Storia di Cristo, 1921; 4ª ed., corr., 1923.
,, —— Story of C.; tr., 1923.
,, PARKER (J.) The inner life of C., 3v, 1889–90.
,, PHILLIMORE (*Mrs.* J. S.) *By an unknown disciple [*fiction*], 1920.
,, PIEPENBRING (C.) The hist. J.; tr., 1924.
,, PINDER (U.) Speculum passionis Domini nostri I. C. &c., 1507.
,, RASHDALL (H.) J., human & divine, 1922.
,, RAWLINSON (A. E. J.) New Test. doct. of the C., 1926.
,, REYNOLDS (E.) Works: Life of Christ &c., 1678.
,, SAELDEN HORT (Der): alemann. Gedicht v. Leben J. &c.; hrsg. H. Adrian, 1927.
,, SARTORIUS (C. F.) Caussarum cur C. scripti nihil reliq. disq., 1815.
,, SCHENCKE (J. H.) De Christi scriptis, 1687.
,, SCHUBART (W.) Das Weltbild Jesu, 1927.
,, SCHULTHESS (J.) De uno argumenti pro divinitate J. &c., 1828.
,, SCHURÉ (E.) Fr. Sphinx to C.; tr., 1928.
see SCHWEITZER (A.) Mystery of the Kingdom of God; tr. Lowrie, 1925.
,, —— Quest of the hist. J.; tr., 2nd Eng. ed., 1922.
,, SCOTT (E. F.) Ethical teaching of J., 1925.
,, SERLE (A.) Horæ solitariæ: names & titles of J. C., 1868.
,, SICHEM (C. v.) De Kindsheyd onses Heeren I. C., 1617.
,, SPENCER (F. A. M.) Civilization remade by C., 1928.
,, STALKER (J.) Life of J. C., n. ed., 1891.
,, STEGMANN (J.) Studii pietatis icon, Christognosia &c., 1689.
,, STIER (E. R.) Words of the Lord J.; tr., 8v, 1855–58.
,, —— Words of the risen Saviour &c.; tr., 1869.
,, TAULER (J.) Les exercises sur la vie de J. C.; tr. par J. Talon, 1670.
,, —— Exercitia super vita & passione Salvatoris nostri, 1565; 1572.
,, TAYLOR (J.) The Great Exemplar: life of C., 4th ed., 3p, 1667.
,, TAYLOR (V.) Hist. evidence for the Virgin Birth, 1920.
,, TEMPLE (W.) Christus veritas, 1925.
,, TIMMERMANS (F.) Het Kindeken J. in Vlaanderen, *n.d.*
,, TISSOT (J. J.) Life of J. C.: compositions f. Gospels, w. notes &c.; tr., 2v, 1897.
,, VIGNON (P.) The shroud of C.; tr., 1902.
,, WALDSCHMIDT (E.) & W. LENTZ. Stellung J. im Manichäismus, 1926.
,, WALKER (T.) What J. read, His dependence &c., 1925.
,, WALTER (J. A.) Cod. in Suida mendax de J., 1724.
,, WARSCHAUER (J.) Historical life of Xt., 1927.
,, WESLEY (J.) *J., altogether lovely; letter, 1780.
,, WESLEY (S.) The life of J. C.: an heroic poem, 1697.
,, WILLIAMS (H. W.) Priesthood of C., 1876.
,, WOLLE (C.) Schediasma de J. spirituali in Anglia redivivo &c., 1730.
,, WUJEK (J.) Zywot y nauka pana naszego J. C., 1597.
,, XAVIER (H.) Historia C., *Pers. & Lat.*, 1639.
,, ZANCHIUS (H.) Theses de iis quae de J. C. post union. praed. &c., 1582.
,, ZWINGLI (U.) In Evangel. hist. de Domino Nostro J. C., 1539.

***Jeu** (Le) des eschecs, avec s. invent., sci. & practique. Tr. d'Espagnol [par Delessand]. 8º. 1609

Jeudwine (John Wynne).
Obs. on Eng. criminal law & procedure. 8º. 1920
Religion, commerce, liberty, 1683–1793. 8º. 1925
Studies in empire & trade. 8º. 1923

Jeune (John Frederic Symons-). 800 years of the Order of the hospital of St. John of Jerusalem. [P2576]. 8º. 1922

Jevakhov (*prince* **Nikolai Davidovich**) [Жеваховъ].
Воспоминанія. t1, 1915–17. 8º. Мюнхенъ. 1923

Jever Colloquy, *1576, see* FEUSTKING (J. H.) Hist. Colloquii Ieverensis, 1707.

Jevons (Frank Byron).
The idea of God in early religions. s8º. C. 1910

Jevons (Herbert Stanley). The future of exchange & the Indian currency. 8º. [Allahabad]. 1922

Jew. International Jew (The): the world's foremost problem. Repr. of articles in The Dearborn Independent, May–Oct., 1920. s8º. 1920
,, ,, for v2, *see* JEWISH activities, 1921.
*Kurtze beschreibung &c. v. e. Juden mit Namen Ahasverus (Leyden, 1602, *facs.*), *see* FREYTAG (G.) Bilder, B4, 1925.

Jewel (John), *bp. of Salisbury.*
Apologia eccl. Anglicanae. s8º. Londini. 1584
,, ,, ... s8º. Londini. 1626
The apology of the Church of Eng. [Tr. by Lady Bacon]. s8º. 1635
An expos. upon the 2 Epist. to the Thessalonians. [Ed. J. Garbrand]. s8º. [1583]

Jewell (H. H.) & F. W. Hasluck. The church of Our Lady of the Hundred Gates in Paros. [Byz. Res. Fund]. fol. 1920

Jewellery. *Cat. of an important assemblage of jewellery, 18th cent., Russ. state j., 1927, *see* CATALOGUE.

Jewett (Charles C.) On the construction of catalogues of libraries. 2nd ed. 8º. Wash. 1853

Jewish.
*Aspects of J. life & thought, *see* EPSTEIN (M.) Letters, s1, 1922.
*Essays on J. life & thought, *see* EPSTEIN (M.). Letters, s2, 1924.
*Jewish activities in the U.S. [Internat. Jew, v2. *Repr. f.* Dearborn Independent]. 8º. 1921
*Jewish (The) peril. Protocols of the learned elders of Zion. [*Publ. by S. Nilus. Based on* Joly (M.) Dial. aux enfers, 1864]. 5th ed. 8º. 1921
,, ,, *see* TRUTH about "The Protocols," 1921.
,, ,, ,, WOLF (L.) J. bogey & the forged protocols, 1920.
*Little bk. of J. cookery, *n.d.*, *see* COOKERY.

Jewish Historical Society of England.
Miscellanies. pl. la8º. 1925
Transactions, 1918–20, 1921–23. [v9, 10]. s4º. 1922–24
see WOLF (L.), *ed.* Jews in the Canary Islands; tr. &c., 1926.

Jewish quarterly review. New ser., v5–7 (1914–17). 8º. Phila. [1914–17]

Jewitt (Orlando), *see* HARTSHORNE (C. H.) Illust. of Alnwick, Prudhoe &c. [by O. J.], 1857 ?.

Jewry. Brit. J.: bk. of honour [1914–18], 1922, *see* ADLER (M.), *ed.*

Jews. *Brief answer to objections agst. Jews &c., 1656, *see* COLLIER (T.)
Forms of prayer acc. to custom of Span. &c. Jews, w. Eng. tr. by D. A. De Sola, 3v, 1836–37, *see* TEPHILOTH.
*Short (A) & easie method w. the Jews, 4th ed., 1715, *see* LESLIE (C.)

Jèze (Gaston). Les dépenses de guerre de la France. [C.E. for Int. Peace]. 8º. [1926]

Jiménez (Juan Ramon). Jardines lejanos. [*Poems*]. s8º. 1904
Poesías escojidas, 1899–1917. [Hisp. Soc. of Amer.] 8º. N.Y. 1917
Segunda antolojía poética, 1898–1918. s8º. 1920

Jiménez Catalán (M.) & J. Sinués y Urbiola. Hist. de la Univ. de Zaragoza. 2t. la8º. Zaragoza. 1922–23

Jiménez de la Espada (Marcos), *see* TAFUR (P.) Andanças é viajes, 1435–39; [*ed. w. notes &c. by* M. J. de la E.], 1874.

Jiménez de Quesada (Gonzalo) [QUESADA (G. J. DE); XIMENEZ DE QUESADA (G.)], *see* GRAHAM (R. B. C.) The conq. of New Granada: life of G. J. de Q., 1922.

Jinakīrti Sūri, *disciple of Somasundara.* Gesch. v. Pāla u. Gōpāla; [Text, Übers. &c. v. J. Hertel], *see* KÖNIGL. SÄCHS. GESELLS. Berichte, B69, 1917.

Jireček (Constantin Josef). La civilisation serbe au m. â. Tr. L. Eisenmann. Préf. de E. Denis. 8º. 1920
Gesch. d. Serben, B2i (1371–1537), 1918, *see* GESCHICHTE DER EUROP. STAATEN.
Staat u. Gesellschaft im mittelalt. Serbien: St. z. Kulturgesch. d. 13.–15. Jhdts., T1, 2, 4, *see* KAISERL. AKAD. D. W. z. WIEN. Denkschr., B56, 64, 1913–20.

Jirku (Anton). Der Kampf um Syrien-Palästina im orient. Alt., *see* ALTE ORIENT (DER), 25, 1926.
Die Wanderungen d. Hebräer im 3. u. 2. vorchr. Jahrt., *see* ALTE ORIENT, 24, 1925.

Jirmunsky (Viktor Maksimovich) [Жирмунский].
Валерий Брюсов и наследие Пушкина. la8º. П. 1922

Joachim II, *elector of Brandenburg, see* STEINMÜLLER (P.) Einführ. d. Reform. in Brandenburg durch J. II, 1903.

Joachim, *abbot of Fiore* [GIOCCCHINO; JOACHIM, VON FLORIS; JOACHIM DE FLORE]. L'évangile éternel. Tr. préc. d'une biog. par E. Aegerter. 2t. 8º. 1928
1, Vie de J. de F. 2, L'évang. étern.

Joachim Ernest, *Prince of Anhalt, see* AMLING (W.) Christl. Trostpredigt &c., 1587.

Joachim (Erich) & M. Klinkenborg. Familien-Gesch. d. gräfl. Finck von Finckensteinschen Geschlechts. 2T [T2, Urkunden]. la8°. 1920–21

Joachimi (Albert), *see* AARSSENS (F. v.) Verbaal van de ambassade van A., J. &c. naar Engeland, 1625, 1867.

Joachimus (Joannes Major), *see* MAJOR (J.), *von Joachimsthal.*

Joad (Cyril Edwin Mitchinson).
Common-sense ethics. Pref. A. H. W. Carr. 8°. [1921]
Common-sense theology. 8°. [1922]
The highbrows. s8°. [1922]
Intr. to mod. philosophy. s8°. 1924
Intr. to mod. polit. theory. s8°. O. 1924
Thrasymachus: or the future of morals. s8°. 1925

Joan, *pope* [JOANNA *papissa*].
*Joannae papissae vita, *see* ROSARIUS (S.) Antithesis Christi & Antichristi &c., 1578.
*Viri docti anon. judicium de S. M. J. restituta. s8°. *n.p.* 1703
see DESMARETS (S.) Joanna &c., 1658.
see LABBE (P.) De script. eccl., t1 (Cenotaphium J. P.), 1660.
,, SPANHEIM (F.) De Papa foemina &c., 1691.
,, —— Hist. de la Papesse Jeanne, 2t, 1720.
,, STALENUS (J.) Papissa monstrosa &c., 1639.

Joanna II, *queen of Naples; 1370–1435, see* FARAGLIA (N. F.) Storia d. G. II d'Angiò, 1904.

Joanne. *Collection des Guides-Joanne.* Arles. s8°. 1907
Avignon & ses environs. s8°. 1909
Nîmes. s8°. 1909
Trouville, Honfleur &c. s8°. 1892

Joanne (Adolphe L.)
Géographie du dépt. de Vaucluse. 7e éd. s8°. 1906

Joannes, *de Caulibus, see* DEANESLY (M.) Gospel harmony of J. de C., or S. Bonaventura, 1922.

Joannes, *Climacus, see* BALL (H.) Byzantin. Christentum: 3 Heiligenleben [*i.e.* J. &c.], 1923.

Joannes, *de Falkaberga* [JOANNES PARVUS; JOHANN V. FALKEBERG]. Tres tractatuli, *see* †Gerson (J.) Opera, t5, 1706.

Joannes, *abbot of Fürstenfeld* [JOHANN]. Ein gesprech vom Glück u. ewiger Ordnung, oder schickung, das man Fatum nennet, aller ding. Inns Teütsch transsferiert. [P2439]. s4°. Augsburg, *H. Steiner.* 1544

Joannes, *bp. of Gerona* [J., *Gerundensis*]. Paralipom. Hispaniae, *see* HISPANICA. Rer. Hisp. scr., t1, 1579.

Joannes, *de Irlandia, see* IRLAND (J.)

Joannes, *de Lemmege, see* LEMEGO (J. v.)

Joannes, *de Mirecourt, see* BIRKENMAJER (A.) Verm. Unters. (Ein Rechtfertigungsschreiben J. v. M.), 1922.

Joannes, *Nevelonis, see* JEAN, *le Névelon.*

Joannes, *Parisiensis, Frater Ord. Prædic., d. 1206* [JEAN QUIDORT], *see* GRABMANN (M.) St. zu J. Quidort v. Paris, O. Pr., 1922.

Joannes, *Parvus, see* JOANNES, *de Falkaberga.*

Joannes, *Philosophus, Ozniensis, see* JOHN IV, *of Otzun, patriarch of Armenia.*

Joannes, *abbas Reom., see* JONAS, *Elnon.* Vitae SS. Columbani, Vedastis, J.; red. B. Krusch, 1905.

Joannes *a Rubino, see* ANTONIO MARIA *da Vicenza* & J. *a R.* Lex. Bonavent., 1880.

Joannes, *de Segovia, see* BIBLE: CONCORDANCES. *C. majores sacræ Bibliæ; Alter C. tomus, qui est partium indeclin. [*by J. de S.*], 1540.

Joannes, *Victoriensis.* Liber certarum hist. (Chron. Carinthiæ). Ed. F. Schneider. [Scr. rerum Germ. in usum schol.] 2t. 8°. Hannoverae. 1909–10

Joannes, *Vitoduranus* [JOHANN, *v. Winterthur*]. Chronik. In Verbindung mit C. Brun hrsg. F. Baethgen. [Mon. Germ. Hist. Scr. rerum germ., n.s., t3]. 8°. 1924

Joannes Franciscus, *Brixianus.* Habes isto volumine lector candidiss. quatuor: primum approbatas religiosis quibusqʒ vivendi regulas &c. [Coll. & ordin. per D. Jo. Fran. Brixianū]. [2p.] 4°. [Rothomagi, *Joh. Richard.* 1510]

Joannes Josephus, *bp. of Soissons, aft. abp. of Sens, see* LANGUET DE LA VILLENEUVE DE GERGY (J. J.)

Joannidès (A.) La Comédie-Française de 1680–1920. Tableau des représent. par a. & par pièces. 8°. 1921

Joannis (Georg Christian).
see CONRADUS, *Schirensis.* Chron. Schir., accur. G. C. J., 1716.
,, TOLNERUS (C. L.) Add. ad hist. Palatinam: quibus ad object. [G. C. J.] respondetur, 1709.

João, *de Portel.* Livro do registro das cartas dos beẽs e erãcas q̃ dõ J. de P. teue nestes reinos; [ed.] P. A. de Azevedo, *see* ARCHIVO HIST. PORTUG., v4–7, 1906–9.

João de S. Joseph, *Brother, see* QUEIROZ DA SILVEIRA (J. DE).

Job (Zephaniah), *see* FARMER (S. S.) Wise to win souls; mem. of Z. J., 1857.

Jobson (Frederick James), *D.D.*
America & American Methodism. 8°. [1857]
Australia; w. notes by the way on Egypt, Ceylon, Bombay & the Holy Land. 8°. 1862
Chapel & school architecture. 8°. 1850

Jochelson (Waldemar). Archaeolog. investig. in the Aleutian Islands. [C.I. of Wash., 367]. 4°. Wash. 1925

Jöcher (Christian Gottlieb). De Opheorum vel Orpheorum haeresi. [P426]. s4°. [Lipsiae. 1730]

Jociscus (Andreas), *Silesius.* Oratio de ortu, vita & obitu J. Oporini. Adj. Librorum per J. O. excusorum cat. s8°. Argentorati. 1569

Jodelle (Etienne). Cléopatre captive. Tragédie. s8°. 1925

Joelson (F. S.) The Tanganyika Territory (form. German E. Africa). 8°. [1920]

Joergensen (Johannes).
Sainte Catherine de Sienne. 7e éd. 8°. 1920

Joets (Jules). Les "tailleurs d'ymaiges" de Saint-Omer & les maîtres du 14e au 18e siècle. 8°. Saint-Omer. 1920

Joffre (Alphonse). Mandat de la France sur la Syrie & le Grand-Liban. la8°. Lyon. 1924

Joffre (*le maréchal* **Joseph Jacques Césaire).** Disc. de réception [*on* J. Claretie. Acad. Fr. 19 déc. 1918. P2819]. s8°. 1919
1914–1915. La prépar. de la Guerre & la conduite des opér. s8°. 1920
The 2 battles of the Marne. By J., the ex-Crown Prince of Germany, Marshal Foch, Marshal Ludendorff. 8°. [1927]
see HANOTAUX (G.) & *Lt.-Col.* FABRY. Joffre, 1921.
,, LAUZANNE (S.) Le Père J., 1923.

Jogiches (Leo).
see KAUTSKY (C.) R. Luxemburg, L. J. &c., 1921.
,, RADEK (C.) Rosa Luxemburg, L. J. &c., 1921.

Johann *v. Falkeberg, see* JOANNES *de Falkaberga.*

Johann, *Abt. zu Fürstenfeld, see* JOANNES, *abbot of F.*

Johann Georg, *Herzog zu Sachsen, see* JOHN GEORGE, *duke of Saxony.*

Johann (Johann Christian Jung-), *see* JUNG-JOHANN (J. C.)

Johannesbuch (Das) d. Mandäer. [Hrsg.] v. M. Lidzbarski, 2p *in* 1v. (1, Text; 2, Einl., Übers., Komm.) la8°. Giessen. 1915

Johannessohn (Martin). Der Gebrauch d. Präpositionen in d. Septuaginta, *see* KÖNIGL. GESSELS. D. W. ZU GÖTT. Nachr., Beih., 1925.

Jóhannesson (Alexander). Gramm. d. urnord. Runeninschr. [German. Bibl.; hrsg. W. Streitberg.] s8°. Heidelberg. 1923

Johannet (René).
Anatole France, est-il un grand écrivain? s8°. [1925]
Eloge du bourgeois français. [Cahiers verts, 39]. s8°. 1924

Johannis (Erasmus). De unigeniti Filii Dei existentia, inter E. J. & F. Socinum disput. s8°. *n.p.* 1595

Johannsen (Otto). Geschichte d. Eisens. 2. A. la8°. 1925

Johansen (K. Friis), *see* CORPUS vasorum ant.: Danemark, par C. Blinkenberg &c., 1924–.

Johansen (P.) Phidias & the Parthenon sculptures. Tr. I. Andersen. 8°. 1925

Johansson (Carl Ferdinand). Skt. *nivātá*—'windstill(e), *see* KUNG. HUM. VET.-SAMF. I UPPSALA. Skr., B24, 1927.
Üb. d. altind. Göttin Dhiṣạ̄na &c., *see* KUNG. HUM. VET.-SAMF. I UPPSALA. Skr., B20, 1917.

John. *John Sherman & Dhoya, 1891, *see* YEATS (W. B.)

John VI, *patriarch of Armenia, called the Historian* [JOHN *catholicus*]. Hist. d'Arménie. Tr. par J. Saint-Martin. [*Ed., w.* "Not. s. la vie &c. du Patriarche" *par F. Lajard*]. 8°. 1841
[Hist. of the Armenians. *In Armenian. Ed.* M. Emin. *a. c. b. w.* Lazarus *of Pharp.* Letter, 1853]. 8°. Moskva. 1853

John, *of Austria, son of Charles V, 1547–78, see* BROSCH (M.) Don J. d'A. in d. Niederl., 1576–78, *n.d.*

John, *of Austria, son of Philip IV of Spain, see* HISPANIA. Hispania illustrata: w. papers f. Don J. of A. &c., 1703.

John, *the Baptist.*
see ANANIAS, *the translator.* On Jonah & J., *in Armenian*; ed. B. Sargisean, 1899.
,, CANISIUS (P.) Comment. de verbi Dei corruptelis lib. 1 de J. Bapt. historia &c., 1571.

John, *the Baptist* [*continued*].
see CANISIUS (P.) Comm. de verbi Dei corruptelis lib. 1, de J. B. hist. evangelica &c., 1577.
„ MEAD (G. R. S.) The gnostic J., 1924.
John VI, *catholicus, see* JOHN VI, *patriarch of Armenia.*
John [COLOMBINI], *Saint, see* BELCARI (F.) Prose, t1, Vita d. B. Giov. C., riv. &c. O. Rainaldi, 1843.
John, *of the Cross, Saint.* Aphorismes. Texte établi & tr., & préc. d'une intr. par J. Baruzi. [Bibl. de l'Ecole des Hautes Et. Hisp., fasc. 9]. la8°. Bordeaux. 1924
see BARUZI (J.) St. J. de la Croix & le problème de l'expér. mystique, 1924.
John, *of Damascus, Saint.* Libellus de his qui in fide dormierunt ex Graeco in Lat. versus per L. Nogarolam &c. s4°. [Ratisponę, *Johann Khol*]. 1532
Opera omnia. Ex var. ed., &c. Lat. versa atque annot. illustr. &c. M. Lequien. 2t. fol. Parisiis. 1712
see LUPTON (J. H.) St. J. of D., 1882.
John, *the Deacon* [HOVHANNES *Sarkavag*], *d. 1129.* Alothamatoytz. [Prayer-book. *In Armenian.* Soferq Hayk., v17]. s8°. i Venetik. 1854
[On the priesthood &c.; *in Armenian.* Soferq Hayk., v3]. s8°. i Venetik. 1853
[Panegyrics of Gregory the Illuminator, *by* J., Vardan & John of Ersnka; *in Armenian.* Soferq Hayk., v5]. s8°. i Venetik. 1853
John, *king of England, see* COURT OF KING'S BENCH. Curia Regis rolls, Richard I & J., 1922–26.
John, *of Ephesus.* Lives of the Eastern saints: Syriac text, ed. & tr. E. W. Brooks, p1–3, *see* GRAFFIN (R.) & F. NAU. Patr. Or., t17–19, 1923–26.
John, *of Ernska, see* JOHN *the Deacon.* [Panegyrics of Gregory the Illuminator, by J. &c., *in Armenian*], 1853.
John, *the Evangelist, Saint.* Eccles. Ephesinae de obitu J. apost. narr. Ex vers. Armen. saec. 5. Lat. prod. curavit J. Catergian. [*Arm. & Lat.*; P2792]. 8°. Viennae. 1877
see BIBLE *for Gospel, Epistles & Comm.*
John II, *king of France.* The ransom of J. II, 1360–70; ed. D. M. Broome, *see* CAMDEN MISC., v14, 1926.
see FRANCE. Les Grandes chron. de F.: Chron. de Jean II &c.; publ. R. Delachenal, t3, 4, 1920.
John, *of Irlande, see* IRLAND (J.)
John I, *Mandakouni, patriarch of Armenia, 480–87.* Una lettera tr. dall' Armeno d. E. Teza. [Dagli Atti d. R. Accad. di Padova, v6. P2795]. 8°. Padova. 1890
[Sermons. *In Armenian.* 2nd ed. P2810]. 8°. i Venetik. 1860
John IV, *of Otzun, patriarch of Armenia* [OZNIENSIS]. Opera, per J. B. Aucher Lat. redd. [*Arm. & Lat.*] 8°. Venetiis. 1834
[Oration against the fantastics. *In Armenian*]. 8°. i Venetik. 1807
[Works. *In Armenian. Foll*[d]. *by Works of* Theodor Khertenavor & Sahak catholikos]. 8°. i Venetik. 1833
John, *of Petritzos, see* MARR (N. YA.) I. П., груз. неоплатоникъ 11–12 вѣка, 1909.
John VIII, *pope. For pope Joan, reckoned by some as John VIII, see* JOAN, *pope.*
John XXII, *pope* [JACQUES D'EUSE]. Jean XXII, 1316–34: lettres communes anal. d'ap. les registres dits d'Avignon & du Vatican par G. Mollat &c. [Ecoles Franç. d'Athènes & de Rome]. t2–8. 4°. 1905–24
Jean XXII, 1316–34: lettres secrètes & curiales rel. à la France, extr. des registres du Vatican par A. Coulon. [Ecoles Franç. d'Athènes & de Rome]. t1, ann. 1–4. 4°. 1906
see ALEXANDRE (N.) Apolog. pro J. XXII, 1862.
John XXIII, *pope.*
see HUNGER (C.) Zur Gesch. Papst J. XXIII, 1876.
„ NIEM (T. DE). De vita & fatis Constantin. J. XXIII, 1416, 1697.
„ REINKE (G.) Frankreich u. J. XXIII, 1900.
John, *de Portel, see* JOÃO *de Portel.*
John I, *king of Portugal.*
see EANNES DE ZURARA (G.) Crónica da tomada de Ceuta por J. I.; publ. F. M. Esteves Pereira, 1915.
„ LOPES (F.) F. L., v2, 3, Cron. de J. I, 1921–22.
John IV, *king of Portugal, see* BARRETO (J. F.) Rel. da embaixada a França em 1641 &c., 1918.
John, *Prester.*
see BERMUDEZ (J.) Rel. da embaix. que J. B. trouxe do P. J., 1565, 1875.

John, *Prester* [*continued*].
see CASTANHOSO (M. DE). Hist. das cousas que C. da Gama fez nos reynos do P. J. &c., 1564, 1875.
„ DRESSER (M.) De statu eccl. &c. in Æthiopia sub Praecioso J., 1584 ?.
„ GOES (D. DE). Fides, religio, moresque Æthiopum sub imperio J. &c., 1540.
„ ROSS (*Sir* E. D.) Prester J. & the Empire of Ethiopia, 1926.
John, *of Salisbury, bp. of Chartres.* Epistolæ, 1154–80 [*ed.* J. Mossonus], *see* SYLVESTER II, *pope.* Epistolæ, 1611.
Hist. pontificalis quae supersunt. Ed. R. L. Poole. 8°. O. 1927
The statesman's bk. of J. of S. 4th, 5th, & 6th bks., & sel. f. 7th & 8th bks., of the Policraticus. Tr. w. intr. by J. Dickinson. 8°. N.Y. 1927
see POOLE (R. L.) The early corresp. of J. of S., 1924.
John, *Sarkavag, see* JOHN *the deacon.*
John, *Elector of Saxony.* Der . . . Fursten . . . Johansen, Hertzogē zu Sachsen . . . Georgen, Marggrafen zu Brandenburg &c. Protestation auff dem Reichsstage zu Speyr wider den ersten Artickel desselben Religion. s4°. [Speier ?]. 1529
see LUTHER (M.) Zwo Predigt ü. d. Leiche d. Kurf. J. zu S., 1532.
„ SCHMEIZEL (M.) Quaest an elect. Sax. Johannes ante obitum in castra Pontif. transiverit ?, 1718.
John *of Tarone* [KOZERN *or* GOZERN], *see* MARR (N. YA.) Сказаніе о камолшкосѣ Петрѣ и ученомъ I. К. [*w. text*], 1895.
John, *abp. of Thessalonica, Saint; d. c. 630.* Discours [*Gr. & Lat.*], *see* MARY, *the Virgin.* Homélies mariales byz.; éd. &c. M. Jugie, p2, 1926.
John, *of Thlkouran* [Hovhannes *Thlkourantzin*], *15–16 c.*
see KOSTANEANTZ (K.) H. Th. & his poems [*in Armenian*], 1892.
John, *Vanandetzi, see* BENIK, *Vardapet.*
John, *of Worcester, see* HOWORTH (*Sir* H. H.) Chron. of J. of W. prev. assigned to Florence of W., 1916.
John a Kent & John a Cumber [*play*]; repr., 1923, *see* MUNDAY (A.)
John Albert I, *Duke of Mecklenburg, 1525–76.* Epistola ad Illyricum [*i.e. M. Flacius*] de Osiandrica hæresi. s8°. [Rostock ?. 1556]
see SCHREIBER (H.) J. A. I, Herzog v. M., 1899.
John Casimir, *Count Palatine of the Rhine.* De libro Concordiae a quibusdam theologis ed., admonitio Christiana scr. à theologis in ditione Ioh. Casimiri. s4°. Neustadii in Palat. 1581
John Frederick, *called the Magnanimous, duke of Saxony, & elector.* Des Churfürsten Lands Ordenung von ubermessiger Kleidung (*facs.* 1546), *see* FREYTAG (G.) Bilder, B3, T2, 1924.
Eyn Schreiben &c. s4°. Marburg. 1546
Vorantwortung so. J. F., Hertzog zu Sachsen auff itzt gehaltenem Reichstage zu Speir schrifftlich hat fürwenden lassen, wider Julius Pflugs der sich Electum zur Naumburg that nennen &c. [P2439]. s4°. [Wittemberg, *Georg Rhaw*]. 1542
Warhafftiger Unterricht etzl. Handlungen, die sich Bapst Pauli III Concilii halben, das er gegen Mantua bestimpt hat zw. D. Math. Held u. den Churfürst &c. auff nähist berürter Stende zu Smalkalden gehaltenem tage, zu getragen haben. [*w. add. of:* Bulla Bapst's Pauli III]. s4°. Wittemberg. [*G. Rhaw*]. 1537
see AUGSBURG. Anzeigung u. bekantnus des Glaubens &c. zu Augspurg [*signed* J. F. *&c.*], 1530.
„ CHARLES V, *Emp.* Artickel d. fürgenumen Concilium betreff., Hertzog Hannsen Friderich v. Sachsen überschickt, Antwort H. F. &c., 1533.
John Frederick II, *duke of Saxony, the Intermediate.* Confession u. Bekentnis d. Glaubens d. Fürsten J. F. d. mitlern, Johans Wilhelm, u. Johans Fridrichen d. jüngern hertzogen zu Sachsen &c. ubergeben auffm landtage zu Weimar a. 1549. [Sig. A5–8 & B1–8 *wanting*]. s4°. Königsberg in P. *n.d.* [1550 ?]
Des Durchleucht. J. F. &c. Confutationes &c. [*b. w. Latin version below,* 1559]. s4°. Jhena. 1559
Illustr. Princip. J. F. II suo ac fratrum Joannis Vuilhelmi & Johannis Friderici jun. nomine confutatio praecip. corruptelarum &c. hoc. temp. ad instaurat. regni Antichristi Rom. Pontif. aliarum fanaticarum opinionum contra veram S. Scripturae, Confess. Aug. & Schmalkald. Articul. relig. s4°. Jenae. 1559

John George I., *Prince of Anhalt*, *see* HOYM (C. VON). Erinnerungschrifft etlicher vom Adel u. Städten; sampt darauff erfolgten Verantwortung [*by J. G.*] &c., 1597.

John George I, *elector of Saxony*, *1611–56* [*b. 1585*]. Solida decisio 4 illorum inter aliquos theologos Aug. Conf. controv. capitum &c. Cum mandato J. G. s4°. Lipsiae. 1624

John George II, *elector of Saxony*, *1656–80* [*b. 1613*].
see PFEIFFER (A.) Jahr-Opfer J. G. dem Andern, 1670.

John George, *Prince*, *duke of Saxony* [JOHANN GEORG], *1869–*.
Das Katharinenkloster am Sinai. 8°. L. 1912
König Albert v. Sachsen. 8°. 1922
Streifzüge durch die Kirchen u. Klöster Ägyptens. 8°. L. 1914
Tagebuchblätter aus Nordsyrien. 8°. L. 1912

John Khamé, *Abba*. The life of Abba J. K.; Coptic text ed. & tr. by M. H. Davis, *see* GRAFFIN (R.) & F. NAU. Pat. Or., t14, 1920.

John Salvator, *archduke of Austria* [JEAN ORTH], *see* FAUCIGNY-LUCINGE (A. DE). L'archiduc J.-S., 1911.

John William, *Elector Palatine*, *see* PALATINATE. Electa juris publici hist. Palat. illustr. [In causa ducissae Aurel. contra electorem Palat.], 1700.

John (Augustus E.) A. John. [Plates, w. descr. &c. signed A. B.] la8°. 1923

John (Gwen). The prince. s8°. O. 1923

John (Ivor B.) The Mabinogion. [P2586]. s8°. 1901

John (Wilhelm). Erzherzog Karl, der Feldherr u. seine Armee. Mit Beiträgen v. O. Criste, J. Hirn Ritter v. Hoen u. a. Im Auftr. d. Kuratoriums hrsg. v. W. J. fol. Wien. 1913

John Carter Brown Library. Bibliotheca Americana. Cat. of the J. C. B. Lib. in Brown Univ., Providence, Rhode Island. 2v [*in 4p. Each p. is b. sep., pagin. cont.*] la8°. Providence. 1919–22

John Company, *see* EAST INDIA COMPANY.

John Rylands Library, *Manchester*.
Bulletin. v5–11. la8°. M'ter. 1918–27
Cat. of exhib. illust. hist. of transmission of the Bible, w. intr. sk. by [H. Guppy]. In commem. of 400th ann. of publ. of Tindale's New Test., 1525. 8°. M'ter. 1925
Cat. of exhib. of mediaeval &c. MSS. & jewelled book-covers. 8°. M'ter. 1924
Cat. of exhib. of the earliest pr. eds. of Greek & Lat. classics &c.; w. intr. by [H. Guppy]. 8°. M'ter. 1926
A descriptive cat. of the Latin MSS., by M. R. James. 2v. 4°. M'ter. 1921
John (The) Rylands Library, 1899–1924: record of its hist., &c. By H. Guppy. la8°. M'ter. 1924
see FAWTIER (R.) La Bible hist. toute figurée de la J. R. L., 1924.
,, RIVERS (W. H. R.) Dreams & primitive culture, 1917–18.

Johns (Bennett George). *No appeal. 3v. s8°. 1870
*Once & for ever. Passages in the life of curate of Danbury. 3v. s8°. 1874
*Saved by a woman. 3v. s8°. 1872

Johns (Charles Alex.) Brit. birds in th. haunts. Ed., rev. &c. by J. A. Owen. [repr.] 8°. 1910
Flowers of the field. Rev. & ed. C. Elliott. 8°. 1907
Forest trees of Brit. 10th ed. rev. by G. S. Boulger. 8°. 1912

Johns (*Rev.* Claude Hermann Walter).
Ancient Babylonia. s8°. C. 1913
Assyrian deeds & doc. recording the transfer of property, chiefly of 7th c., B.C. v3, 4, v4 ed. by h. wife, w. biog. sketch [by R. C. Thompson] &c. 8°. C. 1901–23

Johns (David), *see* FREEMAN (J. J.) & D. J. Narr. of the persec. of Xtns. in Madagascar, 1840.

Johns (*Maj.* Richard). The naval & milit. heroes of Gt. Brit., or Calendar of victory. Contin. &c. by P. H. Nicolas. s8°. 1860

Johns (Rowland). Mind you, or Lewys lad & h. friend Shadrach. s8°. [1922]

Johns Hopkins University. REPRINT OF ECONOMIC TRACTS.
see BERKELEY (G.) The querist, 1735–37, 1910.
,, FAUQUIER (F.) Ways & means for raising money &c. (1756), 1915.
,, MASSIE (J.) Natural rate of interest, 1750, 1912.
,, RICARDO (D.) 3 letters on price of gold, 1809, 1903.
,, VANDERLINT (J.) Money answers all things, 1734, 1914.
,, WEST (E.) Applic. of capital to land &c., 1815, 1903.
Studies in hist. & polit. science. s40iv, N.S., 2, 3. 8°. Baltimore. 1922–25
see HSIEH (P. C.) Govt. of China, 1644–1911, 1925. [N.S., 3.]
,, NAKANO (T.) Ordinance power of the Japanese emperor, 1923. [N.S., 2.]
,, THACH (C. C.) The creation of the presidency, 1775–89, 1923. [40iv.]

Johns Hopkins University [*continued*].
Studies in Romance Lit. & Lang. v4, 5. 8°. Baltimore. 1925
see MILLER (M. H.) Chateaubriand & Eng. lit., 1925. [4.]
,, WOODBRIDGE (B. M.) Gatien de Courtilz, Sieur du Verger, 1925. [5.]

Johnson Club. J. C. papers; by var. hands. [2nd ser. ed. G. Whale & J. Sargeaunt]. s8°. 1920

Johnson (A. Forbes). First cent. of printing at Basle. la8°. 1926
French 16th cent. printing. la8°. 1928
The Italian 16th cent. la8°. 1926

Johnson (Alfred Edward Webb-), *see* WEBB-JOHNSON (A. E.)

Johnson (Allan Chester), *see* ABBOTT (F. F.) & A. C. J. Municip. admin. in Roman Emp., 1926.

Johnson (Allen).
The historian & historical evidence. 8°. N.Y. 1926
Jefferson & h. colleagues. 8°. New Haven, *Yale*. 1921

Johnson (Andrew), *Pres. of the U.S. of America*, *see* CHADSEY (C. E.) Struggle betw. J. & Congr. over reconstruct., 1896.

Johnson (Anthony). Hist. acc. of sev. Eng. translations of the Bible. s8°. 1730

Johnson (Arthur Henry). The age of the enlightened despot, 1660–1789. 10th ed. s8°. [1923]
Europe in the 16th cent., 1494–1598. s8°. 1897
,, ,, ...s8°. 1898
,, ,, ...6th ed. s8°. 1914
Hist. of the Co. of the Drapers of London. v3–5. la8°. O. 1922

Johnson (*Capt.* Charles). Gen. hist. of the pirates. Ed., w. pref. by P. Gosse. [2v]. 4°. *Cayme Press*. 1925–27
Gen. hist. of the robberies & murders of the most notorious pirates, to pres. year [*i.e.* 1724]. Ed. L. Hayward. la8°. 1926
Hist. des pirates anglais, avec la vie etc. de Marie Read & Anne Bonny. Tr. sur l'éd. de 1774. Préf. de P. MacOrlan. s8°. [1921]
see GOSSE (P.) Bibliog. of works of C. J., 1927.

Johnson (Charles), *dramatic writer*.
The country lasses. [P2864]. s8°. *Tonson*. 1735

Johnson (Clarence Richard). Constantinople to-day, or The Pathfinder Survey of C. [*By var. wr.*] Under dir. of C. R. J. Foreword by C. F. Gates. 8°. N.Y. 1922

Johnson (Cornelius) [JONSON], *see* FINBERG (A. J.) Chron. list of portraits by C. J., 1922.

Johnson (Douglas Wilson). Battlefields of the World War: W. & S. fronts. [Amer. Geog. Soc. Res. Ser. No. 3 *& Maps, in case, sep.*] 8°. N.Y. 1921

Johnson (Emory Richard). Hist. of domestic & for. commerce of the U.S. By E. R. J., T. W. Van Metre, G. G. Huebner &c. Intr. by H. W. Farnam. [C.I. of W.] repr. 2v [*in* 1]. la8°. W. 1922

Johnson (Frederic), *see* SUFFOLK. S. manorial families; ed. J. J. Muskett, v3, cont. by F. J., 1900–14.

Johnson (Grove).
The student's manual of yeast culture. 8°. [1908]

Johnson (John). A short acc. of Ann Rogers. [Publ. by J. Wesley. P2675]. s8°. Bristol. 1770

Johnson (John), *M.A.*, *vicar of Cranbrook*. *Case (The) of a rector refusing to preach a visit. sermon: being Rev. G. Huntley's defence, 1642, & The case of occasional days &c. [*b. w. h.* Clergyman's vade mecum, p2, 1723]. s8°. *n.p. n.d.*
* Clergyman's vade mecum. 2p. [p1, 5th ed. 2, 3rd ed.] s8°. 1723

Johnson (John Fulde), *see* BRIT. & FOR. ANTI-SLAVERY SOC. Proc. of Gen. Anti-slavery Convention, June 1843; by J., 1843.

Johnson (Joseph). Noble women of our time. 8°. 1886

Johnson (Julia Mehitable). A list of publications of the descendants of Epes Sargent. [Repr. f. Epes Sargent of Gloucester &c.] la8°. *n.p.* [1923]

Johnson (Lionel). The art of T. Hardy. Chap. on the poetry, by J. E. Barton & bibliog. by J. Lane. n. ed. s8°. 1923

Johnson (Martin). Camera trails in Africa. 8°. [1924]

Johnson (P. H.), *F.R.G.S.*, *see* DOUGLAS (A. J. A.) & P. H. J. South Seas of to-day; cruise of yacht St. George, 1926.

Johnson (Reginald Brimley). Fanny Burney & the Burneys. Ed., w. intr. by R. B. J. 8°. [1926]
A new study of Jane Austen interp. thr. "Love & friendship," *see* VILLARD (L.) Jane Austen; tr. V. Lucas &c., 1924.
Some contemporary novelists (men). s8°. [1922]
,, ,, ...(women). s8°. [1920]

Johnson (Reverdy). An argument to establish the illegality of milit. commissions in the U.S. &c. [P2625]. 8°. Baltimore. 1865

Johnson (Richard), *town clerk of Hereford.* Ancient customs of the city of Hereford &c. [*a. tp. lithographed*]. 4o. 1868
Johnson (Richard Francis). Night attacks. s8o. 1886
Johnson (Robert), *of Edinburgh.* Mem. to be communicat. to Mr. R. J. [? *by* Rob. Douglas], *see* MAIDMENT (J.), *ed.* Hist. fragms., p2, 1833.
Johnson (Robert), *writer on photography,* **& A. B. Chatwood.** Photography, artistic & scientific. 8o. 1895
Johnson (Rossiter). Short hist. of the War of Secession, 1861–65. 8o. Boston. 1888
Johnson (Roswell Hill), *see* POPENOE (P.) & R. H. J. Applied eugenics, 1920.
Johnson (S. Webb-), *see* WEBB-JOHNSON (S.)
Johnson (Samuel), *LL.D.* [*Dr.* JOHNSON].

Works. n. ed., w. essay by A. Murphy. 12v. 8o. 1823
„ „ 11v. *la. paper.* la8o. O. 1825
10, 11, Debates in Parl., 1740–43.
Critical opinions. Arr. &c. w. intr. by J. E. Brown. 8o. Princeton. 1926
The fountains: a fairy tale. [repr.] s8o. 1927
Johnson on Shakespeare. Essays &c., sel. w. intr. by W. Raleigh. [repr.] s8o. 1916
Journey to the W. Islands of Scotland & Boswell's Journal of a tour to the Hebrides w. S. J. Ed. R. W. Chapman. 8o. 1924
*The life of R. Savage. Added, the lives of Sir F. Drake & Adm. Blake. By the a. of The rambler. 4th ed. s8o. 1769
Lives of the poets. Ed. Mrs. A. Napier, w. intr. by J. W. Hales. 3v. s8o. *Bohn.* 1900
Poet. works. Coll. by T. Park. s8o. 1805
*The prince of Abissinia [*i.e.* Rasselas]. 5th ed. s8o. 1775
„ „ ....6th ed. s8o. 1783
Rasselas. s8o. 1809
*Taxation no tyranny; ans. to the resolutions &c. of the American Congress. s8o. 1775
see ADDISON (J.) Crit. on Paradise lost; w. remarks on versific. of Milton by S. J., 1805.
see BOSWELL (J.) B.'s note-book (1776–77), rec. partic. of J.'s early life, 1925.
„ —— Life of J., *var. ed.*
„ CHAPMAN (R. W.) Proposals for new ed. of J.'s letters, 1926.
„ *COLLECTION (A) of epitaphs, w. essay on epitaphs by Dr. J., 2v, 1806.
„ COLLINS (A. S.) Authorship in the days of J., 1927.
„ HARMSWORTH (C.) Dr. J. a gt. Englishman, 1923.
„ —— Dr. J.'s house, 1924.
„ HAWKINS (L. M.) Gossip about Dr. J. &c.; ed. F. H. Skrine, 1926.
„ JOHNSON CLUB. J. C. papers [2nd ser.], 1920.
„ LONGMAN (C. J.) A letter of Dr. J. &c., 1928.
„ MATHEWS (ELKIN). Cat. of bks. by or rel. to Dr. J. & h. circle, for sale by E. M., 1925.
„ READE (A. L.) Johnsonian gleanings, p3, 4, The Doctor's boyhood, p5, Life, 1728–35, 1922–28.
„ REYNOLDS (*Sir* J.) J. & Garrick: 2 dialogues, 1927.
„ SERVOIS (J. P.) Notice sur la vie &c. d. S. J., 1823.
„ SPITTAL (J. K.) Contemp. crit. of Dr. J., h. works & biogr., 1923.

Johnson (Samuel), *Rector of Corringham.*
Essay conc. parliaments. Repr. f. 1694 ed. [P2782]. 8o. 1817
Julian the Apostate. s8o. 1782
Works. [*Pref.* Some memorials of S. J.] fol. 1710
Johnson (Samuel), *pastor of Oyo.* Hist. of the Yorubas to the begin. of the Brit. Protectorate. Ed. Dr. O. Johnson. 8o. 1921
Johnson (Stanley Currie). The medal collector: guide to medals & ribbons. s8o. 1921
Johnson (T. H.), *see* DONCASTER. D. Regional Planning Scheme: Rep. prep. for Joint Comm. by P. Abercrombie & T. H. J., 1922.
Johnson (Thomas). A handbook for rebels. Extr. f. speeches of Sir E. Carson &c. [1911–18]. 3rd ed. [P2530]. 8o. [1918]
Johnson (Thomas), *mezzotinter, see* MURDOCK (K. B.) Portraits of I. Mather, w. notes on T. J., 1924.
Johnson (W. Branch). Folktales of Brittany. 8o. [1927]
Folktales of Provence. s8o. 1927
Johnson (William), *Rom. Cathol. priest, see* BAXTER (R.) The successive visibility of the Church &c. agst. W. J., 1660.
Johnson (William Ernest). Logic. 3p. 8o. C. 1921–24
Johnson (William Eugene), [*ps.* PUSSYFOOT]. The Federal Gov. & the liquor traffic. 2nd ed. rev. & enl. s8o. Westerville, Ohio. [1917]
The liquor problem in Russia. s8o. Westerville, Ohio. 1915
Prohibition in Kansas. [P2431]. s8o. Westerville, Ohio. [1918 ?]
Ten years of prohibition in Oklahoma. [P2419]. s8o. [Westerville. 1918 ?]
Johnson (William Percival), *archdeacon of Nyasa.* Nyasa, the gt. water. Intr. by Bp. of Oxford. s8o. 1922
Johnson (Willis Fletcher). The hist. of Cuba. 5v. 8o. N.Y. 1920

Johnsoun (Thomas). Protocol book, 1528–1578. Ed. J. Beveridge & J. Russell. [Scot. Rec. Soc.] 8o. E. 1920
Johnston (Alex. Keith), *the elder, 1804–71.* Atlas to Alison's Hist. of Europe, 1855; libr. ed., 1875, *see* ALISON (*Sir* A.)
The royal atlas of mod. geogr. Add. & corr. to pres. date by T. B. Johnston. n. ed. lafol. E. 1891
Johnston (Alex. Keith), *the younger, see* JOHNSTON (W.) & A. K. J. Map to illust. Russo-Jap. question, 1904.
Johnston (Arthur), *M.D.* [JONSTONUS (A.)]
Poemata omnia. s8o. Middelb. Zeland. 1642
Johnston (Edward).
Writing & illuminating, & lettering. 13th ed. s8o. [1923]
Johnston (George Alexander).
The development of Berkeley's philosophy. s8o. 1923
Internat. social progress: work of the I. Labour Organ. of the League of Nations. 8o. [1924]
Johnston (*Sir* Harry Hamilton).
The backward peoples & our rels. w. them. [The world of to-day]. s8o. 1921
Comparative study of the Bantu & Semi-Bantu languages. v2. s4o. O. 1922
The man who did the right thing. s8o. 1921
Mrs. Warren's daughter. A story of the Woman's movement. s8o. 1920
Story of my life. 8o. 1923
The Veneerings. Novel. s8o. 1922
Johnston (Hugh).
*St. Martin-in-the-Fields past & present. s8o. [1925]
Johnston (J. Caldwell-), *see* CALDWELL-JOHNSTON (J.)
Johnston (Leslie), *see* BEVAN (E. R.) Memoir of L. J., 1921.
Johnston (M. F.) Coronation of a king; ceremonies &c. of all ages. 8o. 1902
Johnston (Mary).
Admiral of the Ocean-Sea. s8o. [1923]
Croatan. s8o. [1924]
The exile. s8o. [1927]
The great valley. s8o. [1926]
Michael Forth. s8o. [1920]
Silver Cross. s8o. [1922]
Sir Mortimer. 2nd impr. [of 1920 reissue]. s8o. *n.d.*
The slave ship. s8o. [1925]
Johnston (Myrtle). Hanging Johnny. s8o. [1927]
Johnston (Robert Matteson). Arms & the race: foundations of army reform. s8o. N.Y. 1915
Johnston (Thomas Brumby), *see* JOHNSTON (A. K.) Royal atlas of mod. geogr.; add. & corr. to pres. date by T. B. J., 1891.
—— **& J. A. Robertson.** Hist. geography of the clans of Scotland. [With map]. 4o. E. 1872
Johnston (*Lt.-Col.* Thomas R. St.), *see* SAINT-JOHNSTON (T. R.)
Johnston (W.) *of Edinb.,* **& A. K. Johnston,** *younger.* Map to illust. Russo-Japan. question. *folded.* 8o. [1904]
Johnston (William), *Amer. novelist.* Les plaisirs de l'obèse, nouvelle; tr. H. Béraud, *see* ŒUVRES libres, 23, 1923.
Johnston (William Alfred). Geology of Fraser River delta map-area. [*With map.* Canada. Geolog. Survey. P2753]. 8o. Ottawa. 1923
Sediment. of the Fraser river delta. [Canada. Geolog. Survey. P2624]. 8o. Ottawa. 1921
Winnipegosis & Upper Whitemouth River areas, Manitoba: pleistocene & recent deposits. [*With map.* Canada. Geolog. Survey. P2753]. 8o. Ottawa. 1921
—— **& W. L. Uglow.** Placer & vein gold deposits of Barkerville, Cariboo dist., B. Columbia. [Canada. Geolog. Survey]. 8o. Ottawa. 1926
Johnstone *of Johnstone, The family of, see* FRASER (*Sir* W.) The Annandale family book of the J., Earls &c. of A., 2v, 1894.
Johnstone (*Miss* C. L.) The Brit. colony in Russia. 8o. [1897]
Johnstone (G. H.) Prosper Mérimée, a mask & a face. 8o. [1926]
Johnstone (James), *of Liverpool.*
Introd. to oceanography. 8o. Liv'l. 1923
The mechanism of life in rel. to mod. physical theory. 8o. 1921
A study of the oceans. 8o. 1926
—— **A. Scott & H. C. Chadwick.** The marine plankton, w. spec. ref. to investig. at Port Erin, Isle of Man, 1907–14. Intr. by Sir W. A. Herdman. 8o. Liv'l. 1924
Johnstone (Sydney James).
Potash. New ed., rev. & enl. by S. J. J. 8o. 1922
Johnston-Lavis (Henry James). Bibliog. of geol. &c. of volcanoes of S. Italy. Comp. w. assist. of Antonia J.-L 2nd ed. by B. M. Stanton, ed. w. pref. &c. by B. B. Woodward. la8o. 1918
***Joint** compositions [*verse*], 1840 ?, *see* LUSHINGTON (*Sir* F.) & H. LUSHINGTON.

Joint Legislative Committee Investigating Seditious Activities, *New York.* Report, 1920, *see* NEW YORK.

Joinville (*le prince* **de)** [†FRANCIS FERD. P. L. M. [D'ORLÉANS], *p. de J.*] *Note s. l'état des forces navales de la France. [P2830]. 8°. 1844

Joinville (Jean de). Memoirs; cont. hist. of the life of Louis IX. Added notes & diss. of M. Du Cange &c. Tr. T. Johnes. 2v. 4°. 1807

Jokai (Mor), *see* BENYOWSKI (*c.* M. A.) Saját emlékiratai és útleirásai. Fordította J. M., 2k, 1888.

Jokl (Norbert). Albanisch, *see* GRUNDRISS d. indogerman. Sprach- u. Altertumskunde, Abt. 2, B3, 1917.

Joliclerc (Eugène). Sous la griffe. s8°. 1922

Joliet (Albert) & F. Mercier. Le musée de Dijon. s8°. [1924 ?]

Joline (Adrian Hoffman). At the library table. 8°. Boston. 1910
Edgehill essays. 8°. Boston. 1911

Jolivet (Alfred).
W. Heinse, sa vie & s. œuvre jusqu'en 1787. 8°. 1922

Jolli (J. G.) *Hist. de Pologne, & du grand-duché de Lituanie, j. present. s8°. Amsterdam. 1698

Jollie (*Mrs.* **Ethel Tawse),** *wife of J. T. Jollie, form. Colquhoun, see* COLQUHOUN (*Mrs.* E.)

Jolliffe (*Sir* **William George),** *see* HYLTON (W. G. J., *baron*).

Jollivet (Gaston). Ma folle jeunesse: choses vues, *see* ŒUVRES libres, 64, 1926.
Le siège de Paris & la Commune, *see* ŒUVRES libres, 80, 1928.

Jolly (Julius), *of Würzburg.* G. Bühler, 1837–98. [Grundr. d. indo-ar. Phil., B1, H1A]. la8°. Str. 1899
Medicin. [Grundr. d. indo-ar. Phil., B3, H10]. la8°. Str. 1901
Recht u. Sitte. [Grundr. d. indo-ar. Phil., B2, H8]. la8°. Str. 1896

Joly (Alexandre). L'industrie à Tétouan, *see* MISSION SCIENT. DU MAROC. Archives, v8, 11, 15, 18, 1906–12.

Joly (Aristide). Benoît de Ste.-More & le roman de Troie, *see* †SOC. DES ANTIQ. DE NORMANDIE. Mém., s3, v7, 1869.
Note sur Benoet du Lac ou le théâtre & la Bazoche à Aix à la fin du 16e. s. 8°. Lyon. 1862
see WACE (R.) La vie de Ste. Marguerite, poème, suivi de l'analyse du Mystère de Ste. M. par A. J., 1879.

Joly (John), *F.R.S.* Radioactivity & the surface hist. of the earth. Halley Lect., 1924. 8°. O. 1924
Reminiscences & anticip. 8°. [1920]
Surface-history of the earth. 8°. O. 1925

Joly (Maurice).
see JEWISH peril: Protocols *based on J.'s Dialogue, 1864,* 1921.
,, TRUTH about "The Protocols" (*publ. by* S. Nilus), 1921.

Jomini (Alexandre de). *Etude diplomat. sur la Guerre de Crimée, 1852–56. Par un Anc. Diplomate [*i.e.* A. de J.] 2t. 8°. St. Pétersb. 1878
Россія и Европа въ эпоху Крымской Войны [*Tr. f.* Etude diplom. sur la Guerre de Crimée, par un anc. diplomate (*i.e.* Jomini). *Extr. f.* Вѣстникъ Европы, 1886, *no tp.*] 8°. [С.-П. 1886]

Jomini (*le baron* **Antoine Henri de).** An expos. of the first princ. of grand milit. combinations &c. With remarks &c. by J. A. Gilbert. 8°. 1825

Jônain (Pierre Abraham).
Dict. du patois saintongeais. 8°. Royan. 1869

Jonas, *Elnon.* Vitae Sanctorum Columbani, Vedastis, Johannis. Rec. B. Krusch. [Scr. rerum Germ. in usum schol.] 8°. Hannoverae. 1905

Jonas, *bp. of Orleans.* Vita recta & antiqua sive qualiter omnes homines vitam Deo placitam ducere oporteat. s8°. Duaci. 1645

Jonas (Justus) [*formerly* KOCH (JODOKUS)]. Annot. in Acta Apostol. s8°. Norembergæ, *I. Petreius.* 1524
Das siebend Capitel Danielis, von des Türcken Gottes lesterung u. morderey. s4°. Wittemberg, [*Hans Lufft.* 1529 ?]
see AUGSBURG. Acta Comiciorum Augustae ex litt. Philippi, J. & aliorum ad M. L.; hrsg. G. Berbig, 1907.
,, ENCHIRIDION oder e. Handbuchlein &c. [nach d. Urdruckke, 1524 zu Erfurt v. J. J. &c. hrsg.], 1848.
,, KNAPP (G. C.) Narr. de J. J., 1817.
,, REINHARD (L.) Comm. de vita &c. J. J. & M. L., 1731.
——, **M. Caelius &c.** Vom Christlichen abschied aus leben d. D. Martini Lutheri bericht durch J. I., M. Celium, u. ander die dabey gewesen, kurtz Zusammengezogen. [P2439]. s4°. Wittemberg, *Georg Rhaw.* 1546

Jonathan, *ben Uzziel, see* HARDT (H. v. D.) Hoseas, ant. Chaldaicâ J. paraphrasi, &c., 1775.

Joncières (Léonce de). Médusa, courtisane venitienne, nouvelle, *see* ŒUVRES libres, t69, 1927.

Joncquel (Octave) & T. Varlet.
L'agonie de la terre. s8°. Amiens. 1922
Les Titans du ciel. s8°. Amiens. 1921

Jondet (Gaston). Atlas hist. de la ville & des ports d'Alexandrie. [Soc. Sultanieh de Géogr. Mém., t2]. fol. Le Caire. 1921
Les ports submergés de l'anc. Île de Pharos, *see* INSTITUT EGYPTIEN. Mém., t9, 1916.

Jon Duan. *J. D.; by a. of "The coming K—— &c., 1874, *see* DOWTY (A. A.) & S. O. BEETON.

Jones & Co., *publishers.* Jones' views of the seats, mansions, castles &c. of Eng., Wales, Scotl. & Ireland. sl, 2 *in* 3v [1i, ii]. la8°. 1829
The above title is taken f. the engraved gen. tp. The 3 vol. containing views of seats &c. in Wales, Scotland & Ireland are wanting.

Jones (Amy Hemingway). Carnegie Endowment for Internat. Peace: organiz. & work, *see* INTERNAT. CONCILIATION, N°. 200, 1924.

Jones (Anna M.), *see* FITZRANDOLPH (H. E.) & M. D. HAY. Rural indust. of Eng. & Wales, v4, Wales, by A. M. J., 1927.

Jones (Arthur).
The period of the industrial revol. s8°. [1914]

Jones (Arthur Stuart Duncan-), *see* DUNCAN-JONES (A. S.)

Jones (C. Sheridan). Bolshevism, its cause & cure. Foreword by F. Harrison. s8°. [1920]
Short life of Washington. s8°. 1920

Jones (Cecil Knight). Hispanic Amer. bibliographies. Comp. by C. K. J., w. crit. notes on sources by J. T. Medina. la8°. Baltimore. 1922

Jones (Chester Lloyd). Mexico & its reconstruction. 8°. 1921

Jones (Clement Wakefield), *C.B.*
Brit. merchant shipping. 8°. 1922

Jones (D.), *Jesuit.* Chapters on casuistry. [*Extr. f. The Month, v8. b. w.* Coleridge (H. J.) Reviews, 1871]. 8°. 1868

Jones (D. Caradog), *see* CARR-SAUNDERS (A. M.) & D. C. J. Survey of soc. struct. of Eng. & Wales illust. by statistics, 1927.

Jones (Daniel), *M.A.*
Phonetic transcriptions of Eng. prose. 2nd ed. s8°. O. 1921
Pronunciation of English. 2nd ed. [repr.] s8°. C. 1919
see TROFIMOV (M. V.) & D. J. Pronunciation of Russian, 1923.

Jones (David Thomas), H. M. Conacher, &c. Rural Scotland dur. the War. By D. T. J., H. M. C., J. F. Duncan, W. R. Scott. App. by J. P. Day & intr. by W. R. Scott. [C.E. for Internat. Peace.] la8°. 1926

Jones (E. Alfred).
The Loyalists of New Jersey: memorials &c. f. Eng. records. [New Jersey Hist. Soc., Coll. 10]. 8°. Newark, N.J. 1927
Mem. of old North Wales. Ed. E. A. J. 8°. 1913
The old plate of the Cambridge colleges. 4°. C. 1910
see FARRER (W. F.) Cat. of coll. of old plate; comp. by E. A. J., 1924.

Jones (E. Stanley).
The Christ of the Indian road. [repr.] s8°. [1927]

Jones (Edgar Rees).
Sel. Eng. speeches f. Burke to Gladstone. s8°. [1913]

Jones (Edward), *Bard, of Henblas.*
Musical and poetical relicks of the Welsh Bards &c. Likewise a hist. of the Bards &c. 4°. 1784

Jones (Emily Beatrix Coursolles), *aft. Mrs. F. L. Lucas.*
Inigo Sandys. s8°. 1924
Quiet interior. s8°. [1920]

Jones (Enid, *Lady*), *wife of Sir Roderick Jones.* *Serena Blandish or the difficulty of getting married. By a Lady of Quality. s8°. 1924
,, ,, ...[*n. impr.*] s8°. 1925

Jones (Ernest), *M.D.*
Essays in applied psycho-analysis. 8°. 1923
Papers on psycho-analysis. rev. & enl. ed. [repr.] 8°. 1920
,, ,, ...3rd ed. 8°. 1923
A psycho-analytic study of Hamlet. Repr. [*no tp.*] 8°. 1922
,, ,, *For a. copy see h.* Essays in applied psycho-analysis, 1923.
Social aspects of psycho-analysis. Lect. by E. J., J. Glover, J. C. Flügel &c. Ed. E. J. s8°. 1924
see FERENCZI (S.) Psycho-analysis & the war neuroses; by S. F., E. J. &c., 1921.

Jones (Ernest Lester). Elem. of chart making, 1916, *see* UNITED STATES: COMMERCE.

Jones (Evan), *mate, see* †TEMPLE (*Sir* R. C.) Wreck of the "Doddington," 1755; repr. of anon. pamph. & acc. by J., 1902.

Jones (George Ellis). Hygiene & war. Intr. by W. H. Burnham. Ed. P. Monroe. [C.E. for Int. Peace.] la8°. Wash. 1917

Jones (Grosvenor Monro). Navigation laws: 1916, *see* UNITED STATES: COMMERCE.

Jones (H. A.), *M.C.* Over the Balkans & S. Russia: hist. of No. 47 Squadron R.A.F. 8°. 1923

see WAR. Hist. of the Gt. W.: War in the air, v2, by H. A. J., 1928.

Jones (H. Chapman).

Intr. to photography. 3rd ed. rev. & enl. s8°. 1895

Jones (*Sir* Harford), *aft. Brydges, see* KAJARS. *Dynasty of the K., tr. f. Pers. MS. [of Abd. Al-Razzaq ibn Najaf Kuli] by H. J. B., 1833.

Jones (Harold Spencer). General astronomy. 8°. 1922

Jones (Harrie Stuart Vedder). Spenser's defence of Lord Grey. [Illinois: Univ. St. in Lang. & Lit., v5iii]. la8°. Urbana. 1919

Jones (Henry), *of Drogheda.* Earl of Essex, *see* INCHBALD (*Mrs.* E.) Brit. theatre, v22, 1808.

Jones (Henry), *D.D., dean of Kilmore.* A remonstrance of divers remarkeable passages conc. the Church & Kingdome of Ireland, presented by H. J. to the H. of C., *see* †SOMERS (J. *b.*) Coll. of tracts, v5, 1811.

Jones (*Sir* Henry), *M.A., of the Univ. of Glasgow &c.* Browning as a philosoph. & relig. teacher. [repr.] s8°. [1912]

A faith that enquires. Gifford lect. 8°. 1922

Tennyson, 1909, *see* BRIT. ACAD. Proc., 1909–10.

see HETHERINGTON (H. J. W.) Life & letters of Sir H. J., 1924.

—— & J. H. Muirhead.

The life & philosophy of Edward Caird. 8°. Glasgow. 1921

Jones (Henry Arthur).

Shakespeare & Germany. 2nd ed. [P2466]. 8°. 1916

Talks w. playgoers. No. 1, Municipal & repertory theatres. Lect. With introd. letter. 2nd ed. [P2466]. 8°. 1913

What is capital? s8°. 1925

Jones (Henry Festing).

Castellinaria & o. Sicilian diversions. [re-issue]. s8°. 1920

Diversions in Sicily. [re-issue]. s8°. 1920

Mount Eryx & o. diversions of travel. 8°. [1921]

see CAMBRIDGE. ST. JOHN, COLL. OF. Samuel Butler Coll.: cat. & comm. by H. F. J. &c., 1921.

Jones (Henry Stuart).

see LIDDELL (H. G.) Greek-Eng. lex.; n. ed. rev. & augm. by H. S. J., pl, 2, 1925–26.

,, ROME. Cat. of anc. sculptures: Palazzo d. Conserv.; ed. H. S. J., 1926.

Jones (Ifano). Hist. of printing & printers in Wales to 1810, & of printers to 1923, also Hist. of printing &c. in Monmouthshire to 1923. la8°. Cardiff. 1925

Jones (Inigo). Designs for masques & plays at Court: descr. cat. of drawings &c. in coll. of the Duke of Devonshire; intr. & notes by P. Simpson &c., *see* WALPOLE SOC., v12, 1924.

see GOTCH (J. A.) I. J.: mod. view, 1927.

Jones (J. Morlais).

The cup of cold water & o. sermons. 8°. 1894

Jones (James Felix). Memoirs: steam-trip to N. of Baghdad, 1846—Anc. Nahrwan canal—Topog. of Nineveh &c. Ed. R. H. Thomas. [Sel. f. Rec. of Bombay Govt. N.S. 43]. la8°. Bombay. 1857

Jones (James P.) Hist. of the S. Staffordshire Regt., 1705–1923. 8°. Wolverhampton. [1923]

Jones (Jean), *see* WALKER-TISDALE (C. W.) & J. J. Butter & cheese, 1920.

Jones (John), *M.B.* Medical, philosoph., & vulgar errors, consid. & refuted. 8°. 1797

Jones (John), *perpetual curate of Cradley, Worcestershire.* Bp. Hall, h. life &c. App., cont. some of h. writings. 8°. 1826

Jones (John), *servant.* John Jones, an old servant: an acc. of h. life wr. by himself, *see* SOUTHEY (R.) Lives &c. of the uneducated poets; ed. J. S. Childers, 1925.

Jones (John), *virtuoso, d. 1882, see* VICTORIA & ALBERT MUS. Cat. of J. Coll., 3p, 1922–24.

Jones (John Andrews). Bunhill memorials. Sacred remin. of 300 ministers &c. buried in Bunhill Fields. Ed. J. A. J. s8°. 1849

Jones (John Bavington). The records of Dover. The charters, record books &c. of the Corpor., w. the Dover Customal. 8°. Dover. 1920

Jones (John Harry). Economics of private enterprise. 8°. 1926

Social economics. 8°. [1919]

Jones (*Sir* John Morris-).

Sir John Rhŷs. [Brit. Acad. P2834]. 8°. [1926]

see EVANS (J. G.) Taliesin: or the critic [*i.e.* Sir J. M.-J.] criticised, 1924.

Jones (*Sir* John Thomas), *1st bart.*

The war in Spain, Portugal, S. of France, 1808–14. Plates. 4°. *n.d.*

Jones (Lance G. E.)

Training of teachers in Eng. & Wales. 8°. 1924

Jones (Llewellyn Rodwell) & P. W. Bryan. North America: hist., econ. & regional geog. 8°. [1924]

Jones (Margaret Sefton-), *see* SEFTON-JONES (M.)

Jones (Maurice), *D.D.*

The four Gospels: th. lit. hist. &c. s8°. 1921

Jones (Michael), *died 1649, see* KERR (A. W. M.) An Ironside of Ireland: career of Lt.-Gen. M. J., gov. of Dublin &c., 1923.

Jones (Neville). The stone age in Rhodesia. Foreword by Sir A. Keith. 8°. 1926

Jones (Owen Thomas). Lead & zinc, N. Cardiganshire & W. Montgomeryshire, *see* GEOLOG. SURVEY. Spec. rep. on min. resources, 20, 1922.

Jones (P. Mansell).

Emile Verhaeren: devel. of h. art & ideas. 8°. Cardiff. 1926

Jones (Peter), *Indian missionary.* A coll. of Ojebway & Eng. hymns &c. s8°. Toronto. 1860

Jones (Philip L.), *see* BILLUPS (R. S.) & P. L. J. Lab. cond. in the shoe ind. in Mass., 1925.

Jones (Robert), *R. A.* Art of skating. Rev. w. add. by W. E. Cormack. s8°. [1855]

A new treatise on artificial fireworks. s8°. 1765

Treatise on skating. 8°. [1772]

Jones (Robert Edmond), *see* MACGOWAN (K.) & R. E. JONES. Continental stagecraft, 1923.

Jones (Robert H.) Asbestos & asbestic. 8°. 1897

Jones (Rufus Matthew).

Fundamental ends of life. s8°. [1924]

The later periods of Quakerism. 2v. 8°. 1921

New studies in mystical religion. Ely Lect., N.Y., 1927. 8°. 1927

The remnant. s8°. [1920]

Jones (Stephen). *Hist. of Poland, to 1795. 8°. 1795

Jones (Stephen K.), *see* HARRIS (J. R.) & S. K. J. The Pilgrim press at Leyden, 1922.

Jones (Susan Carleton), *see* CARLETON (S.), *ps.*

Jones (Sydney R.) Art & publicity, fine printing & design. Ed. G. Holme. [Studio: Spec. Autumn No., 1925]. 4°. 1925

Posters & publicity: fine printing & design. [Studio: Spec. Autumn No., 1926]. la8°. 1926

Posters & their designers. Ed. G. Holme. [Studio: Spec. Autumn No., 1924]. la8°. 1924

Jones (T. Wynne-), *see* WYNNE-JONES (T.)

Jones (Thomas), *Chaplain of St. Saviour, Southwark.* Works. Pref. a short acc. of h. life. 4th ed. 8°. 1775

Jones (W. Lewis).

King Arthur in hist. & legend. [2nd ed.] s8°. C. 1914

Jones (Walter), *J.P.*

Capital & labour duties &c. s8°. Westminster. 1921

Jones (Will Owen). By land & sea: obs. &c. of travel in Gt. Brit. 8°. Lincoln, Nebraska. [1923]

Jones (William), *M.A., Baptist minister.* The dissenter's plea for h. nonconformity. 8°. [1845]

Mem. of the life &c. of the Rev. Adam Clarke. 8°. 1834

Jones (*Sir* William), *the Orientalist.* Works. 6v. 4°. 1799

A Gram. of Persian lang. 5th ed. 8°. 1801

The Indian game of chess, & The Burmha game of chess comp. w. the Indian &c. by Capt. H. Cox, *see* AUNGERVYLE SOC. Reprints, s2, 1883.

Letters chronolog. arrang. from Lord Teignmouth's collection. 2v *in* 1. s8°. *n.p.* 1821

Mem. of the life, studies &c. of G. Horne, bp. of Norwich. 2nd ed. 8°. 1799

Poems consist. chiefly of trans. f. the Asiatick languages. Added, two essays. s8°. O. 1772

Poeseos Asiaticae comment. libri 6. Subj. Limon seu miscell. liber. 8°. Londini. 1774

Poet. works. Coll. by T. Park. 2v. s8°. 1808

Jones (William Henry).

Hist. of the Port of Swansea. s4°. Carmarthen. 1922

Jones (William Henry Samuel). The doctor's oath: essay in the hist. of medicine. 8°. C. 1924
Malaria, a neglected factor in hist. of Greece & Rome. Intr. by Sir R. Ross & conclud. chap. by G. G. Ellett. [re-issue]. s8°. C. [1920]

Jones (William Hiter).
Federal taxes & state expenses. 8°. N.Y. 1887

Jones (William Lloyd-), *see* LLOYD-JONES (W.)

Jones (William Tudor). The making of personality. s8°. 1920
Nature, thought & personal experience. 8°. 1926

Jonescu (Take). Les questions roumaines du temps présent. [*By*] T. J., D. Hurmuzesco, V. Dimitriu &c. Avant-propos de R. Poincaré. s8°. 1921

Jonge (Boudewijn de) [JUNIUS (BALDUINUS); *ps.* PEREGINUS (CONSTANTIUS)]. Conciones 3 super Evangelia festorum totius anni. s4°. Coloniae Agrippinae. 1616
Theatrum principum sanctorum Vet. & Nov. Test. [2p *in* 1v]. s4°. Brux. 1627

Jonge (C. H. de), *see* DE JONGE (C. H.)

Jonghe (Edouard de), *see* VAN OVERBERGH (C.) & E. DE J. Les Bangala (Etat ind. du Congo), 1907.

Jongkind (Johan Barthold), *see* SIGNAC (P.) J., 1819–91, 1927.

Jonker (*Kapitein*), *1630?–89, see* CHIJS (J. A. v. DER). K. J., 1883–85.

Jonnart (Charles Célestin Auguste). Disc. pour la récept. de C. J. [*on* P. Deschanel. Rép. de A. Baudrillart. Acad. Fr., 15 jan. 1925. P2869]. 4°. 1925

Jonson (Ben).
Ben Jonson. Ed. C. H. Herford & P. Simpson. v1–3. 8°. O. 1925–27
1, 2, The man & h. work. 3, A tale of a tub—The case is altered—Every man in his humour—Every man out of his humour.
Catiline his conspiracy. Ed., w. intr., notes & glossary by L. G. Harris. Thesis. [Yale Studies in Eng.; A. S. Cook, 53]. 8°. New Haven [U.S.] 1916
Every man in h. humour, *see* INCHBALD (*Mrs.* E.) Brit. theatre, v5, 1808.
*Every man out of his humour, 1600. [Prep. by F. P. Wilson & W. W. Greg. Malone Society]. 8°. 1920
Timber; or, discoveries on men & manners. s8°. 1898
Volpone, or The fox. Ed. w. introd., notes &c. by J. R. Rea. [Yale Stud. in Eng.; Cook, 59]. 8°. New Haven. 1919
see DRUMMOND (W.) B. J.'s conversations w. W. D. of Hawthornden; ed. &c. R. F. Patterson, 1923.
„ GREENWOOD (G.) B. J. & Shakespeare, 1921.
„ HORACE. On the art of poetry: Lat. text, Eng. prose tr., w. B. J.'s Eng. verse rendering; ed. E. H Blakeney, 1928.

Jonson (Cornelius), *see* JOHNSON (CORNELIUS).

Jónsson (Finnur), *philologist.* AM 623, 4o, Helgensagaer. Udg. F. J. [S. t. u. a. g. n. l., 52]. 8°. København. 1927
Eirspennill. Nóregs Konunga sǫgur-Magnús goði—Hákon gamli. [Norske Hist. K.] 8°. 1916
Norsk-Islandske kultur-og sprogforhold i 9. & 10. årh., *see* KONGELIGT DAN. VID. SELSK. Hist.-fil. Med., B3, 1920–21.
Rímnasafn. Samling af de ældste islandske rimer. [S. t. u. a. g. n. l., 35]. B2. s8°. København. 1913–22

Jonstonus (Arturus), *see* JOHNSTON (A.), *M.D.*

Jonstonus (Joannes), *M.D., Polonus.* De communione vet. Eccl. syntagma. s8°. Amstelædami. 1658

Joos, *van Gent, see* FRIEDLÄNDER (M. J.) Altniederl. Malerei, B3, 1925.

Joos (Wilhelm).
Anatomie d. Messe. 12e A. 8°. Schaffhausen. 1874

Joppi (Ugo). Rovine di Jesolo (Equilium) n. Comune di Cavazuccherina. [P2839]. s8°. S. Donà di Piave. 1898

Jopson (Norman Brooke). Distrib. &c. of the Slavonic peoples & lang. Lect. [P2719]. 8°. [1922]

Jordaens (Jacob), *see* HERDIES (E.) J. J., 1920.

Jordan, *de Borrentrick* [SAXE], *see* JORDAN, *of Saxony, Dominican.*

Jordan, *de Giano, see* THOMAS, *de Eccleston.* Coming of the Friars Minor to Eng. & Germany: chron. of T. of E. & J. of G.; tr. &c. E. G. Salter, 1926.

Jordan, *of Saxony, Dominican.* Briefe (1222–37). Text &c., zugleich Beitr. z. Gesch. d. Frömmigkeit im 13. Jhdt. v. B. Altaner. 8°. L. 1925

Jordan (David Starr).
The care & culture of men. Addresses. 8°. San Francisco. 1903
Fishes. [rev. ed.] la8°. N.Y. 1925

Jordan (*Mrs.* Dorothy), *see* JERROLD (C.) Story of D. J., 1914.

Jordan (George Jefferis). The reunion of the churches: st. of G. W. Leibnitz & h. gt. attempt. 8°. 1927

Jordan (Hermann), *see* IRENAEUS, *St.* Armen. Irenaeusfragm.; hrsg. &c. H. J., 1913.

Jordan (Jan Petr). Gramm. d. wend.-serb. Sprache in d. Oberlausitz. 8°. Prag. 1841
Vollständ. Taschen-Wbch. d. poln. u. deut. Sprachen. N. Abdr. s8°. L. 1884

Jordan (Joannes Christophorus de). De origin. Slavicis, opus chronologico-geogr.-hist. 2t *in* 1v. fol. Vindobonæ. 1745
t2 *has* 3p, *w. sep. pagin.*

Jordan (Louis Henry). Comparative religion. A survey of its recent lit., 1900–09. 2nd ed. rev. & enl. v1. 8°. 1920

Jordan (Max).
Das Königthum Georg's v. Poděbrad. 8°. L. 1861

Jordan de Asso y del Rio (Ignacio), *see* ASSO Y DEL RIO (I. J. DE).

Jordania (Th.)
[Georgian gram. *In Georgian.* P2806]. s8°. Tiflis. 1889

Jordan-Smith (Paul).
On strange altars. A book of enthusiasms. s8°. 1923

Jordanus, *de Saxo, Gen. of the Order of St. Dominic, see* JORDAN, *of Saxony, Dominican.*

Jordell (Daniel), *see* LORENZ (O.) Cat. gén. de la librairie française, t12–27, red. par D. J., 1898–1920.

Joret (Charles). Auguste Duvau, 1771–1831. Publ. par Cte. A. de Laborde. 8°. 1921

Joret (Charles). Fabri de Peiresc humaniste &c. Conf. la8°. Aix. 1894
„ „ *for a. ed., see* PEIRESC (N. DE). Séance publ., 1894.

Jørgensen (Ellen), *see* ANNALES Danici medii ævi; ed. novam cur. E. J., 1920.

Jorisch (Samuel), *see* HÜBNER (JOHANN VALENTIN). De triplici Ebraeorum Cabbala; resp. S. J., 1669.

Jorissen (Theodor).
Histor. bladen. 5e dr. 4v. 8°. Haarlem. 1912
Histor. karakters. 3e dr. 2v. 8°. Haarlem. 1912
1, Abelard en Heloise.—Richelieu en Maria de Medicis.—Charlotte de Corday.
2, A. R. Falck.—De Traditiën van De Chambord.—Daniël Manin.
Histor. studiën. 3e dr. 6v. 8°. Haarlem. 1912

Jorke (Abraham Gottwert). Diss. sistens conjecturas de aetate cod. Alexandrini. Praes. J. S. Semler. [P430]. s4°. Halae Magdeb. [1759]

Jorrocks (John), *ps., see* SURTEES (R. S.)

Josaphat, *Saint, abp. of Polotsk* [JAN KUNCEWICZ], *d. 1623, see* PIUS XI, *pope.* Encycl. letter &c. on 3rd cent. of St. J., 1924.

Josaphat ben Ezra (Juan), *ps., see* LACUNZA (M.)

José, *del Espiritu Santo, see* JOSEPH, *del Espiritu Santo.*

Jose (Arthur Wilberforce), *ed., see* AUSTRALIAN. Illust. A. encyclop., 1925–26.

Joseph, *ben Abraham, Gikatilia, see* PISTORIUS (J.) Artis Cabalisticae t. 1, 1587.

Joseph, *Albo, see* GENEBRARD (G.) R. J. Albonis, R. D. Kimhi &c. argumenta &c., 1566.

Joseph, *of Arimathea.* El libro de Josep Abarimatia, *see* GRAIL. Span. Grail fragments; ed. K. Pietsch, 2v, 1924–25.
I. A.: сказаніе. Грузинскій текстъ; изд. и перев. Н. Марръ. [Тексты &c. по арм.-груз. филол., 2 (Изд. Фак. Вост. Яз. Имп. С.-П. Унив., N°. 5)]. la8°. С.-П. 1900
see ROBINSON (J. A.) 2 Glastonbury legends: King Arthur & St. J., 1926.

Joseph [CALASANZIO], *Saint, see* HUBERT (W. E.) Lebensbilder kath. Erzieher, B1, 1886.

Joseph, *père, Capucin* [JOSEPHUS CAPUZINUS; *i.e.* F. LE CLERC DU TREMBLAY], *see* RICHARD (R.) Vie du véritable père J. &c., 1705.

Joseph, *del Espiritu Santo, Carmelite; d. 1639.* [JOSEPH *a Spiritu Sancto*]. Cursus theologiae mystico-scholast. 6t [5 *&* 6 *wanting.* t1iii w. sep. pagin. b. in 1; 2i, ii w. sep. pagin. b. in 1]. fol. Hispali. 1721–40

Joseph II, *emperor of Germany.* Benigna constitutio Josephina. De causis matrimonialibus, 1791. [*b. w.* Canones eccl., 1768]. s8°. Debrecini. 1801
Joseph II u. Graf Ludwig Cobenzl: ihr Briefwechsel; hrsg. v. A. Beer & J. Fiedler, 2B, *see* FONTES RERUM AUSTRIAC., B53, 54, 1901.
see SCHLITTER (H.) Reise d. Papstes Pius VI nach Wien &c.; Beziehungen J. II z. röm. Curie, 1892.
„ SCHUBERT (A.) Urkunden-Regesten aus d. ehemal. Archiv. d. v. J. II aufgehob. Klöster Böhmens, 1901.

Joseph, *the patriarch.*
see KORAN. Hist. Iosephi Patr. ex Alcorano, 1617.
„ SCHNITZER (M.) Goethes Josephbilder &c., 1921.
Joseph I, *king of Portugal. Works in* PORTUGAL. Recueil des decrets &c., 2t, 1758–61 ; 2e éd., 1761.
Edit. d'expulsion des Jésuites de Portugal [*Fr. & Portug.*] [2.]
Edit par lequel elle abolit les écoles d'humanités des Jésuites &c. [2.]
Edit portant confisc. des biens dont jouissoient les Jésuites [*Fr. & Portug.*] [2.]
Instruction de sa Maj. à s. ministre de Rome [F. Almada de Mendonça], 8 oct. 1757 [*Fr. & Portug.*] [1.]
Jugement du Conseil, chargé d'instruire le procès au sujet de l'attentat commis sur sa personne [*by J. Mascarenhas &c.*] [1.]
Lettres royales portant (après un exposé des crimes d. Jésuites &c.) que tous les biens &c. seront mis en séquestre [*Portug. & Fr.*] [2.]
Manifeste cont. les erreurs de la Cie de Jésus [*Fr. & Portug.*] [2.]
Mém. au pape Clément XIII [Deducçam, *Fr. & Portug.*] [2.]
*Réflexions sur l'attentat, le 3 sept. 1758, contre la vie du roi de P. [2.]
Joseph, *à Spiritu Sancto, see* JOSEPH, *del Espiritu Santo.*
Joseph ben David aben Yachya, *see* JACHIADES (J.)
Joseph ben Gorion, *ps.* De bello Judaico. Deinde decem Judaeorum captivitates & Decalogus cum comm. Aben Esra. Acc. Collectanea quae S. Lepusculus collig. Omnia Hebraicolatina. [S. Munstero interprete. *2 pagins.*] s8°. Basileæ. [1559]
Joseph (Helen Haiman). A book of marionettes. 8°. [1922]
Joseph (Horace William Brindley).
The labour theory of value of Karl Marx. s8°. 1923
Joseph (Michael). Short story writing for profit. Foreword by S. Aumonier. 2nd ed. s8°. [1923]
Joseph (Morris). Judaism as creed & life. 8°. 1903
Joseph (Samuel). Jewish immigr. to the U.S., 1881–1910. 8°. N.Y., *Columbia Univ.* 1914
Joséphine, *empress consort of Napoleon, see* AUBRY (O.) Le roman de Napoléon & J., (*fict.*), 1927.
Joseph-Renaud (Jean). "Au-delà," roman, *see* ŒUVRES libres, 10, 1922.
L'escrime. Préf. de M. Prevost. 8°. [1911]
Josephson (Ernst). Svarta rosor och gula. s8°. [1915]
Josephus (Flavius).
Compendium hystor., *see* MAIMONIDES. Tredecim articuli fidei Iud., 1529.
TRANSLATIONS & REFERENCES.
[Hist. of the war of the Jews & Romans & the destruction of Jerusalem. *In Armenian*]. s4°. Echmiadzin 1787
Works. [Tr. J. Court ?]. Added, C. Noldius's Hist. of Herod the Gt. fol. 1754
Works. Tr. W. Whiston. 4v. 8°. E. 1814
J. [Works. Text] w. Eng. tr. by H. St. J. Thackeray. [Loeb Class. Lib.] [v]1–3. s8°. 1926–28
Œuvres compl. Tr. sous la dir. de T. Reinach [Soc. des Ét. Juives]. t1, 2, 3, 5, 7i. 8°. 1900–26
TRANS. & REFERS. [*continued*].
Vom jüd. Kriege, Buch 1–4, nach d. slav. Übers. deutsch hrsg. v. A. Berendts u. K. Grass, *see* DORPAT UNIV. Acta &c., v5, 1924.
see BESELIN (L. C.) In periocham F. Josephi de Jesu Christo exercit., 1673.
„ BOSIUS (J. A.) Intr. in notit. scr. eccl. J. F. Buddei &c. [exercit. crit. ad. F. J. periocham de J. C.], 1723.
„ BRETSCHNEIDER (C. G.) Capita theolog. Judaeorum dogmat. e F. J. scr. coll., 1812.
„ KREBS (J. T.) Obs. in Nov. Test. e F. J., 1755.
„ WHISTON (W.) Six dissert., 1734.
Joshi (Janardan). Oriental astrology &c. s8°. Allahabad. 1906
Josiah, *king of Judah, see* SIBBES (R.) The saint's cordialls ; sermons [J.'s reformation &c.], 1637.
Jost (Walter). Von L. Tieck zu E. T. A. Hoffmann : Entwicklungsgesch. d. romant. Subjektivismus. [Panzer (F.) & J. Petersen. Deut. Forschungen, H4, 1921]. 8°. Frankfurt a. M. 1921
Joubert (—), *Syndic-gén. du Languedoc.* *Un projet gigantesque en Languedoc au 18e s. Publ. J. Seeker. [Soc. des Bibliophiles Languedoc]. 8°. Montpellier. 1873
Joubert (Felix), *see* SCOTT (R. L.) Cat. of coll. of Europ. arms & armour ; descr. by F. J., 3v, 1924.
Joubert (Joseph), *conseiller de l'Univ. de Paris, see* BEAUNIER (A.) Le roman d'une amitié : J. J. & P. de Beaumont, 1924.
Jouffroy (Théodore Simon). Le cahier vert.—Comment les dogmes finissent—Lettres inéd. [1822–36]. Publ. P. Poux. 8°. [1924]
Jouffroy d'Eschavannes (—).
Traité de la science du blason. s8°. 1885
Jouglet (René). La nuit pathétique, nouvelle, *see* ŒUVRES (Les) libres, t24, 1923.
Jouhandeau (Marcel). La jeunesse de Théophile. s8°. 1921
Jouin (Henry).
A. Coyzevox, & s. contemporains. s8°. 1883
A. Coyzevox, sa vie, s. œuvre &c. Préc. d'une ét. s. l'école franç. de sculpture avant le 17e s. s8°. 1883
Joujou** (Le) des demoiselles, augm. de plusieurs contes de M. V. s8°. Londres. 1773
Joule (James Prescott). Joint scientific papers. [*w.* Dr. Scoresby, Sir L. Playfair & Sir W. Thomson]. Publ. by Physical Soc. of London. 8°. 1887
Scientific papers. Publ. by Physical Soc. of London. 8°. 1884
Joüon des Longrais (Frédéric). La conception angl. de la saisine du 12e au 14e siècle. la8°. 1925
Jourdain (Francis Charles Robert), *see* MULLENS (W. H.), H. K. SWANN & F. C. R. J. Geograph. bibliog. of Brit. ornithology, 1920.
Jourdain (Gabriel Aimé), *see* MÉMOIRES sur les journées de sept. 1792, par J. &c. ; avec notes par F. Barrière, 1881.
Jourdain (*Lt.-Col.* Henry Francis Newdigate) & E. Fraser. The Connaught Rangers, 1st Batt., form. 88th Foot. 3v. la8°. 1924–28
Jourdain (Ignatius), *see* ROSE-TROUP (F.) An Exeter worthy (I. J.) &c., 1897.
Jourdain (Margaret).
Eng. decoration & furniture, 1500–1650. 4°. [1924]
Eng. decoration & furniture, 1760–1820. fol. [1922]
English interiors in smaller houses, 1660–1830. 4°. [1923]
Jourdan (Silvester). Discovery of the Barmudas by Sir T. Gates, Sir G. Sommers &c. (1610), *see* AUNGERVYLE SOC. Reprints, s2, 1884.
Jourdeuil (E.) Chasses & chasseurs de Bourgogne. Avant-prop. de J. des Airelles. s8°. 1924
Jourgnaic Saint-Méard (François de), *see* MÉMOIRES sur les journées de sept. 1792, par J. St. M. ; avec notes par F. Barrière, 1881.
Journal [JOURNALL].
*J. de marche d'un volontaire de 1792, *n.d.*, *see* FRICASSE (J.)
*J. of a lady of quality : narr. of a journey f. Scotland to W. Indies &c., 1774–1776, 1921, *see* SCHAW (J.)
*J. of a party of pleasure to Paris, 1802, *see* PAUL (*Sir* J. D.)
*J. (A) of Parliament, 1648, *see* PARLIAMENT : ANON WORKS.
J. of travels thr. Russia to Constantinople, 1815–6 [*MS.*], *see* CURTIS (C. B.)
Journal de Berlin. Num. 1, 2, Juillet, 1740 (*facs.*), *see* FREYTAG (G.) Bilder, B5, 1925.
Journal de Paris. Jan. 1784–juin 1790. 13t. s4°. 1784–90
Journal des débats, *see* PEREIRE (A.) J. d. d., 1814–1914, 1924.
Journal des économistes.
Sér. 6, t65–89. (Jan. 1920–Juin 1928). 8°. [1920–28]
Journal des savants. N.S., t17–[25]. 4°. 1919–27
Journal des sciences militaires. s8, t1–s9, t48. [*wanting* t10–12 & 29–36 & Dec. 1892]. 8°. [1872]–92
Travaux tactiques publ. par le Journ. des Sc. milit., 3s, 1909–13, *see* TRAVAUX.
Journal des tribunaux, éd. spéc., Nos. 1–24, 1882, *see* PELTZER (L.) & A. PELTZER.
Journal für auserlesene theolog. Literatur. Hrsg. v. J. P. Gabler. [*Contin. of h.* Neustes theolog. Journal, *q.v.*] 6B. s8°. Nürnberg. 1804–11
Journal of botany, British & foreign. v58–65. 8°. 1920–27
Journal of education. v52–59. (1920–27). 4°. 1920–27
Journal (The) of Egyptian archaeology. [Publ. by Egypt Explor. Fund]. v6–13. 4°. 1920–27
Journal of Hellenic studies. v40–47. 4°. 1920–27
„ „ Index to v17–42 & to Suppl. Paper 3. 4°. 1923
Journal of mental science (The). v66–73. 8°. 1920–27
Journal of philology. v34. 8°. 1918
„ „ Index, 1868–1920. 8°. 1923
Journal (The) of philosophical studies. Ed. S. E. Hooper. v1, 2. 8°. 1926–27
Journal of philosophy, psychology & scientific methods. Ed. F. J. E. Woodbridge & W. T. Bush. v6–24. 8°. [Lancaster, Pa.] 1909–27
Journal of political economy. v1–25 (Dec. 1892–Dec. 1917). [v1, 9, *no tp.*] 8°. Chicago. [1893–1917]
Journal of Roman studies. Publ. by the Soc. for the Promotion of Roman studies. v7–16. la8°. 1917–26
Journal of sacred literature. Ed. J. Kitto. v1–2 (1848). New ser., v1–5 [*in* 3]. [s3], v5, 6 [n.s., v5 & s3 ed. H. Burgess]. 8°. 1848–58

Journal of speculative philosophy. v1–14, 22 (1867–80, 1888). la8°. St. Louis & N.Y. 1867–88
Journal of theological studies. v21–28. 8°. O. 1920–27
Journal officiel de la Commune, *see* POINSOT (A. E.) Livre rouge de la Commune; extr. du Journal Offic., 1871.
Journée. La journée des madrigaux (1653), suiv. de la Gazette de tendre & du Carnaval des prétieuses. Intr. &c. par E. Colombey. [Trésor des pièces rares &c.] s8°. 1856
*__Journey__ (A) thr. England, 2v, 1732, *see* MACKY (J.)
Jousset (Paul).
L'Allemagne contemp. illustrée. [*n. ed.*] 4°. *Larousse.* [1922 ?]
L'Espagne & le Portugal illustrés. 4°. *Larousse.* [1908]
La France: géographie illust. 2t. 4°. *Larousse. n.d.*
Jouve (Pierre Jean).
Hôtel-Dieu. Récits d'hôpital en 1915. 8°. Genève. 1918
Paulina 1880. 11e éd. s8°. [1925]
Romain Rolland vivant, 1914–19. 3e éd. 8°. 1920
Trois poèmes, *see* CHANSON (A.) Ecrits &c., 1927.
Jouveau-Dubreuil (G.) Ancient hist. of the Deccan. Tr. V. S. Swaminadha Dikshitar. 8°. Pondicherry. 1920
Conjeevaram inscr. of Mahêndravarman I. [P2525]. 8°. Trichinopoly. 1919
India & the Romans. Tr. Sir R. C. Temple. Repr. f. "Indian antiq.," v52, 1923. [P2730]. la8°. Bombay. 1923
Vedic antiquities. s8°. 1922
Jouvenel (Henry de). La vie orageuse de Mirabeau. s8°. [1928]
Jouvin (*Col.* G.) & *Capitaine* Gillet. Marches & chansons des soldats de France. Rec. par J. Vidal. la8°. [1919]
Jouvin de Rochefort (Albert). Grand plan de Paris &c., 1675, par J. de R., *see* PARIS. Reprod. d'anc. plans, 1908.
Jovanovitch (Vojislav M.)
Српске народне песме: антологија. s8°. Београд. 1922
Jovellanos (G. M. de). Diarios, 1790–1801. Publ. el Inst. de Jovellanos, de Gijón. la8°. 1915
Jovialis, *see* CRAIG (J. D.) J. & Callop. text of Terence, 1927.
Jovy (Ernest).
Discours: plaque comméma. des anc. élèves du collège de Vitry-le-François morts pour la France (1914–1918). [P2520]. 8°. Vitry-le-Fr. 1921
Etudes pascal. [t]1. s8°. 1927
1, P. & St.-Ange: J. Forton, Sieur de St.-A., s. écrits &c.
Pascal & le p. de Frétat. [P2395]. 8°. Vitry-Le-François. 1919
Pascal inédit. [t]1. 8°. Vitry-le-François. 1908
Pascal & St. Ignace. 8°. 1923
Pascal n'a pas inventé le haquet. [*b. w. h.* Pascal & St. Ignace, 1923]. 8°. 1923
Pour le "Memorial day." Allocution aux enfants des écoles, Vitry-le-François. [P2520]. 8°. V.-le-F. 1921
Jowett (Benjamin). Sel. passages f. theolog. writings. Ed. L. Campbell. s8°. 1902
Jowett (William). Mem. of Cornelius Neale. Add. h. remains &c. 8°. 1834
*Verses wr. on var. occasions. s8°. *p.f.p.d.* 1843
Joy (Henry). On the evidence of accomplices. 8°. D. 1836
Joyce (George Hayward), *S.J.*
Principles of logic. 3rd ed. 8°. 1920
Joyce (James).
Chamber music. [*Poems*]. [3rd ed.] s8°. 1923
Dubliners. [*Novel*]. [2nd ed.] s8°. [1922]
Gens de Dublin. Tr. Y. Fernandez &c. Préf. de V. Larbaud. s8°. [1926]
Pomes penyeach. s8°. Paris. 1927
A portrait of the artist as a young man. s8°. [1916]
see GORMAN (H. S.) J. J., h. first 40 yrs., 1926.
Joyce (Patrick Weston). The origin & hist. of Irish names of places. s8°. D. 1869
Short hist. of Gaelic Ireland to 1608. s8°. D. 1924
Joyce (Thomas Athol). Maya & Mexican art. 8°. 1927
see BRIT. MUSEUM: ANTIQ. Guide to Maudslay coll. of Maya sculptures f. Cent. Amer.; [*by* T. A. J.], 1923.
Joyce (Weston St. John). Neighbourhood of Dublin; topog., antiq. &c. Intr. P. W. Joyce. 8°. D. 1912
Joye (George). The exposycion of Daniel, gathered out of Philip Melancthon, Johan Ecolāpadius, Chonrade Pellicane & out of Johan Draconite &c. [*w. text*]. s8°. [1550]
G. J. confuteth Winchesters false articles. [*b. w. h.* Of the unite &c. of the olde chirche, 1543]. s8°. [Wesill in Cliefelande. 1543]
Of the unite & scisme of the olde chirche. [*Tp. wanting*]. s8°. *n.p.* [1543]
Joyeuse, *The family of, see* VAISSIÈRE (P. DE). Messieurs de J. (1560–1615), 1926.

Joynson-Hicks (*Rt. Hon. Sir* William). The Prayer Book crisis. s8°. [1928]
Juan (*Don*), *of Persia* [†ULUGH BEG; URUCH BEG]. Don Juan of Persia, a Shi'ah Catholic, 1560–1604. Tr. & ed. w. intr. by G. Le Strange. 8°. [1926]
Juana Ines [DE ASBAJE], *de la Cruz, 1651–95, see* NERVO (A.) Juana de Asbaje (*w.* Poesias), 1910; 1920.
Juarros (Domingo). Compendio de la hist. de la Ciudad de Guatemala. 2t [*in* 1v]. 8°. Guatemala. 1857
Jubé de la Perrelle (*le gén. baron* Auguste). Lettre d'un français à Lord Stanhope &c. [P2772]. 8°. 1818
Jubilæus Evang.-Luther.: oratio &c., 1617, *see* ROTHENBURG A. D. TAUBER.
*__Jubilee__ (The) of the Methodist New Connexion, 1848; 1851, *see* METHODIST.
Jubilee Singers. *The story of the Jubilee singers. [*w.* Jubilee songs. *Abridg. of G. T. Pike's books.* Note *signed* J. B. T. M.] 6th ed. s8°. 1876
Juda (Leo). Ad Philippenses annot. per L. J. ex ore Zwinglii conceptae, 1528–33, *see* ZWINGLI (U.)
Judah, *ben David, surnamed Haiyūj* [JEHUDA CHAJJUG; JEHUDA HAJJUG]. Two treatises on verbs cont. feeble & double letters. Tr. into Heb. by R. Moses Gikatilia. Ed. w. Engl. tr. by J. W. Nutt. Added, Treatise on punctuation. 8°. 1870
Judah, *ben Samuel, the Levite.* Liber Cosri. Lat. versione & notis illust. J. Buxtorfius Fil. *Heb. & Lat.* s4°. Basileæ. 1660
Judah Loeb, *ben Joshuah* [JUDAS LEO]. Liber bellum in pace (hist. de Semi-Prag. urbis expugn., 1648) [*Heb. & Lat.*], *see* WAGENSEIL (J. C.) Exercit., 1687; 1719.
Judaica seu vet. script. profan. de rebus J. fragm., 1832, *see* MEIER (F. C.), *ed.*
Judas Iscariot, *see* THURSTON (E. T.) J. I., play, 1923.
Judd (Charles Hubbard).
Democracy & Amer. schools. [P2509]. 8°. Chicago. [1918]
Judd (Neil Merton). Archeolog. investig. at Paragonah, Utah, *see* SMITHSONIAN INSTIT. Misc. coll., v70, 1919.
Archeolog. obs. north of the Rio Colorado. [S.I.: Bur. of Amer. Ethnol., Bull. 82]. 8°. Wash. 1926
Judd (Sylvester). Hist. of Hadley &c. Intr. by G. Sheldon. Family genealogies by L. M. Boltwood. [*w. sep. pagin.*] [n. ed.] 8°. Springfield. 1905
Jude, *Saint, Apostle, see* BIBLE: JUDE, *& see* THADDAEUS, *sometimes confounded w. J.*
Judeich (Walther). Kleinasiat. Studien. Griech.-pers. Gesch. d. 4. Jhdts v. Chr. 8°. Marburg. 1892
Judet (Ernest). Georges Louis. 19e éd. s8°. 1925
Le véritable Clémenceau. 8°. Berne. 1920
Judex (Matthias), *see* WIGAND (J.) & M. J. Kirchenhist., 1560, 1855.
Judge (William Quan), *see* PATAÑJALI. Yoga aphorisms, interpr. by W. Q. J., 1912.
Judgment. Poem on the Day of Judgment; ed. H. J. Chaytor, *see* ANGLO-NORMAN. Camb. A.-N. texts, 1924.
Judith.
Judith: mitteldeut. Gedicht aus d. 13. Jhdt. Hrsg. v. R. Palgen. s8°. Halle. 1924
see BIBLE: ANGLO-SAXON. Heptateuchus &c., Hist. J. fragm., Dano-Saxonice; ed. E. Thwaites, 1698.
Judith (*Mme.*) [*i.e.* JUDITH BERNARD DEROSNE]. My autobiography. Ed. P. G'Sell. Tr. Mrs. A. Bell. 8°. 1912
Judson (Harry Pratt). The threat of German world-politics. [P2509]. 8°. Chicago. 1918
Juet (Robert), *see* IVET (R.)
Jügel (Charles). Souvenirs pittoresques du Rhin. obl.8°. Francfort. 1826
Jugend-Internationale. Die 11 Num. d. Kriegsausgabe, 1915–18. Mit Beitr. v. N. Lenin, L. Trotski &c. neudr. la4°. [1921]
Jugoslav. Mem. pres. to Peace Conf. by deleg. of J. members of parl. &c., 1919, *see* PEACE.
*Mem. addr. by the J. socialists to the Internat. Socialist Peace Conf. in Stockholm. [Pref. signed M. Radosevic. P2495]. 8°. [1917]
Jukes, *The family of, see* ADAMS (P. W. L.) Hist. of the J. family of Cound, Shropshire &c., 1927.
Jukes-Browne (Alfred Joseph).
The following are Mems. of G.S.:—
Cretaceous rocks of Britain. With contrib. by W. Hill. 3v. 8°. 1900–4
Geol. of part of E. Lincs. 8°. 1887
Geol. of the co. around Andover. 8°. 1908

Jukes-Browne (Alfred Joseph) [*continued*].
Geol. of the co. S. & E. of Devizes. 8°. 1905
Geol. of the S.W. part of Lincolnshire. 8°. 1885
see PENNING (W. H.) & A. J. J.-B. Geol. of neighb. of Cambridge &c., 1881.
„ WHITAKER (W.) & A. J. J.-B. Geol. of borders of the Wash, 1899.
„ ——, S. B. J. SKERTCHLY & A. J. J.-B. Geol. of S.-W. Norfolk &c., 1893.
—— **& H. J. O. White.** Geol. of the co. around Henley-on-Thames & Wallingford. 8°. 1908
Julia, *Universitas, see* HELMSTEDT.
Julian, *emperor of Rome.*
Epistulae — Leges — Poemata — Fragm. varia. Coll., rec. I. Bidez & F. Cumont. s8°. Paris. 1922
Works. With Eng. tr. by W. C. Wright. [Loeb Class. Lib.] v3. s8°. 1923
Œuvres compl. Texte établi & tr. par J. Bidez. [Coll. des univ. de Fr.] t1, p2. 8°. 1924
see GEFFCKEN (J.) Kaiser J., 1914.
„ JOHNSON (S.) J. A., life &c., 1782.
Julian, *Saint, bp. of Toledo, see* LORENZANA Y BUITRON (F. A.) SS. PP. Toletan. opera, t2, 1785.
Juliana, *anchoress of Norwich, see* THOULESS (R. H.) The Lady J.: psycholog. study, 1924.
Julianus (Salvius), *see* BIENER (F. A.) De S. Juliani meritis in edictum praetorium recte aestimandis, 1809.
Jülich. *Kirchen-Ordnungen d. Christl. reform. Gemeinden in J. &c., 1754, *see* KIRCHEN-ORDNUNG.
Julien (Eugene Louis), *bp. of Arras.* Le prêtre. [Caractères de ce temps]. s8°. [1925]
Julien (Stanislas A.) Exercices prat. d'analyse, de syntaxe & de lexigraphie chinoise. 8°. 1842
Simple exposé d'un fait honorable denaturé dans un libelle récent de M. Pauthier. 8°. 1842
see PAUTHIER (J. P. G.) Suppl. aux Vindiciae Sinicae ou dern. rép. à S. J., 1843.
„ —— Vindic. Sinicae: dern. rép. à S. J. suivie d'un parallèle de sa nouv. tr. de Lao-Tseu &c., 1842.
***Julius** Levine. Novel. By A gentleman with a duster. 3rd ed. s8°. [1927]
Julius, *duke of Brunswick, see* HELMSTEDT. Hist. narr. de introd. Univ. Juliæ &c., 1579.
see LEMCKER (H. C.) Exercit. de corporis doct. J. & Formulae Concordiae conven., 1726.
Julius II, *pope* [GIULIANO DELLA ROVERE].
see DALLA SANTA (G.) Vero testo d. appellaz. di Venezia d. scomun. di G. II, 1900.
„ GOBINEAU (*le c.* J. A. DE). La fleur d'or [J. II] &c., 1923.
„ KLACZKO (J.) Rome & the Renaissance: pontificate of J. II; tr., 1926.
„ LABANDE (L. H.) Avignon au 15e siècle: légation de Ch. de Bourbon & du Card. J. de La R., 1920.
Julius III, *pope, see* PASTOR (L. v.) Hist. of the Popes; tr., v13, 1924.
Julius (Haldeman-), *see* HALDEMAN-JULIUS.
Julius (Nikolaus Heinr.) Bibliotheca Germano-Glottica. [*interleaved*]. s8°. Hamburg. 1817
Jullian (Camille). De la Gaule à la France: nos origines hist. s8°. 1922
Gallia; tableau de la Gaule sous la domin. romaine. 7e éd. s8°. [1927]
Hist. de la Gaule. [t]5–8. la8°. 1920–[26]
5, La civilis. gallo-romaine: état matériel.
6, La civilis. gallo-romaine: état moral.
7, 8, Les empereurs de Trèves, (1) Les chefs, (2) La terre & les hommes.
Jullita, *see* GIULIETTA.
Juncker (Christian). Comm. de vita, scriptis &c. Jobi Ludolfi. Adj. epistolæ clar. virorum; spec. linguæ Hottentotticæ. s8°. Lipsiæ. 1710
Das guldene & silberne Ehren-Gedächtniss M. Lutheri &c. s8°. Franckfurt. 1706
Jung (Alexander). Die Harfe von Discatherine. [*b. w.* Baumann (J. J.) Elem. d. Philos., 1891]. 2B [*in* 1v]. 8°. L. 1885
Panacee u. Theodicee. Illustrationen, Caricaturen d. Gegenwart &c. 2T [*in* 1v]. s8°. L. 1875
Jung (Carl Gustav). Die Psychologie d. unbewussten Prozesse. 2e A. 8°. Zurich. 1918
Psycholog. types or the psych. of individuation. Tr. by H. G. Baynes. 8°. 1923
Jung (Carl Gustav) [*continued*].
Wandlungen u. Symbole d. Libido: Beitr. z. Entwicklungsgesch. d. Denkens. 2. A. 8°. L. 1925
see CORRIE (J.) ABC of J.'s psychology, 1927.
„ VAN DER HOOP (J. H.) Character & the unconscious: psych. of Freud & J.; tr., 1923.
Jung (Franz). Das geistige Russland v. heute. s8°. [1924]
Jung (Jacob Friedrich) [JUNGIUS]. Compend. theologiae thetico-polemicae &c. Acc. Decalogia controv. loco app. [*w. sep. tp. & pagin.*] s8°. Ulmae. 1752
Jung (Johann Heinrich), *called Stilling.*
Lebensgesch. s8°. L. *n.d.*
Jungclaus (E. Rudolf), *see* STADE. Gesch. d. Reg.-Bez. Stade, 1, Die sächs. Gaue; v. E. R. J., 1924.
Jung-Johann (Johann Christian). Diss. de vita ac doctrina Hrabani Magnentii Mauri. Praes. J. F. Buddeo. s4°. Jenae. [1724]
Juni (Ulricus) [JUNIUS]. Errores astrologorum circa thema Christi genethliacum. Præses U. J., resp. J. Wachtel. [P2634]. s4°. Lipsiæ. [1701]
Junius, *ps., a. of* Die Krise d. Sozialdemokratie (1916), 1919, *see* LUXEMBURG (ROSA).
Junius, *junior, ps.*
*The truth about Ireland. s8°. Guernsey. [1921]
Junius *Florilegus, ps., see* YOUNGE (R.)
Junius (Adrianus). Epistolæ, acc. vita & oratio de artium liberalium dignitate. [*Ed.* P. Junius]. [*Portrait wanting*]. s8°. Dordrechti. 1552 [*i.e.* 1602?]
Junius (Balduinus), *see* JONGE (B. DE).
Junius (Christian Friedrich). De Xtn^orum sapientia in evitandis &c. controversiis circa res hujus seculi, dissert. [P2634]. s4°. *n.p.* 1696
Junius (Franciscus), *1545–1602* [†DU JON (FRANÇOIS), *the elder*]. The Apocalyps, or Revelation of S. John w. a brief expos. &c. Tr. s4°. C. 1596
De peccato primo Adami. [*b. w.* Whitaker (W.) Praelectiones, 1599]. s8°. Lugduni Batav. 1595
De theologia vera. [*b. w.* Whitaker (W.) Praelectiones, 1599]. s8°. Lugduni Batav. 1594
see ARMINIUS (J.) Amica cum F. J. de praedestinatione, collatio, 1613.
„ BIBLE: COMPL. TEXTS &C. Bible, The [*Geneva vers.; w.* F. J.'s Annotat^s. upon Revelation], 1599.
„ GRETSER (J.) De jure & more prohib. libros adv. F. J. &c., 1603.
Junius (Franciscus), *1589–1677* [†DU JON (FRANÇOIS), *the younger*]. Glossarium Ulphila-Gothicum; illust. per G. Stiernhielm. [*2nd tp. dated* 1670. *b. w.* Ulfilas, Evangelia, 1671]. s4°. Holmiae. 1671
Junius (Franciscus Janus Jacobus Albertus). De Justino martyre apologeta adv. ethnicos. 8°. Lugd. Batav. 1836
Junius (Isaacus). Antapologia sive animadv. in 16 priora cap. Apologiae Remonstrantium. s4°. Delphis. 1640
Junius (Patricius), *see* NICETAS. Catena graec. patrum in Job, coll. N.; opera P. J., 1637.
Junk (*Oberstlt.-Auditor* **Ernst**). Das Verbrechertum im Kriege. 8°. Wien. 1920
***Junker** u. Pfaffen im Gewande d. Sprichworts &c. V. Verfass. d. "Allotria." 2e A. [P504]. s8°. [1875]
Junker (Carl). Dokumente z. Gesch. d. Europ. Krieges, 1914/16. Gesamm. &c. v. C. J. Abt. 2, Der Krieg mit Italien. B1, bis 31 Aug. 1915. 8°. Wien. 1916
Junker (Hermann).
Works in KAISERL. AKAD. D. W. ZU WIEN. Denkschr.
Bericht ü. d. Grabungen auf d. Friedhof in Turah, 1909–10, mit e. Kapitel v. D. E. Derry, 1913. [56.]
Bericht ü. d. Grabungen auf d. Friedhöfen v. El-Kubanieh-Nord, 1910–11. 3T, 1918–24. [62, 64, 66.]
Ermenne: Bericht ü. d. Grabungen auf. d. Friedhöfen v. E. (Nubien), 1911/12, 1926. [67.]
Das Götterdekret ü. d. Abaton, 1913. [56.]
Die Onurislegende, 1917. [59.]
Papyrus Lonsdorfer I. Ein Ehepakt a. d. Zeit d. Nektanebos, *see* KAIS. AKAD. D. W. ZU WIEN. Sitzb. B197, 1922.
—— **& W. Czermak.** Kordofân-Texte im Dialekt v. Gebel Dair, *see* KAIS. AKAD. D. WISS. ZU WIEN. Sitzb., B174, 1915.
Junod (Henri A.) The life of a S. African tribe. [The Thonga]. 2nd ed. rev. & enl. 2v [1, Soc. life. 2, Mental life]. 8°. 1927
Jupp (James). The Gaiety stage door: 30 years' remin. Intr. by M. R. Philipson. 8°. [1923]

Jürgensen (*Dr.* —).
Free city of Danzig. [P2824]. s8°. [Danzig. 1925]

Jurgiewicus (Andreas). Bellum quinti Evangelii, contra larvatam Harmoniam Genevensium &c. s8°. Coloniae. 1595

Jurien de La Gravière (Jean Pierre Edmund).
La marine des anciens. [2p]. s8°. 1880
1, La bataille de Salamine & l'expéd. de Sicile.
2, La revanche des Perses—Les tyrans de Syracuse.

Jurieu (Pierre). *L'esprit de M. Arnaud tiré de sa conduite & des écrits de luy & de ses disciples, &c.
2p. s8°. Deventer [Rotterdam]. 1684
*La religion des Jésuites, ou réflexions sur les inscrs. du père Menestrier &c. s8°. La Haye. [1689]
TRANSLATIONS.
A crit. hist. of the doctrines & worships of the church f. Adam to Jesus Christ. Tr. 2v. 8°. 1705
The History of the Co. of Trent. 8 bks. Done into English. s8°. 1684
Pastoral letters dir. to the protestants in France &c. Tr. s8°. 1689
see BOSSUET (J. B.) Œuvres, t21–22, 1[–6] avertissement[s] aux Protestans sur lettres du Ministre J. contre L'hist. des variations, 1816.

***Jurisprudentia** sive de jure Belg. c. nobilit. &c., 1668, *see* BELGIQUE.

Jus divinum ministerii evangelici, 1654, *see* LONDON.

Juslenius (Daniel), *bp. of Skara.* Suomalaisen hana-lugum coetus. Fennici lexici tentamen. s4°. Stockholm. 1745

Jusserand (Jules J.) [JUSSERAND (JEAN ADRIEN ANT. JULES)].
Hist. litt. du peuple anglais: 2, De la Renaissance à la guerre civile. 8°. 1904
„ „ Des orig. jusqu'à la Renaiss. 2e éd. rév. 8°. 1896
TRANSLATIONS.
English wayfaring life in the Middle Ages. Tr. L. T. Smith. n. ed. rev. & enl. 8°. [1920]
The school for ambassadors & o. e. 8°. [1924]
"What to expect of Shakespeare": S. lect., 1911, *see* BRIT. ACAD. Procs., 1911.

Just. *Just (A) & modest vindication of the Scots design &c., 1699, *see* DARIEN.
The just vengeance of heaven exemplify'd in a journal found by Capt. Mawson, on the isl. of Ascension, 1730 ?, *see* MAWSON (*Capt.*)

Justa. *De justa reipub. Xtnæ. in reges impios &c. authoritate, 1590, *see* RAINOLDS (W.)

Justi (Ferdinand). Kurd. Grammatik. 8°. St. Petersburg. 1880

Justi (Ludwig). Deut. Malkunst im 19ten Jhdt. Ein Führer durch d. Nationalgalerie. s8°. 1920

Justices. Early treatises on the practice of J. of the Peace in the 15th & 16th cent. (*includ.* Marowe's Reading on the peace in 1503), *see* VINOGRADOFF (*Sir* P.) Oxford st. in social &c. hist., v7, 1924.

Justin, *ps.*
Jaurès patriote. Idées sur la défense nationale. s8°. 1920

Justin, *Martyr, Saint.*
[Works] Τοῦ ἁγίου Ἰουστίνου φιλοσόφου καὶ μάρτυρος. Ζήνᾳ καὶ Σερήνῳ. Λόγος παραινετικὸς πρὸς Ἕλληνας &c. fol. Lutetiae, *ex offic. R. Stephani.* 1551
De sacris Christianorum publ. saec. 2 narr. [*Gr. & Lat.*] s8°. Halae Magdeb. 1724
First apology. Pref. by J. Kaye. [Anc. & Mod. Lib. of Theolog. Lit.] 8°. [1889]
see BURGER (C. G.) Antiq. lit. Evangel.-Luther. ex J. M. demonst., 1755.
see DODWELL (H.) Explic. of passage in dialogue of J. M. w. Tryphon conc. immortality of souls, 1708.
„ GOODENOUGH (E. R.) The theology of J. M., 1923.
„ JUNIUS (F. J. J. A.) De J. martyre apologeta adv. ethnicos, 1836.
„ LAGRANGE (M. J.) St. J., 1914.
„ RAU (J. J.) Diatribe de philos. J. &c., 1733.

Justinian I, *emperor of the East.*
Codicis D. N. J. libri 12. 4°. Lugduni. 1593
Impp. Justiniani, Justini, Leonis novellae constit. Justiniani edicta. Opus diligentia A. Scrimgeri restitutum &c. [*In Greek. Ed., w. notes, by H. Stephanus*]. fol. [Geneva]. 1558
Institutes. With tr., notes &c. by T. C. Sandars. 6th ed. 8°. 1883
J. & Eudociae Augustae opera quaedam anecdota. Gr. & Lat. cura A. M. Bandini. [Graecae Eccl. vet. mon. ex Bibl. Medicea, t1]. 8°. Florentiae. 1762
see APELLUS (J.) De actionibus ex Instit. J., 1526.
„ CUJAS (J.) Opera, 11t, 1758–83.
„ HEGENDORFF (C.) Compend. titulorum cod. I. exegeses, 1529.
„ KIRCHMAIER (G. C.) Opusc. 6 rariss. de Latin. Digest. & Instit. J., 1772.
„ MEIER (G. T.) Cod. canonum Eccl. univ. à J. confirmatus, 1663.

Justinianus (Benedictus), *see* GIUSTINIANO (B.)

Justinus, *the historian.* Epitoma hist. Philipp. Pompei Trogi. Ex rec. F. Ruehl. Acc. Prologi in Pompeium Trogum ab A. de Gutschmid rec. s8°. L., *Teubner.* 1915
Hist. ex Trogo Pompeio lib. 44, cum notis I. Vossii. s8°. Lugd. Bat., *Elzevir.* 1640
Hist. Philippicæ. Ex rec. J. G. Graevii. Notæ J. Bongarsii &c. 8°. Lugd. Bat. 1683
see ARTOPOEUS (J. G.) Elenchus errorum a J. c. res Judaicas admiss., 1695.
„ SCHUDT (J. J.) Compendium hist. Jud., ad ductum J. &c., 1700.

***Justitia** Britannica &c., 1584, *see* BURGHLEY (W. C., *baron*).

***Justizwesen (Das)** d. Sowjetrepublik, 1920, *see* RUSSIA: SOVIET REPUBLIC.

Justus, *of Ghent, see* JOOS, *van Gent.*

Jusué (Eduardo). Tablas para la reducción d. cómputo árabe y d. hebraico al cristiano &c. [R. Acad. de la Hist. Mem. hist. esp., t48]. 8°. 1918

Jüterbock (Jacob v.) [†JACOBUS *de Clusa;* JACOBUS *de Paradyso*]. [Sermones de sanctis. *f. 1a.* Incipiūt sermones notabiles & formales per Iacobum Cartusieñ domus extra muros Erfordeñ vicariū &c. auctorisati per Calixtū tercium, 1455. *f. 254a.* Expliciūt sermones notabiles &c. *Ends f. 254b* cui soli est honor & gł̄a in secula Amen Et sic est finis]. fol. [Speier, *Printer of Gesta Christi*]. *n.d.* [c. 1475 ?]
254 leaves, sign. a–q, [r–z, Z], A–G in eights, H1–6. The letters r–z & Z are in MS.
see WESSEL (J.) Opera omnia; acc. J. de P. tract. aliquot, 1617.

Jutland, Battle of. Battle of J., 30th May–1st June 1916. Official despatches, w. App. [Cmd. 1068. *Plates in case sep.*] 8°. [1920]
The fighting at J.: personal experiences &c., 1921, *see* FAWCETT (F. W.) & G. W. W. HOOPER, *edd.*
*Narr. of Battle of J., 1924, *see* DEWAR (*Capt.* A. C.) &c.

Juusten (Paulus), *bp. of (1) Wyborg, (2) Abo.* Chron. episcop. Finland. (12–16 c.), *see* PORTHAN (H. G.) Opera sel., d1, 2, 1859–62.

Juvenal.
A. Persi Flacci & D. J. Juv. saturae, cum add. Bodleianis. Rec. &c. S. G. Owen. 2a ed. s8°. O. [1907]
J. Satirae 16, Persii Satirae 6. la8°. Lond., *Chiswick Press.* 1845
Satirae; w. lit. prose tr. & notes by J. D. Lewis. 2nd ed. 2v. 8°. 1882
Satiræ 16. Rec. & illust. &c. a G. A. Ruberti. Adj. A. Persii Flacci Satiræ ex rec. G. L. Kœnig. 8°. O. 1835
Thirteen satires, w. comm. by J. E. B. Mayor. [repr.] 2v. 8°. 1900–01
TRANSLATIONS.
Les satyres de J. & de Perse, en Lat. & Fr. s8°. 1671
Satires. Tr., w. notes rel. to laws &c. of Greeks &c. 2nd ed. 8°. 1745
Satires. Tr. w. notes [by S. Dunster]. [*w. text*]. 8°. 1777
Satires. Texte établi & tr. par P. de Labriolle & F. Villeneuve. [Coll. des univ. de France]. 8°. 1921

K

K. (D. P. P.) Discursus de modo peregrinationes bene inchoandi & absolv., 1670, *see* DISCURSUS.
K. (L. S. P.) Der Theolog. Facultät Informat v. Pietismo; eingeholet v. L. S. P. K., 1711, *see* LEIPZIG, *Univ.*
Kaab-Akbar. The life of the Prophet Abraham; related by Caab-Ekbaar, *see* WALDRON (F. G.) Shakspearean misc., 1802.
Kaap de Goede Hoop, *see* CAPE COLONY & CAPE OF GOOD HOPE.
Kaatz (Hugo). Die Weltanschauung Fr. Nietzsches. Tl. [P2478]. 8°. Dresden. 1892
Kabel (Adriaan van der), *see* CAZENOVE (Q. J. R.) Le peintre Van der Kabel &c., 1888.
Käber (E.) Die Idee d. europ. Gleichgewichts in d. publizist. Lit., 16–Mitte 18. Jhdts. 8°. 1907
Kabinette. Die grosse Politik d. europ. K., 1871–1914, 1922–27, *see* GROSSE.
Kabris (Joseph), *Vice-Roi des Iles Ste.-Christine.* Précis du séjour de J. K. dans les Iles de Mendoça. [P2622]. s8°. *n.p.* [c. 1818]
Kachanov, *ps.*, *see* KARJANSKY (N.)
Kachovskaya (Irène). Souv. d'une révolutionnaire. Tr. M. Livane & J. Newman. Avant-propos de J. N. 2e éd. s8°. 1926
Kadich (Heinrich *Edler* **v.)** Mähr. Adel; bearbt. v. H. v. K., *see* SIBMACHER (J.), *ed.* Wappenbuch, B4x, 1899.
Kadlec (Charles). Les Magyars & la Républ. Tchéco-Slovaque. [P2425]. 8°. Prague. 1919
Kadmin (N.), *ps.*, *see* ABRAMOVICH (N. YA.)
Kaeckenbeeck (Georges Silvain François Charles). Internat. rivers, *see* FOREIGN OFFICE. Handbooks, No. 149, 1920.
Kaehler (Martin), *see* KÄHLER (M.)
Kaff (Siegmund). Konsumvereine in Österreich, *see* UNTERSUCHUNGEN ü. Konsumver., 1923.
Kaffir. *Introd. remarks to a Narr. of the irrupt. of the K. hordes into the Cape of Good Hope, 1834–35, pl, 1835, *see* GODLONTON (R.)
Kagawa (Toyohiko). Before the dawn. Tr. f. Japanese by I. Fukumoto & T. Satchell. 8°. 1925
Kagelmacher (Ernst). F. M. Visconti u. König Sigismund, 1413–31. [P2728]. 8°. 1885
Kahan (Aron). New scheme for settlement of reparations problem. [P2708]. 8°. 1923
Kahan-Coates (Zelda). The life & work of F. Engels. s8°. 1920
Kahil (Jean M. N.), *Bey.*
Syriens et Arabes. [P2411]. 8°. Caire. 1919
Kahl (Ludwig Martin). De Lollardis seculi 14 testibus veritatis. Praes. J. G. Walchio. [P443]. s4°. Jenae. 1732
Kahl (Wilhelm). Dreibund-Treubund, *see* DEUTSCHE Reden in schwerer Zeit, 26, 1915.
Kähler (Martin), *theologian.* Sententiarum quas de conscientia ediderint theologi enarr. Diss. fasc. 1. 8°. Halis Sax. [1860]
Kahn (Gustav). Fantin-Latour. 8°. 1926
Kahn (Otto Hermann). Reflections of a financier. Intr. by J. H. Thomas. 8°. 1921
Kahn (Rosy). Die Graphik d. Lucas van Leyden. la8°. Str. 1918
Kaisenberg (Moritz von) [*ps.* MORITZ VON BERG-NESSELRÖDEN]. Die Mem. d. Baronesse Cecile de Courtot. 2e verb. A. 8°. L. 1899

Kaiser (Georg).
Der Brand im Opernhaus. 8°. Potsdam. 1922
Die Bürger v. Calais. 8°. Potsdam. 1920
Claudius—Friedrich u. Anna—Juana. [3 Einakter]. 8°. Potsdam. 1921
Europa. Spiel u. Tanz. 8°. Potsdam. 1920
Die Flucht nach Venedig. 8°. 1923
Das Frauenopfer. 8°. Potsdam. 1922
Gas. 2T. 8°. Potsdam. 1920–22
Der Geist d. Antike. 8°. Potsdam. [1923]
Der gerettete Alkibiades. 8°. Potsdam. [1920]
Hölle Weg Erde. [Dram. Wille, B2]. s8°. Potsdam. 1919
Die jüdische Witwe. 8°. Potsdam. 1920
Kanzlist Krehler. 8°. Potsdam. 1922
Kolportage. s8°. 1924
König Hahnrei. 8°. Potsdam. [1923]
Konstantin Strobel (Der Zentaur). 8°. Potsdam. 1920
Die Koralle. 8°. Potsdam. 1920
Nebeneinander. 8°. Potsdam. [1923]
Noli me tangere. 8°. Potsdam. 1922
Zweimal Oliver. 8°. 1926

Kaiser (Gottlieb Philipp Christian).
Monogrammata theol. Christ. dogm. 8°. Erlangae. 1819

Kaiser (Leonhard), *see* KEYSER (L.)
Kaiserhaus, *Wien*, *see* VIENNA.
Kaiserlich Deutsches Archäologisches Institut.
Bibliog. z. Jahrbuch, 1918/19–1926. [5p]. la8°. 1924–27
German. Denkmäler d. Frühzeit. Hrsg. v. d. Röm.-Germ. Komm. d. Deut. Arch. Inst. [T]1. 4°. Frankfurt a. M. 1923
1, Denkmäler d. Wangionengebietes, bearbt. v. G. Behrens.
Jahrbuch, mit d. Beiblatt Archäolog. Anzeiger. B31–41. 4°. 1916–27
„ „ Ergänzungsheft 11. la8°. 1927
see BLÜMEL (C.) Griech. Bildhauerarbeit, 1927. [11.]
„ „ Register, B21–30, 1906–15; bearbt. v. L. Malten. 4°. 1921

ATHENISCHE ABTEILUNG.
Mitteilungen. B40, 42–51, 1915, 1917–26. 8°. 1915–27
Tiryns, d. Ergebnisse d. Ausgrab. d. Inst. 2B. 4°. Athen. 1912
1, Die Hera v. Tiryns, v. A. Frickenhaus—Die "geometrische" Nekropole, v. W. Müller u. F. Oelmann.
2, Die Fresken d. Palastes, v. G. Rodenwaldt, mit Beitr. v. R. Hackl u. N. Heaton.

RÖMISCHE ABTEILUNG.
Mittheilungen-Bullettino. B30–41. la8°. Rom. 1915–26
see GERMANIA Romana: e. Bilder-Atlas hrsg. v. d. Röm.-Germ. Komm. d. Deut. Arch. Inst., 1922.

Kaiserliche Akademie der Wissenschaften zu Wien.
Almanach, 1914–27. s8°. Wien. 1914–27
DENKSCHRIFTEN. Phil.-hist. Klasse. B55–57, 59–64, 66, 67. 4°. Wien. 1913–26
Augapfel (J.) Babylon. Rechtsurkunden a. d. Regierungszeit Artaxerxes I u. Darius II, 1917. [59.]
Berthold, *of Tuttlingen*, *see* Erben (W.)
Birnbaum (A.) Vitruvius u. d. griech. Architektur, 1914. [57.]
Bittner (M.) Die heil. Bücher d. Jeziden &c., *&* Nachtrag, 1913. [55.]
Buberl (P.) Die Miniaturenhss. in d. Nationalbibl. in Athen, 1917. [60.]
Erben (Wilhelm). Berthold v. Tuttlingen, Registrator &c. Kaiser Ludwigs d. Baiern., 1923. [66.]
Fiebiger (O.) & L. Schmidt. Inschriftensammlung z. Gesch. d. Ostgermanen, 1917. [60.]
Gerstinger (H.) Bruchstücke e. ant. Komm. z. Archäologie d. Thukydides, 1926. [67.]
Hopfner (T.) Der Tierkult d. alt. Ägypter, 1913. [57.]
—— Üb. d. kopt.-sa'id. Apophthegmata Patrum Aegyptiorum, 1918. [61.]
—— Üb. Form u. Gebrauch d. griech. Lehnwörter in d. kopt.-sa'id. Apophthegmenversion, 1918. [62.]
Jireček (C. J.) Staat u. Gesellschaft im mittelalterl. Serbien, Tl, 2, 4, 1912–19. [56, 64.]
Junker (H.) Bericht ü. d. Grabungen auf d. Friedhöfen v. El-Kubanieh-Nord, 1910–11; 3T (T3, Das Kloster am Isisberg), 1919–22. [62, 64, 66.]
—— Bericht ü. d. Grabungen d. K. Akad. d. Wiss. in Wien auf d. Friedhof in Turah, 1909–10, mit e. Kapitel v. D. E. Derry, 1912. [56.]
—— Ermenne: Bericht ü. d. Grabungen auf d. Friedhöfen v. E., 1911–12, 1926. [67.]
—— Das Götterdekret ü. d. Abaton, 1913. [56.]
—— Die Onurislegende, 1917. [59.]
Karabacek (J. v.) Abendländ. Künstler zu Konstantinopel im 15. u. 16. Jhrh. &c., 1918. [62.]
Keil (J.) & A. v. Premerstein. Ber. ü. e. 3. Reise in Lydien &c., 1914. [57.]
Kopko (P.) Apostolus Bybl. saec. 14. gramm.-krit. analys., 1912. [55.]
Kubitschek (W.) Itinerarstudien, 1919. [61.]
—— Die Kalenderbücher v. Florenz, Rom u. Leyden, 1915. [57.]
Lach (R.) Sebastian Sailer's "Schöpfung" in d. Musik, &c., 1916. [60.]
—— W. A. Mozart als Theoretiker, 1918. [61.]
Mžik (H. v.) Afrika, n.d. arab. Bearb. d. Γεωγραφικὴ ὑφήγησις d. C. Ptolemæus v. Muḥammad ibn Mūsā al-Ḫwārizmi, 1916. [59.]
Oberhummer (E.) Die Brixener Globen v. 1522, 1926. [67.]
Paldus (J.) Milit. Aufnahmen d. Hapsburg. Länder, 1763–85, 1924. [63.]
Reich (N.) Papyri jurist. Inhalts in hierat. &c. Schr. aus d. Brit. Mus., Tl, 1914. [55.]
Schmidt (P. W.) Die Personalpronomina in d. austral. Sprachen &c., 1919. [64.]
Šufflay (M. v.) Städte u. Burgen Albaniens, 1924. [63.]
Thucydides, *see* Gerstinger (H.)
Torczyner (H.) Altbabylon. Tempelrechnungen, 1913. [55.]

Kaiserliche Akademie der Wissenschaften zu Wien [*continued*].

Schriften d. Sprachenkommission. Bl. 8°. Wien. 1909
see Reinisch (S. L.) Das persönl. Fürwort u. d. Verbalflexion in d. chamitosemit. Sprachen, 1909. [1.]

Sitzungsberichte.
B176–181, 183–191, 193, 194, 197, 200–203. 8°. Wien. 1916–28
„ „ Register zu d. B181–200. [2p]. 8°. Wien. 1927–28

Aristophanes, *see* Holzinger (C. v.)
Aristotle, *see* Arnim (H. v.)
Arnim (H. v.) Die 3 aristotel. Ethiken, 1924. [202.]
—— Sprachl. Forsch. z. Chronol. d. Platon. Dialoge, 1913. [169.]
—— Z. Entstehungsgesch. d. aristotel. Politik, 1924. [200.]
Augustine, *St.*, *see* Kalinka (E.)
Battisti (C.) Mundart v. Valvestino, 1913. [174.]
Bauer (A.) Die Herkunft d. Bastarnen, 1918. [185.]
Becker (P. A.) Bonaventure des Periers als Dichter &c., 1924. [200.]
—— C. Marot's Liebeslyrik, 1917. [184.]
—— Mellin de Saint-Gelais, 1924. [200.]
Beers (R.), *see* Garcia (Z.)
Biró (L. A.) Magyar. Sprach- u. Gesangaufnahmen (31. Mitt. d. Phonogr.-Archivs-Komm.), 1914. [173.]
Bittner (M.) Studien z. Laut- u. Formenlehre d. Mehri- Sprache, 4, 5i–iii, 1914–15. [174, 176, 178.]
—— Studien z. Šhauri- Sprache in d. Bergen v. Dofâr a. Pers. Meerb., 4p, 1916–17. [179, 183.]
—— Vorstudien z. Gramm. u. z. Wbche d. Soqoṭri-Sprache, 1–3, 1913–18. [173, 186.]
Bliemetzrieder (F. Pl.) Zu d. Schr. Ivos v. Chartres (†1116), 1917. [182.]
Bretholz (B.) Z. Gesch. d. kais. Akad. d. Wiss. in Wien, 1914. [176.]
Commodianus, *see* Martin (J.)
Czermak (W.) Kordufānnub. Studien, 1919. [177.]
Desperiers (J. B.), *see* Becker (P. A.)
Domaszewski (A. v.) Bellum Marsicum, 1924. [201.]
Engelberti (U.), *see* Grabmann (M.), *below*.
Ettmayer (C.) Ber. ü. Phonogr.-Aufnahmen d. Grödner Mundart (53. Mitt. d. Phonogr.-Archivs-Komm.), 1920. [191.]
—— Ü. das Wesen d. Dialektbildung, erläut. an d. Dialekten Frankreichs, 1924. [66.]
Euripides, *see* Lesky (A.)
Feder (A. L.) St. zu Hilarius v. Poitiers, 3, 1913. [169.]
Frutolf. Breviarium de musica & Tonarius; veröff. v. C. Vivell, 1916. [188.]
Gamillscheg (E.) Olten. Mundarten, 1919. [190.]
Garcia (Z.) Bibl. patrum Latin. Hispan., hrsg. v. G., 2i, 1913. [169.]

For preceding parts see, †Hartel (W. v.)

Geiger (B.) Die Amaša Spantas, 1916. [176.]
Geyer (R.), *see* Ja'far ibn Muḥammad.
Goldbacher (A.) Krit. Beitr. z. 41., 42. u. 43. Buche d. T. Livius, 1919. [193.]
—— Z. Kritik v. Ciceros Schr. De officiis, 1, 2, 1921–22. [196.]
Graber (G.) Der Eintritt d. Herz. v. Kärnten am Fürstenstein zu Karnburg, 1919. [190.]
Gröger (O.) 36. Mitteilung d. Phonogramm-Archivs-Kommission; Schweizer Mundarten, 1914. [176.]
Hatzidakis (G. N.) Ἄγγελος &c., 1914. [173.]
Herzog (E.) Französ. Phonogrammst., 1 (Nr. 25 d. Berichte d. Phonogr.-Arch.-Komm.), 1913. [169.]
Hilary, *St.*, *bp. of Poitiers*, *see* Feder (A. L.)
Hirsch (H.) Die echten &c. Stiftungsurkunden d. Abtei Banz, 1919. [189.]
Hofler (A.) Abhängigkeitsbeziehungen, 1917. [181.]
—— Naturwiss. u. Philosophie, 1, 2, 1920–21. [191, 196.]
Holzinger (C. v.) Aristophaneshss. d. Wiener Hofbibl., B2, 1913. [169.]
Hrozny (F.) Das Getreide im alt. Babylon, T1, 1914. [173.]
Idelsohn (A. Z.) Phonogr. Gesänge u. Aussprachsproben d. Hebrä. d. jemen., pers. u. syr. Juden, 1917. [175.]
Ja'far ibn Muḥammad ibn Ja'far, *al-Tayālisī*. Mukâṭarah; hrsg. R. Geyer, 1927. [203.]
Jagić (V.) Ein Beitr. z. altkirchenslav. Evangelientexte (Evang. Bucovinense), 1916. [180.]
—— Zum altkirchenslaw. Apostolus, 1, Grammat. u. Krit.; 2, 3, Lexical., 1919–20. [191, 193, 197.]
Junker (H.) Papyrus Lonsdorfer I. Ein Ehepakt a. d. Zeit d. Nektanebos, 1921. [197.]
—— & W. Czermak. Kordofân-Texte im Dialekt v. Gebel Dair, 1913. [174.]
Kalinka (E.) Die ält. erhalt. Abschr. d. Verzeichn. d. Werke Augustins, 1925. [203.]
—— Aus d. Werkstatt d. Hörsaals, 1922. [197.]
Karabacek (J. v.) Zur orient. Altertumskunde, 5, 6, 7, 1915–17. [178, 184–5.]
Kirste (J.) Orabazes, 1917. [182.]
Kraft (V.) Grundformen d. wiss. Methoden, 1926. [203.]
Krälitz Greifenhorst (F. v.) Osman. Urk. in türk. Sprache 15. Jhrh., 1922. [197.]

Kaiserliche Akademie der Wissenschaften zu Wien [*continued*.

Sitzungsberichte [*continued*].

Kreibig (J. K.) Über d. Quantität d. Urteils, 1919. [190.]
Kreichgauer (D.) Die Astronomie i. d. gr. Wiener Hs. aus Mexiko, 1917. [182.]
Kubitschek (W.) Zur Gesch. v. Städten d. röm. Kaiserreiches, H1, 1917. [177.]
Lach (R.) Gesänge russ. Kriegsgefangener, 1917–26. [183, 203.]
—— Konstruktionsprinzip d. Wiederholung in Musik, Sprache u. Lit., 1925. [201.]
—— Vergleich. Kunst- u. Musikwiss., 1925. [201.]
—— Die vergleich. Musikwiss., i. Methoden &c., 1924. [200.]
Lesky (A.) Alkestis, 1925. [203.]
Loserth (J.) J. von Wiclif u. G. Peraldus, 1916. [180.]
—— J. von Wiclif u. R. Grosseteste, 1918. [186.]
Maimun ibn Kais, *called al Asha*. Zwei Gedichte; hrsg. R. Geyer, 1921. [192.]
Mally (E.) Stud. z. Theorie d. Möglichkeit u. Ahnlichkeit, 1922. [194.]
Martin (J.) Commodianea, 1917. [181.]
Maver (H.) Einfluss d. vorchristl. Kulte auf d. Toponomastik Frankreichs, 1914. [175.]
Meinong v. Handschuchsheim (A.) Üb. emotionale Präsentation, 1917. [183.]
—— Z. Erweise d. allgem. Kausalgesetzes, 1918. [189.]
Meringer (R.) Mittelländ. Palast, Apsidenhaus u. Megaron, 1916. [181.]
Meyer-Lübke (W.) Roman. Namenstudien, 2, 1917. [184.]
Minor (J.) Studien zu Novalis, 1, 1913. [169.]
Much (R.) Der Name Germanen, 1920. [195.]
Murko (M.) Bericht, Volksepik d. bosn. Mohammedaner, 1914. [173.]
—— Bericht, Volksepic in Bosnia u. Herzegowina, 1915. [176.]
—— 37. Mitt. d. Phonogramm-Archivs-Komm.; Bericht ü. phonogr. Aufnahmen ep. Volkslieder i. mittl. Bosnien u. i. d. Herzegowina, 1915. [179.]
Nagl (A.) Die Rechentafel d. Alten, 1914. [177.]
Novalis, *ps.*, *see* Minor (J.)
Nowotny (E.) Römerspuren nördlich d. Donau, 1918. [187.]
Ottenthal (E.) Die gefälschten Magdeburg. Diplome u. M. Goldast, 1919. [192.]
Peitz (W. M.) Liber diurnus, I, 1918. [185.]
Pfaff (I.) B. Walther von Walthersweil als Romanist d. 16ten Jhdts., 1918. [186.]
Pfalz (A.) Beitr. z. Kunde d. bayer.- österr. Mundarten, H1, 1918. [190.]
—— & H. Voltelini. Forsch. z. d. deut. Rechtsbüchern, 3H, 1919–24. [191, 201.]
Plato, *see* Arnim (H. v.)
Pollak (H. W.) Phonet. Untersuch., 2, Akzent u. Aktionsart. (52. Mitt. d. Phonogr.-Archivs-Komm.), 1919. [192.]
Radermacher (L.) Beitr. z. Volkskunde aus d. Gebiete d. Ant., 1918. [187.]
—— Die Erzählungen d. Odyssee, 1915. [178.]
—— Hippolytos u. Thekla, 1916. [182.]
—— Zur Gesch. d. griech. Komödie, 1, 2, 1924. [202.]
Rhodokanakis (N.) Die Inschr. an d. Mauer v. Koḥlān-Timna, 1924. [200.]
—— Kataban. Texte z. Bodenwirtschaft, 1919. [194.]
—— Studien z. Lexikogr. u. Gramm. d. Altsüdarab., 1, 2, 1915–17. [178, 185.]
Roretz (C.) Z. Analyse v. Kants Philos. d. Organischen, 1922. [193.]
Rosthorn (A. v.) Die Anfänge d. chines. Geschichtschreibung, 1920. [193.]
—— Das Tsch'un-tsch'iu und s. Verfasser, 1919. [189.]
Saint-Gelais (M. de), *see* Becker (P. A.)
Schenkl (H.) Beitr. z. Textgesch. d. Reden d. Themistios, 1919. [192.]
Schleifer (J.) Sahid. Bibel-Fragm., Brit. Mus., 3, Psalmenfragm., 1914. [173.]
Schlitter (H.) Gründ. d. kais. Akad. d. Wiss., 1921. [197.]
Schlosser (J. v.) Mat. z. Quellenkunde d. Kunstgesch., 10H, 1914–20. [177, 179, 180, 184, 189, 192, 195, 196.]
Schuchardt (H. E. M.) Das Baskische u. d. Sprachwiss., 1925. [202.]
—— Berber. Hiatustilgung, 1916. [182.]
—— Die roman. Lehnwörter im Berber., 1918. [188.]
Schürr (F.) Romagnolische Dialektst., 1, 2, 1918–19. [187, 188.]
—— Romagnol. Mundarten, 1917. [181.]
Schwarz (A. Z.) Die hebrä. Hss. d. Hofbibl. zu Wien, 1914. [175.]
Seemüller (J.) Deutsche Mundarten, 5, 1918. [187.]
Singer (H.) Die Dekretalensammlung d. Bernardus Compostellanus antiquus, 1914. [171.]
—— Neue Beitr. ü. d. Dekretalensammlungen vor u. nach Bernhard v. Pavia, 1913. [171.]
Singer (S.) Wolfram's Stil u. der Stoff d. Parzival, 1916. [180.]
Srbik (H. *Ritt.* v.) Ein Schüler Niebuhrs: W. H. Grauert, 1914. [176.]

Kaiserliche Akademie der Wissenschaften zu Wien [*continued*].
SITZUNGSBERICHTE [*continued*].
Steffenhagen (E.) Die Entwickl. d. Landrechtsglosse d. Sachsenspiegels, 11, 12, 1922–23. [194, 195.]
Stein (O.) Megasthenes u. Kauṭilya, 1921. [191.]
Steinhauser (W.) Beitr. z. Kunde d. bairisch-österreich. Mundarten, 1922. [195.]
Stur (J.) Die slaw. Sprachelemente in d. Ortsnamen d. deut.-österr. Alpenländer, 1914. [176.]
Tayālisī, Al-, *see* Ja'far ibn Muḥammad.
Uhlirz (M.) Genesis d. 4 Prager Artikel, 1914. [175.]
Vivell (C.) Comm. anon. in Micrologum Guidonis Aretini, 1917. [185.]
Wachstein (B.) Hebr. Grabsteine, 13.–15. J., in Wien &c., 1916. [181.]
Waschnitius (V.) Perht, Holda u. verwandte Gestalten, 1913. [174.]
Wellesz (E.) Ballet-Suiten v. J. Heinrich u. A. A. Schmelzer, 1914. [176.]
Werner (H.) Die melod. Erfindung im frühen Kindesalter, 1917. [182.]
Wessely (C.) Sahid. Papyrusfragm. d. paulin. Briefe, 1914. [174.]
Wilhelm (A.) Att. Urkunden, T2, 3, 1916–25. [180, 202.]
—— Neue Beitr. z. gr. Inschriftenkunde, T3, 4, 6, 1913–21. [179, 183.]
Winkler (E.) Franz. Dichter d. M.-a., 2, Marie de France, 1918. [188.]
—— Französ. Dichter d. M.- a., 1, Vaillant, 1918. [186.]
Wlassak (M.) Anklage u. Streitbefestigung: Abwehr geg. P. Lotmar, 1920. [194.]
—— Anklage &c. im Kriminalrecht d. Römer, 1917. [184.]
—— Judikationsbefehl d. röm. Prozesse &c., 1921. [197.]
—— Klass. Prozessformel, T1, 1924. [202.]
—— Zum röm. Provinzialprozess, 1919. [190.]
see FONTES RERUM AUSTRIAC.: österreich. Geschichtsquellen; hrsg. v. d. Histor. Commission d. K. A. d. W., 1865–1909.
„ ÖSTERREICH. Mittelalt. Bibliothekskataloge Ö.'s, B1, 1915.

Kaiserlich-Königliches Kunsthistoriches Hofmuseum.
see MÜLLER (D. H.) Südarab. Alterthümer im K. H., 1899.

Kaiserlich-Königliches Münz- u. Antiken-Kabinet zu Wien.
Die ant. Gold- u. Silber-Monumente. Beschr. v. J. Arneth. fol. Wien. 1850
Die Cinque-Cento Cameen u. Arb. d. B. Cellini u. s. Zeitgen. im K.-K. M.- u. A.-Cab. zu Wien. Beschr. v. J. Arneth. fol. Wien. 1858

Kaiser-Wilhelm-Dank. Unterm Eisernen Kreuz, 1914–16. Kriegsschriften d. K.-W.-D. Verein d. Soldatenfreunde. H47, 49, 58–68, 79, 80. 8°. [1916–17]
Aereboe (F.) Die Landwirtschaft u. d. Krieg, 2T, 1916. [49, 67, 68.]
Ardenne (*Baron* A. v.) Die Befreiung v. Galizien, 1916. [66.]
—— Kämfe nach d. Winterschlacht an d. Masurischen Seen. Deut. Armeen in Westgalizien u. d. Karpathen, 1916. [62.]
Bremen (W. v.) Deutscher Kriegshumor, B2, 1916. [65.]
Evers (E.) Feldpostbriefe aus d. Osten, 1916. [59.]
Kalau v. Hofe (E.) Kriegszug d. Kreuzers Emden, 1916. [60, 61.]
Spohn (K.) Stellungskrieg im Westen &c., H3, 4, 1917. [79, 80.]
Sternfeld (R.) Kaiser Wilhelm I in uns. Zeit, 1916. [47.]
Würfel (G.) Englands Kohle als Kampfmittel, 1916. [63, 64.]
Zylka (J.) Westrussland in militärgeograph. Hinsicht, 1916. [58.]

Kajars. *The dynasty of the Kajars, tr. f. Pers. MS. [of 'Abd Al-Razzaq ibn Najaf Kuli] by Sir H. Jones Brydges [assisted by D. Shea]. Pref. succinct acc. of hist. of Persia. 8°. 1833

Kak (Ram Chandra). Antiq. of Bhimbar & Rajauri, *see* INDIA: ARCH. SURVEY. Mem. 14, 1923.

Kalaidovich (Konstantin Fedorovich). Истор. и хронолог. опытъ о посадникахъ новгородскихъ [–1478]. s4°. Москва. 1821

Kálal (Karel). La Slovaquie, terre de l'avenir. [P2403]. 8°. Prague. 1919

Kalankatouatzi (Moses), *see* MOSES KALANKATOUATZI.

Kalau (Abraham), *see* CALOVIUS (A.)

Kalau (Daniel). Arausio supremo imperio vindicata. Præs. J. P. Ludewig. recusa. [P2746]. s4°. Halæ Vened. 1739

Kalau vom Hofe (E.) Kriegszug d. Kreuzers Emden, *see* KAISER-WILHELM-DANK. Kriegsschr., H60, 61, 1916.

Kalemkearean (Grigoris). [Hist. of Armenian journalism. *In Armenian.* v1]. [P2816]. s8°. Vienna. 1893
[Studies of Lemberg codices. 1, Bischoff, Old Lemberg laws.

Kalemkearean (Grigoris) [*continued*].
2, Kohler, Law of the Armenians (*w. sep. pagin.*) Tr. *in Armenian by* G. Kalemkear]. s8°. Vienna. 1890
see DANIEL. Die 7. Vision D.'s; Arm. Text m. deut. Übers. v. G. K., 1892.

Kalet (Anna). Effect of the War on working children in Germany, 1921, *see* UNITED STATES: LABOR.

Kalff (Gerrit). Van zeevarende luyden en zee-poëten. 8°. 's-Gravenhage. 1915

Kālidāsa. Śakuntalā, a Sanskrit drama. Ed. w. notes, crit. & explan. by Monier Williams. 2nd ed. 8°. O. 1876
Sakuntala. Prep. for stage by K. N. D. Gupta. New vers. wr. by L. Binyon, w. introd. essay by R. Tagore. 8°. 1920
see JONES (*Sir* W.) Wks., v6, Sacontalá (tr.), 1799.

Kālidās Nāg, *see* NÂG (KÂLIDÂS).

Kalinin (M. I.) Речи и беседы М. И. К. кн. 1, 2. [P2724]. la8°. Москва. 1919

Kalinka (Ernst). Aus d. Werkstatt d. Hörsaals, *see* KAIS. AKAD. D. WISS. ZU WIEN. Sitzber., B197, 1922.

Kalinsky (Ivan Plakidovich). Церковно-народный мѣсяцесловъ на Руси. [I.R.G.O. Зап. по отд. этнографіи, т7]. 8°. С.–П. 1877

Kalinsky (Johann Gottlieb). Vaticinia Chabacuci & Nachumi itemque Jesaiæ, Micheæ & Ezechielis oracula obs. ex hist. Diodori Siculi circa res Sardanapali illust.; adj. comm. de lessu Jeremiæ in obitum Josiæ. Præmitt. præf. J. F. Burgii. s4°. Vratislaviæ. 1748

Kalisch (Moritz M.)
A Hebrew gram. 2p [p1, rev. ed.] 8°. 1863–65

Kaliski (Julius). Die Unterbilanz d. ersten Revolutionsjahres: zum 9 Nov. [Sonderheft d. Firn]. [P2410]. 8°. 1919

Kalkar (Christian Andreas Hermann). Gesch. d. röm.-kathol. Mission. Deut. A. bearb. v. A. Michelsen. 8°. Erlangen. 1867

Kalkar (Otto). Ordbog til det ældre danske Sprog, 1300–1700. B5. 8°. 1908–18

Kalken (Frans van). Madame de Bellem, la "Pompadour des Pays-Bas." 8°. Brux. 1923

Kalkoff (Paul). Anfänge d. Gegenreform. in d. Niederlanden. [Verein f. Ref.-gesch., Jhrg. 21, Nr. 79, 81]. 2T. 8°. Halle a. S. 1903
Briefe, Depeschen u. Berichte ü. Luther v. Wormser Reichstage 1521. Aus d. Engl., Ital. u. Span. übers. &c. v. P. K. [Ver. f. Ref.-gesch., Jhrg. 15, Nr. 59]. 8°. Halle. 1898
Erasmus, Luther u. Friedrich d. Weise. [Ver. f. Ref.-gesch., Jhrg. 37 (Nr. 132)]. 8°. L. 1919
Der grosse Wormser Reichstag v. 1521. 8°. [Darmstadt. 1921]
Kard. Schiner, ein Mitarbeiter Aleanders auf d. Wormser Reichstage. [Archiv f. Ref.-gesch., Jhrg. 18, H3–4]. 8°. L. 1921
Luther u. d. Entscheidungsjahre d. Reformation. 8°. München. 1917
Vermittlungspolitik d. Erasmus &c., *see* ARCHIV F. REFORMATIONSGESCH., Jhrg. 1, 1904.
Das Wormser Edikt u. d. Erlasse d. Reichsregiments &c. [Hist. Bibl., B37]. 8°. München. 1917

Kalkschmidt (Eugen). Der Goldmacher J. F. Böttger u. d. Erfindung d. europ. Porzellans. 13. A. s8°. St. [1926]

Kall (Abraham), *of Flensburg.* Diss. de codd. MSS. Biblico-Hebr., maxime Erffurtens. Praes. J. H. Michaelis. [P430]. s4°. Halae Magdeb. [1706]

Kallas (Aino Julia Maria), *wife of Dr. O. P. Kallas, Estonian Ambassador.* An Estonian novelist: F. Tuglas. [Extr. f. Slavonic Rev.] [P2876]. la8°. [1927]
The white ship. Estonian tales. Tr. A. Matson. Foreword by J. Galsworthy. s8°. [1924]

Kallas (Oskar). Estonian folklore. [From Folk Lore, June 1923. P2738]. 8°. [1923]

Kállay (Béni). Die Orientpolitik Russlands. Aus d. Ungar. v. J. B. Schwicker. 8°. Budapest. 1878

Kallstenius (Gottfrid). Jonas Rugmans Saml. av isländ. talesätt, *see* KUNG. HUM. VET.-SAMF. I UPPSALA. Skr., B22, 1927.

Kalmár (Antal). Uj dualizmus. 8°. 1909

Kalpaschnikoff (Andrew). A prisoner of Trotsky's. With foreword by D. R. Francis. 8°. N.Y. 1920

Kalteisen (Henrik), *erkebiskop, d. 1465.* Kopibog [*Latin*]. Udj. ved A. Bugge. [Norske Hist. K.] 8°. 1899

Kalyaev (Ivan Platonovich). И. П. К. Процессъ. Стихотворенія &c. [P2716]. s8°. *n.p.* 1905

Kamal-Ud-Din (*Khwaja*).
The ideal prophet. 8°. Woking. [1925]
India in the balance: Brit. rule & the Caliphate. s8°. Woking. [1922]
The sources of Christianity. 8°. Woking. [1924]

Kamarovsky (*count* **Leonid Alekseevich**).
Война или миръ? [P847]. s8°. Одесса. 1895

Kambo (Saverio). Grottaferrata e il Monte Cavo. [Italia artistica, 86]. la8°. Bergamo. [1924 ?]
Il Tuscolo e Frascati. [Italia artist., 84]. 4°. Bergamo. [1920]

Kamehameha III, *king of the Hawaiian Islands, see* HAWAII.
Statute laws of K.; passed by Houses of Nobles &c., 1845–46, v1, 1846.

Kamenev (L. B.) [*i.e.* LEV BORISOVICH ROSENFELD].
Ленинизм или Троцкизм? *see* TROTSKY (L.) 1917, 1924.
Die Sowjetrepublik in d. kapitalist. Umzingelung. (Rede, März, 1921). [P2570]. s8°. L. 1921
see SOWJETRUSSLAND u Polen; Reden v. K. &c., 1920.

Kamensky (Anatolii Pavlovich).
Мебель.—Бѣлая ночь. [P2392]. s8°. Москва. 1917

Kamensky (Petr Valer.) Врачеванiе бѣдности. Опытъ историч. изслѣдованiя. ч1. [P2452]. 8°. Москва. 1909
Значенiе торговопромышленныхъ трестовъ на западѣ и у насъ. [P2452]. 8°. Москва. 1909

Kames (Henry Home, *lord*).
*Essays on the principles of morality & nat. religion. 8°. E. 1751
*Intr. to the art of thinking. s8°. E. 1761
see ANDERSON (G.) Anal. of sentiments cont. in Sopho &c., 1755.
„ BLAIR (H.) Obs. upon Anal. of sentiments cont. in Sopho &c., 1755.
see BONAR (J.) *Estimate of the profit &c. of relig.: illust. w. ref. to Essays on morality &c. [*by* H. H., Ld. K.], 1753.
„ EDWARDS (J.) Remarks on Essays on the principles of morality &c. [by K.], 1758.

Kami (N. Nura), *see* NURA KAMI (N.)

Kaminka (Avgust Isaak).
Труды русскихъ ученыхъ за границей. Сборникъ Акад. группы въ Берлинѣ подъ ред. А. И. К. т1. 8°. [Berlin]. 1922

Kaminsky (Dmitri Nikolaevich Bantish), *see* †BANTISH-KAMINSKY.

Kamkov (Boris), *see* RUSSIA: SOVIET REPUBLIC. Теорiя и практика совѣтскаго строя, в1, 1919.

Kammerer (A.) Essai sur l'hist. ant. d'Abyssinie: le royaume d'Aksum &c. la8°. 1926

Kampen (Nicolaas Gottfried van). Hist. & topog. of Holland & Belgium. Tr. W. G. Fearnside. Illust. by W. H. Bartlett. 8°. [1837]

Kamper (Jar.) & Zd. Wirth. Topogr. d. hist. u. Kunstdenkm.: Polit. Bez. Mies, *see* BOHEMIA. Topographie d. hist. u. Kunstdenkmale, B30, 1911.

Kampf (Der) in Genua. 1, G. Tschitscherin, Rede auf d. Konf. in G., am 10. Apr. 1922. 2, Mem. d. Russ. Delegation. [P2685]. 8°. Hamburg. 1922

Kampf (Arthur), *see* ROSENHAGEN (H.) A. K. (Knackfuss), 1922.

***Kampflieder;** hrsg. v. d. Kommunist. Jugend Deutschlands. [P2570]. s8°. L. 1921

Kandel (Isaac Leon). Education in Gt. Brit. & Ireland, *see* UNITED STATES: EDUCATION.

Kane (John). List of officers of the Royal Reg. of Artillery, 1763 to present time. [*MS. add. to 1839*]. sm. fol. Greenwich. 1815

Kane (*Sir* **Robert).** Inaug. address deliv. at opening of Queen's Coll., Cork. [P2558]. 8°. D. 1849

Kang-He, *emperor of China, see* BOUVET (J.) Ist. de l'Imp. de la Cina; tr., 1710.

Kann (Alphonse). The A. K. coll. Sold, Amer. Art Assoc., Jan. 6–8, 1927. [*Illust. cat.*] 2p. 4°. N.Y. 1927

Kann (Réginald). Le Protectorat marocain. s8°. 1921

Kannenberg (Carl). Kleinasiens Naturschätze, seine wicht. Tiere, Kulturpflanzen &c. Mit. Beitr. v. Prem.-Lieut. Schäffer. 8°. 1897

Kannengiesser (Hans), *pasha.* Gallipoli, 1915. Einführ. v. Marschall L. v. Sanders Pascha. 8°. 1927

Kanner (Heinrich).
Kaiserl. Katastrophen-Politik. 8°. Wien. 1922

Kanovitch (Abraham). The will to beauty: cont. of philos. of Schopenhauer & Nietzsche. [2nd pr.] 8°. N.Y. [1923]

Kant (Immanuel).
Gesamm. Schriften. Hrsg. v. d. Königl. Preuss. Akad. d. Wiss. B9 (Abtlg. 1, Werke, B9), B13 (Abtlg. 2 [Briefwechsel] B4), B16, 17 (Abt. 3 [Handschriftl. Nachlass], B3, 4). 8°. 1914–26
I, 9, Logik—Physische Geographie—Pädagogik. II, 4 (13) Briefwechsel B4, Anmerkungen u. Register. III, 3 (16) Logik. III, 4 (17) Metaphysik, T1.
Der einzig mögliche Beweisgrund zu e. Demonstration d. Daseyns Gottes. s8°. Königsberg. 1763
Versuch d. Begriff d. negativen Grössen in d. Weltweisheit einzuführen. [*b. w. h.* Einzig mögl. Beweisgrund d. Daseyns Gottes, 1763]. s8°. Königsberg. 1763
Vorlesungen ü. Psych. Mit e. Einl.: K.'s myst. Weltanschauung, hrsg. v. C. du Prel [*b. w.* Du Prel (C.) Geheimwiss., 1890–91]. 8°. L. 1889

TRANSLATIONS.
Essays & treatises on moral, polit., relig. &c. subjects. [Tr.] 2v. 8°. 1798–99
The metaphysic of morals. Tr. 2v *in* 1. s8°. 1799
Prolegomena & metaphys. foundations of nat. science. Tr. w. biog. & intr. by E. B. Bax. 2nd ed. rev. s8°. *Bohn.* 1891

see BECK (J. S.) Principles of crit. philos. f. wks. of K.; tr., 1797.
„ CASSIRER (E.) K.'s Leben u. Lehre, 1921.
„ ERDMANN (B.) Die Idee v. Kants Kritik d. reinen Vernunft, 1917.
„ EWING (A. C.) K.'s treatment of causality, 1924.
„ KEYSERLING (H., *Graf* v.) Menschen als Sinnbilder (K. d. Sinneserfasser), 1926.
„ MONTGOMERY (E.) Die Kant'sche Erkenntniss-lehre, 1871.
„ RORETZ (C.) Z. Analyse v. K.'s Philosophie d. Organischen, 1922.
„ SCHOLZ (H.) Religionsphilos. d. Als-ob: e. Nachprüfung K.'s u. d. idealist. Positivismus, 1921.
„ SERRA (R.) Scritti ined., 1923.
„ SMITH (N. K.) Comm. on K.'s "Critique of pure reason," 2nd ed., rev., 1923.
„ STORR (G. C.) Annotat. ad philos. K. doctrinam, 1793.
„ VAIHINGER (H.) Philos. des Als Ob; mit Anhang ü. K. &c., 1911; 1923.
„ WARD (J.) A study of K., 1922.
„ WEBB (C. C. J.) K.'s philos. of relig., 1926.

Kantakuzin (*Princess*), *see* CANTACUZÈNE (*Pcss.*)

Kanteletar, taikka Suomen Kansan wanhoja lauluja ja wirsiä, 1864, *see* LÖNNROT (E.)

Kantemir (*prince* **Antiokh Dmitrievich),** *1708–44.*
Сочиненiя, письма &c. Со статьею о Кантемирѣ &c. В. Я. Стоюнина. 2t. 8°. С.-П. 1867–68
Satyres, tr. avec l'hist. de sa vie [*by O. de Guasco*]. s8°. Londres. 1750

Kantor (R. M.)
В погоне за Нечаевым. 8°. П. 1922

Kantorovich (A. Ya.), *see* SHTEIN (B. E.) & A. YA. K. Русский экспорт, 1923.

Kantorowicz (Ernst). Kaiser Friedrich d. Zweite. la8°. 1927

***Kanuri** songs. Tr. & intr. note by J. R. Patterson. Pref. by H. R. Palmer. la8°. [Lagos. 1926]

Kapitalistische (Die) Welt u. d. Kommunist. Internat., 1920, *see* KOMMUNISTISCHE INTERNATIONALE.

Kaploun (Albert). Psychologie gén. tirée de l'ét. du rêve. s8°. Lausanne. 1919

Kaplun (S.) Охрана труда за 2г. пролетарской револ., 1917–19. [P2459]. 8°. Москва. 1920

Kaplun-Kogan (Wlad. W.) Die jüd. Wanderbewegungen in d. neu. Zeit, 1880–1914. 8°. Bonn a. Rh. 1919
Russ. Wirtschaftsleben seit d. Herrschaft d. Bolschewiki nach russ. Zeitungen. Mit Einl. hrsg. v. K.-K. 2e A. 8°. L. 1919

Kapnist (Vasily Vasilevich), *1757–1824.*
Избранныя сочиненiя. Изд. И. Глазунова. 8°. С.-П. 1907
Ябеда, *see* BUNIN (I. A.) Русскiе писатели, 1921.

Kapp (Alexander).
Comm. de hist. educationis. 4°. Hammoniae. 1834

Kapp (Friedrich) & J. Goldfriedrich. Gesch. d. deut. Buchhandels. Im Auftr. d. Borsenvereins d. deut. Buchhändler hrsg. v. d. Hist. Komm. desselben. 4B. 8°. L. 1886–1913
1, bis in d. 17e Jhdt.; von F. K. 2, 1648–1740, v. J. G. 3, 1740–1804; v. J. G. 4, 1805–89; v. J. G. [*w. gen, indexes, added later*].

Kapp (Wolfgang).
see BERNSTEIN (R.) Der Kapp-Putsch u. s. Lehren, 1920.

Kappes (Mathias). Aristoteles-Lexikon. Erklär. d. termini technici. 8°. Paderborn. 1894

Kappstein (Theodor). Schleiermachers Weltbild u. Lebensanschauung. s8°. München. 1921

Kapras (Johann). Evol. hist. de l'état Tchéco-Slovaque. [P2426]. 8°. Prague. 1919
The Peace League of George Poděbrad king of Bohemia. [P2425]. 8°. Prague. 1919
Prussian Upper Silesia & the Czech state. [P2425]. 8°. Prague. 1919
Karabacek (Josef v.) Abendländ. Künstler zu Konstantinopel im 15. u. 16. Jhdt., 1, 1458–81, 1918, *see* KAIS. AKAD. D. WISS. ZU WIEN. Denkschr., B62, 1918.
Zur orient. Altertumskunde, 5 (Problem oder Phantom), 6 (Koranfragm.), 7 (Gesch. Suleimans), 1915–17, *see* KAISERL. AKAD. D. WISS. ZU WIEN. Sitzungsber., B178, 184, 185, 1916–18.
Karabchevsky (Nikolai Platonovich) [KARABTSCHEVSKY]. La révolution & la Russie. Souv. & impress. s8°. 1921
Karácsonyi (Janos). The histor. right of the Hungarian nation to territ. integrity. [P2567]. s8°. 1920
Karajić (Vuk Stefanović). Српске народне песме. Из збир. К. и друг. [v]1. 8°. [Београд. 1923]
Karakashean (A. M.) [Crit. hist. of the Armenians. *In Armenian.* pl, 2]. la8°. Kostantnoupolis & Tiflis. 1880–95
[Gram. of mod. Armenian. *In Armenian*]. s8°. K.-polis. 1885
Karaman (Ljubo). Pitanje odstranjenja zgrade stare biskupije u Dioklecijanovoj Palači u Splitu, *see* BULLETTINO DI ARCH. &C. DALM., 43, Suppl., 1920.
Karamianz (N.), *see* KÖNIGL. BIBL., *Berlin.* Verzeichniss d. arm. Hss. d. K. B., v. N. K., 1888.
Karamzin (Nikolai Mikhailovich).
Бедная Лиза. Рисунки М. Добужинского. s8°. П. 1921
Избранныя сочиненія. ч2, Письма русс. путешественника. 2ᵉ, исправ. изд. И. Глазунова. 8°. С.-П. 1910
Повѣсти. 5ое изд. s8°. С.-П. 1887
Karapet, *Sasnatzi, bp. & vardapet, 13 c.* [Panegyric on St. Mesrop. *In Armenian.* Ed. M. Ter Movsesean. *Extr. f.* Ararat, 1897. P2814]. s8°. Vagharshapat. 1897
Karatov (F. V.) Павелъ I, его жизнь &c. [P2388]. s8°. Лондонъ. 1903
Kardec (Allan) [*i.e.* H. L. D. RIVAIL]. Filosofía espirit. El libro de los espíritus. Tr. de la 16ª ed. franc. s8°. Barcelona. 1871
Karekin (*le père*), *see* ZARBHANALEAN (K.)
Karelin (—).
Злые сплетни на угнетенных. [P2723]. 8°. Москва. 1919
Karelin (Grig. Silich). Путешествія по Каспійскому морю. [I.R.G.O. Записки по общей геогр., 10]. 8°. С.-П. 1883
Karel van de Woestijne (Peter Eduard Marie).
Goddelijke verbeeldingen. s8°. A. 1918
Karénine (Wladimir).
G. Sand, sa vie & s. œuvres. [t]4, 1848–76. 8°. [1926]
Karg (M. Ad. Fr. F.) Synopsis hist. relig. & eccl. Xtnae. [*Foll. by* Litium relig. enarr. *w. sep. tp. & pagin.*] ed. 2ª emend. 8°. Lipsiae. 1823
Karjansky (N.) [*ps.* KACHANOV].
Чехо-Словаки въ Россіи. 8°. Москва. 1918
Karlfeldt (Erik Axel). Flora och Bellona. 3ᵉ uppl. 8°. [1918]
Flora och Pomona. 3ᵉ uppl. 8°. [1918]
Fridolins lustgård och Dalmålningar på rim. 7ᵉ uppl. s8°. [1917]
Fridolins visor och andra diktor. 8ᵉ uppl. s8°. [1917]
Vildmarks- och kärleksvisor. 7ᵉ uppl. 8°. [1920]
Karlgren (Anton). Bolshevist Russia. Tr. A. Barwell. 8°. [1927]
Karlgren (Bernhard). Sound & symbol in Chinese. s8°. 1923
Karlinger (Hans). Alt-Bayern. Bilderb. la8°. München. 1922
Die hochroman. Wandmalerei in Regensburg. Mit e. techn. Exkurs v. M. Doerner. la8°. München. 1920
Die roman. Steinplastik in Altbayern u. Salzburg, 1050–1260. Bearb. H. K. 4°. Augsburg. 1924
Karlsberg (Bernhard). Der Einfluss d. Seeschiffahrt auf Deutschlands Zahlungsbilanz [1918–], *see* MEERWARTH (R.) &c. Probleme, 1924.
Karlsruhe, *see* BADISCHER KUNSTGEWERBE-VEREIN. Alte u. neue Fächer aus d. Wettbewerbung u. Austellung zu K., 1891.
Karlström (Sigurd). Old Eng. compound place-names in -ing. Inaug. diss. 8°. Uppsala. 1927
Karman, e. buddhist. Legendenkranz, 1925, *see* ZIMMER (H.), *ed.*
Karmin (Otto). Sir Francis D'Ivernois, 1757–1842. Sa vie, s. œuvre & s. temps. Préc. d'une notice s. s. père F. H. d'Ivernois &c. 8°. Genève. 1920
Kärntner Geschichtsquellen, 811–1269; hrsg. v. A. v. Jaksch, *see* CARINTHIA. Mon. hist. duc. Car., B3, 4, 1904–15.

Karo (Georg). Die Schachtgräber v. Mykenai, *see* KAIS. DEUT. ARCH. INST. Athen. Abt. Mitt., B40 (1915), 1927.
Károlyi (*count* **Michael**). Fighting the world: the struggle for peace. Tr. E. W. Dickes. 8°. 1924
Gegen eine ganze Welt: mein Kampf um den Frieden. 8°. München. 1924
Karpenko-Kary (Ivan) [TOBILEVICH (Iv. KARPOV.)]
Збірныкъ драмат. творивъ. 8°. Херсонъ. 1886
Karpinski (Louis C.) Hermann von Helmholtz. [Repr. f. The Scient. Monthly, July 1921. P2621]. 8°. *n.p.* [1921]
Karpinsky (V. A.) Два года борьбы. [P2722]. s8°. Москва. 1919
На чьей стороне справедливость? Крестьянская беседа в 2 действиях. [P2723]. 8°. Москва. 1919
Народное просвещение и советская власть. [P2722]. s8°. Москва. 1919
Karpovich (P. V.) *Карповичъ и Балмашевъ передъ судомъ. [P2389]. s8°. Берлинъ. 1902
see RUSSIA. Избіеніе русской молодежи, 1902.
Karr (J. B. Alphonse).
Agathe & Cécile. n. éd. [*b. w. h.* Contes & nouv., 1852]. s8°. 1856
Devant les tisons. [*b. w. h.* Sous les tilleuls, 1857]. s8°. 1853
Les femmes. [*b. w. h.* "Lettres écr. de m. jardin," 1853]. s8°. 1855
Lettres écr. de m. jardin. s8°. 1853
La pêche en eau douce & en eau salée. n. éd. s8°. 1878
Sous les tilleuls. n. éd. s8°. 1857
Voyage autour de mon jardin. [Coll. Nelson]. s8°. [1913]
Karrer (Otto), *S.J.* Der heil. Franz v. Borja, General d. Gesellschaft Jesu, 1510–72. 8°. Freiburg i. B. 1921
Karsky (Evfimii Fedorovich). Gesch. d. weissruss. Volksdichtung u. Lit. [Grund. d. slav. Philol.] 8°. 1926
Karsky (Isetor), *ps.*, *see* MARKHLEVSKY (YU.)
Karst (Josef). Hist. Gramm. d. Kilikisch-Armen. 8°. Str. 1901
Gesch. d. Hellenismus. 2ᵉ A. B2. 8°. L. 1926
Karsten (Rafael). Blood revenge, war & victory feasts among the Jibaro Indians of East. Ecuador. [S.I. Bureau of Amer. Ethnol., Bull. 79]. 8°. Wash. 1923
The civiliz. of the S. American Indians. Pref. by E. Westermarck. 8°. 1926
Karte. *Geograph. Gen. Karte &c., 1788, *see* GEOGRAPHISCHE.
Kartikov (M. N.) Русские песни: изборник народной лирики. la8°. Вологда. [1922]
Kaser (Kurt). Das späte Mittelalter. 2ᵉ A. 8°. St. 1925
Käser-Kesser (H. A.), *see* KESSER (H.)
Kasiski (F. W.) Die Geheimschr. u. d. Dechiffrir-Kunst. 8°. 1863
Kasperkowitz (Carl), *see* BEUTHEN. Die deut. Stadt B.; hrsg. K. K., 1925.
Kasperl, *ps.*, *see* LA ROCHE (J.), *called Kasperl.*
Kassner (Rudolf).
Der Dilettantismus. s8°. Frankfurt a. M. [1910]
Kastan (Isidor). Berlin wie es war. [10. bis 11. A.] 8°. 1925
Kastren (Matthias Alex.), *see* CASTREN (M. A.)
Katabanische Texte z. Bodenwirtschaft, 1919, *see* RHODOKANAKIS (N.)
Katalanische Lyrik d. Gegenwart: deut. Auslese, 1923, *see* GROSSMANN (R.)
Katalog [*see also* VERSTEIGERUNG].
Auctions-Kat. e. Samml. v. Mobiliaren, Kupferstichen &c. aus d. Besitze d. Frau Bar. B. [16–19 März, 1920; Wien.] Firma Glückselig u. Wärndorfer. [*Illust. b. w.* Kolisch (R.) Versteig., 1921]. 4°. Wien. 1920
K. e. Sammlung v. Kupferstichen &c. Versteig., 1925 &c., *see* GILHOFER (H.) & H. RANSCHBURG.
Katancsich (Petrus Matthias). De Istro ejusque adcolis comm. &c. s4°. Budae. 1798
see BIBLE: CROATIAN. Sveto pismo Starog' [*& Novog'*]; tr. M. P. K., 1831.
Katanov (Nikolai Fedorovich).
Мусульманскія легенды. Тексты и переводы. [I. Akad. Nauk. Записки, t75]. 8°. С.-П. 1894
Katechetische. Aelteste katechet. Denkmale d. evang. Kirche, 1527–29, 1844, *see* HARTMANN (J.), *ed.*
***Katechismus** d. Christl. Lehre z. Gebr. in d. Evang. Kirchen u. Schulen d. Königl. Braunschw. Züneb. Churlande. 2ᵉ A. s8°. Hannover. 1791
Katherdzean (Hovseph), *see* CATERGIAN (J.)
***Katholicismus** (Der) u. d. mod. Staat. [P2656]. 8°. 1873
Katholisch [KATHOLISCHE]. *K. u. Ultramontan. Z. Orientierung. V. e. entschied. Katholiken &c. [P2694]. 8°. München. [1868]

Katholisch [KATHOLISCHE] [*continued*].
*Erklärung d. Gebräuche u. Ceremonien uns. heil. k. Kirche, 1856, *see* ERKLÄRUNG.
Stimmen aus d. K. Kirche über d. Kirchenfragen d. Gegenwart. 2B. s8°. München. 1870
Döllinger (J. J. I. v.) Üb. d. Unfehlbarkeitsadresse u. Die neue Geschäftsordnung d. Concils. [1ii.]
Friedrich (J.) Das päpstl. gewährbistete Recht d. deut. Nation &c. [2ii.]
Hötzl (P. de A.) Ist Döllinger Häretiker? [1iii.]
Huber (J. N.) Die Freiheiten d. französ. Kirche. [1v.]
—— Das Papstthum u. d. Staat. [1i.]
Liaño (E. St. A. de). Das grosse Kirchl. Gebrechen uns. zeit. [1vi.]
Reinkens (J. H.) Ueber papstl. Unfehlbarkeit. [2iii.]
Schmitz (C.) Ist d. Papst. persönl. unfehlbar? etc. [1iv.]
Vatican Council. Wie es auf d. Concil zugeht. [2i.]

Kato (Genchi). St. of the development of relig. ideas am. the Jap. people as illust. by Jap. phallicism, *see* ASIATIC SOC. OF JAPAN, s2, v1, Suppl., 1924.
The Warongo or Jap. analects, *see* ASIATIC SOC. OF JAPAN. Trans., v45ii, 1917.

Katona (István) [KATONA (STEPHANUS)]. Hist. crit. prim. Hungariae ducum &c. 8°. Pestini. 1778
Hist. pragmatica Hungariae. 2p *in* 2v. 8°. Budae. 1782–84
see CANONES. Canones eccl. &c., coll. a K., 1768.

Katsuawa Shunshō, *see* SHUNSHO (K.)

Kaudern (Walter). Ethnogr. studies in Celebes: results of exped., 1917–20. 1, Structures & settlements. 2, Migrations of the Toradja. 3, Musical Instruments. pl–3. 8°. [Göteberg. 1925–27]

Kauffer (E. McKnight). The art of the poster, its origin &c. Arr. & ed. E. McK. K. sm. fol. 1924

Kauffmann (Angelika), *aft. wife of A. Zucchi, see* MANNERS (*Lady* V.) & G. C. WILLIAMSON. A. K., h. life & works, 1924.

Kaufman (Herbert). The song of the guns. [P2561]. 8°. 1914

Kaufmann (Carl Joseph). German West Prussia. Reprod. f. docs. illust. hist. dur. Polish period. Coll. by K. J. K. fol. [1926 ?]
Das staatsrechtl. Verhältnis Danzigs zu Polen, 1454–1793 u. 1807–14. [P2497, 2525]. 8°. Danzig. 1920

Kaufmann (Georg). Zwei kathol. u. 2 protestant. Universitäten v. 16.–18. Jhdt., *see* KÖNIGL. AKAD. D. W. ZU MÜNCHEN. Phil. Kl., Sitz., 1920.

Kaufmann (Johann), *of Nürnberg, 1532–96, see* MULLER (J. P.) Diss. qua J. K. vita & merita percensentur, 1722.

Kaufmann (Paul). Licht u. Schatten bei d. deut. Arbeiterversicherung. [P2409]. 8°. 1912

Kaul (Gōvind), *Paṇḍit, see* HĀTIM TILAWŌNU. H.'s tales &c.; recorded w. the assist. of Pandit G. K. by Sir A. Stein, 1923.

Kaulbach (Anna van Gogh-), *see* GOGH-KAULBACH (A. v.)

Kaulen (Franz). Gesch. d. Vulgata. 8°. Mainz. 1868
Hdbch. d. Vulgata. 8°. Mainz. 1870

Kaunitz (*Graf*) [†KAUNITZ-RIETBERG (WENZEL ANTON v.) *prince*], *see* KÜNTZEL (G.) Fürst Kaunitz-Rittberg als Staatsmann, 1923.

Kauṭilya [CHĀNAKYA; VISHṆUGUPTA]. Abhdlg. d. Hrn. Weber über 100 Sprüche d. C. [*With text & tr. no tp.* Auszug aus d. Monatsbericht d. Königl. Akad. d. Wiss. zu Berlin. P1262]. 8°. [1864]
Arthaśāstra. Tr. R. Shamasastry. Intr. note by J. F. Fleet. 2nd ed. 8°. Mysore. 1923
see BHAṬṬA-SVĀMIN. Comm. on K.'s Artha-Śāstra, 1925–26.
„ NÂG (K.) Les théories diplomat. de l'Inde anc. & l'Arthaçâstra [*attrib. to* K. (326–298 B.C.)], 1923.
„ STEIN (O.) Megasthenes u. K., 1921.

Kautsky (Carl).
Delbrück u. Wilhelm II. Ein Nachwort zu m. Kreigsbuch. [P 2456]. 8°. [1920]
Die deutschen Dokumente z. Kriegsausbruch. Sammlung d. v. K. K. zusammengest. amtl. Aktenstücke. Hrsg. v. M. Montgelas u. W. Schücking. 4B. 8°. Charlottenburg. 1919
Die Internationale. 8°. Wien. 1920
Die Internationale u. Sowjetrussland. s8°. [1925]
Der Kommunismus in d. deut. Reformation, *see* VORLÄUFER d. neueren Sozialismus, 6e A., B2, 1921.
Der polit. Massenstreik. s8°. 1914
R. Luxemburg, K. Liebknecht, L. Jogiches: ihre Bedeutung f. d. deut. Sozialdemokratie. [P2617]. s8°. *n.p.* [1921]
Sozialdemokrat. Bemerkungen z. Uebergangswirtschaft. 8°. L. 1918
T. More, *see* VORLÄUFER d. neueren Sozialismus, 2e A., B3, 1922.
Von d. Demokratie z. Staats-Sklaverei: e. Auseinandersetzung mit Trotzki. s8°. 1921
TRANSLATIONS.
Are the Jews a race? Tr. f. 2nd German ed. 8°. [1926]

Kautsky (Carl) [*continued*].
TRANSLATIONS [*continued*].
Documents allemands rel. à l'orig. de la Guerre. Tr. C. Jordan. 4t. 8°. 1922
Foundations of Christianity. Tr. f. 13th German ed. la8°. [1925]
Georgia, peasant republic. Tr. H. J. Stenning & rev. by author. s8°. [1921]
The guilt of William Hohenzollern. [Tr.] 8°. [1920]
The labour revolution. Tr. H. J. Stenning. s8°. 1925
Outbreak of the World War. German doc. coll. by K. K. & ed. by M. Montgelas & W. Schücking. Tr. by C.E. for Int. Peace. la8°. N.Y. 1924
Terrorisme et communisme. Contrib. à l'hist. des révolutions. Tr. par Mme. N. Stchoupak. s8°. [1919]
Thomas More & h. Utopia, w. hist. intr. Tr. H. J. Stenning. 8°. 1927
see BUKHARIN (N.) K. K. u. Sowjetrussland: e. Antwort, 1925.
„ DELBRÜCK (H.) K. u. Harden, 1920.
„ HELMOLT (HANS F.) K., d. Historiker &c., 1920.
„ LENIN (N.) Пролетарская революция и ренегат К. Каутский, 1919.
„ —— Die proletar. Revol. u. d. Renegat K., 1919.
„ MONTGELAS (M. M. K. D. *Graf* v.) Glossen z. K.-Buch, 1920.
„ SCHIEMANN (T.) Deutschlands u. Wilhelms II. Schuld am Ausbruch d. Weltkrieges: Entgegung an C. K., 1921.
„ TROTSKY (L.) Terrorismus u. Kommunismus: anti-K., 1920.

Kautz (Nathaniel Friedrich). De relig. Xtnae. in Polonia initiis diss. Praes. G. Lengnich. ed. 2a. [P2741]. s4°. Lipsiae. 1735
Praecipua &c. religionis evang. in Polonia fata [1522–72]. [P2443]. s4°. Hamburgi. 1738

Kautzsch (Rudolph) & E. Neeb. Die Kunstdenkmäler d. Stadt u. d. Kreises Mainz. B2, Kirchl. Kunstdenkmäler d. Stadt Mainz. T1, Der Dom zu Mainz. [Kunstdenkmäler Hessen]. la8°. Darmstadt. 1919

Kavanagh (Colman).
The symbolism of "Wuthering Heights." [P2420]. s8°. [1920]

Kavanagh (T. Henry).
The verdict. p2. [P2832]. 8°. Lucknow. 1877

Kaviraj (Krishnadas), *see* KRISHNADAS KAVIRAJ.

Kavkaz, [*see also* CAUCASUS].
Сборникъ матеріаловъ для описанія мѣстностей и племенъ Кавказа, в1–39, 1881–1908, *see* SBORNIK.

Kavraisky (Fedor Fedorovich).
Die Lachse d. Kaukasus. [*In Russ.*] 2 Lief. la8°. Тифлисъ. 1896–97

Kawādh I, *k. of Persia, see* KOBAD.

Kawakami (Karl Kiyoshi). What Japan thinks. [*By var. a.*] Ed. K. K. K. s8°. N.Y. 1921

Kawerau (Gustav).
Works in Verein f. Ref.-gesch. Schr. 8°. Halle &c. 1898–1917
Hieronymus Emser, 1898. [15 (Nr. 61).]
Luther in kath. Beleuchtung: Glossen zu H. Grisars Luther, 1911. [29 (Nr. 61).]
Luthers Gedanken ü. d. Krieg, 1916. [34 (Nr. 124).]
Luthers Schriften nach d. Reihenfolge d. Jahre verzeichnet &c., 1917. [35 (Nr. 129).]
Paul Gerhardt, 1907. [24 (Nr. 93).]
Die Versuche, Melanchthon z. kath. Kirche zurückzuführen, 1902. [19 (Nr. 73).]

Kawerau (Waldemar).
Works in Verein f. Ref.-gesch. Schr. 8°. Halle. 1889–92
Hans Sachs u. d. Reform., 1889. [7 (Nr. 26).]
Die Reformation u. d. Ehe, 1892. [10 (Nr. 39).]
T. Murner u. d. deut. Reform., 1891. [8 (Nr. 32).]
T. Murner u. d. Kirche d. M.-a., 1890. [8 (Nr. 30).]

Kawraisky, *see* KAVRAISKY.

Kay (David Miller).
The Semitic religions. Croall lect., s22. s8°. E. 1923

Kay (Stephen).
A statement of the Kaffer's case. [P2658]. 8°. 1837

Kaye (F. B.), *see* CRANE (R. S.) & F. B. K. Census of Brit. newspapers &c., 1629–1800, 1927.

Kaye (George Rusby). Astronom. instruments in the Delhi museum, *see* INDIA: ARCH. SURVEY. Mem., No. 12, 1921.
A guide to the old observatories [founded by Jai Singh] at Delhi; Jaipur; Ujjain; Benares. 8°. Calcutta. 1920
Hindu astronomy, *see* INDIA: ARCH. SURVEY. Mem. 18, 1924.
see INDIA: ARCH. SURVEY. Index to Annual reports of the Director Gen. of Arch. in I.; by G. R. K., 1924.

Kaye (John), *bp. of (1) Bristol, (2) Lincoln.* The eccl. hist. of the 2nd & 3rd c. illust. f. Tertullian. 8°. [1889]
Writings &c. of Clement of Alexandria. 8°. [1890]

Kaye (*Sir* **John William**). Hist. of the war in Afghanistan. n. ed. rev. 3v. s8°. 1857
,, ,, ...3rd ed. 3v. s8°. 1874
*Long engagements: tale of the Affghan Rebellion. s8°. 1846
Kaye (Michael W.) The king's indiscretion. s8°. [1920]
Kaye (Walter J.), *junior*.
Grasse (Riviera) & its vicinity. s8°. [1912]
Kaye-Smith (Sheila), *wife of Rev. Penrose Fry*.
The end of the House of Alard. [repr.] s8°. [1923]
The George & the Crown. s8°. [1925]
Green apple harvest. s8°. [1920]
,, ,, ...[repr.] s8°. [1924]
Iron & smoke. s8°. [1928]
Isle of Thorns. [repr.] s8°. [1924]
Joanna Godden. s8°. [1921]
Joanna Godden married & o. s. s8°. [1926]
Little England. [repr.] s8°. [1924]
Spell Land. [repr.] s8°. [1924]
Starbrace. [repr.] s8°. [1923]
Sussex gorse. [repr.] s8°. [1923]
,, ,, ...[repr.] s8°. [1925]
Tamarisk Town. [repr.] s8°. [1924]
The tramping Methodist. s8°. [1922]
Kay-Shuttleworth (*Sir* **James P.**), *1st bart., see* SMITH (FR.) Life & work of Sir J. K.-S., 1923.
Kazakam. *К Казакам &c., 1919, *see* RUSSIA: SOVIET REP.
Kazaver (Christophorus). Diss. de tuba stentorea. Praes. J. H. Mullero. [P447]. s4°. [Altorfi Noric. 1713]
Kazimirski (Albin de Biberstein). Dialogues franç.-persans; préc. de la gramm. persane & suiv. d'un vocab. fr.-persan. &c. [*b. in 2v. pagin. cont.*] 8°. 1883
Dict. arabe-franç. 2t. 8°. 1860
Kazin (V.), N. Lyashko & G. Sannikov.
Цветы труда. Сборник. s8°. Москва. 1923
Kazinczy (Ferencz), *1759–1831, see* GAAL (M.) K. F. élete &c., 1898.
Keable (Robert).
Lighten our darkness. s8°. [1927]
The mother of all living. Novel of Africa. s8°. [1921]
Numerous treasure. s8°. 1925
Peradventure. [3rd impr.] s8°. [1922]
Recompence. Sequel to "Simon called Peter." s8°. 1924
Simon called Peter. s8°. 1921
Keach (Benjamin).
Τροπολογία: a key, to open Scripture metaphors. fol. 1779
Keane (*Lt.-Col. Sir* **John**). The zealots: over-regulation & its bearing on national waste. [P2509]. 8°. 1921
Kearton (Cherry). Photographing wild life across the world. la8°. [1923]
Shifting sands of Algeria. la8°. [1924]
Kearton (Richard). At home with wild nature. 8°. 1922
A naturalist's pilgrimage. s8°. [1926]
Keary (William). An hist. review of papal & conciliar infallibility. 2nd ed. s8°. 1827
Keatinge (Gerald Francis).
Agricult. progress in W. India. s8°. 1921
Keats House Committee, *Hampstead*. The John Keats Memorial volume. Issued by the K.H.C. [incl. The Warton lect., by E. de Selincourt, & A bibliog. by T. J. Wise]. [Ed. G. C. Williamson]. la8°. 1921
Keats (John).
Cat. of a loan exhib. comm. death of J. K., 1821–1921, Public Library, Boston, Feb.–March 1921. s8°. Boston. 1921
Endymion. Type-facs. of 1st ed. Intr. & notes by H. C. Notcutt. 8°. 1927
John Keats (The) Memorial volume, 1921, *see* KEATS HOUSE COMMITTEE.
Poet. works. Mem. by Ld. Houghton. 8°. 1866
,, ,, Ed., w. mem., by Lord Houghton. 5th ed. s8°. 1890
Poems. [Everyman's Library. repr.] s8°. [1906]
Poems. Ed. w. intr. & notes by E. de Sélincourt. 4th ed. rev. 8°. [1920]
see BALDWIN (D. L.), L. N. BROUGHTON &c. Concordance to poems of J. K., 1917.
,, BLUNDEN (E.) Shelley & K. as they struck their contemporaries, 1925.
see COLVIN (*Sir* S.) J. K.: h. life, poetry &c., 2nd ed., 1918.
,, DE SÉLINCOURT (E.) Keats lect., 1921.
,, FAUSSET (H. I'A.) K.: a st. in development, 1922.
,, GARROD (H. W.) K., 1926.
,, HUDSON (W. H.) Studies in interpretation; K., Clough &c., 1896.
,, LOWELL (A.) J. K., 2v, 1925.
,, MURRY (J. M.) K. & Shakespeare: st. of K.'s poetic life f. 1816–20, 1925.
,, NOTCUTT (H. C.) An interpret. of K.'s Endymion, 1919.
,, —— Story of Glaucus in K.'s Endymion, 1921.
,, PRICE (C.) K.'s finales: Hyperion, & the eve of St. Mark, 1922.
,, WIEL (T.) Versioni da Th. Gray, J. K. &c., 1906.

Keay (Frank Ernest).
Hist. of Hindī literature. s8°. Calcutta. [1920]
Keble (John).
The Christian Year. 26th ed. s8°. O. 1845
,, ,, ...s8°. 1873
,, ,, w. Collects & series of medit[s]. &c. sel. f. wks. of H. P. Liddon. 8°. 1886
*Lyra innocentium. 3rd ed. s8°. O. 1846
*The Psalter of David in Eng. verse. s8°. O. 1839
Kebra Nagast. The Queen of Sheba & her only son Menyelek: hist. of the departure of God & His ark f. Jerusalem to Ethiopia &c. Compl. tr. of the Kebra Nagast, w. intr. by Sir E. A. W. Budge. [Medici Soc.] 8°. 1922
Keder (Nils). Nummorum in Hibernia cusorum indagatio. Acc. Cat. numm. Anglo-Saxon. & Anglo-Danic. Musei Kederiani. s4°. Lipsiae. 1708
Keele (Joseph). Prelim. rep. on clay & shale deposits of Ontario. [Canada: Geol. Survey]. 8°. Ottawa. 1924
—— **& L. H. Cole.** Rep. on struct. materials, St. Lawrence River &c. [Canada: Geol. Survey]. 8°. Ottawa. 1922
Keeling (E. H.) Adv. in Turkey & Russia. 8°. 1924
Keeling (William), *B.D., fellow of St. John's Coll., Camb., see* PRAYER-BOOK. Liturgiae Brit., arr. by K., 2nd ed., 1851.
Keen (Frank Noel). Towards internat. justice: essays on internat. organis. & the League of Nations. Intr. by G. Murray. s8°. [1923]
Keene (John Harrington).
Fishing tackle, its materials &c. s8°. [1886]
Keeping up w. science, 1924, *see* SLOSSON (E. E.), *ed.*
Keferstein (Christian). Üb. d. Halloren als e. kelt. Colonie &c. 8°. Halle. 1843
Kegel (Daniel Otto). Machærologia, disput. de gladio in sacramentorum reverentiam deponendo. Praes. C. T. Wideburgio. [P437]. s4°. Helmstadii. [1709]
Kegel (Martin). Away from Wellhausen: contr. to new orientat. in O.T. study. Tr. M. Nolloth. s8°. 1924
Kehler (Henning).
The red garden. Tr. F. Toksvig. s8°. N.Y. 1922
Kehler (James Howard). Open letter to the nation w. regard to a peace plan. s8°. N.Y. 1915
Kehr (Georg Jacob), *1692–1740*. Saraceni, Hagareni & Mauri quinam sint? [P2666]. s4°. Lipsiae. [1723]
Kehr (Paul Fridolin). Die ält. Papsturkunden Spaniens; erläut. &c. P. K., *see* KÖNIGL.-PREUSS. AKAD. Abh., Phil.-hist. Kl., 1926.
Das Erzbistum Magdeburg u. d. erste Organis. d. christl. Kirche in Polen, *see* KÖNIGL.-PREUSS. AKAD. Abh., Phil.-hist. Kl., 1920.
Das Papsttum u. d. katalan. Prinzipat bis z. Verein. mit Aragon, *see* KÖNIGL.-PREUSS. AKAD. Abh., Phil.-hist. Kl., 1926.
Papsturkunden in Spanien: Vorarb. zur Hisp. Pontificia, *see* KÖNIGL. GESELL. D. W. ZU GÖTTINGEN. Abh., N.F., 18, 1926.
Regesta Pontificum Romanorum. Jubente Reg. Soc. Gottingensi congressit P. F. K.
Germania pontificia. v2i, ii. la8°. Berolini. 1923–27
2i, ii, Provincia Maguntinensis auctore A. Brackmann.
Italia pontificia. v5–7 [6i, ii, 7i, ii]. la8°. Berolini. 1911–25
5, Aemilia, sive prov. Ravennas. 6, Liguria sive prov. Mediolan. 7, Venetiæ & Histria.
Rom u. Venedig bis ins 12. Jhdt., *see* QUELLEN U. FORSCH. aus ital. Archiv. &c., B19, 1927.
Kehrer (Hugo). Francisco de Zurbarán. la8°. München. [1918]
Die got. Wandmalerei in d. Kaiser-Pfalz zu Forchheim, *see* KÖNIGL. AKAD. D. W. ZU MÜNCHEN. Abh. Phil.-hist. Kl., B26, 1914.
Span. Kunst v. Greco bis Goya. la8°. München. 1926
Kehrmann (Carl). Die "Capita agendorum": Reformverhandl. in Konstanz. [P2727]. 8°. München. 1903
Frankreichs innere Kirchenpolitik, 1378–1409. [P2727]. 8°. Jena. 1890
Keighley, *see* CARNEGIE LIBRARY, *Keighley*.
Keil (Bruno). Beitr. z. Gesch. d. Areopags, *see* KÖNIGL.-SÄCHS. GESELLS. D. W. Berichte, phil.-hist. Kl., B71, 1919.
Keil (Carl Friedrich).
Biblical comm. on Ezekiel. Tr. J. Martin. 2v. 8°. E., *Clark*. 1876
The Bk. of Daniel. Tr. M. G. Easton. 8°. E., *Clark*. 1872
The Bks. of Ezra, Nehemiah, & Esther. Tr. S. Taylor. 8°. E., *Clark*. 1873
Comm. on Joshua. Tr. J. Martin. 8°. E., *Clark*. 1857

Keil (Carl Friedrich) *[continued]*.

Comm. on the Bks. of Kings. Tr. J. Murphy. Suppl. by Comm. on Chronicles, by E. Bertheau ; tr. J. Martin. 2v. 8º. E., *Clark*. 1857

Manual of hist.-crit. intr. to Old Test. Tr., w. notes f. Bleek &c. by G. C. M. Douglas. 2v. 8º. E., *Clark*. 1869–70

—— **& F. Delitzsch.** Bibl. comm. on Samuel. Tr. J. Martin. 8º. E., *Clark*. 1891
Joshua, Judges, Ruth. Tr. J. Martin. 8º. E., *Clark*. 1865
The Pentateuch. Tr. J. Martin. 3v. 8º. E., *Clark*. 1864–65

Keil (Friedrich Siegmund). M. Luther's merkwürdige Lebens-Umstände &c. 4T. *in* 2v. [*pag. of 1–2 & 3–4 cont.*]. s4º. L. 1764

Keil (Josef) & A. v. Premerstein. Ber. ü. e. 3. Reise in Lydien u. d. angrenz. Gebiete Ioniens, 1911, 1914, *see* KAIS. AKAD. D. W. Z. WIEN. Denkschr., B57, 1915.

Keilhau (Wilhelm). Norge & Verdenskrigen. [C.E. for Internat. Peace]. 8º. 1927

Keilinschriftliche Bibliothek: Sammlung v. assyr. u. babylon. Text. in Umschr. u. Übers. Hrsg. v. E. Schrader. B6ii. 8º. 1915
6ii, Texte zur assyr.-babylon. Religion, v. P. Jensen, Lief. 1.

Keiller (Alexander), *see* CRAWFORD (O. G. S.) & A. K. Wessex f. the air, 1928.

Keilschrifttexte. Keilschrifttexte aus Assur hist. Inhalts, 2H, 1911–22, *see* MESSERSCHMIDT (L.) & O. SCHRÖDER.
Keilschrifttexte aus Assur relig. Inhalts, B1, 2, 1919–23, *see* EBELING (E.)
Keilschrifttexte aus Boghazköi ; Autographien v. H. H. Figulla &c., 1916–23, *see* BOGHAZKÖI.

Keim (*Generalleutnant* August).
Prinz Max v. Baden u. d. Kriegskabinett. 8º. [1922]

Keimer (Ludwig). Die Gartenpflanzen im alten Ägypten. B1. 8º. Hamburg. 1924

Keimer (Samuel). A brand pluck'd from the burning : case of S. K. [*Foll. by* A letter f. John Lacy to Th. Dutton &c., *w. sep. pagin.; tp. missing*]. s8º. [1718?]

*Kein Vertrauen zur deutschen Regierung ! Von Germanicus. [P2492]. 8º. [1920]

Keiser (Albert). The influence of Xty. on the vocab. of old Eng. poetry. [Illinois : Univ. St., v5]. la8º. Urbana. 1919

Keith (Alexander). Scot. ballads : evid. of authorship &c., *see* ENG. ASSOC. Essays, v12, 1926.
see GREIG (G.) Last leaves of traditional ballads &c., coll. G. G. ; ed. A. K., 1925.

Keith (*Sir* Arthur), *F.R.S.*

The antiquity of man. [4th imp.] 8º. 1920
„ „ n. ed. rev. 2v. 8º. 1925
Conc. man's origin. Pres. addr., Brit. Assoc., 1927 &c. s8º. 1927
The engines of the human body. 2nd ed. rev. & enl. 8º. 1925
The human body. [Home Univ. Lib.] [repr.] s8º. [1920]
Nationality & race. Boyle lecture. [P2428]. 8º. O. 1919
Report on the Galilee skull, *see* TURVILLE-PETRE (F.) Researches in prehist. Galilee, 1927.
see AVEBURY (J. L., *1st b.*) Life-work of Ld. A. : essays by Sir B. Mallet, Sir A. Keith &c., 1924.
„ UR excavations, v1, Al-'Ubaid : rep., w. ch. by Sir A. K. &c., 1927.

Keith (Arthur Berriedale).

Buddhist philosophy in India & Ceylon. s8º. O. 1923
Constit., admin. & laws of the Empire. [Brit. Emp. ; ed. H. Gunn, v3]. 8º. 1924
Dominion home rule in practice. s8º. 1921
The Karma-Mīmāṁsā. s8º. 1921
The relig. & philos. of the Veda & Upanishads. [Harvard Orient. Ser., v31, 32]. 2v. la8º. Camb., *Mass.* 1925
Responsible govt. in the Dominions. 2nd ed. rewr. & rev. to 1927. 2v. 8º. O. 1928
The Sanskrit drama in its origin &c. 8º. O. 1924
War govt. of the Brit. Dominions. [C.E. for Int. Peace]. la8º. O. 1921
see DICEY (A. V.) & A. B. K. Digest of the laws of Eng. w. ref. to confl. of laws, 3rd ed., 1922 ; 4th ed., 1927.

Keith (Charles P.)
Chronicles of Pennsylvania, 1688–1748. 2v. 8º. Phila. 1917

Keith (Chester). Queen's knight. s8º. [1920]

Keith (George), *rector of Edburton.* An exact narr. of the proc. at Turners-Hall, 1696, w. disputes &c. betw. G. K. & Quakers. [P2652]. s4º. 1696
A journal of travels f. New Hampshire to Caratuck, North America. s4º. 1706
The standard of the Quakers examined, or an ans. to the Apology of R. Barclay. s8º. 1702

Keith (George, *Baron*), *10th Earl Marischal, see* CUTHELL (*Mrs.* E. E.) The Scottish friend of Fred. the Gt., the last Earl Marischall, 2v, 1915.

Keith (George Keith Elphinstone, *visct.*), *admiral.* Keith papers. Letters &c. Ed. W. G. Perrin. [Navy Records Soc., v62]. v1. 8º. 1927

Keith (George S.) Fads of an old physician. Sequel to Plea for a simpler life. 8º. 1897

Keith (James), *C.E.* A new chapter in the hist. of labour. 48 hours' week in Scotch engineering trade &c. la8º. 1893

Keith-Falconer (Adrian). The Oxfordshire Hussars in the Great War (1914–18). 8º. [1927]

Keith-Roach (Edward), *see* LUKE (H. C.) & E. K.-R. Hdbk. of Palestine, 1922.

Kekelidze (Kornil. Semenovich) [CECELIDZE]. Іерусалимскій канонарь 7 вѣка. Грузинская версія. la8º. Тифлисъ. 1912
[Hist. of Georg. lit. *In Georgian*]. v1. la8º. Tiflis. 1923
see ARCHIERATIKON. Древне-груз. архіерат. ; изд. К., 1912.

Kekewich (Granville). Cadet & o. sketches. [*no tp.*] s8º. [1921]

Kekewich (*Col.* Robert George), *see* O'MEARA (*Lt.-Col.* W. A. J.) K. in Kimberley : defence of the Diamond Fields, Oct. 1899–Feb. 1900, 1926.

Kekule von Stradonitz (Reinhard). Die griech. Skulptur. [Hdbchr. d. Staatl. Museen zu Berlin]. 3e A. bearb. v. B. Schröder. s8º. 1922

Kelat, *see* KHELAT.

Kelemina (Jakob). Gesch. d. Tristansage nach d. Dichtungen d. M.-a. 8º. Wien. 1923

Kelke (Will. Henry Hastings).
Epitome of company law. s8º. 1904

Kelland (Philip). Lectures on the princ. of demonstr. mathematics. s8º. E. 1843

Keller (Albert Galloway), *see* SUMNER (W. G.), A. G. K. &c. Sci. of society, 4v, 1927.

Keller (Elizabeth Leavitt).
Walt Whitman in Mickle Street. s8º. N.Y. 1921

Keller (Gottfried), *novelist.* Briefe u. Tagebücher, 1861–90. Hrsg. E. Ermatinger. 8º. St. 1916
A village Romeo & Juliet. [Tr.] Intr. by E. Wharton. s8º. 1915

Keller (Heinrich), *geographer, see* EBEL (J. G.) Atlas to E.'s travellers' guide thr. Switzerland, cont. views &c. & K.'s map, 1819 ?.

Keller (Jacob), *jesuit* [*ps.* HERCYNIANUS (FABIUS)]. Protocoll. d. Colloquii, 1615 Jar, zu Newburg a. d. Donau, zw. J. Keller u. J. Heilbrunner gehalten. [P437]. s4º. Dilingen. [1615]
see HEILBRUNNER (J.) Colloquium Neuberg., zw. J. H. u. J. K., 1616.

Keller (Otto). Illustr. Gesch. der Musik. 3e umgearb. &c. A. 8º. München. [1907]

Keller (Paul). Ferien vom Ich. Roman. 8º. Breslau. [1915]

Kellermann (Benzion).
Die Ethik Spinozas : ü. Gott u. Geist. 8º. 1922

Kellermann (Bernhard). Der 9. November. Roman. s8º. 1921
Schwedenklees Erlebnis. 8º. 1923
Yester u. Li. Gesch. e. Sehnsucht. [143.–152. A.] s8º. [1922]

Kellgren (Johan Henrik), *see* CYRIAX (E. F.) Elem. of K.'s manual treatment, 1903.

Kellio (Miklos) [*ps.* LABSANZKY (JOANNES)]. *Extractus brevis &c. quo demonst. acatholicorum praedicantium, è regno Hung. proscriptio &c. s8º. Tyrnaviae. 1721

Kellner (Leon), P. Arnold & A. L. Delisle. Austria of the Austrians & Hungary of the Hungarians. s8º. 1914

Kellner (Oskar Johann). The scientific feeding of animals. Tr. by W. Goodwin. s8º. 1915

Kellogg (Edward). A new monetary system. Ed. M. K. Putnam. 3rd ed. s8º. N.Y. 1868

Kellogg (Remington). Appar. new toothed Cetacean f. S. Carolina, 1923, *see* SMITHSONIAN INST. Misc. Coll., v76, 1925.

Kellogg (Samuel H.)
Grammar of the Hindi lang. 2nd ed. rev. 8º. 1893

Kellogg (Vernon Lyman). Amer. Nat. C'tee on Intellectual co-op. [Repr. f. Educat. Record. P2870]. 8º. [Wash.] 1927
Herbert Hoover. 8º. N.Y. 1920
Human life as the biologist sees it. [Colver Lect., 1921]. s8º. N.Y. 1922
Milit. selection & race deterior., *see* BODART (G.) Losses of life &c., 1916.

Kellor (Frances Alice).
Immigration & the future. 8º. N.Y. [1920]
—— **& A. Hatvany.** Protocol for the pacific settlement of internat. disputes in rel. to the sanction of war. 8º. [*p.p.* N.Y. 1925]

Kells, *Book of*, *see* SULLIVAN (*Sir* E.) The Book of K.; descr. by S., w. 24 plates in colours, 2nd ed., 1920.

Kelly, *publishers*.
Hdbk. to the titled, landed & official classes, 1878, 1891, 1920–23, 1928. s8°. 1878–[1927]
1878 *ed. has t.* K's Hdbk. to the upper ten thousand.
Kelly's Customs tariffs. la8°. 1910
DIRECTORIES.
Cornwall. Ed. A. L. Kelly. la8°. 1923
DIRECTORIES [*continued*].
Devonshire. Ed. A. L. Kelly. la8°. 1923
Gloucester. la8°. 1923
Ireland. [10th ed.] la8°. [1905]
Monmouthshire. Ed. A. L. Kelly. la8°. 1923
Somerset. la8°. 1923
South Wales. Ed. A. L. Kelly. la8°. 1923

Kelly (Arthur), *see* ABERCROMBIE (P.), S. KELLY & A. K. Dublin of the future, 1922.

Kelly (Francis M.) & R. Schwabe. Historic costume: fashion in Western Europe, 1490–1790. la8°. [1925]

Kelly (Howard Atwood) & W. L. Burrage.
American medical biographies. la8°. Baltimore. 1920

Kelly (Hugh), *dramatic writer.*
False delicacy: a comedy. 8°. 1768
*The school for wives, *see* †INCHBALD (*Mrs.* E.) Mod. theatre, v9, 1811.

Kelly (John), *rector of Copford.* A pract. gram. of the ant. Gaelc, called Manks. 4°. 1804

Kelly (Robert). Rep. of trial of R. K. for murder of Head-Constable Talbot, at the Dublin Comm. Court, Oct. 1871. Rep. by J. Hill, rev. by W. O'Brien. la8°. D. 1873

Kelly (Samuel). Autobiog. of an 18th century seaman. Ed. C. Garstin. 8°. [1925]

Kelly (Sydney), *see* ABERCROMBIE (P.), S. K., & A. KELLY. Dublin of the future, 1922.

Kelly (Walter Keating). Hist. of Russia. 2v. s8°. *Bohn.* 1854–55

Kelly (William), *theological writer.*
Lect. introd. to the Pentateuch. s8°. 1871

Kelman (Janet Harvey). Labour in India: cond. of Ind. women in mod. industry. 8°. [1923]

Kelmscott Press, *see* CLARK (W. A.), *jr.* Library of W. A. C.: K. & Doves Presses, 1921.

***Kelpie's** (The) fiddle-bow. Tr. f. the German by A. H. H. s4°. [1892]

Kelpius (Johannes), *d. 1708.* Hymn bk.; tr. C. Witt, *facs. of MS.*, *see* PENNSYLVANIA. Ch. music &c. in P. in 18th c., v1, 1926.

Kelsen (Hans), *see* ÖSTERREICH. Verfassungsgesetze d. Republik Deutschösterreich, 4T, 1919–20; Bundesverfassung, 1920.

Kelsey (Francis Willey). Excav. at Carthage, 1925. Rep. [Amer. J. of Arch., Suppl.] 8°. N.Y. 1926

Kelvin (William Thomson, *baron*).
see KING (A. G.) K. the man: biog. sketch, 1925.
„ MURRAY (D.) Ld. K. as prof. in the old college of Glasgow, 1924.
„ RUSSELL (A.) W. T. Lord K., 1924.
—— **& P. G. Tait.** Sketch of elementary dynamics. 8°. E. 1864

Kemal (Ismail), *see* ISMAIL KEMAL, *Bey.*

Kemal (Mustaphā), *Pasha*, *see* KIAZIM (O.) L'aventure Kémaliste, 1921.

Kemaly (Ghalib), *see* GHALIB KEMALY.

Kemble (Charles), *tragedian.* Point of honour, *see* INCHBALD (*Mrs.* E.) Brit. theatre, v24, 1808.

Kemble (Frances Anne), *aft. Mrs. Butler* [FANNY KEMBLE]. The day after the wedding. Interlude, adapted fr. the French. [P2582]. s8°. *Lacy. n.d.*

Kemeny (Zsigmond), *1816–75*, *see* BEKSICS (G.) K. Z. &c., 1883.

Kémeri (Sándor). Promenades d'Anatole France. Préf. de P. L. Couchoud. [3e éd.] 8°. [1927]

Kemmerer (Edwin Walter). High prices & deflation. Intr. by F. A. Vanderlip. s8°. Princeton. 1920
Postal savings: hist. &c. st. of postal savings bank system of the U.S. 8°. Princeton. 1917

Kemnicius (Martinus), *see* CHEMNITZ (M.)

Kemp (Emily Georgiana). Chinese mettle. 8°. 1921

Kemp (Harry Hibbard).
Tramping on life, an autobiog. narrative. 8°. [1923]

Kemp (Joannes Theodorus van der).
Memoir of K., missionary in S. Africa. 4th ed. 8°. 1813

Kemp (John). Shooting & fishing in Lower Brittany. s8°. 1859

Kemp (P. H. van der). Het Nederl.-Ind. bestuur in 1817. [2d]. la8°. 's-Gravenhage. 1913–15
[1], Tot het vertrek d. Englischen. [2], In het midden v. 1817.

Kemp (P. H. van der) [*continued*].
Oost-Indië's herstel in 1816. la8°. 's-Gravenhage. 1911
Sumatra in 1818, naar oorspronkelijke stukken. la8°. 's-Gravenhage. 1920
De teruggave der Oost-Ind. koloniën, 1814–16. la8°. 's-Gravenhage. 1910

Kemp (William), *actor.* Nine daies wonder, 1600, *see* CHETTLE (H.) Kind-hartes dreame, 1592, 1923.

Kempe (Alfred John). Investig. of antiq. of Holwood Hill, Keston, *see* DUNKIN (J.) Outlines of hist. &c. of Bromley, 1815.

Kempel (Ernst). Das Hs.-Verhältnis u. d. Sprache d. altfranz. Heldengedichtes Maugis d'Aigremont, *see* ROMANISCHE FORSCHUNGEN, B33, 1915.

Kempen (Martin von) [KEMPIUS (M.)] Charismatum sacrorum trias, sive Bibl. Anglorum theologica, cum app. de Regia Soc. Londin. s4°. [Konigsberg ?]. 1677
Diss. de statu Armeniae eccl. & polit. [P2644]. s4°. [Jena. 1665]

Kempis (Thomas à).
De imitatione Christi libri 4. Opera H. Sommalii. s8°. Venetiis. 1680
De Christo imitando &c. Interpr. S. Castellione. Adj. Liber quartus Lat. redditus & De Sacramento vulgò inscr. s8°. Cantab. 1685
De imitatione Christi lib. 4. fol. Parmae, *typ. Bodonianis.* 1793
De imitatione Christi libri 4. s8°. Londini, *G. Pickering.* 1851
Opuscula. s8°. Venetiis, *Stephan. Sabiensis.* 1535
TRANSLATIONS.
[Imitation of Christ. *In Armenian.* Tr. Hohannes vardapet of Cple.] s8°. Hamstelrodami. 1696
„ „ s8°. Romae. 1705
„ „ s8°. i Venetik. 1786
Livro da comunhaõ. Tr. por Diago Vaz Carrilho. s8°. Trangambar. 1726
TRANSLATIONS [*continued*].
The Christian's pattern, the Imitation of Christ. Corr. by J. Wesley. s8°. 1815
Imit. de Jésus Christ; tr., *see* BUCHON (J. A. C.) Choix d'ouvr. myst., 1840.
Della imitazione di Cristo lib. 4, tr. col testo a fronte da L. Rotelli. la8°. Roma. 1883
see ERHARD (T. A.) Polycrates Gersen. contra scutum K.: apol. pro J. Gersene, protoparente lib. de Imit. Christi, 1729.
„ LAUNOY (J. DE). Opera, t4ii, De autore lib. De imit. Xti., 1732.
„ WESLEY (J.) Companion f. the altar; extr. f. T. à K. by J. W., 5th ed., 1755.

Kempius (Martinus), *see* KEMPEN (M. VON).

Kempling (William Bailey).
Shakespeare memorials of London. s8°. [1923]

***Kempton-Wace** letters. [*Fiction*]. s8°. 1903

Ken (Thomas), *bp. of Bath & Wells.* *A manual of prayers for the scholars of Winchester Colledge. s8°. 1709
Prose works: Coll. & ed., w. not. by W. Benham. 8°. [1889]
Selections f. poet. wks. s8°. 1857
see JACKSON (T.) Lib. of Xtn. biog., v12, T. K., by W. Hawkins, 1840.
„ SANCROFT (W.) Proc. & tryal in case of abp. of Canterbury, bp. of B. & W. &c., 1688, 1689.

Kenckel (Stephan). Diss. de hæresi Novatiana, eique oppos. Conciliis Carthag. & Rom. s4°. Argentorati. 1651

Kendall (George), *D.D.*, *see* BAXTER (R.) Apology agst. the modest exceptions of T. Blake & the digress. of G. K. (in his book agst. Mr. Goodwin), 1654.

Kendall (John) [*ps.* DUM-DUM].
The crackling of thorns. s8°. 1906
A fool's paradise. s8°. 1910
In the hills & o. views. s8°. Bombay. *n.d.*
Odd numbers. s8°. 1913
Rhymes of the East & re-collected verses. s8°. 1905

Kendall (Percy Fry) & H. E. Wroot.
Geology of Yorkshire. 2v. 8°. *p.f.a.* 1924

Kendall (William Converse). The pikes, 1917, *see* UNITED STATES: COMMERCE.

Kendon (Frank). Mural paintings in Eng. churches dur. the M.A. s8°. [1923]

Kendrew (Wilfrid George).
The climates of the continents. 8°. O. 1922

Kendrick (Albert Frank). Book of old embroidery. With articles by A. F. K., L. F. Pesel & E. W. Newberry. Ed. by G. Holme. [Studio Spec. No.] 4°. 1921
Cathedral Church of Lincoln. s8°. 1922
see VICTORIA & ALBERT MUSEUM. Textiles f. burying-grounds in Egypt; by A. F., v1, 1920.
—— **& C. E. C. Tattersall.** Hand-woven carpets, oriental & European. 2v. 4°. 1922

Kendrick (Jack), *see* HODSON (S.) & J. K. Auction bridge, 1924.
Kendrick (Peter Richard), *R.C. abp. of St. Louis, Missouri.* De ordinationibus Anglic., *see* MIGNE (J. P.), *ed.* Theol. cursus, t25, 1860.
Kendrick (Thomas Downing).
The axe age: Brit. prehist. 8°. [1925]
The Druids: Keltic prehist. 8°. [1927]
Kenealy (*Miss* Arabella). Feminism & sex-extinction. 8°. [1920]
Kenealy (Edward Vaughan Hyde).
The Testament of Jesus. s8°. Watford. 1901
see TICHBORNE CASE. Trial at bar of Sir R. C. D. T. for perjury; ed. Dr. K., Intr. & 8v, 1875–80.
Kenilworth. Concise hist. of K. Castle. [*b. w.* Marchetti (G.) Offic. mem^s. &c., 1801]. 3rd ed. [P2494]. s8°. B'ham. 1790
Kenilworth (Walter Winston).
Psychic control thr. self-knowledge. 4th ed. 8°. N.Y. *n.d.*
Keniston (Ralph Hayward).
Garcilaso de la Vega. [Hispanic Soc.] s8°. N.Y. 1922
List of works for study of Hispanic-Amer. hist. [Hispanic Soc.] s8°. N.Y. 1920
see GAUDALAJARA. Fuero de G. (1219); ed. H. K., 1924.
Kennard (A. S.), *see* BRIT. MUS. OF NAT. HIST.: ZOOLOGY. Synonymy of Brit. non-marine Mollusca; by K. &c., 1926.
Kennard (Joseph Spencer).
Goldoni & the Venice of his time. 8°. N.Y. 1920
Kennedy (*Sir* Alexander Blackie William).
Petra, its hist. & monuments. 4°. 1925
Kennedy (Arthur G.) Bibliog. of writings on the Eng. language f. the beg. of printing to 1922. la8°. Camb. [*Mass.*] 1927
see TATLOCK (J. S. P.) & A. G. K. Concordance to compl. wks. of Chaucer &c., 1927.
Kennedy (Aubrey Leo). Old diplomacy & new, 1876–1922. Intr. by Sir V. Chirol. 8°. 1922
Kennedy (Benjamin Hall), *ed., see* LATIN. *Public school L. gram. [& primer], 1866–72.
Kennedy (Geoffrey Anketell Studdert) [*ps.* WOODBINE WILLIE]. Rough rhymes of a padre. [9th ed.] s8°. [1920]
Kennedy (James), *librarian, New Coll., Edinb., see* HALKETT (S.) & J. LAING. Dict. of anon. & pseud. Eng. lit., n. & enl. ed. by J. K. &c., v1–4, 1926–28.
Kennedy (John), *D.D.* On the Bk. of Jonah. s8°. 1895
Kennedy (John), *of Ballygerda, labourer.* Rep. of trials of J. K., J. Ryan & W. Voss for the murder of E. Butler, at Carrickshock, 14th Dec. 1831. By J. Mongan. 8°. D. 1832
Kennedy (John Pitt). Anal. of projects for the relief of the poor of Ireland. [P2556]. 8°. 1837
Instruct; employ; don't hang them, or Ireland tranquilized without soldiers &c. [P2556]. 8°. 1835
Kennedy (Margaret).
The constant nymph. [n. impr.] s8°. 1924
„ „ [n. impr.] s8°. 1925
The ladies of Lyndon. s8°. [1923]
A long week-end. s8°. 1927
Red sky at morning. s8°. [1927]
„ „ [n. impr.] s8°. [1927]
Kennedy (Matthew), *LL.D.* A chronolog., genealog. & hist. diss. of the Stuarts. s8°. Paris. 1705
Kennedy (Melville T.) The Chaitanya movt.: st. of the Vaishṇavism of Bengal. s8°. Calcutta. 1925
Kennedy (Rankin).
The book of electr. installations &c. 3v. la8°. [1921]
Kennedy (William Paul McClure).
The constit. of Canada. la8°. 1922
Kennet (White), *bp. of Peterborough.* The charity of schools for poor children. Sermon, St. Sepulchers, May 16, 1706. 8°. 1706
*A memorial to Protestants on the 5th of Nov., happy deliverance of James I, 1605. [*b. w.* Lloyd (W.) Chron. acc. of Pythagoras, 1699]. s8°. 1713
Kennett (Austin). Bedouin justice: laws & customs am. Egyptian B. s8°. C. 1925
Kennett (Robert Hatch), *D.D.*
Deuteronomy & the Decalogue. s8°. C. 1920
Kenney (James F.), *see* CANADA: CANADIAN ARCHIVES. Cat. of pictures in the Public Archives of C.; intr. & notes by J. F. K., p1, 1925.
Kenney-Herbert (*Col.* A. R.), *see* HERBERT (*Col.* A. H. C. K.)
Kennicott (Benjamin), *D.D.*
Ed. Vet. Test. Heb. brevis defensio. [P543]. 8°. Oxonii. 1782
Epistola ad Michaelis de censurâ primi t. Bibl. Heb. [P543]. 8°. Oxonii. 1777
*A letter to a friend, occas. by a French pamph. [P543]. 8°. 1772
Remarks on sel. passages in the Old Test.: Added, 8 sermons. 8°. O. 1787

Kennicott (Benjamin), *D.D.* [*continued*].
A sermon, May 19, 1765. With notes on Psalms 48 & 49. 8°. O. 1765
10 annual accounts of the collation of Hebrew MSS. of the Old Test., 1760–69. [*b. w. h.* 2 dissert. &c., 1747]. 8°. O. 1770
Two dissert. on the tree of life &c. 2nd ed. w. app. 8°. O. 1747
see DUMAY (J. A.) New & faithful tr. of letters to B. K. &c., 1773.
„ RUTHERFORTH (T.) A letter to K., def. of Sam. Pentateuch &c., 1761.
Kenning (George), *see* WOODFORD (A. F. A.), *ed.* K.'s Masonic cyclop., 1878.
Kenny (Courtney Stanhope).
Outlines of criminal law. 12th ed. 8°. C. 1926
Sel. of cases illust. of Eng. criminal law. [repr.] 8°. C. 1903
„ „ ....5th ed. 8°. C. 1922
***Kensington** garden, poem, 1722, *see* TICKELL (T.)
Kensington (*Maj.* Edgar). Artillery machines, *see* CROFTON (M. W.) & E. K. Tracts on mechanics, 1881.
Kensington (Hugh Edwardes, *6th baron*). Partic., w. plans &c. of St. Bride's estate, incl. Skomer Island &c., sale by Knight, Frank & Rutley, 8th Sept. 1920. By dir. of Ld. K. fol. 1920
Kent. East Kent records. Cal. of unpubl. deeds &c. in Libr. of Lambeth Palace, w. App. Ed. I. J. Churchill. [Kent Arch. Soc. Records Branch, v7]. 8°. 1922
East Kent regional planning scheme: prelim. survey. Prep. by P. Abercrombie & J. Archibald. 4°. Liverpool. 1925
Visitations of K., 1530–31, by T. Benolte & 1574 [& 1592], by R. Cooke. Ed. W. B. Bannerman. [Harleian Soc., 74, 75]. 2p. la8°. 1923–24
Kent Archaeological Society. Archæologia Cantiana: Trans. of the K.A.S. v34–39. 8°. 1920–27
v36 *cont.* Index of papers, v20–35.
Records Branch. v1, 5, 7–[11]. 8°. Canterbury. 1912–27
see CANTERBURY. Cal. of instit. by Chapter of C. Sede vacante; C. E. Woodruff, 1923. [8.]
„ KENT. E. Kent records; ed. I. J. Churchill, 1922. [7.]
„ LYDD. Mon. inscr. in churchyard &c. of All Saints', L.; by L. L. Duncan, 1927. [11.]
„ ROCHESTER. Index of wills proved in R. Consistory Court, 1440–1561; comp. by L. L. Duncan &c., 1924. [9.]
„ —— Parish reg. &c. in diocese of R.; intr. by W. E. Buckland, 1912. [1.]
„ STROOD. Churchwardens' acc. of St. Nicholas, S.; transcr. &c. H. R. Plomer, 2p, 1927. [5.]
„ TENTERDEN. Kentish mon. inscr. at T.; ed. L. L. Duncan, 1919.
„ TWYSDEN (*Sir* R.) The T. Lieutenancy papers, 1583–1668; ed. &c. G. S. Thomson, 1926. [10.]
Kent or Romney Marsh Sheep-Breeders' Association.
Flock book. v7–21, 24 (1901–18). 8°. 1901–18
Kent (A. S.) Old Tartar trails. 8°. Shanghai. 1919
Kent (Charles Foster). Makers & teachers of Judaism to death of Herod the Gt. s8°. [1911]
The work &c. of the Apostles. [repr.] s8°. 1920
Kent (Francis Saville), *see* ROAD, *Somerset.* *Road murder [*of F. S. K.*]: by a Barrister-at-Law, 1860.
Kent (Henry), *publisher, see* SHOPKEEPER'S & tradesman's assistant &c., 1768.
Kent (John). Records & reminisc. of Goodwood & Dukes of Richmond. 8°. 1896
Kenton (James).
A token to the memory of J. Wesley. [P2658]. 8°. 1791
Kent's directory [of London], 1769. List of names & places of abode. Also lists of the lord-mayor &c. 37th ed. s8°. 1769
Kentzinger (Antoine de). Doc. hist. rel. à l'hist. de France, tirés des archives de Strasbourg. 2t. 8°. Str. 1818–19
Kenworthy (*Lt.-Comm. Hon.* Joseph Montague).
Will civilisation crash? Intr. by H. G. Wells. 8°. [1927]
—— **& G. Young.** Freedom of the seas. 8°. [1928]
Kenya. Hdbk. of K. Colony, & the K. Protectorate, 1920, *see* ADMIRALTY: NAVAL INTELL. DIV.
Kenyon (C. F.), *see* CUMBERLAND (G.), *ps.*
Kenyon (Edith C.) The old violin. s8°. 1887
Kenyon (George), *Wesleyan minister.* A life worth living. Mem. of Mrs. Kenyon. By her husband. s8°. [1885]
Kenyon (George Kenyon, *2nd baron*).
Obs. on the Roman Cath. question. 3rd ed. 8°. 1810
Kenyon (*Capt.* Lionel Richard). Recent develop. of field artillery *matériel* on the Continent. [Repr. f. Proceed. Royal Art. Instit., v28 & 29]. 8°. Woolwich. 1903

Kenyon (Sarah), *wife of G. Kenyon, see* KENYON (G.) A life worth living, 1885.

Kephart (Horace).
Our Southern highlanders: S. Appalachians &c. 8°. N.Y. 1922

Kepler (Johann). Nativitet. Ihrer fürstl. Exc. d. Herzogen v. Friedland (*facs. of MS.*), *see* FREYTAG (G.) Bilder, B4, 1925.
Die Zusammenklänge d. Welten &c. Hrsg. u. übers. v. O. J. Bryk. 8°. Jena. 1918
see FÖRSTER (W.) J. K. Vortrag, 1872.

Keppler (Paul Wilhelm v.), *bp. of Rottenberg, see* HASSL (G.) P. W. v. K., Rottenburgs gr. Bischof, 1927.

Keppner (Franz J. A.) Kurze Gesch. d. musikal. Ideen. [*b. w.* Brendel (F.) Grundzüge, 4e A., 1855]. s8°. Freiburg. 1856

Ker (William Paton).
The art of poetry. Lect. [P2424]. 8°. O. 1920
The art of poetry: 7 lects. s8°. O. 1923
Coll. essays. Ed. w. intr. by C. Whibley. 2v. 8°. 1925
English lit.: mediaeval. [Home Univ. Lib. repr.] s8°. [1926]
Hazlitt, *see* ENGLISH ASSOC. Essays &c., v8, 1922.
The humanist ideal, *see* ENGLISH ASSOC. Essays & studies, v6, 1920.
see CHAMBERS (R. W.) W. P. K., 1855–1923, 1925.

Kerby (William Moseley). The life, diplom. career & lit. activities of N. G. Léonard. la8°. Paris. 1925

Kerchove de Denterghem (*cte.* Charles de). L'industrie belge pend. l'occup. allem., 1914–18. [C.E. for Internat. Peace]. la8°. [1927]

Kerckerinck zur Borg (Engelbert, *Frhr.* von) & R. Klapheck. Alt-Westfalen. Die Bauentwickl. Westfalens seit d. Renaissance. [Veröff. d. Westf. Komm. f. Heimatschutz, 1]. 4°. St. [1912]

Kerckhoffs (Aug.) Cours complet de Volapük, avec vocab. 7e éd. corr. &c. s8°. 1886

Kercselich (Balthasar Adam), *de Carbavia.* De regnis Dalmatiae, Croatiae, Sclavoniae notitiae præliminares. fol. Zagrabiae. [1771]

Kerdaniel (Edouard L. de).
Un auteur dramat. du 15e s.: A. de La Vigne. 8°. 1923

Kerékgyártó (Árpád). Tíz év magyarország legujabb történetéből, 1840–49. 2 osztály. s8°. Budapest. 1874

Keren ha-Yesod (The) book. Colonis. problems of Eretz-Israel (Palestine) Found. Fund. s8°. 1921

Kerensky (Aleksandr Fedorovich).
Allied policy tow. Russia. [P2405, 2426]. 8°. 1920
Soviet Russia in 1919. [P2405]. 8°. 1920

Kerényi (Carl). Die griech.-oriental. Romanliteratur in religionsgesch. Beleuchtung. 8°. Tübingen. 1927

Kerguelen Trémarec (Yves Joseph de). Rel. de 2 voyages dans les mers australes & des Indes, 1771–74. 8°. 1782

Kerkherdere (Joannes Gerardus).
Prodromus Danielicus. s8°. Lovanii. [1711]

Kermode (Josephine), [*ps.* CUSHAG]. Manx melodies. s8°. 1922

Kermötzi (J.) *Conf. fidei Xtnae. sec. Unitarios in Transylvania &c. [*by J. K.*], 1782, *see* TRANSYLVANIA.

Kern (Berthold). Das Problem d. Lebens in krit. Bearbeitung. 8°. 1909

Kern (Fritz). Gottesgnadentum u. Widerstandsrecht im früh. M. A. la8°. L. 1914

Kern (Johann Friedrich). De vita, obitu, scriptisque T. Ittigii diss. [P600]. s4°. Lipsiae. 1710

Kern (Oskar).
Johann Rist als weltlicher Lyriker. 8°. Marburg. 1919

Kern (Otto). Inscript. Graecae. Coll. O. K. [Tabulae in usum scholarum; ed. J. Lietzmann, 7]. la8°. Bonnae. 1913
see ORPHEUS. Orphicorum fragm. coll. O. K., 1922.

Kerner (A. Justinus C.), *see* HOWITT (A. M.) Pioneers: life & wks. of J. K. (*adapted fr. the Ger.*) &c., 1883.

Kerner (Anton), *Ritter von Marilaun.* Pflanzenleben.
3e A. neubearb. v. A. Hansen. Neudr. 3B. la8°. L. 1921–22

Kernick (E. F. Cory).
Reg. of changes of names dur. the War. fol. [1919 ?]

Kernohan (J. W.) The co. of Londonderry in 3 cent. w. notices of the Ironmongers' estate. la8°. Belfast. 1921

Kero, *monachus S. Galli.* Interpret. regulae S. Benedicti theotisca, notis illustr. J. G. Scherzius, *see* SCHILTER (J.) Thesaurus antiq., t1, 1728.

Kerp (Heinrich). Landeskunde v. Skandinavien (Schweden, Norwegen u. Dänemark). s8°. L. 1904

Kerr (Albert Boardman). Jacques Cœur, merchant prince of the M.A. 8°. N.Y. 1927

Kerr (Alexander Blacker), *ps., see* KING-HALL (*Miss* M.)

Kerr (Alfred). Newyork u. London. 20 Kapitel nach d. Weltkrieg. s8°. 1923

Kerr (Archibald W. M.) An Ironside of Ireland: career of Lt.-Gen. M. Jones, gov. of Dublin &c., 1647–49. Intr. by J. W. Kernohan. 8°. [1923]

Kerr (Cecil), *see* LOTHIAN (C. C., *march. of*). C., March. of L.: a mem.; ed. C. K., 1922.

Kerr (James), *M.D.* Fundamentals of school health. la8°. [1926]

Kerr (John Graham). Evolution. 8°. 1926

Kerr (*Adm.* Mark Edward Frederic), *R.N.*
Land, sea, & air. Reminiscences. la8°. 1927

Kerr (Michael Crawford). Memorial addresses on life &c. of M. C. K. Deliv. in House of Representatives, 1876 &c. la8°. Wash. 1877

Kerr (Philip) & L. Curtis.
The prevention of war. 8°. New Haven, *Yale.* 1923

Kerr (Robert), *F.R.S.E.* Gen. hist. & coll. of voyages & travels. v18. 8°. 1824
18, Hist. sketch of the progress of discovery &c.—Cat. of voyages & travels—Index to v1–17.

Kerr (Thomas Henry). The Golf-House tragedy; the trial of T. H. K. Cape Times Weekly Ed., Feb. 5th, 1908. [*Extr.*] fol. [Cape Town. 1908]

Kerr (Wilfred Brenton).
The reign of terror, 1793–94. 8°. Toronto. 1927

Kerr (William John Bewglass). Higham Ferrers & its castle & park. 8°. Northampton. [1925]

Kershaw (George Bertram).
Sewage purification & disposal. 8°. C. 1915

Kershaw (N.)
Anglo-Saxon & Norse poems. Ed. & tr. by N. K. 8°. C. 1922
Stories & ballads of the far past. Tr. f. the Norse, w. intr. & notes by N. K. 8°. C. 1921

Kershaw (S.), *see* DUMVILLE (J.) & S. K. The worsted industry, 1924.

Kersten (Curt). N. Lenin, s. Leben u. Werk. [P2456]. 8°. 1920

Kerviler (G. de). La navig. intérieure en France pend. la Guerre. [C.E. for Int. Peace]. 8°. [1926]

Kessel (J.) Les captifs. 53e éd. s8°. [1926]
L'équipage. 32e éd. s8°. [1924]
La steppe rouge. 29e éd. s8°. [1923]

Kessel (Johann Hubert). Geschichtl. Mittheilungen ü. d. Heiligthümer d. Stiftskirche zu Aachen. 8°. Köln. 1874

Kesser (Hermann) [KÄSER-KESSER (H. A.)]
Kaiserin Messalina. Tragödie. 8°. 1914
Die Peitsche: erzaehl. Dichtung. 8°. Frauenfeld. [1919]
Die Stunde d. Martin Jochner. Roman. s8°. 1921

Kessler (Harry, *Graf* v.)
Germany & Europe. 8°. New Haven. 1923

Kessler (Johann), *see* SCHIESS (T.) J. K.'s Sabbata, St. Galler Ref.-chron., 1523–39, 1911.

Kester (Robert).
Les Anglais & nous. Préf. du Gén. Verraux. s8°. 1921

Ketham (Joannes de). The Fasciculus medicinae of J. de K.: facs. of 1st (Venet.) ed. of 1491; w. intr. by K. Sudhoff, tr. & adapted by C. Singer. [Monumenta medica, 1]. fol. Milan. 1924
see FASCICULO. Fasc. di medicina [*sometimes attr. to J. de K.*], 1493, w. intr. by C. Singer, 2p, 1925.

Kett (George). Poetical works. [final rev. *MS. corr. by a.*] 8°. 1911

Ketteler (Wilhelm Emmanuel, *Frhr.* von), *bp. of Mainz.*
Das allgem. Concil u. s. Bedeut. f. uns. Zeit. [P2692]. 8°. Mainz. 1869
Die Anschauungen d. Cultusministers Falk u. d. kathol. Kirche. 5e A. [P2692]. 8°. Mainz. 1874
Der Bruch d. Religionsfriedens. 2te A. [P2696]. 8°. Mainz. 1875
Der Culturkampf geg. d. kathol. Kirche &c. [P2696]. 8°. Mainz. 1874
*Frhr. v. K. u. d. übr. Bischöfe d. Minorität als Märtyrer d. Ueberzeugung. [P2695]. 8°. Mainz. 1875
Kann ein Jesuit v. s. Oberen z. e. Sünde verpflichtet werden? Corr. mit Frhr. von Starck. [P520]. 8°. Mainz. 1874
Die Minorität auf d. Concil. Antw. auf Lord Acton's Sendschr. [P2695]. 8°. Mainz. 1870
Das unfehlbare Lehramt d. Papstes. [P2692]. 8°. Mainz. 1871
Die Unwahrheiten d. röm. Briefe v. Concil. [P2692]. 8°. Mainz. 1870
see FRIEDBERG (E.) Die preuss. Gesetzentwürfe ü. d. Stell. d. Kirche z. Staat: Brief an W. E. Frhrn. v. K., 1873.

Kettell (Samuel). Specimens of American poetry, w. crit. & biogr. notices. 3v. s8°. Boston. 1829

Kettenbach (Heinrich von). Ein Sermon [*on Luke xxi*, 33]. H. v. K. Barfüssers, wider die falschen Aposteln, die da haben gepredigt die Prelaten mögen das haylig Ewangelium verwandeln. s4°. *n.p.* [1523]
Ain sermon oder predig von der Christl. kirchen &c. [P2539]. s4°. *n.p.* 1522
Vergleychung des allerheyl. herren, u. vatter des Bapsts, gegen dem seltzamen frembden gast in der Christenheyt genant Jesus &c. [P2539]. s4°. *n.p.* 1523

Ketterer (Johann Adam).
Karl d. Grosse u. d. Kirche. 8°. München. 1898

Kettering. Compotus of the manor of K., 1292, w. intr., tr. & notes by C. Wise. 8°. Kettering. 1899

Kettle (Tilly), *see* Milner (J. D.) T. K., 1735–86, 1927.

Kettlewell (John).
*Of Christian communion &c. 3p [*sep. pagin.*] s4°. 1693

Kettner (Carl Ernst). De Joh. Fabri episc. Vienn. vita & scriptis. Praes. C. E. K., resp. A. C. Cleemann. [P596]. s4°. Lipsiae. 1737

Kettner (Friedrich Ernst). Hist. dicti Johannei de Trinitate 1 Joh. v. 7, una cum apologia B. Lutheri. s4°. Francofurti. 1713
Des Ministerii zu Frankfurt a. M., zu Lübeck &c. judicia u. responsa v. d. Ehe mit d. Weibes Schwester [1708]. D. Druck überlassen v. F. E. K. s4°. Quedlinburgh. *n.d.*

Kettridge (J. O.) Dict. franç.-angl., angl.-franç. de termes &c. techniques & gén. usités en finance &c. 8°. Londres. [1924]
French-Eng. & Eng.-Fr. dict. of technical terms &c. used in civil, mechanical, electrical &c. engineering. 2v [*pagin. cont.*] la8°. [1925]

Keuffel (Georg Gottfried). Hist. orig. & progr. scholarum inter Christianos. Acc. J. Hildebrandi Oratio de fundat. Acad. Juliae. s8°. Helmstadii. 1743

Keulisch (Hans Heinrich).
Heiliger Sontags Übungen. s8°. St. 1654

Kew, *Royal Botanic Gardens, see* Index Kewensis, Suppl., 1921–26.

Kew chuen, *see* Haou Kew Chuen.

Key. *Key (The) of heaven or a posey of prayers sel. f. Cath. authors, 17th ed. Added, Gother's Instructions &c. s8°. 1831
The Key of Paradise, opening the gate to eternal salvation. impr. ed. s8°. D. 1844

Key (Axel). Schulhygien. Untersuch. Deut. Bearb. hrsg. v. L. Burgerstein. 8°. Hamburg. 1889

Key (Helmer). European bankruptcy & emigration. 8°. [1924]
The new colonial policy. Tr. E. Classen. 8°. [1927]

Key (Pierre Van Rensselaer). Enrico Caruso: a biog. By P. V. R. K., in collab. w. B. Zirato. 8°. 1923

Key (Thomas Hewitt). The alphabet—Terentian metres—Good, better, best, well. 2nd issue. s8°. 1849
A Latin gramm. 2nd ed. corr. & enl. 8°. 1858

Key (Wilhelmine Marie Euteman), *Ph.D.* Heredity & social fitness. Differential mating in a Pennsylvania family. [C.I. of Wash., Publ. 296]. la8°. Wash. 1920

Keynes (Geoffrey Langdon).
Bibliography of Sir Th. Browne, Kt., M.D. la8°. C. 1924
Bibliog. of the wr. of W. Harvey, M.D. la8°. C. 1928
Bibliog. of William Blake. [Grolier Club]. 4°. N.Y. 1921
see Blake (W.) Pencil drawings; ed. G. K., 1927.

Keynes (John Maynard).
The econ. conseq. of Mr. Churchill. s8°. *Hogarth Press.* 1925
The econ. conseq. of the Peace. [repr.] 8°. 1920
The end of laissez-faire. s8°. 1926
A revision of the Treaty. Sequel to Econ. conseq. of the peace. 8°. 1922
A short view of Russia. s8°. 1925
Tract on monetary reform. 8°. 1923
Tract on monetary reform. [repr.] 8°. 1924
A treatise on probability. 8°. 1921
see Lévy (R. G.) La juste paix (*incl.* Une aberration: le livre de M. K.), 1920.
„ Manchester Guardian. Reconstr. in Europe; ed. J. M. K., sect. 1–12, 1922–23.
„ Warnecke (F.) The Treaty: comments of Wilson, K. &c., 1924.

Keysell (Thomas Owen), *1814–62, see* MacCullagh (T.) The earnest life: mem. of K., 1867.

Keyser (Arthur).
*People & places: a life in 5 continents. 8°. 1922
Trifles & travels. 8°. 1923

Keyser (Cassius Jackson). Mathemat. philos.: a study of fate & freedom. 8°. N.Y. [1922]

Keyser (Edouard). La Baraka. s8°. [1921]

Keyser (Erich). Die Bevölkerung Danzigs u. i. Herkunft im 13. u. 14. Jhdt. [Pfingstblätter d. hans. Geschichtsvereins, 15]. 8°. Lübeck. 1924
Die Entstehung v. Danzig. 8°. Danzig. 1924

Keyser (Lienhart) [Kaiser], *see* Roth (L.) L. K., e. evang. Martyr aus d. Innviertel, 1900.

Keyserling (Eduard, *Graf* **v.)**
Abendliche Häuser. Roman. s8°. 1923

Keyserling (Hermann, *Graf* **v.)**
Deutschlands wahre polit. Mission. 3e A. s8°. Darmstadt. 1921
Das Ehe-buch: eine neue Sinngebung. Hrsg. v. H. K. 8°. Celle. [1925]
Das Gefüge d. Welt: Versuch e. krit. Philos. 2e A. s8°. Darmstadt. 1920
Individuum u. Zeitgeist. Rede. [P2763]. 8°. L. 1909
Menschen als Sinnbilder. 8°. Darmstadt. 1926
Die neuentsteh. Welt. s8°. Darmstadt. 1926
Philosophie als Kunst. s8°. Darmstadt. 1920
Politik — Wirtschaft — Weisheit. s8°. Darmstadt. 1922
Das Reisetagebuch e. Philosophen. 7e A. 2B [*pagin. cont.*] s8°. Darmstadt. 1923
Schöpferische Erkenntnis. s8°. Darmstadt. 1922
Das Spektrum Europas. s8°. Heidelberg. [1928]
Unsterblichkeit: Kritik d. Beziehungen zw. Naturgeschehen u. menschl. Vorstellungswelt. 3e, neu durchgearb. A. s8°. Darmstadt. 1920
Was uns Not tut. Was Ich will. 2e A. [P2406]. s8°. Darmstadt. 1920
Wiedergeburt. 8°. Darmstadt. 1927
Translations.
The book of marriage. New interp. by 24 leaders of contemp. thought. Arr. & ed. by H. K. [Tr.] 8°. [1927]
Travel diary of a philosopher. Tr. J. H. Reece. 2v. 8°. 1925
„ „ .... 8°. [1927]
The world in the making [*w.* Autobiog. sketch]. Tr. M. Samuel. 8°. [1927]
see Feldkeller (P.) Graf K. Erkenntnisweg z. Übersinnl., 1922.
„ Hupfeld (R.) Graf H. K., Vortrag, 1922.

Keyte (John Charles). Andrew Young of Shensi. 8°. [1924]

Kéza (Simon de). De orig. & gestis Hungarorum lib. duo. In lucem emittit J. Podhradczky. 8°. Budae. 1833

Khakhanov (Aleksandr S.), *see* Barlaam & Josaphat. Б. и І., Груз. текстъ, съ перевод. и пред. изд. А. Х., 1902.

Khalathean (Grigor). Moses of Khoren. [*In Armenian.* P2809]. s8°. Vienna. 1898
see Bible: Armenian. Книги Паралипоменонъ въ древн. арм. переводѣ; *ed.* G. K., 1899.

Khamé (John), *Abba, see* John Khamé.

Khan (Shafaat Ahmad). Anglo-Portuguese negotiations rel. to Bombay, 1660–77. [repr.] la8°. [1922]
Doc. on 17th c. Brit. India, in Public Rec. Office. [P2737]. 8°. 1924
The East India trade in the 17th c. &c. 8°. 1923
Sources for hist. of Brit. India in 17th cent. 8°. 1926
see Marshall (J.) J. M. in India: notes &c. in Bengal, 1668–72; ed. &c. S. A. K., 1927.

Khanenko (Nikolai Danilovich), *1691–1760.* Дневникъ, 1727–53. Приложеніе къ "Кіевская Старина." 8°. Кіевъ. 1884

Khanikov (Nikolai).
Mém. s. la partie mérid. de l'Asie Cent. 4°. 1861

Kharkov. *Топогр. описаніе Харьковск. намѣстничества &c., 1788, 1888, *see* Zagorovsky (N.)
Харьковскій календарь на 1888 г. въ 2 кн. [3 *pagin.*] 8°. Харьковъ. 1887
Харьковскій сборникъ. Лит.-научное приложеніе къ Харьковск. Календарю. B2 [2 *pag.*] 8°. Харьковъ. 1888
Includes Zagorovsky (N.) Топогр. описаніе Харьковск. намѣстничества (1788).

Kharkov University [Charkov], *see* Naukovii zbirnik. Науковий збірник: the scient. mag. of the C. chair of Ukrainian hist., 1927.

Kharoṣṭhī. Kharoṣṭhī inscriptions discov. by Sir A. Stein in Chinese Turkestan. Transcr. & ed. by A. M. Boyer, E. J. Rapson & E. Senart. 2p. sm. fol. O. 1920–27

Khashero Jadhava, *see* Jadhava (K.)

Khatisean (Gabr.) [Educ. thoughts. *In Armenian.* v1. P2801]. s8°. Tiflis. 1882

Kheiri (Sattar).
Ind. Miniaturen d. islam. Zeit. la8°. [1921]
Islam. Architektur. la8°. [1923]

Khelat [Kelat]. Mem. on K. & Sind frontier affairs, 1876, *see* Merewether (W. L.)

Khemnitser (Ivan Ivanovich). Сочиненія и письма. Съ біог. стат. Я. Грота. [П. А. Н.] 8°. С.-П. 1873

Khevenhüller-Metsch (*Fürst* **Johann Josef**). Aus der Zeit Maria Theresias: Tagebuch, 1742–76. Hrsg. v. R. Graf. K.-M. u. H. Schlitter. [B5–7]. 8º. Wien. 1914–25

Khilkov (D.) О свободы. [P810]. s8º. *n.p. n.d.*

Khilkov (*prince* **Grigory**). Сборникъ князя Хилкова. [*Hist. doc.*, 1493–1743]. la8º. П. 1879

Khiryakov (A. M.) Человек, которого зовут Антоном. Жизнь Калмыка. s8º. Москва. 1924

Khlopin (Grigory Vitalevich). Самоубійства &c. среди учащихся русскихъ учебныхъ Заведеніи. [P2446]. 8º. С.-П. 1906

Khodasevich (Vladislav).
Из еврейских поэтов. s8º. П. 1922
Статьи о русской поэзіи. s8º. П. 1922

Khoklov (Ivan) [Хохловъ]. Статейный списокъ посольства въ Бухарію И. Х. (1620–22), *see* KHILKOV (*pr.* G.) Сборникъ, 1879.

Khokumn. *Khokumn Qristoneakan [Christian Meditation. *Tr. into Armenian by* Johannes, Vardapet]. s8º. [Venice. 1136=1688]

Khosrov, *bp. of Andsewatsia, the Great, d. 972.* [Comm. on the eucharistic liturgy. *In Armenian.* P2812]. 8º. S. Lazar Venet. 1869

Khosrovik, *the Translator.* Khosrovik Thargmanitch. [8 cent. *Ed.* G. Hovsephean. *2 pagin.*] 8º. Vagharshapat. 1899
see DASHEAN (H.) Short bibliog. st., *in Armenian*, pl, K. &c., 1895.

Khrimean, *Hairik, catholicus of Armenia.* [MEKERTICH KHRIMEAN]. The meeting of the kings. Arm. text & Eng. version by P. Tonapetean & L. Binyon; w. biog. sketch. 8º. 1915

Khrisanth, *metropolitan of Neopatras, see* CONTARINI (C.)

Khronika [Хроника], *see* CHRONICA.

Khuda Baksh Library, *see* PATNA ORIENTAL PUBL. LIB.

Khūshḥāl Khān; *1613–91.*
Dīwān i Khūshḥāl Khān. [*Pushtu MS.*] la8º. *n.d.*

Khvostova (Ekaterina A.), *see* SUSHKOVA (E. A.)

Kiaran, *St., abbot of Clonmacnois, see* CIARAN.

Kiazim (Omer). L'aventure Kémaliste, un danger. s8º. 1921

Kibalchich (Nikolai Ivanovich), *d. 1881.* Н. И. Кибальчичъ. [Матеріалъ для біог.] [P2390]. s8º. Carouge (Genève). 1899

Kidd (Benjamin). A philosopher with nature. 8º. [1921]

Kidd (Beresford James). Doc. illust. of the hist. of the Church. Ed. B. J. K. v1, 2. s8º. 1920–23
1, to A.D. 313. 2, 313–461.
Churches of Eastern Christendom, 451 to pres. time. 8º. [1927]
Hist. of the Church to A.D. 461. 3v. 8º. O. 1922

Kidd (George Balderston). Χριστοφάνεια. Manifestations of the Son of God under O. Test. Ed. O. T. Dobbin. 8º. 1852

Kidd (James), *D.D.* A diss. on the eternal sonship of Christ. n. ed. w. introd. biograph. & theolog. by R. S. Candlish. s8º. 1872

Kidd (John), *M.D.* Adaptation of external nature to man. [Bridgewater treatises. 3rd ed.] 8º. 1834

Kidd (William), *bookseller.* Picturesque companion to the Isle of Thanet. Rev. &c. by J. Jones. s8º. [1840 ?]

Kidder (Alfred Vincent). Intr. to the study of southwestern archaeol.; w. acc. of excav. at Pecos. [Phillips Acad. Papers of S.-W. Exped., No. 1]. 4º. New Haven. 1924
—— **& S. J. Guernsey.** Archeolog. explor. in N.-E. Arizona. [S.I., B. of E., Bull. 65]. 8º. Wash. 1919

Kidder (Richard), *bp. of Bath & Wells.* Life of R. K., D.D., bp. of Bath & Wells. Wr. by himself. Ed. A. E. Robinson. [Somerset Record Soc., v37]. 8º. *p.f.s.o.* 1924

Kiddier (William).
The brushmaker & h. craft &c. s8º. *Pitman.* [1923]

Kiderlen-Wächter (Alfred v.) Kiderlen-Wächter Briefwechsel u. Nachlass. Hrsg. E. Fäckh. 2B. 8º. 1924

Kidson (Frank). The Beggar's opera, its predecessors & successors. s8º. C. 1922

Kidston (Robert). Fossil plants of the carbonif. rocks of Gt. Brit., sect. 1, *see* GEOLOG. SURVEY OF ENG. &c. Mem.: Palæontology, v2, 1923–25.

Kiefer (F. J.) Die Sagen d. Rheinlandes. 2e A. s8º. Mainz. 1867

Kielland (Alex. Lange). Samlede digterverker. Standardutg. Indledn. &c. av P. L. Stavnem. Textrev. ved A. H. Winsnes. 5B. s8º. 1919
1, Novelleter—Garman & Worse—For Scenen—Nye Novelletter.
2, Arbeidsfolk—Else—Skipper Worse.
3, To Novelletter—Gift—Fortuna.
4, Sne—Tre Par—Betty's Formynder—Sankt Hans Fest.
5, Professoren—Jacob—Mennesker og Dyr—Tillæg.

Kielmannsegg (Auguste Charlotte, *Gräfin* **von).** Mem. ü. Napoleon I. Hrsg. G. Aretz. 8º. Dresden. [1927]

Kielstra (E. B.) Sumatra's Westkust, 1819–88; & Bijdrage door P. H. van der Kemp, *see* BIJDRAGEN tot de taal &c. v. Ned. Ind., volg 5, d2–7, 10, 1887–94.

Kiepert (Heinrich). Karte v. Klein-Asien. la8º. 1854
see ROBINSON (E.) Maps to accompany Biblical researches in Palestine of E. R. &c., drawn by H. Kiepert, 1856.

Kierkegaard (Søren A.) [*ps*s. JOH. CLIMACUS; VIGILIUS HAUFNIENSIS]. Psychologie d. Sünde, d. Bekehrung u. d. Glaubens. [Der Begriff d. Angst—Philosoph. Bissen]. Uebers. &c. v. C. Schrempf. 8º. L. 1890
Samlede Værker: udgivne af A. B. Drachmann, J. L. Heiberg & H. O. Lange. 2en Udg. B1–9. 8º. 1920–27
Das Tagebuch des Verführers. [Übers. v. M. Dauthendey]. s8º. L. 1903
see BEYER (H.) S. K., 1925.
„ HÖFFDING (H.) S. K. als Philosoph; übers. v. Dorner & Schrempf, 3e deut. A., 1922.

Kiesling (*Oberstleut.* **Hans v.**) Mit Feldmarsch. Von der Goltz in Mesopotamien u. Persien. 8º. L. 1922

Kiesling (Johann Georg). De variis Waldensium veritatis testium nominibus & sectis. Diss. s4º. Jenae. 1739

Kiesling (Johann Rudolph).
De disciplina clericorum. s8º. Lipsiae. 1760
De insanabili Eccl. Rom. c. aquae transsubstantionem in s. Eucharistia, scepticismo, contra P. Aresium. s8º. Lipsiae. 1772
De Leontio episcopo Antiocheno [P597]. s4º. Erlangae. [1762]
Diss. de ritibus sepulchral. Xtn. fidem indic. [P2635]. s4º. Wittenbergae. [1736]
Hist. concert. Graecorum Latinorumque de esu sanguinis & carnis morticinae. s8º. Erlangae. 1763
Hist. concert. Graec. Latinorumque de Transsubstantiatione. s8º. L. 1754
Hist. de usu symbolorum. s8º. Lipsiae. 1753
see LÖSCHER (V. E.) Fortsetzung d. Hist. Motuum V. E. L., bis auf 1601, 1770.

Kieslinger (Franz).
Die Glasmalerei in Österreich. s8º. Wien. *n.d.*

Kiessling (Adolph) & U. v. Wilamowitz-Möllendorff. Philologische Untersuchungen. H25–30. 8º. 1920–25
Contin. as Neue philol. Unters; hrsg. W. Jaeger, *q.v.*
25, Reinhard (L.) Die Anakoluthe bei Platon.
26, Strache (H.) Eklektizismus des Antiochus v. Askalon.
27, Klingner (F.) De Boethii Consolatione philos.
28, Fränkel (E.) Plautinisches im Plautus.
29, Snell (B.) Die Ausdr. f. d. Begriff d. Wissens in d. vorplaton. Philos.
30, Geissler (P.) Chronologie d. altatt. Komödie.

Kiessling (Georg Nicolaus). Th. Munzeri doctr. & facta & G. Arnoldi admissos lapsus exponit, praes. V. E. Loeschero, resp. G. N. K. s4º. Vittembergae. [1708]

Kiev. Типографія К.-Печерской Лавры; состав. Ѳ. Титовъ, т1 & Прилож., 1916–18, *see* TITOV (F. I.)

Kievskaya starina.
Кіевская старина: ежемѣсячный историч. журналъ. т1–19 [Январь & Фев. 1882 *wanting*]. 8º. Кіевъ. 1882–87
see KHANENKO (N. D.) Дневникъ, 1727–53, приложеніе къ К. С., 1884.

Kilber (Henricus), *S.J.* Analysis Biblica, seu univ. Scripturæ Sacræ analytica expos. 2a ed., annot. aucta. 2t. 8º. Lutetiae Paris. 1856
Theologia dogm.-polem.-scholastica. Tract. I, De Deo uno & trino. s8º. Wirceburgi. 1767
Tract. de fide, *see* MIGNE (J. P.), *ed.* Theol. cursus, t6, 1862.

Kilchevsky (V. A.) Богатства и доходы духовенство. [P849]. s8º. Москва. 1907

Kildare (County) Archaeological Society.
Journal. v1–9 (1891–1921). 8º. D. 1895–1921

Kilgour (P.), *see* WOODHOUSE (T.) & P. KILGOUR. The jute industry &c., 1921.

Kilham (Alexander), *Wesleyan minister.* The life of A. K. [by himself]. Added, extracts of letters in favour of reform wr. to K. [Ed. w. pref. by J. Grundell & R. Hall]. s8º. Nottingham. [1799]
see BLACKWELL (J.) *Life of Rev. A. K., one of founders of Methodist New Connexion, 1797, 1838.

Kilian, *Saint.* *In disem puchleine ist czu wysen das hochwirdig heylthum in Wirtzpurg das man do pfligt zu weisen alle Jar an Sant Kyligās tag.
[*facs. repr.*] s4º. [Würzburg ?, *Hans Mayr.* 1483. *repr. n.d.*]
see SERAVIUS (N.) S. K. gesta, 1598.

Kilian (Lucas), *see* FUGGER, *Fam. of.* Fuggerorum et Fuggerarum imagines [L. & W. K. ampl. &c.], 1618.
Kilian (Wolfgang), *see* FUGGER, *Fam. of.* Fuggerorum et Fuggerarum imagines [L. & W. K. ampl. &c.], 1618.
Kiliani (Richard), *see* PLÄNE u. Versuche z. Währungssanierung; Beitr. v. R. K. &c., 1923.
Killebrew (Joseph Buckner), *see* TENNESSEE. Introd. to resources of T.; by J. B. K. &c., 1874.
Killen (Alice M.) Le roman terrifiant, de Walpole à A. Radcliffe, & son infl. sur la litt. franç. j. 1840. 8°. 1923
Killen (William D.), *see* ULSTER. The plea of presbytery &c. by ministers of the General Synod of U. [W. D. K. *& others*], 1843.
Killigrew (Thomas), *the elder.* The parson's wedding (1664), *see* SUMMERS (M.), *ed.* Restoration comedies, 1921.
Killmare. *Exact rel. (An) of the persecut. &c. sustained by the Protest. of K., 1689, *see* ORPEN (R.)
Kilmacolm. Oor ain braw lads frae K.: tribute, 1915, *see* ROBERTSON (J.), *ed.*
Kilmarnock. Burns holograph MSS. in K. Monument Mus., 1889, *see* BURNS (R.)
Kilmarnock (William Boyd, *4th earl of*), *executed 1746.* The trials of K., George, earl of Cromarty, & Arthur, Ld. Balmerino, for high treason, 1746. W. acc. of the lives of K. & Balmerino. [P536]. s8°. [1746]
see CUMBERLAND (W. A., *d. of*). *Book of chron. &c.; added, an abstr. of the life of K., 1746 ?.
,, FOSTER (J.) Behaviour of Earl of K., after h. sentence &c., 1746.
Kilwardby (Robert), *d. 1279, see* BIRKENMAJER (A.) Verm. Unters. (Brief K.'s an Peter v. Conflans &c.; 1277), 1922.
Kimball (Fiske), *see* JEFFERSON (T.) T. J., architect; w. essay & notes by K., 1916.
Kimedoncius (Jacobus).
see HUBER (S.) Disput. 2ª contra Calvinistas, & praesertim Synopsin K., 1593.
,, —— Theses, Christum esse mortuum pro peccatis &c.; acc. confut. thes. K., 1592.
Kimhi (David), *see* DAVID, *ben Joseph Kimchi.*
Kimmel (Ernst Julius).
De Rufino Eusebii interprete libri 2. 8°. Gerae. 1838
Kimmins (Charles William). Children's dreams. s8°. 1920
Kinahan (G. Henry). Handy-book of rock names. s8°. 1873
Kincaid (Charles Augustus) & *Rao Bahadur* **D. B. Parasnis.**
Hist. of the Maratha people. v2, 3. 8°. 1922–25
Kinck (Hans E.) Præsten. s8°. 1905
Kindervater (Johann Heinrich). Disput. de Augustanae Conf. nomine & causis. [P2642]. s4°. Jenae. 1702
Kindle (Edward Martin). Recent & fossil ripple-mark, *see* CANADA: GEOLOG. SURVEY. Museum Bull., No. 25, 1917.
King Edward's School, *Birmingham.*
Records. [Dugdale Soc., 4]. v1. la8°. 1924
1, The "Miscellany" vol.; w. intr. by W. F. Carter.
King (Agnes Gardner). Islands far away. Intr. by Sir E. Im Thurn. 8°. 1920
Kelvin the man: biog. sketch. Intr. by Sir D. Macalister. 8°. [1925]
King (Basil). The happy isles. s8°. [1924]
King (Charles), *LL.D.* Hist. of the N.Y. Chamber of Commerce, 1856, *see* NEW YORK CHAMBER OF COMM. Charter &c., 1856.
King (David), *M.D.* An histor. sketch of the Redwood Lib. & Athenaeum, in Newport, R.I. [P2623]. 8°. Boston. 1860
King (David Barty). Scheme for dealing w. tuberculous persons in London. Foreword by W. Osler. la8°. 1915
King (Dougall Macdougall). Nerves & personal power: princ. of psych. appl. to conduct & health. Intr. by Rt. Hon. W. L. M. King. 8°. [1922]
King (Georgiana Goddard).
Brief acc. of the military orders in Spain. [Hispanic Soc. of Amer.] s8°. N.Y. 1921
A citizen of the twilight: José Asuncion Silva. [Bryn Mawr notes &c., 4]. s8°. Bryn Mawr, Penn. 1921
Mudéjar. [Bryn Mawr notes &c., 8]. s8°. Bryn Mawr. 1927
The play of the Sibyl Cassandra [*by* Gil Vicente]. [Bryn Mawr notes &c., 2]. s8°. Bryn Mawr, Penn. 1921
Pre-Romanesque churches of Spain. [Bryn Mawr notes &c., 7]. s8°. Bryn Mawr, Penn. 1924
Sardinian painting. [v]1. s8°. Bryn Mawr, Penn. 1923
1, Painters of the gold backgrounds.
The way of Saint James. [Hispanic Soc. of Amer.] 3v. s8°. N.Y. 1920
see STREET (G. E.) Unpubl. notes & repr. papers, w. essay by G. G. K., 1916.

King (Gregory). Staffordshire note book, 1679–80; annot. &c. by G. P. Mander, *see* STAFFORDSHIRE. Coll., N.S., v21, 1920.
King (Harriet Eleanor Hamilton).
The disciples. 12th ed. s8°. 1890
King (Henry), *bp. of Chichester.*
Poems. Ed. J. Sparrow. la8°. *Nonesuch Press.* 1925
King (Josiah). Mr. Blount's Oracles of reason, examined &c. The Holy Scriptures &c. asserted against deism & atheism. s8°. Exon. 1698
King (*Lt.-Col.* **Lancelot N. F. I.)** Graphical methods of plotting f. air photographs. [War Office]. 8°. 1925
King (Leonard William). [A hist. of Babylonia & Assyria. v1]. Hist. of Sumer & Akkad. [repr.] la8°. 1916
King (*Mrs.* **Maria M.)** Real life in the spirit land. 5th ed. v1. 8°. Hammonton, N.J. 1892
King (Moses), *publisher.* K.'s views of the Panama Canal, 1913, *see* MILLS (W. W.)
King (P. S.) & Co. Cat. of Parl. Papers, 1801–1900, 2nd suppl., 1911–20, 1922, *see* PARLIAMENTARY PAPERS.
King (Paul). In the Chinese customs service: personal record of 47 yrs. 8°. [1924]
see KING (V.) & P. K. The raven on the skyscraper, 1925.
King (Paul), *Minorite, see* BEELING (R.) Vindic. Cathol. Hiberniae lib. duo: confut. lib. quem P. K. publ. [*i.e.* Epist. nobilis Hiberni &c.], 1650.
King (Peter King, *1st baron*). Enquiry into the constit. &c. of the primitive church. s8°. 1839
King (R. W.), *see* FARNHAM (D. T.), J. A. HALL &c. Profitable science in industry, 1925.
King (Robert), *diocesan curate, Armagh.* Mem. intr. to early hist. of Primacy of Armagh. 2nd ed., *p.f.s.o.* sm. fol. Armagh. 1854
King (Rupert William).
The translator of Dante; H. F. Cary, 1772–1844. 8°. 1925
King (Tom), *of Covent Garden.* *Tom K—g's: or, the Paphian grove, w. humours of Covent Garden &c. 2nd ed. 8°. 1738
King (Veronica) & Paul King. The raven on the skyscraper: st. of mod. Amer. portents. 8°. [1925]
King (W. A. H.) Chelsea porcelain. 4°. 1922
King (W. B. R.), *see* WEDD (C. B.) & W. B. R. K. Geology of co. around Flint &c., 1924.
King (William), *bp. of Derry, abp. of Dublin, see* BOYSE (J.) Remarks on late discourse of W., bp. of D., conc. the inventions of men &c., 1694.
King (William), *LL.D., princ. of St. Mary Hall, Oxford.*
*Oratio in theatro Sheldon. hab., 1749, die dedic. Bibl. Radcliv. s4°. 1750
*Tres oratiunculae hab. in domo Convoc. Oxon. [*degree of D.C.L. conferred upon James, Duke of Hamilton; George Henry, Earl of Lichfield; & J. Boyle, Earl of Orrery, each w. sep. tp. & pagin.*] s4°. [1743]
King (William), *LL.D., student of Christ Church, Oxford; 1663–1712.* A journey to London—Dialogues of the dead, *see* MISCELLANY (A) of the wits; sel. pieces by W. K. &c., 1920.
King (William Joseph Harding).
Mysteries of the Libyan desert. 8°. 1925
***Kingdomes** (The) briefe ans. to the late declar. of Hse. of Commons, Feb. 11, 1647, 1648, *see* PARL.: ANON. WORKS.
King-Hall (*Lady***).** What the Blounts did. s8°. [1922]
King-Hall (*Miss* **Magdalen)** [*ps.* A. B. KERR; CLEONE KNOX].
*The diary of a young lady of fashion, 1764–65. By Cleone Knox. Ed. by h. kinsman, A. B. Kerr. [6th impr.] s8°. [1925]
I think I remember: random recoll. of Sir Wickham Woolicomb. s8°. [1927]
King-Hall (W. Stephen R.) [*ps.* ETIENNE].
The uncharted sea. s8°. 1926
Western civilisation & the Far East. 8°. [1924]
Kinglake (Alex. William). Eothen. n. ed. s8°. 1891
,, ,, ...n. ed. s8°. 1896
King's College, *London, see* MATTHEWS (W. R.), *ed.* K.' Coll. lect. on immortality, 1920.
King's (The) Royal Rifle Corps chronicle. Ed. Lt.-Col. R. Byron. 1914–18 [5v. 1915 *wanting*]. 8°. Winchester. 1915–19
Kingsford (*Mrs.* **Anna),** *form. Bonus; wife of A. G. Kingsford.*
The perfect way in diet. 2nd ed. s8°. 1885
Kingsford (Charles Lethbridge). Add. material for the hist. of the Grey Friars, London, *see* COLLECTANEA FRANCISCANA, v2, 1922.

Kingsford (Charles Lethbridge) [*continued*].
Early hist. of Piccadilly, Leicester Sq., Soho &c. Based on plan drawn in 1585. 8°. C. 1925
Prejudice & promise in 15th cent. England. 8°. O. 1925
Story of the Royal Warwickshire Regiment (formerly the 6th Foot). 8°. [1921]
see LONDON TOPOG. SOC. Drawings of buildings in area descr. in " The early hist. of Piccadilly &c., by C. L. K.," 1926.
,, STONOR, *Fam. of.* Stonor letters &c., 1290–1483, 2v, 1919 ; suppl. (1314–1482), 1923.

Kingsford (Hugh Sadler).
Seals. [*b. w.* Cunningham (W.) Mon., 1920]. s8°. 1920

Kingsford (S. M.)
Psychical research for the plain man. s8°. 1920

Kingsley (Charles).
C. K., h. letters & memories of h. life. Ed. by h. wife. s8°. 1890
The good news of God : sermons. [Works, v24]. 8°. 1885
Poems. s8°. 1889
Two years ago. s8°. 1886
The water-babies. s8°. 1891
Westward Ho ! s8°. 1885
,, ,, ... s8°. 1893

Kingsley (Rose Georgina).
Eversley gardens & others. 8°. 1907

Kingsmill (Joseph). British rule & Brit. Christianity in India. 8°. 1859

Kingston (*The duchess of*), *1720–88* [*born* ELIZ. CHUDLEIGH ; †HERVEY (ELIZ.), *countess of Bristol, calling herself d. of K.*]
Authentic detail of particulars rel. to the late D. of K. 8°. 1788
Trial of the Duchess of Kingston. Ed. L. Melville. [Notable Brit. trials]. 8°. E. [1927]

Kingston (Charles).
Dramatic days at the Old Bailey. 8°. [1923]
Famous judges & famous trials. 8°. [1923]
A gallery of rogues. 8°. [1924]
Rogues & adventuresses. 8°. [1928]

Kingston-upon-Hull. *Further obs. on the improvements in the maintenance of the poor in K.-upon-H. [*b. w.* Thompson (T.) Tithes indef., 3rd ed., 1796]. 8°. Hull. 1801

Kingsway. Opening of K. & Aldwych, 1905, *see* LONDON COUNTY COUNCIL.

Kinnaird (Arthur Fitzgerald Kinnaird, *10th baron*).
In memoriam A. F., 10th Lord K. [P601]. s8°. *n.p.* [1887]

Kinnoul (William Hay, *3rd earl of*). Note of letters taken out of trunk that came to Dumbeath, w. letters f. the Earl of Kinnoul &c., 1649, *see* MAIDMENT (J.), *ed.* Hist. fragm. rel. of Scot. affairs, p2, 1833.

Kinross (John), *architect.* Details f. Ital. buildings chiefly Renaissance. la. fol. E. 1882

Kinsky (*Graf* **Stefan**). Der Congress v. Soissons ; nach &c. d. Berichten d. Kaiserl. Botschafters S. K., 2B, *see* FONTES RERUM AUSTRIAC., B32, 38, 1871–76.

Kipling (Rudyard).
Address, July 7, 1926, *see* ROY. SOC. OF LIT. Essays &c., n.s., v6, 1926.
The art of fiction. [P2847]. 8°. 1926
A choice of songs f. the verse of R. K. s8°. [1925]
The day's work. [repr.] s8°. 1918
Debits & credits. 8°. 1926
,, ,, ...[repr.] 8°. 1926
Le don de William, *see* ŒUVRES libres, No. 47, 1925.
The Irish Guards in the Great War. Ed. & comp. f. th. diaries & papers by R. K. [repr.] 2v. 8°. 1923
The jungle book. [repr.] s8°. 1922
Kim. [repr.] 8°. 1920
Land & sea tales for Scouts & Guides. 8°. 1923
Letters of travel (1892–1913). 8°. 1920
The light that failed. [repr.] s8°. 1920
The phantom 'rickshaw, 1892, *see* Under the deodars, *below.*
Puck of Pook's Hill. [repr.] 8°. 1920
Rewards & fairies. [repr.] 8°. 1919
Soldiers three—The story of the Gadsbys—In black & white. [repr.] 8°. 1920
Le taureau qui pensait, *see* Œuvres libres, 84, 1928.
Twenty poems. s8°. [1918]
Under the deodars. [Wheeler's Ind. Rly. Lib. No. 4]. 8°. Allahabad [London]. *n.d.* [1888]
Under the deodars—The phantom 'rickshaw—Wee Willie Winkie & o. s. s8°. 1892
Verse. Inclusive ed., 1885–1918. 8°. [1922]
,, Inclusive ed., 1885–1926. 8°. [1927]
Wee Willie Winkie, 1892, *see* Under the deodars, *above.*
see CHEVRILLON (A.) 3 ét. de litt. angl. ; La poésie de R. K. &c., 1921 ; tr., 1923.
,, MARTINDELL (E. W.) Bibliog. of works of R. K., 1881–1921, 1922.
,, NOAILLES (*ctsse.* M. DE). A R. K. [*poem*], 1921.
,, SAINT ANDREWS. 2 poems by R. K. &c., 1926.
,, SERRA (R.) Scritti ined., 1923.

Kipling (Rudyard) & C. Graves. Q. Horati Flacci Carminum librum quintum a R. Kipling & C. Graves angl. redditum, & var. notis &c. ed. A. D. Godley. ed. altera. O. 1920

Kipling (Thomas), *see* BIBLE : NEW TEST. (GREEK). Codex Th. Bezae ; ed. K., 2p, 1793.

Kipp (Friedrich).
Silvester v. Schaumberg, d. Freund Luthers. 8°. L. 1911

Kipping (Robert).
Masting, mast-making, & rigging of ships. 14th ed. s8°. 1877

Kipshidze (Ios. Alekseevich). Дополн. свѣдѣнія о чанскомъ языкѣ, *see* MARR (N. YA.), *ed.* Матер. по яфет. яз., 3, 1911.

Kirakos, *of Gandsak* [CYRIAQUE]. [Hist. of Armenia (–1264). *In Armenian.* Ed. G. Hovhannisean Erevanetzi. P2815]. s8°. i Moskova. 1858

Király (János). Magyar alkotmány-és jogtörténet. kl. 8°. 1908

Kirby (William), *rector of Barham,* **& W. Spence.**
Intr. to entomology. 5th ed. 4v. 8°. 1828

Kirby (William), *of Niagara, Ont.,* *see* RIDDELL (W. R.) W. K. [poems, w. biog., apprec. &c.], 1923.

Kirby (William Forsell).
Brit. butterflies, moths & beetles. 7th ed. s8°. 1910

Kirch (Hermann Joseph). Die Fugger u. d. schmalkald. Krieg, *see* JANSEN (M.), H. GRAUERT &c. St. z. Fugger-Gesch., H5, 1915.

Kircheisen (Friedrich Max). Bibliog. du temps de Napoléon ; comprenant l'hist. des Etats-Unis. t2, pl. 8°. 1912
Napoleon I, s. Leben u. s. Zeit. B4, 5. 8°. München. 1922–25

Kircheisen (Gertrude) [*Frau* G. ARETZ].
Katharina II. s8°. München. 1919
Napoleon & h. women friends. Tr. E. & C. Paul. 8°. [1927]

Kirchenampt. Teutsch Kirchēampt &c., 1525, 1848, *see* STRASSBURG.

Kirchengesang. Kirchengesanng Teutsch u. Lat. &c., 1560 ; 1570, *see* WOLFGANG, *Count Palatine.* Kirchenordnung, 1560 ; 1570.

Kirchen-Gesangbuch, *see* GESANGBUCH.

Kirchengesänge.
K. mit Orgelbegleitung. 2H. *b. in 1v.* fol. Prag. 1832–33
*Kirchengeseng, darinnen die Heubtartickel des Christl. glaubens kurtz verfasset u. ausgeleget sind. [Evangel. Kirchen in Behemen u. Merhern. *Tr. f. Bohemian by M. Tham, Joh. Geletzky & P. Herbertus. Foll. by* Geistliche Lieder, nach ordnung d. Jahrzeit, *w. sep. tp. & pagin. Tp. of* Kirchengeseng *in facs. Binding dated 1573*]. s4°. *n.p.* 1566
,, ,, [*a. ed.*] Kirchengesänge &c. s4°. *n.p.* 1606

***Kirchenhistoria,** 1560, 1855, *see* WIGAND (J.) & M. JUDEX.

Kirchenlatein Wbch., 1926, *see* SLEUMER (A.), *ed.*

Kirchen-Ordnung [KIRCHENORDNUNG; KIRCHEN-ORDNUNGEN].
*Corpus juris Evang. eccl., oder Samml. evang.-Luther. u. reform. K.-O. &c., 1737–8, *see* CORPUS.
*K.-O. im Churfurstenthum zu Brandenburg &c., 1533 ; 1540 ; 1543, *see* BRANDENBURG.
K.-O. u. Glaubens-Bekäntniss &c., *see* FRANCE. La discipline eccl., 1711.
K., wie die unter d. Christl. König Edward VI. in Londen, i. d. niderlend. Gemeine Christi, geordnet &c. worden. Durch J. v. Lasco in Lat. beschr. ; aber durch M. Micronium in e. kurtze Sum̃ verf. u. verdeut. s8°. Heidelberg. 1565
K. wie es inn d. Herrn Wolffgangs Furstenthumben u. Landen gehalten worden, 1570, *see* WOLFGANG, *Count Palatine.*
K. wie es mit d. Christenl. Leer &c., 1560, *see* WOLFGANG, *Count Palatine.*
K., wie es mit d. Christl. Lehre &c. gehalten wirdt, 1569, *see* FREDERICK III, *Elector Palatinate.*
*K.-O. d. Christl. reform. Gemeinden in Jülich, Cleve, Berge u. Marck ; wie auch Religions-Vergleiche [*sep. tp. & pagin.*] u. Neben-Recessen &c. zw. Friederich Wilhelmen v. Brandenburg u. Philipp Wilhelmen, Pfaltzgr. bey Rhein &c. [*sep. tp. & pagin.*] s4°. Duisburg a. R. 1754
*O. d. evang. Kirchen in Franckreich &c., 1563, *see* ORDNUNG.

Kircher (Athanasius), *Jesuit.* Lingua Ægyptiaca restituta : op. tripart. una cum suppl. &c. 4°. Romae. 1643
With 2nd *engrav. tp. dated* 1644.
Prodromus Coptus, sive Aegyptiacus &c. s4°. Romae. 1636

Kircher (Rudolf). Engländer. 8°. Fr. a. M. 1926
Fair play : Sport, Spiel u. Geist in England. 8°. Fr. am M. 1927
Powers & pillars : port. of Brit. personalities. Tr. by C. Vesey of " Engländer " (w. rev. & add.) 8° [1928]

Kirchhofer (Melchior).
The life of Guillaume Farel. [Tr.] s8°. 1837

Kirchhoff (Albrecht). Die Anfänge kirchl. Toleranz in Sachsen: August der Starke u. die Reformirten. 2 Vorträge. 8°. L. 1872
Gesch. d. reform. Gemeinde in Leipzig, 1700–25. 8°. L. 1874

Kirchlich-polit. (Die) Gesetzgebung [Preussen] d. Jahre 1873–75. Hrsg. u. erl. v. e. Mitgliede d. H. d. Abgeordneten. s8°. Berlin. 1875

Kirchmaier (Georg Caspar). De rebus moribusque Judaeorum, 1676, *see* SCHLÄGER (C. J.) Diss. fasc. 1, 1742.
Opuscula 6 rariss. de Latinitate Digestorum & Institutionum Justiniani. Coll. G. S. Madihn. s8°. Halae. 1772

Kirchmaier (Georg Wilhelm). Oratio de M. Lutheri oraculo: Bellum Smalcaldicum &c. [P2627]. s4°. Wittebergæ. 1755

Kirchmeyer (Thomas) [*ps.* T. NAOGEORGUS], *see* NAOGEORGUS (T.)

Kirchner (Timotheus). Thesaurus explic. omnium articul. &c. Catholicae, orthodoxae &c. doct. Christ. quae huc aetate controversa sunt. Ex M. Lutheri operibus coll. &c. par T. K. fol. Francofurti ad Moenum. 1566
see ANHALT. Das die 42 Anhalt. Argument wider der Ubiquisten Trewme noch fest stehen, Verantw. uff K. &c., 1584.
„ WIGAND (J.), T. HESHUSIUS & T. K. Erinnerung &c., 1572.
——, **N. Selneccer & M. Chemnitz.** Apologia oder Verantwortung d. christl. Concordien Buchs. fol. Heydelberg. 1583

Kirchoff (Hermann), *see* STENZEL (A.) Seekriegsgesch. in i. wichtigsten Abschnitten &c., T6, 1919–20, von H. K., 1921.

Kirchwey (Freda), *ed.* Our changing morality: a symposium. [By B. Russell *& others*]. 8°. 1925

Kireev (A.) Краткое изложеніе славянофильск. ученія. [P2445]. s8°. С.-П. 1896

Kireevsky (Ivan Vasilevich), *see* GERSHENSON (M. O.) Историч. записки (И. В. К., &c.), 1923.

Kirk of Scotland, *see* CHURCH OF SCOTLAND.

Kirk (Arthur).
Intr. to the hist. study of New High German. s8°. M'ter. 1923

Kirk (John), *Congregational minister.* Orig. titles of hymns sung in Wesleyan-Meth. congreg. & names of a. s8°. 1854

Kirk (*Lt.-Col.* John William Carnegie).
A Brit. garden flora. 8°. 1927

Kirk (Kenneth Escott). Conscience & its problems. 8°. 1927
Ignorance, faith & conformity. 8°. 1925
Some principles of moral theology &c. 8°. 1920

Kirk (William F.) Productivity costs in common-brick industry, *see* UNITED STATES: LABOR. Bull. 356, 1924.

Kirkaldy (Adam Willis).
Brit. shipping, its hist. &c. 2nd impr. s8°. 1919
Economics & syndicalism. s8°. C. 1914
Wealth, its production &c. 8°. [1920]
see GIBSON (A. H.) Brit. finance dur. & after the War, 1914–21; ed. A. W. Kirkaldy, 1921.
see GRIER (*Miss* L.) & *Miss* A. ASHLEY. Brit. labour &c., p2, ed. by A. W. K., 1921.
„ MACLEOD (*Sir* C. C.) & A. W. K. Trade, commerce &c. of the Empire, 1924.

Kirkby (John). *The capacity & extent of the human understanding exempl. in case of Automathes. s8°. 1745

Kirkconnel (Watson).
Internat. aspects of unemployment. 8°. [1923]

Kirkcudbright. *Minute bk. kept by the War committee of the Covenanters in the stewartry of K., 1640–41. 8°. Kirkcudbright. 1804

Kirkes (William Senhouse). Handbook of physiology. *For later ed. see* Halliburton (W. D.)

Kirkland (Edward Chase).
The Peacemakers of 1864. 8°. N.Y. 1927

Kirklington. The parish registers of K., Co. of York, 1568–1812. Transcr. by H. B. McCall. [Yorks. Parish Reg. Soc., 35]. *p.p.* 8°. [Leeds]. 1909

Kirkman (Frederick Bernulf Beevor) & H. G. Hutchinson. Brit. sporting birds. [*By var. wr.*] Ed. F. B. K. & H. G. H. 4°. 1924

Kirkpatrick (James), *of Belfast.* *An hist. essay upon the loyalty of Presbyterians in Gt. Brit. & Ir. f. Reformation to 1713. 3p *in* 1v. s4°. 1713

Kirkpatrick (John), *Treasurer of the Great Hospital, Norwich.* Streets & lanes of Norwich. Pr. f. MS. coll. of A. Norris. Ed. W. Hudson. Added, Early maps, w. intr. by W. T. Bensly. [Norfolk & Norwich Arch. Soc.] fol. Norwich. 1889

Kirkpatrick (*Col.* William). A vocab. Persian, Arabic, & Eng. Being p7 of the New Hindui gram. & dict. 4°. 1785

Kirkstall, *abbey.* Coucher book of the Cistercian abbey of K., Co. of York. Ed. W. T. Lancaster & W. P. Baildon. [Thoresby Soc., 8]. 8°. Leeds. 1904
*Hist. of K. Abbey, w. engr. by W. Mulready &c., 1847, *see* MULREADY (W.)

Kirkwood (*Rev.* J.) Troon & Dundonald, w. th. surroundings. s8°. Kilmarnock. 1875
„ „ 2nd ed., rev. & extended. s8°. Kilmarnock. 1876

Kirkwood (Kenneth P.), *see* TOYNBEE (A. J.) & K. P. K. Turkey, 1926.

Kirn (Paul). Friedrich d. Wiese u. d. Kirche. 8°. L. 1926

Kirnbauer v. Erzstätt (Joh. E.) Niederösterr. Adel, Abthlg. 1, A–R; bearbt. v. J. E. K. v. E., *see* SIBMACHER (J.), *ed.* Wappenbuch, B4iv, 1901.

Kirsch (Georg Wilhelm). Chrestomathia Syriaca. Cum Lexico Syriaco &c. [*w. sep. tp. & pagin.*] s8°. Hofae. 1789

Kirste (Johann). Orabazes, 1917, *see* KAISERL. AKAD. D. WISS. ZU WIEN. Sitzungsber., B182, 1918.

Kirwan (Patrick). The dawn of English drama. 8°. 1920

Kirwan (Thomas).
see BURROWES (P.) Speeches on trials of E. Sheridan & K., under the Convention Act &c., 1812.
„ BUSHE (C. K.) Speeches of B. in cases of E. Sheridan & K., committed for violat. of Convent. Act, 1812.

Kis (Stephanus), *Szegedinus.* Assertio vera de Trinitate contra quorundam deliramenta quæ ex Serueti &c. opinionibus &c. publ. sunt. s8°. Genevæ. 1573
Tabulae analyt., quibus exemplar illud san. sermonum de fide &c. [*b. w. h.* Theologiae sincerae loci &c., 1585]. fol. Schaphusiae. 1592
Theologiae sincerae loci communes de Deo et homine. fol. Basileae. 1585

Kiselev (*Graf* Pavel Dmitrievich), *see* ZABLOTSKY-DESYATOVSKY (A. P.) Графъ П. Д. К. и его время, 4т, 1882.

***Kisses:** fragm. &c. on the kiss (1803), 1884, *see* SECUNDUS (J.)

Kisskalt (Wilhelm). Privatversicherung u. deut. Zahlungsbilanz, *see* MEERWARTH (R.), W. K. &c. Probleme, 1924.

Kist (Nicolaas Christiaan). Disput. inaug. de commut. quam Constantino M. auctore, societas subiit Christiana. 8°. Trajecti ad Rhenum. [1818]

Kistemaeckers (Henry). L'exilée: pièce. [P2730]. la8°. 1913

Kistemaker (Johann Hyacinth). Comm. de nova exegesi praecipue Vet. Test. ex collat. scr. Graec. & Rom. s8°. Monasterii. 1806

Kit, *Kinde, of Kingstone.* *Westward for smelts. Ed. J. O. Halliwell. [Percy Soc., 78. *a. c. b. w.* Gotham. Merry tales &c., 1840]. s8°. 1848

Kit-Cat Club. The Kit-Cat Club. [Portraits] f. orig. paintings of Sir G. Kneller by Mr. Faber. fol. [1735]

Kitchener (Horatio Herbert Kitchener, *1st viscount*).
see ARTHUR (*Sir* G.) Life of Ld. K., 3v, 1920.
„ CONDER (C. R.) & H. H. K. Map of W. Palestine, spec. ed., by T. Saunders, 1882.
„ ESHER (R. B. B., *2nd visct.*) The tragedy of Lord K., 1921.
„ GERMAINS (V. W.) The truth about K., 1925.

Kitchin (Finlay Lorimer), *see* LAMPLUGH (G. W.) & F. L. K. On the mesozoic rocks in coal explorat. in Kent, 1911.
see LAMPLUGH (G. W.), F. L. K. &c. Concealed mesozoic rocks in Kent, 1923.

Kitchin (George William), *dean of Winchester.*
Winchester. [Hist. towns]. 4th ed. s8°. 1893

Kitchin (James George).
The Bible student in the Brit. Museum. s8°. 1893

Kitchiner (William). The cook's oracle. n. ed. s8°. 1843

Kite (Elizabeth S.) Beaumarchais & the War of Amer. Independence. Foreword by J. M. Beck. 2v. s8°. Boston [U.S. 1918]

Kitson (Arthur).
Money problems. With a crit. by H. Withers. s8°. 1920

Kitson (Charles Herbert).
Evolution of harmony. 2nd ed. 8°. O. 1924

Kittel (Abraham). Disput. de ant. funerarum ritu. Sub praes. Æ. Strauchii. ed. 3ª. [P431]. s4°. *n.p.* 1666

Kittel (Gerhard). Sifre zu Deuteronomium. L. 1. 8°. St. [1922]

Kittel (Rudolf). Gesch. d. Volkes Israel. B3, Die Zeit d. Wegführ. nach Babel u. d. Aufricht. d. neu. Gemeinde, H1. 8°. St. 1927
Gestalten u. Gedanken in Israel. 8°. L. [1925]

Kitto (Franklin Hugo). The Peace River Country, Canada. [P2872]. 8°. Ottawa. 1927

Kitto (John). The pictorial hist. of Palestine &c. v1. Bibl. hist. la8°. 1844
see JOURNAL OF SACRED LIT., 1848–58.

Kittredge (George Lyman). Arthur & Gorlagon [*Lat. text, w. 4 vers. of the Werewolf's tale, & notes &c.*], *see* HARVARD UNIV. St. &c. in philol., v8, 1903.
The authorship of the Eng. Romaunt of the Rose, *see* HARVARD UNIV. St. &c. in philol., v1, 1892.

Kiupelian (Ambrosios) [QIUPHELEAN]. [Turkish-Armenian-French dict. *In Armenian*]. s8°. i Vienna. 1883

Kiyoshi Nakarai, *see* NAKARAI (KIYOSHI).

Kiyotsugu (Kwan-ami). Sotoba-Komachi, *see* PERI (N.) Cinq No; tr., 1921.

Kizevetter (Aleksandr Aleksandrovich). Девятнадцатый вѣкъ въ ист. Россіи. [P2445]. s8°. Ростовъ-на-Дону. [1905]
Русское общество въ 18ᴹᵀ ст. 2ᵉ изд. [P2445]. s8°. Ростовъ-на-Дону [1905]

Kjær (A.) Festskrift tilegnet Førstebibliothekar A. Kjaer av Venner, 26. Sept. 1924 [*by var. a.*] 8°. 1924

Kjaer (S.) Hygienic cond. in printing trades, *see* UNITED STATES: LABOR. Bull. 392, 1925.

Kjeldeskriftfondet, *see* GATHORNE-HARDY (G. M.) Bodø-saken; Brit. diplom. corresp. (K.), 1926.

Kjellberg (Anders Lennart). St. zu d. ant. Dacheindeckungen, *see* KUNG. HUM. VET.-SAMF. I UPPSALA. Skr., B24, 1927.

Klaczko (Julian). Rome & the Renaissance: the pontificate of Julius II. Auth. tr. by J. Dennie. 8°. N.Y. 1926

Klaeber (Frederick), *see* BEOWULF. B. & The fight at Finnsburg; ed., w. intr. &c. by F. K., 1922.

Klaiber (Christoph Benjamin). Diss. de damnatione improborum aeterna. Resp. Th. F. Fronmueller. s4°. Tubingae. [1824]

Klaiber (Theodor). Die deut. Selbstbiographie. 8°. St. 1921

Klapheck (Richard), *see* KERCKERINCK ZUR BORG (E., *Frhr.* v.) & R. K. Alt-Westfalen, 1912.

Klapka (Geörgy), *1820–92*. Emlékeimböl. Függelékül: Gróf Teleki László levelei. 8°. 1886

Klaproth (Heinrich Julius v.) Aperçu des entreprises des Mongols en Géorgie & en Arménie dans le 13ᵉ siècle, *see* SOCIÉTÉ ASIAT. Nouv. journ., t12, 1833.
Asia polyglotta. [*Foll. by* Leben d. Budd'a, nach mongol. Nachr. *paged 121–44*]. 4°. Paris. 1823
„ „ Sprachatlas. fol. Paris. 1823
Chrestomathie Mandchou ou recueil de textes Mandchou. 8°. 1828
Mém. sur l'intr. & l'usage des caractères chinois au Japon &c. Extr. du Nouv. journal asiatique. [P2561]. 8°. 1829
Vocab. & gramm. de la langue géorgienne. Publ. par la Soc. Asiat. p1, Vocab. géorg.-fr. & fr.-géorg. 8°. 1827
see HEDIN (S.) South. Tibet: researches, 1906–8, v9iv, Eine chin. Beschr. v. Tibet, v. J. K., nach Amiot's Übers. bearb., 1922.
„ TIMKOVSKI (G.) Voyage à Péking; tr. publ. avec corr. (Aperçu statist. &c.) par K., 1827.
„ Yü. Inschrift des Yü; übers. u. erkl. v. J. v. K., 1811.

Klarwill (Victor v.), *ed.*, *see* FUGGER, *Fam. of.* F.-Zeitungen, 1568–1605, 1923; tr., 2s, 1924–26.

Klary (C.) Guide de l'amateur photographe. s8°. [1888]

***Klassenkampf (Der)** des Proletariats, 1911, *see* HELPHAND (A.)

Klasson (V. N.), *ed.* Депутаты 1ᴴ думы подъ судомъ. Дѣло по обвиненію потомственныхъ дворянъ С. Муромцева, кн. П. Долгорукова, Н. Гредескула, кн. Д. Шаховскаго &c. 8°. С.-П. [1908 ?]

Klatt (B.), *see* MURET (E.) & D. H. SANDERS. Encyclop. Eng.-Germ. & Germ.-Eng. dict., p1, Eng.-Germ. by K., 1913.

Klausner (Joseph). Jesus of Nazareth. His life, times &c. Tr. H. Danby. 8°. 1925

Klaxon, *ps.* Heather mixture. s8°. E. 1922

Klee (Kaspar), *see* BECK (H.) K. K. v. Gerolzhofen, 1901.

Kleemann (Samuel). Die Lorenzianer. 8°. 1926

Klein (*le gén.* ——), *see* HIRSCHAUER (*le gén.* A. E.) & K. Paris en état de défense, 1927.

Klein (Armin). Posture clinics [*& exercises*], *see* UNITED STATES: LAB. Children's Bur., Publ. 164, 165, 1926.

Klein (*l'abbé* **Félix**). Madeleine Sémer, convertie & mystique, 1874–1921. 11ᵉ éd. rev. 8°. 1923

Klein (Franz), *see* MISES (L.) & F. K. Geldtheoret. u. geldrechtl. Seite d. Stabilisierungsproblems, 1923.

Klein (Herman). Musicians & mummers. la8°. [1925]
The reign of Patti. 8°. [1920]

Klein (Johann). De August. Confess. oratio. Ed. a J. E. Kappio. [P2642]. s4°. Lipsiae. 1730

Klein (Julius). The Mesta: Span. econ. hist., 1273–1836. [Harvard Econ. St., 21]. 8°. Cambridge [U.S.] 1920

Klein (Philip).
Prison methods in N.Y. State. 8°. N.Y., *Columbia Univ.* 1920

Klein (Samuel). Tentamen juris eccl. Evang. August. conf. addictorum in Hungaria. 8°. Lipsiae. 1840

Klein (Sydney T.) The way of attainment. 8°. 1924

Kleinasien. Reisen im südwestl. K., B2, *see* PETERSEN (E.) & F. v. LUSCHAN. Reisen in Lykien Milyas &c., 1889.

Kleine Texte für theolog. u. philol. Vorlesungen u. Übungen. Hrsg. H. Lietzmann. T129–158. s8°. Bonn. 1914–1927
Aufhauser (J. B.) Buddha u. Jesus in i. Paralleltext.; v. J. B. A., 1926. [157.]
Bilabel (F.) Klein. Historikerfragm. auf Papyrus. [149.]
Bonwetsch (G. N.), *ed.* Texte z. Gesch. d. Montanismus, 1914. [129.]
Callimachus. Fragmenta nuper reperta ed. R. Pfeiffer. [145.]
Carmina Burana: deut. Lieder d. C. B.; hrsg. F. Lüers. [148.]
Celsus, *the philosopher.* Ἀληθὴς λόγος; excuss. O. Glöckner, 1924. [151.]
Cratippus, *the historian.* Cl. Hellenicorum fragm. Oxyrhynchia ed. J. H. Lipsius, 1916. [138.]
Epistola. Epistula Apostolorum; hrsg. v. H. Duensing. [152.]
Fudali. Muhammedan. Glaubenslehre: d. Katechismen d. F. u. d. Sanusi; übers. &c. M. Horten, 1916. [139.]
Gorgias, *of Leontium.* G. Helena; rec. O. Immisch, 1927. [158.]
Götze (Alb.) Ausgew. hethit. Texte. [153.]
Götze (Alf.) Proben hoch- u. niederdeutscher Mundarten, 1922. [146.]
Günter (H.) Die röm. Krönungseide d. deut. Kaiser, 1915. [132.]
Hiller v. Gärtringen (F. W., *Frhr.*) Hist. griech. Epigramme. [156.]
Jäger u. Prinzessin: e. neuarab. Märchen aus Jerusalem; [hrsg.] E. Littmann. [150.]
Lindische Tempelchronik (Die); neu bearbt. v. C. Blinkenberg, 1915. [131.]
Liturgische Texte. T10, 11.
10, Einführung in d. Röm. Brevier; v. H. Lietzmann. [141.]
11, Taufe u. Firmung nach d. Röm. Missale, Rituale u. Pontificale; hrsg. v. I. Herwegen. [144.]
Lokotsch (C.) Türk. Volkstümliche u. Volkspoesie, mit Anm. versehen v. K. L., 1917. [140.]
Luther (M.) 95 Thesen nebst d. Sermon v. Ablass u. Gnade &c., 1917. [142.]
Octavia, *wife of Nero, emp. of Rome.* Octavia praetexta, cum elementis comm. ed. C. Hosius. [147.]
Orpheus. Lamellae aureae Orphicae; ed. comm. instr. A. Olivieri, 1915. [133.]
Riess (L.), *ed.* Engl. Verfassungsurkunden 12–13. Jhdts. [155.]
Schröder (O.) Novae comoediae fragm., 1915. [135.]
Seneca (L. A.) D. Claudii apotheosis; ed. O. Rossbach. [154.]
Slotty (F.) Vulgärlatein. Übungsbuch, 1918. [143.]
Tosefta. Der Tosephtatraktat roš haššana, mit Bemerkungen v. P. Fiebig, 1914. [130.]
Ungnad (A.) Türk. Nachrichten aus Zeitungen zusamm. mit Anmerkungen, 1916. [136.]
Virgilius Maro (P.) Bucolica; ed. C. Hosius, 1915. [134.]
Wilamowitz-Möllendorff (U. v.), *ed.* Vitae Homeri et Hesiodi &c., 1916. [137.]

Kleine (Engbert Gerard Frederik Hendrik Smit), *see* VLUCHTIG (P.), *ps.*

Kleinmichel (Marie, *Countess*), *wife of Count Nicholas Kleinmichel.* Memories of a shipwrecked world. Tr. V. Le Grand. 8°. [1923]
Souv. d'un monde englouti. [3ᵉ éd.] s8°. [1927]

Kleinpaul (Rudolf).
Das Fremdwort im Deutschen. 3ᵉ verb. A. s8°. L. 1910

Kleinschmidt (Beda), *O.F.M.*
Die Basilika San Francesco in Assisi.
2B. (2, Die Wand-Malereien; hrsg. R. Boving). fol. 1915–26

Kleintitschen (P. August). Mythen u. Erzählungen e. Melanesierstammes aus Paparatava, Neupommern, Südsee. Gesamm., mit Einl. &c. v. P. A. K. [Anthropos-Bibl., B2iv]. 8°. Mödling bei Wien. [1924]

Kleinwächter (Friedrich F. G.) Der Untergang d. oesterreich.-ungar. Monarchie. 8°. L. 1920

Kleiser (Grenville). Similes & th. use. 8°. N.Y. 1925

Kleist (Heinrich von). Germania an ihre Kinder (1813 ?, *facs.*), *see* FREYTAG (G.) Bilder, B5, 1925.
see BERTRAM (E.) H. v. K.: Rede, 1925.
„ CASSIRER (E.) Idee u. Gestalt: K. &c., 2. A., 1924.

Klemm (Johann Christian). Concilii a Benedicto XIII in Laterano hab. examen, praes. J. C. K., exponent C. F. Cuhorst & J. G. Waiblinger. 2p [p2, resp. J. B. Erhardo]. [P436]. s4°. Tubingae. [1729]–30

Klener (Rudolph Ernest), *see* STREITWOLF (F. G.) & R. E. KLENER. Libri symbolici eccl. catholicae, 2t, 1838; 1848.

Klenk (Konraad von). Hist. verhael, of beschr. van de voyagie gedaen onder de suite van K. aan Zijne Majesteyt van Moscovien. s4°. Amsterdam. 1677

Kleutgen (Joseph), *Jesuit.* Instit. theol. in usum scholarum. v1, De ipso Deo. [*No more publ.*] 8°. Regensburg. 1881

Klibanski (Herm. O.) Die Gesetzgebung d. Bolschewiki. Übers. u. bearb. v. H. K. 8°. L. 1920

Klickmann (Flora), *wife of E. Henderson-Smith.*
The flower-patch among the hills. [repr.] s8°. [1924]
The home art bk. of fancy stitchery. Ed. F. K. 5th imp. 8°. [1913 ?]

Klinckowström (Axel).
Bland vulkaner & fågelberg, reseminnen f. Island & Färöarna. 2[v]. la8°. Stockholm. 1911
Damen med djävulshuvudena. s8°. [1921]
Dollarfurstinnans jakt. s8°. [1922]
Filmstjärnans arv. s8°. [1922]
Gift-skatten. Äventyrsroman. s8°. [1921]
Den hemlighetsfulla fotbollen. s8°. [1920]
Olof Trätälja. Sorgespel. 8°. [1908]

Klinckowström (Carl, *Graf* **v.),** *see* GULAT-WELLENBURG (W. v.), C. v. K. &c. Physikal. Mediumismus, 1925.

Kling (Christian Friedrich). Descr. Summae theolog. T. Aquinatis succincta. [*Progr.*] s4°. Bonnae. 1846

Klinger (Friedrich Maximilian v.) Faustus: h. life &c.; tr., *see* BORROW (G.) Wks., v15, 1924.

Klinger (Max), *see* AVENARIUS (F.) M. K. als Poet, mit e. Briefe &c., 1919.

Klingner (Fritz). De Boethii Consol. philos., *see* KIESSLING (A.) & U. v. WILAMOWITZ-MÖLLENDORFF. Philolog. Unters., H27, 1921.

Klingsor (Tristan), *ps., see* LECLERE (T.)

Klinkenborg (Melle), *see* JOACHIM (E.) & M. K. Familien-Gesch. d. gräfl. Finck v. Finckensteinschen Geschlechts, 1920–21.

Klinkmüller (Walter). Ein deut. Offizier im revolut. Russland: m. Fluchtabenteuer. s8°. 1918

Klio: Beiträge z. alten Geschichte. Hrsg. v. C. F. Lehmann-Haupt u. E. Kornemann. B16–21. la8°. L. 1920–27
„ „ ....Beihefte. 14–19. 8°. L. 1923–26
see AUGUSTUS (C. J. C. O.), *emp.* Mon. Antioch.; hrsg. &c. W. M. Ramsay, 1927. [19.]
„ ENSSLIN (W.) Zur Geschichtschr. u. Weltanschauung d. Ammianus Marcellinus, 1923. [16.]
„ BISINGER (J.) Agrarstaat in Platos Gesetzen, 1925. [17.]
„ HEICHELHEIM (F.) Die auswärt. Bevölkerung im Ptolemäerreich, 1925. [18.]
„ LEHMANN-HARTLEBEN (C.) Die ant. Hafenanlagen d. Mittelmeeres, 1923. [14.]
„ SCHUR (W.) Die Orientpolitik d. Kaisers Nero, 1923. [15.]

Kloos (Willem). Verzen. 1. 3edr. 8°. A. 1917

Klose (Martin). Der Roman v. Claris u. Laris in s. Bezieh. z. altfr. Artusepik d. 12. u. 13. Jhdts. &c. [Zeitschr. f. rom. Phil., Beih. 63]. 8°. Halle a S. 1916

Klossowski (Erich).
Honoré Daumier. 2e verb. A. 4°. München. 1923

Klostermann (Erich) & W. Bauer. Die Evangelien, *see* LIETZMANN (H.), *ed.* Hbch. z. N.T., B2i, 1919.

Klosterneuburg. Urkundenbuch d. Stiftes K. bis z. Ende d. 14. Jhdt.; bearb. v. H. Zeibig, T2, *see* FONTES RERUM AUSTRIAC., B28, 1868.

Klotsche (Ernest Heinrich). The supernatural in Euripides, *see* NEBRASKA UNIV. Studies, v18, 1918.

Klüber (Johann Ludwig). Die ehel. Abstammung d. fürstl. Hauses Löwenstein-Wertheim v. d. Kurfürsten Friedrich d. Siegreichen v. d. Pfalz. Hrsg. J. Mülhens. 8°. Frankfurt a. M. 1837

Kluchevsky (Vasily Osigovich).
Добрые люди древней Руси. [P2392]. s8°. Москва. 1916
Значеніе преподобнаго Сергія для русскаго народа &c. [P2499]. s8°. Москва. 1915
Курсъ русской исторіи. ч5. 8°. П. 1921
Сборник статей. 1, 3. 8°. П. 1918
1, Опыты и исследования. 3, Отзывы и ответы.
Характеристика царя Ивана Грознаго. [*Extract f.* Курсъ Русской исторіи]. [P2392]. s8°. Москва. 1917
TRANSLATION.
Hist. of Russia. Tr. C. J. Hogarth. v4. 8°. 1926

Kluchnikov (Yu V.) [KLYUCHNIKOV].
На великомъ историч. перепутьи. 8°. Берлинъ. 1922
see SMENA VEKH. Смѣна Вѣхъ: сборникъ статей: Ю. В. К. &c., 1922.
—— **& A. Sabanin.** Международная политика новейш. времени в договорах, нотах и декларациях. 2ч. la8°. Москва. 1925–26

Kluck (*Gen.* **Alex. H. R. von).** Der Marsch auf Paris u. d. Marneschlacht 1914. 8°. 1920
The march on Paris & the battle of the Marne, 1914. 8°. 1920

Kluge (Friedrich). Angelsächs. Lesebuch zusammengestellt u. mit Glossar versehen v. F. K. 4e A. 8°. Halle. 1915

Kluge (Theodor). Materialien z. e. Lazischen Gramm., Dialektes v. Trapezunt. [Aus d. Nachr. d. K. Gesells. d. Wiss. zu Gött., 1913]. 8°. Gottingen. 1913

Klugkist (Wilhelm Schmidt-), *see* SCHMIDT-KLUGKIST (W.)

Klügling (Carl Friedrich Heinrich), *see* HARLESS (G. C.) Brevior notitia litt. Rom. [*foll. by* Additamenta, scr. K., 1819], 1803–19.

Klüpfel (Carl). Gesch. u. Beschr. d. Univ. Tübingen. 8°. Tübingen. 1849

Klutschak (Franz).
Der Führer durch Prag. 6e A. s8°. Prag. 1852

Klyuchnikov, *see* KLUCHNIKOV.

Klyuev (Nikolai A.) Ленин (*poetry*). s8°. Москва. 1924
Четвертый Рим. [P2269]. s8°. П. 1922

Kmet (Andrej), *1841–1908, see* MEDVECKÝ (K. A.) A. K., rím.-katolícky kňaz &c., 1913.

Kmety (Károly). A magyar közjog tankönyve. 3 javitott kiadás. 8°. 1905

***Knack** (A) to know a knave, 1594, *see* COLLIER (J. P.), *ed.* Five old plays, 1851.

Knackfuss (Hermann) & M. G. Zimmermann. Allgem. Kunstgesch. B1, 3. [1, 3e A.; 3, 2e A.] la8°. Bielefeld. 1910–14
1, Kunstgesch. d. Altertums u. d. Ma., v. M. G. Zimmermann.
3, Kunstgesch. d. Barock, Rokoko u. d. Neuzeit, v. M. G. Zimmermann *&* W. Gensel.

Knapp (Albert).
Evang. Gesangbuch. Hrsg. A. K. s8°. L. 1855

Knapp (Andrew) & W. Baldwin. The new Newgate calendar. 5v. [v3, 1810, pr. for Nuttall &c.] 8°. *Cundee. n.d.*–1810
„ „ ....6v. 8°. [1826?]

Knapp (Arthur William).
Cocoa & chocolate, th. hist. &c. 8°. 1920
Cocoa & chocolate industry: tree, bean, beverage. s8°. *Pitman.* [1923]

Knapp (Georg Christian). Narr. de Justo Jona conditaeque ab eo evangel. Halensis ecclesiae primordiis. 4°. Halis Sax. 1817

Knapp (Georg Friedrich). Staatliche Theorie d. Geldes. 3e A. 8°. München. 1921
State theory of money. Abridged ed., tr. H. M. Lucas & J. Bonar. 8°. 1924
see DÖRING (H.) Geldtheorien seit K., 1922.

Knapp (Jacob). Autobiography. Intr. essay, by R. Jeffery. s8°. N.Y. 1868

Knapp (Johann Georg), *see* FRANCKE (G. A.) Denkmal d. weil. Herrn G. A. Francken von J. G. K., 1770.

Knapski (Grzegorz) [CNAPIUS (GREGORIUS)]. Thesaurus Polonolatinogræcus, seu promptuarium linguae Latinæ et Graecæ. ed. 2a. [t1]. fol. Cracoviæ. 1643

Knauss (Robert).
Die deut., engl. u. französ. Kriegsfinanzierung. 8°. 1923

Knauth (Christian), *Pastor.* D. oberlausitzer Sorberwenden umständl. Kirchengesch. &c. 8°. Görlitz. 1767

Knauth (Oswald Whitman). The policy of the U.S. towards indust. monopoly. 8°. N.Y., *Columbia Univ.* 1913

Knauz (Nándor). Az országos tanács és országgyülések törtenete, 1445–52. 8°. 1859

Knebel (Johannes Wilhelm). Kaiser Friedrich II u. Honorius III (1220–27). Diss. s8°. Münster. 1905

Kneller (*Sir* **Godfrey),** *bart.*
see BAKER (C. H. C.) Lely & K., 1922.
„ KIT-CAT CLUB. [Portraits] f. paintings of Sir G. K. by Mr. Faber, 1735, *n.d.*

Knickerbocker (The), or New-York monthly magazine. v18–20 (July 1841–Dec. 1842), 48–54 (July 1856–Oct. 1859). 8°. N.Y. 1841–59

Knight (Alfred Ernest).
Hutchinson's pop. botany. 2v. la8°. [1912]
—— **& E. Step.**
The living plant in leaf, flower & fruit. la8°. *n.d.*

Knight (*Capt.* **C. W. R.)**
The bk. of the golden eagle. la8°. [1927]
Wild life in the tree tops. la8°. [1921]
Knight (Charles), *publisher.* *The working-man's companion. The results of machinery &c. [*Attrib. to Lord Brougham*]. s8°. 1831
Knight (Edward Frederick). Remin.: wanderings. 8°. 1923
Sailing. s8°. 1893
The Union-Castle & the War, 1914–19. la8°. 1920
Knight (Errol Lorne), *see* STEFÁNSSON (V.) The adv. of Wrangel Island; wr. by S. w. collab. of J. I. Knight upon diary of E. L. K., 1926.
Knight (Francis). Biog. of J. B. Knight, 1785–1859. 8°. [1908]
Knight (Francis A.) & L. M. Dutton.
Devonshire. s8°. C. 1910
Knight (George Alex. Frank). Nile & Jordan: archæol. & hist. inter-rel. betw. Egypt & Canaan to A.D. 70. la8°. 1921
Knight (*Mrs.* **Helen C.)**
Lady Huntington & her friends. s8°. N.Y. [1853]
Knight (Henrietta), *baroness Luxborough, see* LUXBOROUGH (H., *Lady*).
Knight (John Baverstock), *see* KNIGHT (F.) Biog. of J. B. K., 1785–1859, 1908.
Knight (John Irvine), *see* STEFÁNSSON (V.) The adv. of Wrangel Island; wr. by S. w. collab. of J. I. K., 1926.
Knight (Louie M.), *see* DUTTON (L. M.)
Knight (Melvin M.) Econ. hist. of Europe to end of Middle Ages. 8°. [1927]
Knight (William Angus), *prof. of Moral Phil. at St. Andrews.*
Studies in philosophy & lit. s8°. 1879
Knight (William Stanley Macbean). Life & works of H. Grotius. [Grotius Soc. Publs., No. 4]. 8°. 1925
Knight, Frank & Rutley, *auctioneers, For Catalogues of estates sold by K. & Co., see under the names of owners &c.*
Knighton (William), *LL.D.* Private life of an Eastern king, w. Elihu Jan's story of the private life of an East. Queen. Ed. w. intr. & notes by S. B. Smith. [repr.] s8°. 1921
Knightsbridge, Chapel of the Holy Trinity, *see* HOLY TRINITY, *Knightsbridge.*
Knipstro (Johann), *see* BAHLOW (F.) J. K., d. erste Gen.-supt. v. Pommern-Wolgast, 1898.
Knittel (John). Aaron West. s8°. [1921]
Knöbel (Jacobus Burckhardus) & J. C. Schüz. Examen quietismi. Præs. J. W. Jægero. Adject. D. Speneri judic. [P2630]. s4°. Tubingae. [1715]
Knoblauch (Edward) [KNOBLOCK], *see* BENNETT (E. A.) & E. K. Mr. Prohack, 1927.
Knoch (August). Hildersheim, *see* DEUTSCHLAND. D.'s Städtebau, 1921.
Knoche (Herman). Vagandi mos: Reiseskizzen e. Botanikers, 1, Die Kanarische Inseln. la8°. Str. [1923]
Knoche (Walter). Die Osterinsel. Zusammenfassung d. chilen. Osterinselexped., 1911. 8°. Concepción. 1925
Knoedler (M.) & Co. Loan exhib. of Dutch masters of the 17th cent., Nov. 1925. [*Catalogue*]. 8°. N.Y. [1925]
Knogler (Christoph). Disput. de habitibus morum: ex lib. 7 ad Nicomachum conscr. &c., propos. à M. Conrado, resp. C. K. [P522]. s4°. Witebergae. 1595
Knollys (Henry). Eng. life in China. s8°. 1885
*From Sedan to Saarbruck. By an officer of the R. A. [*i.e.* H. K.] s8°. 1870
Knonau (Gerold Meyer v.), *see* MEYER VON KNONAU (G.)
Knop (Joseph Adalbert).
Die Paradoxie d. Willens. [P2491]. 8°. L. 1863
Knopf (Rudolf). Einführ. in d. N.T. Bibelkunde d. N.T. Gesch. u. Relig. d. Urchr. 8°. Giessen. 1919
see LIETZMANN (H.) Hdbch. z. N. Test., Ergzb. 1, Die Lehre d. 12 Apostel &c.; erkl. v. R. K., 1920.
Knöppel (Alois). Bernhard H. Overberg, *see* HUBERT (W. E.) Lebensbilder kath. Erzieher, B5, 1896.
Der selige P. Canisius, *see* HUBERT (W. E.) Lebensbilder kath. Erzieher, B7, 1897.
Knorr (Georg Wolfgang). Sammlung v. Merckwürdigkeiten d. Natur u. Alterthümern d. Erdbodens welche petrif. Cörper enthält. [*T1 cont. text & 58 plates, numbered I–XXXVIII. 2nd tp.* Lapides diluvii univ. testes]. fol. Nürnberg. 1755
Knorr (Levin Georg Carl Wilhelm Wintzingeroda-, *Frhr.* **v.),** *see* WINTZINGERODA-KNORR (L. G. C. W., *Frhr.* v.)

Knorr von Rosenoth (Christian). Kabbala denudata &c. Tr. libri Sohar, Apparatus &c. 2t. s4°. Sulzbaci & Francofurti. 1677–84
Knorringa (H.) Emporos; trade & trader in Greek lit. la8°. Amsterdam. 1926
Knötel (Richard).
Handbuch d. Uniformkunde. s8°. L. 1896
Knottnerus-Meyer (Theodor). Birds & beasts of the Roman Zoo. Tr. B. Miall. 8°. [1927]
Knowles, *The family of, see* HARVEY (F.) Genealog. table of fam. of Sheridan, LeFanu & K., 1875.
Knowles (George William), *barrister, see* QUAKERS & peace; intr. &c. by G. W. K., 1927.
Knowles (James Sheridan).
Caius Gracchus. [Dolby's Brit. theatre]. s8°. [1823]
Dramatic works. 3v [*v1 & 2 wanting*]. 8°. 1843
The hunchback: a play. n. & rev. ed. [P2583]. s8°. 1847
The love-chase: a comedy. [P2588]. s8°. [1840]
Virginius. [Dolby's Brit. theatre]. s8°. [1824]
Knowles (John A.) Henry Gyles, glass-painter of York, *see* WALPOLE SOC. 11th ann. vol., 1922–23.
A Jesse window in York Minster. [Repr. f. "York. Herald"]. [P2489]. 8°. York. 1920
Knowles (Josephine Pitcairn).
The upholstered cage. s8°. [1912]
Knowles (*Sir* **Lees),** *ed.* A gift of Napoleon, being a sequel to letters of Cap. E. Lutyens, St. Helena, 1820–23. 8°. 1921
Knowles (Lilian Charlotte Anne). The econ. development of the Brit. Overseas Empire, 1763–1914. 8°. 1924
The indust. & commercial revolutions in Gt. Brit. dur. 19th c. [London Sch. of Econ^s. St^s., No. 61]. 4th (rev.) ed. 8°. 1926
Knowlittle (John), *ps.* [*i.e.* ARTHUR H. PATTERSON].
The cruise of the "Walrus" on the Broads. s8°. [1923]
Through Broadland in a Breydon punt. s8°. Norwich. 1920
Knox (Alexander), *1757–1831.* *Essays on the polit. circumstances of I., wr. dur. admin. of Earl Camden, w. App. &c. By a gentleman of the N. of Ireland. 8°. D. 1798
see JEBB (J.), *bp.* 30 yrs. corr. betw. J. & K., 2v, 1834.
Knox (*Col. Sir* **Alfred William Fortescue).**
With the Russian Army, 1914–17. 2v. 8°. 1921
Knox (Cleone), *ps., see* KING-HALL (*Miss* M.)
Knox (Edmund Arbuthnott), *bp. of Manchester.* On what authority? Review of found. of the Xtn. faith. 8°. 1922
Knox (Edmund George Valpy) [*ps.* EVOE].
It occurs to me. s8°. [1926]
Knox (Howard V.) The philosophy of William James. s8°. 1914
Knox (John), *the Reformer.* An answere to a great number of blasphemous cavillations written by an anabaptist &c. s8°. *T. Charde.* 1591
Book of Common order of Ch. of Scot. known as J. K.'s Liturgy &c., 1868, *see* CHURCH OF SCOTLAND.
see CARLYLE (T.) Early kings of Norway; also, essay on portraits of J. K., 1882.
„ MULOT (R.) J. K., 1505–72: e. Erinnerungsblatt z. 4. Zentenarfeier, 1904.
Knox (Joseph).
The fixation of atmospheric nitrogen. 2nd ed. s8°. 1921
Physico-chemical calculations. 5th ed. (w. log. tables). s8°. [1924]
Knox (Ronald Arbuthnott).
Memories of the future. Mem., 1915–72, wr. in 1988 by Opal, Lady Porstock. [*Satire*]. s8°. [1923]
An open-air pulpit. 8°. 1926
Other eyes than ours. s8°. [1926]
Sanctions: a frivolity. s8°. [1924]
The three taps. s8°. [1927]
The viaduct murder. s8°. [1925]
see HENRY VI, *k. of Eng.* Miracles; acc. & tr. of 23 miracles f. MS. in B.M., w. intr. by R. K. &c., 1923.
Knox (Vicesimus). Liberal education. 11th ed. 2v. s8°. 1795
*Personal nobility. s8°. 1794
Knox (Wilfred Lawrence). The Catholic Movt. in the Ch. of England. 8°. [1923]
St. Paul & the Ch. of Jerusalem. la8°. C. 1925
Knox (*Maj.-Gen. Sir* **William George).** The flaw in our armour. With intr. by Earl Roberts. s8°. 1914
Knudsen (K. A. Wieth-), *see* WIETH-KNUDSEN (K. A.)
Knutsford (Sydney Holland), *2nd visct.*
In black & white. 8°. 1926
Knuttel (J. A. N.), *see* VRIES (M. DE), L. A. TE WINKEL &c., *edd.* Woordenboek der Nederl. taal, d3ii, iii, door K., 1913–20.

Knuttel (Willem Pieter Cornelis), *see* KONINKLIJKE BIBL. Cat. van de pamfletten verzam. bewerkt door K., d1-9, 1889-1920.

Knyajnin (V. N.) А. А. Блок. s8º. П. 1922

Knytlinga Saga, *see* SQGUR DANAKONUNGA, 2, 1919-25.

Koahipau, *native Hawaiian subject*, *see* HAWAII. Corr. on subject of K., 1846.

Koaliczió (A) tervei és alkotásai 1906-09 ; összeszedte Papharaszti, 1909, *see* PAPHARASZTI.

Kobad I, *king of Persia, A.D. 487* [KAWĀDH], *see* CHRISTENSEN (A.) Kawadh I & le communisme mazdakite, 1925.

Kobayashi (Ushisaburo), *D.C.L.* Milit. industries of Japan. [C.E. for Int. Peace]. la8º. N.Y. 1922

War & armament loans of Japan. [C.E. for Int. Peace]. la8º. N.Y. 1922

War & armament taxes of Japan. [C.E. for Int. Peace]. la8º. N.Y. 1923

Kobbe (Gustav). The compl. opera book. 8º. [1922]

Köbel (Jakob). Die Legende d. heiligen Herzog Ruprecht, 1524. [Wiedergeg. v. F. Falk]. s8º. [Mainz. 1887]

Tischzucht (facs. 1492), *see* FREYTAG (G.) Bilder, B2, 1924.

København. *Københavns Kirkesag, 1890-1915. Festskrift. 8º. København. 1915

Köber (Raphael).
Schopenhauer's Erlösungslehre. [P2523]. 8º. L. [1881]

Köberle (Justus). Die Papyri v. Assuan u. d. Alte Test. [*Extr. f.* Neue Kirchl. Zeitschr., Jhrg. 19]. 8º. Erlangen. 1908

Köbner (Richard). Die Anfänge d. Gemeinwesens d. Stadt Köln. la8º. Bonn. 1922

Koch (Christian Nicolaus). Comm. de legationibus eccl. vet. Christianorum. Cum praef. J. G. Walchii. s8º. Jenae. 1750

Koch (Eduard Emil). Gesch. d. Kirchenlieds &c. d. christl. insbes. d. deutsch-evang. Kirche. 2e verm. A. 2T *in* 4v. 8º. St. 1852-53

Koch (Jodokus), *see* JONAS (J.)

Koch (Johann).
Gesanglehre f. Gymnasien &c. 8º. Frauenfeld. 1856

Koch (Johann), *theologian*, *see* COCCEJUS (JOHANNES).

Koch (Joseph). Durandus de S. Porciano O.P. [Beitr. z. Gesch. d. Philos. d. M.-A., B26i]. T1. 8º. Münster i. W. 1927

Koch (Julius Lud. Aug.) Vom Bewusstsein in Zuständen sog. Bewusstlosigkeit. [P2491]. 8º. St. 1877

Koch (Max). R. Wagner ; hrsg. E. Hofmann. 2T. s8º. 1907-15

see VOGT (F.) & M. KOCH. Gesch. d. deut. Lit., 3B, 1918-20.

Koch (Robert).
Was wissen u. können uns. Aerzte ? [P2491]. 8º. L. 1885

Koch (Rudolf).
Das Schreiben als Kunstfertigkeit. 2. A. 4º. L. 1924

Koch (Theodore Wesley). La Bibliothèque publ. de Petrograd. [*Extr.* de la Revue des Bibliothèques, avr.-sept. 1923]. la8º. 1923

Les livres à la Guerre. Préf. par Maréchal Foch. Intr. by B. E. Stevenson. Tr. A. Doysié. 8º. 1920

Köcher (Johann Christoph).

Bibl. theol. symbolicae et catecheticae, itemque liturgica &c. 2p *in* 1v [p2, *cont.* Conspectus *w. sep. pagin.*] s8º. Guelpherbyti [p2, Jenae]. 1751-56

Breviarium & missale Romanum variationum Eccl. Rom. in doct. testes. [P2635]. s4º. Jenae. 1755

Catechet. Gesch. d. päbstl. Kirche [*a. c. b. w. h.* Einl., 1752]. s8º. Jena. [1753]

Catechet. Gesch. d. reform. Kirchen. [*a. c. b. w. h.* Catech. Gesch. d. päbstl. Kirche, 1753]. s8º. Jena. 1756

Catechet. Gesch. d. Waldenser, Böhm. Brüder, Griechen, u. a. Secten &c. [*b. w. h.* Catech. Gesch. d. päbstl. Kirche, 1753]. s8º. Jena. 1768

Conspectus theologiae univ. &c. s8º. Guelpherbyti. 1749

De idolatria litteraria. s8º. Hanoverae. 1738

Die drey letzte u. vornehmste Glaubens-Bekentnisse d. Böhm. Brüder, &c. s8º. Franckfurt. 1741

Einleitung in die catechet. Theol. &c. s8º. Jena. 1752

Obs. sel. controversias inter Pontificios & Protestantes illust. 2 fasc. *in* 1v. s8º. Jena. 1767-70

Kochkurov (Nikolai), *see* VESELY (ARTEM), *ps.*

Kochs (Ernst).
Paul Gerhardt : Leben u. Lieder. neue A. s8º. L. 1926

Kock (Ebbe). Om hemföljd. I svensk rätt t. o. m. 1734 års lag. 8º. Lund. 1926

Kock (Theodor).
Comic. Attic. fragmenta. Ed. T. K. 3v. 8º. L. 1880-88

Kockström (V. R.) Kurze Gramm. d. finn. Sprache. Bearb. v. K. Suomalainen. s8º. Helsingfors. 1876

Koebel (William Henry). Argentina, past & present. la8º. 1910

The new Argentina. 8º. 1923

Koebel (William Henry) [*continued*].
South America. Painted by A. S. Forrest, descr. by W. H. K. 8º. [1912]

see ANGLO-SOUTH AMER. HANDBOOK ; ed. W. H. K., 1921 ; 1922.

Koeber (Raphael), *see* KÖBER (R.)

Koebner, *see* KÖBNER.

Koecher, *see* KÖCHER.

Kœchlin (Raymond). Les ivoires gothiques franç. 2t & Planches, *b. separately.* s4º. 1924

Koeck (Peter), *see* COECK (P.)

Koeckriz (Franciscus), *called* FABER (F.) Primitiae Silesiacae, sive Sabothus & Silesia. Cui praemitt. J. Fechneri Progr. ejusdem augmenti. Usui publ. restituit Q. A. T. A. V. A. [*In verse. b. w.* Du Moulin (P.) De monarchia temp. pontif. Rom., 1716]. s8º. Lipsiae. 1715

Koehler (René). Ophiurans of the Philippine Seas &c. Tr. by A. H. Clark. [S.I.: U.S. Nat. Mus., Bull. 100]. 8º. Wash. 1922

Koenig (Alma Johanna), *see* KÖNIG (A. J.)

Koeppen (Adolphus Louis). The world in the Middle Ages, w. 6 maps f. hist. atlas of C. Spruner. fol. N.Y. 1854

Koeranides [COERANIDES], *see* UNION ACAD. INTERNAT. Cat. des mss. alchim. grecs., t1, 2, 1924-27.

Koffka (Kurt). Growth of the mind : intr. to child-psychology. Tr. R. M. Ogden. 8º. 1924

Koganeï (Yoshikiyo). Kurze Mitth. ü. Untersuch. an leb. Aino. [*Extr. fr.* Archiv. für Anthropologie, B24]. 4º. [Braunschweig. 1896]

Kögler (Ignatz) [KOEGLERUS]. Notitiae S. S. Bibliorum Judaeorum in imperio Sinensi. Ed. 2a., Seriem chronolog. &c. add. C. T. de Murr. 8º. Halae ad Salam. 1805

Kogutowicz (Károly), *see* BATKY (Z.) & K. K. Ethnogr. map of Hungary, 1919 ; Index, 1919.

Kohl (Heinrich). Kasr Firaun in Petra. [Deut. Orient-Gesell., Wiss. Veröffentl., 13. *b. w.* Borchardt (L.) Grabdenkmal d. K. Nefer-ir-ke-re, 1909]. fol. L. 1910

see PUCHSTEIN (O.) Boghasköi : d. Bauwerke ; v. O. P. unter Mitwirkung v. H. K. &c., 1912.

„ WIEGAND (T.) Baalbek, B3, v. H. K. &c., 1925.

—— & C. Watzinger. Antike Synagogen in Galilaea. [Deut. Orient-Gesell., Wiss. Veröffentl., 29]. fol. L. 1916

Kohl (Johann Georg). Am Wege. Blicke in Gemüth u. Welt. in Aphorismen. 8º. Bremen. 1866

Kohl (Johann Peter). Introd. in hist. & rem lit. Slavorum, sive hist. crit. Cod. sacri & Ephremi Syri &c. Acc. 2 sermones E. Syri. [*b. w.* Berger (F. L. v.) Opusc., 1725]. s8º. Altonaviae. 1729

Köhler & Volckmar, *publishers*, *see* DEUT. LITERATUR-KATALOG, 1927 ; bearb. &c. v. K. & V., 1927.

Köhler (Carl), *artist*, *see* SICHART (E. v.) Prak. Kostümkunde : nach C. K., bearb. v. E. v. S., 2B, 1926.

Kohler (Charles). Mélanges p. s. à l'hist. de l'Orient latin & des Croisades. la8º. 1906

Köhler (Johann Georg Wilhelm). Disput. de cod. Virgilii adhuc incogn. [P445]. s4º. Jenae. 1771

Kohler (Josef). Law of the Armenians, *in Armenian*, *see* KALEMKEAREAN (G.), *tr.* Lemberg codices, 1890.

Köhler (K. F.), *booksellers, Leipzig* [K. ANTIQUARIUM]. Cat. d'une coll. de livres sur les peuples Slaves. [No. 75]. 8º. L. [1862]

Periodica 1-14 [*in* 2v]. 8º. L. 1925-27

Köhler (Ludwig von). Die Staatsverwaltung d. besetzten Gebiete. [C.E. for Int. Peace]. B1. (Belgien). la8º. St. 1927

Kohler (Pierre). Madame de Staël & la Suisse. la8º. 1916

Köhler (Walther Eric).

Bibliogr. Brentiana. 8º. 1904

Brentiana u. a. Reformatoria, *see* ARCHIV F. REFORMATIONSGESCH., Jhrg. 9-11, 1912-14.

Die Gnosis. s8º. Tübingen. 1911

Luther u. d. Lüge. [Verein f. Ref.-Gesch. Schr., Jhrg. 30 (Nr. 109/10)]. 8º. L. 1912

Luthers Schrift An d. christl. Adel deut. Nation : e. Beitr. 8º. Halle a. S. 1895

Wie Luther d. Deutschen das Leben Jesu erzählt hat. [Verein f. Ref.-gesch. Schr., Jhrg. 35 (Nr. 127/28)]. 8º. L. 1917

Köhler (Wilhelm), *see* SCHWERTFEGER (B.) Zur europ. Politik, B1, 5, bearb. v. W. K., 1919.

Köhler (Wolfgang). Aus d. Anthropoidenstation auf Teneriffa, 2, Opt. Unters., 3, Intelligenzprüfungen, 4, Nachweis einfacher Strukturfunktionen, v. W. K., *see* KÖN.-PREUSS. AKAD. Abh., Phys.-math. Klasse, 1915, 1917 & 1918.

Köhler (Wolfgang) [*continued*].
The mentality of apes. Tr. f. 2nd rev. ed. by E. Winter. 8°. 1925
Die phys. Gestalten in Ruhe u. im stationär. Zustand. 8°. Erlangen. [1924]

Kohlhaas (Etta Federn-), *see* FEDERN-KOHLHAAS (E.)

Kohlius (Joannes Petrus), *Kiloniensis.* Eccl. Graeca Lutheranizans. Adj. Joh. Quistorpii De Christianismo Graec. hodiern. opposītu Leoni Allatio. s8°. Lubecae. 1723

Kohlrausch (Heinrich Friedrich Theodor). Deut. Gesch. f. d. Schulen bearb. 10e verm. A. 8°. Elberfeld. 1833

Kohlreiff (Gottfried). Chronologia Liphrat Katon &c. Acc. via nova ad indag. eclipsas, praes. in priscis Sin. libris not. s8°. Labecae. 1732
Defensio restit. antiq. temp. Acc. def. contra Des Vignoles. s8°. Hamburgi. 1728

Kohlreiff (Matthias Erasmus). Computus Julio-Constantinianus diss. Praes. Æ. Strauchio. [P446]. s4°. Wittebergae. 1662

Kohn (Albin) & R. Andree. Sibirien u. das Amurgebiet. Gesch. u. Reisen, Landschaften u. Völker zw. Ural u. Beringstrasse. 2e A. 2B *in* 1v. (1, Sibirien, v. A. Kohn; 2, Amurgebiet, v. R. Andree). 8°. L. 1876

Köhne (Max).
Russlands geistige Entwicklung. [P2685]. 8°. 1918

Koizumi (Gunji). Lacquer work. Foreword by Lt.-Col. E. F. Strange. la8°. 1923

Kokhmansky (P. V.) Москва въ декабрѣ 1905. 8°. Москва. 1906

Kokovtsev (V. N.), *see* MARCHAND (R.) Un livre noir: diplomatie, 1910–14, t2, Rapports de Sazanof & de K., 1923.

Kolb (Annette). Das Exemplar. Roman. 8°. 1922

Kolb (Franz).
see BERNE. Handlung oder Acta gehaltner Disput. zu B. [*betw. B. Haller, F. K. & o.*], 1528.
„ ECK (J. v.) Ein Sentbrieve an ein frum Eidgnossschafft, betreff. die ketzer. disput. F. K. u. B. Hallers zu Bern, 1528.
„ RATSCHLAG. R. halltender Disput. zu Bernn [*w.* Schlussreden *by* F. K. &c.], 1528.

Kolb (Georg Friedrich). The condition of nations; w. statistics. Tr., ed. &c., to 1880, by Mrs. Brewer, w. notes &c. by E. W. Streeter. la8°. [1880]

Kolb (H.), *see* BORRMANN (R.), *ed.* Aufnahmen mittelalterl. Wand-u. Deckenmalereien in Deut.; unter Mitw. v. H. K. &c., 2B, 1897–1914.

Kolbasenko (Ivan Step.) Станица Срѣтенская. [I.R.G.O. Приамурск. отд., 5ii]. 8°. Хабаровскъ. 1899

Kolbassine-Tchernoff (Olga). Les prisons soviet. Mém. de Mme. K.-T. [P2620]. 8°. 1922

Kolbe (Hermann). Üb. d. natürl. Zusammenhang d. organ. mit d. unorgan. Verbindungen (1859). Hrsg. E. v. Meyer. 8°. L. 1897

Kolbe (Walther). Beitr. z. syr. u. jüd. Gesch.: Untersuch. z. Seleukidenliste u. z. d. Makkabäerbüchern. la8°. St. 1926

Kolben (Peter) [KOLBE; KOLET]. Déscr. du Cap de Bonne-Espérance, tirée des mém. de P. Kolet [*sic, by* J. Bertrand]. 3t. s8°. Amsterdam. 1742

Kolchak (*adm.* Aleksandr Vasilevich).
see BUREVOI (K.) Колчаковщина, 1919.
„ KING (J.) Three bloody men: K. &c., 1919.
„ KONSTANTINOV (M. M.) Последние дни Колчаковщины (1919–20), 1926.
„ ZENZINOV (V.) Государств. переворотъ адм. К. въ Омскѣ, 1919.

Kölcsey (Ferencz), *1790–1838.*
Válogatott szónoki müvei (1812–37). 3ik kiadás. s8°. 1900
see GAAL (M.) K. F. élete &c., 1898.

Kolde (Theodor). Die deut. Augustiner-Congregation u. J. v. Staupitz. 8°. Gotha. 1879
Luther u. d. Reichstag zu Worms, 1521. [Verein f. Ref.-gesch. Schr., Jhrg. 1, Nr. 1]. 8°. Halle. 1883
Das relig. Leben in Erfurt beim Ausgange d. M.-a. [Verein f. Ref.-gesch. Schr., Jhrg. 16, Nr. 63]. 8°. Halle. 1898
see AUGSBURG CONFESSION. Die A. Konf., kurz erläut. v. T. K., 1896.

Koldewey (Friedrich). Heinz v. Wolfenbüttel. [Verein f. Ref.-gesch. Schr., Jhrg. 1, Nr. 2]. 8°. Halle. 1883

Koldewey (Robert). Die hettit. Inschrift gefunden in d. Königsburg v. Babylon am 22. Aug. 1899. [Deut. Or.-Gesells., Wiss. Veröff., 1]. fol. L. 1900
Das Ischtar-Tor in Babylon. Nach d. Ausgrabungen durch d. Deut. Or.-Gesell. [Deut. Or.-Gesells., Wiss. Veröff., 32]. fol. L. 1918

Koldewey (Robert) [*continued*].
Die Pflastersteine v. Aiburschabu in Babylon. [Deut. Or.-Gesells., Wiss. Veröff., 2. *b. w. h.* Hettit. Inschr., 1900]. fol. L. 1901
Die Tempel v. Babylon u. Borsippa. [Deut. Or.-Gesells., Wiss. Veröff., 15]. fol. L. 1911

Köler (Johann David), *see* FINCKLER (G. E.) Sacra Sodalitas B. Mariae V. in Monte ad Vetus Brandenburgum; praes. J. D. K., 1745.

Kolet (Pierre), *see* KOLBEN (P.)

Kolhapur (*Shri* Shahu Chhatrapati, *Maharaja of*), 1874–1922. *see* LATTHE (A. B.) Memoirs of S. C., 2v, 1924.

Kolisch (Robert), *Bankier.* Versteigerung v. Mobiliar, Skulpturen &c., Gemälden &c. aus d. Nachlass R. K. [Wien, Mai 17–23, 1921]. Selbstverlag, Glückselig u. Wärndorfer. [*Illust.*] 4°. Wien. 1921

Kolkmann (Joseph). Die Charakterlosigkeit in Deutschland. [P2471]. 8°. Loebau W. Pr. 1878

Kollar (Jan). Sláwy dcera. Lyricko-epická báseň. 3e wydanj. s8°. w Pešti. 1832

Kollegiya Vostokovedov pri Aziatskom Muzee Ross. Akad. Nauk, *see* IMPERATORSKAYA AKAD. NAUK.

Kollesberg (Theodor Dantscher, *Ritter* **von),** *see* DANTSCHER V. KOLLESBERG (T., *Ritter*).

Kollin (Conrad). Eversio Lutherani Epithalamii. [sex libr.] s4°. [? Coloniae]. 1527

Kollmann (Franz). Das Zeppelinluftschiff: s. Entwicklung &c. la8°. 1924

Kollontay (Aleksandra M.) Die Arbeiterin u. Bäuerin in Sowjet-Russland. [P2758]. s8°. L. 1921
The workers' opposition in Russia. [P2690]. s8°. [1923]
see TSETKIN (K.), A. K. &c. Роза Люксембург &c., 1921.

Köln [COLN; KÖLNER]. Christl. u. Cathol. gegenberichtung eyns erwird. Dhomcapitels zu Cöllen, 1544, *see* CHRISTLICHE.
Quellen z. Gesch. d. köln. Handels u. Verkehrs im M.-a., 3B, 1917–23, *see* KUSKE (B.), *ed.*
Die Stadt Cöln unter preuss. Herrschaft, 1815–1915. Hrsg. v. d. Stadt Cöln. [2B in 3T. 1i, ii]. la8°. Cöln. 1915–16
1i, v. E. Gothein. 1ii, v. G. Neuhaus. 2, *by var. a.*
Verz. d. Gemälde d. Städt. Mus. Wallraf-Richartz zu Cöln. s8°. Cöln. 1904
see ALTKATHOLIKEN. Verhandl. d. 2. Altkath. Congr. z. K., 1872.

Kolnai (Aurel). Psychoanalysis & sociology. Tr. by E. & C. Paul. s8°. [1921]

Kolobov (Ivan). Русская свадьба Олонецкой губ. [? *Extr. fr.* Живая Старина]. [P2399]. la8°. *n.p.* [1915?]

Kolokolov (Nikolai). Стихотворения. [P2698]. 8°. [Москва]. 1920

Kolosov (A.) Александръ II, его личность &c. [P2388, 2445]. s8°. Лондонъ. 1902
Александръ III, его личность. [P2388, 2445]. s8°. Лондонъ. 1902

Kolpensky (V.) Якутская ссылка и дело Романовцев. [P2698]. 8°. П. 1920

Kolpinska (Anna). I precursori d. Rivoluzione Russa. Con L'anima d. Russia, di N. Berdiaev e La Russia e il principio di nazionalità, di U. Zanotti-Bianco. s8°. 1919

Kölsch (Adolf).
Die Verwandlungen d. Lebens. s8°. Zürich. 1919

Kolsrud (Oluf). 100 "Gamle Bunde-regler" &c. (17 & 18 c.) [Norske Hist. K. Norske folkeminne, 1]. 8°. 1914

Koltchak, *see* KOLCHAK.

Koltsov (Aleksei Vasilevich). Стихотворенія. Съ статьею пис. В. Бѣлинскимъ. 4oe изд. К. Солдатенкова. 8°. Москва. 1863

Komarov-Kurlov (*General*), *chief of Russian secret police.* Das Ende d. russ. Kaisertums. Persönl. Erinnerungen. 8°. 1920

Komitet Russkoi Knigi. Русская зарубежная книга. [Труды Ком. Р. Кн., вып. 1]. ч1, 2 *in* 1*v.* [ч2, под ред. С. П. Постникова]. 8°. Прага. 1924

Kommission f. d. Gesamtkatalog d. Wiegendrucke, *see* GESAMTKATALOG.

Kommission zur Herausgabe Elsässicher Geschichtsquellen, *see* STRASSBURG. Regesten d. Bischöfe v. S., B1, 1908.

Kommunistische. *Kampflieder; hrsg. d. K. Jugend Deut., 1921, *see* KAMPFLIEDER.
*Manifest d. K. Partei, 1848, *see* MANIFEST.

Kommunistische Internationale (Die), *see* INTERNATIONALE (L').

Komnenos (P.) Συμβολαὶ εἰς τὰς προσπαθείας πρὸς ἑνώσειν τῶν ἐκκλησιῶν. τεῦχος Α'. Ἀγγλικανικαὶ Χειροτονίαι. Ἐκδ. δαπ Κ. Χρυσοστόμου. [P2577]. 8°. ἐν Κ -πόλει. 1921

Kondakov (Nikodim Pavlovich). Rec. d'études dédiées à la mém. de N. P. K. [*w. life by G. V. Vernadskij & bibliog. of wks.*] sm. fol. Prague. 1926
The Russian icon. Tr. E. H. Minns. 4°. O. 1927
see Tolstoy (*c.* I. I.) & N. P. K. Русс. древности, 2, 4, 6, 1889–99.

Koner (Wilhelm), *see* Guhl (E.) & W. K. La vie antique, p2, La vie des Romains; tr., 1885.

Kongeligt Danske Videnskabernes Selskab.
Biologiske Meddelelser. B1–6. 8°. København. 1917–27
Each mem. has sep. tp. & pagin.
Filosofiske Meddelelser. B1. 8°. København. 1920–24
Each mem. has sep. tp. & pagin.
Høffding (H.) Begrebet analogi, 1923. [1.]
—— Bemaerk. om d. Platon. Dial. Parmenides, 1920. [1.]
—— Plato's Bøger om Staten, 1923. [1.]
—— Relation som Kategori, 1921. [1.]
Kroman (K.) Math. & theory of science, 1920. [1.]
Historisk-filologiske Meddelelser. B1–13. 8°. København. 1918–27
Each mem. has sep. tp. & pagin.
[Amenemope]. Weisheitsbuch d. A., aus d. Papyrus 10474 d. B. M. hrsg. &c. v. H. O. Lange, 1925. [11.]
Arason (Jón). Relig. digte; F. Jonsson, 1918. [2.]
Arnim (H. v.) Xenophons Memorabilien u. Apol. d. Sokrates, 1923. [8.]
Benedictsen & Christensen. Dialectes d'Awromān & de Pāwä, 1921. [6.]
Blinkenberg (C. S.) Fibules grec. & orientales, 1926. [13.]
—— Hades's munding, 1919. [2.]
—— L'image d'Athana Lindia, 1917. [1.]
—— Lindiaka, 2–5, 1925–26. [11, 12.]
—— Le temple de Paphos, 1924. [9.]
Brunot (F.) Expression des rel. & des modalités en fr., 1922. [4.]
Christensen (A.) Contes persans en lang. pop., 1918. [1.]
—— Le règne du roi Kawādh I & le communisme mazdakite, 1925. [9.]
—— Smeden Kāväh og det gamle persiske rigsbanner, 1919. [2.]
—— Textes ossètes, 1921. [6.]
—— Xavāṣṣ-i-āyāt, magie du Coran, 1920. [3.]
Cortsen (S. P.) Etrusk. Standes- u. Beamtentitel, durch d. Inschr. beleuchtet, 1925. [11.]
Dhātupātha. The Pāli D. & the Dhātumañjūsā; Andersen & Smith, 1921. [4.]
Drachmann (A. B.) Sagunt u. d. Ebro-Grenze, 220–18, 1920. [3.]
Hammerich (L. L.) Zur deut. Akzentuation, 1922. [7.]
Heiberg (J. L.), *ed.* Glossae medicinales, 1924. [9.]
—— Mathematici Graeci minores; ed. J. L. H., 1927. [13.]
Hude (C.) Oraisons funèbres de Lysias & de Platon, 1917. [1.]
Jensen (I. H.) Älteste Alchymie, 1921. [4.]
Jespersen (O.) De 2 hovedarter av gramm. forbindelser, 1921. [4.]
—— Negation, 1917. [1.]
Jónsson (F.) Norsk-Islandske kultur-og sprogforhold i 9. og 10. årh, 1921. [3.]
Kristensen (M.) " Nokkur blöð ur Hauksbók " undersøgt &c., 1925. [9.]
Lansing Papyrus; hrsg. u. erkl. v. A. Erman u. H. O. Lange, 1925. [10.]
Nilsson (M. P.) Anfänge d. Göttin Athene, 1921. [4.]
—— Übernahme u. Entwick. d. Alphabets durch d. Griechen, 1918. [1.]
Nyrop (K.) Études de gramm. fr., 1919–27. [2–4, 8, 9, 12.]
—— Gueules, et ords hist., 1921. [4.]
—— Hist. étymol. de 2 mots fr. (haricot, parvis), 1918. [2.]
Ohrt (F.) Danske Besværgelser mod Vrid & Blod, 1922. [6.]
Østerberg (V.) Prince Hamlet's age, 1924. [8.]
Pallis (S. A.) Babylonian akītu festival, 1926. [12.]
Pedersen (H.) La 5e declin. lat., 1926. [11.]
—— Formes sigmat. du verbe latin, &c., 1921. [3.]
—— Groupement des dialectes indo-europ., 1925. [11.]
Poulsen (F.) Aus. e. alt. Etruskerstadt, 1927. [12.]
—— Delphische Studien 1, 1924. [8.]
—— Ikonograph. Miscellen, 1921. [4.]
—— Vases grecs, rec. acq. par la glyptothèque de Ny-Carlsberg, 1922. [5.]
Sarauw (C.) Entstehungsgesch. d. Goeth. Faust, 1917. [1.]
—— Goethes Augen, 1919. [2.]
—— Goethes Faust i aarene 1788–9, 1919. [2.]
—— Niederdeut. Forschungen, 1921–24. [5.]
—— Zur Faustchronol., 1925. [10.]
Schütte (G.) Jysk og Østdansk Artikelbrug, 1922. [7.]
Theophilus. Niederdeut. Spiel v. T.; C. Sarauw, 1923. [8.]
Thomsen (V.) Inscrip. de la trouv. d'or de Nagy-Szent-Miklós, 1917. [1.]
Thordarson (O.) Málhljoða—og málskrúðrit &c., 1927. [13.]
Tuxen (P.) Forestillingen om Sjælen i Rigveda &c., 1919. [2.]
Tzetzes (I.) De metris Pindarisis comm.; ed. Drachmann, 1925. [9.]

Kongeligt Danske Videnskabernes Selskab [*continued*].
Mathematisk-fysiske Meddelelser. B1–7. 8°. København. 1917–27
Each mem. has sep. tp. & pagin.
Oversigt, 1920–27. [6v.] 8°. København. 1921–27
Skrifter, Naturvidensk & mathemat. Afd. Række 8. B1–11. 4°. København. 1915–27
Each mem. has sep. tp. but pagin. contin.

Kongeligt Nordisk Oldskrift-Selskab. Aarbøger for nordisk Oldkyndighed. 1867–76. [1868, 70 *wanting*]. 8°. Kjøbenhavn. [1867–76]
Mémoires. nouv. sér., 1914–19, 1920–25. 8°. Copenhague. 1920–26
see Konungs-Skuggsjá. Speculum regale, H1, 1920.

Koni (Anatoly Fedorovich).
Петербург. Воспоминания старожила. s8°. П. 1922
С. Ю. Витте: отрывочные воспом. s8°. Москва. 1925

König (Alma Johanna). Der heilige Palast. s8°. Wien. 1923

König (Friedrich Eduard). Gesch. d. alttest. Religion. 3e u. 4e neubearb. A. 8°. Gütersloh. 1924
Theologie d. Alt. Test. 1e u. 2e A. 8°. St. 1922

König (Georg). Heptas casuum conscientiae misc. [*b. w.* Dannhauer (J. C.) Liber conscientiae, t1, 1669]. s4°. Norimbergae. 1655

König (Heinrich Conrad). Schediasma de hominum inter feras educat. statu nat. solitario. [P1035]. s4°. Hanoveræ. 1730

König (Hermann Caspar), *see* Bokelmann (J. C.) Bibl. Agendorum; ausgefertigt v. H. C. K., 1726.

König (Johann Friedrich). Diss. de principio salutis nostræ primo &c. Præs. J. F. K., def. J. Marci. [P2636]. s4°. Rostochii. 1664
Nucleus theolog. positivae &c. Publ. à M. C. Reineccio. ed. 2a. s8°. Lipsiae. 1706
Theologia positiva acroamatica. ed. 6a. [*b. w.* Fecht (J.) Lect. theol., 1722]. s8°. Rostochii. 1680
„ „ ....ed. 7a. s8°. Rostochii. 1684

Königer (Albert Michael), *see* Ehrhard (A.) Beitr. z. Gesch. d. christl. Alt. &c., Festgabe A. E. dargebr.; hrsg. v. A. M. K., 1922.

Königliche Akademie der Wissenschaften zu München [Königl. Bayer. Akad. d. Wiss.] Abhandlungen d. philosoph.-philolog. u. histor. Klasse. B26–31. 4°. München. 1912–22
Amira (C. v.) Die german. Todesstrafen, 1922. [31.]
Bissing (F. W. v.) Beitr. z. Gesch. d. assyr. Skulptur, 1912. [26.]
Boll (F.) Antike Beobacht. farbiger Sterne; mit e. Beitr. v. C. Bezold, 1916. [30.]
Bulle (H.) Archaisierende griech. Rundplastik, 1918. [30.]
Dhaṇavāla. Bhavisatta Kaha; hrsg. H. Jacobi, 1918. [29.]
Döberl (M.) Bayern u. d. wirtschaftl. Einigung Deutschlands, 1915. [29.]
Ephesus, *Synod of, 431.* Neue Aktenstücke z. E. Konzil v. 431; [hrsg.] E. Schwartz, 1920. [30.]
Geiger (W.) & M. Geiger. Pāli Dhamma, &c., 1921. [31.]
Grauert (H.) M. Heinrich d. Poet in Würzburg, 1912. [27.]
Haribhadra Sūri. Sanatkumāracaritam; hrsg. H. Jacobi, 1921. [31.]
Hartig (O.) Die Gründung d. Münchener Hofbibl., 1917. [28.]
Hümmerich (F.) Quellen &c. z. Fahrt d. ersten Deutschen nach d. portug. Indien, 1505–6, 1918. [30.]
Kehrer (H.) Got. Wandmalereien in d. Kaiser-Pfalz z. Forchheim, 1912. [26.]
Laufer (B.) Chines. Schattenspiele; üb. W. Grube; hrsg. &c. B. L., 1915. [28.]
Lehmann (P.) Corveyer Studien, 1919. [30.]
Lehmann (W.) Vokab. d. Rama-Sprache &c., 1914. [28.]
Reinmar *von Hagenau.* Lieder, [hrsg.] C. v. Kraus, 3T, 1919. [30.]
Riezler (S.) & C. v. Wallmenich, *edd.* Akten z. Gesch. d. bair. Bauernaufstandes 1705/6, 3T, 1912–15. [26, 29.]
Rockinger (L.) Die hs. Grundlage d. Ausg. d. kaiserl. Land u. Lehenrechts, 1. Drittel, 1913. [26.]
Sambhala. Der Weg nach S.; übers. u. hrsg. A. Grünwedel, 1915. [29.]
Traube (L.) Palaeograph. Forsch., T5, Autographa d. Jo. Scotus, 1912. [26.]
Mathemat.-physikal. Klasse. Sitzungsberichte. B[43–51]. 8°. München. 1914–22
Philos.-philolog. u. hist. Klasse. Sitzungsberichte, 1914–27. 8°. München. 1914–27
Amira (C. v.) Grosse Bilderhs. v. Wolframs Willehalm. [1917.]
—— Die Neubauersche Chronik. [1918.]
Athanasius, *St.*, *see* Schwartz (E.)

Königliche Akademie der Wissenschaften zu München [*contd.*]
Philos.-philolog. u. hist. Klasse. Sitzungsberichte [*continued*].
Bäumker (C.) Petrus de Hibernia, d. Jugendlehrer d. T. v. Aquino, u. s. Disput. vor König Manfred. [1920.]
Bernard, *de Ventadour*, *see* Vossler (C.)
Bissing (F. W. v.) Beitr. z. Gesch. d. altägypt Baukunst. [1923.]
—— Die Datierung d. Petrieschen Sinaiinschr. [1920.]
—— Denkmäler z. Gesch. d. Kunst Amenophis IV. [1914.]
—— Ein Hauskauf im 4. Jahrtausend vor Chr. [1920.]
—— Reliefs v. Sonnenheiligtum d. Rathures. [1914.]
—— Urspr. u. Wesen d. pers. Kunst. [1927.]
Bitterauf (T.) Z. Entstehungsgesch. d. Bonapartismus. [1915.]
Blümner (H.) Fahrendes Volk im Altertum. [1918.]
Borinski (C.) Braun als Trauerfarbe. [1918.]
—— Deutung d. Piero di Cosimo zugeschr. Prometheus-Bilder. [1920.]
—— Nochmals d. Farbe Braun. [1920.]
—— Weltwiedergeburtsidee i. neueren Zeiten, T1. [1919.]
Davidsohn (R.) Vorstellungen v. alt. Reich i. d. neuere deut. Gesch. [1917.]
—— Wirtschaftskrieg im M.-a. [1915.]
Distinctiones monast. & morales (13 c.), *see* LEHMANN (P.)
Döberl (M.) Rheinbundverfassung u. bayer. Konstit. [1924.]
Ehrle (F.) Ehrentitel d. scholast. Lehrer. im M.-a. [1919.]
Fischer (H.) Ü. d. Entsteh. d. Nibelungenliedes. [1914.]
—— Üb. Gottfried v. Strassburg. [1916.]
Geiger (W.) & M. Geiger. Die 2. Dekade d. Rasavāhinī. [1918.]
Grabmann (M.) Neu aufgef. lat. Werke deut. Mystiker. [1921.]
—— Neu aufgef. Werke d. Siger v. Brabant u. Boetius v. Dacien. [1924.]
—— Studien zu Johannes Quidort v. Paris, O. Pr. [1922.]
—— Des U. Engelberti Abhdlg. De pulchro. [1925.]
Habich (G.) Üb. 2 Prometheus-Bilder angebl. v. Piero di Cosimo. [1920.]
Hartig (O.) C. Schorer v. Memmingen u. s. "Sprachverderber." [1921.]
Heisenberg (A.) Aus d. Gesch. u. Lit. d. Palaiologenzeit. [1920.]
—— Ikonograph. Studien, lateran. Sarkophag, Nr. 174. [1921.]
—— Das Kreuzreliquiar d. Reichenau. [1926.]
—— Neue Quellen z. Gesch. d. lat. Kaisertums u. d. Kirchenunion.
1, Epitaphios d. N. Mesarites auf s. Bruder Johannes. [1922.]
2, Unionsverhandlungen v. 30. Aug. 1206, Patriarchenwahl u. Kaiserkrönung in Nikaia, 1208. [1923.]
3, Bericht d. N. Mesarites ü. die polit. u. kirchl. Ereignisse, 1214. [1923.]
Herbig (G.) Die Geheimsprache d. Disciplina Etrusca. [1923.]
—— Kleinasiat.-etrusk. Namengleichungen. [1914.]
Hillebrandt (A.) Freiwill. Feuertod in Indien u. d. Somaweihe. [1917.]
—— Ü. d. Anfänge d. ind. Dramas. [1914.]
Hirzel (R.) Die Person im Altertum. [1914.]
Hülsen (C.) Samml. röm. Renaissance—Inschr. aus d. Augsburger Koll. K. Peutingers. [1920.]
Jacob (G.) Schanfarà-Studien, 2T. [1914, 1915.]
Joannes, *Parisiensis*, *Frater Ord. Praedic.*, *see* Grabmann (M.)
Kaufmann (G.) Zwei kathol. u. 2 protestant. Universitäten v. 16.–18. Jhdt. [1920.]
Kranzmayer (E.) Schwäb.-Bair. Mundarten am Lechrain. [1927.]
—— Synonyma f. Kinn u. Stirne in d. Mund. Altbayerns. [1927.]
Külpe (O.) Zur Kategorienlehre. [1915.]
Lehmann (P.) Aufgaben u. Anregungen d. lat. Philol. im M.-a. [1918.]
—— Bücherverzeichnis d. Dombibl. v. Chur, 1457. [1920.]
—— Fuldaer Studien. 2 Folg. [1925, 1927.]
—— Holländ. Reisefruchte, 1–3. [1920.]
—— Mittelalt. Hss. d. K. B. Nationalmus. zu München. [1916.]
—— Mittellat. Verse in Distinctiones monast. &c. v. Anf. d. 13. Jhdts. [1922.]
—— Wert u. Echtheit e. Beda abgesproch. Schrift. [1919.]
Leidinger (G.) Bernardus Noricus. [1917.]
—— Unters. z. Passauer Geschichtschreibung d. M.-a. [1915.]
Lotz (W.) Gab es e. geldwirtschaftl. Verfassung d. Staatsfinanzen unter d. Karolingern ? [1926.]
Mayr (A.) Ü. d. vorröm. Denkmäler d. Balearen. [1914.]
Müller (C.) Luthers Äusserungen ü. d. Recht d. bewaffn. Widerstands gegen d. Kaiser. [1915.]
Muncker (F.) Anschauungen v. engl. Staat u. Volk. i. d. deut. Lit., T1, 2. [1918, 1925.]
—— Neue Lessing-Funde. [1915.]
Otto (W.) Z. Lebensgesch. d. jüng. Plinius. [1919.]
—— Z. Prätur d. jüng. Plinius. [1923.]
Paul (H.) Üb. Kontamination auf syntakt. Gebiete. [1919.]
—— Umschreibung d. Perfektums im Deut. mit haben u. sein. [1918.]
Prutz (H. G.) Die Briefe Jeanne d'Arcs. [1914.]
—— Friedensidee im M.-a. [1915.]
—— Der Kampf um d. Leibeigenschaft in Livland. [1916.]
—— Kurlands deut. Vergangenheit. [1918.]

Königliche Akademie der Wissenschaften zu München [*contd.*]
Philos.-philolog. u. hist. Klasse. Sitzungsberichte [*continued*].
Prutz (H. G.) Neue Stud. z. Jungfrau v. Orléans. [1917.]
—— Z. Gesch. d. Jungfrau v. Orléans : d. Loire-Feldzug, 1429. [1920.]
—— Z. Gesch. d. Jungfrau v. Orléans : Krönungszug n. Rheims. [1923.]
—— Z. Gesch. d. polit. Komödie in Deutschland. [1919.]
Rehm (A.) Griech. Windrosen. [1916.]
—— Neue Beitr. z. Kenntnis d. ant. Wasseruhren. [1920.]
—— Das 7. Buch d. Nat. Quaest. d. Seneca u. d. Kometentheorie d. Poseidonios. [1921.]
—— Zur Chronologie d. miles. Inschr. d. 2. Jhdts. v. Chr. [1923.]
Riezler (S.) Die Landnahme d. Baiuwaren. [1920.]
Robert (C.) Archäolog. Miszellen. [1916.]
Sachs (C.) Musikinstrumente Birmas u. Assams im K. Ethnogr. Mus. zu München. [1917.]
Scherman (L.) Z. altchines. Plastik. [1915.]
Schröder (E.) Der Dichter d. deut. "Eraclius." [1924.]
Schulte (A.) Der hohe Adel im Leben d. mittelalt. Köln. [1919.]
Schwartz (E.) Eine fing. Korresp. mit Paulus d. Samosatener. [1927.]
—— Die sog. Gegenanathematismen d. Nestorius.—Zur Schriftstellerei Theodorets. [1922.]
—— Der sog. Sermo major de fide d. Athanasius. [1924.]
Sieveking (J.) Hermeneut. Reliefstudien. [1920.]
—— Röm. Soldatenrelief. [1919.]
Spiegelberg (W.) Ägyptol. Mitteilungen. [1925.]
—— Demotica 1. [1925.]
—— Erklär. d. dreisprach. Priesterdekretes zu Ehren d. Ptolemaios Philopator. [1925.]
—— & W. Otto. Neue Urkunde zu d. Siegesfeier d. Ptolemaios IV &c. [1926.]
Vollmer (F.) Kürzung durch Tonanschluss im alt. Latein. [1917.]
—— Lesungen u. Deutungen, 1, 2. [1918, 1919.]
—— Die Prosodie d. lat. Komposita mit pro- u. re-. [1922.]
—— Studien zu d. röm. Kochbuche v. Apicius. [1920.]
—— Üb. d. sog. Iambenkürzung bei d. sken. Dichtern d. Römer. [1924.]
—— Zur Gesch. d. lat. Hexameters. [1917.]
Vossler (C.) Minnesang d. Bernhard v. Ventadorn. [1918.]
—— Peire Cardinal, Satiriker aus d. Za. d. Albigenserkr. [1916.]
—— Sprachgemeinschaft u. Interessengemeinschaft. [1924.]
Wecklein (N.) Epikrit. z. Homer. Frage. [1923.]
—— Die Homer. Hymnen u. d. griech. Tragiker. [1920.]
—— Textkrit. Stud. z. d. griech. Tragikern. [1921.]
—— Textkrit. Stud. z. Ilias. [1917.]
—— Textkrit. Stud. z. Odyssee. [1915.]
—— Ü. Zenodot u. Aristarch. [1919.]
—— Ü. Zusätze u. Auslassung v. Versen im Homer. Texte. [1918.]
Wenger (L.) Praetor u. Formel. [1926.]
—— Ü. Papyri u. Gesetzesrecht. [1914.]
—— Z. cippus Abellanus. [1915.]
Wilcken (U.) Beitr. z. Gesch. d. korinth. Bundes. [1917.]
Wolters (P. H. A.) Archäol. Bemerkungen 2. [1915.]
Zenodotus, *see* Wecklein (N.)
REFERENCES.
see BRIEFE u. Akten z. Gesch. d. 30jähr. Krieges, N.F., T2, B2, 1918.
„ DROYSEN (J. G.) Aktenstücke &c. z. Gesch. d. Frankfurter Nationalversamml., 1924.

Königliche Bibliothek [*Berlin*]. Verzeichniss d. arm. Hss. d. Königl. Bibl. zu Berlin. Von N. Karamianz. [Hss. Verzeichnisse, B10]. 4°. 1888

Königliche Gesellschaft der Wissenschaften [GÖTTINGEN]. Abhandlungen. Philolog.-hist. Klasse. N.F., B3ii, 13–18. 4°. & la8°. 1901–25
Bang (W.) & J. Marquart. Osttürk. Dialektstudien, 1914. [N.F., 13.]
Ephesus, *2nd Synod of*. Akten d. E. Synode v. 449 ; hrsg. J. Flemming, 1917. [15.]
Evagrius, *Ponticus*. [Text & German tr. &c.] ; v. W. Frankenburg, 1912. [N.F., 13.]
Herrmann (A.) Alte Geog. d. unt. Oxusgebiete, 1914. [15.]
Jacobsthal (P.) Aus d. Arch. Inst. d. Univ. Göttingen, I, Göttinger Vasen, 1912. [14.]
Kehr (P. F.) Papsturkunden in Spanien, 1i, ii, 1926. [18.]
Körte (G.) Aus d. Arch. Inst. d. Univ. Göttingen, 2, G. Bronzen, 1917. [16.]
Kraus (C. v.) Zu d. Liedern Heinrichs v. Morungen, 1917. [16.]
Lidzbarski (M.) Mandäische Liturgien ; mitgeteilt, übers. &c. v. M. L., 1920. [17.]
Marquart (J.) Ērānšahr nach d. Geog. d. Moses Xorenac'i, 1901. [3ii.]
Meyer (W.) Preces d. mozarab. Liturgie, 1914. [15.]
Moritz (B.) Sinaikult in heidn. Zeit, 1917. [16.]
Nöldeke (T.) Untersuch. z. Achiqar-Roman, 1913. [N.F., 14.]

Königliche Gesellschaft der Wissenschaften [*continued*].
Abhandlungen. Philolog.-hist. Klasse [*continued*].
Oldenberg (H.) Ṛgveda; Textkritik u. exeget. Noten, 7.–10. Buch, 1912. [13.]
—— Zur Gesch. d. altind. Prosa, 1917. [16.]
Petersen (E.) Rhythmus, 1917. [16.]
Rabel (E.) Papyrusurkunden d. Univ. zu Basel, 1917. [16.]
Rüff (H.) Das rhein. Osterspiel d. Berliner Hs., 1925. [18.]
Schwietering (J.) Die Demutsformel mittelhochdeut. Dichter, 1920. [17.]
Sethe (K. H.) Sarapis u. d. sogen. κάτοχοι d. S., 1913. [14.]
Thurneysen (R.) Zu irisch. Hss. u. Litt.-denkmälern, 2 Ser., 1912–13. [14.]
Wellhausen (J.) Krit. Anal. d. Apostelgesch., 1914. [15.]
Wendel (C.) Überlief. &c. d. Theokrit-Scholien, 1920. [17.]
Nachrichten. Geschäftl. Mittheilungen, 1894–1922. [*b. w.* Nachrichten: phil.-hist. Klasse]. 8°. Gottingen. 1895–1923
Nachrichten. Philolog.-histor. Klasse, 1894–1927. 8°. Göttingen. 1895–1928
Beihefte *bound w. the* Nachrichten *for the years mentioned.*
Borchling (C.) Mittelniederdeut. Hss. in d. Norddeutschl., Rheinlanden &c., 1898, 1913.
Johannessohn (M.) Gebrauch d. Präpositionen in d. LXX, 1925.
Lütkemann (L.) & A. Rahlfs. Hexaplar. Randnoten zu Isaias 1–16, 1915.
Rahlfs (A.) Verzeichnis d. griech. Hss. d. Alten Test., 1914.
Rüge (W.) Ält. kartograph. Material in deut. Bibl., 1916.
Wiederhold (W.) Papsturkunden in Frankreich, 1906, 1907, 1910, 1911, 1913.
REFERENCES.
see FRAGMENTA Burana; hrsg. W. Meyer [Festschr.], 1901.
„ GAUSS (C. F.) Werke; hrsg. v. d. Königl. Gesells. d. Wiss. zu G., B1–11, 1870–1927.
„ GÖTTINGISCHE GELEHRTE ANZEIGEN.
„ KEHR (P. F.) Regesta Pontificum Roman., 1911–27.

Königliche Museen, *Berlin, see* KÖNIGLICHES MUSEUM.

Königliche Nationalgalerie, *Berlin* [NATIONALGALERIE], *see* JUSTI (L.) Deut. Malkunst im 19ten Jhdt., Führer durch d. N., 1920.

Königliches Kunstgewerbemuseum, *Berlin* [STAATL. KUNSTGEWERBEMUSEUM], *see* SCHMITZ (H.) Bildteppiche, 1921.

Königliches Museum, *Berlin* [KÖNIGLICHE MUSEEN]. Erklär. Verzeichniss d. Abgüsse ant. Werke, v. K. Bötticher. 2e rev. A. s8°. 1872
Guide to the Pergamon Museum. Tr. M. McM. Honan. s8°. Berlin. 1904
Mitteilungen aus d. ägypt. Sammlung. B3. fol. 1921
see SACHS (C.) Die Musikinstrumente d. alt. Ägyptens, 1921. [3.]
REFERENCES.
see GOLDSCHMIDT (F.) Die ital. Bronzen d. Renaissance u. d. Barock, T1, 1914.
„ KEKULE V. STRADONITZ (R.) Die griech. Skulptur (Hdbchr. d. Staatl. Museen z. B.), 1922.
„ LE COQ (A. v.) Chotscho: Facs.-Wiedergaben d. wichtig. Funde d. ersten Kön. Preuss. Exped.; im Auftr. d. Generalverwaltung d. K. M., 1913.
„ RUMOHR (C. F. L. F. v.) Briefe an Bunsen ü. Erwerbungen für d. Berliner Museum; mitgeteilt v. F. Stock, 1925.
„ SCHUBART (W.) Papyri Graecae Berolin.: coll. W. S., 1911.
„ WULFF (O.) Altchristl. u. mittelalterl. byz. u. ital. Bildwerke, Ergänzungsband; bearbt. O. W. u. W. F. Volbach, 1923.

Königlich-Preuss. Akademie d. Wiss. zu Berlin. Abhandlungen (Phil.-hist. Klasse), 1913–27. 4°. 1915–27
„ „ (Phys.-math. Klasse), 1913–26. 4°. 1913–27
P.-h.=Phil.-hist.; P.-m.=Phys.-math.
Aichel (O.) Kausale Studie z. ontogenet. u. phylogenet. Geschehen am Kiefer. [1918 (P.-m. Kl.)]
Andreas (W.) Russ. Diplomatie u. Politik Fr. Wilhelms IV v. Preussen. [1926 (P.-h. Kl.)]
Bang (W.) Vom. Köktürk. z. Osman., Mittlg. 1–4. [1917, 1919, 1921 (P.-h. Kl.)]
Berend (E.) Proleg. z. hist. krit. Gesamtausg. v. Jean Pauls Werken. [1927 (P.-h. Kl.)]
Brackmann (A.) Zur Gesch. d. Hirsauer Reformbewegung im 12. Jhdt. [1927 (P.-h. Kl.)]
Branco (W.) Bericht ü. Urteile betreff. "Ziele vulkanolog. Forsch." [1914 (P.-m. Kl.)]
—— Ein Betracht. ü. d. ält. Säuger d. Trias-u. Liaszeit. [1915 (P.-m. Kl.)]
Brandl (A.) Zur Geographie d. altengl. Dialekte. [1915 (P.-h. Kl.)]
Bresslau (H.) Ält. Salzburg. Annalistik. [1923 (P.-h. Kl.)]
—— Aus d. ersten Zeit d. gr. abendländ. Schismas. [1919 (P.-h. Kl.)]

Königlich-Preuss. Akademie d. Wiss. zu Berlin [*continued*].
Abhandlungen [*continued*].
Brockelmann (C.) 'Alī's Qiṣṣa'i Jūsuf, d. ält. Vorläufer d. osman. Lit. [1916 (P.-h. Kl.)]
Cōic conara fugill; hrsg., übers. &c. R. Thurneysen. [1925 (P.-h. Kl.)]
De Groot (J. J. M.) Sinolog. Seminare u. Bibliotheken. [1913 (P.-h. Kl.)]
—— Der Thūpa, d. heil. Heiligtum d. Buddhismus in China. [1919 (P.-h. Kl.)]
Delitzsch (F.) Sumer.-akkad.-hett. Vokabularfragm. [1914 (P.-h. Kl.)]
Diels (H.) Entdeckung d. Alkohols. [1913 (P.-h. Kl.)]
—— Üb. d. v. Prokop beschr. Kunstuhr v. Gaza. [1917 (P.-h. Kl.)]
Engler (A.) Beitr. z. Entwicklungsgesch. d. Hochgebirgsfloren, Saxifragen. [1915 (P.-m. Kl.)]
Erdmann (B.) Berkeley's Philos. im Lichte s. wiss. Tagebuchs. [1919 (P.-h. Kl.)]
—— Die Idee v. Kants Kritik d. reinen Vernunft. [1917 (P.-h. Kl.)]
—— Die philosoph. Grundlagen v. Helmholtz' Wahrnehmungstheorie. [1921 (P.-h. Kl.)]
Erman (A.) Ägypt. Schülerhss. [1925 (P.-h. Kl.)]
—— Ein Fall abgekürzter Justiz in Ägypten. [1913 (P.-h. Kl.)]
—— Reden, Rufe &c. auf Gräberbildern d. alt. Reiches. [1918 (P.-h. Kl.)]
—— Röm. Obelisken. [1917 (P.-h. Kl.)]
Euler (L.) L. E.'s u. J. H. Lamberts Briefwechsel (1758–72); hrsg. K. Bopp. [1924 (P.-m. Kl.)]
Ferri (S.) Alc. iscriz. di Cirene. [1925 (P.-h. Kl.)]
Fick (R.) Einiges ü. Vererbungsfragen. [1924 (P.-m. Kl.)]
—— Üb. d. Entst. d. Gelenkformen mit Tierversuchen. [1921 (P.-m. Kl.)]
Ginzel (F. K.) Histor. Sonnenfinsternisse &c. [1918 (P.-m. Kl.)]
Goldman (E. E.) Vitalfärb. am Zentralnervensystem. [1913 (P.-m. Kl.)]
Goldziher (I.) Stellung d. alt. islam. Orthodoxie zu d. ant. Wissenschaften. [1915 (P.-h. Kl.)]
Grapow (H.) Üb. d. Wortbildungen mit e. Präfix m- im Ägypt. [1914 (P.-h. Kl.)]
Gräven (H.) Leibnizens Bildnisse; hrsg. &c. C. Schuchhardt. [1916 (P.-h. Kl.)]
Gressmann (H.) Vom reichen Mann u. armen Lazarus &c. [1918 (P.-h. Kl.)]
Griffith (F. L.) Nubian texts of the Xtn. per. [1913 (P.-h. Kl.)]
Haberlandt (G.) Gedächtnisrede auf S. Schwendener. [1919 (P.-m. Kl.)]
Heeg (J.) Pseudodemokrit. Studien. [1913 (P.-h. Kl.)]
Hellmann (G.) Beitr. z. Erfindungsgesch. meteorolog. Instrumente. [1920 (P.-m. Kl.)]
—— Entwickl. d. meteorolog. Beobachtungen in Deutschland. [1926 (P.-m. Kl.)]
—— Die Meteorologie in d. deut. Flugschriften &c. d. 16 Jhdts. [1921 (P.-m. Kl.)]
—— Versuch e. Gesch. d. Wettervorhersage im 16 Jhdt. [1924 (P.-m. Kl.)]
Helm (R.) Eusebius' Chronik u. i. Tabellenform. [1923 (P.-h. Kl.)]
Helmreich (G.) Handschriftl. Studien zu Meletius. [1918 (P.-h. Kl.)]
Hero, *of Alexandria.* Belopoiika; Gr. u. Deut. v. H. Diels &c. [1918 (P.-h. Kl.)]
Herzfeld (E.) Aufnahme d. sasanid. Denkmals v. Paikūli. [1914 (P.-h. Kl.)]
Heusler (A.) Anfänge d. isländ. Saga. [1913 (P.-h. Kl.)]
Hilzheimer (M.) Tierknochen aus d. Gruben d. Lossower Ringwalls bei Frankfurt a. O. [1922 (P.-h. Kl.)]
Hintze (O.) Gedächtnisrede auf G. v. Schmoller. [1918 (P.-h. Kl.)]
—— Gedächtnisrede auf R. Koser. [1915 (P.-h. Kl.)]
Holl (C.) Augustins innere Entwicklung. [1922 (P.-h. Kl.)]
—— Entst. d. 4 Fastenzeiten in d. griech. Kirche. [1923 (P.-h. Kl.)]
Jensen (C.) Neoptolemos u. Horaz. [1918 (P.-h. Kl.)]
Kehr (P. F.) Die alt. Papsturkun. Spaniens. [1926 (P.-h. Kl.)]
—— Das Erzbistum Magdeburg &c. [1920 (P.-h. Kl.)]
—— Das Papsttum u. d. katalan. Prinzipat &c. [1926 (P.-h. Kl.)]
Köhler (W.) Aus d. Anthropoidenstation auf Teneriffa, 2–4. [1915, 1917 & 1918 (P.-m. Kl.)]
Krüger (E.) & D. Krencker. Ausgrabung d. sog. röm. Kaiserpalastes in Trier. [1915 (P.-h. Kl.)]
Kuhn (F.) Dschong lun d. Tsui Schi (2 Jahrh. n. Chr.) [1914 (P.-h. Kl.)]
Kurrelmeyer (W.) Doppeldrucke in i. Bedeut. f. d. Textgesch. v. Wielands Werken. [1913 (P.-h. Kl.)]
Lachmann (C. C. F. W.) Briefe an K. L., 1814–50; hrsg. &c. A. Leitzmann. [1915 (P.-h. Kl.)]
Le Coq (A. v.) Türk. Manichaica aus Chotscho. II, III. [1919, 1922 (P.-h. Kl.)]

Königlich-Preuss. Akademie d. Wiss. zu Berlin [*continued*].
Abhandlungen [*continued*].
Mahnke (D.) Neue Einblicke in d. Entdeckungsgesch. d. höh. Analysis. [1925 (P.-m. Kl.)]
Meyer (E.) Gemeinde d. neu. Bundes im Lande Damaskus. [1919 (P.-h. Kl.)]
—— Röm. Manipularheer. [1923 (P.-h. Kl.)]
Meyer (K.) Bruchstücke d. ält. Lyrik Irlands. [1919 (P.-h. Kl.)]
—— Üb. d. ält. irische Dichtung, 2H. [1913 (P.-h. Kl.)]
Mittwoch (E.) Zur Entstehungsgesch. d. Islam. Gebets &c. [1913 (P.-h. Kl.)]
Möller (G.) 2 ägypt. Eheverträge aus vorsaït. Zeit. [1918 (P.-h. Kl.)]
Moritz (B.) Beitr. z. Gesch. d. Sinaiklosters im M.-a. [1918 (P.-h. Kl.)]
Müller (C.) Beitr. z. Gesch. d. Verfassung d. alt. Kirche. [1922 (P.-h. Kl.)]
Müller (F. W. K.) 2 Pfahlinschr. aus d. Turfanfunden. [1915 (P.-h. Kl.)]
—— Uigurica, 3. [1920 P.-h. Kl.)]
Pelissier (R.) Mischär-Tatar. Sprachproben. [1918 (P.-h. Kl.)]
—— Mokšamordvin. Texte, gesamm. im Nordosten d. Gouv. Tambov. [1926 (P.-h. Kl.)]
Penck (A.) Die Höttinger Breccie u. d. Inntalterrasse nördl. Innsbruck. [1920 (P.-m. Kl.)]
Petersen (J.) Entst. d. Eckermanns. Gespr. &c. [1924 (P.-h. Kl.)]
Philo, *Byzantius.* Belopoiika; Gr. u. Deut. v. H. Diels &c. [1918 (P.-h. Kl.)]
—— Exzerpte aus P.'s Mechanik B. 7 u. 8; Gr. & Deut. v. H. Diels &c. [1919 (P.-h. Kl.)]
Philodemus. P. Über d. Götter, 1. [*&* 3.] Buch; gr. Text u. Erläut. v. H. Diels. [1915–16 (P.-h. Kl.)]
Plaumann (G.) Der Idioslogos. [1918 (P.-h. Kl.)]
Porphyry. P., "Gegen d. Christen," 15 Bücher; hrsg. A. v. Harnack. [1916 (P.-h. Kl.)]
Rothmann (M.) & E. Teuber. Aus d. Anthropoidenstation auf Teneriffa, 1, v. M. R. & E. T. [1915 (P.-m. Kl.)]
Rubner (M.) Üb. d. Wasserbindung in Kolloiden. [1922 (P.-m. Kl.)]
Sachau (C. E.) Die Chronik v. Arbela. [1915 (P.-h. Kl.)]
—— Verzeichnis muhammedan. Dynast. [1923 (P.-h. Kl.)]
—— Vom Klosterbuch d. Šâbuštî. [1919 (P.-h. Kl.)]
—— Zur Ausbreitung d. Christentums in Asien. [1919 (P.-h. Kl.)]
Schäfer (H.) Nubische Texte im Dialekte d. Kunûzi. [1917 (P.-h. Kl.)]
Schneider (H.) Uhland u. d. deut. Heldensage. [1918 (P.-h. Kl.)]
Schubring (W.) Das Mahānisīha-Sutta. [1918 (P.-h. Kl.)]
Schuchardt (H. E. M.) Zur Kenntnis d. Baskischen v. Sara (Labourd). [1922 (P.-h. Kl.)]
Schuchhardt (C.) Die sogen. Trajanswälle in d. Dobrudscha. [1918 (P.-h. Kl.)]
Seler (E.) Beobacht. &c. in d. Ruinen v. Palenque. [1915 (P.-h. Kl.)]
—— Quetzalcouatl-Fassaden yukatek. Bauten. [1916 (P.-h. Kl.)]
—— Die Ruinen v. Uxmal. [1917 (P.-h. Kl.)]
Sethe (K.) Die Ächtung feindl. Fürsten, Völker u. Dinge auf altägypt. Tongefassscherben. [1926 (P.-h. Kl.)]
Seuffert (B.) Proleg. zu e. Wieland-Ausgabe, 7. [1921 (P.-h. Kl.)]
Spranger (E.) Die wiss. Grundlagen d. Schulverfassungslehre &c. [1927 (P.-h. Kl.)]
Singer (S.) Arab. u. europ. Poesie im M.- a. [1918.]
Stieda (W.) J. Bernouilli in s. Bezieh. z. preuss. Herrscherhause u. z. Akad. d. Wiss. [1925 (P.-h. Kl.)]
Strahl (H.) & E. Ballmann. Embryonalhüllen u. Plazenta v. Putorius furo. [1915 (P.-m. Kl.)]
Struve (G.) Neue Elem. d. inn. Saturnstrabanten. [1918 (P.-m. Kl.)]
Stumpf (C.) Die Attribute d. Gesichtsempfindungen. [1917 (P.-h. Kl.)]
—— Empfindung u. Vorstellung. [1918 (P.-h. Kl.)]
—— Spinozastudien. [1919 (P.-h. Kl.)]
Stutz (U.) Päpstl. Diplom. unter Leo XIII &c. [1925 (P.-h. Kl.)]
Tangl (M.) Bonifatiusfragen. [1919 (P.-h. Kl.)]
Unwerth (W. v.) Proben deutschruss. Mundarten aus d. Wolgakolonien u. d. Gouvt. Cherson. [1918 (P.-h. Kl.)]
Virchow (H.) Gesichtsmuskeln d. Schimpansen. [1915 (P.-m. Kl.)]
Waldeyer-Hartz (W. v.) Gedächtnisrede auf A. Brauer. [1918 (P.-m. Kl.)]
—— Die Intraparietalnähte. [1917 (P.-m. Kl.)]
Waldschmidt (R.) & W. Lentz. Stellung Jesu im Manichäismus. [1926 (P.-h. Kl.)]
Wartburg (W. v.) Zur Benennung d. Schafes i. d. roman. Sprachen. [1918 (P.-h. Kl.)]
Wegehaupt (H.) Florent. Plutarchpalimpsest, *w. facs.* [1914 (P.-h. Kl.)]
Wellmann (M.) Die Georgika d. Demokritos. [1921 (P.-h. Kl.)]
Wenkebach (E.) Beitr. z. Textgesch. d. Epidemienkomm. Galens, T1. [1927 (P.-h. Kl.)]

Königlich-Preuss. Akademie d. Wiss. zu Berlin [*continued*].
Abhandlungen [*continued*].
Wenkebach (E.) Das Proömium d. Komm. Galens zu d. Epidemien d. Hippokrates. [1918 (P.-h. Kl.)]
—— Pseudogalen. Komm. zu d. Epidemien d. Hippokrates. [1917 (P.-h. Kl.)]
—— Unters. ü. Galens Komm. z. d. Epidemien d. Hippokrates. [1925 (P.-h. Kl.)]
Wiegand (T.) 8er Bericht ü. d. v. d. Staatl. Mus. in Milet u. Didyma untern. Ausgrab. [1924 (P.-h. Kl.)]
Will (L.) Kolloidale Subs. als Energiequelle f. d. mikros. Schusswaff. d. Coelenteraten. [1914 (P.-m. Kl.)]
Deutsche Texte d. M. a.; hrsg. v. d. K.-P. Akad. d. Wiss. B26, 27, 29, 31. 8°. 1920–27
see CONRAD, *v. Helmsdorf.* Der Spiegel d. menschl. Heils, 1924. [31.]
,, SAELDEN HORT (Der): alemann. Gedicht v. Leben Jesu &c., 1927. [26.]
,, TROY. Der Göttweiger Trojanerkrieg, 1926. [29.]
,, WERNHER, *Swiss poet.* Marienleben, 1920. [27.]
Sitzungsberichte, 1914–27. la8°. 1914–27
1922–1927 *each in 2p.*, Philos.-hist. Klasse *&* Physikal.-math. Klasse, *each w. sep. tp. & pagin.* [*b. in 1v*].
REFERENCES.
see GRIMM (J. L. C.) & W. GRIMM. Briefwechsel mit K. Lachmann, 2v, 1927.
,, LEIBNITZ (G. W., *Frhr.* v.) Sämtl. Schr. u. Briefe, *in prog.*, 1923 &c.

Königlich-Preussische Staatsarchiven.
Publicationen. B72, 90. la8°. L. 1898
see FREDERICK II, *of Prussia.* Briefwechsel m. Grumbkow u. Maupertuis (1731–59); hrsg. v. R. Koser, 1898. [72.]
,, —— Briefwechsel, Nachträge, 1917. [90.]

Königlich-Preussische Turfan Expedition.
see GRÜNWEDEL (A.) Alt-Kutscha: archäol. u. relig. Forsch. an Tempera-Gemälde aus Buddhist. Höhlen, 1920.
,, LE COQ (A. v.) Auf Hellas Spuren in Ostturkistan: Berichte &c. d. 2. u. 3. Deut. T.-Exped., 1926.
,, —— Die buddhist. Spätantike in Mittelasien, 6T, 1922–28.
,, —— Chotscho: Facs.-Wiedergaben d. wichtig. Funde d. ersten K. P. E. nach T., 1913.
,, —— Von Land u. Leute: Berichte &c. d. 4. Deut. Turfanexped., 1928.

Königlich-Preussisches Historisches Institut in Rom.
see CARDAUNS (L.) Von Nizza bis Crépy, 1923.
,, HILTEBRANDT (P.) Die kirchl. Reunionsverhandl. d. 17. Jhdts.: Ernst August v. Hannover u. d. kath. Kirche, 1922.

Königlich-Sächsische Gesellschaft d. Wiss. zu Leipzig.
Abhandlungen. B18v, 30ii, 33iv. la8°. 1899–1919
see GELZER (H.) Genesis d. byz. Themenverfass., 1899.
,, GROHMAN (A.) Æthiop. Marienhymnen; hrsg. &c. v. A. G., 1919. [33iv.]
,, STUDNICZKA (F.) Symposion Ptolemaios II, 1914. [30ii.]
Berichte ü. d. Verhandlgn. d. G. d. W.: Philol.-hist. Classe. B66–78. 8°. L. [1914–26]
see POGGENDORFF (J. C.) Biogr.-lit. Hdwbh. f. Mathematik &c.; hrsg. v. d. Sächs. Akad., B5, 1926.

Königsmarck (Maria Aurora, *Gräfin* **von).**
see BURG (P.) Die schöne Gräfin Königsmarck, 1919.
,, PALMBLAD (V. F.) A. K. u. ihre Verwandten, 6T, 1848–53.

Koning (Wilhelm Arnold). Specimen de Gerardi Zutphan. vita, scriptis & meritis. 8°. Trajecti a. R. 1858

Koninklijke Akademie van Wetenschappen. Verhand. Afd. lett. N. Reeks. d10ii. la8°. 1909
see MEULEN (R. VAN DER). De Holland. Zee-en Scheeptermen in het Russ., 1909. [N. Reeks, 10ii.]

Koninklijke Bibliothek ['s GRAVENHAGE]. Cat. van de pamfletten-verzameling berustende in de K.B. Door W. P. C. Knuttel., d9, Alfab. register, 1486–1795. s4°. 's Gravenhage. 1920
see BYVANCK (A. W.) Princ. mss. à peint., 1924.

Koninklijk Instituut voor de Taal-, Land & Volkenkunde van Nederlandsch Indië. Gedenkschrift. Uitg. ter gelegenheid v. het 75-jarig bestaan, 4 juni, 1926. la8°. 's Gravenhage. 1926
see BIJDRAGEN tot de taal-, land-en volkenkunde &c.: Tijdschrift van het Kon. Inst., 1853–.
,, BRANDES (J. L. A.) Beschr. van Tjandi Singasari &c.; uitg. door het Kon. Inst. &c., 1909.

Koninklijk-Nederlandsch Aardrijkskundig Genootschap. Nomina geographica Neerlandica. Onder red. van I. Dornseiffen, J. H. Gallée &c. 5d. [*in* 2v]. 8°. A. [2–5, Leiden]. [1885]–1901

Konitza (M.) The Albanian question. [P2485]. 8°. *n.p.* 1918

Konkle (Burton Alva). George Bryan & the constit. of Pennsylvania, 1731–91. 8°. Phila. 1922

Konkol (Marek). Коммуна 71 года. Перев. съ польскаго. [P2398]. 8°. П. 1918

Konkordienbuch, *see* Concordia.

Konopnicka (Marya). Písničky. Přeložil O. F. Babler. 8°. Olomouc. 1923

Konovalova (K. A.), *ed.*, *see* Russia: Sov. Rep. Народное образование в Р. С. Ф. С. Р., 1923.

Konow (Sten). Das ind. Drama. [Grundr. d. indo-ar. Phil., B2, H2, D]. la8°. 1920

Konrad (P.) Dr. A. Moibanus. [Verein f. Ref.-gesch. Schr., Jhrg. 9, Nr. 34]. 8°. Halle. 1891

Konstantin Konstantinovich, *see* Constantine Constantinovich, *grand duke*.

Konstantinov (M. M.) Последние дни Колчаковщины. Материал подготовлен к печати М. М. К. С прилож. статьи А. А. Ширямова. 8°. Москва. 1926

Konstantius (Jiři), *see* Constantius (J.)

Konstitutsionno-Demokraticheskaya Partiya, *see* Shershenevich (G. F.) Программа, 1905.

Konungs-Skuggsjá. Speculum regale. Udg. af det Kong. Nordiske Oldskriftselskab. [H1, Tekst]. la8°. Kjöbenhavn. 1920

see Flom (G. T.) Language of the K.S. (Speculum regale), 2p, 1921–24.

Kool (Jaap). Tänze d. Naturvölker. s8°. 1921

Koop (Albert J.) & H. Inada. Japanese names & how to read them: manual for art-collectors &c. la8°. 1923

Koosen (Johann Heinrich). Der Streit d. Naturgesetzes mit d. Zweckbegriffe. [*b. w.* Strümpell (L. H.) Herbarts Philos., 1834]. 8°. Königsberg. 1845

Kooverba (Manhar), *Mahrani of Panna*. Lady Hardinge of Penshurst. A tribute. 8°. [1915]

Kopff (August). Die Einstein. Relativitätstheorie. [P2684]. s8°. L. 1920

Grundzüge d. Einstein. Relativitätstheorie. 8°. L. 1921

Kopisch (August), *see* Picchioni (L.) La Div. Commedia illust. da A. K. &c., 1846.

Kopitar (Bartholomæus). Glagolita Clozianus &c. Brevi gramm. et lexico illustr. ed. &c. 4°. Vindobonae. 1836

see Hesychius, *of Alexandria*; Hesychii Glossographi discipulus Russus sec. 12–13; ed. B. K., 1839.

Kopitar (Jernej). *Gramm. d. slav. Spr. in Krain, Kärnten u. Steyermark. s8°. Laibach. 1808

Köpke (Balthasar). Dialogus de templo Salomonis. s8°. Amstelaedami. 1698

Kopko (Peter). Apostolus Bybliensis saec. 14. gramm.-krit. analys., 1912, *see* Kais. Akad. d. W. zu Wien. Denkschr., B55, 1917.

Köpp (Friedrich). Üb. d. Bildnis Alexanders d. Grossen. [52. Progr. z. Winckelmannsfeste d. Arch. Gesells.] 4°. 1892

see Aubin (H.) Gesch. d. Rheinlandes; v. H. A., Th. Frings, J. Hansen & F. K., 2B, 1922.

Köppel (Emmy), *see* Hartwig (G.), *ps.*

Köppen (Alfred).

Die mod. Malerei in Deutschland. la8°. Bielefeld. 1925

Koppen (Luise). Katharina v. Bora, Luthers Frau. 2e A. s8°. Bielefeld. 1923

Koppius (Franciscus). Vitae ac gesta abbatum Adwerdensium. [P2755]. 8°. Groningen. [1850]

Korablev (Vasily Nikolaevich). Славянскій съѣздъ въ Прагѣ 1908г. [P2452]. 8°. С.-П. 1908

Koran.

Hist. Iosephi Patriarchae ex Alcorano, Arab. Cum vers. Lat. & scholiis T. Erpenii & alphab. Arab. s4°. Leidae. 1617

[The Koran *in Arabic*]. 8°. [Bombay. 1282=1865]

Corani textus Arab. Rec. &c. G. Fluegel. nova impr. la8°. Lips. 1881

Translations.

The life of Mahomet; w. the Alcoran at large. Tr. into French by the Sieur de Ryer. Now English'd. 8°. 1718

L'Alkoran. Tr. textuelle par Fatma Zaide. 8°. Lisbonne. 1861

The K. Tr., w. notes [&] prelim. disc. by G. Sale, n. ed., w. mem. of [S.] 8°. 1861

„ „ ....[Chandos Class.] s8°. *n.d.*

„ „ Tr. G. Sale. With explan. notes f. app. comm., & S.'s prelim. discourse. Intr. by Sir E. D. Ross. 8°. [1921]

Le Koran analysé, d'ap. la tr. de M. Kasimirski & les obs. de savants orient., par J. La Beaume. [Bibl. Orient., t4]. la8°. 1878

Koran [*continued*].

Translations [*continued*].

Koran. verhalen in het Maleisch; Gerth v. Wijk, *see* Tijdschrift voor Ind. taal &c., d35, 36, 1893–94.

Qouran. [*In Armenian*, w. Life of Mohammed. Tr. L. Larentz. 2p (*pagin. contin.*) P2802]. s8°. K. polis. 1911

Le K.: tr. des Sourates essentielles par J. C. Mardrus. 8°. 1926

see Christensen (A.) Xavāṣṣ-i-āyāt, magie des versets du C., 1920.

„ Marracci (L.) Alcorani textus univ. descr., 4p, 1698.

„ —— Refutatio Alcorani, 1698.

„ Nöldeke (T.) Gesch. d. Qorāns, 2e A, T1–3i, 1909–26.

„ Storey (C. A.) Persian lit., p1, Qur'ānic, 1927.

Körber (Kurt). Kirchengüterfrage u. schmalkald. Bund. [Verein f. Ref.-Gesch. Schr., Jhrg. 30 (Nr. 111/12)]. 8°. L. 1912

Korczok (Anton).

Die griech.-kath. Kirche in Galizien. 8°. L. 1921

Kordgien (G. C.), *see* Sauer (C. M.) & G. C. K. Portugies. Konvers.-Gramm., 1887.

Kordouba (Myron). Le territoire et la population de l'Ukraine. 8°. Berne. 1919

Korea, *see* Corea.

Koreff (David Ferdinand), *1783–1851*, *see* Martin (M.) Un aventurier intellectuel, le dr. K., 1925.

Korevo (Nikolai Nikolaevich) [Korewo]. The Finnish question. Lect., 1910. [*a. c. in* P2451]. 8°. St. Petersb. 1911

Korf (*count* Modest Andreevich). Восшествіе на престолъ Николая I. изд. 3e (1oe для публики). la8°. С.-П. 1857

Жизнь Графа Сперанскаго. Изд. Имп. Публ. Библ. 2t *in* 1v. la8°. С.-П. 1861

Korff (*Baron* Sergei Aleksandrovich).

Autocracy & revolution in Russia. 8°. 1923

The constit. of the Cossacks. [P2403]. 8°. Paris. 1919

Russia's foreign relations dur. last half cent. 8°. 1922

Kori (Torahiko). The toils of Yoshitomo. A tragedy of anc. Japan. [Eng. version assist. by H. M. Sainsbury]. s8°. [1922]

Koriun, *see* Gorium.

Kornacher (Johann Heinrich). De subita &c. coelestis doct. in Aug. Conf. cont. propag. Sub praes. G. Hecking. [P484]. s4°. Heilbronnae. [1730]

Kornemann (Ernst). Kaiser Hadrian u. d. letzte grosse Historiker v. Rom. la8°. L. 1905

Mausoleum und Tatenbericht des Augustus. 8°. L. 1921

Körner (C. Theodor). Drei deut. Gedichte, 1813 (*facs.*), *see* Freytag (G.) Bilder, B5, 1925.

Körner (Emil). Erasmus Alber. [Quellen &c. aus d. Gesch. d. Reformationsjhdts., B15]. 8°. L. 1910

Körner (Friedrich).

Der Menschengeist. 2 Abt. [*in 1v pagin. cont.*] 8°. L. 1870

Körner (George).

Philol.-krit. Abh. v. d. Wend. Sprache &c. s8°. L. 1766

Körner (Gustav). Das deutsche Element i. d. V. S. v. Nordamerika, 1818–48. 2e A. mit Zusätzen &c. 8°. N.Y. 1884

Körner (Johann Gottfried).

Epitome controversiarum theolog. s8°. Lipsiae. 1769

Körner (Josef). Romantiker u. Klassiker: d. Brüder Schlegel in i. Bezieh. zu Schiller u. Goethe. 8°. 1924

Kornilov (Aleksandr Aleksandrovich).

Годы странствий М. Бакунина. 8°. Ленинград. 1925

Молодые годы М. Бакунина. [Семейство Бакуниныхъ, 1]. 8°. Москва. 1915

Обществ. движеніе при Александрѣ II (1855–81). 8°. Москва. 1909

Kornilov (Lavr Georgevich). Кашгарія или Восточный Туркестанъ. Подъ ред. Ген.-Лейт. Сахарова составилъ К. la8°. Ташкентъ. 1903

Korolenko (Vladimir Galaktionovich).

Полное собраніе сочиненіи. 9t *in* 4v. s8°. С.-П. 1914

Домъ No. 13 (эпизодъ изъ Кишиневскаго погрома). 2e изд. [P2716]. s8°. Лондонъ. 1903

Домъ No. 13, *see* Gorky (M.) Протестъ, *n.d.*

Исторія моего современника. 5t. s8°. Москва. 1922

Невольный убійца. Разсказъ. [P846]. s8°. С.-П. 1888

Письма К. к И. П. Белоконскому. 1883–1921. s8°. Москва. 1922

Трагедія генерала Ковалева и нравы военной среды. [P2446]. 8°. Москва. 1906

Translations.

La gelée—En mauvaise société—Le rève de Makar. [Tr.] 8°. 1922

see Gorky (M.) Reminisc. of my youth [*incl.* V. G. K.], tr., 1924.

„ Myakotin (V. A.) "Задруга": памяти К., под. ред. М., 1922.

Korostovets (Ivan Yakovlevich).
Россія на Дальнемъ Востокѣ. la8°. Пекинъ. 1922
Страница изъ ист. Русской дипломатіи. Русско-япон. переговоры въ Портсмутѣ въ 1905. изд. 2e. la8°. Пекинъ. 1923
Pre-war diplomacy. Russo-Jap. problem. Treaty signed at Portsmouth, U.S.A., 1905. 8°. 1920
—— **& E. Hauer.** Von Cinggis Khan zur Sowjetrepublik. Kurze Gesch. d. Mongolei. la8°. 1926

Korostovets (Vladimir Konstantinovich). Neue Väter—Neue Söhne: 3 russ. Generationen. Übers. v. M. v. Busch. [B1]. 8°. 1926

Korsakov (I.) Голодъ въ Совѣтской Россіи и его причины. [P2578]. 8°. Юрьевъ. 1922

Körte (Alfred). Zu neueren Komödienfunden, see Königl.-Sächs. Gesells. Berichte, phil.-hist. Kl., B71, 1919.

Korte (August). Die Konzilspolitik Karls V, 1538–43. [Verein f. Ref.-gesch. Schr., Jhrg. 22, Nr. 85]. 8°. Halle a. d. S. 1905

Körte (Gustav). Aus d. Arch. Inst. d. Univ. Göttingen, 2, Göttinger Bronzen, see Königliche Gesells. d. Wiss. zu Göttingen, Abhlgn., B16, 1917.

Korthals-Altes (J.) Sir C. Vermuyden: life-work in land-reclamation. With notes on pres. condit. of drainage &c. la8°. 1925

Kortholt (Christian), *the elder.*
De lectione Bibliorum in linguis vulgo cognitis &c. comm. s4°. Ploena. 1692
De persecutionibus eccl. primævæ sub imperat. ethn. liber. [*b. w. h.* Hist. eccl. N.T., 1697]. s4°. Kiloni. 1689
De variis Scripturae edit. tractatus. s4°. Kiloni. 1686
Disq. anti-Baronianae. Una cum A. Tribbechovii exerc. ad. Baronii Annales [*w. sep. tp. & pagin.*] s4°. Lipsiae. 1708
Erörterung d. streit. Frage: Ob d. Pabst d. röm. Reich von denen Griechen auff d. Deutsche gebracht habe? &c. [P2670]. s4°. Jena. 1660
Hist. eccl. Novi Test., usque ad sec. 17 &c. s4°. Lipsiae. 1697
Pastor fidelis. s8°. Hamburgi. 1696
„ „ Add. De 'Ορθοτομία verbi divini; publ. C. Kortholtus [Nepos]. s8°. Lemgoviae. 1748
Tract. de orig. &c. philosophiae barbaricae, Chaldaicae, Aegypt., Persicae, Indicae, Gallicae. s4°. Jenae. 1660

Kortholt (Christian), *the younger.* Comm. de eccl. suburbicariis. Praes. C. K., resp. J. G. Walthero. [P432]. s4°. Lipsiae. 1730

Korzybski (Alfred). Manhood of humanity. The science & art of human engineering. 8°. N.Y. 1921

Kosch (Mekhithar), see Mekhithar, *Gosh.*

Kosch (Wilhelm).
P. Martin v. Cochem. [2e A. P2522]. 8°. 1921

Kościuszko (Tadeusz), see Gardner (M. M.) K.: a biog., 1920.

Koser (Reinhold). Gesch. Friedrichs d. Grossen. 6. u. 7. A. 4B. [B4, 4. u. 5. A.] 8°. St. 1914–25
Zur preuss. u. deut. Gesch. Aufsätze u. Vorträge [1888–1908]. 8°. St. 1921
see Hintze (O.) Gedächtnisrede auf R. K., 1915.

Koshelev (Aleksandr Ivanovich).
Записки (1812–83). Съ семью приложеніями. 8°. Berlin. 1884

Koshits (Ivan A. Porai-), see Porai-Koshits (I. A.)

Koskenniemi (Weikko Antero). Gedichte. Aus d. Finn. üb. v. J. J. Meyer. s8°. Dresden. [1907]

Kossak (Sophia) [*Mme.* S. Kossak-Szczucka]. The blaze. Remin. of Volhynia, 1917–19. Tr. s8°. [1927]

Kossovich (Kaetan Andreev). Четыре статьи изъ Зендавесты, see Imperat. Russ. Arch. Obsch. Труды Восточ. отд., ч8, 1864.

Kossuth (Ferencz). K. F. harmincz parlamenti beszéde. Életrajzi adatokkal kisére Hentaller L. &c. 8°. 1906
A kiegyezésröl. [P2398]. 8°. 1907

Kossuth (Lajos), see Áldor (I.) K. L. élete, 1892.

Kostaneantz (Karapet). [Les études armén. en Europe. Liste des livres &c. rel. à l'Armenie dep. 13e siècle. *Tp. & intr. in Armenian*]. 8°. Tiflis. 1910
[Hovhannes Thlkourantzin & his poems. *In Armenian.* P2806]. s8°. Tiflis. 1892
Лѣтопись на камняхъ. Собр.-указатель армянск. надписей. [Bibl. armeno-georgica, 2. *a. tp. in Armenian*]. la8°. С.-П. 1913
[New coll. of mediaeval Armenian poetry &c. Bks. 1 & 2. P2801]. s8°. Tiflis. 1892
"Роза и соловей." Къ полож. армянъ въ 16 вѣкѣ, по стихотв. Григорія Ахтамарскаго. Изъ "Древн. восточныхъ," т4. 4°. Москва. 1913
see Sharakan. Шараканъ богослужебные каноны &c., подъ ред. К., 1914.
„ Thomas, *of Medzoph.* Hist. (*in Armenian*); ed. K. K., 1892.

Kostantin, *Erznkatzi.* [K. E. & his poetry. *In Armenian.* Ed. H. M. Potourean. P2815]. s8°. Venetik. 1905
see †Tchobanian (A.), *tr.* Trouvères arm., 1906.

Kostenko (Lev Theofan.) Путешествіе въ Бухару русской миссіи въ 1870. s8°. С.-П. 1871
Хивинское ханство. [*Extr. fr.* Военный Сборникъ, 1874. P2386]. 8°. [1874]

Köster (Adolf). Die stille Schlacht. Kriegsberichte aus d. Gr. Hauptquartier. 8°. München. 1915

Köster (Albert).
Die deut. Lit. d. Aufklärungszeit. 8°. Heidelberg. 1925
Prolegomena zu e. Ausg. d. Werke Th. Storms, see Königl. Sächs. Gesells. Berichte, B70, 1918.
—— **& J. Petersen.** Gesch. d. deut. Lit., B1, see Schneider (H.) Heldendichtung &c. 1925.

Köster (August). Das antike Seewesen. 1e A. 8°. 1923
Schiffahrt u. Handelsverkehr d. östl. Mittelmeeres im 3. u. 2. Jahrtaus. v. Chr., see Alte Orient, Beih. 1, 1924.
Seefahrten d. alt. Ägypter. 8°. [1926]

Köster (Friedrich Burchard). Meletemata in Zachariae prophetae cap 9–14. s8°. Gottingae. 1818

Köster (Herm. L.)
Gesch. d. deut. Jugendliteratur. 4. A. 8°. Braunschweig. 1927

Koster (W. J. W.) Tractatus Graeci de re metrica ined. [Tract. Urbinas, Nicetas de metris &c.] Cong., rec. &c. K. [Nouv. Coll. de textes &c.; Assoc. G. Budé]. 8°. 1922

Köstler (Rudolf). Wörterbuch z. Codex juris canonici. Lief. 1. 8°. München. [1927]

Kostomarov (Nikolai Ivanovich). Русская исторія. 2 отд. *in* 3v [1i, ii *pagin. cont.*] 8°. С.-П. 1873–74
„ „ ....[*10–17 c.*] 2oe изд. 2т. 8°. С.-П. 1880–81

Kostüme. Zur Gesch. d. K.; Bogen nach Zeichnungen, *n.d.*, see Braun (L.) *&c.*

Kotagiri plates of r. of Rudramamba, A.D. 1273, see Hyderabad Arch. Ser., No. 6, 1925.

Kotas (Walther Hjalmar).
Die skandinav. Lit. seit 1870. s8°. Wiesbaden. 1925

Koteliansky (Samuel Solomonovich), see Chekhov (A.) Life & letters of A. T.; tr. & ed. S. S. K. & P. Tomlinson, 1925.
see Chekhov (A.) Lit. & theatr. reminisc. [*by var. a*[s]*.*]; tr. & ed. S. S. K., 1927.

Kotenev (Anatol M.)
Shanghai: its mixed court & council. la8°. Shanghai. 1925
Shanghai: its municipality & the Chinese. la8°. Shanghai. 1925

Kotlyarevsky (Ivan Petrovich). Виргилиева Енеида на украинскаго мову перелыцевана. s8°. Житоміръ. 1886

Kotlyarevsky (Nestor Aleksandrovich).
Девятнадцатый век; отраженіе его основных мыслей. s8°. П. 1921
Лермонтовъ, личность поэта &c. 5oe изд. 8°. П. 1915
Литературныя направленія Александровской эпохи. 3e изд. 8°. П. 1917
Наше недавнее прошлое въ истолкованіи художниковъ слова xix в. 8°. П. 1919
Н. В. Гоголь. 1829–42. 4oe изд. 8°. П. 1915
Холмы родины. 8°. Берлинъ. 1923

Kotlyarevsky (Sergei Andreevich). Бюджетное право. [Инст. Совет. Права]. la8°. Москва. [1924]

Kotoshikhin (Grigor) [Cotossichin (Grigori Carpofsson)]. Beskrifning om muschofsche rijkets staat. Förswänskat 1669. Samtida skildring af 1600–talets ryska samfundslip utg. af G. Adde. s4°. Stockholm. 1908

Kötschke (Hermann). Unser Reichskanzler [*i.e.* T. v. Bethmann Hollweg]. 5e Auflage. 8°. [1921]

Kotsipinsky (Ant.) Писньи, думки и шумки русского народа на Подоли, Украини &c. Списаны &c. А. К. s8°. Кіевъ. 1885

Kottabos. [Trin. Coll. Dublin]. Ed. R. Y. Tyrrell. v1–4, No. 1 [*no more publ*[d]*.*]; N.S., v1, Nos. 1–3, 6–11, v2, Nos. 1–6, 10, 12 (1869–95). 8°. D. 1873–95

Kottenkamp (Franz), see Lichtenberg (G. C.), *elder.* W. Hogarth's Zeichnungen &c.; nebst e. Biog. v. F. K., 3e verb. A., 1873.

Kotter (Christoph) [Cotterus (C.)] Lux in tenebris, hoc est prophetiae donum, in regno Bohemiae &c. Subm. de statu eccl. in terris per C. Cotterum, C. Poniatoviam, N. Dabricium, 1616–56. [*4 pagins.* Ed. J. A. Komensky]. s4°. *n.p.* 1657

Kotvich (Vladislav Lyudv.) Краткій обзоръ ист. &c. Монголіи. Приложеніе къ картѣ Монголіи, составл. по даннымъ И. Я. Коростовца. [P2532]. 8°. С.-П. 1914
Русскіе архивн. док. по сношеніямъ съ Ойратами въ 17 и 18 вв. [*Extr. f.* Р. Акад. Наукъ, Извѣстія, 1919. P2860]. la8°. Петроградъ. 1921

Kotzde (Wilhelm).
Frau Harke. Roman. 4e A. s8°. St. 1926
Die Wittenbergisch Nachtigall. 5e A. s8°. St. 1924

Kotzebue (August F. F. v.) Lovers' vows: [" *Das Kind d. Liebe* "], by Mrs. Inchbald, *see* INCHBALD (*Mrs.* E.) Brit. theatre, v23, 1808.
Pizarro. Tragic play. [Tr.] [Dolby's Brit. theatre]. s8°. 1824
The wise man of the East; [tr.] by Mrs. Inchbald, *see* †INCHBALD (*Mrs.* E.) Mod. theatre, v7, 1811.

Kötzschke (Rudolf). Grundzüge d. deut. Wirtschaftsgesch., 2e A., *see* GRUNDR. D. GESCHICHTSWISS.; Meister, 2i, 1921.

Kouchnire (M.), *see* KUSCHNIR (M.)

Koukline (G. A.), *see* KUKLIN (G. A.)

Kouli Khan. *Kouli Khan; or, the progress of error. [*A satire on King George IV*]. 3rd ed. [P424]. 8°. [1820]

Kourken (A.), *see* KURKEN.

Kouyoumdcan (Michael), *see* ARLEN (M.), *ps.*

Kovachich (Martin Georg). Vestigia comitiorum apud Hungaros, usque ad hodiernum diem celebratorum. s8°. Budæ. 1790
" " ....Suppl. 3t. s8°. Budæ. 1798–1801

Kovács (Aloysius).
The authenticity of the Hungarian census on the data of the mother-tongue. Tr. J. György. [P2519]. 8°. [Pest. 1920 ?]
Can Roumanian rule in East-Hungary last? [P2567]. s8°. 1920
The development of the population of Hungary since Turkish rule. [P2519]. 8°. [Pest. 1920 ?]
" " ....[2567]. s8°. 1921
The establishment of 3 states. [P2567]. s8°. 1920
" " 2nd ed. *w. t.* Three nationality states. [P2567]. s8°. 1921
Peoples of Hungary. 2nd ed. [P2567]. s8°. 1921
see AJTAY (J.), B. JANCSÓ & A. K. The Transylvanian question, 1921.

Kovalenko (P.) Книжка политич. грамоты. 13e изд. s8°. Москва. [1924]

Kovalenskaya (Aleksandra Grigorevna). Крутиковъ. Разсказъ. 3e изд. [P846]. s8°. С.-П. 1886
Назарычъ. Разсказъ. [P846]. s8°. С.-П. 1887

Kovalensky (Mikhail Ivanovich). Житіе Сковороды. Съ предисловіемъ Н. Ө. Сумцова. [P535]. la8°. Кіевъ. 1886

Kovalev (*gen.*), *see* KOROLENKO (V. G.) Трагедія ген. К., 1906.

Kovalevsky (Maksim Maksimovich). Ист. полицейской администраціи и полицейск. суда въ англійск. графствахъ, до смерти Эдуарда III &c. 8°. Прага. 1877
Customs of the Ossetes; comp. f. K.'s Contemp. customs &c. & tr. by E. Delmar Morgan, *see* ROYAL AS. SOC. Journal, n.s., v20, 1888.

Kovalevsky (Petr). N. S. Leskov, peintre méconnu de la vie nat. russe. 8°. 1925

Koyré (A.) Essai sur l'idée de Dieu &c. chez Descartes. [H. E.: Sci. relig., 33]. 8°. 1922

Kozlov (Petr Kuzm.) Краткие отчеты Экспед. по исследов. Северной Монголии в связи с Монголо-Тибет. Экспед. П. К. К. [Акад. Наук. С.С.С.Р.] 8°. Ленинград. 1925
Монголия и Амдо и мертвый город Хара-Хото Экспедиция Р. Геогр. общ. в нагорной Азии. la8°. Москва. 1923
see YETTS (W. P.) Disc. of K. exped., 1926.

Kozminsky (Isidore).
Magic & science of jewels & stones. 8°. N.Y. 1922

Krabbe (Greger), *see* TANK (G.), *ed.* Akershusregisteret af 1622, optaget af G. K. &c., 1916.

Krabbe (Hugo). The mod. idea of the State. Auth. tr. & intr. by G. H. Sabine & W. J. Shepard. 8°. N.Y. 1922

Krabbe (Knud H.) L'organe sous-commissural du cerveau chez les mammifères, *see* KONG. DAN. VIDENSKAB. SELSKAB. Biolog. Medd., 5, 1925.

Kraelitz (Friedrich), *see* KRÄLITZ-GREIFENHORST (F. v.)

Krafft (Carl Friedrich). Diss. de Confess. August. Germ. & Lat., 1530. [P2642]. s4°. Gottingae. [1741]

Krafft (Hugues).
A trav. le Turkestan russe. fol. 1902

Krafft (Johann Melchior). Hist. Nachricht v. d. 1534 in Wittenberg, bey H. Lufften hrsg. u. gedr. verdeutschten Bibel M. Lutheri &c. s4°. Altona. 1735

Krafft (Johann Wilhelm). Diss. de haeresi Audianorum. Praes. J. J. Schrödero. [P434]. s4°. Marburg. [1716]

Krafft (Ulrich). Das ist der geistlich streit gemacht &c. durch U. K. aussgeteilt in Sermones durch die fiertzigtegigen fastenn &c. s4°. [Strassburg ?, *Lunrat Kerner* ?. 1517 ?]

Krafft (Ulrich) [*continued*].
Das ist die arch Noe: leret wie gott Noe gebotten hatt die Arch zu bauwen &c. [*b. w. h.* Das ist der geistlich streit &c. 1517]. s4°. [St[r]assburg, *Lunrat Kerner.* 1517]

Krafft von Dellmensingen (*Gen.* Konrad). Der Durchbruch um Isonzo. [Schlachten d. Weltkrieges, B12a, b]. 2T. 8°. Oldenburg i. O. 1926
Die Führung d. Kronpr. Rupprecht v. Bayern auf d. linken deut. Heeresflügel bis z. Schlacht in Lothringen, Aug. 1914. 8°. 1925

Kraft (Friedrich Carl). Disput. de I. Bugenhagii in res scholasticas emendatas meritis. [*Progr.*] s4°. Hamburgi. 1829

Kraft (Friedrich Wilhelm). Allgem. Bücherverzeichniss u. Hauptregister, 1746–1756 in 100 Stücken. s8°. L. 1758
Allgem. Bücherverzeichniss u. Hauptregister ü. d. letzten 4 Bände. [*b. w.* Allgem. Bücherverzeichniss, 1758]. s8°. L. 1759
Ehrengedächtniss d. F. W. Krafts. [*b. w.* Allgem. Bücherverzeichniss, 1758]. s8°. [Leipzig]. 1759
Neue theolog. Bibliothek. Stück 1–140. [*b. in* 14B. St. 131–140 *called* Anhang]. s8°. Leipzig. 1746–59

Kraft (Viktor). Die Grundformen d. wiss. Methoden, 1926, *see* KAIS. AKAD. D. WISS. ZU WIEN. Sitz., Phil.-hist. Kl., B203, 1927.

Krag (Thomas P.), *1868–1913.* Ulf Ran. s8°. 1914

Krag (Vilhelm).
Major v. Knarren og H. Venner. s8°. Kristiania. 1911

Krahe (Hans). Die alt. balkanillyr. geog. Namen. [Indogerm. Bibl., Abt. 3, B7]. s8°. Heidelberg. 1925

Krak, *publisher.* Krak's blaa bog: 3000 nulev. danske mænd & kvinders levnedsløb. 8°. Kjøbenhavn. 1918

Krälitz-Greifenhorst (Friedrich v.) Osman. Urk. in türk. Spr., 2. Hälfte d. 15. Jhdt., *see* KAISERL. AKAD. D. W. ZU WIEN. Sitz., B197, 1922.
Sprachprobe e. arm.-tatar. Dialektes in Polen. [Aus Wiener Zeitschr. f. d. K. d. Morgenlandes, B26. P2803]. 8°. Wien. *n.d.*
see MITTEILUNGEN Z. OSMAN. GESCH.; hrsg. v. F. K. &c., 1921–25.

Kraljević (Marko). Ballads. Tr. by D. H. Low. 8°. C. 1922

Kramář (Vincenc).
Mariae Verkündigung v. Rembrandt. 4°. Prag. 1926

Kramer (Lüdertus) [CRAMERUS]. Religio Moscovitica. [Disc. hist.-theolog.] [P2443]. s4°. Giessae. 1661

Kramer (Matthias). Nieuw Engelsch Woordenboek. Eng.-Ned. & Ned.-Eng. Bewerkt door F. P. H. Prick v. Wely. 9e dr. 2d *in* 1v. s8°. Gouda. 1921

Krämer (Philipp). Buben. Erzählungen. s8°. [1920]

Kramers (Hendrik Antonie). Intensities of spectral lines, *see* KONG. DANSKE VIDENSK. SELSKAB. Skrifter, Række 8, B3, 1919.
—— **& H. Holst.** The atom & the Bohr theory of its structure. Foreword by Sir E. Rutherford. [Tr. Lindsay]. 8°. 1923

Krammer (Mario). Quellen z. Gesch. d. deut. Königswahl u. d. Kurfürstenkollegs. 2. A. H1. s8°. L., *Teubner.* 1925

Krandievskaya (Nataliya Vasil.) [VOLKENSHTEIN (N. V.)]
Отъ лукаваго: книга стиховъ. s8°. Москва. 1922

Krane (Friedrich Bruno). Die Ziele d. Bolschewismus &c. [P2486; 2574]. s8°. München. 1920

Kranold (Joan. Theophil. Kuno). De anno Hebraeorum jubilaeo. Comm. [P2655]. 4°. Göttingae. [1827]

Krantz (Albertus). Regnorum Aquilonarium, Daniæ, Sueciæ, Noruagiæ, chronica. Acc., Dithmarsici belli hist., C. Cilicio autore. Cum præf. J. Wolffii. fol. Francofurti ad Moenum. 1583
Wandalia. [*b. w. h.* Regnorum Aquilon. chron., 1583]. fol. Hanoviæ. 1619

Krantz (Charles Camille Julien), *see* EXHIBITIONS: CHICAGO. Rapports publ. sous la dir. de C. K., 1894.

Kranz (C. Anton), *see* WEBER (J. C.) Die Fische Deutschlands u. d. Schweiz; Text v. C. A. K., 1870.

Kranz (Walther), *see* DIELS (H.) Fragm. d. Vorsokratiker, B3, Wortindex v. W. K. &c., 1922.

Kranzmayer (Eberhard). Die schwäb.-bair. Mundarten am Lechrain & Die Synonyma f. Kinn u. Stirne, *see* KÖN. AKAD. D. W. ZU MÜNCHEN. Sitz., Phil. &c. Kl., 1927.

Krapf (Johann Ludwig). Elements of the Kisuáheli lang. w. spec. ref. to Kiuika dial. 8°. Tübingen. 1850

Krapp (George Philip).
The Eng. language in America. 2v. 8°. N.Y. 1925

Krasikov (P. A.) На церковном фронте (1918–23). 8°. Москва. 1923
Krasin (Leonid Borisovich).
Внешняя торговля С.С.С.Р. [P2823]. 8°. Москва. 1924
Krasinski (*count* **Nap. A. Zygmunt).** Iridion. Tr. F. Noyes. Ed. w. intr. by G. R. Noyes. 8°. 1927
The un-divine comedy. Tr. H. E. Kennedy & Z. Umińska. Pref. by G. K. Chesterton. Intr. by A. Górski. 8°. [1924]
Krasnii arkhiv. Красный архив: истор. журнал под ред. В. В. Адоратского &c. [Централ. Архив Р.С.Ф.С.Р.] т2–26. la8°. Москва. 1923–28
Krasnov (Petr Nikolaevich) [KRASSNOFF]. Отъ двуглаваго орла къ красному знамени 1894–1921. Романъ. 4t. s8°. Берлинъ. 1921
Comprendre c'est pardonner. Roman, tr. par O. Vitali & H. Iswolsky. s8°. 1925
De l'aigle impérial au drapeau rouge. Roman. Tr. 8°. 1926
From the two-headed eagle to the red flag, 1894–1921. Tr. f. 2nd Russ. ed. 4v. 8°. 1923
Krasnoyarsky (I. P.), *see* KUZNETSOV (I. P.)
Krassin (L. B.), *see* KRASIN (L. B.)
Krassnoff (Pierre), *see* KRASNOV (P. N.)
Kraus (Carl v.) Zu den Liedern Heinrichs v. Morungen, *see* KÖNIGLICHE GESELLS. D. W. ZU GÖTTINGEN. Abh., B16, 1917.
see REINMAR *von Hagenau.* Lieder [hrsg.] C. v. K., 3T, 1919.
Kraus (Franz Xaver), *see* HAUVILLER (E.) K.: Lebensbild, 1904; 2e A., 1905.
Kraus (Herbert). Das Recht d. Minderheiten. s8°. 1927
Kraus (Oskar). Franz Brentano. Mit Beitr. v. C. Stumpf u. E. Husserl. 8°. München. 1919
Krause (Carl Christian Friedrich). Einleit. in d. Wissenschaftslehre. Hrsg. v. P. Hohlfeld u. A. Wünsche. 8°. L. 1884
Krause (Friedrich Ernst Aug.) Cingis Han, d. Gesch. s. Lebens nach d. Chin. Reichsannalen. la8°. Heidelberg. 1922
Gesch. Ostasiens. 3T. (T3, Index). la8°. Göttingen. 1925
Ju-Tao-Fo. Die relig. u. philos. Systeme Ostasiens. 8°. München. 1924
„ „ Beiheft: Terminologie u. Namenverzeichnis. [*Lithographed*]. 8°. München. 1924
Krause (Fritz). In d. Wildnissen Brasiliens. Bericht &c. d. Leipzig. Araguaya-Exped., 1908. 8°. L. 1911
Krause (Gregor) & C. With. Bali. 2. A. 4°. Hagen. i. W. 1922
Krause (Johann Friedrich).
Opuscula theologica. 8°. Regiomonti. 1818
*Quaeritur utrum &c. theologi recent. &c. a Lutheri mente &c. defecerint. [Festum seculare Acad. Albertinae. 2p]. [P2629]. s4°. Regiomonti. [1817]
Krause (Johannes Henricus). Tractatus memorab. circa incrementum &c. eccl. usque ad finem sec. 17, 3 diss. propos. [3p *in* 1v]. s4°. Lipsiae. 1703
Krause (Lorenz Jacob). Stemmatographia Augusta Saxonica. Sub moder. J. D. Koeleri. [P444]. s4°. Altorfii. [1731]
Krauss (*Gen.* **Alfred).**
Moltke, Benedek u. Napoleon. 8°. Wien. 1901
Die Ursachen uns. Niederlage. Erinn. &c. aus d. Weltkrieg. 8°. München. 1920
Krauss (Friedrich), *see* WEEBER (J. C.) & F. K. Liedersammlung, 5H, 1852–54.
Krauss (Samuel). Synagogale Altertümer. 8°. 1922
see MONUMENTA Hebr. &c., B5, Geschichte; v. S. K., 1913–14.
Krausse (Alexis S.) Russia in Asia, 1558–1899. 2nd ed. 8°. 1900
Krebs (Burkhard), *decanus Patav.*, *see* LEIDINGER (G.) Unters. z. Passauer Geschichtschreib., 1915.
Krebs (Johann Carl). De stylitis. [P432]. s4°. Lipsiae. [1753]
Krebs (Johann Tobias).
Obs. in Nov. Test. e Flavio Josepho. 8°. Lipsiae. 1755
Krebs (Léonce) & H. Moris. Campagnes dans les Alpes pendant la Révolution, 1792–[96]. [2t]. la8°. 1891–1895
Krebs (Ludwig Alexander).
Natürl. Gottesgelehrsamkeit. s8°. Giessen. 1771
Krebs (Manfred). Konrad III von Lichtenberg, Bischof v. Strassburg (1273–99). la8°. Frankfurt a. M. 1926
see STRASSBURG. Regesten d. Bischöfe, B2, hrsg. A. Hessel u. M. K., 1928.
Krebs (Norbert). Die Ostalpen u. d. heut. Österreich. 2e wesentl. erweit. A. d. " Länderkunde d. österreich. Alpen." 2B. 8°. St. 1928
Krehbiel (Henry Edward). A book of operas. Their hist., plots & music. [*&* A 2nd book of o.] 2v *in* 1. s8°. N.Y. 1919
Krehl (August Ludwig Gottlob). Praef. de doctoratu Lutheri. [*Progr.*] [P2627]. s4°. [Lipsiae. 1846]

Kreibig (Jos. Klem.) Über d. Quantität d. Urteils, 1919, *see* KAISERL. AKAD. D. W. ZU WIEN. Sitz., B190, 1919.
Kreichgauer (Damian). Die Astronomie in d. gr. Wiener Hs. aus Mexico, 1917, *see* KAISERL. AKAD. D. W. ZU WIEN. Sitz., B182, 1918.
Krekshin (Petr Nikiforovich), *1684–1763.* Записки, *see* SAKHAROV (I. P.) Записки &c., 1841.
Krell (Max). Die Entfaltung. Novellen an d. Zeit. Hrsg. v. M. K. 8°. 1921
Krell (Nicolaus) [CRELLIUS (N.)], *see* ENGELCKEN (C. H.) Hist. N. Crellii, &c. 1727.
Krementz (Philippus), *bp. of Ermeland*, *see* GRÜNERT (J.) Meine Verhandl. mit P. K. ü. d. päpstl. Unfehlbark., 1872.
Kremer (Alfred *Frhr.* **v.)** The Orient under the Caliphs. Tr. by S. Khuda Bukhsh. 8°. Calcutta. 1920
Krencker (Daniel).
see KRÜGER (E.) & D. K. Vorbericht üb. d. Ergebnisse d. Ausgrabung d. sog. röm. Kaiserpalastes in Trier, 1915.
„ PUCHSTEIN (O.) Boghasköi: d. Bauwerke; v. O. P. unter Mitwirkung v. H. Kohl u. D. K., 1912.
„ WIEGAND (T.) Baalbek: Ergebnisse d. Ausgrab. u. Unters., 1898 bis 1905, B2, 3, von D. K. &c., 1923–25.
Kretschmayr (Heinrich). Venedig, B2, 1920, *see* GESCHICHTE D. EUROPÄ. STAATEN.
Kretschmer (Ernst). Die Ideale u. d. Seele. [P2477]. 8°. L. 1900
Kretzer (Max). Das Mädchen aus der Fremde. s8°. L. [1913]
Meister Timpe, sozialer Roman. 8e A. s8°. L. *n.d.*
Die Sphinx in Trauer. Roman. s8°. Dessau. 1921
Kretzschmar (Hermann).
Musikal. Zeitfragen. 10 Vorträge. 8°. L. 1903
Krey (August Charles). The First Crusade. Accounts of eyewitnesses &c. 8°. Princeton. 1921
Kreymborg (Alfred).
Puppet plays. Pref. by G. Craig. s8°. [1923]
Krieg. Die Bayern im Grossen Kriege, 1914–18, 1923, *see* BAIERN.
Krieg (Der): Illust. Chronik. d. Krieges 1914/18. [H93–112 *in* 1v]. 5. Jahrg. la8°. St. 1919
Krieg (Der) zur See, 1914–18. Hrsg. v. Marine-Archiv. Bearb. v. E. v. Mantey. 8°. 1920–25
Der Kreuzerkrieg in d. ausländ. Gewässern; bearb. v. E. Raeder, 2B.
Der Krieg in d. Nordsee; bearb. v. O. Groos, B1–5. [*Maps to* B5 *in sep. case.*]
Der Krieg in d. Ostsee; bearb. v. R. Firle, B1.
Krieger (Albert), *see* BADEN. Regesten d. Markgrafen v. B. &c., 1050–1515, B4, bearb. v. A. K., 1915.
Krieger (Herbert W.) Coll. of prim. weapons & armor of the Philippine Islands in U.S. Nat. Mus. [S.I.: U.S. Nat. Mus., Bull. 137]. 8°. Wash. 1926
Material culture of people of S.-E. Panama. [S.I.: U.S. Nat. Mus., Bull. 134]. 8°. Wash. 1926
Krieger (Hermann). Aus Münchens dunklen Tagen. Zusammenbruch d. Räte-Republik. s8°. Vlotho. 1919
Kriegs-Depeschen, 1914–17. W. T. B. [B1–7] (1.–41. Kriegsmonat, Aug. 1914–Dez. 1917). [Monat 35 *wanting*]. la8°. 1914–18
Kriegsflotten. Taschenbuch d. K., 1915, *see* TASCHENBUCH.
Kriegsgeschichtliche Einzelschriften. Hrsg. v. Grossen Generalstabe. B9 (H. 49 & Atlas, H. 50). 8°. 1913–14
IX, 49, Erfahrungen aussereurop. Kriege n. Zeit; 2, Aus d. russ-japan. Kriege, 1904–5.
„ 50, Der Balkankrieg 1912/13, H. 1.
Kriegspresseamt. Handbuch d. Auslandpresse, 1918; bearb. v. d. Auslandstelle d. K., 1918, *see* HANDBUCH.
Kriegsschuldfrage (Die). Hrsg. v. Börsenverein d. Deut. Buchhändler &c. s8°. L. 1925
Krigel (Abraham). De Oscis. [P2587]. s4°. Lipsiae. 1736
Diss. de spongiarum apud veteres usu. Præses A. K., resp. S. G. Haenischius. [P1035]. s4°. Lipsiae. 1734
Krijanich (Yury Gasparovich), *1617–82.* Historia de Siberia 1680 (*Lat. & Russ.*), *see* TITOV (A. A.) Сибирь въ XVII вѣкѣ, 1890.
see BELOKUROV (S. A.) Ю. К. въ Россіи, 1901.
Krilov (Ivan Andreevich). Басни. s8°. С.-П. 1835
Басни. Съ біог. автора, нап. П. А. Плетневымъ. 23e изд. 8°. С.-П. 1887
Fables. Tr. C. F. Coxwell. s8°. [1920]
„ „ Tr. into Eng. verse w. pref. by B. Pares. 8°. [1926]
see GROT (YA. K.) Лит. жизнь К., 1868.

Krishnadas Kaviraj. Chaitanya's pilgrimages & teachings. Fr. h. contemp. Bengali biog. the Chaitanya-charit-amrita: Madhya-lila [*by* K. K.] Tr. J. Sarkar. s8°. Calcutta. 1913

Krishnagar. Procs. of the Comm. of Circuit at K. &c., v1–3, 1772, *see* Bengal Records, 1926.

Krishna Sastri (*Hosākote*), *see* Indian. S. Ind. inscriptions, v3, p3; ed. & tr. by H. K. S., 1920.

Krishnaswami Ayyangar (S.)
South India & her Muhammadan invaders. 8°. 1921

Kristeller (Paul). Florentin. Zierstücke in Kupferstich aus d. 15. Jhdt. 25 Tafeln. Hrsg. P. K. [Graph. Gesells., 10]. fol. 1909
Exercitium super Pater Noster. Hrsg. P. K. [Graph. Gesells. Veröff. 6]. fol. 1908
Eine Folge venezian. Holzschnitte aus d. 15. Jhdt. im Besitze d. Stadt Nürnberg. 16 Tafeln. Hrsg. P. K. [Graph. Gesells., 9]. fol. 1909
Giulio Campagnola, Kupferstiche u. Zeichnungen. 22 Tafeln. Hrsg. P. K. [Graph., Gesells. 5]. fol. 1907

Kristensen (Marius). "Nokkur blöð úr Hauksbók," undersøgt &c. med. hensyn til dets sprogform, *see* Kong. Dan. Vid. Selsk. Hist.-fil. Medd., 9, 1924–25.

Kritischer Jahresbericht über d. Fortschritte d. romanischen Philologie. Hrsg. v. K. Vollmöller. B13, 1911–12. la8°. Erlangen. 1915

Kritopoulos (Metrophanes), *patriarch of Jerusalem.* Confessio Cathol. & Apostol. in Oriente Eccl. Ed. & Lat. don. a J. Horneio. [With an epistle f. H. Coringius. *Gr. & Lat.*] s4°. Helmestadii. 1561 [*for* 1661]

Krivtsov (Nikolai Ivanovich).
see Gershenzon (M. O.) Декабристъ К., 1923.

Krizhanich (Y. G.), *see* Krijanich (Y. G.)

Kroeber (Alfred Louis). Anthropology. 8°. [1923]
Handbook of the Indians of California. [S.I.: Bureau of Amer. Ethnology, Bull. 78]. 8°. Wash. 1925
Peoples of the Philippines. [Amer. Museum of Nat. Hist., Hdbk. ser., No. 8]. s8°. N.Y. 1919

Kroeger (Alice Bertha), *see* Mudge (I. G.) New guide to reference bks.; based on 3rd ed. of Guide to study &c. of ref. bks. by A. B. K., 1923.

Krogvig (Anders), *see* Norsk biografisk Leksikon: redaktion: E. Bull, A. K. &c., B1–3, 1923–26.

Krohn (Martinus Ludolphus). De Samosatenianis neotericis, quorum mentio fit in Augustana confessione. [P2587]. s4°. Jenae. 1730

Kroll (Wilhelm).
Studien z. Verständnis d. röm. Lit. 8°. St. 1924

Krom (Nicolaas Johannes). Inleiding tot de Hindoe-Javaansche kunst. 2d. la8°. 's-Gravenhage. 1920

Kroman (Kristian Frederik Vilhelm). Laws of muscular action, *see* Kongeligt Dan. Vid. Selsk. Biol. Med., B1, 1917–19.
Mathematics & the theory of science, *see* Kong. Dan. Vid. Selsk. Filos. Med., B1, 1920–24.

Kromayer (Hieronymus).
Polymathia theologica. s4°. Lipsiae. 1669
Theologia positivo-polemica in qua controv. Lutheranis cum Pontificiis, Calvinianis, &c. tract. Praef. Διάσκεψις articulorum fidei &c. Rec. una cum praef. A. Pfeifferi & tabulis mnemon. J. C. Köhleri. 2p *in* 1v [p2, a D. V. Alberti ed.] s4°. Lipsiae. 1711

Kromayer (Johann Abraham) [Kromayerus (I. A.)] Filia matri obstetricans; de usu linguae Arab. in addisc. Ebraea & explic. Script. S., in libro Jobi &c. s4°. Francofurti. 1707

Kromayer (Johannes). Antike Schlachtfelder. Bausteine zu e. ant. Kriegsgesch. B4, Lief. 1, 2, v. J. K. u. G. Veith. 8°. 1924–26
4, Schlachtfelder aus d. Perserkriegen &c., bis Augustus.

Krömeke (Franz), *see* Sertürner (F. W. A.) F. W. S., d. Entdecker d. Morphiums, hrsg. v. F. K., 1925.

Kronberg (Hartmuth v.), *see* Cronberg (H. v.)

Krone (Rudolf). Lazarus v. Schwendi, 1522–84, s. kirchenpolit. Tätigkeit &c. [Verein f. Ref.-gesch. Schr., Jhrg. 29, Nr. 106/7]. 8°. L. 1912

Kronenberg (M. E.), *see* Nijhoff (W.) & M. E. K. Nederland. bibliogr. van 1500 tot 1504, 1923–27.

Kronenberg (Moritz). Gewalt u. Gedanke: e. Untersuchung üb. deut. Kriegsschuld u. Sühne. 8°. Charlottenburg. 1920

Kröner (Walther). Das Rätsel v. Konnersreuth: St. eines Parapsychologen. 8°. München. 1927

Krones (Franz Xaver), *Ritter v. Marchland.* Österreich. Gesch. Neubearb. v. K. Uhlirz. Hrsg. &c. v. M. Uhlirz. [Samml. Göschen]. 4B. (1, 2, 3e A.; 3, 4, 2e A.) s8°. 1915–23

Kronfeld (Ernst Moritz). Der Krieg im Aberglauben u. Volksglauben. 8°. München. [1915]

Krook (Gudmund), *see* Berg (N.) Exercit. de statu eccl. & relig. Moscovit. prop. praes. N. B., resp. M. G. K., 1704.

Kropotkin (*prince* **Petr Aleksandrovich).** Отъѣздъ П. А. К. изъ Англіи въ Россію и его письма [1917–20]. [*Extr. f.* На чужой сторонѣ, No. 4. P2749]. 8°. *n.p. n.d.*
Ethics: origin & development. Auth. tr. by L. S. Friedland &c. 8°. [1924]

Krüdener (Barbara Juliane von). *Valérie, ou lettres de G. de Linar à Ernest de G. 2t *in* 1v. s8°. Londres. 1804

Krug (Wilhelm Traugott). Comm. acad. partim ad theolog. partim ad philos. spect. 8°. Lipsiae. 1838
Entwurf e. n. Organon's d. Philosophie. 8°. Meissen. 1801

Krüger (Emil) & D. Krencker. Vorbericht üb. d. Ergebnisse d. Ausgrabung d. sog. röm. Kaiserpalastes in Trier, *see* Königl. Preuss. Akad. Abh. (Phil.-hist. Kl.), 1915.

Krüger (Hermann Anders).
Kaspar Krumbholtz. Roman. s8°. Braunschweig. 1921

Krüger (Jeremias). Tract. de eruditionis obstaculis ex parte parentum. [P2671]. s4°. Jenae. 1723

Krüger (O.), *see* Zereteli (G. F.) Papyri russ. u. georg. Sammlungen, 1, Lit. Texte, bearb. v. G. Z. & O. K., 1925.

Krüger (Paul), *Dr.Jur.*, *see* Codex Theodosianus, rec. P. K., fasc. 1, 2. Lib. 1–8, 1923–26.

Kruif (Paul de), *see* De Kruif (P.)

Krumbacher (Carl). Письмо въ стихахъ съ акростихомъ [Гирарда къ Стаматію. Оттискъ. P2811]. 8°. С.-П. 1901

Krumbholtz (M. Jonas). De rebus in agris relictis Hebraeorum vet. [P2587]. s4°. Wittenbergae. 1696

Krummel (Leopold). Utraquisten u. Taboriten: böhm. Reform. im 15. Jhdt. [P2728]. 8°. Gotha. 1871

Krump (Epiphanias). Quaest. quodlibetales cum parergis in 4 libr. Sententiarum J. Duns Scoti &c. Præs. E. K., defend. G. Kistler & J. C. Scheyringer. [P599]. s4°. Ingolstadii. [1709]

Krupp (Alfred), *see* Berdrow (W.) A. K., 2B, 1927.

Krupskaya (Nadejda Konstantinovna).
Воспитание молодежи в Ленинском духе. 8°. [Ленинград]. 1925

Krusch (Bruno). Passiones vitaeque sanctorum aevi Merovingici et antiquiorum aliquot. Ed. B. K. & W. Levison. [Mon. Germ. Hist. Script. rer. Merov. t7]. [t5]. 4°. Hannoverae. 1920

Krusenstern (Adam Johann v.) Wörter-Sammlungen aus d. Sprachen e. Völker d. östl. Asiens u. d. nordwest-Küste v. Amerika. 4°. St. Petersburg. 1813

Krutch (Joseph Wood).
Edgar A. Poe: a st. in genius. 8°. 1926

Krzistanowic, *see* Krzystanowicz.

Krziz (Carolus). Introd. ad sacr. hist. Bohemiae &c. s8°. Vetero-Pragae. 1764

Krzystanowicz (Stanisław) [Krzistanovvic], *see* Polonia. Respublica Poloniæ &c., div. aut. (S. K. &c.), 1627.

Kubitschek (Josef Wilhelm). Grundriss d. ant. Zeitrechnung. [Hdbch. d. Alt.-Wiss., Abtlg. 1, T7]. 8°. München. 1928
Itinerarstudien, 1919, *see* Kais. Akad. d. W. zu Wien. Denkschr., B61, 1919.
Die Kalenderbücher v. Florenz, Rom u. Leyden, 1915, *see* Kais. Akad. d. W. zu Wien. Denkschr., B57, 1915.
Zur Gesch. d. Städten d. röm. Kaiserreiches, H1, 1916, *see* Kais. Akad. d. W. zu Wien. Sitz., Phil.-hist. Kl., B177, 1917.
—— **& S. Frankfurter.** Führer durch Carnuntum. [Österr. Arch. Inst.] 6. A. s8°. Wien. 1923

Ku Chou Pien, Association for the Publ. of.
see Takata (T.) Hsiao Ku Fu Fan, *n.d.*
,, —— Ku Chou Pien, *n.d.*

Kuchuk-Ioannesov (Khristofor Ivanovich). Старинныя армянскія надписи и стар. рукописи въ пред. юго-зап. Руси &c. [*Extr. f.* И. М. А. О. Труды Восточ. Ком., т2. P2805]. 4°. [С.-П. *n.d.*]
Старинныя армянскія рукописи &c., наход. въ пред. Россіи. Отт. изъ Древностей Восточн., т4. [*b. w.* Foucher (A.) Madone, bouddh., 1910]. fol. Москва. 1912

Kück (Eduard) & H. Sohnrey. Feste u. Spiele d. deut. Landvolks. 3. neubearb. A. s8°. 1925

Kuczynski (Robert René). Post-war labor cond. in Germany, *see* UNITED STATES: LABOR, Bull. 380, 1925.
Ein Reichsfinanzprogramm für 1920. [P2409]. 8°. Tübingen. 1920

Küfstein, *The family of, see* KÜFSTEIN (C. F. F., *Graf* v.) Studien z. Familiengesch., T3, 1915.

Küfstein (Carl F. F., *Graf* **v.)**
Studien z. Familiengesch. T3. la8°. Wien. 1915

Kugelgen, *family of, see* KÜGELGEN (L. v.) G. v. K., u. d. 7 Künstler d. Familie, 1924.

Kügelgen (Gerhard v.), *see* KÜGELGEN (L. v.) G. v. K., 1924.

Kügelgen (Helene Marie von), *wife of Gerhard v. K., form. Zoege v. Manteuffel, 1774–1842.* H. M. v. K.: e. Lebensbild in Briefen. Hrsg. v. i. Enkelinnen A. & E. v. Kügelgen. 9e A. 8°. St. [1928]

Kügelgen (Leo v.) Gerhard v. Kügelgen u. d. and. 7 Künstler d. Familie. 3. umgearb. A. la8°. St. [1924]

Kügelgen (Wilhelm G. A. v.)
Jugenderinnerungen e. alten Mannes. s8°. Ebenhausen. 1913

Kugler (Bernhard). Wallenstein, *see* VIRCHOW (R.) & F. v. HOLTZENDORFF. Sammlung, H180, 1873.

Kugler (Franz Theodor). Gesch. Friedrichs d. Grossen. Gezeichnet v. A. Menzel. la8°. L. 1840

Kugler (Franz Xaver), *S. J.* Von Moses bis Paulus: Forsch. z. Gesch. Israels. la8°. Münster. 1922

Kuhl (*Gen.* **Hermann v.)** Der deut. Generalstab in Vorbereitung u. Durchführung d. Weltkrieges. 2e neubearb. A. 8°. 1920
see GERMANY: REICHSTAG. Ursachen d. Zusammenbruchs: Entst. d. Offensive v. 1918; Gutachten d. Gen. v. K. &c., 1923.

Kuhlmann (Quirin), *see* LIEFMANN (G.) Diss. de fanat. Silesiorum & spec. Q. K., 1733.

Kuhn (Alfred).
Das alte Spanien: Landschaft, Gesch., Kunst. la8°. [1925]

Kuhn (Franz). Das Dschong lun d. Tsui Schi, e. Konfuzian. Rechtfertigung (2 Jahrh. n. Chr.), *w. text & tr., see* KÖN. PREUSS. AKAD. Abhdln., Phil.-hist. Kl., 1914.
see HAOU KEW CHUEN. Eisherz u. Edeljaspis; üb. K., 1927.

Kühn (Joachim). Diss. de lotionibus & balneis Graec., 1695, *see* SCHLÄGER (C. J.) Diss. fasc. novus, 1744.

Kühnel (Ernst). Francesco Botticini. la8°. Str. 1906
Maurische Kunst. la8°. 1924
Miniaturmalerei im islam. Orient. la8°. 1922

Kuhnenfeld (F. M. L., *baron* **Kuhn von),** *see* KUHN VON KUHNENFELD (F. M. L., *b.*)

Kühner (Georg Friedrich).
Lamarck: die Lehre v. Leben. 8°. Jena. 1913

Kuhnt (Joachim), *see* ROTHER, *König.* K. R.; hrsg. v. T. Frings & J. K., 1922.

Kuhn von Kuhnenfeld (F. M. L., *baron*). Strateg. importance of Euphrates Valley Rly. Tr. C. W. Wilson. 2nd ed. [P2714]. 8°. 1873

Ku Hung-Ming, *M.A., of Peking.* Vox clamantis. Betrachtungen über d. Krieg &c. [Übers. &c. H. Nelson]. 8°. L. 1920

Kuinoel (Chr. Theoph.) [KÜNOEL], *see* VELTHUSEN (J. C.), C. T. K. &c., *edd.* Comm. theologicae, 6v, 1794–99.

Kuka (Mehrjibhai Nosherwanji).
Wit, humour & fancy of Persia. 8°. Bombay. 1923

Kuklin (G. A.) Итоги революц. движенія въ Россіи за сорокъ лѣтъ (1862–1902). Сборникъ программъ &c. s8°. Женева. 1903
Матеріалы къ изученію ист. революц. движенія въ Россіи. т1 (1800–54). s8°. Женева. 1905

Kukučin (Martin), *ps.* [*i.e.* MATEJ BENCÚR]. Sobrané spisu. Sv. 1. s8°. v Turčianskom Sv. Martine. 1910

Kukula (Richard Cornelius). Persius u. Nero. [Text u. Übers. d. 1. Satire, & Krit.-exeget. &c. Streitfragen]. 8°. Graz. 1923

Kulakov (G. V.)
Конституция С.С.С.Р. &c. [P2824]. s8°. Москва. [1923]

Kulakovsky (Yulian Andreevich).
Исторія Византіи. 395[–717]. 3т *in* 2v. la8°. Кіевъ. 1910–15
Прошлое Тавриды. [Имп. Арх. Комм.] изд. 2ое. 8°. Кіевъ. 1914

Kulczynski (Ignatius). Specimen Eccl. Ruthenicae &c. [Ed. I. Markinov]. 8°. Parisiis. [1859]

Kulish (Panteleimon Aleksandrovich).
Записки о южной Руси. т1. 8°. С.-П. 1856

Küller (Jo van Ammers-), *see* AMMERS-KÜLLER (Jo v.)

Kullmann (Eduard Franz Ludwig). Prozess K., Würzburg, Okt. 1874; v. St. Gätschenberger. [P505]. s8°. Würzburg. 1874

Kulmbach. Kulmbach; hrsg. v. Stadtrat K., *see* DEUTSCHLAND. Deutschlands Stadtebau, 1926.

Kulp (Daniel Harrison), *Jr.* Country life in South China: sociology of familism. v1 (Phenix Village, Kwantung). 8°. N.Y. 1925

Külpe (Oswald). Vorlesungen ü. Psychologie. Hrsg. K. Bühler. 8°. L. 1920
Zur Kategorienlehre, *see* KÖNIGL. AKAD. D. W. ZU MÜNCHEN. Phil. Kl., Sitz., 1915.

Kultur (Die) d. mod. England &c., B1–6, 1912–14, *see* SIEPER (E.), *ed.*

***Kulturwerk** (Das) Sowjet-Russlands, 1920, *see* RUSSLAND.

Kümmel (August), *see* WESTFALEN. Bau- u. Kunstdenkm., 36, Kreis Altena, gesch. Einl. v. A. K., 1911.

Kümmel (Otto). Die Kunst Ostasiens. la8°. 1921
Das Kunstgewerbe in Japan. 2e A. 8°. 1919
Ostasiat. Gerät. Ausgewählt &c. v. K. Einführ. v. E. Grosse. la8°. 1925

Kümmerly & Frey. Taschen-Atlas d. Schweiz. 3e A. v. Wagners Taschenatlas. 8°. Bern. [1920]

Kun (A. A.) Очерки Шагрисебзскаго бекства. [I.R.G.O. Записки по отдѣл. этнограф.. 6i]. 8°. С.-П. 1880

Kun (Bela). Was wollen die Kommunisten? [P2426]. 8°. Hamburg. [1919]
see BIZONY (L.) 133 Tage ungar. Bolschewismus: die Herrschaft B. K. &c., 1920.

Kuncewicz (Jan), *see* JOSAPHAT, *St., abp. of Polotsk.*

Kungliga Vitterhets-, Hist.-och Antiqvitets-Academi, *Stockholm, see* OXENSTIERNA (*c.* A.) Skrifter och brefvexling, Afd. 1, B4, 6, 7, 1909–26.

Kungligt Humanistiska Vetenskapssamfundet i Lund.
Skr. 5–7, 9. 8°. Lund. 1923–27
see EKWALL (E.) Eng. place-names in *-ing*, 1923. [6.]
,, GARNIER, *de Pont Sainte-Maxence.* Vie de St. Thomas le Martyr, 1922. [5.]
,, HIMYARITES. Bk. of the H.; ed., w. intr. &c., by A. Moberg, 1924. [7.]
,, NILSSON (M. P.) Minoan-Mycenaean relig. &c., 1927. [9.]

Kungligt Humanistiska Vetenskaps-Samfundet i Uppsala.
Skrifter. B3i, 20–24. 8°. Uppsala. 1893, [1917–27]
Almquist (H.) Holstein-Gottorp, Sverige & d. Nord. Ligan, 1713–14, 1918. [21.]
Danielsson (O. A.) Zu d. lyd. Inschr., 1917. [20.]
Ekblom (R.) Der Wechsel (j)e—o im Slav., 1925. [22.]
—— Z. Entw. d. Liquidaverbindungen im Slav., 1927. [24.]
—— Z. Physiol. d. Akzentuation langer Silben im Slavo-Baltischen, 1927. [22.]
Friesen (O. v.) Om d. svaga preteritum i germ. språk, 1925. [22.]
—— Om lasningen av codices gotici Ambrosiani, 1927. [24.]
Hagendahl (H.) D. Perfektformen auf -ere u. -erunt, 1923. [22.]
Hägerström (A.) D. röm. Obligationsbegriff, B1, 1927. [23.]
Hahr (A.) Skandin. adelsborgar, 1927. [24.]
Hammer (B.) Humanistisk psykol., 1927. [24.]
Hesselman (B. I.) Språkformen i MB I, 1927. [24.]
Johansson (C. F.) Skt. *nivātá*-'windstill(e), 1927. [24.]
—— Üb. d. altind. Göttin Dhiṣáṇa &c., 1917. [20.]
Kjellberg (A. L.) St. zu d. ant. Dacheindeckungen, 1927. [24.]
Lagercrantz (O.) Euripides Hippolytus, 1922. [21.]
Noreen (E.) St. rör. Eufemiavisorna, 1923–27. [22.]
Persson (P.) Bemerk. zu d. kl. Schr. d. Tacitus, 1927. [24.]
Petrini (E.) Psykol. analyser, 1918. [20.]
Phalén (A.) Ueb. d. Relativität d. Raum- u. Zeitbestimmungen, 1922. [21.]
Reuterskiöld (C. A.) Den svenska förvaltningsrättens system, 1927. [24.]
Rudberg (G.) Forsch. zu Poseidonios, 1918. [20.]
Rugman (J.) Saml. av isländska talesätt (17 c.), 1927. [22.]
Samuelsson (J.) Ad Valerium Flaccum, 1927. [24.]
Sjögren (H.) Ad Ciceronis Epist. ad Atticum adnot., 1927. [24.]
Staaf (E. S.) Sur une lauda de Jacopone da Todi, 1927. [24.]
Stave (E.) Om källorna till 1526 års ofversättning af Nya Test., 1893. [3i.]
Thörnell (G.) Ad Scriptores Hist. Augustae & Ammianum Marcellinum adnot., 1927. [24.]
Upsala: Kongl. Univ. Festskr., 1927. [24.]
Wadstein (E.) Fries. Lehnwörter im Nordischen, 1922. [21.]
—— On the orig. of the English, 1927. [24.]
Westman (C. G.) Häradsnämnd & häradsrätt, 1927. [24.]
Wiklund (C. B.) Lapp. Studien 1–3, 1927. [24.]
Wittrock (G.) Gustaf Adolfs krigföring i Tyskland, 1632, 1927. [24.]
Zachrisson (R. E.) Eng. pronunc. as taught by W. Bullokar, 1927. [22.]
—— Romans, Kelts & Saxons in anc. Brit. (400–600), 1927. [24.]

Künoel (Chr. Theoph.), *see* KUINOEL (C. T.)
Kunstdenkmäler (Die) im Freistaat Hessen, *see* HESSEN.
Kunsthistorisches Museum in Wien. Publikationen aus d. Sammlungen f. Plastik u. Kunstgewerbe. Hrsg. v. J. Schlosser. B1, 3. 4°. Wien. 1919–20
see PLANISCIG (L.) Die Estensische Kunstsammlung, B1, 1919. [1.]
„ SCHLOSSER (J.) Die Sammlung alt. Musikinstrumente, 1920. [3.]
Künstle (Carl).
Ikonographie d. Heiligen. la8°. Freiburg i. B. 1926
Künstler-Inventare, 16.–18. Jhdt.; hrsg. A. Bredius, T7 & Register, 1921–22, *see* BREDIUS (A.)
Künstler-Monographien.
Nos. 46, 70, 107, 110–117. la8°. Bielefeld. 1921–27
see ALTEN (W. v.) Max Slevogt, 1926. [116.]
„ BIERMANN (G.) Louis Corinth, 2e A., 1922. [107.]
„ BÖHN (M. VON). C. Spitzweg, 1921. [110.]
„ OSTINI (F., *baron* v.) Böcklin, 7e A., 1921. [70.]
„ —— Fritz Erler, 1921. [111.]
„ —— Thoma, 3e A., 1923. [46.]
see ROSENHAGEN (H.) Arthur Kampf, 1922. [112.]
„ SCHMITZ (H.) Hans Baldung, 1922. [113.]
„ VOGEL (J.) Otto Greiner, 1925. [114.]
„ WOLF (G. J.) Altdorfer, 1925. [115.]
„ ZÖGE V. MANTEUFFEL (K.) Die Künstlerfam. Van de Velde, 1927. [117.]
Kunstschutz im Kriege; hrsg. v. Paul Clemen, 2B, 1919, *see* CLEMEN (P.)
Küntzel (Georg). Fürst Kaunitz-Rittberg als Staatsmann. 8°. Fr. am Main. 1923
Kuntziger (Marthe). Lambert Lombard. s8°. Turnhout. 1920
Kununga. Kununga ok höfdinga styrilse. Hoc est regum &c. instit. ab incerto auct. conscr. In Lat. vertit notisque illust. J. Schefferus. [*w. text*]. fol. Holmiae Svecorum. 1669
Kunz (Josef L.) Bibliogr. d. Kriegslit. 8°. [1920]
Das Problem von d. Verletzung d. belg. Neutralität. [P2521]. 8°. Wien. 1920
Künzelsauer (Das) Fronleichnamspiel v. Jahr 1479. Hrsg. A. Schumann. 8°. Öhringen. [1926]
Kupfer (Carl F.)
Sacred places in China. 8°. Cincinnati. [1911]
Kuplevasky (Nikolai Osip.) Манифестъ Александра I 1816г. о переименованіи Финляндск. правительств. совѣта въ Имп. Финляндск. сенатъ. [P2451]. 8°. С.-П. 1910
Küppers (Ignaz). Der Apoxyomenos d. Lysippos u. d. griech. Palästra, *see* VIRCHOW (R.) & F. v. HOLTZENDORFF. Samml., H191, 1873.
Kuprin (Aleksandr Ivanovich).
Звѣзда Соломона. [Разсказы]. 8°. Гельсингфорсъ. 1920
Мирное житіе—Памяти Чехова, *see* SBORNIK. Сб. товар. "Знаніе," 2, 3, 1904–05.
Пѣгія лошади, *see* RUSSKII. Р. сборникъ, 1920.
TRANSLATIONS.
Le bracelet de Grenats. Tr. H. Mongault. s8°. 1922
TRANSLATIONS [*continued*].
Le caniche blanc & autres contes. Tr. H. Mongault. s8°. 1924
Sulamite. Tr. par M. Semenoff & S. Mandel. Suppl. au Monde Nouveau. s8°. [1922?]
„ „ ......2e éd. s8°. 1922
Les voleurs de chevaux, nouvelle, *see* ŒUVRES libres, t58, 1926.
Kurchinsky (M. A.) Европейскій хаосъ, *see* DORPAT UNIV. Acta &c., B, v7, 1926.
Kurken (A.) [KOURKEN]. Brief gramm. of the Eng. lang. [*in Armenian*]. 8°. Venice. 1853
Kurlov (*General* **Komarov-**), *see* KOMAROV-KURLOV.
Kurlov (*gen.* **P. G.)**
Гибель императ. Россіи. la8°. Berlin. 1923
Kurmis (A.), *ed.*
Jānis Čakste. [*By var. a.*] la8°. Riga. 1928
Kuropatkin (*gen.* **Aleksei Nikolaevich) & N. P. Linevich.**
Русско-Японская война. Из дневников А. Н. К. и Н. П. Л. С пред. М. Н. Покровского. [Центрархив]. la8°. Ленинград. 1925
Kurrelmeyer (William). Die Doppeldrucke in i. Bedeutung f. d. Textgesch. v. Wielands Werken, *see* KÖN.-PREUSS. AKAD. Abhdln., Phil.-hist. Kl., 1913.
Kürschner (Joseph), *see* DEUTSCHER LITTERATUR KALENDAR; hrsg. K. &c., 1917–28.
Kurskij (D. I.) Советская юстиция. Сборник статей под ред. К. [P2724]. la8°. Москва. 1919
Kurth (Godefroid).
La cité de Liège au moyen-âge. 2t. 8°. Brux. 1909–10
Hist. poét. des Mérovingiens. la8°. 1893
St. Boniface (680–755). 2e éd. s8°. 1902

Kurth (Julius).
Der chines. Farbendruck. 4°. Plauen im Vogtland. 1922
Kurtscheid (Bertrand). Das neue Kirchenrecht. Ergz. zu Heiners Kathol. Kirchenrecht. 2e verb. A. 8°. Paderborn. 1921
Kurtschinsky (M. A.), *see* KURCHINSKY (M. A.)
Kurtz [KURTZE; KURTZER; KURZE].
*Kurtz Bekentnis u. Artickel v. heil. Abendmal ubergeben in jüngsten Landtag zu Torgaw, 1574, *see* TORGAU.
*Kurtze beschreibung v. e. Juden &c., 1601, *see* JEW.
*Kurtze Christliche u. Einfeltige widerholung d. Bekentnis, 1571, *see* SACHSEN.
*Kurtze Hist. d. Evangel. Emigranten aus d. Ertz-Stifft Saltzburg, 1733, *see* SALZBURG.
*Kurtze Nachricht v. denen Academien u. Universitäten überhaupt. [*b. w.* Leipzig. Kurtze Nachr., 1709]. s8°. Halle. [1709?]
*Kurtze Nachricht v. d. Stadt Halle, 1709, *see* HALLE.
*Kurtze Nachricht v. d. Stadt Leipzig, 1709, *see* LEIPZIG.
*Kurtze u. warhafftige erzelung, welcher massen den Frantzös. u. Niderl. verjagten Christen &c., 1598, *see* DATHENUS (P.)
*Kurtzer (Ein) ausszug, aus d. Bepstl. rechten d. Decret u. Decretalen, 1530 [1584], *see* SPENGLER (L.)
*Kurtzer Ausszug u. einfeltige entwerffung d. Formulae Concordiae, 1589, *see* FORMULA CONCORDIAE.
*Kurtzer u. warhafftiger Bericht v. d. letzten Verfolgung der evang. Prediger in Ungaren &c., 1683, *see* UNGARN.
*Kurze Gesch. d. evang. luther. Kirche in Ungarn, 1794, *see* TEKUSCH (J. M.)
Kurze &c. Nachricht v. d. unter d. Böhm.-Mähr. Brüder bekanten, Kirche &c., 1757, *see* BÖHMISCH-MÄHRISCHEN BRÜDER.
Kurtz (Johann Heinrich).
Church hist. Tr. J. Macpherson. 3v. s8°. 1888–90
„ „ ......2nd ed. 3v. s8°. 1891–93
Kuruma (Samezo). Konsumvereine in Japan, *see* UNTERSUCHUNGEN ü. Konsumvereine, 1923.
Kuryłowicz (Jerzy). Traces de la place du ton en gathique. [H.E., 244]. 8°. 1925
Kurz (Marcel). Alpinisme hivernal: le skieur dans les Alpes. Préf. de E. Sauvage. 8°. 1925
Kuschevsky (Ivan Afanasievich), *1847–76.* Николай Негорев или благополучный Россиянин. Роман. s8°. Москва. 1923
Kuschnir (M.) L'Ukraine, l'Europe orientale et la Conférence de la Paix. 8°. 1919
Kuske (Bruno).
Gesch. d. rhein. Städte. Überblick. 8°. Essen. 1922
Quellen z. Gesch. d. kölner Handels u. Verkehrs im M.-a. [Gesells. f. Rhein. Gesch. Publ., 33]. 3B. 8°. Bonn. 1917–23
Kutorga (Mikhail Semenovich). О днѣ и праздникѣ Новаго Года у Аѳинянъ. [I. Akad. Nauk. Записки, т8]. 8°. С.-П. 1865
Kutscher (Artur). Frank Wedekind: s. Leben u. s. Werke. 2B. s8°. München. 1922–27
Kutshev (Stanislav). Очеркъ ист. общ.-государств. строя Польши. Переводъ съ польскаго подъ редак. Н. В. Ястребова. 8°. С.-П. 1907
Kutzner (E. G.) Ukrainische Siedelungen. Ein Beitr. z. Siedelungs- u. Hausgesch. la8°. 1922
Kuusinen (Otto Wilhelm).
The Finnish revolution. [P2419]. s8°. 1919
Die Revol. in Finnland. [P2569]. 8°. Hamburg. 1921
Kuyper (Abraham). Disq. exhib. J. Calvini & J. à Lasco de Eccl. sentent. inter se compositionem &c. 8°. Hagae Com. 1862
Kuzmin (Mikhail Alekseevich).
Глиняные голубки: 3а кн. стихов. изд. 2ое. s8°. П. 1923
Крылья: повесть. изд. 4ое. s8°. [Berlin]. 1923
Параболы: стихотворения, 1921–22. s8°. П. 1923
Плавающие: путешествующие. Роман. изд. 3е. s8°. П. 1923
Сети: первая книга стихов. изд. 3е. s8°. Петрополис. 1923
Тихий сраж: роман. изд. 2ое. 8°. П. 1924
—— **& V. Voinov.** Д. П. Митрохин. 4°. Москва. 1922
Kuzmin-Karavaev (Vladimir Dm.) Изъ эпохи освободительнаго движенія. 2t *in* 1v (1, до 17 Окт. 1905. 2, -8 Іюля 1906). 8°. С.-П. 1907
Kuzminskaya (Tatiana Andreevna). Ma vie: récit dicté par une paysanne [Anissia] à T. A. K. Revu & corr. par L. Tolstoi. Tr. &c. par C. Salomon. [Cahiers verts, 28]. s8°. 1923
Моя жизнь дома и в Ясной Поляне. Предисл. М. А. Цявловского. 2ое изд. [2ч. (1, 1846–62. 2, 1863–64)]. 8°. [Москва]. 1927
Мои понятия о советских хозяйствах. [P2600]. s8°. Москва. 1919
О продовольствии. [P2723]. 8°. Москва. 1919
Kuznetsov-Krasnoyarsky (Innokent Petrovich), *ps.* [*i.e.* KRASNOYARSKY]. Историч. акты xvii столѣтія (1633–99). Матеріалы для ист. Сибири. 2 вып. [in 1v]. la8°. Томскъ. 1890–97

Kuzovkov (D.) Муниципализация жилищ и квартальные хозяйства в Москве. 8°. [Москва]. 1920

Kvačala (Ján). Komenský. 8°. Turčiansky Sv. Martin. 1914

Kvinoel (Christian Theophil). Obs. ad. N.T. ex libris apocryphis V.T. 8°. Lipsiae. 1794

Kvitka (A.) Записки казачьяго офицера. Война 1877–78г. la8°. С.-П. 1903

Kvitki (Grigory Fedorovich) [*ps.* Грицькій Основъяненко]. Сочиненія Л. Ө. К. Малороссійскія повѣсти разсказанныя Г. Основъяненкомъ. Подъ редакц. А. А. Потебни. 2t. 8°. Харьковъ. 1887

Kyd (Thomas). The Spanish tragedy. Ed. w. pref. &c. by J. Schick. s8°. 1898

Kyd (Thomas) [*continued*].
*The Spanish tragedy, w. adds., 1602. [Repr. of enl. version, prep. under dir. of W. W. Greg. Malone Soc. repr.] s4°. 1925

Kyle (Harry M.) The biology of fishes. 8°. 1926

Kyle (Melvin Grove). Moses & the monuments: light f. archaeology on Pentateuchal times. Stone Lect., 1919. 8°. 1920

Kyligan, *Saint, see* Kilian, *Saint.*

Kym (Andreas Ludwig).
Üb. die menschl. Seele. [P2473]. s8°. 1890

Kyösti (Larin), *ps.* [*i.e.* Gösta Larson].
Dikter. Ofvers. af G. Castren &c. s8°. Helsingfors. [1908]

Kyser (Hans). Das Aprikosenbäumchen: Novellen. s8°. 1920

L

L. (*l'abbé*). *Hist. de la républ. de Venise, par l'a. L., 12t, 1758–68, *see* Laugier (M. A.)

L. (*Major*). *Breakfasts, luncheons &c., 1887, *see* Breakfasts.

L. (A.) *Eines recht-evang. treumeinenden Dieners unparthey. Nachricht den Pietismus in Halle betreffend, 1708, *see* Pietismus.

L. (D.) Notices reg. metr. vers. of the Psalms, 1842, *see* Laing (D.)

L. (E. D.), *J.C., see* L'Allouette (E. de), *juris consulte.*

L. (G. A.) *St. of Winchelsea church, 1927, *see* Leigh (G.)

L. (G. G.) Novissima Sinica; ed. G. G. L. [*i.e.* Leibnitz], 1699, *see* Sinica.

L. (*Rev.* **J.**) *Methodism unmasked: Wesley's doct. proved false &c., 1828, *see* Methodism.

L. (M. D.) Antiguedad &c. del Bascuenze, 1728, *see* Larramendi (Manuel de).

L. (M. R.) The sporting party &c., 1865, *see* Lahee (M. R.)

L. (R.) The Bishop of Oxford's charge &c., 1712, *see* Laurence (Roger).

L. (V. A.) Адмиралъ П. С. Нахимовъ, герой севастоп. войны. [P848]. s8°. Москва. 1902

Laache (Rolv).
Cromwell og Puritanerne i samtidens folkelige satire. [P2415]. s4°. [1920]
Cromwell's regiment. [Særtrykk av "Kirke og Kultur," 1925. P2769]. 8°. 1925
Friherre C. Bonde om Cromwell, 1655–56. [Særtryk av Festskr. til A Kjaer. P2851]. la8°. [Christiania. 1924]
Kavallerer og puritanere efter slaget paa Marston Moor. [P2784]. 8°. [1924]
H. Wergeland & h. strid med Prokurator Praëm. [Norske Vid.-Akad. Skr.] B1, 1828–31. la8°. Oslo. 1927
Slaget paa Marston Moor, 2den Juli, 1644. [P2683]. 8°. 1923

Labadie (—), *religieux convers de la Congrég. de St. Maur.*
*Les aventures de Pomponius. [La regence du duc d'Orléans]. s8°. Rome. 1724

Labadie (Jean de), *1619–74, see* Blechschmid (C.) Matæologiam Labadianam &c., 1717.

Laban (Ferdinand). Die Schopenhauer-Literatur. [*b. w.* Fechner (G. T.) Tagesansicht &c., 1879]. 8°. L. 1880

Laband (Paul). Das Staatsrecht d. deut. Reiches. 5e neub. A. B4. la8°. Tübingen. 1914

Labande (Léon Honoré). Avignon au 15e siècle: légation de Ch. de Bourbon & du Card. J. de La Rovère. [Publ. par ordre de Pr. Albert I de Monaco]. la8°. Monaco. 1920
Le palais des papes & les mons. d'Avignon au 14e siècle. 2t. 4°. Marseille. 1925
see Monaco. Inventaires du Palais de M., 1604–1731; publ. avec intr. &c. par L. H. L., 1918.

La Batut (Guy de).
La cour de Monsieur, frère de Louis XIV. 8°. [1927]
Le plaisir singulier, *see* Œuvres libres, 80, 1928.

Labaume (Eugène). Rel. compl. de la campagne de Russie en 1812. 5e éd. 8°. Londres. 1816

La Baume (François de), *bp. of Halicarnassus, see* Favre (P. F.) Lettres édif., s. la visite de La B. à la Cochinchine en 1740, 1746.

Labayru y Goicoechea (Estanislao Jaime de). Hist. gen. del señorio de Bizcaya. 6t. fol. 1895–1903

Labbe (Philippe). De scriptoribus eccl. quos attigit R. Bellarminus diss. 2t [t1, *incl.* Cenotaphium Joannae Papissae t2 *has title*: Diss. philol. de scr. eccl. &c. *&* *incl.* Diatriba de Aimoino]. s8°. Parisiis. 1660

Labbé de la Mauvinière (Henri). Poitiers & Angoulême, St. Savin, Chauvigny. [Villes d'art célèb.] 2e éd. la8°. 1925

Labé (Louise) [Charlin (L.), *aft. Perrin, called Labé*]. Debate between Folly & Cupid (1550). [Tr.] by E. M. Cox. 8°. 1925
see Aynard (J.), *ed.* Les poëtes lyonnais, 1924.
„ O'Connor (D.) L. L., sa vie & son œuvre, 1926.

La Beaume (Jules), *see* Koran. Le K. analysé, d'ap. la tr. de M. Kasimirski & obs. de savants orient. par J. La B., 1878.

La Bédollière (Emile de) [†Gigault de La Bedollière (E.)]
Les industriels: métiers & professions en France. Dessins par H. Monnier. 8°. 1842
Mœurs & vie privée des Français dans les prem. siècles de la Monarchie. 3t. 8°. 1855

La Bédoyère (*le cte.* **Charles A. François de**) **&** *le baron* **A. de Maricourt.** Idylle & drame, 1790–1815: G. de Chastellux & C. de La Bédoyère. 8°. 1924

La Bédoyère (Charles Angélique François Huchet, *comte* **de),** *1786–1815, see* La Bédoyère (*c.* C. A. F. de) &c. Idylle & drame: G. de Chastellux & C. de La B., 1924.

La Bédoyère (Georgine, *comtesse* **de),** *wife of C. A. F. Huchet, cte. de La Bédoyère, form. Chastellux; 1790–1871, see* La Bédoyère (*c.* C. A. F. de) &c. Idylle & drame: G. de C. & C. de La Bédoyère, 1924.

Labellarte (Arcangelo). Apollo in Parnasso poeta dell' Infante Reale. [P2765]. s8°. [Napoli. 1775]

Labenski (*comte* **Xavier**) [*ps.* Jean Polonius], *see* Asse (E.) Les petits romantiques: J. P. &c., 1900.

La Berthier (—). The abominations of the Jesuits exposed &c. Tr. G. Russell. s8°. [1820]

Labessade (Léon de). Les ruelles du 18e s. Préf. par A. Dumas fils. 2p [*pagin. cont.*] 8°. 1879

Labiche (Eugène Marin).
Théâtre complet. Préf. par E. Augier. t2. s8°. 1892
Théâtre complet. t2. s8°. [1922]

La Bigne (Margarinus de). Maxima bibliotheca vet. Patrum & antiq. scriptorum eccl. primo quidem a M. de la B. in lucem ed. Deinde celeb. in Univ. Colon. doctorum studio aucta &c. Hac tandem ed. Lugdun., ad eandem Coloniensem exacta, novis authoribus &c. locupletata [*by* J. Despont]. 28t (t1, Index materiarum, t28, Index locorum S. Script.) la. fol. Lugduni, Genuae. 1677–1707

La Bissachère (Pierre Jacques Lemonnier de). Rel. sur le Tonkin & la Cochinchine (1807). Publ. avec intr. &c. par C. B. Maybon. 8°. 1920

Labitte (Charles).
Etudes litt. Avec notice de Sainte-Beuve. 2t. 8°. 1846

La Blanchère (René Du Coudray de). Terracine: essai d'hist. locale. [Bibl. des Ecoles Franç. d'Athènes & de Rome, fasc. 34]. 8°. 1884

La Boëssière (*le marq.* **de**). Consid. sur les guerres de l'Ouest pend. la Révol. fr. [*b. w.* Duchemin Descepeau (J.) Lettres sur la Chouannerie, t2, 1827]. 8°. 1827

Laborde (*le comte* **Alexandre de**). Etude sur la Bible moralisée illustrée, *see* Bible: Compl. Texts &c. La B. moralisée, t5, 1927.
La mort chevauchant un bœuf. Orig. de cette illust. dans livres d'heures de la fin du 15e siècle. 4°. 1923
Notice sur le fichier Laborde: artistes des 16–18 s. 4°. 1927

Laborde (*le cte.* **Alexandre L. J. de**). Voyage pittor. & hist. de l'Espagne, réimpr. du texte, *see* Revue hispanique, t63, 1925.

Laborde (*le marq.* **Leon E. S. J. de).** Notices des émaux, bijoux &c. dans les galeries du Louvre. p2. s8°. 1853
2, Doc. & glossaire.
see LABORDE (*le cte.* A. DE). Notice s. le fichier L., 1927.

La Borde (Vivien de). *Du témoignage de la vérité dans l'Église. [*b. w.* Opstraet (J.) Theologus Christ., 1697]. s8°. *n.p.* [Paris ?.] 1714

Laboubnia, *see* LABUBNA.

Laboulaye (Édouard) [*le dr.* R. LEFEBVRE; LEFEBVRE LABOULAYE (E. RENÉ)]. Les États-Unis & la France. [P2830]. 8°. 1862
see FRANCE. Grand coutumier de France; n. éd. par E. L. &c., 1868.

Labour.
L. & capital in Parliament. Prep. by the L. Res. Dept. 8°. 1923
L. & industry. Lect. by P. Alden, J. B. Baillie &c. [M'ter, Univ. of: Publ., No. 137]. 8°. M'ter. 1920
L. & the new social order. Rep. on reconstruction. [P2465]. 8°. [1918]
,, ,, ...rev. [P2465]. 8°. [1918]
L. as an internat. problem: essays by G. N. Barnes &c., 1920, *see* SOLANO (E. J.), *ed.*
*L. Party's aim. A crit. &c. By 7 members of the L.P. s8°. [1923]

Labour Commission to Ireland. Report. [P2530]. 8°. [1921]

Labour (The) gazette: prep. &c. at Ministry of Labour. v18 (No. 1-9, Jan.-Sept., 1918). fol. [1918]

Labour, Ministry of.
Industrial reports. Nos. 1-4. [P2563]. 8°. 1917-19
Rep. of an inquiry into condit. of boy labour on the docks at Liverpool. [P2749]. 8°. 1920

Labour Research Department. The Press; prep. by the L.R.D. [Studies in lab. & cap., v2]. 8°. 1922
*Wages, prices & profits, report prep. by L.R.D., 1922, *see* WAGES.
see LABOUR & capital in Parliament, 1923.

Labour who's who (The), 1927. 8°. [1927]

La Bourdonnais (B. F. Mahé de).
Mém. hist. Publ. par s. petit-fils. 2e éd. 8°. 1828
see CREPIN (P.) M. de La B., 1699-1753, 1922.

La Brache (Helga de), *see* BLOMQUIST (F. A.) H. de La B.: bidrag till svensk rätts-och samhällshist., 1877.

Labrador. Newfoundland & L. pilot, 5th ed., 2v. *&* Suppl. 4, 1917-22, *see* ADMIRALTY.

La Brète (Jean de), *ps.*
Les deux sommets. Roman. 2e éd. s8°. [1920]
Mon oncle et mon curé. Intr. par Mme. Félix-Faure-Goyau. s8°. *Nelson.* [1910]

Labriola (Arturo).
Le 2 politiche, Fascismo e riformismo. 8°. Napoli. 1924
Il socialismo contemp., con app.: La dittatura d. prolet. &c. 8°. Napoli. 1922

Labriolle (Pierre de).
Hist. de la litt. latine chrét. 8°. 1920
,, ,, ...2e éd., rev. & augm. 8°. 1924
Hist. & lit. of Xty. f. Tertullian to Boethius. Tr. H. Wilson. Intr. foreword by Card. Gasquet. 8°. 1924

La Bruyère (Jean de). Œuvres. Texte, notices, lexique &c. par G. Servois. [G. é. de la F.]
3e éd. rev. &c. 5t in 6 [*t3 in 2p*; *t5*, "n. éd. 2e tir." 8°. 1922
Les caractères. s8°. [1910]
see MORILLOT (P.) La B., 2e éd., 1921.

Labruzzi (Carlo), *1765-1817*, *see* ASHBY (T.) Dessins de C. L., 1903.

Labry (Raoul). Autour du Moujik. 8°. 1923
Une législation communiste. Rec. des lois, décrets &c. du gouvt. bolchéviste. 8°. 1920

Labsanzky (Joannes), *ps.*, *see* KELLIO (MIKLOS).

Labubna [LABOUBNIA]. Lettre d'Abgar, ou hist. de la convers. des Edesséens par L. Tr. s. la vers. arm. du 5e s. [P2808]. 8°. Venise. 1868

Labusquette (Robert de).
Autour de Dante. Les Béatrices. la8°. [1921]

La Calprenède (Gauthier de Costes, *seigneur* **de)** [†COSTES (G.)]
*Faramond, roman. 4t. s8°. 1753
see SEILLIÈRE (E.) Le romancier du grand Condé: G. de C., Sieur de la C., 1921.

Lacau (Pierre). Les statues "guérisseuses" dans l'anc. Egypte, *see* ACAD. D. INSCR.: FOND. PIOT., Mon., t25, 1921-22.

Lacava (Michele).
Topografia e storia di Metaponto. la8°. Napoli. 1891

Lacenaire (Pierre François), *ps.* [*i.e.* P. F. GAILLARD]. Lacenaire après sa condamn. [*b. w. h.* Méms., 1836]. 8°. 1836
Méms., révélations & poésies. 2v [*in* 1]. 8°. 1836
Procès complet de L. & de ses complices. 8°. 1836

Lacerda (José de). New dict. of Portuguese & Eng. languages. la8°. Lisboa. 1871
Novo dicc. geral das linguas Ingleza e Portugueza. la8°. 1866

Lacey (Thomas Alex.) The Anglo-Catholic faith. s8°. [1926]
Gregory IX & Greek ordinations. [P2690]. s8°. 1898

Lach (Robert). *Works in* KAISERL. AKAD. D. WISS. ZU WIEN.
Gesänge russ. Kriegsgefangener, 1917-26. [Sitz., 183, 203.]
Das Konstruktionsprinzip d. Wiederholung in Musik, Sprache u. Lit., 1925. [Sitz., 201.]
Sebastian Sailer's "Schöpfung" in d. Musik (1750-1800), 1916. [Denkschr., 60.]
Vergleich. Kunst- u. Musikwissenschaft, 1925. [Sitz., 201.]
Die vergl. Musikwissenschaft, Methoden u. Probleme, 1924. [Sitz., 200.]
W. A. Mozart als Theoretiker, 1918. [Denkschr., 61.]

La Chambre (François de), *see* ILHARAT DE LA CHAMBRE (F.)

La Chavignerie (Emile Bellier de), *see* BELLIER DE LA CHAVIGNERIE.

La Chénaye (B. de).
Abécédaire de flore ou langage des fleurs. 8°. 1811

La Chesnais (Pierre Georget). Les peuples de la Transcaucasie pend. la Guerre & devant la paix. s8°. 1921

Lachèvre (Frédéric). Le Casanova du 17e s.: P.-C. Blessebois, Normand (1646 ?-1700 ?). 8°. 1927
Claude Le Petit & La muse de la cour (1657). Avec hist. des gazettes concurrentes &c. 8°. 1922
Les dern. libertins: F. Payot de Lignières, Mme. Deshoulières, Chaulieu, La Fare &c. la8°. 1924
Mélanges. 8°. 1920
Les recueils coll. de poésies libres & satir. publ. dep. 1600 j. la mort de Théophile (1626). Suppl., add. & corr. 4°. 1922
Les successeurs de Cyrano de Bergerac: G. de Foigny &c. 8°. 1922
see BLOT (C. DE C., *baron* DE). Chansons libertines; [Intr. &c. *signed* F. L.], 1919.
,, CYRANO DE BERGERAC (S.) Œuvres libertines; notice biog. par F. L.], 1921.
,, HÉNAULT (J. DE). Œuvres, notice par F. L., 1922.

Lachmann (Carl C. F. W.) Briefe an K. L., 1814-50; hrsg. &c. A. Leitzmann, *see* KÖNIGL. PREUSS. AKAD. D. WISS. Abhdl. (Phil.-hist. Klasse), 1915.
see BIBLE. NEW TEST. [GREEK]. Nov. Test. Gr. & Lat. rec. C. L., 2v, 1842-50.
,, GRIMM (J. L. C.) & W. GRIMM. Briefwechsel mit K. L., 2v, 1927.

Lachmann (Johann) [LACHAMANN], *see* SUABIA. Genotigter u. fremdt eingetrag. schrifft: Syngramma der predigere [J. L. &c.] ynn Schwaben, zu Oecolampadio, 1596.

Lachmann (Thérèse Pauline Blanche), *aft. wife of marq. Araujo de Païva*, *see* PAÏVA (T. P. B., *marquise* DE).

Lackington (James). The confessions of J. L. Added letters on daughters at boarding schools. s8°. 1804
Mems. of the 45 first yrs. of life of L. by himself. 7th ed. corr. s8°. 1794

Lackmann (Adam Heinrich). De computatione annorum per hiemes. [P446]. s4°. Kilonii. 1744
De edendis Lucae Lossii &c. epistolis. Inspersa: Lucae Backmeisteri, De morte Caroli V epistola. [P484]. s4°. Hamburgi. 1719

La Colombrière (Marc de Vulson, *sieur* **de),** *see* VULSON (M. DE).

Lacombe (François), *Commissionaire de police à Montpellier.*
*Dict. de la langue romane, ou du vieux lang. françois. [*re-issue w. new tp. &c.*] s8°. 1768
Dict. du vieux langage françois. Suppl. s8°. 1767

Lacombe (Rose) [LACOMBE (CLAIRE)], *see* LACOUR (L.) 3 femmes de la Révol., 1900.

Lacombe de Prezel (Honoré). Dict. iconologique ou introd. à la connoissance des peintures, sculptures, &c. [*b. w.* Frederick II. Dict. politique, 1762]. s8°. Gotha. 1758

Lacomblé (E. E. B.), *see* PERLES de la poésie franç. contemp. 10e éd., rev. & mise à jour par L., 1920 ?.

Lacordaire (J. B. Henri), *see* CHOCARNE (B.) Inner life of L.; tr., 1883.

Lacoste (*Mme.* **Euphémie),** *see* BOUCHARDON (M. P. G.) Mme. L., 1927.

Lacour (Léopold). Trois femmes de la Révolution: Olympe de Gouges, Théroigne de Méricourt, Rose Lacombe. 8°. 1900

La Cour de La Pijardière (Louis de), *see* LA PIJARDIÈRE.

Lacour-Gayet (Georges).

Antonin le Pieux & son temps (138–161). 8°. 1888
Bonaparte: membre de l'Institut. 8°. 1921
Guillaume II le vaincu. 8°. [1920]
Napoléon, sa vie, s. œuvre, s. temps. Préf. du Maréchal Joffre. 4°. [1921]
Saint-Germain des Prés & la Coupole. s8°. [1924]
see ROUMANIE. La R.: Conférences faites à l'Union Fr. [par L.-G. &c.], 1920.

Lacretelle (Jacques de). Une belle journée, *see* ŒUVRES (Les) libres, t27, 1923.
La Bonifas. 29e éd. s8°. [1925]
Silbermann. 37e éd. s8°. 1922

La Croix (— de), *secretary to the French Embassy at Constantinople.* Etat présent des nations & églises grecque, armén., & maronite en Turquie. s8°. 1715. [1695]

Lacroix (Alfred). Déodat Dolomieu, 1750–1801. Sa vie adv.—sa captivité—s. œuvres &c. 2t. 8°. 1921

Lacroix (*le général* Henri de). Le Maréchal Foch. s8°. [1921]

La Croix (Jacques Vincent de). A review of the constit. of the princ. states of Eur., & of the U.S. Tr. by [E. Ryves]. 2v. 8°. 1792

Lacroix (Paul). Le château de Jarnac, bataille de Jarnac. [P2515]. 8°. 1855
Les gouverneurs de L'Angoumois. [Extr. du Bull. de la Soc. archéol. &c. de la Charente, 1875]. [P2515]. 8°. 1876

Lacroix (Silvestre François). Elem. treatise on the diff. & integral calculus. Tr., w. app. & note. 8°. C. 1816

La Croix de Ravignan (Gustave F. Xavier de).
Clément XIII & Clément XIV. 8°. 1854
„ „ ....Vol. suppl. Doc. hist. &c. 8°. 1854

La Croze (Mathurin Veyssière de). Hist. du Christianisme des Indes. s8°. La Haye. 1724

Lactantius (Lucius Coelius Firmianus). [Opera. Ed. Joannes Andreae episc. Alderieñ. *fol. 2a beg.* Johannis Andree Episcopi Alerieñ . . . epistola. *ff2a–11a table of rubrics; f11b–13a* Lact. Firm. errata &c. *f. 13b blank; f14a* Lactantii Firmiani institutionū divinar. adversū gentes Libri primi prefatio. *Ends on f223a* Aspicis illustris lector quicunq; libellos &c.]
fol. [Romae. *Conr. Sweynheym & Arn. Pannartz.* 1470]
224 leaves, 1st & last blank; a 1–12; b–x in eights, y 1–12, fol. 11a illuminated. Capitals supplied in red & blue.
see MOUNTAIN (J. H. B.) Summary of the writings of L., 1839.
„ SIBYLLINE ORACLES. Fragmenta quæ apud. L. reper., 1817.
„ SPYKER (H. J.) Spec. de pretio Instit. divinis L. statuendo, 1826.

Lacunza (Manuel) [*ps.* J. J. BEN EZRA]. Venida del Mesias en gloria &c. 3t [*pagin. cont.*] s8°. [Madrid. *c.* 1812]

Lacurie (*l'Abbé*), *hon. canon of La Rochelle.* Notice sur le pays des Santones, à l'époque de la domin. romaine. [P2515]. 8°. Saintes. 1851

La Curne de Sainte-Palaye (Jean Bapt. de). Dict. histor. de l'anc. langage françois. Suivi des Curiositez franç. pour suppl. aux dict., par A. Oudin [1656, *w. sep. tp. & pagin. in* t10]. 10t. 4°. Niort. [1875–82]

Lacy (James), *see* *Some remarks on the dialogue between Philalethes & Philotemus & J. L.'s answer &c., 1705.

Lacy (John), *a pseudo-prophet, see* KEIMER (S.) A brand pluck'd f. the burning, *folld. by* A letter f. J. L. &c., 1718.

Ladd (William). An essay on a congress of nations for the adj. of internat. disputes. Repr. f. orig. ed. of 1840, w. intr. by J. B. Scott. [C.E. for Int. Peace]. la8°. N.Y. 1916

Ladell (Arthur Randolph). Richard Baxter, puritan & mystic. Pref. by W. H. Frere. 8°. 1925

Laderchi (Giacomo). Acta Sanct. Xt. martyrum vindicata. 2p *in* 1v. s4°. Romae. 1723

Ladies' Annual register, 1799. [*tp. missing*]. 8°. [1799]

Ladies' diary (The), or Woman's almanack, 1800–08. [1804 *wanting. b. w.* Gentleman's diary, 1800–08]. s8°. [1800–08]

Ladies (The) invention; being £1000 for 6d., to the fortunate &c. [*b. w.* Postman, *after* No. 547, Dec. 1698]. fol. [1698]

Ladislaus VII, *king of Poland, see* VLADISLAUS VII.

Lado. Ладо. Сборникъ литерет.-обществ. [P2452]. 8°. С.-П. 1911

Lady Margaret Hall, *Oxford, see* OXFORD.

Lady (A) of Quality, *ps.* *Serena Blandish, 1925, *see* JONES (ENID, *Lady*).

Laelius (Laurentius) [LOELIUS (L.)] De animarum statu post mortem contra Purgatorium pontificium. s4°. Witebergae. 1596

Laelius (Laurentius) [LOELIUS (L.)] [*continued*].
Theses, de communicatione idiomatum reali. Resp. J. Gryphio. [P2612]. s4°. Witebergae. 1595
Theses de sacramento Coenae Dominicae contra Pontificios. Resp. W. Firnhabero. s4°. Witebergae. 1597
see HUNNIUS (E.) De regno Christi propositiones, def. L. L., 1597.

Laenen (*le chanoine* Joseph). Les archives de l'état à Vienne au p. de vue de l'hist. de Belgique. [Commission Roy. d'Hist.] 8°. Brux. 1924

Laënnec (René Théophile Hyacinthe). Trans. of sel. passages f. De l'auscultation médiate (1st ed.) With biog. by Sir W. Hale-White. 8°. 1923
see ROUXEAU (A.) L. après 1806, 1920.

Laer (Arnold Johan Ferdinand van), *see* VAN LAER (A. J. F.)

Laerne (C. F. van Delden). Brazilië en Java: Koffiecultuur, *see* BIJDRAGEN TOT DE TAAL &C. V. NED. IND., volg. 4, d9, 1885.

La Escosura (Patricio de), *see* ESCOSURA (P. DE LA).

Lafage (Léon). La maison brulée, nouvelle, *see* ŒUVRES libres, t69, 1927.

La Fare (Charles Auguste, *marq.* de), *1644–1712.* *Mém. & réflex. sur les évènemens du r. de Louis XIV. Par Mr. L. M. D. L. F. s8°. Rotterdam. 1716
see LACHÈVRE (F.) Dern. libertins, 1924.

La Farge (Mabel), *see* ADAMS (H.) Letters to a niece &c., w. a niece's mem. by M. La F., 1920.

La Farge (Oliver), *see* TULANE UNIV. Tribes & temples: exped. to Middle Amer., 1925; *by* Blom & La F., 2v, 1926–27.

Lafargue (Marc). Corot. 8°. 1925

Lafargue (Paul). Der Jesuitenstaat in Paraguay T. Campanella, *see* VORLÄUFER d. neu. Sozialismus, 2e A., B3, 1922.

Lafargue (Philip), *ps., see also* PHILPOT (J. H.)

La Faye (Antoine de).
De vita & obitu T. Bezae, ὑπομνηματιον. 8°. Genevæ. 1606

La Faye (Jacques de), *ps.* [*i.e. Mlle.* DE SARDENT].
La Princesse Mathilde, 1820–1904. 8°. 1928

Lafaye (Marcel). Le chemin du désir, *see* ŒUVRES libres, 39, 1924.

Lafayette, *brigantine, see* HAWAII. In Admiralty: adjustment in case of L., 1844.

Lafayette (*le gén.*), *1757–1834, see* REGNAULT-WARIN (J. B. J. I. P.) Hist. du Gén. L. en Amér., 1832.

La Fayette (*Mme.* de), *1634–93* [MOTIER (MARIE MADELEINE), *ctsse. de La Fayette*]. Hist. de Mme. Henriette d'Angleterre. Intr. par E. Henriot. s8°. 1925
Lettres de M.-M. Pioche de La Vergne, Ctsse. de L., & de G. Ménage. Intr., notes &c. par H. Ashton. 8°. Liv'l. 1924
see ASHTON (H.) Mme. de La F., sa vie & s. œuvres, 1922.
„ MAGNE (É.) Mme. de L., 7e éd., 1926.

——, J. Regnauld de Segrais, & F., *duc* **de La Rochefoucauld.**
La princesse de Clèves. Intr. par Mme. Félix-Faure-Goyau. s8°. London. [1913]
The princess of Cleves. Tr. H. Ashton, w. intr. [Broadway Trans.] s8°. [1925]

Lafenestre (Georges). La peinture italienne. t1 [1, jusqu'à la fin du 15e s. *no more publ.*] 8°. [1885]

Laffan (Robert George Dalrymple). Hist. of Serbia—Yugoslav movt.—Yugoslavia to date, *see* BUCHAN (J.), *ed.* Nations of to-day, Yugoslavia, 1923.

Laffleur de Kermaingant (Pierre Paul), *see* TRÉPORT (LE), *abbey of.* Cartulaire de St.-Michel du T.; [publ.] par P. L. de K., 1880.

La Fléchère (Jean Guillaume de), *see* FLETCHER (J. W.)

La Flesche (Francis). The Osage tribe: rite of the chiefs; sayings of the ancient men, *see* SMITHSONIAN INST.: BUR. OF ETHN. Rep. 36, 1921.
The Osage tribe: rite of vigil, *see* SMITHSONIAN INST.: BUR. OF ETHN. Rep. 39, 1925.

Lafontaine (August Heinr. Julius). Marie Menzikof & Fédor Dolgorouki: hist. russe en forme de lettres. Tr. I. de Montolieu. 2t. s8°. 1804

La Fontaine (Jean de).

Contes & nouvelles. n. éd. rev. s8°. 1870
TRANSLATIONS.
Forty-two fables. Tr. E. Marsh. 8°. 1924
More fables. Tr. E. Marsh. 8°. 1925
see BOILLOT (F.) Impr. sensorielles chez La F., 1926.
„ HALLAYS (A.) J. de La F., 1922.
„ POURTALÈS (G. DE). De Hamlet à Swann, 1924.

La Force (Bertrand Nompar de Caumont, *duc* **de).**
Le grand Conti. 8°. 1922
Lauzun : un courtisan du Grand Roi. 8°. 1919
Le maréchal de La Force (1558–1652). [t]1. 8°. 1924
Vie amoureuse de la Grande Mademoiselle. 2[t]. s8°. [1927]

La Force (Charlotte Rose de Caumont de). Les jeux d'esprit, ou la promenade de la Psse. de Conti à Eu. Publ. Le Marq. de La Grange. [Trésor des pièces rares &c.] s8°. 1862

La Force (Jacques Nompar de Caumont, *1er duc* **de),** ***maréchal de France***, *see* LA FORCE (B. N. DE C., *duc* DE). Le maréchal de L. F., t1, 1924.

La Forge (Jean de). La joueuse dupée : comédie (1664), *see* FOURNEL (V.) Contemp. de Molière, t3, 1875.

Laforgue (Jules). Œuvres complètes. [t]1–5. 8°. 1922–25
1, 2, Poésies. 3, Moralités légendaires.
4, Lettres, 1, 1881–82 ; intr. &c. de G. Jean-Aubry.
5, Lettres, 2, 1883–87 ; notes de G. Jean-Aubry.
see CUISINIER (J.) J. L., 1925.
„ RUCHON (F.) J. L., 1860–87 : sa vie, s. œuvre, 1924.

La Fortelle (— de), *lieutenant du Roi.* La vie milit., polit. & privée de demoiselle C. G. L. A. A. T. Eon ou d'Eon de Beaumont. 8°. 1779

Lafosse (*l'abbé*) [LAFOSSE DE CHAMPDORAT]. De Deo ac divinis attributis, *see* MIGNE (J. P.), *ed.* Theol. cursus, t7, 1861.

Lafrensen (Niclas), *the younger*, *see* LEVERTIN (O.) N. L. &c., 4e uppl., 1920.

La Fresnaye (Roger de), *see* ALLARD (R.) R. de La Fresnay, 1922.

Lafuente y Alcántara (Emilio), *see* AJBAR MACHMUÂ. Crónica anón. del s. xi ; tr. y anot. por E. L. y A., 1867.

La Fuÿe (Marguerite Allotte de), *see* ALLOTTE DE LA FUŸE (M.)

La Gabelentz (H. Conon de), *see* GABELENTZ (H. C. V. DER).

La Garde (*comtesse* **Brevern de),** *see* BREVERN DE LA GARDE.

Lagarde (Paul Anton de), *form. P. S. Bötticher.* Materialien z. Kritik u. Gesch. d. Pentateuchs. Hrsg. P. de L. 2B *in* 1v (1, Der Pentateuch arab. 2, Die Genesis arab.) 8°. L., *Teubner.* 1867
Ueb. d. Verhältnis d. deut. Staates z. Theol., Kirche u. Relig. [P2695]. 8°. Göttingen. 1873
*Zur Urgesch. d. Armenier. [P2812]. 8°. 1854
see BIBLE : COPTIC. Der Pentateuch kopt. ; hrsg. P. de L., 1867.
„ —— : PSALMS. Psalterium juxta Hebr. Hieronymi e recogn. P. de L., 1874.

Lagardelle (Hubert). Le socialisme ouvrier. s8°. 1911

Lagden (*Sir* **Godfrey Yeatman).** The native races of the Empire. Ed. & partly wr. by Sir G. L. [Brit. Emp. : survey ; ed. H. Gunn, v9]. 8°. [1924]

Lâge de Volude (*la marquise* **Béatrix Stéphanie de),** *née d'Ambliment*, *see* REINACH-FOUSSEMAGNE (*la ctsse.* H. DE). Une fidèle : la marq. L. de V., 1764–1842, 1908.

Lagercrantz (Otto). Euripides Hippolytus, *see* KUNG. HUM. VET.-SAMF. I. UPPSALA. Skr., B21, 1922.

Lagerheim (Lars Magnus). Litterae Gothicae ab Asia oriundae &c. Diss. ; præs. N. H. Sjöborg. s4°. Londini Goth. [1805]

Lagerholm (Åke), *ed.*, *see* LYGISǪGUR. Drei l., 1927.

Lagerlöf (Selma).
Antikrists mirakler. Roman. 6e uppl. s8°. [1918]
Bannlyst. Berättelse. s8°. [1918]
Charlotte Löwensköld. s8°. 1925
Herr Arnes penningar. 9e uppl. s8°. [1922]
Kejsarn av Portugallien. Värmlandsberätt. s8°. [1922]
Körkarlen. Berättelse. s8°. [1922]
Kristuslegender. 11e uppl. s8°. [1920]
Legender. Berättade. 8e uppl. s8°. [1920]
Osynliga länkar. Berättelser. 11e uppl. s8°. [1922]
Troll och människor. 2a saml. s8°. [1921]
Z. Topelius, utveckling och mognad. s8°. [1920]

TRANSLATIONS.
The emperor of Portugallia. Tr. V. S. Howard. 8°. [1917]
The Holy City : Jerusalem, 2 Tr. V. S. Howard. s8°. 1918
Jans Heimweh. [Übers. v. P. Klaiber]. s8°. München. [1915]
Jérusalem, [2], En terre sainte. Texte fr. d'A. Bellessort. s8°. [1914]
Mårbacka. Tr. V. S. Howard. 8°. [1924]
The tale of the manor & o. sketches. Tr. C. Field. s8°. [1923]
Thy soul shall bear witness! Tr. s8°. [1921]
Le vieux manoir. Tr. M. Hélys. s8°. 1911

La Gervaisais (*le marq.* **Nicolas Louis Marie Magon de).**
*L'auteur du système (1720–1825). [P2764]. 8°. 1825

Lagneau (Jules). De l'existence de Dieu. s8°. 1925

La Gorce (Pierre de). Hist. relig. de la Révolution franç. t4, 5 [t4, 5e éd.]. 8°. 1921–23
La Restauration : Louis XVIII. s8°. [1926]
„ „ [t2], Charles X. s8°. [1928]
see CHEVRILLON (A.) Disc. pour la récept. de A. C. (Rép. de P. de la G.), 1921.

La Gourdaine (Jean Pierre Norblin de), *see* NORBLIN DE LA GOURDAINE (J. P.)

La Grange (Charles Varlet de), *see* VARLET DE LA GRANGE (C.)

Lagrange (*le cte.* **Joseph Louis).**
see NIELSEN (N.) Recherches s. les équations de L., 1923.
„ —— Sur l'opér. itérative des équations de L., 1924.
„ VASSALLI-EANDI (A. M.) Notice abr. de la vie & des écrits de L., 1871.

Lagrange (Marie Joseph). St. Justin. s8°. 1914

La Grèze (Jean de). Serafina. Roman. s8°. 1926

La Guérinière (François de).
Le grand d'Espagne. Roman. s8°. 1922

Laguille (Louis). Hist. de la province d'Alsace j. mariage de Louis XV. 3p *in* 1v. fol. Str. 1727

Laguna (Grace Andrus de), *see* DE LAGUNA (G. A.)

Lagus (J. J. Guilielmus). Studia Latina Provincialium disput. 8°. Helsingforsiae. [1849]

La Harpe (Jean François de). Earl of Warwick ; [*tr.*] T. Franklin, *see* INCHBALD (E.) Brit. th., v19, 1808.

La Haumerie (Crosset de), *ps.*, *see* COLONNA (F. M. P.)

La Haye [*place*], *see* HAGUE.

La Haye (Jean de), *Baron de Coutaux.* Les Mém. & recherches de France & de la Gaulle Acquitanique &c., 1643, *see* BOUCHET (J.) Annales d'Aquitaine &c., 1644.

La Haye (Joannes de), *Franciscan*, *see* BIBLE : LATIN. Biblia maxima vers. ex ling. orient. &c. ; authore J. de la H., 19t, 1660.

La Haye (Léon), *see* LIÉGE. Invent. analyt. des chartes de la Colleg. de St. Jean l'Évangél, par L. L., t1, 1921.

La Haye (Petrus de), *see* TRENT, *Council of.* Catechismus Conc. Tridentini ; opera P. D. L. H. P. [*i.e.* P. de la H.], 1830.

Lahee (*Miss* **M. R.)** The sporting party & Owd Neddy Fitton's visit to th' Earl of Derby : a Lancashire sk. [P2850]. s8°. 1865
see DINSMORE (W.) Lancs. novelists : L., *n.d.*

Lahondès (Jules de). Les monuments de Toulouse, hist., arch., beaux-arts. 8°. Toulouse. 1920

Lahore. Cat. of paintings in the Cent. Museum, L. By S. N. Gupta. 8°. Calcutta. 1922
Journals & diaries of assistants & Resident at L., 1846–49, *see* PUNJAB. P. govt. rec., v4, 1911.
Polit. diaries of Resident at Lahore, 1847–49, *see* PUNJAB : P. govt. rec., v3, 4, 1909–11.
Polit. diaries of R. G. Taylor, P. Sandys &c., 1847–49, *see* PUNJAB : P. govt. rec., v6, 1915.

Lahorgue (Pierre Marie).
La Bretagne au feu (25 Mars–11 Nov. 1918). 8°. Pau. 1919

La Horie (*Général* **Victor Claude Alex. Fanneau de),** *see* LE BARBIER (L.) Le gén. de La H., 1766–1812, 1904.

Lahovary (Jean). Betty B . . ., *see* ŒUVRES libres, 81, 1928.
Monsieur de Bargeaud, *see* ŒUVRES libres, 58, 1926.

Laible (Joseph). Gesch. d. Stadt Konstanz u. i. Umgeb. 2e A. 8°. Konstanz. 1921

Laidler (Harry Wellington). Hist. of socialist thought. 8°. 1927
Recent developments in the Amer. labor movement. [P2734]. s8°. N.Y. 1923
Socialism in thought & action. s8°. N.Y. 1920
—— **& N. Thomas,** *edd.* New tactics in social conflict : symposium, by H. E. Barnes & others. s8°. N.Y. 1926

Laidler (W.), *see* HART (I. B.) & W. LAIDLER. Elem. aeron. sci., 1923.

Laieikawai, *Hawaiian romance*, *see* HALEOLE (S. N.)

Laigue (Louis A. M. P. de). Les doges Sébastien et Pierre Ziani. [Extr. de la Revue d'hist. diplom. P2837]. la8°. 1906

Laincel (Anthoine de), *see* TAMIZEY DE LARROQUE (J. P.) Not. sur le livre de raison de L., 1895.

Lainé (*le vte.* **Joseph Louis Joachim),** *1767–1835*, *see* PERCEVAL (E. DE). Un advers. de Napoléon, le vte. L., 2t, 1926.

Lainez (Diego), *see* ORLANDINUS (N.) Hist. Soc. Jesu, p2, Lainius, 1620.

Laing (Bertram M.) A study in moral problems. 8°. [1922]

Laing (David). *Notices reg. the metr. version of the Psalms, Church of Scot. [Signed D. L. From App. to Baillie's Letters &c., v3]. s8°. E. 1842

Laing (David), *architect.*
Hints for dwellings : designs for cottages &c. 4°. 1800

Laing (Francis Henry). Lord Bacon's "philosophy" examined. Added, The mental process of experience: Essay. s8°. [1877]

Laing (Janet). Wintergreen. s8°. [1921]

Laing (John), *Librarian of the New College Lib., Edinburgh, see* HALKETT (S.) & J. L. Dict. of anon. & pseudon. Eng. Lit., n. ed., v1–4, 1926–28.

Laing (Malcolm), *see* GRAHAM (P.) Essay on authenticity of poems of Ossian, objections of M. L. refuted, 1807.

Lainius (Jacobus), *see* LAINEZ (D.)

Lair (Jules). Etude sur la vie & la mort de Guill. Longue-Epée, Duc de Normandie. fol. 1893

Laird (John). A study in moral theory. 8°. [1926]
A study in realism. 8°. C. 1920

Laistner (Max Ludwig Wolfram). Greek economics. [*Extracts*]. Intr. & tr. by M. L. W. L. 8°. 1923

Lajard (J. B. Félix), *see* JOHN VI, *patr. of Armenia.* Hist. d'Arm.; tr. J. Saint-Martin. Not. s. la vie du P., par F. L., 1841.

La Jonquière (Clément de). La bataille de Jemappes. [Publ. s. la dir. de la Sect. Hist. de l'Etat-Major de l'Armée]. la8°. 1902

Lake (Cuthbert). Notes on the will of H. Cloker, 1573, & St. Magnus the Martyr & th. conn. w. the Co. of Coopers. la8°. 1924

Lake (*Sir* H. Atwell). Narr. of the defence of Kars, hist. & military. 8°. 1857

Lake (John), *bp. of (1) Sodor & Man, (2) Bristol, (3) Chichester, see* SANCROFT (W.) Proc. & tryal in case of abp. of Canterbury, bp. of C. &c., 1688, 1689.

Lake (Kirsopp). Landmarks in the hist. of early Xtny. 8°. 1920
The religion of yesterday & to-morrow. 8°. [1925]
see FOAKES-JACKSON (F. J.) & K. L., *edd.* Beginnings of Xty., p1, v1–3, 1920–26.

Lake (Philip) & R. H. Rastall.
Textbook of geology. 3rd ed., 2nd impr. 8°. 1922

Laking (*Sir* Guy Francis), *bart.* Cat. of the coll. of arms & armour & objects of art formed by G. F. L. Sold by Christie, Apr. 19, 1920. [*Illust.*] la8°. 1920
A record of European armour & arms thr. 7 centuries. v2–5. 4°. 1920–22
see WALLACE COLL. Europ. armour & arms; by G. F. Laking, 1900; 4th ed., 1910.

Lakshmisa, *Dēvapura.* The Jaimini Bharata, a Canarese poem, w. tr. & notes by D. Sanderson. Chap. 1–11. 8°. Bangalore. 1852

Lalande (André). Vocabulaire technique & crit. de la philos. Publ. &c. A. L. [Soc. franç. de philos.] n. éd. rev. & augm. 2t. la8°. 1928

La Laurencie (Lionel de).
Les créateurs de l'opéra français. 8°. 1921

Lallā Yōgiswarī [LAL DĔD]. Lallā-Vākyāni, or The wise sayings of Lal Děd, a mystic poetess of ancient Kashmir. Ed. w. tr., notes & vocab. by Sir G. Grierson & L. D. Barnett. [R.A. Soc., v17]. 8°. 1920
The word of Lalla the prophetess: sayings. Done into Eng. verse & annot. by Sir R. C. Temple. 8°. C. 1924

Lallemant (Louis), *Jesuit, see* BRÉMOND (H.) Hist. litt. du sentiment relig. en France, t5, L'école du Père L. &c., 1920.

Lalli (Giov. Batt.), *see* VIRGILIUS MARO (P.) Eneide travestita di G. B. L., 2t, 1796.

L'Allouette (Edmond de). *Apologie catholique contre les libelles &c. faictes par les Liguez perturbateurs du repos du Royaume de France &c. s8°. [Paris ?]. 1585
[*Also ascr. to P. de Belloy*].

Lalore (*l'abbé* Charles).
see BASSE-FONTAINE. Cartul. de B. F.—Chartes de Beauvoir; [publ. &c.] par l'abbé L., 1878.
,, MONTIÉRAMEY. Cartul.; [publ. &c.] par C. L., 1890.
,, MONTIER-LA-CELLE. Cartul.; [publ. &c.] par C. L., 1882.

Lalou (René). Hist. de la litt. franç. contemp. s8°. 1924

Lama (Friedrich *Ritter* von). Papst u. Kurie in ihr. Politik nach d. Weltkrieg. 8°. Illertissen. 1925
see CRISPOLTI (F.) Don Bosco; nach F. C. bearb. v. F. R. v. L., 1922.

Lamandé (André).
La vie gaillarde & sage de Montaigne. s8°. [1927]

Lamansky (Vladimir Ivanovich).
О нѣкоторыхъ славянск. рукописяхъ въ Бѣлградѣ, Загребѣ и Вѣнѣ. [I. Akad. Nauk. Записки, t6]. 8°. С.-П. 1864

Lamarche (Hippolyte) [DUMAS DE LAMARCHE (H.)] L'Algérie, son infl. s. la France &c. [*Imperf.* P2830]. 8°. 1846

La Marche (Olivier de). Le Chevalier delibéré [1483] (Schiedam c. 1498), facs., *see* PICOT (E.) & H. STEIN. Recueil, 1923.

Lamarck (Jean Bapt.)
see KÜHNER (G. F.) L., die Lehre v. Leben, 1913.
,, PERRIER (E.) L., 1925.

La Mare (Philibert de). De vita, moribus & scr. G. Philandri Castilionii epistola. [*b. w.* Andres (J. F.) Vida de S. Orencio, 1648]. s4°. [Dijon ?]. 1667

Lamarre (Augustin Frederic), *see* CARRARA (A. F. X.) C., l'assassin du garçon de recettes L. (1897), *n.d.*

Lamartine (Alphonse de) [†LAMARTINE DE PRAT (M. L. A. DE)].
Les confidences. n. éd. s8°. 1856
Graziella. s8°. 1919
,, Texte établi d'ap. l'éd. déf. &c. Intr. par G. Charlier. s8°. 1926
Harmonies poét. & relig. s8°. 1920
Méditations poétiques. n. éd., publ. avec intr. &c. par G. Lanson. [G.E. de la F.] 2e tir. 2t. 8°. 1922
Nouv. confidences. n. éd. [*b. w. h.* Les confidences, 1856]. s8°. 1856
see BARTHOU (L.) L., orateur, 1918.
,, BORDEAUX (H.) Amours du temps passé: J. Charles & A. de L., 1923.
,, —— Voyageurs d'Orient, t2, L. &c., 1926.
,, VINET (A. R.) Et. sur la litt. fr. au 19e s., t2, L. & V. Hugo, 1916.

Lamas Carvajal (Valentin), *see* LOPEZ-AYDILLO (E.) & J. PALACIOS. L. C.: est. biog. y crit., con. sel. de sus composiciones, 1925.

Lamase (Martial de Pradel de), *see* PRADEL DE LAMASE (M. DE).

Lamase (*le chevalier* Pradel de), *see* PRADEL DE LAMASE.

La Mauvinière (Henri Labbé de), *see* LABBÉ DE LA MAUVINIÈRE (H.)

La Mazelière (*le marq.* Antoine Rous de).
Le Japon, hist. & civilisation. t1–8. s8°. 1907–23
1, Le Japon ancien.
2, Le Japon féodal.
3, Le Japon des Tokugawa.
4, Le Japon mod., 1, La révol. & la restaur., 1854–69.
5, ,, ,, 2, La transform. du Japon, 1869–1910.
6, ,, ,, 3, La transform. du Japon (*suite*).
7, 8, Le Japon comme Gr. Puissance.

Lamb (Charles).
The essays of Elia & Eliana. s8°. *Bohn.* 1889
see BOOK. B. (The) of the ranks & dignities of Brit. society (1805) [attr. to L.), 1924.
,, DANIEL (G.) Recoll. of C. L., 1927.
see LUCAS (E. V.) Life of L., 5th ed., 2v, 1921.
,, MANNING (T.) Letters to C. L.; ed. G. A. Anderson, 1925.
,, WHERRY (G. E.), *ed.* Cambridge & C. L., 1925.

—— & Mary A. Lamb.
Poetry for children. Ed. &c. R. H. Shepherd. s8°. 1872

Lamb (Harold). Genghis Khan. 8°. [1928]

Lamb (Horace). Higher mechanics. 8°. C. 1920

Lamb (*Gen.* John), *see* LEAKE (I. Q.) Mem. of life & times of L., officer of the Revol., & h. corresp., 1850.

Lamb (*Sir* John Cameron). The life-boat & its work. 8°. 1911

Lamballe (*la princesse* de), *see* CABANÈS (A.) La P. de L. intime &c., *n.d.*

Lambard (William). Eirenarcha: or of the office of Justices of Peace. Gathered 1579, & now rev. &c. s8°. 1594

Lambe (John), *called Doctor Lambe.* *A briefe descr. of the notorious life of J. L. &c. *la. paper.* s4°. Amsterdam. 1628

Lambe (Lawrence Morris). The Hadrosaur Edmontosaurus f. the Upper Cretaceous of Alberta. [Canada. Geol. Survey. P2513]. 8°. Ottawa. 1920

Lambeau (Lucien).
L'Abbaye-aux-Bois de Paris: add. à notice du 9 déc. 1905, *see* PARIS: COMM. MUNIC. DU VIEUX P. Procès-verb., 1920.
Les Carmes déchaussés de la rue de Vaugirard, *see* PARIS. COMM. MUNIC. DU VIEUX P. Procès-verb., 1918.
La Chapelle-Saint-Denis. s4°. 1923
Charonne. t2. s4°. 1921
Le cimetière de Picpus, 1794–1921, *see* PARIS: COMM. MUNIC. DU VIEUX P. Procès-verb., 1920.
La Villette. 8°. 1926

Lambert (—), *dramatist.* La magie sans magie: comédie (1661), *see* FOURNEL (V.) Contemp. de Molière, t1, 1863.

Lambert (André), *see* BERLEPSCH (H. E. v.) Motive d. deut. Architektur; hrsg. v. A. L. &c., Abtlg. 1, 1890.

Lambert (C. H.) Dicc. de paralelos, concordancias y analogías bíblicas. 8°. 1871

Lambert (Elie). Tolède. [Villes d'art célèb.] la8°. 1925

Lambert (François), *of Avignon.*

Comm. de causis excæcationis &c. s8°.[Strassburg?. 1530?]
De regno, civitate & domo Dei, per F. L. coll. & per G. Geldenhaurium recogn. &c. s8°. In vet. Vangionum Vormatia [*S. Wagner.* 1538]
Farrago omnium fere rerum theologic. [Lib. paradoxorum s8°. *n.p. n.d.* [1525]?
In Cantica Cantic. Salomonis libellum comm. s8°. Norimbergæ. 1524
In divi Lucæ evang. comm. s8°. [Norembergae, *Ioh. Petreius.* 1524]
In Iohelem prophetam comm. s8°. *n.p.* [Strasburg?]. *n.d.* [1525?]
In primum 12 prophetarum nempe Oseam comm. [*With text*] Ejusdem lib. de arbitrio hominis. s8°. Argentorati, *apud I. Hervagium.* 1525
see BAUM (J. W.) F. L. v. A., 1840.

Lambert (Gustave), 1824–71, *see* DOUBLET (E.) G. L.: s. projet de voyage au Pôle—sa mort, 1922.

Lambert (Henri). Le nouveau contrat social, ou l'organis. de la démocratie individualiste. 8°. 1920
Pax economica: liberté des échanges internat. 8°. Brux. 1920

Lambert (J. Malet). 2000 years of gild life; w. acc. of the gilds &c. of Kingston-upon-Hull, 14th to 18th cent. *la. paper.* 4°. Hull. 1891

Lambert (Johann Heinrich), *see* EULER (L.) L. E.'s u. J. H. L.'s Briefwechsel (1758–72), 1924.

Lambert (Lionel).

The King's castle & the King's Free Chapel, in Stafford. [P2756]. s8°. *n.d.*
Izaak Walton & the royal deanery of Stafford. s8°. Stafford. 1926
The Royal Free Chapel of Stafford. s8°. Clapham. [1927]
St. Mary's & the College quarter of Stafford. s8° B'ham. 1925
St. Mary's, the Chapel of the Mayor &c. of Stafford. [*b. w. h.* St. Mary's & the College quarter, 1925]. s8°. [1925]
St. Mary's the town church of Stafford & Q. Elizabeth's grant. [P2756]. s8°. *n.d.*
Short hist. of the College of Stafford w. the Ch. of St. Mary. s8°. Guildford. 1923

Lambert (Lion Lambert). Catéchisme du culte judaique, en héb., franç. & allem. s8°. Metz. 1818

Lambert (Roger). Lexique hiéroglyph. la8°. 1925

Lambert (Uvedale). Blechingley: parish hist. w. acc. of family of De Clare. 2v. 4°. 1921

Lambertenghi (Giulio Porro-), *see* PORRO-LAMBERTENGHI (G.)

Lamberti (Arcangelo). Rel. de la Colchide, *see* BERNARD (J. F.), *ed.* Rec. de voy., t7, 1725.

Lambertus, *Hersfeld.* [ASCHAFNABURG]. Opera. Rec. O. Holder-Egger. Acced. Annales Weissenburg. [Scr. rer. Germ. in usum schol.] 8°. Hannoverae. 1894

Lambertz (Max) & G. Pekmezi.
Lehr- u. Lesebuch d. Albanischen. s8°. Wien. [1913]

Lambeth. Conf. of bishops at Lambeth Palace, July 5 to Aug. 7, 1920. Encycl. letter f. the bishops &c. 8°. 1920
Lucubrationes L., 1729, *see* MAICHELIUS (D.)
Princ. mss. à peintures du L. Palace; [*by*] E. G. Millar, *see* SOC. FRANÇ. DE REPROD. DE MSS. À PEINTURES. Bull., Années 8, 9, 1924–25.
[Testamenta Lambethana, a compleat list of the wills &c. in the reg. of L., extr. by Dr. Ducarel (1779). *MS. copy of p1 of the 1854 ed. Names only*]. fol. *n.d.*

Lambinet (Pierre). Recherches sur l'orig. de l'imprimerie. 8°. Brux. an vii. [1799]

Lambley (Kathleen). The teaching & cultiv. of the French lang. in Eng. dur. Tudor & Stuart times. 8°. M'ter. 1920

Lamborn (Edmund Arnold Greening).
Expression in speech & writing. s8°. O. 1922
see HUGHES (T. H.) & E. A. G. L. Towns & t.-planning, 1923.
—— & G. B. Harrison.
Shakespeare, the man & h. stage. s8°. 1923

Lambotte (*Sir* **Paul).** Flemish painting bef. the 18th cent. Tr. H. B. Grimsditch. Ed. G. Holme. [Studio. Autumn No.] 4°. 1927
Henri Evenepoel. la8°. Brux. 1908
L'œuvre de A. Stevens. Cat. de l'expos. organisée par la Soc. Roy. des Beaux-Arts &c., avr.-juin, 1907. Et. illustrée. la8°. 1907

Lambrecht (Nanny).
Die eiserne Freude. Roman. 5e A. s8°. 1915

Lambrino (*Mme.* **S.),** *see* FLOT (MARCELLE).

Lambs, The, *Club.* Annals of the Lambs, London & New York. 8°. N.Y. 1899

Lambsdorff, *see* LAMSDORF.

Lambsprinck (Joannes), *alchemist, 15c.* [LAMBSPRING]. Book of Lambspring conc. the philos. stone, *see* HERMETIC MUSEUM, v1, 1893.

Lambton (Arthur). My story. 2nd ed. 8°. [1925]

Lamennais (Félicité de). Words of a believer. Tr. w. intr. by W. G. Hutchison. 8°. 1905
see DUINE (F.) L., sa vie, ses idées, &c., 1922.

***Lamentationes** Germanicæ Nationis. s4°. *n.p.* [1526?]

Lameth (Théodore de), *1756–1854.* Mémoires. Publ. avec intr. &c. par E. Welvert. 8°. 1913
Notes & souvenirs, fais. suite à ses Mémoires. Publ. par E. Welvert. 8°. 1914

La Mettrie (Julien Offray de). L'homme machine suivi de L'art de jouir. Intr. & notes de M. Solovine. s8°. 1921

Lami (François), *Benedictine monk, see* LAMY (F.)

Lami (Stanislas). Dict. des sculpteurs de l'école franç. au 19e s. t4, N-Z. la8°. 1921

Lamindus Pritanius, *ps., see* MURATORI (L. A.)

Lamm (Carl Johan). Das Glas v. Samarra. [Forsch. z. islam. Kunst; hrsg. F. Sarre, 2, Die Ausgrab. v. Samarra, B4]. 4°. 1928

Lamm (Martin). Swedenborg. St. öfver hans utveckling till mystiker &c. 8°. [1915]
Upplysningstidens romantik. Den mystiskt sentimentala strömningen i Svensk litt. 2d. la8°. [1918–20]

Lammasch (Heinrich), *see* LAMMASCH (M.) & H. SPERL. H. L., seine Aufzeichnungen &c., 1922.

Lammasch (Marga) & H. Sperl. H. Lammasch, s. Aufzeichnungen, s. Wirken u. s. Politik. Hrsg. v. M. L. & H. S., mit Beitr. v. H. Bahr, &c. la8°. Wien. 1922

Lammers (Thorvald), *ed.*
Norske folkeviser, tekst & toner. [2p. 1, 4e opl.] s8°. 1902–23

La Mothe le Vayer (François de), *the elder.* Notitia historicorum select. or animadv. upon Gr. & Latin historians. Tr. by W. D['Avenant]. s8°. O. 1678

Lamouche (Léon). La Bulgarie. s8°. 1923

Lampe (Friedrich Adolf). Comm. Evangelii sec. Joannem. 3t. 4°. Amstelodami. 1724–26
Delin. theologiae activae. s4°. Trajecti ad Rhenum. 1727
Hist. Eccl. Reformatae in Hungaria & Transylvania &c. s4°. Trajecti ad Rhenum. 1728
Synopsis hist. sacrae & eccl. s8°. Francofurti ad Moenum. 1722
„ „ ed. altera auctior &c. s8°. Trajecti ad Rhenum. 1726

Lampe (Johann Friedrich), *see* WESLEY (J.) *Hymns on the gt. festivals [*tunes by J. F. L.*], 2nd ed., 1753.

Lampel (Joseph), *see* VIENNA. Quellen z. Gesch. d. Stadt Wien, Abt. I, B7, 8 *&* Abt. II, B4; bearb. v. J. L., 1914–23.

Lampen (Ernest Dudley). Château d'Oex: life & sport in an Alpine valley. s8°. [1910]

Lampérez y Romea (Vicente). Arquitectura civil española de los s. I al XVIII. 2t. la8°. 1922
The cathedral of Burgos. [Hispanic Soc.] s8°. Barcelona. *n.d.*
Los grandes monasterios españoles. s8°. 1920

Lamphere (George N.)
The U.S. govt.: its organiz. &c. 8°. Phila. 1880

Lamplugh (George William), *F.G.S.* Economic geol. of the Isle of Man. [Mems. of G.S.] 8°. 1903
Geol. of the Isle of Man. [Mems. of G.S.] 8°. 1903
Iron ores &c., by L. &c., *see* GEOLOG. SURVEY. Spec. rep. on min. resources, 12, 1920.
see WEDD (C. B.) & W. B. R. KING. Geol. of co. around Flint &c., w. contrib. by G. W. L. &c., 1924.
—— & W. Gibson. Geol. of the co. around Nottingham. [Mems. of G.S.] 8°. 1910
Geol. of the co. betw. Newark & Nottingham. [Mems. of G.S.] 8°. 1908
Geol. of the Melton Mowbray district & S.E. Notts. [Mems. of G.S.] 8°. 1909
—— & F. L. Kitchin. On the mesozoic rocks in some of the coal explorat. in Kent. [Mems. of G.S.] 8°. 1911
—— —— & J. Pringle. Concealed mesozoic rocks in Kent. [Mem. of G.S.] 8°. 1923
—— & B. Smith. The water supply of Notts f. underground sources. With chap. on rainfall by H. R. Mill. [Mems. of G.S.] 8°. 1914

Lamporecchi (Ranieri). Mém. sur la persécution qu'on fait souffrir en France à M. Libri. Préc. d'une lettre de chev. Del Rosso. 2e éd. 8°. Londres. 1850

Lampridius (Antonius), *ps., see* MURATORI (L. A.)

Lampros (Paulos). Ἀνέκδοτα νομίσματα κοπέντα ἐν Γλαρέντσᾳ (1346–64). [P2768]. la8°. Ἀθήνησιν. 1876
Ἀνέκδοτα νομίσματα κοπέντα ἐν Πέραν, 1421–43. [P2768]. la8°. Ἀθήνησιν. 1872
Νομίσματα καὶ μετάλλια τῆς Ἑπτανήσου Πολιτείας &c. [1800–13]. [P2768]. la8°. Ἀθήνησιν. 1884
Νομίσματα τῆς νήσου Ἀμοργοῦ &c. [P2768]. la8°. Ἀθήνησιν. 1870
Νομίσματα τῶν ἀδελφῶν Μαρτίνου καὶ Βενεδίκτου β' Ζαχαρίων δυναστῶν τῆς Χίου, 1314–29. [P2768]. la8°. Ἀθήνησιν. 1884
Lampugnanus (Pompeius). J. Lipsii in C. Cornelium Tacitum notæ cum MS. cod. Mirandulano collatæ. [*b. w.* Ens (G.) Rerum Hung. hist., 1604]. s8°. Bergomi. 1602
Lamsdorf (*Count* **Vladimir Nikolaevich)** [LAMZDORF]. Дневник, 1886–90. Под ред. Ф. А. Ротштейна. 8°. Москва. 1926
see BURTSEV (V. L.) Der Zar u. d. ausw. Politik ; [geheime Memor. d. Graf. L. &c. ; tr.], 1910.
Lamy (Bernard). *Apparatus Biblicus: or an introd. to Holy Scr. [Tr. R. Bundy]. 4°. 1723
Lamy (Étienne), *see* CHEVRILLON (A.) Disc. pour la récept. de A. C. [*on* E. L.], 1921.
Lamy (François), *Benedictine monk, see* FÉNÉLON (F. DE S. DE LA M.) Réfut. des erreurs de B. de Spinosa par F., L. &c., 1703.
Lamy (Hugues). L'abbaye de Tongerloo dep. sa fond. jusqu'en 1263. [Univ. de Louvain: Rec. de trav., fasc. 42]. 8°. Louvain. [1914]
Lanark. Eccl. records. Sels. f. reg. of presbytery of L., 1623–1709. [Ed. J. Robertson. Abbotsford Club]. 4°. E. 1839
Lancashire. Calendar of persons commem. in monument. inscript. & abstracts of wills cont. in books rel. to Lancs. & Cheshire. Comp. & ed. by F. C. Beazley. [Record Soc. for Publ. of Doc. rel. to L. & Cheshire, v76]. 8°. 1922
Lancashire registers. Ed. J. P. Smith. [Cath. Record Soc., v23]. v4. 8°. *p.p.* 1922
4, Brindle & Samlesbury.
Lancashire (The) & Cheshire naturalist: a monthly journal. Ed. W. M. Tattersall &c. v12–17. [*No more publ.*] 8°. M'ter. 1919–25
Lancaster (Henry Carrington). Pierre Du Ryer, dramatist. [C.I. of Wash., Publ. 171]. la8°. Wash. 1913
Lancaster (John). The life of Darcy, Lady Maxwell, of Pollock: comp. fr. Diary (1768–1810). 2v. s8°. 1821
„ „ ....2nd ed. 8°. 1826
Lancaster (W. T.), *ed., see* THORESBY (R.) Letters addr. to R. T., 1912.
Lancelot, *of Denmark* [LANSELOOT]. A beautiful play of Lancelot of Denmark. Tr. f. Middle Dutch [w. intr.] by P. Geyl. s8°. The Hague. [1923]
Lancelot, *of the Lake, hero of romance.* *Li chantari di Lancellotto. Ed. w. intr. notes & gloss. by E. T. Griffiths. 8°. O. 1924
Lançarote, *see* GRAIL. Span. G. fragm.; ed. K. Pietsch, 2v, 1924–25.
see BOULENGER (J.) Romans de la Table Ronde, t1, 2, 1922–23.
Lancelot (Claude) [*ps.* TRIGNY (DE)]. *Grammaire gén. &c. [Par le sieur D. T.] n. éd. s8°. Brux. 1676
Nouv. methode pour appr. la langue espagnole. [*b. w. h.* Gramm., 1676]. 6e éd. s8°. Brux. 1687
Nouv. methode pour appr. la langue ital. [*b. w. h.* Gramm., 1676]. 3e éd. s8°. Brux. 1677
Lancet (The). 1920–27. [*2v annually*]. la8°. 1920–27
Lanchester (Henry Vaughan). Art of town planning. 8°. 1925
Lanci (Fortunato), *see* MARCOLINI (C.) Degli ordinamenti ond 'ebbe informata Dante la prima cantica d. Div. Comm. investig. di F. L., 1855, 1856.
Lancia (Andrea). Novelle, sec. 14. [*Ed.* G. Papanti. *a. c. in* P2277]. s8°. Bologna. 1873
Lanciani (Rodolfo Amedeo). Le antichità del territorio Laurentino n. reale Tenuta di Castelporziano, *see* REALE ACCAD. D. LINCEI. Mon. ant., v16, 1906.
L'itinerario di Einsiedeln e l'ord. di Benedetto canonico, *see* REALE ACCAD. D. LINCEI. Mon. ant., v1, 1890.
La villa Adriana. [P2844]. s8°. 1906
Wanderings thr. anc. Roman churches. la8°. 1925
Lanciano (Cristoforo da). Pagine di musica relig. in 21 pezzi per organo. la8°. *n.d.*
Lancicius (Nicolaus), *see* LANCZYCKI (N.)

Lanckoroński (Carl *Graf*). Städte Pamphyliens u. Pisidiens. Unter Mitwirkung v. G. Niemann u. E. Petersen; hrsg. L. 2B. (1, Pamphylien. 2, Pisidien). fol. Wien. 1890–92
Lancret (Nicolas), *see* WILDENSTEIN (G.) L., 1924.
Lanczycki (Nikołaj) [LANCICIUS (N.)]
Meditationes. s8°. Leodii. 1672
Opusc. spiritual. 2t. fol. Ingolstadii. 1724
Land & Water [THE COUNTY GENTLEMAN & L. & W.] [*War articles, by H. Belloc &c.*] Oct. 17, 1914–Dec. 28, 1916. [4v. *no tp.*] sm. fol. 1914–16
Landau (J. L.) Short lect. on mod. Hebrew lit. f. M. H. Luzzatto to S. D. Luzzatto. 8°. Johannesburg. 1923
Landau-Aldanov (Mark Aleksandrovich) [ALDANOV (M. A.)]
Передъ концомъ, *see* RUSSKII. Р. сборникъ, 1920.
Современныя проблемы. Сборникъ статей М. А. А., Ю. Делевскаго [*& others*]. 8°. Парижъ. [1921]
Sainte Hélène. Tr. du ms. Russe par M. Hirchwald. s8°. 1921
Landauer (Gustav). Aufruf z. Sozialismus. 3e A. 8°. 1920
Landauer (Ignacio Bauer), *see* BAUER LANDAUER (I.)
Lan-Davis (Cyril Frederick).
Telephotography. 2nd ed. by L. B. Booth. s8°. 1921
Landázuri (Joaquín José de). Hist. de Guipúzcoa. 2t. 8°. 1921
Lande (Aleksandr Solomonovich), *see* IZGOEV (A. S.)
Landenberg (Hugo von), *bp. of Constance, see* HOHENLANDENBERG (H. v.)
Landenberger (Emil). Durch Central Amerika. 8°. St. 1922
Lander (Richard L.), *see* CLAPPERTON (H.) Journal of 2nd exped.; add. journal of R. L. from Kano to the sea-coast, 1829.
Landi (Ortensio) [*ps.* ANONIMO, *di Utopia*; PHILALETHES *Polytopiensis*]. *Comment. d. più notabili &c. cose d'Italia & altri luoghi, di lingua Aramea in Ital. tr. Aggionto, Cat. d. inventori d. cose che si mangiani &c. da M. Anonymo di Utopia composto. [*Cat. has sep. tp. b. w.* Firenzuola (A.) Prose, 1548]. s8°. [Vinegia]. 1548
Forcianae quaestiones, in quibus var. Ital. ingenia explic., *see* PYRCKMAIR (H.) De arte peregrin., 1591.
*Lettere di molte valorose donne [I. Sforza &c.], n. quali appare non esser alli huomini inferiori. s8°. Vinegia. 1548
Novelle. Ristamp. e. corr., prec. d. sua vita [& Cat. d. opere]. [*la. paper*]. 8°. Lucca. 1851
Landini (Placido). Istoria dell' oratorio e d. ven. arciconfraternita di Santa Maria d. Misericordia, Firenze [*& in* Toscana]. Accresciuta, corr., e con note d. P. Pillori &c. [2p in 1v]. la8°. Firenze. 1843
***Landlords,** Land laws & Land leagues in Scotland; by Aliquis, 1881, *see* SCOTLAND.
Landman (T.), *see* CUNDALL (L. B.) & T. L. Wales, 1925.
Landogna (Francesco). Maestri e scolari pisani n. Studio di Bologna, sec. 12–14, *see* ARCHIVIO STOR. ITAL., a. 84i, 1926.
Landoni (Teodorico), *see* ARETINO (P.) Lettere scritte a P. A., emendate per cura di T. L. &c., 2v, 1873–75.
Landor (Robert Eyres). Sel. f. R. L. Ed. E. Partridge. 8°. 1927
see PARTRIDGE (E.) R. E. L., 1927.
Landor (Walter Savage).
Complete works. Ed. T. E. Welby. v1–8. 8°. 1927–28
1–8, Imaginary conversations.
Letters of a Conservative, means of saving Eng. Church, addrest to Lord Melbourne. [P2777]. s8°. 1836
The Pentameron & o. imagin. conversations. Ed. w. pref. by H. Ellis. s8°. 1889
Pericles & Aspasia. Pref. by H. Ellis. s8°. *Scott.* [1890]
see BAILEY (J. C.) Unpopularity of L., 1925.
„ MASON (A. H.) W. S. L., poète lyrique, 1924.
„ WISE (T. J.) & S. WHEELER. Bibliog. of writings of W. S. L., 1919.
Landormy (Paul). La vie de Schubert. s8°. 1928
Landre (Jeanne). Angèle & Ouistiti, *see* ŒUVRES libres, 6, 1921.
Les idylles de Pont-aux-Muses, *see* ŒUVRES libres, 72, 1927.
Landry (Lionel). La sensibilité musicale. 8°. 1927
see CLERC (H.) & L. L. Le tentateur, 1928.
Landsberger (Artur). Hass. Roman e. Deutsch-Engländers aus 1950. s8°. München. 1915
Landsberger (Benno). Assyr. Handelskolonien in Kleinasien aus d. 3 Jahrt., *see* ALTE ORIENT., B24, 1925.
Landsberger (Franz). Breslau. s8°. L. 1926
Landsberger (Julius).
Fabulae aliquot Aramaeae. [P2590]. s8°. Berolini. 1846
Landseer (*Sir* **Edwin H.)** Cat. of the eng. works of E. L., coll. by C. G. Lewis, sold by auction by Southgate & Barrett. [P2852]. 8°. 185[illegible]

Landstad (Magnus Brostrup).
Norske Folkeviser, saml. og udg. af M. B. L. 8°. 1853
Landt (J. L.) Coke as a household fuel in Central Canada. la8°. Ottawa. 1925
Landtman (Gunnar). Kiwai Papuans of Brit. New Guinea. Intr. by A. C. Haddon. 8°. 1927
Landtsperger (Joannes), *see* MÜLLER (J.), *otherwise* LANDTSPERGER.
Landucci (Luca). A Florentine diary, 1450–1516. Contin. by an anon. writer till 1542. Notes by I. del Badia. Tr. A. de R. Jervis. 8°. 1927
Land-Waiter in the port of Poole, *ps.* Poems on several subjects, 1741, *see* PRICE (H.), *ed.*
Lane (Edward William). Manners & customs of the mod. Egyptians. 5th ed., ed. E. S. Poole. 2v. 8°. 1871
Lane (Franklin Knight), *Secretary of the Interior, U.S.*
Letters. Ed. A. W. Lane & L. H. Wall. 8°. [1923]
Lane (*Sir* Hugh Percy), *see* GREGORY (A.) H. L.'s life & achievement, 1921.
Lane (John), *F.C.A.* Masonic records, 1717–1894: being lists of lodges &c. Introd. by W. J. Hughan. 2nd ed. 4°. 1895
Lane (Rose Wilder). The peaks of Shala: wanderings among the hill tribes of Albania. 2nd impr. 8°. 1924
Lane (*Lt.-Col.* William Horsburgh).
Babylonian problems. Intr. by S. Langdon. 8°. 1923
Lane-Poole (Stanley). The Moors in Spain. By L.-P. w. collab. of A. Gilman. [Story of the Nations]. 4th ed. 8°. 1890
Laney (Benjamin), *bp. of Ely &c., see* HOBBES (T.) A letter about liberty &c.; w. obs. by L., 1676.
Lanfranc, *abp. of Canterbury, see* MACDONALD (A. J.) L.: st. of h. life, work & writing, 1926.
Lanfredini, *The family of, see* MANSFIELD (M.) A fam. of decent folk, 1200–1741, L. of Florence, 1922.
Lanfrey (Pierre).
Hist. de Napoléon [*to end of 1811*]. n. éd. 5t. s8°. 1880
Lang (Andrew).
A batch of golfing papers. By A. L. & o. Ed. R. Barclay. s8°. [1892]
The blue poetry book. 7th impr. s8°. 1918
The bk. of dreams & ghosts. re-issue. s8°. 1899
Coll. of ballads. Ed. w. intr. & notes by A. L. [repr.] s8°. [1910]
Old friends. Essays in epistolary parody. n. imp. s8°. 1913
The origin of terms of human relationship, 1908, *see* BRIT. ACAD. Proc., 1907–08.
Poet. works. Ed. Mrs. Lang. 4v. 8°. 1923
32 ballades in blue china. s8°. 1885
The yellow fairy book. n. impr. s8°. 1924
see ARABIAN NIGHTS. A.N. entertainments; sel. &c. A. L., 1921.
Lang (August). Der Heidelberger Katechismus. [Verein f. Ref.-gesch. Schr., Jhrg. 31 (Nr. 113)]. 8°. L. 1913
Joh. Calvin: e. Lebensbild zu s. 400. Geburtstag. [Verein f. Ref.-gesch. Schr., Jhrg. 26 (Nr. 99)]. 8°. L. 1909
Lang (Cosmo Gordon), *abp. of York, see* DAVIDSON (R. T.) Prayer Book measure: sp., 1927.
Lang (Emil), *see* SPILLMAN (W. J.) & E. L. Law of diminishing returns, p2, Law of the soil by L., 1925.
Lang (Henry R.) Contrib. to restor. of text of the Poema del Cid, *w. text, see* REVUE HISPAN., t66, 1926.
Lang (John Dunmore).
Cooksland in N.-E. Australia. s8°. 1847
Phillipsland. s8°. E. 1847
Lang (Marx). La Nouv. Calédonie, s. climat, s. ressources nat. &c. Préf. de G. Moussu. 8°. 1925
Lang (Paul). Litt. contemp. de la Suisse franç. & de la Suisse ital. [P2732]. 8°. Londres. 1923
Die schweiz. Tellspiele. [P2732]. 8°. London. 1924
Lang (*Sir* Peter Redford Scott), *see* DEWAR (D.) Accounts; comm. by Sir P. R. S. L., 1926.
Lang (William Dickson).
see BRIT. MUS. OF NAT. HIST.: GEOLOGY &c. Fossil Bryozoa: Cretaceous Bryozoa, v3, 4, 2p, by W. D. L., 1921–22.
,, ——: ZOOLOGY. Handbk. of Brit. mosquitoes; by W. D. L., 1920.
Lang (Wolfram), *see* SYNESIUS, *of Cyrene.* Traumbuch; übers. &c. v. W. L., 1926.
Langa (Langa). Up against it in Nigeria. 8°. [1922]
Langdale (Alban) [LANGDAILUS]. Catholica confut. impiae cuiusdam determinationis D. N. Ridlei, post disputat. de Eucharistia in Acad. Cantab. habitae. 8°. Lutetiae. 1556
Langdale (Henry Bickersteth, *baron*). Judgment in the case of the Skinners' Comp. vers. the Irish Soc. & others. [P524]. 8°. [1838]
Langdale (Marmadake Langdale, *baron*), *1598–1661, see* SUNDERLAND (F. H.) M., Ld. L. & some events of h. time, 1926.
Langdon (Stephen). Ausgrabungen in Babylonien seit 1918; üb. F. H. Weissbach, *see* ALTE ORIENT, B26, 1927.
The Babylonian epic of creation. Restored f. tablets of Assur. Transcr., tr. & comm. by S. L. 8°. O. 1923
Excavations at Kish. The Herbert Weld &c. Exped. to Mesopotamia. v1, 1923–24. 4°. Paris. 1924
Le poème sumérien du Paradis, du déluge & de la chute de l'homme. [*w. text & tr.*] 8°. 1919
Sumerian epic of Paradise, the Flood & the Fall of Man. [Univ. of Pa., Babyl. Sect., v10, No. 1]. 4°. Phila. 1915
Lange (Carl). Der Kronprinz. s8°. L. [1921]
Lange (Carl Heinrich). Instit. stili Romani. s8°. Lubecae. 1745
Lange (Christian L.) Hist. de l'internationalisme. [Inst. Nobel Norvégien. Publ., t4]. [t]1 (–1648) [*no more publ.*] 4°. Kristiania. 1919
Russia, the Revol. & the War: acc. of a visit to Petrograd & Helsingfors in March, 1917. [C.E. f. Int. Peace. P2676]. la8°. Wash. 1917
Lange (Friedrich Albert). Hist. of materialism. Auth. tr. by E. C. Thomas. Intr. by B. Russell. 3rd ed. 3v [*in 1. sep. pagin.*] 8°. 1925
Lange (Hans Ostenfeldt), *see* AMENEMOPE. Weisheitsbuch d. A.; hrsg. &c. v. H. O. L., 1925.
Lange (Joachim), *1670–1744.*
Abfertigung d. sog. Vollständigen Timothei Verini V. E. Löscher's &c. [*b. w. h.* Comm. de vita &c. Pauli, 1718]. s4°. Halle. 1719
Antibarbarus orthodoxiae dogm.-hermeneuticus, sive systema dogmatum evangelic. adv. P. J. Spenerum &c. 2p *in* 1v. s4°. Berolini [p2, Hallae]. 1709–11
Apologet. Erläuterung d. neu. Hist. bey d. evang. Kirche v. 1689–1719, z. Endigung d. Sectir. Fabel-Wesens v. Pietismo &c. [*b. w. h.* Comm. de vita &c. Pauli, 1718]. s4°. Halle. 1719
Auffrichtige Nachricht v. d. Unrichtigkeit d. sog. Unschuldigen Nachrichten z. waren Unterscheid. d. Orthodoxie &c. Pseudorthodoxie, &c. [7T *each w.* "Anhang" *on V. E. Löscher;* T7 *is in* 2 Ordnungen]. [P2610]. s4°. L. 1707[–8]
Caussa Dei & relig. Judæis revelatae adv. sic dictum naturalismum &c. [*b. w. h.* Caussa Dei & relig. nat. &c., 1727]. s8°. Halae Sax. 1726
Caussa Dei & relig. nat. adv. atheismum, & pseudophilosophiam &c. ed. 2a. auctior. s8°. Halae Sax. 1727
Caussa Dei ac relig. revel.; & quidem Christianae adv. Judæos; nec non Evangelicae adv. Socinianos & pontificios &c. s8°. Halae Sax. 1727
Comm. de vita & epistolis Pauli. isag. in Acta Apost. & Pauli epistolis &c. Acc. app. apolog. T. Verino [*by V. E. Löscher*] opposita. s4°. Halae Magdeb. 1718
Disput. de indulgentiis, qua M. Lutheri theses 95 illust. [P484]. s4°. Halae Magdeb. 1718
Hist. eccl. a mundo condito ad sec. 18. ed. 2a. s8°. Halae Magdeb. 1731
J. Langens Lebenslauf v. ihm selbst verfasset. Nebst e. Anh. väterl. Warnung v. d. Herrenhut. Kirchenwesen u. Missionswercke. [*b. w.* Fischer (E. R.) Vita I. Gerhardi, 1723]. s8°. Halle. 1744
see FERBER (J. J.) Exercit. 2a de fanat., barbara malitia J. L. &c., 1711.
,, ZIEROLD (J. W.) Synopsis verit. div., &c.; suff. Idea theol. Schelguig., aut. J. L., 1706.
Lange (Johann Michael) [LANGIUS]. Ad J. G. Bajeri Compend. theolog. moral. suppl. s8°. Jenae. 1700
Tract. de nuptiis & divortiis. [P2745]. s4°. Berolini. 1716
Lange (Johann Peter). Theolog.-homilet. Bibelwerk. Hrsg. v. L. Des Alten Test. 20T [*in* 8v]; Des Neuen Test. 16T [*in* 6v]. 8°. Bielefeld. 1861–78
Lange (Lorenz). Journal, 1721–22, *see* BELL (J.) Travels, v2, 1788.
Journal cont. ses négoc. à la cour de la Chine, 1721–22, *see* BERNARD (J. F.), *ed.* Rec. de voy., t8, 1727.
Journal du voyage à la Chine, *see* BERNARD (J. F.), *ed.* Rec. de voy., t5, 1734.
Lange (Maurice). Le comte A. de Gobineau, ét. biog. & crit. Préc. d'une notice biog. [de M. L.] par C. Pfister. 8°. Str. 1924
Lange (Willy). Gartengestaltung d. Neuzeit. Unter Mitwirkung v. O. Stahn. 3e A. la8°. L. 1912
Langebek (Jacob), *ed.* Scr. rerum Danic. medii aevi. *For a. ed. of t1, see* VITAE sanct. Dan.; nov. ed. crit. cur. M. C. Gertz, 1908–12.

L'Angelier (Pierre Emile), *see* SMITH (*Miss* M. H.) Trial for alleg. poisoning of L'A., 1857.

Langemack (Gregorius). Diss. de hymno Erhalt uns Herr bey deinem Wort &c. [P2645]. s4°. Kiloni. 1709

Hist. catecheticae, oder gesamm. Nachrichten zu e. catech. Hist. 3T *in* 2v. [T3, mit Vorrede v. J. W. Löpern; z. Druck übergeben v. M. D. J. Geismaro &c.] s8°. Stralsund [Greifswald]. 1729–40

Langen (Joseph). Das vatican. Dogma in s. Verhältn. z. N.T. u. d. patrist. Exegese. [P2692]. 8°. Bonn. 1871

Langenbeck (Georg).
De Sadducæis. [P2587]. s4°. [Wittenberg]. 1680

Langenbeck (Hermann), *of Göttingen.* Über Atom u. Monade. Inaug.-Abhdl., Göttingen. [P2491]. 8°. Hannover. 1858

Ueber das Geistige. [P2491]. 8°. 1868

Langenbeck (Wilhelm).
Gesch. d. Norddeutschen Lloyd. s8°. L. 1921

Langenes (Bernardt). Verhael van de reyse by de hollandt. schepen gedaen naer Oost Indien &c.; ghedruckt voor B. L. (1597), *see* HOUTMAN (C. DE). Eerste schipvaart der Nederlanders naar Oost-Indië, d2, 1925.

Langenheim (Johann Christian). Catalogus diss. theol.-exeget.-philol. &c. ed. 2ª. 2p. s8°. Lipsiae. 1739–59
Each v. has 36p, w. sep. tps. dated 1738–70, but pagin. cont.

Langensee (Andreas). Judicium Lutheri de Eccl. Rom. vindicatum. Diss., praes. J. F. Buddeo, subjicit A. L. [P2742]. s4°. Jenae. [1717]

Langer (Eduard). Bibliographie d. österr. Drucke d. 15. u. 16. Jhdts. Hrsg. E. L. B1, H1, bearb. v. W. Dolch, mit Anh., v. I. Schwarz. [*no more publ*ᵈ.] 8°. Wien. 1913

Langermann (F. E.), *see* WHEELER-BENNETT (J. W.) & F. E. L. Inform. on the problem of security, 1917–26, 1927.

Langfeld (Herbert Sidney). The aesthetic attitude. 8°. N.Y. 1920
see PRINCE (M.) Problems of personality: st. pres. to M. P.; ed. H. S. L. &c., 1925.

Langford-James (Richard Lloyd). Dict. of the Eastern Orthodox Ch. Pref. by J. Gennadius. 8°. [1923]

Långfors (Arthur), *see* JEANROY (A.) & A. L. Chansons satiriques &c. du 13ᵉ s., 1921.

Langguth (Christian August). De mumiis avium in labyrintho apud Sacaram repetitis, prolusio &c. 4°. Vitebergae. [1803]

Langham (William). The garden of health, conteyning the vertues &c. of simples & plants &c. [*The table has sep. sign. a–d4*]. 8°. 1579

Langhansen (Christian) [LANGHANSEN (CHRISTOPH)]. Diss. de mense vet. Hebraeorum lunari. Praes. C. L., resp. J. A. Rinneberg. [P446]. s4°. Jenae. [1713]

Langhansen (Christoph), *see* LANGHANSEN (CHRISTIAN).

Langhorne (John). The fables of flora [*in verse*]. Life of the a., by F. Blagdon. s8°. 1804

Poet. works. Collated by T. Park. 2v. s8°. 1806

Langhorne (William), *M.A.* Job. A poem. 4°. 1760

Langhout (Joh.) The economic conquest of Acheen by the Dutch. Pref. by Gen. H. N. A. Swart. Intr. by A. G. van Sluys. 8°. The Hague. 1924

Langie (André). Cryptography. Tr. J. C. H. Macbeth. s8°. 1922

Langius (Joannes), *physician of Lemberg.* Oratio J. L., Encomium theologicæ disputationis doctorum I. Eckii, Andreæ Carolstadii ac M. Lutheri cōplectens. s4°. Lipsiæ. 1519

Langius (Joannes Michael), *see* LANGE (J. M.)

Langlade (Jacques).
Le Puy & le Velay. [Villes d'art célèb.] 8°. 1921

Langland (William) [W. LANGLEY]. The vision & creed of Piers Ploughman. Ed. T. Wright. 2nd & rev. ed. 2v. [*pagin. cont.*] s8°. 1887
see CHADWICK (D.) Soc. life in days of Piers Plowman, 1922.
,, CHAMBERS (R. W.) Long Will, Dante, & the righteous heathen, 1924.

Langlès (Louis Matheiu), *see* SAVARY (C. E.) Gramm. de la lang. arabe, aug. de contes a. par l'éditeur [L. M. L.], 1813.

Langlet Du Fresnoy, *see* LENGLET DU FRESNOY.

Langley Ærodynamical Laboratory. Advisory Comm. on the L.A.L. [Hodgkins Fund], 1913, *see* SMITHSONIAN INST. Misc. coll., v62, 1923.

Langley (Batty). Builder's complete assistant. 4th ed. 8°. *n.d.*

Langley (Edmund de), *see* HAYTHORNTHWAITE (J. P.) Life of E. de L. &c., 1927.

Langley (John Henry). Sacred hymns, with addr. to young men. s8°. 1776

Langley (Thomas), *see* VERGILIUS (P.) An abridgement of the worke of P. V., by T. L., 1551.

Langlois (Charles Victor). Les hôtels de Clisson, de Guise & de Rohan-Soubise au Marais. la8°. 1922

Medieval France: companion to Fr. st., by L. &c., 1922, *see* TILLEY (A.), *ed.*

La vie en France au m. âge. [3t.] 8°. 1924–27

Langlois (Eustache Hyacinthe). Mém. s. la peinture s. verre, vitraux des églises de Rouen. [*Extr.* Soc. d'Emul. de Rouen]. [P2515]. 8°. Rouen. 1823

Langlois (Victor). Descr. of the Armen. monast. of St. Lazarus, Venice. [Tr. F. Schröder. P2816]. s8°. Venice. 1874

Langsdorf (Georg Heinrich *Frhr.* v.) Exped. ao inter. do Brasil, 1825–29, *see* INSTITUTO HIST. E GEOG. BRAZIL. Revista, t38, 39, 1875–76.

Langshaw (Harold). Socialism: & the hist. function of Liberalism. Pref. by C. Trevelyan. 8°. [1925]

Langson (Mary), *see* WESLEY (J.) *Short acc. of the death of M. L., 1775.

Langton (Robert), *d. 1524.* The pilgrimage of R. L., transcr w. intr. by E. M. Blackie. 8°. Camb., Mass. 1924

Langton (Stephen), *card., abp. of Canterbury.*
see POWICKE (F. M.) S. L. (Ford lect.), 1928.
,, SCHMID (O.) Über verschiedene Eintheilungen d. H. Schrift insbes. ü. d. Capitel-Eintheilung S. L.'s im 13 Jhdt., 1892.

Langtry (Lillie), *wife of Edw. Langtry, née Emilie Charlotte Le Breton, aft. Lady de Bathe.* The days I knew. Foreword by R. Le Gallienne. 2nd ed. 8°. [1925

Language.
*The l. & sentiment of flowers, 1866, *see* FLOWERS.
*The l. of flowers: added, Calendar of f., 6th ed. rev., 1838, *see* FLOWERS.
*The l. of flowers: alphabet of floral emblems, 1857, *see* FLOWERS.
*The l. of flowers: illust. by K. Greenaway, 1884, *see* FLOWERS.
*The l. of flowers: w. illust. poetry, 1851, *see* FLOWERS.

Languedoc. Bibl. hist. du L.: ét. & doc. sur l'hist. relig. écon. &c.; publ. J. Guiraud, *see* PROUILLE. Cartul. de Notre-Dame de P., 2t, 1907.

Langues (Les) du monde. Par un groupe de linguistes sous la dir. de A. Meillet & M. Cohen. [Coll. Linguist.; publ. Soc. de Ling. de Paris, 16]. la8°. 192

Languet (Hubert) [LANGUETUS].
see BRUTUS (S. J.), *ps.* Vindiciae contra tyrannos, *sometime attrib. to L.*, 1660.
,, SIDNEY (*Sir* P.) Corresp. of P. S. & H. L.; ed. W. A. Bradley, 1912.

Languet de la Villeneuve de Gergy (Jean Joseph), *bp. of Soissons, aftw. abp. of Sens.* De vero eccl. sensu circa sacr. caeremon. usum, acc. diss. J. A. Assemani De sacris ritibus. 4°. Romae. 175

De vero eccl. sensu c. sacr. cæremoniarum usum, *see* MIGNE (J. P.), *ed.* Theol. cursus, t26, 1859.

Lanier (Sidney).
Florida: scenery, climate & hist. s8°. Phila. [188

Lankester (*Sir* Edwin Ray).
Great & small things. s8°. [1923]
The kingdom of man. 8°. 1911
Science f. an easy chair. 5th ed. s8°. [1911]
,, ,, ...9th ed. s8°. [1916]
,, ,, ...13th ed. s8°. [1919]
,, ,, s2. 3rd ed. s8°. [1920]
Secrets of earth & sea. s8°. [1920
see LECTURES. Lect. on edu- [*repr. w. t.*] Science educ., ed. Sir E. R., 191

Lanman (Charles). Biog. annals of the Civil Govt. of the U.S. dur. its 1st c. la8°. Wash. 187

Dict. of the U.S. Congress, & Gen. Govt. 5th ed. rev. la8°. Hartford. 186

Lannert (Gustav L:son). An investig. into the lang. of Robinson Cruso, as compared w. that of o. 18th c. works. 8°. Uppsala. 19

Lanning (George) & S. Couling. The hist. of Shanghai pl. [*no more publ.*] 8°. Shanghai. 19

Lannoy (Charles de), *prof. à l. Univ. de Gand,* **& H. Vand Linden.** Hist. de l'expansion colon. des peuples europ. Néerlande & Danemark (17ᵉ & 18ᵉ s.) 8°. Brux. 19

Lanoë (Julien). Vacances. 8°. [192

Lanoë-Villène (Georges). Le livre des symboles. Dict. de symbol. & de mythologie. [t]1, 2 (A–B). 8°. 19

Lanoye (F. de) [†TUGNOT DE LANOYE (FERDINAND)].
La Sibérie. n. éd. s8°. 18

Lans (Jean). *Spongia qua absterguntur convitia & maledic Equitis Poloni contra Jesuitas. Anagramma aut. San recta salus. [*Ed.* S. Resca]. s8°. Ingolstadii. 15

Lansburgh (Alfred). Die Politik d. Reichsbank u. Reichsschatzanweisungen nach d. Kriege. [V. f. Sozialpol., B166ii]. 8°. München. 1924
Lansbury (George). What I saw in Russia. s8°. [1920]
Your part in poverty. s8°. [1917]
Lansdell (K. A.) Weeds of S. Africa. [P2820, 2849, 2870]. 4p. 8°. Pretoria. 1923–27
Lansdowne (Henry Charles Keith Petty-Fitzmaurice, *5th marq. of*), *see* FORREST (*Sir* G. W.) The admin. of Marq. of L. as Viceroy &c. of India, 1888–94, 1894.
Lansdowne (Henry William Edmund Petty-Fitzmaurice, *6th marq. of*) [KERRY (*earl of*)]. The first Napoleon: some unpubl. doc. f. the Bowood Papers. Ed. Earl of K. 8°. 1925
The secret of the Coup d'Etat. Unpubl. corr. of Pr. Louis Napoleon, MM. de Morny, de Flahault &c., 1848–52. Ed. w. intr. by the Earl of K., & a study by P. Guedalla. 8°. 1924
see PETTY (*Sir* W.) P. papers: unpubl. wr. of P.; ed. f. Bowood papers by Marq. of L., 2v, 1927.
Lanseloot, *see* LANCELOT.
Lansing Papyrus. Papyrus L.: e. ägypt. Schulhs. d. 20. Dyn.; hrsg. u. erkl. v. A. Erman u. H. O. Lange, *see* KONG. DAN. VID. SELSK. Hist.-fil. Medd., 10, 1924–25.
Lansing (Robert).
The Big Four, & others of the Peace Conference. 8°. 1922
Notes on sovereignty. [C.E. for Int. Peace]. la8°. Wash. 1921
The Peace negot. A personal narr. 8°. 1921
Lanson (Gustave).
Esquisse d'une hist. de la tragédie franç. 8°. N.Y. 1920
Hist. illust. de la litt. franç. 2t. 4°. [1923]
Manuel bibliog. de la litt. fr. mod., 16–19s. n. éd. rev. & corr. 8°. 1925
Lantenay (Ant. de), *ps., see* BERTRAND (A.-L.)
Lantier (Raymond). Inventaire des mon. sculptés pré-chrét. de la Péninsule ibérique. pl. 8°. Bordeaux. 1918
1, Lusitanie: Conventus Emeritensis.
see POINSSOT (L.) & R. L. Mosaïques de la "maison d'Ariadne" à Carthage, 1924.
Lantsheere (Antoine Carlier de), *see* CARLIER DE LANTSHEERE (A.)
Lanuza (Vincencio Blasco de), *see* BLASCO DE LANUZA (V.)
Lanza (Anton Maria).
Angelo Musco. [*a. c. in* P2517]. la8°. Milano. 1920
Lanzoni (Francesco). Le origini d. diocesi ant. d'It. [Studi e testi, 35]. la8°. 1923
***Laou-seng-urh,** or, An heir in h. old age. A Chinese drama. [Tr. Mr. Davis, w. brief view of Chinese drama]. s8°. 1817
Laou-Tsze. Lehrsaal des Mittelreiches: enthaltend d. Encyclopädie d. chines. Jugend &c. Hrsg., übers. & erläut. v. C. F. Neumann. 4°. München. 1836
see HARLEZ (C. DE). L., 1884.
,, WATTERS (T.) Lao-Tzu, 1870.
,, WIEGER (L.) Taoïsme, t2, Les pères du système t., L. &c. [*Chinese & French*], 1913.
Lapaquellerie (Yvon). Amoret. s8°. 1922
Lapauze (*Mme.* **Henry),** *see* †LESUEUR (DANIEL), *ps.*
Lăpedatu (Alex.) Istoriografia română ardeleană, *see* ACADEMIA ROM. Disc., 55, 1923.
see ROMSTORFER (K. A.) Cetatea Sucevii, descrisă pe propiilor cercetări făcute între 1895 & 1904; publ. &c. cu o. not. istor. de A. L., 1913.
La Peña y Reyes (Antonio de), *see* PEÑA Y REYES (A. DE LA).
La Pérouse (Jean François Galaup, *cte.* **de).** A voyage round the world, 1785–88, by the Boussole &c., under the command of J. F. G. de La P. Publ. under sup. of L. A. Milet-Mureau. Tr. 3rd ed. 3v. 8°. 1807
see BELLESSORT (A.) La P., 1926.
La Péruse (Jean Bastier de) [†BASTIER DE LA PÉRUSE], *see* BANACHEVITCH (N.) J. B. de La P., 1923.
La Peyrère (Isaac de) [I. PEYRERIUS]. Relations de l'Islande & du Groenland, *see* BERNARD (J. F.), *ed.* Recueil, t1, 1713, 1731.
see HILPERT (J.) Disq. de Praeadamitis anon. exercit. auct. [*La P.*] opposita, 1656.
,, PYTHIUS (J.) Resp. exetastica ad tract. [*by I. de la P.*] Praeadamitae, 1656.
La Piana (George). Foreign groups in Rome dur. the first cent[s]. of the Empire. [*Extr. f.* Harvard theolog. rev., 1927]. 8°. Camb., *Harvard.* 1927
Lapide (Hippolithus a), *ps., see* CHEMNITZ (B. P. v.)
Lapidoth-Swarth (Hélène), *see* SWARTH (H.)

La Pijardière (Louis de La Cour de), *see* MONTPELLIER. Rec. de pièces rel. au Siège de M., 1622; réunies & préc. d'une préf. par M. de La P., 1875.
La Place (Pierre de). Comm. de l'estat de la relig. & république, 1556–61, *see* BUCHON (J. A. C.) Choix de chron. &c., 1884.
La Placette (Jean), *pasteur de l'église franç. de Copenhagen.* Obs. hist.-eccl. vet. eccl. sensus c. pontificis Rom. potestatem in defin. fidei rebus. s8°. Amstelodami. 1695
*Of the incurable scepticism of the Ch. of Rome. [*Tr. by abp. T. Tenison*]. [P2661]. s4°. 1588 [*i.e.* 1688]
Traité de la restitution. s8°. Amsterdam. 1696
Laporte (Albert). En Suisse le sac au dos. 8°. [1869]
Lapparent (Albert de). Cours de minéralogie. la8°. 1884
Précis de minéralogie. 7e éd. s8°. 1921
Traité de géologie. 2e éd. rev. & augm. la8°. 1885
Lappo-Danilevskaya (Nadejda Aleksandrovna).
Русскій баринъ. Романъ. 8°. П. 1915
Laprade (William Thomas), *see* ROBINSON (J.) Parl. papers, 1774–84; ed. W. T. L., 1922.
La Primaudaie (F. Elie de). Etudes sur le commerce au moyen âge: hist. du commerce de la Mer Noire &c. 8°. 1848
La Primaudaye (Pierre de). Academie françoise, instit. des mœurs &c. 3e éd. s8°. Basle. 1587
Lapshin (Ivan Ivanovich). Заветные думы Скрябина. s8°. П. 1922
Философские взгляды А. Н. Радищева. s8°. П. 1922
Laptev (S.) В старой роте. Драма. [P2698]. s8°. [Москва]. 1921
Lapthorne (Richard), *of Hatton Garden.* The Portledge papers: extr. f. letters of R. L. to R. Coffin, 1687–97. Ed. R. J. Kerr & I. C. Duncan. Pref. by Sir E. Gosse. 8°. 1928
La Puente y Acevedo (José Fernandez), *see* FERNANDEZ DE LA PUENTE Y ACEVEDO (J.)
La Quintinie (Jean de). The compleat gard'ner: or, direct. for cultivating fruit- & kitchen-gardens &c. Added, Treatise of orange-trees &c. [*sep. pagin.*] Engl. by J. Evelyn. [2v in 1]. fol. 1693
Lara, *House of, see* SALAZAR Y CASTRO (L. DE). Hist. genealog. de la Casa de L., 3t, 1696–97; Pruebas &c., 1694.
Laran (Jean).
see DUPLESSIS (G.) &c. Cat. de la coll. des portraits franç. &c. conserv. au Dépt. des Estampes de la Bibl. Nat., t7, commencé par G. D., cont. par J. L., 1911.
,, MARCEL (H.) Chassériau; 48 planches, not. par J. L., 1911.
Larat (Jean). Bibliog. crit. des œuvres de C. Nodier. Suivie de docs. inéd. 8°. 1923
see NODIER (J. E. C.) Moi même &c., avec intr. s. le roman personnel par J. L., 1921.
Larbaud (Valery).
A. O. Barnabooth, son journal intime. 8°. 1923
Fermina Marquez. s8°. [1920]
Jaune, bleu, blanc. 5e éd. s8°. [1927]
Larcena (Jean). Le séjour à Sens du pape Alex. III (1163–65). [P2818]. 8°. Sens. 1925
Larchanz, *see* GUILLAUME, *d'Orange.* L., chançon de Willelme, 1908.
Larco (Renzo). La Russia e la sua rivoluzione. 8°. Bari. 1920
Larden (Walter). Argentine plains & Andine glaciers. 8°. 1911
Larentz (Leuon), *see* KORAN. Qouran (*in Armenian, w. life of Mohammed*; tr. L. L.), 2p, 1911.
Larg (David Glass). Mme. de Staël: la vie dans l'œuvre (1766–1800). la8°. 1924
Largent (*le r. p.* **Augustin).** Saint Jérôme. 8e éd. s8°. 1922
Largillières (René).
Six saints de la région de Plestin. 8°. Rennes. 1922
see FAVART (C. S.) & R. L. Polichinelle, 1924.
Largillierre (Nicolas de), *see* PASCAL (G.) L., 1928.
Larguier (Leo). La journée d'un célibataire, nouv., *see* ŒUVRES libres, t33, 1924.
Un pur amour, *see* ŒUVRES libres, t7, 1922.
Larguier des Bancels (Jacques). Le goût & l'odorat. 8°. 1912
Intr. à la psychologie: l'instinct & l'émotion. 8°. 1921
Laribé (Michel Augé-), *see* AUGÉ-LARIBÉ (M.)
La Rigaudie (Pierre Chilhaud de), *see* CHILHAUD DE LA RIGAUDIE (P.)
Larin (Yu.), *ps., see* LURE (M.)
La Rive (Auguste de).
A. P. de Candolle: vie & travaux. s8°. 1851
Larminie (Margaret Rivers), *ps.* [*i.e. Mrs.* R. C. TRAGETT]. Soames Green. s8°. 1925
Larmor (*Sir* **Joseph),** *see* CAVENDISH (*Hon.* H.) Scientific papers, v2, w. contrib. by Sir J. L. &c., 1921.
Larnec (Jean). Colette, sa vie, s. œuvre. 5e éd. s8°. [1927]

La Roca (Juan Ant. de Vera y Figueroa, *conde* **de),** *see* VERA Y FIGUEROA (J. A. DE), *conde de la Roca.*
La Rocca (Luigi). La cessione del r. di Sardegna alla casa Sabauda, *see* REGIA DEPUT. Miscellanea, t41, 1905.
La Roche (Johann), *called Kasperl ; d. 1807, see* GUGITZ (G.) Der weiland Kasperl (J. La R.) [*w. texts*], 1920.
La Roche (Mazo de). Possession. s8°. 1923
La Roche d'Allery (Pietro de Lucas, *conte* **di),** *see* ROCHE D'ALLERY (P. DE L., *conte* DELLA).
La Rochefoucauld (Armand de), *5e duc de Doudeauville, see* DOUDEAUVILLE.
La Rochefoucauld (François de), *cardinal.* De l'autorité de l'Église en ce qui concerne la foy & la religion. 2e éd. rev. & augm. s8°. 1604
La Rochefoucauld (François, *duc* **de),** *see* SCHULZ (F.) Aphorismen : Nachlese zu La R., 1793.
La Rochefoucauld (*le vte.* **J. Fr. de),** *comte de Surgères ; 1734–88.* *Ramassis. [Sur la dispute—De l'éduc.—Lettre p. s. à l'éloge de M. le Cte. de Maurepas, *w. sep. tp.*—De l'ambition —De l'amitié—De la fatuité—Sur le soleil—Sur l'humeur &c.—De l'amour—De la crapule—Lettres 51 & 52, *each w. sep. pagin. No gen. tp.*] s8°. [c. 1783]
La Rochelle (Pierre Drieu), *see* DRIEU LA ROCHELLE (P.)
La Rogerie (H. Bourde de), *see* BOURDE DE LA ROGERIE (H.)
La Romana (Pedro Caro y Sureda, *3rd marq.* **de),** *see* ROMANA (P. C. Y S., *3rd marq.* DE LA).
La Roncière (Charles Bourel de). Un atlas inconnu de la dern. expéd. de Drake. [Extr. du Bull. de géogr. hist. &c. No. 3, 1909. *a. c. in* P2731]. la8°. 1909
La découverte de l'Afrique au moyen âge : cartographes & explorateurs. [Soc. Roy. de Géogr. d'Egypte. Mém., t5, 6, 13]. 3t. 4°. Le Caire. 1924–27
La Roncière (Emile Clément de). Procés complet d'E. C. de La R., accusé d'une tentative nocturne de viol sur la personne de M. de Morell. 8°. 1835
La Roque (F. Bisson de), *see* BISSON DE LA ROQUE (F.)
La Rose de Rosimond (Claude). Le nouveau festin de Pierre (1669), *see* FOURNEL (V.) Contemp. de Molière, t3, 1875.
Larousse, *publishing firm.*
Atlas départemental. Texte par G. Treffel. fol. [1914]
Larousse mensuel illustré. Revue encyclop. univ. Publ. s. la dir. de C. Augé. [t1–6]. 4°. *n.d.*
1, 1907–10. 2, 1911–13. 3, 1914–16. 4, 1917–19.
5, 1920–22. 6, 1923–25.
„ „ Table gén., 1907–25. 4°. [1926]
Larousse universel. Nouv. dict. encyclop. Publ. sous la dir. de C. Augé. 2v. la8°. [1924]
Petit Larousse illust. : nouv. dict. encyclop. Publ. s. la dir. de C. Augé. 8°. 1922
La Rovère (Julien de), *see* JULIUS II, *pope.*
Larra (Mariano José de) [*ps.* FIGARO], *see* MARTINEZ RUIZ (J.) Rivas y L., 1921.
Larramendi (Manuel de). *De la antiguedad y universalidad del Bascuenze en España &c. Su author M. D. L. s8°. Salamanca. [1728]
Larrey (*le baron* **Félix Hippolyte),** *see* BÉRENGER-FÉRAUD (L. J. B.) Le baron H. L., 1899.
Larroque (Matthieu de). Hist. de l'Eucharistie. 2e éd. rev. & corr. 3p[*in* 2v. *pagin. cont.*] s8°. Amsterdam. 1671
The hist. of the Eucharist. Done into Engl. by J. W[alker]. s4°. 1684
Larrouy (Maurice), *see* †MILAN (R.), *ps.*
Larrubiera (Alejandro). El amor en peligro. s8°. [1923]
Larsen (Anton). Dict. of Dano-Norweg. & Eng. lang. 4th ed. 8°. Copenhagen. 1910
Larsen (Hanna Astrup). Knut Hamsun. s8°. [1923]
Larsen (J. Anker).
Martha & Mary. Tr. A. G. Chater. 8°. 1926
The philosopher's stone. Tr. A. G. Chater. s8°. 1924
„ „ ....[3rd printing]. 8°. N.Y. 1924
De vises sten. 8°. 1923
Larsen (Sofus Chr.) The discovery of N. America 20 years before Columbus. la8°. Copenhagen. 1925
Larson (Gösta), *see* KYÖSTI (L.), *ps.*
Larsson (Carl).
Andras barn. 32 målningar med text af C. L. fol. [1913]
Ett hem. 25 målningar med text af C. L. 3e uppl. obl.4°. [1910]
Larssons. Ett album bestående af 32 målningar och med text teckningar af C. L. 2a uppl. fol. [1910]
Spadarvet. Mitt lilla lantbruk. s8°. [1919]

Larsson (Hans). La logique de la poésie. Tr. de E. Philipot. Préf. de E. Boutroux. 8°. 1919
Larsson (Yngve). Inkorporeringsproblemet. Stadsområdets förändringar. 2d. 8°. [1912]
Lartet (Louis). Explor. géolog. de la Mer Morte, de la Palestine & de l'Idumée. Obs. dur. l'expéd. scient. du Duc de Luynes. 4°. [1877]
Lartigue (Alfred Charlemagne), *see* DELACOUR (A.), *ps.*
Larudan (*l'abbé***),** *see* FRANCS-MAÇONS. *Les Francs-Maçons écrases ; tr. du Lat. [? *or rather wr. by* l'abbé L.], 1762.
Larwood (Jacob) & J. C. Hotten.
Hist. of signboards. *la. paper copy.* la8°. 1867
La Sablière (Marguerite Rambouillet de), *see* MENJOT D'ELBENNE (*le vte.* S.) Mme. de la S., s. pensées chrét. & s. lettres à l'abbé de Rancé, 1923.
La Sagra (Ramon de), *see* SAGRA (R. DE LA).
La Sale (Antoine de) [LA SALLE]. The fifteen joys of marriage. Tr. R. Aldington, w. intr. 8°. [1926]
see NÈVE (J.) A. de la Salle : vie &c., suivi du Réconfort de Madame du Fresne & du Paradis de la Reine Sybille, par La S., 1903.
La Salle (Jean Baptiste de).
see DELAIRE (A.) St. J.-B. de la S., 1659–1719, 7e éd., 1923.
„ HUBERT (W. E.) Lebensbilder kath. Erzieher, B2, 1887.
La Salle de Rochemaure (*le duc* **de).**
Gerbert, Silvestre II. la8°. Rome. 1914
Las Almenas (*conde* **de).** Mediaeval &c. works of art f. Spain [coll. of Cde. de L. A.] Cat. wr. by M. S. Byne & A. Byne &c. [Amer. Art. Assoc.] la8°. N.Y. 1927
Las Casas (Bartolomé de), *bp. of Chiapa* [†CASAS (B. DE LAS)].
An acc. of the 1st voy. & disc. made by the Spaniards in America ; cont. rel. of th. cruelties on the Indians &c. Added, The art of travelling [*sep. pagin.*] 8°. 1699
La destrucción de las Indias & Refut. de Las Casas [*by* B. Vargas Machuca]. s8°. Paris. *n.d.*
see PIO (M.) Allegatione &c., cavata d. vita di B. d. C., 1621.
Las Cases (M. J. A. E. D., *cte.* **de),** *marq. de La Caussade* [LAS CASAS ; *ps.* A. LE SAGE]. Atlas hist., généalog., chronolog. & géogr., avec des augm. & des annots. par le Chev. Marchal. atlas fol. Brux. 1853
Mémorial de Sainte-Hélène. Journal de la vie privée et des conversations de Napoléon à S. H. 8p *in* 4t. 8°. Londres. 1823
see NAPOLEON I. Recueil de pièces authentiques sur le captif de Ste.-Hélène ; suivis de lettres de Comte L. C &c., 12t, 1821–25.
Lascelles (Brian Piers), *see* HORT (*Sir* A. F.), *ed.* B. P. L. mem. [*by var. wr.*], 1924.
Lascelles (E. C. P.), *see* EMMERSON (H. C.) & E. C. P. L. Guide to Unemploy. Insur. Acts, 1926.
—— & S. S. Bullock.
Dock labour & decasualisation. 8°. 1924
Lascelles (T. W.) Engraving. s8°. [1920]
Lasch (Richard), *see* BUSCHAN (G.) Illustr. Völkerkunde, B1 Amerika-Africa v. R. L. &c., 1922.
Lasco (Joannes a), *1499–1560, bp. of Veszprin.* Defensio verae &c. doctrinae de Christi incarnatione adv. Mennonem Simonis Anabapt. doctorem &c. s8°. Bonnae. 1545
Forma ac ratio tota eccl. ministerii in peregrin. eccl. Londini 1555, *see* FORMA.
Kirchenordnung, wie die in Londen, i. d. niderlend. Gemeine Christi, geordnet worden, durch M. Micronium verdeut. 1564, *see* KIRCHENORDNUNG.
Purgation, *see* DATHENUS (P.) Kurtze &c. erzelung &c. 1598.
see BULLINGER (H.) Absoluta de sacramentis tract. ; adj. ejusdem argumenti epistola per J. a L., 1551.
„ KUYPER (A.) Disq. exhib. J. Calvini & J. à L. de eccl. sent. &c., 1862.
La Serna (Juan Hurtado y J. de), *see* HURTADO Y J. DE L. S. (J.)
La Serre (Puget de). The mirrour which flatters not. F. th Fr. by T. C. [*i.e.* T. Cary]. s8°. 163
La Servière (Joseph de), *S.J.* Les anc. missions de la Co. d Jésus en Chine, 1552–1814. 8°. Chang-Hai. 192
La nouv. mission du Kiang-Nan, 1840–1922. 8°. Chang-Hai. 192
Lasicki (Joannes) [LASICIUS ; LASITIUS]. De eccl. disciplina moribus &c. fratrum Bohem. memorabilia cont. &c. cur admon. J. A. Comenii. s8°. Amstelaedami. 166
De Russorum, Moscovitarum & Tartarorum relig., sacrificiis nuptiarum, funerum ritu &c. Adj. : De Livonia & pace con inter regem Poloniæ & ducem Moscoviæ. s4°. Spiræ. 158

La Sizeranne (Robert de). Béatrice d'Este & sa cour. 8°. [1920]
César Borgia & le duc d'Urbino, 1502–03. 8°. 1924
La peinture anglaise contemp., 1844–91. 8°. [1922]
Le vertueux Condottière, F. de Montefeltro, Duc d'Urbino, 1422–82. 8°. 1927
Lask (Emil). Gesammelte Schriften. Hrsg. E. Herrigel. Geleitwort v. H. Rickert. 3B. 8°. Tübingen. 1923–24
Lasker (Bruno). The Brit. system of labor exchanges, *see* UNITED STATES: LABOR, Bull. 206, 1916.
Lasker (Emanuel). Common sense in chess. s8°. 1896
Laski (Albertus), *Palatine of Sieradz.* De novis rebus Polonicis ad relig. pertin. Epistola A. L. ad novos in Polonia ministros responsoria. Acc. altera epist. s8°. [Dilingae]. 1571
Laski (Harold Joseph).
Communism. [Home Univ. Lib.] s8°. [1927]
Foundations of sovereignty & o. essays. 8°. [1921]
A grammar of politics. 8°. [1925]
„ „ .....[repr.] 8°. [1926]
Karl Marx, an essay. [P2705]. 8°. 1921
On the study of politics. [P2848]. 8°. O. 1926
Polit. thought in England f. Locke to Bentham. [Home Univ. Lib.] s8°. N.Y. [1920]
The state in the new social order. 8°. 1922
Laskine (Edmond).
L'Internationale & le Pangermanisme. 8°. 1916
Le socialisme suivant les peuples. s8°. 1920
Las Navas (*conde* de). The Royal Palace, Madrid. [Hispanic Soc.] s8°. Barcelona. *n.d.*
La Sorsa (Saverio). Fiabe e novelle d. popolo pugliese. Pref. di A. Mari. v1. 8°. Bari. 1927
Lassalle (Ferdinand J. G.) Gesammelte Reden u. Schriften. Hrsg. &c. E. Bernstein. 12B. 8°. 1919–20
1, Der ital. Krieg—Franz v. Sickingen.
2, Die Verfassungsreden—Das Arbeiterprogramm u. d. anschliessenden Verteidigungsreden.
3, 4, Die Agitation für d. allgem. deut. Arbeiterverein, 1863–4—Polemik—Aktenstücke.
5, L.'s ökonom. Hauptwerk.
6, Philos.-lit. Streifzüge.
7, 8, Die Philos. Herakleitos d. Dunklen v. Ephesos.
9–12, Das System d. erworbenen Rechte.
Nachgelassene Briefe u. Schriften. Hrsg. v. G. Mayer. 6B. 8°. St. 1921–25
1, Briefe von u. an L. bis 1848.
2, L.'s Briefwechsel v. d. Revol. v. 1848 bis z. Beginn. s. Arbeiteragitation.
3, Briefwechsel zw. L. u. Marx, nebst Briefen v. F. Engels &c.
4, L.'s Briefwechsel mit Gräfin S. v. Hatzfeldt.
5, L.'s Briefwechsel, 1862–64.
6, Schriften d. Nachlasses u. Briefwechsel mit K. Rodbertus.
see BERNSTEIN (E.) F. L.: e. Würdigung d. Lehrers u. Kämpfers, 1919.
„ BORDEAUX (H.) Amours du temps passé: H. de Doenniges & F. L., 1923.
„ ONCKEN (H.) L.: e. polit. Biog., 4e A., 1923.
Lassar-Cohn (*Dr.*) Gold- u. Papiergeld: die Bedeutung d. Goldwährung im Leben d. Gegenwart u. das Eisen. s8°. L. 1922
Lassen (Christian). Hist. of Indian Commerce. Tr. K. P. Jayaswal & A. Banerji-Sastri, *see* BIHAR & ORISSA RESEARCH SOC. Journal, v10, 1924.
Instit. linguae Pracriticae. [Excursus &c. *w. sep. pag.*] 8°. Bonnae ad Rhenum. 1837
see BURNOUF (E.) & CHR. LASSEN. Essai sur le Pali, 1826.
Lasserre (Pierre).
Cinquante ans de pensée française &c. s8°. [1922]
La jeunesse d'E. Renan: hist. de la crise relig. au 19e siècle. 2t. 8°. 1925
La nuit tarbaise: roman, *see* ŒUVRES libres, t64, 1926.
Philosophie du goût musical. [Cahiers verts, 11]. s8°. 1922
La promenade insolite. s8°. 1922
Renan & nous. [Cahiers verts, 18]. s8°. 1923
The spirit of French music. Tr. D. Turner. s8°. 1921
Lasso (Orlando di) [ORLAND DE LASSUS; ROLAND DE LATTRE; ROLAND DE LASSUS], *see* CLOSSON (E.) R. de L., 1919.
Lassota von Stablau (Erich), *see* LISKE (J.) Viajes de extranjeros por España y Portugal en los s. 15, 16, y 17: E. L. de S. (1580–84) &c., 1878.
Lassus (Roland de), *see* LASSO (O. DI).
Lasswitz (Kurd).
Gustav Theodor Fechner. 2T [*in* 1v]. 8°. St. 1896
Lasteyrie (Robert de). L'architecture relig. en France à l'époque goth. Publ. M. Aubert. 2t. la8°. 1926–27
Lasturel (Pierre). L'affaire gréco-ital. de 1923. 8°. 1925

La Tailhède (Raymond de). Poésies. 8°. 1926
***Late** voyage (A) to Holland, 1691, *see* HOLLAND.
Lateau (Anne Louise), *1850–83.* *Ein Besuch bei L. L., in Bois d'Haine. 5e verb. &c. A. [P505]. s8°. Dülmen. [1874]
see MAJUNKE (P.) L. L., ihr Wunderleben &c., 1875.
„ SCHÜRMANN (H.) Petrus ü. Papstthum; Anhange: L. L., 1875.
„ SCHWANN (T.) Mein Gutachten ü. d. Versuche, die an d. Stigmatisirten L. L. angestellt wurden, 1875.
Latermann (Joannes), *see* MILENTA (C.) Judicia theologorum orthodox. de lite Regiomonti à C. M. J. L. mota &c., 1648.
La Tessonnerie (Gillet de), *see* GILLET DE LA TESSONNERIE.
Latham (Charles). In Eng. homes. *For continuation &c. see* † TIPPING (H. A.) Eng. homes.
Latham (H. M.), *see* LAYARD (G. S.) Cat. raisonné of engr. Brit. portraits; arr. by H. M. L., 1927.
Latham (Henry) [*ps.* PRESBYTER CICESTRENSIS], *vicar of Fittleworth.* Anthologia Davidica; or metr. tr. of Bk. of Psalms. s8°. 1846
Latham (Lewis), *1555–1655, see* AUSTIN (J. O.) Ancestral dict. [descendants of L. L.], 1891.
Lathbury (*Rev.* Thomas). A hist. of the Eng. episcopacy f. period of Long Parl. to Act of Uniformity &c. 8°. 1836
Memorials of Ernest the Pious, 1st duke of Saxe-Gotha. s8°. 1843
State of Popery & Jesuitism in Eng., Reformation to 1829. s8°. 1838
Lathrop (George Parsons). Represent. poems of living poets, Amer. & Eng. Sel. by the poets. Intr. by G. P. L. [Pref. by J. L. Gilder]. 8°. 1886
Latif (Shah Abdul), *1689–1752, see* GIDVANI (M. M.) S. A. L., 1922.
Latimer (Hugh), *bp. of Worcester, see* JACKSON (T.) Lib. of Xtn. biog., v5, H. L., by W. Gilpin, 1838.
Latimer (John). Annals of Bristol in the 18th cent. 8°. *p. f. the a.* [Frome]. 1893
Annals of Bristol in the 19th cent. 8°. Bristol. 1887
„ „ ....1887–1900. 8°. Bristol. 1902
Hist. of the Soc. of Merchant Venturers of Bristol, w. acc. of anterior merchants' guilds. la8°. Bristol. 1903
Latin. Early Lat. hymns, 1922, *see* WALPOLE (A. S.), *ed.*
The 100 best L. hymns, 1926, *see* PHILLIMORE (J. S.), *ed.*
Public school L. grammar &c. [*Ed.* B. H. Kennedy]. 8°. 1872
Public school L. primer. [*Ed.* B. H. Kennedy]. s8°. 1866
Latina. *Reflexiones priv. de ling. L. in sacris eccl. cathol. usu &c., 1845, *see* RÁCZ (A.)
Latinitas. *Incipit exercitium latinitatis per compos. quorundam verborum in fabulis coll., *n.d., see* EXERCITIUM.
Latino (Anatolio).
Gli Armeni e Zeitun. 2v in 1. 8°. Firenze. 1897
Latishev (Vasily Vasilevich). Житія св. епископовъ Херсонскихъ. [I. Akad. Nauk. Mém., s8, t8iii]. la8°. С.-П. 1906
Hagiographica Graeca ined. ed. B. L. [I. Akad. Nauk. Mém., s8, t12ii]. la8°. St. Pétersb. 1914
Inscr. antiquæ oræ septentrion. Ponti Euxini Graecæ & Lat. [Soc. Arch. Imp. Russ.] [2a ed.] v1. 4°. Petropoli. 1916
Latomus (Bartholomæus). De docta simplicitate primæ Eccl. & de usu calicis in synaxi &c., adv. insultationem J. Andreæ responsio. s4°. Coloniæ. 1559
see BUCER (M.) Scripta duo adversaria D. B. L. & M. B. de dispensatione &c., 1544.
„ CROCUS (C.) De vera Christi eccl. libelli duo, alter à C. C. alter à J. L., *n.d.* [c. 1545].
Latorre (Germán). Relaciones geográficas de Indias (Conten. en el Archivo Gen. de Indias de Sevilla). La Hispano-América del s. 16. [2v]. la8°. Sevilla. 1919–20
[1], Colombia—Venezuela—Puerto Rico—Repub. Argentina.
[2], Virreinato de Nueva Esp.
see ARCHIVO GEN. DE INDIAS. Cat.: cuadro gen. de la document., por P. Torres Lanzas y G. L., 1918.
La Torre (Jorge Corredor), *see* CORREDOR LA TORRE (J.)
Latouche (Henri de), *see* THABAUD DE LATOUCHE (H. J. A.)
La Touche (Jean Claude Hippolyte Méhée de), *see* MÉHÉE DE LA TOUCHE.
La Touche (Thomas Henry Digges). Bibliog. of Indian geology, p2–4. [India. Govt. Publ.] la8°. Calcutta. 1921–26
La Touloubre (Louis Ventre, *seigneur* **de),** *dit Artefeuil, see* ARTEFEUIL.

La Tour, *maison* **de,** *see* FLACCHIO (E.) Généalogie de la maison de La T., 3t, 1709.

La Tour (Charlotte de), *ps., see* CORTAMBERT (*Mme.* L.)

La Tour (Marie Jacqueline de), *wife of Charles Amador de la T., see* SOULIÉ (M.) La grande avent., roman d'une Paris. [M. de La T.], 1927.

La Tour (Maurice Quentin de). Cat. de la coll. M. Q. de La T. à St.-Quentin, par E. Fleury. Ed. du Louvre. [P2736]. 8º. 1919
see ERHARD (H.) La T.: 89 Nachbildungen &c., mit Einführung &c., 4e A., 1920.
„ TOURNEUX (M.) La T.: biog. crit., 1904.

Latour (Thérèse Louis). Princesses, dames & aventurières du règne de Louis XIV. s8º. 1923
Princesses, ladies & adventuresses of the reign of Louis XIV. [Tr. by W. D. Burrard]. 8º. 1924

La Tour (*le maréchal* **Victor Amédée Sallier de),** *see* SALLIER DE LA TOUR.

La Tour d'Auvergne-Lauraguais (*le card.* **Hugues Robert Jean Charles de),** *1768–1851, see* LESUEUR (E.) Le card. de La T. d'A.-L., 1927.

La Tour du Pin (*la marquise* **Henriette Lucie de).** Journal d'une femme de cinquante ans, 1778–1815. Publ. par Comte A. de Liedekerke-Beaufort. [23e éd.] 2t. 8º. 1924–25
Recoll. of the Revolution & Empire. Ed. & tr. by W. Geer. 8º. 1921

La Tramerye (Pierre L'Espagnol de).
The world-struggle for oil. Tr. by C. L. Leese. 8º. [1924]

La Trémoille (Louis Charles Marie, *11e duc* **de),** *1863–1921.*
Rapp. (22 juil. 1919) s. la rôle &c. de la métallurgie en France, 1919, *see* FRANCE: CHAMBRE DES DÉPUTÉS.

Latrobe (Christian Ignatius). Journal of a visit to S. Africa in 1815–16 w. acc. of settlements of United Brethren near Cape of Good Hope. 4º. 1818

La Trobe (John Antes). The music of the Church, congregat. & choral. 8º. 1831

Latsis (M. Ya.) [Лацис (М. Я.) *ps.* Судрабс]. Два года борьбы на внутреннем фронте. [P2458]. 8º. Москва. 1920
Чрезвычайные комиссии по борьбе с контр-революцией. [P2697]. 8º. Москва. 1921

Latte (Kurt). Heiliges Recht. Untersuchungen zur Gesch. d. sakralen Rechtsformen in Griechenland. 8º. Tübingen. 1920

Lattes (Alessandro). F. de Aguirre e S. Maffei, *see* REGIA DEPUT. Miscellanea, t44, 1909.

Lattey (Cuthbert Charles). Texts illust. anc. ruler-worship. Texts, w. explan. [P2756]. s8º. 1924

Latthe (A. B.) Memoirs of H. H. Shri Shahu Chhatrapati, Maharaja of Kolhapur [1874–1922]. 2v. 8º. Bombay. 1924

Latude (Henry Masers de). Memoirs of the Bastille. By L. & Linguet. Tr. w. intr. by J. & S. F. M. Whitham. 8º. 1927
see LINGUET (S. N. H.) Mem. de Linguet & de L. &c.; avec notes par F. Barrière, 1884.

Latvia. Mém. sur la L. prés. par la Délégation lettone à la Conf. de la paix. [P2417]. fol. [1919]

Latvian Economist (The). [v1–7iv]. (May 1920–Apr. 1927). [*no more publ.*] 4º. [Riga]. 1920–27

Latyschev, *see* LATISHEV.

Latzarus (Louis). La vie paresseuse de Rivarol. s8º. 1926

Latzarus (Marie Thérèse). Litt. enfantine en France dans la 2e moitié du 19e s. la8º. 1923

Laubat (*le marq.* **Louis de Chasseloup-),** *see* CHASSELOUP-LAUBAT.

Laubert (Manfred).
Die preuss. Polenpolitik, 1772–1914. 8º. [1920]

L'Aubespine (Gabriel), *bp. of Orleans* [ALBASPINÆUS]. Opera varia. Acc. A[1] elogium auctore C. Paulino. 4º. Neapoli. 1770

Laubreaux (Alin). Hist. canaque, *see* ŒUVRES libres, 56, 1926.

Lauck (William Jett).
Polit. & indust. democracy, 1776–1926. 8º. N.Y. 1926

Laud (William), *abp. of Canterbury.* Relation of conf. betw. L. & Fisher the Jesuit, w. ans. to such exceptions as A. C. takes agst. it. 3rd ed. rev. sm. fol. 1673
see COLLINS (W. E.), *ed.* Lect. on L., w. bibliog. of L. lit. & the L. Exhib. cat. &c., 1895.
„ DUNCAN-JONES (A. S.) Abp. L., 1927.
„ PYM (J.) Speech to the Lords, upon delivery of the articles to the Commons, agst. W. L. &c., 1640.
„ STILLINGFLEET (E.) Rational acc. of grounds of Protestant relig. vindic. of [L.'s] Relation of a Conf. &c., 1681.

Lauda, *see* LODI.

Laudario (Il) dei Disciplinati di S. Croce di Urbino; [ed.] G. Grimaldi, *see* MONACI (E.) Studj romanzi, v12, 1915.

Laudensis (Orfinus), *see* ORFINUS, *Laudensis.*

Lauderdale (John Maitland, *1st earl of***),** *see* MACKENZIE (W. C.) Life &c. of J. Maitland, Duke of L., 1923.

Laudi (Le) del Piemonte, v1, 1891, *see* GABOTTO (F.) & D. ORSI, *edd.*

Laue (Max von).
Die Relativitätstheorie. B2. 8º. Braunschweig. 1921

Lauer (Hans Erhard).
Rudolf Steiner's Lebenswerk. 8º. Basel. 1926

Lauer (Max).
Gramm. d. class. armen. Spr. [*a. c. in* P2801]. 8º. Wien. 1869

Laufenberg (Heinrich) & F. Wolffheim.
Nation u. Arbeiterklasse. [P2509]. 8º. Hamburg. 1920
—— **& F. Wolffheim.** Revolutionärer Volkskrieg oder konter-revol. Bürgerkrieg. [P2410]. 8º. Hamburg. 1919

Laufer (Berthold). Chines. Schattenspiele; üb. W. Grube; hrsg. u. eingeleitet v. B. L., 1915, *see* KÖNIGL. AKAD. D. W. ZU MÜNCHEN. Abhdlgn., B28, 1917.
see MILARASPA. Milaraspa: Tibet. Texte in Auswahl übertr. v. B. L., 1922.

Lauff (Joseph v.) Sinter Klaas. Roman v. Niederrhein. s8º. 1922

Laugherne (Hugh), *curate of St. Nicholas, Warwick, see* FIELD (W.) Second letter, in reply to remarks &c. made by the vicar & curate (*i.e.* H. L.) of St Nicholas, 1791.

Laughlin (James Laurence).
Latter-day problems. s8º. N.Y. 1909
Principles of money. 8º. N.Y. 1903
Study of polit. economy. s8º. N.Y. 1885

Laughter. *Essay on l., 1769, *see* ESSAY.

Laughton (L. G. Carr). Old ship figure-heads & sterns. 4º. 1925
—— **& V. Heddon.** Great storms. 8º. [1927]

Laugier (Marc Antoine). *Hist. de la républ. de Venise, j. présent par l'abbé L. 12t. s8º. 1758–1768

Laumonier (Paul). Ronsard, poète lyrique: ét. hist. & litt. 2e éd. rev. & corr. la8º. 1923

Launay (Adrien). Mémorial de la Soc. des Missions-étrangères. 2p. la8º. 1912–16

Launay (*vte.* **Charles de),** *ps., see* GIRARDIN (*Mme.* E. DE).

Launay (Louis de). Un amoureux de Mme. Récamier. Le journal de J. J. Ampère. 8º. 1927
Le christianisme. 8º. 192[illegible]
Géologie de la France. 8º. 192[illegible]

Launceston. A hdbk. of L., Tasmania. 8º. Launceston. [1922]

Launoy (Jean de). Opera omnia, auctoris vita &c. aucta [*Ed.* F. Granet]. 5t *in* 10 [t1i, ii, *pag. contin.* t5 contain. Epistolae]. fol. Coloniae Allobrogum. 1731–3[illegible]
Epistolae omnes. Acc. indices. fol. Cantabrigiae. 168[illegible]

Laura [†LAURA DE SADE?], *see* COLONNA (S.) *Sonetti &c. d M. L. in risposta di F. Petrarca, 1740.

Lauraguais (*le card.* **Hugues Robert J. C. de La Tour d'Auvergne-),** *see* LA TOUR D'AUVERGNE-LAURAGUAIS.

Laurana (Francesco), *see* BURGER (F.) F. L., 1907.

Laurana (Luciano), *see* COLASANTI (A.) L. L.: 24 riprod. co[illegible] testo e cat., 1922.

Laurand (Louis). Manuel des études grecques & latines. 8 fasc. *in* 1v. 8º. 1918–2[illegible]

Laure (*Lt.-Col.* **Emile).**
La victoire franco-espagn. dans le Rif. 8º. [1927]

Laurenberg (Petrus) [LAUREMBERG (P.)], *see* HARTNACCIUS (D. Hist. univ. eccl. &c. juxta ord. P. L. Chron. obs., 1686.

Laurence (John), *rector of Yelvertoft, see* LAWRENCE (J.)

Laurence (Richard), *abp. of Cashel, see* SAXONY. Visit. of th[illegible] Saxon reformed church in 1527–28 &c.; [ed.] R. L., 1839.

Laurence (Roger). *The Bishop of Oxford's [*i.e.* W. Talbot's] charge consid. in ref. to the independency of the Churc[illegible] upon the State &c. By the a. of Lay-baptism invalid [*i.* R. L.] 8º. 171[illegible]

Laurencin (F. P. *Graf***).** Zur Gesch. d. Kirchenmusik bei [illegible] Italienern u. Deutschen. [*b. w.* Brendel (F.) Grundzüg[illegible] 4e A., 1855]. s8º. L. 185[illegible]

Laurencin (Marie), *see* ALLARD (R.) M. L., reprod. de pein[illegible]tures &c., 1921.

Laurens (Jean Paul), *see* THIERRY (J. N. A.) 1er [2e & 3e] récit des temps mérovingiens, avec 6 dessins de J. P. L., 3[illegible] 1881–83.

Laurent (Camille J. Fernand-), *see* FERNAND-LAURENT.

Laurent (Jacques), *see* MOLESME. Cartul. de l'abbaye de M[illegible] 916–1250; rec. de doc[s]., publ. avec intr. par J. L., 2[illegible] 1907–11.

Laurent (Joseph). L'Arménie entre Byzance & l'Islam dep. la conquête arabe j. 886. [Ecoles Franç. d'Athènes & de Rome, 117]. 8°. 1919
Byzance & les Turcs Seldjoucides dans l'Asie occident. j. 1081. [Annales de l'Est, 27e année, fasc. 1]. 8°. 1913
Laurent (Marcel). Nos gouvernements de Guerre. Viviani.—Briand.—Ribot.—Painlevé.—Clemenceau. s8°. 1920
Le juge à l'œil de lynx, nouvelle, *see* ŒUVRES libres, t57, 1926.
Laurent (Paul), *see* NARBONNE. Livre vert de l'archevêché de N.; publ. par P. L., 1886.
Laurent (Pierre). La poésie bretonne contemp. 8°. 1902
Laurentian Library, *Florence, see* ANZIANI (N.) Bibl. Mediceo-L., 1872.
see PROVENZALISCHE Liederhs. Cod. 42 d. L. Bibl., 1872.
Laurentius (Gaspar) [LAURENT (GASPARD)]. Catholicus veterum in omnibus fidei Christianae articulis consensus &c., *see* CORPUS & syntagma confessionum fidei &c., 1654.
Laurentius (Jacobus). Catechesis Heidelberg. orth. contra censuram & Excalvinizationem J. Andreae. s8°. Amstelredami. 1625
Laurent-Vibert (R.) Routiers, pélerins & corsaires aux échelles du Levant. [Busbec &c. Voyages]. s8°. 1923
Lauret (Christophe). Hazoar, sive illust. prophetarum de plenitudine temp. Messiae. [*b. w.* Joseph ben Gorion. De bello Jud., 1559]. s8°. Parisiis. 1610
Laurie (Arthur Pillans). The pigments & mediums of the old masters, w. chap. on microphotographic st. of brushwork. 8°. 1914
Laurie (Maxwell). The black blanket. s8°. [1921]
Laurie (Richard Holmes). Fredonia; or, the U.S. of N. Amer., incl. Canadian Prov. &c. Publ. R. H. L. [*Map only*]. *folded* 8°. 1830
L.'s New plan of London &c. Survey by J. Outhett. *folded* 8°. 1821
L.'s Survey of the country around London. *folded* 8°. 1829
[Map of] America. Publ. 1828, add. &c., 1830. *folded* 8°. [1830]
Laurie (Thomas). Dr. Grant & the Mountain Nestorians. 8°. Boston [Mass.] 1853
Laurie (William Alexander). Mem. of J. Burnes, *see* BURNES (J.) Notes on h. name &c., 1851.
Laurie (William Ferguson Beatson). Orissa, incl. an acc. of Brit. connexion w. the Temple of Jagannáth &c. s8°. 1850
Our Burmese Wars & relations w. Burma: an abstract, 1824–26 & 1852–53. 2nd ed. 8°. 1885
Pegu, being a narr. of events during Burmese War, 1852–53 &c. 8°. 1854
Laurier (*Sir* Wilfrid), *see* SKELTON (O. D.) Life & letters of Sir W. L., 2v, 1922.
Laurin (Carl G.) Folklynnen. 8e uppl. 8°. [1920]
Konsthistoria. 6e tillökade uppl. 8°. [1918]
Kulturhistorisk bilderbok, 1400–1920. 2a uppl. 8°. [1919]
Lauris (Georges de). Une conquête, *see* ŒUVRES libres, 27, 1923.
Laurissenses. Annales L. maiores & Einhardi, *see* FRANCI. Annal. regni Fr.; Kurze, 1895.
Lauro (Pietro). De le lettere di M. P. L. Modonese il primo libro. [Lib. 2° *wanting*]. s8°. Venetia. 1553
Laursen (L.), *see* DANMARK. Danmark-Norges traktater, 1523–1750; udg. af L. L., B1–7, 1905–26.
Lauserus (Polycarpus), *see* GRETSER (J.) Panegyricus, Honorarium Polyc. Lauserianum &c., 1606.
Lautard (Jean Baptiste). Hist. de l'Académie de Marseille, 1726–1826. 2p. 8°. Marseille. 1826–29
Lautenbach (Samuel). *Controv. inter theologos Wittenberg. de regeneratione & electione explic. E. Hunnii, P. Leyseri &c., cum refut. argumentorum quae S. Huber attulit. [P2610]. s4°. Francoforti a. M. 1594
Lautensack (Paul L.), *see* ZELTNER (G. G.) De P. L. fanatici Noriberg. fatis & placitis &c., 1716.
Lauterbach (Julius). 1000£ Kopfpreis—tot oder lebendig. Fluchtabenteuer &c. s8°. [1917]
Lauterbach (Paul).
Aegineten. Gedanke u. Spruch. [P2470]. s8°. L. [1891]
Lauterwar (Christian). Wider das Interim. Papistische Mess, Canonem vnnd Meister Eissleuben. s4°. *n.p.* 1549
Lautrec (Henri de Toulouse), *see* COQUIOT (G.) L., ou 15 ans de mœurs Paris., 1885–1900, 1921.
Lauvrière (Emile). La tragédie d'un peuple: hist. du peuple acadien de s. orig. à nos jours. [3e éd.] 2t. 8°. 1922
Lauwereyns de Roosendaele (L. de). Comment Saint-Omer fit retour à la France en 1677 (1676–80). s8°. Saint-Omer. 1893
Lauwick (Hervé). Portrait de jeune fille, roman, *see* ŒUVRES libres, 38, 1924.
Laux (Johann Joseph). Der heilige Bonifatius, Apostel d. Deutschen. s8°. Fr. im B. 1922
Lauzanne (Stéphane Joseph Vincent).
Works in ŒUVRES libres.
Comptes-tu, public?, 1927. [74.]
Dans le royaume des journaux, 1925. [47.]
Le diable aux yeux bleus, 1922. [7.]
Une partie de poker à Washington, 1925. [54.]
Le Père Joffre, 1923. [26.]
Sa majesté la presse, 1924. [32.]
La table qui parle, choses entendues, 1922. [12.]
La vieille dame aux billets, 1926. [60.]
Lauzun (Antonin-Nompar de Caumont, *duc* **de),** *1633–1723, see* LA FORCE (B. N. DE C., *duc* DE). L.: un courtisan du Grand Roi, 1919.
Lavagna, *Conti di, see* SCORZA (A.) Arbor sive genealogia fam. S., & aliarum Comitum Lavaniae, *&* Suppl.; Ital. tr., 1611.
Lavagno (Francesco). Convito nuziale dato da G. Visconti, 1368. [Nozze Callori—De Viry. N119]. fol. Torino. [1884]
La Vaissière (Robert de).
Anthologie poét. du 20e s. 2t. s8°. [1923]
Laval, *The house of, see* DU CHESNE (A.) Hist. genealog. de la maison de Montmorency & de L., 2p, 1624.
Laval (M. de). Une âme de lumière: le Baron Fr. d'Yvoire. Préf. d'H. Bordeaux. s8°. [1923]
Lavalle (Juan Bautista).
El Perú y la Gran Guerra. 8°. Lima. 1919
Lavallée (Joseph), *marq. de Bois-Robert, see* MUSÉE NAPOLÉON. Galerie, rédigée par L., 10t, 1804–15.
Lavallée (Théophile). Hist. de la maison royale de Saint-Cyr, 1686–1795. la8°. 1856
La Vallière (Louise Françoise, *duchesse* **de)** [*Mde.* DE LA V. &c.]
see BOSSUET (J. B.) Sermon prononcé à la profession de Mde. de la V., 1732.
„ FERVAL (C.) The martyr of love: life of L. de La V.; tr., 1914.
„ MEYRAC (A.) L. de La V., 1926.
Lavaquery (*l'abbé* E.)
Le Cardinal de Boisgelin, 1732–1804. 2[t]. la8°. [1921]
Lavardin (Henri Charles de Beaumanoir, *Marquis* **de),** *see* BEAUMANOIR (H. C. DE).
Lavater (Johann Caspar).
Predigt. Ps. 37, 10–15. [P2649]. s4°. [Zürich]. 1777
Lavater (Ludwig). De ritibus & institutis eccl. Tigurinæ opusc. s8°. *n.p.* [Tiguri ?. 1559]
Lavaterus (Joannes Rodolphus), *of Zürich.* Κατάβασις εἰς ᾅδου: Hoc est, De descensu Jesu Christi ad inferos. s8°. Francofurti. 1610
Lavauzelle (Roger Marty-), *see* MARTY-LAVAUZELLE (R.)
Lavedan (Henri) [*ps.* MANCHECOURT].
La belle hist. de Geneviève. s8°. 1920
Gaudias. 2t. s8°. [1921]
Les grandes heures. s3–5. 4 sept. 1915–sept. 1918. s8°. 1918–20
Irène Olette. s8°. [1920]
Madame Lesoir. 2t. s8°. [1925]
Panteau. 2t. s8°. [1923]
Servir: pièce. [*Foll. by* La chienne du roi: pièce, *w. sep. tp. & pagin.* P2752]. la8°. 1913
Laveille (*Mgr.* Auguste). Madame Carré de Malberg, fondatrice de la Soc. des Filles de St. François de Sales (1829–91). 8°. 1917
Laveleye (Emile de). De l'avenir des peuples cathol., étude d'écon. soc. [P520]. 8°. 1875
Le parti clérical en Belgique. [P2505]. s8°. Brux. 1874
La propriété collective du sol en diff. pays. [Extr. de la Revue de Belgique]. la8°. Brux. 1886
Laver (James).
A stitch in time. [*Poem*]. la8°. *Nonesuch Press.* 1927
see SHERINGHAM (G.) & J. L. Design in the theatre, 1927.
Laverendrye (Pierre Gaultier de Varennes de). Journals & letters of P. G. de V. de La V. & h. sons, w. corr. touching the search for the Western Sea. Ed. w. intr. &c. by L. J. Burpee. [Champlain Soc.] 8°. Toronto. 1927
Lavers (*Rev.* William), *of Honiton, Devon, see* ELLIOTT (J. S.) Mem. of W. L., 1848.
Lavery (*Sir* John).
see ROSS (R.) & C. E. MONTAGUE. Brit. artists at the front, p2, Sir J. L., 1918.
„ SPARROW (W. S.) J. L. & h. work, 1922.
Laviano (Enzo Valentini, *conte* **di),** *see* VALENTINI (E.)

La Vicomterie de Saint-Samson (Louis) [*ps. Le père* PARENNIN *or* PARRENIN]. Le code de la nature, poëme de Confucius. Tr. & comm. par le Père Parennin [*or rather wr. by P.* P2760]. 8°. Londres. 1788

Lavigerie (*le card.*) [†ALLEMAND LAVIGERIE (CH. MARTIAL)]. *see* BERTRAND (L. M. E.) Le centen. du card. L. (*in h.* Devant l'Islam). [1926].
„ JAMMES (F.) L., 1927.

Lavignac (Albert). Encyclopédie de la musique & dict. du conservatoire. pliv, v, 2i, ii. la8°. 1920–26

La Vigne (André de), *see* KERDANIEL (E. L. DE). Un auteur dramat. du 15e s.: A. de La V., 1923.

La Ville (Pierre de). Disc. sommaire de ce qui est arrivé en Moscovie, 1611. Suivi d'une Lettre du Tzar Michel au Sultan Achmet, 1613. [*b. w.* Boussingault (A.) Théâtre de Moscovie, 1859]. s8°. 1859

La Villehervé (Bertran de). Fr.-Th. de Baculard d'Arnaud: s. théâtre & s. théories &c. la8°. 1920

La Villemarqué (*le vte.* **Hersart de).** Barzaz-Breiz: chants pop. de la Bretagne. Rec., tr. &c. par L. n. éd. 8°. 1923

Lavington (Frederick). The English capital market. 8°. [1921]

Lavington (George). *The enthusiasm of Methodists & Papists compar'd. 3p *in* 1v. 8°. 1749–51

Lavis (Henry James Johnston-), *see* JOHNSTON-LAVIS (H. J.)

Lavisse (Ernest). Hist. de France contemp., dep. la Révol. j. 1919. 10t. 4°. [1920–22]
1, La Révolution, 1789-92; par P. Sagnac.
2, La Révolution, 1792–99; par G. Pariset.
3, Le Consulat & l'Empire, 1799–1815; par G. Pariset.
4, La Restauration, 1815–30; par S. Charléty.
5, La Monarchie de juillet, 1830–48; par S. Charléty.
6, La Révolution de 1848—Le Second Empire, 1848–59; par C. Seignobos.
7, Le déclin de l'Empire & l'établ. de la 3e Républ., 1859–75; par C. Seignobos.
8, L'évol. de la 3e Républ., 1875–1914; par C. Seignobos.
9, La Grande Guerre; par H. Bidou, A. Gauvain, C. Seignobos —Conclusion gén.; par E. Lavisse.
10, Tables gén.

Lavizari (Pietro Angelo). Storia d. Valtellina in dieci libri descr. 2t. s8°. Capolago. 1838

Lavoisne (C. V.) & C. Gros. A new genealog., hist. & chronolog. atlas &c. fol. 1809

Lavrenev (Boris).
Ветер, рассказы. 2^oe изд. 8°. Ленинград. [1926]
Сорок первый. Со вступит. статей П. Медведева, автобиог. &c. s8°. Харков. [1926]

Lavrentiev Chronicle. Повѣсть временныхъ лѣтъ по Лаврентiевскому списку. Изд. А. К. (*Facsimile*). 4°. С.–П. 1872

Lavrin (Janko).
Dostoevsky & h. creation. A psycho-crit. study. s8°. [1920]
Gogol. s8°. [1925]
Ibsen & h. creation: psycho-crit. st. s8°. [1921]
Tolstoy: a psycho-crit. study. s8°. [1924]

Lavrov (Petr Lavrovich) [*ps.* П. Миртовъ].
Историческiя письма. 4^e изд. s8°. С.–П. 1906
П. Л. Л. Статьи, воспоминания &c. [*By* E. L. Radlov *& others*]. 8°. П. 1922

Lavrovsky (Petr Alekseevich). Коренное значенiе въ названiяхъ родства у Славянъ. [I. Akad. Nauk. Записки, t12]. 8°. С.–П. 1867

***Law** student's guide (The), 1827, *see* LEIGH (P. B.)

Law list (The). 1915, 1923, 1925, 1926. s8°. [1915–26]

Law Quarterly Review (The). v36–43. 8°. 1920–27

Law, *Family of, see* FAIRLEY (J. A.) Lauriston Castle, 1925.

Law (*Sir* **Algernon),** *ed., see* ELLENBOROUGH (E. L., *2nd b.*), India under Lord E., 1926.

Law (*Miss* **Alice),** *F.R.Hist.S.* Emily J. Brontë & the authorship of "Wuthering Heights." s8°. Altham. [1925]
Patrick Branwell Brontë. s8°. [1924]

Law (Bimala Charan). Buddhist conception of spirits. Foreword by S. Krishnaswami Aiyangar. 8°. Calcutta. 1923
Histor. gleanings. Foreword by B. M. Barua. 8°. Calcutta. 1922
Life & work of Buddhaghosa. Foreword by Mrs. C. A. F. Rhys Davids. 8°. Calcutta. 1923
Some Kṣatriya tribes of anc. India. Foreword by A. B. Keith. la8°. Calcutta. 1923
see PUGGALA-PAÑÑATTI. Design. of human types (P.-N.); tr. B. C. L., 1924.

Law (Ernest).
Card. Wolsey at Hampton Court. s8°. 1923
Commonwealth or Empire: which should it be? s8°. 1921
Hampton Court gardens. 8°. 1926
King Henry VIII's Newe Wyne Seller at Hampton Court. s8°. 1927
The London Museum at Kensington Palace. s8°. 1912
Shakespeare's garden, Stratford-upon-Avon. 8°. 1922

Law (Henry), *C.E.* Rudiments of the art of constr. common roads. [Prec. by Gen. survey of metropol. roads, by S. Hughes], w. remarks on macadamised roads, by Gen. Sir J. F. Burgoyne. s8°. 1861–62

Law (Hugh Alexander). Anglo-Irish lit. Foreword by A. E. [*i.e.* G. W. Russell]. s8°. 1926
see MURRAY (R. H.) & H. A. L. Ireland, 1924.

Law (John), *of Lauriston, see* THIERS (L. A.) The Mississippi Bubble: mem. of J. L., 1864.

Law (Narendra Nath). Aspects of anc. Indian polity. Foreword by A. B. Keith. 8°. O. 1921

Law (William), *a. of* "*A serious call*" *&c.*
An humble, earnest &c. address to the clergy. 8°. 1761
*The nature & design of Xty. Extr. f. a late a. [*i.e.* W. L. *by* J. Wesley]. 9th ed. [P2536]. s8°. Bristol. 1771
A practical treatise upon Xtn. perfection. 8°. 1726
A reply to the bishop of Bangor's [Hoadly] ans. to the represent. of the ctee. of Convocation. 8°. 1719
A serious call to a devout & holy life. 8°. [1890]
The way to divine knowledge: sev. dialogues &c. 8°. 1752
see HOBHOUSE (S.) W. L. & 18th cent. Quakerism, incl. letters &c., 1927.

Law (William John). Some remarks on the Alpine passes of Strabo. [*a. c. in* P320]. 8°. 1846

Law (William Smalley). Oundle's story: hist. of the town & school. s8°. [1922]

La Wall (Charles Herbert).
4000 years of pharmacy. 8°. Phila. [1927]

Lawes (Charles Bennett), *see* BELT (R.) *Review of the B. trial [B. *v.* L.]; by an Outsider, 1882.

Lawes (*Sir* **John Bennet),** *1st bart. & Sir* **J. H. Gilbert.** Rothamstead mems. on agric. science. v9–13. la8°. Harpenden. 1919–28

Lawes (Lewis E.) Man's judgment of death: oper. & effect of capital punishment. 8°. N.Y. 1924

Lawler (Catherine), *alias Kate Webster, see* WEBSTER (K.)

Lawless (*Hon.* **Emily).**
Ireland. [Story of the Nations]. 3rd ed. 8°. 1889
The point of view. [*Poems*]. s8°. *p.p.* 1909

Lawlor (H. C.) The monastery of Saint Mochaoi of Nendrum. Foreword by R. A. S. Macalister. 8°. Belfast. 1925

Lawlor (Hugh Jackson), *see* BERNARD, *St., abbot of Clairvaux.* Life of St. Malachy of Armagh; [tr., w. intr.] by H. J. L., 1920.

Lawne (William), *see* CALVIN (J.) An abridgement of the Instit. of the Xtn. relig., by W. L.; tr., 1585; 1586.

Lawrence, *Saint & Martyr, see* MADERUS (J. J.) De S. L. martyre &c., 1688.

Lawrence [O'Toole], *Saint, abp. of Dublin, see* O'HANLON (J.) Life of St. L. O'T, 1857.

Lawrence (Amos), *1786–1853.* Extracts f. diary & corr., w. brief acc. of h. life. Ed. W. R. Lawrence. 8°. Boston [Mass.] 1855

Lawrence (Arnold Walter). Later Greek sculpture & its influence &c. la8°. 1927

Lawrence (C. E.) Lass of the sword. s8°. 1923
Mr. Ambrose. s8°. 1922
The old man's wife. s8°. 1926
Pilgrimage. [2nd ed.] s8°. [1914]

Lawrence (Charles P.), *F.S.I.* Economic farm buildings. Intr. note by Sir T. Middleton. 8°. 1919

Lawrence (David).
The true story of Woodrow Wilson. 8°. [1924]

Lawrence (David Herbert) [*ps.* DAVISON (LAWRENCE H.)]
Aaron's rod. s8°. [1922]
Birds, beasts & flowers. Poems. 8°. [1923]
England, my England. s8°. [1924]
Fantasia of the unconscious. s8°. N.Y. 1922
Kangaroo. s8°. [1923]
The ladybird—The fox—The captain's doll. s8°. [1923]
The lost girl. s8°. [1920]
Mornings in Mexico. 8°. 1927
Movements in European hist. 8°. O. 1925
The plumed serpent (Quetzalcoatl). 8°. [1926]

Lawrence (David Herbert) [*ps.* DAVISON (LAWRENCE H.)] *contd.*
Psychoanalysis & the unconscious. s8°. N.Y. 1921
Psychoanalysis & the unconscious. 8°. [1923]
St. Mawr—The princess. s8°. [1925]
Sea & Sardinia. 8°. [1923]
Sons & lovers. [4th impr.] s8°. [1924]
Studies in classic Amer. lit. 8°. [1924]
Touch & go. Play. s8°. 1920
Women in love. [repr.] s8°. [1927]
—— & M. L. Skinner.
The boy in the bush. 2nd impr. s8°. [1924]
Lawrence (*Mrs.* **Emmeline**), *wife of F. W. Pethick Lawrence, see* VOTES FOR WOMEN; ed. F. & E. P. L., v3–7, 1909–14.
Lawrence (Frederick William Pethick).
Unemployment. s8°. [1922]
see VOTES FOR WOMEN; ed. F. & E. P. L., v3–7, 1909–14.
Lawrence (H. W.) & B. L. Dighton.
French line engravings of the late 18 cent. 4°. 1910
Lawrence (*Sir* **Henry Montgomery**), *see* PUNJAB. P. govt. rec., v3 (Diaries of Resid. at Lahore, 1847–48), 1909.
Lawrence (John), *rector of Yelvertoft* [LAURENCE]. The gentleman's recreation: or the 2nd part of the Art of gardening improved. Added, New &c. way to find a meridian line &c. by E. Laurence. s8°. 1716
Lawrence (John Laird Mair Lawrence, *1st b.*), *see* PUNJAB. P. govt. rec., v3 (Diaries of resid. at Lahore, 1847–48), 1909.
Lawrence (Margery H.)
Miss Brandt: adventuress. 2nd ed. s8°. [1923]
Lawrence (*Col.* **Thomas Edward**). Cat. of an exhib. of paintings &c. illustr. L.'s "Seven pillars of Wisdom," w. pref. by B. Shaw & T. E. L. Leicester Galls. s8°. 1927
Revolt in the desert. [2nd impr.] 8°. 1927
,, ,, ...[4th impr.] 8°. 1927
,, ,, ...[5th impr.] 8°. 1927
Seven pillars of wisdom: a triumph. la8°. 1926
see BRIT. MUSEUM. Carchemish: rep. on excav. at Jerablus; by C. L. Woolley & T. E. L., p2, 1921.
,, GRAVES (R.) L. & the Arabs, 1927.
,, THOMAS (L.) With L. in Arabia, 1924; 4th ed., 1925; 16th ed., 1927.
Lawrence (Thomas Joseph). Princ. of internat. law. 7th ed., rev. by P. H. Winfield. 8°. 1927
The society of nations. Its past, present &c. 8°. N.Y. 1919
Lawrence (*Sir* **Walter Roper**), *1st Bart.* The India we served. 8°. [1928]
Lawrence (William Beach). Discourses & reviews princ. on polit. econ. [*Each Disc. &c. h. sep. tp. & pagin.*] 8°. N.Y. 1834
The Treaty of Washington. Letters. 8°. Providence. 1871
W. B. L. vs. R. H. Dana, Jr., &c. [Circuit Court of U.S. Distr. of Mass.] Bill in Equity.—Arguments &c. [*b. w. h.* Treaty of Washington, 1871]. [3p *in* 1v]. la8°. Boston. 1868
Lawrence (William John). The mystery of Lodowick Barry. [Repr. f. Studies in Philol., v14. P2847]. 8°. Chapel Hill [U.S.A.] 1917
Physical cond. of the Eliz. public playhouse. 8°. Camb., *Mass.* 1927
Pre-Restoration stage studies. 8°. Cambridge, *Harvard.* 1927
Lawrence (William Richards), *see* LAWRENCE (A.) Extracts f. diary &c., w. brief acc. of h. life; ed. W. R. Lawrence, 1855.
Lawrence (William Witherle). Mediaeval story & the beg. of soc. ideals of Eng.-speaking people. [Columbia Univ. Lect.] 2nd ed. 8°. N.Y. 1926
Lawry (Walter). Friendly & Feejee islands: a missionary visit. Ed. E. Hoole. s8°. 1850
Laws.
*Laws (The) & customs, rights, liberties, & privileges, of the city of London. s8°. 1765
Laws (The) of the earliest Eng. kings, 1922, *see* ATTENBOROUGH (F. L.), *ed.*
Laws (The) of the kings of England, 1925, *see* ROBERTSON (A. J.), *ed.*
Lawson (George), *rector of More, Salop, d. 1678.* An expos. of the Ep. to the Hebrewes. sm. fol. 1662
Lawson (*Lieut.-Gen. Sir* **Henry**), *K.C.B.* Report [*&* 2nd rep.] on the Irish situation. [P2530]. 8°. [1921]
Lawson (John Cuthbert). Tales of Ægean intrigue. 8°. 1920
Lawson (Leonard Axel). The relation of Brit. policy to the declar. of the Monroe doct. [Columbia Univ. St. in hist. &c., 103i]. 8°. N.Y. 1922
Lawson (P. H.), *ed., see* MORRIS (R. H.) Siege of Chester, 1643–46, 1924.

Lawson (William D.) Wesleyan local preachers: biog. illust. By the a. of Tyneside Celebrities. s8°. Newcastle-upon-Tyne. 1874
Lawton (Harold Walter).
Terence en France au 16e s. Éditions & trads. 8°. 1926
Lawton (Lancelot). The Russ. Revolution, 1917–26. 8°. 1927
Laxdaela Saga.
L.S. Tr. M. A. C. Press. [Temple Class.] s8°. 1925
Lay (Wilfrid). Man's unconscious spirit: psychoanalysis of spiritism. s8°. [1921]
Layamon. Layamon's Brut. Sel., ed. w. intr., notes &c. by J. Hall. 8°. O. 1924
Layard (*Rt. Hon. Sir* **Austen Henry**). The massacre of St. Bartholomew &c. [Repr. f. Huguenot Soc., 1887]. 8°. 1888
Layard (George Somes). Cat. raisonné of engraved Brit. portraits f. altered plates. Fr. notes of L., arr. by H. M. Latham. Intr. by Marq. of Sligo. 4°. 1927
The headless horseman, P. Lombart's engraving: Charles or Cromwell? Intr. by C. Dodgson. la8°. 1922
Layard (Nina Frances). Notes on some Eng. paxes. [Repr. f. Archaelog. Journ., v61. P2621]. 8°. 1904
Laynez (Diego), *see* LAINEZ (D.)
Laynez (James), *jesuit, see* RULE (W. H.) Celebr. Jes., v1, 1852.
Layritius (Joannes Jacobus). De articulis Svobac. Augustanae Conf. fundamento. Disput. s4°. Wittenbergae. 1719
Layriz (Johann Christoph) [†LAYRITZ].
De exilio poetarum. [P445]. s4°. Baruthi. [1706]
Layton (Edwin J.) Thomas Chippendale. 4°. 1928
Layton (G.) Castle-Barnard, a poem. s8°. Barnard Castle. 1823
Layton (Walter Thomas). Intr. to the study of prices, w. spec. ref. to hist. of 19th c. [repr. w. add. chap. &c.] s8°. 1920
Laz (Joseph François Bonabe Jégou, *cte.* **du),** *see* JÉGOU.
Lazak (Stephan), *see* SUMMA. *Summa univ. theol. Christ. sec Unitarios, [*by S. L.?*], 1787.
Lazard (Lucien), *see* MONIN (H.) & L. L. Sommier des biens nat. de Paris; publ. M. & L., t1, 2, 1920.
Lazarev, *The family of, see* MSEREANTZ (G.) Records of lives & works of L. family [*in Armenian*], 3p, 1856.
Lazarevsky Institut Vostochnikh Yazikov.
Каталогъ книгъ и рукоп. Библ. Л. И. В. Я. 8°. Москва. 1888
Собраніе высоч. указовъ и актовъ, относ. до Московск. Арм. Л. И. В. Я. [*In Russ. & Armenian*]. 8°. С.-П. 1839
Эминскій этнограф. сборникъ. вып. 9. la8°. Tiflis. 1913
see ADJARIAN (H.) Провинціал. словарь арм. языка, 1913 [9].
,, BARLAAM & JOSAPHAT. Б. и І., Груз. текстъ, съ перевод. и пред. изд. А. Хахановъ (Л. И. Вост. Яз. Труды. вып. 9), 1902.
,, BIBLE: ARMENIAN. Книги Паралипоменонъ въ древн. арм. переводѣ; *ed.* G. Khalatheantz, 1899.
,, SHARAKAN. Шараканъ богослужебные каноны &c., 1914.
Lazarevsky (Ivan). Среди коллекціонеровъ. 3e изд. s8°. П. 1922
Lazari (Vincenzo). Del traffico e d. condiz. d. schiavi in Venezia nei tempi di mezzo, *see* REGIA DEP. DI STORIA PATRIA. Misc., t1, 1862.
Lazarillo (—).
Giov. Papini. [*a. c. in* P2517]. la8°. Milano. 1920
Salvator Gotta. la8°. Milano. 1919
Lázaro (Angel). Jacinto Benavente, de su vida y de su obra. 8°. [1925]
Lazarus, *of Pharp* [*Parb*].
[Hist. of Armenia, *in Armenian*]. 8°. i Venetik. 1793
[,, ,, *a. ed. w.* Letter, *in Arm.*] s8°. i Venetik. 1891
[Letter to Vahan Mamikonian. *In Armenian.* Ed. M. Emin. *a. c. in* P2813]. 8°. Moskva. 1853
Lazienkowski Palace, *Warsaw, see* WARSAW.
Lazikean (Arsen). [*Poem on Mekhithar. In Armenian.* P2800]. s8°. Venetik. 1900
Lazistan. [**Lazistan, Armenia & Kurdistan. tp. wanting. In Armenian.* P2799]. la8°. *n.p.* 1893 ?
Lazzareschi (Eugenio). Un ambasciatore lucchese a Vienna: G. B. Domenico Sardini, 1751–59. 8°. Lucca. 1918
Viareggio. [P2860]. 4°. Milano. *n.d.*
Lazzari (Alfonso). I "ricordi di governo" di Alfonso II d'Este, duca di Ferrara, *see* ARCHIVIO STORICO ITAL. Anno 78, v1, 1920.
Lazzari (Maria Domenica), *called Addolorata, see* BRENTANO (C.) A. K. Emmerich, D. L. &c., 1874.
Lazzarini (Vittorio).
L'avvocato dei carcerati poveri a Venezia. [*Extr. f.* R. Istit. Ven., t70ii. P2836]. 8°. Venezia. 1911
I Foscari. [Nozze Foscari-Meloncini]. [N123, 135]. la8°. Padova. 1895
Un inscriz. Torcellana d. sec 7.

Lazzarini (Vittorio) [*continued*].
[*Extr. f.* R. Istit. Ven., t73ii. P2840]. 8º. Venezia. 1914
Storia di un trattato tra Venezia, Firenze e i Carraresi, 1337–99. [Estr. d. N. Arch. Ven., t18. P2840]. 8º. Venezia. [1899]
Il testamento del doge Andrea Dandolo [1354. Estr. d. N. Arch. Ven., n.s., t7. P2840]. 8º. Venezia. 1904
I titoli dei dogi di Venezia. [Estr. d. Nuovo Arch. Ven., n.s., t5. P2835]. 8º. Venezia. 1903
see BERTANZA (E.) & V. L. Il dialetto veneziano, 1891.

Lazzeri (Gerolamo). Mario Mariani. la8º. Milano. 1919
Lea (Hermann). Thomas Hardy's Wessex. 8º. 1913
Lea (John). Romance of bird life. 8º. 1921
see COUPIN (H.) & J. L. Romance of animal arts & crafts, 1913.
Lea (Thomas Simcox), *D.D.*, *see* BOND (F. B.) & T. S. LEA. Prelim. investig. of the Cabala &c., 1917.
—— & F. B. Bond. Materials for the study of the apostolic gnosis. pl, 2. 8º. O. 1919–22
Leabhar Chlainne Suibhne (16 c.): acc. of MacSweeney families in Ireland, 1920, *see* WALSH (P.), *ed.*
Leach (Arthur Francis). Milton as a schoolboy & schoolmaster. [From Brit. Acad. Proc. v3, P2411]. 8º. [1908]
Some results of research in hist. of educ. in England &c., 1914, *see* BRIT. ACADEMY. Proc., 1913–14.
Leach (Henry Goddard).
Angevin Britain & Scandinavia. 8º. C. [Mass.], *Harvard.* 1921
Leach (J. A.) Australian nature studies. 8º. Melbourne. 1922
Leacock (Stephen). College days. s8º. 1923
The garden of folly: a picture of the world we live in. 8º. 1924
My discovery of England. s8º. 1922
Winsome Winnie & o. new nonsense novels. s8º. 1921
see MACARTHUR (P.) S. L. [biog. sk., extr. f. wr. & an apprec. &c.], 1923.
Lead (Jane) [LEADE], *see* JÄGER (J. W.) Diss. de J. L. vita, visionibus &c., 1712.
Leadbeater (Charles Webster). The astral plane. s8º. 1895
Leaf (Charlotte Mary), *wife of Walter Leaf*, *see* SYMONDS (M.) Out of the past, w. acc. of Janet C. Symonds, by Mrs. L., 1925.
Leaf (Horace). Under the Southern Cross: rec. of a pilgrimage. Intr. by Sir A. C. Doyle. 8º. [1923]
Leaf (Lotta). The poet's garden &c. *p.f.p.c.* s8º. 1916
Leaf (Walter). Banking. [Home Univ. lib.] s8º. [1926]
A Byzantine Pleiad. [Agathias &c.] s8º. E. 1920
Little poems f. the Greek. [Tr. by W. L.] 2s. s8º. 1922
Quatrains fr. the Greek. [*p.p.*] s8º. E. 1919
see STRABO. S. on the Troad; ed. w. tr. & comm. by W. L., 1923.
Leaf (*Mrs.* Walter), *see* LEAF (CHARLOTTE MARY).
League of Nations.
The econ. consequences of the League. The World Econ. Conf. Intr. by Sir A. Salter. Articles by [*var. a.*] 8º. [1927]
Greek refugee settlement. Tr. 8º. Geneva. 1926
Internat. credits. (The "Ter Meulen" Scheme). [P2519]. 8º. [1921]
*League (The) of Nations; ed. S. P. Duggan, 1919, *see* DUGGAN (S. P. H.)
*League (The) of Nations. The covenant expld. With introd. by G. Murray. [P2405]. 8º. [1920]
League (The) of Nations & China. Extrs. f. speeches by Vsct. Bryce, H. E. C. T. Wang &c., 1919. [P2487]. s8º. 1919
League (The) of Nations starts. An outline by its organisers. [R. B. Fosdick *& others*]. 8º. 1920
OFFICIAL PUBLICATIONS.
Compte rendu—Minutes of the 12th [— 14th] session [1921] of the Council of the L. of N. [*In French & Eng.*] fol. [Lausanne &c. 1921]
Conférence Internat. du Travail. 2e session., Gênes; juin-juillet 1920. [*Fr. & Eng.*] fol. Genève. 1920
For 1st session see special catalogue of Parliamentary papers.
Currencies after the War: conditions in various countries. 8º. [1920]
Internat. Conf. on traffic in women & children, Geneva, 1921. Gen. rep. *&* Records [*in 1v. French & Eng.*] fol. [Geneva. 1921]
Mém. sur la superposit. des taxes, par B. P. Blackett. [*Fr. & Eng.* P2687]. fol. [Lausanne. 1921]
Monthly summary. v1–7 (1921–27). fol. [1921–27]
Official journal—Journal officiel. [*In Eng. & Fr.*] Years 1–8 (1920–27). la8º. & fol. Geneva. 1920–[27]
,, ,, Spec. suppl. No. 1–39, 41–52, 62. la8º. & fol. London & Geneva. 1920–28
Aaland Islands. [1, 3.]
Constitution of Danzig. [7.]
Court of Internat. Justice. [2.]

League of Nations [*continued*].
OFFICIAL PUBLICATIONS [*continued*].
Official journal—Spec. suppl. [*continued*].
Index to Off. journal, 1920–27. [10, 12, 22, 31, 41, 52, 62.]
Minutes of Sessions of the Council: Index, 1921. [8.]
Poland & Lithuania. [4.]
Records of 4th Assembly, 1923, *&* Index. [13–20.]
,, ,, 5th Assembly, 1924, *&* Index. [23–30.]
,, ,, 6th Assembly, 1925. [33–39.]
,, ,, 7th Assembly, 1926, *&* Index. [44–51.]
see Records *below for 1st–3rd Assemblies.*
,, of Spec. Session, Mar. 1926. Plenary meetings & Meetings of Comm. [42.]
Resolutions &c. [5, 6, 9, 11, 21, 32, 43.]
Permanent Mandates Commiss. Minutes of 1st–11th session[s], Geneva, 1921–27. [*Fr. & Eng.* 1st sess. *in* P2687. Index, sess. 1–10, 2p]. fol. [Geneva. 1921–27]
Procès-verb. de la sess. extraord. du Conseil, Haute-Silésie, 29 août–12 oct., 1921. [*Fr. & Eng.* P2687]. fol. [Lausanne. 1921]
Protection des minorités en Lettonie. Mém. du Dr. Walters. [*Fr. & Eng.* P2687]. fol. [Lausanne. 1922]
Records of the 1st[–3rd Assembly]. Plenary Meetings [*&* Committees], 1920–22. 4º. *&* fol. Geneva. 1920–22
For Records *of later* Assemblies *see* Offic. journal &c. Suppl. *above.*
Répertoire des organisat. internat. Hdbk. [*in Fr.*] la8º. Genève. 1921
Rep. by the Secretary-Gen. to 1st [& 2nd] Assembly on the work of the Council [1920–21; *in 1v*]. fol. [Lausanne. 1920–21]
Rep. of experts on traffic in women & children. 2p. fol. 1927
Rep. of the Secretary &c. on Jewish questions. [P2701]. 4º. 1921
Treaty series. Publ. of treaties &c. registered w. the Secretariat. Suppl. to the Official journal. [*In Fr. & Eng.*] v1–68. 4º. 1920–28
,, ,, ...Gen. index, v1–39. 4º. 1927
COMMITTEE [*& INSTITUTE*] ON INTELLECTUAL CO-OPERATION.
Bulletin of the Internat. University Information Office, 1924, 1925. 8º. Geneva. 1924–25
Index bibliographicus: internat. cat. of sources of curr. bibl. inform. Ed. M. Godet. 8º. Geneva. 1925
Internat. Inst. of Intellectual Co-operation. [P2878]. s8º. 1927
Notable books publ. in var. countries dur. 1924, 1925. s8º. Paris. 1926–27
see ZIMMERN (A. E.) Learning & leadership, 1927.
PERMANENT COURT OF INTERNATIONAL JUSTICE.
Advisory Comm. of Jurists. Doc. pres. to Comm. rel. to existing plans for establ. of a Permanent Court of Internat. Justice. fol. 1920
Advisory Comm. of Jurists. Procès-verbaux of the Proc. of the Comm., June 16th–July 24th 1920, w. Annexes. fol. The Hague. 1920
Doc. conc. action taken by the L. of N. under article 14 & adoption by the Assembly of the Statute of the Permanent Court. fol. [1921]
REFERENCES.
see GENEVA INSTITUTE OF INTERNAT. AFFAIRS. Problems of peace: lects., 1926, 1927.
,, INTERNAT. FINANCIAL CONF.
,, MUNCH (P.), *ed.* Les origines & l'œuvre de la Soc. des Nations, t1, 2, 1923–24.
,, ROUMANIA. Agrarian reform in R. & case of Hungarian optants in Transylvania bef. L. of N., 1927; *Fr. ed.*, 1927.
,, THRACE. Mém. sur la T., adr. à la Soc. des Nat. par le Comité Turc de la T., 1922.
,, WILLOUGHBY (W. W.) Opium as internat. problem: Geneva conf., 1925.
League of Nations Union.
The first assembly: study of proc. &c. s8º. 1921
Unemployment in its nat. & internat. aspects; rep. of confer., London, 1924, *see* INTERNATIONAL LABOUR OFFICE.
see also GENEVA INSTITUTE OF INTERNAT. AFFAIRS.
Leake (Hugh Martin). The bases of agricult. practice & econ. in the U.P., India. Foreword by J. Mackenna. 8º. C. 1921
Land tenure & agric. production in the tropics. 8º. C. 1927
Leake (Isaac Q.)
Mem. of the life & times of Gen. J. Lamb. 8º. Albany. 1850
Leake (*Rear-Adm. Sir* John), *1656–1720*, *see* LEAKE (S. M.) Life of Sir J. L.; ed. G. Callender, 2v, 1920.
Leake (Stephen Martin), *F.S.A.*, *1702–73* [MARTIN-LEAKE]. The life of Sir John Leake, Rear-Adm. Ed. G. Callender. [Navy Records Soc., 52, 53]. 2v. 8º. 1920
Leake (William Martin). Researches in Greece. 4º. 1814
Leakey (James Shirley). In Chancery. Betw. G. G. Daugars, plaintiff, & A. H. Rivaz, J. S. L. &c., def. Ans. of L. [Fr. Church in London]. 8º. *n.d.* [1858 ?]
Leal de Castro (Rogue). Cartas, sobre la representacion del arzobispo de Valencia a la Cortes 20 oct. 1820. [*each w. sep. pagin.*] s8º. 1820

Leamington.
The vicinity of L.; guide &c. s8°. Leamington. [1844 ?]

Leang-Li (T'ang), *see* T'ANG (L. L.)

Lear (Edward). Queery Leary nonsense. A Lear nonsense book. Ed. Lady Strachey. Intr. by the Earl of Cromer. la8°. [1911]

Lear (P. G.) & L. O. The strange &c. adv. of 4 authors in search of a character. [Cayme Press Pamph., No. 2]. 8°. *Cayme Press*, Kensington. 1926

Learned (Marion Dexter). Guide to the MS. mat. rel. to Amer. hist. in the German State archives. [C.I. of Wash., Publ. 150]. la8°. Wash. 1912

Leary (Lewis Gaston). Andorra, the hidden republic. s8°. 1912

Leask (J. C.) & H. M. McCance.
Regimental records of The Royal Scots. s4°. D. 1915

Leatham (Isaac). Gen. view of the agric. of the E. Riding of Yorks. &c. [*b. w.* Rennie (G.) &c. Gen. view, 1794]. s4°. 1794

Leathes (Stanley). The people in the making. s8°. 1921
The people of adventure. s8°. 1920
The people on its trial. s8°. 1923

Léautaud (Paul) [*ps.* MAURICE BOISSARD].
Le théâtre de M. Boissard, 1907–23. 3e éd. s8°. [1926]

Leavell (R. H.), *see* UNITED STATES: LABOR. Negro migration in 1916–17: reps. by L. &c., 1919.

Leavitt (Sturgis Elleno). Argentine lit.: bibliog. [Univ. of N. Carolina: St. in Lang. & Lit., No. 1]. la8°. Chapel Hill. 1924

Leb. ספר לב טהור, 1753, *see* SEPHER.

Lebaigue (Charles). Dict. latin-français, suiv. d'un app. s. la métrologie &c. 53e éd. la8°. 1924

Le Barbier (Louis).
Le général de La Horie, 1766–1812. s8°. 1904

Lebasteur (Henri). Le Prince de Ligne & les poètes français. [P2717]. 8°. Brux. 1921

Lebedev (Gerasin). A gramm. of the East Indian dialects w. dialogues. 4°. 1891

Lebedev (P. I.), *see* POLYANSKY (V.), *ps.*

Lebègue (Henri), *see* UNION ACAD. INTERNAT. Cat. des mss. alchim. grecs, t1, Les Parisini, décr. par H. L., 1924.

Lebensbeschreibungen. Auserlesene Lebensb. heil. Seelen &c., 3B, 1733–43, *see* TERSTEEGEN (G.)

Lebeuf (Jean). Diss. sur l'hist. eccl. & civile de Paris &c. 3t. s8°. 1739–43
t3 *cont.* Vie de Charles V, par Christine de Pisan.
Mém. conc. l'hist. civile & eccl. d'Auxerre & de s. anc. diocèse. Avec add. de nouv. preuves &c. par M. Challe [&] M. Quantin. 4t. la8°. Auxerre. 1848–55

Lebey (André). Jean L. de Tinan. s8°. 1921

Lebiez (Paul) & Aimé Barré. *L. & B. [*Murder of Mme. Gillet &c. by P. L. & A. B., 1878. no tp.* P2826]. s8°. [Sceaux. *n.d.*]

Lebisii (Daniel). Diss. de Melchisedeco. Sub praes. C. Hoffmani. [P431]. s4°. Jenae. [1669]

Leblan (Eugène), *see* ISABEY (L.) & E. L. Villas, maisons &c. comp. sur les motifs des habitations de Paris mod., 1864.

Le Blanc (Augustin), *ps., see* SERRY (J. H.)

Leblanc (Georgette), *afterwards Mme. Maurice Maeterlinck.* Mes conversations avec La Duse, *see* ŒUVRES libres, 66, 1926.

Leblanc (Henri). La Grande Guerre. Iconographie—bibliog.—doc. divers. Coll. de H. L. 8t. la8°. 1916–22

Le Blanc (Hubert), *of Amsterdam.* Le Czar Pierre I en France. [*Satire*]. 2t. s8°. Amsterdam. 1741

Leblanc (Maurice). La dent d'Hercule Petitgris, nouvelle, *see* ŒUVRES libres, 42, 1924.
"813." 2p. s8°. 1921
1, La double vie d'Arsène Lupin.
2, Les trois crimes d'Arsène Lupin.

Le Blanc (Thomas), *Jesuit.* Psalmorum Davidic. analysis: adjung. comm. 6t [*in* 3v]. fol. Coloniae Agrippinae. 1744

Le Blanc de Beaulieu (Louis). Disputationes, *see* DU MOULIN (P.) Thesaurus disput., v2, 1661.

Le Blon (Jakob Christoffel), *1667–1741, see* SINGER (H. W.) J. C. Le Blon, 1901.

Le Blond (*Mrs.* Aubrey). The old gardens of Italy: how to visit them. 2nd ed. rev. s8°. 1926

Leblond (Marius) & Ary Leblond. L'amour sur la montagne, roman, *see* ŒUVRES (Les) libres, 24, 1923.
La croix du sud: nouvelle, *see* ŒUVRES libres, 64, 1926.
L'Ophélia. s8°. 1922
Ulysse, Cafre; ou, l'hist. dorée d'un noir. s8°. [1924]

Leblond (Victor). L'art & les artistes en Ile-de-France au 16e s. (Beauvais & Beauvaisis). [Soc. Acad. de l'Oise &c. Publ.: doc. t6]. 8°. 1921
see BEAUVAIS. Cartul. de la maladrerie de S. Lazare de B., 1922.
,, —— Cartul. de l'Hôtel-Dieu de B., 1919.
,, —— Censier de l'Hôtel-Dieu de B., 1316, 1919.
,, —— Obituaire de l'Hôtel-Dieu de B., 1292, 1919.

Le Bon (Gustave).
Les civilisations de l'Inde. la8°. 1887
Le déséquilibre du monde. s8°. 1923
Psychologie des temps nouveaux. s8°. 1920
Psychologie du socialisme. 4e éd. rev. 8°. 1905
TRANSLATIONS.
The crowd. 4th impr. s8°. 1903
The world in revolt: psychological st. of our times. Tr. B. Miall. 8°. [1921]

Le Bossu (Jacobus). Animadv. in propos. L. Molinae de concordia liberi arbitrii cum gratiae donis, *see* REGINALD (A.) De mente Conc. Trid., 1706.

Le Bouthillier de Rancé (Armand Jean), *see* CHATEAUBRIAND (*le vte.* F. R. DE). Congrès de Vérone &c.; suivie de la Vie de R., *n.d.*

Le Bouvier (Gilles), *dit Berry.* Armorial de France, Angleterre &c., 1450. Publ. &c. par M. Vallet (de Viriville). 8°. 1886

Le Braz (Anatole). Pâques d'Islande. s8°. [1914]
Le sang de la sirène. s8°. [1901]

Le Bret (Johann Friedrich).
Acta Eccl. Graecae annor. 1762 et 63, sive de schismate recentiss. comm. s8°. Stutgardiae. 1764
De Eccl. Wirtemberg. renascentis calamitatibus. Def. G. W. Hegel &c. [P441]. s4°. Tubingae. [1793]
De orig. &c. Eccl. Wirtemberg. Def. G. T. F. Breitschwerdt, C. H. Roesslin &c. p1 & 2ii. [P441]. s4°. Tubingae. [1790–91]
De primitiva Eccl. Wirtemberg. repurgatae disciplina &c. Def. C. P. F. Leutwein &c. [P441]. s4°. Tubingae. [1792]
De spectro Jansenismi in Tuscia. Præs. Le B., disput. J. H. Harter [*& others.* P2630]. s4°. Tubingæ. [1789]
De variis proselytismi relig. formis. Praes. J. F. Le B. Disput. C. F. Weeber &c. [P433]. s4°. Tubingae. [1787]
Diss. de statu praes. eccl. Graecae in Dalmatia quae ritum Slavo-Servicum sequitur. s4°. Stutgardiae. [c. 1765]
*Pragmat. Gesch. d. so beruf. Bulle in Coena Domini &c. [Part of Vorrede *wanting*]. 2e verb. A. 4T. *in* 1v. 8°. Frankfurt. 1772–73

Le Breton (André). La jeunesse de Victor Hugo. s8°. [1928]
Le théâtre romantique. s8°. *n.d.*

Le Breton (Nöel), *sieur de Hauteroche.* Crispin médecin: comédie (1673), *see* FOURNEL (V.) Contemps. de Molière, t2, 1866.

Le Brigant (Jacques). Elémens de la langue des Celtes Gomérites, ou Bretons. s8°. Strasbourg. 1779

Le Brun (Pierre), *prêtre de l'Oratoire.* Explic. litt., hist., dogmat. &c. Missæ. A J. A. Dalmaso Lat. redd. 4t [*in* 2v]. s4°. Venetiis. 1770

Le Cacheux (Paul), *see* HENRY VI, *king of England.* Actes de la Chancellerie d'H. VI conc. la Normandie sous la domin. angl., 1422–35, t2, 1908.

Le Camus (Hieronymus), *ps., see* †SIMON (R.)

Lecanu (*l'abbé*). Hist. des évêques de Coutances, dep. la fondation de l'évêché. [*a. c. in* P1406]. 8°. Coutances. 1839

Le Cardonnel (Georges) & P. Lièvre.
Études sur E. Montfort. s8°. 1920

Le Cardonnel (Louis), *see* RICHARD (P. P. J.) Le poète L. Le C., 1925.

Le Cène (Charles). *An essay for a new tr. of the Bible. [Tr.] by H. R., a minister of the Ch. of E. [*i.e.* Hugh Ross]. 8°. 1702
see GOUSSET (J.) Consid. sur le projet d'une nouv. version franç. de la Bible, 1698.

Lecène (Paul). L'évol. de la chirurgie. s8°. 1923

Lecesne (Paul Louis), *see* PARL.: H. OF COMMONS. Rep. of debate, June 1825, on deportation of L &c. f. Jamaica, 1825.

Le Charpentier (Constant). Monsieur Hamon: médecin & solitaire de Port-Royal (1618–87). la8°. Mamers. 1924

Lechat (Henri). Dolorosa, tête grecque (Musée de Lyon), *see* ACAD. DES INSCR.: FOND. PIOT. Mon., t23, 1918–19
Epidaure. Restaur. & descr. des princ. mons. du sanctuaire d'Asclépios. Relevés & restaur. par A. Defrasse. fol. 1895

Le Cheminant (Keith).
Colonial & foreign banking systems. s8°. 1924

Lechler (Gotthard Victor). Johannes Hus: e. Lebensbild. [Verein f. Ref.-gesch. Schr., Jhrg. 7, Nr. 28. *a. c. bound sep.*] 8º. Halle. 1889
John Wycliffe & his Engl. precursors. Tr. by Prof. Lorimer. n. ed. 8º. [1884]

Lecky (William Edward Hartpole). Clerical influences: Irish sectarianism & Eng. govt. Ed. w. intr. by W. E. G. Lloyd & F. C. O'Brien. s8º. D. 1911

Le Claire (*l'abbé* Jacques Marie).
L'anc. paroisse de Guer. 8º. *p.p.* Hennebont. 1915

Le Clerc (Alexia), *see* ALEXIA (*Le Clerc*).

Leclerc (*le gén.* Charles Emmanuel), *see* BOUVET DE CRESSÉ (A. J. B.), *ed.* Hist. de la catastrophe de St.-Domingue, avec corresp. des gén. L. &c., 1824.

Le Clerc (Jean), *of Amsterdam, 1657–1736.*
Hist. des Provinces-Unies des Pays Bas, avec les princ. médailles & leur explic. 3t [2, 3 *wanting*]. fol. Amsterdam. 1723
The "Explic. des médailles" *forms a sep. part w. sep. tp. & pagin. & is b. w.* t1.
*Sentimens de quelques théologiens de Hollande sur l'Hist. crit. du Vieux Test. par R. Simon. s8º. Amsterdam. 1685
Twelve diss. out of L.'s Genesis; done out of Latin by Brown. s8º. 1696
see BURY (A.) *Hist. vindic. [*attrib. to Le C.*] of The naked gospel [*by* B.], 1691.
„ JACOBI (J.) Hist. eccl. Arminianae a E. S. Cypriano adv. J. Clerici object. def., 1726.
„ MAJUS (J. H.) Repet. examen Hist. crit. textus N.T. a R. Simonio, exam. artis crit. J. Clerici, &c., 1708.
„ NEWTON (*Sir* I.) Two letters to Mr. Le C. &c., 1754.
„ †SIMON (R.) [SIMONVILLE]. Hist. crit. du Vieux Test. v2, *for* Réponse à J. Le C. &c., 1685 &c.

Le Clerc (Léon). Le mobilier normand. fol. [1924]

Leclerc (Marc). La passion de notre frère le Poilu. Préf. de R. Bazin. s8º. 1916

Le Clerc de Beauberon (Nicolas François). Tract. de gratia, pars dogmat. *&* App., *see* MIGNE (J. P.), *ed.* Theol. cursus, t10, 1861.

Leclercq (Henri Maurus). Hist. de la Régence pendant la minorité de Louis XV. 3t. 8º. 1921
see CABROL (F. M.) Dict. d'arch. chrét. &c., t4–7ii, publ. F. C. & H. L., 1920–27.

Leclère (Adhémard). Cambodge. Fêtes civiles & relig. [Annales du Mus. Guimet, Bibl. de vulg., t42]. 8º. 1916

Lèclere (Léon). La question d'Occident. Les pays d'Entre Deux de 843–1921. 8º. Brux. 1921

Leclere (Tristan) [*ps.* TRISTAN KLINGSOR].
Cézanne. Tr. J. B. Manson. s8º. [1925]

L'Ecluse (Charles de), *see* L'ESCLUSE (C. DE).

Le Coconnier (Louis) *& others.* Rec. de disc. en faveur de l'Islam &c. Comité "La France & l'Islam." [P2702]. la8º. 1921

Le Cointe (Paul). L'Amazonie brésilienne. 2t. la8º. 1922

Lecomte (Georges). La lumière retrouvée. Roman. s8º. 1923
Le mort saisit le vif. Roman. s8º. 1925
La vie amoureuse de Danton. s8º. [1927]

Lécomte (Jules). Les lettres de Van Engelgom. Intr. & notes de H. d'Almeras. s8º. 1925

Lecomte (Louis), *Jesuit.*
*Censure de quelques propos. des PP. Le Comte & Le Gobien. Refutée par les écrits des Dominiquains & des Franciscains miss. de la Chine. [*Foll. by the* Propositions, *w. sep. pagin.*] [P2559]. s8º. *n.p.* 1700
*Éclairciss. sur la dénonc. faite à N.S.P. le pape des Nouv. mém. de la Chine, comp. par L. le C. [P2559]. s8º. *n.p.* 1700
Lettera al seren. Duca del Maine int. alle cerimonie d. Cina. [*b. w.* Montecatini (B.) Discrepanze, 1700]. s8º. [Colonia ?]. 1700
*Lettre à monsgr. le duc Du Mayne sur les cérémonies de la Chine. [P2559]. s8º. *n.p.* 1700
Mem. & remarks in 10 years travel thr. China. Tr. 8º. 1738
Propositions extr. des livres du P. Le Comte, *see* Censure *above.*
see LE GOBIEN (C.) Acte de protest. signifié aux Sieurs Syndic. &c. de la Fac. de Théol. de Paris, par le père G., L. Le C. &c., 1700.
„ —— *Lettre s. les propos. [*advanced by L. L.*] déferées par M. Priou, 1700.
„ —— Second Parallele des propos. du père Le C. &c., *n.d.*
„ PARIS: UNIVERSITY. *Réflexions s. la censure de la Fac. de Théol., contre Nouv. mém. s. l'état prés. de la Chine [*by L. L.*] &c., 1700.

Leconfield (Charles Henry Wyndham, *3rd baron*). Cat. of. Americana & MSS. largely f. lib. of 9th Earl of Northumberland, at Petworth House. Sold by Sotheby, Apr. 1928. [Illust.] la8º. 1928
Cat. of the Petworth coll. of pictures in p. of Ld. L. By C. H. C. Baker. la8º. 1920

Leconfield (Charles Henry Wyndham) [*continued*].
Cat. of tapestry &c., the property of Ld. L., &c. Sold by Christie, June 28, 1923. [*Illust.* P2748]. 8º. 1923

Le Conte (Joseph). Sight. 3rd ed. s8º. 1895

Leconte de Lisle (Charles Marie).
Dern. poèmes. [Œuvres]. s8º. *n.d.*
Poèmes antiques. [Œuvres]. s8º. *n.d.*
Poèmes barbares. [Œuvres]. s8º. *n.d.*
Poèmes tragiques. [Œuvres]. éd. rev. & augm. s8º. *n.d.*

Le Coq (Albert v.) Auf Hellas Spuren in Ostturkistan. Berichte &c. d. 2. u. 3. Deut. Turfan-Exped. 8º. L. 1926
Die buddhist. Spätantike in Mittelasien. [Ergebnisse d. Kgl. Preuss. Turfan-Exped.] 6T. fol. 1922–28
1, Die Plastik. 2, Die Manichaeischen Miniaturen. 3, Die Wandmalereien. 4, Atlas d. Wandmalereien *&* Beschreibender Text. 5, 6, Neue Bilderwerke.
Chotscho. Facsimile-Wiedergaben d. wichtig. Funde d. ersten Kön. Preuss. Exped. nach Turfan in Ost-Turkistan. Im Auftr. d. Generalverwaltung d. Kön. Museen aus Mitteln d. Baessler-Inst. hrsg. v. A. v. Le C. [Ergebnisse d. Kgl. Preuss. Turfan-Exped.] la. fol. 1913
Türk. Manichaica aus Chotscho. II, III, *see* KÖNIGL. PREUSS. AKAD. D. WISS. Abhdl. (Phil.-hist. Klasse), 1919, 1922.
see HEDIN (S.) South. Tibet: researches, 1906–08, v8iii, 2 osttürk. Ms.-Karten, unter Mitw. v. A. v. Le C., 1922.
„ —— South. Tibet: researches, 1906–08, v9ii, Osttürk. Namenliste, mit Erkl., v. A. v. L., 1922.

Lecoq (Louis). Les deux paradis: conte, *see* ŒUVRES libres, 54, 1925.

Le Corbusier (—).
L'art décoratif d'aujourd'hui. [8e éd.] la8º. [1926]
Towards a new architecture. Tr. f. 13th Fr. ed., w. intr. by F. Etchells. la8º. 1927

Le Couteur (John Dolbel). Eng. mediaeval painted glass. [Rev. &c. G. McN. Rushforth. Hist. mon. of Eng.] 8º. [1926]

Le Couvreur (Adrienne), *see* SOREL (C.) La vie amoureuse d'A. L., 1925.

Lectures. Lectures [*by var. a.*] on education, deliv. at the Royal Institution, 1854.
„ „ [*repr., w. t.*] Science & educ. Ed. E. Ray Lankester. s8º. 1917
Lectures on foreign churches deliv. in Edinb. & Glasgow, 1845 [& 46] in conn. w. objects of Comm. of Free Ch. of Scot. [*by var. a.*] s1, 2. s8º. E. 1845–46

Ledieu (Paul). Diderot & Sophie Volland. 8º. [1925]

Ledner (Emil). Erinnerungen an Caruso. Vorw. v. L. Blech. 8º. Hannover. [1922]

Ledrain (Eugene), *de la Bibl. Nationale, see* BIBLE: FRENCH. La Bible, tr. L., v5, 6, 1889–90.

Le Drou (Pierre Lambert).
De contritione & attritione diss. 4. s4º. Monachii. 1708
Trias patrum, sive moralis Xtna., quam, præs. P. L. L., propugn. P. Worms. [P2659]. s8º. Lovanii. 1679
see MICHEL (A.) Discussio theol. 4 diss., quas in puncto contrit. & attrit. posuit Le D., 1710.

Ledsham. The parish reg. of L., Co. of York, 1539–1812. Ed. J. W. Clay. [Yorks. Parish Reg. Soc., 26]. 8º. [Leeds]. *p.p.* 1906

Ledwich (Edward). Hist. & antiq. of Irishtown & Kilkenny, *see* VALLANCEY (C.) Coll. de rebus Hib., v2, 1781.
Obs. on Irish antiq., ship-temple nr. Dundalk &c., *see* VALLANCEY (C.) Coll., v3, 1783.
St. of Irish antiq.—Round towers in Ireland—Dunamase & Shean Castle, *see* VALLANCEY (C.) Coll., v2, 1781.

Lee, *Kent.* Register of all marriages, christenings & burials in the Church of S. Margaret, Lee, 1579–1754. Ed. L. L. Duncan &c. [Lewisham Antiq. Soc.] sm. fol. [*p.p.*] Lee. 1888

Lee (Arthur Hamilton Lee, *1st visct.*) *of Fareham.* Cat. of the pictures &c. at 18 Kensington Palace Gardens coll. by Visct. & Visctss. L. of F. Descr. by T. Borenius. 2v. 4º. *p.p.* [O. 1923]–26

Lee (Arthur J.), *of Sewardstone, see* VICTORIA & ALBERT MUSEUM. Flat ornament: sels. by A. J. L., s1, 1910.

Lee (E. Craven), *see* HOBBS (T. G.) Luton par. church; intr. by E. C. L., 1924.

Lee (Frederic E.) The Russian cooperative movement, 1920, *see* UNITED STATES: COMMERCE.

Lee (Frederick George).
Lyrics of light & life. Ed. L. 2nd ed. enl. s8º. 1878

Lee (Gabriel Warton). Brit. carboniferous Trepostomata, *see* GEOL. SURV. OF ENG. &c. Mem.: Palæontology, v1iii, 1912.

Lee (Henry), *of Virginia, the Elder.* Memoirs of the War in the South. Dept. of the U.S. n. ed., w. rev. & biog. of the a. by R. E. Lee. 8°. N.Y. 1872

Lee (Hetty). New methods in the junior Sunday school, based on Froebelian principles. 7th ed. s8°. *n.d.*

Lee (Ida), *see* MARRIOTT (*Mrs.* C. B.)

Lee (Ivy Ledbetter). U.S.S.R. (Union of Soc. Soviet Rep.) A world enigma. 8°. [1927]

Lee (John), *D.D.* Lect. on the hist. of the Ch. of Scot. Ed. W. Lee. 2v. 8°. E. 1860

Memorial for the Bible societies in Scot. [Edinb. Bible Soc.] [*a. issue w. enlarged app.*] 8°. E. 1824

Lee (John), *M.A.*

Management: st. of indust. organiz. 8°. 1921

Lee (Marie Esther), *aft. wife of Graf A. H. K. L. v. Waldersee, see* WALDERSEE (*Gräfin* M. E. v.)

Lee (Nathaniel). Rival queens, *see* INCHBALD (*Mrs.* E.) Brit. theatre, v6, 1808.

Theodosius, a tragedy, *see* NEW Eng. theatre, v10, 1777.

Lee (Rachel Fanny Antonina), *see* GORDON (L. H.) Apology for conduct of the Gordons; corr. &c. w. Mrs. Lee, 1804.

Lee (*Gen.* Robert Edward), *Confederate States Army.*

see DRINKWATER (J.) Robert E. Lee: play, 1923.

„ MAURICE (*Maj.-Gen. Sir* F. B.) R. E. L., 1925.

„ RILEY (F. L.) Gen. R. E. L. after Appomattox, 1922.

„ WILSON (W.) R. E. L.: apprec., 1924.

Lee (Robert Warden), *see* JENKS (E.), *ed.* Digeste de droit civil angl.; tr., 2e éd., 2t, 1923.

Lee (Samuel), *D.D., canon of Bristol: 1783–1852.* Biblia Sacra polyglotta, 3p, 1829–31, *see* BIBLE: COMPLETE TEXTS &c.

A letter to John Bellamy on h. new tr. of the Bible. 8°. C. 1821

Sylloge librorum orient.: cui praemittitur Disp. de necessitate studii ling. Biblic. &c. auctore J. Jahn. Contexuit S. L. 8°. Cantab. 1821

Lee (*Sir* Sidney).

King Edward VII. Biography, 9 Nov. 1841–6 May, 1910. 2v. 8°. 1925–27

A life of William Shakespeare. 3rd ed. of rev. version. 8°. 1922

see ENGLISH (THE) ASSOCIATION. Year's work in Eng. studies, 1919–20; ed. S. L., 1921.

see PARSONS (J. D.) Sir S. L. & absolute proof, 1920.

„ SHAKESPEARE ASSOC. St. in the First Folio, 1925.

Lee (Sophia), *a. of "The chapter of accidents."* The chapter of accidents, *see* †INCHBALD (*Mrs.* E.) Mod. theatre, v9, 1811.

Lee (Vernon), *ps.* [*i.e.* VIOLET PAGET]. For Maurice: 5 unlikely stories. s8°. [1927]

Genius loci: notes on places. [3rd ed.] 8°. 1908

The golden keys & o. essays on the genius loci. 8°. [1925]

The handling of words & o. st. in lit. psychology. s8°. [1923]

Satan the waster. s8°. 1920

Lee (Willis Thomas). Early mesozoic physiography of S. Rocky Mts., 1918, *see* SMITHSONIAN INSTIT. Misc. coll., v69, 1921.

Leech (John), *artist.* Early pencillings f. Punch. 4°. [1864]

Leechman (John). Logic. 2nd ed. enl. s8°. Glasgow. 1845

Leeds. L. Parish church reg. [1572]–1757. [Ed. G. D. Lumb. Thoresby Soc., 1, 3, 7, 10, 13, 20]. 6v. 8°. Leeds. 1891–1914

Reg. of the chapels of the parish ch. of L., 1724–63 &c. 1st & 2nd books. Transcr. & ed. G. D. Lumb. [Thoresby Soc., 23]. 8°. Leeds. 1916

Leeds Grammar School. Admission books, 1820–1900. Ed. & annot. by E. Wilson. [Thoresby Soc., 14]. 8°. Leeds. 1906

Leeds University. Calendar, 1926–27. s8°. Leeds. 1926

Leeds (Edward Thurlow). Oxford tradesmen's tokens, *see* SALTER (H. E.), *ed.* Surveys &c., 1923.

see ACHESON (A.) Shakespeare's sonnet story; w. app. incl. a mon. on the Crosse Inn & the Tavern of Oxford, by E. T. L., 1922.

Leem (Knud). De Lapponibus Finmarchiae comm., una cum J. E. Gunneri notis & E. J. Jessens. Tractatu de Finnorum Lapponumque Norvegic. relig. pagana. [*w. sep. pagin. Dan. & Lat.*] 4°. Kiøbenhavn. 1767

see RASK (E. C.) Ræsonn. Lapp. Sproglære, Omarb. af K. L.'s Lapp. Gramm., 1832.

Leenhof (Friedrich von).

Der Himmel auff Erden. s8°. Amsterdam. 1706

Lees (Beatrice Adelaide). Alfred the Great, 848–899. [Heroes of the nations]. [repr.] 8°. N.Y. 1919

Lees (James Cameron), *see* MACLEAN (N.) Life of J. C. L., 1922.

Lees (Robert James). Through the mists, or autobiog. of a soul in paradise. 8°. 1898

Lees-Smith (Hastings Bertrand). A guide to parl. & official papers. [London School of Econ. P2750]. 8°. 1924

Second chambers in theory & practice. 8°. [1923]

Leete (Mary Mather). The children's bureau of Cleveland, *see* UNITED STATES: LAB. Children's Bur., No. 177, 1927.

Leeuw (Aart van der). Mythe van een jeugd. 8°. 1921

Leeuwen (Joannes van), *of Amsterdam.*

Octaviae querela: carmen. 8°. Amstelodami. 1857

Le Faivre (Paul). Soleil levant, soleil couchant. Angl.–Etats-Unis–Japon. s8°. 1921

Le Fanu, *The family of.*

see HARVEY (F.) Genealog. table of fam. of Sheridan, L. &c., 1875.

„ LE FANU (T. P.) Memoir of the Le F. family, 1924.

Lefanu (Alicia). Memoirs of the life & wr. of Mrs. F. Sheridan, w. remarks upon a late life [*by* J. Watkins] of R. B. Sheridan &c. 8°. 1824

Le Fanu (Joseph Sheridan).

The house by the churchyard. s8°. D. 1904

Madam Crowl's ghost & o. t. of mystery. Coll. & ed. M. R. James. s8°. 1923

Le Fanu (Thomas Philip). Memoir of the Le Fanu family; f. mat. coll. by W. J. H. Le Fanu. la8°. *p.p.* [M'ter. 1924]

Le Fanu (William Joseph Henry), *see* LE FANU (T. P.) Memoir of the Le Fanu family; f. mat. coll. by W. J. H. Le F., 1924.

Le Fanu (William Richard).

Queen Anne's Bounty: its hist. & work. 8°. 1921

Lefebure (Victor). The riddle of the Rhine—Chemical strategy in peace & war. Intr. by Sir H. Wilson. 8°. 1921

Lefebvre (Gustave). Un bas-relief grec dans un tombeau égypt., *see* ACAD. D. INSCR.: FOND. PIOT. Mon., t25, 1921–22.

Lefebvre (Jacques), *seigneur de Saint-Remy.* Mémoires, 1407–35, *see* BUCHON (J. A. C.) Choix de chron., 1875.

Le Febvre (Jean), *avocat en la Cour de Parlement, see* FOURNIVAL (R. DE). La vieille; tr. J. L. (14 c.), 1861.

Lefèbvre (Raymond), *see* MAXE (J.) Cahiers de l'anti-France, 4, "Clarté," s. initiateurs, R. L. &c., 1922.

Lefebvre du Preÿ (Ed.), *ed., see* SAINT-OMER. L'arrondissement de St.-O., 1924.

Lefevre (*Mrs.*) An extract of letters by Mrs. L. [By J. Wesley. *no tp.*] [P2542]. s8°. [Bristol. 1773]

Lefèvre (Frédéric). Le mépris Sauveur—Scala Dei—Consomption. Essais. s8°. 1920

Le Fèvre (Jacques), *d'Étaples,* [FABER (JACOBUS), *Stapulensis*], *1455–1537.* Comm. initiatorii in 4 Evangelia. [*w. text*]. fol. 1526

see FISHER (*card.* J.) Confutatio secundae discept. per J. F. habitę &c., 1519.

„ GRAF (C. H.) La vie & les écrits de J. L. d'E., 1842.

Le Fèvre (Jacques), *docteur de la Sorbonne.* Motifs invincibles pour convaincre ceux de la religion prétendue reformée. s8°. 1682

Nouveau recueil de tout ce qui s'est fait pour & contre les Protestans, en France. [4p *in* 1v]. s4°. 1686

p2, Liste des temples. 3, Recüeil de ce qui s'est fait dep. la revoc. de l'Edit de Nantes. 4, La revoc. de l'Edit de Nantes.

Lefèvre (Louis Raymond).

Vie de Cyrano de Bergerac. 8°. [1927]

Le Fèvre de La Boderie (Gui) [BODERIANUS (GUIDO FABRICIUS)]. Dict. Syro-Chaldaicum, *see* BIBLE. Biblia sacra, t6, 1572.

Lefèvre-Deumier (Jules). Les vespres de l'abbaye du Val. Introd. par G. Brunet. [*& Notice bibliogr.* Bibl. romantique]. 8°. [1924]

Leffingwell (Georgia Williams). Social & private life at Rome in the time of Plautus & Terence. 8°. N.Y., *Columbia Univ.* 1918

Leffler (Anna Carlotta), *aft. Fru Edgren.* Sommerdrømme. Oversættelse ved O. Borchsenius. [2v]. s8°. 1914

Lefranc (*l'abbé* A.)

Olivier de Clisson, connétable de France. 8°. 1898

Le Franc (Marie). Grand Louis l'innocent. 52e éd. s8°. 1927

Le Franc de Pompignan (Jean Georges), *bp. of Puy, aft. abp. of Vienne.* Controv. pacif. sur la foi des enfants & des adultes ignorants, *see* MIGNE (J. P.), *ed.* Theol. cursus, t6, 1862.

Lefrançois-Pillion (Louise). Les sculpteurs de Reims. 8°. 1928

Lefroy (Augustus Henry Frazer).
Hist. & institutes of Roman law. 8°. Toronto. [1915]
Jurisprudence. [Repr. f. Law Quart. Rev., Apr. 1911. P2463]. 8°. Toronto. [1911]

Lefroy (*Mrs.* **Anne**), *form. Rickman, see* HILL (C.) Good company in old Westminster &c.: early recoll. of A. L., 1925.

Lefroy (George Alfred), *bp. of (1) Lahore, (2) Calcutta, see* MONTGOMERY (H. H.) Life & letters of G. A. L., 1920.

Lefroy (*Gen. Sir* **John Henry**). Diary of a magnetic survey of a portion of Canada chiefly in the N.W. territories, 1842–44. la8°. 1883
Report on the regimental & garrison schools of the army, & on milit. libraries &c. 8°. 1859
see BOXER (E. M.) Answer to a pamphlet wr. by L., 1862.
„ WOOLWICH. Offic. cat. of Museum of Artillery; by J. H. L., 1864.

Lefroy (William), *Dean of Norwich.*
"Christian science." Sermons. s8°. 1903

Lefuse (M.) The life & times of Arabella Stuart. 8°. [1913]

Lega d. teologia mod. colla filosofia &c., 1787, *see* BONOLA (R.)

Legacy. Legacy (The) of Israel: essays by Sir G. A. Smith &c., 1927, *see* BEVAN (E. R.) & C. SINGER, *edd.*
Legacy (The) of the Middle Ages; [*by var. wr.*], 1926, *see* CRUMP (C. G.) & E. F. JACOB, *edd.*

Le Gal (Etienne).
Ne confondez pas. . . . Préf. de L. Cledat. s8°. 1927
Ne dites pas. . . . Mais dites. . . . Préf. de E. Bourciez. s8°. 1926

Le Gallienne (Richard). The romantic '90s. 8°. 1926

Le Gallo (Emile). Les Cents-jours. 8°. 1924

Legard, *The family of, see* LEGARD (*Col. Sir* J. D.) The Legards of Anlaby & Ganton, 1926.

Legard (*Col. Sir* **James Digby**). The Legards of Anlaby & Ganton: th. neighbours &c. la8°. 1926

*__Legatio__ Romam M.L. &c., 1688, *see* SFONDRATI (*il card.* C.)

Legazpi (Miguel López de), *see* LÓPEZ DE LEGAZPI (M.)

*__Legend (The)__ of Maandoo, 2nd ed., 1893, *see* ABBOTT (*Col.* J.)

Legenden. Nachträge zu d. L., 1879–88, *see* HORSTMANN (C.)

Legendre (A. F.) La civilis. chinoise mod. 8°. 1926

Legendre (Maurice). Las Jurdes: ét. de géographie humaine. [Bibl. de l'Ecole des H. E. Hisp., fasc. 13]. 8°. Bordeaux. 1927

*__Legends__ of the Dunbars &c., 1854, *see* MASSON (P. A.)

Léger (Charles). Ève de Balzac d'ap. des docs. inéd. 8°. 1926

Léger (Jean). Algem. Gesch. d. Waldenser, oder d. evang. Kirchen in d. Thälern v. Piemont. Übers. v. H. F. Frhrn. v. Schweinitz. Mit e. Vorrede v. S. J. Baumgartens. 2 Bücher *in* 1v. s4°. Breslau. 1750

Leger (Louis), *prof. au Collège de France.*
Les anc. civilis. slaves. [Coll. Payot]. s8°. 1921
La mythologie slave. 8°. 1901
Prague. [Villes d'art célèb.] la8°. 1907

Leges. Leges eccl. regni Hungariae & provinciarum adjac., 3t, 1785–1827, *see* BATTHYAN (I. DE), *ed.*
Leges Francorum Salicae & Ripuar., 1720, *see* ECKHART (J. G. v.)

Legg (Leopold G. Wickham). Matthew Prior: his public career & corr. 8°. C. 1921
see BRITISH. Brit. diplom. instructions, 1689–1789, v2, 4, ed. L., 1925–27.

Legge (*Miss* **Helen Edith**).
The Divinity School, Oxford: a guide. 8°. O. 1923

Legge (James Granville). The millennium. 8°. O. 1927

Leggett (Bernard). Wireless telegraphy, w. spec. ref. to the quenched-spark system. 8°. 1921

Legh, *The family of, see* NEWTON (EVELYN, *Lady*). Lyme Letters, 1660–1760, 1925.

Legion, *ps.* *Letter to Duke of Richmond, Chairman of Slavery Comm. of H. of Lords, cont. exposure of character of the evidence on the colonial side &c. 8°. [1832]
*Second letter to Duke of Richmond, cont. analysis of anti-slavery evidence &c. [*b. w. h.* Letter, 1832]. 8°. 1833

Légion d'Honneur, *see* PALAIS DE LA LÉGION D'HONNEUR.

Legionnaire 17889, *ps.* *In the Foreign Legion, 1915, *see* ROSEN (E.)

Legislative. *On legislative ignorance. [P2558]. 8°. 1837

Legnano (Giovanni da), *see* COOPLAND (G. W.) Unpubl. work of J. of L.: Somnium of 1372, 1925.

Le Gobien (Charles), *Jesuit.*
Acte de protestation signifié aux Sieurs Syndic, doyen & docteurs de la Fac. de Théol. de Paris, 18 Oct. 1700, par le père Gobien, L. Lecomte, &c. [*no tp.* P2559]. s8°. *n.p.* [c. 1700]

Le Gobien (Charles), *Jesuit* [*continued*].
*Censure de quelques propos. des PP. Le Comte & Le G., 1700, *see* LECOMTE (L.)
*Lettre à un docteur de la Faculté de Paris sur les propos. [*advanced by L. Lecomte*] déferées en Sorbonne par M. Priou. [P2559]. s8°. *n.p.* 1600 [*i.e.* 1700]
*Parallele de quelques propos. déferées au S. Siege & à la Sorbonne &c. [*no tp.* P2559]. s8°. *n.p. n.d.* [c. 1701]
*Remarques d'un docteur en théol. sur la protest. des Jésuites; avec une réponse contre la censure de Sorbonne. [*no tp.* P2559]. s8°. *n.p.* [1709]
Réponse aux remarques de M.*** sur la protest. du père le Gobien. [P2559]. s8°. *n.p.* MVCC. [1700]
*Second Parallele des propos. du père Le Comte avec quelques autres propos., adr. à M. le Syndic de la Fac. de Théol. de Paris. [P2559]. s8°. *n.p. n.d.*
see ALEXANDRE (N.) *Apol. d. Dominicains; rép. à l'éclairc. du p. Le G., 1699.
„ PARIS: UNIVERSITY. *Réflexions s. la censure de la Fac. de Théol., contre Hist. de l'édit de l'emp. de la Chine [*by C. Le G.*] &c., 1700.

Le Goff (Marcel). A. France à La Béchellerie: propos & souv., 1914–24, avec doc. inéd. s8°. 1924

Le Goffic (Charles Henri). L'âme bretonne. s4. s8°. 1924
L'illustre Bobinet. s8°. [1922]
Poésies complètes, 1889–1914. s8°. [1922]
see AUDIAT (G.) C. Le G., 1922.

Legouis (Emile).
Bacchic elem. in Shakespeare's plays. [Brit. Acad. Ann. Sh. lect. 1926. P2833]. 8°. [1926]
Dans les sentiers de la renaiss. anglaise. s8°. 1925
Edmund Spenser. s8°. 1923
G. C. de Beaurieu & s. élève de la nature, 1763. Taylorian Lect., 1925. 8°. O. 1925
Spenser. [Lect.] s8°. London. 1926
William Wordsworth & Annette Vallon. s8°. 1922
Wordsworth in a new light. 8°. Camb., *Harvard.* 1923

—— **& L. Cazamian.** Hist. de la litt. anglaise. 8°. 1924
Hist. of Eng. lit. Tr. H. D. Irvine [*&* (v2) W. D. MacInnes]. 2v. 8°. 1926–27

Legouvé (G. J. B. Ernest W.)
L'art de la lecture. n. éd. rev. &c. s8°. [1897]

Legrain (Georges). Statues & statuettes de rois & de particuliers. [Cat. gén. des antiq. égypt. du Musée du Caire. Service des antiq. de l'Egypte]. 3t *&* Ind. fol. Le Caire. 1906–25

Legrain (Léon). Mission en Susiane: sous la dir. de R. de Mecquenem &c.: empreintes de cachets élamites, par L. L., *see* DÉLÉGATION EN PERSE, t16, 1921.

Le Grand (Antoine), *Philosophical Writer.*
Hist. haeresiarcharum. s8°. Duaci. 1728
Man without passion or the wise stoick (*sic*). Engl. by G. R. s8°. 1675

Legrand (Emile). Bibliographie albanaise, 15e siècle à 1900. Compl. & publ. par H. Gûys. [Œ. posth., N°. 5]. 8°. 1912
Bibliographie hellénique: descr. raisonnée des ouvrages publ. par des Grecs au 18e s. Compl. & publ. par L. Petit & H. Pernot. t1. la8°. 1918
Nouv. dict. grec moderne-français. s8°. [1882]

Legrand (Louis), *Sulpicien.* Notiones prævia de natura, auctore & antiq. eccl. [Tract. de eccl., diss. 1], *see* MIGNE (J. P.), *ed.* Theol. cursus, t4, 1859.
Tract. de Incarnatione Verbi divini, *see* MIGNE (J. P.), *ed.* Theol. cursus, t9, 1841.

Legrand (Philippe E.) La poésie alexandrine. s8°. 1924

Le Gras (Joseph). Casanova, adventurer & lover. Tr. A. F. Steuart. 8°. [1923]

Le Gras (N.) Véritable disc. d'un logement de gens-d'armes, Ham [1654]; O. Thorel &c., *see* SOC. DES ANTIQ. DE PICARDIE. Mém., s4, t8, 1916.

Legré (Ludovic). La botanique en Provence au 16e s. [4p *in* 3v]. 8°. Marseille. 1899–1901
Hugues de Solier, 1899.
L. Anguillara—P. Belon—C. de l'Escluse—A. Constantin, 1901. [*b. w.* L. Rauwolff].
L. Rauwolff—J. Raynaudet, 1900.
P. Pena & M. de Lobel, 1899.
La botanique en Provence au 18e s.—Pierre Forskal et le Florula Estaciensis. [*b. w. h.* La botanique &c.: H. de Solier, 1899]. 8°. Marseille. 1900
L'indigénat en Provence du Styrax officinal—Pierre Pena et Fabri de Peiresc. [*b. w. h.* La botan. en Prov.: P. Pena &c., 1899]. 8°. Marseille. 1901

Legros (Alphonse). Cat. of paintings &c. by A. L. (1837–1911), f. coll. of F. E. Bliss. Apprec., by C. Ricketts. Pref. to etchings, by C. Dodgson. la8°. 1922

Legros (G. V.)
La vie J. H. Fabre. Préf. de J. H. F. 2e éd. s8°. 1919
„ „ suivie du répertoire gén. analyt. des Souv. entomolog. Préf. de J. H. F. la8°. 1924

Legros (Lucien A.) Economy of human effort in rel. to indust. fatigue. [P2833]. 8°. 1926
Skill—in relation to production. Address. [P2784]. 8°. [1925]
Technical & non-techn. management. [P2873]. 8°. [1927]
—— **& H. C. Weston.** Design of machinery in rel. to the operator, *see* INDUST. FATIGUE RES. BD. Rep. 36, 1926.

Le Guennec (Louis). Notice s. la commune de Plougonven (Finistère). s8°. Morlaix. [1922]

Leguina y Vidal (Enrique de), *baron de la Vega de Hoz.* Glosario de voces de armería. 8°. 1912

Leguizamón (Martiniano), *see* URQUIZA (J. J. DE). U., el juicio de la posteridad [*comp. by L.*], 2p, 1921.

Lehfeldt (Robert Alfred), *D.Sc.* Money. s8°. 1926

Lehmann (Carl). Junge deutsche Dramatiker. 8°. L. 1923
Ludendorffs Schuld an d. milit. Katastrophe. [P2426]. 8°. L. 1920
Vom Drama uns. Zeit. ; n. Folge. 8°. L. 1924

Lehmann (Christoph) [LEHMANNUS]. Florilegium politic. auct. Das ist : Ernewerter polit. Blumen-garten, &c. s8°. Franckfurt. 1640

Lehmann (*Dr.* Edvard), *see* CHANTEPIE DE LA SAUSSAYE (P. D.) Lehrbuch d. Religionsgesch., 4e A., hrsg. A. Bertholet u. E. L., 2B, 1925.

Lehmann (Johann Georg). Gesch. d. Herzogthums Zweibrücken &c. 8°. München. 1867

Lehmann (Johann Jacob). Oratio de Scylla morali. Acc. diss. de fructibus ex repurgata per Lutherum relig. [P484]. s4°. Jenae. 1717

Lehmann (Oskar). Die tachygraph. Abkürzungen d. griech. Hss. [*b. w. a. c. of* Gardthausen (V.) Griech. Palaeog., 1879]. 8°. L. 1880

Lehmann (Paul).
Works in KÖNIGL. AKAD. D. WISS. ZU MÜNCHEN. Phil. Kl., Sitz.
Aufgaben u. Anregungen d. lat. Philol. d. M.-a. [1918.]
Ein Bücherverzeichnis d. Dombibl. v. Chur, 1457. [1920.]
Corveyer Studien. [1920.]
Fuldaer Studien, 2F. [1925, 1927.]
Holländ. Reisefruchte, 1–3. [1920.]
Mittelalt. Hss. d. K.B. Nationalmuseums zu München. [1916.]
Mittelalt. Verse in Distinctiones monast. & morales v. Anf. d. 13. Jhdts. [1922.]
Wert u. Echtheit e. Beda abgesproch. Schrift. [1919.]
Franciscus Modius als Handschriftenforscher. 8°. München. 1908
Joh. Sichardus u. d. v. ihm benutzt. Bibl. u. Hss. 8°. München. 1911
Die Parodie im Mittelalter. 8°. München. 1922
Parodistische Texte : Beispiele z. latein. Parodie im M.-a. Hrsg. P. L. 8°. München. 1923
Pseudo-ant. Lit. des M.-A. [Anh., Pyramus—&c. Dicht. d. Matthaeus v. Vendôme &c., Heroiden d. Baudri de Bourgueil]. la8°. L. 1927
Vom M.-A. u. v. d. latein. Philol. d. M.-A. 8°. München. 1914

Lehmann (Rosamond). Dusty answer. s8°. 1927

Lehmann (Walter). Altmexikan. Kunstgesch. la8°. 1922
Kunstgesch. d. alten Peru. Von W. L. unter Mitarbeit v. H. Doering. 4°. 1924
Vokabular d. Rama-Sprache nebst gramm. Abriss, 1914, *see* KÖNIGL. AKAD. D. W. ZU MÜNCHEN. Abhdlgn., B28, 1917.

Lehmann-Hartleben (Carl). Die ant. Hafenanlagen d. Mittelmeeres. [Klio, Beiheft 14]. la8°. L. 1923

Lehmann-Haupt (Carl F.) [*ps.* C. F. LEHMANN]. Armenien einst u. jetzt. Reisen &c. B1, 2i. la8°. 1910–26
Armenien u. Nordmesopotamien. [Vortrag. P2810]. 8°. [1900]
Der Krieg u. d. Deutschtum im Auslande, *see* DEUTSCHE Reden in schwerer Zeit, 28, 1915.
Šamaššumukîn, König v. Babylonien, 668–648 v. Chr. Inschriftl. Material ; hrsg., übers. u. erl. v. C. F. L. [*3 pagin.* Originaltexte, *lithogr.*] 4°. L. 1892

Lehner (Alfons). Tafeln z. Bestimmen d. Mineralien auf chem. Wege &c. s8°. 1921

Lehnert (Maximilian). Robinsonaden. Sammlung v. Abenteurergesch. früh. Jhdte. Bearbt. u. hrsg. v. M. L. 5B [*in* 4v. 2, 3 *in* 1]. s8°. Charlottenburg. [1916–20]
1, Der deut. Robinson. 2, 3, Die ostfriesländ. Robinsonin. 4, Der kurländ. Robinson u. d. venetian. Robinsonin sowie d. niedersäch. Robinson. 5, Der böhm. Robinson sowie d. holländ. Robinson.

Lehr (Henry). Les Protestants d'autrefois. Sur mer & outre mer. 8°. 1907

Lehrberg (Aron Christian) [Лербергъ].
Изслѣдованія, служащіе къ объясненію древней русской исторіи. Изд. на нѣмецкомъ языкѣ по опредѣленію И. Акад. Наукъ. Перевелъ Д. Языковъ. 4°. С.–П. 1819

Lehrbuch. *Lehrbuch d. Brandenb.-Preuss. Gesch., 1825, *see* BRANDENBURG.
Lehrbuch d. Philosophie, 2B, 1925, *see* DESSOIR (M.), *ed.*

Lehrs (Max). Holzschnitte d. erst. Hälfe d. 15. Jhdts. im Kön. Kupferstichkabinett zu Berlin. 22 Tafeln. Hrsg. M. L. [Graph. Gesellschaft, 7]. fol. 1908
Katalog d. Kupferstiche M. Schongauers. [Sonderausg. d. " Gesch. &c. Kat. d. Deut. &c. Kupferstichs im 15. Jhdt.," B5]. 4°. Wien. 1925

Leib (Bernard). Rome, Kiev & Byzance. Rapports relig. des Latins & des Gréco-Russes, sous le pontif. d'Urbain II, 1088–99. la8°. 1924

Leib (Johann) [LEIBIUS]. Jubilæum catholicum, sive narr. de statu relig. temp. Caroli V. [P483]. s4°. Norimbergae. 1618

Leibnitz (Gottfried Wilhelm, *Frhr.* **v.)**
WORKS.
Sämtl. Schriften u. Briefe. Hrsg. v. d. Preuss. Akad. d. Wiss. Reihe 1, B1, 2. Reihe 2, B1. 4°. Darmstadt. 1923–27
Reihe 1, Allg. polit. u. histor. Briefwechsel, B1, 2, 1668–79.
Reihe 2, Philos. Briefwechsel, B1, 1663–85.
Collectanea etymologica, illust. ling. vet. Celt., Germ., Gallicae &c. Cum pref. J. G. Eccardi. 2p *in* 1v. s8°. Hanoverae. 1717
Defensio Trinitatis—2 epist. ad Loeflerum, de Trinitate &c.—Remarques sur le livre d'un Antitrinitaire anglais &c., *see* MIGNE (J. P.), *ed.* Theol. cursus, t8, 1860.
Epistolarum pentas una cum totidem responsionibus S. Clarckii &c. Notis illust. N. Engelhard. [N. E. otium]. s8°. Groningae. 1740
Otium Hanoveranum sive Misc. ex ore & schedis L. cum rebus ad hist. Brunsvic. pertin. operam navaret J. F. Fellerus. Add. Epist. Gallicae amoebeæ L. & Pelissonii de tolerantia &c. Praem. suppl. vitae L. [J. F. Felleri]. [*b. w. h.* Collect. etym. &c., 1717]. s8°. Lipsiae. 1718
TRANSLATIONS.
The early mathematical MSS. of L. Tr., w. crit. & hist. notes by J. M. Child. [*& 2 essays by* C. I. Gerhardt]. 8°. Chicago. 1920
see CANZ (I. G.) Philos. L. &c. usus in theol., 2t, 1739.
„ DILTHEY (W.) Gesammelte Schr., B3, L. u. s. Zeitalter &c., 1927.
„ GRÄVEN (H.) L.'s Bildnisse, 1916.
„ JORDAN (G. J.) Reunion of the churches : L. & h. gt. attempt, 1927.
„ LOEWE (V.) Ein Diplomat &c., E. Spanheim, 1629–1710 : mit Anhang : Aus d. Briefwechsel zw. S. u. L., 1924.
„ SCHMALENBACH (H.) L., 1921.
„ SINICA. Noviss. Sinica hist. nostri temporis illust. ; ed. G. G. L., 1699.

Leicester.
Index to wills &c. proved in Archdeaconry Court of L., 1660-1750 &c. ; transcr. &c. H. Hartopp, 1920, *see* BRIT. REC. SOC., Ind. Lib., v50, 1920.
The old Town Hall Library of L. Cat. &c. comp. by C. Deedes, J. E. Stocks [&] J. L. Stocks. s4°. O. 1919
Records of the borough of L. : extr. f. archives of the Corp., 1603–88. Ed. H. Stocks, w. assist. of W. H. Stevenson. 8°. C. 1923
Register of the Freemen of L., 1196–1770, incl. apprentices sworn, 1646–1770. Abstr. f. the Borough Records & ed. by H. Hartopp. [Records of the Borough of L., N.S., v1]. 8°. Leicester. 1927

Leicester Fields, *London.* Registers of the churches of the Tabernacle, Glasshouse Street & Leicester Fields, 1688–1783. Ed. W. & S. Minet. [Huguenot Soc. of London, v29]. 4°. Frome. 1926

Leicester (*Sir* Peter), *bart., d. 1678* [LEYCESTER]. Hist. antiq., in 2 bks. The first treating of Gt.-Brit. & Ireland, the 2nd cont. remarks conc. Cheshire. Annexed, transcr. of Domesday-book conc. Cheshire. fol. 1673

Leicht (Pier Silverio). Breve storia del Friuli. s8°. Udine. 1923
Elementi rom. nella costituz. longobarda, *see* ARCHIVIO STOR. ITAL. Anno 81, 1925.
Romani e germani in un giuramento carolingio, *see* ARCHIVIO STOR. ITAL., Anno 85, v1, 1927.
see FRIULANO. Parlamento Friulano : p. c. di P. S. L., v1 (1228–1429), p1, 1917.

Leichtentritt (Hugo). Händel. 8°. St. 1924

Leidinger (Georg). Bernardus Noricus, *see* KÖNIGL. AKAD. D. W. ZU MÜNCHEN. Phil. Kl. Sitz., 1917.
Unters. z. Passauer Geschichtschreibung d. M-a., *see* KÖNIGL. AKAD. D. W. ZU MÜNCHEN. Phil. Kl. Sitz., 1915.

Leidinger (Georg) [*continued*].
see BAIERN. Bayer. Chroniken des 14. Jhdts.; hrsg. G. L., 1918.
„ MÜNCHEN. Miniaturen aus Hss. d. Kgl. Hof- u. Staats-bibl. in M.; hrsg. G. L., H3–8, 1913–24.

Leigh (Edward), *M.A. of Magdalen Hall, Oxford.* Annot. upon all the New Test. &c. fol. 1650
Select. obs. conc. the Roman & Greek Emperors. The first 18 by E. L.; the others by Henry Leigh. Also French proverbs. 3rd ed. corr. s8°. 1670
Three diatribes. 1, of travel. 2, of money. 3, of measuring distance. s8°. 1671

Leigh (Gertrude). *Guide to Winchelsea. [*Signed* G. A. L. P2877]. s8°. 1927
*Story of Winchelsea church. [*Signed* G. A. L. P2877]. [3rd ed.] 8°. [1927]

Leigh (Henry), *see* LEIGH (E.) Select obs. conc. the Roman &c. emp., 1670.

Leigh (*Rev. the Hon.* **James Wentworth),** *D.D., dean of Hereford.* Other days. Pref. by O. Wister. 8°. [1921]

Leigh (Mary Augusta Austen-), *see* AUSTEN-LEIGH (M. A.)

Leigh (P. Brady). *The law student's guide; Inns of Court &c. 8°. 1827

Leigh (Richard Arthur Austen-), *see* ETON COLLEGE. Register, 1698–1790, ed. R. A. A. L., 2v, 1921–27.

Leigh-Bennett (Ernest).
Handbook of the early Christian Fathers. 8°. 1920

Leighton House. [*Account of*]. [P2702]. 4°. [c. 1917]

Leighton (Alexander). The court of Cacus, or the story of Burke & Hare. 2nd ed. s8°. 1861

Leighton (Frederic Leighton, *baron***),** *see* RHYS (E.) F., Ld. L., h. life & work, 3rd ed., repr., 1900.

Leighton (J. & J.), *booksellers.* Cat. of books &c. offered for sale by J. & J. L. n.s. Nos. 3–6 *in* 1v. 8°. *n.d.*

Leighton (Joseph Alexander).
Typical modern conceptions of God. s8°. 1901

Leighton (Marie Connor). The silent clue. s8°. 1921

Leighton (Rachel), *see* WILLIAMS WYNN (C., *Lady*). Corr. of Lady W. W. & h. 3 sons, 1795–1832; ed. R. L., 1920.

Leighton (Robert), *(1) bp. of Dumblane, (2) abp. of Glasgow, 1611–84, see* MURRAY (T.) Life of R. L., 1828.

Leighton (Robert). The complete book of the dog. 8°. 1922

Leijonhufvud (Sigrid). Trå kvinnoöden från Karolinska tiden (Brigitta Scherzenfeldt, 1684–1736—Lovisa v. Burghausen, 1697–1733). 8°. [Stockholm. 1907]

Leimbach (Carl L.), *ed.* Die deutschen Dichter d. Neuzeit u. Gegenwart. B10, Lief. 1, 2. [*no more publ.*] 8°. L. [1906–09]

Leinster. L. east & west; [*by var. wr.*], 1922, *see* FLETCHER (G.), *ed.*

Leinster (Edward Fitzgerald, *7th duke of***).** Cat. of old French & Eng. furniture &c. of L. &c. Auct. by Christie &c., May 13, 1926. [Illust. P2859]. 8°. 1926
Cat. of old masters sold by orders of trustees &c. Auct. by Christie &c., May 14, 1926. [Illust.] 8°. 1926

Leip (Hans). Godekes Knecht. Roman. s8°. L. 1925

Leiper (Robert Thompson) & E. L. Atkinson. Parasitic worms, *see* BRIT. ANTARCTIC EXPED., 1910–13. Zoology, v2, 1914–20.

Leipoldt (Johannes). Jesus u. die Frauen. Bilder aus d. Sitten-gesch. d. alt. Welt. 8°. L. 1921

Leipzig.
Cat. of Brit. sec. of Internat. Exhib. of Book Industry &c., *see* EXHIBITIONS.
*Kurtze Nachricht v. d. Stadt L., u. absonderlich v. d. Univ. s8°. [Halle ?. 1709 ?]
Stadt (Der) L. Fewerordnung, Vernewert Anno 1568, *see* FREYTAG (G.) Bilder, B4, 1925.
UNIVERSITY.
*Endlicher Bericht u. Erklerung d. Theologen beider Univ. L. u. Wittemberg. Auch d. superint. d. Kirchen in d. Churfürsten zu Sachsen Landen belangend die Lere &c. Mit Christl. Erinnerung &c. v. d. streittigen Artickeln so Flacius Illyr. &c. s4°. Wittemberg. 1570
Fragstück u. Antwort, oder erklerung d. Theologen in d. 3 Univ. zu L., Wittenberg u. Jhena. Von d. Wittembergischen Grundfest, Newen Catechismo, Exegesi, Dressnischen Consens &c. s4°. Dresden. 1581
Herrn (Der) Theologen in d. 3 löbl. Univ. L., Wittemberg u. Ihena bestendiger wahrhafft. Bericht aus was ursachen die Prediger zu Zerbst, biszhero d. Christl. Werck d. Concordien &c. entgegen gesetzt haben. [P2437]. s4°. *n.p.* 1586
Progr. publ. Acad. Lips. de inst. Jubileo Evang. eccl. Saxonicae &c. [P483]. s4°. [Lipsiae]. 1617
Theolog. (Der) Facultät Informat v. Pietismo. Eingeholet v. L.S.P.K. [P2630]. s8°. Franckfurt. 1711

Leipzig Disputation, 1519, *see* ECK (J. v.) Authent. Text d. L. D. (1519); hrsg. Seitz, 1903.

Leischner (Carl Ferdinand).
Taschenbuch z. Selbsterlernung d. Reitkunst. s8°. L. 1826

Leisentrit (Johann). Catholicum hymnologium Germanicum orthodoxae vereque Apostolicæ eccl. Rev., auctum & elab. a J. L. *Germ.* 2T. [T2 *has title* Das ander T. Christl. cathol. Gesengen]. s8°. Budissin [Buntzen]. 1584

Leiser (Polycarp), *see* LEYSER (P.)

Leiser (Walter). Die Juden im Heer. [P2484]. 8°. 1919

Leitch (Cecil). Golf simplified. s8°. [1924]

Leites (K.) Recent econ. develop. in Russia. Ed. H. Westergaard. [C.E. for Int. Peace]. 8°. O. 1922

Leith (Charles Kenneth).
Economic aspects of geology. 8°. 1922
The Mesabi iron-bearing district of Minnesota. [U.S. Geolog. Survey Monograph, 43]. 4°. Wash. 1903
see VAN HISE (C. R.) & C. K. L. Geology of Lake Superior region, 1911.
„ —— & —— Pre-Cambrian geology of North Amer., 1909.

Leitschuh (Franz Friedrich), *b. 1865.* Bamberg. s8°. L. 1914

Leitzmann (Albert), *see* BEETHOVEN (L. v.) Berichte d. Zeitgenossen, Briefe &c.; gesamm. &c. v. A. L., 2B, 1921.

Le-Ke. Il Li-ki o istituzioni &c. d. Cina ant. Tr., com. e note di C. Puini. la8°. Firenze. 1883
Tre capitoli del "Li-Ki" conc. la relig. Tr., comm. e note [di] C. Puini. la8°. Firenze. 1886

Le Laboureur (Jean). Hist. &c. du voyage de la royne de Pologne [Marie de Gonzague], & du retour de Mme. la mareschalle de Guébriant, par la Hongrie &c. Avec discours. 3p [*in* 1v. *sep. pagin.*] 8°. 1648

Le Laé (Claude-Marie), *1745–91.* La vie & les œuvres comiques de C-M. Le Laé. [*Ed.*] G. Esnault. [t1]. 8°. 1921

Leland (Charles Godfrey).
Drawing & designing. 4th ed. 8°. 1904
Leather work: pract. manual. 8°. 1892
Manual of wood carving. Rev. J. J. Holtzapffel. 8°. 1890
„ „ ....3rd ed. 8°. 1894
The minor arts. s8°. 1880

Leland (John), *the antiquary.* The assertion of King Arthure; tr. by R. Robinson f. L.'s Assertio inclytissimi Arturii, w. Lat. orig.; ed. &c. W. E. Mead, *see* MIDDLETON (C.) Famous hist. of Chinon of England &c., 1925.
Itinerary. Publ. by T. Hearne. Pref. L.'s New-Year's gift. Subj. disc. conc. antiq. found in Yorks. &c. 3rd ed. 9v. 8°. O. 1768–69

Leland (Waldo Gifford) & N. D. Mereness. Intr. to Amer. offic. sources for econ. &c. hist. of World War. [C.E. for Int. Peace]. la8°. New Haven, Conn. 1926
see VAN TYNE (C. H.) & W. G. L. Guide to archives of govt. of U.S. in Washington, 2nd ed., 1907.

Lelandais (Pierre). Ces honnêtes gens, *see* ŒUVRES libres, 80, 1928.

Lelarge (André). Paul Louis Courier, Parisien. 8°. 1925

Leleux (Charles). Le poison à travers les âges. Les empoisonneurs. s8°. 1923

Lelewel (Joachim). Essai hist. sur la législ. polon., 930–1430, *see* MALTE-BRUN (C.) Tableau, 1830.
Hist. de la Lithuanie & de la Ruthénie j. 1569. Tr. E. Rykaczewski. 8°. 1861

Lelewer (Georg), *see* EXNER (F.) Krieg u. Kriminalität in Österreich; Beitr. ü. d. Kriminalität d. Militärpersonen, v. G. L., 1927.

Lelièvre (Matthieu). The Alpine missionary or life of J. L. Rostan. Tr. by A. J. French. s8°. 1869
Hist. du Méthodisme dans les Iles de la Manche. s8°. 1885

Leliwa (*Graf***)** [LELIV].
Русско-польскія отношенія. 8°. Лейпцигъ. 1895

Le Long (Isaac). Boek-Zaal d. Nederduitsche Bybels &c. 2de. Uitg. 2p *in* 1v. [*pagin. cont.*] s4°. Hoorn. 1764

Le Long (Jacques). *Discours histor. sur les princ. éditions des Bibles polyglottes. Par l'auteur de la Bibl. Sacrae. s8°. 1713

Lelong (Jean). La vie & les œuvres de Loyseau. la8°. 1909

Le Long (Jean), *d'Ypres, see* JEAN, *d'Ypres.*

Lely (*Sir* **Frederic Styles Philpin).** Suggestions for the better governing of India. s8°. 1906

Lély (Gilbert). Chefs-d'œuvre des poètes galants du 18e s. Préf. de G. La Flize. s8°. 1921

Lely (*Sir* **Peter),** *see* BAKER (C. H. C.) L. & Kneller, 1922.

Lély (Pierre). La guirlande. Poèmes. s8°. *n.d.*

Lema (*Marqués* **de).** Spain since 1815. Lect. s8°. C. 1921

Le Maire (Nicolas). Sanctuarium profanis occlusum, sive de SS. Bibliorum prohibitione in lingua vulgari tractatus. Lat. prodit. s4°. Herbipoli. 1662

Lemaistre (J. G.)
*Rough sketch of mod. Paris: letters, 1801–02. 8°. 1803

Le Maistre de Sacy (Isaac Louis). *Les enluminures du fameux almanach des PP. Jésuites, La déroute &c. des Jansenistes; ou Triomphe de Molina Jésuite sur S. Augustin [*by L. I. Le M. de S.*] Avec L'onguant pour la brûlure ou Le secret d'empescher aux Jésuites de brûler des livres [*by J. Barbier d' Aucour*] & Réponse touch. les règles de la conduite des Saints Pères dans la composition de leurs ouvrages [*by A. Arnauld*]. [*w. sep. pagin*]. s8°. Liège. 1683

Lemaître (Frédérick), *see* SILVAIN (E.) F. L., 1926.

Lemaitre (Jules).
Literary impressions. Tr. A. W. Evans. s8°. 1921
Un salon, pièce, *see* ŒUVRES libres, 33, 1924.
see BORDEAUX (H.) J. L., 1920.
,, MORICE (*l'abbé* H.) J. L., 1924.

Le Mans [†MANS]. Cartul. de l'évèché du Mans, 965–1786. Publ. par le comte Bertrand de Broussillon &c. [Soc. des Archives Hist. du Maine]. 8°. au Mans. 1908
Cartul. du Chapitre Royal de Saint-Pierre-de-la-Cour, du Mans. Publ. par le vte. Menjot d'Elbenne & L. J. Denis. [*&* Introd. *w. tp.* Le Chapitre Royal &c., 1910. Soc. des Archives Hist. du Maine]. 8°. au Mans. 1903–10
Chartularium abbatiæ S. Vincentii Cenoman. Liber primus. [*no tp.*] 4°. *n.p.* [1886]

Le Marchant (*Sir* **Denis).**
Mem. of Maj.-Gen. Le Marchant. *f.p.c.* 8°. 1841

Le Marchant (*Maj.-Gen.* **John Gaspard),** *see* LE MARCHANT (D.) Mem. of J. G. Le M., 1841.

Le Masson (Alexandre). Venise en 1848 & 1849. 8°. 1851

Lemcke (Johannes). Vincent Placcius u. s. Bedeut. f. d. Anon. u. Pseudon.-Bibliog. la8°. Hamburg. 1925

Lemcker (Heinrich Christian). Exercit. de corporis doct. Julii & Formulae Concordiae convenientia. [P2643]. s4°. Helmstadii. [1726]

Lemego (Jan van) [LEMMEGE (JAN VAN); JOHANNES DE LEMMEGE]. Kroniek, *see* BENNINGE (S.) Kroniek, 1e & 2e deel (Kroniek Jan van L.); uitg. &c. J. A. Feith, 1887.

Le Mercier d'Erm (Camille). Les hymnes nat. des peuples celt. Publ. avec tr. par Le M. d'E. 3e éd. s8°. Dinard. 1920

Lémery (Hélène).
La voie passionnée. Avant-dire de P. Claudel. s8°. [1925]

Le Mesurier, *the family of, see* LE MESURIER (T. A.) Short mem. (1899), 1925.

Le Mesurier (L.) Common-sense economics. s8°. 1922

Le Mesurier (Thomas Augustus). Short mem. of the Le Mesurier family, 1899. [Repr. P2786]. 8°. [Gloucester, Mass. 1925]

Le Metel de Bois-Robert (François), *1592–1662*. La belle invisible: tragi-comédie (1656), *see* FOURNEL (V.) Contemp. de Molière, t1, 1863.
Epistres en vers. Ed. crit. avec comm. &c. par M. Cauchie. [Soc. des Textes Franç. Mod.] t1. s8°. 1921
see MAGNE (E.) Le plaisant Abbé de B., 1592–1662, 2e éd., 1909.

Lemeur (J.), *see* HABERT (L.), J. L. &c. Consultation, 1717.

Lemierre (Georges), *see* THÉVENIN (L.) & G. L. Les étapes d'un livre, 1922.

Le Mire (Aubert) [A. MIRAEUS]. Bibl. eccl. sive nomenclatores VII veteres. S. Hieronymus, Gennadius Massil., Ildefonsus Tolet., Sigebertus Gemblac., S. Isidorus Hispal., Honorius Augustod., Henricus Gandav. A. M. illust. [Pars altera, 1494 ad usque temp. nostra; A. vanden Eede publ.] 2p *in* 1v. fol. Antverpiae. 1639–49

Lemke (Mikhail). 250 дней въ царской ставкѣ (25 Сент. 1915–2 Іюля 1916). 8°. Петербургъ. 1920

Lemm (Oscar v.) Aegypt. Lesestücke m. Schrifttafel u. Glossar. T1 [*no more publ.*] la8°. L. 1883

Lemmege (Jan van), *see* LEMEGO (J. v.)

Lemmens (Leonardo), *ed.* Acta S. Congreg. de Propaganda Fide pro Terra Sancta, p1, 2, 1622–1847, *see* GOLUBOVICH (G.) Bibl. bio-bibliog., n.s., t1, 2, 1921–22.

Lemmi (Francesco). Diplomatici Sardi (1789–96), *see* REGIA DEPUT. Miscellanea, t50, 1922.
Il Risorgimenti. [Guide bibliograf.] s8°. 1926

Lemmi (Francesco) [*continued*].
La rivol. piemontese, 1821: nuovi doc. a cura di F. L. &c., *see* REGIA DEPUT. S. GLI STUDI DI STORIA PATRIA &C. Bibl., v11, 1923.
see FIORINI (V.) & F. L. Periodo Napoleonico, 1799–1814, *n.d.*

Lemoine (Angélina), *b. 1843*, *see* BOUCHARDON (P.) A. L. & sa mère, 1928.

Lemoine (Jean). Madame de Sévigné, sa famille & s. amis, d'ap. des docs. inéd. [t]1. 8°. [1926]

Lemoisne (Paul André). Les soirées du Louvre: aquarelles d'E. Giraud, *see* SOC. DE L'HIST. DE L'ART FRANÇ. Bull. 1920.
see DUPLESSIS (G.) &c. Cat. de la coll. des portraits franç. &c. conserv. au Dépt. des Estampes de la Bibl. Nat., t6, commencé par G. D., cont. par P. A. L., 1907.
,, LOUVRE. La peinture, école franç., 14–16s., par P. A. L., 1927.

Lemon (Mark), *see* DICKENS (C.) Unpubl. letters to M. L., 1927.

Lemonnier (Camille).
Le bestiaire. s8°. 1893
C'était l'été. . . . s8°. 1900
Claudine Lamour. n. éd. s8°. 1903
Comme va le ruisseau. 3e éd. s8°. 1903
L'hallali. s8°. [1906]
Les peintres de la vie. s8°. 1888
Poupées d'amour. 3e éd. s8°. 1903
Thérèse Monique. s8°. 1882
see DES OMBIAUX (M.) Prem. romanciers nationaux de Belgique, L. &c., 1919.

Lemonnier (Henry), *prof. d'hist. à l'Ecole des Beaux-Arts.* Etude hist. sur la condit. privée des affranchis aux 3 prem. siècles de l'Emp. rom. 8°. 1887
see ACAD. ROYALE D'ARCHITECTURE. Procès-verbaux, 1671–1793; publ. par L., t6–9, 1744–93, 1920–26.

Le Monnier (Joseph).
Guingamp, Avaugoir & Penthièvre. la8°. [Rennes. 1923]

Lemonnier (Léon). L'amour interdit. s8°. [1925]

Lemonnyer (J.) Les journaux de Paris pend. la Commune. Revue bibliog. compl. de la presse paris., 19 mars–27 mai [1871]. 8°. [1871]

Lémonon (Ernest), *see* MÉRIGNHAC (A.) & E. LÉMONON. Le droit des gens & la Guerre de 1914–18, 2t, 1921.

Lemordant (Jean Julien), *see* CHANCEREL (J.) J. J. L., 1920.

Lemos (Thomas de). Acta omnia Congregationum ac Disput. quæ sunt celebratæ in causa &c. de auxiliis divinæ gratiæ. [*Ed.* J. H. Serry ?]. fol. Lovanii. 1702

Le Moy (Arthur). L'Anjou. 8°. 1924

Lemoyne (André). Poésies. 4v. s8°. [1883–97]

L'Empereur (Constantin), *see* MISHNAH. Talumudis Babylon. Cod. Middoth s. de mensuris Templi; opera C. L'E., 1630.

Lempfert (Rudolf Gustav Karl). Meteorology. s8°. [1920]

Le Nain (Antoine), *see* BURLINGTON F.A. CLUB. Illust. cat. of pictures by the brothers Le N., 1910.

Le Nain (Louis). Rapp. s. la vie acad., 1914–18. [Extr. des Bull. de l'Acad. roy. de Belgique]. [P2818]. 8°. Brux. 1919
Rapp. s. l'état du Palais des Acad. ap. le départ des Allemands. [P2818]. 8°. Brux. 1919

Le Nain (Louis), *painter, 1593–1648*, *see* BURLINGTON F.A. CLUB. Illust. cat. of pictures by the brothers Le N., 1910.

Le Nain (Mathieu), *see* BURLINGTON F.A. CLUB. Illust. cat. of pictures by the brothers Le N., 1910.

Le Nain de Tillemont (Louis Sébastien). Eccl. mem. of the six first c., w. a chronolog. table &c. 2v. fol. 1733–35

Lenclos (Ninon de), *see* MAGNE (E.) N. de L., 1925.

Lencqvist (Christian Erich). De superstitione vet. Fennorum &c. s4°. Aboæ. 1782

Lenel (Walter). Die Entstehung d. Vorherrschaft Venedigs an d. Adria, mit Beitr. z. Verfassungsgesch. 8°. Str. 1897
Studien z. Gesch. Paduas u. Veronas im 13. Jhdt. s8°. Str. 1893

Le Nepvou de Carfort (*cte.* **Henri).**
Hist. de Du Guay Troüin, le corsaire. 8°. [1922]

Lenéru (Marie).
Les affranchis. [Pièce]. Préf. de F. Gregh. s8°. 1926
Le bonheur des autres. [Préc. de La Vivante]. Préf. de Mme. J. Balde. s8°. [1925]
Journal. Avec préf. de F. de Curel. 2t. s8°. [1921]
La paix. Préf. de Mme. de Noailles. s8°. 1922
Saint-Just. Préc. d'une intr. de M. Barrès. s8°. 1922

Le Neve (John). Monumenta Anglicana: inscr. on mon. of eminent persons. 5v. 8°. 1717–19
[1], 1700–15. [2], 1650–79. [3], 1680–99. [4], 1600–49. [5], Suppl., 1650–1718.
The vol. are here numbered in order of their appearance; that numbered [1] *was issued as a "specimen."*

Lenfant (Jacques).
Hist. of the Co. of Constance. Tr. 2t. s4º. 1730
Préservatif contre la réunion avec le Siège de Rome : ou apologie contre le livre de Mlle. de B[eaumont] &c. 4t. s8º. Amsterdam. 1723

Lengenbrunner (Johannes). Erinnerung, Was v. M. Luther, s. Lehr &c. zu halten sey. [P2436]. s4º. Ingolstatt. 1576

Lengherand (Georges). Voyage., à Venise, Rome, Jérusalem &c., 1485–86, avec intr. &c. par le Marq. de Godefroy Ménilglaise. [Sóc. d. Bibl. Belges]. la8º. Mons. 1861

Lenglet Du Fresnoy (Nicolas). Chronolog. tables of univ. hist. Tr. 2p. 8º. 1762
A new method of studying hist. Added, Diss. of Sc. Maffei conc. use of inscr. & medals. [Tr.] by R. Rawlinson. 2v. 8º. 1728
v2 *is* A catalogue of principal historians.
see MICHAULT (J. B.) Mém. p. s. à l'hist. de la vie de l'abbé L. du F., 1761.

Lengnich (Gottfried). De Prussorum in August. Conf. meritis oratio. [P2642]. s4º. Gedani. [1730]

Lenin (N.), *ps.* [*i.e.* VLAD. ILICH ULYANOV].
Собрание сочинений. [Под ред. Л. Б. Каменева]. т1–19 [7i, ii, 11i, ii, 12i, ii, 14i, ii]. 8º. Москва. *n.d.*–1925
Собрание сочинений. т4, Искра, 1900–03. 8º. Москва. 1920
*В. И. Ульянов, краткая біографія. [P2455]. s8º. Харьков. 1919
Великий почин. изд. 2ºᵉ. [P2722]. s8º. Москва. 1919
Две речи по внешкольному образованию (Мая 1919). [P2724]. la8º. Москва. 1919
Задачи русск. Соціальдемократовъ. изд. 2ᵉ, съ предислов. [P2716]. s8º. Женева. 1902
Новая эконом. политика, Статьи и речи. 8º. Москва. [1923]
О професс. союзах, о текущем моменте &c. 2ᵉ. изд. [P2698]. 8º. П. 1921
Объ аграрной программѣ Икса. Отвѣтъ. [P2715]. s8º. Женева. 1903
Письмо к рабочим и крестьянам по поводу победы над Колчаком. [P2600]. s8º. Москва. 1919
Письмо къ товарищу о нашихъ задачахъ. [P2716]. s8º. Женева. 1904
Пролетарская революция и ренегат К. Каутский. [P2396]. 8º. С.–П. 1919
Речь на съезде работниц. [P2722]. s8º. Москва. 1919
Речь по работе в деревне. [P2724]. la8º. Москва. 1919
Тезе Ленина о буржоаској демократији &c. [P2455]. s8º. Москва. 1919

TRANSLATIONS.
Aufgaben d. Proletariats in uns. Revolution. [P2569]. 8º. Wien. 1921
Die drohende Katastrophe &c. Uebers v. S. Liebknecht. [P2492]. 8º. Wien. 1920
Die gegenw. Lage Sowjet-Russlands (Rede). [P2570]. s8º. L. 1921
Die grosse Initiative. [P2462]. 8º. 1920
„ „ [P2521]. 8º. Wien. 1920
Der Imperialismus als jüngste Etappe d. Kapitalismus. 8º. Hamburg. 1921
Kundgebungen. [P2495]. 8º. 1920
"Left Wing" Communism, an infantile disorder. s8º. [1920]
Die Lehren d. Revolution. 8º. Wien. 1921

TRANSLATIONS [*continued*].
La lutte pour le pain. [P2392]. s8º. *n.p. n.d.*
La maladie infantile du communisme. s8º. 1920
Materialism & empirio-crit. [Tr. D. Kvitko. Coll. wks., v13]. 8º. 1927
Die nächsten Aufgaben d. Sowjet-Macht. [P2407]. 8º. [1918]
Die Politik d. kommunist. Partei Russlands. [Anh. : Thesen z. Referat &c. P2711]. s8º. L. 1921
Les problèmes présents du pouvoir des soviets. [P2398]. 8º. Genève. [1918]
Die proletar. Revolution u. d. Renegat Kautsky. [P2457]. 8º. Wien. 1919
Die Rote Armee. Das Militärprogr. d. proletar. Revol. v. L.—Die Organis. d. Roten Armee v. T. [P2457]. 8º. [1920]
Speech at the 3rd All-Russia Trade Union Congress. [P2466]. 8º. Moscow. 1920
Die Stellung d. Kommunisten z. mittleren Bauerntum. [P2521]. 8º. Moskau. 1919
La tâche des représentants de la gauche de Zimmerwald &c. [P2398]. 8º. Genève. [1918]
Towards soviets. [P2419]. s8º. [1918 ?]
Das Verhältnis d. Arbeiterklasse z. Bauerntum. [P2570]. s8º. L. 1921
Die Vorbedingungen u. d. Bedeut. d. neu. Politik Sowjet-Russlands. (Üb.d.Naturalsteuer). [P2570]. s8º. L. 1921
Die Wahlen z. konstituier. Versammlung u. d. Diktatur d. Proletariats. [P2462]. 8º. 1920
Die Weltlage u. d. Aufgaben d. Kommunist. Internat. Rede 19 Juli 1920. [P2462]. 8º. 1920
Werden die Bolschewiki die Staatsmacht behaupten ? [P2521]. 8º. Wien. 1921
Will the Bolsheviks maintain power ? s8º. [1922]
Zur Agrarpolitik d. Bolschewki. [P2569]. 8º. Wien. 1921
Zur Frage der Diktatur. [P2521]. 8º. Wien. 1921

REFERENCES.
see BOURDEAU (J.) Tolstoï, L. & la Révol. Russe, 1921.
„ BOX (P. H.) Three master builders, 1925.
„ CHARASCH (A.) Lenin, 1920.

Lenin (N.), *ps.* [*i.e.* VLAD. ILICH ULYANOV] [*continued*].
REFERENCES [*continued*].
see DRAHN (E.) L., e. Bio-Bibliographie, 1924.
„ EASTMAN (M.) Marx, L. & the sci. of revolution, 1926.
„ FARBMAN (M. S.) After L. : new phase in Russia, 1924.
„ FÜLÖP-MILLER (R.) L. & Gandhi ; tr., 1927.
„ GORKY (M.) L. et le paysan russe, 1924.
„ —— V. I. Lénine, 1920.
„ GUILBEAUX (H.) Le portrait de V. I. L., 1924.
„ —— W. I. L. : e. treues Bild s. Wesens ; Übertr., 1923.
„ KERSTEN (C.) N. L., s. Leben u. Werk, 1920.
„ KLYUEV (N. A.) Ленин (*poetry*), 1924.
see MORIZET (A.) Chez L. & Trotski, Moscou 1921, 1922.
„ NOLDE (*Baron* B. E.) L.'s Räte-Republik, 1920.
„ —— Le règne de L., 1920.
„ PLATTEN (F.) Reise L.'s durch Deut. (1917), 1924.
„ SOLSKY (V.) Ленинъ, 1921
„ SOWJETRUSSLAND u Polen Reden v. Kamenev, L &c., 1920.
„ STALIN (J.) Leninism ; tr. 1928.
„ TERNE (A. M.) Въ царств Ленина, 1922.
„ TROTSKY (L.) L. ; tr., 1925
„ ZINOVIEV (G.) Н. Л., 1919
„ —— N. Lénine, 1924.
„ —— Die Wetpartei d Leninismus ; l[tr.], 1924.

Lennep (Jacob van).
De Roos van Dekama. 16ᵉ dr. 8º. Leiden. *n.d*

Lennox, *The family of, see* FRASER (*Sir* W.) The L., 2v, 1874

Lennox (Matthew Stewart, *4th earl of*) ; *1516–71, see* MAHO (*Maj.-Gen.* R. H.) Mary Q. of Scots : st. of the Lenno narr., 1924.

Le Noble (E.) [†LE NOBLE DE TENNELIÈRE (EUSTACHE), *baro de Saint George*]. *L'esprit de Gerson, ou instruction catholiques, touch. le Saint Siége. s8º. Londres. 171

Le Noble (Pierre). *Hist. du père La Chaize, Jesuite &c [Jean danse mieux que Pierre &c., pl, 2]. 2p. s8º. Cologne. 171

Lenormand (Henri René). *Works in* ŒUVRES libres.
Fidelité, nouvelle, 1923. [30
L'homme & ses fantômes, pièce, 1924. [41
Le sacrifice d'Abraham, nouvelle, 1922. [11
Théâtre complet. éd. déf. 5t. s8º. 1921–2
1, Les ratés—Le temps est un songe. 2, Le simoun—I mangeur de rêves. 3, Le dent rouge—Une vie secrèt 4, L'homme & s. fantômes—A l'ombre du mal. 5, Le lâch

Lenormant (François). La divination & la science des pr sages chez les Chaldéens. 8º. 187

Lenôtre (André) [LE NOSTRE], *see* GUIFFREY (J. J.) A. Le N. ét crit., 1912.

Lenotre (G.), *ps.* [*i.e.* GOSSELIN (L. L. T.)].
Les agents roy. en France au temps de la Révol. & de l'Empire. L'affaire Perlet. 8º. 1922
Babet l'empoisonneuse . . . ou l'empoisonnée [*i.e.* E. ctsse. de Normont]. s8º. 1927
Le drame de Varennes, juin 1791 ; d'ap. des doc. inéd. & les rel. des témoins oculaires. [38ᵉ éd.] 8º. 1921
La femme sans nom. [Mme. de Douhault]. s8º. 1922
Le Jardin de Picpus. [Pèlerinages de Paris révol.] [12ᵉ éd.] s8º. 1928
Martin le Visionnaire (1816–34). s8º. 1924
La Mirlitantouille : épisodes de la Chouannerie bretonne. [5ᵉ éd.] 8º. 1925
Monsieur Charette, le roi de Vendée. 8º. [1924]
Le mysticisme révol. Rob spierre & la " Mère de Dieu 8º. 192
Paris révolutionnaire. n. éd. 8º. 19
Paris révolutionnaire : vieil maisons, vieux papiers. [3ᵉ éd.] s5. s8º. 19
La proscription des Girondins s8º. [192
Le roi Louis XVII & l'énigr du Temple. 8º. 19
TRANSLATIONS.
The Dauphin (Louis XVII the riddle of the Templ [Tr.] F. Lees. 8º. 19
Paris in the Revolution. T by H. N. Williams. 8º. [192
Two Royalist spies of t French Revol. [*i.e.* L. Fauch Borel & C. F. Perlet]. Tr. Miall. 8º. [192
The woman without a na [Mme. de Douhault]. Tr. Ashley. s8º. [192

Le Nourry (Denis Nicolas). Apparatus ad Bibl. max. v patrum, et antiq. script. eccles. 2t. fol. Parisiis. 1703–17

Lenroot (Katherine F.), *see* UNITED STATES : LAB. Illegit. a child-welfare problem, p2, Boston & Mass., by E. Lundberg & K. F. L., 1921.

—— & E. O. Lundberg. Juvenile courts at work, *see* UNIT STATES : LAB. Children's Bur., Publ. 141, 1925.

Lens (A. R. de). Derrière les vieux murs en ruines. Rom marocain. s8º. 19

Lensæus (Joannes). De fidelium animarum purgatorio libri De limbo patrum liber 3ᵘˢ. s8º. Lovanii. 15
De una Christi in terris eccl. libri sex. s8º. Lovanii. 15

Lensky (Z. Stencel-), *see* STENCEL-LENSKY (Z.)

Lents (Robert Emilyanovich). Изслѣдованія въ восточной Персіи и Хератскомъ владѣніи. ч1. [I. Akad. Nauk. Записки, t13]. 8°. С.-П. 1868

Lentz (Wolfgang), *see* WALDSCHMIDT (E.) & W. L. Stellung Jesu im Manichäismus 1926.

Lenygon (Francis). Furniture in England f. 1660 to 1760. [2nd impr.] fol. [1920]

Lenz (Adolf). Der Wirtschaftskampf d. Völker u. s. internat. Regelung. 8°. St. 1920

Lenz (Harald Othmar). Botanik d. alt. Griechen u. Römer, deutsch in Auszüg. aus. d. Schr. nebst Anmerk. 8°. Gotha. 1859
Gemeinnützige Naturgesch. 6. A. bearb. v. O. Burbach. B1–3 [B2, 3, 5. A.]. 8°. Gotha. 1875–84
1, Die Säugetiere. 2, Die Vögel. 3, Die Reptilien, Amphibien, Fische u. wirbellosen Thiere.
Mineralogie d. alt. Griechen u. Römer. [*b. w. h.* Zoologie d. alt. Gr. &c., 1856]. 8°. Gotha. 1861
Zoologie d. alt. Griechen u. Römer, deutsch in Auszügen. nebst Anmerk. 8°. Gotha. 1856

Lenz (Kurt) & W. Fabian. Die Friedensbewegung. 8°. 1922

Lenz (Max). Geschichtsschreib. u. Geschichtsauffass. in Elsass z. Zeit d. Reformation. [Verein f. Ref.-gesch. Schr., Jhrg. 12 (Nr. 49)]. 8°. Halle. 1895
Kleine hist. Schriften. B2, Von Luther zu Bismarck. 8°. München. 1920
König Sigismund u. Heinrich V v. England. [*a. c. in* P2727]. 8°. 1874
Luthers Tat in Worms. [Verein f. Ref.-gesch. Schr., Jhrg. 39 (Nr. 134)]. 8°. L. 1921

Lenzi (Furio). San Domnio, vesc. e martire di Salona, *see* BULLETTINO DI ARCH. &C. DALM., 36, Suppl., 1913.

Leo III, *emp. of the East, the Isaurian.* Manual of later Roman law: the Ecloga ad Procheiron mutata. Founded upon Ecl. of L. III & Constantine V, & Procheiros nomos of Basil I, of Macedonia. Tr. E. H. Freshfield. 8°. C. 1927
Manual of Roman law: the Ecloga. Publ. by Emp. L. III & Constantine V, A.D. 726. [Tr.] E. H. Freshfield. 8°. C. 1926
Rev. man. of Roman law, founded upon the Ecloga. [Tr.] E. H. Freshfield. 8°. C. 1927

Leo VI, *emperor of the East, see* VASILEV (A. A.) Византія и Арабы: Л. VI &c., 867–959, 1902.

Leo, *Hebræus, see* ABRAVANEL (LEON).

Leo I, *pope, "the Great," Saint, see* GRIESBACH (J. J.) Diss. locos theol. ex L. M. sistens, 1768.

Leo III, *pope, see* FABER (J. G.) De Leone III, pontif. Rom., 1748.

Leo X, *pope* [GIOVANNI DE' MEDICI].
Bulla cōtra errores Martini Lutheri et sequacium [Exurge Domine] (1520 *facs.*), *see* FREYTAG (G.) Bilder, B3, T1, 1924.
see DU BOULAY (N.) *Vies des papes Alex. VI & L. X; par D. B., 1751.
,, FERRAJOLI (A.) La congiura dei cardinali contro L. X, 1919.
,, GOBINEAU (*le c.* J. A. DE). La fleur d'or [L. X] &c., 1923.
,, LUTHER (M.) Assertio omnium articul. M. L. per bullam L. X nov. damnatorum, 1521.
,, MAYER (J.) Eccl. papaea Lutheranae reform. patrona; de pontificiis L. X processum adv. Lutherum improb. &c., 1698.
,, MAYER (J. F.) Triga diss., 1, De pontificiis L. X adv. Lutherum &c., 1907.

Leo XI, *pope, see* PASTOR (L. v.) Gesch., B12, 1605–21, 1927.

Leo XII, *pope, see* GUADET (J.) Esquisses s. Pie VII, suiv. d'une not. sur l'élection de L., 1829.

Leo XIII, *pope.* Constit. apost. de prohib. & censura lib. [P2789]. la8°. Romae. 1897
see BONGHI (R.) L. e l'Italia, 1878.
,, CRISPOLTI (C.) & G. AURELI. Politica di L. XIII &c., 1912.
,, STUTZ (U.) Päpstl. Diplom. unter L. XIII, 1925.

Leo (Heinrich). Comment. de carmine vestusto Hibernico in S. Patricii laudem scripta. [*Progr.*] s4°. Halis Saxonum. 1845

Leo (Jacobus Jehuda), *see* JACOB JUDAH ARYEH.

Leo (Ulrich). Studien z. Rutebeuf. Entwicklungsgesch. u. Form d. Renart le Bestourné &c. [Z. f. roman. Phil. Beiheft, 67]. 8°. Halle. 1922

Leodiensia. Testamenta Leod., 1913, *see* TESTAMENTA.

Leodius (Andreas Fabricius). Harmonia Conf. Augustanae, doctrinae Evang. consensum declarans. Adj., Caroli V de eadem Conf. judicium. fol. Coloniae. 1573

Leodius (Hubertus Thomas), *see* THOMAS (H.), *Leodius.*

Leofric Collectar. The L.C. compared w. the Collectar of St. Wulfstan, w. kindred doc. of Exeter & Worcester. Ed. &c. f. papers of E. S. Dewick by W. H. Frere. [Henry Bradshaw Soc., v56]. v2. 4°. 1921

Leon (*Fray* Luis de). Poesías orig. s8°. 1928
see BELL (A. F. G.) L. de L., 1925.
,, FITZMAURICE-KELLY (J.) Fray L. de L.: biogr. fragment, 1921.

Leon (Moses Pereira de), *see* PEREIRA DE LEON (M.)

León (Ricardo). Amor de caridad. 4ª ed. s8°. 1926
Humos de rey. Novela. s8°. [1923]
La voz de la sangre; ensayos españoles, con prologo de A. Maura y Montaner. s8°. [1921?]

Léonard (Nicolas Germain), *see* KERBY (W. M.) Life, diplom. career & lit. activities of L., 1925.

Leonard (Robert Maynard). *The pageant of Eng. poetry. 1150 poems & extr. s8°. 1909
The pageant of Eng. prose. 500 passages. s8°. 1920

Leonard (William Arthur). Music in the W. Church. 8°. 1872

Léoncel, *see* VIENNE. Chartes de St.-Maurice de V., de l'abbaye de L. &c.; publ. U. Chevalier, 1912.

León Dominguez (Luis). Los cuentos de Andalucia. s8°. [1924]

Leonhard (Susanne), *see* DRAHN (E.) & S. L. Unterird. Lit. im Revol. Deut. währ. d. Weltkrieges, 1920.

Leonhard (Thomas), *see* REISER (A.) Vindiciae evang.-Thomisticae, contra T. L. &c., 1669.

Leoni (Pierleone), *d. 1492, see* SORDINI (G.) Piero de' Medici e P. L., 1906.

Leoni (Pompeo), *see* HISP. SOC. OF AMER. P. L. in coll. of H. S., 1928.

Leoniceno (Niccoló) [†NICOLAUS, *Leonicenus*]; *1428–1524.* Libellus de epidemia (Venice), 1497, *facs., see* SUDHOFF (C.) Earliest pr. lit. on syphilis, 1925.

Leonico Tomeo (Nicola) [†LEONICUS THOMAEUS (NICOLAUS)]; *1456–1531, see* GASQUET (F. A.) Card. Pole & h. early friends [*i.e.* N. L. T. &c. *w. h.* letters to P.], 1927.

Léon-Martin (Louis). *Works in* ŒUVRES libres.
Le G. V. C., 1924. [41.]
L'honorable carrière de Mlle. Angèle, 1922. [9.]
Passe . . . pair . . . & gagne . . . 1926. [63.]
Le trio en sol majeur, 1923. [21.]

Leonov (Leonid Maksimovich).
Барсуки. 8°. Ленинград. 1925
Вор. Роман. 8°. Москва. 1928
Конец мелкого человека. s8°. Москва. 1924
Петушихинский пролом. s8°. 1923
Рассказы. s8°. Москва. 1926
Туатамур. s8°. Москва. 1924

Leontev (Konstantin Nikolaevich), *1831–91.*
Страницы воспоминаний. Редакция &c. П. К. Губера. 8°. С.-П. 1922

Leontius, *of Phrygia, bp. of Antioch, see* KIESLING (J. R.) De L. doxologiae eccles. hoste, 1762.

Leontius, *praefectus mon. S. Sabae.* S. Gregorii vita, *see* GREGORY II, *pope.* Libri 10 Explan. eccl., 1791.

Leontovich (Fedor Ivanovich). Къ ист. права русскихъ инородцевъ. Древній монголо-калмыцкій или ойратскій уставъ взысканій. (Цааджинъ-Бичикъ). 8°. Одесса. 1879

Leopardi (*il conte* Giacomo).
Canti. Ed. corr. [*b. w. h.* Prose, 1886]. s8°. Napoli. 1884
Prose, scelte ed annot. C. Durando. ed. 3ª. s8°. Torino. 1886
Puerili e abbozzi vari. A cura di A. Donati. 8°. Bari. 1924
Versi—Paralipomeni della Batracomiomachia. A cura di A. Donati. 8°. Bari. 1921
TRANSLATIONS.
Giacomo Leopardi. [*Works*] Deutsch v. P. Heyse. 2T. *in* 1v. s8°. 1878
Poems. Ed., w. intr. & notes & a verse-tr. by G. L. Bickersteth. 8°. C. 1923

Leopold IV, *Margrave of Austria, Saint, 1073–1136.* *Leopold der Heilige, Schutzpatron v. Oesterreich. Eine geistl. &c. Legende. 8°. Wien. 1835

Leopold, *Prince of Bavaria* [LEOPOLD MAXIMILIAN JOSEF MARIA ARNULF], *see* WOLBE (E.) Gen.-Feldmarschall Pr. L. v. B.: e. Lebensbild, 1920.

Leopold I, *king of the Belgians, 1790–1865, see* CORTI (E. C.) L. I of Belgium: secret pages of Europ. hist.; tr., 1923.

Léopold II, *k. of the Belgians.*
see DAYE (P.) La polit. coloniale de L. II, 1918.
,, HARRY (G.) L. II, 1920.

Leopold I, *emperor of Germany, 1640–1705.* *The Emperor's [*i.e.* L.'s] manifesto; right of the house of Austria to the crown of Spain. [Tr.] 8°. 1701

Leopold (J. H.) Verzen. 2e dr. s8°. Rotterdam. 1920

Leopold (Werner). Die religiöse Wurzel v. Carlyles liter. Wirksamkeit, dargest. an s. "State of Germ. lit. (1827)." [Stud. z. Engl. Philol., 62]. 8°. Halle. 1922

Lepage (P. C.) La décoration primitive afrique. 42 planches accomp. d'une préf. & d'une table descr. 4°. [1922 ?]

Lepanto, *Battle of.* [Descrizione. *Ed.* F. Corazzini. Nozze Corazzini-Brenzini. N134.] 8°. [Firenze. 1899]

Le Pappe de Trévern (Jean Franç. Marie). An ans. to G. S. Faber's Difficulties of Romanism. Tr. F. C. Husenbeth. 8°. 1828

*Discussion amicale sur l'établ. & la doctrine de l'Église angl. &c. sur la Réformation par un licencié de la Maison & Société de Sorbonne. 2t. 8°. Londres. 1817

Le Paulmier (Claude Stéphen). L'Orviétan. Hist. d'une famille de charlatans du Pont-Neuf [*i.e.* Contugi] aux 17e & 18e s. 8°. [1893]

Le Pays (René), *sieur du Plessis-Villeneuve, 1636–90.* Amitiez, amours et amourettes. dern. éd. s8°. Amsterdam. 1678

Nouv. œuvres, suivies du Dialogue de l'amour & de la raison. Intr. & notes de A. de Bersaucourt. s8°. 1925

Portrait de l'a. des Amitiez &c. [*b. w. h.* Amitiez, 1678]. s8°. Amsterdam. 1678

see REMY (G.) Un précieux de province au 17e s.; R. de Le P., 1925.

Lepel-Gnitz (Juliet v.) Ein Stradivarius. Novelle. s8°. 1878

Lepell (W. H. Ferd. Carl *Graf.* **v.)** *Verzeichniss d. Schriften d. Grafen L. v. Zinzendorf. s8°. Stettin. 1824

Le Pelletier (Anatole), *see* NOSTRADAMUS (M.) Les Oracles de M. de N. Éd. A. Le P., 1867.

Le Petit (*Dr.* **—).** Erklärg. d. hogarth. Kupferstiche, 14e Lfg., 1835. *This forms part of* LICHTENBERG (G. C.) Erklärg. hogarth. Kupferstiche, 1794–1835, *q.v.*

Le Petit (Claude), *see* LACHÈVRE (F.) C. Le P. & La muse de la cour 1657, 1922.

Le Petit (Mathurin), *Jesuit.* Rel. des Natchez, 1730, *see* BERNARD (J. F.), *ed.* Recueil de voy., t9, 1737.

Lépicié (Nicolas Bernard), *see* GASTON-DREYFUS (P.) Cat. raisonné de l'œuvre de N. P. L., 1922.

Lepidoptera. *Accentuated list of the Brit. L. Publ. by the Entomolog. Soc. of Oxf. & Camb. 8°. 1858

Le Plat (Josse), *ed.* Canones & decreta Co. Tridentini, 1779, *see* TRENT, *Council of.*

Le Pluche (Noel Ant.), *see* PLUCHE (N. A.)

Le Poittevin (Alfred). Une promenade de Bélial & œuvres inéd. Préc. d'une intr. sur la vie &c. d'A. Le P. par R. Descharmes. s8°. 1924

Lepp (Friedrich). Schlagwörter d. Reformationszeitalters. [Quellen &c. aus d. Reformationsjhdts., B8]. 8°. L. 1908

Lepper (John Heron). Fifty yrs. of masonry in East Antrim, 1800–50. [*From* Trans. Quatuor Coronati Lodge, v35]. la8°. [1922]

Le Prévost (Gabriel). Entre rayons & ombres, sous le ciel d'Albion: poésies. s8°. 1895

Lepsius (Johannes). Deutschland u. Armenien, 1914–18. Sammlung diplomat. Aktenstücke. Hrsg. &c. J. L. 8°. Potsdam. 1919

see GROSSE. Die gr. Politik d. europ. Kabinette, 1871–1914; Samml., hrsg. v. J. L. [*& others*], 1922–27.

Lepusculus (Sebastianus), *see* JOSEPH BEN GORION, *ps.* De bello Judaico &c.: acc. Collectanea quae S. L. collig., 1559.

Le Queux (William). The fatal face. s8°. [1926]

In secret. s8°. [1920]

Mademoiselle of Monte Carlo. s8°. 1921

Lerberg (Aron C.), *see* LEHRBERG (A. C.)

Lerberghe (Charles van).

La chanson d'Eve, augm. de poèmes inéd. 8°. 1926

Lerch (Eugen). Das invariable Participium praesentis d. Franz., *see* ROMANISCHE FORSCH., B33, 1915.

Lerch (*General-Major* **Theodor von).** Krit. Betracht. ü. d. letzten Kämpfe a. d. deut. Westfront. Vortrag. [P2702]. la8°. Wien. 1919

Lerda de Tejada (Miguel M.) Comercio esterior de México desde la conq. hasta hoy. la8°. Mexico. 1853

Leri (João de), *see* LÉRY (J. DE).

Lérins, *abbey of.* Cartul. de l'abbaye de L. Publ. par H. Moris, E. Blanc. [Soc. des Lettres &c. des Alps-Marit.] pl. 4°. St.-Honorat de Lérins. 1883

Lermina-Flandre (Juliette). Salomé, reine de Chalcis, *see* ŒUVRES libres, 37, 1924.

Lermite (Pierre), *ps.* La grande amie. [Roman]. la8°. *n.d.*

Lermontov (Mikhail Yurevich). Сочиненія. Приведенныя въ порядокъ С. С. Дудышкинымъ. 2т. 8°. С.-П. 1863

Собраніе сочиненій. 2т. 8°. Берлинъ. 1921

see BITSILLI (P. M.) Этюды о русс. поэзии: место Л. в ист. русс. поэзии, 1926.

Lermontov (Mikhail Yurevich) [*continued*].

see KOTLYAREVSKY (N. A.) Лермонтовъ, 1915.

,, SUSHKOVA (E. A.) Записки, 1812–41, 1928.

Lerner (Nikolai Osipovich). Царское Село в поэзии. Со статьей Э. Ф. Голлербаха. Редакция Н. О. Лернера. 8°. С.-П. 1922

Le Rossignol (James Edward).

What is socialism? s8°. N.Y. [1921]

Le Rouge (Gustave), *see* CAZALS (F. A.) & G. LE R. Les derniers jours de P. Verlaine, n. éd., 1923.

Leroux (Désiré). La vie de B. Palissy. 8°. 1927

Leroux (Emmanuel). Le pragmatisme amér. & anglaise: ét. hist. & crit. Suivie d'une bibliog. méthod. 8°. 1923

Leroux (Gaston). Le fantôme de l'opéra. s8°. [1910]

Rouletabille chez les Bohémiens. 2p. s8°. [1923]

1, Le livre des ancêtres. 2, La pieuvre.

The slave bangle. Tr. H. Bennett. s8°. [1925]

Le Roux (Hugues) [*i.e.* R. C. HENRI LE ROUX, *dit Hugues Le Roux*]. Te souviens-tu. . . . s8°. [1920]

Leroux-Cesbron (C.) Le château de Neuilly. 8°. 1923

Le Roux de Lincy (A. J. V.) Chants hist. & populaires [1408–72]. Publ. avec intr. &c. par Le R. de L. [Trésor des pièces rares &c.] 8°. 1857

Le Roy (Alexandre), *bp. of Alinda.*

La relig. des primitifs. 5e éd. s8°. 1925

Leroy (Édouard).

L'exigence idéaliste & le fait de l'évol. 8°. [1927]

Leroy (Maxime). La vie véritable du comte Henri de Saint-Simon (1760–1825). [Cahiers verts, 54]. s8°. 1925

Le Roy (Thomas). Curieuses recherches du Mont-Sainct-Michel. Publ. E. de Robillard de Beaurepaire. [Extr. des Mém. de la Soc. des Antiq. de Normandie]. 2t. 8°. Caen. 1878

Lerroux (Alejandro), *see* GARCÍA CARRAFFA (ALB.) & ART. G. C. L., 1918.

Léry (Jean de) [LERI (J. DE); LERIUS (A. J.)] Istoria de viagem á Brazil; tr. T. de Alencar Araripe, *see* INSTITUTO HIST. &C. BRAZ. Rev., t52, 1889.

Voyage au Brésil, 1556–58. Intr. par C. Clerc. 8°. 1927

Léry (Maxime), *see* ANTOINE (A. P.) & M. L. Les chevaux de bois, 1923.

Le Sage (Alain René).

Œuvres choisies. Avec figures. 16t. 8°. 1810

Crispin rival de son maître—Turcaret, *see* THÉÂTRE choisi du 18e s., t1, 1914.

Hist. de Gil Blas de Santillane. n. éd. rev. & corr. t1, 2. s8°. Londres. 1769

Turcaret or the financier; tr., *see* ALDINGTON (R.) Fr comedies of 18th c., 1923.

see HEINZ (H.) Gil Blas u. d. zeitgenöss. Leben in Frankreich, 1916.

Lesage (Charles).

Napoléon I, créancier de la Prusse, 1807–14. 8°. 1924

Lesca (Giuseppe), *see* DANTE ALIGHIERI. Lectura D.: c. [illegible] del Purgatorio letto da G. L., 1919.

Lescallier (*le baron* **Daniel).** Vocab. des termes de marine anglois & franç. n. éd. 2p [*in* 1v]. 8°. Londres. 178[illegible]

Lescarbot (Marc). Nova Francia: a descr. of Acadia, 1606. Tr. P. Erondelle. Intr. by H. P. Biggar. [Broadway Travellers]. 8°. [1928

L'Escluse (Charles de), *botanist, 1526–1609,* [CLUSIUS; †L'ECLUSE].

see HUNGER (F. W. T.) C. de L'E., Nederland. kruidkundige, 1927.

,, LEGRÉ (L.) La botanique en Provence au 16e s.: L Anguillara &c., 1901.

Lescun (Jean de), *comte de Comminges, dit le bâtard d'Armagnac* *see* JAURGAIN (J. DE). 2 Comtes de Comminges béarnai au 15e s.: J. de L. &c., 1919.

Lescun (Odet d'Aydie, *seigneur* **de),** *see* AYDIE (O. D').

Lescure (Mathurin F. Adolphe de).

Les amours de Henri IV. 8°. 186[illegible]

Lesguillon (*Madame* **Hermance).**

L'homme. Réponse à Alex. Dumas fils. s8°. 187[illegible]

Leskien (August). Hdbch. d. altbulgar. (altkirchenslav. Sprache. 4e A. 8°. Weimar. 190[illegible]

,, ,, [Indogerman. Bibl., Abt. 1, Reihe 1, B15]. 6e A. 8°. Heidelberg. 192[illegible]

Zur neusten Gesch. d. slaw. Sprachforschung. Abdruck. [P2428]. 8°. 186[illegible]

Leskov (Nikolai Semenovich) [LYESKOV (N.); *ps.* M. STEBNITZKY].

Ein absterbendes Geschlecht. Familienchron. d. Fürsten Protosanow. [Deut. v. J. v. Guenther]. s8°. München. [1925]
Am Ende d. Welt. [Deut. v. E. Müller &c.] Nebst e. Biog. L.'s v. E. M. s8°. München. [1927]
The cathedral folk. Tr. I. F. Hapgood. s8°. [1924]
Charaktere u. Sonderlinge. [Deut. v. E. Müller &c.] s8°. München. [1927]
The enchanted wanderer. Tr. A. G. Paschkoff. Intr. by M. Gorky. s8°. 1926
Geschichten aus alter Zeit. [Deutsch v. E. Müller]. s8°. München. [1924]
Geschichten aus d. Grossstadt. [Deutsch v. J. v. Guenther & E. Müller]. s8°. München. [1924]
Geschichten v. Lande. [Deutsch v. H. v. Heiseler & J. v. Guenther]. s8°. München. [1924]
Die Klerisei. [Deut. v. A. Luther]. s8°. München. [1927]
Legenden. [Deutsch v. J. v. Guenther & E. Müller]. s8°. München. [1924]
Militär. Geschichten. [Deut. v. E. Müller]. s8°. München. [1925]
The sentry & o. stories. [The Lady Macbeth—The Toupee artist—On the edge of the world]. Tr. A. E. Chamot. Introd. by E. Garnett. s8°. 1922
see KOVALEVSKY (P.) N. S. L., peintre méconnu de la vie nat. russe, 1925.

Lesky (Albin). Alkestis, d. Mythus u. d. Drama, 1925, *see* KAIS. AKAD. D. W. ZU WIEN. Sitz., Phil.-hist. Kl., B203, 1927.

Lesley (*Mrs.* **Susan Inches**). Recoll. of my mother. [Mrs. A. J. Lyman]. [repr.] 8°. [Boston (Mass.)] 1886

Leslie (Charles), *M.A., 1650–1722.*
The case of the regale & of the pontificat. 2nd ed. s8°. 1702
*A disc. proving the divine instit. of water-baptism. [P2652]. s4°. 1697
*Disc. shewing who are qualify'd to admin. baptism &c. By a. of Water-baptism [*i.e.* C. L. *b. w. h.* Hist. of sin &c., 1698]. s4°. 1698
*An essay conc. the divine right of tythes. By a. of The snake in the grass [*i.e.* C. L. *b. w.* Lloyd (W.) Chron. acc. of Pythagoras, 1699. *tp. & last few leaves missing*]. s8°. 1700
*Five disc. by the a. of The snake in the grass [C. L.] *viz.* On Water-baptism; Episcopacy; Prim. heresie of the Quakers; Reflections on the Quakers; Socinian Trinity. s8°. 1700
*Hist. of sin & heresie. s4°. 1698
*Prim. heresie revived in Quakers. [*b. w. h.* Hist. of sin &c., 1698. *a. c. in* P2652]. s4°. 1698
*Satan disrob'd; or the Quakers last shift; in reply to T. Ellwood's Answer. 2nd ed. w. improv. [*b. w. h.* Hist. of sin &c., 1698]. s4° 1698
*A short & easie method w. the Deists. [Added, Letter to a Deist &c. *w. sep. pagin.*] 4th ed. s8°. 1711
*A short & easie method w. the Jews. [*b. w. h.* Short &c. method w. the Deists, 4th ed., 1711]. 4th ed. corr. s8°. 1715

Leslie (H. W.) "The Royal Mail" war book: oper. of ships of the R.M. Steam Packet Co., 1914–19. 8°. 1920

Leslie (John), *bp. of Ross.* [LESLÆUS; LESLEY]. Pro libertate impetranda, oratio. Ad. Elizabetham Angliae reginam. s8°. Parisiis. 1574

Leslie (*Lt.-Col.* **John Henry).** Hist. roll of women of the Brit. Emp. to whom Milit. Medal has been awarded, 1914–18. 5p *in* 1v. la8°. Sheffield. 1919–20
Origin &c. (1805–61) of Madras Horse artillery. [P2592]. 8°. Leicester. 1907
The story of a Brit. flag captured at Quatre Bras 1815. [P2603]. la8°. [1911]
see MASONIC CALENDAR for the Punjab district, 1893, 1894, 1895–96, ed. J. H. L., 1893–96.

Leslie (Shane).
George the Fourth. [3rd impr.] 8°. 1926
Henry Edward Manning, h. life & labours. 8°. 1921
Mark Sykes: h. life & letters. Intr. by Rt. Hon. W. Churchill. 8°. 1923
The Oppidan. s8°. 1922
Poems. la8°. *Cayme Press.* 1928
see HENRY VI, *k. of Eng.* Miracles: acc. & tr. of 23 miracles f. MS. in B.M., w. intr. by R. Knox & S. L., 1923.
,, SHEPHARD (*Brig.-Gen.* G. S.) Memoirs; ed. S. L., 1924.

Leslie (*count* **Walter),** *see* TAVERNER (P.) Cæsarea legatio quam mand. Imp. Leopoldo I ad Portam Ottomam suscepit &c. W. comes de L., 1668.

Lesne (Emile). Hist. de la propriété eccl. en France. 2t *in* 4. [2i–iii.] 8°. Lille. 1910–28

Lesort (André).
see CLERMONTOIS. Chartes du C.; [publ. avec intr. par] A. L., 1904.
,, SAINT-MIHIEL. Chron. & chartes; publ. A. L., 1909–12.

Lespinasse (René de), *see* NEVERS. Cartul. de St.-Cyr de N.; [*publ.*] par R. de L., 1916.

L'Espine (Jean de), *see* ACTES. Acts of the dispute & conf., Paris, 1566, betw. 2 doctors & [J. de l'E. & H. Du Rosier]; tr., 1602.

Lesquier (Jean). L'armée romaine d'Egypte, d'Auguste à Dioclétien, *see* INSTITUT FRANÇ. D'ARCH. DU CAIRE. Mém., t41, 1918.
see LEXOVIENNES. Etudes lex. par G. Besnier, J. L. &c., 2t, 1915–19.

Less (Gottfried). The authenticity &c. & credibility of the New Test. Tr. by R. Kingdom. 8°. 1804
Hdbch. d. Xtl. Religions-Theorie. 3e umgearb. A. s8°. Göttingen. 1789
Opuscula theolog., exeget. & homiletici argumenti. ed. auct. s8°. Gottingae. 1780

Lessey (Theophilus), *see* HANNAH (J.), *D.D.* Mem. of the life & corr. of J. L., 1842.

Lessing (Gotthold Ephraim). Sämtl. Schriften. Hrsg v. K. Lachmann. 3e A., besorgt durch F. Muncker. B22–23. 8°. 1915–24
22i, Berichtigungen u. Nachträge. 22ii, Verzeichnis d. Drucke. 23, Register; bearb. v. H. Guggenheimer &c.
Fabeln. s8°. L. 1844
Laokoon. s8°. St. 1873
Laokoon. [*w.* Anhang (Uebersetzungen)]. Hrsg. v. R. Gosche. s8°. 1876
see MUNCKER (F.) Neue Lessing-Funde, 1915.

Lessing (Johann Gottfried). Vindici[ae] Reformationis Lutheri a Novatorum praejudiciis. [P2628]. s4°. Vitembergæ. 1717

Lessing (Otto). Modern architectural ornaments. fol. 1884

Lessio (Leonardo), *Jesuit.*
De justitia et jure &c. libri 4. fol. Brixiae. 1696
De summo bono & æterna beatitudine hominis libri 4. s8°. Antverpiae. 1616
Hygiasticon: or a treatise of the means of health & long life. [Tr.] T. Smith. Ann., Cornaro's Benefits of a sober life [*w. sep. tp. & pagin.*] 8°. 1742
Quæ fides & religio sit capessenda, *see* MIGNE (J. P.), *ed.* Theol. cursus, t3, 1860.
Tract. de justitia, *see* MIGNE (J. P.), *ed.* Theol. cursus, t15, 1861.

Lesskow (Nikolai), *see* LESKOV (N. S.)

Lessona (Michele). Volere è potere. s8°. Firenze. 1869
—— & C. Avalle. Diz. univ. di scienze, lettere ed arti. la8°. Milano. 1875

Lester (George). Grimsby Methodism (1743–1889) & the Wesleys in Lincolnshire. Note by Dr. Rigg. [*la. paper*]. 8°. 1890
Lord Tennyson & the Bible. s8°. [1891]

Lestock (*admiral* **Richard).** *An authentic acc. of the late exped. to Bretagne conducted by R. L. & lieut-gen. St. Clair. [P608]. s8°. 1747
see WEST (*capt.* T.) Defence agst. L.'s charge rel. to h. conduct off Toulon, 1746.

Lestocq (Nic. de), *see* L'ETOILE (P. DE). *L'ombre de M. Thiers, ou rép. à la diss. de L. sur la transl. de S. Firmin &c., 1712.

Le Strange (Guy).
Spanish ballads. Chosen by G. Le S. s8°. C. 1920

L'Estrange (Hamon), *the elder.* The alliance of divine offices, exhib. the liturgies of the Ch. of England since the Reformation &c. fol. 1659
,, ...2nd ed. fol. 1690

Lesueur (Émile). Le cardinal de La Tour d'Auvergne-Lauraguais (1768–1851). 8°. 1927

Le Sueur (Eustache), *see* ROUCHES (G.) E. Le S., 1923.

Le Sueur (Jean François), *see* FOUQUE (O.) Révolutionnaires de la musique, 1882.

Lesurques (Joseph), *see* DELAYEN (G.) L'affaire du courrier de Lyon: procès de L., &c., 1905.

Lesvignes (Marcel). Rita, championne d'Italie, *see* ŒUVRES libres, t47, 1927.

Letarouilly (Paul Marie).
Edifices de Rome mod. pl, 2 *in* 1v. 4°. Liége. 1849–53
,, ,, Planches. la. fol. Liége. 1843–*n.d.*

Letchworth Village, *Eastern New York State Custodial Asylum.* Ann. rep. of Board of Managers, 11th, 13th, 15th–18th. 8°. Albany. 1920–27

Letellier (Albert). Bossuet notre plus grand écrivain. 8°. 1920

Le Tellier (Charles Maurice), *abp. of* (*1*) *Nazianzus,* (*2*) *Rheims.* Ordonnance pour l'approb. des reguliers dans s. diocése. [*Prec. by* Diatriba theologica, *sep. pagin.*] s8°. Reims. 1697
Requeste pres. au Parlement, le 10 Jan. 1698, contre la remonstrance publ. par les Jesuites sur son ordonnance du 15 Juillet 1697. [*b. w. h.* Ordonnance &c., 1697]. s8°. *n.p.* 1698

Letellier (L.) Louis Bouilhet, 1821–69. Sa vie & ses œuvres d'ap. des doc. inéd. s8°. 1919

Le Tellier (Michel), *see* ALEXANDRE (N.) *Apol. d. Dominicains : rép. au livre du p. le T. &c., 1699.

Lethaby (William Richard). Form in civilization : coll. papers on art & labour. s8°. 1922
Londinium, architecture & crafts. 8°. [1923]
Westminster Abbey re-examined. 8°. 1925
see PAGE (A.) The Foundling Hospital, w. intr. by W. R. L., 1926.

Lethbridge (Alan). Germany as it is to-day. s8°. [1921]

Lethem (G. J.) Colloquial Arabic, Shuwa dialect of Bornu, Nigeria &c. Gram. & vocab. s8°. 1920

Leti (Gregorio) [*ps. abbate* GUALDI].
Hist. di Elisabetta reg. d'Inghilterra. p2. s8°. Amsterdamo. 1683
L'hist. de la vie du pape Sixte V. Tr. [par L. A. Peletier]. n. éd. rev. & augm. 2t *in* 1v. s8°. 1698
*Le nepotisme de Rome. Tr. 2p [*in* 1v]. s8°. *n.p.* 1664
Il nipotismo di Roma : or, The hist. of the popes nephews. [Tr.] 2p. s8°. 1669
La vie d'Elizabeth, d'Angeterre. Tr. [*Illust.*] 2p. s8°. Amsterdam. 1694
see CONCLAVI. C. de' pontefici romani [*attrib. to G. L.*], 1668.

L'Etoile (Pierre de), *abbé de Saint-Acheul d'Amiens.* *L'ombre de M. Thiers, ou rép. à la diss. de M. Lestocq s. la transl. de S. Firmin le Confesseur. Avec une crit. de la vie de S. Salve. [*w. sep. pagin.*] s8°. Liege. 1712
*Remarques crit. s. le livre de M. Lestocq, Justific. de la transl. de S. Firmin. [*b. w. h.* L'ombre de M. Thiers, 1712]. s8°. 1714

Letopis. Лѣтопись Сибирская &c. изд. 17в., 1821, *see* SIBERIA.
Полное собранiе русс. лѣтописей, *see* ARKHEOGRAFICHESKAYA KOMM.

Le Tourneur (Pierre), *see* CUSHING (M. G.) P. Le T., 1908.

Le Tourneux (Nicolas), *abbé.* *De la meilleure manière d'entendre la sainte messe. s8°. 1681

Le Tréport, *abbey of, see* TRÉPORT (LE).

Letschius (Johannes Christianus) & M. Hanke. Diss. Nestorianismi hist. complect. Praeses J. C. Letschius. Resp. M. H. s4°. Wittebergae. 1688

Letsome (Sampson).
The preacher's assistant. 2p [*interleaved*]. 8°. [1753]
1, A series of texts preached upon & publ. since the Restoration &c.
2, An hist. register of authors ; added lists of abp. & bp., 1660–1753.

Letter.
*L. (A) conc. the late Act of Parl. rel. to eccl. small dues, 1750, *see* PARLIAMENT : ANON. WKS.
*L. (A) f. a gentleman at Edinb. conc. affairs in Scotland &c., 1745, *see* SCOTLAND.
*L. from Legion to Duke of Richmond &c., 1832, *see* LEGION, *ps.*
*L. (A) f. the Assembly of divines in Eng. to the Assembly in Scot., w. the ans., 1643, *see* ENGLAND.
*L. (A) f. the bp. of Rochester to the earl of Dorset conc. his sitting in the late Eccl. Comm. *&* Second letter, 1688–9, *see* SPRAT (T.) bp.
*L. (A) of resolution conc. Origen &c., 1661, *see* RUST (G.)
*L. on the Belgic Revolution, tr., 1831, *see* VAN DER WEYER (S.)
*L. (A) to a friend, occas. by a French pamph., 1772, *see* KENNICOTT (B.)
*L. (A) to J. Wesley occ. by his Calm addr. to Amer. colonies, 1775, *see* EVANS (C.)
*L. (A) to Mrs. Campbell of Barbreck &c., 1830, *see* CAMPBELL (F. W.)
*L. (A) to the Earl of Mulgrave ; by a dissatisfied gentleman, 1836, *see* NORMANBY (C. H. P., *1st marq. of*), *2nd earl of Mulgrave.*
*L. (A) to the people of Ireland on tythes, 1758, *see* TITHES.
*L. (A) to the Rev. T. T. Churton, 1841, *see* WILSON (H. B.)
*L. to the Rt. Hon. T. B. C. Smith suggest. extending to Ireland reforms adopted in Eng., 1844, *see* SMITH (*Rt. Hon.* T. B. C.)
*L. (A) to Visc. Melbourne &c. on admin. of Earl Mulgrave, &c., 1836, *see* WALLACE (T.)
*Second l. f. Legion to Duke of Richmond &c., 1833, *see* LEGION, *ps.*
*Second (A) l. to the people of Ireland on tythes, 1758, *see* TITHES.
*Third (A) l. to the people of Ireland on tythes, 1758, *see* TITHES.

Lettera.
L. d'un filarmonico o. paral. tra L. Todi e L. Marchesi, 1791, *see* N. (N.)
L. scr. al p. Clemente XI da pp. d. Co. di Gesù d. Cina, con risp. dell' Imperador &c., 1701, *see* JESUITS.

Lettere.
*L. ad un' abate di qualità int. alla Lettera di L. di Cicè, s. idolatrie &c. d. Cina, 1701, *see* CICE (L. DE).
L. di cortigiane del sec. 16. [*Ed.* L. A. Ferrai. Operette ined. &c., pubbl. d. Libreria Dante in Firenze, 9]. 8°. [Firenze. 1884]
*L. di 2 mandarini di Corea e due barbassori del Giappone conc. la principessa de' Fangadi. s8°. " Odessa." 3529
*L. di molte valorose donne &c., 1548, *see* LANDI (O.)
L. di 13 huomini illust. &c., 1565, *see* PORCACCHI (T.)
L. ined. di illust. Italiani dei sec. 18 e 19 al G. Gradenigo, 1856 *see* GRADENIGO (G.)
*L. sui primi libri a stampa dell' Italia superiore, 1794, *see* BONI (M.)
Sette l. ined. d'illust. Italiani dei sec. 18 e 19, *see* TESSIER (A.)

Letters.
*A general's l. to h. son on minor tactics, 1918, *see* PILCHER (T. D.)
*A general's l. to h. son on obt. h. commission, 1917, *see* PILCHER (T. D.)
*Girq thlthotz. [Book of letters of the patriarchs. (Sahak Mesropean, lib. 5). *In Armenian*]. 8°. Tiflis. 1901
*L. f. a lady who resided in Russia, 1775, *see* WARD (*Mrs.*)
*L. from Jersey, 1830, *see* JERSEY.
L. f. the Cttee. of Estates at Newcastle &c., 1646, *see* SCOTLAND PARL.
*L. of Britannicus on Mr. Grattan's bill for relief of Roman Catholics &c., 1813, *see* BRITANNICUS, *ps.*
L. on the Amer. Revol., 1774–6, 1925, *see* WILLARD (M. W.), *ed.*
*L. on Theron & Aspasio &c., 1768, *see* SANDEMAN (R.)
Sel. l. betw. the Duchess of Somerset, Lady Luxborough &c. 2v, 1778, *see* HULL (T.), *ed.*
*Two l., conc. farther advantages &c. nec. on taking Cape Breton 1746.

Lettieri (Niccolo). Istoria dell' ant. cittá di Suessola, e de castello d'Arienzo. 2p [*pagin. cont.*] 8°. Napoli. 177[illegible]
p2 *has tp.* Ist. del vecchio &c. castello d'Arienzo.

Lettonie [LETTONE].
*Démocratie (La) l. au travail. Ed. E. Despréaux [Bull. N°. 3]. [P2564]. 8°. 192[illegible]
*Droits (Les) de la L. à faire partie de la Soc. des Nations. [P2563]. 8°. Genève. 192[illegible]
*L. (La). Pays de transit & d'exportation. Ed. par le Bureau Letton d'Inform. à Paris. [P2739]. 8°. 192[illegible]
*L. (La) (Latvija). [*By var. a.* A. Bihlmans &c. Revue Belg[illegible] d'import. & d'export.] 4°. Brux. 192[illegible]
*L. (La) historique. Ed. E. Despréaux. Bull. N°. 2. [P2564]. 8°. 192[illegible]
*L. (La) : situation écon. [P2876]. 8°. Riga. 192[illegible]
*République (La) de L. : doc., traités & lois. 1. Ed. par le Bureau d'Inform. à Paris. 8°. 192[illegible]
Traités conclus entre la L. & l'Esthonie en 1923. [P2750]. la8°. [192[illegible]]

Lettre.
*L. à M. de L. C. P. D. B. sur le livre intitulé Hist. Flagellantium *n.d.*, *see* DU CERCEAU (J. A.)
*L. à M. l'Abbé sur le Concordat de 1817, 1817, *see* DILLON (H.).
*L. à M.** touch. les honneurs que les Chinois rendent au philo[illegible] Confucius & à leurs ancêtres, 1700, *see* CHINOIS.
*L. à Mgr. Dechamps sur sa 2e réponse à l'évêque d'Orléans, 187[illegible] *see* DECHAMPS (*Card.* V. A. I.)
*L. à Mgr. le duc Du Mayne s. les cérémonies de la Chine, 170[illegible] *see* LECOMTE (L.)
*L. de messieurs des missions étrang. au Pape sur les idolatries & chinoises, 1700, *see* SÉMINAIRE DES MISSIONS ETRANG.
*L. de Pekin sur le génie de la langue chinoise &c., 1773, *see* CIB[OT] (P. M.)
*L. de quelques eccl. du Brabant à l'archévêque de Cambray & 1715, *see* FÉNÉLON (F. DE S. DE LA M.), *abp.*
*L. d'un evesque anglois, c. 1718, *see* GASTRELL (F.), *bp.*
*L. sur les caractères chinois &c., 1773, *see* CIBOT (P. M.)

Lettres.
*L. de M*** à un ami au sujet du quiétisme, 1733, *see* PHELYPEA[UX] (*l'abbé* J.)
*L. d'un François à un catholique angl., 1734, *see* PA[R] (FRANÇOIS DE).
*L. écr. de Londres sur les Anglois, 1734, *see* VOLTAIRE.
L. édif. & cur. conc. l'Asie &c., avec rel. nouv. des missions &c publ. s. la dir. de L. Aimé-Martin, 4t., 1838–43, *see* JESUITS.
L. & pièces conc. les changemens actuels de Portugal, à l'éga[rd] des Jésuites [*Fr. & Port.*], *see* PORTUGAL. Rec. de decre[ts] apostol. &c., p1, 1758.
*L. philosoph., serieuses &c., 1733, *see* SAUNIER DE BEAUMONT (–
Plus (Les) jolies l. d'amour, 1919, *see* PÈNE (A. DE).

Letts (C. Hubert). The 100 best pictures. Arr. & ed. C. H. L. 6th ed. fol. 19[illegible]

Letts (Malcolm). Admin. of criminal law in Flanders, 15th cent. [Repr. f. L.Q. Review, 1925. P2784]. 8°. 19[illegible]
Bruges & its past. 8°. Bruges. 19[illegible]
" " .... 2nd ed. rev. & enl. 8°. Bruges. 19[illegible]

Leuba (James Henry).
Psychology of relig. mysticism. 8°. 19[illegible]

Leuba (Jeanne). L'aile de feu. Roman. s8°. [1920]
Un royaume disparu. Les Chams & leur art. Préf. de L. Finot. la8°. 1923
Leubnitz (Friedrich), *see* STIEDA (W.) Prof. F. L., 1917.
Leuckfeld (Johann Georg). Hist. Heshusiana: Leben u. Schr. T. Hesshusiana. Benebst e. genealog. Nachr. v. den Olearien. s4°. Quedlinburg. 1716
Leudet (Maurice).
Emperor of Germany at home. Tr. V. Taylour. 8°. 1898
Leumann (Carlos Alberto).
La vida victoriosa. s8°. Buenos Aires. 1922
Leupold (Benjamin). Diss. inaug.: initia relig. Xtnae. in Silesia ante Micislai I temp. s4°. Halae Magdeb. 1758
Leuridant (Félicien).
Une ambassade du Prince de Ligne en Angleterre, 1660. [P2498]. 8°. Brux. *n.d.*
Les collations de cures & de bénéfices de la maison de Ligne. [Extr. des "Annales du Cercle Archéol. d'Ath," t7]. [P2703]. la8°. Brux. 1921
Une éducation de prince au 18e s. Charles Joseph de Ligne. Doc. inéd. [Acad. Roy. de Belg. Mém., 18i]. la8°. Brux. 1923
Un pélerin belge à Notre-Dame de Lorette au 17e s. [P2498]. 8°. Brux. *n.d.*
Le Prince de Ligne, Mme de Staël & C. Murray. [P2509; 2717]. 8°. Brux. 1920
Le tribunal de prem. instance d'Ath en 1787. [P2498]. 8°. [Brux. 1921]
Le vieux château & la "Cense du Parc" à Belœil. [P2498]. 8°. Brux. *n.d.*
Leuschner (Kurt). Ant. Furetière u. s. Streit mit d. französ. Akad., *see* ROMANISCHE FORSCH., B34, 1915.
Leusden (Jan). Philologus Hebræo-mixtus unà cum Spicilegio philologico. [*w. sep. tp.*] ed. 2a. s4°. Ultrajecti. 1682
Philologus Hebraeus cont. quaest. Heb. circa Vet. Test. Heb. ed. 5. s4°. Basileae. 1739
Leusser (Hermann). Ein Jahrzehnt deut.-amer. Politik, 1897–1906. [Hist. Zeitschr., Beiheft 13]. 8°. München. 1928
Leuthner (Carl). Russ. Volksimperialismus. s8°. 1915
Leuwis (Dionysius de) *de Rickel* [DIONYSIUS *Carthusianus*]. Liber &c. de 4 hominis novissimis, nempè, morte &c. Ejusdem colloquium de partic. judicio animarum &c. ed. recogn. s8°. Coloniae. 1614
Levaillant (Maurice). Splendeurs & misères de M. de Chateaubriand. 3e éd. 8°. [1922]
Levainville (J.)
Rouen pend. la Guerre. [C.E. for Int. Peace]. 8°. [1926]
Levasseur (Guillaume), *sieur de Beauplan.* Descr. de l'Ukraine. n. éd. publ. par le pr. A. Galitzin. s8°. 1861
Le Vasseur (Jòsua). Disputationes, *see* DU MOULIN (P.) Thesaurus disput., v2, 1661.
Le Vayer de Boutigny (Roland). Traité de l'autorité des rois t. l'admin. de l'église. s8°. Londres. 1753
Levchenko (Mikhail Mikhailovich).
Опытъ русско-украйнскаго словаря. 8°. Кіевъ. 1874
Level (Maurice). L'ombre. Roman. s8°. [1921]
Vieilles filles, nouvelle inéd., *see* ŒUVRES libres, 16, 1922.
Leven (Alexander Leslie, *1st earl of***).** *Glorious &c. battel at York, 1644, *see* MAIDMENT (J.), *ed.* Hist. fragm., p1, 1833.
Levenson (A. A.) Москва; изд. А. А. Л., 1912, *see* MOSCOW.
Levenstein (Adolf). Die Arbeitfrage. Mit bes. Berücksichtigung d. sozialpsycholog. Seite d. mod. Grossbetriebes &c. 8°. München. 1912
Lévêque (Raphaël). Le problème de la vérité dans la philos. de Spinoza. Préf. de M. Pradines. 8°. Str. 1923
Lever (Charles James). Charles O'Malley. 2v. 8°. 1865
*Cornelius O'Dowd upon men, women, & o. things. [s1]. s8°. E. 1864
Harry Lorrequer. 17th ed. s8°. *n.d.*
„ „ Intr. by L. Melville. [Everyman's Lib.] s8°. [1907]
Lever (Christopher). The historie of the Defenders of the Catholique Faith: the state of religion in Eng. &c. dur. the r. of Henry VIII, Edward VI, Marie, Elizabeth & James &c. [*Engraved tp. missing*]. 8°. 1627
Leverhulme (William Hesketh Lever, *1st baron***).** Art coll. of Visct. L. Sold Feb. 9–March 4, 1926, Anderson Galleries, N.Y. 7p [*in 1v*]. la8°. N.Y. 1926
What is capital? Address. [P2487]. s8°. *n.d.*
see LEVERHULME (W. H. L., *2nd visct.*) Visct. L., 1927.
Leverhulme (William Hulme Lever, *2nd visct.***)**
Visct. Leverhulme. By h. son. 8°. 1927
Leverson (Montague Richard), *see* HUME (E. D.) Béchamp or Pasteur? founded upon MS. by M. R. L., 1923.
Levertin (Oscar).
Carl von Linné. 3e uppl. s8°. [1908]
Diktare och drömmare. 5e uppl. s8°. [1919]
Dikter. 3e saml. 2a uppl. s8°. [1920]
Essayer. 2d. s8°. [1920]
För och mot. Artiklar i dagens frågor. s8°. [1920]
Från Gustaf III: s dagar. 4e uppl. s8°. [1916]
Gustaf III, som dramatisk författare. 4e uppl. s8°. [1920]
Johan Wellander. 2a uppl. s8°. [1908]
Kung Salomo och Morolf. Dikter. [*b. w. h.* Dikter, 2a uppl., 1920]. s8°. [1919]
Legender och visor. Dikter. 8e uppl. s8°. [1919]
N. Lafrensen d. y. och förbindelserna mellan svensk och fransk målarkonst på 1700–t. 4e uppl. s8°. [1920]
Nordisk litt. s8°. [1918]
Nya dikter. [*b. w. h.* Legender &c., 8e uppl., 1919]. s8°. [1920]
Resebref. 4e uppl. s8°. [1920]
Sista dikter. [*b. w. h.* Dikter, 2a uppl., 1920]. s8°. [1920]
Sista noveller. 5e uppl. s8°. 1921
Studier öfver J. Callot. 3e uppl. s8°. [1920]
Teater och drama under Gustaf III. 4e uppl. s8°. [1920]
Ungdomsnoveller. 4e uppl. s8°. [1920]
Utländsk konst. s8°. [1920]
Utländsk litt. s8°. [1922]
Levesque (Geneviève).
La situation internat. de Dantzig. 8°. 1924
Levesque de Burigny (Jean). *Traité de l'autorité du pape &c. 4t. s8°. La Haye. 1720
Lévesque de Pouilly (Jean Simon). *Vie de M. de L'Hôpital, chancelier de France. s8°. Amsterdam. 1767
Levey (R. M.) A coll. of the dance music of Ireland. Arr. for piano forte by R. M. L. 3rd ed. 4°. *n.d.*
Levey (Sivori).
Britishers! & o. songs for the war. [P2585]. s8°. 1914
Levi (Adolfo). Il concetto del tempo &c. n. filos. di Platone. la8°. Torino. [1920]
La filosofia di Giorgio Berkeley. la8°. Torino. 1922
Sulle interpretazioni immanentist. d. filos di Platone. la8°. Torino. [1921]
Levi (Alda). *Works in* REALE ACCAD. D. LINCEI. Mon. ant.
Bassorilievi in marmo trov. in Villazzano, 1920. [26.]
Camere sepolcrali scop. in Napoli dur. i lavori d. dir. Roma-Napoli, 1926. [31.]
L'Iside Barberini, 1922. [28.]
Ruderi di terme romane trov. a Baja, 1922. [28.]
Levi (Cesare). Dante "dramatis persona," *see* ARCHIVIO STOR. ITAL. Anno 79, v1, 1921.
Virginia Reiter. [*a. c. in* P2517]. la8°. Milano. 1920
Levi (David), *tr., see* TEPHILOTH. Form of prayers acc. to Span. & Portug. Jews, 1789.
Levi (Eugenia). Per la congiura contro Venezia nel 1618. [P2835]. 8°. Venezia. 1899
Levi (Ezio). Troveri ed abbazie, *see* ARCHIVIO STOR. ITAL. Anno 83, v1, 1925.
Lévy (Isidore). Recherches sur les sources de la légende de Pythagore. [H.E.: Sci. Relig., 42]. 8°. 1926
Levi (Moses). Hist. relig. Judæorum eorumque demigrationis &c. [*b. w.* Simon (R.) Hist. crit. Vet. Test., 1681]. s4°. Amstelodami. 1681
Levi (Paul). Unser Weg wider d. Putschismus. Mit e. Artikel v. K. Radek als Anhang. 2e A. [P2526]. 8°. 1921
see TSETKIN (K.), P. L. &c. Роза Люксембург, 1921.
Levi (Riso). Billiards: strokes &c. 3v *in* 1 [*pagin. cont.* 1, 3rd ed.] 8°. [1904–06 ?]
Levi (Ugo). I monumenti d. dialetto di Lio Mazor. la8°. Venezia. 1904
Levick (G. Murray). Nat. hist. of the Adélie penguin, *see* BRIT. ANTARCTIC EXPED., 1910–13. Zoology, v1, 1914–16.
Levillain (Léon). Le Formulaire de Marculf & la crit. mod., *see* ECOLE (L') des Chartes. Bibl., t84, 1923.
Levillier (Roberto). Nueva cron. de la conq. del Tucuman. t1, 1542–63. la8°. Buenos Aires. 1926
Levine (Israel). Francis Bacon, 1561–1626. s8°. [1925]
Levine (Louis). Syndicalism in France. Intr. by F. H. Giddings. [Columbia Univ.] 2nd rev. ed. of "The labor movement in France." 8°. N.Y. 1914
Levinge, *The family of, see* LEVINGE (*Sir* R. G. A.) Jottings for early hist. of L. fam., p1, 1873.
Levinge (*Sir* Richard George Augustus), *7th bart.* Jottings for early hist. of the Levinge family. pl. *p.f.p.c.* 8°. D. 1873
Levingston (*Sir* Henry); *d. 1463,* [LEVYINGSTOUN]. Procuratory to Sr. J. ye Rosse of ye Hawkehed, 1460, *see* MAIDMENT (J.) & R. PITCAIRN. Nugae derelictae, 1822.
Levinsen (Georg Marius Reinold). Bryozoerne i. d. danske Kridtformation; udg. af K. B. Nielsen & Th. Mortensen, *see* KONG. DAN. VID. SELSK. Skrifter, Række 8, B7, 1920–25

Levinstein (Herbert).
The Brit. dyestuff industry. Conference. [P2430]. s8°. 1919
Lévis (*card.* **Philippe de)**, *see* FICHET (G.) Poème comp. en l'honneur du card. P. de L., 1473, facs., 1923.
Levison (Sarah Rachel), *see* RACHEL (*Mme.*)
Levison (Wilhelm), *see* KRUSCH (B.), *ed.* Passiones vitaeque sanct. aevi Merov., t5, 1920.
Levita (Elias), *see* ELIJAH, *Ben Asher, the Levite.*
Levot (Prosper Jean). Hist. de la ville & du port de Brest [-1792]. 3t. 8°. Brest. 1864–66
Lévy (Arthur).
Napoléon intime. Préc. d'une ét. par F. Coppée. s8°. [1910]
Levy (E. Lawrence).
Birmingham theatrical remin., 1870–1920. 8°. B'ham. [1920]
Levy (Emil). Provenzal. Suppl.-Wörterbuch. Berichtig. u. Ergänz. zu Raynouards Lexique Roman.
B7, 8, R–Z. 8°. L. 1915–24
Lévy (Eugène). Mrs. Besant & the present crisis in the Theosoph. Soc. Pref. by M. E. Schuré. Tr. C. E. S.
s8°. 1913
Lévy (Isidore). La légende de Pythagore de Grèce en Palestine. [H.E., 250]. 8°. 1927
Lévy (Raphael Georges). La juste paix ou la verité sur le Traité de Versailles. [*Includ.* Une aberration : le livre de M. Keynes]. 8°. [1920]
Levy (Reuben). Persian lit. : an introd. s8°. 1923
The 3 dervishes & o. Persian tales &c. For most part tr. f. Bodl. MSS. s8°. [1924]
Levy (Roger). Trotsky. s8°. 1920
Levy (S.)
Jewish theology. Repr. f. Jewish Chron. [P2431]. s8°. 1920
Levy (Stanley Isaac). Modern explosives. s8°. [1920]
Lévy-Bruhl (Lucien). L'âme primitive. 8°. 1927
How natives think. Tr. L. A. Clare. 8°. [1926]
Jean Jaurès : esquisse biog. n. éd. suivie de lettres inéd.
6e éd. s8°. 1924
Primitive mentality. Auth. tr. by L. A. Clare. 8°. [1923]
Levyingstoun (*Sir* **Henry)**, *d. 1463, see* LEVINGSTON (*Sir* H.)
Lévy-Schneider (Léon). L'applic. du Concordat par un prélat d'anc. régime, Mgr. Champion de Cicé, 1802–10. la8°. 1921
Lewandowski (Maurice). Comment l'Allemagne a su se faire payer. Lille sous l'occup. allem. Avec lettre de M. Delesvalle. s8°. 1923
Lewes. The song of Lewes. [*Lat. & Eng.*] Ed. w. intr. & notes by C. L. Kingsford. s8° O. 1890
Lewes House, *see* BEAZLEY (J. D.) The L.H. coll. of anc. gems, 1920.
Lewes (George Henry). Life of Goethe. 3rd ed. rev. 8°. 1875
Lewicky (E.), *see* LEVITSKY (E.)
Lewin (Joseph). Earthquakes. s8°. Liv'l. 1926
Lewin (Percy Evans). Resources of the Empire. [Brit. Emp. : survey ; ed. H. Gunn, v4]. 8°. [1924]
see ROYAL COLONIAL INST. Sel. list of rec. publs. illust. constit. rels. betw. var. parts of Brit. Emp. ; comp. by E. L., 1926.
Lewin (Thomas Herbert). Manual of Tibetan. Prep. w. ass. of Yapa Ugyen Gyatsho. obl.8°. Calcutta. 1879
Lewis, *island.* The islands of N. Harris & S.H. &c. for sale, 1925, *see* HARRIS, *island.*
Lewis *of Puente, see* PUENTE (LUIS DE LA).
Lewis (*Mrs.* **Agnes Smith)**, *see* AḤIḲAR. The story of A., [*ed.*] L. &c., 2nd ed., 1913.
Lewis (Albert Buell). Block prints f. India for textiles.
[P2752]. 4°. Chicago. 1924
New Guinea masks. [P2736]. 8°. Chicago. 1922
Lewis (Alfred Henry).
Nation-famous New York murders. s8°. N.Y. [1914]
Lewis (Arthur M.)
Struggle betw. sci. & superstition. s8°. Chicago. [1915]
Lewis (C. A.) Broadcasting from within. [2nd ed.] 8°. [1924]
Lewis (C. T. Courtney).
George Baxter, the picture printer. la8°. [1924]
„ „ Suppl., *w. t.* The picture printer price list.
s8°. [1924]
Lewis (Charles B.), *see* APOLLONIUS, *Tyrius.* Altfranzös. Prosavers. d. A.-Romans ; hrsg. C. B. L., 1915.
Lewis (Charles G.), *see* LANDSEER (E. H.) Cat. of engr. works of E. L., coll. by C. G. L., 1855.
Lewis (Cleona), *see* MOULTON (H. G.) & C. L. The French debt problem, 1925.

Lewis (D. B. Wyndham).
At the sign of the Blue Moon. 3rd ed. s8°. [1925]
François Villon : a documented survey. Pref. by H. Belloc.
8°. 1928
Lewis (Ernest Dorman), *see* MACLAUGHLIN (A. C.), W. A. SLADE & E. D. L. Writings on Amer. hist., 1903, 1905.
Lewis (*Mrs.* **Ethelreda).** The harp. [*Novel*]. s8°. [1924]
see HORN (A. A.), *ps.* The life & works of A. A. H. ; ed. E. L., v1, 1927.
Lewis (*Sir* **George Cornewall)**, *2nd Bart.* On the origin of the Romance lang., cont. exam. of Raynouard's theory.
2nd ed. 8°. 1862
Lewis (George Griffin). The practical book of oriental rugs.
5th ed. 8°. Phila. 1920
Lewis (George Pitt-), *see* PITT-LEWIS (G.)
Lewis (George Randall). The stannaries : st. of Eng. tin miner. [Harvard Econ. st., v3]. 8°. Camb. [*Mass.*] 1924
Lewis (Gilbert Newton).
Anatomy of science. 8°. New Haven. 1926
Lewis (Griffith George), *see* AIDE-MÉMOIRE to milit. sciences ; ed. [L. &c.], 2nd ed., rev., 3v, 1853–62.
Lewis (Harry Reynolds).
Poultry keeping. 2nd rev. ed. s8°. Phila. [1919]
Lewis (Helen Prothero) [*Mrs.* JAMES J. G. PUGH].
The hill beyond. s8°. [1925]
Lewis (Henry), *see* MIRKUS (J.) Darn o'r Ffestifal (Liber festialis), gyda rhagymadrodd &c. gan H. L., 1925.
Lewis (Isabel Martin). Splendours of the sky. s8°. 1920
Lewis (J. Sydney). Old glass & how to collect it. [w. cat. of prices at recent sales]. [3rd ed. rev.] 8°. 1925
Lewis (John Frederick). Hist. of the Apprentices' Lib. of Phila., 1820–1920. la8°. Phila. 1924
Lewis (L. W. P.), *M.A.*
Pract. hints on the teaching of Latin. s8°. 1919
Lewis (P. Wyndham), *see* LEWIS (WYNDHAM).
Lewis (Samuel Savage), *see* MIDDLETON (J. H.) The L. coll. of gems & rings &c., 1892.
Lewis (Sinclair).
Babbitt. Intr. by H. Walpole. s8°. [1922]
„ „ [3rd impr.] s8°. [1922]
„ „ [The Travellers' Lib.] s8°. [1926]
Elmer Gantry. s8°. [1927]
The job. s8°. [1926]
Main Street. Story of Carol Kennicott. 8th pr. s8°. [1920]
Mantrap. s8°. [1926]
Martin Arrowsmith. s8°. [1925]
Our Mr. Wrenn. s8°. [1923]
The trail of the hawk. s8°. [1923]
Lewis (W. R. Sunderland).
Cubwood. Intr. by W. de la Mare. s8°. [1924]
Lewis (William), *teacher of chess.* Fifty games at chess. 8°. 1832
Lewis (Wyndham) [LEWIS (P. WYNDHAM)].
The art of being ruled. 8°. 1926
The lion & the fox : the hero in Shakespeare's plays. 8°. 1927
Tarr. s8°. 1918
Time & Western man. 8°. 1927
Lewis (Z.), *domestic sec. of United For. Mission. Soc., see* AMERICAN MISSION. REGISTER, by Z. L., v1, 1821.
Lewishon (Ludwig). The spirit of modern German lit. Lect., Univ. of Wisconsin. s8°. N.Y. 1916
Lewisohn (Sam Adolph).
The new leadership in industry. s8°. [1926]
Lewy (Julius). Die Chronologie d. Könige v. Israel u. Juda.
8°. Giessen. 1927
Lex. Lex Dei sive Mosaic. & Rom. legum collatio ; ed. F. Blume, 1833, *see* COLLATIO.
Lexicon [LESICON].
*Lesicon Románescu-Látinescu-Ungurescu-Nemtescu. Seu lex. Valachico-Lat.-Hung.-Germ., a pluribus auctoribus.
8°. Budae. 1825
*Lexicon Graecum (*Gr.-Lat.*), *see* BIBLE. Biblia sacra, t6, 1572.
Lexington (Henry de), *bp. of Lincoln ; d. 1258, see* GROSSETESTE (R.) Rotuli R. G., & Rotulus H. de L., Episc. Lincoln., 1254–59 ; ed. F. N. Davis, 1914.
Lexoviennes. Etudes lexov. 2[t]. la8°. 1915–19
1, Par G. Besnier, R. Lantier, J. Lesquier, A. Moisy, R. Quéru, R. N. Sauvage. 2, Par G. Huard, V. Lahaye, J. Lesquier.
Ley (Hans). Die litterar. Tätigkeit d. Lady Craven. Inaug.-Diss. [P2862]. 8°. Erlangen. 1904
Ley (John), *prebendary of Chester, see* BIBLE. COMPL. TEXTS &c. Annot. upon the O. & N.T. : by [J. L. &c.], 2nd ed., 2v., 1651.

Leyden. Bronnen tot de gesch. d. Leidsche Univ.; uitg. v. P. C. Molhuysen, d4–7, 1920–24, *see* MOLHUYSEN (P. C.)
Stadsrekeningen van L., 1390–1434. Uitg. door A. Meerkamp van Embden. [Hist. Genoots. Werken., s3, 32, 34]. 2d. 8°. A. 1913–14
see BRONCHORST (E.) Diarium, sive adversaria omnium quae gesta sunt in Acad. L., 1591–1627, 1898.

Leynez (Diego), *see* LAINEZ (D.)

Leys (Norman). Kenya. Intr. by G. Murray. 8°. 1924

Leyser (Polycarp) [LEISER], *of Dresden.* Ein Christl. Bedencken, was v. d. Exorcismo bey d. Tauff &c. zu halten sey. [P2438]. s4°. Magdeburg. 1591
„ „ ....[*a. ed.* P2626]. s4°. *n.p.* 1591
Examen 10 doc. Adami Conzen, quae Lutheranis meditanda proposuit. Resp. J. Wincklero. [P483]. s4°. Lipsiae. 1618
Kurtzer Bericht auff die, unter D. Hoffmann's Namen wieder die zu Dresden gedr. Christl. Concordiam, ausgesprengte Beschüldigung. [*b. w.* Hoffmann (D.) Abtr. etl. Schr., 1597]. s4°. Dressden. 1597
Oratio jubilæa de Rom. pontificis blasphema tyrannide. [P483]. s4°. Lipsiae. 1618

Leyser (Polycarp), *of Helmstadt* [LYSERUS]. Diss.: hist. Conciliorum Moguntin. Praes. J. A. Schmidio. [P2647]. s4°. Helmstadii. [1713]

Leyser (Polycarp), *of Leipzig, the younger* [LYSER]. Disput. de cetis. [P1035]. s4°. Lipsiae. [1680]

Lhéritier (Michel). Tours & la Guerre: ét. écon. & soc. Par M. L., avec concours de C. Chautemps. [C.E. for Internat. Peace]. 8°. [1926]
see DRIAULT (E.) & M. L. Hist. diplomat. de la Grèce de 1821 à nos jours, t1–5, 1925–26.

L'Hermite (François Tristan). Les amours & a. poésies choisies. Préf. &c. par P. Camo. 8°. 1925
La mort de Seneque. Tragédie. Ed. crit. publ. J. Madeline. [Soc. des Textes Franç. Mod.] s8°. 1919
Le parasite (1654), *see* FOURNEL (V.) Contemp. de Molière, t3, 1875.

Lhomel (Georges de). Docs. p. s. à l'hist. de Berck. la8°. Abbeville. 1913
La vicomté de Montreuil-sur-Mer. 8°. Montreuil-sur-Mer. 1904
see MONTREUIL-SUR-MER. Cartul.; publ. par G. de L., 1904.
„ —— Rec. [& Nouv. rec.] de doc. p. s. à l'hist. de M., 1000–1782; publ. par G. de L., 2t, 1907–10.

L'Hôpital (Winefride de), *wife of René de l'H., née Bentley.* Westminster Cathedral & its architect. Intr. by W. R. Lethaby. 2v. [*pagin. cont.*] la8°. [1919]

L'Hospital (Michel de), *chancelier de France* [†L'HOPITAL (M. DE)], *see* LÉVESQUE DE POUILLY (J. S.) *Vie de M. de L'H., 1767.

Lhotzky (Heinrich). Das Buch d. Ehe. s8°. Königstein. [1921]

L'Huillier (*Dom* A.) St. Thomas de Cantorbéry. 2t. 8°. 1891–92

Liang, *dynasty, see* TCHANG (M.) Tombeau des L., fam. Siao, pl, 1912.

Liaño (Enrique Sant' A. de). Das grosse kirchl. Gebrechen unser. Zeit, 1870, *see* KATHOLISCH. Stimmen aus d. K. Kirche, B1, 1870.

Libanius. Opera. Rec. R. Foerster. v9–12. s8°. Lips., *Teubner.* 1921–27
9, Characteres epistolici, proleg. ad epistulas, cur. E. Richtsteig. 10, Epistulae, 1–839. 11, Epistulae, 840–1544, una cum pseudepigr. et Basilii cum Libanio commercio epist.—Fragmenta. 12, Index nom. propr., congessit E. Richtsteig.

Libedinsky (Yury).
A week. Tr., w. intr. by A. Ransome. s8°. [1923]

***Libelle** (The) of Englyshe polycye: poem, 1436; ed. Sir G. Warner, 1926, *see* ENGLISH.

Libellus. Incipit l. de raptu anime Tundali &c., 1483, *see* TUNDALE.
*L. supplex Imperatoriae Maj. &c., 1570, *see* BELGAE.

Libens (Joannes). Theses proleg. ad sacram scr. Praes. J. L., propugn. J. de Wysel, J. v. Hove. [P2659]. s8°. Lovanii. 1720

Liber.
Liber de causis, *ascr. to Aristotle, see* ARISTOTLE: SPUR. WORKS.
Liber diurnus, *see* PEITZ (W. M.) L. d.: Beitr., 1, 1918.
Liber diurnus, ou rec. des formules usitées par la Chancellerie pontif. du 5e au 11e s. Publ. &c. par E. de Rozière. Suppl. 8°. 1869
Liber feodorum. *This is the alternative t. of* *Testa de Nevill, *q.v.*
Liber hymnorum in metra noviter redact., 1501, *see* BEBELIUS (H.)
Liber instrument. memorialium, &c., 1884–6, *see* GUILLEMS, *Seigneurs de Montpellier.*

Liber [*continued*].
Liber Marchiane ruine: poema storico d. sec. 14; pubbl. da C. Cantu, *see* REGIA DEP. DI STORIA PATRIA. Misc., t5, 1868.
Liber margarita Davitica, 1471?, *see* MARGARITA.
Liber Pontificalis prout exstat in cod. ms. Dertusensi, textum compl. hactenus ex parte ined. Pandulphi. Ed. &c. a J. M. March. Acc. Mem. eccl. Romae. 4°. Barcinone. 1925

Liberal Evangelicalism: an interpretation. By Members of the Church of England. 3rd ed. 8°. [1923]

Liberal Industrial Inquiry.
Britain's indust. future. Report. 8°. 1928

Liberal Publication Department. Ten yrs. of Tory govt., 1895–1905. Home affairs. 8°. 1905

***Liberties** (The) of England asserted, 1714, *see* ENGLAND.

Libertin (Charles), *Jesuit, see* GENNADIUS, *patr. of Cple. in the 15 c.* De praedestinatione; Lat. don. & comm. illust. C. L., 1681.

Libertini (Guido). Di alc. rec. scoperte n. necropoli di S. Luigi a Caltagirone, *see* REALE ACCAD. D. LINCEI. Mon. ant., v28, 1922.
Le isole Eolie nell' antichità greca e romana. [R. Instit. di Studi Prat. &c.] la8°. Firenze. 1921

Liberty (The) bell. By Friends of freedom. [Coll. of articles on slavery, in prose & verse]. s8°. Boston. 1852

Librarian (The) internat. directory of booksellers: Clegg's successor; ed. A. J. Philip, 1927, *see* DIRECTORY.

Libraries. The uses of l.: [lect. *by var. wr.*], 1927, *see* BAKER (E. A.), *ed.*

Library (A) of Xtn. biog., 12v, 1837–40, *see* JACKSON (T.)

Library (The). A quarterly review of bibliog. Ed. A. W. Pollard. s4, v1–8. [*Incorporating* Trans. of Bibliog. Soc., s2, v1–8]. 8°. [1921–28]

Library Association.
Handbook for 1924, 1926, 1928. la8°. [1924–28]
The L.A. record. v22–24 (1920–22). la8°. 1921–23
„ „ ......Ed. A. Esdaile. New ser., v1–5. la8°. 1923–27
L.A. year book, 1921, 1922. 8°. 1921–22
The Roll of Honour of Brit. librarians. Suppl. to the L.A. Record, N.S., v3, No. 9. la8°. 1925
Subject index to periodicals, 1917–22, 1926. Issued by the L.A. [6v; 1917–19, *b. in* 2v]. 4°. 1920–28
No index of names issued for 1920–22, 1926.

Libres. Les œuvres libres, 1921–28, *see* ŒUVRES.

Libri symbolici eccl. cathol., 2t, 1838, *see* STREITWOLF (F. G.) & R. E. KLENER.

Libri (Guglielmo), *see* LAMPORECCHI (R.) Mém. sur la persécution &c., 1850.

Libro. Libro (Il) dei setti savj di Roma, 1864, *see* SEVEN SAGES.
Libro de los Tres Reyes de Oriente. Publ. in facs. f. MS. in Library of the Escorial by A. M. Huntington. [Hisp. Soc. of Amer.] la8°. N.Y. 1904
Libro d'oro d. nobilità ital. vol. 6, 1923–25. s8°. [1925]
Libro d'oro (Il), Venice, 1623. The golden book: legends of saints &c. Tr. Mrs. F. Alexander. 8°. 1905

Libros de caballerias, 1924, *see* TENREIRO (R. M.), *ed.*

Liburnio (Niccolò). Lo verde antico d. cose volgari. [*Imperfect, Leaf A2 wanting,* H1 *in MS.*] s8°. [Venetia. 1524]

Libya. A hdbk. of L., 1920, *see* ADMIRALTY.

Lichačov (Nikolaus), *see* ZERETELI (G. F.), *ed.* Papyri russ. u. georg. Sammlungen, 4, Kome-Aphrodito Papyri d. Sammlung L., 1927.

Lichfield.
The Gild of St. Mary, L. Ordinances & o. doc. Ed. F. J. Furnivall. [E.E.T.S., E.S., 114]. 8°. 1920
The gt. register of L. Cathedral, Magnum reg. album; ed. H. E. Savage, *see* STAFFORDSHIRE. Coll. for hist. of S., 1924, 1926.
*Hand guide to L. cathedral, 8th ed., 1906, *see* HARRADINE (C.)
*A short acc. of L. Cathedral; partic. of the painted glass &c. 3rd ed. w. add. 8°. Lichfield. 1823

Lichnowsky (Carl Max, *Fürst* v.) Auf d. Wege z. Abgrund. London. Berichte, Erinnerungen &c. 2B. 8°. Dresden. 1927
Heading for the abyss. [Tr. S. Delmer]. 8°. 1928
Meine Londoner Mission 1912–14 u. Eingabe an d. preuss. Herrenhaus. [P2409]. 8°. [1919]
see MACCURDY (*Rt. Hon.* C. A.) Guilty! L.'s disclosures, 1918.
„ SÄNGER (A.) Die Schuld d. deut. Regierung am Kriege; Nachtrag zu Meine Lond. Mission, v. L., *n.d.*

Lichnowsky (Mechtild), *wife of Carl Max, Fürst v. Lichnowsky.*
Geburt. 3e A. 8°. 1922
Der Kampf m. d. Fachmann. s8°. Wien. 1925
Der Stimmer. 8°. L. 1917

Lichtenberg (Georg Christoph), *the elder.* Erklärg. d. hogarth. Kupferstiche. 14 Lief. *in* 2v. [Lief. 13 *has t.*: J. P. Lyser's Erklärg. d. hogarth. Kupferstiche. Lief 14: Dr. Le Petit's Erklärg. d. hogarth. Kupferstiche]. s8º. Göttingen. 1794–1835
Gedanken u. Maximen. Mit e. biogr. Einl. v. E. Grisebach. s8º. L. 1871
Vermischte Schriften. Neue verm., Original-Ausgabe. 8B [*in* 3v]. s8º. Göttingen. 1844–67
B7 & 8 have add. tp. "G. C. L.'s Briefe; hrsg. v. C. W. Lichtenberg."
W. Hogarth's Zeichnungen. Nach d. Orig. in Stahl gestochen. Mit d. Erkl. Nebst e. Biog. Hogarth's v. F. Kottenkamp. [w. a pref. by L. Gantter]. 3e verb. A. 8º. St. 1873

Lichtenberger (André).
Biche. s8º. 1920
Chez les Graffougnat. s8º. [1923]
Des enfants dans un jardin. s8º. [1927]
Des voix dans la nuit, *see* Œuvres libres, 81, 1928.
La folle aventure. éd. déf. s8º. 1924
Lolotte & s. vieux roi, *see* Œuvres libres, 59, 1926.
M. de Migurac, ou le marquis philosophe. éd. définitive. s8º. 1922
Redemption. [Livre mod. illust.] 8º. 1924
Sang basque, *see* Œuvres libres, 53, 1925.

Lichtenberger (Henri). Rel. betw. France & Germany. A report. [C.E. for Int. Peace]. 8º. Wash. 1923
The Ruhr conflict. [C.E. for Int. Peace. P2750]. la8º. Wash. 1923

Lichtwark (Alfred). Briefe an d. Komm. f. d. Verwaltung d. Kunsthalle [Reisebriefe]. Hrsg. G. Pauli. 2B. s8º. Hamburg. 1924

Licino (Giov. Batt.) *Rime d diversi celebri poeti dell' età nostra. Nuov. racc. &c. [*by* G. B. L.] 8º. Bergamo. 1587

Lickute Kadmoniot: z. Gesch. d. Karaismus, 1860, *see* Pinsker (S.), *ed.*

Liddell (Henry George), *dean of Christ Church,* **& R. Scott.** Greek-Eng. lex. New ed. rev. & augm. by H. S. Jones, w. ass. of R. McKenzie &c. pl, 2. A–διαλέγω. 4º. O. 1925–26
Lexicon abr. f. L. & S.'s Greek-Eng. lexicon. 25th ed. rev. 8º. O. 1892

Liddell (Robert Scotland).
Fifty thousand miles of sun. 8º. 1925

Liddell-Hart (*Capt.* **Basil Henry),** *see* Hart (*Capt.* B. H. L.)

Liddil (James Andrew). [*ps.* Dick Liddil], *see* James (F.) *Trial of F. J.; w. confess. of D. L. &c., 1898.

Liddon (Henry Parry), *see* Keble (J.) Christian Year, w. medit. &c. sel. f. wks. of L., 1886.

Lido. Relaz. s. regolarizz. d. porto di L. fol. Venezia. 1874

Lidwina, *Saint, d. 1433, see* †Huysmans (J. K.) Ste. L. de Schiedam, 3e éd., 1901.

Lidzbarski (Mark). Mandäische Liturgien; mitgeteilt, übers. u. erkl. v. M. L., *see* Königl. Gesells. d. W. zu Göttingen. Abh., N.F., B17, 1921.
see Ginza. G., d. grosse Buch d. Mandäer, übers. u. erkl. v. M. L., 1925.
„ Johannesbuch. Das J. d. Mandäer; [hrsg.] M. L., 1915.

Lie (Jonas Lauritz Idemil), *1833–1903.*
Lodsen og hans Hustru. 5e Opl. s8º. 1880
Rutland. s8º. 1880
Samlede digterverker. Standardutgave. Inleid. av V. Erichsen. Oplysninger og varianter ved P. Bergh. 10B. s8º. 1920–21
1, Den Fremsynte—Fortællinger og Skildringer—Tremasteren "Fremtiden."
2, Lodsen og hans Hustru—Faustina Strozzi.
3, Thomas Ross—Adam Schrader—Grabows Kat.
4, Rutland—Ole Bull—Gaa paa!
5, Livsslaven—Familien paa Gilje—En Malstrøm.
6, Otte Fortællinger—Stemninger—Kommandørens Døttre.
7, Et Samliv—Maisa Jons—Onde Magter.
8, Trold I–II—Niobe—Lystige Koner.
9, Naar Sol gaar ned—Dyre Rein—Lindelin—Faste Forland.
10, Wulffie & Comp.—Naar Jernteppet falder—Ulfvungerne—Østenfor Sol og vestenfor Maane—Eventyr—Digte og Sange.

Lie (M. Sophus), *1842–99.* Vorlesungen ü. continuierl. Gruppen mit geometr. u. a. Anwendungen. Hrsg. G. Scheffers. la8º. L. 1893

Lieb (Sylvester), *see* Hillinger (J. G.) Memoria Aquilina: Leben C. A. aus S. L.'s Ms., 1731.

Liebaert (Paul), *see* Ehrle (F.) & P. L. Specimina cod. Lat. Vatican., ed. 2a, 1927.

Liebenam (Willy). Forsch. z. Verwaltungsgesch. d. röm. Kaiserreichs.
B1. Die Legaten in d. röm. Prov. [*no more publ.*] 8º. L. 1888

Lieber (Maxim), *see* Clark (B. H.) & M. L., *edd.* Gt. short stories of the world, 1926.
—— **& B. C. Williams.** Great stories of all nations. 158 sh. stories, sel. by M. L. & B. C. W. 8º. [1927]

Liebermann (Felix). Texte u. Forschungen z. engl. Kulturgesch. Festgabe für F. L., dargebracht v. H. Böhmer, A. Brandl &c. 8º. Halle. 1921

Liebert (Arthur). Das Problem d. Geltung. 2e A. 8º. L. 1920

Liebhard (Ludwig). Brevis &c. inter Protestantes invariatae August. Conf. addictos & Calvino-reformatos hist. s4º. Francofurti. 1672

Liebich (Bruno). Zur Einführ. in d. ind. einheim. Sprachwiss. [*Extr. f.* Heidelberg. Akad. d. Wiss. Sitzb., 1919]. [H1–4 *in 1v*]. 8º. Heidelberg. 1919

Liebig (Hans, *Frhr.* **v.)** Bethmann-Hollweg — Erzberger — Scheidemann. [Reichsverderber, T1]. 8º. [1922]
Die Politik v. Bethmann Hollwegs. 2T *in* 1v [*pagin. cont.*] 8º. München. 1919

Liebig (Justus, *Frhr.* **v.)** [*Baron* Liebig]. Über d. Constit. d. organ. Säuren (1838). Hrsg. v. H. Kopp. 8º. L. 1891

Liebknecht (Carl Paul Aug. Frdr.)
Das Zuchthausurteil gegen K. L. Wörtl. Wiedergabe d. Prozessakten, Urteile u. Eingaben L. Hrsg. v. d. Kommunist. Partei. Deutsch. 8º. 1919
Судъ надъ К. Либкнехтомъ. [P2397]. 8º. П. 1918
see Kautsky (C.) R. Luxemburg, K. L. &c., 1921.
„ Radek (C.) Rosa Luxemburg, K. L. &c., 1921.
„ Schumann (H.) K. L., 1923.
„ Zinovev (G.) & L. Trotzky. K. L. u. R. Luxemburg, 1920.

Liebknecht (Johann Georg). Fest. Reformationis Evangel. Orat. de Luthero &c. [P484]. s4º. Giessae. [1717]

Liebknecht (Wilhelm).
Zum Jubeljahr d. Märzrevolution. 8º. 1898

Liebmann (Otto). Gedanken u. Thatsachen. H1. 8º. Str. 1882
„ „ 2e A. 2B [B1 *wants* H1. B2ii *b. separately*]. la8º. Str. 1899–1904
Die Klimax d. Theorieen. 8º. Str. 1884
Ueb. d. individ. Beweis f. d. Freiheit d. Willens. 8º. St. 1866
Weltwanderung. Gedichte. s8º. St. 1899

Liebrecht (Henri) & G. Rency. Hist. illust. de la litt. belge de langue fr. 8º. Brux. 1926

Liebrechts (*le maj.* **Charles).** Congo. Suite à mes souv. d'Afrique, 1889–1908. 8º Brux. 1920

Liebusch (Georg). Skythika, etymolog. u. krit. Bemerk. ü. alte Bergrelig. u. spät. Fetischismus &c. 8º. Camenz. 1833

Liechtenstein, *The House of, see* Ströhl (H. G.) Das Wappen d. Fürstentums L., 1913.

Liefmann (Gottlieb). Diss. de fanaticis Silesiorum & spec. Q. Kuhlmanno. Præs. G. Wernsdorfio. ed. 4. [P2631]. s4º. Wittenbergae. 1733

Liefmann (Robert). Internat. cartels, combines & trusts. Intr. by C. T. Hallinan. s8º. [1927]

Liefrinck (F. A.) Het eiland Bali, *see* Tijdschrift voor Ind. taal &c., d33, 1890.

Liége.
2 livres d'heures néerland.; repr. des miniatures &c., Bibl. de l'Univ. de L., 1924 ?, *see* Heures.
Invent. analyt. des chartes de la Colleg. de Ste. Croix à L.; par E. Poncelet. [C.R. d'H. de Belg.] t2. 8º. Brux. [1921]
Invent. analyt. des chartes de la Collég. de St. Jean l'Évangél à L.; par L. Lahaye. [C.R. d'H. de Belg.] t1. 8º. Brux. 192

Liegnitz. Die Stadt L. Hrsg. Charbonnier, Dr. Elsner &c. la8º. 1927

Lieh-tzu [Lie-tzeu], *see* Wieger (L.) Taoïsme, t2, Les pères du système t., L. &c. [*Chinese & French*], 1913.

Lienert (Meinrad). Frohfarbenfähnlein: Gesch. aus d Bergland. s8º. Frauenfeld. 191
Der jauchzende Bergwald: Geschichten. 3. A. s8º. Frauenfeld. 191

Lienhart (Theobald). De antiq. liturgiis & de disciplina Arcani tract. 8º. Argentorati. 182

Lier (Helperus Ritzema van). Dissert., *see* Pap (J.) Disp. 1784.

Liestøl (Knut) & M. Moe.
Norske folkeviser fra middelalderen. 2et Opl. s8º. 191

Lietz (Hermann). Das 15e Jahr in Deut. Land-Erziehungs Heimen. T2. [P2502]. 8º. L. 191
Über die Deut. Land-Erziehungs-Heime: Urteile ü. d. D.L E.-H. u. d. "Deut. Nationalschule" v. H. L. 2e Folge. Hrsg v. d. Freunden d. D.L.-E.-H. [*By var. wr.*] 8º. *n.p.* 191

Lie-tzeu, *see* Lieh-tzu.

Lietzmann (Hans). Einführung i. d. Röm. Brevier, *see* KLEINE TEXTE, T141, Liturg. Texte, T10, 1917.
Handbuch zum Neuen Testament. In Verbindung mit W. Bauer &c. Hrsg. v. H. L. B1i–iii [*in 1v*], 2i, ii [*in 1v*], 3i, ii [*in 6T. b. sep.*], 4i–iii [*b. sep. Each part has sep. tp. & pagin. except B1iii*]. 8°. Tübingen. 1910–23
1i, Neutestamentl. Grammatik ; v. L. Radermacher.
1ii, iii, Die hellenist.-röm. Kultur—Die urchristl. Lit. ; v. P. Wendland, 2. u. 3. A.
2i, Die Evangelien ; erklärt v. E. Klostermann.
2ii, Die Evangelien, 2, Johannes ; erklärt v. W. Bauer.
3i, Die Briefe d. Apostels Paulus, T1, An d. Römer, T2, An d. Korinther I, II, 2e A., T3, An d. Galater ; erklärt v. H. Lietzmann.
3ii, Die Briefe des Apostels Paulus, T1, An d. Kolosser, Epheser, An Philemon, 2, An d. Thessalonicher I, II, An d. Philipper, 3, An Timotheus I, II, An Titus ; erklärt v. M. Dibelius.
4i, Die Apostolgesch. ; erklärt v. E. Preuschen.
4ii, Die Katholischen Briefe ; erklärt v. H. Windisch.
4iii, Der Hebräerbrief ; erklärt v. H. Windisch.
Bd. 3i, T2 An d. Korinther I, II *is numbered* 9.
„ „ 2e, völlig neubearb. A. B6. 8°. Tübingen. 1925
6, Das Johannesevangelium ; erklärt v. W. Bauer.
„ „ Ergänzungsband, Die apostol. Väter. 8°. Tübingen. 1920–23
1, Die Lehre d. 12 Apostel—Die 2 Clemensbriefe ; erkl. v. R. Knopf.
2, Briefe d. Ignatius v. Antiochia u. d. Polykarpbrief ; erkl. v. W. Bauer.
3, Der Barnabasbrief ; erkl. v. H. Windisch.
4, Der Hirt d. Hermas ; erkl. v. M. Dibelius.
Petrus u. Paulus in Rom. 2e neubearb. A. 8°. 1927
Tabulae in usum scholarum ; ed. sub cura J. L., 1910–27, *see* TABULA.

Lieure (J.) La gravure dans le livre & l'ornement. [La gravure en France au 16e s.] 4°. 1927

Lieven (*Fürst* Anatol Pawlowitsch), *see* BRAATZ (K. W. v.) Fürst A.P.L. im Kampfe gegen d. balt. Separatismus &c.,1926.

Lieven (*princess* Doroteya Khristoforovna). Unpubl. diary & polit. sketches. Ed. H. W. V. Temperley. 8°. 1925

Lièvre (Auguste François). Hist. des Protestants & des églises réformées du Poitou. 3t. 8°. Poitiers. 1856–60

Lièvre (Pierre), *see* LE CARDONNEL (G.) & P. L. Etudes sur E. Montfort, 1920.

Life [LYFE].
*Life (The) & death of M. Luther &c., 1641, *see* ADAMUS (M.)
*Life & defence &c. of E. Bonner, bp. of London, 1842, *see* TOWNSEND (G.)
Life & its maintenance. A symposium on biological problems. [*By var. wr.*] s8°. 1919
*Life (The) of God in soul of man, 1748 ; 1777, *see* SCOUGAL (H.)
*Life of J. Sage, 1714, *see* GILLANE (J.)
*Life (The) of Mr. A. Pedan, 1788, *see* PEDEN (A.)
*Life (The) of that incomparable man F. Socinus &c. ; tr., 1653, *see* PRZYPKOWSKI (S.)
*Life (The) of Will. Bedell, bp. of Kilmore, 1685, *see* BURNET (G.)
Lyfe (The) of St. Radegunde ; ed. F. Brittain, 1926, *see* RADEGUNDA, *St.*

***Light** (The) of other days : some remin. By the a. of "50 years of London society." 8°. [1924]

Light (Henry). Travels in Egypt, Nubia, Holy Land, Mt. Libanon & Cyprus, 1814. 4°. 1818

Lightfoot (John), *botanist.*
Flora Scotica. 2v. [*pagin. cont.*] 8°. 1777

Lightfoot (Joseph Barber), *bp. of Durham.*
Biblical essays. [2nd ed.] 8°. 1904
Colossians & Philemon : rev. text, notes &c. 9th ed. 8°. 1890
Galatians. 7th ed. 8°. 1881
Philippians : rev. text, notes &c., by L. 8°. 1891

Lightfoot (Peter), *see* HOWGRAVE-GRAHAM (R. P.) P. L., monk of Glastonbury &c., 1922.

Lighthall (William Douw). Lt.-Gen. Garret Fisher : a forgotten loyalist. [*From* Royal Soc. of Canada, Trans., sect. 2, 1922]. [P2703]. la8°. [Montreal. 1922]

Lightley (J. W.) Jewish sects &c. in time of Jesus. [Fernley Lect.] 8°. [1925]

Lightning Rod Conference. Report. Ed. G. J. Symons. 8°. 1882

Ligne, *House of, see* LEURIDANT (F.) Les collations de cures & de bénéfices de la maison de L., 1921.

Ligne (Charles Joseph, *prince* **de).**
Coup d'œil sur Belœil & jardins de l'Europe. Intr. & notes par Cte. E. de Ganay. n. éd. 8°. 1922
Les embarras. Pièce. s8°. [1914]
Lettres de Fédor à Alphonsine. s8°. Brux. 1921
Ma Napoléonide. s8°. 1921

Ligne (Charles Joseph, *prince* **de)** [*continued*].
Mém. Ed. du centenaire, par E. Gilbert. s8°. 1914
Mém. & lettres. n. éd. augm. de doc. inéd. 8°. 1923
Mém. du prince Eugène de Savoie. Écrits par lui-meme [*not by E. but by L.*] 2e réimpr. 8°. 1811
*Mem. of Prince Eugene of Savoy. Written by himself, [*not by E. but by L.*] Tr. W. Mudford. 8°. 1811
Préjugés militaires. Ed. du centenaire, par le baron de Heusch. s8° 1914
see GILBERT (O. P.) The Prince of L. ; tr. J. McCabe, 1923.
„ LEBASTEUR (H.) Le Pr. de L. & les poètes fr., 1921.
„ LEURIDANT (F.) Une éducation de prince au 18e s. : C. J. de L., 1923.
„ —— Le prince de L., Mme. de Staël & Caroline Murray, 1920.
„ OULIÉ (M.) Le Prince de L., 1926.

Ligne (Claude-Lamoral, *prince* **de).**
see LEURIDANT (F.) Une ambassade du Prince de L. en Angleterre, 1660, *n.d.*
„ —— Un pélerin belge à N.-Dame de Lorette au 17e siècle, *n.d.*

Ligne (*pcsse.* Hedwige de), *wife of prince Eugène de Ligne, née pcsse. Lubomirska.* Souv., 1815–50 ; publ. Pcsse. Ch. de Ligne. 2e éd. 8°. Brux. 1923

Lignières (François Payot de), *see* PAYOT DE LIGNIÈRES (F.)

Liguori (Alfonso Maria de), *Saint.*
Expos. & def. of points of faith defined by the C. of Trent, w. a refut. of the errors of the pretend. reformers &c. w. obj. of P. Sarpi. Tr. s8°. D. 1846
Homo apostolicus instructus ad audiendas confessiones. ed. 7a. 3t. s8°. Mechliniae. 1824
*Life of St A. M. L. [*tp. wanting*]. s8°. 1880
Morale systema, *see* MIGNE (J. P.), *ed.* Theol. cursus, t11, 1861.
Praxis confessarii, *see* MIGNE (J. P.), *ed.* Theol. cursus, t22, 1860.
see BUSENBAUM (H.) Theologia moralis, nunc aucta à A. de L., 3t, 1757.

Liguoro (Antonio di), *see* NOZZE. Coppola-Caracciolo. Vari compon. [ed. A. di L.], 1725.

Li Kang-ki. Kiao-ou li-lio [*comp. by Li K.-ki*] publ. par ordre de Tcheou Fou ; tr., 1917, *see* TCHEOU FOU.

***Like** as the damaske rose &c. : verses on man's mortalitie &c., 1925, *see* VERSES.

Liliencron (Detlev, *Frhr.* **v.)** Kriegsnovellen. s8°. [1912]

Lilienfein (Heinrich).
Die feurige Wolke. Roman. 1.–5. A. s8°. St. 1919

Lilienfeld. Todtenbuch d. Cisterc.-Stiftes L. ; mitgetheilt v. H. Zeissberg, *see* FONTES RERUM AUSTRIAC., B41i, 1879.

Lilienthal (Michael). Bibl. Archivarius d. heil. Schr. Alten Test. &c. [*& N. Test. b. together*]. s4°. L. 1745–46
Bibl. exeget. Bibliothec : Verzeichniss &c. 2te A. s8°. Königsberg i. P. 1748
De Machiavellismo literario &c. s8°. Regiomonti. 1713
Theolog.-homilet. Archivarius &c. s4°. Königsberg. 1749

Lilienthal (Theodor Christoph). Diss. de Pelagianismo. Praes. J. G. Walchio. [P434]. s4°. Jenae. [1738]
Schediasma hist.-theolog. de canone missae Gregoriano. s8°. Lugd. Batav. 1740

Lilii (Camillo). Dell' historia di Camerino parte prima [-seconda]. 2p *in* 1v. 4°. [Venice? *or* Macerata?. 1670?]
This book was never finished ; p1 is incomplete, wanting tp., pages 219–224 & all after p. 256, as in all copies known.

Lilius (Carolus Gustavus). Animadv. in Fennicam Bibliorum sacr. versionem. s4°. Aboae. [1826]

Liljefalk (Axel). Kong Frederik VIII. 8°. København. [1912]

Lill (Georg). Deut. Plastik. 8°. 1925

Lille. Chambre des comptes de L. : cat. des chartes du sceau de l'audience, t1, 1915, *see* NELIS (H.), *ed.*
Franchises, lois & coutumes de la ville de L. : anc. ms. cont. chartes &c. ; publ. &c. Brun-Lavainne, 1842, *see* ROISIN (J.)

Liller Kriegszeitung. Auslese aus Nr. 1–40. Hrsg. v. [P. O.] Hoecker & [G.] von Ompteda. 8°. [1915]

Lilley (A. E. V.) & W. Midgley.
Book of studies in plant form. enl. ed. 8°. 1902

Lilley (Henry T.) & A. T. Everitt.
Portsmouth parish church. 8°. Portsmouth. [1921]

Lillie (D. G.) Cetacea, *see* BRIT. ANTARCTIC EXPED., 1910–13. Zoology, v1, 1914–16.
see HARMER (S. F.) & D. G. L. List of collecting stations, 1914.

Lillie (Frank Rattray).
Problems of fertilization. s8°. Chicago. [1919]

Lillo (George). Fatal curiosity, *see* INCHBALD (E.) Brit. th., v11, 1808.
George Barnwell. Tragedy. [P2575]. 8°. 1777
„ „ *a. ed., see* INCHBALD (E.) Brit. th., v11, 1808.
Lily (William) & J. Colet. *A short introd. of grammar of Latin [ed. by J. Ward]. s8°. 1825
Lima. *Sumario del concilio provinc., que se celebro en la ciudad de los reyes [*i.e.* Lima], 1575. s8°. Sevilla. 1614
Liman von Sanders (*General* **Otto K. V.)**
Fünf Jahre Türkei. 8°. [1919]
Limay (Paul Ratouis de), *see* RATOUIS DE LIMAY (P.)
Limborch (Philippus van). Comm. in Acta Apostol. & in Epist. ad Rom. & ad Hebraeos. fol. Roterodami. 1711
Historia Inquisitionis. Cui subjungitur Liber sententiarum Inquis. Tholosanæ, 1307–23 [*w. sep. pagin.*] fol. Amstelodami. 1692
Theologia christiana, ad praxin pietatis &c. directa. ed. 3ª. folio. Amstelædami. 1700
see CATTENBURGH (A. VAN). Spicilegium theologiae Christ. P. a L., 1726.
Limbourg. Invent. des chartes &c. des duchés de Brabant & de L. &c., p1, t1–7, 1910–17, *see* VERKOOREN (A.)
***Limburg** manœuvre of Aug. 1914, 1919, *see* CANDID (*Capt.*), *ps.*
Limerick (The) curfew murders of Mar. 7th, 1921. The case of Michael O'Callaghan. [P2560]. 8°. 1921
Limpsfield [LYMPSFIELD]. *Lympsfield & its environs, 1838, *see* STREATFIELD (T.)
Lin (Thomas). *Short (A) survey of A friendly conf. betw. a countrie-man & h. nephew [*by L.*], 1711 ?, *see* MACMILLAN (*Rev.* J.)
Linacre (Thomas). De emendata structura Latini sermonis libri 6. s8°. Venetiis, *P. Manutius.* 1557
„ „ Recognita a J. Camerario. Acc. Libellus ejusdem Camerarii de arte grammatica &c. [Annotat. C. Landsidelii]. s8°. Lipsiae. 1573
Linant de Bellefonds (A.) Carte hydrograph. de la Basse Égypte & d'une partie de l'Isthme de Suez. folded la8°. [1856 ?]
Linar (Gustave de), *ps., see* KRÜDENER (B. J. v.) Valérie, ou lettres de G. de L., 1804.
Linares Rivas (Manuel).
La fuente amarga. Comedia. s8°. 1910
Linati (Carlo). Pubertà ed altre storie. 8°. Milano. 1926
Sulle orme di Renzo [Promessi sposi]. Pagine di fedeltà lombarda. [P2427]. s8°. 1919
Sulle orme di Renzo, e altre prose lombarde. [n. ed.] 8°. Milano. 1927
Linck (Johann) [LINCCIUS (J.)] Circulus philosophiae &c. diss. s4°. Wittebergae. 1628
Linckenheld (Emile). Les stèles funéraires en forme de maison chez les Mediomatriques & en Gaule. 8°. Str. 1927
Lincoln.
Calendars of administr. in Consistory Court of L., 1540–1659. Ed. C. W. Foster. [L. Rec. Soc., v16]. la8°. Horncastle. 1921
„ „ *for a. ed., see* BRIT. REC. SOC. Ind. Lib., v52, 1921.
Catalogue of MSS. of L. Cathedral Chapter Library. Comp. by R. M. Woolley. 8°. O. 1927
Chapter acts of the Cathedral Church of St. Mary of L., 1547–59. Ed. R. E. G. Cole. [Lincoln Rec. Soc., v15]. 8°. Horncastle. 1920
Lincoln wills reg. in Distr. Probate Registry at L. Ed. C. W. Foster. [Lincoln Rec. Soc., v5]. 8°. Lincoln. 1914
Offic. guide, Lincoln, city & cathedral. s8°. Lincoln. [1921]
Parish reg. of City of L. Marriages, 1538–1754. Ed. C. W. Foster. [Lincoln Rec. Soc. Parish Reg. Sect.] la8°. Horncastle. 1925
Parish reg. of St. Peter at Gowts, Lincoln, 1538–1837. Ed. R. C. Dudding. [Lincoln Rec. Soc.: Par. Reg. Sect., v8]. 8°. Horncastle. 1923
State of the church in reigns of Eliz. & James I as illust. by docs. rel. to the diocese of L. Ed. C. W. Foster. [Lincoln Rec. Soc., v23]. v1. la8°. [Horncastle]. 1926
Lincoln Record Society.
Parish Register Section. v6–9. la8°. Horncastle. 1921–25
see BOURNE. Parish reg., 1562–1650, 1921. [7.]
„ GAINSBOROUGH. Parish reg., v1, 1564–1640, 1920. [6.]
„ LINCOLN. Parish reg.: marriages, 1538–1754, 1925. [9.]
„ —— Parish reg. of St. Peter at Gowts, 1538–1837; 1923. [8.]
Publications. v3, 5, 6, 9, 11, 15–19, 22, 23. la8°. 1912–26
v2 (Lincoln episc. records, 1571–84)=Canterbury & York Soc., extra part, *q.v.*
v7 (Lincoln, Visitations of relig. houses, v1)=Canterbury & York Soc., v17, *q.v.*
v20 (Rotuli R. Gravesend, 1258–79)=Canterbury & York Soc., v31, *q.v.*

Lincoln Record Society [*continued*].
see DOMESDAY. Lincs. D.; tr. &c. C. W. Foster &c., 1924. [19.]
„ GROSSETESTE (R.) Rotuli R. G., 1235–53, 1914. [11.]
„ HUGH, *of Wells, bp.* Rotuli, 1209–35, 3v, 1912–14. [3, 6, 9.]
„ LINCOLN. Cal. of admin. in Consistory Court, 1540–1659, 1921. [16.]
„ —— Chapter acts of the Cath., 1547–59, 1920. [15.]
„ —— L. wills reg. in Distr. Probate Reg., v1, 1271–1526, 1914. [5.]
„ —— State of the church in r. of Eliz. & James I, v1, 1926. [23.]
„ LINCOLNSHIRE. Earliest L. Assize Rolls, 1202–9, 1926. [22.]
„ —— Final concords, v2, 1244–72 &c., 1920. [17.]
„ STENTON (F. M.), *ed.* Transcripts of charters rel. to the Gilbertine houses of Sixle, Ormsby &c., 1922. [18.]
Lincoln (Abraham), *president of the U.S.*
Last speech in Springfield in campaign of 1858. [Ed. O. R. Barrett]. 4°. Chicago. 1925
see ALLPORT (H. R.) A. L., 1923.
„ BACHELLER (I.) A man for the ages [A. L.: *fiction*], 1920.
„ BALLARD (*Brig.-Gen.* C. R.) Military genius of A. L., 1926.
„ BARTON (W. E.) Life of A. L., 2v, 1925.
„ —— The soul of A. L., 1920.
„ CHITTENDEN (L. E.) Recoll. of Pres. L. & h. administ., 1891.
see DRINKWATER (J.) A. L., a play, 13th impr., 1921.
„ HERNDON (W. H.) & J. W. WEIK. H.'s Lincoln, 3v, *n.d.*
„ MACCLURE (A. K.) A. L. & men of war-times, 1892.
„ PITMAN (B.) Assassination of L. & trial, 1865.
„ ROVER (W. W.) A. L. in 1848 secessionist, *n.d.*
„ SANDBURG (C.) A. L., Prairie years (–1860), 2v, 1926.
„ STEPHENSON (N. W.) L., acc. of h. personal life &c., 1924.
Lincoln (Charles), *warden of Mass. State Prison, see* BIGELOW (G. T.) & G. BEMIS. Rep. of trial of A. Rogers for murder of C. L., 1844.
Lincoln (Levi), *see* AMERICAN ANTIQUARIAN SOC., Proc., 1868.
Lincoln (Mary Johnson), *wife of David A. Lincoln.*
Mrs. L.'s Boston cook book. 8°. Boston. 1899
Lincolnshire. The earliest L. Assize Rolls, 1202–09. Ed. D. M. Stenton. [Lincoln Rec. Soc., v22]. la8°. 1926
Final concords of the Co. of Lincoln. v2, 1244–72, w. add., 1176–1250. Ed. C. W. Foster. [Lincoln Rec. Soc., v17]. 8°. Horncastle. 1920
v1, *ed. by W. O. Massingberd, was publ. in 1896, not by the Lincoln Rec. Soc.*
L. Domesday &c.; tr. & ed. C. W. Foster &c., 1924, *see* DOMESDAY.
L. parish registers. Marriages. Ed. T. M. Blagg. v11. 8°. 1921
Lincolnshire Grazier (A), *ps., see* HORNE (T. H.)
Lincoln's Inn. The Hon. Soc. of Lincoln's Inn: Quincent. celebr. la8°. 1922
Lind (James), *see* ROLLESTON (H. D.) J. L., pioneer of naval hygiene, 1915.
Lind (Jenny), *aft. Frau Otto Goldschmidt, see* MAUDE (*Mrs.* J. M. C.) Life of J. L., 1926.
Lind (Jens). Geograph. distrib. of some Arctic Micromycetes, *see* KONG. DAN. VID. SELSK. Biolog. Medd., B6, 1927.
see JESSEN (K.) & J. L. Det danske Markukrudts Hist., 1922–23.
Lindanus (W. D.), *bp. of* (*1*) *Roermond,* (*2*) *Ghent.* Concordia discors &c. Inserta est Censure Jeremiae patr. Constantinop. de Conf. August. epitome. s8°. Coloniae. 1583
De optimo Scripturas interpretandi genere libri 3. s8°. Coloniae. 1558
Dubitantius de vera certaque, per Christi Jesu Evangelium, salutis æternæ via libris 3 instructus. s8°. Coloniae. 1571
Tabulae passim hæreseon anasceuasticæ, atque analyticæ. Quibus subtexitur Sectæ Lutheranæ trimembris epitome per F. Staphylum &c. [*sep. tp. & pagin.*] s4°. Antverpiae. 1562
see FEUERLEIN (J. W.) Observ. in August. Confess. sing. art. cum praef. de W. L. concordia discorde &c., 1742.
Lindau (Hans). Die Theodicee im 18. Jhdt. 8°. L. 1911
Lindbergh (*Col.* **Charles),** *see* VALE (C.) Spirit of St. Louis: 100 poems, 1927.
Lindblom (Gerhard). The Akamba in Brit. E. Africa. 2nd ed., enlarg. la8°. Uppsala. 1920
Linde (Richard). Die Niederelbe. 4ᵉ A. la8°. Bielefeld. 1913
„ „ ....6. Aufl. la8°. Bielefeld. 1924
Linden (Fritz van der), *see* VAN DER LINDEN (F.)
Linden (Joannes Georgius zur). Comm. de jejuniis & sacris caerimoniis ex 3 parabolis Christi V Lucae extremo. s8°. Jenae. 1732

Lindenau (Ernst). Was man wissen muss v. Bolschevismus. 3. A. [P2408]. 8º. Nürnberg. 1919
Lindfors (Anders Otto). Reg. Acad. Lundensis hist., ad 1739. 2p [*in 1v. 2 pagin.*] s4º. Lundae. 1809–21
Lindhard (J.) Function of the motor end-plates in skeletal muscles, *see* KONG. DAN. VID. SELSK. Biog. Medd., 4, 1923–25.
Lindinger (Johann Simeon). De Ebraeorum vet. arte medica, de daemone & daemoniacis. s8º. Servestae. 1774
Lindische Tempelchronik (Die); neu bearbt. v. C. Blinkenberg, *see* KLEINE TEXTE, T131, 1915.
Lindisfarne Gospels.
see BIBLE. ANGLO-SAXON. The Lindisfarne Gospels: plates f. Cotton MS. in Brit. Mus., w. intr. by E. G. Millar, 1923.
„ BROWN (G. B.) Arts in early Eng., v5, The Gospels of L. &c., 1921.
Lindley (Mark Frank). The acquisition & govt. of backward territory in internat. law. 8º. 1926
Lindores. Cowmpt of geir belong. to the Abbacie of L., 1530, *see* MAIDMENT (J.) & R. PITCAIRN. Nugae derelictae, 1822.
Dispute—Abbot &c. of L. & inhabitants of Newburgh (1309), *see* ABBOTSFORD CLUB. Misc., v1, 1837.
Lindquist (Axel Martin), *see* CONRAD, *v. Helmsdorf.* Spiegel d. menschl. Heils; hrsg. v. A. L., 1924.
Lindquist (Gustavus Elmer Emanuel). The Red Man in the U.S. Soc., econ. & relig. life. Under dir. of L. Foreword by C. H. Burke. 8º. N.Y. [1923]
Lindsay (Alexander Dunlop).
Karl Marx's Capital: intr. essay. s8º. 1925
Lindsay (*Lady* Anne), *see* BARNARD (*Lady* A.)
Lindsay (Caroline Blanche Elizabeth, *Lady*).
From a Venetian balcony &c. s8º. 1903
Lindsay (*Sir* David) [LYNDSAY].
Poet. works. n. ed. rev. 2v. s8º. E. 1871
Lindsay (Harry Alex. Fanshawe) & C. M. Harlow.
Report on lac & shellac. 8º. Allahabad. 1921
Lindsay (Jack). Loving mad Tom: Bedlamite verses of 16th & 17th cent. Foreword by R. Graves. Texts ed. &c. J. L. Musical transcr. by P. Warlock. 4º. 1927
Lindsay (James Bowman), *see* MILLAR (A. H.) J. B. L. & o. pioneers of invention, 1925.
Lindsay (*Sir* John), *see* RENWICK (R.) & *Sir* J. L. Hist. of Glasgow, 1921.
Lindsay (Kenneth). Social progress & educat. waste. "Free-place" & scholarship system. Intr. by Visct. Haldane. 8º. 1926
Lindsay (Norman). Poetry in Australia, 1923. Pref. by N. L. s8º. Sydney. 1923
Lindsay (Samuel McCune), *see* ITALY: CODES &c. Constit. of I. (1848); tr. &c. by S. M. L., 1894.
Lindsay (Thomas M.) Letters of Principal T. M. Lindsay to Janet Ross. [1906–14. Ed. Janet Ross]. 8º. 1923
Lindsay (Thomas Somerville). Plant names. s8º. 1923
Lindsay (Vachel). Coll. poems. 8º. 1923
The Daniel jazz & o. poems. s8º. 1920
The golden book of Springfield. s8º. N.Y. 1920
Lindsay (Wallace Martin). Early Latin verse. 8º. O. 1922
Early Welsh script. 8º. O. 1912
Die latein. Sprache. Übersetz. v. H. Nohl. 8º. L. 1897
Palaeographia Lat. Ed. W. M. L. [St. Andrews Univ. Publs., 14, 16, 19, 20]. pl-5. 8º. 1922–27
see CORPUS. The C. gloss., 1921.
—— & H. J. Thomson.
Anc. lore in medieval Latin glossaries. 8º. 1921
Lindsey, *Lincolnshire.* Lincolnshire Domesday & the L. survey; tr. & ed. C. W. Foster &c., 1924, *see* DOMESDAY.
Lindsey (Theophilus), *see* MACLACHLAN (H.) Letters of T. L., 1920.
Lindsey (W. H.) A season at Harwich, w. excursions by land & water &c. 2p *in* 1v. 8º. 1851
Lindt (Willem van der), *see* LINDANUS (W. D.)
*__Lines__ in memory of J. Wesley, 1786, *see* WESLEY (J.)
Linevich (N. P.), *see* KUROPATKIN (*gen.* A. N.) & N. P. L. Русско-Япон. война, 1925.
Lingard (John), *D.D.*
Antiq. of the Anglo-Saxon Church. 2nd ed. 8º. Newcastle. 1810
Lingay (J.), *prof. de litt. à l'Athénée de Paris, see* GUILLIÉ (S.) Hist. du cabinet des Tuileries &c. [*attrib. to* S. G. *& also to* J. L.], 1815.
Lingendes (Claude de), *Jesuit, see* NOUET (J.), F. ANNAT *& others.* Responses aux Lettres Provinciales &c., 1668.
Lingke (Johann Theodor).
M. Luther's merkwürdige Reisegesch. 4º. L. 1769
Linguet (Simon Nicolas Henri). *Hist. impartiale des Jésuites, j. leur prem. expulsion. 2t. s8º. *n.p.* [Madrid?]. 1768
Mém. de L. & de Latude, suivis de doc. divers sur la Bastille & de fragm. conc. la captivité du Baron de Trenck. Avec notes &c. par F. Barrière. s8º. 1884
Memoirs of the Bastille; tr. &c. by J. & S. F. M. Whitham, *see* LATUDE (H. M. DE). Mem.; tr., 1927.
Linius (Martin), *1634–1712, see* COCHEM (MARTIN v.)
Linke (Eva Hoffmann-), *see* HOFFMANN-LINKE (E.)
Linnaeus (Carl).
Genera plantarum. ed. 6ª aucta. 8º. Holmiae. 1764
see JACKSON (B. D.) L.: h. life adapted f. Swedish of T. M. Fries & brought down to pres. time, 1923.
„ LEVERTIN (O.) C. v. L., 3ᵉ uppl., 1908.
Linnankoski (Johannes).
The song of the blood-red flower. [Tr.] s8º. [1920]
Linnebach (Carl). Deutsche u. französ. Okkupationsmethoden, 1871–73—1920–?. 8º. 1925
*__Linotype__ (The) composing machine. 8º. *n.d.*
Linschoten-Vereeniging. Werken uitg. door de L.-V. 17–29. 8º. 's-Gravenhage. 1919–27
see GERRITSZOON (H.) Beschr. van d. Samoyeden Landt & Hist. du pays nommé Spitsberghe, 1924. [23.]
„ HAMEL (H.) Verhaal van het vergaan van het jacht De Sperwer &c., 1653–66, 1920. [18.]
„ HOUTMAN (C. DE). De eerste schipvaart der Nederlanders naar Oost-Indië, d2, 1925. [25.]
„ HUDSON (H.) Reize onder Nederland. vlag &c., volgens het journaal van R. Juet &c., 1921. [19.]
„ MOLSBERGEN (E. C. G.) Reizen in Zuid-Afrika in de Hollandse tijd, d3, 1922. [20.]
„ NOORT (O. VAN). Reis, 1598–1601, 2d, 1926. [27, 28.]
„ NOUHUYS (J. W. VAN). De eerste Nederl. Transatlant. stoomvaart in 1827 van Zʳ Mˢ Stoompakket Curaçao, d1, 1927. [29.]
„ TASMAN (A. J.) De reizen v. T. & F. J. Visscher, 1919. [17.]
„ WIEDER (F. C.) De reis van Mahu & de Cordes door de Straat v. Magalhães, 1598–1600, 3d, 1923–25. [21, 22, 24.]
„ —— De stichting van New York in Juli 1625, 1925. [26.]
Linschoten (Jan Huygen van). Voyage au Waeigatz *&* Second voy., 1594–95, *see* BERNARD (J. F.), *ed.* Recueil, t4, 1718; t3, 1732.
Linska de Castillon (Louis Frédéric de), *dit* PRADO. *Prado. [*Murder of Marie Aguetant, trial &c.*, 1888. *no tp.* P2826]. s8º. [Sceaux. *n.d.*]
Linskill (*Miss* Mary).
Tales of the North Riding. n. ed. s8º. 1893
Lintilhac (Eugène).
Vergniaud: le drame des Girondins. 8º. 1920
Linton (Arthur). 25 Consecration prayers. With notes & intr. by A. L. s8º. 1921
Linton (*Mrs.* E. Lynn), *wife of W. J. Linton.*
Under which lord? n. ed. s8º. [1881]
Linton (William James).
The hist. of wood-engraving in America. 4º. 1882
Lintott (E. Barnard).
Art of water colour painting. 8º. 1926
Lintrup (Søren), *bp. of Viborg* [LINTRUPIUS (SEVERINUS)]. Anglia Lutheranizans. [P444]. s4º. [Helmstadt?]. 1710
Lionardi (Alessandro).
Dialogi d. inventione poetica &c. s4º. Venetia. 1554
Lionello (Giov. Batt.) Brieven van L. & Suriano uit Den Haag aan Doge & Senate van Venetie, 1616–18, benevens verslag van Trevisano betref. zijne zending naar Holland in 1620. [*In Ital. & Dutch.* Hist. Genoots. Werken., N.S., 37]. 8º. Utrecht. 1883
Lionne (Artus de), *bp. of Rosalie* [LYONNE], *see* JESUITS. Rel. de ce qui s'est passé à la Chine en 1697–99, à l'occas. d'un établ. que L. a fait à Nien-Tcheou, 1700.
Lionne (Hugues de), *marq. de Berny, see* GRAMONT (A. *duc* DE). Corr. inéd. de G. & de L., 1650, 1925.
Liotard (Jean Etienne), *see* FOSCA (F.) L., 1702–89, 1928.
Lipinska (Mélanie). Hist. des femmes médecins, dep. l'antiq. j. nos jours. 8º. 1900
Lipman, *of Mühlhausen.* Carmen memoriale—Liber Nizzachon, [*Hebr. & Lat.*], *see* WAGENSEIL (J. C.) Tela ignea Satanae &c., 1681.
Li Po [LI TAI-PO]. Works. Done into Eng. verse by S. Obata. With intr. &c. 8º. 1923
Lippert & Schmidt, *booksellers.* Catalog v. Werken aus d. Gesammtgebiete d. Theologie. 8º. 1847

Lippert von Granberg (Josefine).
Sicania. Blätter [*poems*]. 8°. Wien. 1897

Lippi (Lippo), *see* GIGLIOLI (O. H.) Fra F. L., 1921.
see SORDINI (G.) La tomba di F. L., 1904.

Lippi (Lorenzo) [*ps.* PERLONE ZIPOLI]. Il Malmantile racquistato. [*Pref.* Vita di L. L., da F. Baldinucci *in MS.*] s8°. Firenze. 1749
Malmantile racquistato. s8°. Londra. 1779

Lippi (Mattia Giuseppe). Vita di Papa Innocenzo XI. Ed. con aggiunte a cura del p. G. Berthier. la8°. 1889

Lippmann (Walter). The phantom public. 8°. N.Y. [1925]
Public opinion. 8°. 1922

Liprandi (Ivan Petrovich). Краткое обозрѣніе существующихъ въ Россіи расколовъ, ересей и сектъ &c. 2^oe^ изд. s8°. Лейпцигъ. *n.d.*

Liprando, *king of the Lombards, see* LIUDPRANDUS.

Lipsius (Justus).
Conc. the fate of the Antients; tr., *see* ZANCHIUS (H.) Doctrine of predestination, 1769.
De bibliothecis syntagma. la8°. Antverpiae. 1602
De Cruce libri 3 cum notis. Acc. e praelect. G. Calixti: De vera forma crucis app. & G. Cassandri epistola [*w. sep. pagin.*] s8°. Brunsvigae. 1640
,, ,, Ed. ult. castig. s8°. Amstelodami. 1670
Dispunctio notarum Mirandulani codicis ad Cor. Tacitum. [*b. w. h.* De bibl. syntagma, 1602]. la8°. Antverpiae. 1602
Variarum lectionum libri 4. s8°. Antverpiae. 1569
see ANDERTON (B.) Sk. f. a library window [J. L. &c.], 1922.
,, BERNEGGER (M.) J. L. Politicorum libri 2–6 cap. in aphorismos resol.; praes. M.B., 1616–17.
,, BEZA (T.) De vera pronuntiatione Gr. & Lat. linguae (J. L. de recta pronunt.), 1587.
,, ESTIENNE (HENRI). De Lipsii Latinitate palaestra 1, 1695.
,, LAMPUGNANUS (P.) J. L. in C. C. Tacitum notae cum cod. Mirandulano coll. a P. L., 1602.

Lipsius (Justus Hermann). Lysias' Rede geg. Hippotherses u. d. attische Metoikenrecht, *see* KÖNIGL.-SÄCHS. GESELLS. D. WISS. Berichte, phil.-hist. Kl., B71, 1919.

Lipsius (Richard Adelbert). Luthers Lehre v. d. Busse. [Sep.-Abdr. aus d. Jhbn. f. prot. Theol., 18. Jhrg.] 8°. Braunschweig. 1892

Lipský (E.) Josef Ressel, příspěvky k životopisu Slavného vynálezce. 8°. Vydalo. 1924

Lipson (Ephraim).
Hist. of the woollen & worsted industries. 8°. 1921
Intr. to the econ. hist. of England. [v]1, The Middle Ages. 2nd impr. 8°. 1920
,, ,, ... 3rd ed. 8°. 1923

Liptzin (Solomon). Shelley in Germany. 8°. N.Y. 1924

Liria, Palacio de, *Madrid, see* ALBA (M. DEL R., *dss.* DE). Cat. de las colecciones, 1898.

Lis (Charles du), *see* DU LIS (C.)

Lis (Jan) [LYS], *see* OLDENBOURG (R.) J. L.; riprod. con testo e cat., 1921.

Lisander. *A tragi-commicall hist. of our times, under the borrowed names of L. & Calista; tr., 1627, *see* AUDIGUIER (V. D').

Liset (Abraham). Amphithalami, or, the accountants closet &c. 2p [*b. w.* Collins (J.) Merchants-accompts, 1675]. fol. 1684

Lisieux. Etudes lexov., 2t, 1915–19, *see* LEXOVIENNES.

Lisio (Giuseppe), *ed.* Orazioni scelte del sec. 16. (B. Calvalcanti, G. Guidiccioni, I. Nardi, Lorenzino de' Medici, G. della Casa, P. Paruta). Rid. a buona lez. &c. par G. L. 8°. Firenze. 1897

Liske (Javier). Viajes de extranjeros por España y Portugal en los siglos 15, 16 y 17. [N. de Popielovo, 1484; J. Dantiscus (de Curiis), 1519–31, E. Lassota de Steblovo, 1580–84, J. Sobieski, 1611]. Coll. de J. L. Tr. y anot. por F. R. s8°. 1878

L'Isle (Guillaume de), *geographer.* Lettre t. la Californie—Lettre t. le Mississippi &c., *see* BERNARD (J. F.), *ed.* Recueil, t3, 4, 1715–32.

Lissauer (*Dr.* —) A. v. Haller u. s. Bedeutung f. d. deut. Cultur, *see* VIRCHOW (R.) & F. v. HOLTZENDORFF. Samml., H189, 1873.

List.
List of officers of the Roy. Reg. of Artillery, 1763 to pres. time, 1815, *see* KANE (J.)
List (A) of the officers of the army, & marines, a succession of colonels, & list of officers on half-pay. 8°. Dublin. 1789
List (A) of the officers of the Army, the Marine Forces, &c., 1784, 1799, 1804, 1808, 1811, 1817, 1819, 1823, 1826, 1832, 1836, 1839, 1847, 1850, 1852, 1856–59, 1864–67. [War Office]. 8°. 1784–1867

List [*continued*].
*List (A) of pr. service books &c., 1850, *see* DICKINSON (F. H.)
List of Regular Lodges Masonic, 1920, 1921, 1924, *see* FREEMASONS.
List. of treaties, &c., rel. to commerce &c. betw. Gt. Brit. & For. Powers, 1927, *see* ENGLAND.

List & Francke, *booksellers.* Cat. d'une coll. de livres embrass. les litt. hongr. & transylvan., bibl. de E. de Nagy à Pesth. 8°. Leipzig. 1870

List (Friedrich), *polit. economist.* Kl. Schriften. Hrsg. &c. v. F. Lenz. T1, Zur Staatswiss. u. polit. Ökon. s8°. Jena. 1926
Über den Wert u. d. Bedingungen e. Allianz zw. Grossbrit. u. Deutschland. Einleit. v. O. Jöhlinger. [P2684]. s8°. L. [1920]

List (Guido). Die Armanenschaft d. Ario-Germanen. 2^e^ A. 2T. 8°. Wien. [1911–21]
Das Geheimnis der Runen. 2^e^ A. s8° Wien. 1912
Die Namen d. Völkerstämme Germaniens. 2^e^ A. 8°. Wien. 1909

Lister (A. Lindsay), *see* BADSWORTH, *ps.*

Lister (Arthur), *see* BRITISH MUSEUM OF NAT. HIST.: ZOOLOGY. Monograph of the Mycetozoa, by A. L., 3rd ed., rev. by G. Lister, 1925.

Lister (George A.), *see* CARR (H. R. C.) & G. A. L., *edd.* Mountains of Snowdonia, 1925.

Lister (John). Early Yorkshire woollen trade. Extr. f. Hull Customs' Rolls & transcr. of the Ulnagers' Rolls. Ed. J. L. [Yorks. Arch. Soc. Rec. Ser., 64]. 8°. 1924

Lister (Joseph Lister, *1st baron***).** Six papers. With biog. & notes by Sir R. J. Godlee. s8°. 1921
see CHEYNE (W. W.) L. & h. achievement, 1925.

Lister (Thomas). Opposition dangerous. [P2515]. 8°. 1798

Listing (Johann Benedikt). Beitrag z. physiol. Optik. Hrsg. v. O. Schwarz. 8°. L. 1905

Liszt (Ferencz). Die Legende v. d. heil. Elisabeth: Oratorium nach Worten v. O. Roquette. Klavierauszug. 3. A. la8°. L. *n.d.*
see POURTALÈS (G. DE). Vie de F. L., 28e éd., 1926.
,, SCHRADER (B.) F. L., 2e A., 1921.
,, WALLACE (W.) L., Wagner & the Princess, 1927.

Li Tai-po, *see* LI PO.

Litanies. Irish litanies: text & tr., 1925, *see* PLUMMER (C.), *ed.*
Litanies for the choirs of the United Brethren. [*b. w.* Liturgic hymns, 1811]. rev. & enl. 2nd ed. s8°. M'ter. 1811

Litchfield (Frederick).
Antiques: genuine & spurious. la8°. 1921
Pottery & porcelain. 4th ed., new, compl. rev. &c. la8°. 1925

Literae, *see* LITTERAE.

Literarischer Verein in Stuttgart. Verzeichnis: Publicationen, 1839–1918 (No. 1–266). 8°. St. [1921]
[*Publications*]. 107, 111, 113, 116, 251–270. 8°. Tübingen. 1871–73; 1909–27
see BIBLE: GERMAN. Die 1e deutsche Bibel [c. 1466]; hrsg. v. W. Kurrelmeyer, B6–10, 1909–15. [251, 254, 258, 259, 266].
,, BOLTE (J.) Drei Schauspiele vom sterb. Menschen, 1927. [269/270.]
,, CHARLOTTE ELIZABETH, *dsse. d'Orléans.* Briefe, 1707–15, 1871. [107.]
,, COLUMELLA (L. J. M.) De re rust.; übers. H. Österreicher, 2B, 1914. [263, 264.]
,, DURMART, *le Galois.* Li romans de D. le G., 1873. [116.]
,, FLAYDER (F. H.) Ausgewählte Werke, 1925. [267/8.]
,, LOGAU (F. v.) Sämmtl. Sinngedichte, 1872. [113.]
,, MATTHISSON (F.) Gedichte, 2B, 1912–13. [257, 261.]
,, OTTO II, *bp. of Freising.* Der Laubacher Barlaam, 1913. [260.]
,, PYRAMUS. Drei deut. Pyramus-Thisbe-Spiele (1581–1607), 1911. [255.]
,, SCHALLENBERG (C. v.) Ein österreich. Lyriker d. 16 Jhdt., 1910. [253.]
,, SPANGENBERG (W.) Anbind-oder Fangbriefe, 1914. [262.]
,, TERENCE. Eunuchus; übers. v. Hans Neidhart 1486, 1915. [265.]
,, TRIMBERG (H. v.) Der Renner, B3 & 4, 1909–12. [252, 256.]
,, WELLER (E.) Die ersten deut. Zeitungen, 1872. [111.]

Literarisches Centralblatt f. Deutschland. Jhrg. 71–77. la8°. L. 1920–26
Beilage zum L. C. f. D., 1900, *see* SCHÖNE LITERATUR (DIE).
Jahresberichte d. Lit. Zentralblattes. 1. [*in* 24B] & 2. Jahrgang 1924–25. Hrsg. W. Frels. 8° & 4°. L. 1926

Literary year-book (The).
Ed. M. Meredith. 1921, 1922. 8°. [1921–22]
see WHO'S WHO IN LITERATURE: cont. of bibliogr. sect. of Lit. year-bk., 1924 &c.

Literature. Outline of l., 1923, *see* DRINKWATER (J.), *ed.*

Lith (Johann Wilhelm von der). Diss. de superstitione jubilaei pontif. [P436]. s4°. Halae Magdeb. [1700]

Lithuania. Econ. & financial condit. of the L. Republic at beg. of 1922. [P2750]. la8°. [1922]

The Lithuanian-Polish dispute. 3v *in* 2. 4°. 1921–23
1, 2nd assembly of League of Nat., Geneva, 1921.
2, Corr. betw. League of Nat. & L. Govt., Dec. 1921–July 1922.
3, Corr. betw. L. Govt. & League of Nat. & Conf. of Ambassadors, Aug. 1922–July 1923; w. intr. statements.

see MEMEL. Question of M.: dipl. & o. doc., 1919–23, 1924.

Lithus (Christianus Simon), *Misenus, ps.*, *see* STENIUS (S.)

Litta (*il conte* Pompeo). Armory of celeb. Ital. families; descr. armorial bearings of the "Celeb. famiglie ital."; by W. Dickinson, w. Suppl. (1880). [*MS. b. w.* Tettoni (L.) &c. Dict., *n.d.*] fol. *n.d.*

Litta-Visconti-Arese (Pompeo, *duca*), *1856–*. Monsignor Villarosa. s8°. [1914]

Litterae [LITERAE].

Literae humaniores, an appeal to teachers. [P2690]. s8°. 1911

Litterae apostolicae div. Roman. pontificum pro officio Inquisit. &c., 1579, *see* EYMERICUS (N.) Directorium Inquisit., 1578.

*Litteræ apostolicæ, quibus institutio &c. S.J. cont., 1568, *see* JESUITS.

Little [LYTTEL &c.]

Little ark (A): 17th-c. verse, 1921, *see* THORN-DRURY (G.)

*Little bk. of Jewish cookery, *n.d.*, *see* COOKERY.

Little bk. of modern verse, ed. J. B. R., 1913, *see* RITTENHOUSE (J. B.), *editor.*

*Little more nonsense, 1923, *see* DAVIES (R.)

*Lyttel booke of nonsense, n. ed., 1925, *see* DAVIES (R.)

Little Review, The; or, an inquisition of scandal. N°. 13, 18 July 1705. [*b. w.* Post Man, 1704–08]. s4°. 1705

Little (Andrew George). Friar Henry of Wodstone & the Jews, *see* COLLECTANEA Franciscana, v2, 1922.

Some recently disc. Franciscan doc^s. & th. rel. to the 2nd life by Celano & the Speculum Perfectionis. [Brit. Acad.] la8°. [1926]

see FITZMAURICE (E. B.) & A. G. L. Mat. for hist. of Franciscan Prov. of Ireland, 1230–1450; ed. F. & L., 1920.

„ TOUT (T. F.) Essays in medieval hist.: pres. to T.; ed. A. G. L. &c., 1925.

Little (O. H.) Geogr. & geol. of Makalla, S. Arabia. With 2 app. by G. Stefanini & P. Pallary. [Min. of Finance, Egypt. Survey: Geol.] la8°. Cairo. 1925

Little (Thomas), *Esq., ps.*, *see* MOORE (T.), *the poet.*

Littledale (Willoughby A.), *see* GRANTS. Coll. of misc. g., crests &c.; ed. W. A. L., 2v, 1925–26.

Littlefield (George Emery). Early Boston booksellers, 1642–1711. [Club of Odd Vol.] 8°. *p.p.* Boston, *U.S.* 1900

Littlejohns (John), *R.B.A.*

see RICHMOND (L.) & J. L. Art of painting in pastel, 1920.

„ —— & —— Technique of water-colour painting, 1925.

Littler (Laurie). Poems. s8°. Amersham. 1923

Littleton (Alfred Henry). A catal. of 100 works illust. the hist. of music printing, 15 to 17 cent., in lib. of L. la8°. 1911

Littmann (Enno). Greek & Lat. inscr.—Semitic inscr., *see* PRINCETON UNIV. Syria, div. 3, 4, §A, by E. L. &c., 1914–21.

Jäger u. Prinzessin: e. neuarab. Märchen aus Jerusalem, *see* KLEINE TEXTE, 150, 1923.

see NIELSEN (D.), *ed.* Hdbch. d. altarab. Altertumskunde, B1, 1927.

Littré (M. P. Emile). Dict. de la langue française. 4t. 4°. 1881

Liturgia [LITURGIARUM].

L., seu liber precum comm. juxta usum Eccl. Anglic. &c., 1696, *see* PRAYER-BOOK.

L. Anglic., ó lib. de oracion comun, 1906, *see* PRAYER BOOK.

L. antiq. Hispanica Gothica Isidoriana Mozarabica Toletana mixta illustr. Adj. vet. mon. [Tractatus coll. &c. J. Pinius]. 2t. fol. Romae. 1746

L. Mozarabica, *see* MOZARABIC BREVIARY.

L. sanct. apostol. Adaei & Maris [*in Syriac*], 1890, *see* ADAEUS.

L. Tigurina: Bk. of C.P. &c., 1693, *see* PRAYER-BOOK: ADAPTATIONS.

Liturgiarum orient. coll. 2t, 1716, *see* RENAUDOT (E.) *the younger.*

Liturgie.

L. (La) &c. selon l'usage de l'église anglic., 1703, *see* PRAYER-BOOK.

L. (La) selon l'usage anglic., 1721, *see* PRAYER-BOOK.

„ „ ....1834, *see* PRAYER-BOOK.

Liturgies [LITURGIC; LITURGICAL; LITURGY].

Illust. of the Liturgy: drawings by C. O. Skilbeck, notes &c., by P. Dearmer, 1912, *see* DEARMER (P.)

Liturgic hymns of the United Brethren. Tr. fr. German. rev. & enl. 2nd ed. s8°. M'ter. 1811

Liturgy & hymns for use of United Brethren. n. & rev. ed. s8°. 1849

*Liturgy (A) coll. princ. f. the Bk. of C.P. for the use of the 1st Episcopal Ch. in Boston; together w. the Psalter. 8°. Boston [Mass.] 1785

Liturgy (The) of the Eastern Orthodox Church [*includ.* Lit. of Chrysostom]. Intr. & note by H. H. M. 8°. 1916

The Samaritan l.; ed. A. E. Cowley, 2v, 1909, *see* SAMARITAN.

***Liturgik** oder Erklärung d. gottesdienstl. Handlungen d. Kathol. Kirche &c., 1857, *see* SCHAMM (J.)

Litvinov-Falinsky (Vladimir Petrovich). Какъ и для чего страхуются рабочіе. Полный текстъ новыхъ законовъ. [P2452]. 8°. С.-П. 1912

Litzmann (Berthold). C. Schumann, e. Künstlerleben n. Tagebüchern u. Briefen. 3B [B1, 4. n. durchgeseh. A.; B2, 4. unveränd. A.; B3, 3. durchgeseh. A.] 8°. L. 1910

Ernst v. Wildenbruch. B2, 1885–1909. la8°. 1916

Liu Chai-lien. The Arabian prophet: life of Mohammed f. Chinese & Arabic sources. Tr. I. Mason. App. on Chinese Mohammedanism. Foreword by S. M. Zwemer. 8°. Shanghai. 1921

Liudprandus, *bp. of Cremona.* Werke [*Lat.*] Hrsg. J. Becker. [Scr. rerum Germ. in usum schol.] 8°. Hannover. 1915

see BECKER (J.) Textgesch. L.'s, 1908.

Liudprandus, *king of the Lombards; 712–44* [ALIPRANDO; LIPRANDO; LUITPRAND], *see* ACQUA (C. DELL'). Del piede L.: diss. doc., 1883.

see MARTENS (W.) Polit. Gesch. d. Langobard. unter L., 1880.

Li Ung Bing. Outlines of Chinese hist. Ed. J. Whiteside. 8°. Shanghai. 1914

Liveing (Susan). A 19th cent. teacher, J. H. Bridges. Pref. by L. T. Hobhouse & intr. by P. Geddes. 8°. 1926

Liverpool, *see* WALKER ART GALLERY.

Liverpool University. INSTITUTE OF ARCHAEOLOGY, *see* ANNALS OF ARCHAEOL. & ANTHROPOL.; ed. J. L. Myres, 1908–.

Liverpool (Cecil George Savile Foljambe, *1st e. of [2nd cr.]*), *aft. Baron Hawkesbury.* Evelyn pedigrees & memoranda. fol. *p.p.* 1893

see YEATMAN (J. P.), *Sir* G. R. SITWELL & C. J. [*sic*] S. F. Feudal hist. of Co. of Derby, v1–5, 1886–1907.

Lives.

Bethada Náem nÉrenn: lives of Irish saints, 2v, 1922, *see* PLUMMER (C.), *ed.*

*Lives of eminent Russian prelates, 1854, *see* RUSSIAN.

[*Lives of the holy fathers, *in Armenian*]. 2v. i Venetik. 1855

*Lives (The) of the most eminent mod. painters since, or omitted by M. de Piles, 1754, *see* BURGESS (J.)

*Lives (The) of the most famous Eng. poets, 1687, *see* WINSTANLEY (W.)

*Lives of the most remarkable criminals, condemn'd 1720 to pres. time. 3v. s8°. 1735

*Lives of the Serbian saints, 1921, *see* YANICH (V.) & C. P. HANKEY.

*Varq en vkayabanouthiunq Srbotz. [Lives & martyrology of the saints. *In Armenian*]. 2v. 8°. Venetik, *Mekhitharist Press.* 1874

Livesey (W.) The mining crisis. s8°. 1921

Livet (Guillaume), *see* BISSON (A.) & G. L. Nick Carter, pièce, 1910.

Livingston, *The family of*, *see* LIVINGSTON (E. B.) L's. of Callendar & their princ. cadets, 1920.

Livingston (Edwin Brockholst).

The captain of Stirling Castle. s8°. Paisley. 1927

The Livingstons of Callendar & their princ. cadets: hist. of an old Stirlingshire family. n. ed. rewr. & enl. la8°. E. 1920

Livingston (*Lady* Jean), *wife of W. Livingston, aft. Visct. Kilsyth*, *see* CLAVERHOUSE (J. G., *viscountess Dundee*).

Livingston (Robert R.), *see* BEMIS (S. F.), *ed.* Amer. Secr. of State, v1, L., by M. L. Bonham, 1927.

Livingstone (David), *see* DOLMAN (A.) In the footsteps of L.: diaries &c.; ed. J. Irving, 1924.

Livingstone (Richard Winn).

Greek genius & its meaning to us. 2nd ed. 8°. O. 1915

The legacy of Greece. Essays by G. Murray, W. R. Inge, & J. Burnet *& others.* Ed. R. W. L. s8°. O. 1921

The pageant of Greece. [Sel. f. Gr. wr., w. sk. of th. lives &c.] Ed. R. W. L. s8°. O. 1923

Livingstone (William Pringle). A Galilee doctor: career of Dr. D. W. Torrance of Tiberias. 8°. [1923]
Livinus, *Saint, see* HEILMANN (J. D.) Commentatiuncula de S. L., 1813.
Livre.
*Livre (Le) de la chasse du Gr. Seneschal de Normandye &c., 1858, *see* BRÉZÉ (J. DE).
*Livre des merveilles: Marco Polo, Odoric de Pordenone, Mandeville, Hayton &c. [*partly comp. in 1351 by Jean le Long d'Ypres*]. Reprod. de 265 miniatures du ms. fr. 2810. 2t. s4°. *n.d.*
Livre des privilèges de Manosque, 1169–1315, 1894, *see* MANOSQUE.
*Livre d'or de la noblesse phanariote & des familles princ. de Valachie & de Moldavie. Par E. R. R. 2e éd. 4°. Athènes. 1904
Livre (Un) noir: diplomatie d'avant-guerre d'ap. les doc. des archives russes, 1910–14, 2t, 1922–23, *see* MARCHAND (R.)
Livre (Le) noir & les Etablissements de Dax; [*ed. &c.*] F. Abbadie, 1902, *see* DAX.
Livre vert de l'archevêché de Narbonne; publ. P. Laurent, 1886, *see* NARBONNE.
Livy [*Patavius*; †LIVIUS (TITUS); TITE LIVE; TITO LIVIO; TITU LIVIU].
Rerum gestarum populi Romani libri triginta, castigatiores autore J. Sobio. L. Flori epitome; index rerum &c. [*Engr. border to tp. MS. notes &c.*] fol. [Coloniae, *Jo. Soter.*] 1525
Hist. quod extat. Ex rec. I. F. Gronovii. s8°. Amstelodami, *Elzevir.* 1678
TRANSLATIONS.
Le deche di T. L. delle hist. romane. Tr. J. Nardi, e nuov. riv., corr. &c. da F. Turchi, con suppl. d. 2a deca &c.. fol. Venezia. 1734
Hist. of Rome. Tr. G. Baker. 3rd ed. 6v. 8°. 1822
Istoria romana; tr. N. Locusteanu şi I. S. Petrescu. [Acad. Rom.] t4, 5, Cărţile 31–45. la8°. 1911–15
Livy. With Eng. tr. by B. O. Foster. [Loeb Class. Lib.] [v]2–4, s8°. 1922–26
see GOLDBACHER (A.) Krit. Beitr. z. 41., 42. u. 43. Buche d. T. L., 1919.
Lizerand (Georges). Le dossier de l'affaire des Templiers. Ed. & tr. par G. L. s8°. 1923
Lizier (Augusto).
Marcello Filosseno, poeta trivigiano. 8°. Pisa. 1893
Lizlov (Andrei Ivanovich). Скиѳская исторія; отъ А. Л. написана 1692, изд. Н. Новиковымъ. изд. 2ое. 3ч *in* 1. 8°. Москва. 1787
Llana (Manuel Gonzalez), *see* GONZALEZ LLANA (M.)
Llandaff. Some acc. of the condit. of the fabric of Ll. Cathedral; by the Bp. of L., 2nd ed., 1860, *see* OLLIVANT (A.), *bp.*
Llewelyn (*Mrs.* **Penderel).**
Hymns tr. f. Welsh. [*w. text*]. s8°. 1850
Llewelyn (Thomas), *LL.D.* Hist. & crit. remarks on the Brit. tongue & its conn. w. o. languages, founded on Welsh Bible. 8°. 1769
Llorente (Juan Antonio). Disc. sobre una constit. relig. Su autor un Americano. Los da á luz J. A. L. [*Foll. by notes signed* J. A. Grassot. *w. sep. pagin.*] s8°. Paris. 1820
Diss. sobre el poder que los reyes Españoles ejercieron hasta el s. xii en la division de obispados &c. s4°. 1810
Hist. crit. de la Inquisicion de España &c. 10t [t10 *missing*]. s8°. 1822
Lloyd, *The family of, of Lloyd's Neck, Long Island, New York.*
Papers of the L. family of the manor of Queens Village, Lloyd's Neck, 1654–1826, 2v, 1927, *see* NEW YORK HIST. SOC., Coll.
Lloyd (Alfred Henry). The will to doubt. s8°. 1907
Lloyd (Bertram), *ed.* The great kinship: anthol. of humanitarian poetry. 8°. [1921]
Lloyd (C. M.) The reorganis. of local gov. Essays, w. introd. by S. Webb. With appendix. [P2426]. 8°. 1919
Trade unionism. 2nd ed., rev. & enl. s8°. 1921
Lloyd (Charles), *poet.* Desultory thoughts in London, Titus & Gisippus, w. o. p. s8°. 1821
*Isabel. A tale. 2v. s8°. 1810
Poems. s8°. 1823
Poet. essays on character of Pope & on lang. &c., fit for poetry. s8°. 1821
Lloyd (E. M. H.) Experiments in State control at the War Office & Ministry of Food. [C.E. for Int. Peace]. la8°. O. 1924
Stabilisation: econ. policy for producers & consumers. s8°. [1923]
Lloyd (Francis) & Charles Tebbitt.
How to utilise the Volunteers. [P2831]. 8°. 1879
Lloyd (Frank), *see* BRIT. MUS.: ANTIQ. F. L. coll. of Worcester porcelain, 1923.
Lloyd (Hannibal Evans). Alexander I, Emp. of Russia. 8°. 1826
see TURNER (J. M. W.) Pictur. views of Eng. & Wales, descr. by H. E. L., 2v, 1832–38.
Lloyd (J. A. T.) Prestige. s8°. [1920]
Lloyd (Nathaniel).
Garden craftmanship in yew & box. la8°. 1925
Hist. of Eng. brickwork. Intr. by Sir E. L. Lutyens. 4°. 1925
Lloyd (Reginald), *see* BRAZIL. 20th c. impressions of B.: Director-in-Chief R. L., 1913.
Lloyd (Roger B.) The approach to the Reformation. Intr. by Bp. of Manchester. s8°. [1925]
Lloyd (W. Francis), *see* AUSTIN (B.) & W. F. L. Secret of high wages, 1926.
Lloyd (Will L.) The red book, illust. legisl. manual of the State, cont. portraits & biog. &c. 8°. Albany. 1892
Lloyd (William), *bp. of (1) St. Asaph, (2) Lichfield & Coventry, (3) Worcester.* *Chronolog. acc. of life of Pythagoras &c., w. epistle to Dr. Bentley about Porphyry's & Jamblichus's Lives of P. s8°. 1699
Sermon at the funeral of Sir Edmund-Bury Godfrey, Oct., 1678. 8°. 1678
see MACKENZIE (*Sir* G.) A defence of the Royal line of Scotland in ans. to [L.], 1685.
,, SANCROFT (W.), *abp. of Canterbury.* Proc. & tryal in case of abp. of Canterbury, bp. of St. A. &c., 1689.
Lloyd George (*Rt. Hon.* **David).**
Coal & power. Rep. of an enquiry presided over by D. Ll. G. s8°. [1924]
The Great War. Speech, 1914. [P2488]. s8°. 1914
Is it peace? 8°. [1923]
*The man who didn't win the War: exposure of Lloyd Georgism. By Centurion. s8°. 1923
see LANSING (R.) The Big Four, 1922.
see RAYMOND (E. T.) Mr. L. G.: a biog., 1922.
,, ROBERTSON (J. M.) Mr. L. G. & Liberalism, 1923.
,, ROPSHIN (V.) Open letter to L. G., 1922.
,, SUTHERLAND (W.) 1916–1920: Ll.-G. Coalition, 1920.
,, TERRAIL (G.) Le combat des trois: la Confér. de la paix, 1922.
Lloyd-Jones (William).
Havash! frontier adventures in Kenya. 8°. [1925]
Lloyd's, *see* GREY (H. M.) Lloyd's, 1922.
see WRIGHT (C.) & C. E. FAYLE. Hist. of Ll., 1928.
Llwyd (Richard). Poems. 2v [*in* 1]. s8°. Chester. 1804
Loane (George Green). Short hdbk. of literary terms. s8°. [1923]
Lobb (R.), *ed., see* AMBULATOR: or pocket companion round London, 6th ed., 1793.
Lobel (Edgar), *see* ALCÆUS, *of Mitylene.* Ἀλκαίου μέλη, ed. E. L., 1927.
L'Obel (Matthias de). In G. Rondelletii Pharmaceuticam offic. animadv. Acc. auctaria, in antidotaria vulgata censurae & Simplicium medicamentorum explic., adversariorumque vol. [*by* P. Pena & M. de L'O.] & illust. &c. [*2 pagin.*] sm. fol. Londini. 1605
see LEGRÉ (L.) La botanique en Provence au 16e s.: P. Pena & M. de L., 1899.
Löber (Christian) [LOEBERUS]. Defensio doct. de omnibus concedenda Script. lectione, occasione bullae anti-Quesnellianae. Præs. J. F. Buddeo. [P2630]. s4°. Jenae. 1715
Löber (Christoph Heinrich) [LOEBERUS]. Indiculus hist. eccl. præprimis ad ephoriam Orlamundanam spect. Cum præf. C. Sagittarii. [P2649]. s4°. Jenæ. 1685
Vindiciæ sacramenti baptismi, contra Quakeros. Def. N. Beck. [P2632]. s4°. Jenæ. 1689
Löber (Gotthilf Friedmann). Obs. ad hist. vitae & mortis J. C. imprimis Bengelii sentent. s8°. Altenburgi. 1767
Lobera y Abio (Antonio). El porqué de todas las ceremonias de la iglesia y sus misterios. Cartilla de prelados &c. n. ed. 8°. Barcelona. 1791
Lobley (Joseph Albert). The Church & the churches in S. India: Portuguese missions in the 16th c. 8°. C. 1870
Löbnitz (Wilhelm Müller-), *see* MÜLLER-LÖBNITZ (W.)
Lobo (Jeronymo). A voyage to Abyssinia. With 15 diss. by M. Le Grand. Tr. S. Johnson. Add. var. o. tracts by same a. [Ed. by G. Gleig]. 8°. 1789
Lobsien (Wilhelm). Der Halligpastor. Roman. s8°. 1920
Lobwasser (Ambrosius). Psalmen Davids, nach frantzös. Melodey u. Reymen art in Teutsche reymen &c. gebracht durch A. Lobwasser D. s8°. Herborn. 1601
,, ,, [*a. ed.*] Sampt etl. a. Psalmen u. geistl. Liedern &c. [*b. w.* Bible: German. Das Newe Test., 1621]. 8°. Herborn. 1616
,, ,, [*a. ed., w. tunes*]. Auch andere Psalmen [*w. sep. tp.*] Samt d. Catechismo. [*3 pagin.*] s8°. Amsterdam. 1698
Local preachers magazine & Christian family record. Organ of Wesleyan Methodist Local Preachers Mutual Aid Assoc. v6–27 [v21 (1871) *&* 25 (1875) *wanting*]. 8°. 1856–77

Locard (Edmond).
L'enquête criminelle & les méthodes sci. s8º. 1920

Locatelli (Pasino). Illustri Bergamaschi: studi crit.-biogr. Pittori. [pl]. s8º. Bergamo. 1867

Locatelli (Tommaso). Feste spettacoli e costumi di Venezia. [Estr. d. Venezia e le sue lagune. P2768]. la8º. Venezia. 1847

Loccenius (Joannes). Hist. rerum Suecic., usque ad Caroli Guatavi obitum deductæ libri 9. [Obs. & notæ hist., *w. sep. pagin.*] s8º. Upsaliæ. [1662]
Hist. Suecanae, usque ad Carolum XI deductae, libri 9. ed. 2ª auct. &c. Acc. Antiq. Sueo-Gothic. libri 3 eod. auct. [ed. 4ª *w. sep. tp. & pagin.*] s4º. Francofurti. 1676

Loch (*Sir* Charles Stewart). A gt. ideal & its champion. Papers &c. by L. [Ed. A. Clay]. s8º. [1923]

Loch (Sydney).
see NANKIVELL (J. M.) & S. L. Ireland in travail, 1922.
,, —— & —— River of a 100 ways: life in war-devastated areas of East. Poland, 1924.

Locher (Johann), *see* SCHOTTENLOHER (C.) H. Schobser, mit Anhang: Wer ist J. L. v. München?, 1925.

Lochmaier (Michael). Parrochiale curatorum &c. Ed. a M. L. 8º. [Parrhisieñ Lutecia], *M. N. de la barre.* [1513]

Lochmer (Šandor). Englesko-Hrvatski rječnik. [Eng.-Croatian dict.] 8º. u Senju. 1906

Lochner (Christoph Moritz).
De Martino Luthero. [P2587]. s4º. [Altdorf]. 1730

Lochner (Jacob Hieronymus), *see* FECHT (J.) Diss. de suggestionibus Satanae; praes. J. F., resp. J. H. L., 1706.
—— **& J. Vogt.** Observ. Anglicarum delectum primum subm. J. H. L. & J. V. [P444]. s4º. Bremae. [1714]

*Loci communes rerum theologic., 1521, *see* MELANCHTHON (P.)

Lock (Henry Osmond). The conquerors of Palestine thr. 40 centuries. Intr. by Visct. Allenby. 8º. 1920

Lock (Robert Heath). Recent progr. in study of variation, heredity & evolution. Rev. by L. Doncaster. Biog. note by B. S. Woolf. 8º. 1920

Lock (Walter). St. Paul the master-builder. 3rd ed. s8º. [1910]
see BIBLE: COMPL. TEXTS &c. Internat. Crit. Comm.: Pastoral Epistles; by W. L., 1924.

Locke (D. M.) Cast not a stone. s8º. 1927

Locke (George Herbert).
The Queen's Rangers: issued in conn. w. the present. of the colours to the Public Lib. of Toronto. [P2740]. la8º. [1923]
When Canada was New France. s8º. Toronto. 1920

Locke (John), *the philosopher.*
Works. 12th ed. 9v. 8º. 1824
,, With essay & notes by J. A. St. John. 2v. s8º. *Bohn.* 1854
Corresp. of J. L. & E. Clarke. Ed., w. biog. study by B. Rand. 8º. O. 1927
Essay conc. human understanding. 10th ed. w. add. 2v. 8º. 1731
,, ,, Abridged & ed. A. S. Pringle-Pattison. 8º. O. 1924
Sev. papers rel. to money, interest & trade &c. s8º. 1696
1, Some consid. of the conseq. of the lowering of interest &c., 2nd ed., corr., 1696, *w. sep. tp. & pagin.*
2, Short obs. on a paper, intit., For encour. the coining silver money in Eng., *w. sep. pagin.*
3, Further consid. conc. raising the value of money &c., 2nd ed., corr., 1695, *w. sep. tp. & pagin.*
see JÄGER (J. W.) Judicium de 2 adversariis J. L. & P. Poireto, 1708.
,; STILLINGFLEET (E.) Ans. to L.'s Second letter, 1698.

Locke (Richard). The Western Rebellion. Repr. f. the Somerset Arch. &c. Soc. [facs. of 1782 ed.] 8º. Taunton. 1888
,, ,, ...[repr.] [P2705]. 8º. Taunton. 1912

Locke (William John).
The coming of Amos. s8º. [1924]
The great Pandolfo. s8º. [1925]
The house of Baltazar. s8º. [1920]
Idols. [Pop. ed.] s8º. [1927]
The kingdom of Theophilus. s8º. [1927]
Moordius & Co. s8º. [1923]
The mountebank. s8º. 1921
The old bridge. s8º. [1926]
The red planet. [5th ed.] s8º. 1920
The rough road. [repr.] s8º. [1925]
Stories near & far. s8º. [1926]
The tale of Triona. s8º. 1922
Where love is. s8º. [1926]

Locker (Edward Hawke).
Views in Spain. [*wanting 6 plates*]. 4º. 1824

Lockerby (William). Journal of W. L., trader in the Fijian Islands, 1808–09; w. intr. & o. papers. Ed. E. Im Thurn & L. C. Wharton. [Hakluyt Soc., Ser. II, 52]. 8º. 1925

Locker-Lampson (Frederick), *see* BIRRELL (A.) F. L.-L.; character sketch w. letters &c., 1920.

Locker-Lampson (Godfrey Lampson Tennyson).
Cat. of anc. Greek coins coll. by G. L. L. Comp. by E. S. G. Robinson. 4º. 1923
On freedom. 8º. 1911
Oratory Brit. & Irish, the Gt. Age (1760–1832). Ed., w. notes by L.-L. 8º. 1918
Outline of financial procedure in H. of C. s8º. 1924
,, ,, 2nd rev. ed. s8º. 1924
A soldier's book of love poems, arranged by L.-L. s8º. 1917
Thoughts in middle life. s8º. 1919

Lockey (Joseph Byrne).
Pan-Americanism, its beginnings. 8º. N.Y. 1920

Lockhart (Douglas) [*ps.* ROBERT BIRKHILL]. Seeds of war: polit. st. of Austria, Hungary, Czecho-Slovakia &c. Intr. by Hon. A. Herbert. [2nd ed.] 8º. 1925

Lockhart (J. G.)
Mysteries of the sea.: bk. of strange tales. 8º. [1924]
Peril of the sea: shipwrecks &c. 8º. 1924

Lockhart (John Gibson).
Anc. Span. ballads. Tr. [w. intr. &c.] n. ed. s8º. 1870
Hist. of Napoleon. [Everyman's Lib.] [repr.] s8º. [1909]
Life of Burns. [Everyman's Lib.] s8º. [1907]

Lockie (John), *publ.* Edinburgh guide. s8º. 1900

Lockitt (Charles Henry).
The rel. of French & Eng. society, 1763–93. 8º. 1920

Lockton (William). The treatment of the remains at the Eucharist after Holy Communion &c. 8º. C. 1920

Lockyer (*Sir* Joseph Norman).
Elem. lessons in astronomy. [repr. w. corr.] s8º. 1919
see CORTIE (A. L.) Sir N. L., 1921.
,, NORMAN LOCKYER OBSERVATORY.

Lockyer (William James Stewart).
Apparatus for broadening spectra. [Repr. f. R. Astr. Soc., v85. P2769]. 8º. *n.p.* 1924
The Hill Observatory, Salcombe Regis. [Repr. f. Trans. of Devon. Assoc. P2489]. 8º. [1920]
On the relationship betw. solar prominences & the corona. [Repr. f. R.A.S., v82. P2705]. 8º. [1922]
Recent obs. of some bright-hydrogen-line stars. [Repr. f. Roy. Astr. Soc., v84. P2738]. 8º. [1924]
Spectroscopic & magnitude obs. of *o* (Mira) Ceti, 1924. [Repr. f. R.A.S., v84. P2754]. 8º. [1924]
Spectrum of ϕ Persei. [Repr. f. R.A.S., v85. P2785]. 8º. [1925]
see NORMAN LOCKYER OBSERVATORY. Hdbk. to the N. L. Obs.; by L., 1921.

Locman [LOKMAN]. Fables de L. expliq. par 2 trad. franç. avec dict. analyt. par A. Charbonneau. 2e tirage. s8º. 1864
Fabulae L[i]. & quaedam dicta Arabum c. interpret. Lat. T. Erpenii, ejusdemque notulis & stricturis J. Golii. [*Extr.*] s4º. *n.p. n.d.* [1615 ?]
see ERPENIUS (T.) Gramm. Arabica cum fabulis L. (*Arab. & Lat.*), 1748.

Lóczy (Louis), *ed.* A geograph., econ. & soc. survey of Hungary. [Hung. Geog. Soc. P2519]. 8º. Budapest. 1919

Loder (*Sir* Edmund Giles), *bart., see* PEASE (*Sir* A. E.) E. L.: a mem., 1923.

Loder (*Capt.* John de Vere). Truth about Mesopotamia, Palestine & Syria. Foreword by Ld. R. Cecil. s8º. [1923]
see BOOTHBY (R. J. G.), J. DE V. L. &c. Industry & the state, 1927.

Löder (Johann Heinrich), *see* BOHEMI. Protestatio B., 1415; hrsg. J. H. L., 1712.

Lodge (Edmund). Illust. of Brit. hist., biog. & manners, Henry VIII–Ja. I exhib. in papers f. MSS. of the families of Howard, Talbot, Cecil; cont. great part of the corr. of Eliz. & h. ministers w. G., 6th Earl of Shrewsbury dur. years in wh. Mary, Q. of Scots, remained in h. custody, w. notes &c. 3v. 4º. 1791

Lodge (Eleanor Constance). Account book of a Kentish estate, 1616–1704. [Cheyncecourt &c. *Toke fam. estate*]. Ed. E. C. L. la8º. 1927
Gascony under Eng. rule. 8º. [1926]

Lodge (Gonzalez). Lexicon Plautinum. v1. la8º. Lipsiae. 1924

Lodge (Henry Cabot).
The Senate & the League of Nations. 8º. N.Y. 1925
see ROOSEVELT (T.) Sel. f. corresp. of R. & H. C. L., 1884–1918, 2v, 1925.

Lodge (*Sir* Oliver Joseph).
Atoms & rays: intr. to mod. views. 8º. 1924
Electrical precipitation. 8º. 1925
Ether & reality: functions of the ether of space. s8º. [1925]
Evolution & creation. s8º. [1926]
Making of man; st. in evolution. [repr.] s8º. [1924]
Raymond revised. New & abbrev. ed. of Raymond or Life & death. 8º. [1922]

Lodge (*Sir* Oliver Joseph) [*continued*].
Science & human progress. 8º. [1927]
The substance of faith allied w. science. 10th ed. 8º. [1910]
The survival of man. s8º. [1915]
Talks about wireless. 8º. [1925]
The War & after. s8º. [1915]
see MURCHISON (C.), *ed.* Case for & agst. psychical belief, by Sir O. L. &c., 1927.
„ UNIV. COLL., *London.* Centenary addresses [by Sir O. L. &c.], 1927.

Lodge (Raymond), *see* LODGE (*Sir* O. J.) Raymond revised, 1922.
Lodge (*Sir* Richard). Gt. Brit. & Prussia in the 18th cent. Ford lect., Oxf., 1922. 8º. O. 1923
Lodge (Thomas), *see* HARMAN (E. G.) The Ctsse. of Pembrokes Arcadia &c. (with chap. on T. L.), 1924.
Lodi. Statuta caligariorum et sartorum civit. Laudae; ed. A. Ceruti, *see* REGIA DEP. DI STORIA PATRIA. Misc., t7, 1869.
Lodoicus *Granatensis, see* LUIS, *de Granada.*
Lodovico, *duca di Savoia ; 1402–65, see* LOUIS, *duke of Savoy.*
Lods (Adolphe). Jean Astruc et la crit. bibl. au 18e s. Not. biog. par P. Alphandéry. [Extr. de la Rév. d'hist. &c. rélig.] 8º. Str. 1924
Loehr (August Octav v.), *see* LÖHR (A. O. v.)
Loelius (Laurentius), *see* LAELIUS (L.)
Loen, *see* LÖN.
Loening (Otto), *see* LÖNING (O.)
Loew (Elias Avery), *aft.* LOWE, *see* LOWE (E. A.)
Loewe (Herbert). Mediæval Hebrew minstrelsy. 16 Zemiroth arr. by R. L. Henriques. Tr. [w. notes &c.] by H. L. Foreword by J. H. Hertz. 8º. 1926
Some mediaeval Heb. poesy. Foreword by Sir H. Allen. s8º. [1927]
see CAMBRIDGE: GIRTON COLL. Cat. of pr. bks. &c. in the Mary Frere Heb. Lib.; by H. L., 1915.
Loewe (Victor). Ein Diplomat u. Gelehrter, E. Spanheim, 1629–1710. Mit Anhang: Aus d. Briefwechsel zw. S. u. Leibniz. 8º. 1924
Loewenfeld-Russ (Hans), *see* LÖWENFELD-RUSS (H.)
Löffler (Carl).
Schwäb. Buchmalerei in roman. Zeit. 4º. Augsburg. 1928
Loftie (William John). Kensington Palace. 8º. 1898
The Latin year: coll. of hymns. Comp. by L. s8º. 1873
Loftus (Pierse). The creed of a Tory. 8º. [1926]
Loga (Valerian v.)
Die Malerei in Spanien v. 14. bis 18. Jhdt. la8º. 1923
Logan (J. D.) & D. G. French.
Highways of Canadian lit., 1760–1924. 8º. Toronto. [1924]
Logan (James), *F.R.G.S.*
Ulster in the X-Rays. Intr. by Ld. E. Hamilton. s8º. [1923]
Logan (James), *chief justice of Pennsylvania.* Corresp. of J. L. & T. Story, 1724–41. Ed. N. Penney. 8º. Phila. 1927
Logan (James Richardson), *F.G.S.* The ethnology of the Indian archipelago. 8º. Singapore. 1850
Logan (John), *poet.* Poems. 3rd ed. 8º. 1789
Poet. works. Coll. by T. Park. [*b. w.* Smollett (T. G.) Poet. wks., 1807]. s8º. 1807
Logau (Friedrich v.) Sämmtl. Sinngedichte. Hrsg. G. Eitner. [Lit. V. in St. 113]. 8º. [Tübingen]. 1872
Loggan (David). Oxonia illustrata, sive collegiorum &c. scenographia. fol. Oxon. 1675
Logia Jesu [SAYINGS OF JESUS]. The sayings of Jesus f. Oxyrhynchus. Ed. w. intr., comm. &c. by H. G. E. White. s8º. C. 1920
***Logica,** sive ars cogitandi, 1677, *see* ARNAULD (A.) & P. NICOLE.
Loginovsky (K. D.) Свадебныя пѣсни &c. казаковъ вост. Забайкалья. [I.R.G.O. Зап. приамурск. отд., 5ii]. 8º. Хабаровскъ. 1899
Logio (George Clenton). Hist. [of Bulgaria] dur. the War, *see* BUCHAN (J.), *ed.* Nations of to-day, B. & Romania, 1924.
Löher (Franz von). Kretische Gestade. s8º. Bielefeld. 1877
Lohmeyer (Carl), *see* SILLIB (R.) & C. L. Heidelberg, 1927.
Löhr (August Octav v.) Karl Domanig, *see* SITTE (H.) Vergessenes Parthenonbild &c., 1915.
Loire. *Les châteaux de la Loire. [Guides Bleus. Dir. M. Monmarche]. 6e éd. s8º. 1919
„ „ ....7e éd. s8º. 1923
***Loisirs** (Les) d'un étranger au Pays Basque, 1901, *see* WEBSTER (W.)
Loisy (Alfred).
Les Actes des Apôtres. la8º. 1920
„ „ Tr. nouv. avec intr. & notes. s8º. 1925
L'Apocalypse de Jean. la8º. 1923
L'église & la France. s8º. 1925
L'Epitre aux Galates. s8º. 1916

Loisy (Alfred) [*continued*].
Essai hist. sur le sacrifice. la8º. 1920
L'Evangile selon Luc. la8º. 1924
La morale humaine. s8º. 1923
La paix des nations & la religion de l'avenir. [P2435]. s8º. 1919
Le quatrième Evangile. 2e éd. refondue. Les épitres dites de Jean. la8º. 1921
Relig. & humanité. s8º. 1926
see BIBLE: FRENCH. Les livres du Nouv. Test.; tr. avec intr. &c. par A. L., 1922.

***Loix** (Les) de la galanterie (1644). [*Intr. by L. Lalanne.* Trésor des pièces rares &c.] s8º. 1855
Lokhvitsky (Aleksandr Vladimirovich).
Губернія ея земскія и правительств. учрежденія. ч1. 8º. С.-П. 1864
Lokotsch (Carl). Etymolog. Wbch. der europ. (german., roman. & slav.) Wörter oriental. Urspr. 8º. Heidelberg. 1927
Türk. Volkstümliche u. Volkspoesie, 1917, *see* KLEINE TEXTE, T140, 1917.
Loliée (Frédéric). "La Païva." La légende & l'hist. de la Marquise de Païva. 8º. [1920]
***Lollards** (The), acc. of the witnesses for the truth in Eng. betw. 1400 & 1546. [Relig. Tract Soc.] p1–12 *in* 1v. [p1, 2, 2nd ed. p13 & 14 wanting, *no tp.*] s8º. [1843]
Lomax (Montague).
The experiences of an asylum doctor. 8º. [1921]
Lomax (W. J.) The ambassador's kiss. s8º. [1925]
Lombard (Jacques). Les amants damnés. s8º. 1922
Lombard (Jean), *see* JESUITS. Voyages &c., t1, Mission de Cayenne &c. [J. L. &c.], 1857.
Lombard (Lambert), *see* KUNTZIGER (M.) L. L., 1920.
Lombard (Mich.), *see* *SUMMA univ. theol. Christ. sec. Unitarios [*by M. L.?*], 1787.
Lombard (Paul). Le cabaret du Nervoso. s8º. [1922]
Féodor-le-Brutal, nouvelle, *see* ŒUVRES libres, 57, 1926.
Le village en folie, nouvelle, *see* ŒUVRES libres, 12, 1922.
Lombardia. Chronicon marchiae Tarvisinae et L., 1207–70, *see* MURATORI. Rerum Ital. scr., t8iii, 1916.
Lombardo (Alberto).
Los Estados-Unidos: notas &c. de viaje. 8º. Mexico. 1884
Lombart (Pierre), *see* LAYARD (G. S.) The headless horseman, P. L.'s engraving: Charles or Cromwell?, 1922.
Lomba y Pedraja (J. R.)
Teatro ant. a Lope de Vega. Sel. por L. y P. 8º. 1924
Lombroso (Cesare). L'homme criminel. Tr. Regnier & Bournet. Atlas. 2e éd. la8º. 1888
Lombroso (Gina). L'anima d. donna. s8º. Bologna. [1920]
Lomellini (Gianni). La battaglia di Montebello (1859). 8º. [Montebello. 1906]
Lomonosov (Mikhail Vasilevich). Письма, *see* GROT (YA. K.) Письма Л. и Сумарокова &c., 1862.
see MENSHUTKIN (B. N.) М. В. Л., 1911.
„ PEKARSKY (P. P.) Извѣстія для біографіи Л., 1865.
Lön (Johann Michael von), *1694–1776, see* SIEBER (S.) J. M v. L., 1922.
Lönborg (Sven). Dike och Eros. Människor och Makter forntidens Aten. 2d. 8º. 192(
Klass. Filologi. Efterskrift till [*& b. w. h.*] Dike och Eros, d2 8º. 192
Lonchay (Henri) & J. Cuvelier. Corr. de la cour d'Espagne sur les affaires des Pays-Bas au 17e s. [C. R. d'H. de Belg. t1, 2. 4º. Brux. 1923–2
1, Corr. de Philippe III, 1598–1621.
2, Corr. de Philippe IV avec l'infante Isabelle, 1621–33.

London.
Anonymous Works [*i.e. works in wh. London is the catchword*
Calendars &c.
Ambulator: or, pocket companion round London, 6th ed [ed. R. Lobb], 1793; 11th ed., 1811, *see* AMBULATOR.
Antiqs. of L.: chiefly f. works of T. Pennant, 1814, *se* PENNANT (T.)
*Antiqs. (The) of L. & Westminster, by N. B., 1722, *se* BAILEY (N.)
Calendar of early Mayor's Court rolls, among the archives the Corp. of the City of London, A.D. 1298–1307. Ed. A. F Thomas. la8º. C. 192
Calendar of Plea & Memoranda Rolls pres. in Archives of th Corp. of L., 1323–64. Ed. A. H. Thomas. la8º. C. 192
Complete (A) guide to all persons who have trade &c. v London: cont. names of streets, stage-coaches, places abode &c. 7th ed. s8º. 17
*Gallant news for L., 1647, *repr., see* HARTSHORNE (E. S. Mem. of Holdenby, 1868.
*Golden guide to London. 4th ed. rev. s8º. 18
Introductions to London, 1926, *see* DAWSON (L. H.), *ed.*
London anecdotes: inventors & discoverers. s8º. 18

London [*continued*].

Anonymous Works—Calendars &c. [*continued*].

*London (The) printers lamentation, or, the press opprest &c. [*no tp.*] 8°. [1660]

For a. ed. see HARLEIAN Misc., v3.

Map drawn in 1585 to illust. lawsuit conc. Geldings Close. [London Top. Soc. *b. w.* Den Wyngaerde (A. van) View (c. 1550), 1881–2]. atl. fol. 1925

„ „ *see* KINGSFORD (C. L.) Early hist. of Piccadilly &c., based on plan drawn in 1585, 1925.

Mod. practice of the London hospitals. 3rd ed., w. index of diseases &c. s8°. 1770

New plan of London & its environs. Engraved by S. W. Cooke. folded s8°. [*in case*]. 1823

*Records of old L. &c. w. descr. letterpress by W. G. H., 1888, *see* HABERSHON (W. G.)

Survey of London. [Comm. for the Survey of the Memorials of Greater London & London County Council]. v7–12. 4°. 1921–27

7, Parish of Chelsea, p3 ; by W. H. Godfrey.

8, Parish of St. Leonard, Shorditch ; drawings &c. by G. Topham Forrest ; ed., w. hist. intr. &c., by Sir J. Bird.

9, Parish of St. Helen, Bishopsgate, p1 ; by M. Reddan & A. W. Clapham.

10, Parish of St. Margaret, Westminster, p1 ; drawings &c. by G. T. Forrest ; ed., w. hist. notes by M. H. Cox.

11, Parish of Chelsea, p4, The Royal Hospital ; by W. H. Godfrey.

12, Cromwell House, Highgate ; by P. Norman.

*View (A) of London & Westminster : or, the town spy. 2p [*in* 1v ; *tp. of* p2 *dated* 1725]. s8°. 1728

Civic &c. Institutions.

Addresses [&c.] pres. from the Court of Common Co. to the king, resol. granting freedom of the city &c., 1760–70 [*&* 1769–78, 2p *in* 1v]. s8°. [1778]

Hdbk. of ceremonials &c. : rev. ed. of the bk. of cerem. of the city of L., as repr. in proof in 1882. 8°. 1906

Order (The) of the hospitalls of K. Henry VIII & K. Edward VI, viz. St. Bartholomew's, Christ's, Bridewell, St. Thomas's. By the Maior &c. of L. s8°. 1557 [repr. c. 1700 ?]

Provincial Assembly.

Jus divinum ministerii evangelici ; or the Divine right of the gospel ministry : divided into two parts. Publ. by the Prov. Assembly of London. s4°. 1654

see MARTIN (J.), S. PETTO &c. The preacher sent : in ans. to Jus divinum minist. evang. by the Prov. Ass. of L. &c., 1658.

London & Middlesex Archaeological Society. Transactions. N.S., v3–5. 8°. 1917–28

London Argus (The) : weekly journal &c. of public life. v15–18 (Apr. 1904–Apr. 1906). [*b. in* 2v]. 4°. [1904–06]

London Assurance (The), *see* STREET (G. S.) The L.A., 1720–1920, 1920.

London Cabinet & Upholstery Trades Federation. London furniture. 4°. 1925

London Chamber of Arbitration. Rules. [P2871]. 8°. 1892

London Chronicle (The). v106 (July–Dec. 1809), 108 (July–Dec. 1810). 4°. 1809–10

v106 *wants* Nos. 7913–4, 7937, 7947, 7963. v108 *wants tp.*, index & Nos. 8041, 8082 & 8095.

London Churches Commission, City of. Report, 1919. sm. fol. 1919

London County Council.

Conference on local govt. Proc. fol. 1896

L.C.C. Gazette : the official organ of the L.C.C. v25–32. fol. 1920–27

London parks & open spaces. Foreword by Sir J. Bird. 8°. 1924

London statistics, 1915–20. [Comp. by the Clerk of the Council]. v26, la8°. 1921

Opening of Kingsway & Aldwych by H.M. the King, 18th Oct. 1905. la8°. [1905]

Proposed demolition of 19 City churches. Report. 8°. [1921]

Record of service in the Great War, 1914–18, by members of staff. 8°. 1922

see BRAINES (W. W.) *Site of the Globe Playhouse, Southwark ; publ. by arr. w. the L.C.C., 2nd ed., 1924.

„ BURT (C.) Mental & scholastic tests, 2nd impr., 1922.

„ LONDON. Survey of L., 1921–27.

„ SAINT OLAVE'S. St. O. : hist. assoc. &c., 1918.

London, Declaration of. D. of L. Coll. of offic. papers & docs. rel. to the internat. naval confer., Dec. 1908–Feb. 1909. Intr. by E. Root. Ed. J. B. Scott. [C.E. for Int. Peace]. la8°. N.Y. 1919

see NAVAL WAR COLLEGE, *Wash.* Internat. law topics : D. of L. of Feb. 26, 1909, 1910.

London Devonian Association, *see* DEVONIAN YEAR BOOK, 1926.

London Directory of Brit. manufacturers &c., 1921, 1924, 1928. la8°. [1921–28]

London, Edinburgh & Dublin philosophical magazine & journal of science. 6th ser., v39–50, 7th ser., v1–5. 8°. [1920–28]

London Gazette, The, Dec. 31, 1751–Dec. 30, 1755. Nos. 9124–9541. [9160, 9489 *wanting* ; 9126–28, 9131, 9458 *are also wanting, but dates are consecutive*]. sm. fol. 1752–55

„ „ [*Supplements, mostly beg.*] Whitehall. This day &c., 23 Oct. 1702, 2 Nov. 1702, 13 Mar. 1703, 14 & 16 July 1705, 21 & 30 Aug. 1705, 28 May 1706. [*b. w.* Post Man, 1702–08]. sm. fol. *E. Jones.* 1702–06

„ „ The L.G. extraordinary, Oct. 16, 1759. sm. fol. 1759

London Journal, The. No. 82 (Feb. 18, 1720), 179 (Dec. 29, 1722) [*b. w.* Post Man, 1720–24], 512 (May 24, 1729). fol. 1720–29

London Library, *1785.* Catalogue. [*w. Prospectus headed* L.L. Society]. 8°. 1786

London Library. Cat. of the L.L. By C. T. Hagberg Wright & C. J. Purnell. 2v. 4°. 1913–14

„ „ Suppl. (1914–15). By C. T. H. Wright & C. J. Purnell. 4°. 1915

„ „ Suppl. (1913–20). By C. T. H. Wright & C. J. Purnell. 4°. 1920

Subject index of the L.L. By C. T. Hagberg Wright & C. J. Purnell. v2, Add., 1909–22. 4°. 1923

see WRIGHT (C. T. H.) La " London Library," 1925.

„ —— The L.L., 1926.

„ —— The soul's dispensary : early yrs. of the L.L., 1922.

London Mercury (The). Ed. J. C. Squire. v1–17. la8°. [1920–28]

London Missionary Society. Reports, 1795–1814. 8°. [1814]

see SMITH (J.) Rep. of proc. agst. J. S., tried on a charge of aiding &c. in rebellion of Negro slaves, 1824.

London Museum, The.

Catalogues. No 1, London & the Vikings. 8°. 1927

see LAW (E.) The L.M. at Kensington Palace, 1912.

London Post, The [*formerly* The London Slip of News]. No. 32 (Aug. 16–18, 1699), 466 (Aug. 21–24, 1702). [*b. w.* Daily Courant, No. 85 &c., 1702–03]. fol. 1699–1702

London quarterly review (The). v1–60 (1853–83), 133–149 (1920–28). 8°. 1853–1928

London School of Economics & Political Science.

Calendar, 1920–21—1927–28. 8°. 1920–27

see BAL KRISHNA. Commercial rel. betw. India & Eng., 1601–1757, 1924.

„ DALTON (H.) Princ. of public finance, 1923.

„ KNOWLES (L. C. A.) Indust. &c. revol. in Gt. Brit. dur. the 19th cent., 4th ed., 1926.

„ LEES-SMITH (H. B.) Second chambers in theory & practice, 1923.

„ MALINOWSKI (B.) Argonauts of the West. Pacific, 1922.

„ MESS (H. A.) Factory legisl., 1891–1924, 1926.

„ MORLEY (F.) Unemployment relief in Gt. Brit., 1924.

„ PILLAI (P. P.) Econ. condit. in India, 1925.

„ STELLING (C. D.), *ed.* Yea & nay : lect. & counter-lect. at London Sch. of Econ., 1923.

London Topographical Society. Drawings of buildings in area descr. in " The early hist. of Piccadilly &c., by C. L. Kingsford." 4°. 1926

London topograph. record incl. 20th[–26th] ann. rep. of L.T.S. v13, 14. 8°. 1923–28

see CAPON (W.) Views of Westminster, 1801–15, w. descr. ; annot. by P. Norman, 1923–24.

„ HOLLAR (W.) Drawings, 1922.

„ LONDON. Map drawn in 1585 to illust. lawsuit conc. Geldings Close, 1925.

„ MERIAN (M.) View of London (1638), 1922.

„ TALLIS (J.) T.'s London street views (1839) : Bond St., Div. 1, 1921.

London University. Cat. of the MSS. & autograph letters in the Univ. library, Central building ; w. descr. of the MS. life of Edward, Prince of Wales, by Chandos. Comp. by R. A. Rye. 8°. 1921

Cat. of works dealing with study of Western palaeography in U. of L. Comp. by J. Wilkes & A. D. Lacey. 8°. 1921

Univ. of London O.T.C. Roll of War service, 1914–19. 8°. 1921

see BIRKBECK COLLEGE.

„ RANDERSON (W.) Albert Kahn Travelling Fellowships : Rep., 1923–24, 1926.

„ RATAN TATA FOUNDATION.

London (Charmian Kittredge), *wife of Jack London.* The new Hawaii. Cont. My Hawaiian aloha, by Jack London. 8°.1923

London (Jack).
L'esprit de Porportuk, see ŒUVRES libres, 55, 1926.
Island tales. s8º. [1920]
Le jeu du ring, see ŒUVRES libres, 71, 1927.
My Hawaiian aloha, see LONDON (C. K.) The new Hawaii, 1923.
Londonderry (Charles W. Stewart [*aft. C. W. Vane*], *3rd marq. of*), *1778–1854*. Narr. of the Peninsular War, 1808–13. 4º. 1828
Narr. of the war in Germany & France, 1813–14. 4º. 1830
Story of the Peninsular War: w. contin. by G. R. Gleig. s8º. *n.d.*
Londonderry (Edith, *marchioness of*), *wife of 7th marquess, form. Hon. E. Chaplin*. Henry Chaplin: memoir. 8º. 1926
Londres (Albert). La Chine en folie, choses vues, see ŒUVRES libres, 30, 1923.
*Long engagements; tale of the Affghan Rebellion, 1846, see KAYE (*Sir* J. W.)
Long (Basil S.), see VICTORIA & ALBERT MUSEUM. Jones Coll.; p3, Paintings & miniatures, by L., 1923.
Long (Constance Ellen).
Coll. papers on the psychology of phantasy. 8º. 1920
Long (Frances Louise), see CLEMENTS (F. E.) & F. L. L. Experimental pollination, 1923.
Long (Isaac Le), see LE LONG (I.)
Long (Roger). The music speech at public Commencement in Cambridge, July 6, 1714. [P2868]. s8º. 1714
Long (Thomas), *prebendary of Exeter*. An exercitation conc. the use of our Lord's Prayer. [*b. w. h.* A rebuke &c., 1704]. s8º. 1658
A rebuke to E. Calamy, a. of the Abridgment of Baxter's life. s8º. Exon. 1704
Long (W. H.) A dict. of the Isle of Wight dialect. s8º. 1886
Long (Walter Hume Long, *1st viscount*), *of Wraxall*.
Memories. 8º. 1923
Longard (Leonhard Caspar).
Symbola ad doct. de digammo Aeolica. 8º. Bonnae. 1837
Longchamp (F. C.) L'estampe & le livre à gravures. Guide de l'amateur. [Un siècle d'art suisse, 1730–1830]. la8º. Lausanne. [1920]
Manuel du bibliophile suisse. Typographie &c. dans l'illust. du livre du 16–20 s., suivi d'une bibliogr. gén. la8º. 1922
Longden (*Maj.* **Alfred Appleby).** Art of the Empire, see SALMON (E.) Lit. of the Emp. &c., 1924.
Longden (Henry Isham). Hist. of the Washington family. Repr. f. The genealogist's mag. s8º. Northampton. 1927
Longe (Francis Davy). The wage-fund theory &c. [P2598]. 8º. 1866 [*repr.* Baltimore. 1904]
Longfellow (Henry Wadsworth). Poet. works [pref. not. by W. M. Rossetti]. s8º. *Suttaby. n.d.*
„ „ ....Oxford ed. s8º. 1916
The Song of Hiawatha. s8º. Boston [Mass.] 1855
see GOGGIO (E.) L. & Dante, 1924.
Longfield (Robert). Rep. on legisl. measures to facilitate commercial contracts resp. occup. of land in Ireland. [P2554]. 8º. D. 1851
Longford (Joseph Henry). Japan, see BUCHAN (J.), *ed.* Nations of to-day, 1923.
Longhi (Pietro).
see RAVÀ (A.) Contrib. alla biog. di P. L., 1911.
„ SYMONDS (J. A.) A Venet. painter, P. L., 1889.
„ UZANNE (O.) P. L., 1924.
Longhi (Roberto).
Piero d. Francesca. Tr. J. Chuzeville. la8º. 1927
Longhurst (Albert Henry). Pallava archit., pl, see INDIA: ARCH. SURVEY. Mem. 17, 1924.
Longhurst (Margaret H.) English ivories. 4º. [1926]
see VICTORIA & ALBERT MUS. Cat. of carvings in ivory, pl, 1927.
Longi (Jo. Ru.), *i.e. J. R. Longipollus*, see RUBIUS (JOHANN).
Longin (Emile). Baux à ferme & vente des chastellenies &c. du Pays de Beaujollois, 1528–1604. 8º. Lyon. 1907
Longinov (Mikhail Nikolaevich). Русскій театръ въ Петербургѣ и Москвѣ (1749–74). [I. Akad. Nauk. Записки, t23]. 8º. С.-П. 1873
Longinus (Dionysius Cassius).
Libellus de sublimitate. Rec. A. O. Prickard. s8º. O. [1906]
On the sublime. Tr. w. notes by W. Smith. 5th ed. s8º. 1757
„ „ w. tr. by W. H. Fyfe [Loeb Class. Lib.], 1927, see ARISTOTLE. Poetics, 1927.
see WILKE (A. L.) "Ὕψος script. divin. e Longini excelsa disciplina expensum, 1758.

Longipollus (J. Rubius), see RUBIUS (JOHANN).
Longland (John), *bp. of Lincoln*, see LONGLONDE.
Longlonde (John), *bp. of Lincoln* [LONGLAND]. Benedictional. Ed. R. M. Woolley. [Henry Bradshaw Soc., v64]. 8º. 1927
Longman (Charles James). A letter of Dr. Johnson & some 18th-cent. imprints of the House of Longman. la8º. *p.f.p.c.* 1928
Longman (Sibyl). The church's year in the Sunday Kindergarten. 3rd ed. 8º. [1924]
Longmans, *publishing firm* [LONGMANS, GREEN, & CO.]
see COX (H.) & J. E. CHANDLER. House of L., w. rec. of th. bicentenary celebrations, 1724–1924, 1925.
„ LONGMAN (C. J.) Letter of Dr. Johnson & some 18 c. impr. of the House of L., 1928.
Longnon (Auguste). Doc. parisiens sur l'iconographie de S. Louis. Publ. A. L. 8º. 1882
Les noms de lieu de la France. Publ. par P. Marichal [&] L. Mirot. fasc. 1–3. 8º. 1920–27
Longo (Bartolo), see PAYAN (A.) Le sanctuaire de Notre Dame &c., d'ap. les écr. de B. L., 1894.
Longo (Egidio). Introd. alla mascara e ballo. [Nozze Marchese–Caracciola]. [N125]. 8º. Napoli. 1677
Longo (Michele). Giambattista Vico. 8º. Torino. 1921
Longobardus (Nicolaus), see JESUITS. Recent. de ampl. regno Chinae [a N. L., 1598], 1601.
Longolius (Christophorus).
see BECKER (P. A.) C. de L., s. Leben &c., 1924.
„ OSORIO DA FONSECA (J.) H. Osorii in G. Haddonum libri tres; ed. 3ª acc. C. L. oratio, 1576.
Longpont. Cartul. du prieuré de Notre-Dame de L. de l'Ordre de Cluny, 11ᵉ–12ᵉ s. Publ. avec intr. & notes. la8º. Lyon. 1879
Longrais (Frédéric Joüon des), see JOÜON DES LONGRAIS (F.)
Longrigg (Stephen Hemsley).
Four cent. of mod. Iraq. 8º. O. 1925
Longueil (Christophle de), see LONGOLIUS (C.)
Longuet (André). L'origine commune des religions. la8º. 1921
Longueval (Jacques). *Tractatus de schismate. Ex Gallico Latine redditus &c. s8º. Lovanii. [1718]
Longueville (Thomas) [*ps.* THE PRIG].
*The platitudes of a pessimist. 8º. 1897
Longus [*Longo*], see GAMBARA (L.) Expositi (tr. f. L.), 1581.
Longworth de Chambrun (Clara), see CHAMBRUN (C. L. DE).
Longy (*le Lieutenant*).
La campagne de 1797 sur le Rhin. 8º. 1909
Lonicer (Johann). Contra Romanistam fratrem Augustinū Alveldeñ Franciscanū Lipsicū Canonis Biblici publicū lictorē & tortorē eiusdem. s4º. Vvittenbergae. 1520
Lonicer (Johann Adam), see BRY (J. T.) 4ª pars Iconum viros virtute &c. illust. repraes.; opera & studio [J. A. L.], 1599.
Löning (Otto). Die Freie Stadt Danzig—K. Ollmert, Das Saargebiet. [P2749]. 8º. Münster i. W. 1923
Lönnrot (Elias). Kanteletar taikka Suomen Kansan wanhoja lauluja ja wirsiä. Toinen painos. 8º. Helsingissä. 1864
Löns (Hermann).
Das zweite Gesicht: e. Liebesgesch. 8º. Jena. 1926
Lonsdale (Frederick).
The last of Mrs. Cheyney. Comedy. [2nd impr.] 8º. [1926]
Spring cleaning. Play. 8º. [1925]
Lonsdorf (Otto *von*), *bp. of Passau, 1254–65*, see SCHMID (U.) O. v. L., 1903.
Loo, *abbey of St. Pierre*, see STOOP (P. DE). Notice sur l'abbaye de L., 1843.
Loofs (Friedrich). Paulus v. Samosata: e. Unters. z. altkirchl. Lit.- u. Dogmengesch. [Texte u. Unters. z. Gesch. d. altchr. Litt., B44v]. 8º. L. 1924
Looker (Samuel J.)
Dawn & sunset gold. Poems. [P2503]. s8º. 1920
Thorns & sweet briar. Love & nature lyrics w. satires. [P2520]. s8º. [1917]
***Looking-glass (A)** for all lordly prelates, 1636, see PRYNNE (W.)
Loomans (Charles).
De la connaissance de soi-même. 2ᵉ éd. s8º. 1883
Loomis (Roger Sherman). Illust. of medieval romance on tiles f. Chertsey Abbey. [Univ. of Illinois. St. in lang. &c., v2ii]. 8º. [Urbana]. 1916
Looney (J. Thomas), *ed.*, see OXFORD (E. DE V., *earl of*). Poems, 1921.
Loos (Anita) [*i.e. Mrs.* JOHN EMERSON].
"Gentlemen prefer blondes." s8º. N.Y. 1925
„ „ ....[2nd impr.] s8º. [1926

Loos (Josef). Slownik slowenskej, madarskej a nemeckej reči. [v]3. s8°. Peši. 1871

Looy (Jacobus van). Feesten. 3e dr. 8°. 1920
Jaapje. 5e dr. 8°. A. 1922
Proza. 5e dr. 8°. A. 1922

Lop (S. Ferdinand-), *see* FERDINAND-LOP (S.)

Łopaciński (Boleslas), *see* CHARLES [*de Saxe*], *duke of Courland.* C. de S.: sa vie, corr. &c.; publ. B. L., 1870.

Lo Parco (Francesco). Tideo Acciarini, umanista marchigiano d. sec. 15, con s. Carmina e un Libellus ined. 8°. Napoli. 1920

Lopatin (B.) Польскія политич. партіи. [P2450]. 8°. С.-П. 1906

Lopatin (Herman Aleksandrovich). Г. А. Лопатин (1845–1918). Автобиография. Письма. Статьи и стихотворения &c. Подготовил к печати А. А. Шилов. 8°. П. 1922

Löpelmann (Martin). Il diletteuole essamine de' Guidoni, Furfanti &c., 1598, *see* ROMANISCHE FORSCH., B34, 1915.
Das Weihnachtslied d. Franz. u. d. übr. roman. Völker, *see* ROMANISCHE FORSCH., B33, 1915.

Loperraez Corvalan (Juan). Descr. hist. del obispado de Osma, con cat. de s. prelados. 3t. la8°. 1788
t3 has t. Col. diplomática citada en la Descr. hist. &c.

Lopes (Fernão).
Chron. de el-Rei D. Fernando. 3v. s8°. 1895–96
Chron. of F. L. & Gomes Eannes de Zurara. With tr. extracts &c. by E. Prestage. 8°. Watford. 1928
F. L. [v.] 1, Cron. de D. Pedro e D. Fernando. 2, 3, Cron. de D. João I. [Antol. portug. Intr. &c. por J. de Magalhães Lima]. 3v [*v1, 2a ed.*] s8°. Paris. 1921–22
see BELL (A. F. G.) F. L., 1921.

Lopes (José M.), E. R. Bensley &c. Nuevo dicc. inglés-esp. y esp.-ingl. n. ed., aumentado &c. con supl. por M. de La Torre &c. [2p]. la8°. Paris. *n.d.*

Lopes de Castanheda (Fernam), *see* ALVAREZ PEREIRA (N.) Chron. [*attrib. to F. L.*], 1911.

Lopes de Santiago (Diogo), *see* SANTIAGO (D. L. DE).

Lopes de Sousa (Pero). Diario da navegação, 1530–32, *see* INSTITUTO HIST. E GEOG. BRAZIL. Rev., t24, 1861.

Lopes Vieira (Afonso). Verso e prosa. s8°. Paris. 1925

Lopez (Dominicus), *see* SOCINUS (F.) De Sacrae Scr. auctoritate [*wrongly attrib. to D. L.*], 1588.

Lopez (José Castro y), *see* CASTRO Y LOPEZ (J.)

Lopez (Santiago). Nueva guia de caminos para ir desde Madrid. 4a ed. corr. s8°. 1828

Lopez (Tomás), *see* CASTANEDA Y ALCOVER (V.) Rel. geogr., topogr. &c. de Reino de Valencia, hechas en el siglo 18 a ruego de T. L., Prov. of V., 2p, 1921–22.

Lopez-Aydillo (Eugenio) & J. Palacios.
Lamas Carvajal: est. biog. y crit. con sel. s8°. 1925

Lopez de Ayala (Ignacio). Hist. de Gibraltar. 8°. 1782

Lopez de Ayala (Jeronimo), *see* CEDILLO (J. L. DE A. A., *conde* DE).

Lopez de Ayala (Pedro). Poesias. Publ. por A. F. Kuersteiner. [Hispanic Soc. of Amer.] 2t. s8°. N.Y. 1920
see UHAGON (F. R. DE). Libros de cetreria de P. L. de A. &c., noticias, 1889.

Lopez de la Huerta (José). Exámen de los sinónimos de la lengua castell. 4a ed. corr. s8°. Barcelona. 1819

López de Legazpi (Miguel), *see* COLECCIÓN de docs. inéd. de Ultramar, s2, t2, 3, Filipinas, Exped. de L. (1559–67) &c., 1886–87.

López de Vallalobos (Ruy), *see* VALLALOBOS (R. L. DE).

Lopez Mezquita (José Maria), *see* FRANCÉS (J.) J. M. L. M., 1920.

Lopis Stunica (Jacobus). Annot. contra Erasmum in defens. tralationis Novi Test.
sm. fol. [In Acad. Complutensi. *A. G. de Brocario.* 1520]

Lopukhin (Aleksei Aleksandrovich). Докладная записка директора департ. полиціи Л. 1905. Съ предисловіемъ Н. Ленина. [P2390]. s8°. Женева. 1905
Изъ итоговъ служебнаго опыта. [P849]. s8°. Москва. 1907
A second tp. has Настоящее и будущее русс. полиціи.
Отрывки из воспоминаний. С предисл. М. Н. Покровского. s8°. Москва. 1923

Lopukhin (Ivan Vladimirovich), *1756–1816.* The Rite of reception into the degree of a Spiritual Knight acc. to I. V. L. Tr. B. Telepneff. [P2734]. s8°. *n.d.*

Lorck (J. Etienne). Altbergamask. Sprachdenkmäler (9–15 Jhdt.) Hrsg. &c. v. J. E. L. [Roman. Bibl., 10]. s8°. Halle a. S. 1893

Lorck (Josias). Bibl. Biblica Würtenberg. ducis olim Lorckiana. Ed. J. G. C. Adler. [5p *in* 1v]. s4°. Altonae. 1787

*__Lord__ bishops none of the Lords bishops, 1640, *see* PRYNNE (W.)

Lord (Arthur). Plymouth & the Pilgrims. s8°. Boston [Mass.] 1920

Lord (Arthur Ritchie). The princ. of politics. Evol. of polit. ideas. s8°. O. 1921

Lord (John Holt). Squire Brooke. A mem. of Edward Brooke; w. extracts f. h. diary. s8°. 1872

Lord (Robert Howard). Origins of the war of 1870: new doc. f. German archives. [Harvard Hist. St., v28]. 8°. Camb. [U.S.A.] 1924
The second partition of Poland. St. in diplomatic hist. [Harvard Hist. St., v23]. 8°. Camb. [U.S.A.] 1915
see HASKINS (C. H.) & R. H. L. Some problems of the Peace Conf., 1920.

Lord (William Barry). Crab, shrimp & lobster lore. s8°. 1867
Sea fish & how to catch them. [P2596]. s8°. [1862]
„ „ ....[2nd ed.] s8°. [1863]
The silkworm book. s8°. 1867

Lorde (André de) & H. Bauche. Les drames célèbres du Grand-Guignol. [t]1. s8°. 1924
1, Le château de la mort lente—La grande épouvante—La laboratoire des hallucinations.

Lord's Prayer, *see* CHAMBERLAYNE (J.) Oratio Dominica in div. linguas versa, 1715.

Lorentowicz (Jean).
Ladislas Reymont: son œuvre. 8°. Varsovie. [1924]

Lorentz (Friedrich) [LORENZ].
The life of Alcuin. Tr. J. M. Slee. s8°. 1837

Lorentz (*Dr.* Friedrich). Gesch. d. pomoranischen (kaschubischen) Sprache. la8°. 1925

Lorentz (Hendrik Antoon). Clerk-Maxwell's electromagnetic theory. Rede lect. s8°. C. 1923
see ADLER (F.) Ortszeit &c.: Unters. ü. d. L. u. Einstein. Kinematik, 1920.

——, A. Einstein & H. Minkowski. Das Relativitätsprinzip. Eine Samml. v. Abhdln. 8°. L. *Teubner.* 1920
„ „ 4e verm. A. 8°. L. *Teubner.* 1922

——, ——, —— & H. Weyl. Princ. of relativity: coll. of orig. memoirs. Notes by A. Sommerfeld. Tr. W. Perrett & G. B. Jeffery. 8°. [1923]

Lorenz (Charlotte), *see* UMBREIT (P.) & C. LORENZ. Der Krieg u. d. Arbeitsverhältnisse: d. gewerbl. Frauenarbeit, v. C. L., 1928.

Lorenz (Hermann), *1864–*, *see* KLEEMAN (S.) Die Lorenzianer, 1926.

Lorenz (Ludwig).
Die besten deut. Geschichtswerke. 10 Listen. s8°. L. 1919

Lorenz (Otto), *libraire.* Cat. gén. de la librairie française réd. par D. Jordell. t27–29. 8°. 1920–27
27, Table des matières, 1913–15.
28, 1916–18, 2p, Auteurs—Matières.
29, 1919–21.

Lorenz (S.) Taylorsystem u. Arbeiterschaft. [P2522]. 8°. Wien. [1921]

Lorenzana y Buitron (Francisco Antonio), *card.* SS. PP. Toletanorum quotquot extant opera. Opera &c. F. de Lorenzana. 3t. fol. Matriti-Romæ. 1782–93
1, Montani, S. Eugenii III & S. Ildephonsi opuscula. 2, S. Juliani & S. Eulogii opuscula &c. 3, R. Ximenii de Rada opera; app., Series regum Hisp., Concilia Tolet., Cat. praesulum *&* Descr. templi Tolet., auct. B. Ortizio.

Lorenzen (M.) Gammeldanske krøniker. Udg. M. L. [Samfund t. u. a. g. n. l., 18]. s8°. 1887–1913

Lorenzen (Vilhelm), *see* CLEMMENSEN (M.) & V. L. Kallundborg Kirke, 1922.

Lorenzetti (Giuseppe).
Fra Paolo Sarpi. Dramma. 8°. Venezia. 1867
Paolo Sarpi: cenni biogr. [P2840]. 8°. Venezia. 1867

Lorenzi (Giovanni Battista). Il sogno di Alcesindo Misiaco, canto per la nasc. di Filippo &c. [P2767]. 8°. Napoli. 1747

Lorenzo, *Don, called Il Monaco, Camaldolese monk, see* SIRÉN (O.) Don Lorenzo Monaco, 1905.

Lorenzo [*de' Medici*], *the elder, 1448–92.* Canti carnascialeschi sec. l'esempl. Riccardiano, *see* BIAGI (G.) Bibl. umanistica, s1, 1–2, 1925.
*La compagnia del Mantellaccio [*sometimes attrib. to L.*], 1489, 1861, *see* COMPAGNIA.
see RHO (E.) L. il M., 1926.

Lorenzo (Giuseppe de). Leonardo da Vinci e la geologia. [Ist. di St. Vinc. Pubbl., v3]. 8°. Bologna. [1920]
Shakespeare e il dolore d. mondo. 8°. Bologna. [1921]

Lorenzo (Tina di), *aft. wife of Armando Falconi, see* SERRETTA (E.) T. di L., 1920.
Lorenzoni (Giovanni), *see* ITALY: GOVT. PUBLS. INCH. PARL. s. condiz. d. contadini, v6, Sicilia, t1, Relaz. d. G. L., 1910.
Loret (Victor), *see* GAILLARD (C.) Recherches sur les poissons repr. dans quelques tombeaux égypt.; par C. G. avec collab. de V. L. &c., 1923.
Loreto. Trāslatio miraculosa Eccl. beate Marie virginis de L. [*Foll. by*: Diuisiones decem nationum totius christianitatis, *imperf., for a. ed. of which, see* DIVISIONES]. s8°. *n.p. n.d.* [c. 1500 ?]
Lorette (Louis). La taille Lorette. 3e éd. 8°. 1921
Lorgeou (Edouard), *see* NANG TANTRAI. Les entretiens de N. T.; tr. du siamois par E. L., 1924.
Loria (Gino). Le scienze esatte ne l'ant. Grecia. 2a ed. riv. s8°. Milano. 1914
Lorich (Jodocus). Oratio de absurditatibus, quae seq. ex errore circa modum existentiae Christi in Sacramento Eucharistiæ. s4°. Ingolstadii. 1590
Positiones theolog. de caeremoniis eccl. in genere &c. s4°. Ingolstadii. 1590
Speculum imperfectionis in vita & moribus Christianis. s4°. Ingolstadii. 1590
Lorimer (*Miss* H. L.) Hist. of Serbia, *see* BUCHAN (J.), *ed.* Nations of to-day, Yugoslavia, 1923.
Lorimer (*Miss* Norma Octavia). Alec's mother. s8°. [1925]
A mender of images. s8°. [1920]
The path of love. s8°. [1921]
The shadow of Egypt. s8°. [1923]
The white sanctuary. s8°. [1924]
Lorimer (Peter).
The Scottish Reformation, hist. sketch. s8°. 1860
Lorin (Henri). Bordeaux la Gironde. 8°. 1921
L'Égypte d'aujourd'hui, le pays & les hommes. [Soc. Roy. de Géog. d'Égypte]. la8°. 1926
Loring (Andrew). The rhymers' lexicon. Comp. & ed. A. L. With intr. by G. Saintsbury. 2nd ed. rev. 8°. *n.d.*
Loring (F. H.) Atomic theories. 8°. [1921]
Lorinser (Franz).
Vor dem Concil. 2e A. [P2692]. 8°. Breslau. 1869
Loriot-Lecaudey (—), *see* FLERS (R., *marq.* DE) & G. A. DE CAILLAVET. La vendetta, drame lyr., d'ap. une nouvelle de L.-L., 1911.
Loris-Melikov (Ivan). La Révolution russe & les nouv. républiques transcaucas. Préf. de A. Thomas. 8°. 1920
Loris-Melikov (*graf.* Mikhail Tarielovich Tainov). Сущность и значеніе конституціи Л.-М. [P2390]. s8°. Лондонъ. 1901
The Russ. constitution [*in Russian*]. s8°. Лондонъ. 1893
see NEMIROVICH-DANCHENKO (V. I.) На кладбищахъ, 1921.
„ TCHMSHKEAN (S. B.) Poem on death of L. M., 1889.
Lorme (Marie de), *see* DELORME (MARION).
L'Orme (Robert de), *see* ROBERT, *de L'Omme.*
Lorrain (Claude), *see* CLAUDE, *le Lorrain.*
Lorrain (Jean). Monsieur de Phocas. Roman. 18e éd. s8°. *n.d.*
Lorraine. Bibliogr. lorraine, 1913–19. Revue du mouvt. intellect., artist. & écon. 8°. Nancy. 1921
Lorraine (Charles de), *see* GUISE (C. DE).
Lorraine (Renée de), *Consort of William V, duke of Bavaria, see* RENÉE, *de Lorraine.*
Lorris (Guillaume de) & Jehan de Meung. Le roman de la rose. Publ. E. Langlois. t2–4. (2–4 Texte-Notes). [S.d.a.t.f.] 8°. 1920–22
Der Roman v. d. Rose. [Bearb. v. J. Gregor [*based on*] Ubers. v. H. Fährmann (1839). s8°. Wien. [1922]
„ „ [Übers. v. H. Fährmann, v. J. Gregor neu bearb.; erläut. Text schrieb E. Winkler, w. facsimiles of French MS.] 4°. [1921]
see DURANTE, *Ser.* Il Fiore, imité du Roman de la Rose, 1881.
„ KITTREDGE (G. L.) The authorship of the Eng. Romaunt of the Rose, 1892.
„ TATLOCK (J. S. P.) & A. G. KENNEDY. Concordance to Chaucer & Romaunt of the rose &c., 1927.
Lort de Sérignan (*le cte.* Arthur de). Un conspirateur milit. sous le Prem. Empire: le gén. Malet. s8°. 1925
Napoléon & les grands généraux de la Révol. & de l'Emp. 8°. 1914
Loryot (François). Les secretz moraux conc. les passions du cœur humain. s4°. 1614
Losch (Philipp). Gesch. d. Kurfürstentums Hessen, 1803–66. 8°. Marburg. 1922 [1921]
Lösche (Georg). Zur Gegenreformation in Schlesien: Troppau Jägerndorf, Leobschütz. [Verein f. Ref.-gesch. Schr., Jhrg. 32, 33 (Nr. 117/18, 123)]. 2T. 8°. L. 1915–16
Löscher (Caspar). De latrociniis quae in publ. scr. solent committere haeretici diss. s4°. Martisburgi. [1674]
Löscher (Friedrich Hermann). Schule, Kirche u. Obrigkeit im Reformations-Jhdt. [Verein f. Ref.-Gesch. Schr., Jhrg. 43 (Nr. 138)]. 8°. L. 1925
Löscher (Valentin Ernst).
Auserlesene Samml. d. Schrifften v. Zustand d. Seele nach d. Tod &c. s8°. Dressden. 1735
Ausführl Hist. motuum. zw. d. Evangel-luther. u. Reformierten &c. 2e verm. A. 3T *in* 1v. [*Foll. by* Heilsame Worte, oder Friedfert. Anrede & Kurtze Beantwortung d. Beschuldigungen &c., *each w. sep. pagin.*] s4°. Franckfurt. 1723–24
„ „ Fortsetzung, bis auf 1601, v. J. R. Kiesling. [Beylagen, *w. sep. pagin.*] 4°. Schwabach. 1770
Breviarium theolog. exegeticae &c. s8°. Vitembergae. 1719
Kurtze Rettung d. Reformations-Wahrheiten gegen d. Melod. Einwürffe [*i.e.* Bernd's Einfl. d. göttl. Warheiten]. s4°. L. 1729
Literator Celta. Cur. J. A. Egenolf. s8°. Lipsiæ. 1726
Praenotiones theolog. contra naturalistarum & fanatic. omne genus, atheos, deistas, &c. Ed. 5a emmend. s8°. Vitembergae. 1752
Vollständige Reformations-Acta u. Doc. 3T *in* 2v. [T1, 2 *are b. in 1v*]. s4°. L. 1720–29
Zulängl. Unterricht vom wahren Christenthum &c. Neue verm. Ed. s8°. Dresden. *n.d.*
see ENGELHARDT (M. v.) V. E. L., 1853.
„ KIESSLING (G. N.) Th. Munzeri doctr. &c., praes. V. E. L., 1708.
„ LANGE (J.) Abfertigung d. sog. Vollständ. Timothei Verini Löschers, 1719.
„ —— Apologet. Erläut. d. neu. Hist. bey d. evang. Kirche, 1689–1719: Timotheus Verinus (*by Löscher*) abgefertiget, 1719.
„ —— Auffricht. Nachr. v. d. Unrichtigkeit d. sog. Unschuldig. Nachr., 7T [*each w.* "Anhang" *on L.*], 1707–8.
„ —— Comm. de vita &c. Pauli, acc. app. T. Verino oppos., 1718.
„ THEOLOGISCHE ANNALES &c., 1701–50, 5B, 1715–54.
Löschke (Carl Julius). Merkwürdige Begebenheiten aus d. schles. u. brandenburg.-preuss. Gesch. z. Gebr. in Volksschulen. 2. verm. A. s8°. Breslau. 1843
Loserth (Johann).
Acten &c. z. Gesch. d. Gegenreform. in Innerösterr. (1578–90); gesamm. &c. v. J. L., *see* FONTES RERUM AUSTRIAC., B50, 1898.
Das Archiv des Hauses Stubenberg, *see* HISTORISCHER VEREIN F STEIERMARK. Beitr., J. 35, 1906.
Johann von Wiclif u. Guilelmus Peraldus, 1916, *see* KAIS. AKAD D. W. ZU WIEN. Sitz., B180, 1917.
Johann von Wiclif u. Robert Grosseteste, 1918, *see* KAIS. AKAD D. W. ZU WIEN. Sitz., B186, 1921.
Ueb. d. Bezieh. zw. engl. u. böhm. Wiclifiten. [*Extr. f.* Inst. f österr. Gesch., Mitthlg. 12. P2729]. 8°. [1891
see MAXIMILIAN II, *emp.* Registratur M., 1547–51; hrsg. v J. L., 1896.
Losius (Johann Justus). De defectu judicii logici in scriptor. eccl., *see* VIRORUM &C. molimina theolog., 1761.
Losky (Constantin). La souveraineté ukrainienne dans son passé &c. [P2426]. 8°. Stockholm. 1919
Losowski (A.), *see* LOZOVSKY (A.)
Loss (Jeremias). Diss. de epispasmo Judaico, 1654, *see* SCHLÄGER (C. J.) Diss. fasc. nov., 1744.
Loss (Lucas) [LOSSIUS (L.)] Annot. in Gramm. P. Melanthonis Latinam &c. s8°. Franc[ofurti]. 1559
Catechismus. Item: Objectiones cum earum solutionibus. s8°. Francoforti. [1553
„ „ ....[*a. ed.*] s8°. Lipsiae. 1563
Trostschrifft für die jenigen welchenn ihr Vatter, Mütter, Ehegemahel, Kinder &c. verscheiden. [P2436]. s4°. Franckfurt am Mein. 156
see LACKMANN (A. H.) De edendis L. L. &c. epistolis, 1719
Lossada Dias (Demetrio). Gen. Juan Vicente Gómez, Präsident v. Venezuela &c. [P2754]. 8°. [1924
Lossing (Benson John). The pictorial field-book of the war of 1812. la8°. N.Y. 1868
Lossius (Lucas), *see* LOSS (L.)
Lossky (Nikolai Onufrievich). Handbuch d. Logik. Aut Übers. n. d. 2e A. v. W. Sesemann. 8°. L. *Teubner.* 1927
The world as an organic whole. Tr. N. A. Duddington. 8°. O. 1928
Lost. *Lost (The) dominion, 1924, *see* CARTHILL (AL.), *ps.*
Lost (The) mutton found!! or, the R——l Fly-by-night; A poem. 2nd ed. [P425]. 8°. [1820 ?
Lot (Ferdinand).
La fin du monde ant. & le début du M.Â. 8°. 1927
L'impôt foncier & la capitation personnelle sous le Bas-Emp & à l'époque franque. [H.E., 253]. 8°. 192

Lote (Georges). Napoléon & le romantisme franç., *see* ROMANISCHE FORSCHUNGEN, B33, 1915.

Lote (René), *see* HANOTAUX (G.) Hist. de la nation française, t5, Hist. des sci., v2, Hist. de la philos.; par R. L. &c., 1924.

Lothaire II (III), *emperor of Germany, see* URKUNDEN d. deut. Könige &c., B8, 1927.

Lothaire, *king of Italy, see* MAIOCCHI (R.) Un diploma ined. di Re L. rig. Como (20 agosto 949), 1896.

Lothaire, *king of Lorraine.* Epistolae ad divortium L. pertin., *see* DUMMLER (E. L.), *ed.* Epist. Merow. et Karol. aevi, t4, 1925.

Lothian (Cecil Chetwynd, *Marchioness of*), *wife of 7th Marquess of Lothian; form. Talbot.* Cecil, Marchioness of Lothian: a mem. Ed. C. Kerr. 8°. [1922]

Lothrop (Samuel Kirkland). Tulum: archæolog. st. of east coast of Yucatan. [C.I. of Wash.] 4°. Wash. 1924

Loti (Pierre) [*i.e.* JULIEN VIAUD].

Un jeune officier pauvre: fragm. de journal intime rassemblés par son fils S. Viaud. s8°. 1923
Journal intime, 1878–81. Publ. S. Viaud. s8°. 1925
Lettres à Mme. Juliette Adam (1880–1922). s8°. [1924]
La mort de notre chère France en Orient. [11e éd.] s8°. [1920]
La mort de Philæ. s8°. 1920
Ramuntcho. s8°. 1899
Suprêmes visions d'Orient: fragm. de journal intime. [17e éd.] s8°. 1921

TRANSLATIONS.
Egypt. Tr. W. P. Baines. 8°. [1909]
The Sahara. Tr. by M. Laurie. 8°. [1921]
Siam. Tr. W. P. Baines. 8°. [1923]
see MALLET (F.) P. L., s. œuvre, 1923.
,, SERBAN (N.) P. L.: sa vie & son œuvre, 1920; 2e éd., 1924.

Lotmar (Philipp), *see* WLASSAK (M.) Anklage u. Sreitbefestigung: Abwehr geg. P. L., 1920.

Lotter (Tobias Conrad). Mappa geog. repraes. regnum Poloniae &c. folded s8°. Aug. Vindel. 1772

Lotus Club, *New York, see* ELDERKIN (J.) Brief hist., 1895.

Lotz (Walther). Die deut. Staatsfinanzwirtschaft im Kriege. [C.E. for Int. Peace]. la8°. St. 1927
Gab es e. geldwirtschaftl. Verfassung d. Staatsfinanzen unter d. Karolingern?, *see* KÖNIGL. AKAD. D. W. Z. MÜNCHEN. Philos.-philol. Kl., Sitz., 1926.
Valutafrage u. öffentl. Finanzen in Deutschl. [V. f. Sozialpol., B164i]. 8°. München. 1923
see SINZHEIMER (L.) & W. L. Geist. Arbeiter, T2, 1922.

Lotze (R. Hermann). Mikrokosmus. 3e A. 3B. s8°. L. 1876–80
Outlines of the philos. of relig. s8°. 1887
see HÄGER (A.) L. Kritik der Herbart. Metaphysik u. Psychologie, 1891.

Loubet (Emile), *pres. of the French Republic, see* SIMOND (E.) Hist. de la 3e Républ., t4, Prés. de M. L., 1922.

Loubier (Hans). Der Bucheinband, bis z. Ende d. 18. Jhdts. 2e, umgearb. u. verm. A. la8°. L. 1926
Buch u. Bucheinband. [*By var. wr.*] Aufsätze u. graph. Blätter z. 60. Geburtstage v. H. L. [Hrsg. M. J. Husung]. 4°. L. 1923
Die neue deut. Buchkunst. la8°. St. 1921

Löuen, *see* LOUVAIN.

Louis II, *king of Bavaria.*
see BÖHM (G. v.) L. II, 1922.
,, DÖRING (O.) Das Tagebuch König L. II, 1921.
,, DURIEUX (L.) Le roi vierge, 1927.

Louis, *dauphin de France, son of Louis XIV.* Hist. de France comp. par le Dauphin, d'ap. les leçons de Bossuet & revue par lui. 3t. 8°. Versailles. 1821

Louis III, *king of France.* 'Επινίκιον rhythmo Teut. L. acclamatum, cum Nortmannos 883 vicisset; illustr. J. Schilter, *see* SCHILTER (J.) Thesaurus antiq., t2, 1727.

Louis IX, *king of France.*
see JOINVILLE (J. DE). Memoirs: cont. hist. of the life of L. IX, 2v, 1807.
,, LONGNON (A.) Doc. paris. sur l'iconographie de S. L., 1882.
,, RAMSEY (R. W.) Dante & St. L., 1924.

Louis XI, *king of France.*
see CHAMPION (P.) Louis XI, 2t, 1927.
,, FORT (P.) Ballades franç., [29], L. XI, [*play*], 1922.
,, —— Ballades franç., 31, Les compères du roi L. (L. XI homme considérable), [*play*], 1923.
,, MANDROT (B. DE), *ed.* Dépêches des ambassadeurs milanais en France sous L. XI, t3, 4 (1465–66), 1920–23.
,, PICOT (E.) & H. STEIN, *edd.* Rec. de pièces histor. impr. s. le règne de L. XI, 2t, 1923.

Louis XIII, *king of France, see* MONTPELLIER. Rec. de pièces rarissimes rel. au Siège de M. par L. XIII en 1622, 1875.

Louis XIV, *king of France.*
*The great Bastard, Protector of the little one. [Prince James Edw. Francis Stuart]. Done out of French. [P2663]. s4°. Cologne. 1689
*Les héros de la Ligue, ou process. monacale conduitte par L. XIV, pour la conversion des Protestans &c., 1691, *see* DUSART (C.)
A king's lessons in statecraft: L. XIV: Letters to h. heirs, w. intr. & notes by J. Longnon. Tr. H. Wilson. 8°. [1924]
Mémoires, 1661 & 1666, suivis des Réflex. sur le métier de roi, des Instruct. au Duc d'Anjou &c. Intr. &c. par J. Longnon. s8°. 1923
The spirit of France, & the politick maxims of L. XIV. [Tr. f. Dutch. P2663]. s4°. 1689
see BERTRAND (L. M. E.) L. XIV, 1923; 86e éd., 1927.
,, BRADBY (G. F.) Gt. days of Versailles: court life in later yrs. of L. XIV, 1927.
,, CROUSAZ-CRÉTET (P. DE). Paris sous L. XIV, t1, 2, 1922–23
,, FORESTER (C. S.) L. XIV, 1928.
,, HASSALL (A.) L. & zenith of Fr. monarchy, 1925.
,, HAUTECOEUR (L.) L'hist. des châteaux du Louvre & des Tuileries sous L. XIV, 1927.
,, LA FARE (C. A., *marq.* DE). Mém. &c. sur les princ. évènemens du r. de L. XIV, 1716.
,, MAGNE (E.) Le Grand Condé & le Duc d'Enghien; lettres inéd. sur la cour de L. XIV, 1660–67; publ. &c. par E. M., 1920.
,, ROUEN. Sereniss. pr. Franciae Delphino Xenia Coll. Rothomag. soc. Jesu., 1639.
,, WILLIAM III, *king.* K. W. or K. L., 1689.

Louis XV, *king of France.*
Corr. de L. XV & du Maréchal de Noailles. Publ. &c. avec intr. par C. Rousset. 2t [*in* 1v]. 8°. 1865
see ARGENSON (*le marq.* D'). Autour d'un ministre de Louis XV, 1923.
,, CARRÉ (H.) France sous L. XV, 1891.
,, DUMAS (A.) L. XV, & sa cour, 2t, 1866.
,, LECLERCQ (H. M.) Hist. de la Régence &c., 3t, 1921
,, MOUFFLE D'ANGERVILLE (—). Vie privée de L. XV, 1921; tr., 1924.
,, RICCI (S. DE). Les chasses royales de L. XV: peintures par J. B. Oudry, 1921.
,, VIENNA. Trat. de paz, concl. entre el Rey de Fr. &c. (1738), 1739.

Louis XVI, *king of France.*
see ANGOULÊME (*la dsse.* D'). Narr. of journey of L. XVI &c. to Varennes; tr., 1823.
,, COUTHON (G.) Opinion s. le jugement de L., préc. d'une lettre secrète de L. à Fr. Guillaume, de Prusse, 1833.

Louis XVII, *king of France, 1785–95.*
see ALMÉRAS (H. D'). Le petit Capet dans sa prison du Temple, 1924.
,, AUBRY (O.) Le roi perdu (L. XVII retrouvé), 1924.
,, LENOTRE (G.) The Dauphin (L. XVII): riddle of the Temple; tr., 1922.
,, —— Le roi L. XVII & l'énigme du Temple, 1921.

Louis XVIII, *king of France.* Narr. of journey to Bruxelles & Coblentz in 1791; tr., *see* FRENCH REVOLUTION. Royal mems. &c., 1823.
Relation d. dispos. funèbres &c., Toulon, pour la mém. de L. [&*] Discours par le chan. Michel, 7 oct. 1824. [P2772]. 8°. [Toulon. 1824?]
see LUCAS-DUBRETON (L.) L. XVIII, 1925.
,, PIUS VII, *pope.* Concordat entre le Pape & le Roi [*L. XVIII*], 1817.

Louis I, *emp. of Germany, & king of the Franks* [LOUIS LE DEBONNAIRE; LOUIS LE PIEUX; LUDOVICUS PIUS; LUDWIG DER FROMME], *see* FRANCE. Les grandes chron. de Fr., t4, Louis le D. à Louis V, 1927.

Louis IV, *emp. of Germany* [LUDWIG *der Bayer*]. Chronica L. IV, *see* BAIERN. Bayer. Chron. d. 14. Jhdts.; hrsg. G. Leidinger, 1918.
see †BÖHMER (J. F.) Regesta Imp., 1314–47, 1839–65.
,, MARSILIO *da Padova.* Def. pacis sive apologia pro L. IV, 1599.

Louis [*Gonzaga*], *Saint, see* GONZAGA (ALOYSIUS).

Louis, *duc d'Orléans, 1372–1407, see* GERSON (J.) Opera, t5 (Narr. cædis Ducis Aurelian.), 1706; ed. 2a, 1728.

Louis VI, *Elector Palatine, 1576–83, see* SCHECHSIUS (P.) Kurtzer Bericht &c.: ein stück Pfaltzgrave L. S. G. Testaments die Religion betreffend &c., c. 1585.

Louis, *prince of Parma, see* BODONI (G. B.) Pel battesimo di L., iscrizioni, 1774.

Louis, *duke of Savoy, d. 1465.*
see CHIAPUSSO (F.) Di uno statuto concesso dal duca L. di S. alla città di Susa nel 2 luglio 1462, 1880.
„ SARACENO (F.) Doc. ined. del regno di L., d. di S., 1874.
Louis II, *landgrave of Thuringia, called the Leaper, see* REINHARD (C. F.) Comm. in qua fabula de L. II refellitur &c., 1737.
Louis Bonaparte, *king of Holland ; aft. cte. de Saint-Leu.*
see COLENBRANDER (H. T.) Schimmelpenninck & Koning L., 1911.
„ GARNIER (A.) *Mém. sur la cour de L. N. &c., 1828.
Louis Philip Marie Ferdinand Gaston d'Orléans, *cte. d'Eu, see* ORLÉANS (GASTON D').
Louis William I, *margrave of Baden, 1655–1707, see* HASPEL (J. D.) De Wilhelmis felicibus [L. W. I &c.], 1694.
Louis (Georges), *see* JUDET (E.) G. L., 19e éd., 1925.
Louis (Henry), *M.A., see* ANDREW (G. W.), *ed.* Fuel, [*w.*] section on coal, lignite &c. by H. L., 1924.
Louis (*le baron* **Joseph** [Louis] **Dominique),** *1755–1837, see* GIGNOUX (C. J.) Vie du Baron L., 1928.
Louis (Paul). Anc. Rome at work: econ hist. [Hist. of Civiliz. Tr. E. B. F. Wareing]. 8o. 1927
La crise du socialisme mondial de la 2e & la 3e Internationale. s8o. 1921
Les crises intérieures allem. pend. la Guerre. 8o. 1916
Hist. de la classe ouvrière en France (1789–1926). 8o. 1927
Louisa Isabella, *of Orleans, q. consort of Louis I, of Spain* [LOUISE ELISABETH D'ORLÉANS], *see* PIMODAN (*cte.* C. DE). L.-E. d'O., r. d'Espagne, 1709–42, 1922.
Louise, *princess, of Belgium, eldest daughter of Leopold II.*
My own affairs. Tr. by M. M. C. ffoulkes. 8o. 1921
Louise Elisabeth, *d'Orléans, q. consort of Louis I, of Spain, see* LOUISA ISABELLA, *of Orleans.*
Louise Victoria Alexandra Dagmar, *princess royal, duchess of Fife.* Cat. of pictures sold by order of the Pcss. Royal; also pictures &c. the property of Col. H. H. Mulliner &c. Sold by Christie, July 18, 1924. [*Illust.* P2748]. 8o. 1924
Louisiana. *Relation de la L. ou Mississippi, par un officier de Marine, *see* BERNARD (J. F.), *ed.* Recueil, t5, 1734.
see TULANE UNIV. OF L.
Loukaris (Cyril), *see* LUCAR (C.)
Loureiro (João). Cartas escr. do Rio de Janeiro, 1828–42, *see* INSTITUTO HIST. &C. BRAZIL. Rev., t76ii, 1914.
Lourié (Ossip) [OSSIP-LOURIÉ]. La Révolution Russe. s8o. 1921
Loutchisky (Ivan). L'état des classes agricoles en France à la veille de la Révol. s8o. 1911
La petite propriété en France av. la Révol. & la vente des biens nat. s8o. 1897
Louter (Jan de). Le droit internat. public positif. [C.E. for Int. Peace]. 2t. la8o. O. 1920
Loutfut (Adam), *see* LULLY (R.) Book of the ordre of chyvalry; tr. & pr. by Caxton, w. A. L.'s Scot. transcr., 1926.
Louth (County) Archaeological Society.
Journal. v3, 4. la8o. Dundalk. [1912–20]
Lou Tö-ming [LOU YUAN-LANG], *see* PELLIOT (P.) Le Chou king en caractères anc. & le Chang chou che wen [par L. Tö-ming], 1916.
Louvain.
Actes ou procès-verbaux des séances tenues par le conseil de l'Univ. de L. Publ. A. van Hove. t2 (1445–55). 4o. Brux. 1917
Cat. (Les) des livres reprouvez &c. 1550, *see* Ordonnance (L') & edict de l'emper. Charles V &c., *see below.*
Condemnatio doctr. librorũ M. L., per quosdam magistros nostros L., & Colonieñ, facta. Responsio L. s4o. Vuittenbergae, *M. Lotther jun.* 1520
Invent. des archives de l'Univ. de L. &c., 1817–35, 1917, *see* NELIS (H.)
Ordenung u. Mandat Keiser C. V.; Item ein Reg. d. verbottenen Büchern, Vermanung d. Rectors d. Univ. zu L., &c., 1550 ?, *see* CHARLES V, *emp. of Germ.*
Ordonnance (L') & edict de l'emp. Charles V renouvelle 1550, pour l'extirpation des sectes & erreurs &c. Avec le Cat. des livres reprouvez & prohib. Et aussi des bons livres qui se deburõt lire &c. [*w. sep. tp. & pagin.*] s4o. Louvain. 1550
L'Université de Louvain à trav. 5 siècles. Et. hist.; publ. avec intr. par L. van der Essen, avec le concours de E. van Cauwenbergh, F. Claeys-Boúúaert &c. fol. Brux. 1927
Zwen u. dreissig Artickel die allgemeinen Religion u. Glauben belangend, v. d. Theologen d. hohē Schül zu Löuen, &c. [P2439]. s4o. *n.p.* 1545
Louvel (Louis Pierre), *1783–1820, see* LUCAS-DUBRETON (J.) L. le régicide, 1923.
Louvet (Louis Eugène). La Cochinchine religieuse. 2t. 8o. 1885
Louvet de Couvray (Jean Baptiste). Mémoires, *see* DUMOURIEZ (*gén.* C. F.) Suite des Mém. du Gén. D. &c., 1886.
Louvie (Paul), *ps.* [*i.e.* HENRY DE BERNADOTTE]. Des fleurs, des larmes & du sang. Préf. de J. Aicard. s8o. 1919
Louville (Charles Auguste d'Allonville, *marq.* **de),** *1668–1731.* Mém. secrets sur l'établ. de la maison de Bourbon en Espagne [Pièces div.–Buenos-Ayres en 1710. Mém. de le duc du Maine dans l'aff. des princes légitimés &c. *in* v2]. 2t. 8o. 1818
Louvre [*see also* MUSÉE DES ARTS DÉCORATIFS].
Crystal cups in the L. chiefly Italian. 31 photographs]. atl. fol. *n.d.*
Musée Nat. du Louvre. Cat. des peintures exposées. [p]1, 3. s8o. 1922–24
1, École fr.; par G. Brière.
3, Écoles flam., holland., allemande & angl.; par L. Demonts.
Notice des tableaux dans les galleries du Musée Nat. du L. 3p *in* 1v [1, 17e éd.; 2, 10e éd.; 3, 4e éd.] s8o. 1873–74
Peinture (La) au Musée du L. Publ. J. Guiffrey. [11p]. la8o. [1927 ?]
École allemande, par L. Réau. [5.]
„ anglaise, par M. Nicolle. [7.]
„ espagnole, par M. Nicolle. [6.]
„ flamande, par E. Michel. [3.]
„ française, 14–16s., par P. A. Lemoisne. [8.]
„ „ 17s., par C. Terrasse. [9.]
„ „ 19s. [p1], par L. Hautecoeur. [11.]
„ „ 19s [p2], par P. Jamot. [12.]
„ hollandaise, par C. Misme. [4.]
Écoles ital., 13–15s., par L. Hautecoeur. [1.]
„ „ 16–18s., par G. Rouchès. [2.]
see ALGÉRIE. Musées &c. archéolog. de l'A. &c.: Musée Afr. du L.; par A. Héron de Villefosse, 1921.
„ CORPUS vasorum antiq., France: Musée du L.; par E. Pottier, 1922–.
„ DREYFUS (C.) Objets d'art du 18 s., 2v, 1923.
„ GEFFROY (G.) Musées d'Europe: palais du L., archit., nobilier, objets, 1909.
„ LABORDE (*le marq.* L. E. S. J. DE). Notices des émaux &c. dans les galeries du L., p2, Doc. & gloss., 1853.
„ MARQUET DE VASSELOT (J. J.) *& Mdlle.* M. J. BALLOT. Chinese ceramics, 2v, 1922.
„ MIGEON (G.) L'art japonais, 1927.
„ —— L'Orient musulman, 2v, 1922.
„ POTTIER (E.). Cat. d. vases ant. de terre cuite, p1, 1896.
„ RAFFAËLLI (J. F.) Mes promenades au Musée du L., 2e éd., rev. & augm., 1913.
Louÿs (Pierre). Poësies. 8o. 1927
see REVUE DES LIVRES ANCIENS; dir. P. L., 2v, 1913–17.
Lovat (Simon Fraser, *12th Lord*), *see* FRASER (*Sir* W.) Papers [P. rel. to S., Ld. L. &c.]; ed. J. R. N. Macphail, 1924.
Lovato de' Lovati [LOVATUS, *Patavinus*]. Epistole ined. di L. e d'altri a lui. [Ed.] C. Foligno. [Estr. d. Studi medievali. P2840]. 8o. Torino. [1906]
Love (Albert Gallatin), *see* UNITED STATES: ARMY. Medical Dept. in the World War, v15, 2p, by A. G. L. &c., 1921–25.
Love (John), *of the Gables, Northwood.* Cat. of coll. of Chinese porcelain. Sold by Christie, May 1927. [P2870]. 8o. 1927
Loveday (J.), *see* INDUST. FATIGUE RESEARCH BD. Rep., 10; by J. L. &c., 1920.
Lovejoy (Arthur O.), *see* DRAKE (D.) Essays in crit. realism; by D. D., A. O. L. &c., 1920.
Lovelace (Mary Caroline, *countess of*), *wife of the 2nd Earl of L.* A portrait mis-named Lady Byron. Repr. f. The Connoisseur, Oct. 1917. 8o. 1918
Ralph, Earl of Lovelace. A memoir. 8o. [1920]
Lovelace (Ralph Gordon N. Milbanke, *2nd earl of*). Astarte; fragm. of truth conc. Byron. n. ed., with addit. letters, ed. by Mary Ctss. of L. 8o. 1921
see LOVELACE (M. C., *ctss. of*). R., Earl of L.: a mem., 1920.
Lovelace (Richard).
Poems. Ed. C. H. Wilkinson. 2v. la8o. O. 1925
see HARTMANN (C. H.) The cavalier spirit & its infl. on L., 1925.
Lovelace (Richard), *ps., see* COLOMB (G. H.)
Lovell (Robert), *poet.* Poet. works. Coll. by T. Park. [*b. w.* Moore (J. H.) Poet. works, 1808]. s8o. 1808
Lover of Free Grace, *ps.* *Question (The), What is an Arminian ? answered, 1770, *see* WESLEY (J.)
Lover (Samuel). Handy Andy. [Everyman's Lib.] s8o. 1907
Lovett (*Sir* **Verney**), *K.C.S.I.* A hist. of the Indian Nationalist movement. [3rd ed.] 8o. 1921
India, *see* BUCHAN (J.), *ed.* Nations, 1923.
Lovibond (Edward). Poet. works. Coll. by T. Park. [*b. w.* Shaw (C.) Poet. works, 1807]. s8o. 1807

Loving mad Tom: Bedlamite verses (16 & 17 c.), 1927, *see* LINDSAY (J.), *ed.*
Loviot (Louis), *see* REVUE DES LIVRES ANCIENS; réd. L. L., 2v, 1913–17.
Low (Barbara). Psycho-analysis: Freudian theory. Intr. by E. Jones. s8°. [1920]
Low (George Carmichael). The lit. of the Charadriiformes, 1894–1924, w. class. of the order &c. 8°. 1924
Low (Hilda Lucy Adelaide), *aft. wife of Sir W. A. Mount, Bt., see* Low (W. M.) Some descents of 2 19th c. sisters [*i.e.* H. L. A. L. &c.] f. Edward III, of Eng., 1922.
Low (Ida Mary Ursula), *see* Low (W. M.) Some descents of 2 19th c. sisters [*i.e.* I. M. U. L. &c.] f. Edward III, of Eng., 1922.
Low (*Capt.* James). A gramm. of the T,hai, or Siamese lang. 4°. Calcutta. 1828

Löw (Johann Friedrich) [LOEW]. Brev. stricturae in F. Riberae scriptum ant-apologeticum. Praes. C. M. Pfaffio. [P598]. s4°. Tubingae. 1753
Low (William Malcolm). Some descents of 2 19th c. sisters f. Edward III, k. of England. la. fol. *p.p.* 1922
Lowe (Boutelle Ellsworth).
The internat. protection of labor. 8°. N.Y. 1921
Lowe (Edward Joseph).
Nat. hist. of new & rare ferns. la8°. 1865
Lowe (Elias Avery), *form. Loew.* Die ält. Kalendarien aus Monte Cassino. 8°. München. 1908
The Beneventan script: hist. of the S. Ital. minuscule. la8°. O. 1914
Codices Lugdun. antiq. Le script. de Lyon. [Doc. paléograph. &c. de la Bibl. de Lyon, fasc. 3 & 4]. 4°. Lyon. 1924
Studia palaeographica, *see* KÖNIGL. AKAD. D. WISS. ZU MÜNCHEN. Phil.-philol. Kl. Sitz., 1910.
see BOBBIO MISSAL (THE): notes & studies; by A. Wilmart, E. A. L. &c., 1924.
„ FRY (R. E.) & E. A. L. Eng. handwriting, 1926.
—— & E. K. Rand. A 6th-c. fragment of the Letters of Pliny the Younger: a st. of 6 leaves of an uncial MS. in Pierpoint Morgan Libr., N.Y. [C.I. of Wash.] 4°. Wash. 1922
Lowe (F. Gordon). G. L. on lawn tennis. s8°. [1924]
Lowe (George). Josef Holbrooke. s8°. 1920
Lowe (William Henry). A Hebrew grammar. 2nd ed. s8°. 1889
Lowell (Abbott Lawrence). The govt. of France, Italy & Germany. [*Abr. of h.* Govt. &c. in Contin. Europe]. 8°. Cambridge [U.S.] 1914
Greater European governments. 8°. C. [U.S.A.] 1918
Lowell (Amy). John Keats. 2v. 8°. [1925]
Tendencies in mod. Amer. poetry. [repr.] 8°. O. [1921]
see AYSCOUGH (F.) Fir-flower tablets: poems tr. f. Chinese by F. A.; Eng. versions by A. L., 1922.
„ BRYHER (W.) A. L., crit. apprec., 1918.
Lowell (James Russell).
The Biglow Papers. Pref. note by E. Rhys. s8°. [1892 ?]
Commem. of the centenary of the birth of L. la8°. N.Y. 1919
The Eng. poets: Lessing, Rousseau: essays. [Camelot Classics]. s8°. [1888]
My study windows. Intr. by R. Garnett. [Camelot Classics]. s8°. [1886]
Poems.
2v. s8°. Boston [Mass.] 1849
„ ......Oxf. ed. s8°. 1912
Löwenberg (Jakob). Vom goldnen Überfluss: Auswahl aus neuern deut. Dichtern f. Schule &c. Hrsg. v. J. L. [6. A.] s8°. L. [1923]
Lowenfeld (Henry) & M. Lowenfeld. Back to prosperity: new aspect of practical life. s8°. 1923
Löwenfeld-Russ (Hans). Die Regelung d. Volksernährung im Kriege. [C.E. for Int. Peace]. la8°. Wien. 1926
Löwenheim (Louis). Die Wissenschaft Demokrits u. i. Einfluss auf d. mod. Naturwiss. Hrsg. Leopold Löwenheim. [*pages 1–48 originally issued as* Beilage zu H4 d. Archivs f. Gesch. d. Phil., B26]. 8°. 1914
Löwenstein (Fritz E.) Die Handzeichnungen d. japan. Holzschnittmeister. 4°. Plauen im Vogtland. 1922
Löwenstein (Rudolf).
Kindergarten. 5e verb. A. 4°. Hamburg. [1905]
Löwenstein (Siegfried), *see* ERZBERGER (M.) Der Prozess E.-Helfferich: Rechtsgutachten mit e. Begleitwort v. L., 5. A., 1921.
Löwenstein-Wertheim, *House of, see* KLÜBER (J. L.) Eheliche Abstammung d. fürstl. Hauses L.-W. v. d. Kurfürsten Friedrich d. Siegreichen v. d. Pfalz; hrsg. v. J. Mülhens, 1837.
Löwenthal (Johann Jacob). Morphy's games of chess: w. notes by L. s8°. *Bohn.* 1872

Lower (Mark Antony). Mem. of Seaford. 8°. 1855
Lowes (John Livingston).
Convention & revolt in poetry. s8°. [1919]
The road to Xanadu: st. in ways of the imagination. 8°. [1927]
Lowey (H.) Die myst. Bezeichnungen Jesu Christi als Siloë, Schiloh u. Piscis. 8°. Paderborn. 1888
Lowie (Robert Heinrich). Primitive religion. 8°. 1925
Primitive society. 8°. 1921
Lowis (Douglas W.), *D.D.*
Hist. of the Ch. in France, 950–1000. 8°. [1926]
Löwis of Menar (August v.)
Die Brünhildsage in Russland. [Palaestra, 142]. 8°. L. 1923
Löwis of Menar (Carl Waldemar von). Burgenlexikon für Alt-Livland. Mit Plänen u. Ansichten. [*w. sep. tp.* Gesells. f. Gesch. &c. d. Ostseeprov.] 8°. Riga. 1922
Lowndes (*Mrs.* Belloc-).
Bread of deceit. s8°. [1925]
From the vasty deep. s8°. [1920]
Good old Anna. 4th ed. s8°. 1916
The lonely house. s8°. 1920
Some men & women. s8°. [1925]
The story of Ivy. s8°. [1927]
The Terriford mystery. s8°. [1924]
"Thou shalt not kill." s8°. [1927]
What really happened. s8°. [1926]
What Timmy did. s8°. [1921]
Lowndes (William Thomas). The bibliographer's manual of Eng. lit. n. ed. rev. &c. w. App. by H. G. Bohn. 4v. s8°.1864
Lowth (Robert). *A short introd. to Eng. gram. s8°. 1787
Lowth (Simon). *Histor. collections conc. Church affairs; right to dispose of bishops &c. Added: Obs. upon Dr. Hody's The case of the sees vacant &c. [*b. w.* Kettlewell (J.) Of Christ. commun., 1693]. s4°. 1696
see PRESBYTER (A) OF THE CHURCH OF ENG. Independent power of the Ch. &c.: suppl. to bk. by S. L., 1716.
Lowth (William), *prebendary of Winchester.* Comm. upon Daniel & the 12 minor prophets. 2v *in* 1. s4°. 1726
Comm. upon Ezekiel. s4°. 1723
Comm. upon Isaiah. s4°. 1714
Comm. upon Jeremiah. s4°. 1718
Comm. upon the Prophets; being cont. of Bp. Patrick. 3rd ed. fol. 1730
„ „ ....n. ed. corr. by J. R. Pitman. 4°. 1822
Lowther (H. C.) Principle of skating turns. s8°. 1900
Lowther (James William), *see* ULLSWATER (J. W. L., *1st visc.*)
***Loyalist's (The)** house that Jack built. [P2557]. 8°. [1819 ?]
The above is fr. the half-t.; there is a 2nd t.: The Brit. constit. triumphant &c.
Loyal Orange Institution of England. Ritual of introd. to the Orange Order. [P524]. 8°. 1877
Loyautlander, *ps.* Die heutige Sibille oder unterschiedene Geheimnisse auff die letzte Zeit &c. aus d. Wälschen u. a. Sprachen übergesetzt hrsg. v. L. [P2443]. s4°. *n.p.* 1667
Loyd (Lewis R. W.) Lundy, its hist. & natural hist. 8°. 1925
Loyola (Ignatius), *Saint.*
Manresa: spiritual exercises of I. n. ed. s8°. [1881]
*Narratio miracul. an. 1623 Munebregae Bilbilensium ad imaginem I. de L. [*b. w.* *Thronus justitiæ &c., 1624]. s8°. Coloniae Agrippinae. 1624
Spiritual exercises, w. med. & prayers by Father L. Siniscalchi. Tr. s8°. [1864]
see BERINGER (J.) Flosculi blasphemiarum ex 3 concionibus I. L., 1612.
„ BÖHMER (H.) L. u. d. deut. Mystik, 1921.
„ BOUHOURS (D.) *La vie de S. Ignace, 1680; 1688.
„ GOTHEIN (E.) I. v. L., 1885.
„ HENAO (G. DE). Averig. de Cantabria [é ignacianas: Genealogia de S. I. &c.], 7t, 1894–95.
see JAPONIA. The Theater of Japonia's constancy &c. Also the miracles of S. I. at Munebrega &c., 1624.
„ JESUITS (The) gospel acc. to I. L., 1679.
„ JOVY (E.) Pascal & St. I., 1923.
„ MAFFEI (G. P.) De vita & moribus I. L. libri 3, 1586; *& in h.* Opera omnia, t2, 1747.
„ —— Hist. Indic. lib. 16, acc. I. L. vita, 1593.
„ ORLANDINUS (N.) Hist. Soc. Jesu, p1, Ignatius, 1620.
„ RIBADENEIRA (P. DE). Vita I. L., 1598.
„ SEDGWICK (H. D.) I. L., 1923.
Loyseau (Charles), *see* LELONG (J.) La vie & les œ. de L., 1909.
Łoza (Stanisław). Słownik architektów i budowniczych Polaków &c. 8°. Warszawa. 1917
Lozano (Christoval). Los reyes nuevos de Toledo: descr. las cosas desta ciudad &c. s8°. Barcelona. 1744
Lozano Muñoz (Francisco). Crón. de la prov. de Jaén, 1867, *see* ESPAÑA. Crón. gen., v9, 1865 &c.
Lozano y Casela (Pablo), *see* CEBES. Parafrasis arabe de la Tabla de C.; tr. &c. por L., 1793.

Loziński (Władysław). Salon i kobieta (z estetyki i z dziejów życia towarzyskiego). Wydal M. Treter. 8°. Lwów. 1921
Życie Polskie w dawnych wiekach. Wydanie 4e przejrzał &c. M. Treter. la8°. Lwów. 1921

Lozovsky (Aleksandr) [LOSOWSKI]. Der internat. Rat d. Fach- u. Industrie-Verbände. [P2522]. 8°. Hamburg. 1921

Lozynsky (Michel). Décisions du Conseil Suprême [des Alliés] sur la Galicie orientale. Doc. avec intr. par M. L. [P2401]. 8°. 1919
Notes sur les relations ukraino-polonaises en Galicie (1895–1919). [P2402]. 4°. 1919
L'Ukraine occidentale (Galicie). L'invasion polonaise. [P2401]. 8°. 1919

Lubābu 'l-Albāb: an early Persian anthology, 1921, *see* MUḤAMMAD 'AWFĪ

Lubbertus (Sibrandus). De papa Romano libri 10. s8°. apud Aeg. Radaeum in Acad. Francker. 1594

Lubbock (Alfred Basil).
The Colonial clippers. 2nd ed. 8°. Glasgow. 1921
The China clippers. 4th ed. 8°. Glasgow. 1919

Lubbock (Percy).
The craft of fiction. 8°. [1921]
„ [3rd impr.] 8°. [1922]
Earlham. 8°. [1922]
„ [3rd impr.] 8°. [1922]
George Calderon. A sketch. 8°. 1921
The region cloud. 8°. [1925]
Roman pictures. 8°. [1923]

Lubecensis. Bibliotheca L., 12v, 1725–31, *see* BIBLIOTHECA.

Lübeck. Die Bau- u. Kunstdenkmäler d. Freien u. Hansestadt Lübeck. Hrsg. v. d. Baubehörde [Denkmalrat]. B2–4. la8°. Lübeck. 1906–28
Bekentnuss u. Erklerung auffs Interim durch Lübeck, Hamburg, Lüneburg &c. Superintendenten, Pastorn u. Predigern zu Christl. u. notwendiger unterrichtung gestellet. [*b. w.* Charles V. Der Röm. Kaiserl. M. erklärung &c., 1548]. s4°. Magdeburgk. *M. Lotther.* [1549]
Lübeck; hrsg. v. Senat d. Freien u. Hansestadt L.; bearb. F. W. Virck, *see* DEUTSCHLAND. D.'s Städtebau, 1921.

Lubieński (Stanisław), *bp. of Plock.*
Hist. reformationis Polonicae. s8°. Freistadii. 1685

Lubin (Isador) & H. Everett. The British coal dilemma. s8°. 1927

Luboff (Edouard), *LL.D.*, *see* RAINE (G. E.) Bolshevik Russia; by R. in collab. w. E. L., 1920.

Lubomirska (*pcsse.* **Hedwige de**), *aft. wife of prince Eugène de Ligne, see* LIGNE (*pcsse.* H. DE).

Luca (Pasquale de). Alfredo Baccelli. la8°. Milano. 1920

Lucan. De bello civili. Cum Grotii &c. notis, accur. C. Schrevelio. s8°. Lugd. Batav. 1669
La guerre civile (La Pharsale). Texte établi & tr. par A. Bourgery. [Coll. des univ. de France]. t1. 8°. 1926
M. Annaei L. Belli civilis lib. 10. Ed. A. E. Housman. 8°. O. 1927
see DANTE ALIGHIERI. Lectura D., D. e. L.; conferenza da V. Ussani, 1917.

Lucar (Cyril), *patriarch of (1) Alexandria, (2) Constantinople.*
Conf. Christ. fidei, adj. gemina ejusdem conf. &c. s8°. [Iasii Moldaviae]. 1645
The colophon dated 1642.
see SMITH (T.) Miscellanea: De vita &c. C. L. &c., 1686.

Lucas, *van Leyden* [†HUYGENS (LUKAS) *van Leyden*; JACOBSZ (L.)], *see* BALDASS (L.) Die Gemälde d. L., 1926.
see KAHN (R.) Die Graphik d. L. van L., 1918.

Lucas, *bp. of Tuy.* Crónica de España. Prim. ed. del texto romanceado, prep. &c. por J. Puyol. [Real Acad. de la Hist.] la8°. 1926

Lucas (—), *physician at the Hague, see* FÉNELON. Réfut. des erreurs de Spinosa; avec la vie de S. par J. Colerus, augm. de particul. tireés d'une vie par [L.], 1703.

Lucas (A.), *chemist, Survey Dept., Labor., Cairo.*
Anc. Egyptian materials. 8°. 1926

Lucas (Arthur). John Lucas, portrait painter, 1828–74. Mem. Arranged &c. by A. L. fol. [1910]

Lucas (Arthur F.) The legal minimum wage in Mass. [Annals of Amer. Acad. of Polit. &c. Sc., v130, Suppl.] 8°. Phila. 1927

Lucas (Charles), *M.P.* Polit. constit. of Gt. Brit. & Ireland, asserted &c. & addr. & letters to the free-citizens of Dublin. v1. 8°. 1751

Lucas (*Sir* Charles Prestwood). The Empire at war. Ed. for the R. Colonial Inst. by L. 5v. 8°. 1921–26
The Gold Coast & the War. [P2427]. s8°. 1920

Lucas (*Sir* Charles Prestwood) [*continued*].
Hist. geography of the Brit. Colonies [Dominions & Dependencies]. v4ii, v7ii. s8°. O. 1915–16
4, S. Africa, p2, Hist. of the Union of S.A.
7, India, p2, Hist. under the govt. of the Crown, by P. E. Roberts.
„ „ ....3rd ed. v5ii. s8°. O. 1923
5, Canada, p2, Hist., 1763–1921, by H. E. Egerton.
The partition & colonization of Africa. 8°. O. 1922
The story of the Empire. [Brit. Emp.: survey; ed. H. Gunn, v2]. 8°. 1924

Lucas (Daniel B.) Nicaragua: war of the filibusters, w. intr. chap. by L. Baker—Nicaraguan Canal, by W. A. MacCorkle—Monroe doct. by J. F. McLaughlin. 8°. Richmond, Va. 1896

Lucas (David), *see* HOLMES (*Sir* C. J.) Constable, Gainsborough & L. &c., 1921.

Lucas (Edward Verrall).
Advisory Ben. s8°. [1923]
Cambridge & C. Lamb, *see* WHERRY (G. E.), *ed.* Cambridge & C. L., 1925.
Edwin Austin Abbey, R.A. Record of h. life & work. 2v. la8°. 1921
Encounters & diversions. s8°. [1924]
Events & embroideries. s8°. [1926]
The friendly town. Comp. by L. [2nd ed.] s8°. [1905]
„ „ [10th ed.] s8°. [1918]
Genevra's money. s8°. [1922]
Giving & receiving: essays & fantasies. s8°. [1922]
Highways & byways in Sussex. [repr.] 8°. 1921
Life of C. Lamb. [5th ed. rev.] 2v. s8°. [1921]
A little of everything. 5th ed. s8°. [1916]
The open road. Comp. by E. V. L. 9th ed. s8°. [1906]
The phantom journal & o. essays &c. s8°. [1919]
Rose & Rose. s8°. [1921]
Roving east & roving west. 8°. [1921]
Verena in the midst. s8°. [1920]
Vermeer of Delft. Intr. by Sir C. J. Holmes. 8°. [1922]
A wanderer among pictures. 8°. [1924]
A wanderer in Paris. 15th ed. s8°. [1920]
„ „ 21st ed. s8°. [1924]
A wanderer in Rome. 8°. [1926]
Zigzags in France & var. essays. s8°. 1925

—— **& E. Lucas.** 300 games & pastimes: suggest. for children's games. [8th impr.] 8°. 1922

Lucas (Elizabeth), *see* LUCAS (E. V.) & E. L. 300 games &c, 1922.

Lucas (Emily B. C.), *wife of F. L. Lucas, see* JONES (E. B. C.)

Lucas (Franciscus), *of Bruges.* Rom. correctionis in Latinis Bibliis ed. Vulgatae jussu Sixti V. recogn., loca insigniora. s8°. Antverpiae. 1603
see BIBLE: LATIN. Biblia Sacra Vulg. [*foll. by* Rom. correct. loca insigniora à F. L.], 1603.
„ HUGO, *de Sancto Charo, Card.* Sacr. Bibl. vulgatæ ed. concord.; rec. & emend. à F. L., 1768.
„ —— Sacr. Bibl. Vulg. ed. concord. &c., rec. à F. L., 1825.

Lucas (Frank Laurence). Euripides & h. influence. Intr. by R. W. Livingstone. s8°. [1924
Seneca & Elizabethan tragedy. 8°. C. 1922

Lucas (Frederic Augustus). Animals of the past. [Amer. Mus. of Nat. Hist., Hdbk. ser., No. 4]. 5th ed. s8°. N.Y. 192[illegible]

Lucas (Jean Maximilien). The oldest biog. of Spinoza [*i.e.* La vie de feu Mr. de Spinosa, *attrib. to J. M. L.*] Ed. w tr., intr. &c. by A. Wolf. 8°. 192[illegible]

Lucas (John), *portrait painter; 1807–74, see* LUCAS (A.) J. L. mem., 1910.

Lucas (Netley). Crooks: confessions. Foreword by J. C. Goodwin. 8°. [1925

Lucas (Paul) [*ps. Le Père* SIMPLICIEN], *see* FRANCE. ANON. WORKS. L'Etat de la France &c.; [*ed.* N. Besongne, *u. add. & corr. by* Simplicien], 5t, 1727.

Lucas (Pietro de), *see* ROCHE D'ALLERY (P. DE L., *conte* DELLA)

Lucas (Richard), *D.D.* Extr. f. Enquiry after happiness, *se* WESLEY (J.) Xtn. lib., v40, 41, 1754.

Lucas (St. John Welles). Certain persons. s8°. E. 192[illegible]
The Oxford book of French verse, 13th–19th cent. Chosen by St. J. L. s8°. O. 192[illegible]
„ „ 13th–20th cent. Chosen by St. J. L. s8°. O. 192[illegible]

Lucas-Dubreton (Jean).
Le Comte d'Artois, Charles X. 8°. [1927]
La disgrâce de N. Machiavel, 1469–1527. 2e éd. s8°. 1913
Louis XVIII. la8°. [1925]
Louvel le régicide. s8°. 1923
La Restauration & la Monarchie de Juillet (1814–48). 8°. [192[illegible]
S. Pepys. Tr. H. J. Stenning. 8°. [192[illegible]
La vie d'Alex. Dumas père. 3e éd. s8°. 192[illegible]

Lucca. Bandi lucchesi del sec. 14, 1863, *see* BONGI (S.), *ed.*
Inventari del vescovato, d. cattedrale e di a. chiese di L. Pubbl. P. Guidi e E. Pellegrinetti. [Studi e testi, 34]. fasc. 1. la8°. 192[illegible]
see SCHIAPARELLI (L.) Il cod. 490 d. Bibl. Cap. di L. &c. 1924.

Lucchi (Lorna de'). Anthology of Ital. poems [*Ital. & Eng.*], 13th–19th c. Sel. & tr. by L. de' L. Pref. by C. Foligno. s8°. 1922

Luccock (John). Gram. & vocab. of the Tupi lang.; coll. & tr. f. works of Anchieta & Figueira &c., *see* INSTITUTO HIST. E GEOG. BRAZIL. Revista, t43, 44, 1880–81.

Luce (Alfred Fabre-), *see* FABRE-LUCE (A.)

Luce (Arthur Aston). Bergson's doctrine of intuition. Donnellan Lect., 1921. s8°. 1922

Monophysitism, past & present: st. in Christology. s8°. 1920

Luce (Siméon). Jeanne d'Arc à Domremy: recherches crit. sur la orig. de la mission de La Pucelle. la8°. 1886

Lucena (João de), *Jesuit.* Vida do F. de Xavier. 2v [*v1, 2ª ed.*] s8°. Paris. 1921

Lucena (Luis Seco de), *see* SECO DE LUCENA (L.)

Lucerna (Roman). Morphologie d. Montblancgruppe, 1914, *see* PETERMANNS MITT. Ergnzb., 39, 1915.

Lucian, *of Samosata.*

Colloquia selecta, & Timon. Cebetis Thebani tabula &c. Gr. & Lat. Notis illust. T. Hemsterhuis. s8°. Amstelædami. 1708

Lucianus. Ed. N. Nilén. v1, fasc. 2, Libelli XV–XIX [*pagin. cont.*] s8°. L., *Teubner.* 1923

„ „ Prolegomena [H1, *no tp.*] s8°. L., *Teubner.* [1927]

TRANSLATIONS.

Lucien. Tr. N. Perrot, Sr. d'Ablancourt. 2p [*t2 wanting*]. s8°. 1664

L.; w. Eng. tr. by A. M. Harmon. [Loeb Class. Lib.] v3, 4. s8°. 1921–25

see MELANCHTHON (P.) Necessarias esse ad omne studiorum genus artes dicendi &c. Item Lucianus opusc. ad indoctum &c., 1523.

„ MORE (*Sir* T.) Latina opera (Luciani Necromantia, &c.), 1566.

Luciane (*Comte* F. C. de Mareschal de), *see* MARESCHAL DE LUCIANE (*Comte* F. C. DE).

Luciani (Luigi). Human physiology. [Tr.], w. pref. by J. N. Langley. v5. 8°. 1921

5, Metabolism—temperature—reproduction &c.; ed. M. S. Pembrey.

***Lucien Greville ;** by a cornet, 3v, 1833, *see* PETTIGREW (T. L.)

Lucifer, *bp. of Cagliari, see* COLEMAN (A. M.) Biblical text of L. of C. (Acts), 1927.

Lucilius (Caius). Carminum reliquiae. Rec. enarr. F. Marx. v2, Comm. 8°. L. 1905

Lucillus, *of Tarrha.* Coll. proverbiorum, *see* ÆSOP, 1505.

Lucinière (*gén. de* Cornulier-), *see* CORNULIER-LUCINIÈRE (*gén. de*).

Lucius (Ludwig), *see* MAGDEBURG CENTURIES. Hist. eccl.; per L. L. rec., 1624.

Lück (Stephan).

Gesang- u. Gebetbuch f. d. Diözese Trier. s8°. Trier. 1847

Lucka (Emil).

Otto Weininger, s. Werk &c. 8°. Wien. 1905

Lücken (Gottfried v.) Die Anfänge d. Burgund. Schule: d. Antike in d. Baukunst d. 12. Jhdt. 4°. Basel. [1922]

Luckenbach (Hermann). Kunst u. Gesch. Hrsg. H. L. Gesamtausgabe. la8°. München. 1923

Luckenbill (Daniel David). Anc. records of Assyria & Babylonia. [Ed.] D. D. L. [Anc. records; gen. ed. J. H. Breasted, s1]. v1, 2. 8°. Chicago. [1926–27]

1, 2, Hist. records of Assyria.

Annals of Sennacherib [Univ. of Chicago: Or. Inst. publ. v2]. 4°. Chicago. [1924]

Lückes (Eva C. E.) Lect. on gen. nursing. s8°. 1884

Luckey (Leonard W. A.) Whence comest thou? Whither goest thou? 8°. Boston, *Mass.* 1927

Luckiesh (Matthew). Artificial light. 8°. [1920]

Lucknow. Cat. of coins in the Prov. Museum, Lucknow. By C. J. Brown. Coins of the Mughal emperors. [Publ. for United Prov. Govt.] 2v. la8°. O. 1920

see HIRANANDA SHASTRI. Some sculptures in Prov. Mus., L., 1922.

Luco (Juan Bernardo Diaz de), *see* DIAZ DE LUCO (J. B.)

Luçon, *Diocese.* Ordonnances synodales du dioceze de L., 1685, *see* BARILLON (H. DE).

Lucretius.

De rerum natura libri 6. 4°. Lond., *Tonson.* 1712

„ „ Recog., adnot. crit. instr. C. Bailey. ed. 2ª. s8°. O. [1921]

„ „ Lat. u. Deut. v. H. Diels. 2B. 8°. Berlin. 1923–24

„ „ Notes & tr. by H. A. J. Munro. 4th ed. finally rev. v2, Explan. notes, w. intr. essay on scient. signif. of L., by E. N. da C. Andrade. 8°. 1928

TRANSLATIONS.

De la nature. Texte établi & tr. par A. Ernout. [Coll. des univ. de France]. s8°. 1920

De rerum natura. [Text], w. Eng. tr. by W. H. D. Rouse. [Loeb Class. Lib.] s8°. 1924

Lucretius [*continued*]

TRANSLATIONS [*continued*].

The nature of things. Tr., accomp. w. the orig. text. By J. M. Good. 2v. 4°. 1805

Translations f. L. by R. C. Trevelyan. s8°. [1920]

Von d. Natur d. Dinge. Mit d. Lat. Text nach Wakefield's Ausgabe. 2B [*in* 1v]. 8°. L. 1821

see SANTAYANA (G.) 3 philos. poets: L., Dante &c., 3rd impr., 1922.

Lucy (*Sir* Henry William). The diary of a journalist. 3v (2, Later entries; 3, Fresh extracts). 8°. 1920–23

Lucy (William), *bp. of St. David's.*

*A treatise of the nature of a minister. s4°. 1670

Lüdeke (Henry). L. Tieck u. d. alte engl. Theater. 8°. Frankfurt a. M. 1922

Lüdeke (Johann Friedrich). Tabulae synopticae in Theses theolog. S. J. Baumgarten. [*b. w.* Baumgarten (S. J.) Theses theol., 1758]. ed. 2ª. s8°. Halae. 1760

Lüdemann (Heinrich). Die Vorherrschaft d. Geistes. [*b. w.* Drew (A.) Das Ich, 1897]. 8°. 1899

Ludendorff (Erich).

Kriegführung u. Politik. 8°. 1922

Urkunden d. Obersten Heeresleitung ü. i. Tätigkeit 1916/18. Hrsg. E. L. 2ᵉ A. 8°. 1921

TRANSLATIONS.

The General Staff & its problems. Rel. betw. the High Command & the German Imp. Govt. Tr. F. A. Holt. 2v. 8°. [1920]

The 2 battles of the Marne, by L. &c., 1927, *see* JOFFRE (*le mar.* J. J. C.)

see BECKER (G.) Trois conf. sur L., 1920.

„ BUAT (E.) Hindenburg & L. stratèges, 1923.

„ —— L., 1920.

„ DELBRÜCK (H.) L., Tirpitz &c., 1920.

„ —— L.'s Selbstporträt, 1922.

„ LEHMANN (C.) L.'s Schuld, 1920.

„ VENI VIDI, *ps.* L. in Bayern, 1924.

Lüders (Gerhard). De progressu emend. per Lutherum relig. Praes. G. Wernsdorfio. [P484]. s4°. Vitembergae. [1717]

Lüders (Heinrich), *orientalist, see* GRUNDRISS. G. d. indo-ar. Philol. u. Altertumskunde; hrsg. v. H. L. & J. Wackernagel, 3B, 1896–1920.

Ludewig (Hermann Eduard). The lit. of Amer. local hist.: bibliog. essay. 8°. N.Y. 1846

Ludewig (Johann Peter von). De jure clientelari German. in feudis & coloniis. ed. 2ª. s4°. Halae Sal. 1737

Jubelrede v. d. Wohlthaten &c. auf d. Augsburg. Reichs-Tage. [P484]. s4°. Halle. [1730]

see KALAU (D.) Arausio supremo imperio vindic.; præs. L., 1739.

„ SCHÖNBECK (J. C.) Diss. de jure postarum heredit.; præs. L., 1704.

Ludhiana. Records of the Ludhiana agency [1808–15], *see* PUNJAB. P. govt. records, v2, 1911.

Lüdinghausen (Bernhard Georg Herm. Heinr. Rob. Ferd., *Frhr.* v.) Die Schuld am deut. Zusammenbruch. Tagebuchblätter [v. L.] Hrsg. O. Baumgarten. [P2410]. 8°. Tübingen. 1919

Ludlow (Edmund). Imprisonment & death of Charles I: extr. f. Mem. of L. &c., *see* AUNGERVYLE SOC. Reprints, s1, 1882.

Ludlow (Edmund), *ps.* Letter to Sir E. S. [*i.e.* Seymour] comparing the tyranny of 4 years of K. Charles w. 4 years of late abdic. King &c. [*Postcript wanting.* P2663]. s4°. Amsterdam. 1691

Three tracts publ. at Amsterdam in 1691 & 92 under the name of letters of General Ludlow to Sir E. Seymour & o. persons etc. [ed. by F. Maseres]. 4°. 1812

Ludolf (Hiob), *the elder.*

Ad suam Hist. Aethiop. Comm. fol. Francofurti ad Moenum. 1691

Appendix 2ª ad Hist. Aethiop. cont. Diss. de locustis &c. [*b. w. h.* Ad suam hist. Comm., 1691. fol. Francofurti ad Moenum. 1694

Epistolae Samaritanæ Sichernitarum ad J. L. cum Lat. vers. & annot. [*b. w.* Cellarius (C.) Horae Sam., 1682]. s4°. Cizae. 1688

Gramm. Æthiopica. ed. 2ª. Acced. Prosodia &c. fol. Francofurti ad Moenum. 1702

Gramm. linguae Amharicae. fol. Francofurti ad Moenum. 1698

Lexicon Aethiopico-Lat. ed. 2ª. fol. Francofurti ad Moenum. 1699

Lexicon Amharico-Latinum. [*b. w. h.* Gramm. linguae Amharicae, 1698]. fol. Francofurti ad Moenum. 1698

Relatio nova de hodierno Habessiniae statu. Add. Epistolis regiis ad Soc. Indiae Orient. &c. [*b. w. h.* Ad suam hist. Comm., 1691]. fol. Francofurti ad Moenum. 1693

see CLAUDIUS, *king of Ethiopia.* Conf. fidei, Lat. vers. I. L., 1702.

„ JUNCKER (C.) Comm. de vita &c. J. L. &c., 1710.

Ludorff (A.) Die Bau- u. Kunstdenkmäler v. Westfalen, hrsg. v. A. L., 1906–12, *see* WESTFALEN.

Ludovici (Albert).
An artist's life in London & Paris, 1870–1925. 8°. [1926]

Ludovici (Anthony Mario).
A defence of conservatism. 8°. [1927]
The false assumptions of "democracy." 8°. [1921]
Lysistrata or woman's future &c. s8°. [1924]
Man's descent from the gods; case agst. prohibition. 8°. 1921
Personal remin. of A. Rodin. 8°. 1926
Too old for dolls. s8°. 1920
Woman: a vindication. 8°. 1923

Ludovici (Christian), *see* MISHNAH. Text. Talmudicus tract. de primitiis &c. publ. disput. tuebitur C. L., 1696.

Ludovici (Jacob Friedrich). Obs. de privilegiis studiosorum ad Petrum Rebuffum. [*b. w.* Rebuffi (P.) Privilegia &c., 1585]. s8°. Halæ Magd. 1705

Ludus Coventriæ; ed. K. S. Block, 1922, *see* COVENTRY PLAYS.

Ludwig (Albert), *see* ARNOLD (R. F.), *ed.* Das deut. Drama; in Verbindung mit J. Bab, J. L. &c., 1925.

Ludwig (Carl), *prof. of anatomy, see* FREY (M. v.), *ed.* Abhandlgn. ü. d. Speichel v. C. L. &c. (1851), 1890.

Ludwig (Emil).
Bismarck: Gesch. e. Kämpfers. 8°. 1927
Bismarck: e. psycholog. Versuch. 4e A. 8°. 1912
Genie u. Charakter: 20 männl. Bildnisse. 8°. 1927
Goethe: Gesch. e. Menschen. 3B. 8°. St. 1920
Kunst. u. Schicksal: 4 Bildnisse. 8°. 1927
Der Menschensohn: Gesch. e. Propheten. 8°. 1928
Napoleon. 8°. [1926]
R. Dehmel. s8°. 1913
Tom u. Sylvester. Ein Quartett. 8°. 1928
Wilhelm II. 8°. 1926
TRANSLATIONS.
Bismarck: story of a fighter. Tr. E. & C. Paul. 8°. [1927]
„ „ [2nd impr.] 8°. [1927
Bismarck. The trilogy of a fighter. [3 plays. Tr.] 8°. [1927]
Genius & character. [Tr. K. Burke &c.]. 8°. [1927]
Kaiser Wilhelm II. Tr. E. C. Mayne. 8°. [1926]
„ „ 4th impr. 8°. [1926]
Napoleon. Tr. E. & C. Paul. 8°. [1927]
„ „ [2nd ed.] 8°. [1927]
„ „ [3rd ed.] 8°. [1927]
The Son of Man. Tr. E. & C. Paul. 8°. [1928]

Ludwig (Fritz).
Der Cowboy u. d. Geigenfee u. a. Erzählungen. s8°. L. [1894]

Ludwig (Otto). Sämtl. Werke. Unter Mitwirk. d. Goethe- u. Schiller-Arch. &c. hrsg. P. Merker. B4, 5. 8°. München. 1922
4, Gedichte; hrsg. H. H. Borcherdt. 5, Die Torgauer Heide —Die Rechte d. Herzens—Des Fräulein v. Scuderi—Die Pfarrrose; hrsg. E. Schmidt.

Luffman (John). Brief acc. of the island of Antigua &c.: letters, 1786–88. 2nd ed. rev. s8°. [1788]

Lufft (Hans), *see* ZELTNER (G. G.) Hist. d. Bibel-Version M. Lutheri in der Beschr. d. Lebens &c. H. Luffts &c., 1727.

Lugal-e ũg me-lám-bi ner-gál, *see* RADAU (H.) Nin-Ib: determiner of fates acc. to Sumerian epic Lugal-e &c., 1910.

Lugar (Robert). The country gentleman's architect: designs for farm houses &c. 4°. 1807

Lugard (*Sir* **Frederick John Dealtry).** The Dual mandate in Brit. tropical Africa. 8°. E. 1922
„ „ ....3rd ed. 8°. E. 1926

Lugli (Giuseppe). La Villa Sabina di Orazio, *see* REALE ACCAD. DEI LINCEI. Mon. ant., v31, 1926.

Lugo (*card.* **Juan de).** Tract. de Eucharistiæ sacramento, *see* MIGNE (J. P.), *ed.* Theol. cursus, t23, 1860.

Lugones (Leopoldo).
El libro de los paisajes. s8°. Buenos Aires. 1917

Lugo-Viña (Ruy de). Un internacionalista representativo: C. de la Torriente. 8°. Paris. [1924]

Lugt (Frits). Les marques de coll. de dessins & d'estampes, avec notices hist. sur les collectionneurs, les coll. &c. la8°. Amsterdam. 1921

Luhn (Johann Bernhard). M. F. Beckii memoria. Resp. E. Weidio. [P595]. s4°. Wittembergae. [1703]

Luick (Carl). Gesch. d. heim. engl. Versarten. [Sonderabdr. v. Paul's Grundr. d. german. Philol.] 2e verb. A. [P2703]. la8°. Str. 1905
Histor. Gramm. d. engl. Sprache. Bliii–vi, Hl [*pagin. cont.*] 8°. L. 1920–21

Luiga (G. E.)
Die Agrarreform in Eesti. [P2710]. s8°. Helsingfors. 1920

Luigi Amedeo Giuseppe Maria F. F., *duke of the Abruzzi.* La "Stella Polare" nel Mare Artico, 1899–1900. 3a ed. la8°. Milano. 1903

Luigini (Federigo), *da Udine.* Il libro d. bella donna. [*Ed.* C. Téoli. Bibl. rara, v23]. s8°. Milano. 1863

Luis *de Granada* [LODOICUS *Granatensis*]. Flores ex omnibus eius opusculis spiritualibus excerpti, & in 8 partes distrib. Coll. & interpret. M. ab Isselt. s8°. Coloniae. 1588
see MARTINEZ RUIZ (J.) De G. a Castelar, 1922.

Luiso (Francesco Paolo). Per la biog. di Bonagiunta Orbicciani da Lucca, *see* ARCHIVIO STOR. ITAL., anno 85, v2, 1927.
see DANTE ALIGHIERI. Lectura D.: c. 21 del Paradiso letto da F. P. L., 1912.

Luithold (Waremund). Vom tag zu Hagenaw, u. wer verhinderet hab, das kein gesprech von vergleichung der Religion, daselbst für gangen ist. s4°. *n.p.* 1540

Luitprand, *king of the Lombards, see* LIUDPRANDUS.

Lukach (Harry Charles), *see* LUKE (H. C.)

Lukács (Georg). Die Theorie d. Romans. s8°. 1920

Luke, *Saint & Evangelist, see* BIBLE *for Gospel & Comm., & Life.*

Luke, *Stylites, Saint, see* DELEHAYE (H.) Saints stylites, 1923.

Luke (Harry Charles) [LUKACH].
Anatolica. 8°. 1924
Bibliog. of Sierra Leone, prec. by essay on origin &c. of the Colony &c. 2nd ed. enl. s8°. 1925
Cyprus under the Turks, 1571–1878. s8°. 1921
Mosul & its minorities. 8°. 1925
Prophets, priests & patriarchs. Sects of Palestine & Syria. 8°. [1927]
The Yezidis of Mosul. [Repr. f. Ind. Antiquary, v54. P2851]. 4°. Bombay. 1925
see BERTRAM (*Sir* A.) & H. C. L. Rep. of Comm. apptd. to inquire into Orthodox Patriarchate of Jerusalem, 1921.
„ CYPRUS. Hdbk. of C.; ed. by H. C. L. & D. J. Jardine, 1920.
„ SPANISH Franciscan's narr. of a journey to the Holy Land; tr. & ed. H. C. L., 1927.

—— & E. Keith-Roach.
Handbook of Palestine. Intr. by Sir H. Samuel. s8°. 1922

Lukomsky (A. S.) Воспоминанія ген. А. С. Л. Періодъ Европ. войны &c. 2т. 8°. Berlin. 1922
Erinnerungen. Zeit d. Europ. Krieges. Anfang v. Russlands Verfall. Kampf mit d. Bolschewisten. Uebers. A. v. Hamm. 2B. 8°. 1923

Lukomsky (Georgy Kreskentevich) [LOUKOMSKI].
Егор Нарбут художник-график. s8°. Берлин. 1923
Москва и деревня въ гравюрахъ &c. 1800–50 &c. 8°. [Берлинѣ. 1922]
Московыя въ представленіи иностранцевъ 16–17в. 4°. [Берлинъ. 1922]
St. Petersburg: e. Gesch. d. Stadt u. i. Baudenkmäler. 8°. München. [1923]
La vie & les mœurs en Russe, de Pierre le Grand à Lénine. 4°. 1928.
Zarskoje Sselo: Innenräume u. Möbel. 4°. 1924
see CALZINI (R.) G. L., 1923.

Luks (H. T.), *see* GRIEBEN'S REISE-BIBL., B29, 13e A. neu bearbt. v. H. T. L., 1882.

Lukyanov (Aleksandr Aleksandrovich). Кузнецъ, *see* SBORNIK. Сб. товар. знаніе, 4, 1905.

Lullus, *Saint, abp. of Mentz.* Briefe, *see* BONIFACE, *St.* Briefe d. heil. B. u. L. (*Latin*); hrsg. v. M. Tangl., 1916.
see LAMBERTUS, *Hersfeld.* Opera (Vita Lulli); rec. O. Holder-Egger, 1894.

Lully (Jean Baptiste de), *see* REVUE MUSICALE, jan. 1925, No. spéc., L. & l'opéra franç., 1925.

Lully (Raymond), *1236–1315.* Blanquerna: a 13th cent. romance. Tr. f. the Catalan by E. A. Peers. la8°. 1925
The book of the lover & the beloved. Tr. w. intr. essay, by E. A. Peers. s8°. 1923
The book of the ordre of chyvalry. Tr. & pr. by W. Caxton f. Fr. vers. of L.'s "Le libre del orde de cavayleria." With A. Loutfut's Scot. transcr. Ed. A. T. P. Byles. [E.E.T.S., 168]. 8°. 1926
Opera ea quae ad adinventam ab ipso artem universalem pert. &c. Acc. V. de Valeriis aureum in artem Lulli generalem opus. s8°. Argentorati. 1617
see AGRIPPA (H. C.) In Artem brevem R. L. comm., 1533.
„ PERROQUET (A.) La vie & le martyre du docteur R. L., 1667.
„ WAITE (A. E.) R. L., 1922.

Lumb (A. D.) The platinum metals. 8°. 1920

Lumb (T. W.) Notes on the Greek anthology. s8°. 1920

Lumbroso (Alberto). Origini econ. e diplomat. d. Guerra Mondiale. v1. 8°. Milano. 1926

Lumbroso (Giacomo). Notizie s. vita di Cassiano Dal Pozzo, con ricordi e lettere, *see* REGIA DEP. DI STORIA PATRIA. Misc., t15, 1874.

Lumisden, *Family of, see* LUMSDEN.

Lummer (Otto). Contrib. to photographic optics. Tr. & augm. by S. P. Thompson. 8°. 1900
Lummis (Charles Fletcher). The wonderland of the old South-West (Mesa, Cañon & Pueblo). 8°. [1926]
Lumsden, *Family of* [LUMISDEN; LUMSDAINE], *see* LUMSDEN (H. W.) Mem. of the families of L. &c., 1889.
Lumsden (E. S.) The art of etching. 8°. 1925
Lumsden (Henry William). Mem. of the families of Lumsdaine, Lumisden or Lumsden. la8°. E. 1889
Lumsden (Thomas). A journey f. Merut in India to London, 1819–20. 8°. 1822
Luna (Pedro Martinez de) [BENEDICT XIII, *antipope*], *see* ARCHIV F. LIT. U. KIRCHENGESCH., B6, 7 (Ehrle, Neue Mat. z. Gesch. P. v. L. *&* Die Kirchenrechtl. Schriften P. v. L.), 1892–1900.
Lunacharsky (Anatoli Vasilevich).
Драм. произведения. 2г. 8°. Москва. 1923
Vasilisa the Wise. A dram. fairy tale. Auth. tr. by L. A. Magnus. 8°. [1922]
Lunardi (Vincenzo). An acc. of the first aërial voyage in Eng., in a ser. of letters to G. Compagni. 8°. 1784
Lund. Acta Univ. Lundensis. Lunds Univ. Arsskrift, *see* THYRÉN (J. C. W.) Den första väpnade neutraliteten, *n.d.*
Lund (C. Wesenberg-), *see* WESENBERG-LUND (C.)
Lund (Hans), *teacher of Danish language.* A new method of learning Danish & Norwegian lang. With key. n. ed. s8°. 1909
see BEGTRUP (H.), H. L. &C. Folk high schools of Denmark, 1926.
Lundberg (Emma Octavia). Illegit. as a child-welfare problem, p2, Boston & Mass., by L. &c., 1921, *see* UNITED STATES: LABOR.
State commissions for study &c. of child-welfare laws, *see* UNITED STATES: LAB. Children's Bur., Publ. 131, 1924.
Unemployment & child welfare, *see* UNITED STATES: LAB. Children's Bur., Publ. 125, 1923.
see LENROOT (K. F.) & E. O. L. Juvenile courts at work, 1925.
—— & M. E. Milburn. Child dependency in Dist. of Columbia, *see* UNITED STATES: LAB. Children's Bur., 140, 1924.
Lundblad (O.) Quellenhydracarinen auf Møens Klint, *see* KONG. DAN. VID. SELSK. Biolog. Medd., B6, 1926.
Süsswasseracarinen aus Dänemark, *see* KONG. DAN. VID. SELSK. Skr., Raekke 8, B6, 1920.
Lundegård (Axel), *see* AHLGREN (E.) Saml. skr., b5, Moderd, av E. A. & A. L., b6, Dramatik, av E. A. & A. L., 1919–20.
Lundqvist (K. G.) Hist. Dikter ur d. Svenska Litt. s8°. [1902]
Lundy's Lane Historical Society. Publ., *see* CRUIKSHANK (E. C.), *ed.* Doc. hist. of the campaign upon the Niagara frontier, 1812[–14], 9p, 1896–1908.
Lungershausen (Johann Jacob). Diss. prior [& posterior]. Mysteria Christianismi contra [Toland's] Xtny not mysterious. [P2743]. s4°. Jenæ. 1713–14
Luniński (Ernest). Napoleon. Legiony i księstwo Warszawskie. Ilustracje. [*Polish & French*]. obl. 4°. Warszawa. *n.d.*
Lunn (Arnold). A hist. of ski-ing. 8°. 1927
The mountains of youth. 8°. 1925
Roman converts. 8°. 1924
Lunn (*Sir* Henry Simpson). Ægean civilizations. Ed. L. Lect[s]. by Dr. Caton, L. R. Furneaux &c. [*Fr.* Proc. of Hellenic Travellers' Club, 1910–12]. 8°. 1925
J. Wesley: essay, Trin. Coll. [P449]. 8°. D. 1885
The love of Jesus. Manual of prayer &c. s8°. 1911
Reunion & Lambeth. John Wesley's [*supposed*] message to the bishops, 1920. Intr. letter by L. s8°. 1920
Lunt (George). The origin of the late war. [repr.] s8°. N.Y. 1867
Lunt (William Edward), *see* NORWICH. The Valuation of N., ed. W. E. L., 1926.
Lun Yu, *see* CONFUCIUS. Works, orig. text w. tr., v1 [Lun yu], 1809.
Lupas (I.) Nicolae Popea & I. M. Moldovanu, *see* ACADEMIA ROM. Disc., 48, 1920.
Lupi (Clemente). Necrologia, *see* ARCHIVIO STOR. ITAL. Anno, 77, v1, 1919.
Lupi (Diotesalvi), *see* LUPI (M.) Mem. p. s. a. vita d. m. m. D. L., gen. d. fanteria venez., 1865.
Lupi (Mario). Mem. p. s. a. vita d. m. m. D. Lupi; pubbl. G. Finazzi, *see* REGIA DEP. DI STORIA PATRIA. Misc., t6, 1865.
Lupis (Antonio). L'Eroina Veneta: Elena Lucretia Cornara Piscopia. s4°. Venetia. 1689
Lüpke (Theodor v.), *see* WIEGAND (T.) Baalbek: Ergebnisse d. Ausgrab. u. Unters., 1898 bis 1905, B2, v. D. Krencker, T. v. L. &c., 1923.

Luplau Janssen (C.) La surface de la planète Jupiter, 1919–24, *see* KONG. DAN. VID. SELSK. Skr., Række 8, B11, 1926.
Lupoldus, *de Bebenberg, see* EGLOFFSTEIN (L. DE), *bp. of Bamberg.*
Lupset (Thomas), *lecturer in Rhetoric at Oxford.* An exhortation to yonge men (1529); hrsg. E. Wolffhardt, *see* ARCHIV F. D. ST. D. NEU. SPR., B142, 1921.
Lupton (Donald). London & the countrey carbonadoed &c. (1632), *see* AUNGERVYLE SOC. Reprints, s2, 1883.
Lupton (Frederick), *solicitor.* Law relating to dogs. 8°. 1888
Lupton (Joseph Hirst). St. John of Damascus. s8°. 1882
Lupus (Christianus), *see* VIANE (F. v.) & C. L. Relatio, 1693.
Lupus (Marius), *see* LUPI (MARIO).
Lupus (Servatus), *Ferrariensis* [LOUP (S.)] Epistolae, *see* DÜMMLER (E. L.), *ed.* Epist. Merow. et Karol. aevi, t4, 1925.
Lure (M.) [*ps.* Ларинъ (Ю.)]
Составъ пролетаріата. [P2391]. 8°. П. 1918
Lurine (Louis), *see* ALHOY (P. M.) & L. L. Les prisons de Paris, 1846.
Luschan (Felix von). Entstehung u. Herkunft d. ion. Säule, *see* ALTE ORIENT (DER), Jhrg. 13, 1912.
Rassen u. Völker, *see* DEUTSCHE Reden in schwerer Zeit, 33, 1915.
see PETERSEN (E.) & F. v. L., *edd.* Reisen in Lykien Milyas u. Kibyratis, 1889.
Luscinius (Ottomarus), *see* NACHTIGALL (O.)
Luserna (Carlo Francesco Manfredi, *conte* **di).** Memorie, 1551–1631; ed. V. Promis, *see* REGIA DEP. DI STORIA PATRIA. Misc., t18, 1879.
see PROMIS (V.) Ambasciata di L. a Praga nel 1604, 1877.
Lushington (*Sir* Franklin) & Henry Lushington. *Joint compositions. [*Verse. no tp.*] s8°. [*p.p.* 1840 ?]
Lushington (Henry), *see* LUSHINGTON (*Sir* F.) & H. L. Joint compositions, 1840 ?.
Lushington (*Rt. Hon.* Stephen), *judge of the Arches & Admiralty Courts, see* PARL.: H. OF COMMONS. Rep. of debate, June 1825, on L.'s motion resp. deport. of L. C. Lecesne &c. f. Jamaica, 1825.
Lusignan (Charlotta v.), *see* CHARLOTTE, *q. of Cyprus.*
Lusk (Clayton R.), *see* NEW YORK. Revolutionary radicalism; Rep. of the Legisl. Comm., [Chairman, C. R. L.], 1920.
Lutetian Society, *see* VOLTAIRE. La Pucelle; new tr., rev. &c. by E. Dowson, 2v, 1899.
Luthard (Christoph). Disput. Bernensis, 1528, ad exam. propositarum explic. Et contra adversarios, praecipuè J. Schuler defensio. &c. Libri duo. 2 lib. *in* 1v. fol. Bernae. 1660
Luthardt (Christoph Ernst). Apolog. lects. on the fundamental truths of Xty. Tr. S. Taylor. s8°. E. 1865
Apolog. lects. on the moral truths of Xty. Tr. S. Taylor. 4th ed. s8°. E. 1889
Apolog. lects. on the saving truths of Xty. Tr. S. Taylor. s8°. E. 1868
Luther (Arthur). Alt-Dorpat u. d. russ. Geistesleben. 2e A. [P2485]. s8°. 1920
Luther (Catharina), *wife of M. Luther* [*geb.* C. v. BORA].
see KOPPEN (L.) K. v. Bora, 2e A., 1923.
,, MAYER (J. F.) Diss. de C. conjuge L., 1710.
Luther (Hans), *father of M. Luther, see* MAYER (J. F.) De parentibus D. Lutheri, 1708.
Luther (*Dr.* Hans), *Oberbürgermeister,* **P. Mitzlaff & E. Stein.** Die Zukunftsaufgaben d. deut. Städte.; hrsg. v. H. L. &c. 8°. 1922
Luther (Martin).
Catalogus oder Register aller Bücher u. schrifften D. M. L., 1518–1533. Mit e. Vorrhede. s8°. Wittemberg. [1533]
*Curieuser Geschichts-Calender M. Lutheri &c. 3rd impr. s8°. L. 1698
*Defensio vitae &c. M. L. contra imput. calumnias a G. F. Damiani. Suscepta &c. a Veritatis quodam amante. s8°. *n.p.* 1755
*Historia B. L., oder hist. Nachr. &c. Aus Mathesii Hist. Seckendorffs Lutheranismo &c. s8°. Augspurg. 1750
*Lutherus sui ipsius proditor: der durch sich selbst entlarvte Luther &c. s8°. Öhringen. 1717
*Nöthige &c. Unterredung. Erstes Gespräche gehalten v. M. Luthero u. U. Zwinglio. [Vorrede *signed* Philander u. Agathocles P2627]. s4°. Franckfurt. 1720
Verzeichung u. Register aller Bücher u. schrifften M. L., 1518–28. s8°. *n.p.* 1528
*Von d. Papstthumb zu Rome: wider M. Luther. s4°. *n.p. n.d.* [c. 1535]
COLLECTED WORKS [*Lat. & Germ. in order of date of publ.*]
Prima [*&* Secunda] pars operum M. L. 2p in 1v [*pagin. cont.*] s4°. *n.p.* [1520]
Tomus 1(–7) omnium operum. 7t. fol. Witebergae. 1545–57

Luther (Martin) [*continued*].
COLLECTED WORKS [*continued*].
Der erste (& Der anden) Theil der Bücher &c. d. M. L. deren viel weder in den Wittenberg, noch Jhen. Tomis zufinden, Zusamen getragen [*by* J. Aurifaber]. 2T. fol. Eisleben. 1564–65
Werke. Krit. Gesamtausgabe. B10, Abt. 1ii, 17ii, 21, 31ii, 35, 39i, 44, 48, 51–54. la8°. Weimar. 1914–28
„ „ Die Deutsche Bibel. B4, 5. la8°. Weimar. 1914–23
„ „ Tischreden. B5, 6. la8°. Weimar. 1919–23
CATECHISMS [*in chronolog. order; see also* TRANS. & REFERENCES].
Catechismus, lectu digniss., latinus factus per V. Obsopœum. Adjecti sunt alii quoque gemini Catechismi J. Brentii, eodem interprete. s8°. Hagonæ [*J. Secerius*]. 1529
Deudsch Catechismus. s4°. Wittemberg, *G. Rhaw*. 1529
Parvus Catechismus pro pueris in schola. s8°. Ratisponæ, *I. Khol. n.d.* [c. 1530]
Parvus catechismus pro pueris in schola. s8°. [Vuittebergae]. 1531
Catechismus minor pro trivialibus scholis latinitate donatus &c. s8°. Norimbergæ, *F. Peypus*. 1532
Enchiridion. Der kleine Catechismus für die gemeine Pfarherrn u. Prediger. s8°. L. [1566]
Catechesis M. L. parva. Gręcolatina. Accesserunt sententię aliquot Patrū Graecolat.: Narrationes item Apocryphae de Christo, Maria, &c. His adj. Prochori de Joanne theologo & evangelista hist.: Omnia Graecolat. descr. & ed. studio M. Neandri. s8°. Basileae. [1567]
Catechesis minor, Germanice, Latine, Graece & Ebraice edita studio & opera J. Claii. s8°. Wittebergæ. 1572
Catechismus minor M. L. [*Latin & Icelandic*]. s8°. Hoolum. 1708
Emblemat. Catechismus. s8°. Augspurg. 1713
Katechismus. Mit e. Erkl. u. 72 Lieder; [hrsg.] v. J. G. Herder. s8°. Halle. [1809]
Kleiner Katechismus. Erkl. v. K. H. Caspari. s8°. Erlanger. 1856
Catechism for the people, pastor & preacher. Reprod. of ed. pr. at Frankfort-on-Main, 1553. Ed. W. H. Rylands. [Holbein Soc.] fol. 1892
Die beiden Katechismen M. L. in Zusammenhang. Hrsg. O. Müller. 8°. Gotha. 1901
Kleiner Katechismus nach d. ältest. A. in hochdeut., niederdeut. u. lat. Sprache. Ed. &c. K. Knoke. obl.8°. Halle a. S. 1904
Grosser Katechismus. Textausgabe &c. Einleit. v. J. Meyer. [Quellenschr. z. Gesch. d. Prot., H12]. 8°. L. 1914
TISCHREDEN.
Colloquia oder Tischreden. Gemehret durch Y. Aurifabern. fol. Franckfurt am Mayn. 1574
This ed. has at the end Propheceyung M. L. Zur erinnerung &c. zur Christl. Busse &c. zusamen getragen d. G. Walther, 1573, *w. no pagin.*
SINGLE WORKS &c. [*Lat. & Germ.*]
Acht Sermon. M. L. von im geprediget zů wittemberg, v. d. Messen, Bildnussen &c. [P2539]. s4°. Wittemberg. 1523
Acta & res gestae D. M. L. in Comitijs Principū Vuormaciæ a. 1521 [*w. portrait after Cranach*]. s4°. *n.p.* [1521]
Acta F. M. L. apud Dominū Legatum Apostolicum Augustæ. s4°. [Wittenberg? 1518?]
Ad Schedulam inhibitiōis sub nomine Episcopi Misneñ ed. sup sermone de Sacramento Eucharistie M. L. Responsio. [*With the* Schedula, 24 Jan. 1520]. s4°. [Wittenberg? 1520]
Adversus execrabilem Antichristi bullam. s4°. Wittembergae [*M. Lotther*]. 1520
An den Christl. Adel deut. Nation: v. d. Christl. standes besserung. [*sig. A–M3, foll. by* Hie nach volget so Doctor M. L. jüngst gemacht hat &c. sig. K. *n.p. n.d.*] s4°. Wittenberg. [1520]
„ „ Bearb. &c. v. K. Benrath. [Verein f. Ref.-gesch. Schr., Jhrg. 1, Nr. 4]. 8°. Halle. 1884
An d. durchleuchtigen Hochgebornen Fürsten &c. Albrechten, Marggraffen zu Brandenburg &c. Ein Sendbrieff. s4°. Wittemberg [*N. Schirlentz*]. 1532
An d. herren Deütschs Ordens: das sye falsche keüschheit meyden, &c. ermanung. s4°. Wittemberg. 1524
Antwort deitsch M. L. auff König Heynrichs v. Engelland büch. s4°. [Wittenberg. 1522]
Appellatio F. M. L. ad Concilium [*b. w. h.* Acta, 1518]. s4°. [Wittenberg? 1518?]
Appelation [L.] odder beruffung an ain Christl. frei Conciliū v. d. Bapst Leo. Wittembergk M.D.XX. s4°. [Eilenburg? 1520]
Articuli qui exhibendi fuerant in Concilio Mantuae &c. [Articuli Smalcald. &c.] s8°. Vitebergae. 1579
Assertio omnium articul. M. L. per Bullam Leonis X noviss. damnatorum. s4°. *n.p.* [1521]
Auff das Vermeint Keiserlich Edict, Ausgangen im 1531 jare, nach d. Reichstage d. 1530. Glosa. s4°. Wittemberg [*N. Schirlentz*]. 1531
Auff des konigs zu Engelland lester schrifft Titel, M. L. Antwort. s4°. [Wittemberg]. 1527
Auserl. erbaul. kleine Schriften, mit Einleit. dargelegt von J. J. Rambach. s8°. 1743
Auslegung d. Episteln u. Evangelien v. Advent bis auff Ostern. Anderweit corr. durch M. L. s4°. [Magdeburg, *M. Lotther*]. 1532
Ein Brieff an den Card. Ertzbisschoff zu Mentz. s4°. [Nuremberg? 1530?]

Luther (Martin) [*continued*].
SINGLE WORKS &c. [*continued*].
Christ-Luther. Unterredung ü. J. Deutschmanns Tractat, Der Christ-Luther. Kirchen Prediger Beichte &c. Vorred P. J. Speners. s4°. Franckfurt a. M. 1699
Ein Christl. Urtheyl M. L. v. s. eygen Büchern. Sampt e. Unterricht, was darzu gehöre wenn man in d. heil. Schr. recht studien &c. will. s4°. [Strassburg. 1578]
Confessiones fidei duæ, altera M. Lutheri, altera I. Bugenhagii denuo recogn. & latinæ ed. s8°. Vitebergae. 1539
Contra Henricum regem Angliæ. [*Border to tp. by L. Cranach?*]. s4°. Wittembergae. 1522
Contra malignum Iohannis Eccii judicium, super aliquot articulis, a fratribus quibusdam ei suppositis, Martini Lutheri defensio &c. [P2444]. s4°. *n.p.* [Leipzig, *M. Lotter*. 1519?]
Corpus librorum M. L. & aliorum praecipuorum in eccl. Vuiteberg., de verbis Domini, Hoc est corpus meum &c. [Ed. H. Boyer]. fol. Ursel. 1563
Das eyn Christliche versammlung odder gemeyne recht &c. habe, alle lere tzu urteylen &c., Grund u. ursach aus der schrifft. M. L. [*8 leaves; tp. wanting.* P2539]. s4°. [Wittemberg? 1523]
Das Jhesus Christus eyn geborner Jude sey. [*Decor. border to tp.* P2539]. s4°. Wittemberg. 1523
De abroganda Missa privata M. L. sententia. [*Decor. border dated 1519*]. s4° *n.p. n.d.* [1522?]
43 leaves, sig. A–L3 in fours.
De bonis operibus liber. Denuo recogn. [*Border to tp. by L. Cranach*]. s4°. Vvittembergae [*Johann Grunenberg*]. 1521
De captivitate Babylonica eccl. praeludium M. L. [*40 leaves; sig. a–k. Portrait by Cranach on a1 verso*]. s4°. *n.p.* [1520]
„ „ [*a. issue. sig. A–L. no portrait*]. s4°. Vuittembergae. *n.d.* [1520]
De constituendis scholis liber donatus Latin. [*Pref. by Melanchthon*]. s8°. Hagoniæ, *J. Secerius. n.d.*
De libertate Xtn. Cum notis, præs. P. Antonio, sistit M. Heise. [P2629]. s4°. Halae Magdeb. 1706
De servo arbitrio M. L. ad Erasmū. Acc. insuper index &c. [*b. w.* Erasmus (D.) De libero arbitrio, 1524]. s8°. [Augustæ Vindelic. 1526]
De votis monasticis M. Lutheri iudicium. s4°. Vvittembergae. [1521]
*Deutsche Messe u. Ordnūg Gotes diensts, zu Wittemberg fürgenomen. [Vorrede M. Luther]. s4°. *n.p.* 1526
Deuttung d. Munchikalbs czu Freyberg M. L., *see* MELANCHTHON (P.) Deuttung d. czwo grewl. Figuren, 1523.
Disputatio, pro declar. virtutis indulgentiarum, 1517, *see* Theses *below.*
Die drey Symbola oder Bekentnis des glaubens Christi inn der kirchen eintrechtig gebraucht. [*Decor. border to tp.*] s4°. Wittemberg [*J. Weis*]. 1538
Duo M. L. fragmenta. 1, Ad J. Reuchlini, De arte caballistica lib. 3, 1517. 2, Ad Erasmi Adnot. in Nov. Test., 1516. Collegit & ed. J. Justus von Einem. [P442]. s4°. Helmaestadii. 1730
Ein einfeltige weise zu Beten, fur einen guten freund. s4°. [Wittemberg, *Hans Lufft*]. 1535
Epistola Lutheriana ad Leonem X. Diss. de libertate christiana per autorem recog. Wittenbergae. s4°. *n.p.* [Basel, *A. Petri?* 1521]
Epistolas 8 ex autographis rec. C. G. Schwarzius. s4°. Altorfii. 1740
Erbieten. s4°. [Wittenberg? 1521?]
[*Two leaves: Title pr. in 3 lines, without border*].
Etliche warhafftige weissagung, u. fürneme spruche d. Doctor M. Luthers durch I. Amsterdamum zusamengebracht. [P2441]. s4°. Magdeburgk. 1552
Exempel einen rechten Christlichen Bischoff [*N. v. Amsdorf*] zu weihen. Geschehen zu Neumburg a. 1542, 20. Ian. D. M. L. s4°. Wittemberg. [1542]
Fünff schoner Christl. Sermon gepred. durch M. L. zu Wittemberg. 1523. Jare. [*Portrait on back of tp.* P2539]. s4°. [Wittemberg?]. 1523
Geistl. Lieder. Mit e. n. Vorrede M. L. [*Foll. by* Psalmen u geistl. Lieder &c. *pagin. contin.*] s8°. L. 1560
Geistl. Lieder mit Singweisen. Hrsg. P. Wackernagel. n. A. 8°. St. 185[illegible]
Hertzog Georg zů Sachszen M. L. Sendbrieff. Auch Antwort &c. s4°. [Wittenberg?] 152[illegible]
In Cantica Canticorum, brevis enarratio. s8°. Wittenbergæ. *I. Luft.* 1539
In epistolam S. Pauli ad Galatas comm. ex praelectione M. L. coll. [*2 pagin.*] s8°. Vitebergae, [*J. Luft*]. 153[illegible]
Iudicium M. Lutheri, de Erasmo. P. Melanchthonis de Erasmo & Luthero elogion. Ratio discendi per eundem tradita. Eiusdem, Quo judicio Augustinus ac reliqui doctores legendi sint. D. M. Lutheri ad W. F. Capitonem epist. s4°. *n.p.* [1522?
Judicium M. L. de votis, scr. ad episc. &c. Vuittembergeñ. Eccl. s4°. Vuittembergae. [1521
Die kleine antwort auff H[erzog] Georgen nehestes buch. s4°. Wittemberg [*H. Lufft*]. 153[illegible]
Kurtz bekentnis L., vom heiligen Sacrament. s4°. Wittenberg, *Hans Lufft*. 154[illegible]

Luther (Martin) [*continued*].
SINGLE WORKS &c. [*continued*].
Eine kurtze vnderweysung wie man bychtē sol. s4°. Basel, *Adam Petri*. 1519
Die letzte Predigt D. M. L. zu Wittenberg den xvij. Januarii 1549. [Rom. xii. *Ed. w. pref. by S. Tucher*]. s4°. *n.p.* 1549
Loci communes ex scriptis ipsius latinis forma Gnomologica & Aphoristica coll. &c. à T. Fabricio. s4°. Magdeburgi. 1594
Passio oder das leiden Jhesu Christi: gepred. durch M. L. Auch ain Sermon uber d. Evangelium Luce an d. 18. Von d. Gleychssner u. Zölner. [*Portrait on back of tp.* P2539]. s4°. Wittemberg. *n.d.* [1522]
Ein predig M. L., das man kinder zur Schůlen halten solle. s4°. *n.p.* 1530
Eine Predigt. D. M. L. Das man Kinder zur Schulen halten solle. [*a. ed. w. different pref. & decor. border to tp.*] s4°. Wittemberg, [*N. Schirlentz*]. 1541
Ein predig v. d. betrachtung d. heil. lyden Christi. [*Decor. border & woodcut on tp.*] s4°. [Basel, *Adam Petri*, 1519]
Ein Predigt v. d. Engeln. s4°. Wittemberg [*H. Lufft*]. 1535
Eine predigt D. M. L., newlich zu Leiptzig gethan. s4°. Wittemberg. 1545
Resolutio Lutheriana super propositione decia tertia: de potestate pape: per autorē locupletata. [P2444]. s4°. [Lipsiæ, *Melchior Lottherus*]. 1519
Resolutiones Lutheriane super propositionibus suis Lipsiae disputatis. [*w. the 13 Propositions & epistle addr. to Georgius Spalatinus.* P2444]. s4°. Lipsiae, *ex aedibus Vuolffgangi monacensis*]. 1519
Die Schmalkald Artikel, 1537, nach L.'s Autograph &c. Hrsg. K. Zangemeister. 4°. Heidelberg. 1883
Sententia M. Luth. de adiaphoris ex scriptis illius coll. per J. Westphalum. s8°. *n.p.* 1549
Sermo de digna praeparatione cordis suscipiendo Sacramēto Eucharistiae. s4°. [Wittenburgii, *Joh. Grunenberg*. 1519]
Sermo de meditatione Dominicę Passionis in lat. versus. [*woodcut on tp*]. s4°. Wittembergę. 1521
Sermo de penitentia. s4°. [Augustę, *in edibus S. Otmar*. 1518 ?]
Ornamental border on tp. Six leaves sig. A1–6.
„ „ *a. ed. w. woodcuts in border & centre of tp.* s4°. *n.p. n.d.* [1518 ?]
Ain Sermon, Am pfingstag dz evāgelium Joa. xiiij. [P2539]. s4°. Wittemberg. *n.d.* [1522]
Ain sermō. Am Sontag nach d. auffart des herren Jesu daz Evangelium Joha. am xv. Wañ da koñen wirt der tröster den ich senden wird. [P2539]. s4°. *n.p. n.d.* [Augsburg. 1522 ?]
Ein Sermon oder Predig von d. ablass u. gnade. s4°. *n.p.* [1518]
Ain Sermon. Secundū Lucam am 16. vō dem verdampten reyche man, Uñ des seligē armen Lazaro kürtzlich gepred. zů Witten. 1522. [*A garbled version*]. s4°. [Augsburg ? 1523 ?]
Ein Sermon [*on Matt. ix. 1–8*] v. Christlicher gerechtigkeit, gepredigt zu Marpurg, 1528. [Vorrede N. Galli]. s4°. Regenspurg, *Hans Khol*. 1554
Ain Sermon v. d. hochwirdigen Sacrament. Und v. d. Bruderschaffteu. s4°. [Augspurg, *S. Ottmar*. 1520]
Large Woodcut of the Eucharist on tp. Thirteen leaves A–C in fours+1 leaf.
Ain Sermō v. d. unrechten Mammon Luce am xvi. [*w. portrait by Cranach*]. s4°. [Wittenberg ? 1522]
Das tauff buchlin verdeutscht durch M. L. [*Altered by L. f. Ch. of Rome service. Decor. border to tp.* Sig. A–C4. C4 *blank*]. s4°. Vuittemberg [*N. Schirlentz*]. 1523
„ „ [*a. ed. w. woodcut on tp. & at end. Decor. border to dedic. on fol. B4.* Sig. A–C2. P2539]. s4°. Vuittemberg [*Erfurt pr* ?]. 1523
[*Theses*]. Disputatio, pro declaratione virtutis Indulgentiarum. 8°. [Wittenberg ? 1517]
Theses [*broadsheet*], 1517 (*facs.*), *see* FREYTAG (G.) Bilder, B3, T1, 1924.
Theses adv. Indulgentias &c. 1517. Ed. 2ª. [P442]. s4°. Vitembergae. [1717]
L.'s 95 Thesen samt s. Resolutionen sowie d. Gegenschr. v. Wimpina-Tetzel, Eck u. Prierias u. d. Antworten L.'s daruf. Krit. A. v. W. Köhler. 8°. L. 1903
95 Thesen nebst d. Sermon v. Ablass u. Gnade, 1517 &c., *see* KLEINE TEXTE, T142, 1917.
Der thewre schöne Spruch Mosi, Gene. XV. Abraham gleubete d. Herrn &c. Verdeudscht durch A. Otho. s4°. [Northausen ? 1552]
Trostunge an die Christen zu Halle uber Er Georgen [Winckler] yhres predigers tod. s4°. Wittemberg, *H. Lufft*. 1527
Fourteen leaves; sig. A–D2 in fours.
Uber d. Erst Buch Mose predigete M. L. sampt eyner vnderricht wie Moses zu leren ist. [*With text*]. s4°. *n.p.* [Wittemberg ?] 1527
Ein unterrichtūg wie sich d. Christen in Mosen sollen schicken. s8°. Wittemberg. 1526
Ursach u. anttwortt das iunkgfrawē Kloster gotlich vlassen mugē. [P2539]. s4°. Wittemberg. 1523
Vermanūg an die geistlichen versamlet auff d. Reychsstage zů Augspurg a. 1530. s4°. [Nürmberg, *Georg Wachter*. 1530]

Luther (Martin) [*continued*].
SINGLE WORKS &c. [*continued*].
Vom Kriege wider die Türcken. s4°. *n.p.* [Wittenberg, *H. Weiss* ?]. 1529
Von anbeten des Sacraments, des hailigen leichnams Christi. [*Woodcut on tp.*] s4°. *n.p.* 1523
Von bayder gestalt des Sacraments zunehmen: und ander neüerūg. D. M. L.'s maynūg. Vuittemberg. s4°. [Nuremberg ? 1522]
17 leaves, sig. A–C in fours; D1–2; E1–3.
Von d. Freyheyt eyniss Christen menschen. s4°. Vuittembergae. 1520
„ „ (1520, *facs.*), *see* FREYTAG (G.) Bilder, B3, T1, 1924.
Von d. grewel der Stilmesse, so man den Canon nennet. s4°. Wittenberg. 1525
Von d. newen Eckischenn Bullen vnd lugen. s4°. Vuittemberg. [1520]
Von d. winckelmesse u. Pfaffen Weihe. s4°. Wittenberg [*N. Schirlentz*]. 1533
Von ordenung gottis dienst yñ der gemeyne. [P2539]. s4°. Wittemberg. 1523
Warum des Bapsts und seyner Jungerñ bucher von D. M. L. vorbrāt seynñ. Lass auch anczeygen wer do will warumb sie D. M. L. bucher verbrennet habeñ. s4°. Wittembergk. 1520
Ein weyse Christlich Mess zu halten vñ zum tisch Gottis zu gehen. [*Tr. by* P. Speratus]. s4°. Wyttemberg. 1524
Widder d. Bullen des Endchrists: D. M. L. s4°. Vuittembergk. 1520
Widder d. Verkerer u. felscher Keyserlichs mandats. [P2539]. s4°. *n.p.* 1523
4 leaves, last page blank. Decor. border to tp.]
Wider d. Bapstum zu Rom vom Teuffel gestifft. [*Foll. by 2 plates:* Papa agit gratias *&* Papa dat concilium &c.] s4°. Wittemberg, *H. Lufft*. 1545
Wie sich M. Luther u. H. Zwinglin In d. Sum Christlicher Leer, gleichförmig ze sein, befundē habē, Uff dem gesprech zu Marpurg in Hessen Jüngst gehalten. s4°. *n.p.* 1529
Zwo predigt auff 1. Thess. 4. D. M. L. gethan vber d. leiche d. Chürfursten Hertzog Friderichs zu Sachsen. Item, eyne tröstunge an Chürfursten v. Sacksen gedechtnis &c. [*Tr.*] Georgius Spalatinus. s4°. *n.p.* 1525
Zwo Predigt uber d. Leiche d. Kürfursten-Hertzog Johann zu Sachssen. s4°. Wittemberg [*N. Schirlentz*]. 1532
TRANSLATIONS.
A la noblesse chrét. de la nation allem. t. la réform. de la chrétienté. [Tr.] Notice hist. par F. Kuhn. s8°. 1879
[Catechism; tr. into Arabic by S. Negri; ed. J. H. Callenberg]. s8°. [Halle ?] *n.d.*
Comm. on Galatians. Added life of the a. &c. by E. Middleton. Tr. 8°. 1807
„ „ Pref., Life by E. Middleton. new ed. rev. 8°. 1836
„ „ With life &c. by E. Middleton. n. ed. corr. 8°. 1864
Hymns of the Reformation. Added life by P. Melancthon, by [H. J. Fry]. s8°. 1845
Le livre de la liberté chrét., avec l'épitre dédic. au pape Léon X. [Tr.] Notice hist. par F. Kuhn. s8°. 1879
On the bondage of the will. wr. in ans. to Erasmus on free-will. Tr. H. Cole. 8°. 1823
Spiritual songs; f. the German, by J. Hunt. s8°. 1853
Table talk. Tr. by W. Hazlitt. n. ed., add. Life of M. L. by A. Chalmers &c. s8°. *Bohn*. 1857
REFERENCES.
see ADAMUS (M.) The life & death of M. L.; Eng. by T. Hayne, 1641.
„ ADRIAN VI, *pope*. Eyn Bepstl. Breve d. radt czu Bamberg gesand widder d. L., 1523.
„ —— Breve ad Fridericum adv. L., 1523.
„ —— Legatio A. VI ad Conventum Nuremberg, 1522; [*pref. by L.*], 1538.
„ ALBERT (F. R.) Briefwechsel H. v. Einsiedel mit L. &c., 1908.
„ ALBRECHT (O.) L.'s Katechismen, 1915.
„ ALLEN (J. W.) Polit. conceptions of L., 1924.
„ ANDREÆ (J.) Collatio cathol. &c.; repetitio doct. L., 1582.
„ ANTON (A.) De Pathmo L. in arce Warteburg: animadv. adv. Card. Pallavicinum, ed. 5ª, 1710; ed. nov., 1730.
„ BAIER (J. W.), *the elder*. Diss. qua dialogi Erbermanni ani inter L. & Arium excut., 1673.
„ BAIER (J. W.), *the younger*. De informatione catechetica aphorismi, ad praef. catech. L., 1698.
„ BALDUIN (F.) De disput. L. cum diabolo in controv. de priv. missâ, 1605.
„ —— Hyperaspistes Lutheri &c., 1603.
„ BAUER (C.) L. u. d. Papst, 1910.
„ BAUMGARTEN (S. J.) Erläut. d. klein. Catechismi M. L., 1764.
„ BECK (M.) Versio Lutheri vindicata, 1696–8.
„ BEHR (J. A.) Catechismus: das ist d. durch Bilder erklärte Cat., 1718.
„ BENRATH (C.) L. im Kloster, 1505–25, 1905.
„ BERBIG (G.) G. Spalatin u. s. Verhältnis zu M. L. auf Grund i. Briefwechsels 1525, 1906.
„ BERGER (A. E.) M. L. in kultur. Darstellung, 3T, 1895–1921.

Luther (Martin) [*continued*].
REFERENCES [*continued*].
see BERNHARD (G. F.) Diarium oder Tag-Register, Zeit d. Auffenthalts M. L. auf Coburg, 1530, 1730.
,, BERNHARDT (E.) Wie L. beruhiget u. tröstet, 1831.
,, BERNHOLD (J. B.) De charact. pseudoprophet. in M. L., 1731.
,, BIBLIANDER (T.) De mysteriis salutiferae passionis &c. Iesu ; adj. M. L. oratio de reform. eccl., 1551.
,, BÖHMER (H.) L. im Lichte d. neu Forsch., 1906 ; 5e A., 1918.
,, —— L.'s erste Vorlesung, 1924.
,, BOYSEN (P. A.) Diss. de cod. Gr. N.T. & consilio quo usus est L., 1723.
,, BRANDENBURG (E.) & G. EBERLEIN. Vorträge [L.'s Anschauung v. Staate u. d. Gesellschaft], 1901.
,, BRAUNSCHWEIG. *Bekenntnisse v. d. Sacramente d. lives unde blodes Christi, 1534.
,, BRÜSTLEIN (J.) L.'s Einfl. auf d. Volksschulwesen &c., 1852.
,, BUCER (M.) Præf. in 4. tomum Postillae Lutheranæ, 1527.
,, BÜDDEMANN (B. H.) Ἱστορούμενα de Reformat. L. minist. instit., 1717.
,, CAROLUS (A. D.) De relig. L., 1685.
,, CAZAL (G.) De quadripertita justitia libri 3, L. &c. opiniones, 1563.
,, CHÂTEILLON (S.) De haereticis an sint perseq. Luteri &c. sententiae, 1554.
,, CHLADENIUS (M.) Jubilaea [L.], 1718.
,, COCHLÆUS (J.) Adv. latrocinantes & raptorias cohortes Rusticorum : M. L. &c., 1525 ?
,, —— Articuli. CCCCC. M. L. &c., 1526.
,, —— Comm. de actis & scriptis M. L. &c., 1549.
,, —— Ex compendio act. M. L. caput ult. &c., 1548.
,, —— Hist. de actis & scr. M. L. &c., 1565.
,, —— Wie verkerlich widder Georgen, Hertzogen zu Sachssen &c. M. L. den sibenden Psalm verdewtzscht, &c., 1529.
,, DIETERICH (J.) Discursus de actis Colloquii Marpurg. &c., 1627.
,, DOELSCHIUS (J.) Contra doctrinalem &c., pro M. L., 1525.
,, ECK (J. v.) Christenl. erhaltung wider L., 1530.
,, —— Disputatio J. E. & M. Lutheri in studio Lipsensi &c., 1519.
,, —— Des heil. Concilij tzu Costenitz entschuld., in M. L. &c., 1520.
,, —— M. L.'s Underricht an Kurfursten von Sachssen &c., 1519.
,, —— Prima (*&* secunda) pars op. contra L., 1530–1.
,, ECKHARD (P. J.) Vindiciae L. & Melanchthonis, 1738.
,, EGRANUS (J. S.) Apolog. resp. contra dogmata [*dedic. by* M. Eleutherius, *i.e.* L.], 1518.
,, EMPSYCHOVIUS (H.) Demonstratio Lutherum idem docuisse &c., 1617.
,, EMSER (H.) Annotat. uber L.'s naw Test., 1524 ; 29.
,, ERASMUS (D.) Contenta in hoc libello E. R. epist. ad Ducē Fridericū, positiones M. L. &c., 1519 ?.
,, —— Hyperaspistes diatribæ adv. Servum arbitrium M. L., 1526.
,, ERDMANN (D.) L. u. s. Beziehungen zu Schlesien, insbes. zu Breslau, 1887.
,, EXUSTIO. *Exustionis antichristianorum decretalium acta, 1521.
,, FABRICIUS (J. A.) Centifolium Lutheranum, sive notitia script. de L., 1728.
,, FECHT (J.) Diss. de versione L. Germ., 1709.
,, FEUERLEIN (J. W.) Bibl. symbolica evang. lutherana, 1752 ; aucta, 2p, 1768.
,, FICKER (J.) L., 1516 : Rede, 1918.
,, FISHER (*card.* J.) Assert. Lutheranae confut., 1525.
,, —— Defensio Regie assert. cōtra Babylonicam captivitatē [*of L.*], 1525.
,, —— Sacri sacerdotii defensio contra L., 1525.
,, FÖRER (L.) Septem characteres M. L. &c., 1626.
,, FORIS (F.) Examen Reformationis L. &c., 1696.
,, FÖRSTER (J.) Vindiciae L., 1609.
,, FRANCK (C. F.) Imag. ingen. morumq. L. &c., 1789.
,, FRÖBING (J. C.) Lutherus ; seu hist. Ref., 1811.
,, GASPARIN (*le cte.* A. DE). L. & la Réf., 1873.
,, GERBER (J.) De Latinitate L. oratio, 1754.
,, GESANGBUCH. *Neue (Das) verm. Deutsche u. Wend. Gesangbuch, M. L. u. a. Gesänge, 1719.
,, GESNER (S.) Orthodoxa confess. de persona &c. Jesu Chr., extr. ex Dei Verbo, & L. &c. testimoniis, 1604.
,, GIESE (G. C.) Hist. Nachr. v. d. Bibelübers. M. L., 1771.
,, GÖRING (A.) M. L. quae classica Graec. Latinorumque scripta commendavit tractanda, &c., 1817.
,, GÖTZE (G. H.) De domesticis L., 1707.
,, —— De reliquiis L., 1703.
,, —— Diss. : L.'s Schuhe sind nicht allen Dorf-Priestern gerecht, 1750.
,, GÖZ (J. A.) Gesch.-lit. Überblick ü. L.'s Vorschule &c., 1824.
,, GÖZE (J. M.) Vergleich. d. Orig.-Ausg. d. Uebers. d. heil. Schr. v. L., 1517–45 &c., 1777–9.
,, GREFIUS (N.) L. reformator, 1650.
,, GRETSER (J.) De jure & more prohib. libros &c., examen libelli M. L. &c., 1603.

Luther (Martin) [*continued*].
REFERENCES [*continued*].
see HAMBACH (J. N.) Diatr. de orig. perverse sentiendi licentiae ex Bibl. vers. M. L., 1749.
,, HAMBURG : STAATS-U. UNIV.-BIBL. Die deut. Bibel : Ausstell. z. Jubelfeier d. Luth. N.T., 1522, 1922.
,, HÄNTZSCHEL (J. G.) Medit. de theopneustia L., 1732.
,, HARDT (H. V. DER). Oratio de fontium Hebr. interp. L., 1690.
,, HARNACK (C. G. A. v.) M. L. u. d. Grundlegung d. Reform., 1928.
,, HEBENSTREIT (J. B.) Panegyricon pro jubilæo seculari L., 1617.
,, HEIDELBERG CATECHISM. Catechismus, item M. L. meynung v. Brodtbrechen &c., 1596.
,, HELMSTADT. ACAD. JULIA. Progr. de invictis L., 1717.
,, HENRY VIII, *k. of Eng.* Ad Saxoniae principes de coercenda &c. Lutherana factione & L. ipso epist., 1523.
,, —— Assertio septem sacrament. adv. M. L., 1521.
,, HERBORN. Trewhertzige &c. Warnung v. d. zu Herborn nachgedr. Bibel M. L., 1598.
,, HERRNSCHMID (J. J.) Comm. hist. de vita M. L., 1742.
,, HERTZBERGER (A. O.) Etliche Propheceysprüche M. L. &c., 1552.
,, HIRTZWIG (H.) Lutherus : drama, 1617.
,, HORWEIN (J. T.) Diss. de vaticiniis & de v. L., 1755.
,, HOYNOVIUS (D.) Exercit. de causis, quibus impulsus L. &c., 1695.
,, JACOBI (J. A.) Eichenlaub auf Luther's Grab gestreut, 1818.
,, JANI (J. H.) Comm. de L. Biblici stud. instauratore, 1730.
,, JÄNICHEN (J. C.) Caussas a L. susceptae Reform. exhib. J., 1755.
,, JONAS (J.) & M. CAELIUS. Vom Christl. Abschied M. L. &c., 1546.
,, JUNCKER (C.) Das guldene &c. Ehren-Gedächtniss M. L., 1706.
,, KALKOFF (P.) Erasmus, L. & Fried. d. Weise, 1919.
,, —— L. u. d. Entscheidungsjahre d. Ref., 1917.
,, KAWERAU (G.) L. in kath. Beleuchtung : Glossen zu H. Grisars L., 1911.
,, —— L.'s Gedanken ü. d. Krieg, 1916.
,, —— L.'s Schr. nach d. Reihenfolge d. Jahre verzeichnet &c., 1917.
,, KEIL (F. S.) M. L.'s merkwürd. Lebens-Umstände &c., 4T, 1764.
,, KETTNER (F. E.) Hist. dicti Joh. de Trinitate, cum apol. L., 1713.
,, KIRCHMAIER (G. W.) Oratio de M. L. oraculo : Bellum Smalcaldicum &c., 1755.
,, KIRCHNER (T.) Thesaurus explic. omnium articul. &c. ; ex M. L. operibus coll., 1566.
,, KÖHLER (W. E.) L. u. d. Lüge, 1912.
,, —— L.'s Schr. An d. christl. Adel deut. Nation, 1895.
,, —— Wie L. d. Deutschen d. Leben Jesu erzählt hat, 1917.
,, KOLDE (T.) L. u. d. Reichstag zu Worms, 1521, 1883.
,, KOLLIN (C.) Eversio L. Epithalamii, 1527.
,, KOTZDE (W.) Die Wittenbergisch Nachtigall (*fiction*), 5e A., 1924.
,, KRAFFT (J. M.) Hist. Nachr. v. d. 1534 bey H. Lufften hrsg. u. gedr. verdeut. Bibel M. L., 1735.
,, KRAUSE (J. F.) Quaeritur utrum &c. theologi recent. qui omnem script. sacrae interpret. ad rationem revocent a L. mente defec., 1817.
,, KREHL (A. L. G.) Praef. de doctoratu L., 1846.
,, LANGE (J.) Disput. de indulgentiis, qua M. L. theses 95 illust., 1718.
,, LANGENSEE (A.) Judicium L. de Ecclesia Rom. vindic., 1717.
,, LANGIUS (J.) Oratio : encomium theolog. disput. I. Eckii, A. Carolstadii & M. L. &c., 1519.
,, LENGENBRUNNER (J.) Erinnerung, M. L., s. Lehr &c., 1576.
,, LENZ (M.) Kl. hist. Schr., B1, v. L. z. Bismarck, 1920.
,, —— L.'s Tat in Worms, 1921.
,, LESSING (J. G.) Vindic. Reform. L., 1717.
,, LIEBKNECHT (J. G.) Orat. de L. &c., 1717.
,, LINGKE (J. T.) M. L.'s merkwürdige Reisegesch., 1769.
,, LIPSIUS (R. A.) L.'s Lehre v. d. Busse, 1892.
,, LOCHNER (C. M.) De M. L., 1730.
,, LÜDERS (G.) De progressu emend. per L. relig., 1717.
,, LYRA (J. W.) L.'s Deut. Messe u. Ordnung in i. liturg. u. musikal. Bestandteilen, 1904.
,, MACKINNON (J.) L. & the Reformation, v1, 2, 1925–28.
,, MANN (C.) Wie &c. ist L. der grosse Bibel-Uebersetzer geworden ?, 1835.
,, MARITAIN (J.) 3 réformateurs : L. &c., 1925.
,, MARSCHALCK (H.) V. d. Namen L. wz er bedeut &c., 1523.
,, MATTHESIUS (J.) Hist. v. M. L. anfang, lehr &c., 1564.
,, MAYER (J. F.) Eccl. papaea Lutheranae reform. patrona, 1698.
,, —— Triga diss., De pontificiis adv. L. &c., 1707.
,, MECHLER (Æ.) Catechismus &c., 1574.
,, MELANCHTHON (P.) De disput. inter M. & L. super justific. [1536], 1783.

Luther (Martin) [*continued*].
REFERENCES [*continued*].
see MELANCHTHON (P.) Didymi Faventini adv. T. Placentinum pro M. L. oratio, 1521.
„ —— Hist. de vita & actis M. L., 1548; 1557.
„ —— M.-Kompend.: Samml. Lehrsätze M. in L.'s Werken; hrsg. J. Haussleiter, 1902.
„ —— Oratio ü. d. Leich M. L.; verdeutscht durch C. Creutziger, 1546.
„ —— Vita M. L., ed. 2a, 1746.
„ MEYDERLIN (P.) Evang. Luther. Cathol. Ætern.: Klare Beweisung &c., 1621.
„ MÖHRING (G. V.) De primordiis emend. per L. relig., 1708.
„ MÖLLER (J. G.) D. L. ut confess. in Comitiis Wormat. 1521 conspic., 1693.
„ —— D. L. ut martyrem in persecut. illust., 1693.
„ MORE (*Sir* T.) Latina opera (Resp. ad epist. Lutheri &c.), 1566.
„ MOSELLANUS (P.) Strena Lips. vel eulog. Lutheri Lipsia papisticum, 1609.
„ MÜLLER (C.) L. ü. d. Recht d. bewaffn. Widerstandes gegen d. Kaiser, 1915.
„ NEUMANN (J. G.) Orationes 2, 1, De nummo aureo quo L. Carolostadium ad certamen provoc. perhibetur, 1692.
„ NEUMAYR (F.) Frag: ob. L. nicht besser gethan hätte, wann er d. Fastnacht hätte abgeschafft &c.?, 1757.
„ *NICHTS neues, e. Schmehkarte ü. L. Rand-Glösslein Gen. iv, 1, 1693?.
„ OECOLAMPADIUS (I.) Urtayl u. maynung &c., 1521.
„ —— Die verdeutscht antwort, der, die Eck in s. Sendbrieff an d. Bischoff zu Meyssen hat die ungelarten L. Thumhern genandt, 1520.
„ PALM (J. G.) Hist. d. deut. Bibelübers. L., 1517–34, 1772.
„ PANZER (G. W.) Zusätze zu s. Entwurf e. Gesch. d. deut. Bibelübers. M. L., 1517–81, 1791.
„ PARIS. *Confut. determin. doctorū Parrhis. contra M. L., 1523.
„ PEUCER (D.) De epist. L. de interpret. comm., 1736.
„ PFEFFERKORN (G. M.) Etl. Lutheraner &c. Urtheile v. L., 4e A., 1730.
„ PREGITZER (G. C.) M. L. de univ. eccl. optime merit. &c., 1720.
„ RAITHIUS (B.) Vindiciae vers. S. Bibl. Germ. M. L. labore ed., 1676.
„ RAM (P. F. X. DE). Disq. hist. de iis quae contra L. Lovan. theologi egerunt a.1519, 1843.
„ REINHARD (L.) Comm. de vita J. Jonae & M. L., 1731.
„ RICHTER (J. G.) Sing. M. L. de matrimonio sentent., 1752.
„ RISCH (A.) L.'s Bibelverdeutschung, 1922.
„ RÖBER (P.) & J. STEGMANN. Disput. de indulg. pontif.: Propos. quas 1517 promulg. M. L., 1702.
„ ROGGE (C.) L. u. d. Kirchenbilder, 1912.
„ ROSSEEUW ST. HILAIRE (E. F. A.) Études (L. &c.), 1863.
„ ROST (F. W. E.) De div. spiritu eorum quae L. &c. fecerunt, 1817.
„ SAGITTARIUS (C.) Diss. pro doct. L. de missa &c., 1684.
„ SALMON (G.) M. L.: sermon, 2nd ed., 1883.
„ SCHALLER (F.) Exam. scrupulorum circa L. Jubiléum, 1630, 1631.
„ SCHAMELIUS (J. M.) Evang. Lieder-Comm. &c., dabey Abdr. d. Gesang-Buchs L., 1724.
„ SCHEEL (O.) Entwicklung L. [–1516], 1910.
„ SCHERER (G.) Der L. Bettler Mantel, 1588.
„ SCHLOSSER (J. L.) L. Lutheranus &c., 1739.
„ SCHUBERT (H. v.) L.'s Frühentwicklung (bis 1517/9), 1916.
„ SCHULTZE (B.) Perspic. explic. doct. Xtnae. sec. ord. 5 cap. Catech. maj. in Telugicam versa, 1747.
„ SCHWARZ (F. I.) De silentio L., 1778.
„ SCHWENDER (F.) De excelso &c. L. animo, 1827.
„ SCHWOB (S.) Register aller Bücher u. Schriften M. L. &c., 1573.
„ SEEBERG (R.) Lehrb. d. Dogmengesch., B4, i, Die Lehre L.'s, 1917.
„ SELNECCERUS (N.) Recitationes, 4, De autoritate L. & Philippi, 1581.
„ SEMMT (J. G.) Judic. L. de vi oblig. quam Decalogus habeat, 1791.
„ SERARIUS (N.) De L. magistro, 1604.
„ SIMONIUS (J.) Triumphus secul.: oratio: per L. ministerium liberat. eccl., 1618.
„ SMEND (J.) Das evangel. Lied v. 1524, 1924.
„ SOTHEBY (S. L.) Unpubl. doc. &c. in autograph of M. L., 1840.
„ SPANGENBERG (C.) Warhafft. Lere v. d. Erbsünde M. L. &c., 1572.
„ SPENGLER (L.) Bekendnis, mit Vorrhede L., 1535.
„ STALLBAUM (J. G.) De instaurat. sacr. per L., 1840.
„ STAPHYLUS (F.) Defensio pro trimembri theol. L. &c., 1559.
„ —— Theol. L. trimembris epitome, 1558.
„ STIGEL (J.) De viro sancto M. L. (*Lat. & Germ. verse*), 1546.
„ STRACKE (E.) L. s. grosses Selbstzeugnis 1545, 1926.
„ STRASS (J. F. V. D.) Mem. Thaumasiandri L. renovata, 1661.

Luther (Martin) [*continued*].
REFERENCES [*continued*].
see SUABIA. Genot. u. fremdt eingetrag. schr. &c. [Vorrede *by* M. L.], 1526.
„ TARNOVIUS (J.) Tres Eliæ: compar. Eliæ, Joh. Bapt., M. L., 1618.
„ TARNOVIUS (P.) Panegyr. de visitat. per L. ministerium &c., 1618.
„ †ULENBERG (C.) Gesch. d. luther. Reformatoren, B1, 1836.
„ —— Hist. de vita &c. prædicantium Lutheran. &c., 1622.
„ ULRICH (J. D.) Diss. de autoritate L. in eccl., 1748.
„ VELTKIRCH (I.) Confut. libelli F. Aug. Alveld., pro M. L., 1520.
„ VENT (H. W.) De causis Reform. L. praepar., 1816.
„ VILLERS (C. F. D. DE). Essay; added, life of L.; tr. 1806.
„ VOGEL (E. G.) Bibl. biograph. L., 1851.
„ WALCH (C. W. F.) Comm. de L. disputatore &c., 1754. [P442].
„ WALTHER (W.) L. im neu. röm. Gericht, 4H, 1884–92.
„ WEICKHMANN (J. S.) De Concil. Trident. ex morte L. triumphante, 1746.
„ WERNLE (P.) Der evangel. Glaube, B1, L., 1918.
„ WERNSDORF (E. F.) Liturgia L. servans exemplum ant. eccles., *n.d.*
„ WILL (R.) La lib. chrét., le principe de la piété chez L., 1922.
„ WITTROCK (J.) Diss. de Reform. L. &c., 1722.
„ ZEIBICH (C. H.) Electa hist. vitae & mortis M. L., 1746.
„ ZELTNER (G. G.) Hist. d. gedr. Bibel-Version &c. L., 1727.
„ ZÜRICH. Orthod. Tigur. eccl. ministr. confessio, cum resp. ad M. L. calumnias, 1545.

Lutheraner. *Der Christl. L. stellet vor die Kirchen-Historien vom J. 1370, u. was v. selbiger Zeit darinnen ergangen &c. s4º. [Wittemberg]. 1717

Lutherani. *Canoni indocti L., 1519?, *see* OECOLAMPADIUS (J.)

Lütiens (Wilhelm Friedrich). Diss. de relig. Ruthenorum hodierna. Praes. J. G. Feuerlino. [*a. c. in* P426]. s4º. Gottingae. [1745]

Lütkemann (Leonhard) & A. Rahlfs. Hexaplar. Randnoten zu Isaias 1–16, aus e. Sinai-Hs. hrsg. v. L. L. & A. R., *see* KÖNIGL. GESELLS. D. W. ZU GÖTTINGEN. Nachr., philol.-hist. Kl., 1915, Beiheft.

Lutosławski (Wincenty). Üb. d. Grundvoraussetzungen &c. d. individualist. Weltanschauung. [P2785]. 8º. Helsingfors. 1898
The world of souls. Pref. by W. James. 8º. 1924

Lutta (C. Martin). Der Dialekt von Bergün &c. [Zeitschr. f. roman. Philol., Beih. 71]. 8º. Halle (Saale). 1923

Lutterbeck (Johann Anton Bernhard).
An Pabst Pius IX. [P2692]. 8º. Giessen. 1870
Die Clementinen u. ihr Verhältniss z. Unfehlbarkeitsdogma. [P2694]. 8º. München. 1872
Lebensepoche Baader's u. Charakteristik s. Systems d. Philos. [P2483]. 8º. Würzburg. 1860

Lutterworth lect. on Xty. & language; by var. a.; foreword &c. by Ld. Braye, 1913, *see* BRAYE (A. T. T. V.-C., *5th b.*)

Lutyens (*Sir* Edwin Landseer), *see* WEAVER (L.) L. houses & gardens, 1921.

Lutyens (Engelbert), *see* KNOWLES (*Sir* L.) A gift of Napoleon, sequel to letters of Capt. E. L., St. Helena, 1820–23, 1921.

Lutz (Hermann). Lord Grey & the World War. Tr. E. W. Dickes. 8º. [1928]
Lord Grey u. d. Weltkrieg: Schlüssel z. Verständ. d. brit. amtl. Aktenpubl. ü. d. Kriegsausbruch, 1914. la8º. 1927

Lutz (Jules). Les verrières de l'anc. église St.-Etienne à Mulhouse. [Suppl. au Bull. du Musée hist. de M., t29]. la8º. Mulhouse. 1906

Lützelberger (Hans), *see* HOLBEIN (H.) The dance of death; enl. facs. of orig. wood engravings by H. L. in 1st ed., Lyons, 1547, 1916.

***Lux** in tenebris, hoc est donum prophetiae &c., 1657, *see* KOTTER (C.)

Lux (Johann Philipp). Judæorum religio sec. Rom. poetas. Præs. J. C. Reuchlin, subj. a J. P. L. [P2744]. s4º. Argentorati. [1749]

Lux (William). *Poems on sev. occasions: *viz.* The garden, The phaenomenon &c. s8º. O. 1719

Luxborough (Henrietta, *Lady*), *wife of Robert Knight of Barrells, aft. cr. Baron Luxborough.* Letters to W. Shenstone [1739–56]. 8º. 1775

Luxembourg. Dénombrements des feux des duché de L. & comté de Chiny. Publ. avec add. &c. de J. Vannérus. [C. R. d'H. de Belg.] tl. 4º. Brux. 1921
1, Doc. fiscaux, 1306–1537, réunis par J. Grob.

Luxembourg [*continued*].
Inventaire des chartes & cartul. du L., t2–4, 1915–17, *see* VERKOOREN (A.)

Luxembourg (*le maréchal* **de**). Pacta u. Verbündnus d. Herzogs v. L. so er mit Satan getroffen; aus d. Fr. üb., 1680, *facs.*, *see* FREYTAG (G.) Bilder, B3ii, 1924.

Luxembourg (Madeleine Angélique de Neufville de Villeroy, *dsse.* **de),** *marq. de Boufflers, see* BUFFENOIR (H.) La maréchale de L., 1707–87, 1924.

Luxemburg (Rosa).
Briefe aus d. Gefängnis. [P2524]. s8°. [1920]
Frau R. L. sogenannte Junius-Broschüre. Die Krise d. Sozialdemokratie, von Junius (1916). [P2408]. 8°. [1919]
Накопленіе капитала. Перевод III. Двoлайцкого под ред. Н. Бухарина. la8°. [Москва]. 1921
see KAUTSKY (C.) R. L. &c., 1921.
„ RADEK (C.) R. L. &c., 1921.
„ TSETKIN (K.), A. KOLLONTAI &c. P. Л., 1921.
„ ZINOVEV (G.) & L. TROTZKY. K. Liebknecht u. R. L., 1920.

Luyckx (Bonifaz Anton), *O.P.* Die Erkenntnislehre Bonaventuras. [Beitr. z. Gesch. d. Philos. d. M-a's, B23iii, iv]. 8°. Münster i. W. 1923

Luyken (Max). Generalfeldmar. v. Mackensen. Von Bukarest bis Saloniki. Nach Miterlebtem u. an Hand v. Urkunden dargestellt v. M. Luyken. 8°. München. 1920

Luynes (Honoré T. P. J. d'Albert, *duc* **de),** *1802–67.*
see BABELON (E.) Cat. de la Coll. de L. [Bibl. Nat.], monnaies grec., t1, 2, 1924–26.
„ LARTET (L.) Explor. géolog. de la Mer Morte &c., expéd. du duc de L., 1877.

Luzarches (Robert de), *fl. 1220, see* ROBERT, *de Luzarches.*

Luzigni (*Marquis* **de**). *Corresp. d'un jeune militaire, ou Mém. de L. & d'Hortense de Saint-Just, 2t, 1778–79, *see* BOURGOING (*b.* J. F.) & L. A. M. DE MUSSET.

Luzio (Alessandro).
Carlo Alberto e G. Mazzini: st. &c. di stor. del Risorgimento. 8°. Torino. 1923
I carteggi dell' Archivio Gonzaga rifl. l'Inghilterra. [Estr. d. Atti d. R. Accad. d. Sci. di Torino, v53, 2p. P2784]. 8°. [1917–18]
Dalle Riforme allo statuto di Carlo Alberto, *see* ARCHIVIO STOR. ITAL., a. 84i, 1926.
G. Mazzini carbonaro. Nuovi doc., con pref. e note. s8°. Torino. 1920
Garibaldi, Cavour, Verdi. Nuova ser. di st. &c. sulla storia del Risorgimento. 8°. Torino. 1924
Inizi del regno di Carlo Alberto: nuovi doc. [Estr. d. Mem. d. R. Accad. di Torino, s2, t66]. la8°. Torino. 1923
La missione Malaguzzi a Vienna, 1865–6 per la cess. del Veneto. [Estr. d. Risorgimento ital., N.S., v15–16]. la8°. Torino. 1923
Ult. giorni di Carlo Alberto: doc. ined. [Estr. d. Atti d. R. Accad. di Torino, v59]. *no tp.* 8°. [Torino. 1924]

Luzzatto (Rahel), *aft. wife of J. Morpurgo, see* MORPURGO (R.)

Luzzatto (Samuel Davide), *see* LANDAU (J. L.) Sh. lect. on mod. Hebrew lit. f. M. H. Luzzatto to S. D. L., 1923.

Lvov (F. A.) Лиходѣи бюрократич. самовластья какъ непосредств. виновники первой Русско-Японской войны. la8°. С.-П. 1906

Lvov-Rogachevsky (Vasily Lv.)
Новейшая русская литература. la8°. Москва. 1919

Lyall (*Sir* **Charles James),** *1845–1920.* Some aspects of anc. Arabian poetry, *see* BRIT. ACAD. Proc., 1917–18.
see BRIT. ACAD. Proc., v9, Obit. not., by R. A. Nicholson, 1919–20.

Lyashko (N.), *see* KAZIN (V.), N. L. &c. Цветы труда, 1923.

Lyatsky (Evgeny Aleksandrovich).
Гончаровъ: жизнь, личность &c. изд. 3ᵉ. 8°. Стохгольмъ. 1920

Lyautey (*le gén.* **Hubert).** Disc. de réception [*on* H. Houssaye]. Réponse de Mgr. Duchesne. [Acad. Fr., 8 juillet, 1920. P2819]. s8°. 1921
Lettres du Tonkin & de Madagascar (1894–99). 2t. la8°. 1920
Paroles d'action: Madagascar—Sud-Oranais—Oran—Maroc (1900–26). Préf. de L. Barthou. 8°. 1927
see BRITSCH (A.) Le maréchal L., 1921.
„ GEORGES-GAULIS (B.) La France au Maroc (l'œuvre du gén. L.), 1919.

Lybyer (Albert Howe). The govt. of the Ottoman Empire in the time of Suleiman the Magnificent. [Harvard Hist. St., v18]. 8°. Camb. [U.S.] 1913

Lycophron. Alexandra. With Eng. tr. & explan. notes by G. W. Mooney. s8°. 1921
see CALLIMACHUS. C. & L.; tr. by A. W. Mair, 1921.

Lydd. Monumental inscr. in the churchyard &c. of All Saints', Lydd, Kent. By L. L. Duncan. Ed. A. Finn. [Kent Arch. Soc. Records Br.] 8°. Ashford. [1927]

Lyde (Lionel William).
The continent of Europe. [2nd ed.] 8°. 1924
see BARTHOLOMEW (J. G.) Atlas of econ. geography; intr. by L., 1914.
„ VRIJ (M. P.) Internat. rivers. Reply to L., 1920.

Lydekker (Richard).
see BRITISH MUS. OF NAT. HIST. Cat. of fossil birds; by R. L., 1891.
„ —— Cat. of fossil Reptilia & Amphibia; by R. L., 4p, 1888–90.
„ HARMSWORTH, *publ. firm.* H. natural hist., 3v, 1910–11.

Lydenberg (Harry Miller).
Hist. of the New York Public Library. la8°. N.Y. 1923

Lydgate (John). A lytell treatyse of the horse, the sheep & the ghoos. Pr. by W. de Worde, c. 1499. [Facs. ed. F. Jenkinson]. la8°. C. 1906
see BOCCACCIO (G.) L.'s Fall of princes, 4p, 1923–27; 4p, 1924–27.
„ *COURT of sapience; [*sometimes attrib. to J. L.*]; krit. Textausgabe v. R. Spindler, 1927.
„ MACCRACKEN (H. N.) L. canon, 1907.
„ ——, *ed.* Lydgatiana, 1911–13.

Lydiat (Thomas) [LYDYAT]. Defensio tract. de variis annorum formis, contra J. Scaligeri obtrect. [*b. w. h.* Emend. temp. 1609]. s8°. 1607
Emendatio temporum, compend. facta. s8°. Lond. 1609

Lydin (M.) Material z. Erl. d. Parteikrise in d. Socialdem Arbeiterpartei Russlands. [P2715]. 8°. Genf. 1904

Lydius (Balthasar). Waldensia; id est conservatio verae eccl., demonstrata ex confess. cum Taboritarum tum Bohem &c. [2p *in* 1v. p2 *wanting tp.*] s8°. Roterodami. 1616

Lydwina, *Saint, of Schiedam, see* LIDWINA, *St.*

Lydyat (Thomas), *see* LYDIAT.

Lyebedeff (Herasim), *see* LEBEDEV (ERASIN).

Lyell (*Sir* **Charles).** Man. de géologie élém. Tr. M. Hugard. 5ᵉ éd. 2t. 8°. 1856–57
Princ. de géol. Tr. T. Meulien. 4p. s8°. 1843–48

Lyell (Denis D.) Hunting trips in N. Rhodesia &c. 4°. 1910
Mem. of an African hunter, w. ch. on E. India. 8°. 1923
Wild life in C. Africa. 8°. 1913

Lyell (James P. R.) Early book illustration in Spain. Intr by K. Haebler. 4°. 1926
The sentence of Pontius Pilate. [P2577]. 8°. 192

Lyell (Thomas). The ins & outs of Mesopotamia. 8°. 1923

Lyell (W. D.) The house in Queen Anne Sq. s8°. 1920

Lyeskov (Nicolai), *see* LESKOV (N. S.)

Lyfe, *see* LIFE.

Lygisǫgur. Drei lygisǫgur. Egils saga einhenda ok Ásmundar berserkjabana—Ála flekks saga—Flóres saga konungs ok sona hans. Hrsg. Å. Lagerholm. [Altnord. Saga-Bibl. 17]. 8°. Halle (Saale). 192

Lykeus, *ps., see* POPPER (J.)

Lyly (John), *the Euphuist.* Campaspe (1584), *see* ADAMS (J. Q.) Chief pre-Shakespearian dramas, 1925.

Lyman (Anne Jean), *form. Robbins, see* LESLEY (S. I.) Recoll of my mother [*Mrs.* A. J. L.], 1886.

Lyman (*Col.* **Theodore),** *naturalist.* Meade's headquarters 1863–65. Letters of L. Sel. & ed. G. R. Agassiz. [Mass. Hist. Soc.] la8°. Boston. 192

Lyme letters, 1660–1760, 1925, *see* NEWTON (E., *Lady*).

Lympsfield, *see* LIMPSFIELD.

Lynch (Arthur). Ethics: an expos. of principles. 8°. 192
Science: leading & misleading. 8°. [192

Lynch (Bohun). Isles of illusion: letters f. the South Sea Ed. B. L. s8°. 192
Max Beerbohm in perspective. With pref. letter by M. B. 8°. 192

Lynch (*Col.* **Charles),** *U.S. Army, see* UNITED STATES: ARMY Medical Dept. in the World War, v1, 8; prep. by C. L. &c 1923–25.

Lynch (Henry Finnis Blosse). The importance of Persia, *see* PERSIA SOCIETY. Lect., 1912.
see TONAPHETEAN (P.) Armenia by L. (*in Arm.*), 1902.

Lynd (Robert). The art of letters. 8°. 19
Books & authors. s8°. [192
The passion of labour. s8°. 19
The peal of bells. s8°. [192

Lynd (Sylvia). The swallow dive. s8°. [1921]
Lynde (*Sir* Humphrey). Via tuta. The safe way: leading all Christians to the true anc. catholike faith in the Ch. of Eng. s8°. 1629
Lyndewode (William), *bp. of St. David's.* Provinciale seu Cōstit. Anglie Cū summariis, atque iustis annotat. politissimus characteribus: summaq. accuratiōe rursum revise, atq. impresse. [*Prec. by Pref. & 3 tables. Ed.* J. Badius Ascensius]. 2p [p2 *wanting*]. fol. Cura atq. diligentia W. Hopylii. In inclyta Parisiorū Acad. Impēsis honesti mercatoris Londoñ: W. Bretton. 1505.
The imprint w. date 1505 is taken f. the colophon of p1: the pref. of Badius is dated 1506.
Lynkeus, *ps., see* Popper (J.)
Lynn (J. M.) A short hist. of Methodism on the Armagh circuit. 2nd ed. s8°. Belfast. 1885
Lyon, *see* Lyons.
Lyon (David Gordon), *see* Reisner (G. A.), C. S. Fisher & D. G. L. Harvard excav. at Samaria, 1908–10, 2v, 1924.
Lyon (John Henry Hobart). A study of The newe metamorphosis, wr. by J. M., Gent., 1600. [Columbia Univ. St. in Eng.] 8°. N.Y. 1919
Lyon (Laurance). *The path to peace. By the a. of "The pomp of power." 8°. [1923]
*The pomp of power. 8°. [1922]
*Where freedom falters. By the a. of The pomp of power. 8°. 1927
Lyon (P. H. B.) France. Newdigate Prize Poem, 1919. [P2435]. s8°. O. 1919
Lyonnet (Henry). Mlle. Molière (Armande Béjart). [Acteurs &c. d'autrefois]. 8°. 1925
Lyonnet (Jean Baptiste), *bp. of (1) Saint-Flour, (2) Valence.*
App. ad tract. De justitia & jure, *see* Migne (J. P.), *ed.* Theol. cursus, t15, 1861.
Tract. de contractibus in gen. & in partic., *see* Migne (J. P.) *ed.* Theol. cursus, t16, 1859.
Lyons. Art (L') lyonnais: exposition. Cat. par J. Billiet, avec préf. d'H. Focillon. s8°. Lyon. 1925
Cartul. lyonnais. Doc. inéd. pour servir à l'hist. des anc. prov. de Lyonnais, Forez &c. Rec. & publ. par M. C. Guigue. [Acad. des Sci. &c. de Lyon]. 2t. 4°. 1885–93
1, Doc. antér. à 1255. 2, Doc., 1255–1300.
*Recherche des antiq. &c. de L., 1673, *see* Spon (J.)
see Hennezel (H. d'). Le Musée Hist. des Tissus de la Ch. de Commerce de L., 1922.
,, Lowe (E. A.) Codices Lugdun. antiq., 1924.
Université de Lyon.
Annales de l'U. de L.
see Chevalier (J.) Essai sur la formation de la nationalité &c. au pays de Galles, 1923.
,, Courant (M.) L'Asie Cent. aux 17e & 18e siècles, 1912.
Lyons (A. Neil) [Lyons (Alb. Michael N.)]
Fifty-fifty. s8°. [1923]
A market bundle. s8°. [1921]
Lyons (George A.)
Some recoll. of Griffith & h. times. s8°. D. 1923
Lyons (*Sir* Henry George), *see* Brit. Antarctic (Terra Nova) Exped., 1910–13: Misc. data; comp. by H. G. L., 1924.
Lyons (Vyvyan Ashleigh). Wages & Empire. s8°. 1920
Lyra. Lyra Anglicana, 1879, *see* Baynes (R. H.)
Lyra Apostolica. [*Poems by J. W. Bowden, J. Keble, J. H. Newman &c.*] 5th ed. s8°. Derby. 1841
Lyra Graeca: remains of all Gk. lyric poets f. Eumelus to Timotheus excepting Pindar. [Text], newly ed. & tr. by J. M. Edmonds. [Loeb Class. Lib.] 3v. s8°. 1922–27
1, Terpander, Alcman, Sappho & Alcaeus.
2, Stesichorus, Ibycus, Anacreon & Simonides.
3, Corinna — Bacchylides — Timotheus — Anon. fragments — Folk-songs & Scolia w. acc. of Greek lyric poetry.
Lyra (Justus Wilhelm). Luthers Deut. Messe u. Ordnung in i. liturg. u. musikal. Bestandteilen &c. erl. Mit Erörter. u. liturg. Melodien &c., hrsg. v. M. Herold. 8°. Gütersloh. 1904
Lyra (Nicolaus de), *see* Nicolaus, *de Lyra.*
Lyrical. Lyrical ballads w. a few o. poems [*by* Coleridge & Wordsworth], 1798. [Noel Douglas Replicas]. 8°. [1926]
Lyrics. L. f. the old song books, 1927, *see* Duncan (E.), *ed.*
L. of light & life, 1878, *see* Lee (F. G.), *ed.*
Lys (Jan), *see* Lis (J.)
Lysaght (Sydney Royse). My tower in Desmond. s8°. 1925
Poems of the unknown way. s8°. 1901
Lyschinska (Mary J.), *see* Breymann (H. J. J. S.) H. S.-B., Brief. &c.; zusammeng. u. erl. v. M. J. L., 2B, 1922.
Lysen (A.), *see* Grotius (H.) H. G.: essays on h. life &c.; sel. by A. L., 1925.
Lyser (Christian). Consensus non consensus quin potius dissensus Lutheran. & Jansenist., contra falsas Molinistarum imput. [P441]. s4°. Lipsiae. 1673
Lyser (Johann) [Aletophilus Germanus, *ps.*] Discursus inter polygamum & monogamum de polygamia. Prodit lat. cum præf. &c. C. Vigilis. [P2633]. s4°. 1673
Lyser (Polycarp), *see* Leyser (P.)
Lysias, *the orator.* Discours. Texte établi & tr. par L. Gernet & M. Bizos. [Coll. des univ. de France]. t1. 8°. 1924
Orationes [*in Greek*], *see* Oratores. Orationes horum rhetorum, p1, 1513.
Orationes. Rec. &c. C. Hude. s8°. O. [1913]
see Dobson (W. S.), *ed.* Oratores Attici, t2, L., t13, Antiphontis, L. &c. interpret. Lat., 1828.
,, Hude (C.) Oraisons funèbres de L. &c., 1917.
,, Lipsius (J. H.) L.'s Rede geg. Hippotherses u. d. att. Metoikenrecht, 1919.
Lysippos, *the sculptor, see* Küppers (I.) Apoxyomenos d. L. u. d. griech. Palästra, 1873.
Lysle (Andrea de Roever). Mod. rational pract. Eng.-Ital. dict. 2v (v2, Nuovo diz. ital.-ingl.) s8°. Torino. 1913–15
Lyttelton (*Hon.* Alfred), *see* Lyttelton (*Hon.* E. S.) A. L., 1917; n. ed., abr., 1923.
Lyttelton (*Dame* Edith Sophy), *wife of Hon. Alfred Lyttelton, form. Balfour.* Alfred Lyttelton: acc. of h. life. 3rd impr. 8°. 1917
,, ,, ... n. ed. abr. s8°. 1923
Florence Upton, painter. s8°. 1926
The Sinclair family. s8°. 1925
Lyttelton (*Rev. the Hon.* Edward), *7th son of 4th baron Lyttelton.*
Letters on education. s8°. C. 1922
Memories & hopes. 8°. 1925
Lyttelton (George Lyttelton, *1st baron*), *1709–73.* Obs. on the conversion &c. of Paul. [*b. w.* Jenyns (S.) Internal evid. of Xtn. relig., 1799]. 9th ed. s8°. 1799
Poet. works. Coll. by T. Park. s8°. 1805
Lyttelton (Lucy Caroline), *see* Cavendish (*Lady* Fred.)
Lyttelton (*Gen. Sir* Neville Gerald).
Eighty years: soldiering, politics, games. 8°. [1927]
Lyttleton, *The family of, see* Wyndham (*Hon.* M. M.) Chron. of the 18th cent., Sir T. L. & h. family, 2v, 1924.
Lyttleton (*Sir* Thomas), *3rd bart.; 1686–1751, see* Wyndham (*Hon.* M. M.) Chron. of the 18th cent., L. &c., 2v, 1924.
Lytton (*Lady* Constance), *see* Lytton (*Hon.* N. S.) The Eng. country gentleman, *w. chap. on L.*, 1925.
Lytton (Edward G. Earle Lytton Bulwer Lytton, *1st baron*), *see* Frost (W. A.) B. Lytton, errors of h. biographers, 1913.
Lytton (*Hon.* Neville Stephen).
The English country gentleman. 8°. [1925]
The press & the General Staff. 8°. [1921]
Lyubavsky (Matvei Kozmich). Исторія западныхъ Славянъ (прибалтійскихъ, Чеховъ, и Поляковъ). изд. 2ое 8°. Москва. 1918
Очеркъ исторіи Литовско-русскаго государства до Люблинской уніи. Изд. И. Общ. Ист. и Древностей Росс. la8°. Москва. 1910
Lyubich-Koshurov (I. A.) Картины боевой жизни на дальнемъ Востокѣ. Въ Боевомъ огнѣ. Разсказъ. [P847]. s8°. 1904–05
Lyutnya. *Лютня II. Потаенная литература XIX ст. 2ое изд. s8°. Лейпцигъ. *n.d.*

M

M. (A.) *An anthology of mod. verse; chosen by A. M., 1921, *see* METHUEN (A.)

M. (A.) *Il matrimonio Grimani-Mocenigo, 1910, *see* MOCENIGO (A.)

M. (D. R. H. Q.) *Le divorce satyrique, 1664, *see* PALMA CAYET (P. V.)

M. (F.) Coup d'œil rapide s. Costa Rica, 1849, *see* COSTA RICA.

M. (H.), *Hungarus, ps., see* ROTARIDES (JÁNOS).

M. (I. D.) *Dialogues rustiques d'un prestre de village &c., 1616, *see* DIALOGUES.

M. (J.) *Nugae derelictae, q. coll. J. M. & R. P., 1822, *see* MAIDMENT (J.) & R. PITCAIRN.

M. (J.), *Gent., a. of* The newe metamorphosis, *see* LYON (J. H. H.) A st. of The n. m., 1600, 1919.

M. (J. B. T.). *Story of the J. singers [note *signed* J. B. T. M.], 1876, *see* JUBILEE SINGERS.

M. (Juan F.) *Poems by a slave in Cuba [J. F. M.]; tr. R. R. Madden, w. hist. of early life wr. by himself. Prefixed, 2 pieces descr. of Cuban slavery &c. by R. R. M[adden]. 8º. 1840

M. (M. B. L.) L'art de conserver sa santé; tr. M. B. L. M. [*i.e.* Bruzen de La Martinière], 1766, *see* SCHOLA SALERNITANA.

M. (R.) *Sion's prospect in its first view; by a minister of Christ, R. M., 1653, *see* MOSSOM (R.)

M. (R. C.) *Journal of a tour in Persia, 1824–25, 1828, *see* MONEY (R. C.)

M. (V. S.) *A memoir of Howard Marsh, 1921, *see* MARSH (H.)

M. (W. J.) Biblia &c., 1834, *see* MIKLOS (W. J.)

Ma (Yin Ch'u). Finances of the city of New York. 8º. N.Y., *Columbia Univ.* 1914

Maak (Richard Karlovich) [MAACK], *see* IMPERATORSKOE RUSS. GEOG. OBS. Атласъ къ путешествiю на Амуръ [*by M.*], 1859 ?.

Maandoo. *The legend of M., 1893, *see* ABBOTT (*Col.* J.) The T'Hakoorine, 2nd ed., 1893.

Maar (Harko G. de), *see* DE MAAR (HARKO G.)

Ma'arrath Gazzê, *see* ME'ÂRATH GAZZÊ.

Maas (Mabel). The two flames. s8º. [1922]

Maas (Nicolaes), *see* MAES (N.)

Maasen (Wilhelm). Hans Jacob Fugger (1516–75). Hrsg. P. Ruf. 8º. München. 1922

Maass (Johann Gerhard Ehrenreich).
Versuch ü. d. Leidenschaften. 2T. s8º. Halle. 1805–07

Mabbe (James).
see ALEMAN (M.) The rogue, or, The life of Guzman de Alfarache; done into Eng. by J. M., 1623, 4v, 1924.
„ ROJAS (F. DE). Celestina &c.; tr. J. M., 1631; ed. &c. H. W. Allen, 1923.

Mabbott (Thomas Ollive), *ed., see* PINKNEY (E. C.) Life & works: mem. & poems &c., 1926.

Mabie (Hamilton Wright). Educat. exchange w. Japan: obs., 1912–13. [C.E. for Inter. Peace. P2676]. la8º. Wash. 1914

Mabillon (Jean). De liturgia Gallicana lib. 3. Acc. disq. de cursu Gallicano. 4º. Parisiis. 1729
Praefationes in Acta Sanct. Ejusdem diss. 5. 1, De pane eucharist. azymo & fermentato. 2, De cultu Sanct. ignot. ed 2ª. 3, De vet. reliquiis discern. 4, De vocibus Missae &c. in Regula S. Benedicti adhib. 5, De primario Romarici Montis instituto. s4º. Tridenti. 1724
see RUINART (T.) Vita J. M.; tr., 1714.

Mabinogion. The M. Tr. by Lady C. Guest. [Intr. by R. Williams. Everyman's Lib. repr.] s8º. [1906]
see JOHN (I. B.) The M., 1901.

Mabuse (Jean) [*i.e.* JAN GOSSART], *see* SEGARD (A.) J. G. dit M., 1923.

Macadam (Elizabeth), *M.A.*
Equipment of the social worker. s8º. [1925]

Macafee (Daniel). The anatomy of popery, incl. letters to O'Connell. 8º. Belfast. 1860

MacAfee (Helen), *see* PEPYS (S.) P. on the Restoration stage, 1916.

Macaire, chanson de geste, *see* GUESSARD (F.) Anc. poëtes, t9, 1866.

Macalister (*Sir* Donald), *of Tarbert.* Romani versions. Intr. by Dr. J. Sampson. [Gypsy Lore Soc., Monogr., 5]. 8º. E. 1928

Macalister (Donald Alexander). Field gunnery. s8º. 1915
„ „ ....[2nd ed.] s8º. 1916
„ „ ....[3rd ed.] s8º. 1917
see HILL (J. B.) & D. A. M. Geol. of Falmouth & Truro &c., 1906.
„ MOOR (C. G.) Recognition of minerals, w. monogr. on geology &c. by D. A. M., 1909.
„ USSHER (W. A. E.), G. BARROW & D. A. M. Geol. of co. around Bodmin & St. Austell, 1909.

Macalister (Robert Alex. Stewart).
The archaeology of Ireland. 8º. [1928
A century of excav. in Palestine. 8º. [1925
Ireland in pre-Celtic times. la8º. D. 192
The Lat. & Irish lives of Ciaran. [Ed., w. intr. &c.] by M [Tr. of Xtn. lit., s5]. s8º. 192
Present & future of archaeology in Ireland. Address. [P2784]. 8º. D. [1925
Text-book of European archaeology. v1, Palaeolithic period. la8º. C. 192

MacAll (Robert Stephens), *1792–1838.* Discourses on spec occ., w. life by R. Wardlaw. 2v. 8º. 184

MacAlmon (Robert). Explorations. [*Poems*]. 8º. 192

Macan (Reginald Walter). *Hellenikon: sonnets afte Herodotus. [P2794]. 8º. O. *p.p.* 189

Macanaz (Joaquin Maldonado), *see* MALDONADO MACANAZ (J.)

MacAndrew (John). Cat. of coll. of objects of art &c. forme by J. M., sold by Christie &c., Dec., 1925. 8º. 192

Macara (*Sir* Charles Wright). How the cotton indust. wa internationalised. [P2878]. s8º. M'ter. 192
In search of a peaceful world. s8º. M'ter. 192
Mod. indust. tendencies. s8º. M'ter. 192
Recollections. 8º. 192
Social & industrial reform. s8º. M'ter. 191

Macarius, *of Egypt, saint, the elder.* 50 geistl. Homilien Übers. v. D. Stiefenhofer. 8º. Kempten. 191
Fifty spiritual homilies. [Tr. w. intr.] by A. J. Mason. s8º. 192
Macarii anecdota. 7 unpubl. homilies of M. Ed. G. L. Marriott. [Harvard Theolog. St., 5]. 8º. Camb. [U.S.] 191

Macarius, *a Sancto Elia.* Instit. patrologiae. [*b. w.* Introd. ad hist. litt. theol., 1781]. s8º. Graecii. 178
Introd. ad hist. litt. theologiae. s8º. Græcii. 178

MacArthur (Peter). Stephen Leacock. [Biog. sk., extr. wr. &c.] s8º. Toronto. [192

MacArthur (*Sir* William), *1809–87, see* MACCULLAGH (T.) S W. M'A.; a biog., 1891.

Macartney (Carlile Aylmer).
The social revolution in Austria. 8º. C. 192

Macartney (Maxwell H. H.) Five years of Europ. chaos. 8º. 192

Macartney (Mervyn Edmund), *F.S.A.* Recent Eng. domest architecture. Spec. issue of the Archit. Review. E M. E. M. [v5]. sm. fol. [192

Macassey (*Sir* Lynden). Labour policy—false & true. 8º. [192

Macaulay (Rose).
A casual commentary. s8º. [1925]
Crewe train. s8º. [1926]
Dangerous ages. s8º. [1921]
Mystery at Geneva. s8º. [1922]
Non-combatants & others. s8º. [191
Orphan Island. s8º. [192
Potterism. s8º. [192
Told by an idiot. s8º. [192

Macaulay (Thomas Babington Macaulay, *baron*).
Works. Albany ed., n. impr. 12v [v11, 12, 1st impr.] 8º. 1898–1916
1–6, Hist. of Eng.
7–10, Essays & biographies.
11, 12, Speeches, poems & misc. wr.
Crit. & hist. essays. 4th ed. 3v. 8º. 1846
Lays of ancient Rome. n. ed. 8º. 1874
Sels. fr. writings. Ed. w. notes by G. O. Trevelyan. s8º. 1876
see ALLPORT (H. R.) M., 1917.
see COURTHOPE (W. J.) M comparison of Dante Milton, 1908.
„ HARINGTON (E. C.) T reformers of the An Church & M.'s Hist. Eng., 1849.
„ SITWELL (*Sir* G. R.) Count life in 17th cent.: no upon M.'s caricature of t country squires, 1901.
„ TREVELYAN (*Sir* G. Life & letters of M., impr., 2v, 1923.

MacBain (Alex.) Place names, Highlands & islands of Sco land. Notes & foreword by W. J. Watson. 8º. Stirling. 19

MacBain (Howard Lee) & L. Rogers.
The new constit. of Europe. 8º. N.Y. 19

Macbean (Lachlan), *see* BUCHANAN (D.) Confessions &c.; w. h. letters & life by L. M., 1919.
MacBeth (Ann), *see* SWANSON (M.) & A. M. Educat. needlework, n. ed., 1913.
Macbeth (Robert W.), *see* WEDMORE (F.) Notes on Velasquez & Titian in the etchings of R. W. M., 1888.
Macbeth (Roderick George). Policing the plains. Royal N.-W. Mounted Police. 8o. 1921
MacBey (James), *see* SALAMAN (M. C.) J. McB., 1924.
Macbrair (Robert Maxwell). Sketches of a missionary's travels in Egypt, Syria & W. Africa. 8o. 1839
Macbride (Ernest William). Intr. to the study of heredity. [Home Univ. Lib.] s8o. [1924]
Macbride (Mackenzie). Arran of the Bens &c. 8o. 1910
MacBride (Peter). Psycho-analysts analysed. Intr. by Sir H. B. Donkin. s8o. 1924
MacBride (Robert Medill). Spanish towns & people. 8o. 1926
MacBurney (Isaiah). The students' hdbk. of anc. hist. Intr. essay by Sir J. Stoddart. s8o. 1856
MacCabe (Joseph). The existence of God. s8o. 1913
Robert Owen. s8o. 1920
Spiritualism. A pop. hist. f. 1847. 8o. [1920]
Maccabees.
see DRUSIUS (J.) Liber Hasmonaeorum, *Gr. & Lat.*, cum notis &c., 1600.
„ KOLBE (W.) Beitr., Untersuch. z. d. M.-Büchern, 1926.
„ STRIGELIUS (V.) Libri duo M., c. 1575.
„ WERNSDORF (G.) Comm. de fide hist. libr. M., 1747.
MacCallum (J. L.) James Annand, M.P. A tribute. With intr. by J. W. Crombie. s8o. 1908
MacCallum (James Dow). Lord Morley's criticism of Eng. poetry & prose. Diss. 8o. [Princeton ?. 1921?]
MacCallum (*Sir* Mungo William). The dramatic monologue in the Victorian period. [*From* Proc. of Brit. Acad.: Warton lect. 16. P2818, 2821]. 8o. [1925]
MacCalmont (*Maj.-Gen. Sir* Hugh). Memoirs. Ed. & compl. by C. E. Callwell. 8o. 1924
MacCance (H. M.), *see* LEASK (J. C.) & H. M. McC. Regimental records of The Royal Scots, 1915.
MacCance (*Capt.* Stouppe), *see* CARY (A. D. L.) & S. McC., *edd.* Regimental records of the R.W. Fusiliers, 2v, 1921–23.
MacCann (William Sidney). Geology & mineral deposits of Bridge River map-area, B.C. [Canada. Geol. Survey]. 8o. Ottawa. 1922
MacCarron, Stewart & Co., *Ltd., publishers, see* ALLEN (P. S.) Stewart's hand book of the Pacific Islands, 1920.
MacCarthy, *The family of, see* MACCARTHY (S. T.) The MacCarthys of Munster, 1922.
MacCarthy (Justin), *Mrs.* **Campbell Praed & M. Menpes.**
The grey river. fol. 1889
MacCarthy (Samuel Trant).
The MacCarthys of Munster. s8o. Dundalk. 1922
Three Kerry families. [Mahony—Conway—Spotswood]. s8o. Folkestone. [1925]
The Trant family. [*w.* Suppl.] 8o. Folkestone. [1924–26]
MacCarthy Mór, *see* BUTLER (W. F. T.) Gleanings f. Irish hist.: [the lordship of MacC. Mór] &c., 1925.
MacCartney (Richard Hayes).
Songs from a watch-tower. s8o. Chicago. 1919
Maccas (Léon). La question gréco-albanaise. 8o. Nancy. 1921
MacCaul (Alex.), *D.D.* Acc. of Rabbinic authorities, *see* PRIDEAUX (H.) Hist. conn. of O. & N. Test. &c., 2v, 1865.
Maccheronee di 5 poeti ital. del sec. 15. T. Odassi—Anonimo Padovano—B. Mantovano—G. G. Alione—Fossa Cremonese. Con app. di 2 sonetti in dial. bergamasco. 8o. Milano. 1864
MacCheyne (Robert Murray).
see BONAR (A. A.) Memoir & remains of R. M. M., 1892.
„ —— & R. M. M. Narr. of a mission of inquiry to the Jews &c., 1839.
Macchioni (Bartolomeo). Descr. d. famiglia Cilnia fatta d. E. Camurrini, esaminata d. B. M. 8o. Napoli. 1688
Macchioro (Vittorio). Le terme romane di Agnano, *see* REALE ACCAD. D. LINCEI. Mon. ant., v21, 1912.
Zagreus: st. sull'Orfismo. 8o. Bari. 1920
MacClean (Frank), *see* CAMBRIDGE: FITZWILLIAM MUS. McC. coll. of Greek coins, v1, 2, 1923–26.
MacClean (John Robinson), *see* CAMBRIDGE: FITZWILLIAM MUS. McC. coll. of Greek coins, v1, 2, 1923–26.
MacClees (Helen), *see* METROPOL. MUSEUM OF ART, *N.Y.* Daily life of the Greeks & Romans as illust. by the class. coll.; by H. M., 1924.
MacClelland (Nancy). Historic wall-papers, to the intr. of machinery. Intr. by H. Clouzot. la8o. Phila. 1924
Pract. book of decor. wall-treatments. 8o. Phila. 1926
MacClenaghan (Barbara). The Springs of Lavenham & the Suffolk cloth trade in 15 & 16 c. 8o. Ipswich. [1924]
MacClintock (John), *D.D.* Sketches of eminent Methodist ministers. With portraits. la8o. N.Y. 1854
—— **& J. Strong.** Cyclopædia of Biblical, theolog. & eccl. lit. [*&* Suppl.] 12v (v11, 12, Suppl., v1, 2) [v10 *wanting*]. 8o. N.Y. 1867–91
MacClintock (Walter). Old Indian trails. 8o. 1923
MacClure (Alexander Kelly). Abraham Lincoln & men of war-times. Intr. by A. C. Lambdin. 8o. Phila. 1892
MacClure (*Sir* Robert J. Le Mesurier). The North-West passage. Capt. M'Clure's despatches f. H.M.S. "Investigator." [P2404]. 8o. 1852
MacClure (Victor). Nicolette of the Quarter. s8o. [1923]
Ultimatum. s8o. [1924]
MacClymont (James Roxburgh).
Essays in hist. geography. 8o. 1921
Essays on early ornithology &c. 8o. 1920
MacConmara (Denis), *see* MACNAMARA (D.)
MacConnell (Frederick Vavasour), *see* CHUBB (C.) Birds of Brit. Guiana, based on the coll. of F. V. M., 2v, 1916–21.
MacConnell (Richard George). Portions of Portland Canal & Skeena Mining Divisions, B.C. [Canada. Geol. Survey]. 8o. Ottawa. 1913
MacConnell (Thomas).
Signs of the times. 3rd ed. [P2782]. 8o. 1835
MacCorkle (William Alex.) The Nicaraguan Canal, *see* LUCAS (D. B.) Nicaragua &c., 1896.
MacCormick (John).
The island of Mull, its hist. &c. s8o. Glasgow. [1923]
MacCosh (James).
An exam. of Mill's philos. 2nd ed. w. add. 8o. N.Y. 1869
Realistic philos. defended. 2v. s8o. 1887
Maccovius (Joannes) [MAKOWSKY]. Distinctiones & regulae theolog. &c. Studio F. Cnutii. [*b. w.* Wollebius (J.) Compendium, 1657]. s8o. Amstelodami. 1663
MacCown (Chester Charlton), *see* SOLOMON, *king of Israel.* The testament of S. ed. by C. C. MacC., 1922.
MacCrackan (William Denison). The new Palestine. Foreword by Visct. Bryce. 8o. [1922]
MacCracken (Henry Mitchell).
H. M. M.: in memoriam. [*By var. a.*] 8o. N.Y. 1923
MacCracken (Henry Noble). The Lydgate canon, *see* PHILOL. SOC. Trans., 1907.
Lydgatiana; ed. M., *see* ARCHIV F. D. ST. D. NEU. SPR., B126, 127, 129–131, 1911–13.
MacCreiche, *Saint, see* PLUMMER (C.) Misc. hagiogr. Hibern., 1925.
MacCrie (Thomas), *D.D., the elder, 1772–1835.* Hist. of the progr. & suppr. of the Reformation in Italy in the 16th c.: incl. sketch of the Reform. in the Grisons. 2nd ed. enl. 8o. E. 1833
Lives of A. Henderson [by T. McC.] & J. Guthrie, 1846, *see* HENDERSON (A.)
Vindic. of the Covenanters, in a rev. of "Tales of my landlord" [by Sir W. Scott]. 4th ed. s8o. E. 1845
MacCrie (Thomas), *D.D., the younger, 1797–1875.* Annals of Engl. Presbytery, to the pres. time. s8o. 1872
Sketches of Scot. Ch. History. 4th ed. s8o. E. [1846]
MacCrindle (J. W.) Anc. India as descr. by Ktesias the Knidian; being a tr. of the abridg. of h. "Indika" by Phôtios &c. With intr., notes & ind. [Anc. India, v3]. 8o. Calcutta. 1882
Ancient India as descr. in classical lit. Coll. of Gr. & Lat. texts, extr. f. Herodotus, Strabo &c. Tr. & annot. by J. W. M'C. 8o. Westminster. 1901
MacCuirtin (Hugh), *see* MACCURTIN (H.)
MacCullagh (*Capt.* Francis).
Bolshevik persecution of Xty. 8o. 1924
A prisoner of the Reds, in Siberia. 8o. 1921
MacCullagh (Thomas). The earnest life: mem. of T. O. Keysell. s8o. 1867
Sir William M'Arthur: a biogr. 8o. 1891

MacCulloch (John Arnott). The misty isle of Skye. Intr. by Macleod of Macleod. [3rd ed.] 8º. Stirling. 1927
R. L. Stevenson & The Bridge of Allan &c. 8º. Glasgow. 1927
see MYTHOLOGY of all races; ed. J. A. M. &c., v4, 7, 1925–27.

Macculloch (John Ramsay).
Dict. of commerce & commercial navig. 8º. 1844
Disc. on the rise &c. of polit. econ. 2nd ed. [P2782]. 8º. E. 1825

MacCunn (John).
Ethics of citizenship. [6th ed.] s8º. Glasgow. 1921
The making of character. [repr.] s8º. C. 1921
The polit. philosophy of Burke. 8º. 1913

MacCurdy (*Rt. Hon.* Charles Albert). Guilty! Prince Lichnowsky's disclosures. [P2484]. 8º. [1918]

MacCurdy (Edward). The lays of a limpet. s8º. 1920
Leonardo & war. Estr. d. "Raccolta Vinciana," fasc. 10. [P2786; 2849]. 8º. Milano. 1919
Leonardo da Vinci. [R. Inst. of Gt. Brit. *Repr.* P2773; 2847]. 8º. 1920
The mind of Leonardo da Vinci. 8º. [1928]

MacCurdy (George Grant). Human origins: a manual of prehistory. 2v. 8º. N.Y. 1924

MacCurdy (James Frederick). History, prophecy & the monuments. 2v. 8º. N.Y. 1894

MacCurdy (John Thomson).
Common princ. in psychology & physiology. 8º. C. 1928
Problems in dynamic psychology. s8º. C. 1923
Psychology of emotion. 8º. O. 1925

MacCurtin (Hugh) [MACCUIRTIN (H.)], *see* BEGLY (C.) Engl.-Irish dict., 1732.

MacDaniel (Walton Brooks).
Roman private life & its survivals. s8º. [1925]

MacDermot (Edward Terence).
Hist. of the Gt. Western Railway. v1, 1833–63, 2p. 8º. 1927

MacDiarmid (Duncan Stewart). Life of Lt.-Gen. Sir J. M. Grierson. Foreword by Earl Haig. 8º. 1923

Macdonagh (Michael). The Reporters' Gallery. 8º. [1920]

Macdonald, *The clan of, see* MACDONALD (A.) Family mem. of the M. of Keppoch, 1885.

Macdonald (Alan John).
Lanfranc: st. of h. life, work & writing. 8º. 1926

Macdonald (Alexander), *F.R.G.S., war correspondent.*
*Why Gordon perished. By a war correspondent. 8º. 1896

Macdonald (Alexander K.) Picturesque Paraguay. 8º. [1911]

Macdonald (Angus), *M.D., of Taunton.* Family mem. of the Macdonalds of Keppoch. Ed. C. R. Markham. Notes by C. E. Stuart, Cte. d'Albanie. 8º. 1885

Macdonald (Anne). Bud & adventure. School story. s8º. [1926]

MacDonald (Arthur). Anthropometry of soldiers. Repr. f. Med. Record, Dec. 14, 1918. [P2427]. s8º. N.Y. [1918]
Criminology. Intr. by C. Lombroso. s8º. N.Y. 1893
Scots & Scot. infl. in Congress. [*Extr. f.* Metron, v1, N. 2. P2682]. 8º. Rovigo. 1920

MacDonald (Donald), *fellow of the Linnean Soc.*
Fruit culture & utility. s8º. 1924

Macdonald (Donald), *minister of the Free Church, Edinkillie.*
Introd. to the Pentateuch. 2v. 8º. E. 1861

MacDonald (Donald Francis). Sediment. form. of the Panama Canal Zone. [S.I., U.S. Nat. Mus. Bull. 103]. 8º. Wash. 1919

MacDonald (*le maréchal* Etienne J. J. A.), *duc de Tarente.*
Développement de la propos. faite dans la séance du 3 de ce mois. [Chambre des pairs, 10 déc. 1814]. [P2772]. [*no tp.*] 8º. *n.p.* [1814]
Recoll. Ed. C. Rousset. Tr. S. L. Simeon. n. & rev. ed. s8º. 1893

MacDonald (Frederick Charles), *see* HARFORD (J. B.) & F. C. M. H. C. G. Moule, bp. of Durham; biog., 1922.

Macdonald (George), *curator of Hunterian Coin Cabinet, Glasgow.* The evolution of coinage. s8º. C. 1916
The silver coinage of Crete. [P2411]. 8º. 1919
„ „ *For a. copy see* BRIT. ACAD. Proc., v9, 1919–20.

Macdonald (George), *LL.D.* Violin songs. s8º. 1884
see BULLOCH (J. M.) Centennial bibliog. of G. M., 1925.
„ MACDONALD (GREVILLE.) G. M. & h. wife, 1924.

Macdonald (George Ranald). Spanish-Eng. & Eng.-Span. commercial dict. 2nd ed. rev. & enl. s8º. [1920]

Macdonald (Greville), *M.D.* George Macdonald & h. wife. Intr. by G. K. Chesterton. la8º. [1924]
How Jones found his enemy. s8º. 1916
The north door. s8º. 1920

Macdonald (J. N.)
A political escapade: Fiume & d'Annunzio. 8º. 1921

Macdonald (*Rev.* James). Mem. of the Rev. J. Benson. 8º. 1822

Macdonald (*Rt. Hon.* James Ramsay).
*The man of to-morrow: J. R. Macdonald. By Iconoclast. 8º. 1923
Margaret Ethel Macdonald. [repr.] s8º. [1924]
Parliament & democracy. s8º. [1920]
A policy for the Labour Party. s8º. [1920]
Socialism: crit. & constructive. s8º. 1921
„ „ [rev. ed.] 8º. [1924]

Macdonald (John), *footman, of Inverness-shire.* Mem. of an 18th cent. footman. Travels (1745–79). Intr. by J. Beresford. 8º. [1927]

Macdonald (John), *F.R.S.* A treatise on telegraphic communication, marine code & o. naval signals. 8º. 1808

Macdonald (*Rt. Hon. Sir* John Alec), *1815–91.* Correspondence. Sel. made by Sir J. Pope. 8º. Toronto. [1921]

Macdonald (*Rt. Hon.* John Archibald Murray), *M.P.*
K. Marx & the present unrest. [P2617]. s8º. [1922]

Macdonald (John Ronald Moreton). Third Republic, *see* BUCHAN (J.), *ed.* Nations, 1923.

Macdonald (L. M.), *wife of Rev. Ewan M., see* MONTGOMERY (L. M.)

Macdonald (Louisa), *wife of George Macdonald, form. Powell, see* MACDONALD (G.) George Macdonald & h. wife, 1924.

Macdonald (Margaret Ethel), *wife of J. Ramsay Macdonald.*
see HERBERT (L.) Mrs. R. M., 1924.
„ MACDONALD (J. R.) M. E. M., 1924.

Macdonald (*marshal* Stephen J. A.), *see* MACDONALD (*le mar.* ETIENNE J. J. A.)

Macdonald (T. D.) Gaelic proverbs & proverb. sayings, w. Eng. tr. s8º. Stirling. [1926]

MacDonald (Walter), *D.D.* Remin. of a Maynooth professor. Ed. D. Gwynn. [2nd impr.] 8º. [1926]
Some ethical questions of peace & war, w. spec. ref. to Ireland. s8º. 1919

Macdonald (William), *prebendary of Salisbury, see* DOUGLAS (J.) Sel. works, w. biograph. mem. by W. M., 1820.

MacDonald (William), *prof. of hist. in Brown Univ.* From Jefferson to Lincoln. [Home Univ. Lib.] s8º. N.Y. [1913]
The intellectual worker & h. work. s8º. [1923]
Reconstruction in France. 8º. 1922

MacDonald (William Bell).
Sketch of a Coptic gramm. [*lithogr.*] 8º. E. 1846

Macdonell (Alastair Ranaldson), *15th chieftain of the clan Glengarry, see* ROUGHEAD (W.) G.'s way &c., 1922.

Macdonell (Arthur Anthony). India's past: survey of lit., relig., lang. & antiqs. s8º. O. 1927
Lect. on compar. religion. 8º. Calcutta. 1925
Vedic grammar. [Grundr. d. indo-ar. Phil., B1, H4]. la8º. Str. 1910

Macdonell (*Sir* John). Hist. trials. Ed. R. W. Lee. Pref by Ld. Shaw of Dunfermline. 8º. O. 1927

Macdonnel (D. E.) Dict. of quotations, taken f. Lat., Fr., Greek, Span., & Ital. lang. Tr. into Eng. 9th ed. rev. &c. s8º. 1826

MacDougal (Daniel Trembly) & F. Shreve. Growth in trees & massive organs of plants. [C.I. of Wash.] la8º. Wash. 1924

MacDougall (Alexander William).
The Maybrick case. 8º. 1891

MacDougall (Frank Lidgett). Sheltered markets: value of Empire trade. Pref. by Sir R. Horne. s8º. 1925

MacDougall (William).
The Amer. nation: its problems &c. 8º. [1925]
Anthropology & history. Boyle lect., 1920. [P2433]. 8º. 1920
Character & the conduct of life. 8º. [1927]
Ethics & some mod. world problems. s8º. [1924]
The group mind. Princ. of collective psychol. &c. 8º. C. 1920
Intr. to soc. psychology. 14th ed., w. 3 suppl. chapters. s8º. [1919]
„ „ 15th ed. s8º. [1920]
„ „ 16th ed. s8º. [1921]
„ „ 18th ed. s8º. [1923]
Janus: the conquest of war. s8º. [1927]
National welfare & nat. decay. s8º. [1921]
Outline of abnormal psychology. 8º. [1926]
Outline of psychology. 8º. [1923]
Physiological psychology. [Temple primers]. [repr.] s8º. 192[illegible]
see PRINCE (M.) Problems of personality: st. pres. to M. P.; ed. W. McD. &c. 1925.

MacDowall (Arthur). Nature & men. s8º. [1923]

MacDowall (Robert John Stewart). The mind. [By var. a. Lectures. Ed. R. J. S. M. Intr. by E. Barker. s8º. 192[illegible]

MacDowall (Stewart Andrew). Evolution, knowledge & revelation. Hulsean Lect., 1923–24. s8°. C. 1924
Mace (Arthur Cruttenden).
see CARTER (H.) & A. C. M. Tomb of Tut-ankh-Amen, v1, 1923.
„ REISNER (G. A.) & A. C. M. Early dynastic cemeteries of Naga-ed-Dêr, p2 by M., 1909.
Mace (Aurelia Gay) [*ps.* AURELIA]. *The Aletheia: princ. of Shakers. 8°. Farmington, Maine. 1899
Mace (Herbert). Adventures among bees. s8°. [1923]
Macedo (Francisco). Collationes S. Thomae et Scoti in tertium sententiarum, cum differentiis &c. fol. Patavii. 1680
Macedo Soares (José Carlos de). Brazil & the League of Nations. Intr. by Ld. Phillimore. 8°. Paris. 1928
Macedonia. A hdbk. of M., 1920, *see* ADMIRALTY: NAVAL INTELL. DIVISION.
Macedonio (Marcello). Le nove muse di M. M. Racc. da P. Macedonio. 8°. Napoli. 1614
MacElroy (Robert MacNutt). Amer. hist. as an internat. study. Inaug. address, Oxford, 1926. [P2821]. 8°. O. 1926
Grover Cleveland: auth. biog. 2v. 8°. 1923
MacEvoy (Charles). The paper wedding. s8°. [1921]
The Three Barrows. Play. s8°. 1924
MacEvoy (James).
Smoky River Coal Field. [P2771]. 8°. [Ottawa. 1925]
MacEwen, *The family of, see* MACEWEN (R. S. T.) Clan Ewen, 1904.
MacEwen (R. S. T.) Clan Ewen. 8°. Glasgow. 1904
MacEwen (William), *F.R.S.* The growth & shedding of the antler of the deer. 8°. Glasgow. 1920
MacFadden (Gertrude Violet). The preventive man. s8°. 1920
The Roman way. s8°. [1925]
Macfall (C. Haldane C.)
The book of Lovat Claud Fraser. 4°. 1923
Macfarlan (Duncan), *D.D.* The revivals of the 18th c., Cambuslang. With 3 sermons by G. Whitefield &c. s8°. [1847]
MacFarlane (John), *M.A., M.Com.*
Econ. geography. 3rd ed. 8°. 1927
Macfarlane (John Muirhead).
The evol. & distrib. of fishes. 8°. N.Y. 1923
Macfarlane (William Charles).
A short acc. of Dorchester. [P2846]. 8°. O. 1883
Macfarren (George). Winning a husband. Interlude. [P2583]. s8°. *Cumberland.* [1828]
MacFee (William). Command. 2nd impr. s8°. [1923]
Race. s8°. [1924]
Sunlight in New Granada. 8°. 1925
Macfie (Ronald Campbell).
Heredity, evolution & vitalism. 8°. Bristol. 1912
Sunshine & health. [Home Univ. Lib.] s8°. [1927]
MacFirbis (Duald). On the Fomorians & the Norsemen. Irish text, w. tr. & notes by A. Bugge. [Norske Hist. K.] 8°. Christiania. 1905
MacGee (Thomas D'Arcy), *see* BRADY (A.) T. D. M., 1925.
Macgeorge (Bernard Buchanan).
Cat. of library of B. B. M. *p.f.p. use.* la8°. Glasgow. 1906
Cat. of the library of M. Sold by auction by Sotheby, July 1924. [Illust.] la8°. [1924]
MacGhee (Robert James). *The Church of Rome: h. moral theology. A rep. on "the books & doc. on the papacy" depos. in the Univ. Libr., Camb. &c. [Ed. E. Baines]. 8°. 1853
The complete notes of the Doway Bible & Rhemish Test. 8°. D. 1837
MacGiffert (Arthur Cushman), *D.D.*
The God of the early Xtns. s8°. E. 1924
MacGilchrist (John), *M.D.* Remarks on Present state of medicine. Review of Prof. Bennett's lect. 2nd ed. [P2576]. 8°. E. 1856
MacGill (Caroline E.) Hist. of transportation in the U.S. bef. 1860. Prep. under dir. of B. H. Meyer by C. E. M. *& others.* [C.I. of Wash.]. la8°. Wash. 1917
MacGill (Hamilton Montgomerie). Songs of the Xtn. creed & life. [*Greek & Lat.*] Sel. & tr. by H. M. G. 8°. 1876
MacGill (J. F.) British grasses. [Ed. J. F. M.] Publ. by McGill & Smith, Ltd., Ayr. la8°. Ayr. [1920]
MacGill (Nettie Pauline). Infant-welfare work in Europe, 1921, *see* UNITED STATES: LAB.
The welfare of children in bitum. coal mining communities in W. Virginia, *see* UNITED STATES: LAB. Children's Bur., Publ. 117, 1923.

MacGill (Patrick). Lanty Hanlon. s8°. 1922
Maureen. s8°. 1920
Moleskin Joe. s8°. 1923
Songs of Donegal. s8°. 1921
Macgill (Thomas), *Merchant, of Glasgow.* Travels in Turkey Italy & Russia, 1803–06, w. acc. of some of the Greek islands. 2v. s8°. 1808
MacGill & Smith, *Ltd., Ayr, see* MACGILL (J. F.), *ed.* Brit. grasses, 1920.
Macgillivray (Evan James).
Copyright cases, 1919. [P2490]. 8°. 1920
MacGilvary (Margaret).
The dawn of a new era in Syria. 8°. N.Y. [1920]
MacGovern (*Mrs.* Janet B. Montgomery). Among the head-hunters of Formosa. Pref. by R. R. Marett. 8°. [1922]
MacGovern (William Montgomery).
Jungle paths & Inca ruins. 8°. [1927]
Manual of Buddhist philos. v1, Cosmology. 8°. 1923
To Lhasa in disguise: acc. of a secret exped. thr. Tibet. 8°. [1924]
MacGowan (John), *Baptist minister.*
Infernal conference: or, dialogues of devils. s8°. 1839
*Priestcraft defended. A sermon occ. by the expulsion of 6 gentlemen f. Univ. of Oxford. By the Shaver. 12th ed. s8°. 1771
„ „ ....[P2511]. 8°. Halifax. 1815
MacGowan (Kenneth). The theatre of to-morrow. 8°. [1923]
—— **& R. E. Jones.** Continental stagecraft. 8°. 1923
MacGrath (*Mrs.* Arthur T.), *see* FORBES (ROSITA).
MacGrath (*Sir* Patrick Thomas). Newfoundland, *see* BUCHAN (J.), *ed.* Nations, Brit. Amer., 1923.
MacGregor (Alasdair Alpin). Wild Drumalbain, or, the road to Meggernie & Glen Coe. 8°. [1927]
MacGregor (Alexander), *M.A., of West Church, Inverness.* Highland superstitions. Foreword by I. Cameron. 8°. Stirling. 1922
MacGregor (George), *F.S.A., Scot.* Hist. of Burke & Hare & of the Resurrectionist times. 8°. Glasgow. 1884
MacGregor (James Comyn).
Basuto traditions. [P2584]. s8°. [Cape Town. 1905]
MacGregor (Jessie). Gardens of celebrities & celeb. gardens in & around London. la8°. [1919]
MacGregor (John Marshall). Leaves of Hellas: essays on aspects of Greek lit. 8°. 1926
MacGregor (M.) Iron ores &c. by M. &c., *see* GEOLOG. SURVEY OF ENG. &c. Spec. rep. on min. resources, 11, 1920.
Macgregor (Malcolm), *ps., see* MASON (W.)
MacGregor (Marshall), *see* MACGREGOR (J. M.)
MacGuire (Constantine Edward), *see* MOULTON (H. G.) & C. E. M. Germany's capacity to pay, 1923.
MacGuire (James William). Geog. dict. of Virgin Islands of U.S., 1925, *see* UNITED STATES: COMMERCE, DEPT. OF.
Mach (Ernst). Hist. & root of princ. of the conservation of energy. Tr. & annot. by P. E. B. Jourdain. s8°. Chicago. 1911
Principles of physical optics. Tr. J. S. Anderson & A. F. A. Young. 8°. [1926]
Machado (Antonio).
see MACHADO (M.) & A. M. Desdichas de la fortuna o J. Valcárcel, 1926.
„ —— & —— Juan de Mañara, 1927.
Machado (Cyrillo Volkmar). Coll. de mem. rel. ás vidas d. pintores, e escultores &c. portug. &c. [1823]. Seg. de notas p. Dr. J. M. Teixeira de Carvalho & Dr. V. Correia. 8°. Coimbra. 1922
Machado (Manuel) & A. Machado. Desdichas de la fortuna o Julianillo Valcárcel. Tragicomedia. 8°. [1926]
Juan de Mañara. Drama. 8°. 1927
Machado de Assis (Joaquim Maria). Attendant's confession—Fortune-teller—Life, *see* GOLDBERG (I.), *tr.* Brazilian tales, 1924.
Machar (J. S.) The jail: exper. in 1916. Auth. tr. by P. Selver. s8°. O. 1921
Machard (Alfred). Minuit, Chrétiens!, *see* ŒUVRES libres, 16, 1923.
La noce à papa, *see* ŒUVRES libres, 5, 1921.
Machatschek (Fritz). Landeskunde d. Sudeten- u. Westkarpatenländer. 8°. St. 1927
Landeskunde v. russ. Turkestan. 8°. St. 1921
Machault (Guillaume de) [MACHAUT]. Œuvres. Publ. par E. Hœpffner. [Soc. d. a. t. f.] t3. 8°. 1921

Machault (Jacques de). Hist. of the miss. of the Soc. of Jesus estab. in Persia by A. of Rhodes. Tr. Sir A. T. Wilson. [Extr. f. Bull. of Sch. of Or. St., v3, p4, *q.v.* P2821]. 8°. 1925

Machen (Arthur).
The Canning wonder [1753]. 8°. 1925
The chronicle of Clemendy. s8°. 1925
The hill of dreams. [repr.] s8°. [1922]
The house of souls. [repr.] s8°. 1923
The London adventure or the art of wandering. 8°. [1924]
Things near & far. s8°. [1923]

Machen (John Gresham). The origin of Paul's religion. J. Sprunt Lect. 8°. [1921]

Machiavelli (Niccolò).
Hist. fiorentine. 8°. [Firenze]. 1532
Tutte le opera. 2t. 4°. Londra. 1747
TRANSLATIONS.
[Works]. The hist. of Florence—The prince &c. [Tr. H. Nevile]. [*no gen. tp.*] fol. 1680
,, Tr. &c. [by H. Nevile]. 3rd ed. fol. 1720
see BROSCH (M.) M. am Hofe &c. Maximilians I, *n.d.*
see JANNI (E.) M., 1927.
,, LEWIS (W.) The lion & the fox, Shakespeare's plays (infl. of M. &c.), 1927.
,, LUCAS-DUBRETON (J.) La disgrâce de N. M., 1469–1527, 2e éd., 1913.
,, PREZZOLINI (G.) Vita di N. M. fiorentino, 1927.
,, TOFFANIN (G.) M. e il "Tacitismo," 1921.

Machin (Alfred). The ascent of man. 8°. 1925
Machin (John), *1624–64, see* WOLSELEY (*Sir* C.) Narr. of life of J. M., 1671.
Machuel (Louis). Méthode pour l'ét. de l'Arabe parlé. 5e éd. s8°. Alger. 1900
Macias (Juan Manuel). Cuba in revolution. [P2845]. 8°. 1871
Maciej, *z Miechowa.* Tractatus de duabus Sarmatiis Asiana & Europiana & de contentis in eis. s4°. [Auguste Vindel. 1518]
Maciejowski (Samuel) [MATIEOVIUS (S.)], *bp. of Cracow, see* ORICHOVIUS (S.) Pro eccl. Christi ad S. M., 1546.
Maciel (Ant. Vicente Mendes), *see* CONSELHEIRO (A.)
MacIlvaine (Charles Petit), *bp. of Protestant Episc. Ch., Ohio.*
The evidences of Xty. 9th ed. s8°. N.Y. [1832]
MacIlwain (Charles Howard).
The Amer. Revolution. 8°. N.Y. 1923
MacInerny (M. H.) St. Mochta & Bachiarius. [Repr. f. "The Irish eccles. record," 1923]. 8°. D. [1924]
MacInnes (C. M.) The early Eng. tobacco trade. s8°. 1926
Macintosh (Charles), *naturalist: 1839–1922, see* COATES (H.) C. M., 1924.
Macintosh (Jessie), *see* MACLACHLAN (*Mrs.* J.)
MacIntosh (William Carmichael). Monograph of the Brit. marine Annelids. [Ray Soc.] v4. 2p. fol. 1922–23
The resources of the sea. Effects of trawling &c. off Scot. shores. 2nd ed. 8°. C. 1921
MacIver (David Randall-), *see* RANDALL-MACIVER (D.)
Maciver (Robert Morrison).
The elements of soc. science. 3rd ed. s8°. [1926]
The modern state. 8°. O. 1926
Mack (James Logan). The border line f. Solway Firth to the North Sea along Marches of Scotland & Eng. la8°. E. 1924

Mackail (Denis).
According to Gibson. s8°. [1923]
Bill the bachelor. s8°. 1922
The flower show. s8°. [1927]
The fortunes of Hugo. s8°. [1926]
Greenery Street. s8°. [1925]
,, ,, [new impr.] s8°. [1925]
The majestic mystery. s8°. [1924]
What next? s8°. 1920

Mackail (John William).
Allan Ramsay & the romantic revival, *see* ENGLISH ASSOC. Essays &c., v10, 1924.
The alliance of Latin & Eng. studies. [P2718]. 8°. 1923
Bentley's Milton. [Warton lect.; f. Proc. of Brit. Acad., v11. P2737]. 8°. [1924]
Classical studies. 8°. [1925]
The classics. Address, Class. Assoc. [P2718]. 8°. 1923.
Collins, & the Eng. lyric in the 18th c., *see* ROY. SOC. OF LIT. Essays &c.: Trans., N.S., v1, 1921.
J. L. Strachan-Davidson, Master of Balliol. 8°. O. 1925
The life of William Morris. n. impr. 2v *in* 1. s8°. 1922
The Pilgrim's progress: lect., Roy. Inst., March 14, 1924. s8°. 1924
Shakespeare after 300 years: lect., *see* BRIT. ACAD. Proc., 1915–16.
Studies of Eng. poets. 8°. 1926
The study of poetry. Disc. [P2466]. 8°. 1915
Virgil & h. meaning to the world of to-day. s8°. [1923]
What is the good of Greek? Lect. [P2738]. 8°. 1924
see ERASMUS (D.) Against war; intr. by J. W. M., 1907.

—— & G. Wyndham.
Life & letters of George Wyndham. 2v. 8°. [1925]

Mackall (Leonard L.) Servetus notes. Repr. f. Contrib. ded. to Sir W. Osler. [P2433]. 8°. [N.Y.] 1919
Mackarness (Frederic Coleridge), *see* GOOCH (G. P.) F. M., a brief memoir, 1922.
MacKay (Bertram Reid). Beauceville Map-area, Quebec. [Canada. Geol. Survey. P2624]. 8°. Ottawa. 1921
MacKay (C. D.)
The French garden. Pref. by W. B. Thomas. s8°. [1909 ?]
Mackay (Charles).
The Thames & its tributaries. 2v [v2 *wanting*]. 8°. 1840
Mackay (Dorothy Louise). Les hôpitaux & la charité à Paris au 13e s. la8°. 1923
Mackay (*Capt.* E. J. H.), *see* VINCENT (L. H.) & E. J. H. M. Hébron, 1923.
Mackay (Francis Alexander) [FITZHUGH (FRANCIS), *ps.*] The crook & the sword, The heir of Lorn & o. poems. s8°. E. 1853
Lays & poems on Italy. s8°. 1862
Poems, pastorals & songs. coll. & rev. ed. s8°. E. 1866
Mackay (John Henry). Der Freiheitsucher. Psychologie e. Entwickelung. 2e (Privat-) A. 8°. 1921
Mackay (Robert A.) The unreformed Senate of Canada. Intr. by G. M. Wrong. 8°. 1926
Mackay (William), *see* INVERNESS. Records of I.; ed. W. M. &c., v2, 1924.
Mackcoull (James) [J. MOFFAT].
*Memoir of life & trial of J. M., w. append. 8°. E. 1822
MacKeachan (John) [*ps.* JOHN HECTORSON].
Sport of fishing. 8°. 1923
Mackean (William Herbert). Christian monasticism in Egypt, to close of 4th cent. 8°. 1920
Mackee (Thomas Hudson). The national conventions & platform of all political parties. 3rd ed. rev. & enl. s8°. Baltimore. 1900
Presid. inaugurat., 1789–1893, w. addresses, hist. notes &c. 8°. Wash. 1893
Mackellar (C. D.) Scented isles & coral gardens: Torres Straits, German New Guinea & Dutch East Indies. 8°. 1912
MacKelvie (William), *D.D.* *Memorials of the union of the Secession & Relief Churches now United Presbyterian Church, 1847. s8°. E. 1847
MacKendrick (*Col.* William Gordon) [*ps.* THE ROADBUILDER]. The destiny of the Brit. Empire & the U.S.A. With app., Who are the Japanese? 5th ed. rev. 8°. 1925
Mackenna (Robert William). Through flood & fire. s8°. [1925]

MacKenna (Stephen).
An affair of honour. s8°. [1925]
The commandment of Moses. s8°. [1923]
The confessions of a well-meaning woman. s8°. [1922]
Due reckoning. 3rd & last part of "The realists." s8°. 1927
The education of Eric Lane. s8°. N.Y. [1921]
Lady Lilith. 1st part of The sensationalists. s8°. [1920]
The oldest god. s8°. [1926]
The secret victory. 3rd part of The sensationalists. s8°. [1921]
Soliloquy. s8°. [1922]
Sonia between two worlds. 13th ed. s8°. [1918]
To-morrow & to-morrow. s8°. [1924]
The unburied dead. s8°. [1928]
Vindication. s8°. [1923]
While I remember. 8°. [1921]

MacKenna (Theobald), *see* SHEEHY (P.) Union a plague: ans. to M.'s Mem. on the projected union, 1799.
Mackensen (A. L. F. August, *Feldmarschall* **v.),** *see* LUYKEN (MAX). Mackensen: von Bukarest bis Saloniki: nach Miterlebtem &c. dargestellt v. M. L., 1920.
Mackenzie (Agnes Mure). Lost Kinnellan. s8°. [1927]
The quiet lady. s8°. [1926]
The women in Shakespeare's plays. 8°. 1924
Mackenzie (*Sir* Alex.), *explorer, d. 1820.*
see WADE (M. S.) M. of Canada: life & adv., 1927.
,, WOOLLACOTT (A. P.) M. & h. voyageurs, 1927.
,, WRONG (H.) Sir A. M., explor. &c., 1927.
Mackenzie (Alexander), *of the Legislative Council, Madras.*
How India is governed. s8°. 1882
Mackenzie (Arthur Henderson). State exams. in Scot. schools. [Bur. of Educ., India. Pamph. No. 9. P2497]. 8°. Calcutta. 1921
see DUNCAN (H. S.) & A. H. M. Training of teachers, 1919.
Mackenzie (Charles Francis). A Turkish manual. s8°. 1879
Mackenzie (Charles Frederick), *missionary bp. of S. Africa, see* GOODWIN (H.) Mem. of M., 2nd ed., 1865.

Mackenzie (Compton).
The altar steps. s8°. [1922]
Coral. s8°. [1925]
Fairy gold. s8°. [1926]
The heavenly ladder. s8°. [1924]
The old men of the sea. s8°. [1924]
The parson's progress. s8°. [1923]
Rich relatives. s8°. 1921
The seven ages of woman. s8°. [1923]
The vanity girl. s8°. [1920]
Vestal fire. s8°. [1927]

Mackenzie (D. R.), *F.R.G.S.* The spirit-ridden Konde: inhab. of Lake Nyasa region. 8°. 1925

Mackenzie (David). The emigrant's guide; 10 years' exper. in Australia. s8°. 1845

Mackenzie (Donald Alexander).
Anc. civilizations. 8°. 1927
Anc. man in Britain. Foreword by G. E. Smith. 8°. 1922
Buddhism in pre-Xtn. Brit. 8°. 1928
Egypt. myth & legend. 8°. [1913]
Footprints of early man. s8°. 1927
Indian myth & legend. 8°. [1913]
The migration of symbols & th. rel. to beliefs & custom. 8°. 1926
Myths of Babylonia & Assyria. 8°. [1915]
Myths of China & Japan. 8°. [1923]
Myths of Crete & Pre-Hellenic Europe. 8°. [1917]
Myths of pre-Columbian America. 8°. [1926 ?]

Mackenzie (Frederick Arthur).
Korea's fight for freedom. 8°. [1920]
The mystery of the Daily Mail. 8°. 1921
Serving the King's Men: Salvation Army. [P2242]. 8°. 1918
see THAW (H. K.) Trial of H. T.; ed. F. A. M., 1928.

Mackenzie (*Sir* George), *Lord Advocate, of Rosehaugh, 1636–91.* A defence of the Royal line of Scotland &c. in ans. to the bp. of St. Asaph [W. Lloyd]. s8°. 1685

Mackenzie (H. Millicent), *wife of J. S. M., form. Hughes.* Freedom in education: meaning, value &c. s8°. [1924]

Mackenzie (Hector Graham Gordon) & G. Rhodes. Health & the mind. s8°. [1921]

Mackenzie (Henry), *a. of "The man of feeling."* Anecdotes & egotisms, 1745–1831. Ed., w. intr. by H. W. Thompson. 8°. 1927
see HIGHLAND SOCIETY. Report on authenticity of poems of Ossian, 1805.

Mackenzie (*Sir* James), *M.D.* The future of medicine. 8°. 1919
see WILSON (R. M.) The beloved physician: Sir J. M., 1926.

Mackenzie (*Col.* James Stuart Fraser). Brit. orchids. 4°. [1918]

Mackenzie (John Stuart). Arrows of desire. Essays on our nat. character & outlook. 8°. [1920]
Outlines of social philos. [repr.]. 8°. [1921]
Ultimate values. s8°. [1924]

MacKenzie (Kenneth), *ed., see* ÆSOP. Ysopet-Avionnet, 1919.

Mackenzie (Kenneth Donald). Confusion of the churches: problem of reunion. 8°. 1925

MacKenzie (N. M. W. J.) The men of the Hudson's Bay Company. 8°. Fort William. [1921]

Mackenzie (Osgood Hanbury).
A hundred years in the Highlands. 8°. 1921
,, ,, ...pop. ed. 8°. 1924

Mackenzie (Peter). Lectures & sermons. Arranged & introd. by J. Dawson. s8°. 1897

MacKenzie (Roderick D.), *see* PARK (R. E.), E. W. BURGESS & R. D. McK. The city, 1925.

Mackenzie (William Cook). Life & times of J. Maitland, Duke of Lauderdale, 1616–82. 8°. 1923

Mackenzie (William Douglas).
The ethics of gambling. n. & enl. ed. s8°. 1911

Mackenzie (William Mackay). The mediaeval castle in Scotland. Rhind. lects., 1925–26. 8°. 1927
see BARRON (D. G.) Castle of Dunnottar, w. descr. of bldgs. by W. M. M. &c., 1925.

MacKerrell (John).
Gram. of the Carnátaca lang. 4°. Madras. 1820

MacKerrow (Ronald Brunlees). A note on the teaching of "Eng. lang. & lit." [Eng. Assoc., Pamph. 49. P2683]. 8°. 1921
Eng. gram. & grammars, *see* ENGLISH ASSOC. Essays, v8, 1922.
Intr. to bibliog. for literary students. 8°. O. 1927

Mackie Ethnological Expedition to Cent. Africa. Report.
see ROSCOE (J.) The Bagesu &c., 1924. [3.]
,, —— The Bakitara, 1923. [1.]
,, —— The Banyankole, 1923. [2.]

Mackie (J. B.) Life & work of D. McLaren. 2v. 8°. 1888

Mackie (*Sir* Peter Jeffery), *Bart.* The keeper's book: duties of a gamekeeper. With ch. by Ld. M. Graham, Capt. H. S. Kennedy &c. [16th ed.] 8°. 1924

MacKillop (A. D.), *see* MACKILLOP (M.) & A. D. MACK. Efficiency methods, 2nd impr., 1920.

MacKillop (M.) & A. D. MacKillop. Efficiency methods: intr. to scientific management. 2nd impr. s8°. 1920

Mackinlay (*Lt.-Col.* George). The Magi. How they recognised Christ's Star. Pref. by W. M. Ramsay. 8°. 1907
see WAR OFFICE. Text book of gunnery [by G. M.], 1897.

MacKinley (William), *pres. of the U.S., see* RHODES (J. F.) The McK. & Roosevelt admin., 1897–1909, 1922.

Mackinnon (James), *Ph.D.* Constit. hist. of Scotland, to the Reformation. By J. M. assist. by J. A. R. Mackinnon. 8°. 1924
Luther & the Reformation. v1, 2. 8°. 1925–28
Social & indust. hist. of Scotland, to the Union. 8°. 1920

Mackinnon (James A. R.), *see* MACKINNON (J.) Constit. hist. of Scotland; by J. M. assist. by J. A. R. M., 1924.

Mackintosh (Alexander), *of Forfar.* The muster roll of the Forfarshire or Ld. Ogilvy's Regt., raised on behalf of the Hse. of Stuart, 1745–46, w. biog. sketches. 8°. Inverness. 1914

Mackintosh (C. W.) The new Zambesi trail: 2 journeys to N.-W. Rhodesia, 1903 & 1920. 8°. 1922

Mackintosh (Herbert B.) Pilgrimages in Moray. s8°. Elgin. 1924

Macklin (Charles). The man of the world. [Dolby's Brit. theatre]. s8°. [1824]
Man of the world, *see* INCHBALD (*Mrs.* E.) Brit. theatre, v14, 1808.

Macknight (James), *treasurer of the Abbotsford Club, see* DRUMMOND (J.) *Mem. of Sir Ewen Cameron of Locheill &c.; [ed. J. M.], 1842.

MacKnight (W. A.) Ireland under the Ulster legend: statist. tables, w. notes &c. Foreword by S. Bryant. [P2530]. 8°. 1921

Mackworth (*Lady* Margaret Haig), *wife of Sir H. Mackworth, see* RHONDDA (M. H. M., *2nd viscountess*).

Macky (John).
*Journey thr. England. 2v [1, 5th ed., 2, 3rd ed.] 8°. 1732

MacLachlan (Herbert). Letters of Theophilus Lindsey. [M'ter. Univ. Hist. ser., No. 37]. s8°. M'ter. 1920

Maclachlan (*Mrs.* Jessie) [MACINTOSH (JESSIE)]. Proceed. at trial for murder, 1862. [Return, H. of C.] fol. 1863
The Sandyford murder case: trial of Mrs. M. at Glasgow Circuit Court, Sept., 1862. s8°. Glasgow. 1862
Trial of J. M'L. Ed. W. Roughead. [Notable Brit. trials]. [2nd ed.] 8°. E. [1925]

Maclagan (Eric). The appreciation of sculpture. [From Proc. of Brit. Acad. P2818, 2821]. 8°. [1925]
A romanesque relief in York Minster. [From Proc. of Brit. Acad. P2731, 2821]. 8°. [1923]
see VICTORIA & ALBERT MUSEUM. Cat. of Ital. plaquettes; by E. M., 1924.

Maclagan (O. F.)
Mutual defence of nations. 6th ed. enl. s8°. [1915]

Maclagan (Robert Craig). Our ancestors, Scots, Picts & Cymry, & their traditions. 8°. 1913
Scot. myths: notes on S. hist. &c. 8°. E. 1882

Maclaine (James), *see* ALLEN (*Rev. Dr.*) Acc. of behaviour of J. M. fr. his condemn. to his execut., 1750.

Maclaren (Alex.), *D.D.*
The unchanging Christ & o. sermons. s8°. 1889

MacLaren (Archibald Campbell). Cricket old & new. Pref. by Hon. F. S. Jackson. s8°. 1924

MacLaren (Duncan), *see* MACKIE (J. B.) Life &c. of D. M., 2v, 1888.

MacLaren (Eva Shaw).
Elsie Inglis. Pref. by L. Ashwell. s8°. 1920

Maclaren (J. Malcolm).
Gold: its geol. occur. & geog. distrib. la8°. 1908

MacLaren (Jack). My crowded solitude. [2nd impr.] 8°. [1926]

Maclaren (W. A.) Rubber, tea & cacao, w. sect. on coffee, spices & tobacco. Comp. &c. by W. A. M. Intr. by Sir E. Geddes & H. E. Miller. [Resources of the Empire, v5]. 4°. 1924

MacLauchlan (Henry). The Watling Street, w. enl. plans &c. f. surveys made by dir. of the Duke of Northumberland. [*b. w. h.* The Roman Wall &c., 1857]. la. fol. [1857]

MacLaughlin (Andrew Cunningham). Report on the diplomatic archives of the Dept. of State, 1789–1840. [C.I. of Wash.] rev. ed. la8°. Wash. 1906
Sixteen causes of war. [Univ. of Chicago. War papers, 4]. [P2509]. 8°. Chicago. [1918]

MacLaughlin (A. C.) *contin.*, **W. E. Dodd &c.** Source problems in U.S. hist., by A. C. M., W. E. D., M. W. Jernegan, A. P. Scott. s8°. N.Y. [1918]
——, **W. A. Slade & E. D. Lewis.** Writings on American hist. 1903. Bibliog. [C.I. of Wash.] la8°. Wash. 1905
MacLaughlin (J. Fairfax). The Monroe doctrine, *see* LUCAS (D. B.) Nicaragua &c., 1896.
MacLaurin (Charles), *F.R.C.S.E.* Mere mortals: medico-hist. essays, 2nd ser. s8°. [1925]
Post mortem: essays, hist. & medical. s8°. [1923]
Maclaurin (John), *Lord Dreghorn.* *Essays in verse. 8°. [1769]
MacLaurin (John), *minister of the North West Church, 1693–1754, see* JACKSON (T.) Lib. of Xtn. biog., v10, J. McL., by J. Gillies, 1839.
MacLean, *The family of* [MCLEAN], *see* MACLEAN (A.) *Breif [*sic*] genealog. acc. of ffamily of McL., 1872.
MacLean (Alexander). *Breif [*sic*] genealog. acc. of the ffamily of McLean f. 1st settlement in the Isl. of Mull &c. la8°. E. 1872
MacLean (Annie Marion). Mod. immigration. 8°. Phila. [1925]
Maclean (Catherine Macdonald), *M.A.*
Dorothy & William Wordsworth. 8°. C. 1927
Maclean (Magnus). Electricity & its pract. applications. n. & enl. ed. 8°. 1923
Maclean (Norman).
Life of J. C. Lees, K.C.V.O., D.D. 8°. Glasgow. 1922
Maclear (George Frederick). A hist. of Xtn. missions dur. the M. Ages. s8°. C. 1863
MacLearn (Frank Harris). Palaeontology of the Silurian rocks of Arisaig, Nova Scotia. [Canada. Geolog. Survey]. 8°. Ottawa. 1924
see DOWLING (D. B.), S. E. SLIPPER & F. H. M. Investig. in the gas & oil fields of Alberta &c., 1919.
MacLennan (John Cunningham). Rep. on some sources of Helium in the Brit. Empire. [Canada. Geol. Survey. P2513]. 8°. Ottawa. 1920
Maclennan (Malcolm), *D.D.* Pronouncing & etymolog. dict. of Gaelic lang. G.-Eng.—Eng.-G. 8°. E. 1925
MacLeod (Addison). Plays & players in modern Italy. 8°. 1912
MacLeod (*Sir* **Charles Campbell) & A. W. Kirkaldy.** Trade, commerce & shipping of the Empire. [Brit. Emp.: survey; ed. H. Gunn, v7]. 8°. [1924]
MacLeod (Donald), *D.D.*
Mem. of Norman Macleod. [2nd ed.] 8°. 1877
Macleod (Flora Abigail). The vigil of hope: thoughts & prayers for mothers. s8°. 1923
Macleod (John). Manual da hist. constit. da Inglaterra. Versão dir. do orig. por T. D. Travessa. s8°. Rio de Janeiro. 1922
Macleod (*Sir* **John Lorne).** Scot. kingship, its antiq. & continuity. [P2710]. s8°. E. [1923]
Macleod (Norman), *D.D., the younger, 1812–72, see* MACLEOD (D.) Mem. of N. M., 1877.
MacLeod (Walter), *of the Scottish Hist. Society.* Royal letters & o. hist. doc. sel. f. family papers of Dundas of Dundas. Ed. W. M. 4°. E. 1897
Macler (Frédéric).
La chaire d'Arménien à l'École Spec. des Lang. Or. viv.: leçon d'ouv., 1911. [P2803]. 8° 1912
Miniatures armén.: vies du Christ, peintures ornement., 10e au 17e siècle. 4°. 1913
Moïse de Khoren & les travaux d'A. Carrière. [Extr. de la Revue archéol., s3, t41; P2790]. la8°. [1902]
Note s. un nouv. ms. d'une chron. samarit. [Extr. de la Revue des et. juives, 1905; P2790]. 8°. [1905]
Rapp. s. une mission scient. en Arménie (1909). [*Extr. f.* Nouv. arch. des miss. scient., n. s., fasc. 2]. 8°. 1910
Le texte armén. de l'Évang. d'ap. Matthieu & Marc. [Annales du Musée Guimet: Bibl. d'études, 28]. 8°. 1919
see ABAS, *Mar, called Katina.* Extr. de la chron., essai de crit. par M., 1903.
MacLintock (William Francis Porter), *see* MUSEUM OF PRACT. GEOL. Guide to coll. of gemstones: by M., 1912.
MacMahon (*Miss* **Ella).** John Fitzhenry. s8°. [1920]
Wind of dawn. s8°. [1927]
MacMahon (Percy Alexander).
Combinatory analysis. 2v. la8°. C. 1915–16
New mathematical pastimes. 8°. C. 1921
MacManus, *The sept of, see* SOTHERAN (C.) Genealog. mem. rel. to fam. of S. & s. of M., 1871.
MacMaster (John). Short hist. of the royal parish of St. Martin-in-the-Fields. 8°. 1916
MacMaster (John Bach) & F. D. Stone, *edd.* Pennsylvania & the Federal Constit., 1787–88. [Hist. Soc. of Pa.] la8°. [Phila.] 1888
Macmath (William), *F.S.A.* The Gordons of Craichlaw. Ed. T. Fraser. With biog. sketch [*of* W. M.] by F. Miller [*sep. tp.*], & 2 app. [Memorial vol.] la8°. Dalbeattie. 1924
see MILLER (F.) M. song & ballad MS., 1925.
MacMechan (Archibald). Canadian lit.: the beginnings, *see* ENG. ASSOC. Essays, v12, 1926.
Sagas of the sea. s8°. [1923]
MacMichael (Harold Alfred).
Hist. of the Arabs in the Sudan. 2v. 8°. C. 1922
Macmillan, *publishers.* Hist. atlas of mod. Europe. Maps illust. of recent hist. &c. Ed. F. J. C. Hearnshaw. la8°. 1920
Macmillan (A. S.) Somerset epitaphs. [Somerset folk ser., no. 18, 25]. 2s. s8°. 1924–26
Macmillan (*Sir* **Frederick).** The Net book Agreement 1899 & The Book War 1906–8, incl. narr. of dispute betw. The Times Book Club & The Publishers' Assoc. by E. Bell. 8°. *pr. f. the a.* 1924
Macmillan (Harold), *see* BOOTHBY (R. J. G.) &c. Industry & the state, 1927.
MacMillan (*Rev.* **John),** *of Edinburgh.* *A short survey of A friendly conf. betw. a countrie-man & h. nephew, [a follower of Mr. M.; *by T. Lin. b. w.* Covenant, National C. &c., 1712]. [*tp. wanting*]. s4°. *n.p.* 1711 ?
MacMillan (William), *Ph.D.*, **& J. A. Stewart.**
The story of the Scottish flag. la8°. Glasgow. 1925
Macmillan (William Miller).
The Cape colour question: hist. survey. 8°. [1927]
Macmorran (Kenneth M.) Handbook for churchwardens & church councillors. s8°. [1921]
MacMunn (*Lt.-Gen. Sir* **George Fletcher).**
Pike & carronade. s8°. 1912
see WAR. Hist. of Gt. War based on offic. docs., Milit. oper., Egypt & Palestine; by Sir G. M. &c., v1, 1928.
Macmunn (Nora Eileen) & G. Coster.
Europe, a regional geog. s8°. O. 1922
Macmurray (John), *see* STREETER (B. H.) Adventure; by B. H. S., J. M. &c., 1927.
MacMurray (John Van Antwerp). Treaties & agreements w. & conc. China 1894–1919. Comp. & ed. by J. V. A. M. [C.E. for Internat. Peace]. 2v. la8°. N.Y. 1921
MacMurray (William). Records of 2 City parishes: docs. ill. of hist. of SS. Anne & Agnes, Aldersgate, & St. John Zachary, London, f. 12th cent. Comp. &c. W. McM. la8°. 1925
MacMurry (Charles Alex.) Teaching by projects. A basis for purposeful study. 8°. N.Y. 1920
MacMurtrie (Douglas Crawford). Abstract-cat. of lit. on the war blinded. [P2501]. la8°. Baltimore, Md. 1919
Experience in the re-educ. of disabled soldiers in Gt. Brit. [P2430]. 8°. *n.p.* [1919]
Macnaghten (Hugh).
50 years of Eton, in prose & verse. 8°. [1924]
Macnaghten (*Sir* **Melville Leslie).** Days of my years. 8°. 1914
MacNair [MCNAIR], *The family of,* [MCNEAR; MCNEIR], *see* MACNAIR (J. B.) McNair, McNear, & McNeir genealogies, 1923.
MacNair (Harley Farnsworth). Mod. Chinese hist.: sel. readings. Extracts to illust. China's internat. rel. dur. past 100 years. 8°. Shanghai. 1923
MacNair (James Birtley). Citrus products, p1, 2, *see* FIELD COLUMBIAN MUS. Botan. ser., v6, 1926–27.
McNair, McNear, & McNeir genealogies. 8°. Chicago. 1923
MacNair (John Frederick Adolphus). Prisoners their own warders. Convict prison at Singapore. By McN., ass. by W. D. Bayliss. 8°. 1899
—— **& T. L. Barlow.** Oral tradition f. the Indus. Comprised in tales; added, explan. notes. rev. & corr. 4°. Brighton. 1908
MacNair (Mary Wilson), *see* UNITED STATES: LIBRARY OF CONGRESS. List of Amer. doctoral diss. pr. in 1919[–26], 1921–28.
MacNair (William Lennox), *see* CAMBRIDGE. Demosthenes demobilised: Camb. Union Soc. debates, 1919–20, 1920.
Macnally (Leonard). Fashionable levities, *see* †INCHBALD (*Mrs.* E.) Mod. theatre, v10, 1811.
Macnamara (Brinsley). The clanking of chains. s8°. D. 1920

Macnamara (Denis) [*MacConmara*]. The adventures of a luckless fellow; tr. f. Gaelic by P. A. Ussher, *see* MERRIMAN (B.) The midnight court &c., 1926.
MacNamara (John) *of Cratelagh* [MACNAMARRA]. The several informations of J. M., M. Fitzgerald & James Nash rel. to the horrid popish plot in Ireland &c., 1680. [P525]. sm. fol. 1680
Macnamara (Margaret). Yesterday. Hist. comedy. 8°. 1926
Macnamara (Rachel Swete). Golden dishes. s8°. [1923]
The green shoes of April. s8°. [1919]
Jealous gods. s8°. [1921]
Stolen fruit. s8°. [1922]
Macnaught (D.), *LL.D.*
The truth about Burns. s8°. Glasgow. 1921
MacNaught (John Campbell).
The Celtic Church & the See of Peter. 8°. O. 1927
Macnaughton (S.) Four-Chimneys. s8°. [1912]
MacNear [McNEAR], *see* MACNAIR.
MacNeile (Alan Hugh).
Intr. to the study of the New Test. 8°. O. 1927
New Test. teaching in the light of St. Paul's. s8°. C. 1923
Problems of the future life. [Moorhouse Lect., 1925]. 8°. 1925
St. Paul, h. life, letters & Xtn. doctrine. s8°. C. 1920
MacNeill (*Maj.* Douglas), *see* BURMAH. Maps & plans to accomp. Rep. & Gazetteer of B.; by D. M., 1883.
MacNeill (F. M.) Iona: a hist. of the island. s8°. 1920
MacNeill (John [Eoin]). Celtic Ireland. 8°. D. 1921
MacNeill (John Gordon Swift). Studies in the constit. of the Irish Free State. 8°. D. 1925
MacNeill (P.) Prestonpans & vicinity. s8°. Tranent. 1902
MacNeill (Ronald). Ulster's stand for union. 8°. 1922
MacNeir [McNEIR], *see* MACNAIR.
MacNicol (Nicol). Making of mod. India. s8°. 1924
MacNicoll (David). Works, incl. poet. remains. Prefixed mem. by James Dixon. 8°. 1837
Mâcon. Cartul. de Saint-Victor de Mâcon connu s. le nom de Livre enchainé. Publ. s. les auspices &c. de l'Acad. de Mâcon par C. Ragut. [Doc. inéd.] 4°. Mâcon. 1864
Macon (Gustave). Chantilly: le château &c. s8°. [1924]
Maconochie (*Sir* Evan). Life in the Indian Civil Service. 8°. 1926
Mac-Orlan (Pierre). La cavalière Elsa. 17e éd. s8°. 1921
La chant de l'équipage. Roman. s8°. [1918]
Macoun (James Melville) & M. O. Malte. Flora of Canada, *see* CANADA: GEOLOG. SURVEY. Museum bull., No. 26, 1917.
Macovetsky, *see* MAKOVETSKY.
MacOwan (Peter), *1795–1870.* A man of God: or mem. of P. M'O. comp. f. h. letters. Ed. G. Osborn. s8°. 1873
MacPhee (Allan). The econ. revol. in Brit. West Africa. 8°. 1927
Macpherson (A. G. H.) Cat. of a loan exhib. of old naval prints. [Illust.] la8°. 1924
MacPherson (Edward). Polit. hist. of the U.S. dur. the period of reconstruction, 1865–1870. 3rd ed. 8°. Wash. 1880
Macpherson (Hector), *the younger.*
Mod. astronomy, its rise & progress. s8°. 1926
Macpherson (James), *see* OSSIAN *for the poems wh. M. professed to have tr. f. Gaelic of O.*
Macpherson (James), *captain in the army of Prince Charles Edward.* Hist. of the present rebellion in Scotland; taken f. the rel. of J. M., who was an eye-witness. [P2779]. 8°. 1745
Macpherson (*Sir* John), *Bart., 1745–1821, Gov. General of India, see* HASTINGS (*Rt. Hon.* W.) Letters to Sir J. M., [1775–87], 1927.
Macpherson (Stewart). The musical educ. of the child. 8°. [1916]
Macpherson (*Maj.-Gen. Sir* William Grant). Hist. of the Great War based on offic. docs.: medical services, gen. hist. by Maj.-Gen. Sir W. M., 3v, 1921–24; Surgery, 2v, 1922, *see* WAR.
Macquarie (*Maj.-Gen.* Lachlan). The Macquarie Book, the life & times of M. [By J. H. M. Abbott, H. Wilson & C. H. Bertie. Art in Australia, No. 10]. 8°. Sydney. 1921
Macquarrie (Hector). How to live at the front. s8°. Phila. [1917]
Over here. Impressions of Amer. by a Brit. officer. s8°. Phila. 1918
Macqueen (John Fraser), *Barrister-at-Law.* Pract. treatise on the appellate jurisdiction of the House of Lords & Privy Council. With pract. on parl. divorce. 8°. 1842
Macquer (Philippe). Compendio cronológico de la hist. ecles. que contiene de las iglesias de oriente y occidente &c. Tr. por B. Zapata y Merino. 4t. s8°. 1791–94
Macqueron (Henri). Iconographie du Dépt. de la Somme. Cartes, vues, armoiries, portraits &c. 8°. Abbeville. 1886
Macquoid (Percy) & R. Edwards. Dict. of Eng. furniture. Gen. intr. by H. A. Tipping. 3v. fol. 1924–27
Macquoid (*Mrs.* Percy). Cat. of old Eng. furniture &c., prop. of Mrs. M. Sold by Christie, June 1925. [*Illust.*] 8°. 1925
MacRae (John Findlay), *see* CASLON (H. W.) & Co., *Ltd.* 2 cent. of typefounding: annals of Letter Foundry establ. by W. Caslon, 1720: [text by J. F. McR.], 1920.
Macready (*Rt. Hon. Gen. Sir* Cecil Frederick Nevil).
Annals of an active life. 2v. 8°. [1924]
Macready (William). The bank note, *see* †INCHBALD (*Mrs.* E.) Mod. theatre, v9, 1811.
*The village lawyer, 1792, *see* DUBLIN. Vol. of farces, 1792.
MacRitchie (David) & W. H. Stevenson. Great & Little Britain, *see* JESPERSON (O.) Logic & grammar &c., 1924.
Macrizi, *see* MAKRIZI.
Macrobius [MACROBE; M. AMBROSIUS AURELIUS THEODOSIUS]. Opera. Acc. notae integrae J. Pontani, J. Meursii, J. Gronovii. s8°. Lugduni Batav. 1670
see WHITTAKER (T.) M. &c., 1923.
Macropedius (Georgius). Hecastus, 1539, *see* BOLTE (J.) 3 Schauspiele, 1927.
Macself (A. J.) Gladioli. 8°. [1925]
Grass: pract. bk. on g. for lawns & sports &c. 8°. [1924]
MacSweeney, *The family of, see* WALSH (P.), *ed.* Leabhar Chlainne Suibhne: acc. of the M. families in Ireland, w. pedigrees, 1920.
MacSwiney (Terence James), *see* O'HEGARTY (P. S.) Sh. mem. of T. MacSwiney, 1922.
MacTaggart (*Mrs.* Ann). Constantia, a tragedy, & Valville, a drama. s8°. 1824
Mactaggart (John).
The Scottish Gallovidian encyclopedia. 8°. 1824
MacTaggart (John McTaggart Ellis). The nature of existence. 2v [v2 ed. C. D. Broad]. 8°. C. 1921–27
MacTyeire (Holland Nimmons). A hist. of Methodism, in Europe & America. 8°. Nashville, Tenn. 1884
Macveigh (James). Scot. family hist.: acc. of all Scot. families &c. 3v. la8°. Dumfries. 1891
Macwatt (John). The primulas of Europe. 8°. 1923
Macwhirter (John), *R.A.* Landscape painting in water-colour. Intr. by E. Bale. [repr.] obl. 8°. [1915]
MacWilliam (H. D.), *see* ELCHIES (P. G., *Ld.*) Letters, w. mem. &c. by M., 1927.
MacWilliam (John Morell).
The birds of the island of Bute. 8°. 1927
Mad. *Mad Tipperary, 1890, *see* TIPPERARY.
Madách (Imre). Az ember tragédiája. Drámai költemény. 16ik kiadás. s8°. 1904
Madan (Falconer).
The Bodleian Library at Oxford. s8°. [1919]
Books in MS. Intr. to th. study & use. 2nd ed. rev. 8°. 1920
Oxford outside the guide-books. s8°. O. 1923
R. Burton & the Anatomy of Melancholy. Papers by Sir W. Osler, Prof. E. Bensly &c. Ed. F. M. [Oxf. Bibliogr. Soc., Proc. &c., v1, p3, 1925]. la8°. O. 1926
see BODLEIAN LIBRARY. Summary cat. of Western MSS. in the B.L., w. ref. to the Oriental MSS. &c.; by F. M. &c., v2i, 6, 1922–24.
„ DANIEL (C. H. O.) The Daniel Press; mems. of C. H. O. D., w. bibliog. of the Press, 1845–1919, [by F. M.], 1921.
Madan (Martin).
A coll. of Psalms & hymns &c. 4th ed. s8°. 1765
„ „ ....6th ed. w. app. s8°. 1769
Madariaga (Iuan de). Vida del San Bruno, patriarca de la Cartuxa &c. [2p *in* 1v. *pagin. cont.*] s4°. Valencia. 1596
Madariaga (Salvador de). Arceval y los Ingleses. s8°. 1925
Englishmen, Frenchmen, Spaniards: essay in compar. psychol. Pref. note by A. Zimmern. 8°. 1928
Genius of Spain & o. essays on Span. contemp. lit. 8°. O. 1923
La jirafa sagrado o el buho de plata. Novela. s8°. [1925]
Shelley & Calderon & o. essays on Eng. & Spanish poetry. [The case of Wordsworth]. 8°. 1920
Madathanas (Henricus), *ps., see* MYNSICHT (ADRIANUS).
***Mädchen** (Die) v. Tanagra, 1925, *see* TANAGRA.
Madden (*Rt. Hon.* Dodgson Hamilton). Chapter of mediaeval hist.: the fathers of the lit. of field sport & horses. 8°. 1924
Madden (*Maj.-Gen. Sir* George Allan). Services of G. A. M.; comp. f. authentic doc.; by a friend. 8°. 1815

Madden (Richard Robert).
Island of Cuba: resources &c. s8°. 1849
see M. (J. F.) Poems by a slave in Cuba; tr. R. R. M., prefixed, 2 pieces descr. of Cuban slavery by R. R. M., 1840.

Madden (Samuel), *D.D., Rector of Drummully.* *Reflect. & resolut. proper for the gentlemen of Ireland as to th. conduct for the service of th. country. 8°. D. 1738

Madden (Thomas), *minister of Aldersgate Street Chapel, London.* A new coll. of hymns. s8°. 1811

Maddison (Eugen). Die nationalen Minderheiten Estlands. [P2871]. 8°. Reval. 1926

Maddoks (Mikhail Egorovich), *see* CHAYANOVA (O. E.) Театр М. в Москве, 1776–1805, 1927.

Madeley (Helen M.) History as a school of citizenship. s8°. 1924

Madelin (Louis).
La bataille de France, 21 mars–11 nov. 1918. 8°. [1920]
Le chemin de la victoire. 2[t]. s8°. [1920]
[L'Europe napoléon.]: Soc. des Etudes Hist. [P2577]. 8°. 1921
La France du Directoire. Conférences. s8°. [1922]
Le maréchal Foch. s8°. [1925]
TRANSLATIONS.
Danton. Tr. by Lady M. Lloyd. 8°. 1921
The French Revolution. Tr. [3rd impr.] 8°. [1922]
see HANOTAUX (G.) Hist. de la nation franç., t4, Hist. polit., v2 (De 1515 à 1804), par L. M., 1924.

Maden (J.), *see* DIXON (E. E. L.), J. M. &c. Geol. of the Carlisle &c. dist., 1926.

Mader (Carl). Freiburg im Breisgau: Stadtgeogr. la8°. Karlsruhe i. B. 1926

Mader (Felix). Oberpfälz. Klöster u. Wallfahrtskirchen. la8°. Augsburg. 1924
Passau. la8°. Augsburg. 1925
Stadt- u. Dorfkirchen d. Oberpfalz. la8°. Augsburg. 1926

Maderno (Carlo), *see* MUÑOZ (A.) C. M.: 35 riprod. con testo &c., 1921.

Maderus (Joachimus Joannes). De S. Laurentio martyre ejusque monasterio prope Scheningam &c. [P597]. s4°. Helmstadi. 1688

Madis (Alex.), *see* MIRANDE (Y.) & A. M. Simone est comme ça, comédie inéd., 1923.

Madison (James), *pres. of the United States.* The debates in the Federal Convention of 1787 wh. framed the constit. of the U.S. Rep. by J. M. Internat. ed. G. Hunt & J. B. Scott, eds. [C.E. for Int. Peace]. la8°. N.Y. 1920
Letters & o. writings. Publ. by order of Congress. 4v. 8°. Phila. 1865
Papers: corresp., reports of debates &c. Publ. H. D. Gilpin. 3v [*pagin. cont.*] 8°. N.Y. 1844
see BEMIS (S. F.), *ed.* Amer. Secr. of State, v3, M., by C. E. Hill, 1927.

Mádl (Karel B.) Topogr. d. hist. u. Kunstdenkm. im polit. Bez. Kolin, *see* BÖHMEN. Topograph. d. hist. u. Kunstdenkmale, B1, 1898.

Madras.
MISCELLANEOUS GOVT. PUBL^S.
Admin. of the M. Presidency. Report, 1919/20–1926/27. fol. Madras. 1921–28
Calendar of Madras despatches, 1744–55. By H. Dodwell. 8°. Madras. 1920
Hist. of services of gazetted & o. officers in the Civil Dept. Corr. up to 1st July 1920, 1922–1927. 8°. Madras. 1920–27
Report regarding possibility of introd. land & agric. banks into M. Pres. 2v. fol. Madras. 1895–97
see SWAMIKANNU PILLAI (L. D.) Indian ephemeris, 700–1799, vli, 6, 1922.
„ WALCH (G. T.) Engineering works of the Kistna Delta, 2v, 1899.
ARCHAEOLOGICAL SURVEY OF S. INDIA.
Annual report of the Arch. Dept., S. Circle. fol. Madras. 1920–21
Epigraphy progress Report of the Assistant Arch. Superintendent, Southern Circle. fol. Madras. 1919–27
1922/23– *have t.* Ann. rep. on South-Ind. epigr.
CENSUS, 1921, *see* INDIA: CENSUS.
CENTRAL MUSEUM.
Cat. of exhibits in the Econ. Products Sect., except wood specimens. By S. N. C. Ayyar. 8°. Madras. 1921
FORT ST. GEORGE, RECORDS OF.
Despatches from England, 1701–21. [6v]. fol. Madras. 1925–28
Despatches to England, 1701–2—1710–11. fol. Madras. 1925
Diary & consultation book of 1696–1703. [8v]. fol. Madras. 1921–27
Letters f. F. St. G. for 1693–94, 1694, 1696, 1698, 1699–1700, 1700–1, 1702. [7v]. fol. Madras. 1920–23

Madras [*continued*].
MISCELLANEOUS GOVT. PUBL^S. [*continued*].
LEGISLATIVE DEPT.
Madras Code. Suppl. to 4th ed. la8°. Madras. 1925
PUBLIC WORKS DEPT.
Administration report[s], pl, 1918/19–1925/26. fol. Madras. 1920–26
Classified list & distribution return of establishment corr., 1920–1925. 8°. Madras. 1920–26
UNIVERSITY.
Historical ser. v2. 8°. [Madras]. 1924
see AIYAR (R. S.) Hist. of Nayaks of Madura, 1924. [2.]

Madrid. Expós. Historico-Europea, 1892, *see* EXHIBITIONS.
REAL BIBLIOTECA.
Catálogo. t5. la8°. [1918]
see MENÉNDEZ PIDAL (R.) Crónicas gen. de España. 3ª ed. 1918. [5.]
see MUSEO ARQUEOLÓGICO, *Madrid.*

Madrolle (Antoine M.) *Mémorial cathol. à l'usage des royalistes reconnus libéraux. [P2764]. 8°. 1826

Madrolle (Claudius). Chine du Nord & vallée du Fleuve Bleu: Corée. 2e éd. s8°. 1913

Madryn Castle. Illust. partic. w. plans of the M.C. estate: Knight, Frank & Rutley auction, 28th June 1910. By order of the Trustees. fol. 1910

Maercker (*Komm. Gen.-Maj.*), *see* MÄRCKER (*Komm. Gen.-Maj.*)

Maes (Nicolaes) [MAAS], *see* VALENTINER (W. R.) N. M., 1924.

Maes (Pierre). Georges Rodenbach, 1855–98. s8°. 1926

Maestri (I) dell' arte, No. 17–24, 1919–20, *see* SAPORI (F.)

Maeterlinck (L.)
Une école préeyckienne inconnue. 4°. 1925
L'énigme des primitifs français. s8°. [1923]
Namur Martins ou Le Maître de Flémalle. Nouv. doc. 8°. Brux. 1913

Maeterlinck (Maurice).
Le bourgmestre de Stilmonde suivi de Le sel de la vie. s8°. 1920
Le grand secret. s8°. 1921
Le malheur passe: pièce, *see* ŒUVRES libres, 54, 1925.
Marie-Victoire: pièce, *see* ŒUVRES libres, 74, 1927.
Le miracle de Saint Antoine. Farce. s8°. 1920
Morceaux choisis. Intr. par Mme. G. Leblanc. [Coll. Nelson]. s8°. [1910]
La puissance des morts: pièce, *see* ŒUVRES libres, 64, 1926.
La vie de l'espace. s8°. 1928
La vie des termites. s8°. 1927
TRANSLATIONS.
The great secret. Tr. B. Miall. s8°. [1922]
The life of the bee. Tr. A. Sutro. [pocket ed. repr.] s8°. 1910
The life of the white ant. Tr. A. Sutro. 8°. [1927]
Old-fashioned flowers & o. open-air essays. Tr. A. Teixeira de Mattos. s8°. 1906
The wrack of the storm. Tr. A. Teixeira de Mattos. s8°. 1916
see ROSE (H.) M.'s symbolism; the blue bird &c., 1910.

Maev (Nikolai Aleksandrovich). Путеводитель отъ Петербурга до Ташкента. [P2399]. la8°. С.–П. 1870

Maeztu (Gustavo), *see* FRANCÉS (J.) G. de M., 1920.

Maffei (*il march* **Francesco Scipione).** *Animadv. in hist. theolog. dogmatum &c. de divina gratia a S. M. elaboratam. s4°. Francofurti ad Moenam. 1749
„ „ de divina gratia, libero arbitrio et praedestinatione &c. Ex Italico Lat. reddidit F. Reiffenbergius cujus Diss. de divina gratia & [Maffeii] opuscula acc. fol. Francofurti. 1756
Opere dramm. e poesie varie. A cura di A. Avena. [Scr. d'It., 104]. 8°. Bari. 1928
*La Verona illustrata. Prem. la vita d. m. S. M. 2p. 8°. Verona. 1771
see LATTES (A.) F. de Aguirre e S. M., 1909.
„ LENGLET DU FRESNOY (N.) New method of studying hist.; added, Diss. of M. conc. use of inscr. & medals; tr., 2v, 1728.

Maffei (Giovanni Pietro). De vita & moribus Ignatii Loiole libri 3. s8°. Mediolani. 1586
Hist. ab excessu Gregorii XIII libri 3. Sixti V pontific. compl. [*b. w. h.* Opera omnia, t2, 1747]. s4°. Bergami. 1747
Historiarum Indicarum libri 16 &c. Acc. Ignatii Loiolae vita, postremo recognita. Adjecta est carta geogr. [*missing*]. fol. Coloniae Agripp. 1593
Opera omnia Lat. scripta. Acc. M. vita, P. A. Sevassio auctore. 2t. s4°. Bergami. 1747

Mafra (Ginés de). Libro d. descubr. d. estrecho de Magellanes, *see* MAGELLAN (F.) Descr. &c., 1920.

Magaillans (Gabriel), *see* MAGELLAN (G. DE).

Magalhaens Gandavo (Pedro de). Hist. da prov. Santa Cruz, 1576, *see* COLLECÇÃO de opusc. reimpr., 1875.
Hist. da Prov. Sãta Cruz, vulg. Brasil, 1576, *see* INSTITUTO HIST. E GEOG. BRAZIL. Rev., t21, 1858.
Magallanes (Fernando), *see* MAGELLAN (F.)
Magallon (Xavier de). L'ombre. s8°. 1921
Magazin für d. Kirchen- u. Gelehrten Geschichte d. Kurfürstenthums Pfalz. Hrsg. v. D. L. Wundt. B1–2. s8°. Heidelberg. 1789–90
Magazin für d. neueste Gesch. d. evangel. Missions u. Bibelgesellschaften &c. [Hrsg. M. Blumhardt]. 1er Jhrg. 1816–1856. [Bibelblätter *have sep. pagins.*] 8°. Basel. 1816–56
Continued as: Evangelisches Missions-Magazin. Neue Folge. Hrsg. v. A. Ostertag &c. Jhrg. 1–27 [16, 19 & 20 *wanting*]. 8°. Basel. 1857–83
Magazin für d. pfälzische Geschichte. Hrsg. v. D. L. Wundt u. J. L. C. Rheinwald. Mit Bez. auf d. Mag. f. d. Kirchen- &c. Gesch. [*q.v.*] B1. s8°. Heidelberg. 1793
Magazine (The) of American history, w. notes & queries. v1–29. 8°. N.Y. 1877–93
Magazines. *How to write for the magazines, 1900, *see* How.
Magdeburg [MEYDEBURG].
*Aussführl. u. gründtl. Bericht: Was sich bey vergangner Beläger &c. d. Statt M. verloffen; darbey Herrn Gen. Grafen v. Tylli Warnungsschreiben &c., 1631 (*facs.*), *see* FREYTAG (G.) Bilder, B4, 1925.
*Confessio & apologia pastorum &c. eccl. M. a. 1550. s4°. Magdeburgi, *M. Lotther.* [1550]
Der von Magdeburgk Entschüldigung, Bit, u. gemeine Christl. erinnerunge. [P2440]. s4°. Magdeburgk. 1549
Der von Magdeburgk widerlegung u. verantwortung alles ungrundts u. unglimpffs, in ihrer unchristl. Belagerung v. d. Magdeburg. Baalspfaffen &c. [P2441]. s4°. Magdeburgk, *M. Lotther.* 1551
Methodus doctr. Christi sicut in eccl. M. traditur, 1561, *see* WIGAND (J.)
Ursach u. handelung: In d' Keyserl. Löbl. u. Christl. Statt Meydeburg, Ein Christlich wesen u. wandel belangende &c. Durch die Christl. gemeynen u. versamlungen Offentlichen gehandelt u. beschlossen, 1524. s4°. Maydeburg. [1524]
Magdeburg Centuries. Centuriae Magdeburgenses, seu hist. eccl. Novi Test. cum var. theolog. continuationibus ad haec nostra tempora [*by* M. Flacius; J. Wigandus; M. Judex; B. Faber]. [*Ed.* J. J. Hauckins]. 4v. 4°. Norimbergæ. 1757–75
Hist. eccles. integram eccl. Christ. condit. exponens: per studiosos &c. viros in urbe Magdeburgica congesta [*by* M. Flacius, J. Wigandus, M. Judex & B. Faber]; per L. Lucium rec. 13 cent. *in* 3v. fol. Basileae. 1624
see BRUNUS (C.) Adv. novam hist. eccl. [Magd. Cent.], 1565.
Magee (William), *abp. of Dublin, 1766–1831, see* HARE (E.) Refut. of charges agst. Methodists, advanced by M., 1810.
Magellan (Ferdinand). Descr. de los reinos, costas &c. desde el Cabo de Buena Esperanza hasta los Leyquios. Libro que trata del descubr. &c. del estrecho que se llama de Magallanes, por G. de Mafra y Descr. de parte del Japón (Anon.) [Real Soc. Geog.] la8°. 1920
see HILDEBRAND (A. S.) M.: life & times &c., 1925.
,, PHILIPPINE ISLANDS. Celebración d. 4° centen. d. descubr. de Filipinas por F. de M., 1921.
,, PIGAFETTA (A.) Rel. du prem. voyage autour du monde par M., 1519–22; éd. J. Denucé, 1923.
Magellan (Gabriel de), *Jesuit* [MAGAILLANS; †MAGALHAENS]. New history of China. Done out of French. 8°. 1688
Magelone, *see* MAGUELONNE.
Magendie (Maurice). Du nouveau sur l'Astrée. la8°. 1927
La politesse mondaine & les théories de l'honnêteté en France, 1600–60. 2t. 8°. [1925]
Magenta (Carlo). Alfonso Corradi: commem., *see* REGIA DEP. DI STORIA PATRIA. Misc., t30, 1893.
see DELL' ACQUA (C.) In memoria del Comm. Prof. C. M., 1895.
Mager (Fritz). Kurland: e. allg. Siedlungs-, Verkehrs- u. Wirtschaftsgeogr. la8°. Hamburg. 1920
Maggi (Francesco Maria). Syntagmatωn linguarum orient. quae in Georgiae regionibus audiuntur 2 lib. fol. Romae. 1670
Maggi (Girolamo), *see* PROMIS (C.) Vita di G. M. d'Anghiari, ingegnere milit., poeta &c. d. sec. 16, 1862.
Maggini (Francesco). La mostra dantesca alla Laurenziana di Firenze, *see* ARCHIVIO STOR. ITAL. Anno 79, v1, 1921.
Maggiorotti (Margherita). In Piemonte, 1637–1642: contrasti n. reggenza di Maria Cristina e l'opera dei nunzi papali. 8°. Castello. 1923

Maggs Bros.
Autograph letters, hist. docs., & authors' orig. MSS. [Cat. 449]. s4°. 1924
Autograph letters, doc., MSS. &c. [Cat. 433, 436, 445 *in* 1v]. 8°. 1922–23
Autograph letters, signed doc. & MSS. [Cat. 386, 399, 417. P2616]. 8°. 1919–21
Bibliotheca incunabulorum. [Cat. 402]. 8°. 1921
Book bindings. [Cat. 407. P2616]. 8°. 1921
Book bindings. [Cat. 489]. s4°. [1927]
Books on art &c. [Cat. 437]. 8°. 1923
Books &c. on old medicine &c. [Cat. 426, *b. w.* Books on art &c., 1923]. 8°. 1922
Books pr. in Spain & Span. bks. [Cat. 495]. 8°. 1927
Eng. literature, 14–18 c. [Cat. 446]. 8°. 1924
Eng. lit. & printing, 15–18 c. 4p *in* 2v. [Cat. 477, 481, 503, 505]. 8°. 1926–28
Eng. lit. of the 19th & 20th c. [Cat. 443–4]. 2p *in* 1v. 8°. 1923
Engraved portraits &c. [Cat. 392, 398, 408, 420]. [P2615]. 8°. 1920–22
Engravings, etchings &c. [Cat. 430, 438, 447 & 466 *in 1v*]. 8°. 1922–25
Illum. MSS. & miniatures. [Cat. 404]. [P2615]. 8°. 1921
MSS., incunables &c. [Cat. 395, *b. w.* Bibl. incunab., 1921]. 8°. 1920
Sel. of books, MSS., engravings &c. [Cat. 500]. fol. 1928
Shakespeare & Shakespeareana, 1623–1923. 8°. 1923
,, ,, [Cat. 493]. la8°. 1927
see CAMOENS (L. DE). C. & s. temps: [cat. d'une expos. en comm. du 4e cent. de C., 1524–1924], 1925.
,, RICCI (S. DE). Cat. d'une coll. des éd. orig. de Ronsard, 1925.

Magi, *legend, see* SARGISEAN (B.) Fable of the 3 M. in Arm. sources (*in Arm.*), 1910.
Magic [MAGICK]. Magic casement (The): anthology of fairy poetry, 1908, *see* NOYES (A.), *ed.*
*A system of magick, 1728, *see* DEFOE (D.)
Magini (Giovanni Antonio), *see* ALMAGIÀ (R.) L'Italia di G. A. M. &c., 1922.
Mägiste (Julius). Rosona murde pääjooned, 1925, *see* DORPAT UNIV. Acta &c., B, v7, 1926.
Magna. *The M. Charta of Methodism invalid: hist. & invalid. of Wesley's deed poll set forth &c., by a solicitor, 1835, *see* METHODISM.
Magna Charta. Magna Charta, made in 9 Henry III &c., w. obs. f. Coke. Tr. E. Cooke. s8°. 1680
Magnasco (Alessandro), *see* FERRI (A.) A. M.: 40 riprod. con testi &c., 1922.
Magne (Emile).
Un ami de Cyrano de Bergerac, le Chevalier de Lignières. 8°. [1920]
Une amie inconnue de Molière [*i.e.* Honorée de Bussy], suivi de M. & l'Université. s8°. 1922
La fin troublée de Tallemant des Réaux. 3e éd. s8°. 1922
Le Grand Condé & le Duc d'Enghien. Lettres inéd. à Marie-Louise, Reine de Pologne, sur la cour de Louis XIV, 1660–67. Publ., avec intr. &c. par E. M. 8°. 1920
La joyeuse jeunesse de Tallemant des Réaux. s8°. 1921
Mme. de Chatillon (Isabelle-Angélique de Montmorency). s8°. 1910
Mme. de Lafayette en ménage. 7e éd. s8°. 1926
Ninon de Lanclos. Portr. & doc. inéd. la8°. 1925
Le plaisant Abbé de Boisrobert, fondateur de l'Académie Franç., 1592–1662. 2e éd. s8°. 1909
Scarron & s. milieu. n. éd. augm. de doc. inéd. s8°. 1924
Voiture & les années de gloire de l'Hôtel de Rambouillet, 1635–48. s8°. 1912

Magnien (Edouard). Mortel, ange ou démon. [*Play on* Ld. Byron]. 2t. 8°. 1836
Magnin (Joseph) [PIERRE JOSEPH MAGNIN], *see* DELABROUSSE (L.) J. M. & s. temps, 1824–1910, 2t, 1924.
Magno (Celio). Rime di C. M. et O. Giustiniano [*w. sep. pagin.*] s4°. Venetia. 1600
***Magnum** speculum exemplorum &c., 2t, 1605, *see* SPECULUM.
Magnus Saga, *see* JÓNSSON (F.), *ed.* Eirspennill, 1916.
Magnus (Julius). Die neuen internat. Vertr. d. Deut. Reichs; mit Erläut. hrsg. v. J. M. [B]1. 8°. 1926
1, Deut.-russ. Vertr. v. 12. Okt. 1925; O. Mersmann-Soest & P. Wohl, 1926.
Magnus (Laurie), *M.A.* Dict. of Europ. lit. la8°. 1926
Eng. lit. in its foreign rel., 1300–1800. 8°. [1927]
Jubilee bk. of the Girls' Public Day School Trust, 1873–1923. 8°. C. 1923
—— & Cecil Headlam. Prayers f. the poets. s8°. 1899
Magnus (Leonard Arthur).
The heroic ballads of Russia. 8°. 1921
Magnus (Olaus), *abp. of Upsala* [OLAUS DE GROOTE].
Hist. de gentibus Septentrion. &c. 4°. Romae. 1555
Magnus (Paul). Die Pilze (Fungi) v. Tirol, Vorarlberg &c.; bearbt. P. M., 1905; Nachtrag, 1926, *see* DALLA TORRE (C. W. v.) &c. Flora, &c., B3, 1905–26.

Magnus (Valerianus), *see* STEGMANN (J.) Brev. disqu., an & quomodo Evangelici Pontificios, ac nominatim V. M. refutare queant, 1633.

Magnussen (Johannes).
Dansk-Norsk-Engelsk ordbog. 8°. København. 1902

——, O. Madsen & H. Vinterberg.
Engelsk-Dansk Ordbog. 8°. København. 1909

Magnusson (Leifur). Housing by employers in the U.S., *see* UNITED STATES: LAB. Bull. 263, 1920.

Magrath (John Richard). The Flemings in Oxford: doc. f. Rydal papers, 1650–1700. Ed. M. [Oxf. Hist. Soc. v79]. v3, 1691–1700. 8°. 1924
The Queen's College. 2v. la8°. O. 1921

Magre (Maurice).
L'appel de la bête. Roman. s8°. [1920]
Arlequin. Comédie. 8°. 1927
Les colombes poignardées. 7e éd. s8°. 1927
L'ingrate: comédie, *see* ŒUVRES libres, 50, 1925.
La luxure de Grenade: roman. s8°. [1926]
La mort enchaînée. Légende dramatique. s8°. [1920]
La porte du mystère. Poésies. s8°. 1924
Priscilla d'Alexandrie. Roman. s8°. [1925]
Vie des courtisanes, variétés, *see* ŒUVRES (Les) libres, 23, 1923.

Magson (Egbert H.) How we judge intelligence: value of an interview. [Brit. Journ. of Psych. Monogr. suppl., 11]. la8°. C. 1926

Maguelonne [MAGELONE], *see* PIERRE, *de Provence, for var. vers. of* *Hist de Pierre de Provence & de la belle M.

Maguire (Thomas Miller).
The American Civil War, 1861–65. [P2593]. s8°. D. 1893

Maguire (Yvonne), *M.A.* The women of the Medici. 8°. 1927

Magyar. M. Békeküldöttség. Delegation of Hungary. [P2604]. la8°. *n.p.* 1920
Struggle &c. of M. Reformed Ch. in Transylvania under the Roumanian heel. [P2576]. 8°. Budapest. 1921

Magyar Földrajzi Társaság [HUNGARIAN GEOG. SOC.] Appeal to the geog. societies of the world. [P2519]. 8°. Budapest. 1919
see LÓCZY (L.), *ed.* Geog., econom. & soc. survey of Hungary, 1919.

Magyar Gazdaszövetség. Ertekezések a társadalmi tudományok köréből. 8°. Budapest. 1909

Magyar Királyi Belügyministerium. 1907 évi XIX törvényczikk az ipari és kereskedelmi alkalmazottaknak betegség és baleset esetére való biztositásáról. Hivatalos kiadás. [P2397]. 8°. 1911

Magyar Tudományos Akademia.
Archæologiai értesitö. Uj folyam. k33–41. la8°. 1913–27
Értekezések a történelmi tudományok köréből. k23, 24 (k23, 24 *have 10sz. each*). 8°. 1915–18
Történeti szemle. Szerkeszti Angyal Dávid &c. évfolyam 2–12. 8°. 1913–26

REFERENCES.
see MARCZALI (H.) Az 1790/1-diki országgyules, 2k, 1907.
„ REVUE DES ÉT. HONGR. & FINNO-OUGR., 1923–27.
„ VÁMBÉRY (Á.) A török faj.: ethnolog. és ethnogr. tekintetben, 1885.

Mahābhārata.
Nalus, carmen Sanscritum e M. Ed., Lat. vertit, & adnot. illust. F. Bopp, 1819, *see* NALOPĀKHYĀNA.
Selections f. the M. Ed. F. Johnson. 8°. 1842
TRANSLATIONS.
The M. Tr. into Eng. prose. Publ. by Protap Chandra Roy. Adi Parva *&* Sabha Parva [*in 1v. sep. tp. & pagin.*] 8°. Calcutta. 1884
TRANSLATIONS [*continued*].
A prose Eng. trans. of the M. Ed. & publ. by M. N. Dutt. 3v. la8°. Calcutta. 1895
Tales from the Mahábhárata. [*Verse*], by S. Rice. 8°. [1924]
see OLDENBERG (H.) Das M., s. Entsteh., Inhalt, Form, 1922.
„ TEMPLE (*Sir* R. C.) The projected illust. M. 1923.

Mahaffy (John Pentland). Alexander's Empire. By M., w. collab. of A. Gilman. [Story of the nations]. 5th ed. 8°. 1890

Mahaim (Ernest). Le secours de chomage en Belg. pend. l'occup. allem. [C.E. for Int. Peace]. 8°. [1926]

Mahan (Alfred Thayer), *see* TAYLOR (C. C.) Life of Admiral M., 1920.

Mahan (Asa). The phenomena of spiritualism; expl. & exposed. s8°. 1875

Mahānisīha-Sutta, *see* SCHUBRING (W.) Das M.-S., 1918.

Mahendravarman I, *see* JOUVEAU-DUBREUIL (G.) Conjeevaram inscr. of M. I, 1919.

Mahlau (Ludwig).
Gesch. der freien Stadt Danzig. 8°. Danzig. 1921

Mahler (Georg), *see* DUNS (J.) Theolog. D. Scoti; elucid. per G. M., 1702.

Mahler (Gustav), *see* STEFAN (P.) G. M.: Persönlichkeit u. Werk, n. verm. &c. A., 1920.

Mahn (C. A. F.) Die Werke d. Troubadours, in Provenz. Sprache. Bl. s8°. 1846

Mahn (Georg). Der Tempel v. Boro-Budur. Eine buddhist. Studie. s4°. L. 1919

Mahnke (Dietrich). Neue Einblicke in d. Entdeckungsgesch. d. höh. Analysis, *see* KÖN.-PREUSS. AKAD. Abhdln., Phys.-math. Kl., 1925.

Mahon (*Maj.-Gen.* **Reginald Henry).** The indictment of Mary Queen of Scots, f. MS. in Univ. Lib. at Camb. With comments on authorship &c. 8°. C. 1923
Life of Gen. the Hon. James Murray. With biog. sk. of the family of Murray of Elibank. 8°. 1921
Mary Queen of Scots: Lennox narrative &c. 8°. C. 1924

Mahony, *Family of, see* MACCARTHY (S. T.) Three Kerry families, 1925.

Mahony (Francis Sylvester) [*ps.* FATHER PROUT]. Reliques of F. P. Coll. by O. Yorke. n. ed. rev. s8°. *Bohn.* 1862

Mahu (Jacob), *see* WIEDER (F. C.) De reis v. M. &c., 1598–1600, 3d, 1923–25.

Mahzor [MACHSOR], *see* MAIMONIDES. Symbolum fidei Jud. è R. Mose Ægyptio: praecationes pro defunctis, è lib. M., 1569.

Maichelius (Daniel). Lucubrationes Lambetanae: mon. lit. ex Bibl. Gul. Wakii coll. &c. s8°. Tubingae. 1729

Maidment (James), *d. 1879.* Cat. of library of J. M. Sold by T. Chapman & Son, April–May, 1880. la8°. E. 1880
Hist. fragments rel. to Scotish affairs, 1635–64. [Ed. J. M.] [3p]. 8°. E. 1833
Balcarres (A. L., *1st e.*) Acc. of any accession to the late engagement &c., 1649. [3.]
„ —— Letter to Charles II, 1653. [3.]
„ —— Proposals to Charles II, 1654. [3.]
Burns (J.) Mem., 1644–61, 1832. [1.]
Charles II. Instruct. to Earl of Balcarres &c., 1654; Maidment, 1833. [3.]
Cochrane (*Sir* J.) Rel. of partic. in negoc. since coming to Hamburgh, 1649. [2.]
Douglas (R.) Diary, when w. Scot. army in England, 1644. [1.]
[Dumbeath]. Note of letters that came to D. &c., 1649. [2.]
Edinburgh. Coll. by a private hand at E., 1650–61. [2.]
Johnson (R.) Mem. to be communicat to R. J. [? *by* R. Douglas], *n.d.* [2.]
[Scotland]. Declar. of inhabitants of the hill countreys, 1653. [3.]
Solemn League & Covenant. Burning, May 29, 1662. [2.]
Spreul (J.) Some remark. passages of the Lord's Providence, 1635–64, 1832. [2.]
Wodrow (R.) Mem. &c. rel. to Alex. Henderson, 1723. [3.]
York. Glorious & miraculous battel at Y., 1644. [1.]
see STEVENSON (T. G.) Bibliog. of J. M., 1817–78 [*w.* App., Notices of sale of M. coll., 1880], 1883.

—— & R. Pitcairn.
*Nugae derelictae, quas coll. J. M. & R. P. 8°. E. 1822
Alexander, *king of Scotland.* Confirmatio terrarum S. Joh. Bapt. Torphaphyn.
Arbuthnot, *family of.* Inventory of titles, 1206–1483.
Balfour (R., *5th b.*), *of Burleigh.* Memoir, 1821.
Buchan (W. C., *earl of*). Charter, land of Drumry, ante 1233.
Edward III. Letter for pardon to Cecil de Ridgeway, 1358.
Fleming (*Dame* E.) Inventar of ye gudis &c., 1578.
Flodden Field. *Batayle of Floddon-felde [*w.* Notes regard. death &c. of James IV], 1820.
Galloway (*Sir* J.) Sir J. G., h. prophesy, 1649.
Haddington (T. H., *1st e.*) Instrument of resign. of ye Templelands, 1614.
Haxton (—) *of Rathillet.* Speech & last words, 1680.
*Heraldic verses, ante 1565.
Levingston (*Sir* H.) Procuratory, to Sr. J. Hawkehed, 1460.
Mylne (R.) Excerpt [rel. to Temple lands, 1488], f. A perfect inventor &c., 1702.
Saint Giles, *Edinb.* Charter in favor of W. de Prestoune, 1454.
Symsoun (J.) Cowmpt of ye geir belong. to Abbacie of Lindores, 1530.

Maier (August Richard). Niclaus Gerhauert v. Leiden, e. niederl. Plastiker d. 15 Jhdt. la8°. Str. 1910

Maier (Bartholomæus). Exerc. ad repet. hist. eccl. 1, De Jubilæo Romano, Lælio Zechio opposita. Praes. B. Gualthero, resp. B. M. [P483]. s4°. Jenae. 1617

Maier (Christophorus). Octo fidei controversiae, difficult. redeundi ad eccl. cathol. s8°. [Cologne]. 1622

Maierus (Michael), *of Rendsburg, the alchemist.* The golden tripod: 3 chem. tracts; ed. M. (1618), *see* HERMETIC MUSEUM, 2v, 1893.
A subtle allegory conc. secrets of alchemy, *see* HERMETIC MUSEUM, v2, 1893.
Maignien (Edmond). Bibliographie hist. du Dauphiné, pend. la Révol. Franç. 3t. 8°. Grenoble. 1891
Maigron (Louis).
Le romantisme & la mode, d'ap. des doc. inéd. 8°. 1911
Maigrot (Charles), *see* *ACTA causae rituum seu ceremon. Sinensium: complect. Mandatum C. M. &c., 1715.
Maillard (E.) L'art à Nantes au 19 s. la8°. [1888]
Mailles (Jacques de) [LE LOYAL SERVITEUR]. *Hist. du chevalier Bayard & de plusieurs choses mem. adv. en France &c., 1489–1524. [Ed., w. annot. by T. Godefroy]. s4°. 1616
Hist. du Seigneur de Bayart. Par le L. S. Transcr. de l'éd. paris. de 1527. [Intr. by O. H. Prior]. 8°. 1927
Maillol (Aristide), *see* DENIS (M.) A. M., 1925.
Mailly (François de), *abp. of Rheims.* Epistola [*on Bull Unigenitus*] ad princ. Galliae regentum è Gallico in Lat. conv. [*&* Epistola encyclica (*on acc. of h. letter being burnt by order of Parl.*) P2659]. s8°. Lovanii. [1718]
Mailros, *see* MELROSE.
Maimbourg (Louis) [MAIMBURGIUS]. A peaceful method for re-uniting Protestants & Catholicks in matters of faith, of the Eucharist &c. [Tr. by T. W.] s8°. Paris. 1671
see BAYLE (P.) *Nouv. lettres de l'a. de la Crit. gén. de l'Hist. du Calvinisme de M., 2t, 1685.
„ BEZA (T.) De Juvenilibus T. B. poematis epistola ad N. C. qua M. &c. confutantur, 1683.
„ BOILEAU (J.) *Remarques d'un théologien sur le "Traité historique" &c. par M., 1688.
„ SPANHEIM (F.), *the younger.* Hist. imaginum restituta præcipue adv. L. M. [*in his* "Hist. eccl."], 1686.
Maimbourg (Théodore), *escuyer.* Lettre cont. les choses qui l'ont obligé de quitter la communion de l'Eglise Romaine. s8°. 1659
Maimon (Abraham). Historia, quam ex Arab. in Heb. ling. conv. A. M. [*Heb. & Lat.*], *see* WAGENSEIL (J. C.) Exercit., 1687; 1719.
מעשה של ירושלמי ומעשה רבי בוסטנאי.
[P468]. s8°. [Verona. 1647?]
Maimonides [†MOSES BEN MAIMON]. De idolatria liber cum interpret. Lat. & notis Dionysii Vossii.
[*2 leaves wanting after tp.*] s4°. Amsterdami. 1642
De sacrificiis liber. Acc. Abarbanelis exordium, comm. in Leviticum & M. Tract. de consecratione calendarum &c. [*Tr.*] L. de Compiegne de Veil. s4°. Lond. 1683
Exerc. acad.: M. Maimonidis tract. De circumcisione, cum interpret. Lat. & annot. exhib. C. Walther, resp. C. Rausch. [P2666]. s4°. Regiomonti. [1705]
The reasons of the laws of Moses. From the "More Nevochim" of M. With notes, diss. & life by J. Townley. 8°. 1827
Symbolum fidei Judaeorum è R. Mose Ægyptio. Praecationes pro defunctis, è lib. Mahzor. 613 legis praecepta e more Nebuchim. Interp. G. Genebrardo. [*b. w.* Joseph ben Gorion. De bello Jud., 1559]. s8°. Parisiis. 1569
Tredecim articuli fidei Iudaeorum. Item Compendium elegans hystoriar. Iosephi. Item decem captivitates Iudaeorum. Per S. Munsterum. Heb. & Lat. leg. exar. s8°. [Vuormaciæ. *Peter Schoef[f]er*]. 1529
see BUXTORFIUS (J.), *elder.* Instit. epist. Hebr.; acc. var. epist. R. Majemonis &c., 1629.
„ COHEN (A.) Teachings of M., 1927.
„ FROMMANN (E. A.) Diss. qua philosophemata quaed. M. cum rec. sententiis coll., 1745.
„ ROTH (L.) Spinoza, Descartes & M., 1924.
Maimun ibn Kais, *called al-Asha.* Zwei Gedichte v. Al-'Ašâ; hrsg., übers. &c. v. R. Geyer, 2, Waddi' Hurairata, 1921, *see* KAIS. AKAD. D. W. Z. WIEN. Sitzber., B192, 1921.
Mainage (Th.)
Les religions de la préhist.; l'âge paléolith. la8°. 1921
Maine (Anne Louise Bénédicte de Bourbon, *dsse.* **du),** *see* MAUREL (A.) La Dsse. du M., 1928.
Maine (*Sir* Henry J. Sumner).
Ancient law. 9th ed. 8°. 1883
„ „ Intr. & notes by Sir F. Pollock. [repr.] 8°. 1920
Maine (Louis Auguste de Bourbon, *duc* **du),** *see* SAUTAI (M.) La bataille de Malplaquet d'après les corr. du duc. du M. à l'Armée de Flandre, 1904.

Mainland (T.), *see* HEDDLE (J. G. F. M.) & T. M. Orkney & Shetland, 1920.
Mainov (Vladimir Nikolaevich).
Результаты антропологич. изслѣдованій среди Мордвы-Эрзй [I.R.G.O. Зап. по отд. этнографіи, т11]. 8°.С.–П. 1883
Maintenon (*Mme.* de).
see LAVALLÉE (T.) Hist. de la maison roy. de St.-Cyr, 1686–1795, 1856.
„ SAINT-RENÉ TAILLANDIER (*Mme.*) Mme. de M.: l'énigme de sa vie auprès du Gr. Roi, 1920; tr., 1922.
Mainwaring (*Sir* Henry), *see* MANWARING (G. E.) Life & works of Sir H. M., 2v, 1920–22.
Mainwaring (John). *Memoirs of the life of G. F. Handel. Added, cat. of h. works &c. s8°. 1760
Mainz. Gedenkblaetter z. Gutenbergfeier, M., 1887, *see* GUTENBERG (J.)
Maiocchi (Rodolfo). Un diploma di Re Lotario rig. Como (20 agosto 949), *see* REGIA DEP. DI ST. PATRIA. Misc., t34, 1896.
F. Barbavara dur. la reggenza di Caterina Visconti, *see* REGIA DEP. DI ST. PATRIA. Misc., t35, 1898.
Maïoli (Thomas), *see* HOBSON (G. D.) M., Canevari &c., 1926.
Maior (Georg), *see* MEIER (GEORG), *prof. of theology, Wittenberg.*
Maior (Joannes), *von Joachimathal, see* MAJOR.
Maiorescu (Titu Liviu), *see* BOGDAN-DUICĂ (G.) T. L. M., 1921.
Maire (—). Topog. de Paris; plan (1808), reimp. [&] nomencl. des rues sous la Révol., par A. Franklin, 1816, *see* PARIS. Reprod. d'anc. plans, 1908.
Maire (Gilbert). Henri Bergson. s8°. [1926]
Mairey (A.), *see* FALLEX (M.) & A. M. Géog. d'après-Guerre: la face nouv. du monde, 1922.
Mairhofer (Theodor), *ed.* Urkundenbuch d. August. Chorherren-Stiftes Neustift in Tirol, *see* FONTES RERUM AUSTRIAC., B34, 1871.
Mais (Stuart Petre Brodie).
Books & their writers. s8°. 1920
Caged birds. s8°. 1922
Orange Street. s8°. 1926
Prunello. s8°. 1923
Quest sinister. s8°. 1922
Uncle Lionel. s8°. 1920
Maiseau (Raymond Balthazar), *see* FRANCE. Enquête faite par ordre du Parl. d'Angleterre, pour constater les progrès de l'indust. en F.; [ed. & tr. R. B. M.], 1825.
Maison (La) des jeux académiques, 1665, *see* SOREL (C.)
***Maisons** de l'ordre des Chartreux: vues & notices, 4t, 1913–19, *see* CHARTREUX.
Maistre (*le cte.* Joseph de). La franc-maçonnerie: mém. inéd., 1782. Publ. avec intr. par E. Dermenghem. s8°. 1925
Letters on the Spanish Inquisition, w. notes by J. Fletcher. 8°. 1838
Œuvres compl. n. éd., notice par Sainte-Beuve. s8°. *n.d.*
Sur la maxime qu'un honnête homme ne change jamais de religion, *see* MIGNE (J. P.) Theol. cursus, t5, 1841.
see VULLIAUD (P.) J. de M., franc-maçon, 1926.
Maistre (*le général* Paul), *see* BORDEAUX (P.) Le gén. M., 1923.
Maitland Club, *see* CHURCH OF SCOTLAND. Acts & proc. of the general assemblies of the Kirk of S. fr. 1560, 1839–45. [49.]
Maitland (A. Gibb) & A. Montgomery. The geol. & mineral industry of W. Australia. (W.A.: Geol. Survey). 8°. Perth. 1924
Maitland (Ella Fuller) & *Sir* F. Pollock, *bart.*
The Etchingham Letters. 3rd ed. s8°. 1900
Maitland (Frances), *see* HINKSON (*Mrs.* K. T.) & F. M. Bk. of flowers, 1909.
Maitland (Frederic William). The constit. hist. of Eng. Lect. [Ed. H. A. L. Fisher]. [repr.] 8°. C. 1920
Domesday Book & beyond. 3 essays on early hist. of Eng. [repr.] 8°. C. 1921
Maitland (*Sir* Richard), *Lord Lethington, 1496–1586.* The Maitland folio MS. cont. poems by Sir R. M., Dunbar, Douglas, Henryson & others. Ed. W. A. Craigie. [Scot. Text Soc., N.S., 20]. v2. 8°. E. 1927
The Maitland quarto MS. cont. poems by Sir R. M., Arbuthnot & others. Ed. W. A. Craigie. [Scot. Text Soc., N.S., 9]. 8°. E. 1920
Maître de Flémalle (Le), *see* FLÉMALLE (*Meister* VON).
Maitre (Léon), *see* QUIMPERLÉ, *abbey of.* Cartul. de l'abbaye de Ste.-Croix de Q.; publ. par L. M. &c., 1896.
Maittaire (Michael). *Stephanorum hist., vitas & libros complectens. 2t *in* 1v. s8°. Londini. 1709
Majano (Benedetto da), *see* BENEDETTO, *da Majana.*

Majendie (*Sir* Vivian Dering). Guide bk. to the Explosives Act, 1875. With remarks upon the Explosive Substances Act, 1883. 11th ed. s8°. [1902]
Up among the Pandies. s8°. 1859
Majenza (Michele). La natura e l'amore n. Divina Commedia. la8°. Caltanissetta. 1922
Majerus (Johannes). Gentis Hungaricae prima incunabula. [P2443]. s4°. Wittebergæ. 1676
Major (Albany F.) Surrey, London & the Saxon conquest. Address. [P2493]. 8°. 1920
—— **& E. J. Burrow.** The mystery of Wansdyke: record of research &c. [*w.* App. *by var. wr.*] 4°. Cheltenham. 1926
Major (Charles).
When knighthood was in flower. s8°. [1924]
Major (Emil). Erasmus v. Rotterdam. 8°. Basel. [1926?]
Major (Georg), *professor at Wittemberg, see* MEIER (G.), *1502–74.*
Major (Henry Dewsbury Alves). A resurrection of relics. A Modern churchman's defence in a charge of heresy. s8°. O. 1922
see BURGE (H. M.), *bp.* Doct. of the resurrection of the body: doc. rel. to quest. of heresy agst. M., 1922.
Major (Joannes), *of Arras, Jesuit, see* *MAGNUM speculum exemplorum var. notis &c. illust. per quendam patrem e S. J. [*i.e.* J. M.], 1605.
Major (Joannes), *von Joachimsthal.*
Epicedion Justi Menii. [P2468]. s4°. Witebergae. [1558 ?]
Operum pars prima [2ª & 3ª]. [3p *in* 2v]. s8°. Wittebergæ. 1566–74
see JENA *University.* Jubilæa Acad. Jen. festiv. celebr. orat. 5 [*by J. M. & others*], 1618.
Major (Johann Tobias). De oratione pro defunctis, diss. prior Hugoni Grotio &c. opposita. [P436; 2635]. s4°. Jenae. 1649
Exegematum locorum diffic. Πραξαποστόλων 2p *in* 1v. s8°. Jenae. 1647–49
Majumdar (P.) Swaraj. s8°. Calcutta. [1921]
Majunke (Paul). Louise Lateau, ihr Wunderleben &c. im deut. Kirchenconflicte. 2ᵉ Aufl. [P2657]. 8°. 1875
Majus (Joannes Henricus), *the elder.*
Introd. ad studium philologic., critic. & exegetic. &c. [*b. w. h.* Theol. evang., 1701]. s4°. Gissae. *n.d*.[1701 ?]
Oeconomia judiciorum divin. sub. Nov. Test. 2p *in* 1v. s4°. Francofurti a. M. 1717
Oeconomia judiciorum divin. per Vet. Test. libros. 3p. s4°. Francofurti a. M. 1712–14
Œconomia temp. Novi Test. [*b. w. h.* Œcon. temp. Vet. T., 1706]. s4°. Francofurti a. M. 1708
Œconomia temp. Vet. Test. s4°. Francofurti a. M. 1706
Repet. examen Hist. crit. textus Novi Test. a. R. Simonio &c. Auctum introd. & examine artis crit. J. Clerici & Novi spec. Biblic. emendat. &c. M. Meibomii. [App., Diss. de inspir. libr. sacr. &c. *w. sep. pag.*] s4°. Francofurti ad Moenum. 1708
Theologia evangelica ex pericopis Evangeliorum dominical. & festival. s4°. Gissae Hass. 1701
Majus (Joannes Henricus), *the younger.* Diss. de Zabiis, 1716, *see* SCHLÄGER (C. J.) Diss. fasc. nov., 1744.
Makeev (Nicholas) & V. O'Hara.
Russia. Intr. by H. A. L. Fisher. 8°. 1925
Makepeace (Walter), G. E. Brooke & R. St. J. Braddell, *edd.* 100 years of Singapore, 1819–1919. 2v. 8°. 1921
Makgill (J. D.) & E. Winch. Captain Joan. s8°. [1923]
Makhnovets (Vlasimir Petrovich), *see* AKIMOV (V. P.)
Maklakov (Vasily Alekseevich).
Толстой и Большевизмъ. [P2499]. s8°. Парижъ. 1921
La chute du rég. tsariste. Interrogatoires des ministres, conseillers &c. de la Cour Imp. Russe par la Comm. Extr. du Gouvt. Prov. de 1917. Préf. de B. M. Tr. J. & L. Polonsky. 8°. 1927
„ „ *For compl. Russ. originals, see* SCHEGOLEV (P. E.)
Makoldy (Joseph de). Pictures of Transylvania. Pref. by Count Albert Apponyi; w. pen & pencil by J. de M. 8°. Budapest. 1920
Makovetsky (H.) [MACOVETZKY]. Directory for Russ. & for. businessmen. Ed. H. M. *& others.* 8°. Petrograd. 1924
Makovsky (Sergei). В. Сѣровъ. s8°. Берлинъ. 1922
Силуэты русскихъ художниковъ. 8°. Прага. 1922
Peasant art of Subcarpathian Russia. Explan. text by S. M. Pref. by J. Gordon. 4°. Prague. [1926]
Makowsky (J.), *see* MACCOVIUS (J.)
Makram Ebeid (W.)
Complete independence *v.* the Milner scheme. [P2562]. 8°. 1921

Makrizi. Descr. hist. & topog. de l'Egypte; tr. P. Casanova, p4i, *see* INSTITUT FR. D'ARCH. OR. DU CAIRE. Mém., t4i, 1920.
El-Mawâ'iz wa'l-i'tibâr fî dhikr el-Khiṭaṭ wa'l-Athâr; éd. G. Wiet, t3–5i, *see* INSTITUT. FR. D'ARCH. OR. DU CAIRE. Mém., t46, 49, 53i, 1922–27.
Hist. regum Islamiticorum in Abyssinia. Interpret. est & una cum Alulfedae descr. regionum. Nigrit. e codd. Bibl. Leid. Arabice ed. F. T. Rinck. s4°. Lugduni Batav. 1790
Maksheev (Aleksci Ivanovich). Географ. свѣдѣнія книги большаго чертежа о Киргизскихъ степяхъ и Туркестанскомъ краѣ. [I.R.G.O. Зап. по отдѣл. этног., 6ii]. 8°. С.–П. 1880
Maksimov (Sergei Vasilevich).
Годъ на сѣверѣ. 3ᵉ изд. 8°. С.–П. 1871
Maksimovich (Karl Ivanovich). Амурскій край. [I. Akad. Nauk. Записки, t2]. 8°. С.–П. 1862
Maksimovich (Nikolai Ivanovich). Днѣпръ и его бассеинъ. [*&* Приложеніе]. [2t]. 4°. Кіевъ. 1901
Makushev (Vikenty Vasilevich).
Изслѣдованія объ историч. памятникахъ &c. Дубровника [*imperf.* I. Akad. Nauk. Записки, t11]. 8°. С.–П. 1867
Итал. архивы и хранящіеся въ нихъ мат. для Славянской ист. [I. Akad. Nauk. Записки, t16, 19]. [3p]. 8°. С.-П. 1870–71
1, Флорентинскій архивъ. 2, Неаполь и Палермо. 3, Неаполь, Бари, Анкона.
Malabar. A gram. of the Malabar lang. Tamul. By Eng. miss. of Madras. 2nd ed. s8°. Madras. 1789
Malachy [*O'Morgair*], *Saint, bp. of Down & Connor, abp. of Armagh, see* BERNARD, *St., abbot of Clairvaux.* Life of St. M. of Armagh; [tr., w. intr.] by H. J. Lawlor, 1920.
Malagodi (Olindo), *see* GIOLITTI (G.) Mem. d. mia vita; con studio di O. M., 2v, 1922.
Malagola (Carlo). L'istituz. d. rappres. diplom. di Venezia alla corte di Pietroburgo, e una relaz. [*by* F. Foscari] s. Marina russa. [Nozze Sacripante-Vitutii–Lovatelli. N123]. la8°. Venezia. 1906
Le Lido de Venise. la8°. Venise. 1909
Malagrida (Gabriele). Procès-verbal de condamn. de G. M. Jésuite *&* Exécution, 3 sept. 1758 [*2 pagin.*], *see* PORTUGAL. Rec. de decrets &c., p2, 1761.
see PARISOT (P.) Lettre cont. une rel. de l'exécution du p. M., 22 sept. 1761, 1761.
Malaguzzi Valeri (Francesco). La corte di Lodovico il Moro. [v3, 4]. 4°. Milano. 1917–23
3, Gli artisti lombardi. 4, Le arti industr., la letteratura, la musica.
Donati Bramante: 31 riprod., con testo e cat. 8°. 1924
Guido Reni. s8°. Firenze. [1921]
Leonardo da Vinci e la scultura. [Istit. di Studii Vinciani, v5]. la8°. Bologna. [1922]
Malan (Solomon Caesar). Bp. Ellicott's new tr. of the Athanasian Creed. [P2658]. 8°. 1872
Malaspina (Giovanni). Gli escavi di Julia Concordia [*i.e.* Concordia Sagittaria] &c. [Estr. d. Ateneo Veneto, 1885. P2840]. 8°. Venezia. 1885
Malaspina (Spinetta), *see* BIADEGO (G.) Tre doc. Scaligeri rig. S. M., 1915.
Malatesta (Marc Antonio Pandolfo), *see* MOREA. L'origine d. M.; [*dedic. signed* M. A. P. M.], 1686.
Malay. A gram. of the Malay tongue. Comp. fr. Bowrey's Dict. 4°. 1800
Illust. guide to Fed. Malay States. Ed. C. W. Harrison. [3rd impr.] s8°. [1920]
see also BRITISH MALAYA.
Malberg (*Mme.* Caroline Carré de), *see* CARRÉ DE MALBERG (*Mme.* C.)
Malcolm III, *king of Scotland, see* GEDDES (J.) Life of St. Margaret of Scotland, w. acc. of M. III, 1794.
Malcolm (Charles A.) The piper in peace & war. Foreword by the Duke of Atholl. 8°. 1927
Malcolm (David).
Genealog. mem. of the House of Drummond. s8°. E. 1808
Malcolm (*Sir* John). Hist. of Persia (Modern). Ed. &c. M. H. Court. sm. fol. Lahore. 1888
*Sketches of Persia. 2v. s8°. 1827
Malcolm (John), *of Poltalloch.* Descr. cat. of drawings by old masters forming coll. of J. M.; by J. C. Robinson. *p.p.* la8°. 1869
Malcolm (Wyatt), *see* CAMSELL (C.) & W. M. Mackenzie river basin, 1919.

Malden (Henry), *M.A.* On connecting vowels in Greek. [*Extr. f.* Philol. Soc. Trans., 1862–63]. 8°. [1863]
Malden (Richard Henry).
Problems of the New Test. to-day. s8°. O. 1923
Malden (Walter J.)
Actual farming: processes & practice. 3v. 8°. 1925
Grassland farming, pastures & leys. la8°. 1924
Maldonado Macanáz (Joaquin). Crón. de la prov. de Búrgos, 1866, *see* ESPAÑA. Crón. gen., v10, 1865.
Maldonatus (Joannes), *Jesuit.* Comm. in quatuor Evangelistas. 2t *in* 1v. fol. Mussiponti. 1596–97
see PRAT (J. M.) M. & l'Univ. de Paris, 16. s., 1856.
Mâle (Emile). L'art relig. du 12e s. en France. 4°. 1922
„ „ ....2e éd. rev. & corr. 4°. 1924
Malebranche (Nicolas). Dialogues on metaphysics & on religion. Tr. M. Ginsberg. Pref. by G. D. Hicks. 8°. [1923]
see STIELER (G.) N. M., 1925.
*__Malefactor's__ Register, or the Newgate & Tyburn calendar, 1700–79. v1–4 [no more publ.: *extra illust.*] 8°. [1779?]
Malès (Gabriel), *see* DUCHÊNE (A.) G. M. & la reconst. financ. de la France ap. 1789, 1923.
Malet, *Château, Monaco.* Descr. cat. of Château Malet, residence of Sir E. Malet &c. [With App., Cat. of plants, by Lady E. Malet &c. *w. sep. tp. & pagin.*] la8°. *p.f.p.c.* 1898
Malet (*le gén.* **Claude François).**
see LORT DE SÉRIGNAN (*cte.* A. DE). Un conspirateur milit. s. le Prem. Emp.: le gén. M., 1925.
„ MASSON (F.) La vie & les conspir. du Gén. M., 1754–1812, 3e éd., 1920.
Malet (*Rt. Hon. Sir* **Edward Baldwin),** *see* MALET, *Château, Monaco.* Descr. cat. of C. M., 1898.
Malet (*Lady* **Ermyntrude),** *see* MALET, *Château.* Descr. cat. [w. App., Cat. of plants, by Lady M. &c.], 1898.
Malet (Lucas), *ps.* Da Silva's widow & o. s. s8°. [1922]
The dogs of want. s8°. [1924]
The survivors. s8°. [1923]
The tall villa. s8°. [1920]
Malfante (Antonio), *d. 1450, see* LA RONCIÈRE (C. DE). La découv. de l'Afr. au m. â., t3, 1927.
Malgorn (G.) Lexique techn. anglais-fr. Avec la collab. de M. Desmarets. s8°. 1920
Malharro (Victorina).
De amor y de dolor. s8°. Buenos Aires. 1919
Malheiro (Alexandre). Longe da vista . . . 8°. 1913
Malherbe (François de). Poésies. Publ. d'ap. éds. rev. par M. & disposé par P. Martinon. Intr. par M. Allem. s8°. 1926
see FAGUET (E.) Hist. de la poésie fr., t1, Au temps de M., 1923.
„ GOSSE (E.) M. & the class. reaction in 17 c., 1920.
Malibran (Maria Felicita), *née Garcia, see* FLAMENT (A.) Une étoile en 1839: la M., 1928.
Malikov (Aleksandr Kapit). На задворкахъ Фабрики-Край безъ будущаго (по волжскимъ степямъ). 8°. Москва. 1902
Malinjak (Nicolaus). De eccl. Russa orthodoxa a Ruthenis adjuvanda &c. [P2424]. 8°. Pragae. 1912
Malinowski (Bronislaw). Argonauts of the Western Pacific. Pref. by Sir J. G. Frazer. [R. Mond Exped. to New Guinea, 1914–18]. la8°. 1922
Classific. particles in the lang. of Kiriwina. [P2621]. 8°. *n.p. n.d.*
Crime & custom in savage society. 8°. 1926
Sex & repression in savage society. 8°. 1927
Malins (William). A plan for addit. national defences. 8°. 1848
Malkhasean (St.) [Historians of the Armenians. *In Armenian.* Ed. St. M.] v1ii, 2i. la8°. Tiflis. 1909–13
see AGATHANGELUS. Hist., 1909 [1ii].
„ MOSES, *of Choren.* Hist., 1913 [2i].
Mallarmé (Stéphane).
Les dieux antiques. Nouv. mythologie d'ap. G. W. Cox &c. 2e éd. s8°. [1925]
Igitur ou la Folie d'Elbehnon. [Préf. *signed* E. Bonniot]. 3e éd. 8°. 1925
Poésies. Ed. compl., cont. plusieurs poèmes inéd. 26e éd. s8°. [1924]
S. M. in Eng. verse. By A. Ellis. Intr. by G. Turquet-Milnes. s8°. [1927]
see DUJARDIN (E.) De S. M. au prophète Ezéchiel &c., 1919.
„ ROYÈRE (J.) M., 1927.
Malleson (Miles). The fanatics. Comedy. s8°. 1924
Young heaven, & 3 o. plays. s8°. 1918
Mallet (*Sir* **Bernard),** *see* AVEBURY (J. L., *1st b.*) Life-work of Ld. A.: essays by Sir B. M. &c., 1924.
Mallet (Charles), *Canon of Rouen.*
see ARNAULD (A.) *Cont. de la Nouv. défense &c.: contre le livre de M., 1682.
„ —— *Nouv. déf. de la tr. du N.T.; contre le livre de M., 1680.
Mallet (*Sir* **Charles Edward).**
Hist. of the Univ. of Oxford. 3v. 8°. O. 1924–27
Mallet (David). Poet. works. Coll. by T. Park. s8°. 1805
Mallet (Dominique). Les rapports des Grecs avec l'Egypte (525–331), *see* INSTITUT FRANÇ. D'ARCH. ORIENT. DU CAIRE. Mém., t48, 1922.
Mallet (*Mme.* **Étienne),** *see* BRÖLEMANN (H. A.) Cat. of coll. of illum. MSS., sold by order of Mme. E. M., 1926.
Mallet (Frédéric). Pierre Loti, s. œuvre. s8°. 1923
Malleterre (*le général* **Pierre Marie Gabriel).** De la Marne à l'Yser. La victoire des forces morales &c. s8°. 1915
Un peu de lumière sur les batailles d'août-sept. 1914. [P2711]. s8°. 1917
Mallett (Marguerite).
A white woman among the Masai. 8°. [1923]
Mallik (Devendra Nath). The elements of astronomy. 8°. C. 1921
Optical theories. Lect. 2nd ed. rev. 8°. C. 1921
Malling (Mathilda). Manden, Hustruen & Lord Byron. Roman. s8°. København. 1912
Malloch (E. S.), *see* BLIZARD (J.) & E. S. M. Gas producer trials w. Alberta coals, 1921.
Mallock (William Hurrell). Is life worth living? 2nd ed. 8°. 1879
Memoirs of life & literature. 8°. 1920
Mallory (George Leigh), *see* PYE (D.) G. L. M., 1927.
Mallory (Walter H.) China: land of famine. [Amer. Geogr. Soc., Spec. Publ. No. 6]. la8°. N.Y. 1926
Mallouf (N.) Dict. franç.-turc. 2e éd. s8°. 1856
Mally (C. W.)
The maize stalk borer. [P2820]. 8°. Cape Town. 1920
Mally (Ernst.) Studien z. Theorie d. Möglichkeit u. Ähnlichkeit, 1922, *see* KAIS. AKAD. D. W. ZU WIEN. Sitzber., B194, 1923.
Malmesbury (James Harris, *1st earl of*), *see* HARRIS (JAS.) Works; w. life by h. son, M., 1841.
Malmesbury (William, *of*). De gestis regum & Hist. nov., *see* SAVILE (*Sir* H.) Rerum Angl. scr., 1596; 1601.
Malmignati (*Countess***).**
Through inner deserts to Medina. 8°. [1925]
Malmström (Bernhard Elis). Grunddragen af Svenska vitterhetens hist. Föreläsningar. 5d [d3 *wanting*]. 8°. Örebro. 1866–68
Malo (Henri).
Les corsaires dunkerquois & Jean Bart. t2, 1662 à 1702. s8°. 1914
Les dern. corsaires: Dunkerque (1715–1815). 8°. 1925
Dunkerque, ville héroïque. s8°. 1918
La gloire du Vicomte de Launay, Delphine Gay de Girardin. 8°. 1925
La grande guerre des corsaires: Dunkerque (1702–15). 8°. 1925
Une muse et sa mère: Delphine Gay de Girardin. 8°. 1924
Nos 3 ports du Nord. Dunkerque, Calais & Boulogne. 8°. 1920
see DOSNE (*Mme.* S. E.) Mém. de Mme. D.; publ. avec. intr. &c. par H. M., 2t, 1928.
Malon (Benoît). La morale sociale. s8°. [1895]
Malone Society. Collections. v2, p2. s4°. 1923
[PUBLICATIONS]. s4°. 1920–26
see CHRISTMAS PRINCE (THE), 1607–8, 1922 [1923].
„ GREENE (R.) *The [comicall hist. of] Alphonsus, King of Aragon, 1599, 1926.
„ —— Friar Bacon & Friar Bungay, 1594, 1926.
„ —— *The Scot. hist. of James IV, 1598, 1921.
„ GREG (W. W.) 2 Elizabethan stage abridgements: the Battle of Alcazar & Orlando Furioso, 1922 [1923].
„ JONSON (BEN). *Every man out of his humour, 1600, 1920.
„ MARSTON (J.) Antonio & Mellida & Antonio's revenge, 1602, 1921.
„ MUNDAY (A.) John a Kent & John a Cumber, 1923.
„ *WELSH (THE) embassador (*c.* 1623), 1920 [1921].
Malone (Kemp). Lit. hist. of Hamlet. [Anglist. Forsch.; hrsg. J. Hoops, H59]. [v]1. 8°. Heidelberg. 1923
Malone (William), *see* HOYLE (J.) Rejoynder to Mr. M.'s reply [to J. Usher] conc. Reall Presence, 1641.
Malorossiiskii.
Полный Малороссійскій пѣсенникъ, 1874, *see* RUSSIA.
Malory (*Sir* **Thomas).** La morte d'Arthur. Abr. & rev. by E. Conybeare. s8°. 1868
Le morte d'Arthur. [Everyman's Lib.] [repr.] 2v. s8°. [1908]

Malory (*Sir* **Thomas**) [*continued*].
The most anc. & famous hist. of Prince Arthur &c. Newly refined &c. [Tr. M. *Imperf.* 3p *in* 1v]. s4°. 1634
see CHAMBERS (*Sir* E. K.) Sir T. M., 1922.
,, SCUDDER (VIDA D.) Le morte D'arthur; the bk. & its sources, 1921.

Malraux (André), *see* CHANSON (A.) Ecrits; par A. C., A. M. &c., 1927.

Malsagov (S. A.) An island hell: a Soviet prison in the Far North. Tr. F. H. Lyon. s8°. 1926

Maltbie (Milo Roy). Eng. local govt. of to-day. [Columbia Univ. St. in hist. &c., v9i]. 8°. N.Y. 1897

Maltby (Isaac). Treatise on courts martial & milit. law. 8°. Boston [U.S.] 1813

Malte-Brun (Conrad) [†BRUUN (MALTHE CONRAD)]. Tableau de la Pologne anc. & mod. [Législ. polon. 930–1430, par J. Lelewel.—Litt. anc. de la Pologne, par M. Podczaszynski]. n. éd., augm. &c. par L. Chodzko. 2t. 8°. 1830

Malthe. *Malthe, Corse, Minorque & Gibraltar. [*b. w.* Curti (L.) Mém. justif. &c., 1796. *no tp.*] s8°. 1797

Malther (Henry). Saadia Gaon, h. life & works. 8°. Phila. 1921

Malthus (Thomas Robert).
see BONAR (J.) M. & h. work, 2nd ed., 1924.
,, GRIFFITH (G. T.) Population problems of age of M., 1926.

Malvenda (Petro de). Lettres & mém. de F. de Vargas, de P. de M. &c. t. le Co. de Trente, 1700, *see* VARGAS (F. DE).

Malvezzi (Aldobrandino). Il risorgimento ital. in un carteggio di patrioti lombardi, 1821–60. Lettere ined. di C. Arconati Visconti &c. A cura di A. M. 8°. Milano. 1924

Malvezzi (*il marchese* **Virgilio**). Chiefe events of the monarchie of Spain, 1639. Tr. R. Gentilis. s8°. 1647

Malynes (Gerard de). The ancient sea-laws of Oleron, Wisby & the Hanse-towns. Taken out of Les us [*sic*] & coutumes de la mer [*by* G. de M.] & rendred into Eng. by G. Miege. [*b. w.* Burroughs (*Sir* J.) Soveraignty &c., 1686]. fol. 1686

Mamachi (Tommaso Maria). De animabus justorum in sinu Abrahae &c. libri 2. 2t [*pagin. cont.*] 8°. 1766

Mameli (Goffredo).
Poesie. Note e pref. di P. Bardazzi. 8°. Milano. [1924]

Mamiani (*il conte* **Terenzio**). Teorica d. religione e d. stato &c. 8°. Firenze. 1868
see SANTANGELO (G. B.) Alc. versi sicil., seg. da una lettera sull' inno a S. Sofia, di T. M., 1878.

Mammetractus, *ps., see* MARCHESINUS (J.)

***Mamotrectus** super Bibliam, 1479, *see* MARCHESINUS (J.)

Man. *Man (The) who didn't win the War, 1923, *see* LLOYD-GEORGE (*Rt. Hon.* D.)
*Man (The) who never understood. s8°. [1924]

Man: a monthly record of anthropological science. Publ. under dir. of Anthropological Institute. [v]20–27. la8°. [1920–27]

Man, *Isle of.* *Compl. hist. of the Isle of Man, *see* SEACOME (J.) Hist. of House of Stanley, 1821.
Constit. of the I. of Man, p3 of Report of Comm. of Inq., 1792, w. App. & o. docs. Ed. R. Sherwood. [Manx Soc., 31]. 8°. Douglas. 1882
Manorial roll of the I. of Man, 1511–15. Tr. T. Talbot. Pref. by G. F. Clucas. With app. la8°. 1924
*Six day's tour thr. the I. of Man. By a stranger. s8°. Douglas. 1836

Man (Edward Howard). The arts of the Andamanese & Nicobarese. With obs. by A. Lane Fox. [*Extr. f.* Journal of Anthrop. Inst., v7, 1878. P2601]. 8°. 1878

Man (John), *of Reading.*
Hist. & antiq. of Reading. 4°. Reading. 1816

Manacorda (Giuseppe). Studi Foscoliani. 8°. Bari. 1921

Manandian (Yakob [Agop]). Beitr. z. alban. Gesch. [Moses d. Utier (Kalankatuaci)]. Inaug.-Diss., Univ. Jena. 8°. L. 1897
Davith Anyalthi khndire. [*In Armenian. Extr. f.* Ararat, 1904. *b. w.* George, *of Pisidia.* Vetzoreayq, 1900]. 8°. Vagharshapat. 1904
—— **& H. Adjarean.** Rec. martyrology of Armenians, 1155–1843. 8°. Vagharshapat. 1903

Mance (*Brig.-Gen.* **Harry Osborne**). The railway systems of W. Africa. Lect. [P2564]. 8°. 1913

Manceaux (Jean Baptiste). Hist. de l'abbaye & du village d'Hautvillers. 3t. 8°. Epernay. 1880

Manchée (W. H.) The Westminster City Fathers (The Burgess Court of W.), 1585–1901. 8°. 1924

Manchester.
Extracts f. M. churchwardens' accounts, 1664–1710; by E. Broxap, *see* CHETHAM MISC., N.S., v4, 1921.
Latin verses &c. by scholars of M. Grammar School, 1640 & 1750–1800; ed. A. A. Mumford, *see* CHETHAM MISC., N.S., v4, 1921.
*M. al mondo: contemplation of death &c., 6th impr. enl., 1655, *see* MANCHESTER (H. M., *1st e. of*).
ART GALLERY.
Cat. of pictures, w. descr. notes & illust. Comp. by W. Stanfield. la8°. M'ter. [1894]
UNIVERSITY.
Calendar, 1921-22, 1922–23. 8°. M'ter. 1921–22
Cat. of the Freeman Lib. Comp. by J. Tait. 8°. M'ter. 1894

Manchester Guardian (The).
Hist. of the War. v8, 9. fol. 1919–20
Reconstruction in Europe. Ed. J. M. Keynes. sect. 1–12 [*in 1v. no tp. issued*]. fol. [1922–23]
see MILLS (W. H.) M. G., cent. of hist., 1921.

Manchester (Charles Montagu, *1st duke of*), *1660–1722.* [*Letter to S. Valier &c., 1697, with* Relaz. d. G. Venier, 1697. *Ed.* V. Rizzo. Nozze Wiel-Lawley. N137]. fol. [Venezia]. 1890
[*Letters conc. his embassy to Venice, 1697. Ed.* V. Rizzo. Nozze Wiel-Lawley]. [N119]. fol. Roma. [1890]

Manchester (Henry Montagu, *1st earl of*). *Manchester al mondo: Contemplation of death & immortality. 6th imp. enl. w. Latine sentences rendered into Eng. s8°. 1655

Manchon (J.) Le slang. Lexique de l'Anglais familier &c. Et sur la prononciation &c. s8°. 1923

Manchuria. Econ. hist. of M. Comp. in commem. of the Bank of Chosen [*by* T. Hoshino. Foreword by S. Minobe]. 8°. Seoul. 1920
M.: land of opportunities. Comp. & publ. by T. F. Logan. rev. ed. 8°. N.Y. 1924
N. Manchuria & the Chinese E. Railway. [*By var. a.* Intr. signed G. Diky]. 4°. Harbin, China. 1924

Mancini (Enrico Fossa), *see* FOSSA MANCINI (E.)

Mancini (Girolamo). *Works in* ARCHIVIO STOR. ITAL.
Contrib. dei Cortonesi alla coltura ital., 1923. [79ii.]
Cosimo Bartoli (1503–72), 1918. [76ii.]
Giov. Tortelli cooperatore di Niccolò V nel fondare la Bibl. Vaticana, 1920. [78ii.]
Gregorio Tifernate, 1925. [81.]
Necrologia: G. M., 1925. [83i.]

Mancini (Giulio). Viaggio per Roma [1620–26]. Hrsg. L. Schudt. [Röm. Forsch., 4]. 8°. L. 192[illegible]

Mancini (Hortense), *dsse. Mazarin, see* MAZARIN (H. MANCINI *dsse.*)

Mancini (Marie), *aft. wife of Prince Colonna, Constable o[f] Naples, see* PLÉDY (L.) Brouage &c.—M. M. à Brouage 1925.

Mancini (Pasquale Stanislao). Sopra il disegno di legge pe[r] la soppress. d. corpor. relig. in Roma. Discorsi. [P520]. 8°. 187[illegible]

Mandacuniese (Giovanni), *see* JOHN I, *Mantagouni, patr. o[f] Armenia.*

Mandäische Liturgien; mitgeteilt, übers. &c. v. M. Lidzbarski 1920, *see* LIDZBARSKI (M.)

Mandalay. *Mandalay massacres. Upper Burma dur. r. o[f] King Theebaw. [By W. H. Wootton & o.] [P2845]. 8°. Rangoon. 188[illegible]

Mandarini. *Lettere di duo m., 3529, *see* LETTERE.

Mandarini (Enrico), *see* BIBLIOTECA ORATORIANA, *Naples.* codici ms. d. Bibl. O. illust. da E. M., 1897.

Mandelkern (Solomon). Hist. Chrestomathie d. russ. Litt bis auf die neueste Zeit. [*2nd tp. in Russian*]. 8°. Hannover. 189[illegible]

Mandell (C. Creighton) & E. Shanks.
Hilaire Belloc. Intr. by G. K. Chesterton. s8°. [191[illegible]

Mandelshtam (Osip Emilevich).
Tristia. [*In Russian*]. s8°. II. 192[illegible]

Mander (Gerald P.), *see* BRIDGEMAN (C. G. O.) & G. P. M The Staffs. hidation, 1920.
—— **& T. Pape.** Some Ridware armorial glass, *see* STAFFORDSHIRE. Coll. for hist. of S., 1923, 1924.

Mander (Jane). The strange attraction. s8°. [192[illegible]

Mandeville (Bernard). The fable of the bees: or, privat[e] vices, publick benefits. With comm. by F. B. Kaye. 2v. 8°. O. 192[illegible]

Mandeville (*Sir* **John**). M.'s travels. Tr. f. the French [of] J. d'Outremeuse. Ed. P. Hamelius. [E.E.T.S., 153, 154] 2v [*in 1*]. 8°. 1919–[illegible]
The voiage & travaile of Sir J. M. 8°. *Woodman & Lyon.* 17[illegible]

Mandeville (*Sir* **John**) [*continued*].
The voiage & travaile of Sir J. M. Repr. f. ed. of 1725; w. intr., notes & gloss. by J. O. Halliwell. 8°. 1866
" " ....[re-impr.] 8°. 1883
" " With the Journal of Frier Odoricus. [Intr. by J. Bramont. Everyman's Lib.] s8°. [1928]
see CORDIER (H.) Mélanges, t1, J. de M. &c., 1914.
Mandrot (Bernard de). Dépêches des ambassadeurs milanais en France sous Louis XI & François Sforza. Publ. B. de M. [Soc. de l'Hist. de F.] t3, 4. 8°. 1920–23
3, 1465. 4, 1465–66, par C. Samaran.
Manek (Franz), G. Pekmezi & A. Stotz.
Albanes. Bibliographie. 8°. Wien. 1909
Manenti (Cipriano). Estr. d. Historie (1325–76), *see* MURATORI (L. A.) Rerum Ital. scr., t15v, 1920.
Manenti (Luca di Domenico). Cronaca (1174–1413), *see* MURATORI (L. A.) Rerum Ital. scr., t15v, 1920.
***Manes** Sturmiani sive epicedia scripta in obitum Ioan. Sturmii a diversis amices &c. s8°. Argentorati. 1590
Manes (Alfred). Mietverlust-Versicherung. 8°. 1908
Manet (Edouard), *see* BLANCHE (J. E.) M., 1925.
see DURET (T.) Hist. de E. M. & de s. œuvre, n. éd., 1919.
" WALDMANN (E.) E. M., 1923.
Manfred, *king of Naples & Sicily, see* BÄUMKER (C.) Petrus de Hibernia, Jugendlehrer d. T. Aquino, u. seine Disput. vor König M., 1920.
Manfredi (Carlo Francesco), *see* LUSERNA (C. F. M., *c.* DI).
Manfredi (Manfredo Emanuele), *see* VENEZIA. Basilica di S. Marco in V.: restauri &c. (*signed* M. E. M. &c.), 1904–8.
Manfredini (Vincenzo). Regole armoniche. la8°. Venezia. 1775
Manfrin (Pietro). Il comune e l'individuo in Italia. s8°. 1879
Manfroni (Camillo). Ginevra, Berna e Carlo Emanuele I (1589–92) &c., *see* REGIA DEP. DI ST. PATRIA. Misc., t31, 1894.
Storia d. marina ital. dur. la Guerra Mondiale, 1914–18, con doc. ined. &c. 8°. Bologna. 1923
Mangasarian (M. M.)
What is Christian Science? [P2688]. 8°. [1922]
Mangels (H.) Paraguay. Wirtschaftl., naturgesch. &c. Abhandlungen. 2e A. 8°. München-Freising. 1919
Mangenot (Eugène), *see* DICTIONNAIRE. D. de théologie cathol., sous la dir. de A. Vacant, cont. sous celle de E. M., t6–8, 1920–25.
Manger (J.-B.) L'Entente cordiale. Rev. d'Hist. de la Guerre Mond.: Extr. [P2876]. 8°. 1927
Mangey (Thomas), *see* CARPZOV (J. B.) De Λόγῳ Philonis non Johanneo, adv. T. M., 1739.
Mangin (*Général* **Charles Marie Emmanuel).**
Comment finit la Guerre. [7e éd.] 8°. [1920]
Des hommes & des faits. s8°. [1923]
see DUTRÈB (M.) & P. A. DE GRANIER DE CASSAGNAC. Mangin, 1920.
" HANOTAUX (G.) Le général M., 1925.
" —— Hist. de la nation franç., t8, Hist. milit. & navale, par M. &c., 1927.
Mangles (James), *see* IRBY (*Hon.* C. L.) & J. M. Travels in Egypt &c., 1844.
Mango (*Mrs.* J. A.), *see* SNEYD (R.) Cat. of old Eng. &c. furniture; also the property of Mrs. M. &c., 1924.
Manhar Kooverba, *see* KOOVERBA (M.)
Manhart (Franciscus Xavier), *see* MANNHARDT (F. X.)
Manhattan Club.
[Constit., rules & list of members]. s8°. [N.Y. 1898]
***Mani** morte, ossia lettera &c., 1765, *see* FLORIO (F.)
Manichaeus, *see* BURKITT (F. C.) Relig. of the Manichees, 1925.
***Manifest** d. Kommunist. Partei, 1848 (*facs.*), *see* FREYTAG (G.) Bilder, B5, 1925.
Manilius (Marcus). Astronomicon liber 4. Rec. & enarr. A. E. Housman. 8°. Londinii. 1920
Manin (Daniele).
see JORISSEN (TH.) Hist. Karakters, 2, D. M., 1912.
" PASCOLATO (A.) M. e Venezia nel 1848–49, 1916.
" TREVELYAN (G. M.) M. & the Venetian Revol. of 1848, 1923.
Manin (*il conte* **Leonardo).** Illustr. d. medaglie dei dogi di Venezia denom. Oselle. ed. 2a. la8°. Venezia. 1847
Manington (George), *F.R.G.S.* The West Indies, w. Brit. Guiana & Brit. Honduras. 8°. [1925]
Manini Ferranti (Giuseppe). Compendio d. storia sacra e politica di Ferrara. 6t *in* 3v. 8°. Ferrara. 1808–10

Manitius (Maximilian). Gesch. d. latein. Lit. d. Mittelalters. [Müller (I. E. P. v.) Hdbch. d. Altertumswiss., B9, Abt. 2, T2]. T2. la8°. München. 1923
Manley (*Sir* **Roger).** Hist. of the rebellions in Eng., Scot. & Ireland, 1640–85. 3p *in* 1v [*pag. cont.*] s8°. 1691
Manlius (Jacobus), *see* MENNEL (J.)
Manly (John Matthews). Lok-Sounday, *see* HARVARD UNIV. St. in philol. &c., v1, 1892.
Manly anniversary st. in language & lit. [*By var. wr.* Chicago Univ.] 8°. Chicago. 1923
The miracle play in med. Eng., *see* ROY. SOC. OF LIT. Essays, N.S., v7, 1927.
Obs. on the lang. of Chaucer's Legend of good women, *see* HARVARD UNIV. St. &c. in philol. &c., v2, 1893.
—— & E. Rickert.
Contemp. Amer. lit. Bibliographies &c. s8°. [1922]
Manly (Thomas). Ozotype. s8°. 1901
Mann (Carl). Wie &c. ist Luther d. grosse Bibel-Uebersetzer geworden? [P2622]. s8°. St. 1835
Mann (Charles A.)
Paper money, the root of all evil &c. s8°. N.Y. 1872
Mann (Charles Edward). The Sargent family & the old Sargent homes. [Cape Ann in story &c., 5]. 8°. Lynn. 1919
Mann (Charles Riborg). The Amer. spirit in educ. [Bur. of Ed. Bull. No. 30]. [P2412]. 8°. Wash. 1919
Mann (Claus). Vor dem Leben. s8°. Hamburg. [1925]
Mann (Eliza), *see* FENNEL (J.) A tribute to mem. of E. M., 1819.
Mann (F. O.) London & suburban. Poems. s8°. 1925
Mann (G. A.) The develop. of the will-power. 8°. Paris. 1912
Mann (Heinrich).
Die Armen. s8°. L. [1917]
Die Göttinnen. [3B]. s8°. München. *n.d.*
Im Schlaraffenland. s8°. L. *n.d.*
Die Jagd nach Liebe. s8°. München. *n.d.*
Die kleine Stadt. s8°. München. [1922]
Der Kopf. s8°. 1925
Liliane u. Paul. s8°. 1926
Macht u. Mensch. s8°. München. [1919]
Mutter Marie. s8°. 1927
Professor Unrat. s8°. L. *n.d.*
Mann (Horace K.), *of Newcastle-on-Tyne.* Lives of the popes in the Middle Ages. v13, 14. 8°. 1925–28
9–14, Innocent II to Benedict XI, 1130–1305 (13, 14, 1216–54).
The portraits of the Popes, *see* BRIT. SCHOOL AT ROME. Papers, v9, 1920.
Mann (Jacob). The Jews in Egypt & in Palestine under the Fatimid Caliphs. 2v. 8°. O. 1920–22
Mann (James Saumarez), *1893–1920.* An administrator in the making. Ed. by h. Father [J. S. M.] 8°. 1921
Mann (Thomas).
Bekenntnisse d. Hochstaplers Felix Krull. Buch der Kindheit. s8°. St. 1924
Bemühungen: neue Folge d. Gesamm. Abhandl. u. kl. Aufsätze. s8°. 1925
Der kleine Herr Friedemann u. a. Novellen. s8°. [1921]
Pariser Rechenschaft. 8°. 1926
Unordnung u. frühes Leid. s8°. [1926]
Der Zauberberg. 2B. s8°. 1925
" " [81. bis 95. A.] s8°. [1927]
TRANSLATIONS.
Buddenbrooks. [Tr. H. T. Lowe-Porter]. 2v. 8°. 1924
The magic mountain. Tr. H. T. Lowe-Porter. 2v. 8°. [1927]
see ELOESSER (A.) T. M., s. Leben u. s. Werk, 1925.
" JACOB (G.) Das Werk T. M.'s: Bibliog., 1926.
Mann (Thomas), *a waterman.* The honest waterman. Life & character of T. M. s8°. 1825
Mann (Tom). Memoirs. 8°. 1923
Mannerheim (*Gen.* **Gustavus Charles),** *b. 1869, see* KING (J.) Three bloody men: M. &c., 1919.
Manners (Nicholas). A full confut. of John Fletchers Appeal &c. [*b. w.* Horne (M.) An investig. &c., 1809]. s8°. Hull. 1789
Remarks on the writings of the Rev. J. Wesley. [P2667]. s8°. Hull. 1788
Some particulars of the life &c. of N. M. [P2667]. s8°. York. 1785
Manners (*Lady* **Victoria) & G. C. Williamson.**
Angelica Kauffmann. 4°. [1924]
Mannhardt (Franz Xavier) [MANHART (FRANCISCUS XAVIER)].
De ingenua indole probabilismi, see MIGNE (J. P.), *ed.* Theol. cursus, t11, 1861.
Liber singularis de antiq. Christianorum. s8°. Augustæ Vindelic. 1767
Mannhardt (Wilhelm). Wald- u. Feldkulte. 2e A. besorgt v. W. Heuschkel. 2B. 8°. 1904–5
Manniche (Peter), *see* BEGTRUP (H.), H. LUND & P. M. Folk high schools of Denmark, 1926.

Mannin (Ethel Edith) [*Mrs.* J. A. PORTEOUS].
Hunger of the sea. [3rd impr.] s8°. [1926]
Pilgrims. 8°. [1927]
Sounding brass. s8°. 1925
Manning (*Miss* Anne). The household of Sir T. More. s8°. 1906
Manning (Frederic). Life of Sir W. White. Intr. by Ld. G. Hamilton. 8°. 1923
Manning (Frederick George). The Bermondsey murder: trial of M. & Maria M. for murder of P. O'Connor. 8°. 1849
Manning (*card.* Henry Edward), *abp. of Westminster.* The centenary of St. Peter & the Gen. Council. [P2694]. 8°. 1867
Die vatikan. Dekrete. *Uebersetz.* 8°. Mainz. 1875
see LESLIE (S.) H. E. M., h. life & labours, 1921.
„ STRACHEY (L.) Eminent Victorians, 1920.
Manning (Henry Parker). The fourth dimension: coll. of essays sel. &c. w. intr. & ed. notes by M. s8°. [1921]
Manning (Percy). Sport & pastime in Stuart Oxford, *see* SALTER (H. E.), *ed.* Surveys &c., 1923.
Manning (Robert), *prof. in the Eng. Coll. at Douai.*
*Case (The) stated, betw. the Church of Rome & the Ch. of Eng. [*controverting The Case stated, by Leslie or Spinckes*]. 2p. 8°. [Antwerp ?] 1721
*England's conversion & reformation compared. 4 dialogues. s8°. Antwerp. 1725
see TRAPP (J.) Ch. of Eng. def. agst. Ch. of Rome; ans. to England's conversion &c. [*by M.*], 1727.
Manning (Samuel), *LL.D.*
*Spanish pictures. la8°. [1870]
„ „ [*a. issue w. author's name on tp.*] la8°. [1870]
Manning (Thomas).
Letters to Charles Lamb. Ed. G. A. Anderson. 8°. 1925
Manning (William Ray). Arbitration treaties among Amer. nations to close of 1910. [C.E. for Int. Peace]. la8°. N.Y. 1924
Diplomatic corr. of the U.S. conc. independence of Lat.-Amer. nations. [C.E. for Int. Peace]. v1–3. la8°. N.Y. 1925
Mannlich (Johann Christian v.) Rokoko u. Revolution. Lebenserinnerungen, 1741–1822. [Tr., hrsg. E. Stallreither. 3e A.] s8°. 1923
Manno (Antonio).
Works in REGIA DEP. DI STORIA PATRIA. Misc.
Alcuni cat. di ant. librerie piemontesi; pubbl. A. M., 1880. [19.]
Annali e scritti di G. Spano, 1879. [18.]
E. Ferrero commem. [*w.* Bibliog.], 1909. [44.]
Eugenio Cais di Pierlas, 1904. [40.]
Il lavoro quadragen. d. Barone G. Claretta, indicato da A. M., 1900. [36.]
L. Fontana, ricordi, 1909. [44.]
P. Micca ed il gen. conte Solaro d. Margarita: ricerche 3 sull' assedio di Torino del 1706, 1883. [21.]
Relaz. e doc. sull' assedio di Torino nel 1706; racc. &c. da A. M., 1878. [17.]
Sull' assedio di Torino nel 1706: ricerche 2, 1880. [19.]
Manolesso (Emilio Maria). Hist. nova, successi d. guerra Turchesca, la congiura d. duca de Nortfolch contra la regina d'Inghilterra; la guerra di Fiandra &c.; l'uccisione d'Ugonotti &c. da 1570 s. all' hora pres. 8°. Padoua. 1572
Manoscritti, miniature &c., vend. 1927, 1927, *see* HOEPLI (U.)
Manosque. Livre des privilèges de Manosque. Cartul. municipal lat.-provençal, 1169–1315. Publ. M. Z. Isnard, suivi de Remarques philol. sur le texte provençal, par C. Chabaneau. 4°. Digne. 1894
Manouk, *see* MEKHITHAR, *of Sebaste.*
Manrique (Gervasio). Soria, la ciudad d. alto Duero: leyendas y tradic. de su prov. s8°. 1926
Manrique (Jorge). Coplas por la muerte de su padre, primera ed. crit. publ. R. Foulché-Delbosc. [Bibl. Hisp.] s8°. *n.d.*
see BARAHONA (D.) Glosa a la obra de J. M. 1541. [repr. 1902].
Manrique (Sebastian). Travels, 1629–43. Tr., w. intr. & notes by C. E. Luard & H. Hosten. [Hakluyt Soc., s2, 59]. v1, Arakan. 8°. O. 1927
Mans, *see* LE MANS.
Mansbridge (Albert). The older univ. of England: Oxford & Cambridge. 8°. 1923
Mansel (Henry Longueville), *dean of St. Paul's.* Limits of relig. thought. Bampton Lect., 1858. 8°. 1858
Phrontisterion, 1852, *see* GORDON (G.), *ed.* Three Oxf. ironies, 1927.
Mansfeld.
Bedencken, das diese Proposition oder Lehre, nicht nütz, not noch war sey &c. Das gute werck z. seligkeit nötig sind. Gestellet durch die Prediger zu M. &c. [P2442]. s4°. [Magdeburgk, *M. Lotther.* 1553]

Mansfeld [*continued*].
Bericht d. Prediger in d. Graffschafft Manssfelt, der Irrungen halben [*of* P. Eber & G. Meier]. [P2436]. s4°. [Eisleben, *Andreas Petri.* 1568]
Kurtzer Bericht, Wes sich die Prediger, in M., in irem Synodo zu Eisleben 1562 &c. in Deutscher u. Latein. sprach, ausgegangenen Confession halben wider alle Secten einhellig vergliechen haben. [P2436]. s4°. Eisleben, *Urban Ganbisch.* 1563
*Mansfeld. (Der) Theologen, Bericht u. Bekentnis v. d. Wittenberg. Catechismo. [*b. w.* Wittenberg. *Christl. Fragstück &c. 1571]. s4°. *n.p.* 1571
Propositiones quibus vera ac simplex doct. de peccato originali explicatur &c. Coll. a quibusdam verbi Dei ministris, ex com. Mansfeldensi pulsis &c. [*b. w.* Flacius (M.) Defensio, 1575]. s4°. *n.p.* 1576
Mansfield College, *Oxford.* M. C., its origin & opening. [*By var. a.* W. B. Selbie &c.] 8°. 1890
Mansfield (Catherine Hope), *see* BRYNE (M. St. C.) & C. H. M. Somerville College, 1879–1921, 1921.
Mansfield (Charlotte). Strings. s8°. [1920]
Via Rhodesia: journey thr. S. Africa. la8°. 1911
Mansfield (Katherine), *ps.* [*i.e.* KATHERINE MIDDLETON MURRY, *née* KATHLEEN BEAUCHAMP].
Bliss, & o. s. s8°. [1920]
„ „ .... [repr.] s8°. [1921]
The doves' nest & o. s. s8°. [1923]
The garden party & o. stories. s8°. [1922]
In a German pension. [n. ed.] s8°. 1926
Journal [1914–22]. Ed. J. M. Murry. 8°. 1927
Something childish & o. s. 8°. 1924
see STONEHILL (C. A.) &c. Bibliog. of mod. a., s2, 1925.
Mansfield (Leslie), *see* GLOAG (J.) & L. M. The house we ought to live in, 1923.
Mansfield (M.) A family of decent folk, 1200–1741. The Lanfredini of Florence. la8°. Florence. 1922
Mansi (Giovanni Domenico), *abp. of Lucca.* Sacrorum conciliorum nova &c. coll. t36, 48–53. fol. Parisiis & Arnhem. 1915–27
36, Synodi occident., 1610–1719.
48, Synodi occident., 1860–7.
49–53, SS. Œcumenici Concilii Vaticani.
Mansi (Giuseppe). Locuplet. bibliotheca moralis. 4t. fol. Augustae Vindelic. 1732
Mansilla (Lucio V.) Una excursion á los Indios Ranqueles. 2t. s8°. Buenos Aires. 1907
Die letzten wilden Indianer d. Pampa. s8°. L. 1925
Manson (Marie Françoise Clarisse). *Le coin du voile levé s. l'affaire Fualdès: confess. &c. de Mme. M. &c. [*b. w.* Fualdès (A. B.) Hist. &c. des assass. de F., t2, 1818]. 8°. 1819
Mant (Richard), *bp. of (1) Killaloe, (2) Down, Connor & Dromore.* Anc. hymns f. the Roman breviary &c. s8°. 1837
The Book of Psalms in an Eng. metr. vers. w. notes. 8°. O. 1824
Mantegazza (Paolo). Un giorno a Madera. s8°. 1910
Mantegazza (Vico). L'Isola d'Elba. s8°. Milano. 1920
Mantegna (Andrea).
see BORENIUS (T.) Four early Ital. engravers, 1923.
„ BRIT. MUS.: PRINTS, DRAWINGS &C. Book of drawings form. ascr. to M. in B.M., 1923.
„ FIOCCO (G.) L'arte di A. M., 1927.
Mantellaccio. *La compagnia del M., 1489, 1861, *see* COMPAGNIA.
Manteuffel (Kurt Zoege v.), *see* ZÖGE VON MANTEUFFEL (K.)
Mantey (Eberhard v.), *see* KRIEG (Der) zur See, 1914–18; hrsg. v. Marine Archiv: Bearb. E. v. M., 1920–25.
Manteyer (Georges de). Austria's Peace offer, 1916–17. Ed G. de M. With introd. letter by Prince Sixte de Bourbon. [Tr.] 8°. 192[illegible]
Manton (Thomas), *1620–77.* Pract. comm. &c. on the Epistle of James. Lect[s]. s8°. 165[illegible]
see JACKSON (T.) Lib. of Xtn. biog., v9, T. M., by W. Harris 1838.
Mantoux (Paul). The indust. revol. in the 18th cent.: begin of mod. factory system in Eng. Rev. ed., tr. M. Vernon. 8°. [1928
Mantzius (Carl). Hist. of theatrical art in anc. & mod. times Tr. by C. Archer. v6. la8°. 192[illegible]
Manu, *see* JONES (*Sir* W.) Works, v3, Ordinances of Menu tr., 1799.
Manual [MANUEL].
Manual for the use of the legislature of the State of New York 1869, 70, 71, 75, 92, 1869–92, *see* NEW YORK: ANON. WKS.
*Manual of prayers for Winchester Colledge, 1709, *see* KEN (T.)
*Manuel [*sic*] (A) of controversies demonstr. the truth of Cath relig. &c., 1654, *see* TURBERVILLE (H.)

Manuale. Manuale scholarium : acc. of life in med. university. Tr. f. Lat. R. F. Seybolt. 8°. C. 1921
Manuel [*see also* MANUAL]. Manuel d'archéologie française. 1, Architecture relig. [2e éd. augm.], 2p [*pagin. cont.*] 8°. 1919–20
Manuel de doct. des égl. des Frères-Moraves, 1743, *see* NITSCHMANN (D.)
Manuel II [*Palaeologus*], *emperor of the East.* Homélie [*Grec & Lat.*], *see* MARY, *the Virgin.* Homélies mariales byz., éd. &c. M. Jugie, 1922.
see SCHLUMBERGER (G. L.) Un empereur de Byzance [*i.e.* M.] à Paris & à Londres, 1916.
Manuel (D. G.), *B.D.* Dryburgh Abbey in light of its hist. & eccl. setting. 8°. E. 1922
Manuel (Juan). Count Lucanor: or the 50 pleasant tales of Patronio. Tr. J. York. Intr. by J. B. Trend. [Broadway Trans.] s8°. [1924]
Le comte Lucanor. Tr. par le cte. L. Ostrorog. 8°. 1925
Manuel de Mello (Francisco), *see* MELLO (F. M. DE).
Manuel di San Giovanni (Giuseppe).
Works in REGIA DEP. DI STORIA PATRIA. Misc.
Un episodio d. storia d. Piemonte n. sec. 13, eretici valdesi e bagnolesi & ant. signori di Bagnolo, 1874. [15.]
Notizie e doc. rig. la chiesa e prepositura di S. Maria di Vezzolano nel Monferrato, 1862. [1.]
Notizie stor. di Pagno e Valle Bronda, presso Saluzzo, 1889. [27.]
Tre doc. rig. G. Benso di Santena, 1869. [7.]
see CARUTTI (D.) Il barone G. M. di S. G.: notizia, 1887.
Manuk, *see* MEKHITHAR, *of Sebaste.*
Manung. Manūg (Eyn) d cristēheit widd die durkē (1454), *see* TÜRKENKALENDAR.
Manuscript writing & lettering, 1918, *see* HOGG (J.), *publ.*
***Manuscrit** de l'Ile d'Elbe, 1820, *see* MONTHOLON (*gén.* C. J. F. T. DE).
Manuzio (Aldo Pio), *the elder.* Grammaticæ instit. Græcæ. s4°. Venetiis, *Aldus.* 1515
Orthographiæ ratio &c. s8°. Venetiis, *Aldus.* 1591
Manwaring (Elizabeth Wheeler). Ital. landscape in 18th cent. England. Infl. of C. Lorrain & S. Rosa, 1700–1800. 8°. N.Y. 1925
Manwaring (George Ernest). The dress of the Brit. seaman f. the Revol. to 1748. [Repr. f. The Mariner's mirror, v10, 1924. P2750]. la8°. [1924]
The life & works of Sir Henry Mainwaring. Ed. G. E. M. &c. [Navy Rec. Soc., 54, 56]. 2v. 8°. 1920–22
see ROGERS (W.) A cruising voyage round the world; intr. &c. by G. E. M., 1928.
„ TEONGE (H.) Diary; ed. G. E. M., 1927.
Manx ballads & music, 1896, *see* MOORE (A. W.), *ed.*
Manx Society. Publications. v30, 31. 8°. Douglas. 1880–82
Manx miscellanies. Ed., w. pref. & notes by W. Harrison. v2, 1880. [30.]
see MAN, *Isle of.* Constit. of the Isle of Man; ed. R. Sherwood, 1882. [31.]
Manzano (Francesco di), *count.* Annali del Friuli o. recolta d. cose storiche. Compil. dal co. F. di M. 7v (7, Aggiunta all'epoca 6). 8°. Udine. 1858–79
Manzi (Guglielmo). Disc. sopra gli spettacoli, le feste ed il lusso degli' Ital. nel sec. 14. 8°. 1818
Testi di lingua ined. tr. dá codici d. Bibl. Vaticana. 8°. 1816
Manzini (Amerigo).
Emma Gramatica. [*a. c. in* P2517]. la8°. Milano. 1920
Ruggero Ruggeri. [*a. c. in* P2517]. la8°. Milano. 1920
Manzoni (*il conte* Alessandro).
Carteggio di A. M. a cura di G. Sforza e G. Gallavresi, p2, 1822–31. 8°. Milano. 1921
I promessi sposi. 3t. 8°. Livorno. 1827
„ „ .... 8°. Milano. 1908
„ „ ....n. ed. a cura di A. Cerquetti. s8°. Milano. 1917
Manzoni intimo. 3v. [1, 2, *ed.* M. Scherillo; 3, *ed.* G. Gallavresi]. s8°. Milano. 1923
1, Vittoria e Matilde Manzoni: mem. di V. Giorgini-Manzoni.
2, Lettere ined. dir. alle figlie Vittoria e Matilde &c.
3, 94 lettere e 17 postille ined. alla moglie Teresa &c.
TRANSLATIONS.
The betrothed, w. intr. by R. Sabatini. 8°. *n.d.*
see BELLEZZA (P.) Curiosità manzoniane, 1923.
„ GALLETTI (A.) A. M., il pensatore e il poeta, 2v, 1927.
„ LINATI (C.) Sulle orme di Renzo [Promessi sposi], 1919; n. ed., 1927.
„ RUBERTIS (A. DE). Documenti M., 1926.
„ SANCTIS (F. DE). M.: studi e lezioni, 1922.
„ TONELLI (L.) M., 1928.

Manzoni (Giacomo). Annali tipografici torinesi del sec. 15, *see* REGIA DEP. DI STORIA PATRIA. Misc., t4, 1863.
Manzoni (Luigi). Chi fu il maestro d. Pinturicchio. [Nozze Steinmann-Gerstfeldt. N. 134]. 8°. [Perugia. 1901]
Manzoni (Matilde), *see* MANZONI (A.) Manzoni intimo, v1, Vittoria e M. Manzoni: mem. di V. Giorgini-Manzoni, 1923.
Manzoni (Renzo). El Yèmen. Tre anni nell' Arabia felice, 1877–80. la8°. 1884
Manzoni (Vittoria), *see* GIORGINI-MANZONI (V.)
***Maori** mementos: ser. of addresses pres. by the native people to Sir G. Grey, 1855, *see* GREY (*Sir* G.)
Map (Walter). De nugis curialium. Tr. M. R. James, w. hist. notes by J. E. Lloyd. Ed. E. S. Hartland. [Cymmrodorion Rec. Ser., No. 9]. 8°. 1923
„ „ (Courtiers' trifles). Engl. by F. Tupper & M. B. Ogle. la8°. 1924
see GRAIL. La queste del Saint Graal [*? by* W. M.]; ed. A. Pauphilet, 1923.
Mappae Arab., 1926–27, *see* MILLER (K.), *ed.*
Maps. Cat. of maps publ. by the Geogr. Sect., Gen. Staff, 1920, *see* WAR OFFICE.
[Misc. maps, 18–20 cent. *b. in* 7v]. la. fol. *var. d.*
Maquarie (Arthur). The Uffizi A.B.C. Drawn by L. Symington. 8°. Florence. 1908
Maquet (Auguste). La belle Gabrielle. 3[t]. s8°. [1922]
see SIMON (G. M. S. C.) Hist. d'une collabor.: A. Dumas & A. M., 1919.
Mar (John Erskine, *6th* [*or 11th*] *earl of*), *1675–1732, see* PHILIPS (J.) Earl of Mar marr'd: farce, 3rd ed., 1716.
Marais (Jeanne). Le mariage de l'adolescent. Roman. Préface d'A. Brisson. s8°. 1920
Marais (Johannes Stephanus).
Colonisation of N. Zealand. 8°. 1927
Marak (Janko).
Kroat.-deutsches Wörterbuch. 3e A. s8°. Wien. [1920]
Marakkayar (Ahmad Tambi), *Muhi-ud-Din, see* AHMAD TAMBI MARAKKAYAR.
Maramaldo (Fabrizio), *see* VASSALLO (C.) F. M. e gli Agostiniani in Asti, 1890.
Maran (Prudent). *Divinitas J. C. manifesta in Scripturis & traditione. Opera &c. unius ex Monachis Congr. S. Mauri. 4p *in* 1v. fol. Parisiis. 1746
Maran (René). Batouala. Vérit. roman négre. s8°. [1921]
Batouala. Tr. 8°. 1922
Journal sans date, roman, *see* ŒUVRES libres, 73, 1927.
Marande (Max de).
Morguy la sorcière. Roman basque. s8°. 1924
Maranelli (Carlo) & G. Salvèmini. La questione dell' Adriatico. 2a ediz. ampl. & corr. s8°. [1919]
Marangone (Luigi), *see* VENEZIA. Per il restauro d. Capella d. Rosario n. SS. Giov. e Paolo, 1910.
Marangoni (Guido). Maestri contemp. dell' arte ital. s1. la8°. Bergamo. [1923]
Marangoni (Matteo). Il Caravaggio. la8°. Firenze. [1922]
Marat (Jean Paul). Appel à la nation contre le ministre des finances &c. [*no tp.*] [P2774]. 8°. *n.p.* 1790
see PHIPSON (S. L.) J. P. M., h. career before the Revol., 1924.
Marbach. Annales M. qui dicuntur. (Cron. Hohenburg. cum cont. & addit. Neoburg.) Acc. Annales Alsatici brev. Rec. H. Bloch. [Scr. rer. Germ. in usum schol]. 8°. Hannover. 1907
Marbach (Gotthard Oswald).
Gedächtnissrede auf Benedict v. Spinoza. 8°. Halle. 1831
Marbault (—). *Essai s. le commerce de Russie avec l'hist. de ses découv. 8°. Amsterdam. 1777
Marbecke (John) [MARBECKE]. A dialogue betweene youth & old age [*tp. missing & otherwise imperf. b. w.* Wimbledon (R.) A sermon, 1579]. s8°. [1584?]
Marble (*Mrs.* Annie Russell).
The Nobel Prize winners in literature. 8°. N.Y. 1925
Marburg [MARPURGENSES]. *Brevis rel. colloq. authoritate Wilhelmi Hessiae landgravii, inter theologos M. & Rintelenses, Cassellis Jul. [1661] habiti. s8°. *n.p.* [1662?]
Die 15 M. Artikel v. 3. Oct. 1529 als Facsimile veröffentl. v. H. Heppe. 2e A. 4°. Kassel. 1854
Urkundensammlung ü. d. Verfassung &c. d. Univ. M. unter Philipp d. Grossmüthigen. Hrsg. v. B. Hildebrand. 4°. Marburg. 1848
Marçais (Georges), *see* GSELL (S.), G. M. &c. Hist. d'Algérie, 1927.

Marcel (Gabriel). Un homme de Dieu. 4 actes. [Les cahiers verts, 51]. s8°. 1925
L'iconoclaste: pièce, *see* REVUE HEBDOM. Suppl.: coll. nouv. 13, 1923.
Notice sur quelques cartes rel. au royaume de Siam, *see* FOURNEREAU (L.) Le Siam anc., t1 (Musée Guimet, 27), 1895.
Marcel (Guillaume). Tablettes chronolog. cont. l'état de l'Eglise, les Conciles &c. s8°. 1682
„ „ .... s8°. Amsterdam. 1714
Marcel (Henry). Chassériau. 48 planches, notices par J. Laran, intr. par H. M. s8°. [1911]
Marcel (Jean Jacques). Alphabet irlandais préc. d'une notice hist. &c. 8°. Nivose, an XII. [1804]
Marcellinus, *the rhetorician.* De Thucydidis vita &c., *see* THUCYDIDES. Hist. belli Pelop., 1869.
Marcello (Alvise). Notizie che A. M. mandò colla pianta di Canea, 1688, *see* MARCELLO (AND.) Sopra alc. carte &c., 1881.
Marcello (Andrea). Una mostra di cavalleria in Bologna, 1508. [P2837]. la8°. Bologna. 1887
Sopra alcune carte ms. [Rel. di M. Marcello (1660)—Rel. d. N. Marcello di Sebenico (1646)—Not. che Alvise Marcello mandò (1668). P2836]. 8°. Venezia. 1881
Marcello (Angelo). Relaz. di A. M.: tornato da capitanio a Padova (1660). [Ed. L. Michiel. Nozze Marcello-Zon. N122]. 8°. Padova. 1858
Marcello (Marino). Rel. di M. M. Provveditore gen. d. tre isole di Levante (1660), *see* MARCELLO (AND.) Sopra alc. carte &c., 1881.
Marcello (Nicolò). Rel. di N. M. tornato di Sebenico (1646), *see* MARCELLO (AND.) Sopra alc. carte &c., 1881.
Marcello (Pietro). Lettera di P. M. ad Alvise zen provveditore del Zante (1758). [Nozze Marcello-Grimani. N135]. la8°. Venezia. 1894
Marcellus, *Empiricus* [MARCELLUS, *Burdigalensis*]. De medicamentis liber; rec. M. Niedermann, *see* CORPUS medic. Lat., v5, 1916.
Marcellus (Christophorus), *abp. of Corfu, see* PATRICIUS PICCOLOMINEUS (A.) Sacr. cæremoniarum libri 3 a M. primum ed., 1750.
Marcère (Emile L. G. H. de). Une ambassade à Constantinople [de Descorches de Sainte-Croix]: polit. orient. de la Révol. Fr. 2t. 8°. 1927
Marcet de La Roche Arnaud (Martial). Mém. d'un jeune Jésuite, ou conjur. de Mont-Rouge devélop. par des faits. 4e éd. 8°. 1828
March (Ausias), *see* PAGÈS (A.) Comm. des poésies d'A. M., 1925.
March (Charles Henry Gordon-Lennox, *earl of***).**
Records of the old Charlton Hunt. s4°. 1910
March (Joseph M.), *ed., see* LIBER Pontificalis, cod. ms. Dertus., 1925.
March (Lucien). Mouvement des prix & des salaires pend. la Guerre. [C.E. for Internat. Peace]. la8°. [1926]
Marchadier (A.-L.) & A. Goujon.
Les poisons méconnus. s8°. 1921
Marchal (Henri). Guide archéol. aux temples d'Angkor. 8°. 1928
Marchal (Sappho). Costumes & parures khmèrs d'ap. les devatâ d'Angkor-Vat. Av.-prop. de V. Goloubew. 8°. 1927
Marcham (Frank). The King's Office of the Revels, 1610–22. Doc. in Brit. Mus., transcr. by F. M., w. pref. by J. P. Gilson. la8°. 1925
Marchand (A.) Les chemins de fer de l'Est & la Guerre de 1914–18. la8°. 1924
Marchand (*l'abbé* **F.),** *see* DOUVRES. Chartes de la tour de D., 1250–1624; par F. M., 1891.
Marchand (Jean), *see* JEAN (R.) J. R.: reprod. de peintures &c. *&* ét. crit., 1920.
Marchand (Prosper), *see* FAULTRIER (J.) Cat. libr. bibl. J. F., digestus à P. M., 1709.
Marchand (René). Lettre au président Poincaré, *see* RUSSIE. Pour la R. socialiste, 1918.
Un livre noir. Diplomatie d'avant-guerre d'ap. les doc. des archives russes, nov. 1910–juil. 1914. 2t. 8°. [1922–23]
1, 1910–12, 3 rapports de Nekloudof, la corresp. d'Isvolsky.
2, [1913–14], Corresp. d'Isvolsky & de Benckendorf, Rapports de Sazonof & de Kokovtsef, Confér. milit. franco-russes &c.
see ROMIEU (J.) Livre noir [*by R. M.*] & Livre jaune, 1922.
Marchandon (Charles). *M. [Murder of Marie Cornet by C. M., 1885. *no tp.* P2826]. s8°. [Sceaux. *n.d.*]

Marchant (*l'abbé* **J.)** Notices sur Rome, les noms rom. & les dignités rom. 8°. 1869
Marchant (Jacques), *see* MARCHANTIUS (J.)
Marchant (*Sir* **James).**
Anthology of Jesus. Arr. & ed. J. M. s8°. [1926]
The claims of the coming generation. By var. writers [Dean Inge, Sir A. Newsholme &c.], arranged by J. M. s8°. 1923
The coming renaissance. [*By var. wr.*] Ed. J. M. Intr. by W. R. Inge. 8°. 1923
The control of parenthood. By J. A. Thomson, L. Hill &c. Intr. by Bp. of Birmingham. Ed. M. s8°. 1920
The future of Xty. [*By var. wr.*] Ed. M., w. intr. by A. C. Headlam. 8°. [1927]
The future of the Church of Eng. Essays by the Dean of Winchester, Bp. of Manchester, F. W. Dwelly &c. Ed. M. 8°. 1926
Medical views on birth control. By H. Crichton-Miller, L. Hill &c. Intr. by Sir T. Horder. Ed. M. 8°. 1926
see IMMORTALITY; by Sir F. Petrie, F. M. Cornford &c.; ed. M., 1924.
Marchantius (Jacobus), *of Liége, theologian.*
Hortus pastorum. fol. Patavii. 1749.
Resolutiones pastorales de praeceptis, vitiis capitalibus, sacramentis &c. ed. 2a. s8°. Montibus. 1648
Märchen, Schwänke u. Fabeln, 1925, *see* TEGETHOFF (E.), *ed.*
Marchenko (M.) [MARTCHENKO]. La catastrophe austro-hongr. Souv. d'un témoin oculaire. Préf. de L. Barthou. s8°. 1920
Un voyage en Perse pend. la révol. russe. Les agissements allemands. Préf. de M. A. Le Chatelier. s8°. 1920
Marchesan (Angelo). Treviso medievale. 2v. la8°. Treviso. 1923
Marchesi (Vincenzo). Storia docum. d. rivol. e d. difesa di Venezia, 1848–49, tratta da fonti ital. & austriache. la8°. Venezia. [1916]
Marchesi Buonaccorsi (Georgio Viviano). Mem. stor. dell' ant. &c. Accad. de' Filergiti di Forli &c. 8°. Forli. 1741
Marchesinus (Joannes) [*ps.* MAMMETRACTUS]. [*Mamotrectus super Bibliam. *Sig.* A–C, Tabula principaliū vocab. *sig.* a1 &c., Prologus autoris &c.—Tractat' de orthographia.—Tractatus de accentu &c.—De antiphonis &c.—Hymni.—De sermonibus & omelies.—Legenda sanctorum. *Last leaf cont.* Tabula librorum &c.] 8°. [Venetiis. per Nic. Jenson. 1479]
Sig. A–C *in eights*, a–y *in eights*, 1–7 *in eights* & *2 leaves without sig.*
see BEBELIUS (H.) Liber hymnorum—Annot. in quasdam vocabulorum interpretationes Mammetracti, 1501.
Marchetti (Giovanni), *abp. of Ancyra.* Offic. mem. of juridical exam. into miraculous events at Rome, 1796–97. Tr. B. Rayment. [P2494]. s8°. 1801
Marchetti (Vincenzo Salvagnoli-), *see* SALVAGNOLI-MARCHETTI (V.)
Marchi (Alessandro), *ed., see* PADOVA. Cenni stor. s. famiglie di P. &c., 1842.
Marchi (Emilio de).
Demetrio Pianelli. Romanzo. s8°. Milano. [1919]
Marchiane. Liber M. ruine: poema storico d. sec. 14, 1868, *see* LIBER.
Marchlewskii (Julius), *see* MARKHLEVSKY (YULY).
Marchmont (Alexander Hume, *2nd earl of***),** *Baron Polwarth.* Corr. (1718–20), *see* HIST. MSS. COMM., Polwarth MSS., v2, 1916.
Marchmont (Arthur W.) By right of sex. s8°. [1923]
"His majesty." s8°. [1923]
A millionaire mystery. s8°. 1924
Marciano (Girolamo). Descr., orig. e successi d. prov. d'Otranto; con aggiunte d. D. T. Albanese. la8°. Napoli. 1855
Marcinowski (Jaroslaw).
Works in HATTINGBERG (H. v.) Nerv. Mensch, B8–11, 1924.
Die Gefühlszerrissenheit d. neurot. Psyche. [9.]
Minderwertigkeitsgefühle. [10.]
Probleme u. Praxis d. geschlechtl. Aufklärung. [8.]
Schuldgefühle. [11.]
Marcion, *of Sinope.* The gospel of the Lord: an early version. Tr. by J. H. Hill. s8°. Guernsey. [1891]
see HARNACK (C. G. A.) M.: d. Evangelium v. fremden Gott, 1921.
„ —— Neue Studien zu M., 1923.
„ SCHELLING (F. W. J. v.) De M. Paullinarum Epist. emendatore, 1795.
Märcker (*Kdr. Gen.-Maj.* **Ludwig Rudolf Georg)** [MAERCKER]. Vom Kaiserheer z. Reichswehr. 8°. L. 192[illegible]
Marcks (Erich). Deutschland u. England in d. grossen europ Krisen seit d. Reformation. [P2409]. 8°. St. 190[illegible]

Marcolini (Camillo), *Count di Cantoceto.* Degli ordinamenti ond' ebbe informata Dante la 1ª cant. d. Div. Comm. investig. di F. Lanci, 1855. [Estr. dall' Encicl. contemp., v3. P2787]. 8º. [Fano. 1856]
Notizie stor. d. provincia di Pesaro e Urbino. la8º. Pesaro. 1868

Marconi (Pirro). Antinoo, *see* REALE ACCAD. D. LINCEI. Mon. ant., v29, 1923.

Marcoreos, *Venetian painter, see* BRANCALEONE (N.)

Marcos (Angel Revilla), *see* REVILLA MARCOS (A.)

Marcoureau de Brécourt (Guillaume). Le jaloux invisible (1666)—L'ombre de Molière (1674), *see* FOURNEL (V.) Contemp. de Molière, t1, 1863.

Marcovitch (Lazare). Serbia & Europe, 1914–20. [Articles publ. in La Serbie, 1916–19]. Ed. w. pref. by L. M. 8º. [1920]

Marculfus, *monachus.*
see LEVILLAIN (L.) Le Formulaire de M., 1923.
,, SMITH (T.) M., 1836.

Marcus, *a Sancto Antonio Paduano, Augustiniam.*
Kraynska Gramm. 2ᵉ verb. A. s8º. Laybach. 1783

Marcus (Benjamin). Mykur hayem. Mistranslations &c. of the Old Test. s8º. D. 1846

Marcus (Joseph). Labor condit. in Porto Rico, 1919, *see* UNITED STATES: LAB.

Marcuse (Ludwig).
G. Büchner u. s. besten Bühnenwerke. s8º. [1921]

Marczali (Henrik).
Az 1790/1-diki országgyülés. [M. Tud. Akad.] 2k. 8º. 1907
Magyarország története II József Korában. 2ik kiadás. k1, 2. 8º. 1885

Marden (Charles Carroll), *see* APOLLONIUS, *Tyrius.* Libro de A.; ed. M., p2, 1922.

Marden (*Maj.-Gen.* **Thomas Owen).** Short hist. of the 6th Division, Aug. 1914–March 1919. Ed. T. O. M. 8º. 1920

Mardochaeus, *see* MORDECAI BEN NISAN.

Mardrus (J. C.)
see KORAN. Le K., tr. des Sourates essent., par J. C. M., 1926.
,, SHEBA, *The queen of.* The Q. of S.; tr. into Fr. f. h. Arabic text by J. C. M.; Eng. vers. by E. P. Mathers, 1924.

Maréchal (Bernard). Concordantia sanct. patrum eccl. Gr. & Lat. 2t *in* 1v. fol. Venetiis. 1767

Maréchal (Joseph), *S.J.* Etudes sur la psychologie des mystiques. t1. 8º. Bruges. 1924

Marengo (Emilio). Un' ant. pergamene d. R. Archivio di Stato in Genova, *see* REGIA DEP. Misc., t48, 1915.

Mareš (Franz) & J. Sedláček. Topogr. d. hist. u. Kunstdenkm. Polit. Bez. Wittingau, *see* BÖHMEN. Topographie d. hist. u. Kunstdenkmale &c., B10, 1904.

Maresch (Leopold). Das grosse Sterben an der Wolga. Tagebuchskizzen e. Kommunisten. 8º. Wien. 1922

Mareschal (*barão* **Wenzel de).** Correspondencia [1822], *see* INSTITUTO HIST. &C. BRAZIL. Rev., t80, 1917.

Mareschal de Luciane (F. C. de). Les premiers maréchaux de Savoie, *see* REGIA DEP. DI STORIA PATRIA. Misc., t26, 1887.
Les Savoyards à la bataille de Bulgnéville (1431), *see* REGIA DEP. Misc., t49, 1918.

Maresius (Samuel), *see* DESMARETS (S.)

Maret (Henri Louis Charles), *bp. of (1) Sara, (2) Lepanto.* Le Pape & les Évêques: déf. du livre sur le Concile gén. &c. [P2656]. 8º. 1869

Marett (Robert Ranulph).
Anthropology. [Home Univ. Lib.] [repr.] s8º. [1919]
The birth of humility. Inaug. lect. 8º. O. 1910
The diffusion of culture. Frazer lect. s8º. C. 1927
The threshold of religion. 3rd ed. s8º. *n.d.*

Marev (P.) Полит. борьба крестьянства, *see* GORN (VL.), V. MECH & CHERAVANIN. Борьба обществ. силъ, в3, 1907.

Margaret [*Beaufort*], *countess of Richmond & Derby, 1441–1509, see* ROUTH (E. M. G.) Lady Margaret, 1924.

Margaret, *St. of Cortona, see* NUTI (M.) M. da C., la sua legenda e la storia, 1923.

Margaret, *queen consort of Humbert, k. of Italy* [*M. of Savoy*].
see SALAZAR (F. Z.) M. of Savoy; h. life &c., 1914.
,, TISSOT (E.) Le livre des reines: Victoria, M. de Savoie &c., 1896.

Margaret, *duchess of Parma, 1522–86* [MARGARET *of Austria*]. Corr. franç. avec Philippe II. Ed. J. S. Theissen. [Hist. Genoots. Werken, s3, 47]. t1 (1565–67). 4º. Utrecht. 1925

Margaret [*of Savoy*], *marchioness of Monferrato, see* SOPETTO (E.) M. di S., march. di M., 1295–1313, 1907.

Margaret, *St., queen consort of Malcolm, k. of Scotland, see* GEDDES (J.) Life of St. M. of Scotland &c., 1794.

Margaret [*de Valois*], *1553–1615; queen consort of Henry IV, king of France.* La ruelle mal assortie. [Trésors des pièces rares &c.] s8º. 1855
see NAUD (J.) Château d'Issy & s. hôtes; M. &c., 1926.
,, PALMA CAYET (P. V.) *Le divorce satyrique, ou les amours de M. de V. sous le nom de D. R. H. Q. M., 1664.

Margaret, *St., Virgin & Martyr, see* WACE (R.) La vie de Ste. M., poème, suivi de l'analyse du Mystère de Ste. M. par A. Joly, 1879.

Margarita. [*Beg.* fol. 1 *verso*]. In nomine sanctissime & individue trinitatis . . . Liber margarita Davitica nuncupatus: ex Hieronimo: Augustino: Ac Cassiodoro: originaliter ac sũmarie sumptus. Ip̄m regalem exponēs prophetam David felicitᵉ incipit. fol. [Augsburg, *G. Zainer.* 1471 ?]
[122 *numbered leaves without sig.* 34 *ll. to a full page. The last two leaves unnumbered, containing the table, are missing in this copy.*]

Margaritov (V. P.) Камчатка и ея обитатели. [I.R.G.O. Записки приамурск. отд., 5i]. 4º. Хабаровскъ. 1899

Margate. *M. delineated; including Ramsgate &c. 10th ed. s8º. [1829]

Margery, *psychic medium* [*i.e. Mrs.* L. R. G. CRANDON]. Margery—Harvard—Veritas: st. in psychics. [*By*] M. W. Richardson &c. 8º. Boston. 1925

Marggraff (Johann Georg). Vet. praedestinatorum hist. exhibens dissert. [P434]. s4º. *n.p.* 1714

Margherita *of Savoy, see* MARGARET, *q. consort of Humbert, k. of Italy.*

Margoliouth (David Samuel).
Analecta orient. ad Poeticam Aristoteleam. [Poetica Arab. interp. Abu Bashar, Poetica Avicennae &c.] Ed. M. s8º. Londini. 1887
Arabic papyri of the Bodleian. W. transcr. & tr. by M. fol. 1893
Avicenna, *see* PERSIA Soc. Lect., 1914.
The Homer of Aristotle. s8º. O. 1923
The relations betw. Arabs & Israelites prior to the rise of Islam. [Brit. Acad. Schweich lect., 1921]. 8º. 1924
The Syro-Armenian dialect. [From Journ. of R. Asiat. Soc. P2794]. 8º. 1898
Two S. Arabian inscr. [Fr. Proc. of Brit. Acad., v11. P2784]. 8º. [1925]

Margoliouth (*Mrs.* **Jessie Payne),** *wife of D. S. Margoliouth, see* PAYNE SMITH (R.) Thesaurus Syriacus; Suppl., coll. &c. by J. P. M., 1927.

Margueritte (Ève Paul). La folle poursuite. s8º. [1922]

Margueritte (Lucie Paul). Les colombes. s8º. *n.d.*
La déception amoureuse. s8º. *n.d.*

Margueritte (Paul).
L'album secret. s8º. [1922]
La faiblesse humaine. s8º. [1910]
La maison brûle. 8º. [1921]
Nous, les mères. . . . [24ᵉ éd.] s8º. [1922]
Le sceptre d'or. 2t. s8º. [1921]

Margueritte (Victor).
Un cœur farouche. s8º. [1921]
Le compagnon. s8º. [1923]
Le couple. [La femme en chemin]. s8º. [1924]
La femme en chemin: roman, *see* ŒUVRES libres, 5, 1921.
La garçonne. s8º. [1922]
Le soleil dans la geôle. s8º. [1921]
Ton corps est à toi. [Vers le bonheur]. s8º. [1927]

Margulies (Manuil Sergeevich). Год интервенции, 1918–19. [Летопись револ., No. 11]. 2кн. s8º. Берлин. 1923

Margutti (Albert, *Frhr.* **v.)** The Emp. Francis Joseph & his times. 8º. 1921
La tragédie des Habsbourg: mém. d'un aide de camp. s8º. 1924
Vom alt. Kaiser. Personl. Erinn. an Franz Joseph I. 4ᵉ A. s8º. L. 1921

Marheinecke (Philipp Conrad). Instit. symbolicae doct. Catholic., Protest. &c. summam &c. exhib. ed. 3ª auct. s8º. Berolini. 1830

Mari (Giovanni).
Vocabolario Hoepli d. lingua ital. 2v. s8º. Milano. 1913

Maria. Memoirs of M., a Persian slave, 2v, 1790, *see* MEMOIRS.

Maria *de la Visitacion, prioress, mon. of the Anunciada at Lisbon, see* GEDDES (M.) The Church hist. of Ethiopia &c., 1696.

Maria Christina, *consort of Alfonso XII of Spain, see* CHRISTINA.

Maria Christina, *of Savoy, wife of Ferdinand II, king of the Two Sicilies; see* CROCE (B.) M. C. di Savoia, 1924.

Maria Clementina, *consort of James Edward* [*Stuart*], *"the old Pretender," see* WOGAN (C.) Female fortitude: seizure, escape & marriage of Pcss. Clementina Sobiesky, 1722.

Maria Deodata, *Cistercian Order, see* DEODATA (M.), *ps.*
Maria Josefa Amalia, *q. c. of Ferdinand VII, k. of Spain, see* HÄBLER (K.) M. J. A., Kön. v. Sp., 1892.
Maria Laach, *see* STIMMEN AUS M. L.
Maria Theresia, *queen of Hungary & Bohemia.*
see GAAL (M.) M. T., 1900.
„ KHEVENHÜLLER-METSCH (J. J.), *prince.* Aus d. Zeit M. T., B5-7, 1914–25.
Mariage. *Du m. des enfans de famille. [Du droit des pères &c. *b. w.* Du Tilliot (J. B. L.) Mém. p. s. à l'hist. de la fête des Foux, 1741]. 4°. *n.p. n.d.*
Le m. des sept arts &c.: poèmes fr. du 13e s.; ed. A. Långfors, 1923, *see* JEAN, *le Teinturier.*
Mariana (Juan de), *jesuit.* De rege & regis institutione libri 3. Ejusdem de ponderibus & mensuris liber [*w. sep. tp. & pagin.*] ed. 2a. s8°. [Mentz ?] 1611
Hist. de rebus Hispaniæ libri 30. Acc. J. E. Minianiæ contin. novæ libri 10. 4t. fol. Hagæ-Comitum. 1733
Hist. gen. de España. Comp., emend. &c. por J. de M. 16a impr. 2t. 4°. Valencia. 1794
Hist. gen. de España. Nueva ed., cont. la cont. del P. Miñana tr., y la Narr. de los sucesos desde el año 1600, cont., hasta el de 1808. 9t. s8°. 1828
t7, 8 *have t.* Cont. de la Hist. gen. &c. t9 *has t.* Narr. de los sucesos princ. &c.
Mariani (Lucio).
Works in REALE ACCAD. D. LINCEI. Mon. ant.
Antichità cretesi, 1895. [6.]
Aufidena, 1901. [10.]
Statue mutile di Teseo ed il Minotauro, 1897. [7.]
see BONI (G.) & L. M. Rel. int. al consolid. &c. dell' Arco di M. Aurelio in Tripoli, 1915.
Mariani (Mario), *see* LAZZERI (G.) M. M., 1919.
Mariani (Valerio). Il Palazzo Massimo alla Colonne. s8°. [1926]
see COZZA (A.) & V. M. Nuovi scavi d. stadio palat., 1895.
Mariano (Raffaele). Il problema relig. in Italia. 8°. 1872
Roma nel medio evo. 8°. 1873
Máriássy (Béla). A szabadelvüség multja, jelene és jövöje. 8°. Györ. 1896
Mariátegui (Eduardo de). Crón. de la prov. de Toledo, 1866, *see* ESPAÑA. Crón. gen., v1, 1865 &c.
Mária y Campos (Ricardo de), *see* MEXICO. Datos mercantiles; compil. por R. de M. y C., 1892.
Maribas, *see* ABAS, *Mar, called Katina.*
Marich (László Szögyény-), *see* SZÖGYÉNY-MARICH (L.)
Marichal (Paul). Remarques sur la Cartul. de Gorze, *see* SOC. NAT. DES ANTIQ. DE FR. Mettensia, t3, 1902.
see METZ. Cartulaire; publ. P. M., 2t, 1903–8.
Maricourt (*le baron* **André de).** Foch, une lignée—une tradition—un caractère. s8°. [1920]
L'Oise dévastée. 4e éd. s8°. 1920
see LA BÉDOYÈRE (*c.* C. A. F. DE) & *le baron* A. DE M. Idylle & drame: G. de Chastellux & C. de La Bédoyère, 1924.
Marie, *princess of Battenburg, see* ERBACH-SCHÖNBERG (*princess* M. *of*).
Marie, *de France, see* WINKLER (E.) Franz. Dichter d. M., 2, M. de F., 1918.
Marie, *de l'Incarnation, Carmelite* [*Mme.* BARBE ACARIE], *see* BROGLIE (E. DE) La B. M. de l'I., Mme. A., 1566–1618, 5e éd., 1921.
Marie, *de l'Incarnation, Ursuline* [MARIE GUYARD, *aft.* MARTIN].
see BELLESSORT (A.) Reflets de la vieille Amérique (Une grande française), 1923.
„ BRÉMOND (H.) Hist. litt. du sentiment relig. en France, t6, M. de l'I. &c., 1922.
Marie, *de Lorraine, wife of Louis d'Orléans, duc de Longueville, aft. q. c. of James V of Scotland, see* MARY, *of Lorraine.*
Marie, *q. c. of Ferdinand, king of Roumania, see* MARTINEAU (E.) Roumania & h. rulers, 1927.
Marie, *empress consort of Alexander III, emperor of Russia* [MARIE FEODOROVNA; *Princess* DAGMAR].
see POLIAKOFF (V.) The Empress M. of Russia & h. times, 1926.
Marie Anne Christine Victoire [*of Bavaria*], *consort of Louis, dauphin of France, see* COLLAS (É.) La belle-fille de Louis XIV, *n.d.*
Marie Antoinette, *queen consort of Louis XVI, king of France.*
see CAMPAN (*Mme.* J. L. H.) Méms. sur la vie privée de M. A., 2t, 1823.
see HEIDENSTAM (O. G. DE). Letters of M. A., Fersen &c.; tr., 1926.

Marie Antoinette, *queen consort of Louis XVI* [*continued*].
see MUNIER-JOLAIN (J.) Le card. Collier & M.-A., 1927.
„ NOLHAC (P. DE). M.-A., dauphine, 1906.
see NOLHAC (P. DE). La reine M.-A., 4e éd., 1925.
„ SÉGUR (*m.* P. DE). M.-A., 2e éd., 1920.
Marie Charlotte, *daughter of Leopold I, king of the Belgians, see* CHARLOTTE, *empress of Mexico.*
Marie Feodorovna, *empress consort of Alexander III, emp. of Russia, see* NICHOLAS II, *emp. of Russia.* Lettres de N. II & de sa mère [M. F.], 3e éd., 1928.
Marie Louise, *empress consort of Napoleon I.* Private diaries. Intr. & comm. by F. Masson. 8°. 1922
Marie Louise, *princess, daughter of Prince Christian of Schleswig-Holstein.* Letters f. the Gold Coast. 8°. [1926]
Marie Sophia Frederika Dagmar, *princess, daughter of Christian IX, k. of Denmark, see* MARIE, *empress of Russia.*
Marie (Aristide). Bibliog. des œuvres de G. de Nerval, avec hist. de s. livres. [Œ. compl.] 8°. 1926
Mariéjol (Jean-H.) Catherine de Médicis (1519–89). 8°. 1920
Mariès (Louis). Le De Deo d'Eznik de Kołb, éts. de crit., *see* REVUE DES ÉT. ARMÉN., t4, 1924.
Mariéton (Paul). Hellas [*poems*]. s8°. Paris. 1889
Marignan (Albert). Un historien de l'art franç.: L. Courajod. [t]1, Les temps francs. 8°. 1899
Marillac (*le maréchal* **Louis de),** *see* VAISSIÈRE (P. DE). L'affaire du Maréchal de M., 1630–32, 1924.
Marillier (Henry Currie), "Christie's," 1766–1925. la8°. 1926
Hist. of the Merton Abbey Tapestry Works, founded by W. Morris. 4°. 1927
see BEARDSLEY (A.) Early work; pref. note by M., 1912.
Marimonti (Giuseppe), *see* FRISI (A. F.) Mem. stor. d. città di Monza, cont. da G. M., 1841.
***Marine** vocabulary, *see* STRATICO (S.), *ed.* Vocab. di marina, v3, 1814.
Marine-Archiv, *see* KRIEG. Krieg (Der) zur See, 1914–18; hrsg. v. M.-A., 1920–25.
Marine Research Society. Publ. No. 2. la8°. Salem, Mass. 1923
see DOW (G. F.) & J. H. EDMONDS. Pirates of the New Eng. coast, 1630–1730, 1923. [2.]
Marine Society, *see* HANWAY (J.) An acc. of the M.S., 6th ed. [*& List of subscribers*], 1759.
Marinella (Lucrezia). Due brevi novelle di L. M. e A. Abati. [*Ed.* A. Tessier. P2787]. 8°. Venezia. 1854
Marinelli (Giovanni), *prof. of geography at Padua.* Venezia n. storia d. geografia: disc. 8°. Venezia. 1889
Marinelli (Olinto). Le condiz. fisiche attuali, *see* FILIPPI (F. DE). Rel. sci. d. Spediz. Ital. n. Himàlaia &c., s2, v4, 1928.
Mariner's Mirror, The. Journal of the Society for Nautical Research. v6–13. 8°. 1920–27
Marineus (Lucius). De rebus Hisp., *see* HISPANICA. Rer. H. scr., t2, 1579.
Marini (Gaetano Luigi). Gli atti e mon. de' fratelli arvali. 2p [*pagin. contin.*] 4°. Roma. 1795
Marini (Riccardo Adalgisio). Medaglie e medaglisti sabaudi del Rinascimento, *see* REGIA DEPUT. Misc., t46, 1912.
Statuti di Villafranca Piemonte (1384) con altri doc. e mem. (1001–1620); ed. M., *see* REGIA DEPUT. Misc., t49, 1918.
Marinis, *Libreria* **de.** Vendita all 'asta d. coll. prov. d. L. de M., Maggio [*&* Nov.-Dic.] 1925 [& 17–19 Giugno, 1926], n. lib. U. Hoepli. 3p. 8°. Milano. [1925–26]
Marino (Giovanni Battista). L'Adone. A cura di G. Balsamo-Crivelli. s8°. Torino. [1922]
Marinoni (C. P. L.) Lady Montagu Wortley. Studio stor.-biogr. 2p *in* 1v. 8°. Lovere. 1903–4
Marinov (D.) Народна вѣра и религиозни народни обичаи (книга 7 отъ Жива-Старина); събралъ Д. М., *see* SBORNIK. Сборникъ за народни умотвор., кн. 28, 1914.
Marion (Marcel). Dict. des institut. de la France aux 17e & 18e s. 8°. 1923
Marion (Séraphin). Rel. des voyageurs franç. en Nouv. France au 17e s. 8°. 1923
Marion Dumersan (Théophile), *see* DUMERSAN (T. M.)
Maris, *see* ADAEUS. Liturgia s. apost. A. & Maris [*in Syriac*], 1890.
Maris (Matthew), *see* FRIDLANDER (E. D.) M. M., 1921.
Mariscal (Francisco de Sierra y), *see* SIERRA Y MARISCAL (F. DE).
Mariscal (Ignacio). Don Nicolás Bravo ó clemencia Mexicana. Drama. 8°. México. 1895
Maritain (Jacques). Primauté du spirituel. s8°. [1927]
Trois réformateurs: Luther—Descartes—Rousseau. s8°. [1925]

Mariti (Giovanni).
Travels in Cyprus. Tr. C. D. Cobham. s8°. Nicosia. 1895
Marivaux (Pierre C. de C. de). The game of love & chance; tr., *see* ALDINGTON (R.) French comedies of 18th c., 1923.
La provinciale. Introd. de P. Chaponnière. 8°. Genève. 1922
Marjoribanks (Norman Edward) & A. K. G. Ahmad Tambi Marakkayar. Rep. on Indian labour emigr. to Ceylon & Malaya. fol. Madras. 1917
Mark, *of Ephesus, see* EUGENIKOS (M.), *abp. of Ephesus.*
Mark, *Saint & Evangelist* [*see* BIBLE: MARK *for Gospel &c.*]
Div. liturgia S. Marci. Clementis P. R De ritu missae. Acc. divini horarum officii declar. Gr. & Lat. s8°. Parisiis. 1583
Mark, *The family of* [MARKE], *see* YARKER (J.) Geneal. of the fam. of M., 1898.
Mark (John), *of West Didsbury, see* YARKER (J.) Geneal. of fam. of M., 1898.
Market Harborough. Parish records, to 1837. By J. E. Stocks, assisted by W. B. Bragg. [2v]. 8°. 1890–1926
Markevich (Boleslav Mikhailovich).
Полное собранiе сочиненiй. 11t. s8°. С.-П. 1885
Markham (*Mrs.*), *ps., see* BELLOC (H.) Mrs. M.'s new hist., intr. to curr. hist. &c., 1926.
Markham (*Sir* **Albert Hastings**), *see* MARKHAM (M. E.) & F. A. M. Life of Sir A. H. M., 1927.
Markham (Christopher A.) The "new" pewter marks & old pewter ware, dom. & eccles. 2nd ed. rev. & enl. la8°. 1928
Markham (*Sir* **Clements Robert).** The lands of silence. Hist. of Arctic & Antarctic explor. la8°. C. 1921
Markham (F. A.), *see* MARKHAM (M. E.) & F. A. M. Life of Sir A. H. Markham, 1927.
Markham (Gervase) [MARKAM], *see* LYON (J. H. H.) A st. of The newe metamorphosis, wr. by J. M., Gent. [? Markham], 1600, 1919.
Markham (M. E.) & F. A. Markham.
Life of Sir A. H. Markham. 8°. C. 1927
Markham (Violet R.) [*aft. Mrs.* CARRUTHERS]. A woman's watch on the Rhine. Sk. of the occupation. 8°. [1920]
Markhlevsky (Yuly) [*ps.* KARSKY (ISETOR)]. Was ist Bolschewismus? [P2458]. 8°. Moskau. 1919
see TSETKIN (K.), YU. M. &C. Роза Люксембург, 1921.
Markos (Georg), *see* *SUMMA univ. theol. Christ. sec. Unitarios, [*by G. M. ?*], 1787.
Markov (Evgeny Aleksandrovich).
Очерки Кавказа. изд. 3°. la8°. С.-П. *n.d.*
Markovich (O. V.)
Украiнськi приказки, прислiвъя и таке инше. Збiрники О. В. Марковича и других. Спорудив М. Номис. la8°. С.-П. 1864
Markow (Alexis), *of Kertch.* Das Wachstum d. Bevölkerung &c. in Preussen, 1824–85. [Neumann (F. J.) Beiträge, B3]. 8°. Tübingen. 1889
Marks (Arthur Houlton).
Hist. notes on Lincoln's Inn Fields. s8°. [1922]
Marks (F. Helena). The sonata: its form & meaning as exemplified in piano sonatas by Mozart. 8°. [1922]
Marks (Montagu). Cyclopædia (The) of home arts. Ed. &c. M. M. s4°. 1899
Marks (Phoebe Sarah), *aft. wife of Prof. W. E. Ayrton, see* AYRTON (*Mrs.* H.)
Marlay (Charles Brinsley), *see* CAMBRIDGE: FITZWILLIAM MUSEUM. Cat. of pictures in the M. bequest; comp. by W. G. Constable, 1927.
Marlborough (John Churchill, *1st duke of***).**
see ATKINSON (C. T.) M. & the rise of the Brit. Army, 1921.
,, SAUTAI (M.) Une opération milit. d'Eugène & de M., 1905.
,, TAYLOR (F.) The wars of M., 1702–9, 2v, 1921.
Marle (Raimond van). Development of the Ital. schools of painting. v1–10. la8°. The Hague. 1923–28
v6, Iconogr. index to v1–5.
La peinture romaine au moyen-âge, s. développement du 6e j. la fin du 13e s. la8°. Str. 1921
Recherches sur l'iconogr. de Giotto & de Duccio. la8°. Str. 1920
Simone Martini & les peintres de s. école. la8°. Str. 1920
Marliave (Joseph de). Les quatuors de Beethoven. Publ. avec intr. &c. par J. Escarra. Préf. de G. Faure. 8°. 1925
Marlorat (Augustin). A catholicke & eccl. exposition of St. John. Tr. by T. Timme. fol. 1575
see BIBLE: FRENCH. Nouv. Test., avec annot. &c. par A. M., 1563.
Marloth (Rudolf). The flora of South Africa: w. synopt. tables of the genera of the higher plants.
v2 [*in* 2 *sect., b. sep., pagin. cont.*] la8°. Capetown. 1925
Marlow (Isaac). A treatise of the Holy Trinunity. s8°. 1690
Marlowe (Christopher).
Edward the Second, 1594. [Prep. under dir. of W. W. Greg. Malone Soc. repr.] s4°. 1925
see CRAWFORD (C.) The M. concordance, [p2, 3], 1912–13.
,, ELLIS-FERMOR (U. M.) C. M., 1927.
,, HOTSON (J. L.) Death of C. M., 1925.
see SEATON (E.) M.'s map, 1924.
,, SYKES (H. D.) Authorship of the "Taming of a Shrew" &c., & the add. of M.'s "Faustus," 1920.
,, THIMME (M.) M.'s "Jew of Malta," 1921.
Marlowe (Christopher), *M. A.* The Fen country. 8°. [1925]
Marmer (Harry Aaron). The tide. 8°. N.Y. 1926
Marmery (J. Villin).
Progress of science. Intr. by S. Laing. 8°. 1895
Marmion, *Family of, see* MARMYUN.
Marmitta (Giacomo), *1504–61.*
Rime. [*Ed.* L. Spaggi Marmitta]. 8°. Parma. 1564
see RONCHINI (A.) Not. biogr. int. a J. M., *n.d.*
Marmont (*le maréchal*) [†VIESSE DE MARMONT (A. F. L.), *duke of Ragusa*], *see* RAPETTI (P. N.) La défection de M. en 1814, 1858.
Marmontel (Jean François).
Mémoires. Intr. par F. Barrière. s8°. 1891
Marmora Oxoniensia &c., 1676, *see* PRIDEAUX (H.)
Marmyun, *The family of, see* BANKS (*Sir* T. C.) Hist. of the fam. of M. &c., 1817.
Marne. Der M.-Feldzug, *see* WELTKRIEG (DER), 1914 bis 1918; bearb. im Reichsarchiv, B3, 4, 1926.
The 2 battles of the Marne, 1927, *see* JOFFRE (*le mar.* J. J. C.)
Maroc. Le M. chez les auteurs anc., 1924, *see* ROGET (R.)
Residence Gén. de la France au M., *see* MISSION SCIENTIF. DU MAROC.
Sources (Les) inéd. de l'hist. du M., 1905 &c., *see* CASTRIES (*c.* H. DE).
Maronitica. *De eccl. Maronitica, 1810–11, *see* SCHNURRER (C. F.)
Marot (Clément) [MAROTUS].
Pseaulmes 50 de David; mis en vers fr. par C. M. s8°. Lyon. 1548
see BECKER (P. A.) C. M.'s Liebeslyrik, 1917.
,, —— C. M., Leben u. Dichtung, 1926.
,, —— C. M.'s Psalmenübers., 1920.
see COLLETET (G.) Les trois M., 1871.
,, GUY (H.) Hist. de la poésie fr. au 16e s., t2, Marot & s. école, 1926.
,, VILLEY (P.) M. & Rabelais, avec table chron. des œuvres de M., 1923.
—— & T. Beza. Les Pseaumes mis en rime franç. [*b. w.* Bible: French. Le Nouv. Test. &c., 1563].
s8°. [Genève], *J. Bonnefoy.* 1563
Marot (Jean), *see* COLLETET (G.) Les trois M., 1871.
Marot (Michel), *see* COLLETET (G.) Les trois M., 1871.
Marouzeau (Jules). Dix années de bibliog. class., 1914–24. Publ. J. M. pl. la8°. 1927
Le Latin. 10 causeries. s8°. Toulouse. 1923
L'ordre des mots dans la phrase latine. 1, Les groupes nominaux. 8°. 1922
Marowe (Thomas). Early treatises on the pract. of Justices of the Peace in the 15th & 16th cent. (*includ.* M.'s Reading on the peace in 1503), *see* VINOGRADOFF (*Sir* P.) Oxford st., v7, 1924.
Mar-People (*Sir* **Martin),** his coller of esses, 1590, repr., 1923, *see* DAVIES (*Sir* JOHN).
Marprelate (Martin), *see* COOPER (T.) An admonition wherein are ans. the untruethes by M. M. &c., 1589.
Marpurgenses, *see* MARBURG.
Marquand (Allan).
Benedetto & Santi Buglioni. la8°. Princeton. 1921
Giovanni della Robbia. la8°. Princeton. 1920
Luca della Robbia. la8°. Princeton. 1914
Marquard (Alfred). Das hohe Lied v. Holz. 4°. St. [1927]
Marquardt (Martha). P. Ehrlich als Mensch u. Arbeiter: Erinn. (1902–15). Einführung v. R. Koch. 8°. [1924]
Marquart (Josef). Ērānšahr nach d. Geog. d. Ps. Moses Xorenac 'i, *see* KÖNIGL. GESELLS. D. WISS. Abhlgn. Phil.-hist. Kl., N.F., B3ii, 1901.
see BANG (W.) & J. M. Osttürk. Dialektstudien, 1914.

Marques Perdigao (João da Purificação), *bp. of Pernambuco.* Itinerario das vizitas feitas na sua dioceze, 1833–40, *see* INSTITUTO HIST. & GEOG. BRAZIL. Revista, t55, 1892.

Marquet (Jean). Lettres de Guerre d'un Annamite, *see* ŒUVRES libres, t9, 1922.

Marquet de Vasselot (Jean J.) Un ivoire chrétien réc. acquis par le Musée du Louvre, *see* ACAD. DES INSCR.: FOND. PIOT. Mons. &c., t28, 1925–26.

Répertoire des catalogues des musées de prov., *see* SOC. DE L'HIST. DE L'ART FR. Bull., 1923.

—— & *Mdlle.* **M. J. Ballot.** Chinese ceramics. [Louvre Museum. Doc. d'Art]. [2v]. s4°. 1922

Marquina (Eduardo). El beso en la herida. s8°. 1920

Marr (George S.) Periodical essayists of the 18th c. w. extr. 8°. [1923]

Marr (Nikolai Yakovlevich).

Агіограф. матеріалы по грузинск. рукописямъ Ивера. [Имп. Р. Арх. Общ.: Отт. изъ Зап. Восточ. отд., т13]. 2ч *in* 1v. la8°. С.–П. 1900–1

1, 5 пергамен. рукописей. 2, Житіе Св. Варлаама Сирокавказскаго.

Арабское извлеч. изъ сир. хроники Марибаса. [Отт. изъ Зап. Вост. Отд. И. Р. Арх. Общ., т14. P2804]. la8°. С.–П. 1902

Аркаунъ, монгол. названіе христіанъ. [P2804]. la8°. С.–П. 1905

Боги Языч. Грузіи. [Отт. изъ Зап. Вост. Отд. И. Р. Арх. Общ., т14. P2798]. la8°. С.–П. 1901

Возникновеніе &c. древне-груз. свѣтской лит. [*Extr. f.* Журналъ Мин. Нар. Просвѣщ., ч326. P2811]. 8°. *n.p.* [1899]

Грамм. древнеармянск. языка. Этимологія. la8°. С.–П. 1903

Грамм. чанскаго (лазскаго) яз., съ хрестом. и слов., 1910, *see his* Матеріалы &c. *below.*

Грузинскій изводъ сказки о трехъ остроумн. братьяхъ изъ "Русуданіани". [*With text*]. Изъ Восточ. Замѣтки. [*b.w.h.* Сказаніе, 1895]. fol. С.–П. 1895

Грузинскія приписки греч. Евангелія изъ Коридіи. [*Extr. f.* Изв. Имп. Акад. Наукъ, 1911. P2797]. la8°. [С.–П. 1911]

Древнеармянская хрестоматія, съ арм.-русс. словаремъ. 8°. С.–П. 1893

Древнегрузинскіе одописцы (12. в.). Пѣвецъ Давида Строителя—Пѣвецъ Тамары. Груз. текстъ, изсл. &c. Н. М. [Тексты &c. по арм.-груз. филол., 4 (Изд. фак. восточ. яз., No. 5)]. la8°. С.–П. 1902

Еще о словѣ "челеби." [Отт. изъ Зап. Восточ. отд. Имп. Р. Арх. Общ., t20 *& other extr.* P2797]. la8°. С.–П. 1911

Замѣтки по текстамъ св. Писанія въ древн. перев. арм. и груз. [*Extr. f.* Христ. востокъ. P2798]. la8°. [1913]

Изъ лингвист. поѣздки въ Абхазію. [*Extr. f.* Изв. Имп. Акад. Наук, 1913. P2798] la8°. С.–П. 1913

Изъ лѣтней поѣздки въ Арменію, 10–16. [Отт. изъ зап. вост. отд. И. Р. Арх. Общ., т6 *& o. extracts.* P2796]. la8°. [С.–П.] *n.d.*

Изъ поѣздки въ Турецкій Лазистань. [*Extr. f.* Изв. Имп. Акад. Наукъ, 1910. 2p. P2797]. la8°. С.–П. 1910]

Изъ поѣздки на Аѳонъ. [*Extr. f.* Журналъ Мин. Народн. Просвѣш. ч322. P2813]. 8°. 1899

Изъ поѣздокъ въ Сванію. [*Extr. f.* Христ. востокъ. P2798]. la8°. [С–П. 1913]

Исторія Грузіи. [P2809]. s8°. Спб. 1906

Іоаннъ Петрицскій, груз. неоплатоникъ 11–12 вѣка. [Отт. изъ Зап. Вост. отд. И. Р. Арх. Общ., t19. P2797]. la8°. С.–П. 1909

Крещеніе Армянъ, Грузинъ, Абхазовъ и Алановъ св. Григоріемъ. Араб. версія. la8°. С.–П. 1905

Критика и мелкія статьи. [Тексты &c. по арм.-груз. филол., 5]. la8°. С.–П. 1903

Къ вопр. о задачахъ арменовѣдѣнія. Рѣчь. [P2811, 2813]. 8°. С.–П. 1899

Къ вопр. о полож. абхазск. языка среди яфетич., *see* MARR (N. YA.) Мат. по яфет. яз., 5, 1912.

Къ столѣтію дня рожд. М. И. Броссе. [P2804]. la8°. С.–П. 1902

Матеріалы по яфетич. Языкознанію. [*Ed. M.*], 1–6, 8, 9, 11 [*in* 3v]. 8°. С.–П. 1910–20

Beridze (V.) Груз. глоссарій, 1912. [6.]
Charaya (P. G.) Объ отнош. абхазск. яз. къ яфет., 1912. [4.]
Chkonia (I.) Груз. глоссарій, 1910. [1.]
Kipshidze (I. A.) Доп. свѣдѣнія о чанск. яз., 1911. [3.]
Marr (N. Ya.) Грамм. чанск. (лазскаго) яз., 1910. [2.]
—— Къ вопр. о полож. абхазск. яз. среди яфет., 1912. [5.]
—— Яфетич. Кавказ, 1920. [11.]
Onian (A.) Сборникъ сванскихъ названій деревьевъ и растеній, 1917. [8.]
—— Сванскіе тексты на лашхск. нарѣчіи, 1917. [9.]

Мудрость Балавара, груз. версія душепол. ист. о Варлаамѣ и Іоасафѣ. [Отт. изъ Зап. вост. отд. И. Р. Арх. Общ., т3. P2796]. la8°. [С.–П. 1899 ?]

Marr (Nikolai Yakovlevich) [*continued*].

Надпись Епифанія, катол. Грузіи. [*Extr. f.* Изв. Имп. Акад. Наукъ, 1910. P2797]. la8°. [С.–П. 1910]

Новые матеріалы по арм. эпиграфикѣ. Отт. изъ Зап. вост. отд. И. Р. Арх. Общ., т8. P2796]. la8°. С.–П. 1893

О начальной ист. Арменіи Анонима. Объ источн. ист. Моисея Хорен. [P2796]. la8°. *n.d.*

О раскопкахъ и работахъ въ Ани, 1906. [Тексты и разысканія по арм.-груз. филол. (С.–П. унив.), кн. 10]. la8°. С.–П. 1907

Объ единствѣ задачъ арм.-грузинской филол. [P2803]. 8°. Тифлисъ. 1902

Опредѣл. языка второй категоріи Ахеменидск. клинообразныхъ надписей по данн. Яфетич. языкознанія. [Имп. Р. Арх. Общ: Отдѣл. отт. изъ Зап. Вост. Отд., т22]. la8°. С.–П. 1914

Основн. таблицы къ грамм. древне-грузинск. языка. 4° С.–П. 1908

Отзывъ о сочиненіи Е. С. Такайшвили. Отт. изъ Сборника отчетовъ &c. за 1907. P2803]. 8°. С.–П. 1908

Раскопки въ Ани въ 1904. [P2797]. la8°. С.–П. 1906

Сказаніе о католикосѣ Петрѣ и ученомъ Іоаннѣ Козернѣ [*With text*]. Изъ сборн. фак. Восточ. Яз. Восточ. Замѣтки. fol. С.–П. 1895

Яфетич. элем. въ языкахъ Арменіи, 1, 6, 7. [*Extr. f.* Изв. Имп. Акад. Наукъ, 1911–14 *& o. extr^s.* P2797–8]. la8°. [С.–П. 1911–14]

[Summer travels in Armenia. Tr. *into Armenian* by O. Anofean. P2809]. s8°. Vienna. 1892

see ACTA Iberica SS. tergemin. martyrum Speusippi &c.; explic. ed. & Ross. vertit N. M., 1906.

,, ANTIOCHUS [STRATIG]. Плѣненіе Іерусалима, 614; изд Н. М., 1909.

,, JERUSALEM. Синодикъ Крестн. мон.: груз. текстъ изд. Н. М., 1914.

,, SAINT PETERSBURG. Кат. груз. рукописей, Имп. Публ. Библ., 1900.

,, VARTAN, *called the Great.* Сборники притчъ Вардана: матеріалы; *ed.* Н. М., 3ч, 1894–99.

,, YAFETICHESKY INST. Яфет. сборник [*by* N. M. &c.], 1, 2, 1922–23.

Marr (Timothy), *see* FAIRBURN (J.) Acc. of murders of families of M. & Williamson, 1811.

Marra (Ferrante della), *duca della Guardia, see* DELLA MARRA.

Marracci (Lodovico). Alcorani textus universus descriptus. Prodromus totum priorem tomum implens. [4p *in* 1v]. fol. Patavii. 1698

Refutatio Alcorani. fol. Patavii. 1698

Marradi (Giovanni).

Poesia d. riscossa. [P2418]. 8°. Firenze. 1918

Marriage. Book (The) of m.: new interp. by 24 leaders of contemp. thought; tr., 1927, *see* KEYSERLING (H., *Graf* v.), *ed.*

*Marriage laws of Soviet Russia, 1921, *see* Russia.

Marriage (Ernest). Elem. telephotography. 8°. 1901

Marrier (Martinus) & A. Du Chesne. Bibl. Cluniacensis, SS. Patrum Abb. Clun. vitæ, miracula, scripta &c. Ex Ms. codd. coll. M. M. & A. Quercetanus, qui eadem disposuit, ac notis illust. (1614). fol. Matiscone. 1915

Marriott (Charles). The grave impertinence. s8°. [1921]

Mod. Eng. architecture. 8°. 1924

Mod. movements in painting. 8°. 1920

An order to view. s8°. [1922]

Marriott (*Mrs.* Charles Bruce), *form. Miss Ida Lee.*

Capt. Bligh's second voyage to the South Sea. 8°. 1920

Early explorers in Australia, from log-books &c., incl. Diary of A. Cunningham, 1817–18. 8°. 1925

see HARE (R. H. A.) Voyage of the Caroline, 1827–28; w. ch. on early hist. of N. Tasmania &c. by I. Lee, 1927.

Marriott (Horace), *D.D.* The Sermon on the Mount. Pref. by [W. Lock]. 8°. 1925

Marriott (J. W.)

One-act plays of to-day. Sel. by J. W. M. s8°. [1924]

Marriott (*Sir* John Arthur Ransome).

The constit. in transition, 1910–24. s8°. O. 1924

Economics & ethics. 8°. [1923]

Empire settlement. s8°. 1927

Europe & beyond. World politics, 1870–1920. 8°. 1921

The mechanism of the mod. State: treatise on the science & art of govt. 2v. 8°. O. 1927

Second chambers. n. ed. rev. &c. 8°. O. 1927

Syndicalism, econ. & polit. [P2500]. s8°. [1920]

Marriott (*Rt. Hon. Sir* William Thackeray). The Khedivial family: corresp. betw. M. & Sir E. Vincent. [P2830]. 8°. 1889

***Marrow** (The) of alchemy, 2p [in 1v], 1654–55, *see* STARKEY (G.)

Marrow, *The family of, see* KING EDWARD'S SCHOOL, *Birmingham.* Records, v1, w. intr. [*on the* M. family], by W. F. Carter, 1924.

Marryat (*Capt.* **Frederick**), *R. N.*
Mr. Midshipman Easy. [repr.] s8°. [1923]
Peter Simple. Intr. by D. Hannay. [repr.] s8°. 1911
„ „ Illust. by J. A. Symington. Intr. by D. Hannay. s8°. 1925

Marsala (Vincenzo Maria). Il probabilisimo sostenuto &c.: stato eccl. [P2767]. 8°. Palermo. 1757

Marschalck (Hans). *Eyn edles schönes lieplichs Tractätlein von d. reynen hyml. ewigen wort &c. s4°. [Augsburg. c. 1524]
Von dem weyt erschollē Namē Luther, wz er bedeūt. u. wie er wirt miszbraucht. Marschalk Strapburg. s4°. *n.p.* 1523

Marschall von Bieberstein (Christian) [MARSCHALCH À B.] Exercit. de Rom. pontificibus ex German. gente creatis. Praes. J. C. Wagenseilio. [P2670]. s4°. Altdorfi Noric. 1683

Marschlins (Meta von Salis-), *see* SALIS-MARSCHLINS (M. VON).

Marsden (Antony). The man in the sandhills. s8°. [1927]

Marsden (John Buxton). Mem. of the life & labours of Rev. S. Marsden. Ed. J. B. M. s8°. 1858

Marsden (Joshua), *missionary.* The narr. of a mission to Nova Scotia & the Somers Islands &c. 2nd ed. s8°. 1827

Marsden (Margaret), *see* HOLDEN (W.), J. ASHCROFT &c. Trial &c. of J. A., W. H. &c. for murder of M. M. &c., 1817.

Marsden (Richard). Cotton spinning, w. append. on steam engines & boilers. s8°. 1884

Marsden (*Rev.* **Samuel**), *see* MARSDEN (J. B.) Mem. of Rev. S. M.; ed. J. B. M., 1858.

Marsden (Victor E.) Jews in Russia. [P2523]. 8°. [1920 ?]
see NILUS (S.) Protocols of the elders of Zion; tr. M., 1923.

Marsden (William), *F.R.S.* Bibl. Marsden. philol. et orient. Catalogue. 4°. 1827

Marselaer (Fridericus de).
Legatus libri duo. s4°. Antverpiae. 1626

Marsennus (Martinus), *see* MERSENNE (MARIN).

Marsh (A.), *see* BEHN (A.) The ten pleasures of marriage [wr. by M., 1682], 1922.

Marsh (Charles Fielding). The four-post bed. s8°. [1927]

Marsh (Edward Howard), *see* BROOKE (R.) Coll. poems: w. mem. [by E. M.], 7th impr., 1920.

Marsh (Frank Burr). English rule in Gascony (1199–1259), w. spec. ref. to the towns. [Univ. of Michigan]. 8°. 1912

Marsh (Frederick Haward), *see* MARSH (HOWARD).

Marsh (Herbert), *bp. of (1) Llandaff, (2) Peterborough.* Conseq. of neglecting to give the Prayer book w. the Bible; w. matter rel. to B. & F. Bible Soc. 4th ed. s8°. 1812
see MILNER (I.) Strictures on publ. of M., reply to h. obj. agst. Brit. & For. Bible Soc., 1813.

Marsh (Howard) [FREDERICK HAWARD MARSH]. A mem. of Howard Marsh. [Pref. *signed* V. S. M.] 8°. 1921

Marsh (John Fitchett). On engraved & pretended portraits of Milton. [Extr. f. Trans. of Hist. Soc. of Lancs. &c., v12, 1859–60]. 8°. Liv'l. 1860

Marsh (Narcissus), *provost of Trin. Coll., Dublin, 1678–83, see* WHITE (N. J. D.) Four good men, N. M. &c., 1927.

Marsh (*Lt.-Col.* **William Lockwood**), *see* VIVIAN (E. C.) Hist. of aeronautics, w. sect. on progr. in aeroplane design by M., 1921.

Marshall (*Mrs.* **Agnes B.**)
Cookery book. rev. & enl. ed. s8°. [1897]

Marshall (Alfred). Elem. of economics of industry: being v1 of Elem. of economics. 3rd ed. 8°. 1899
Industry & trade. [2nd ed.] 8°. 1919
Memorials of A. M. [*by var. a.*] Ed. A. C. Pigou. 8°. 1925
Money, credit & commerce. 8°. 1923
Official papers. 8°. 1926
see SCOTT (W. R.) *A. M., 1842–1924, 1926.

Marshall (Archibald).
The Allbright family. s8°. [1926]
Anthony Dare. s8°. [1923]
Anthony Dare's progress. s8°. [1925]
Big Peter. s8°. [1922]
The Clintons, & others. s8°. [1920]
The education of Anthony Dare. s8°. [1924]
The Hall & the Grange. [3rd impr.] s8°. [1921]
Pippin. s8°. [1923]
Sir Harry. s8°. [1920]
A spring walk in Provence. 8°. [1920]
The squire's daughter. [repr.] s8°. [1922]
That island. s8°. [1927]
see VACHELL (H. A.) & A. M. Mr. Allen, 1926.

Marshall (Arthur), *architect.* Specimens of antique carved furniture & woodwork. fol. 1888

Marshall (Bruce). The stooping Venus. s8°. [1925]

Marshall (Chapman Frederick Dendy).
The Brit. post office, to 1925. la8°. 1926

Marshall (Charles Henry Tilson) & G. F. L. Marshall. A monograph of the Capitonidae or scansorial barbets. 4°. 1870–71

Marshall (Dorothy). Eng. poor in the 18th cent. 8°. 1926

Marshall (Edward), *vicar of Sandford St. Martin, Oxford.* Acc. of the parish of Sandford, Oxon. s8°. O. 1866

Marshall (Frederick Henry). Discovery in Greek lands: princ. excav. &c. of last 50 yrs. s8°. C. 1920

Marshall (*Maj.-Gen.* **George Frederick Leycester**), *see* MARSHALL (C. H. T.) & G. F. L. M. Monogr. of the Capitonidae &c., 1870–71.

Marshall (George William). Coll. for genealog. acc. of the family of Comberbach. 8°. 1866

Marshall (Henry Rutgers). The beautiful. 8°. 1924

Marshall (John), *of the East India Co.; 164½–77.* John Marshall in India: notes & obs. in Bengal, 1668–72. Sel. &c. by S. A. Khan. 8°. 1927

Marshall (John), *of the U.S., see* BEMIS (S. F.), *ed.* Amer. Secr. of State, v2, M., by A. J. Montague, 1927.

Marshall (John A.) Amer. Bastile: illegal arrests &c. of Amer. citizens dur. Civil War. 6th ed. 8°. Phila. 1870

Marshall (*Sir* **John Hubert**). Annual report, 1918/19, pl, 1921, *see* INDIA: ARCH. SURVEY.
Conservation manual. Hdbk. for archaeolog. officers &c. [India. Govt. Publ.] 8°. Calcutta. 1923
Excavations at Taxila: Stupas & monasteries at Jauliāñ, *see* INDIA: ARCH. SURVEY. Mem., No. 7, 1921.
see INDIA: ARCH. SURVEY. Index to Annual rep. of the Director Gen. (Sir J. M.), 1902–16, 1924.

Marshall (Leon Carroll). Readings in industrial society. [*From var. a.*] [5th impr.] 8°. Chicago. [1920]

Marshall (Thomas Maitland), *see* BOLTON (H. E.) & T. H. M. Coloniz. of N. America, 1492–1783, 1920.

Marshall (William Elliot). Amongst the Todas. 8°. 1873
Another issue w. title A phrenologist amongst the Todas &c.

Marshfield.
Parish registers of M., Gloucestershire. la8°. *p.p.* 1893

Marshman (John Clark), *see* CONFUCIUS. Works; pref. a diss. by J. M., 1809.

Marshman (Joshua). A defence of the deity & atonement of Jesus Christ, in reply to Ram-Mohun Roy. 8°. 1822

Marsh's Library, Dublin, *see* WHITE (N. J. D.) Account, 1926.

Marsi (Antonio). I drammi pastorali. A cura di I. Palmarini. 2v. s8°. Bologna. 1887–88

Marsilio, *da Padova.*
Defensor minor. Ed. C. K. Brampton. 8°. B'ham. 1922
Defensor pacis sive apologia pro Ludovico IIII Imp. Bavaro. Tractatus, de translatione imperii. Ed. castigatior &c. s8°. *Ex bibliopolio Comeliniano.* 1599
[Prefixed is tp. & pref. of the ed. of F. Gomarus, print. by J. Wechelus. Frankfort 1592.]
see HURAUT (A.) Étude, 1892.
„ TOOLEY (M. J.) The authorship of the Defensor pacis, 1926.
„ WEISSENBURGER (W.) Antilogia Papae (M. de Padua de transl. Imperii), 1555.

Marsilio (Giovanni). Defensio in favorem responsi octo propos. cont. adv. quod scripsit Bellarminus, *see* PAUL V, *pope.* Controversiae, 1607.
see SERVANTIO (G.) Difesa d. potestà &c. eccl. contro le 8 propos. di un dottore incogn. [*i.e.* G. M.] &c., 1606.

Marsin (M.) [MERSEN (M.)] A clear & brief explan. upon the chief points in the New Test., what is faith that justifies &c. [*b. w. h.* Two sorts of latter days, 1699]. s8°. 1697
Two sorts of latter days proved from Scripture. [*2 pagin.*] s8°. 1699

Marsland (Ellis), *see* MONSON (*Maj.* E. C. P.) & E. M. Air raid damage in London, 1923.

Marsollier (Jacques).
*Hist. de l'Inquisition. s8°. Cologne. 1693
Hist. du ministère du card. Ximenez. s8°. Toulouse. 1694

Marstaller (Leonardus), *see* GERLACHER (T.) *von Billican.* Apologia ad epistolam L. M. &c., 1524.

Marston. Churchwardens' accounts of M., Spelsbury, Pyrton. Ed. F. W. Weaver & G. N. Clark. [Oxf. Rec. Soc., 6]. 8°. O. 1925

Marston (John), *dramatist.* *Antonio & Mellida & Antonio's revenge, 1602. [*w. facs. tps.* Malone Soc.] s4°. [O.] 1921
The scourge of villanie (1599). [Bodley Head Quartos]. s8°. [1925]
see LYON (J. H. H.) A st. of The newe metamorphosis, wr. by J. M., Gent. [? Marston], 1600, 1919.

Marston (Maurice). Sir Edwin Chadwick (1800–90). 8°. [1925]
Marston (Philip Bourke), *see* OSBORNE (J. C.) P. B. M., 1926.
Marstrander (Carl J. S.), *ed., see* ROYAL IRISH ACAD. Dict. of Ir. lang., fasc. 1, 1913.
Martchenko (M.), *see* MARCHENKO (M.)
Marteau (—), *see* BLOCHET (E.) Notices sur les mss. persans &c. de la coll. M., 1923.
Martel (Édouard Alfred).
Les Cevennes & la région des Causses. la8°. 1890
Martel (Tancrede). Ce que coûtent les rêves. Roman. s8°. 1921
L'intrigue dans l'amour ; le duc d'Epernon. s8°. 1925
Julien et Marguerite de Ravalet (1582–1603). 8°. 1920
Martelli (Lodovico) [MARTELLO].
Rime volgari [& Tragedia]. s8°. Venetia. 1533
Martellière (Jean). Pierre de Ronsard, gentilhomme vandomois. Préf. de G. Hanotaux. s8°. 1924
Marten (Clarence Henry Kennett), *see* WARNER (G. T.) & C. H. K. M. Groundwork of Brit. hist., repr., 1923.
Marten (Maria), *see* CURTIS (J.) Authentic &c. hist. of murder of M. M. in the Red Barn ; added, trial of W. Corder, 1834.
Martens (F. de) [MARTENS (FEDOR FEDOROVICH)].
Современное международное право &c. 2t. 8°. С.-П. 1882–83
Le conflit entre la Russie & la Chine. [P535]. la8°. Brux. 1880
see DANEWSKY (V.) La Russie & l'Angl. dans l'Asie Centrale : obs. sur M., 1881.
Martens (Friedrich) [MARTEN]. Hispan. Reise-Beschreibung de anno 1671. Hrsg. W. Junk. 8°. 1925
Journal d'un voyage au Spitzbergen &c. ; tr., *see* BERNARD (J. F.), *ed.* Recueil, t2, 1715 ; 1732.
Martens (Georg Friedrich von). Nouv. recueil gén. de traités &c. Cont. du grand rec. de M. par H. Triepel.
s3, t8–17. 8°. Leipzig. 1915–27
„ „ ....s3, Table gén., t1–10. 8°. L. 1922
Martens (Kurt). Die deut. Lit. unsrer Zeit in Charakteristiken u. Proben. 8°. München. 1922
Schonungslose Lebenschronik, 1870–1900.
3e Aufl. 8°. Wien. 1921
Martens (Wilhelm). Polit. Gesch. d. Langobardenreichs unter Liutprand (712–44). 8°. Heidelberg. 1880
Martí (José), *see* MÉNDEZ (I.) J. M.: estudio, 1925.
Martial, *the poet.*
TRANSLATIONS.
Epigrams. Tr. into prose, w. verse tr. f. Eng. poets.
[repr.] s8°. *Bohn.* 1904
„ „ With Eng. tr. by W. C. A. Ker. [Loeb Class. Lib.] v2. s8°. 1920
„ „ Transl. & imitations, by A. L. Francis & H. F. Tatum. 8°. C. 1924
The 12 books of epigrams. Tr. J. A. Pott & F. A. Wright, w. an intr. [Broadway Trans.] 8°. [1925]
Martial-Piéchaud (—), *see* PIÉCHAUD (M.)
Martin, *The family of, see* MAXWELL-LYTE (H. C.) Burci, Falaise & M., 1919.
Martin, *St., abp. of Braga, see* ECKHARD (T.) Codices manuscripti Quedlinburg. &c., 1723.
Martin, *of Tours, Saint.* Professio fidei cath. de Trinitate, *see* GALLIA. *Vet. aliq. G. theol. scripta, 1586.
see SEVERUS (S.) Saint M. ; *tr.* &c. par P. Monceaux, 1926.
„ —— St. M. of T. ; [tr.] M. C. Watt, 1928.
„ TREUER (G. S.) Untersuch. d. Ursprungs u. d. Bedeut. d. Märtens-Mannes &c., 1733.
Martin (A.) M.'s annals of crime, or New Newgate Calendar.
v1, 2. 8°. 1837–38
Martin (A.), *bibliographer, see* SAULNIER (E.) & A. M. Bibliog. des travaux, 1866–97, sur l'hist. de la France, 1500–1789, fasc. 1, 1927.
Martin (A. D.) The Prophet Jonah: the book & the sign. Intr. note by A. S. Peake. s8°. 1926
Martin (*le baron* **Alexandre**), *de Gray.* Opinion sur le projet de loi rel. à la liberté de la presse. [P2772, 2866]. s8°. 1817
Martin (Arthur Patchett).
The Queen in the I. of Wight. 8°. 1898
Martin (Asa Earl) & H. H. Shenk.
Pennsylvania hist. told by contemporaries. 8°. N.Y. 1925
Martin (B. Kingsley). The triumph of Lord Palmerston: public opin. in Eng. bef. the Crimean War. 8°. 1924
Martin (*Sir* **Benjamin**). Raisons qui ont porté le gouv. de la Gr. Bret. à former une colonie dans la Georgie, *see* BERNARD (J. F.), *ed.* Recueil, t9, 1737.
Martin (Carl). Landeskunde v. Chile. 2. verm. A., umgearbt. v. J. Brüggen, W. Drascher &c., u. v. d. Hrsg. Chr. Martin. la8°. Hamburg. 1923
Martin (Charles Emanuel).
Intr. to st. of the Amer. constit. 8°. N.Y. 1926
Policy of the U.S. as regards intervention.
8°. N.Y., *Columbia Univ.* 1921
Martin (Conrad), *bp. of Paderborn.* Katechismus d. röm.-kathol. Kirchenrechts. 2e Aufl. 8°. Münster. 1875
I lavori del Concilio Vaticano. Vers. dal Tedesco per E. Pick. [P2694]. 8°. Roma. 1873
Omnium Concilii Vaticani quae ad doct. &c. pert. doc. coll.
ed 2a. 8°. Paderbornae. 1873
Der wahre Sinn d. Vatikan. Lehrentscheid. ü. d. unfehlb. päpstl. Lehramt. 3e A. [P2693]. 8°. Paderborn. 1871
see BONOLA (R.) *Auch eine Enthüll. od. ein alt. Buch geg. d. neu. Irrungen ; hrsg. v. K. M., 1871.
Martin (Corneille). Généalogies &c. des forestiers & comtes de Flandre, avec descr. de leurs vies &c. Ornées de portraicts &c. par P. Balthasar. sm. fol. Anvers. 1580
Martin (Edward A.) Short acc. of the nat. hist. & antiq. of Croydon. 8°. Croydon. 1923
Martin (Edward James). The Biblical text of Firmicus Maternus. [Extr. f. Journal of theol. st., v24. P2705]. 8°. 1923
Life & criticism. s8°. *p.p.* [O.] 1927
The trial of the Templars. s8°. [1928]
Martin (Edward Sandford).
Life of J. H. Choate f. h. letters &c. 2v. 8°. 1920
Martin (Ernst). Goethe in Strassburg, *see* VIRCHOW (R.) & F. v. HOLTZENDORFF. Vorträge, H135, 1871.
Martin (*l'abbé* **Eugène**). St. Colomban. 2e éd. s8°. 1905
Martin (Eveline C.) Brit. West African settlements, 1750–1821: local admin. 8°. 1927
Martin (Everett Dean).
Psychology, what it has to teach &c. s8°. [1926]
Martin (François), *de Vitré.* Descr. du premier voyage faict aux Indes Orient. par les François. s8°. 1609
Martin (Franz). Schloss Hellbrunn bei Salzburg. 8°. Wien. 1927
Stift St. Peter in Salzburg. 8°. Wien. 1927
Martin (Gaston). Carrier & sa mission à Nantes. 8°. 1924
Martin (Geoffrey).
Mod. chemistry & its wonders. [2nd ed.] s8°. [1922]
Martin (Germain). Les finances publ. de la France & la fortune privée, 1914–25. 8°. 1925
see HANOTAUX (G.) Hist. de la nation franç., t10, Hist. écon. & financière ; par G. M., 1927.
Martin (Gregory). A discoverie of the manifold corruptions of the Holy Scr. by the heretikes, English Sectaries &c.
s8°. Rhemes. 1582
see RAINOLDS (J.) Summe of the conference between J. R. & J. Hart &c., w. def. *agst.* G. M., 1588.
Martin (Henry), *admin. de la Bibl. de l'Arsenal.* Les joyaux de l'enluminure à la Bibl. Nat. Avant-propos du Cte. A. de Laborde. fol. 1928
La miniature franç. du 13e au 15e s. fol. 1923
Le style de Louis XIV. 8°. [1925]
Le style de Louis XV. 8°. [1925]
Martin (Hugh).
Ireland in insurrection. Pref. by P. Gibbs. s8°. 1921
Martin (J. W.) [*ps.* " THE TRENT OTTER "].
Coarse fish angling. [re-issued]. 8°. [1924]
Martin (Jacques), *Benedictine.* *Explic. de plus. textes diffic. de l'Ecriture. Par le R. P. Dom * * * religieux Bénédictin. 2p *in* 1t. s4°. 1730
Martin (John), *minister at Edgefield, Norfolk,* **S. Petto & F. Woodall.** The preacher sent: or a vindic. of the liberty of publ. preaching, in ans. to 1, Jus divinum ministerii evang., by the Provinc. Assembly of London, 2, Vindiciæ ministerii evang., by J. Collings. s8°. 1658
Martin (John), *painter ; 1789–1864, see* PENDERED (M. L.) J. M., h. life & times, 1923.
Martin (Josef). Commodianea, 1917, *see* KAIS. AKAD. D. W. ZU WIEN. Phil.-hist. Kl. Sitz., B181, 1928.
Martin (Kingsley).
The Brit. public & the General Strike. s8°. 1926
Martin (Louis Claude). Colour & methods of colour reproduction, w. chap. on colour printing & photography by W. Gamble. 8°. 1923
A forgotten poet of the 17th cent. [N. Wanley], *see* ENG. ASSOC. Essays, v11, 1925.

Martin (*Lt.-Col.* **Lawrence**), *U.S. Army*, *see* TREATIES. T. of peace, 1919–23; maps comp. &c. by M., 2v, 1924.
Martin (Louis), *M.D.*, *see* SCHOLA SALERNITANA. L'école de Salerne avec tr. burlesque du Dr. M. (1650); n. éd., rev. &c. par P. Le Duc, 1875.
Martin (Louis Léon-), *see* LÉON-MARTIN (L.)
Martin (Maria), *see* CORDER (W.) Trial of W. C. for the murder of M. M., 1828.
Martin (Marie), *form. Guyard*, *see* MARIE, *de l'Incarnation.*
Martin (Marie Françoise Thérèse), *see* THERESA, *St.*, *of Lisieux.*
Martin (Marietta). Un aventurier intellectuel: le docteur Koreff (1783–1851). la8°. 1925
Martin (Percy Falcke).
Egypt—old & new: a pop. acc. 8°. [1923]
The Sudan in evolution. Foreword by Gen. Sir F. R. Wingate. 8°. 1921
Martin (Rudolf), *prof. of anthropology at Zürich.*
Die Inlandstämme d. Malay. Halbinsel &c. la8°. Jena. 1905
Martin (Samuel). Relig. divisions consid. &c. Sermon: annexed peculiarities of Methodism, f. wr. of J. Wesley. [P2535]. s8°. Glasgow. 1768
Martin (Stuart). The mystery of Mormonism. 8°. [1920]
Martin (Thomas Ignace), *see* LENOTRE (G.) M. le Visionnaire (1816–34), 1924.
Martin (Victor), *see* SILINGARDI (G.) Les négoc. du nonce S. rel. à publ. du Concile de Trente en France, 1599–1601: doc.; thèse par V. M., 1919.
Martin (William). Hist. de la Suisse. 8°. 1926
Martin (*Paymaster Rear-Admiral* **William Ernest Russell**).
Adv. of a naval paymaster. 8°. 1924
Martin (*Vice-Adm. Sir* **William Fanshawe**), *Bart.*
Mem. on naval reserves. [P2831]. 8°. 1860
Martin Alonso (Aurelio). Diez y seis años de regencia (Maria Cristina de Hapsburgo-Lorena, 1885–1902). s8°. Barcelona. 1914
Martin-Chauffier (Louis). L'épervier: roman. s8°. 1925
Martindale (Adam). Divinity-knots unloosed. s8°. 1649
Martindale (Cyril Charlie), *S.J.* Bernard Vaughan, S.J. 8°. 1923
Richard Philip Garrold, S.J. Memoir. s8°. 1921
Martindale (Louisa), *M.D.*
The woman doctor & h. future. 8°. [1922]
Martindale (William). Coca, cocaine & its salts. s8°. 1886
Martin de Herrera (*Card.* **José**), *abp. of Santiago de Compostela.*
Constit. sinodales. Dadas y publ. por J. M. de H. en el Sínodo Diocesano, 12–14 Julio, 1909. 3ª ed. 8°. Santiago. 1909
Martindell (Ernest Walter). Bibliog. of works of R. Kipling, 1881–1921. 8°. 1922
Martin Du Gard (Maurice). De Sainte-Beuve à Fénelon: H. Brémond. 3e éd. s8°. [1927]
Martin Du Gard (Roger). Jean Barois. 30e éd. s8°. 1921
Le testament du père Leleu: farce. [Répert. du vieux-colombier]. 4e éd. s8°. [1923]
Les Thibault. p1–5 [in 6v]. s8°. 1922–28
1, Le cahier gris. 2, Le pénitencier. 3, La belle saison, 2v. 4, La consultation. 5, La Sorellina.
Martineau (Alfred).
Dupleix & l'Inde française, 1722–1754. [t]1–4. 8°. 1920–28
Les orig. de Mahé de Malabar. [Extr. de la Rev. de l'hist. des colonies fr.] 8°. 1917
see PONDICHÉRY. Corr. du Conseil Supér. de P. &c.; publ. avec intr. par A. M., t1, 2, 1920.
Martineau (Alice). The herbaceous garden. Intr. by W. Robinson. 4th ed., rev. & enl. 8°. 1923
Martineau (David). The pedigree of the Martineau family, descended f. Gaston Martineau. la8°. *p.f.p.c.* 1907
Martineau (Edith), *wife of Philip Martineau.* Gardening in sunny lands, the Riviera, California, Australia. Intr. by E. Wharton. 8°. [1924]
Roumania & her rulers. 8°. [1927]
Martineau (Gaston), *see* MARTINEAU (D.) Pedigree of the M. family, descended fr. G. M., 1907.
Martineau (George). Sugar, cane & beet. s8°. [1910]
Martineau (Harriet). Demerara, a tale. 2nd ed. s8°. 1832
Eastern life. n. ed. s8°. [1875]
see BOSANQUET (T.) H. M.: essay in comprehension, 1927.
Martineau (James).
A study of religion, its sources &c. 2nd ed. rev. 2v. s8°. O. 1889
see UPTON (C. B.) Dr. M.'s philosophy, 1905.
Martineau (John), *writer of "Letters f. Australia," see* MARTINEAU (V.) J. M., the pupil of Kingsley, 1921.
Martineau (*Mrs* **Philip**), *see* MARTINEAU (EDITH).

Martineau (René). Léon Bloy: souv. d'un ami. s8°. 1921
Martineau (Violet).
John Martineau, the pupil of Kingsley. 8°. 1921
Martinelli (Giuseppe), *see* ALBERTI DI VILLANOVA (*il cte.* F.) Nuovo diz. portat. ital.-fr. & fr.-ital. compend. per G. M., 7ª ed., 1853.
Martinenche (Ernest).
L'Espagne & le romantisme français. 8°. 1922
Martinengo (Evelina).
Storia d. liber. d'Italia, 1815–70. 2ª ed. s8°. Milano. 1915
Martinengo Cesaresco (*ctss.* **Evelyn L. H.**) The Madonna of the scales. [*Poem.* P2844]. s8°. O. 1905
see GREEK. A sheaf of Gr. folk songs; intr. note by Ctss. E. M. C., 1922.
Martines (Joan). Portolan atlas: J. M. en Messina 1582. Facs., w. intr. by E. L. Stevenson. [Hisp. Soc. of Amer.] atl. fol. N.Y. 1915
Martinet (Marcel). La maison à l'abri. 4e éd. s8°. [1919]
Martinez (Albert B.) Baedeker of the Argentine Republic. 4th ed. s8°. Barcelona. 1914
Martínez (Eugenio Agacino y), *see* AGACINO Y MARTÍNEZ (E.)
Martinez (Vincenzo), *Veneziano.* Il natale di Telemaco. Poemetto. [Feste p. la nasc. d. princ. Carlo. P2765]. 8°. [Napoli ?]. 1775
Martínez Añíbarro y Rives (Manuel). Intento de un dicc. de autores de la prov. de Burgos. la8°. 1889
Martínez de Ripalda (Juan).
De ente supernat. disp. theolog. n. ed. expurg.
3t (1, 2, n. ed.) fol. 1, 2, Lugduni; 3, Coloniae Agripp. 1648–66
t3, Adv. articulos olim a Pio V &c. damnatos, Lib. 2 Ad Disp. De ente Supernat. Appendix, et t3.
Tractatus theolog. &c. de virtutibus fide, spe, et charitate. Opus posthum. ed. 2ª. fol. Lugduni. 1680
Martínez Ruiz (J.) [*ps.* AZORIN].
Antonio Azorín. s8°. 1913
Las confesiones de un pequeño filósofo. s8°. 1904
De Granada a Castelar. s8°. 1922
Doña Inés. 2ª ed. s8°. [1926]
Una hora de España (entre 1560 y 1590). [2ª ed.] s8°. [1925]
Los pueblos. s8°. 1919
Un pueblecito. Riofrío de Ávila. s8°. 1916
Los Quinteros y otras paginas. s8°. [1925]
Rivas y Larra: razón soc. del romanticismo en España. s8°. 1921
Los valores literarios. 8°. 1913
see MULERTT (W.) Azorín, z. Kenntnis span. Schr., 1926.
Martínez Sierra (Gregorio). Ignacio Zuloaga. 8°. [1920]
Julio Romero de Torres. [*Intr. by* G. M. S.] 8°. [1919]
Plays. 2v. [v1, Eng. vers. by J. G. Underhill, w. crit. apprec. of the plays by H. G. Barker; v2, Eng. vers. by H. & H. G. Barker]. s8°. 1923
1, The cradle song—The lover—Love magic—Poor John—Mme. Pepita.
2, The Kingdom of God—The two shepherds—Wife to a famous man—The romantic young lady.
Santiago Rusiñol. 8°. [1918]
Martinez y Delgado (Francisco). Hist. de la ciudad de Medina Sidonia. Publ. con notas J. M. Enrile y Mendez. 8°. Cadiz. 1875
Martínez y Martínez (Matías Ramón). El libro de Jerez de los Caballeros. 8°. Sevilla. 1892
Martini (Fausto Maria), *see* ALOISIO (N. D'). F. M. M., 1919.
Martini (Ferdinando).
A Pieriposa. Novella all' antica. s8°. Milano. 1923
Confessioni e ricordi (Firenze granducale). s8°. Firenze. 1922
Martini (Giovanni Battista). Esemplare o sia saggio di contrappunto fugato. 2p. 4°. Bologna. 1774–[75]
Storia d. musica. 3t. 4°. Bologna. 1757–81
Martini (Gottlieb Ernst). Sacrificium missae pontif. liturgiis or. ignotum. Praes. J. G. Jano. [P436]. s4°. Vitembergae. [1725]
Martini (Jacob). Synopsis totius relig. Photinianorum novorum ex Volkelio, Ostorodo &c. repetitae &c. s8°. Wittebergae. 1633
Martini (Mario Maria).
La passione di Fiume. Diarî &c. s8°. [1919]
Martini (Martinus), *S.J.* Rel. de la Tartarie orientale [*tr. f. h.* Novus Atlas Sin.], *see* BERNARD (J. F.), *ed.* Recueil, t3, 1715; t4, 1732.
Sinicæ hist. decas prima. Res à gentís orig. ad Christum natum gestas complexa. s4°. Monachii. 1658
" " ....s8°. Amstelædami. 1659
see SPATHARY (N. G.) Описаніе первыя ч. вселенныя имен. Азіи &c. [*mostly tr. f. M.*], 1910.

Martini (Simon), *called Memmo, see* MARLE (R. VAN). S. M. & les peintres de s. école, 1920.
Martinie (A. H.) La sculpture. [L'art fr. dep. 20 ans]. 8°. 1928
Martin-Leake (Stephen), *see* LEAKE (S. M.)
Martino (Pierre).
Parnasse & symbolisme (1850–1900). s8°. 1925
Martin Saint-Léon (Etienne). Hist. des corporations de métiers, j. leur suppression en 1791 &c. 3e éd. rev. & augm. 8°. 1922
Martins (Nabur), *see* MAETERLINCK (L.) N. M. ou Le Maître de Flémalle: nouv. doc., 1913.
Martinus [*Strepus*], *abp. of Gnesen* [MARTINUS *Oppaviensis*; M. *Polonus*; STREBSKI (M.)] Chron. d. Kaiser u. Päpste in deut. Uebers. d. 14. Jhdts.; hrsg. San-Marte (A. Schulz), pl, *see* ARCHIV. F. D. ST. D. NEU. SPR., B23, 1858.
Martinus (Johannes), *of Groningen.* Praxeos populariter concionandi rudimenta. Add. Centuria textuum [Praxeos concion. gymnasmata, *w. sep. tp. & pagin.*] s8°. Groningæ. 1651
Martir Rizo (Juan Pablo).
Hist. de la ciudad de Cuenca. sm. fol. 1629
Martius (Johannes Heinr.), *see* JACOBI (C. F.) & J. H. M. De lotionibus Mohammed. exercit. prima, 1706.
Martna (M.)
Estland, die Esten u. d. estn. Frage. 8°. Olten. [1919]
Martonne (Emmanuel de). La Roumanie. Conférence. [*Extr. du* Bull. de la Soc. de Géogr. de Lille. P2737]. 8°. Lille. 1920
Martorell (Juan), *see* VAETH (J. A.) Tirant lo Blanch: st. of its authorship, princ. sources &c., 1918.
Martov (L.), *ps.* [*i.e.* YU. O. TSEDERBAUM]. Down with executions. From Russian by E. I. Z. [P2405]. 8°. [1919]
——, **P. P. Maslov & A. Potresov,** *editors.* Обществ. движенiе въ Россiи въ началѣ xx° вѣка. Подъ редакц. Л. М., П. М. и А. П. 2t (t2i, ii). la8°. С.-П. 1909–10
Marty (Paul).
Etudes sur l'Islam & les tribus du Soudan. 4t. la8°. 1918–21
1, Les Kounta de l'Est—Les Berabich—Les Iguellad.
2, La région de Tombouctou (Islam Songaï)—Dienné, le Macina & dépendances (Islam Peul).
3, Les tribus Maures du Sahel & du Hodh.
4, La région de Kayes—Le pays Bambara—Le Sahel de Nioro.
Marty-Lavauzelle (Roger).
Les manœuvres de l'Est en 1911. 8°. [1912]
Les manœuvres de l'Ouest en 1912. 8°. 1913
Les manœuvres de Picardie en 1910. 8°. [1911]
Martyn (Francis).
Homilies on the Bk. of Tobias. 2nd ed. rev. s8°. 1822
Martyn (Thomas), *B.D., F.R.S.* *A chronolog. series of engravers &c. [*Interleaved; MS. notes &c.*] s8°. C. 1770
Flora rustica, figures of plants useful or injurious in husbandry, drawn & engr. by F. P. Nodder, w. descr. &c. by T. M. 4v. [v2–4 *wanting*]. 8°. 1792–94
see ROUSSEAU (J. J.) Letters on the elem. of botany; tr., w. notes & 24 letters by T. M., 2nd ed., 1787; 38 plates w. explan. &c., 1788.
Martyr (Peter). Tractatio de sacramento Eucharistiæ, habita in celeb. univ. Oxon. Ad hec Disput. de eodē Eucharistiae sacram. habita a. 1549 [*w. sep. tp. & pagin.*] s4°. Londini. [1549]
see BRENTZ (J.) De majestate J. C. & de vera praesentia &c., resp. P. Martyri, 1562.
„ SMITH (R.) Diatriba de hominis justific. adv. P. M., 1551.
***Martyrdom (The)** of an Empress, 2nd ed., 1899, *see* CUNLIFFE-OWEN (*lady* M.)
Märtyrerakten, *see* PREMERSTEIN (A. v.) Zu d. sog. alexandrin. Märtyrerakten, 1923.
Martyrologium.
*M. Romanum. Ad novam kalendarii rationem &c. restitutum. Gregorii xiii jussu ed. Acc. notationes atque Tract. de Martyrologio Rom. auctore Cæsare Baronio. 8°. Venetiis. 1597
M. Romanum Gregorii XIII jussu ed. Urbani VIII & Clementis X auctor. recogn. & a Benedicto XIV auctum, & castig. [*2 pagin.*] s4°. Coloniae Agripp. 1751
„ „ .... 8°. Antverpiae. 1771
M. Romanum Gregorii XIII jussu ed. &c. a. 1749 Benedicti XIV labore auctum &c. ed. 6. Taurin. s8°. Taurini. 1911
Vetustius occid. eccl. m. D. Hieronymo a Cassiodoro, Beda &c. tributum, nuncupandum Romanum. 4°. Lucae. 1668
Martyrology [MARTYROLOGE]. The Roman martyrologe set forth by the comm. of Gregory XIII &c. Tr. by G. K[eynes]. 2nd ed. [*Ed. by* W. B.] s8°. S. Omers. 1667

Martyrs. Some authentic acts of the early m.; tr., 1927, *see* OWEN (E. C. E.)
Marucchi (Orazio). Guida arch. dell' ant. Preneste. 8°. 1885
Marutas, *Saint, bp. of Tagrit* [MARUTHAS]. Acta Sanct. martyrum orient. & occid. in 2 partes distrib. Acc. Acta S. Simeonis Stylitae S. E. Assemanus recensuit &c. [*Syr. & Lat.*] 2p. fol. Romae. 1748
Marvá (*General* **José).** Le génie à Mélilla. 8°. Madrid. 1909
The engineer troops in the campaign of Melilla (1909). Tr. by G. M. W. Macdonogh. [*From* R. E. Profess. papers, s4, v2. P2704]. la8°. Chatham. 1910
Marvaud (Angel). Le territoire de la Sarre, s. évol. écon. & soc. s8°. [1924]
Marvell (Andrew).
A. M., 1621–78. Tercent. tributes by A. Birrell, H. H. Henson, E. Gosse *& others.* Ed. W. H. Bagguley. s8°. 1922
*Flagellum parliamentarium: sarcastic notices of Members of Parl, 1661–78, *see* AUNGERVYLE Soc. Reprints, s1, 1881.
Misc. poems. [*repr. of 1681 ed.*] la8°. 1923
Poems & letters. Ed. H. M. Margoliouth. 2v. 8°. O. 1927
*The Rehearsal transpros'd: animadv. upon a book [by S. Parker] intitd "A preface &c." s8°. 1672
A short hist. essay t. gen. councils, synods, &c. 3rd ed. s8°. 1703
see ELIOT (T. S.) Homage to Dryden: 3 essays [A. M. &c.], 1924.
Marvin (Charles). Eye-witnesses' acc. of the Campaign agst. the Akhâl-Tekke Turcománs. Alphab. index, by W. E. Gowan. 8°. Calcutta. 1883
The Russian advance towards India. Alphab. index, by W. E. Gowan. [*b. w. h.* Russ. adv., 1882]. 8°. Lahore. 1883
Marvin (Dwight Edwards).
The antiquity of proverbs. s8°. 1922
Marvin (Francis Sydney).
England & the world: essays [by W. J. Perry, R. G. Collingwood &c.] arr. & ed. by F. S. M. 8°. 1925
The evolution of world-peace. Essays arranged & ed. by F. S. M. 8°. O. 1921
India & the West. 8°. 1927
The living past: a sketch of Western progress. 4th ed. s8°. O. 1920
The living past: a sketch of Western progress. 4th ed. [repr.] s8°. O. 1923
Science & civiliz. Essays [*by var. a.*] arr. & ed. by F. S. M. 8°. 1923
Western races & the world. Essays [*by var. wr.*] arr. & ed. by F. S. M. 8°. 1922
see STAWELL (F. M.) & F. S. M. Making of the Western mind, 1923.
Marvin (Walter Taylor).
Introd. to systematic philosophy. 8°. N.Y. 1903
Marvy (Louis), *see* THACKERAY (W. M.) Landscape painters of Eng.; engr. by L. M., 1850.
Marwick (*Sir* **James David).** Charters &c. rel. to Glasgow, 1175–1707; ed. M., 2v, 1894–1906, *see* GLASGOW.
Marwitz (Alexander von der), *see* VARNHAGEN VON ENSE (*Frau* R. A. F.) Rahel u. A. v. d. M. in ihr. Briefen (1809–1813), 1925.
Marx (Carl).
Zur Kritik d. polit. Ökonomie. Hrsg. K. Kautsky. 9e A. s8°. St. 1922
TRANSLATIONS.
The civil war in France. Prec. by 2 manifestoes of the International [1870]. Hist. intr. by R. W. Postgate. [repr.] 8°. 1921
The eighteenth Brumaire of Louis Bonaparte. Tr. E. & C. Paul. s8°. 1926
REFERENCES.
see BEER (M.) Life & teaching of K. M.; tr., 1921.
„ CUNOW (H.) Die M. Gesch.- Gesells.- u. Staatstheorie &c., 2B, 1920–21.
„ DESLINIÈRES (L.) Délivrons-nous du Marxisme, 1923.
„ EASTMAN (M.) M., Lenin & the sci. of revolution, 1926.
„ GUILLAUME (J.) K. M. Pangermaniste, 1915.
„ HYNDMAN (H. M.) Economics of socialism; M. made easy, 1922.
„ JOSEPH (H. W. B.) Labour theory of value of K. M., 1923.
„ LASKI (H. J.) Karl Marx, an essay, 1921.
REFERENCES [*continued*].
see LASSALLE (F. J. G.) Nachgelassene Briefe &c., B3, zw. L. u. M. &c., 1922.
„ LINDSAY (A. D.) K. M.'s Capital: intr. essay, 1925.
„ MACDONALD (*Rt. Hon.* J. A. M.) K. M. & the present unrest, 1922.
„ MAUTNER (W.) Der Bolschewismus; Unters. s. Verhältnisses z. Marxismus, 1920.
„ MITRANY (D.) M. v. the peasant, 1927.
„ MÖGLICH (A.) Sinn d. Sozialismus; M. Gedankenwelt, 1920.
„ NICHOLSON (J. S.) Revival of Marxism, 1920.
„ RYAZANOV (T.), *ed.* K. M., man, thinker & revolutionist: symposium, 1927.
„ SALTER (F. R.) K. M. & mod. socialism, 1921.
„ SCOTT (J. W.) C. M. on value, 1920.
„ SOREL (G.) Décomposition du Marxisme, 1910.
„ WILLIAM (M.) Social interp. of hist.: refut. of M. econ. interp., 1922.

Marx (Carl) & F. Engels. Aus d. liter. Nachlass K. M. u. F. E., 1841–50. Hrsg. v. F. Mehring. 3e A. 3B. 8°. St. 1920
K. M. u. F. E. ueb. d. Diktatur d. Proletariats &c. [Nachwort v. E. Drahn. P2457]. 8°. 1920
Marx (Claude Roger-), *see* Roger-Marx (C.)
Marx (Henry). G. de Porto-Riche. s8°. 1924
Un homme en marche: pièce. [2e éd.] s8°. 1923
Marx (Magdeleine). Woman. Intr. by H. Barbusse. Tr. A. S. Seltzer. s8°. [1921]
***Mary** Hamilton. By a niece of the late Miss Austen. [Pref. *by* H. V. M.] s8°. 1927
Mary, *duchess of Burgundy, consort of Maximilian I, archduke of Austria, aft. emp. of Germany, see* Maximilian I, *emp. of Germany.* Deffense de Mgnr. le Duc & Mme. la Dsse. d'Austriche &c. (1477 ou 78), facs. &c., 1923.
Mary [*Gonzaga*], *queen consort of Vladislaus IV, king of Poland, see* Le Laboureur (J.) Hist. &c. du voyage de la royne de Pologne &c., 1648.
Mary II, *queen of Gt. Brit. & Ireland.* Letters of 2 queens. [Mary II & Anne. Ed.] by Hon. B. Bathurst. 8°. [1924]
see Cambridge. Lacrymæ Cantab. in obitum M., 169 4/5.
Mary, *queen consort of George V, king of Gt. Brit. & Ireland, see* Woodward (K.) Queen M., 1927.
Mary, *of Guise, see* Mary, *of Lorraine, q. c. of James V of Scotland.*
Mary, *of Lorraine, queen consort of James V of Scotland* [Mary, *of Guise*]. Foreign corr. with M. de L. f. the Balcarres papers, 1537–[57]. Ed. M. Wood. [Scot. Hist. Soc., s3, v4, 7]. 2v. 8°. E. 1923–25
Scot. corr. of M. of L., 1542–60. Ed. A. I. Cameron. [Scot. Hist. Soc., s3, v10]. 8°. E. 1927
Mary [*de' Medici*], *queen consort of Henry IV, king of France* [Marie de Médicis], *see* Jorissen (Th.) Hist. Karakters, 1, Richelieu en M. de M., 1912.
Mary [*of Modena*], *queen consort of James II, k. of Gt. Brit.*
see Alberti (G.) Dispacci, 1673, rel. al matrim. di M. B. E. D'Este con G. Stuart, 1890.
„ Sandford (F.) Hist. of the coron. of J. II & Q. M., 1687.
Mary, *of Nimmegen.* A marvelous hist. of Mary of N. Tr. f. Middle Dutch by H. M. Ayres, w. intr. by A. J. Barnouw. s8°. The Hague. [1923]
Mary, *queen of Scots* [M. Stuart].
Mary Q. of S. & the Babington plot; ed. f. orig. docs. by J. H. Pollen. [Scot. Hist. Soc., s3, v3]. 8°. E. 1922
Trial of M., Q. of S. Ed. A. F. Steuart. 8°. E. [1923]
see Ascoli (G.) La Gr. Bret. dev. l'opinion fr., App., Poèmes publ. à l'occas. de la mort de M., 1927.
„ Barnestapolius (O.) Maria Stuarta &c., 1588.
„ Bjørnson (B.) M. S. i Skotland, 4e udg., 1879; 5e udg., 1892; 6e udg., 1902.
„ Drinkwater (J.) M. S.: play, 1921; rev. ed., 1922.
„ Gordon (J. W.) M., Q. of S. & h. execution, 1927.
„ Lodge (E.) Illust. of Brit. hist. &c., corr. of Eliz. &c. w. G., 6th earl of Shrewsbury, M. in custody, 3v, 1791.
„ Mahon (*Maj.-Gen.* R. H.) The indictment of M., w. comments on the authorship &c., 1923.
„ —— M. Q. of Scots: Lennox narr. &c., 1924.
„ Meyer-Cohn (M.) G. Buchanan als Publizist &c. M. S., 1913.
„ Mumby (F. A.) Fall of M. S., 1921.
„ Rait (R. S.) & A. I. Cameron, *edd.* King James's secret: negot. rel. to execut. of M., 1927.
„ Saint John (J.) M. q. of S., a tragedy, 1811.
„ Scotus (R.) Summarium rationum quibus Elizabethae persuaserunt occidendam esse M. S. &c., 1588.
„ Vondel (J. van den). Werken, d14, Maria Stuart (play, 1646), *n.d.*
„ Walker (A.) *M. Q. of Scots: a narr. & defence, 1889.
Mary, *the Virgin.*
Altengl. Marienlegenden aus MS. Vernon; hrsg. C. Horstmann, *see* Archiv f. d. St. d. neu. Spr., B56, 1876.
Le glorie di M. e di S. Giuseppe. Dedicato a Maria Teresa dai P. P. della Congr. Mechit. di S. Antonio. [*in Arm.*] sm. fol. Trieste, *Stamp. Mechit.* 1780
Homélies mariales byzantines: textes grecs éd. & tr. en Lat. par M. Jugie:
[1], Abraham d'Ephèse—Abbé Théognoste—S. Euthyme—M. Psellos—Néophyte le reclus—Manuel II Paléologue—G. Scholarios. [2], Théodote d'Ancyre—Chrysippe, prêtre de Jérusalem — S. Jean, archevêque de Thessalonique — S. Euthyme, patr. de Constantinople — Nicolas Cabasilas — Georges Scholarios, *see* Graffin (R.) & F. Nau. Patr. orient, t16, 19, 1922–26.
*In die assumptionis M. gloriosę genitricis Dei Marię. [*A sermon in MS.*] [P2539]. s4°. *n.p. n.d.* [c. 1522]
*Liber de miraculis Sanctae Mariae. Publ. at Vienna, 1731, by B. Pez [*ascr. to* Potho]. Repr., w. intr., notes &c. by T. F. Crane. [Cornell Univ. St. in Romance Lang. &c., v1]. 8°. Ithaca. 1925
Poem on the Assumption; ed. J. P. Strachey, *see* Anglo-Norman. Camb. A.-N. texts, 1924.
see Agreda (M. de). La Cité mystique de Dieu: vie de M., 2e éd, 6t, 1862.
„ —— Vie divine de M., 1884.
„ Benedict XIV, *pope.* De festis Jesu Christi & B.M.V., 1859.
„ Berceo (G. de). Los milagros de N. Señora, 1, 1926.
„ Berlan (F.) Intr. d. stampa in Milano a prop. d. Miraculi de la V.M., 1469, 1884.
„ Bernegger (M.) Hypobolimaea M. camera, seu Idolum Lauretanum &c., 1619.
„ Billuart (C. R.) Tract. de mysteriis Chr. & B. Virginis, 1860.
„ Bordonio (H.) Devoto libro chiamato Recitoria Virginis, 1529.
„ Budge (*Sir* E. A. T. W.) 110 miracles of M.; tr. f. Ethiopic MSS. in B.M. &c., 1923.
„ —— Legends of M. &c.; tr. f. Ethiopic MSS. by B., 1922.
„ Clagett (W.) Disc. conc. worship of B.V., 1686.
„ Dante Alighieri. Laude ined. in onore di Nostra Donna, 1854.
„ Goldschmidt (A.) Got. Madonnenstatuten in Deut., 1923.
„ Grohmann (A.), *ed.* Æthiop. Marienhymnen, 1919.
„ Hamon (A. J. M.) *Notre-Dame de France, 7v, 1861–66.
„ Hickes (G.) Speculum B.V., 1686.
„ Horicke (Petrus van den). B. virgo Maria a peccato orig. &c. immunis, 1672.
„ Loreto. Trãslatio miraculosa beate M. virginis de L., *n.d.* [c. 1500].
„ Maynard (M. U.) La sainte Vierge, 2e ed., 1877.
„ Millon (A.) Grandes Madones bretonnes, 1922.
„ Officia. Officium B.M. virg. &c., 1797.
„ Quatrelles, *ps.* Légende de la Vierge de Münster, 1881.
„ Ryckel (J. G. A.) Hodoeporicon Marianum, 1634.
„ Wernher, *Swiss poet.* Das Marienleben d. Schweizers W. [Bearbtg. d. Vita B.M. et Salvatoris rhythmica]; hrsg. v. M. Päpke &c., 1920.
„ Widenfeldt (A.) *Wholesome advices f. the B.V.; tr., 1687.
„ York. Horae Eboracenses: Prymer or Hours of the B.V. &c., 1920.
Mary Christine, *archduchess of Austria.* Briefe an Leopold II &c., *see* Fontes rerum Austriac., B48i, 1896.
Mary Jane Battista, *consort of Charles Emm. II, duke of Savoy, see* Contessa (C.) Progetti econ. d. 2a Madama Reale di Sav. fond. sopra un contratto nuziale, 1678–82, 1915.
Mary Josepha Amelia, *q. c. of Ferdinand VII, k. of Spain, see* Maria Jesefa Amalia.
Mary Louisa [de Bourbon], *q. consort of Louis, k. of Etruria, see* Villa-Urrutia (W. R., *marq.* de). La reina de Etruria, 1923.
Mary Louisa, *queen consort of Philip V, k. of Spain, see* Rossi (G.), *of Ventimiglia.* M. L. in Nizza, nel sett., 1701, 1895.
Mary Magdalene.
see Fisher (*card.* J.) Confut. secundae disceptat. per J. Fabrum Stapulensem habitę in qua 3 fæminis partiri molitur quae consuetudo unicę tribuit Magdalenae, 1519.
„ Horstmann (C.) Nachtr. zu d. Legenden, p2, 1882.
„ Saelden Hort (Der): alemann. Gedicht v. Leben Jesu, Johannes d. Täufers u. d. Magdalena; hrsg. H. Adrian, 1927.
„ Southwell (R.) M. M.'s funerall teares (1634), 1823.
Maryland Historical Society, *see* Carroll (C.) Journal, dur. visit to Canada in 1776, 1876.
Marylebone. Registers of marriages of St. Mary le Bone, Middlesex, 1775–1812; ed. W. B. Bannerman. [Harleian Soc. Reg., 51–57]. p3–9. la8°. 1921–27
Public Library.
Cat. & guide to books in Children's Dept. 8°. 1927
Marzio (Cornelio di). Il Fascismo all' estero. s8°. Milano. 1923
Mas (Emile). La Champmeslé. 8°. 1927
Masaniello, *1623–47* [†Aniello (Tommaso), *of Amalfi, called M.*], *see* Capasso (B.) La casa e la famiglia di M., 1919.
Masařik (Josef). Böhm. Schulgramm. 3e A. 8°. Prag. 1883
Masaryk (Tomáš Garrigue), *president of the Czechoslovak Republic.* At the eleventh hour: milit. situation. [Pref. by R. M. Burrows & R. W. Seton-Watson]. [P2518]. la8°. 1916
The making of a state: mem. &c., 1914–18. Eng. version &c. w. intr. by H. W. Steed. la8°. [1927]
Das neue Europa. Autor. Übertr. a. d. Tschech. v. E. Saudek. 8°. 1922
О большевизмѣ. Переводъ подъ редак. Б. Соколова. [P2569]. s8°. Прага. 1921

Masaryk (Tomáš Garrigue) [*continued*].
Pres. M. in Paris, Brussels & London, Oct. 1923. [Speeches, w. replies &c.] 4°. Prague. 1924
Die Welt-Revolution. Erinnerungen &c., 1914–18. [Übertr. v. C. Hoffmann]. 8°. 1925
see HERBEN (JAN). T. G. M., 1919.
„ ZIMKA (C.) T. M., wie man Präsident wird, 1923.
Mascall (Edward James).
The statement of the duties of customs & excise. 8°. 1809
Mascardi (Mario). Vita di Fr. Baracca. s8°. Genova. 1925
Mascaregnas (Fernand Martinz). Tractatus de auxiliis divinae gratiae ad actus supernat. fol. Lisibone. 1604
Mascarenhas (Joseph de), *duke de Aveiro, see* JOSEPH I, *k. of Port.* Jugement du Conseil Souverain, procès au sujet de l'attentat commis sur sa personne [*by* J. M. &c.], 1761.
Mascaró (F. Condeminas), *see* CONDEMINAS MASCARÓ (F.)
Mascovius (Georgius). Disput. de majestate divina Christi hominis. Præs. M. Hafenreffer. [P2612]. s4°. Tubingae. 1607
***Masculine** cross; hist. of anc. & mod. crosses. Also acc. of phallic faiths &c. s8°. *p.p.* 1904
Masefield (John).
Coll. poems. s8°. 1923
Enslaved & o. poems. s8°. 1920
Esther. Tragedy. Adapted & tr. f. French of J. Racine. s8°. 1922
The everlasting mercy. s8°. 1921
Gallipoli. [n. ed.] 8°. [1924]
*J. M. Synge: a few personal recoll. w. biogr. notes. [*repr.*] s8°. Letchworth. 1916
King Cole. With drawings by J. Masefield. *limited ed.* 8°. 1921
„ „ ....s8°. [1923]
A king's daughter. Tragedy in verse. s8°. [1923]
Melloney Holtspur. [Play]. s8°. 1922
The midnight folk. s8°. [1927]
Odtaa. Novel. s8°. [1926]
Pompey the Great, *see* PLAYS of to-day, v2, 1925.
Right Royal. s8°. 1920
Salt-water ballads. [7th ed.] s8°. 1920
„ „ [8th ed.] s8°. 1921
Sard Harker. s8°. [1924]
„ „ [n. impr.] s8°. [1924]
Sel. poems. s8°. 1922
Shakespeare & spiritual life. Romanes lect., 1924. 8°. O. 1924
The taking of Helen. 8°. 1923
The trial of Jesus. [A play]. s8°. [1925]
Tristan & Isolt. Play in verse. 8°. [1927]
With the living voice. Address, Scot. Assoc. for the Speaking of Verse. 8°. C. [1925]
see BIGGANE (C.) J. M.: study, 1924.
„ RACINE (J.) Berenice; tr. J. M., 1922.
„ WHITEHOUSE (J. H.), *ed.* Ruskin the prophet &c.; by J. M. &c., 1920.
„ WILLIAMS (I. A.) Bibliographies of mod. a., No. 2, J. M., 1921.
Masefield (Muriel), *wife of Charles Masefield.* Story of Fanny Burney. Intr. to diary &c. of Mme. d'Arblay. 8°. C. 1927
Masenius (Jacobus), *Jesuit, see* CARPZOV (S. B.) Examen novae praxeos &c., à J. M. propos., 1677.
Maseras (Alfons). A la deriva. 8°. Barcelona. 1921
Maseres (Francis). Tracts on the resol. of affected algebraic equations by Halley's, Raphson's & Newton's methods. s8°. 1800
Mashafa Sĕnkĕsâr, *see* SYNAXARIUM. Bk. of the saints of the Ethiopian Ch.; tr. of the Ethiopic S. [M. S.] by Sir E. A. W. Budge, 4v, 1928.
Mashtotz. Ritual of Armenian Church, *var. ed., see* ARMENIAN.
Masini (Antonio). Bologna perlustrata. 3ª impr. accresc. &c. 3p [*in 1v*]. 8°. Bologna. 1666
Masius (Andreas). Syrorum peculium *&* Gramm. linguae Syr., *see* BIBLE. Biblia sacra, t6, 1572.
Maskell (Alfred), *see* BRASSEY (T. B., *e.*) *Cat. of works of art &c. at Normanhurst Court, Battle, prop. of Lord B., 1878–81.
Maskell (William). The anc. liturgy of the Church of Eng. acc. to uses of Sarum, Bangor, York, Hereford, & the Roman lit. in par. columns, w. notes &c. 2nd ed. 8°. 1846
Maskelyne (Anthony Story), *see* TALLOW CHANDLERS. Records of Co. of T.C., London; [coll. & arr. by A. S. M. &c.], 1897.
Maslov (Petr Pavlovich) [MASSLOV].
Аграрный вопросъ въ Россіи. 3е изд. 8°. С.–П. 1906
see MARTOV (L.), P. M. &c., *edd.* Обществ. движеніе въ Россіи, 2г, 1909–10.
Maslov (Sergei S.)
Россія послѣ 4 лѣтъ революціи. [2t]. s8°. Парижъ. 1922
Russia after 4 yrs. of revol. Tr. A. G. Paschkoff. 8°. 1923
La Russie après 4 ans de révol. Tr. A. V. Eisenstadt. 8°. 1922
Masom (William Frederick). Glossary of sel. words & phrases f. the Court Leet records, 1550–1624 &c., *see* SOUTHAMPTON. C. L. records, Suppl., 1908.
see HAYES (B. J.) & W. F. M. Tutorial Lat. grammar, 10th impr., 1912.

Mason (Alfred Edward Woodley).
The house of the arrow. s8°. [1924]
No other tiger. [repr.] s8°. [1927]
The Royal Exchange. Note on occas. of bicent. of the R.E. Assurance. s8°. 1920
Running Water. s8°. [1925]
The summons. s8°. [1920]
The winding stair. s8°. [1923]
Mason (Arthur James). A guide to the anc. glass in Canterbury Cathedral. [P1786]. 8°. Canterbury. 1925
What became of the bones of St. Thomas? s8°. C. 1920
Mason (Augustus H.)
W. S. Landor, poète lyrique. 8°. 1924
Mason (Charles Welsh) [MASON (CHARLES HENRY ALAN WELSH)]. Chinese confessions. 8°. 1924
Mason (Daniel Gregory). Contemp. composers. s8°. N.Y. 1918
The romantic composers. s8°. N.Y. 1926
Mason (Francis), *archdeacon of Norfolk.* The authority of the Church in making canons & constit. conc. things indifferent. Sermon, 1605. [*b. w.* Bradford (S.) Credibility &c., 1700]. s4°. 1707
Of the consecration of the bishops in the Ch. of England: with their succession, jurisdiction &c. sm. fol. 1613
Mason (James). Fra Angelico. 8°. [1907]
Mason (John), *Nonconformist minister.*
Self-knowledge. 16th ed. pref. mem. of the a. s8°. 1809
Mason (John), *rector of Water-Stratford.* *Spiritual songs. With Song of Songs. In Eng. verse. 2nd ed. corr., w. poem on Dives & Lazarus. [*w. sep. tp. & pagin.*] s8°. 1685
Spiritual songs & Penitential cries by T. Shepherd. s8°. 1859
Mason (John Mitchell). A plea for catholick communion. 2nd ed. w. corr. 8°. N.Y. 1816
Mason (Michael H.) The Arctic forests. 8°. 1924
Mason (N.), *see* ANGELUS A S. FRANCISCO.
Mason (Rupert), *see* SHERINGHAM (G.) & R. B. MORRISON. Robes of Thespis; ed. for R. M. by G. S. &c., 1928.
Mason (William), *poet* [*ps.* MALCOLM MACGREGOR]. Satirical poems publ. anon. by W. M., w. notes by H. Walpole (1779). Ed., w. exposé of the mystification &c. by P. Toynbee. la8°. O. 1926
Mason (William Albert).
A hist. of the art of writing. 8°. N.Y. 1920
Mason (William Hayley). Goodwood: w. cat. of pictures in gallery of Duke of Richmond, rec. of G. races &c. 8°. 1839
Mason (William Shaw). Descr. & arch. sketch of the Grace-Mausoleum in the Queen's Co. taken f. the statist. acc. of Ireland. [*Ed. S. Grace. extra-illust.*] 8°. [*p.p.*] D., *Faulkner Press.* 1819
Survey of Tullaroan, or Grace's Parish in the Co. of Kilkenny; taken f. the statist. acc. of Ireland. [*Ed. S. Grace. extra-illust.*] 8°. [*p.p.*] D., *Faulkner Press.* 1819
Masonic. M. Calendar for the Punjab district for 1893, 1894, 1895–96. Ed. J. H. Leslie. s8°. Bombay. 1893–96
M. roll of honour: names of brethren who fell dur. the Gt. War, 1914–18, 1921, *see* FREEMASONS.
Masonic Year Book, 1921, 1922, 1926–1928. s8°. 1921–28
Maspero (*Sir* Gaston) [MASPERO (GASTON CAMILLE CHARLES)], *see* BIBLIOTHÈQUE ÉGYPTOLOGIQUE; publ. sous la dir. de M., t25, 1914.
„ CAIRO. Guide to C. Museum, by G. M., 1908.
„ CORDIER (H.) Bibliog. des œuvres de G. M., 1922.
„ DAVIS (T. M.) Excavations: Bibân el Molûk; Notes on Iouiya & Touiyou, by G. M., 1907.
„ SERVICE DES ANTIQ. DE L'ÉGYPTE. Temples immergés: doc. [ed. G. M. &c.], t1, 1920.
Maspero (Henri).
La Chine antique. [Hist. du monde, t4]. 8°. 1927
Maspero (Jean) [MASPERO (JACQUES JEAN GASTON)]. Hist. des patriarches d'Alexandrie, 518–616. Revu & publ. par A. Fortescue & G. Wiet. [H. E., 237]. 8°. 1923
Papyrus grecs d'époque byzantine. [Cat. gén. des antiqs. égypt. du Musée du Caire. Service des Ant. de l'Eg.] 3t. fol. Le Caire. 1911–16
—— **& G. Wiet.** Matériaux p. s. à la géogr. de l'Egypte, s1, *see* INSTITUT FRANÇ. D'ARCH. OR. DU CAIRE. Mém., t36, 1919.
Masquelez (Alfred Emile Alexis Eugène). Etude sur la castramétation des Romains & sur leurs instit. milit. 8°. 1864
***Mass** des unmassgebl. Bedenckens &c., 1692, *see* PIETISTS.
Massa (Giovanni Andrea). *La Sicilia in prospettiva. Da un relig. d. Comp. di Giesú. 2p [p2 *wanting*]. s4°. Palermo. 1709

Massa (Isaac). Beschryvinghe van der Samoyeden Landt. [*Tr. I. M.*], [1612/13]; uitg. door S. P. L'Honoré Naber, 1924, *see* GERRITSZOON (H.)
Hist. des guerres de la Moscovie (1601–10). [*Dutch & Fr.*] Publ., avec d'autres opusc. sur la Russie & des annot., par le Pr. M. Obolensky & A. van der Linde. [*Dutch & Fr.*] 2t [*in* 1v]. 8°. Brux. 1866
The opusc. are: Massa's Descr. regionum Siberiæ, Samojediæ, Tingoësiæ & itinerum e Moscovia &c. versus eo ducentium &c., *&* La légende de Demetrius; tr. nouv. l'an 1606, *w. sep. tp.*
—— **& Elias Herkman.** Сказанія М. и Г. о смутномъ времени въ Россіи. Изд. Археограф. Комм. Приложеніе (1) Портретъ И. Массы (1635), (2) Планъ Москвы (1606), (3) Планъ двора Лжедимитрія I. fol. [1874]
Massa (Maria Teresa Cybo, *dssa.* **di),** *see* SFORZA (G.) Il pr. Eugenio Francesco di Savoia e il suo fidanz. con M. T. Cybo, dssa. di M., 1909.
Massa (Simon). Chron. Fuchsio-Lupino-Oltardinum sive annales Hungarici & Transsilvanici, quibus ex lucubrationibus A. Gunesch &c. quaedam adj. J. Ziegler. Ed. J. Trausch. 2p *in* 1v. s4°. Coronae. 1847–48
Massa (Teodoro). Le consuetudini d. città di Bari. la8°. Bari. 1903
Massabuau (Joseph). L'état contre la nation. 8°. 1922
Massachusetts. Journals of House of Representatives of M., 1715–[24]. [Mass. Hist. Soc.] [v1–5]. la8°. [Camb., Mass.] 1919–24
Massachusetts Historical Society.
Collections. v75, 76. la8°. Boston. 1922–23
Broadsides, ballads &c. printed in Massachusetts, 1639–1800. [75.]
see STORER (M.) Numismatics of Massachusetts, 1923. [76.]
Proceedings. v52–55 (Oct. 1918–June 1922). la8°. Boston. 1919–23
A sh. account of the M.H.S. Orig. prep. by C. C. Smith, w. Act of Incorporation, list of officers & members &c., 1791–1918. 8°. Boston. 1918
see ADAMS (H.) Mont-Saint-Michel &c., 1919.
„ COOLIDGE (T. J.) T. J. C., 1831–1920: an autobiog., 1923.
„ LYMAN (*Col.* T.) Meade's headquarters, 1863–65: letters; sel. &c. G. R. Agassiz, 1922.
„ MASSACHUSETTS. Journals of House of Representatives of M., 1715–24, v1–5, 1919–24.
„ PRESCOTT (W. H.) Corr., 1833–47; transcr. &c. R. Wolcott, 1925.
„ WINTHROP PAPERS, v1, 1498–1628, 1925.
Massam (J. A.), *District Commissioner, Kenya.*
Cliff-dwellers of Kenya. 8°. 1927
Massard (Emile) & G. Dallier. Pierre Coignard ou Le Forçat-Colonel. Roman vécu s. la Restauration. 8°. *n.d.*
Massari (Giuseppe), *1821–84, see* GIOBERTI (V.) & G. M. G.-M., carteggio, 1838–52; pubbl. &c. G. Balsamo-Crivelli, 1920.
Massé (Gertrude C. E.) Bibliog. of 1st editions of bks. illust. by W. Crane. Pref. by H. Sumner. 8°. 1923
Massé (Henri Jean Louis Joseph).
The pewter collector. s8°. 1921
—— **& C. K. Scott.** Bk. of old carols [*w. music*]. Ed. M. & S. v1. la8°. 1910
Massee (George). Brit. fungi, w. chap. on lichens. 8°. [1911]
Masséna (*le maréchal* **André),** *duc de Rivoli, prince D'Essling.*
see AMIC (A.) Hist. de M., 1864.
„ CAMPREDON (*Gén.* J. D. M. DE). Doc. milit.: défense du Var &c.: lettres des Gén. M. &c.: annot. &c. C. Auriol, 1889.
„ GACHOT (E.) Hist. milit. de M.: la campagne d'Helvétie, 1799, 1904.
Massenet (Jules Émile Frédéric), *see* SCHNEIDER (L.) M. (1842–1912), 1926.
Masse-priests. *The supplication of certaine M.-p., 1604, *see* SUPPLICATION.
Massèra (Aldo Francesco). Sonetti, burleschi e realistici, dei primi due secoli. A cura di A. F. M. [Scr. d'It., 88, 89]. 2v. 8°. Bari. 1920
Nuôvi sonetti di Cecco Angiolieri, *see* MONACI (E.) Studj romanzi, v13, 1917.
Masseron (Alexandre). Assise. la8°. 1926
Masses (Federico Beltran), *see* BELTRAN MASSES (F.)
Massey (Charles Carleton). Thoughts of a mod. mystic. Sel. f. wr. of C. C. M. Ed. W. F. Barrett. 8°. 1909
Massey (*Sir* **Edward),** *see* HYETT (*Sir* F. A.) Notes on portraits of Sir E. M., 1923.
Massey (William Thomas). Allenby's final triumph. 8°. 1920
Massi (Ercole). Descr. compend. dei musei dell' ant. scultura greca e rom. nel Palazzo Vaticano &c. 3a ed., ampl. e corr. s8°. 1888
Massi (Francesco). Poesie ital. e lat. 8°. 1843
Massie (James William). Liberty of conscience &c. s8°. 1847
Massie (Joseph). Governing causes of the natural rate of interest, 1750. [J. H. Univ. Repr. of econ. tracts. P2619]. 8°. [Baltimore. 1912]
Massignon (Louis). Essai sur les orig. du lexique technique de la mystique Musulmane. [Textes hallagiens, *w. sep. pagin.*] la8°. 1922
La passion d'al Hallaj, martyr mystique de l'Islam, exécuté à Bagdad le 26 mars 922. 2t. la8°. 1922
Massillon (Jean Baptiste), *bp. of Clermont.* Sermons & morceaux choisis. Préc. de s. éloge. s8°. 1848
Sermons. 2v. 8°. [1889–90]
Massimo (Camillo Vittorio), *prince d'Arsoli.* Notizie istor. d. Villa Massimo alle Terme Diocleziane, con un' app. di doc. 4°. Roma. 1836
Massinger (Philip).
Dramatic works of M. & Ford. Intr. by H. Coleridge. [Ford's works *have sep. pagin.*] n. ed. la8°. [1848]
A new way to pay old debts. [Dolby's Brit. theatre]. s8°. 1824
„ „ ed. w. crit. essay &c., by B. Matthews, *see* GAYLEY (C. M.) Repres. Eng. comedies, v3, 1914.
„ „ *see* INCHBALD (*Mrs.* E.) Brit. theatre, v6, 1808.
A new way to pay old debts. Ed. A. H. Cruickshank. 8°. O. 1926
see CHELLI (M.) Le drame de M., 1923.
„ —— Et. sur la collab. de M. avec Fletcher & s. groupe, 1926.
„ CRUICKSHANK (A. H.) M. & 'The two noble kinsmen,' 1922.
„ —— P. M., 1920.
Massingham (Harold John). *Dogs, birds & others. Nat. hist. letters f. Spectator, chosen w. intr. &c. by H. J. Massingham, pref. by J. St. L. Strachey. 8°. [1921]
Downland man. Intr. by G. E. Smith. 8°. [1926]
In praise of England. 8°. [1924]
Poems about birds: M. Ages to pres. day. Chosen & ed., w. intr. &c. by H. J. M. Pref. J. C. Squire. 8°. [1922]
Some birds of the countryside. 8°. [1921]
Massingham (Henry William). H. W. M.: sel. f. writings. Ed. w. pref. &c. by H. J. Massingham, w. intr. essays by J. L. Hammond &c. 8°. [1925]
Massis (Henri) [*ps.* AGATHON].
Défense de l'Occident. s8°. [1927]
La vie d'Ernest Psichari. s8°. [1916]
Masslov (Peter), *see* MASLOV (P. P.)
Masson (Frédéric). Revue d'Ombres. Près de la Princesse Caroline, 1803–5—Dern. jours de Murat, mai–oct. 1815—L'envers d'une conspiration, Grenoble, 1816. 8°. [1921]
La vie & les conspirations du Gén. Malet, 1754–1812. 3e éd. 8°. [1920]
see MARIE LOUISE. Private diaries: intr. & comm. by F. M., 1922.
Masson (Georges Armand). Paul Fort. s8°. [1922]
Masson (Jean Papire).
see RONZY (P.) Bibl. crit. des œuvres impr. & ms. de M., 1924.
„ —— Un humaniste italianisant: P. M., 1924.
Masson (Paul). Marseille pend. la Guerre. [C.E. for Int. Peace]. la8°. [1926]
see BOUCHES-DU-RHÔNE; encyclop. départ. publ. sous la dir. de P. M., 1913–28.
Masson (Phoebe Ann). *Legends of the Dunbars, & o. p. By one of their desc. [*i.e.* P. A. M.] la8°. 1854
*Sir Ninian; a tale of chivalry, & o. p. By the author of "Legends of the Dunbars" [*i.e.* P. A. M.] la8°. *p.f.p.c.* 1860
Massorah [†MASORAH]. The M. compiled f. MSS. alphabet. & lexic. arranged by C. D. Ginsburg. 4v. [1, 2, Text, 3, Suppl., 4 *has t.*: The M. tr. into Eng. w. comm.] fol. 1880–1905
Massow (Wilhelm F. Ph. v.), *see* DEUTSCH. Verfassung (Die) d. Deut. Reichs; mit Sachregister &c. v. W. v. M., 1919.
Massuet (Pierre).
Hist. de la guerre présente. 2t. 8°. Amsterdam. 1736
Massy (Anne L.), *see* BRIT. ANTARCTIC EXPED., 1910–13: Zoology, v2, Mollusca, p2, 3; by M., 1914–20.

Mast (Samuel Ottmar). Changes in shape, color, & pattern in fishes &c. [Fr. Bull. of Bur. of Fisheries, v34, 1914]. [P2702]. la8°. Wash. 1916

Master Mercury, The. No. 11, Sept. 11, 1704. [*b. w.* Post Man, 1704–08]. s4°. 1704

Master Printers annual (The) & typogr. year book, 1925, 1926. Ed. R. A. Austen-Leigh & G. T. Meynell. 8°. [1925–26]

Masterman (Charles F. Gurney). England after war. 8°. [1922]
How England is governed. s8°. [1921]
The new Liberalism. s8°. [1920]

Masterman (George Frederick).
Seven eventful years in Paraguay. 2nd ed. 8°. 1870

Mastermañ (John Howard B.), *M.A.* The dawn of mediæval Europe, 476–918. 4th ed. s8°. [1919]

***Masterpieces** of modern German art, 2v, c. 1885, *see* GERMAN.

Masters (David). How to conquer consumption. Intr. by Sir B. Bruce-Porter. 8°. 1926
The romance of excavation. s8°. [1923]
Wonders of salvage. 8°. [1924]

Masters (Edgar Lee). Domesday book. [Verse]. 8°. 1921

Mastri (Pietro). La via delle stelle. Poema lirico, 1923–27. s8°. Milano. 1928

Mastricht (Petrus von), *the elder.* Theoretico-practica theologia. ed. nov. emend. & auct. Acc. Hist. eccl.: Idea theologiae moralis &c.
2t *in* 1v. [*pagin. contin.*] s4°. Trajecti ad Rhenum. 1715

Mastrofini (*l'abbé*). Discussion sur l'usure, *see* MIGNE (J. P.), *ed.* Theol. cursus, t16, 1859.

Masuccio, *Salernitano* [MASSUCCIO], *see* FISCHER (R.) Quellen zu Romeo u. Julia, 1922.

Mata (Pedro). La catorce. Ni amor ni arte—La condenación del P. Martin—Cuesta abajo. Novelas. s8°. 1923
Corazones sin rumbo. 11ª ed. s8°. 1920
Un grito en la noche. Novela. 30ª ed. s8°. 1921
Una ligereza. s8°. [1925]

Mataratius (Franciscus), *see* MATURANZIO (FRANCESCO).

Matějček (A). Die böhm. Malerei d. 14. Jhdts. s8°. L. 1921

Matějka (Bohumil). Topogr. d. hist. u. Kunstdenkm. im polit. Bez. Laun, *see* BÖHMEN. Top. &c., B2, 1897.
Topogr. d. hist. u. Kunstdenkm. im polit. Bez. Raudnitz, *see* BÖHMEN. Top. &c., B4, 27, 1900–10.

Matejko (Jan), *see* WITKIEWICZ (S.) Matejko, 1911.

Materiali [Матеріалы].
*М. для ист. гоненія студентовъ при Александрѣ II, *n.d.*, *see* ALEXANDER II.
*М. по вопр. о порядкѣ изд. касоющ. финл. законовъ, 1910, *see* FINLAND.
М. по ист. франко-русск. отношении, 1910–14, 1922, *see* RUSSIA. *Anon. works.*
М. по университ. вопросу, 1902–4, *see* STRUVE (P.), *Editor.*
М. по яфетич. Языкознанію, 1910–12, *see* MARR (N. YA.), *ed.*
Сборникъ м. для описанія мѣстностей и племенъ Кавказа, в1–39, 1881–1908, *see* SBORNIK.

Materialien betr. d. Friedensverhandlungen, 1919, T1–7, 9–12 & Beih. 1, 1919–21, *see* VERSAILLES, *Treaty of.*

Matériaux pour l'hist. positive & philos. de l'homme. [FONDÉ] par G. de Mortillet [*cont. by* E. Cartailhac &c.] Année[s] 1864–88. 22v. 8°. 1865–88
cont. as L'Anthropologie, *q.v.*

Mathematical Association, *see* NEWTON (*Sir* I.) I. N.: memorial vol. ed. for M.A. by W. J. Greenstreet, 1927.

Mathematici Graeci minores; ed. J. L. Heiberg, *see* KONG. DAN. VID. SELSK. Hist.-fil. Medd., B13, 1927.

Mather (Cotton), *D.D., F.R.S.*
Essays to do good. n. ed. impr. by G. Burder. s8°. 1807
India Christiana. A discourse, w. instruments rel. to the design of propagating our religion &c. [*Includ. Letter f. J. E. Grundler in Lat. & Eng.*] s8°. Boston, Mass. 1721
The life & death of John Eliot, first preacher to the Indians in America &c. 2nd ed. s8°. 1691
Life of John Eliot, *see* WESLEY (J.) Xtn. lib., v50, 1755.
Student & preacher. Added transl. of M.'s famous Latin preface &c. Rev. &c. by a Lover of the Gospel. s8°. 1789
see FABYAN (F. W.) Ill. cat. of Americana &c., 1920.
„ HOLMES (T. J.) The M. lit., 1927.
„ MATHER (S.) Life of Dr. C. M.; abr. f. acc. by S. M., *n.d.*
„ WENDELL (B.) C. M., the Puritan priest, 1926.

Mather (Frank Jewett). The portraits of Dante comp. w. measurements of h. skull &c. [Princeton Monographs, 10]. la8°. Princeton. 1921

Mather (Increase). De successu Evangelii apud Indos occident. in Nova-Anglia epistola. [*b. w.* Sinica. Noviss. Sinica hist., 1699]. s8°. Ultrajecti. 1699

Mather (Increase) [*continued*].
The order of the Gospel, prof. & pract. by the churches in New England &c. s8°. Boston [*Mass.*], repr. London. 1700
Sermons wherein the Beatitudes are opened & applied in 15 disc. Added: A Sermon conc. the assurance of the love of Christ. 2nd ed. s8°. Boston, repr. Dublin. 1721
see FABYAN (F. W.) Ill. cat. of Americana &c., 1920.
„ HOLMES (T. J.) The M. lit., 1927.
„ MURDOCK (K. B.) I. M., the foremost Amer. Puritan, 1925.
„ —— Portraits of I. M., 1924.

Mather (Loris Emerson). The Rt. Hon. Sir W. Mather, 1838–1920. [*By var. a.* J. F. Baddeley &c.] Ed. L. E. M. la8°. [1925]

Mather (Marshall) [MATHER (JAMES MARSHALL)]. John Ruskin: h. life & teaching. 3rd ed. rev. s8°. 1890

Mather (Richard), *see* HOLMES (T. J.) The M. lit., 1927.

Mather (Samuel), *D.D.* Life of Dr. Cotton Mather. Abridged f. acc. by S. M. s8°. *n.d.*

Mather (*Rt. Hon. Sir* **William).**
Educ. & duty. [Addr. M'ter Univ. P2489]. 8°. M'ter. 1908
Educ. & soc. problems. Bolton Educ. Soc. Addr. [P2485]. s8°. Bolton. 1908
"Getting on." Address. [P2489]. 8°. M'ter. 1908
The relation of educ. to industry. [Brit. Assoc., 1915. P2489]. 8°. M'ter. 1915
see MATHER (L. E.) Sir W. M., 1838–1920, 1925.

Mathesius (Johann), *see* MATTHESIUS (J.)

Matheson (Annie). A plain friend [*i.e.* Eliz. Fry]. Foreword by Lady B. Balfour. s8°. [1920]

Matheson (Cyril). A cat. of publ. of Scot. hist. &c. clubs & societies, & of papers rel. to Scot. hist. issued by H.M.S.O. &c., 1908–27. With a subject-index. 8°. Aberdeen. 1928

Matheson (M. Cécile).
Citizenship: intr. handbook. 3rd & rev. ed. s8°. 1918

Matheson (Percy Ewing). The growth of Rome. s8°. 1922
The life of H. Rashdall, dean of Carlisle. 8°. 1928

Mathew (Arnold Harris). Life & times of Rodrigo Borgia, Pope Alex. VI. 8°. [1924]

Mathew (Frank). An image of Shakespeare. 8°. [1922]

Mathew (Theobald). *Forensic fables. By O. s8°. 1926
*Further forensic fables. By O. s8°. 1928

Mathews (Basil Joseph). The clash of colour. [9th ed.] s8°. 1925

Mathews (Charles James), *1803–78.*
The Dowager. Comedy. [P2582]. s8°. *Lacy. n.d.*

Mathews (Elkin), Ltd. Cat. of bks. by or rel. to Dr. Johnson & h. circle, for sale by E. M. [Comp. by A. W. Evans], w. intr. by J. Drinkwater. 8°. 1925

Mathews (Gregory M.)
The birds of Australia. 12v. fol. 1910–27
„ „ Suppl. No. 1–3, Check list of birds of Australia. 3p. fol. 1920–24
„ „ No. 4, 5, Bibliography of birds of Australia [*b. w.* Check list *above*]. 2p. fol. 1925

Mathews (Lucia Elizabeth), *see* VESTRIS (*Madame*).

Mathews (*Admiral* **Thomas),** *1676–1751.* Acc. of the action in the Mediterranean; added, M. D. Court's letter. [*In reply to Adm. R. Lestock's "Recapitulation"*]. [P2778]. 8°. 1745
The answer & defence of adm. M. to the charge exhib. agst him. [*a. c. in* P608]. s8°. 174
The charge agst. T. M. [P608]. s8°. 174
Remarks on the evidence &c. on his trial. [P608]. s8°. 174
see also AMBROSE (J.); NORRIS (J.); WEST (TEMPLE) *fo evidence at their trials in connexion w. same engagement.*

Mathieson (William Law).
Brit. slavery & its abolition, 1823–38. 8°. 192
England in transition, 1789–1832. 8°. 192
English church reform, 1815–40. 8°. 192

Mathiez (Albert), *prof. au lycée Voltaire.*
Autour de Danton. 8°. 192
Danton & la paix. s8°. 191
Un procès de corruption sous la Terreur. L'affaire de la Cie des Indies. la8°. 192
La Révolution française. 3t. s8°. 1922–2
see CAHEN (L.) & A. M. Les lois franç. de 1815 à nos jour 2e éd., 1919.

Mathorez (Jules). Les étrangers en France sous l'Anc. régim Hist. de la formation de la population franç. 2t. la8°. 1919–2

Matieovius (Samuel), *see* MACIEJOWSKI (S.)

***Matilda**: tragedy, 1811, *see* FRANCKLIN (T.)

Matilda, *of Magdeburg* [MECHTILDE], *see* ANCELET-HUSTACHE (J.) M. de M., 1207–82 : ét. de psych. relig., 1926.

Matilda, *countess of Tuscany ; 1046–1125, see* CONTELORIO (F.) M. cssae. genealogia, 1657.

Matisse (Henri), *see* FAURE (E.) H. M. ; par E. F., J. Romains &c., 1923.

Matlekovits (Sándor). Közös vámterület és a gazdasági elválás Ausztriától. 8°. 1905

Maton (William George) & *Rev.* T. Rackett. A descr. cat. of Brit. testacea. [Fr. Trans. of Linnean Soc., v8. *b. w. h.* Hist. acc., 1804]. 4°. [1807]

An hist. acc. of testaceological writers. [Fr. Trans. of Linnean Soc., v7]. 4°. [1804]

Matons (Marcel Grosdidier de), *see* GROSDIDIER DE MATONS (M.)

Matorohanga, Te, *see* SMITH (S. P.), *tr.* Lore of the Whare-wānanga ; wr. down by H. T. Whatahoro f. teachings of Te M., 2p, 1913–15.

Matos Fragoso (Juan de). El ingrato agradecido. Ed. H. C. Heaton. [Hisp. Soc. of Amer.] s8°. N.Y. 1926

Matricula & acta Hungarorum in univ. Ital. stud. ; ed. A. Veress, 1915–17, *see* HUNGARI.

Matsunami (Niichirō). Immunity of state ships as a contrib. towards unific. of laws &c. 8°. 1924

Mattei (Giuseppe). Compendio d. storia d. persecuzione mossa contro la Cattolica relig. nell' Imp. d. Cina, 1784. s8°. Firenze. 1789

Mattei (Saverio). *Il natal d'Apollo. Compon. dram. p. festig. la nasc. di Princ. Ered. d. Sicilie. [P2765]. 8°. Napoli. 1775

Matter (Hans). Engl. Gründungssagen v. Geoffrey of Monmouth bis z. Renaiss. 8°. Heidelberg. 1922

Matter (Paul). Cavour & l'unité ital. 3[v]. 8°. 1922–27

Matteson (David Maydole). List of MSS. conc. Amer. hist. in European libraries. [C.I. of Wash.] la8°. Wash. 1925

Matthaei (Georg), *Pfarrer zu Cöln.*
Wendische Grammatik. s8°. 1721

Matthaei (Louise Ernestine).
Germany in revol. First phase. s8°. 1920

Matthaeus, *Vindocinensis* [MATTHIEU *de Vendôme*]. Ars versificatoria, *see* FARAL (E.) Les arts poét. du 12 & 13 s., 1924.
see LEHMANN (P.) Pseudo-ant. Lit. des M.-A. [Anh., Pyramus-&c. Dicht. d. M. &c.], 1927.

Matthaeus (Antonius), *see* VOET (J.) Oratio funebr. in orbit. A. M., 1710.

Mattheos, *vardapet, see* MATTHEW.

Matthesius (Johann) [MATHESIUS]. Historien v. M. Luther's anfang, lehr, leben u. sterben &c. [*b. w.* Spangenberg (C.) Catechismus, 1547]. s4°. Nürnberg. 1564

Matthew, *Saint & Evangelist, see* BIBLE *for Gospel & Comm.*

Matthew, *vardapet, disciple of Mekhitar* [MATTHEOS]. [Meditations on the Passion of Christ. *In Armenian*]. s8°. i Venetik. 1759

Matthew (Patrick). Emigration fields, N. America, the Cape, Australia & New Zealand. 8°. E. 1839

Matthew (*Sir* Tobias), *see* SUTCLIFFE (M.) The Unmasking of a masse-monger [*Sir T. M.*] &c., 1626.

Matthews (Bache). Hist. of the Birmingham Repertory Theatre. [Intr. by B. V. Jackson, & contrib. by B. Shaw, J. Drinkwater &c.] 8°. 1924

Matthews (George F.), *ed., see* YEAR BOOKS. Y.B. of Probates, v5, 6, 1909–11.

Matthews (James Brander) [*ps.* ARTHUR PENN]. The Englishing of French words by M. & Dialectal words in Blunden's poems &c. by R. Bridges. [S.P.E. Tract No. 5]. 8°. 1921
Essays on English. s8°. N.Y. [1921]
Poems of Amer. patriotism. s8°. N.Y. 1882

Matthews (John), *ed., see* YEAR BOOKS. Y.B. of Probates, v5, 6, 1909–11.

Matthews (Philip W.) The Bankers' Clearing House. Pref. by R. Holland-Martin. 8°. 1921
Hist. of Barclays Bank, Ltd. &c. Ed. A. W. Tuke. la8°. 1926

Matthews (R. Borlase). Electro-farming : or the applic. of electricity to agric. 8°. 1928

Matthews (Walter Robert).
The Gospel & the modern mind. s8°. [1925]
King's College lectures on immortality. By J. F. Bethune-Baker, A. Caldecott &c. Ed. M. s8°. 1920
Studies in Xtn. philosophy. Boyle lect. 1920. 8°. 1921

Matthews (William Henry). Mazes & labyrinths. 8°. 1922

Matthias I [*Corvinus*], *king of Hungary.*
see BEKSICS (G.) Mátyás király birodalma és Magyar. jövöje, 1905.
„ HEVESY (A. DE). La bibliothèque du roi M. C., 1923.

Matthias, *Neoburgensis.* Chronik. Hrsg. A. Hofmeister. [Mon. Germ. Hist. Scr. rerum Germ., N.S., t4i]. [t]1. 8°. 1924

Matthias (Leo). Genie u. Wahnsinn in Russland. 8°. 1921

Matthieu (Pierre), *Historian.* *Hist. des dern. troubles de France. Soubs les regnes des Roys Henry III, Henry IV & Louys XIII. [5 livres]. dern. ed. [Livre 5 *has sep. tp. & pagin.*] s8°. *n.p.* 1613
*Hist. véritable des guerres entre les deux maisons de France & d'Espagne, j. 1598. [*b. w. h.* Hist. des dern. troubles &c., 1613]. s8°. *n.p.* 1606
Remarques d'estat de M. de Villeroy trad. en Italien. [*Fr. & Ital.*] Item L'essence de la langue franç. par L. Parent. [pl]. s8°. Franequer. 1652
see HENRY IV, *king of France.* Recueil des Edicts & Articles, 1613.

Matthison (Friedrich). Gedichte. Hrsg. G. Bölsing. [Lit. V. in St. 257, 261]. 8°. Tübingen. 1912–13

Mattingly (Harold).
Roman coins, to fall of the Western Emp. 8°. [1928]
see BRIT. MUS. : COINS &c. Coins of the Roman Empire in the B.M. ; w. intr. by H. M., v1, 1923.
—— **& E. A. Sydenham.** The Roman imperial coinage. With intr. &c. v1, 2. 8°. 1923–26

Mattox (William Courtney). Building the Emergency Fleet : U.S. Shipping Bd. Emergency Fleet Corp. 8°. Cleveland [U.S.] 1920

Maturanzio (Francesco) [MATARATIUS (F.)] F. Mataratii de componendis versibus, hexametro & pentametro opusculum. Item Jacobi Sentini de quibusdam lyricis versibus app. 8°. [Nurnbergae, *Joan. Stucks.* 1520]

Matveev (*graf* Andrei Artamonovich), *1666–1728.* Записки, *see* SAKHAROV (I. P.) Записки &c., 1841.

Matz (Bertram Waldrom).
The inns & taverns of " Pickwick." 8°. [1921]

Maubourguet (J. M.)
Le Périgord méridional, à 1370. Thèse. la8°. Cahors. 1926
see CADOUIN, *abbey.* Cartulaire, préc. de notes sur l'hist. écon. du Périgord mérid. &c. par J. M. M., 1926.

Mauceri (Enrico). Siracusa. s8°. Firenze. 1921

Mauceri (Luigi). Topog. di Imera e avanzi d. tempio di Bonfornello, *see* REALE ACCAD. D. LINCEI. Mon. ant., v18, 1907.

Mauclair (Camille), *ps.* [*i.e.* C. FAUST].
Antoine Watteau (1684–1721). s8°. [1920]
Claude Monet. Tr. J. L. May. 8°. [1925]
Étreindre, roman inéd., *see* ŒUVRES libres, t28, 1923.
Florence. s8°. 1923
Hist. de la miniature féminine franç. Le 18e siècle—L'Emp. —La Restauration. 8°. 1925
L'Orient vierge. Roman. [n. éd.] s8°. *n.d.*
Un peintre hollandais contemp. : Antoon van Welie. 8°. 1924
Le théâtre, le cirque, le music-hall & les peintres du 18e s. à nos jours. Préf. de C. M. 4°. [1926]
La vie de Sainte Claire d'Assise d'ap. les anc. textes. [8e éd.] s8°. [1924]

Mauclère (Jean). Tiotis aux yeux de mer. s8°. [1925]

Maude (Aylmer). Authorized life of Marie C. Stopes. s8°. 1924
Family views of Tolstoy. [Articles obt. by R. Fülöp-Miller]. Ed. A. M. Tr. L. & A. Maude. 8°. [1926]
Russian tales. Tr. A. M. s8°. [1927]
The teaching of Tolstoy. [P643]. s8°. M'ter. 1900

Maude (Cyril) & C. H. Towne.
The actor in room 931. s8°. [1927]

Maude (*Lt.-Gen. Sir* Frederick Stanley), *K.C.B., see* CALLWELL (*Maj.-Gen. Sir* C. E.) Life of Sir S. M., 1920.

Maude (*Mrs.* Jenny Maria Catherine), *O.B.E., wife of Raymond Maude.* Life of Jenny Lind. Told by h. daughter, Mrs. R. M. 8°. [1926]

Maude (Joseph Hooper).
The foundations of the Eng. Church. s8°. [1909]

Maudslay (Alfred Percival), *see* BRITISH MUSEUM : ANTIQ. Guide to M. coll. of Maya sculptures f. Cent. Amer., 1923.

Maugham (William Somerset).
The Casuarina tree. s8°. 1926
The circle. Comedy. s8°. 1921
Landed gentry. Comedy. s8°. 1913
Our betters. Comedy. s8°. 1924
The painted veil. [n. impr.] s8°. [1925]
Smith. Comedy. s8°. 1913
The tenth man. Tragic comedy. s8°. 1913
The trembling of a leaf. Little stories of South Sea Islands. s8°. 1921
The unknown. Play. s8°. 1920

Maughan (Cuthbert).
Trade term definitions. [2v]. s8°. 1925
v2 *has t.*: Commodity market terms.

Maughan (H. Hamilton), *see* LITURGY of E. Orthodox Ch.; intr. by M., 1916.

Maugis, *d'Aigremont, see* KEMPEL (E.) Hs.-verhältnis u. Sprache d. M. d'A., 1915.

Maugridge (John) [MAWGRIDGE]. *The life &c. of J. M., executed for the murder of Capt. Cope. [P2828]. s8°. 1708

Maul (Dietrich). Leben u. Werke d. Malers C. Bentum. la8°. Str. 1915

Maulbronn [MAULBRUN].
Epitome colloquii inter Friderici Palatini Elect. & Chr. Ducis Wirtenberg. theologos, de majestate hominis Christi, deq. vera ejus in Eucharistia præsentia, M. instituti, per Wirtenb. theologos perscripta. [*b. w.* Andrae (J.) Assertio piae &c. doct., 1565]. s8°. *n.p.* 1564
Protocoll das ist, Acta oder Handlungen des Gesprechs, zw. den Pfältz. u. Wirtemberg. Theologen v. d. Ubiquitet des Leibes Christi &c. zu M. gehalten. Item der Wirtemb. Theologen Bericht, samt der Pfältz. Theologen Gegenbericht. [*pagin. contin.*] s4°. Heidelberg. 1565
Protocoll des Gesprächs zw. d. Pfältz. u. Würtenberg. Theologen im Aprill 1564, zu M. gehalten. [*Foll. by* Christl. Erklärung d. Würtenberg. Theologen Bekanndtnuss v. d. Maiestet d. Menschen Christi &c., *w. sep. tp. & pagin.*] s4°. Tübingen. 1565
Protocollum hoc est Acta colloquii inter Palatinos & Wirtebergicos theologos, de ubiquitate &c. corporis Christi &c. a. 1564 M. habiti. Item Wirtebergicorum theologorum de hoc colloquio epitome [*w. sep. tp. & pagin.*] s4°. Heidelbergae. 1566

Mauldon (F. R. E.) Study in soc. economics: the Hunter River Valley, N. S. Wales. 8°. Melbourne. 1927

Maule (*Sir* John Blossett) *see* BURN (R.) Justice of the Peace &c., 30th ed., v5 by J. B. M., 1869.

Mauler (*Frau* Melanie v.) Meine Leiden in russ. Gefangenschaft. Erlebnisse [*compiled by*] V. Franiel. s8°. [1917]

Maunder (E. Walter). Astronomy without a telescope. 8°. 1902

Maunsell (Francis Richard). The geography of Eastern Turkey in Asia. [P2591]. s8°. Aldershot. 1894

Maunsell (*Maj.* Manuel Charles). Eng.-French & Fr.-Eng. artillery & naval techn. terms. 3rd ed. s8°. 1917

Maupassant (Guy de).
Clair de lune. [Œ. illus.] s8°. *n.d.*
Mlle. Fifi. [Œuvres illust.] s8°. [1925]

TRANSLATIONS.
Bel-Ami. Tr. M. Laurie. 8°. [1923]
Boule de suif & o. s. Tr. M. Laurie. 8°. [1926]
A life. Tr. M. Laurie. 8°. [1924]
Tales from M. [Tr.] Pref. by R. B. Cunninghame Graham. 8°. 1926
„ „ [2nd impr.] 8°. [1927]

TRANSLATIONS [*continued*].
Yvette & o. s. Tr. Mrs. J. Galsworthy, w. pref. by J. Conrad. s8°. [1920]
see BOYD (E. A.) G. de M., biog. study, 1926.
„ DEFFOUX (L.) & E. ZAVIE. Le groupe de Médan: G. de M. &c., 1920.
„ RIDDELL (A. R.) Flaubert & M.: literary relationship, 1920.
„ SHERARD (R. H.) Life, work & fate of G. de M., 1926.

Maupertuis (Pierre Louis Moreau de).
see FREDERICK II, *king of Prussia.* Briefwechsel m. G. & M., 1731–59; hrsg. R. Koser, 1898.
„ —— Briefwechsel, Nachträge, Briefwechsel F. mit M. &c., 1917.

Maura Gamazo (Gabriel).
Carlos II y su corte. t2, 1669–79, la8°. 1915
Hist. crít. d. reinado de Don Alfonso XIII dur. la regencia de María Cristina de Austria. 2t. 8°. Barcelona. [1919–25]

Maurel (André). La Dsse. du Maine, reine de Sceaux. 8°. [1928]
Souv. de litt., *see* ŒUVRES libres, No. 44, 1925.
Paysages d'Italie. [t]1–4. s8°. 1913[–22]
A month in Rome. Tr. H. Gerard. s8°. N.Y. 1919

Maurenbrecher (Wilhelm). Don Carlos, *see* VIRCHOW (R.) & F. v. HOLTZENDORFF. Samml., H90, 1869.

Maurepas (*le comte* Jean Frédéric Phelypeaux de) [†PHELYPEAUX DE MAUREPAS (J. F.)], *see* LA ROCHEFOUCAULD (*le vte.* J. FR. DE). *Ramassis [Lettre p. s. à l'éloge de M. &c.], c. 1783.

Maurer (Louis). L'expéd. de Strasbourg en sept. 1681. Corresp. offic. Préf. de A. Chuquet. 8°. 1923

Maurey (Max), *see* DUVERNOIS (H.) & M. M. L'éternel printemps, comédie, 1925.

Mauri (*conte* Luigi de) [E. SARASINO]. Flores sententiarum. Racc. di 5000 sentenze, proverbi e motti lat., con tr. ital. s8°. Milano. 1926

Mauriac (François).
Le baiser au lépreux. s8°. 1922
La chair & le sang. s8°. 1920
Le désert de l'amour. [Cahiers verts, 50]. s8°. 1925
„ „ [64e éd.] s8°. 1925
Destins. [Cahiers verts, n.s., 8]. s8°. 1928
„ „ [23e éd.] s8°. 1928
Le fleuve de feu. Roman. s8°. 1923
Genitrix. s8°. 1924
Préséances. [3e ed.] s8°. 1921
Thérèse Desqueyroux. s8°. 1927
La vie de Jean Racine. 8°. [1928]

Maurice, *Prince of Anhalt-Dessau, see* PREITZ (M.) Prinz M. v. D., in siebenjähr. Kriege, 1912.

Maurice, *elector of Saxony, 1521–53.* Unnser v. Gotts genaden Moritzen &c. warhafftiger bericht, welcher gestalt sich Hertzog Heinrichs von Braunschweigk u. s. sones Carln Ergebunge [1545] zugetragen. [P2439]. s4°. Leipzig. 1546
see BARTENSTEIN (J. C.) Diss. de bello Carolo V a M. illato, 1709.

Maurice (C. Edmund). Bohemia, to found. of Czecho-Slavak Republic, 1918. [Story of the Nations]. 2nd ed. rev. 8°. [1922]

Maurice (*Maj.-Gen. Sir* Frederick Barton).
Forty days in 1914. 2nd ed. 8°. 1920
Governments & war. 8°. 1926
Milit. effort of Brit. Emp. in the Gt. War, *see* BUCHAN (J), *ed.* Nations, Gt. Brit., v1, 1923.
Milit. operations [1914–18], *see* BUCHAN (J.), *ed.* Nations France, 1923.
Robert E. Lee, the soldier. 8°. 192[illegible]
see RAWLINSON (H. S., *1st b.*) Life; ed. M., 1928.

—— **& *Sir* G. Arthur.** Life of Lord Wolseley. Foreword by Gen. Sir R. Wingate. 8°. 192[illegible]

Maurice (*Sir* J. Frederick). Milit. hist. of the Campaign of 1882 in Egypt. [War Office. Intelligence Branch]. [*Map in case*]. [n. ed. rev.] 8°. [1908]

Maurice (J. Frederick Denison), *1805–72.* The kingdom of Xt.; hints to a Quaker. 4th ed. 2v. 8°. 189[illegible]
Mediaeval philosophy. 2nd ed. s8°. 185[illegible]
Reasons for not joining a party in the Church. Letter to S. Wilberforce &c. [P2788]. 8°. 184[illegible]

Maurice (Jules). Constantin le Grand: l'orig. de la civilis. chrét. 8°. [192[illegible]

Maurice (Matthias). Mon. of mercy, or Congregational ch. a Rowel. s8°. 172[illegible]

Maurice (Michael). Not in our stars. s8°. [192[illegible]

Maurice-Pouquet (Jeanne), *see* POUQUET (J. M.)

Mauritius, *bp. of Burgos, 1213–1238, see* SERRANO (L.) Do[illegible] M., 1922.

Mauritshuis, *see* HAGUE (THE).

Mauro (Giovanni), *see* CAPORALI (C.) Rime piacevoli [illegible] C. C., del M. &c., 1588.

Maurois (André).
Les Anglais. Préc. d'une opin. sur les Français par C. Washburn, tr. A. M. s8°. [1927]
Ariel; ou, la vie de Shelley. [Cahiers verts, 22]. s8°. 1923
„ „ [46e éd.] s8°. 1923
Ariel. A Shelley romance. Tr. E. D'Arcy. s8°. 1924
Bernard Quesnay. 16e éd. s8°. [1926]
„ „ Tr. B. W. Downs. s8°. [1927]
Dialogues sur le commandement. 8°. 1924
Lesdiscours du docteur O'Grady. [7e éd.] s8°. 1922
Essai sur Dickens. [Cahiers verts]. s8°. 1927
Études anglaises: Dicken[s] Walpole, Ruskin & Wilde, jeune litt. s8°. 19[illegible]
General Bramble. Tr. J. Ca[r]tier & R. Boswell. s8°. 19[illegible]
La hausse & la baisse, [s.] Œuvres libres, 13, 1922.
Meïpe ou la délivrance. s8°. 19[illegible]
Quatre études angl. Mme. [du] Deffand & H. Walpole Lord Byron & le dém[on] de la tendresse—De Rusk[in] à Wilde—La jeune li[tt.] anglaise. 8°. 19[illegible]
Vie de Disraeli. 68e éd. s8°. 19[illegible]
„ „ 174e éd. s8°. 19[illegible]
Voyage au pays des Articoles 18e éd. s8°. [19[illegible]

Mauron (Charles). The nature of beauty in art & lit. [illegible] & pref. by R. Fry. s8°. 19[illegible]

Maurras (Charles Marie Photius).
Les Amants de Venise, G. Sand & Musset. n. éd. [28e éd.] s8°. *n.d.*
Anatole France, politique & poète. s8°. 1924
Anthinéa: d'Athènes à Florence. n. éd. s8°. [1926]
Barbarie & poésie. 8°. 1[illegible]
Le démocratie relig.: dilemme de M. Sangnier—polit. relig.—l'Action fra[nç.] & la relig. cath. 8°. 1[illegible]
Enquête s. la monarchie, sui[vie] de Une campagne royal[iste]

Maurras (Charles Marie Photius) [*continued*].
au Figaro & Si le coup de force est possible [par C. M. & H. Dutrait-Crozon]. 8°. 1924
Inscriptions. [*Poèmes*]. s8°. 1921
Kiel & Tanger, 1895–1905. La République Franç. dev. l'Europe, 1905–13–21. [3e éd.] 8°. 1921
Le mauvais traité, de la victoire à Locarno. 2v. 8°. [1928]
La musique intérieure. [Cahiers verts, 52]. 8°. 1925
La naissance du poème, souvenirs, *see* ŒUVRES libres, 42, 1924.
Romantisme & révolution. Ed. déf., avec une préf. nouv. de L'avenir de l'intelligence—A. Comte—Le romantisme féminin — Mdlle. Monk — L'invocat. à Minerve—Trois idées polit.: Chateaubriand, Michelet, Sainte-Beuve. 8°. 1922
Tombeaux. 8°. 1921
see GWYNN (D.) The "Action Française" condemnation, 1928.
,, THIBAUDET (A.) Les idées de C. M., 1920.

Maurus (Rabanus). De clericorum instit. & ceremoniis eccl. ex Vet. & Novo Test. ad Heistulphum archiepisc. libri 3. Eiusdem ad Otgarium episc., Pœnitentium liber [*& other works*]. [*b. w.* Suso (H.) Opera omnia, 1555]. s8°. Coloniae, *J. Prael.* 1532
Epistolae, *see* †DÜMMLER (E. L.), *ed.* Epist. Merow. et Karol. aevi, t4, 1925.
see JUNG-JOHANN (J. C.) Diss. de vita ac doctr. Hrabani Magnentii Mauri, 1724.
,, SCHELL (F. J.) S. Hrab. M. de sacramentis eccl. doct., 1845.

Maury (Lucien). Stockholm et Upsal. la8°. 1913

Mauthner (Fritz).
Mrs. Socrates. [Tr. J. W. Hartmann]. s8°. 1927
Wörterbuch d. Philosophie. 2. verm. Aufl. 3B. 8°. L. 1923

Mautner (Wilhelm). Der Bolschewismus. Zugleich e. Unters. s. Verhältnisses z. Marxismus. 8°. 1920

Mauvinière (Henri Labbé de la), *see* LABBÉ DE LA MAUVINIÈRE (H.)

Maver (Hans). Einfl. d. vorchristl. Kulte auf d. Toponomastik Frankreichs, 1914, *see* KAIS. AKAD. D. W. Z. WIEN. Sitzb., B175, 1916.

Mavor (James). The Russian Revolution. la8°. [1928]

Mavrogordato (John). England in the Balkans, *see* ANGLO-HELLENIC LEAGUE. Publ. No. 24, 1916.

Maw (Elizabeth), *see* INGHAM (S. C. J.) An innercourt worshipper: memorials of E. M., 1888.

Mawdsley (J. B.) St. Urbain Area, Charlevoix Dist., Quebec. [Canada: Geol. Survey. P2874]. 8°. Ottawa. 1927

Mawe (Thomas) & J. Abercrombie. Every man his own gardener. 23rd ed., w. impr. by J. Main. s8°. 1829

Mawer (Allen).
The chief elements in Eng. place-names. [Eng. Place-Name Soc., v1, p2]. 8°. C. 1924
Eng. place-name study. [Fr. Proc. of Brit. Acad., v10]. 8°. [1921]
Place-names & hist. R. S. Watson Memor. Lect., 1922. Publ. for the Survey of Eng. Place-names. [P2688]. 8°. Liv'l. 1922
Place-names of Northumberland & Durham. [Camb. Arch. &c. Ser.]. 8°. C. 1920
The Vikings. s8°. C. 1913

—— & F. M. Stenton.
Introd. to the survey of Eng. place-names. [Chap. by O. G. S. Crawford, E. Ekwall &c. Eng. Place-Name Soc., v1, p1]. p1. 8°. C. 1924
Place-names of Beds. & Hunts. [Eng. Place-Name Soc., v3]. 8°. C. 1926
Place-names of Bucks. [Eng. Place-Name Soc., v2]. 8°. C. 1925
Place-names of Worcestershire. By A. M. & F. M. S. in collab. w. F. T. S. Houghton. [Eng. Place-Name Soc., v4]. 8°. C. 1927

Mawgridge (John), *see* MAUGRIDGE (J.)

Mawson (*Capt.*) Just (The) vengeance of heaven exemplify'd in a journal lately found by Capt. Mawson on the isl. of Ascension &c. [P536]. s8°. [1730 ?]

Mawson (Christopher Orlando Sylvester), *see* ROGET (P. M.) Internat. Thesaurus of Eng. words &c.; founded upon R.'s work, w. add. &c. by M., 1925.

Mawson (*Sir* **Douglas**), *see* HURLEY (F.) Argonauts of the South: in the Antarctic w. Sir D. M. &c., 1925.

Mawson (E. O.) Pioneer irrigation: manual for farmers in the colonies, w. add. chapters on light railways by E. R. Calthrop. 8°. 1904

Max, *prince of Baden.* Erinnerungen u. Dokumente. 8°. 1927
Die moral. Offensive: Deutschlands Kampf um sein Recht. 8°. St. 1921
see KEIM (*Generalleutnant* A.) Pr. M. v. B. u. d. Kriegskabinett, 1922.

Max (Heinrich). Der Starnberger See. obl. s8°. München. [1892]

Maxe (Jean), *ps.* L'anthologie des défaitistes. [*Cont.* Les cahiers de l'anti-France, 1–10]. Préf. de E. Buré. 2t. s8°. 1925
Les cahiers de l'anti-France. Le bolchevisme litt. [6 Nos. *in* 1v, *pagin. cont.*] s8°. 1922
De Zimmerwald au Bolchevisme. Menées internat. pend. la Guerre, 1914–20. 8°. 1920

Maxfield (Thomas), *assist. chaplain to the Ctss. of Huntingdon.* A coll. of psalms & hymns. Extr. by M. 3rd ed. s8°. 1778

Maxfield (Thomas), *Roman Cath. priest.* Brevis narr. martyrii T. M. (1616), *see* ABBOTSFORD CLUB. Misc., v1, 1837.

Maxima bibliotheca veterum Patrum &c., 28t, 1677–1707, *see* LA BIGNE (M. DE).

Maximilian I, *elector of Bavaria; 1573–1651, see* BRIEFE u. Akten zur Gesch. d. 30jähr. Krieges, N.F., Die Politik M. I v. B. u. s. Verbündeten, T2, B2, bearbt. v. W. Goetz, 1918.

Maximilian I, *emp. of Germany, 1459–1519* [*form. archduke of Austria*]. Deffense de Mgnr le Duc & Mme la Dsse d'Austriche &c. (Bruges 1477 ou 78), facs. &c., *see* PICOT (E.) & H. STEIN. Recueil, 1923.
see BALDASS (L.) Der Künstlerkreis Kaiser M., 1923.
,, HIRTH (G.) Kulturgeschl. Bilderbuch aus 4 Jhdtn., B1, *includ.* Kayser M.'s Triumph, 1923.
,, MAYER (T.) Die Verwaltungsorganis. M. I, 1920.
,, SCHWEINITZ (J. S. v.) Diss. de Caes. M. I pontif. max. affectante, 1716.

Maximilian II, *emperor of Germany, 1527–76.* Die Registratur Erzherzog M., 1547–51; hrsg. v. J. Loserth, *see* FONTES RERUM AUSTRIAC., B48ii, 1896.
see BIZARI (P.) Pannonicum bellum sub M. II, 1573.

Maximilian, *emperor of Mexico, 1832–67.*
see CORTI (*cte.* E. C.) M. u. Charlotte v. M., 2B, 1924; tr. C. A. Phillips, 2v, 1928; tr. J. Vernay, 2t, 1927.
,, MESSERVY (G. P.) The quick-step of an emperor, 1921.
,, WERFEL (F.) Juarez u. M., Dramat. Hist., 1924.

Maximilian A. F. W., *Prinz von Baden, see* MAX, *pr. of Baden.*

Maximilian Franz, *of Austria, elector of Cologne, 1756–1801, see* BRAUBACH (M.) M. F. v. Österreich, 1925.

Maximus, *Saint, abbot & confessor.* Scholia in Gregorium theologum, *see* SCOTUS (JOHN), *Erigena.* De div. naturae, 1681.

Maxiriarth, *ps., see* HARTZENBUSCH (E.)

Max-Müller (Friedrich). A Sanskrit gramm. for beginners. 2nd ed. rev. 8°. 1870

Maxon (William Ralph). New Selaginellas f. West. U.S., *see* SMITHSONIAN INST. Misc. coll., v72, 1922.

Maxse (Frederick Ivor). Seymour Vandeleur. Story of a Brit. officer, being mem. of V. [ed. de luxe]. la8°. 1905

Maxse (L. J.) The great Marconi mystery, *see* †NATIONAL REVIEW, May, 1913.

Maxwell, *The family of, see* FRASER (*Sir* W.) Mem. of the M. of Pollok, 2v, 1863.

Maxwell (Constantia). The colonisation of Ulster. [*Repr. f.* History, 1916]. 8°. *n.p.* [1916]
The foundations of mod. Ireland. p1, Civil policy of Henry VIII, & the Reformation. [Texts for students, No. 27. P2573]. s8°. 1921
Irish hist. f. contemp. sources, 1509–1610. 8°. [1923]
The plantation of Ulster. [Repr. f. Sewanee rev., Apr. 1923. P2731]. 8°. *n.p.* 1923
A short bibliog. of Irish hist. [Histor. Assoc. Leaflet 23 rev.] [P2563]. 8°. 1921
Short hist. of Ireland. s8°. D. [1925]

Maxwell (Darcy, *Lady*), *wife of Sir W. Maxwell, of Pollok, 4th bart., d. 1810, see* LANCASTER (J.) Life of D. Lady M., 2v, 1821; 2nd ed., 1826.

Maxwell (Donald). Unknown Norfolk. 8°. [1925]

Maxwell (Gordon Stanley).
The authors' Thames: a lit. ramble. 8°. [1924]

Maxwell (*Rt. Hon. Sir* **Herbert E.**), *of Monreith, 7th bart.*
Inter alia: a Scot. calendar of crime & o. e. 8°. Glasgow. 1924
Life of Wellington. 3rd ed. 2v. 8°. 1900
The Lowland Scots regiments, th. origin, character &c. prev. to 1914. la8°. Glasgow. 1918
Memories of the months. 7th ser. s8°. 1922
60 years a Queen. The story of Her M. reign. sm. fol. [1897]

Maxwell (J. H.) Guide book to the stewartry of Kirkcudbright. [3rd ed.] 8°. Castle-Douglas. 1878

Maxwell (James), *of Paisley.*
Divine miscellanies; or sacred poems &c. s8°. B'ham. 1756

Maxwell (*Sir* John), *Bart.*, *Ld. Pollock*, *see* POLLOCK (*Sir* J. M., *Lord*).
Maxwell (W. Harold), *see* SWEET & MAXWELL, *Ltd.* Compl. law bk. cat., v1, Bibliog. of Eng. law to 1650, 1925.
Maxwell (William Babington).
The case of Bevan Yorke. s8º. [1927]
Children of the night. s8º. [1925]
The day's journey. s8º. [1923]
Elaine at the gates. s8º. [1924]
„ „ [n. impr.] s8º. [1924]
Fernande. s8º. [1925]
Gabrielle. s8º. [1926]
A little more. 2nd ed. s8º. [1923]
A man & his lesson. s8º. [1919]
A remedy against sin. s8º. [1920]
Spinster of this parish. s8º. [1922]
Maxwell-Lefroy (H.) Insects injurious to books & paper. [Repr. f. Eastern Printers' Year Book. P2851]. v1. la8º. Calcutta. [1907]
Maxwell-Lyte (*Sir* Henry Churchill), *K.C.B.* Burci, Falaise & Martin. [Repr. f. Somersets. Arch. Soc., v65]. [P2576]. 8º. 1919
Hist. notes on the use of the Great Seal of England. la8º. 1926
see DUNSTER. Doc. & extr. illust. hist. of Honour of D.; sel. & ed. Sir H. C. M.-L., 1917–18.
„ RECORD OFFICE (PUBLIC). Cat. of MSS. &c., w. descr. &c. notes by Sir H. C. M.-L., 9th ed., 1922; 10th ed., 1924.
May, *Isle of.* Rec. of the priory of the I. of M., 1868, *see* STUART (J.), *ed.*
May (Arthur S.)
Marriage à la mode: a surrogate's tales. 8º. [1925]
May (C. J. Delabére). How to identify Persian rugs. s8º. 1920
May (*Major-Gen. Sir* Edward Sinclair).
Achievements of field artillery. 8º. Woolwich. 1893
Cavalry & Horse Artillery. [P2593]. s8º. D. 1896
Changes & chances of a soldier's life. 8º. [1925]
Geography in relation to war. 8º. 1907
May (James Lewis).
Anatole France, the man & h. work. 8º. [1924]
May (Norman).
Hist. of & guide to the Isle of Wight. s8º. [1884]
May (Stacy), *see* HAMILTON (W. H.) & S. M. Control of wages, 1923.
May (Stella Burke). Men, maidens & mantillas. 8º. 1924
May (Thomas). Excav. on the Romano-Brit. civitas at Wilderspool, 1899–1900. [P2404]. 8º. Liv'l. 1901
Pottery found at Silchester, deposited in Reading Museum. la8º. Reading. 1916
The Roman fortifications at Wilderspool. [P2404]. 8º. Liv'l. 1899
Mayakovsky (Vladimir Vladimirovich).
Вещи этого года до 1 Августа 1923. s8º. Берлин. 1924
Избранный Маяковский. s8º. Берлин. 1923
Испания, Океан, Гаванна, Мексика, Америка. s8º. Москва. 1926
Maybon (Charles B.), *ed.*, *see* LA BISSACHÈRE (P. J. L. DE). Rel. sur le Tonkin & la Cochinchine (1807), 1920.
Maybon (Pierre B.)
Essai sur les associations en Chine. la8º. [1925]
Maybrick (*Mrs.* Florence Elizabeth), *see* MACDOUGALL (F. E.) M. case, 1891.
Maycock (Alan Lawson). The Inquisition, to the Great Schism. Intr. by R. Knox. 8º. [1926]
Maydeburg, *see* MAGDEBURG.
Maydon (H. C.) Simen: its heights & abysses. 8º. 1925
Mayence (Fernand). La légende des francs-tireurs de Louvain. Rép. au mém. de Prof. Meurer. s8º. Louvain. 1928
see CORPUS vasorum antiq. Belgique, fasc. 1: Bruxelles, Mus. Roy. du Cinquant., fasc. 1; par F. M., 1926.
Mayenne. Documents sur la ville de M., 1906, *see* GROSSE-DUPERON (A. P. A.), *ed.*
Mayer (Anton). Peregrinus Windesprang. Roman. s8º. 1926
Mayer (August Liebmann).
Alt-Spanien. 4º. München. [1920]
„ „ [2e verm. A.] 4º. München. [1922]
El Greco: Leben &c. des D. Theotocopuli. [2e verm. A.] 8º. München. 1916
Il Greco. [Bibl. d'arte illust.] 8º. 1921
Mittelalterl. Plastik in Spanien. sm. fol. München. [1922]
Segovia, Avila u. El Eskorial. s8º. L. 1913
Toledo. s8º. L. 1910
see PRADO. Meisterwerke d. Gemäldesamml.; einleit Text v. A. L. M., 1922.
Mayer (Charles).
Trapping wild animals in Malay jungles. 8º. [1922]
Mayer (Georg), *see* AGRICOLA (THEOPHILUS), *ps.*
Mayer (Gustav). Friedrich Engels. B1 & Ergzb. (Schr. d. Frühzeit). la8º. 1920
Mayer (Johann Friedrich), *prof. of theology, Wittenberg.*
Bibliotheca Biblica sive diss. de notitia auctorum qui in S. Script. comm. scrips. ed. altera. s4º. Francofurti. 1709
Comm. in Zachariam. Ed. cur. M. B. Wybers. [*b. w.* Schudt (J. J.) Compendium hist. Jud., 1700]. s8º. Francofurthi. 1722
De Jo. Tezelio, diss. J. F. M. & P. Schöppich. [P484]. s4º. Wittebergae. 1717
De morte Caroli V imp. evangelica. [P595]. s4º. Lipsiae. 1682
De parentibus D. Lutheri [Hans & Margaretha]. [P2438]. s4º. Gryphiswaldiæ. 1708
De pietistis eccl. vet. comm. Acc. diss. M. Casauboni de enthusiasmo precatorio. s4º. Regusa. 1716
Disput. de indulgentiis pontif. Resp. J. H. Balthasare. [P437]. s4º. Gryphiswaldae. [1711]
Diss. de Catharina Lutheri conjuge. Praes. J. F. M., resp. M. Richey. ed. 4ª. [P442]. s4º. Hamburgi. 1710
Ecclesia papaea Lutheranae reformationis patrona &c.; sive diss. de pontificiis Leonis X processum adv. Lutherum improbantibus &c. Acc. oratio de morte Caroli V imperat. s4º. Lipsiae. 1698
Hist. versionis Germ. Bibliorum M. Lutheri. Acc. mantissa de tr. Bibl. Germ. ante Lutherum &c. s4º. Hamburgi. [1750 ?]
Tract. de osculo pedum pontificis Romani. ed. 2ª. [P2670]. s4º. Lipsiae. 1714
Triga dissert. theol. ed. 3ª. [P484]. s4º. Gryphiswaldae. 1707
see HALL (J.) Roma irreconciliabilis, & Syllabum autorum &c. add. J. F. M., 1706.
Mayer (Theodor). Die Verwaltungsorganis. Maximilians I: Ursprung u. Bedeutung. 8º. Innsbruck. 1920
Mayerling. *Das Drama v. Mayerling. [Tod d. Kronpr. Rudolf u. d. Bsse. M. Vetsera. Denkschr. d. Baronin Helene Vetsera &c.] s8º. Reichenberg. 1921
Mayew (Richard), *bp. of Hereford.* Registrum R. M., episc. Hereford., 1504–16. Ed. A. T. Bannister. [Canterbury & York Soc., 27]. 8º. 1921
Mayflower. Souv. of the "M." tercentenary, nos. 1–4, 1920, *see* HARRIS (J. R.), *ed.*
Mayhew (Arthur). Education of India: Brit. educ. policy (1835–1920). 8º. 1926
Mayhew (Henry). The Lower Rhine & its scenery. Rotterdam to Mayence. Illust. by B. Foster. Descr. by H. M. la8º. 1860
The Upper Rhine: scenery &c. Mayence to Lake Constance Illust. B. Foster. Descr. by H. M. la8º. 1860
The wonders of science, or young Humphry Davy. [repr.] s8º. *n.d*
Maylander (Alfred). Food situation in C. Europe, 1917, *see* UNITED STATES: LAB., Bull. 242, 1918.
Maynard (François de) [MAINARD (F.)]
Odes & sonnets. Intr. par F. Gohin. s8º. [1925]
Poésies. Recueil de 1646 &c., avec notice &c. par F. Gohin. s8º. 1927
Maynard (George Darell) & G. A. Turner. Anthropol. notes on Bantu natives f. Portuguese East Africa. [S. African Instit for Medical research]. [P2380]. 4º. Johannesburg. 1914
Maynard (*l'abbé* Michel Ulysse). La sainte Vierge. 2e éd préc. d'un Bref de Pie IX. la8º. 1877
Maynard (Theodore). Our best poets, English & American. 8º. [1924]
Mayne (Ethel Colburn). Blindman. s8º. 1919
Byron. 2nd ed. rev. 8º. [1924]
Inner circle. s8º. 1925
Nine of hearts. s8º. [1923]
Maynooth. Proc. of Anti-M. conf. 1845, 1845, *see* THELWALL (A. S.), *ed.*
Mayo (Charles), *rector of Bechingstoke.* A chronol. hist. of the European states, w. discov. & settlements 1678–1792 &c., also biogr. sk. of sovereigns &c. fol. Bath. 1793
Mayo (Katherine). The isles of fear. Truth about the Philippines. 8º. 1925
Mother India. 8º. [1927]
see IYER (C. S. R.) Father India: reply to Mother India 1927.
Mayo (Lawrence Shaw). John Wentworth, Governor of New Hampshire, 1767–75. la8º. Camb., *Mass.* 1921
Mayo (Margarita), *see* PÉREZ GALDÓS (B.) G.: selecc. hecha por M. M., 1922.
Mayol (Joseph). Summa moralis doctrinæ Thomisticæ circa Decalogum, & Apps., *see* MIGNE (J. P.), *ed.* Theol. cursus t13, 14, 1861.
Mayor (F. M.) The rector's daughter. s8º. 192-

Mayor (John Eyton Bickersteth). Cambridge in the 17th cent. [Ed. J. E. B. M.] 3p. s8°. C. 1855–71
1, Nicholas Ferrar; two lives by h. brother John & by Dr. Jebb.
2, Autobiog. of Matthew Robinson.
3, Life of Bp. Bedell by h. son.
Spain, Portugal, the Bible. s8°. C. 1892
The Spanish Reformed Church. Sermon. [P505]. s8°. C. 1895

Mayow (John). Medico-physical works. Tr. of the Tractatus 5 medico-physici, 1674. [Old Ashmolean repr., 5]. s8°. O. 1926

Mayr (Albert). Üb. d. vorröm. Denkmäler d. Balearen, *see* KÖNIGL. AKAD. D. W. ZU MÜNCHEN. Phil. Kl., Sitz., 1914.

Mayr (Cherubinus). Gemini justitiae actus, restitutio &c., juxta mentem Joannis Duns Scoti scholastice declarati &c. Præs. A. Holzmann: resp. C. M. s8°. [Passau ?. 1718]
Ordinis hierarch. descensus & ascensus, à tonsura ad episcopatum &c. cum sel. assert. theolog. ex J. Duns Scoto expos. s8°. Salisburgi. [1726]

Mayran (Camille). L'épreuve du fils. s8°. [1921]
Hiver. [Cahiers verts, 63]. s8°. 1926

Mayrhofer (Johannes). Konnersreuth. 8°. Regensburg. [1927]

Maza (Francisco F. de la), *see* MEXICO. Código de coloniz. &c. de la Repúbl. Mexicana; formado por F. F. de la M., 1893.

Mazade (Fernand). Anthol. des poètes fr. des orig. à nos jours. t2. 4°. [1926?]

Mazarin (*le card.*) [†MAZZARINI (GIULIO), *card.*] Lettere a G. Giustiniani, patrizio di Genova; ed. V. Ricci, *see* REGIA DEP. DI ST. PATRIA. Misc., t4, 1863.
see ALAZARD (J.) L'abbé L. Strozzi, corr. artist. de M. &c., 1924.
,, FEDERN (C.) M., 1922.
,, GUALDO PRIORATO (*il conte* G.) Hist. of managements of Card. M.; tr., t1, p1, 1671.
,, SAGREDO (*c.* A.) G. M. ritratto da un suo contemp., prec. da una nota stor. di A. S., 1844.

Mazarin (Hortense Mancini, *dsse.***),** *see* HARTMANN (C. H.) The vagabond duchess; H. M., 1926.

Mazaroz (Jean Paul). La revanche de la France par le travail &c.; t3, chap. 2, La Franc-Maçonnerie &c. 8°. 1880

Mazaud (Emile). Dardamelle, pièce, *see* ŒUVRES libres, 15, 1922.
La folle journée, comédie. 3e éd. s8°. [1920]
Voltigeur: pièce, *see* ŒUVRES libres, 49, 1925.

Mazdak, *c. 470–531 A.D.* [MAZDEK], *see* CHRISTENSEN (A.) Kawādh I & le communisme mazdak., 1925.

Maze (*abbé* **Camille).**
Etude sur le langage de la banlieue du Havre. 8°. 1903

Mazel (G. Vial-), *see* VIAL-MAZEL (G.)

Mazel (Henri). Effect of the War upon the Fr. merchant marine, *see* GIDE (C.), *ed.* Effects of War upon Fr. econ. life, 1923.

Mazeline (Guy). Piège du démon. 3e éd. s8°. [1927]

Mazois (François), *b. 1783.* Le palais de Scaurus. Préc. d'une notice biogr. par M. Varcollier. 4e éd. 8°. 1869

Mazon (André). Gramm. de la langue tchèque. 8°. 1921
Lexique de la Guerre & de la Révol. Russie, 1914–18. 8°. 1920

Mazzatinti (Giuseppe).
Note per la storia d. città di Alba. s8°. Alba. 1888
—— **& A. Sorbelli.** Inventari dei mss. d. biblioteche d'Italia. v26–38. la8°. Firenze. 1918–28
v26–38 *by* A. Sorbelli *only.*

Mazzella (Scipione). Descr. del regno di Napoli, con nota de' fuochi &c. s4°. Napoli. [1586]
Sito et antichità di Pozzuolo. [*w.* Opusculum de Balneis Puteolorum &c. (*by G. Elisio*); *sep. tp., pagin. cont., 1606*]. Agg. un Apparato delle statue ritrov. n. Cuma [*by A. Ferro; sep. tp. & pagin., 1606*]. s8°. Napoli. 1606

Mazzetti (Francesco). A tutti i chierici regolari &c. [*no tp.*] [P2766]. 8°. Napoli. 1763

Mazzinghi (*count* **Giuseppe),** *1768–1844.* Three sonatas for piano-forte &c. Op. 14. [*b. w.* Corelli (A.) Twelve concertos, 1790 ?]. 4°. [1800 ?]

Mazzini (Giuseppe).
Essays: sel. f. the writings of M. [Ed. W. Clarke]. s8°. [1887]
Letters to an English family, 1844–[72]. Ed. w. intr. by E. F. Richards. 3v. 8°. 1920–22
Scritti ed. & ined. [Ed. nazionale]. v1–46. 8°. Imola. 1906–26
Epistolario, v1–24. [5, 9–12, 14, 15, 18–20, 23, 24, 26–28, 30, 32, 33, 35, 37, 40, 42, 44, 45].
Letteratura, v1–5. [1, 8, 16, 21, 29].
Politica, v1–17. [2–4, 6, 7, 13, 17, 22, 25, 31, 34, 36, 38, 39, 41, 43, 46].

Mazzini (Giuseppe) [*continued*].
see BARATTA (M.) G. M. ed il confine orientale d'Italia, 1919.
,, HINKLEY (E.) M.: story of a gt. Italian, 1924.
,, LUZIO (A.) Carlo Alberto e M., 1923.
,, —— G. M. carbonaro: nuovi doc. d. archivi di Milano &c., con pref. &c., 1920.
,, SALVEMINI (G.) Mazzini, 1920.
,, SANCTIS (F. DE). Mazzini, 1920.
,, VOSSLER (O.) M.'s polit. Denken u. Wollen, 1927.

Mazziotti (Matteo). La congiura dei Rosaroll. St. storico con doc. ined. s8°. Bologna. [1920]

Mazzoleni (Alberto), *see* FINAZZI (G.) Di alcuni mss. conc. la storia d. Concilio di Trento, racc. M., 1865.

Mazzone di Miglionico (Marc Antonio). I fiori della poesia dichiarati &c. da l'opere di Virgilio, Ovidio & Horatio. Con frasi volg., Similitudini &c. 2p *in* 1v. 8°. Venetia. 1593

Mazzoni (Guido). I bóti d. SS. Annunziata in Firenze. [Nozze Rambaldi-Bertolini, N121]. s8°. Firenze. 1923
Il nome di Dante e le 2 società ital. intitolate da lui, *see* ARCHIVIO STOR. ITAL. Anno 79, v1, 1921.
see PETTORELLI (A.) G. M. da Modena, 1925.

Mazzuchelli (*il conte* **Giovanni Maria).** Vita di J. Bonfadio, *see* BONFADIUS (J.) Op., p1, 1746.

Meacham (*Miss* **M. I.)** The Kate Greenaway coll. of M. Sold, Dec. 12, Anderson gall. [P2856]. 8°. N.Y. 1921

Mead (Charles Williams). Old civilizations of Inca land. [Amer. Museum of Nat. Hist. Hdbk. ser., No. 11]. s8°. N.Y. 1924

Mead (G. R. S.) The gnostic John the baptizer; sel. from the Mandaean John-book w. studies on J. &c. 8°. 1924
Simon Magus: an essay. la8°. 1892

Mead (Richard). Medica sacra; sive de morbis insign. qui in Bibliis memorantur, comm. ed. nov. 8°. Lugduni Batav. 1759
Monita & præcepta medica. [*b. w. h.* Medica sacra, 1759]. 8°. Parisiis. 1757
Oratio Harveiana, 1723. Adj. diss. de nummis a Smyrnæis in medicorum honorem percussis. [*b. w. h.* Medica sacra, 1759]. 8°. Londini. 1725
see WINTRINGHAM (C.) Notationes & obs. in R. M. Monita &c., 1773.

Meade (G. Willoughby-), *see* WILLOUGHBY-MEADE (G.)

Meade (*Gen.* **George Gordon),** *U.S. Army*, *see* LYMAN (*Col.* T.) M.'s headquarters, 1863–65; letters; sel. &c. G. R. Agassiz, 1922.

Meadmore (W. S.) South Place Sunday popular concerts (1887–1927). 8°. 1927

Meager (Leonard). The Eng. gardener, or, a sure guide to young planters &c. 3p [*in 1v. plates 17 & 18 wanting*]. 8°. 1670

Meagher (George A.) Figure & fancy skating. Pref. by Earl of Derby. s8°. 1895

Meakin (*Lieut.* **Walter).** The 5th North Staffords & the North Midland Territorials (46th & 59th Div.), 1914–19. la8°. Longton, *Staffs.* 1920

Meaño (Luis F. Blanco), *see* BLANCO MEAÑO (L. F.)

Means (Philip Ainsworth). Hist. of the Span. conquest of Yucatan & of the Itzas. [Peabody Mus. of Amer. arch. &c., Harvard Univ. Papers, v7]. 8°. C., Mass. 1917
A survey of anc. Peruvian art. [*Extr. f.* Trans. of Connecticut Acad., v21]. 8°. New Haven. 1917

Me'ârath Gazzê. Book of the Cave of treasures [*wrongly ascr. to Ephraim, the Syrian*]. Tr. f. Syr. text by Sir E. A. W. Budge. 8°. 1927

Mears (Eliot Grinnell). Mod. Turkey, 1908–23. 8°. N.Y. 1924

Meath (Reginald Brabazon, *12th earl of***).**
Memories of the 19th cent. 8°. 1923
Memories of the 20th cent. 8°. 1924

Meautys (*Sir* **Thomas),** *see* BUNTEN (A. C.) Sir T. M. & h. friends, 1918.

Meaux, *see* RECUEIL. R. des hist. de la Fr., Obituaires, t4, Prov. de Sens, t4 (Diocèses de M. &c.), 1923.

Meaux (*Mr.* **de),** *see* BOSSUET (J. B.)

Mecatti (Giuseppe Maria). Storia geneal. d. nobiltà e cittadinanza di Firenze. t1. [*no more publ.?*] s4°. Napoli. 1754
In 3p. w. sep. tp. p1, 2, 1753.

Mech (V. D.) Силы реакціи—Либеральная &c. буржуазія, *see* GORN (VL.), V. M. & CHERAVANIN. Борьба обществ. силъ, в1, 4, 1907.

Mecham (J. Lloyd). Francisco de Ibarra & Nueva Vizcaya. 8°. Durham, *Carolina.* 1927

Mechel (Christian v.), *see* CRANACH (L.) Stammbuch &c.; hrsg. v. C. v. M., 1814.

Mechitar, *of Sebaste*, *see* MEKHITAR.

Mechitarists, *see* MEKHITARISTS.
Mechler (Ægidius). Catechismus: allenthalben gericht auf d. Catech. M. Luth. Item Bekentnis d. Glaubens u. Lere Æ. M. s8°. Witteberg. 1574
Mechnikov (Ilya Ilich), *see* METCHNIKOFF (ELIE).
Mecklenburg. Meklenburg. Urkundenbuch. Hrsg. v. d. Verein f. M. Gesch. &c. 11B. 4°. Schwerin. 1863–78
Mecklenburg (John Albert, *1st duke of***),** *see* JOHN ALBERT I, *duke of Mecklenburg.*
Mecklin (John Moffatt). The Ku Klux Klan. 8°. N.Y. 1924
Mecquenem (Roland de). Fouilles de Suse, 1914, 1921, 1922. [*Extr. f.* Revue d'Assyriologie, v19]. sm. fol. 1922
Meda (Filippo), *see* MUSSIO (G.) F. M., giornalista ministro, 1919.
Meddelelser om Grønland. Udg. af Komm. for Ledelsen af de Geolog. &c. Undersøgelser i Grønland. B39, 40. la8°. 1914–23
see THALBITZER (W.), *ed.* The Ammassalik Eskimo, 2p, 1914–1923. [39, 40.]
Meddygon Myddveu, *see* MYDDVAI.
Mede (Joseph). Gründl. Beweiss dass Kirchen z. christl. Gottesdienst verordnet in u. v. d. Apostel Zeit. her gewesen seyn geführet. Übers. u. mit Vorrede versehen v. H. L. Benthem. [P2638]. s4°. Hannover. 1706
Medeiros e Albuquerque (José). Vengeance of Felix, *see* GOLDBERG (I.), *tr.* Brazilian tales, 1924.
Meder (Joseph). Die Handzeichung. la8°. Wien. 1919
Handzeichnungen alter Meister aus d. Albertina u. aus Privatbesitz. Hrsg. J. M. Neue Folge. fol. Wien. 1922
Medhurst (Walter Henry), *D.D., the elder, 1796–1857.* China: its state & prospects, w. spec. ref. to spread of Gospel. 8°. 1838
Mediaeval [MEDIEVAL]. M. contrib. to mod. civilisation: lect., 1921, *see* HEARNSHAW (F. J. C.), *ed.*
M. France: companion to Fr. st., *by var. a.*, 1922, *see* TILLEY (A.), *ed.*
Medical Directory (The). 1909, 1922, 1927. 8°. [1909]–27
Medical Research Committee. National Health Insurance. Alcohol: its absorption into & disappearance f. blood under diff. conditions. [By E. Mellanby]. [P2577]. 8°. 1919
see also NATIONAL HEALTH INSURANCE.
Medical Research Council, *see* INDUSTRIAL FATIGUE RESEARCH BOARD.
Medici, *The family of.*
see BRINTON (S.) Golden age of the M., 1434–94, 1925.
„ BROSCH (M.) Albizzi u. M., 1908.
„ CONTI (G.) Firenze dopo i M., 1921.
„ MAGUIRE (Y.) Women of the M., 1927.
„ NOBLE (M.) Mem. of house of M., 1428–1737, 1797.
„ PIERACCINI (G.) La stirpe de' M. di Cafaggiolo, trasmiss. eredit. dei caratteri biol., 3v, 1924–25.
„ TRAPESNIKOFF (T.) Porträtdarstellungen d. Mediceer d. 15. Jhdts., 1909.
„ YOUNG (G. F.) The M., 3rd ed., repr., 2v, 1926.
Medici (Giovanni de'), *1567–1621, see* SOMMI PICENARDI (G.) G. de' M. &c., 1907.
Medici (Girolamo Casio de'), *see* CASIO DE' MEDICI (G.)
Medico-Legal Society. Transactions, 1919–20. Ed. R. H. Wellington &c. v14. 8°. 1921
Medin (*il conte* **Antonio),** *see* DANTE ALIGHIERI. Lectura D.: c. 13 dell' Inferno letto da A. M., 1905.
Medina (José Toribio). Dicc. de anónimos y seudónimos hispanoamer. 2t. la8°. Buenos Aires. 1925
see JONES (C. K.) Hisp. Amer. bibliog., w. crit. notes on sources by J. T. M., 1922.
Medinaceli (Luis [Fernandez de Cordova-Figueroa de la Cerda v. Salabert], *17th duke***),** *see* PAZ Y MELIA (A.) Series de los mas import. doc. del archivo y bibl. del Duque de M.; publ. par P. y M., s2, 1922.
Mediolanenses. Annales M., *see* FREDERICK I, *emp. of Germany.* Gesta F. in Lombardia (Annal. M. maiores), 1892.
Meditations. Medit. on life &c. of Christ; ed. C. D'Evelyn, 1921, *see* CHRIST.
Mediterranean. M. pilot, 5v, *&* Suppl. 2, 3, 5–7, 1913–22, *see* ADMIRALTY.
Medland (W. M.) & C. Weobly. Coll. of remark. &c. criminal trials &c. Pref., Essay on reprieve & pardon, & biog. sk. of Lord Eldon &c. 3v. 8°. 1803–5
Medler (Nicolaus), *see* DANZ (J. T. L.) Epistolae P. Melanchthonis ad N. M. &c., 1825.
Medley (Dudley Julius).
Orig. illust. of Eng. constit. hist. 8°. [1910]
Student's manual of Eng. constit. hist. 6th ed. rev. 8°. O. 1925
Medley (Samuel). Hymns. s8°. 1800

Medolago, *Family of, see* VAERINI (B.) Scritt. di Bergamo d. fam. M. &c., publ. A. Alessandri, 1873.
Medvecký (Karol A.) Andrej Kmeť, 1841–1908. Životopis. 8°. [v Turčianskom Sv. Martine]. 1913
Medvedev (Pavel). Драмы и поэмы Ал. Блока из ист. их создания. s8°. Ленинград. 1928
Medvedev (Silvestr [Semen]), *1641–91.* Записки, *see* SAKHAROV (I. P.) Записки &c., 1841.
Medwall (Henry). Fulgens & Lucres (c. 1490). Intr. note by S. de Ricci. [H. E. Huntington Facs. Repr., 1]. 8°. N.Y. 1920
„ „ Ed. F. S. Boas & A. W. Reed. s8°. O. 1926
see REED (A. W.) Early Tudor drama, M. &c., 1926.
Meehan (C. P.), *tr., see* O'DALY (D. DE R.) The Geraldines &c. (1655), 1847.
Meek (Alexander), *D.Sc.* Essentials of zoology &c. 8°. 1922
Meek (C. K.) Northern tribes of Nigeria: ethnogr. acc. w. rep. on 1921 census. 2v. 8°. 1925
Meek (Seth Eugene).
Works in FIELD COLUMBIAN MUSEUM.: Zool. ser.
Annot. list of fishes in fresh waters of Costa Rica, 1914. [10.]
New species of fishes f. Costa Rica, 1912. [10.]
—— & S. F. Hildebrand.
Works in FIELD COLUMBIAN MUS.: Zool. ser.
Descr. of new fishes f. Panama, 1912. [10.]
Fishes of fresh waters of Panama, 1916. [10.]
Marine fishes of Panama, 2p, 1923–25. [15.]
New species of fishes f. Panama, 1913. [10.]
Meerman (Gerard), *see* BOWYER (W.) Origin of printing; substance of M.'s acc., 1774.
—— & J. Meerman, *see* BYVANCK (A. W.) Princ. mss. à peint. de la Bibl. Roy. & du Musée Meermanno-Westreenianum à La Haye, 1924.
Meerwarth (Rudolf), W. Kisskalt & B. Karlsberg. Probleme d. deut. Zahlungsbilanz. [V. f. Sozialpol., B167i]. 8°. München. 1924
Mees (Josina A. Mees-), *see* SIMONS-MEES (J. A.)
Meester (Johan de). Geertje. 4e dr. 2d *in* 1v. 8°. Bussum. 1921
Megasthenes, *see* STEIN (O.) M. u. Kauṭilya, 1921.
Megglé (Armand). Le domaine colonial de la France, s. ressources &c. s8°. 1922
Mégroz (Rodolphe Louis). Francis Thompson. 8°. [1927]
A talk w. J. Conrad & a crit. 8°. 1926
The 3 Sitwells. 8°. 1927
Walter de la Mare. 8°. 1924
Mehedinți (S.) Caracterizarea etnogr., prin. munca și uneltele, *see* ACADEMIA ROM. Disc. 47, 1920.
Méhée de la Touche (Jean Claude Hippolyte). Hist. de la révol. de Pologne en 1791, avec exam. de la nouv. constit. 2e éd. s8°. 1792
Mehta (*Sir* **Ferozshah),** *see* MODY (H. P.) Sir P. M.: polit. biog., 2v, 1921.
Mehta (S. S.) Monograph on Mirabai, the saint of Mewad. 8°. [Bombay. 1920]
Meh Tse, *Chinese philosopher.* The social teachings of M. T. [tr.] L. Tomkinson, 1927, *see* ASIATIC SOC. OF JAPAN, Trans., s2, v4, 1927.
Meibom (Heinrich), *the younger.* De incubatione in fanis deorum (1659), *see* SCHLÄGER (C. J.) Diss. fasc. 1, 1742.
Meibomius (Marcus), *see* MAJUS (J. H.) Repet. examen &c., spec. Bibl. emend. M. M. &c., 1708.
Meier (Carl Ernst). Westfäl. Wasserburgen, 15 Steinzeichnungen. 4°. Münster. 1913
Meier (Friedrich Carl). Judaica seu vet. script. profan. de rebus Judaicis fragm. Coll. F. K. M. 8°. Jenae. 1832
Notiones vet. Ebraeorum de rebus post mortem futuris. Diss. [*b. w. h.* Judaica]. 8°. Jenae. 1832
Meier (Gebhard Theodor). Codex canonum Eccl. univ. à Justiniano confirmatus. Ed. nova cura M. Cum ejusdem de coll. canonum hist. rel. *Gr. & Lat.* [*b. w.* Kritopoulos (M.) Confessio, 1661]. s4°. Helmestadi. 1663
Meier (Georg) [MAJOR (G.)], *prof. of theology, Wittenberg, 1502–74.*
Primus [— Tertius] tomus operum G. M. 3t [t2 *has tp.* Homeliae &c., 1563]. fol. Witebergae. 1563–70
De arbore consanguinitatis &c. regulae & tabellae. [*b. w.* Melanchthon (P.) Explic. Proverb., 1551]. s8°. Wittebergae, *J. Craton.* 1551
De orig. & autoritate verbi Dei &c. [*b. w.* Augsburg Confession. Conf. fidei, 1542]. s8°. Witembergae, *J. Sufft.* 1550
Ewiger Göttlicher Allmecht. Mayestat Declaration. Wider Carl und Bapst Paulum III. s4°. *n.p.* [c. 1546]
„ „ ....[*a. ed.*] s4°. *n.p.* [c. 1546]

Meier (Georg) [MAJOR (G.)] [*continued*].
Homeliae in Epistolas dierum dominic. et festorum, 1563, *see* Opera, t2, *above*.
Refut. horrendae prophanationis coenae Domini. Cum praef. P. Melanchthon. [*b. w.* Melanchthon (P.) Explic. Proverb., 1551]. s8°. Witebergae, *V. Creutzer*. 1551
Vita S. Pauli Apostoli. [*Foll. by* Euthalii de temp. praedic. S. Pauli &c. *Gr. & Lat.*] s8°. Wittembergae. 1556
„ „ *see* GUDE (G. F.) De eccl. Ephesinae statu &c., 1732.
see AMSDORFF (N.) Ein kurtzer vnterricht auff G. M. Antwort &c., 1552.
„ BRAUNSCHWEIG. Christl. Bedencken auff M. Repetition &c., 1568.
„ MANSFELD. Bericht der Prediger der Irrungen halben &c., 1568.
„ SCHLÜSSELBURG (C.) Haereticorum cat., lib. 7, Maioristarum argumenta, 1599.
„ †ULENBERG (C.) Gesch. d. luther. Reformatoren, B2, 1837.
„ —— Hist. de vita &c. Melanchthonis, M. &c., 1622.

Meier (Georg August). Dionysii Areopagitae & mysticorum saec. 14 doct. inter se compar. Diss. 8°. Halis. [1845]

Meier (I. I.) Tabeera Nordhusana i. e. deflagratio qua Nordhusa periit, carmine heroico descr. &c. [P444]. s4°. Nordhusa. 1712

Meier (Johann Christian Wilhelm). Diss. de effectibus concionum methodisticarum haud miraculosis nec mirabilibus. s4°. 1758

Meier (Paul Jonas). Die Stadt Goslar. s8°. St. 1926

Meier-Gräfe (Julius).
Cézanne. Tr. J. Holroyd-Reece. 4°. 1927
Courbet. 3. Aufl. la8°. München. 1924
Dostoevsky, the man & h. work. Tr. H. H. Marks. la8°. 1928
Spanische Reise. 2e A. 8°. 1923
Spanish journey. Tr. J. Holroyd-Reece. 8°. [1926]
Vincent. 2B. 4°. München. [1921]
Vincent Van Gogh. A biog. study. Tr. J. H. Reece. 2v. 4°. 1922

Meijer (Jacob). Disput.: Institutum Mosaicum in Hebraeorum de rebus post mortem futuris opinionibus. 8°. Groningae. 1825

Meijer (Willem).
Spinoza: een levensbeeld. [P2416]. la8°. [1915]
see SPINOZA (B. DE). Spinozana, 1897–1922, benevens een Levensb. omt. Dr. W. M., 1922.

Meikle (James).
Places & place-names round Alyth. 8°. Paisley. 1925

Meikle (John James). Claims of M. Rep. of comm. app. to inquire into. [*b. w.* Chemis (L.) Regina v. L. C., 1889]. fol. [Wellington. 1907]

Meilhac (Henry). Bibliothèque de H. M. [*Sale catalogue*]. [P2603]. la8°. [1922]

Meillet (Antoine) [MEILLET (PAUL JULES A.)], *b. 1866*.
De la compos. en arménien. [Extr. des Mém. de la Soc. de Ling. de Paris, t18. P2798]. 8°. 1913
De quelques évangéliaires armén. accentués. [Extr. des Mém. Orient., Congr. de 1905. P2804]. la8°. 1905
Linguistique historique &c. la8°. 1921
Le Slave commun. la8°. 1924
3 confér. sur les Gâthâ de l'Avesta. [Museé Guimet]. s8°. 1925
see LANGUES (Les) du monde; sous la dir. de A. M. &c., 1924.

—— & A. Vaillant.
Gramm. de la langue serbo-croate. 8°. 1924

—— & *Mme.* H. de Willman-Grabowska.
Gramm. de la langue polon. 8°. 1921

Meilleure. *De la meill. man. d'entendre la messe, 1681, *see* LE TOURNEUX (N.)

Mein (Susan), *aft. wife of Lt.-Col. W. Sibbald, see* SIBBALD (*Mrs.* S.)

Meincke (David). Osiandrismum in pietismo renatum, præs. G. Wernsdorfio, disput. excutiet D. M. [P2587]. s4°. Wittembergæ. 1707

Meinecke (Friedrich). Deutsche Kultur u. Machtpolitik im engl. Urteil, *see* DEUTSCHE Reden in schwerer Zeit, 29, 1915.
Weltbürgertum u. Nationalstaat. 3e A. 8°. München. 1915

Meiner (Annemarie). Das deut. Signet. 4°. L. 1922

Meinertzhagen (Dan) & R. P. Hornby. Bird life in an Arctic spring. Diaries of D. M. & R. P. H. [*&* The Mottisfont birds & t. master (D. M.)] s8°. 1899

Meinhard II, *count of Tyrol.* Meinhards II, Urbare d. Grafschaft Tirol; v. O. v. Zingerle, *see* FONTES RERUM AUSTRIAC., B45i, 1890.

Meinhard, *bp. of (1) Ykeshola, (2) Riga, see* WITTE (H.) Exemplum non simulatae relig. in M., 1689.

Meinhart (Roderich). Wiener Totentanz. Roman. s8°. L. 1921

Meinhold (J. Wilhelm). Mary Schweidler, the amber witch. Tr. Lady Duff Gordon. s8°. 1846
Sidonia v. Bork, d. Klosterhexe. 2B. s8°. L. [1924?]

Meinike (Joachim). Disput. de reliquiis Christi & sanctorum. Sub. præs. S. Niemanni. [P2635]. s4°. Jenæ. 1666

Meinong von Handschuchsheim (Alexius) [A. MEINONG].
Über emotionale Präsentation, 1917, *see* KAISERL. AKAD. D. W. ZU WIEN. Sitz., B183, 1924.
Zum Erweise d. allgem. Kausalgesetzes, 1918, *see* KAISERL. AKAD. D. W. ZU WIEN. Sitz., B189, 1919.

Meintel (Johann Georg).
Diss. crit. de orig. vocis Teuton. Kirche. s4°. *n.p.* 1755
Probe e. crit. Polyglotten-Bibel, Conferenzen ü. d. ersten 3 Cap. des 1. Buchs Mose [*&* Cap. 4. biss z. Ende. 3T *in* 2v]. 4°. Nürnberg. [1761]–69
T2 *has t.:* Fortges. crit. Polyglotten-Conferenzen.
T3, Crit. Polyglotten-Conf.

Meinwerk, *bp. of Paderborn.* Leben. [*Lat.*] Hrsg. F. Tenckhoff. [Scr. rerum Germ. in usum schol.] 8°. Hannover. 1921

Meis (Angelo Camillo de).
see CROCE (B.) Ricerche &c. Desanctisiani, 9, Carteggio ined. di A. C. de M., 1915.
„ VECCHIO-VENEZIANI (A. DEL). La vita e l'opera di A. C. de M., 1921.

Meisl (Josef). Gesch. d. Juden in Polen u. Russland. B1–3. 8°. 1921–25

Meisner (Balthasar). Collegium Adiaphoristicum; controv. circa Adiaphora inter nos & Calvinianos. Ed. alt. emend. s4°. Wittebergae. 1663
Medit. sacræ in Evangelia dominicalia. s8°. Wittebergæ. 1619
Philosophia sobria: consid. quaest. quas Calviniani moverunt &c. 3p. s8°. Giessae Hessorum. [p3, Wittenberg]. 1611–1623

Meisner (Basilius). De Judaeorum flagellandi ritibus. Praes. J. Hilperto. [P2666]. s4°. Helmaestadi. 1652

Meisner (Heinrich Otto), *ed., see* WALDERSEE (*Graf* A. v.) Denkwürdigkeiten, 3B, 1923.

Meisner (Johann), *prof. of theology at Wittenberg.* Tractatus de Origene & Origenianis. ed. 2a. s4°. Wittenbergæ. 1712

Meissner (Bruno). Assyr. Jagden, *see* ALTE ORIENT (DER), Jhrg. 13, 1911.
Babylonien u. Assyrien. 2B. s8°. Heidelberg. 1920–25
Grundzüge d. babylonisch-assyr. Plastik. [Der Alte Orient, Jhrg. 15]. 8°. L. 1915

Meissner (Rudolf), *see* RHEINISCHE Beitr. &c. zur german. Philol. u. Volkskunde; hrsg. T. Frings, R. M. &c., 1922–26.

Meister (Aloys). Die deut. Presse im Kriege &c. 8°. Münster i. W. 1916
Deut. Verfassungsgesch., b. ins 14. Jhdt., 2e A., 1913, *see* GRUNDR. D. GESCHICHTSWISS., 2iii, 1913.
Grundzüge d. hist. Methode, 2e A., 1913, *see* GRUNDR. D. GESCHICHTSWISS., 1vi, 1913.
see GRUNDRISS D. GESCHICHTSWISSENSCHAFT; hrsg. v. A. M., 1912–22.

Meister von Flémalle, *see* FLÉMALLE (*Meister* VON).

Mejov (Vladimir Izmailovich). Систематъ. каталогъ русскимъ книгамъ. 8°. С.-П. 1869

Mekerchus (Adolphus), *see* BEZA (T.) De vera pronuntiatione Gr. & Lat. linguae &c. (A. M. de vet. & recta pronunt. ling. Gr. comment), 1587.

Mekertich Khrimean, *see* KHRIMEAN, *Hairik.*

Mekhithar, *Anetzi.* Patmouthiun. [Hist. *in Armenian*; *ed.* Kh. Patkanean, *see* SEBEOS]. Hist., 1879.

Mekhithar, *Gosh* [MKHITHAR, *Coss, Goche, Kosch*]. Arakq. [Fables *in Armenian*]. s8°. i Venetik. 1854
Choix de fables attr. à M. G.; tr. par F. Macler. [Extr. du Journ. Asiat. P2791]. 8°. 1902
[Code of laws of the Armenians. *In Armenian.* Ed. V. Bastamean]. la8°. i Vagharshapat. 1880

Mekhithar, *physician, of Her.* [Balm for fevers. *In Armenian*]. 8°. i Venetik. 1832

Mekhithar, *vardapet of Sebaste.*
see ALBERTUS *Magnus.* Girq Eraneloyn Alperti; [tr. by M.], 1729.
„ AUCHER (P.) *Brief acc. of the M. Soc. &c., 1835.
„ LAZIKEAN (A.) Poem on M. (*in Armenian*), 1900.

Mekhitharists.
Abriss d. Gesch. d. Wiener Mekhit. Congreg. [P2812]. 8°. Wien. 1887
*Brief (A) acc. of the M. Soc. &c., 1835, *see* AUCHER (P.)
Cat. d. armen. Hss. in d. M.-Bibliothek zu Wien. Von J. Dashian. 4°. Wien. 1895

Mekhitharists [*continued*].
[Cat. of the publs. of the Mekhitharist Press, 1716–1893. *In Armenian.* P2800]. s8°. Venetik-S. Lazar. 1893
„ „ [*a. ed.*] 1716–1910. [P2815]. s8°. Venetik-S. Lazar. 1910
„ „ [Triest & Vienna, 1776–1895. *In Armenian.* P2800]. s8°. Vienna. 1895
[*List & spec. of type*, 1716–1898, *M. Press. In Armenian.* P2803, 2807]. 8°. Venetik. 1898
[M. jubilee, San Lazaro, Venice, 1701–1901. *In Armenian. By* L. Alishan, S. Sarean *& others*]. la8°. [Venice. 1901]
see MARY, *the Virgin.* Le glorie di M. &c.; dai P. P. d. Congr. M. di S. Antonio, Trieste, 1780.

Meklenburgisches Urkundenbuch, 11B, 1863–78, *see* MECKLENBURG.

Mekum (Friedrich) [†MYCONIUS (F.)], *see* SCHERFFIG (P.) F. M. v. Lichtensfels: e. Lebensbild, 1909.

Melanchthon (Philipp).
Operum P. M. tomi quinque. 5t *b. in* 2. fol. Basileae, *I. Hervagius.* 1541
Omnium operum P. M. pars 1[–4]. [Ed. C. Peucer]. 4p *in* 4v. fol. Wittebergae. 1562–64
Aliquot insign. loc. Terrae Sanctae explic., *see* Peucer (C.) De dimensione terrae &c., 1544.
Annot. in Epistolam ad Rhomanos unam & ad Corinthios duas. s8°. Argentorati, *I. Hervagius.* 1523
Antwort auff das Buch Andreae Osiandri v. d. Rechtfertigung d. Menschen. s4°. Witteberg. 1552
Apologia Confessionis. *For editions issued as part of the Augsburg Conf., see* AUGSBURG CONFESSION.
*Catechesis cont. explicationem simplicem & brevem &c. contextam ex Corpore doctrinæ Christ. Ed. in Acad. Witeberg. &c. s8°. Witebergæ. 1571
„ „ ....[*a. ed. w. index*]. s8°. *n.p.* 1571
„ „ contextam ex scriptis P. M. s8°. Witebergæ. 1572
Catechesis puerilis recogn. [*b. w.* Loss (L.) Catechismus &c., 1553]. s8°. Lipsiae. 1549
Comm. in epistolam Pauli ad Romanos. s8°. [Vitebergae, *J. Clug*]. 1532
Consilia sive judicia theologica &c. Ed. studio Chr. Pezelii. s8°. Neustadii. 1600
Corpus doctrinæ Christ. s8°. Lipsiae. 1569
„ „ ....[*a. ed.*] s8°. Argentorati. 1580
De artibus liberalibus oratio à P. M. Tubingae habita. s4°. [Hagenau. Ex charisio T. Anshelmi. 1517]
De conjugio piae commonefactiones. [*b. w. h.* Explic. Proverb., 1551]. s8°. Wittebergae, *J. Craton.* 1551
De dialectica libri quatuor recogniti. s8°. [Vitebergæ, *I. Clug.*] 1533
*De disput. inter M. & Lutherum super justificatione [1536]. [Rector Acad. Lips. indicit. P2742]. s4°. [Lipsiae. 1783]
De Eccl. auctoritate & de vet. scriptis libellus. [*b. w. h.* Explic. Proverb., 1551; *a. c. b. w.* Augsburg Confession. Conf. fidei, 1542]. s8°. Vitebergae. *J. Klug.* 1550
De Erasmo—Ratio discendi &c., *see* LUTHER (M.) Iudicium, 1522?.
De legibus oratio, *see* ALCIATUS (A.) De ponderibus &c., 1530.
De locorum theolog. P. M. orthodoxa puritate &c. assertio &c. aliquot doctorum [M. Lutheri &c.]. s4°. [Gorlicii]. 1580
De rebus adiaphoris epistola concionatorum Hamburg. ad P. M. & responsio [1549]. s8°. *n.p. n.d.* [1550?]
De vita et actis Lutheri comm. Adjectum est epigramma de Fonte Lutheri. [P2443]. s4°. Vitembergae. 1700
Declamationum M. quae ab ipso & aliis in Acad. Witeberg. recitatae ac editae sunt, nunc primum in 3 tomos distinctae opera M. J. Richardii. 3t. s8°. Argentorati, *T. Rihelius.* [1570]
1, Philosophicus. 2, Medicus ac Juridicus. 3, Theologicus.
Declamatiunculæ duæ in Pauli doctrinam. Ejusdem epistola ad J. Hessum. s8°. [Argentorati, *J. Hervagius.* 1522]
Defensio P. M. contra Joannem Ekium. [P2444]. s4°. [Lipsi, *Wolfgangus Monacensis.* 1519]
Deuttung der czwo grewliche Figuren Bapstesels czu Rom [durch P. M. deuttet] u. Munchkalbs zu Freyberg ynn Meysszen [deuttung M. Luthers] funden. [*w. woodcuts.* P2539]. s4°. Wittemberg. 1523
Didymi Faventini adv. Thomam Placentinum [*i.e.* H. Emser] pro M. Luthero oratio. s8°. *n.p.* [1521]
Elementorum rhetorices libri duo. Adjectæ: Epistolæ contrariæ Pici & Hermolai Barbari una cum dispositione. P. M. 2p [*pagin. cont.*] s8°. Lipsiæ. 1547
Enarr. brevis concionum libri Salomonis cui titulus est Ecclesiastes. [*b. w. h.* Explic. Proverb. Salom., 1551]. s8°. Vitebergae, *J. Klug.* 1550
Epigrammata P. M. selectiora, formulis precum, historiis, paraphrasi dictorum divin., &c. insignia coll. a M. Petro Hegelundo. Iconibus exorn. a S. Feyerabend. s4°. Francoforti ad Moenum. 1583
Epistola de Lipsica Disputatione. s4°. [Leipzig?. 1519]
„ „ [*a. ed.* P2444]. s4°. [Wittenberg. 1521?]

Melanchthon (Philipp) [*continued*].
Epistola in qua respondetur Flacio Illyrico. s8°. Vittebergæ, *J. Klug.* 1549
Epistolarum liber. Antehac nunquam ed. s8°. Lugd. Bat., *Elzevir.* 1647
Epistolarum P. M. liber primus. Ed. a C. Peucero. [*&* Alter libellus epist. P. M. *2p in 1v. sep. pagin*]. s8°. Witebergae. 1570–74
Epitome renovatæ eccl. doctrinæ ad illust. principem Hessorū. s8°. *n.p. n.d.* [1524]
Examen eorum qui audiuntur ante ritum publicae ordinationis, qua commendatur eis ministerium Evangelii. Traditum Vuitebergae 1554. s8°. Witebergae. 1556
„ „ ....[*a. ed.*] s8°. Witebergae. 1559
„ „ ....[*a. ed.*] s8°. Witebergae. 1577
Explic. Proverbiorum Salomonis in schola Witemberg. recens dictata. s8°. Francoforti, *P. Brubach.* 1551
*Farrago aliquot epigrammatum P. Melanchthonis & aliorū quorundam erudit. s8°. Haganoæ, *J. Secerius.* 1528
Grammatica Græca. Jam denuo recognita &c. s8°. Haganoæ, *J. Secerius.* 1527
„ „ ....s8°. Basileæ, *N. Brylinger.* 1538
Grammatica Latina, ab auth. nuper aucta & recog. s8°. Norembergæ, *J. Petreius.* 1529
Historia de vita & actis M. Lutheri. Adjecta sunt a J. Policario Carmina quædam de beneficiis quae Deus per L. orbi terrarum contulit. s8°. [Apud Thuringiæ Hieræfordiam (Erfurt), *G. Sthurmerus*]. 1548
„ „ Adj.: De obitu ejus brevis narr. s8°. *n.p.* 1557
In Evangelia quae usitato more diebus dominicis & festis proponuntur, annot. P. M. Recogn. & auctae. s8°. Lipsiae. 1552
*Kurtzer Bericht wie P. M. sein Leben hie auff Erden geendet &c. Geschrieben v. d. Professoribus d. Universitet Witteberg &c. [P2442]. s4°. Nürnberg, [*Valentin Newber*]. 1560
Liber cont. continua serie epistolas P. M. scriptas annis 38 ad J. Camerar., studio hujus ed., curante eum exprim. E. Vœgelino. 8°. Lipsiæ. [1569]
Loci communes, das ist die furnemesten Artikel christl. lere. Aus d. Latin verdeutscht durch J. Jonam. 8°. Wittenberg. 1536
*Loci communes rerum theologicarum seu hypotyposes theologicae. s8°. Wittembergae. 1521
„ „ ....[*a. ed.*] s4°. Vitebergae. 1541
Melanchthon-Kompend.: e. unbekannte Sammlg. eth., polit. u. philos. Lehrsätze M. in Luthers Werken. [Hrsg.] J. Haussleiter. 8°. Greifswald. 1902
Necessarias esse ad omne studiorum genus artes dicendi P. M. declamatio. Item Luciani opusc. ad. indoctum & multos libros ementem. s8°. Hagenoa, *J. Secerius. n.d.* [1524?]
Oratio dicta cum decerneretur gradus magisterii A. Winclero Vratisla & aliis viris, 1535. [*b. w.* Alesius (A.) Responsio &c. 1535]. s8°. *n.p.* 1535
Oratio dicta in funere Friderichi Saxoniae ducis.—Oratio de legibus.—De gradibus.—Praef. in Æschinis & Demosthenis orationes.—Oratio Critiae contra Theramenem ex Xenophonte. [P2541]. s8°. Hagonae. 1525
Oratio uber Leich des. Ehrw. h. D. M. L. Verdeudscht durch D. C. Creutziger. s4°. Wittemberg, *G. Rhaw.* 1546
Orationes, epitaphia & scripta, quae edita sunt de morte P. M. omnia, cum narr. &c. edita à professoribus Acad. Vuiteberg. s8°. Vitebergae. 1561
Ein schrifft an ein erbare Stadt, von anrichtung d. Latin. Schuel. s4°. Wittemberg. [1543]
Sententia de cœna Domini, ex scriptis ejus coll. per J. Westphalum. s8°. Noribergae. 1557
Sententiæ Sanct. Patrum de Coena Domini, recitatæ & ed. Vuitebergæ. [*b. w. h.* Examen eorum qui audiuntur ante ritum &c., 1577]. s8°. Witebergæ. 1574
Sermo habitus apud iuventutem acad. Wittemberg. de corrigendis adulescentiæ studiis. s4°. [Vuittenburgij, *J. Grunenberg.* 1518]
Supplementa Melanchthoniana. Werke P. M. die im Corpus Reform. vermisst werden. Hrsg. v. d. M.-Komm. d. Verein f. Reformationsgesch. Abt. 5, T1, Abt. 6, T1. la8°. L. 1915–26
5i, Schriften z. prakt. Theol.; hrsg. P. Drews u. F. Cohrs, T1, Katechet. Schr., 1915.
6i, Briefwechsel; hrsg. O. Clemen, B1, 1926.
Syntaxis, ab auth. recogn. Item De periodis, De prosodia. s8°. [Norimbergæ, *I. Petreius*]. 1529
Ursach warumb die Stende, so der Augspurg. Confession anhangen &c. Auch warumb das vermeindte Trient. Concilium weder zu besuchen, noch darein zu willigen sey gestellet auss Churfürstlichem befelh. s4°. [Nürmberg, *J. v. Berg & U. Neuber*]. 1546
Below title is a woodcut represent. the elector of Saxony.
Vita M. Lutheri. Adj. Petri Mosellani Narr. de disput. Lips. 1519. Adj. præf. & annot. C. A. Heumannus. ed. 2ª. [P2627]. s4°. Gottingae. 1746
see AUGSBURG. Acta Comiciorum Augustae ex litt. Philippi &c. ad M. L.; hrsg. G. Berbig, 1907.
„ †CALINICH (R.) Kampf u. Untergang d. Melanchthonismus in Kursachsen, 1570–74, 1866.
„ CAMERARIUS (J.) De P. M. ortu, &c., 1566; 1696.

Melanchthon (Philipp) [*continued*].
see CAMERARIUS (J.), *the elder*. Vita P. M., 1655.
,, —— De vita M., bibl. libr. M. &c., 1777.
,, CLEMEN (O.) Studien zu M. Reden u. Gedichten, 1913.
,, COCHLAEUS (J.) *Ein Sendbrieffe, wider P. M., 1544.
,, COGLER (J.) Imagines elegantissimae, ad intellig. doct. Xtnae. locos coll., ex praelect. P. M. &c., 1558.
,, COHRS (F.) P. M., Deutschlands Lehrer, 1897.
,, CROCUS (C.) De vera Christi eccl. lib.; alter a J. Latomo libello De eccl. P. M. resp., c. 1545.
,, DANZ (J. T. L.) Epistolae P. M. ad J. Stigelium, 1824.
,, —— Epistolae P. M. ad Nic. Medlerum &c., 1825.
,, ECK (J.) Excusatio E. ad ea que falso &c., 1519.
,, ECKHARD (P. J.) Vindiciae Lutheri & M., 1738.
,, EURIPIDES. Tragoediae; Lat. soluta orat. redd. &c. e praelect. P. M., 1558.
,, FLACIUS (M.) *Illyricus*. Epistola apologetica, item duo somnia Philippi &c., 1549?.
,, —— Responsio ad epist. P. M., 1549.
,, HAUSSLEITER (J.) Aus d. Schule M.: theol. Disp. &c. zu Wittenberg, 1546–60, 1897.
,, JOYE (G.) Expos. of Daniel, out of P. M., &c., 1550.
,, KAWERAU (G.) Die Versuche, M. z. kath. Kirche zurückzuführen, 1902.
,, LOSS (L.) Annot. in Gramm. P. M. Lat., 1559.
,, MOSELLANUS (P.) Tabulae de schematibus & tropis; item. Rhetorices P. M. tab., 1527.
,, MYLIUS (M.) Chronologia scriptorum P. Melanchthonis, 1582.
,, OSIANDER (L.) De studiis Verbi div. minist. priv. recte instit. admon.; acc. Alia P. M. &c., 2p, 1733.
,, PARIS, *University of*. Determinatio super doct. Lutheriana & Apologia *by* P. M., 1521.
,, —— Determin. secunda super Apologiam P. M., 1521.
,, PEUCER (C.) Tract. hist. de P. M. sententia, De controv. Coenae Domini &c., 1596.
,, PEZEL (C.) Argumentorum et object., de artic. doct. Xtnę., cum respons., quae extant in scr. P. M., 9p, 1578–89.
,, RATISBON. Actes of the disputaciō in cowncell of Empyre holden at Regenspurg; pref. of P. M., set forth by P. M. &c.; tr., 1542.
,, REINHARD (L.) Comm. (Unumstössl. Beweis dass P. M. wegen d. Conf. zu Augspurg unterredet &c.), 1731.
,, SCHMIDT (H.) Narr. de morbo obituque M. &c., 1860.
,, SCHMIDT (J. A.) Progr. de corporibus doct. Philippicae &c., 1706.
,, SCHOTT (A. H.) Mem. P. M. &c., 1717.
,, SELL (C.) P. M. u. d. deut. Reformation bis 1531, 1897.
,, SELNECCERUS (N.) Recitationes: 4, De autoritate Lutheri & Ph., 1581.
,, SOTHEBY (S. L.) Unpubl. doc. &c. in the autograph of P. M., 1840.
,, STALLBAUM (J. G.) De P. M. libror. sacror. interprete, 1856.
,, STAPHYLUS (F.), *the elder*. Defensio pro Trimembri theologia M. Lutheri contr P. M. &c., 1559.
,, STRIGELIUS (V.) In epitomen philos. moralis P. M. ὑπομνήματα, 1582.
,, —— In P. M. libellum de anima notae &c., 1590.
,, —— Loci theologici quibus loci comm. P. M. illustrantur, 1582–84.
,, †ULENBERG (C.) Gesch. d. luther. Reformatoren, B2, 1837.
,, —— Hist. de vita &c. M., 1622.
,, VIRGILIUS MARO (P.) Opera una cum annot. P. M., 1547.
,, VOLLANDUS (J. I.) Merita P. M. in rem lit. Noribergensium, 1719.
,, WEGSCHEIDER (J. A. L.) P. M. epistolae 13, 1827.
,, WITTENBERG. Libelli Calviniani, Tract. hist. de P. M. sententia de controv. Coenae à C. Peucero scr. refut., 1597.
,, WOLFART (J. F.) De P. M. eoque per Scrip. S. interpret. de Sacrorum instaur., 1824.
,, WORMS. Abschied der gesandten Augspurg. Conf., zum Colloquio inn Wormbs, [signed P. M. &c.], 1557.
,, —— Colloq. Wormaciense instit. A.D. 1540 &c., 1542.

Melanchthonus (J.), *ps.*, *see* CHAMBRUN (J. P. DE).

Melanesia. Essays on the depopul. of M., 1922, *see* RIVERS (W. H. R.), *ed.*

Mélanges d'hist. offerts à H. Pirenne, 2t., 1926, *see* PIRENNE (H.)

Melani (Alfredo). Palladio, 1508–80. la8°. Milano. 1928

Melania, *Saint, 383–439* [MÉLANIE], *see* GOYAU (G.) Sainte M., 10e éd., 1921.

Mélas (George M.) Ex-king Constantine & the War. 8°. [1920]
The Turk as he is. 8°. [Hove. 1922]

Melato (Macario Padua), *ps.*, *see* AMAT (F.)

Melato (Maria), *see* BONTEMPELLI (M.) M. M., 1921.

Melba (*Mme.*) Melodies & memories. 8°. [1925]

Melbourne (Elizabeth, *viscountess*), *1752–1818*, *see* AIRLIE (M., *ctss. of*). In Whig society, 1775–1818: f. corresp. of E. &c., 1921.

Melbourne (William Lamb, *2nd visc.*)
see WALLACE (T.) *A letter to M. &c. on admin. of Earl Mulgrave, 1836.
,, —— *3 letters addr. to Visc. M. &c., 1835.

Melchers (B.), *see* FUHRMANN (E.) & B. M. China, 2B, 1921.

Melchet (*Rt. Hon.* **Alfred Moritz Mond,** *baron*), *see* MOND.

Melchizedec, *king of Salem*.
see LEBISII (D.) Diss. de M. &c., 1669.
,, OUTREIN (J. D'). Diss. de M. non Henocho &c., 1713.
,, QUANDT (J. J.) Examen controv. de sacerdotio M., 1735.

Meldahl (F.) Venedig: Hist. og Mindesmærker. 4°. 1903
,, ,, ...Suppl. *w. t.* Venedigs Kirker. 4°. 1903

Meldrum (David Storrar).
Rembrandt's paintings, w. essay on h. life &c. la8°. [1923]

Meldrum (George). Sermon agst. toleration of episcopacy, *see* SAGE (J.) The reasonableness of toleration &c., 1705.

Meldrum (Neil).
Forteviot: hist. of a Strathearn parish. 8°. Paisley. 1926

Meleager [M. GADARENUS; MELEAGRO DA GADARA].
Compl. poems. Tr. F. A. Wright. s8°. [1924]

Melendez Valdes (Juan). Poesias. 3t. s8°. Valladolid. 1797

Meletius, *of Tiberiopolis*, *see* HELMREICH (G.) Handschriftl. Studien zu M., 1918.

Meleusippus, *see* ACTA Iberica SS. tergemin. martyrum M. &c.; ed. &c. N. Marr, 1906.

Melgunov (Grigory Valerianovich). О южномъ берегѣ Каспiйскаго моря. [I. Akad. Nauk. Записки, t3, 1863]. 8°. С.-П. 1863

Melgunov (Serg. Petr.) Red terror in Russia. [Tr.] 8°. 1925

Melho (Philippus de). Eenige Psalmen Davids, en andere lofzangen, in Tamul. overgeset door P. de M. s8°. Clombo. 1755

Melicof (Jean Loris-), *see* LORIS-MELIKOV (I.)

Mélida (Joseph Ramón), *see* RAMÓN MÉLIDA (J.)

Mélingue (Étienne Marin), *see* TRUFFIER (J.) M.: le comédien &c., 1925.

Melish (John). Traveller's directory thr. the U.S. [*Extra maps wanting*]. 5th ed. s8°. Phila. 1819

Melissander (Caspar). Einhellige Bekentnis vieler Theologen u. fürnemer Kirchen in etl. Fürstenthumen &c. d. alt. Augspurg Confession &c. Von d. Newen Catechismo &c. s4°. Jhena. 1572
Epithalamion. Erklerung d. Geheimnuss Christi &c. so im Ehestandt fürgebildet &c. dem David Dürnbacher &c. in Reime verfast. 8°. Lavingen. 1567

Melissus (Paulus), *ps.* [*i.e.* PAUL SCHEDE], *see* NOLHAC (P. DE). Un poète rhénan ami de la Pléiade, P. M., 1923.

Melito, *Saint, bp. of Sardis*, *see* WOOG (C. C.) De M. S. in Asia episcopo, 1734.

Mell (Anton). Regesten z. Gesch. d. Familien v. Teufenbach in Steiermark, 1074–1547, *see* HISTORISCHER VEREIN F. STEIERMARK. Beitr., J34, 1905.

Melland (Frank Hulme). In witch-bound Africa. Primitive Kaonde tribe & th. beliefs. 8°. 1923

Mellard, *Family of*, *see* READE (A. L.) The M. &c., 1915.

Mellarède (Pietro), *plenipotentiary of Savoy at Congress of Utrecht, 1659–1730*. Rel. s. corte d'Inghilterra [*in French*]; pubbl. D. Carutti, *see* REGIA DEP. DI STORIA PATRIA. Misc., t24, 1885.

Mellen (Grenville). Book of the U.S. 8°. N.Y. 1839

Meller (Simon).
Peter Vischer d. Ältere u. s. Werkstatt. la8°. L. 1925

Meller (Walter Clifford). The Boy Bishop & o. essays on forgotten customs &c. 8°. 1923
A knight's life in the days of chivalry. 8°. 1924
Old times: relics, talismans, forgotten customs &c. 8°. [1925]

Mellicensis. Anonymus M. de scriptoribus eccl., *see* PEZ (B.) Bibl. Benedictino-Mauriana, 1716.

Mellius Freirius, *see* MELLO FREIRE DOS REIS (P. J. DE).

Mello (Francisco de), *see* MELO (F. DE).

Mello (Francisco Manoel de), *1608–66* [MELO]. Apologos dialogaes. Com noticia da vida &c. do author por A. Herculano. 3v *in* 1. 8°. 1900
Carta de guia de casados (1651). Com estudo crit., notas &c. por E. Prestage. 2a ed. rev. s8°. Porto. 1923
see PRESTAGE (E.) D. F. M. de Mello, 1922.

Mello (*Cap.* **Froilano de) & J. F. St. A. Fernandes.** Révision des champignons appart. au genre Nocardia. [As. Soc. of Bengal, Mem., v7, No. 2. P2751]. 4°. Calcutta. 1919

Mello Freire dos Reis (Pascoal José de) [MELLIUS FREIRIUS]. Hist. juris civilis lusitani liber singularis. 2ª ed. 8º. Olisipone. 1794

Instit. juris civilis lusitani liber i (–iv). [4v]. 8º. Olisipone. 1789–93

Instit. juris criminalis lusitani liber singularis. 8º. Olisipone. 1794

Mellone (Sydney Herbert) & M. Drummond. Elements of psychology. s8º. 1907

Mellor (Joseph William). Intr. to mod. inorg. chemistry. n. impr. s8º. 1920

Mellor (Stanley A.) Jesus of Nazareth. Addresses on the historical Jesus. 8º. Liv'l. 1926

Melnik (I. S.), *editor.* Сибирь ея современное состоянiе &c. Сборникъ статей [*by var. a.*] 8º. С.–П. 1908

Melnikov (Juvenal Dmitrievich), *see* NEVSKY (V.) Харьковское дело М., 1921.

Melnikov (Pavel Ivanovich) [*ps.* PECHERSKY (ANDREI)], *1819–1883.* Въ лѣсахъ. 4ч. *2v. in* s8º. Москва. 1875

Melnikova-Papoushkova (N. F.) Антологiя русской поэзiи 20 ст. [v]l. s8º. въ Прагѣ. 1920

Melo (Francisco de), *conde de Assumar* [MELLO], *see* BARRETO (J. F.) Rel. da embaixada a França em 1641 &c. [Rel. da viag. que fiz. F. de M. &c.], 1918.

Melodius (Christianus), *ps., see* BERND (ADAM).

Melrose Abbey. Chronica de Mailros, e cod. in Bibl. Cotton. serv. ed. [J. Stevenson. Bannatyne Club]. 4º. E. 1835

Melrose (Thomas Hamilton, *earl of*), *see* HADDINGTON (T. H., *1st earl*).

Melton (F. E.) Local lore, an introd. to history. s8º. [1927]

Melville, *Family of, see* AMHERST (H. A., *4th e.*) Cat. of pr. bks. &c. & 3rd portion of M. papers, 1926.

Melville (Andrew), *principal of New College, St. Andrews.* Comm. in Pauli Epistolam ad Romanos, e cod. ms. ed. curis G. L. Alexander, 1849, *see* FERME (C.) Logical analysis &c., 1850.

Melville (*Col.* **Charles Henderson).** Life of Gen. the Rt. Hon. Sir Redvers Buller, V.C. 2v. 8º. 1923

Melville (Fred Jones). Egypt [Stamps of]. s8º. 1915

Melville (H. L. Leydie), *see* BRANDES (J. L. A.) Beschr. van Tjandi Singasari &c.; samengesteld door H. L. L. M. &c., 1909.

Melville (Henry Dundas, *1st visct.*) Trial, by impeachment, of Ld. M., for high crimes & misdemeanors, 29th Apr. to 17th May, 1806. impartial ed. 8º. E. 1806

Melville (Herman).

Works. Standard ed. 16v. 8º. 1922–24

1, Typee.
2, Omoo.
3, 4, Mardi.
5, Redburn.
6, White jacket.
7, 8, Moby Dick.
9, Pierre.
10, The piazza tales.
11, The confidence man.
12, Israel Potter.
13, Billy Budd & o. prose pieces.
14, 15, Clarel: a poem & pilgrimage in the Holy Land.
16, Poems.

The apple-tree table & o. sketches. Intr. note by H. Chapin. 8º. Princeton. 1922

John Marr & o. poems. Intr. note by H. Chapin. 8º. Princeton. 1922

Mardi & a voyage thither. 2v. s8º. [1927]

Moby-Dick or the whale. Intr. by V. Meynell. s8º. [1920]

,, ,, ...[repr.] s8º. [1922]

see FREEMAN (J.) H. M., 1926.

,, WEAVER (R. M.) H. M., mariner & mystic, 1921.

Melville (Lewis), *ps.* [*i.e.* L. S. BENJAMIN].

Beau Brummell: h. life & letters. la8º. 1924
Lady Suffolk & h. circle. 8º. 1924
Life & letters of J. Gay. 8º. 1921
Life & letters of T. Smollett, 1721–71. 8º. [1926]
Regency ladies. 8º. 1926
The South Sea Bubble. 8º. 1921
The Star of Piccadilly: mem. of William Douglas, 4th duke of Queensberry (1725–1810). 8º. 1927

see KINGSTON (*duchess of*). Trial; ed. L. M., 1927.
,, †WELLESLEY (R. C. W., *marquis*). The Wellesley Papers, 1760–1842; by the editor of "The Windham Papers" [*i.e.* L. M.], 2v, 1914.
,, †WINDHAM (*Rt. Hon.* W.) The Windham Papers, 1750–1810; [ed. L. M.], 2v, 1913.

Mély (Fernand de). Les dieux ne sont pas morts. la8º. [1927]

Les primitifs & leurs signatures. [t1] Les miniaturistes. 4º. 1913

Melzi (B.) Nuovo diz. inglese-ital. [*& ital.-ingl.*] 2p *in* 1v. s8º. Milano. 1916

Member of the Inner Temple, *ps.* *Temple Bar: the city Golgotha, 1853, *see* WILSON (J. H.)

Memel.

*Memorandum on the M. question. [P2749]. 8º. [1922 ?]

The question of Memel. Diplom. & o. doc. f. Versailles Peace Conf. till ref. of the quest. by Conf. of Ambassadors to Council of League of Nations, 1919–23, incl. hist. sk. of Memel Region &c. [Lithuanian Min. for For. Affairs]. 4º. 1924

Suppl. to the publ. "The Memel problem." Replies by Lithuan. organis. &c. [*no tp.* P2682]. 8º. 1923

Memmo (Simon), *see* MARTINI (S.), *called Memmo.*

Memoir.

M. annexed to an atlas cont. plans of princ. battles, &c. dur. war in the Span. Peninsula &c., 1841, *see* WYLD (J.)

*M. (A) of the Serampore translations for 1813 &c., 1815, *see* SERAMPORE.

*M. of a map of countries between Black Sea & Caspian, 1788, *see* ELLIS (G.)

Mémoire.

M. justif. de l'a. des Mém. hist. &c. de Vénise, 1796, *see* CURTI (L.)

M. sur la Latvia, 1919, *see* LATVIA.

M. sur la Thrace, adr. à la Soc. des Nat. par le Comité Turc de la T., 1922, *see* THRACE.

Mémoires.

*M. & réflex. sur les princ. évènemens du r. de Louis XIV, 1716, *see* LA FARE (C. A., *marq.* DE).

M. hist. & crit. pour l'hist. de Troyes, t1, 1774, *see* GROSLEY (P. J.)

M. hist. & géogr. sur les pays situés entre la Mer Noire & la Mer Caspienne. [*Extr. f.* B. Edwards—Mém. de G. E. J. de Sainte-Croix—Extr. d'un voy. en 1784 *by* A. B. F. de Baert &c.] 4º. 1797

Another ed. was issued in 1798 w. title Voyages histor. & géogr., *q.v.*

*M. hist. & polit. sur la républ. de Venise, 2p, 1795, *see* CURTI (L.)

*M. p. s. à l'hist. de la vie &c. de l'abbé Lenglet du Fresnoy, 1761, *see* MICHAULT (J. B.)

M. p. s. à l'hist. de Pierre III, emp. de Russie, 1763, *see* GOUDAR (A. DE).

M. p. s. à l'hist. des hommes ill., *see* NICERON (J. P.) Nachrichten v. d. Begebenheiten u. Schriften &c.; ubers., 24T, 1749–71.

M. secrets de Bachaumont [*ed.* L. P. de Bachaumont *& others*]. Revus & publ. avec des notes &c. par P. L. Jacob. [*Abr. ed.*] s8º. 1874

*M. sur la cour de Louis Napoléon & sur la Hollande, 1828, *see* GARNIER (A.)

M. sur les journées de sept. 1792, par Jourgniac de St.-Méard, Mme. la marq. de Fausse-Lendry, l'abbé Sicard, & G. A. Jourdan. Suivis des délibér. prises par la Commune de Paris, & des procès-verb. de la mairie de Versailles. Notes par F. Barrière. s8º. 1881

Memoirs.

*Compleat m. of the life of that impostor W. Morrell &c., 1694, *see* SETTLE (E.)

*M., cont. acc. of the House of Stanley, 1783, *see* SEACOME (J.)

*M. of a sergeant in the 43rd Light Inf. Reg. previously to & during the Peninsular War. 2nd ed. s8º. 1839

*M. of Maria, a Persian slave. 2v. s8º. 1790

M. of Mrs. William Veitch, Thomas Hog of Kiltearn, Henry Erskine & John Carstairs. s8º. 1846

*M. (The) of that great favourite card. Woolsey &c., 1706, *see* CAVENDISH (G.)

*M. of the antiq. of Great-Brittain rel. to the Reformation &c. Prefix'd a preface on Steven's first addit. vol. to Dugdale's Monastichon Anglic. in defence of the late bp. Burnet. s8º. 1713

*M. of the court of France & city of Paris; tr., 2p., 1702, *see* FRANCE.

*M. of the family of Taafe, 1856, *see* TAAFE, *Family of.*

*M. of the green-room [*tp. & pages 1–14 wanting*]. s8º. [c. 1815]

M. of the late war: narr. of Capt. Cooke &c., 1831, *see* COOKE (J.)

Memorabilien. Eine philos.-theolog. Zeitschrift. Von H. E. G. Paulus. 8 Stücke [*w. sep. tp. & pagin., b. in 2v*]. 8º. L. 1791–96

Memorandum.

*M. addr. by the Jugoslav socialists &c., 1917, *see* JUGOSLAVS.

*M. conc. Portuguese rights &c. on W. coast of Africa. [P2846]. 8º. 1883

*M. on the Memel question, 1922 ?, *see* MEMEL.

M. pres. to Peace Conf. conc. Serbians &c., 1919, *see* PEACE.

M. pres. to Peace Conf. in Paris, by deleg. of Jugoslav members of parl. &c., 1919, *see* PEACE.

Memorial [MÉMORIAL].

M. catholique à l'usage des royalistes, 1826, *see* MADROLLE (A. M.)

*M. (A) of God's last 29 years wonders in England, 1689, *see* ENGLAND: ANON. WKS.

*M. (A) to Protestants on the 5th of Nov. &c., 1713, *see* KENNET (W.) *bp.*

Memorials.

M. of aff. of state in reigns of Eliz. & James I, 3v, 1725, *see* WINWOOD (*Sir* R.).

M. of old Dorset, 1907, *see* PERKINS (T.) & H. PENTIN, *edd.*

M. of old N. Wales, 1913, *see* JONES (E. A.), *ed.*

Memorials [*continued*].
M. of the late war. 2v. s8°. E. 1828
*M. of the union of the Secession & Relief Churches &c., 1847, *see* MacKelvie (W.)

Memorie. M. di un terrazzano di Rivoli, 1535–86; [*ed. D. C. Promis*], *see* Regia Dep. di Storia Patria. Misc., t6, 1865.

Men. Men of 1914 [Builders of Our Nation], publ. annually. 8°. Chicago. 1915
Men of the time. Dict. of contemp. 8th ed. rev. &c. by T. Cooper. s8°. 1872

Mena (Pedro de) [Mena y Medrano (P. de)], *see* Orueta y Duarte (R. de). Vida y obra de M. y. M., 1914.

Mena (Ramon). Filigranas o marcas transpar. en papeles de Nueva España, siglo 16. s8°. Mexico. 1926

Ménage (Gilles) [Aegidius Menagius], *see* La Fayette (*Mme.* de). Lettres de M.-M. &c., Ctsse. de L., & de G. M., 1924.

Menander, *the poet.* Fabularum reliquiae. Cum praef., notis crit., comm. exeget. 3[um] ed. J. van Leeuwen. s8°. Lugd. Batav. 1919
Le laboureur de M. Fragm. inéd. déchiffrés, tr. &c. par J. Nicole. 8°. Bâle. 1898
M.; with Eng. tr. by F. G. Allinson. [Loeb Class. Lib.] s8°. 1921
Das Schiedsgericht (Epitrepontes). Erklärt v. U. v. Wilamowitz-Möllendorff [*w. text & tr.*] 8°. 1925

Ménant (Joachim). Babylone & la Chaldée. la8°. 1875

Mena y Medrano (Pedro de), *see* Mena (P. de).

Mencelius (Hieronymus), *see* Menzel (H.)

Mencius, *see* Wu Ting-Fang. Confucius & M., address, 1901.

Mencken (Henry Louis). The American language: development of English in U.S. la8°. [1922]
Americana, 1925. Ed. H. L. M. 8°. 1925
A book of prefaces. [4th ed.] 8°. [1922]
Notes on democracy. 8°. [1927]
Prejudices. s1–4. s8°. [1921–25]

Menco, *abbot of Werum, see* Emo, *abbot of Werum.* Kronijken van E. en M. &c.; uitg. door H. O. Feith &c., 1866.

Menczel (Philipp).
Als Geisel nach Sibirien verschleppt. s8°. 1916

Mendel (Gregor Johann).
Experiments in plant-hybridisation. [Tr., repr.] 8°. C. 1925
Versuche ü. Pflanzenhybriden. 2 Abhdlgn. (1866 & 1870). Hrsg. E. v. Tschermak. 4. A. 8°. L. 1923

Mendeleev (Dmitry Ivanovich). Дополненія къ познанію Россіи. [*b. w. h.* Къ познанію Россіи, 1906]. 8°. С.-П. 1907
Къ познанію Россіи. 3e изд. 8°. С.-П. 1906

Mendelson (N. M.), *see* Brodsky (N. L.), N. M. M. & N. P. Sidorov. Хрестоматия, ч1–3, 1922–23.

Mendelssohn (Moses). Schriften zur Philos., Aesthetik u. Apologetik. Mit Charakteristik M.'s. Hrsg. v. M. Brasch. 2e A. 2B. 8°. L. 1881

Mendenhall (Dorothy Reed). Milk, *see* United States: Lab. Children's Bur., Publ. 163, 1926.

Mendes Silva (Rodrigo). Catalogo real y genealogico de España. Ref. & anadido en esta ult. impr. &c. 8°. 1656
Poblacion general de España. la8°. 1645

Méndez (Isidro). José Martí: estudio biog. 8°. Paris. [1925]

Méndez Bejarano (Mario). Dicc. de escritores, maestros y oradores naturales de Sevilla. t1, 2i, 3. la8°. Sevilla. 1922–25
1, A–Ll. 2i, M–S.
3, T–Z, Hebreos y Musulmanes, Ap. y Ind.
Hist. de la Juiverie de Séville. 8°. 1922

Mendham (Joseph).
An index of prohibited bks. by command of Gregory XVI in 1835. s8°. 1840
Life & pontificate of Pius V. 8°. 1832
The literary policy of the Ch. of Rome exhib., in an acc. of her damnatory catalogues. 2nd ed. enl. 8°. 1830
Mem. of the Council of Trent. 8°. 1834
„ „ Suppl. [*b. w.* Mem., 1834]. 8°. 1836
see Index. I. librorum prohibitorum a Sixto V; ed. J. M., 1835.

Mendonça Furtado (Tristão de). A embaixada de T. de M. F. á Holanda em 1641. Com. doc. por E. Prestage. 8°. Coimbra. 1920

Mendoza (Antonio de), *1491?–1552, Viceroy of Mexico, see* Aiton (A. S.) A. de M., 1927.

Mendoza (Bernardino de), *anbassador; c. 1540–1604, see* Morel-Fatio (A.) Etudes sur l'Esp., s4, B. de M. &c., 1925.

Mendoza (Catalina), *1542–1602, see* Morel-Fatio (A.) Etudes sur l'Esp., s4, Une mondaine contempl., Doña C. de M., 1925.

Menendez Pidal (Maria Goyri de), *see* Goyri de Menendez Pidal (M.)

Menéndez Pidal (Ramón). Crónicas gen. de España descr. por R. M. P. [Cat. de la Real Biblioteca, t5]. 3ª ed., con emmiendas &c. la8°. [1918]
Estudios literarios. s8°. [1920]
Floresta de leyendas heroicas españolas. Comp. par R. M. P. Rodrigo, el último Godo. 2t. s8°. 1925–26
Oríg. del Español, hasta el siglo xi. [Rev. de Filol. Esp., an. 1]. 8°. 1926
Poesía juglaresca y juglares. 8°. 1924

Menéndez y Pelayo (Marcelino) [Menéndez Pelayo].
Antologia de poetas lír. castellanos. t14. s8°. 1916
14, Boscán y Garcilaso de La Vega, con estudio crít. por J. Rogerio Sánchez.
G. Núñez de Arce: est. biog.-crít. s8°. [c. 1890]

Meneses (Alexeie de), *see* Menezes (A. de).

Menestrier (Claude François), *Jesuit.* Philosophia imaginum, *i.e.* sylloge symbolorum e lingua Gall. in Lat. tr. figurisque ornata. s8°. Amstelodami. 1695
see Jurieu (P.) La religion des Jésuites, ou réfl. sur les inscr. du père M., 1689.

Méneville (Félix Édouard Guérin-), *see* Guérin-Méneville.

Ménez (François).
L'envoûté. Préf. de C. Le Goffic. s8°. [1923]

Menezes (Alexeie de), *abp. of (1) Goa, (2) Braga.* J. F. Raulin Hist. Eccl. Malabaricae, cum Diamperitana Synodo apud Indos Nestorianos, coacta ab A. de M., 1599. E Lusitano in Lat. versa. Acc. Liturgia Malabarica, diss. variae &c. 4°. Romae. 1745
see Gouvea (A. de). Hist. orient. des grans progrès &c. par A. de M. &c., 1609.

Menezes (Jozé Cezar de). Idéa da população da capitania de Pernambuco &c., 1774, *see* Rio de Janeiro. Bibl. Nac. Annaes, v40, 1923.

Mengozzi (Guido). La città ital. nell' alto medio evo. Periodo langobardo-franco. la8°. [1914]

Meninski Mesgnien (Franciscus a), *see* Mesgnien Meninski (F. a).

Menippée, *see* Satire Menippée.

Menius (Justus), *see* Maior (J.) Epicedion rev. vir. J. M. &c., 1558?.

Menjot d'Elbenne (*le vte.* **Samuel).** Madame de la Sablière, s. pensées chrét. & s. lettres à l'abbé de Rancé. 8°. 1923
see Le Mans. Cartul. du Chapitre Royal de St.-Pierre-de-la-Cour; publ. par le vte. M. d'E. &c., *& Introd.:* Le Chapitre Royal &c., 1903–10.

Mennel (Jacob) [Manlius (Jacobus)]. De inclito atq. apud Germanos rarissimo actu eccl. Kaleñ. Augusti Auguste celebrato 1518. [*at the installation of Albert, Marquis of Brandenburg &c. as a Cardinal*]. s4°. [Augsburg. 1518]

Menner (Robert James), *ed., see* Purity; a Mid. Eng. poem, 1920.

Menno (S.), *see* Simons (Menno).

Mennonisten. Christl. Glaubens-Bekentnus d. waffenlosen Mennonisten. s8°. Amsterdam. 1664

Menochio (Giovanni Stefano), *see* Bible: Latin. Biblia maxima vers. ex ling. orient. &c. cum annot. J. M. &c., 19t, 1660.

Menologion. Menologium Graecorum. In 3 partes div. nunc primum Graece & Lat. prodit. 3p [*in 1v*]. fol. Urbini. 1727

Menpes (Mortimer), *see* MacCarthy (J.), *Mrs.* C. Praed & M. M. The grey river, 1889.

Mensch (Hermann). On the Eng. transl. of the Bible. 4°. Neustadt-Eberswalde. 1862

Menschheit. Dämmerung &c.; hrsg. v. K. P., 1919, *see* Pinthus (K.)

Mensching (Gustav). Das heil. Schweigen. 8°. Giessen. 1926

Menshutkin (Boris Nikolaevich).
М. В. Ломоносовъ. la8°. [С.-П.] 1911

Menteith, *Earldom of, see* Monteith.

Mentelberg (Anna de Crignis-), *see* Crignis-Mentelberg (A. de).

Mentienne (Adrien). Hist. de Bry-sur-Marne des temps préhist. au 20e s. la8°. 1916

Mentz (Georg). Hss. der Reformationszeit, ausgewählt v. G. M. [Tabulae in us. scholarum, ed. J. Lietzmann, 5]. la8°. Bonn. 1912

Mentzel (O. F.) Life at the Cape in mid-18th c.: biog. of R. S. Allemann (1784). Tr. M. Greenlees. 8°. Cape Town. 1919

Mentzer (Balthasar) [Mentzerus], *prof. of theology (1) Marburg, (2) Giessen, (3) Marburg.*
Apologia primae (ex 14) disput. Anti-pistorianae pro div. Sacr. Scr. auctoritate adv. scr. J. Pistorii. [*b. w. h.* Disputationes, 1601]. s8°. Marpurgi. 1602

Mentzer (Balthasar) [MENTZERUS] [*continued*].
Disput. 14 de controv. Christ. doctr. capitibus oppos. capitibus libri à J. Pistorio : Wegweiser &c. s8°. Marpurgi. 1601
Exegesis Augustanae Conf. ed. 2ª. s8°. Giessae Hass. 1615
„ „ ed. ult. &c. s8°. Francofurti ad Moenum. [1644]
Quæstio : num sponsis, ante solennem in ecclesia copulationem &c., concumbentibus, publ. poenitentia justè imponatur. 4ª rec. [P2633]. s4°. Wittebergæ. 1702

Mentzer (Balthasar), *Consistorial-Rath in Hannover.* A vindic. of the Lutheran relig. f. the charge of popery. Tr. by a Presbyter. s8°. 1720

Menzel (Adolf Friedrich Erdman). Illust. des œuvres de Frédéric le Grand. Préf. & notice par L. Gonse. Texte explic. par L. Pietsch. 2t. sm. fol. Londres. [1882]

Menzel (Hieronymus) [MENCELIUS (H.)] Cristl. Bericht aus was ursachen, oder wie fern sich ein Pfarherr, anderer Pfarkinder nicht annehmen &c. [P2468]. s4°. [Eisleben]. 1561
Erklerung d. Weinmar. Bekentnis halben &c. [P2665]. s4°. [Eisleben]. *n.d.*
Kurtze verzeichnis etl. grober Irrthumbe &c. [P2665]. s4°. *n.p. n.d.*

——, H. Roth, A. Fabricius & Z. Praetorius. Auff d. verleumb. C. Spangenbergs u. auffs. Furshlag. [P2665]. s4°. Eisleben. 1573

Menzel (Wilhelm Friedrich), *see* HERMIAS, *the philosopher.* Spec. theol. quo exhib. Ἑρμείου Διασυρμὸς τῶν ἔξω φιλοσόφων [*Gr. & Lat.*], 1840.

Menzel (Wolfgang), *1798–1873.*
Gesch. Europas, 1789–1815. 2e A. 2B. s8°. St. 1866
Was hat Preussen f. Deutschland geleistet ? 8°. St. 1870

Menzies, *The family of.* Illust. partic. & plans of the M. estates, auction by Knight, Frank & Rutley, 29 May 1914. fol. 1914

Menzies (Archibald). Journal of Vancouver's voyage, Apr. to Oct., 1792. Ed., w. botan. &c. notes by C. F. Newcombe & biog. note by J. Forsyth. [Archives of Brit. Columbia. Mem., No. 5]. 8°. Victoria, B.C. 1923

Menzies (*Mrs.* Stuart). Modern men of mark. 8°. 1921

Menzies (W. J. M.) The salmon. la8°. 1925

Menzies (William), *jun.*
Windsor Park & Forest. la8°. Windsor. [1904]

Mer Noire. Mém. hist. & géogr. sur les pays situés entre la M. N. &c., 3p, 1797, *see* MÉMOIRES.

Merand (Friedrich). Als engl. Missionar v. China in d. Heimat. s8°. [1918]

Meraviglia (Rudolf Johann). Böhm. Adel, *see* SIBMACHER (J.), *ed.* Wappenbuch, B4, ix, 1886.

Méray (Antony). La vie au temps des libres prêcheurs. 2e éd. augm. 2t. 8°. 1878

Mercado (Hector Díaz), *see* DÍAZ MERCADO (H.)

Mercator (Gerardus), *see* AVERDUNK (H.) & J. MÜLLER-REINHARD. G. M. u. d. Geogr. unter s. Nachkommen, 1914.

Mercer (Andrew). Hist. of Dunfermline. s8°. Dunfermline. 1828

Mercer (John Edward), *bp. of Tasmania.*
Alchemy, its science & romance. s8°. 1921

Mercer (T. W.) Co-operative policy in rel. to munic. trading. [Repr. f. Leicester Co-op. Mag., 1926. P2763]. 8°. M'ter. 1927
The Co-operative Union. 3rd ed. [P2763]. 8°. M'ter. 1925

Merchant-Taylors-Hall. Hist. cat. of the pictures, herse-cloths & tapestry at M.T.H., w. list of the sculptures & engr. By F. M. Fry. la8°. 1907

Mercier (*Card.* Désiré J.), *abp. of Malines.* Cardinal Mercier's own story. [Tr.] Intr. by F. Mayence. 8°. [1920]
see MALINES. Conversations at M., 1921–25, 1927.
„ NOËL (L.) Le Card. M., 1920.
„ RAMAEKERS (G.) Le gr. card. belge, D. J. M., 1851–1926, 1926.

Mercier (Fernand), *see* JOLIET (A.) & F. M. Musée de Dijon, 1924 ?.

Mercier (*Mrs.* Jerome). Campanella, die kleine Geigerin. [Tr.] A. v. Lagerström. s8°. L. 1879

Mercier (Louis). Petites Géorgiques. s8°. 1923

Mercier (Louis), *consul de France.*
La chasse & les sports chez les Arabes. 8°. 1927

Mercier (Louis Sébastien). De J. J. Rousseau, consid. comme l'un des prem. auteurs de la Révol. 2t. 8°. 1791
Le nouv. Paris. 6t. [*in* 3]. 8°. 1797

Mercker (Johannes). Christl. Unterweisung v. d. Freyheit zu lehren &c. s8°. [Essen ?]. 1703
Christl. Unterweisung v. d. Gemeinschafft d. Heiligen wie auch v. d. Ceremonien &c. s8°. [Essen ?]. 1703
Christl. Unterweisung v. d. unmittelbahren Offenbahrungen, Enthusiasmo, Handlungen d. Sacramenten &c. s8°. [Essen ?]. 1703

Mercure de France. Série moderne, t137–205. 8°. 1920–28

Mercure historique & polit., *see* PRESENT STATE (THE) OF EUROPE ; done f. orig. [M. hist. &c.], 1692–1712.

Mercure hollandois (Le), cont. les choses les plus remarquables de toute la terre, 1673–77. s8°. Amsterdam. 1675–78

*__Mercurius__ Belgicus &c., 1685, *see* RYVES (B.)

" Mère de Dieu " (La), *ps., see* THÉOT (C.)

Meredith (George).
The adv. of Harry Richmond. n. ed. s8°. 1886
Beauchamp's career. n. ed. s8°. 1886
Diana of the Crossways. s8°. 1890
The egoist. [repr.] s8°. [1925]
The ordeal of Richard Feverel. n. ed. s8°. 1885
The shaving of Shagpat, & Farina. n. ed. s8°. 1889
Vittoria. s8°. 1914
see ELLIS (S. M.) G. M., h. life & friends in rel. to h. work, 2nd ed., 1920.
see FORMAN (M. B.) Bibliog. of wr. in prose & verse of G. M., 1922.
„ —— Meredithiana : Suppl. to the bibliog. of M., 1924.
„ GALLAND (R.) G. M., 1828–78, 1923.
„ GRETTON (M. S.) Writings & life of G. M., 1926.
„ PRIESTLEY (J. B.) G. M., 1926.
„ STRONG (A. T.) Three st. in Shelley, & essay on nature in M., 1921.

Meredith (Mary), *see* WEBB (*Mrs.* M.)

Merejkovsky (Dmitri Sergeevich).
Л. Толстой и Достоевскій. 2т (1, изд. 3е ; 2, изд. 2ое). la8°. С.-П. 1903
1, Жизнь и творчество Л. Т. и Д.
2, Религія Л. Т. и Д.
Смерть царевича Алексѣя : сцены, *see* RUSSKII. Р. сборникъ, 1920.
Тайна Трехъ, Египетъ и Вавилонъ. s8°. Прага. [1925]
Царевичъ Алексѣй. Трагедія. s8°. Prague. [1921]
TRANSLATIONS.
Akhnaton, king of Egypt. Tr. N. A. Duddington. s8°. 1927
December the fourteenth. Tr. N. A. Duddington. s8°. [1923]
The forerunner. [Tr.] [repr.] s8°. [1924]
Joseph Pilsudski. [*in Fr.*] [P2495]. 8°. 1921
Michel Angelo, roman, *see* ŒUVRES libres, 38, 1924.
Le Mufle-Roi (L'avènement du Cham). Tr. par D. Roche. [6e éd.] s8°. 1922
La naissance des dieux. Toutankhamon en Crète. Tr. Dumesnil de Gramont. s8°. 1924
Quatorze décembre. Roman. Tr. M. de Gramont. s8°. 1922
Le règne de l'Antéchrist. [Le peuple crucifié—La croix & le pentagramme—Tolstoï & le Bolchevisme—Carnet de notes]. Z. Hippius : Mon journal sous la terreur. D. Philosophoff : Notre évasion. Tr. [6e éd.] s8°. 1921

——, Z. N. Gippius, D. V. Filosofov & V. A. Zlobin. Царство Антихриста [*articles on Bolshevism*]. s8°. München. 1921

Mereness (Newton Dennison), *see* LELAND (W. G.) & N. D. M. Intr. to Amer. sources for econ. &c. hist. of World War, 1926.

Merewether (*Sir* William Lockyer). Mem. on Kelat & Sind frontier affairs. [App. *w. sep. pag.*] fol. [Kurracher. 1876]

Merguet (Hugo). Lexikon zu Vergilius, mit Angabe sämtl. Stellen. la8°. L. 1912

Merian (Matthäus), *the elder, 1593–1650* [MERION]. View of London. [Engr. by M. M., f. " Neuwe archont. cosmica, durch J. L. Gottfried, 1638. London Topog. Soc. *Publ.*] obl. fol. 1922

Merian-Genast (Ernst). Voltaire u. d. Entwicklung d. Idee d. Weltlit., *see* ROMANISCHE FORSCH., B40, 1927.

Merici (Angela), *see* ANGELA [*Merici*], *St.*

Meridies (Wilhelm). H. Stehr : s. Werk u. s. Welt [*by var. a.*] Hrsg. v. W. M. 8°. Habelschwerdt. 1924

Mérignhac (A.) & E. Lémonon. Le droit des gens & la Guerre de 1914–18. Préf. de L. Bourgeois. 2t. 8°. 1921

Mérimée (Prosper) [*ps.* CLARA GAZUL].
Carmen. s8°. 1925
Le carrosse du Saint-Sacrement. 8°. Neuilly. 1921
Chron. du règne de Charles IX. Ornée par E. Toudouze. la8°. 1889
„ „ s8°. *Nelson.* [1912]
see JOHNSTONE (G. H.) P. M., a mask & a face, 1926.
„ TRAHARD (P.) Jeunesse de M., 2t, 1925.
„ VINOGRADOFF (A. K.) М. въ письмахъ к Соболевскому, [*w. facs. of letters*], 1928.

Meringer (Rudolf). Mittelländ. Palast, Apsidenhaus u. Megaron, 1916, *see* KAIS. AKAD. D. W. ZU WIEN. Phil.-hist. Kl. Sitz., B181, 1928.

Merino Álvarez (Abelardo).
Marruecos. [Real Soc. Geogr.] 8°. 1921
La sociedad abulense dur. el sig. 16. La nobleza. Discursos, R. Acad. de la Hist. la8°. 1926

Merion (Matthew), *see* MERIAN (M.)

Meriton (George), *gent.*
Guide to surveyors of the high-ways &c. s8°. 1694

Merkel (Carlo). Una pretesa dominaz. provenzale in Piemonte nel sec. 13, *see* REGIA DEP. DI STORIA PATRIA. Misc., t26, 1887.
see CIPOLLA (C.) Commem. del prof. C. M., 1900.
Merkel (Wolfgang Andreas). De variis juris patronatus adquirendi modis. s4°. Jenae. [1731]
Merker (Paul). Neuere deut. Literaturgesch. 8°. St. 1922
Merklas (V.) Geographie d. Königr. Böhmen. s8°. Prag. 1852
Merlani (Adolfo).
S. Caterina da Bologna. [P2497]. 8°. Bologna. 1912
Merlant (Joachim). De Montaigne à Vauvenargues. Essais sur la vie intér. & la culture du moi. s8°. 1914
Merle d'Aubigné (Jean Henri). Geneva & Oxford, discourse, Geneva, 1842. Intr. by E. Bickersteth. s8°. 1843
Rome & the Reformation; or, a tour in the S. of France. s8°. 1844
see UNGARN. Gesch. d. evangel. Kirche in U.; Einl. v. M. d'A., 1854.
Merlet (Lucien), *see* TIRON. Cartul. de l'abbaye de la Ste.-Trinité de T.; publ. & annoté par L. M., 2t, 1883.
Merlin. La estoria de Merlin, *see* GRAIL. Span. Grail fragments; ed. K. Pietsch, 2v, 1924–25.
see BOULENGER (J.) L'hist. de M. &c., 1922.
„ MONMOUTH (G., *of*). The Vita Merlini: [Lat. text w. Eng. tr., ed.] J. J. Parry, 1925.
„ SCHURÉ (E.) M. l'enchanteur: légende dramat., 1924.
Merlin, *ps. of a writer in "The Referee," see* MURRAY (D. C.)
Merlin (Alfred). Statuette de terre cuite peinte trouvée à Carthage, *see* ACAD. DES INSCR. FOND. PIOT. Mon., t24, 1920.
Merlin (Antoine Christophe), *de Thionville, see* MERLIN (R.) M. de T., 2t, 1927.
Merlin (Charles). Traité sur les paroles &c. des 7 Sacrements, *see* MIGNE (J. P.) Theol. cursus, t21, 1841.
Merlin (Roger).
Merlin de Thionville, d'ap. des doc[s]. inéd. 2t. 8°. 1927
Merlinus liberatus, Almanack for 1800–8. By J. Partridge. [1804 *wanting. b. w.* Gentleman's diary, 1800–8]. s8°. 1800–8
Merlo (Clemente). Del potere metafonetico palatilizzante di lat. Ū-Ŭ, *see* MONACI (E.) Studj romanzi, v13, 1917.
Merriam (Charles Edward) & H. E. Barnes. Hist. of polit. theories, recent times. Contrib. by students of W. A. Dunning. Ed. M. & B. 8°. N.Y. 1924
Merriam (Clinton Hart). Classific. &c. of Pit River Ind. tribes of California, *see* SMITHSONIAN INST. Misc. Coll., v78, 1926.
Merrick (George Charles). Hausa proverbs. s8°. 1905
Merrick (James). The Psalms, tr. &c. in Eng. verse. 2nd ed. s8°. Reading. 1766
Merrick (Leonard) [*form.* L. MILLER]. The actor-manager. Intr. by W. D. Howells. s8°. [1918]
A chair on the boulevard. Intr. by A. N. Lyons. s8°. [1919]
The man who was good. Intr. by J. K. Prothero. s8°. [1920]
Quaint companions. Intr. by H. G. Wells. s8°. [1918]
Merrill (Elmer Truesdell). Essays in early Xtn. hist. 8°. 1924
Merrill (George Edmands). The parchments of the faith. 8°. 1894
Merrill (George Perkins). Contrib. to a hist. of Amer. state geolog. & nat. hist. surveys. [*By var. wr.*] Ed. &c. by M. [S.I: U.S. Nat. Mus., Bull. 109]. 8°. Wash. 1920
Handbook &c. of gems & precious stones in the U.S. Nat. Mus. By M., assist. by M. W. Moodey & E. T. Wherry. [S.I.: U.S. Nat. Mus., Bull. 118]. 8°. Wash. 1922
Merrill (L. R.), *see* GRIMALD (N.) Life & poems; by L. R. M., 1925.
Merrill (Stuart). Poèmes (1887–97). Les gammes—Les fastes—Petits poèmes d'automne—Le Jeu des épées. 2e éd. s8°. 1897
Les quatre saisons. Poèmes. s8°. 1890
Merriman (Brian). The midnight court [*by* B. M.] & The adv. of a luckless fellow [*by* D. Macnamara]. Tr. f. Gaelic by P. A. Ussher. Pref. by W. B. Yeats. 8°. 1926
Merriman (Nathaniel James), *bishop of Grahamstown.* The Kaffir, the Hottentot &c. Passages of missionary life f. journals of M. s8°. 1853
Merriman (Roger Bigelow).
The rise of the Spanish Empire. v3. 8°. N.Y. 1925
Merritt (Abraham). The moon pool. s8°. N.Y. 1919
Merritt (Leonidas) & Alfred Merritt, *see* GATES (F. T.) Truth about Rockefeller & the Merritts, *n.d.*
Merry (The) tales of the Wise Men of Gotham; Halliwell, 1840, *see* GOTHAM.
Mersen (M.), *see* MARSIN (M.)
Mersenne (Marin) [MARSENNUS (MARTINUS)], *see* AMAMA (S.) Anti-barbarus biblicus; acc. resp. ad censuras M. M., 1656.

Mersmann-Soest (O.) & P. Wohl. Die deut.-russ. Vertr. v. 12. Okt., 1925, *see* MAGNUS (J.), *ed.* Die neu. internat. Vertr., B1, 1926.
Mervelles de Rigomer, *see* JEAN, *author of R.*
Mervyn, *The family of, see* DRAKE (*Sir* W. R.) Notes of fam. of M. of Pertwood, 1873.
Merwin (Samuel). Silk, a legend: journals & corr. of Jan Po. s8°. 1924
Merx (E. O. Adalbert), *see* HEIDELBERG UNIV. H. Professoren aus d. 19. Jhdt. [*by* A. M. &c.], 1903.
Méry (Joseph P. A.) Les damnés de l'Inde. n. éd. s8°. 1885
Meryon (Charles).
see DELTEIL (L.) & H. J. L. WRIGHT. Cat. rais. of etchings of C. M., 1924.
„ DODGSON (C.) Etchings of C. M., 1921.
„ GEFFROY (G.) C. M., 1926.
Merz (Aloysius). Frag, was ist d. Pabst? beatw. [P436]. s4°. Augsburg. [1782]
Merz (Hieronymus). Hist. vitae & controv. V. Strigelii &c. Praes. C. E. Weismanno. [P599]. s4°. Tubingae. [1732]
Mesa Ortiz (Rafael M.)
Colombianos ilustres. t2, 3. la8°. Bogotá. 1917–19
Mesarites (Joannes), *1162–1207, see* MESARITES (N.) Epitaphios auf s. Bruder J. 1207.
Mesarites (Nikolaus). Bericht ü. d. polit. u. kirchl. Ereignisse d. 1214, *Gr. text, see* KÖNIGL. AKAD. D. W. ZU MÜNCHEN. Phil. Kl., Sitz., 1923.
Epitaphios auf s. Bruder Johannes; [1207], *Gr. text, see* KÖNIGL. AKAD. D. W. ZU MÜNCHEN. Phil. Kl., Sitz., 1922.
Mesa y Lopez (Rafael). Antologia de los mejores poetas castellanos. Intr. y com. de R. M. y L. s8°. [1913]
Mescheryakov (N. L.) В меньшевистском раю, из впечатлений поездки в Грузию. [P2698]. 8°. [Москва]. 1921
Кооперация и социализм. Сборник статей. 8°. Москва. 1920
Современная кооперация. изд. 2[oe]. 8°. Москва. [1924]
Meschîchâ-Sechâ [MEŠÎḤÂ-ZEKHÂ]. Die Chronik v. Arbela, *see* SACHAU (C. E.), *ed.*
Meschinello (Giovanni). *La chiesa ducale di S. Marco. 2t *in* 1v. 8°. Venezia. 1753
Mesgnien Meninski (Franciscus a). Instit. linguae Turcicae cum rudimentis parall. ling. Arabicae & Persicae. Ed. altera. 2t. 4°. Vindobonae. 1756
Mešîḥâ-zekhâ, *see* MESCHÎCHÂ-SECHÂ.
Meskovsky (Aleksei) [MIESKOWSKI]. Lehrbuch z. pract.-theoret. Erlernung d. Russ. Spr.
2[e] A. T1. 8°. St. Petersburg. 1888
„ „ Schlüssel. [*b. w.* Lehrbuch]. 8°. St. P. 1890
Mesmer (Franz Anton), *see* INCE (R. B.) F. A. M., h. life & teaching, 1920.
Mesopotamia. Geology of M., 1920, *see* ADMIRALTY.
Mesrop, *episkopos, see* TER-MOVSESEAN (M.)
Mesrop *Maschdotz, c. 354–441* [MESROB].
see ADJARIAN (H.) St. M. & invent. of writing [*in Armen.*], 1907.
„ GORIUN *the admirable.* G.'s Lebensbeschr. d. hl. M., übers. &c., 1841.
„ —— Life of St. M. [*in Armenian*], 1854.
„ ISAAC, *the Great, patriarch of Armenia.* Hist. of Sahak & M. &c. [*in Armenian*], 1853.
„ KARAPET, *Sasnatzi.* Panegyric on M. [*in Armen.*]; ed. M. Ter-Movsesean, 1897.
Mess (Adolf v.) Caesar, s Leben, s. Zeit u. s. Politik &c. la8°. 1913
Mess (Henry A.) Factory legislation & its admin., 1891–1924. [London Sch. of Econ[s]. St[s]., No. 84]. 8°. 1926
Mess (Johann Jacob). Sammlung symbol. Bücher d. reform. Kirche. 3T *in* 1v. s8°. Neuwied. 1828–46
1, Die helvet. Confess., deutsch.
2, Die Conf. d. reform. Kirche in Deutschland.
3, Die Conf. d. reform. Kirche ausserhalb Deutschlands u. d. Schweiz.
***Message** (The) of man. Bk. of ethical scriptures. 2nd ed. s8°. 1895
Messager (Le) de Thalie: feuilletons inéd. de crit. dram. (1780–81), 1925, *see* CASANOVA (J.)
Messe. *De la meill. man. d'entendre la m., 1681, *see* LE TOURNEUX (N.)
*Deutsche M. u. Ordnūg Gotes diensts, zu Wittemberg fürgenomen, 1526, *see* LUTHER (M.)

Messenius (Johan). Scondia illustr., seu chronologia de rebus Scondiae, hoc est Sueciae, Daniae, Norvegiae &c. Ed. J. Peringskiöld usque 1612.
15t *in* 2v [t14 *not publ*d.] fol. Stockholmiae. 1700–05
t1–8, Scondia illustr. ad 1612. t9, Hist. sanctorum &c. 10, De rebus Finnonum, Livonum, & Curland. ad 1628. 11, 12, Analect. Scondic. liber 1, 2 (1656). 13, Censura de Hist. Scondiae. 14, "Perditus." 15, Epitome Scondiae illustr. sive Chronologia.

Messer (August).
Erläut. zu Nietzsches Zarathustra. s8°. St. 1922
Oswald Spengler als Philosoph. s8°. St. 1922

Messeri (Antonio), *see* DANTE ALIGHIERI. Lectura D., Il c. 32 dell' Inferno letto da A. M., 1917.

Messerschmidt (Leopold) & O. Schröder. Keilschrifttexte aus Assur hist. Inhalts. Autographien v. L. M. [& O. Schröder. Deut. Or.-Gesell., Wiss. Veröff., 16, 37]. 2H. fol. L. 1911–22

Messervy (George P.) The quick-step of an emperor: Maximilian of Mexico. 8°. 1921

Messie (Petrus), *see* MEXIA (PEDRO).

Messina. Pandetta d. gabelle e dei diritti d. curia di M.; ed. Q. Sella, *see* REGIA DEP. DI STORIA PATRIA. Misc., t10, 1870.

Messina (Maria). La casa nel vicolo. s8°. Milano. 1921
Le pause della vita. s8°. Milano. 1926

Messmer (Jos.) Die stigmatisierte Seherin T. Neumann. Persönl. Eindrücke v. Konnersreuth. 3e A. 8°. Luzern. 1927

Meston (James Scorgie Meston, *1st baron***).** India at the crossways. Rede lect., 1920. s8°. C. 1920
see ILBERT (*Sir* C.) & *Ld.* M. New constitution of India; Lects., 1923.

***Mestre.** [Cento città, 21. P2860]. 4°. Milano. *n.d.*

Mestre (Ed.) Quelques résultats d'une compar. entre les caractères chin. mod. & les Siao tchouan. [H.E.: Sci. relig., 40]. 8°. 1925

Mestrezat (Jean) & *le père* **F. Véron.** Actes d'une conférence tenue au sujet d'une dame en 1624 entre M. & V. [*b. w.* Drelincourt (C.) Dialogues, 1660]. s8°. 1655

Métais (Charles). Églises & Chapelles du dioc. de Chartres; publ. par C. M. sl. 8°. Chartres. 1897

Metamorphosis. *M. Anglorum sive mutationes var. regum, 1653, *see* ANGLI.

Metastasio (Peitro A. D. B.)
see DELLA CORTE (A.) Paisello &c.—l'estetica musicale di P. M., 1922.
„ RUSSO (L.) Metastasio, 1921.

Metcalf (Henry Clayton), *see* TEAD (O.) & H. C. M. Personnel admin., 1920.

Metcalf (Maynard Mayo). The Opalinid ciliate infusorians. [S.I.: U.S. Nat. Mus., Bull. 120]. 8°. Wash. 1923

Metcalfe (Alfred). Guide to St. Peter's Church, Dorchester. s8°. Dorchester. 1907

Metcalfe (Charles C.) Practical electric wiring for lighting installations. [repr.] 8°. 1919

Metcalfe (Harvey). The evolution of spiritualism. Intr. by M. Metcalfe & pref. by Sir A. C. Doyle. 8°. [1925?]

Metcalfe (John Henry), *see* WILCOX (A. M.) Royal descent, 1892.

Metchnikoff (Elie) [MECHNIKOV (ILYA ILICH)]. Исторія развитія Nebalia. [I. Akad. Nauk. Записки, t13]. 8°. С.-П. 1868
The nature of man: st. in optimistic philosophy. Eng. tr., ed. P. C. Mitchell. [2nd ed.] 8°. [1904]
see METCHNIKOFF (O. N.) Жизнь И. И. М., 1926.
„ —— Life of E. M.; tr. 1921.
„ —— Vie d'E. M., 1845–1916, 1920.

Metchnikoff (Olga N.) [MECHNIKOVA]. Жизнь И. И. Мечникова. 8°. Москва. 1926
Life of Elie Metchnikoff. Tr., w. pref. by Sir R. Lankester. 8°. 1921
Vie d'E. Metchnikoff, 1845–1916. 8°. 1920

Metford (James). A gen. disc. of simony. s8°. 1682

Metge (Bernat), *see* PAR (A.) Sintaxi Catalana segons los escrits de B. M. (1398), 1923.

Methley, *Yorks.* Reg. of the parish church of M., 1560–1812. Transcr. & ed. G. D. Lumb. [Thoresby Soc., 12]. 8°. Leeds. 1903

Methodism.
*The Magna Charta of M. invalid: hist. & invalid. of Wesley's deed poll set forth &c. By a solicitor. [P449]. 8°. 1835
*M. in 1879. Impressions &c. s8°. 1879
*M. unmasked: Wesley's doct. proved false &c., & the calumnies of Mr. Holroyd ans. &c. By the Rev. J. L. [P449]. 8°. Scarborough. 1828

Methodist.
*Discipline & ritual of Bethany Independent M. church of Baltimore. s8°. Baltimore. 1872
Formole di pubbl. preghiere ad uso delle chiese evang. metod. d'Italia. 8°. Padova. 1874
*Jubilee (The) of the M. New Connexion. 2nd thousand. s8°. 1848
„ „ ....3rd thousand. s8°. 1851
Letters &c. of the M. Ctee., 1812. [*MS.*] sm. fol. [1812]
Lives of early M. preachers, 6v, 1865–66, *see* JACKSON (T.), *ed.*

Methodist Conference.
Minutes of the M.C. f. the first held in London by J. Wesley, 1744. v1 (–1798). 8°. 1812
„ „ ....1744–1878. 21v. [1–5, repr.] 8°. 1862–78
„ „ Hdbk. & Index of the Minutes, 1744–1890, by C. E. Wansbrough. Introd. by G. Osborn. 8°. 1890
Minutes of the M.C. in Ireland. 3v. s8°. Dublin. 1864–67
Minutes of several conversations between J. Wesley & the preachers in connect. w. him &c. s8°. 1797
Minutes of several conversations at ann. conferences, 1808–12. [*b. w.* Minutes, 1797]. s8°. 1808–12
The Minutes *for* 1810–12 *have sep. tps. & pagins.*

Methodist Episcopal Church. Ritual. 8°. N.Y. 1851
see HYMNS. H. for use of M.E. Ch., 1849.

Methodists [METHODISTES].
Annual rep. of the state of the missions, 1812–17, *see* WESLEYAN METHODIST MISSIONARY SOCIETY.
*Essai sur les classes d'expérience chrét. en usage chez les M.-Wesleyens. Par un élève de F. Neff. [P2538]. s8°. 1851
*Hist. (The) constit. & conf. of faith of the Calvinistic M. in Wales. Tr. [by D. Davies]. 2nd ed. s8°. Chester. 1834
see COKE (T.) Statement of receipts &c. for the support of missions establ. by the M. Soc. for conversion of Negroes &c., 1794.

Methodius, *Saint, patriarch of Constantinople.* Vita S. Theophanis confess. ed. B. Latyšev. [*Greek.* I. Akad. Nauk. Mém., s8, t13iv]. la8°. Petrograd. 1918

Methodius, *Saint, abp. of Moravia.*
see HILFERDING (A. F.) Собраніе соч., т1, Кириллъ и М., 1868.
„ STREDOWSKY (J. G.) Sacra Moraviae hist. sive vita M. &c. 1710.

Methodius, *Saint, bp. of (1) Olympus & Patara, (2) Tyre.* Þe bygynnyng of þe world & þe ende of worldes, *see* TREVISA (T.) Dialogus &c.; [tr.] J. T.; intr. by A. J. Perry, 1925.
see SIXT (J. A.) Comment. de M. Tyri episcopo, 1787.

Methodus confessionis. Ad haec xii articul. fidei explanatio. s8°. Antverpiæ. 1556

Methuen (A.) An anthology of mod. verse. Chosen by A. M[ethuen]. Intr. by R. Lynd. s8°. [1921]
„ „ ....8th ed. s8°. [1922]

Methuen (Paul Sanford Methuen, *3rd baron***).** Corsham Court, 1903. [Cat. of pictures &c., w. acc. of the house & hist. of the family]. 8°. [1903]

Metlinsky (Ambrosii Lukyan). Народныя южнорусскія пѣсни. 8°. Кіевъ. 1854

Metropolitan Museum of Art, *New York.*
Bulletin. v17–22. 8°. [N.Y. 1922–27]
Nov. & Dec. 1922 & Oct. & Dec. 1923, Dec. 1924, March 1926 have 2nd parts.
Daily life of the Greeks & Romans as illust. by the class. coll.; by H. McClees. 8°. N.Y. 1924
Shapes of Greek vases. [P2707]. la8°. N.Y. 1922
EGYPTIAN EXPEDITION. Robb. de Peyster Tytus Mem. Ser. v2–5. la. fol. N.Y. 1922–27
see DAVIES (N. DE G.) Tomb. of Puyemrê at Thebes, 2v, 1922–23. [2, 3.]
„ —— Tomb of 2 sculptors at Thebes, 1925. [4.]
„ —— 2 Ramesside tombs at Thebes, 1927. [5.]
see DEAN (B.) Helmets & body armor in mod. warfare, 1920.

Metscher (Heinrich). Casual-Nexus zw. Leib u. Seele &c. Inaug.-Diss., Bern. [P2477]. 8°. [Dortmund. 1896]

Mettenleiter (Dominicus). Die sonntägl. Episteln d. kathol. Kirchenjahres. [*b. w. h.* Sonntägl. Evang., 1856]. s8°. Schauffhausen. 1856
Die sonntägl. Evangelien d. kathol. Kirchenjahres. s8°. Schaffhausen. 1856

Mettenses [METTENSIA], *see* METZ.

Metternich (*Fürst* Clemens W. N. Lothar von), *1775–1859.*
M.-Hartig: Briefwechsel d. Staatskanzlers aus d. Exil, 1848–51. Hrsg. &c. v. F. Hartig. 8°. Wien. 1923
see BIBL (V.) M. in neu. Beleuchtung: s. geheimer Briefwechsel mit Wrede [1831–34], 1928.
„ PALÉOLOGUE (G. M.) Romantic diplomat, M. &c., 1926.
„ —— Talleyrand, M. &c., 1924.
„ SRBIK (H., *Ritter* v.) M., d. Staatsmann u. d. Mensch., 2B, 1925.

Metternich (*Princess* **Pauline**), *wife of Prince Richard Metternich.* The days that are no more. 8°. 1921

Metz [METTENSES]. Annales M. priores. Prim. rec. B. de Simson. Acced. addit. Annalium M. post. [Scr. rerum Germ. in usum schol.] 8°. Hannoveræ. 1905

Cartul. de l'Evêché de M.; publ. P. Marichal, *see* SOC. NAT. DES ANTIQ. DE FR. Mettensia, t4, 5, 1903–08.

Coll. Emmery & Clouët-Buvignier sur l'hist. de M. & de la Lorraine à la Bibl. Nat.: invent. publ. H. Omont, *see* SOC. NAT. DES ANTIQ. DE FR. Mettensia, t7, 1919.

Mettensia, t1–8, 1897–1927, *see* SOC. NAT. DES ANTIQ. DE FR.

Metz (Rudolf). George Berkeley: Leben u. Lehre. 8°. St. 1925

Metzger (Hélène).
Les concepts scientif. Préf. de A. Lalande. 8°. 1926

Metzler (Johannes Guilhelmus). Disput. hist.-politica, aliquammulta dubia cont. [P2641]. s4°. Argentorati. 1617

Metzner (Johannes Gottfried), *see* PFEIFFER (J. G.) & J. G. M. Eruditum θαυμαστόν in aetate tenera, 1696.

Meulen (A. J. van der). Platen-atlas voor de Vaderlandsche gesch. Door A. J. van der M. mid medewerking van M. ten Bouwhuys. 2e herz. druk. sfol. Groningen. [1912]

Studies over het ministerie van Van de Spiegel. 8°. Leiden. 1905

Meulen (R. van der). De Hollandsche Zee-en Scheeptermen in het Russisch. [*Extr. f.* Verhandel. d. Kon. Akad. van Wet. te Amsterdam. Afd. Lett., N. Reeks, d10]. la8°. 1909

see VRIES (M. DE) &c. Woordenboek der Nederl. taal, d13, bewerkt door R. van der M., 1924.

Meung (Jean de), *called Clopinel.* A demonstration of nature, made to the erring alchemists &c., *see* HERMETIC MUSEUM, v1, 1893.

Meunier (Constantin).
see DEMOLDER (E.) C. M., 1901.
,, DEVIGNE (M.) C. M., 1919.

Meunier (Dauphin). Autour de Mirabeau: docs. inéd. Préf. de L. Barthou. 8°. 1926

Meunier (Léon).
Hist. de la médecine. Préf. par G. Ballet. 8°. 1924

Meunier (*Mme.* **Stanislas**), *née Levallois.*
La conquête du diamant. Préf. de G. Geffroy. s8°. [1921]

Meunier (Stanislas). Les glaciers & les montagnes. s8°. 1920

Meurer (Christian). Die Grundlagen d. Versailler Friedens u. d. Völkerbund. 8°. Würzburg. 1920

Meurer (M.) Pflanzenbilder. Ornamental verwerthbare Naturstudien f. Architekten &c. [Ser. 1, 10H *in* 1v]. fol. Dresden. [1896–99]

Meuret (F. C.) Annales de Nantes. 2t. 8°. Nantes. [1830–31]

Meurgey (Jacques). Hist. de la paroisse Saint-Jacques-de-la-Boucherie. Préf. de C. Jullian. la8°. 1926

Meuschen (Johann Gerhard), *see* BOSIUS (J. A.) Intr. in notit. scr. J. F. Buddei, J. G. M. &c., 1723.

Meusel (Carl Heinrich).
Doct. Joannis Scoti Erigenae &c. [P2655]. 4°. Budissae. 1869

Meux (Valerie Susie, *Lady*), *wife of 3rd bart.* Theobald's Park, Waltham Cross, Herts. Cat. &c. of furniture &c. Waring & Gillow will sell, May 1911. sm. fol. 1911

Mévil (André). De la Paix de Francfort à la Conf. d'Algésiras. 2e éd. s8°. 1909

Mew (Egan). Battersea enamels. la8°. [1926]

Mew (James) & J. Ashton. Drinks of the world. 8°. 1892

Mewar, *The family of, see* STRATTON (J. P.) Chitor & the M. fam., 1881.

Mexia (Pedro) [MESSIE (PETRUS)]. Hist. Imp. y Cesarea, desde Julio Cesar hasta el Emp. Carlos V. sm. fol. Anvers. 1578

The rarities of the world. Tr. by J. B[aildon], gent. s4°. 1651

Mexican petroleum, 1922, *see* PAN AMER. PETROLEUM &c. Co.

Mexicana. Lira m., 1879, *see* PEZA (J. DE D.), *ed.*

Mexicanos. Hombres ilust. m., 4t, 1873–74, *see* GALLO (E. L.), *ed.*

Mexico.
Carta geogr. gen. de la Republ. M. Comenzada en 1878 por la Comm. Geogr.-Explor. Atlas topogr. de los alrededores de puebla. Hoja 1–9 [13 *maps & tp. in case*]. folded 8°. [1883]
,, ,, [reduc.], s3, letra AP. obl.8°. [1883]
Código de coloniz. y terrenos baldíos de la Repúbl. M., 1451–1892. Formado por F. F. de la Maza. 8°. México. 1893
Código postal de los estados unidos m. ed. ofic. 8°. Mexico. 1884
Datos mercantiles. Comp. por R. de Mária y Campos. 8°. México. 1892
La deuda exterior de M. 8°. Mexico. 1926
Discurso[s], 1884–92, *n.d.*, *see* DIAZ (P.)

Mexico [*continued*].
Expos. que hace el Secr. de Fomento sobre la coloniz. de la Baja California. [P2721]. 8°. México. 1887
*General descr. data [Pan-American Union]. [P2562]. 8°. W. 1921
Hdbk. (A) of M. [maps *in case*], 1919, *see* ADMIRALTY: NAVAL INTELL. DIV.
Informe que el Gen. H. Charles, comand. d. "Gendarmeria Fiscal" pres., 1886–7. la8°. México. 1888
Informe que el Min. de Hacienda, M. Dublan, pres. sobre el empréstito de £10,500,000. [P2721]. 8°. Mexico. 1888
Informe que rinde el Secretario de Fomento sobre coloniz. y terrenos baldíos. [*Pref. signed* C. Pacheco]. 8°. México. 1885
Leyes constitut. de M. dur. el s. 19: discurso pronuncío el Lic. J. M. G., 1901, *see* GAMBOA (JOSÉ M.)
Mem. pres. por el Ministro de Fomento, L. Robles Pezuela, de los trábajos ejecut., 1865. la8°. México. 1866
M. & the Caribbean; Clark Univ. addresses, 1920, *see* BLAKESLEE (G. H.), *ed.*
President's message, Sept. 16, 1882. [P2720]. 8°. Mexico. 1882
La primera guerra entre M. y Francia. Prol. de A. de la Peña y Reyes. [Arch. Hist. Diplom. Mexicano, 23]. 8°. Mexico. 1927
Secretaria de Est. de Relac. Exter.—Inglaterra. Tratado de amistad &c. [P2720]. 8°. [Mexico ?. 1889]

Meydeburg, *see* MAGDEBURG.

Meyderlin (Petrus). Evangelium Lutherano Catholicum Æternum. Klare Beweisung &c., dass die Hauptlehr Augspurg. Conf. v. der Gerechtigkeit des Glaubens bekannt gewesen sey &c. [P2438]. s4°. Kempten. 1621

Meyen (Fritz). Ibsen—Bibliographie. Bearb. v. F. M. Mit e. Einführ. Ibsen u. Deutschl. v. Dr. W. Möhring. [Nord. Bibliog., H1]. la8°. Braunschweig. 1928

Meyendorff (Peter v.) Peter v. Meyendorff, e. russ. Diplomat an d. Höfen v. Berlin u. Wien. Briefwechsel, 1826–63. Hrsg. &c. O. Hoetzsch. 3B. 8°. 1923

Meyer, *publishing firm.* Meyers grosses Konversations-Lexikon. 6e gänzl. neubearbt. u. verm. A. Kriegsnachtrag. 3T. la8°. L. 1916–20
Meyers Handlexikon. 8e gänzl. veränd. u. neubearbt. A. 8°. L. 1921
Meyers Lexikon. 7e A. B1–8. la8°. 1924–28

Meyer (Alfred). L'abbé Bernier, apôtre de La Vendée, évêque d'Orléans. 8°. 1923

Meyer (Arnold Oskar). Der brit. Kaisertitel z. Zeit d. Stuarts. [Abdr. aus Quellen &c. aus ital. Archiven &c., B10. P2859]. la8°. Rom. 1907
Clemens VIII u. Jakob I v. Eng. [Abdr. K. P. Hist. Inst. in Rom. Quellen &c., B7ii]. [P2837]. la8°. Rom. 1904
Einiges ü. d. ital Volkscharakter. [Aus d. Mitt. d. Schles. Gesells. für Volkskunde, H21. P2838]. 8°. Trebnitz. 1909
England & the Catholic Church under Q. Elizabeth. Auth. tr. by J. R. McKee. 8°. 1916

Meyer (Balthasar Henry), *see* MACGILL (C. E.) Hist. of transport. in U.S. bef. 1860; prep. under dir. of B. H. M., 1917.

Meyer (Eduard), *prof., Berlin Univ.*
Der Amerikan. Kongress u. d. Weltkrieg. 8°. 1917
Blüte u. Niedergang d. Hellenismus in Asien. 8°. 1925
England: s. staatl. &c. Entwickl. u. d. Krieg gegen Deutschl. 6. u. 7. A. 8°. St. 1915
Die Gemeinde d. neu. Bundes im Lande Damaskus, *see* KÖNIGL. PREUSS. AKAD. D. WISS. Abh., Phil.-hist. Kl., 1919.
Gesch. d. Altertums. Bii & Nachtrag, 2i, 3i, 4, 5. [1ii, 5, 3e A.; 2i, 2e neubearb. A.; 3i, 4, 2e unveränd. A., n. Abdr.] 8°. St. 1913–28
Hist. de l'antiquité. Tr. E. Combe. t3. la8°. 1926
3, La Babylonie & les Sémites.
Kleine Schriften. 2B [B1, 2e A.] 8°. Halle. 1924
Der Papyrusfund v. Elephantine. 3e A. 8°. L. 1912
Preussen u. Athen. Rede, 15. Okt. 1919. [P2432]. 8°. 1919
Das röm. Manipularheer, *see* KÖN.-PREUSS. AKAD. Abh., Phil.-hist. Kl., 1923.
Spenglers Untergang d. Abendlandes. 8°. 1925
Ursprung u. Anfänge d. Christentums. 3B. 8°. St. 1921–23

Meyer (Eduard Lorenz) & O. L. Tesdorpf. Hamburg. Wappen u. Genealogien. [*Enl. ed. of* M.'s Wappenbuch hamburg. Senatoren &c. & T.'s Wappenbuch hamburg. Familien]. la8°. Hamburg. 1890

Meyer (Erich).
Deutsch-Evangel. im Orient. [P2503]. s8°. [1916]

Meyer (Ernst Christopher).
Infant mortality in N.Y. city, 1885–1910. 8°. N.Y. 1921

Meyer (George v. Lengerke), *see* HOWE (M. A. DE W.) G. v. L. M., life & public services, 1920.

Meyer (Gertrud).
Tanzspiele u. Singtänze. 8e A. s8°. L. [1921]
Volkstänze, gesamm. v. G. M. 6e A. obl.8°. L. 1921

Meyer (Gustav), *prof. at the Univ. of Graz.* Kurzgefasste albanes. Gramm., mit Lesestücken u. Glossar. 8°. L. 1888

Meyer (Hans). Das deut. Kolonialreich. 2B. la8°. L. 1909–10
1, Ostafrika u. Kamerun. 2, Togo, Südwestafrika, Schutzgebiete in d. Südsee u. Kiautschougebiet.

Meyer (Herman Henry Bernard), *see* UNITED STATES: LIB. OF CONGRESS, *for bibliographies compiled under the direction of M.*

Meyer (Johann Caspar). Disquis. de Siculis Gallorum vesperis. [P444]. s4°. Baruthi. [1690]

Meyer (Johann Friedrich von). Hades. Theorie d. Geisterkunde &c. s8°. Franckfurt a. M. 1810

Meyer (Jonas Daniel). Mém. sur l'orig. de la différence rel. à l'usage de la langue flamande ou wallonne dans les Pays-Bas. [*Extract*]. 4°. 1825

Meyer (Jürgen Bona). A. Schopenhauer als Mensch u. Denker, *see* VIRCHOW (R.) & F. v. HOLTZENDORFF. Vorträge, H145, 1872.

Meyer (Kuno). Bruchstücke d. ält. Lyrik Irlands, *see* KÖNIGL. PREUSS. AKAD. D. WISS. Abhdl. (Phil.-hist. Klasse), 1919.
German gram. for schools. 2nd ed. 2p. 8°. 1889
Miscellanea Hibernica. [Univ. of Illinois. St. in lang. &c., v2iv]. la8°. [Urbana]. 1917
Üb. d. ält. irische Dichtung, 2H, *see* KÖN.-PREUSS. AKAD. Abhdln., Phil.-hist. Kl., 1913.

Meyer (Leo). Unters. ü. d. Sprache v. Einfisch im 13. Jhdt., *see* ROMANISCHE FORSCH., B34, 1915.

Meyer (Lodewijk), *M.D.* *Philosophia Scripturae interpres. 3. ed. & app. J. Camerarii aucta; cum notis &c. J. S. Semleri. 8°. Halae Magdeb. 1776

Meyer (Martin). Grundskizze zu e. System d. Ethik. 8°. 1923

Meyer (Paul). De l'expansion de la langue fr. en Ital. pend. le m.-â. [Estr. d. Atti d. Congr. int. di sci. stor., 1903, v4. P2790]. la8°. Roma. 1904

Meyer (Richard). Vorles. ü. d. Gesch. d. Chemie. la8°. L. 1922

Meyer (Richard Moritz). Die Weltliteratur im 20. Jhdt. 2e A., fortgeführt v. P. Wiegler. 8°. St. 1922

Meyer (Theodor Knottnerus-), *see* KNOTTNERUS-MEYER (T.)

Meyer (Wilhelm), *aus Speyer, prof. in Göttingen.* Gesammelte Abhandl. z. mittellatein. Rythmik. 2B. 8°. 1905
Gottes Wort in eiserner Zeit. Folge 3. Lief 2–6. s8°. Marburg. 1916–18
Die Preces d. mozarab. Liturgie, 1914, *see* KÖNIGL. GESELLS. D. WISS., GÖTTINGEN. Phil.-hist. Kl., B15, 1917.
see FRAGMENTA Burana; hrsg. v. W. M., 1901.

Meyer (Wilhelm Josef), *ed.*, *see* AELLEN (H.) Schweiz. Zeitgenossen-Lex., 1921.

Meyer (*Sir* William), *G.C.I.E.*, *see* LOVETT (*Sir* V.) India, w. sect. on econ. based on contrib. by Sir W. M., 1923.

Meyer-Cohn (Marie). George Buchanan als Publizist &c. Maria Stuarts. Inaug.-Diss. 8°. Heidelberg. 1913

Meyer-Lübke (Wilhelm). Das Katalan., s. Stellung z. Span. u. Provenzal. 8°. Heidelberg. 1925
Roman. etymolog. Wörterbuch. 8°. Heidelberg. 1911 [1920]
Roman. Namenstudien, 2, 1917, *see* KAISERL. AKAD. D. W. ZU WIEN. Sitzungsber., B184, 1918.

Meyerson (Emile).
De l'explication dans les sciences. 2t. 8°. 1921

Meyer-Steineg (Theodor) & C. Sudhoff. Gesch. d. Medizin im Überblick. 2e durchges. A. 8°. Jena. 1922

Meyer von Knonau (Gerold). Die evangel. Kantone u. d. Waldenser, 1663–64. [Verein f. Ref.-Gesch. Schr., Jhrg. 28 (Nr. 103/4)]. 8°. L. 1911

Meyjes (R. Posthumus), *see* TASMAN (A. J.) De reizen v. T. & F. J. Visscher; uitg. door R. P. M., 1919.

Meynadier (Robert).
Les étapes de la royauté d'Alphonse XIII. s8°. 1914

Meynardus, *see* MEINHARD.

Meynell (*Mrs.* Alice), *wife of Wilfrid Meynell.*
Poems. compl. ed. s8°. 1923
see STONEHILL (C. A.) &c. Bibliog. of mod. a., s2, 1925.

Meynell (Esther H.), *see* †MOORHOUSE (E. H.), *ps.*

Meynell (Viola). Narcissus. 2nd impr. s8°. [1916]
Young Mrs. Cruse. s8°. 1924
,, ,, ...2nd impr. s8°. 1925

Meynell (Wilfrid). The man Disraeli. Rev. ed. of "Benjamin Disraeli." 8°. [1927]

Meyrac (Albert). Louise de La Vallière. 8°. [1926]
see SAINT-SIMON (*le duc* DE). Le Régent; notes &c. par A. M., 2s, 1923–25.

Meyrat (J.) Dict. national des communes de France, d'Alsace-Lorraine & d'Algérie &c. [12e éd.] s8°. [1921]

Meyrick (Edward). Micro-lepidoptera, 1927, *see* B.M. NAT. HIST.: ZOOLOGY. Insects of Samoa, p3ii, 1927.

Meyrick (Frederick). Is dogma a necessity? s8°. 1883

Meyrink (Gustav). Des deut. Spiessers Wunderhorn. Gesamm. Novellen. 3T *in* 1B. 8°. München. 1925
Der Engel vom westl. Fenster. 8°. L. [1927]
Wachsfigurenkabinett. s8°. München. [1918]

Mézard (*le chevalier*). Du principe conservateur, *see* CONSTANT (B.) &c. Mél. polit. &c., t1, 1829.

Mezger (Gottlob Immanuel Siegfried). De statu animae post mortem recentiores controv. s4°. Tubingae. [1758]

Mezger (Paul). Sacra hist. de gentis Hebraicae ortu &c. lib. 5. fol. Augustae Vindel. 1700

Mézières (P. J.)
La voix des morts. Préf. de J. Péricard. s8°. 1926

Mezzabarba (Antonio).
Rime. [*Dedic. by* F. Marcolini]. 8°. [Vinegia. 1536]

***Mezzo** infall. per imparare a montare a cavallo &c. [P2755]. 8°. Milano. 1816

Miaban. Nstotz. [*In Armenian. Extr. f.* Ararat, 1893. P2792]. 8°. *n.p.* 1893
see HERESIES. Girq herdsouadzotz (book of h.; ed. M., *in Arm.*), 1892.

Miall (Stephen). The structure of the atom. [P2576]. 8°. 1922

Miari (*il conte* Fulcio). Il nuovo patriziato Veneto dopo [1646]. 8°. Venezia. 1891
Venetia anticha. [Officj e regimenti &c.] la8°. Venetia. 1890

Mic (Constant). La commedia dell' arte ou le théâtre des comédiens ital. des 16e–18e s. la8°. 1927

Micanzio (Fulgenzio). *Vita del Padre Paolo dell' Ordine de' Servi. s8°. Venetia. 1658

Micard (Etienne Jean Philippe Nicolas) [*ps. vcte.* CISTERNI]. Un écrivain acad. au 18e s.: A. L. Thomas (1732–85). la8°.1924

Miccà (Pietro), *see* MANNO (A.) P. M. ed il gen. conte Solaro d. Margarita: assedio di Torino, 1706, 1883.

Michael, *Maleinos, Saint.* Vie & office de M. M., suiv. du traité ascét. de Basile le Maléinote. Texte grec publ. L. Petit. [P2790]. la8°. 1903

Michael, *suffraganeus Moguntinus, see* HELDING (M.)

Michael, *Metrop. of (1) Novgorod, (2) St. Petersburg, see* MIKHAIL.

Michael VIII [*Palaeologus*], *emperor of Constantinople, see* CHAPMAN (C.) M. P., restaurateur de l'emp. byz., 1261–82, 1926.

Michael, *St., the Archangel, see* DOBIACHE-ROJDESTVENSKY (O.) Le culte de St. M. & le moyen âge latin, 1922.

Michael, *bp. of Sidonien, see* HELDING (M.), *bp. of Merseburg.*

Michael, *de Ungaria.* Sermones M. de V. s8°. [Parisiis], *J. Petit.* 1501
Sig. A 1–8; a–o in eights.

Michael Angelo, *1475–1564.*
see CLEMENT (C.) Michelangelo; tr., 1885.
,, FREY (D.) M.: 29 riprod. con testo e cat., 1923.
,, GOBINEAU (*le c.* J. A. DE). La fleur d'or [M.-A. &c.], 1923.
,, HOFFMANN (R.) M.: d. Decke d. Sixtin. Kapelle, 1925.
,, REYMOND (M.) M.-A., 1920.
,, STEINMANN (E.) Der Jeremias d. M., 1894.

Michael Theodorovich, *emperor of Russia, 1613–45.*
see BERKH (V.) Царствованіе М. Ө., 2ч., 1832.
,, LA VILLE (P. DE). Disc., suivi d'une lettre du Tsar M au Sultan Achmet, 1613, 1859.

Michael (Wolfgang). Engl. Gesch. im 18. Jhdt. B2. la8°. 192

Michaelis (Caroline), *aft. Senhora de Vasconcellos; b. 1851.*
see RIBEIRO (B.) & C. FALCÃO. Obras; n. ed., pref. po C. M. de V., 2v, 1923.
,, VICENTE (G.) Autos portugueses &c.; ed. facs. con intr de C. M., 1922.

Michaelis (Christian Benedict). Tract. crit. de variis lectioni bus N. Test. s4°. Halae Magdeb. 174

Michaelis (Clara). Polit. Zitatenbuch. 8°. Halle a. d. S. [192

Michaelis (Henriette). Diz. pratico ital.-tedesco e ted.-ital. 13a ed. 2p. 8°. Lipsia. 190

Michaelis (Johann David).
Abh. v. d. Ehegesetzen Mosis. 2e verm. Aufl. s4°. Göttingen. 17
Cat. scriptorum M. usque ad 1787. [*b. w. h.* Neue Or. Bib T1–4, 1786–87]. s8°. Goettingae. [178
Comment. in Soc. Reg. Scient. Gotting., 1758–62[–68], praelect ed. 2 auct. [2p *in* 1v]. s4°. Bremae. 17
Diss. de punctorum Hebraic. antiquitate. Praes. C. B. Michaeli [P431]. s4°. Halae Magdeb. [173

Michaelis (Johann David) [*continued*].
Gedanken ü. d. Lehre d. heil. Schrift v. Sünde u. Genugthuung. Neue A. s8°. Göttingen. 1779
Glossarium Chrestomathiae Syriacae. Annot. &c. auctum a J. C. C. Doepke. s8°. Gottingae. 1829
Gramm. Syriaca. 4°. Halæ. 1784
Neue oriental. u. exeget. Bibl. [*Continued by T. C. Tychsen*]. 9T *in* 3v. s8°. Göttingen. 1786–93
Oriental. u. exeget. Bibl. 24T [*in* 7v]. [T24 *cont.* Siebenfaches Register *by* J. C. Schmidt *&* J. W. Stüber]. s8°. Frankfurt a. M. 1771–89
Suppl. ad lexica Hebr. [Ed. T. C. Tychsen]. 6p *in* 2v. 4°. Gottingae. 1792
Syntagma comment. 2p [*in* 1v]. 4°. Goettingae. 1759–67
Verm. Schriften. 2T *in* 1v. s8°. Frankfurt a. M. 1766–69
Zerstreute Kleine Schriften. [*b. w. h.* Verm. Schr. 1766–69]. 3 Lief. s8°. Jena. 1793–95

Michaelis (Karin). Das Geheimnis (Gunhilds Wanderjahre). Roman. s8°. Potsdam. 1927

Michaud (Eugene), *see* BORDEAUX (H.) Voyageurs d'Orient, t2, M. &c., 1926.

Michault (Jean Bernard). *Mém. pour servir à l'hist. de la vie &c. de l'abbé Lenglet du Fresnoy. [Dédic. *signed* G*** P***, *i.e.* J. B. M.] s8°. Londres. 1761

Michault (Pierre). *Le doctrinal du temps present [vers 1484]. Not. de E. Droz. [Livres à grav. imp. à Lyon au 15e siècle, 2a. *b. w.* Abuzé (L') en court (c. 1484), 1925]. 4°. Lyon. 1925

Michaut (Gustave Marie Abel).
Anatole France. 5e éd., rev. s8°. 1922
Les débuts de Molière à Paris. 8°. 1923
Hist. de la comédie romaine. [p2], Plaute. 2t. 8°. 1920
La jeunesse de Molière. 8°. 1922
Pages de crit. & d'hist. litt. 19e s. s8°. 1910
Sainte-Beuve. [G. E. Fr.] s8°. 1921

Michaux-Bellaire (E.), *b. 1857.* Conférences, *see* MISSION SCI. DU MAROC. Archives, v27, 1927.
Le Gharb, *see* MISSION SCI. DU MAROC. Archives, v20, 1913.
Les habous de Tanger, 2t, *see* MISSION SCI. DU MAROC. Arch., v22, 23, 1914.
see MISSION SCI. DU MAROC. Archives, v11, 15 (*for several o. works by M.-B.*), 1907–8.

Michel. *Ein new Klaglied Teutsche M. genannt wider alle Sprachverderber [1637? *facs.*], *see* FREYTAG (G.) Bilder, B4, 1925.

Michel (*le chanoine*). Discours, 7 oct. 1824, *see* LOUIS XVIII. *Rel. d. dispos. fun.; Toulon, 1824.

Michel (André). Hist. de l'art dep. les prem. temps chr. j. nos jours. Publ. sous la dir. de M. t6i, ii, 7i, ii. la8°. [1921–24]
6i, ii, L'art en Europe au 17e s.
7i, ii, L'art en Europe au 18e s. pl, 2.

Michel (Augustinus), *Theologian.* Discussio theolog. 4 diss., quas in puncto contritionis & attritiones posuit P. L. Le Drou. s4°. Augustae Vindel. 1710

Michel (Carl Ludwig). Comm. de jure indicendi luctum publ. [P428]. s4°. Altorfii. 1766

Michel (Edouard). Abbayes & monastères de Belg.; import. &c. dans le dévelop. du pays. s8°. Brux. 1923
see LOUVRE. La peinture, école flam., par E. M., 1927.

Michel (Francisque), *1809–87.* Deux années du r. de H. II, roi d'Angleterre (1173–74). [P2523]. 8°. Poitiers. 1841
Wade. Lettre s. une tradition angl. du m. âge. [P2532]. 8°. 1837

Michel (Michel Georges-), *see* GEORGES-MICHEL.

Michel (Oskar). Hdbch. deut. Zeitungen, 1917. Bearb. im Kriegspresseamt v. O. M. la8°. 1917

Michelet (Carl Ludwig), *see* CHLEBIK (F.) Philos. d. Bewussten &c. nach Hegel u. C. L. M., 1870.

Michelet (Jules).
see GUÉHENNO (J.) L'évangile éternel: M., 1927.
,, MAURRAS (C.) Romantisme &c., éd. déf., M. &c., 1922.
,, MONOD (G.) Vie & pensée de J. M., 1798–1852, 2t, 1923.
see RUDLER (G.) M., historien de Jeanne d'Arc, 2t, 1926.
,, VINET (A.) Et. sur la litt. franç. au 19e s., t3, M. &c., 1924.

Micheli (Domenico), *doge of Venice, d. 1130* [MICHIEL], *see* MONTICOLO (G. B.) Patto d. Maggio 1122? giur. d. doge D. M. a. comun. d. Bari, 1899.

Micheli (Francesco), *abp. of Ravenna, 1333–42* [MICHIEL], *see* PASOLINI DALL' ONDA (P. D.) F. M., 1876.

Micheli (Giovanni) [MICHIEL]. I dispacci di G. M. ambasc. veneto in Inghilt. (1554–57). Deciferati da P. Friedmann. Rettific. &c. di L. Pasini. 8°. Venezia. 1869

Michelis (Friedrich B. F.) Der häret. Charakter d. Infallibilitätslehre. [P2657]. 8°. Hannover. 1872
Eine kathol. Antw. a. d. päpstl. Encyklika v. 5ten Feb. [P2693]. 8°. Bonn. 1875

Michell (Harold).
Introd. to the geography of Sierra Leone. 8°. 1919

Michell (Robert). E. Turkestan & Dzungaria, & rebellion of the Tungans &c., 1862–66. [*no tp.* P535]. 8°. [1871?]
Rep. on overland trade betw. Russia & China. [India Office: Polit. &c. Dept. *no tp.* P535]. 8°. [1871]

Michell (Thomas), *F.R.G.S.* Analysis of laws that affect position of Brit. residents in Russia. [P2714]. 8°. St. P. 1871
Hist. of the Scot. exped. to Norway in 1612. 8°. 1886

Michels (Paul). Paderborn, *see* DEUTSCHLAND. D.'s Städtebau, 1921.

Michels (Victor), *see* GRUNDRISS d. indogerm. Spr. &c., Abt. 2, B2i, Germanisch, v. V. M. &c., 1927.

Michelson (Truman).
Works in SMITHSONIAN INST. Bur. of Ethn. Rep.
Autobiog. of a Fox Ind. woman. [40.]
Mythical orig. of White Buffalo Dance of Fox Indians. [40.]
Notes on Fox mortuary customs & beliefs. [40.]
Notes on Fox society known as "Those who worship the Little Spotted Buffalo." [40.]
Tradit. orig. of the Fox society known as "The singing around rite." [40.]
Contrib. to Fox ethnology. [S.I.: Bur. of Amer. Ethn., Bull. 85]. 8°. Wash. 1927
The Owl sacred pack of the Fox Indians. [S.I.: Bur. of Ethnol., Bull. 72]. 8°. Wash. 1921

Michiel (Francesco), *abp. of Ravenna, see* MICHELI (F.)

Michieli (Adriano Aug.) La laguna di Venezia ed i suoi caratteri econ., *see* QUADERNI geograf., N11, 1919.

Michigan. UNIVERSITY OF M.
HUMANISTIC SERIES. v10ii, 16, 21. la8°. N.Y. 1923–27
see NICOMACHUS, *Gerasinus.* Intr. to arithmetic; tr. M. L. D'Ooge, 1926. [16.]
,, SANDERS (H. A.) & C. SCHMIDT. The Minor Prophets in the Freer coll. &c., 1927. [21.]
,, WORRELL (W. H.) 2 Coptic homilies & a magical text in the Freer Coll., 1923. [10ii.]
Univ. of M. Cat. of the officers & students, 1866–67, with a descr. 8°. Ann Arbor. 1867
The William L. Clements Library of Americana at the Univ. of M. 8°. Ann Arbor. 1923
see HAYDEN (R.) The Senate & treaties, 1789–1817, 1920.

Michon (Etienne). Un décret de dème de Cholargos rel. aux Thesmophories, *see* ACAD. DES INSCR. Mém. &c., s1, t13i, 1923.
Isis, Horus & Serapis &c., bas-relief du Louvre, *see* ACAD. D. INSCR.: FOND. PIOT. Mon., t25, 1921–22.
Tête de jeune homme de la frise du Parthénon (Louvre), *see* ACAD. DES INSCR.: FOND. PIOT. Mon., t23, 1918–19.

Michon (Georges).
L'alliance franco-russe, 1891–1917. 8°. 1927

Michon (L. A. Joseph). Des céréales en Italie sous les Romains. Thèse. 8°. 1859

Mickiewicz (Adam). Chefs-d'œuvre poét. Tr. par lui-même & par s. fils, & suivis du Livre de la nation polon. &c. Avec vie de l'a. par L. Mickiewicz. s8°. 1924
Corresp. (1820–55). Publ. L. Mickiewicz. 8°. [1924]
Dziady. Sceny dramat. 8°. Kraków. 1901
Forefathers' Eve (Prologue & scenes I–V). Tr. D. P. Radin. Ed. G. R. Noyes. 8°. 1925
Konrad Wallenrod & o. writings. Tr. J. Parish &c. 8°. Berkeley, Cal. 1925
see SZPOTANSKI (S.) A. M. & le romantisme, 1923.
,, TLUCHOWSKI (O. S.) A. M., 1922.

Mickle (William Julius).
Poet. works. Coll. by T. Park. s8°. 1808

Micklem (Edward Romilly). Miracles & the new psychology: healing miracles of the New Test. [n. impr.] s8°. 1922

Micks (William Lawson). Acc. of the constit., admin. & dissolution of the Congested Distr. Board f. Ireland, 1891–1923. 8°. D. 1925

Micoletzky (H.), *see* MIKOLETZKY.

Micrælius (Johann). Hist. ecclesiast. Ed. cura D. Nartnacci & contin. adorn. 5a ed. s4°. Lipsiae. 1699

Micronius (Martin), *see* KIRCHENORDNUNG, wie die unter d. Christl. König Edward VI in London; durch J. v. Lasco in Lat. beschr.; aber durch M. M. verdeut. &c., 1565.

Middelburg. Bronnen tot de gesch. v. M., dl, 2 (1217–1574), 1923–26, *see* UNGER (W. S.)
Onderzoek van's Konings wege ingesteld omtrent de M. beroerten, 1566–67. Uitg. door J. van Vloten. [Hist. Genoots. Werken., N.S., 18]. 8°. Utrecht. 1873

Middeldorpf (Heinrich), *see* BIBLE: SYRIAC. Codex Syriaco-hexapharis; ed. &c. H. M., 2p, 1735.

Middendorf (Aleksandr Fedorovich). Барaбá. [I. Akad. Nauk. Записки, t19]. 8°. С.–П. 1871

Middendorf (E. W.) Das Muchik oder die Chimu-Sprache. Anh. ü. d. Chibcha-Spr. la8°. L. 1892
Das Runa Simi, oder die Keshua-Sprache. la8°. L. 1890

Middlemiss (Charles Stewart). Geol. of Idar State, *see* INDIA: GEOL. SURVEY. Mem., v44i, 1921.

Middlesex.
M. parish registers: Marriages, v8, ed. T. Gurney. 8°. 1927
A petition of the freeholders of M., pres. to H. Majesty, 24th May, 1769. [*b. w.* London: Civic inst. Addr. &c., 1778]. s8°. [1769]

Middle Temple. Suppl. to Cat. of printed bks. in Lib. of the M.T. Alphabet. arr., w. index of subjects by H. A. C. Sturgess, 1914–24. la8°. 1925

Middleton (A. Safroni-), *see* SAFRONI-MIDDLETON (A.)

Middleton (Christopher), *writer of romance.* The famous hist. of Chinon of England. Added, The assertion of King Arthure, tr. R. Robinson f. Leland's Assertio, w. Lat. orig. [*sep. pagin.*] Ed. w. intr. &c. by W. E. Mead. [E.E.T.S., 165]. 8°. 1925

Middleton (Conyers). A free inquiry into the miraculous powers in Xtian ch. 3rd ed. s4°. 1749
A letter f. Rome shewing an exact conformity betw. popery & paganism. 4th ed. 8°. 1741
see BOWYER (W.) Origin of printing; substance of M.'s Diss., 1774.
,, WESLEY (J.) Letter to C. M. occ. by h. Free inq., 1749.

Middleton (Edgar Charles). Kingdom of the air. s8°. [1919]

Middleton (Erasmus), *see* LUTHER (M.) Comm. on Galatians; life of a. &c. by E. M., 1807.

Middleton (George).
The annals of Prestwich: chron. record. s8°. M'ter. 1902

Middleton (John Henry). The Lewis coll. of gems & rings of C.C. Coll., Camb. W. intr. essay on anc. gems. 8°. 1892

Middleton (Richard) [MIDDLETON (RICHARD BARHAM)], *see* SAVAGE (H.) R. M., the man & h. work, 1922.

Middleton (Thomas), *dramatist, see* PASTOR (A.) Un embajador de España en la escena inglesa, 1925.
—— **& W. Rowley.** The Spanish gipsy (1661); ed. w. crit. essay &c. by H. B. Clarke, *see* GAYLEY (C. M.) Repres. Eng. comedies, v3, 1914.

Middleton (Thomas Hudson). Food production in war. [C.E. for Int. Peace]. la8°. O. 1923

Midgley (W.), *see* LILLEY (A. E. V.) & W. M. Bk. of studies in plant form, enl. ed., 1902.

Midland Railway (South). Map of the S. Midland lines, session 1846. folded s8°. 1846

Midrash. ספר מדרש רבות.
[2v *in* 1]. fol. [Frankfurt on the Oder. 1711–12]
see STRACK (H. L.) & P. BILLERBECK. Komm. z. Neu. Test. aus Talmud u. M., 3B, 1922–26.

Mieg (Johann Rudolf). *Monumenta pietatis & lit. virorum in republica & lit. illustrium selecta.
2p *in* 1v. s4°. Francofurti ad Moenum. 1701

Mieg (Ludwig Heinrich). Diss. de Rom. pontif. infallibilitate. Præs. P. Werenfelsio. [P2670]. s4°. Basileæ. 1684

Miege (Guy). *Present state of Gt. Brit. & Ireland &c., also pres. state of H.M.'s dominions in Germany. 8th ed., corr. & enl. [*5 pagin. Scotland & Germany have sep. tp.*] 8°. 1738
see MALYNES (G. DE). Anc. sea-laws of Oleron &c.; taken out of Les us & coutumes de la mer [*by* G. de M.] & rendred into Eng. by G. M., 1686.

Mielcke (Christian Gottlieb). Anfangs-Gründe e. littau. Sprachlehre; v. Ruhig hrsg. Gramm. z. Grunde gelegt &c. [*b. w. h.* Littau.-deut. Wbch., 1800]. s8°. Königsberg. 1800
Littauisch-deut. u. Deut.-littau. Wbch., das v. Ruhig hrsg. zu Grunde gelegt &c. 2T *in* 1v. s8°. Königsberg. 1800

Mielert (Fritz).
Das schöne Westfalen. B1–4. la8°. Dortmund. 1920–[26 ?]
Westfalen, Münsterland—Industriegebiet—Sauerland—Siegerland. la8°. Bielefeld. 1923

Mielke (Hellmuth) & H. J. Homann.
Der deut. Roman d. 19. u. 20. Jhdts. 5e A. 8°. Dresden. 1920

Mieses (Matthias).
Die jiddische Sprache. Hist. Gramm. 8°. 1924

Mieskowski (Aleksei), *see* MESKOVSKY (A.)

Miethe (Käthe). Die Smaragde d. Pharao: e. Abenteuerfahrt v. Nil z. Roten Meer. la8°. [1923]

Migeod (Frederick William Hugh).
Across equatorial Africa. 8°. 1923
Through Brit. Cameroons. 8°. 1925

Migeon (Gaston).
L'art japonais. [Musée du Louvre. Doc. d'art]. 8°. [1927
Les arts musulmans. la8°. 1926
Le Caire, le Nil & Memphis. la8°. 190
L'Orient musulman. [Musée du Louvre. Doc. d'art]: [2v]. s4°. 192

Migieu (Barbe Charlotte de), *aft. wife of Ch. Richard Montaugé see* MONTAUGÉ (B. C. DE M. DE).

Miglionico (Marc Antonio Mazzone di), *see* MAZZONE D MIGLIONICO (M. A.)

Migne (J. P.), *ed.* Theologiae cursus completus.
28t. la8°. Lutetiae Paris. 1841–6
Alexandre (N.) De justa bonorum temporal. ab eccles. posses —Apolog. pro Joanne XXII—De investituris episc. & abbat. [18
—— De Noachidarum praeceptis—De præceptis moral. legi Mosaicæ *& o. disserts.* [15
—— De oratione Dominica. [17
—— De symbolo fidei—De symbolo Apostol. [6
—— De tradition. non scriptis. [26
—— Tract. de peccatis. [11
Allacci (L.) De utriusque eccl. occident. & orient. in dogmat de purgatorio perpetua consensione. [18
Antoine (P. G.) De obligationibus spec. certorum statuum offic. [16
—— De sacris Xtn. ritibus. [19
Assemanus (J. A.) De ritibus sacris. [26
Ballerini (P. & G.) De vi ac ratione primatûs Roman. ponti &c.—De potestate eccl. summorum pontif. &c. [3
Barth (F. J.) De statuto principis. [16
Baudeau (N.) Anal. de l'ouvr. du Pape Benoît XIV sur l béatifications &c. [8
Benedict XIV. De festis Jesu Christi & B. Mariæ Virginis. [26
—— De Missæ sacrificio. [23
—— De synodo dioecesana. [25
Beusch (G.) Tract. de pactis & contractibus in genere. [16
Billuart (C. R.) De consensu ad matrimon. requisito. [25
—— De fine propter quem instituta fuit circumcisio—I intentione ministri sacramentorum. [21
—— De statu religioso. [16
—— Tract. de actibus humanis—Tract. de passionibus. [11
—— Tract. de mysteriis Christi & B. Virginis. [8
Biner (J.) De jure primarum precum & instit. [18
—— Diss. juridica de usuris. [16
Bona (J.) De sacrificio Missæ tract. asceticus &c. [23
Boyer (P. D.) Apol. du St.-Office dans les décisions sur prêt à interêt—Lettre de l'a. de la Défense de l'Eglise. [16
Brocardus, *theologian.* Tract. de conscientia. [1
Camus (J. P.) Appropinquatio protestant. ad eccl. Cat Roman. [
Cano (F. M.) De locis theologicis. [
Carboneano (P. de). De proposit. ab eccl. damnatis. [
Chardon (C.) Hist. des sacrements. [2
Charles [*Borromeo*], *St.* Monita ad confessores. [2
Chrismann (P. N.) Regula fidei cath. & coll. dogmat. crede dorum. [
Collet (P.) De censuris—De irregularitatibus. [1
—— De purgatorio—De indulgentiis—De jubilæis. [1
—— Tract. de pœnitentia. [2
Corradus (P.) *De controv. inter Catholicos agitatis &c. [
—— Praxis dispensat. apostol. [1
Delorme (—) De Immaculata &c. [2
Dens (P.) Tract. de quatuor novissimis. [
Devie (A. R.) Litteræ monitoriæ c. quoddam opus de mutu [1
Devoti (G.) De hierarchia eccl. [
Domat (J.) Traité des lois. [1
Drouin (R. H.) De bonitate & licitate matrimonii—De solemn ad contractum matrimonii requistis—De ritibus matrimo conferendi. [2
—— De sacramentis in genere. [2
Du Jardin (T.) De officio sacerdotis &c. [2
Estrix (Æ.) Logistica probabilitatum &c. [1
Eustratius. De statu animarum post mortem &c.; [tr. Allacci]. [1
Gautier (J.) De hæresibus—De conciliis—De summis pontif De S. Patribus. [
Gerdil (*card.* G. S.) De adoranda humanite Christi—De cu Sacri Cordis Jesu. [

Migne (J. P.), *ed.* Theol. cursus compl. [*continued*].
Goldhagen (H.) Meletema de relig. Hebr. sub lege nat. [15.]
Gonzalez (T.) De recto usu opinionum probabilium. [11.]
Hallier (F.) De sacris electionibus &c. [24.]
Holden (H.) Divinæ fidei analysis &c.—De schismate in genere. [6.]
Hooke (L. J.) De vera religione. [2, 3.]
Ilharat de la Chambre (F.) Intr. à la théologie. [26.]
Kendrick (P. R.) De ordinat. Anglic. [25.]
Kilber (H.) Tract. de fide. [6.]
Lafosse (*l'abbé*). De Deo ac div. attributis. [7.]
Languet de la Villeneuve de Gergy (J. J.) De vero eccl. sensu c. sacr. cæremoniarum usum. [26.]
Le Clerc de Beauberon (N. F.) Tract. de gratia, pars dogmat. [10.]
Le Franc de Pompignan (J. G.) Controv. pacif. sur la foi des enfants &c. [6.]
Legrand (L.) Notiones prævLiæ de natura &c. eccl. [4.]
—— Tract. de Incarnatione Verbi divini. [9.]
Leibnitz (G. W., *Frhr.* v.) Defensio Trinitatis &c.—2 epist. ad Loeflerum &c.—Remarques sur le livre d'un Antitrinitaire angl. [8.]
Lessio (L.) Quæ fides & religio sit capessenda. [3.]
—— Tract. de justitia. [15.]
Liguori (A. M. de'). Morale systema &c. [11.]
—— Praxis confessarii. [22.]
Lugo (J. de). Tract. de Eucharistiæ sacramento. [23.]
Lyonnet (J. B.) App. ad tract. De justitia & jure. [15.]
—— Tract. de contractibus in gen. & in partic. &c. [16.]
Maistre (*cte.* J. M. de). Sur la maxime qu'un honnête homme ne change jamais de relig. [5.]
Mannhardt (F. X.) De ingenua indole probabilismi. [11.]
Mastrofini (*l'abbé*). Discussion sur l'usure. [16.]
Mayol (J.) Summa moralis doctr. Thomisticæ circa Decalogum *&* App. [13, 14.]
Merlin (C.) Traité sur les paroles &c. des 7 Sacrements. [21.]
Molanus (J.) De hist. sacr. imaginum &c.—Oratio de Agnis Dei. [27.]
Montagne (C. L.) De censuris, seu notis theolog. &c. [1.]
—— Tract. de gratia. [10.]
—— Tract. de opere 6 dierum. [7.]
Moser (G.) De impedimentis matrimonii—Coll. declar. ac decret. Rom. pontif. &c. [25.]
Muzzarelli (A.) De regula mor. opinionum pro confessariis. [11.]
Paris, Univ. of. Censure de la Fac. de Théol. de P. contre Emile (1762). [2.]
Patuzzi (G. V.) De præceptis fidei & de vitiis fidei oppositis. [6.]
—— Prodromus ad univ. morum theol. &c.—De ratione humana &c.—De virtutibus moralibus &c. [11.]
Pauwels (J.) Tract. de casibus reservatis. [18.]
Perrone (G.) De dæmonum cum hominibus commercio—De mundo—De homine. [7.]
—— Tract. de cultu sanctorum. [8.]
—— Tract. de Eucharistia. [26.]
—— Tract. de ordine—De coelibatu eccl.—Tract. de matrimonio. [25.]
—— Utrum hæretici &c. sint extra Xti. eccl.—De Protestantismo—An extra Cath. eccl. detur salus—De tolerantia. [6.]
Petau (D.) De angelis—De sex dierum opificio. [7.]
Petit-Didier (M.) De auctoritate &c. summ. pontif. [4.]
Piacevich (F. X.) De primatu Roman. eccl. contra schismat. orient. [5.]
Regnier (C.) Tract. de eccl. Christi. [4.]
Reiffenstuel (A.) De beneficiis eccl., jure patronatus &c.—De immunitate eccl. [18.]
Sainte-Beuve (J. de). Tract. de sacramento Unctionis infirm. extremae. [24.]
Sanchez (T.) Compend. totius tract. s. matrimonii sacramento T. S. [ab. E. L. Soarez] ordine alphabet. dispos. [25.]
Soarez (E. L.), *see* Sanchez (T.) *above.*
Söttler (J. G.) De officiis sacerdot. & pastoral. [25.]
Suarez (F.) De horis canonicis, & laude Dei per cantum &c. [18.]
—— De simonia—De oratione, 3p. [17.]
—— Juris naturæ & gentium &c., cum notis Guarini. [15.]
—— Tract. de legibus, & legislatore Deo. [12, 13.]
Tertullian. De praescript. adv. haereticos. [1.]
Thomas, *a Jesu.* De unione schismat. cum eccl. cath. procuranda. [5.]
Thomas, *ex Charmes.* De castitate in usu matrimonii servanda. [25.]
Thomassin (L.) De adventu Christi. [8.]
Tournély (H.) De baptismo. [21.]
—— & P. Collet. De subjecto sacramentorum. [21.]
Valsecchi (A.) De spiritu philos. [6.]
Véron (F.) De regula fidei cathol. [1.]
—— Methodus compend. praetensam Reform. erroris convincendi. [5.]
Vincent, *of Lerins, St.* Commonitorium. [1.]
Vogler (J.) Juris-cultor theol. c. obligat. restitut. in gen. &c. [15.]

Migne (J. P.), *ed.* Theol. cursus compl. [*continued*].
Walenburch (A. *&* P. van). De controversiis tract. gen.—Professio fidei catholicae. [1.]
Witasse (C.) Tract. de confirmatione. [21.]
—— Tract. de S. Trinitate. [8.]
Zaccaria (F. A.) Antifebronius vindic. seu suprema rom. pontif. potestas &c. [27.]
—— De usu librorum liturg.—De usu inscript. xtn. [5.]
Zanolini (A.) Disputat. de festis & sectis Judaeorum. [26.]
Zech (F. X.) Rigor moderatus doctr. pontif. circa usuras. [16.]

Mignet (François Auguste Marie). Hist. de la Révol. Fr., 1789–1814. [Coll. Nelson]. 2t. s8°. [1914]

Mignot de Montigny (Etienne), *see* BOURDE DE LA ROGERIE (H.) Voyageurs en Bretagne: voyage M. de M., 1752, 1925.

Miguélez (*Padre*), *O.S.A.*, *see* ESCURIAL. Cat. de los códices esp. de la biblioteca del E.; [*comp. &c. by*] P. M., t1, 2, 1917–25.

Mijer (Pieter). Batiks, & how to make them. 8°. 1919

Mikaëlian (Nerses Ter-), *see* TER-MIKAËLIAN.

Mikhail, *priest.* Оброна вѣрному чл҃вку (выдержки); А. Петровъ, *see* IMP. AKAD. NAUK. Сборникъ, т97, 1921.

Mikhail, *Metrop. of (1) Novgorod, (2) St. Petersburg, see* RUSSIAN. Lives of emin. R. prelates, M. &c., 1854.

Mikhail Feodorovich, *see* MICHAEL THEODOROVICH.

Mikhailov (Mikhail Illar).
Записки (1861–62). Ред. А. А. Шилова. 8°. П. 1922

Mikhailov (Mikhail Ivanovich). Домашный &c. бытъ Зырянъ. [? *Extr. f.* Журналъ Мин. Внутр. Дѣлъ, c. 1851. P560]. 8°. [С.-П. c. 1851]
О земледѣліи &c. у Зырянъ устьсысольскаго уѣзда [? *Extr. f.* Журналъ Мин. Внутр. Дѣлъ, c. 1851. P560]. 8°. [С.-П. c. 1851]
Промыслы Зырянъ &c. [*Extr. f.* Журналъ Мин. Внутр. Дѣлъ, c. 1851. P560]. 8°. [С.-П. c. 1851]
Физическія и нравственныя свойства Зырянъ. [? *Extr. f.* Журналъ Мин. Внутр. Дѣлъ, c. 1851. P560]. 8°. [С.-П. c. 1851]

Mikhailovsky (Nikolai Konstantinovich).
Что такое прогресс? Под ред. Иванова-Разумника. s8°. П. 1922

Mikkola (Jooseppi Julius).
Urslav. Grammatik. T1. 8°. Heidelberg. 1913

Miklos (W. Jankovich), *see* BIBLE: HUNGARIAN. Biblia tudnüllik a' szentitás különb és eredeti magyar fordításainak öt példái; esmérteti W. J. M. [*i.e.* Miklos ?], 1834.

Miklosich (Franz).
Etymolog. Wörterbuch d. slav. Spr. la8°. Wien. 1886
Lexicon Palaeoslovenico-Graeco-Lat. emend. auctum ed. F. M. la8°. Vindobonae. 1862–65
see NESTOR, *the annalist.* Chronica ed. F. M., 1860.

Mikoczi (Josephus).
Otiorum Croatiae liber unus. 8°. Budae. 1866

Mikoletzky (Heinrich) [MICOLETZKY]. Die freileb. Süsswasser- u. Moornematoden Dänemarks, *see* KONG. DAN. VID. SELSK. Skrifter, Række 8, B10, 1925–26.

Mikszáth (Kálmán) [*ps.* SCARRON].
A jó palócok. 2 füz *in* 1v. s8°. *n.d.*
Club és folyosó. 5ik kiadás. 8°. 1904
Tavaszi rügyek. 2ik kiadas. 8°. Budapest. 1893
Urak és parasztok. 6ik kiadás. 8°. 1904

Milan (Luis), *see* TREND (J. B.) L. M. & the vihuelistas, 1925.

Milanese (Giovanni). La chiesa di San Nicolò in Treviso. n. ed. 8°. Treviso. 1904

Milani (Luigi Adriano). Il piombo scritto di Magliano, *see* REALE ACCAD. D. LINCEI. Mon. ant., v2, 1893.
Reliquie di Firenze ant., *see* REALE ACCAD. D. LINCEI. Mon. ant., v6, 1895.

Milano. *Chronica di M. dal 948 al 1487; ed. G. Porro Lambertenghi, *see* REGIA DEP. Misc., t8, 1869.
Statuti d. strade ed acque del contado di M., fatti 1346; ed. G. Porro Lambertenghi, *see* REGIA DEP. Misc., t7, 1869.
ARCHIVIO STORICO DEL COMUNE DEL MILANO, *see* VINCI (L. DA). Racc. Vinciana, fasc. 1–12, (1905–25), 1906–26.

Milano (Euclide). La leggenda e la storia del luogo di Auçabech, *see* REGIA DEPUT. Miscellanea, t42, 1906.

Milaraspa [MILA]. Milaraspa. Tibet. Texte in Auswahl übertragen v. B. Laufer. 4°. Hagen i. W. 1922
see RAS CHUNG PA. Le poète tibétain M.; tr. J. Bacot, 1925.

Milbiller (Joseph). Gesch. d. Königr. Bayern. 5e verbess. A. n. bearb. v. A. Mengein. s8°. München. 1827

Milbourne (Luke). Mysteries in religion vindicated, agst. Socinians &c. s8°. 1692
Psalms of David, in Eng. metre. Tr. L. M. [*pages 97–120 missing, pages 73–96 in duplicate*]. s8°. 1698

Milburn (Mary E.), see LUNDBERG (E. O.) & M. E. M. Child dependency in Dist. of Columbia, 1924.
Milburn (Robert Gordon). The theology of the real. 8º. 1925
Miles (Clement A.) Christmas in ritual & tradition, Xtn. & pagan. [2nd ed.] 8º. [1913]
Miles (Eustace Hamilton). How to remember. s8º. [1901]
Through the day: health &c. s8º. [1923]
see SCHMIDT (F. A.) & E. H. M. The training of the body, 1901.
Miles (Favell Mary, *Lady*), *wife of Sir Charles W. M.*
The red flame. 2nd ed. s8º. [1921]
Red, white & grey. s8º. [1921]
Miles (Henry Downes). The Anglo-Indian word-book. s8º. 1858
Miles (John Charles).
see JENKS (E.), *ed.* Digeste de droit civil anglais; par E. J., J. C. M. &c.; tr., 2e éd. 2t, 1923.
„ —— Digest of Eng. civil law, bk. 2iii, Law of quasi-contract & tort, 1908–10.
Miles (Walter Richard).
Alcohol & human efficiency. [C.I. of Wash.] la8º. Wash. 1924
see BENEDICT (F. G.), W. R. M. &c. Human vitality &c., 1919.
Milhaud (Gaston). Descartes savant. 8º. 1921
Milinda. Les questions de M. Tr. du pali avec intr. & notes par L. Finot. 8º. 1923
Milioutine, *see* MILUTIN.
Military chronicle (Royal), 1810–17, *see* ROYAL MILIT. CHRON.
Military Historical Society of Massachusetts. Papers. v2. Boston. 1886–95
see POPE (*maj.-gen.* J.) Virginia campaign of Gen. P. in 1862, 1886; n. ed., 1895.
Militsina (Elena Dmietrievna) & M. E. Saltikov. The village priest & o. stories. Tr. by B. L. Tollemache. Intr. by C. H. Wright. s8º. [1918]
Mill (Anna Jean). Mediaeval plays in Scotland. Thesis. [St. Andrews Univ. Publ., 24]. 8º. E. 1927
Mill (David). Oratio de var. virorum doct. in antiq. erroribus, 1727, *see* SCHLÄGER (C. J.) Diss. fasc. 1, 1742.
Mill (Hugh Robert). Life of Sir E. Shackleton. 8º. 1923
Mill (James). Elements of polit. economy. 8º. 1821
Mill (John), *D.D.*
see BIBLE. NEW TEST. [GREEK]. N.T.; studio &c. J. M., 1707.
„ PFAFF (C. M.) Diss. crit. de J. M. coll. var. Nov. Test. lectionum &c., 1709.
„ WHITBY (D.) Addit. annot. to N. Test.; & app. ent. Exam. variantium lect. J. M. in Nov. Test., 1710.
Mill (John), *minister in Shetland, see* WILLCOCK (J.) A Shetland minister of the 18th c.: passages in life of J. M., 1897.
Mill (John Stuart). Autobiography. 3rd ed. 8º. 1874
„ „ w. app. of unpubl. speeches & pref. by H. J. Laski. s8º. [1924]
Principles of polit. economy. Ed., w. intr. by Sir W. J. Ashley. n. impr. 8º. 1920
Système de logique déductive & inductive. Tr. 2t. 8º. 1866
see MACCOSH (J.) An exam. of M.'s philos., 1869.
Millais, *The family of, see* PAYNE (J. B.) Lineage & pedigree of f. of M., 1331–1865, 1865.
Millar (A. H.), *LL.D.* Haunted Dundee. 8º. Dundee. 1923
James B. Lindsay & o. pioneers. Foreword by Sen. Marconi. 8º. Dundee. 1925
Millar (Alexander), *see* WHITE (G.) Pract. designing: contrib. by A. M. &c., 1893; 2nd ed., 1894.
Millar (Eric George). Eng. illum. MSS., 10–13 c. fol. Paris. 1926
Eng. illum. MSS. of the 14th & 15th cent. fol. Paris. 1928
Princ. mss. à peintures du Lambeth Palace, *see* SOC. FRANÇ. DE REPROD. DE MSS. À PEINTURES. Bull., Année 8, 9, 1924–25.
see BIBLE: ANGLO-SAXON. The Lindisfarne Gospels; intr. by M., 1923.
Millar (James), *rector of Upcerne, Dorset, see* VOLTAIRE. Mahomet; [*tr.*] M., 1808.
Millard (Christopher Sclater), *see* †MASON (STUART), *ps.*
Millard (Thomas Franklin Fairfax). Democracy & the Eastern Question. 8º. [1919]
Millardet (Georges). Linguistique & dialectologie romanes. [Soc. des Langues Rom., Publ. spéc. 28]. 8º. Montpellier. 1923
Recueil de textes des anc. dialectes landais, avec intr. gram. &c. 4º. 1910
Millay (Edna St. Vincent).
Renascence & o. poems. [4th ed.] 8º. N.Y. 1921
Second April. [3rd ed.] 8º. N.Y. 1921

Mille & un contes, récits &c. arabes, 3t, 1924–27, *see* BASSET (R.)
Mille (Pierre).
Le bol de Chine ou divagations sur les beaux-arts. s8º. 1920
Dans trois cents ans, *see* Œ. libres, 7, 1922.
Le député, nouvelle, *see* Œ. libres, 47, 1925.
La détresse des Harpagon. s8º. [1923]
„ „ *for a. ed., see* Œ. libres, 14, 1922.
L'écrivain. [Caractères de ce temps]. s8º. [1925]
L'illustre Partonneau. s8º. [1924]
Le Maréchal Butler, *see* Œ. libres, 11, 1922.
Mes trônes, choses vues, *see* Œ. libres, 21, 1923.
Myrrhine, courtisane & martyre, *see* Œ. libres, 1, 1921.
La nuit d'amour sur la montagne. s8º. [1920]
Où est le cadavre?, *see* Œ. libres, 68, 1927.
Sacerdos in æternum, *see* Œ. libres, 25, 1923.
La victoire . . . & la retraite, *see* Œ. libres, 31, 1924.
Milleker (Felix). Gesch. d. Stadt Pančevo. s8º. Pančevo. 1925
Kurze Gesch. d. Stadt Belacrkva (Weisskirchen) im Banat, 1355–1918. 3e A. 8º. Bela Crkva. 1927
Millenium Hall. *A descr. of M. Hall, 1762, *see* MONTAGU (*Lady* B.) & *Mrs.* S. SCOTT.
Miller (Agnes). The Colfax book-plate. [3rd impr.] s8º. 1927
Miller (Alexandre). Essai sur l'hist. des institut. agraires de la Russie Cent. du 16e au 18e s. Préf. de G. L. Duprat. 8º. 1926
Miller (Anne, *Lady*), *wife of Sir John Miller, bart., see* HESSELGRAVE (R. A.) Lady M. & the Batheaston lit. circle, 1927.
Miller (E. B.), *see* CORNFORD (M. E.) & E. B. M. Cal. of MSS. in W. Salt Library, Stafford, 1921.
Miller (Edward), *Mus.D.* Psalms for the use of parish churches: words sel. f. vers. of Tate & Brady, by G. H. Drummond. Music sel. &c. [w. Pref.] by E. M. la8º. 1790
Miller (Frank).
A. Cunningham's contrib. to Cromek's Remains of Nithsdale & Galloway song. [Repr. f. Trans. of Dumfriesshire &c. Nat. Hist. &c. Soc., 1920]. [P2706]. 8º. [E.] 1920
Andrew Crosbie, advocate, a reputed original of Paulus Pleydell in Guy Mannering. [Repr. f. Trans. of Dumfries. &c. Nat. Hist. &c. Soc., 1919. P2523]. 8º. [1919
„ „ ....2nd ed. 8º. Annan. 1925
A bibliog. of the parish of Annan, w. biog. mem. 8º. Dumfries. 1925
The Macmath song & ballad MS. [P2847]. 8º. 1925
see MACMATH (W.) The Gordons of Craichlaw; w. biog. sk. by F. M., 1924.
Miller (Gerrit Smith), *jr.*
Works in SMITHSONIAN INST. Misc. Coll.
Remains of mammals f. caves in Haiti, 1922. [74.
Telescoping of the Cetacean skull, 1923. [76.
Miller (Herbert Adolphus). Races, nations & classes: psychol of domination & freedom. s8º. Phila. [1924
Miller (Hugh). Edinburgh & its neighb., geolog. & hist. w. geol. of the Bass Rock. 8º. E. 188[illegible]
First impressions of Eng. & its people. 3rd ed. E. 185[illegible]
Geol. of the country around Otterburn & Elsdon. [Mems of G.S.] 8º. 188[illegible]
Scenes & legends of the N. of Scotland. 3rd ed. s8º. E. 185[illegible]
Miller (Hugh Crichton).
The new psychology & the parent. s8º. [1922
The new psychology & the teacher. s8º. [1921
see MARCHANT (*Sir* J.), *ed.* Med. views on birth control; by H. C.-M. &c., 1926.
„ ROUSE (R.) & H. C. M. Xtn. experience & psycholog processes, 1920.
Miller (Joe), *1684–1738.* J. M.'s jests. 8º. 1739 [repr.] *n.d.*
Miller (Konrad). Mappae Arabicae d. 9.–13. Jhdts. in arab Urschr., lat. Transkr. &c. Hrsg. v. K. M. Bl, 2, 3, 6. 4º. St. 1926–2
1i, Die Karten d. Mittelmeeres (Islam-Atlas, Nr. 6); ii, Di Weltkarte des Idrisi v. 1154; iii, Die kleine Idrisikarte v 1192 n. Chr.
2, Die Länder Europas u. Afrika's im Bilde d. Araber, mi Beih.: Islamatlas Nr. 3 Magreb u. Nr. 4 Ägypten.
3, Die arab. Kartendarstellung v. Vorder- u. Mittelasie [Islam-Atlas, Nr. 1, 2, 5, 7–12].
6, Idrisi-Atlas, 336 photograph. Wiedergaben.
Weltkarte des Castorius, genannt Die Peutinger'sche Tafel. [*Facsimile*]. fol. Ravensberg. 188
Miller (Leslie William). Essentials of perspective. obl.8º. 188
Miller (Meta Helena). Chateaubriand & Eng. lit. [John Hopkins St.] 8º. Baltimore, Md. 192
Miller (Patrick). The deep end. s8º. [1927
The natural man. s8º. 192
Miller (Philip). The gardener's & botanist's dict. Corr. b T. Martyn. 2v [*in 4*]. fol. 180

Miller (René Fülöp-), *see* FÜLÖP-MILLER (R.)
Miller (Robert), *vicar of St. Nicholas, Warwick.*
see FIELD (W.) Letter, in ans. to charges ag. Dissenters by R. M., 2nd ed., 1791.
,, —— Second letter, in reply to remarks &c. by [R. M.] &c., 1791.
Miller (S. N.), *M.A.* The Roman fort at Balmuildy (Summerston, nr. Glasgow) on the Antonine Wall. Acc. of excav. 8°. Glasgow. 1922
Miller (W. Henry-), *see* HENRY-MILLER (W.)
Miller (Wilhelm). What England can teach us about gardening. la8°. N.Y. 1911
Miller (William), *barrister.*
The English in Athens bef. 1821. [P2845]. 8°. 1926
Essays on the Latin Orient. 8°. C. 1921
Hist. of the Greek people, 1821–1921. Intr. G. P. Gooch. s8°. [1922]
The Latin Orient. [Helps for students, No. 37]. s8°. 1920
Mediaeval Rome, 1073–1600. 8°. 1901
The Ottoman Empire & its successors, 1801–1922. Rev. &c. ed. of The O. Emp., 1801–1913. s8°. C. 1923
,, ,, Rev. &c. ed., 1801–1927. s8°. C. 1927
Trebizond, the last Gk. Empire. s8°. 1926
The Turkish restoration in Greece, 1718–97. [Helps for students, No. 38. P2573]. s8°. 1921
Millet (Gabriel). L'école grec. dans l'archit. byz. [H.E.: Sci. relig., 26]. 8°. 1916
Monuments de l'Athos. Relevés avec le concours de l'armée franç. d'Orient & de l'Ecole Fr. d'Athènes. Publ. G. M. [Mon. de l'art byzantin, 5]. [t]1. fol. 1927
Millet (Jean François), *artist, see* SENSIER (A.) Vie & œ. de J. F. Millet, 1881.
Millet (Philippe).
La délivrance de Zacouren. Roman. s8°. [1922]
Millet (René). Les Almohades. Hist. d'une dynastie berbère. Préc. d'une lettre du mar. Lyautey & d'une préf. par G. Guiot. 8°. 1923
Millett (Fortescue William). Rep. on recent Foraminifera of the Malay Archipelago coll. by A. Durrand. [Extr. f. Roy. Micr. Soc. Journal, 1898–1904, *in* 1v]. 8°. 1898–1904
Milleville (Henry J. G. de). Armorial hist. de la noblesse de France. Rec. &c. par un comité, publ. par M. la8°. 1845
Millevoye (Charles Hubert), *see* BRONTË (C.) Early essay [*on* M.'s La chute des feuilles]; intr. by M. H. Spielmann, 1924.
Millhouse (John). English-Italian & Ital.-Eng. dictionary. n. ed. w. add. & improv. by F. Bracciforti. 2v. s8°. *n.d.*
Milliet (Paul), *1844–1918.* Recueil Milliet. Textes grecs & lat. rel. à l'hist. de la peinture anc.; publ., tr. & comm. par A. Reinach, t1. Avant-propos par S. Reinach. la8°. 1921
Milligan (George), *D.D.*
Here & there among the papyri. s8°. 1922
see MOULTON (J. H.) & G. M. Vocab. of the Greek Test., p4–6, 1920–26.
Millin (Sarah Gertrude). The dark river. s8°. 1919
God's step-children. s8°. 1924
Mary Glenn. s8°. 1925
The South Africans. s8°. [1926]
Millman (Robert Malcolm). The verb of the Japanese written lang. Pref. by T. Matsumura. s8°. Tokyo. [1921]
Millon (*l'abbé* A.) Les grandes Madones bretonnes: mois de Marie hist. 8°. Rennes. 1922
Mills (Arthur Frederick Hobart) [*ps.* PLATOON COMMANDER].
Pillars of salt. s8°. [1922]
Ursula Vanet. s8°. [1921]
Mills (Arthur Hobart). The danger game. s8°. [1926]
Mills (*Lady* Dorothy R. M.)
The arms of the sun. s8°. [1924]
The dark gods. s8°. [1925]
The laughter of fools. s8°. [1920]
Phoenix. s8°. [1926]
The road to Timbuktu. 8°. [1924]
Mills (Ernestine). The domestic problem. s8°. [1925]
Mills (Frederick Cecil). Contemp. theories of unemployment & unempl. relief. 8°. N.Y., *Columbia Univ.* 1917
Mills (*Rev.* J.), *of Loughborough.* Mem. of the life &c. of the "Ven." Robert Peck &c. s8°. 1856
Mills (J. Travis). Great Britain & the U.S. Review of their hist. relations. [P2424]. 8°. 1920
Mills (James Philip). The Ao Nagas. Foreword by H. Balfour. Suppl. notes & bibliog. by J. H. Hutton. 8°. 1926
The Lhota Nagas. Intr. & notes by J. H. Hutton. 8°. 1922
Mills (John). Within the atom: pop. view of electrons & quanta. s8°. [1922]
Mills (John Saxon). The Genoa Conference. 8°. [1922]
Life & letters of Sir H. Herkomer. 8°. 1923
The press & communic. of the Empire. Foreword by Vsct. Burnham. [Brit. Empire: survey; ed. H. Gunn, v6]. 8°. [1924]
—— **& M. G. Chrussachi.** The question of Thrace. Greeks, Bulgars & Turks. [P2422]. obl.8°. 1919
Mills (Joseph Trueman). Stockgrove estate, nr. Leighton Buzzard. [For sale by Knight &c. By dir. of exec. of M. P2861]. fol. 1924
Mills (L. A.) Brit. Malaya, 1824–67. App. by C. O. Blagden. [Roy. A. Soc.] 8°. Singapore. 1925
Mills (Stephen). Taxation in Australia. 8°. 1925
Mills (Thomas), *of Sandhurst, Berks.*
The fateful sea-gull. 8°. Reading. [1919]
Mills (William Haslam).
The Manchester Guardian. Century of hist. 8°. 1921
Mills (William Wirt). King's views of the Panama Canal. [Text by W. W. M.] obl.8°. [1913 ?]
Millspaugh (Arthur Chester). The Amer. task in Persia. 8°. 1926
Millspaugh (Charles Frederick) & L. W. Nuttall. Flora of Santa Catalina Island, Cal., *see* FIELD COLUMBIAN MUSEUM. Botan. ser., v5, 1923.
Milman (Arthur), *M.A.*
Eng. & Scotch hist. ballads. Ed. M. s8°. 1871
Milman (Helen) [*Mrs.* CALDWELL CROFTON].
My roses. [3rd ed.] 8°. 1901
Miln (Louise Jordan). It happened in Peking. s8°. [1926]
Milne (Alan Alexander).
First plays. [3rd impr.] s8°. 1920
Four plays. [To have the honour—Ariadne, or business first—Portrait of a gentleman in slippers—Success]. s8°. 1926
A gallery of children. Illust. by Saida. [2nd ed.] 4°. [1925]
Now we are six. 8°. [1927]
,, ,, [3rd ed.] 8°. [1927]
The Red House mystery. s8°. [1922]
Second plays. s8°. 1921
Success. s8°. 1923
Three plays [The great Broxopp, The Dover Road, The truth about Blayds]. 8°. 1923
When we were very young. 10th ed. s8°. [1925]
Milne (Duncan Grinnell-), *see* GRINNELL-MILNE (D.)
Milne (J. Grafton). Hist. of Egypt under Roman rule. [Hist. of Eg., v5]. 3rd ed. rev. & enl. 8°. [1924]
Milne (*Mrs* Leslie) [M. L. MILNE]. An elementary Palaung gramm. Introd. by C. O. Blagden. s8°. O. 1921
The home of an eastern clan: Palaungs of the Shan States. 8°. O. 1924
Milne (William), *D.D., see* PHILIP (R.) Life & opinions of W. M., missionary to China, 1840.
Milne (William C.) A retrospect of the Protestant mission to China. 8°. Malacca. 1820
Milner (Alfred Barrow). History of Micheldever. 8°. Paris. 1924
Milner (Alfred Milner, *viscount*).
Questions of the hour. 8°. [1923]
see MAKRAM EBEID (W.) Complete independence *v.* M. scheme, 1921.
Milner (Dennis). Higher production, by a bonus on national output &c. s8°. [1920]
Milner (Isaac), *dean of Carlisle.* Strictures on publ^s. of Rev. H. Marsh: reply to h. objections agst. the B. & F. Bible Soc. 8°. 1813
Milner (James D.) Tilly Kettle, 1735–86, *see* WALPOLE SOC., v15, 1927.
Milner (John), *bp. of Castabala.* Hist. & survey of antiq. of Winchester. 2nd ed. corr. & enl. 2v [*in* 1]. 4°. Winchester. [1809]
Milner (Joseph Thorpe). Mem. of the Rev. Joseph Hollingworth &c. s8°. Sheffield. 1836
Milner (Thomas), *M.A., F.R.G.S.* The life, times & corresp. of Rev. Isaac Watts, D.D. 8°. 1845
Milner-Gibson-Cullum (Gery). Mary Beale. [Repr. f. Suffolk Instit. Proc.] [P2708]. 8°. Ipswich. 1918
see CARMICHAEL (M.) Inscr. in old Brit. cemetery of Leghorn, 1906.
Milnes (Alfred). Economics for to-day: elem. view. s8°. 1920
Milton (John).
POETICAL WORKS [*in order of publ.*]
Poems, 1645. type-facs. s8°. O. 1924
Minor poems. [*Facs. repr. of* Poems, both Eng. & Lat., 1645, *omitting the Lat. poems.* Noel Douglas Replicas]. 8°. [1926]
Poet. works. With a life of the a. by W. Hayley. 3v. la. fol. 1794–97
Poet. works. Coll. by T. Park. 4v. s8°. 1805
Poet. works. s8°. 1832

Milton (John) [*continued*].
POETICAL WORKS [*in order of publ. cont.*].
Poet. works. Life &c. by G. Gilfillan. 2v. 8°. E. 1853
Poet. works. [Life by J. Mitford. Aldine ed.] 3v. s8°. 1886–8
Poet. works, w. intr. mem., notes &c. [" Albion " Ed.] 8°. 1896
Poems, Eng., Lat., Greek & Ital., arr. in chronolog. order, w. pref. by H. J. C. Grierson. 2v. 8°. *Florence Press*. 1925
SINGLE & MISC. WORKS. [*Poet. & prose*].
Areopagitica & o. tracts. s8°. 1900
Εἰκονοκλάστης, in ans. to a book intitl'd Εἰκὼν Βασιλική, the portracture of K. Charles I &c. s8°. Amsterdam. 1690
On the morning of Christ's nativity. M.'s hymn w. illust. by W. Blake & note by G. Keynes. 4°. C. 1923
Paradise lost. Facs. reprod. of 1st ed., w. intr. by D. Masson. 8°. 1877
" " ....9th ed. s8°. 1711
" " From text of T. Newton. 4°. B'ham, *Baskerville*. 1759
" " ....With acc. of a. & h. wr. s8°. 1789
" " An extract with notes. [*Ed.* John Wesley]. s8°. 1791
Paradise regain'd. Added, Samson Agonistes. s8°. 1680
" " ....la8°. B'ham, *Baskerville*. 1759
*Portraits, prints & writings of J. M. [By G. C. Williamson]. Exhib. at Christ's Coll., Camb. [Milton Tercent.] [2nd ed.] 8°. [C.] 1908
" " By Dr. Williamson. With app. & index by C. Sayle. [repr.] *large paper copy, p. f. p. c.* la8°. [C.] 1908
Pro Populo Anglicano defensio contra Claudii anonymi, alias Salmasii defensionem regiam. s8°. Londini. 1651
Some newly discov. stanzas wr. by J. M. on engr. scenes illust. Ovid's Metamorphoses. [*Ed.*] H. C. H. Candy. 8°. [1924]
The tercentenary of Milton's birth. Lines by G. Meredith. Oration by A. W. Ward. Milton & music by Sir F. Bridge. [From Brit. Acad. Proc., v3. P2411]. 8°. 1908
TRANSLATION.
Paradise lost. In Hebrew blank verse by J. E. S[alkinson]. 8°. [Vienna. 1871]
REFERENCES.
see ADDISON (J.) Crit. on Paradise lost ; w. remarks on versific. of M. by S. Johnson, 1805.
" CAMBRIDGE : CHRIST'S COLLEGE. Early eds. of M.'s wks. in Ch. Coll. library, 1921.
" COOPER (L.) Concord. to Lat., Gr. & Ital. poems of M., 1923.
" CORSON (H.) Intr. to wks. of M. ; autobiog. passages, Comus, Lycidas & Samson Agonistes, w. notes &c., 1914.
" COURTHOPE (W. J.) Macaulay's comparison of Dante & M., 1908.
" DOWDEN (E.) M. in the 18th c., 1701–50, 1908.
" GARROD (H. W.) M.'s lines on Shakespeare, 1926.
" GEFFROY (M. A.) Ét. s. les pamphlets de M., 1848.
" HAVENS (R. D.) Influence of M. on Eng. poetry, 1922.
" HOLMES (E.) Some notes on M.'s use of words, 1924.
" JEBB (*Sir* R. C.) Samson Agonistes & the Hellenic drama, 1908.
" LEACH (A. F.) M. as a schoolboy &c., 1908.
" MACKAIL (J. W.) Bentley's Milton, 1924.
" MARSH (J. F.) On engraved & pretended portraits of M., 1860.
" MUTSCHMANN (H.) M.'s eyesight & chronol. of wks., 1924.
" —— Orig. of " Paradise Lost," 1924.
" —— Secret of J. M., 1925.
" SALMASIUS (CL.) C. S. ad J. M. responsio, 1660.
" SAURAT (D.) La pensée de M., 1920.
" SEDULIUS (C.) The Easter song ; w. intr. &c. incl. schedule of M.'s " debts," by G. Sigerson, 1922.
" SYMMONS (C.) Life of J. M., 1822.

Milyukov (Pavel Nikolaevich). Исторія второй русской революціи. t1. вып. 1–3. 8°. Софія. 1921–24
Россія на переломѣ : больш. періодъ русск. revол. 2т. 8°. Парижъ. 1927
TRANSLATIONS.
Bolshevism : an international danger. 8°. [1920]
The case for Bessarabia. Docs. on Roumanian occupation. [2nd ed. P2848]. 8°. [1919]
Constit. govt. for Russia. [P2452]. s8°. N.Y. 1908

Milyutin (Dmitry Alekseevich), *1816–1912, see* NEMIROVICH-DANCHENKO (V. I.) На кладбищахъ, 1921.

Milyutin (N. A.) Проекты постановки соц. обеспечения трудящихся, в3. [P2499]. s8°. 1918
Руководство по составлению отчетов местных собесов. [P2458]. 8°. Москва. 1919

Milyutin (V. P.)
Народное хозяйство Советской России. [P2822]. la8°. Москва. 1920
La nationalisation de l'industrie (Oct. 1918). [P2392]. *n.p.* [1919 ?]
Die Volkswirtschaft in Sowjetrussland. [P2492]. 8°. Wien. 1920

Mīmāmsā-Sutra, *see* KEITH (A. B.) The Karma-Mīmāmsā, 1921.

Mimosa, *ps.* *Under Eastern skies. s8°. Rangoon. 1901

Mimpriss (Robert). The treasury harmony &c. of the 4 Evangelists &c. 4°. [1855]

Mims (Stewart Lea). Colbert's West India policy. [Yale Hist. St., 1]. 8°. New Haven. 1912

Minadoi (Giovanni Tommaso). Hist. d. guerra fra Turchi & Persiani &c., con una lettera all' Ill. Sig. M. Corrado int. Tauris &c. 8°. Venetia. 1588

Minaev (—). Изъ ист. рабочаго класса. Подъ ред. Н. А. Рожкова. [P2448]. 8°. Москва. 1906

Minaev (Ivan Pavlovich).
Свѣдѣнія о странахъ по верховьямъ Аму-Дарьи. 8°. С.-П. 1879
see PĀTIMOKKHA-SUTRA. Пратимокша-сутра ; изд. &c. И. М., 1869.

Miñana (José Manuel de).
see MARIANA (J. DE). Hist. de rebus Hisp. ; acc. J. E. M. contin. novæ libri 10, t4, 1733.
" —— Hist. gen. de España ; nueva ed. cont. la cont. del P. M. tr., 9t, 1828.

Mind (The) ; by var. a. : lectures, *see* MACDOWALL (R. J. S.), *ed.*

Mind : a quarterly review. N.S. 29–36. 8°. 1920–27
" " Index, v13–32 (1904–23). 8°. [1924]

Mind Association, *see* ARISTOTELIAN Soc. Suppl. vol. 3–6 : papers read at joint session[s] of A. Soc., Mind Assoc. &c., 1923–26.

Mindon, *king of Burma, see* DUROISELLE (S.) Pageant of King M., 1865 ; reprod. f. contemp. doc., 1925.

Miner (Clarence Eugene). The ratification of the Fed. constit. by the State of N.Y. [Columbia Univ.] 8°. N.Y. 1921

***Minerva,** or, the art of weaving. Wr. in verse by R. C. s4°. 1677

Minerva. Jahrbuch d. gelehrten Welt.
Jhrg. 25–29. [28, 29 *each in* 4B *incl.* Geogr. Reg.] 8°. 1921–28

Mingarelli (Giovanni Luigi) [MINGARELLIUS (Jo. ALOYSIUS)].
Anecdotorum fasc., sive S. Paulini Nolani, Anon. Scriptoris, Alani Magni, ac Theophylacti opuscula aliquot. J. A. M. ed., praef. &c. add., Gr.-Lat. redd. 4°. Romae. 1756

Minghetti (Marco). Alcune lettere ined. di M. M. e di Giosuè Carducci a E. Masi. [*Ed.* G. Albertotti. Nozze Bonasi-Bruni. N122]. 8°. Padova. 1910
Carteggio tra M. M. e Gius. Pasolini, 1846–59. Per cura di Guido Pasolini. 2v. 8°. Torino. 1924–26

Mîng sîn paò Kiân. [*Precious mirror for enlightening the heart. Chinese moral precepts*]. 8°. *n.p. n.d.*

Ming-tsiao tchong-jenn, *ps.* La brise au clair de lune : roman chinois [*by* M.] ; tr. G. Soulié de Morant, 1925, *see* HAOU KEW CHUEN.

Miniana (José Manuel de), *see* MIÑANA (J. M. DE).

Minieri Riccio (Camillo). Cenno storico d. Accad. Pontaniana. [P2859]. la8°. Napoli. 1876

Minin (S. K.)
Кто такие коммунисты ? [P2722]. s8°. Москва. 1919
Религия и коммунизм. [P2723]. 8°. Москва. 1919
Страшный казак. Сон ген. Деникина. [P2722]. s8°. Москва. 1919
Чего они хотят ? &c. [P2722]. s8°. Москва. 1919

***Mining** in Egypt ; by an Egyptologist, *n.d.*, *see* EGYPT.

Mining manual (The) & mining year book, 1926. By W. E. Skinner. 8°. 1926

***Ministère** (Le) vengé ; par un Constitutionnel Salarié, 1818, *see* THIÉRY (A.)

Ministry of Agriculture & Fisheries, *see* BOARD OF AGRICULTURE.

Ministry of Health, *see* HEALTH, MINISTRY OF.

Ministry of Munitions, *see* MUNITIONS, MINISTRY OF.

Minkowski (Hermann), *see* LORENTZ (H. A.), A. EINSTEIN & H. M. Das Relativitätsprinzip, 1920 ; 4e verm. A., 1922.

Minnelieder aus Österreich : Dichtungen d. 12. bis 14. Jhdts., 1921, *see* GRUNSTEIN (L.)

Minnesangs (Des) Frühling, *see* HALBACH (K.) Walther v. d. Vogelweide u. d. Dichter v. M. F., 1927.

Minns (Ellis Hovell). St. Cyril really knew Hebrew. [*Extr. f.* Mélanges en l'honn. de P. Boyer. P2859]. la8°. Paris. 1925

Minns (*Miss* Susan), *see* DANCE OF DEATH. Coll. of S. M. : books &c. illust. of " The dance of death," sold, May 1922, Amer. Art Galleries, 1922.

Minocchi (Salvatore). L'ombra di Dante. s8°. Firenze. 1921

Minor (The) theatre : coll. of farces &c., v4, *see* FOOTE (S.) The commissary &c., 1794.

Minor (Jacob). Goethes Fragmente v. Ewigen Juden u. v. wiederkehr. Heiland. s8°. St. 1904
Studien zu Novalis, 1, Z. Textkritik d. Gedichte, 1911, *see* KAIS. AKAD. D. W. ZU W. Sitzb., B169, 1913.

Minotto (Antonio S.) Monumenti a V. de' Rambaldoni e. P. Castaldi in Feltre. la8°. Feltre. 1869
see TREVISO. Codex Trivis., 996–1318 ; cur. A. S. M., 1874–75.

Minsky (Nikolai Mikhailovich) [*i.e.* N. M. VILENKIN].
Изъ мрака къ свѣту, избран. стихотворенія. s8°. Берлинъ. 1922

Minto (Antonio). Lamine di bronzo fig. a Sbalzo di arte paleoetrusca, *see* REALE ACCAD. D. LINCEI. Mon. ant., v28, 1922.
Populonia, la necropoli arcaica. [R. Istit. di Studi Super. &c.] la8°. Firenze. 1922
Le terme romane di Massaciuccoli, *see* REALE ACCAD. D. LINCEI. Mon. ant., v27, 1921.

Minto (Gilbert Elliot, *1st earl of***).** Speech in House of Peers, Apr. 11, 1799 &c. resp. an union betw. Gt. Brit. & Ireland. [P2555]. 8°. D. 1799

Minto (Gilbert John Elliot-Murray-Kynynmound, *4th earl of***),** *see* BUCHAN (J.) Lord M.: a mem., 1924.

Mintslov (Sergei Rudolfovich).
Закатъ. Романъ. s8°. Берлинъ. 1926

Minty (E. Arden). Some acc. of the hist. of Petersfield. s8°. 1923

Minucci (Andrea), *of Serravalle.* Descr. di un viaggio fatto 1549 da Venezia a Parigi, con cenni biogr. &c. dell' ab. J. Bernardi, *see* REGIA DEP. DI STORIA PATRIA. Misc., t1, 1862.

Minucci (Minuccio), *abp. of Zara.* Hist. degli Uscochi, -1602, e contin. dal P. M. Paolo, -1616. s8°. Venetia. 1683

Minucius Felix (Marcus). Octavius, & C. Cypriani De idolor. vanitate nova ed. Nic. Rigaltii obs. s4°. Lutetiae. 1643
see BAYLIS (H. J.) M. F. & h. place am. the early Fathers, 1928.

Minuti (Antonio), *of Piacenza.* Vita di M. Attendolo Sforza; ed. G. Porro Lambertenghi, *see* REGIA DEP. DI STORIA PATRIA. Misc., t7, 1869.

Minutti (Rodolfo). Letteratura tedesca. s8°. Milano. 1889

Minuvshie godi. Минувшіе годы: журналъ: Октябрь & Ноябрь. 8°. С.-П. 1908

Miolo (Gianbernardo), *di Lombriasco.* Cronaca [985–1569, *Latin*], *see* REGIA DEP. DI STORIA PATRIA. Misc., t1, 1862.

Miomandre (Francis de).
L'aventure de Thérèse Beauchamps. Bois orig. de R. Grillon. 8°. *n.d.*
Ce monde de rosée, *see* Œ. libres, 35, 1924.
Ces petits messieurs, *see* Œ. libres, 6, 1921.
. . . d'amour & d'eau fraîche. s8°. 1913
Le dictateur, *see* Œ. libres, 66, 1926.
L'enfant prodigue & s. père, *see* Œ. libres, 41, 1924.
Figures d'hier & d'aujourd'hui. 8°. [1911]
Le jeu de l'amour & de la danse, *see* Œ. libres, 16, 1922.
Le mariage de Geneviève. s8°. 1920
Le pavillon du mandarin. s8°. 1921
Les taupes. s8°. 1922

Mion (Francesco). Storia giuridica d. ant. diritto di nomina alla sede patriarcale di Venezia. [P2843]. sm. fol. Venezia. 893

Mira, *see* MIRABAI.

Mira (Giuseppe Maria), *see* SALVO-COZZO (G.) Giunte e corr. alla lett. A d. Bibliog. sicil. di M., 1881.

Mira (Jenaro Alenda y), *see* ALENDA Y MIRA (J.)

Mira (Lluis Fullana), *see* FULLANA MIRA (L.)

Mirabai, *of Mewad* [MIRA], *1498–1563, see* MEHTA (S. S.) Monograph on M., 1920.

Mirabeau (Honoré G. Riquetti, *cte.* **de),** *1749–91.* *Corr. pour servir de suite à l'Hist. secrette de la cour de Berlin. 8°. Postdam [*sic*]. 1789
see JOUVENEL (H. DE). La vie orageuse de M., 1928.
„ MEUNIER (D.) Autour de M.: docs. inéd., 1926.

Mirabello (Carlo Ignazio Montagnini, *conte* **di),** *see* MONTAGNINI (C. I.)

***Mirabilis** liber: qui prophetias &c. preteritas, presentes & futuras aperte demonstrat. [Sensuyt la seconde partie de ce livre]. *p1 in Latin, p2 in French.* s8°. [Paris ?, *au Pellican en la rue St. Jacques, E. de Marnef* ?. 1530 ?]

Miraflores (*el marques* **de)** [†PANDO FERNANDEZ DE PINEDO ALAVA Y DÁVILA (M.)] Vida del general español D. S. Davila y Daza, prec. de una hojeada de las 3 princ. cuestiones polit.-relig. y soc. la8°. 1857

Miralles de Imperial (Adolfo). Crón. de la prov. de Castellon de la Plana, 1867, *see* ESPAÑA. Crón. gen., v7, 1865 &c.

Miranda (Luigi).
Da Hegel a Croce e da Jellinek a Chiovenda. 8°. Bari. 1921

Miranda (Salustio). Novella di Battista Abbraccia il Porco. [*Ed.* A. Tessier. P2787]. 8°. Venezia. 1854

Mirande (Yves) & A. Madis. Simone est comme ça, comédie, *see* ŒUVRES libres, 22, 1923.

Mirbeau (Octave). Des artistes. 2s. s8°. [1922–24]
Un gentilhomme. s8°. [1920]
Les 21 jours d'un neurasthénique. s8°. 1901

Mircesco (V.) Gram. de la langue roumaine, préc. d'un aperçu hist., par A. Ucini. s8°. 1865

Mirepoix. Cartul. de M. [*Ed. w.* Intr. hist. *by*] F. Pasquier. 2t. 4°. Toulouse. 1921

Mirepoix (Lévis). Le seigneur inconnu. s8°. [1922]

Mirkus (John) [MIRK; MYRE]. Darn o'r Ffestifal (Liber festialis): allan o Lawsgrif Hafod 22, td. 80–195, gyda rhagymadrodd a nodiadau gan H. Lewis [*sep. tp. & pagin.*], *see* CYMMRODORION. Trans., 1923–24, 1925.
Instructions for parish priests. Ed. E. Peacock. [E.E.T.S., 31]. 8°. 1868
„ „ Rev. 1902 [by F. J. Furnivall. E.E.T.S., 31]. 8°. 1868 [repr. 1902]

Miró (Gabriel).
El angel, el molino, el caracol del faro &c. s8°. [1921]
El humo dormido. s8°. 1919
Libro de Sigüenza. s8°. Barcelona. [1921]

Miron (Robert), *see* MIRON DE L'ESPINAY (A.) R. M. &c., 1922.

Miron de L'Espinay (Albert). R. Miron & l'admin. municipale de Paris, 1614–1616—Le tiers aux Etats-Gèn. de 1614—L'ambassade franç. en Suisse, 1617–72 [*i.e.* 27]. 8°. 1922

Mirot (Léon). Une propriété rurale de la famille Gobelin: la Cour-Roland, *see* SOCIÉTÉ DE L'HIST. DE PARIS &C. Mém., t47, 1924.

Mirrlees (Hope). The counterplot. [2nd impr.] s8°. [1924]
Lud-in-the-mist. s8°. [1926]
Madeleine, one of love's Jansenists. [2nd impr.] s8°. [1919]
see HARRISON (*Miss* J. E.) & H. M. The book of the bear, 1926.

Mirrors. M. (The) of Downing Street, 2nd ed., 1920, *see* DOWNING STREET.
*M. (The) of Washington, 1921, *see* WASHINGTON.

Mirsky (Boris) [MIRKINE-GETZEVITCH]. Les Juifs & la Révolution Russe. Préf. de S. Reinach. 8°. [1921]

Mirsky (*prince* **Dmitri Svyatopolk-).**
Русская лирика: маленькая антологія. s8°. Парижъ. 1924
Contemp. Russian lit., 1881–1925. 8°. 1926
Hist. of Russian lit. (-1881). 8°. 1927
Mod. Russian lit. s8°. 1925
Pushkin. s8°. 1926
see VERSTI. Версты; ред. С.-М. &c., 1926.

Mirtov (P.), *ps., see* LAVROV (P. L.)

Mirza Husain ʻAlī, *see* BAHĀ 'U 'LLĀH.

Misʻar ibn al-Muhalhil (Abu Dulaf), *see* ABU DULAF.

Miscellanea.
M. de la Républ. Tchécoslovaque, 1919, *see* TCHÉCOSLOVAQUE.
M. di storia ital., 1862–1928, *see* REGIA DEPUT. DI STORIA PATRIA.
*M. Duisburgensia, edita, inedita, &c. ad incrementum rei lit. [*Ed.* D. Gerdes]. 2t. s8°. Amstelodami & Duisburgi. [1732]–35
M. hagiographica Hibernica, 1925, *see* PLUMMER (C.), *ed.*
*M. juris publ. curiosa de novemviratu. Ob d. Neunte Electorat eingeführt werden könne? &c. [P2746]. s4°. *n.p.* 1692

Miscellanea genealogica et heraldica. Ed. A. W. Hughes Clarke. 5th ser., v3, 4. la8°. 1918–22

***Miscellanea Groningana** in Misc. Duisburgensium cont. publ. [Ed. D. Gerdes]. 4t. s8°. Amstelodami &c. 1736–45
„ „ *Scrinium antiquarium sive Misc. G. nova. t1, 2 [*in* 1v]. s4°. Groningae. [1748]–1751

Miscellany. M. of Hebrew lit., 1872, *see* SOC. OF HEBREW LIT.
M. (A) of the wits. Sel. pieces by W. King, J. Arbuthnot & o. hands. Intr. by K. N. Colvile. 8°. 1920

Mischief. *Reply (A) to the mischief of impositions &c., 1681, *see* CLAGETT (W.)

Misciattelli (Piero). Saggio biog. sopra S. Filippo Neri, *see* STRONG (E.) Chiesa nuova, 1923.

***Miseries** (The) & great hardships of the inferiour clergy &c., 1722, *see* STACKHOUSE (T.)

Mises (Ludwig). Die Gemeinwirtschaft: Unters. ü. d. Sozialismus. 8°. Jena. 1922
—— **& F. Klein.** Die geldtheoret. u. geldrechtl. Seite d. Stabilisierungsproblems. [V. f. Sozialpol., B164, T2]. 8°. München. 1923

Mish (Mikhail Ignatevich) [Мышъ]. Положеніе о земскихъ учрежденіяхъ со всѣми узаконеніями. изд. 2ое исправл. 8°. С.-П. 1884

Mishnah.
Duo codd. Talmudici Avoda Sara & Tamid. Paraphrasi Lat. redditi a G. Peringero. [P431]. s4°. Altdorfi Noric. 1680
Duo tituli thalmudici Sanhedrin & Maccoth, cum excerptis ex Gemara; annotat. illust. à J. Coch &c. [*Heb. & Lat.*] s4°. Amsterodami. 1629
J. C. Wagenseilii Sota; liber Mishnicus de uxore adulterii suspecta una cum libri en Jacob excerptis Gemarae vers. Lat., & comm.

Mishnah [*continued*].
perpetuo illust. Acc. correctiones Lipmannianæ. [*w. sep. pagin.*] s4°. Altdorfi Noricorum. 1674
Schekalim : tract. Talmud. de modo &c. siclum mense Adar offerendi, &c., Lat. don. & comm. illust. à J. Wülfero. [P1015]. s4°. Altdorfi Noric. 1680
Talumudis Babylonici Codex Middoth sive de mensuris Templi una cum vers. Lat. &c. opera C. L'Empereur. s4°. Lugduni Batavorum. 1630
Text. Talmudicus tract. de primitiis, & comm. ejus à Rambano confectus cum vers. Lat. & annot. publ. disput. tuebitur C. Ludovici, resp. T. A. Nicandro [*&* T. Brock, *&* G. I. Musculo]. 3p. [P427]. s4°. Lipsiae. 1696
Tractate Berakoth (Benedictions), M. & Tosephta. Tr. w. intr. & notes by A. L. Williams. s8°. 1921
Tractate Shabbath. Tr. w. explan. notes by W. O. E. Oesterley. s8°. 1927
Tractatus Talmudicus de cultu quotidiano templi. [*Heb. & Lat.*] Notis illust. &c. C. Iken. s4°. Bremæ. 1736
see ABOTH. Ethics of the Fathers; tr. w. intr. to Talmud, by R. Young, 1852.
„ TOSEFTA.

Miskjian (Hovhannes) [MISKGIAN (J.); MISQDJEAN].
Manuale lexicon Armeno-Lat. ad usum schol. 8°. Romae. 1887
„ „ *a. interleaved copy w. MS. add. by F. C. Conybeare.*
Manuale lexicon Latino-Armenum ad usum schol. 8°. Romae. 1893

Mislenta (Coelestinus). Judicia theologorum orthodox. de lite Regiomonti à C. M. J. Latermanno mota &c. [P2671]. s4°. Thorunii. [1648]

Misme (Clotilde), *see* LOUVRE. La peinture, école holland., par C. M., 1927.

Misqdjean, *see* MISKJIAN.

Misra (C. S.) Cultiv. of lac in the plains of India, *see* AGRIC. RESEARCH INST., *Pusa*. Bull. No. 142, 1923.

Miss Tiverton goes out. By the a. of The house made w. hands. [2nd impr.] s8°. [1925]

Missa [MISSAE]. Missa Gothica seù Mozarabica, 1770, *see* MOZARABICA.
Missae propriae festorum ord. eremitarum S. Augustini, auctor. Clement X rev., corr. &c. [*b. w.* Missale Rom., 1799]. fol. Matriti. 1789

Missal [MISSALE; *see also* OFFICIA].
Missal for the laity. [*2 pagin.*] s8°. *n.d.*
Missale Alexandrinum S. Marci in quo Eucharistiae Liturgiae omnes antiq. ac recentes eccl. Ægypti, Graece, Coptice, Arabice, & Syriace exhibentur. J. A. Assemanus rec., Lat. convertit &c. s4°. Romae. 1754
„ „ *for a. ed., see* ASSEMANUS (J. A.) Codex liturgicus eccl. univ., t7, 1754.
[Missale Lubicense. *Fol. 1 blank. Fol. 2a (unnumbered) beg.* Januarius habet dies xxx &c. *Last fol. (numbered* ccii) *ends* Gl'ia in excelsis deo. *Printed in double columns, 38ll. to the col. except the leaves of the Canon quire, which are in single cols. of 19ll.*] fol. [Speyer: *Peter Drach.* c. 1495]
For full collation see Reichling (D.) App. ad Hainii-Copingeri Repertorium, fasc. 3, page 60, *but fol. 16 (blank) is wanting & the Canon quire has 9 leaves instead of 10.*
M. Romanum. s8°. Venetiis. 1576
„ „ .... la8°. Venetiis. 1766
„ „ ex decr. Conc. Tridentini restitutum, Pii V jussu ed. &c. [Commune Sanctorum *w. sep. pagin.* & Missae propriae SS. Hispanorum *&* Ord. eremit. S. Augustini, *each w. sep. tp. & pagin.*] fol. Matriti. 1799
Office divin ou Misesl [*sic*] Rom. à l'usage des laiques. [*2 pagin.*] n. ed. s8°. Avignon. 1786
Ordinary (The) of the Mass, Vespers &c. In Lat. & Eng. s8°. 1794
*Pocket (A) missal for the use of the laity. s8°. 1836
*Roman (The) M. for the use of the laity. s8°. *n.d.*
Sherborne (The) M., 1920, *see* SHERBORNE MISSAL.
Taufe u. Firmung nach d. Röm. M., Rituale &c.; hrsg. I. Herwegen, *see* KLEINE TEXTE, T144, Liturg. Texte, T11, 1920.

Missen (L. R.) Hist. of the 7th (Ser.) Bn. Prince of Wales's (N. Staffs. Regt.), 1914–19. s8°. C. 1920

Mission Archéologique de Perse. Mémoires, t15–18, 1914–27, *see* DÉLÉGATION EN PERSE.

Mission Archéologique en Arabie. II [1909–10], El-'Ela, d'Hégra à Teima, Harrah de Tebouk, par RR. PP. Jaussen & Savignac. [Soc. Franç. des Fouilles Archéol. 2t, 1, Texte. 2, Atlas]. la8°. 1914
„ „ Suppl., Coutumes des Fuqarâ, par RR. PP. Jaussen & Savignac. la8°. 1914 [1920]
„ „ III, [1909–12], Les châteaux arabes de Qoṣeir 'Amra, Ḥarâneh & Ṭûba, par RR. PP. Jaussen & Savignac. [Soc. Franç. des Fouilles Archéol. *&* Atlas, avec 58 planches]. la8°. 1922

Mission Archéologique (La) Française au Caire. Mémoires. t20. 4°. Le Caire. 1928
Rochemonteix (M. *marq.* de). Le Temple d'Edfou; publ. E. Chassinat, t3. [20.]

Mission Scientifique du Maroc [*aft.* RÉSIDENCE GÉN. DE LA RÉP. FR. AU MAROC]. Archives marocains. v10–15, 18–24, 26, 27, 30–32. 8°. 1907–27
10, 30–32, Aḥmad ibn Khālid. Kitâb elistiqṣâ. &c., t1–4; tr. A. Graulle, E. Fumey &c., 1907–27.
11, 15, 18, Misc. 1907–12.
12, 13, Ahmad *al Wanscharīsī.* La pierre de touche des fétwas, 2t, 1908–9.
14, Slouschz (N.) Hebræo-Phéniciens & Judéo-Berbères, 1908.
18, Misc., 1912.
19, Ibn 'Askar. La "Daouhat An-Nâchir"; tr. de A. Graulle, 1913.
20, Michaux-Bellaire (E.) Le Gharb, 1913.
21, 24, Muhammad al-Qâdirî. Nachr al-Mathânî; tr. de A. Graulle &c., 2t, 1913–17.
22, 23, Michaux-Bellaire (E.) Les habous de Tanger, 2t (1, Texte arabe; 2, Analyses & extr.), 1914.
26, 'Abd al-Ḥaqq *al-Bâdisî.* El-Maqṣad (Vies des saints du Rîf); tr. annot. de G. S. Colin, 1926.
27, Michaux-Bellaire (E.) Conférences, 1927.
Villes & tribus du Maroc. Doc. & renseignements publ. sous les auspices de la Résidence générale. t4–7. la8°. 1918–21
4–6, Rabat et s. région, t2, Les villes après la conquête. 3, Les tribus. 4, Le Gharb (Les Djebala). 7, Tanger & sa zone; publ. par la Dir. des Affaires Indigènes &c.
see also REVUE DU MONDE MUSULMAN.

Missionary (The) controversy: discussion, evidence & report. [Wesleyan Meth. Miss. Soc.] 8°. 1890

Missionary Conference. General M. Conf. held in Allahabad, 1872–73. [Ed. J. Barton *& others*]. 8°. 1873

Missionary notices, 1816–80, *see* WESLEYAN MISSIONARY NOTICES.

Missionary Society, *see* LONDON MISSIONARY SOC.

Missions. *Lettre de messieurs des missions étrangères au Pape sur les idolatries &c. chinoises, 1700, *see* SÉMINAIRE DES MISSIONS ETR.

Missionsnachrichten der Ostind. Missionsanstalt zu Halle, 1849–65, *see* DÄNISCHE MISSIONARIEN.

Misson (François Maximilien). *Les prophètes protestants. Avec préf. de A. Bost. [*a.c. in* P524]. 8°. [Melun. 1847]

Mistler (Jean). Madame de Staël & M. O'Donnell, 1805–17, d'ap. des lettres inéd. 8°. [1926]

Mistral (Frederi). Calendal. Texte & tr. s8°. *n.d.*
Les îles d'or. Texte & tr. s8°. *n.d.*
Mireille. Texte & tr. s8°. *n.d.*
Nerte. Texte & tr. s8°. 1910
Les olivades. Texte & tr. s8°. [1912]

Mistruzzi (Vittorio). Giov. Cotta, *see* GIORNALE STOR. D. LETT. ITAL. Suppl. 22, 1924.

Mitchell (Abe). Essentials of golf. Ed. &c. J. Martin. 8°. [1927]

Mitchell (Alexander Ferrier). The Westminster Assembly, its hist. &c. Baird lect. s8°. 1883

Mitchell (Charles Ainsworth). Science & the criminal. s8°. 1911

Mitchell (Donald Grant) [*ps.* IK MARVEL], *see* DUNN (W. H.) Life of D. G. M., 1922.

Mitchell (Frank William Drew).
A key to health & long life. 2nd ed. s8°. 1922

Mitchell (Frederick Scott-), *see* SCOTT-MITCHELL (F.)

Mitchell (J. Murray). The Zend-Avesta & the relig. of the Pârsîs. [P505]. s8°. *n.d.*
see EVANGELICAL ALLIANCE. The relig. condition of Christendom, 1885.

Mitchell (*Major-Gen.* **John),** *1785–1859.*
Life of Wallenstein. s8°. Frankfort o. M. 1841

Mitchell (John Kearsley). Self help for nervous women. 8°. 1909

Mitchell (John Malcolm), *see* CARNEGIE UNITED KINGDOM TRUST. Public library system of Gt. Brit. & Ir., 1921–23, 1924.

Mitchell (Ogilvie). The talking machine industry. s8°. [1922]

Mitchell (Peter Chalmers). *Rep. on the propaganda library, 1917, *see* WAR OFFICE.

Mitchell (Philip Henry). Nutrition of oysters. [Fr. Bull. of the Bur. of Fisheries, v35]. [P2702]. la8°. Wash. 1917

Mitchell (Robert McBurney). Heyse & h. predecessors in the theory of the Novelle. [N.Y. Univ.] 8°. Fr. a. M. 1915

Mitchell (Samuel Augustus). An accompaniment to M.'s reference & distance map of United States. 8°. Phila. 1836
see YOUNG (J. H.) M.'s Ref. & distance map of the U.S., 1836.

Mitchell (Thomas Walker).
Medical psychology & psych. research. s8°. [1922]
The psychology of medicine. s8°. [1921]
Mitchell (Wesley Clair). Internat. price comparisons &c., *see* UNITED STATES: LABOR.
see EDIE (L. D.), *ed.* Stabilization of business; by W. C. M. &c., 1923.
Mitchell-Hedges (F. A.), *see* HEDGES (F. A. M.)
Mitchison (Naomi). Cloud cuckoo land. s8°. [1925]
The conquered. Intr. by E. Barker. s8°. [1923]
When the bough breaks & o. s. s8°. [1924]
Mitford (John), *vicar of Benhall.* Sacred specimens sel. f. the early Eng. poets, w. pref. verses by J. M. s8°. 1827
Mitford (Mary Russell), *see* HILL (C.) M. R. M. & her surroundings, 1920.
Mithra, *see* GEDEN (A. S.) Sel. passages illust. Mithraism; tr., w. intr., 1925.
Mitius (Otto). Dürers Schlosshofansichten u. d. Cadolzburg bei Nürnberg. sm. fol. L. 1922
Mitman (Carl W.) Cat. of the mechan. engineering coll. in the U.S. Nat. Mus.: Motors, locomot. & self-propell. vehicles. [S.I.: U.S. Nat. Mus., Bull. 119]. 8°. Wash. 1922
Cat. of the watercraft coll. in the U.S. Nat. Mus. Comp. &c. C. W. M. [S.I.: U.S. Nat. Mus., Bull. 127]. 8°. Wash. 1923
Some pract. aspects of fuel economy, 1923, *see* SMITHSONIAN INST. Misc. Coll., v76, 1925.
Mitrany (D.) Marx v. the peasant, *see* CANNAN (E.) London essays, 1927.
The problem of internat. sanctions. s8°. 1925
*__Mitre__ (The), a sacred poem, 1757, *see* PERRONET (E.)
Mitre (Bartolomé), *president of the Argentine Republic.* Arengas. Col. de discursos parl., polít. &c., 1848–1902. 3ª ed. 3t. s8°. Buenos Aires. *n.d.*
t3, *cont. an* estudio biográf. por J. J. Viedma.
Hist. de Belgrano y de la independencia Argentina. 4t. s8°. Buenos Aires. 1927–28
Hist. de San Martín y de la emancipacíon Sudamericana. 3ª ed. 6t. s8°. Buenos Aires. *n.d.*
see NACION (LA). Suppl.: Centenario de B. M., 1921.
Mitrofanov (A.)
Комитеты деревенской бѣдноты. [P2455]. s8°. Москва. 1918
Первое Мая—праздник труда. [P2455]. s8°. [Киев. 1919]
Mitrokhin (Dmitri Isidorovich), *see* KUZMIN (M.) & V. VOINOV. Д. И. М., 1922.
Mitrophanow (Igor), *see* BREDON (J.) & I. M. The moon year, 1927.
Mittag (Johann Gottfried). Merkw. Leben u. Thaten Annae Ivanownae, Kayserin aller Reussen. [*b. w.* Moscovia gloriosa, 1741]. s8°. Grimma. 1741
Mitteilungen z. osmanischen Geschichte. Hrsg. v. F. Kraelitz u. P. Wittek. B1 (1921–22), 2i, ii (1923–25). 8°. Wien. 1922–25
Mittelalterliche Bibliothekskataloge; Hrsg. v. d. Kgl. Preuss. Akad., d. Kgl. Gesell. d. Wiss. in Göttingen &c. la8°. Wien. 1915
see ÖSTERREICH. Ma. Bibliothekskat. Ö.'s, B1, 1915.
Mittelalterliches Hausbuch: Bilder-Hs. d. 15. Jhdts.; Vorwort v. A. Essenwein, 1887, *see* HAUSBUCH.
Mitternacht (Johann Sebastian). Diss. de loco Joh. XXI, 22 & quaest. an Johannes Martyrium subierit &c. s8°. Numburg. 1665
Mittler (Theodor). De schismate in Eccl. Rom. sub pontif. Benedicti IX. [P2759]. s8°. Turici. 1835
Mitton (G. E.), *aft. wife of Sir J. G. Scott.*
The lost cities of Ceylon. 8°. 1916
The two-stringed fiddle. s8°. 1919
—— **&** *Sir* **J. G. Scott.** A frontier man. s8°. 1923
Mittwoch (Eugen). Zur Entstehungsgesch. d. Islam. Gebets u. Kultus, *see* KÖN.-PREUSS. AKAD. Abhdln., Phil-hist. Kl., 1913.
see BURCHARDT (H.) Aus d. Jemen, bearb. v. E. M., 1926.
Mitzlaff (Paul), *see* LUTHER (H.), P. M. &c. *edd.* Die Zukunftsaufgaben d. deut. Städte, 1922.
Miyamori (Asataro). Tales of the Samurai, & "Lady Hosokawa," a hist. drama [*by* Kido Okamoto]. enl. & rev. ed. s8°. Yokohama. [1922]
Mizler (Stephan Andreas). De vet. Celtarum Celia, Oelia & Zytho, ad illust. Flori locum. [*b. w.* Jäger (A.) De lingua vet. Europae, 1686]. s4°. [Wittenbergae. 1695]
Mjøen (Jon Alfred). Race hygiene. 8°. 1914
Mkhithar, *see* MEKHITHAR.
Mkrttchean (Galoust). [Echmiadzin inscriptions. *In Armenian.* Banaser *publ.* P2817]. 8°. Paris. 1906
Moberg (Carl Axel), *see* HIMYARITES. Bk. of the H.: fragm. of Syriac work; ed., w. intr. & tr. by A. M., 1924.
Moberly (*Brig.-Gen.* **Frederick James),** *see* WAR. Hist. of the Gt. War: campaign in Mesopotamia; comp. by F. J. M., 4v, 1923–27.
Möbius (Carl August). Der Bau d. Eozoon canadense &c. [Abdr. aus Palaeontographica, B25. P2875]. 4°. Cassel. 1878
Möbius (Georg). Theologia canonica, *i.e.* sel. canones theologici &c. s8°. Lipsiae. 1687
Mocatta (Frances). Thine shall be mine. s8°. 1926
Mocenigo, *The family of, see* MOCENIGO (A.) Il matrimonium Grimani-M., 1910.
Mocenigo (A.) *Il matrimonio Grimani-Mocenigo nel 1766. [*Pref. signed* A. M. P2843]. fol. *n.p.* [1910]
Mocenigo (Alvise), *doge of Venice, see* TIEPOLO (P.) Comm. data a P. T. 1571, 1845.
Mocenigo (Filippo Nani), *see* NANI MOCENIGO (F.)
Mocenigo (Giovanni), *1552–1612.* Due anni alla corte di Carlo Emanuele I duca di Savoia. Da dispacci al Senato di G. M., 1583–85. [Ed. V. Ceresole. Nozze Caïs de Pierlas-Mocenigo. N135]. la8°. Venezia. 1884
Mocenigo (Lazaro), *b. 1624, see* GOZZI (G.) L. M., 1884.
Moch (Gaston). La relativité des phénomènes. s8°. 1921
Mochta, *St., bp. of Louth, see* MACINERNY (M. H.) St. M. & Bachiarius, 1924.
Mocket (Richard). *Doctrina & politia Eccl. Anglic., a Edovardo VI, Elizabetha stabilitæ & a Jacobo contin. Ejusdem Eccl. apologia praef. s4°. Londini. 1617
Mockler (Edward). Grammar of the Baloochee lang. as spoken in Makrān. s8°. 1877
Mockler-Ferryman (Augustus Ferryman), *see* OXFORDSHIRE & Bucks. Light Infantry chron., 1914–15; w. war rec. of o. battn. of the regiment; comp. & ed. by A. F. M.-F.; v24, 1919 ?.
Mocquereau (André), *see* PALÉOGRAPHIE MUSICALE, 11v [v8–11, sous la dir. de Dom. A. M.], 1900–12.
Mocsáry (Lajos). A válság, vezényszó-polit., vemzetisége kérdés. [P2399]. 8°. Eger. 1905
Modena. Cronaca M. (1588–1636), *see* SPACCINI (G. B.)
Descr. de' quadri del ducale appartamento di Modena. 8°. Modena. 1784
Modena (Leo). סוד ישרים*. [2p. P468]. s8°. Verona. [1652]
Hist. of the rites, customes &c. of the present Jews. Tr. by E. Chilmead. s8°. 1650
*Recede a malo: libellus anon. de lusu; *Heb. & Lat.* illust. à A. Pfeiffern, *see* SENNERT (A.) Ebraismus, 1666.
Modern.
*Masterpieces of mod. German art, 2v, c. 1885, *see* GERMAN.
*Mod. antiques: farce, 1792, *see* O'KEEFFE (J.)
Mod. Brit. poetry, 1920, *see* UNTERMEYER (L.), *ed.*
Mod. Eng. essays, [1870–1920], 5v, 1922, *see* RHYS (E.), *ed.*
Mod. (The) Eng. house, 1927, *see* PHILLIPS (R. R.)
Mod. France: companion to French st., 1922, *see* TILLEY (A.), *ed.*
Mod. practice of the London hospitals, 3rd ed., 1770, *see* LONDON.
Mod. (The) teacher: essays on educ. aims & methods, [*by var. a.*], 1921, *see* BAIN (A. W.), *ed.*
Modern Humanities Research Association. Bibliography of Eng. lang. & lit., 1921; ed. A. C. Paues, 1922, *see* BIBLIOGRAPHY.
Research Series: v1, *see* LA FAYETTE (*Mme.* DE). Lettres &c., 1924. [1.]
Modern Language Association, *see* YEARBOOK OF MOD. LANG., 1920.
Modern Language Association of America.
Monograph Series. No. 2. 8°. N.Y. 1927
see ALBRIGHT (E. M.) Dram. publ. in Eng., 1580–1640, 1927. [2.]
Publications. v35–42 (N.S., v28–34). 8°. Baltimore. 1920–27
see TANNENBAUM (S. A.) Probl. in Shakspere's penmanship, 1927.
Modern language review. v15–22. 8°. C. 1920–27
Modern philology. v17–24. la8°. Chicago. [1920–27]
*__Modes__ & manners of the 19th cent.; tr. M. Edwardes, 3v, 1909, *see* BÖHN (M. v.)
*__Modest__ (A) address to the Commons of Gt. Brit. &c. occas. by the ill-success of our pres. naval war w. France &c. [P527]. 8°. 1756
Modi (Jivanji Jamshedji).
Anthropolog. papers. 2p. s8°. Bombay. [1912]–18
The funeral ceremonies of the Parsees. 2nd ed. [P2423]. 8°. Bombay. 1905

Modi (Jivanji Jamshedji) [*continued*].
Memorial papers. 4°. Bombay. [1922]
The relig. ceremonies & customs of the Parsees. s8°. Mazagon, Bombay. 1922
Modius (Franciscus), *see* LEHMANN (P.) M. als Handschriftenforscher, 1908.
Modona (Aldo Neppi), *see* NEPPI MODONA (A.)
Mody (H. P.) Sir Pherozeshah Mehta. Polit. biog. 2v [*pagin. cont.*] 8°. Bombay. 1921
Modzalevsky (Boris Lvov.)
Пушкин под тайным надзором. 8°. С.-П. 1922
see PUSHKIN (A. S.) Новые материалы о дуэли и смерти П., Б. Л. М. &c., 1924.
Moe (Jörgen I.), *see* ASBJÖRNSEN (P. C.) & J. I. M. Norweg. fairy tales; tr., 1924.
Moe (Moltke), *see* LIESTØL (K.) & M. M. Norske folkeviser fra middelalderen &c., 1919.
Moebius (Johannes). De prodigiis quibusdam quæ annunciasse dicuntur nativitatem Christi. Præses J. M., resp. J. D. König. [P2634]. s4°. *n.p.* 1685
Moerkerken (P. H. van), *jr.* De dans des levens. s8°. A. [1912]
Moerlin (Joachim), *see* MÖRLIN (J.)
Moes (E. W.) Iconographia Batava. Beredeneerde lijst van geschilderde en gebeeldhouwde portretten van N.-Nederlanders. 2d. la8°. Amsterdam. 1897–1905
Moffat (James), *ps.*, *see* MACKOULL (J.)
Moffat (John Smith), *see* MOFFAT (R. U.) J. S. M., missionary, 1921.
Moffat (Robert Unwin).
John Smith Moffat, C.M.G., missionary. 8°. 1921
Moffatt (James), *D.D.*
The approach to the New Test. [Hibbert Lect., s2]. 8°. 1921
The Presbyterian Churches. 8°. [1928]
see BIBLE: COMPL. TEXTS &c. Internat. Crit. Comm.: Hebrews; by J. M., 1924.
,, EXPOSITOR'S YEARBOOK (THE), 1925; ed. J. M., 1926.
Moffett (Lacy I.), *see* GEE (N. G.), L. I. M. &c. List of Chinese birds, 1926.
Mogg (Edward). Mogg's Brighton Railway & Brighton, Lewes, Shoreham, & Worthing guide. s8°. 1841
Moggridge (John Traherne). Contrib. to the flora of Mentone & Riviera. 3rd ed. la8°. 1874
Möglich (Alfred). Der Sinn d. Sozialismus. Marxist. Gedankenwelt. [P2492]. 8°. 1920
Mohl (*Mme.* Mary Elizabeth), *form. Clarke*, *see* SMITH (M. E.) Une Anglaise intellect. en France: Miss M. C., 1927.
Mohl (Ottmar v.) Fünfzig Jahre Reichsdienst. Lebenserinnerungen. la8°. L. [1920]
Möhler (Johann Adam).
The life of St. Anselm. Tr. H. Rymer. s8°. 1842
see VIGENER (F.) 3 Gestalten aus d. mod. Katholizismus, M. &c., 1926.
Mohnike (Gottlieb Christian Friedrich). Urkundl. Gesch. der sogen. Professio fidei Tridentinae &c. s8°. Greifswald. 1822
Zur Gesch. des ungar. Fluchformulars [Conf. nov. Cathol.] &c. Mit e. Anhange betreff. d. öffentl. Uebertritt d. Königinn Christine v. Schweden. [*b. w. h.* Urkundl. Gesch., 1822]. s8°. Greifswald. 1823
Mohr (Andreas), B. Staub & D. Scheffer. Amphibolia beatitudinis decisionibus theolog. ad mentem I. Duns Scoti determinata &c. s8°. Salisburgi. 1663
—— & A. Stumph. Graphis theologica humanitatis ad mentem J. Duns Scoti deducta &c. [*b. w. h.* Amphibolia beatit. &c., 1663]. s8°. Salisburgi. [1665]
Mohr (Fritz). Nervosität u. organ. Leiden, *see* HATTINGBERG (H. v.) Nerv. Mensch., B5, 1924.
Möhring (Gottfried Victor). De primordiis emend. per Lutherum relig. Praes. G. Wernsdorfio. [P484]. s4°. Vitembergae. [1708]
Mohun (Charles Mohun, *baron*), *see* HAMILTON (J. H., *4th duke of*). Duel betw. J. d. of H. & C. Lord Mohun, 1713.
Moibanus (Ambrosius), *see* KONRAD (P.) Dr. A. M.: Beitr. z. Gesch. d. Kirche &c. Schlesiens, 1891.
Moidrey (Joseph de). Carte des préfectures de Chine & de leur popul. chrét. en 1911, *see* VARIÉTÉS sinolog., No. 35, 1913.
La hiérarchie catholique en Chine, en Corée & au Japon, 1307–1914, *see* VARIÉTÉS sinolog., No. 38, 1914.
Moir (David Macbeth). Poet. works. Ed. T. Aird, w. mem. of the a. 2nd ed. 2v. s8°. E. 1860
Sketches of the poet. lit. of the past half-cent. s8°. E. 1851
Moir (J. Reid).
The antiquity of man in East Anglia. 8°. C. 1927
Moissenet (Léon). Obs. on rich parts of lodes of Cornwall. Tr. J. H. Collins. 8°. 1877
Moister (Roger), *patriarch of Wyoming, 1783–1859*, *see* MOISTER (W.) Mem. of R. M., 1883.
Moister (William).
Barnabas Shaw. s8°. 1877
Conversations on Wesleyan missions. s8°. 1869
A hand book of Wesleyan missions. s8°. [1883]
A hist. of Wesleyan missions. Introd. by E. Hoole. 2nd rev. ed. s8°. 1871
Mem. of missionary labours in W. Africa & the W. Indies. s8°. 1850
Mem. of R. Moister. s8°. 1883
Missionary martyrs. s8°. 1885
Missionary worthies, Wesleyan Miss. Soc. s8°. 1885
The West Indies, enslaved & free. s8°. 1883
Mojžischek (Leo).
Lehrb. d. tschech. Sprache, &c. 3e A. s8°. Wien. *n.d.*
Mokshagundum Visvesvaraya (*Sir*), *see* VISVESVARAYA (*Sir* M.)
Molanus (Gerardus Walterus), *see* BOSSUET (J. B.) & G. W. M. Super reunione protest. cum eccl. Cath. tract., 1782.
Molanus (Joannes). De hist. sacr. imaginum & picturarum—Oratio de agnis Dei, *see* MIGNE (J. P.), *ed.* Theol. cursus, t27, 1843.
Molbech (Christian). Bidrag til en Hist. &c. af de danske Bibeloversættelser, fra det XVIde. Aarh. 4°. Kiøbenhavn. [1840]
Molchanov (Aleksandr Nikolaevich). По Россiи. Изд. картограф. заведенiя А. Ильина. la8°. С.-П. 1884
Moldovanu (Ioan M.), *see* LUPAS (I.) N. Popea & I. M. M., 1920.
Molé (*le cte.* Louis Mathieu), *1781–1855.* Essais de morale & de polit. 2e éd. [*Foll. by*] Vie de M. Molé, prem. prés. du Parl. de Paris. [*w. sep. pagin.*] 8°. 1809
see NOAILLES (H. DE). Le cte. M., t1–3, 1922–24.
,, —— Life & mem. of Count M., v1, 2, 1923–25.
Molé (Mathieu), *1584–1656*, *see* MOLÉ (*le cte.* L. M.) Essais de morale &c.; [*foll. by*] Vie de M. M., 1809.
Molema (S. M.) The Bantu past & present. 8°. E. 1920
Molesme. Cartul. de l'abbaye de Molesme, 916–1250. Rec. de doc. &c., avec intr. &c. par J. Laurent. [Comm. des Antiq. de la Côte-d'Or]. 2t. 4°. 1907–11
Molesworth (*Mrs.* Mary Louisa).
Little Miss Peggy. Pictures by W. Crane. s8°. 1924
Molhuysen (Philipp Christiaan). Bronnen tot de gesch. der Leidsche Univ. Uitg. d. P. C. M. [Rijks Gesch. Publ., 45, 48, 53, 56]. d4–7, 1682–1811. 4°. 's-Gravenhage. 1920–24
see HAGUE (THE). Bibl. du Palais de la Paix, Cat.; par P. C. M. &c., 1916.
—— & P. J. Blok. Nieuw nederlandsch biografisch woordenboek; onder redactie van M. & B. &c. d5–7. la8°. Leiden. 1921–27
Molière (J. B. P. de).
Œuvres, avec remarques &c. par M. Bret. [*Illust. by Moreau*]. 6t. 8°. 1773
Œuvres, avec des notes de tous les commentateurs. t1–3. 8°. 1861
Œuvres. Notice par Sainte-Beuve. 2t [*in* 1v]. s8°. 1894
TRANSLATIONS.
Plays f. M. by Eng. dramatists; w. intr. by H. Morley. 8°. 1883
see DONNAY (M.) Molière, 1921.
,, FOURNEL (V.) Le théâtre au 17e siècle: la comédie (M. &c.), 1892.
,, GENEST (E.) & E. DUBERRY. La maison de M., 1922.
see HÉMON (F.) Cours de litt., 6, M., 1922.
,, MAGNE (E.) Une amie inconnue de M., suivi de M. & l'univ., 1922.
,, MICHAUT (G. M. A.) Les débuts de M. à Paris, 1923.
,, —— La jeunesse de M., 1922.
,, TAILHADE (L.) De Célimène à Diafoirus &c., 1913.
,, TIERSOT (J.) La musique dans la comédie de M., 1922.
,, TILLEY (A.) M., 1921.
Molina (Christoval de), *see* THAYER OJEDA (T.) Las biog. de los 2 " C. de M." por C. A. Romero, 1920.
Molina (Luis) [†MOLINA (LUDOVICUS)]. Concordia liberi arbitrii cum gratiæ donis divina præscientia &c. ad nonnullos primae partis Thomae articulos [& App., 1589, *b. w.* Concordia]. s4°. Olyssipone. 1587–89
see LE MAISTRE DE SACY (I. L.) Les enluminures du fameux almanach des Jésuites intitulé La déroute des J. ou triomphe de M., 1683.
Molina (Tirso de), *ps.*
T. de M. Seleccion por S. G. Gaya. s8°. 1922

Molinet (Jean). Le Temple de Mars (c. 1476), facs., *see* PICOT (E.) & H. STEIN. Recueil, 1923.

Molineus (Petrus), *see* DU MOULIN (PIERRE), *the Elder*.

Molinos (Miguel). A brief treatise conc. daily communion. Tr. [*b. w. h.* Spiritual guide, 1688]. s8°. *n.p.* 1678 [*i.e.* 1688]
Manuductio spiritualis una cum tract. De quotidiana communione &c., in Lat. ling. tr. a A. H. Franckio. [*b. w.* Kempis (T. a) De Christo imit., 1685]. s8°. Lipsiae. 1687
The spiritual guide which disintangles the soul &c. Tr. s8°. *n.p.* 1688
see INNOCENT XI, *pope*. Decretum contra M. de M., 1687.
,, JÄGER (J. W.) Examen theolog., in quo M. de M. placita revocantur, 1709.

Molins (W. Jaime).
La ciudad única: Potosí. s8°. Buenos Aires. 1922
Naturaleza. Cuentos y relatos. s8°. Buenos Aires. 1922

Molitor (Wilhelm). Brennende Fragen. s8°. Mainz. 1874

Molitvoslov. Молитвословъ. s8°. С.-П. 1882

Moll (Albert). Hypnotism. 3rd ed. s8°. *n.d.*

Moll (Carl Bernhard), *see* HYMNARIUM. Blüthen latein. Kirchenpoesie, Vorw. v. M., 1861.

Moll (Willem). Comm. ad quaest. " de modo laudes divinas hymnorum concentu praedicandi " &c. 4°. Lugd. Batav. 1823

Mollat (Guillaume), *see* JOHN XXII, *pope*. Jean XXII, 1316–34: lettres communes anal. d'ap. les registres dits d'Avignon &c. par G. M. &c., t2–8, 1905–24.

Möller (Georg). 2 ägypt. Eheverträge aus vorsaït. Zeit, *see* KÖNIGL.-PREUSS. AKAD. Abh. (Phil.-hist. Kl.), 1918.

Moller (Hendrik), *see* MULLER (H.)

Møller (Hermann).
Indoeurop.-semitisk sammenlign. glossarium. 8°. 1909
Vergleichendes indogerman.-semit. Wörterbuch. 8°. Göttingen. 1911

Möller (J. C.), *see* HANSEN (H. P.) & J. C. M. La Guerre Europ. & la quest. du Slesvig, 1918.

Moller (Johann), *of Flensburg*. Bibl. septentrionis eruditi &c. A. Bartholini Lib. de scr. Danorum, Norwag.; J. Schefferi Suecia lit.; J. Molleri Introd. ad hist. Slesvic. & Holsat., ejusdem Praef nova. s8°. Lipsiae. 1699
Introductio in ducatuum Cimbricorum Slesvicensis & Holsatici hist. &c. 2p *in* 1v. s8°. Hamburgi. 1699

Möller (Johann Gottlieb). D. Lutherum ut confessorem in Comitiis Wormat. 1521 conspicuum. Præses J. G. M., resp. J. Schmidt. [P2629]. s4°. Rostochii. [1693]
D. Lutherum ut martyrem in persecutionibus illustrem. Præses J. G. M., resp. C. Arndio. [P2629]. s4°. Rostochii. [1693]

Møller (Poul), *see* FIBIGER (J. A. G.) & P. M. Immunisation &c., 1927.

Möller (Wilhelm). Hist.-krit. Bedenken gegen d. Graf-Wellhausen. Hypothese. 8°. Gütersloh. 1899

Mölling (Christoph Jacob). Pseudo-Vetus Test. Praes. J. A. Schmidio disquis. submittit C. J. M. [P432]. s4°. Helmstadii. [1797]

Mollison (Theodor). Technik u. Methoden d. phys. Anthropologie, *see* HINNEBERG (P.) Die Kultur d. Gegenwart, T3 v, 1923.
see FISCHER (E.) & T. M. Allgem. Anthropologie, 1923.

Molloy (Francis). Lucerna fidelium seu fasc. decerptus de doctrina Christiana. [*In Irish*]. s8°. Romae. 1676

Molmenti (Pompeo Gherardo).
I banditi d. Rep. Veneta. 2ª ed. riv. &c. s8°. Firenze. 1898
Curiosità di storia veneziana. [*incl.* L. Cornaro e la vita sobria—Relaz. di F. Pannocchieschi &c.] s8°. Bologna. [1920]
Un curioso processo d. sec. 18. [Estr. d. Arch. Veneto, t35i. P2852]. la8°. *n.p.* [1888]
Discuss. sul bilancio d. pubbl. istruzione. [P2838]. 8°. 1911
I nemici di Venezia. Polemiche racc. ed annot. da E. Zorzi. s8°. Bologna. [1924]
Gli spogliatori di Venezia artistica. [Dagli Atti d. R. Istit. Veneto, Ser. 7, t8. P2852]. 8°. Venezia. 1897
see VENEZIA. *Sventramento di V.—Delendae Ven. di P. G. M. &c., 1887.

Molnár (Albert), *see* PARIZ (F.) Dict. Lat.-Hungar. &c. [t2, olim studio A. M. &c.], 1801.

Molnar (Franz). Liliom. [*Play*]. Eng. text & intr. by B. F. Glazer. s8°. N.Y. [1922]
Plays. [Liliom—Husbands & lovers—Fashions for men—The swan]. Eng. & intr. by B. F. Glazer. 8°. [1927]

Molo (Walter Rud. M. von).
Im Zwielicht d. Zeit. Bilder aus uns. Tagen. s8°. München. 1922
Der Roman meines Volkes. 3T [*in* 1v]. s8°. München. 1924
Till Lausebums. Lustspiel. s8°. München. 1921
Das Volk wacht auf. Roman. s8°. München. 1921
see ELSTER (H. M.) W. v. M. u. s. Schaffen, 1920.

Molsbergen (E. C. Godée). Reizen in Zuid-Afrika in de Hollandse tijd. Uitg. door M. [Linschoten-V., 20]. d3. 8°. 's-Gravenhage. 1922
3, Tochten naar het Oosten, 1670–1752.
De stichter van Hollands Zuid-Afrika, Jan van Riebeeck, 1618–77. la8°. A. 1912

Molsdorf (Wilhelm). Führer durch d. symbol. u. typolog. Bilderkreis d. christl. Kunst. d. Mittelalters. 8°. L. 1920

Moltedo (Guido). L'assedio di Maccalè: camp. d'Africa, 1895–96. s8°. 1901

Molteno (*Sir* James Tennant).
The dominion of Afrikanderdom: recoll. 8°. [1923]
Further South African recoll. 8°. [1926]

Moltherus (Johannes). Malleus obstinationis Judaicae. Acc. &c. cat. praecip. Jud. gentis doctorum. s8°. Francofurti. 1600

Moltke (Helmuth C. B., *Graf* v.)
Briefe ü. Zustände u. Begebenheiten in d. Türkei, 1835–39. 8°. 1917
Erinnerungen, Briefe, Dokumente, 1877–1916. Hrsg. &c. v. Eliza v. Moltke. 8°. St. 1922
H. v. M.: ein Lebensbild nach s. Briefen &c. Hrsg. v. H. M. Elster. 8°. St. 1923
M.'s Military corresp. 1870–71 publ. by the Pruss. Gen. Staff. 1st sect., The War to the battle of Sedan. Précis by Spenser Wilkinson. 8°. O. 1923
see HÖNIG (F. A.) 24 hours of M.'s strategy: battles of Gravelotte & St. Privat; tr., 1895.
,, KRAUSS (A.) M., Benedek u. Napoleon, 1901.
,, WHITTON (*Lt.-Col.* F. E.) M., 1921.

Molza (Francesco Maria), *1489–1544*. Quattro novelle da una stampa rarissima del sec. 16. 8°. Lucca. 1869
Rime, *see* BROCARDO (A.) Rime, 1538.

Mommers (Joannes Mauritius), *see* SCHLOSSER (J. L.) Lutherus Lutheranus Luthero reformato J. M. M. oppositus &c., 1739.

Mommsen (Theodor). Comment. ludorum saecularium quint., imp. Augusto, *see* REALE ACCAD. D. LINCEI. Mon. ant., v1, 1890.
—— **& C. G. A. Harnack.** Zu Apostelgesch. 28, 16. (princeps peregrin.) [*Extr. f.* K. Preuss. Akad. d. Wiss. Phil.-hist. Cl. Sitz., 1895; P2793]. la8°. 1895

Monachus Sangall, *see* CHARLEMAGNE *for work on C. by M. S.*

Monaci (Ernesto). Studj romanzi. Ed. a cura di E. M. [v]10–13. 8°. 1913–17
v11 *has no tp. & no* " indice."
Bartholomaeis (V. de). Avanzi di un canzoniere provenzale del sec. 13, 1915. [12.]
—— Ritmo volgare lucchese del 1213, 1915. [12.]
Bertoni (G.) Discussioni etimologiche, 1917. [13.]
—— La " sestina " di Guilhem de Saint Grigori, 1917. [13.]
—— Note su Peire d'Auvergne, 1917. [13.]
—— Sordello e Reforzat, 1915. [12.]
Filzi (M.) Contrib. alla sintassi dei dialetto ital., 1914. [11.]
Laudario (Il) dei Disciplinati di S. Croce di Urbino; [ed.] G. Grimaldi, 1915. [12.]
Massèra (A. F.) Nuovi sonetti di C. Angiolieri, 1917. [13.]
Merlo (C.) Del potere metafonetico palatilizzante di lat. Ū-Ŭ, 1917. [13.]
Ovidio (F. d'). *Bevanda* e *vivanda* e lor comitive, 1913. [10.]
Pieri (S.) Appunti toponomastici, 1913. [10.]
Toppino (G.) Il dialetto di Castellinaldo, p2, 1913. [10.]
Vignoli (C.) Il folk-lore di Castro dei Volsci, 1917. [13.]

Monacis (Laurentius de). Chronicon de rebus Venetis ad 1354. Acc. Carmen de Carolo II & Anon. Scr. de causis belli exorti inter Venetos, & ducem Ferrar. Pref. illustr. F. Cornelius. s4°. Venetiis. 1758

Monaco. Doc. histor. rel. à la princ. de M., 3t, 1888–91, *see* SAIGE (M. J. J. G.)
Inventaires du Palais de Monaco, 1604–1731. Publ. avec intr. &c. par L. H. Labande. la8°. Monaco. 1918

Monaco (Gioseppe). Trionfi epitalamici. [Nozze Minutolo—Pinelli]. [N125]. 8°. Napoli. 1688

Monaco (*Don* Lorenzo), *see* LORENZO, *Don, called Il Monaco*.

Monahan (Francis John). Early hist. of Bengal. Pref. by Sir J. Woodroffe. 8°. 1925

Monardes (Nicolas). Joyfull newes out of the newe founde worlde. Eng. by J. Frampton, 1577. Intr. by S. Gaselee. [Tudor Trans., s2, v9, 10]. 2v. 8°. 1925

Monastical. *The hist. of monast. conventions & milit. instit. w. a survey of the court of Rome. Coll. by J. S. s8°. 1686

Monastier. Cartul. de l'abbaye de St-Chaffre du Monastier, suivi de la Chronique de St.-Pierre du Puy & app. de chartes. Publ. par U. Chevalier. 8°. 1884

Monatte (Pierre), T. Argence & A. Herclet.
Left wing trade-unionism in France. s8°. [1922]

Moncada (R. de), *see* TEJERA (J. P.) & R. DE M. Bibl. del Murciano, t1, 1922.

Moncalm (—). The origin of thought & speech. Tr. G. S. Whitmarsh. 8°. 1905

Monceaux (Paul).
Hist. litt. de l'Afrique chrétienne, dep. les origines j. l'invasion arabe. t5–7. la8°. 1920–23
5, Saint Optat & les premiers écrivains donatistes.
6, Litt. donatiste au temps de St. Augustin.
7, St. Augustin & le Donatisme.
St. Cyprien. s8°. 1914
see BATIFFOL (P.), P. M. &c. L'église & le droit de guerre, 2e éd., 1920.
„ SEVERUS (S.) St. Martin: récits [tr.] avec intr. par P. M., 1926.

Moncel (Henri), *see* DOUDAN (X.) Des révolutions du goût; intr. par H. M., 1924.
see GIRARD (H.) & H. M. Bibliogr. des œuvres de E. Renan, 1923.

Monckhoven (D. van). Photographic optics. Tr. 8°. 1867
Pop. treatise on photography. Tr. W. H. Thornthwaite. 2nd ed. rev. s8°. 1867

Monckton (*Capt.* **Charles Arthur Whitmore).** Last days in New Guinea: being further exper. of a New G. resident magistrate. 8°. 1922
Some experiences of a New Guinea resid. magistrate. 8°. 1921

Monckton (Horace Woollaston). Berkshire. s8°. C. 1911

Monckton (*Gen.* **Robert),** *see* NORTHCLIFFE (A. C. W. H., *1st baron*). The N. Coll. [papers of M. &c.]; pres. to Govt. of Canada, 1926.

Moncorvo Bandeira de Mello (Emilia), *see* CARMEN DOLORES, *ps.*

Moncrieff (Robert Hope), *see* HOPE (A. R.), *ps.*

Moncur-Sime (A. H.), *see* SIME (A. H. M-.)

Mond (*Rt. Hon.* **Alfred Moritz),** *1st baron Melchet.* Industry & politics. 8°. 1927

Mondain-Monval (J.), *see* MONVAL (J.)

Monde nouveau (Le). Revue mensuelle internat.
3e–5e année (jan. 1921–juin 1923). la8°. [1921–23]
„ „ Suppl. s8°. 1922
see ENGELBERTS (F. J.) Souvenirs de famille; tr., 1922.
„ KUPRIN (A. I.) Sulamite; tr., 1922 ?.

Mondella (Francesco). Isifile, tragedia. s8°. Verona. 1582

Mondino, *da Luzzi, see* MUNDINUS.

Mone (Franz Joseph). Gesch. d. Heidenthums im nördl. Europa. T1, Die Religionen d. finn., slaw. u. scandinav. Völker. 8°. L. 1822

Monet (Claude), *see* GEFFROY (G.) C. M., sa vie &c., 1922.
see MAUCLAIR (C.), *ps.* C. M., tr. J. L. May, 1925.

Moneta, *Cremonensis.* Adv. Catharos et Valdenses libri 5. Ed. T. A. Ricchinius. fol. Romae. 1743

Monetarius (Hieronymus), *see* MÜNZER (H.)

Monetary Conference (Internat.) Proc. of the I.M.C., Paris, Apr.–July, 1881. Pr. by order of the Sec. of State. la8°. Cincinnati. 1881

Money (*Sir* **Leo George Chiozza).**
The peril of the white. 8°. 1925
The triumph of nationalization. 8°. 1920

Money (Robert Cotton). *Journal of a tour in Persia, 1824–25. By R. C. M. 8°. 1828

Monferrato (Bianca, *dssa.* **di).** Inventario dei beni mobili di B. [1519]; *ed.* P. Giacosa, *see* REGIA DEPUT. Miscellanea, t42, 1906.

Monferrato (Guglielmo VII, *marchese* **di),** *see* BOZZOLA (A.) Un capitano di guerra &c. G. VII di M. (1254–92), 1922.

Mongan (James), *see* KENNEDY (J.) Report of trials of J. K., J. Ryan &c. for the murder of E. Butler; by J. M., 1832.

Monglond (André). La jeunesse de Ramond, *see* CHRONIQUE DES LETTRES FR., t4, 1926.

Mongolo. Монголо—ойратскіе 1640 г. &c.: Калмыцкій текстъ &c., 1880, *see* GOLSTUNSKY (K. F.)

Mongrédien (Georges). Étude sur la vie & l'œ. de N. Vauquelin, seigneur des Yveteaux, précepteur de Louis XIII (1567–1649). la8°. 1921
see VAUQUELIN (N.) Œuvres compl.; publ. G. M., 1921.

Mongton Chih Hsu, *see* HSU (M. C.)

Monhemius (Joannes), *see* HESSELS (J.) Tractatus pro invoc. Sanctorum contra J. M. &c., 1568.

Moniage Guillaume. Altfranzös. Prosafassung d. M. G.; *ed.* G. Schläger, *see* ARCHIV. F. D. ST. D. NEU. SPR., B97, 98, 1896–97.

Monica, *Sister.* Angela Merici & h. teaching idea, 1474–1540. Intr. by J. F. Regis Canevin. 8°. N.Y. 1927

Monicke (C. H.) Notes & queries on the Ormulum [*w. spec. of text & Eng. tr.*] 4°. L. 1853–54

Monier (Camille). Résumé de sociologie. s8°. 1904

Monier (Léonard), *Jesuit* [MOSNIER]. Rel. de l'Arménie, *see* BERNARD (J. F.), *ed.* Recueil, t6, 1729.

Monier (Raoul). Reliquiae, *see* BERNARD (J. M.) Œ., t1, 1923.

Monier-Williams (*Sir* **Monier).** Hindústání primer. s8°. 1860
A pract. gram. of the Sanskrit lang. 4th ed. enlarged. 8°. O. 1877

Monier-Williams (Monier Faithfull), *see* TALLOW CHANDLERS, CO. OF, *London.* Rec. of Worshipful Co. of T. Ch.; ed. under dir. of M.-W., 1897.

Monier-Williams (Montagu Sneade Faithfull).
Figure-skating. 8°. 1898
—— & S. F. Monier-Williams.
Combined figure-skating. s8°. 1883

Monier-Williams (Stanley F.), *see* MONIER-WILLIAMS (M. S. F.) & S. F. M.-W. Combined figure-skating, 1883.

Monimenta medii ævi ex Bibl. Reg. Hanov., 2v, 1757–64, *see* WALCH (C. W. F.)

Monin (Henry), *b. 1854,* **& L. Lazard.** Sommier des biens nationaux de la ville de Paris. Publ. par H. M. & L. L. [Publs. rel. à la Rév. Fr.] t1, 2. la8°. 1920

Monk of St. Augustine's (A). *Pax: Vatican Decrees & Cath. allegiance, 1874, *see* GLADSTONE (*Rt. Hon.* W. E.)

Monk (George), *1st duke of Albemarle, 1608–70.*
see CORBETT (*Sir* J. S.) M., 1908.
„ SANDFORD (F.) Order & ceremonies for the interment of George, d. of A., 1670.

Monkbretton, *priory.* Abstr. of the chartularies of the priory of Monkbretton. Ed. J. W. Walker. [Yorkshire Archæol. Soc. Record Ser., v66]. 8°. 1924

Monkhouse (Allan Noble).
The conquering hero. Play. s8°. 1923
First blood. Play. s8°. 1924
Mary Broome, *see* PLAYS of to-day, v2, 1925.
The words & the play, *see* ENG. ASSOC. Essays &c., v11, 1925.

Monkhouse (William Cosmo). A few words about Hogarth, *see* HOGARTH (W.) Works, 1872.

***Monkraven**: the story of h. betrayal, 3v, 1886, *see* ARAMIS, *ps.*

***Monk's** (The) hood pull'd off; tr., 1671, *see* DU MOULIN (P.)

Monlaur (Reynès). Les dieux s'en vont. [7e éd.] 8°. [1922]

Monmarché (Marcel). Vallée du Rhône, Cévennes, Lyonnais &c. [Guides Bleus]. s8°. 1923
see LOIRE. *Les châteaux de la L.; dir. M. M., 6e éd., 1919; 7e éd., 1923.
„ MUIRHEAD (F.) & M. M., *edd.* Brittany, 1925.
„ —— „ —— N.-E. France, 1922.
—— & L. Tillion. Le pays de France: aspects de la nature, richesses mon. &c. Publ. s. la dir. de M. & T. 3t. 4°. [1925]

Monmouth (Geoffrey *of***).** The Brit. hist. Tr. by A. Thompson. n. ed. rev. & corr. by J. A. Giles. 8°. 1862
The Vita Merlini. [Lat. Text w. Eng. tr., ed.] J. J. Parry. [Univ. of Illinois, 10iii]. la8°. Urbana. 1925
see MATTER (H.) Engl. Gründungssagen v. G. of M. bis z. Renaiss., 1922.

Monmouth (James, *duke of***)** [FITZROY (JAMES)], *aft. Scott. d. of Buccleuch, see* MANLEY (R.) Hist. of the rebellions, 1640–85, 1691.

Monnaies. Cat. de m. franç. (956–1496), pl, 1927, *see* CATALOGUE.

Monnier (*Mme.*), *see* DELSART (H. M.), *ps.*

Monnier (Henry), *prof. of Bordeaux, see* DUGUIT (L.) & H. M. Constitutions & lois de la France, 4e éd., 1925.

Monnier (Philippe). Venice in the 18th c. Tr. 8°. 1910
Venise au 18e s. [13e éd.] 8°. 1923

Monod (Gabriel). La vie & la pensée de J. Michelet, 1798–1852. Préf. de C. Bémont. [H.E., 235, 236]. 2t. 8°. 1923

Monod (Pierre), *1586–1644, see* VALLE (D.) P. M. e le sue relaz. col Card. Richelieu, 1910.

Monpersan (Louis de).
*La politique des Jésuites. s8°. Londres. 1688

Monro (Harold). Some contemp. poets, 1920. s8°. [1920]

Monro (*maj.-gen.* **Robert).** Letter conc. affairs in Ireland, *see* ARGYLL (A. C., *m. of*). Speech, 1646.

Monroe (James), *president of the U.S.*
see BEMIS (S. F.), *ed.* Amer. Secr. of State, v3, M., by J. W. Pratt, 1927.
„ MADISON (J.) *Exam. of the Brit. doct. &c., 2nd ed., cont. letter f. [*M.*] to Ld. Mulgrave, 1806.
„ MONROE DOCTRINE, *in Subject-Index.*
Mons. *Mons, Anzac & Kut; by an M.P., 1919, *see* HERBERT (*Hon.* A. N. H. M.)
Mons (Anna), *see* SEMEVSKY (M. I.) Царица Катерина Алексѣевна, А. и Виллимъ М., 1692–1724, изд. 2ое., 1884.
Mons (Villim), *see* SEMEVSKY (M. I.) Царица Катерина Алексѣевна. Анна и В. М., 1692–1724, изд. 2ое., 1884.
Monson (*Maj.* E. C. P.) & E. Marsland. Air raid damage in London: rec. of effect of aircraft attack &c. Prep. by E. C. P. M. & E. M. 8o. 1923
Monson (*Sir* William). Naval tracts. [*Extr. f.* Churchill, Voyages, v3, pages 163–560]. sm. fol. 1703
Monson-Fitzjohn (G. J.), *F.R.Hist.S.*
Quaint signs of olde inns. 8o. 1926
Mont (Pol de). Lentesotternijen & Twee eerste idyllen. volksuitg., 3e dr. s8o. Antwerpen, 1920
see ANTWERP. Peinture anc. au Musée royal &c., préc. d'un Guide histor. &c. par M., 1914.
Montagnacco (Antonio), *see* FLORIO (F.) Le mani morte, ossia lettera all' a. del Ragionamento int. ai beni poss. dalle chiese [*i.e.* A. M.], 1765.
Montagne (Claude Louis).
Works in MIGNE (J. P.), *ed.* Theol. cursus.
De censuris, seu notis theolog. & de sensu proposit. 1860. [1.]
Tract. de gratia 1861. [10.]
Tract. de opere sex dierum 1861. [7.]
Montagnini (Carlo Ignazio), *conte di Mirabello.* Dell' ant. legislaz. ital. sulle manimorte, *see* REGIA DEP. DI STORIA PATRIA. Misc., t19, 1880.
Montagnini (*il conte* Luigi), *see* COMINO (F.) Il conte L. M., cenni, 1885.
Montagu (*Lady* Barbara) & *Mrs.* S. Scott. *A descr. of Millenium Hall. By A gentleman on h. travels. s8o. 1762
Montagu (Charles), *1st duke of Manchester, see* MANCHESTER.
Montagu (Edward Montagu, *2nd baron*) *of Boughton, 1616–84.* Letter, w. narr., June 1647, *repr., see* HARTSHORNE (E. S.) Mem. of Holdenby, 1868.
Montagu (*Mrs.* Eliz.), *wife of E. Montagu.* Mrs. M., "queen of the blues," h. letters & friendships, 1762–1800. Ed. R. Blunt, f. material left by E. J. Climenson. 2v. 8o. [1923]
Montagu (*Lady* Mary Wortley), *d. of 5th earl* [*aft. 1st duke*] *of Kingston.* Letters dur. travels in Europe, Asia & Africa. Added, poems by the same a. n. ed. 2v. s8o. 1789
Letters (1709–62). [Intr. by R. B. Johnson. Everyman's lib.] [2nd ed.] s8o. [1906]
see MARINONI (C. L. P.) Lady M. W., 2p, 1903–4.
Montagu (Richard), *bp. of (1) Chichester, (2) Norwich* [MOUNTAGUE], *see* YATES (J.) Ibis ad Caesarem, ans. to M.'s Appeale, 1626.
Montague (Andrew Jackson). John Marshall, *see* BEMIS (S. F.), *ed.* Amer. Secr. of State, v2, 1927.
Montague (Charles Edward).
Disenchantment. s8o. 1922
Fiery particles. s8o. 1923
Right off the map. s8o. 1927
The right place: a book of pleasures. s8o. 1924
Rough justice. s8o. 1926
see ROSS (R.) & C. E. M. Brit. artists at the front, p2, 1918.
Montaigne (Michel).
De l'institution des enfants. éd. crit., avec intr. &c. par G. Michaut. 8o. 1924
L'esprit de M., maximes, pensées &c. 2t. s8o. Berlin. 1753
Les essais de M. Publ. d'après l'éd. de 1588 avec les variantes de 1595 & une notice &c. par H. Motheau et D. Jouaust. 7t. s8o. 1886–89
„ „ ....4t. s8o. [1912]
„ „ Publ. par F. Strowski, F. Gebelin &c. d'ap. l'exempl. de Bordeaux, avec variantes, notes &c. t4, Les sources des Essais, annot. &c. par P. Villey. 4o. Bordeaux. 1920
TRANSLATIONS.
Essays. [Tr. C. Cotton]. 7th ed. 3v. 8o. 1759
TRANSLATIONS [*continued*].
Essays. Tr. C. Cotton. Ed. w. notes by W. C. Hazlitt. 3v. 8o. 1893
„ Tr. G. B. Ives. Intr. by G. Norton. 4v. 8o. Cambridge, [*Mass.*] 1925
„ Tr. E. J. Trechmann. Intr. by J. M. Robertson. 2v. s8o. 1927
see BOUILLIER (V.) La renommée de M. en Allemagne, 1921.
„ LAMANDÉ (A.) La vie gaillarde & sage de M., 1927.
„ MERLANT (J.) De M. à Vauvenargues, 1914.
„ PRÉVOST (J.) Vie de M., 8e éd., 1926.
„ TAYLOR (G. C.) Shakespere's debt to M., 1925.

Montale (Eugenio). Ossi di seppia. 8o. Torino. 1925
Montalto, *The family of, see* GENNARO (G. A. DI). Della famiglia M., 1735.
Montanaro (A. F.) Hints for a bush campaign. s8o. 1901
Montandon (George). Aïnou, Japonais, Bouriates, *see* ANTHROPOLOGIE (L'), t37, Atlas, 1927.
Montanelli (Giuseppe), *see* RUBERTIS (A. DE). V. Gioberti e la Costituente di G. M., 1923.
Montanismus. Texte z. Gesch. d. M.; hrsg. N. Bonwetsch, 1914, *see* KLEINE TEXTE, T129, 1914.
Montanius (Claudius Ludovicus), *see* MONTAGNE (C. L.)
Montanus, *abp. of Toledo, see* LORENZANA Y BUITRON (F. A.) SS. PP. Toletan. opera, t1, 1782.
Montanus (Arias Benedictus), *see* ARIAS MONTANO (BENITO).
Montanus (Hieronymus). Theses de descensu Christi ad inferos & eiusdem ad coelos ascensu. [P2437]. 4o. Ingolstadii. 1587
Montanus (Reginaldus Gonsalvus), *see* GONSALVIUS MONTANUS (R.)
Montaugé (Barbe Charlotte de Migieu de), *see* ARMAGNAC (M. M. D'). Le vie & les entretiens d'une femme du monde au 18e s., d'ap. souv. &c. de B. C. de M. de M., 1762–97 &c., 1924.
Montbas (Jean-François Barton, *baron* **de).** Au service du roi. Mémoires. Intr. &c. par le Vcte. de Montbas. 8o. 1926
Montbel (*le baron* Guillaume Isidore).
Le Duc de Reichstadt. 8o. 1832
Montbéliard (Frederick, *count of*), *see* FREDERICK, *duke of Würtemberg.*
Monteagle (*Rt. Hon.* Thomas Spring-Rice, *1st baron*). Letter to Abp. of Dublin on the Eccl. Titles Act &c. [P2554]. 8o. D. 1851
Monte Carlo, *Monaco.* *The odds at Monte Carlo. Analysed by Scrutator. s8o. [1924]
Monte Cassino, *see* LOWE (E. A.) Ält. Kalendarien aus M. C., 1908.
Montecatini (Balthasar). *Discrepanze, o' contradiz. int. al fatto tra' mod. impugnatori de' riti cinesi [*foll. by* Nota d' alc. discrep. &c. circa i punti cap. di questa causa *&* Nota d' alc. fatti &c. [*each w. sep. tp. & pagin.*] s8o. Colonia. MCCC [*for* 1700]
Montefeltro (*il conte* Antonio di), *see* VISCONTI (B.), *d. of Milan.* Trattato fra B. V., A. di M., la Rep. di Firenze &c., 1884.
Montefiore (Claude Joseph Goldsmid).
The Old Testament—& after. 8o. 1923
The Synoptic Gospels. Ed. w. intr. & comm. by C. G. M. 2nd ed. rev. 2v. 8o. 1927
Montégut (Emile).
Le maréchal Davout, s. caractère &c. s8o. 1882
Les Pays-Bas. 2e éd. s8o. 1884
Montégut (Henri de), *see* VIGEOIS. Cartul. de l'abbaye de V. en Limousin, 954–1167; publ. &c. M. de M., 1907.
Monteil (Charles). Les Bambara du Ségou & du Kaarta: ét. d'une peuplade du Soudan franç. [Gouvt. Gén. de l'Afr. Occid. Fr.] 8o. 1924
Monteith, *Earldom of* [MENTEITH], *see* FRASER (*Sir* W.) The red book of M., 2v, 1880.
Monteith (John). The parish of Glencairn. s8o. Glasgow. 1876
Monteith (Mary E.) The fringe of immortality. s8o. 1920
Montelius (Oscar). Die ält. Kulturperioden im Orient u. in Europa. [B]2, Babylonien, Elam, Assyrien. 4o. Stockholm. 1923
Bibliogr. de l'arch. préhist. de la Suède pend. le 19e s. [Soc. des Antiq. de Suède]. s8o. Stockholm. [1875]
Kulturgesch. Schwedens, bis z. 11ten Jhdt. la8o. L. 1906
see HILDEBRAND (E.), *ed.* Sveriges hist.; under medverkan af O. M. &c., 10 Afd., 1903–10.
Montellano (Mariano Ortiz de), *see* ORTIZ DE MONTELLANO (M.)
Montemagno (Giovane Buonaccorso da), *younger.*
Prose ined. alcune per G. B. C. Giuliari. s8o. Bologna. 1874
Montemarte (Francesco di), *Cte. di Corbara.* Cronaca (1333–1400), *see* MURATORI (L. A.) Rerum Ital. scr., t15v, 1920.
Montemayor (Jorge de). La Diana. s8o. Paris. *n.d.*
Montenegrin (The) bulletin. Publ. by the Montenegrin Comm. f. Nat. Union. No. 1–5 (Dec. 1917–Sept. 1918). 8o. 1917–18
„ „ *see also* BULLETIN MONTÉNÉGRIN, No. 1, 1917.
Montenegro. A hdbk. of Serbia, M. &c., 1920, *see* ADMIRALTY, NAVAL INTELL. DIV.
Montesauro (Natale) [†MONTESAURUS (NATALIS)]. De dispositionibus (Verona?), 1498, *facs., see* SUDHOFF (C.) Earliest pr. lit. on syphilis, 1925.

Montesinos (Ferando de). Memorias antig. hist. del Peru. Tr. & ed. by P. A. Means. Intr. by Sir C. R. Markham. [Hakluyt Soc., s2, 48]. 8°. 1920
Montesinos (J. F.)
Die mod. span. Dichtung. 8°. L., *Teubner*. 1927
Montesquieu (Charles de Secondat, *baron* **de).**
Œuvres. n. éd., rev., corr. & augm. 3t. 8°. Londres. 1771–72
Œuvres compl. Préc. de la vie de cet auteur. 5t. 8°. Lefévre. 1820
*De l'esprit des loix. nouv. éd. rev. 4t [t3 *missing*]. s8°. Londres. 1757
Persian letters. Tr. by J. Davidson, w. an intr. [Broadway tr[s].] s8°. [1923]
see FOURNOL (E.) Bodin, prédécesseur de M.: ét. s. théories polit. de la République & de l'Esprit des lois, 1896.
Montesquiou (Robert de) [*i.e. le cte.* R. DE MONTESQUIOU-FEZENSAC]. Les pas effacés. Mémoires. Publ. par P. L. Couchoud. 3t. s8°. 1923
see CLERMONT-TONNERRE (E. DE). M. & Proust, 1925.
Montessori (Maria).
Dr. M.'s own handbook. 4th impr. s8°. 1920
see CLAREMONT (C. A.) Review of M. lit., 1919.
,, FYNNE (R. J.) M. & h. inspirers, 1924.
Montessus de Ballore (*le vte.* **R. de),** *see* INDEX GENERALIS: ann. gén. des universités &c.; publ. s. la dir. de R. de M. de B., 1921.
Montet (Albert de). Extr. de docs. rel. à l'hist. de Vevey, *see* REGIA DEP. Misc., t22, 1884.
Montet (Pierre). L'art phénicien, trouvailles de Byblos, *see* ACAD. DES INSCR.: FOND. PIOT. Mon. &c., t27, 1924.
Les Egyptiens à Byblos, *see* ACAD. D. INSCR.: FOND. PIOT. Mon., t25, 1921–22.
Les scènes de la vie privée dans les tombeaux égypt. de l'anc. empire. la8°. Str. 1925
Monteverdi (Claudio Zuan Antonio).
see PRUNIÈRES (H.) M.; tr., 1926.
,, SCHNEIDER (L.) Un précurseur de la musique ital.: C. M., 1567–1643, 1921.
Montfordius (Basilius), *ps.*, *see* CURIO (C. S.)
Montfort (Eugène), *b. 1877.*
Un cœur vierge. Roman. s8°. [1920]
L'oubli des morts. 4e éd. s8°. [1923]
La Turque. Préf. de F. Carco. n. éd. s8°. [1925]
see LE CARDONNEL (G.) & P. LIÈVRE. Etudes sur E. M., 1920.
Montfort (Simon de), *the younger, earl of Leicester, 1208 ?–65, see* BATEMAN (S.) S. de M., h. life & work, 1923.
Montgelas (Max M. K. D., *Graf* **v.)** Case for the Central Powers: impeachment of the Versailles verdict. Tr. C. Vesey. 8°. [1925]
Glossen z. Kautsky-Buch. Mit Anhang: Die franz.-russ. Militärkonvention. [P2410]. 8°. Charlottenburg. 1920
see KAUTSKY (C.) Deut. Dokumente z. Kriegsausbruch; hrsg. v. M. M. &c., 4B, 1919; (*Fr.*) tr. C. Jordan, 4t, 1922; (*Eng.*) tr., 1924.
Montgomery (A.), *see* MAITLAND (A. G.) & A. M. Geol. & mineral industry of W. Australia, 1924.
Montgomery (*Maj.-Gen. Sir* **Archibald Armar),** *K.C.M.G.*
The story of the 4th Army, Aug. 8th to Nov. 11th, 1918. Foreword by Gen. Rawlinson. [*w.* Maps, *bound separately*]. 4°. [1920]
Montgomery (Bo-Gabriel de). Brit. & continental labour policy, 1900–22. 8°. 1922
Issues of European statesmanship. 8°. [1926]
Montgomery (Edmund).
Die Kant'sche Erkenntnisslehre. 8°. München. 1871
Montgomery (Henry Hutchinson), *bp. of Tasmania, aft. Secretary of S.P.G.*
C. J. Corfe. Intr. by M. N. Trollope. s8°. 1927
Life & letters of G. A. Lefroy, Bp. of Calcutta &c. 8°. 1920
Montgomery (James), *poet.* Xtn. psalmist; or, Hymns, sel. & orig., w. introd. essay. 8°. Glasgow. 1825
Journal of voyages &c. by Daniel Tyerman & G. Bennet, visit to S. Sea Islands, China, India &c. Compiled by J. M. 2v. 8°. 1831
Montgomery (James Alan), *see* BIBLE: COMPL. TEXTS &c. Internat. Crit. Comm. Daniel; by J. A. M., 1927.
Montgomery (L. M.), *wife of Rev. Ewan Macdonald.*
Anne's house of dreams. s8°. [1917]
Montgomery (Marshall). Friedrich Hölderlin & the German Neo-Hellenic movt. pl. 8°. 1923

Montgomery (Thomas Hartley). [Queen *v.* T. H. M., Omagh assizes, 1873. Rep. of trial: evidence & charge. *no tp.* 2v. *pagin. cont.*] fol. 1873
Montgomery (William), *B.D.*
St. Augustine: aspects of h. life & thought. 8°. 1924
Montgomeryshire. Colls. hist. & archaeolog. rel. to M. & its borders. [Powys-Land Club]. v37–39. 8°. Welshpool. 1915–20
Montgon (Charles Alexander de). Mémoires, publ. par lui-même. Cont. les diff. négociat. dont il a été chargé dans les cours de France, d'Espagne & de Portugal &c. 6t (t6, Pièces justific. *w. 5 pagin.*) s8°. *n.p.* 1750
Month (The). v135–150. (Jan. 1920–Dec. 1927). 8°. 1920–27
Montherlant (Henry de).
Aux fontaines du désir. [21e éd.] s8°. 1927
Les bestiaires. [34e éd.] s8°. 1926
Chant funèbre pour les morts de Verdun. s8°. 1925
Le songe. [Roman]. s8°. 1922
Monthly chronicle (The). v1–4, 1728–31. 8°. 1728–31
Monthly Criterion (The), *see* CRITERION (THE).
Monthly labor review. [U.S. Dept. of Labor. Bureau of Labor statistics]. v12–25 (1921–27). 8°. Wash. 1922–27
,, ,, Subject index, v1–12 (1915–20). Prep. by K. Klager & E. M. Pursglove. 8°. Wash. 1923
Monthly mercury, *see* PRESENT STATE (THE) OF EUROPE, or The hist. & polit. m. m., 1692–1712.
Monthly musical record (The). v46–57. la8°. [1916–27]
Monthly register, The, or Mem. of the affairs of Europe &c. v1–5 [v1, No. 1 *wanting*]. s4°. 1703–7
Vol. 1 *cont.* A suppl. to the M.R. for Dec.: A manifesto shewing right of Charles III to Span. monarchy.
Montholon (*le gén.* **C. J. F. T. de),** *marq. de Montholon-Sémonville.* *Manuscript de l'Ile d'Elbe. Des Bourbons en 1815. Publ. par le Comte ******** (Bertrand) [*i.e.* M.] 8°. Londres. 1820
see NAPOLEON I. Méms. &c. écrits à St. Hélène par les généraux qui ont partagé sa captivité [G. Gourgaud & M.], 1823.
Monti (Agostino Maria de'). Compendio di mem. hist. d. città di Savona &c. s8°. 1697
Monti (Antonio), *see* BERTARELLI (A.) & A. M. Tre sec. di vita milanese, 1927.
Monti (Solone), *see* DANTE ALIGHIERI. Lectura D., Il c. 30 del Purgatorio letto da S. M., 1910.
Monti (Vicenzo), *see* BUSTICO (G.) V. M., la vita, 1921.
Monticelli (Adolphe).
see ARNAUD D'AGNEL (G.) & E. ISNARD. M.: sa vie & s. œuvre, 1824–86, 1926.
,, COQUIOT (G.) M., 1925.
Monticolo (Giovanni Battista). La costituz. d. doge Pietro Polani (1143) circa la processio scolarum. [Estr. d. R. Accad. dei Lincei: Classe di sci. &c., v9. P2840]. la8°. 1900
Il patto del Maggio 1122 ? giurato d. doge D. Michiel a. comunità di Bari. [R. Accad. dei Lincei, Rendiconti, Cl. di sc. mor. &c. Estr. d. v8. P2840]. la8°. 1899
Montiéramey. Cartul. de l'abbaye de M. [Publ. &c.] C. Lalore. 8°. 1890
Montier-la-Celle. Cartul. de M.-la-C. [Publ. &c.] C. Lalore. 8°. 1882
Montiers (André).
Les petites " visionnaires." Roman. s8°. 1923
Montigny (—). *Stratagems of chess. From the French, rev. &c. [*2 pag.*] s8°. 1817
Montigny (Maurice).
En voyageant avec Mme. de Sévigné. 8°. [1920]
Montijn (A. M. M.) A new principle of internat. law. [P2507]. 8°. The Hague. 1919
Montijo, *House of, see* ALBA (J. S. F.-J., *17th duke* DE). Noticias hist. y geneal. de los estados de Montijo y Teba, 1915.
Montizambert (E.) Unnoticed London. s8°. 1922
Montlosier (François Dominique de Reynaud, *cte.* **de),** *see* MADROLLE (A. M.) *Mém. catholique, relig. de M. &c., 1826.
Montluc (Blaise de), *see* BROQUA (*cte.* DE). Le maréchal de M., 1924.
Montmartre. Recueil des chartes de l'abbaye royale de M. Publ. &c. par E. de Barthélemy. la8°. 1883
Montmollin (Georges de). Mém. sur le Comté de Neuchâtel en Suisse. 2t [in 1v]. s8°. Neuchâtel. 1831
Mont-Morel.
Cartul. de M.-M. Publ. M. Dubosc. 4°. Saint-Lo. 1878

Montmorency, *The house of, see* Du Chesne (A.) Hist. généalog. de la maison de M. &c., 2p, 1624.
Montmorency (Charlotte Marguerite de), *princesse de Condé, see* Condé (C. M. de M., *psse.* de).
Montmorillon (R. de). Le voile tombe. s8º. 1924
Montorgueil (Georges). La vie à Montmartre. Illust. de P. Vidal. 4º. [1899]
Le vieux Montmartre. s8º. [1925]
Montoto (Santiago), *see* Colección de doc. inéd. para la hist. de Ibero-Amér.; recop. por S. M., t1, 2 (2, Nobiliario d. sig. 16), 1927–28.
Montpellier. Cartul. de l'Univ. de M. Publ. s. les auspices du Conseil de l'Univ. de M. 2t [2, Fac. de Méd. &c.; avec intr. par J. Calmette]. 4º. Montpellier. 1890–1912
Rec. de pièces rel. au Siège de M. par Louis XIII, 1622. Réunies & préc. d'une préf. par M. de La Pijardière. s8º. Montpellier. 1875
see Guillems, *Seigneurs de M.*
Montpensier (*Mlle.* **de)** [Anne Mary Louisa (*d'Orléans*), *duchess de Montpensier*], *see* La Force (B. N. de C., *duc* de). Vie amoureuse de la Grande Mlle., 2t, 1927.
Montpensier (Antoine Marie Philippe Louis [*d'Orléans*], *duc* **de),** *1824–90* [†Antony Marie Philip Louis (*d'Orleans*), *Duke de Montpensier*], *see* Giraud (—). Considerations resp. marriage of the D. of M., w. ref. to the Treaty of Utrecht, 1847.
Montreuil-sur-Mer. Cartul. de la ville de M.-sur-Mer. Publ. G. de Lhomel. la8º. Abbeville. 1904
*G.H.Q. (M.-sur-M.), 1920, *see* Fox (*Sir* F.)
Rec. [*&* Nouv. rec.] de doc. p. s. à l'hist. de M.-sur-Mer, 1000[–1782]. Suppl. au Cartul. municipal. Publ. G. de Lhomel. [2t]. la8º. Compiègne. 1907–10
Montrose (James Graham, *1st marq. of***),** *see* Wishart (G.) *I. G.: De rebus, sub imperio J. M. &c. gestis, comm., 1647.
Montucci (Antonio), *see* Morrison (R.) & A. M. A parallel betw. the two Chinese dict., 1817.
Monumenta.
M. cartographica, v1, 2, 1925–26, *see* Wieder (F. C.), *ed.*
M. Erphesfurtensia saec. 12–14, *see* Sankt Peter, *abbey, Erfurt.*
M. Hebraica. M. Talmudica. Hrsg. v. S. Funk &c. B1, 2i, ii, 5. 4º. Wien. 1913–14
1, Bibel u. Babel; bearb. v. S. Funk. 2, Recht; v. S. Gandz. 5, Geschichte; v. S. Krauss.
M. hist. ducatus Carinthiae, 811–1269, *see* Carinthia.
M. hist. Norveg., 1880, *see* Storm (G.), *ed.*
M. Hungarorum in Polonia (1575–1668). v1. la8º. Budapest. 1918
see Bathory (I.), *king of Poland.* Rationes curiae S. B. hist. Hung. &c. illust. (1576–86); ed. A. Veress, 1918.
M. medica. Under the gen. ed. of H. E. Sigerist. v1–4. fol. 8º. *&* la8º. Milan. 1924–25
see Canano (J. B.) Musculorum humani corporis picturata dissectio, 1541 ?; facs., 1925. [4.]
„ Fasciculo. Fasc. di medicina [*sometimes attr. to J. de Ketham*], 1493, 1925. [2.]
„ Ketham (J. de). Fasc. medicinae: facs. of ed. of 1491; tr. &c., 1924. [1.]
„ Sudhoff (C.) Earliest pr. lit. on syphilis, 10 tract., 1495–8, in facs., 1925. [3.]
*M. pietatis & literaria virorum illustrium, selecta, 2p, 1701, *see* Mieg (J. R.)
Monumenta Germaniae Hist.
Auctores antiquissimi. t15. 4º. Berolini. 1919
see Aldhelm, *St., bp. of Sherborn.* Opera, 1919. [15.]
Carmina Cantab.; ed. K. Strecker, 1926, *see* Cambridge.
Diplomata regum et imperatorum Germ.
see Urkunden d. deut. Könige u. Kaiser, B5i, 8, 1926–27.
Epistolae.
see Dümmler (E. L.), *ed.* Epist. Merowingici et Karolini aevi, t4, 1925. [Epist., t6.]
Epistolae selectae. t1–4. 8º. 1916–26
see Boniface, *St.* Briefe d. heil. B. u. Lullus; hrsg. v. M. Tangl., 1916. [1.]
„ Froumundus. Die Tegernseer Briefsamml.; hrsg. v. K. Strecker, 1925. [3.]
„ Gregory VII. Register, 1–2, 1920–23. [Epist. sel., t2i, ii.]
„ Hampe (C.), *ed.* Die Aktenstücke z. Frieden v. S. Germano, 1230, 1926. [4.]
Leges.
Legum sectio 1. Legum nationum German. t5ii, Lex Baiwariorum (ed. Ernestus liber Baro de Schwind). 4º. Hannoverae. 1926

Monumentia Germaniae Hist. [*continued*].
Leges [*continued*].
Legum sect. III. Concilia. t2, Suppl. (Libri Carolini sive C. M. Capit. de imaginibus; rec. H. Bastgen). 4º. Hannoverae. 1924
Legum sectio IV. Constit. et Acta publica imperatorum & regum. t6i, 8. 4º. Hannoverae. 1910–27
6i, 1325–1330; ed. J. Schwalm.
8, 1345–48; ed. K. Zeumer & R. Salomon.
Necrologia Germaniæ,
see Necrologia Germaniae, t4, 1920.
Poetæ Latini.
see Poetæ Lat. aevi Carolini, t4ii, iii, 1923.
Scriptores. Scriptorum t30, p2, fasc. 1. fol. Lipsiae. 1926
—— Nova ser. t1–4i. 8º. 1922–24
see Cosmas, *Pragensis.* Chronik d. Böhmen, 1923. [n.s., 2.]
„ Henricus, *Surdus.* Die Chronik Heinrichs Taube &c., 1922. [n.s., 1.]
„ Joannes, *Vitoduranus.* Chronik, 1924. [n.s., 3.]
„ Matthias, *Neoburgensis.* Chronik, t1, 1924. [n.s., 4i.]
Scriptores rerum Germ. in usum schol.
see Abbo, *monk of St. Germain.* De bello Parisiaco, 1871.
„ Adamus, *Bremensis.* Hamburg. Kirchengesch., 3e A., 1917.
„ †Albertus, *de Bezanis.* Chronica, 1908.
„ Altaich. Annales Altah. maiores, 1891.
„ Arnoldus, *abbot of Lübeck.* Chron. Slavorum, 1868.
„ Baiern. B. Chroniken des 14. Jhdts., 1918.
„ Boniface, *St.* Vitae, 1905.
„ Bruno, *Magdeburg.* De bello Saxon. liber, 1880.
„ Burchardus, *Ursperg.* Chronicon, 1916.
„ Canute, *the Great.* Cnutonis regis gesta, 1865.
„ Carmen de bello Saxonico &c., 1889.
„ †Chronicon. Chron. Moguntinum, 1885.
„ Codagnello (J.) Annales Placentini, 1901.
„ Coloniensis. Chron. Regia Colon. &c., 1880.
„ Cyrinus [Arbeo], *episc. Frising.* Vitae SS. Haimhrammi & Corbiniani, 1920.
„ Ditmarus, *bp. of Merseburg.* Chronicon, 1889.
„ †Eginhard. Annales, 1845.
„ —— Vita Karoli Magni, 1863.
„ Fontenelle. Gesta abbatum F., 1886.
„ Franci. Annales regni Francorum, 1895.
„ Frederick I, *emp. of Germany.* Gesta F. in Lombardia &c., 1892.
„ Fulda. Annales F. &c., 1891.
„ Gislebert *of Mons.* Chronicon Hanon., 1869.
„ Godefridus *Viterb.* Gesta Friderici I & Heinr. VI, 1870.
„ Guelph. Mon. Welforum antiqua, 1869.
„ Helmoldus. Cronica Slavorum, 1909.
„ Henricus *Ymera.* Chron. Lyvoniae, 1874.
„ Henry IV, *emp. of Germany.* Vita H. IV Imp. 1855.
„ Herbordus. Dialogus de vita Otton. episc. Babenberg., 1868.
„ Hildesheim. Annales H., 1878.
„ Joannes, *Victoriensis.* Liber certarum hist., 2t, 1909–10.
„ Jonas, *Elnon.* Vitae SS. Columbani, Vedastis, Johannis, 1905.
„ Lambertus, *Hersfeld.* Opera; acced. Annales Weissenburgenses, 1894.
„ Liudprandus, *bp. of Cremona.* Werke, 3e A., 1915.
„ Marbach. Annales Marbac.; acc. Annales Alsat. brev., 1907.
„ Meinwerk, *bp. of Paderborn.* Leben, 1921.
„ Metz. Annales M. priores, 1905.
„ Nithardus. Historiarum libri 4, 1907.
„ Norbert, *St., abp. of Magdeburg.* Vita Bennonis II, episc. Osnabrug., 1902.
„ Novalese, *Abbey.* Chron. Nov., 1846.
„ Otto, *bp. of Frisingen.* Chronica &c., 1912.
„ —— O. & Rahewini Gesta Frid. I, 1884.
„ Otto *de S. Blasio.* Chronica &c., 1912.
„ Paulus, *diaconus.* Hist. Langobard, 1878.
„ —— Hist. romana, 1879.
„ Porta (J.) Lib. de coronatione Karoli IV, 1913.
„ Regino, *Prumiensis.* Chronicon, 1890.
„ Rembert, *St.* Vita Anskarii &c., 1884.
„ †Richer, *French chronicler, 10th cent.* Hist. libri IV, 1839.
„ Saint Bertin, *abbey.* Annales Bert., 1883.
„ Sankt Peter, *abbey, Erfurt.* Mon. Erphesfurt., 1899.
„ Walramus, *of Schwarzenberg.* Liber de unitate eccl. conserv., 1883.
„ Wippo. Werke, 1915.
„ Xanten. Annales X. & Annales Vedast., 1909.
Scriptores rerum Merovingicarum.
see Krusch (B.), *ed.* Passiones vitaeque sanct. aevi M., t5, 1920.
Monumenta Reformationis Belgicae. t1. la8º. Lugd. Bat. 1882
see Œconomica. Het oudste Nederlandsche verboden boek, 1523: œcon. xtna.; uitg. Toorenbergen, 1882.

Monumenti. M. di storia patria d. prov. Modenesi: ser. d. cronache, t16, 1911, *see* SPACCINI (G. B.)
M. antichi ined., ovvero Notizie s. antichità e belle arti di Roma, per l'anno 1787. [*By* G. A. Guattani]. la8°. 1787
Monuments de l'art byzantin. Publ. sous Min. de l'Instr. Publ. &c. [t]5. fol. 1927
see MILLET (G.) Mon. de l'Athos, t1, 1927. [5.]
Monumentum Ancyranum, *see* AUGUSTUS (C. J. C. O.), *emperor of Rome.*
Monumentum Antiochenum: neugefund. Aufzeichnung d. Res gestae divi Augusti &c.; hrsg. W. M. Ramsay &c., 1927, *see* AUGUSTUS (C. J. C. O.), *emp.*
Monval (Jean) [MONDAIN-MONVAL (J.)] Soufflot: sa vie, son œuvre, son esthétique (1713–80). la8°. 1918
see SOUFFLOT (J. G.) Corresp. avec les directeurs des batiments &c.; publ. M., 1918.
Monypenny, *The family of, see* VAN DE PUT (A.) The M. breviary, 1922.
Moodey (Margaret W.), *see* MERRILL (G. P.) Handbook &c. of gems &c. in U.S. Nat. Museum; by G. P. M., assist. by M. W. M. &c., 1922.
Moodie (John Wedderburn Dunbar). Camp. in Holland in 1814, *see* COOKE (J.) Mem. of the late war &c., v2, 1831.
Moody (Campbell N.) The mind of the early converts. 8°. [1920]
Moody (Francis W.) Lect. & lessons on art. [9th ed.] 8°. 1898
Moody (John). The masters of capital: Wall Street. [Chron. of Amer. ser., v41]. 8°. New Haven, *Yale.* 1919
The railroad builders. Welding of the States. [Chron. of Amer. ser., v38]. 8°. New Haven, *Yale.* 1919
Moog (Willy). Die deut. Philos. d. 20. Jhdts. 8°. St. 1922
Mookerji (Radhakumud), *see* MUKERJI (R.)
Moon (Parker Thomas).
Imperialism & world politics. [repr.] 8°. N.Y. 1927
The labor probl. & the Social Catholic movement in France. 8°. N.Y. 1921
Syllabus on internat. relations. 8°. N.Y. 1925
Moon (Robert Oswald). Hippocrates & h. successors in rel. to the philosophy of th. time. Fitzpatrick Lect. s8°. 1923
Moonan (George Aloysius), *see* HAYDEN (M.) & G. A. MOONAN. Sh. hist. of the Irish people, 1921.
Mooney (John). Eynhallow: the holy island of the Orkneys. 8°. Kirkwall. 1923
Moor (C. G.) The recognition of minerals, w. monogr. on geology &c. by D. A. MacAlister. 8°. [1909]
Moor (John Frewen). The future state of animals. Coll. by J. F. M. 2nd ed., ed by E. Carrington. s8°. Winchester. 1899
Moore (*Sir* Alan Hilary), *Bart.* Last days of mast & sail: essay in nautical comparative anatomy. la8°. O. 1925
Moore (Alfred Finley), *see* ABBOT (C. G.) & A. F. M. Obs. of the total solar eclipse of May 20, 1919, 1920.
—— **& L. H. Abbot.** The brightness of the sky, *see* SMITHSONIAN INSTIT. Misc. coll., v71, 1920.
Moore (Arthur William), *M.A.*
Manx ballads & music. 8°. Douglas, I. of M. 1896
Moore (Blaine Free). Econ. aspects of the commerce &c. of the Netherlands, 1912–18, 1919, *see* UNITED STATES: COMMERCE.
Moore (Clifford Herschel). Pagan ideas of immortality dur. Early Roman Empire. s8°. Cambridge, [U.S.] 1918
Moore (E. Hamilton) [*aft. Mrs.* E. H. GORDON].
The flame & o. p. s8°. 1910
The fountain of ablutions & o. p. s8°. C. 1921
An idyll & o. p. s8°. 1912
Moore (Edward), *of Abingdon.* Foundling, *see* INCHBALD (E.) Brit. th., v14, 1808.
The gamester. [Dolby's Brit. th.] s8°. [1823]
The gamester, *see* INCHBALD (E.) Brit. th., v14, 1808.
Poet. works. Coll. by T. Park. s8°. 1806
see CASKEY (J. H.) The life & wks. of E. M., 1927.
Moore (Edward), *principal of St. Edmund Hall, Oxford.* The "DXV" prophecy in the Div. Commedia. [P2838]. 8°. O. 1901
Moore (Elwood S.) Coal. 8°. N.Y. 1922
Moore (Francis), *physician, see* VOX STELLARUM: or, A loyal almanack, 1800–8.
Moore (George), *novelist.*
The apostle. Drama. 8°. 1923
Avowals. 8°. 1924
The Brook Kerith. A Syrian story. [7th ed. rev.] 8°. 1927
Celibate lives. [n. ed. *of* In single strictness]. 8°. 1927
The coming of Gabrielle. A comedy. 8°. [*p.p.*] 1920
Confessions of a young man, 1886. Ed. & annot. by G. M., 1904, & again in 1916. [n. & rev. ed.] s8°. [1926]
Conversations in Ebury Street. 8°. 1924
Esther Waters. [repr.] s8°. 1920
„ „ [n. impr.] s8°. [1926]

Moore (George), *novelist* [*continued*].
Héloïse & Abélard. 2v. 8°. *p.p.* 1921
„ „ Fragments [*b. w.* v2]. 8°. *p.p.* 1921
„ „ .... 8°. 1925
„ „ [2nd impr.] 8°. 1926
Impressions & opinions. 2nd impr. 8°. 1914
In single strictness. 8°. [*p.p.*] 1922
Memoirs of my dead life. [2nd ed.] s8°. 1906
Pure poetry: an anthology. Ed. G. M. la8°. 1924
Ulick and Soracha. 8°. *Nonesuch Press.* 1926
see FREEMAN (J.) Portrait of G. M. [*add.*: G. M.: a bibliogr., by H. Danielson], 1922.
„ WILLIAMS (I. A.) Bibliographies of mod. a., No. 3, G. M., 1921.
Moore (George Edward). Philosophical studies. 8°. 1922
Moore (George Foot). Judaism in the 1st cent. of the Xtn. era. 2v. la8°. Camb. [Mass.] 1927
see MYTHOLOGY of all races; ed. L. H. Gray & G. F. M., v4, 7, 11, 1920–27.
Moore (Henry), *Wesleyan minister, 1751–1844.*
The life of John Wesley; incl. life of Charles Wesley &c. 2v. 8°. 1824
The life of Mary Fletcher. 3rd ed. 8°. 1818
„ „ 11th ed. 8°. 1844
Sermon preached in Bristol, 30th Jan. 1791, on death of Rev. J. Easterbrook. [P2537]. s8°. 1791
Sermons. With a mem. s8°. 1830
Thoughts of the eternal Sonship. [P2543]. 8°. B'ham. 1817
see SMITH (*Mrs* M. A.) Life of H. M., 1844.
Moore (J. B.) *of Salisbury, see* BROWN, *publisher, of Salisbury* B.'s hdbk. &c. to Salisbury cathedral, 1884.
Moore (J. J.), *of the Royal Navy.*
The Brit. mariner's vocabulary &c. 8°. 1801
Moore (James Carrick). Campaign of the Brit. army in Spain commanded by Sir J. Moore. 4th ed. 8°. 1809
Moore (*Lt.-Gen. Sir* John).
see BROWNRIGG (B.) Life & letters of Sir J. M., 1923.
„ WOLFE (C.) The burial of Sir J. M. &c., 1825.
Moore (*Sir* John Henry), *Bart.*
Poet. works. Coll. by T. Park. s8°. 180[illegible]
Moore (*Sir* Jonas). A new systeme of the mathematicks cont. arith., geom., trig., cosmog., navig., doctr. of th sphere, astr. tables, geog. [Ed. W. Hanway & J. Potenger] [*v1 in 3p; v2 in 4p, w. sep. pag.*] 2v. 4°. 168
Moore (N. Hudson), *wife of S. P. Moore.*
Old glass, European & Amer. 8°. [1926
Moore (Olin Harris). The Young King, Henry Plantagene (1155–83), in hist., lit. & tradition. [Ohio State Univ.] 8°. Columbus, *Ohio.* [192
Moore (Thomas), *curator of the Botanic Garden, Chelsea.*
Brit. wild flowers. n. ed. of The field botanist's companion 8°. 186
Moore (Thomas), *the poet* [*ps.* THOMAS LITTLE].
Poet. works. Ed. A. G. Godley [Oxford ed. *Thin*]. s8°. O. 1910
Diary: selection ed. w. intr. by J. B. Priestley. s8°. C. 1925
*Intercepted letters: or, the twopenny post-bag &c. s8°. 1813
Life of Lord Byron, *see* BYRO (*Lord*). Works, v1–6, 1832.
Poet. wks. of the late Thom. Little. 14th ed. s8°. 18
see BYRON (*Lord*). Letters &c w. life by M., 2v, 1830.
Moore (Thomas Sturge).
Danaë, Aforetime, Blind Thamyris. [Poems]. 8°. 19
Tragic mothers. 8°. 19
Moore (Thomas Verner). P. B. Shelley: intr. to the study character. 8°. Princeton, N.J. [192
Moore-Anderson (Arthur P.), *M.D.* Sir Robert Anderso K.C.B., LL.D. A tribute & memoir. Pref. by J. S. Holde s8°. 19
Moorhouse (James), *bp. of (1) Melbourne, (2) Manchester, s* RICKARDS (E. C.) Bp. M. of Melbourne &c., 1920.
Moorman (Frederic William). Place-names of the We Riding of Yorkshire. [Thoresby Soc., 18]. 8°. *p.p.* Leeds. 19
Mooyer (Ernst Friedrich). Üb. d. angebl. Abstammung normann. Königsgeschlechts Siziliens v. d. Herzogen Normandie. 4°. Minden. 18
Verzeichniss d. deut. Bischöfe seit 800. Nebst e. Anhange Würdenträger e. Abteien u. Ritterorden enthalt. 8°. Minden. 18
Mopsuestinus (Theodorus), *see* THEODORE, *bp. of Mopsuestia.*
Moquot (Estienne). La guerre ministrale, au descouv. de pretendue harmonie &c. des Calvinistes, Lutheriens, &c. s8°. Poictiers. 16

Mor (Antonio) [Moor (A.); Moro (Antonio); More (*Sir* Anthony)], *see* Hisp. Soc. of Amer. M. in coll. of H.S., 1927.

Mora (Angelo Herreros de), *see* **Herreros de Mora (A.)**

Mora (Pedro de Rojas, *conde* **de),** *see* Rojas (P. de).

Mora Bhatta Dandekara, *see* Wilson (J.) An exposure of the Hindu relig. in reply to M. B. D.; pref. a tr. of [*h.*] tract, 1832.

Moraes (Francisco Teixeira de). Rel. dos tumultos na cidade de S. Luiz do Maranhão &c. (1692), *see* Instituto Hist. e Geog. Brazil. Rev., t40, 1877.

Morale. *Morale (La) pratique des Jésuites, t1, 1649; 2e éd., 8t, 1682–1735, *see* Jesuits.

Morales (Luis de), *see* Hisp. Soc. of America. Cat. ser., 1925–26.

Morand (Paul).

Bouddha vivant. [Chron. du 20e siècle, 2, 15e éd.] s8o. 1927
L'Europe galante. s8o. 1925
Fermé la nuit. 89e éd. s8o. 1923
Lewis & Irène. Roman. s8o. 1924
La nuit de Putney Common, nouvelle, *see* Œuvres libres, 15, 1922.
Ouvert la nuit. [126e éd.] s8o. 1922
Poèmes, 1914–24. Lampes à arc—Feuilles de température suivis 25 poèmes sans oiseaux. s8o. 1924
Rien que la terre: voyage. [Cahiers verts, 65]. s8o. 1926
Tendres stocks. Préf. de M. Proust. 10e éd. s8o. 1923
Translations.
Closed all night. [Tr. G. P. C., C. B. P., & H. M. 2nd ed.] s8o. 1925
Green shoots. Tr. H. I. Woolf; intr. by A. B. Walkley & pref. by M. Proust. s8o. 1923
Open all night. Tr. H. B. V. [2nd ed.] s8o. 1923

Morandi (Luigi). Prose e poesie ital.: scelte e annot. da L. M. s8o. Città di Castello. 1901

Morando (Cesare). Rime. 8o. Genova. 1599

Moranville (Luigi Selliers di), *see* Selliers di Moranville (L.)

Moras (Anne Marie), *ctsse. de Courbon* [†Peirenc de Moras (A. M.), *ctsse. de Courbon*], *see* Mouhy (C. de F., *chev.* de). Mém. d'A. M. de M., 4p, 1740.

Morata (Olympia Fulvia). Lettere, [1540–55], *see* Paladino (G.) Opusc. &c. di Riform. ital., v2, 1927.
see Bonnet (J.) Vie d'O. M., 3e éd., 1856.

Moratin (L. F. de).
La derrota de los pedantes y poesías. s8o. Paris. *n.d.*

Moraves. Manuel de doct. des égl. des Frères-M., 1743, *see* Nitschmann (D.)

Moravian [Moravians]. Church constit. [Ratio disciplinae] of Bohemian & M. Brethren, 1864, *see* Seifferth (B.), *ed.*
*Hist. (The) of the M., f. their first settlem. at Herrnhaag &c. Tr. f. the German. [*b. w.* Rimius (H.) Cand. narr., 2nd ed., 1753]. 8o. 1754

Morawski (Joseph de). Proverbes français antér. au 15e siècle. Ed. J. M. s8o. 1925

Moray. *Survey of the province of M.; hist., geogr. & polit. 8o. Aberdeen. 1798

Moray (*Sir* Robert), *1608–73*, *see* Robertson (A.) Life of M., 1922.

Morbio (Carlo), *see* Porro-Lambertenghi (G.) Breve commem., 1882.

Morcelli (Stefano Antonio). Africa Christiana in tres partes tributa. 3v. fol. Brixiae. 1816–17
Lexicon epigraph. Morcell. [*Ed. & augm. by* F. Schiassi]. 3v. fol. Bononiae. 1835–38
„ „ vocibus italicis digestum. fol. Bononiae. 1843

Morcuende (Federico Ruiz), *see* Ruiz Morcuende (F.)

Mordacq (Jean Jules Henri). La durée de la prochaine guerre. Note de gén. Langlois. [P2704]. la8o. 1912

Mordaunt (Elinor).

Alas, that spring— s8o. [1922]
The dark fire. s8o. [1927]
The further venture book. 8o. [1926]
Laura Creichton. s8o. [1921]
The little soul. s8o. [1920]
Old wine in new bottles. s8o. [1919]
People, houses & ships. s8o. [1924]
Reputation. s8o. [1923]
Short shipments. s8o. [1922]

Mordecai ben Nisan [Mardochaeus]. Notitia Karaeorum ex M. Karaei recentioris tractatu. Cum vers. Lat., notis &c. ed. J. C. Wolfius. Acc. J. Triglandi diss. de Karaeis. s4o. Hamburgi. 1714

Mordell (Albert). The erotic motive in literature. 8o. N.Y. 1919

Morden (*Sir* John). *Sir J. Morden & h. College, w. Suppl. s8o. 1925

Morden (William J.) Across Asia's snows & deserts. Intr. by R. C. Andrews. 8o. N.Y. 1927

Mordovtsev (Daniil Lukich), *1830–1905.*
Десятилѣтіе русскаго земства, 1864–75. 8o. С.–П. 1877
Полное собраніе историч. романовъ &c. Съ крит.-біог. очеркомъ состав. П. В. Быковымъ. [32p in 6v]. 8o. [С.–П. 1914]

More books, *see* Boston, Mass.: Pub. Lib. Bulletin, s6, 1926–.

More (George), *Esq.* Principles for yong princes. s4o. 1629

More (Gertrude), *see* Baker (A.) Inner life & wr. of Dame G. M.; rev. &c. by B. Weld-Blundell, v1, 1910.

More (Hannah).
Letters. Sel. w. intr. by R. B. Johnson. 8o. 1925
Letters to Z. Macaulay. Ed. A. Roberts. s8o. 1860
Percy, *see* †Inchbald (E.) Mod. th., v7, 1811.

More (Henry), *the Platonist.*
An explan. of godliness &c. 4o. 1660
De J. Boehmio judicium H. M. &c., *see* Jäger (J. W.) Examen theol. myst., 1709.
Enchiridion ethicum. ed nova; cui acc. auctoris epistola ad V. C. (quae apologiam complectitur pro Cartesio). s8o. Amstelodami. 1679
Tract. de anima. [*b. w.* Sandius (C.) Tract., 1671]. s8o. Roterodami. 1677

More (James A.), *see* Watson (J. A. S.) & J. A. M. Agriculture, 1924.

More (Louis Trenchard).
The dogma of evolution. 8o. Princeton. 1925

More (Paul Elmer).
The Christ of the New Test. 8o. Princeton. 1924
Christ the Word. 8o. Princeton. 1927
The relig. of Plato. 8o. Princeton. 1921

More (*Sir* Thomas), *Lord High Chancellor of England.*

Dialogue conc. Tyndale. Reprod. in black letter facs. f. coll. ed. (1557) of M.'s Eng. works. Ed. w. mod. version & essay by W. E. Campbell. Hist. intr. &c. by A. W. Reed. la8o. 1927
The historie of the life & death of Edward V &c.: w. the tyrannical gov. of Richard III &c. s8o. 1641
Last letters. Intr. by Card. Gasquet. Ed. w. connecting narr. by W. E. Campbell. s8o. 1924
Omnia Latina opera (Utopia, Luciani Necromantia, Hist. Richard III, Resp. ad epist. Lutheri &c.) fol. Lovanii. 1566
Sel. f. Eng. works & f. Lives by Erasmus & Roper. Ed. P. S. & H. M. Allen. s8o. O. 1924
Utopia, a mendis vindic. s8o. A, *Blaeuw*. 1629
Utopia. s8o. 1639
Utopia; tr., *see* Morley (H.) Ideal commonwealths, 1885.
„ „ Tr. into mod. Eng. by G. C. Richards. s8o. O. 1923
see Bray (R.) Sir Th. More's house at Chelsea: [play], 1926.
see Dudok (G.) Sir T. M. & h. Utopia, 1923.
„ Delcourt (J.) Essai sur la langue de Sir T. M. d'ap. s. œuvres angl., 1914.
„ Greenwood (*Sir* G. G.) Shakspere signatures & "Sir Thomas More," 1924.
„ Hoddesdon (J.) Hist. of the life &c. of Sir T. M.; coll. by J. H., 1662.
„ Kautsky (C.) T. M. & his Utopia; tr., 1927.
„ Manning (A.) The household of Sir T. M., 1906.
„ Pico della Mirandola (G.) T. Morus' Picus Erle of Mirandula; tr., 1908–9.
„ Pollard (A. W.) Shakespeare's hand in the play of Sir T. M.: papers, w. text of the Ill May Day scenes, ed. W. W. Greg, 1923.
„ Stapleton (T.) Tres Thomae &c., 1588.
„ Wahllius (J.) Diss. de T. Moro, 1686.

Morea. *L'origine d. M. [Dedic. *signed* M. A. Pandolfo Malatesta]. 2p *in* 1v (p2, Descr. d. 8. provincie). s8o. Venetia. 1686

Moréas (Jean). Œuvres. [t]1, 2. 8o. 1923–26
1, Les Syrtes—Les Cantilènes—Le pèlerin passionné—Enone au clair visage & Sylves—Eriphyle & Sylves nouv.
2, Les stances—Iphigénie.
Contes de la vieille France. 4e éd. s8o. 1910
Les stances, les 7 livres. 8o. Lyon. 1923
Trois nouveaux contes de la vieille France. s8o. 1921
see Rouveyre (A.) Souv. de mon commerce: Gourmont, Apollonaire, M. &c., 1921.

Moreau (Félix) & J. Delpech. Les règlements des assemblées législ. Ed. & tr. par M. & D. Préf. de C. Benoist. 2t. 8o. 1906–7

Moreau (Hégésippe). Le Myosotis, petits contes & petits vers [1838]. 8o. Lyon. 1920

Moreau (Jean Michel), *see* Hind (A. M.) Fragonard, M. le jeune & Fr. engravers, 1913.

Moreau (*le gén.* Jean Victor), *see* Picard (E.) Bonaparte & M., 1905.

Moreau (Luc Albert), *see* Allard (R.) L. A. M.: reprod. de peintures &c., préc. d'une ét. crit., 1920.

Moreau de Jonnès (Alexandre). Adventures in wars of the Republic & Consulate. Tr. f. ed. of 1893 by Brig.-Gen. A. J. Abdy. 8°. 1920
La Prusse, son progrès polit. & social. Suivi d'un Exposé économ. & statist. des réformes dep. 1806 tr. de l'allemand de Dieterici. 8°. 1848
Moreau-Nélaton (Etienne), *see* CHANTILLY: MUSÉE CONDÉ. Crayons franç. du 16e s.: intr. par E. M.-N., 1910.
Morehouse (Edward W.), *see* ELY (R. T.) & E. W. M. Elem. of land econ., 1924.
Morel (*lt.-col.*) La Légion étrangère: rec. de doc. &c. 8°. 1912
Morel (*l'abbé* **E.),** *see* COMPIÈGNE. Cartul. de l'abbaye de St.-Corneille de C.; publ. M., t1, 1904.
Morel (*l'abbé* **Gustave),** *see* CALVET (J.) L'abbé G. M.; tr., 1913.
Morel (Maurice). Marinette. Roman. s8°. [1922]
Moreland (William Harrison). Dutch sources for Indian hist.: 1590 to 1650. [Extr. f. Journal of Ind. hist. *No tp.* P2731]. 8°. [1923]
From Akbar to Aurangzeb: st. in Indian econ. hist. 8°. 1923
Morel-Fatio (Alfred).
La comedia espagnole du 17e s. 2e éd. rev. s8°. 1923
Etudes sur l'Espagne. s4. 8°. 1925
Morell (John Reynell). Russia self-condemned. Secret & ined. doc. conn. w. Russ. hist. &c. Tr. & ed. J. R. M. 8°. 1854
Morell (Marie de), *see* LA RONCIÈRE (E. C. DE). Procés d'E. C. de La R., accusé d'une tentative nocturne de viol sur la personne de M. de M., 1835.
Morelles (Cosmas) [MORRELLES (C.)] Relatio colloquii Francofurt. 1609 inter nonnullos Calvinianae religionis ministros & R. P. C. M. &c. s4°. Coloniae Agrippinae. 1610
Morellet (*l'abbé* **André).** Lettres inéd. sur l'hist. polit. & litt. des ann. 1806 & 1807, p. faire suite à s. Mém. 8°. 1822
Morelli (Domenico) & E. Dalbano. La scuola napoletana di pittura nel sec. 19 &c. A cura di B. Croce. 8°. Bari. 1915
Morelli (Giovanni). Della pittura ital. [t1]. Le gallerie Borghese e Doria Pamphili in Roma. la8°. Milano. 1897
Moreno (Francisco Fernandez), *see* FERNANDEZ MORENO (F.)
Moreno (Francisco P.) Viaje á la Patagonia Austral. 2a ed. t1. [*Frontispiece missing*]. la8°. Buenos Aires. 1879
Moreno (Giuseppe). Inni religiosi. s8°. 1889
Moreno Nieto (José). Gram. de la lengua arábiga. 8°. 1872
Morenos (David Levi). L'emigraz. peschereccia pel lavoro n. Adriatico. [P2842]. la8°. Venezia. 1916
Morente (Antonio Jaén), *see* JAÉN MORENTE (A.)
Moresini (Andrea), *see* MOROSINI (A.)
Moresinus (Thomas). Papatus, seu, depravatae religionis origo & incrementum &c. s8°. Edinburgi. 1594
Moresthe (Georges).
Vilna & le problème de l'Est européen. s8°. 1922
Moret (Alexandre). Fragm. du mastaba de Shery, prêtre, *see* ACAD. D. INSCR.: FOND. PIOT. Mon., t25, 1921–22.
Le Nil & la civilisation égypt. 8°. 1926
The Nile & Egypt. civilization. [Tr. M. R. Dobie]. 8°. 1927
—— **& G. Davy.** Des clans aux empires. L'organis. chez les primitifs & dans l'Orient anc. 8°. 1923
From tribe to empire: soc. organiz. am. primitives & in the anc. East. [Tr. V. G. Childe.] 8°. 1926
Moreti (Juan José). Hist. de ciudad de Ronda. 8°. Ronda. 1867
Moretti (Marino).
Conoscere il mondo. s8°. Milano. 1919
Guenda. Romanzo. s8°. Milano. [1919]
L'isola dell' amore. Romanzo. s8°. Milano. 1920
Mia madre. Pref. di A. Panzini. s8°. Milano. [1925]
Nè bella nè brutta. Romanzo. s8°. Milano. 1921
I puri di cuore. s8°. Milano. [1923]
Il trono dei poveri. s8°. Milano. 1928
La voce di Dio. Romanzo. s8°. Milano. 1921
Moretto (*Il*), *see* BONVICINO (A.)
Moretus, *Family of, see* ANTWERP. Cat. of the Plantin-Moretus Museum, by M. Rooses, 3rd ed., 1921.
Moreux (*l'abbé* **Théodore).**
Astronomy to-day. Tr. C. F. Russell. s8°. [1926]
L'Atlantide a-t-elle existé? 8°. 1924
Morgagni (Giov. Batt.)
Adversaria anatomica omnia. [*var. tp.*] fol. Venetiis. 1762
De sedibus & causis morborum per anatomen indagatis libri 5. 2a ed. 2t. fol. Patavii. 1765
Epistolæ anatomicæ 18 [*or rather 20*] ad scripta pertin. A. M. Valsalvae &c. 2p [*in 1v. pagin. cont.*] fol. Bassani. 1764

Morgagni (Giov. Batt.) [*continued*].
Epistolæ anatomicæ 2 novas obs. & animadv. compl. [*b. w. h.* Adversaria, 1762]. fol. Venetiis. 1762
Opuscula misc. 3p [*in 1v. sep. tp. & pagin.*] fol. Venetiis. 1763
Morgan (Arthur Eustace).
Tendencies of mod. English drama. 8°. 1924
Morgan (Bayard Quincy). A bibliography of German lit. in Eng. tr. [Wisconsin Univ.] 8°. Madison. 1922
Morgan (Caro).
A mixed bag. [Sh. stories & Tr. f. Horace]. s8°. [1926]
Morgan (Claude). Un peuple en fermentation, ou Beograd, cité mod., *see* ŒUVRES libres, No. 79, 1928.
Morgan (Conwy Lloyd).
Emergent evolution. Gifford Lect., 1922. 8°. 1923
Life, mind & spirit. [Gifford lect. (Emergent evol.), 2]. 8°. 1926
Morgan (Edward Delmar). The old channels of the Lower Oxus. [From Journ. of Roy. Geog. Soc., 1878. P2714]. 8°. 1879
see PALLADY, *archimandrite.* Exped. thr. Manchuria f. Pekin in 1860; tr. by E. D. M., 1872.
Morgan (Frederick Cecil). Hdbk. of Artillery matériel. 7th ed. rev. by W. B. Caddell. s8°. 1913
Morgan (Henry Arthur), *Master of Jesus Coll., Cambridge, see* MORGAN (I. L. O.) Mem. of H. A. M., 1927.
Morgan (Iris L. Osborne). Memoirs of H. A. Morgan, Master of Jesus Coll., Camb., 1885–1912. 8°. 1927
Morgan (J.), *Gent.* Phoenix Britannicus. Being a misc. coll. of scarce & curious tracts &c. Nos. 1–4 *in* 1v. 4°. 1731
Morgan (Jacques Jean Marie de). L'humanité préhistor.: esquisse de préhist. gen. s8°. 1921
La préhistoire orientale. 3t. la8°. 1925–27
1, Généralités. 2, L'Égypte & l'Afrique du Nord; publ. L. Germain. 3, L'Asie antérieure; publ. L. Germain.
Prehistoric man. [Tr. J. H. Paxton & V. C. C. Collum]. la8°. 1924
Les premiers temps de l'Égypte, *see* ACAD. D. INSCR.: FOND PIOT. Mon., t25, 1921–22.
Morgan (*Rev.* **James),** *M.A.* The importance of Tertullian in develop. of Christian dogma. s8°. 1928
Morgan (James), *Wesleyan preacher.* The life & death of Mr. Thomas Walsh. s8°. 1762
Morgan (*Brig.-Gen.* **John Hartman).**
John, Viscount Morley: apprec. & reminisc. 8°. 1924
The present state of Germany. Lect., w. intr. s8°. 1924
see ROBINSON (G. E.) Publ. authorities & legal liability intr. on Remedies agst. the Crown, by J. H. M., 1925.
Morgan (John Hill). Paintings by J. Trumbull at Yale Univ. of hist. scenes &c. in Amer. Revol. 4°. New Haven, *Yale.* 192
Morgan (John Pierpoint). Byzantine enamels in P. M.'s coll. By O. M. Dalton, w. note by R. Fry. [Repr. f. Burlington Mag.] 4°. 191
Morgan (Robert Burns). Elementary graphs. s8°. 190
Readings in Eng. social hist. f. contemp. lit. [–1837]. Ed. R. B. M. 5v. s8°. C. 1921–2
„ „ ....[n. ed. *in* 1v]. 8°. C. 192
Morgan (Sydney), *Lady Morgan, wife of Sir T. C. Morgan*
*Le Morganiche: lettere scr. da un Italiano a Miledi M sopra var. articoli rel. a Milano &c. 8°. Edimburgo. 182
Morgan (Thomas Hunt). A critique of the theory of evolution Lect., 1916. 8°. Princetown. 191
Evolution & genetics. 8°. Princeton, *N.J.* 192
Heredity & sex. 2nd rev. ed. 8°. N.Y. 191
The physical basis of heredity. 8°. Phila. [191
The theory of the gene. 8°. New Haven, *Yale.* 192
Morgan (William), *D.D.*
The nature & right of religion. 8°. E. 192
Morgan (William), *F.R.S., see* SOC. FOR EQUITABLE ASSURANCES. Deed of settlement, w. addresses by W. M. &c 1833.
Morgan (William Thomas). English polit. parties & leaders in the r. of Q. Anne, 1702–1710. [Yale Hist. Publ. Misc. 7]. 8°. New Haven, *Yale.* 192
***Morganiche** (Le): lettere scr. da un Italiano a Miledi Morga &c. rel. a Milano &c., 1824, *see* MORGAN (S.)
Morgen (Curt von). Meiner Truppen Heldenkämpfe. 8°. 192
Morgenland. Darstellung aus Gesch. u. Kultur d. alt. Orient Hrsg. W. Schubart. H12–14. 8°. L. 192
For earlier parts, see ALTE ORIENT. Beihefte.
see EHRENBERG (V.) Karthago, 1927. [14
„ SCHARFF (A.) Grundzüge d. ägypt. Vorgesch., 1927. [12
„ SCHUBART (W.) Das Weltbild Jesu, 1927. [13

Morgenthau (Henry). Les faits les plus horribles de l'hist. [P2709]. 8°. 1918
Mori (Attilio). Toscana. s4°. Torino. 1927
Mori (Gustav), *see* Frankfort. Frankfurter Urkundenbuch z. frühgesch. d. Buchdrucks; hrsg. v. G. M. &c., 1920.
Moriarty (*Capt.* H. A.), *R.N., C.B., see* Admiralty. South Indian Ocean pilot, orig. comp. by M., 3rd ed., 1911.
Morice (Charles). Il est ressuscité! n. éd. avec préf. de l'auteur. s8°. 1913
Morice (*l'abbé* Henri).
Jules Lemaitre. Préf. par J. Gahier. s8°. 1924
Morier (James Justinian). The adv. of Ḥājī Bābā of Ispahan. Tr. into Persian by Ḥājī Shaykh Aḥmad-i Kirmānī; ed. w. notes by D. C. Phillpott. 2nd ed. 8°. Calcutta. 1924
The adv. of Hajji Baba of Ispahan. s8°. 1925
Mories (A. S.) Christ's secret doctrine &c. s8°. 1917
Mörike (Eduard). Der Schatz. s8°. Grünwald-München. [1922]
Das Stuttgarter Hutzelmännlein. 8°. München. 1920
Morillot (Paul). La Bruyère. 2e éd. s8°. 1921
Scarron & le genre burlesque. la8°. 1888
Morin (Etienne) [Morinus (Stephanus)]. Exercit. de lingua primaeva, ejusque appendicibus. s4°. Ultrajecti. 1694
Morin (Jean). Comm. hist. de disciplina in admin. sacramenti poenitentiae 13 primis seculis in eccl. occid. &c. obs. Quae Judaei antiq. &c. tradunt de poenitentia &c. Complures libelli &c. ex antiq. cod. eruti. [*2 pagin.*] fol. Antverpiae. 1682
see Antiquitates. Eccl. Orient. antiq. M. &c.; praef. est M. vita, 1682.
„ Hottinger (J. H.) Exercit. Anti-Morinianae: de Pentateucho Samaritano, 1644.
Möring (Carl). Alexander papa VIII pseudonymus. Præs. C. Kortholt. [P2670]. s4°. Kiloni. 1690
Morinus (Stephanus), *see* Morin (E.)
Moris (Henri). *see* Krebs (L.) & H. M. Campagnes dans le Alpes, 1792–96, 2t, 1891–95.
see Lérins, *abbey of.* Cartul. de l'abbaye de L.; publ. par H. M. &c., pl, 1883.
Morisanus (Josephus). De protopapis & deutereis Graecorum & Catholicis eorum eccl. diatriba. la8°. Neapoli. 1768
Morison (James), *the Hygeist, see* Bulloch (J. M.) Centenary of J. M., 1925.
Morison (James L.) Allenby's first attempt on Jerusalem. [Bulletin 33, Dept. of Hist. &c., Queen's Univ., Kingston, Canada]. [P2425]. 8°. Kingston [Ont.] 1919
Morison (John Lyle), *D.Litt.* The 8th Earl of Elgin. Chapter in 19th-cent. imperial hist. 8°. 1928
Morison (Samuel Eliot).
The maritime hist. of Mass., 1783–1860. 8°. Boston. 1921
Oxford hist. of the U.S., 1783–1917. 2v. 8°. 1927
Sources & doc. illust. the Amer. Revol., 1764–88, & the formation of the federal constit. Sel. & ed. M. s8°. O. 1923
Morison (Stanley). The art of the printer. 250 title & text pages sel. f. bks. in the Roman letter, 1500–1900. 4°. 1925
Caractères de l'écriture dans la typographie. Tr. la. paper copy. sm. fol. 1927
On type faces: examples of use of type for printing of bks. With intr. essay &c. by S. M. 4°. 1923
Type designs of the past & present. 8°. 1926
Morison (*Sir* Theodore), *see* India. Brit. I.; by an Indian Mahomedan, w. foreword by Sir T. M., 1926.
Morisot (Berthe), *see* Fourreau (A.) B. M., 1925.
Moritz (Bernhard). Arabien. Studien z. physikal. u. histor. Geographie d. Landes. 4°. Hannover. 1923
Beiträge z. Gesch. d. Sinaiklosters im M.-a. nach arab. Quellen, *see* Königl. Preuss. Akad. d. Wiss. Abhdl. (Phil.-hist. Kl.), 1918.
Der Sinaikult in heidn. Zeit, *see* Königl. Gesells. d. W. zu Göttingen. Abhdlgn., B16, 1917.
Moritz (Carl Philipp). Anton Reiser. Novel. Tr. P. E. Matheson. s8°. [1926]
Reisen e. Deutschen in Italien, 1786–88. 3T. s8°. 1792
Travels in England, 1782. Repr. of Eng. tr., 1795, w. intr. by P. E. Matheson. [Oxf. Misc.] s8°. 1924
Morizet (André). Chez Lénine & Trotski, Moscou 1921. Préf. de L. Trotski. s8°. [1922]
Morkill (John William), *see* Platt (G. M.) & J. W. M. Rec. of the parish of Whitkirk, 1892.
Mörl (Gustav Philipp). Vindiciae doct. Lutheranorum de gratia praedestinationis quam Feuerlinus, 4 concionibus propugnavit; nuper vero Dom. de Vallone impugnandam suscepit. [*b. w.* Mitternacht (J. S.) Diss., 1665]. s8°. Noribergae. 1702

Mörl (Maria von), *see* Brentano (C.) A. K. Emmerich, M. v. M. &c., 1874.
Morland (George), *painter.*
see Henderson (B. L. K.) M. & Ibbetson, 1923.
„ Huth (L.) Cat. of mezzotint portr. aft. Reynolds & engr. aft. G. M., 1905.
Morley (Christopher). Thunder on the left. s8°. 1926
Morley (Edith Julia). J. Warton: compar. of h. Essay on Pope w. h. ed. of Pope's works, *see* English Assoc. Essays &c., v9, 1924.
Morley (F. V.), *see* Quillinan (*Mrs.* D.) Dora Wordsworth, her book; [intr. &c.] by F. V. M., 1924.
Morley (Felix). Unemployment relief in Gt. Brit.: st. in state socialism. [London Sch. of Econ. &c.] 8°. 1924
Morley (Henry), *prof. of Eng. Lit. at Univ. Coll., London.*
A bundle of ballads. Ed. w. intr. &c. by H. M. s8°. 1918
Ideal commonwealths: Plutarch's Lycurgus—More's Utopia—Bacon's New Atlantis—Campanella's City of the sun, & a frag. of Hall's Mundus alter & idem. Intr. by H. M. 8°. 1885
Morley (James Wycliffe Headlam-), *see* Headlam-Morley (J. W.)
Morley (John Morley, *viscount***).** John Morley: Irish record. [Pall Mall gazette "extra," No. 23]. 2nd ed. [P2750]. la8°. [1886]
see Bigelow (J.) Lest we forget: Gladstone, M. & the Confed. Loan of 1863, 1905.
„ Hirst (F. W.) Early life & letters of J. M., 2v, 1927.
„ MacCallum (J. D.) Ld. M.'s criticism of Eng. poetry & prose, 1921.
„ Morgan (J. H.) J., Visct. M., 1924.
Morley (Silvano Griswold).
The inscriptions at Copan. [C.I. of Wash.] 4°. Wash. 1920
Morley (Thomas). A plaine & easie intr. to practical musicke. la8°. 1608
Mörlin (Joachim). Disput. tres, pro tertio usu legis contra fanaticos. 8°. *n.p.* [1566]
Themata de imagine Dei in homine. Et brevis tract. M. Kemnitii. [P2626]. s4°. Witebergae. 1570
see Wigand (J.), J. M. &c. De peccato orig. scripta &c., 1571.
Mornay (Charlotte de), *Madame Du Plessis-Marly, wife of P. de Mornay.* A Huguenot family in the 16 cent. Memoirs of P. de Mornay. Wr. by h. wife. Tr. L. Crump, w. intr. [Broadway Trans.] 8°. [1926]
Mornay (Philippe de), *seigneur du Plessis-Marly.*
De veritate relig. Christ. liber; adv. atheos, epicureos, ethnicos, Judaeos, Mohumedistas &c. s8°. Antverpiae. 1583
The mysterie of iniquitie: that is to say the hist. of the Papacie. Engl. by S. Lennard. sm. fol. 1612
A treatise of the Church. Rev. & enl. by the a. Tr. 8°. 1606
A woorke conc. the trewnesse of the Xtn. relig.; begunne to be tr. by Sir P. Sidney & finished by A. Golding, 1587, *see* Sidney (*Sir* P.) Defence of poesie &c.; ed. A. Feuillerat, 1923.
see Brutus (S. J.), *ps.* Vindiciae contra tyrannos &c., *sometimes attrib. to M.*, 1660.
„ Mornay (C. de). A Huguenot family in the 16 cent.: mems. of P. de M.; wr. by h. wife; tr., w. intr., 1926.
Mörne (Arvid). Ett liv. s8°. [1925]
Mornet (Daniel). Hist. de la litt. & de la pensée franç., (12–19s.) [n. éd. rev. &c.] 8°. [1927]
Hist. de la litt. & de la pensée franç. contemp., (1870–1925). s8°. 1927
La pensée franç. au 18e siècle. s8°. 1926
Morning chronicle (The). Jan. 18–July 6, 1797 (No. 8510–8652). [Apr. 11, 21; May 15; June 12 *wanting*]. fol. [1797]
***Morning-Exercise** (The) against popery; or, The principal errors of the Church of Rome detected &c. in Southwark by sev. ministers of the gospel. [*Names added in MS.*] s4°. 1675
Morny (Charles Auguste L. J., duc de).
see Boulenger (M.) Le duc de M., créateur de Deauville, 1925.
„ —— Le Duc de M. [Figures du passé], 1925.
Morone (*le card.* Giovanni), *see* Constant (G.) La légation du card. M., 1563, 1922.
Morone (Girolamo). Lettere ed orazioni latine; ed. D. Promis e G. Müller, *see* Regia Dep. Misc., t2, 1863.
see Müller (J.) Doc. conc. la vita pubbl. di G. M., 1865.
Morones (Luis N.), *see* Retinger (J. H.) M. of Mexico: hist. of the labour movt., 1926.
Moroni (*il conte* Antonio). Ragionamento storico int. a. città di Bergamo. 4°. Bergamo. 1791

Morosini (Andrea) [MORESINI]. L'imprese &c. di Terra Santa, et l'acquisto fatto d. Imp. di Constantinopoli d. Repub. di Venetia. [Tr. d. Lat.] s4°. Venetia. 1627

Morosini (Francesco), *1618–94.*
see MOROSINI (Z.) F. M., 1885.
„ VENETE. Successi d. armi v. in Levante, 1685, sotto. F. M., 1686.

Morosini (Zaccaria).
Francesco Morosini. [P2842]. la8°. Venezia. 1885

Morphy (Paul Charles), *see* LÖWENTHAL (J. J.) M.'s games of chess: w. notes by L., 1872.

Morpurgo (Rahel), *wife of J. Morpurgo, form. Luzzatto, see* SALAMAN (N.) R. M. & contemp. Hebrew poets in Italy, 1924.

Morrah (Herbert Arthur).
The Oxford Union, 1823–1923. 8°. 1923

Morre (*Dr.* **G.**) Descr. of princ. tombs in the old church at Delft. Tr. D. Goslings. 5th ed. [P2757]. s8°. Delft. 1912

Morrell (William), *of Banbury, Surgeon* [*ps*s. WILL. BOWYER; HUMPHREY WICKHAM], *see* SETTLE (E.) *Compleat mem. of life of impostor W. M., died, Jan. 3, 169½, 1694.

Morrell (William Wilberforce). Notices of Wesleyan Methodism in Masham, 1796–1896. [P2576]. 8°. 1896
Notices of Wesleyan Methodism in Selby 1744–1892. [P2594]. 8°. Selby. 1892

Morrelles (Cosmas), *see* MORELLES (C.)

Morris (Charles). Heroes of discovery in America. 2nd ed. rev. s8°. Phila. [1919]

Morris (Charles Richard) & M. Morris.
Hist. of polit. ideas. s8°. [1924]

Morris (E. J. McCarthy). Motionism, or the world's true religion. s8°. [1919]

Morris (Earl H.) Prelim. acc. of antiq. of region betw. the Mancos & La Plata Rivers in S.-W. Colorado, *see* SMITHSONIAN INST. B. OF ETHNOLOGY. Rep., 33, 1919.

Morris (Edward Patrick Morris, *1st baron*), *see* DOMINIONS (THE) & depend. of the Emp.; [*by Ld. M. &c.*], 1924.

Morris (Francis Orpen). Hist. of Brit. birds. 3rd ed., rev. corr. & enl. 6v. la8°. 1891
Natural hist. of nests & eggs of Brit. birds. 2nd ed. 3v. la8°. 1870–71

Morris (Gedeon), *the younger.* Relatorios e cartas [1636–44; *tr.* J. Hygino], *see* INSTITUTO HIST. E GEOG. BRAZIL. Revista, t58, 1895.

Morris (Guy Wilfred) & L. S. Wood. The English-speaking nations; development of the commonwealth ideal. 8°. O. 1924
The golden fleece: intr. to indust. hist. of England. s8°. O. 1922

Morris (Homer Lawrence). Parl. franchise reform in Eng., 1885–1918. 8°. N.Y., *Columbia Univ.* 1921

Morris (John Edward), *M.A., D.Litt., see* NORTHAMPTONSHIRE. Copy of papers rel. to musters, beacons &c. (1586–1623); intr. by J. E. M., 1926.

Morris (John Williams). Mem. of the life & wr. of the Rev. Andrew Fuller. n. ed. corr. 8°. 1826

Morris (*Capt.* **Joseph**). German air raids on Gt. Brit., 1914–18. 8°. [1925]

Morris (*Sir* **Lewis**). Works. s8°. 1890

Morris (Lloyd R.) The rebellious puritan: portrait of Mr. Hawthorne. 8°. 1928

Morris (Marmaduke Charles Frederick). Benjamin Fawcett, colour printer & engraver. 8°. 1925
Yorkshire remin. 8°. 1922

Morris (*Mrs.* **Mary**), *wife of C. R. Morris, see* MORRIS (C. R.) & M. M. Hist. of polit. ideas, 1924.

Morris (Reginald Owen). Contrapuntal technique in the 16th c. la8°. O. 1922
Foundations of pract. harmony & counterpoint. 8°. 1925

Morris (Richard), *LL.D.* Hist. outlines of Eng. accidence. n. ed. s8°. 1883
Specimens of early English, w. intr., notes &c. by R. M. & W. W. Skeat. 4th ed., p2, 1298–1393. s8°. O. 1898

Morris (Rupert Hugh). The Siege of Chester, 1643–46. Ed. &c. by P. H. Lawson. 8°. Chester. 1924

Morris (W. H.) Elementa Latina. 29th impr. s8°. 1905

Morris (W. S.) *Hist. & topog. of Wye. 8°. Canterbury. 1842

Morris (William), *poet.*
Communism. [Fabian tract, 113]. [repr. P2877]. 8°. 1923
Early romances in prose & verse. [repr.] s8°. [1920]
The Earthly Paradise. 2nd ed. [p1, 2 *in* 1v]. s8°. 1868
Old French romances, done into

Morris (William), *poet* [*continued*].
Eng. by W. M. Intr. by J. Jacobs. [n. ed.] s8°. 1914
see DRINKWATER (J.) W. M.: a crit. study, 1912.
„ GLASIER (J. B.) W. M. & early days of the Socialist movement, 1921.
„ JACKSON (H.) W. M., rev. &c. ed., 1926.
see MACKAIL (J. W.) Life of W. M., 1922.
„ MARILLIER (H. C.) Hist. of the Merton Abbey Tapestry Works, founded by W. M., 1927.
„ SPARLING (H. H.) The Kelmscott Press & W. M., 1924.
„ VIDALENC (G.) W. M., 1920.

Morris (William Alfred). The early Eng. county court. [Univ. of Cal., Publ. in hist., 14ii, pp89–230]. la8°. Berkeley, *Cal.* 1926
The mediæval Eng. sheriff, to 1300. [M'ter Univ. Publs.] 8°. M'ter. 1927

Morris (William O'Connor). Villars. [P2593]. s8°. D. 1892

Morrison (Alfred). Coll. of engravings formed, 1860–68, by A. M. Annotated cat. & index to portraits by M. Holloway. la8°. *p.p.* 1868
Exhib. of Japanese screens held at gall. of the R. Soc. of Brit. Artists, July 1910. Illust. cat. 8°. 1910

Morrison (Charles Clayton). The outlawry of war: constructive policy for world peace. 8°. Chicago. 1927

Morrison (David McLaren). Imp. federation. [P2846]. 8°. 1889

Morrison (Emmeline).
Good grain. s8°. [1921]
Jack River's wife. s8°. [1927]
Light fingers. s8°. [1927]
Not for a day. s8°. [1926]
There was a veil. s8°. [1923]
Three of a kind. s8°. [1924]
When the play began. s8°. [1925]

Morrison (Lewis Albert). Appreciation of English, w. note on the art of the essay & passages for study. s8°. [1923]

Morrison (R. Boyd), *see* SHERINGHAM (G.) & R. B. M. Robes of Thespis, 1928.

Morrison (Robert), *D.D.* Chinese miscellany: orig. extracts from Chinese authors, w. tr. &c. 4°. 1825
A gramm. of the Chinese lang. 4°. Serampore. 1815
A view of China for philolog. purposes. 4°. Macao. 1817
—— **& Antonio Montucci.** A parallel betw. the two intended Chinese dict. With M.'s Horae Sinicae, a new ed. &c. 4°. 1817

Morrison (Steinie). Trial. Ed. by H. F. Moulton. 8°. [1922]

Morrone (Joseph Maria). Vocabulary of the Cochin-Chinese lang., *see* DU PONCEAU (P. E.) Diss., 1838.

Morsbach (Lorenz). Mittelengl. Originalurkunden v. d Chaucer-Zeit bis z. Mitte d. 15. Jhdts. s8°. Heidelberg. 192

Morscovius (Petrus). Politia eccl. quam vulgo agendam vocant, sive forma regiminis exter. eccl. in Polonia. Rec & diss. praelim. de agendis eccl. &c. adj. G. L. Œderus. s4°. Francofurti. 174

Morse, *Family of, see* MORSE (W. I.), *ed.* Genealogiae or data conc. families of M. &c., 1925.

Morse (A. H.)
Radio: beam & broadcast, its story & patents. 8°. 192

Morse (C. F.) *A gramm. of the Bulgarian lang., w. exercise &c. [by C. F. M. aided by C. Vasiliev]. [2p *in* 1v]. 8°. Constantinople. 1859–6

Morse (Harry Havelock). The Acadian hunter, or Jean Breau Ed. & pr. pr. by W. Inglis Morse. 8°. [1927

Morse (Hosea Ballou). Chronicles of the East India Company trading w. China, 1635–1834. 4v. 8°. O. 192

Morse (Robert), *of Clarges St.* Cat. of coll. of prints &c formed by R. M.; sold by T. Dodd, May, 1816. [*MS prices*]. 4°. [1816

Morse (William Inglis). Genealogiae or data conc. the familie of Morse, Chipman, Phinney, Ensign & Whiting. Ed W. I. M. 8°. Boston, Mass. 192

Morselli (Enrico) & S. De Sanctis. Biografia di un bandito Giuseppe Musolino. la8°. Milano. 190

Morselli (Ercole Luigi), *see* FRATTINI (A.) E. L. M., 1920.

Mort (Frederick), *D.Sc.* Dumbartonshire. s8°. C. 192

Mortara (Giorgio). La salute pubbl. in Italia dur. e dop la Guerra. [C.E. for Internat. Peace]. la8°. Bari. 192

Mortensen (Carl). Dansk litteraturhist. 4e udg. 8°. 191
Litteraturudvalg for gymnasiet. H4–6. 8°. 192

Mortensen (Hans). Litauen. 8°. Hamburg. 192
Siedlungsgeographie d. Samlandes. 8°. St. 192

Mortet (Charles). Les origines & les débuts de l'imprimeri [Soc. Fr. de Bibl.] 4°. 192

Mortier (Alfred). Un dramaturge pop. de la Renaiss. ital. Ruzzante (1502–42). 2t. (2, Œuvres compl.; tr. A. M.) la8°. 1925–2

Mortier (*Mme.* **Alfred**), *see* AUREL, *ps.*
Mortier (D. A.) Hist. abrégée de l'Ordre de Saint-Dominique en France. 8°. Tours. 1920
Hist. des Maîtres généraux de l'Ordre des Frères Prêcheurs. t8, Index gen. 8°. 1920
Mortier (*le maréchal* **Ed. Ad. Casimir Joseph**), *duc de Trévise, see* DESPRÉAUX (*le col.* F.) Le maréchal M., t3, 1920.
Mortier (Pierre). Le verbe aimer, comédie, *see* ŒUVRES (Les) libres, 19, 1923.
Mortillet (Gabriel de), *see* MATÉRIAUX POUR L'HIST. DE L'HOMME, fondé par M., 1865–88.
Mortimer (Geoffrey), *ps., see* GALLICHAN (W. M.)
Mortimer (George).
Aluminium; its manufacture &c. s8°. [1920]
Mortoft (Francis). F. M.: his book: travels thr. France & Italy, 1658–59. Ed. M. Letts. [Hakluyt Soc., s2, 57]. 8°. 1925
Morton, *The earldom of.* Registrum Honoris de M. Anc. charters of earldom of M. w. o. orig. docs. [Bannatyne Club]. 2v. 4°. E. 1853
Morton (G. F.)
Childhoods fears: psycho-analysis &c. 8°. [1925]
Morton (H. V.) May Fair. s4°. 1927
Morton (*Card.* **John**), *see* JENKINS (C.) Card. M.'s register, 1924.
Morton (John Maddison). The sentinel, a musical burletta. Pref. by biogr. sketch of Mme. Vestris. [P2583]. s8°. [1837?]
Wooing one's wife. Farce. [P2582]. s8°. *Lacy. n.d.*
Morton (Michael) & P. Traill. Woman to woman. s8°. [1924]
Morton (Thomas), *bp. of (1) Chester, (2) Lichfield & Coventry, (3) Durham.* De pace inter Evangelicos procuranda sententiae quatuor a T. Dunelm, Jo. Sarisb. &c. Traditae J. Duraeo &c. s8°. Londini. 1638
*Exact discoverie of Romish doctrine in the case of conspiracie &c. [P2660]. s4°. 1605
A full satisfaction conc. a double Rom. iniquitie; hainous rebellion &c. 3p [*p3 w. sep. pagin.*] [P2660]. s4°. 1606
Of the instit. of the Sacrament. 8 bks. discovering the superstitions &c. of the Romish Masse &c. 2p [*in 1v*]. sfol. 1631
Secunda pars Apologiae Catholicae, judicem Eccl. demonstrans. s8°. Londini. 1606
Morton (Thomas), *dramatist.*
Works in INCHBALD (*Mrs.* E.) Brit. theatre, v25, 1808.
Cure for the heartache.
School of reform.
Speed the plough.
Way to get married.
A Roland for an Oliver. Farce. [P2582]. s8°. *Lacy.* 1826
Secrets worth knowing, *see* †INCHBALD (E.) Mod. th., v3, 1811.
Zorinski, *see* †INCHBALD (E.) Mod. th., v3, 1811.
Morton (William Cuthbert). The language of anatomy. Ed. w. intr. by R. Bridges. [S.P.E. Tract No. 9]. 8°. 1922
Mortreuil (Théodore).
La Bibliothèque Nat., orig. & accroissements. 8°. 1878
Morungen (Heinrich v.), *12c., see* KRAUS (C. v.) Zu d. Liedern H.'s v. M., 1917.
Morus (Samuel Friedrich Nathanael). Comm. exeget.-hist. in suam Theologiæ Christ. epitomen. Ed. &c. C. A. Hempel. 2t. 8°. Halæ Saxonum. 1797–98
Epitome theologiæ Christ. s8°. Lipsiæ. 1789
see DATHE (J. A.) & S. F. N. M. Disput. in Aquilae reliquias interpret. Hoseae, 1757.
Moscherosch (Hans Michael) [*ps.* PHILANDER V. SITTEWALD], *see* HARTIG (O.) C. Schorer u. s. "Sprachverderber" [*sometimes attr. to M.*], 1921.
Moschini (Giovanni Antonio) & E. A. Cigogna. *Memoria d. trasporto d. osse di P. Sarpi a San Michele di Murano. [P2835]. 8°. Venezia. 1828
Moschopoulos (Emanuel) [M. MOSCHOPULUS]. Carrés magiques, texte grec & tr., *see* TANNERY (P.) Mém^s. scient., t4, 1920.
Moschus (Joannes) [†JOHN, *Moschus, called Eucrates*]. Il prato spirituale, volgariz. di F. Belcari, *see* BELCARI (F.) Prose, t3–5, 1843–44.
Moscovia. *Moscovia gloriosa. Das unter Petro I blühende Moscau &c. s8°. Erfurt. 1741
*Respublica M. & urbes. [*Taken f. A. Guagninus & o. writers*]. s8°. Lugduni Batav. 1630
Moscow [MOSCOU; MOSKVA].
Archives princ. de Moscou du Min. des Affaires Étrangères. fol. Moscou. 1898
Conférence de M. pour la limitation des armements, [1922]. 8°. Moscou. 1923

Moscow [MOSCOU; MOSKVA] [*continued*].
Moscow (The) Art Theatre ser. of Russ. plays; tr., s1-2, 1923–24, *see* SAYLER (O. M.), *ed.*
Москва. Изд. А. А. Левенсонъ. [*Russian, German & French text*]. fol. Москва. [1912]
О греч. кондакарѣ 12–13 в. М. Синодальной библ. &c., 1869, *see* AMFILOKHY (A.)
Октябрьские дни в М. и районах, 1922, *see* RUSSIA: SOVIET.
*Récit du sanglant &c. massacre dans M.; tr. par le prince A. Galitzin, 1869, *see* RUSSELL (W.)
see TRETYAKOV GALLERY.
Moscrop (Thomas). The kingdom without frontiers: a missionary survey. 8°. [1910]
Moseley (Sydney Alexander). The convict of to-day. s8°. [1927]
The much chosen race! s8°. [1922]
Mosellanus (Petrus). Narr. de disput. Lipsiensi 1519, *see* MELANCHTHON (P.) Vita M. Lutheri, ed. 2^a, 1746.
Strena Lips. vel eulogium Lutheri Lipsia-papisticum. Studio J. Forsteri. [P2629]. s4°. Witebergae. 1609
Tabulae de schematibus & tropis P. M. Item. Rhetorices P. Melanchthonis tabulae. Item. Libelli Erasmi de duplici copia scilicet rerum & verborum, tabulae. s8°. Norimbergae, *Ioh. Petreius.* [c. 1527]
Moser (G.) De impedimentis matrimonii—Coll. declar. ac decret. Rom. pontif. c. varia dubia matrimon. concern., *see* MIGNE (J. P.), *ed.* Theol. cursus, t25, 1860.
Moser (Johann Jacob). Von d. teutschen Religions-Verfassung &c. s4°. Franckfurt. 1774
see CORPUS. *Corpus juris Evang. eccl. &c.; mit e. Vorrede J. J. M., 1737–38.
Moser (*General* **Otto v.**)
Feldzugsaufzeichnungen, 1914–18. 8°. St. 1920
Preparation & conduct of tactical rides & tours on the ground. Tr. by the Gen. Staff, War Office. 8°. 1911
Moses, *of Choren.*
[*Works* (Hist., Geog. &c.) *in Armenian*]. 2nd ed. 8°. i Venetik. 1865
[Armenian hist. *In Armenian. Ed.* Kh. Dz. Stephane. Notes *w. sep. pagin.*] s8°. S. Peterbourg. 1889
Hist. d'Arménie. Texte & tr. fr. par P. E. Le Vaillant de Florival. 2t *in* 1v. 8°. Venise. 1841
[Hist. of the Armenians. *In Armenian. Ed.* M. Abelean & S. Harouthiunean. (Historians of Arm.; ed. St. Malkhasean, v2i)]. la8°. Tiflis. 1913
see AUCHER (P.) Anc. weights &c. *by* Epiphanius, M. &c., *in Armenian*, 1821.
„ CARRIÈRE (A.) Abgar leg. in M.'s Hist.; tr. *into Arm.*, 1897.
„ —— M. & les généal. patriarcales, 1891.
„ —— Nouv. sources de M., 1893.
„ KHALATHEAN (G.) M., *in Arm.*, 1898.
„ MACLER (F.) M. & les travaux d'A. Carrière, 1902.
„ MARQUART (J.) Ērānšahr nach d. Geog. v. M., *w. text & tr.*, 1901.
„ MARR (N. YA.) О начальной ист. Арменіи Анонима, объ источн. ист. М. Х., *n.d.*
„ SARGISEAN (B.) Hist. of Sylvester & sources of M. (*in Arm.*), 1893.
Moses, *ben Joseph Kimchi.* Ὁδοιπορία ad scientiam &c. Item introd. D. Binjamin f. D. Judae; annot. illust. authore C. L'Empereur. [*Hebr. & Lat.*] s8°. Lugd. Batav., *Elzevir.* 1631
Moses, *Kalankatouatzi* [MOSES CALANKAT; MOSES, *of Uti*]. [Hist. of the Armeno-Albanians. Ed. M. Emin. *In Armenian*]. 8°. Moskva. 1860
„ „ [*a. ed.* Galérie hist. arm. *Ed.* G. V. Chahnazarian]. 2v. s8°. Paris. 1860
see MANANDIAN (Y.) Beitr. z. alban. Gesch. (M. d. Utier), 1897.
Moses, *the Lawgiver.*
see ASATIR (THE): Samaritan bk. of the "Secrets of Moses & story of the death of M.; intr., tr. &c. by M. Gaster, 1927.
„ COLLATIO. Lex Dei sive Mosaic. & Rom. legum collatio, *var. ed.*
„ MAIMONIDES. Reasons of the laws of M.; f. the "More Nevochim" of M., 1827.
„ MICHAELIS (J. D.) Abhandlung v. d. Ehegesetzen M., 1768.
„ OOSTERZEE (J. J. VAN). M.: a biblical study; tr., 1876.
„ SCHUMANN (G. A.) Vita M., p1, De infantia M., 1826.
Moses, *ben Nachman.* Disput. R. Mosis Nachmanidis cum Fr. Paulo [*Hebr. & Lat.*], *see* WAGENSEIL (J. C.) Tela ignea Satanae &c., 1681.
Moses, *Xorenaci, see* MOSES, *of Choren.*

Moses (Bernard). The intellect. background of the Revol. in S. Amer., 1810–24. [Hisp. Soc. of Amer.] s8°. N.Y. 1926
Spain's declining power in South America, 1730–1806. 8°. Berkeley, 1919
Spanish colonial lit. in S. America. [Hisp. Soc. of Amer.] s8°. N.Y. 1922
Moses (Robert). The Civil Service of Gt. Brit. 8°. N.Y., *Columbia Univ.* 1914
Moses (William Stainton).
Spirit teachings. Memorial ed. 8°. 1898
Mosheim (Johann Lorenz von).
De auctoritate Concilii Dordraceni paci sacra noxia. Ed. 3ª corr. [P2643]. s4°. Helmstadii. 1726
De Beghardis & Beguinabus comm. Ed. G. H. Martini. 8°. Lipsiae. 1790
De poenis haereticorum cum S. Iavorskio disput. s4°. Helmstadii. 1731
Diss. ad hist. eccl. pertin. Ed. 3ª acc. & emend. 2v. s8°. Altonae. 1767
An eccl. hist., antient & mod. to the beg. of the pres. century. Tr., w. notes, by A. Maclaine. n. ed. 6v [v6 *wanting*]. 8°. 1790
Elementa theologiae dogmaticae. Ed. 3ª rev. &c. a C. E. de Windheim. 2v. s4°. Norimbergae. 1781
Erzählung d. neuesten chines. Kirchengesch. s8°. Rostock. 1748
Institutes of eccl. hist. Tr. w. notes by J. Murdock & H. Soames. Ed. & brought down to pres. time by W. Stubbs. 3v. 8°. 1863
Versuch e. unpart. u. gründl. Ketzergesch. s4°. Helmstaedt. 1746
Vindiciae antiquae Christian. disciplinae adv. J. Tolandi Nazarenum. De vita, fatis & scriptis J. Tolandi comm., praef. praemisit J. F. Buddeus. Ed. 2ª auct. 2p *in* 1v. s8°. Hamburgi. 1722
—— & J. M. Gesner. Epistolae amoebææ. Ed. C. A. Klotz. s8°. Lipsiae. 1770
Moskovsky Armyansky Laz. Inst. Vost. Yazikov, *see* LAZAREVSKY INST. VOST. YAZIKOV.
Moskovsky Glavnii Arkhiv. М. Г. Архивъ Мин. иностранн. дѣлъ. (Виды Архива &c.) Изд. Комм. печатанія Государств. Грамотъ &c. fol. Москва. 1898
Moskovsky Pushkinist. М. П. 1, 1837–1927. Статьи и материалы под ред. М. Цявловского. s8°. Москва. 1927
Moslem (The) world to-day; by var. wr., 1925, *see* MOTT (J. R.), *ed.*
Mosler (Alexander). In d. Sturmtagen d. russ. Revolution. Meine Befreiung. s8°. 1918
Mosley (*Sir* **Oswald**), *2nd bart.*
Hist. of Castle &c. of Tutbury. 8°. 1832
Mosnier (Léonard), *see* MONIER (L.)
Moss (Geoffrey). Defeat. s8°. 1924
New wine. s8°. [1927]
Sweet pepper. s8°. [1923]
Whipped cream. s8°. [1926]
Moss (*Rev.* **Lemuel**).
Annals of the U.S. Xtn. Commission. la8°. Phila. 1868
Moss (Richard Waddy). The range of Christian experience. Fernley Lect. 8°. 1898
Moss (Rosalind). The life after death in Oceania & the Malay Archipelago. 8°. 1925
Mosse (Rudolf), *publisher.* Almanach, 1921. 8°. [1920]
Mosso (Angelo). La necropoli di Molfetta, *see* REALE ACCAD. D. LINCEI. Mon. ant., v20, 1910.
Villaggi preist. di Caldare e Cannatello pr. Girgenti, *see* REALE ACCAD. D. LINCEI. Mon. ant., v18, 1907.
Mossom (Robert), *bp. of Derry.* The preacher's tripartite in 3 bks. [*sep. pagin^s.*] 3v. fol. 1657
*Sion's prospect in its first view. By a minister of Christ &c., R. M. 8°. 1653
Most (Johann Joseph), *see* ROCKER (R.) J. M.: Leben e. Rebellen, 1924.
Mostaert, *The family of, see* PIERRON (S.) Les M., 1912.
Mostaert (Franz), *1525–56, see* PIERRON (S.) Les Mostaert, 1912.
Mostaert (Gilles), *1525–1601, see* PIERRON (S.) Les Mostaert, 1912.
Mostaert (Jan), *dit le maitre d'Oultremont: 1499–1555, see* PIERRON (S.) Les M., 1912.
Mostyn (Llewellyn Nevill Vaughan Lloyd-Mostyn, *3rd baron*). Cat. of illumin. & o. MSS. Sold by Sotheby, 13 July 1920. [*b. w. h.* Cat. of pr. bks., 1920]. la8°. 1920
Cat. of pr. books the prop. of Lord M. Sold by Sotheby, April 16, 1920. [*Illust.*] la8°. 1920
Mostyn (*Admiral* **Savage**). Minutes of a Court-Martial, [1745] enq. into conduct of commanders of Hampton Court & Dreadnought [*i.e. M. & T. Fowke*]. [P2778]. 8°. 1745

Moszkowski (Alexander). Der Abbau d. "Unendlich." [Beil. zu H1, 2 d. Archivs f. system. Phil., B19. Bibl. f. Phil., B27]. 8°. 1925
Einstein: Einblicke in s. Gedankenwelt. 8°. Hamburg. 1921
Einstein the searcher, h. work explained f. dialogues w. Einstein. Tr. by H. L. Brose. 8°. [1921]
Moszkowski (Max). Auf neuen Wegen durch Sumatra. Forschungsreisen, 1907. 8°. 1909
***Mot** (Un) sur la philippique de Chateaubriand, 1818, *see* CHATEAUBRIAND (F. R. DE).
Motenebbi, *see* AḤMAD IBN ḤUSAIN (ABŪ AL-JAIYIB), *al-M.*
Mothersole (Jessie).
Agricola's road into Scotland. s8°. [1927]
Czechoslovakia. 8°. [1926]
Hadrian's Wall. s8°. 1922
In Roman Scotland. s8°. [1927]
The Saxon Shore. 8°. [1924]
Motherwell (William).
Poems, narrative & lyrical. s8°. Glasgow. 1832
Motion. *An humble motion unto hir maiesties privie counsell &c., 1590, *see* PENRY (J.)
Motivi. Мотивы орнаментовъ (12–17 c.), в1, *see* STROGANOVSKOE TSENTRALN. UCHILISCHE.
Motley (John Lothrop). Rise of the Dutch Republic. [Everyman's Lib.] 3v. s8°. [1906]
Motokiyo (Se-ami). Oimatsu—Atsumori—Ohara go kô—Aya no tsuzumi [*attr. to M.*], *see* PERI (N.) Cinq Nô, tr., 1921.
Mott (*Sir* **Frederick Walker**). Alcohol & its rel. to prob. in mental disorders, *see* STARLING (E. H.) Act. of alcohol on man, 1923.
The brain & the voice in speech & song. s8°. 1910
Mott (John Raleigh). The Moslem world to-day. [*By var. wr.*] Ed., w. foreword by J. R. M. s8°. [1925]
Mott (Lewis Freeman). Ernest Renan. s8°. N.Y. 1921
Motta (Luigi).
Flames on the Bosphorus. Tr. H. Zimmern. s8°. [1920]
Mottaz (Eugène). Dict. hist., géogr. & statist. du Canton de Vaud. 2v. la8°. Lausanne. 1914–21
Mottini (G. Edoardo). La pittura ital., da Leonardo al Tiepolo. 8°. Milano. 1927
Mottram (Ralph Hale).
The crime at Vanderlynden's. s8°. 1926
Our Mr. Dormer. 8°. 1927
Sixty-four, ninety-four! s8°. 1925
The Spanish farm. Pref. by J. Galsworthy. s8°. 1924
The Spanish farm trilogy, 1914–18. [*Cont.* The Spanish farm—Sixty-four, ninety-four!—The crime at Vanderlynden's &c.] [repr.] s8°. [1927]
Mouchanoff (Marie v.) [*geb. Gräfin* NESSELRODE, *aft.* M. v. KALERGIS, *aft.* M. v. M.], *see* PHOTIADÈS (C.) La "Symphonie en blanc majeur": M. K., 1822–74, 1924.
Mouchembert (*le sieur* **de**). Essais polit. & militaires. s8°. 1627
Mouëtte (Germain). Travels in Fez & Morocco, *see* STEVENS (J.) New coll. of voyages &c., v2, 1711.
Mouffle d'Angerville (—). Private life of Louis XV. Annot &c. by A. Meyrac. Tr. H. S. Mingard. 8°. [1924
Vie privée de Louis XV. Publ. & annotée par A. Meyrac repr. 8°. 192
Mouhib, *see* MUHIBB.
Mouhy (Charles de Fieux, *chevalier* **de)** [†FIEUX (CH. DE), *chev. de Mouhy*]. *Mém. d'Anne Marie de Moras, Ctsse. de Courbon. 4p [*in* 2v]. s8°. La Haye. 174
Moule (Handley Carr Glyn), *bp. of Durham.*
Outlines of Christian doctrine. s8°. 189
" " .... revised. s8°. 189
see HARFORD (J. B.) & F. C. MACDONALD. H. C. G. M.: biog., 1922.
" RIDLEY (N.) Brief declar. of the Lord's Supper; repr., w intr. & life by H. C. G. M., 1895.
Moule (Henry Joseph).
Dorchester antiquities. s8°. Dorchester. 190
Moule (Thomas), *see* WINKLES (B.) & H. WINKLES. Architect &c. illust. of cathedral churches &c. of Eng. &c., w. descr. by T. M., 3v, 1836–42.
Moulin (Alfred). L'Afrique à travers les âges. [Chap. complém.: La Guerre mondiale en Afr.] 8°. [1920
Moulin (Stéphane). La carrière d'un marin au 18s.: Josep de Flotte (1734–92). la8°. Gap. 192
Moult (Thomas). The comely lass. s8°. 192
Snow over Elden. s8°. 192
see SPENCER (W. T.) Forty years in my bookshop, ed., w intr., by T. M., 1923.

Moulton (Harold Glenn).
Principles of banking. 3rd impr. 8°. Chicago. [1921]
Principles of money & banking. 4th impr. 8°. Chicago. [1920]
The War & indust. readjustments. [P2465]. 8°. Chicago. [1918]
see BASS (J. F.) & H. G. M. America & balance sheet of Europe, 1922.
—— **& C. Lewis.** The French debt problem. s8°. N.Y. 1925
—— **& C. E. McGuire.** Germany's capacity to pay: st. of the reparation problem. s8°. 1923
Moulton (Hugh Fletcher). The life of Ld. Moulton. Pref. by the Earl of Birkenhead. 8°. [1922]
see MORRISON (S.) Trial of Steinie Morrison, ed. by H. F. M., 1922.
Moulton (James Hope). A grammar of N.T. Greek. v2, Accidence & word-formation, p2, Accidence. Ed. W. F. Howard. [*pagin. cont.*] 8°. E. 1920
—— **& G. Milligan.** The vocab. of the Greek Test. p4–6 [*by* G. M. *only*]. 4°. 1920–26
Moulton (John Fletcher Moulton, *1st baron*).
Address at St Mary's Hospital. [P2566]. 8°. 1911
Address, Liverpool Board of Legal Studies. [P2566]. 8°. 1912
The aim of techn. educ. Address. [P2566]. 8°. 1911
The Chinese labour ordinance. Speech. [P2566]. 8°. 1904
Evidence before R. Comm. on vivisection, July 1907. [P2566]. 8°. 1907
Government by cabinet; speeches by J. F. M., H. J. Tennant &c. [P2566]. s8°. 1905
The House of Lords, a plea for deliberation &c. Repr. f. Contemp. Rev. [P2566]. 8°. *n.d.*
Law & manners. Address. [P2566]. 8°. 1912
Old-age pensions. [Repr. f. Fortnightly Rev. P2566]. 8°. 1892
The training &c. of the chemical engineer. Lect. [P2566]. 8°. 1920
The trend of invention in chemical industry. [P2566]. 8°. 1904
see MOULTON (H. F.) Life of Ld. M., 1922.
Moulton (Richard Green).
Shakespeare as a dramatic thinker. 8°. N.Y. 1924
see BIBLE: COMPL. TEXTS. Mod. reader's (The) Bible; ed. w. intr. & notes by R. G. M., 1910; repr., 1912.
Moulton (William Fiddian).
The hist. of the English Bible. 2nd ed. rev. s8°. [1884]
The Methodist comm. on the New Test. 2nd ed. s8°. 1894
Mounier (Jean Joseph), *d. 1806.* Recherches sur les causes qui ont empêché les François de devenir libres &c. 2t [*in* 1v]. 8°. Genève. 1792
Mounin (Abraham), *see* BOUCHET (J.) Annales d'Aquitaine &c. augm. de pièces rec. par A. M., 1644.
Mount (Hilda Lucy Adelaide, *Lady*), *wife of Sir W. A. Mount, Bt., see* LOW (H. L. A.)
Mountain craft; ed. G. W. Y., 1920, *see* YOUNG (G. W.)
Mountain (Jacob Henry Brooke).
Summary of the writings of Lactantius. 8°. 1839
Mountaine (Dydymus), *ps., see* HILL (T.)
Mount Cashell (Stephen, *2nd earl*), *see* WILMOT (C.) An Irish peer on the Continent, 1801–3: narr. of tour of S., 2nd Earl Mt. C. thr. France &c., 1920.
Mount Edgcumbe (Ernest Augustus Edgcumbe, *3rd earl of*).
Extracts f. a journal kept dur. revol. at Palermo, 1848. 2nd ed. 8°. 1850
Extracts f. journal kept dur. the Roman revol. [*b. w. h.* Extr. &c. 1850]. 2nd ed. 8°. 1849
Mount Everest Expedition.
see BRUCE (*Brig.-Gen. Hon.* C. G.) Assault on Mt. E., 1922; by C. G. B. & o. members of the Exped., 1923.
„ HOWARD-BURY (*Lt.-Col.* C. K.) Mount Everest: the reconnaissance, 1921; by C. K. H.-B. & o. members of the Mt. E. Exped., 1922.
Mount-Stephen (George Stephen, *1st Baron*). Cat. of mod. pictures &c. property of Ld. Mt.-S., S. H. Day &c., sold by Christie, May 19, 1922. [*Illust.*] 8°. [1922]
Mouravit (Gustave).
Peiresc le lettré &c. Conf. [P2833]. 8°. Aix-en-Prov. 1896
Mouret (Félix), *see* CORPUS vasorum antiq.: France, fasc. 6, Coll. Mouret (fouilles d'Ensérune), 1927.
Mourey (Gabriel).
Essai sur l'art décoratif français mod. 4e éd. 8°. 1921
Mourj [MOURTCH] [*monthly magazine in Armenian*].
Dec. 1892–Dec. 1894 [in 2v. Oct. 1894 *wanting*]. la8°. Tiflis. 1892–94
Mousley (Edward Opotiki). An Empire view of the Empire tangle. Pref. by Rt. Hon. W. F. Massey. s8°. 1921
The secrets of a Kuttite. Story of Kut &c. s8°. 1921

Mousset (Albert).
L'Espagne dans la polit. mondiale. 8°. 1923
La Petite Entente. Préf. de J. Brunhes. 3e éd. s8°. 1923
Un témoin ignoré de la Révol. Le Cte. de Fernan Nuñez, ambass. d'Esp. à Paris, 1787–91. 8°. 1924
Moussorgsky (Modeste Petrovich). Boris Godounov. A national music drama. n. ed. rev. &c. by N. Rimsky-Korsakov. Eng. tr. by R. Newmarch. [P2420]. s8°. 1908
see RIESEMANN (O. v.) Monogr. z. russ. Musik, B2, 1926.
Moustafa, *see* MUSTAFA.
Mouttet (Alexandre), *see* TAMIZEY DE LARROQUE (P.) & A. M. Autour de Peiresc, 1898.
Mouvement pacifiste (Le), 1912–19, *see* PEACE MOVEMENT (THE).
Mowat (John Lancaster Gough). *Notes on the Oxfordshire Domesday. [Signed J. L. G. M.] 8°. O. 1892
Mowat (Robert Balmain).
The diplomacy of Napoleon. 8°. 1924
Diplom. rel. of Gt. Brit. & the U.S. 8°. 1925
Hist. of European diplomacy, 1815–1914. 8°. 1922
Hist. of Europ. diplomacy, 1914–25. 8°. 1927
New hist. of Gt. Brit. s8°. 1923
see OAKES (*Sir* A. H.) & R. B. M. Gt. Europ. treaties of the 19th c.; ed. Sir A. O. & R. B. M., 1921.
„ PLUNKET (I. L.) & R. B. M. Hist. of Europe, E. & the mod. world, 1492–1914, by R. B. M., 1927.
Mowbray (Lawrence), *of Leeds.*
Narr. conc. the bloody popish conspiracy. [P525]. sm. fol. 1679
Mowinckel (Sigmund). Psalmenstudien. 1, Åwän u. d. individuellen Klagepsalmen. 2, Das Thronbesteigungsfest Jahwäs u. d. Ursprung d. Eschatologie. [Videnskapsselskapets Skrifter]. [2v]. la8°. Kristiana. 1922
Mowrer (Ernest R.) Family disorganiz.: intr. to a sociolog. analysis. [Univ. of Chicago]. 8°. Chicago. [1927]
Moxon (Joseph). A tutor to astronomy & geography &c. 5th ed. corr. & enl. 8°. 1699
Moxon (Reginald Stewart). The doctrine of sin. 8°. [1922]
Moya (Matthæus de) [*ps.* GUIMENIUS (AMADEUS)]. Opusculum, singularia theologiæ moralis complectens, adv. quorundam expost. contra Jesuit. opiniones. ed. noviss. corr. &c. s8°. Coloniae Agrippinæ. 1665
see PARIS: UNIV. Censura Facult. theolog. Paris. in lib. A. G., 1666.
Mozarabic Breviary. Liturgia Mozarabica: tractatus, doc. &c., 1740, *see* PINIUS (J.)
Missa Gothica seù M. &c. explan. ad usum Mozárabum Sacelli Toleti á Card. Ximenio erecti &c. fol. Angelopoli. 1770
see MEYER (W.) Preces d. mozarab. Liturgie, 1917.
„ SCHIAPARELLI (L.) Note paleog.: Data e proven. d. cod. 89 d. Bibl. Capit. di Verona (l'Orazionale M.), 1924.
Mozart (J. C. Wolfgang Amadeus).
Chefs d'œuvre: pianoforte works ed. C. Potter, No. 3, p2; 18, p1; 37; 42 [*& o. wks., var. ed.*] [*b. w.* Beethoven (L. v.) Rondo, Andante &c.] 4°. London. *n.d.*
Lettres. Tr. avec. intr. & notes par H. de Curzon. 8°. 1888
see CORBETT-SMITH (A.) Nat. opera hdbks., 5, 6 (Magic flute, Marriage of Figaro), 1922.
„ HUSSEY (D.) W. A. M., 1928.
see JAHN (O.) W. A. M., neubearb. v. H. Abert, 6. A., 2T, 1923.
„ LACH (R.) W. A. M. als Theoretiker, 1918.
„ MARKS (F. H.) The sonata as exemplified in piano s. by M., 1922.
„ PROCHÁZKA (R., *Frhr.* v.) M. in Prag, 1892.
„ PROD'HOMME (J.-G.) M., rac. par ceux qui l'ont vu (1756–91), 1928.
Mozelius (Fridericus). Diss. de relig. armorum apud Suio-Gothos. Praes. J. Ihre. [P2743]. s4°. Stockholmiae. [1752]
Mozley (Francis Woodgate). The Psalter of the Church: Septuagint Psalms compared w. Hebrew &c. s8°. C. 1905
Mozley (John Kenneth). The impassibility of God: survey of Xtn. thought. s8°. C. 1926
Mr. *Mr. Buchanan's admin. on eve of the Revol., 1866, *see* BUCHANAN (J.)
*Mr. Wesley's dangerous tenets exposed, *n.d.*, *see* WESLEY (J.)
Msereantz (Grigor). [Records of the lives & works of members of the Lazarev family. *In Armenian.* 3p *in* 1v]. la8°. i Moskoua. 1856
Msereantz (Levon). [Armenian dialectology. Tr. *into Armenian* by G. Menevishean. P2814]. s8°. Vienna. 1899
Армянская діалектологія. Рѣчь. Отт. изъ Этногр. обозрѣнія, кн. 36. [P2813]. 8°. Москва. 1898
Къ интерпрет. ванск. надписей. [*Extr.* P2813]. 8°. *n.p. n.d.*

Msereantz (Levon) [*continued*].
Этюды по армянской діалектологіи. ч1, Мушск. діал. &c. [& Дополненія &c. *w. sep. pagin.* Изъ Учен. Зап. Имп. Моск. Унив., в24. P2813]. 8°. Москва. 1897

Msereantz (Mser), *magistros.* [Hist. of the patriarchs of Echmiadzin, 1763–1831. *In Armenian*]. 8°. i Moskoua. 1876
[The last hours of czar Nicholas I. *In Armenian*]. 8°. i Moskoua. 1855

Mtusu (Daniel), *see* FRASER (D.) Autobiog. of an African, D. M.; retold by D. F., 1925.

Mu'allakāt [MOALLAKAT; MO'ALLAGĀT], *see* JONES (*Sir* W.) Works, v4, The Moallakat, *text & tr.*, 1799.

Much (Rudolf). Der Name Germanen, 1920, *see* KAIS. AKAD. D. WISS. ZU WIEN. Sitzungsber., B195, 1923.

Mücke (Johann Heinrich) & G. L. Pflaum. Diss. hist. de tribus capitulis Co. Calchedon. s4°. Lipsiae. [1766]

Muckle (Friedrich).
Das Kulturideal d. Sozialismus. 8°. München. 1919

Muddiman (Henry), *1629–92, see* MUDDIMAN (J. G.) The King's journalist [*i.e.* H. M.], 1659–89, 1923.

Muddiman (J. G.) The King's journalist [*i.e.* H. Muddiman], 1659–89: st. in reign of Charles II. 8°. 1923

Mudge (Isadore Gilbert). New guide to reference books. Based on 3rd ed. of Guide to study &c. of ref. bks. by A. B. Kroeger as rev. by I. G. M. [Amer. Lib. Assoc.] 8°. Chicago. 1923
—— **& M. E. Sears.** A George Eliot dictionary. 8°. 1924

Mudge (*Col.* William), *F.R.S.* Acc. of operations for accompl. a trigonometrical survey of England & Wales, 1784[–1809]. Rev. f. Philos. Trans. [of Roy. Society]. 3v. 4°. 1799–1811
1, 1784–96; by M. & I. Dalby. 2, 1797–99; by M. *only.* 3, 1800–09; by M. & T. Colby.

Mudgett (Herman Webster), *see* HOLMES (H. H.)

Mudie (Robert). *Hist. acc. of H.M.'s [*i.e.* George IV] visit to Scotland. 8°. E. 1822

Mudrony (Soma). A vámkérdés megoldása. [P2393]. 8°. 1896

Muel (Léon). Gouvernements, ministères & constit. de la Fr., 1789–1895. D'ap. les doc. offic. Préf. de E. Boulanger. 5e éd. rev. [*3 pagins.*] 8°. 1895

Muelverstedt (Georg Adalbert v.), *see* MÜLVERSTEDT (G. A. v.)

Mufaḍḍal ibn Muḥammad, *al-Ḍabbī.* The Mufaḍḍalīyāt. Anthology of anc. Arabian odes comp. by Al-M., acc. to recension & w. comm. of Abū Muḥammad al-Qāsim ibn Muḥammad al-Anbārī. Ed. C. J. Lyall. 2v. 4°. O. 1918–21

Mufazzal ibn Abū al-Fazaïl [MOUFAZZAL IBN ABIL-FAZAÏL]. Hist. des sultans mamlouks; texte arabe publ. & tr. par E. Blochet, p2, *see* GRAFFIN (R.) & F. NAU. Pat. Or., t14, 1920.

Mugford (W. E.), *see* DEVONSHIRE. Abstracts of the exist. transcr. of the lost parish-reg. of Devon, 1596–1644; by R. Granville & W. E. M., v1, 1908.

Mügge (Maximilian A.) The War diary of a square peg. With a dict. of War words. 8°. 1920

Muggenthaler (Hans). Kolonis. & wirtschaftl. Tätigkeit e. deut. Zisterzienklosters im 12. u. 13. Jhdt. 8°. München. 1924

Muggleton (Lodowick). M.'s last will & testament. With his bounty to Oliver's porter &c. [P2434]. s8°. *pr. for D. M.* 167?
see REEVE (J.) & L. M. A list of books &c., 1843.

Muggletonians. *True (A) representation of the absurd &c. principles of the M., 1694, *see* WILLIAMS (J.), *bp. of Chichester.*

Mugna (Antonio).
La chiesa. Conferenze nel 1870. 8°. Rovigo. 1887

Mugnone, *see* FAYTINELLI (P. DE').

Muḥammad, *the Prophet.*
see AMEER ALI, *Seyd.* Spirit of Islam, w. life, 1922.
,, KORAN. The life of M.; w. the Alcoran; tr., 1718.
,, LIU CHAI-LIEN. Arabian prophet: life of M. fr. Chinese & Arabic sources; tr. I. Mason, 1921.
,, MUḤAMMAD 'ALĪ, *Maulvi.* Muhammad the Prophet, 1924.
,, PRIDEAUX (H.) The true nature of imposture in life of M., 1697; 1718.

Muḥammad Abduh, *Sheikh.* Rissalat al Tawhid: exposé de la relig. musulmane. Tr., avec intr. sur la vie &c. du Cheikh M. par B. Michel &c. 8°. 1925

Muḥammad 'Alī, *pasha of Egypt, see* DRIAULT (E.) M. A. & Napoléon, 1807–14 &c., 1925.

Muḥammad 'Alī, *Maulvi.*
Muhammad the Prophet. s8°. Lahore. [1924]

Muḥammad al-Qâdirî [ABÛ 'ABDALLAH MUḤAMMAD IBN AL-ṬAYYIB]. Nachr al-Mathânî; tr. de A. Graulle, E. Michaux-Bellaire &c., 2t, *see* MISSION SCIENT. DU MAROC. Arch. maroc., t21, 24, 1913–17.

Muḥammad 'Awfī, *see* NICHOLSON (R. A.) St. in Islamic poetry [Lubábu 'l-Albáb: early Persian anthology; *by* M. A. &c.], 1921.

Muḥammad bin 'Abdulla Hassan, *mullah of Somaliland, see* JARDINE (D.) The Mad Mullah of Somaliland, 1923.

Muhammad Hayat Khan, *Malik, see* PUNJAB: GOVT. PUBL. Customary law of Pakpattan & Dipalpur Tahsils of the Montgomery District; comp. by M., 1925.

Muḥammad ibn Aḥmad ibn Iyās, *al-Miṣri.* Account of the Ottoman conquest of Egypt in year A.H. 922 (1516). Tr. f. 3rd vol. of the Arabic chron. of M. by W. H. Salmon. [Orient. Trans. Fund, N.S., v25]. 8°. 1921

Muḥammad ibn 'Alī ibn Misbāh, *see* IBN 'ASKAR.

Muhammad ibn eš-Šāfi 'i, *see* FUDĀLĪ.

Muḥammad ibn Mūsā, *al-Ḥwārizmi, see* MŽIK (H. v.) Afrika, n. d. arab. Bearb. d. Ptolemaeus v. M. ibn M. al-H., 1916.

Muḥammad ibn Sirin, *al-Basri* [AḤMAD IBN SIRIN]. Achmetis Oneirocriticon. Rec. F. Drexl. [Bibl. Teubner.] s8°. Lipsiae. 1925

Muhammad Ibrahim, *see* FLEISCHER (H. L.) Gramm. d. pers. Spr.; nach Mirza M. I.'s Gramm., 1875.

Muhammad Shafi (M.), *see* SHAFI (M. M.)

Muhammedanus precans, 1666, *see* HENNINGSEN (H.)

Muḥibb, *Efendi* [MOUHIB], *see* BAREILLES (B.) Un Turc à Paris 1806–11; voyage &c. de M., 1920.

Muhle (Hendrich) [MUHLIUS (HENRICUS)].
Diss. hist. theologicae &c. s4°. Kiliae. 1715

Muhleman (Maurice Louis).
Monetary systems of the world. rev. ed. s8°. N.Y. 1897

Mühlmann (Carl). Der Kampf um die Dardanellen, 1915. Bearb. C. M. [Schlachten d. Weltkrieges, B16]. 8°. Oldenburg. 1927

Muilenburg (James). Embassy of E. van Weede, Ld. of Dykvelt, to England in 1687, *see* NEBRASKA UNIV. Studies, v20, 1920.

Muinuddin Nadwi, *Maulavi, see* BANKIPORE. Cat. of Arabic & Pers. MSS. in Or. Publ. Lib. at B.; v12, by M. M. N., 1927.

Muir (Dorothy). Hist. of Milan under the Visconti. 8°. [1924]

Muir (Edwin). Latitudes. 8°. [1924]
The marionette. 8°. 1927

Muir (G.), *publisher.*
Muir's Malta almanack & directory, 1855. s8°. [Malta. 1854]

Muir (James Hamilton).
Glasgow in 1901. Illust. by M. Bone. s8°. Glasgow. 1901

Muir (John), *D.C.L.* *Index to Muir's Sanskrit texts, pl, 2. Comp. by G. B. 8°. 1861

Muir (Ramsay).
America the golden. 8°. 1927
The expansion of Europe. 3rd ed. 8°. 1922
Liberalism & industry. s8°. 1920
Politics & progress: survey. s8°. [1923]
A short hist. of the British Commonwealth. 2v. 8°. 1920–22
,, ,, 2nd ed. v1. 8°. 1922
Trade unionism & the Trade Union Bill. With app. on legal pos. of T. unions by W. A. Jowitt &c. s8°. [1927]
see EUROPA YEAR BOOK; ed. R. M. &c., 1926 &c.
,, PHILIPS' *publishing firm.* New histor. atlas for students; intr. &c. by R. M., 1920.

Muir (*Sir* Richard D.), *Public Prosecutor, see* FELSTEAD (S. T.) Sir R. M.: a mem., 1927.

Muirchu, *Maccu Mactheni, see* PATRICK, *St.* Writings & life [*by* M.; ed. &c.] N. J. D. White, 1920.

Muirhead (Findlay).
Belgium & the Western front, Brit. & Amer. s8°. 1920
England. Ed. F. M. 2nd ed. 2nd impr. s8°. 1924
—— **& M. Monmarché.**
Brittany. Ed. F. M. & M. M. s8°. 1925
North-East. France. Ed. F. M. & M. M. s8°. 1922

Muirhead (John Henry). Contemp. Brit. philosophy. Personal statements by J. B. Baillie, B. Bosanquet, J. Ward &c. Ed. J. H. M. s1, 2. 8°. 1924–25
see JONES (H.) & J. H. M. Life & philos. of E. Caird, 1921.

Mukerji (Dhan Gopal). My brother's face. 8°. [1925]

Mukerji (Radhakamud). Local government in anc. India. Foreword by Marq. of Crewe. [Mysore Univ.] 2nd ed. rev. & enl. 8°. O. 1920
Men & thought in anc. India. [Lucknow Univ.] s8°. 1924
The rural economy of India. 8°. 1926

Mukherji (Panchanandas). Co-operative movt. in India. Foreword by J. T. Donovan. 3rd ed. re-wr. & enl. 8°. Calcutta. 1923

Mula (*card.* **Marco Antonio da**), *1505–1570.* Orazione latina d. M. A. da M. ambasc. a Pio IV. Pubbl. & in ital. rid. [Nozze Mula-Bentivoglio di Aragona. N129]. 8°. Venezia. 1846

Mulai Ahmed el Raisuni, *see* RAISUNI, *El.*

Mulcaster (Richard), *c. 1532–1611.*
Elementarie [1582]. Ed. E. T. Campagnac. 8°. O. 1925

Mulertt (Werner). Azorín (José Martínez Ruiz), z. Kenntnis span. Schr. 8°. Halle (Saale). 1926

Mülertz (Andreas Faaborg). De causis propagatae celeriter in Dania reformationis. Diss. s8°. Havniae. 1817

Mulford (Prentice), *1834–91.* The gift of the spirit: sel. f. essays of P. M. Pref. & intr. by A. E. Waite. [2nd rev. ed.] s8°. [1903]
„ „ .... s8°. 1905
The gift of understanding: essays. Intr. by A. E. Waite. 8°. 1907

Mulgan (Alan E.) Home. A New Zealander's adventure. Pref. note by J. C. Squire. 8°. 1927
see SHRIMPTON (A. W.) & A. E. M. Maori & Pakeha, 1921.

Mulholland (Rosa), *aft. Lady Gilbert, wife of Sir John T. Gilbert, see* DUBLIN. Cal. of anc. records; ed. Lady G., v14–18, 1909–22.

Mülinen (E., Graf von). Beiträge z. Kenntnis d. Karmels. [Sep. aus d. Z. d. Deut. Palästina-Vereins, B30–31]. 8°. L. 1908

Mulinen (W. Frédéric de).
Hist. de Berne, 1191–1891. 8°. Berne. 1891

Mullens (Joseph). Ten years missionary labour in India, 1852–61. 8°. 1863

Mullens (William Herbert) & H. Kirke Swann. Bibliog. of Brit. ornithology. Suppl. Chronolog. list of Brit. birds, by H. K. S. 8°. 1923
—— —— **& F. C. R. Jourdain.** Geograph. bibliog. of Brit. ornithology to end of 1918. Arr. under counties. 8°. 1920

Müller (Adam Lebrecht). Gradus damnationis aeternae, d. i. Deutl. Untersuchung &c. Tractat P. J. Spener Von d. Ursachen d. Verdammniss. [*b. w. h.* Gradus vitae aeternae, 1733]. s8°. Jena. 1735
Gradus vitæ æternæ od. Deutl. Untersuchung &c. s8°. Jena. 1733

Müller (Adolf). Leben d. Erasmus v. Rotterdam. Mit. einl. Betracht. 8°. Hamburg. 1828

Müller (Andreas), *of Greiffenhagen, see* 'ABD ALLAH IBN 'UMAR IBN MUḤAMMAD IBN 'ALĪ, *al Baidhāwī.* Hist. Sinensis ed., Lat. reddita a A. M. &c., 1689.

Muller (August). De Hermannis eruditione & virtute claris comm. in hon. J. G. Hermanni. [P596]. s4°. Vitembergae. 1746

Müller (Balthasar). Das LXIII Capit. d. Propheten Esaiæ in 5 Predigten einfeltig erkleret. s4°. Eissleben. 1604

Müller (Carl), *b. 1852, prof. in (1) Breslau, (2) Tübingen.*
Beitr. z. Gesch. d. Verfassung d. alt. Kirche, *see* KÖNIGL. PREUSS. AKAD. D. WISS. Abhdl. (Phil.-hist. Klasse), 1922.
Luthers Äusserungen ü. d. Recht d. bewaffn. Widerstands gegen d. Kaiser, *see* KÖNIGL. AKAD. D. WISS. ZU MÜNCHEN. Phil. Klasse, Sitz., 1915.

Müller (Caspar Jacob). De convers. Pomeranorum. Praes. F. Wokenio. [P2646]. s4°. Lipsiae. [1726]

Müller (David). De quarta bestia Danielis, cap. 7, diss. [P483]. s4°. Tubingae. 1617

Müller (David), *historian.* Gesch. d. deut. Volkes. 20e verb. A., besorgt v. R. Lange. 8°. 1910

Müller (David Heinrich). Südarab. Alterthümer im Kunsthistor. Hofmuseum. Hrsg. M. fol. Wien. 1899

Müller (Erich), *see* LESKOV (N. S.) Am Ende d. Welt, nebst e. Biog. L.'s v. E. M., 1927.

Müller (Ferdinand), *of St. Petersburg.* Unter Tungusen u. Jakuten. Erlebnisse &c. d. Olenék-Exped. d. K. Russ. Geog. Gesells. 8°. L. 1882

Muller (Frederik). Cat. diss. & orationum juridic., 1600–1866, in acad. Neerlandiae, Germaniae & Sueciae, venales apud F. M. 8°. Amstelodami. 1867
Cat. diss. & orationum theologic. ab a. 1650 ad 1850 in acad. Neerlandiae, Germaniae, Sueciae &c. coll. a F. M. Acc. 2 indices. Cur. J. G. van Slee. 8°. Amstelodami. 1867

Müller (Friedrich), *Gymnasiallehrer in Schässburg.* Siebenbürg. Sagen. Gesammelt &c. v. F. M. 8°. Kronstadt. 1857

Müller (Friedrich), *Postmeister.* Grosses deutsches Ortsbuch. 3e umgearb. A. la8°. Barmen. 1926

Müller (Friedrich), *prof., of Vienna.*
Beitr. z. Conjug. d. armen. Verbums. [P2792]. 8°. Wien. 1863
Urspr. d. gruzin. Schr. [*a. c. in* P2807]. 8°. Wien. 1897
see BASMADJIAN (K. J.) [F. M.: obit. not., *in Armenian*], 1898.

Müller (Friedrich W.) Die anthropolog. Ergebnisse d. vorgeschichtl. Gräberfeldes v. Abusir el-Meleq. [Deut. Orient-Gesell., Wiss. Veröffentl., 27]. fol. L. 1915

Müller (Friedrich Wilhelm Karl), *of Berlin.* Uigurica, 3, Uigur. Avadāna—Bruchstücke (1–8), 1922, *see* KÖNIGL. PREUSS. AKAD. Abhandl., Phil.-hist. Klasse, 1920.
2 Pfahlinschr. aus d. Turfanfunden, *see* KÖNIGL. PREUSS. AKAD. D. WISS. Abhdl., Phil.-hist. Klasse, 1915.

Müller (Fritz), *1875–.*
Kramer & Friemann. Eine Lehrzeit. s8°. Hamburg. [1919]

Müller (Georg). Eine Predigt, v. d. zweien Sacramenten, d. Osterlam im Alten: u. heil. Abendtmal im N. Test. [P2613]. s4°. Jhena. 1590

Müller (Gerhard Friedrich). Извѣстія о запорожск. Козакахъ. [*Extr. f.* Соч., 1760. *b. w. h.* О началѣ &c. Козаковъ, 1760]. s8°. *n.p.* [1760]
„ „ *For Germ. ed.* Nachr. v. d. Caporog. Cosacken, *see* †MÜLLER (G. F.) Samml., B4, 1760.
О началѣ &c. Козаковъ. [*Tr. f.* Gottsched's Das Neueste &c. *Extr. f.* Соч., 1760]. s8°. *n.p.* [1760]
„ „ *For Germ. ed.* Von d. Urspr. d. Cosacken, *see* †MÜLLER (G. F.) Samml., B4, 1760.
Lebensbeschr. d. Gen.-Feldm. Graf B. P. Scheremetew, mit Erläut. ü. d. Gesch. Peters d. Gr. Übers. v. H. L. C. Bacmeister. 8°. St. Petersburg. 1789

Müller (Giuseppe), *ingegnere.* Idrografia dei porti di Lido &c. [*Map*]. fol. Venezia. 1874

Müller (Giuseppe), *prof. at Turin, see* MÜLLER (JOSEPH).

Müller (Gottlieb). Schediasma: efficaciam precum haud esse praedeterminatam. [*b. w.* Baier (J. W.) Compend., 1750]. s8°. Vitembergae. 1747

Müller (Gustav Adolf). Brennende Welten. Roman aus d. Zeit d. Völkerkriegs. s8°. L. [1916]

Muller (Hendrik), *van Zutphen* [MOLLER (H.)], *see* IKEN (J. F.) Heinrich v. Zütphen, 1886.

Müller (Henry R.) The Whig party in Pennsylvania. [Columbia Univ.] 8°. N.Y. 1922

Müller (Hermann Fr.) Dionysios, Proklos, Plotinos: hist. Beitr. z. neuplaton. Philos. [Beitr. z. Gesch. d. Philos. d. M.-a., B20, iii–iv]. 8°. Münster i. W. 1918

Müller (Iwan E. P. v.) Hdbch. d. Altertumswissenschaft. In neuer Bearb. hrsg. v. W. Otto.
B1vii, 3, Abt. 1i, 5, Abt. 1i, 9, Abt. 2ii. 8°. München. 1923–28
see HOMMEL (F.) Ethnol. u. Geog. d. alt. Orients, H2, 1926. [III, 1, i.]
„ KUBITSCHEK (W.) Grundriss d. ant. Zeitrechnung, 1928. [1vii.]
„ MANITIUS (M.) Gesch. d. lat. Lit. d. Ma., T2, 1923. [9, 2ii.]
„ WINDELBAND (W.) Gesch. d. abendländ. Philos. im Altertum, 4e A., bearbt. v. A. Goedeckemeyer, 1923. [5, 1i.]

Müller (Jacob S. Worm-), *see* WORM-MÜLLER (J. S.)

Muller (James Arthur).
Stephen Gardiner & the Tudor reaction. 8°. [1926]

Müller (Joannes) *otherwise* LANDTSPERGER. Ain Sendbrieff: an alle Regiment d. Teütscher Nacion, &c. s4°. [1526]

Müller (Johan Bernard). Les mœurs & usages des Ostiackes, *see* BERNARD (J. F.), *ed.* Recueil de voy., t8, 1727.

Müller (Johann Conrad). Ueb. d. Gesch. u. d. Lehrbegrif d. protest. Religionspartheyen u. Sekten. s8°. Breslau. 1789

Müller (Johann Georg), *Dotensis-Misnicus.* Disput. de Eccl. Maronitarum. [P2644]. s4°. Jenae. [1668]

Muller (Johann Gottfried). De lingua August. Confess. authentica &c. [P2642]. s4°. Jenae. [1748]

Muller (Johann Paul). Diss. qua J. Kaufmanni vita & merita percensentur. Praes. G. G. Zeltnero. [P597]. s4°. Altdorfi. [1722]

Müller (Johann Stephan). Introd. in theologiam revelatam usu philos. Dariesianae adornata. s8°. Francofurti. 1770

Müller (Johann Tobias D. I. P.) Die symbol. Bücher d. evangel.-luther. Kirche, deutsch u. latein. 3e durchgesch. A. 8°. St. 1868

Müller (Joseph), *prof. at Univ. of Turin.* Doc. conc. la vita pubbl. di G. Morone, *see* REGIA DEP. DI STORIA PATRIA. Misc., t3, 1865.

Müller (Lydia). Der Kommunismus d. mähr. Wiedertäufer. [V. f. Ref.-gesch. Jahr. 45, H1 (Nr. 142)]. 8°. L. 1927

Müller (Moritz). Über d. " Weisheit letzten Schluss ! " [P2476]. 8°. 1886
Müller (Nikolaus). Georg Schwartzerdt, d. Bruder Melanchthons. Festschrift. [Verein f. Reformationsgesch., Jhrg. 25 (Nr. 96/97)]. 8°. L. 1908
Müller (P. E.) Bidrag til d. jydske Hedesletters Naturhist. [*w. résumé in French*], *see* KONG. DAN. VID. SELSK. Biol. Medd., 4, 1923–25.
Müller (Peter), *Jurisconsult.*
De numo confessionario. ed. 6a. [P2638]. s4°. Jenæ. 1693
De osculo sancto comm. [P2633]. s4°. Jenæ. 1718
Müller (Philipp), *see* AUGSBURG CONFESSION. Concordia &c. ed. a P. M., 1705.
Muller (Pieter Lodewijk). Gesch. van onzen tijd sedert 1848. 3d. 8°. Haarlem. 1903–21
Muller (Samuel), *archivaris v. Utrecht, see* UTRECHT. Registers & rekeningen v. Bisdom Utrecht; uitg. door S. M., 2d, 1889–91.
——, **J. A. Feith & R. Fruin.** Handleiding voor het ordenen en beschrijven van archieven. [Vereen. v. Archivarissen]. 2e dr. la8°. Groningen. 1920
Müller (Sophus). Bronzealderens kunst i Danmark. Udg. paa Carlsberg Fondets bekostning. Intr. & sommaire en Français. fol. Kjøbenhavn. 1921
Müller (Venanz).
Die Lüge vom Hohenzollernsegen. 8°. Diessen. 1920
Müller (Walter) & F. Ölmann. Die " geometrische " Nekropole, *see* KAISERL. DEUT. ARCH. INST. ATHEN. ABTHLG. Tiryns, B1, 1912.
Müller (Wilhelm), *of Dessau; 1794–1827.* Gedichte. Vollständige krit. A., mit Einleit. &c.; besorgt v. J. T. Hatfield. s8°. *n.d.*
Müller (Wilhelm), *praeceptor in Weinsberg.*
Gesch. Württembergs. s8°. St. 1862
Müller (Wilhelm Max), *Ph.D., 1862–1919.* Egyptian mythology. [*Re-issue of the Egypt. part of v12 of* Mythology of all races]. 8°. [1924]
Egyptolog. researches. [C.I. of Wash.] [v1], 3. 4°. Wash. 1906–20
1, Results of a journey in 1904.
3, Bilingual decrees of Philae.
Müller-Freienfels (Richard).
Philos. der Individualität. 2e durchges. A. 8°. L. 1923
Psychologie d. deut. Menschen u. s. Kultur. 8°. München. 1922
Müller-Guttenbrunn (Adam), *see* GRUBER (F. E.) A. M.-G., der Erzschwab, 1921.
Müller-Löbnitz (Wilhelm). Die Sendung d. Oberstleutn. Hentsch, 8–10 Sept. 1914. 2e A. 8°. 1922
Müller-Lyer (Franz). Phasen d. Liebe: e. Sociologie d. Verhältnisses d. Geschlechter. [2e A.] 8°. München. 1921
Hist. of social development. Tr. E. C. Lake &c. Intr. by L. T. Hobhouse &c. 8°. [1920]
Müller-Meiningen-Hof (Ernst H.) Das deut. Urheber- u. Verlagsrecht. 2B. s8°. München. 1901–7
Müller-Reinhard (J.), *see* AVERDUNK (H.) & J. M.-R. G. Mercator u. d. Geogr. unter s. Nachkommen, 1914.
Mullerus (Vitus).
Disput. de religione Christiana. s4°. Tubingæ. 1586
Mullick (Gosto Behary). Lord Northbrook & h. mission in India. Lect. rev. & enl. 8°. Calcutta. 1873
Mulliner (*Col.* H. H.) Cat. of coll. of old Eng. furniture, tapestry &c., sold by Christie &c., July 10, 1924. [*Illust.*] 8°. 1924
Cat. of coll. of old Eng. silver &c. of the 17th & 18th cents., sold by Christie &c., July 9, 1924. [*Illust.*] 8°. 1924
see LOUISE VICTORIA ALEX. DAGMAR, *pcss. royal.* Cat. of pictures &c.; also pictures &c., prop. of M., 1924.
„ TOWNSHEND PAPERS. Cat. of pr. bks. &c., Eng. bookbindings prop. of M. &c., 1924.
Mullins (Claud).
The Leipzig trials. Intr. by Sir E. Pollock. 8°. 1921
London's story. s8°. 1920
Mulot (R.) John Knox, 1505–72. [Verein f. Ref.-gesch. Schr., Jhrg. 22, Nr. 84]. 8°. Halle a. d. S. 1904
Mulready (William). *Hist. of Kirkstall Abbey, w. engravings f. orig. drawings by W. M. &c. 8°. 1847
Multatuli, *ps., see* DEKKER (E. D.)
Multscher (Hans), *see* GERSTENBERG (K.) H. M., 1928.
Mulvany (William Thomas), *1806–85, see* BLÖMERS (K.) W. T. M., 1922.

Mülverstedt (Georg Adalbert v.) [MUELVERSTEDT], *see* SIBMACHER (J.), *ed.* J. S.'s gr. Wappenbuch, B1–7, 1856–1912, *list of contents for var. parts* bearbt. v. G. A. v. M.
Mumby (Frank Arthur). The fall of Mary Stuart: narr. in contemp. letters. 8°. 1921
George III & the American Revolution: the beginning. 8°. 1924
Mumford (Edith E. Read). Dawn of character in the mind of the child. n. & rev. ed. s8°. 1925
Mumford (James).
The Catholic Scripturist. 4th ed. corr. s8°. *n.p.* 1767
Mumford (Lewis). Story of utopias: ideal commonwealths & social myths. Intr. by H. W. van Loon. 8°. [1923]
„ „ ....[2nd printing]. 8°. N.Y. [1923]
Mun (*cte.* Adrien Albert Marie de) [MUN (ALBERT DE)].
Combats d'hier & d'aujourd'hui. 6s. & suppl. to s1 (1900–14). [s1, 3, 2e éd.; s2, 3e éd.] s8°. [1910–16]
Mun (Thomas). England's treasure by forraign trade. [Repr. f. ed. of 1664]. 8°. O. 1928
Munby (*Lt.-Col.* Joseph Ernest), *C.M.G.* A hist. of the 38th (Welsh) Division. By the G.S.O's. I of the Div. Ed. J. E. M. s8°. 1920
Munch (Andreas). Digte, gamle og nye. s8°. Christiania. 1848
Munch (P.) Les origines & l'œuvre de la Soc. des Nations. [*By var. wr.*] t1, 2. la8°. Copenhague. 1923–24
Munch (Peder Andreas). Pavelige nuntiers regnskabs-og dagbøger, førte under tiende-opkraevningen i Norden 1282–1334. Med Anhang &c. [Norske Hist. K.] 8°. 1864
München.
Aktenstücke d. Ordinariates d. Erzbisthums M. u. Freising betreff. d. allgem. Vatic. Conc., B1, 1871, *see* VATICAN COUNCIL.
Illust. Katalog d. K. Glyptothek zu M. Von P. Wolters. s8°. München. 1912
Miniaturen aus Hss. d. Kgl. [Bayer.] Hof- u. Staatsbibl. in M. Hrsg. G. Leidinger. H3–8. fol. München. 1913–24
3, Turnierbuch Herzog Wilhelms IV v. Bayern.
4, Drei armen. Min.-Hss. (cod. arm. 1, 6 u. 8); erläut. v. E. Gratzl.
5, Perikopenbuch Kaiser Heinrichs II.
6, Evangeliarium aus d. Domschatze zu Bamberg.
7, Gebetbuch d. Herzogin Sibylla v. Cleve; erläut. v. H. Reiners.
8, Regensburg-Prüfeninger Buchmalerei d. 12. u. 13. Jhdts.; dargest. v. A. Boeckler.
Das Miniaturen Kabinett d. M. Residenz. Vorwort u. krit. Kat. v. H. Buchheit u. R. Oldenbourg. fol. München. 1921
Mittelalt. Hss. d. K. Bayer. Nationalmus., v. P. Lehmann, *see* KÖNIGL. AKAD. D. WISS. ZU MÜNCHEN. Phil. Kl., Sitz., 1916.
Münchner (Das) Spiel v. 1510, *see* BOLTE (J.) 3 Schauspiele, 1927.
Prozesse (Die) d. Geiselmordes im Luitpold-Gymn. in M. vor d. Volksgericht, 1920, *see* PROZESSE.
see SACHS (C.) Musikinstrumente Birmas &c. im K. Ethnogr. Mus., 1917.
„ SCHERMAN (L.) Z. altchines. Plastik, Neuzugänge im M. Ethnogr. Museum, 1915.
Munchmeier (Tobias Dieterich). Hist. saec. 2. fabulis variorum maculata. Praes. J. A. Schmid. [P432]. s4°. Helmstadii. [1706]
Muncker (Franz). Anschauungen v. engl. Staat u. Volk i. d. deut. Lit., T1, 2, *see* KÖNIGL. AKAD. D. W. ZU MÜNCHEN. Phil. Kl., Sitz., 1918 & 1925.
Neue Lessing-Funde, *see* KÖNIGL. AKAD. D. W. ZU MÜNCHEN. Phil. Kl., Sitz., 1915.
Munday (Anthony). Fidele & Fortunio, comedy (1584); *ed.* F. Flügge, *see* ARCHIV. F. D. ST. D. NEU. SPR., B123, 1909.
John a Kent & John a Cumber. [Prep. by M. St. C. Byrne & ed. W. W. Greg. Malone Soc. repr.] s4°. 1923
Mundinus [MONDINO *da Luzzi*]. Anathomia, 1316; tr., *see* FASCICULO di med., *ed.* C. Singer, 1925.
Mundy (Godfrey Basil). Life of Rodney. n. ed. s8°. 1836
Mundy (Matthew), *see* ROSE-TROUP (F.) Rev. M. M., 1–4, 1894.
Mundy (Peter). Travels in Europe & Asia, 1608–67. Ed. Sir R. C. Temple. [Hakluyt Soc. II, 55]. v4. 8°. 1925
4, Travels in Europe, 1639–47.
Mundy (Talbot). The ivory trail. s8°. 1920
Om. s8°. [1925]
Ramsden. s8°. [1926]
Municipal handbook of city of Auckland, 1922, *see* AUCKLAND.
Munier-Jolain (J.) Le cardinal Collier [Rohan] & Marie-Antoinette. Éd. augm., préc. d'une vie de l'abbé Georgel, avec pages de s. méms. Préf. de M. Henri-Robert. 8°. 1927

Munitions, Ministry of. History of the M. of M. 8v. 8°. 1920–22
1, Indust. mobilisation, 1914–15. 2, General organisation &c. 3, Finance & contracts. 4, Supply & control of labour, 1915–16. 5, Wages & welfare. 6, Man power & dilution. 7, Control of materials. 8, Control of indust. capacity & equipment.

Münnich (*Count* **Burkhard Christoph v.**), *Fieldmarshal; 1683–1767* [†MUENNICH].
see HALEM (G. A. v.) Vie du comte de M., tr., 1807.
„ HEMPEL (C. F.) Leben &c., 1742.

Muñoz (Antonio). Carlo Maderno: 35 riprod. con testo e cat. a cura di A. M. 8°. [1921]
Francesco Borromini; 30 riprod. con testo e catalogo. 8°. [1921]
G. L. Bernini. 8°. [1925]
Pietro da Cortona; 32 riprod. con testo e catalogo. 8°. [1921]

Muñoz (Francisco Lozano), *see* LOZANO MUÑOZ (F.)

Muñoz (Manuel Henao y), *see* HENAO Y MUÑOZ (M.)

Muñoz y Gaviria (José). Islas de Fernando Poo, Corisco y Annobon, 1871, *see* ESPAÑA. Crón. gen., v12, 1865 &c.

Muñoz y Romero (Tomás). Dicc. bibliog.-hist. de los ant. reinos, prov., ciudades, villas &c. de España. la8°. 1858

Munro, *The family of, see* ROSS (A.) Hist. sk. of anc. Ross-shire fam.: M. of Culcairn &c., 1884.

Munro (Dana Gardner). The five Republics of C. America. Ed. D. Kinley. [C.E. for Internat. Peace]. la8°. N.Y. 1918

Munro (Hector Hugh) [*ps.* "SAKI"]. Beasts & super-beasts. Intr. by H. W. Nevinson. [coll. ed.] s8°. [1926]
The chronicles of Clovis. Intr. by A. A. Milne. [coll. ed.] s8°. [1926]
The square egg & o. sketches, w. 3 plays. With a biog. by h. sister. 8°. [1924]
The unbearable Bassington. Intr. by M. Baring. [coll. ed.] s8°. [1926]

Munro (Hugh Andrew Johnstone), *fellow of Trin. Coll., Cambridge, see* LUCRETIUS. De rerum nat.; notes & tr. by M., 4th ed. rev., v2, Explan. notes, 1928.

Munro (Innes). A narr. of the milit. oper. on the Coromandel Coast agst. the French, Dutch & Hyder Ally Cawn, 1780–84 &c. 4°. 1789

Munro (James). A Gaelic primer &c. s8°. Glasgow. 1828

Munro (Robert). Prehist. Britain. s8°. [1919]

Munro (William Bennett).
The gov. of American cities. 3rd ed. 8°. N.Y. 1923
The gov. of European cities. 8°. N.Y. 1919
Governments of Europe. [repr.] 8°. N.Y. 1926

Munsell (Joel). Chronology of paper & papermaking. 8°. Albany [N.Y.] 1857

Munster. Munster. [*By var. wr.*], 1921, *see* FLETCHER (G.), *ed.*

Munster (George FitzClarence, *1st earl of*). Camp. of 1809 in Portugal, *see* COOKE (J.) Mem. of the late war &c., v2, 1831.
Letter from Toulon. [*Repr. f.* U. Service journal, June 1830]. *no tp.* 8°. [1830]

Munster (Sebastian).
see BIBLE: MATTHEW. Evang. sec. M. in ling. Hebr. & annot. S. M., 1557.
„ ELIJAH, *ben Asher, the Levite.* Gramm. Hebraea per S. M. versa & illust., 1543.

Münsterberg (Hugo). Die Willenshandlung: e. Beitrag z. physiolog. Psychologie. 8°. Freiburg i. B. 1888
see MÜNSTERBERG (M.) H. M., h. life & work, 1922.

Münsterberg (Margaret).
Hugo Münsterberg, h. life & work. 8°. N.Y. 1922

Muntaner (Ramon). Chronicle. Tr. f. Catalan by Lady Goodenough. [Hakluyt Soc., s2, 47, 50]. 2v. 8°. 1920–21
Crónica. Pref. per J. Coroleu. 8°. Barcelona. 1886
see RAHOLA (C.) En R. M.: l'home—la crónica, 1922.

Muntz (William James Stephens). Rome, St. Paul & the early church: infl. of Roman law &c. s8°. 1913

Munyay (Lajos). *Hist. Eccl. Evang. August. Confess. addictorum in Hungaria, praecipue in 13 oppidis Scepusii. 8°. Halberstadt. 1830

Münz (I.) Die jüd. Ärzte im Mittelalter. 8°. Frankfurt a. M. 1922

Münz (Sigmund). Weltkongress u. Weltgericht. Appell an d. hohen Geister aller Völker. s8°. Wien. 1919

Münzer (Friedrich).
Römische Adelsparteien u. Adelsfamilien. 8°. St. 1920

Münzer (Hieronymus) [MONETARIUS (H.)] Itinerarium Hispanicum, 1494–95, *see* REVUE HISPAN., t48, 1920.

Münzer (Thomas).
see AURBACH (C. W.) Diss. de eloquentia inepta T. M., 1716.
„ BLOCH (E.) T. M. als Theologe d. Revolution, 1921.
„ KIESSLING (G. N.) Th. M. doctr. & facta &c., 1708.
„ ZIMMERMANN (J.) T. M., 1925.

Murad (Friedrich). Ararat u. Masis. Stud. z. armen. Altertumskunde u. Litt. [P2808 & P2811]. 8°. Heidelberg. 1901

Murasaki (*Lady*) [FUJIWARA (MURASAKI)].
The tale of Genji. Tr. A. Waley. [p1–4]. 8°. [1925–28]
2, The sacred tree. 3, A wreath of cloud. 4, Blue trousers.

Murashû *Sons, of Nippur, 464–404 B.C.* Business doc. of M. S. dated in reign of Darius II. [Ed. w. pref.] by A. T. Clay. [Univ. of Pa.] 4°. Phila. 1912

Murat (Amélie). Bucoliques d'été. s8°. 1920

Murat (Caroline), *queen of Naples; 1782–1839, see* MASSON (F.) Revue d'ombres: près de la Psse. Caroline, 1803–5 &c., 1921.

Murat (Joachim), *king of Naples.* Lettres & doc. pour servir à l'hist. de M., 1767–1815. Publ. par le prince Murat, avec intr. & notes par P. Le Brethon. t8. 8°. 1914
see MASSON (F.) Revue d'ombres: dern. jours de M., mai–oct. 1815 &c., 1921.
„ REBOUL (F.) Campagne de 1813, t1, Commandement de M., déc. 1812–jan. 1813, 1910.

Murat (*princesse* **Lucien**). Vie amoureuse de la Grande Catherine de Russie. s8°. [1927]

Muratori (Giovanni Francesco). Iscrizioni romane dei Vagienni, *see* REGIA DEP. DI STORIA PATRIA. Misc., t8, 1869.

Muratori (Ludovico Antonio) [*ps.* VALDESIO (FERDINANDO)].
Annali d'Italia sino all' anno MDCCL. Colle pref. critiche di G. Catalani.
ed. 2ª Romana. 12t [*each in 2p*]. 8°. Roma. 1786–88
„ „ Cont. sino ai giorni nostri dall 'A. G. O. V. [*i.e.* Giuseppe Oggeri Vincenti].
ed. prima. t13–15 [*each in 2p*]. 8°. Roma. 1789–90
„ „ Tavole cronologiche &c. 8°. Roma. 1786
De corona ferrea, qua Rom. imperatores in Insubribus coronari solent, comm. [*b. w.* Fontanus (J.) De corona ferrea &c., 1719]. s8°. Mediolani. 1719
De ingeniorum moderatione in relig. negotio &c.
ed. 3ª Veneta castig. s4°. Venetiis. 1741
De Paradiso, non expectata corporum resurrectione justis a Deo conlata, adv. T. Burneti librum De statu mortuorum. 4°. Veronae. 1738
De superstitione vitanda sive censura voti sanguinarii in honorem Immaculatae Conceptionis Deiparae emissi. [*b. w. h.* De ingen. moderatione, 1741]. ed. 2ª. s4°. Mediolani. 1742
Diss. sopra le Antichità Italiane. Comp. e tr. nell' Ital. favella. Opera postuma, data in luce d. G. F. Soli Muratori. 3ª ed. 3t [*each in 2p*]. 8°. Roma. 1790
Epistolario, 1691–[1750]. Ed. &c. da M. Campori. 14[t. *pagin. cont.*] la8°. Modena. 1901–22
F. Valdesii epistolae, sive app. ad librum A. Lampridii De superstitione vitanda &c. [*b. w. h.* De ingen. moderatione, 1741]. s4°. Mediolani. 1743
Lettere ined.; *ed.* A. Ceruti *&* G. Biadego, *see* REGIA DEP. Misc., t8, 18, 28, 1869–90.
Relation des missions du Paraguai. [Tr. *Added* Lettres de G. Cattaneo. *pagin. cont.*] s8°. 1754
A rel. of the missions of Paraguay. Tr. [*w.* Letters of C. Cattaneo on h. voy. f. Cadiz to Paraguay (1729–30) &c.] s8°. 1754
Rerum Italicarum Scriptores. Indice sistem. d. Cronache astesi (Muratori, R.I.S., XI) di Oggero Alfieri, G. e S. Ventura, comp. da C. Merkel &c., *see* REGIA DEP.: Misc., t23, App., 1884.
„ „ Indice sistem. d. Hist. rerum in Italia gest. (Muratori, R.I.S., IX) di Ferreto de' Ferreti, comp. da G. Filippi &c., *see* REGIA DEP.: Misc., t23, App., 1884.
„ „ Indices chronolog.; scr. J. Calligaris, J. Filippi, C. Merkel; operis moderamen sibi suscep. C. Cipolla, A. Manno, *see* REGIA DEP.: Misc., t24, App., 1885.
„ „ 500–1500. n. ed., riv., ampliata e corr. con la dir. di G. Carducci e V. Fiorini. t2i, 8iii, v, 11v, 13i, iii, 15v, 17i, 19iii, 24iii, v, vi, 28iii.
4°. Città di Castello. 1905–27
Aretino (L.) Hist. Florent. pop. & Rerum suo temp. gest. comm. [19iii.]
Azzurrinio (B.) Chronica breviora aliaque mon. faventina; a A. B. coll. [28iii.]
Cataluccio (M. di). Ricordi (1422–58). [15v.]

Muratori (Ludovico Antonio) [*continued*].
Rerum Ital. Scriptores [*cont.*]
Chronicon. C. marchiae Tarvisinae et Lombardiae, 1207–70. [8iii.]
Confortus, *de Custodia*. Framm. di storia vicentina, 1371–87. [13i.]
Gatari (G. & B.) Cronaca carrarese, 1318–1407. [17i.]
Manenti (C.) Estr. d. Historie (1325–76). [15v.]
Manenti (L. di Domenico). Cronaca (1174–1413). [15v.]
Montemarte (F. di). Cronaca (1333–1400). [15v.]
Neocastro (B. de). Hist. Sicula, 1250–93. [13iii.]
Nicolaus, *Smeregus*. Annales civitatis Vincentiae, 1200–1312. [8v.]
Petri (A.) Il diario romano, 1404–17. [24v.]
Pistoia. Storie Pistoresi [Annales P.], 1300–48; a cura di S. A. Barbi. [11v.]
Priuli (G.) I diarii, 1494–1512, v1. [24iii.]
Silvestro (T. di). Diario (1482–1514). [15v.]
Subiaco. Chron. Sublacense, 593–1369; a cura di R. Morghen. [24vi.]
Urbevetanæ. Ephemerides Urbevetanæ dal Cod. Vaticano Urbinate 1745 (1342–69), v1. [15v.]
Verona. Veronae rythmica descr. [2i.]

Muratov (Pavel Pavlovich).
Древне-русская иконопись въ собранiи И. С. Остроухова. — 4°. Москва. 1914
Les icones russes. la8°. [1927]
Морали. Рассказы. s8°. Берлин. 1923
Эгерiя. Романъ. s8°. Берлинъ. 1922

Muraviev (*Count* Mikhail Nikolaevich), *see* Chukovsky (K.) Поэт и палач (Некрасов и М.), 1922.

Murch (Jerome).
Biograph. sketches of Bath celebrities &c. 8°. 1893

Murchison (Carl). Case for & agst. psychical belief. By Sir O. Lodge, Sir A. C. Doyle &c. Ed. C. M. 8°. Worcester, *Mass.* 1927

Murchison (Claudius Temple).
Resale price maintenance. 8°. N.Y., *Columbia Univ.* 1919

Murdoch (Alexander).
Ochiltree, its hist. & remin. s8°. Paisley. [1921]

Murdoch (James), *M.A.* Hist. of Japan. v3, The Tokugawa epoch, 1652–1868. Rev. & ed. J. H. Longford. la8°. 1926

Murdoch (Walter). Alfred Deakin: a sketch. 8°. 1923

Murdock (Kenneth Ballard). Handkerchiefs f. Paul: verses of Puritan Massachusetts. By B. Tompson, J. Wilson &c., w. o. poems by S. Torrey &c. Repr. Ed. &c. K. B. M. 8°. Camb., *Mass.* 1927
Increase Mather, the foremost Amer. Puritan. 8°. Cambridge [*Mass.*] 1925
Portraits of Increase Mather, w. notes on T. Johnson. la8°. *f.p. distr.* Cleveland. 1924

Muret (Edward) & D. H. Sanders. Encyclopædie Eng.-Germ. & Germ.-Eng. dict. [Toussaint-Langenscheidt Method]. abrdg. ed. [*2nd tp. in Germ.*] 2p. la8°. [1913]
1, Eng.-Germ. by B. Klatt, rev. by E. Klatt.
2, Germ.-Eng., n. ed. by H. Baumann.

Muret (Maurice).
L'évolution belliqueuse de Guillaume II. s8°. 1917
La littérature allemande pend. la Guerre. s8°. 1920

Murgoci (G. M.) La population de la Bessarabie. Préf. par Em. de Martonne. [P2464]. 8°. 1920

Murgotten (Francis Clark), *see* Aḥmad ibn Yaḥyā, *al Balādurī*. Origins of the Islamic state; tr., w. notes by F. C. M., p2, 1924.

Muriel (Domingo). Hist. del Paraguay, 1747–67. Tr. &c. por P. Hernández. [Los Jesuítas en el Rio de La Plata 1586–1830, 2]. s8°. 1918

Murillo (Bartolomé Estéban).
see Alfonso (L.) M., el hombre &c., 1886.
„ Williamson (G. C.) M., 1902.

Murko (Matthias).
Works in Kaiserl. Akad. d. Wiss. zu Wien. Sitzungsber.
Bericht ü. e. Reise z. Studium d. Volksepik in Bosnien u. Herzegowina, 1913, 1915. [176.]
Bericht, Volksepik d. bosn. Mohammedaner, 1913. [173.]
37. Mitt. d. Phonogramm-Archivs-Komm.; Bericht ü. phonogr. Aufnahmen ep. Volkslieder i. mittl. Bosnien u. i. d. Herzegowina, 1915. [179.]

Murlin (John).
Sacred hymns. 3rd ed. s8°. High-Wycombe. 1788

Murner (Thomas), *b. 1475.* De augustiniana hieronymianaꝗ reformatione poetarum. s8°. Argentine. 1509
*Hier vürt angezeigt dz unchristlich frevel, ungelört u. vurecht-lich vss rieffen uñ fürnemen einer loblichen herrschafft von Bern ein disput. zu halten &c. s4°. Luzern. 1528
Schelmenzunst. [*Facs. Ed.* H. Rupé. Schr. z. deut. Lit.; hrsg. G. Müller, B3]. 8°. [Augsburg. 1926]
*Von den fier ketzeren Prediger ordē̃s der observantz zü Bern im Schweytzer land verbrañt, in dē jar noch Christi geburt. M.CCCCC.IX uff dē nechstē donderstag noch Pfingsten. Mit figürlin. 8°. [Strassburg. 1510]
see Baden. Die disputacion vor den xij orten einer lobl. eidtgnoschafft &c., *by T. M.*, 1527.

Murphy (Arthur).
Works in Inchbald (*Mrs.* E.) Brit. theatre, v15, 1808.
All in the wrong. | Know your own mind.
Grecian daughter. | The way to keep him.
The way to keep him. [Dolby's Brit. th.] s8°. 1823

Murphy (*Lieut.-Col.* Charles Cecil Rowe).
Soldiers of the Prophet. 8°. 1921

Murphy (*Mrs.* Claudia Quigley). Coll. of cookery books. Sold, Apr. 19, 1926, Anderson Gall. [P2856]. 8°. N.Y. 1926

Murphy (Gwendolen). A bibliography of Eng. character-books, 1608–1700. [Bibliog. Soc. Suppl. to Trans. N°. 4]. 8°. 1925
A cabinet of characters. Chosen & ed. by G. M. 8°. 1925

Murphy (John), *D.Litt.*
Primitive man: h. essential quest. 8°. O. 1927

Murphy (Robert Cushman). Bird islands of Peru. 8°. N.Y. 1925

Murray, *The family of.*
see Cook (W. B.) M. of Touchadam & Polmaise; genealog. chart, 1907.
„ Mahon (*Maj.-Gen.* R. H.) Life of Hon. J. Murray, w. biog. sketch of fam. of M. of Elibank, 1921.
„ Skeet, *Family of.* Hist. of the families of S. &c., 1906.

Murray (*Hon.* Alexander), *see* Whitehead (P.) *Case of the Hon. A. M., 1751.

Murray (Alex. Stuart), *keeper of Greek & Roman Antiq., B.M.*
Manual of mythology. s8°. 1873

Murray (Andreas), *of Hamburg.* Ex antiq. orientali de Kinaeis. Resp. G. P. Speckio. [P2666]. s4°. Jenae. [1717]

Murray (Andrew), *F.R.I.B.A.* Recent architect. works of the Corp. of London. [*Extr. f.* Public Works. *No tp.*] 4°. *n.p. n.d.*

Murray (*Gen. Sir* Archibald James). Despatches, June 1916–June 1917. [*w.* Maps *in case*]. la8°. 1920

Murray (Arthur Turnour). Fables f. the Russ., Gr., French & Latin. Tr. into Eng. verse by A. T. M. s8°. Aberdeen. 1920

Murray (C. J.), *B.A.*, *see* Clarke (G. H.) & C. J. M. Gram. of the German lang., 1906.

Murray (Caroline), *1750–1831*, [Murray (Marie C.)], *see* Leuridant (F.) Le Pr. de Ligne, Mme. de Staël & C. M., 1920.

Murray (David), *LL.D., F.S.A.Scot.*
The David Elder Infirmary, Govan. la8°. Glasgow. 1927
Early burgh organiz. in Scotland. v1 (Glasgow). 8°. Glasgow. 1924
Evidence reg. Sheriff Court records. 8°. Glasgow. 1926
Lord Kelvin as prof. in the old college of Glasgow. [*Repr. f. h.* Mem. of the old college &c.] 4°. Glasgow. 1924
Scot. local records & rep. of Depart. Comm. of 1925 on Sheriff Court records. 8°. Glasgow. 1927

Murray (David), *Ph.D., LL.D.* Japan. n. ed. rev. by J. H. Longford. s8°. [1920]

Murray (David Christie). Guesses at truths. 8°. 1908

Murray (David Leslie). Disraeli. 8°. 1927

Murray (Douglas Stuart). Notes on the early hist. of Blithfield, *see* Staffordshire. Coll., N.S., v21, 1920.

Murray (*Sir* Evelyn), *see* Murray (*Sir* George E. P.)

Murray (G. Gilbert A.)
The classical trad. in poetry. C. E. Norton Lect. 8°. 1927
Essays & addresses. 8°. [1921]
Five stages of Greek religion. Lect., Columbia Univ., 1912. [2nd ed.] 8°. O. 1925
1st ed. h. title, Four stages of Gr. relig.
Hamlet & Orestes: lect., 1914, *see* Brit. Acad. Proc., 1913–14.
The problem of foreign policy. s8°. 1921
The rise of the Greek epic. 3rd ed. rev. & enl. 8°. O. 1924
Satanism & the world order. [P2486]. s8°. [1920]
The Stoic philosophy. [Conway Lect. 4th impr.] s8°. 1921
see League of Nations. The L. of N.; intr. by G. M., 1920.
„ Livingstone (R. W.), *ed.* Legacy of Greece, essays by M. &c., 1921.

Murray (G. W.) English-Nubian comparative dict. [Harvard Afr. Sts., v4]. 4°. [O.] 1923
Murray (George), *of Magdalen Hall.* Oxford (The) Ars poetica [*attrib. to G. M.*], 1853, *see* GORDON (G.), *ed.* Three Oxf. ironies, 1893.
Murray (*Lord* **George),** *1694–1760, see* DUKE (W.) L. G. M. & the Forty-Five, 1927.
Murray (*Sir* **George Evelyn Pemberton),** *K.C.B.*
The Post Office. 8°. [1927]
Murray (Grace A.), *wife of Keith Murray.*
Personalities of the 18th cent. 8°. 1927
Murray (*Sir* **Hubert),** *K.C.M.G.* Papua of to-day, or an Australian colony in the making. 8°. 1925
Murray (James), *M.A.*
Kilmacolm: a parish hist., 1100–1898. 4°. Paisley. 1898
Murray (*Gen. the Hon.* **James),** *see* MAHON (*Maj.-Gen.* R. H.) Life of Hon. J. M. &c., 1921.
Murray (*Sir* **James),** *b. 1850.* Cat. of pictures &c., property of Sir J. M. Sold by Sotheby. [*Illustr.*] 8°. 1927
Murray (*Sir* **John),** *K.C.B., b. 1841,* **& L. Pullar.** Bathymetrical survey of the Scot. fresh-water lochs, under dir. of M. & P., 1897–1909. Rep. on scient. results.
6v [v4–6, Plates]. 8°. E. 1910
Murray (John Wilson), *b. 1840, see* SPEER (V.) Mems. of a gt. detective, J. W. M., 1904; 1905.
Murray (*Mrs.* **Keith),** *see* MURRAY (GRACE A.), *wife of Keith Murray.*
Murray (*Miss* **Margaret Alice).**
Anc. Egyptian legends. [repr.] s8°. [1927]
Excav. in Malta. With chap. by G. C. Thompson.
2p. la8°. 1923–25
The witch-cult in W. Europe. 8°. O. 1921
see PETRIE (*Sir* W. M. F.), G. BRUNTON & M. A. M. Lahun II, 1923.
Murray (Mungo), *of Edinburgh.* Trial of M. for assaulting T. Sydserf, comedian, 4 & 11 June 1669, *see* ABBOTSFORD CLUB. Misc., v1, 1837.
Murray (Richard), *dean of Ardagh.* Outlines of the hist. of the Cath. Church in Ireland. s8°. 1840
Murray (Robert F.) Poems: w. mem. by A. Lang. s8°. 1894
Murray (Robert Henry). Dublin University & the new world. Memorial disc. 8°. 1921
Hist. of polit. science. 8°. C. 1926
Hist. of the VIII King's Royal Irish Hussars, 1693–1927. Foreword by Sir B. T. Mahon. 2v. la8°. C. 1928
Ireland, 1494–1603, 1603–1714, 1714–1829. [3p in 1v. Helps for students of hist., 33–35]. s8°. 1920
Polit. consequences of the Reformation. 8°. 1926
Science & scientists in the 19th cent. Intr. by Sir O. Lodge. 8°. [1925]
see ANGLICAN essays; by Abp. of Armagh, R. H. M. &c., 1923.
—— **& H. A. Law.** Ireland, *see* BUCHAN (J.), *ed.* Nations, 1924.
Murray (Sinclair). The crucible. s8°. [1925]
Sands of fortune. s8°. 1927
Murray (*maj.* **Stewart L.)** The reality of war: intr. to "Clausewitz." Note by S. Wilkinson. 8°. 1909
Murray (T. C.) Aftermath: play. s8°. D. 1922
Birthright. Play. s8°. D. [1911]
Maurice Harte. Play. s8°. D. 1912
Murray (Thomas), *of Edinburgh, LL.D.* The life of Robert Leighton, abp. of Glasgow. s8°. E. 1828
Murray (William H.), *see* CUMMING (C. F. G.) The inventor of the numeral-type for China [*i.e.* W. H. M.], 1899.
Murray's Handbooks. Algeria & Tunis; by Sir R. L. Playfair. 5th ed. rev. s8°. 1895
India, Burma & Ceylon. 10th ed., repr. s8°. 1920
" " ....12th ed. s8°. 1924
Spain; by R. Ford.
3rd ed. rev. 2p [*in* 4v. *pagin. cont.*] s8°. 1855
Syria & Palestine. Ed. M. Brodrick. rev. ed. s8°. 1903
Murry (John Middleton).
Aspects of literature. 8°. 1920
Countries of the mind. Essays in lit. criticism. 8°. 1922
Discoveries: essays in lit. crit. 8°. [1924]
Keats & Shakespeare: st. of K.'s poetic life f. 1816 to 1820. 8°. 1925
The life of Jesus. 8°. [1926]
" " [2nd impr.] 8°. [1926]
The problem of style. 8°. 1922
The things we are. Novel. 8°. [1922]
To the unknown god. Essays. 8°. [1924]
The voyage. s8°. [1924]
Murry (Katherine Middleton), *née Kathleen Beauchamp, see* MANSFIELD (KATHERINE), *ps.*

Murshidabad. Proc. of Controlling Council of Revenue at M., 27th Sept. 1770–2 Mar. 1774, v1–12, 1919–24, *see* BENGAL: GOVT. PUBL.
Mursinna (Samuel). Primae lineae encyclopaediae theologicae &c.
2t *in* 1v [t1, ed. 2ª auct.] s8°. Halae Magdeburg. 1784–94
Musa (Antonius), *the Roman physician.* De herba vettonica liber, *see* CORPUS medicorum Lat., v4, 1927.
Musa (Antonius) *of Wittenberg.* Singularia de viris eruditione florentibus &c. [*b. w.* Steinhoffer (J. U.) Græcia sacra, 1784]. s8°. Wittebergae. 1778
Musaeus (Joannes), *prof. of theology at Jena.* Collegium controversiarum Becano, Wendelino, Crellio, aliisque Socinianis oppositum. s4°. Jena. 1701
Praelectiones in epitomen Formulae Concordiae &c. s4°. Jenae. 1701
Spinosismus: hoc est tractatus theologico-politicus. s4°. Witebergæ. 1708
Musatti (Eugenio).
La donna in Venezia. 8°. Padova. 1891
Muscio (Bernard). Vocational guidance—Vocational selection, *see* INDUST. FATIGUE RESEARCH BD. Rep. No. 12, 16, 1921–22.
Musco (Angelo), *see* LANZA (A. M.) A. M., 1920.
Musculus (Andreas).
Betbüchlin [*b. w.* Luther (M.) Enchiridion, 1566]. s8°. [1568]
Precationes ex vet. orthodoxis doctoribus; ex eccl. hymnis &c. coll. & rec. & auctæ. s8°. Lipsiae. 1575
Responsio ad virulentum &c. scriptum ex meris calumniis &c. conflatum F. Staphyli, ed. ab A. M. s4°. *n.p.* [1558]
Musculus (Wolfgang).
In ambas ad Corinthios Epist. comm. 2p *in* 1v. fol. Basileae. 1566
In Davidis Psalterium comm. Ed. postrema fol. Basileae. 1599
In Epist. Pauli ad Romanos comm. fol. Basileæ. 1611
In Epist. ad Philippenses, &c. comm. [*b. w. h.* In Cor. comm., 1566]. fol. Basileae. 1565
In Esaiam comm. fol. Basileae. 1570
In Evang. Matthaeum comm. 3t [*in 1v. pagin. cont.*] fol. Basileae. [1551]
" " ....Acc. index. fol. Basileae. 1567
In Genesim Mosis comm. fol. Basileae. [1600]
In Johannis Evangelium comm. [*b. w. h.* In Matthaeum Comm., 1567]. fol. Basileae. 1580
Loci communes theologiae sacrae. Ed. ultima. fol. Basileae. [1599]
see COCHLAEUS (J.) In prim. M. Anticochlaeum replica J. C., 1545.
" —— Sacerdotii ac sacrificii novae legis defensio adv. W. M. Arrosiones, 1544.
Musée Condé, *see* CHANTILLY.
Musée de l'Armée, *Paris, see* PARIS.
Musée des Arts Décoratifs, *Paris.* Expos. d'orfévrerie franç. civile du 16ᵉ siècle au début du 19ᵉ, avr.–mai 1926. s8°. 1926
Cinquante ans de peinture franç., 1875–1925, mai–juillet, 1925. s8°. 1925
Le décor de la vie sous le Second Empire. s8°. 1922
Musée du Jeu de Paume, *see* PARIS: M. DU J. DE P.
Musée Napoléon. Galerie du Musée N., publ. par Filhol, & rédigée par Lavallée [livr. 1–9 *by* Caraffe]. 10t. la8°. 1804–15
t1 *has 2nd tp.* Cours hist. & élém. de peinture.
see †LANDON (C. P.) Annales du musée &c., 1801–15.
" MUSÉE ROYAL DE FRANCE, ou coll. gravée, 1827.
Musée National Suisse, *Zurich, see* ZURICH.
Musée Royal de France. M. R. de F., ou coll. gravée des chefs-d'œ. de peinture & sculpt. dont il s'est enrichi dep. la Restaur. Texte réd. par A. Jal. Publ. Mᵐᵉ Filhol. [*la. paper*]. 4°. 1827
For the coll. to which this is a suppl., see MUSÉE NAPOLÉON.
Musée Royal de La Haye, *see* HAGUE (THE).
Museo Arqueológico, *Madrid.* Falcata Iberica. [Hispanic Soc. of Amer.] [P2699]. la8°. N.Y. *n.d.*
Muséon (Le): études philolog. &c.
nouv. sér., v15, 3ᵉ sér., t1 [=t33], 34–38. 8°. 1914–25
Museo Nazionale [*form.* REAL MUSEO BORBONICO]. Racc. de' monumenti del R. M. B.; publ. da R. Gargiulo. 4°. Napoli. 1825
Museo Nazionale di Palermo, *see* SALINAS (A.) Sigilli di Creta nel M. N. di P., 1883.
Muses library. *The hist. &c. medley: or M. l., 1738, *see* COOPER (E.)
Museu Paulista. Annaes. t1, Commem. do prim. centen. da indep. nac. 8°. São Paulo. 1922

Museul Național de Antichități, *Bucharest, see* BUCHAREST.
Museum.
*Museum Casimirianum &c., p1, 1771, *see* FROMMANN (E. A.), *ed.*
Museum historico-philologico-theologicum, 1728–32, *see* HASE (T.)
Museum of painting &c., drawn & etched by Réveil, v1–6, 1828–30, *see* DUCHESNE (J.)
***Museum Duisburgense.** [*Contin. of* Symbolae litterariae Haganae, *q.v.*] Constructum a. J. P. Berg. s8°. Hagae Com. & Duisburgi. 1782–85
Museum Haganum hist.-philol.-theol. extructum a N. Barkey. 4t. Hagae-Comitum. 1774–80
Museum of Practical Geology & Geological Survey. Guide to the coll. of gemstones: by W. F. P. MacLintock. 8°. 1912
see RUDLER (F. W.) Hdbk. to a coll. of minerals of Brit. Islands, mostly f. Ludlam coll., 1905.
Musgrave (*Sir* Richard). Mem. of the rebellions in Ireland from the arrival of the English &c. 4°. D. 1801
Musgrave (*Sir* William), *bart.* Cat. of coll. of Eng. portraits by an eminent collector [W. M.] Sold by Mr. Richardson, 1800, [*MS. prices*]. 8°. [1800]
Music. Dict. of mod. m. & musicians, 1924, *see* HULL (A. E.), *ed.*
Musical antiquary (The). [Ed. G. E. P. Arkwright]. v1–4 (Oct. 1909–July 1913). [*no more publ.*] la8°. [1910–13]
Musical Society (Internat.) Rep. of the 4th Congress, London, 29 May–3 June 1911. la8°. 1912
Musil (Alois). Arabia Deserta: topog. itinerary. [Amer. Geog. Soc., Oriental explor. &c., No. 2]. la8°. N.Y. 1927
The middle Euphrates: topog. itin. [Amer. Geog. Soc., Oriental explor. &c., 3]. la8°. N.Y. 1927
The Northern Ḥeğâz: topog. itinerary. [Amer. Geog. Soc., Oriental explor. &c., No. 1]. la8°. N.Y. 1926
Musil (Robert).
Die Schwärmer. Schauspiel. s8°. Dresden. [1921]
Muskett (Joseph James), *see* SUFFOLK. S. manorial families; ed. J. J. M. & F. Johnson, v1–3iii, 1900–14.
Musoni (Francesco). Gli Sloveni (Jugoslavi occident.), *see* QUADERNI geograf., N. 10, 1919.
Muspratt (Edmund Knowles). My life & work. 8°. 1917
Mussard (Pierre). *Les conformitez des cérémonies mod. avec les anc. s8°. 1667
Mussatus (Albertinus). Il principato di Giacomo da Carrara primo signore di Padova. [Ed. L. Padrin. Nozze Squarcina-Rossi]. 8°. Padova. 1891
Musset (L. C. Alfred de).
Les caprices de Marianne. 8°. 1906
Comédies & proverbs. 3t. s8°. 1897–1900
La confession d'un enfant du siècle. s8°. *n.d.*
Poésies nouvelles, 1836–52. s8°. Londres. [1913]
Premières poésies, 1829–35. n. éd. s8°. 1865
„ „ . . . . n. éd. s8°. 1867
see MAURRAS (C.) Les amants de Venise, G. Sand & M., 28e éd., *n.d.*
Musset (Louis Alex. Marie de), *marq. de Cogners, see* BOURGOING (*b.* J. F.) & L. A. M. DE M. *Corr. d'un jeune militaire &c., 1778–79.
Mussio (Giovanni).
F. Meda, un giornalista ministro. la8°. Milano. 1919
Musso (Cornelio), *bp. of* (1) *Forlimpoli.* (2) *Bitonto.* Conciones Evangel. de Dominicis aliquot & festis totius anni &c. Opera &c. M. ab Isselt. 2t. s8°. Coloniae. 1603
Mussolini (Benito), *b. 1883.*
I discorsi d. rivoluzione. Pref. di I. Balbo. 2a ed. s8°. [1923]
Il mio diario di guerra, 1915–17. s8°. Milano. [1923]
Mussolini as revealed in h. polit. speeches, 1914–23. Sel., tr. & ed. by Barone B. Quaranta di San Severino. 8°. 1923
see BOX (P. H.) Three master builders &c., 1925.
„ DANESE (O.) M., 1922.
see GODDEN (G. M.) M.: the birth of the new democracy, 1923.
„ GÜTERBOCK (F.) M. u. d. Fascismus, 1923.
„ ROSSATO (A.) M., 1922.
„ RUSSO (D.) M. & le Fascisme, 1923.
„ SARFATTI (M. G.) Dux [*i.e.* M.], 1926.
„ —— Life of B. M.; tr., 1925.
Mussorgsky (Modest Petrovich), *see* MOUSSORGSKY.
Mustafa Kamel, *pasha.* Lettres égypt. franç. addr. à Mme. J. Adam, 1895–1908. 1e éd. s8°. Cairo. [1909]
Mustapha Chéréf [MOUSTAPHA].
Le traité turc & le droit. [P2712]. 8°. *n.p.* [1920]
Mustoxidi (T. M.) Hist. de l'esthétique française, 1700–1900. Suivie d'une bibliogr. gén. à 1914. Préf. de A. Lalande. 8°. 1920
Mut (Vicente), *see* DAMETO (J.) & V. M. *The anc. & mod. hist. of the Balearick Islands; tr., 1716.
Mutanabbi, *see* AḤMAD IBN ḤUSAIN (ABŪ AL-JAIYIB), *al-M.*
Muthesius (Hermann). Landhaus u. Garten: Beispiele neuzeitl. L. &c. mit Text hrsg. v. H. M. la8°. München. 1907
Mutinelli (Fabio). Storia arcana ed aneddot. d'Italia racc. dai veneti ambasciatori. 3v. la8°. Venezia. 1855–58
Mutiny. Mutiny records (corresp. & reps.), 4p, *see* PUNJAB. P. govt. rec., v7, 8, 1911.
Press-list of "Mutiny papers," 1857, 1921, *see* INDIA: GOVT. PUBL.: RECORD DEP.
Mutschmann (Heinrich). Milton's eyesight & the chronol. of h. wks., *see* DORPAT UNIV. Acta & comment., B, v5, 1924.
Orig. of "Paradise Lost," *see* DORPAT UNIV. Acta &c., B, v5, 1924.
The secret of John Milton. [Acta &c. Univ. Dorpat., B, v8ii]. 8°. Dorpat. 1925
Muurling (Wilhelm). Comm. de Wesseli Gansfortii cum vita &c. pl. 8°. Trajecti ad Rhenum. 1831
Muys (Gottfried). Griechenland u. d. Orient. 8°. Köln. 1856
Muzet (Alphonse). La Roumanie nouvelle. 8°. 1920
Muzio (Girolamo), *Giustinopolitano.* [MUTIO]. Egloghe. s8°. Vinegia. 1550
see TOCCO (V.) Un progetto di confed. ital. (G. M., 1572), 1924.
Muzzarelli (Alfonso). De regula moralium opinionum pro confessariis, *see* MIGNE (J. P.), *ed.* Theol. cursus, t11, 1861.
Muzzey (David Saville).
An American history. rev. ed. s8°. Boston. [1921]
The U.S. of America. 2[v]. 8°. Boston. [1922–24]
Myakotin (Venedikt Aleksandrovich). "Задруга": памяти Вл. Г. Короленко. [*By var. as.*] Под ред. В. А. М. 8°. Москва. 1922
Идея земскаго собора въ русскомъ прошломъ и настоящемъ. [P2445]. 8°. С.-П. [1905]
Myasnikov (A.)
Беспартийная конференция. [P2722]. s8°. Москва. 1919
Myasoedov (Sergei Nikolaevich), *1866–, see* FREINAT (O. G.) Правда о дѣлѣ М. и др., 1918.
Myatlev (T. P.) Просвѣтит. чтенія по исторіи Русс. страны. 2ч [*each in 3p b. together*]. 8°. С.-П. 1911
1, Происхожденіе самобытной русской народности и Россія въ стародавнія врем.
2, Исторія Русс. государетва и Православ. церкви. [-1175].
Myconius (Friedrich), *see* MEKUM (F.)
Myddvai, *Caermarthenshire.* Le plus ancien texte des Meddygon Myddveu, 1913 [*w. text & Fr. tr.*], *see* DIVERRES (P.)
Myechow (Matthias de), *see* MACIEJ, *z Miechowa.*
Myers (Alfred Edward Cecil).
Our coast defence organ. [P2596]. s8°. 1908
Myers (Charles Samuel). Improved methods in an iron foundry, *see* INDUST. FATIGUE RES. BD. Rep., 3, 1919.
Indust. psychology in Gt. Brit. 8°. [1926]
Mind & work. s8°. 1920
Myers (Denys Peter). Manual of colls. of treaties & of colls. relating to treaties. [Harvard Bibliog. lib. ser., v2]. 8°. C. 1922
Myers (Frederic W. H.) Coll. poems, w. autobiog. & crit. fragments. Ed. E. Myers. 8°. 1921
Essays classical & modern. 8°. 1921
Wordsworth. [Eng. men of letters]. [repr.] s8°. [1919]
see DALLAS (H. A.) Mors janua vitae?: discuss. of communic. purport. to come fr. F. W. H. M., 1910.
Myers (Harriet Williams). Western birds. 8°. N.Y. 1922
Myers (James), *of Whitby.* Remains, w. acc. of his life by J. Watkins. s8°. 1830
Myers (Leopold Hamilton). The Clio. s8°. [1925]
The Orissers. [*Fiction. Limited ed.*] la8°. [1922]
„ „ [repr.] s8°. 1923
Myles (William).
Chronolog. hist. of the Methodists. 4th ed. enl. 8°. 1813
Mylius (Georg), *of Augsburg, called also* MILLER *or* GERING.
Augustanæ conf., quæ eccl. evangelic. noviss. temp. symbolum &c. est explicatio. 2p *in* 1v. s4°. Ienæ. 1596
De abrogatione exorcismi in baptismo. Praes. G. M., resp. J. Hofstetterus. [P2673]. s4°. Jenae. 1591
Disput. de Christo exaltato, ex Esa. 53. M. Henricus resp. [P2612]. s4°. Jenae. 1589
In epistolam Pauli ad Romanos &c. s8°. Jenæ. 1595
Πρόδρομος disput. ex Epist. Paulina ad Romanos &c. Resp. J. Maior. [P2640]. s4°. Jenae. 1590
Spongia abstersoria pro Conf. Augustana. Præs. G. M., resp. J. Pflaumius. s4°. Jenae. 1591
see BALDUIN (F.) Leichpredigt bey d. Leichbegängnuss G. M., 1607.
„ HUTTER (L.) Oratio de vita &c. G. M., 1607.

Mylius (Johann Christoph). Bibl. anonymorum et pseudon. Cum praef. G. Stollii. [*b. w.* Placcius (V.) Theatrum, 1708]. 2p. fol. Hamburgi. 1740
see Jena. Das in 1738 &c. blühende Jena &c., 1738–50.

Mylius (Martinus).
*Chronologia script. P. Melanchthonis. s8°. Gorlicii. 1582

Mylius-Erichsen (L.), *1872–1907.* Fra Klit og Hav. s8°. 1912

Mylling (Thomas), *bp. of Hereford.* Registrum T. M., 1474–92. Ed. A. T. Bannister. [Canterbury & York Soc., v26]. 8°. 1920

Mylne (Robert), *of Balquharage.* Excerpt [rel. to Temple lands, 1488] f. A perfect inventor &c., 1702, *see* Maidment (J.) & R. Pitcairn. Nugae derelictae, 1822.

Mylne (Robert), *of Edinburgh, the younger.* Memoir of J. Geddy, *see* Abbotsford Club. Misc., v1, 1837.

Mynsicht (*count* **Adrianus a)** [*ps.* Henricus Madathanas]. The Golden Age restored (1621), *see* Hermetic museum, v1, 1893.

Myrc (John), *see* Mirkus (J.)

Myres (John Linton). Address, 1919, *see* Anglo-Hellenic League. Publ., No. 39, 1919.
The dawn of history. [Home Univ. Lib.] [repr.] s8°. [1924]
Political ideas of the Greeks. 8°. 1927
see Annals of archaeol. & anthropol., v1–14, 1908–27.

Myron, *the sculptor, see* Rossi (F.) Mirone & Policleto, 1922.

Myrriam (Paul). Le magicien. s8°. 1926

***Myself** not least. Being the personal remin. of " X." 8°. [1925]

Mysore. Archaeological Dept. Annual report, 1921, w. Govt. review. fol. Bangalore. 1922
*Narr. sketches of the conq. of the M., effect. in the capt. of Seringapatam & death of Tippoo. 4th ed. [P2825]. s8°. Bath. 1803

Mysore Archaeological Series.
Archit. &c. in Mysore, No. 2, 3. la8°. Bangalore. 1919
see Narasimhachar (R.) The Kesava temple at Belur, 1919. [2.]
,, —— The Lakshmidevi temple at Dodda-Gaddavalli, 1919. [3.]

***Mysteria** Patrum Jesuit. ex scriptis &c., 1633, *see* Schoppe (C.)

Mystery.
*M. (The) of iniquity working in the dividing of Protestants &c., 1689, *see* Protestants.
*M. of the good old cause unfolded (1660), 1883, *see* Parliament.

Mystic rose (The) f. the garden of the king: fragm. of the vision of Sheikh Haji Ibrahim of Kerbela; [*tr. or rather wr.*] by F. L. Cartwright, 1899; 1925, *see* Cartwright (*Sir* F. L.)

Mythographi Graeci. ed. 2ª. v1. s8°. L., *Teubner.* 1926
1, Apollodori bibliotheca—Pediasimi lib. de xii Herculis lab. Ed. R. Wagner.

Mythologie asiatique illustrée. [*By var. a.* Avant-propos par P. L. Couchoud]. 4°. 1928

Mythology. Mythology of all races. Ed. L. H. Gray & G. F. Moore. v4, 7, 8, 11. la8°. Boston [U.S.] 1920–28
4, Finno-Ugric, Siberian; by U. Holmberg.
7, Armenian; by M. H. Ananikian. African; by A. Werner.
8, Chinese; by J. C. Ferguson. Japanese; by M. Anesaki.
11, Latin America; by H. B. Alexander.

Mytton Hall, *see* Hick (J.) Cat. of princ. paintings &c. at M.H., 1893.

Mžik (Hans v.) Afrika, n. d. arab. Bearb. d. Γεωγραφικὴ ὑφήγησις d. C. Ptolemæus v. Muhammad ibn Mūsā al-Ḫwārizmi, mit Anhang Ptolemäus &c. von J. Fischer, 1916, *see* Kaiserl. Akad. d. W. zu Wien. Denkschr., B59, 1917.

N

N. *De controversiis inter Catholicos agitatis &c. 1861, *see* De &c.

N. (*abbas*). *Epistolae abbatis N. ad episc. N. quibus demonstratur æquitas Constitutionis Unigenitus &c. [*of* Clement XI]. Acc. Declar. Sacræ Facult. Theol. Lovan. [*b. w.* Ranst (F. van). Veritas &c., 1715]. s8°. Lovanii. [1716]

N. (D.), *E.T.* *Dictionarium Lat.-Armenum, 1695, *see* Nierszesovicz (D.)

N. (J.) *Biog. anecd. of Hogarth, 2nd ed., 1782; 3rd ed., 1785, *see* Nichols (J.)

N. (N.) *Lettera d'un filarmonico, o. paralello tra Luigia Todi e Luigi Marchesi. [P2839]. s8°. [Venezia. 1791]

N. (N.) *Ein Sendbrieffe an e. fürnemen Thumbherren d. Stiffts Eychstat v. D. J. Cochles &c. [*signed N. N.*], 1544, *see* Cochlaeus (J.)

N. (N.) *Successi d. armi venete in Levante, 1685, 1686, *see* Venete.

N. (N. N.) *Hist. persecutionum eccl. Bohemicae (Pref. *signed* N. N. N.), 1648, *see* Bohemia.

N. (P.) *An exact abridgment of all the trials &c., 1690, *see* Trials.

N. (S.) *A concordance to the Holy Scripture, 1662, *see* Newman (S.)

N. (S. K.) W. Nicholson: [descr. &c. *signed* S. K. N.], 1923, *see* Nicholson (W.)

N. (T.) *Analecta sacra nova, 1617, *see* Roth (David).

Naamregister. Naamreg. van de gecommitt. Raden in de Coll. ter Admiraliteit &c., 1784, *see* Holland: Admiraliteit.
Naam-reg. van de predikanten &c., 1784, *see* Holland.

Naayem (J.) Les Assyro-Chaldéens & les Arméniens massacrés par les Turcs. s8°. 1920

Näbe (Friedrich August Adolph).
Compend. hist. eccles. &c. 8°. Lipsiae. 1832

Nabokov (Konstantin). The ordeal of a diplomat. 8°. [1921]

Nabonne (Bernard). Maïténa. Roman. s8°. 1927

Nachmanides, *see* Moses, *ben Nachman.*

Nachricht. *Historische N. v. Brüder-Gesangbuche d. J. 1778, 1835, *see* Historische.
Kurze &c. N. v. d. unter d. Böhm.-Mähr. Brüder bekanten Kirche &c., 1757, *see* Böhmisch-Mähr.-Brüder.

Nachrichten. N. v. d. Begebenheiten u. Schriften berümt. Gelehrten &c., 24T, 1749–71, *see* Niceron (J. P.)
*N. v. e. Hallischen Bibliothek. [*Ed.* S. J. Baumgarten]. 8B *in* 4 (48 Stück.) s8°. Halle. 1748–51

Nachrichten von d. Königl. Gesells. d. Wiss zu Göttingen, 1894–, *see* Königliche Gesellschaft d. Wiss. zu G.

***Nächste** (Der) Weltkrieg, 1916, *see* Wencker (F.)

Nachtigall (Ottomar) [Luscinius (Ottomarus)]. Allegoriae Psalmorum Davidis &c. [Psalterium D. latinitate redditum]. s8°. apud Augustam. 1524

Nachtmahl. Form wie das heilig Nachtmal J. C. in Heidelberg &c. gehalten wird, 1564, *see* Frederick III, *Elector Palatine.*

Nacion (La). Suppl. Centenario de B. Mitre. [*by var. authors*]. fol. Domingo. 1921

Nadal (Victor). Le château de Chambord. Guide. Revu par J. A. Grenouillot. 4ᵉ éd. [P2435]. s8°. Blois. 1907

Nadejda, *ps.* *Once I had a home. Diary &c. of Nadejda, Lady of Honour to the Empress of Russia &c. [2nd impr.] 8°. [1927]

Nadir Shah, *shah of Persia.*
see Abraham III, *catholicus of Echmiadzin.* Mon. hist. & celui de N. (18 c.), 1876.
,, Jones (*Sir* W.) Works, v5, Hist. de N. S. & Introd. to the life of N. S., 1799.

Nadler (Josef). Die Berliner Romantik, 1800–14. 8°. [1920]
Von Art u. Kunst d. deut. Schweiz. s8°. L. 1922

Nadler (Tobias). Diss. de 3 codd. MSS. Hebr. [Ebnerianis]. Praes. J. A. M. Nagelio. [P430]. s4°. Altorfii. [1749]

Naeff (Top). School-idyllen. 12ᵉ dr. 8°. *n.d.*
Voor de Poort. 5ᵉ dr. 2d *in* 1v. 8°. A. 1921

Nafḥatᵘ 'l-Yaman: " Breezes f. Yemen " [coll. of Arabic stories &c.]; tr. w. philol. &c. notes, p1, 1907, *see* Aḥmad ibn Muḥammad, *al-Yamanī.*

Nâg (Kâlidâs). Les théories diplomat. de l'Inde anc. & l'Arthaçâstra [*attrib. to* Kautilya (326–298 B.C.)] la8°. 1923

Nagl (Alfred). Die Rechentafel d. Alten, 1914, *see* Kais. Akad. d. W. zu Wien. Sitz., Phil.-hist. Kl., B177, 1917.

Nagonio (Giovanni Michele), *see* Pingonio (G. M.)

Nagy (Estienne de), *see* List & Francke. Cat. d'une coll. compos. la bibl. de E. de N., 1870.

Nahid *Bey.* Zeineb la courtisane, *see* Œuvres libres, No. 75, 1927.

Nahmmacher (Conrad). Diss. de syncretismo philos. & theol. revelatae. s4°. Helmstadii. 1755

Naidenov (S.) Авдотьина жизнь, *see* Sbornik. Сб. товар. " Знаніе," 4, 1905.

Naile, *Saint, see* Plummer (C.) Misc. hagiogr. Hibern., 1925.

Naim *Bey.* Memoirs. Turkish offic. doc. rel. to the deportations &c. of Armenians. Comp. by A. Andonian. Intr. by Visct. Gladstone. s8°. [1920]

Nair (*Sir* **Chettur Sankaran).**
Gandhi & anarchy. s8°. Indore. [1922 ?]

Nairn (Katharine), *aft. wife of T. Ogilvy.*
Trial. Ed. W. Roughead. 8°. E. [1926]

Nairne (Alexander). The faith of the New Test. s8°. 1920
see BIBLE. COMPL. TEXTS &c. Cambridge Bible: Hebrews; intr. & notes by A. N., 1921.

Nairne (W. P.) Gilmour of the Mongols. 8°. [1924]

Nakano (Tomio), *Ph.D.* Ordinance power of the Japanese emperor. [Johns Hopkins Univ.] 8°. Baltimore. 1923

Nakarai (Kiyoshi). Relations betw. the govt. & Xtianity in Chosen. [P2620]. 8°. *n.p.* [1921]

***Naked** (The) truth, p2, 3, 1681, *see* HICKERINGILL (E.)

Nakhimov (*admiral* **Pavel Stepanovich),** *see* L. (V. A.) Адмиралъ П. С. Н., 1902.

Nala & Damayanti, *var. ed*[s]., *see* NALOPĀKHYĀNA.

Naldini (Lamberto). La "tallia militum soc. tallie tuscie" nella 2ª metà del sec. 13, *see* ARCHIVIO STOR. ITAL. Anno 78, v2, 1920.

Nalopākhyāna [NALA & DAMAYANTI; NALUS; †MAHABHARATA —*Nalopākhyāna*]. La légende de Nala & Damayanti. Tr., avec intr., notes & vocab. par S. Lévi. 8°. 1920
Nalopákhyánam: story of Nala, an episode of the Mahábhárata, w. vocab. & impr. version of Milman's tr. by Monier Williams. 2nd ed. rev. 8°. O. 1879
Nalus, carmen Sanscr. Ed., Lat. vertit &c. F. Bopp. 8°. Londini. 1819

Nalson (John), *1638–86.* A true copy of the journal of the High Court of Justice for the tryal of K. Charles I &c., w. introd. sm. fol. 1684

Namias (Angelo). Parnaso modenese. Liriche scelte di poeti m. contemp. s8°. Modena. 1880

Nana, *Syrian* [NONNUS *of Nisib*]. [Expos. of the Gospel of John. *In Armenian.* Ed. Q. A. Tchraqean]. s8°. Venetik. 1920

Nance (R. Morton).
Sailing-ship models. Intr. text by R. M. N. 4°. 1924

Nangle (Edward), *1799–1883, see* SEDDALL (H.) E. N., the apostle of Achill, 1884.

Nangle (*capt.* **Walter Chidisck),** *see* PALLISER (E. M.) & W. C. N. The volunteer in the field, 1861.

Nang Tantrai. Les entretiens de N. T. Tr. du siamois par E. Lorgeou. 8°. 1924

Nani (Floriano). Il transito di S. Filippo Neri. Poema. [*b. w.* Casio de' Medici (G.) Libro, 1528]. s8°. Bologna. 1623

Nani Mocenigo (Filippo). Di alcune fonti venez. [Estr. d. Ateneo Veneto, a. 26. P2841]. 8°. Venezia. 1903
Poeti vernacoli venez. d. sec. 19. [P2859]. 8°. [Venezia. 1886]

Nanjo (F.), *see* BRINKLEY (F.), F. N. & Y. IWASAKI. An unabr. Jap.-Eng. dict., 1896.

Nankivell (Joice M.) & S. Loch.
Ireland in travail. s8°. 1922
The river of a hundred ways: life in E. Poland. s8°. [1924]

Nannucci (Vicenzio).
Analisi crit. dei verbi ital. 8°. Firenze. 1843

Nansen (Fridtjof). Armenia & the Near East. 8°. [1928]
Russia & peace. s8°. [1923]
Sporting days in wild Norway. Intr. by W. B. Johnson. 8°. [1925]
see HELLAND-HANSEN (B.) & F. N. Temperature variations in N. Atlantic &c., 1920.

Nansen (Joseph).
Julies Tagebuch. Roman. [66.–73. A.] s8°. [1921]

Naogeorgus (Thomas) *ps.* [*i.e.* KIRCHMEYER (THOMAS)].
Agriculturae sacrae libri 5. s8°. Basileae. [1550]
Mercator, 1540, *see* BOLTE (J.) 3 Schauspiele, 1927.
Tragoedia nova Pammachius. Cum praef. luculenta. s8°. Augustæ. 1539
see THEOBALD (L.) Leben u. Wirken d. Tendenzdramatikers T. N. seit s. Flucht aus Sachsen, 1908.

Napier (*Gen. Sir* **Charles James),** *1782–1853, see* HOLMES (T. R.) Sir C. N., 1925.

Napier (Elma). Nothing so blue. 8°. *Cayme Press.* 1927

Napier (*Lt.-Col. Hon.* **Henry Dundas).** Experiences of a military attaché in the Balkans. la8°. [1924]

Napier (*Gen. Sir* **William Francis Patrick),** *1785–1860.* Hist. de la guerre dans la Péninsule &c., 1807–1814. Tr. revue, corr. &c. par M. Dumas. 13t. 8°. 1828–44

Napier (*Gen. Sir* **William Francis Patrick)** [*continued*].
*Strictures on passages in N.'s Hist. of the Peninsular War wh. rel. to Gen. Beresford. Added, Sir B. D'Urban's Rep. of operations in the Alemtejo &c., 1811 [*sep. pagin.*] 2nd ed. 8°. 1835

Naples. In Regis Caroli Borboni et Amaliae Saxonicae nuptis Reg. Nap. Acad. obseq. officium. [Orat. J. B. Vici &c. N126]. 8°. Neapoli. 1738
*Obs. on a journey to N., 1691, *see* EMILIANE (G. D').
see BIBLIOTECA ORATORIANA, *Naples.*

Napoleon I, *emperor of the French.*
Bulletins offic. de la Grande Armée, dictés par N.; rec. par A. Goujon, 2t, 1822, *see* Recueil de pièces authent., t8, 9 *below.*
Corr. inéd. conservée aux Archives de la Guerre. Publ. E. Picard & L. Tuetey. t5, 1812. la8°. 1925
Dict.-Napoléon, ou Rec. des opinions &c. de l'Emp. N. Intr. & notes par Damas Hinard. 2ᵉ éd. 8°. 1854
Discours sur les vérités & les sentiments &c. Publ. par le gén. Gourgaud. [*b. w.* Delfico (M.) Vérité sur les Cent Jours &c., 1825]. 8°. Brux. 1826
*Hist. de N. d'ap. MM. de Norvins, le Cte de Las-Cases & gén. Gourgaud. n. éd. s8°. 1837
Lettres inéd. (An VIII–1815). Publ. L. Lecestre. 2ᵉ éd. 2t. 8°. 1897
Méms. p. s. à l'hist. de France sous N. écrits à St Hélène par les généraux qui ont partagé sa captivité [G. Gourgaud & C. J. F. T. de Montholon] & publ. sur les mss. corr. de sa main. 4t *in* 2v. 8°. 1823
Recueil de pièces authent. sur le captif de Ste.-Hélène, de mém. & doc. écrits &c. par N., suivis de lettres de Comte Bertrand, Comte Las Cases &c. [12t]. 8°. 1821–25
The following have additional tp.:—
6, 7, Mém. p. s. à l'hist. de la vie privée &c. de l'Emp. N. en 1815; par le baron Fleury de Chaboulon.
8, 9, Bulletins offic. de la Gr. Armée, dictés par l'Emp. N. & rec. par A. Goujon.
10, 11, N. dans l'exil &c., tr.; by B. E. O'Meara.
12, Hist. de la vie polit., milit. & privée de N. Bonaparte; par Chennechot.
Tombeau de Nap. I, érigé dans le dome des Invalides par M. Visconti. s8°. 1853
*Vie de Napoléon, avec détails sur maladie & mort. s8°. Genève. 1822
see ABRANTÈS (L. J., *duc.*) Autobiog. &c. [*w. 2nd tp.*: Home & court life of N.], 4v, 1893.
„ ANTOMMARCHI (C. F.) Mém. ou dern. momens de N., 2t, 1825.
„ ARCHAMBAULT (T.) Cat. des reliques, prov. de Ste. Hélène, 1924.
„ AUBRY (O.) Le roman de N. B. & Joséphine (*fict.*), 1927.
„ BALLARD (*Brig.-Gen.* C. R.) N.: an outline, 1924.
„ BARTON (D. P.) Bernadotte & N., 1763–1810, 1921.
„ BEAUCHAMP (A. DE). Hist. des malheurs de Pie VII sous N., 1814.
„ BITTERAUF (T.) Zur Entstehungsgesch. d. Bonapartismus, 1915.
„ BOUCHOT (H.) La toilette à la cour de N., 1810–15, 1895.
„ BOURRIENNE (L. A. FAUVELET DE). Méms. s. N. &c., 10t, 1829.
„ BROADLEY (A. M.) Coll. Nap.: cat. of autographs, hist. doc[s]. &c.; comp. by W. V. Daniell, 1905.
„ BURNAND (R.) & F. BOUCHER, *edd.* L'hist. de N. racont. par les gr. écrivains, 1922.
„ CABANÈS (A.) Dans l'intimité de l'Emp., 1924.
„ CHATEAUBRIAND (*le vte.* F. R. DE). De Buonaparte &c., 1814.
„ CHENNECHOT (L. E.) Hist. de la vie de N., 1825.
„ COHEN (L.) N. anecdotes, 1925.
„ COLIN (J.) L'éduc. milit. de N., 1900.
„ CONARD (P.) N. & la Catalogne, 1808–14, t1, 1910.
„ COUDERC DE SAINT-CHAMANT (H.) N., s. dern. armées, 1902.
„ DRIAULT (E.) Mohamed Aly & N., 1807–1814 &c., 1925.
„ —— N. & l'Europe: le Gr. Empire, 1809–12, 1924.
„ ESSLING (*pr.* D'). Coll. de monnaies &c., N. I &c., 1927.
„ FAIN (*le baron* A. J. F.) Ms. de 1813 p. s. à l'hist de N., 2ᵉ ed., 2t, 1825.
„ FAURE (E.) Napoléon, 1921.
„ FISHER (H. A. L.) N., 1924.
„ FLEURY DE CHABOULON (*le b.* P. A. E.) Mém[s]. p. s. à l'hist. de N. en 1815, 2t, 1822; 3p, 1901.
„ FOURNIER (A.) N. I: a biog.; tr. A. E. Adams, 2nd ed., v1, 1912.
„ —— Zur Textkritik d. Korresp. Napoleons I, 1903.
„ GABORY (É.) N. & la Vendée, 1914.
„ GALLAIS (J. P.) Hist. du dix-huit Brumaire & de Buonaparte, 2ᵉ éd., 2p, 1814.
„ GEOFFROY DE GRANDMAISON (C. A.) L'Espagne & N., t2, 1809–11, 1925.
„ GUEDALLA (P.) N. & Palestine, 1925.
„ GUÉRARD (A. L.) Reflections on N. legend, 1924.
„ GUILLIÉ (S.) *Hist. du cabinet des Tuileries &c. & de la conspiration qui a ramené Buonaparte en France, 1815.
„ GUILLON (E.) N. & la Suisse, 1803–15, 1910.
„ KIELMANNSEGG (A. C., *Gräfin* v.) Mem. ü. N. I, 1927.

Napoleon I, *emperor of the French* [*continued*].
see KIRCHEISEN (F. M.) Bibliog. du temps de N., t2, pl, 1912.
„ —— N., s. Leben u. s. Zeit, B4, 5, 1922.
„ KIRCHEISEN (G.) N. & h. women friends; tr., 1927.
„ KNOWLES (*Sir* L.) A gift of N., sequel to letters of Capt. E. Lutyens, St. Helena, 1820–23, 1921.
„ KRAUSS (A.) Moltke, Benedek u. N., 1901.
„ LACOUR-GAYET (G.) Bonaparte : membre de l'Institut, 1921.
„ —— N., sa vie, s. œuvre, s. temps, 1921.
„ LANFREY (P.) Hist. de N. [–1811], n. éd., 5t, 1880.
„ LANSDOWNE (H. W. E. P.-F., *6th marq. of*), *ed.* The 1st N. : some unpubl. doc[s]. f. the Bowood Papers, 1925.
„ LAS CASES (M. J. A. E. D., *cte. de*). Mém. de Sainte-Hélène &c., 8p, 1823.
„ LESAGE (C.) N. I, créancier de la Prusse, 1807–14, 1924.
„ LÉVY (A.) N. intime, 1910.
„ LIGNE (C. J.) Ma Napoléonide; publ. F. Leuridant, 1921.
„ LORT DE SÉRIGNAN (*le cte.* A.) N. & les gr. généraux de la Révol. &c., 1914.
„ LOTE (G.) N. & le romantisme franç., 1915.
„ LUDWIG (E.) N., 1926; tr., 1927.
„ LUNIŃSKI (E.) N.: legiony i ksiestwo Warszawskie, *n.d.*
„ MOWAT (R. B.) Diplomacy of N., 1924.
„ MUSÉE NAPOLÉON. Galerie, publ. Filhol &c., 10t, 1804–15.
„ NAPOLÉON III. Des idées Napol., 1839.
„ O'MEARA (B. E.) N. in exile, 5th ed., 2v, 1822; tr., 2t, 1822–25.
„ PERCEVAL (E. DE). Un advers. de N., le vte. Lainé, 2t, 1926.
„ PHIPPS (*Col.* R. W.) Armies of the 1st Fr. Republic & the rise of the marshals of N. I, 1926.
„ PICARD (E.) Bonaparte & Moreau, 1905.
„ PLUMPTRE (A.) Narr. of 3 yrs. residence in France: incl. partic. resp. early life of [N.], 3v, 1810.
„ PROUDHON (P. J.) Comm. sur les Méms. de Fouché, [&] parallèle entre N. & Wellington, 3e éd., 1900.
„ REGNAULT-WARIN (J. B. J. I. P.) Cinq mois de l'hist. de France, 1815.
„ RICHARDSON (H. N. B.) Dict. of N. & h. times, 1920.
„ ROSE (J. H.) Life of N., 8th ed. rev., 1922.
„ RÜDER (F. A.) Leben &c. d. Kaisers N., 1827.
„ RÜSTOW (F. W.) Die erst. Feldzüge Nap. Bonaparte's in Ital. u. Deut., 1796–97, 1867.
„ RÜTHER (E.) N. u. Polen, 1806–12, 2T, 1901–2.
„ SECKENDORFF (C. v.) N. I u. Pius VII, 1873.
„ SFORZA (G.) Gli antenati di N. I in Lunigiana, 1915.
„ TRUMPER (*Lt.-Com.* V. L.) Hist. sites, Palestine, w. acc. of N.'s exped. to Syria, 1921.
„ TUCKETT (J. E. S.) N. & freemasonry, 1914.
„ VANDAL (A.) L'avènement de Bonaparte, 2t, 1912.
„ VIGNALI (A. P.) Descr. of V. Coll. of relics of N., 1924.
„ WALISZEWSKI (K.) La Russie: le règne d'Alex. Ier, t2, La guerre patriot. & l'héritage de N., 1812–16, 1924.
„ WARNER (G. T.) How wars were won: st. of N.'s times, 1915.
„ WILKINSON (H. S.) Defence of Piedmont: prelude to st. of N., 1927.

Napoleon III, *emperor of the French.*
Des idées Napoléoniennes. 8°. 1839
see GUEDALLA (P.) The 2nd Empire: Bonapartism—The prince &c., 1922.
„ LANSDOWNE (H. W. E. P.-F., *6th marq. of*), *ed.* Secret of the Coup d'Etat: unpubl. corr. of L. N. &c., 1848–52, 1924.
„ MARX (C.) The 18th Brumaire of L. B.; tr., 1926.
„ ONCKEN (H.) N. III u. d. Rhein, 1926.
„ PAPIERS secrets & corr. du Second Empire, 9e éd., 1875.
„ SIMPSON (F. A.) L. N. & the recovery of France, 1848–56, 1923.
„ VIEL-CASTEL (*c.* H. DE). Méms. s. le r. de N. III, 1851–64; 6t, 1883–84; 3e éd., 1883–85.

Napoli (Giuseppe de).
Altamura. [Cento città, 94. P2860]. 4°. Milano. *n.d.*

Naquet (J. Alfred). La loi du divorce. s8°. 1903

Narasimhachar (*Rao Bahadur* **R.)** The Kesava temple at Belur. [Mysore Archæol. Ser.] la8°. Bangalore. 1919
The Lakshmidevi temple at Dodda-Gaddavalli. [Mysore Archaeol. Ser.] la8°. Bangalore. 1919

Narasu (*P.* **Lakshmi).** A study of caste. s8°. Madras. [1922]

Nārāyana Rāva, *see* WILSON (J.) A second exposure of the Hindu relig., in reply to N. Ráo &c. 1832.

Narbonne. Livre vert de l'archevêché de N. Publ. P. Laurent. 8°. 1886

Narbut (Egor), *see* LUKOMSKY (G. K.) E. H., 1923.

Narducci (Luigi). Notizie biogr. d. Pietro Antoniutti. [Nozze Serravallo—De Concina. N129]. la8°. Udine. 1884

Narekatzi (Anania), *see* ANANIAS, *of Narek.*

Nariman (G. K.) Lit. hist. of Sansk. Buddhism, fr. Winternitz, S. Levi, Huber. 8°. Bombay. 1920

Narodnaya Volya, *see* BOGUCHARSKY (V. YA). Литература партіи Народной Воли, 1905; 2B, 1907.

Narodniya. Народныя южнорусскія пѣсни, 1854, *see* METLINSKY (A. L.)

Narodny Komissariat Finansov, *see* RUSSIA.

Narracio. Quedam narr. de Groninghe, de Thrente, de Covordia &c. sub div. episc. Traject., 1888, *see* TRAJECTENSES.

Narrative.
*N. of the Battle of Jutland, 1924, *see* DEWAR (*Capt.* A. C.) &c.
*N. of the Russ. milit. exped. to Khiva under Gen. Perovsky in 1839; tr., 1867, *see* PEROVSKY (*Gen.* V. A.)
*N. sketches of the conquest of Mysore &c., 1803, *see* MYSORE.
*Second n. of the signal victory under command of Duke of York, 3rd June 1665, 1665, *see* JAMES II, *k. of Gt. Brit.*

Narratori. Narratori contemp., 2v, 1921, *see* ROSA (G. T.), *ed.*

Nase (Johann) [NASS; NAS]. Concordia alter u. newer &c. Glaubensstrittiger lehren &c. s4°. [München]. 1583
Examen chartaceæ Lutheranorum Concordiæ, Aussmusterung u. Widerlegung dess Nagel newgeschmidten Concordi Buchs &c. [*Dir. agst. the wr. of J. Andreæ*]. s4°. Ingolstadt. 1581
Sextæ centuriæ prodromus: Das ist, Ein Vortrab u. Morgengab, d. sechstē hunderts Evāgeloser warheit &c. s4°. *n.p.* 1574

Nash (*capt.* **Edward).** Jackson's strategy. [P2596]. s8°. 1904
The principles of strategy. s8°. 1905

Nash (Joseph), *artist, see* EXHIBITIONS: LONDON, 1851. Dickinsons' pictures of the gt. E. of 1851; fr. originals by N. &c., 2v, 1854.

Nash (Paul). Paul Nash. [Descr. &c. *signed* A. B. Contemp. Brit. artists]. la8°. 1923

Nash (Roy). Conquest of Brazil. 8°. [1927]

Nash (Thirza). The ex-gentleman. s8°. 1925

Nash (William Giles). America: its discovery. la8°. 1924

Násir al-Din, *king of Oude* [NUSSIR-U-DEEN], *see* KNIGHTON (W.) Priv. life of an East. king: N.-u-D. &c., 1921.

Näsman (Reinhold E.)
Historiola linguae Dalekarlicae. s4°. Upsaliae. 1733

Nasmith (David), *1799–1839, see* CAMPBELL (J.) Mem. of D. N., 1844.

***Naspo** Bizaro con la zonta del lamento &c., 1620, *see* CARAVIA (A.)

Naṡr al-Dín, *Khwājar.* The Turkish jester; tr. G. Borrow, 1884, *see* BORROW (G.) Wks., v16, 1924.

Nass (Lucien), *see* CABANÈS (A.) & L. N. La névrose révolutionnaire, 2t, 1925.

Nassarre y Ferriz (Blas Antonio), *see* RODRIQUEZ (C.) Bibl. univ. de la polygraphia española; publ. N. y F., 1738.

Nassau (Louis, *count of*) [LODEWIJK VAN NASSAU; † LOUIS, *count de Nassau*]. Corresp. van & betref. L. van N. & andere onuitg. doc. Verzameld door P. J. Blok. [Hist. Genoots. Werken., 47]. 8°. Utrecht. 1887

Nast (Christian Friedrich). Diss. De usu vers. Lat. vet. in Eccl. Xtiana occas. cod. Stuttgard. Præs. J. F. Le Bret. [P2645]. s4°. Tubingae. [1786]

Nast (Johann). Hist.-crit. Nachrichten v. d. 6 ersten teutschen Bibel-Ausgaben &c. s8°. St. 1767
Litter. Nachr. v. d. hochteut. Bibelübers. s8°. St. 1779

Natal, *Colony of.* Natal (Maj. Jackson's ser.), *maps.* Sheets 36, 38, 38a, 39, 1902, *see* TRANSVAAL.
N. province. Descr. guide & official hand-book. Ed. A. H. Tatlow. la8°. Durban. 1911

Natali (Giulio). Idee, costumi, uomini d. settecento. 2[a] ed. s8°. Torino. 1926

Natali (J. B.) Nos géorgiques. [Soc. des Sci. hist. & nat. de la Corse]. tirage spéc. 8°. Bastia. 1921

Natanson (Jacques).
Comedies in ŒUVRES libres.
L'âge heureux, 1923. [23.]
Les amants saugrenus, 1925. [45.]
Le greluchon délicat, 1926. [61.]
L'infidèle éperdu, 1926. [66.]

Natesan (Ganapathi Agraharam). What India wants. Autonomy within the Empire. s8°. Madras. [1917]

Nathan, *the Babylonian, Rabbi, see* ABOTH. Ethics of the Fathers [*falsely attrib. to R. N.*]; tr. R. Young, 1852.

Nathan (Manfred), *K.C.* The renascence of internat. law. [Grotius Soc. Publ[s]., No. 3]. 8°. 1925
S. Africa f. within. 8°. [1926]
S. African literature. s8°. Cape Town. 1925

Nation (The). [*American*]; journal devoted to polit., lit., science & art. v110–113. 4°. N.Y. 1920–21

Nation (The) & The Athenaeum. v26–42. 4°. 1919–28
[From Feb. 19, 1921, The Athenaeum was incorporated w. the Nation.]

National. *Nat. (The) portrait gallery of disting. Americans; w. biog. sketches by celeb. a. 4v. la8°. Phila. 1865
*Nat. prosperity & industrial peace. [Repr. f. The Round Table, Sept. 1921]. [P2564]. 8°. 1921
National Anc. Monuments year book. Foreword by Rt. Hon. S. Baldwin. Intr. by Earl of Crawford & Balcarres. Ed. J. Swarbrick. 8°. 1927
National Art-Collections Fund.
17th–23rd ann. report[s]. 4°. 1921–27
National Art Library, *see* VICTORIA & ALBERT MUSEUM.
National Art Survey of Scotland. v1. fol. [E.] 1921
see SCOTTISH. Examples of Scot. archit. f. 12th to 17th c.: reprod. f. N.A.S. drawings; ed. Sir R. R. Anderson &c., 1921. [1.]
National Assembly of the Church of England.
Report of proc., 1920. 8°. 1921
Report of the Cathedrals Comm. 2p [*in* 1v]. Report & Apps. 8°. 1927
Nationalbibliothek, *Wien, see* VIENNA.
National Birth-Rate Commission. Problems of population & parenthood. 2nd report & chief evidence taken by N.B.-R.C., 1918–20. 8°. 1920
National Civic Federation. Profit sharing by Amer. employers &c. Rep. of the N.C.F. 8°. N.Y. [1921]
National Council of Public Morals, *see* COMMITTEE ON VENEREAL DISEASE.
National Gallery.
see HOLMES (*Sir* C. J.) Old masters &c.: the N.G., v1–3, 1923–27.
,, —— & C. H. C. BAKER. Making of the N.G., 1824–1924, 1924.
,, HUTTON (E.) Sienese school in the N.G., 1925.
,, PEERS (*Mrs.* C. R.) Early Northern painters, 1922.
National Gallery, Millbank, *see* TATE GALLERY.
National Health Insurance. Medical Research Comm. Rep. upon anaerobic bacteria & infections. 8°. 1919
M.R.C. Rep. on accessory food factors (Vitamines). 8°. 1919
National Institute of Industrial Psychology.
Journal. Ed. C. S. Myers. v1–3 (1922–27). 8°. 1923–27
National Institute of Social Sciences (The). Reconstruction after the War. Journal. [Amer. Soc. Sci. Assoc.] v4. 8°. Boston. 1918
National Library of Ireland. Subject index of bks. added, 1904–15, & of those in gen. coll. prior to 1894. fol. D. 1926
National Library of Wales. Bibliog. of R. Owen, 1771–1858. 2nd ed. rev. 8°. Aberystwyth. 1925
Bibl. Celtica: reg. of publ. rel. to Wales & the Celtic peoples &c., 1914–18. 8°. Aberystwyth. 1923
Calendar of deeds & doc. Comp. by F. Green. 2v. 8°. Aberystwyth. 1921–27
1, Coleman deeds. 2, Crosswood deeds.
Calendar of Wynn (of Gwydir) papers, 1515–1690. [Intr. by J. Ballinger]. la8°. Aberystwyth. 1926
Cat. of MSS. By J. H. Davies. v1, Addit. MSS. in the coll. of Sir J. Williams. 8°. Aberystwyth. 1921
National Museum of Wales, *see* NORTH (F. J.) Coal &c. in Wales, 1926.
National Political Union. Anatomy. Proc. resp. legisl. interference. [P2782]. 8°. 1832
National Portrait Gallery. Illust. list of portraits. 8°. 1925
National review (The). v75–91. 8°. [1920–28]
National Republican Convention, *see* UNITED STATES: REPUBL. NAT. CONV.
National Rifle Association, *see* HUMPHREY (A. P.) & T. F. FREMANTLE. Hist., 1859–1909, 1914.
National Union of Scientific Workers. On the encouragement of fundamental research. [P2762]. 8°. 1924
National Union of Women's Suffrage Societies, *see* COMMON CAUSE, THE, 1910–12.
National Unionist Association. Looking ahead. Re-statement of Unionist principles &c., w. 3 speeches by S. Baldwin. 8°. [1924]
National-Versammlung (Die) in Wort u. Bild. [P2406]. s8°. St. 1919
Natoli (Luigi). Il primo sogg. di G. Balsamo a Parigi e un amore di Lorenza, *see* SOCIETÀ SICIL. Arch., n.s., 46, 1925.
Nator. Letter copy book of Supervisor of Rajshahi at N., 1769–72, 1925, *see* BENGAL.
Natorp (Paul). Üb. Platos Ideenlehre. 2e A. 8°. 1925
Nattier (Jean Marc), *see* NOLHAC (P. DE). N., 1925.
***Natural** (The) hist. of bees; tr., 1744, *see* RÉAUMUR (R. A.)
Natural history. Journal of the American Museum. v21–27. 8°. N.Y. 1921–27

Nature. *Spectacle de la n.: or N. display'd; tr., 7v, 1736–48, *see* PLUCHE (N. A.)
Nature: weekly illust. journal of sci. v105–120. la8°. 1920–27
***Naturgemässe** (Die) Lösung d. grössten Lebensräthsels. [P2473]. s8°. Zürich. 1871
Naturwissenschaftlich-Medizin. Verein in Innsbruck.
Berichte. Jhrg. 40. 8°. Innsbruck. 1926
see MAGNUS (P.) Die Pilze: Nachtrag, 1926. [40.]
Nauck (August), *see* WALKER (R. J. B.) Addenda scenica, suppl. to N.'s Fragments, 1923.
Naud (Joseph). Le château d'Issy & ses hôtes. La reine Margot, les Contis &c. la8°. 1926
Naudé (Gabriel). Advis pour dresser une bibliothèque. Réimpr. s. la 2e éd. (1644). s8°. 1876
Instructions conc. erecting of a library. Interpreted by Jo. Evelyn. s8°. 1661
Polit. consid. upon refin'd politicks & the master-strokes of state. Tr. by Dr. King. s8°. 1711
Naudeau (Ludovic). Les dessous du chaos russe. s8°. [1920]
La jolie fille de Dublin, *see* ŒUVRES (Les) libres, 25, 1923.
Naue (Julius). Die Hügelgräber zwischen Ammer- u. Staffelsee. 4°. St. 1887
Naukovii zbirnik. Науковий збірник. The scientific mag. of the Charkov chair of Ukrainian hist. No. 5–7 *in* 1v. 8°. Харків. 1927
Naumann (Emil). L. van Beethoven, *see* VIRCHOW (R.) & F. v. HOLTZENDORFF. Vorträge, H117, 1870.
Naumann (Hans). Die deut. Dichtung d. Gegenwart, 1885–1924. 2. A. 8°. St. 1924
Naumann (Johann Gottfried) [†NAUMANNUS]. Diss. de Jephtigenia, Jud. XI, 39 &c. Praeses J. G. N.; resp. J. G. Günther. s4°. Lipsiae. [1712]
Diss. de Θυγατροθυσία Jiphtachi. Resp. A. Ermannus. [*b. w. h.* Diss. de Jephtigenia &c., 1712]. s4°. Lipsiae. 1711
Naumburg. Adv. Synodi Tridentinae restitut. à Pio IV. Pontif. indictam, opposita gravamina. Proposita in Naoburgico conventu Principum &c. E Germ. in Lat. conversa à L. Tuppio. s4°. Argentorati. 1565
Naval. *How to become a n. officer &c., rev. ed., 1907, *see* How.
N. (The) miscellany. Ed. W. G. Perrin. [Navy Rec. Soc., 63]. v3. 8°. 1928
*Naval sketch-bk., 2v, 1826, *see* GLASCOCK (W. N.)
Naval annual (The) [BRASSEY'S NAVAL & SHIPPING ANNUAL]. 1894, 1920/21, 1921/22, 1927. Ed. A. Richardson & A. Hurd. 8°. 1894–[1926]
Naval War College, *Washington.* The Declaration of London of Feb. 26, 1909. 8°. Wash. 1910
Navar (Tiburtius). Manuductio ad praxim executionis litt. S. Poenitentiariæ. s8°. Parisiis. 1691
Navarre (Octave). Le théâtre grec. s8°. 1925
Navarro (A. de Gusmão), *see* GUSMÃO-NAVARRO (A. DE).
Navenne (Ferdinand Henry de). Rome & le palais Farnèse pend. les 3 dern. siècles. 2t. 8°. 1923
Naville (Edouard). The higher criticism in rel. to the Pentateuch. Tr., w. intr. by J. R. Mackay. s8°. E. 1923
The Law of Moses. Tr., w. pref. by H. Wace. s8°. 1922
La reine Aahmès, *see* ACAD. D. INSCR.: FOND. PIOT. Mon., t25, 1921–22.
see DAVIS (T. M.) Excavations: Biban el Molûk; The funeral papyrus of Iouiya, w. intr. by E. N., 1908.
,, DOUMERGUE (E.) Moïse & la Genèse d'ap. les trav. de E. N., 1920.
Navy.
Coll. of all such statutes &c. as rel. to the Admiralty, Navy &c., 1742, *see* ADMIRALTY.
*Gloria Britannica: acc. of the Royal Navy &c., 1696, *see* GLORIA.
*Obs. & proposals conc. the navy. [P2778]. 8°. 1745
Regulations &c. rel. to H.M.'s service at sea. Establ. by H.M. in Council. 5th ed. 4°. 1745
Navy Records Society. *Publications.* 52–63. 8°. 1920–28
see CAMBRIDGE: MAGDALENE COLL. Descr. cat. of naval MSS. in Pepysian Lib.; ed. J. R. Tanner, v4, 1923. [57.]
,, KEITH (G. K. E., *visct.*) K. papers, v1, 1927. [62.]
,, LEAKE (S. M.) Life of Sir J. Leake; ed. G. Callender, 2v, 1920. [52, 53.]
,, MANWARING (G. E.) Life & works of Sir H. Mainwaring, 2v, 1920–22. [54, 56.]
,, NAVAL miscellany (The); ed. W. G. Perrin, v3, 1928. [63.]
,, PEPYS (S.) Naval minutes; ed. J. R. Tanner, 1926. [60.]
,, SAINT VINCENT (J. J., *1st earl of*). Letters, 1801–04; ed. D. B. Smith, 2v, 1922–27. [55, 61.]
,, SPENCER (G. J. S., *2nd earl*). Private papers, 1794–1801; ed. H. W. Richmond, v3, 4, 1924. [58, 59.]

Nayler (James), *1618–60, see* Brailsford (M. R.) A Quaker f. Cromwell's army: J. N., 1927.

Naylor (Henry Darnley), *see* Horace. Odes & epodes; study by N., 1922.

Neal (Daniel). Hist. of the Puritans, or Prot. Non-Conformists. 4v. 8º. D. 1755

Neale, *The family of, see* Neale (J. A.) Suppl. to Charters &c. of Neales of Berkeley &c., 1927.

Neale (Cornelius), *see* Jowett (W.) Mem. of C. N., add. h. remains, sermons, allegories &c., 1834.

Neale (Erskine). *Dark deeds. By the a. of "The gaol chaplain." 8º. [1849]

Neale (James), *F.S.A.*
The Abbey Church of St. Alban, Herts. *p.f.s.* la. fol. [1877]

Neale (James), *M.A.* Select hymns. s8º. 1763

Neale (John Alexander). Suppl. to Charters & records of Neales of Berkeley, Yate & Corsham. la8º. 1927

Neale (John Ernest). The Commons' privilege of free speech in Parl., *see* Pollard (A. F.) Tudor studies, 1924.

Neale (John Mason). Hymnal noted, 1851–56; 7th ed., 1877, *see* Hymnal.
Hymni ecclesiae e breviariis &c. desumpti. Coll. &c. J. M. N. s8º. Oxonii. 1851
Notes ecclesiolog. & picturesque on Dalmatia, Croatia, Istria, Styria &c. s8º. 1861

Neale (John Preston). Views of seats of noblemen & gentlemen in Eng., Wales, Scot. & Irel. From drawings by J. P. N. 11v (1–6. s2. 1–5). 4º. 1818–1829

Neale (Reginald Edgar).
Electricity. 2nd impr. rev. s8º. *Pitman. n.d.*

Neame (*Lt.-Col.* Philip).
German strategy in the Gt. War. 8º. 1923

Neander (Michael) *of Sorau.*
see Luther (M.) Catechesis parva; ed. M. N., 1567.
,, Pindar. Aristologia Pindarica; ed. M. N., 1556.

Near East (The) year book & who's who, 1927. Ed. H. T. M. Bell. 8º. 1927

Neave (David), *see* Parkes (K.) Etchings &c. of D. N., *n.d.*

Nebbia (Ugo). La 14ª esposiz. d'arte a Venezia, 1924. la8º. Bergamo. [1924]

Neblette (C. B.) Photography. 8º. 1927

Nebolsin (Pavel Ivanovich), *see* Grigorev (V. V.) Разборъ сочиненія Н., c. 1856.

Nebraska. Laws, joint resolutions &c. passed by the Legisl. Assembly of N., 1887. 8º. Lincoln, Neb. 1887

Nebraska University. Bibliog. contrib. f. the lib. of the Univ. of N. No. 6. 8º. Lincoln, Neb. 1926
see Gable (J. H.) Learned &c. publs. of the Univ. of N., 1871–1926, 1926. [6.]
Univ. studies. v14–24. 8º. Lincoln, Nebraska. 1914–25

Nebuchadnezzar II, *king of Babylon, see* Weissbach (F. H.) Die Inschriften N. II im Wâdī Brîsā &c.; hrsg. u. übers. v. W., 1906.

Nechaev (Sergy Gennadievich), *see* Kantor (R. M.) В погоне за Н., 1922.

Nechvolodov (Aleksandr). Сказанія русской землѣ. 4ч. 8º. 1913
L'Emp. Nicholas II & les Juifs: essais sur la Révol. Russe. Tr. I. M. Narischkina. 8º. 1924

Necker (Jacques). Sur le compte rendu au roi en 1781: nouv. éclairc. par N. [*in ans. to the* "Réponse" *of C. A. de Calonne*, 1788]. s8º. Lyon. 1788
see Haussonville (G. P. O. de C., *cte.* d'). Mme. de Staël & N. d'ap. corr. inéd., 1925.

Necrologia Germaniae. [Mon. Germ. Hist.] t4. 4º. 1920
4, Diœcesis Passaviensis; ed. M. Fastlinger, compl. J. Sturm.

Nédeff (*lieut.-col.* N.) Les opérations en Macédoine: l'épopée de Doïran, 1915–18. Tr. Goetzmann. 8º. Sofia. 1927

Nederland. Klein plakkaatboek van N., 1919, *see* Blécourt (A. S. de) & N. Japikse.
Staatsblad van het Koningrijk d. Nederlanden, 1813–21, *see* Staatsblad.
Het verheerlykt N., of Kabinet v. hedendaagsche gezigten. 9d. [d8, 9 *wanting*]. 8º. *I. Tirion.* 1745–74

Nederlandsch Aardrijkskundig Genootschap, *see* Koninklijke Nederl. Aardrijksk. Genoots.

Nederlandsch Indië. Neerlands Ind.: land & volk, gesch & bestuur &c., 2d, 1913, *see* Colijn (H.), *ed.*
De Volken van Nederl. I., 2d, 1920–21, *see* Eerde (J. C. van), *ed.*

Nederlandsche (De) Geloofsbelijdenis. [Belydenisse d. gheloofs]. Naar d. druk v. 1562 uitg. door A. v. d. Linde. s8º. Nijmegen. 1864
Oudste (Hed) N. verboden boek 1523; Oeconomica Christiana, 1882, *see* Oeconomica.

Nederlandsche Uitgeversbond. Het Nederl. boek, 1925. 8º. 1925

Nediani (Tommaso). Ravenna. s8º. Firenze. 1921

Neeb (Ernst), *see* Kautzsch (R.) & E. N. Kunstdenkmäler d. Stadt &c. Mainz, B2i, 1919.

Needham (John), *of Bristol.*
Hymns devotional & moral. s8º. Bristol. 1768

Needham (Joseph), *ed.* Science, religion & reality. [By] Earl Balfour, B. Malinowski, C. Singer [*& o. wr.*] 8º. 1925
,, ,, ...[3rd impr.] 8º. 1926

***Needs** (The) of Europe, 1921, *see* Europe.

Neera, *ps.* [*i.e. Signora* Radius].
Addio! 11ª ed. s8º. Milano. 1904

Neerlandicus. Codex diplomaticus N., 1852–63, *see* Codex.

Neerlands Indië, *see* Nederlandsch Indië.

Neesen (Johann Maria Balduin). Diss. de advocatis eccles. Præs. P. Gallade. [P2636]. s4º. [Heidelberg ?]. 1768

Nefer-ʾir-keʒ-reʿ, *k. of Egypt, see* Borchardt (L.) Grabdenkmal d. Königs N., 1909.

Neff (Felix). *Vie de F. N. s8º. Londres. 1836

Negri (Ada).
Finestre alte. s8º. [1923]
Il libro di Mara. s8º. Milano. [1920]
Le strade. s8º. Milano. [1926]
see Fabbri (E.) A. N., 1921 ?.
,, Frattini (A.) A. N., 1919.

Negri (Salomon) [†Sulaimán ibn Yakúb]. Mem. Negriana, hoc est S. N. vita, olim ab ipsomet conscr. nunc access. illust. & ejusdem Tractatio de vers. N. T. Turc. &c. Ed. G. A. Freylinghausen. s4º. Halae Salicae. 1764

Negro.
*Inquiries rel. to negro emancipation. [P2755]. 8º. 1829
The negro in Chicago: st. of race rels. &c., 1922, *see* Chicago Comm. on Race Relations.
Negro slavery; or, view of state of soc. in U.S. & W. Indies. 4th ed. [P2761]. 8º. 1824

Neilissow (Constantin). De digammate. [*b. w.* Longard (L. C.) Symbola &c., 1837]. 8º. Petropoli. 1854

Neill (Alexander Sutherland). A dominie in doubt. s8º. 1921

Neill (Robert M.) Microscopy in the service of man. [Home Univ. Lib.] s8º. [1926]

Neilos, *bp. of Tamasso.* Τυπικὴ διάταξις τῆς κατὰ τὴν νῆσον Κύπρον μονῆς τῆς ὑπεραγίας Θεοτόκου, Μαχαιράδος ἐπιλεγ. Ἐπιμελείᾳ τοῦ κυρίου Εφραίμ. 8º. Ἐνετίησιν. 1756

Neilson (George). Birkenside & the stewardship of Scotland. [Repr. f. Berwickshire Nat. Club, v24. P2428]. 8º. E. [1920 ?]
A bundle of ballads, *see* English Assoc. Essays &c., v7, 1921.

Neilson (William Allan). The origins & sources of The Court of love [*form. attrib. to Chaucer*]. [Harvard studies &c.] 8º. Boston [U.S.] 1899

Nejedlý (Zdeněk). Frederick Smetana. s8º. [1924]

Nekludov (A.) Diplomatic reminisc., 1911–17. Tr. f. French by A. Paget. 8º. 1920
see Marchand (R.) Un livre noir: diplom. d'avant-guerre, 1910–14, t1, 3 rapps. de N. &c., 1922.

Nekrasov (Nikolai Alekseevich). Избранные стихотворения для дѣтей. Ред. Н. Ашукина. la8º. Москва. 1923
Н. Воспоминания Н. П. Некрасовой. Статьи Б. Эйхенбаума, В. Евгеньева-Максимова, А. Гизетти, Э. Голлербаха. s8º. [Ленинград]. 1928
Н. Неизд. стихотворения, варианты и письма. s8º. П. 1922
Петербургские углы. Со вступит. статьей В. Евгеньева-Максимова. 8º. П. 1921
Стихотворенія. Изд. К. Солдатенкова и Н. Щепкина. s8º. Леіпцигъ. 1859
see Chukovsky (K.) Н., как художник, 1922.
,, —— Поэт и палач (Н. и Муравьев), 1922.
,, Polyansky (V.) Н. А. Н., 1921.
,, Sakulin (P. N.) Н., 1928.
,, Tissot (E.) N. A. N., *n.d.*

Nelis (Hubert). Chambres des comptes de Flandre & de Brabant. Invent. des comptes en rouleaux. [*b. w.* Verriest (L.) Inventaire, 1915]. 8º. Brux. 1914
Chambre des comptes de Lille. Cat. des chartes du sceau de l'audience. t1. 8º. Brux. 1915
Inventaire des archives de l'Université de l'état, à Louvain & du Collège philos., 1817–35. [*b. w.* Verriest (L.) Inventaire, 1915]. 8º. Brux. 1917

Nelson (Ernesto). Las bibliotecas en los Estados Unidos. [C.E. for Int. Peace]. 8º. 1927
Nelson (Horatio Nelson, *viscount*).
see ALLEN (J.) Life of N., 1857.
,, BRIT. MUS.: MSS. MSS. &c. exhib., N. centenary, 1905.
,, SOUTHEY (R.) Life of N.; ed. w. intr. &c. by G. Callender, 1922.
,, VERRUA (P.) O. N. nel pensiero &c. d. Foscolo e d. Canova, 1919.
,, WESTWOOD (A.) M. Boulton's medal &c., also N.'s reception, 1802, 1926.
Nelson (James Fraser) & J. F. Edwards.
Life & teaching of Tukārāma. 8º. Madras. 1922
Nelson (James Henry). The Madura country: manual comp. by o. of Madras Govt. 5p [in 1v. *sep. pagin.*] 8º. Madras. 1868
Nelson (Robert). The life of George Bull, bp. of St. David's, w. hist. of controversies. 2nd ed. s8º. 1714
Nelson (*Sir* **Thomas James),** *see* RICHMOND PARK. Extr. f. recs. of Parl. &c. rel. to transfer &c. of R. P., 1649–60; ed., w. intr. by N., 1883.
Nemény (Wilhelm).
Petersburg, 1920. [P2522]. 8º. München. 1921
Nemesius, *bp. of Emesa.*
see DASHEAN (H.) Short bibliog. st. &c., *in Armenian*, pl, N. &c., 1895.
,, TEZA (E.) Natura dell' uomo di N. e le vecch. tr. in Ital. & Armeno, 1892.
,, —— Nemesiana, Natura dell' uomo in Arm., 1893.
Nemirovich-Danchenko (Vasily Ivanovich).
На кладбищахъ. (Воспоминанія). 8º. Ревель. [1921]
Соловки. Воспоминанія и разсказы. [P846]. s8º. С.-П. 1888
Némirowsky (Irène). L'enfant génial, *see* ŒUVRES libres, 70, 1927.
Le malentendu, *see* ŒUVRES libres, 56, 1926.
Nemours (Gaston de Foix, *duc* **de),** *1489–1512, see* POGGI (V.) I presunti avanzi d. mausoleo di G. di F. in Savona, 1894.
Nemours (Jacques de Savoie, *duc* **de),** *1531–85, see* BORDEAUX (H.) Amours du temps passé: A. d'Este & J. de N., 1923.
Nennius, *abbot of Bangor.* Hist. Britonum, *see* BERTRAM (C. J.) Brit. gentium ant. scr.: N. &c., 1757.
Neocastro (Bartolomaeus de). Hist. Sicula, 1250–93; a cura di G. Paladino, *see* MURATORI (L. A.) Rerum Ital. scr., t13iii, 1921.
Neon, *ps.* *The great delusion: aircraft in peace & war. Pref. by A. H. Pollen. 8º. 1927
Neophytus, *the recluse, 1134–c. 1220.* Homélies [*Grec. & Lat.*], *see* MARY, *the Virgin.* Homélies mariales byz., éd. &c. M. Jugie, 1922.
Neoplatonism. Sel. passages illust. N.; tr., 1923, *see* DODDS (E. R.), *ed.*
Neoportus (Mauritius), *see* NEWPORT (M.)
Neoptolemus *Parianus, see* JENSEN (C.) N. u. Horaz, 1919.
Nepos (Cornelius). Œuvres. Texte établi & tr. par A. M. Guillemin. [Coll. des univ. de France]. 8º. 1923
Vitae. Rec. &c. E. O. Winstedt. s8º. O. [1904]
***Nepotisme (Le)** de Rome, tr., 1664, *see* LETI (G.)
***Nepotismus** theologice expensus. Quando n. sub Innocentio XII abolitus fuit. [Hist. nepotismi]. s8º. *n.p.* [1692?]
Neppi Modona (Aldo).
Cortona etrusca e romana. 8º. Firenze. 1925
Nerger (Carl August). S. M. S. Wolf. s8º. [1918]
Neri (Ferdinando).
Il Chiabrera e la Pleiade francese. s8º. Torino. 1920
Neri (Filippo), *Saint.*
see BACCI (P. J.) Vita di F. N., 1859.
,, MISCIATTELLI (P.) Saggio biog. sopra San F., 1923.
,, NANI (F.) Transito di S. F. N., poema, 1623.
Nernst (Walther). The new heat theorem. Tr. f. 2nd German ed. by G. Barr. 8º. [1926]
Nero, *emperor of Rome.*
see KUKULA (R. C.) Persius u. N., 1923.
,, SCHUR (W.) Die Orientpolitik d. Kaisers N., 1923.
Nero, *ps.* *Nero vanquished. [*Satire on George IV*]. [P425]. 8º. [1820]
Nerses IV, *Glayetsi, patriarch of Armenia.* Opera in Lat. conversa studio J. Cappelletti. 2v *in* 1. 8º. Venetiis. 1833
Nerses *Lampronensis, St.* [Consid. of church order & expos. of the sacrament. *In Armenian*]. 8º. i Venetik. 1847
[Municipal laws. *In Armenian.* Ed. K. H. Basmadschean. Banaser *publ.* P2817]. 8º. Paris. 1907

Nerses *Lampronensis, St.* [*continued*].
[Orations, letters & sermons *in Armenian*], *see* GREGORY IV, *cath. of Arm.* Letters, 1865.
see GREGORY *Skevratzi.* [Panegyric of St. N., *in Armenian*], 1854.
Nerses I, *the Parthian, patriarch of Armenia.* [Hist. of N., *in Armenian*]. (Soferq Hayk., v6, 7). 2v *in* 1. s8º. i Venetik. 1853
Nerses, *Shnorhali, the Gracious, 1102–73.* Banq tchaphav. [Poems, *in Armenian*]. s8º. i Venetik. [1279=1830]
[Life of St. Sargis general (& of his son Martiros), tr. by N. *In Armenian.* Soferq Hayk., v16]. s8º. i Venetik. 1854
Patmouthiun varoutz. [Hist. (12 c.) *in Armenian.* Soferq Hayk., v14]. s8º. i Venetik. 1854
see VETTER (P.) N. S.'s Kirchenlieder, 1899.
Nerva, *emp. of Rome* [NERVA MARCUS COCCEIUS], *see* HENDERSON (B. W.) 5 Roman emperors, 1927.
Nervo (Amado).
Almas que pasan. [Obras compl., 5]. s8º. [1920]
El Bachiller—Un Sueno—Amnesia — El Sexto Sentido. [Obras, 13]. s8º. [1920]
Ellos. [Obras, 9]. s8º. [1920]
Juana de Asbaje. s8º. 1910
,, ,, [Obras, 8]. s8º. 1920
Pascual Aguilera—El donador de almas. [Obras, 6]. 8º. 1920
Las voces, Lira heroica y o. poemas. [Obras, 3]. s8º. 1920
see ESTRADA (G.) Bibliog. de A. N., 1925.
Nesbit (C. M.) The net, *see* SCHOFIELD (S.) The marble god & o. plays, 1926.
Nesbit (E.), *aft. Mrs. Hubert Bland.*
The incredible honeymoon. s8º. [1921]
The phoenix & the carpet. s8º. 1908
The story of the amulet. [2nd impr.] s8º. 1912
To the adventurous. s8º. [1923]
Wings & the child. s8º. [1913]
The wonderful garden. [repr.] s8º. 1912
Nesbitt (Alexander). Notes on the hist. of glass-making. Intr. to cat. of coll. of glass &c. formed by F. Slade. fol. *p.f.p.d.* 1869
Nesbitt (Florence). Standards of publ. aid to children, *see* UNITED STATES: LAB. Children's Bur. Publ. 118, 1923.
Nesmond (Henri de), *bp. of Montauban; abp. of (1) Albi, (2) Toulouse, see* BASNAGE DE BEAUVAL (J.) Traité des préjugez, ou rép. aux lettres &c. de N. &c., 1701.
Nesmy (Jean). Les quatre saisons de la forêt. s8º. 1922
Nesse (Christopher) [NESS]. An antidote against Arminianism. Repr. by R. Stodhart, w. pref. & mem. of the a. s8º. 1835
Nesterov (Mikhail Vasilevich).
see EVREINOV (N. N.) Нестеров, 1922.
,, GLAGOL (S.) М. В. Н.: жизнь и творчество, 1914?.
Nestor, *the annalist.* Средній текстъ лѣтописи Н., *see* VOSKRESENSKAYA LETOPIS. Лѣтопись &c., 1856.
Chronica N. Textum Russico-Sloven. ed. F. Miklosich. 8º. Vindobona. 1860
Russ. Annalen in i. slavon. Grundspr. vergl., übers. u. erkl. v. A. L. Schlözer. 5T. [*in* 3v]. 8º. Göttingen. 1802–9
Nestorius, *patriarch of Constantinople.* The Bazaar of Heracleides. Tr. f. the Syriac & ed. w. intr. &c. by G. R. Driver & L. Hodgson. 8º. O. 1925
see SCHWARTZ (E.) Die sog. Gegenanathematismen d. N., 1922.
Netchvolodow, *see* NECHVOLODOV.
Netherlands.
[*Engraved views of Holland,* 18c. *no tp.*] 8º. *n.p. n.d.*
8 maps or plans of fortified towns in the N. &c. dur. Austrian War of Succession. *MS.* Maps, 6]. folded fol. c. 1746
A manual of N. India (Dutch East Indies), 1920, *see* ADMIRALTY: NAVAL INTELL. DIV.
Netherlands East-Indies. Yearbook of the Netherlands East-Indies, 1920. la8º. *n.p.* 1920
Netolitzky (Aug.), *see* BURGERSTEIN (L.) & A. N. Handbuch d. Schulhygiene, 1912.
Netscher (Pieter Marinus). Gesch. v. d. kolonien Essequebo, Demerary & Berbice. [Prov. Utrechtsch Genoots.] la8º. 's Gravenhage. 1888
Nettelbladt (Daniel). Initia hist. litter. juridicae univ. ed. 2ª auct. s8º. Halae Magd. 1774
Nettelbladt (F. *Frhr.* **von).**
Suaheli-Dragoman. Gespräche, Wbch. &c. s8º. L. 1891
Netter (Nathan). Israël & s. Talmud à trav. l'hist. la8º. 1926
Netter (Thomas), *Waldensis.* Doctrinale antiq. fidei cathol. eccles. Ad vetera exemplaria recog. &c. a B. Blanciotti. [3t]. fol. Venetiis. 1757–59
2, De sacramentis; 3, De sacramentalibus.

Nettleship (Richard Lewis). Lectures on the Republic of Plato. Ed. Ld. Charnwood. [2nd ed., repr.] 8°. 1925
Nettleton (J. A.) Manufacture of whisky & plain spirit. 8°. Aberdeen. 1913
Netto (Coelho), *ps.* [*i.e.* ANSELMO RIBAS]. The pigeons, *see* GOLDBERG (I.), *tr.* Brazilian tales, 1924.
Neubau (Robert).
Kriegsgefangen—ü. England entflohen ! s8°. [1917]
Neubauer (Adolf). The 53rd chap. of Isaiah, acc. to Jewish interpreters. 2v. s8°. O. 1876–77
1, Texts, ed. A. N. 2, Tr. by S. R. Driver & A. N.; w. intr. to the tr. by E. B. Pusey.
Neubauer (Ernst Friedrich). Comm. de Giessens. studio contra Socinianorum deprav. [P444]. s4°. Halae Magd. 1731
Nachr. v. d. itztleb. Evang.-luther. u. Reform. Theologen in Deutschland &c. s4°. Züllichau. 1743
Neubecker (Friedrich Carl).
Russ. u. oriental. Eherecht. [P2526]. 8°. L. 1921
Neubour (Georg Philipp Anton). Diss. qua Athalarici edictum de elig. papa &c. illust. Praes. C. A. Heumanno. [P445]. s4°. Gottingae. [1740]
Neuburg (Philipp Ludwig, *Pfalzgraf* **v.),** *d. 1614, see* SPERL (A.) Pfalzgraf P. L. v. N., s. Sohn Wolfgang Wilhelm u. d. Jesuiten, 1895.
Neuburg (Wolfgang Wilhelm v.), *see* SPERL (A.) Pfalzgraf Philipp Ludwig v. Neuburg, s. Sohn W. W. u. d. Jesuiten, 1895.
Neuburger (Albert). Die Technik d. Altertums. 8°. L. 1919
Neuchatel. Liturgy used in churches of N.: w. a letter f. Dr. Jablonski, conc. liturgies: added, the form of prayer introd. into Ch. of Geneva. 8°. 1712
Neucom (Alexius). Disp. de invocatione Sanctorum. [P2587]. s4°. Tubingae. 1592
Neue [NEWE].
Neue Bibliotheck v. selt. Büchern &c., 1776–82, *see* HUMMEL (B. F.), *ed.*
Neue oriental. u. exeget. Bibliothek, 1786–93, *see* MICHAELIS (J. D.)
Neue Österreichische Biographie, 1815–1918. Begründet v. A. Bettelheim, A. Fournier &c. Geleitet v. A. B. Abt. 1, B1–5, Abt. 2. 8°. Wien. 1923–28
Neue theolog. Bibliothek, 10B, 1760–69, *see* ERNESTI (J. A.)
*Neue (Das) verm. Deutsche u. Wend. Gesangbuch, 1719, *see* GESANGBUCH.
*Newe Zeytung Die Widerteuffer zu Münster belangende, 1535, *see* WIDERTEUFFER.
Neue Beyträge v. alt. u. neu. theolog. Sachen, 1751–61, *see* UNSCHULDIGE NACHRICHTEN V. ALT. U. NEU THEOLOG. SACHEN.
Neue Jahrbücher für d. klass. Altertum, Gesch. u. deut. Litt. u. für Pädagogik. Hrsg. v. J. Ilberg. Jhrg. 1918–24, B41–54. 8°. L. 1918–24
Each Jhrg. has 2B, w. sep. tp.
Neuere Geschichte der Evangel. Missions Anstalten, 1776–1848, *see* DÄNISCHE MISSIONARIEN.
Neues Repertorium f. Bibl. & morgenl. Litteratur. Hrsg. v. H. E. G. Paulus. 3T *in* 1v. 8°. Jena. 1790–91
***Neueste.** N. Gesch. d. reform. Kirche in Pfalz, 1791, *see* HÖFFELEIN (C. A. H.)
N. theolog. Bibliothek &c., 4B, 1771–76, *see* ERNESTI (J. A.)
Neues theologisches Journal. [*Contin. of* Döderlein's Auserles. theolog. Bibl., *q.v.*] Hrsgg. v. H. C. A. Hänlein & C. F. Ammon. 4B. s8°. Nürnberg. 1793–94
,, Hrsgg. v. C. F. Ammon, H. C. A. Hänlein & H. E. G. Paulus. 7B. s8°. Nürnberg. 1795–98
For continuation see: NEUESTES THEOLOG. JOURNAL.
Neuestes theologisches Journal. [*Contin. of* Neues theolog. Journal]. Hrsg. v. J. P. Gabler. 12B. s8°. Nürnberg. 1798–1803
B7–9 *have add. title*: Journal für theol. Lit., B1–3.
For continuation, see JOURNAL FÜR AUSERLESENE THEOLOG. LIT.
Neufchâteau (*le cte.* Nic. L. François de), *see* NIVERNAIS (L., *duc* DE). Œ. posth.; publ. N. F. de N., 1807.
Neuhauss (Georg), *see* KÖLN. Die Stadt Cöln, 1815–1915, 1ii, v. G. N., 1916.
Neuilly (Ange Achille Charles Brunet, *cte.* **de),** *1777–1868, see* BROSTER (D. K.) The happy warrior [*i.e.* Cte. de N.], 1926.
Neukirch (Albert). Der niedersächs. Kreis u. d. Kreisverfassung bis 1542. 8°. L. 1909
Neuman (Henry) & G. Baretti.
Dict. of Spanish & Eng. lang. 4th ed. 2v. 8°. 1823

Neumann (Alfred). König Haber. Erzählung. s8°. St. 1927
Der Teufel. Roman. 8°. 1927
Neumann (Carl Friedrich), *see* LAOU-TSZE. Lehrsaal des Mittelreiches; hrsg. &c. v. C. F. N., 1836.
Neumann (Friedrich Julius), *prof. at (1) Freiburg, (2) Tübingen.* Beiträge z. Gesch. d. Bevölkerung in Deutschland &c. B2, 3. 8°. Tübingen. 1887–89
see FRANKENSTEIN (K.) Bevölk. &c. im Kreise Schmalkalden, 1887. [2.]
,, MARKOW (A.) Wachstum d. B. &c. in Preussen &c., 1889. [3.]
Neumann (Georg Paul). The German Air Force in the Gt. War. Tr. J. E. Gurdon. 8°. [1921]
Neumann (Heinrich), *see* UNTERSUCHUNGEN ü. Preisbildung, Abt. C.; Beitr. v. H. N., 1920.
Neumann (Johann Friedrich Wilhelm). *Bibliotheca juris imperantium quadripartita &c. s4°. Noribergae. 1727
Neumann (Johann Georg), *theologian.*
Orationes 2. [P442]. s4°. Wittenbergae. [1692]
Primitiae diss. acad. cum novo app. & vita autoris. [*3 pagins.*] s8°. Wittenbergae. 1716
Programmata acad. theolog. & hist. argumenti. ed. 3ª. s4°. Wittenbergae. 1722
Neumann (Theresia).
see MAYRHOFER (J.) Konnersreuth, 1927.
,, MESSMER (J.) Die stigmatisierte Seherin T. N.: persönl. Eindrücke v. Konnersreuth, 3ᵉ A., 1927.
,, SCHMID (F.) Die Wahrheit ü. d. Wunder v. Konnersreuth, 1927.
Neumann (Wilhelm), *of Riga.* Riga u. Reval. [Berühmte Kunststätten, 42]. s8°. L. 1908
Neumann Rizzi (Ignazio). *Di alcuni scritti pubbl. da E. A. Cicogna, 1807–50. [*Pref. signed* N. P2787]. 8°. Venice. [1850]
Neumayr (Franz). Frag: Luth. Gewissens-Ruhe &c. [P2629]. s4°. München. 1759
Frag: ob Luther nicht besser gethan hätte, wann er die Fastnacht hätte abgeschafft, u. nicht d. Fasten ? [P2629]. s4°. München. 1757
Neumayr (Melchior). Erdgesch. 3ᵉ A. auf Grund d. v. B. Uhlig hrsg. 2ᵗᵉⁿ A. neu bearb. v. F. E. Suess. B1, Dynam. Geologie. la8°. L. 1920
Neumeister (Erdmann). *Articulus de justificatione a corruptelis Haferungianis assertus &c. s8°. 1732
Neuordnung (Die) d. deut. Finanzwirtschaft. Hrsg. v. H. Herkner, mit Beitr. v. G. Cohn &c. [V. f. Sozialpol. 156ii, iii]. T2, 3. 8°. München. 1918
Ne-user-reᶜ, *king of Egypt, see* BORCHARDT (L.) Grabdenkmal d. Königs N., 1907.
Neuss. Neuss am Rhein. Bearb. &c. im Auftr. d. Stadtverwalt. v. G. Entner. 4°. Düsseldorf. 1926
Neuss (Wilhelm). Die katalan. Bibelillustration um die Wende d. ersten Jhdts. u. die altspan. Buchmalerei. 4°. Bonn. 1922
Neustift. Urkundenbuch d. Augustiner Chorherren-Stiftes N.; hrsg. v. T. Mairhofer, *see* FONTES RERUM AUSTRIAC., B34, 1871.
Neuville (Albert de). Gilles Demarteau. s8°. Turnhout. 1920
Nève (Félix). Valère André, prof. d'hébreu. [P2684]. s8°. Louvain. 1846
Nève (Joseph). Antoine de la Salle: vie & ouvrages d'ap. des docˢ. inéd., suivi du Réconfort de Madame du Fresne *&* du Paradis de la reine Sibylle &c. par A. de la S. s8°. 1903
Nevers. Cartul. de Saint-Cyr de Nevers. [*Publ. &c.*] par R. de Lespinasse. la8°. Nevers. 1916
Neveux (Pol). Golo. Roman. s8°. 1925
Nevile (*Sir* Henry) [NEVILLE], *see* WINWOOD (*Sir* R.) Mems. of aff. of state, negotiations of N. &c., 3v, 1725.
Nevill (Ralph Henry).
Brit. military prints. la8°. 1909
Echoes old & new. 8°. 1919
Eng. country house life. 8°. [1925]
Floreat Etona: anecdotes &c. of Eton College. 8°. 1911
London clubs. 8°. 1911
Mayfair & Montmartre. 8°. 1921
Old Eng. sporting prints. Ed. G. Holme. 4°. *Studio.* 1923
Paris of to-day. 8°. 1924
Romantic London. 8°. [1928]
Unconventional memories. Europe—Persia—Japan. 8°. 1923
The world of fashion, 1837–1922. 8°. [1923]
Yesterday & to-day. 8°. [1922]
Neville (Eric Harold). The fourth dimension. 8°. C. 1921
Neville (Francis de). The Christian & catholike veritie: the conversion of F. de N. &c. 8°. 1642
Neville (Margot). Marietta is stolen. s8°. [1922]

Neville-Polley (Leonard Joseph). John Dalton. s8°. 1920

Nevin (John Williamson).
The mystical presence. 8°. Phila. 1846

Nevins (Allan). Amer. social hist. as recorded by Brit. travellers. 8°. [1924]
The American states, 1775–89. 8°. N.Y. 1924

Nevinson (Christopher Richard Wynne). C. R. W. Nevinson. [*Letterpress by* O. S. Contemp. Brit. Artists]. la8°. 1925
The roads of France. [P2422]. sm. obl. 8°. [1918]

Nevinson (Henry Wood). Changes & chances. 8°. [1923]
More changes, more chances. 8°. [1925]
Original sinners. s8°. [1920]

Nevinson (*Mrs.* Margaret Wynne), *wife of H. W. Nevinson.*
Life's fitful fever: memories. 8°. 1926

Nevsky (V. I.) Братья казаки &c. [P2722]. s8°. Москва. 1919
Харьковское дело Ювеналия Мельникова, *see* Blagoev (D.) От группы Благоева &c., 1921.

—— **& S. Ravitsch.** Arbeiter—u. Bauernuniversitäten in Sowjetrussland. [P2521]. 8°. Hamburg. 1921

Nevzorov (N.) Этимологія и синтаксисъ русскаго и новаго церковно-славянск. языка. изд. 2°е. 8°. Казань. 1879

New [Newe].
*New & faithful tr. of letters f. Mr. l'abbé * * * to B. Kennicott &c., 1773, *see* Dumay (J. A.)
New calendar (The) of great men, 1920, *see* Harrison (F.), *ed.*
*New coll. (A) of hymns for Xtns. of all denom[s]., 1792, *see* Hymns.
*New coll. (A) of voyages & travels into sev. parts of the world &c., 1711, *see* Stevens (*capt.* J.), *ed.*
New Congregational hymn book, *n.d.*, *see* Hymn.
New Decameron (The). [*Tales by var. a.*] v3–5. s8°. O. 1925–27
*New dict. (A) of terms anc. & mod. of the canting crew, *n.d.*, *see* Dictionary.
New English theatre. v10, Cato, Theodosius, Siege of Damascus, Douglas, Zara. s8°. 1777
*New guide (A) to Cheltenham, 1834 ?, *see* Cheltenham.
New historians (The): booklet about the authors of the chron. of Amer., 1920, *see* Chronicles: Chron. of Amer.
New internat. year book. For 1919–1922. Ed. F. Moore Colby. la8°. N.Y. 1920–23
*New Jerusalem (The): a hymn, 1852, *see* Jerusalem.
New past (The) & o. essays on the development of civilisation, 1925, *see* Carter (E. H.), *ed.*
*New pilgrim's (The) progress; or, a journey to Jerusalem [*a satire on Queen Caroline*]. [P2600]. 8°. 1820
New pocket dict. of Eng. & Dutch lang., 1894, *see* Pocket-Dictionary.
*New univ. Eng. & Ital. dict., 2p, 1849, *see* English.
New (A) univ. hist. of arts & sciences, 2v, 1769, *see* Universal.
*Newe metamorphosis (The): [*poem*], 1600, *see* Lyon (J. H. H.) A st. of The newe metamorphosis, wr. by J. M., Gent., 1919.

New age (The). Weekly review. Ed. A. R. Orage &c. v28–34 (Nov. 1920–Oct. 1924). fol. 1921–24

New College, *Edinburgh.* Cat. of the library in the N.C., Edinburgh. 8°. E. 1846

New College, *Oxford, see* Oxford.

New Criterion (The), *see* Criterion (The).

New East (The). A monthly review of thought &c in the E. & W. Worlds. v1, 2 (June 1917–June 1918). la8°. Tokyo. [1917–18]

New Europe (The). A weekly review of foreign politics. v14–16 (Jan.–Oct. 1920). 8°. 1920

New monthly magazine & universal register. v1–14. 8°. 1814–20
contin. as New monthly mag. & literary journal, *q.v. in 1913 Cat.* v6–10, 12 want frontispieces, v7 *wants tp.*

New Russia (The). A weekly review of Russian politics. Ed. by The Russ. Liberation Comm. v1–3 (1920). 8°. 1920

New Spalding Club.
see Banff, *co. of.* Records of co. of B., 1660–1760; comp. by J. Grant, 1922.
,, Inverness. Records of I.; ed. W. Mackay & G. S. Laing, v2, 1924.

New state of Europe, The. No. 18 (Aug. 5–7, 1701). [*b. w.* Daily Courant, No. 85 &c., 1702–03]. s4°. 1701

New statesman (The). A weekly review of politics & lit. v1–30 [18 *wanting*]. 4°. 1913–28

New Sydenham Society. Publications. v22. 8°. 1864
see Donders (F. C.) Anomalies of accommod. & refraction of the eye; tr., 1864. [22.]

New World (The). Monthly internat. review. v2 (Dec. 1919–May 1920). la8°. [1920]

Newall (William). Cat. of coll. of objects of art, Renaissance period, formed by W. N. Sold by Christie, June 27, 1922. [*Illust.*] la8°. 1922

***Newark** as a publishing town, 1898, *see* Blagg (T. M.)

Newark, *New Jersey.*
Public Library.
Chemistry: bks. & periods. rel. to c. [P2686]. 8°. *n.p.* [1921]
Printing & allied indust. [P2686]. 8°. Newark. 1922

Newberry (Percy Edward), *see* Davis (T. M.) Excav.: Bibân el Molûk; Descr. of objects, by N., 1907.

Newbigin (Marion Isabel).
Canada, the Great river, lands, & men. 8°. [1927]
Economics [Romania], *see* Buchan (J.), *ed.* Nations of to-day, Bulgaria & R., 1924.
Former Austro-Hung. lands—Econ. & resources of Yugoslavia, *see* Buchan (J.), *ed.* Nations of to-day, Yugoslavia, 1923.
Frequented ways: land forms, climates &c. of W. Europe &c. 8°. 1922
The Mediterranean lands. 8°. [1924]
see Glasgow. The City of G., its origin &c.; M. I. N., ed., 1921.

Newbold (Ethel M.) Human factor in accidents, *see* Indust. Fatigue Res. Bd.: Rep. 34, 1926.

Newbold (John Turner Walton). Capitalism & counter-revolution. [P2756]. s8°. [1919]

Newbolt (*Sir* Francis George), *K.C.* *Clifton College 40 yrs. ago. Diary of a præpostor. 8°. 1927

Newbolt (*Sir* Henry John).
The book of Cupid: anthology. Intr. by H. N. 8°. 1909
The book of good hunting. 8°. 1920
The book of the Grenvilles. 8°. 1921
Eng. anthology of prose & poetry, 14th–19th c[s]. 2p [p2, Notes & indices; p1, repr.] s8°. 1922
The future of the Eng. lang., *see* Roy. Soc. of Lit. Essays, N.S., v3, 1923.
Peacock, Scott & Robin Hood, *see* Roy. Soc. of Lit. Essays, N.S., v4, 1924.
Poetry & time, *see* Brit. Acad. Proc[s]., 1918.
Some poets & their scenery, *see* Roy. Soc. of Lit. Essays, N.S., v5, 1925.
Story of the Oxf. & Bucks. Light Infantry. 8°. [1915]

Newbolt (Michael Robert).
Edmund Rich, abp. & saint. 8°. 1928

Newbolt (William Charles Edmund).
Years that are past. Recoll[s]. 8°. [1921]

Newborough (Maria Stella Petronilla, *Lady*), *form. known as M. S. P. Chiappini.* Memoirs. Tr. H. M. Capes, w. intr. by B. D'Agen. 8°. 1914

Newbury (William *of*).
Rerum Anglicarum libri 5. s8°. Antverpiæ. 1567

Newcastle [*upon Tyne*]. Early deeds rel. to N. [Ed. A. M. Oliver. Surtees Soc., v137]. 8°. Durham. 1924
Extracts f. the N. upon T. Council minute book, 1639–56. [Intr. &c. by M. H. Dodds]. 8°. Newcastle u. T. 1920
Letters f. the Com. of Estates at N. & Com. of Scotland &c., 1646, *see* Scotland: Parl.

Newcastle Chronicle, The. Nos. 1540–1696 (Jan. 4, 1794–Dec. 31, 1796). [Nos. 1576, 1612, 1631, 1641 = Sept. 13, 1794; May 23, Oct. 3, & Dec. 12, 1795 *wanting*]. la. fol. Newcastle-upon-Tyne, 1794–96

Newcastle upon Tyne Records Committee.
Publications. v1, 4. 8°. Newcastle u. T. 1920–24
see Newcastle. Extrs. f. Council minute book, 1639–56, 1920. [1.]
,, Northumberland. N. monuments, 1924. [4.]

Newcastle (Henry Pelham Archibald Douglas Pelham-Clinton, *7th d. of*). Cat. of old Eng. silver-gilt plate &c., prop. of N. Sold by Christie, July 1921. [*Illust.*] 8°. 1921

Newcastle (Margaret Cavendish, *duchess of*), *2nd wife of 1st duke.* The life of W. Cavendishe, Duke of Newcastle. fol. 1667
see Newcastle (W. C., *1st duke*). The cavalier & h. lady: sel. f. works of 1st Duke & Duchess of N., 1872.

Newcastle (William Cavendish, *1st duke of*), *1592–1676.* The cavalier & h. lady. Sel. f. works of 1st Duke & Duchess of Newcastle. Ed. w. intr. essay by E. Jenkins. s8°. 1872
*Confut. of the Earle of N.'s reasons for taking under h. command &c. Popish recusants &c. [*b. w.* Truths discov., 1646]. s8°. 1643
A gen. system of horsemanship &c. [Tr. by J. Brindley?]. 2v *in* 1. fol. 1743
see Newcastle (M. C., *dss. of*). Life of W. C., D. of N., 1667.

Newcomb (Harvey). A cyclopedia of missions &c. rev. ed. 8°. N.Y. 1855

Newcomb (Rexford).
The volute in archit. &c. 8°. Urbana. 1921

Newcomb (Simon). A crit. exam. of our financial policy dur. Southern Rebellion. s8°. N.Y. 1865
A plain man's talk on the labor question. s8°. N.Y. 1886
Principles of polit. economy. 8°. N.Y. 1886

Newcome (Henry), *Rector of Middleton, Lancashire.* Transubstantiation discuss'd. 2p *in* 1v. s4°. 1705

Newcome (William), *D.D., bp. of (1) Dromore ; (2) Ossory ; (3) Waterford.* An harmony of the Gospels &c. fol. D. 1778

Newcomer (Mabel). Separation of state & local revenues in the U.S. [Columbia Univ. Studies in hist. &c., 76ii]. 8°. N.Y. 1917

Newdigate-Newdegate (*Sir* Francis). Cat. of rare &c. books, prop. of Sir F. N.-N., sold by Sotheby, Jan. 1920. [Illust. P2853]. la8°. [1920]

Newe, *see* NEUE.

Newell (*Mrs.* Harriet), *wife of Rev. S. Newell.* Memoirs. Also, Sermon on h. death by L. Woods. 2nd ed., w. acc. of Amer. Missionary Soc. s8°. 1816
Memoirs. With app. s8°. 1827

Newell (Samuel), *1784–1821, see* JACKSON (T.) Lib. of Xtn. biog., v4, 1838.

New-England.
*Farther (A) brief &c. narr. of the late wars in N.E., 1676, *see* DRAKE (S. G.) The old Indian chron., &c., 1867.
*New (A) & farther narr. of the state of N.-E., by N. S., 1676, *see* DRAKE (S. G.) The old Indian chron. &c., 1867.
N.E. (The) states, 4v, 1897, *see* DAVIS (W. T.), *ed.*
*News from N.-E., a true & last acc., 1676, *see* DRAKE (S. G.) Old Ind. chron., 1867.
*Present (The) state of N.-E. w. respect to the Indian war, 1675, & Cont. &c., 1676, *see* DRAKE (S. G.) Old Ind. chron. &c., 1867.
*True (A) acc. of the most consid. occurrences in the warre, 1676, *see* DRAKE (S. G.) Old Ind. chron., 1867.
*War (The) in N.-E. visibly ended [by R. H. *i.e.* Hutchinson], 1677, *see* DRAKE (S. G.) Old Ind. chron., 1867.
see SOC. FOR PRESERV. OF N.E. ANTIQ.

New England Company. Hist., from 17th cent., incl. rep. of proc., 1869–70. 8°. 1871
Rep. of proc[s]., 1871–72. 8°. 1874

New-England Society. [Proceedings], 68th anniv. celeb., N.Y., 1873. [P2625]. 8°. *n.d.*
see TOOKE (J. H.) Memorial to J. H. T., unveiled by the N.E. Soc., 1920.

Newes, *see* NEWS.

Newest (Th.), *see* GOLDZIER (HANS).

Newfoundland. French treaty rights in N. Case for the colony stated by Sir J. S. Winter, P. J. Scott & A. B. Morine. 8°. 1890
N. & Labrador pilot, 5th ed., 2v, & Suppl. 4, 1917–22, *see* ADMIRALTY.

Newgate.
*Annals of N., or malefactors register, 4v, 1776, *see* VILLETTE (J.)
Malefactor's register, or the N. &c. cal., 1700–79, 1779, *see* MALEFACTOR'S register.
Martin's annals of crime, or New N. cal., v1, 2, 1837–38, *see* MARTIN (A.)
New & compl. N. cal. ; or, Malefactor's univ. register, 8v, 1818, *see* JACKSON (W.)
The new N. cal., 5v, *n.d.* ; 6v, 1826, *see* KNAPP (A.) & W. BALDWIN, *edd.*

Newgate magazine (The), or malefactors monthly chronicle. v2 [pages 523–844 & 109–168]. 8°. 1766

New Guinea, *see also* NIEUW GUINEA.

Newhall (Richard Ager). Eng. conquest of Normandy, 1416–24. 8°. New Haven, *Yale.* 1924

Newington Longeville, *priory.* Newington Longeville charters. Transcr. & ed. w. intr. by H. E. Salter. [Oxf. Rec. Soc., v3]. 8°. O. 1921

New Jersey Historical Society. Collections. v10. 8°. Newark, N.J. 1927
see JONES (E. A.) The Loyalists of N.J., 1927. [10]

Newland (Jane), *see* WESLEY (J.) *Sh. acc. of the life & death of J. N., 1790.

Newman (Bertram). Cardinal Newman. 8°. 1925

Newman (*Maj.* E. W. Polson). The Mediterranean & its problems. Foreword by Ld. E. Gleichen. 8°. [1927]

Newman (Edward), *F.L.S.* A hist. of Brit. ferns. 8°. 1840

Newman (Ernest).
Elgar. [2nd ed.] s8°. 1920
A musical critic's holiday. 8°. [1925]
A musical motley. s8°. 1919
" " [rev. ed.] 8°. N.Y.1925
The piano-player & its music. s8°. 1920
The unconscious Beethoven. 8°. [1927]
Wagner as man & artist. [2nd Amer. ed.] la8°. N.Y. 1924

Newman (*Sir* George).
A century of medicine at Padua. [P2592]. 8°. 1922

Newman (*Card.* John Henry).
The Arians of the 4th c. &c. 8°. 1833
The Benedictine centuries. [*Extr. f.* The Atlantis, v2]. 8°. [c. 1860]
Callista. n. impr. s8°. 1923
*The Church of the Fathers. s8°. 1840
Essay on the development of Xtn. doctrine. 2nd ed. 8°. 1846
Letter to Bp. of Oxford, on occas. of No. 90 in Tracts. [P2788]. 8°. O. 1841
*Letter to R. W. Jelf, D.D., in explan. of No. 90 in Tracts. By the a. [*i.e.* N. P2788]. 8°. O. 1841
On the Roman Breviary &c., *see* TRACTS for the times, No. 75, 1836.
Poetry, w. ref. to Aristotle's Poetics. Ed., w. intr. & notes by A. S. Cook. s8°. Boston [U.S. 1891]
Sel. adapted to the seasons of the eccl. year f. the parochial & plain sermons. 3rd ed. 8°. 1886
see BARRY (W. F.) The Turks, Card. N., & the Council of Ten, 1919.
" NEWMAN (B.) Card. N., 1925.
" TRACTS. T. for the Times : some doc. conn. w. No. 90, 1841.
" WISEMAN (N. P. S.) Letter to N. upon passages in h. letter to Dr. Jelf, 3rd ed., 1841.

Newman (John P.) The thrones & palaces of Babylon & Nineveh. 8°. N.Y. 1876

Newman (Louis Israel).
Jewish infl. on Xtn. reform movts. 8°. N.Y. 1925

Newman (Samuel). *A concordance to the Holy Scripture. By S. N. fol. C. 1662

Newman (V. Winthrop). Illust. cat. of drawings of naval &c. subjects. Coll. of V. W. N. Sold, Amer. Art Assoc., Nov. 30, 1921. [P2855]. 8°. N.Y. [1921]

New Netherland, *see* HENRY E. HUNTINGTON LIBRARY. Doc. rel. to New N., 1624–26 ; tr. & ed. A. J. F. van Laer, 1924.

Newport (Maurice) [NEOPORTUS (MAURITIUS)]. S. Principi Carolo II votum candidum. ed. 3ª recogn. s8°. Londini. 1676

News [NEWES]. *Newes from Scotland : life & death of Dr. Fian, a noted sorcerer &c. (1591), *see* JAMES I, *k. of Gt. Brit.* Dæmonologie, 1924.

Newsham (J. C.) Crops & tillage. Pref. by Ld. Bledisloe. 8°. [1921]

Newsholme (*Sir* Arthur), *K.C.B.*
Elem. of vital statistics. n. ed. rewr. 8°. [1923]
Health probl. in organized society. 8°. 1927
The Ministry of Health. 8°. 1925
Prohibition in America. s8°. 1921
Public health & insurance : Amer. address. 8°. Baltimore. 1920
see MARCHANT (*Sir* J.) Claims of coming generation ; by var. wr. [Dean Inge, Sir A. N. &c.], 1923.

Newski (W.), *see* NEVSKY (V. I.)

New South Wales. Ann. rep. of Dept. of Mines, 1919, 1920. fol. Sydney. 1920–21
Financial statement of Sir A. A. C. Cocks, Colonial Treasurer, 1922, 1923, 1924. fol. Sydney. 1922–24
Financial statement of Hon. J. T. Lang, Premier & Colonial Treasurer, 1925, 1926. fol. Sydney, 1926–27
Official year book, 1918–1924, 1925–26. 8°. Sydney. 1920–25
Report of Dept. of Public Works, year ending June 1919–22, 1925, 1926. fol. Sydney. 1920–27
see CHAPMAN (F.) & W. HOWCHIN. Foraminifera of the permo-carbonif. limestones of N.S.W. [Geolog. Survey : Palæontology, No. 14], 1905.

Newspapers. Tercentenary handlist of Eng. & Welsh n., &c., 1920, *see* TIMES (THE).

Newte (Horace Wykeham Can).
The gentle bigamist. s8°. [1920]
The master beast, 1888–2020. 8°. 1907

Newth (George Samuel). Text-book of inorganic chemistry. n. & enl. ed. s8°. 1923

Newton (Adelaide Leaper), *see* BAILLIE (J.) Memoir of A. L. N., 1871.

Newton (Alfred), *prof. of Zoology at Cambridge, see* WOLLASTON (A. F. R.) Life of A. N., 1921.

Newton (Alfred Edward). The amenities of book-collecting &c. 8°. 1920
A magnificent farce & o. diversions of a book-collector. 8°. 1921

Newton (Arthur Percival). Federal & unified constitutions : coll. of constit. doc[s]. Ed., w. hist. intr. by A. P. N. 8°. 1923
Select docs. rel. to the unific. of S. Africa. Ed., w. intr., by A. P. N. 2v. 8°. 1924

Newton (Arthur Percival) [*continued*].
Travel & travellers of the Middle Ages. [*By var. wr.*] Ed. A. P. N. 8°. 1926
Tudor reforms in the royal household, *see* POLLARD (A. F.) Tudor studies, 1924.
The universities & educ. systems. [Brit. Emp.: survey; ed. H. Gunn, v10]. 8°. 1924

Newton (Augustus). The case of Thomas Smethurst, trial &c. for murder & bigamy. s8°. 1859

Newton (Edwin Tulley), *F.G.S.* The vertebrata of the forest bed series of Norfolk & Suffolk. [Mems. of G.S.] 8°. 1882
The vertebrata of the Pliocene deposits of Britain. [Mems. of G.S.] 8°. 1891

Newton (Evelyn, *Lady*), *wife of Th. Wodehouse Legh, 2nd baron Newton.* Lyme letters, 1660–1760. 8°. 1925

Newton (George) *of Taunton.* A sermon at the funeral of Joseph Aleine, *see* ALLEINE (J.) Life, 1672.

Newton (Henry Chance). The Old Vic & its assoc. Foreword by G. Dance. s8°. [1923]

Newton (*Sir* **Isaac).**
The chronology of the anc. kingdoms amended. [*Ed.* J. Conduitt]. s4°. 1728
Isaac Newton, 1642–1727. Mem. vol. [*by var. a.*] ed. for Mathematical Assoc. by W. J. Greenstreet. [With bibliog. & list of portraits]. 8°. 1927
Mathemat. principles of nat. philos. Tr. by A. Motte. 3v. 8°. 1803
Obs. upon Daniel & the Apocalypse of St. John. [Ed. B. Smith]. 2p *in* 1v [*pagin. contin.*] s4°. 1733
„ „ [*a.c. b. w. h.* Chronol., 1728]. 2p. s4°. 1733
Two letters to Mr. Le Clerc: upon I John, v. 7, *&* I Timothy, iii. 16. [P490]. 8°. 1754
see BRODETSKY (S.) Sir I. N., 1927.
„ HORNE (G.) *The theol. & philos. in Cicero's Somnium Scipionis explained: N. system &c., 1751.
„ SNOW (A. J.) Matter & gravity in N.'s physical philos., 1926.

Newton (John), *rector of St. Mary, Woolnoth.* Letters & sermons; w. a rev. of eccl. hist. & hymns. [Ed. by T. Haweis]. 6v. s8°. 1787

Newton (Richard Bullen). Eocene Mollusca f. Nigeria. With app. on the Foraminifera by E. Heron-Allen &c. [Geolog. Survey of Nigeria. Bull. No. 3]. la8°. *n.p.* 1922

Newton (Robert), *D.D., Wesleyan minister, see* JACKSON (T.) Life of R. N., 1855.

Newton (Wilfrid Douglas). Green ladies. s8°. [1919]

New York, *city & state.*
ANON. WORKS & MISC. PUBLS.
Historic N.Y.; [*by var. wr.*], 2v, 1899, *see* GOODWIN (M. W.), *ed.*
Letter (A) f. the Comm. of the Assoc. of N.Y. to the Lord Mayor &c. of London, 5th May 1775. [*Facs. w. intr.* P2417]. 4°. 1920
Manual for the use of the legislature of the State of N.Y. Prep. by the Sec. of State. 1869, 1870, 1871, 1875, 1892. s8°. Albany. 1869–92
Minutes of Comm. & of 1st Commission for detecting &c. conspiracies in State of N.Y., Dec. 1776–Sept. 1778; added, Minutes of Council of Appointment, Apr. 1778–May 1779, 2v [*pagin. cont.*], *see* NEW YORK HIST. SOC. Coll., v57–58, 1924–25.
Papers rel. to 1st settlement of N.Y. by the Dutch, cont. list of immigrants, 1657–64, f. "Doc. hist. of N.Y." & Descr. &c. of New Netherland f. "Wassenaer's Hist. van Europa." *la. paper.* 2v *in* 1. 8°. *p.p.* E. 1888
*Picture (The) of N.Y., 1828, *see* GOODRICH (A. T.)
Report of Prison Survey Comm. 4°. Albany, N.Y. 1920
Revolutionary radicalism; its hist., purpose & tactics. Rep. of the Joint Legislative Comm. investig. seditious activities, filed Apr. 24, 1920, in the Senate of the State of N.Y. [Chairman, C. R. Lusk]. 2p *in* 4v. 8°. Albany. 1920
Stichting (De) van, N.Y. in Juli 1625, *see* WIEDER (F. C.), *ed.*
see LLOYD, *The fam. of.* Papers of the L. fam. of the manor of Queens Village, Lloyd's Neck, N.Y., 1654–1826, 2v, 1927.

Departments of State &c.
ASSEMBLY OF THE STATE OF N.Y.
Proc. of the Judiciary Comm. of the Assembly in investig. as to qualifications of L. Waldman, A. Claessens &c. to retain their seats. [Legisl. Doc. No. 35]. 3v. [v1 *wants tp.*] 8°. Albany. 1920
BOARD OF COMMISS. OF THE DEP. OF PUBLIC PARKS.
First ann. rep. la8°. N.Y. 1871
CENSUS.
Census of the State of N.Y. for 1865 & 1875. 2v. fol. Albany. 1867–77
LAWS.
Revised statutes of the State of N.Y. 3v [v3, 3rd ed.] 8°. Albany. 1829–48
Statutes at large of the State of N.Y. Ed. J. W. Edmonds. 5v. 8°. Albany. 1863

New York, *city & state* [*continued*].
Departments of State &c. [*continued*].
LIBRARY [NEW YORK STATE].
Bulletin. v24–31. la8°. N.Y. 1920–27
see LYDENBERG (H. M.) Hist. of N.Y. Publ. Library, 1923.
UNIVERSITY OF THE STATE OF NEW YORK.
Ottendorfer mem. series, *see* MITCHELL (R. M.) Heyse &c., 1915.
see ROCHESTER UNIV., *N.Y.*

New York Academy of Science [*form.* LYCEUM OF NATURAL HIST.], *see* FAIRCHILD (H. LE R.) Hist. of the N.Y. Acad., 1887.

New York Chamber of Commerce. Charter & by-laws w. a hist. of the C. of C. of the St. of N.Y. [*by* C. King]. 8°. N.Y. 1855

New York Historical Society. Collections. Publication Fund Ser. [v52–60]. 8°. N.Y. 1921–27
Colden (C) Letters & papers, v3–7, 1743–75. [52–56.]
Lloyd. Papers of the L. family of the manor of Queens Village, Lloyd's Neck, N.Y., 1654–1826, 2v. [59, 60.]
New York. Minutes of Committee & 1st Commission for detecting & defeating conspiracies, Dec. 1776–Sept. 1778; added, Minutes of Council of Appointment, Apr. 1778–May 1779, 2v. [57, 58.]

New York Times, *see* DAVIS (E. H.) Hist. of the N.Y.T., 1851–1921, 1921.

New York Tribune (The), *see* CONGDON (C. T.) Tribune articles, 1857–63, 1869.

New York Zoological Society.
see BEEBE (C. W.) The Arcturus adv.: N.Y. Zoolog. Soc.'s 1st oceanogr. exped., 1926.
„ —— Galápagos: world's end, 1924.
„ —— Monograph of pheasants, 4v, 1918–22.
„ ——, G. I. HARTLEY &c. Tropical wild life in Brit. Guiana, v1, 1917.

New Zealand.
CENSUS.
Results of a census, 1916. 12p *&* App. A–E [*in 1v*] fol. Wellington. 1918
„ „ ......Rep. fol. Wellington. 1920
Results of a census, 1921. 15 p. *&* App. A–F [*in 1v.*] fol. Wellington. 1921–25
„ „ ......Gen. rep. fol. Wellington. 1925
MISC. GOVT. PUBLS. & ANON. WORKS.
Handbook on the dominion of N.Z. [P2755]. 8°. 1924
Local authorities handbook, 1926, 1927. Compiled in Census &c. Office. 1st, 2nd issue[s]. 8°. Wellington, N.Z. 1926–27
*N.Z.: an illust. descr. &c., 1924, *see* FANNING (L. S.)
N.Z. official year-book, 1921–1928. 8°. Wellington. 1922–27
N.Z. pilot, 9th ed., *&* Suppl. 3, 1919–22, *see* ADMIRALTY.
Royalty in N.Z. Offic. souv. of visit of T.R.H. The Duke & Duchess of York, 1927. la8°. 1927
War effort of N.Z. [*By var. wrs.*] Ed. Lt. H. T. B. Drew. [Offic. hist. of N.Z.'s effort in Gt. War, v4]. 8°. Auckland. 1923
STATISTICS [*see also* CENSUS *above*].
Rep. on the vital statistics of N.Z., 1921–25. fol. Wellington. 1922–26
Statist. rep. on local government in N.Z. for 1921–24. fol. Wellington. 1923–25
Statist. rep. on the population &c. of N.Z. for 1921–1925/26. fol. Wellington. 1922–26
Statist. rep. on trade & shipping in N.Z., 1921–26 [1925 & 1926 *in* 2p]. fol. Wellington. 1922–27
Statistics of the Dominion of N.Z., 1917, Suppl. to v2; 1918 & App. to v3; 1919, 1920. fol. Wellington. 1918–22
1918–20 *in 4v. each year.*

Nexø (Martin Andersen).
Bornholmer Noveller. s8°. 1913
Ditte: daughter of Man. Tr. A. G. Chater & D. Thirsk. s8°. 1922

Ney (Joseph Napoléon), *duc d'Elchingen.* Doc. inéd. sur la campagne de 1815. Publ. par le Duc d'E. [*tp. missing*]. 8°. 1840

Ney (Julius). Pfalzgraf Wolfgang, Herzog v. Zweibrücken u. Neuburg. [Verein f. Ref.-gesch. Schr., Jhrg. 29, Nr. 106/7]. 8°. L. 1912

Ney (*le maréchal* **Michel),** *prince de la Moskowa, see* BONNAL (*gén.* H.) La vie milit. du mar. N., t3, 1914.

Nibelungenlied.
see FISCHER (H.) Entstehung, 1914.
„ HEMPEL (H.) Nibelungenst., B1, 1926.
„ HEUSLER (A.) Nibelungensage u. N., 1921.
„ TONNELAT (E.) La Chanson des N.: compos. & form., 1926.

Niblack (*Rear-Adm.* **Albert Parker),** *U.S. Navy.* Why wars come, or forms of govt. & for. policies in rel. to causes of wars. s8°. Boston, Mass. 1922

Niboyet (Paulin) [*ps.* FORTUNIO], *see* STOCKHOLM. S. pittoreskt album; *letterpress signed* P. N., 1857.
Nicasio, *pastor' arcade, ps.* Per le vittorie, 1717, contro il Turco, sotto Eugenio di Savoja canzone. [N125]. 8º. Lucca. 1717
Niccodemi (Dario).
La morte in maschera. Romanzo. s8º. Milano. [1920]
Niccolotti Pescatori. *Relazione verid. d. modo che si tiene nel creare il Gastaldo grande de' N. P., 1762, *see* RELAZIONE.
Nice. Catéchisme du diocèse de N. publ. par ordre de D. Galvano, évêque. s8º. Nice. 1839
Obituaire de l'anc. cathédrale de N.; publ. & annoté par E. Cais de Pierlas, *see* REGIA DEP. DI STORIA PATRIA. Misc., t34, 1896.
see SAINT-PONS. Chartrier de l'abbaye de Saint-Pons hors les murs de N., 1913.
Niceforo (Alfredo). Les classes pauvres. Recherches anthropolog. &c. 8º. 1905
Le génie de l'argot. s8º. 1912
Les indices numér. de la civilisation & du progrès. s8º. [1921]
Niceforo (Nicola). La Sicilia e la costit. del 1812, *see* SOCIETÀ SICIL. Arch., n.s., 44–46, 1922–25.
Nicephorus, *Saint, Patriarch of Constantinople.* Chronologia sec. Graecorum rationem. Conversa in serm. Lat. & explic. à I. Camerario. Add. Narr. Camerarii De Synodo Nicaena. Omnia recognita procur. E. Voegelino. s4º. Lipsiae. 1573
Opuscula hist. Ed. C. de Boor. Acced. Ignatii diac. vita N. [*in Greek*]. s8º. L., *Teubner.* 1880
Niceron (Jean Pierre). Nachrichten v. d. Begebenheiten u. Schriften berümten [*sic*] Gelehrten: [übers., u.] mit Zusätzen hrsg. [T1–15] v. S. J. Baumgarten. [T16–22 *by* F. E. Rambach. T23–24 *by* C. D. Jani].
24T *in* 12v. s8º. Halle. 1749–71
This is a tr. of Mémoires p. s. à l'hist. des hommes ill., *q.v.*
Niceta, *of Remesiana, see* BURN (A. E.) The hymn Te Deum & its author [*i.e.* N.?], 1926.
Nicetas, *bp. of (1) Serra & (2) Heraclea.* Catena Graec. patrum in beatum Iob, collectore N. Graecè nunc ed. & Lat. versa opera P. Junii. Acc. Textus Iobi. [Textus Iobi *has sep. pagin.*] fol. 1637
De metris, *see* KOSTER (W. J. W.), *ed.* Tract. Graeci, 1922.
see CORDIER (B.) & P. POSSINUS. Symbol. in Matthaeum &c. t2, Catena patrum Graec 30, coll. Niceta &c., 1547.
Nichiren, *Japanese Buddhist, 1222–82, see* SATOMI (K.) Japanese civilization: Nichirenism &c., 1923.
Nicholas, *prince, of Greece, b. 1872.* My 50 years. 8º. [1926]
Nicholas, *of Guildford, see* OWL (THE) & THE NIGHTINGALE [*possibly by N. of G.*], 1922.
Nicholas, *Saint, bp. of Linköping, see* REMBERT, *St.* S. Anscharii vita &c. & versio vetus Suecica quam dedit S. N., 1677.
Nicholas, *Saint, bp. of Myra.* Hagios Nikolaos. Der hlg. N. in d. griech. Kirche. Texte u. Untersuch. v. G. Anrich. 2B (1, Die Texte [*Greek lives &c.*] 2, Prolegomena, Unters., Indices). 8º. L., *Teubner.* 1913–17
Nicholas I, *pope.* Epistolae, *see* DUMMLER (E. L.), *ed.* Epist. Merow. et Karol. aevi, t4, 1925.
see PERELS (E.) Papst N. I u. Anastasius, 1920.
Nicholas V, *pope, see* MANCINI (G.) G. Tortelli cooperatore di N. nel fondare la Bibl. Vaticana, 1920.
Nicholas I, *emperor of Russia.*
see BLUDOV (*count* D. N.) Les dern. heures de N. I; tr., 1855.
,, KORF (*count* M. A.) Восшествіе на престолъ Н. I, 1857.
,, MSEREANTZ (M.) [The last hours of N. I, *in Armenian*], 1855.
,, SIROECHKOVSKY (B. E.) Междуцарствие 1825г, и восстание декабристов в переписке &c. [Н.] &c., 1926.
Nicholas II, *emperor of Russia.*
Дневникъ [1890–1906]. 8º. Берлинъ. 1923
Первый юбилей Н. II (1894–1904). [P2400]. s8º. Берлинъ. 1905
Переписка Вильгельма II с Н. II, 1923, *see* WILLIAM II, *Germ. emp.*
Переписка Н. и Александры Романовых, 1914–[17]. т3–5, с предисл. М. Н. Покровского. 8º. Москва. 1923–27
Полное собраніе рѣчей Николая II, 1894–1906. [P2446]. s8º. С.-П. 1906
*Последние дни последнего царя. [P2758]. s8º. Москва. 1922
*Царь Переводъ съ англійскаго. [P810]. s8º. *n.p.* 1905
Lettres de N. II. & de sa mère. Tr., intr. &c. de P. L. Léon. 3e éd. s8º. [1928]
see ALEXANDRA FEDOROVNA, *emp. c.* Письма къ Н. II [*Russ. & Eng.*], 2t, 1922.

Nicholas II, *emperor of Russia* [*continued*].
see BENCKENDORFF (*Count* P.) Last days at Tsarskoe Selo; tr., 1927.
,, GARDENIN (YU.) Юбилей Н. послѣдняго, *n.d.*
,, GILLIARD (P.) 13 years at the Russ. court: last yrs. of N. II &c.; tr. F. A. Holt, 1921.
,, —— Le tragique destin de N. II, 1921.
,, HANBURY-WILLIAMS (*Maj.-Gen. Sir* J.) Emp. N. II as I knew him, 1922.
,, NECHVOLODOV (A.) L'Emp. N. II & les Juifs; tr., 1924.
,, SCHEGOLEV (P. E.), *ed.* Отречение Н. II: воспом. очевидцев, док., 1927.
,, SEMENNIKOV (V. P.) Монархия перед крушением, 1914–17; бумаги Н. II &c., 1927
,, WILLIAM II, *German emp.* The Kaiser's letters to the Tsar; ed. &c. N. F. Grant, 1920.
Nicholas (*Sir* Edward). Nicholas papers: corr. of Sir E. N. Ed. Sir G. F. Warner. [Roy. Hist. Soc., III, 31]. v4, 1657–60. 8º. 1920
see EVELYN (J.) Mems. &c.; subj., private corr. betw. Charles I & Sir E. N., 1818.
Nicholas (Innocent). Vocab. of Eng. & Tamul words: added coll. of dialogues & rudiments of grammar. 8º. Madras. 1820
Nicholas (William), *D.D.*
Christianity & Socialism. Fernley Lect. 8º. 1893
Nicholas Mikhailovich, *grand duke.* L'empereur Alexandre I. Essai d'étude hist. t1. 4º. St. Pétersbourg. 1912
see ALEXANDER I, *emp. of Russia.* Corresp. de l'emp. A. I avec sa sœur Catherine, 1805–18; [publ. avec intr. par] N. M., 1910.
Nicholl (*Rt. Hon. Sir* John), *LL.D., Judge of Arches Court.* The judgment, Dec. 11, 1809, Kemp, ag. Wickes, clerk, for refus. to bury infant child &c. [P527]. 8º. 1826
Nichols (Beverley).
Are they the same at home? 8º. [1927]
,, ,, [2nd impr.] 8º. [1927]
Crazy pavements. s8º. [1927]
Patchwork. [2nd impr.] s8º. [1927]
Prelude. A novel. [2nd impr.] s8º. [1920]
Self. s8º. 1922
Twenty five: candid recoll. [2nd impr.] s8º. [1926]
,, ,, [4th impr.] s8º. [1926]
Nichols (*Capt.* George Herbert Fosdike) [*ps.* QUEX].
The 18th division in the Great War. 8º. 1922
London Town. Intr. by A. Bennett. s8º. 1926
Pushed & the return push. s8º. E. 1919
Nichols (James), *Printer.*
Calvinism & Arminianism compared. 8º. 1824
Nichols (John), *F.S.A., printer.* *Beiträge zu W. Hogarth's Lebensbeschreibung. Nebst e. Verzeichnisse s. Kupferstichwerks. Aus d. Engl. mit Abkürzung, [*by Crayen*]. 8º. L. 1783
*Biog. anecdotes of William Hogarth; & a cat. of h. works &c. [*By N. assisted by G. Steevens & I. Reed*]. 8º. 1781
,, ,, ...2nd ed. 8º. 1782
,, ,, [*a. copy corrected by author to form "copy" for 3rd ed.*]
,, ,, ...3rd ed. 8º. 1785
,, ,, [*a. copy w. MS. corrections by author*].
—— **& G. Steevens.** The genuine works of William Hogarth illust. w. biog. anecdotes, a chron. cat. & comm. 2v. 4º. 1808
Nichols (John), *of the English Seminary, Rome.* The oration & sermon made at Rome, Maie 1578. Now brought into the Eng. tongue. Herein also is answered an infamous libell agst. J. N. s8º. 1581
Nichols (John Gough). London pageants. 8º. 1837
Nichols (John Treadwell). Fishes of the vicinity of New York City. Intr. by W. K. Gregory. [Amer. Mus. of Nat. Hist., Hdbk. ser., No. 7]. 8º. N.Y. 1918
Nichols (Robert). The assault & o. war poems, f. "Ardours & endurances." s8º. 1918
Fantastica: The smile of the sphinx & o. tales of imagin. s8º. 1923
Invocation: war poems &c. [P2596]. s8º. 1915
Nichols (Rose Standish).
Spanish & Portuguese gardens. s4º. [1925]
Nicholson (*Mrs.* Asenath). The Bible in Ireland. [*Abridg. of*] Ireland's welcome to the stranger &c. Ed. w. intr. by A. T. Sheppard. 8º. [1926]
Nicholson (C. A.) The dancer's cat. s8º. 1925
To be a lady. s8º. 1927
Nicholson (D. H. S.) The marriage-craft. s8º. [1924]
The mysticism of St. Francis of Assisi. 8º. [1923]

Nicholson (John Henry). The re-making of the nations. 8º. 1925
Nicholson (Joseph Shield).
Elements of polit. economy. 2nd ed. [repr.] 8º. 1922
The revival of Marxism. s8º. 1920
Nicholson (Peter). The student's instructor in drawing & working the 5 orders of architecture. 3rd ed. augm. 8º. 1810
Nicholson (Reynold Alleyne).
The idea of personality in Ṣúfism. s8º. C. 1923
St. in Islamic mysticism. 8º. C. 1921
St. in Islamic poetry. [Lubábu 'l-Albáb: early Persian anthology; *by* Muḥammad 'Awfí—The meditations of Ma'arri]. 8º. C. 1921
Translations of Eastern [Arabic & Persian] poetry & prose. 8º. C. 1922
see THORNTON (F. DU P.) & R. A. N. Arab. reading book, 1907.
Nicholson (Sydney Hugo), *organist of Westminster Abbey, see* GARDNER (G. L. H.) & S. H. N., *edd.* Manual of Eng. church music, 1923.
Nicholson (*Maj.* **Walter Adams).** Artillery fire. s8º. 1907
Nicholson (Watson). Anthony Aston, stroller & adventurer. App. Aston's Brief suppl. to Cibber's Lives; & sketch of life of A. A., wr. by himself. s8º. South Haven, Michigan. 1920
Hist. sources of Defoe's Journal of the plague year. s8º. Boston, Mass. 1919
Nicholson (William), *artist.* W. Nicholson. [Plates, w. descr. &c. signed S. K. N.] la8º. 1923
Nicholson (William), *bp. of Gloucester.* A plain expos. of the catechism of the Ch. of England. s4º. 1671
***Nichts** neues, sondern e. alte papist. Legend v. Cainischen Messia, e. Schmehkarte ü. Lutheri Rand-Glösslein Gen. iv, 1 [*b. w.* Fecht (J.) Hist. Coll. Emmending., 1694]. s8º. St. Annenberg. [1693?]
Nicius Erythræus (Janus), *see* ERYTHRÆUS (J. N.)
Nickalls (E. Patteson). The challenge of life. s8º. 1927
Piper's Hill & o. poems. s8º. [1922]
Nickerson (Hoffman). The Inquisition: polit. & milit. study. Pref. by H. Belloc. 8º. 1923
Nicodemi (Giorgio). Il Moreto da Brescia. s8º. Firenze. 1921
Pittori lombardi. 26 riprod. con testo e cat.; a cura di G. N. 8º. [1922]
Nicodemus, *see* HORSTMANN (C.) Nachträge zu d. Legenden, p2, 1882.
Nicodemus, *Gospel of.* Evangelium N. ausz dem latein gebracht. s4º. *n.p.* [c. 1530]
Evangelium N. in altschoft. Mundart aus MS. Harl. 4196 (14 J.) v. C. Horstmann, *see* ARCHIV F. D. ST. D. NEU SPR., B53, 57, 1874–77.
see BIBLE: ANGLO-SAXON. Heptateuchus, Evang. N. &c., Anglo-Sax.; ed. E. Thwaites, 1698.
Nicol (E.) Les Alliés & la crise orientale. s8º. 1922
Nicol (J. W.) Brush-drawing: hdbk. for teachers &c. 4º. 1901
Nicolai (Jeremias). Theologiae e solis sacris literis concinn. libri 4. s8º. Hamburgi. 1604
Nicolai (Joannes). Sel. quaedam antiquitates eccl.: mores Xtn. vet. in conventibus & templis. s8º. Tubingae. 1705
Nicolai (Laurentius), *Jesuit.* Confessio Christiana de via Domini, quam Christianus populus in 3 regnis septentr. Daniæ, Sueciæ & Norvegiæ constantes confessus est. s4º. Cracoviæ. 1604
Nicolai (Melchior). Consid. 4 quaest. controv. de profundissima κενώσει Jesu Christi. ed. 2ª. s4º. Tubingae. 1676
Nicolai (Philipp). Comm. de regno Christi, vaticiniis accomodat. libri duo. [*b. w.* Camerarius (J.) Hist. narr., 1605]. 2p *in* 1v. s8º. Francoforti ad Moenum. 1597
Fundamentorum Calvinianae sectae cum vet. Arianis & Nestorianis communium detectio. [P2632]. 8º. Tubingæ. 1586
Theoria vitae aeternae oder hist. Beschr. d. gantzen Geheimnisses v. ewigen Leben. Mit e. Vorrede v. J. D. Arcularias. [5ᵉ A.] s4º. Franckfurt a. M. 1707
Nicolai (*Oberst* **Walter).** Geheime Mächte. Internat. Spionage u. i. Bekämpfung im Weltkrieg &c. 8º. L. 1924
Nicolas (F. J.), *see* CANADA: GOVT. PUBL. Index to rep., 1906–10 & summary rep., 1905–16; comp. by F. J. N., 1923.
Nicolas (J. B.) Dialogues persans-franç. &c. 2ᵉ éd. 8º. 1869
Nicolas (*Sir* **Nicholas Harris),** *see* THISTLE, *The Order of the.* Statutes; ed. &c. Sir N. H. N., 1828.
Nicolas (Yvon). The belief in personal immorality. [Cayme Press]. 8º. Kensington. 1925
Nicolaus, *von Leiden, see* GERHAERT (N.)
Nicolaus, *Leonicenus, see* LEONICENO (N.)
Nicolaus, *de Lyra.* Postilla seu expositio super Psalterium Daviticum & hymnos &c. 4º. [Lugduni, *Anthon. du Ry.* 1516]
see BIBLE: LATIN. Biblia maxima, cum annot. N. de L. &c., 19t, 1660.
„ —— Biblia Sacra &c. & postilla N. L. &c., 1634.
Nicolaus, *physicus.* Anatomia [12 c.]; tr., *see* CORNER (G. W.) Anatom. texts, 1927.
Nicolaus, *Smeregus.* Annales civit. Vincentiae, 1200–1312; a cura di G. Soranzo, *see* MURATORI (L. A.) Rerum Ital. script., t8v, 1921.
Nicolaus (Melchior), *see* FORER (L.) Manuale Lutheranorum, adv. M. N. Symbolum Luther. male vindicatum, 1628.
Nicole (Georges). La peinture des vases grecs. la8º. 1926
Un vase du style de Meidias, nécrop. d'Ensérune, *see* ACAD. DES INSCR.: FOND. PIOT. Mon., t27, 1924.
Nicole (Jules). Cat. d'œuvres d'art conserv. à Rome, époque imp.: texte du pap. lat. 7 de Genève transcr. & comm. [P2790]. la8º. Genève. 1906
Nicole (Pierre) [*ps.* BARTHELEMI].
*Les prétendus reformez convaincus de schisme p. s. de réponse à Consid. sur les lettres circulaires de l'assemblée du clergé de France 1682. [*by Jean Claude*]. s8º. 1684
„ „ ....2ᵉ éd. rev. s8º. 1684
see ARNAULD (A.) & P. N. *Logica, sive ars cogitandi, 1677.
„ AUBERT DE VERSÉ (N.) L'avocat des protes. contre N., 1686.
„ CLAUDE (J.) La défense de la Réformation contre le livre: Préjugez &c., 1673, 1683.
„ PASCAL (B.) Pensées, suiv. d'un choix des pensées de N. & de s. traité de la paix, 1861.
Nicoletti (Giuseppe). Illust. d. chiesa e scuola di S. Rocco in Venezia. la8º. Venezia. 1885
In mem. d. G. N. morto 1911. [P2836]. 8º. [Venezia?. 1911]
Nicoli Cristiani (Federico). Della vita &c. di L. Gambara. Agg. notizie int. á pittori bresciani. la8º. Brescia. 1807
Nicolini (Fausto).
Works in ARCHIVIO STOR. ITAL.
La famiglia dell' Abate Galiani, 1918. [76ii.]
La lettera di G. Boccaccio a Fr. de' Bardi, 1924. [82ii.]
Per la biog. di G.-B. Vico, 1925. [83ii.]
L' "Istoria civile" di P. Giannone ed i suoi crit. rec. [Estr. d. Atti d. Accad. Pontan., v37. P2789]. la8º. Napoli. 1907
Nicoll (Allardyce).
British drama: hist. survey. 8º. [1925]
The development of the theatre. 4º. [1927]
Dryden & h. poetry. s8º. [1923]
Dryden as an adapter of Shakespeare. [Sh. Assoc. Papers., No. 8]. 8º. [1922]
Hist. of early 18th cent. drama, 1700-50. 8º. 1925
Hist. of late 18th cent. drama (1750–1800). 8º. C. 1927
Hist. of Restoration drama, 1660–1700. 8º. C. 1923
„ „ 2nd ed. 8º. C. 1928
Intr. to dramatic theory. s8º. [1923]
Studies in Shakespeare. s8º. 1927
Nicoll (*Mrs.* **Allardyce)** [JOSEPHINE CALINA].
Shakespeare in Poland. [Sh. survey, 1]. s4º. 1923
Nicoll (*Sir* **William Robertson).** Dickens's own story: side-lights on h. life & personality. 8º. 1923
The garden of nuts: mystical expos. w. essay on Xtn. mysticism. 2nd ed. 8º. 1905
see DARLOW (T. H.) W. R. N.: life & letters, 1925.
Nicolle (Marcel), *see* LOUVRE. La peinture, école angl. [*& espagn.*], par M. N., 2p, 1927.
Nicolls (Ferdinando), *see* ROSE-TROUP (F.) An Exeter worthy & his biographer [F. N.], 1897.
Nicolson (*Hon.* **Harold G.).**
Byron: the last journey, April 1823–April 1824. 8º. 1924
Paul Verlaine. 8º. [1921]
Some people. 8º. 1927
Swinburne. [Eng. Men of Letters]. 8º. [1926]
Swinburne & Baudelaire, *see* ROY. SOC. OF LIT. Essays &c., n.s., v6, 1926.
Tennyson: aspects of h. life, character & poetry. 8º. 1923
Nicolson (*Hon.* **Victoria Mary),** *see* SACKVILLE-WEST (V.), *aft. wife of Hon. Harold G. Nicolson.*
Nicolson (William), *bp. of (1) Carlisle; (2) Derry, abp. of Cashel* [NICHOLSON]. The Eng. hist. library. 3p. s8º. 1696–99
The Scot. histor. library &c. s8º. 1702
Nicol-Speyer (Alexander), *see* HUBERICH (C. H.) & A. N.-S., *edd.* Germ. legisl. for Belgium, 17 ser. &c., 1915–19.
Nicomachus, *Gerasinus.* Intr. to arithmetic. Tr. M. L. D'Ooge. With st. in Greek arithmetic by F. E. Robbins & L. C. Karpinski. [Univ. of Michigan]. la8º. N.Y. 1926
Nicon, *6th Patriarch of Moscow; 1605–81* [NIKON], *see* THORNTON (R.) Life of N., 1854.
Nidhámí-i-'Arúdí, *Samarqandí, see* AḤMAD IBN 'UMAR.

Niebergall (Friedrich).
Prakt. Theologie. B2. 8°. Tübingen. 1919
Niebuhr (Barthold Georg), *see* SRBIK (H. *Ritt.* v.) Ein Schüler N.'s: W. H. Grauert, 1914.
Niederheitmann (Friedrich). Cremona: acc. of Ital. violin-makers & th. instruments. Tr. w. notes &c. by W. H. Quarrell. 8°. 1894
Niederländische Akten u. Urkunden z. Gesch. d. Hanse u. z. deut. Seegesch., B1, 1913, *see* HÄPKE (R.)
Niederle (Lubor). Manuel de l'antiq. slave.
2t (1, L'hist. 2, La civilisation). la8°. 1923–26
Niedermayer (Andreas). Mecheln u. Würzburg. Skizzen &c. Katholiken-Versamml. in Belgien u. Deutschland.
s8°. Freiburg im Br. 1865
Niedieck (Paul).
Begegnungen mit Menschen u. Tieren. 2e A. s8°. 1921
Niedner (Chr. Wilhelm). Philosophiae Hermesii Bonnensis explic. &c. [P2755]. 8°. Lipsiae. 1838
Niedner (Otto). Die Kriegsepidemieen d. 19 Jhdts. 8°. 1903
Niekamp (Johann Lucas). Kurtzgefasste Missions-Gesch.: Evang. Miss.-Berichte aus Ost-Indien, 1705–36. Mit Vorrede G. A. Franckens. s4°. Halle. 1740
Hist. missionis evang. in India orientali. In ling. Lat. tr. a I. H. Grischovio. Praef. praem. G. A. Franckius.
s4°. Halae. 1747
Niel (P. G. J.) Portraits des personages français les plus illustres du 16e siècle. Rec. publ. avec notices par N.
2s *in* 1v. fol. 1848–56
Each Notice has sep. pagin.
Nielsen (Ditlef). Handbuch d. altarab. Altertumskunde. In Verbindung mit F. Hommel u. N. Rhodokanakis, hrsg. D. N., mit Beitr. v. A. Grohmann u. E. Littmann.
B1. 4°. Kopenhagen. 1927
Nielsen (Fred K.) American & Brit. claims arbitration under spec. agreem. concl. betw. the U.S. & Gt. Brit., Aug. 18, 1910. Rep. of F. K. N. 8°. Wash. 1926
Nielsen (Harald). Af Tidens Træk, litt. Afhandl. 8°. 1909
Holberg i Nutidsbelysning: en æstetisk Undersøgelse. 8°. 1923
Vej og Sti: æstet. Afhandlinger. 8°. 1916
Nielsen (Lauritz). Dansk Bibliografi, 1482–1550, med særligt Hensyn til dansk Bogtrykkerkunsts Hist. 4°. 1919
Nielsen (Niels).
Works in KONG. DAN. VID. SELSK. Math.-fys. Medd.
Recherches s. l'équation de Fermat, 1922. [4.]
Recherches s. les équations de Lagrange, *& o. p.*, 1923. [5.]
Sur l'opération itérative des équations de Lagrange, 1924–25. [6.]
Nielsen (Peter). The black man's place in S. Africa.
s8°. Cape Town. 1922
Niem (Theodoricus de), *bp. of (1) Verden, (2) Cambray.* De vita & fatis Constantin. Johannis Papae XXIII, 1416, *see* †HARDT (H. V. D.) Rerum Conc. Const. t2, 1697.
Niemann (Alfred). Kaiser u. Revolution. Ereignisse im Grossen Hauptquartier. 8°. [1922]
Wanderungen mit Kaiser Wilhelm II. 2. A. 8°. L. 1924
Niemann (George), *see* LANCKOROŃSKI (C. *Graf*). Städte Pamphyliens u. Pisidiens; unter Mitw. v. G. N., 2B, 1890–92.
Niemann (Walter). Die Musik d. Gegenwart u. d. letzten Vergangenheit bis z. d. Romantikern &c. 9e–12e A. 8°. [1920]
Niemeier (Johann Barthold). De conjugiis prohibitis dissertationes [1–10]. Acc. suppl. cum indice. [*Each diss. w. diff. resp. & sep. tp. in 1v*]. s4°. Helmestadi. [1699–]1705
De fanaticorum palinodia, diss. præs. J. H. v. Elswich.
[P2631]. s4°. Vitembergæ. 1714
Tract. de disciplina eccl. in 4 diss. digestus. Acc. J. Sirmondi Hist. poenitentiae publ. s4°. Hannover. 1703
Niemeyer (August Hermann). Die Universität Halle nach i. Einfl. auf Theol. s8°. Halle. 1817
Niemeyer (Paul).
Die Erkältungskrankheiten. 2e A. [P2461]. s8°. *n.d.*
Niemojewski (Jan) [NIEMOJEVIUS (JOANNES)], *see* SOCINUS (F.) De Coena Domini, unà c. ejusdem adv. scr. J. N. defensione, 1618.
Niemöller (Heinrich). Reformationsgesch. v. Lippstadt. [Verein f. Ref.-gesch. Schr., Jhrg. 24, Nr. 91].
8°. Halle a. d. S. 1906
Nienburg (Bertha M.) The status of women in the govt. service in 1925, *see* UNITED STATES: LAB. Women's Bur., No. 53, 1926.
The woman home-maker in the city, Rochester, N.Y., 1920. [Bur. of Census. P2763]. 8°. Wash. 1923

Nieper (Hieronymus). Quietismi revolut. in Quietistis 14[1] & hujus sec. [P2630]. s4°. Helmestadi. 1696
Nieremberg (Juan Eusebio).
De origine Sacræ Scr. libri 20. fol. Lugduni. 1641
A treatise of the diff. betwixt the temporal & eternal. Tr. V. Mullineaux. 8°. *n.p.* 1672
Nieri (Idelfonso).
Cento racconti popolari lucchesi. 8°. Livorno. 1906
Nierszesovicz (Deodatus), *bp. of Trajanopolis.* [D. N. E. T.]
*Dict. Lat.-Armenum super Sacr. Scrip. & lib. dic. offic. eccles. Arm. s4°. Romae. 1695
Niess (Joannes), *see* HUGO (H.) Pia desideria: quatuor noviss. M. Raderi & J. N., 1673.
Nieto (David) [DAVID BEN PHINEHAS], *see* AMZALAK (M. B.) D. N., 1923.
Nieto (Ishac), *the younger, see* SEPHER. ספר לב טהור, *w. tr. by* I. N., 1753.
Nieto (José Moreno), *see* MORENO NIETO (J.)
Nietzsche (*Frau* **Elis. Förster**), *see* FÖRSTER-NIETZSCHE.
Nietzsche (Friedrich August Ludwig). Epist. Petri posterior, auctori suo imprimis contra Grotium vindicata &c.
8°. Lipsiae. 1785

Nietzsche (Friedrich Wilhelm).
Werke, B15–20 [15, 16, 2e Abt., B7, 8; 17–19, 3e Abthlg. B1–3, B15, 3e A.] 8°. L. 1910–26
15, Ecce homo—Der Wille z. Macht, Buch 1 u. 2.
16, Der Wille z. Macht, Buch 3 u. 4.
17–19, Philologica. 20, Register.
Also sprach Zarathustra. [T1 *in* P2475]. 8°. Chemnitz. 1883
" " ....T4 [*b. w. h.* Fröhliche Wiss., 1887]. 8°. L. 1891
" " ....[T]2, 3 *in* 1v. 8°. Chemnitz. 1883–84
Dionysos-Dithyramben. [*wanting tp. b. w. h.* Fröhl. Wiss., 1887].
8°. [L. 1888 ?]
Die fröhl. Wissenschaft. [*b. w. h.* Morgenröthe, 1881].
8°. Chemnitz. 1882
" " ....Neue A., mit e. Anhange: Lieder d. Prinzen Vogelfrei. 8°. L. 1887
Die Geburt d. Tragödie. [*b. w. h.* Unzeitgemässe Betrachtungen, 1873–76]. 2e A. 8°. L. 1874
Götzen-Dämmerung. [*b. w. h.* Jenseits v. Gut u. Böse, 1886].
8°. L. 1889
Jenseits von Gut u. Böse: Vorspiel e. Philosophie d. Zukunft.
8°. L. 1886
Menschliches, Allzumenschliches. Anhang: Vermischte Meinungen u. Spruche. 2B [in 1v.] 8°. Chemnitz. 1878–79
Morgenröthe. Gedanken ü. d. moral. Vorurtheile.
8°. Chemnitz. 1881
Unzeitgemässe Betrachtungen. 4 St. [4, 2e A.] 8°. L. 1873–76
1, Strauss, d. Bekenner u. Schriftsteller.
2, Vom Nutzen u. Nachtheil d. Historie für d. Leben.
3, Schopenhauer als Erzieher.
4, Wagner in Bayreuth.
Der Wanderer u.s. Schatten. [*b. w. h.* Menschliches, &c., 1878–79].
8°. Chemnitz. 1880
Zur Genealogie der Moral. [*b. w. h.* Jenseits v. Gut u. Böse, 1886].
8°. L. 1887
TRANSLATIONS.
The birth of tragedy, or Hellenism & pessimism. Tr. by W. A. Haussmann. [Comp. wks., v1; Levy]. [2nd ed.] s8°. 1910
N. as critic, philosopher, &c. Selections f. h. works, comp. by T. Common. 8°. 1901
The N.-Wagner corresp. Ed. E. Foerster-Nietzsche. Tr. C. V. Kerr. Intr. H. L. Mencken. la8°. [1922]
Sel. letters. Ed. with pref. by O. Levy. Auth. tr. by A. M. Ludovici.
8°. 1921
see ANDLER (C.) N., sa vie & sa pensée, t1–3, 5, 1920–22.
" EISNER (C.) Psychopathia spiritualis: F. N. u. d. Apostel d. Zukunft, 1892.
" EWALD (O.) N. Lehre in ihren Grundbegriffen, 1903.
" FÖRSTER-NIETZSCHE (*Frau* E.) The lonely N.; tr., 1915.
" HANSSON (O.) F. N., s. Persönlichkeit &c., *n.d.*
" KAATZ (H.) Weltanschauung F. N., T1, 1892.
" MESSER (A.) Erläut. zu N.'s Zarathustra, 1922.
" RICHTER (R.) F. N., s. Leben u. s. Werk, 1922.
" RIEHL (A.) F. N., Künstler u. Denker, 1898.
" SALIS-MARSCHLINS (M. v.) Philosoph u. Edelmensch: e. Beitrag z. Charakteristik F. W. N., 1897.
" SCHELLWIEN (R.) Max Stirner u. F. N., 1892.
" STRECKER (C.) N. u. Strindberg, 1921.
" TÜRCK (H.) N. u. s. philosoph. Irrwege, 1891.
" VAIHINGER (H.) Philos. des Als Ob; mit Anhang ü. Kant u. N., 1911; 1923.
" WEIGAND (W.) F. N., psych. Versuch, 1893.
" WRIGHT (W. H.) What N. taught, 1915.
" ZERBST (M.) Nein u. Ja! Antworf auf H. Türck's Fr. Nietzsche, 1892.

Nieuhof (Jan). Legatio batavica ad magnum Tartariae chamum Sungteium.
2p [*w. sep. pagin.*] fol. Amstelodami. 1668

Nieuwenhuis (Ferd. Jac. Domela). Oratio de varia mutatione quam in patria nostra subiit Eccl. Lutherana.
8°. Trajecti ad Rhenum. 1845

Nieuwentydt (Bernard). L'existence de Dieu démontrée par les merveilles de la nature. [*Tr. f. the Dutch by* P. Noguez].
3p *in* 1v. 4°. Amsterdam. 1727

Nieuw Guinea. N.G., ethnograph. & natuurkundig onderzocht &c. in 1858 door e. Ned. Ind. Comm., *see* BIJDRAGEN tot de taal &c. v. Ned. Ind., volg. 2, d5, 1862.

Nieva (Alfonso Pérez), *see* PÉREZ NIEVA (A.)

Nievo (Ippolito), *see* BULFERETTI (D.) I. N., 1831–61, versi e prose, 1925.

Niger (Hieronymus), *1492–1557, see* SADOLETO (*il card.* J.) Epistol. append., H. N. vitae, epist. &c., 1767.

Niger (N. G. Radulescu-), *see* RADULESCU-NIGER (N. G.)

Nightingale (B.) Early stages of the Quaker movement in Lancashire. 8°. [1921]

Nightingale (Florence).
see COOK (*Sir* E. T.) Life of F. N., repr., 2v, 1914; abridged & rev. by R. Nash, 1925.
„ HALL (E. F.) F. N., 1920.
„ STRACHEY (L.) Eminent Victorians, 1920.

Nightingale (James E.) On the succession of the abbesses of Wilton &c. [From Wilts. Arch. Mag., v19. P2515].
8°. [Devizes]. 1881

Nigond (Gabriel). Sophie Arnould: pièce, *see* REVUE HEBDOM. Suppl., No. 6, 1922.

Nigra (Costantino), *see* CAVOUR. Il carteggio Cavour-Nigra, 1858–61, v1-3, 1926–28.

Nihilismus. *Was ist der Nihilismus? Von e. Eingeweihten.
[P2620]. s8°. L. 1881

Nihusius (Bartoldus), *bp. of Myra.* Anticriticus, de fabrica Crucis Dominicæ incertam G. Calixti opinionem esse indicans. [*b. w.* Lipsius (J.) De Cruce, 1640]. s8°. Coloniae Agripp. 1644

Niise (Nicolai de), *see* DENYSE (N.)

Nijegorodets, *ps.*
Русскіе коммунисты-духоборы. [P848]. s8°. Москва. 1906

Nijhoff (M.) De wandelaar. Verzen. 8°. A. 1916

Nijhoff (Martinus). De Anglophobie van Nic. Witsen &c. [Overdr. uit Het Boek. P2874]. 8°. [1925]
Fondscatalogus, 1853–1926. 8°. 's-Gravenhage. 1927

Nijhoff (Wouter) & M. E. Kronenberg. Nederl. bibliographie van 1500 tot 1540. la8°. 's-Gravenhage. 1923
„ „ Aanvulling 1, 2 [*in* 1v].
la8°. 's-Gravenhage. 1925–27

Nijni-Novgorod [NIJEGOROD]. Отчетный ежегодник Н. ярмарки 1922, 1923. la8°. [Москва]. 1923–24

Nikisch (Arthur), *see* CHEVALLEY (H.) A. N., Leben u. Wirken, 1922.

Nikitenko (Aleksandr Vasilevich), *1804–77.* Моя повѣсть о самомъ себѣ &c. Записки и дневникъ (1804–77). Изд. 2ое подъ редак. М. К. Лемке. 2t. la8°. С.–П. 1904–5

Nikitin (Athanasius) [†ATHANASIUS, *son of Nikita*]. Fahrt ü. d. drei Meere. Reise e. russ. Kaufmannes nach Ostindien, 1466–72. Übers., mit Einl. &c. v. K. H. Meyer. s8°. L. [1920]

Nikitine (Nicolas). Le matin, nouv. [tr. par L. Bernstein & L. Desormonts], *see* ŒUVRES libres, 34, 1924.

Nikolsky (Yurii).
Тургеневъ и Достоевскій. Исторія одной вражды. s8°. Софія. 1921

Nikonovskaya letopis. Лѣтописный сборникъ, имен. патріаршею или никон. лѣт. (продолженіе). [Полное соб. русс. лѣт. изд. Арх. Комм. т 12]. 4°. С.–П. 1901

Niles (Blair). Casual wanderings in Ecuador. 8°. 1923

Nilostonsky (Robert). Der Blutrausch d. Bolschewismus.
3. A. 8°. Lorch. [1925]

Nilsøn (Jens), *bp., 1538–1600.* Visitatsbøger og reiseoptegnelser, 1574–97. Udg. ved Y. Nielsen. [Norske Hist. K.]
8°. 1885

Nilsson (Martin P.)
Die Anfänge d. Göttin Athene, *see* KONG. DAN. VID. SELSK. Hist.-fil. Med., B4, 1921–22.
Hist. of Greek religion. Tr. F. J. Feilden. Pref. by Sir J. G. Frazer. 8°. O. 1925
Imperial Rome. Tr. G. C. Richards. 8°. 1926
Minoan-Mycenæan relig. & its survival in Greek relig. [Kungl. Hum. Vetenskapssamf. i Lund, Skr. 9]. 8°. Lund. 1927
Primitive time-reckoning. 8°. Lund. 1920

Nilsson (Martin P.) [*continued*].
Timbres amphoriques de Lindos &c. [Acad. Roy. des Sci. &c. de Dan. Extr. du Bull., 1909. Explor. de Rhodes (Fond. Carlsberg) 5]. 8°. Copenhague. 1909
Die Übernahme u. Entw. d. Alphabets durch d. Griechen, *see* KONG. DAN. VID. SELSK. Hist.-fil. Med., B1, 1917–18.

Nilus, *Saint.* Libellus de primatu Romani Pontificis. A M. Flacio Illyr. in Lat. conversus, cum praef. ejusdem. [*Gr. & Lat.*] s8°. Francofurti. 1555

Nilus, *bp. of Tamasso, see* NEILOS, *bp. of Tamasso.*

Nilus (Sergei). Protocols of the learned elders of Zion. Tr. V. E. Marsden. [P2719]. 8°. 1923
see TRUTH (The) about "The Protocols," 1921.

Nimmo (Joseph), *jr.* Compar. rates of wages in U.S. & in for. countries, 1882, *see* UNITED STATES: STATISTICS.

Nineteenth Century (The). v87–103. la8°. 1920–28

Ninian (*Sir*). *Sir N., a tale of chivalry, &c., 1860, *see* MASSON (P. A.)

Nioradze (George).
Der Schamanismus bei d. sibir. Völkern. 8°. St. 1925
see BEKOEV (G.) Das Ossenland [*rev. of N.'s* Bergossen &c.], 1924.

Niox (*le gén.* **Gustave Léon**). Expéd. du Mexique, 1861–67: récit polit. & milit. 8°. 1874
Géographie. 5, L'expansion europ. Empire Brit., Asie—Afrique—Océanie. 3e éd. s8°. *n.d.*
see PARIS: MUSÉE DE L'ARMÉE. Résumé des fastes milit. de la France: guide [par] Gen. N., 1920.

Nippold (Otfried). Development of internat. law after the World War. Tr. A. S. Hershey. [C.E. for Int. Peace].
la8°. 1923

Nisard (Jean Marie Napoléon Désiré), *see* AGRONOMES (Les) lat.: Caton, Varron, Columelle, Palladius; publ. M. N., 1877.

Nisbet (Mary), *aft. wife of Th. Bruce, 7th/11th Earl of Elgin & Kincardine, see* ELGIN & KINCARDINE (M., *ctss. of*).

Nissardi (Filippo), *see* TARAMELLI (A.) & F. N. L'altipiano d. Giara di Gesturi in Sardegna, 1907.

Nisser (Wilhelm). Michael Dahl & the contemp. Swedish school of painting in Eng. 4°. Uppsala. 1927

Nistor (Ioan). Un capitol din vieata culturată a Românilor din Bucovina, 1774–1857, *see* ACADEMIA ROM. Disc., 44, 1916.
Der nationale Kampf in d. Bukowina, mit besond. Berücks. d. Rumänen u. Ruthenen. Ausg. d. Rumän. Akad.
la8°. București. 1919
Românii & Rutenii in Bucovina. [Anexă: Bemerk. de I. Budai-Deleanu]. Ed. Acad. Române. la8°. București. 1915
see HURMUZAKI (E. DE). Doc. priv. la ist Românilor, v19i, Coresp. diplom. si rap. consulare austriace, 1782–97; publ. I. I. N., 1922.

Nithardus, *S. Richarii abbas.* Hist. des fils de Louis le pieux. Éd. & tr. Ph. Lauer. 8°. 1926
Hist. libri 4. Acced. Angelberti rhythmus de pugna Fontanetica. [Scr. rer. Germ. in usum schol.]
ed. 3a rec. E. Müller. 8°. Hannoverae. 1907

Nitschmann (David), *Moravian bp.* *Manuel de doctrine des églises des Frèves-Moraves. s8°. Londres. 1743

Nitti (Francesco Saverio). The decadence of Europe: the paths of reconstruction. Tr. F. Brittain. 8°. [1923]
La decadenza dell' Europa—Le vie d' ricostruzione.
8°. Firenze. [1922]
L'Europa senza pace. la8°. Firenze. [1921]
Peaceless Europe. [Tr.] 8°. 1922
They make a desert. Tr. F. Brittain. 8°. 1924

Nitze (William Albert) & E. P. Dargan.
Hist. of French lit. 8°. [1923]

Nitzsch (*Dr.*), *see* WESTFALEN. Bau- u. Kunstdenkm., 30, Kreis Halle, gesch. Einl. v. Dr. N., 1909.

Nitzsch (Carl Immanuel). De testamentis 12 patriarcharum.
[P2645]. s4°. Vitebergae. [1810]
Urkundenbuch d. Evang. Union mit Erläut. hrsg. v. N.
8°. Bonn. 1853

Nivarius (Eustachius). Oratio habita Romæ coram Julio XII [pro agendis gratiis propensissima confirmationis gratia].
s4°. [Bononiae, *per Benedictū Hectorē.* 1506]

Nivelle (*gén.* **Robert Georges**), *see* PIERREFEU (J. DE). L'offensive du 16 avril: vérité sur l'affaire N., 1919.

Nivernais (L., *duc* **de).** Œuvres posthumes. Publ. à la suite de son éloge par N. F. de Neufchâteau. 2t. 8°. 1807

Nixon (John Alexander). The debt of medicine to the fine arts. Addr. [*From* Bristol medico-ch. j.] 8°. Bristol. [1923]

Niẓāmī, *Ganjavī* [†ILYĀS IBN YŪSUF (ABU MUḤAMMAD), *called Niẓāmī, Ganjavī*]. Haft paikar (the 7 beauties). Cont. the life & adv. of King Bahrām Gūr &c. Tr., w. comm. by C. E. Wilson. 2v [1, Tr. 2, Comm.] s8º. 1924
Nizámí-i-'Arúḍí, *of Samarqand.* Chahár Maqála. Rev. tr., foll. by abridg. tr. of Mírzá Muḥammad's notes to the Persian text by E. G. Browne. [Gibb Mem. Ser., v11ii]. 8º. 1921
Nizamu-d Dīn, *see* ZAFAR HASAN (*Maulvi*). Guide to N.-d Dīn [*& Life*], 1922.
Nizier du Puitspelu, *see* TISSEUR (C.)
No. *No appeal, 3v, 1870, *see* JOHNS (B. G.)
Nō. Cinq Nō; tr., 1921, *see* PERI (N.)
Nō (The) plays of Japan; [tr. &c.] by A. D. Waley, 1921, *see* WALEY (A. D.)
Noah, *patriarch, see* DREXEL (H.) Noe architectus arcæ &c., 1652.
Noailles, *the family of, see* LENOTRE (G.) Le Jardin de Picpus, 1928.
Noailles (Adrien M. de Noailles, *duc* **de),** *1678–1766, see* LOUIS XV, *king of France.* Corr. de L. XV & du Maréchal de N.; publ. C. Rousset, 2t, 1865.
Noailles (Amblard Marie Raymond Amédée, *vte.* **de),** *b. 1856.* La mère du Grand Condé, C. M. de Montmorency, psse. de Condé, 1594–1650. 8º. 1924
Noailles (Anna Maria Helena, *ctsse.* **de),** *form. Coesveldt, see* OSBORNE (C. C.) A. M. H., ctsse. de N., 1918.
Noailles (*Marq.* **Hélie de).** Le comte Molé, 1781–1855. Sa vie, ses mém. t1–3. 8º. 1922–24
Life & memoirs of Count Molé, 1781–1855. Ed. by the Marq. de N. v1, 2. 8º. 1923[-25]
Noailles (*le card.* **Louis Anton de).** Appellations-Instrument v. 3. April 1717. Übers. v. J. M. Heineccio. *Fr. & Germ.* [P436]. s4º. Halle i. Magdeb. 1718
see BASNAGE DE BEAUVAL (J.) Traité des préjugez, ou réponse aux lettres de N., 1701.
,, GASTRELL (F.) Lettre d'un évesque angl. à Mgr. le card. de N., c. 1718.
Noailles (*ctsse.* **Mathieu de)** [*i.e.* ANNE ELISABETH, *pcsse. de Brancovan*].
A Rudyard Kipling. s8º. [1921]
Les forces éternelles. éd. rev. & corr. s8º. [1921]
L'honneur de souffrir. [Cahiers verts, 69]. s8º. 1927
,, ,, [28e éd.] s8º. 1927
Parmi les lettres qu'on n'envoie pas, see ŒUVRES libres, 2, 1921.
Parmi les lettres qu'on n'envoie pas, nouvelle, *see* ŒUVRES libres, 14, 1922.
Poème de l'amour. s8º. 1924
see JAMMES (F.) Œ., t5, L'évol. spirituelle de Mme. de N., 1926.
,, PLÉIADE (LA): [*poems by* Ctsse. de N. &c.], 1921.
Noake (John). Worcester sects. s8º. 1861
Nobbs (Eric A.)
Guide to the Matopos. 1st impr. 8º. Cape Town. 1924
Nobel (Alphons). Handbuch d. Staatsmanns. Im Anhang ein Personalregister d. Politiker d. Welt, bearb. v. G. Schultze. 8º. München. 1923
Nobili (Riccardo). The gentle art of faking. s8º. 1922 [1921]
*Nobilitá et antichitá d. famiglia Capece, 1687, *see* CAPECE (B.)
Noble (*Sir* **Andrew),** *K.C.B.* Artillery & explosives. 8º. 1906
Noble (Arthur Henry), *see* SHERLOCK (R. L.) & A. H. N. Geol. of co. around Beaconsfield, 1922.
Noble (John). British S. Africa & the Zulu war. Paper, R.C.I. [P2832]. 8º. 1879
Noble (Joseph). Gazetteer of Lincolnshire, hist., topogr. & antiq. 8º. Hull. 1833
Noble (Mark). An hist. genealogy of the royal house of Stuarts fr. Robert II to James VI. 4º. 1795
Mem. of the illust. house of Medici, 1428–1737 &c. 8º. 1797
see FLINDALL (J. M.) Amateur's pocket companion: books mentioned in wks. of N. &c., 1813.
Noble (Richmond Samuel Howe). Shakespeare's use of song, w. the text of the princ. songs. 8º. 1923
Noble (Sam), *A.B.* 'Tween decks in the 'seventies. An autobiog. Foreword by Rear-Adm. A. P. Davidson. 8º. [1925]
Noble (Thomas) & T. Rose. The counties of Chester, Derby, Leicester, Lincoln, & Rutland, illust. f. drawings by T. Allom. With hist. &c. descr. by T. N. & T. R. 4º. [1836]
Noblesse belge (La). Annuaire 1913. Publ. Baron de Troostembergh [& A. de Ridder]. 2p [*in 1v*]. 8º. Brux. 1913
Noch. Ночь революціи, трагедія. [P2453]. 8º. *n.p. n.d.*
Nocq (Henry). Le poinçon de Paris: rép. des maîtres-orfèvres dep. le moyen-âge j. la fin du 18e siècle. [v1, A–C]. 4º. 1926

Nodier (J. E. Charles).
Contes fantastiques. n. éd. acc. de notes. s8º. 1850
Moi-même. Ouvrage inéd. avec intr. sur le roman personnel par J. Larat. s8º. 1921
Nouvelles, suiv. des Fantaisies du dériseur sensé. n. éd. acc. de notes. s8º. 1859
Romans. n. éd. acc. de notes. s8º. 1850
Souv. de jeunesse, suiv. de Mlle. de Marsan & La neuvaine de la Chandeleur. 5e éd. s8º. 1850
Souv. de la Révol. & de l'Empire. n. éd. avec notes &c. 2t. s8º. 1850
see LARAT (J.) Bibliog. crit. des œuvres de N.; suivie de docs. inéd., 1923.
,, PINGAUD (L.) La jeunesse de C. N.: les Philadelphes, 1914.
Nöding (Kaspar). Leitfaden bei'm Unterricht in d. hess. Gesch. 2e verm. A. s8º. Marburg. 1824
Noel (*Hon.* **Baptist Wriothesley).** The state of the Metropolis. Letter to the bp. of London. 3rd ed. enl. s8º. 1835
Noel (*Hon.* **Charles).** *A narr. of the prosec. of C. Noel on inform. of Charles, earl of Romney, charg. C. N. w. permitt. an assembly f. relig. worship at h. mansion &c. [P527]. 8º. Maidstone. [1816]
Noël (L.) Le Card. Mercier. s8º. Turnhout. 1920
Noël (Pierre). L'Allemagne & les réparations. 8º. 1924
Noel (*Hon.* **Roden B. W.),** *4th s. of 1st e. of Gainsborough, see* SYMONDS (J. A.) & E. HICKEY. The poetry of N., 1901.
Noer (Marie Esther, *Fürstin* **v.),** *see* WALDERSEE (*Gräfin* M. E. v.)
Nofri (Gregorio) & F. Pozzani. La Russia com' è. Pref. di F. Turati. 2a ed. s8º. [1921?]
Nogales (Rafael de). Four years beneath the crescent. Tr. M. Lee. Intr. by E. Davis. 8º. 1926
Nogaret de la Valette & de Foix (Henri de), *duc de Candale, see* CANDALE (HENRI, *duc* DE).
Nogaro (Bertrand) & L. Weil. La main-d'œuvre étr. & coloniale pend. la Guerre. [C.E. for Int. Peace]. 8º. [1926]
Noguchi (Yone). Utamaro. Tr. M. E. Maitre. la8º. 1928
Nohl (Johannes). The Black Death: chron. of the Plague. Comp. f. contemp. sources. Tr. C. H. Clarke. 8º. [1926]
Der schwarze Tod: e. Chronik d. Pest, 1348–1720. Bearb. v. J. N. s8º. Potsdam. 1924
Noke (Charles J.) & H. J. Plant.
Pottery: hist., processes &c. s8º. [1924]
Nola (Paulinus, *bp. of***),** *see* PAULINUS, *Saint, bp. of Nola.*
Nolan (Frederick). An inquiry into the integrity of the Greek vulgate. 8º. 1815
Nolan (*Dom* **Patrick).**
Monetary hist. of Ireland. p1, 2. s8º. 1926–28
Nolde (*Baron* **Boris Emanuilovich).** Lenins Räte-Republik. Übers. v. R. Paderstein. [P2457]. 8º. 1920
Петербургская миссия Бисмарка, 1859–62. Россия и Европа в началѣ царствованія Александра II. la8º. Прага. 1925
Le règne de Lénine. s8º. 1920
Nöldeke (Theodor). Gesch. d. Qorāns. 2e A. bearb. v. F. Schwally. T1–3i. 8º. L. 1909–26
1, Über d. Ursprung d. Qorāns. 2, Die Sammlung d. Qorāns. 3, Gesch. d. Qorāntexts, v. G. Bergsträsser.
Untersuch. z. Achiqar-Roman, 1913, *see* KÖNIGL. GESELLS. D. WISS. ZU GÖTT. Abhlgn., N.F., 14, 1913.
Noldius (Christianus). Concordantiae particularum Ebræo-Chaldaic. J. G. Tympius rec. &c. 4º. Jenae. 1734
Hist. of Herod the Gt., *see* JOSEPHUS (F.) Works; tr., 1754.
Nolhac (Pierre de).
Ausonia Victrix. s8º. [1922]
Disc. pour la récept. de P. de N. [*on* E. Boutroux. Rép. de M. Donnay. Acad. Fr., 18 jan. 1923. P2869]. 4º. 1923
Marie-Antoinette, dauphine. s8º. [1906]
Nattier: peintre de Louis XV. 8º. 1925
Un poète rhénan ami de la Pléiade, P. Melissus. 8º. 1923
La reine Marie-Antoinette. [4e éd.] 8º. [1925]
Ronsard & l'humanisme. [H.E., 227]. 8º. 1921
Tableaux de Paris pend. la Révol. franç., 1789–92: 64 dessins de J. L. Prieur. fol. 1902
Versailles & la cour de France. 8º. 1925
La vie amoureuse de Pierre de Ronsard. s8º. [1926]
Nollekens (Joseph F.) [OLD NOLLEKENS].
see SAYERS (J.) Hints to N. on h. modelling a bust of Ld. G****** le, 1808.
,, SMITH (JOHN T.) N. & h. times; ed. & annot. by W. Whitten, 2v, 1920.
Nolleroth (Johann Peter). Comm. de sacramentis. Præf. &c. J. E. Schubert. [P2634]. s4º. Gryphiswaldiæ. 1770
Nolli (Giov. Batt.) New plan of Roma, 1748. Foreword by [J. S.] [*Extr. f.* The Mask, v11]. 8º. [1925]

Nolloth (Charles Frederick). The Christian faith. Essays. Ed. N. [Xtn. Evid. Soc.] s8°. 1922
The Fourth Evangelist. 8°. 1925
Nolloth (Henry Edward).
Beverley & its Minster. [repr. P2872]. 8°. [1915]
Nolly (Emile), *ps.* [*i.e. Cap.* DÉTANGER]. La barque annamite. Roman de mœurs tonkin. [3e éd.] s8°. [1921]
Nolten (Rudolph August). Diatribe litt. de genuinis hist. Russ. fontibus. s4°. Lipsiae. [1739]
Nölting (Johann Heinrich Vincenz) [NOELTINGIUS]. Antiq. Damascenae ex Act. 9, 1–25 illust. Praes. J. E. I. Walchio. [P431]. s4°. Jenae. [1757]
*__Nomad__ (A) in North Amer., 1927, *see* BEN ASSHER, *ps.*
Nombela (Julio). Crón. de la prov. de Navarra, 1868, *see* ESPAÑA. Crón. gen., v8, 1865 &c.
Nomenclator ó dicc. de la ciudades, villas &c. de España, 1789, *see* ESPAÑA. E. div. en prov. &c., t2, 1789.
Nomis (M.), *ps.*, *see* SIMONOV (M. T.)
Nonconformist. *Reasonable (A) acc. why some n. ministers judge it sinful to perform th. minist. acts in publick, 1679, *see* COLLINGES (J.)
Nonesuch Press. Nonesuch books. Handlist &c. s8°. [1925]
Nonnen (Nicolaus), *see* HASE (T.) Museum hist.-philol.-theolog., 2v, 1728–32.
Nonnosus, *abbot of Attel in Bavaria.* Psalterium Davidis in 3 partes distrib., explan. lit. & mystica dilucidatum &c. Acc. Cantica Canticorum Salomonis. [*w. sep. tp. & pagin.*] 3p *in* 2v. s4°. 1741–42
pl, Pedeponti, 2, Straubingae, 3, Augusta Vindel.
Nonnus, *of Nisib, see* NANA, *Syrian.*
Nonnus, *of Panopolis.* Scholien zu 5 Reden d. Gregor v. Nazianz, [hrsg.] A. Manandian, *see* ZEITSCHR. F. ARM. PHILOL., B1, 1903.
Noort (Olivier van). Reis om de wereld, 1598–1601. Uitg. door J. W. Ijzerman. [Linschoten-Vereeniging, 27, 28]. 2d. 8°. 's-Gravenhage. 1926
Noortdonck (Borluut de), *see* BORLUUT DE NOORTDONCK (—).
Nopcsa (Franz, *Baron*). Albanien: Bauten, Trachten u. Geräte Nordalbaniens. la8°. 1925
Noppen (J. G.) Westminster Abbey & its anc. art. la8°. [1926]
Noppus (Hieronymus) [NOPUS], *see* COLLINUS (M.), *Gurimenus.* De summa Xtnae. relig. brevia quædam axiomata, olim ab H. N. tradita &c., 1543.
Norayr, *Biuzantatzi* [†PIUZANTATZI (N. N.)] [Armenian word-enquiry. *In Armenian*]. 8°. K-polis. 1880
[Crit. of Nouparean tr. of V. Hugo's Notre Dame. *In Armenian. b. w. h.* Arm. word.-enq., 1880]. 8°. K-polis. 1884
see QNNASER. Q. [The Enquirer, mag. for hist., lit. &c. of Armenia; ed. N. N. P., No. 1, 2], 1887.
Norberg (Matthias). Selecta opuscula acad. Ed. J. Norrmann. 3p. s8°. Londini Gothorum. 1817–19
see BIBLE: SYRIAC. Cod. Syr.-Hexaplaris Ambrosiano-Mediolan.; ed. & Lat. vers. a M. N., 1787.
Norbert, *Saint, abp. of Magdeburg* [IBURGENSIS]. Vita Bennonis II, episcopi Osnabrug. Rec. H. Bresslau. [Scr. rerum Germ. in usum schol.] 8°. Hannoverae. 1902
Norblin de La Gourdaine (Jean Pierre), *see* BATOWSKI (Z.) Norblin, 1911.
Nordal (Sigurður). Om Olaf den helliges saga. En krit. undersøgelse. 8°. 1914
Norden (Eduard), *see* GERCKE (A.) & E. N. Einl. in d. Altertumswiss., 3B, 1914–27.
see VIRGILIUS (P. M.) Aeneis Buch 6, erkl. v. E. N., 1916.
Norden (Hermann). White & black in East Africa. 8°. 1924
Nordenskiöld (Erland). Compar. ethnographical studies. [Tr.] [v]1–6 [v6 *in* 2p]. 8° [Göteborg. 1919–25]
1, Ethno-geogr. anal. of material culture of 2 Indian tribes in the Gran Chaco.
2, Changes in material culture of 2 Indian tribes.
3, Ethnography of South-America seen f. Mojos in Bolivia.
4, Copper & bronze ages in S. America.
5, Deductions suggested by geogr. distrib. of Post-Columbian words used by Indians of S. America.
6i, Secret of the Peruvian quipus.
6ii, Calculations w. years & months in the Peruvian quipus.
Indianer u. Weisse in Nordostbolivien. 8°. St. 1922
Nordhausen; hrsg. v. Magistrat N.; bearb. v. Geissler, *see* Deutschland. D.'s Städtebau, 1921.
Nordhoff (Charles).
Politics for young Americans. s8°. N.Y. 1875
Nordin (Carolus Jacobus a). Diss. Gothland. cum Suecis div. tempor. conjunct. adumbrans. [P2648]. s4°. Upsaliae. [1832]

Nordiska Museet, *Stockholm.* Träsniderimönster i allmogestil hemt. ur N. M. af W. Oldenburg. fol. [1893]
Nordmann (Charles). Einstein & l'univers. s8°. [1921]
Einstein & the universe. Tr. by J. McCabe. Pref. by Visc. Haldane. 8°. [1922]
Notre maître le temps: les astres & les heures, Einstein ou Bergson? 8°. [1924]
Le royaume des cieux: un peu du secret des étoiles. 8°. [1923]
Noreen (Adolf Gotthard). Altschwed. Gramm., mit Einschluss d. Altgutnischen. 8°. Halle. 1904
Vårt språk. Nysvensk gramm. i utförlig framställning. B1, 3, 7 [*No more publ.*] 8°. Lund. [1903–19]
Noreen (Erik). Studier rör. Eufemiavisorna, 1, Textkrit. anmärk. til Flores & Blanzaflor, 2, Hertig Fredriks Textkritik, *see* KUNG. HUM. VET.-SAMF. I UPPSALA. Skr., B22, 1923–27.
Norfolk. Copy of the poll for knights of the shire for the Co. of N., 12th–20th July 1802. 8°. Norwich. [1802]
Narr. &c. of the proc. at the election for knights of the shire, for the Co. of N., July 12th to 28th Aug. 1802. [*b. w.* Norfolk. Copy of poll, 1802]. 8°. Norwich. 1802
N. Parish Reg.: Marriages (1559–1837). Ed. A. R. Vaughan Daubeny. v11. 8°. 1926
Norfolk & Norwich Archaeological Society, *see* KIRKPATRICK (J.) Streets &c. of Norwich, 1889.
Norfolk (Thomas Howard, *4th duke of*), *see* MANOLESSO (E. M.) Hist. nova, congiura d. duca de N., 1572.
Norgate (Kate). Richard the Lion Heart. 8°. 1924
Norge [NORGES]. Danmark-Norges traktater, 1523–1750, *see* DANMARK.
Norge, 1814–1914. Øket folkeutgave av nationalverket Norge i det 19 aarhundrede. [*By var. wr.*] 3B. fol. 1914
Norges indskrifter med de aeldre [*& yngre*] Runer, 1891–1924, *see* BUGGE (S.)
Norie (John William). Directions for sailing to & from the coast of Brazil &c., descr. of coasts & harbours of S. Amer. &c. 2nd ed. pl. 8°. 1830
Falconer improved &c. Mariner's new & compl. naval dict. in 2p, 1, Vocab. of Brit. marine, 2, Mod. French marine dict. 3rd ed. rev., corr. &c. by J. W. N. 8°. 1804
Norinsky (K. M.) Воспоминания, *see* BLAGOEV (D.) От групиы Благоева &c., 1921.
Noris (*card.* **Enrico).** Hist. Pelagiana & dissert. de synodo V Oecumenica &c. Additis Vindiciis August. 3p [*in 1v*]. fol. Patavii. 1673
Nørlund (N. E.) Stirlings Interpolationsrække, *see* KONG. DAN. VID. SELSK. Skr., Række 8, B7, 1920–25.
Norman Lockyer Observatory. Hdbk. to the N. L. Observatory. Compl. by W. J. S. Lockyer. [P2524]. s8°. 1921
Norman (Bruce). The black pawn. s8°. [1927]
The thousand hands. s8°. [1926]
Norman (Clarence H.) The revolutionary spirit in mod. lit. & drama. [P2426]. 8°. 1920
Norman (*Capt.* **Francis Martin).** The food of plants in ref. to Peruvian guano & w. recoll. of the Chincha islands. [P2846]. 8°. 1880
Norman (*Mrs.* **George),** *ps.* [*i.e. Mrs.* G. BLOUNT]. Morning. s8°. [1927]
Norman (Mark William). Popular guide to geology of the Isle of Wight, w. note on its rel. to that of the Isle of Purbeck. 8°. Ventnor. [1887]
Norman (Philip), *F.S.A.* East Acton Manor House. [Ed. P. N. Survey of Mem. of Greater London, 7]. 4°. [1921]
Scores & annals of the West Kent Cricket Club (1812–96), w. acc. of Chislehurst & Bromley &c. la8°. 1897
see LONDON. Survey of L., v12, Cromwell House, Highgate; by P. N., 1926.
,, VICTORIA & ALBERT MUSEUM. Cat. of drawings of old London; by P. N., 1921.
Normanus, *ps.* *Illust. acc. of St. Bartholomew's Priory Church, Smithfield &c. 8°. [1874]
Normanby (Constantine Henry Phipps, *1st marq. of*), *2nd earl of Mulgrave.* *A letter to the earl of Mulgrave. By a dissatisfied gentleman. [P2566]. 8°. D. 1836
Speech, H. of Lords, 27 Nov. 1837, on motion of Earl of Roden ref. to Ireland]. 2nd ed. [P2552]. 8°. 1837
see WALLACE (T.) *A letter to Visc. Melbourne &c. on admin. of Earl M. in rel. to defective applic. of the law &c., 1836.

Normand (Gilles), *see* Tisserand (E.) G. N., 1922.
Normand (Suzanne). La maison de laideur & de lésine, *see* Œuvres libres, 65, 1926.
Normandy (Robert [Curthose], *d. of*), *see* Robert [*Curthose*], *d. of Normandy.*
Normanhurst Court. *Catalogue of works of art &c. at N.C., 1878, *see* Brassey (T. B., *e.*)
Normanton (Sidney James Agar, *4th earl*). Cat. of old French furniture, property of Earl of N. & decor. furniture &c. property of Visct. Ednam &c., sold by Christie, July 16, 1925. 8°. [1925]
Norme e regole d. giuoco Gilét alla Greca, 1901, *see* Gilet alla Greca.
Normont (Elisabeth, *ctsse.* **de)** [*ps.* Babet], *see* Lenotre (G.) Babet l'empoisonneuse, 1927.
Noronha (Eduardo de). Hist. das toiradas. obl.8°. Lisboa. 1900
Nor-qnar. [*New lyre*: Ashel-shirini. *Ed.* Z. Sargsean. *In Armenian.* P2792]. 8°. Shoushi. 1891
Norris (Anthony), *see* Kirkpatrick (J.) Streets &c. of Norwich; pr. f. MS. coll. of A. N., 1889.
Norris (Frank). The pit. [repr.] s8°. *n.d.*
Norris (Henry Handley). A pract. expos. of the tendency & proc. of the Brit. & For. Bible Soc. begun in a corresp. betw. N. & J. W. Freshfield &c. Ed. N. 2nd ed. w. add. notes. 8°. 1814
*The principles of the Jesuits, in a coll. of extracts f. their own authors &c. 8°. 1839
Norris (Herbert). Costume & fashion. v1, 2. la8°. 1924–27
1, Evol. of Europ. dress thr. earlier ages.
2, Senlac to Bosworth, 1066–1485.
Norris (John), *rector of Bemerton.* A treatise on Xtn. prudence. Extr. f. N. by J. Wesley. 3rd ed. [P2536]. s8°. Bristol. 1749
see Dodwell (H.) Explication: letter to J. Norris &c., 1708.
Norris (Kathleen). Barberry Bush. s8°. [1927]
Martie the unconquered. s8°. 1918
Sisters. s8°. 1919
Norris (*capt.* **Richard).** Minutes taken at a court-martial on H.M. ship Torbay Jan. 1744 &c., being an enquiry into the conduct of R. N. in engagement under Adm. Mathews &c. 11 Feb. 1743 [1744]. [P608]. s8°. 1745
Norris (William Edward). Tony the exceptional. s8°. [1921]
The triumphs of Sara. s8°. 1920
Nors (P.) The court of Christian VII of Denmark. Ed. E. Steen. 8°. [1928]
Norsk [Norske].
Aarskatalog over norsk litt. 1924, 1925, 1925–26, see Aarskatalog.
Ældre norske sprogminder, 1–3, 1911–15, *see* Hannaas (T.), *ed.*
Norsk biografisk Leksikon. Redaktion: E. Bull, A. Krogvig, G. Gran. B1–3. la8°. 1923–26
Norsk bokfortegnelse, 1911–20, 1923–24, *see* Haffner (H. J.)
Norske folkeviser, 1923, *see* Lammers (T.)
Norske folkeviser fra middelalderen, 1919, *see* Liestøl (K.) & M. Moe.
Norske folkevisor, 3. [N. folkeskrifter 68]. s8°. 1920
Norske Herredags-Dombøger, 1893–1911, *see* Thomle (E. A.), *ed.*
Norske Historiske Kildeskriftfond.
see Bugge (E. S.) Norges indskrifter med de aeldre Runer, B1–3, 1891–1924.
,, —— Norges indskrifter med de yngre Runer, 1902–06.
,, † Ceallachan *of Cashel, King of Munster,* Caithreim Cellachain Caisil, 1905.
,, Daae (L.) Matrikler over Nord. Studerende, 1885.
,, Glostrup (N. S.) Visitatser i Oslo og Hamar Stifter 1716–37, 1895.
,, Hannaas (T.), *ed.* Ældre norske sprogminder, 1–3, 1911–15.
,, Historiske Samlinger, B1–3, 1900–14.
,, Jónsson (F.) Eirspennill: Nóregs Konunga sǫgur—Magnús góði—Hákon gamli, 1916.
,, Kalteisen (H.) Kopibog; udg. A. Bugge, 1899.
,, Kolsrud (O.) 100 "Gamle Bunde regler," 1914.
,, MacFirbis (D.) On the Fomorians &c., 1905.
,, Munch (P. A.) Pavelige nuntiers regnskabs-og dagböger, 1282–1334, 1864.
,, Nilssøn (J.) Visitatsbøger &c., 1574–1597, 1885.
,, Prebensen (N.) & Hj. Smith. Christian V norske Lov, 1687, 1887.
,, Ranessøn (S.) S. R. proces, 1877.
,, Skulerud (O.) Cat. of Norse MSS., 1918.
,, Søfrenssøn (S.) Memorialbog, 1564–99, 1898.
,, Stavanger Domkapitels protokol, 1571–1630; udg. A. Brandrud, 1901.
,, Storm (G.), *ed.* Historisk-topogr. Skrifter om Norge &c., 16e Aarh., 1895.
,, —— Islandske Annaler indtil 1578, 1888.

Norske Historiske Kildeskriftfond [*continued*].
see Storm (G.) Mon. hist. Norveg., 1880.
,, —— Otte brudstykker af d. aeldste saga om Olav den Hellige, 1893.
,, —— Regesta Norveg., 1898.
,, Stub (N.) Optegnelsesbøger, 1895.
,, Sverris saga; utg. G. Indrebø, 1920.
,, Tank (G.) Akershusregisteret af 1622, 1916.
,, Thomle (E. A.) Norske Herredags-Dombøger (1578–1623), 1893–1911.
Norske Videnskaps-Akademie i Oslo. II. Hist.-Filos. Klasse. 1927, No. 5. la8°. Oslo. 1927
see Laache (R.) H. Wergeland & h. strid med Prokurator Praëm, B1, 1828–31, 1927. [5.]
see Eitrem (S.), *ed.* Papyri Osloenses, fasc. 1, 1925.
Norsworthy (Naomi) & M. T. Whitley.
The psychology of childhood. 8°. N.Y. 1920
North Sea pilot, 4p, Suppl. 6, *&* Not. to mariners, 1914–22, *see* Admiralty.
North (Alfred John). Descr. cat. of nests & eggs of birds in Australia & Tasmania. [Australian Mus., Cat. No. 12]. la8°. Sydney. 1889
North (Francis), *1st baron Guilford, 1637–88, see* Bedloe (W.) Exam. of W. B., rel. to Popish Plot, taken by Sir F. N., 1680.
North (Frederick John). Coal, & coalfields in Wales. [Nat. Mus. of Wales]. 8°. Cardiff. 1926
North (Laurence). The Golightlys, father & son. s8°. 1912
Northall (John). Travels through Italy. 8°. 1766
North American review. v211–225. la8°. N.Y. 1920–28
Northampton. Quarter Sessions records of the co. of N. (a.d. 1630, 1657, 1657–58). Ed. J. Wake, w. intr. by S. A. Peyton. [N. Record Soc., 1]. 8°. Hereford. 1924
Northampton (Henry Howard, *1st earl of*). A defensative agst. the poyson of supposed prophecies &c. Newly revised &c. sm. fol. 1620
Northamptonshire. Copy of papers rel. to musters, beacons, subsidies &c. in N. (1586–1623). Ed. J. Wake. Intr. by J. E. Morris. Genealog. note by H. I. Longden. [Northants. Rec. Soc., Publ., v3]. la8°. Kettering. 1926
Northamptonshire Record Society.
[Publications]. v[1], 3. 8°. Hereford *&* Kettering. 1924–26
see Northampton. Quarter Sessions records, 1924. [1.]
,, Northamptonshire. Copy of papers rel. to musters &c., 1926. [3.]
***Northanger Abbey,** 4v, 1818, *see* Austen (J.)
Northbrook (Thomas George Baring, *1st earl of*). Descript. cat. of the coll. of pictures belonging to N. Dutch, Flemish & Fr. schools, by W. H. J. Weale; Ital. & Span. schools by J. P. Richter. 4°. 1889
see Mullick (G. B.) Lord N. & h. mission in India, 1873.
Northcliffe (Alfred Charles William Harmsworth, *1st baron*). My journey round the world, 16 July 1921–26 Feb. 1922. Ed. C. & St. J. Harmsworth, w. intr. &c. 8°. [1923]
The N. Collection [papers of Gen. R. Monckton, Brig.-Gen. Townshend &c.] Pres. to the Govt. of Canada by Sir L. Harmsworth. [Publ. Archives of Canada]. 8°. Ottawa. 1926
see Owen (L.) The real Lord N., 1902–22, 1922.
,, Pemberton (M.) Lord N., mem., 1922.
Northcote (Hugh). Xty. & sex problems. 2nd ed. rev. & enl. 8°. Phila. 1920
Northcote (James), *R.A.*
One hundred fables, orig. & selected. 2nd ed. s8°. 1829
Northcote (James Spencer).
The Roman catacombs. 2nd ed. s8°. 1859
Northern. N. looking glass, 1825–26, *see* Glasgow looking glass.
N. numbers. Being sel. f. certain living Scot. poets. [Foreword *signed* C. M. G.] s8°. E. [1920]
Northesk (David John Carnegie, *10th earl of*). Cat. of the Rosehill coll. of prehist. & ethnol. objects, the property of 10th E. of N. Sold by Christie, July 14, 1924. [*Illust.* P2748]. 8°. 1924
North Georgia Gazette, The, & winter chronicle [1819–20]. [Ed. Sir E. Sabine]. 4°. 1821
North Staffordshire Railway. Map of the N.S. Lines, incorp. 1846. *folded.* s8°. *C. F. Cheffins.* [1846?]
Map show. course of N.S.R. & Trent & Mersey canal. *folded.* s8°. [1848]

Northumberland. Hist. of N.: under dir. of N. Co. Hist. Committee. v11, 12, 4°. Newcastle-upon-Tyne. 1922–26
11, The parishes of Carham, Branxton, Kirknewton, Woolner, & Ford; by K. H. Vickers.
12, The parishes of Ovingham, Stamfordham & Ponteland; by M. H. Dodds.
Northumbrian mon., or, shields of arms, effigies & inscr. in churches &c. of N. [Ed. w. intr. by C. H. Hunter Blair. Newcastle upon Tyne Records Comm., v4]. 8°. N. upon T. 1924

Northumberland, *ship, see* TRUE. *True &c. narr. of action betw. N. & French men of war, 1745.

Northumberland (Alan Ian Percy, *8th duke of***).** Cat. of miniatures, property of the D. of N. Comp. by J. J. Foster. *p.p.* la8°. 1921
see CONSPIRACY agst. Brit. Empire, 1921.
„ SHERBORNE MISSAL (The): reprod. f. Missal executed betw. 1396 & 1407, in lib. of Duke of N. at Alnwick Castle, 1920.

Northumberland (Charlotte Florentia Percy, *duchess of***).**
Castles of Alnwick & Warkworth &c. From sketches by C. F., d. of N., 1823. 4°. [1824]

Northumberland (Elizabeth Percy, *duchess of***),** *wife of Sir Hugh Smithson, aft. 1st duke of Northumberland (3rd cr.); 1716–76.*
Diaries of a duchess: extracts, [1752–74]. Ed. J. Greig. Foreword by the Duke of Northumberland. 8°. 1926

Northumberland (Henry Percy, *8th earl of***),** *see* *CRUDELITATIS Calvinianae exempla duo recentiss. ex Anglia; cont. mortem comitis N., 1585.

Northumberland (Henry Percy, *9th earl of***),** *1564–1632, see* LECONFIELD (C. H. W., *3rd b.*) Cat. of Americana & MSS. f. lib. of E. of N., 1928.

Northumberland (Hugh Percy, *2nd duke of***),** *see* SPILSBURY (J.) Coll. of 50 prints f. ant. gems in coll. of Earl Percy &c., engr. by J. S., 1785.

Northumbrian. N. mon., or, shields of arms &c. in churches &c. of N., 1924, *see* NORTHUMBERLAND.

Northup (Clark Sutherland). Reg. of bibliog. of the Eng. lang. & lit. Contrib. by J. Q. Adams & A. Keogh. la8°. New Haven. 1925

Northup (George Tyler). Ten Spanish farces of the 16th–18th c., w. notes &c. Ed. G. T. N. s8°. 1924

North-West Frontier Province [India]. Administration report, 1917/18–1925/26. fol. Peshawar *&* Delhi. 1919–27

Norton (Andrews). Evidences of the genuineness of the Gospels. 2nd ed. 2v. 8°. 1847

Norton (Arthur P.) A star atlas & telescopic handbook (epoch 1920). n. & enl. ed. 4°. 1919

Norton (*Lt.-Col.* **Edward Felix).**
The fight for Everest: 1924. la8°. 1925

Norton (Henry Kittredge).
The Far Eastern Republic of Siberia. 8°. [1923]

Norton (John), *of Boston, U.S.A.* A brief & excellent treatise cont. the doctrine of Godliness. s8°. 1468 [*i.e.* 1648]

Norton (Thomas), *of Bristol.* Believe-me, or the Ordinal of alchemy, *see* HERMETIC MUSEUM, v2, 1893.

Norton (Thomas James).
Constit. of the U.S.: its sources &c. s8°. [1923]

Norvins (*le baron* **de),** *see* NAPOLEON I. Hist. de N. d'ap. M. de N. &c., 1837.

Norway.
Norway's shipping losses dur. the War, to June 1917. Tr. & summ. from "Sjöforklaringer over norske skibes krigsforlis." [*By W. Archer.* P2687]. fol. 1918
A hdbk. of N. & Sweden, 1920, *see* ADMIRALTY: NAVAL INTELL. DIV.
Norway pilot, 3p, *&* Suppl. 4, 6, 1914–22, *see* ADMIRALTY.
see also NORWEGEN.

Norway year book (The), 1924. Ed. S. C. Hammer. s8°. Christiania. [1923]

Norway (Arthur Hamilton).
Naples past & present. 6th ed. s8°. [1924]

Norwegen. Handbuch für d. West- u. Nordküste N. 3e A. 2T & Ergänzungen. 8°. 1919–21
1, Von Lindesnes bis Drontheim.
2, Von Drontheim bis zur Murman-Küste.

Norwich. The valuation of N. Ed. W. E. Lunt. 8°. O. 1926

Norwich, *Connecticut.* The Norwich Jubilee: rep. of celebr., Sept. 1859, w. hist. doc. Comp. by J. W. Stedman. 8°. Norwich, Conn. 1859

Norwid (Cypryan Kamil). Pisma zebrane. tA [in 2v, *pagin. cont.*], C, E. s8°. 1911[–12]

Norwood (Gilbert). The art of Terence. 8°. O. 1923

***Nos** poètes: J. Barbey d'Aurevilly—T. Corbière &c. [*By var. a., w. specimens*]. 2t. 8°. *n.d. &* 1925

Nosek (Vladimír). Great Britain & the Czecho-Slovaks. [P2425]. 8°. Prague. 1919
The spirit of Bohemia: survey of Czechoslovak hist., music & lit. 8°. [1926]

Noske (Gustav). Von Kiel bis Kapp. Zur Gesch. d. deut. Revolution. 8°. 1920

Noskov (I.)
Амурскій край въ коммерч. &c. отношеніяхъ. 8°. С.-П. 1865

Nösselt (Johann August). Bibliotheca Nösseltiana. Catalogus. Divend. auctionis lege. s8°. Halis. 1810
Diss. providentiae divinae vestigia in vindicanda per Pacem Passav. 1552 & Augustanam 1555 sacr. Evang. libertate exponens. Praes. S. J. Baumgarten. [P442]. s4°. Halae Magdeb. [1755]
Exercit. ad Sacr. Script. interpret. s8°. Halae. 1803
Opusc. ad interpret. Sacr. Script.
fasc. 1[–3] (fasc. 1, 2, ed. 2a auct.) s8°. Halae. 1785–1817
T3 has title: Opusc. ad hist. eccles. fasc. 3 *&* add. tp. Tres commentationes &c.

Nossig (Alfred), *see* RODITSCHEW (J. F.) & A. N. Bolschewismus u. Juden, 1922.

Nostradamus (M.) [†NOSTREDAME (MICHEL DE)]. Les Oracles de M. de N. Éd. ne varietur, par A. Le Pelletier. 2t. 8°. 1867

Notari (Umberto), *see* VALORI (G.) N., 1920.

Notarq Hayotz 1393–1467; coll. &c. L. Firlalemean, 1892, *see* ARMENIA.

Notcutt (Henry Clement). The Faerie Queen & its critics, *see* ENG. ASSOC. Essays, v12, 1926.
An interpret. of Keats's Endymion. 8°. [Capetown. 1919]
The story of Glaucus in Keats's Endymion. [P2737]. 8°. [Capetown. 1921]

Note.
*Note book of an Oxonian, late member of Brazen Nose Coll., 1831, *see* OXONIAN, *ps.*
*Note (The) of hand, or trip to Newmarket, 1774, *see* CUMBERLAND (R.)
*Note s. l'état des forces nav. de la France, 1844, *see* JOINVILLE (*le prince* DE).

***Notebooks** (The) of a spinster lady, 1878–1903, 1919, *see* HOLLAND (*Miss* C.)

Noter (Raphaël). Légumes & fruits des cinq parties du monde. 2[t]. s8°. 1923

Notes. *Notes on painted glass in Canterbury Cath., 1897, *see* CANTERBURY.
*Notes on the Oxfordshire Domesday, 1892, *see* MOWAT (J. L. G.)

Notes & queries.
Ser. 12, v6–12, Ser. 13, v1; v146–154. s4°. 1920–28
The numbering in Series was discontinued with v146.
„ „ Gen. index to Ser. 11 (1910–15), v1–12. s4°. 1920
„ „ „ „ Ser. 12 (1916–23), v1–12. s4°. High Wycombe. 1924

Notestein (Wallace). The winning of the initiative by House of Commons. [Brit. Acad. Raleigh Lect. From Proc. of B.A. P2834]. 8°. [1926]
see PARLIAMENT: II, H. OF C.: GEN. COLL. Commons debates for 1629 ed. & intr. by W. N. &c., 1921.

***Nothwendige** Gedancken d. evang. Prediger in Teutschland üb. d. Exulanten auss Ungarn &c., 1683, *see* UNGARN.

***Notices** reg. metr. vers. of the Psalms received by Ch. of Scot., 1842, *see* LAING (D.)

***Notitia** hist.-lit. de libris ab artis typogr. inventione ad a. (M.D.) impressis &c., 2p, 1788–89, *see* BRAUN (P. I.)

Notiziario archeologico, Anno 1, 2, 1915–16, *see* ITALY: MIN. DELLE COLONIE.

Notker, *Labeo.* Psalterium Davidicum notis illustr. J. Schilterus, *see* SCHILTER (J.) Thesaurus antiq., t1, 1728.

***Notre-Dame** de France, 1861–66, *see* HAMON (A. J. M.)

Notre-Dame & Ste-Marguerite de La Presle, *see* PRESLE (LA).

Notre-Dame de Longpont, *priory of, see* LONGPONT.

Notre-Dame-des-Ardents, *Arras, see* ARRAS.

Nott (*Sir* **William),** *see* INDUS. *Recoll. of the 1st camp. west of the Indus &c. under Sir W. N., 1845.

Nott-Bower (*Sir* **John William).**
Fifty-two years a policeman. 8°. 192[6]

Notti (Gherardo delle), *see* HONTHORST (G. J.)

Nottinghamshire. Nottinghamshire parish registers. Marriages. Ed. T. M. Blagg &c.
v20, Thurgarton Wapentake, final part. 8°. 191[illegible]

Nötzel (Carl). Das Leben Dostojewskis. 8°. L. 1925
Die soziale Bewegung in Russland. 8°. St. 1923

Nouagaran. Manual of canticles, *in Armenian*, 1794, *see* ARMENIAN.

Nouaillac (Joseph), *see* GUÉNIN (G.) & J. N. L'Anc. Régime & la Révol., 1715–1800, 1921.

Nouet (Jacques), F. Annat & others. *Responses aux Lettres Provinciales publ. par le secrétaire du Port-Royal contre les pp. de la Co. de Jesus sur le sujet de la morale des dits pères. s8°. Liége. 1668

Nouhuys (J. W. van). De eerste Nederl. Transatlant. stoomvaart in 1827 van Zr Ms Stoompakket Curaçao. [Linschoten-Vereeniging, 29]. dl. 8°. 's-Gravenhage. 1927
1, Het journaal.

Noussanne (Henri de).
The Kaiser as he is. Tr. W. Littlefield. 8°. N.Y. 1905
Le véritable Guillaume II. s8°. [1904]

Nouveau. Nouveau recueil de farces franç. des 15. & 16. s., 1880, *see* PICOT (É.) & K. NYROP.

Nouvel. Nouvel annuaire de France, géogr. statist. des 86 départemens &c. p. s. de texte explic. à l'atlas portatif de F. rédigé par A. Bret. s8°. [1836 ?]

***Nouvelle** défense de la tr. du Nouv. Test. imprimée à Mons, 1680, *see* ARNAULD (A.)

Nouvelle revue (La). Sér. 4, t14 (juillet–déc. 1914). la8°. 1914

Nouvelle revue du Midi, *see* PELADAN (J.) J. P. [*By var. a.* N. R. du M., No. 10 (Spécial)], 1924.

Nouvelle revue française (La). Revue mensuelle de litt. & de crit. t14–30. 8°. 1920–28

***Nouvelles** lettres de l'a. de la Critique gén. de l'Hist. du Calvinisme de Mr. Maimbourg, 2t, 1685, *see* BAYLE (P.)

Nouvelle Société Helvétique, *London.* Helvetic bibliog. [Ed. P. Lang. P2736 ; 2755]. 8°. Olten. [1923]

Nova.
*Nova cartilha da doutrina Christaã &c. s8°. Trangambar. 1733
*Nova Indica, sive memor. virtus Xtian. 61 in Japonia, 1639, 1644, *see* INDICA.

Nova Acta historico-ecclesiastica, 1758–71, *see* ACTA HISTORICO-ECCL.

Nova Guinea. N. G. Uitkomsten d. nederland N.-G.-Exped. in 1903[–20]. Onder Leiding v. A. Wickmann, [H. A. Lorentz & A. F. Herderschee].
v6iii, 7, 9, 13, 14i, ii, 15i, ii, 16i, ii. 4°. Leiden. 1922–28
6iii, Géologie. 7, 16i, ii, Ethnographie. 9, 13, 15i, ii, Zoologie. 14i, ii, Botanique.

Novak (Grgo). Topog. i etnog. rimske prov. Dalmacije, 1918, *see* BULLETINO DI ARCH. &C. DALM., 39, Suppl., 1919.

Novalese, *Abbey.* Chronicon N. Ex rec. Bethmanni, rec. fecit G. H. Pertz. [Scr. rerum Germ. in usum schol.] 8°. Hannoverae. 1846

Novalis, *ps.* [*i.e.* F. L. v. HARDENBERG], *see* MINOR (J.) Studien zu N., 1, 1911.

Novaro (Angiolo Silvio). Dio è qui. 8°. Milano. 1927

Nova Scotia. N. S. (S.-E. coast) & Bay of Fundy pilot, 7th ed., 1921, 1922, *see* ADMIRALTY.
*Selections f. the public doc. of N. S. Ed. T. B. Akins. Tr. by B. Curren. 8°. Halifax. 1869

Novati (Francesco). Necrologia, *see* ARCHIVIO STOR. ITAL., anno 76, v1, 1918.

Novela (La) picaresca, 1922, *see* RUIZ MORCUENDE (F.)

Novella d'incerto autore d. sec. 15. Da un cod. palatino. [*Ed.* G. Molini]. 8°. Firenze. 1834

Novelle. N. d'incerti autori del sec. 14. [Ed. F. Zambrini]. s8°. Bologna. 1861
Il Novellino, the 100 old tales. Tr. E. Storer, w. intr. [Broadway Trans.] 8°. [1925]

Novellieri. Tesoro dei novellieri ital. scelti dal 13° al 19° sec., 2p, 1847, *see* TESORO.

Novello (Vincent), *see* CLARKE (M. C.) Life & labours of V. N., 1864.

Novels. Great short n. of the world, 1927, *see* CLARK (B. H.), *ed.*

November night. By the a. of "The house made with hands." s8°. [1928]

Novgorod. Новгородскія лѣтописи [911–1824]. Изд. Археографической Коммиссіи. la8°. С.–П. 1879

Novgorodtsev (Pavel Ivanovich).
Объ обществ. идеалѣ. изд. 3e. в1. 8°. [Berlin]. 1921

***Novi ecclesiastico-scholastici annales** Evangelicorum August. & Helvet. Confess. in Austriaca Monarchia. [Ed. S. Ambrosius]. 3v *or* cursus *b. in* 2. (v1 *has* 4t ; 2, 3, *have* 2t *each*). s8°. Schemniczii [v2, Neosolii]. 1793–95

Novik (Dmitri), *see* OUDARD (G.) & D. N. Les verts, 1928.

Novikov (Nikolai Ivanovich), *see* LIZLOV (A. I.) Скиѳская ист. ; изд. Н. Н., 3ч, 1787.

Novus Homo, *ps.*, *see* BECANUS (MARTINUS).

Nowack (Wilhelm). Die kleinen Propheten ; übers. u. erklärt. [Götting. Handkomm. z. Alt. Test., III, 4].
3e neu verb. A. la8°. Göttingen. 1922

Nowak (Carl Friedrich). The collapse of C. Europe. [Tr.] Intr. by Visct. Haldane. 8°. 1924
Sanssouci. s8°. L. [1908]
Der Sturz d. Mittelmächte. la8°. München. 1921
Der Weg z. Katastrophe. s8°. [1919]

Nowell (Alexander), *dean of St. Paul's.* Catechismus. Lat. explic. [*Ed. w. pref. by W. Jacobson*]. 8°. O. 1844
Christianae pietatis prima instit., Gr. & Lat. scr. [*Gr. tr. by* W. Whitaker]. s8°. Londini. 1687

Nowell (Thomas), *D.D.* An answer to Pietas Oxon. [*by Sir R. Hill. b. w.* Hill (*Sir* R.) Pietas Oxon, 2nd ed., 1768]. 8°. O. 1768

Nower (Francis), *see* GUILLIM (J.) Display of heraldry, 4th ed., added, Register of Knights of the Garter &c., by F. N., 1660.

Nowotny (Eduard). Römerspuren nördl. d. Donau., 1918, *see* KAISERL. AKAD. D. WISS. ZU WIEN. Sitzungsber, B187, 1918.

Nowotny z Luže (Frantissek). Biblioteka českých Biblj &c. od trináctého wéku az do léta 1810. s8°. *n.p. n.d.* [c. 1815]

Noyes (Alfred).
Collected poems. v3, 4. s8°. E. 1920–27
3, The lord of misrule—Tales of the Mermaid tavern—The wine-press—The search-lights—A Belgian Christmas eve—A salute from the fleet. 4, [Misc. poems].
The hidden player. s8°. [1924]
The magic casement. Anthology of fairy poetry. Ed., w. intr. by A. N. 8°. [1908]
Robin Hood. *Play.* 8°. E. 1926
Sel. verse incl. A victory dance &c. 8°. E. 1921
Some aspects of mod. poetry. 8°. [1924]
Some characteristics of mod. lit., *see* ROY. SOC. OF LIT. Essays, N.S., v3, 1923.
Songs of Shadow-of-a-leaf & o. poems. s8°. E. 1924
The torch bearers. [Poem]. 2v. s8°. E. 1922–25
v2 *has title* The book of earth.

Nozière (Fernand). Notre amour, pièce, *see* ŒUVRES libres, 70, 1927.

Nozze.
N.B.—The following list consists only of anonymous "per nozze," and of those which merely contain congratulatory poems or letters. These are arranged below under the names of the bride & bridegroom. See various authors for prose works &c. & consult typed list.

Appaiato—Benissimo. Gli sposi [*by* A. C. Vigodarzere. N127]. 8°. [Padova. 1866]
Balzan—Piazza. *Versi di Dr. Turazza.* [N127]. 8°. Padova. [1857]
Bariola—Francesconi. Ronda-album. [*Contribs. by P. Rota &c.* N119]. fol. 1885
Barucchello—Turazza. Sogno d'una fanciulla. [*Ed.* C. Ederle]. [N127]. 8°. *n.p.* [1866]
Benissimo—Appaiato. Gli sposi [*by* A. C. Vigodarzere. N127]. 8°. [Padova. 1866]
Biasini—Gaudio. La donna : cantico *di L. C.* [N127]. 8°. Padova. 1863
Biasini—Gaudio. Versi di G. C. [N127]. 8°. [Padova. 1863]
Bolzon—Cenzatti. [*Doc. conc. Asolo,* 1509. N139]. la8°. [Asolo. 1886]
Cantilena—Testolini. *Versi di F. Doglioni.* [N127]. 8°. Belluno. 1864
Caracciolo—Coppola. Vari compon. [*by var. a.; ed.* A. di Liguoro]. [N126]. 8°. Firenze. 1725
Carli—Zambelli. *Versi di T. Mestre &c.* [N127]. 8°. Verona. 1846
Cenzatti—Bolzon. [*Doc. conc. Asolo,* 1509. N139]. la8°. [Asolo. 1886]
Chizzolini—Tagliavacca. Rime *di* G. L. [N127]. 8°. Brescia. 1847
Clerle—Ravenna. Fiori ! [N127]. 8°. Karia. 1866
Coppola—Caracciolo. Vari compon. [*by var. a.; ed.* A. di Liguoro]. [N126]. 8°. Firenze. 1725
Della Stufa—Ridolfi. [*Due doc. &c.* N134]. 8°. S. Miniato. 1918
Emo Capodilista—Venier. [Allo sposo *by* G. Cittadella. N127]. s8°. [Padova. 1867]
Federici—?. Lettera [*by* C. Marcolini. P2787]. 8°. *n.p. n.d.*
Francesconi—Bariola. Ronda-album. [*Contrib. by P. Rota &c.* N119]. fol. 1885
Gaddi—Pepoli. [Alla sposa *verse by* E. Fiorioli. N127]. 8°. Firenze. 1868

Nozze [*continued*].
Gaudio—Biasini La donna : cantico *di L. C.* [N127]. 8º. Padova. 1863
Gaudio—Biasini. Versi di G. C. [N127]. 8º. [Padova. 1863]
Margherita, *pssa*—Umberto, *pr.* *Verses.* [N127]. 8º. [Belluno. 1868]
Occioni—Valerio. *Versi di A. Cesare Sorgato.* [N127]. 8º. Padova. 1867
Penso—Venturini. Paterni ammonimenti. [N127]. 8º. [Venezia. 1861]
Penso—Venturini. *Versi di G. Penso.* [N127]. 8º. Venezia. 1861
Pepoli—Gaddi. [Alla sposa *verse by* E. Fiorioli. N127]. 8º. Firenze. 1868
Piazza—Balzan. *Versi di Dr. Turazza.* [N127]. 8º. Padova. [1857]
Ragazzini—Sacchetto. [Due sonetti, *by* G. Cittadella. N127]. 8º. Padova. [1866]
Ravenna—Clerle. Fiori ! [N127]. 8º. Adria. 1866
Riario—Rospigliosi. Componimenti [*by var. a.; ed.* T. Ridolfi. N126]. 8º. 1740
Ridolfi—Della Stufa. [*Due doc.* N134]. 8º. S. Miniato. 1918
Rinaldi—Vecelli. [Alla sposa : carme *by* G. B. S. N127]. 8º. Treviso. 1867
Romiati—Sanmartin. Alla sposa [*verses by A. Sacchetti.* N127]. 8º. [Padova. 1866]
Romiati—Sanmartin. Il rito nuziale [*verse.* N127]. 8º. Padova. 1866
Romiati—Sanmartin. *Versi. [N127]. 8º. [Padova. 1866]
Rospigliosi—Riario. Componimenti [*by var. a.; ed.* T. Ridolfi. N126]. 8º. 1740
Sacchetto—Ragazzini. [Due sonetti, *by* G. Cittadella. N127]. 8º. Padova. [1866]
Sanmartin—Romiati. Alla sposa [*verses by A. Sacchetti.* N127]. 8º. [Padova. 1866]
Sanmartin—Romiati. Il rito nuziale [*verse.* N127]. 8º. Padova. 1866
Sanmartin—Romiati. *Versi. [N127]. 8º. [Padova. 1866]
Tagliavacca—Chizzolini. Rime *di* G. L. [N127]. 8º. Brescia. 1847
Testolini—Cantilena. *Versi di F. Doglioni.* [N127]. 8º. Belluno. 1864
Turazza—Barucchello. Sogno d'una fanciulla. [*Ed.* C. Ederle. N127]. 8º. *n.p.* [1866]
Umberto *pr.*—Margherita, *ssa.* *Verses.* [N127]. 8º. [Belluno. 1868]
Valerio—Occioni. *Versi di A. Cesare Sorgato.* [N127]. 8º. Padova. 1867
Vecelli—Rinaldi. [Alla sposa : carme *by* G. B. S. N127]. 8º. Treviso. 1867
Venier—Emo Capodilista. [Allo sposo *by* G. Cittadella]. [N127]. s8º. [Padova. 1867]
Venturini—Penso. Paterni ammonimenti. [N127]. 8º. [Venezia. 1861]
Venturini—Penso. *Versi di G. Penso.* [N127]. 8º. Venezia. 1861
Wallner—Zeiner. [Canzonetta *by* C. Zeiner. N127]. 8º. Verona. 1867
Wallner—Zeiner. [La rosa, *versi by* G. Rogger. N127]. 8º. [Verona. 1867]
Wallner—Zeiner. [L'ultimo sogno : versi. N127]. 8º. [Verona. 1867]
Zambelli—Carli. *Versi di T. Mestre &c.* [N127]. 8º. Verona. 1846
Zeiner—Wallner. [Canzonetta *by* G. Zeiner. N127]. 8º. Verona. 1867
Zeiner—Wallner. [La rosa, *versi by* G. Rogger. N127]. 8º. [Verona. 1867]
Zeiner—Wallner. [L'ultimo sogno : versi. N127]. 8º. Verona. 1867

Nubilonio (Cesare). Cronaca di Vigevano, 1584 ; p. c. di C. Negroni, *see* REGIA DEP. Misc., t29, 1892.

Nuél (M.), *ps., see* SCHNITZER (M.)

Nugae. *Nugae derelictae, q. coll. J. M. & R. P., 1822, *see* MAIDMENT (J.) & R. PITCAIRN.

Nugent (*Sir* Charles B. P. Hodges).
Imperial defence. [P2831]. 8º. [1884]

Nugent (Margherita). Alla Mostra d. Pittura Ital. del' 600 e 700 [Palazzo Pitti], note e impress. 8º. [Firenze]. 1925

Nugent (Robert Craggs-Nugent, *earl*). *Farther consid. upon a reduct. of the land-tax. [P2783]. 8º. 1751

Numerical. Book of the numerical sayings, p2 ; tr. A. D. Jayasundere, 1925, *see* ANGUTTARA-NIKĀYA.

Numismatic (The) chronicle & Journal of the Royal Numismatic Society. Ser. 4, vol. 19, 20, s5, v1–5. 8º. 1919–26

Nunes (José Joaquim). Cantigas d'amigo dos trovadores galego-portugueses. Ed. crit. acomp. de intr., com. &c. por J. J. N. v2, Texto. s8º. Coimbra. 1926

Nuñez (Lucio Maria). *Cenni storici : ricordo del 2º centen. d. canonizz. di S. Caterina da Bologna. [P2497]. 8º. [Bologna. 1912]

Nuñez Cabeça de Vaca (Alvar). Comentarios de A. Nunes C. de V. [*by P. Hernandes,* 1555] ; tr. T. de Alencar Araripe, *see* INSTITUTO HIST. E GEOG. BRAZIL. Revista, t56, 1893.

Nuñez de Arce (Gaspar).
see CASTILLO Y SORIANO (J. DEL). N. de A. : apuntes para su biog., 1904.
„ MENÉNDEZ Y PELAYO (M.) G. N. de Arce : est. biog.-crít., c. 1890.

Núñez de Arenas (Manuel). Ramón de la Sagra, reformador social, *see* REVUE HISPANIQUE, t60, 1924.

Nunn (Henry Preston Vaughan).
An introd. to eccl. Latin. s8º. C. 1922

Nunn (Thomas Percy). Relativity & gravitation. 8º. 1923

Nuova. *Nuova guida angel. perpet. romana ; tr. in Armeno da G. d'Elia, 1725, *see* ROMA.

Nuova antologia di scienze, lettere ed arti.
6ª ser. v205–244 (della raccolta 289–322). 8º. 1920–25
7ª ser. v245–260 („ „ 323–338). 8º. 1926–28
The vol. no. 224–28 are missed in enumeration of s6, *and* 312 "della raccolta" *is repeated.*

Nuova Sirena (La), *ps., see* HASSE (F.)

Nuovo Patto (Il), *see* PROVENZAL (G.) Il cinquantennio (1870–1920), scritti che Il N. P. consacra &c., 1921.

Nura Kami (N.) *& others.* [Comm. on Sir E. Satow's Jesuit Mission press in Japan, w. list of his works &c. *In Japanese*]. 4º. [Tokyo. 1926]

Nürnberg [NUREMBERG]. Neŭw Ordenunge der bettler halben, In der statt Nürnberg hoch von nöten beschehen Im 1522. [*Arms on tp.* P2539]. s4º. *n.p. n.d.* [Nürnberg ?. 1522 ?]
[*Nuremberg Chronicle, *Latin*], 1493, *see* SCHEDEL (H.)
Der Predicanten zu N. [W. Linck, A. Osiander &c.] schrifft an Ruprecht v. Moshaim Dechant zu Passau verteutscht. s4º. *n.p.* [1539]
*Verhandl. d. Altkatholiken-Versamml. f. N. &c., 1871, 1872, *see* ALTKATHOLIKEN.
see PANZER (G. W.) Litter. Nachr. v. d. allerält. gedr. deut. Bibeln aus d. 15. Jhdt. in d. öffent. Bibl., N., 1777.

***Nut-Brown Maid (The).** The notbrowne mayde [*poem*], *see* CAPELL (E.) Prolusions, 1760.
„ „ *f. a. ed., see* †PRIOR (M.) Poems on sev. occasions, 1713 ; Poet. works, v3, 1807.

Nuti (Mariano).
Margherita da Cortona : la sua legenda &c. s8º. [1923]

Nutt (Alfred).
The legends of the Holy Grail. [P2586]. s8º. 1902

Nutt (David). Cat. of foreign theol. on sale by D. N. [*& App., w. sep. pagin.*] 8º. 1837

Nutt (John W.), *see* JUDAH *ben David, Haiyūj.* Two treatises on verbs &c. ; ed., w. Eng. tr., by N., 1870.

Nuttall (G. Clarke). Beautiful flowering shrubs. la8º. [1920]
Ye flower-lover's booke. s8º. 1911

Nuttall (Lawrence William), *see* MILLSPAUGH (C. F.) & L. W. N. Flora of Santa Catalina Island, 1923.

Nuttall-Smith (George Nuttall) [*form.* SMITH]. Chron. of a Puritan family in Ireland : Smith (form.) of Glasshouse. By G. N. N.-S. f. notes coll. by R. W. Smith &c. 8º. 1923

Nutting (Charles Cleveland). Amer. hydroids, p3, The Campanularidæ & the Bonneviellidæ. [S.I. : U.S. Nat. Mus., Spec. Bull.] fol. Wash. 1915

Nyasaland. A hdbk. of Port. N., 1920, *see* ADMIRALTY : NAVAL INTELL. DIV.

Nyassa Company. Handbook of N.C. 8º. 1898

Nyerup (Rasmus), *see* COPENHAGEN. Cat. libr. Sanskrit. ; scr. E. N., 1821.

Nyèssen (D. J. H.) The passing of the Frisians : anthropography of Terpia. la8º. The Hague. 1927

Nygaard (M.) Norrøn syntax. la8º. Kristiania. 1905

Nyren (Carl). Crisis evang.-polit. scr. Confess. fid. exhib. Holmiae Quakerorum. [P2646]. s4º. Regiomonti. 1783

Nyrop (Kristoffer).
Works in KONG. DAN. VID. SELSK. Hist.-fil. Med.
Études de gramm. franç., 1919–27. [2–4, 8, 9, 12.]
Gueules, et ords hist., 1921–22. [4.]
Hist. étymol. de 2 mots français (haricot, parvis), 1918–19. [2.]
France. Tr. J. de Coussange. s8º. [1916]
The kiss & its hist. Tr. W. F. Harvey. 8º. 1901
see PICOT (E.) & K. N. Nouv. recueil de farces franç. des 15ᵉ & 16ᵉ s., 1880.

Nys (Ernest). Christine de Pisan & ses princ. œuvres. 8º. Brux. 1914

Nyström (Anton). Judarne förr och nu, samt Judefrågan i östra Europa. 8º. 1919

O

O., *ps.* Forensic fables & Further f. f., 1926–28, *see* MATHEW (T.)

O. (E. v.) Gesch. Übersicht d. slav. Spr., 1837, *see* OLBRECHT (E. VON).

O. (L.) The strange &c. adv. of 4 authors in search of a character, 1926, *see* LEAR (P. G.) & L. O.

O*** (R******, *E—l* of),** *see* WALPOLE (*Sir* R.), *aft. 1st e. of Orford.*

O. (W.) *Some acc. of the life &c. of C. Cotton [*signed* W. O., *i.e.* W. Oldys], *see* WALTON (I.) Compl. angler, 1760.

Oahu, *see* HAWAII.

Oakeley (Hilda Diana).
History & progress & o. essays &c. 8°. [1923]

Oakenfull (J. C.) Brazil past, present & future. s8°. 1919

Oakes (*Sir* Augustus Henry) & R. B. Mowat, *edd.* The great European treaties of the 19th c. Intr. by Sir H. E. Richards. 2nd impr. s8°. O. 1921

Oakeshott (Ronald). Cut & come again. s8°. [1923]

Oakley (Amy). Hill-towns of the Pyrenees. 8°. 1924

Oakley (Thomas Pollock). Eng. penitential discipline & Anglo-Saxon law in th. joint influence. [Columbia Univ.] 8°. N.Y. 1923

Oates (*Lt.-Col.* W. Coape), *D.S.O.* The Sherwood Foresters in the Great War, 1914–18. The 2/8th Battalion. s8°. Nottingham. 1920

Obbard (Robert). Mem. of Hafiz, 1921, *see* HAFIZ, *Shīrāzī.*

Obdam (*Adm.* Jacob van Wassenaer-), *see* WASSENAER-OBDAM.

Obenauer (Carl Justus).
Goethe in s. Verhältnis zur Religion. 8°. Jena. 1921

Ober (Frederick Albion). Guide to the W. Indies, Bermuda & Panama. 3rd rev. ed. s8°. 1921

Oberholser (Harry Church). New E. Indian birds, Turdidae &c., 1923, *see* SMITHSONIAN INST.: Misc. Coll., v76, 1925.
New Timaline birds f. the E. Indies, 1922, *see* SMITHSONIAN INSTIT.: Misc. Coll., v74, 1925.

Oberhummer (Eugen). Die Brixener Globen v. 1522; hrsg. E. O., *see* KAISERL. AKAD. D. W. IN WIEN. Denkschr., 67, 1926.

Ober-Lausitz. *Neue (Das) verm. Deut. u. Wend. Gesangbuch, z. Gebr. d. evang. O.-L. schen Kirchen, 1719, *see* GESANG-BUCH.

Obermaier (Hugo). Fossil man in Spain. Intr. by H. F. Osborn. [Hispanic Soc. of Amer.] 8°. New Haven. 1924
see BREUIL (H.), H. O. &c. La Pileta à Benaojan, 1915.

—— & *el conde* de la Vega del Sella.
La cueva del Buxu (Asturias). la8°. 1918

—— & P. Wernert. Las pinturas rupestres del barranco de Valltorta (Castellón). la8°. 1919

Oberschlesien. *Die Abstimmung in O. Polnischer Terror &c. 8°. *n.p.* [1921]

Obey (André), *see* AMIEL (D.) & A. O. La souriante Mme. Beudet; pièce, 1922.

Obichnoe pravo. Обычное право. в2, Мат. для библіографіи. la8°. Ярославь. 1896

Obizzi (*il march.* Pio Enea degli), *see* DEGLI OBIZZI (*il m.* P. E.)

Obninsky (Viktor Petrovich).
Лѣтопись русской револ. т3, Дума и револ. вып. 2, Внѣ закона.—Хроника, Апр.-Іюль 1906 [*w. sep. pagin. b. w. h.* Полгода русс. револ., вып. 1, 1906]. la8°. Москва. 1907
Полгода русской революціи. Сборникъ матеріаловъ (1905–6). вып. 1. la8°. Москва. 1906

Obolensky (*prince* Dmitry Aleksandrovich).
Мои воспоминанія о В. К. Еленѣ Павловнѣ. 8°. С.-П. 1909

Obolensky (*prince* Ivan), *see* VLADIMIROV (V.) Revol. in Finland under pr. O.; tr., 1911.

Obolensky (Leonid Egorovich).
Максимъ Горькій и причины его успѣха. s8°. С.-П. 1903

Obradović (Dosithei).
Првенацъ. Изд. С. Илійћъ. s8°. у Карлштадту. 1830

Obrecht (Ulrich). Alsatic. rerum prodromus. [v1. *No more publ.*] s4°. Argentorati. 1681

Obregón (Alvaro), *president of the Republic of Mexico, see* DILLON (E. J.) President O., 1922.

O'Brien (*Capt.* Donat Henchy), *R.N.* My adventures during the late war: 1804–27. 2v. 8°. 1839

O'Brien (Edward J.) & J. Cournos.
The best short stories of 1924. 1, English. s8°. [1925]
„ „ 1925. 1, English. s8°. [1926]
„ „ 1926. 1, English (w. Irish suppl.); ed. E. J. O'Brien. s8°. [1927]
„ „ 1927, w. yearbook; ed. E. J. O'Brien. 2v (1, Eng.; 2, Amer.) s8°. 1928

O'Brien (Eris M.) Life & letters of Archpriest J. J. Therry. Intr. M. Kelly. 8°. Sydney. 1922

O'Brien (Frank P.) Amer. pioneer life, a coll. of books &c. publ. by Beadle & Adams. Sold, Anderson Gall. [P2856]. 8°. N.Y. 1920

O'Brien (Frederick). Mystic isles of the South Seas. 8°. 1921

O'Brien (George). Econ. hist. of Ireland f. the Union to the famine. 8°. 1921
Essay on mediæval econ. teaching. 8°. 1920
Essay on the econ. effects of the Reformation. 8°. 1923
Labour organization. s8°. [1921]

O'Brien (James Thomas), *bp. of Ossory, Ferns & Leighlin.* A charge deliv. to the clergy of the dioceses of Ossory, Ferns, & Leighlin at h. prim. visit. in 1842. 2nd ed. 8°. 1843

O'Brien (John), *R.C. bp. of Cloyne.* *Focaloir Gaoidhilge-Sax-Bhéarla, or Irish-Eng. dict. 4°. Paris. 1768

O'Brien (Kathleen). John-Barbara. s8°. [1926]

O'Brien (Sibyl Wilbur), *see* WILBUR (S.)

O'Brien (William), *M.P. for Cork [to 1895].*
Edmund Burke as an Irishman. 8°. D. 1924
Evening memories. 8°. D. 1920
The Irish cause & the Irish "Convention." Rep. of speech in H. of Commons. [P2487]. s8°. D. 1917
The Irish revolution & how it came about. 8°. 1923
see UNITED IRELAND. U.I. on Spencer, Trevelyan & Gladstone, value of O'B.'s denials, 1888.

Obschestvo izucheniya Amursk. kraya [Общ. изученія А. края]. Записки. т1 (*4 pagin.*) 8°. Владивостокъ. 1888

Observantz. *Von. d. fier Ketzeren Prediger Ordē d. O. &c., 1510, *see* MURNER (T.)

Observationes.
*Obs. ad moralem Libr. Sacr., 1796, *see* HEBENSTREIT (C. W.)
*Obs. quaedam de infallibilitatis eccl. subjecto. [P2693]. 8°. Neapoli. 1870

Observations.
*Further obs. on the improvements of the maintenance of the poor in Kingston-upon-Hull, 1801, *see* KINGSTON-UPON-HULL.
*Obs. addr. to the shipping, the agricult. & the commerc. interests on the impolicy of the free trade syst. pursued by H.M. ministers. [P448]. 8°. Newcastle. 1826
*Obs. & proposals conc. the navy, 1745, *see* NAVY.
*Obs. & reflect. on a war w. Russia, 1791, *see* RUSSIA.
*Obs. d'un journaliste sur "Du système polit.," 1818, *see* AUBERT DE VITRY (F. J. P.).
*Obs. on a journey to Naples, 1691, *see* EMILIANE (G. D').
*Obs. on the Duke of Richmond's plans of fortific., 1794, *see* GLENIE (J.)
*Obs. on the 3 last vol. of the Roman hist. of E. Gibbon, 1788, *see* GIBBON (E.)
*Obs. upon a pamph. An analysis of the moral & relig. sentiments &c. 1755, *see* BLAIR (H.)
*Short obs. on a commutation of tithes for gov. annuities, 1798, *see* TITHES.

Observator, The.
v10, No. 61, Aug. 1, 1711. [*b. w.* Post Man, 1709–11]. fol. 1711

Obvinitelnii. Обвинительный актъ по дѣлу о револ. пропагандѣ въ имперіи, 1877, *see* RUSSIA.

O'Callaghan (Edmund Bailey), *see* NEW YORK. Papers rel. to 1st settlement by the Dutch, cont. list of immigrants f. "Doc. hist. of N.Y." &c., v1, 1888.

O'Callaghan (J.) Dual evolution: idealism & realism f. viewpoint of humanism. 8°. 1921

O'Callaghan (John Cornelius). The green-room, gleanings f. the writing-desk of a literary agitator. [*Engr. tp. dated 1845*]. 2nd ed. 8°. D. 1844

O'Callaghan (Michael), *see* LIMERICK. L. curfew murders of Mar. 7th, 1921: case of M. O'C., 1921.

O'Casey (Sean). The plough and the stars. Tragedy. s8°. 1926
Two plays. Juno & the paycock—The shadow of a gunman. 8°. 1925
„ „ ....[repr.] 8°. 1926

Occam (William), *see* OCKHAM (W.)

Occioni-Bonaffons (Giuseppe). Di un epistolario femminile ined. n. Quiriniana di Venezia. [Estr. d. R. Istit. Veneto, s6, t6. P2840]. 8°. [Venezia. 1888]
Doc. rel. a Fiesso d'Artico (Prov. di Venezia, 1792–97). [Nozze Médail—Occioni-Bonaffons. N129]. la8°. Venezia. 1905
Insurrezioni pop. a Rovigno n. Istria (1752–96). [*Extr. fr.* R. Istit. Ven., Atti, t1, Ser. 7. P2838]. 8°. Venezia. 1890
La liturgia slava n. Istria. [P2840]. 8°. Venezia. 1893
Nil sub sole novum. Storie di campanili veneziani. [Estr. d. Ateneo Ven., anno 26. P2840]. 8°. Venezia. 1903
I pregiudizi nel pass. e n. pres. [Estr. d. Ateneo Ven. P2836]. 8°. Venezia. 1889

Occom (Samson). A sermon at the execution of Moses Paul, an Indian. Added, Obs. on lang. of the Muhhekaneew Indians, by J. Edwards. [*w. sep. tp. & pagin.*] repr. s8°. 1788

Ocean highways: the geographical review. Ed. C. R. Markham. [*cont. of* Our ocean highways]. n.s. v1. la8°. 1874
This was cont. w. title Geographical magazine, 1874–78, *q.v.*

Ocellus, *Lucanus.* "O. L."; Text u. Komm. v. R. Harder. [Neue philol. Unters.; hrsg. W. Jaeger, H1]. 8°. 1926

Öchelhäuser (Adolf v.) [†Oechelhaeuser].
Das Heidelberger Schloss. 4e A. s8°. Heidelberg. 1920

Ochino (Bernardino) [Occhine].
Certaine godly &c. sermons of faith &c. Tr. out of Italian into English by W. Phiston. s4°. 1580
De purgatorio dialogus. s8°. [Tiguri. 1555]
Dialogi 30 in 2 libros divisi, primus de Messia, secundus de Trinitate [*wanting*]. s8°. Basileae. 1563
Liber de corporis Christi præsentia in Coenæ Sacramento. Cui adj: Labyrinthos de divina praenotione & libero seu servo hominis arbitrio [*w. sep. tp. & pagin.*] s8°. Basileæ. [1561]
Sermons (to the number of 25) conc. the predestination & election of God &c. Tr. by A. C. [*i.e. A. Cooke, afterwards Bacon*]. s8°. *John Day.* [*ca.* 1555]
see Benrath (C.) B. O. v. Siena, ein Beitrag z. Gesch. d. Reform. &c., 1875.

Ochorowicz (Julijan). Mental suggestion. Pref. by C. Richet. Tr. J. Fitzgerald. 8°. N.Y. [1891]

Ochs (Peter), *1752–1821.* Korr.; hrsg. G. Steiner, B1, *see* Quellen z. Schweizer Gesch. N.F., Abtlg. 3, B1, 1927.

Öchsli (Wilhelm). Hist. of Switzerland, 1499–1914. Tr. E. & C. Paul. 8°. 1922

Ockham (David). The Eng. Dreyfus case. [Miss V. Douglas-Pennant. P2773]. 2nd ed. 8°. [1922]

Ockham (William) [Occam; Occamus &c.] De imperatorum & pontif. potestate. Ed. C. K. Brampton. 8°. O. 1927
Dialogus inter militem & clericum, *see* Trevisa (J.) Dialogus &c.; [tr.] by J. T.; intr. &c. by A. J. Perry, 1925.

O'Connell (Daniel). Trial of D. O'C. &c. [Suppl. to the Weekly Dispatch, Feb. 4, 11, 18 & 25]. la. fol. 1844
see Fagan (W.) Life & times of D. O'C., 2v, 1847–48.

O'Connor (Dorothy). Louise Labé. la8°. 1926

O'Connor (*Rt. Hon. Sir* James).
Hist. of Ireland, 1798–1924. 2v. 8°. 1925

O'Connor (James Arthur), *see* Bodkin (T.) 4 Irish landscape painters, J. A. O'C. &c., 1920.

O'Connor (Murroghoh), *ps.?* A pastoral in imitation of the first Eclogue of Virgil. [P2868]. 8°. 1719

O'Connor (Vincent Clarence Scott). An Eastern library [Patna Oriental Pub. Lib.] With 2 cat. of its Persian & Arabic MSS. comp. by Abdul Muqtadir & Abdul Hamid. s8°. Glasgow. 1920
A vision of Morocco, the far west of Islam. 8°. [1923]

O'Conor (Charles), *of Benanagare.* Reflect. on hist. of Ireland dur. heathenism &c., *see* Vallancey (C.) Coll. de rebus Hib., v3, 1782.
2nd [*& 3rd*] letter on heathen state &c. of Ireland, *see* Vallancey (C.) Coll. de rebus Hib., v3, 4, 1783–84.

O'Conor (Norreys Jephson). Changing Ireland: lit. background of the Irish Free State, 1889–1922. s8°. C. [Mass.] 1924

Octavia, *wife of Nero, emperor of Rome.* Octavia praetexta, cum elementis comm. ed. C. Hosius, *see* Kleine Texte, 147, 1922.

Octavian, *emperor, hero of romance.* *Romance of O., abr. f. MS. in Bodleian by J. J. Conybeare (1809); ed. w. add. notes by E. M. Goldsmid, *see* Aungervyle Soc. Reprints, s1, 1882.

O'Daly (Daniel) [Dominicus de Rosario]. The Geraldines, earls of Desmond & Persecution of the Irish Catholics. Tr. [Rise of the Geraldines &c., 1655]. s8°. 1847
see Prestage (E.) Frei Domingos do Rosario, diplom. e politico, 1595–1662, 1926.

Odassi (Tifi), *see* Maccheronee di 5 poeti ital del sec. 15: T. O. &c., 1864.

Odds. *A few odds & ends for cheerful friends, 1870, *see* Collier (J. P.)

Odd Volumes, The Club of, *Boston, U.S.* Cat. of exhib. illust. var. interests of book buyers, 1450–1600. 8°. Boston, *Mass.* 1922
Providence meeting, May 20, 1908. 8°. *n.p.* 1908
10th anniv. exhib., Boston Art Club, Feb. 17–24, 1897. 8°. [Cambridge, *U.S.* 1897]
see Littlefield (G. E.) Early Boston booksellers, 1642–1711, 1900.

Odd Volumes, Sette of. [List of members, rules &c., *w.* Bibliog. of privately pr. opuscula &c, 1910–14, 1923–25, 1927. Booklets 34–37, 40, 47, 49, 50, 51]. s8°. [1904–27]
Opuscula &c.
see Cooke (C. W.) Automata old & new, 1893.
,, Gould (*Lt.-Comm.* R. T.) J. Horrox, astronomer, 1923.
,, —— The sea-serpent, 1926.
,, Heron-Allen (Ed.) Codex Chiromantiae, Codicillus I, Chirognomy, 1883.
,, —— Inaug. addr., 25th Oct. 1927, 1927.
,, —— Memoranda of memorabilia in corr. of Marq. de Sévigné &c., 1928.
,, Hildesley (A.) The press gang, 1925.
,, Holland (V.) Mediæval courts of love, 1927.
,, Rosedale (H. G.) The Spanish match, 1908.
,, Sebastian (L. B.) Manor of Pellipar, 1919.
,, —— Old City Co.: Skinners' Co., 1906.
,, Symons (A. J. A.) Frederick Baron Corvo, 1927.
Quatrains coll. f. the misc. publ. &c. of The S. of O. V. [Foreword by J. Todhunter]. s8°. 1905
Year-boke, 28th year, 1905–6. s8°. [1906]

Ode (Jacob). Comm. de angelis. s4°. Trajecti ad Rhenum. 1739

Odelem (Johann Philipp).
De re monetali Ebræorum. s4°. Helmestadi. [1699]

Odell (George C. D.)
Annals of the New York stage. 2v. la8°. N.Y. 1927
Shakespeare from Betterton to Irving. 2v. 8°. N.Y. 1920

Oder (Eugen). Corpus hippiatric. Graec.; ed. E. O. &c., 2v, 1924–27, *see* Corpus.

Öder (Georg Ludwig) [Oederus].
see Morscovius (P.) Politia eccl.; rec. & diss. praelim. de agend. eccl. &c. adj. G. L. O., 1745.
,, Racovian Catechism. Cat. Racov.; rec. &c. G. L. O., 1739.

Öder (Johann Ludwig) [Oederus]. Diss. prodromum hist. Bogomilorum crit. exhib. [P2648]. s4°. Gottingae. [1743]

Odessa. National Library.
see Poprujenko (M. G.) О Город. Публ. Библ., 1830–1910, 1911.
,, Tüneewa (A.) Miniaturausg. in d. Staatsbibl. in O., 1926.

Odgers (William Blake). A digest of the law of libel & slander &c., 5th ed. by the author, J. B. Eames & Walter B. Odgers. la8°. 1911

Odinot (Paul). Le monde marocain. 8°. 1926

Odle (*Mrs.* Alan), *see* Richardson (D. M.)

Odle (E. V.) The history of Alfred Rudd. Novel. s8°. [1922]

Odo, *called Beatus, bp. of Cambray.* Canonis missæ expos., *see* Wild (J.) Examen ordinandorum &c., 1589.

Odo, *abbot of Cluny, Saint.* Vie de St. Grégoire, évéque de Tours (10c.), *see* Gregory, *of Tours.* Hist. eccl. des Francs, t1, 1859.

Odoevtsev (Irina). Двор чудес: стихи (1920–21). s8°. П. 1922

Odom (William).
Beauchief Abbey, Sheffield. s8°. Sheffield. 1927
Mem. of Sheffield: its cathedral & parish churches. 8°. Sheffield. 1922

Odom (William Macdougal). A hist. of Italian furniture f. 14th to early 19th c. 2v. fol. N.Y. 1919

Odon, *count of Savoy, d. c. 1060, see* Fontaines (M. L. C. de P. de G., *ctsse.* de). Hist. de la Ctsse. de Savoie; n. éd., avec notices &c. [*incl.* Le comte O.] par C. Buet, 1889.

O'Donnell (Charles James).
The lordship of the world. 3rd ed. 8°. [1925]

O'Donnell (Elliot), *see* Webster (K.) Trial of K. W.; ed. E. O'D., 1925.

O'Donnell (*le comte* Maurice), *see* Mistler (J.) Mme. de Staël & M. O'D., 1805–17, 1926.

O'Donoghue (Edward Geoffrey). Bridewell Hospital: palace, prison, schools, to end of the reign of Eliz. 8°. [1923]

O'Donoghue (Freeman M.), *see* Brit. Museum: Prints &c. Engraved Brit. portraits; by F. M. O'D., v5, 1922.

O'Donovan (Gerald). Conquest. s8°. 1920
The holy tree. s8°. 1922
How they did it. s8°. [1920]
Vocations. s8°. 1921
Odoricus [*Matthuissi*], *a Minorite monk.* Voyages en Asie au 14e siècle. Publ. avec. intr. & notes par H. Cordier. [Rec. de voyages & de docs. p. s. à l'hist. de la géogr., 10]. la8°. 1891
see MANDEVILLE (*Sir* J.) Voiage &c.; with Journal of Frier O. [Everyman's lib.], 1928.
O'Duffy (Eimhar). King Goshawk & the birds. [repr.] s8°. 1926
O'Dwyer (*Sir* **Michael Francis**).
India as I knew it, 1885–1925. 8°. 1925
Oechelhaeuser (Adolf v.), *see* ÖCHELHÄUSER (A. v.)
Oechsli (Wilhelm), *see* ÖCHSLI (W.)
Oecolampadius (Joannes) [ECOLAMPADE; HAUSSCHEIN (J.)]
*Canoni indocti Lutherani. [Argumentum epistolae. Eccio, respondent Canonici indocti, quatenus & qua ratione sint Lutherani]. s4°. *n.p. n.d.* [Wittenberg ?. 1519 ?]
Clare u. Christl. antwortung etl. hochgelerten &c. zů Hall in Schwaben versamlet über die wort dess nachtmals &c. s4°. *n.p.* 1526
De genuina verborum Domini, Hoc est corpus meum. [*b. w.* Zwingli (U.) De vera & falsa relig., 1525]. s8°. [Basileæ. 1525]
In epistolam ad Hebræos explan. &c. s8°. Argentorati, *M. Apiarus.* 1538
In epist. B. Pauli Apost. ad Rhomanos adnot. s8°. Basileae, *A. Cratander.* 1525
In epistolam Ioannis primam demegoriae, hoc est homiliæ 21. s8°. Basileæ, *A. Cratander.* 1524
,, ,, denuo per auth. recogn. s8°. [Basileae, *A. Cratander*]. 1525
In Hieremiam comm. libri 3. Eiusdem in Threnos Hieremiæ enarr. s4°. Argentinæ. 1533
In Jesaiam hypomnematon, hoc est, Comm. libri 6. s4°. Basileae. 1525
,, ,, [*a. ed. foll. by* In Jeremiam—In Ezechielem—In Job—In Danielem—In Min. prophetas, *each w. sep. tp. & pagin.*] fol. Genevæ. 1558–67
In prophetam Ezechielem comm. per V. Capitonem æditus. De obitu O. Epist. Grynæi. De vita ejus V. Capitonis. [*b. w. h.* In Hieremiam proph. comm. libri 3, 1533]. s4°. Argentorati. 1534
Oecolampadii urtayl u. maynung, auch a. reden &c. Mart. Luther belangend, auss dem latein. s4°. *n.p.* 1521
Quod non sit onerosa christianis confessio paradoxon. s4°. [Augustæ Vindelic., *Grimm & Wyrsung.* 1521]
*Die verdeutscht antwort, der, die Eck in s. Sendbrieff an d. Bischoff zu Meyssen hat die ungelarten Luther. Thumhern genandt. s4°. *n.p.* 1520
see STRAUSS (J.) Das der war leyb Christi im Sacramēt sey &c. erklerūg auff J. Hauszscheyn &c., 1527.
,, SUABIA. Genotigter u. fremdt eingetrag. schrifft &c. der predigere ynn Schwaben, zu O., 1526.
Oeconomica. Hed oudste Nederland. verboden boek 1523. Oeconomica Christiana. Summa d. godl. Scrifturen. Uitg. door J. J. van Toorenenbergen. [Mon. Reform. Belg., t1]. la8°. Leiden. 1882
Œconomos (Lysimaque). The martyrdom of Smyrna & East. Christendom. Evidence &c., comp. &c. by. L. Œ. 8°. 1922
The tragedy of the Xtn. Near East; app., The Smyrna holocaust, by C. Dobson, *see* ANGLO-HELLENIC LEAGUE, No. 50, 1923.
Oeconomy, *see* ECONOMY.
***Oecumenica** cathedrae apostol. authoritas, 1689, *see* REDING (A.)
Œdenburg, *see* SOPRON.
Oederus (Joannes Ludovicus), *see* ÖDER (JOHANN LUDWIG).
Oehlke (Waldemar), *see* ÖHLKE (W.)
Oelmann (Franz), *see* ÖLMANN (F.)
Oelsnitz (A. B. E. v. der), *see* ÖLSNITZ (A. B. E. V. DER).
Oemler (Marie Conway).
The butterfly man. [7th impr.] s8°. 1920
His wife-in-law. s8°. N.Y. [1925]
Shepherds. s8°. 1926
A woman named Smith. s8°. 1920
Oer (Reiner). Quæstio de differentia inter Calvinistas, Pelagianos & Catholicos in negotio prædestinationis. [*b. w.* Becanus (M.) De triplici sacrificio &c., 1610]. s8°. Moguntiæ. 1609
Oertelius (Joannes Gottofridus), *see* ÖRTEL (J. G.)
Oesterley (William Oscar Emil). Immortality & the unseen world: st. in O.T. religion. 8°. 1921
The Jewish background of the Xtn. liturgy. 8°. O. 1925
The sacred dance: st. in comparative folklore. s8°. C. 1923
—— **& G. H. Box.** A sh. survey of the lit. of Rabbinical & mediaeval Judaism. s8°. 1920
Oesterreich (T. Konstantin), *see* ÖSTERREICH (T. K.)

Œuvres (Les) libres. Rec. litt. mensuel ne publiant que de l'inéd. [No.] 1–86. s8°. [1921–28]
***Of** educ., espec. of young gentlemen, 3rd impr., 1677, *see* WALKER (O.)
Ofeïcoff, *ps.* La Macédoine au point de vue ethnograph., hist. et philolog. s8°. Philippoli. 1887
Offa, *king of the Mercians; d. 796, see* HEWLETT (J. H.) O.'s dyke, 1924.
Offel (Horace van). Le roi de la jetée, roman, *see* ŒUVRES libres, 36, 1924.
Offer. *Dit Boeck wort genaemt: Het offer des Heerē, Om het inhout van sommige opgeofferde kinderen Gods &c.: Item, Liedtboecrken trackteerende van het Offer des Heeren [*w. sep. tp. & pagin.*] s8°. Harlinghen. 1599
Officers died in the Gt. War, 1914–19, 1919, *see* WAR OFFICE.
Officia [OFFICE; OFFICIUM].
Divine (The) office for the use of the laity. 4v [*each v. has 2 pagin.*] s8°. *n.p.* 1763
Etrennes spirituelles cont. l'office lat. & franç. [*by* T. de Hansy]. s8°. *Th. de Hansy.* 1755
Eucologe ou livre à église à l'usage de diocèse d'Arras &c. cont. l'office &c. s8°. Lille. 1837
Office (L') de la quinzaine de Paques, en latin & en franç. s8°. Lille. 1824
Office (L') de la semaine sainte &c. Tr. nouv. s8°. 1685
Office (L') de la semaine sainte & de l'octave de Pasque en latin & en franç. &c. n. éd. [*Engr. tp., w. date* 1684]. 8°. 1691
Officia nova in Breviario Rom. [*sev. pagin.*] s8°. Antverpiae, *Plantin.* 1678
Officium B. Mariae Virginis, nuper reform. & Pii V jussu ed. Acc. Canones brev. in Kal. Greg. s8°. Parisiis, *J. Kerver.* 1583
Officium B. Mariae virg. &c. s8°. Londini. [1631]
Officium B. Mariae virg. &c. s8°. Antverpiae, *Plantin.* 1797
Officium Hebdomadae Sanctae. s8°. Mechliniae. 1843
Le petit Paroissien rom., cont. L'Office divin. n. éd. s8°. 1774
Official. Official German doc. rel. to World War; tr., v1, 2, 1923, *see* GERMAN.
Official Year Book of the Ch. of Eng., 1921, *see* CHURCH.
Official army register, *U.S.A., see* UNITED STATES: ARMY.
Officium, *see* OFFICIA.
Offley, *Family of, see* HUNTER (J.) Alienation & recovery of estates of O. of Norton in 1745, 1841.
O'Flaherty (Liam). The informer. s8°. [1925]
Life of Tim Healy. 8°. [1927]
Oganovsky (N. P.)
Очерки по экономич. географии С.С.С.Р. 2ое изд. la8°. Москва. 1924
Ogawa (Gotaro).
Conscription system in Japan. [C.E. for Int. Peace]. la8°. N.Y. 1921
Expenditures of the Russo-Jap. War. [C.E. for Int. Peace]. la8°. N.Y. 1923
Ogawa (Mimei). Rose & Witch & o. stories. Tr. &c. M. B. McKenney & S. N. Yoshioka. 8°. San Francisco. [1925]
Ogburn (William Fielding). Social change w. resp. to culture & orig. nature. s8°. [1923]
Ogden (Charles Kay), *see* BEST (R. H.) & C. K. O. Problem of the contin. school, 1914.
—— **& I. A. Richards.** The meaning of meaning: influence of language upon thought &c. Intr. by J. P. Postgate & suppl. essays by B. Malinowski & F. G. Crookshank. 8°. 1923
Ogden (Robert Morris). Psychology & education. 8°. [1926]
Ogg (David). Europe in the 17th cent. 8°. 1925
Ogg (Frederic Austin).
The governments of Europe. rev. ed. 8°. N.Y. 1920
—— **& W. R. Sharp.** Econ. develop. of mod. Europe. Suppl. chap. by W. R. Sharp. rev. ed. 8°. N.Y. 1926
Ogier de Cavoye, *see* CAVOYE.
Ogilbeus (Joannes), *see* OGILVIE (JOHN).
Ogilby (John), *misc. writer.* The entertainment of Charles II, in h. passage thr. the city of London to h. coronation: added, a brief narr. of h. coronation &c. fol. 1662
see FORDHAM (*Sir* H. G.) J. O. (1600–76), h. Britannia &c., 1925.
Ogilvie (Alexina). Profitable proverbs. 25 wood cuts illust. as many proverbs. [Foreword by R. Davies]. la8°. *Cayme Press.* 1923
Ogilvie (*Sir* **George**). A true acc. of the preserv. of the regalia of Scotland, 1701, *see* SCOTLAND. Papers rel. to regalia of S., 1829.
Ogilvie (J. N.), *D.D.* Castle memories: Edinburgh Castle. 2nd ed. s8°. E. 1911
Ogilvie (John), *Jesuit* [OGILBEUS (JOANNES)]. Relatio incarcerationis & martyrii P. J. Ogilbei, denuo recusa. s8°. Moguntiae. 1616

Ogilvie (Will). The Overlander & o. verses. s8°. Glasgow. 1913
Whaup o' the rede. Ballad. 8°. Dalbeattie. 1909
Ogilvie (William). Right of property in land, *see* BEER (M.) Pioneers of land reform, 1920.
Ogilvie-Grant of Grant (Trevor), *see* STRATHSPEY (T. O.-G. OF G., *Baron*).
Ogilvy, *The family of, see* AIRLIE, *House of.*
Ogilvy (David), *Lord Ogilvy & titular Earl of Airlie.* Orderly bk. of Ld. O.'s regt., army of Pr. Ch. Ed. Stuart, 10 Oct. 1745–21 Apr. 1746. Explan. notes by Sir B. Seton, *see* SOC. OF ARMY HIST. RESEARCH. Spec. No. of v2, 1923.
Ogilvy (James S.) A pilgrimage in Surrey. 2v. 4°. 1914
Ogilvy (*Mrs.* **Katharine),** *wife of T. Ogilvy, see* NAIRN (K.)
Ogilvy (Margaret), *aft. Barrie, see* BARRIE (*Sir* J. M.) M. O.; by h. son, 1896; 1921.
Oglethorpe (*Gen.* **James Edward),** *see* BRUCE (H.) Life of Gen. O., 1890.
Ogorodnikov (Evlampy Kirillovich). Прибрежья Ледовит. и Бѣлаго морей & съ нхъ притоками. [I.R.G.O. Зап. по отд. этнографіи, т7]. 8°. С.–П. 1877
O'Grady (Hugh). Strafford & Ireland: hist. of h. Vice-Royalty w. acc. of h. trial.
2v. [*pagin. cont., v2 no tp.*] 8°. D. 1923
O'Grady (Standish Hayes), *see* BRIT. MUSEUM: MSS. Irish MSS., v1, by S. H. O'G., 1926.
Ohanian (Armen). Dans les griffes de la civilis. s8°. 1921
O'Hanlon (*canon* **John).** The life of St. Laurence O'Toole, archb. of Dublin. s8°. D. 1857
O'Hara (Kane). Midas. Musical burletta. [P2583]. s8°. *n.d.*
O'Hara (Valentine J.) Esthonia. [*Repr. f.* "Rev. of reviews," Sept., 1922. P2730]. la8°. [Bournemouth. 1922]
see MAKEEV (N.) & V. O. Russia, 1925.
O'Haran (Denis Francis), *D.D., administrator of St. Mary's Cathedral, Sydney, see* CONINGHAM (A.) *Secret hist. of the C. case [petition for divorce, D. F. O'H., co-respondent], 1901.
O'Hart (John). Irish pedigrees; origin & stem of the I. nation. s8°. D. 1878
Ôhasama (Schûej), *see* ZEN. Z.: Ausgewählte Stücke d. Zen-Textes übers. &c. v. S. Ô., 1925.
O'Hegarty (Patrick Sarsfield). A short mem. of Terence MacSwiney. With chap. by D. Corkery. s8°. D. 1922
The victory of Sinn Féin. s8°. D. 1924
O'Hier de Grandpré (Louis Marie Joseph, *conte*), *see* GRANDPRÉ (L. M. J., *conte* O'H. DE).
Öhlenschläger (Adam G.) Nord. Oldsagn, bearb. til Almeenlæsning af O. [Skole-Udg.] 8°. 1853
see ANDERSEN (V.) A. Oehlenschläger, 3v, 1899–1900.
Öhler (Gustav Friedrich) [OEHLER]. Vet. Testam. sententia de rebus post mortem futuris. 8°. Stuttgartiae. 1846
Öhler (Richard), *see* NIETZSCHE (F. W.) Werke, B20, Register; v. R. Ö., 1926.
Öhlke (Waldemar). Deut. Lit. seit Goethes Tode & ihre Grundlagen. 8°. Halle. 1921
Öhlmann (Ernst), *ed., see* SEYDLITZ (E. v.) Hdbch. d. Geog., 1914.
Ohnet (Georges). Journal d'un bourgeois de Paris pend. la Guerre de 1914[–18]. fasc. 12–17 [*in* 2v]. s8°. *n.d.*
Le maître de forges. Pièce. 30ᵉ éd. s8°. 1905
La ténébreuse. 2ᵉ éd. s8°. 1901
Ohrt (Ferdinand). De danske Besværgelser mod Vrid og Blod, *see* KONGELIGT DAN. VID. SELSK. Hist.-fil. Med., B6, 1921–22.
Ó Huiginn (Tadhg Dall). A bhfuil aguinn dár chum T. D. Ó H., 1550–91. [Bardic poems. Ed. E. Knott. Irish Text Soc., v22, 23]. 2v. 8°. Lúndain. (1920–21) 1922–26
Oimenepthah I, *king of Egypt* [SETI I], *see* SOANE (*Sir* J.) MUSEUM. An acc. of the sarcophagus of S. I; by E. A. W. Budge, 1908.
Oireachtas (The) companion &c., 1928, *see* FLYNN (W. J.)
Ojeda (Tomás Thayer), *see* THAYER OJEDA (T.)
Ojetti (Ugo).
As they seemed to me. Tr. H. Furst. Intr. by G. d'Annunzio. s8°. [1928]
Cose viste [1921–23]. s8°. Milano. 1923
Mio figlio ferroviere. Romanzo. s8°. Milano. 1922
Raffaello e altre leggi. s8°. Milano. 1921
see PALAZZI. I palazzi &c. che non sono più del re; pref. di U. O., 1921.
„ PARIBENI (R.), P. FEDELE, &c. Ambasciate &c. a Roma; pref. d. U. O., 1927.
„ PITTI, *Palace.* La pittura ital.; [*by*] U. O. &c., 1924.
Ojetti (Ugo) [*cont.*] **& L. Dami.** Atlante di storia dell' arte ital. t1. 4°. Milano. [1924?]
Okakura (Kakasu) [OKAKURA-KAKUZO].
The book of tea. s8°. 1906
Okakura (Yoshisaburo). The Japanese spirit. Intr. by G. Meredith. n. ed. s8°. [1909]
Okamoto (Kido). Lady Hosokawa: hist. drama, *see* MIYAMORI (A.) Tales of the Samurai, enl. & rev. ed., 1922.
O'Keeffe (John).
Castle of Andalusia, *see* INCHBALD (E.) Brit. th., v22, 1808.
*The farmer, *see* DUBLIN. Vol. of farces, 1792.
Fontainbleau, *see* INCHBALD (E.) Brit. th., v22, 1808.
Lie of a day, *see* †INCHBALD (E.) Mod. th., v10, 1811.
*Modern antiques, *see* DUBLIN. Vol. of farces, 1792.
*Peeping Tom of Coventry, *see* DUBLIN. Vol. of farces, 1792.
Wild oats, *see* INCHBALD (E.) Brit. th., v22, 1808.
O'Kelly (Seumas). Hillsiders. s8°. D. 1921
Okely (Francis). The distinguished pre-eminence of the Son of Man, a hymn. [P504]. s8°. Northampton. 1776
The indispensable necessity of faith; disc. [*b. w. h.* Mem. of Behmen, 1780]. s8°. Northampton. 1781
Mem. of the life & writings of Jacob Behmen. s8°. 1780
Okey (Thomas). Italian studies, their place in mod. educ. Address. [P2420]. s8°. C. 1919
The story of Avignon. [Med. Towns Ser.] [2nd & rev. ed.] s8°. 1926
Venice & its story. [3rd ed.] 8°. 1904
Okill (J.) Internal-combustion engines. s8°. *Pitman.* [1922]
Ökumenische (Das) Concil, 1869–70, *see* VATICAN COUNCIL.
Olaf I [*Tryggvasch*], *king of Norway, see* NORDAL (S.) Om Olaf den helliges saga, 1914.
Olaf II [*Haraldsson*], *king of Norway, Saint, see* STORM (G.), *ed.* Otte brudstykker af d. aeldste saga om O., 1893.
Ólafsson (Eggert), *see* HERMANNSSON (H.) E. O.: biog. sk., 1925.
Ólafsson (Jón). Life, wr. by himself about 1661, w. cont. by another hand to h. death in 1679. Tr. f. Icelandic ed. of S. Blöndal by B. S. Phillpotts. [Hakluyt Soc., s2, 53]. v1. 8°. 1923
Olai (Ericus). Hist. Suecorum Gothorumque a J. Loccenio iterum ed. [*b. w.* Loccenius (J.) Hist., 1662]. s8°. Holmiæ. 1654
Olavarría y Ferrari (Enrique de). El arte lit. en México: noticias biog. y crit. 2ª ed. s8°. *n.d.*
Poesías líricas mejicanas de I. Prieto, Rosas y o. a. Col. &c. por O. y F. s8°. 1878
see AMERICANISTS. Crón. del 11° Congreso Internat. de Americanistas, Mexico, 1895, escr. por E. de O. y F., 1896.
Olbers (Levinus). Diss. topogr. de territorio Vestrogothiae Flundre. Præs. E. M. Fant. [P2641]. s4°. Upsaliae. [1788]
Olbrecht (E. von). *Geschichtl. Übers. d. slav. Sprache u. d. slav. Lit. Bearb. u. hrsg. v. E. v. O. 8°. L. 1837
Old.
Old English ballads, 1553–1625, 1920, *see* ROLLINS (H. E.), *ed.*
*Old (The) black cock &c. in jeopardy. [*Satire on George IV*]. 2nd ed. [P425]. 8°. 1820
*Old halls, manors, & families of Derbyshire, 4v, 1892, *see* TILLEY (J.)
Old Poor Robin, 1800–8, *see* POOR ROBIN.
Old Bailey. Select trials at the Sessions-House in the Old Bailey, 1720–41, 2nd ed., 4v, 1742; 1741–64, 4v, 1764, *see* TRIALS.
Old Etonian Association, *see* ETON COLLEGE. E. Register, p7, 1899–1909, 1922.
Oldcastle (*Sir* **John),** *styled Lord Cobham, d. 1417, see* GILPIN (W.) Lives of Wicliff, Ld. Cobham &c., 1765.
Olden (Sarah Emilia). Shoshone folk lore as disc. f. J. Roberts on Wind River Ind. Reserv. in Wyoming. s8°. Milwaukee, Wis. [1923]
Oldenbarnevelt (Johan van), *see* BARNEVELD (JAN VAN OLDEN).
Oldenberg (Hermann). Das Mahabharata, s. Entsteh., s. Inhalt, s. Form. 8°. Göttingen. 1922
Ṛgveda; Textkrit. u. exeget. Noten, 7ᵉˢ bis 10ᵉˢ Buch, 1912, *see* KÖNIGL. GESELLS. D. W. ZU GÖTTINGEN. Abh., N.F., 13, 1914.
Die Weltanschauung d. Brāhmana-Texte. 8°. Göttingen. 1919
Zur Gesch. d. altind. Prosa, *see* KÖNIGL. GESELLS. D. W. ZU GÖTTINGEN. Abh., B16, 1917.

Oldenbourg (Rudolf). Domenico Feti. 25 riprod. con testo e cat. 8º. [1921]
Jan Lys. 26 riprod. con testo e cat. 8º. [1921]
see MÜNCHEN. Das Miniaturenkabinett d. M. Residenz; Vorwort &c. v. H. Buchheit u. R. O., 1921.
Oldenburg (Sergei Fedorovich), *see* IMPER. RUSS. GEOG. OBSCH. Сказочн. Ком., под ред. С. Ф. О., 1926–27.
Oldenburg (Wilhelm), *see* NORDISKA MUSEET, *Stockholm.* Träsniderimönster, af W. O., 1893.
Oldendorp (Christian Georg Andreas). Gesch. d. Mission d. evang. Brüder auf d. Caraib. Inseln S. Thomas, S. Croix & S. Juan. Hrsg. J. J. Bossart. 2T *in* 1v. s8º. Barby. 1777
Oldfather (William Abbot), *ed.*
see ÆSOP. Ysopet-Avionnet, 1919.
„ SENECA (L. A.) Index verborum quae in S. fabulis reperiuntur a G. A. O. &c. confectus, 3p, 1918.
Old Felstedian Society, *see* FELSTED SCHOOL.
Oldham (Charles), *F.Z.S.*, *see* COWARD (T. A.) & C. O. Birds of Cheshire, 1900.
Oldham (John). Spencer's ghost, a satyr, *see* DRYDEN (J.) MacFlecknoe, &c., 1709.
Works, with remains.
[4p. *each w. sep. tp. & pagin. & date* 1694]. s8º. 1695
Oldham (John Haslope).
Christianity & the race problem. [3rd ed.] 8º. 1924
„ „ ....[4th ed.] 8º. [1925]
Oldham (Richard Dixon). The Cutch earthquake of 16th June 1819, *see* INDIA: GEOL. SURVEY. Mem., v46ii, 1926.
The structure of the Himalayas, & of the Gangetic plain, *see* INDIA: GEOL. SURVEY. Mem., v42ii, 1917.
Oldknow (Samuel), *see* UNWIN (G.) S. O. & the Arkwrights, 1924.
Old-Latin Biblical Texts. No. 7. s4º. O. 1924
see IRENAEUS, *St.* Novum Test.: quotations in Old-Lat. version; ed., w. intr. &c. by W. Sanday & C. H. Turner, 1924. [7.]
Oldmeadow (Ernest James). Coggin. s8º. 1919
The hare. s8º. 1920
Wildfang. s8º. 1922
Oldnorsk Læsebog med Gloss., 1863, *see* UNGER (C. R.)
Oldoino (Ercole). Orlando. Agg. argomenti d'incerto a. 8º. Venetia. 1598
Oldschool (Oliver), *ps.*, *see* DENNIE (J.)
Oldys (William). *Some acc. of the life &c. of C. Cotton, *see* WALTON (I.) Compl. angler, 1760.
Olearius, *Family of*, *see* LEUCKFELD (J. G.) Hist. Heshusiana &c.; geneal. Nachr. v. d. O., 1716.
Olearius (Gottfried), *assessor to the Leipsic Consistory.* Comm. de redemptione ex inferno &c. ex Oseae 14. s4º. Jenae. 1742
Obs. sacræ ad Evang. Matthaei. 4º. Lipsiæ. 1743
Olearius (Joannes), *prof. of Greek at Leipzig.* De stilo Novi Test. liber, auctus a J. C. Schwartz. Acc. J. H. Boecleri De lingua Nov. Test. orig. diss. s8º. Coburgi. 1731
Synopsis errorum Socinian. Præs. J. O., resp. M. Wolfgang *& others.* [P2743]. s4º. Lipsiæ. 1685
Olearius (Johann), *general superintendent at Weissenfels.*
Universa theologia positiva, polemica, exegetica & moralis. s4º. Halae Saxon. 1678
O'Leary (*Rev.* **De Lacy).**
Arabia before Muhammad. 8º. 1927
Arabic thought & its place in history. 8º. 1922
Compar. grammar of Semitic lang. 8º. 1923
Fragmentary Coptic hymns f. the Wadi n-Natrun. Ed. w. tr. & notes by De L. O'L. 4º. 1924
A short hist. of the Fatimid Khalifate. 8º. 1923
Oleggio (Giovanni Visconti), *d. 1366.*
see SIGHINOLFI (L.) La signoria di G. da O. in Bologna, 1355–60, 1905.
„ SORBELLI (A.) La signoria di G. V. a Bologna e le sue rel. con la Toscana, 1901.
Olevianus (Caspar), *Trevirus.* Expos. symboli apostolici, desumpta ex concionibus catecheticis G. O. T. s8º. Francofurti. 1576
„ „ [*a. ed. b. w.* Daneau (L.) Orat. Domin. explic., 1583]. s8º. Francofurti. 1584
An expos. of the Symbole of the Apostles &c. Sermons of G. O., tr. by J. Fielde. [*imperfect*]. s8º. 1582
In epistolam Pauli ad Galatas notæ, ex concionibus G. Oleviani excerptae & à T. Beza ed. s8º. Genevae. 1578
Olgin (Moissaye Joseph).
Guide to Russian lit., 1820–1917. 8º. N.Y. 1920

Oliger (Livario), *ed.*, *see* COZZA (*card.* L.) Vita e diarii, 1654–1729, 1925.
Olimpo degli Alessandri (Caio Baldassare) [OLYMPO]. Aurora. Libro primo d'amore. s8º. [Vinetia, *Tomaso di Salo*]. *n.d.*
Olin (Stephen), *D.D.*, *President of the Wesleyan Univ.*
Works. 2v (1, Sermons; 2, Lectˢ.) s8º. N.Y. 1854
Oliphant (E. H. C.) The plays of Beaumont & Fletcher: attempt to determine th. respective shares &c. 8º. New Haven, *Yale.* 1927
Oliphant (Francis William).
A plea for painted glass. s8º. O. 1885
Oliphant (*Mrs.* **Margaret Oliphant).** La ville enchantée. Tr. par H. Brémond. Intr. par M. Barrès. s8º. 1911
Phoebe, junior: a last chronicle of Carlingford. s8º. [1877]
Olivares (*el conde* **de),** *1587–1645* [OLEVARES; †GUZMAN (GASPAR DE), *duke de San Lucar de Baramada, count de Olivares*], *see* VERA Y FIGUEROA (J. A. DE). L'hist. du ministère du comte-duc [d'O.] &c., 1673.
Olivarius (Christiernus). De vita & scriptis Pauli Eliae vulgo Povel Vendekaabe. 8º. Havniae. 1741
Oliveira (Antonio Corrêa d'), *see* CORRÊA D'OLIVEIRA (ANTONIO).
Oliveira Martins (Joaquim Pedro).
The England of to-day. Tr. C. J. Willdey. s8º. 1896
Portugal contemporaneo. 3ª ed. 2t. s8º. 1895
Oliver & Boyd's Edinburgh Almanac [*form.* O. & B.'s New E. A.] 1843–44. 2v *in* 1. s8º. E. [1843–44]
Oliver, *Family of*, *see* OLIVER (*Maj.-gen.* J. R.) The O.'s of Cloghanodfoy &c., 3rd ed., 1904.
Oliver (Francis Wall). The exploitation of plants. [*By var. a.*] Ed. F. W. O. s8º. 1917
Oliver (Frederick Scott).
A. Hamilton. [Pop. ed.] s8º. *Nelson.* [1909]
*A draft bill entitl. An Act to amend the provision for the govt. of England, Scotland & Ireland. [P2380]. 4º. *n.d.*
Ordeal by battle. abridged ed. s8º. 1916
Oliver (George), *D.D.*, *rector of South Hykeham; 1782–1867.*
Golden remains of the early masonic writers. Intr. essay & notes by G. O. 5v. s8º. 1847–49
1, Masonic institutes, by var. a., intr. essay &c. by O.
2, Masonic princ., by Wᵐ. Calcott.
3, Masonic persecutions, by var. a., intr. essay by G. O.
4, Sermons, by J. Inwood.
5, Masonic morality, by T. M. Harris.
Oliver (*major-gen.* **John Ryder).** The Olivers of Cloghanodfoy &c. 3rd ed. [P2596]. s8º. 1904
Oliver (*capt.* **Samuel Pasfield).** Les Hovas &c. de Madagascar. [P2601]. 8º. Guernesey. 1869
Oliver (William), *artist.* Scenery of the Pyrenees. la. fol. 1842
Oliverius *Scholasticus* [OLIVERUS *Coloniensis*]. Rel. de exped. Damiatina [1217–19], *see* COLOGNE. Chron. &c.; rec. G. Waitz, 1880.
Olivers (Thomas). A defence of Methodism. [P2533]. s8º. 1785
A scourge to calumny. s8º. 1774
Olivet (*l'abbé* **d')** [†THOULIER D'OLIVET (P. J.)] Delectus comm. in M. T. Ciceronis opera omnia, ad ed. J. A. Ernesti accommodatus. Ex ed. J. O. 3t. [t2, 3 *pagin. cont.*] 8º. Londini. 1819
Olivey (Hugh P.)
North Curry: anc. manor & hundred. 8º. Taunton. 1901
Oliveyra (Francisco Xavier de). A pathetic disc. on the pres. calamities of Portugal. Tr. from French. 2nd ed. 8º. 1756
Olivier (Ad.) Carolles, Granville, Avranches & leurs environs. Mont Saint-Michel. Guide illust. s8º. 1922
Olivier (Eugène), G. Hermal & R. de Roton. Manuel de l'amateur de reliures armoriées franç. s1–13. la8º. 1924–28
Olivier (Paul). L'écouteuse de morts, nouv., *see* ŒUVRES libres, 33, 1924.
Olivier (Sydney Olivier, *1st baron*) [OLIVIER OF RAMSDEN].
The anatomy of African misery. 8º. 1927
Ollier (Edmund), *see* DORÉ (P. G.) Cassell's D. gallery: w. mem. of D., crit. essay, & letterpress by E. O., 1887 ?.
Ollivant (Alfred), *grandson of A. Ollivant, bp. of Llandaff.*
The brown mare & o. st. of Eng. under the cloud. s8º. [1916]
The next step. s8º. [1919]
One woman: 2nd part of a romance of Sussex. s8º. [1921]
Owd Bob. [repr.] s8º. *n.d.*
Redcoat captain. s8º. 1907
Ollivant (Alfred), *bp. of Llandaff.* Did the success of the evang. movement of 18th cent. consist in the propag. of dissent? Enquiry sugg. by an article in "Church Quarterly Review," July 1877 *&* Reply to Short notice &c. *in* 1v. 8º. O. 1877
Some acc. of the condition of the fabric of Llandaff Cathedral. 2nd ed. 4º. 1860

Ollivier (*Mme.* **Marie Thérèse Emile).** Emile Ollivier, sa jeunesse, d'ap. s. journal &c. s8°. 1918

Ollivier (O. Emile). L'église & l'état au Concile du Vatican. 2t [1, 4e éd., 2, 3e éd.] s8°. *n.d.*
see OLLIVIER (*Mme.* M. T. E.) E. O., sa jeunesse, d'ap. s. journal &c., 1918.

Ollmert (Carl). Das Saargebiet, *see* LÖNING (O.) Die Freie Stadt Danzig, 1923.

Ölmann (Franz) [OELMANN], *see* MÜLLER (W.) & F. O. Die "geometrische" Nekropole [Tiryns], 1912.

Olmedo (José Joaquín de). Odes, *see* BELLO (A.) Odes of B., O. &c.; intr. by E. C. Hills, 1920.

Olmet (Luis Anton del) & J. de Torres Bernal.
Los grandes Españoles. [v11]. Palacio Valdés. 8°. 1919
„ „ [v12]. Maria Guerrero. 8°. 1920

Olminsky (M.), *ed.* Из эпохи "Звезды" и "Правды" (1911–14). 8°. Москва. 1921
О воспоминаниях Н. Д. Богданова, *see* BLAGOEV (D). От группы Благоева, 1921.

Olmsted (Frederick Law). Fred. L. Olmsted, landscape architect, 1822–1903. Ed. F. L. Olmsted, Jr. & T. Kimball. [v]1. 8°. N.Y. 1922

Ölrichs (Johann). Germaniae litt. opuscula hist. philol.-theol. [*by var. a.*] emend. ed. I. O. 2t. s8°. Bremae. 1772–74

Olrik (Axel).
Danmarks heltedigtning: en oldtidsstudie. 2d. 8°. 1903–10
1, Rolf Krake og den aeldre Skjoldungfejden.
2, Starkad den gamle og den yngre Skjoldungraekke.
Danske folkeviser i udvalg. Under medvirkning af I. Falbe-Hansen. Saml. 1. s8°. 1918
Folkelige afhandlinger. Udvalgte og udg. af H. Ellekilde. 8°. 1919
Ragnarök, d. Sagen v. Weltuntergang. Untersucht v. A. O. Übertragen v. W. Ranisch. 8°. 1922

Olschki (Leo S.) Bibl. Savonaroliana: œuvres de Fra G. Savonarola. Cat. 39. s8°. Florence. 1898

Olsen (Magnus), *see* BUGGE (S.) Norges indskrifter; udg. ved S. B. & M. O., 3B, 1891–1924.

Olshausen (Hermann). Bibl. comm. on the Gospels & the Acts. Tr. [H. B. Creak]. 4v [1, 4th ed. 2–4, 5th ed.] 8°. E., *Clark.* 1864–65
Bibl. comm. on St. Paul's Ep. to Galatians, Ephesians, Colossians & Thess. Tr. 3rd ed. 8°. E., *Clark.* 1864
Opuscula theologica ad crisin &c. N. Test. pert. s8°. Berolini. 1834

Ölsnitz (A. B. E. v. der). Herkunft u. Wappen d. Hochmeister d. Deut. Ordens, 1198–1525. 8°. Königsberg i. Pr. 1926

Olsson (K. G.), *see* HEDIN (S.) South. Tibet: researches, 1906–8, v6ii, Les obs. astronom., &c. par K. G. O., 1918.

Olsvig (Viljam). Holberg og England. 8°. 1913

Olthusius (J.), *see* HOLTHUSIUS (J.)

Oltramare (Paul). L'hist. des idées théosophiques dans l'Inde. t2, La théosophie bouddhique. [Annales du Mus. Guimet, Bibl. d'ét., t31]. 8°. 1923

Olufsen (O.) The second Pamir exped., *see* PAULSEN (O.) Studies on the vegetation of the Transcaspian Lowlands [*&* Pamir], 2v, 1912–20.

Ὀλύμπια Δώματα, or, Almanack, 1880–83, 1805. By T. Wing. [*b. w.* Gentleman's diary, 1800–3, 1805]. s8°. 1800–5

Olver (George William). Life & death, the sanctions of the law of love. [Fernley Lect.] 8°. 1878
see POSNETT (J. L.) Notes on O.'s Fernley Lect., 1878.

Olympianus, *fabulist.* Fabellae Olympianeae. [*Extr. b. w.* Msereantz (M.) Last hours of Nicholas I, 1855]. 8°. *n.p. n.d.*

Olympo (Baldassare), *see* OLIMPO DEGLI ALESSANDRI (C. B.)

O'Mahony (The) [PIERCE CHARLES DE LACY O'MAHONY]. Bulgaria & the powers. With Serbo-Bulgarian treaty (1912) &c. [P2600]. 8°. D. 1915

O'Malley (Lewis Sidney Steward). Hist. of Bengal, Bihar & Orissa under Brit. rule. s8°. Calcutta. 1925

Oman (Carola). Princess Amelia. s8°. [1924]

Oman (*Sir* **Charles William Chadwick).**
Castles. la8°. *G.W.R.* 1926
Column & line in the Peninsular War, 1910, *see* BRIT. ACADEMY. Proc., 1909–10.
England bef. the Norman Conquest. [Hist. of Eng., ed. C. Oman, v1]. 4th ed. 8°. [1919]
„ „ ....5th ed. 8°. 1921
Hist. of Eng. n. & rev. ed. s8°. [1921]

Oman (*Sir* **Charles William Chadwick)** [*continued*].
Hist. of England. v3–6 [*var. ed.*] 8°. 1921–25
see INNES (A. D.) Eng. under Tudors, 6th ed., 1920. [4.]
„ ROBERTSON (C. G.) Eng. under the Hanoverians, 6th ed., 1923. [6.]
„ TREVELYAN (G. M.) Eng. under the Stuarts, 11th ed., 1924; 12th ed. rev., 1925. [5.]
„ VICKERS (K. H.) Eng. in the later Middle Ages, 3rd ed., 1921. [3.]
Hist. of the art of war in the Middle Ages. 2nd ed. rev. & enl. 2v. 8°. [1924]
A hist. of the Peninsular War. v6 (Sept. 1812–Aug. 5, 1813). 8°. O. 1922
The unfortunate Col. Despard & o. studies. 8°. 1922

Oman (John Wood). Book of Revelation, theory of the text: rearr. text & tr: comm. s8°. C. 1923
Grace & personality. 3rd ed. rev. 8°. C. 1925

Omar, *pasha, see* ARBUTHNOT (G.) Herzegovina; or Omer Pacha & the Xtn. rebels, 1862.

Omar Kkayyam. Rubáiyát of O. K., rendered into Eng. verse by E. Fitzgerald, w. drawings by E. Vedder [& Biog. sk. of E. F., by M. K.] 8°. Boston [Mass.] 1894
see PLIMMER (H. G.) Omariana, *n.d.*
„ VARESI (M. A.) 'Umar Khayyám, 1922.

Omar Kiazim, *see* KIAZIM (OMER).

O'Meara (Barry Edward). Napoléon dans l'exil, ou, l'écho de Ste.-Hélène; tr., 2t, *see* NAPOLEON I. Rec. de pièces authent., t10, 11, 1822–25.
Napoleon in exile; or, a voice f. St. Helena: opinions &c. of N. on the events of h. life. 5th ed. 2v. 8°. 1822

O'Meara (*Lt.-Col.* **Walter Alfred John).** Kekewich in Kimberley: defence of the Diamond Fields, Oct. 1899–Feb. 1900. Foreword by Sir R. Baden-Powell. 8°. 1926

Omer, *St., bp. of Thérouanne, see* DUSAUTOIR (A.) St. O. & s. successeurs, 1924?.

Omessa (Charles) & Henri Omessa.
La dern. Tsarine. Révélations d'A. Dobrowitz. s8°. 1920

Omichund [AMI CHAND], *see* †TEMPLE (*Sir* R. C.) Side-lights on O., 1919.

Omodeo (Adolfo). Paolo di Tarso. 8°. Messina. [1922]

Omond (Thomas Stewart). English metrists: sk. of Eng. prosodical crit. &c. 8°. O. 1921

Omont (Henri).
see METZ. Coll. sur l'hist. de M. &c. à la Bibl. Nat.; publ. O., 1919.
„ POIRIER (*Dom* G.) Rapport de Dom P. sur la réunion à Paris des cartul. par H. O., 1909.
„ VENICE. Deux registres de prêts de mss. de la Bibl. de S. Marc (1545–59); [ed. H. O.], 1888.

Ompteda (Christian Fr. Wilh., *Frhr.* **v.)** In the King's German Legion. Mem. of Baron O. dur. the Napoleonic Wars. [Ed. Baron L. v. Ompteda]. 8°. 1894

Ompteda (Georg, *Frhr.* **von).** Der neue Blaubart. s8°. 1919

On. *On chanting, by the compilers of "Congreg. Ch. music" &c., 1854, *see* CHANTING.
*On legislative ignorance, 1837, *see* LEGISLATIVE.
*On the necessity of a gen. arming in Eng. &c., 1859, *see* ENGLAND.

Onasander, *see* ONOSANDER.

Once. *Once & for ever, 3v, 1874, *see* JOHNS (B. G.)
*Once I had a home, 2nd impr., 1927, *see* NADEJDA, *ps.*

Oncieu, *The house of, see* DOUVRES. Chartres de la tour de D., 1250–1624: doc. &c. [*mainly on hist. of H. of E.*]; par F. Marchand, 1891.

Oncken (Hermann).
Deut. Vergangenheit u. Zukunft. [P2848]. 8°. München. 1926
Grossherzog Friedrich I. v. Baden u. d. deut. Politik v. 1854–71. Hrsg. v. d. Bad. Hist. Komm. Bearb. v. H. O. 2B. 8°. 1927
The historical Rhine policy of the French. Intr. by F. Schevill. s8°. N.Y. 1923
Die hist. Rheinpolitik d. Franzosen. 8°. St. 1922
Lassalle: e. polit. Biog. 4e durchgearb. A. 8°. St. 1923
Napoleon III u. d. Rhein: Urspr. d. Krieges v. 1870–1. [Einltg. z. "Rheinpolitik Napoleons III v. 1863–70, 1926]. la8°. 1926
Die Rheinpolitik Napoleons III, 1863–70, u. d. Urspr. d. Krieges v. 1870–1. Nach d. Staatsakten v. Österr., Preussen &c. 3B. la8°. 1926
Weltgesch. u. Versailler Friede. [P2526]. 8°. Frankfurt a. M. 1921

Oncken (Wilhelm). Aristoteles u. s. Lehre v. Staat; *for a. copy see* VIRCHOW (R.) & F. v. HOLTZENDORFF. Vorträge, H103, 1870.

One-act plays of to-day, 1924, *see* MARRIOTT (J. W.), *ed.*

O'Neddy (Philothée), *ps., see* DONDEY (THÉOPHILE).

O'Neil (Alfred). Annals of Brechin cricket, 1849–1927. 8°. Brechin. 1927

O'Neil (Owen Rowe). Adventures in Swaziland. Story of a S. African Boer. 8°. [1921]

O'Neill (Eugene).
All God's chillun got wings—Desire under the elms—& Welded. [Plays]. s8°. [1925]
Beyond the horizon *&* Gold: 2 plays. s8°. [1924]
The great god Brown incl. The fountain, The dreamy kid & Before breakfast. [*Plays*]. s8°. [1926]
The hairy ape & o. plays [*i.e.* Anna Christie & The first man]. s8°. [1923]
The moon of the Caribbees & 6 o. plays of the sea. Intr. by St. J. Ervine. 8°. [1923]
Plays: 1st series. The straw—The emperor Jones—Diff'rent. Intr. by C. E. Bechhofer. s8°. [1922]

O'Neill (Herbert Charles).
The Royal Fusiliers in the Gt. War. 8°. 1922

O'Neill (J. J.) Prelim. rep. on the economic geol. of Hazelton district, B.C. [Canada: Geol. Survey. P2513]. 8°. Ottawa. 1919
see Canadian Arctic Exped. Rep., v11, A, Geol. of Arctic coast of C., west of Kent Pen., by J. J. O'N., 1924.

O'Neill (Moira), *ps.* [*i.e.* Nesta Higginson].
More songs of the Glens of Antrim. s8°. E. 1921
Songs of the glens of Antrim. 5th impr. s8°. E. 1900

Onely (Richard), *see* Pope (A.) Messiah [text, *w.* tr. into Latin verse by R. O.], 1749.

Ongania (Ferdinando), *publisher, see* Venezia. Doc. per la storia di San Marco, 1886.

Ongaro (Max). Come è caduto il Campanile di S. Marco. [Estr. d. Nuova Rassegna tecnica internaz., N. 15. P2838]. 8°. Prato. 1904

***Onguant** pour le brülure, 1683, *see* Barbier d'Aucour (J.)

Onian (Arsen) [Wonyan (A.)]
Сборникъ сванск. названій деревьевъ и растеній, *see* Marr (N. Ya). Матеріалы, 8, 1917.
Сванскіе тексты на лăшхск. нарѣчіи, *see* Marr (N. Ya.) Матеріалы, 9, 1917.

Onions (Oliver). Cut flowers. [2nd impr.] s8°. 1927
Ghosts in daylight. s8°. 1924
Peace in our time. 3rd impr. s8°. 1924

Onkelos. Thargum, hoc est paraphrasis O. Chaldaica in sacra Biblia ex Chaldaeo in Lat. versa, additis annot. autore P. Fagio. Pentateuchus. t1. sm. fol. Argentorati. 1546

Ono (Giichi). Expenditures of the Sino-Japanese War. [C.E. for Int. Peace]. la8°. N.Y. 1922
War & armament expenditures of Japan. [C.E. for Int. Peace]. la8°. N.Y. 1922

Onofrio (J. B.) Essai d'un glossaire des patois de Lyonnais, Forez & Beaujolais. 8°. Lyon. 1864

Onosander. The general: text, w. Eng. tr. by members of the Illinois Greek Club [Loeb Class. Lib.], 1923, *see* Æneas, *Tacticus*.

Onslow (Huia), *2nd son of 4th Earl Onslow* [Onslow (Victor Alex. Herbert Huia)], *see* Onslow (M.) Huia O.: a mem., 1924.

Onslow (Muriel), *wife of Huia Onslow.*
Huia Onslow: a memoir. 8°. 1924

Ontario Historical Society, *see* Simcoe (J. G.) Corr. &c., 1789–94, 2v, 1923–24.

Ontario Library Association.
*The O.L.A.: an hist. sketch, 1900–25. 8°. Toronto. 1926

Onus ecclesiae, 1531, *see* Ebser (J.), *bp. of Chiemsée.*

Oordt (Adriaan van).
Warhold. 2e dr. 2d *in* 1v. 8°. Bussum. 1912

Oost (Joseph van), *see* Van Oost (J.)

Oosterzee (Jan Jacob van). Christian dogmatics. Tr. by J. W. Watson & M. E. Evans. 2nd ed. 8°. 1878
Moses: a biblical study. Tr. by J. Kennedy. 8°. E. 1876
Oratio de scepticismo, hodiernis theologis caute vitando. 8°. Roterodami. 1863
Theolog. & homilet. comm. on Gospel of St. Luke. Ed. J. P. Lange. Tr. S. Taylor. 2v. 8°. E., *Clark*. 1862–63

Opdyke (George). Offic. doc., addresses &c. of G. O., mayor of New York, 1862–63. 8°. N.Y. 1866

Open (The) road: bk. for wayfarers, 9th ed., 1906, *see* Lucas (E. V.)

***Ophiolatreia**: acc. of serpent-worship &c. s8°. *p.p. n.d.*

Opie (*Mrs.* **Amelia)**, *wife of John Opie.* The father & daughter, a tale in prose: w. an Epistle & o. poet. pieces. s8°. 1801

Opisanie. *Описаніе Тибета, 1828, *see* Bichurin (J.)

Opmeer (Petrus ab), *the elder.* Officium Missae, apud Eccl. temp. 4 primorum concil. gen. in usu fuisse hist. assertio. s8°. Antverpiæ. 1570

Oporinus (Joannes), *see* Jociscus (A.) Oratio de ortu, vita & obitu J. O., 1569.

Oppé (Adolf Paul). Thomas Rowlandson, h. drawings & water-colours. Ed. G. Holme. [The Studio]. 4°. 1923
Water-colour drawings of J. S. Cotman, w. comm. Ed. G. Holme. [Studio (The)]. la8°. 1923
see Sharp (C. J.) & A. P. O. The dance, 1924.

Oppenbusch (Michael van). Exercit. in qua religio Moscovitarum delineata. [*b. w.* Hesterberg (J.) Eccl. Waldens., 1668]. s4°. Argentorati. 1667

Oppenheim (E. R.), *see* Hague (The). Bibl. du Palais de la Paix: cat., par O. &c., 1916.

Oppenheim (Edward Phillips).
The devil's paw. s8°. [1921]
Gabriel Samara. s8°. [1926]
The great impersonation. s8°. [1920]
Harvey Garrard's crime. s8°. [1927]
Jacob's ladder. s8°. [1921]
The light beyond. s8°. [1928]
Madame. s8°. [1927]
Miss Brown of X.Y.O. s8°. [1927]
The profiteers. s8°. [1921]
Stolen idols. s8°. [1925]
The yellow crayon. s8°. *n.d.*

Oppenheim (K. A.)
Россия в дорожном отношении. la8°. Москва. 1920

Oppenheim (Lassa Francis Lawrence). The future of internat. law. [C.E. for Int. Peace]. la8°. O. 1921
International law. 3rd ed., ed. R. F. Roxburgh. 2v. 8°. 1920–21

Oppenheimer (Franz). The state, its hist. &c. viewed sociologically. Auth. tr. by J. M. Gitterman. 8°. [1923]

Oppenheimer (Heinrich).
The constit. of the German Republic. 8°. 1923

Oppenheimer (Reuben), *see* Flexner (B.) & R. O. Legal aspect of the juvenile court, 1922.

Oppermann (A.), *ingénieur, see* Bouches-du-Rhône; encyclop. départ., t8, par P. Masson, A. O. &c., 1926.

Oppermann (Hans). Zeus Panamaros. [Religionsgesch. Versuche, B19iii]. 8°. Giessen. 1924

Opstraet (Johannes). Theologus Christianus sive ratio studii & vitæ instituenda a theologo. s8°. Lovanii. 1697

Optatianus Porphyrius (Publilius), *see* Porphyrius (P. O.)

Optatus, *Saint, bp. of Mela.* Libri sex de schismate Donatist. adv. Parmenianum. s8°. *n.p. ex. Bibliopolio Commeliniano.* 1599
see Monceaux (P.) Hist. de l'Afrique chrétienne, t5, St. O. & les prem. écr. donatistes, 1920.

Opuscoli interessanti l'umanità &c. [Dubbi &c. s. la libertà d. commercio &c.] 8°. [1730]

***Opuscula** miscella quaedam juris publici, 1725, *see* Berger (F. L. v.)

Oracles. *Réponse à l'Hist. des o. &c., 1709, *see* Baltus (J. F.)
*Suite de la réponse à l'Hist. des o. &c., 1709, *see* Baltus (J. F.)

Orage (Alfred Richard), *see* Douglas (*Maj.* C. H.) Credit-power & democracy, w. comm. on the included scheme by A. R. O., 1920; 2nd ed., 1921.

O'Rahilly (Cecile).
Ireland & Wales: their hist. & lit. rels. 8°. 1924

Oram (Samuel Marsh). Poet. works. Coll. by T. Park. [*b. w.* Moore (J. H.) Poet. works, 1808]. s8°. 1808

Orange River Colony, *see* Transvaal. T. & O. R. C.: Rep. of Director of educ., 1900–4, 1905.

***Oratio** in theatro Sheldon. hab., 1749, *see* King (W.)

Orationes horum rhetorum, 1513, *see* Oratores.

Oratores. Oratores Attici, 16t, 1828, *see* Dobson (W. S.), *ed.*
Orationes horum rhetorum. [1], Æschinis, Lysiae, Alcidamantis, Anthisthenis Demadis, item Æschinis vita [*&*] Lysiae vita. [2], Orationes infra scriptorum rhetorum Andocidis, Isæi, Dinarchi, Antiphontis Lycurgi, Gorgiae, Lesbonactis, Herodis. [3], Isocratis orationes; Alcidomantis contra dicendi magistros. Gorgiae de laudibus Helenae. Aristidis de laudibus Athenarum; Eiusdem de laudibus urbis Romae [*in Greek*]. 3p *in* 2v. fol. [Venetiis *in aedibus Aldi* &c. 1513]

Oratoriana, Biblioteca, *Naples, see* Biblioteca Oratoriana.

Oratzoytz, 1899. [Almanac, *in Armenian*]. s8°. i Vagharshapat. [1899]

Orazioni scelte del secolo 16, 1897, *see* Lisio (G.), *ed.*

Orbelian (Stephanus), *bp. of Siuniq, fl. 1287.* Patmouthiun Tann Sisakan. [Hist. of Sisak, *i.e.* Siuniq, *in Armenian.* Ed. M. Emin]. 8°. Moskva. 1861

Orbicciani (Bonagiunta), *see* URBICIANI (B.)

Orbigny (Alcide d'), *see* HERON-ALLEN (E.) A. d'O., h. life & work, 1917.

Orcutt (William Dana).
In quest of the perfect book. 8°.]1926]

Orczy (*baroness* Emmuska). The celestial city. s8°. [1926]
Nicolette. s8°. [1922]
Pimpernel & Rosemary. s8°. [1924]
Sir Percy hits back. s8°. [1927]
Unravelled knots. s8°. [1925]

Ord (Hubert). Chaucer & the rival poet in Shakespeare's sonnets. s8°. 1921

Orde-Browne (*Maj.* Granville St. J.), *see* BROWNE (*Maj.* G. ST. J. O.)

Ordelaffi (Francesco dei), *see* EMERTON (E.) Humanism & tyranny (Tyranny of F. dei O., *early sources*), 1925.

*__Ordem__ (A) da salvaçaõ ou a doutrina Christaã. s8°. Tranquebar. 1712

Orden de ros-asanah y kipur, nuev. corr., 5466 [*i.e.* 1700], *see* TEPHILOTH.

Ordenaçoens do Sen. Rey D. Affonso V, 5 livros, 1792, *see* PORTUGAL. Coll. da legisl. &c. do reino de P. &c.

Order of admin. of the Lord's Supper &c. as used by the Wesleyan Methodists. With app. 8°. 1848

Ordinance (An) of the Lords & Commons for excluding such members as have deserted Parl., 1644, *see* PARLIAMENT: ANON. WORKS.

Ordinary (The) of the Missal &c. (Lat. & Eng.), 1794, *see* MISSAL.

*__Ordinatio__ eccl. regnorum Daniæ &c., 1537, *see* DANIA.

Ording (Fr.)
Riksarkivar M. Birkeland, hans liv og virke. la8°. 1919

Ordnance [ORDNANCE SURVEY &c.] O. Survey atlas of England & Wales. obl. fol. 1922
O. Survey atlas of Scotland. obl. fol. Southampton. 1924
O. Survey: map of Roman Britain. folded. 8°. 1924
see CRAWFORD (O. G. S.) Air survey and archæology, 1924.

Ordnung [*see also* KIRCHEN-ORDNUNG]. *O. d. evang. Kirchen in Franckreich, so gehalten wird &c. [*Tr.*] s8°. Heydelberg. 1563

Ordo Prophetarum, 1922, *see* YOUNG (C.)

Oreffice (Pellegrino).
Giacomo Favretto. [P2841]. 8°. Venezia. 1899

O'Reilly (Antonio Bernal de), *see* BERNAL DE O'REILLY (A.)

O'Reilly (M. M.), *see* HOLLINGWORTH (E. J.) & M. M. O'R. Anglo-Saxon cemetery at Girton Coll., Cambridge, 1925.

Orella (J. Ant. de Camino y), *see* CAMINO Y ORELLA.

Orellana (Fernando Pizarro y), *see* PIZARRO Y ORELLANA (F.)

Orelli (Conrad von). The Old Test. prophecy of the consummation of God's Kingdom. Tr. J. S. Banks. 8°. E., *Clark.* 1889
The prophecies of Isaiah. Exp. by O. Tr. J. S. Banks. 8°. E., *Clark.* 1889

Oren (Nicolaus), *see* ORESME (N.)

Orenburgsky (Sergei Gussiev). The land of the children. Tr. N. N. Selivanova. 8°. 1928
The land of the fathers. Tr. N. N. Selivanova. 8°. [1925]

Orencio, *San* [ORENS ORENTIUS], *see* ORIENTIUS, *Saint, bp. of Auch.*

Oresme (Nicholaus), *bp. of Lisieux* [OREN (N.)] Epistola Luciferi ad spirituales. [*Ed.* M. Flacius]. [P2528]. s8°. [Magdeburgae. 1549]

Orestano (Francesco). Nuovi principi. la8°. [1925]

Orfali (Gaudence). Capharnaüm & ses ruines: d'ap. les fouilles accomp. à Tell-Houm par la Custodie Franciscaine de Terre Sainte, 1905–21. fol. 1922

Orfinus, *Laudensis.* Poema de regimine et sapientia potestatis; nunc primum ed. A. Ceruti, *see* REGIA DEP. DI STORIA PATRIA. Misc., t7, 1869.

Orford (Edward Russell, *earl of*), *1653–1727*, *see* ALLYN (R.) Narr. of victory obt. by fleet, La-Hogue, 1692; added letters wr. by Adm. R. &c., 1744.

Organ (Edward J.)
The Gold Coast cocoa industry. [P2563]. 8°. Bournville. 1921

Orgemont (Pierre d'), *see* FRANCE. Les Grandes chron. de F.: Chron. des règnes de Jean II & de Charles V [*sometimes attrib. to* P. d'O.]; publ. R. Delachemal, t3, 4, 1920.

Oriani (Alfredo).
No. Romanzo. s8°. Bari. 1920
Olocausto. Romanzo. s8°. Bari. 1918
Punte secche: 2ª serie di Fuochi di bivacco. 8°. Bari. 1921
Vortice. Romanzo. s8°. Bari. 1918
see PENTIMALLI (G.) A. O., 1921.
,, SERRA (R.) Scritti ined. (Abbozzo di un saggio su A. O.), 1923.

Oribasius. Coll. medic. reliq., v1, libri 1–8; ed. J. Raeder, *see* CORPUS medic. Graec., v6i, 1, 1928.
Synopsis ad Eustathium—Libri ad Eunapium; ed. J. Raeder, *see* CORPUS medic. Graec., v6iii, 1926.

Orichovius (Stanislaus).
Chimæra: sive de Stancari funesta regno Poloniæ secta. 8°. *n.p.* [Cracow ?]. 1562
,, ,, ...[*a. ed.*] s8°. Coloniae. 1563
De lege cœlibatus contra Syricium in concilio habita oratio. Ejusdem Ad Julium III supplicatio de approbando matrimonio à se inito. Item: De bello adv. Turcas &c. Ad Sigismundum Turcica 2ª. s8°. Basileæ. 1551
Fidei catholicae conf. Petricoviæ in synodo &c. a. 1552. s8°. Cracoviæ. [1561]
,, ,, [*a. ed. b. w. h.* Chimæra &c., 1563]. s8°. Coloniae. 1563
In Warszaviensi Synodo pro dignitate sacerdotali oratio. s8°. Cracoviae. 1561
,, ,, [*a. ed. b. w. h.* Chimæra, 1563]. s8°. Coloniæ. 1563
Pro eccl. Christi ad S. Matieovium episc. Crac. s8°. Cracovie. 1546

Oriens christianus: röm. Halbjahrhefte. Hrsg. v. Priestercoll. d. deut. Campo Santo unter Schriftleit. v. A. Baumstark. Jahrg. 1, 2 [*in* 1v]. la8°. Rom. 1901–2

Oriental Ceramic Society.
Transactions, 1921/22–1926/27. 4°. *f.p.c.* 1923–28

Oriental Club (The).
Annals, 1824–58. Ed. S. Wheeler. 8°. *p.f.p.c.* 1925

Oriental Texts Society, *see* SOCIETY FOR THE PUBL. OF OR. TEXTS.

Oriental Translation Fund.
PUBLICATIONS, *see* DIDASCALIA.
,, ,, ...N.S., v25–28. 8°. 1921–27
see ABU 'ALĪ AL-MUḤASSIN AL-TANŪKHĪ. [27, 28.]
,, ASATIR (THE). [26.]
,, MUḤAMMAD IBN AḤMAD IBN IYĀS. [25.]

Orientalische.
Neue Or. u. exeget. Bibliothek, 9T, 1786–93, *see* MICHAELIS (J. D.)
Or. u. exeget. Bibl., 24T, 1771–89, *see* MICHAELIS (J. D.)
Or. u. occidental. Sprachmeister &c., 1748, *see* FRITZ (J. F.)

Orientalische Bibliographie. B25 (für 1911). 8°. 1917–22

Orientalists. Eminent or., Indian, Europ., Amer. s8°. Madras. [1922]

Orientius, *Saint, bp. of Auch* [ORENCIO; ORENS; ORENTIUS], *see* ANDRES (J. F.) Vida de San Orencio obispo de Aux &c., 1648.

Origen [ORIGENES ADAMANTIUS].
Opera omnia et quae ejus nom. circumfer. Lat. versa. Ex recent. ed. Paris. Caroli Delarue. 3t. fol. Venetiis. 1743
Werke. B6–8, Homilien. Hrsg. W. A. Baehrens. [Die griech. christl. Schr.] la8°. L. 1920–25
Contra Celsum libri 8. Et Gregorii Neocæsar. Thaumaturgi panegyricus in O. A D. Hoeschelio ed. &c. [*Gr. & Lat. 2 pagin.*] s4°. Augustæ Vindelic. 1605
De oratione libellus. Ex cod. MS. Coll. Trin. Cantab. [*Foll. by* Diadochus, Sermo contra Arianos. *pagin. cont.*] s4°. [Basileae. 1694]
In sacras Scr. comm. quæcumque Græce reperiri potuerunt. P. D. Huetius Græca primus maxima ex parte edidit, Lat. interpret. adj. &c. Cui præfixit Origeniana, vita &c. 2p. fol. Rothomagi. 1668
Philosophumena [*form. attrib. to O.*], *see* HIPPOLYTUS, *St., bp. of the Port of Rome, for text & tr.*
see FAYE (E. DE). Esquisse de la pensée d'O., 1925.
,, —— O., sa vie &c., v1, 2, 1923–27.
,, —— O. & h. work; tr., 1926.
,, FISCHER (P.) Comm. de O. theologia & cosmologia, 1846.
,, GREGORY, *Thaumaturgus.* Address to O.; [tr., w. intr.] by W. Metcalfe, 1920.
,, —— Panegyricus ad O., 1722.
,, HORBIUS (J. H.) Hist. Origeniana, 1670.
,, MEISNER (J.) Tractatus de O. &c., ed. 2ª, 1712.
,, PARKER (S.) Free & impartial censure of Platonick philos., w. acc. of O. hypothesis &c., 1667.
,, RUST (G.) *Letter of resolution conc. O., 1661.
,, WEICKHMANN (J. S.) De schola O. sacra, 1744.
,, ZORN (P.) Diss. de eunuchismo O., 1708.

Original.
*Orig. letters to an honest sailor, 1746, *see* WAGER (*adm. sir* C.)
*Orig. (The) papers & letters rel. to the Scots & Suppl., 1700, *see* DARIEN COMPANY.

Original [*continued*].
*Orig. poems in the moral &c. styles, 14th ed., 1833, *see* HUGMAN (J.)
Orig. pr. records of Amer. vessels captured, 1803–11, 1926, *see* AMERICAN.
Orig. sacred hymns, 1776, *see* THOMSON (*Rev.* G.)
***Origine** (Dell') de' barbari, che distrussero &c. l'imp. di Roma onde hebbe principio Venetia, *see* ZENO (N.) Dell' orig. di Venetia, 1558.
Orioli (Leonardo).
Descr. storica di Ravenna. la8º. Ravenna. 1836
O'Riordan (Conal Holmes O'Connell) [*ps.* NORREYS CONNELL].
Adam of Dublin. s8º. [1920]
In London. s8º. [1922]
Married life. s8º. [1924]
Rowena Barnes. s8º. [1923]
Orissa, *see* BIHAR & ORISSA *for Govt. publ*ˢ.
Oriundi (Federico Paleologo). I Corsi nella fanteria italiana di Venezia. 8º. Venezia. 1912
Orla-Jensen (Sigurd). Lactic acid bacteria, *see* KONG. DAN. VID. SELSKAB. Skr., Række 8, B5, 1919.
Orlandini (Giovanni). La gondola. [P2842]. la8º. [Venezia. 1903]
Storia d. magistrature Venete. Saggio. [P2836]. 8º. Venezia. 1898
Orlandinus (Nicolaus). Hist. Soc. Jesu pars prima [& secunda]. 2p *in* 1v. [p3–6 wanting]. fol. Antverpiae. 1620
1, Ignatius ; *ed.* F. Sacchini. 2, Lainius, auctore F. Sacchino.
Orlando (Vittorio Emanuele). Contrib. alla storia di Partinico, *see* SOCIETÀ SICIL. Arch., n.s., 44, 1922.
see LANSING (R.) The Big Four, 1922.
Orleans. Saint Joan of O. Scenes f. the 15th cent. Mystère du Siège d'Orléans. Sel. & tr. by J. Evans. Text ed. P. Studer. s8º. O. 1926
Orléans, *The House of.* Deux inventaires de la Maison d'O., 1389 & 1408. Publ., & préc. d'une intr. [*by*] F. M. Graves. 8º. 1926
Orléans (Charles, *duc* **d'),** *1391–1465.* Poésies. Ed. P. Champion. [Class. franç. du m. â.] t1. s8º. 1923
Orléans (Gaston d'), *comte d'Eu* [†LOUIS PHILIP MARIE FERD. GASTON [D'ORLÉANS], *cte. d'Eu*]. Viagem militar ao Rio Grande do Sul (1865), *see* INSTITUTO HIST. &C. BRAZIL. Rev., t85, 1921.
Orléans (Louis Philippe Joseph, *duc* **d'),** *1747–93* [PHILIPPE EGALITÉ], *see* BRITSCH (A.) La jeunesse de P.-E., 1747–85, 1926.
Orléans (Louise Elisabeth d'), *q. consort of Louis I, of Spain, see* LOUISA ISABELLA, *of Orleans.*
Orléans (Philippe, *duc* **d'),** *1640–1701, brother of Louis XIV, see* LA BATUT (G. DE). La cour de Monsieur, frère de Louis XIV, 1927.
Orléans (Philippe, *duc* **d'),** *1674–1723, regent of France.*
see LECLERCQ (H. M.) Hist. de la Régence &c., 3t, 1921.
„ SAINT-SIMON (*le duc* DE). Le Régent, ses filles &c., 2s, 1923–25.
Orléans (*le père* **Pierre Joseph d').** Hist. de M. Constance [*i.e.* C. Phaulkon], ministre du Roy de Siam & de la dern. révolution. s8º. Tours. 1690
Hist. des deux conquerans tartares qui ont subjugué la Chine [&* Hist. de Sevagi & de son successeur &c., *w. sep. pagin.*] Par le R. P. J. D. . . . [Hist. & remarques curieuses, t1]. s8º. 1690
„ „ *f. a. ed., see* BERNARD (J. F.), *ed.* Rec. de voy., t7, 1725.
Hist. des révolutions d'Espagne. Rev. & publ. par les PP. Rouillé & Brumoy. 4t. s8º. La Haye. 1734
Orléans (Valentine [*de Milan*], *duchesse* **d')** [VISCONTI (V.)], *see* CAMUS (J.) La venue en France de V. V. & l'invent. de ses joyaux apportés de Lombardie, 1900.
Orlers (Jan). Beschr. der Stadt Leyden. 2. druck vergroot met een 3. deel &c. 8º. Leyden. 1641
Orlovsky (K. F.), *see* GOLOVIN (K. F.)
Ormanian (Malachia). Il reversurus ovvero la Turchia ed il Papato. [Estr. d. Rev. giurid., 2i, ii. [P520]. 8º. Roma. 1872
Orme (Robert). *Hist. of the milit. trans. of the Brit. Nation in Indostan from 1745. Pref. a diss. on Mahomedan conquerors in I. 2nd ed. corr. 2v. 4º. 1775–78
„ „ 4th ed. [repr.] 3v. [v2 *in 2 sections, sep. tp.* v3, Maps]. la8º. Madras. 1861–62
Orme (William), *see* OWEN (J.) Works, v1, cont. Mem. of the life & wr. &c. of J. O. by W. O., 1826.
Ormerod (Henry Arderne). Piracy in the anc. world, essay in Mediterranean hist. 8º. Liv'l. 1924
Ormesby Psalter, *see* BIBLE : PSALMS. 2 E. Anglian Ps. at Bodl. Lib., Oxf. : O. Ps. &c., 1926.
Ormesson (Wladimir d'). La 1ᵉ mission officielle de la France aux États-Unis : C.-A. Gérard, 1778–79. 8º. 1924
Ormin, *canon Regular of the Order of St. Augustine, see* MONICKE (C. H.) Notes & queries on the Ormulum [*w. spec. of text & Eng. tr.*], 1853–54.
Ormonde (James Butler, *1st duke of***),** *see* RUSSELL (C. W.) & J. P. PRENDERGAST. The Carte MSS. [Ormonde papers &c.] in Bodleian Lib. : rep., 1871.
Orna (Adolphe O.) A French girl in London. [*Tr.*] s8º. [1922]
Ornament. *Flat o. : pattern bk. of designs, *n.d., see* FLAT.
Ornhjälm (Claudius), *see* ARRHENIUS (C.)
Ornstein-Brodsky (Nadja). Das Referendum in d. Praxis. 25 Jahre Gemeindeabstimmung in Zürich. 8º. Wien. 1922
Orobio (Balthasar de), *see* FÉNÉLON (F. DE S. DE LA M.) Réfut. des erreurs de B. de Spinosa. [*Foll. by* Certamen philos. adv. J. Bredenburg, meditab. I. O.], 1703.
Orologio (Galeazzo Dondi-), *see* DONDI-OROLOGIO (G.)
Or-ongle (F. d').
Segovia viejo y Segovia nuevo. 8º. Segovia. 1888
Oronte. Un jardin sur l'O., 1922, *see* BARRÈS (M.)
Orosius (Paulus). Extracts fr. Alfred's Orosius. Ed. H. Sweet. 2nd ed. s8º. O. 1901
see PAULI (R.) Life of Alfred, tr. ; app., Alfred's version of O., tr. Thorpe, 1902.
O'Rourke (Horace T.), *see* DUBLIN. D. Civic Survey : Report ; prep. by H. T. O'R. &c., 1925.
Orozco y Berra (Manuel). Hist. antigua y de la conquista de Mexico. 4t [& plates, 4º]. 8º. Mexico. 1880
Orpen (*Mrs.* **Adela E.),** *wife of Goddard H. Orpen.* Mem. of the old emigrant days in Kansas, 1862–65, also of a visit to Paris in 1867. 8º. E. 1926
Orpen (Goddard Henry). Ireland under the Normans. v3, 4. 1216–1333. 8º. O. 1920
Orpen (Richard). *An exact relation of the persecutions &c. sustained by the Protestants of Killmare. By a Principal Manager in that action. [P1451]. 8º. 1689
Orpen (*Sir* **William).**
An onlooker in France, 1917–19. la8º. 1921
Outline of art. Ed. Sir W. O. la8º. [1923]
Sir W. Orpen. [Plates, w. descr. &c. *signed* R. P.] la8º. 1923
Stories of old Ireland & myself. 8º. 1924
Orphans. *Case (The) of orphans consider'd, w. remarks on our Courts of Wards &c. 8º. 1725
Orpheus. The Bk. of the Orphic Hymns. Extr. f. Hermann's ed. Pr. in uncial letters. 8º. 1827
Lamellae aureae Orphicae ; ed. comm. instr. A. Olivieri, *see* KLEINE TEXTE, T133, 1915.
Orphicorum fragmenta coll. O. Kern. 8º. Berolini. 1922
see EISLER (R.) O.—the fisher : comp. st. in Orphic & early Xtn. cult symbolism, 1921.
„ MACCHIORO (V.) Zagreus : st. sull' Orfismo, 1920.
Orr (Robert Low). Lord Guthrie, a memoir. With 2 ch. by Ld. G. 8º. [1923]
Orran, *see* OSSIAN. Poems of Ossian, O., Ulin & o. bards ; ed. H. & J. M'Callum, 1816.
Orrinsmith (*Mrs.* **Lucy).** The drawing-room. s8º. 1878
Ors (Eugenio d').
El Valle de Josafat. Tr. de R. Marquina. s8º. [1921]
Glosas. Páginas del Glosari de Xenius (1906–17). Vers. castellana de A. Maseras. s8º. 1920
Orsato (Reprandino). Alcune sonetti. Ed. A. Mabellini. [P2867]. s8º. Torino. 1884
Orsay (Francesca de Villarosa, *comtesse* **d'),** *wife of Comte Max de Grimaud d'Orsay.* Ce que je peux écrire : mémoires. la8º. 1927
Orsbridge (Philip). *Hist. views of ye exped. of H.M.'s ships &c. agst. the Havannah, under Sir G. Pocock &c. obl. fol. [1762]
Orsi (Delfino), *see* GABOTTO (F.) & D. O., *edd.* Laudi d. Piemonte, v1, 1891.
Orsi (Paolo). *Works in* REALE ACCAD. D. LINCEI. Mon. ant.
Anathemata di una città siculo-greca a Terravecchia di Grammichele (Catania), 1907. [18.]
Camarina, campagne archeol., 1899–1903, 1904. [14.]
Caulonia, (1) campagne archeol., 1912–15 ; (2) mem., 1914–23. [23, 29.]
Città greca a Terravecchia pr. Grammichele di Catania, 1897. [7.]
Di una anon. città siculo-greca a Monte S. Mauro, pr. Caltagirone, 1910. [20.]

Orsi (Paolo) [*continued*].
Works in Reale Accad. d. Lincei. Mon. ant. [*cont.*]
Gela : scavi, 1900–5 [*&* Tavole], 1906. [17.]
Megara Hyblaea, 1917–21, 1921. [27.]
Messana : necrop. rom. di S. Placido e alt. scop., 1910–15, 1916. [24.]
Necropoli preellen. calabresi di Torre Galli e di Canale, Ianchina, Patariti, 1926. [31.]
Necrop. sicula di Pantalica, *&* di M. Dessueri, 1912. [21.]
Necrop. sicula pr. Siracusa, 1893. [2.]
Scavi int. a l'Athenaion di Siracusa, 1912–17, 1918. [25.]
Thapsos, 1895. [6.]
—— **& F. S. Cavallari.** Megara Hyblaea, *see* Reale Accad. d. Lincei. Mon. ant., v1, 1890.
Orsini, *house of, see* Sansovino (F.) Hist. di Casa O., 1565.
Orsini (Luigi). Il Tempio Malatestiano. [*With Fr. & Eng. tr.*] s8º. Firenze. 1927
Orsini (Niccolò), *count of Pitigliano & Nola, see* Hill (G. F.) Medals of N. O., 1926.
Ortega Rubio (Juan). Hist. de Madrid y de los pueblos de su prov. 2t. la8º. 1921
Ortega y Gasset (José). El espectador. [2t.] s8º. 1916–17
Örtel (Johann Gottfried) [Oertelius (I. G.)] Harmonia ll. Orientis & Occidentis speciatimque Hungaricae cum Hebraea expos. a J. Hlivai. s8º. Wittebergae. 1746
Theologia Aethiopum ex liturgiis fidei conf., aliisque scr. congesta &c. [*a. c. b. w. h.* Harmonia ll., 1746]. s8º. Wittebergae. 1746
Ortelius (Abraham). Epitome theatri Orteliani. [94 maps, w. descr.] obl. s8º. Antwerpiae. 1589
Orth (Jean), *see* John Salvator, *archduke of Austria.*
Orth (Samuel Peter). The armies of labor. Organized wage-earners. [Chron. of Amer., v40]. 8º. New Haven, *Yale.* 1919
Our foreigners. Americans in the making. [Chron. of Amer., v35]. 8º. New Haven, *Yale.* 1920
Örthel (Ludwig), "*Frhr. v. Egloffstein,*" *see* Schramek (T.) "Frhr. v. Egloffstein," 1925.
Orthodoxa Tigurinae eccl. ministrorum conf. &c., 1545, *see* Zürich.
Orthodoxographia theologiae sacro sanctae ac syncerioris fidei doctores numero 76 &c. [*Ed.* J. Heroldt]. fol. Basileae. [1555]
***Orthographia** Ungarica, 1549, 1908, *see* Biró (M.)
Ortí y Lara (Juan Manuel). La Inquisicion. Ed. corr. 8º. 1877
Ortiz (Alberto). Parnaso nicaragüense. Antología. Comp. por A. O. s8º. Barcelona. *n.d.*
Ortiz (Luis G.) Poesias. s8º. Mexico. 1856
Ortiz de Montellano (Mariano). Apuntes para la liquidacion de la deuda contraida en Londres. 8º. México. 1886
Ortiz de Zuñiga (Diego). Anales ecles. y seculares de Sevilla, 1246–1671. Ilust. y corr. por A. M. Espinosa y Carzel. 5t. 8º. 1795–96
Ortizius (Blasius). Summi templi Tolet. descr., *see* Lorenzana y Buitron (F. A.) PP. Tolet. opera, t3, 1793.
Ortmann (Otto). Physical basis of piano touch & tone. 8º. 1925
Ortner (Eugen). Gott Stinnes. Pamphlet gegen d. vollkomm. Menschen. 8º. Hannover. [1922]
Orton (Job). The pract. works of J. O. Pref. mem. of the a. 2v. 8º. 1842
—— **&** *Sir* **J. Stonhouse.** Letters to T. Stedman [*& ed. by him*]. 2v. [*v1 wanting.* v2 *has add. tp.* Letters f. Sir J. Stonhouse]. s8º. Shrewsbury. 1800
Orton (William Aylott). Labour in transition. Brit. industrial hist. since 1914. 8º. [1921]
Orueta y Duarte (Ricardo de).
Berruguete y su obra. [*Span. & French*]. s8º. 1917
La vida y la obra de P. de Mena y Medrano. la8º. 1914
Orvar-Odds Saga, *see* Björner (E. J.) Schediasma hist.-geogr. de Varegis &c. [*app.* Vita Oddi Jaculatoris ant. carmine ab ipso descr., *extr. f.* Orvar-Odds saga], 1743.
Orvieto [*see also* Urbevetanæ]. Cronaca d'O., 1342–63. [Ed. G. Antimaco]. s8º. Milano. 1845
Orwin (Charles Stewart) & W. R. Peel.
The tenure of agricultural land. 8º. C. 1925
Ory (Eugène).
Causeries sur Pont-à-Mousson. 8º. Pont-à-Mousson. 1880
Osbaldeston (George). Autobiography. Ed. w. comm. by E. D. Cumming. Intr. by Sir T. Cook. 4º. [1926]
Osborn (George), *D.D., Wesleyan minister.*
Outlines of Wesleyan bibliogr. 8º. 1869
,, ,, ...[*a. copy interleaved*]. 8º. 1869
see MacOwan (P.) A man of God, 1873.
Osborn (Henry Fairfield). Man rises to Parnassus: crit. epochs in the prehist. of man. 8º. Princeton, N.J. 1927
Men of the old stone age; th. environment, life & art. 3rd ed., w. notes &c. on archaeology of Spain & N. Africa. 8º. 1921
Osborn (Lucretia Perry).
Washington speaks for himself. 8º. N.Y. 1927
Osborn (Max). Berlin. 2e A. s8º. L. 1926
Osborne (Algernon Ashburner). Speculat. on the N.Y. Stock Exchange, Sept., 1904–March, 1907. 8º. N.Y., *Columbia Univ.* 1913
Osborne (Charles Churchill).
A. M. H. Comtesse de Noailles. [P2734]. s8º. 1918
Philip B. Marston. 8º. *p.p.* 1926
Osborne (Ethel E.), *M.Sc., see* Indust. Fatigue Research Bd. Rep., 2, 19; by E. E. O., 1919–22.
Osborne (Sidney). The problem of Upper Silesia. 8º. 1921
The Saar question: a disease spot in Europe. 8º. [1923]
The Upper Silesian question & Germany's coal problem. 2p [*in 1v. pagin. cont.*] 8º. 1920
Osborne (Walter Fredrick), *see* Bodkin (T.) 4 Irish landscape painters, W. F. O. &c., 1920.
Osborne (Walter V.)
Trade unions & party politics. [P2484]. 8º. [1911]
Osbourne (Lloyd). Wild justice: stories of the South Seas. [n. ed.] s8º. 1922
see Stevenson (R. L.) & L. O. The wrong box, n. impr., 1911.
,, Williams (*Mrs.* I.) Cat. of books, Stevensoniana, prop. of L. O. &c., 1923.
Osburn (William). The antiq. of Egypt. 8º. 1847
Doct. errors of the apostol. &c. fathers. 8º. 1835
Osebergfundet. Utg. av d. Norske Stat under red. av A. W. Brøgger, Hj. Falk, H. Schetelig. 3B. fol. 1917–28
Ösfeld (Max v.) [Oesfeld]. Die Kirchenpolit. Reformgesetze Preussens v. 1873. Erl. &c. v. M. v. O. 8º. Breslau. 1873
Osgood (Charles Grosvenor). A concordance to the poems of Edmund Spenser. Comp. & ed. by C. G. O. [C.I. of Wash., Publ. 189]. 4º. Wash. 1915
Osgood (Herbert Levi).
The American colonies in the 18th c. 4v. 8º. N.Y. 1924
see Fox (D. R.) H. L. Osgood, an American scholar, 1924.
Osgood (Wilfred Hudson).
Works in Field Columbian Museum. Zool. ser., v10.
Diagnoses of new E. Afr. mammals, 1910.
Four new mammals f. Venezuela, 1914.
Further new mammals f. B.E. Africa, 1910.
Mammals f. coast & islands of N. South America, 1910.
Mammals f. W. Venezuela & E. Colombia, 1912.
Mammals of an exped. across N. Peru, 1914.
Mammals of Collins-Day S. Amer. exped., 1916.
New mammals f. Brazil & Peru, 1915.
New Peruvian mammals, 1913.
A peculiar bear from Alaska, 1909.
O'Shaughnessy (Edith Coues), *wife of Nelson O'Shaughnessy.* Viennese medley. [*Fiction*]. s8º. [1925]
O'Shiel (Kevin Roantree).
The making of a republic. s8º. D. 1920
Osiander (Andreas), *the elder, 1498–1552.*
Apologia contra libellum Scelerati cuiusdam & Zwingliani Nebulonis, elegiaco carmine conscriptum. s4º. *n.p.* 1544
*Bedencken auf das Interim. Von einem &c. Herrn [A. Osiander *the Elder*] einem Erbarn Radt seiner Oberkeit uberreicht. [P2440]. s4º. *n.p.* 1584 [*i.e.* 1548]
Beweisung: das ich nun über die 30 jar, alweg einerley Lehr, v. d. Gerechtigkeit d. Glaubens gehalten hab &c. [P2441]. s4º. Künigsperg in Preussen. 1552
Coniecturae de ultimis temporibus. s4º. Norimbergæ. 1544
Die gantze evang. histori. Das ist: Das heilig Evangelion nach d. inhalt d. vier Evägelisten &c. s4º. [Franckfurt a. Meyn. 1541]
Harmoniae Evangelicae lib. III graece et latine. Item: Annot. liber unus [*w. no pagin.*] fol. Basileae, *Froben.* 1537
Ain schöne Sermon [*on John II 1, 11*] gepredigt zü Nüremberg v. A. O. s4º. [Nüremberg]. 1523
Was zu Marpurgk in Hessen, vom Abendtmal &c. vergleicht sey worden. s4º. *n.p.* [Marburg ?. 1529]
see Alesius (A.) Refutatio errorum quos sparsit nuper A. O. in libro &c. 1552.
,, Flacius (M.) Kurtze &c. erzelung d. argument O. v. d. gerechtigkeit d. glaubens, 1552.
,, Hamburg. Responsio ministrorum eccl. quae est Hamburgi & Luneburgi ad conf. A. O., 1553.
,, John Albert I, *Duke of Mecklenburg.* Epistola ad Illyricum de Osiandrica hæresi, 1556.
,, Meincke (D.) Osiandrismum in pietismo renatum exc. D. M., 1707.

Osiander (Andreas), *the elder, 1498–1552* [*continued*].
see MELANCHTHON (P.) Antwort auf d. Buch A. O. v. d. Rechtfertigung, 1552.
,, ROTTINGUS (M.) Testimonium M. R. contra falsam A. O. de justific. sententiam &c., 1551 ?.
,, SCHLÜSSELBURG (C.) Haeretic. cat., lib. 6, Osiandristarum argumenta, 1598.
,, ULENBERG (C.) Hist. de vita &c. Melanchthonis, O. &c., 1622.
,, —— Gesch. der luther. Reformatoren, B2, 1837.

Osiander (Andreas), *the younger, 1562–1617.*
Apologia contra mendacia &c. cujusdam Ingolstadiensis : Secunda peccata cujusdam Wirtembergici in def. Responsi ad Analysin &c. [*b. w. h.* Resp. ad Anal., 1593]. s4°. Tubingae. 1595
Defensio Responsi ad Analysin G.-Valentinianam contra G. de Valentia apolog., Peccata cujusdam Lutherani. [*b. w. h.* Resp. ad Anal., 1593]. s4°. Tubingae. 1594
Responsum ad Analysin G. Valentiani de eccl. &c. s4°. Tubingae. 1593
Tractatus de omnipraesentia Christi, in quo ad ubiquitatis confut. per quendam Christianum Waldensem respondetur. s4°. Tubingae. 1587

Osiander (Johann Adam). Diss. de addit. cod. Cantabrig. post verba Christi Matth. 20, 28. Praes. J. A. O. ventil. publ. exponent G. I. S. Mezger &c. [P430]. s4°. Tubingae. [1755]
Diss. de successione episcopali. Præs. C. M. Pfaffio, def. J. A. O. [P2636]. s4°. Tubingæ. 1720

Osiander (Lucas), *the elder, 1534–1604.*
De ratione concionandi. [*b. w.* Grynæus (J. J.) Synopsis &c., 1579]. s8°. Tubingæ. 1582
De studiis Verbi divini ministrorum priv. recte instit. admon. Rec. &c. G. B. S[charf]. Acc. Alia P. Melanchthonis & C. Crucigeri nec non ined. epistolarum decas. 2p *in* 1v. s4°. Francofurti. 1733
Gründtl. Bericht. Auff. S. Huber's Lästerschrifft (Notwendige entdeckung &c.) in deren er L. O. mit Gewalt will z. e. Calvinisten machen. Sampt d. Predigt L. O. &c. s4°. Tübingen. 1596
Justa defensio orthodoxae veritatis in libro Concordiae &c. compreh. de 4 theologicis c. omnipraesentiam & omnipotentiam carnis Christi. s4°. Tubingae. 1622
Verantwortung wider die zwo Gifftspinnen G. Scherern, u. C. Rosenbusch, beide Iesuiter : welche auss der Christlichen Warnung lauter Gifft gesagen &c. s4°. Tübingen. 1586
see NASE (J.) Sextae centuriae prodromus &c., die vermeinten Hosnädrin. ableynung beläget J. N., 1574.
,, ROSENBUSCH (C.) Antwort auf L. O. Schmachschrift &c., 1586.

Osiander (Lucas), *the younger, 1571–1638.*
Abriss. u. Muster d. treffl. Kleinods so die Jesuiter in d. zu Durlach Colloquio erfochten haben &c. [P2608]. s4°. Tübingen. 1614
Enchiridion controvers., quas Augustanae Conf. theologi habent cum Calvinianis. s8°. Tubingæ. 1605
Enchiridion controvers. relig. [*b. w.* Hutter (L.) Compend. loc. theolog. &c., 1619]. 3p. s8°. Wittebergae. 1614–15
Scultetus atheus. Præs. & aut. L. O., resp. L. Osiandro, fil. [P599]. s4°. Tubingae. 1620

Osius (Hieronymus). Icones catecheseos Christianae, item virtutum ac vitiorum carmine elegiaco expos. s8°. Vitebergæ. 1565

Osler (*Sir* William), *Bt.*
Evolution of mod. medicine. la8°. New Haven, *Yale*. 1921
Incunabula medica : st. of earliest pr. medical bks., 1467–80. [Bibl. Soc. Illust. monogr., 19]. 4°. 1923
R. Burton : the man, h. bk., h. library, 1926, *see* MADAN (F.) R. Burton &c.
see CUSHING (H.) Life of Sir W. O., 2v, 1925.

Osloenses. Papyri Osloenses, fasc. 1, 1925, *see* EITREM (S.), *ed.*

Osmaston (F. P. B.) Cromwell. Drama. s8°. 1906

Osorio da Fonseca (Jeronimo), *bp. of Silves* [H. OSORIUS].
H. Osorii in G. Haddonum libri tres. s4°. Olissipone. 1567
,, ,, ed. 3ª. Acc. C. Longolii oratio. s8°. Dilingae. 1576

Ossat (*le card.* Armand d'). Lettres. Avec notes de M. Amelot de la Houssaie. n. éd. corr. 2t. 4°. 1698

Ossendowski (Ferdinand Antoni).
Beasts, men & gods. [repr.] 8°. 1923
The fire of desert folk : journey thr. Morocco. Eng. text by L. S. Palen. 8°. 1926
Man & mystery in Asia. By F. O. in collab. w. L. S. Palen. 8°. 1924
*Um F. Ossendowski : Zur Authentizität &c. 8°. Frankfurt. 1925

Osservationi d. lingua volg. di div. huomini illustri : Bembo, Gabriello &c., 1562, *see* SANSOVINO (F.), *ed.*

Ossian.
Works. Tr. J. Macpherson. 3rd ed. 2v. 8°. 1765
Fingal, an anc. epic poem. Tr. by J. Macpherson. 2nd ed. 4°. 1762

Ossian [*continued*].
Fingal, an anc. epic poem. Rendered into heroic verse by E. Cameron. 4°. 1777
Fragments of anc. poetry coll. in Highlands &c. & tr. f. Gaelic &c. 1760 ; repr. of 1st O. publ. of J. Macpherson, *see* AUNGERVYLE Soc. Reprints, s1, 1881.
The poems of O. &c. Cont. the poet. wks. of J. Macpherson ; w. notes & illust. by M. Laing. 2v. 8°. E. 1805
Poems, in orig. Gaelic, w. lit. tr. into Lat. by R. Macfarlan. A diss. on authenticity of the poems by Sir J. Sinclair, & tr. of Abbé Cesarotti's diss. on authenticity of O., w. notes &c. by J. M'Arthur. 3v. 8°. 1807
Poems of O., Orran, Ulin, & o. bards. Coll. & ed. by H. & J. M'Callum. 8°. Montrose. 1816
The poems of O. Tr. J. Macpherson. s8°. E. 1830
see BLACK (G. F.) Macpherson's O. &c., bibliog., 1926.
,, GRAHAM (P.) Essay on authenticity of poems of O., 1807.
,, GRANT (J.) Thoughts on orig. &c. of the Gael, & obs. on poems of O., 1814.
,, HIGHLAND SOCIETY. Report on authenticity of poems of Ossian, 1805.
,, SHAW (W.) Enq. into authentic. of poems ascr. to O., 1781.

Ossiannilsson (Karl Gustav).
Amerikaner & Byzantiner. 8°. [1905]
Barbarskogen. Roman. 8e uppl. 8°. [1919]
Belgiens fångknekt och Tysklands ! s8°. [1917]
Förrädare. Skädespel. Efter Barbarskogen. s8°. [1917]
Gustavus Adolphus Magnus. Roman. 2d. 8°. [1916]
Hemmet och hemlandet. Dikter. 8°. Lund. [1915]
Kärleksdikter. s8°. [1918]
Masker : diktsamling. 8°. [1900]
Örnar : diktsamling. 8°. [1902]
Samlade dikter. 4d. s8°. [1920]
Svart & hvitt (med dramat Jörgen Kock) : dikter. 8°. [1904]
Sven Hedin—adelsman ! 8°. [1917]
Thomas Thorild. Skädespel. s8°. [1917]
Tidsdikter. 8°. Lund. [1916]
Tigerhuden. Skädespel. s8°. [1908]

Ossington (John Evelyn Denison, *visct.*) & *Sir* H. B. W. Brand. Decisions of the Rt. Hon. E. Denison & H. B. W. B. on points of order &c., by E. G. Blackmore. 8°. Adelaide. 1892

Ossip-Lourié, *see* LOURIÉ (O.)

Ostafevsky. Остафьевскій архивъ князей Вяземскихъ, 1899–1913, *see* VYAZEMSKY (*pr.* P. A.)

Osten (H. H. von der), *see* VON DER OSTEN (H. H.)

Ostende. *Hist. remarquable & vérit. de ce qui s'est passé au siège de la ville d'O. [*Dedic. signed* Jeremie Perier]. s8°. 1604

Ostendorfer (Hans). Turnierbuch Herzog Wilhelms IV v. Bayern [1541], *see* MÜNCHEN. Miniaturen ; hrsg. G. Leidinger, H3, 1913.

Ostendorfer (Michael), *see* DODGSON (C.) O. & the beautiful Virgin of Regensburg, *n.d.*

Ostenfeld (Carl E. Hansen). Contrib. to W. Australian botany, p3, *see* KONG. DAN. VID. SELSK. Biol. Medd., B3, 1921–22.
The flora of Greenland, *see* KONG. DAN. VID. SELSK. Biol. Medd., B6, 1926.

Ostenso (Martha). The passionate flight. s8°. [1926]

Østerberg (V.) Prince Hamlet's age, *see* KONG. DAN. VID. SELSK. Hist.-fil. Medd., B8, 1923–24.
Studier over Hamlet-teksterne. [v]1. 8°. Kjøbenhavn. 1920

Osterhout (Winthrop John Vanleuben).
The nature of life. s8°. N.Y. [1924]

Ostermann (*Graf* Andree Ivanovich) [OSTERMANN (HEINR. JOH. FRIEDR. v.)], *see* HEMPEL (C. F.) Merkw. Leben u. Fall A. Grafens v. O., 1742.

Österreich [DEUTSCHÖSTERREICH].
Beiträge z. Statistik Deutschösterreichs [d. Republik Österreich]. Hrsg. v. d. Statist. Zentralkommission. H1–5 [in 1v]. la8°. Wien. 1919–20
Entwurf d. Organisation d. Gymnasien u. Realschulen in Ö. Vom Minist. d. Cultus. la8°. Wien. 1849
Evangel. Ö. &c., 1732–44, *see* RAUPACH (B.)
Mittelalt. Bibliothekskat. Ö. Hrsg. v. d. K. Akad. d. Wiss. in Wien. B1, Niederösterr. ; bearb. v. T. Gottlieb [*no more publ.*] la8°. Wien. 1915
Oesterreich u. d. Papstwahl 1740. Samml. v. Dokumenten aus d. MS. Acta legationis Romanae Josephi Episcopi Gurcensis [*i.e.* J. M. v. Thun]. 8°. München. 1875
Statist. Handbuch f. d. Republik Ö. ; hrsg. v. d. Statist. Zentralkomm., 1920–21, *see* STATISTISCHES HANDBUCH &c.
*Um Österreichs Weltstellung. Von e. Grossösterreicher. [P2735]. 8°. Wien. 1909
Die Verfassungsgesetze d. Republik Deutschösterreich. Mit hist. Übersicht &c. hrsg. H. Kelsen. 4T. [1–3 *b. together*]. s8°. Wien. 1919–20
,, ,, Bundesverfassung (Textausgabe). [*b. w.* T4]. s8°. Wien. 1920

Österreich (Traugott Konstantin) [OESTERREICH]. Occultism & mod. science. Tr. f. 2nd Germ. ed. s8°. 1923

Österreichische [-EN ; -ER].
Neue Ö. Biographie, 1815–1918, Abt. 1, B1–4, Abt. 2, 1923–27, *see* NEUE.
Österr. Erbfolge-Krieg, 1740–48. Nach d. Feld-Acten u. a. authent. Quellen bearbt. in d. kriegsgeschichtl. Abth. d. k. u. k. Kriegs-Archives. 8B [*in* 9v. 1i, ii]. la8°. Wien. 1896–1905
Österr. Kunsttopographie. B16, 18–21. 4°. Wien. 1919–27
see BUBERL (P.) Denkmale d. polit. Bezirkes Hallein, 1927. [20.]
„ FREY (D.) Denkmale d. polit. Bezirkes Baden, 1924. [18.]
„ —— Denkmale d. polit. Bezirkes Schärding, 1927. [21.]
„ —— Denkmale d. Stiftes Heiligenkreuz, 1926. [19.]
„ TIETZE (H.) Die Kunstsammlungen d. Stadt Salzburg, 1919. [16.]

Österreichische Gesellschaft f. Archaeolog. Erforschung Kleinasiens, *see* PETERSEN (E.) & F. v. LUSCHAN. Reisen in Lykien Milyas &c., 1889.

Österreichisches Archäologisches Institut in Wien.
see KUBITSCHEK (J. W.) & S. FRANKFURTER. Führer durch Carnuntum, 6. A., 1923.
„ RIEGL (A.) Spätröm. Kunst-Industrie, 2T, 1901–23 ; n. A., 1927.

Österreichisches Jahrbuch 1923. Nach amtl. Quellen. 5e Folge. s8°. Wien. 1924

Österreichisches Museum, *Wien*, *see* VIENNA.

Osterspiel. Das rhein. O. d. Berl. Hs. MS. germ. fol. 1219 ; hrsg. v. H. Rüff, 1925, *see* KÖNIGL. GESELL. D. WISS. ZU GÖTTINGEN. Abh., N.F., 18, 1926.

Osteuropa-Institut in Breslau. Quellen u. Studien.
Abt. 1ii, 5i, ii, 6i. Abt. Sprachwiss &c., H1. 8°. L. 1920–26
see GOGEL (S.) Die Ursachen d. russ. Revol. v. Jahre 1917, 1926. [Abt. Spr., H1.]
„ HAASE (F.) Die relig. Psyche d. russ. Volkes, 1921. [5ii.]
„ KLIBANSKI (H.), *ed.* Die Gesetzgebung d. Bolschewiki, 1920. [1ii.]
„ MORTENSEN (H.) Litauen, 1926. [5i.]
„ WINKLER (H.) Die altaische Völker u. Sprachenwelt, 1921. [6i.]

Ostiani (Luigi Francesco Fè d'), *see* FÈ D'OSTIANI (L. F.)

Ost-Indien. Der Königl. Dänische Missionarien aus O.-I. Berichten, 1735–70, *see* DÄNISCHE MISSIONARIEN.

Ostini (Fritz, *Baron* **v.)**
Böcklin. [Knackfuss, 70]. 7e A. la8°. Bielefeld. 1921
Fritz Erler. [Knackfuss, 111]. la8°. Bielefeld. 1921
Thoma. [Knackfuss, 46]. 3e A. la8°. Bielefeld. 1923

Ostorodt (Christoph). Unterrichtung v. d. vornem. Hauptpuncten d. Christl. Relig., d. Confession d. Gemeinen im Königr. Polen &c. s8°. Rackow. 1612
see PORTUM (J. AD). Orthod. fidei def. adv. C. O. &c., 1613.

Ostrander (Isabel Egenton) [*ps.* CHIPPERFIELD (ROBERT ORR)].
Annihilation. s8°. [1923]
The Black Joker. s8°. [1925]
The heritage of Cain. s8°. [1922]
How many cards ? s8°. [1922
Impulse. s8°. [1924]
The man in the jury box. s8°. [1921]
The sleeping cat. s8°. [1926]
The trigger of conscience. s8°. [1922]
The twenty-six clues. s8°. [1921]
Unseen hands. s8°. [1921]

Ostroukhov (I. S.)
see MURATOV (P. P.) Древне-русс. иконопись въ собраніи О., 1914.
„ TRETYAKOV GALLERY. Москов. Городская Худож. Галлерея П. и С. М. Третьяковыхъ : текстъ И. С. О. &c., 2t, 1909.

Ostrovsky (Aleksandr Nilovaevich), *1823–86*. Enough stupidity in every wise man [tr. P. Kasherman], *see* SAYLER (O. M.) Moscow Art Theatre ser. of Russ. plays, s2, 1924.
see DOLGOV (N.) А. Н. О. жизнь &c., 1923.

Ostwald (Wilhelm). The sci. foundations of analyt. chemistry. Tr. G. M'Gowan. 3rd ed. 8°. 1908

Ostwald (Wolfgang). An introd. to theoret. & appl. colloid chemistry. Tr. M. H. Fischer. 8°. N.Y. 1917

Oswald, *Abbot, O.S.B.*, *see* HUNTER-BLAIR (*Rt. Rev. Sir* D.)

Oswald (Felix) & T. D. Pryce.
Introd. to the study of terra sigillata. 4°. 1920

Oswaldus (Johannes).
Ex hist. eccl. de J. Rokyczana famoso Calixtinorum in Bohemia pontifice. s4°. Atdorfii Noric. 1718

Oswell (George Devereux).
Sketches of rulers of India. 4v. 8°. O. 1908

Otero (Jose Pacifico). L'Argentine dev. l'hist. Préf. de A. Croiset. t1. s8°. [1922]

Otes (Samuel), *the elder*. An explan. of the Epistle of Saint Jude. Sermons. Publ. by S. Otes, his sonne. 4°. 1633

Otfried, *of Weissenburg*. Volumen Evangeliorum in 5 lib. distinct. a J. Schiltero Lat. donatum &c. notis auctum J. G. Scherzio, *see* SCHILTER (J.) Thesaurus antiq., t1, 1728.
see STADE (D. v.) Specimen lect. antiq. Francic. O[1]. libris Evangel., 1708.

Othen (Nathanael), *see* WESLEY (J.) *A short acc. of N. O., shot in Dover-Castle, 1757, *n.d.* [1757?].

Other. *Other (The) door. Novel. By A gentleman with a duster. s8°. [1926]
*Other people's money. By a Trustee. 2nd ed. rev. s8°. 1921

Othlonus. Vita Bonifatii, *see* BONIFACE, *St.* Vitae ; rec. W. Levison, 1905.

Otho (Johann Heinrich).
Lexicon Rabbinico-philolog. s8°. Genevae. 1675

Otinel. Chanson de geste, *see* GUESSARD (F.) Anc. poëtes, t1, 1859.

Ötinger (Friedrich Christoph). Inquisitio in sensum communem & rationem &c. Acc. Nova analysis musica. [*w. sep. pagin.*] s8°. Tubingae. 1752
Theologia ex idea vitae deducta. s8°. Francofurti. 1765

Otis (James). Silent Pete. s8°. N.Y. 1886

Otkliki. Отклики. B1. [P2446]. 8°. С.-П. 1906

Otrokocsi (F. Foris), *see* FORIS (F.) *Otrokocsi*.

Ott (Andreas C.) Das altfranz. Eustachiusleben (L'Estoire d'Eustachius, *see* ROMAN. FORSCHUNGEN, B32, 1913.

Otte (Friedrich). China, wirtschaftspolit. Landeskunde, 1927, *see* PETERMANNS MITT. Ergnzb., 42, 1927.

Otte (Johann Heinrich) [OTTIUS (J. H.)]
Annales Anabaptistici. s4°. Basileae. 1672
Examinis perpetui in Annales Caes. Baronii centuria I [II, III]. 3p [*in* 1v]. s4°. Tiguri. 1676

Ottenthal (Emil). Die gefälschten Magdeburger Diplome u. Melchior Goldast, 1919, *see* KAIS. AKAD. D. W. Z. WIEN. Sitzber., B192, 1921.

Otter (*Sir* John Lonsdale).
Nathaniel Woodard : memoir. 8°. [1925]

Otter (William). Life & remains of Rev. E. D. Clarke. 4°. 1824

Öttingen (Arthur J. v.) Abhandl. ü. Thermometrie v. Fahrenheit, Réaumur, Celsius, hrsg. v. Ö. 8°. L. 1894

Ottley, *The family of*, *see* OTTLEY (J. E.) Records of an anc. family, 1923.

Ottley (Jane Emily). Records of an ancient family [*i.e.* Ottley]. s8°. [1923]

Ottley (Robert Lawrence).
St. in the Confessions of St. Augustine. 8°. 1919

Otto I, *bp. of Bamberg, d. 1139, Saint.*
see EBBO *S. Michaelis Monachus*. Life of O., Apostle of Pomerania, 1060–1139 ; by E. & Herbordus ; [tr. &c.] C. H. Robinson, 1920.
„ HERBORDUS. Dial. de vita O. ; rec. fecit G. H. Pertz, 1868.

Otto, *author of Eraclius* [OTTE], *see* SCHRÖDER (E.) Der Dichter d. deut. E., 1924.

Otto, *bp. of Frisingen* [*Freising*], *d. 1158*. Chronica sive hist. de duabus civitatibus. Rec. A. Hofmeister. [Scr. rerum Germ. in usum schol.] ed. 2a. 8°. Hannoverae. 1912
O. & Rahewini Gesta Friderici I Imp. [Scr. rerum Germ. in usum schol.] ed. 2a. rec. G. Waitz. 8°. Hannoverae. 1884

Otto II, *bp. of Freising, d. 1220*. Der Laubacher Barlaam, e. Dichtung O. II. v. F. (1184–1220). Hrsg. A. Perdisch. [Lit. V. in St., 260]. 8°. Tübingen. 1913

Otto III, *emperor*, *see* SICKEL (T. v.) Erläuterungen zu d. Diplomen O. III, 1891.

Otto *von Lonsdorf*, *see* LONSDORF (O. v.)

Otto *de S. Blasio*. Chronica. Ed. A. Hofmeister. Acced. ex chron. univ. Turicensi excerpta. [Scr. rerum Germ. in usum schol.] 8°. Hannoverae. 1912

Otto, *Truchsess v. Waldburg*, *see* WALDBURG (O. v.)

Otto (Antonius). Einfalt. Von den newen Rumpelgeistern &c. [P2468]. s4°. *n.p.* 1583

Otto (Eberhard). Tractatio juris gentium de titulo imp. Russorum &c. Ed. noviss. s4°. Halae Magdeb. 1724

Otto (Emil). First German book. 5th ed. s8°. Heidelberg. 1875
German conversation-grammar. 20th ed. 8°. Heidelberg. 1882
„ „ Key. Rev. by H. Runge. 20th ed. s8°. 1902

Otto (Rudolf). Aufsätze, d. Numinose betreffend. 8°. St. 1923
Das Heilige : ü. d. Irrationale in d. Idee des Göttlichen &c. 12e A. 8°. St. 1924
The idea of the holy : inq. into the non-rational factor in the idea of the divine &c. Tr. J. W. Harvey. 8°. 1923
see HODGSON (L.) Place of reason in Xtian apologetic [*incl. crit. of O.'s* " Das Heilige "], 1925.

Otto (Walter). Kulturgesch. d. Altertums. 8°. München. 1925
Z. Lebensgesch. d. jüng. Plinius, *see* KÖNIGL. AKAD. D. W. ZU MÜNCHEN. Phil. Kl., Sitz., 1919.
Zur Prätur d. jüng. Plinius, *see* KÖNIGL. AKAD. D. W. ZU MÜNCHEN. Phil. Kl., Sitz., 1923.
see MÜLLER (I. E. P. v.) Hdbch. d. Altertumswiss.; in neuer Bearb. hrsg. v. W. O., 1923 &c.
,, SPIEGELBERG (W.) & W. O. Neue Urkunde zu d. Siegesfeier d. Ptolemaios IV &c., 1926.
Otto (Walter F.) Die Manen oder v. d. Urformen d. Totenglaubens. 8°. 1923
Ottokar (Niccolo). L'istituz. d. priorato a Firenze, *see* ARCHIVIO STOR. ITAL. Anno 82, v1, 1924.
Ottolini (Angelo). Giovanni Prati. s8°. Messina. [1919]
Pietro Verri e i suoi tempi. Con la ristampa dei s. scritti ined. 8°. 1921
see ANTONA-TRAVERSI (C.) & A. O. Ugo Foscolo, 4v, 1927–28.
Ottoni (Theophilo Benedicto). Circular, 1860–61, reprod. &c. por B. de Magalhães, *see* INSTITUTO HIST. &C. BRAZIL. Rev., t78ii, 1916.
Otway (Thomas).
Compl. works. Ed. M. Summers. 3v. la8°. Bloomsbury, *Nonesuch Press*, 1926
*The cheats of Scapin: farce [*tr. f.* Molière's Fourberies de Scapin], *see* DUBLIN. Vol. of farces, 1792.
The orphan, *see* INCHBALD (E.) Brit. th., v12, 1808.
Venice preserved. [Dolby's Brit. th.] s8°. 1823
,, ,, [*a. ed.*], *see* INCHBALD (E.) Brit. th., v12, 1808.
Oud Batavia, 3d, 1922–23, *see* BATAVIA.
Oudard (Georges). La meilleure maîtresse, *see* ŒUVRES libres, 46, 1925.
—— **& D. Novik.** Les verts: choses vues, *see* ŒUVRES libres, 80, 1928.
Oudin (Antonin). Curiositez françoises pour suppl. aux dictionnaires, 1656, *see* LA CURNE DE SAINTE-PALAYE (J. B. DE). Dict., t10, 1882.
Oudney (Walter), *see* DENHAM (D.), H. CLAPPERTON & W. O. Travels in N. & C. Africa (1822–24), 1826.
Oudry (Jean Bapt.), *see* RICCI (S. DE). Les chasses royales de Louis XV: peintures par J. B. O., 1921.
Oudshoorn (J. van). Willem Mertens' levensspiegel. 2. dr. s8°. Rotterdam. 1920
Ouida, *ps.* Under two flags. new impr. s8°. 1919
Oukhtanes, *of Ourha, bp. of Edessa* [UKHTANES]. [Hist. of Armenia. *In Armenian.* 2p *in* 1v]. 8°. Vagharshapat. 1871
Ould (Charles Woodrooffe). William S. Royce. Intr. by Rt. Hon. J. H. Thomas. 8°. [1925]
Ould (E. A.), *see* PARKINSON (J.) & E. A. O. Old cottages &c. in Shropshire &c. intr. & descr. notes &c. by E. A. O., 1904.
Oulié (Marthe). Le Prince de Ligne. 8°. [1926]
Ou Li Yu-chan, *see* CUNHA (S. A.)
Oulmont (Charles). Le verger, le temple & la cellule: essai sur la sensualité dans les œuvres de mystique relig. Préf. de É. Boutroux. s8°. 1912
Oulton (Andrew Newton), *see* IRELAND: LAWS &C. Index to statutes in force in I., 1310–1844, 2v, 1839–45.
Oulton (*Miss* L.), *see* AUSTEN (J.) The Watsons: a fragm. by J. A., concluded by L. O., 1923.
Oultremont (*le maître* d'), *see* MOSTAERT (J.)
Oulx. Della pubbl. del cartario dell' ant. abbadia d'O. fatta da Berta e Rivautella, e d. cod. Peralda, 1882, *see* BERNARDI (J.)
Sui cartolari d. prevostura d'O., 1904, *see* COLLINO (G.)
***Our** parish; by one who has never been out of it, 1884, repr., 1925, *see* GEERING (T.)
Ouseley (Gideon), *1762–1839.*
see ARTHUR (W.) Life of G. O., 1876.
,, REILLY (W.) A mem. of G. O., 1847.
Ouspensky, *see* USPENSKY.
Outamaro [UTAMARO, YUSUKÉ KITAGAWA], *see* NOGUCHI (Y.) Utamaro; tr., 1928.
Outghersz (Jan). Nieuwe volmaeckte beschr. d. Strate Magellani, *see* WIEDER (F. C.) De reis v. Mahu &c., 1598–1600, d2, 1924.
Outhett (John), *see* LAURIE (R. H.) New plan of London &c., 1821.
Outline.
Outline of art, 1923, *see* ORPEN (*Sir* W.), *ed.*
Outline of literature, 1923, *see* DRINKWATER (J.), *ed.*
Outline of science, 2v, 1921–22, *see* THOMSON (J. A.), *ed.*
Outline of a vocabulary of langs. in W. & C. Afr., 1841, *see* AFRICA.

Outram (James).
In the heart of the Canadian Rockies. 8°. N.Y. 1923
Outrein (Johannes d'). De clangore Evangelii diss. 15. [*b. w. h.* Diss. de Melchizedeco &c., 1713]. s8°. Amstelodami. 1713
Diss. de Melchizedeco non Henocho & obs. misc. in sel. sacri codicis loca. s8°. Amstelodami. 1713
Ovando (Nicolao de), *see* JANE (L. C.) The govt. of O. in Española (1501–9): treatment of the Indians, 1923.
Overall (William Henry), *see* ATKINS (S. E.) & W. H. O. Some acc. of the W. Co. of Clockmakers, 1881.
Overberg (Bernhard Heinrich), *see* KNÖPPEL (A.) B. H. O., d. Lehrer d. Münsterlandes, 1896.
Overbergh (Cyr. van), *see* VAN OVERBERGH (C.)
Overburg (Robert William). The Jesuits. s8°. 1846
Overbury (*Sir* Thomas), *the elder.* Misc. works in verse & prose; w. mems. of h. life. 10th ed. s8°. 1756
Sir T. Overbury, h. Wife. With add. of new characters &c. 15th impr. s8°. 1632
see INGERSLEBEN (I.) Das Elisabethan. Ideal d. Ehefrau b. O. (1613), 1921.
,, JAMES I. *Truth brought to light, p2, Arraign. of Sir J. Ellis &c. about murther of O. (1615), 1692.
,, PARRY (*Sir* E. A.) The O. mystery, 1925.
Overell (Lilian). A woman's impressions of German New Guinea. 8°. 1923
Overkampf (Georg Wilhelm). Comm. de ratione status Curiae Romanae c. usum Lat. ling. in sacris cultuque publico. s8°. Ienae. 1732
Overseas Englishman (An), *ps.* *England, 1922, *see* ENGLAND.
Overseas Trade, *Dept. of.* Report on econ. condit. in France, rev. to June 1924 by J. R. Cahill. 8°. 1924
see EXHIBITIONS: PARIS. Reports on &c. the industrial arts at Internat. Exhib. of Mod. Decor. & Indust. Arts, 1925; w. intr. survey, 1927.
Overton (George L.) Clocks & watches. s8°. *Pitman.* 1922
Overton (Grant Martin). Portrait of a publisher [*i.e.* W. W. Appleton] & The 1st 100 yrs. of the Hse. of Appleton, 1825–1925. 8°. N.Y. 1925
Overvoorde (J. C.), *see* DORT. Rekeningen van de gilden van Dordrecht, 1438–1600; [uitg.] door J. C. O., 1894.
Oviatt (Edwin).
The beginnings of Yale (1701–26). 8°. New Haven. 1916
Ovid.
Tristium liber 2. Ed., w. intr., tr., & comm. by S. G. Owen. 8°. O. 1924
TRANSLATIONS.
[Works. v1]. Fasti, Tristia, Pontic Epistles, Ibis, Halieuticon. Lit. tr. into prose by H. T. Riley. s8°. *Bohn.* 1859
[Works. v3]. Heroides, Amours, Art of Love, Remedy of Love, & minor wks. Lit. tr. into prose by H. T. Riley. s8°. *Bohn.* 1881
L'art d'aimer. Texte établi & tr. par H. Bornecque. [Coll. des univ. de Fr.] 8°. 1924
The lover's handbook. Tr. F. A. Wright, w. intr. s8°. [1923]
Metamorphosis Englished &c. By G. S[andys]. [*With index*]. fol. 1640
,, ,, Herscheppinge; vertaelt door J. v. Vondel (1671), *see* VONDEL (J. VAN DEN). Werken, d28–30, *n.d.*
,, ,, Tr. by Dryden, Addison, Garth &c. Publ. by Sir S. Garth. 3rd ed. v1. s8°. 1727
,, ,, Lit. tr. into prose by H. T. Riley. s8°. *Bohn.* 1876
The mirror of Venus. Tr. F. A. Wright. [Broadway trans.] 8°. [1925]
Tristia—Ex Ponto. With Eng. tr. by A. L. Wheeler. [Loeb Class. Lib.] s8°. 1924
see BÄHRENS (E.) Poetæ Lat. minores, v2ii, Ovidi Nux, 1923.
,, BELLORI (G. P.) Pitture ant. del sepolcro de' Nasonii &c., 1680.
,, CAMERARIUS (J.) Comment. de exordio versus O.: Exitus acta probat, 1572.
,, FOURNIVAL (R. DE). La vieille, dern. amours d'O.; tr., 1861.
,, HEINZE (R.) O.'s eleg. Erzählung, 1919.
,, MAZZONE DI MIGLIONICO (M. A.) Fiori d. poesia dich. &c. da l'op. di Virgilio, O. &c., 1593.
,, MILTON (J.) Some newly discov. stanzas by M. on engr. scenes illust. O.'s Metamorphoses; [*ed.*] H. C. H. Candy, 1924.
,, RAND (E. K.) O. & h. infl., 1926.
,, ROSTAGNI (A.) Ibis: storia di un poemetto greco, 1920.
,, SLATER (D. A.) Towards a text of the Metamorphosis of O., 1927.
Ovidio (Francesco d'). *Bevanda* e *vivanda* e lor comitive, *see* MONACI (E.) Studj romanzi, v10, 1913.
Ovsyaniko-Kulikovsky (Dmitry Nikolaevich).
Л. Н. Толстой какъ художникъ. B1. [P643]. 8°. С.-П. 1899

Ovsyannikov (N.), *ed.*
Москва в Октябре. Сборник, под ред. Н. О. s8º. Москва. 1919
Owd weighver, Th', *ps., see* CLEGG (J. T.)
Owen (Charles), *D.D.* The character & conduct of ecclesiastics, taken f. a MS. of C. O. [*by* F. B.] Added, a short acc. of Eng. historians. s8º. Shrewsbury. 1768
Owen (*Maj.-Gen.* Charles Henry).
Europe's mad dog. [P2590]. s8º. 1915
Owen (Collinson). The Rockingham diamond. s8º. [1923]
Zero. s8º. [1927]
Owen (David John). The Port of London. 4º. 1927
Owen (Edward Charles Everard). Some authentic acts of the early martyrs. Tr. w. notes &c. by E. C. E. O. 8º. O. 1927
Owen (Frances Mary). Essays & poems. 8º. 1887
Owen (Goronwy), *called Goronwy Ddu o Fôn; 1723–69, see* CYMMRODORION. Trans., Session, 1922–23, Suppl. vol., G. O. & h. bicentenary, 1924.
Owen (Harold). Common sense about the Shaw. Crit. of "Common sense about the War" by B. Shaw. s8º. [1915]
Disloyalty: the blight of pacifism. s8º. 1918
Owen (*Mrs.* Jean A.), *aft. Mrs. Visger,* **& G. S. Boulger.**
The country month by month. Notes by Ld. Lilford. [n. ed.] 8º. [1914]
Owen (John). The hoarding. s8º. [1923]
The idealist. s8º. [1922]
Owen (John), *D.D., 1616–83.*
Works. Ed. T. Russell. Mem. by W. Orme. v1, cont. the life & wr. of O. &c. 8º. 1826
Works. Ed. W. H. Goold, w. life by A. Thomson. 24v. 8º. E. 1862
Exercitations conc. a day of sacred rest &c. 2nd ed. s8º. 1671
Extracts f. works, *see* WESLEY (J.). Xtn. lib., v17–19, 1752.
The principles of the doctrine of Christ: in 2 short Catechismes. s8º. 1645
The true nature of a gospel church & its gov. &c. [With pref. signed J. C., *i.e.* Isaac Chauncy ?]. s4º. 1689
A vindic. of the animadv. on fiat lux. Principles of the Roman Ch. as to moderation, unity & truth &c. s8º. 1664
see BAXTER (R.) Catholick communion &c., J. O.'s 12 arguments, 1684.
,, HAMMOND (H.) An answer to the animadv. [of J. Owen] on the diss. t. Ignatius's Epistles &c., 1654.
,, SHERLOCK (W.) *A disc. about church-unity &c., ans. to Dr. O. &c., 1681.
Owen (Leonard V. D.) Connect. betw. England & Burgundy dur. 1st half of the 15th cent. Stanhope Essay, 1909. s8º. O. 1909
Owen (Louise). The real Lord Northcliffe. Personal recolls., 1902–22. s8º. 1922
Owen (*Lady* Marguerite Cunliffe-), *see* CUNLIFFE-OWEN.
Owen (R. Jones). The practice of perfumery &c. s8º. 1870
Owen (Robert), *the Socialist, 1771–1858.* The marriage system of the new moral world. 3rd ed. s8º. Leeds. 1839
see COLE (G. D. H.) R. O., 1925.
,, MACCABE (J.) R. O., 1920.
,, NATIONAL LIBRARY OF WALES. Bibliog. of R. O., 2nd ed., 1925.
Owen (Robert Dale), *1801–77.* Footfalls on the boundary of another world. Ed. & rev., w. intr. &c., by A. MacArthur. s8º. *n.d.*
Owen (Sidney George), *see* OVID. Tristium liber 2; ed., w. intr., tr. & comm. by O., 1924.
Owen (W. Powell-), *see* POWELL-OWEN (W.)
Owen's College, *Manchester, see* MANCHESTER: UNIVERSITY.
Owl (The) & the nightingale. [*Possibly by Nicholas of Guildford*]. Ed. w. intr., texts, notes, tr. & glossary by J. W. H. Atkins. 8º. C. 1922
Owsepian (G.), *see* HOVSEPHEAN (G.)
Owst (G. R.) Preaching in mediaeval England: intr. to sermon MSS., c. 1350–1450. 8º. C. 1926
Oxberry (William). Dramatic biography & histrionic anecdotes. 5v & N.S. v1. s8º. 1825–27
The printed tp. of v1–3 dated 1835; engr. tp. of v4 dated 1839.
Oxenham (John), *ps.* Chaperon to Cupid. s8º. [1924]
The perilous lovers: an idyll of Sercq. s8º. [1924]
Scala sancta. s8º. [1925]
Oxenstierna (*Count* Axel). Skrifter och brefvexling. Utg. af Kungl. Vitterhets-Hist. och Antiqvitets-Akad.
1a Afdlgn., B4, 6, 7 (Bref, 1628–29, 1631, 1632). 8º. 1909–26
Oxford [*&* OXFORD UNIVERSITY].
*Academia: or, The humours of the Univ. of O., 1716, *see* D'ANVERS (A.)
*Act (An) at O.: comedy, 1704, *see* BAKER (TH.)
Cat. of all graduats &c., 1659–88 [w. App. to 1699]. s8º. O. 1689

Oxford [*continued*].
Cat. of all graduats, 1659–1770; added chancellors, high-stewards &c., 1659–1770, also burgesses, 1603–1770. 8º. O. 1772
*College rhymes, v1–3, 1860–62, *see* COLLEGE.
Concise O. dict.; adapt. f. the O. Dict., 1911, *see* FOWLER (H. W.) & F. G. F.
Facs. of letters of O. Welshmen [in the Bodl. Libr. Ed. R. Ellis]. [P2699]. 4º. [O. 1903]
Hymns for the use of Univ. of O. in St. Mary's Ch. s8º. O. 1872
Liber albus civitatis Oxon. Abstract of wills, deeds & enrolments. By W. P. Ellis. Intr. & notes by H. E. Salter. la8º. O. 1909
Mediaeval archives of the Univ. of O. Ed. H. E. Salter. [Oxf. Hist. Soc., 70, 73]. v1, 2. 8º. O. 1920–21
Munimenta Civitatis Oxonie. Ed. H. E. Salter. [Oxf. Hist. Soc., 71]. 8º. Devizes. 1920
Oxford (The) Ars poetica [*attrib. to G. Murray*], 1853, *see* GORDON (G.), *ed.* Three Oxf. ironies, 1927.
Oxford (The) book of ballads, repr., 1924, *see* QUILLER-COUCH (*Sir* A. T.)
Oxford (The) book of Eng. prose, 1925, *see* QUILLER-COUCH (*Sir* A. T.)
Oxford (The) book of French verse, 13–19c., 1924; 13–20c., 1926, *see* LUCAS (ST. J. W.)
Oxford (The) bk. of med. Lat. verse, 1928, *see* GASELEE (S.), *ed.*
Oxford (The) book of Portuguese verse, 1925, *see* BELL (A. F. G.)
Oxford (The) bk. of Russ. verse, 1924, *see* BARING (*Hon.* M.)
Oxford (The) book of Scandinavian verse, 1925, *see* GOSSE (*Sir* E.) & W. A. CRAIGIE.
Oxford City properties, 1926, *see* SALTER (H. E.), *ed.*
Oxford (The) English dictionary. Ed. Sir J. A. H. Murray, H. Bradley, W. A. Craigie, C. T. Onions. v10i, ii. 4º. O. 1926–28
Oxford index of therapeutics, 1921, *see* SORAPURE (V. E.), *ed.*
Oxford (The) packet; cont. 1, News f. Magdalen Coll. [*wanting*]; 2, Antigamus, by T. Sawyer; 3, Vindic. of the Oxford ladies. [P2868]. s8º. 1714
Oxford tracts on economic subjects. No. 1–28 [*in* 1v]. 8º. [1920]
Oxford song book (The), 1919, *see* BUCK (P. C.), *ed.*
Oxford University calendar, 1810, 1921, 1923–27. s8º. O. 1810–[1927]
Oxford University roll of service. Ed. by E. S. Craig & W. M. Gibson. 8º. O. 1920
Oxforder (Das) Buch deut. Dichtung, neu. A., 1927, *see* FIEDLER (H. G.), *ed.*
Records of mediæval O. Coroners' inquests, the walls of O. &c. Ed. H. E. Salter. la8º. O. 1912
*Round about "The Mitre" at O., 1924, *see* SPIERS (R. A. H.)
Several (The) papers, laid bef. the lords in Parl. rel. to the riots at O. on the Prince's birthday. [P2606]. fol. 1717
Surveys and tokens, 1923, *see* SALTER (H. E.), *ed.*
*Tres oratiunculae hab. in domo Convoc. Oxon., 1743, *see* KING (W.)
see POOLE (*Mrs.* L.) Cat. of portraits in Univ. &c., v2, 3, 1925; 26.
ALL SOULS COLLEGE.
see BUCKLER (B.) *Compl. vindic. of the mallard of A.S. Coll. agst. suggest. of Mr. Pointer, 1750; 2nd ed., 1751.
ASHMOLEAN MUSEUM.
see CORPUS vasorum antiquorum. Gt. Brit., fasc. 3, Oxford, A. Mus.; by J. D. Beazley, 1927.
,, HOGARTH (D. G.) Hittite seals w. ref. to the A. Coll., 1920.
,, PRIDEAUX (H.) Marmora Oxon., &c., 1676.
BRASENOSE COLLEGE.
*Brasenose ale, 1878, *see* WARD (T. H.), *ed.*
CHRIST CHURCH.
Carmina quadragesimalia ab Ædis Christi Oxon. alumnis composita &c. [Ed. C. Este & A. Parsons]. 2v [*in 1*]. s8º. Glasguæ. 1757
see WREN (*Sir* C.) "Tom Tower" C.C.: letters of W. to J. Fell, set forth & annot. by W. D. Caröe, 1923.
LADY MARGARET HALL.
Lady Margaret Hall: a short hist. [*By var. wr.*] s8º. 1923
MERTON COLLEGE.
Merton muniments. Sel. & ed. by P. S. Allen & H. W. Garrod. [Oxf. Hist. Soc.] 4º. O. 1928
Registrum annalium Collegii M., 1483–1521. Ed. H. E. Salter. [Oxf. Hist. Soc., 76]. 8º. O. 1923
NEW COLLEGE.
Adderbury "Rectoria": manor at A. belong. to N.C.: account rolls &c., 1926, *see* HOBSON (T. F.), *ed.*
A facs. of 5 pages from the Bk. of the steward of the Hall, 1386–7. fol. O. 1886
see HORNCHURCH PRIORY. Kalendar of doc. in poss. of N.C., 1923.
ORIEL COLLEGE.
The Dean's reg. of Oriel, 1446–1661. Ed. G. C. Richards & H. E. Salter. [Oxf. Hist. Soc., v84]. 8º. O. 1926
Oriel Coll. records. [Ed.] by C. L. Shadwell & H. E. Salter. [Oxf. Hist. Soc., v85]. 8º. O. 1926
RADCLIFFE LIBRARY.
see KING (W.) Oratio, 1749, die dedic. Bibl. Radcliv., 1750.
ST. JOHN'S COLLEGE.
see CHRISTMAS PRINCE (THE): [acc. of the St. J.'s Coll. revels, held, 1607–8, f. MS. in the Coll. Library; prep. by F. S. Boas], 1923.

Oxford [*continued*].
UNIVERSITY PRESS.
*Some account of the Oxford Univ. Press, 1468–1921. 8°. O. 1922
„ „ ....1468–1926. [2nd ed.] 8°. O. 1926
see HART (H.) Rules f. compositors &c., 1921.
WADHAM COLLEGE.
see DIXEY (F. A.) Early connex. of the Royal Soc. w. W.C. &c., 1912.

Oxford Almanack, 1728, 1745, 1750–53, 1755–58, 1760–65, 1767–74, 1777, 78, 1790, 1792, 1800, 1802, 1803, 1811, 1814–16, 1818–20. [1728, 1758 *want calendar*; 1770–74, 1777–78 & 1802 *want all text*]. [Prints]. la. fol. O. [1727–1819]

Oxford Bibliographical Society.
Proceedings & Papers. v1, p3, la8°. O. 1926
see MADAN (F.) R. Burton & the Anat. of Melancholy; papers, ed. F. M., 1926. [iiii.]

Oxford Dante Society (The). A record of 44 years, 1876–1920. Comp. by P. Toynbee. s8°. O. 1920

Oxford historical & literary studies. Issued under the dir. of C. H. Firth & W. Raleigh. v11, 12. 8°. O. 1920–21
see EVELYN (J.) Early life & education, 1920. [11.]
„ SEYMOUR (ST. J. D.) Puritans in Ireland, 1647–61, 1921. [12.]

Oxford Historical Society.
Publications. v70–85. 8°. O. 1920–26
see GUNTHER (R. W. T.) Early science in Oxford, 2v, 1923. [77, 78.]
„ HEARNE (T.) Remarks &c., v11, 1921. [72.]
„ MAGRATH (J. R.) Flemings in Oxford, v3, 1924. [79.]
„ OXFORD. Mediaeval archives of Univ. of O.; ed. H. E. Salter, v1, 2, 1920–21. [70, 73.]
„ —— Munimenta Civitatis Oxonie; ed. H. E. Salter, 1920. [71.]
„ —— MERTON COLLEGE. M. muniments; sel. &c., by P. S. Allen &c., 1928.
„ ——: —— Registrum annalium Coll. M., 1483–1521, 1923. [76.]
„ ——: ORIEL COLL. Dean's reg., 1446–1661, 1926. [84.]
„ ——: —— O.C. records, 1926. [85.]
„ POOLE (*Mrs.* R.) Cat. of portraits in the poss. of the Univ. &c. of Oxford, v2, 3, 1926. [81, 82.]
„ SALTER (H. E.), *ed.* Chapters of the Augustinian canons, 1922. [74.]
„ —— Oxford City properties, 1926. [83.]
„ —— Snappe's formulary & o. records, 1924. [80.]
„ —— Surveys & tokens, 1923. [75.]

Oxford magazine (The).
v38–42 (Oct. 1919–June 1924). 4°. O. 1919–24

Oxford Philosophical Society, 1683–90, *see* PHILOSOPHICAL SOC. OF O.

Oxford University Entomological Society.
see LEPIDOPTERA. *Accentuated list of the Brit. L.; publ. by the Entomolog. Soc. of Oxford & Cambridge, 1858.

Oxford University Press, *see* OXFORD: UNIV. PRESS.

Oxford, Worcester & Wolverhampton Railway.
Map. *folded* 8°. 1851

Oxford (Edward De Vere, *17th earl of*), *1550–1604.*
Poems. With biog. notice, intr. to the poems & notes by J. T. Looney. 8°. [1921]
see WARD (B. M.) The 17th Earl of O., f. contemp. docs., 1928.
„ WARD (*Col.* B. R.) The mystery of "Mr. W. H.": [*Shakespeare identified w. E. de V.*], 1923.

Oxford (Robert Harley, *1st earl of*). The answer of O. to the articles of impeachment &c. [P2606]. fol. [1715]
*Articles of impeachment of high treason &c. against O. [P2606]. fol. [1715]

Oxford & Asquith (Emma Alice Margaret, *countess of*) [MARGOT ASQUITH], *see* ASQUITH (E. A. M.)

Oxford & Asquith (*Rt. Hon.* **Herbert Henry,** *1st earl of*), *see* ASQUITH (*Rt. Hon.* H. H.)

Oxfordshire. O. & Buckinghamshire Light Infantry chron., 1914–15. Ann. rec. of 1st & 2nd battalions, form. 43rd & 52nd L. I., w. war rec. of o. batt. of the regiment. Comp. & ed. Lt.-Col. A. F. Mockler-Ferryman. v24. 8°. [1919 ?]
Chantry certificates & Edwardian inventories for O., 1919; 1920, *see* GRAHAM (R.), *ed.*
Some pedigrees f. the visitation of O., made by J. Philipott & W. Riley, 1634. [Repr. f. Misc. Geneal. & Heraldica]. la8°. 1913

Oxfordshire Record Society.
Oxfordshire record series. v1–9. 8°. O. 1919–27
see BARNETT (H.) Glympton: hist. of Oxf. manor, 1923. [5.]
„ COOKE (A. H.) Early hist. of Mapledurham, 1925. [7.]
„ GRAHAM (R.), *ed.* Chantry certificates & Edwardian inventories; ed. &c. R. G., 1919. [1.]
„ HOBSON (T. F.), *ed.* Adderbury "Rectoria," 1926. [8.]
„ JEFFERY (R. W.) Manors & advowson of Gt. Rollright, 1927. [9.]
„ MARSTON. Churchwardens' acc. of M., Spelsbury, Pyrton, 1925. [6.]
„ NEWINGTON LONGEVILLE. N.L. charters; transcr. &c. H. E. Salter, 1921. [3.]
„ WOOD (A. à) & R. RAWLINSON. Parochial coll.; transcr. &c. F. N. Davis, 2p, 1920–22. [2, 4.]

Oxholm (Axel H.) Forest resources of Norway, 1922, *see* UNITED STATES: COMMERCE.

Oxilia (Ugo Giuseppe), *see* CRESCI (M.) Storia ital. [1524–46]; comm. U. G. O., 1907.

Oxley (Thomas). Facilography, system of easy, expeditious writing &c. App. shewing a univ. system of stenography &c. 2nd ed. 4°. 1816

Oxley (William). The philosophy of spirit, illust. by a new version of the Bhagavat Gítá. 2nd ed. s8°. M'ter. 1903

Oxonian, *ps.* *Note book of an Oxonian, late member of Brazen Nose College. s8°. [*p.p.*] 1831

Oxonian, *ps.* *Wesleyan classics, or biogr. sketches &c. by Oxonian, 1870, *see* WESLEYAN.

***Oxoniana,** 4v, 1807 ?, *see* WALKER (J.)

Oxyrhynchus papyri (The). Ed., w. tr. & notes, by B. P. Grenfell & A. S. Hunt. [Egypt Explor. Soc.] p15–17. la8°. 1922–27
see CRATIPPUS, *the historian.* C[1]. Hellenicorum fragm. O. &c., 1916.
„ HELLENICA. Oxyrhynchia; ed. E. Kalinka, 1927.
„ —— Oxyrhynchia cum Theopompi & Cratippi fragm.; rec. B. P. Grenfell & A. S. Hunt, 1909.

Ozaki (*Mme.* **Yukio).** Romances of old Japan. Rendered into Eng. f. Jap. sources. la8°. [1919]

Ozenfant (Amédée) & C. Jeanneret.
La peinture mod. [5e éd.] la8°. [1925]

Ozerov (Ivan Khrist.) Атласъ діаграммъ по экономич. вопросамъ. 8 вып. *in 1v.* 8°. Москва. 1908–9
Какъ расходуются въ Россіи народныя деньги? s8°. Москва. 1907
Русскій бюджетъ. [*b. w. h.* Атласъ діаграммъ, 1908–9]. s8°. [Москва. 1907]
Что должны имѣть въ виду рабочіе. [P2448]. 8°. Москва. 1906
Фабричные комитеты или какъ рабочему добиться лучшихъ условій труда? изд. 2ое. [P2448]. 8°. Москва. 1906

Ozerov (Vladislav Aleksandrovich).
Сочиненія. 5ое изд. 3ч. *in 1v.* 8°. С.-П. 1928

Ozolin (Ian A.)
The oldest Europ. nation. Latvia. [P2503]. s8°. [1920]
„ „ ....2nd ed. rev. [P2710]. s8°. [1920]

Ozzòla (Leandro). G. P. Pannini: pittore. 50 tavole, con intr. di L. O. la8°. Torino. 1921
La litografia ital. 1805–70. 4°. 1923

P

P* (***M.* **de).** Hist. acc. of pres. troubles in Persia &c.; tr., 1756, *see* PEYSSONEL (C. C. DE).

P* (***Mr.* **de).** *Recherches philos. sur les Américans, 3t, 1771, *see* PAUW (C.)

P. (D. B.) *Reformation (A) of a cath. deformed, 1604, *see* BISHOP (WILLIAM), *bp. of Chalcedon.*

P. (D. M.) Dict. iconologique, 1758, *see* LACOMBE DE PREZEL (HONORÉ).

P. (E. C.) *Eng. medieval embroidery, 1848, *see* HARTSHORNE (C. H.)

P. (E. R. D. T.) *Apologia pro J. Gersonio, 1676, *see* RICHER (EDMOND).

P* (G***).** *Mém. p. s. à l'hist. de la vie &c. de l'abbé Lenglet du Fresnoy. [Dédic. *signed* G*** P***], 1761, *see* MICHAULT (J. B.)

P. (J.) Three godly treatises, 1632, *see* PRESTON (J.)

P. (J.), *Somerset Herald.* *Cat. of Chancellors of Eng. &c., 1636, *see* PHILIPOT (J.)

P** (J. F.)** Aix anc. & mod., 1833, *see* AIX-EN-PROVENCE.

P. (*p.* M.) *La Trappe mieux connue, 1834, *see* †PÉQUIGNY (P.)

P. (P. D. K. S. T.) Concordia, seu sacra cœnæ theoria sacra, 1776, *see* CONCORDIA.

P. (R.) *Nugae derelictae q. coll. J. M. & R. P., 1822, *see* MAIDMENT (J.) & R. PITCAIRN.

P. (R.) Sir W. Orpen: [*descr. &c. signed R. P.*], 1923, *see* ORPEN (*Sir* W.)

P. (S. P.) *Ad Regis Galliae consiliarios, exhortatio; tr. S. P. P. faciebat, 1561, *see* GALLIA.

P. (W.) *Address (An) to Protestants, 2nd ed., 1692, *see* PENN (WILLIAM).

Pacca (*il card.* **Bartolommeo),** *see* CONSALVI (*card.* E.) & B. P. Corr. ined. dei card. C. e. P. nel tempo del Congr. di Vienna, 1814–15, 1903.

Pace (Biagio). *Works in* REALE ACCAD. D. LINCEI. Mon. ant.
- La basilica di Salemi, 1916. [24.]
- Ricerche cartaginesi, con contrib. di R. Lantier, 1925. [30.]
- Il tempio di Giove Olimpico in Agrigento, 1922. [28.]
- Vasi fig. con rifl. d. pittura di Parrasio, 1922. [28.]

Pace (Edward George). Ideas of God in Israel. 8°. 1924

Pacheco (Felix). Presidente Harding. Discurso. [P2752]. 4°. Rio de Janeiro. 1923

Pacher (Friedrich), *see* SEMPER (H.) Michael u. F. P., 1911.

Pacher (Michael).
see SEMPER (H.) M. u. F. P., i. Kreis u. i. Nachfolger, 1911.
„ TIETZE (H.) M. P. u. s. Kreis, 1921.

Pacheu (Jules). L'expérience mystique & l'activité subconsciente. s8°. 1911
Jacopone de Todi, auteur présumé du Stabat Mater, 1228–1306. [*w. texts*]. s8°. 1914

Pachom (Georg August) [PACHOMIUS]. Synopsis logomachiarum &c. Acc. C. Forstneri De dissidiis theologorum epistolæ. [Ed. I. I. Sartorius, *w. sep. pagin.*] s8°. Francofurti. 1726

Pachomius, *St., abbot of Tabenna, see* BOUSSET (W.) Apophthegmata (Unters. zur Vita P.), 1923.

Pachtere (Félix Georges de). La table hypothécaire de Veleia. Et. sur la propriété foncière dans l'Apennin de Plaisance. [H. E., 228]. 8°. 1920

Pachtler (G. M.) Die Hymnen d. Kathol. Kirche in Versmasse übers. s8°. Mainz. 1853

Pacific Islands. P.I. pilot, 5th ed., 3v, *&* Suppl. 1–3, 1918–22, *see* ADMIRALTY.

Pacific Ocean. Our journal in the P.; by officers of H.M.S. Zealous, 1873, *see* EARDLEY-WILMOT (*Sir* S. M.), *ed.*

Pacificus (Hermannus), *see* EPHESUS, *1st synod.* Synodus Ephesina &c.; adj. theses H. P., 1581.

Paciotto (Francesco). Lettere a Guidobaldo II, duca d'Urbino, ed. & annot. da C. Promis, *see* REGIA DEP. DI STORIA PATRIA. Misc., t12, 1871.
see PROMIS (C.) Vita di F. P. da Urbino, archit. d. sec. 16, 1863.

Pacius (Julius), *see* CORVINUS (J. A.) Posthumus P. &c., 1659.

Packard (Francis Randolph). Life & times of A. Pare, 1510–90. With new tr. of h. Apology & acc. of h. journeys &c. 8°. 1922
see SCHOLA SALERNITANA. The sch. of Salernum, Eng. version by Sir J. Harington: hist. of school, by F. R. P., 1922.

Packard (Frank Lucius). The four stragglers. s8°. [1923]
The red ledger. s8°. [1926]

Padelford (Frederick Morgan). Early 16th century lyrics. Ed. F. M. P. s8°. Boston [*Mass.*] 1907

Paderborn. Paderborn; hrsg. v. Magistrat P. bearb. Michels, *see* DEUTSCHLAND. D.'s Stadtebau, 1921.

Padiglione (Il) di re Alfonso, versi, 1904, *see* ALFONSO, *k. of Aragon &c.*

Padova.
- Cenni stor. s. famiglie di Padova e s. mon. dell' univ. [*Ed.* A. de Marchi]. Prem. un tratt. sull' arte araldica. [*By* L. J. Grotto degli Erri]. fol. Padova. 1842
- Inscriz. dell' Univ. di P. che ricordano studenti vicentini (*16 & 17 c.*) [Nozze Tasin-Pedezza]. [N. 46]. la8°. [Vicenza]. [1891]
- Monografie stor. s. Studio di P. Contrib. del. R. Ist. Veneto di Sci. [By A. Favaro *& others*]. 8°. Venezia. 1922
- Statuten d. Juristen-Univ. P., 1331; hrsg. H. Denifle, *see* ARCHIV F. LIT.-U. KIRCHENGESCH. D. M.-A., B6, 1892.

Padua (Macario), *ps., see* AMAT (F.), *abp. of Palmyra.*

Paes de Abreu (Bartholomeu), *see* TAUNAY (A. D' E.) Um grande bandeirante: B. P. de A. (1674–1738), 1922.

Paetow (Louis John), *ed., see* GARLAND (J.) Morale scolarium, 1927.

Pagan (*le cte.* **Blaise François de).** Hist. & geogr. descr. of the country & river of the Amazones. Tr. W. Hamilton. s8°. 1661

Paganini (Nicoló).
see ESCUDIER (M. & L.) Vies &c. des cantatrices, & Vie de P., 1856.
„ FÉTIS (F. J.) Biog. notice of N. P. &c., 1876.
„ PROD'HOMME (J. G.) P., 1908.

Pagano (Giovanni). Storia di Ferdinando II, 1830–1850. [3 lib. *in* 1v]. 8°. Napoli. 1853

Paganuzzi (Giovanni Battista). Iconografia d. trente parrocchie di Venezia. fol. *n.p.* 1821

Page (Anne). The Foundling Hospital & its neighbourhood. Intr. by W. R. Lethaby. 4°. 1926

Page (*Hon.* **Arthur),** *Judge of the High Court of Judicature, Fort William, Bengal, see* GANGARAM, *Brahmin.* Trial of G. & Sew Prasad; ed. A. P., 1927.

Page (Harlan), *see* HALLOCK (W. A.) Mem. of H. P., 1835.

Page (J. A.) Guide to the Qutb, Delhi. 8°. Calcutta. 1927
An hist. mem. on the Qutb, Delhi, *see* INDIA: ARCH. SURVEY. Mem., No. 22, 1926.

Page (Jesse). Schwartz of Tanjore. 8°. 1921

Page (John), *minstrel.* Siege of Rouen. Krit. Textausg. nebst Einleit. &c. v. H. Huscher. 8°. L. 1927

Page (Mabel), *see* TUCKER (C. L.) Trial of T. for murder of M. P., 1907.

Page (Thomas Walker). Making the tariff in the U.S. By T. W. P. w. aid of the Inst. of Economics. s8°. N.Y. 1924

Page (Walter Hines). A publisher's confession. Intr. by F. N. Doubleday. s8°. 1924
see HENDRICK (B. J.) Life & letters of W. H. P., 3v, 1922–25; repr., 1924.

Page (William), *of Lincoln's Inn, F.S.A.*
London, its origin & early development. 8°. 1923
St. Albans. s8°. 1920

Pageant. *P. (The) of Eng. poetry, 1909, *see* LEONARD (R. M.), *ed.*
P. (The) of Eng. prose: 500 passages &c., 1920, *see* LEONARD (R. M.), *ed.*

Pagenstecher (Rudolf), *see* SIEGLIN (E. v.) Exped. E. v. S.: Ausgrabgn. in Alexandria, B2iii, Die griech.-ägypt. Samml. E. v. S.; bearb. v. R. P., 1913.

Page-Roberts (William), *dean of Salisbury.*
Law & God. 5th ed. s8°. 1878

Pages de défense protestante, t1, 1923, *see* VIÉNOT (J.)

Pages actuelles, 1914[–19]. Nos. 137–141. s8°. 1919–21
- Bourelly (*gén.*) Campagne d'Égypte & de Syrie contre les Turcs, 1919. [137.]
- Bucaille (V.) Denys Cochin, 1922. [138.]
- Geoffroy de Grandmaison (C. A.) La croix-rouge française, 1921. [140–41.]
- Pinon (René). L'Europe nouv. & le catholicisme, 1921. [139.]

Pagès, *Family of, see* AGEORGES (J.) Une famille franç. au 19ᵉ s.: les Pagès & les Bordes-Pagès, 1920.

Pagès (Amédée).
Comm. des poésies d'A. March. [H. E., 247]. 8°. 1925

Pagès (Georges), *see* BOURGEOIS (E.) & G. P. Orig. & responsabilités de la Grande Guerre, 1921.

Pagès (Jean Pierre). De la responsabilité ministérielle &c., *see* CONSTANT (B.) &c. Mél. polit. &c., t2, 1829.

Pagès (Léon). Bibliog. japon. ou Cat. des ouvr. rel. au Japon, dep. le 15ᵉ siècle. 4°. 1859

Paget (*Sir* **Richard Arthur Surtees),** *Bart.* The nature of human speech. On the use of italic, by H. W. Fowler. Reviews & notes by R. Bridges. [S.P.E., Tract 22]. 8°. O. 1925
Vowel resonances. [P2688]. 8°. 1922

Paget (Stephen), *F.R.C.S.* The faith & works of Christian Science. [repr., w. add.] 8°. 1909
Henry Scott Holland. Mem. &c. ed. by S. P. 8°. 1921
I have reason to believe. 8°. 1921

Paget (Walburga, *Lady*).
Embassies of other days, & further recoll. 2v. 8°. 1923
In my tower. 2v. 8°. 1924

Pagine Istriane. Periodico. Annata 3. la8°. Capodistria. 1905

Pagitt (Ephraim). Christianographie or the descr. of the multitude & sundry sorts of Christians in the world not subject to the pope. 2nd ed. inlarged. [*3 pagin.*] s4°. 1636

Paglia (Ludovico). Ist. d. cittá di Giovenazzo, con un raguaglio ist. d. D. L. Sagarriga, vita d. N. Paglia &c. Date in luce d. D. G. Frammarini. 8°. Napoli. 1700

Paglia (Nicoló), *see* PAGLIA (L.) Ist. d. Giovenazzo, con vita di N. P. *by* L. Sagarriga, 1700.

Pagliaini (Attilio), *see* CATALOGO gen. d. libreria ital., Indice, v3, 1922; Suppl. 2, v1, A–K, 1925.

Pagliarino (Battista). Cron. di Vicenza dal princ. di questa città sino al Dom. Veneto, 1404. s4°. Vicenza. 1663

Pagninus (Santes). Thesauri Heb. linguae epitome; cui acc. gramm. libellus, *see* BIBLE: POLYGLOT. Biblia sacra, t6, 1572.
see BIBLE: LATIN. Biblia; Habes in hoc libro . . . utriusq. instrum. nov. tr. aeditam a . . . S. P., 3p, 1528.

Pahr, *Family of, see* HAHR (A.) Die Architektenfamilie P., 1908.

Paijkull (Carl Wilhelm).
A summer in Iceland. Tr. M. R. Barnard. 8°. 1868

Pailleron (Edouard). Meisjesdroomen, naar E. P., *see* HALL (J. N. VAN). De viool van Cremona &c., 1882.

Pailleron (Marie Louise). Le cercueil de Mlle. de Saint-Cast, *see* ŒUVRES libres, 24, 1923.
Le coucou, *see* ŒUVRES libres, 48, 1925.
François Buloz & s. amis: les écrivains du 2nd Empire. 8°. 1924

Paillot (Fortuné). Amant ou maîtresse? s8°. [1922]
Le diable par la queue. s8°. [1924]
Les époux scandaleux. Roman. s8°. [1921]

Pain (Barry Eric Odell). The death of Maurice. s8°. [1920]
Marge Askinforit. s8°. [1920]

Pain (William), *architect.*
The pract. builder. 4th ed. rev. 4°. 1787

Paine (Albert Bigelow).
Joan of Arc, Maid of France. 2v. 8°. N.Y. 1925

Paine (Martyn).
Physiology of the soul & instinct &c. 8°. N.Y. 1872

Paine (Ralph Delahaye). The fight for a free sea. War of 1812. [Chron. of Amer. ser., v17]. 8°. New Haven, *Yale.* 1920
The ships & sailors of old Salem. 8°. 1924

Paine (Thomas), *polit. writer.*
Agrarian justice, *see* BEER (M.) Pioneers, 1920.
La crise américaine. Tr. [P2760]. 8°. an 2e [1794]
Le siècle de la raison. Tr. F. Lanthenas. [P2760]. 8°. an 2e [1793]
see BEST (M. A.) T. P., 1927.
,, DREW (S.) Remarks on "The age of reason," 1820.
see GOULD (F. J.) T. P., 1925.
,, HAMMOND (C.) Pilgrimage of T. P. &c. in the spirit world, 1852.
,, INGERSOLL (R. G.) Orations (T. P. &c.), 1881.
,, TAYLOR (T.) Answer to the 1st [& 2nd] part[s] of Age of reason, 1796.

Paine (William Worship). The menace of socialism. s8°. [1925]

Painlevé (Paul), *see* LAURENT (M.) Nos gouvernments de Guerre: P. &c., 1920.

***Painted** windows. A study in relig. personality. By A gentleman with a duster. s8°. [1922]
,, ,, ...2nd ed. s8°. [1922]

Painters' Company, *London* [PAINTER-STAINERS COMPANY OF LONDON], *see* ENGLEFIELD (W. A. D.) Hist. of P.-S. Co. of L., 1923.
see PITMAN (W. H.) The W. Co. of P.: its hall, pictures, & plate, 1906.

Pais (Ettore).
Fasti triumphales populi Romani. Ed. & illust. da E. P. 2p. la8°. Roma. 1920
Imperialismo romano e politica ital. s8°. Bologna. [1920]
Italia antica. Ricerche di storia e di geogr. storica. 2v. Bologna. [1922]
Ricerche s. storia e sul diritto pubblico di Roma. [Vol. di complemento d. storia crit. di Roma]. s4. la8°. 1921
Storia d. colonizz. di Roma antica. v1. la8°. 1923
Storia di Roma dalle orig. all' iniz. d. guerre Puniche. 3a ed. v3–5. la8°. 1927–28
3, Dalla cacciata d. re all' invas. Gallica.
4, Dall' invas. d. Galli all' intervento d. Romani n. Campania.
5, Dalla resa di Napoli all' intervento di Pirro—Roma alla testa d. Confederazione Italica.
Storia di Roma dur. le Guerre Puniche. 2v. la8°. 1927

Paish (*Sir* George). The road to prosperity. Foreword by Sir J. Stamp. 8°. 1927

Paisiello (Giovanni Gregorio Cataldo), *see* DELLA CORTE (A.) P., con una tavola tematica &c., 1922.

Paiva (Mosseh Pereyra de). Notisias dos Judeos de Cochim. [*Facs. of 1687 ed.*] Nov. publ. com intr. de M. B. Amzalak. 4°. Lisboa. 1923

Païva (Thérèse Pauline Blanche, *marquise* **de),** *née Lachmann, aft. wife of A. Villoing, later ctsse. Henckel, see* LOLIÉE (F.) "La Païva": la légende & l'hist. de P., 1920.

Paiva de Andrade (Diogo de), *the elder* [PAYVA (JACOBUS)]. De soc. Jesu orig. lib. contra Kemnicii cujusd. petulantē audaciā, *see* JESUITS. Epist. Indicae, 1566.

Pajitnov (K. A.) [PASHITNOV]. Die Lage d. arbeit. Klasse in Russland. Autor. Übers. v. M. Nachimson, mit e Anhang v. M. N. s8°. St. 1907
Положеніе рабочаго класса въ Россіи. [*a. c. in* P2448]. 8°. 1906

Pakington (Mary). The house with twisty windows, *see* SCHOFIELD (S.) The marble god & o. plays, 1926.
The true likeness. Fantasy. 8°. 1928

Pakraduni (Arsenio). Le due sorelle, framm. d. Haik. [*In Arm. & Ital.*] Tr. [E. Teza. *a. c. in* P2797]. la8°. Venezia. 1905

Palache (John Garber). Four novelists of the old régime: Crébillon, Laclos, Diderot, Restif de la Bretonne. 8°. N.Y. 1926

Palacios (Jose), *see* LOPEZ-AYDILLO (E.) & J. P. Lamas Carvajal: est. biog. y crit., 1925.

Paladino (Giuseppe). Opusc. e lettere di Riformatori ital. d. cinquecento. A cura di G. P. [Scr. d'It., 99]. v2. 8°. Bari. 1927
2, Actio in pontifices Romanos et eorum asseclas [by A. Paleario]—Lettere di Olimpia morata—Epistole di Celio Secondo Curione.

Paladinos da linguagem. [Antol. portuguesa; organiz. por A. de Campos]. 3v [v1, 2a ed.] s8°. Paris. 1922–26

Palaephatus, *the Grammarian.* De non credendis historiis, *see* ÆSOP, 1505.
Von d. unglaubl. Begebenheiten. Übers. &c. v. J. D. Büchling. s8°. Halle. 1791

Palaestra. Untersuch. u. Texte aus d. deut. u. engl. Philologie. Hrsg. A. Brandl &c. [B]139, 142, 143, 154. 8°. L. 1923–27
see GUY, *of Warwick.* G. of W.; hrsg. G. Schleich, 1923. [139.]
,, HEIDRICH (H.) John Davies of Hereford u. s. Bild v. Shakespeare's Umgebung, 1924. [143.]
,, LÖWIS OF MENAR (A. v.) Die Brünhildsage in Russland, 1923. [142.]
,, PRINZ (J.) John Wilmot, e. of Rochester, 1927. [154.]

Palafox y Mendoza (Juan de), *bp. of (1) Puebla de Los Angeles, (2) Osma.* Hist. de la conquête de l'empire de la Chine par les Tartares, *see* BERNARD (J. F.), *ed.* Recueil, t6, 1729.
The hist. of the conquest of China by the Tartars. Rendred Eng. s8°. 1671
see JESUITS. *Morale pratique &c., t4, Hist. de Palafox [by A. Arnauld], 1718.

Palairet (Elie). Obs. philol.-crit. in sacros Nov. Foed. libros. 8°. Lugd. Batav. 1752

Palais de la Légion d'Honneur. Exposition rétrospect. des maréchaux de France. [P2699]. 4°. 1922

Palais de la Paix, *see* HAGUE (THE).

Palais des Beaux Arts, *Paris.*
Expos. du paysage franç. Catalogue. 8°. 1925
Venise aux 18–19 siècles. Expos. [*Fr. & Ital.*] s8°. 1919
see PRUD'HON (P. P.) Expos. P. P. P.: catalogue, 1922.

Palamenghi-Crispi (Tommaso). Francesco Crispi: polit. interna. Diaro e doc. 8°. Milano. 1924

Palampet. Inscriptions at P., *see* HYDERABAD. Arch. Ser., No. 3, 1919.

Palat (Barthélemy Edmond) [*ps.* PIERRE LEHAUTCOURT].
La Grande Guerre sur le front occidental. [t]6–12. 8°. 1920–27
6, La victoire de la Marne, 5–13 sept. 1914.
7, La course à la mer, 14 sept.–15 oct. 1914.
8, La ruée vers Calais, 15 oct.–13 déc. 1914.
9, Les offensives de 1915, déc. 1914–déc. 1915.
10, La ruée sur Verdun, 5 août 1915–30 juin 1916.
11, Bataille de la Somme, juil. 1916–jan. 1917.
12, L'année d'angoisse, 1917.

Palatinate [PALATINATUS]. Catechesis relig. Xtnae. quae trad. in eccl. &c. P., 1563, *see* HEIDELBERG CATECHISM.
Electa juris publici hist. Palatinam illust. [Contin. actorum in causa Sereniss. dominae ducissae Aurelian. contra electorem P. *b. w.* Freher (M.) Orig. Palat., 1686]. 2p. s4°. [Frankfort. 1700]

Palatine anthology: coll. of poems &c. rel. to Lancs. & Cheshire, 1850, *see* HALLIWELL-PHILLIPPS (J. O.), *ed.*

Palatinus. La passion du P. Mystère du 14e s. Ed. par G. Frank. [Class. franç. d. m.-â.] s8°. 1922

Palau y Dulcet (Antonio). Manual del librero hispanoamericano. 7t. 4°. Barcelona. 1923–27

Palazzechi (Aldo). Il codice di Perelà. s8º. Firenze. [1920]

***Palazzi** (I) e le ville che non sono più del re. Di G. de Abate [*& o. writers*]. Con pref. di Ugo Ojetti. 4º. Milano. 1921

Palazzo dei Conservatori, *see* ROME. Cat. of the anc. sculptures in municipal coll. of R.: Sculptures of the P. dei C., 1926.

Paldjean (Aleksandr). [Hist. of the Cath. doct. of the Armenians & their accord w. the Rom. Church. *In Armenian*]. 8º. Vienna. 1878

Paldus (Josef). Die milit. Aufnahmen im Bereiche d. Habsburg. Länder, 1763–85, 1919, *see* KAISERL. AKAD. D. W. ZU WIEN. Denkschr., B63, 1924.

Paleario (Aonio) [*i.e.* ANTONIO DALLA PAGLIA]. Actio in pontifices Romanos et eorum asseclas, *see* PALADINO (G.) Opusc. &c., v2, 1927.

The benefit of Christ's death. Intr. by Rev. J. Ayre. s8º. [1847]

Opera. Rec. & diss. de vita &c. A. P. praem. F. A. Hallbauer. s8º. Jenae. 1728

see BONNET (J.) A. P., 1863.

Palen (Lewis Stanton).

The White Devil of the Black Sea. s8º. [1924]

Palencia (Angel González), *see* HURTADO Y J. DE LA SERNA (J.) & A. G. P. Hist. de la lit. españ., 1921–22; 2ª ed., 1925.

Palencia (Isabel O. de) [BEATRIZ GALINDO].

El sembrador sembró su semilla. Novela. s8º. 1923

Paleocapa (Pietro). Dello stato ant., d. vicende &c. d. estuari veneti. 8º. Venezia. 1867

Paléographie musicale. Les principaux manuscrits de chant grégorien, ambrosien, mozarabe, gallican publ. en facsimilés phototypiques par les Bénédictins de Solesmes [v8–11, sous la dir. de Dom A. Mocquereau]. 2e série (Monumentale). 11v [v7 *wanting*]. 4º. Solesmes. 1900–12

see ANTIPHONALE. Antiphon. Missarum S. Gregorii, cod. 47, Chartres, 1912. [11.]

,, —— Antiphon. Missarum S. Gregorii, cod. 239, Laon, 1909. [10.]

,, —— Le cod. 121 de la Biblioth. d'Einsiedeln, Antiph. S. Gregorii, 1894. [4.]

,, —— Antiph. officii monast. écrit par le B. Hartker, 1900. [1.]

,, ANTIPHONARIUM. Antiphon. Ambrosianum du Mus. Brit., 2p, 1896–1900. [5, 6.]

,, —— Antiphonaire monastique, cod. 601, Lucques, 1906. [9.]

,, —— Antiphon. tonale Missarum, cod. H. 159, Montpellier, 1901–5. [8.]

,, GRADUALE. Le Répons-Graduel Justus ut palma &c., 1891–92. [2, 3.]

Paléologue (G. Maurice) [MAURICE GEORGES P.]

L'art chinois. n. éd. 8º. [1910]

Le roman tragique de l'Empereur Alexandre II. [8e éd.] s8º. [1923]

La Russie des Tsars pend. la Grande Guerre. 3t. 8º. [1921–22]

Talleyrand, Metternich, Chateaubriand. 8º. [1924]

TRANSLATIONS.

An ambassador's memoirs. By M. P. Tr. F. A. Holt. 3v. 8º. 1923–25

Cavour. Tr. I. F. D. & M. M. Morrow. la8º. 1927

The romantic diplomat: Talleyrand—Metternich—Chateaubriand. Tr. A. Chambers. 8º. [1926]

The tragic romance of Alexander II of Russia. Tr. A. Chambers. 8º. [1926]

Paleotimus (Lucius). Antiquitatum sive originum eccl. summa &c. [Ed. S. Sciugliaga]. s4º. Augustae Vindel. 1767

Paleotti (Gabriele), *cardinal, see* TRENT, *Council of.* Acta Co. Tridentii 1562 & 63 &c., 1842.

Palestine. Rep. of Comm. apptd. by Govt. of P. to inq. into affairs of Orthodox Patriarchate of Jerusalem, 1921, *see* BERTRAM (*Sir* A.) & H. C. LUKE.

Report on P. admin. [Govt. of P. rep.], July 1920–Dec. 1921. 8º. 1922

Palestine Exploration Fund.

see ARMSTRONG (G.) Map of Palestine, 1890.

,, CONDER (C. R.) & H. H. KITCHENER. Map of W. Palestine, spec. ed., by T. Saunders, 1882.

Palestrina (Giovanni Pierluigi da) [GIOVANNI BATTISTA PIETRO LUIGI *da Palestrina*], *see* PYNE (Z. K.) G. P. da P., h. life & times, 1922.

Paley (*la pcsse.*), *wife of grand duke Paul Alexandrovitch.*

Mem. of Russia, 1916–19. 8º. 1924

Souvenirs de Russie, 1916–19. Préf. de P. Bourget. s8º. [1923]

Paley (G. A.) Paul Redway. Pref. by D. MacCarthy. s8º. 1923

Paley (William), *archdeacon of Carlisle, see* ALEXANDER (G. G.) Archdeacon P. as a jurist, 1918.

Palgrave, *The family of, see* PALMER (C. J.) & S. TUCKER, *edd.* P. fam. mems., 1878.

Palgrave (*Sir* **Francis**), *1788–1861.* Coll. hist. works. Ed. Sir R. H. I. Palgrave. v3–10. la8º. C. 1921–22

3, 4, Hist. of Normandy & of Eng., v3, 4.

5, Hist. of the Anglo-Saxons.

6, 7, Hist. of the Eng. Commonwealth: Anglo-Saxon period, 2p.

8, Truths & fictions of the Middle Ages: The merchant & the friar—Norfolk family.

9, 10, Reviews, essays & o. writings.

Palgrave (Francis Turner). The golden treasury of the best songs &c. in Eng. s8º. 1872

Palgrave (*Sir* **Robert H. Inglis**). Dict. of polit. economy. Ed. H. Higgs. [n. ed.] 3v. 8º. 1925–26

Palgrave (William Gifford). A year's journey thr. C. & E. Arabia, 1862–63. 6th ed. 8º. 1871

Pali Text Society.

see PUGGALA-PAÑÑATTI. Design. of human types (P.-P.); tr. B. C. Law, 1924.

,, SANYUTTA-NIKAYA. The Book of the Kindred Sayings (Sanyutta-Nikāya); tr. Mrs. Rhys Davids &c., p2, 3, 1922–24.

,, THERAGĀTHĀ. Psalms of the early Buddhists; [tr. &c.] Mrs. Rhys Davids, 2v, 1909–13.

Palissy (Bernard), *see* LEROUX (D.) La vie de B. P., 1927.

Palizzolo Gravina (Vincenzo), *barone di Ramione.* Il blasone in Sicilia ossia racc. araldica. fol. Palermo. 1871–75

Palk (*Sir* **Robert**), *see* HIST. MSS. COMM. Palk MSS., Rep., 1922.

Palkovič (Giri) [PALKOWITSCH]. Böhmisch-deutsch-lat. Wörterbuch &c. 2B. 8º. Prag. [B2, Pressburg]. 1820–21

Palladio (Andrea). The architecture of A. P. in 4 books. Added, notes &c. by Inigo Jones. Rev. & publ. by G. Leoni. Tr. [by N. Du Bois. *Eng., Ital. & French, w. sep. tp. & pagin.* L'architettura di A. P.—L'architecture de A. P. &c.] [2v]. fol. 1715

see BARICHELLA (V.) A. P. e la sua scuola, 1880.

,, MELANI (A.) P., 1508–80, 1928.

Palladius, *bp. of (1) Helenopolis, (2) Aspona* [P. HELENOPOLITANUS]. The dialogue conc. the life of Chrysostom. [Tr. w. intr.] by H. Moore. [Tr. of Xtn. Lit., s1, Greek Texts]. s8º. 1921

Dialogus de vita S. Joannis Chrysostomi. Ed. w. rev. text, intr. &c. by P. R. Coleman-Norton. 8º. C. 1928

see BUTLER (E. C.) Authorship of Dial. de vita Crysostomi [*attr. to P.*], 1908.

Palladius Rutilius Taurus Æmilianus, *see* AGRONOMES (Les) latins: Caton, P. &c. (*Lat. & Fr.*); Nisard, 1877.

Pallady, *archimandrite.* Exped. thr. Manchuria f. Pekin to Blagovestchensk in 1860. Comp. f. Journal of [P.] & tr. by E. D. Morgan. [P2714]. 8º. 1872

Pallares (Jacinto). Legislacion federal compl. d. derecho civil mexicano. Col. form. por J. Vazquez Tagle, H. Díaz Mercado &c. Bajo la dir. y con est. d. J. P. 8º. Mexico. 1897

,, App. de 1897 [*b. w. above*]. 8º. Mexico. 1898

Pallary (P.) Terrestrial Mollusca f. Makalla, *see* LITTLE (O. H.) Geog. &c. of Makalla, 1925.

Pallas (Carl). Briefe u. Akten z. Visitationsreise d. Bischofs Johannes VII v. Meissen im Kurf. Sachsen, 1522, *see* ARCHIV F. REFORMATIONSGESCH., Jhrg. 5, 1908.

Pallavicino (Cosimo). Versi et regole de la nuova poesia toscana [A. Renieri &c. *Ed. C. P.*] 8º. 1539

Pallavicino (*il card.* **Sforza**). Pensieri e profili. A cura di M. Ziino. 8º. Napoli. 1927

Vera Concilii Trident. hist., contra falsam P. Suavis Polani narr. Latine reddita à J. B. Giattino. 3t. 4º. Antverpiae. 1670

,, ,, ...3p *b. in 1.* fol. Antverpiae. 1673

see ANTON (A.) De Pathmo Lutheri in arce Warteburg: animadv. adv. P., ed. 5ª, 1710; ed. nov., 1730.

Pallegoix (Jean Baptiste), *bp. of Mallos.*

Descr. du royaume Thai ou Siam. 2t. s8º. 1854

Pallin (William Alfred).

A treatise on epizootic lymphangitis. 8º. [1904]

Pallis (Svend Aage). The Babylonian akītu festival, *see* KONG. DAN. VID. SELSK. Hist.-fil. Medd., B12, 1926.

Mandæan studies. [Tr. f. Danish ed. (1919) by E. H. Pallis]. 8º. [1927]

Palliser (Edward Mathew) & *Capt.* **W. C. Nangle.**

The volunteer in the field. [P2593]. 8º. 1861

Palm (Johann Georg). Hist. d. deut. Bibelübersetzung D. M. Lutheri, 1517–34. Hrsg. &c. J. M. Goezen. 4º. Halle. 1772

Palm (Johann Heinrich). Diss. de bellis Domini. Praes. J. C. Becmano, resp. J. H. P. [P444]. s4º. Francofurti a. Viad. [1696]

Palm (Johann Jacob). Handbibl. d. theol. Litt. 3 Abth. *in* 2v. [*pagin. contin.*] s8°. Erlangen. 1792–93

Palma (Justus de), *Florentinus.* Austriacae Austeritatis, ejusdemque contin. confirmatio &c. [*b. w.* Tököly (I.) Austriaca austeritas &c., 1671]. s4°. [Viennae. 1673]

Palma Cayet (Pierre Victor). *Le divorce satyrique, ou les amours de Marquerite de Valois sous le nom de D. R. H. Q. M. [*i.e.* P. V. P. C.?], *see* HENRY III, *king of Fr.* Rec. de div. pièces, 1664.

Palmblad (Vilhelm Fredrik). Aurora Königsmark u. ihre Verwandten. Aus d. Schwed. 6T [*in* 3v]. s8°. L. 1848–53

Palmer (Charles), *Deputy Sergeant of the House of Commons.* A coll. of sel. aphorisms & maxims &c. la8°. 1848

Palmer (Charles John) & S. Tucker, *edd.* Palgrave fam. memorials. la8°. Norwich. *f.p.d.* 1878

Palmer (Edward Henry).
The Arabic manual. 2nd ed. s8°. 1885
Concise dict. Eng.-Persian. Compl. & ed. by G. Le Strange. s8°. 1883
„ „ ....3rd impr. s8°. 1906
Concise dict. of the Persian lang. 2nd ed. s8°. 1884
„ „ ....7th impr. s8°. 1906

Palmer (George), *commander.* The migration from Shinar; or the earliest links betw. the old and new continents. s8°. 1879

Palmer (Gladys Louise). Labor rel. in lace &c. industries in U.S., *see* UNITED STATES: LAB., Bull. 399, 1925.

Palmer (Howard). The Freshfield glacier, Canadian Rockies, 1924, *see* SMITHSONIAN INST.: Misc. Coll., v76, 1925.

Palmer (H. P.) Old Somerset. s8°. 1925

Palmer (John Leslie). The happy fool. s8°. [1922]
Studies in the contemp. theatre. 8°. 1927

Palmer (*Hon.* **Robert Stafford Arthur),** *see* RIDDING (*Lady* L. E.) The life of R. P., 1888–1916, 1921.

Palmer (Samuel), *artist, see* BINYON (L.) Followers of W. Blake: S. P. &c., 1925.

Palmer (Thomas Francis), *ed., see* SOMERSET RECORD SOC. Collectanea 1, 1924.

Palmer (William), *of Rugeley.* Ὁ ἐναγὴς ἰατρός; ἤτοι ἡ δίκη τοῦ Ου. Π.. ὑπὸ Χ. Β. Καβουρ. [*b. w.* Xenos (S. Th.) Ἡ Κιβδηλεία, t2, 1860]. 4°. ἐν Λονδίνῳ. 1860
The Queen *v.* Palmer. Verbatim rep. of trial of W. P., May 14 &c., 1856. 8°. 1856
see FLETCHER (G.) Life &c. of Dr. W. P., 1925.

Palmer (William Mortlock). Cambridgeshire doctors in the olden time, 1466–1827. [From Camb. Antiq. Soc. Communic., v15. P2618]. 8°. [C. 1911]
College dons, country clergy, & univ. coachmen. (Early Probate records). [From Camb. Antiq. Soc. Communic., v16. P2618]. 8°. [C.] 1913

Palmeri (Niccolo). Somma d. storia di Sicilia. 8°. Palermo. 1850

Palmerin, *of England, hero of romance, see* TENREIRO (R. M.) Libros de caballerías, sel. por T., 1924.

Palmerius (Johannes), *ps., see* HOTMAN (FRANÇOIS).

Palmerius (Matthias) [†PALMIERI (MATTEO) *Florentino*].
Libro del poema chiamato Citta di vita. Transcr., w. pref. by M. Rooke. [Smith Coll. St. in mod. lang., v8, No. 1, 2]. pl, Bks. 1–2xv. 8°. Northampton, Mass. 1927
La vita di Niccola Acciaioli; fatta volgare da D. Acciaioli, *see* UBALDINI (G. B.) Ist. de gli Ubaldini &c., 1588.

Palmerston (Emily, *visctess.*), *wife of 3rd Visc. Palmerston, formerly Countess Cowper, see* AIRLIE (MABELL, *countess of*). Lady P. & her times, 2v, 1922.

Palmerston (Henry John Temple, *3rd visct.*)
see BERNHARDT (T.) Lord P., Vortrag, 1870.
„ GUEDALLA (P.) Palmerston, 1926.
„ MARTIN (B. K.) Triumph of Lord P., 1924.

Palmieri (Aurelius), *O.S.A.* La politica asiatica dei Bolscevichi. [v]1, Cina—Giappone—India—Persia. la8°. Bologna. [1924]

Palmieri (Enzo). Borgese. 8°. Napoli. [1928]

Palmieri (Giuseppe). Cenno storico milit., 1859–61. 8°. *n.p. n.d.*

Palomeque (Francisco de Paula Romero y), *see* ROMERO Y PALOMEQUE.

Paltock (Robert). *Life & adv. of Peter Wilkins. 8°. 1925

Paltov (Vladimir).
„Взглядъ и нѣчто" о дворянствѣ. 8°. Москва. 1904

Paludan-Müller (Frederik), *see* ANDERSEN (V.) P.-M., 2B, 1910.

Paludanus (Joannes) [BROEK (J. VAN DEN)], *1565–1630, of Louvain.* Vindiciæ theologicæ adv. verbi Dei corruptelas. 2p *in* 1v. s8°. Antverpiæ. 1620

Pamler (Caspar) [PAMMLER]. Colloquium oder Gesprech in Schneeberg 1608 &c. [P2608]. s4°. L. 1610

Pamparato (Stanislao Cordero di), *see* CORDERO DI PAMPARATO (S.)

Pamphile (Le), *ps., see* AURIGNY (G. D').

Pan, *ps., see* BERESFORD (L.)

Panaev (Avdotya Yakovlevna), *1819–93.*
Воспоминания 1824–70. Исправл. изд. под редакц. &c. К. Чуковскаго. s8°. Ленинград. 1927
Семейство Тальниковых. Повесть. Прил.: К. Чуковский "П. и Некрасов" &c. 2. изд. s8°. Ленинград. 1928
see CHUKOVSKY (K.) Жена поэта, 1922.

Panaev (Ivan Ivanovich), *1812–62.* Литерат. воспоминания. Под ред. Иванова-Разумника. s8°. Ленинград. 1928
Очерки изъ Петербургской жизни новаго поэта. [P846]. 8°. С.-П. 1888
Сегодня и завтра. Повѣсть. [P846]. 8°. С.-П. 1888

Pan American Petroleum & Transport Company.
Mexican petroleum. s8°. N.Y. 1922

Pan American Scientific Congress (Second), Dec. 27, 1915–Jan. 8, 1916. Recomm. on internat. law & offic. comm. thereon. Ed., w. intr. matter by J. B. Scott. [C.E. for Int. Peace]. la8°. N.Y. 1916

Pan-American Union, *see* MEXICO. Gen. descr. data &c., 1921.

Panaretoff (Stephen).
Near Eastern affairs & conditions. 8°. 1922

Pañchatantra, *see* HERTEL (J.) Das P.: s. Gesch. u. s. Verbreitung, 1914.

Pancrazi (Pietro), *see* PAPINI (G.) & P. P. Poeti d'oggi, antologia &c., 1920; 2ª ed., 1925.

Pandiani (Emilio). La cacciata d. Austriaci da Genova, 1746, *see* REGIA DEPUT. DI STORIA PATRIA. Misc., t51, 1924.

Pando Fernandez de Pinedo Alava y Dávila (Manuel), *see* MIRAFLORES (*el marq.* DE).

Pandulphus, *Pisanus* [ALETRINUS], *see* LIBER Pontificalis prout exstat in cod. ms. Dertusensi, textum gen. compl. hactenus ex parte ined. P.: ed. &c. a J. M. March, 1925.

Panecius (Nicolaus). Jacobi Apost. Epist. versio Arab., cum interpret. &c. Nisselii &c. Cura &c. N. P. [P2671]. s4°. Wittenbergae. 1694

Panella (Antonio).
Works in Archivio Stor. Ital.
Commem. di P. Villari e bibl., 1918. [a. 76ii.]
La crisi di regime d'un comune merid. [*i.e.* Aquila], 1925. [a. 81.]
Firenze e il secolo crit. d. fortuna di Dante, 1921. [a. 79i.]
L'Italia e la questione romana [1858–59], 1922. [a. 80.]

Panelli (Domenico de), *archbp. of Lydda.* Encore le Pape & l'Inquisition! Hist. d'un archev. détenu pend. 10 ans dans les cachots du St.-Office: lettre de Mgr. de P. Tr. &c. par J. T. Cetto. [P505]. s8°. 1874

Pange (*Cte.* **Jean de)** [*ps.* SONGY (JEAN)], *see* RHÉNANIE, LA. La R.: conf. [*by P. &c.*], 1922.

Pange (*Ctsse.* **Jean de),** *née Pauline de Broglie* [*ps.* SONGY].
Le beau jardin. s8°. [1923]

Pange (*comte* **Maurice de).**
Les Lorrains & la France au m.-â. 8°. [1919]

Pangerl (Matthias). Die beiden ält. Todtenbücher d. Benedictinerstiftes St. Lambrecht in Obersteier; mitg. v. M. P., *see* FONTES RERUM AUSTRIAC., B29, 1869.
Urkundenbuch d. Cistercienserstiftes Goldenkron in Böhmen; bearbt. v. M. P., *see* FONTES RERUM AUSTRIAC., B37, 1872.

Panin (M.) Кустарничество и партійная организація. [P2716]. s8°. Женева. 1904

Panin (*graf* **Nikita Petrovich),** *1770–1837.* Матеріалы для жизнеописанія Н. П. П. (1770–1837). Изд. А. Брикнера. t3 (1798). 8°. С.-П. 1890

Panizza (Oskar). Der Illusionismus u. d. Rettung d. Persönlichkeit. [*b. w.* Rulf (J.) Wiss. d. Weltgedankens &c., T2, 1888]. 8°. L. 1895
Visionen d. Dämmerung. 8°. München. 1923

Panizzi (Andrea), *see* ROSSI (G.) Sopra un poemetto sul preteso dir. cosciatico [*by* P., 1713], 1906.

Panizzi (*Sir* **Anthony),** *principal librarian of the Brit. Museum, see* REFORM CLUB. Cat. of Panizzi pamphlets, 1920.

Pankhurst (Christabel).
America & the War. Speech. [P2484]. 8°. [1914]

Pankhurst (E. Sylvia).
Delphos: future of internat. language. s8°. [1927]
——, P. Lynch & M. O'Callaghan.
Rebel Ireland. [P2756]. s8°. [1919]

Pankratov (Vasily Semenovich).
С царем в Тобольске. s8º. Ленинград. 1925

Pannini (Gian Paolo), *see* OZZOLA (L.) G. P. P.: pittore: 50 tavole, con intr., 1921.

Pannone (Adolfo). Lo Stato borbonico: diritto pubblico napol. dal 1734 al 1799. v1. 8º. Firenze. 1924

Panofsky (Erwin).
Die deut. Plastik, 11.–13. Jhdt. 2B. 4º. München. [1924]

Pansa (Francesco). Istoria dell' ant. Repubbl. d'Amalfi &c. Con lo registro di archivi [*w. sep. pagin.*] 2t. 8º. Napoli. 1724

Pansier (P.) Hist. du livre & de l'imprimerie à Avignon du 14e au 16e s. 3t. la8º. Avignon. 1922

Pantaleon (Heinrich). Martyrum hist., *see* FOX (J.) Rerum in eccl. gestarum comm., p2, 1563.

Panteleoni (Maffeo). Memorandum [*Fr. & Eng.*], *see* INTERNAT. FINANCIAL CONF. Paper 13vi, 1920.

Pantu (Zach. C.) Orchidaceele din România. Ed. Acad. Române. 8º. București. 1915

Pantusov (N. N.) Фергана по Запискамъ султана Бабера. [I.R.G.O. Записки по отдѣл. этнограф., 6i]. 8º. С.–П. 1880

Panunzio (Constantine Maria).
The soul of an immigrant. s8º. N.Y. 1921

Panvinio (Onofrio). De ritu sepeliendi mortuos apud vet. Xtnos. & eorundem coemeteriis liber iterum ed. cum præf. J. G. Jochii. [P2635]. s4º. Francofurti. 1717
see GRETSER (J.) Apologia pro Gregorio VII; acc. de vita &c. Greg. ex libro 4º O. P., 1609?.

Panyity (Louis S.) Prospecting for oil & gas. 8º. N.Y. 1920

Panzacchi (Enrico). Nel mondo d. musica. Impressioni &c. s8º. Firenzi. 1895

Panzani (Gregorio), *see* PLOWDEN (C.) Remarks on memoirs of G. P., 1794.

Panzer (Georg Wolfgang).
Aelteste Buchdruckergesch. Nürnbergs. Verzeichnis, bis 1500. 4º. Nürnberg. 1789
Annalen d. ältern deut. Litt. oder Beschr. d. Bücher welche bis 1526 in deut. Spr. gedruckt worden sind. 2B *&* Zusätze, 1802. [*b. w.* B1]. 4º. Nürnberg. 1788–1805
Ausführl. Beschreib. d. ältesten Augsburg. Ausgaben d. Bibel. s4º. Nürnberg. 1780
Litter. Nachr. v. d. allerält. gedr. deut. Bibeln aus d. 15. Jhdt. in d. öffent. Bibl., Nürnberg. 4º. Nürnberg. 1777
Versuch e. kurzen Gesch. d. röm. cathol. deutschen Bibelübersetzung. s4º. Nürnberg. 1781
Zusätze zu s. Entwurf e. vollst. Gesch. d. deut. Bibelübers. M. Luthers, 1517–81. 8º. Nürnberg. 1791

Panzini (Alfredo).
Le damigelle. s8º. Milano. 1926
Diario sentimentale [d. Guerra], luglio 1914 [–nov. 1918]. [2v.] s8º. [1923–24]
Il diavolo n. mia libreria. 8º. [1920]
Dizionario mod. Suppl. ai diz. ital. 3a ed., rinnov. &c. 8º. Milano. 1918
„ „ 4a ed., rinnov. e aum. la8º. Milano. 1923
Donne, madonne e bimbi. s8º. Milano. 1921
Io cerco moglie! s8º. Milano. 1920
Il libro di lettura d. scuole popolari. s8º. 1920
La Madonna di Mamà. s8º. Milano. [1919]
Matteo Maria Boiardo. s8º. Messina. 1918
Il mondo è rotondo. s8º. Milano. 1920
Novelle d'ambo i sessi. s8º. Milano. [1920]
Il padrone sono me! s8º. Milano. [1925]
La Pulcella senza pulcellaggio. s8º. Milano. [1925]
Santippe. s8º. Milano. [1919]
I tre Re con Gelsomino buffone del Re. Romanzo. 8º. Milano. [1926]
La vera istoria dei tre colori. s8º. Milano. [1924]
see FABBRI (E.) A. P., *n.d.*

Paoletti (Pietro). Raccolta di doc. ined. p. s. a. storia d. pittura veneziana nei sec 15 & 16. Fasc. 1, J. Bellini. fol. Padova. 1894

Paoli (Betty), *see* SCOTT (A. A.) B. P., an Austrian poetess of the 19th cent., 1926.

Paoli (*il gen.* Pasquale de') [P. PAOLI]. Lettere ined.; con avvertenze &c. di N. Bianchi, *see* REGIA DEP. DI STORIA PATRIA. Misc., t19, 1880.
see BOSWELL (J.) Journal of a tour to Corsica; & mem. of P. P.; ed. &c. S. C. Roberts, 1923.

Paolino, *da San Bartolommeo* [JOANNES PHILIPPUS WERDIN *or* WESDIN].
Alphabeta Indica. s8º. Rome. 1791
De antiq. & affinitate ling. Zend., Samscradam. & Germ. diss. s4º. [Patavii]. 1798
De veteribus Indii diss. [*b. w. h.* India Orient. Xtna., 1794]. s4º. Romae. 1795
India Orient. Christiana &c. s4º. Romae. 1794
Sidharubam seu grammatica Samscrdamica; cui acc. diss. hist.-crit. in linguam S. 4º. Romae. 1790

Paolucci (Giuseppe), *poet.* Arte pratica di contrappunto. 3t. 4º. Venezia. 1765–72

Paon (Le): anc. poème chinois. Tr. Tchang Fong, suivi d'une ét. de l'évol. poét. en Chine. s8º. 1924

Pap (Josephus) [PAP DE FAGARAS (J.)] Disp., qua demonstr., non esse contra naturam Dei effecisse mundum, in quo mala insunt &c. Acc. dissert 4, J. C. Schwab, H. R. van Lier, T. Spaan, W. L. Brown. 4º. Lugd. Batav. 1784

Papa (Jo. Christian), *see* ROHT (R.) Attila Hunnorum rex; resp. J. C. P., 1671.

Papa (Pasquale), *see* DANTE ALIGHIERI. Lectura D.: c. 34 dell' Inferno da P. P., 1900.

Papa (Ulisse). Il genio e le opere di A. Bonvicino (Il Moretto). [Estr. d. Emporium, v7]. la8º. Bergamo. 1898

Papadopoli, *Family of, see* CASTELLANI (G.) & G. CERESOLE. Saggio di una bibliog. nuziale d. fam. P., 1905.

Papadopoli (*il conte* Nicolò) [PAPADOPOLI ALDOBRANDINI].
Alessando Pascolato. Commemorazione. [P2411]. 8º. Venezia. 1908
Le monete di Venezia descr. ed illust. 3p [*in* 4v, 3i, ii]. la8º. Venezia *&* Milano. 1893–1919
La tariffa Veneta del 1543. [P2516]. la8º. Milano. 1904

Papadopoulos (Chrysostomos), *abp. of Athens.*
Τὸ ζήτημα περὶ τοῦ κύρους τῶν Ἀγγλικαν. χειροτονιῶν. [P2849]. 8º. ἐν Ἱεροσολύμοις. 1925

Papai (Franciscus Pariz), *see* PARIZ (F.), *Pápai.*

Papal. *Papal infallibility. Reasons why a R.C. cannot accept the doctrine. By a Roman Catholic layman. 8º. 1876
*Papal (The) power; tr., 2v, 1825, *see* DAUNOU (P. C. F.)
Papal registers. Cal. of entries in P.R., illust. the hist. of Gt. Brit. & Ir. [Cal. of St. Papers]. Papal letters, v11 (1455–64). la8º. 1921

Papanek (Georgius). Compendiata hist. gentis Slavae. De regno regibusque Slavorum quam compendiavit G. Fándly. Add. notis &c. a G. Szklenar. s8º. Tyrnaviae. 1793

Pape. *Traité de l'autorité du pape &c., 4t, 1720, *see* LEVESQUE DE BURIGNY (J.)

Pape (Franz Sigismund). Hist. sec. 4. & 5. fabulis var. macul. Praes. J. A. Schmidio. [P432]. s4º. Helmstadii. [1713]

Pape (T.), *F.S.A., see* MANDER [G. P.) Some Ridware armorial glass, 1924.

Papen (Johann Ludwig).
Diss. inaug. de simonia. s4º. Helmstadii. 1799

Paperna (Geras. Abramovich). Б. Спиноза, его жизнь и философ. дѣятельность. [P2400]. s8º. С.–П. 1895

Papers. Papers for the present. Issued for the Cities Comm. of the Sociological Soc. No. 6, 7, 10–15 [*in* 1v]. 8º. [1919–21?]
6, Public health in the indust. age. By P. Geddes.
7, The 3rd alternative, p1.
10, A gardener of paradise [*i.e.* P. Geddes; by G. Sandeman].
11, Sir Ronald Ross's story: st. in 3rd alternative.
12, The war-mind, the business-mind &c.
13, Theology, poetry & civics. [By V. V. Branford].
14, Earth, hell & the 3rd alternative.
15, Body, mind & spirit.
Papers on inter-racial problems: ed. G. Spiller, 1911, *see* RACES CONGRESS (UNIV.)
Papers rel. to the regalia of Scotland, 1829, *see* SCOTLAND.

Papharaszti. A koalicziò tervei és alkotásai 1906–1909. Összeszedte Papharaszti. 8º. 1909

Papiers secrets & corresp. du Second Empire. réimpr. compl. &c., rec. par A. Poulet-Malassis. 9e éd. 8º. 1875

Papin-Dupont (Léon), *see* DUPONT (L. P.)

Papini (Giovanni).
Pane e vino, con Solil. sulla poesia. 8º. Firenze. [1926]
Storia di Cristo. 8º. Firenze. [1921]
„ „ 4a ed., corr. 8º. Firenze. [1923]
TRANSLATIONS.
Four & twenty minds. Essays sel. & tr. by E. H. Wilkins. 8º. [1923]
Hist. du Christ. Tr. de P. H. Michel. s8º. 1922
A man—finished (Un uomo finito). Tr. by M. P. Agnetti. 8º. [1924]
TRANSLATIONS [*continued*].
The story of Christ. Tr. M. P. Agnetti. 7th ed. 8º. [1923]
„ „ 8th ed. 8º. [1923]
„ „ Tr. D. C. Fisher. 8º. N.Y. [1923]
The Amer. ed. has t. The life of Christ.
see GIULIOTTI (D.) & G. P. Diz. dell' omo salvatico, v1, 1923.
„ LAZARILLO (—). G. P., 1920.

—— **& P. Pancrazi.** Poeti d'oggi, 1900–20. Antologia comp. da G. P. e P. P., con notizie biog. &c. 8º. Firenze. [1920]
„ „ 2a ed., rev. &c. 1900–25. 8º. Firenze. [1925]

Papini (Roberto).
Le arti a Monza nel 1923. la8°. Bergamo. [1923]
Fra Giovanni Angelico. 4°. Bologna. 1925
Papinianus (Æmilius), *see* CUJAS (J.) Opera, t4 (Comm. in lib. quaest. Æ. P.), 1777.
Papis (Giuseppe). Serenata a 3 voce per fest. M. B. d'Erberstein. [N125]. 8°. Nap. 1714
Papists. *Practical (The) divinity of the P. &c., 1676, *see* CLARKSON (D.)
Papotti (Tiberio). Elogi di illustri Imolesi. 8°. Imola. 1829–42
Each Elogio *has sep. tp. & pagin.*
Notizie int. alla vita &c. di alcuni illust. Imolesi, sec. 18. s8°. Imola. 1834
Pappafava (Vladimir). La théorie gén. des ondes & la liberté de l'éther. [Extr. de la Revue Jurid. Internat. de la Radio-électricité. P2784]. 8°. 1925
Pappus (Johann).
Epitome hist. eccl. Nov. Test. Recogn. & contin. studio E. Bohemi. s8°. Wittebergae. 1626
Hist. eccl. de conversionibus gentium, persecutionibus eccl. &c. epitome. s8°. Argentorato. 1584
„ „ ed. 3a emend. [*w. t.* Epitome hist. eccles.] s8°. Witebergae. 1612
see BEZA (T.) De hypostatica 2 in Christi naturarum unione &c., discept. T. B. cum J. P., 1579.
„ FECHT (J.) Hist. Colloquii Emmending., 1590; protocoll. &c. J. P. a calumniis J. Pistorii vindic. &c., 1694.
„ GRETSER (J.) De jure & more prohib. libros adv. J. P. &c., 1603.
Pappus (Leonardus). *Rerum Germanic. 1617–43 gestarum epitome. Ed. alt. & c. priore contin. s8°. *n.p.* 1655
Päpstliche [BEBSTLICHEN; BEPSTLICHEN]. *Kurtzer (Ein) auszug aus d. Bepstl. rechten der Decret u. Decretalen, 1530 [1584], *see* SPENGLER (L.)
Verteütschtē (Die) Text aus den Bebstl. Rechten. s4°. *n.p.* [c. 1530]
Papstthumb. *Von dem P. zu Rome wider M. L. &c., *n.d.* [c. 1535], *see* LUTHER (M.)
Papyri. Papyri Osloenses, fasc. 1, 1925, *see* EITREM (S.)
Papyri russ. u. georg. Sammlungen, 1, 4, 1925–27, *see* ZERETELI (G. F.), *ed.*
Par (Anfós). Sintaxi Catalana segons los escrits en prosa de Bernat Metge (1398). [Zeitschr. f. roman. Philol., Beiheft 66]. 8°. Halle (Saale). 1923
Parabosco (Girolamo). Delle lettre amorose di G. P. Libro secondo con alcune sue novelle & rime. [*b. w.* Firenzuola (A.) Prose, 1548]. s8°. Vinegia. 1548
Il primo libro d. lettere famigl. di G. P. & Il primo libro de' suoi madrigali [*w. sep. tp. & pagin. b. w.* Lauro (P.) De le lettere, 1553]. s8°. Vinegia. 1551
Rime. s8°. Venetia. 1547
Paracelsus (A. T.)
see CLARKE (J. H.) Hahnemann & P., 1923.
„ SENDIVOGIUS (M.) New light of alchymie &c.: also Nine books of the nature of things; tr., 1650.
„ SPANN (E.) P. u. s. Jünger, Dichtung, 1921.
„ SPUNDA (F.) P., 1925.
„ STILLMAN (J. M.) P., h. personality &c., 1920.
Paradin (Claude). Devises héroïques. s8°. Lion. 1557
Paradis. Le poème sumérien du P., 1919, *see* LANGDON (S.)
Paradise. *Key (The) of P., 1844, *see* KEY.
Paradise (Viola Isabel). Child labor & wk. of mothers in oyster & shrimp canning commun., Gulf Coast, 1922, *see* UNITED STATES: LABOR.
Paradowska (Marguerite). Yaga. 2e éd. s8°. 1888
***Paraguay.** A concise hist.; & causes of the present war w. Brazil. 8°. 1867
Parallele. *Parallele de quelques propos. &c., *n.d.*, *see* LE GOBIEN (C.)
Second Parallele des propos. du père Le Comte &c., *n.d.*, *see* LE GOBIEN (C.)
Parasnis (*Rao Bahadur* Dattatraya Balavant).
Poona in bygone days. 8°. Bombay. 1921
see KINCAID (C. A.) & D. B. P. Hist. of the Maratha people, v2, 3, 1922–25.
Parchevsky (K.), *see* BOJNEV (B.) & K. P. Русс. лирика, в1, 1920.
Parchon (Solomon ben Abraham Ben), *see* SOLOMON.
Parco (Francesco lo), *see* LO PARCO (F.)
Pardaillan de Gondrin (Louis Henri de), *abp. of Sens, see* BURLUGUAY (J.) Toilette de M. l'archevesque de Sens, ou réponse au Factum &c., 1669.
Pardi (Giuseppe). Disegno d. storia demogr. di Livorno, *see* ARCHIVIO STOR. ITAL. Anno 76, v1, 1918.
Pardieu (*commandant* F. de). Etude crit. de la tactique & des nouv. réglements allemands. 8°. 1910
Pardo (Filippo), *abp. of Manila, see* JESUITS. *Morale pratique &c., t5, Hist. de la persécution de P. &c. [*by A. Arnauld*], 2e éd., 1717.
Pardo-Bazán (Emilia). Cuentos de amor. s8°. 1911
La madre naturaleza. s8°. 1910
Los pazos de Ulloa. s8°. *n.d.*
Pardoe (Julia S. H.) The beauties of the Bosphorus. Drawings by W. H. Bartlett. 4°. 1839
Paré (Ambroise), *1510–90, see* PACKARD (F. R.) Life & times of A. P.: w. tr. of h. Apology & acc. of h. journeys &c., 1922.
Pareau (Louis Gerlach).
Initia institutionis Christ. moralis. 8°. Groningae. 1842
Parekh (Manilal C.), *see* GRAY (R. M.) & M. C. P. Mahatma Gandhi, 1924.
Parennin (*le père*), *ps.*, *see* LA VICOMTERIE DE SAINT-SAMSON (L.)
Parent (Louis). L'essence de la langue franç. [p1], *see* MATTHIEU (P.) Remarques d'estat, 1652.
Parenthood. The control of p.; by J. A. Thomson &c., 1920, *see* MARCHANT (*Sir* J.), *ed.*
Parenzo (Aldo). Almanacchi Veneti. la8°. Venezia. 1897
Pares (*Sir* Bernard). A hist. of Russia. la8°. [1926]
Pareto (Vilfredo). Traité de sociologie gén. Ed. franç. par P. Boven, rev. par l'a. v2. [*pagin. cont.*] la8°. 1919
Pareus (David).
A comm. upon the Divine Revelation of John. Tr. by E. Arnold. sm. fol. 1644
Historia Palatina: comitum Palatinorum Rheni vitae &c. s8°. Francofurti. 1633
In Hoseam prophetam comm.; cum tr. triplici, Lat. ex Hebræo, et Chaldæo Thargum Jonathæ, nec non Gr. LXX. Præmitt. προλεγόμενα de prophetis &c. 4°. Heidelbergae. 1616
Irenicum, sive de unione & synodo Evangelic. conciliando liber. s4°. Heidelbergae. 1614
Methodus totius controv. ubiquitariae. [P2743]. s4°. Neostadii Palat. 1586
Misc. catechetica, *see* URSINUS (Z.) Opera, t3, 1612.
Operum theolog. exegetic. t1i–iv. [*b. in 2v.* p3 *has 2 pagin.*] fol. Francofurti. 1647
Oratio de Jesuitarum strophis circa canonem Script. &c. s8°. [Heidelberg ?. 1602 ?]
Rettung der zur Newstadt an der Hardt in anno 87. u. 91. getruckten Teutschen Bibel, wider D. Jacobi Andreae u. anderer darwider aussgesprengte &c. Lesterungen &c. s4°. Amberg. 1592
see HUTTER (L.) Irenicum vere Xtnum. &c.: Irenici D. Parei consilia refellens, 1616.
„ URSINUS (Z.) Corpus doct. orthod., absol. D. P., 1612.
Parfusius (Dominicus). Lapis angularis, seu princip. Xtnae. relig. mysteria a Judaeorum perfidia vindicata &c. s8°. Vindobonae. 1756
Pargiter (Frederick Eden).
Ancient Indian hist. tradition. 8°. 1922
see ROYAL ASIATIC SOC. OF GT. BRIT. &C. Cent. vol.; comp. & ed. F. E. P., 1923.
Pargiter (*Maj.* R. B.) & H. G. Eady.
The army & sea power. Hist. outline. 8°. 1927
Paribeni (Roberto).
Works in REALE ACCAD. D. LINCEI. Mon. ant.
Necropoli barbarica di Nocera Umbra, 1918. [25.]
Necropoli del territ. capenate, 1906. [16.]
I quattro tempietti di Ostia, 1914. [23.]
Ricerche nel luogo dell' ant. Adulis (Colonia Eritrea), 1907. [18.]
Ricerche nel sepolcreto di Haghia Triada pr. Phaestos, 1904. [14.]
Vasi ined. del Museo Kircheriano, 1904. [14.]
see SAVIGNONI (L.) &c. & R. P. Nuovi st. & scop. in Gortyna, 1907.
——, P. Fedele &c. Ambasciate e ambasciatori a Roma. Pref. di U. Ojetti. 4°. Milano. 1927
—— & P. Romanelli. Studii e ricerche archeol. nell' Anatolia merid., *see* REALE ACCAD. D. LINCEI. Mon. ant., v23, 1914.
Parigi, *see* PARIS.
Parini (Giuseppe). The day. Poem. Tr., w. intr. &c. by H. M. Bower. s8°. 1927
Paris [PARIGI].
*Confut. determinationis doctorū Parrhis. contra M. L[uther] ex eccl. doctoribus desumpta denuo recogn. &c. Adj.: Disput. Groningæ habita, cū 2 epistolis &c. s8°. Basileæ. 1523
*Journal of a party of pleasure to P., 1802, *see* PAUL (*Sir* J. D.)
P. & its environs: 200 views. Drawings under dir. of A. Pugin, engr. under C. Heath. 2v *in* 1. 4°. 1831

Paris [PARIGI] [*continued*].
*Paris in 1815 [*poem*], 1817, *see* CROLY (G.)
Reprod. d'anc. plans de P. Notice[s] par A. Bonnardot. *6p in 1v*; la. fol. *A. Taride.* [1908]
P. vers 1551, par O. Truschet & G. Hoyau. Notes par J. Cousin.
P. au 17s., 1652, par J. Gomboust.
P. vers 1675, par Jouvin de Rochefort.
P. en 1710, par le sieur Bullet, rev. par Jaillot.
P. au 18s., par L. Bretez [dit Plan de Turgot], 1734–39.
P. sous Napoléon I, publ. par Maire.
*Rough (A) sketch of mod. P., 1803, *see* LEMAISTRE (J. G.)
Sommier des biens nat. de la ville de P., t1, 2, 1920, *see* MONIN (H.) & L. LAZARD.
*Vero, Il, successo occorso n. città di Parigi contra l'Armiraglio, e suoi seguaci Ugonotti &c. s8°. Venetia. 1572
What really happened at P.: Peace Conf., 1918–19, by American delegates, 1921, *see* HOUSE (E. M.) & C. SEYMOUR, *edd.*
CIVIC INSTITUTIONS &c.
Alcuni arresti del Parl. di Parigi [*on the Jesuits, in French & Ital.*], con note. [P2767]. 8°. Verona. [1761]
Registres des délibér. du Bureau de la ville de P. [Hist. gén. de P.] t15, 1610–14; éd. L. Le Grand. 4°. 1921
COMMISSION MUNICIPALE DU VIEUX PARIS.
Procès-verbaux. Année[s], 1917–23. 4°. 1922–26
Année[s] 1918, 1920–23 *contain* "Annexes" *as under*:—
1918, Formigé (J. C.) & J. Formigé. Les arènes de Lutèce. Lambeau (L.) Les Carmes dechaussés de la Rue de Vaugirard.
1920, Lambeau (L.) L'Abbaye-aux-Bois de Paris: add. à notice du 9 déc. 1905.
1921, Tesson (L.) Le Mont Valérien: hist., 1400–1845 &c. Lambeau (L.) Le cimetière de Picpus, 1794–1921.
1922, Comméм. du 25 anniv., 27 jan. 1923. Villain (G.) Le Palais: études &c.
1923, Gerards (E.) Un captage de la nappe de l'argile plastique &c. Grimault (A.) Compte rendu des fouilles effect. p. la constr. de la chemin de fer Métrop. No. 7.
MUSÉE DE L'ARMÉE.
Cat. des armes &c. de souverains franç. & étr.; par J. Robiquet. Préf. du Gén. Niox. s8°. 1916
Résumé des fastes milit. de la France du 14e au 20e s. Guide à la Sect. hist. [par] Gén. Niox. s8°. [1920]
MUSÉE DU JEU DE PAUME.
see BÉNÉDITE (L.) Expos. de l'art belge, 1923.
„ —— Expos. de l'art suisse, 1924.
„ EXHIBITIONS: ROUMANIAN. Expos. de l'art roumain, 1925.
SECRÉTARIAT D'ETAT DES POSTES & DES TÉLÉGRAPHES.
Annuaire offic. des abonnés aux réseaux téléphoniques de la région de P., 1923–24. la8°. [1923]
UNIVERSITY OF PARIS.
Bibliothèque de la Faculté des Lettres. s2. [t]6. la8°. 1926
see CHELLI (M.) Collab. de Massinger avec Fletcher &c., 1926. [II, 6.]
*Case (A) of conscience, propos'd to, & decided by 40 doctors of the Faculty of P., in favour of Jansenism, 1703, *see* JANSENISM.
Cat. de la Bibliothèque de l'Univ. de P. 2, Cartulaires. [P2469]. 8°. 1907
Censura Fac. theolog. Paris. in lib. A. Guimenii, 1666, *see* JESUITS. Théologie morale, 1666.
Censure de la Fac. de Théologie de P. contre Emile (1762), *see* MIGNE (J. P.), *ed.* Theologiæ cursus, t2, 1862.
*Censure de quelques proposit. des PP. Le Comte & Le Gobien, publ. sous le nom de la Fac. de Théol. de P. &c., 1700, *see* LE COMTE (L.)
Determinatio secunda almę fac. theolog. P. super Apologiam Melanchthonis pro Luthero scr. [*b. w. h.* Determinatio theolog., 1521]. s4°. [Vvittembergae. 1521]
Determinatio theolog. fac. P. super doctrina Lutheriana hactenus per eam visa. Apologia pro Luthero adv. decretū Paris. [*by P. Melanchthon*]. s4°. Vvittembergae. 1521
*Entretien d'un docteur de la maison de Sorbonne &c., 1703, *see* ENTRETIEN.
*Propositions soutenues &c. par quelques docteurs de la Fac. de Théol. de P. [*no tp.* P2559]. s8°. *n.p. n.d.* [c. 1700]
*Réflexions s. la censure, publ. sous le nom de la Fac. de Théol. de P., contre Nouv. mém. sur l'état prés. de la Chine [*by L. Lecomte*] —Hist. de l'édit de l'emp. de la Chine [*by C. Le Gobien*]—Lettre des cérémonies de la Chine. [P2559]. s8°. *n.p.* MVCC. [1700]
Vie (La) univ. à P. Publ. sous les a. du Conseil de l'Univ. par P. Boyer, M. Caullery &c. la8°. 1918
REFERENCES.
see FRANKLIN (A.) Recherches s. la Bibl. de la Fac. de Méd. de P., 1864.
„ COLISÉE, *Paris.*
„ MUSÉE DES ARTS DÉCORATIFS.

Paris (François de). *Cantique sur le miracle operé en la personne de Mlle. Hardoüin, par B. F. de Paris. [*b. w. h.* Lettres &c., 1734]. s8°. *n.p. n.d.*
*Eclaircissemens sur les miracles de M. Paris, où l'on répond

Paris (François de) [*continued*].
aux difficultez formées par l'archévêque de Paris. [*b. w. h.* Lettres &c., 1734]. 2p. s8°. Paris. 1733
*Lettres d'un François dans lesquelles, à l'occ. des vertus &c. de M. de Paris, on combat les principes des Jésuites &c. s8°. Brux. 1734

Paris (François Edmond). Souv. de marine. Coll. de plans ou dessins de navires & de bateaux anc. & mod. 3p [p1, 2e tirage]. fol. 1884–1910

Paris (Gaston). Cat. de la bibl. G. P. Par L. Barrau-Dihigo. livr. 1. [H.E, 200]. 8°. 1912

Paris (John), *ps.* Banzai! (Hurrah!). s8°. [1925]
A Japanese Don Juan & o. p. 8°. [1926]
Kimono. [2nd impr.] s8°. [1921]
Sayonara (Good-bye). s8°. [1924]

Paris (Matthew).
see EDWARD *the Confessor.* La estoire de St. Ædward le Rei, w. some pages of the MS. of life of St. Alban [*by M. P.?*], 1920.
„ JAMES (M. R.) Drawings of M. P., 1926.

Paris (Pierre).
Promenades archéol. en Espagne. [v2]. s8°. 1921
La sculpture antique. n. éd. 8°. [1889]

Parise. Parise la duchesse, chanson de geste, 2e éd., rev., *see* GUESSARD (F.) Anc. poëtes, t4, 1860.

Pariselle (H.) Les instruments d'optique. s8°. 1923

Pariset (Georges), *see* LAVISSE (E.) Hist. de France contemp., t2, La Révol., 1792–99; t3, Le Consulat & L'Emp., 1799–1815, par G. P., 1920–21.

Parish, *family of, see* EHRENBERG (R.) Das Haus P. in Hamburg, 1925.

Parish (E.) Agric. experiment. [Union of S. Africa. P2820]. 8°. Pretoria. 1922

Parisi (Pasquale). Il giornale e il giornalismo. s8°. [1920]

Parisien (Un), Relig. de la Cie. de Jésus, *ps.* *La perspective practique, 1642, *see* DUBREUIL (J.)

Parisot (Pierre) ["*Le père Norbert,*" *ps.*, PLATEL (PIERRE CUREL)]. Lettre cont. une rel. de l'exécution du p. Malagrida, 22 sept. 1761, *see* PORTUGAL. Recueil de decrets &c., p2, 1761.
see FAVRE (P. F.) Lettres édifiantes, p. s. de contin. aux Mém. hist. du père Norbert, 1746.

Parisot (Robert). Hist. de Lorraine. t2, 3. 8°. 1922–24
„ „ ....Index gén. 8°. 1924
Le royaume de Lorraine sous les Carolingiens (843–923). 8°. 1898

Pariz (Ferenz), *Pápai.* Dict. Lat.-Hungaricum &c., labore P. Bod. [t2, Dict. Ungaro-Lat.-Germ., olim studio A. Molnár, F. P. Pápai & P. Bod conscr., emend. &c. J. C. Eder]. ed nova. 2t *in* 1v. 8°. Posonii. 1801
Rudus redivivum seu breves rerum eccl. Hungar. juxta & Transylvanicarum inde a prima reformatione comment. [*Leaves wanting after E12 are supplied in MS.*] s8°. Cibinii. 1684

Park (Joseph Hendershot).
The Eng. Reform Bill of 1867. 8°. N.Y., *Columbia Univ.* 1920

Park (Mungo), *see* HEWITT (W. H.) M. P., 1923.

Park (Robert Ezra), E. W. Burgess & R. D. McKenzie. The city. Bibliog. by L. Wirth. [Univ. of Chicago. St. in urban sociology]. s8°. Chicago. [1925]

Park (Thomas), *F.S.A.* Brit. poets. Suppl. 12v. s8°. 1808–09
For the volumes of Brit. poets; ed. T. P., *other than the* Suppl., *see under following names:—For list in order of issue see* Lowndes (W. T.) Bibliogr. manual *under Poets.*

Addison (J.), 1805–7.
Akenside (M.), 1805.
Armstrong (J.), 1807.
Bampfylde (J.), 1808.
Beattie (J.), 1805.
Blair (R.), 1807.
Bruce (M.), 1807.
Burns (R.), 1807.
Butler (S.), 1806.
Churchill (C.), 1807.
Collins (W.), 1805.
Cotton (N.), 1806.
Cunningham (J.), 1805.
Denham (*Sir* J.), 1807.
Dryden (J.), 1806.
Dyer (J.), 1807.
Garth (*Sir* S.), 1808.
Gay (J.), 1806.
Glover (R.), 1806.
Goldsmith (O.), 1805.
Gray (T.), 1805.
Green (M.), 1808.
Hamilton (W.), 1805.
Hammond (J.), 1805.
Headley (H.), 1808.
Hoyland (F.), 1808.
Jago (R.), 1808.
Jenyns (S.), 1807.
Johnson (S.), 1805.
Jones (*Sir* W.), 1808.
Langhorne (J.), 1806.
Logan (J.), 1807.
Lovell (R.), 1808.
Lovibond (E.), 1807.
Lyttelton (G., *b.*), 1805.
Mallet (D.), 1805.
Mickle (W. J.), 1808.
Milton (J.), 1805.
Moore (E.), 1806.
Moore (*Sir* J. H.), 1808.
Oram (S. M.), 1808.
Parnell (T.), 1807.
Perowne (T.), 1807.
Philips (J.), 1807.
Pope (A.), 1805.
Prior (M.), 1807.
Russell (T.), 1808.
Scott (J.), 1808.
Shaw (C.), 1807.
Shenstone (W.), 1806.

Park (Thomas), *F.S.A.* [*continued*].

Smollett (T. G.), 1807.	Thompson (W.), 1807.	Warton (J.), 1805.
Somerville (W.), 1806.	Thomson (J.), 1805.	Warton (T.), 1805.
Swift (J.), 1806–7.	Tickell (T.), 1807.	Watts (I.), 1807.
	Waller (E.), 1806.	Young (E.), 1806.

Sonnets, & o. small poems. 8°. 1797

Parker (Alfred D.) Sentimental journey in & about Lichfield. 8°. Lichfield. 1925

Parker (David W.) Calendar of papers in Washington archives rel. to the territories of the U.S. (to 1873). [C.I. of Wash.] la8°. Wash. 1911

Guide to materials for U.S. hist. in Canadian archives. [C.I. of Wash.] la8°. Wash. 1913

see BELL (H. C.), D. W. P. &c. Guide to Brit. West Ind. archive materials &c., 1926.

Parker (De Witt Henry).

The analysis of art. 8°. New Haven, *Yale*. 1926

Parker (Edward Harper).

1000 yrs. of the Tartars. 2nd ed. rev. 8°. 1924

Parker (Edwin B.) America's part in advancing the admin. of internat. justice, *see* INTERNAT. CONCILIATION, No. 203, 1924.

Parker (Eric). An angler's garland. s8°. 1920

Hesketh Prichard, D.S.O., hunter &c. 8°. [1924]

Playing Fields. 8°. [1922]

Parker (Frank Rowley). The powers, duties & liabilities of an election agent &c. in Eng. & Wales, includ. law &c. of election petitions. 3rd ed., ed. O. F. Dowson. 8°. 1920

Parker (George), *M.A., M.D.*

The early hist. of surgery in Gt. Britain. s8°. 1920

Parker (George), *of Oxford, see* STALKER (J.) & G. P. Treatise of japaning &c., 1688.

Parker (George Howard) & R. E. Sheldon. The sense of smell in fishes. [Fr. Bull. of the Bur. of Fisheries, v32]. [P2702]. la8°. Wash. 1913

Parker (*Sir* Gilbert). Carnac. s8°. [1922]

No defence. s8°. [1920]

Tarboe. s8°. [1927]

Parker (H. W.)

Library classific. & numbering system. 3rd ed. 8°. N.Y. 1926

Parker (*capt.* Harry). Illust. cat. of Amer. & Brit. naval & marine prints &c. prop. of P. Sold, Jan. 6, 1922, Amer. Art Assoc. [P2855]. 8°. N.Y. [1922]

Parker (Henry), *of Lincoln's Inn, 1604–52, see* STATIONERS COMPANY, *London.* *To the High Court of Parl.: the humble remonstrance of the Co. of S., 1643.

Parker (Henry), *of Lincoln's Inn, 18th cent.* Hist. of the War in India betw. Surajah Dowla, Nabob of Bengal & the English. 4°. 1789

Parker (Henry Michael Denne). The Roman legions. 8°. O. 1928

Parker (John). Who's who in the theatre: biog. record of contemp. stage. Comp. &c. by P. 4th ed. rev. & enl. s8°. 1922

Parker (John Henry).

Excavations in Rome, 1870–71. [P2706]. 8°. 1871

Parker (Joseph), *Independent minister.*

The inner life of Christ. 3v. [*var. ed.*] 8°. 1889–90

The People's Bible: disc. upon Holy Scr. 25v [19, 21 *wanting*]. 8°. 1885–95

Parker (*Mrs.* Katherine). "My Ladie Dundie": h. life &c. Pref. by C. S. Terry. 8°. Paisley. 1926

Parker (Leslie Henry), *see* PARTINGTON (J. R.) & L. H. P. The nitrogen industry, 1922.

Parker (Robert). De politeia eccl. libri tres. [lib. 3, *w. sep. pagin.*] s4°. *n.p.* 1616

Parker (Samuel), *bp. of Oxford* [*ps., Mr.* BAYES]. A free & impartial censure of the Platonick philos. w. acc. of Origenian hypothesis conc. preexistence of souls, in two letters. [*sep. tp.*] 2nd ed. s8°. O. 1667

see EUSEBIUS. Eccl. hist. of E., Socrates &c.; tr., w. acc. of lives &c., by P., 3rd ed. rev., 1729.

„ MARVELL (A.) *The Rehearsal transpros'd: animadv. upon [P.'s] "A preface &c.," 1672.

Parker (Samuel), *of Trinity Coll., Cambridge.* Letter to Mr. Bold conc. the resurrection of the same body [*sep. tp. & pagin.*], *see* SOCRATES, *Scholasticus.* Eccl. hist. of S. &c.; abr. by S. P., pl, 1707.

Parker (William). The late Assembly of Divines Conf. of faith examined as it was presented &c. unto the Parl. [*With the text*]. s8°. 1651

Parker (William), *A.B.* The Paris Bourse & French finance w. ref. to organ. speculat. in N.Y. 8°. N.Y., *Columbia Univ.* 1920

Parker (William Belmont).

Argentines of to-day. [Hisp. Soc. of Amer.] 2v. s8°. Buenos Aires. 1920	Paraguayans of to-day. [Hisp. Soc.] s8°. 1921
Casual letters from S. America. [Hisp. Soc.] s8°. 1921	Peruvians of to-day. [Hisp. Soc.] s8°. Lima, Peru. 1919
Cubans of to-day. [Hisp. Soc.] s8°. N.Y. 1919	Uruguayans of to-day. [Hisp. Soc.] s8°. 1921

Parkes (*Sir* Henry), *1815–96; Australian statesman.*

Stolen moments. Poems. s8°. Sydney. 1842

Parkes (Joan).

Travel in England in the 17th cent. 8°. [O.] 1925

Parkes (Joseph). The governing charter of the borough of Warwick, 1694, w. letter. 8°. 1827

see BUCKLEY (J. K.) J. P. of Birmingham & part wh. he played in Radical Reform movt., 1825–45, 1926.

Parkes (Kineton). The etchings & dry-point engravings of David Neave. [P2490]. 8°. [1920 ?]

The painter-poets. Sel. &c. by K. P. s8°. [1890]

Sculpture of today. 2v. 8°. 1921

Parkes (U. W. A.) Text-book on the artistic anatomy of the human form. la8°. 1923

Parkes (William Henry). New revelations in astronomy & gravitation. [P2773]. 8°. 1925

Parkhouse (A. W.) Practical polishing & staining. la8°. 1922

Parkhurst (Helen). Education on the Dalton plan. Intr. by T. P. Nunn, & contrib. by R. Bassett. s8°. 1923

Parkinson (Edward). The city of Downe. 8°. Belfast. 1928

Parkinson (James), *architectural woodworker,* **& E. A. Ould.**

Old cottages, farm houses, & o. half-timbered buildings in Shropshire, Herefordshire & Cheshire. Photogr. by J. P. Intr. & descr. notes &c. by E. A. O. la8°. 1904

Parkinson (John), *apothecary.* A garden of pleasant flowers. Chosen & arr. by A. H. Hyatt. s8°. 1904

„ „ ....s8°. 1907

Theatrum botanicum: the theater of plants: or, an herball. [*Engraved tp.*] fol. 1640

Parkinson (Maude Rea). Twenty years in Romania. 8°. [1921]

Parkman (Francis), *the younger; 1823–93.*

France and England in N. Amer.

[3], La Salle & the discovery of the Great West. [n. lib. ed.] 8°. Boston. 1922

Earlier ed. have title: The discovery of the Great West.

[7], Montcalm & Wolfe. [n. lib. ed.] 2v. 8°. 1906

Montcalm & Wolfe. 2v. s8°. [1908]

Parkman (George), *see* WEBSTER (J. W.) Rep. of case of W. indicted for murder of G. P.; by G. Bemis, 1850.

Parkossius (Jacobus). Antiquiss. de orthographia Polonica libellus. Opera G. S. Bandtkie ed. s8°. Posnaniae. 1830

Parks (*Mrs.* George Richmond), *see* ROBINS (*Miss* ELIZ.)

Parlement (Le) interallié. (Sessions 1–4, 2p). [P2597]. 8°. [1917]

Parliament.

ANONYMOUS WORKS.

All the severall ordinances, directions & votes of the Lords & Commons in Parl. for the establ. of presbyteriall gov. [*w. sep. tp. as below.* P2653]. s4°. 1646

[1], Directions for electing &c. of ruling-elders, 1645.

[2], Ordinance w. rules & conc. suspension f. the Lord's Supper, 1645.

[3], Ordinance for giving power to all the classicall presbyteries, 1645.

[4], Ordinance for keeping scandalous persons f. the Lord's Supper, 1646.

[5], Ordinance for setling of presbyteriall gov., 1646.

[6], Ordinance for ordin. of ministers by classicall presbyters, 1646.

*Blot (The) on Parl., 1923, *see* ARCANUM, *ps.*

Catalogue (A) of the dukes, marquesses, earles &c. that sit in this Parl., begun 3. Nov. 1640. s8°. 1640

Catalogue (A) of the names of the knights for the counties, citizens &c. for this Parl., begun 3. Nov. 1640. [*b. w.* Cat. of dukes &c., 1640]. s8°. 1640

*The character of the Parl., commonly called the Rump, begun Nov. 23, 1640. s8°. 1721

Declar. (A) in Parl. in ans. to the King's declar. conc. Hull. [P2571]. s8°. 1642

For the King's reply to the above Declar., *see* CHARLES I. H.M. ans. &c., 1642.

Declar. (A) &c. in Parl. how sev. commissions have been granted to Papists &c. w. names of some rebels in Ireland &c. [P2571]. s8°. 1642

Parliament [*continued*].
ANONYMOUS WORKS [*continued*].
Declar. (A) of Parl. of Commonwealth of Eng., conc. the settlement of Scotland &c. [P2571]. s8º. 1652
Declar. (A) of the L. & C. &c. conc. the miserable distractions &c. [P2571]. s8º. 1642
Declar. (A) of the L. & C., w. add. reasons, annexed H.M.'s speech, March 1641. [P2571]. s8º. 1641
*Former ages never heard of &c., or, a brief review of the most materiall Parl. transact. beg. Nov. 3, 1640. s8º. 1656
His M.'s ans. to petition of the L. & C., pres. at York, June 17, 1642, *see* CHARLES I.
*Journall (A) of Parl., or, a survey of the P.'s proceedings, Apr. 20–May 26, 1648. No. 1 [*no more publ.*] 8º. [1648]
*Kingdomes (The) briefe ans. to the late declar. of Hse. of Commons, Feb. 11, 1647, touching reasons of th. no further addr. to the king. s4º. 1648
Labour & capital in Parl., 1923, *see* LABOUR.
*Letter (A) conc. the late Act of P. rel. to Eccl. small dues. [P2669]. s8º. 1750
Message (A) sent f. both Houses to the Kings M., 16 March 1641, conc. spec. matters. [P2571]. s8º. 1642
*Mystery of the good old cause briefly unfolded in cat. of members of the Long Parl. &c. (1660), *see* AUNGERVYLE Soc. Reprints, s2, 1883.
New declar. (A) of both Houses, sent to the Kings M., 16th March, upon h. removall f. Huntington to York &c., 1641. [P2571]. s8º. 1642
Ordinance (An) of the L. & C. for excluding such members as have deserted the Parl. &c. [*b. w.* Hurtado de Mendoza (A.) Fiestas, 1670]. s4º. 1644
Parlement (The) of the thre ages: allit. poem. [Sel. Early Eng. poems; ed. I. Gollancz, 2]. 8º. 1915
Petition (The) of both Houses &c. to H.M. conc. h. intended going to Ireland. [P2571]. 8º. 1642
Petition (The) of both Houses to the K.M. at Yorke, March 26, 1642, w. h. ans. thereunto &c. [P2571]. s8º. 1642
*Vindic. (A) of the imprisoned &c. Members &c., 1649, *see* PRYNNE (W.)
*Vindic. (A) of the last Parl. In 4 dialogues between Sir Simon & Sir Peter. 8º. 1711
GENERAL COLLECTIONS & DEBATES [*in order of date of publ.*]
Catalogue (A) & coll. of ordinances, proclamations &c., Dec. 1653–Sept. 1654. [*Comp. by H. Scobell*]. sm. fol. 1654
Debates in P., 1740–43, *see* JOHNSON (S.) Wks., v10, 11, 1825.
Précis of offic. papers: abstracts of all Parl. returns dir. to be printed by both Houses.
1880, 2p, 1881, 2p [*each p. b. sep.*] 8º. 1880–82
Parl^y. Debates, H. of Lords, Nov. 13, 1918; H. of C., Oct. 23–Nov. 18, 1918. Armenia. [P2384]. 8º. 1918
REFERENCES.
see FRANCE. Enquête faite par ordre du Parl. d'Angleterre, de l'indust. en F.; tr., 1825.
,, PERFECT DIURNALL of some passages in Parl., 1644–48.
,, STOCK (L. F.), *ed.* Proc. & debates of Brit. Parl. resp. N. Amer., v1, 2, 1542–1702, 1924–27.

II, House of Commons.
GENERAL COLLECTIONS.
Journals of the H. of C. v175–182. fol. 1920–27
,, ,, Gen. index, v166–175 (1911–20). fol. [1923]
PROCEEDINGS REL. TO SPECIAL SUBJECTS, OR ON SPECIAL DATES [*in chronological order*].
Commons debates for 1629 crit. ed. & intr. dealing w. Parl. sources &c. Ed. by W. Notestein & F. H. Relf. [Univ. of Minnesota]. la8º. Minneapolis. 1921
Remonstrance (A) of the state of the kingdom, 15 Dec. 1641. 8º. 1641
Abstract (An) of several examinations in co. of Monmouth & Hereford deliv. in to the H. of C., reported by Sir J. Trevor at a Conf. to prevent the growth of popery. [P525]. sm. fol. 1680
Substance of debate, May 1823, on motion for mitigation & abolition of slavery, w. pref. & app. [P2761]. 8º. 1823
Auth. report of debate, June 1825, on Mr. Buxton's motion rel. to demolition of the Methodist Chapel &c. in Barbadoes & the expulsion of Mr. Shrewsbury &c. [P2762]. 8º. 1825
Report of debate, June 1825, on Dr. Lushington's motion resp. the deportation of L. C. Lecesne & L. Escoffery f. Jamaica. [P2762]. 8º. 1825

Parliament [*continued*].
II, House of Commons [*continued*].
REFERENCES.
see EAST INDIA COMPANY. 5th Rep. f. Sel. Comm. of H. of C. on affairs of E.I. Co., 1812; ed. W. K. Firminger, 3v, 1917–18.
,, GLANVILL (*Sir* J.) Reports of certain cases [1623–24], 1775.
,, SLAVERY. Analysis of rep. of Comm. of H. of C. on extinction of s., 1833.

III, House of Lords.
HIST. MSS. COMMISSION [*& Cont.*]
Manuscripts of the H. of Lords. N.S., v6–8, 1704–10, *see* HIST. MSS. COMM., Lords, *House of.*
REFERENCES.
see CAROLINE, *queen.* Proceedings in H. of L., *var. ed.*
,, INTERNAT. COMMUNICATION BILL. Minutes of evidence; minutes of proceedings, 1872.
,, LEGION, *ps.* Letter [*& 2nd letter*] to Duke of Richmond, Chairman of Slavery Comm. of H. of L., 1832–33.
,, OXFORD. Sev. papers. laid bef. the lords rel. to riots at O. on the Prince's birthday, 1717.

Parliamentary. Parl. Debates (Official report). [H. of Commons]. s5, v129–220. 8º. 1920–28
Parl. Debates (Official report). [H. of Lords]. s5, v38–70. 8º. 1920–28
Parl. (The) gazetteer of Ireland, 3v, 1845, *see* IRELAND.
Parliamentary Papers. Cat. of Parl. papers, 1801–1900. 2nd Suppl., 1911–20. 4º. *King.* [1922]
Parmegiano, *see* FRÖHLICH-BUM (L.) P. u. d. Manierismus, 1921.
Parmelee (Julius Hall), *see* DIXON (F. H.) & J. H. P. War admin. of the rlys. in U.S. & Gt. Brit., 2nd ed., 1919.
Parmelee (Maurice). Blockade & sea power: the blockade, 1914–19. 8º. [1924]
Parmentier (Henri). Les sculptures chames au Musée de Tourane. [Ars Asiatica, 4]. fol. 1922
Parmoor (Charles Alfred Cripps, *1st baron***),** *see* EUROPE. Needs of E.: rep. of Internat. Econ. Conf., 1920: addresses by P. &c., 1921.
Parn (Francisque). La nymphe en danger. s8º. 1926
Parnaso.
P. antillano, 1916, *see* BAZIL (O.), *ed.*
P. brasileiro, *n.d.*, *see* COSTA (A.), *ed.*
P. chileno, 1910, *see* †DONOSO (A.)
P. cubano: sel. compos. poet., 1920, *see* VALLE (A. DEL), *ed.*
P. boliviano, *n.d.*, *see* BLANCO MEAÑO (L. F.), *ed.*
P. dominicano, 1916, *see* BAZIL (O.), *ed.*
P. ecuatoriano, *n.d.*, *see* BRISSA (J.), *ed.*
P. español contemp., 1914, *see* BRISSA (J.), *ed.*
P. mexicano, 2t, *n.d.*, *see* ESTEVA (A. A.) & J. PABLO RIVAS, *edd.*
P. nicaragüense, *n.d.*, *see* ORTIZ (A.), *ed.*
P. peruano, 1915, *see* †GARCÍA CALDERÓN (V.)
P. salvadoreño, 1917, *see* ERAZO (S. L.), *ed.*
P. venezolano. Sel. composiciones poét. col. por C. B. A. 2ª ed. aum. por J. Gonzalez Gamargo. 2t. s8º. Barcelona. [1918]
Parnasse (Le) satyrique du 15ᵉ s., 1905, *see* SCHWOB (M.), *ed.*
Parnell (Charles Stewart).
see ERVINE (ST. J. G.) Parnell, 1925; pop. ed., 1928.
,, PARNELL (J. H.) C. S. P., 1916.
,, ROBBINS (*Sir* A. F.) P., the last 5 years, 1926.
Parnell (Emma Jane), *aft. wife of 5th earl Darnley, see* DARNLEY (E. J., *ctss. of*).
Parnell (John Howard). C. S. Parnell: mem. 8º. 1916
Parnell (Thomas), *archdeacon of Clogher.*
Poet. works. Coll. by T. Park. s8º. 1807
Poet. works. [Life by J. Mitford. Aldine ed.] s8º. [1866]
see CRUICKSHANK (A. H.) T. P., or what was wrong w. the 18th cent., 1921.
*"**Parnellites** at work, or a bloody assize." [P2560]. s8º. 1886
Parny (E. Désiré de Forges, *vcte.* **de).** Opuscules.
4ᵉ éd. corr. & augm. 2p. [*p2 & tp. wanting*]. s8º. [Paris. 1784]
Parodi (Dominique).
Traditionalisme & démocratie. 2ᵉ éd. s8º. 1924
Parodi (Ernesto Giacomo), *see* DANTE ALIGHIERI. Lectura D.: c. 2 del Paradiso letto da E. G. P., 1911.
Paroissien romain. Cont. l'Office de tous les Dimanches & des Saints de l'année. [*Lat. & Fr.*]
éd. nouv., augm. s8º. Malines. [1881]
Le petit P. rom., cont. l'Office divin, 1774, *see* OFFICIA.
Parolino (Carlo Roncalli), *see* RONCALLI PAROLINO (C.)

Parona (Carlo Fabrizio). Fossili d. secondario e d. terziario, *see* FILIPPI (F. DE). Rel. sci. d. Spediz. Ital. de F. n. Himàlaia &c., s2, v6, 1928.
Trattato di geologia, con spec. rig. a. g. d'Italia. Collab. per la geol. stor., G. Dal Piaz, R. Fabiani, M. Gortani. 2a ed. 8o. Milano. 1924
Paronean (Souqias), *see* BARONIAN (S.)
Parr (Elnathan). Plaine expos. upon 8–11 ch. of the Epist. of St. Paul to the Romans &c. 8o. 1618
Parra (Porfirio).
Pacotillas. Novela mexicana. 8o. Barcelona. 1900
Parreidt (Johann Heinrich). De auro Judaico. Disput. J. H. P. & C. G. Wincklerus. [P431]. s4o. Lipsiae. [1743]
Parrenin (*le père*), *ps.*, *see* LA VICOMTERIE DE SAINT-SAMSON.
Parrhasios, *c. 400 B.C.*, *see* PACE (B.) Vasi fig. con rifl. d. pittura di P., 1922.
Parrhisienses, *see* PARIS.
Parrillis (Giuseppe de), *ed.* Componimenti poet. [Nozze Orsini—Caracciola]. [N125]. 8o. Napoli. 1711
Parrington (Vernon Louis).
Main currents in Amer. thought. v1. 8o. N.Y. 1927
1, The colonial mind, 1620–1800.
Parrot (J. L. von). Versuch e. Entwicklung d. Sprache, Abstammung, Gesch., Mythologie &c. d. Liwen, Lätten, Eesten &c. Nebst e. Topographie &c. d. Landes z. Anfang d. 13. Jhdts. [Vergleich. Tafeln d. Declin. u. Conjug. d. europ. Stammsprachen u West-, Süd- Asiatischer (*by* R. C. Rask)]. 2B. 8o. St. 1828
Parrott (Thomas Marc).
The problem of Timon of Athens. [P2717]. 8o. 1923
Parry (Albert William).
Educ. in Eng. in Middle Ages. s8o. 1920
Parry (*Sir* C. Hubert H.), *Bart.*
The evolution of the art of music. 7th ed. s8o. 1920
,, ,, ... 8th ed. s8o. 1923
Studies of great composers. 10th ed. 8o. *n.d.*
see GRAVES (C. L.) H. P., h. life & works, 2v, 1926.
Parry (Edward), *of Chester.* Royal visits & progresses to Wales & Border Counties of Cheshire, Salop, Hereford & Monmouth. 2nd ed. 4o. 1851
Parry (*Sir* Edward Abbott). Berrington. s8o. [1928]
The drama of the law. 8o. [1924]
The Overbury mystery. 8o. [1925]
The seven lamps of advocacy. 8o. [1923]
Vagabonds all. 8o. [1926]
What the judge thought. 8o. [1922]
Parry (Methold Sidney). Ireland's claim to independence, how Eng. met this claim in 1782. [P2530]. s8o. [1921]
Parry (Reginald St. John). Cambridge essays on adult education. [*By var. wr.*] Ed. P. 8o. C. 1920
Henry Jackson, O.M. 8o. C. 1926
The Pastoral Epistles. With intr., text & comm. 8o. C. 1920
Parsey (Arthur). Art of miniature painting on ivory. s8o. 1831
Parson (William), *see* BAINES (E.) Hist., dir. &c. of Co. Pal. of Lancaster: dir. dept. by W. P., 2v, 1824–25.
Parsons (*Mrs.* Clement).
Recommended gift books for children. n. ed. 8o. [1928]
Parsons (Edward), *see* SIMPSON (D.) Plea for the deity of Jesus; w. mem. of the a. &c. by E. P., 1812.
Parsons (Elsie Clews). Folk-lore f. the Cape Verde Islands. [Amer. Folk-Lore Soc., Mem., v15]. 2p. 8o. Cambridge, Mass. 1923
Parsons (Frederick Gymer).
The earlier inhabitants of London. 8o. [1927]
Parsons (James), *M.D.* Remains of Japhet: hist. enq. into affinity &c. of Europ. langs. 4o. 1767
Parsons (John Denham). The great taboo in Engl. literary circles. [P2423; 2520]. 8o. 1919
Sir Sidney Lee & absolute proof. [P2520]. 8o. 1920
Stratford upon Avon gravestones & inscriptions. [P2520]. 8o. [1920]
William Shakespeare. "Another's name." [P2520]. 8o. [1920]
Parsons (*Sir* John Herbert).
Intr. to st. of colour vision. 8o. C. 1915
Parsons (Robert), *the Jesuit* [PERSONS: *ps.* N. DOLEMAN].
An answer to the fifth part of Reportes by Sir E. Cooke conc. the municipall lawes of Eng. which do apperteyne to spiritual power and jurisdiction. s4o. *n.p.* [St Omer ?]. 1606
A Christian directory, guiding men to eternall salvation. Rev. corr. & augm. [The Preface: cont. notes upon a false ed. by M. E. Buny]. s8o. [London ?]. 1650

Parsons (Robert), *the Jesuit* [PERSONS: *ps.* N. DOLEMAN] [*contd.*]
*De persecutione Anglicana comm., a Colleg. Anglic. Romano ed. &c. Add. litteris Gregorii XIII hortatoriis. s8o. Ingolstadii. 1582
*De persecutione Anglicana libellus &c. s8o. Romae. 1582
The Jesuit's [*i.e. R. P.*] memorial, for the intended reform. of England; w. intr. &c. by E. Gee. s8o. 1690
see STRONG (*Mrs.* E.) Note on a copy of the Responsiones of R. P., 1920.
,, SUTCLIFFE (M.) The subversion of R. P., his work &c., 1606.
Parsons (Theophilus), *the younger.* Personal & property rights of a citizen of the U.S. 8o. Hartford. 1878
Slavery. Its origin, infl. & destiny. [P2756]. s8o. Boston [Mass.] 1863
Parthenius, *patriarch of Constantinople.* Decretum synodale super Calvin. dogmatibus, in epistola, Cyrilli nomine ed. &c. [*Gr. & Lat.*] s8o. Parisiis. 1643
Parthenopæus, *Hereticus, ps.*, *see* GORDON (WILLIAM).
Partington (Hannah), *see* HOLDEN (W.), J. ASHCROFT *&c.* Trial & convict. of J. A., W. H. &c. for murder of M. Marsden & H. P., 1817.
Partington (James Riddick).
Chemical thermodynamics. 8o. 1924
—— & L. H. Parker. The nitrogen industry. 8o. 1922
Partington (S. W.) The Toll Bars of Manchester, incl. the Toll Bridges. 8o. M'ter. 1920
Partington (Wilfred). Smoke rings & roundelays: blendings f. prose & verse. Compiled by W. P. s8o. [1924]
Partridge (Eric). The French Romantics' knowledge of Eng. lit., 1820–48, acc. to contemp. Fr. mem., letters &c. la8o. Paris. 1924
R. E. Landor: biog. & crit. sk. 8o. 1927
Partridge (John), *see* MERLINUS LIBERATUS. Almanack, 1800–8.
Partridge (Silvester), *ps.*, *see* INFALLIBLE ASTROLOGER, THE: or Mr. S. P.'s prophesie &c., No. 1, 1700.
Partsch (Joseph). Die Stromgabelungen d. Argonautensage, *see* KÖNIGL.-SÄCHS. GESELLS. Berichte, phil.-hist. Kl., B71, 1919.
Paruta (Paolo). Di una lega proposta da Filippo II [1592]. Dispacci. [Nozze Comello—Totto. N. 129]. la8o. Venezia. 1864
Parvus, *ps., a. of Klassenkampf d. Proletariats &c.*, *see* HELPHAND (A.)
Pascal (André). Le moulin de la galette, comédie, *see* ŒUVRES libres, 36, 1924.
Pascal (Blaise) [*ps.* LOUIS DE MONTALTE].
Œuvres. Publ. avec doc. compl., intr. & notes par L. Brunschvicg. [G. é. de la Fr.] t12–14. 8o. 1921
Études sur P., par M. Blondel, L. Brunschvicg, J. Chevalier &c. [Revue de métaphys. &c. No. spéc.] 8o. 1923
PENSÉES.
Pensées sur la religion. n. éd. augm. de sa vie &c. s8o. 1761
Pensées, fragm. & lettres. Publ. par P. M. Faugère. 2t. 8o. 1844
Pensées. Sa vie par Mme. Périer. Choix des Pensées de Nicole & de s. traité de la paix. s8o. 1861
Pensées. Préf. d'E. Boutroux. Intr. par V. Giraud. s8o. [1913]
Pensées sur la vérité de la relig. chrét. Par J. Chevalier. 2t. 8o. 1925
PROVINCIALES.
Les Provinciales. éd. nouv. augm. de la vie de l'a. [par Mme. Perier]. s8o. Cologne. 1698
Les lettres provinciales. Ed. H. F. Stewart. s8o. M'ter. 1920
Lettres écr. à un provincial; préc. de l'hist. des L. prov. d'ap. l'éd. de 1754 & obs. litt. par F. de Neufchâteau. s8o. *n.d.*
TRANSLATIONS.
*An answer to the Provinciall Letters publ. by the Jansenists, under the name of L. Montalt, agst. the doctrine of the Jesuits &c. s8o. Paris. 1659
TRANSLATIONS [*continued*].
Life [*by Mme.* G. Perier], w. h. letters rel. to the Jesuits. Tr. into Eng. by W. A[ndrews]. 2v. 8o. 1744
Les provinciales, or, the mystery of Jesuitisme. 2nd. ed. corr. w. add. s8o. 1658
Provincial letters. Tr., added, A view of the hist. of the Jesuits &c. 8o. 1816
Provincial letters; w. a biog. pref. [Anc. & Mod. Lib. of Theolog. Lit.] 8o. [1889]
Thoughts on relig. &c., *see* WESLEY (J.) Xtn. lib., v23, 1753.
REFERENCES.
see BARRÈS (M.) Dante, P. &c., 1923.
,, BRÉMOND (H.) En prière avec P.: sermon, 1923.
,, BRUNSCHVICG (L.) Génie de P., 1924.
,, CHAMAILLARD (E.) P., mondain & amoureux, 1923.
,, CHEVALIER (J.) P., 1923.
,, COLERIDGE (H. J.) Reviews of fam. bks., 1, Provincial Letters, 1871.
,, DARMESTETER (*Mme.* J.) Portrait of P., 1927.
,, GIRAUD (V.) La vie héroïque de B. P., 1923.
,, JESUP (E.) Lives of John Picus & of Mons. P., 3rd ed., *n.d.*

Pascal (Blaise) [*ps.* LOUIS DE MONTALTE] [*continued*].

REFERENCES [*continued*].

see JOVY (E.) Etudes pascaliennes, t1, 1927.
,, —— P. & le p. de Frétat, 1919.
,, —— P. & St. Ignace, 1923.
,, —— P. inédit, t1, 1908.
,, —— P. n'a pas inventé le haquet, 1923.

REFERENCES [*continued*].

see NOUET (J.), F. ANNAT & *others.* *Responses aux Lettres provinciales &c., 1668.
,, SOLTAU (R. H.) P., man & message, 1927.

Pascal (Georges). Largillierre. 8º. [1928]

Pascal (Yves). Bel oiseau sans ailes . . ., *see* ŒUVRES libres, 84, 1928.

Paschale (Ludovico). Rime volgari. s8º. Vinegia. 1549

Paschali (Giulio Cesare). Salmi di Davidde, tr., poetica parafrase, pel sig. G. C. P. [*Foll. by* Rime spirituale aggiunto il primo canto del suo Universo. *w. sep. pagin. & tp.*] s8º. Geneva. 1592

Paschalius (Carolus), *see* PASQUALE (CARLO), *viscount di Quente.*

Pascoe (Edwin Hall). Geolog. notes on Mesopotamia w. spec. ref. to occurr. of petroleum, *see* INDIA: GEOL. SURVEY. Mem., v48, 1922.

Oil-fields of Burma—Petroleum occurr. of Assam & Bengal—Petroleum in Punjab & N.-W. Frontier Prov., *see* INDIA: GEOLOG. SURVEY. Mem., v40, 1920.

Pascolato (Alessandro), *1841–1904.* Manin e Venezia nel 1848–49. Pagine postume a cura di M. P. Pascolato. s8º. Milano. [1916]

I profughi veneti e lombardi a Venezia nel 1848. [P2411]. 8º. Venezia. 1901

see CASTELNUOVO (E.) Commem. di P., 1905.
,, PAPADOPOLI (N.) A. P., 1908.
,, TRUFFI (F.) Commem. di A. P., 1907.

Pascoli (Gabriel) *da Ravenna.* La pazzesca pazzia de gl' huomini e donne di corte innamorati. s8º. Venetia. 1608

Pascoli (Giovanni).

Canti di Castelvecchio. 2ª ed. la8º. Bologna. 1903
Fior da fiore: prose e poesie. 7ª ed. accresc. 8º. Milano. [1921]
Limpido rivo: prose e poesie. 2ª ed. s8º. Bologna. [1920]
Poemi del Risorgimento. Inno a Roma—Inno a Torino. 8º. Bologna. [1921]
Poesie varie, racc. da Maria. 3ª ed. 8º. Bologna. 1920
Sul limitare. Poesie e prose per la scuola ital. Scelte da G. P. 2ª ed. 8º. Milano. 1902
Traduzioni e riduzioni racc. e riordin. da Maria. 2ª ed. 8º. Bologna. 1920
see BORGESE (G. A.) Risurrezioni (Il P. minore &c.), 1922.
,, CROCE (B.) G. P.; studio crit., 1920.

Pascu (G.) Sufixele Românești. Ed. Acad. Române. la8º. București. 1916

Pasella (Guido). A. Betrone. la8º. Milano. 1920

Pashitnov (K. A.), *see* PAJITNOV (K. A.)

Pashkevich (V. V.)

Лекарств. растения, их культура и сбор. 8º. Москва. 1924

Pasi (Francesco). Trois lettres annuelles du Japon, 1603, 1604–5, 1606, 1609, *see* JESUITS.

see JESUITS. Litteræ annuae Iapon. a F. P. &c., 1604.
,, ——. *Rec. de ampliss. regno Chinae; item de morte Taicosamae Iap. monarchae [a F. P.], 1601.

Pasiadès [IASIADÈS], *see* DEMANGEL (R.) Un nouvel alabastre du peintre P., 1923.

Pasini (Alberto), *see* CALDERINI (M.) A. P., pittore: 49 tavole con intr., 1916.

Pasini (Ferdinando). L. Pirandello. 8º. Trieste. 1927

Pasini (Giuseppe). De praecipuis SS. Bibliorum linguis & vers. diss. s8º. Patavii. 1716

Pasini (Luigi). Delle scritture in cifra usate d. rep. di Venezia. 8º. [Venezia]. 1872

see MICHELI (G.) Dispacci di G. M. (1554–57); rettific. &c. di L. P., 1869.

Paske-Smith (Montague Bentley Talbot), *H.B.M. Consul, Nagasaki.* A glympse of the " English House " & Eng. life at Hirado, 1613–23. 8º. Kobe. 1927

Paskhales (Demetrios P.) Νομισματικὴ τῆς νήσου Ἄνδρου. [*Extr. f. t3* Διεθνοῦς ἐφημ. τῆς νομισμ. Ἀρχαιολογίας]. [P2749]. 8º. ἐν Ἀθήναις. 1898

Pasolini Dall' Onda (*il conte* Giuseppe), *see* MINGHETTI (M.) Carteggio tra M. M. e G. P., 1846–59, 2v, 1924–26.

Pasolini Dall' Onda (Pietro Desiderio). Francesco Michiel arcivesc. di Ravenna n. sec. xiv. [Nozze Bianchi—Michiel. N129]. la8º. Ravenna. 1876

Pasolini Dall' Onda (Pietro Desiderio) [*continued*].

I genitori di T. Tasso. Note stor. [*w.* Rime di T. in vita &c. di Porzia de' Rossi, Lettere scelte di B. Tasso &c.] la8º. 1895

Ravenna e le sue grandi mem. 8º. 1912

Gli statuti di Ravenna ordinati e descr. s8º. Firenze. 1868

Pasolino (Serafino).

Huomini illustri di Ravenna. fol. Bologna. 1703

Pasor (Georgius). Syllabus Græco-Latinus Novi Test. vocum. Adj.: Idea de septem N.T. dialectis. ed. 5ª. aucta. s8º. Francofurti. 1663

Pasquale (Carlo), *viscount di Quente* [PASCHALIUS (C.)] Christianarum precum libri 2. [*b. w.* Beza (Th.) Psalmorum Davidis libri 5, 1580]. s8º. Cadomi. [Caën], *J. le Bas.* 1592

Pasquali Alidosi (Giov. Niccolò), *see* ALIDOSI (G. N. P.)

Pasquaris (G. M.) Gabriele d'Annunzio. la8º. Milano. 1923

Pasquet (D.) Essay on the origins of the House of Commons. Tr. R. G. D. Laffan. Pref. & add. notes by G. Lapsley. s8º. C. 1925

Pasqui (Angelo). Scavi nel territ. falisco (Narce &c.), *see* REALE ACCAD. D. LINCEI. Mon. ant., v4, 1894.

La villa Pompeiana d. Pisanella pr. Boscoreale, *see* REALE ACCAD. D. LINCEI. Mon. ant., v7, 1897.

Pasqui (Ubaldo), *see* AREZZO. Doc. per la storia d. città di A. &c.; racc. per cura U. P., 2v, 1899–1916.

Pasquier (Etienne), *1529–1615.* *Le catechisme des Jésuites. s8º. Villefranche. 1602

Pasquier (Félix), *see* MIREPOIX. Cartul. de M.; [*ed. w.* Intr. hist. *by*] F. P., 2t, 1921.

Passagni (Leandro).

Il violino. Manualetto pratico. s8º. Milan. [1898]

Passamonti (Eugenio). Cesare Balbo e la rivol. del 1821 in Piemonte, *see* REGIA DEP. S. GLI STUDI DI STORIA PATRIA &C. Bibl., v12, 1926.

Passau. Abdruck des Passaw. Vortrags so den andern Monats tag Augusti Anno etc. LII. auffgericht worden. [*beg.* Wir Ferdinand &c. 22 leaves: sig. A–F. P2441]. s4º. *n.p.* [1552]

Passé (Le). Былое: журналъ. 1907, *see* BILOE.

Passerini (Carlo Tesi-), *see* TESI-PASSERINI (C.)

Passerini (Giuseppe Lando).

Il ritratto di Dante. s8º. Firenze. 1921

Passerini (*conte* Luigi). Geneal. e storia della famiglia Altoviti. 8º. Firenze. 1871

Passini (Grete), *see* URBANITZKY (G. v.), *ps.*

***Passio** I. C. ex evangel. textu deprompta &c., 1507, *see* JESUS CHRIST.

Passion (La) du Palatinus, 1922, *see* PALATINUS.

Passional Christi u. Antichristi, Wittenberg, 1521, (*facs.*), *see* FREYTAG (G.) Bilder, B3, T1, 1924.

Passionale. Das Stuttgarter P.; 1923, *see* BÖCKLER (A.)

***Passionate** remonstrance made by his Holinesse upon the late proc. &c. (*satire*, 1641), 1884, *see* URBAN VIII, *pope.*

Passiones vitaeque sanct. aevi Merovingici, t1–5, 1896–1920, *see* KRUSCH (B.), *ed.*

Passos (John Dos), *see* DOS PASSOS (J.)

Passow (Carl). Beitr. z. Gesch. d. deut. Universitäten im 14. Jhdt. [*Progr.*] s4º. 1836

Pastè (Romualdo). Storia doc. dell' abbazia di S. Andrea di Vercelli, 1219–1466, *see* REGIA DEP. DI STORIA PATRIA. Misc., t38, 1902.

Pasternak (Boris). Рассказы. 8º. Москва. 1925

Сестра моя жизнь. s8º. Берлин. 1923

Темы и варьяции: 4ая кн. стихов. s8º. Москва. 1923

Pasteur (Louis).

Œuvres. Réunies par P. Vallery-Radot. t1–4. la8º. 1922–26

1, Dissymétrie moléculaire. 2, Fermentations & générations dites spontanées. 3, Etudes sur le vinaigre & sur le vin. 4, Etudes sur la maladie des vers a soie.

see DESCOUR (L.) P. & h. work, tr., 1922.
,, HUME (E. D.) Béchamp or P.?: lost chapter in hist. of biology, 1923.

***Pastime** papers, 1885, *see* SAUNDERS (F.)

Paston Letters. Sel. f. Paston Letters as transcr. by Sir J. Fenn. Arr. & ed. A. D. Greenwood. 8º. 1920

see BENNETT (H. S.) The P.'s & their England, 1922.

Pastor (Antonio R.) Un embajador de España en la escena inglesa [*i.e.* D. Sarmiento de Acuña condado de Gondomar. Del Homenaje a M. Pidal, t3. P2851]. la8º. 1925

see SANTILLANA (I. L. DE M., *marq.* DE). Letter to Don Peter, constable of Portugal; intr. &c. by A. R. P. &c., 1927.

Pastor (Ludwig v.) Erläuterungen u. Ergänz. zu Janssens Gesch. d. deut. Volkes; hrsg. v. L. v. Pastor. B10, H3. 8°. Freiburg im Br. 1920

Veit (A. L.) Kirche u. Kirchenreform in d. Erzdiözese Mainz, 1517–1618, 1920. [10iii.]

Gesch. d. Päpste seit d. Ausgang d. Mittelalters. B7–12. 8°. Freiburg im Br. 1920–27

7, Pius IV, 1559–65. 8, Pius V, 1566–72. 9, Gregor XIII, 1572–85. 10, Sixtus V, Urban VII, Gregor XIV u. Innozenz IX, 1585–91. 11, Klemens VIII, 1592–1605. 12, Leo XI u. Paul V, 1605–21.

Hist. des Papes dep. la fin du moyen âge. Tr. A. Poizat. [4e éd.] t11. 8°. [1925]

Hist. of the Popes f. close of Middle Ages. [Tr.], ed. R. F. Kerr. v13–16. 8°. 1924–28

Pastorello (Ester). Tipografi, editori, librai a Venezia n. sec. 16. la8°. Firenze. 1924

Pastori (Giacomo). Il Card. Ferrari. la8°. Milano. 1919

Pastorini, *Signor, ps., see* WALMESLEY (CHARLES), *bp. of Rama.*

Pastorius (Joachimus). Florus Polonicus, seu Polon. hist. epitome nova [–1576]. s8°. Lugd. Batav. 1641

Pastourelle (La) dans la poésie occitane du m.-â.; textes & tr., avec intr. &c., 1923, *see* AUDIAU (J.), *ed.*

Pastre (Louis). Elém. de gramm. catalane. Préf. de J. S. Pons. s8°. Perpignan. [1926?]

Pastrnek (Franz). Chrvatsko-hlaholský rukopis Sienský. [*Extr. f.* Král. České Spol. Náuk, 1900. P2811]. 8°. v Praze. 1900

Pasvolsky (Leo). The economics of communism, w. ref. to Russia's experiment. s8°. N.Y. 1921

Russia in the Far East. s8°. N.Y. 1922

Patañjali. The Yoga aphorisms of P. Interpr. by W. Q. Judge, assis. by J. H. Connelly. s8°. N.Y. 1912

Pataroli (Lorenzo). Series Augustorum, Augustarum, Cæsarum &c., a C. J. Cæsare ad Carolum VI cum eorundem imaginibus ex numismatum. ed. 3a. 8°. Venetiis. 1740

Patch (Howard Rollin). The goddess Fortuna in med. lit. 8°. Camb., *Mass.* 1927

Patch (Richard). The trial of R. P. for murder of Isaac Blight at the Sessions House, Newington, Apr. 1806. 8°. 1806

Patent Rolls.

Calendar of the Patent Rolls. [C. of S. P.] 5v. la8°. 1924–26

Edward VI.
1, 1547–48. 2, 1548–49. 3, 1549–51. 4, 1550–53. 5, w. App., 1547–53.

Pater (Walter Horatio).

Appreciations; w. an essay on style. s8°. 1924

Marius the Epicurean. [pocket ed.] s8°. 1924

see BENSON (E.) P.'s Marius, 1885.

,, STONEHILL (C. A.) &c. Bibliog. of mod. a., s2, 1925.

Paterno (Lodovico). Le nuove fiamme: sonetti, canzoni, stanze &c. s8°. Venetia. [1561]

Paternò Castello (Maria Ricci), *see* RICCI PATERNÒ CASTELLO (M.)

Paterson (Arthur Henry).

George Eliot's family life & letters. 8°. [1928]

The homes of Tennyson. Painted by H. Allingham. 8°. 1905

The weapon of the strike. Foreword by Sir W. P. Rylands & A. Henderson. s8°. 1922

Paterson (Daniel), *see* FORDHAM (*Sir* H. G.) P.'s Roads, 1738–1825, 1925.

Paterson (Donald Rose), *M.D.*

Early Cardiff: street names &c. 8°. Exeter. 1926

Paterson (Isabel). The singing season. s8°. [1925]

Paterson (Marcus), *M.D.*

The shibboleths of tuberculosis. 8°. 1920

Paterson (Robert Gildersleeve). Wage-payment legisl. in the U.S., *see* UNITED STATES: LABOR. Bull. 229, 1918.

Paterson (Thomas Frederick).

East Bergholt, in Suffolk. 8°. *p.f.p.c.* C. 1923

Paterson (William Paterson). The nature of religion: Gifford lect., 1924–25. 8°. [1925]

see PRAYER. The power of prayer: sel. of Walker Trust essays; ed. W. P. P. &c., 1920.

Paterson-Smyth (John), *see* SMYTH (J. P.)

*__Path__ (The) to peace, 1923, *see* LYON (L.)

Pathelin (Pierre), *fictitious character.* Le farce de maître P., avec tr. en vers mod., & préc. d'un prologue, par E. Fournier. s8°. 1872

Maistre P. P.: farce du 15e siècle. Ed. R. T. Holbrook. [Class. franç. du m. â.] s8°. 1924

see CONS (L.) L'auteur de la farce de Pathelin [? G. Alecis], 1926.

*__Patiala__ & the Great War: hist. of the services of the premier Punjab state. 8°. *p.f.p.c.* 1923

Patience: an alliterative version of Jonah by the poet of Pearl. [Sel. Early Eng. poems; ed. I. Gollancz, 1]. 8°. 1913

see PEARL. Pearl, Cleanness, Patience &c.; reprod. in facs.; intr. by Sir I. Gollancz, 1923.

Pātimokkha-sutra [PRĀTIMOKSHA-SUTRA].

Пратимокша-сутра, буддійскій служебникъ, изд. и перевед. И. Минаевымъ. [I. Akad. Nauk. Записки, t16]. 8°. С.–П. 1869

Patin (Charles) [C. PATINUS]. Introd. ad hist. numismatum. Lat. versa. s8°. Amstelædami. 1683

Patin (Gui). Lettres du temps de la Fronde (1649–50). Intr. & notes de A. Thérive. s8°. 1921

Patkanov (Kerope Petrovich). О названіяхъ древнихъ армянскихъ мѣсяцевъ, *see* IMPERAT. RUSS. ARCH. OBSCH. Труды Восточ. отд., ч16, 1872.

Patkanov (Serafim Keropovich). Опытъ географіи &c. Тунгусскихъ племенъ Сибири. 2ч (ч1 *has* 2B *w. sep. pagin.*) [I.R.G.O. Записки по отдѣл. этнограф., 33i, ii]. 8°. С.-П. 1906

Patmore (Coventry K. D.) Courage in politics, & o. essays, 1885–96. s8°. 1921

see BURDETT (O.) The idea of C. P., 1921.

Patna. The diaries of 3 surgeons of P., 1763, 1909, *see* FIRMINGER (W. K.), *ed.*

Patna Oriental Public Library [KHUDA BAKSH LIB.], *see* O'CONNOR (V. C. S.) An Eastern lib., w. cat. of Pers. & Arabic MSS., 1920.

Paton (Diarmid Noel). On the proposed internat. scheme of North Sea fishery investig. [P2600]. 8°. E. 1902

Paton (Herbert James). The good will. 8°. [1927]

Paton (Lewis Bayles). Spiritism & the cult of the dead in antiquity. 8°. [1921]

Paton (Raymond). The autobiog. of a blackguard. s8°. [1923]

Paton (Stewart), *M.D.* Signs of sanity & the princ. of mental hygiene. 8°. N.Y. 1922

Paton (William Agnew). The econ. position of the U.K., 1912–18, 1919, *see* UNITED STATES: COMMERCE.

Patono (Benedetto), *see* ROBERTO (G.) B. P. di Meirano (1763–1830) e i suoi Mém. p. s. à l'hist. de la dern. guerre des Alpes, 1905.

Patouillet (Louis), *see* COLONIA (D. DE). *Dict. des livres Jansénistes &c.; [nouv. éd. augm. par L. P.], 1755.

Patres.

Analysis operum S.S. Patrum & script. eccl., 18t, 1780–96, *see* SCHRAM (D.)

Bibliotheca vet. patrum antiq. script. eccl., 14t, 1765–81, *see* GALLANDIUS (A.)

De optima legendorum eccl. patrum methodo &c., 1742, *see* VIGNEUL-MARVILLE (-DE), *ps.*

*Ephemeridum S. Patrum bono cum Deo edendarum institutum & scopus. [1–5 (Jan.–Majus) in 1v]. s4°. Flensburgi. 1708

Maxima bibliotheca vet. Patrum &c., 28t, 1677–1707, *see* LA BIGNE (M. DE).

Patriarchs. De testamentis 12 p., 1810, *see* NITZSCH (C. I.)

Hebrew text [*& tr.*] of 1 of the Test. of the 12 p. [Naphtali]. By M. Gaster. [Repr. f. Proc. of Soc. f. Bibl. Arch. P2810]. 8°. 1894

The testaments of the 12 p. Tr. into Lat. by R. Grosseteste, now Englished. s8°. 1638

,, ,, ...s8°. Glasgow. 1666

*__Patricia__ Brent, spinster, 1918, *see* JENKINS (H.)

Patricius Piccolomineus (Augustinus), *bp. of Pienza & Montalcino.* Sacrarum cæremoniarum libri tres, & a Marcello primum ed. Nunc innumeris mendis purgati & comm. aucti, auctore J. Catalano. 2t. fol. Romae. 1750–51

Patrick, *Saint, Apostle of Ireland.*

S. P. adscripta opuscula. Rec. &c. opera & studio J. Waraei. s8°. Londini. 1656

Writings & life [*by* Muirchu. Ed. w. intr. &c.] by N. J. D. White. [Tr. of Xtn. lit., s5]. s8°. 1920

see ARCHDEKIN (R.) Vitae &c. P., 1671.

see CZARNOWSKI (S.) Le culte des héros &c.: St. P., 1919.

,, LEO (H.) Comm. de carmine Hib. in S. P. scripta, 1845.

,, RIGUET (*l'abbé*). St. P., 1911.

,, THYRAEUS (G.) Discursus panegyrici de nominibus &c. S. P., 1617.

Patrick (David), *see* CHAMBERS, *publ. firm.* Encyclopaedia, n. ed., 1923–25.

Patrick (Diana). Call it a day! s8°. [1927]

Firefly. s8°. [1926]

Patrick (John), *D.D., Preacher to the Charterhouse.* *A full view of the doctrines &c. of the anc. Church rel. to Eucharist. [P2661]. s4°. 1688
see CHILLINGWORTH (W.) Mr. C.'s bk. called The relig. of Protestants &c. made more gen. useful &c. [*by* J. P.], 1867.

Patrick (Simon), *bp. of (1) Chichester, (2) Ely.*
Works incl. autobiogr. Ed. A. Taylor. 9v. 8°. O. 1858
The Book of Job paraphras'd [—Bk. of Psalms, 4th ed.—Proverbs of Solomon—Bk. of Ecclesiastes—Song of Solomon. *each w. sep. tp., pagin. cont.*] s4°. 1710
A comm. upon Genesis. 3rd ed., corr. s4°. 1704
A comm. upon Exodus. s4°. 1697
A comm. upon Leviticus. s4°. 1698
A comm. upon Numbers. s4°. 1699
A comm. upon Deuteronomy. s4°. 1700
A comm. upon Joshua, Judges & Ruth. s4°. 1702
A comm. upon the 2 Bks. of Samuel. s4°. 1703
A comm. upon the 2 Bks. of Kings. s4°. 1705
A comm. upon Chronicles, Ezra, Nehemiah & Esther. s4°. 1706
see LOWTH (W.) Comm. upon the larger & lesser Prophets; being cont. of Bp. P., 3rd ed., 1730; n. ed., 1822.

Patrizi (Maurizio Luigi). Il Caravaggio e la n. critica d'arte. la8°. Recanati. 1921

Patrizio Veneto. *Delle accoglienze usate dai Viniziani ai principi esteri, 1840, *see* GIACHETTI (V.), *ed.*

Patroni (Giovanni). Nora: colonia fenicia in Sardegna, *see* REALE ACCAD. D. LINCEI. Mon. ant., v14, 1904.
Vasi arcaici d. Puglie nel Museo Naz. di Napoli, *see* REALE ACCAD. D. LINCEI. Mon. ant., v6, 1895.
see CASTELFRANCO (P.) & G. P. Stazione palus. di Campo Castellaro, 1916.

Patry (Raoul). Le régime de la liberté des cultes dans le dépt. du Calvados, 1795–1802. 8°. 1921
La relig. dans l'Allemagne d'aujourd'hui. 8°. 1926

Patten (Marjorie), *see* BRUNNER (E. DE S.), G. S. HUGHES & M. P. Amer. agricult. villages, 1927.

Patten (Robert). Hist. of the rebellion in 1715, w. orig. papers &c. of the principal noblemen &c. concern'd in it. 3rd ed. [P2779]. 8°. 1745

Patten (Simon Nelson). The theory of social forces. [Suppl. to Annals of Amer. Acad. of Polit. &c. Sci., 1896]. 8°. Phila. 1896

Patterson (Arthur H.), *see* KNOWLITTLE (J.), *ps.*

Patterson (Charles Brodie).
Dominion & power: st. in spiritual sci. 8°. 1908

Patterson (David).
The provincialisms of Belfast &c. [P519]. 8°. Belfast. 1860

Patterson (J. G.) A Zola dict.: characters of the Rougon-Macquart novels, w. biog. &c. intr. &c. 8°. 1912

Patterson (J. R.), *ed., see* KANURI songs; tr. &c., 1926.

Patterson (*Lt.-Col.* John Henry). With the Judæans in the Palestine campaign. 8°. [1922]

Patterson (Leonard). Mithraism & Christianity. St. in comparative religion. s8°. C. 1921
Theodore of Mopsuestia & mod. thought. s8°. 1926

Patterson (Malcolm), *see* SAINT ANDREWS. St. A., poems by R. Kipling &c., drawings & etchings by M. P., 1926.

Patterson (Marjorie). A woman's man. s8°. 1920

Patterson (R. F.), *ed., see* DRUMMOND (W.) B. Jonson's conversations w. D., 1923.

Patterson (William Morrison). The rhythm of prose. [Columbia Univ.] 2nd ed. 8°. N.Y. 1917

Patti (Adelina Maria Clorinda) [*Baroness* ROLF CEDERSTRÖM], *see* KLEIN (H.) The reign of P., 1920.

Pattison (Samuel Rowles). Rise & progress of relig. life in England. s8°. 1864

Patton (M. J.) Nat. resources of Quebec. [Canada: Dept. of Int. P2874]. 8°. Ottawa. 1923

Patuzzi (Giovanni Vincenzo). De praeceptis fidei & de vitiis fidei oppositis, *see* MIGNE (J. P.), *ed.* Theol. cursus, t6, 1862.
Prodromus ad univ. morum theologiam—De ratione humana—De virtutibus moralibus &c., *see* MIGNE (J. P.), *ed.* Theol. cursus, t11, 1861.

Paudler (Fritz). Die hellfarbigen Rassen u. i. Sprachstämme, Kulturen u. Urheimaten. 8°. Heidelberg. 1924

Pauer (Rupert Gottlieb). Exercit. de novis fanaticorum quorundam purgatoriis. Sub præs. T. Ittigii, resp. R. G. P. [P2631]. s4°. Lipsiæ. [1703]

Paues (Anna C.), *see* BIBLIOGRAPHY of Eng. lang. & lit., 1921; ed. A. C. P., 1922.

Paul, *apostle & saint, see* BIBLE: PAUL &C.

Paul III, *pope.*
*Bulla Antichristi de retrahendo populo Dei in ferream Aegiptiacæ servitutis fornacem &c. [*Pref. by* Flacius Illyr. P2528]. s8°. *n.p.* 1549
Bulla indict. SS. gen. Concilii, [1536]. s4°. [Rome. 1536]
Concilium delectorum cardinalium &c. de emendanda eccl., Paulo III ipso jubente conscriptum & exhib. 1538. [Signed C. Card. Contarenus *& others*]. s4°. Coloniae, *Melchior Novesianus.* 1538
Ein Sendbrieff u. vermanung zum fride Röm. K. M., durch Legaten den Cardinal von Visen vberantwort [26 Aug. 1542]. Darauff: Römischer K. M. Antwort [18 Oct. 1542]. Newlich aus d. Latein verdeutscht 1543. [P2439]. s4°. [Nuremberg. 1543 ?]
see BROSCH (M.) Zu d. Confl. Karls V mit P. III, *n.d.*
,, CAPASSO (C.) Paolo III, 1534–49, v1, 1924.
,, FLACIUS (M.) Epist. de morte P. III, 1578.
,, SCHMALKALD, *League of.* Causae quare synod. indict. a P. III recus. principes &c., 1537.

Paul IV, *pope.*
see BROSCH (M.) P. IV gegen Karl V. &c., *n.d.*
,, PASTOR (L. v.) Hist. of the Popes; tr., v14, 1555–59, 1924.

Paul V, *pope.*
Controversiae memorabilis inter P. V & Venetos de excommunicatione contra eosdem Venetos Romae promulgata 17 Aprilis 1606 acta & scripta varia [*each w. sep. tp.; 2 pagin.*] s8°. In villa San Vincentiana. 1607
The famous Bull in Caena [*sic*] Domini publ. at Rome every Maundy Thursday against hereticks &c. s4°. *n.p.* 1688
see BECANUS (M.) *Supplicatio ad Imperatorem &c., contra P. V, 1613.
,, LEMOS (T. DE). Acta omnia Congregat. ac Disput. coram P. V &c., 1702.
,, PASTOR (L. v.) Gesch. d. Päpste, B12, 1927.
,, SERVANTIO (G.) Difesa d. potestà &c. eccl. contro le 8 propos. di un dottore incogn. sopra il Breve di censure d. papa P. V, 1606.

Paul I, *emperor of Russia, see* KARATOV (F. V.) II. I, 1903.

Paul, *of Samosata, bp. of Antioch.* Eine fing. Korresp. mit P. d. S., *w. Gr. text, see* KÖN. AKAD. D. W. ZU MÜNCHEN. Sitz., Phil. &c. Kl., 1927.
see BARDY (G.) P. de S.: ét. hist., 1923.
,, LOOFS (F.) Paulus v. S.: Unters. z. altkirchl. Lit.- u. Dogmengesch., 1924.
,, SCHNIZLIN (J. G. C.) Diss. de haeresi P. S. &c., 1741.

Paul Vladimir, *of Cracow* [PAULUS VOLADIMIRUS]. Demonstratio cruciferis de Prussia oppos., 1415, *see* †HARDT (H. V. D.) Rerum Conc. Const. t3, 1698.

Paul (Adolf Georg). The language of birds. Comedy. Tr. A. Travers-Borgstroem. Intr. H. C. Shelley. s8°. 1922

Paul (Cedar), *see* PAUL (E.) & C. P.

Paul (Eden) & C. Paul. Communism. [P2563]. 8°. 1921
Creative revolution: st. of communist ergatocracy. 8°. [1920]

Paul (Hermann). Üb. Kontamination auf syntakt. Gebiete, *see* KÖNIGL. AKAD. D. W. ZU MÜNCHEN. Phil. Kl., Sitz., 1919.
Die Umschreibung d. Perfektums im Deutschen mit haben u. sein, *see* KÖNIGL. AKAD. D. W. ZU MÜNCHEN. Phil. Kl., Sitz., 1918.

Paul (*Sir* John Dean). *Journal of a party of pleasure to Paris in 1802. 8°. 1802

Paul (Pierre). Le card. M. de Polignac, 1661–1741. la8°. 1922

Paul (Robert Bateman) [*ps.* JAMES HAMLEY TREGENNA].
Journal of a tour to Moscow, in summer of 1836. s8°. 1836

Paul-Boncour (Joseph). Le fédéralisme écon. 2e éd. Préf. de M. Waldeck-Rousseau. 8°. 1901

Paulding (James Kirke), *see* HEROLD (A. L.) J. K. P., versatile American, 1926.

Paulhan (Fr.)
Les transformations sociales des sentiments. s8°. 1920

Pauli (Gustav). Inkunabeln d. deut. u. niederländ. Radierung. Hrsg. G. P. [Graph. Gesells. Veröff. 8]. fol. 1908

Pauli (Reinhold). Life of Alfred the Gt. App., Alfred's version of Orosius, w. tr. &c. by B. Thorpe. s8°. *Bohn.* 1902

Paulin (George). No struggle for existence—no natural selection. Exam. of Darwinian theory. 8°. E. 1908

Paulinier (Pierre Antoine Justin), *bp. of Grenoble, abp. of Besauçon.* Le concile œcumén. 8°. 1869

Paulinus, *patriarch of Aquileia, d. 802, see* SAVORGNAN (C. G. DI B.) Enrico, duca, S. Paolina &c., 1903.

Paulinus, *Saint, bp. of Nola.* Carmen 11–13 in S. Felicem, *see* MINGARELLI (G. L.) Anecdotorum fasc., 1756.

Paullain (Valérand) [POLLANUS]. Antidotus V. P., *see* DATHENUS (P.) Kurtze u. warhafft. erzelung &c., 1598.

Paulli (Simon). Comment. de abusu tabaci & herbae theé &c. s4°. Argentorati. 1665
Paullin (Charles Oscar) & F. L. Paxson. Guide to the materials in London archives for the hist. of the U.S. since 1783. [C.I. of Wash.] la8°. Wash. 1914
Paullo (Ambrogio da), *see* AMBROGIO, *da Paullo.*
Paul-Margueritte (Lucie), *see* MARGUERITTE (LUCIE PAUL).
***Paul's** letters to h. kinsfolk, 1816, *see* SCOTT (*Sir* W.)
Paulsen (Friedrich). Schopenhauer—Hamlet—Mephistopheles. 3 Aufsätze z. Naturgesch. d. Pessimismus. s8°. St. 1926
Paulsen (Ove).
St. on the vegetation of Pamir. la8°. Copenhagen. 1920
St. on the vegetation of the Transcaspian Lowlands. la8°. Copenhagen. 1912
Paulsen (Rudolf). Gespräche des Lebens. Gedichte. s8°. 1911
Im Schnee d. Zeit. Gedichte. s8°. 1922
Lieder aus Licht u. Liebe. 8°. 1912
Paulsiek (K.) Deutsches Lesebuch für Vorschulen. Neu bearb. v. C. Muff.
Abt. 1 (f. Octava). 13e A. d. n. Bearb. 8°. 1907
Paulus, *Ægineta.* Paulus Aegineta, libri 1–7, 2p; ed. L. L. Heiberg., see CORPUS MEDICORUM GRAECORUM, v9i, ii, 1921–24.
Paulus, *abbot of Altenzelle, see* BACHMANN (P.)
Paulus, *Burgensis, see* PAULUS, *de Sancta Maria.*
Paulus, *de Castro, see* CUJAS (J.) Opera, t5 (in lib. 1 Pauli ad edict. comm.), 1777.
Paulus, *diaconus.* Gedichte; krit. u. erkl. Ausg. v. K. Neff. [Traube (L.), *ed.* Quellen &c. z. lat. Philol. d. M-A., B3iv]. la8°. München. 1908
Hist. Langobardorum. [Scr. rerum Germ. in usum schol.] 8°. Hannoverae. 1878
Hist. Romana [Scr. rerum Germ. in usum schol.] 8°. Berolini. 1879
Paulus, *Samosatenus, see* PAUL, *of Samosata, bp. of Antioch.*
Paulus, *de Sancta Maria, bp. of (1) Carthagena, (2) Burgos.*
Contra perfidiam Judaeorum, *see* BIBLE: LATIN. Biblia Sacra &c., t6, 1634.
De nomine tetragrammato, *see* DRUSIUS (J.), *elder.* Tetragrammaton, 1634.
Paulus (Heinr. Eberhard Gottlob).
Historia Cerinthi. 2p *in* 1v. 8°. Jenae. [1795]
see BIBLIOTHEK. Bibl. v. Anzeigen u. Auszügen kl. akad. Schriften &c., 1790–92.
Paulus (Joseph), *see* ENCYCLOPÆDIE van Nederl.-Indië, 2e druk; samengesteld door J. P., d3, 4, 1919–21.
Paulus (Nikolaus). Gesch. d. Ablasses im Mittelalter. 2B [*in 1v*]. 8°. Paderborn. 1922–23
Pauly (August Friedrich v.) Real-Encyclopädie d. class. Altertumswiss. Neue Bearbtg. begonnen v. G. Wissowa; hrsg. v. W. Kroll. B10ii, 11. la8°. St. 1919–22
Real-Encyclopädie d. class. Altertumswiss. Neue Bearbtg., begonnen v. G. Wissowa; hrsg. W. Kroll u. K. Witte. 2e Reihe, B1, 2. Ra-Sila. 8°. St. 1920–23
Paunat. Fragments de cartul. du monastère de P. [Publ.] par R. Poupardin & A. Thomas. [Extr. des Annales du Midi, t18, 1906. P2469]. 8°. Toulouse. 1906
Pausanias. Descr. arcis Athenarum. Ed. O. Jahn. ed. 2a recog. ab A. Michaelis. 4°. Bonnae. 1880
Descr. Græciae. Rec. L. Dindorfius. Graece et Latine cum indice. la8°. Parisiis, *Didot.* 1845
Descr. of Greece. [Text] w. Eng. tr. by W. H. S. Jones & H. A. Ormerod. [Loeb Class. Lib.] v2. s8°. 1926
Pauthier (J. P. Guillaume). Vindiciae Sinicae. Dern. rép. à S. Julien suivie d'un parallèle de sa nouv. tr. de Lao-Tseu &c. 8°. 1842
„ „ Suppl. [P2565]. 8°. [1843]
see JULIEN (S. A.) Simple exposé d'un fait honorable, libelle de M. P., 1842.
Pauw (Cornelius), *1739–99.* *Recherches philos. sur les Américains. Par Mr. de P***. Avec. diss. sur l'Amérique par Dom Pernety. 3t. s8°. Londres. 1771
Pauw (Napoléon de), *see* ARTEVELDE, *The family of.* Cartul. hist. & généalog. des A.; [*ed.*] par N. de P., 1920.
Pauwels (Josephus). Tract. de casibus reservatis, *see* MIGNE (J. P.), *ed.* Theol. cursus, t18, 1862.
Pavanello (Giuseppe). La strada e il traghetto d. Fossetta. 8°. Venezia. 1906
Pavani (Giuseppe). Un vescovo belga in Italia nel sec. 10: Raterio di Verona. 8°. Torino. 1920
Pavet de Courteille (Abel Jean Baptiste). Dict. turk-oriental. [*Turkish-Fr. Founded on a Turk. orig. known as Abushkah*]. la8°. Paris. 1870
Pavia (Luigi).
Gramm. d. lingua spagnuola. 2a ed. 8°. Roma. 1901
Pavie (André). Revivre. Roman. s8°. 1921
Pavlov (Ivan Petrovich). Conditioned reflexes: investig. of physiolog. activity of the cerebral cortex. Tr. & ed. G. V. Anrep. la8°. 1927
Pavlovitch (Michel). Found. of imperialist policy. s8°. [1922]
Pàvry (Jal Dastur Cursetji). Zoroastrian doct. of a future life. [Columbia Univ.] 8°. N.Y. 1926
Pawlyn (John S.) Bristol Methodism in John Wesley's day &c. s8°. Bristol. [1877]
Fallen on the field: mem. of A. H. Clegg, missionary to the Gambia. s8°. 1889
Pax. *The Vatican Decrees & Cath. allegiance; reply to Gladstone's polit. expost., 1874, *see* GLADSTONE (*Rt. Hon.* W. E.)
Paxson (Frederic Logan). Hist. of the American frontier, 1763–1893. 8°. Boston, Mass. 1924
Recent hist. of the U.S. 8°. Boston [U.S.] 1921
see PAULLIN (C. O.) & F. L. P. Guide to materials in London archives for hist. of U.S. since 1783, 1914.
Paxton (*Sir* Joseph), *see* HORTICULTURAL REGISTER (THE); [ed.] J. P. &c., v1, 2, 1831–33.
Payan (Auguste). Le sanctuaire de Notre Dame du Rosaire à Val de Pompei, d'ap. les écrits de B. Longo. 2t *in* 1v. s8°. Valle di Pompei. 1894
Paycocke, *The family of, see* POWER (E.) The Paycockes of Coggeshall, 1920.
Payer (Friedrich). Von Bethmann Hollweg bis Ebert. Erinner. &c. 8°. Fr. am M. 1923
Payne (Albert Henry), *see* BICKNELL (W. I.) Illust. London: views engraved by A. H. P., 2p, 1846–47.
Payne (C. H.) Scenes & characters f. Indian hist. Comp. &c. w. notes by P. s8°. 1925
Payne (Edward John), *fellow of Univ. Coll., Oxford.*
Hist. of European colonies. s8°. 1877
Payne (*Rev.* George), *LL.D.*
The doctrine of original sin. 8°. 1845
Elements of mental & moral science. 8°. 1828
„ „ ....4th ed. 8°. 1856
Lectures on Xtn. theology: w. mem. by J. Pyer, & remin. by R. Wardlaw. 2v. 8°. 1850
Payne (James Bertrand). Lineage &c. of family of Millais, 1331–1865. Extr. fr. "Armorial of Jersey." fol. *p.p.* 1865
Payne (John), *a. of "The Masque of Shadows."* Nature & h. lover & o. poems. Intr. by T. Wright. 8°. Olney. 1922
The Quatrains of Ibn et Tefrid. Intr. by T. Wright. 8°. Olney. 1921
The way of the winepress. Intr. by T. Wright. 8°. 1920
Payne (Nevil).
*The fatal jealousie. Tragedy. [? *by* N. P.] 8°. 1673
Payne Smith (Robert), *dean of Canterbury; 1819–95.*
Thesaurus Syriacus: Suppl. coll. &c. by J. P. Margoliouth. 4°. O. 1927
Payot (Jules). La conquête du bonheur. 3e mille. 8°. 1921
L'éducation de la volonté. 3e éd. 8°. 1895
Payot de Lignières (François, *sieur*), *1626–1704.*
see MAGNE (E.) Un ami de Cyrano de Bergerac, le Chev. de L., 1920.
„ LACHÈVRE (F.) Derniers libertins, 1924.
Payro (Roberto J.) Divertidas aventuras del nieto de Juan Moreira. 8°. Barcelona. [1918]
Pays-Bas.
Confession de foy, faicte d'un commun accord par les fideles qui conversent és pays bas, 1561, 1855, *see* CONFESSION.
Corr. de la cour d'Espagne sur les Pays-Bas au 17e s., t1, 2, 1923–27, *see* LONCHAY (H.) & J. CUVELIER.
*Exposé hist. de l'état de l'église réformée des Pays-Bas &c. 8°. Amsterdam. 1855
Payson (*Rev.* Edward). *Life of Rev. E. P. s8°. [1833]
Payva (Jacobus), *see* PAIVA DE ANDRADE (D. DE).
Paz (Jacobus Alvarez de), *see* ALVAREZ DE PAZ (JACOBUS), *Jesuit.*
Pazaurek (Gustav E.)
Kunstgläser d. Gegenwart. la8°. L. 1925
Paz Soldán (Mariano Felipe).
Hist. del Perú independiente (1822–27). t2. 8°. 1919

Paz y Melia (Antonio). Series de los mas importantes doc. del archivio y bibl. del Duque de Medinaceli. Publ. par P. y M. s2, Bibliografica. fol. [1922]

Peabody (Elizabeth Palmer). Crimes of the House of Austria &c. Coll. & ed. by E. P. P. s8°. N.Y. 1852

Peabody (Francis Greenwood).
The Apostle Paul & the mod. world. 8°. N.Y. 1923

Peabody (Frederick W.), see Riley (W.), F. W. P. &c. Faith, falsity &c. of Xtn. Science, 1926.

Peace.
Mem. pres. to the Peace Conf. in Paris, by deleg. of Jugoslav members of parl. repres. districts occup. by Ital. army. [P2687]. fol. [Paris. 1919?]
Mem. pres. to the Peace Conf. in Paris conc. claims of Serbians, Croatians & Slovenes [*& o. memoranda b. together as below*]. sm. fol. *n.p.* [1919]
Albania—Dalmatian Question—Frontiers betw. Serbians &c. & Italy—Goritza & Gradiska—Istria—Milit. effort of Serbians &c.—North Frontier—Riyeka (Fiume)—Serbians & Roumanians in the Banat—Serbo-Bulgarian relations—Triest.
*Peace againe in Sion &c., England & Scotland united, the Scots departure f. Newcastle. [*b. w.* Truths discovery, 1646]. s8°. 1641
*Peace in Europe; by Augur, 1927, see Poliakoff (V.)

Peace movement (The). Organ of the Internat. Peace Bureau in Berne, 1912–19. 8°. Berne. 1912–19
1912–13, *issued fortnightly.* 1914, *monthly.* 1915–19, *have t.* Le mouvement pacifiste *& are in French, issue irregular.*

Peace with Ireland Council. [*Leaflets &c.,* by G. K. Chesterton *& others.* P2530]. 8°. [1920–21]

Peace (Charles). C. P., or the adv. of a burglar. la8°. *n.d.*
see Gaskell (N. K.) The career of C. P., 1906.

Peacey (Howard). El Dorado. Play. s8°. O. 1925
The Fifth of November. Play. s8°. 1924
Warren Hastings [play]. s8°. *Cayme Press.* 1928

Peach (Benjamin Neeve). Monogr. on the higher Crustacea on the carbonif. rocks of Scotland, see Geolog. Survey. Mem.: Palæontology, v1i, 1908.

Peach (L. du Garde). Wind o' the Moors, see Clarke (A. K.) 3 one-act plays, 1925.

Peacham (Henry). The worth of a penny: or a caution to keep money. s8°. 1695

Peachey (George C.)
Memoir of Will. & John Hunter. 8°. Plymouth. 1924
William Bromfield, 1713–1792. [Repr. f. R. Soc. of Med., Proc., v8. P2852]. la8°. 1915

Peacock (John), *author of "Songs of praise."*
Songs of praise. s8°. 1776

Peacock (Reginald), *bp. of (1) St. Asaph, (2) Chichester* [Pecock].
Collectanea quaedam, see Fox (J.) Comm., 1554.
The donet. Ed. & coll. w. The poore mennis myrrour, by E. V. Hitchcock. [E.E.T.S., 156]. 8°. 1921
The folewer to the Donet. Ed., w. intr. on P.'s lang. & style, by E. V. Hitchcock. [E.E.T.S., 164]. 8°. 1924
The reule of Crysten religioun. Ed. W. C. Greet. [E.E.T.S., 171]. 8°. 1927

Peacock (Thomas Love). Crotchet Castle. s8°. 1831
Nightmare Abbey. Repr. f. ed. of 1818. s8°. 1923
Peacock's Four ages of poetry—Shelley's Defence of poetry—Browning's Essay on Shelley. Ed. by H. F. B. Brett-Smith. [Percy Repr. No. 3]. 8°. O. 1921
see Newbolt (*Sir* H. J.) P., Scott & Robin Hood, 1924.
„ Priestley (J. B.) T. L. P., 1927.
„ Wright (H.) Assoc. of T. L. P. w. Wales, 1926.

Peacock (W.)
English prose. Chosen & arr. by W. P. 5v. s8°. [1921–22]
English prose f. Mandeville to Ruskin. Chosen & arr. by W. P. [7th impr.] s8°. [1921]
Sel. Eng. essays. Chosen & arr. by W. P. [repr.] s8°. [1922]

Peake (Arthur Samuel). Brotherhood in the Old Test. John Clifford lect., 1923. s8°. [1923]
A comm. on the Bible. Ed. A. S. P., w. assist. of A. J. Grieve. 8°. 1920
The People & the Book: essays on the O.T. by H. R. Hall, S. A. Cook &c. Ed. A. S. P. s8°. O. 1925
The Revelation of John. [Hartley lect.] s8°. [1920]

Peake (Harold). The bronze age & the Celtic world. 4°. 1922
The English village: orig. & decay of its community. 8°. 1922

Peake (Harold) [*contd.*] **& H. J. Fleure.**
Apes & men. [Corridors of time, 1]. 8°. O. 1927
Hunters & artists. [Corridors of time, 2]. 8°. O. 1927
Peasants & potters. [Corridors of time, 3]. 8°. O. 1927
Priests & kings. [Corridors of time, 4]. 8°. O. 1927

Pear (Tom Hatherley).
Remembering & forgetting. 8°. [1922]

Pearce (Charles E.) Madame Vestris & h. times. 8°. [1923]

Pearce (Ernest Harold), *bp. of Worcester.* Hartlebury Castle, w. notes on bishops who lived in it &c. 8°. 1926
Thomas de Cobham, bp. of Worcester, 1317–27: st. f. h. register w. acc. of h. life. 8°. 1923
Walter de Wenlok, abbot of Westminster. 8°. 1920
William de Colchester, abbot of Westminster. s8°. 1915

Pearce (Ethel Katharine).
Typical flies. Photographic atlas. 2s. la8°. C. 1915–21

Pearce (Joseph Pearce).
Reveries in a village church. la8°. 1921

Pearce (Samuel), *Baptist minister, 1766–99.*
see Fuller (A.) Mem. of S. P., *n.d.*
„ Jackson (T.) Lib. of Xtn. biog., v4, S. P., by A. Fuller, 1838.

Pearce (Villiers).
The life of V. P. [*by himself.* P2827]. 8°. 1856

Pearce (William Howard), see Hoby (J.) Mem. of W. Yates, w. abr. of h. life of P., 1847.

Pearcey (Fred. Gordon). Foraminifera of the Scot. Nat. Antarctic Exped. [Extr. f. Royal Soc. of Edinb. Trans., v49. P2875]. 4°. E. 1914

Peard (W. H.), see Bagshaw (J. F. G.) Pract. banking; w. ch. on bank book-keeping by P., 1920.

Pearl: Eng. poem of the 14th c., re-set in mod. Eng. by I. Gollancz. 8°. 1918
*Pearl: Eng. poem of the 14th c. Ed. w. mod. rendering, w. Boccaccio's Olympia, by Sir I. Gollancz. s8°. 1921
Pearl, Cleanness, Patience & Sir Gawain. Reprod. in facs. f. MS. Cotton Nero A. x. in the Brit. Mus. Intr. by Sir I. Gollancz. [E.E.T.S., 162]. la8°. 1923

Pearl (Raymond). Alcohol & mortality, see Starling (E. H.) Action of alcohol on man, 1923.
Biology of death. Lect., Lowell Inst., 1920. 8°. Phila. [1922]
Biology of population growth. 8°. 1926

Pears (*Maj.-Gen. Sir* **Thomas Townsend).** Extract f. overland journey to India in 1837. Added, Sh. acc. of h. life &c. [*Typescript*]. sm. fol. [1924?]

Pearse (*Mrs.* **Cecilia**), *wife of Godfrey Pearse, form. Candia.*
The enchanted past. 8°. 1926

Pearse (Patrick H.) Coll. works. Polit. writings & speeches. 8°. D. 1922

Pearson (A. F. Scott). Thomas Cartwright & Elizabethan Puritanism, 1535–1603. 8°. C. 1925

Pearson (*Lt.-Col.* **Alfred**). The early fortifications of Rome. [P2838]. 8°. Rome. 1877

Pearson (Alfred Chilton). Verbal scholarship & the growth of some abstract terms. [P2595]. s8°. C. 1922

Pearson (*Sir* **Arthur**), *1st bart.*
The conquest of blindness. s8°. [1921]

Pearson (Charles Henry).
Constitut. question in Victoria. [P2832]. 8°. [1879]

Pearson (Edmund Lester). Murder at Smutty Nose & o. murders. 8°. 1927

Pearson (Hesketh). Modern men & mummers. 8°. [1921]
*The whispering gallery. Leaves f. a diplomat's diary. [repr.] 8°. [1926]

Pearson (Hugh Nicholas), *dean of Salisbury.* A diss. on the propag. of Christianity in Asia. Pref. a view of the progress of the gospel in diff. nations &c. 4°. O. 1808

Pearson (John), *bp. of Chester.*
Critici sacri: sive annot. doct. virorum in Vet. ac Nov. Test. &c. [Ed. J. P., A. Scattergood, F. Gouldman & R. Pearson]. ed. nova. 9t. fol. Amstelaedami. 1698
An expos. of the Creed. 11th ed. corr. [*w. portrait*]. fol. 1723
„ „ n. ed. rev. by J. Nichols. 8°. [1854]
„ „ ....6th ed. 8°. O. 1877
„ „: w. anal. by W. H. Mill. v1. 8°. [1890]
Opera posthuma chronologica &c. Cur. &c. H. Dodwellus. [*3 pagin.* s4°. Londini. 1687–88]

Pearson (John), *F.R.S., Surgeon.* The life of W. Hey. [w. extracts f. h. wr.] 2nd ed. 2v. 8°. 1823

Pearson (Karl).
Charles Darwin, 1809–82, see University Coll., *Lond.* Questions, No. 12, 1923.

Pearson (Karl) [*continued*].
Francis Galton, 1822–1922, *see* UNIV. COLL., *Lond.* Questions, No. 11, 1922.
King Robert the Bruce, 1274–1329; skull & portraiture. [Offpr. f. Biometrika, v16]. sm. fol. [1925]
Life, letters & labours of F. Galton. 2v. 4°. C. 1914–24
Mendelism & the problem of mental defect. 3, On graduated char. of m. d. &c., 1914, *see* UNIV. COLL., *Lond.* Questions, No. 9, 1914.
On the skull & portraits of G. Buchanan. la8°. 1926
The science of man. Address, Brit. Assoc., 1920, *see* UNIV. COLL., *Lond.* Questions, No. 10, 1920.
Pearson (Peter Henry). Schools of Scandinavia &c., 1919, *see* UNITED STATES: EDUCATION.
Pearson (R. O.), *see* RANWORTH. R. rood screen; drawn by P., *n.d.*
Peasant art of Subcarpathian Russia, 1926, *see* MAKOVSKY (S.)
Pease, *The family of, see* FOSTER (S. B.) Pedigrees of P. of Hutton &c., 1890.
Pease (*Sir* Alfred Edward), *bart.* Edmund Loder: a memoir. With contrib. by St. G. Littledale, C. G. A. Nix &c. 8°. 1923
Pease (Howard). Northumbria's decameron. 8°. [1927]
Peasenhall. *The Peasenhall murder case, 1902, *see* GARDINER (W.)
Pecchiai (Pio). La Brianza. [P2860]. 4°. Milano. *n.d.*
Pecchio (*il conte* Giuseppe). Vita di U. Foscolo. Intr. &c. di P. T. Mattiucci. [Doc. di storia lett. ital., 2]. s8°. Città di Castello. 1915
Pechat i Revolutsiya. Печать и Революция. Журнал лит., искусства &c. под ред. А. В. Луначарского &c. [Р.С.Ф.С.Р.] 1922, кн. 7, 8 (Сент.-Дек.); 1923, кн. 1, 2, 4; 1924, кн. 1–6. la8°. Москва. 1922–24
Pechey (John). The compleat herbal of physical plants. s8°. 1694
Peck (Annie Smith), *F.R.G.S.* The South American tour: a descr. guide. n. & rev. ed. 8°. [1924]
Peck (Emelyn Foster). Adoption laws in U.S., *see* UNITED STATES: LABOR. Children's Bur., Publ. 148, 1925.
Peck (George). Life & times of Rev. G. Peck, wr. by himself. s8°. N.Y. 1874
Peck (Robert), *1782–1855, see* MILLS (J.) Mem. of R. P., 1856.
Peck (William), *astronomer.* The constellations & how to find them. la8°. *n.d.*
Peckard (Peter), *dean of Peterborough.* Memoirs of the life of N. Ferrar. 8°. C. 1790
Peckham (Joannes), *abp. of Canterbury* [PECHAM], *see* SPETTMANN (H.) Die Psychologie d. J. P., 1919.
Peckham (W. D.), *see* SUSSEX. Thirteen custumals of S. manors &c.; tr. & ed. W. D. P., 1925.
Pecock (Reynold), *see* PEACOCK (REGINALD).
Pecquet (Pierre), *1584–1656, see* ALIX (F.) Un moine bibliophile au 17ᵉ s.: P. P., 1912.
Pedan (Alexander), *see* PEDEN (A.)
Peddie (Alexander), *M.D.* Recoll. of Dr. J. Brown, w. sel. f. h. corresp. 8°. 1893
Peddie (John Taylor). Capitalism is socialism w. econ. adjustments. Foreword by G. C. Vyle. s8°. 1926
Cause of econ. & soc. unrest. s8°. 1927
Peddie (Robert Alexander). Conspectus incunabul. Index cat. of 15 c. books w. references to Hain &c. pl (A–B). 8°. 1910
Peddie (William). Colour vision. 8°. 1922
Peden (Alexander) [PEDAN (A.)] *The life of Mr. A. P., minister of the Ch. of Scot. [P2675]. s8°. *n.p.* 1788
Pedersen (Holger).
Works in KONG. DAN. VIDENSKAB. SELSK. Hist.-filol. Medd.
La 5ᵉ déclinaison lat., 1926. [11.]
Les formes sigmat. du verbe latin & le probb. du futur indo-européen, 1920–1. [3.]
Le groupement des dialectes indo-europ., 1925. [11.]
Pedersen (Johs.) Israel, its life & culture. [Tr.] 8°. [1926]
***Pedigree** of the fam. of Tristram, of Belbroughton, Worcs., 1904, *see* TRISTRAM.
Pedler (*Mrs.* Margaret). The barbarian lover. s8°. [1923]
Bitter heritage. s8°. [1927]
The lamp of fate. [repr.] s8°. *n.d.*
Red ashes. s8°. [1924]
Yesterday's harvest. s8°. [1926]
Pedraza (Cristòbal). Rel. de var. suc. en Honduras, 1539, *see* SERRANO Y SANZ (M.) Rel. hist., 1916.
Pedrell (Felipe).
Cancionero musical pop. español. 4t. 8°. Valls. [1918–22]
Pedro (Valentín de). El Arlequín Azul. s8°. [1923]
España renaciente. Opiniones &c. s8°. 1922
Los mejores cuentos venezolanos. Prol., sel. y notas de V. de P. s8°. Barcelona. 1923
Peebles. Charters & docs. rel. to the Burgh of P., w. extr. f. the records, 1165–1710. [Ed. W. Chambers, Scottish Burgh Rec. Soc.] 4°. E. 1872
Peeblesshire. Hist. of Peeblesshire; [*by var. a.*], 3v, 1925–27, *see* BUCHAN (J. W.), *ed.*
Peel (Albert), *M.A.* The Brownists in Norwich & Norfolk about 1580, w. A treatise of the Church & the Kgdm. of Christ, by R. H. [*i.e.* Robert Harrison?]. [*b. w. h.* First Congreg. Churches, 1920]. 8°. C. 1920
The first Congregat. Churches, 1567–81. 8°. C. 1920
100 eminent Congregationalists, 1530–1924. s8°. [1927]
Peel (*Hon.* Arthur George Villiers).
The econ. impact of America. 8°. 1928
The financial crisis of France. 8°. 1925
see PEEL (*Rt. Hon. Sir* **R.**) Private letters; ed. G. P., 1920.
Peel (*Mrs.* Charles S.)
A hundred wonderful years, 1820–1920. 8°. [1926]
Peel (Ethel), *see* PEEL (*Lady* G. A.) Recoll.; comp. by h. daughter, E. P., 1920.
Peel (*Hon.* George), *see* PEEL (*Hon.* A. G. V.)
Peel (*Lady* Georgina Adelaide), *daughter of 1st Earl Russell.* Recoll. Comp. by h. daughter, E. Peel. la8°. 1920
Peel (*Rt. Hon. Sir* Robert), *2nd bart., 1788–1850.* Bibl. Hibernicana: cat. of a sel. Irish library, coll. for R. P. 8°. D. 1823
Private letters. Ed. G. Peel. 8°. 1920
see WALLACE (T.) *3 letters addr. to Sir R. P. &c., 1835.
Peel (William Ralph), *see* ORWIN (C. S.) & W. R. P. The tenure of agricult. land, 1925.
Peele (George), *see* GREG (W. W.) 2 Elizabethan stage abridgements: the Battle of Alcazar &c., 1922.
***Peeping Tom** of Coventry: comic opera, 1792, *see* O'KEEFFE (J.)
Peerage. *Biograph. p. of Gt. Brit., 3v, 1808–9, *see* BRYDGES (*Sir* S. E.)
*Biograph. p. of Ireland &c., 1817, *see* BRYDGES (*Sir* S. E.)
***Peers** (The), or the people. [*sgd.* A Reformer]. [P2782]. 8°. 1834
Peers (Gertrude Katherine), *wife of Charles Reed Peers.* Early Northern painters: st. in the Nat. Gallery. 8°. 1922
The saints in story. 8°. 1910
Peers (Edgar Allison).
Angel de Saavedra, Duque de Rivas: crit. study, *see* REVUE HISPANIQUE, t58, 1923.
Elizabethan drama & its mad folk. 8°. C. 1914
Rivas & romanticism in Spain. 8°. 1923
Spanish mysticism, a prelim. survey. 8°. 1924
St. of the Spanish mystics. v1. 8°. 1927
see FINCH (M. B.) & E. A. P. Origins of French romanticism, 1920.
Peet (Thomas Eric). Egypt & the Old Test. 8°. Liv'l. 1922
—— **& C. L. Woolley.** The city of Akhenaten. With chapters by B. Gunn & P. L. O. Guy. [Egypt. Explor. Fund. Mem. 38]. pl. 4°. 1923
Peez (Ernst Alex. v.)
England u. d. Kontinent. 9ᵉ A. [P2495]. 8°. 1915
Peggs (James). A hist. of the Baptist Miss. establ. in [Orissa], *see* STERLING (A.) Orissa, 1846.
The infanticide's cry to Britain. 4th ed. [P2759]. 8°. 1844
Pegna (Francesco), *see* EYMERICUS (N.) Directorium Inquisit. cum scholiis F. P. & F. P. Disput. de auctor. Inq., 1578.
Péguy (Charles Pierre). Œuvres complètes. [t9]. 8°. 1924
9, Œuvres posthumes: Note conjointe sur M. Descartes préc. de la note sur M. Bergson.
Le mystère de la charité de Jeanne d'Arc. t2. s8°. [1926]
see THARAUD (J.) & J. THARAUD. Notre cher P., 2t, 1926.
Peichich (Christophorus). Speculum veritatis inter Orientalem & Occid. Eccl. refulgens. Auctum Latinè. s8°. Venetiis. 1725
Peignot (E. Gabriel). Répertoire bibliogr. univ. 8°. 1812
Peintres. *Quelques p. suisses, 1921, *see* SUISSE.
Peirce (Hayford) & R. Tyler. Byzantine art. 8°. 1926
Peirce (James). A paraphrase &c. on Colossians, Philippians & Hebrews. Annexed, crit. diss. on partic. texts. With a paraph. & notes on the 3 last chap. of the Hebrews &c. by J. Hallett. [*5 sep. tp. & pagin.*] 2nd ed. s4°. 1733
Peirce (Paul Skeels), *see* FISK (G. M.) & P. S. P. Internat. commercial policies, 1923.

Peirenc de Moras (Anne Marie), *ctsse. de Courbon, see* MORAS (A. M.)

Peiresc (Nicolas Claude de Fabri, *seigneur* **de).**
Corresp. avec plus. missionnaires & religieux de l'O. des Capucins, 1631–37. Rec. par Apollinaire de Valence; préf. par P. Tamizey de Larroque. la8°. 1891
Corresp. inéd. avec J. Aleandre &c. Publ. Fauris de St.-Vincens. [Extr. des Annales encycl. *b. w.* Boissard (H.) Disc., 1867]. 8°. 1819
Fêtes de P., nov. 1895. Discours &c. 8°. Aix. 1896
Lettre inéd. au Card. de Sourdis [1622]. Intr. par A. de Lantenay. la8°. Bordeaux. 1878
Notes inéd. sur points d'hist. nat. Publ. P. Tamizey de Larroque [Extr. du Bull. de la Soc. Sci. &c. des Basses-Alpes, 1895–96]. 8°. Digne. 1896
Séance publ. pour l'érection d'un mon. à P., Aix, 11 mai 1894. [Iconographie, par M. Guillibert. Biog. *by* C. Joret]. 8°. Aix. 1894
see BOISSARD (H.) Discours: P., 1867.
,, GUIBERT (J.) Dessins du Cabinet Peiresc de la Bibl. Nat., 1910.
,, JORET (C.) Fabri de P. humaniste &c., 1894.
,, LEGRÉ (L.) L'indigénat en Provence du Styrax officinal: P. Pena & P., 1901.
,, MOURAVIT (G.) P. le lettré &c., 1896.
,, RICCI (S. DE). Un nouv. ms. de P., 1900.
,, TAMIZEY DE LARROQUE. Deux jardiniers émérites—Peiresc & V. Robin, 1896.
,, —— Le livre de raison du muet de Laincel d'ap. les mss. de P., 1895.
,, —— P., abbé de Guitres, 1893.
,, —— & A. MOUTTEL. Autour de P., 1898.
,, WRIGHT (C. T. H.) N. Fabri de Peiresc, 1926.

Peitz (Wilhelm M.) Liber diurnus: Beitr. z. Kenntn. d. ältest. päpstl. Kanzlei vor Gregor d. Grossen, I, *see* KAISERL. AKAD. D. W. ZU WIEN. Sitz., 185, 1918.

Peixotto (Ernest Clifford).
Through Spain & Portugal. 8°. N.Y. 1922

Pejacsevich (Franciscus Xaverius) *a Verocza.* Hist. Serviae seu colloquia XIII de statu regni &c. a s. VII ad XV. Opus posth. &c. la. fol. Colocæ. 1799

Pekarsky (Petr Petrovich). Дополнит. извѣстія для біог. Ломоносова. [I. Akad. Nauk. Записки, t8]. 8°. С.-П. 1865
Мат. для ист. журнальной и литературной дѣятельности Екатерины II. [I. Akad. Nauk. Записки, t3]. 8°. С.-П. 1863
Новыя извѣстія о В. Н. Татищевѣ. [I. Akad. Nauk. Записки, t4]. 8°. С.-П. 1864
О жизни и трудахъ К. И. Арсеньева. [I. Akad. Nauk. Записки, t20]. 8°. С.-П. 1871
Редакторъ &c. въ русс. журналѣ, 1755–64. [I. Akad. Nauk. Записки, т12]. 8°. С.-П. 1867

Peking Society of Natural History.
Bulletin. v1. la8°. [Peking]. 1926
see GEE (N. G.), L. I. MOFFETT & G. D. WILDER. Tentative list of Chinese birds, 1926. [1.]

Pekmezi (Georg).
see LAMBERTZ (M.) & G. P. Lehr- u. Lesebuch d. Albanischen, 1913.
,, MANEK (F.), G. P. & A. STOTZ. Albanes. Bibliog., 1909.

Pel (Albert). *Pel, l'horloger de Montreuil. [*no tp.* P2826]. s8°. [Sceaux. *n.d.*]

Péladan (Joséphin) [JOSEPH AIMÉ P.]
Les dévotes d'Avignon. Roman. s8°. 1922
Hist. & légende de Marion de Lorme. Avec une document. iconograph. &c. de E. Magne. 8°. 1927
J. Peladan. [*By var. a.*] [Nouv. Revue du Midi, No. 10 (Spécial)]. la8°. Nimes. 1924
La torche renversée. Roman. s8°. [1925]

Pelagius, *the heresiarch.*
see BRADWARDINUS (T.), *abp. of Canterbury.* De causa Dei contra Pelagium &c., 1618.
,, SOUTER (A.) Character & hist. of P.'s comm. on Epistles of St. Paul, 1916.
,, TEXTS & STUDIES, v9i, ii, P.'s expos. of 13 epistles of St. Paul; intr. [by A. Souter], 1922–26.
,, VOSSIUS (G.) Hist. de controv., quae P. &c. moverunt, 1655.

Pelargus (Christophorus). Articuli de persona Christi repet. brev. Suscepta a C. P.; resp. J. Mullero. [P2612]. s4°. [Frankfurt.] 1598
Locorum theol. pene omnium ἐξέτασις. s4°. Francofurti. 1596

Pelecier (*le gén.*) Un raid de cavalerie. Épisode de la première bataille de la Marne. Avant-propos du gén. Fonville. s8°. 1921

Pelecius (Joannes) [PELECYO], *Jesuit, see* *THRONUS justitiae &c., ex 4 S. J. patribus desumptus J. P. &c., 1624.

Pelegromius (Simon). Synonymorum sylva, olim a S. P. coll. &c. e Belgarum sermone in Anglicanum transfusa &c. per H. F. Acc. Synonyma quædam poetica &c. s8°. Londini. 1650

Pelerzi (*le père* **E.)**
Les grottes de Loungmen (Honan). 8°. [Shanghai. 1923]

Pelham (Camden), *ps.* The chronicles of crime, or the New Newgate Calendar. [repr.] 2v. 8°. 1891

Pelham (Evelyn Georgiana), *see* CUST (*Lady* E.) & E. G. P. Edward, 5th Earl of Darnley &c.; ed. Lady E. C. & E. G. P., 1913.

Pelham (Peter), *see* WHITMORE (W. H.) Notes conc. P. P. & h. successors, 1867.

Pelicanus (Cunradus), *see* PELLICANUS (CONRADUS).

Pélissier (Jean).
Dix mois de guerre dans les Balkans, 1912–13. 8°. 1914

Pélissier (Léon G.) L'alliance milano-allem. à la fin du 15e s.: l'ambass. d'H. Brasca à Maximilien (1498), *see* REGIA DEP. DI STORIA PATRIA. Misc., t35, 1898.

Pelissier (Robert). Mischär-Tatar. Sprachproben, 1919, *see* KÖNIGL. PREUSS. AKAD. Abhdl., Phil.-hist. Kl., 1918.
Mokšamordvin. Texte, gesammelt im Nordosten d. Gouv. Tambov, *see* KÖNIGL.-PREUSS. AKAD. Abhandl., Phil.-hist. Kl., 1926.

Pelivan (Ion G.)
Chronologie de la Bessarabie 1812–1919. [P2464]. 8°. 1920
The economic state of Bessarabia. [P2464]. 8°. Paris. 1920
L'état économ. de la Bessarabie. [P2464]. 8°. 1920

Pelka (Otto). Altchristl. Ehedenkmäler. la8°. Str. 1901
Bernstein. 8°. 1920

Pell (Charles Edward). The law of births & deaths. Variation in the degree of animal fertility. 8°. [1921]
The riddle of unemployment & its solution. s8°. [1922]

Pellapra (E. L. M. F.), *pcsse. de Chimay, see* CHIMAY (E. L. M. F. P., *pcsse.* DE).

Pellegrin (*Col.* **F. L. L.)** La vie d'une armée p. la grande Guerre. Préf. du Gén. Mangin. s8°. 1921

Pellegrin (Simone). Le Prince Charmant est mort. s8°. 1922

Pellegrini (Gius. Salvatore).
Giovinezza, giovinezza. . . . Romanzo. s8°. Firenze. 1923

Pelleprat (Pierre), *see* JESUITS. Voyages &c., t1, Mission de Cayenne &c. [P. P. &c.], 1857.

Pellett (Frank Chapman).
Productive bee-keeping. 2nd ed. rev. 8°. Phila. [1918]

Pellicanus (Conradus). Comm. Bibliorum & illa brevia quidem ac catholica.
5t. *b. in 3* [*the tps. vary*]. fol. Tiguri, *Froschoverus.* 1533–38
In quatuor Evangelia & Apostol. Acta comm. [*w. 5 pag.*] fol. Tiguri, *Froschower.* 1537
Psalterium Davidis Pelicani opera elab. s8°. Argentorati. 1527

Pelliot (Paul). A propos des Comans. [Extr. du Journal asiat., avr.–juin 1920]. 8°. 1920
Le Chou king en caractères anc. & le Chang chou che wen [par Lou Tö-ming], *see* ACAD. DES INSCR. &C. Mém. conc. l'Asie Or., t2, 1916.
Chrétiens d'Asie cent. et d'Extrême-Or. [Extr. du T'oung-pao, s2, v15. P2859]. la8°. Leide. 1914
see GUIMET: Bull. archéol. du Musée G., fasc. 2, Asie centr. &c., 1921.

Pellissier-Guys (Henri), *see* BOUCHES-DU-RHÔNE. Encyclopédie départ., t10, Le mouvt. social; par H. P.-G. &c., 1923.

Pellisson-Fontanier (Paul), *see* LEIBNITZ (G. W. v.) Otium Hanoveranum &c.; add. Epist. &c. P. de tolerantia, 1718.

Pellizza (Giuseppe), *1868–1907, see* SAPORI (F.) Maestri, No. 19, 1920.

Pellizzari (Achille). Su la vetta, pagine d'arte e di vita. 10a ed. 3v [v3, 6a ed.] 8°. Firenze. [1920]

Pellizzi (Camillo).
Problemi e realtà del Fascismo. 8°. Firenze. [1924]

Pelly (George). Trial, before Governor of Oahu, G. P. vs. R. Charlton, action of trespass on case for slander. [P2776]. 8°. [1844]
see CHARLTON (R.) Exposure of villany &c. of R. C., 1844.

Pelly (Russell G.), *see* BOLTON (E. R.) & R. G. P. Oils, fats, waxes & resins, 1924.

Pelsaert (Françoys). Jahangir's India: the Remonstrantie of F. P. Tr. W. H. Moreland & P. Geyl. 8°. C. 1925

Peltier (Roger). Abel Hermant, s. œuvre. s8°. 1924

Peltzer (Armand).
see PELTZER (L.) & A. P. The P. case, 1928.
,, —— & —— Le procès P., 1882.

Peltzer (Léon) & A. Peltzer.
The Peltzer case. By G. Harry. 8°. [1928]
[Le procès P. Journ. des Tribunaux, éd. spéc. No. 1–24, 24 Nov.–23 Déc. 1882]. fol. [Brux. 1882]

Pelzer (Auguste). Un traducteur inconnu: P. Gallega (1250–67), *see* EHRLE (F.) Miscell., v1, 1924.

Pemberton, *The family of, see* PEMBERTON (*Maj.-Gen.* R. C. B.) P. pedigrees, 1923.

Pemberton (A. C.) The complete cyclist. By A. C. P., Mrs. H. Williamson &c. Ed. B. F. Robinson. 8°. 1897

Pemberton (Henry), *Jr.* Shakspere & Sir Walter Ralegh. Ed. S. L. Pemberton. s8°. Phila. 1914

Pemberton (*Sir* Max). The diamond ship. s8°. 1912
Lord Northcliffe: a mem. 8°. [1922]

Pemberton (Max Joseph). Hindoo Khan. s8°. [1922]

Pemberton (*Maj.-Gen.* Robert Charles Boileau). Pemberton pedigrees. Ed. R. Pemberton. la8°. Bedford. 1923

Pemble (William). A briefe introd. to geography. [*b. w. h.* Vindiciæ fidei, 1635]. sm. fol. 1635
De formarum origine [*&* De sensibus internis. *b. w. h.* Vindiciæ fidei, 1635]. sm. fol. 1635
A summe of moral philos. [*b. w. h.* Vindiciæ fidei, 1635]. sm. fol. [1632]
Vindiciæ fidei. [W. a dedic. epistle by R. Capel & an address by G. Walter]. 3rd ed. sm. fol. 1635

Pembrige (Christopher). Annals of Ireland, *sometimes attrib. to P., see* †GILBERT (J. T.) Chartularies of St. Mary's Abbey, v2, 1884.

Pembroke (Anne Herbert, *countess of***),** *see* RAINBOW (E.) Sermon pr. at funeral of A. &c., 1677.

Pembroke (Mary Herbert, *countess of***).** Poem on Our Saviour's Passion. Pref. by the ed. [R. G. B.] 8°. 1862

Pembroke (Reginald Herbert, *15th earl of***).** Cat. of armour, sold by Sotheby, 14th June 1923. [Illust. P2851]. la8°. 1923

Pembroke (William Herbert, *3rd earl of***).** Poems of W. H. & Sir B. Rudyard (1660). 2nd ed. s8°. 1817

Pen. *Whole (The) art of p. making, *n.d., see* WHOLE.

Pena (Leonardo). Hist. du Chili. s8°. 1927

Pena (Petrus).
see LEGRÉ (L.) La botanique en Provence au 16e s.: P. P. &c., 1899.
,, —— L'indigénat en Provence du Styrax officinal: P. P. & F. de Peiresc, 1901.
,, L'OBEL (M. DE). In G. Rondelletii Pharmaceut. offic. animadvers.; acc. Simplic. medicament. explic. [*by* P. P. & M. de L'O.] &c., 1605.

Peñaranda (Gaspar de Bracamonte y Guzman, *conde* **de),** *see* HISPANIA. Hispania illustrata: w. papers f. the Conde de P. &c., 1703.

Peña y Reyes (Antonio de la). Don M. E. de Gorostiza y la cuestion de Texas: doc. prec. de una notic. biog. por La P. y R. 8°. Mexico. 1924
Lucas Alaman: el reconocimiento de nuestra independ. por España &c. Intr. por La P. y R. 8°. Mexico. 1924
see MEXICO. Prim. guerra entre M. y Francia; prol. de A. de la P. y R., 1927.

Penck (Albrecht). Die Höttinger Breccie u. d. Inntalterrasse nördl. Innsbruck, *see* KÖN.-PREUSS. AKAD. Abh., Phys.-math. Klasse, 1920.
Was wir im Kriege gewonnen u. was wir verloren haben, *see* DEUTSCHE Reden in schwerer Zeit, 23, 1915.

Pendered (Mary Lucy). Corisande. s8°. [1926]
John Martin, painter, h. life & times. 8°. 1923

Pendlebury (*Mrs.* Mary), *form. Gribble, see* GRIBBLE (J. D. B.) Hist. of the Deccan; ed. &c. by M. P., 1924.

Pendrill (Charles). London life in the 14th cent. 8°. [1925]
Wanderings in medieval London. 8°. [1928]

Pène (Annie de). Les plus jolies lettres d'amour. Rec. & publ. par A. de P. 8e éd. s8°. 1919

Penhallow (Samuel). The hist. of the wars of New-England w. the Eastern Indians, 1703–26. [Mem. of S. P. by N. Adams; pref. by B. Colman]. s4°. Cincinnati. 1859

Peninsula. Mem. annexed to an atlas cont. plans of princ. battles &c. dur. war in the Span. P. &c., 1841, *see* WYLD (J.)

Penka (Carl). Die Herkunft d. Arier. N. Beitr. z. hist. Anthropologie d. europ. Völker. 8°. Wien. 1886

Penman (John Simpson).
Irresistible movt. of democracy. 8°. 1923

Penn (Richard). Maxims & hints for an angler, added, Maxims &c. for a chess player. n. ed. enl. s8°. 1839

Penn (William), *founder of Pennsylvania.* *An address to Protestants for the promotion of virtue & charity. By W. P. a Protestant. 2nd ed. corr. 2p [*pagin. cont.*] s8°. 1692
W. P.'s first charter, 1682. [Facs.] Ed. A. C. Myers. 4°. Phila. 1925
see HARRISON (G. L.) The remains of W. P.: Pa.'s plea &c., 1882.

Penna (Lorenzo). Li primi albori musicali per li principianti d. musica figurata. 3 libri. 5a impr. s4°. Bologna. 1696

Pennant (Thomas). Antiq. of London: views & hist. descr. &c. chiefly f. works of T. P. [Dedic. signed J. Coxhead]. 8°. 1814
A journey f. London to the Isle of Wight. 2v. 4°. 1801
Some account of London. [*Large paper: extra illustrated*]. 4th ed. [*b. in* 6v]. fol. 1805
Tour f. Alston-Moor to Harrowgate & Brimham Crags. [*b. w. h.* Tour f. Downing &c., 1801]. s4°. 1804
Tour f. Downing to Alston-Moor. s4°. 1801

Pennell (*Mrs.* Eliz. Robins), *wife of J. Pennell, see* PENNELL (J.) & E. R. P. The Whistler journal, 1921.

Pennell (Joseph). The adventures of an illustrator: works shown at the Anderson Gall. la8°. N.Y. [1925]
The graphic arts: modern men & mod. methods. 8°. Chicago. 1921
A little book of London. [re-issue]. 8°. [1911]
see DODGSON (C.) & J. P. The Senefelder Club, 1922.
,, VAN DYKE (J. C.) The new New York; illust. by J. P., 1909.
—— & E. R. Pennell. The Whistler journal. 8°. Phila. 1921

Pennell (*Mrs.* Theodore). Children of the Border. s8°. 1926

Penney (Norman), *see* FELL (S.) Household account book of S. F.; ed. N. P., 1920.

Penniman (Josiah Harmar).
A book about the English Bible. 8°. N.Y. 1919

Penning (William Henry), *F.G.S., see* WHITAKER (W.), W. H. P. &c. Geol. of the N.W. part of Essex &c., 1878.
—— & A. J. Jukes-Browne. Geol. of the neighb. of Cambridge. With palaeont. app. by R. Etheridge. [Mems. of G.S.] 8°. 1881

Pennsylvania. Church music & musical life in P. in the 18th cent. [Penn. Soc. of Colon. Dames of Amer., Publ. 4]. v1, 2. la8°. Phila. 1926–27
v1 *incl*s. facs. of MS. of Hymn bk. of J. Kelpius; tr. C. Witt.

UNIVERSITY OF P.
Babylonian Exped. of the U. of P. Ser. D.: Researches & treatises. Ed. H. V. Hilprecht. v5i, ii. 8°. Phila. 1910
see HILPRECHT (H. V.) Earliest version of Babylonian Deluge story & the Temple Library of Nippur, 1910. [Ser. D. 5i.]
,, RADAU (H.) Nin-Ib, 1910. [Ser. D. 5ii.]

MUSEUM.
Babylonian Section.
Publ. 2i, 4i, v9i, 10i, 11iii. 4°. Phila. 1912–19
see BARTON (G. A.) Sumerian business &c. doc., 1915. [9i.]
,, CHIERA (E.) Lists of personal names f. Temple school of Nippur, v3, 1919. [11iii.]
,, LANGDON (S.) Sumerian epic of Paradise, the Flood &c., 1915. [10i.]
,, MURASHÛ *Sons, of Nippur.* Business doc. of M. S.; [ed.] A. T. Clay, 1912. [2i.]
,, POEBEL (A.) Historical texts, 1914. [4i.]

REFERENCES.
see SEYBERT COMM. ON SPIRITUALISM. Prelim. report of Comm. app. by Univ. of P. to investigate mod. spiritualism &c., 1920.

Pennsylvania Academy of the Fine Arts. Cat. of the memorial exhib. of portraits by T. Sully. [Biog. notes by A. C. Myers &c.] 2nd ed. la8°. Phila. 1922

Pennsylvania Society of the Colonial Dames of America.
Publications. 4. la8°. Phila. 1926–27
see PENNSYLVANIA. Church music &c. in P. in 18th cent., v1, 2, 1926–27. [4.]

Penny (Frank). The Church in Madras: hist. of the eccl. &c. action of the East India Co. v3, 1835–61. 8°. 1922

Penny (*Mrs.* Frank E. F.)
Diamonds. s8°. [1920]
Living dangerously. s8°. [1925]
One of the best. s8°. [1923]
Pulling the strings. s8°. [1927]
A question of colour. s8°. [1926]
The Swami's curse. s8°. [1922]

Penny (John), *see* HALL (J.) *Hist. of J. H., executed for murder of J. P., 1741.

Penrose (Claude Quayle Lewis).
Poems, w. biograph. preface. la8°. 1919

Penry (John). *Humble motion (An) with submission unto H.M. privie counsell. Consid. that eccl. discipline were reformed after the worde of God &c. s8°. *n.p.* 1590
see PIERCE (W.) J. P., h. life, times & wr., 1923.

Pensa (Girolamo). Epigrammi toscani. [*Lat., w. Ital. verse.*] 8°. Monte Regale. 1570

Penshurst. Rep. on MSS. at P. Place, v1, 1925, *see* HIST. MSS. COMM.

Penson (Lilian M.) The colonial agents of the Brit. W. Indies. 8°. 1924

Penson (*Sir* Thomas Henry). Economics of everyday life: 1st bk. of economic study. 2p [p1, repr.] s8°. C. 1920–21

Pentimalli (Giuseppe). Alfredo Oriani. s8°. Firenze. 1921

Pentin (Herbert), *see* PERKINS (T.) & H. P., *edd.* Mem. of old Dorset, 1907.

Penton (Stephen). Apparatus ad theologiam, in usum acad. 1, Generalis. 2, Specialis. s8°. 1688

Penty (Arthur Joseph). Guilds, trade & agriculture. s8°. [1921]
Post-industrialism. Pref. by G. K. Chesterton. s8°. [1922]
Protection & the social problem. s8°. [1926]
Towards a Xtn. sociology. s8°. [1923]

Penzer (Norman Mosley). Annotated bibliogr. of Sir R. F. Burton. Pref. by F. G. Baker. la8°. 1923
Non-ferrous metals & o. minerals. Intr. by Sir E. Geddes & Sir R. Redmayne. [Resources of the Empire, v8ii.] 4°. 1924

Penzig (Otto). Monte Generoso, a botanico-geogr. sk. Eng. by R. M. B. [P2848]. 8°. Alexandrie. 1900

Penzig (Rudolph). Schopenhauer u. d. menschl. Willensfreiheit. [P2505]. s8°. Halle. [1879]

***People** & places: a life in 5 continents, 1922, *see* KEYSER (A.)

People's Art Union, *see* HISTORICAL. Hist. gallery of portraits &c. of celeb. men, 4v, 1835?.

People's Year Book & Annual of the English & Scottish wholesale societies, 1921–28. 8°. M'ter. 1921–28

Pepin I, *king of Aquitaine, see* CHARTES & diplômes rel. à l'hist. de France, t8, Rec. des actes de P. I &c., 814–48; publ. L. Levillain, 1926.

Pepin II, *king of Aquitaine, see* CHARTES & diplômes rel. à l'hist. de France, t8, Rec. des actes de P. II &c., 814–48; publ. L. Levillain, 1926.

Pepoli (Taddeo), *d. 1347, see* RODOLICO (N.) Dal Comune alla Signoria: saggio sul governo di T. P. in Bologna, 1898.

Pepys, *The family of, see* WHITEAR (W. H.) More Pepysiana: notes on the diary & genealogy of the family, 1927.

Pepys (Samuel).
Acc. of Charles II.'s escape. Dictated to S. P. by the King. [*Extr. no tp.*] [P2622]. s8°. *n.p. n.d.*
Diary. Transcr. by M. Bright. Ed., w. add. by H. B. Wheatley. [repr.] s8°. *Bohn.* 1913
Everybody's Pepys. Diary, 1660–69, abr. & ed. by O. F. Morshead. 8°. 1926
Naval minutes. Ed. J. R. Tanner. [Navy Rec. Soc., v60]. 8°. 1926
Pepys on the Restoration stage. [Extracts &c.] By H. McAfee. 8°. New Haven. 1916
Private corr. & misc. papers, 1679–1703. Ed. J. R. Tanner. 2v. 8°. 1926
see CAMBRIDGE: MAGDALENE COLL. Bibl. Pepysiana: descr. cat. of lib. of S. P., p3, Med. MSS.; by M. R. James, 1923.
,, —— Descr. cat. of naval MSS. in Pepysian Lib. at M.C.; ed. J. R. Tanner, v4, 1923.
,, GASELEE (S.) Span. books in lib. of S. P., 1921.
,, LUCAS-DUBRETON (J.) S. P.; tr., 1924.
,, ROLLINS (H. E.), *ed.* Pepysian garland; ballads 1595–1639, chiefly f. coll. of S. P., 1922.
,, TANNER (J. R.) Mr. P., intr. to Diary & later life, 1925.
,, WHEATLEY (H. B.) S. P. & the world he lived in, 5th ed., 1907.
,, WHITEAR (W. H.) More Pepysiana, 1927.

Pera. Statuti d. colonia genovese di P., ed. V. Promis, *see* REGIA DEP. DI STORIA PATRIA. Misc., t11, 1870.

Peragallo (Prospero). Colonia ital. in Portogallo, sec. 14–16, *see* REGIA DEP. DI STORIA PATRIA. Misc., t40, 1904.

Peraldus (Gulielmus), *see* LOSERTH (J.) J. von Wiclif u. G. P., 1916.

Peramas (Josephus Emmanuel). De vita & moribus 13 virorum Paraguaycorum. 8°. Faventiae. 1793

Pératé (André). Versailles. 5th ed. 8°. 1922

Perceval, *le Gallois, Knight of the Round Table, see* GOLTHER (W.) Parzival u. d. Gral in d. Dichtung d. M-a's &c., 1925.
see SCHRÖDER (F. R.) Die Parzivalfrage, 1928.

Perceval (*Hon.* Arthur Philip). An apology for the doctrine of apostol. succession & w. an app. on Engl. orders. s8°. 1839

Perceval (Émile de). Un adversaire de Napoléon: le vte. Lainé (1767–1835) & la vie parlement. au temps de la Restauration. 2t. 8°. 1926

Perceval (George). Hist. of Italy. 2v. 8°. 1825

Perche. Chartes servant de pièces justif. à la Géogr. &c. du P.; publ. par le vte. de Romanet, 1890–1902, *see* ROMANET (*le vte.* DE).

Percin (*le gén.* Alexandre). Deux hommes de Guerre. Sarrail & Gallieni. [P2493]. 8°. 1919
Le massacre de notre infanterie, 1914–18. s8°. [1921]

Percival (A. Blayney). A game ranger's note-book. Ed. E. D. Cuming. [repr.] 8°. 1925

Percival (G. Arncliffe). The electric lamp industry. s8°. [1920]

Percival (John), *bp. of Hereford, see* TEMPLE (W.) Life of Bp. P., 1921.

Percival (John), *prof. of agric. botany, Univ. Coll., Reading.*
The wheat plant: a monograph. la8°. [1921]

Percival (MacIver).
The chintz book. la8°. [1923]
The fan book. 8°. [1920]
The glass collector. Guide to old English glass. 2nd ed. s8°. *n.d.*
Old English furniture & its surroundings, f. the Restoration to the Regency. 4°. 1920
The walnut collector. 8°. 1927

Percival (Robert). Account of the Cape of Good Hope. 4°. 1804

Percy, *Family of.* Percy bailiff's rolls of the 15th c. [Ed. J. C. Hodgson. Surtees Soc., v134]. 8°. Durham. 1921

Percy (*le baron* Pierre François). Journal des campagnes du baron P., chirurgien (1754–1825). Publ. avec intr. par E. Longin. 8°. 1904

Percy (Thomas), *bp. of Dromore.*
The hermit of Warkworth: a Northumberland ballad, 1771, *see* AUNGERVYLE SOC. Reprints, s2, 1883.
Reliques of anc. Eng. poetry. 3v. s8°. 1765
,, ,, ...4th ed. 3v. s8°. 1794
,, ,, w. some few of later date. n. ed. 3v. 8°. 1839
,, ,, [Everyman's Lib.] 2v. s8°. [1906]
Thomas Percy u. W. Shenstone: Briefwechsel aus d. Entstehungszeit d. Reliques. Hrsg. mit Einl. &c. v. H. Hecht. 8°. Str. 1909
see BALDERSTON (K. C.) Hist. & sources of P.'s Memoir of Goldsmith, 1926.

Perdigon, *de Lespéron, troubadour.* Chansons. Éd. H. J. Chaytor. [Class. fr. du m. â.] s8°. 1926

Perdou de Subligny (Adrien Thomas). La folle querelle, comédie (1668), *see* FOURNEL (V.) Contemp. de Molière, t3, 1875.

Perdrizet (Paul). Antiquités de Leontopolis, *see* ACAD. D. INSCR.: FOND. PIOT. Mon., t25, 1921–22.
La plus anc. descr. de la Lorraine [*f. B. de Glanville*]. [P2601]. 8°. Nancy. 1909

Pereda (José Maria de). Pedro Sanchez. 4ª ed. s8°. 1923

Pereda (Vicente de). Juan de Castilla. 8°. 1925

Pereda y Salgado (Antonio), *c. 1608–78, see* HISP. SOC. OF AMER. P. in coll. of H.S., 1928.

Père de la Comp. de Jésus, *ps., see* CIBOT (P. M.)

Perefixe (Hardouin de) [†BEAUMONT DE PEREFIXE].
Hist. du roy Henry le Grand. s8°. 1662
see STEPHENS (E.) *A disc. conc. the Powder-Plot &c. coll. out of P. &c., 1674.

Peregrinandi. De arte peregrinandi lib. 2, 1591, *see* PYRCKMAIR (H.)

Peregrinus (Constantius), *ps., see* JONGE (BOUDEWIJN DE).

Pereira (Fernandes), *see* FRANCISCO *dos Prazeres Maranhão.*

Pereira (*Brig.-Gen.* George). Peking to Lhasa: narr. of journeys in Chinese Empire. Comp. by Sir F. Younghusband f. notes & diaries supplied by Maj.-Gen. Sir C. Pereira. 8°. 1925

Pereira (Nuno Alvarez), *see* ALVAREZ PEREIRA (N.)

Pereira da Costa (Francisco Augusto). Folk-lore pernambucano, *see* INSTITUTO HIST. &C. BRAZIL. Rev., t70, 1908.

Pereira de Leon (Moses). Gesch. d. Kolonie v. Suriname, door e. Gezelschap [M. P. de L. *& others*], 1791, *see* SURINAM.

Pereire (Alfred). Le Journal des débats, 1814–1914. 4°. 1924

Perelaer (Michael Theophile Hubert), *see* REES (W. A. VAN) & M. T. H. P. Nederl.-Indie, 4p, 1881–83.

Perels (Ernst). Papst Nikolaus I u. Anastasius Bibliothecarius. Beitr. z. Gesch. d. Papsttums im 9. Jhdt. 8°. 1920

Pérennès (*l'abbé* Henri). Les Psaumes. Tr. & comm. Préf. du R. P. Condamin. 8°. Saint-Pol-de-Léon. [1922]

Peresvet. Пересвет. I. Б. Зайцев, М. Осоргин, Ф. Сологуб, Г. Чулков, М. Цветаева, А. Яковлев. s8°. Москва. 1921

Pérétié (A.) Les medrasas à Fès, *&* Le rais El-Khadir Ghailan, *see* MISSION SCIENT. DU MAROC. Archives, v18, 1912.
see BIARNAY (S.) & A. P. Recherches archéol. au Maroc, 1912.

Perets (Egor Abramovich), *1833–99*.
Дневник, 1880–83. С пред. А. Е. Преснякова. [*Ed.*] А. А. Сергеев. [Центрархив]. la8°. Москва. 1927
Peretz (Isaac Loeb). Bontshe the silent. Tr. w. pref. & glossary by A. S. Rappoport. s8°. [1927]
Pereverzev (V.) Творчество Достоевского. 8°. Москва. 1922
Perevlesskoi (Petr Mironovich).
Грамматика старославянскаго языка. 2°e изд. s8°. С.–П. 1856
„ „ 10°e изд. [*w. title* Славянская грам.] 8°. С.–П. 1879
Pereyra (Carlos). Hist. de América española. 8t. 8°. 1920–26
1, Descubr. y explor. del Nuevo Mundo. 2, El Imperio Español. 3, Méjico. 4, Las Républ. del Plata. 5, Los países antillanos y la Amér. cent. 6, Colombia, Venezuela, Ecuador. 7, Perú y Bolivia. 8, Chile.
Perez (Antonio), *sec. of state to Philip II of Spain* [A. PEREZIUS], *see* FITZMAURICE-KELLY (J.) A. P., 1922.
Pérez (D. Jorge Abad), *see* ABAD PÉREZ (D. J.)
Pérez (Juan), *of Villalvín, see* HISP. SOC. OF AMER. Manuscripts: J. P. & Sol Fernandez, 1324 *&* 1326, MSS. B5 *&* B12, 1927.
Pérez (Luis Marino). Guide to the materials for American hist. in Cuban archives. [C.I. of Wash.] la8°. Wash. 1907
Pérez de Ayala (Ramón).
A. M. D. G. [La vida en los colegios de Jesuitas]. s8°. 1911
Belarmino y Apolonio. Novela. s8°. 1921
El curandero de su honra. 2ª parte de Tigre Juan. s8°. [1926]
Luna de miel, luna de hiel. s8°. 1924
Miguel Viladrich. [*Intr. by* R. P. de A.] 8°. [1920]
Prometeo—Luz de Domingo—La caída de los limones. Novelas poemát. 2ª ed. s8°. 1920
Prometheus: The fall of the house of Limón: Sunday sunlight. Poetic novels of Spanish life. Prose tr. by A. P. Hubbard: poems done into Eng. by G. H. Conkling. s8°. N.Y. [1920]
El sendero andante. Poemas. s8°. 1921
Tigre Juan. 2ª ed. s8°. [1926]
„ „ 3ª ed. s8°. [1927]
Tinieblas en las cumbres. Novela. s8°. 1923
Los trabajos de Urbano y Simona. 2ª ed. s8°. 1924
Perez de Pineda (Juan). Breve tratado de doctrina, 1560. Ahora fielmente reimpreso. s8°. 1852
Perez de Villa-Amil (Genero), *see* VILLA-AMIL (G. P. DE).
Pérez Galdós (Benito).
El amigo manso. 2ª ed. s8°. 1885
Antón Caballero. Comedia. Obra póstuma, refundida por S. y J. Alvarez Quintero. s8°. 1922
Dona Perfecta. s8°. 1919
Episodios nacionales. s8°. 1918–20
III, Bodas reales.
IV, O'Donnell.
Fortunata y Jacinta (Dos hist. de Casadas). 4p. s8°. 1915–18
Galdós: selecc. hecha por M. Mayo. s8°. 1922
Memoranda. s8°. 1906
Miau. s8°. 1907
see WALTON (L. B.) P. G. & the Span. novel of the 19th cent., 1927.
Pérez Lugín (Alejandro).
La casa de la Troya. 25ª ed. s8°. 1922
Currito de la Cruz. Novela. 7ª ed. 2t [*pagin. cont.*] s8°. 1922
Pérez Nieva (Alfonso).
El paje de la duquesa. Novela. s8°. [1926]
Pérez Pastor (Cristóbal).
La imprenta en Medina del Campo. la8°. 1895
La imprenta en Toledo: descr. bibliogr. la8°. 1887
Noticias y docs. rel. a la hist. y lit. españolas, t2, 3, *see* REAL ACAD. ESP. Mem., t11, 12, 1914–16.
Perez Rioja (Antonio). Crón. de la prov. de Soria, 1867, *see* ESPAÑA. Crón. gen., v10, 1865 &c.
Perfall (Anton, *Frhr.* v.)
Förster Söllmann. Roman. 14e A. s8°. 1922
Perfect diurnall (A) of some passages in Parliament &c. Nos. 70 (25 Nov.–2 Dec. 1644), 191 (22–29 Mar. 1647), 204 (21–28 June), 210 (2–9 Aug.), 213 (23–30 Aug.), 215 (6–13 Sept.), 217 (20–27 Sept.), 220 (11–18 Oct.), 228 (6–13 Dec.), 247 (17–24 Apr. 1648), 249 (1–8 May), 257 (26 June–3 July), 273 (16–23 Oct.) [215, 220 *in* P2597]. 8°. 1644–48
Perfect diurnall (A) of some passages &c. of, & in rel. to, the armies in Eng., Ireland & Scot. Nos. 47 (Oct. 21–28, 1650), 58 (Jan. 13–20, 1650/1) *imperf.*, 125 (Apr. 26–May 3, 1652). 8°. 1650–52
Pergamon Museum, *Berlin, see* KÖNIGLICHES MUSEUM, *Berlin*.
Pergaud (Louis). Les rustiques. 6e éd. s8°. 1921
La vie des bêtes: études & nouv., suivies de Lebrac, bûcheron: roman inachevé. Intr. de E. Rocher. 3e ed. s8°. 1923
see ROCHER (E.) L. P., conteur rustique, 1923.
Peri (Noël). Cinq Nô: drames lyriques japonais [par Motokiyo & Kiyotsugu]. Tr. avec préf. &c. par N. P. 8°. 1921

Périer (Gaston Denys).
Moukanda. Lect. sur le Congo &c. 8°. Brux. 1914
Perier (*Mme.* Gilberte), *sister of B. Pascal, see* PASCAL (B.) Life [*by Mme.* G. P.], w. h. letters rel. to the Jesuits; tr., 2v, 1744.
Périgord (Paul). The Internat. Labor Organiz. Intr. by H. M. Robinson. 8°. N.Y. 1926
Perilla (F.) Le Mont Athos. 4°. 1927
Peringer (Gustaf), *aft. Peringer Liljeblad*. De templo Herculis Gaditano, 1695, *see* SCHLÄGER (C. J.) Diss. fasc. 1, 1742.
De Zabiis, 1691, *see* SCHLÄGER (C. J.) Diss. fasc. novus, 1744.
see MISHNAH. Duo codd. Talmudici; paraphrasi Lat. redd. a G. P., 1680.
Péringuey (L.) Inscriptions left by early Europ. navigators on their way to the East. [*From* Annals of the South Afr. Museum, v13]. [P2707]. la8°. 1913
Perito (Enrico). La congiura dei baroni e il Conte di Policastro. Con l'ed. compl. e crit. dei sonetti di G. A. de Petruciis. 8°. Bari. 1926
Perk (Jacques), *1859–81*.
Gedichten. 15e dr. bezorgd door W. Kloos. s8°. A. 1920
Perkins (Oliver Henry). Priv. library of O. H. P. To be sold, Mar. 1926, Anderson Galleries. [*Illust. cat.*] 8°. N.Y. 1926
Perkins (Thomas) & H. Pentin. Memorials of old Dorset. [*By var. wr.*] Ed. T. P. & H. P. 8°. 1907
Perkins (William), *fellow of Christ's College, Cambridge*.
Workes. Newly corr. 3v [v2, *ed.* T. Pickering; v3, *ed.* T. Pierson; v3 *has 2 pagin.*] fol. C. 1608–9
*A brief discourse, taken out of the wr. of H. Zanchius [*conc. election & predestination*]. s8°. 1592
A reformed Catholike: declar. shewing how neere we may come to the Church of Rome &c. s8°. C. 1604
see ABBOT (R.) Defence of Reformed Cath. of W. P., pl, 2, 1606–7.
„ ARMINIUS (J.) Examen modestum libelli quem G. P. ed. &c., 1612.
„ BISHOP (W.) A reformation of a catholike deformed: by W. P. &c., 1604.
Perks (Sydney). Essays on old London. 4°. C. 1927
The hist. of the Mansion House. 8°. C. 1922
Perles de la poésie française contemp. 10e éd., rev. & mise à jour par E. E. B. Lacomblé. s8°. Amsterdam. [1920 ?]
Perlet (Charles Frédéric).
see LENOTRE (G.) Les agents roy. en Fr. au temps de la Révol. & de l'Empire: l'affaire P., 1922.
„ —— 2 Royalist spies of the French Revol. [*i.e.* L. Fauche-Borel & C. F. P.]; tr., 1924.
Perlman (Selig).
A hist. of trade unionism in the U.S. 8°. N.Y. 1923
Permanent Consultative Committee on Official Statistics, *see* STATISTICS.
Permanent Court, *see* HAGUE (THE).
Permanent Mandates Commission, *see* LEAGUE OF NATIONS.
Pernice (Angelo). Un episodio del valore toscane n. guerre di Valacchia, *see* ARCHIVIO STOR. ITAL., Anno 83, v1, 1925.
Pernier (Luigi). Scavi della missione ital. a Phaestos, 1902–3, *see* REALE ACCAD. D. LINCEI. Mon. ant., v14, 1904.
Tumulo con tomba mon. al Sodo presso Cortona, *see* REALE ACCAD. DEI LINCEI. Mon. ant., t30, 1926.
Pernot (Hubert). Études de litt. grecque mod. 8°. 1916
see LEGRAND (E.), L. PETIT & H. P. Bibliogr. hellénique; compl. & publ. par H. P. &c., t1, 1918.
Pernot (Maurice). L'épreuve de la Pologne. [5e éd.] s8°. [1921]
Pérochon (Ernest).
Bernard l'Ours & la torpédo-camionnette. s8°. [1927]
Conte du Chevalier fol qui voulait faire le bonheur d'autrui, nouvelle, *see* ŒUVRES libres, 62, 1926.
Les creux-de-maisons. s8°. [1921]
En se dindinant, *see* ŒUVRES libres, 33, 1924.
The foster mother. Tr. Intr. by R. Le Gallienne. s8°. [1922]
Les gardiennes. s8°. [1924]
Huit gouttes d'opium. 8°. [1925]
Nêne. Préf. de G. Chéral. s8°. [1920]
La parcelle 32. Roman. s8°. [1922]
Sur la pointe des pieds, nouvelle, *see* ŒUVRES libres, 45, 1925.
Perofski (*Gen.*), *see* PEROVSKY (*Gen.* V. A.)
Perojević (Marko). Ninski biskup Teodozije (g. 879–892), *see* BULLETTINO DI ARCH. &C. DALM., 45, Suppl., 1922.
Perot, *de Garbelei*. Divisiones mundi: [*poem*]; ed. O. H. Prior, *see* ANGLO-NORMAN. Camb. A.-N. texts, 1924.
Perotti (Armando). Storie e storielle di Puglia. 8°. Bari. 1923

Perottus (Nicolaus), *see* HORACE: CARMINA. Omnia poemata: N. P. libellus de metris odarum &c., 1573.

Pérouse (Gabriel). La vie d'autrefois à Aix-les-Bains. 8°. 1922

Perovskaya (Sofiya Lvovna), *1854–81*.
*С. Л. Перовская. [P2390]. s8°. Carouge (Genève). 1899
see ASHESHOV (N. P.) С. Перовская, 1920.

Perovsky (*Gen.* Vasily Alekseevich). Narr. of the Russ. milit. exped. to Khiva under Gen. P. in 1839. Tr. for Govt. of India. 8°. Calcutta. 1867

Perowne (Thomas). Poet. works. Coll. by T. Park. [*b. w.* Shaw (C.) Poet. works, 1807]. s8°. 1807

Perrault, *The family of*, *see* HALLAYS (A.) Les P., 1926.

Perrault (Charles). Les hommes illustres qui ont paru en France pend. ce siècle. [*2p in 1v*]. sm. fol. [1696–1700]
see HALLAYS (A.) Les Perrault, 1926.
„ SAINTYVES (P.) Les contes de P. & les récits parallèles, 1923.

Perrault (Claude), *see* HALLAYS (A.) Les Perrault, 1926.

Perrault (Nicolas). *The Jesuits morals. Coll. by a doctor of the Sorbon. Tr. [by E. Tonge]. fol. 1670

Perreau (Joseph). Victoire chère & paix de dupes: précis hist. &c. de la Grande Guerre, 1914–19. 8°. 1919

Perrens (François Tommy). L'église & l'état en France sous Henri IV & la rég. de Marie de Médicis. 2t. 8°. 1872–73

Perret (Frank Alvord).
The Vesuvius eruption of 1906. [C.I.] 4°. Wash. 1924

Perrichet (Lucien). La Grande Chancellerie de France des orig. à 1328. Thèse. la8°. 1912

Perrier (Edmond). Lamarck. s8°. 1925
La terre avant l'hist. Les orig. de la vie & de l'homme. 8°. 1920
The earth before hist.: man's orig. & the orig. of life. [Tr. P. Radin & V. C. C. Collum]. la8°. 1925
Traité de zoologie. fasc. 1–8 [*in 2v*]. [*pagin. cont.*] la8°. [1893–1928]

Perrier (Rémy). La faune de la France en tableaux synopt. illust. fasc. 3, 4, 10. 8°. 1923–26

Perrin (Alice). Government House. s8°. [1925]
The mound. s8°. [1922]
The vow of silence. s8°. [1920]

Perrin (André). De l'assoc. des monnayeurs du St. Empire rom. & des ateliers de Piémont, *see* REGIA DEP. DI STORIA PATRIA. Misc., t13, 1871.
Le trésor de la chapelle du château des Échelles, Commanderie de St. Jean de Jérusalem: invent. inéd. du 16e s.—Docs. sur la prise du château par Lesdiguieres, *see* REGIA DEP. DI STORIA PATRIA. Misc., t34, 1896.

Perrin (Antoine Sainte-Marie), *see* SAINTE-MARIE-PERRIN (A.)

Perrin (E. Sainte-Marie), *see* SAINTE-MARIE-PERRIN (E.)

Perrin (*Mrs.* Henry), *see* BOULGER (G. S.) Brit. flowering plants; illust. by Mrs. H. P., 4v, 1914.

Perrin (Jean Bapt.) Atoms. Auth. tr. by D. Ll. Hammick. 2nd Eng. ed. rev. 8°. 1923

Perrin (Pierre), *dramatist*, *see* POUGIN (A.) Les vrais créateurs de l'opéra franç.: P. & Cambert, 1881.

Perrin (William Gordon). British flags. Their early hist. & develop. at sea. Illust. in colour by H. S. Vaughan. 8°. C. 1922
see NAVAL miscellany (The); ed. W. G. P., v3, 1928.

Perrin Du Lac (F. M.) Voyage dans les 2 Louisianes & chez les nations sauvages du Missouri, 1801–3. 8°. 1805

Perris (George Herbert). A short hist. of war & peace. [Home Univ. Lib.] [repr.] s8°. [1919]

Perromat (Charles).
William Wycherley, sa vie, son œuvre. la8°. 1921

Perrone (*il conte* di), *see* BOGINO (G. L.), P. BALBO & *conte* DI P. Lettere a G. Ferrari, 1883.

Perrone (Giovanni).
Works in MIGNE (J. P.), *ed.* Theol. cursus, 1859–62.
De dæmonum cum hominibus commercio—De mundo—De homine. [7.]
Tract. de cultu sanctorum. [8.]
Tract de Eucharistia. [26.]
Tract. de ordine—De coelibatu eccl.—Tract. de matrimonio. [25.]
Utrum hæretici & schismatici sint extra Christi eccl.—De Protestantismo—An extra Cath. eccl. detur salus—De tolerantia. [6.]
De immaculato B. V. Mariae conceptu. ed. alt. emend. &c. 8°. Monasterii Guestphal. 1848

Perronet (Charles), *see* *DIALOGUE (A) betw. the pulpit & reading desk [*attrib. to* C. P.], 1786; 1795.

Perronet (Edward). *The mitre: a sacred poem. [*wanting tp.*] s8°. *p.pr.* 1757

Perronet (Vincent). Some enquiries chiefly rel. to spiritual beings, opinions of Mr. Hobbes w. regard to sensation &c. 8°. 1740

Perronneau (Jean Baptiste), *see* VAILLAT (L.) & P. RATOUIS DE LIMAY. J. B. P., 1715–83, sa vie & s. œuvre, 1923.

Perroquet (A.) La vie & le martyre du docteur R. Lulle, avec une apol. de s. œuvres. s8°. Vendosme. 1667

Perry (Aaron Jenkins), *see* TREVISA (J.) Dialogus inter milit. &c.; [tr.] T.; intr. by A. J. P., 1925.

Perry (Arthur Reed). Preventable death in cotton manufact. industry, *see* UNITED STATES: LABOR. Bull. 251, 1919.

Perry (Bliss). A study of poetry. s8°. [1922]

Perry (Henry Ten Eyck). The comic spirit in Restoration drama. 8°. New Haven. 1925

Perry (*Capt.* John). Extr. conc. la mer Caspienne &c., *see* BERNARD (J. F.), *ed.* Recueil, t7, 1725.

Perry (Nora). Hope Benham. s8°. Boston [U.S.] 1894

Perry (Ralph Barton). Annotated bibliography of wr. of Will. James. 8°. N.Y. 1920
Gen. theory of value. 8°. 1926

Perry (Walter Copland).
Sicily in fable, hist., art & song. 8°. 1908

Perry (William), *D.D.*
The Scottish Liturgy, its value & hist. 2nd ed. s8°. 1922

Perry (William), *wood carver.*
Treatise on the identity of Herne's oak. s8°. 1867

Perry (William James). Children of the sun: st. in early hist. of civiliz. 8°. [1923]
Growth of civilization. 8°. [1924]
Origin of magic & religion. 8°. [1923]
see MARVIN (F. S.), *ed.* England & the world: essays [by W. J. P. &c.], 1925.

Perrycoste (Frank H.) Some records of Talland parish. Repr. f. "The Cornish Times." s8°. *n.d.*

Perse School, *Cambridge*. Perse playbooks. No. 6. 8°. [1921]
6, Homework & hobbyhorses. New poems by boys of P. Ed. H. C. Cook.
Two plays f. the P.S. Pref. by W. H. D. Rouse, & intr. on "Dramatic teaching in schools" by F. C. Happold. 8°. C. 1921
see GRAY (J. M.) Hist. of P. Sch., Camb., 1921.

Persecution. Greek Patriarchate: "Persecution of the Greeks in Turkey," 1914–18, *see* GREEK.

***Persecutione** (De) Anglic. comm. [*or* libellus], a Colleg. Anglic. Rom. ed. &c., 1582, *see* PARSONS (R.)

***Persecutores** (Ad) Anglos pro catholicis &c., 1589, *see* ALLEN (W.), *card.*

Persia.
Акты относ. до заключ. мира съ Персіею, 1828. [*In Russ. & Armenian.* P2798]. s4°. С.-П. 1828
*Hist. acc. of the pres. troubles in P. &c., by M. de P***; tr., 1756, *see* PEYSSONEL (C. C. DE).
*Journal of a tour in P., 1824–25, 1828, *see* MONEY (R. C.)
*Sketches of P., 2v, 1827, *see* MALCOLM (*Sir* J.)

Persia Committee, *see* PERSIAN (The) crisis, 1912.

Persia magazine (The). Publ. by the Persia Soc. v1, No. 1–3 [*no more publ.*] 8°. 1921

Persia Society. Lectures. [*b. in* 2v]. 8°. [1911–14]
Ameer Ali, *Syed*. Persian culture, 1913.
Browne (E. G.) The lit. of Persia, 1912. [*a. c. in* P2762].
—— Persian press & P. journalism, 1913.
Curzon of Kedleston (G. N. C., *1st earl*). Persian autonomy, 1911.
Durand (*Sir* H. Mortimer). The charm of P., 1912.
Lynch (H. F. B.) The importance of Persia, 1912.
Margoliouth (D. S.) Avicenna, 1914.
Pollock (F.) A little Persian not a dangerous thing, 1913.
Price (M. P.) Journey thr. Azerbaijan & Pers. Khurdistan, 1913.
Sykes (P. M.) Persian manners & customs, 1913.
Turner (G. D.) Main events in Persia, Oct. 1912 to Oct. 1913, 1913.
Waters (G.) Persia: people & lang., 1912.
see PERSIA MAGAZINE, 1921.

***Persian** (The) crisis 1912. Persia Ctee Pamphlet, No. 1. [P2425]. 8°. [1912]

Persicini (Petronio). Di Andrea Brustoloni scultore bellunese. 8°. Padova. 1882

Persicum. *Alphabetum P. &c., 1783, *see* ALPHABETUM.

Persius. P. u. Nero [Text u. Übers. d. l. Satire & Krit.-exeget. &c. Streitfragen], 1923, *see* KUKULA (R. C.)
Satiræ ex rec. G. L. König, *see* JUVENAL. Satiræ 16, 1835.
Satires. Texte établi & tr. par A. Cartault. [Coll. des univ^{s}. de France]. s8º. 1920

Persky (Serge).
La vie & l'œuvre de Dostoievsky. n. éd. rev. 8º. 1924

Person (A) of quality, a native of France, *ps.* *The political mischiefs of popery, 1698, *see* SOULIGNÉ (-DE).

Personal. *P. narr. of a journey f. the Bank to Barnes; by an inside passenger, 1829, *see* JERDAN (W.)
*P. nobility: or, letters to a young nobleman &c., 1794, *see* KNOX (V.)

Personne (Nils). Svenska teatern, 1792–1810. 8º. [1914]

Persons (Robert), *see* PARSONS (R.)

Perspective. *La p. practique; par un Parisien &c., 1642, *see* DUBREUIL (J.)
*Practical p., by a Jesuit of Paris; tr., 7th ed., *n.d.*, *see* DUBREUIL (J.)

Perspicua explicatio doctr. Xtnae. in Telug. versa, 1747, *see* SCHULTZE (B.), *tr.*

Persson (Per). Bemerk. zu d. kl. Schr. d. Tacitus, *see* KUNG. HUM. VET.-SAMF. I UPPSALA. Skr., B24, 1927.

***Persuasive (A)** to the enlargement of psalmody &c., 1763, *see* FINDLAY (R.)

Pert (Camille), *ps.* [*i.e. Mme.* HORTENSE ROUGUEUL, *née Grille*]. La petite Cady. s8º. [1918]

Perthel (Eduard Theophil.)
Oratio de P. P. Vergerio. [P2759]. 8º. Jenae. [1842]

Perthes (Justus), *publisher.* Taschen-Atlas. 52. A. n. bearb. v. H. Habenicht. Mit Not. v. H. Wichmann. s8º. Gotha. 1915

Perticari (Giulio). Delle nozze di Costenzo Sforza e Camilla d'Aragona 1475. [*Ed.* A. Cerni. Nozze Ruggeri-Castagna. N119]. 4º. Pesaro. 1919

Pertsch (Johann Georg), *the younger.* Elementa juris canonici & Protestantium eccl. 2p *in* 1v. s8º. Francofurti. 1731

Pertsch (Johann Wilhelm). Poetarum coronationem, praes. F. C. Hagen, ed. J. W. P. [P445]. s4º. Baruthi. [1705]

Pertwee (Roland). Out to win. [repr.] s8º. [1922]
Rivers to cross. [2nd impr.] s8º. [1926]
The singing wells. s8º. [1923]

Peru: the cradle of South America. A monthly publ., hist., social &c. [*Eng. & Spanish*].
v1, 2 (July 1924–June 1926). 4º. [1924–26]

Perucci (Francesco). Pompe funebri di tutte le nationi del mondo. obl.8º. Verona. [1646]

Perugia. Cat. dei quadri n. Pinacoteca Vannucci in P. 8º. Perugia. 1903

Perugino [†VANNUCCI (PIETRO), *called Perugino*].
see ALAZARD (J.) P.: biog. crit., 1927.
,, GNOLI (U.) Pietro Perugino, 1923.

Peruzzi, *The family of, see* SAPORI (A.) Compagnie d. Bardi e d. P. in Inghilt. n. sec. 13 e 14, 1922.

Pervigilium Veneris. P. V. Lat. & Eng., w. comm. by R. W. Postgate. la8º. 1924

Perzyński (Friedrich).
Von Chinas Göttern. Reisen. la8º. München. [1920]

Peschaud (Marcel-Charles). Politique & fonctionn. des transports par chemin de fer pend. la Guerre. [C.E. for Int. Peace]. la8º. [1926]

Pescio (Amedeo). Settecento genovese. 8º. 1922

Pesente (Giovanni Maria). La battaglia navale di Malaga (24 agosto 1704), narr. da un testimonio oculare [*G. M. P.; ed. V. Poggi*], *see* REGIA DEP. Misc., t36, 1900.

Peshkovsky (A. M.)
Русский синтаксис в научном освещении. изд. 2^{oe}. 8º. Москва. 1920

Peskovsky (M.) Въ странѣ, гдѣ тысячи озеръ. [*Extr. f.* Русскій Мысль, 1887]. 8º. [1887]

Pesl (Ludwig Dan.) Das Dumping. Preisunterbietungen im Welthandel. la8º. München. 1921

Pesni. Пѣсни борьбы. [P2453]. 8º. [Ростовъ на Дону. 1906]
Пѣсни рабочихъ, *see* ROUGET DE L'ISLE (C. J.) Марсельеза, &c., *n.d.*
Пѣсни русскаго народа, 5ч., 1838–39, *see* SAKHAROV (I. P.), *ed.*

Pestalozza (Alessandro). Elementi di filosofia.
3^{a} ed. 4v [*v4 wanting*]. s8º. Milano. 1855–56

Pestalozzi (Johann Heinrich).
P. & h. times: pict. rec. Ed. for cent. of h. death by the Pestalozzianum & the Zentralbibl., Zurich. [Introd. by H. Stettbacher]. la8º. Zurich. 1928
see ALBERTI (C. E. R.) H. P., 1869.

Pestel (Friedrich Ulrich). Exercit. de candore. Praes. F. U. P., resp. filius ejus, F. G. Pestel.
[P428]. s4º. Rintelii. [1740]

Pestoni (Annibale). Manuale dei publici servizi per l'anno 1921. Diz. dei comuni e frazioni. 8º. Milano. 1921

Pétain (Henri Philippe), *maréchal de France.* Rapp. sur les opérations de la 2e armée en Champagne. [*Extr. f.* Archives de la Grande Guerre, 1re année—t4]. [P2707]. la8º. *n.d.*
see FOUCAULT (A.) Une colère du Gen. P. (1917), 1924.

Petau (Denis) [DIONYSIUS PETAVIUS]. De angelis—De sex dierum opificio, *see* MIGNE (J. P.), *ed.* Theol. cursus, t7, 1861.
Rationarium temporum &c. ed. nov. acc. duo opusc. J. Usserii. (1) De chronologia sacra Vet. Test. (2) De Macedonum & Asianorum anno solari. 2p [*in 1v*]. fol. Veronae. 1741
The Opusc. J. U. *has sep. pagin.*

Peter, *Apostle, & Saint.* [*For Canonical Epistles & Comm^{s}., see* BIBLE: PETER].
see DAVID (J.) Antiq. Eccl. Syro-Chald. traditio circa Petri &c. primatum, 1870.
,, RESOCONTO autentico d. disputa, Roma, 19 febb. 1872 int. alla venuta di S. P. in Roma, 1872; tr. by W. Arthur, 1872.
,, STUHLFAUTH (G.) Die apokryphen Petrusgesch. in d. altchristl. Kunst, 1925.
,, XAVIER (H.) Hist. S. Petri, *Pers. & Lat.*, 1639.

Peter *de Aqua Blanca, bp. of Hereford.* Will of (1268); ed. C. E. Woodruff, *see* CAMDEN MISC., v14, 1926.

Peter I, *emperor of Brazil.* Viagem do P. I a Minas-Geraes, 1830–31, *see* INSTITUTO HIST. &C. BRAZIL. Rev., t60, 64, 1897–1901.

Peter II, *emperor of Brazil; 1825–91.* Contrib. para a biog. de P. II, [*by var. wr.*], pl, *see* INSTITUTO HIST. &C. BRAZIL. Revista, tomo esp., 1925.
Trasladação dos restos mortaes de D. Pedro II e de D. Tereza Christina, *see* INSTITUTO HIST. &C. BRAZIL. Revista, tomo esp., 1925.

Peter I, *king of Castile, the Cruel, see* SITGES (J. B.) Mujeres del rey D. Pedro I, 1910.

Peter, *the Hungarian* [UNGARUS; HONGRE], *see* JACOBUS, *de Voragine.* Lég. dorée; [impr.] M. Husz & P. H. (1483), *facs.*, 1924.

Peter [KEDATARTZ], *catholicos of Armenia, see* MARR (N. YA.) Сказаніе о кат. П. &c. [*w. text*], 1895.

Peter, *constable of Portugal, b. 1429, see* SANTILLANA (I. L. DE M. *m.* DE). Letter to P. (c. 1449), w. intr. &c., 1927.

Peter I, *King of Portugal, see* LOPES (F.) F. L., v1, Cron. de D. P. &c., 1921.

Peter I, *emp. of Russia, the Great.*
*Петръ Великій въ его изреченіяхъ. 1ая Серія, [Предисловіе *signed* В. Строевъ]. s8º. 1910
*Geistl. Reglement auf Befehl Petri I, u. mit Bewilligung d. Synodi d. orthod. Russ. Kirche &c. s4º. Dantzig. 1724
Réglement eccl. de Pierre le Grand (1721). Tr., avec intr. & notes par C. Tondini. Ed. accomp. de la tr. lat., 1785, du texte russe orig. &c. [*w. sep. tp. & pagin.*] 8º. 1874
see HAUSSONVILLE (G. P. O. DE C., *cte.* D'). Visite du Czar P. le Gr. en 1717, 1896.
,, LE BLANC (H.) Le Czar P. I en France, *Satire*, 2t, 1741.
,, MÜLLER (G. F.) Lebensbeschr. d. Graf. B. P. Scheremetew, mit Erlaut. ü. d. Gesch. P. d. Gr.; übers. v. H. L. C. Bacmeister, 1789.
,, PLATONOV (S. F.) П. Великий, 1926.
,, VOLTAIRE. *Hist. de Russie sous P. le Gr., 2t, 1759; 2t, 1825.

Peter III, *emperor of Russia.*
see GOUDAR (A. DE). Mem. p. s. à l'hist. de P. III &c. & Suppl., 1763.
,, SALDERN (DE). Hist. de la vie de P. III, 1802.

Peter II, *count of Savoy, see* CARRARD (H.) Une commune vaudoise au 13 s.: les statuts de P. de S. & la charte de Moudon, 1887.

Peter I, *king of Servia, see* SOKOLOVITCH (P. P. DE). P. I de S. & s. calomniateurs, 1909.

Peter (Claude H.), O. B. Peter & A. F. Robbins. Launceston & Dunheved: brief record of 1000 years.
[P2786]. 8º. [Launceston. 1925]

Peter (Hermann), *b. 1837* [H. PETERUS]. Histor. Romanorum reliquiae. Coll., disposuit, rec., praef. est H. P.
v2. 8º. Lipsiae. 1906

Peter (*Generalmajor* **Josef).** Ein deut. Gefangenenlager (Ingolstadt). [P2784]. 8º. L. [1921]

Peter (Otho Bathurst), *see* PETER (C. H.), O. B. P. & A. F. ROBBINS. Launceston & Dunheved, 1925.

Peterborough. A cat. of bks. of theology, chiefly of the Elizabethan age, in the Minster Library, P. s8°. C. 1842

Peterborough Abbey, *see* JAMES (M. R.) Lists of MSS. form. in P.A. library, 1926.

Peterborough Psalter. A Peterborough Psalter & bestiary of 14th c.; descr. by M. R. James. [*Facsimile.* Roxburghe Club.] fol. O. 1921

Peterborough (Charles Mordaunt, *3rd earl of***),** *see* THORNTON (L. H.) Campaigners, 1925.

Peterburjets, *ps.* Очеркъ петербургск. рабочаго движенія 90хъ г. [P2715]. s8°. Лондонъ. 1902

Péterfi (Károly) [PETERFFY]. Sacra concilia eccl. Rom.-Cathol. in regno Hungariae. Acc. regum Hungariae, & sedis apostol. legatorum constit. eccl. 2p. fol. Posonii. 1741–42

Peterkin (Alexander), *the elder.* Records of the Kirk of Scotland, cont. acts & proc. of the General Assemblies f. 1638. v1(1638–54). la8°. E. 1838

see CHURCH OF SCOT. Booke of Universall Kirck of Scot., 1839.

Peterloo. Three acc. of P. by eyewitnesses: Bp. Stanley; Lord Hylton; J. B. Smith &c. Ed. F. A. Bruton. [Manch. Univ.] s8°. M'ter. 1921

Petermann (August Heinrich). Acc. of exped. to Central Africa, under Richardson, Barth &c., 1850–53. Comp. f. offic. &c. materials. la. fol. 1854

Petermann (Julius Heinrich).
Brevis ling. Samarit. gramm. &c. s8°. Berolini. 1873

Petermanns Mittheilungen aus Justus Perthes' geograph. Anstalt. B60ii–73. 4°. Gotha. 1914–27
After B60 only 1 vol. to each year.

Ergänzungsband 39–42 (Heft 181–194). la8°. Gotha. 1915–27
Averdunk (H.) & J. Müller-Reinhard. G. Mercator u. d. Geogr. unter s. Nachkommen, 1914. [39.]
Breitfuss (L.) Erforsch. d. Polargebietes Russ.-Eurasiens, 1925. [41.]
—— Internat. Studiengesells. z. Erforsch. d. Arktis mit d. Luftschiff, 1927. [41.]
Büdel (A.) Transkaukasien, 1926. [41.]
Fickeler (P.) Der Altai, 1925. [40.]
Franze (B.) Die Niederschlagsverhältnisse in Südamerika, 1927. [42.]
Frobenius (H.) Abriss d. Militärgeogr. Europas, T1, 1914. [40.]
Halbfass (W.) Die Seen d. Erde, 1922. [40.]
Hörner (G.) Die Waldvölker, 1927. [42.]
Jäger (F.) Forsch. ü. d. diluviale Klima in Mexico, 1926. [41.]
Jessen (O.) Südwest-Andalusien, 1924. [40.]
Lucerna (R.) Morphologie d. Montblancgruppe, 1914. [39.]
Mercator (G.), *see* Averdunk (H.) &c.
Otte (F.) China, wirtschaftspolit. Landeskunde, 1927. [42.]
Philippson (A.) Reisen &c. im westl. Kleinasien, H5, 1915. [39.]

Petern (*Pater*), *see* PETRE (EDWARD), *jesuit.*

Peters (Charles), *ed.* Home handicrafts. 8°. 1890

Peters (Fred. J.) Cat. of books &c. pert. to the sea, models &c. Sold, Anderson galleries. [*Illust.* P2855]. 8°. N.Y. 1921

Peters (Friedrich), *Pastor at Brunswick.* Ad scriptum, quod theologi Bremenses adv. collectores apologiæ publicarunt responsio. [*b. w.* Chemnitz (M.) De 2 naturis, 1580]. s4°. Lipsiæ. 1585

Bericht v. e. vermeinten Handelwucher. [P2438]. s4°. Hamburg. 1608

Pro libello M. Chemnitii De unione hypostatica naturarum Christi & de communicatione idiomatum a L. Danæo conscr. responsio. Add., Admonitio &c. [*w. sep. tp. & pagin.* Vitebergæ 1584. *b. w.* Chemnitz (M.) De 2 naturis, 1580]. s4°. Lips. 1585

Peters (Hugh). Gods doings & mans duty. Sermon, April 2, 1645. 8°. 1646

see COLOMB (G. H.) Regicide's career; pseudo St. P., 1899.

Peters (John Punnett). The Psalms as liturgies. 8°. [1922]

Peters (Orville Sherwin). Protect. of life & property against lightning, 1916, *see* UNITED STATES: COMM., DEPT. OF.

Petersen (*Pater*), *see* PETRE (EDWARD), *jesuit.*

Petersen (Ad. Stender-), *see* STENDER-PETERSEN (AD.)

Petersen (Axel). Bidrag til de dan. Simuliers Naturhist., *see* KONG. DAN. VIDENSK. SELSKAB. Skr. Raekke, B5, 1918–24.

Petersen (Eugen). Die attische Tragödie als Bild- u. Bühnenkunst. 8°. Bonn. 1915

Rhythmus, *see* KÖNIGLICHE GESELLS. D. WISS. ZU GÖTTINGEN. Abhlgn., B16, 1917.

Petersen (Eugen) [*continued*].
see LANCKOROŃSKI (C. *Graf*). Städte Pamphyliens u. Pisidiens: unter Mitw. v. G. Niemann u. E. P., 2B, 1890–92.

—— & F. v. Luschan. Reisen in Lykien Milyas u. Kibyratis. Ausgeführt auf Veranl. d. Österr. Ges. f. Arch. Erforschung Kleinasiens &c. Hrsg. E. P. u. F. v. L. fol. Wien. 1889

Petersen (Gerlac) [†PETRI (GERLACUS)].
The fiery soliloquy with God. Tr. s8°. 1921

Petersen (Johann Wilhelm), *see* WÄCHTLER (J.) Arcana chiliasmi moderni &c. aus Schr. J. W. P. &c., 1695.

Petersen (Julius). Entst. d. Eckermannschen Gespräche u. i. Glaubwürdigkeit, *see* KÖN.-PREUSS. AKAD. Abhdln., Phil.-hist. Kl., 1924.

„ „ 2e verb. A. [Deut. Forsch., H2]. 8°. Frankfurt a M. 1925

see KOSTER (A.) & J. P. Gesch. d. deut. Literatur, B1, 1925.

Petersen (K. O. Vedel-), *see* VEDEL-PETERSEN (K. O.)

Peterson (M. N.)
Очерк синтаксиса русского языка. 8°. Москва. 1923

Peterson (Margaret) [*Mrs.* A. O. FISHER].

Adventurous youth. s8°. [1925]
Fear shadowed. s8°. [1927]
The feet of death. 2nd ed. s8°. [1927]
Love is enough. s8°. [1920]
Moonflowers. s8°. [1926]
Passionate particles. s8°. 1927
The scent of the rose. s8°. [1923]
„ „ pop. ed. s8°. [1925]

Peterson (Roy Merle). The cults of Campania. [Amer. Acad. in Rome. Papers &c., v1]. 8°. [Rome]. 1919

Peterson (William). Canadian essays &c. 8°. 1915

Pethahiah, *ben Jacob, of Ratisbon* [PETACHIAS]. Peregrinatio [12 c., *Heb. & Lat.*], *see* WAGENSEIL (J. C.) Exercit., 1687; 1719.

Petheram (John). Hist. sketch of progress & pres. state of Anglo-Saxon lit. in England. 8°. 1840

Petherick (Horace). Joseph Guarnerius, h. work & h. master [*i.e.* A. Gisalberti]. s8°. 1906

Petiet (Raynald). Du pouvoir législatif en France dep. Philippe le Bel j. 1789. Avant-propos de M. A. Duverger. 8°. 1891

Petigru (James Louis), *see* GRAYSON (W. J.) J. L. P.: biog. sketch, 1866.

Petit. Petit dict. class. d'hist. naturelle, par B. de St. Pierre &c., 2t, 1827, *see* COLLIN DE PLANCY (J. A. S.)

*Petit sorcier (Le). s8°. [1816]

Petit (Felice de). Gli amplessi del Tebro col Sebeto. [Nozze Cavaniglia—Sforza]. [N125]. 8°. Napoli. 1706

Petit (Henri), *see* CHANSON (A.) Ecrits; par A. C., H. P. &c., 1927.

Petit (Louis). Arménie. [*Extr. f.* Dict. de théol. cath. P2789]. la8°. [1900–5]

see ATHOS. Actes de l'A., 1, publ. L. P., 1903.

„ FLORENCE, *Council of.* Doc. rel. au C. de F.: textes éd. & tr. par L. P., pl, 2, 1923–27.

„ LEGRAND (E.) Bibliogr. hellénique; compl. & publ. par L. P. &c., t1, 1918.

Petit (Louis D.) Repertorium d. verhandelingen en bijdragen betr. de gesch. d. Vaderlands, d3, 1911–20; bewerkt door H. J. A. Ruys. 8°. Leiden. 1928

Petit-Didier (Mathieu), *bp. of Macra.* De auctoritate & infallib. pontificum, *see* MIGNE (J. P.), *ed.* Theol. cursus, t4, 1859.

Diss. hist.-theolog. in qua exam., quaenam mens fuerit conc. Constant. &c. circa auctorit., & infallib. Pontif. &c. In Lat. tr. G. Cartier. 4°. Augustae Vindel. 1738

see COTTA (J. F.) Comm. de fallibili pontificis auct. M. P.-D. oppos., 1732.

Petition (A) of the freeholders of Middlesex, pres. to H. Majesty, 1769, *see* MIDDLESEX.

Petlin (Ivan), *see* POKROVSKY (F. I.) Путешествіе въ Монголію &c., II. II. 1618, 1914.

Petra (Giulio de). Framm. di legge romana scop. a Taranto, *see* REALE ACCAD. D. LINCEI. Mon. ant., v6, 1895.

Petracchi (Celestino). Vita di Arrigo di Suevia, Re di Sardegna, volg. Enzo. s8°. Faenza. 1750

Petrarch.

L'Africa. Ed. N. Festa. la8°. Firenze. [1926]
Carmina incogn. Ex codd. ital. Bibl. ed. G. M. Thomas. 4°. Monachii. 1859
Il Petrarca. Con l'espos. di A. Velutello. s4°. Venetia. 1584
CANZONIERE.
Le rime de P. [*w.* Comp. d. vita di F. P., fatto da sign.

Petrarch [*continued*].

CANZONIERE [*continued*].
giornalisti d'Italia]. [*engr. tp. only*]. 2t. s8°. Londra. 1778
Le rime de P. con note dal P. F. Soave. [*&* Vita del G. Tiraboschi *&* Cat. di princ. ed.] 2v. 8°. Milano. 1805
Le rime. 2v. 8°. Milano. 1828
Raccolta di rime attrib. a F. P. che non si legg. n. s. Canzoniere. 8°. Padova. 1874

TRANSLATIONS.
Some love sonnets of P. Tr. &c. w. biog. intr. by W. D. Foulke. s8°. 1915
see FORESTI (A.) Viaggi de F. P. dall' Italia ad Avignone, 1920.
,, PIETROPOLI (G. P.) Il Petrarca impugnato dal P., 1818.
,, TATHAM (E. H. R.) F. P., h. life & corresp., 2v, 1925–26.

Petrasanta (Silvester) [PETRASANCTA (S. A)].
Symbola heroica. s4°. Amstelaedami. 1682

Petrashevtsi.
Петрашевцы. [Полит. процессы Никол. эпохи.] la8°. Москва. 1907

Petre (Edward), *jesuit* [PATER PETERN ; P. PETERSEN].
Antwort an Pater la Chaisen. [P2743]. s4°. *n.p.* 1688
Neue jesuit. Anschläge wieder d. Protestanten in Engeland. [P2743]. s4°. *n.p.* 1688

Petre (*Hon.* Edward). Notices of Eng. colleges & convents estab. on Continent after dissol. of relig. houses in Eng. Ed. F. C. Husenbeth. 8°. Norwich. 1849

Petre (Francis Turville-), *see* TURVILLE-PETRE (F.)

Petre (Maude D. M.) The ninth Lord Petre. 8°. 1928

Petre (Robert Edward, *9th baron*), *see* PETRE (M. D. M.) The 9th Lord P., 1928.

Petreius (Nicolaus), *Pastor in Aas.* Cimbrorum & Gothorum origines, migrationes &c. s8°. Lipsiae. 1695

Petreius (Theodorus), *see* BELLARMINO (*il card.* R. F. R.) *Doct. Xtna. Arm., in Lat. versa & publ. à T. P., 1667.

Petri (Antonius) [PIETRO DELLO SCHIAVO (ANTONIO DI)]. Il diario romano, 1404–17, *see* MURATORI (L. A.) Rerum Ital. Script., t24v, 1917.

Petri (Fridericus), *Pastor at Brunswick, see* PETERS (F.)

Petri (Georg Carl). Diss. 1–4, de studio magico Judaeorum. Resp. J. G. Thomae, B. H. Magentius &c. [*Each diss. w. diff. resp.* P431]. s4°. Vitembergae. [1727–30]

Petri (Gerlacus), *see* PETERSEN (G.)

Petri (Johann Christoph). De hist. 2 Gadarenorum δαιμονιζομένων comm. [P1035]. s4°. Erfordiae. 1797

Petri (Stanislao). Gli adornatori del libro in Italia. Testo crit. di S. P., pref. di C. Ratta. 2v [v2, 2ª ed.; rec. di R. Biordi e M. Ferrigni]. fol. Bologna. 1923–25

Petriconi (Hellmuth). Die span. Lit. d. Gegenwart seit 1870. s8°. Wiesbaden. 1926

Petricovia. Confessio Cathol. fidei Christiana: vel potius explic. quaedam Conf. a patribus factae in synodo provinciali quae habita est Petrikoviae a. 1551. [*Pres. N. Dziergowski*]. fol. [Moguntiae]. 1557
Fidei cathol. conf., P. in synodo &c. a. 1552, 1563, *see* ORICHOVIUS (S.)

Petrie (Alexander). A hist. of the Cathol. church, 600–1600. [*2 pagin.*] fol. Hague. 1662

Petrie (George), *LL.D., M.R.I.A.* Christian inscriptions in the Irish lang. Coll. &c. G. P. Ed. M. Stokes. [Roy. Hist. & Arch. Assoc. of Ir.] 2v. 4°. D. 1872–78

Petrie (*Sir* William Matthew Flinders).
Amulets. Illust. by Egypt. Coll. in Univ. Coll., London. 4°. 1914
Anc. weights & measures. [Dept. of Egyptology, Univ. Coll.] 4°. 1926
Buttons & design scarabs. [Brit. Sch. of Arch. in Egypt &c.] 4°. 1925
Corpus of prehist. pottery & palettes. [Brit. Sch. of Arch. in Egypt &c.] 4°. 1921
Gerar. [Brit. Sch. of Arch. in Egypt]. 4°. 1928
Glass stamps & weights. [Brit. Sch. of Arch. in Egypt]. 4°. 1926
Hawara portfolio: paintings of the Rom. age, found by W. M. F. P. [Brit. Sch. of Arch. in Egypt &c.] 4°. 1913
Hist. of Egypt to the 16th dynasty. 10th ed. rev. s8°. [1923]
Neglected Brit. hist. [*i.e.* Tysilio's Chron.], *see* BRIT. ACADEMY. Proc., 1917–18.
Objects of daily use with figures f. Univ. Coll., London. [Brit. Sch. of Arch. in Egypt]. 4°. 1927
Prehistoric Egypt, illust. by objects in Univ. College, London. [Brit. Sch. of Arch. in Egypt &c.] 4°. 1920
Relig. life in anc. Egypt. s8°. 1924
The revolutions of civilis. [3rd ed.] s8°. 1922
Social life in anc. Egypt. s8°. 1923
The status of the Jews in Egypt. Foreword by Sir P. Sassoon. s8°. [1922]
Tombs of the Courtiers & Oxyrhynkhos. With chap. by A.

Petrie (*Sir* William Matthew Flinders) [*continued*].
Gardiner, H. Petrie & M. A. Murray. [Brit. Sch. of Arch. in Egypt &c., 1922]. 4°. 1925
see BISSING (F. W. v.) Die Datierung d. Petrieschen Sinaiinschr., 1920.
,, IMMORTALITY; by Sir F. P. &c., 1924.
—— **& G. Brunton.** Sedment. [Brit. Sch. of Arch. in Egypt &c.] 2[v]. 4°. 1924
——, —— **& M. A. Murray.** Lahun II. [Brit. Sch. of Arch. in Egypt &c.] 4°. 1923

Petrini (Edward). Psykolog. analyser, *see* KUNG. HUM. VET.-SAMF. I UPPSALA. Skr., B20, 1918.

Petrocchi (Policarpo). Novo diz. scolast. d. lingua ital. 8°. Milano. [1920]
Nòvo diz. univ. d. lingua ital. 2v. la8°. Milano. 1900

Petrograd, *see* SAINT PETERSBURG.

Petrogubotkomkhoz. Петрогуботкомхоз в 1922, 1923, *see* SAINT PETERSBURG.

Petrolini (—), *actor, see* DESSY (M.) P., 1921.

Petronius Arbiter (Titus).
Cena Trimalchionis, w. Seneca's Apocolocyntosis & sel. of Pompeian inscr. Ed. W. B. Sedgwick. s8°. O. 1925
P., leader of fashion. Tr. & notes by J. M. Mitchell. s8°. 1922
Petronius; w. Eng. tr. by M. Heseltine—Seneca, Apocolocyntosis; w. Eng. tr. by W. H. D. Rouse. [Loeb Class. Lib.] [repr.] s8°. 1916
Le satiricon. Texte établi & tr. par A. Ernout. [Coll. des univ. de France]. 8°. 1922
Satyricon, cum fragm. Albæ Graecæ recup. 1688. s8°. Roterodami. 1693
see HEINSE (J. J. W.) Sämmtl. Werke, B2, Begebenheiten d. Enkolp &c., 1903.

Petrosean (Matthias), *see* BEDROSSIAN (M.)

Petrov (A.) Матеріалы для ист. Угорской Руси, 7, *see* IMP. AKAD. NAUK. Сборникъ, т97, 1921.

Petrov (Grigory).
Письмо Митрополиту Антонію. [P849]. s8°. Berlin. *n.d.*

Petrov (Nikolai Ivanovich).
Очерки изъ ист. украйнской лит. xviii вѣка. 8°. Кіевъ. 1880

Petrov (V.), *see* RUSSIA. Таиные общества [*by P. &c.*], 1926.

Petrovsky (D.)
Красное знамя и братство народов. [P2722]. s8°. Москва. 1919

Petrucci (Fabio Bargagli), *see* BARGAGLI-PETRUCCI (F.)

Petrucci (Giovanni Antonio de'), *conte di Policastro, see* PERITO (E.) La congiura dei baroni e il conte di P.; con l'ed. compl. e crit. dei sonetti di G. A. de P., 1926.

Petrucci (*Card.* Pietro Mattheo), *see* JÄGER (J. W.) Examen theolog., in quo Card. P. placita revocantur, 1709.

Petrus, *de Duisburg.* Chronicon Prussiae; ordinis Teutonici origo & res, 1226–1326, in Prussia gestae, cum cont. usque ad 1435 &c. Access. Privilegia quaedam, item diss. xix antiq. Prussicas complexae auctore C. Hartknoch. 2p [*sep. pagin.*] s4°. Jenae. 1679

Petrus, *de Hibernia, tutor to St. Thomas Aquinas, see* BÄUMKER (C.) P. de H. u. s. Disput. vor König Manfred, 1920.

Petrus, *Lombardus, bp. of Paris.* Epitome in quatuor lib. sententiarum M. P. L. recéns ed. Authore F. C. Spinaeo. s8°. Parisiis. [*Petrus Rathiire*]. 1551
Sententiarum libri 4. s8°. Coloniæ Agripp. 1566
see DANEAU (L.) In P. L. libr. prim. sententiarum comm. triplex &c., 1580.

Petrus, *Pictav.* [PIERRE *de Poitiers*]. Sententiarum lib. 5, *see* PULLUS (R.) Sentent. lib. 8, 1655.

Petrus, *de Rosenheim.* *Sacrarum literarum memoriale pauculis versibus. s8°. [Argentinæ]. 1544
[*Author's name given in acrostic in prologue.*]

Petrus, *Sarnensis.* Hystoria Albigensis. Publ. P. Guébin & E. Lyon. [Soc. de l'Hist. de Fr.] t1. 8°. 1926

Petrus (Franciscus). Suevia eccl., seu clericalia collegia tùm secularia tùm regularia &c. fol. Augustae Vindel. 1699

Petrus (Suffridus), *Leovardiensis.* De scriptoribus Frisiae decades 16. s8°. Franequerae. 1699

Petrusevich (Nikolai Grigorevich). Туркмены между старымъ русломъ Аму-Дарьи; *& o. articles, see* IMPERATORSKOE RUSS. GEOG. OBSCH. Записки Кавказ. отд., кн. 11i, 1880.

Pettazzoni (Raffaello). Stazioni preist. n. prov. di Bologna, *see* REALE ACCAD. D. LINCEI. Mon. ant., v24, 1916.

Pettenkofen (August), *see* WEIXLGÄRTNER (A.) A. P., 2T, 1916.

Pettermand (Carl). Die Konsumvereine, Schweiz, *see* UNTERSUCHUNGEN ü. Konsumver., 1923.

Pettersen (Hjalmar).
Norsk anonym- og pseudonym-lexikon. la8°. 1924

Pettie (George), *see* Guazzo (S.) Civile conversation; 1st 3 bks. tr. by G. P., 1581, 2v, 1925.

Pettigrew (Thomas Lettson). *Lucien Greville. By a cornet in the East India Co.'s service. [*T. L. P.*] 3v. s8°. 1833

Pettit (Charles).
Le fils du grand eunuque. Roman chin. s8°. [1920]
Hist. d'un vieux lettré & de son médecin, roman chin., *see* Œuvres libres, 19, 1923.

Pettit (Walter William), *see* Cumming (C. K.) & W. W. P. Russian-Amer. relations, 1917–20, 1920.

Pettitt (Edward). The visions of government: antimonarch. principles &c. of Commonwealths-men &c. exposed. s8°. 1684

Pettman (Charles). Place names of the Orange Free State. s8°. Queenstown. 1922

Petto (Samuel), *see* Martin (J.), S. P. &c. The preacher sent, 1658.

Pettorelli (Arturo). Guido Mazzoni da Modena, plasticatore. la8°. Torino. 1925
Salvator Rosa: 52 tavole con introd. la8°. Torino. 1924

Pettus (*Mrs.* Daisy Caden), *see* Evans (*Mrs.* R. C.) Letters f. Mexico; arr. w. comments by D. C. P., 1926.

Petty (*Sir* William), *M.D., surveyor-gen. of Ireland to Charles II.* The Petty papers. Unpubl. wr. of P. Ed. f. Bowood papers by Marq. of Lansdowne. 2v. 8°. 1927

Petty-Fitzmaurice (Henry Charles Keith), *5th marq. of Lansdowne, see* Lansdowne (H. C. P.-F., *5th m. of*).

Petworth Collection, *see* Leconfield (C. H. W., *3rd b.*) Cat. of the P.C. of pictures, 1920.

Peucer (Caspar).
Copey d. Schreibens C. P. aus d. Gefengnis zu Leipzig &c., 1579. Bekantnus v. d. 2 streittigen Articuln. [P2611]. s4°. [Zerbst ?]. 1603
De dimensione terræ &c. Descr. locorum Terræ Sanctæ autore Brocardo Monacho; Aliquot insignium loc. Terrae Sanctae explic. &c. per P. Melanthonem. s8°. Wittebergæ. 1554
Hist. carcerum & liberationis divinae. Operâ &c. C. Pezelii. s8°. Tiguri. 1605
In obitum C. Peuceri, carmina epitaphia &c. [P2611]. s4°. Servestae. 1603
Test. C. P.'s von ihme selbs in s. Gefengnuss. [P2611]. s4°. Zerbst. 1603
Test. Latinum C. P. in carcere scriptum. [P2611]. s4°. Servestae. 1603
Tract. hist. de P. Melanchthonis sententia, De controversia Cœnæ Domini cum app. sel. epistol. &c. Philippi &c. Studio Q. Reuteri. s4°. Ambergae. 1596
see Brendel (J.) Des Sendbrieffes an Smyrna, Erklerung uff C. P. bey dess. Begräbnuss, 1603.
„ Eichstadt (H. C. A.) Narr. de C. P. Melanchthonis genero, 1841.
„ Stenius (S.) Oratio, qua C. P. manibus parentatum est, a S. S., 1603.
„ Wittenberg. Christl. u. wolgegründete Widerlegung d. Calvin. Test. so wol auch Confess. u. Leichpredigt C. P. &c., 1603.
„ —— Libelli Calviniani, Tract. hist. de Melanthonis sententia de controv. Coenae à C. P. scr. refut., 1597.

Peucer (Daniel). De epistola Lutheri de interpretatione comm. [P2629]. s4°. Numburgi. 1736

Peutinger (Conrad). Briefwechsel. Gesammelt, hrsg. u. erläut. v. E. König. 8°. München. 1923
see Hülsen (C.) Samml. röm. Renaissance-Inschriften aus d. Augsburger Koll. K. P., 1920.
„ Miller (K.) Weltkarte d. Castorius, gen. Die P.'sche Tafel, *facsimile*, 1888.

Peyran (Charles). Hist. de l'anc. Académie réformée de Sedan. Thèse. 8°. Strasbourg. 1846

Peyran (Jean Rodolphe). An hist. defence of the Waldenses or Vaudois [*in Fr.*] Intr. & app. by T. Sims. 8°. 1826

Peyre (Roger). Les Carraches: biog. crit. 8°. [1924]
Nîmes, Arles, Orange, Saint-Rémy. [Villes d'art célèbres]. 4e éd. rev. la8°. 1923

Peyrolières, Sainte-Foy-de, *see* Sainte-Foy-de-Peyrolières.

Peyrony (D.) Elém. de préhistoire. Préf. du Dr. Capitan. la8°. Ussel. 1923
see Capitan (L.), H. Breuil & D. P. La caverne de Font-de-Gaume (Dordogne), 1910.

Peyser (Ethel), *see* Bauer (M.) & E. P. How music grew, 1925.

Peyssonel (Claude Charles de), *consul gen. of France in Smyrna.* *An hist. acc. of the pres. troubles of Persia & Georgia. In cont. of Mr. Hanway's Hist. to 1753. By M. de P***. Tr. la8°. 1756

Pez (Bernhard). Bibliotheca Benedictino-Mauriana, libri 2. Autore B. P. qui vet. anonymum de script. eccl. addidit &c. s8°. Augustæ-Vindel. 1716

Pez (Bernhard) [*continued*].
Epistolae apologet. pro ord. S. Benedicti adv. libell. " Cura salutis " &c., aut. anonym. S. J. Ed. R. D. P. Mellitus. s8°. Campoduni. 1715
see Mary, *the Virgin.* *Liber de miraculis Sanctae Mariae; publ. at Vienna, 1731, by B. P.; repr., w. intr. &c. by T. F. Crane, 1925.

Peza (Juan de Dios). Lira mexicana: col. de poesías de a. contemp. Prólogo del d. A. Balbin de Unquera. s8°. 1879

Pézard (Maurice). La céramique archaïque de l'Islam & s. orig. [Planches *in case, sep.*] 4°. 1920
Mission à Bender-Bouchir: docs. arch. & épigraph., *see* Délégation en Perse, t15, 1914.
Une nouv. stèle de Séti I, *see* Acad. d. Inscr.: Fond. Piot. Mon., t25, 1921–22.

Pezel (Christoph).
Apologia verae doctrinae de definitione Evangelii opposita Thrasonicis præstigiis &c. I. Wigandi. s4°. Witebergae. 1571
Argumentorum et objectionum, de praecipuis artic. [capitibus] doct. Christianę, cum responsionibus, quae passim extant in scriptis P. Melanchthonis. 9p *in* 8v. s8°. Neostadii. 1578–89
tp. of p1 *wanting.* p4 & 5 *have t.* Quarta [Quinta] pars objectionum & respons. &c. p9 *has t.* Argument. Philippicorum p. ult.
„ „ ....[*a. ed. of* p1 *w. tp.*] s8°. Genevae. 1578
De sacrosancta Cœna Domini tractatus &c. s8°. Bremæ. 1589
Testimonia vet. script. insigniora. De sacramentali verborum Cœnæ interpret. [*b. w. h.* De sacrosancta Cœna, 1589]. s8°. Bremæ. 1590
see Hamelmann (H.) De impostura, fraudulentia &c. C. P., 1592.
„ Peucer (C.) Hist. carcer. & liberationis; operâ C. Pezelii, 1605.

Pezuela (Jacobo de la). Crón. de las Antillas, 1871, *see* España. Crón. gen., v12, 1865 &c.

Pezuela (Luis Robles), *see* Robles Pezuela (L.)

Pfaff (Carl), *historian.* Fürstenhaus u. Land Württemberg &c. 2e verb. A. 8°. St. 1849
Gesch. Wirtenbergs. 2B. 8°. Reutlingen. 1818–20

Pfaff (Christoph Matthäus).
Acta et scripta publica Eccl. Wirtemberg. &c. Rec. &c. C. M. P. s4°. Tubingae. 1720
De formula consensus Helvetica. Diss. [P441]. s4°. Tubingae. *n.d.*
Diss. crit. de genuinis librorum Novi Test. lectionibus, de J. Millii coll. var. lectionum. s8°. Amstelodami. 1709
Diss. de Stercoranistis. Praes. C. M. P., resp. J. S. Heller &c. [P434]. s4°. Tubingae. [1750]
Eccl. evangelicæ lib. symbolici, tria symb. oecumenica, Augustana conf. invar., ejusd. apol., artic. Smalcaldici, uterq. cat. D. Lutheri, Formula Concordiæ. [*& App. b. together*]. s8°. Tubingae. 1730
Instit. hist. eccl. &c. *Foll. by* De liturgiis, missalibus &c. [*sep. pagin.*] s8°. Tubingae. 1721
„ „ ....ed. 2a. aucta. s8°. Tubingae. 1727
Instit. theol. dogmat. & moralis &c. Adj. De gustu spirituali, & De vitiis &c. [*sep. tp. & pagin.*] s8°. Tubingae. 1720
Introd. in hist. theologiae litt. 3p. s4°. Tubingae. 1724–26
Schediasma de Formula Consensus Helvetica. [P426]. s4°. Tubingae. 1723
see Salchlin (J. R.) Stricturae & obs. in C. M. P. Formula Consensus Helvetica, 1723.

Pfaff (Ivo). Bernhard Walther von Walthersweil als Romanist d. 16ten Jhdts., 1918, *see* Kais. Akad. d. W. zu Wien. Sitzber., B186, 1921.

Pfaff (Johann Christoph). Disput. heptas de imputatione divina. ed. 2a. s4°. Tubingae. 1715–16

Pfältzische. Protocoll d. i. Acta oder Handlungen des Gesprechs, zw. d. Pf. u. Wirtemberg. Theologen, Apr. 1564 zu Maulbrun gehalten &c., 1565, *see* Maulbronn.

Pfalz. Neueste Gesch. d. Reform. Kirche in d. Untern Pf., 1791, *see* Höffelein (C. A. H.)

Pfalz (Anton). Beitr. z. Kunde d. bayer.-österr. Mundarten, H1, 1918, *see* Kaiserl. Akad. d. W. zu Wien. Sitzber., B190, 1920.
—— **& H. Voltelini.** Forsch. z. d. deut. Rechtsbüchern. 1, Die Überlief. d. Deutschenspiegels, v. A. P. 2, Der Verf. d. sächs. Weltchronik. 3, Der Sachsenspiegel u. d. Zeitgesch., v. H. V., 1919–24, *see* Kaiserl. Akad. d. W. zu Wien. Sitzber., B191, 201, 1922–25.

Pfandl (Ludwig). Span. Kultur u. Sitte d. 16. u. 17. Jhdts. 8°. [München]. 1924

Pfedteshem (Conrad), *see* Pfettisheim (C.)

Pfefferkorn (Georg Mich.) Etl. Lutheraner wie auch Papisten, Calvinisten, Türcken u. Heyden gute Urtheile v. Luthero &c. [*b. w.* Fabricius (J. A.) Centifolium, 1728–30]. 4e A. s8°. Gotha. 1730

Pfeffinger (Johann), *theologian.* Antwort auff die offentl. Bekentnis d. reinen Lare d. Evangelii u. Confut. d. itz. Schwermerey N. v. Ambsdorff. [P2468]. s4°. Wittemberg. 1558
see AMSDORFF (N. v.) Das D. Pf. seine missethat bösslich leugnet &c., 1559.
Pfeiffer (August), *orientalist.* Introd. in Orientem: de orig. &c. lingg. orient. ed. 3a. s8°. Jenae. 1715
Jahr-Opffer, Hn. Johann Georgen II, Hertzogen zu Sachsen, in 15 Sprachen. [P2671, 2746]. s4°. Wittenberg. 1670
Opera omnia quae extant philologica. 2t *in* 1v. 4°. Ultrajecti. 1704
see MODENA (LEO). Recede a malo, libellus anon. de lusu; illust. A. P., 1665.
Pfeiffer (Christian Gottfried). Diss.: Amicorum omnia communia &c. [P2649]. s4°. Jenae. 1717
Pfeiffer (Franz). Meister Eckhart (Leipzig, 1857). Tr., w. omissions & add. by C. de B. Evans. 8°. 1924
Text h. t. Deut. Mystiker d. 14 Jhdts., *&* Meister E. *is cont. in* B2.
Pfeiffer (Johannes Gottlob) & J. G. Metzner. Eruditum θαυμαστόν in aetate tenera, diss. [P447]. s4°. Lipsiae. [1696]
Pfeiffer (Ida L.) A lady's travels round the world. Tr. W. Hazlitt. s8°. 1852
Visit to Iceland & the Scandinavian North. Tr. Added, Essay on Icelandic poetry &c. 2nd ed. 8°. 1853
Pfeiffer (Joachim Ehrenfried).
Elementa hermeneutica univ. s8°. Jenae. 1743
Instit. hermeneuticae sacrae vet. & recent. s8°. Erlangae. 1771
Pfettisheim (Conrad) [PFEDTESHEM (C.)]. Chron. rimée des guerres de Bourgogne, Strasb. 1477, facs. & tr., *see* PICOT (E.) & H. STEIN. Recueil, 1923.
Pfintzing (Melchior), *see* TITZ (H. G.) Disquis. de inclyto lib. poet. Theuerdanck, 1737.
Pfister (Christian). Les Schweighaeuser & la chaire de litt. grecque de Strasbourg (1770–1855). [Extr. du Bull. de la Fac. des Lettres de Str., 1925–27]. la8°. 1927
Pfister (Johann Christian von).
Übersicht d. Gesch. v. Schwaben. s8°. St. 1813
Pfister (John R. v.), *see* BREWER (C.) & Co. Rep. of case of C. B. & Co. vs. J. R. v. P., 1845.
Pfister (Kurt). Hugo van der Goes. 4°. Basel. 1923
Katakomben Malerei. 4°. Potsdam. 1924
Die primitiven Holzschnitte. la8°. München. 1922
Pfister (Oskar).
Die Behandlung schwer erziehbarer u. abnormer Kinder. s8°. [1921]
Die Liebe vor d. Ehe. 8°. Bern. 1925
Ein neuer Zugang zum alten Evangelium &c. s8°. Gütersloh. 1918
Vermeintl. Nullen u. angebl. Musterkinder. s8°. [1921]
Wahrheit u. Schönheit in d. Psychanalyse. 8°. Zürich. 1918
TRANSLATIONS.
Love in children & its aberrations. Tr. E. & C. Paul. 8°. 1924
Psycho-analysis in the service of educ. Auth. tr. s8°. 1922
Some applications of psycho-analysis. auth. Eng. version. 8°. [1923]
Pflacher (Moses). Disput. de jure vocandi ministros eccl. [P2504]. s4°. Tubingæ. 1585
Die gantze Lehr vom Tod u. Absterben d. Menschen kurtz verfasset u. geprediget. s4°. Franckfurt a. M. 1582
Pflaum (Gottfried Ludwig), *see* MÜCKE (J. H.) & G. L. P. Diss. hist. de 3 capitulis Conc. Calchedon., 1766.
Pflug (Julius), *bp. of Naumburg.*
see JOHN FREDERICK, *Elector of Saxony.* Verantwortung so Johans Friderich &c., wider J. P., 1542.
,, SCHULZE (F.) Disput. de rationibus quibus electio J. P. impugnata & propugnata est, 1750.
Pflugk-Harrtung (Julius A. G. v.) [†HARTTUNG (JUL.)]
1813–15. Illust. Gesch. d. Befreiungskriege. 4°. St. 1912
Pfohl (Ernst). Wirtschafts-Atlas d. Tschecho-Slowak. Staates. obl. fol. Reichenberg i. Böhmen. [1920]
Pfohl (Ferdinand), *see* CHEVALLEY (H.) A. Nikisch; v. F. P. &c., 1922.
Pfordten (Hermann *Frhr.* **v. d.)** Beethoven. 4e A. s8°. L. 1922
Pfuhl (Ernst).
Malerei u. Zeichung d. Griechen. 3B. la8°. München. 1923
Pfungst (Henri Joseph). Descr. cat. of a small coll. princ. of 15th & 16th cent. bronzes. 20 copies pr. 4°. *n.d.*
Phaedrus. Fables. Texte établi & tr. par A. Brenot. [Coll. des univ. de Fr.] 8°. 1924
Fabularum Æsopicarum libri 5. s8°. Londini. 1750

Phaedrus [*continued*].
Fabulae Æsopiae cum N. Perotti prologo et 10 novis fabulis. Recog. &c. I. P. Postgate. s8°. O. [1919]
see FISCHER (J. F.) De Ph. ejusque fabulis prolusio, 1746.
,, FUNCK (J. N.) Pro Ph. ejusque fabulis apologia, 1747.
Phale (Justine de Saint), *see* SAINT PHALE (*Mademoiselle* DE).
Phalén (Adolf). Ueb. d. Relativität d. Raum-u. Zeitbestimmungen, *see* KUNG. HUM. VET.-SAMF. I UPPSALA. Skr., B21, 1922.
Phanariote. *Livre d'or de la noblesse ph. &c., 2e éd., 1904, *see* LIVRE.
Phara, *Saint, see* FARA, *St.*
Pharmani Asman [FARMANI ASMAN]. Hist. de Pharmani Asman tr. de l'arm. par F. Macler. [Extr. de la Rev. des trad. pop. P2803]. 8°. 1906
Phaulkon (Constantine) [*M.* CONSTANCE, *prime minister of the King of Siam*], *see* ORLÉANS (P. J. D'). Hist. de M. Constance &c., 1690.
Phebens (Eggerik Egges). Kronijk, 1565–94. Uitg. door H. O. Feith. [*Lat.* Hist. Genoots. te Utrecht. Werken, N.S., 7]. 8°. Utrecht. 1867
Phelan (Gerald B.)
Feeling experience & its modalities. 8°. 1925
Phelan (William). The hist. of the policy of the Church of Rome in Ireland, to the Great Rebellion. 8°. D. 1827
,, ,, 3rd ed., w. mem. by J. Jebb &c. 8°. 1854
Remains. Biog. mem. by John [Jebb], bp. of Limerick. [*Bound as* Jebb (J.) Works, v8, 9]. 2v. 8°. 1832
Phelps (Anson G.), *see* PRENTISS (G. L.) Sermon on the death of A. G. P.; w. extr. f. h. journal, 1854.
Phelps (Austin), *D.D.* The theory of preaching. la8°. 1882
Phelps (J. J.) Antiq. at Bowdon. Lect. 8°. M'ter. [1926]
Phelps (William Lyon).
Essays on modern dramatists. s8°. N.Y. 1921
Phelypeaux (*l'abbé* **Jean)** [PHELIPEAUX]. *Lettres de M*** à un ami au sujet du quiétisme. [*b. w. h.* Rel. &c., 1732]. s8°. *n.p.* 1733
*Relation de l'orig., du progrès & de la condamnation du quiétisme en France. [2p *in* 1v]. s8°. *n.p.* 1732
Phelypeaux de Maurepas (Jean Frédéric), *see* MAUREPAS (*le cte.* J. F. P. DE).
Pherecydes, *of Syros.*
see DIELS (H.) Zur Pentemychos d. P., 1897.
,, WILAMOWITZ-MÖLLENDORFF (U. v.) P., 1926.
Phidias.
see CARO-DELVAILLE (H.) P. ou le génie grec, 1922.
,, GALLI (E.) Fidia in Etruria, 1921.
,, JOHANSEN (P.) P. & the Parthenon sculpt. 1925.
see SCHRADER (H.) Über P., 1911.
,, SITTE (H.) Zu P., biog. Beitr., 1924.
Phifer (Charles Lincoln). Posthumous essays by Emerson. Purporting to be by automatic writing f. spirit R. W. E. Medium C. L. P., w. intr. 8°. Boston, Mass. 1907
Philadelphus (Hieronymus), *ps., see* CALDERWOOD (DAVID).
Philaletes. *Some remarks on the dialogue between P. & Philotimus &c., 1705, *see* SOME.
Philaletes, *ps. of a. of *Appeal (An) to the public whether a Calvinist can be a minister of the Ch. of Eng., 1780, &c., see* TAYLOR (T.)
Philalethes, *Polytopiensis, ps., see* LANDI (ORTENSIO).
Philalethes (Eirenaeus Philoponos), *ps., see* STARKEY (GEORGE).
Philalethes (Irenaeus), *ps., see* PRZYPKOWSKI (S.)
Philalethes (Irenaeus), *Eleutherius, ps., see* SPANG (W.)
Philalethes Eridairon, *ps., see* HEBENSTREIT (C. W.)
Philander, *ps.* *Nöthige &c. Unterredung: erstes Gespräche v. M. Luthero u. U. Zwinglio [Vorrede *signed* P. u. Agathocles], 1720, *see* LUTHER (M.)
Philandrier (Guillaume) [†PHILANDER (GULIELMUS)], *see* LA MARE (PHILIBERT). De Vita, moribus & scr. G. P., 1667.
Philarchaios, *ps., see* GORDON (J.)
Philargyrius (Junius). Explan. in Bucolica Vergilii, *see* SERVIUS MAURUS HONORATUS. Comm., v3ii, 1902.
Philatelic Literature Society, *see* BIBLIOTHECA Lindesiana, v7, Cat. of the philatelic lib. of the Earl of Crawford; by E. D. Bacon, 1911; Suppl., 1926.
Philby (Harry St. John Bridger). The heart of Arabia: record of travel &c. 2v. 8°. 1922
Southern Nejd: journey in 1918. la8°. Cairo. 1919

Philibert, *Saint, see* JAUD (L.) St. Filibert, 1910.

Philidor (A. D.) [FILIDOR; PHILIDORE; DANICAN (F. ANDRÉ), *called Philidor*]. L'analyze des echecs. [1st ed., w. list of subscribers]. 8º. Londres. 1749

,, ,, [*a. issue, diff. arranged*]. 8º. Londres. 1749

see CHESS. *Easy intr., incl. P.'s analysis, 1820.

Philip, *of Burgundy, bp. of Utrecht, see* GELDENHAUER (G.) Collectanea [De triumph. ingressu P. (1517)—Vita P. (1529) &c.]; uitg. door J. Prinsen, 1901.

Philip III, *duke of Burgundy* [*the Good*], *see* DOUTREPONT (G.) Notice sur le ms. franç.: la croisade par P., 1923.

Philip, *of Cyprus, Prothonotary of the Church of Constantinople.* Chronicon Eccl. Graecae. Ed. Latineque vertit N. Blancardus. H. Hilarius recensuit &c. Acc. app. s8º. Lipsiae. 1687

Philip IV, *king of France* [PHILIPPE LE BEL].

see BONIFACE VIII, *pope.* Acta inter B. VIII, Bened. XI, Clem. V & Ph., 1614.

,, SCHOLZ (R.) Die Publizistik z. Zeit P.'s, 1903.

Philip, *landgrave of Hesse.*

see EELLS (H.) Attitude of M. Bucer toward bigamy of P., 1924.

,, EGELHAAF (G.) & W. DIEHL. Landgraf P. v. H. &c., 1904.

,, MARBURG. Urkundensammlung ü. d. Verfassung &c. d. Univ. M. unter P., 1848.

Philip, *of Leyden, d. 1380, see* HOLLAND. Kronijk van H. van een ongenoemden gestelijke [*sometimes attr. to P.*], 1867.

Philip II, *duke of Savoy* [FILIPPO SENZA TERRA; PHILIPPE SANS TERRE]. *La ribellione di F. S. T. narrata da un contemp.; [*French, ed. E. Bollati*], *see* REGIA DEP. DI STORIA PATRIA. Misc., t16, 1877.

Philip II, *king of Spain.* Ph. II regis Cathol. edictum de librorum prohib. cat. obs. s8º. Antverpiae. 1570

see MARGARET, *duchess of Parma.* Corr. avec P. II; éd. J. S. Theissen, t1, 1925.

,, PARUTA (P.) Una lega proposta da F. II (1592), 1864.

,, WEGG (J.) Decline of Antwerp under P., 1924.

Philip III, *king of Spain, see* LONCHAY (H.) & J. CUVELIER. Corr. de la cour d'Espagne, t1, Corr. de P. III, 1923.

Philip IV, *king of Spain, see* LONCHAY (H.) & J. CUVELIER. Corr. de la cour d'Espagne, t2, Corr. de P. IV avec l'infante Isabella, 1927.

Philip Augustus, *king of France, see* CHARTES & diplômes rel. à l'hist. de France, t6, Rec. des actes de P. A., t1, 1179–94, 1916.

Philip William, *elector Palatine, duke, see* KIRCHEN-ORDNUNG. Kirchen-Ordnungen &c., u. Neben-Recessen zw. Fried. Wilh. v. Brandenburg u. Ph. W., 1666–73, 1754.

Philip (*Rev. Dr.*) The Ghetto in Rome [*& The Ecumen. Council at Rome in 1869*]. 2nd ed. [P505]. s8º. Florence. 1875

Philip (Alexander).

The calendar: its hist. struct. & improvement. 8º. C. 1921

Philip (Alex. J.), *see* DIRECTORY (International) of booksellers &c., 1927.

Philip (John), *D.D.* Researches in South Africa; cond. of native tribes &c. 2v. 8º. 1828

Philip (Robert).

The life & opinions of the Rev. W. Milne. s8º. 1840

Philipot (John), *Somerset Herald.* *Cat. of the Chancellors of Eng., the Lord Keepers of the Gt. Seal & the Lord Treasurers of Eng. By J. P. [*i.e.* Philipot]. 2p [*in 1v, sep. pagin.*] s8º. 1636

see OXFORDSHIRE. Some pedigrees f. the visit. of O., made by J. P. & W. Riley, 1634, 1913.

Philipp (Albrecht), *see* GERMANY: REICHSTAG &C. Das Werk d. Untersuchungsausschusses, Reihe 4, Ursachen d. deut. Zusammenbruchs im Jahre 1918; hrsg. A. P., 1925–26.

Philipp (Hans). Gesch. d. Stadt Templin. 8º. Templin. 1925

Philippart (*Sir* **John**). The Royal Military Calendar, cont. services of every gen. officer in Brit. army &c. 2v. 8º. 1815

Philippe, *Sans Terre, see* PHILIP II, *duke of Savoy.*

Philippe (Charles Louis).

Chroniques du canard sauvage. 9e éd. s8º. 1923

Philippi (Friedrich). Atlas z. weltl. Altertumskunde d. deut. Ma. 134 Taf. mit Erläut. fol. Bonn. 1924

Philippi (Wilhelm). Elektrizität im Bergbau. la8º. L. 1924

Philippine Islands. Celebración del 4º cent. del descubr. de Filipinas por F. de Magallanes: 1521–1921. 8º. Manila. 1921

Mineral resources of the P.I. for 1917 & 1918, 1919 & 1920, 1921–23. [Bureau of Science, Manila]. la8º. Manila. 1920–25

Philipps (Jenkin Thomas). *34 conferences betw. Danish missionaries & Malabarian Bramans, conc. the truth of the Xtn. relig. Tr. by Philipps. 8º. 1719

The hist. of Ernestus the Pious, duke of Sax-Gotha & Bernard the Great, duke of Sax-Weimar; w. short hist. of John William, Prince of Gotha, & genealog. tables. s8º. 1740

Short acc. of the church-govt. of the Muscovites, *see* CATECHISM. The Russian C., 2nd ed., 1725.

Philipps (Ubbo) [UBBE PHILIPZOON], *see* HILMERS (J. H.) Comm. De Ubbone Philippi & Ubbonitis, 1733.

Philippsen (Heinrich). Alt-Schleswig. Beitr. z. Gesch. d. Stadt S. la8º. Schleswig. 1924

Philippson (Alfred). Reisen u. Forsch. im westl. Kleinasien, H5, 1915, *see* PETERMANNS MITT. Ergnzb., 39, 1915.

Philips', *publishing firm* [PHILIP (GEORGE) & SON]. Modern atlas of America: acc. by index-gazet. of the world. fol. *Philip.* 1905

Philips' large scale milit. map of the seat of war in S. Africa. 4th ed. Sheets 1, 2. *folded.* 8º. 1900

Philips' New histor. atlas for students. Intr. &c. by Ramsay Muir. 4th ed. 8º. 1920

Philips (Ambrose) [PHILLIPS]. Distressed mother, *see* INCHBALD (*Mrs.* E.) Brit. theatre, v7, 1808.

Pastorals, epistles, odes & o. p., w. trs. s8º. D. 1768

Philips (John), *a. of " The splendid shilling."*

Poet. works. Coll. by T. Park. s8º. 1807

Poems. Ed. M. G. L. Thomas. 8º. O. 1927

Philips (John), *dramatist.* The Earl of Mar marr'd. A farce. 3rd ed. [P2583]. s8º. 1716

Philips (Katherine), *called " The matchless Orinda."* Poems. Added, Corneille's Pompey & Horace, w. o. tr. [*2 pagin.*] la8º. 1669

Philipson (John). Art & craft of coachbuilding. s8º. 1897

Phillimore & Co., *publishers.*

Parish registers & Phillimore's, 1923. [P2706]. 8º. 1923

Phillimore (John) [*ps.* TWIN]. Motor road transport for commercial purposes. Intr. by Sir H. P. Maybury. 8º. [1921]

Phillimore (John Swinnerton).

The 100 best Latin hymns. Sel. J. S. P. s8º. 1926

Phillimore (*Mrs.* John Swinnerton).

*By an Unknown Disciple. [*Fiction*]. s8º. [1920]

Phillimore (Walter George Frank Phillimore, *1st baron***).**

Droits & devoirs fondamentaux des états. 8º. 1925

Schemes for maintaining general peace, *see* FOREIGN OFFICE. Handbooks, No. 160, 1920.

Phillip (John), *R.A., see* DAFFORNE (J.) Pictures by J. P.; w. descr. & biog. sk., 1877.

Phillips Academy, *Andover, Mass.*

DEPT. OF ARCHAEOLOGY.

Papers of the Southwestern Exped. No. 1. 4º. New Haven. 1924

see KIDDER (A. V.) Intr. to study of s.-w. archaeol.; w. prelim. acc. of excav. at Pecos, 1924.

Phillips (C. M.) Short acc. of the silver plate &c. belong. to the Worshipful Co. of Cooks, London. 8º. 1909

Phillips (Charles), *Comm. of the Insolvent Debtors' Court.*

Curran & h. contemps. 4th ed. 8º. E. 1851

The Queen's case stated. 21st ed. [P425]. 8º. 1820

Phillips (Charles), *M.A.* The new Poland. 8º. [1923]

Phillips (Chester Arthur). Bank credit. 8º. N.Y. 1920

Phillips (*Sir* Claude).

Emotion in art. Ed. M. W. Brockwell. 8º. 1925

Phillips (David Rhys).

Hist. of the Vale of Neath. la8º. Swansea. 1925

Phillips (Georg). De Anglo-Saxonum re judiciaria. Diss. s4º. Gottingae. 1825

Du droit eccl. dans ses sources &c. Suivi d'un essai de bibliographie du droit canon. Tr. [J. P.] Crouzet. 8º. 1852

Phillips (H. W.)

Mod. foreign exchange & foreign banking. 8º. 1926

Phillips (John), *F.R.S.* Illustr. of the geol. of Yorkshire. 2p [pl, 2nd ed.] 4º. 1835–36

The Malvern Hills &c., *see* GEOLOG. SURVEY OF ENG. &c. Mems., v2, p1, 1848.

Phillips (John), *Milton's nephew.* Daveidos, or a spec. of David's Psalms in Eng. metre; w. remarks upon the late translators. s8º. 1698

Phillips (John), *surveyor.* A gen. hist. of inland navigat. &c., abr. f. 4º. ed. & contin. to pres. time. 4th ed. 8º. 1803

Phillips (*Sir* Lionel), *1st bart.* Some reminiscences. 8º. [1924]

Phillips (M.) & W. S. Tomkinson.
Eng. women in life & letters. 8°. O. 1926

Phillips (*Sir* **Percival).** The "Red" dragon & the Black Shirts: true story of the Fascisti movt. 8°. [1922]

Phillips (Philip Lee), *see* UNITED STATES: LIBRARY OF CONGRESS, *for works comp. under dir. of P.*

Phillips (R. Randal).
The book of bungalows. 3rd ed. 8°. [1926]
The mod. Eng. house. [Intr. signed R. R. P.] 4°. [1927]
The servantless house. 8°. 1920
Small country houses of to-day. v3. 4°. 1925
For ser. 1, 2, 1910–19, *see* WEAVER (L.)
Small family houses. 8°. [1924]
—— **& E. Woolrich.** Furnishing the house. la8°. 1921

Phillips (S. M.) Famous cases of circumstantial evidence: w. introd. on the theory of presumptive proof. 8°. Jersey City, [N.J.] 1879

Phillips (Theodore Evelyn Reece), *see* HUTCHINSON & Co., *publishers.* Splendour of the Heavens; ed. T. E. R. P. & W. H. Steavenson, 1923.

Phillips (W. C.), *see* HOOPER (W. H.) & W. C. P. Manual of marks on pottery & porcelain, 1919.

Phillips (Walter Alison).
The Revolution in Ireland, 1906–1923. 8°. 1923
,, ,, ...2nd ed. 8°. 1926

Phillips (Walter C.), *Ph.D.* Dickens, Reade, & Collins, sensation novelists. [Columbia Univ.] 8°. N.Y. 1919

Phillips (Willard). Manual of polit. econ., w. partic. ref. to the U.S. 8°. Boston. 1828

Phillips (William), *F.L.S. &c., 1775–1828.*
Outlines of mineralogy & geology. 4th ed. enl. 8°. 1826

Phillips (William J.) Carols. Orig., music, & conn. w. mystery plays. Foreword by Sir F. Bridge. 8°. [1921]

Phillipson (Coleman). 3 criminal law reformers: Beccaria, Bentham, Romilly. 8°. 1923

Phillott (*Lt.-Col.* **Douglas Craven).**
Colloquial Eng.-Persian dictionary. la8°. Calcutta. [1914]
Domestic Hindustani. s8°. Calcutta. 1919
Eng.-Hind. vocabulary. 2nd ed. enl. 8°. Calcutta. 1917
Higher Persian gramm., w. notes on rhetoric. la8°. Calcutta. 1919
Hindustani exercises, w. notes & trans. 8°. Calcutta. 1912
Hindustani manual. 3rd ed. s8°. Calcutta. 1918
Khazīna-e Muḥāwarāt, or Urdu idioms. Coll. & tr. by Lt.-Col. D. C. P. 8°. Calcutta. 1912
Khwab o Khiyal or "Visions of the past." Offic. text-bk. for exam. of officers by higher standard Hindustani. Ed. w. notes by D. C. P. [3p, *sep. tp. & pagins.*] 8°. Calcutta. 1911
,, ,, Annot. Eng. tr. [3p]. 8°. Calcutta. 1911
1, Sītārāma, *Sūbahdār.* From Sepoy to subadar &c. 2, Sel. f. Rusūm-i-Hind. 3, Selections.
Persian saws & proverbs. [*Extr. f.* As. Soc. of Bengal, Mem., v1. P2751]. 4°. Calcutta. 1906
Urdu rozmarra or "every-day Urdu". Offic. text-bk. for exam. of officers &c. by lower standard Hindustani. Ed. w. notes by D. C. P. 4th ed. [3p, *w. sep. pagin.*] 8°. Calcutta. 1920
,, ,, Annot. Eng. tr. 3rd ed. [3p, *w. sep. pagin.*] 8°. Calcutta. 1919
1, Stories. 2, The Wazir of Lankaran, *w. sep. tp.* 3, Hist. events.
see AḤMAD IBN MUḤAMMAD, *al-Yamanī, al-Shirwānī.* Nafḥat[u] 'l-Yaman; tr., w. philol. & crit. notes by D. C. P., p1, 1907.

Phillpotts (Adelaide Eden). Tomek the sculptor. s8°. [1927]

Phillpotts (Bertha Surtees).
The Elder Edda & anc. Scandinavian drama. 8°. C. 1920

Phillpotts (Eden).
Black, white & brindled. s8°. 1923
The bronze Venus. s8°. 1921
"Cheat-the-boys." s8°. [1924]
Cherry-stones. [Poems]. s8°. 1923
Children of men. s8°. [1923]
The chronicles of St. Tid. s8°. 1917
A Cornish droll. s8°. [1926]
Eudocia. s8°. 1921
The farmer's wife. Comedy. [3rd imp.] s8°. [1924]
George Westover. s8°. [1925]
The green alleys. s8°. [1916]
The grey room. s8°. [1922]
A human boy's diary. s8°. 1924
It happened like that. s8°. [1927]
The jury. s8°. [1927]
The Marylebone miser. s8°. [1926]
Miser's money. s8°. 1920
Orphan Dinah. s8°. 1920
Peacock House & o. mysteries. s8°. [1926]
Pixies' plot. [*Poems*]. s8°. 1912
Redcliff. s8°. [1925]
The Red Redmaynes. s8°. [1923]
The ring fence. s8°. [1928]
Up hill, down dale. Stories. s8°. [1925]
Wild fruit. [*Poems*]. s8°. 1911

Phillpotts (Henry), *bp. of Exeter.* Letters to C. Butler on his Bk. of the Roman Cath. church. 8°. 1825
A suppl. letter to C. Butler on evidence given by Irish Rom. Cath. bishops &c. 8°. 1826

Phillpotts (Marian Hadfield), *wife of J. S. Phillpotts, form. Cordery.* Trans. f. Fr., Germ. & Greek. Ed. J. S. P[hillpotts]. 8°. Winchester. 1925

Philo, *Byzantius.* Belopoiika (4[es] Buch d. Mechanik); Gr. u. Deut. v. H. Diels u. E. Schramm, 1919, *see* KÖNIGL. PREUSS. AKAD. D. WISS. Abhdl. (Phil.-hist. Klasse), 1918.
Exzerpte aus P.'s Mechanik B. 7 u. 8; Gr. u. Deut. v. H. Diels u. E. Schramm, 1920, *see* KÖNIGL. PREUSS. AKAD. D. WISS. Abhdl. (Phil.-hist. Klasse), 1919.

Philo, *Judaeus.*
Opera quae supersunt. v7, Indices, comp. J. Leisegang, p1. 8°. Berolini. 1926
Paralipomena Armena: lib. 4 in Genes.; lib. 2 in Exod.; sermo de Sampsone, de Jona, de angelis Abraamo apparent. Ex Arm. in Lat. tr. per J. B. Aucher. [*b. w.* Philo. Serm. 3, 1822]. 4°. Venetiis. 1826
[Sermons. *In Armenian*]. 8°. Venetik. 1892
Sermones 3 ined. Ex Armen. in Lat. tr. per J. B. Aucher. [*With Arm. text*]. 4°. Venetiis. 1822
see CARPZOV (J. B.) De Λογῳ Philonis non Johanneo, 1739.
,, —— Sacrae exercit. in epist. ad Hebraeos ex P.; praef. Philoniana, 1750.
,, GROSSMANN (C. G. L.) Quaest. P., 2p, 1829.
,, WENDLAND (P.) Krit. &c. Bemerk. zu P., 2p, 1897–8.

Philobiblion (The): a monthly catalogue & lit. journal. v1, 2 (No. 1–24, Dec. 1861–Dec. 1863). [*no more publ.*] 8°. N.Y. [1861–63]

Philodemus, *of Gadara.* Philodemos Über d. Götter, 1. [*&* 3.] Buch; gr. Text u. Erläut. v. H. Diels, *see* KÖNIGL. PREUSS. AKAD. Abhdlg. (Phil.-hist. Kl.), 1915–16.
Üb. d. Gedichte. 5tes Buch. Gr. Text mit Übers. u. Erläut. v. C. Jensen. 8°. 1923

Philoi-D'Or, *ps.* The King the avowed enemy of the Queen. [P425]. 8°. 1820

Philo-Kuriaces (Theophilus), *Loncardiensis, ps., see* YOUNG (THOMAS), *vicar of Stowmarket.*

Philological Society. Transactions, 1907–10. 8°. 1910
The following have sep. pagin.
1907, App., Skeat (W. W.) Evol. of the Canterbury tales. [*sep. tp.*]
1907, App., MacCracken (H. N.) Lydgate canon, 1908. [*sep. tp.*]
1907–10, Suppl., Hodgkin (J.) Proper terms, Bk. of St. Albans &c.

Philologische u. krit. Bibliothek, 2B, 1770–72, *see* SCHMID (C. F.)

Philologus. Suppl.-Bd. 14i, 16ii, 18i, 19i. 8°. L. 1920–27
see BILABEL (F.) Die ionische Kolonisation, 1920. [14i.]
,, CARTELLIERI (W.) Die röm. Alpenstrassen, 1926. [18i.]
,, PREMERSTEIN (A. v.) Zu d. sog. Alexandrin. Märtyrerakten, 1923. [16ii.]
,, TSCHERIKOWER (V.) Hellenist. Städtegrund., 1927. [19i.]

Philon (Frederick). He would be a soldier, *see* †INCHBALD (E.) Mod. th., v8, 1811.

Philosopher's stone, *see* HERMETIC MUSEUM (THE): The p. s. &c., 1678; ed. A. E. Waite, 2v, 1893.

***Philosophia** Scripturae interpres; ed. J. S. Semler, 1776, *see* MEYER (L.), *M.D.*

***Philosophical** theories & phil. experience, 1845, *see* CORNWALLIS (C. F.)

Philosophical Institute of Canterbury [*N.Z.*] Natural hist. of Canterbury. Ed. R. Speight &c. 8°. Christchurch. 1927

Philosophical Society of Australasia, *see* ROYAL SOCIETY OF NEW SOUTH WALES.

Philosophical Society of Oxford. Trans., 1683–90, *see* GUNTHER (R. W. T.) Early sci. in Oxf., v4, 1925.

Philosophie (Die) d. Gegenwart. The philos. of the pres. time; hrsg. A. Ruge. 5 (1913). 8°. Heidelberg. 1915

Philosophumena; form. attrib. to Origen, but now to Hippolytus; tr. f. text of Cruice by F. Legge, v1, 1921, *see* HIPPOLYTUS, *St.*

Philosophy. Contemp. Brit. ph.: personal statements, s1, 2, 1924–25, *see* MUIRHEAD (J. H.), *ed.*
*Ph. (The) of individualism. Bibliog., w. intr. essay. s8°. 1927
*Ph. of the plan of salvation &c., 1847, *see* WALKER (J. B.)

Philostratus. Flavii P[i]. de vitis sophist. libri 2 A. Bomfino interprete. s4°. [Strassburg, *Ex aedib. Schurerianis*]. 1516
P. & Eunapius. The lives of the sophists. [Text], w. Eng. tr. by W. C. Wright. [Loeb Class Lib.] s8°. 1922

Philotimus, *see* *SOME remarks on the dialogue betw. Philaletes & P. &c., 1705.

Philoxeno (Marcello), *see* FILOSSENO (M.)

Philoxenus, *bp. of Mabug.* De Uno e S. Trinitate incorp. et passo: textum Syr. ed. & Lat. vertit M. Brière, *see* GRAFFIN (R.) & F. NAU. Patr. orient., t15, 1927.

Philoxenus (Marcellus), *see* FILOSSENO (M.)

Philpin de Piépape (Nicolas-Joseph), *see* PIÉPAPE (N. J. P. DE).

Philpot (Joseph Henry), *M.D.* [*ps.* PHILIP LAFARGUE].
Maistre Wace: a pioneer in 2 lit. s8°. [1925]
For earlier works, see †LAFARGUE (PHILIP), *ps.*

Philumenus. De venenatis animalibus eorumque remediis; ed. M. Wellmann, *see* CORPUS medicorum Graecorum, v5xi, 1, 1918.

Phin (John), *of New York.* Open air grape culture &c. & the manufacture of domestic wine. 8°. N.Y. 1862

Phinney, *Family of, see* MORSE (W. I.), *ed.* Genealogiae or data, 1925.

Phipps, *Family of, see* PHIPPS (H. R.) Notes on P. families, 2p, 1911.

Phipps (Henry Ramsay). Notes on Phipps & Phip families. 2p. [P2589]. s4°. Lahore. 1911

Phipps (*Col.* **Ramsay Weston).** The armies of the 1st French Republic & the rise of the marshals of Nap. I. The Armée du Nord. 8°. 1926

Phipson (Sidney Lovell). Jean P. Marat, h. career bef. the Revolution. s8°. [1924]

Phleme (Christian Friedrich), *ps., see* HEMPEL (C. F.)

Phœbadius, *Saint.* Contra Arrianos liber, *see* GALLIAE. *Vet. aliq. G. theol. scripta, 1586.

Phœniceus (Heinrich), *ps., see* RHEGIUS (URBANUS).

Phœnix. Phœnix & turtle, *see* †CHESTER (R.) Loves martyr, 1601; w. its suppl. " Diverse poet. essaies " on the Turtle & P. by Shakspere &c.; ed. &c. A. B. Grosart, 1878.
see CYNEWULF. Old English Elene, P. &c.; ed. A. S. Cook, 1919.

Pholien (Fl.) La verrerie au pays de Liège. 8°. Liège. [1900]

Phonetic transcription & translit. Proposals of Copenhagen conf. April 1925. [P2847]. 8°. O. 1926

Phords, *review in Armenian, see* FORDS.

Photiadès (Constantin). La " Symphonie en blanc majeur." Marie Kalergis, née Ctsse. Nesselrode, 1822–74. s8°. [1924]

Photius, *patriarch of Constantinople.* Βιβλιοθήκη. Lib. quos legit P. excerpta &c. D. Hoeschelius prim. ed.; notis in quibus fragm. ined. illust. [*Gr.*] fol. Augustae Vindel. 1601
The Library of P. [Tr., w. pref. & notes] by J. H. Freese. v1. s8°. 1920
see JAGER (J. N.) Hist. de P. [Cath.], 1845.
,, MACCRINDLE (J. W.) Anc. India as descr. by Ktesias; tr. of abridg. of h. " Indika " by P. &c., 1882.
,, SWALUE (E. B.) Disput. de discidio eccl. Xtnae. Ph. auctoritate maturato, 1829.

Photogram, The. v1–11. 8°. 1894–1904

Photograms of the year, 1925. Ann. review for 1926. Ed. F. J. Mortimer. 4°. [1926]

Photographic Quarterly, The. Ed. C. W. Hastings. v1–3 (Oct. 1889–July 1892). 8°. 1889–92

Photography as a sci. implement. Coll. work by A. E. Conrady, C. R. Davidson &c. [2nd impr.]. 8°. 1924

Physical Society of London &c. Discussion of ionization in the atmosphere & its infl. on propag. of wireless signals. la8°. [1924]
see JEANS (J. H.) Rep. on radiation & quantum-theory, 2nd ed., 1924.
,, JOULE (J. P.) Joint sci. papers, 1887.
,, —— Sci. papers; publ. by P. Soc. of L., 1884.

Physician's (A) anthology of Eng. & Amer. poetry, 1920, *see* WOOD (C. A.) & F. H. GARRISON, *edd.*

Physiologus. The Old Eng. Physiologus. Text & prose tr. by A. S. Cook. Verse tr. by J. H. Pitman. [Yale st. in Eng., 63]. 8°. New Haven, *Yale.* 1921
P., tr. w. intr. by J. Carlill [Broadway tr.], *see* REYNARD, *the Fox.* Epic of the beast &c.; tr., 1924.
see CYNEWULF. Old English Elene, P. &c.; ed. A. S. Cook, 1919.

Physiology & national needs [*by var. wr.*], 1919, *see* HALLIBURTON (W. D.), *ed.*

Piacevich (Franciscus Xaverius) [PEJACEVICH], *1713–81.* De primatu Roman. eccl. contra schismat. orient., *see* MIGNE (J. P.), *ed.* Theol. cursus, t5, 1841.

Piaget (Jean). The language & thought of the child. Pref. by E. Claparède. [Tr. M. Warden]. 8°. 1926

Piales d'Axtrez (*lieut.* **Jean Marie Joseph Alfred),** *see* ROMAGNY (*lt.* C.) & P. D'A. Et. somm. des batailles d'un siècle, 1890.

Pian de Carpine (John *of***).** Rel. du voy. en Tartarie, 1246, *see* BERNARD (J. F.), *ed.* Recueil, t7, 1725.

Piasecki (Pawel), *bp. of Kaminietz, of Chelm, & of Przemysl.* [PIASECIUS]. Praxis episcopalis. s8°. Coloniae Agripp. 1615

Piatti (Antonio). A. P. [Artisti viv.] s8°. Torino. [1921]

Piave. The Battle of the P. (June 15–23, 1918). Issued by Supreme Command of Royal Ital. Army. Tr. M. Prichard-Agnetti. la8°. [1921]

Piazzi (Giuseppe). Le opere di F. Raibolini detto il Francia. 8°. Bologna. 1925

Pibrac (Gui Du Faur, *Seigneur* **de),** *see* DU FAUR (G.), *Seigneur de Pibrac.*

Picard (Charles.)
Ephèse & Claros. Recherches sur les sanctuaires & les cultes de l'Ionie du nord. [Bibl. des Ecoles franç. d'Athènes & de Rome, fasc. 123]. la8°. 1922
L'établ. des Poseidoniastes de Bérytos, *see* ECOLE FRANÇ. D'ATHÈNES. Explor. arch. de Délos, fasc. 6, 1921.
Portrait d'homme inconnu, tête de bronze trouvée dans Délos, *see* ACAD. DES INSCR.: FOND. PIOT. Mon., t24, 1920.
La sculpture antique, des origines à Phidias. la8°. 1923
La sculpture antique, de Phidias à l'ére byzantine. la8°. 1926
Tête féminine du Musée d'Alexandrie, *see* ACAD. DES INSCR. &c.: FOND. PIOT. Mons. &c., t28, 1925–26.

Picard (Edmond). Les constantes du droit. Inst. juridiques mod. s8°. 1921

Picard (Emile). Discours & mélanges. 8°. 1922
Mélanges de mathémat. & de phys. la8°. [1924]
Traité d'analyse. 3t. [t1, 2, 3e éd., t3, 2e éd.] la8°. 1908–26
La vie & l'œuvre de J. Tannery. 8°. 1926
see HANOTAUX (G.) Hist. de la nation franç., t14, Hist. des sciences, v1, intr. gén. par E. P., 1924.

Picard (Ernest). Bonaparte & Moreau. L'entente initiale —Les prem. dissentiments—La rupture. 8°. 1905

Picard (Louis Benoit).
The Gil Blas of the Revolution. 3v. s8°. 1825

Picard (Y.) Le collège de Léon. 8°. Morlaix. 1895

Picardie. Archives hist. & eccl. de la P. &c., 1842, *see* ROGER (P. A.), *ed.*

Picardin (Jean). Une idylle au Dworek: roman, *see* ŒUVRES libres, 52, 1925.

Picavet (Camille Georges).
Une démocratie hist.: la Suisse. s8°. 1920

Picavet (François Joseph), *b. 1851, see* HANOTAUX (G.) Hist. de la nation franç., t12, Hist. des lettres, v1, Des origines à Ronsard; par J. Bédier, F. P. &c., 1921.

Picchioni (Luigi). La Divina Commedia illust. da A. Kopisch, G. Picci e M. G. Ponta: cenni crit. di L. P. 8°. Milano. 1846

Picci (Giuseppe). Compendio d. guida allo studio d. belle lettere. 8a ed. s8°. Milano. 1881
see PICCHIONI (L.) La Div. Commedia illust. da G. P. &c., 1846.
,, PONTA (M. G.) Saggio di critica ai nuovi studi sopra Dante del Sig. G. P., 1845.

Piccini (Giulio), *see* JARRO, *ps.*

Piccioni (Luigi). Da Prudenzio a Dante: manuale per la storia d. lett. in Italia dal sec. 4 al s. 13. Con comm. e gloss. 8°. Torino. [1916]

Piccoli (Raffaello). Benedetto Croce: intr. to h. philosophy. Foreword by H. W. Carr. s8°. [1922]

Piccolomini (Alessandro), *abp. of Patras & coadjutor abp. of Siena.* Cento sonetti. [*Ed.* G. Ziletti]. s8°. 1549
La Raffaella, ov. della creanza d. donne: dialogo. [Ed. C. Téoli. Bibl. rara, v1]. s8°. Milano. 1862

Pichard (Louis). Tibulle & les auteurs du Corpus Tibullianum. Texte établi d'ap. la Méthode de crit. verbale de L. Havet par L. P. [H.E., 241]. 8°. 1924

Pichegru (Charles), *see* BOURDEAU (H.) P. a-t-il trahi à Mannheim? sept. 1795, 1909.

Picher (Rodolphe Hector). Rep. on road materials along the St. Lawrence river, f. the Quebec boundary line to Cardinal, Ontario. [Canada: Geol. Survey. P2513]. 8°. Ottawa. 1920

Picherellus (Petrus).
Opuscula theol. s8°. Lugduni Batav. 1729

Pichler (Wolfgang). Diss. de simulatione judicis. s4°. Argentorati. 1658

Pichon (Léon). The new book-illustr. in France. Tr. H. B. Grimsditch. [Studio]. la8°. 1924

Picht (Werner). England nach d. Kriege: Reisebetrachtungen. s8°. München. 1923
Pichtl (Balthasar Johannes). Diss. de computo Thalmudico-Rabbinico; sub praes. Æ. Strauchii. ed. 2ª. [P446]. s4°. Wittebergae. 1661
Pick (Behrendt). Goethes Münzbelustigungen. [Goethe-Gesells. Jhbch., Sonderdr. aus B7. P2503]. 8°. Weimar. 1920
see SVORONOS (J. N.) Les monnaies d'Athènes; terminé par B. P., 1923–26.
Pick (Friedel). Joh. Jessenius. [Beilag: Ad regni Boemiæ &c. ordines de restaur. Prag. Acad. exhort., 1619 *in facs.* St. z. Gesch. d. Med., H15]. la8°. L. 1926
Pick (Ulysse) & Jules Hermann. Vive l'Empire. 4ᵉ ed. [*b. w.* Beslay (F.) Voyage, 1873]. s8°. 1852
Pickard-Cambridge (Arthur Wallace). Dithyramb, tragedy & comedy. 8°. O. 1927
Pickel (Konrad), *see* CELTES (C.)
Pickering (Mary Evelyn), *afterwards wife of W. De Morgan, see* DE MORGAN (M. E.)
Pickering (Timothy), *see* BEMIS (S. F.), *ed.* Amer. Secr. of State, v2, P., by H. J. Ford, 1927.
Pickering & Chatto, *Messrs.* Coll. of rare books of old Eng. lit. [1485–1789]. For sale by P. & C.
12p *&* Addenda pl–8. [*pagin. contin.* Cat. No. 208–220, *b. in* 2v]. 8°. *n.d.*
„ „ 18p *&* Addenda [*pagin. contin.* Cat. No. 226–246, *b. in* 2v]. 8°. [1926–28]
Pickett (Elbert Deets). How prohibition works in American cities. Forew. by Bp. W. F. McDowell. [P2700]. 4°. Wash. [1922]
see ENCYCLOPÆDIA. Cyclopedia of temperance &c.; ed. D. P., 1917.
Pickthall (Marmaduke). The early hours. s8°. [1921]
Sir Limpidus. s8°. [1919]
Pico della Mirandola (Giovanni), *1463–94.* A platonick discourse upon love. [*Tr. T. Stanley, 1651*]. Ed. E. G. Gardner. 8°. Boston, *Merrymount Press.* [1914]
T. Morus' Picus Erle of Mirandula; *tr. f. life by h. son*; *ed.* M. Kullnik, *see* ARCHIV F. D. ST. D. NEU. SPR., B121, 122, 1908–9.
see JESUP (E.) Lives of J. P., 3rd ed., *n.d.*
„ MELANCHTHON (P.) Elementorum rhetorices libri 2, adj. Epistolæ Pici &c., 1547.
Picon-Febres (Gonzalo). Libro raro. Voces, locuciones y otras cosas de uso en Venezuela &c. 2ª ed., aumenta. 8°. Curazao. 1912
Picot (Emile), *see* URECHIĔ (G.) Chronique de Moldavie; tr., notes &c. par E. P., 1878.
—— **& K. Nyrop.** Nouveau recueil de farces franç. des 15ᵉ & 16ᵉ s. s8°. 1880
—— **& H. Stein.** Recueil de pièces histor. imprimées sous le règne de Louis XI, reprod. en fac-similé, avec comm. par E. P. & H. S. [Soc. des Bibliophiles Franç]. [2t. 1, Texte. 2, Fac-similés]. 4°. 1923
Picotti (G. B.) Il nome "Patria" attrib. al Friuli. [Estr. d. Antologia Veneta, a. 1. P2838]. 8°. Feltre. 1900
Picq (*Col.* **Charles Ardant du),** *see* ARDANT DU PICQ.
Pictet (Bénédict). La théologie chrétienne, & la sci. du salut. 2t *in* 1v. s4°. Amsterdam. 1702
Wiclefus, oratio acad. [P600]. s4°. Genevae. 1717
Picton (*Sir* **Thomas),** *see* ROBINSON (H. B.) Mems. of P., incl. h. corr., 2v, 1835.
***Picture** (The) of Quebec & its vicin., 2nd ed., 1831, *see* QUEBEC.
Pictures. 100 best pictures, 6th ed., 1901, *see* LETTS (C. H.)
Picturesque Europe, 5v, 1881–86, *see* EUROPE.
Pidgin (Charles Felton). Quincy Adams Sawyer & Mason's Corner folks. s8°. Boston. 1901
Piéchaud (Martial). Mlle Pascal: comédie, *see* REVUE HEBDOM. Suppl., 1, 1922.
Le sommeil des amants, comédie, *see* REVUE HEBDOM. Suppl., 15, 1923.
Piedrahita (Lucas Fernandez de), *see* FERNANDEZ DE PIEDRAHITA (L.)
Piépape (*gen.* **Léonce de).**
N. J. Philpin de Piépape (1731–93). 8°. 1924
Piépape (Nicolas-Joseph Philpin de), *1731–93, see* PIÉPAPE (*gen.* L. de). P., jurisconsulte &c., 1924.
Piepenbring (Charles). La Christologie biblique & ses origines. la8°. 1919
The hist. Jesus. Tr. L. A. Clare. 8°. [1924]

Pier (Arthur Stanwood). Some consequences of neutrality. [Repr. f. the Boston Transcript]. [P2465]. 8°. [Boston, Mass.] 1915
Pieraccini (Gaetano). La stirpe de' Medici di Cafaggiolo: ricerche s. trasmiss. eredit. d. caratteri biolog. 3v. 4°. Firenze. [1924–25]
Pieraccini (Piero). Note di demografia fiorentina, *see* ARCHIVIO STOR. ITAL., a. 83ii, 1925.
Pierantoni (Augusto). La Chiesa Cattolica nel diritto comune. 8°. Firenze. 1870
Pierantoni (Riccardo).
Die Stärkere. Übers. v. E. Becher. 2B. s8°. St. 1906
Piérard (Louis). The tragic life of Vincent Van Gogh. Tr. H. Garland. la8°. [1925]
Pierce (Edgar).
The philosophy of character. 8°. C., Mass. 1924
Pierce (Edward), *sculptor; c. 1630–98, see* POOLE (R.) E. P., the sculptor, 1923.
Pierce (Thomas), *D.D., Dean of Salisbury.* The sinner impleaded in his own court. Added, The Love of Christ planted upon the very same turf &c. [*w. sep. tp.*: The signal diagnostick]. 3rd ed. 2p [in 1v]. s4°. 1670
Pierce (William).
John Penry, h. life, times & writings. 8°. 1923
Pierce (William), *grocer.* *A full rep. of the gt. gold robbery. [Trial of P. &c.] Illust. by P. Cruikshank. 8°. [1859]
Pieri (Piero). La quest. di Malta e il gov. napoletano (1798–1803), *see* ARCHIVIO STOR. ITAL., Anno 85, v1, 1927.
Taranto nel 1799 e Mgr. Capecelatro, *see* ARCHIVIO STOR. ITAL., Anno 82, v1, 1924.
Pieri (Silvio). *Appunti toponomastici, *see* MONACI (E.) Studj romanzi, v10, 1913.
Pieris (Paulus Edward). Ceylon & the Portuguese, 1505–1658. 8°. Tellippalai. 1920
The Kingdom of Jafanapatam, 1645. Its admin. organis., f. Portuguese archives. 8°. [Colombo]. 1920
The prince Vijaya Pala of Ceylon, 1634–54, f. orig. doc. s8°. Colombo. 1927
Pierius (Urban). Admonitio de libello anno XCI sub studiosorum Vvittenberg. nomine promulgato: quo D. V. P. de Calvinismo purgare conantur. Ed. per aliquot Principum Augustanæ conf. theologos. s4°. Tubingæ. 1592
Brevis repet. doct. orthod. de persona & officio Christi 3 disput.; resp. N. Dethlevus. [P2612]. s4°. Witebergae. 1591
Piero, *di Cosimo.*
see BORINSKI (C.) Die Deutung d. P. di C. zugeschr. Prometheus-Bilder, 1920.
„ HABICH (G.) Üb. 2 Prometheus-Bilder angebl. v. P. di C., 1920.
Piéron (Henri).
Thought & the brain. Tr. C. K. Ogden. 8°. 1927
Pierotti (Ermete). Jerusalem explored, being a descr. of the anc. & mod. city. Tr. T. G. Bonney. 2v. la4°. 1864
Pierre, *Cardinal, see* CARDINAL (PEIRE).
Pierre, *d'Auvergne* [PEIRE, *d'A.*], *see* BERTONI (G.) Note su P. d'A., 1917.
Pierre, *de Provence.*
La belle Maguelonne. Ed. A. Biedermann. 8°. 1913
*Die schöne Magelone. Hyst. v. d. edeln ritter Peter v. Provenz u. d. schönsten Magelona, d. königs v. Naples tochter. Alt. Deut. Bearbt. &c., hrsg. v. H. Degering. s4°. 1922
see BEES (N. A.) Franz.-mittelgr. Ritterroman "Imberios u. Margarone," 1924.
Pierre, *d'Ussel, see* USSEL. Poésies des 4 troubadours d'U.; publ. d'ap. les MSS. par J. Audiau, 1922.
Pierre-Bodin (Richard). Mon amant puéril, nouvelle, *see* ŒUVRES libres, 38, 1924.
Pierrefeu (Jean de). G.Q.G., Secteur 1. éd. déf., rev. & augm. 2t. s8°. [1922]
L'offensive du 16 avril: la vérité sur l'affaire Nivelle. s8°. [1919]
Plutarch lied. Tr. J. E. Jeffery. 8°. 1924
Plutarque a menti. s8°. 1923
Pierre Joseph, *ps., see* HAITZE (P. J. DE).
Pierremont (E.), *see* CHE-KA. Tche-ka: matériaux &c.; [*by var. a.*], tr. E. P., 1922.
Pierre-Quint (Léon).
Comment travaillait Proust. Bibliog. &c. 8°. [1928]
Marcel Proust, sa vie, son œuvre. s8°. [1925]

Pierron (Sander). Guillaume Charlier. la8°. Brux. 1913
Henri Boncquet. la8°. Brux. 1909
Les Mostaert. Jean M., dit le maitre d'Oultrement—Giles & François M.—Michel M. 8°. Brux. 1912

Piers (*Sir* Charles Pigott), *Bart.*
Sport & life in Brit. Columbia. 8°. [1923]

Piers (Harry).
Robert Field, portrait painter. la8°. N.Y. 1927

Piers (*Sir* Henry), *Bart.* Chorogr. descr. of the Co. of West-Meath, 1682, *see* VALLANCEY (C.) Coll., v1, 1770.

Pierson (Allard). Disquis. de realismo & nominalismo, inde ab Anselmo usque ad Gulielmum ab Occamo. 8°. Trajecti ad Rhen. 1854

Pierson (Arthur Tappan).
The divine enterprise of missions. s8°. 1892

***Pietas** Oxoniensis: acc. of expulsion of 6 students, 1768, *see* HILL (*Sir* R.)

Pieters (Charles). Annales de l'imprimerie Elsevirienne, ou hist. de la famille des Elsevier. 8°. Gand. 1851

Pietismus. *Eines recht-evangel. treumeinenden Dieners unparthey. Nachricht &c. den P. in Halle betreff. [*signed* A. L. *b. w.* Frederick IV, *k. of Denmark.* Edict, 1708]. s4°. [Stettin]. 1708

Pietists. *Mass d. unmassgebl. Bedenckens, v. d. Pietisten u. Collegiis pietatis &c. V. e. Liebhaber d. göttl. Warheit. [P2443]. s4°. *n.p.* 1692

Pietri (Francesco de').
Cronologie d. famiglia Caracciola &c. s4°. Napoli. 1605

Pietro (Sano di), *see* SANO DI PIETRO.

Pietro dello Schiavo (Antonio di), *see* PETRI (A.)

Pietropoli (Giovanni Pietro).
Il Petrarca impugnato dal Petrarca. 8°. Venezia. 1818

Pietrucci (Napoleone). Delle illust. donne padovane: cenni biog. 2a ed. 8°. Padova. 1853

Piette (Maximin). La réaction de J. Wesley dans l'évol. du Protestantisme. Préf. d'A. Leger. 2e éd. rev. & augm. 8°. Brux. 1927

Piferrer (Francisco). Nobiliario de los reinos y señoríos de España. Con un dicc. de heraldica por J. Fernandez de La Puente y Acevedo. [6t]. la8°. 1855–60

Pigafetta (Antonio). Rel. du prem. voyage autour du monde par Magellan, 1519–22. Ed. J. Denucé. la8°. Anvers. 1923

Pigalle (Jean-Baptiste), *see* ROCHEBLANE (S.) J.-B. P., 1919.

Piganiol (André). Essai sur les origines de Rome. [Bibl. d. Ecoles Franç. d'Athènes & de Rome, fasc. 110]. la8°. 1917

Piggott (*Sir* Francis Taylor), *Kt.* [*ps.* DAWLISH (HOPE)]. The freedom of the seas, hist. treated, *see* FOREIGN OFFICE. Handbooks, No. 148, 1920.
A village community. s8°. Hong Kong. 1910

Pighius (Albertus). Apologia indicti a Paulo III concilii adv. Lutheranae confoederationis rationes. [*b. w. h.* Controvers. explic., 1542]. fol. Coloniae. 1538
Controvers. præcip. in comitiis Ratispon. tractat. explicatio. fol. Coloniae. 1542
De libero hominis arbitrio &c. lib. 10. [*b. w. h.* Controvers. explic., 1542]. fol. Coloniae. 1542
see BUCER (M.) De vera eccl. reconciliatione &c. responsio ad calumnias A. P. &c., *n.d.*

Pigna (Giov. Batt.) Hist. de principi di Este. 4°. Vinegia. 1572

Pigneirus (Emmanuel), *see* PINHEIRO (MANOEL).

Pignoria (Lorenzo) [L. PIGNORIUS].
Le origini di Padoua. 8°. Padoua. 1625
see VENETA. Squitinio d. libertà V. [*attr. to P.*], 1612.

Pignotti (Guido). I pittori Senesi d. fondazione Biringucci, 1724–1915. 8°. Siena. 1916

Pigott (George West Royston).
The Harrogate Spas, w. introd. essay. s8°. 1853

Pigou (Arthur Cecil).
A capital levy & a levy on war wealth. s8°. 1920
The economics of welfare. 8°. 1920
,, ,, 2nd ed. 8°. 1924
Essays in applied econ. 8°. 1923
Industrial fluctuations. 8°. 1927
Mem. on credit &c., *see* INTERNAT. FINANCIAL CONF. Paper 13iv, 1920.
The political econ. of war. 8°. 1921
A st. in public finance. 8°. 1928
see MARSHALL (A.) Mem. of A. M., ed. A. C. P., 1925.

Pigouchet (Philippe), *see* HEURES. *Beg. f. 1 recto* P. P. &c., 1494.

Pijnacker Hordijk (C.), *see* TRAJECTENSES. Quedam narracio de Groninghe &c.; uitg. C. P. H., 1888.

Pijoan (José). Hist. del arte & el arte al traves de la hist. 3t [1, 3, 2a ed.] 8°. Barcelona. 1915–[25]

Pike (Gustavus D.) *The story of the Jubilee singers; [*abridg. of G. D. P.'s bks*], 1876, *see* JUBILEE SINGERS.

Pike (Oliver Gregory). Farther afield in birdland. 8°. [1911]

Pikler (Blanche) & R. Braun.
List of all Hungarian books in trade. 8°. Budapest. 1925

Piksanov (N. K.)
Два века русской литературы. 8°. Москва. 1923
Старорусская повесть. 8°. Москва. 1923
Тургеневскій кружокъ подъ руковод. Н. К. П. Тургеневскій сборникъ &c. [&] библіографія. 8°. [П. 1922]

Pilate (Pontius).
see LYELL (J. P. R.) Sentence of Pontius P., 1922.
,, WEBER (P. X.) Der Pilatus u. s. Gesch., 1913.

Pilcher (*Maj.-Gen.* Thomas David).
Fire problems. 3rd impr. s8°. 1916
*A general's letters to h. son on minor tactics. s8°. 1918
*A general's letters to h. son on obt. h. commission. s8°. 1917
see CLAUSEWITZ (C. v.) War acc. to C.; ed., w. comm. by T. D. P., 1918.

Pilcius (Casparus). *Examen regularum Pilcianarum, quibus depravat doct. de Coena Domini. [*Beg. w. sig. O.*] s8°. *n.p. n.d.*
see WAGNER (M.), T. FABRI &c. Exam. thesium &c. Zuingl. &c. vulg. per C. P., 1586.

Piles (Roger de), *see* BURGESS (J.) *Lives of the most emin. mod. painters omitted by M. de P., 1754.

Pilgerfahrt (Die) d. träumenden Mönchs, 1926, *see* DEGUILEVILLE (G.)

Pilgrim (H. Guy Ellcock). The geology of parts of Persian prov. of Fars, Kirman & Laristan, *see* INDIA: GEOL. SURVEY. Mem., v48, p2, 1925.

Pilgrim's. *New (The) p.'s progr., 1820, *see* NEW.

Pilkington, *The family of, see* PILKINGTON (*Lt.-Col.* J.) Hist. of Lancs. family of P. &c., 1066–1600, 1894.

Pilkington (*Lt.-Col.* John). Hist. of the Lancs. family of Pilkington & its branches, 1066–1600. 2nd & rev. ed., enl. la8°. Liv'l. 1894

Pilkington (L. G.), *see* FIENNES (G.) & L. G. P. Getting our living, 1924.

Pilkington (*Mrs.* Letitia), *wife of Matthew Pilkington.* Memoirs, 1712–50. [Anecdotes of Swift &c.] Wr. by herself. Intr. by I. Barry. [repr.] 8°. [1928]

Pilkington (Matthew), *vicar of Donabate, Dublin.* Dict. of painters. [*Extra-illust. & extended to 5v, by Richard Bull, w. add. tp. dated* 1784]. 4°. 1770

Pilkington (Matthew), *M.A.* Poems on sev. occasions. Added, The plague of wealth, w. sev. poems not in Dublin ed. Rev. by Dr. Swift. 8°. 1731

Pillai (P. Padmanabha). Econ. condit. in India. Intr. note by G. Slater. [London Sch. of Econ. &c.] 8°. 1925

Pillet (Jean), *chanoine de Gerberoy.* Hist. du château & de la ville de Gerberoy. s4°. Rouen. 1679

Pillet (Maurice L.) L'expédition scientif. & artist. de Mésopotamie & de Médie, 1851–55. [*Under the direction of F. Fresnel*]. la8°. 1922

Pillion (Louise Lefrançois-), *see* LEFRANÇOIS-PILLION (L.)

Pillsbury (John Elliott), *see* UNITED STATES; COAST SURVEY. Gulf Stream explor.; rep. by J. E. P., 1890.

Pilnyak (Boris) [*i.e.* BORIS ANDREEVICH WOGAU].
Былье. s8°. Ревель. 1922
Голый год. Роман. 8°. Берлин. 1922
Иван да Марья: [повести]. s8°. Берлин. 1922
Повесть. s8°. П. 1922
Повести о черном хлебе. s8°. Москва. 1923
TRANSLATIONS.
L'année nue. Tr. L. Bernstein & L. Desormonts. 4e éd. s8°. [1926]
Bielokonskoïé, nouv. [tr. par A. Pierre], *see* ŒUVRES libres, t34, 1924.
Tales of the wilderness. [Tr. F. O'Dempsey]. Intr. by Prince D. S. Mirsky. s8°. 1924

Pilot (Ant.) Spettacoli e feste per l'arrivo dei conti del Nord a Venezia nel 1782. la8°. Venezia. 1914

***Pilot's** guide to the river Thames, &c., 1913, *see* THAMES.

Pilsbry (Henry Augustine). Cirripedia f. the Panama Canal Zone. [S.I.: U.S. Nat. Mus., Bull. 103]. 8°. Wash. 1918

Pilsudski (Joseph), *see* MEREJKOVSKY (D. S.) J. P., 1921.
see SIEROSZEWSKI (W.) J. P., 1921.
,, SZPOTANSKI (S.) Pologne nouv. & son premier Chef d'Etat J. P., 1920.

Pilyaev (M. I.) Старый Петербургъ: разсказы изъ былой жизни столицы. Изд. А. С. Суворина. la8°. С.–П. 1887

Pimentel (Alberto). O descobrimento do Brazil. Romance. 2a ed. riv. s8°. 1900
Pimentel (Eleonora Fonseca), *see* FONSECA PIMENTEL (E.)
Pimodan (*cte.* **C. de).** Louise-Elis. d'Orléans, reine d'Espagne, 1709–42. s8°. [1922]
Pinaut (Jeanne), *see* BELLEM (*Mme.* DE).
***Pinch (A)** of snuff &c., 1840, *see* HILL (B. E.)
Pincier (Johann) [PINCIERUS]. Antidotum adv. Enthusiastarum, Metusiastarum & Synusiastarum cavillos &c. in causa Eucharistica. Acc. P. Melanthonis de eadem re aliquot epistolae. s8°. Basileae. 1561
Pinckney (Thomas), *see* BEMIS (S. F.) P.'s Treaty, 1783–1800, 1926.
Pincott (Frederic). Hindì manual. s8°. 1882
Pindar.
Aristologia Pindarica Græcolat. Acc. Sententiae novem lyricorum. Cum expos. &c. opera M. Neandri. [*Gr. & Lat.*] s8°. Basileæ. [1556]
Carmina cum fragm. selectis. Iterum ed. O. Schroeder. [*Foll. by* Suppl. Pindaricum, 1923, *w. sep. pagin.*] s8°. Lips., *Teub.* 1914–23
Olympia, Pythia, Nemea, Isthmia. [*Gr.*] s8°. [Basileæ. 1556]
Scholia vetera in P. Carmina. Rec. A. B. Drachmann. v3. s8°. L., *Teubner.* 1927
3, Scholia in Nemeonicas & Isthmionicas — Epimetrum—Indices.
TRANSLATIONS.
Odes &c. With intr. & Eng. tr. by Sir J. Sandys. [Loeb Class. Lib.] [2nd rev. ed.] s8°. 1919
TRANSLATIONS [*continued*].
Olympia, Pythia, Nemea, Isthmia. Per P. Melanthonem conv. in Lat. [*b. w. h.* Olympia &c., *Gr.*, 1556]. s8°. Vitebergae. 1563
Pindar [Odes] in Eng. verse. By A. S. Way. 8°. 1922
P., texte établi & tr. par A. Puech. [Coll. des univ. de Fr.] 4t. 8°. 1922–23
1, Olympiques; 2, Pythiques; 3, Néméennes; 4, Isthmiques & fragm.
see DIEHL (E.) Suppl. lyricum, 3e A., 1917.
,, SCHRÖDER (O.) P.'s Pythien, 1922.
,, TZETZES (I.) De metris P. comm.; ed. A. B. Drachmann, 1925.
,, WILAMOWITZ-MÖLLENDORFF (U. v.) Pindaros, 1922.
Pindar (Paul), *ps.*, *see* AKERMAN (J. Y.)
Pindemonte (Ippolito). I sepolcri, *see* FOSCOLO (N. U.) Ult. lettere, 5a ed., 1817.
see SCHERILLO (M.) I. P., e la poesia bardita, 1920.
Pinder (Ulrich). Speculum passionis J. C. [Cum textu quatuor evãgelistarũ & glosis: cum figuris (*by H. L. Schäuffelein*)]. fol. [In civitate im̃periali Nurenbergen. 1507]
Pinder (Wilhelm). Problem d. Generation in d. Kunstgesch. Europas. 8°. [1926]
Pineda (Joannes de), *of Seville.* Ad suos in Salomonem comm. Salomon praevius, id est de rebus S. lib. 8. fol. Lugduni. 1609
Comm. in Ecclesiasten. fol. Antwerpiae. 1620
Pineda (Juan de), *of Medina del Campo.* Libr'o del passo honroso defendido por Suero de Quiñones. Cop. de un lib. antig. de mano por F. J. de P. [Hispanic Soc. of America]. 8°. Salamanca. 1588 [facs. repr. *De Vinne press,* 1902]
Pineda (Juan Perez de), *see* PEREZ DE PINEDA (J.)
Pinedo y Salazar (Julian de).
Hist. de la insigne Orden del Toyson de Oro. 3t. fol. 1787
Pinero (*Sir* **Arthur Wing).** The enchanted cottage. s8°. 1922
The freaks. [repr.] s8°. 1922
His house in order. [n. impr.] s8°. 1919
Playgoers. s8°. [1913]
Pineton de Chambrun (Jacques), *see* CHAMBRUN (J. P. DE).
Pingaud (Léonce). La jeunesse de C. Nodier. Les Philadelphes. 8°. Besançon. 1914
Pingonio (Giovanni Michele) [NAGONIO (G. M.)], *see* SARACENO (F.) Nota sopra un ms. falsam. attrib. a P., 1887.
Pingriff (G. N.) Leicestershire. s8°. C. 1920
Pinheiro (Manoel), *Jesuit* [PIGNEIRUS (E.)]
see JESUITS. Recent. de ampl. regno Chinae; item De statu Xtnae apud magnum regem Mogor [ex litt. H. Xaverii & P. 1598–99], 1601.
,, XAVIER (H.) Hist. Petri, *foll. by* Narr. brevis rerum in regno magni Mogor gest. transcr. ex literis E. P. &c., 1639.
Pinheiro Ferreira (Silvestre). Cartas sobre a revol. do Brazil [1821], *see* INSTITUTO HIST. E GEOG. BRAZIL. Revista, t51, 1888.
Pinius (Joannes). Liturgia Mozarabica. Tractatus, doc. &c. coll. & illustr. J. P. fol. Romae. 1740
see LITURGIA. L. antiq. Hispanic, Gothica, Isidor., Mozarabica &c. mixta illust.; adj. vet mon. [Tractatus coll. &c. J. P.], 2t, 1746.
Pinkerton (Matthew Worth).
Murder in all ages. 8°. Chicago. [1898]
Pinkerton (*Rev.* **Robert).** Extracts of letters on tour in Russia, Poland & Germany to promote the object of the B. & F. Bible Soc. With letter f. prince A. Galitzin to Lord Teignmouth. 8°. 1817
Pinkney (Edward Coote). Life & works. Mem. & compl. text of poems & prose, prep. by T. O. Mabbott & F. L. Pleadwell. 8°. N.Y. 1926
Pinner (Ephraim Moses), *see* PINNER (MORITZ).
Pinner (Erna), *see* PUPPENBUCH. Das Puppenbuch [Puppen d. E. P. &c.], 1921.
Pinner (Moritz [Ephraim Moses]), *see* TALMUD. Compendium d. Hierosolymitan. u. Babylon. T.; uebers. &c. v. M. P., B1, 1832.
Pinnow (Hermann). Gesch. d. deut. Volkes f. d. Mittelklassen höh. Lehranstalten. 2B. 8°. *Teubner.* 1923
Pino (Bernardino). I falsi sospetti; comedia. nuov. posta in luce [*w. declar. by F. Abirelli*]. s8°. Venetia. 1588
Pinon (René). L'empire de la Méditerranée. 8°. 1912
L'Europe nouv. & le catholicisme, *see* PAGES ACTUELLES, no. 139, 1921.
France & Allemagne, 1870–1913. [n. éd.] s8°. 1913
Pinot (Pierre). Le controle du ravitaillement de la population civile. [C.E. for Internat. Peace]. la8°. [1925]
see AUGÉ-LARIBÉ (M.) Agric. & food supply dur. the War: Food s., by P. P., 1927.
Pinsker (Simchah), *ed.* Lickute Kadmoniot. Zur Gesch. d. Karaismus &c. 8°. Wien. 1860
Pinthus (Kurt). Menschheits Dämmerung. Symphonie jüngster Dichtung; hrsg. v. K. P. 8°. [1919]
Pinto (Vivian de Sola).
Sir Charles Sedley, 1639–1701. 8°. 1927
Pinto de Morales (Jorge).
Maravillas del Parnaso &c. [Hispanic Soc.] 8°. Lisboa. 1637. [facs. repr. *De Vinne press.* 1902]
Pinturicchio, *see* MANZONI (L.) Chi fu il maestro d. P., 1901.
Pinza (Giovanni). Monumenti prim. di Roma e del Lazio antico, *see* REALE ACCAD. D. LINCEI. Mon. ant., v15, 1905.
Ricerche su la topog. di Cartagine punica, *see* REALE ACCAD. DEI LINCEI. Mon. ant., t30, 1925.
Pinzi (Cesare). Per l'inaugur. del Museo Civico di Viterbo, 1912, *see* VITERBO.
Pió (Michele). Alleg. per confirmare quanto si scrive nell' annot. all' Avviso di Parnaso [by V. Fulvio]. Cavata d. vita di F. Bartolomeo dalla Casa. [*b. w.* Veneta. Squit. d. libertà, 1612]. s8°. *n.p.* 1621
***Pipe (A)** of tobacco, 1744, *see* BROWNE (I. H.)
Pipe Rolls. Cal. of P.R. of r. of Rich. I for Bucks. & Beds., 1189–99; by G. H. Fowler & M. W. Hughes, *see* BEDFORDSHIRE HIST. REC. SOC. Publ., v7, 1923.
Great Roll of the P. for 32[–34], Hen. II, 1185–86[–1187–88]. [Pipe Roll Soc., 36–38]. la8°. 1914–25
Great Roll of the P. for 14th year of Henry III, 1230. Ed. C. Robinson. [Pipe Roll Soc., N.S., v4]. la8°. Princeton. 1927
Great Roll of the P. for 2nd–5th year[s] of Richard I, 1190–93. Ed. D. M. Stenton. [Pipe Roll Soc., N.S., v1–3]. la8°. 1925–27
Pipe Roll Society. Publications. v36–38, N.S., v1–4. la8°. 1914–27
see PIPE ROLLS. Great Roll, 1185–88, 1914–25. [36–38.]
,, PIPE ROLLS. Great Roll of the P. for 14th year of Henry III, 1230; ed. C. Robinson, 1927. [N.S., 4.]
,, PIPE ROLLS. Great Roll of the P. for 2nd–5th year[s] Richard I, 1190–93; ed. D. M. Stenton, 1925–27. [N.S., 1–3.]
Piper (C. Welborne). First book of the lens. 8°. 1901
Piper (Reinhard). Das Tier in d. Kunst. Neubearb. la8°. München. 1922
Piper (Thomas W.) Offic. rep. of trial of T. W. P. for murder of Mabel H. Young. Sup. Judic. Court of Mass. [1875–76]. 8°. Boston [Mass.] 1887
Pipping (Fredrik Wilhelm). Förteckning öfver i tryck utgifna skrifter på Finska &c. 4°. Helsingissä. 1856–57
Pipping (Heinrich). Arcana Bibliothecae Thomanae Lips. sacra. [*w.* App. superintendentium &c.] s8°. Lipsiae. 1703
Hist. theol. Einl. zu d. Symbol. Schr., *see* AUGSBURG CONFESSION. Concordia Christl. &c., 1703.
Syntagma diss. academ. Praem. vita auctoris. s8°. Lipsiae. 1723
Piqueré (P. J.)
Gramm. d. türk.-osman. Umgangssprache. s8°. Wien. 1870

Piramus, *see* PYRAMUS.
Pirandello (Luigi).
All' uscita—Il dovere del medico—La morsa—L'uomo dal fiore in bocca. 8°. [1926]
L'amica delle mogli. 8°. Firenze. [1927]
Il berretto a sonagli : commedia. n. ed. riv. s8°. Firenze. [1925]
Ciascuno a suo modo. Commedia. s8°. Firenze. [1924]
Come prima meglio di prima. Commedia. s8°. Firenze. 1921
Così è (se vi pare) : parabola in 3 atti. n. ed. riv. s8°. Firenze. 1925
Diana e la tuda. s8°. Firenze. [1927]
E domani, lunedì . . . Novelle. s8°. Milano. [1919]
Enrico IV. Tragedia. s8°. Firenze. 1922
Il giuoco d. parti. n. ed. riv. e corr. s8°. Firenze. 1925
L'imbecille—Lumie di Sicilia—Cecè—La patente. 8°. [1926]
L'innesto. Commedia. n. ed. riv. e corr. s8°. Firenze. [1925]
Ma non è una cosa seria. Commedia. n. ed. riv. e corr. s8°. Firenze. [1925]
Maschere nude, *see var. works above & below.*
Novelle per un anno. v1–12. s8°. Firenze. [1922–28]
1, Scialle nero. 2, La via nuda. 3, La rallegrata. 4, L'uomo solo. 5, La mosca. 6, In silenzio. 7, Tutt'e tre. 8, Dal naso al cielo. 9, Donna Mimma. 10, Il vecchio dio. 11, La giara. 12, Il viaggio.
Pensaci, Giacomino ! commedia. n. ed. riv. s8°. Firenze. 1925
Il piacere dell' onestà : commedia. n. ed. riv. s8°. Firenze. [1925]
Quaderni di S. Gubbio operatore. s8°. Firenze. [1925]
La ragione d. altri : commedia. s8°. Firenze. [1926]
Sagra del Signore della nave—L'altro figlio—La giara. Commedie. s8°. Firenze. [1925]
Sei personaggi in cerca d'autore. Commedia. s8°. Firenze. 1921
La signora Morli, una e due. Commedia. s8°. Firenze. 1922
Tu ridi. Novelle. n. ed. riv. s8°. Milano. 1920
Tutto per bene. Commedia. s8°. Firenze. [1920]
Uno, nessuno e centomila. s8°. Firenze. 1926
L'uomo, la bestia e la virtù. Apologo. s8°. Firenze. 1922
Vestire gli ignudi. Commedia. s8°. Firenze. [1923]
La vita che ti diedi. Tragedia. s8°. Firenze. [1924]
TRANSLATIONS.
Chacun sa vérité, parabole en 3 actes, *see* ŒUVRES libres, 42, 1925.
Each in his own way, & 2 o. plays [*i.e.* The pleasure of honesty—Naked]. Tr. A. Livingston. 8°. [1925]
3 plays. Right you are—Six characters in search of an author—"Henry IV." [Tr. E. Storer & A. Livingston. Ed. A. L.] 8°. 1923
„ „ ....[4th pr.] 8°. [1925]
Vêtir ceux qui sont nus, *see* ŒUVRES libres, N°. 77, 1927.
see FABBRI (E.) P., 1921 ?.
„ PASINI (F.) L. P., *w.* Nota bibliog., 1927.
„ ROST (P.) L. P., 1921.
„ STARKIE (W.) L. P., 1926.
Piranesi (Giovanni Battista).
see GIESECKE (A.) Studien ü. G. B. P., Kap. 1, 2, 1911.
„ HIND (A. M.) P., crit. study, w. list of publ. wks. & cat. of prisons & views, 1922.
Pirchegger (Hans).
Gesch. d. Steiermark. B1, bis 1283. 8°. Gotha. 1920
Pirckheimer (Wilibald) [*ps.* J. F. COTTALAMBERGIUS].
*Eccius dedolatus. s4°. *n.p.* [*Impr. in Utopia.* 1520?]
see ROSENTHAL (E.) Dürers Buchmalereien für P.'s Bibl., 1928.
„ ROTH (F.) W. P.: e. Lebensbild, 1887.
Pirenne (Henri). Hist. de Belgique. t5, 6 [5, 2e éd., rev. & corr.] 8°. Brux. 1926
Mediaeval cities : th. orig. & the revival of trade. Tr. F. D. Halsey. s8°. Princeton. 1925
Mélanges d'hist. offerts à H. P. à l'occasion de sa 40e année d'enseignement à l'univ. de Gand, 1886–1926. 2t. [*pagin. cont.*] la8°. Bruxelles. 1926
Les villes du m. â. s8°. Brux. 1927
see ESPINAS (G.) & H. P. Rec. de doc. rel. à l'hist. de l'industrie drapière en Flandre, p1, t3, 4, 1920–24.
Pirenne (Jacques) & M. Vauthier. La législation & l'admin. allemandes en Belgique. [C.E. for Int. Peace]. la8°. [1926]
Pirie-Gordon (*Lt.-Col.* H.), *ed.*, *see* EGYPTIAN EXPEDITIONARY FORCE. Brief record of the advance, 1917–18, 2nd ed., 1919.
Piron (Alexis), *1689–1773.*
La métromanie. Mem. & notes by G. Masson. s8°. C. 1875
„ „ *for a. ed.*, *see* THÉÂTRE choisi du 18e s., t2, 1914.
Pirquet (Clemens). Volksgesundheit im Krieg. [*By var. wr.*] Hrsg. C. P. [C.E. for Int. Peace]. 2T. la8°. Wien. 1926
Pirrss (O.) [PIRS]. Маленькій Русскій. Пособіе для усовершенствованія въ русск. языкѣ. s8°. Карльсруэ. 1905
Pisa. Constit. facte in div. sess. sacri gen. concilii pisani. s8°. Parrisii, *Jehan Petit.* [1512]
Pisan (Christine de). Hist. de Charles V, *see* LEBEUF (J.) Diss. sur l'hist. de Paris, 1739–43.
see NYS (E.) C. de P. & s. œuvres, 1914.

Pisani (Baldassarre). Gli ossequi d. Muse, nell' acclam. d. Carlo III. [N125]. 8°. Napoli. 1708
Pisani (Carlo). I nostri nonni. [P2852]. 8°. Venezia. 1872
Pisano (Giovanni).
see BRACH (A.) N. & G. Pisano u. d. Plastik d. 14. Jhdts. in Siena, 1904.
„ POPP (A. E.) Nicolo & G. P., 1922.
Pisano (Nicolo), *c. 1206–c. 1280.*
see SUPINO (I. B.) La patria di N. P., 1916.
„ SWARZENSKI (G.) N. P., 1926.
Piscator (Johann), *of Herborn.*
Analysis logica 7 epist. apostolic. quae Catholicæ appellari solent. Una cum scholiis &c. [*b. w. h.* Anal. epist. Pauli, 1594]. s8°. Londini. 1597
Analysis logica Evang. sec. Matthaeum [*wanting pp. 817–832*]. s8°. Sigenæ Nassov. 1597
Analysis logica omnium epist. Pauli. Una cum scholiis &c. ed. 2a. s8°. Londini. 1594
Comm. in omnes libros N.T. Analysis—Scholia—Observat. 2a ed. 4°. Herbornae Nassov. 1621
Kurtzer bericht v. des Herren Abendmal. [P437]. s4°. Herborn. 1589
Pischel (Richard).
Gramm. d. Prakrit-Sprachen. la8°. Str. 1900
Piscopia (Elena Lucrezia Cornara), *see* CORNARA (E. L.)
Pisecius (Thomas) [*ps.* CASTIM (JOSEPHUS)]. Manuductio in viam pacis eccl. s8°. Eleutheropli. 1650
Pissarro (Camille), *see* TABARANT (A.) P. ; tr., 1925.
Pistelli (Ermenegildo).
see DANTE ALIGHIERI. Lectura D., Il c. 14 del Purgatorio letto da E. P., 1909, n. ed. corr., 1922.
„ —— Lectura D.: c. 33 del Paradiso letto da E. P. (1904), n. ed., 1922?.
Pistis Sophia. P. S. Lit. tr. by G. Horner. Intr. by F. Legge. la8°. 1924
P. S. Neu hrsg. m. Einl. &c. v. C. Schmidt. [Coptica, 2]. 8°. Hauniae. 1925
Pistoia. Statuti dell' Opera di S. Jacopo di P. volgar. 1313 da M. di ser G. Bellebuoni, con due inventarj, 1340 e 1401, pubbl. da S. Ciampi. [P2701]. 4°. Pisa. 1814
Storie Pistoresi [Annales P.], 1300–48 ; a cura di S. A. Barbi, *see* MURATORI. Rerum Ital. Script., t11, p5, 1927.
Pistorius (Fritz), *ps.* [*i.e.* ROB. EULE]. Das Volk steht auf ! 1813. 3e A. 8°. [1912]
Pistorius (Johann), *of Nidda.* Artis Cabalisticae tom. 1 in quo praeter P. Ricii libros sunt pene omnes scriptores qui artem comm. suis illust. [*i.e.* R. Joseph, Leo Hebr., Jo. Reuchlin, Archangelus Burgon. & Abraham] ex J. P. bibliotheca. [*No more published*]. fol. Basileae. 1587
see MENTZER (B.) Apologia prim. disput. Anti-pistorianae pro div. Sacr. Script. auct. adv. scr. J. P. &c., 1602.
„ —— Disput. 14 de controv. Christ. doctr. capit. oppos. cap. libri a J. P., 1601.
Pitaval (Der) d. Gegenwart. Almanach interessanter Straffälle. Hrsg. v. R. Frank, G. Roscher, H. Schmidt. B8. 8°. Tübingen. 1914
Pitaval (F. Gayot de) [GAYOT DE PITAVAL (F.)]
Causes célèbres. 20t [t1–10, n. éd. augm.] s8°. 1739–59
Pitcairn (Robert), *see* MAIDMENT (J.) & R. P. Nugae derelictae, q. coll. J. M. & R. P., 1822.
Pitezel (Benjamin F.), *see* GEYER (F. C.) The Holmes-P. case, 1896.
Pithou (Pierre), *the younger* [PITOU]. Le prem. livre des mémoires des comtes heredit. de Champagne & Brie. [*no more publ. la. paper.*] 4°. 1572
see COLLATIO. Mosaycarum & Roman. legum collatio &c., 1654.
Pitigrilli (Segré Dino).
Amalia Guglielminetti. [2a ed.] la8°. Milano. 1922
Pitman (Benn). The assassination of Pres. Lincoln & the trial of the conspirators. Comp. & arr. by B. P. 8°. Cincinnati. 1865
Pitman (*Sir* Isaac).
The phonographic teacher [*& Key*]. [P2421]. s8°. 1894
Pitman (*Sir* Isaac) & Sons, *publishers*, *see* HEELIS (F.), *ed.* P.'s theory & practice of commerce, 1912.
Pitman (Walter Hayward). Acc. of the life & works of S. Luke [patron of the Co. of Painters]. 8°. *pr. for a.* 1889
The W. Co. of Painters &c. : its hall, pictures, & plate. 8°. 1906
Pitollet (Camille). V. Blasco Ibáñez, s. novelas y la novela de su vida. 8°. Valencia. [1921]
V. Blasco Ibáñez, ses romans & le roman de sa vie. 8°. [1921]

Pitonius (Peter). Ein Leychpredig, zu trost allen denen, die da ein ewigs leben in Christo Jesu hoffen. [*On Ps. xc*]. [P2439]. s4°. [Nürnberg, *bey dem Petreio*]. 1542

Pitou, *see* PITHOU.

Pitra (*le card.* Jean Baptiste), *see* BATTANDIER (A.) Le card. J. B. P., 1893.

Pitrou (Robert). F. Schubert, vie intime. 8°. 1928

Pitt (Frances). Animal mind. 8°. [1927]

Shetland pirates & o. wild life studies. 8°. [1923]

Wild creatures of garden & hedgerow. 8°. 1920

Pitt (St. George Lane-Fox). Free will & destiny. With letter on Internat. Moral Educ. Congress &c. by Sir F. Pollock, & app. by F. J. Gould. s8°. 1920

Pitt (*Rt. Hon.* William), *1759–1806.* The beauties of P.; sels. f. h. speeches by A. Howard. s8°. [1834 ?]

see ADAMS (E. D.) Infl. of Grenville on P.'s for. policy, 1787–1798, 1904.

„ ROSE (J. H.) Short life of W. P., 1925.

Pittard (Eugène).

Les races & l'hist.: intr. ethnol. à l'hist. 8°. 1924

Race & hist.: ethnolog. intr. to hist. [Tr. V. C. C. Collum]. 8°. 1926

Pitter (Ruth). First poems. s8°. [1920]

Pitti, *Palace.* La pittura ital. del seicento e del settecento alla mostra di Palazzo Pitti. [*By*] U. Ojetti, L. Dami, N. Tarchiani. 4°. Milano. [1924]

see NUGENT (M.) Alla Mostra d. Pittura Ital. del '600 e '700, note &c., 1925.

Pitt-Lewis (George), *see* FRANCIS-WILLIAMS (B.) & G. P.-L. The Coal Mines Regul. Acts, 1887–1896, 1896.

Pittoni, *Family of, see* PITTONI (L.) Dei P., 1907.

Pittoni (Battista), *see* DOLCE (L.) Imprese di div. principi &c. [di B. P.], 1602.

Pittoni (Laura).

Dei Pittoni, artisti Veneti. 8°. Bergamo. 1907

La libreria di S. Marco. Cenni storici. 8°. Pistoia. 1903

Pitt-Rivers (*Lt.-Gen.*) [†FOX (AUGUSTUS HENRY LANE), *aft. Pitt-Rivers*].

Address to the Anthropolog. sect. of the Brit. Assoc., 1872. [*b. w. h.* Prim. warfare, 1867–9]. 8°. 1872

Primitive warfare. Lect. [R.U.S. Inst.] 3 sect. 8°. *f.p.c.* 1867–69

On some flint implements found in Oxfordshire &c. [*b. w. h.* Prim. warfare, 1867–9]. 8°. *n.d.*

On the disc. of palæolithic implements at Acton. [Fr. Quart. J. of Geol. Soc., 1872. *b. w. h.* Prim. warfare, 1867–69]. 8°. 1872

Short guide to the Larmer Grounds, Rushmore, King John's House, & the Museum at Farnham, Dorset. 8°. [c. 1900]

Pitt-Rivers (George Henry Lane-Fox).

The clash of culture & contact of races. 8°. 1927

World significance of the Russian revol. Pref. by O. Levy. [P2487]. s8°. O. 1920

Pitts (Thomas). *The western martyrology, or bloody assizes, 1678–89, 5th ed., 1705, *see* †WESTERN.

Piucco (Clotaldo). Prime rappresentazioni nei teatri di prosa a Venezia (1848–66). [Nozze Caïs de Pierlas-Mocenigo. N. 134]. 8°. [Venezia. 1884]

Piumati (Giovanni), *see* VINCI (L. DA). Il Codice atlantico di L. da V.; trascriz. diplom. e crit. d. G. P., 4v, 1894–1904.

Pius II, *pope* [ENEA SILVIO PICCOLOMINI; ÆNEAS SYLVIUS PICCOLOMINEUS]. De Bohemorum orig. ac gestis hist., *see* DUBRAVIUS (J.) Hist. Bohemica, 1687.

[Epistolae. *fol. a2 beg.*:—] Epistola sive oratio Pii in Conventu Mantuano. s4°. [Milan, *A. Zarothus.* 1487]

145 *ff. Without pagin.; a1 missing; a, b, c, f, g, i, k, l, m, o, p, q, r, s, t, & u in eights; d, e, h, n in fours; u8 foll. by Tituli (2 leaves).*

Epistole et varii tractatus Pii secūdi pōtificis maximi: ad diuersos in quadruplici vite eius statu trāsmisse: noviter impr. [*Ed. by A. Archintus & revis. by J. Vinzalius.*] 8°. Lugduni, *Venund. ab S. Gueynard.* [*Impr. J. de Vingle*]. 1505

Pius IV, *pope.* Soc. Jesu defensio ex test. et litt. Pii IV, *see* JESUITS. Epist. Indicae, 1566.

see AUGSBURG CONF. Causae cur electores &c. A. C. ad concil. à Pio IV Tridenti indictum, non acc., 1564; 1664.

„ PASTOR (L. v.) Gesch., B7, 1920; tr., ed. R. F. Kerr, v15, 16, 1559–65, 1928.

Pius V, *pope.*

see BARLOW (T.), *bp. of Lincoln.* Brutum fulmen, or the bull of Pius V conc. the damnation of Q. Elizabeth &c., 1681.

Pius V, *pope* [*continued*].

see HIRSCHAUER (C.) Polit. de St. P. V en France, 1566–72, 1922.

„ MENDHAM (J.) Life &c. of P. V, 1832.

„ PASTOR (L. v.) Gesch., B8, 1920.

Pius VI, *pope.*

see DINI (G.) Diario de la peregrinacion apostolica de P. VI &c., 1783.

„ RINIERI (I.) Della rovina di una monarchia: rel. st. tra P. VI e la corte di Napoli, 1776–99, 1901.

„ SCHLITTER (H.) P. VI u. Josef II, 1782–84, 1894.

„ —— Die Reise P. VI nach Wien u. s. Aufenthalt daselbst &c., 1892.

Pius VII, *pope.* Concordat entre le Pape & le Roi [*Louis XVIII*], signé à Rome, 1817. [P2553]. 8°. 1817

see BEAUCHAMP (A. DE). Hist. des malheurs &c. de P. VII sous Napoléon, 1814.

„ GUADET (J.) Esquisses hist. & polit. s. P., 1829.

„ SECKENDORFF (C. v.) Napoleon I u. Pius VII, 1873.

Pius IX, *pope.*

Discorsi [1870–73]. Racc. d. p. Pasquale de Franciscis. 2v. s8°. 1872–73

Discours adressés dans le Vatican aux fidèles de Rome &c. Rec. & publ. par P. de Franciscis. Tr. 3t. 8°. Rome. 1875–76

I doc. citati nel Syllabus ed. per ordine d. Pio IX, &c. Estr. d. Archivio dell' ecclesiastico. 8°. Firenze. 1865

Enciclica di P. IX &c. [*b. w. h.* Encyclica, 1863]. s8°. Torino. 1865

Encyclica P. IX data Dec. 1864. Syllabus errorum &c. s8°. Aug. Taurin. 1865

Die E. u. Syllabus. [*Lat. & Germ.*] Nebst Einl. 2e verm. A. [P2693]. 8°. Köln. 1865

The Encyclical & Syllabus of Pius IX, Dec. 8, 1864, w. introd. [P2694]. 8°. 1865

Encyclique adr. à tous les patriarches, primats &c., 8 déc. 1864. [8e éd. P520]. 8°. 1865

Encyclika v. 21 Nov. 1873. [P504]. s8°. Mainz. 1873

The papal encyclical & syllabus, tr. f. Latin text. Repr. f. The Daily News. Add. Dogmatic decrees of the Vatican Council. [P2565]. 8°. 1875

Lettere pontif. che pron. la scomunica maggiore contro gli usurpatori d'una parte degli stati della Chiesa. [P520]. 8°. [1860]

Der Papst u. d. mod. Ideen. H2, Die Encyclica v. 8. Dec. 1864, nebst Vorw. v. C. Schrader. [P2693]. 8°. Wien. 1865

*P. IX als Papst u. als König dargest. aus d. Acten s. Pontificates. 8°. Wien. 1865

Der Syllabus Pius IX in s. Hauptsätzen. 2te A. [P2694]. 8°. Köln. 1872

see ARTHUR (W.) The modern Jove, 1873.

„ LUTTERBECK (J. A. B.) An Pabst Pius IX, &c., 1870.

„ TESI-PASSERINI (C.) Pio IX e il suo tempo, 3p, 1877–81.

Pius X, *pope* [GIUSEPPE SARTO]. Pro pastorali regimine in patriarchatu Venetiarum ineundo &c. J. card. Sarto adhortatio. [P2842]. la8°. Mantuae. 1894

see CAPECELATRO (*card.* A.) Papa P. X e la Francia, 1907.

Pius XI, *pope* [ACHILLE RATTI]. Climbs on Alpine peaks. Tr. J. E. C. Eaton. Foreword by D. Freshfield, & intr. by L. C. Casartelli. 8°. [1923]

Encyclical letter &c. on 3rd cent. of St. Josaphat, Abp. of Polotsk. [P2733]. 8°. 1924

see BIERBAUM (M.) Papst P. XI, 1922.

„ †PETRARCH. P. e la Lombardia; collabor., A. R. &c., 1904.

Piuzantatzi (Norayr N.), *see* NORAYR *Biuzantatzi.*

Piváný (Eugene).

The case of Hungary. [P2524]. s8°. Budapest. 1919

Hungarian-Amer. hist. connections. Tr. 8°. Budapest. 1927

Pivčević (Ivan). Povijest Poljica, *see* BULLETTINO DI ARCH. &C. DALM., 44, Suppl., 1921.

Pizarro y Orellana (Fernando). Disc. apolog. en gracia &c. de las ordenes milit., *see* CARO DE TORRES (F.) Hist. &c., 1629.

Pizon (Antoine).

Précis d'hist. naturelle. 5e éd. rev. & corr. s8°. 1923

Pizzi (Tomaso). La gara delle muse, per celeb. il nome del re Carlo &c. [P2766]. 8°. Napoli. 1747

Placcius (Vicentius). Theatrum anonym. et pseudonym. Praem. est vita auctoris, scriptore J. A. Fabricio. 3p *in* 1v [p3, Deckherri Conjecturae]. fol. Hamburgi. 1708

see LEMCKE (J.) V. P. u. s. Bedeut. f. d. Anon. &c. Bibliog., 1925.

Place (Francis), *engraver, see* HAKE (H. M.) Contemp. records rel. to F. P., w. cat., 1922.

Place (Francis), *political reformer.* *Essay (An) on the state of the country in resp. to cond. &c. of husbandry labourers. [P2782]. 8°. [1831]

Placentinus (Joannes). Vier nachdenkl. Fragen: 1, von d. Ebbenflut.—2, Wie d. Finsternüsse &c. [P447]. s4°. [Franckfurth a. O.] 1659

Placentinus (Thomas), *ps., see* EMSER (H.)

Placet (Peter), *pseud.*
The string of beads for the Romanisers. s8°. 1844

Placitus (Sextus). Liber medicinae ex animalibus, *see* CORPUS MEDICORUM LAT., v4, 1927.

Plain. *Plain (A) &c. acc. of the conduct & proc. of the rebels at Derby, 4th–6th Dec., 1745, *see* DERBY.
*Plain (A) acc. of genuine Xty., 1761, *see* WESLEY (J.)
*Plain (A) acc. of the people called Methodists, 1749, *see* WESLEY (J.)
*Plain (A) & familiar discourse &c. conc. the Cath. Ch., 1687, *see* FREEMAN (S.)

Plaisans (Guillaume de). [Orationes, *Lat. & Fr.* (1308)], *see* LIZERAND (G.), *ed.* Le dossier de l'affaire des Templiers, 1923.

Plaisted (Arthur Henry). Manor & parish records of Medmenham, Bucks. 8°. 1925

***Plan** & cartes d. villes d'Artois, *n.d., see* BEAULIEU (S. DE).

Plan (Pierre Paul). J. Callot, maître graveur, 1593–1635, suivi d'un cat. chronolog. n. éd. rev. &c., ornée de 96 estampes &c. 8°. Brux. 1914

Planché (Eliza). A hasty conclusion: Burletta. [P2581]. s8°. *Webster.* 1838

Planché (James Robinson).
Captain of the watch. Farce. [P2581]. s8°. *Lacy. n.d.*
Charles XII. Drama. [P2581]. s8°. N.Y. *French. n.d.*
The follies of a night. Comedy. [P2581]. s8°. *Lacy.* [1854]
Grist to the mill. Comic drama. [P2581]. s8°. *Lacy.* [1856]
The Jacobite. Comic drama [P2581]. s8°. *Lacy.* [1854]
Love & fortune. Dram. tableau. [P2581]. s8°. *Lacy.* [1859]
The merchant's wedding. Comedy. [P2863]. 8°. 1828
My heart's idol. Comedy. [P2581]. s8°. [1850]
The mysterious lady. Comedy. [P2581]. s8°. *Lacy.* [1853]
Not a bad judge. Comic drama. [P2581]. s8°. *Lacy.* [1853]
Somebody else. Farce. [P2581]. s8°. *Lacy.* [1853]

Planck (Max). Origin & development of the quantum theory. Tr. H. T. Clarke & L. Silberstein. 8°. O. 1922
A survey of physics: lect. &c. Tr. R. Jones & D. H. Williams. 8°. [1925]
Das Wesen d. Lichts. Vortrag. 2e, unveränd. A. [P2509]. 8°. 1920

Pläne u. Versuche z. Währungssanierung. Beitr. v. E. Wilmersdörffer, R. Kiliani &c. [V. f. Sozialpol., B165ii]. 8°. München. 1923

Planiscig (Leo). Die Estensische Kunstsamml. B1. [Kunsthist. Museum in Wien]. 4°. Wien. 1919

***Plant** (The) of renown, *n.d., see* HAWKER (R.)

Plant (Harold J.), *see* NOKE (C. J.) & H. J. P. Pottery, 1924.

Planté (Francis), *see* DANDELOT (A.) F. P.: une belle vie d'artiste, 1920.

Plantenga (J. H.) L'architecture relig. dans l'anc. Duché de Brabant, 1598–1713. la8°. La Haye. 1926

Plantin (Christoffel). Sept études publ. [sous la dir. de M. Sabbe] à l'occas. du 4e cent. d. C. P. [1520–1920]. 4°. Brux. [1920]
see ANTWERP. Cat. of the Plantin-Moretus Museum, by M. Rooses, 3rd ed., 1921.
,, SABBE (M.) C. P., 1920.
,, THESAURUS Theutonicae ling. &c. [*pref. by* P.], 1573.

Plants. The exploitation of plants; [*by var. a.*], 1917, *see* OLIVER (F. W.), *ed.*

Planudes (Maximus), *see* FREYTAG (F. G.) Narr. M. P. de insigni Aesopi deform., 1717.

Plarre (Ernst Martin). Diss. de justitia armorum Cebennensium. Praes. J. C. Becmano. [P2742]. s4°. Francof. 1704

Plaskitt (F. J. W.) Microscopic fresh water life. 8°. 1926

Plassmann (J. O.) Gesch. d. Stadt. Münster in Westfalen. 8°. Münster i. W. [1925]

Plat (*Sir* **Hugh**), *see* PLATT (*Sir* H.)

Plate, *river.* *Appeal on behalf of Brit. subjects in the River P., 1846, *see* APPEAL.

Platen (August, *Graf* **v.),** *1796–1835.* Der Briefwechsel. Hrsg. P. Bornstein. B3. 8°. München. 1921

Platen (Leontine v. Winterfeld-), *see* WINTERFELD-PLATEN (L. v.)

Plater (William Edward) & H. J. White.
Grammar of the Vulgate. 8°. O. 1926

Platina (Baptista). The lives of the popes: to the accession of Gregory VII. Tr. by W. Benham. [Anc. & Mod. Lib. of Theolog. Lit.] 2v. 8°. [1888]

***Platitudes** (The) of a pessimist, 1897, *see* LONGUEVILLE (T.)

Plato, *Eleus.*
The Hippias major, attrib. to P. Intr. essay &c. by D. Tarrant. 8°. C. 1928
The Laws of P. Text ed. w. intr. notes &c., by E. B. England. [Publ. of Univ. of M'ter, Class. Ser. 3, 4]. 2v. s8°. M'ter. 1921
Phaedo. Ed. w. intr. & notes by J. Burnet. s8°. O. 1911
The Philebus. Rev. text & Eng. notes by E. Poste. 8°. O. 1860
Politia sive de republica lib. 10. Rec. G. Stallbaum. [Opera, v3]. ed. nova. 2v *in* 1. 8°. Gothae. 1858

TRANSLATIONS: WORKS.
Works. A new & lit. version. Tr. H. Cary. v1, Apology of Socrates, Crito &c. s8°. *Bohn.* 1861
Œuvres compl. Texte établi & tr. par M. Croiset &c. t1, 2, 3i, ii, 4i, 8i–iii, 10, 13i. 8°. 1920–26
P. [Text], w. Eng. tr. [Loeb Class. Lib.] [v]2–6, 8–10. s8°. 1921–27
2, Theaetetus—Sophist; by H. N. Fowler.
3, The Statesman—Philebus; by H. N. Fowler—Ion; by W. R. M. Lamb.
4, Laches—Protagoras—Meno—Euthydemus; by W. R. M. Lamb.
5, Lysis—Symposium—Gorgias; by W. R. M. Lamb.
6, Cratylus—Parmenides—Greater Hippias—Lesser Hippias; by H. N. Fowler.
8, Charmides—Alcibiades 1 & 2—Hipparchus—The lovers—Theages—Minos—Epinomis; by W. R. M. Lamb.
9, 10, Laws; by R. G. Bury, v1, 2.

TWO OR MORE WORKS.
Euthyphro, Apology of Socrates, Timaeus, *in Armenian. Pref. signed* A. Souqrean]. 8°. i Venedig. 1877
Euthyphro, Apology of Socrates, & Crito. Ed. w. notes by J. Burnet. s8°. O. 1924
[Laws & Minos *in Armenian; b. w. h.* Euthyphro &c., 1877]. 8°. i Venedig. 1890

EPINOMIS.
The Epinomis. Tr. w. intr. & notes by J. Harward. s8°. O. 1928

PHAEDO.
The Phaedo. Tr. Hon. P. Duncan. s8°. O. 1928

REPUBLIC.
Republic. Tr. H. Spens. [Everyman's Lib.] [repr.] s8°. [1908]
Republic. Tr. J. U. Davies & D. J. Vaughan. [Golden Treasury Ser.] [repr.] s8°. 1923
Republic. Tr. A. D. Lindsay. 4th ed., w. rev. text & enl. intr. s8°. 1926

SYMPOSIUM [OR, CONVIVIUM].
Symposium or Supper. Tr. F. Birrell & S. Leslie. s8°. [1925]

TIMAEUS LOCRUS, *see* TIMAEUS, *Locrus.*

REFERENCES.
see ADAM (J.) Nuptial number of P.: solution &c., 1891.
,, ALCINOUS. Liber de doctrina P., 1497.
,, ARNIM (H. v.) Sprachl. Forsch. z. Chronol. d. Platon. Dialoge, 1912.
,, BISINGER (J.) Der Agrarstaat in P.'s Gesetzen, 1925.
,, CUOCO (V.) P. in Italia (*fiction*), v2, 1924.
,, DUPRÉEL (E.) Légende Socratique & sources de P., 1922.
,, FICINO (M.) Comm. s. i 10 dial. del giusto, tr. C. Spontone, 1590.
,, FRANK (E.) P. u. d. sogen. Pythagoreer, 1923.
,, FRIEDLÄNDER (P.) Der grosse Alcibiades: e. Weg zu P., 2t, 1921–23.
,, GROTE (G.) P. & o. companions of Sokrates, 2nd ed., 3v, 1867.
,, HØFFDING (H.) Bemærk. om Parmenides, 1920.
,, —— Bemerk. ü. Parmenides, 1921.
,, —— P.'s Bøger om Staten, 1923.
,, HUDE (C.) Oraisons funèbres de Lysias & de P., 1917.
,, LEVI (A.) Il concetto del tempo &c. e dell' essere n. filosofia di P., 1920.
,, —— Sulla interpretaz. immanent. d. filos. di Platone, 1921.
,, MORE (P. E.) Religion of P., 1921.
,, NATORP (P.) Über P.'s Ideenlehre, 2e A., 1925.
,, NETTLESHIP (R. L.) Lect. of the Republic of P., 2nd ed., repr., 1925.
,, PARKER (S.) Free & impartial censure of P. philos. &c., 1667.
,, REINHARD (L.) Anakoluthe bei P., 1920.
,, SANTAYANA (G.) Platonism & the spiritual life, 1927.
,, SPEUSIPPUS. Liber de P. definitionibus &c., 1497.
,, TAYLOR (A. E.) Comm. on P.'s Timaeus, 1928.
,, —— Platonism & its infl., 1925.
,, —— P.'s biog. of Socrates, 1917.
,, —— P., the man & h. work, 1926.
,, URWICK (E. J.) The message of P.: re-interp. of the "Republic," 1920.

Platonov (Sergei Fedorovich). Борис Годунов. 8°. П. 1921
Иван Грозный. s8°. Берлинъ. 1924
Петр Великий. 8°. Ленинград. 1926
Hist. of Russia. Tr. E. Aronsberg. Ed. F. A. Golder. 8°. 1925
Platt (A. E.) Hist. of the parish & grammar school of Sedbergh, Yorks. 8°. 1876
Platt (Arthur).
Nine essays. Pref. by A. E. Housman. 8°. C. 1927
Platt (Charles). The psychology of social life. 8°. [1922]
The psychology of thought & feeling. 8°. N.Y. 1921
Things you don't know about cats. s8°. [1924]
Platt (George Moreton) & J. W. Morkill.
Records of the parish of Whitkirk. 4°. Leeds. 1892
Platt (*Sir* Hugh) [PLAT]. The jewel house of art & nature. Added, Disc. of minerals &c. by D. B. s4°. 1653
Platt (*Sir* Thomas Comyn-), *see* COMYN-PLATT (*Sir* T.)
Plattard (Jean). Guillaume Budé, 1468–1540 & les orig. de l'humanisme franç. 8°. 1923
La vie & l'œ. de Scévole de Sainte-Marthe (1536–1623). 8°.1924
Platten (Fritz). Die Reise Lenins durch Deutschland [1917, *w. art^s. by* Krupskaja, Radek & Zinovev]. 8°. [1924]
Platthy (Mathias). Primordia sanctae cathol. &c. eccl. e 4 prim. sec. monumentis propos.
5p [pl, 2 & 4, 5 *have cont. pagin.*] fol. Budae. 1790
Platus (Hieronymus), *Jesuit.* The happiness of a religious state. Wr. in Lat. Tr. [*by* H. More].
s4°. *n.p.* [Saint Omer?]. 1632
Plaumann (Gerhard). Der Idioslogos: Untersuch. z. Finanzverwaltung Ägypt. in hellenist. u. röm. Zeit, 1919, *see* KÖNIGL. PREUSS. AKAD. D. WISS. Abhdl. (Phil.-hist. Klasse), 1918.
***Plausible** (The) arguments of a Rom. priest from antiquity answered &c., 1735, *see* COMBER (T.), *D.D.*
Plautus (Titus Maccius).
Plautus. With Eng. tr. by P. Nixon. [Loeb Class. Lib.]
[v]3. s8°. 1924
3, The merchant—The braggart warrior—The haunted house—The Persian.
Pseudo-Plaute. Le prix des ânes (Asinaria). Texte ét. & tr. par L. Havet & A. Freté. [Coll. des univ. de France]. 8°. [1925]
3 plays. The slip-knot (Rudens)—The crock of gold (Aulularia)—The trickster (Pseudolus). Tr. F. A. Wright & H. L. Rogers. [Broadway Trans.] 8°. [1925]
see ESTIENNE (H.) De Latinitate; de Plauti Latin. &c., 1576.
„ FRÄNKEL (E.) Plautinisches im P., 1922.
„ LEFFINGWELL (G. W.) Social &c. life at Rome in time of P. &c., 1918.
„ LODGE (G.) Lexicon Plautinum, v1, 1924.
„ MICHAUT (G. M. A.) Hist. de la comédie rom., p2, P., 2t, 1920.
Plaw (John). Sketches for country houses, villas &c. 4°. 1800
Player (Cyril Arthur). Arms—& the men. Glimpses at Washington Conf. [P2590]. s8°. Detroit. 1922
Playfair (*Sir* Nigel). Story of the Lyric Theatre, Hammersmith. Intr. by A. Bennett, epilogue by A. A. Milne, contrib. &c. by St. J. Ervine &c. la8°. 1925
Playfair (Philip), *of the Inner Temple, ps.* The Queen & her pawns against the King [George IV] & his pieces.
[P425]. 8°. 1820
Playfair (*Sir* Robert Lambert). Hist. of Arabia Felix or Yemen &c. [Bombay. Sel. f. the Records of the Brit. Govt., N.S., 49]. la8°. Bombay. 1859
see MURRAY'S HANDBOOKS. Algeria &c.; by R. L. P., 1895.
—— **& A. C. L. G. Günther.** The fishes of Zanzibar. 4°. 1866
Playfere (Thomas), *D.D.* The meane in mourning. A Sermon [*on Luke xxiii,* 28. *Foll. by* The pathway to perfection. A Sermon (*on Philip. III,* 14), *sep. tp., pagin. cont.*]. s8°. 1616
Nine sermons [*Foll. by* The sicke mans couch, *w. sep. pagin.*]
s8°. C. 1612
Playford (Henry). *The divine companion; or David's Harp new tun'd. Coll. of psalms, hymns & anthems.
4th ed. w. adds. s8°. 1722
Playford (John).
*The dancing master. [16th ed., *imperf.*] obl. s8°. 1718
see SHARP (C. J.) Country dance bk., p2, 3, 6, The Eng. dancing master, by J. P., 1927.
Playne (Arthur Twisden). Hist. of the parishes of Minchinhampton & Avening. la8°. Gloucester. 1915
Playne (Caroline E.) The neuroses of nations. 8°. [1925]
Plays of to-day. 2v. 8°. [1925]
***Plea** (The) of presbytery &c., 1843, *see* ULSTER.
***Pleasaunt** (The) hist. of Lazarillo de Tormes, *see* HURTADO DE MENDOZA (D.)

Pleasing instructor (The) or entertaining moralist, 1806, *see* FISHER (A.)
Plédy (Lucien). Brouage: ville forte, 16 & 17 siècles—Marie Mancini à Brouage. Préf. de M. Tinayre.
8°. La Rochelle. [1925]
Pleekschan (Jan), *see* RAINIS (J.)
Plehn (Hans). Bismarcks auswärtige Politik nach d. Reichsgründung. Vorwort v. O. Hoetzsch. 8°. München. 1920
Pléiade (La). [*Poems by* Ctsse. de Noailles, P. Camo, C. Derennes, J. Gasquet &c., *w. pref.*, Du rôle positif & de l'avenir de la poësie]. 8°. 1921
see NERI (F.) Chiabrera e la P. franc., 1920.
„ NOLHAC (P. DE). Un poète rhénan ami de la P., P. Melissus, 1923.
Pleito del matrimonio entre T. Guerrero y R. Sepúlveda, 1880, *see* GUERRERO (T.) & R. SEPÚLVEDA.
Plekhanov (Georgii Valentinovich). Годъ на Родинѣ. Полное соб. статей &c., 1917–18. [*w. short biog.*] 2t *in* 1v. 8°. [1921]
Новый походъ противъ русской соціаль-демократіи.
[P2716]. s8°. Женева. 1897
Русскій рабочій въ револ. движеніи. изд. 2^e. [P2715]. 8°. *n.p.* 1902
Vademecum для редакціи "Рабочаго дѣла." Съ предислов. Г. П.
[P2716]. s8°. Женева. 1900
Plener (Ernst, *Frhr.* v.) Erinnerungen.
B2. Parlamentar. Tätigkeit, 1873–91. 8°. St. 1921
***Plenipo** & the devil! An infernal poem. By the a. of the House that Jack built [W. Hone?]. [*A satire on King George IV*]. 2nd ed. [P425]. 8°. 1820
Plessis-Richelieu (François du), *see* RICHELIEU (F. DU P., *seign.* DE).
Plettenberg (*Count* Wolter von), *see* ARBUSOW (L.) W. v. P. u. d. Untergang d. Deut. Ordens in Preussen, 1919.
Plettenbergius (Hunoldus). Notitia congregationum & tribunalium Curiae Romanae. s8°. Hildesii. 1693
Plew (Joannes). Quellenuntersuchungen z. Gesch. d. Kaisers Hadrian, nebst Anhange ü. d. Mon. Ancyranum u. d. kais. Autobiog. 8°. Str. 1890
Plimmer (Henry George).
Omariana. [P2862]. *p.p.* 8°. *n.p. n.d.*
Plimmer (Robert Henry Aders), *see* PLIMMER (V. G.) & R. H. A. P. Vitamins &c., 1922.
Plimmer (*Mrs.* Violet Geraldine) & R. H. A. Plimmer.
Vitamins & the choice of food. 8°. 1922
Pliny, *the elder.* Die geog. Bücher (II, 242–VI Schluss) d. Nat. Hist., m. krit. Apparat hrsg. v. D. Detlefsen. [Quellen u. Forsch. z. alt. Gesch. u. Geog., H9]. 8°. 1904
see DETLEFSEN (D.) Die Anordnung d. geogr. Bücher d. P. u. i. Quellen, 1909.
„ TOPSELL (E.) Elizabethan Zoo: [sel. f. P. Holland's tr. of P. 1601 &c.], 1926.
Pliny, *the younger.* Epistolarum libri decem, in quibus multae habentur epistolae non ante impressae. Tum Graeca corr. &c. [*Imperfect*]. s8°. [Venetiis, *In aed. Aldi &c.* 1508]
Sel. letters. Text, w. notes. Ed. A. J. Church & W. J. Brodribb. 3rd ed. s8°. 1877
TRANSLATIONS.
Œuvres; tr. M. de Sacy avec le texte latin. n. éd. 3t. s8°. 1820
Lettres. Texte établi & tr. par A. M. Guillemin. [Coll. des univ. de Fr.] t1, 2, livres 1–6. 8°. 1927
see LOWE (E. A.) & E. K. Rand. A 6th-c. fragment of the Letters of P.: a st. of 6 leaves of an uncial MS. in P. Morgan Libr., 1922.
„ OTTO (W.) Z. Lebensgesch. d. jüng. P., 1919.
„ —— Zur Prätur d. jungeren P., 1923.
Plitts (Johann Jacob). Bedanken ü. diejen. Menschen welche bald nach ihrem Tode wieder auferwecket.
s8°. Marburg. 1752
Plodi. *Плоды ученія Л. Н. Толстого.
изд. 2^oe. 2кн. [P643]. s8°. Москва. 1896
Plomer (Henry Robert). A dict. of the printers & booksellers in Eng., Scot. & Ireland, 1668–1725. By P., w. help of H. G. Aldis &c. Ed. A. Esdaile. [Bibliog. Soc.]
8°. O. 1922
Eng. printers' ornaments. 4°. 1924
The Kentish feast: Hon. Soc. of Natives of Kent, 1657–1701, *&* Assoc. of Men of Kent &c. [P2786]. 8°. Canterbury. 1916
William Caxton (1424–91). 8°. [1925]
—— **& T. P. Cross.** Life & corr. of L. Bryskett. [Mod. Philol. Monogr., Univ. of Chicago]. 8°. Chicago. [1927]
Plooij (D.), *see* HARRIS (J. R.) & S. K. JONES. The Pilgrim press; w. chap. on locat. of press at Leyden, by D. P., 1922.

Plopper (Clifford H.) Chinese religion seen thr. the proverb. [v]1. 8°. Shanghai. 1926

Ploshinsky (L. O.) Городское или средни состоянiе русскаго народа въ его историч. развитiи. 8°. С.-П. [1852]

*Plot & passion: drama, 1853 ?, *see* TAYLOR (T.)

Plotinus [PLOTIN].

TRANSLATIONS.

Les Ennéades. Tr., accomp. de sommaires, de notes &c., & préc. de la vie de P. avec des fragments de Porphyre &c., par M. N. Bouillet. 3t. 8°. 1857–61

Ennéades. Texte établi & tr. par E. Bréhier. [Coll. des univ. de Fr.] t1–14. 8°. 1924–27

Plotinus. Tr. S. Mackenna. [v2–4]. la8°. 1921–26

2, Psychic & physical treatises, comp. the 2nd & 3rd Enneads.
3, On the nature of the soul, 4th Ennead.
4, The divine mind, 5th Ennead.

see CUMONT (F.) Culte égypt. & le mysticisme de P., 1922.
,, DODDS (E. R.) Sel. passages illust. Neoplatonism; tr. [*f.* P. &c.], 1923.
,, HEINEMANN (F.) P. Forschungen, 1921.
,, INGE (W. R.) The philos. of P., 2nd ed., 2v, 1923.
,, MÜLLER (H. F.) Dionysios, Proklos, P., 1918.

Plott (Thomas) & T. Chudleigh, *Eng. envoys at the Hague.* Dispatches of T. P., 1681–82 & T. C., 1682–85. Ed. F. A. Middlebush. [Rijks Gesch. Publ., Kl. ser., 22]. la8°. s'Gravenhage. 1926

Plötz (Alfred). Sozialanthropologie, *see* HINNEBERG (P.) Die Kultur d. Gegenwart, T3v, 1923.

Plowden (Charles). Remarks on a book ent. Memoirs of G. Panzani. Prec. by an address to Rev. J. Berington. 8°. Liege. 1794

Plowden (Edmund), *serjeant-at-Law.* Abridgment des touts les cases reportez alarge per Mons. P., ovesq, les Exceptions al pleadings & leur responses &c. Composee &c. p T. A[she]. s8°. Londini. [1600 ?]

Plowden (Francis), *LL.D.* An hist. letter to Sir J. C. Hippesley on Catholic claims. 8°. D. 1814

,, ,, A second hist. l. [*b. w. above*]. 8°. Paris. 1815

Plowman (Max). Intr. to st. of Blake. s8°. 1927

Pluche (Noël Antoine). The hist. of the heavens acc. to notions of poets & philosophers comp. w. the doctrines of Moses; orig. of idolatry &c. Tr. by J. B. de Freval. 3rd ed. 2v. s8°. 1752

*Spectacle de la nature: or Nature display'd. Tr. by Mr. Humphreys &c. 7v. [v1, 3rd ed.; v2, 3, 2nd ed.] 8°. 1736–48

The truth of the gospel demonstrated. Pref.: a prelim. disc. [Tr.] 2v. 8°. 1751

[*Pagin. & register are cont. throughout.*]

Plucknett (Theodore F. T.) The Lancastrian constit., *see* POLLARD (A. F.) Tudor st., 1924.

Statutes & th. interp. in 1st half of 14th c. 8°. C. 1922

Plumb (Glenn Edward) & W. G. Roylance. Industrial democracy: a plan for its achievement. 8°. N.Y. 1923

Plume (La), revue de littérat., de crit., & d'art indépendants bi-mensuelle. Année 1–8, 1889–96. 8°. 1889–96

Plumier (Charles).

Nova plantarum Amer. genera. 4°. Parisiis. 1703

Plummer (Charles). Bethada Náem nÉrenn. Lives of Irish saints. Ed. w. intr. tr., &c. by C. P. 2v. O. 1922

Irish litanies. Text & tr. Ed. C. P. [Henry Bradshaw Soc., v62]. 8°. 1925

Miscellanea hagiographica Hibernica: vitae ined. SS. Mac Creiche—Naile—Cranat. Rec. &c. C. P., acced. Cat. hagiogr. Hibern. [Soc. des Bollandistes]. 8°. Bruxelles. 1925

On colophons & marginalia of Irish scribes. [From Proc. of Brit. Acad. P2834]. 8°. [1926]

Plummer (Henry Crozier). An introd. treatise on dynamical astronomy. la8°. C. 1918

Plumon (Eugène). Guides techniques Plumon. Dict. méthod. illust. en plusiers langues. v1, 3, 15i, 28. s8°. [1919–21]

1, Les transports [*Fr. & Eng.*]
3, L'usine [*Fr. & Eng.*]
15i, Indust. textiles & connexes [*Fr., Eng., Germ., Ital.*]
28, Le béton armé [*Fr., Eng., Ital.*]

Plumptre (Anne). Narr. of 3 yrs. residence in France, 1802–05: incl. partic. resp. early life of the Fr. Emperor. 3v. 8°. 1810

Plumptre (James). Four disc. on subjects rel. to the amusement of the stage. 8°. C. 1809

Plunket (Ierne L.) & R. B. Mowat. Hist. of Europe. The Middle Ages, by I. L. P. Europe & the mod. world, 1492–1914, by R. B. Mowat. s8°. O. 1927

Plunkett (*Rt. Hon. Sir* Horace Curzon). The rural life problem of the U.S. [repr.] s8°. N.Y. 1913

see AGRICULTURAL. *A. co-operation, w. intr. by Sir H. P., 1925.

Plüschow (*Kap.-Lt.* Gunther). My escape f. Donington Hall, prec. by acc. of the siege of Kiao-Chow in 1915. Tr. P. de Chary. s8°. 1922

Plutarch.

Liber de sera Numinis vindicta [*Gr. & Lat.*] Acc. fragm. Rec. &c. D. Wyttenbach. 8°. Lugd. Bat. 1772

De liberorum institutione [*Greek. Pref. by Melanchthon in Latin*]. s4°. Parisiis. 1547

TRANSLATIONS.

Lives, w. an Eng. tr. by B. Perrin. [Loeb Class. Lib.] [v]9–11. s8°. 1920–26

Lycurgus; tr., *see* MORLEY (H.) Ideal commonwealths, 1885.

Moralia. [Text], w. Eng. tr. by F. C. Babbitt. [Loeb Class. Lib.] v1. s8°. 1927

The Philosophie commonlie called the Morals. Tr. by Philemon Holland. fol. 1603

The Roman questions of P. Tr. w. essays & comm. by H. J. Rose. 8°. O. 1924

see HIRZEL (R.) Plutarch, 1912.
,, WEGEHAUPT (H.) Florent. P.-palimpsest, 1914.

Plütscho (Heinrich), *see* ZIEGENBALG (B.) & H. P. Merckwürd. Nachricht, Trangebar, 1708–17.

P——m (A. R.) *Burning spear: exper. of Mr. J. Lavender in time of war; recorded by A. R. P——m., 1919, *see* BURNING.

Pniower (Otto). Goethes Faust: Zeugnisse &c. zu s. Entstehungsgesch. 8°. 1899

Pobedonostsev (Konstantin Petrovich). L'autocratie russe: C. P., procureur gén. du Saint-Synode. Méms. polit., corr. offic. &c., 1881–94. 8°. 1927

Истор. изслѣдованія и статьи (17 & 18 c.) 8°. С.-П. 1876

К. П. П. и его корреспонденты. Письма и записки с предисловием М. Н. Покровского. t1i, ii. 8°. Москва. 1923

Письма П. К. Александру III. [Центрархив]. т1, с предисл. М. Н. Покровского. 8°. Москва. 1925

Pocci (Franz, *Graf.* v.) Fest-Kalender in Bildern u. Liedern v. F. v. P., G. Görres &c. [15H. *in* 1*v*. H1. 2e A.] la8°. München. [1835–36]

Geschichten u. Lieder mit Bildern. B1, 2. 8°. [1843]

Pochhammer (Hans). Graf Spee's letzte Fahrt. Erinnerungen an das Kreuzergeschwader. s8°. 1918

Pocket. *A new pocket dict. of Eng. & Dutch lang. Stereotype ed. [2*p*. (p2, Nederduit.-Eng.)] s8°. Leipsic. 1894

*Pocket (A) hymn book for use of Xtns. &c., 1785, *see* WESLEY (J.)

Pocock (Edward), *the elder* [POCOCKIUS].

A comm. on Hosea. fol. O. 1685

A comm. on Joel. fol. O. 1691

A comm. on Micah. fol. O. 1677

Pocock (George), *of Bristol, the elder.* A statement conn. w. ejectment of ministers f. Wesleyan Meth. in Bristol, in 1820. [P449]. 8°. Bristol. [1820]

Pocock (*Adm. Sir* George), *see* ORSBRIDGE (P.) *Hist. view of exped. of H.M.'s ships &c. agst. the Havannah, under command of Sir G. P. &c., 1762.

Pocock (Reginald Innes). A monographic revision of the monkeys of the genus Cercopithecus [*Extr. f.* Proc. of Zool. Soc. 1907]. [P2601]. 8°. 1907

Pocock (Roy Woodhouse), *see* SHERLOCK (R. L.) & R. W. P. Geol. of co. around Hertford, 1924.

—— & D. A. Wray. Geology of the co. around Wem. With contrib. by T. C. Cantrill. [Mem. of G.S.] 8°. 1925

Pocock (Theodore Innes). Geol. of co. around Macclesfield, Congleton, Crewe & Middlewich. With contrib. by G. Barrow &c. & notes on fossils by E. T. Newton. [Mems. of G.S.] 8°. 1906

see GIBSON (W.), T. I. P. &c. Geol. of south. part of Derbys. &c. coal-field &c., 1908.

Pococke (Edward), *canon of Christ Church, see* POCOCK (ED.), *the elder.*

Podczaszynski (Michel). Fragm. sur la litt. anc. de la Pologne, *see* MALTE-BRUN (C.) Tableau, 1830.

Podesta (Francesco). I Genovesi e le pescherie di corallo nei mari di Sardegna, *see* REGIA DEP. DI ST. PATRIA. Misc., t37, 1901.

Podlaha (Anton). *Works in* BOHEMIA. Topographie d. hist. u. Kunstdenkmale.
The following " Polit. Bezirke " &c. *are by* A. P.
Karolinenthal, 1903. [15.]
Kralowitz, 1916. [37.]
Melnik, 1901. [6.]
Mühlhausen, 1901. [5.]
Prag: Hradschin, 1903–4.
Příbram, 1902. [13.]
Rokytzan, 1901. [9.]
Selčan, 1899. [3.]
Weinberge, 1916. [28.]

Podligailov (P. N.) Мѣстное управленіе въ Россіи. 8°. С.-П. 1884

Podvinsky (Yu.) 100 лѣтъ борьбы Польскаго народа за свободу. [P2450]. 8°. Москва. 1907

Poe (Edgar Allen). The bells & o. poems. Illust. by E. Dulac. 4°. [1912]
Poet. works. With notice by J. Hannay. s8°. 1853
see ALLEN (H.) Israfel: Life & times of E. A. P., 2v, 1927.
,, KRUTCH (J. W.) E. A. P.: st. in genius, 1926.
,, QUICKENS (Q.), *ps.* English notes [*attrib. to* E. A. P.], 1920.

Poebel (Arno).
Histor. texts. [Pa.: Univ. of]. 4°. Phila. 1914

Poems.
*Devotional p.; by a clergyman of the country, 1699, *see* DEVOTIONAL.
P. about birds, 1922, *see* MASSINGHAM (H. J.), *ed.*
*P. by a slave in Cuba; tr. R. R. Madden &c., 1840, *see* M. (J. F.)
*P. by J. D., 1633, *see* DONNE (J.)
P. consisting chiefly of tr. f. the Asiatick languages &c., 1772, *see* JONES (*Sir* W.)
P. f. Punch, 1909–20, 1922, *see* PUNCH.
*P. of Amer. patriotism, 1882, *see* MATTHEWS (J. B.)
P. of to-day; an anthology. Publ. for the Eng. Assoc. s2. s8°. 1922
" " ....[repr.] 2s. s8°. 1922
*P. on sev. occasions, 1709, *see* PRIOR (M.)
*P. on sev. occasions: The garden &c., 1719, *see* LUX (W.)
*P. on sev. subjects, by a Land-waiter of Poole, 1741, *see* PRICE (H.)
*P. upon sev. occas., 2nd ed., 1716, *see* GRANVILLE (G.)

Poerio, *The family of, see* CROCE (B.) Una famiglia di patrioti, 1919.

Poesie. *P. di div. autori. s8°. Londra. 1782
P. lombarde ined. del sec. 13, 1856, *see* BIONDELLI (B.), *ed.*
*P. scelte da un canzoniere ined. d. sec. 16. [Nozze Venezze-Mocenigo. N140]. 8°. Padova. 1819

***Poésies** diverses, 1760, *see* FREDERICK II, *of Prussia.*

Poestion (Joseph Calasanz). Lehrbuch d. schwed. Sprache. 2e, verb. u. verm. A. s8°. Wien. [1897]

Poetæ [POETARUM]. Poetæ Latini aevi Carolini. [Mon. Germ. hist.]
t4ii & iii [*in* 1v], rec. K. Strecker. 4°. Berolini. 1923
Poetae minores Graeci, v1, 2, 1814–16, *see* GAISFORD (T.), *ed.*
Poetarum scenic. Graec. Aeschyli &c. fabulae superstites &c., ed. 5a, 1869, *see* DINDORF (C. W.)
Poetarum vet. eccl. opera Xtna &c., 1564, *see* FABRICIUS (G.)

Poëte (Marcel). Paris: l'art à P. s8°. [1924]
Paris: Louvre & Tuileries, places & avenues, mon. divers. 8°. [1925]
Paris: les thermes & les arènes, le Palais & Notre Dame, anc. églises. s8°. [1925]
Une vie de cité: Paris de sa naissance à nos jours. t1, 2 *&* Album. la8°. 1924–27
see SELLIER (H.), A. BRUGGEMAN & M. P. Paris pend. la Guerre, 1926.

Poètes. *Nos poètes, 2t, *n.d. &* 1925, *see* NOS.

Poeti. Poeti d'oggi, 1900–20, 1920; 2a ed. (–1925), 1925, *see* PAPINI (G.) & P. PANCRAZI, *edd.*
Поэты пушкинской поры сборникъ стиховъ, 1919, *see* VERKHOVSKY (Y. N.), *ed.*

***Poetical** dict. (The), 4v, 1761, *see* GOLDSMITH (O.)

Poetry.
P. of common life: sel. &c., 1844, *see* ARNOLD (T.)
P. of Irish hist., 1927, *see* BROWN (S. J.), *ed.*
P. of to-day, 1920, &c., *see* POETRY REVIEW (THE).
Pure p.: an anthology, 1924, *see* MOORE (G.), *ed.*

Poetry review, The. v12–18. 8°. 1921–27
Poetry of to-day. The Poetry review new verse suppl., 1920. 8°. 1920
" " A quarterly " extra " of the Poetry review. n. ser. v1–3. 8°. 1925–27

Poets. Poets of the 19th cent., 1892, *see* WILLMOTT (R. E. A.)
Poets of the Wight, 1922, *see* ARNELL (C. J.), *ed.*
Poets' (The) year, 1922, *see* SHARPLEY (A.)

Poeziya. Поэзія большевистск. дней. s8°. Берлинъ. 1921

Poffenberger (Albert Theodore). Applied psychology. 8°. 1927

Pogány (Josef).
Der weisse Terror in Ungarn. s8°. Wien. 1920

Poggendorff (Johann Christian). Biogr.-literar. Hdwbch. f. Mathematik &c. Hrsg. v. d. Sächs. Akad. d. Wiss. zu Leipzig. B5, 1904–22. Redig. v. P. Weinmeister. la8°. L. 1926

Poggi (Giovanni). Il Reliquiario " del libretto " nel Battistero fiorentino. [P2621]. 8°. Firenze. [1917]

Poggi (Vittorio).
Works in REGIA DEP. DI STORIA PATRIA. Misc.
L'atto di fondaz. del monastero di S. Quintino di Spigno (991), 1901. [37.]
Commem. di M. Staglieno, 1910. [45.]
Cronotassi dei princ. magistrati che ressero &c. il comune di Savona, 1905–13. [41, 45, 47.]
I presunti avanzi del mausoleo di Gastone di Foix in Savona, 1894. [31.]

Pogosky (Aleksandr Thomich).
Злодѣй и петька. Повѣсть. 3e изд. [P846]. s8°. С.-П. 1888
Чему быть того не миновать &c. изд. 2e. [P846]. 8°. С.-П. 1875

Pogue (Joseph Ezekiel), *see* GILBERT (C. G.), J. E. P. &c. Mineral indust. of the U.S., 8p, 1917–23.

Pohlenz (Maximilian). Staatsgedanke u. Staatslehre d. Griechen. s8°. L. 1923

Poidebard (A.)
Au carrefour des routes de Perse. [Voyages]. s8°. 1923

Poincaré (Henri). Œuvres. t1, 2. 4°. 1916–28
1, Publ. P. Appell, avec collab. de J. Drach.
2, Publ. G. Darboux, avec collab. de N. E. Nörlund & E. Lebon.
Calcul des probabilités. Rédact. de A. Quiquet. 2e éd. rev. & augm. [n. tirage]. 8°. 1912 [1923]
Sur la dynamique de l'électron. [Estr., Rendiconti d. Circolo Matemat. di P., t21]. la8°. [Palermo. 1905]

Poincaré (Raymond Nicolas Landry), *president of the French Republic.*
Au service de la France. 9 années de souvs. [t]1–4. 8°. 1926–27
Ernest Renan. s8°. 1923
Hist. politique: chroniques de quinzaine. [t1–3], mars 1920–sep. 1921. s8°. [1920–21]
Messages, discours &c. [t2, 3], 13 nov. 1918–fév. 1920. s8°. 1920–21
Les origines de la Guerre. s8°. [1921]
The origins of the War. [Tr.] 8°. 1922
see FOCH (*mar.* F.) Disc. de récep.; réponse de R. P., 1920.
,, HUDDLESTON (S.) P.: biog. portrait, 1924.
,, SEEHOLZER (H.) R. P., 1922.
,, THIBAUDET (A.) Les princes lorrains [P. &c.], 1924.

Poinsot (Antoine Edmond) [*ps.* GEORGES D'HEILLY; *or* G. D'HEYLLI]. Le livre rouge de la Commune. Extr. du Journal Officiel. s8°. 1871

Poinssot (Louis) & R. Lantier. Les mosaïques de la " maison d'Ariadne " à Carthage, *see* ACAD. DES INSCR.: FOND. PIOT. Mon., t27, 1924.

***Point** (The) of church-unity & schism discuss'd, 1679, *see* CORBET (J.)

Pointer (John), *see* BUCKLER (B.) *Compl. vindic. of the mallard of All Souls College agst. suggest. of Mr. P., 1750; 2nd ed., 1751.

Pointner (Andy). Die Werke d. florent. Bildhauers Agostino d'Antonio di Duccio. la8°. Str. 1909

Poiret (Pierre).
Bibliotheca mysticorum selecta. Præm. J. Gärden Diss. de theol. pacifica. [*a. c. b. w.* Arnold (G.) Hist. & descr. theol. myst. &c., 1702]. s8°. Amstelædami. 1708
De eruditione solida specialiora, 3 tractatibus. s4°. Amstelædami. 1707
Oeconomiae divinae libri sex. Tr. 2t *in* 1v. s4°. Francofurti. 1705
see BOURIGNON (A.) La vie de B., partie par P. P., 1683.
,, JÄGER (J. W.) Epist. ad P., 1708.
,, —— Examen theol., in quo P. Poireti placita revocantur, 1709.
,, —— Exam. theol. nov. & maxime Poireti &c., 1708.
,, —— Judicium de 2 adversariis J. Lookio & P. P., 1708.
,, —— Nova purgatio animae, excocta in cerebro P. P. &c., 1716.

Poirier (*Dom* Germain). Rapport de Dom P. sur la réunion à Paris des cartul. (1798) par H. O. [Extr. de la Revue des Bibl. P2469]. 8°. 1909

Poisson (Raymond). Le baron de la Crasse (1662)—Le poëte basque (1668)—Les faux Moscovites (1668), *see* FOURNEL (V.) Contemp. de Molière, t1, 1863.

Poitevin (Eugene) & R. P. D. Graham. Contrib. to the mineralogy of Black Lake area, Quebec, *see* CANADA: GEOLOG. SURVEY, 1918.

Poitiers. De l'Univ. de la ville de P., extr. d'un anc. ms. &c., 1643, *& o. wks.*, *see* BOUCHET (J.) Annales d'Aquitaine &c., 1644.
Rec. de docs. conc. la commune & la ville de P. t1, 1063–1327; par E. Audouin, avec intr. par P. Boissonnade. [Arch. hist. du Poitou, 44]. la8°. Poitiers. 1923
Poitiers (Aliénor de), *see* ELEANOR, *de Poitiers.*
Poitou (Eugène Louis). Spain & its people. [Tr.] 8°. 1873
Poizat (Alfred). Les poètes chrétiens: scènes de la vie litt. du 4e au 7e s. 8°. 1902
Pokorný (Fr.), *see* CÍSAŘ (J.) Czechoslovak Republ., its econ. &c.; coll. u. dir. of J. C. by F. P. &c., 1920.
Pokorny (Julius).
Altirische Gramm. [Samml. Göschen]. s8°. 1925
Pokrovsky (F. I.) Путешествіе въ Монголію и Китай Ивана Петлина 1618 г. [*Journey of V. Tyumenets. Extr. fr.* I. A. N. Извѣстія отд. русск. яз., t18, 1913. P2532]. 8°. [С.-П. 1914]
Pokrovsky (M. N.) Aus d. Geheim-Archiven des Zaren. [P2569]. s8°. 1919
Русская история с древ. времен.
4т (т1–3, изд. 6oe; 4, изд. 7oe). 8°. Ленинград. 1924–25
see RUSSIA. Царская Россия в Мир. Войне, т1, 1925.
Pokrovsky (V. I.) А. П. Сумароковъ, его жизнь и сочиненія. изд. 2e. la8°. Москва. 1911
Polaczek (Ernst). Strassburg. s8°. L. 1926
Polancus (Joannes). Ispravnik za erei ispovidnici i za pokornici. Prenesen s'latinskog yazika, u slovignski. Dir. per Confessori e per penitenti tr. da ling. Lat. n. Illyrica. [*By* S. Budinic]. s8°. Romae. 1636
„ „ [*a. ed. in Glagolitic characters b. w. above*]. s8°. Romæ. 1635
Poland. *Coup d'oeil s. l'état polit., 1815–30, *see* HOFFMANN (C. A.)
*Hist. of P. to 1795, 1795, *see* JONES (STEPHEN).
*Resurrection of P. 2, For a lasting peace. [P2516]. la8°. Paris. 1915
*Russian invasion of P., 1563; tr. of contemp. acc., 1884, *see* RUSSIAN.
Poland (E. B.)
The Friars in Sussex, 1228–1928. 8°. Hove. 1928
Poland (*Sir* Harry Bodkin), *see* BOWEN-ROWLANDS (E.) 72 years at the bar, mem. [of P.], 1924.
Polani (Pietro), *d. 1148*, *see* MONTICOLO (G. B.) Costituz. d. doge P. P. (1143) c. la process. scolarum, 1900.
Polano (Pietro Soave), *see* SARPI (*Fra* PAOLO).
Polanus (Amandus). De æterna Dei praedestin. didascalia. In qua haec doct. est explicata & à R. Bellarmini &c. depravationibus asserta. ed. 2a. repurg. s8°. Basileae. 1600
Gemmula partitionum theol., *see* FEGUERNEKINUS (I. L.) Enchiridii ed 2a, 1596.
Pole (*Card.* Reginald). De concilio liber [*&* De baptismo Constantini Magni]. 8°. Romae, *P. Manutius.* 1562
De summo Pontifice Christi in terris vicario &c. s8°. Lovanii. 1569
Reformatio Angliae ex decretis R. Poli, anno 1556. [*b. w. h.* De concilio, 1562]. 8°. Romae, *P. Manutius.* 1562
see BIRON (R.) & J. BARENNES. Un prince anglais, card.-légat au 16e s., R. P., 1923.
„ GASQUET (F. A.) Card. P. & h. early friends [*i.e.* N. Leonico Tomeo &c.], 1927.
Pole (William), *F.R.S.* Philosophy of music. 6th ed., w. intr. by E. J. Dent & suppl. essay by H. Hartridge. 8°. 1924
——, A. W. Drayson &c. Handbook of games. Enl. ed. v1. Table games. s8°. 1890
Poley (Arthur Pierre). The hist., law & practice of the Stock Exchange. By A. P. P., asst. by F. H. C. Gould. 3rd ed. rev. 8°. [1920]
The Imperial Commonwealth. Commercial, indust. & soc. hist. f. Tudor period. 8°. 1921
Polheim (Carl). Die lat. Reimprosa. 8°. 1925
Polhill (Edward) [POLHIL]. Christus in corde; or, the myst. union betw. Xt. & believers. s8°. 1788
„ „ ....3rd. ed., ed. T. Cloutt. 8°. 1823
Poliakoff (Vladimir) [*ps.* AUGUR].
Bibliog. list of Eng. books &c. rel. to Brit. infl. in Russia, 1553–1853. [*Type-written*]. 4°. 1922
The Empress Marie of Russia & h. times. 8°. [1926]
*Germany in Europe. s8°. [1927]
*God & politics. s8°. 1928
*Peace in Europe. s8°. [1927]
*Soviet v. civiliz. s8°. [1927]
The tragic bride: story of the Empress Alexandra of Russia. 8°. N.Y. 1927
Policastro (Giovanni Antonio de Petrucci, *conte* **di),** *see* PETRUCCI (G. A. DE').
Police Budget, *see* FURNISS (H.), *ed.* Famous crimes; P.B. ed., v1–8 *in* 2v, *n.d.*
Polidori (Filippo Luigi), *see* SENESE. Statuti Senesi; publ. p. c. di F. L. P. &c., 1863–67.
Polidori (John William). *The vampyre; a tale. [*Foll. by* Acc. of Byron's residence in Mitylene]. 8°. 1819
Polidori Calamandrei (E.) Le vesti d. donne fiorentine nel quattrocento. la8°. Firenze. 1924
Polignac (*le card.* Melchior de), *see* PAUL (P.) Le card. M. de P., 1661–1741, 1922.
Polinovsky (M. B.) Среди босяковъ. изд. 2e. 8°. Одесса. 1902
Poliphilus. Poliphili Hypnerotomachia, 1499, repr. 1904, *see* †COLONNA (F.)
Polish Comm. of work prep. to the Conference of Peace, *see* GDAŃSK. G. & E. Prussia, 1919.
***Politesse** française: princ. de la bonne éduc.; par un groupe de personnalités du monde. s8°. Tours. [1923]
Political.
*Polit. (The) hist. of the devil, *var. ed.*, *see* DEFOE (D).
*Polit. issues of the 19th century, w. statistics. By J. L. J. [P448]. 8°. 1886
*Polit. mischiefs of popery; by a person of quality, a native of France, 1698, *see* SOULIGNÉ (— DE).
Polit. princ. of prime ministers of 19th c., 1926, *see* HEARNSHAW (F. J. C.), *ed.*
*Polit. (The) Queen that Jack loves, 1820, *see* HONE (W.)
*Two polit. squibs, 1660-90 [*i.e.* The ghost *&* An epitaph on the D. of G[rafton], 1883, *see* AUNGERVYLE Soc. Repr., s2, 1883.
Political science quarterly.
v35–42. 8°. Lancaster, Penn. 1920–27
Politicheskiya. Политическія письма, 1898–1908, 3ч, 1908.
Politik. Die grosse Politik d. europ. Kabinette, 1871–1914, 1922–27, *see* GROSSE.
***Politique** (La) des Jésuites, 1688, *see* MONPERSAN (L. DE).
Politzer (Adam). Versteigerung d. Gemäldesamml. A. P. &c., Wien [Dez. 7–9]. Selbstverlag, Glückselig u. Wärndorfer. [*Illust. b. w.* Kolisch (R.) Versteig., 1921]. 4°. Wien. 1920
Polivanov (Aleksei Andreevich), *1855–1920.* Из дневников и воспом. по должности Военного Министра &c. 1907–16. Под ред. А. М. Зайончковского. С пред. М. Павловича. т1. 8°. Москва. 1924
Polivanov (Petr Sergeevich). Алексѣевскій Равелинъ. Отрывокъ изъ воспом. [P810]. s8°. *n.p.* [1903]
Polizei Ordnung. Pfaltzgrave Friderichs auffgerichte Christl. Policey Ordnung, 1565, *see* FREDERICK III, *Elector Palatine.*
Poliziano (Angelo). Annot. doct. virorum in grammaticos, oratores &c. [*b. w.* Priscianus. Instit. gram. &c., 1516]. fol. [Paris]. ab J. & J. B. Ascensio. 1511
Pollaiuolo (Antonio del), *see* BORENIUS (T.) Four early Ital. engravers, 1923.
Pollak (Hans Wolfgang). Phonet. Untersuchungen, 2, Akzent u. Aktionsart. (52. Mitt. d. Phonogr.-Archivs-Komm.), 1919, *see* KAIS. AKAD. D. WISS. Z. WIEN. Sitzber., B192, 1921.
Pollanus (Valerandus), *see* POULLAIN (V.)
Pollard (Albert Frederick). The evol. of Parliament. 8°. 1920
„ „ ....2nd ed. rev. 8°. 1926
Factors in American history. 8°. C. 1925
Henry VIII. n. imp. s8°. 1919
Tudor studies. Pres. to A. F. P., the work of 12 of h. colleagues. Ed. R. W. Seton-Watson. la8°. 1924
Pollard (Alfred William). Eng. miracle plays, moralities & interludes: specimens. Ed., w. intr. &c. by A. W. P. 8th ed. rev. s8°. O. 1927
The found. of Shakespeare's text. [Brit. Acad. P2683]. 8°. 1923
Shakespeare's fight w. the pirates & the problems of the transmission of h. text. 2nd ed. rev. s8°. 1920
Shakespeare's hand in the play of Sir Thomas More. Papers by A. W. P., W. W. Greg, E. M. Thompson &c., w. text of the Ill May Day scenes, ed. W. W. Greg. s8°. C. 1923
—— & G. R. Redgrave. Short-title cat. of bks. pr. in Eng., Scotland, & Ireland & Eng. bks. pr. abroad, 1475–1640. Comp. by A. W. P. & G. R. R. w. help of G. F. Barwick, G. W. Cole &c. [Bibliogr. Soc.] 4°. 1926
Pollard (Hugh B. C.) History of firearms. 4°. [1926]
The secret societies of Ireland, th. rise & progress. 8°. 1922
Pollard (James). Study in mun. govt.: the corp. of Berlin. 2nd ed. rev. s8°. E. 1894
Pollard (Samuel).
In unknown China. Obs. &c. of a missionary. 8°. 1921

Pollard (William), *F.C.I.*, *see* STRAHAN (*Sir* A.) & W. P. The coals of S. Wales, w. spec. ref. to anthracite, 1915.

Pollastrino (Il), *see* POLLIO LAPPOLI (G.)

Pollen (John Hungerford), *the younger*, *S.J.* The English Catholics in the r. of Q. Elizabeth, 1558–80. 8°. 1920

Sources for the hist. of Roman Catholics in Eng., Ireland & Scotland, 1533–1795. [Helps for students, No. 39. *b. w.* Cunningham (W.) Mon., 1920]. s8°. 1921

see MARY, *q. of Scots.* Mary & the Babington plot; ed. by J. H. P., 1922.

Polley (L. J. Neville), *see* NEVILLE-POLLEY (L. J.)

Pollhammer (Carl).

Jacques Callot als Illustrator. la8°. Wien. 1925

Pollicarius (Joannes), *see* MELANCHTHON (P.) Hist. de vita & actes M. Lutheri, adj. a J. P. Carmina, 1548.

Pollio Lappoli (Giovanni), *called* IL POLLASTRINO. Opera d. Diva & Seraphica Catharina da Siena. In rima. In stramotti. Capituli. Sonetti &c. 8°. [Siena. 1505]

Pollius (Joannes), *Wesphalus.* Opuscula piissima & erudit. in primis autem nostræ ætati appositissima. s8°. Tiguri, *Froschouer.* [*c.* 1540]

Pollock (*Rt. Hon. Sir* **Frederick),** *3rd bart.*

Essays in the law. 8°. 1922

Intr. to the hist. of the sci. of politics. n. ed. rev. s8°. 1920

A little Persian not a dangerous thing, 1913, *see* PERSIA SOCIETY. Lect., 1913.

Outside the law: diversions. 8°. *Cayme Press.* 1927

Sir C. P. Ilbert. [From Proc. of Brit. Acad. P2834]. 8°. [1926]

Spinoza's polit. doctrine. [Diss. ex Chronici Spinozani t1 sep. ed.] [P2707]. 8°. Hagae Com. 1921

see MAITLAND (E. F.) & Sir F. P. The Etchingham Letters, 1900.

Pollock (John). Anatole France & Mrs. Grundy, w. passages hitherto unpubl. f. A. F. en pantoufles by J. J. Brousson. 8°. *Cayme Press*, Kensington. 1926

Twelve one-acters. 8°. *Cayme Press*, Kensington. 1926

Pollock (*Sir* **John Maxwell,** *Lord*). Letters to Rev. R. Woodrow, 1703–10. [*Ed. J. Maidment*]. s8°. [*p.p.*] E. 1835

Pollock (Juliet, *Lady*), *wife of 2nd bart.*, *see* POLLOCK (W. H.) & J., *Lady* P. Amateur theatricals, 1879.

Pollock (Margaret A.) Working days: personal records of 16 working men &c. wr. by themselves. Ed. M. A. P. Intr. by Ld. Buckmaster. 8°. [1926]

Pollock (Walter Herries) & J., *Lady* **Pollock.**

Amateur theatricals. s8°. 1879

***Polly** Honeycombe, dram. novel, 1760, *see* COLMAN (G.), *the elder.*

Polman (Jean) [POLMANNUS (JOANNES)]. Breviarium theolog. cont. definitiones &c. terminorum theologic. ed. 6ª. 3p *in* 1v. s8°. Lovanii. 1673

Poln. *Cat. d. Gemeine d. Leute im Königr. P. &c., 1608, *see* RACOVIAN CATECHISM.

Polnische. *Verfassung (Die) d. poln. Republik v. März 1921. [P2600]. 8°. Bromberg. [1921]

Polo (Marco).

De regionibus orient., *see* †GRYNÆUS (S.) Nov. orbis, 1532.

Le livre de M. P. Tr. en fr. mod. & annoté d'ap. les sources chinoises par A. J. H. Charignon. t1, 2. la8°. Pekin. 1924–26

O livro de Marco Paulo—O livro de Nicolao Veneto [escr. p. Pogio] —Carta de Jeronimo de Santo Estevam. Conform. a impr. 1502. Intr. por F. M. E. Pereira. [Bibl. Nac. Reimpr. 2]. 4°. 1922

Il milione. A cura di L. F. Benedetto. [Com. Geog. Naz. Ital., Publ. 3]. fol. Firenze. 1928

Travels. [Repr. of ed. tr. Marsden & rev. Wright]. Intr. by J. Masefield. [repr.] 8°. 1926

see BONVALOT (G.) M. P., 1924.

,, CORDIER (HENRI). Ser Marco Polo, notes & addenda to Sir H. Yule's ed., cont. results of recent research &c., 1920.

,, *LIVRE des merveilles; Marco Polo, reprod. de miniatures, 2t, *n.d.*

Pologne.

*Abrégé chronol. de l'hist. de P., 1763, *see* SCHMID (F. A.)

Constit. de la Répub. de P. du 17 mars 1921. Préf., intr. hist. & tr. par M. Potulicki. [P2730]. la8°. Varsovie. [1921]

*Hist. de P. & Lituanie &c., 1698, *see* JOLLI (J. G.)

Recueil des traités &c. conc. la P., 1762–1862, 1862, *see* ANGEBERG (*cte.* D').

Polonais (Un), *ps.* *Coup d'œil s. l'état polit. de Pologne, 1815–30, 1832, *see* HOFFMAN (C. A.)

Polonaise. Actes & doc. de la Conf. Germano-P., tenue à Vienne du 30 avr.–30 août 1924, 1925, *see* ACTES.

Polonia [POLONICARUM].

Catechesis eccl. quae in regno P. &c., 1609, *see* RACOVIAN CATECHESIS.

Catechesis eccl. in regno P. &c., 1651, *see* RACOVIAN CATECHISM.

Polonia [POLONICARUM] [*continued*].

Charitativi pontificiorum in P. colloquii consilia secretiora &c. Tum ex publ. invitationis archiepiscop. quae Vilnae facta est &c. 4°. [1644]

Confessio fidei Xtnae ed. nom. eccl. P. [*w. comm. by J. Szlichting*], 1642; 1651, *see* APOSTLES' CREED.

Consensus in fide &c. inter eccl. evang. P., Lithuaniae &c., primo Sendomiriae a. 1570, ac demum Wlodislav. generali synodo a. 1583 confirmatus. Acc. Acta &c. synodi gener. Toruniensis. [*b. w.* Camerarius (J.) Hist. narr., 1605]. s8°. Haidelbergae. 1605

Respublica, sive status regni P., Lituaniæ, Prussiæ, Livoniæ &c. div. autorum [S. Krzystanowicz; M. Cromer; A. Guagninus; P. Philippus, *ps.* J. Bellus]. s8°. Lugduni Batav. 1627

Polonius (Jean), *ps.*, *see* LABENSKI (*cte.* X.)

Polonsky (Vyacheslav).

М. А. Бакунин: жизнь &c. t1. 8°. Москва. 1922

Polounine (Arcadius), *see* AUBERT (T.) L'affaire Conradi: plaidoirie pron. pour A. P. dev. Tribunal de Lausanne, 14 & 15 nov., 1923, 1924.

Polovtsev (V. N.) Russian co-oper. & internat. trade. [P2405]. 8°. [1920]

Polozov (Alexandra Létitia de). L'autocratie en Russie. [P2446]. 8°. Nancy. 1907

Poltava. Сборникъ по хозяйств. статистикѣ полтавской губ. t3–7. 4°. Полтава. 1884–88

Polverino (Agnello).

Descriz. ist. d. città d. Cava. 2p *in* 1v. s8°. Napoli. 1716–17

Polwarth (Alexander Hume, *baron*), *see* MARCHMONT (A. H., *2nd earl of*).

Polyaenus.

Strategicon libri 8. Rec. E. Woelfflin. s8°. Lips. 1860

Polyakov (A. S.) Ежегодник петроградских государств. театров. [1918–19]. Под редакц. А. С. П. la8°. П. 1920

О смерти Пушкина. 8°. П. 1922

Polyakov (Vladimir), *see* POLIAKOFF (VL.)

Polyander a Kerckhoven (Joannes). A disput. agst. the adoration of the reliques of saints &c. Tr. H. Hexham. s8°. Dordrecht. 1611

Polyansky (Valeryan), *ps.* [*i.e.* P. I. LEBEDEV].

Н. А. Некрасов. [P2698]. 8°. Москва. 1921

Polybiblion: revue bibliograph. t148–174. 8°. 1920–27

Polybius. Hist. de P. Tr. par V. Thuillier, avec un comm. ou corps de science militaire &c. Par M. de Folard. 6t. 4°. 1727–30

The histories. With Eng. tr. by W. R. Paton. [Loeb Class. Lib.] 6v. s8°. 1922–27

Polycarp, *St.*, *bp. of Smyrna.*

see APOSTOLIC. The Apostolic Fathers; [tr.], v2, 1889; 1909.

,, COTELERIUS (J. B.), *ed.* SS. patrum P. &c. opera; unà cum P. actis &c., 2v, 1724.

,, ITTIG (T.) Bibl. Patrum Apost. Gr.-Lat., 1699.

,, LIETZMANN (H.) Handbuch z. N.T.: Ergänzungsband, 2, Briefe d. Ignatius u. d. Polykarpbrief, erkl. v. W. Bauer, 1920.

Polycletus, *the Sculptor.*

see ANTI (C.) Monumenti P., 1920.

,, ROSSI (F.) Mirone e Policleto, 1922.

Polynesian, The. Publ. weekly. J. J. Jarves, ed. n.s. v1–3 (May 1844–Jan. 1847). fol. Honolulu. 1844–47

Polynesian Society. Memoirs.

v3–5. 8°. Wellington, N.Z. & New Plymouth. 1913–24

see BEST (E.) The Maori, 2v, 1924. [5.]

,, SMITH (S. P.), *ed.* Lore of the Whare-wānanga, or teachings of the Maori College, 2p, 1913–15. [3, 4.]

Poma (Cesare). The Eng. element in Ital. family names. [*Repr. f.* Philol. Soc. Trans., 1920. P2688]. 8°. Hertford. 1922

Pombal (Sebastião José de Carvalho e Mello, *marq.* **de).** *Relaçaõ abbrev. da republica, que os religiosos Jesuitas das Prov. de Portugal, e Hespanha estab. nos Dominios Ultramarinos &c. Relation abrégée &c.; [tr. P. O. Pinault. *Port. & Fr.*], *see* PORTUGAL. Rec. de decrets apostol. &c., p1, *n.d.*; 2nd ed., p1, 1761.

Pombo (Rafael). Fabulas y verdades. la8°. Bogota. 1916

Poesias. Ed. bajo la dir. de A. Gómez Restrepo. 2t. la8°. Bogota. 1916–17

Traducciones poeticas. Ed. bajo la dir. de A. Gómez Restrepo. la8°. Bogota. 1917

Pomey (François Antoine) [POMAI]. Pantheum mythicum. Ed. noviss. corr. &c. s8°. Francofurti. 1732

Traitté fort curieux de la vénerie & de la fauconnerie. Réimpr. de l'éd. orig. Lyon 1671. Texte franç. & allem. s8°. St. [1886]

Pomfret (Henrietta Louisa Fermor, *countess of***)**, *see* HERTFORD (F. S., *ctss. of*). Corr. betw. H. & P., 1738–41, 2nd ed., 1806.

Pomfret (John). Poems upon several occasions; w. acc. of h. life & writings. Added his remains [*sep. tp. & pagin. 4th ed.*] 10th ed. s8°. 1736

Pommier (Jean).
Renan, d'après des doc. inéd. 2e éd. 8°. 1923

***Pomp** (The) of power, 1922, *see* LYON (L.)

Pompadour (*Mme.* **de)**, *see* TINAYRE (*Mme.* M.) La vie amoureuse de Mme. de P., 1924.

Pompen (Aurelius), *O.F.M.* The English versions of the Ship of Fools: early French Renaiss. in England. la8°. 1925

Pompignan (Jean Georges Le Franc de), *see* LE FRANC DE POMPIGNAN (J. G.)

Pompilius (Paulus). Vita Senecae; éd. nouv., intr. & notes, *see* FAIDER (P.) Et. sur S., 1921.

Pomponius. *Les aventures de P., 1724, *see* LABADIE (—).

***Pomps** & vanities. By A Gentleman with a duster. s8°. [1927]

Poncelet (Edouard), *see* LIÉGE. Invent. analyt. des chartes de la Collég. de Ste. Croix, par E. P., t2, 1921.

Ponchon (Raoul). La muse au cabaret. s8°. 1921
see COULON (M.) R. P., 1927.

Pond (E. J.)
Les idées morales & relig. de George Eliot. la8°. 1927

Pondichéry. Cat. des mss. des anc. archives de l'Inde franç. t2, P., 1789–1815. Publ. avec intr. par E. Gaudart. [Soc. de l'Hist. de l'Inde franç.] la8°. 1924
Corresp. du Conseil Sup. de P. & de la Comp. Publ. avec intr. par A. Martineau. [Soc. de l'Hist. de l'Inde Fr.] t1, 2. 8°. Pondichéry. 1920

Poni (P.) Statistica răzesilor. [Academia Rom.] la8°. Bucureşti. 1921

Poniatovia (Christina), *see* PONIATOWSKA (KRYSTYNA).

Poniatowska (Krystyna) [PONIATOVIA (C.)], *see* KOTTER (C.) Lux in tenebris &c.: subm. de statu eccl. in terris per C. Cotterum, C. P. &c., 1616–56, 1657.

Poniatowski (Józef, *prince***)**, *marshal of France.*
Correspondance avec la France. [Soc. Scient. de Poznan. Publ. &c. 1, 2]. [t]1, 2 (1807–9). la8°. Poznan. 1921–23
see SOLTYK (R.) Rel. des opér. de l'armée aux ordres du P. 1809 en Pologne &c., 1841.

Ponsonby (Arthur).
English diaries. A review, 16th–20th c., w. intr. on diary-writing. 8°. [1923]
More Eng. diaries f. 16th to 19th cent., w. intr. on diary reading. 8°. [1927]
Now is the time: an appeal for peace. 8°. [1925]
The Priory & Manor of Lynchmere & Shulbrede: records of Shulbrede Priory, the Village of Lynchmere &c. 8°. Taunton. 1920
Scot. & Irish diaries f. 16th to 19th cent., w. an intr. 8°. 1927
Wars & treaties, 1815–1914. 8°. [1918]

Ponsonby (*Rt. Hon. Sir* **Frederick Edward Grey),** *K.C.B.*
The Grenadier Guards in the Great War, 1914–1918. Intr. by the Earl of Cavan. 3v. 8°. 1920

Ponsonby (Mary Elizabeth, *Lady***)**. M. P., a mem., some letters &c. Ed. by h. daughter M. Ponsonby. 8°. [1927]

Ponsonby (Richard A. B.), *see* PONSONBY-FANE (R. A. B.)

Ponsonby-Fane (Richard A. B.) Anc. capitals & palaces of Japan. [Repr. f. Trans. of Japan Soc., v20]. 8°. [1923]
Haitei Monogatari: the story of the exiled emperors. [Repr. f. Trans. of Japan Soc. of London, v19]. la8°. [1922]
The imperial family of Japan. 8°. Tokyo. 1915
Kiōto in the M. ages, *see* JAPAN SOC. Trans. &c., v23, 1926.
Misasagi: the imperial mausolea of Japan. [Repr. f. Trans. of Jap. Soc. of London, v18]. 8°. [1921]

Pont (Robert). A new treatise of the right reckoning of yeares, & ages of the world &c. 8°. E. 1599

Ponta (Marco Giovanni). Nuovo esperimento s. princ. allegoria d. D. C. di Dante. [*b. w.* Cesare (G. di) Esame d. Div. Comm. &c., 1807]. 2a ed. riv. & corr. 8°. Novi. 1845
Saggio di critica ai nuovi studi sopra Dante del Sig. G. Picci. [*b. w.* Cesare (G.) Esame d. Div. Comm., 1807]. 8°. 1845
see PICCHIONI (L.) La Div. Commedia illust. da M. G. P. &c., 1846.

Pontailler (Guy de), *sire de Talmay, maréchal de Bourgogne, see* DUMAY (G.) Guy de P., 1907.

Pontanus (Georgius Bartholdus) [†PONTANUS Z PRAITENBERKA (JIŘI B.)] Aureum diurnale concionatorum. Cum brevi praxi ad ritè concionandum ex F. Romano & A. Sucquet. Acc. Rituale Rom. &c. [1628 *w. sep. tp. & pag.*] s8°. Coloniae Agrippinae. 1629
Bohaemia pia. Acc. res gestae sub Ludovico. fol. Francofurti. 1608

Pontanus (Joannes Jovianus). Amorum lib. 2—De amore coniugali [*& o. poems*]. Explic. loc. abstrus. auth. P. Summontio. s8°. [Venetiis, *in aed. Aldi & Andr. Soceri.* 1518]

Pontatzin (Stephan E.) [Mod. Arm. fut. destiny. *In Armenian.* P2802]. s8°. K. polis. 1879

Pontault (Sébastien de Beaulieu, *sieur* **de)**, *see* BEAULIEU (S. DE).

Pont-de-Veyle (Antoine de Ferriol, *comte* **de)** [†FERRIOL (A. DE), *count de Pont de Veyle*]. Le somnambule (1739). Comédie. s8°. [1924?]

Ponte (Lorenzo da), *the elder* [L. D'APONTE]. Memorie. Con intr. di S. Paggi. s8°. Milano. [1923]
see RUSSO (J. L.) L. da P., poet & adventurer, 1922.

Ponte (Ludovico de), *jesuit, see* PUENTE (LOUIS DE LA).

Pontey (William). The rural improver. 4°. 1822

Ponti (Ermanno).
Roma: visioni stor. di un secolo fa. 8°. [1925]

Pontier (L. André-), *see* ANDRÉ-PONTIER (L.)

Pontieu. *La fille du Comte de Pontieu. Conte en prose. Versions du 13e & du 15e s. Publ. par C. Brunel. [S. d. a. t. f.] 8°. 1923
" " Ed. C. Brunel. [Class. fr. du m. â.] s8°. 1926

Pontifex. *De summi pontificis infallib. personali. [P2691]. 8°. Neapoli. 1870

Pontificale. P. noviter impressum: ppulchrisq. characteribus diligētissime annotatum. [*Ed.* Jacobus de Lutiis & Joannes Burchardus]. fol. Lugduni, *J. Moilin.* 1511
225ff. 2ff. cont. tp. pref. & tabula at the beginning, & 1f at the end cont. colophon &c.
P. Romanum Clementis VIII primum, nunc denuo Urbani PP. VIII auctoritate recogn. s8°. Matriti. 1773

Pontifices. *Ἀνάμνησις juris quod in approb. pontificibus imperatores habuerunt, cum commemor. vice versa. Add. constitutio Ludovice IIII Imperatoris &c. s8°. Francofurti. 1562

Pontificia. *De pontificia infallib. qualis in Conc. Vatic. defin. proponitur. [P2691]. 8°. Neapoli. 1870

Ponting (Herbert George). The great white South: Capt. Scott's S. Pole exped. & nature life of the Antarctic. Intr. by Lady Scott. [5th impr.] 8°. [1923]
" " ....[6th impr.] 8°. [1924]
In lotus-land Japan. la8°. 1910

Pontissara (Johann de), *see* PONTOISE (J. DE).

Pontmartin (Armand de), *d. 1890, see* VOGÜÉ (E. M. DE). Lettres à P., 1922.

Pontmartin (Henri de), *1844–1916, see* VOGÜÉ (E. M. DE). Lettres à P., 1922.

Pontoise (John de), *bp. of Winchester; d. 1304* [PONTISSARA]. Registrum J. de Pontissara, episc. Wynton., 1282–1304. Transcr. & ed. C. Deedes. [Canterbury & York Soc.] 2v. [*pagin. cont.*] 8°. 1915–24

Pontoppidan (Henrik). Skyer. Fortællinger. s8°. 1906
To Portræter: Isbjørnen—Lille Rødhætte. s8°. 1909

Pontormo (Jacopo da) [CARRUCCI; CARUCCI].
see CLAPP (F. M.) J. Carucci da P., h. life & work, 1916.
" GAMBA (C.) Il P., 1921.

Pontus. Black book: tragedy of P., 1914–22, 1922, *see* BLACK.

Ponz (Vicente Bardavíu), *see* BARDAVÍU PONZ (V.)

Poole, *The family of, see* POOLE (H. R.) The Pooles of Cae Nest, Merionethshire, 1916.

Poole (—). *The Classical collector's vade mecum: introd. to best editions of the Greek & Roman classics. s8°. 1822

Poole (Ernest). Danger. 8°. 1924
Silent storms. s8°. 1927

Poole (George Ayliffe).
The life & times of St. Cyprian. 8°. O. 1840
Sir Raoul de Broc & h. son Tristram. s8°. 1849

Poole (Henry Robert). The Pooles of Cae Nest, Merionethshire. la8°. *p.f.p.c.* Horncastle. 1916

Poole (Joseph).
Telegraphy, telephony & wireless. s8°. [1921]

Poole (*Mrs.* **Rachael**), *wife of R. L. Poole.* Cat. of portraits in poss. of the Univ., colleges, city & county of Oxford.
v2, 3, Portraits in the coll. & halls. 8º. O. 1925
,, ,, *a. ed.* [Oxford Hist. Soc., 81, 82].
v2, 3. 8º. O. 1926
Edward Pierce, the sculptor, *see* WALPOLE SOC. 11th ann. vol., 1922–23.

Poole (Reginald Lane).
The beginning of the year in the Middle Ages. [From Proc. of Brit. Acad., v10. P2565]. 8º. 1921
Benedict IX & Gregory VI, *see* BRIT. ACAD., Proc., 1917–18.
Chronicles & annals: orig. & growth. s8º. O. 1926
The early corresp. of John of Salisbury. [From Proc. of Brit. Acad., v11. P2731]. 8º. [1924]
Essays in hist. Pres. to R. L. P. [w. list of h. works]. Ed. H. W. C. Davis. 8º. O. 1927
Illust. of the hist. of medieval thought &c. 2nd ed. rev. 8º. 1920
Imperial influences on the forms of Papal doc., *see* BRIT. ACAD. Proc., 1917–18.
Léopold Delisle, 1826–1910, *see* BRIT. ACAD. Proc., 1911–12.
see JOHN, *of Salisbury.* Hist. pontific.; ed. R. L. P., 1927.

P'oo Lew Seen [P'OU SOUNG-LIN].
Contes magiques. [Tr.] L. Laloy. [5e éd.] s8º. [1925]
Liao-Chai-Chih-I. [*Chinese. Incomplete*]. s8º. *n.d.*

Pooley (Andrew Melville). Japan's foreign policies. 8º. [1920]

Poor. Some early tracts on poor relief, 1926, *see* SALTER (F. R.), *ed.*

Poor (Charles Lane). Gravitation v. relativity. Prelim. essay by T. C. Chamberlin. 8º. N.Y. 1922

Poore (George Vivian).
A treatise on medical jurisprudence. 2nd ed. 8º. 1902

Poore (**Ida**, *Lady*), *wife of Adm. Sir Richard Poore, form. Graves.* Harbour lights. s8º. [1922]

Poor Robin. Old Poor Robin, an almanack, 1800–8. [1804 *wanting. b. w.* Gentleman's diary, 1800–8]. s8º. 1800–8

Poortenaar (Jan).
An artist in the tropics. Tr. H. Shipp. la8º. [1927]

Poot (Abraham van). Korte hist. van de reformatie d. kerken van Hongaryen en Sevenbergen &c. s8º. t'Amsteldam. 1701

Pope. Histor. (An) disc. of the popes usurped supremacy over princes, 1682?, *see* HISTORICAL.

Pope (Alexander).
Essay on man. Notes by Bp. of Gloucester. s8º. 1771
,, ,, Ed. M. Pattison. 6th ed. s8º. O. 1878
Letters of P. & sev. of h. friends. sm. fol. 1737
Messiah, ecloga sacra. [Text, *w.* Tr. into Latin verse by R. Onely. P2568]. sm. fol. 1749
Poet. works. Coll. by T. Park. 4v. s8º. 1805
Poet. works. [Mem. by A. Dyce. Aldine ed.] 3v. s8º. 1878–87
Poet. works. Ed. w. notes & mem. by Sir A. W. Ward. Globe ed. [repr.] s8º. 1917
Sober advice f. Horace to the young gentlemen about town. Imitated in the manner of Mr. Pope. [By Pope himself]. [P2568]. sm. fol. [1735 ?]
see GRIFFITH (R. H.) A. P.: a bibliog., v1, 2p, 1922–27.
,, LLOYD (C.) Poet. essays on P. &c., 1821.
,, MORLEY (E. J.) J. Warton: compar. of h. Essay on P. w. h. ed. of P.'s works, 1924.
,, STRACHEY (G. L.) P., 1925.

Pope (Alfred). The walks & avenues of Dorchester. [From Dorset Nat. Hist. &c. Club, Proc. 38, 1917. P2706].
8º. Dorchester. 1917

Pope (*maj.-gen.* **John**). Virginia campaign of Gen. P. in 1862. [Milit. Hist. Soc. of Mass., v2]. 8º. Boston. 1886
,, ,, [*n. ed.*] ed. T. F. Dwight. 8º. Boston. 1895

Pope (*Sir* **Joseph**), *C.M.G., of Ottawa, see* MACDONALD (*Sir* J. A.) Corr.: sel. made by J. P., 1921.

Pope (Walter). Memoirs of Mons. Du Vall: a reflexion on the fondness of Eng. ladies tow. French footmen, 1670, *see* †HARLEIAN MISC.

Pope (William Burt). Compendium of Xtn. theology.
2nd ed. rev. & enl. 3v. 8º. 1877–79
Memoir of J. Fernley. [Repr. f. Wesleyan-Methodist Mag.]
s8º. 1874
Mem. of James Heald. s8º. 1876
The person of Christ. Fernley Lect. of 1871, w. 2 add. essays.
3rd ed. 8º. 1885

Popea (Nicolae), *see* LUPAS (I.) N. P. & I. M. Moldovanu, 1920.

Popenoe (Paul) & R. H. Johnson.
Applied eugenics. 8º. N.Y. 1920

Popenoe (Wilson).
Manual of tropical & subtrop. fruits. 8º. N.Y. 1920

Popert (Hermann M.)
Wenn—Ein vaterl. Traum. 5 Aufzüge. 8º. Hamburg. [1922]

Popery.
*Brief (A) hist. of the rise &c. of Popery dur. the 3 yrs & an half of James the 2nd, w. descr. of the 6 Popish pillars. s8º. 1690
*Hist. (The) of Popery, w. alter. & add. By sev. gentlemen. [An abstract, w. improvements, of Weekly Pacquet of advice f. Rome].
2v. 8º. 1735–36
*Political (The) mischiefs of p.; by a person of quality, a native of France, 1698, *see* SOULIGNÉ (— DE).

Popielovo (Nicolas).
see LISKE (J.) Viajes de extranjeros por España y Portugal en los siglos 15, 16, y 17; N. de P. (1484) &c., 1878.

Popish. A coll. of letters & o. writings rel. to the horrid Popish plot &c. Pr. f. originals in hands of G. Treby.
[P529]. fol. 1681
*Hist. (The) of the popish-sham-plots f. r. of Q. Elizabeth.
s8º. 1682
*Popish cruelty display'd by facts. [P2781]. 8º. 1745

Popley (Herbert A.) The music of India. s8º. Calcutta. [1921]

Popol-vuh, *see* RAYNAUD (G.) Les dieux, les héros &c. de l'anc. Guatémala d'ap. Le livre du Conseil [P.-V.], 1925.

Popov (Aleksandr Serafimovich), *see* SERAFIMOVICH (A.), *ps.*

Popov (Georg) [POPOFF].
The Tcheka: the red inquisition. 8º. 1925
Tscheka: d. Staat im Staate. 8º. Frankfurt a. M. 1925
Unter d. Sowjetstern: Alltag, Kultur, Wirtschaft.
8º. Frankfurt a. M. 1924

Popović (Bogdan), *ed.*
Антологија новије српске лирике 4º. изд. 8º. Београд. 1920

Popovics (Alexander). Das Geldwesen im Kriege. [C.E. for Int. Peace]. la8º. Wien. 1925

Popp (Anny E.) Nicolo u. Giovanni Pisano. s8º. L. [1922]

Popp (Hermann). Die Architektur d. Barock-u. Rokokozeit in Deutschl. u. d. Schweiz. 4º. St. 1913

Poppelreuter (Jos.) Der anonyme Meister d. Poliphilo. St. z. ital. Buchillust. &c. la8º. Str. 1904

Popper (Josef) [*ps.* LYNKEUS; POPPER-LYNKEUS].
Phantasieen eines Realisten.
n. verbess. A. [2T *in 1v*]. 8º. Dresden. 1918
see WITTELS (F.) An end to poverty [*expos. of P.'s scheme for universal service*]; tr., 1925.

Poprujenko (M. G.)
Одесская Город. Публ. Библiотека, 1830–1910. la8º. Одесса. 1911

Popular (The) Dod. Ed. by Tommy. 3p *in* 1v. s8º. 1881

Population Conference, World, *see* WORLD POPULATION CONFERENCE.

Por (Odon). Fascism. Tr. E. Townshend. s8º. 1923
Guilds & co-operatives in Italy. Tr. E. Townshend. Intr. by A. E. & App. by G. D. H. Cole. s8º. [1923]

Porai-Koshits (Ivan A.)
Очеркъ исторiи русс. дворянства, 862–1796. 8º. С.–П. 1874

Porcacchi (Tommaso). Lettere di 13 huomini illustri, alle-quali &c. ne sono state aggiunte molte da T. P.
s8º. Vinetia. 1565

Porcari (Stefano). Orazioni, *see* MANZI (G.) Testi, 1816.

***Porcelain** tower (The); comp. by "T. T. T.," 1841, *see* SEALY (T. H.)

Porché (François).
Le chevalier de Colomb. Drame. s8º. 1923
Les commandements du destin. 8º. 1921
La dauphine. Comédie. s8º. 1922
Paul Valéry & la poésie pure. 8º. [1926]
Sonates. s8º. 1923
La vierge au grand cœur, ou la mission &c. de Jeanne d'Arc. [*Play*]. s8º. 1925

Porcia (*conte* **Jacopo di**) [PURLILIARUM (JACOBUS), *comes*]. De liberorum educatione; [*f. 1 verso,* Io. Bapt. Uranii carmen ad lectorem. *f. 2 verso,* De generosa liberorum educatione. *Foll. on f. 17 by*: F. Niger Venetus: Doctor Iacobo &c. foelicitatem].
s4º. [Tarvisii, *per Gerardum de Flandria.* 1492]
[*18 leaves marked with rom. numerals.*]

Porphyrius (Publilius Optatianus). Carmina. Rec. &c. E. Kluge. s8º. L., *Teubner.* 1926

Porphyry, *the philosopher.*
De divinis & dæmonibus, *see* IAMBLICHUS *of Chalcis.* De mysteriis &c., 1497.
P., "Gegen d. Christen," 15 Bücher, Zeugnisse, Fragm. &c.; hrsg. A. v. Harnack, *see* KÖNIGL. PREUSS. AKAD. D. WISS. Abhdl. (Phil.-hist. Klasse), 1916.
see ABÉLARD (P.) Philos. Schr., 1i, Die Glossen zu P., 1919.
,, BARBARO (D.) Exquisitae in P. comm., 1542.

Porphyry, *the philosopher* [*continued*].
see BÄUMKER (C.) & B. SARTORIUS V. WALTERSHAUSEN, *edd.* Glossen d. angebl. Jepa z. Isagoge, 1924.
„ LLOYD (W.) Chronolog. acc. of life of Pythagoras &c., w. epistle about P.'s &c. Lives of Pythagoras, 1699.

Porrée (Jonas).
*Traité des anc. ceremonies. 4e éd. rev. s8°. Rouen. 1673

Porreño (Baltasar), *d. 1639.* Dos tratados histór. toc. al card. Ximénez de Cisneros. [Intr. por el Conde de Cedillo. Soc. de Bibliófilos Esp., 41]. 8°. 1918

Porritt (Arthur). The best I remember. 8°. 1922

Porritt (Edward). The fiscal & diplom. freedom of the Brit. oversea dominions. Ed. D. Kinley [C.E. for Int. Peace]. la8°. O. 1922

Porritt (Norman). The factory king. s8°. [1923]

Porro (Giulio), *see* TRIVULZIANA. Cat. dei codici; ed. p. c. di G. P., 1884.

Porrois, *abbey of, see* PORT ROYAL.

Porro-Lambertenghi (Giulio). Breve commem. del socio Carlo Morbio, *see* REGIA DEP. DI STORIA PATRIA. Misc., t20, 1882.
see CARUTTI (D.) Il Conte G. P. L.: notizia, 1887.

Porta (Johannes) *de Annoniaco.* Liber de coronatione Karoli IV Imp. Ed. R. Salomon. [Scr. rerum Germ. in usum schol.] 8°. Hannoverae. 1913

Porta (Nott da). Catechism' oder informatiū da la vaira relig. Christiana. s8°. Scuol. 1724

Porta (Petro Dominico da), *see* ROSI DA PORTA (P. D.)

Portail (Jean). Fruit d'orage, *see* ŒUVRES libres, 82, 1928.

Portal, *The family of, see* PORTAL (*Sir* W. W.) A. P. & h. descendants, 1925.

Portal (Abraham), *see* PORTAL (*Sir* W. W.) A. P. &c., 1925.

Portal (*Sir* William Wyndham), *2nd bart.* Abraham Portal, 1726–1809, & h. descendants. 8°. Winchester. 1925

Portalis (*le baron* Roger).
Les dessinateurs d'illustr. au 18e s. 2p. 8°. 1877
Henry P. Danloux, peintre de portraits, & s. journal dur. l'émigration, 1793–1809. [Soc. des Bibliophiles franç.] fol. 1910

Portel (João de), *see* JOÃO, *de Portel.*

Portenari (Angelo). Della felicità di Padova, libri nove &c. sm. fol. Padova. 1623

Porteous (Alexander). Forest folklore, mythology & romance. 8°. [1928]

Porteous (*Mrs.* J. A.), *see* MANNIN (E. E.)

Porter (Edmund). Trin—Unus—Deus; or the Trinity & unity of God &c. s8°. 1657

Porter (James), *D.D.* A compendium of Methodism. 4th ed. s8°. Boston [U.S.A.] 1852

Porter (Kirk Harold). National party platforms. Comp. by K. H. P. 8°. N.Y. 1924

Porter (*Sir* Robert Ker). A narr. of the campaign in Russia, 1812. 3rd ed. 8°. 1814
Travels in Georgia, Persia, Armenia, anc. Babylonia &c., 1817–20. [*a. copy w. some plates coloured*]. 2v. 4°. 1822

Porter (Whitworth).
Hist. of the fortress of Malta. s8°. Malta. 1858

Port Erin Biological Station. Spec. publ. No. 1. 8°. Liv'l. 1923
see SMITH (W. C.) Sh. hist. of Irish Sea herring fisheries, 1923. [1.]

Porteus (Beilby), *bp. of (1) Chester, (2) London, 1731–1808, see* HODGSON (R.) *Life of Dr. B. P., 2nd ed., 1812.

Porteus (Thomas Cruddas). Captain Myles Standish: h. lost lands & Lancashire connections. [M'ter Univ. Publ.] s8°. M'ter. 1920
Hist of the parish of Standish, Lancs. la8°. Wigan. 1927

Portfolio (The). By Oliver Oldschool [*i.e.* J. Dennie].
New ser. v1–3, No. 5, Jan. 1806–Jan. 1807. 8°. Phila. 1806–7

Porthan (Henricus Gabriel). Opera selecta. Skrifter i urval. [*Ed.* S. G. Elmgren & A. Schauman]. d1, 2 [*in* 1v. *pagin. cont.*] 8°. Helsingfors. 1859–62
1, 2, Juusten (P.) Chron. episcop. Finland.

Porti marittimi, 1905, *see* ITALY: MIN. D. LAV.

Portigliotti (Giuseppe). I Borgia: Alessandro VI—Cesare—Lucrezia. 8°. Milano. 1921
The Borgias. Tr. B. Miall. 8°. [1928]
Donne d. Rinascimento. 8°. Milano. 1927
Un grande monomane: Savonarola. 8°. Torino. 1902

Portland (William Bentinck, *1st earl of*), *1649–1709.*
see GREW (M. E.) W. B. & William III (Pr. of Orange), 1924.
„ WILLIAM III, *k. of Eng.* Corr. v. W. III en H. W. B., ged. 1, Archief v. Welbeck Abbey, d1, 1927.

Portland (William J. A. C. J. Cavendish-Bentinck, *6th duke of*).
Cat. of pictures belong. to D. of P., at Welbeck Abbey, & London. 4°. 1894

Portledge papers (The), 1687–97; ed. R. J. Kerr & I. C. Duncan, 1928, *see* LAPTHORNE (R.)

Porto (Luigi da), *see* FISCHER (R.) Quellen zu Romeo u. Julia, 1922.

Portolan. Facs. of p. charts belong. to the Hispanic Soc. of Amer., 1916, *see* STEVENSON (E. L.)

Portoneria (Libera), *of Carignano, see* BOSIO (A.) Not. sui sepolcri di Bianca di Monferrato e di L. P., 1870.

Porto-Riche (Georges de).
Anatomie sentimentale. Pages préférées. 3e éd. s8°. [1920]
Théâtre d'amour. 3e ed. s2. s8°. 1922
2, Le vieil homme—Zubiri—Les marchand d'estampes—Les Malefilâtre.
Veux-tu que je sois ta femme? nouvelle, *see* ŒUVRES (Les) libres, 19, 1923.
Le vieil homme. Pièce. s8°. [1911]
Zubiri. Fantaisie. 3e éd. s8°. 1912
see MARX (H.) G. de P.-R., s. œuvre, 1924.

***Port-Royal** (The) of Holy Scr., 1655, *see* HART (J.)

Port Royal, *abbey of.* Cartul. de l'abbaye de Porrois, plus connue sous s. nom mystique Port Royal. [Ed. &c. A. de Dion]. v1, 1204–80. 8°. 1903

Portugal.
Collecçaõ da legislaçaõ ant. e mod. do reino de Portugal. 2p [*in* 13t]. 8°. Coimbra. 1790–95
Coll. chronologica dos assentos das casas da supplic. e do civel, 1t. [II.]
Coll. da legislaçaõ ant. e mod. do reino de P., 3t. [II.]
Ordenaçoens do Sen. Rey D. Affonso V, 5t. [I.]
Repertorio das ordenações, e leis do reino de P., 4t. [II.]
*P. & Gallicia, 2v, 1836, *see* CARNARVON (H. J. G. H., *3rd earl of*).
[Recueil des decrets apostoliques & des ordonnances du roi de P. au sujet des crimes de la Co. de Jésus (conc. la conduite des Jesuites dans le Paraguai &c.)] 2t *&* Suite. s8°. Amsterdam. [1758–61]
„ „ ....2e éd. 2t *&* Suite. s8°. Amsterdam. 1761
t1 & 2 *of the 1st ed. have no gen. tp.* t1 *of the 1st ed. beg.* Relacaõ abbrev. [*Portug. & French*]; t2 *beg.* Recueil de pièces, 1761. *The 2nd ed. has many add. pieces.*
West coast of Spain & P. pilot, *&* Suppl. 1, 1921–22, *see* ADMIRALTY.

Portugiesische. *Gesch. d. ersten p. Entdeckungen unter Infant Heinrich, d. Seefahrer. 1783, *see* FREIRE (F. J.)

Portuguese [PORTUGUEZE].
*Authentic memoirs of the P. Inquisition. Also reflections on popery &c. 8°. 1761
*A compleat acc. of the Portugueze lang.: dict. of Eng. w. P., & P. w. Eng. &c. By A. J. sm. fol. 1701
*Mem. conc. P. rights &c. on W. coast of Africa, 1883, *see* MEMORANDUM.

Portuguese East Africa. A manual of P.E.A., 1920, *see* ADMIRALTY: NAVAL INTELL. DIV.

Portugueza. *Doc. para a hist. da typog. p. (16–17c.), 2v, 1881–82, *see* DOCUMENTOS.

Portum (Jacobus ad). Orthodoxae fidei defensio adv. C. Ostorrodii Instit. relig. ut vocat Christianae &c. 4°. Genevae. 1613

Portus (Garnet Vere). Caritas Anglicana: inq. into relig. & philanthrop. societies in Eng., 1678–1740. Intr. by W. H. Hutton. s8°. 1912

Portusnaonense. Diplomatarium Portusnaon. (1276–1514) &c.; cura J. Valentinelli, *see* FONTES RERUM AUSTRIAC., B24, 1865.

Portwine (Edward). Harbours of refuge on S.E. coast of Eng. [P2846]. 8°. 1849

Poruks (Jānis).
La couronne d'airelles. Tr. R. Ressel. s8°. Riga. 1926
Die reinen Herzens sind. Übers. E. Eckardt-Skalberg. 8°. Riga. [1922]
see BLAUMANIS (R.) Builders of new Rome & o. Lettish tales; [by] R. B., J. P. &c.; tr., 1924.

Poschinger (Heinrich, *Ritter* **v.),** *see* ROBOLSKY (H.) *Bismarck in Frankfurt [*abridged f.* P.'s "Preussen im Bundestag"], 1885.

Poseck (Maximilian v.) Die Deut. Kavallerie 1914 in Belgien u. Frankreich. 2e A. 8°. 1922

Poseidonios, *see* POSIDONIUS *of Apamea.*

Posen. Assert. theol. De trino & uno Deo &c.: ex praelect. Collegii Posnan. excerpt. &c., 1618, *see* SOCINUS (F.)

Posidonius, *of Apamea.*
see HEINEMANN (I.) P.'s metaphys. Schriften, 1921.
„ REHM (A.) Das 7. Buch d. Nat. Quaest. d. Seneca u. d. Kometentheorie d. P., 1921.
„ REINHARDT (C.) Poseidonios, 1921.
„ RUDBERG (G.) Forsch. zu P., 1918.

Positivist review (The). v28–33 [*no more publ.*] 8°. 1920–25
v32 & 33 *have title* Humanity, the Positivist review.
Posnansky (Arthur). Eine præhist. Metropole in Südamerika. [*In German & Spanish*]. Bl. 4°. 1914
Posner (Johann Caspar). Orat. de emend. Sacrorum a Luthero susceptae divinitate. [P484]. s4°. Jenae. [1717]
Posnett (Hutcheson Macaulay).
Hereditary Lords. [P2600]. 8°. 1894
Posnett (J. Leonard). Notes on the Rev. G. W. Olver's Fernley lect. [P2561]. 8°. 1878
Posrednik, *publisher.* Списокъ изданій "Посредникъ" (1885–96). [P2719]. 8°. Москва. 1896
Posse (Hans). Der röm. Maler A. Sacchi. 4°. L. 1925
Posse (Vladimir Aleksandrovich). Рабочія стачки. Очерки, 1, Англія-Америка-Австралія-Японія. 4, Россія. [P2448]. 8°. 1906
Possevino (Antonio), *the Elder.* Bibl. selecta de ratione studiorum ad disciplinas & ad salutem omnium gentium procurandam &c. 2t *in* 1v. fol. Venetiis. 1603
Moscovia. s8°. Vilnæ. 1586
La Moscovia. Tr. di Latino in volgare da G. B. Possevino. [*tp., pref. &c. damaged*]. s8°. Ferrara. 1592
Transilvania (1584). Per cura d. A. Veress. [Fontes rer. Transyl., t3]. la8°. Budapest. 1913
see JAMES (J.) A treatise of the corruption of Scripture by the Church of Rome, w. ans. unto A. P. &c., 1611.
Possidius, *Saint, bp. of Calama.* S. A. Augustini Hipp. Episc. vita rec. notisque illust. opera J. Salinas. Acc. Michaelis III Disq. crit. de var. gestis, dictis &c. Augustino falso attrib. s8°. Augustae Vindel. 1764
Possinus (Petrus). Catena Graec. patrum in Marcum; coll. P. P. qui & adj., titulo Spicilegii, Comm. ad loca sel. quatuor Evang. &c. fol. Romae. 1673
see CORDIER (B.) & P. POSSINUS. Symbolarum in Matthæum &c. 2t, 1546–47.
Post (Charles William). I am well! Mod. practice of nat. suggestion. 2nd ed. 8°. Boston. 1895
Post Boy, The. Nos. 410–412, 414–433, 448, 450, 454, 473–481, 483–488, 492–583, 657, 681, 1147, (Dec. 18, 1697–Aug. 19, 1699, Sept. 17–19, 1702). fol. 1697–1702
Poste. Poste (La) dans les temps anc. & mod., 1924, *see* HEURGREN (P. G.), *ed.*
*Poste per div. parti del mondo con la tariffa. s8°. 1771
Postel (Guillaume). De origin. seu de Hebraicae linguae & gentis antiq., deque var. linguarum affinitate liber. s4°. Parisiis. [1538]
Postgate (John Percival). Flaws in classical research, 1908, *see* BRIT. ACAD.: Proc., 1907–08.
On anc. Greek accentuation. [From Proc. of Brit. Acad. P2821]. 8°. [1925]
Short guide to the accentuation of anc. Greek. 8°. 1924
Translation & translations: theory &c. s8°. 1922
Postgate (Raymond William).
The Bolshevik theory. s8°. 1920
Murder, piracy & treason: select. of Engl. trials. 8°. [1925]
Revolution f. 1789 to 1906. Doc. sel. & ed. w. notes & intr. by R. W. P. 8°. 1920
Posthumus (N. W.) Bescheiden betref. de prov. organis. d. Hollandsche lakenbereiders. Uitg. door N. W. P. [Hist. Genoots. Werken., s3, 38]. 8°. A. 1917
Bronnen tot de gesch. van de Leidsche textielnijverheid, verzameld door P. [Rijks Gesch. Publ.; uitg. in opdr. v. d. Min. v. Onderwijs &c., 49]. d6, 1703–95. 4°. 's-Gravenhage. 1922
Postillae. *Postille majores in Epistolas & Evangelia: tam dominicaliū feriatorumq; dierum &c. s4°. [Basileae, *A. P. de Langendorff*]. 1514
Postma (J.)
Tennyson as seen by his parodists. 8°. Amsterdam. 1926
Post Man, The, & the Historical account, &c. Nos. 102–695 (Dec. 31, 1695–Dec. 30, 1699) [Nos. 152, 270, 386, 403–10 & 473 *wanting.* Nos. 410–19, 431, 508, 510, 554, 630–639 *have been used twice in the numeration & 537 three times, 514 omitted in numbering*]. [4v]. fol. 1696–99
Postnikov (S. P.), *see* KOMITET RUSS. KNIGI. Русс. зарубежн. книга, ч2 под ред. С. П. П., 1924.
Post Office, *see* MURRAY (*Sir* G. E. P.) The P.O., 1927.
Post Office directories.
Dublin, 1847.
Glasgow, 1917–18.
London [w. County suburbs], 1921–28.
Postolakas (Akhilleus).
Κερμάτια συμβολικά. [P2749]. 8°. Ἀθήνησιν. 1880

Pot (Combertus Willem van der). Specimen theolog. de Basilio magno. 8°. Amstelodami. 1835
Potanin (Grigory Nikolaevich). Очерки сѣверо-западной Монголіи. Результаты путешествія 1876–77, по порученію И.Р.Г.О. Bl, 2 [*in* 1v. B2 *has 2 pagin.*] 8°. С.-П. 1881
Potchett (William), *vicar of Grantham, Lincoln.* Popery unchanged &c., being a comm. on a sermon by the bishop of Siga. 8°. Grantham. 1826
Potebnya (Aleksandr Afanasievich).
Объясненія малорусскихъ и сродныхъ народныхъ пѣсень. [2v]. (2, колядки и щедровки). la8°. Варшава. 1887
Potemkin (Petr Ivanovich). La Russie du 17e siècle dans ses rapports avec l'Europe occid. Récit du voyage de P. P., 1668. Préc. d'un aperçu de l'état social par le prince E. Galitzin. s8°. 1855
***Potentia** d'amore, 1528, *see* GUIDALOTTI (D.)
Potesta (Felix). Examen eccl., univ. materiæ morales, casus conscientiae &c. Cum denunciat. ad monitoria &c. ed. noviss. cui acc. App. Thesium Quesnellianarum. 2t *in* 1v. [*pagin. cont.*] s4°. Venetiis. 1733
Potez (Henri).
L'élégie en France avant le romantisme, 1778–1820. s8°. 1898
Potho, *Benedictine, of Prüffling* [BOTHO], *see* MARY, *the Virgin.* *Liber de miraculis Sanctae Mariae; publ., 1731, by B. Pez [*ascr. to* P.]; repr., w. intr. &c. by T. F. Crane, 1925.
Potocki (Antoni). Grottger. 4°. Lwów. 1907
Potonniée (Georges).
Hist. de la découverte de la photographie. la8°. 1925
Potresov (A.), *see* MARTOV (L.), P. MASLOV & A. P., *edd.* Обществ. движеніе въ Россіи, 2t, 1909–10.
Pott (August Friedrich). Allgem. Sprachwiss. u. C. Abels Aegypt. Sprachstudien. [P2506]. 8°. L. 1886
Comm. de ling. Lettic. cum vicinis nexu scr. 4°. Halis. 1841
De Lithuano-Borussicae in Slav. Letticisque linguis principatu comm. [*Progr.*] 4°. Halis Sax. 1837
Pott (David Julius), *ed.* Sylloge comment. theolog. 8v [v6 *wanting*]. s8°. Helmstadii. 1800–7
Pottecher (Maurice). Les joyeux contes de la cigogne d'Alsace &c. 4e éd. s8°. [1920]
Potter (G. W. J.)
A hist. of the Whitby & Pickering Railway. 2nd ed. 8°. 1906
Potter (Harold), *LL.B.*
Intr. to hist. of Eng. law. 2nd ed. partly rewr. 8°. 1926
Potter (John), *bp. of Oxford, abp. of Canterbury.*
A disc. of Church govt. 8°. 1707
Potter (Michael Cresse).
Elem. text-book of agric. botany. 5th ed. s8°. [1919]
Potter (S. Carlyle).
Russia bef. & after the Revol. [P2431]. s8°. 1920
Pottier (Edmond).
Cat. d. vases ant. de terre cuite; Musée du Louvre. pl, les origines. s8°. 1896
Diphilos & les modeleurs de terres cuites grec. 8°. [1909]
Note sur l'Égypte & la plastique grecque, *see* ACAD. D. INSCR.: FOND. PIOT. Mon., t25, 1921–22.
Le problème de l'art dorien. [Extr. de la Bibl. de vulg. du Musée Guimet, t28]. s8°. 1908
Réplique de la "Vénus de Médicis," coll. M. F. Vlasto, *see* ACAD. DES INSCR.: FOND. PIOT. Mon., t23, 1918–19.
Statuettes de terre cuite dans l'antiq. s8°. 1890
see CORPUS vasorum antiq.: France: Musée du Louvre; par E. P., 1922 &c.
—— **& S. Reinach.** La nécropole de Myrina: recherches archéolog. Texte & notices par E. P. & S. R. [Ecole Franç. d'Athènes]. 2t. 4°. 1888
Potton (Edward). A record of the United Arts Rifles, 1914–19. [*By var. wr.*] Ed. E. P. 4°. 1920
Potts (Robert). Liber Cantabr.: aids to poor students &c. Pref., coll. of maxims &c. s8°. C. 1855
P'ou Soung-lin, *see* P'OO LEW SEEN.
Poucel (Benjamin). Les otages de Durazno. Souv. du Rio de la Plata pend. l'intervention anglo-franç., 1845–51. 8°. 1864
Pouchen (Andreas) [POUCHENIUS (A.)] Ad. Iohannis Palmerii [*i.e. F. Hotman*] protest. oppositas Formulae Concordiae responsio. s4°. [Lubecae. 1579]
Theses oppos. blasphemæ disput. tertiae Eusebii Cleberi De unione personali & supernaturali duarum naturarum in Christo. [P2504]. s4°. Tubingæ. 1585
Poucher (William Arthur). Perfumes, cosmetics & soaps, w. espec. ref. to synthetics. 2nd ed. 2v. 8°. 1925–26
Pouchet (Félix Archimède).
The universe. 4th ed. Tr. revised. 8°. 1877

Poueigh (Jean), *see* Séré (O.), *ps.*
Pouget de Saint-André (Henri).
Les auteurs cachés de la Révol. Franç. 8°. 1923
Pougin (Arthur).
Dict. hist. & pittor. du théâtre & des arts &c. la8°. 1885
Les vrais créateurs de l'opéra franç.: Perrin & Cambert. s8°. 1881
Pouilly (Jean Simon Lévesque de), *see* Lévesque de Pouilly.
Poujol (Adolphe), *the elder.*
La girouette de village (1818). Comédie. s8°. [1924?]
Poulet-Malassis (Paul Emmanuel Auguste), *see* Papiers secrets &c. du 2me. Emp.; réimpr., rec. par A. P.-M., 1875.
Poulsen (Frederik).
Aus e. alt. Etruskerstadt, *see* Kong. Dan. Vid. Selsk.: Hist.-filol. Medd., B12, 1927.
Delphische Studien [Kgl. Dan. Vidensk. Selskab: Hist.-filol. Medd. VIII, 5]. Tl. 8°. København. 1924
For a. copy, see Kong. Danske Vid. Selskab.
Delphi. Tr. G. C. Richards. Pref. by P. Gardner. la8°. [1920]
Etruscan tomb paintings. Tr. by I. Andersen. la8°. O. 1922
Ikonograph. Miscellen, *see* Kong. Dan. Vid. Selsk.: Hist.-filol. Medd., B4, 1921–22.
Travels & sketches. Tr. 8°. 1923
Vases grecs réc. acquis par la Glyptothèque de Ny-Carlsberg, *see* Kong. Dan. Vid. Selsk., Hist.-filol. Medd., B5, 1921–22.
Pound (Ezra). Umbra. Early poems of E. P., w. tr. f. G. Cavalcanti &c. s8°. 1920
Pound (*Miss* Louise).
Amer. ballads & songs. Coll. & ed. by L. P. s8°. N.Y. 1922
Poetic origins & the ballad. 8°. N.Y. 1921
Pound (Roscoe). Interpretations of legal history. [Camb. st. in Eng. legal hist.] 8°. C. 1923
Pountney (W. J.) Old Bristol potteries, 1650–1850, w. some pages on the old Chapel of St. Anne, Brislington. Forewords by R. L. Hobson & B. Rackham. la8°. Bristol. 1920
Poupardin (René), *see* Paunat. Fragments de cartul. du monastère de P.; [publ.] par R. P. &c., 1906.
Pouquet (Jeanne Maurice). Le salon de Mme. Arman de Caillavet: s. amis, A. France, Comdt. Rivière &c. Préf. de G. Hanotaux. 8°. [1926]
Pour la Russie Socialiste. Recueil d'articles: Marchand: Préobrajensky: Z., 1918, *see* Russie.
Pourichkevitch, *see* Purichkevich.
Pourrat (Henri). Gaspard des Montagnes. s8°. [1922]
Pourrat (Pierre).
La spiritualité chrétienne. 2t [1, 5e éd., 2, 3e éd.] s8°. 1921
Pourtalès (Guy de). Chopin, ou le poète. 13e éd. s8°. 1927
De Hamlet à Swann: études s. Shakespeare, La Fontaine, Senancour, B. Constant, M. Proust. s8°. 1924
La vie de F. Liszt. 28e éd. s8°. 1926
Poussin (Nicolas), *1594–1665.*
see Grautoff (O.) N. P., s. Werk u. s. Leben, 2B, 1914.
„ Hourticq (L.) De P. à Watteau, 1921.
„ Sutro (E.) N. P., 1923.
Pouthas (Charles H.)
Guizot pendant la Restauration, 1814–30. 8°. [1923]
Poutsma (H.) Characters of the Eng. verb & the expanded form. 8°. Groningen. 1921
Grammar of late mod. English for use of Continental &c. students. 2p [*in 3v*, 2i, ii]. 8°. Groningen. 1904–16
The infinitive, the gerund & the participles of the Eng. verb. 8°. Groningen. 1923
Mood & tense of the Eng. verb. 8°. Groningen. 1922
Poux (Joseph).
La cité de Carcassonne: hist. & descr. la8°. Toulouse. 1922
Poux (Pierre), *ed.*, *see* Jouffroy (T.) Le cahier vert &c., 1924.
Povest. Повѣсть временн. лѣтъ, 1872, *see* Lavrentiev Chron.
Powel (Gabriel). A consideration of the Papists reasons of state & religion, for toleration of Poperie in England. [P2660]. s4°. O. 1604
Theolog. positions conc. the lawfulnesse of borrowing upon usurie &c. s8°. 1605
Powell (Annie E.), *wife of E. Robertson Dodds.* The rom. theory of poetry: exam. in light of Croce's Æsthetic. 8°. 1926
Powell (A. H.), *see* Society for the Protection of Ancient Buildings. Report on old cottages, *n.d.*
Powell (Chilton Latham). Eng. domestic relations, 1487–1653: st. of matrimony &c. 8°. N.Y. 1917
Powell (*Miss* D. L.), *see* Surrey. Co. of S., abstract of par. rec.; comp. by D. L. P., 1928.
Powell (E. Alexander), *correspondent of the New York World.*
Asia at the crossroads. Japan: Korea: China: Philippine Islands. 8°. 1922
By camel & car to the Peacock Throne. 8°. 1923
The map that is half unrolled: Equatorial Africa. 8°. 1926
Powell (Harry J.) Glass-making in England. la8°. C. 1923
Princ. of glass-making, w. tr. on sheet g. by H. Chance, & plate g. by H. G. Harris. s8°. 1883
Powell (James Edward). Payment by results. 8°. 1924
Powell (John Clark). Hist. of Italy, *see* Buchan (J.), *ed.* Nations of to-day, 1923.
Powell (John Undershell). Collectanea Alexandrina: reliq. minores poet. Graec. aet. Ptolemaicae, 323–146 A. C. epicorum, elegiac., lyric., ethic. Ed. J. U. P. 8°. O. 1925
—— **& E. A. Barber.** New chapters in hist. of Greek lit.: recent discoveries, 4th c. B.C. &c. [*By var. wr.*] Ed. J. U. P. & E. A. B. 8°. O. 1921
Powell (John Wesley), *see* Dellenbaugh (F. S.) Romance of the Colorado River, w. ref. to voyage of P., 1902.
Powell (Joseph) & F. Gribble.
The hist. of Ruhleben. 8°. [1919]
Powell (Thomas), *Wesleyan minister.* An essay on apostolic succession, a defence of Protestant ministry &c. 8°. 1838
see Sandwith (H.) Mem. of T. P., 1852.
Powell (Vavasov), *1617–70, see* Jackson (T.) Lib. of Xtn. biog., v12, 1840.
Powell-Owen (W.) The complete poultry book. 8°. [1924]
Power. *Of the power of the Keyes, or of binding & loosing, 1647, *see* Hammond (H.)
Power (*Sir* D'Arcy). The birth of mankind: bibliog. study. [Repr. f. The Library, 1927]. s4°. 1927
Power (Eileen).
Medieval English nunneries c. 1275–1535. 8°. C. 1922
Medieval people. 8°. [1924]
„ „ ....2nd ed. 8°. [1925]
The Paycockes of Coggeshall. s8°. [1920]
see Tawney (R. H.) & E. P., *edd.* Tudor econ. doc., 3v, 1924.
Power (*Lieut.* John E.) Vade mecum for officers & civilians proc. to India. Chap. on langs. & contrib. on sport by G. M. Routh. s8°. 1912
Power (Patrick). Prehistoric Ireland. Manual of Ir. pre-Xtn. archæology. s8°. D. [1923]
Power (Philip Bennet).
Dinah's fiddlestick; & "I quite forgot." 8°. [1890]
Powers (Harry Huntington). The American era. s8°. N.Y. 1920
Powicke (Frederick James). The Cambridge Platonists. 8°. 1926
Life of Richard Baxter, 1615–91. 8°. [1924]
The Rev. Richard Baxter under the cross (1662–91). 8°. [1927]
S. Langton. Ford Lect., Oxf., 1927. 8°. O. 1928
Powicke (Frederick Maurice). Ailred of Rievaulx & h. biographer Walter Daniel. [Repr. f. Bull. of John Rylands Lib., v6]. la8°. M'ter. [1922]
Powley (Edward Barzillai).
The Eng. navy in the Revol. of 1688. 8°. C. 1928
Pownall (Thomas), *governor of Mass. Bay.* Ship-temple, nr. Dundalk, added, Remarks by Lt. Col. Vallancey, *see* Vallancey (C.) Coll. de rebus Hib., v3, 1782.
Powys (Alfred R.), *see* Soc. for Protect. of Anc. Buildings. An old cottage saved; prep. by P., 1921.
Powys (Llewelyn). Black laughter. s8°. 1925
Henry Hudson. 8°. [1927]
Powys (Theodore Francis). Innocent birds. s8°. 1926
The left leg. Cont.: The left leg—Hester Dominy—Abraham men. s8°. 1923
Mark only. s8°. 1924
Mr. Tasker's gods. s8°. 1925
Powys-Land Club, *see* Montgomeryshire. Colls. hist. &c. rel. to M. &c., v37–39, 1915–20.
Poynton (Francis John). Genealog. mem. rel. to the fam. of Blackburne &c. [*b. w.* Grazebrook (H. S.) Fam. of Shenstone, 1890]. 4°. *p.p.* 1874
Poyntz (Sydnam), *see* Scotland: Parl. Letters f. Ctte. of Estates at Newcastle &c., also letters betw. the Comm. of E. &c. & Gen. P., 1646.
Poyssl (Johann Albert). Drei Gedichte (17. J.); *ed.* J. Bolte, *see* Archiv. f. d. St. d. neu. Spr., B122, 1909.

Pozdneev (Aleksei Matveevich).
Монголія и Монголы. Результаты поѣздки въ Монголію, 1892–93. Изд. И.Р.Г.О. t1. la8°. С.-П. 1896
Монгольская лѣтопись "Эрдэнійнъ Эрихэ." Текстъ съ переводомъ &c. заключающ. въ себѣ матеріалы для ист. Халхи съ 1636 по 1736. 8°. С.-П. 1883
Poznańskie Towarzystwo Przyjaciół Nauk [Soc. Scient. de Poznan], *see* Poniatowski (J. *pr.*) Corresp. avec la Fr., t1, 2, 1921–23.
Pozza (Francesco), *see* Ristori (R. J.) P., 1920.
Pozzani (Fernando), *see* Nofri (G.) & F. P. La Russia com'è, 2ª ed., 1921 ?.
Pozzo (Archangelo), *see* Archangelo [*Pozzo*].
Prach (Vojtěch), *see* Herzer (J.) & V. P. Českoněmecký Slovík; [za] pomocí četných odborníků sestavili J. H. a V. P., d2, 3, 1922.
Practica (Ain) oder weyssagung eins bruders Barfüsser ordenns &c., 1523 ?, *see* Dieterich, *friar, Barfüsser.*
Practical. *Pract. (The) divinity of the Papists &c., 1676, *see* Clarkson (D.)
*Pract. instr. on law of landlords & tenants, 1872, *see* Barrister-at-Law, *ps.*
*Pract. perspective, by a Jesuit of Paris; tr., 7th ed., *n.d.*, *see* Dubreuil (J.)
Pract. road engineering, 1910, *see* Boulnois (H. P.), *ed.*
*Practicall (A) catechisme &c., 1632, *see* Rogers (D.)
Pradel de Lamase (*le chevalier* de). Nouvelles notes intimes d'un émigré [1792–1821]. Les grandes journées révolut. [*Ed.* P. & M. de P. de L.] 8°. 1920
Pradel de Lamase (Martial de). L'Hôtel de la Marine, le monument & l'hist. 8°. [1924]
Prado. Meisterwerke d. Gemäldesamml. d. Prado in Madrid. Einl. Text v. A. L. Mayer. la8°. München. 1922
Tapestries & carpets f. the Pardo [*sic*] for exhib. by the Hispanic Soc. of Amer. [Hisp. Soc. of Amer.] sm. fol. N.Y. 1917
Prado, *ps.*, *see* Linska de Castillon (L. F. de).
Prado (Hieronymus) & J. B. Villalpando. In Ezechielem explan. et apparatus urbis &c. Hierosolymitani. 3t. [t1 & 2i *b. together*: t3i, ii, *pagin. cont.*] fol. Romae. 1596–1604
Pradt (D. D. de).
*Antidote au Congrès de Rastadt &c. 8°. Londres. 1798
De la Belgique, 1789–94. [*no tp., b. w. h.* Progrès du gouv. représ., 1817]. 8°. [1820]
Des progrès du gouv. représ. en France, 1817. Article 1er [*no more publ.*] [*no tp., but preceded by tp. of* Mélanges polit. &c., par B. Constant &c., 1829 *inserted*]. 8°. [1817]
Lettre à un électeur de Paris. [*no tp., b. w. h.* Progrès du gouv. représ., 1817]. 8°. [1817]
Préliminaires de la session de 1817. [*no tp., b. w. h.* Progrès du gouv. représ., 1817]. 8°. [1817]
Praed (*Mrs.* Campbell).
see MacCarthy (J.), *Mrs.* C. P. &c. The grey river, 1889.
Praeger (Robert Lloyd). Aspects of plant life w. spec. ref. to Brit. flora. s8°. 1921
Praëm (Jens Obel), *see* Laache (R.) H. Wergeland & h. strid med Prokurator P., B1, 1828–31, 1927.
Praetorius (Abdias), *see* Armenii. *Armeniorum de Trinitate & Filio Dei confessio; A. P. interprete, 1570.
Praetorius (Fridericus). Disput. de simonia. Sub præs. J. Reusneri. [P2638]. s8°. Wittebergae. 1629
Praetorius (Georg Gottfried). Captus erat Gallus, sive victum Franciscum I a Carolo V &c., 1525. Praes. J. P. Roesero. [P444]. s4°. Baruthi. [1692]
Praetorius (Johannes), *see* Prätorius (J.)
Praetorius (Zacharias) [Pretorius]. Antwort auff Spangenbergs Gegenbericht v. d. Heubtsache im Streit u. d. Erbsünde &c. [P2665]. s4°. Eisleben. 1572
see Menzel (J.), H. Roth &c. Auff d. Verleumbdung Spangenbergs &c., 1573.
Pragmatische. Gesch. d. so berufenen Bulle in Coena Domini &c., 4T, 1772–73, *see* Le Bret (J. F.)
Prague [Praag]. *Prague, the capital of the Czechoslovakian Republ. 2nd ed. [P2421]. s8°. Prague. 1919
*Warhafftige Zeitung Aus Praag Darinnen vermeldet wird d. gefährliche Zustandt welcher ü. d. Evangel. Stände hat ergehen sollen, 1618 [*facs.*], *see* Freytag (G.) Bilder, B4, 1925.
Prais, *ps.*, *see* Spir (A.)
Praitenberka (G. B. Pontanus z), *see* Pontanus (J. B.)
Prance (Miles). Ans. to Mrs. Cellier's libel &c. likewise a vindic. of Sir Wm. Waller fr. Popish scandals. [P525]. sm. fol. 1680

Pranckh (Hans, *Frhr.* v.), *see* Arco-Valley (*Graf.* A.) Der Prozess gegen A. A.-V. der den bayer. Ministerpräs. K. Eisner erschossen hat; hrsg. P., 1920.
Pranzini (Henri). *P. [*Murder of Mme. Régine de Montille* &c., 1887. *no tp.* P2826]. s8°. [Sceaux]. *n.d.*
Prasad (Beni). Hist. of Jahangir. Foreword by Shafaat Ahmad Khan. [Allahabad Univ.] 8°. 1922
Prasch (Daniel). Epitaphia Augustana Vindelica conquisita labore &c. D. P. pl, 2 *in* 1v. s4°. [Augustae Vindel.] 1624
Praschkauer (Maximilian). Antimetallism. [P2829]. s8°. 1889
Prášek (Justin V.) Kyros der Grosse, *see* Alte Orient (Der), Jhrg. 13, 1912.
Prat (Jean Marie), *Jesuit.* Maldonat & l'Univ. de Paris au 16me s. 8°. 1856
Prat (Marcelle). Conte Urugayen: nouvelle, *see* Œuvres libres, 67, 1926.
Pratesi (Mario). Il peccato del dottore. s8°. Milano. 1902
Prati (Giovanni), *see* Ottolini (A.) G. P., 1919.
Prātimoksha, *see* Pātimokkha.
Prato (Giuseppe). Fatti e dottrine econ. alla vigilia del 1848: l'Assoc. agraria subalpina e C. Cavour, *see* Regia Dep. s. St. Patria &c. Bibl., v9, 1921.
Il Piemonte e gli effetti d. Guerra s. sua vita econ. &c. [C.E. for Int. Peace]. la8°. Bari. 1925
Prätorius (Johann), *of Zetlingen.* Bekannte &c. Historien v. d. Rübezahl. s8°. L. 1926
Pratt (Anne), *aft. Mrs. John Pearless.* Ferns of Gt. Brit. & th. allies the club-mosses &c. 8°. *n.d.*
Pratt (Edwin A.)
Brit. railways & the Great War. 2v. la8°. 1921
War record of the L. & N.W. Railway. [Extr. f. Brit. Rlys. & the Gt. War]. la8°. 1922
Pratt (Enoch). Comprehensive hist. of Eastham, Wellfleet & Orleans, Co. of Barnstable, Mass., 1644–1844. 8°. Yarmouth [U.S.] 1844
Pratt (James Bissett). Matter & spirit: st. of mind & body in th. rel. to the spiritual life. s8°. [1923]
The relig. consciousness. [repr.] 8°. N.Y. 1926
see Drake (D.) Essays in crit. realism; by D. D., J. B. P. &c., 1920.
Pratt (James E.), *see* Clarke (J. J.) & J. E. P. Outlines of indust. & soc. economics, 1919.
Pratt (John Henry), *archdeacon of Calcutta.*
see Eclectic Society. E. notes, 1798–1814, 2nd ed., 1865.
,, Pratt (J.) & J. H. P. Mem. of Rev. J. Pratt, B.D., 1849.
Pratt (Josiah). The life of D. Brainerd. s8°. 1856
see Pratt (J.), *the younger* & J. H. Pratt. Mem., 1849.
Pratt (Josiah), *the younger* **& J. H. Pratt.**
Memoir of Rev. J. Pratt, B.D. 8°. 1849
Pratt (Julius W.)
Expansionists of 1812. 8°. N.Y. 1925
James Monroe, *see* Bemis (S. F.), *ed.* Amer. Secr. of State, v3, 1927.
Pratt (*Lt.-Col.* Sisson Cooper). Field artillery. Rev. by E. Baker. 6th ed. s8°. 1896
The milit. law examiner, cont. questions set at public exam. 8th ed. rev. & corr. s8°. [1911]
Pratt (Waldo Seldon). New encyclopedia of music & musicians. la8°. 1924
Praty (Richard), *bp. of Chichester.* Episcopal register, Extr., 1438–45; sel. & ed. by C. Deedes, *see* Sussex. Misc. rec., 1905.
Prausnitz (G.) Der Wagen in d. Relig.; s. Würdigung in d. Kunst. la8°. Str. 1916
Pravdin (B.)
Революц. дни въ Кіевѣ. [P2715]. s8°. Женева. 1903
Praviel (Armand). L'assassinat de M. Fualdès. Préf. de M. Prévost. s8°. 1922
L'hist. tragique de la belle Violante [de Batz, *aft. wife of P. de St. Romain*]. s8°. 1924 [1923]
Le massacre de Ramel, *see* Œuvres libres, 78, 1927.
Pravieux (Jules).
Le vicaire & le romancier. s8°. [1922]
Pravilo. Правило къ Бжественному причащенію. [*tp. wanting*]. s4°. Kiev, *Pechersky monastery.* 1868
Pray (Georg), *Jesuit.* Annales regum Hungariae ab 997 ad 1564. 5p. fol. Vindobonae. 1763–70
Annales vet. Hunnorum, Avarum & Hungar. ab an. a. Chr. 210 ad an. Chr. 997. fol. Vindobonae. 1761

Pray (Georg), *Jesuit* [*continued*].
Diss. hist. crit. in Annales vet. Hunnorum, Avarum et Hungar. fol. Vindobonae. 1774
Epistola ad B. Cetto. Acc. Hist. controvers. de rebus Sinicis &c. 8º. Pestini. 1789

Prayer. Forms of prayer acc. to custom of Span. &c. Jews, w. Eng. tr. by D. A. De Sola, 3v, 1836–37, *see* TEPHILOTH.
Power (The) of prayer. Sel. of Walker Trust essays, w. a study of the essays &c. Ed. W. P. Paterson & D. Russell. 8º. 1920

Prayer Book. [BOOK OF COMMON PRAYER].
Arranged in order of publication.
B. (The) of C.P., w. the Psalter &c. [*b. w.* Bible. The Holy Bible, 1625]. s4º. 1621
B. (The) of C.P. &c. w. the Psalter. s8º. E. 1633
Facs. of the black-letter P.B. of 1636, shewing MS. alterations in 1661 & in 1662. fol. 1870
Facsimile of the black-letter P.B., 1636, cont. MS. alterations &c. made 1661 &c. & annexed to Act of Uniformity, 1662 [*called the* Convocation Book]. fol. 1871
B. (The) of C.P. &c. [*b. w.* Bible, 1638]. fol. C., *Buck & Daniel.* 1638
B. (The) of C.P. *b.l.* fol. *Bill & Barker. n.d.* [c. 1662]
Βίβλος τῆς δημοσίας εὐχῆς. [Ψαλτήριον, *w. sep. tp. dated* 1664]. s8º. ἐν τῇ Καντaβριγίᾳ. 1665
B. (The) of C.P., w. Psalter. s8º. *Bill & Barker.* 1673
Liturgia, seu liber p. c., cum Psalterio. s8º. 1696
Liturgie (La), avec Pseaumes. [*w. sep. pagin.* Tr. Jean Durel]. s8º. Londres. 1703
B. of C.P. [*in Eng. & Irish*] w. Psalter [*in Irish*] [*2nd tp.*: Leabhar &c.] 8º. [1712]
B. (The) of C.P. for the use of the Ch. of Scot. With Psalms in metre by James VI [*w. sep. tp.*] s8º. E. 1712
Liturgie (La) &c. n. éd., corr. s8º. A la Haye, *Vaillant.* 1721
B. of C.P., w. Psalter. 4º. O. 1726
Llyfr Gweddi Gyffredin &c. [*b. w.* Bible: Welsh. Y Bibl., 1746] 8º. Caer-Grawnt, *J. Bentham.* 1746
B. (The) of C.P., w. Psalter. [*w. cuts*]. 8º. O., *Baskett.* 1751
B. (The) of C.P.; w. Psalter. s8º. C., *Baskerville.* 1762
B. (The) of C.P.; w. Psalter. Tr. into Manks. s4º. Whitehaven. 1777
B. (The) of C.P. &c. Protest. Episcop. Church, Philadelphia, 1785. s8º. Phila., repr. London. 1789
B. (The) of C.P. &c. acc. to the use of the United Ch. of Eng. & Ireland; w. Psalter s8º. *Reeves.* [1801]
„ „ *w. 2 tps.* s8º. *Reeves.* 1802
Prayers sel. f. the liturgy & tr. into Singhalese by B. Clough. s8º. Colombo. 1819
B. (The) of C.P.; w. Psalter &c.: notes by R. Mant. 4º. O. 1820
Liturgie (La) &c. selon l'usage anglic. s8º. Londres. 1834
B. (The) of C.P., w. notes by H. Stebbing. s8º. 1838
Order (The) for the admin. of the Holy Communion &c. fol. *Pickering.* 1844
Liturgicae Britannicae, the sev. eds. of the B. of C.P., w. the Liturgy for the Ch. of Scot., arr. to shew their variations, by W. Keeling. 2nd ed. 8º. 1851
B. (The) of C.P., with wood cuts f. designs of Dürer, Holbein & others. [*Second engraved tp. dated* 1853]. s8º. *Pickering.* 1855
Booke (The) of C.P. &c. [Scot. liturgies of the reign of James VI]. Ed. G. W. Sprott. s8º. E. 1871
Prayer (The) B. for teachers &c.; w. intr. &c. by A. Barry. s8º. [1882]
First (The) P.B. of K. Edward VI, 1549. 8º. [1890]
P.-B. (The) of Queen Elizabeth, 1559. s8º. [1890]
Liturgia Anglic., ó lib. de oracion comun. [Tr.] s8º. Londres. 1906
Liturgia Britanica. s8º. London, *Bagster. n.d.*
ADAPTATIONS & COMMENTARIES.
B. (The) of C.P. reformed; w. Psalms & Hymns [*w. sep. tp. & pagin.*] rev. & corr. [*Unitarian ed.*, ed. by John Disney]. 2nd ed. s8º. 1802
B. (The) of C.P. rev. acc. to plan of S. Clarke; w. Psalter [*Unitarian*]. 7th ed. s8º. 1823
Liturgia Tigurina: or the Book of C.P. Tr. out of Helvetian by J. C. Werndly. s8º. 1693
P.-B. comm., hist. intr. &c. s8º. 1894
Proposed amendments to text of Psalter. P.B. Commission. s8º. N.Y. 1921
B. of C.P. Bk. of 1662, w. permiss. add. & deviations approved in 1927. [Provisional]. 8º. [1927]
„ „ [Bk. ref. to in P.B. Measure, submitted Mar. 29]. 8º. [1927]
see ARMITAGE (W. J.) Story of Canadian revision of P.B., 1922.
„ BAXTER (R.) A petition for peace w. the reformation of the liturgy &c., 1661.
„ CLARKE (W. K. L.) *The New P.B. explained, 1927.
„ DEARMER (P.) Illust. of the Liturgy: 13 drawings; w. notes & intr. by P. D., 1912.
„ DIRECTORY for the publique worship of God, w. ordinance of Parl. for taking away of B. of C.P. &c., 1646.
„ FRANKFORT ON THE MAIN. *A brieff disc. off the troubles at F. 1554, abowte B. of C.P., 1575.

Prayer Book [*continued*].
see HOOLE (E.) Lady's Tamil bk., cont. portions of B. of C.P., 1859.
„ JOYNSON-HICKS (*Sir* W.) The P.B. crisis, 1928.
„ MARSH (H.) Consequences of neglecting to give the P.B. w. the Bible, 1812.
„ PRYNNE (W.) Short &c. exam. of exuberances in, & ceremon. appurt. to the C.P., 1661.
„ RELTON (M.), *ed.* The new P.B.: lect. [*by var. a.*], 1927.
„ SANDAY (W.) & C. W. EMMET. The Psalms explained: compan. to P.B. Psalter, 1918.
„ TEMPLE (W.) The P.B. crisis, 1928.
„ WHEATLY (C.) Rational illust. of B. of C.P., 1845.

Prayers.
Form of p. acc. to custom of Span. & Portug. Jews; tr. D. Levi, 1789, *see* TEPHILOTH.
Forme (The) of prayers & admin. of the sacraments &c. used in the Engl. congreg. at Geneva & approved by John Calvin. s4º. Geneva. 1643
Prayers of the saints, 1898, *see* HEADLAM (C.), *ed.*

Praz (Mario). Penisola pentagonale. 8º. Milano. 1928

Prazeres Maranhão (Francisco dos), *see* FRANCISCO *dos Prazeres Maranhão.*

Prebensen (N.) & Hj. Smith. Forarbeiderne til Christian V norske Lov af 15 Apr. 1687. Udg. af N. P. & Hj. S. [Norske Hist. K.] 8º. 1887

***Precationes** aliquot privatae & publicae. [*b. w.* Heidelberg Catechism, 1563]. s8º. Heydelbergae. 1563

***Preces** christianae Barmanorum lingua &c., ed. s8º. Romae, *Typis Sac. Congreg. de Prop. Fide.* 1785

Prechtl (Robert). Alkestis. Tragoedie. [3e A.] 8º. [1920]

Precipiano (Humbert Guillaume de), (*1*) *bp. of Bruges,* (*2*) *abp. of Malines, see* ARNAULD (A.) *Très-humble remontrance à H. de P., 1695.

Précis. Précis of offic. papers: abstracts of all Parl. returns &c., 1880–1, 1880–2, *see* PARLIAMENT.

Predelli (Matteo).
In mem. d. cav. R. Predelli. 8º. [Trento. 1910]

Predelli (Riccardo), *1842–1909.* Le reliquie d. Archivio d. Ordine Teutonico in Venezia. [*Extr. f.* R. Ist. Veneto, Atti, t64ii]. 8º. Venezia. 1905
see PREDELLI (M.) In mem. d. R. P., 1910.
„ SEGARIZZI (A.) R. P., 1909.

Prediger-Orden. *Von den fier ketzeren Prediger ordẽs d observantz &c., 1510, *see* MURNER (T.)

Predikanten. Naam-register van de p. &c., 1784, *see* HOLLAND

Preger (Conrad). Pankraz v. Freyberg auf Hohenaschau [Verein f. Ref.-gesch. Schr., Jhrg. 10, Nr. 40]. 8º. Halle. 189[illegible]

Pregitzer (Georg Conrad). M. Lutherum de univ. eccl. optime meritum &c. Præses G. C. P., resp. C. P. Kalbfell. [P2627]. s4º. Tubingæ. 172[illegible]

Pregnon (*l'abbé*). Hist. du pays & de la ville de Sedan. 3t. 8º. Charleville. 185[illegible]

Prehistoric (The) Society of East Anglia. Proceedings, 1908–2[illegible] v1–5. 8º. Ipswich. 1914–2[illegible]
Report on the excav. at Grime's Graves, Weeting, Norfolk 1914. Ed. W. G. Clarke. 8º. 191[illegible]

Preisendanz (Carl). Akephalos d. kopflose Gott, *see* ALT ORIENT. Beih. 8, 1926.

Preisenstein (Jodocus). Ein Leichpredig bey d. Leiche u Begrebnuss L. Rabi &c. [*Foll. by* Threnodia &c.] [P2613]. s4º. Tübingen. 159[illegible]

Preisigke (Friedrich). Sammelbuch griech. Urkunden au Ägypten. Hrsg. im Auftr. d. Wiss. Gesell. in Strassbur v. F. P. [fortgesetzt v. F. Bilabel]. B1–3. la8º. Str. & Berlin. 1915–2[illegible]
Wbch. d. griech. Papyrusurkunden, mit Einschluss d. g Inschriften, Ostraka &c. Hrsg. v. E. Kiessling. 2B. 4º. 1925–2[illegible]

Preiss (Joseph), *see* XAVIER (F.) Vita S. F. X. [*attrib. to J. P.* 1691?.

Preitz (Max). Prinz Moritz v. Dessau im siebenjähr. Kriege. 8º. München. 19[illegible]

Preller (Charles S. Du Riche). Italian mountain geology. 3p [*in 2v.* pl 1 & 2, 3rd ed.] 8º. 1923–[illegible]

Preller (Ludwig). Les dieux de l'anc. Rome: mytholog romaine. Tr. M. L. Dietz. 3e éd. s8º. 18[illegible]
Griech. Mythologie. 4e A., von C. Robert. B2i–iii [*pagin. cont.*] 8º. 1920–[illegible]

Premerstein (Anton v.)
Zu d. sog. Alexandrin. Märtyrerakten. 8º. L. 19[illegible]
see KEIL (J.) & A. v. P. Ber. ü. eine 3. Reise in Lydie &c. 1914.

Prendergast (John Patrick), *see* RUSSELL (C. W.) & J. P. P. The Carte MSS. in the Bodleian Lib., 1871.

Prentice (William Kelly). Greek & Lat. inscr., *see* PRINCETON UNIV. Syria, div. 2, §B, by P., 1922.

Prentiss (George Lewis). A sermon on the death of Anson G. Phelps. With some extr. f. h. journal. (f. priv. distrib.) [P601]. 8°. N.Y. 1854

Prentout (Henri). Caen & Bayeux. 2e éd. rev. 8°. 1921

Les états provinciaux de Normandie. [t1, *publ. as* Acad. Nat. des Sci. &c. de Caen. Mém., n. sér., t1]. 3t. 8°. Caen. 1925–27

Preobrajensky (A.)

Краткая грам. нов. церковно-слав. языка. изд. 11oe. 8°. Москва. 1910

Preobrajensky (Evgeny A.)

Анархизм и коммунизм. 8°. [Москва]. 1921

Le front de l'Oural, *see* RUSSIE. Pour la Russie socialiste, 1918.

О крестьянских коммунах. [P2455]. s8°. Киев. 1919

see BUKHARIN (N.) & E. P. Das ABC d. Kommunismus, 2B, 1920.

Preparation for death, in sev. hymns, 1772, *see* WESLEY (J.) & C. WESLEY.

Presber (Rudolf).

Die Brücken zum Sieg. Kriegsgedichte. s8°. *n.d.*

Presbyter Cicestrensis, *ps., see* LATHAM (H.)

Presbyter of the Church of Eng., *ps., a. of Ans. to Hicks's Xtn. priesthood,* 1709, *see* HANCOCK (J.)

Presbyter of the Church of Eng., *ps., a. of A disc. about church unity,* 1681, *see* SHERLOCK (W.)

Presbyter (A) of the Church of Eng., *ps., a. of The independent power of the church &c.,* 1716, *see* INDEPENDENT.

Presbyterian [*incl.* P. CHURCH ; PRESBYTERIANS].

*Historical (An) essay upon loyalty of P., 1713, *see* KIRKPATRICK (J.)

*History (A) of the union betw. P. & Congregat. ministers in & about London &c., 2nd ed., 1698, *see* TAYLOR (*Rev.* R.)

*Mem. of the union of the Secession & Relief Churches, now the United P. Ch., 1847, *see* MACKELVIE (W.)

P.'s (The) armoury. 3v. 8°. E. 1843–46

1, 2, Gillespie (G.) Works. 3, Rutherford's Lex Rex—Brown of Wamphray's Apologetical relation—Calderwood's Pastor & Prelate—Causes of the Lord's wrath against Scotland.

Rules & forms of procedure in the church courts of the United P. Church adopted 1848. 7th ed. cont. alterations up to May 1863. s8°. E. 1863

Prescott (Frederick Clarke). The poetic mind. s8°. N.Y. 1922

Prescott (H. F. M.) The unhurrying chase. s8°. 1925

Prescott (William Hickling).

Corr., 1833–47. Transcr. & ed. R. Wolcott. [Mass. Hist. Soc.] la8°. [Camb., *Mass.*] 1925

Hist. of the conquest of Mexico ; w. life of Cortés. n. & rev. ed. Ed. J. F. Kirk. 8°. 1878

„ „ ....[repr.] 8°. 1890

„ „ Illust. by K. Henderson. Intr. by T. A. Joyce. 2v. la8°. 1922

Hist. of the conquest of Peru &c. 6th ed. 2v. 8°. 1850

„ „ n. & rev. ed. Ed. J. F. Kirk. 8°. 1890

„ „ ....2v. s8°. *Bohn.* 1902

Hist. of the r. of Ferdinand & Isabella. 3v. 8°. 1838

„ „ n. & rev. ed. Ed. J. F. Kirk. 8°. 1901

„ „ ....3v. s8°. *Bohn.* 1902

„ „ ....8°. *n.d.*

Letters to Gayangos in lib. of Hisp. Soc. of Amer. (1838–60). Ed. w. notes by C. L. Penney. s8°. N.Y. 1927

Present.

*P. state of Eng. as to coin &c., 1697, *see* HODGES (J.)

*P. state of Europe &c., 1752, *see* CAMPBELL (J.), *LL.D.*

*P. state of Gt. Brit. & Ireland, 8th ed., 1738, *see* MIEGE (G.)

*P. state of H.M.'s dominions in Germany, 1737, *see* MIEGE (G.) Pres. state of Gt. Brit. &c., 8th ed., 1738.

*P. state of Scotland, 1738, *see* MIEGE (G.) Pres. state of Gt. Brit., 8th ed., 1738.

Present state (The) of Europe, or The hist. & polit. monthly mercury. Done f. orig. [Mercure hist. & polit.] publ. at the Hague. v1–23 (Nov. 1688–Dec. 1712) [v10, No. 6–12 (June 1699–Dec. 1700), v15–18 (1704–7) *wanting*]. s4°. 1692–1712

v1 *has tp.*: The gen. hist. of Europe, 1688–90. *The place of* v15–18 *is supplied by* The Monthly Register, *q.v.*

Presland (John), *ps.* [*i.e. Mrs.* GLADYS SKELTON].

Dominion. s8°. [1925]

Frustration. s8°. [1925]

Presle (La). Hist. & cartul. du prieuré de Notre-Dame & Ste.-Marguerite de La P. [Publ. &c.] E. Carré. [Extr. de la Revue de Champagne & de Brie. P2469]. 8°. Arcis-sur-Aube. 1893

Press. *Press (The) : prepared by the Labour Research Dept., 1922, *see* LABOUR RESEARCH DEPT.

Press laws of foreign countries, w. app. cont. press laws of India. Ed. M. Shearman & O. T. Rayner. 8°. 1926

Pressensé (Edmond de). The anc. world & Christianity. Tr. by A. H. Holmden. 8°. 1888

Contemporary portraits : Thiers, Strauss, Arnaud de l'Ariège, Dupanloup, A. Monod, Vinet, Verny, Robertson. Tr. by A. H. Holmden. s8°. 1880

Presser (J.) Das Buch "De tribus impostoribus." 8°. A. 1926

Prestage (Edgar).

D. Francisco Manuel de Mello. [Hispanic Soc.] s8°. O. 1922

Diplomat. rel. of Portugal & Eng., 1640–68. [P2773]. 8°. Watford. 1925

Embaixada de T. de Mendonça Furtado á Holanda em 1641 ; ed. E. P., 1920, *see* MENDONÇA FURTADO (T. DE).

Frei Domingos do Rosário [*i.e.* [D. O'Daly], 1595–1662. 8°. Coimbra. 1926

Minor works of Camões. 8°. 1924

Portugal, Brasil e Grã-Bretanha. Lição inaug. [Tr.] 8°. Coimbra. 1925

Portugal, Brazil & Gt. Brit. Lect. [P2718]. 8°. O. 1923

Royal power & the Cortes in Portugal. [P2871]. 8°. Watford. 1927

see CRUS (L. F.), *ed.* Manifesto das ostillidades, 1919.

„ LOPES (F.) Chron. of F. L. & G. Eannes de Zurara, w. tr. extracts &c. by E. P., 1928.

„ SANTA CRUZ DO CASTELLO. Registo, 1536–1628 ; publ. com intr. &c. por E. P. &c., 1913.

„ SÉ. Registo da freguesia da Sé, 1563–1610 ; publ. com intr. &c. por E. P. &c., 2v, 1924–27.

„ SOUSA COUTINHO (F. DE). Corresp. diplom. de F. de S. C. ; publ. E. P. & P. de Azevedo, v1, 2, 1920–26.

Preston [PRESTON EPISCOPI]. Abstract of Court rolls of the manor of P. By C. Thomas-Stanford. [Sussex Rec. Soc., v27]. 8°. 1921

Preston, *The family of, see* GORMANSTON. Cal. of the G. register, 1916.

Preston (Hayter). The house of vanities. [Biog. foreword by H. Macfall. Decor. by C. Lovat Fraser]. s8°. 1922

Preston (John), *master of Emmanuel Coll., C.* *Three godly & learned treatises. Agst. covetousnesse—descr. of spirituall death & life—self-denial. Sermons by J. P. [*sep. tps. & pagins.*] s4°. 1632

Preston (*Lt.-Col.* Richard Martin Peter). The Desert Mounted Corps : cavalry oper. in Palestine & Syria, 1917–18. Intr. by Lt.-Gen. Sir H. G. Chauvel. 8°. 1921

Preston (Sydney), *see* HILL (*Sir* N.) &C. War & insurance, 1927.

Preston (Thomas), *LL.D., 1537–98.* Cambises, King of Percia (*c.* 1584), *see* ADAMS (J. Q.) Chief pre-Shakespearian dramas, 1925.

Prete (Leone del), *see* FAYTINELLI (P. DE'). Rime ; publ., con notizie s. vita dell' autore, da L. del P., 1874.

***Prétendus** (Les) reformez convaincus de schisme, 1684, *see* NICOLE (P.)

Preti (Mattia), *called Il Cavalier Calabrese ; 1613–99.*

see CHIMIRRI (B.) & A. FRANGIPANE. M. P., detto Il Cavalier C., 1914.

Pretorius (Zacharias), *see* PRAETORIUS (Z.)

Preuschen (Erwin). Die Apostelgeschichte ; erkl. v. E. P., *see* LIETZMANN (H.), *ed.* Handbuch z. N.T., B4i, 1912.

see ZEITSCHRIFT F. D. NEUTESTAMENTL. WISSENSCHAFT ; hrsg. v. E. P., 1900 &c.

Preuss (Hugo), *see* SCHMOLLER (G.) W. Rathenau u. H. P., 1922.

Preuss (Julius).

Biblisch-talmud. Medizin. 2e unveränderte A. la8°. 1921

Preuss (Konrad Theodor). Religion u. Mythologie der Uitoto. 2B [*pagin. cont.*] la8°. Göttingen. 1921–23

Preuss (Paul). Die Kokospalme u. i. Kultur. la8°. [1911]

Preussen. Kirchl.-polit. (Die) Gesetzgebung, 1873–75, 1875, *see* KIRCHLICH.

*P.'s protest. Kaiseridee u. Oesterreichs kathol.-polit. Zukunft. [P2695]. 8°. Wien. 1871

Preusser (Conrad). Nordmesopotam. Baudenkmäler, alt-christl. u. islam. Zeit. [Deut. Orient-Gesell., Wiss. Veröffentl., 17]. fol. L. 1911

Preussische (Der) Correspondent. Nr. 1., 2. April. 1813 (*facs.*), *see* FREYTAG (G.) Bilder, B5, 1925.

Preussische Akademie d. Wissenschaften, *see* KÖNIGLICH-PREUSS. AKADEMIE D. WISS. ZU BERLIN.

Preussische Jahrbücher. Hrsg. H. Delbrück &c. B163–212. 8°. 1916–28

Preussisches Historisches Institut in Rom, *see* KÖNIGLICH-PREUSS. HIST. INST. IN ROM.

Prevention of venereal disease, 1921, *see* COMMITTEE ON VENEREAL DISEASE.

Previté-Orton (Charles William), *see* CAMBRIDGE. Index to Tripos lists, 1748–1910 ; comp. by C. W. P.-O., 1923.

Prévost (*l'abbé*). Hist. of Manon Lescaut & the Chevalier des Grieux. Tr., w. intr. by G. D. Gribble. [Broadway Trans.] s8°. [1925]

Prevost (*General* **Augustin**), *1723–86.*
[Journal, 1774. *MS.*] s8°. [1774]

Prévost (Ernest).
Le livre de l'immortelle amie. Poèmes. s8°. 1924
Poèmes de tendresse. s8°. 1920

Prévost (Jean). La vie de Montaigne. 8e éd. s8°. 1926

Prévost (Marcel).
L'art d'apprendre. s8°. [1922]
Los don Juanes. Roman. s8°. [1922]
Missette [*&* Poupette]. s8°. *n.d.*
La nuit finira. Roman. 2[t]. s8°. 1920
La retraite ardente. s8°. [1927]
Sa maitresse & moi. s8°. [1925]

Prévost (Victor Joseph). *Prévost (le gardien de la paix assassin). [P2826]. s8°. [Sceaux. 1898]

Prewett (Frank). Poems. 8°. [1921]

Preyer (William).
Die Erklärung d. Gedankenlesens. [P2507]. 8°. L. 1886

Prezel (Honoré Lacombe de), *see* LACOMBE DE PREZEL (H.)

Prezzolini (Giuseppe).
Amici. s8°. Firenze. [1922]
La coltura ital. 8°. Firenze. 1923
Fascism. Tr. [& w. final chap. by] K. Macmillan. 8°. [1926]
Io credo. 8°. Torino. 1923
Uomini 22 e città 3. s8°. Firenze. [1921]
Vita di N. Machiavelli fiorentino. 8°. Milano. 1927
Vittorio Veneto. s8°. [1920]
see BIBLIOTECA DEI MAESTRI ITALIANI. Guida bibliografica, *n.d.*

Priamure [Приамурье]. Приамурье. Факты, цифрі, наблюденія. Собр. сотрудникали. общеземской организаціи. *With* Приложеніе, *b. sep.* [*Preface by* кн. Г. Львовъ ; *introd. by* Т. Полнеръ. la8°. Москва. 1909

Pribram (Alfred Francis). Aus d. Berichte e. Franzosen ü. d. Wiener Hof, 1671–72. [*Extr. f.* Inst. f. österr. Gesch., Mitthlg. 12. P2729]. 8°. [1891]
Austrian foreign policy, 1908–18. Foreword by G. P. Gooch. s8°. [1923]
The secret treaties of Austria-Hungary, 1879–1914. Eng. ed. by A. C. Coolidge. v1, 2. 8°. C. 1920–21
v1, Texts of the treaties & agreements ; w. tr. by D. P. Myers & J. G. D'A. Paul.
v2, Negot. leading to the treaties of the Triple Alliance, w. doc. app. tr. by J. G. D'A. Paul & D. P. Myers.

Price (Archibald Grenfell). Foundation & settlement of S. Australia, 1829–45. 8°. Adelaide. 1924

Price (Candelent).
Keats' finales : Hyperion, & the eve of St. Mark. s8°. 1922

Price (Frederick George Hilton), *see* PRICE (J. E.) & F. G. H. P. Descr. of remains of Roman buildings at Morton, I. of Wight, 1881.

Price (Henry), *poetical writer.* *Poems on several subjects. By a Land-Waiter in the Port of Poole. [*Comp. by H. P., & cont. h.* Shalum & Hilpa *& o. poems*]. 8°. 1741

Price (Hereward T.)
Volkswirtschaftl. Wörterbuch. T1. s8°. 1926

Price (John Edward) & F. G. H. Price. A descr. of the remains of Roman buildings at Morton, nr. Brading, Isle of Wight. 4°. 1881

Price (Morgan Philips). Journey thr. Azerbaijan & Persian Khurdistan, *see* PERSIA SOCIETY. Lect., 1913.
My remin. of the Russian Revol. 8°. [1921]

Price (*Capt.* **R. K.**) Astbury, Whieldon, & Ralph Wood figures, & Toby jugs. Coll. by R. K. P. Intr. by F. Falkner. 4°. 1922

Price (Richard). Obs. on reversionary payments ; on schemes for annuities &c. New arranged, & gen. intr. by W. Morgan. 6th ed. 2v. 8°. 1803

Price (*Sir* **Uvedale**), *1st bart., see* ROBINSON (P. F.) Village archit. : designs illust. of Essay on the picturesque by P., 1830.

Prichard (H. Hesketh). Sniping in France. Scientific training of scouts &c. Foreword by Gen. Ld. Horne of Stirkoke. 8°. [1920]
see PARKER (E.) H. P., D.S.O., hunter, explorer &c., 1924.

Prichard (James Cowles). Six ethnograph. maps, illustr. of "Nat. hist. of man." 2nd ed. fol. [1861]

Prickett (Marmaduke).
Descr. of the Priory Church of Bridlington. la8°. C. 1831

Prick van Wely (F. P. H.), *see* KRAMER (M.) Nieuw Engelsch Woordenboek ; bewerkt d. P. v. W., 1921.

Pride. *Pride (The) of life ; *ed.* F. Holthausen, *see* ARCHIV F. D. ST. D. NEU. SPR., B108, 1902.

Prideaux (Humphrey), *dean of Norwich.* An histor. connection of the Old & New Test. Added, An acc. of the Rabbinic authorities by A. M'Caul. 2nd ed. rev. &c. by J. T. Wheeler 2v. 8°. 186[5]
A letter to the Deists. [*b. w. h.* The true nature of imposture 1697]. s8°. 169[7]
Marmora Oxoniensia, ex Arundellianis, Seldenianis, aliisque conflata. Rec. & explic. H. P. Appos. Seldeni & Lydiat annot. Acc. S. Ursati De notis Roman. comm. fol. Oxonii. 167[6]
For 2nd ed., 1732, *see* † MAITTAIRE (M.)
The true nature of imposture displ. in the life of Mahomet &c s8°. 169[7]
„ „ w. a disc. annex'd for the vindic. of Xty. f. thi[s] charge &c. [*w. sep. tp.*] 7th ed. 8°. 171[8]

Prideaux (John), *bp. of Worcester, see* PRIDEAUX (M.) A[n] easy &c. introd. &c. Added, A synopsis of Councels, by J. P. (1671), 1672.

Prideaux (Mathias). An easy &c. introd. for reading all sort[s] of histories, 5th ed. Added, A synopsis of Councels by J. Prideaux [*w. sep. tp.* (1671) *& pagin.*] s4°. Oxford. 167[2]

Prideaux (Sarah Treverbian), *see* VICTORIA & ALBERT MUS[EUM] Notes on printing & bookbinding : guide to exhib. of tool[s] &c., by S. T. P., 1921.

Pridik (Alexander). Der Mitregent d. Königs Ptolemaios I[I] Philadelphos, *see* DORPAT UNIV. Acta &c., B–v5, 1924.
Mut-em-Wija, die Mutter Amenhotep's III, *see* DORPA[T] UNIV. Acta &c., B–v5, 1924.

Priel (Jarl). L'affaire Bombille ; nouvelle, *see* ŒUVRES libre[s] 66, 1926.
Cincinnatus au pays des Soviets : roman, *see* ŒUVRES libre[s] 74, 1927.

Prier (Robert). A cristall looking-glass for a proud pharise[e] &c. [Pref. signed R. B.] s8°. 165[.]

Prières dur. la Sainte Messe, oraisons pr. la Confession, [la] Communion &c. [*tp. wanting*]. s8°. *n.p.* [175.]

***Priestcraft** defended ; by the Shaver, 12th ed., 1771, *se[e]* MACGOWAN (J.)

Priestley (John Boynton). Adam in moonshine. s8°. 192[.]
George Meredith. [Eng. Men of Letters]. 8°. 192[.]
Thomas Love Peacock. [Eng. Men of Letters]. 8°. 192[.]

Priestley (Joseph), *LL.D.* Descr. of a chart of biography w[.] cat. of names & dates annexed. n. ed. [P2494]. s8°. 178[.]
see WESLEY (J.) Orig. letters ; pref. addr. to Methodist[s] by J. P., 1791.

Priestley (Joshua).
True womanhood. Mem. of Eliza Hessel. s8°. 18[.]

Priestley (Raymond E.) Glaciology—Physiography (Rober[t]son Bay & Terra Nova Bay regions), 1922–23, *see* BRI[T.] ANTARCTIC EXPED., 1910–13.
see ROYAL ENGINEERS. Work of the R.E. : Signal servic[e] by R. E. P., 1921.

Prieto de Landázuri (Isabel), *see* OLAVARRIA Y FERRARI (E. DE) Poesías líricas mejicanas de I. P. &c., 1878.

Prieur (Jean Louis), *see* NOLHAC (P. DE). Tabl. de Par[is] pend. la Révol., dessins de P., 1902.

Primas (Hermannus), *see* FLACIUS (M.) Quod hoc tempo[re] nulla penitus mutatio &c. contra quoddam scr. &c. p[er] H. P., 1549.

Prime (William Cowper). Tent life in the Holy Land. 8°. 18[.]

Prime ministers. Polit. princs. of notable p. m. of the 19th cent. : lects., 1926, *see* HEARNSHAW (F. J. C.), *ed.*

Primer.
[The Primer set furth by the kinges maiestie & his clergie & 1545. *tp. &c. wanting*]. [repr. 1710
Three primers put forth in the reign of Henry VIII, viz. 1, [A] goodly prymer, 1535. 2, The manual of prayers or t[he] prymer in English, 1539. 3, King Henry's primer, 154[5] Ed. E. Burton. 8°. O. 18[.]

***Primitive** heresie revived in the faith &c. of Quakers, 1698, *see* LESLIE (C.)
***Primordia** Corcyrae, 1738, *see* CORCYRA.
Prince (John Dyneley).
Pract. gram. of the Lettish lang. s8°. 1925
Prince (Morton). Problems of personality. Studies pres. to M. P. Ed. C. MacF. Campbell, H. S. Langfeld, W. McDougall &c. 8°. 1925
Prince (Samuel Henry). Catastrophe & social change: Halifax disaster. [Columbia Univ.] 8°. N.Y. 1920
Prince Edward Island.
*P.E.I., Canada: its resources &c. 8°. Ottawa. 1926
Prince's Plain Cricket Club, *see* WEST KENT C.C.
***Princesse Cloria (The)**: or, The royal romance. Wr. by a person of honour. 2nd ed. la8°. 1665
Princeton University. Holder Tower & the new dining-halls of P.U. With apprec. by R. A. Cram. Repr. f. Architecture. 4°. N.Y. 1918
Syria. Publ. of the P.U. archaeolog. exped. to Syria in 1904–5 & 1909. div. 2, A, B, 3, A, B, 4, A. 4°. Leyden. 1914–22
Div. II, Architecture, by H. C. Butler: §A, Southern Syria. §B, Northern Syria.
Div. III, Greek & Lat. inscr.: §A, S. Syria, by E. Littmann, D. Magie & D. R. Stuart. §B, N. Syria, by W. K. Prentice.
Div. IV, Semitic inscr., by E. Littmann: §A, Nabataean inscr.
see ART STUDIES; ed. by members of Dept. of the Fine Arts at P. &c., v1, 2, 1923–24.
Principes fondamentaux de la doctrine catholique. Tr. de l'anglais. rev. &c. par D. Galvano évêque de Nice. [*b. w.* Nice. Catéchisme du dioc. de N., 1839]. s8°. Nice. 1843
Principles (The) of the Jesuits, 1839, *see* NORRIS (H. H.)
Pring (Martin). Rel. des voyages de P. &c. à la Virginie, 1602–3, *see* BERNARD (J. F.), *ed.* Recueil, t3, 1732.
Pringle (John).
see LAMPLUGH (G. W.), F. L. KITCHIN, & J. P. Concealed mesozoic rocks in Kent, 1923.
„ SHERLOCK (R. L.) Geol. of co. around Aylesbury, w. contrib. by J. P. &c., 1922.
„ —— & A. H. NOBLE. Geology of co. around Beaconsfield, w. contrib. by J. P., 1922.
Print Collectors' Club. Publications. No. 5. la8°. 1926
see ROOKE (N.) Woodcuts & w. engravings, 1926. [5.]
Print-collector's quarterly (The). Ed. Campbell Dodgson. v8–15. s8°. 1921–28
„ „ .... Index, v1–7. s8°. 1917
„ „ .... Gen. index, v1–13. s8°. 1927
Print Society. Publications. No. 1, 3. 4°. 1920–26
see HUBBARD (E. H.) How to distinguish prints, 1926. [3.]
„ —— On making & collecting etchings; wr. by members of the P. Soc.; ed. &c. E. H. H., 1920. [1.]
Printa (Charles). La Bosnie & l'Herzégovine dev. la fut. confér. [*No tp.*; *extr. f.* Questions diplom. &c., t17, 1909. P2753]. 8°. [1909]
Printer. *The London printers lamentation, 1660, *see* LONDON.
Printing. *Hist. (The) of p. in Europe, 1713, *see* WATSON (J.), *printer.*
Prinz (Johannes). John Wilmot, earl of Rochester: life, corresp. &c. & bibliog. of h. works &c. [Palaestra 154]. 8°. L. 1927
Prinzing (Friedrich). Epidemics resulting f. wars. Ed. H. Westergaard. [C.E. for Internat. Peace]. la8°. O. 1916
Prior (Edward Schroder). Eight chapters on Eng. medieval art: st. in Eng. economics. s8°. C. 1922
Prior (George Thurland).
see BRIT. MUS. OF NAT. HIST. Cat. of meteorites; by G. T. P., 1923.
Prior (James), *ps.* [*i.e.* JAMES P. KIRK]. Hyssop. s8°. 1904
Ripple & flood. s8°. 1897
Prior (Matthew).
*Poems on sev. occasions. s8°. 1709
Poet. works. Coll. by T. Park. 3v. s8°. 1807
Poet. works. [Life by J. Mitford. Aldine ed.] 2v. s8°. [1866]
see LEGG (L. G. W.) M. P.: his career & corresp., 1921.
Prior (Oliver Herbert Phelps), *ed.*, *see* ANGLO-NORMAN. Camb. A.-N. texts, 1924.
Prior (W. H.) Notes on the weights & measures of medieval England. [*Extr. f.* Union Acad. Internat. Bull.] 8°. Paris. 1924
Priou (Salomon), *see* LE GOBIEN (C.) *Lettre s. les propos. [*advanced by L. Lecomte*] déferées par M. P., 1700.

Priscianus, *of Lydia, the philosopher.* Expos. Pr. & Marsilii in Theophrastum de sensu ac phantasia & intellectu, *see* IAMBLICHUS *of Chalcis.* De mysteriis &c., 1497.
Institutiones gramaticę: Adj. Libello de xii carminibus. fol. [Paris]. ab I. B. Ascensio, 1516
see DIONYSIUS. Orbis descr. &c. acc. Perigesis P., 1697.
Prison Survey Committee, *New York, see* NEW YORK.
Prison System Enquiry Committee, *see* HOBHOUSE (S.) & A. F. BROCKWAY. Eng. prisons to-day, 1922.
Prisse d'Avenues (A. C. T. Emile). L'art arabe d'ap. les mon. du Kaire. Texte, 1v. Planches, 3v. 4°. & atl. fol. 1877
Pritanius (Lamindus), *ps., see* MURATORI (L. A.)
Pritchard (Thomas Sirrell), *see* BURN (R.) Justice of the Peace &c., 30th ed., v1 by T. S. P., 1869.
Pritzel (Lotte), *see* PUPPENBUCH. Das Puppenbuch [Puppen de L. P. &c.], 1921.
Priuli (Girolamo). I diarii di G. P., 1494–1512; a cura di A. Segre, v1, *see* MURATORI (L. A.) Rerum Ital. script., t24iii, 1912–21.
Priuli (Mafio). Copia di una lettera ven. d'India, 1537. [*Ed. G. A. Moschini f. ed. pr. by F. Marcolino.* Nozze Danese-Buri—Giovanelli. N124]. 8°. Venezia. 1824
Privilegia universitatum, collegiorum &c., 1585, *see* REBUFFI (P.)
Privy Council. Acts of the Privy Council of England, 1613–[17]. [Ed. H. C. Maxwell Lyte *&* J. V. Lyle]. [3v]. la8°. 1921–27
[1], 1613–14. [2], 1615–16. [3], 1616–17.
Probates. Year Books of Probates: Abstracts of Probate Acts in Prerog. Court of Canterbury, v5, 6, 1650–3—Extra vol.: Abstracts of Probates & Sentences, 1620–24; ed. J. &c. Matthews, 1909–11, *see* YEAR BOOKS.
Problems.
P. of mod. science, lect., 1922, *see* DENDY (A.), *ed.*
P. of peace; lect. 1926, 1927, *see* GENEVA INST. OF INTERNAT. RELATIONS.
P. of personality: st. pres. to M. Prince; ed. C. MacF. Campbell &c., 1925, *see* PRINCE (M.)
P. of population & parenthood, 2nd rep. &c. 1918–20, 1920, *see* NATIONAL BIRTH-RATE COMMISSION.
Probst (Anton). Trial of A. P. for murder of C. Dearing &c. at Philadelphia, Apr. 25, 1866. Publ. under supervision of W. B. Mann. 8°. Phila. 1866
Probus (Marcus Valerius). In Vergilii Bucolica & Georgica comm., *see* SERVIUS MAURUS HONORATUS. Comm., v3ii, 1902.
Proby (*Col.* Douglas James), *see* ELTON HALL. Cat. of pictures at E.H. in poss. of Col. D. J. P., by T. Borenius &c., 1924.
Proceedings. P. at laying of the corner stone of the New Capitol, 24th June 1871, *see* ALBANY, *N.Y.*
Processio. *Hist. de ortu et progressu controv. de process. Spir. Sancti, 1772, *see* PROKOPOVICH (T.)
Processus. De processu martyriali quorūdam fidei pugilum, 1619, *see* ROTH (D.) Analecta sacra de rebus Cath. in Hibernia, p3, 1619.
Procès-verbaux de la Commune de 1871, *see* COMMUNE.
Procházka (Rudolph, *Frhr.* **v.)** Mozart in Prag. 8°. Prag. 1892
Prochorus. P. de Johanne theologo & evangelista hist.; S. Castalione interprete, *Gr. & Lat.*, *see* LUTHER (M.) Catechesis parva &c., 1567.
Procksch (Otto). Petrus u. Johannes bei Marcus u. Matthäus. la8°. Gütersloh. 1920
Proclus, *Diadochus.* In Platonicum alcibiadem de anima atq; daemone—De sacrificio & magia, *see* IAMBLICHUS *of Chalcis.* De mysteriis &c., 1497.
see DASHEAN (H.) Short bibliog. st. &c., *in Armenian*, p1, P. &c., 1895.
„ MÜLLER (H. F.) Dionysios, P., Plotinos, 1918.
Proclus, *Saint, patriarch of Constantinople, see* BAUER (F. X.) P. v. Konstantinopel, 1919.
Procopius, *of Caesarea.* P., w. an Eng. tr. by H. B. Dewing. [Loeb Class. Lib.] v4. s8°. 1924
Procopius, *of Gaza, see* DIELS (H.) Über d. v. P. beschr. Kunstuhr v. Gaza, 1917.
Procopowicz, *see* PROKOPOVICH.
Procter (Adelaide Ann).
Legends & lyrics. With intr. by C. Dickens. 8°. 1882
Procter (Thomas), *poet.* *A gorgeous gallery of gallant inventions, 1578. Ed. H. E. Rollins. la8°. Cambridge, *Mass.* 1926
Procter (William Charnock).
The story of sacred song. s8°. [1925]
Proctor (Mary). Evenings with the stars. 8°. [1924]

Proctor (Richard Anthony). Easy star lessons. n. ed. s8º. 1883
How to play whist, w. laws &c. By "5 of clubs" (R. A. P.) 8º. 1885
The stars in their seasons. Maps. 3rd ed. la8º. 1884
The sun. 3rd ed. 8º. 1876
Prodenzani (Simone), *see* DEBENEDETTI (S.) Il "Sollazzo"; contrib. alla stor. d. novella &c. nel trecento, 1922.
Prodgers (Cecil Herbert).
Adv. in Bolivia. Intr. by R. B. C. Graham. 8º. 1922
Adv. in Peru. 8º. [1924]
Prod'homme (Jacques Gabriel). Hector Berlioz, 1803–69, sa vie & s. oeuvres, suivi d'une bibliog. music. & litt. &c. & d'une généalogie de la famille de H. B. Préf. de A. Bruneau. 8º. [1904]
Mozart, rac. par ceux qui l'ont vu (1756–91): lettres, mém. &c., réun. & tr. par P. s8º. [1928]
Paganini. 8º. [1908]
Proeleus (Immanuel). De hostiis & calice venenatis. [P2638]. s4º. Gryphiswaldiæ. 1703
Professio. Brevis orthodoxae fidei professio quae ex præscripto S. Sedis Apostolicae ab orient. ad Romanae eccl. unitatem venientibus facionda proponitur. Jussu Clementis VIII. [*Arabic & Lat. b. w.* Oliveyra (F. X. de). Path. discourse, 1756]. 8º. Romae. 1595
***Profit-sharing** by Amer. employers &c., 1921, *see* NATIONAL CIVIC FEDERATION.
Programm (Das) d. kommunist. Partei Russlands, 1920, *see* RUSSLAND.
Programma publ. Acad. Lips. de inst. Jubileo Evang. eccl. Saxonicae, 1617, *see* LEIPZIG, *University.*
Prohibited books, *see* INDEX.
Pro-Jerusalem Council, *see* JERUSALEM.
Projet. *Un projet gigant. en Languedoc au 18e s.; publ. J. Seeker, 1873, *see* JOUBERT (—).
Prokopovich (Sergei Nikolaevich).
Econ. condition of Soviet Russia. s8º. 1924
Очерки хозяйства советской России. 8º. Берлин. 1923
Союзы рабочихъ и ихъ задачи. [P848]. s8º. [С.-П. 1905]
Prokopovich (Theofan), *1681–1736.* Hist., de ortu & profectu controv. Graecos inter & Latinos de process. Spirit. Sancti &c. s8º. *n.p.* 1767
Tract. de processione Spiritus Sancti. [*Foll. by* Hist. de Controv., *by the editor, w. sep. tp. & pagin.*] 8º. Gothae. 1772
Proletarskie. Пролетарские писатели! антология, 1924, *see* RODOV (S. A.)
Promis (Carlo).
Works in REGIA DEP. DI STORIA PATRIA. Misc.
Biografie di ingegneri milit. ital. dal sec. 14 alla metà del 18, 1874. [14.]
Gl'ingegneri e gli scrittori milit. bolognesi d. 15 e 16 sec., 1863. [4.]
Gl'ingegneri milit. d. Marca d'Ancona, 1550–1650, 1865. [6.]
Gl'ingegneri milit. in Piemonte, 1300–1650, 1871. [12.]
L'Oratorio del Sacramento in Torino, con alcuni mon. archit. del Piemonte e de' sec. 15 e 16, 1871. [13.]
Vita di F. Paciotto da Urbino, archit. d. sec. 16, 1863. [4.]
Vita di Girolamo Maggi d'Anghiari, 1862. [1.]
Promis (Domenico Casimiro).
Works in REGIA DEP. DI STORIA PATRIA. Misc.
Dell' orig. d. zecca di Genova e di alcune sue monete ined., 1870. [11.]
Illust. di una medaglia di Claudio di Seyssel, e n. ricerche sull' Ordine del Collare di Savoia, 1871. [13.]
Monete d. abati di S. Benigno di Fruttuaria, 1870. [10.]
Monete di zecche ital. ined., Mem. 2, 3, 1869–71. [7, 12.]
Monete e medaglie ital., 1871. [13.]
Monete ined. del Piemonte, Suppl., 1868. [5.]
Sigilli italiani illust., 1870. [9.]
Promis (Vincenzo).
Works in REGIA DEP. DI STORIA PATRIA. Misc.
Ambasciata di C. F. Manfredi di Luserna a Praga nel 1604, 1877. [16.]
Brevi sceni s. vita e s. scritti del p. G. Colombo, Barnabita, 1884. [23.]
Cento lettere conc. la storia d. Piemonte, 1544-92; ed. V. P., 1870. [9.]
Cronachette astesi [*Latin*]; ed. V. P., 1870. [9.]
Due inventari d. sec. 17; ed. V. P., 1880. [19.]
Lettere di illust. Italiani; ed. V. P., 1870. [11.]
Monete di zecche ital. ined. o corr., Mem. 4, 1883. [21.]
Sigilli ital., 1874. [15.]
Su un soffitto ant. n. palazzo di S. Giovanni in Torino, 1880. [19.]
Tasse per rifiuto a div. cariche n. Repubb. Fiorentina n. sec. 15, 1877. [16.]
see FERRERO (E.) V. P. e i suoi studii numismatici, 1892.

Promise. *The promisse of matrimonie [Articles de la trêve de Picquigny, 1475, *betw. Edward IV & Louis XI*] (Londres, 1483), facs. &c., *see* PICOT (E.) & H. STEIN. Recueil, 1923.
Propagation. Annales de la p. de la foi, *see* ANNALES &C.
Congreg. Sacra de Prop. Fide, *see* CONGREGATIO.
Proper. *Proper dyaloge (A) betw. a gentillman & a husbandman. *For a. copy see* ROY (W.) & J. BARLOW. "Rede me & be nott wrothe" &c., 1871.
*Proper lessons for the Tories (1716), 1883, *see* AUNGERVYLE Soc. Reprints, s2, 1883.
Propert (Walter Archibald). The Russian ballet in West Europe, 1909–20, w. ch. on the music by E. Goossens. 4º. 1921
Propertius (Sextus). Carmina. Rec. &c. J. S. Phillimore. [2nd ed.] s8º. O. [1907
Catullus, Tibullus, P., 1529; Opera, 1772, *see* CATULLUS (C. V.)
Property.
*P. inviolable: or, some remarks upon a pamph. entit. Prescription sacred. [P2669]. s8º. D. 173
*P. re-asserted in ans. to Property vindicated [? *by John Brett* P2669]. s8º. D. 1640 [*i.e.* 1740
*P. vindicated; or, some remarks upon a pamph., intit. Property inviolable. [P2669]. s8º. D. 173
***Prophetic** voices ab. America. [F. the Atlantic Monthly, Sept 1867]. [P2623]. [*no tp.*] 8º. *n.p. n.d*
Proportional Representation Society of Ireland.
Sligo's "P.R." lead. [P2380]. 4º. D. [1919
***Proposal** (A) for uniform. of weights &c. in Scotland, 1779 2nd ed., 1789, *see* SWINTON (J.)
Propositiones quibus vera ac simplex doctrina de peccat originali explic. &c., 1576, *see* MANSFELD.
Proshloe. Прошлое русской музыки. Матеріалы &c. [*by var. a.* I. П. И. Чайковскій. la8º. Петербург. 192
Prosistas mod., 1922, *see* DIEZ-CANEDO (E.), *ed.*
Prospects. *Various prospects of mankind, nature & providence, 1761, *see* †WALLACE (ROBERT).
Prosper, *of Aquitaine, Saint.* Opuscula, *see* STANISLAUS PLACENTIA. Augustini & Scoti de gratia Xti consensus, v 1768.
Prosperi (Carola).
Il fanciullo feroce. Romanzo. s8º. Milano. 192
Prosser (James). A key to Hebrew Scr. &c. Pref. a sho Heb. gram. 2nd ed. s8º. 184
Prost (Auguste). A. P., vie, œuvres, coll., *see* SOC. NAT. D ANTIQ. DE FR. Mettensia, t1, 1897.
Prost (Claude). Les revêtements céram. dans les mon. musu mans de l'Egypte, *see* INSTITUT FRANÇ. D'ARCH. OR. D CAIRE. Mém., t40, 1916.
Prost (Yvette). Salutaire orgueil. s8º. [192
Pröstler (Johann P. A. E. J. M.) Capitulatio episcopo Ge maniae electo a suis electoribus proposita. [P2587]. s4º. Heidelbergae. 17
Protection of Churches, Central Committee for the, *see* CENTRA COMMITTEE &C.
Protestant.
*Few (A) plain reasons why a Prot. of the Ch. of Engl. should n turn Rom. Cath., 1688, *see* BARLOW (T.)
*Pr. (The) association, wr. in the midst of the tumults, 1780, 178 *see* WESLEY (J.) & C. WESLEY.
*Pr. Jesuitism. By a Protestant. s8º. N.Y. 18
Protestant Dissenters, *see* DISSENTERS.
Protestants.
*Appeal (An) to Pr. of Gt. Brit. &c. on Rom. Cath. q., 1813, APPEAL.
*Memorial (A) to Pr. on the 5th of Nov. &c., 1713, *see* KENN (W.), *bp.*
*Mystery (The) of iniquity working in the dividing of Pr., to t subverting of relig. &c. By a Protestant &c. [P2663]. s4º. 16
*Queries offered by T. W. [*i.e.* Thomas Ward] to the Pr. conc. t Engl. Reformation, 1688, *see* CLAGETT (W.)
Protestatio Bohemorum, 1415, 1712, *see* BOHEMI.
Prothero (Rowland Edmund), *aft. 1st baron Ernle, see* ERN (R. E. P., *1st b.*)
Protocol [PROTOCOLL; PROTOCOLS].
Protocoll d. i. Acta oder Handlungen d. Gesprächs, zwisch den Pfältz. u. Wirtemberg. Theologen &c., 1565, *see* MAU BRONN.
P. of the learned elders of Zion; tr., 1923, *see* NILUS (S.)
*Truth (The) about "The Protocols," 1921, *see* TRUTH.
Protopopesco (Dragosh), *see* CONGREVE (W.) W. C.: a sh of poet. scraps, prose misc. & letters; ed. D. P., 2nd e 1925.

Protopopov (A. D.) Записки, *see* SCHEGOLEV (P. E.) Падение царского режима, т4, 1925.

Prou (Maurice). Manuel de paléographie latine & franç. 4e éd. refondue avec collab. de A. de Boüard. 8o. 1924
„ „ ....Album. 4e éd. 4o. 1924
see SAINT-BENOÎT-SUR-LOIRE. Rec. des chartes de l'abbaye de St. B.-sur-L.; publ. &c. par M. P. &c., t1, 2i, 1900–12.

Proudhon (Pierre Joseph). Comm. sur les Méms. de Fouché, suivis du parallèle entre Napoléon & Wellington. Publ. C. Rochel. 3e éd. 8o. 1900
see BOURGEOIS (N.) Théories du droit internat. chez P., 1927.

Prouille. Cartul. de Notre-Dame de P. Préc. d'une ét. sur l'Albigéisme languedoc. aux 12e & 13e siècles. [Bibl. hist. du Languedoc; publ. J. Guiraud]. 2t. 4o. 1907

Proust (Marcel).
A la recherche du temps perdu. t3–8 [*var. ed.*] s8o. 1920–27
3, Le côté de Guermantes, 1.
4, Le côté de Guermantes, 2, Sodome & Gomorrhe, 1.
5, Sodome & Gomorrhe, 2 [*in* 3t].
6, Sodome & Gomorrhe, 3, La prisonnière, 2t.
7, Albertine disparue, 2t.
8, Le temps retrouvé, 2t.
Les cahiers M. P. 1, Hommage à M. P. [*by var. wr.*] 9e éd. 8o. [1927]
Chroniques. 7e éd. s8o. [1927]
Jalousie: roman, *see* ŒUVRES libres, 5, 1921.
Lettres inéd. Préf. & app. par C. Vettard. s8o. 1926
Précaution inutile, roman, *see* ŒUVRES libres, 20, 1923.
TRANSLATIONS.
The Guermantes way. Tr. C. K. Scott Moncrieff. 2t. s8o. 1925
Swann's way. Tr. C. K. Scott Moncrieff. 2v. s8o. 1922
Within a budding grove. Tr. C. K. Scott Moncrieff. 2v. s8o. 1924
see CLERMONT-TONNERRE (E. DE). Montesquiou & P., 1925.
„ DREYFUS (R.) M. P. à 17 ans, 1926.
„ —— Souvs. sur M. P., avec lettres inéd. de M. P., 1926.
„ GABORY (M.) Essai s. M. P., 1926.
„ GERMAIN (A.) De P. à Dada, 1924.
„ PIERRE-QUINT (L.) Comment travaillait P., Bibliog. &c., 1928.
„ —— M. P., sa vie, son œuvre, 1925.
„ POURTALÈS (G. DE). De Hamlet à Swann, 1924.
„ SCOTT-MONCRIEFF (C. K.), *ed.* M. P.: an Eng. tribute; by J. Conrad, E. A. Bennett &c., 1923.
„ SOUDAY (P.) M. P., 3e éd., 1927.

Prout (Ebenezer). Harmony: its theory & practice. Augener's ed., 5th ed. 8o. *n.d.*

Prout (Samuel).
Sketches in France, Switzerland & Italy. la. fol. 1839

Provana di Collegno (Luigi). La donazione di Teutcario, ossia Cumiana, sec. 9–15, *see* REGIA DEP. Misc., t24, 1885.

Provana di Collegno (Saverio). Notizie e doc. d'alcune Certose del Piemonte, 2v, *see* REGIA DEP. Misc., t32, 37, 1895–1901.

Provence.
*Abrégé de l'hist. de P. s8o. Marseille. 1837
Arrest de la cour du Parlement de P. du 2 Mai 1768. [*b. w.* Le Voyer de Boutigny (R.) Traité de l'autorité des rois &c. 1753]. s8o. Aix. 1768
*Hist. héroïque &c. de la noblesse de P., 4t, 1776–1901, *see* ARTEFEUIL (L. V.)
Rec. des actes des rois de P., 855-928; publ. par R. Poupardin, *see* CHARTES & diplômes rel. à l'hist. de France, t5, 1920.

Provenzal (Giulio), *ed.* Il cinquantennio (1870–1920). Racc. di scritti [*by var. as.*] che Il Nuovo Patto consacra &c. 8o. 1921

Provenzalische. P. (Die) Liederhs. Cod. 42 d. Laurenzian. Bibl., nach E. Stengel, *see* ARCHIV F. D. ST. D. NEU. SPR., B49, 50, 1872.
P. (Die) Liederhs. Cod. 5232 d. Vatican. Bibl., nach E. Stengel, *see* ARCHIV F. D. ST. D. NEU. SPR., B51, 1873.

Providence, *Rhode Island*, *see* DRURY (F. K. W.), *ed.* Techn. & sci. serials in libr. of P., 1921.

***Providences** (The) of God obs. thr. sev. ages tow. this nation, 1691, *see* BETHEL (S.)

Provincial Assembly of London, *see* LONDON.

Provincial Museum, *Lucknow*, *see* LUCKNOW.

***Provinciales** (Les), or, the mystery of Jesuitisme, 2nd ed., 1658, *see* PASCAL (B.)

Provins. Hist. & cartul. des Templiers de Provins. Avec intr. sur les débuts du Temple en France par V. Carrière. la8o. 1919

Provinzialausschuss d. Rheinprovinz. Tausend Jahre deut. Gesch. &c. am Rhein, 1925, *see* SCHULTE (A.), *ed.*

Provisional Emergency Cotton Committee. Crisis in the cotton industry: report of proc. of Prov. E. Cotton Comm., Sept. 1922–May 1923, 2v, 1923, *see* COTTON.

Prozesse (Die) d. Geiselmordes im Luitpold-Gymn. in München vor d. Volksgericht. 8o. München. [1920]

Prudence, *St., bp. of Tarazona*, *see* FLORANES (R. DE). Supresion del obispado de Alaba &c., t2, Carta &c., 1920.

Prudentius (Galindo), *Saint, bp. of Troyes*, *see* SAINT BERTIN, *abbey*. Annales Bertiniani [p2, auct. P.], 1883.

Prudentius Clemens (Aurelius). A. P. C. Th. Pulmanni & V. Giselini operâ emendatus, & in eum V. Giselini commentarius [*w. sep. tp. & no pagin.*] s8o. Antverpiæ. 1564
Carmina. Rec. &c. I. Bergman. [C.S.E. Lat., v61]. 8o. Vindobonae. 1926

Prud'hon (Pierre Paul). Exposit. P. P. Prud'hon. [Palais des Beaux-Arts, Paris]. Catalogue. [P2708]. 8o. 1922
see SOC. DE L'HIST. DE L'ART FRANÇ. Archives, nouv. pér., t13, L'œuvre de P. P. Prud'hon, 1924.

Prugavin (Aleksandr Stepanovich).
Вопіющее дѣло. (Дѣло В. О. Рахова). [P2446]. 8o. Москва. 1906

Prunai (Giovanni Battista). Siena. s8o. Firenze. 1902

Pruneda (Pedro). Crón. de la prov. de Cuenca, 1869, *see* ESPAÑA. Crón. gen., v1, 1865 &c.
Crón. de la prov. de Teruel, 1866, *see* ESPAÑA. Crón. gen., v4, 1865 &c.

Prunel (Louis N.) La renaissance catholique en France au 17e s. s8o. 1921

Prunelé (P. de), *see* TCHANG (M.) & P. DE P. Le père S. A. Cunha, 1914.

Prunières (Henry). Le ballet de cour en France avant Benserade & Lully, suivi du Ballet de la délivrance de Renaud. 8o. 1914
Monteverdi. Tr. M. D. Mackie. 8o. 1926

Prussia. Gdańsk & E. Prussia, 1919, *see* GDAŃSK.
German W. Prussia; reprod. f. docs., 1926, *see* KAUFMANN (C. J.), *ed.*

Prutz (Hans G.) *Works in* KÖNIGL. AKAD. D. WISS. ZU MÜNCHEN. Phil. Kl., Sitz.
Die Briefe Jeanne d'Arcs, 1914.
Die Friedensidee im M.- a., 1915.
Der Kampf um d. Leibeigenschaft in Livland, 1916.
Kurlands deut. Vergangenheit, 1918.
Neue Stud. z. Gesch. d. Jungfrau v. Orléans, 1917.
Z. Gesch. d. Jungfrau v. Orléans: Krönungszug n. Rheims, 1923.
Z. Gesch. d. Jungfrau v. Orleans: d. Loire-Feldzug, 1429, 1920.
Z. Gesch. d. polit. Komödie in Deutschland, 1919.

Pryce (Arthur Ivor), *see* BANGOR. Diocese of B. in the 16th c.: digest of registers of the bishops, 1512–1646; comp. w. intr. by A. I. P., 1923.

Pryce (F. N.), *see* CORPUS vasorum antiq. Gt. Brit.: Brit. Museum, fasc. 2; by A. H. Smith & F. N. P., 1926.

Pryce (T. Davies), *see* OSWALD (F.) & T. D. P. Introd. to the study of terra sigillata, 1920.

Pryde (Anthony), *ps.*, *see* WEEKES (A. R.)

Pryde (James), *see* CHAMBERS. Mathematical tables; ed. J. P., 1921.

Prym (Heinrich Eugen) & A. Socin. Kurd. Sammlungen: Erzähl. u. Lieder hrsg. u. übers. 2 Abt. [*in 1v*]. [*each Abt. has 2p w. sep. tp.*] 8o. St.-Pétersb. 1887–90
1, Dial. d. Ṭûr 'Abdîn, v. E. P. & A. S.
2, Dial. v. Bohtan, v. A. S.

Prynne (William).
The Church of England's old antithesis to new Arminianisme. s8o. 1629
Conscientious &c. quaeres, propounded to the anti-parl. Westminster juncto &c. s8o. 1660
God, no impostor, nor deluder: ans. to Popish &c. cavill, in defence of free-will &c. s8o. 1630
A Gospel plea for the lawfulness &c. of the antient setled maintenance & tenths of ministers &c. 2p [*in* 1v, p2 *dated* 1659]. 8o. 1660
Healthes: sicknesse: disc. proving the drinking &c. of healthes to be sinfull &c. s8o. 1628
Independency examined, unmasked &c. 8o. 1644
A legal vindication of the liberties of England agst. illegal taxes &c. 2nd ed. enl. 8o. 1660
*A looking-glasse for all lordly prelates. s8o. 1636
*Lord bishops none of the Lords bishops: prelat. jurisdict. not of divine institution &c. s8o. 1640
A moderate apology agst. a pretended calumny in ans. to passages in The preheminence of Parlement by J. Howell. 8o. 1644
The perpetuitie of a regenerate mans estate. [*Imperfect, tp. & 1 leaf in MS., part of address "To the Xtn. reader" wanting*]. s8o. 1626
A seasonable vindic. of free-admission & frequent admin. of Holy Communion &c. s8o. 1656
A short exam. of exuberances in, & ceremon. appurtenances to the Common Prayer &c. s8o. 1661

Prynne (William) [*continued*].
The substance of a speech in the Hse. of Commons, 4th Dec. 1648, touching the King's ans. to propos. of both Houses upon the whole treaty &c. s4°. 1649
Suspention suspended, or, the divines of Syon-Colledge late claim &c. [*Mutilated*]. 8°. 1646
Ten considerable quæries conc. tithes &c. [*b. w. h.* Gospel plea, 1660]. 8°. 1659
Twelve considerable &c. questions touching church govt. 8°. 1644
The unbishoping of Timothy & Titus &c.: power of ordination belongs to presbyters as well as bishops &c.
repr., w. add. [*2 pagin.*] 8°. 1661
A vindic. of 4 questions conc. excommunic. & suspention f. the Sacrament &c. 8°. 1645
*A vindic. of the imprisoned &c. Members of the H. of Commons f. aspersions in paper int., An humble ans. of the Gen. Councel &c. s8°. 1649
see CAMPANELLA (T.) T. C., h. advice to the king of Spain &c.; tr. by E. Chilmead, w. pref. by W. P., 1660?.

Prytz (Andreas Johannes). Theses de quæstione: Utrum Muschovitae sint Christiani? s4°. Lipsiæ. 1705

Przybyszewski (Stanislaw).
[Homo sapiens]. [3]v. s8°. L. 1898–1904
1, Ueber Bord. 2, Unterwegs. 3, Im Malstrom.

Przyluski (Jean). La légende de l'emp. Açoka (Açoka-Avadāna) dans les textes ind. & chin. [Musée Guimet. Bibl. d'études, t32]. 8°. 1923

Przypkowski (Samuel) [*ps.* IRENAEUS PHILALETHES]. *The life of that incomparable man F. Socinus Sen. descr. by a Polonian knight. Tr. [by J. Biddle]. s8°. 1653
*Vita Fausti Socini descr. ab equite Polono. Acc. diss. cum cat. operum. s8°. Eleutheropoli. 1651
see HALES (J.) *Anonymi diss. de pace & concordia eccl.; ed. per I. Philalethen, ed. 2a, 1630.

***Psalmi** seu cantica ex sacris literis, in eccl. cantari solita, cum hymnis &c. fol. Witebergae. 1564

Psalmodia. *Ps. Germanica; divine hymns; tr. f. High Dutch [by J. C. Jacobi]. With tunes. s8°. *Young.* 1722
*Ps. Germanica: or, the Germ. psalmody. Tr. f. high German [by J. C. Jacobi. Ed. J. Haberkorn. & Suppl. *w. sep. pagin. Without tunes*]. s8°. 1765
„ „ *a. c.*, w. tunes. s8°. 1765

Psalmodist & Magazine of sacred music. v1. sm. fol. E. 1856

Psalms [*see* BIBLE: PSALMS *for Biblical Ps.*]
*Coll. (A) of psalms & hymns, f. var. authors for use of Christians &c. n. ed. s8°. *Oliver.* 1774
„ „ .... n. ed. s8°. York, *Spence.* 1781
*Coll. (A) of psalms, hymns & spiritual songs for &c. private family. s8°. *Parkhurst.* 1701
Psalms of the early Buddhists; [tr. &c.] Mrs. Rhys Davids, 2v, 1909–13, *see* THERAGĀTHĀ.

Psellus (Michael Constantine).
Chronographie ou hist. (976–1077). Texte établi & tr. par E. Renauld. [Coll. Byzantine; Assoc. Budé]. 2t. 8°. 1926–28
De daemonibus, *see* IAMBLICHUS, *of Chalcis.* De mysteriis &c., 1497.
Homélie sur l'Annonciation [*Grec. & Lat.*], *see* MARY, *the Virgin.* Homélies mariales byz.; ed. &c. M. Jugie, 1922.
P. sur la grande année—Sur les nombres—Sur Diophante [*Greek text & comm.*], *see* TANNERY (P.) Mém. scient., t4, 1920.
Tableau sommaire des anc. dogmes des Chaldéens, *see* DAMASCIUS. Problèmes &c., tr. A. E. Chaignet, t3, 1898.
see ZERVOS (C.) Un philosophe néoplatonicien du 11e s., M. P. sa vie, s. œuvre &c., 1920.

Psichari (Ernest). Terres de soleil & de sommeil. Préf. de Mgr. A. Le Roy. n. éd. s8°. 1917
see GOICHON (A.) E. P., d'ap. doc. inéd., 1921.
„ MASSIS (H.) La vie d'E. P., 1916.

Psichari (Jean N.)
Ernest Renan: jugements & souvenirs. s8°. 1925
Le solitaire du Pacifique. Roman. s8°. 1922
Typesses. Roman. 21e éd. s8°. 1923

Psychical. Case (The) for & agst. psych. belief, by Sir O. Lodge &c., 1927, *see* MURCHISON (C.), *ed.*

Psychology & the sciences, 1924, *see* BROWN (W.), *ed.*

Psychology (International Congress of). 4e Congrès internat. de Psych., 1900. Comte rendu des séances & texte des mém. Publ. P. Janet. la8°. 1901
7th Internat. Congress of Psychology, 1923. Proc. & papers. Ed. Pres. [*i.e.* C. S. Myers]. la8°. C. 1924

Ptaschkina (Nelly Lvovna). Diary. Tr. P. de Chary. 8°. [1923]

Ptolemy, *the geographer.* Anc. India as descr. by P. McCrindle's facs. repr. Ed. w. intr. &c. by S. Majumdar Śâstrî. 8°. Calcutta. 1927
Geographicae enarr. libri octo. Ex B. Pirckeymheri tralatione, à M. Villanovano recog. Adiecta scholia &c. Quinquaginta tabulae adnectuntur &c. la. fol. Lugduni. 1535
Geographiae libri viii Græcé et Latiné. Graeca ad codices Palatinos collata, aucta &c. sunt, Latina infinitis locis correcta. [Bertius (Petrus), *ed.* Theatrum geographiae vet., t1]. fol. Amstelodami. 1619
Die Geographie des P. Hss., Text u. Unters. v. O. Cuntz. la8°. 1923
see HUDSON (J.), *ed.* Geog. vet. scriptores Gr. min., v3, 1712.
„ MŽIK (H. v.) Afrika, n. d. arab. Bearb. d. C. P. v. Muḥammad ibn Mūsā al-Ḫwārizmi, 1916.

Ptolemy II, *called Philadelphus, king of Egypt.*
see PRIDIK (ALEXANDER). Mitregent Königs Ptolemaios II, 1924.
„ STUDNICZKA (F.) Das Symposion P. II, 1914.

Ptolemy IV, *called Philopator, king of Egypt, see* SPIEGELBERG (W.) Erkl. d. dreisprach. Priesterdekretes zu Ehren d. P., 1925.

Pu'amrā, *Theban noble, see* PUYEMRÊ.

Puaux (René).
Constantinople & la question d'Orient. [P2418]. 8°. 1920
Cypris victorieuse, nouvelle, *see* ŒUVRES (Les) libres, t27, 1923.
La femme du rêve. s8°. 1927
La malheureuse Épire. s8°. 1914

***Public.** *Public school Latin grammar, 1872, *see* LATIN.
*Public school Latin primer, 1866, *see* LATIN.
Public Schools Year-Book, 1923, 1927. s8°. [1923–27]

Publicius (Jacobus). Ars memorativa [Gedächtniskunst]. Reprod. Druck d. A. Sorg, Augsburg, 1490. Vorwort v. E. Weil. la8°. Augsburg. 1922

Puccini (Giacomo), *see* FRACCAROLI (A.) Vita di G. P., 1925.
see WEISSMANN (A.) G. P., 1922.

Puccini (Mario). Brividi. s8°. Milano. [1920]
Dove è il peccato è Dio. Romanzo. s8°. Foligno. [1922]

Puccioni (Nello). La Vallombrosa. s8°. Firenze. [1921]

Puchstein (Otto). Boghasköi: d. Bauwerke. Von O. P. unter Mitwirkung v. H. Kohl u. D. Krencker. [Deut. Orient-Gesell., Wiss. Veröffentl., 19]. fol. L. 1912

Puckering (John), *see* SCOTUS (R.) Summarium rationum quibus cancellarius & Puckeringius Elizabethae persuaserunt &c., 1588.

Pudsey (*Sir* George), *recorder of Oxford.*
Speech to the King, Sept. 3, 1687. sm. fol. Oxon. 1687

Puech (Aimé).
Hist. de la litt. grecque chrét. t1, 2. 8°. 1928

Puente (Luis de la), *Jesuit* [LEWIS OF PUENTE]. Meditations upon the mysteries of our holie faith &c. tr. out of Spanish by J. Heigham. The first Tome. 4°. S. Omers. 1619
see *THRONUS justitiae &c. ex 4 S. I. patribus desumptus: P. L. de Ponte &c., 1624.

Puente y Brañas (Ricardo).
Tocar el violon. Zarzuela. 2a ed. 8°. 1884

Pufendorf (Samuel, *Frhr.* v.) [PUFENDORFIUS; PUFFENDORF].
De habitu relig. Xtnae ad vitam civilem liber. Ed. 3a corr. s8°. Bremae. 1697
Exercit. posthuma de consensu & dissensu inter Protestantes. [*b. w. h.* Jus feciale div., 1695]. s8°. *n.p. n.d.*
An introd. to the hist. of the principal states of Europe, begun by Baron P. contin. by Mr. de La Martinière [–1743]. Improved [tr.] by J. Sayer. n. ed. rev. & corr. 2v. 8°. 1764
Jus feciale divinum, sive de consensu & dissensu protestantium. s8°. Lubecae. 1695
see ETTENHUSIUS (J. B.) Epist. ad L. A. Rechenbergium, examen J. W. Jaegeri, In B. P. Jus div. feciale &c., 1698.
„ JÄGER (J. W.) Jus Dei foederale, exam. P. Jus feciale divinum &c., 1698.

Pugachev (Emelyan), *see* ESENIN (S.) Пугачов, *verse*, 1922.
see GROT (YA. K.) Мат. для. ист. П. бунта, 1862–63.

Pugenhag (Joh.), *see* BUGENHAGEN (J.)

Puggala-Paññatti. Designation of human types (P.-P.) [4th wk. of the Abhidhamma Piṭaka]. Tr. by B. C. Law. [Pali Text Soc., Transl. ser., no. 12]. 8°. [1924]

Pugh (Edwin W.)
The secret years. Further adv. of Tobias Morgan. s8°. [1923]

Pugh (*Mrs.* James J. G.), *see* LEWIS (H. P.)

Pughe (William Owen) [IDRISON; †OWEN (W.), *aft.* OWEN PUGHE]. A grammar of the Welsh lang. 8°. 1803

Pugin (Augustus), *see* PARIS. P. & environs: drawings under dir. of A. P., 2v, 1831.

Pugliese (Giulio). Il bolscevismo in Italia. s8°. Firenze. [1920]

Pugliese (Salomone). Condizioni econom. e finanz. d. Lombardia nella prima metà del sec. 18, *see* REGIA DEPUT. DI STOR. PATRIA. Misc., t52, 1924.

Pugnani (Gaetano), *see* CARUTTI (D.) Della famiglia di G. P., 1895.

Puiades (Gerónimo), *see* PUJADES (G.)

Puigblanch (Antonio). The Inquisition unmasked. Tr. by W. Walton. 2v. 8°. 1816

Puig y Cadafalch (J.), A. de Falguera & J. Goday y Casals. L'arquitectura romànica a Catalunya. v2, 3. la8°. Barcelona. 1911–18

Puimrē', *Theban noble, see* PUYEMRÊ.

Puini (Carlo). St. compar. d. istituz. soc. n. ant. civiltà. [R. Ist. di St. Super. &c. *b. w.* Le-Ke. 3 capitoli. 1886]. la8°. Firenze. 1886
Origini d. civiltà sec. la tradiz. e la storia dell' Estr. Oriente. [R. Ist. di St. Super. &c.] la8°. Firenze. 1891
see LE-KE. Il Li-Ki, o istituz. &c. d. Cina ant.; tr., comm. e note di C. P., 1883.
,, —— 3 capitoli del "Li-Ki" conc. la relig.; tr., comm. e note di C. P., 1886.

Puisieux (Roger Brulart, *marq. de Sillery & de***).** Les Suisses & le marq. de P., ambass. de Louis XIV, 1698–1708. Doc. préc. d'une notice hist. par J. de Boislisle. la8°. 1906

Pujades (Gerónimo). Coronica univ. d. principat de Cathalunya. sm. fol. Barcelona. 1609

Pujols, *Barony of, see* GERBEAU (J. B.) Essai hist. sur la baronnie de Pujols en Agenais, 1891.

Pulcher (Appius Claudius), *see* CLAUDIUS PULCHER (A.)

Pulci (Luigi). Il Morgante Maggiore. 3t. s8°. Londra. 1778

Pulgar (Hernando de). Claros varones de Castilla. Ed. y notas de J. Domínguez Bordona. s8°. 1923

Pulitzer (Joseph), *see* HEATON (J. L.) Story of a page: 30 yrs. in editorial col. of New York World [J. P.], 1913.

Pullan (Leighton), *D.D.* Religion since the Reformation. 8 lects. [Bampton]. 8°. O. 1923

Pullar (Laurence), *F.R.S.E., see* MURRAY (*Sir* J.) & L. P. Bathymetrical survey of the Scottish fresh-water lochs, 1897–1909, 6v, 1910.

Pullen (Robert), *cardinal, see* PULLUS (R.), *card.*

Pullen-Burry (Bessie).
Letters from Palestine, Feb.–Apr., 1922. s8°. [1922]

Puller (Timothy). The moderation of the Church of Eng. considered as useful for allaying pres. distempers &c. 8°. 1679

Pulling (Alexander), *the elder.* Crime & criminals. Is the gaol the only preventive? [P2709]. 8°. 1863
Electoral bribery & corruption. [Repr. f. "Law Mag. &c."]. [P2709]. 8°. 1867
Our parliamentary elections. [P2709]. 8°. 1866
Private bill legisl. [P2709]. 8°. 1855

Pullus (Robertus), *Cardinal* [PULLEN (R.)]. Sententiarum lib. viii. Item Petri Pictav. Sententiarum lib. v. [*w. sep. pagin.*] Ed. &c. op. H. Mathoud. fol. Parisiis. 1655

Pulszky (Ferencz).
Deák Ferencz. Jellemrajz. 2ik kiadás. [P2390]. s8°. 1904

Pult (G.) Über Ämter u. Würden in roman. Bünden, *see* ROMAN. FORSCHUNGEN, B32, 1913.

Pulver (Jeffrey).
Biographical dict. of old Eng. music. 8°. 1927
A dict. of old English music & musical instruments. 8°. 1923

Punch. v158–174. la8°. 1920–28
B. Disraeli in cartoons f. Punch. n. & enl. ed. 4°. [1881]
Mr. Punch's Hist. of the Great War. [10th impr.] 8°. 1920
Pictures f. Punch. 6v. 4°. 1894–96
Poems from Punch, 1909–20. With intr. essay by W. B. D. Henderson. repr. s8°. 1922
see DU MAURIER (G. L. P. B.) Eng. soc. at home; f. P., 1880.
see GRAVES (C. L.) Mr. P.'s hist. of mod. Eng., 1841–1914, 4v, 1921–22.
,, LEECH (J.) Early pencillings f. P., 1864.
,, TENNIEL (J.) Cartoons f. P., 1864.
,, THACKERAY (W. M.) Contribs. to P., 1900.

***Punch & Judy,** w. illust. by Cruikshank, dialogue of the puppet-show &c., 6th ed. 1881, *see* COLLIER (J. P.)

Punjab.
Frontier memorandum. [*Signed* Lepel Griffin]. fol. *n.p.* [1876]
Papers rel. to the P. 1847–49. [*a. c. in* P.P. 945]. 4°. [1849]

Government Publications.

ADMINISTRATION REPORTS.
Rep. on the admin. of the P. & its dependencies, 1882/83, 1919/20, 1920/21, 1921/22, 2v. 8°. Lahore. 1884, 1921–23
v1 of 1921–22 *rep. has title*: The Land of the 5 rivers.

Punjab [*continued*].
Government Publications [*continued*].

CUSTOMARY LAW.
Customary law. rev. ed. 8°. Lahore. 1921–26
Ambala D.; by R. B. Whitehead. [10.]
Dera Ghazi Khan Distr.; by W. R. Wilson. [16.]
Gujrat D.; by H. S. Williamson. [9.]
Multan D.; by H. W. Emerson.
Muzaffargarh D.; by J. D. Anderson, rev. ed., 1925.
Pakpattan & Dipalpur Tahsils of the Montgomery D.; by Mohammad Hayat Khan.

DISTRICT GAZETTEERS.
Rohtak D., 1883–84. la8°. Calcutta. *n.d.*

OFFICERS, SERVICES OF.
Hist. of services of officers [gazetted govt. servants]. 40th–43rd, 45th ed. corr. to 1st July 1920–25. 8°. Lahore. 1920–25

RECORDS.
[Punjab govt. records. *No gen. tp. vols. have sep. tp. & pagin.*] 9v *in* 10. la8°. Lahore. 1909–21
1, Rec. of Delhi residency & agency.
2, Rec. of Ludhiana agency.
3, Polit. diaries of Resid. at Lahore, 1847–48.
4, Journ. &c. of assistants to Resid. at Lahore, 1846–47.
5, Polit. diaries of H. B. Edwardes, Lahore, 1847–49.
6, Polit. diaries of R. G. Taylor &c., Lahore, 1847–49.
7i, ii, Mutiny records (corresp.)
8i, ii, Mutiny records (rep.)
9, Sel. f. note-bks. by G. Birch, 1818–21.

Punjab Masonic Calendar, 1893–96, *see* MASONIC CALENDAR.

Punshon (William Morley). Lectures. 8°. 1889

Pupikofer (O.), J. Heierli *& others.* Die Entwickl. der Kunst i. d. Schweiz. Im Auftrag d. Gesells. Schweizer. Zeichenlehrer. Hrsg. v. O. P. &c. la8°. St. Gallen. 1914

Pupin (Michael Idvorsky).
From immigrant to inventor. [repr.] 8°. N.Y. 1926

Puppenbuch (Das). [Puppen d. E. Pinner & L. Pritzel]. 2e Aufl. s8°. 1921

Purcell (Henry), *see* ARUNDELL (D. D.) H. P., 1927.

Purcell (Robert J.)
The spoiling of Wilson. Play. 8°. D. 1918

Purichkevich (Vladimir Mitrofanovich) [POURICHKEVITCH]. Comment j'ai tué Raspoutine: pages du journal. Tr. par L. Krestovsky. [*Pref. letter by B. Maklakoff*]. 8°. [1924]

***Puritanismus** Anglicanus; tr., 1610, *see* BRADSHAW (W.)

Purity. A Middle Eng. poem. Ed., w. intr., notes & glossary by R. J. Menner. [Yale Studies in Eng.; A. S. Cook, 61]. 8°. New Haven [U.S.] 1920

Purliliarum (Jacobus), *comes, see* PORCIA (J. DI), *Count.*

Purnell (Christopher James), *see* LONDON LIBRARY. Catalogue, & Subject index, 1913–23.

Puşcariu (Sextil). Locul limbii române intre limb. romanice, *see* ACADEMIA ROM. Disc., 46, 1920.

Puschin (Ivan Ivanovich) [†PUSHCHIN], *1789–1859.*
Записки о Пушкине и письма [1820–59]. Ред. и биог. очерк С. Я. Штрайха. 8°. Москва. 1927

Pusey (Edward Bouverie).
The Articles treated on in Tract 90 reconsid. & th. interp. vindic. in letter to R. W. Jelf, w. app. f. Abp. Ussher. 8°. O. 1841
Daniel, 9 lects. 3rd ed. 8°. O. 1869
Letter to the abp. of Canterbury on crisis in the Engl. church. 4th ed. 8°. O. 1842
Scriptural views of baptism, 1836, *see* TRACTS for the times, Nos. 67–69, 1836.
What is of faith as to everlasting punishment? reply to Farrar's "Eternal Hope." 3rd ed. 8°. O. 1880
see NEUBAUER (A.) 53 chap. of Isaiah, v2, Tr. by S. R. Driver & A. N., w. intr. to the tr. by E. B. P., 1877.
,, RIGG (J. H.) The character & life-work of Dr. P., 1883.

Pushkin (Aleksandr Sergeevich).
Сочинения. изд. 8ое исправл. &c. подъ ред. П. А. Ефремова. 7t. 8°. Москва. 1882
Гавриiлiада, поэма. Редакцiя Б. Томашевскаго. 8°. П. 1922
Дневникъ А. С. П. (1833–35). [Труды Госуд. Румянцов. Музея, вып. 1]. 8°. Москва. 1923
Неизданный П. собранiе А. Θ. Онѣгина. 8°. П. 1922
Новые материалы о дуэли и смерти П., Б. Л. Модзалевского *& others.* Труды П. Дома при Росс. Акад. Наук. s8°. П. 1924
Письма П. и К П. не вошедшие в изд. Акад. Наук. Собр. М. Цявловский. [Госуд. Акад. Худ. Наук. Тексты &c., вып. 1]. la8°. Москва. 1925
Письма; под ред. Б. Л. Модзалевского. 2т (1, 1815–25; 2, 1826–30) 8°. Москва. 1926–28
Пушкин в мировой лит. Сборник статей [*by var. a.* Научно-исследоват. Инст.] 8°. Ленинград. 1926
Стихотворенiя. s8°. Леипцигъ. 186]
Стихотворенiя П. не вошедшiя въ послѣднее соб. его соч. 2ое изд. 8°. Berlin. 1870

Pushkin (Aleksandr Sergeevich) [*continued*].

Table talk, розсказни за столомъ. s8°. Берлинѣ. 1923

TRANSLATIONS.

Boris Godunóv. Drama. Eng. by A. Hayes. Pref. by C. Nabokoff. s8°. [1925]

see BITSILLI (P. M.) Этюды о русск. поэзии, П. &c., 1926.
,, BLOK (A.), A. F. KONI &c. Пушкин — Достоевский, 1921.
,, FATOV (N. N.) А. С. П. 1921.
,, GERSHENZON (M. O.) Мудрость П., 1919.
,, JIRMUNSKY (V. M.) В. Брюсов и наследие П., 1922.
,, MIRSKY (*pr.* D. S.) P., 1926

see MODZALEVSKY (B. L.) П. под тайным надзором, 1922.
,, MOSKOVSKY PUSHKINIST. М. П., 1, 1837–1927: статьи, 1927.
,, POLYAKOV (A. S.) О смерти П., 1922.
,, PUSCHIN (I. I.) Записки о П.; ред. С. Я. Штрайха, 1927.
,, SAITOV (V. I.) Соболевский друг П., 1922
,, SCHEGOLEV (P. E.) Дуэль и смерть П., изд. 3е. 1928.
,, SOKOLOV (B. M.) М. Н. Раевская в жизни &c. П., 1922.
,, TOMASHEVSKY (B.) П., 1925.

Pussyfoot, *ps., see* JOHNSON (W. E.)

Putherbæus (Gabriel), *see* DUPUYHERBAULT (G.)

Putnam (Bertha Haven). Early treatises on Justices of the Peace in the 15th & 16th cent. (*includ.* Marowe's Reading on the peace in 1503), *see* VINOGRADOFF (*Sir* P.) Oxford st. in social &c. hist., v7, 1924.

Putnam (Eliza Osborn), *see* HEATON (*Mrs.* E. O. P.)

Putnam (George Haven). A prisoner of war in Virginia, 1864–65. Repr., w. addit., f. address, Dec. 7, 1910. 8°. N.Y. 1912

Putnam (G. P.) 's Sons, *see* FLEMMING (L. A.) Putnam's word bk., 2nd ed., 1919.

Putnam (Harrington), *see* TOOKE (J. H.) Memorial to T.; w. intr. statement &c., by H. P., 1920.

Putnam (James Jackson). Addresses on psycho-analysis. Pref. by S. Freud. [Inter. Psycho-Analytical Lib.] 8°. 1921

Putnam (Mary Corinna), *aft. wife of Abraham Jacobi, see* JACOBI (*Mrs.* M. C. P.)

Putnam (Ruth). Life & letters of Mary Putnam Jacobi. Ed. R. P. Foreword by G. H. Putnam. 8°. N.Y. 1925

A mediaeval princess, Jacqueline, Countess of Holland &c., 1401–36. 8°. N.Y. 1904

Putney. Parish reg. of P., Surrey, [1620–1870]. Transcr. by A. C. Hare. Ed. W. B. Bannerman. 3v [*pagin. cont.*] 8°. *p.p.* Croydon. 1913–16

Putschius (Helias). Grammaticae Lat. auctores antiq. Opera H. P. 4°. Hanoviae. 1605

Putsillo (Mikhail Pavlovich). Указатель дѣламъ и рукописямъ относящ. до Сибири. 8°. Москва. 1879

Pütter (Johann Stephan). Systemat. Darstell. d. Pfälz. Religions-Beschwerden &c. 8°. Göttingen. 1793

Putterill (V. A.), *see* THOMSON (M. R. H.), V. A. P., &c. Investig. on export citrus fruit, 1922.

Puxley (W. Lavallin).

Wanderings in the Queensland bush. 8°. [1923]

Puy (Jean), *see* PUY (M.) J. P., reprod. & étude, 1920.

Puy (Michel).

Jean Puy. Reprod. préc. d'une etude. s8°. [1920]

Puycibot (Jausbert de), *see* JAUSBERT, *de P.*

Puyemrê, *Theban noble* [PU'AMRĀ; PUIMRĒ'], *see* DAVIES (N. DE G.) Tomb of P. at Thebes, 2v, 1922–23.

Puy-en-Velay. Chron. de St.-Pierre du Puy &c., *see* MONASTIER. Cartul.; publ. U. Chevalier, 1884.

Puységur (Jacques François de Chastenet, *marq.* **de).** *Etat actuel de l'art &c. milit. à la Chine; [*by* P. &c.], 1773, *see* CHINE.

Puyzieulx (Roger Brulart, *marq. de Sillery & de*), *see* PUISIEUX.

Pycraft (William Playne). Camouflage in nature. 8°. [1926]

The sea-shore. s8°. 1920

Pye (David). G. L. Mallory: memoir. 8°. 1927

Pye (Henry James).

Alfred; an epic poem, in six books. 4°. 1801

see GIBBON (E.) *Obs. on last 3 vol. of Roman hist. of G. [*attrib. to* H. J. P.], 1788.

Pym (John). Speech to the Lords, upon delivery of the articles of the Commons agst. W. Laud, w. copie of the articles. s4°. 1641

Pym (Thomas Wentworth).

More psychology & the Xtn. life. 8°. 1925

Pyne (Zoë Kendrick).

G. P. da Palestrina, h. life & times. 8°. 1922

Pypin (Aleksandr Nikolaevich) & V. D. Spasović.

Исторія славянскихъ литературъ. изд. 2ое тl. 8°. С.-П. 1879

Pyramidentexte, *see* SETHE (K. H.), *ed.* Die altaegypt. P., 1908–22.

Pyramus. Drei deut. P.-Thisbe-Spiele (1581–1607). Hrsg. u. eingel. v. A. Schaer. [Lit. V. in St., 255]. 8°. Tübingen. 1911

Piramus et Tisbé, poème du 12e siècle. Ed. C. de Boer. [Class. Fr. du M. âge]. s8°. 1921

Pyrckmair (Hilarius). De arte peregrinandi lib. 2 [*by H. P. & H. Turlerus*]; item, lib. 2 de regimine iter agentium. Quibus access. Quaestiones forcianae, &c. s8°. [Noribergae]. 1591

Pyre (James Francis Augustin). The formation of Tennyson's style: versific. of the early poems. [Univ. of Wisconsin]. 8°. Madison. 1921

Wisconsin. 8°. N.Y. 1920

Pyrénées. *Hist. des négoc., & du traité de paix des P., 2t, 1750, *see* COURCHETET D'ESNANS (L.)

Pyrton. Churchwardens' acc., 1925, *see* MARSTON.

Pyszka (Hannes). Der Ruhrkrieg. 8°. München. 1923

Pythagoras.

Aurea Pythagoreorum carmina. Latinè conversa &c. auct. T. Marcilio. s8°. Lutetiae. 1585

Aurea verba—Symbola, *see* IAMBLICHUS, *of Chalcis.* De mysteriis &c., 1497.

see FRANK (E.) Plato u. d. sogen. P., 1923.
,, IAMBLICHUS, *of Chalcis.* Life of P. or Pythagoric life &c.; tr. T. Taylor, 1926.
,, LÉVY (I.) La légende de P., 1927.
,, —— Rech sur les sources de la légende de P., 1926.
,, LLOYD (W.) Chronolog. acc. of life of P. &c., 1699.
,, ROSCHER (W. H.) Die hippokrat. Schr. v. d. Siebenzahl u. ihr Verhältn. z. Altpythagoreismus, 1919.

Pythius (Joannes). Resp. exetastica ad tract. [*by I. de la Peyrère*] Praeadamitae. s8°. Lugd. Batav. 1656

Q

Qalqachandy (Abou'l 'Abbâs ebn 'Aly), *see* AḤMAD IBN 'ABD ALLĀH, *al-Ḳalḳashandī.*

Qâsim Hasîr Radavî (*Maulavî*), *see* BÛHÂR LIBRARY. Cat. raisonné of the B.L., begun by M. Q. H. R., 1921.

Qissa'i Yusuf, *see* BROCKELMANN (C.) 'Alī's Qissa'i Jūsuf, d. älteste Vorläufer d. osman. Lit., 1916.

Qiuphelean (Ambrosios), *see* KIUPELIAN (A.)

Qnnaser. [The Enquirer: a mag. for hist., lit. &c. of Armenia. Ed. Norayr N. Piuzantatzi. Lithogr. in cursive Armenian. Nos. 1, 2]. 8°. Stockholm. 1887

Quaderni geografici. Pubbl. mensile dir. d. prof. M. Baratta. N1–11 [*in 1v*]. 8°. Novaro. 1918–19

Baratta (M.) C. Battisti, 1918. [1.]
—— Confine orientale d'Italia, 1918. [3.]
—— G. Mazzini ed il confine orient. d'Italia, 1919. [7.]
Barnes (J. S.) Il futuro stato d'Albania, 1919. [8.]
Bertacchi (C.) L'Armenia, 1918. [2.]
Errera (C.) Congo Belga, 1918. [4.]
—— Italiani e Slavi n. Venezia Giulia, 1919. [9.]

Quaderni geografici [*continued*].

Michieli (A. A.) La laguna di Venezia, 1919. [11.]
Musoni (F.) Gli Sloveni, 1919. [10.]
Sanesi (I.) Spàlato e la quest. dalmatica, 1918. [5.]
Taramelli (T.) Il Massiccio del Grappa, 1918. [6.]

Quadros (Antonio de), *see* JESUITS. Epist. Indicae [*by Q. &c.*], 1566; 3a ed., 1570.

Quaerentes, *see* SEEKERS.

Quæstiones [QUESTIONES]. In hoc libello exponuntur quaestiones 5 Quibus tota doctrina Evangelii compræhenditur propositae Lipsiae futuris doctoribus theologiae [*by* W. Schirmesterus *& others*]. Cui inclusa Oratio &c. [*by* B. Ziegler]. s8°. Lipsiae. 1544

Questiones cum suis argum. in oppos. form. supra evāg. dominic. et solenn. festivit., 1508, *see* VERDELLAY (J. DE).

Questiones naturales antiq. philosophorum tractantes de div. generibus ciborum et potus &c. s4°. [Colonia, *C. de Zyrychzee.* 1505]

Quagliati (Quintino). Deposito sepolcr. in Crispiano pr. Taranto, *see* REALE ACCAD. D. LINCEI. Mon. ant., v26, 1920.
—— **& D. Ridola.** Necrop. arcaica ad incineraz. pr. Timmari nel Materano, *see* REALE ACCAD. D. LINCEI. Mon. ant., v16, 1906.

Quain (Jones). [Anatomical plates. 5 parts, p4 & 5 *wanting*. p2–5 are by J. Q. & W. J. E. Wilson]. atlas fol. 1836–42
Elem. of anatomy. Ed. E. A. Schäfer & G. T. Thane. 3v [*in* 8p *&* App. *var. ed. & impr.*] la8°. 1893–1900

***Quaker** boy (The): autobiog. of R. B. Dillingham, 1910, *see* FOULKE (W. D.)

Quakers.
*Brief acc. of many of the persec. of Q. &c., 1736, *see* BESSE (J.)
*Danger (The) of enthusiasm discov., in an epistle to the Q., 1674, *see* ALLEN (W.), *controv. wr.*
*Disc. (A) proving the divine instit. of water-baptism wherein the Q. arguments are coll., 1697, *see* LESLIE (C.)
*Exam. of a book pr. by the Q., ent. Brief acc. of many persecutions &c., 1741, *see* HAYTER (T.), *bp.*
*Letter to a person lately joined w. the Q., 1748, *see* WESLEY (J.)
*Primitive heresie revived in the faith &c. of Q., 1698, *see* LESLIE (C.)
Quakers & peace [*sel. f. var. a.*] Intr. & notes by G. W. Knowles. [Grotius Soc., Texts for Students, 4]. 8°. 1927
*Vindic. of Brief acc. of many persec. of Q. &c., 1737; 1741, *see* BESSE (J.)

Quandt (Johann Gottlob v.)
Wissen u. Seyn. [P2471]. 8°. Dresden. 1859

Quandt (Johann Jacob). Examen controv. de sacerdotio Melchisedeciano. [P2637]. s4°. *n.p.* 1735

Quaranta (Bernardo, *barone* **di San Severino),** *see* MUSSOLINI (B.) M. as revealed in h. polit. speeches; sel., tr. & ed. by Q., 1923.

Quaranta (Vanni de) [VANNI]. La tragedia infernale. Prima cantica, 1914–15. [ed. pop.] s8°. San Francisco. [1920]

Quaritch (Bernard). Cat. of books in Eng. hist. & lit., to end of 17 c. la8°. 1922
Cat. of bks. pr. in Europe dur. 15 & 16 c. [*Illust.*] pl, Incunabula. la8°. 1923
Gen. cat. of bks. Suppl., 1875–7. 2v. 8°. 1877
Palæography: notes upon hist. of writing & illumination. *p.p.* la8°. 1894

Quarles (Francis). Emblems; with Hieroglyphics of the life of man. s8°. Bristol. 1808
Emblems, divine & moral. n. ed., rev. &c. w. notes by R. Wilson. 2v. s8°. 1824
,, ,, ...s8°. 1845
The school of the heart. [*b. w. h.* Emblems, 1808]. s8°. Bristol. 1808

Quarry (W. Edmund). Dict. of musical compositions & composers; w. bibliog. 8°. N.Y. 1920

Quarterly Indian army list, *see* INDIAN ARMY LIST (QUARTERLY).

Quarterly journal of economics. v1–11, 34–41. [v11, p3 *wanting*]. la8°. Boston *&* Camb., Mass. 1887–1927

Quarterly review.
v233–250 [243 missed in numeration]. 8°. 1920–28

Quatrelles, *ps.* [*i.e.* ERNEST L'EPINE]. Légende de la Vierge de Münster. Illust. par E. Courboin. [*Decor. binding by Sir E. Sullivan*]. 4°. [1881]

Quayle (Thomas).
Poetic diction: st. of 18th cent. verse. 8°. [1924]

Quazza (Romolo). La lotta diplomatica tra Genova e la Spagna &c., *see* ARCHIVIO STORICO ITAL. Anno 78, v1, 1920.

Quebec.
*Picture (The) of Q. & its vicinity. 2nd ed. rev. & corr. s8°. Quebec. 1831
Rapport de l'archiviste [*i.e.* P. G. Roy] de la Prov. de Q. pour 1924–25. la8°. *n.p.* 1925
Vieux manoirs, vieilles maisons. Comm. de mon. hist. de la prov. de Q. sl. la8°. Quebec. 1927

Quedlinburg [QUEDELBURG]. *Bericht v. d. Colloquio d. zu Quedelburg versambleten Theologen. Uber d. Artickel v. d. Ubiquität d. Leibs Christi &c. Item das Judicium D. Heshusij v. d. Apologien &c. [P2437]. s4°. Newstatt an der Hardt, *M. Harnisch.* 1585

Queen. *The Queen [Caroline] & the Mogul [George IV]; a play. [P425]. 8°. 1820
*The Queen in the Moon. [*A satirical poem*]. 2nd ed. [P425]. 8°. 1820

Queen Anne's Bounty, *see* LE FANU (W. R.) Q. A.'s B.: its hist. & work, 1921.

Queensberry (William Douglas, *4th duke of*), *1725–1810* [OLD Q.], *see* MELVILLE (L.) The Star of Piccadilly, 1927.

Queensland. A.B.C. of Queensland statistics, 1921. Comp. by G. Porter. [P2577]. 8°. Brisbane. 1921
Vital statistics, 1916–1918. Nos. 55, 57, 58, 59, 61 [*in 1v*]. fol. Brisbane. 1915–22

Queen's Own Corps of Guides, *see* GUIDES.

Queiroz da Silveira (João de), *bp. of Grão-Pará* [*Fr.* JOÃO DE S. JOSEPH QUEIROZ]. Memorias; com intr. &c. por C. Castello-Branco. s8°. Porto. 1868

Quell (Christian Friedrich). De excommunicationis origine. [P2637]. s4°. Lipsiae. [1759]

Quellen. Q. u. Aufsätze z. russ. Gesch. Hrsg. v. K. Stählin. H1, 2. s8°. L. [1920]
see NIKITIN (A.) Fahrt über d. drei Meere, 1466–72: übers. &c. v. K. H. Meyer, 1920. [2.]
,, STÄHLIN (C.) Jacob v. Stählin, 1920. [1.]
Q. u. Forschungen z. Zeitbestimmung d. ägypt. Gesch. Hrsg. L. Borchardt. B1. fol. 1917
see BORCHARDT (L.) Annalen u. d. zeitl. Festlegung d. alt. Reiches d. ägypt. Gesch., 1917. [1.]
Q. z. Gesch. d. Stadt Wien, Abtlg. 1, B9, 1921, *see* VIENNA.

Quellen u. Darstellungen aus d. Gesch. d. Reformationsjhdts. Hrsg. G. Berbig. B1–18. 8°. Halle (Saale) *&* L. 1906–11
see ALBERT (F. R.) Briefwechsel H. v. Einsiedel mit Luther &c., 1908. [7.]
,, AUGSBURG. Acta Comiciorum Augustae ex litt. Philippi, Jonae & aliorum ad M. L., 1907. [2.]
,, BERBIG (G.) G. Spalatin u. s. Verhältnis zu M. L. auf Grund i. Briefwechsels 1525, 1906. [1.]
,, BUGENHAGEN (J.) Katechismuspredigten, 1525 u. 1532, 1909. [9.]
,, —— Ungedr. Predigten, 1524–29, 1910. [13.]
,, EGRANUS (J. S.) Ungedruckte Predigten, 1519–22, 1911. [18.]
,, GEISENHOF (G.) Bibliotheca Bugenhagiana, 1908. [6.]
,, HEEP (J.) Juan de Valdés, s. Relig. &c., 1909. [11.]
,, KIPP (F.) S. v. Schaumberg, d. Freund Luthers, 1911. [17.]
,, KÖRNER (E.) E. Alber, 1910. [15.]
,, LEPP (F.) Schlagwörter d. Reformationszeitalters, 1908. [8.]
,, NEUKIRCH (A.) Der niedersächs. Kreis u. d. Kreisverfassung bis 1542, 1909. [10.]
,, †RICHTER (M.) D. Erasmus u. s. Stellung zu Luther, 1907. [3.]
,, ROTSCHEIDT (W.) S. Isaak, e. köln. Pfarrer, 1910. [14.]
,, SCHERFFIG (P.) F. Mekum v. Lichtenfels, 1909. [12.]
,, SPALATIN (G.) Spalatiniana, 1908. [5.]
,, THEOBALD (L.) Leben &c. d. Tendenzdramatikers d. Reformationszeit, T. Naogeorgus &c., 1908. [4.]
,, TSCHACKERT (P.) Analecta Corviniana, 1910. [16.]

Quellen u. Forschungen aus Italien. Archiven u. Bibliotheken. Hrsg. v. Preuss. Hist. Inst. in Rom. B17–19. la8°. Rom. 1914–27

Quellen z. Schweizer Gesch. N. F., Abtlg. 3, B1, 3–6; Abtlg. 4, B3. 8°. Basel. 1915–27
Barth (H.) Bibliographie d. schweizer Gesch., B3, 1915. [N.F., Abtlg. 4, B3.]
Buchi (A.), *ed.* Korresp. u. Akten z. Gesch. d. Kard. M. Schiner, 2B, 1489–1527, 1920–25. [N.F., Abtlg. 3, B5, 6.]
Ochs (P.) Korr.; hrsg. G. Steiner, B1, 1927. [N.F., Abtlg. 3, B1.]
Rufer (A.), *ed.* Der Freistaat d. III Bünde u. d. Frage d. Veltlins: Korr. u. Aktenstücke 1796–97, 2B, 1916–17. [N.F., Abtlg. 3, B3, 4.]

Quellenstudien z. hölland. Kunstgesch. Hrsg. unter d. Leitung v. C. Hofstede de Groot. [B]12–15. 8°. Haag. 1919–28
see BREDIUS (A.), *ed.* Künstler-Inventare 16.–18. Jhdt. T6, 7, & Register, 1919–22. [12–15.]

***Quelques** peintres suisses, 1921, *see* SUISSE.

Quenedey (Raymond).
La prison de Jeanne d'Arc à Rouen. 8°. 1923

Quènes, *de Béthune* [BÉTHUNE (CONON DE)]. Les chansons de C. de B. Ed. A. Wallensköld. [Classiques fr. du m.-â., 24]. s8°. 1921

Quennell (Charles Henry Bourne), *see* QUENNELL (M.) & C. H. B. Q., *for works wr. in collab.*

Quennell (Marjorie) & C. H. B. Quennell. Everyday life in Anglo-Saxon, Viking & Norman times. 8°. [1926]
Everyday life in prehistoric times. s8°. [1924]
Everyday life in Roman Britain. 8°. [1924]
Everyday life in the new stone, bronze & early iron ages. s8°. [1922]
Everyday life in the old stone age. s8°. [1921]

Quenstedt (Joannes Andreas). Theologia didact.-polem. sive systema theolog.
4p *in 2v. b. in 1 (each p. has sep. pag.)* fol. Wittebergae. 1691
see RAAB (G.) Disput. de unione fidelium cum Deo mystica; praes. J. A. Q., 1678.
Quental (Anthero de), *1842–91.* Sonnets & poems. Tr. by S. G. Morley. s8°. Berkeley, Cal. 1922
Quentin (*Dom* Henri).
Les martyrologes hist. du m. â. 8°. 1908
Mém. sur l'établ. du texte de la Vulgate. [Coll. Biblica Lat., v6]. 8°. Rome. 1922
Quentin-Bauchart (Pierre). La crise sociale de 1848: les orig. & la Révol. de février. 8°. [1920]
***Querela** Cantab. or remonstrance for banished members &c., 1647; 1685, *see* BARWICK (J.)
Querido (Israel). De Jordaan. Roman. [Amsterdamsch Epos].
3d. [1, 10e dr.; 2, 8e dr.; 3, 9e dr.] s8°. A. *n.d.* & 1919–22
[2], Van nes en zeedijk. [3], Manus Peet.
De oude waereld, het land van Zarathustra; romant. epos, benevens het Boek der toelichtingen &c. 2e dr. 4°. A. 1919
Zegepraal. 2e omgewerkte druk. s8°. A. *n.d.*
Queries. *Q. offered by T. W. [*i.e.* Thomas Ward] to the Protestants conc. the Engl. Reformation, 1688, *see* CLAGETT (W.)
Some q. to Protestants answ. &c., 1686, *see* ALTHAM (M.)
Querini, *Family of, see* OCCIONI-BONAFFONS (G.) Di un epistolario, 1888.
Querist (The), 1735–37, 1910, *see* BERKELEY (G.)
Quesada (Gonzalo Jimenez de), *see* JIMENEZ DE QUESADA (G.)
Quesnel (François), *painter, c. 1544–1619.* Douze crayons, 1927, *see* DIMIER (L.) Hist. de la peinture de portr. en Fr. au 16e s., Suppl., 1927.
Quesnel (Pasquier).
Errores & synopsis vitæ P. Q.: 101 propositiones [*taken f. h.* Réflexions morales &c.] Constitutione Clementis XI damnatæ &c. [*b. w.* Ranst (F. van). Veritas, 1715]. s8°. Antverpiae. 1717
*Hist. abregée de la vie & des ouvrages de Monsr. Arnauld. Ci-devant impr. sous le titre de Question curieuse &c. s8°. Cologne. 1695
see BABENSTUBER (L.) Diss. in quo ostenditur P. Q. &c. errores injuste trib. S. Thomae, 1720.
„ BENITEZ DE LUGO (C.) Concursus Dei praevius & efficax &c.; à Jansenii & Quesnellii erroribus vindic., 5t, 1737.
„ BOSSUET (J. B.) Justific. des Réflexions [*of P. Q.*] sur le Nouv. Test., 1745.
„ BUDDEUS (J. F.) Comm. de Pelagianismo in Eccl. Rom. per bullam anti-Q. triumphante, ed. nova, 1719.
„ DESMARETS (D.) Tableau des papes de Rome pour juger de la constit. de Clém. XI contre les Réflexions par Q., 1714.
„ GORDON (J.) The bull Unigenitus, put forth by Clement XI, agst. Q.'s tr. of the New Test., 1731.
„ JENICHEN (G. F.) Hist. & examen bullae anti-Q., 1714.
„ LÖBER (C.) Def. doct. de omnibus conced. Script. lect., occas. bullae anti-Q., 1715.
„ POTESTA (F.) Exam. eccl., app. Thesium Q., 1733.
„ RANST (F. VAN). Veritas in medio, 1715.
„ VIVA (D.) Quesnellianae theses, 1724.
„ WERNER (J. M.) Diss. sistens examen doct. Q. de eccl. &c., 1717.
Quest (The); a quarterly review. Ed. G. R. S. Mead.
v11–18 (Oct. 1919–July 1927). 8°. 1920–27
Question. *Q. (The), What is an Arminian? answered, 1770, *see* WESLEY (J.)
Q. (La) syrienne, 1919, *see* SYRIENNE.
Questiones, *see* QUAESTIONES.
Quételet (L. Adolphe J.), *see* VAN DRUNEN (J.) A. Q., 1919.
Queteville (Jean de). Recueil de cantiques, à l'usage de la soc. appelée Méthodiste. n. éd. corr. s8°. 1828
Quevedo (F. de) [†GOMEZ DE QUEVEDO VILLEGAS (FRANCISCO)].
Páginas escogidas. Prólogo &c. de A. Reyes. s8°. 1916
Poesias completas. 8°. Barcelona. 1869
Los Sueños. 8°. Paris. *n.d.*
La vida del Buscon [1626. Hisp. Soc. of America, 112]. 8°. N.Y. 1917
TRANSLATIONS.
Choice humorous & satirical works. Tr. R. L'Estrange, J. Stevens, &c. Rev. & ed., w. intr., notes &c. by C. Duff. [Broadway Transl.] 8°. [1926]
TRANSLATIONS [*continued*].
Pablo de Segovia. Tr. Illust. by D. Vierge, w. comm. by J. Pennell, & essay on the life &c. of Q. by H. E. Watts. sm. fol. 1892
Pablo de Segovia (the Spanish sharper). Tr. Intr. by H. E. Watts. 8°. 1927
see TARSIA (P. A. DE). Vida de Q., 1663.
Quex, *ps., see* NICHOLS (*capt.* G. H. F.)

Qui êtes-vous? Annuaire des contemporains, 1924. 8°. [1924]
Quibell (*Mrs.* Annie A.) Egyptian hist. & art w. ref. to museum collections. 8°. 1923
„ „ ....[2nd ed. rev.] 8°. [1926]
Quibell (James Edward) & A. G. K. Hayter. Excavations at Saqqara. Teti Pyramid, North side. [Service des Antiq. de l'Egypte]. fol. Le Caire. 1927
Quicherat (Louis). Dict. français-latin. 16e tirage. 8°. 1871
„ „ Rev. & augm. par É. Chatelain. 45e éd. la8°. *n.d.*
Quick (*Sir* John), *LL.D.* The legisl. powers of the Commonwealth & the states of Australia, w. proposed amendments. la8°. Melbourne. 1919
Quick (Oliver Chase). The Xtn. sacraments. 8°. [1927]
Quickens (Quarles), *ps.* [*i.e.* E. A. POE?]. English notes [1842] being a reply to C. Dickens's "American notes." With crit. comments by J. Jackson & G. H. Sargent. 8°. N.Y. 1920
Quidort (Jean), *see* JOANNES, *Parisiensis, Frater Ord. Prædic.*
Quiétisme. *Lettres de M*** à un ami au sujet du q., 1733, *see* PHELYPEAUX (*l'abbé* J.)
Quiggin (Edmund Crosby). Prolegomena to study of later Irish bards, 1200–1500, *see* BRIT. ACAD. Proc., 1911–12.
Quigley (Harold Scott). Chinese politics & for. powers, *see* INTERNAT. CONCIL., 1927.
Quigley (Hugh). Italy & the rise of a new school of criticism in 18th c., w. spec. ref. to work of P. Calepio. [Univ. of Glasgow.] s8°. Perth. 1921
Lombardy, Tyrol & the Trentino. 8°. [1925]
Passchendaele & the Somme: a diary of 1917. 8°. [1928]
Towards indust. recovery. 8°. [1927]
Quignonius (*card.* Franciscus), *see* QUIÑONES (*il card.* F.)
Quiller-Couch (*Sir* Arthur Thomas) [*ps.*, Q.]
Adventures in criticism. [pocket ed.] s8°. C. 1924
Charles Dickens & other Victorians. 8°. C. 1925
A lect. on lectures. Intr. vol. s8°. 1927
Major Vigoureux. s8°. [1907]
On the art of reading. Lect., 1916–7. 8°. C. 1920
On the art of writing. [pocket ed.] s8°. C. 1923
The Oxford book of ballads. Chosen & ed. by A. Q.-C. [repr.] s8°. O. 1924
The Oxford book of Eng. prose. Chosen & ed. by Sir A. Q.-C. 8°. 1925
The Oxford book of Eng. verse, 1250–1900. [*re-issue*]. s8°. O. 1910
„ „ ....s8°. O. 1912
Shakespeare's workmanship. [4th impr.] 8°. [1923]
Studies in literature. s2. 8°. C. 1922
„ „ [pocket ed.] s1. s8°. C. 1923
„ „ [repr.] s1. s8°. C. 1924
see BRISCOE (W. A.) Byron; addr. & essays by Q. &c., 1924.
Quillinan (*Mrs.* Dorothy), *wife of Ed. Quillinan, form. Wordsworth.* Dora Wordsworth, her book. [Intr. &c.] by F. V. Morley. s8°. 1924
Quimperlé, *abbey of.* Cartul. de l'abbaye de Ste.-Croix de Q. Publ. par L. Maitre & P. de Berthou. 4°. 1896
Quin (Malcolm). Memoirs of a Positivist. 8°. [1924]
Quinault (Philippe). L'amant indiscret: comédie (1654), *see* FOURNEL (V.) Contemp. de Molière, t1, 1863.
Le comédie sans comédie (1654)—Le docteur de verre, *see* FOURNEL (V.) Contemp. de Molière, t3, 1875.
La mère coquette. éd. crit. par E. Gros. 8°. 1926
Théâtre. n. éd., augm. de sa vie &c. 5t. s8°. 1778
see GROS (E.) P. Q., sa vie & s. œuvres, *w. bibliog.*, 1926.
Quinci (Giovanni Battista). Un breve soggiorno di Maria Carolina in Mazara, 1813, *see* SOCIETÀ SICIL. Arch., n.s., 45, 1924.
Quincy (Josiah), *president of Harvard Univ., see* SHAW (*Maj.* S.) Journals; w. life of the a. by J. Q., 1847.
Quinet (Edgar). L'ultramontanisme ou l'Église rom. & la société mod. 8°. 1844
see VINET (A.) Et sur la litt. franç. au 19e s., t3, E. Q. &c., 1924.
Quinn (John). The library of J. Q. To be sold Nov. [& Dec.] 1923, Jan., Feb., Mar. 1924, Anderson Galleries.
5p & Priced list [*in* 2v]. 8°. N.Y. [1923–24]
Quiñones (*il card.* Francisco de) [†QUIGNONIUS (*card.* F.)], *see* BREVIARIUM Romanum &c., 1544.
Quiñones de Benavente (Juan). El Monte Vesuvio. [*b. w.* Alsario dalla Croce (V.) Vesuvius, 1632]. 8°. 1632
***Quinque** novi indices gen. &c., 1623, *see* AQUINAS (T.)
Quint (Léon Pierre-), *see* PIERRE-QUINT (L.)
Quintilian. Institutio oratoria, w. Eng. tr. by H. E. Butler. [Loeb Class. Lib.] 4v. s8°. 1921–22

Quintilian [*continued*].
Instit. oratoriae liber 1. Ed., w. intr. & comm., by F. H. Colson. 8°. C. 1924
Int. alle 2 ediz. Venete 1471 e senz' anno d. Istit. oratorie di Q. &c. [*By* C. C.] [P2839]. s8°. Venezia. 1891

Quinton (René).
L'eau de mer. Milieu organique &c. 2e éd. 8°. 1912

***Quinzaine** (La) angloise à Paris, 1777, *see* RUTLEDGE (J. J.)

Quirini (*il card.* Angelo Maria). Liber sing. de opt. script. editionibus quae Romæ primum prodierunt post typogr. invent. Rec. &c. J. G. Schelhornius. s4°. Lindaugiae. 1761

Quirke (Terence Thomas), *see* COLLINS (W. H.), T. T. Q. & E. THOMSON. Michipicoten iron ranges, 1926.

Quiroga (*Card.* Gaspard de). Index librorum expurg. G. Q. jussu ed., 1584, *see* INDEX.
see INDEX. I. & cat. libr. prohib. mandato G. a Q., 1583.

Quiroga (Pedro de). Libro intit. Coloquios de la verdad. Causas &c. que impiden la doct. e conversión de los Indios de Pirú &c. [1563 ?]. Publ. &c. J. Zarco Cuevas. [Publ. del Centro Oficial de Est. Amer. Bibl. Colon. Amer., t7]. 8°. Sevilla. 1922

Quistorp (Johann), *the younger*, *see* KOHLIUS (J. P.) Eccl. Gr. Luther. ; adj. J. Q. De Xtismo Graec. &c., 1723.

Quistorp (Johann Jacob). De Quackerorum Christi hominis in nobis nativitate. [P2632]. s4°. Rostochii. [1759]

Quiz, *ps.*, *see* EVANS (POWYS).

Quyny (Richard), *see* FRIPP (E. I.) Master R. Q., bailiff of Stratford-upon-Avon & friend of Shakespeare, 1924.

Qvanten (Emil v.)
Sveriges skönaste folkvisor. Utg. E. v. Q. s8°. [1882]

R

R. (D.), *B. of Divin.* *Pract. catechisme, 1632, *see* ROGERS (DANIEL).

R. (E.) *Authentic narr. of depart. of J. Wesley, 1791, *see* RITCHIE (E.)

R. (E.), *D.T.P.* *Apol. pro J. Gersonio, 1676, *see* RICHER (E.)

R. (E. R.) *Livre d'or de la noblesse phanariote &c., 2e éd., 1904, *see* LIVRE.

R. (F.) Viajes de extranjeros por España y Portugal ; coll. de J. L. ; tr. por F. R., 1878, *see* LISKE (J.)

R. (F. E.) *Hist. reminisc. of Dublin Castle, 849–1895, 1895, *see* DUBLIN CASTLE.

R. (J. L.) Hist. de la rep. del Ecuador, t1, 2, 1809–77, 1920–25, *see* ECUADOR.

R. (K.), *ps.* *Царь Іудейскій, 1914, *see* CONSTANTINE CONSTANTINOVICH, *grand duke*.

R. (W.) *Essay on psalmody [*pref. signed* W. R.], 1775, *see* ROMAINE (W.)

Raab (Georg). Disput. de unione fidelium cum Deo mystica quam duce Christo. Praeside J. A. Quenstedt. s4°. Wittebergae. [1678]

Raab (Isidor). Urkundenbuch d. Benedictiner-Stiftes Seitenstetten, *see* FONTES RERUM AUSTRIAC., B33, 1870.

Raabe (Berthold). Von der Antike : Führer durch die Lit. vom klass. Alt. s8°. L. 1923

Raabe (Gustav E.), *see* AARSKATALOG over norsk litt. 1924–26 ; forsynet med register av G. E. R., 1925–27.

Raabe (Siegfried).
Zaungäste des Lebens. s8°. München. [1915]

Raabe (Wilhelm). Sämtl. Werke.
Ser. 1, 6B ; Ser. 2, 6B ; Ser. 3, 6B. 8°. [1913–20]
Ser. 1, B1, Die Chronik d. Sperlingsgasse—Der Hungerpastor.
2, Ein Frühling—Halb Mär, halb mehr.
3, Der heilige Born—Nach dem grossen Kriege.
4, Unseres Herrgotts Kanzlei—Verworrenes Leben.
5, Die Leute aus dem Walde—Ferne Stimmen.
6, Drei Federn—Der Regenbogen.
Ser. 2, B1, Abu Telfan—Horacker.
2, Die Kinder von Finkenrode—Christoph Pechlin.
3, Der Dräumling—Deutscher Mondschein—Meister Autor.
4, Krähenfelder Geschichten.
5, Wunnigel—Deutscher Adel—Fabian u. Sebastian.
6, Alte Nester—Prinzessin Fisch.
Ser. 3, B1, Der Schüdderump—Das Horn von Wanza.
2, Villa Schönow—Pfisters Mühle—Anruhige Gäste.
3, Im alten Eisen—Der Lar—Kloster Lugau.
4, Das Odfeld—Gutmanns Reisen.
5, Stopfkuchen—Die Akten des Vogelsangs.
6, Hastenbeck—Altershausen—Nachlese.
see DÖRNENBURG (E.) & W. FEHSE. R. u. Dickens, 1921.
„ FEHSE (W.) W. R.'s Erwachen zum Dichter, 1921.

Raaf (K. H. de) & J. J. Griss. Zeven eeuwen : spiegel d. nederl. letteren, v. 1200 tot heden. 4d. 8°. Rotterdam. 1918–20

Rabagliati (Andrea Carlo Francisco).
Towards life. 8°. Bradford. 1923

Raban (Edward). Record of celebr. of tercent. of intr. of printing into Aberdeen by E. R., 1622. 8°. Aberdeen. 1922

Rabanus, *Magnentius*, *see* MAURUS (RABANUS).

Rabbath (Antoine), *Jesuit*. Docs. inéd. p. s. à l'hist. du Christianisme en Orient.
t2, fasc. 1, 2 [*no more publ.*] 8°. 1910–11

Rabbe (Alphonse).
Album d'un pessimiste. Publ. J. Marsan. s8°. [1924]
Resumé de l'hist. de Portugal. Intr. par R. T. Chatelain. 2e éd. s8°. 1824

Rabbe (P. F.) Au Maroc. Sur les rives du Bou Regreg. Rabat—Salé—Chella. s8°. 1922

Rabe (Heinrich). Deutsch-engl. Satzlexikon d. allg. u. wirtschaftl. Sprache. la8°. St. 1924

Rabe (Johann Jacob), *canon of Staubingen* [RABUS]. Rom : e. Münchener Pilgerfahrt, 1575, beschrieb. v. J. R. Nach e. ungedr. Hs. ; hrsg. v. K. Schottenloher. s8°. München. 1925

Rabel (Ernst). Papyrusurkunden d. Öffentl. Bibl. d. Univ. zu Basel ; hrsg. E. R., *see* KÖNIGLICHE GESELLS. D. WISS. ZU GÖTTINGEN. Abhdlgn., B16, 1917.

Rabelais (François).
Œuvres. 3t. [3, *Bibliog.*, Table, Glossaire &c.] 8°. *Janet.* 1823
Œuvres. Avec variantes, notes & glossaire. [Bibl. Elzevirienne]. 2t. s8°. 1858–72
Œuvres. n. éd., augm. Notes par L. Jacob. s8°. 1861
Œuvres. Ed. nouv., avec des remarques hist. & crit. de Le Duchat & Le Motteux. Publ. P. Favre. 5t. 8°. 1875–80
Œuvres. Ed. crit. publ. par A. Lefranc &c. t3, 4. s4°. 1922
3, 4, Pantagruel.
Œuvres. Avec variantes, notice & glossaire par P. Jannet. [*Vol. 1 has no editor's name*]. 7t. s8°. *Flammarion. n.d.*

TRANSLATIONS.
Works. Tr. Urquhart & Motteux, w. explan. notes by Duchat, Ozell &c. n. ed., rev., w. add. notes. 2v. s8°. *Bohn.* 1854–55
„ „ 2v. s8°. *Bohn.* 1863
Works. Faithfully tr., w. variorum notes &c. & illust. by Doré. 8°. *Moray Press*, Derby. 1894
see ARNSTÄDT (F. A.) F. R. u. s. Traité d'éducation &c., 1872.
„ SAINÉAN (L.) La langue de R., 2t, 1922–23.
„ —— Probl. litt. du 16e s., le 5e Livre &c., 1927.
„ VILLEY (P.) Marot & R., 1923.

Rabener (Justus Gotthart).
Diss. de dæmonibus. [P1035]. s4°. Lipsiae. [1707]

Rabenius (Laurentius G.) Obs. hist. Zigeunorum illust. Praes. E. Fant. [P2671]. s4°. Upsaliae. [1791]

Rabinovich (Isaak Moiselvich). Das Deutsch-russ. Handelsabkommen v. 6 Mai 1921. Mit Anmerk. v. R. [P2595, 2710]. s8°. 1921

Rabizzani (Giovanni). Sterne in Italia. Riflessi nostrani dell' umorismo sentimentale. Pref. di O. Gori. 8°. [1920]

Rabochaya Misl. [Рабочая Мысль]. Отдѣльнос приложеніе къ "Р. М." [P2715]. 8°. П. 1899

Rabochy, *ps.* Рабочіе и интеллигенты въ нашихъ организ. Съ предисл. П. Аксельрода. [P2716]. s8°. Женева. 1904

Rabus (Jakob), *see* RABE (J. J.)

Rabus (Ludovicus). Hist. der heyligen ausserwölten Gottes Zeugen Bekeñern u. Martyrern, warhafftig beschryben durch L. R. 8T *in* 5v. s4°. Str. 1555–58
see PREISENSTEIN (J.) Leichpredig bey d. Begrebnuss L. R., 1593.

Rabut (François), *see* DUFOUR (A. H.) & F. R. Renonciat. du Comte Amédée VI de Savoie au mariage &c., 1878.

Rabutin (François de). Comm. des dern. guerres en la Gaule Belgique, 1551–59, *see* BUCHON (J. A. C.) Choix de chroniques &c., 1884.

Raby (Frederic James Edward). Hist. of Xtn.-Latin poetry, f. beg. to close of M.A. 8°. O. 1927

Racca (Carlo) [*ps.* AKKAR]. Burattini e marionette, il loro teatro ed i loro fantocci. la8°. Torino. [1922]

Raccolta.
R. de parti prese (1517–1697), *n.d.*, *see* VENEZIA.
R. di lirici ital., sino al sec. 18, *see* GIRONI (R.)
R. Vinciana, fasc. 1–12, 1906–26, *see* VINCI (L. DA).

Races Congress (Universal). Papers on inter-racial problems communic. to 1st U.R.C., London, 1911. Ed. G. Spiller. 8°. 1911

Raché (Paul). Wofür kämpfen die Engländer ?, *see* JÄCKH (E. F. W.) Der deut. Krieg, H78, 1916.

Rachel (*Mlle.*), *the actress*, *see* BARTHOU (L.) R., 1926.

Rachel (*Mme.*), *dealer in cosmetics* [†LEVISON (SARAH RACHEL)]. The extraord. life & trial of Mme. R., Cent. Criminal Court, 22–25 Sept. 1868. 8°. [1868]

Rachel (Samuel).
De jure naturae et gentium diss. 2v. la8°. Wash. 1916
1, [Text]; ed. L. v. Bar. 2, Tr., by J. P. Bate. [*tp. in English*].

Racheli (Antonio), *see* VARCHI (B.) Opere: con disc. di A. R. intorno alla filologia del sec. 16, 2v, 1858–59.

Rachfahl (Felix). Bismarcks Engl. Bündnispolitik. [P2620]. 8°. Freiburg im Br. 1922
Wilhelm v. Oranien u. d. niederl. Aufstand. B3. 8°. Haag. 1924

Racine (Jean).
Britannicus. Tragédie; notices &c. par G. Lanson. 7e éd. s8°. 1908
Lettres à son fils. Suivies de lettres de J.-B. Racine à Louis Racine. Intr. & notes de G. Truc. [Coll. des chefs-d'œ. méconnus]. s8°. 1922
Théâtre complet. Avec remarques litt. &c. par F. Lemaistre, préc. &c. la vie &c. de R. par L. S. Auger. s8°. [1869]
Théâtre complet. Ed. var. &c.; publ. par C. Louandre. s8°. 1912
Théâtre. Publ. D. Jouaust. Préf. par V. Fournel. 3t. s8°. [1922]

TRANSLATIONS.
Bernice. Tragedy. Tr. J. Masefield. s8°. 1922
The litigants. Tr., & exper. in rhymed anapaests by W. R. Dunstan. la8°. O. 1928
see BEYLE (M. H.) R. & Shakspeare, 2t, 1925.
„ DARMESTETER (*Mme.* J.) Life of R., 1925.
„ ECCLES (F. Y.) R. in Eng., 1922.
„ FRYE (P. H.) Racine, 1919.
„ MASEFIELD (J.) Esther: tragedy; adapted &c. f. J. R., 1922.
„ MAURIAC (F.) La vie de J. R., 1928.

Racine (Jean-Baptiste), *see* RACINE (J.) Lettres à son fils; suivies de lettres de J.-B. R., 1922.

Rackett (*Rev.* **Thomas).**
see MATON (W. G.) & T. R. Descr. cat. of Brit. testacea, 1807.
„ —— & —— An hist. acc. of testaceol. writers, 1804.

Rackham (Bernard).
see ECCLES (H.) & B. R. Analysed spec. of Eng. porcelain, 1922.
„ VICTORIA & ALBERT MUSEUM. H. Allen coll. of Eng. porcelain; by B. R., 2nd ed., 1923.

—— & H. Read. English pottery, its development to end of 18th cent. With app. on the Wrotham potters by J. W. L. Glaisher. 4°. 1924

Rackham (Richard Belward). The nave of Westminster, 1909, *see* BRIT. ACADEMY. Proc., 1909–10.

Racovian Catechism (*in chronolog. order of publ.*)
*C. d. Gemeine derer Leute die da im Königreich Poln, u. a. Herschaften z. d. Kron Poln gehörig affirmieren u. bekennen &c. Aus d. Poln. verdeut. s8°. Rackaw. 1608
C. eccl. quae in regno Poloniae, &c. affirmant &c. Ante annos 4 Polonice nunc Lat. edita. s8°. Racoviae. 1609
C. eccl. quae in regno Poloniae &c. affirm. neminem alium praeter Patrem &c. Cui acc. F. Socini vita &c. [*wanting*]. s8°. Racoviae. 1651
C. Eccl. Polon., anno 1609 in lucem primum emissa. Iterumque a J. Crellio & nunc a J. Schlichtingio recog. [M. Ruari notae, *w. sep. pagin.*] s8°. Irenopoli. 1659
C. R. seu liber Socinianorum primarius. Rec. &c. G. L. Oederus. s8°. Francofurti. 1739
R. (The) C. [Catechism of the churches of Poland by J. Crellius &c.] Tr. by T. Rees. s8°. 1818
see ARNOLD (N.) Religio Sociniana, seu Cat. Racov. refutata, 1654.
„ OSTORODT (C.) Unterricht v. d. vornem. Hauptpuncten d. Christl. Relig., d. Confession d. Gemeinen im Königr. Polen &c., 1612.
„ SCHMIDT (J. A.) Progr. de Cat. Racov., disput. 15. publ. Anti-Socinianis &c., 1724.

Racowitza (*Frau* **Helene von),** *geb. v. Dönniges*, *see* BORDEAUX (H.) Amours du temps passé: H. de D. & F. Lassalle, 1923.

Rácz (Andreas). *Reflexiones priv. de linguae Lat. in sacris eccl. cathol. usu &c. [P2651]. 8°. Lipsiae. 1845

Rada (Girolamo de). Poesie albanesi [*w. Ital. tr.*] 5v [*b. in* 3]. s8°. Corigliano Calabro. [v5, Napoli]. 1872–77
2–5, Scanderbeccu i pa-faan.

Rada (Joannes de). Controversiæ theologicæ inter S. Thomam & Scotum. s4°. Venetiis. 1599

Radama II, *king of Madagascar*, *see* VINSON (A.) Voyage à Madagascar au couronnement de R. II, 1865.

Radau (Hugo). Nin-Ib: determiner of fates acc. to the gt. Sumerian epic Lugal-e ŭg me-lám-bi ner-gál. [Univ. of Pa.] 8°. Phila. 1910

Radcliffe (*Mrs.* **Ann),** *see* WIETEN (A. A. S.) Mrs. R., her rel. towards romanticism, 1926.

Radcliffe (Charles Bland).
Behind the tides. 2nd ed. 8°. *n.p.* [1889]
Proteus or unity in nature. 2nd ed. 8°. 1877

Radcliffe (John). The confess. of the Xtn. faith, called the creed of Athanasius &c. 8°. 1844

Radcliffe (Lewis).
Caviar, 1916, *see* UNITED STATES: COMMERCE.
The sharks & rays of Beaufort, N. Carolina. [Fr. Bull. of Bur. of Fisheries, v34]. [P2702]. la8°. Wash. 1916

Radcliffe (William). Fishing f. the earliest times. 8°. 1921

Radclyffe (Charles W.) Memorials of Charterhouse. Views taken &c. on stone. fol. 1844

Radde (Gustav). Дауро-Монгольская граница Забайкалья. [*Extract.* P2532]. 8°. *n.d.*

Rade (Paul Martin). Glaubenslehre. 2B *in* 3v. [B1i, ii]. 8°. Gotha. 1924–27

Radegunda, *St.* *The lyfe of Saynt Radegunde. [*Attrib. to* Hy. Bradshaw]. Ed. f. copy in Jesus Coll. Lib. by F. Brittain. s8°. C. 1926
see BRIAND (E.) Hist. de sainte Radegonde &c., 1898.

Radek (Carl).
На службе германской революции. (Перевод с немецкого). 8°. [Москва.] 1921
Портреты и памфлеты. 8°. Москва. 1927
Anarchismus u. Sowjetregierung. [P2457]. 8°. Wien. [1920]
Die auswärt. Pol. d. deut. Kommunismus u. d. Hamburger nat. Bolschewismus. [P2457]. 8°. Wien. [1920]
Die auswärt. Pol. Sowjet-Russlands. [P2522]. 8°. Hamburg. 1921
The development of socialism. [P2487]. s8°. Glasgow. [1920?]
Die Entwicklung d. Welt-Revolution u. d. Taktik d. kommunist. Parteien im Kampfe um d. Diktatur d. Proletariats. [P2457]. 8°. Wien. 1920
In d. Reihen d. deut. Revolution, 1909–19. 8°. München. [1920]
Die innere u. äuss. Lage Sowjetrusslands u. die Aufgaben d. K.P.R. [P2570]. s8°. L. 1921
Die Masken sind gefallen. Antwort an Crispien &c. [P2462]. 8°. 1920
Programm d. sozialist. Wirtschaftsaufbaues. [P2457]. s8°. Wien. 1920
Proletarische Diktatur u. Terrorismus. [P2425]. 8°. Hamburg. [1919]
Rosa Luxemburg, Karl Liebknecht, Leo Jogiches. [P2603]. la8°. Hamburg. 1921
Die russ. Sowjetverfassung. [P2457]. 8°. Wien. [1920]
Theorie u. Praxis d. 2½ Internationale. [P2522]. 8°. Hamburg. 1921
Wege d. russ. Revolution. 8°. 1922
see LEVI (P.) Unser Weg wider d. Putschismus: mit e. Artikel v. C. R., 1921.
„ PROGRAMM d. kommunist. Partei Russlands; mit Einführung v. C. R., 1920.

Rademacher (Arnold), *see* BAUMGARTEN (O.) Geistige &c. Wirk. d. Krieges in Deut., von O. B., A. R. &c., 1927.

Rademaker (Abraham). Kabinet v. nederland. outheden & gezichten verzamelt &c. door A. R. met beschr. in Duitsch, Fr. & Eng. 2d. 8°. 1725

Räder (E.) Kreuzerkrieg, 2B, *see* KRIEG z. See, 1922–23.

Radermacher (Ludwig).
Works in KAISERL. AKAD. D. W. ZU WIEN. Sitzungsber.
Beitr. z. Volkskunde aus d. Gebiet d. Antike, 1918. [187.]
Die Erzählungen d. Odyssee, 1915. [178.]
Hippolytos u. Thekla, 1916. [182.]
Zur Gesch. d. griech. Komödie, 1, 2, 1925. [202.]
Neutestamentl. Grammatik, *see* LIETZMANN (H.), *ed.* Handbuch z. N.T., B1i, 1912.
Probleme d. Kriegszeit im Altertum. Vortrag. [P2493]. 8°. Wien. 1918

Raderus (Matthias), *see* HUGO (H.) Pia desideria: quatuor noviss. M. R. &c., 1673.

Radford (George), *M.A.*
Agricultural co-oper. & organis. 2nd ed. rev. 8°. 1917
Labour & the moneyed man. s8°. [1922]

Radford (John), *Jesuit, 1561–1630.* A Directorie teaching the way to the truth in a briefe & plaine discourse &c. Whereunto a short treatise agst. Adiaphorists, Neuters &c. [*tp. wanting*]. s8º. [Douay?]. 1599]

Radhakrishnan (Sarvepalli). Hindu view of life. 8º. [1927]
Indian philosophy. 2v. 8º. [1923–27]
The philosophy of the Upaniṣads. Foreword by R. Tagore. Intr. by E. Holmes. 8º. [1924]

Radiguet (Raymond). Le bal du comte d'Orgel. 8º. 1924

Radin (Paul). Monotheism am. prim. peoples. Foreword by I. Zangwill. s8º. [1924]
Primitive man as philosopher. 8º. N.Y. 1927
The Winnebago tribe, *see* SMITHSONIAN INSTIT.: BUR. OF ETHN. Rep. 37, 1923.

Radinus Todischus (Thomas). In Philippū Melāchthonē Lutheranę hæreseos defensorem oratio. s8º. [Romae. 1522]

Radischev (Aleksandr Nikolaevich), *1749–1802, see* LAPSHIN (I. I.) Философ. взгляды Р., 1922.

Radlov (Ernst Lvovich).
Очерк ист. русской философии. 2ºе изд. la8º. П. 1920
see LAVROV (P. L.) П. Л. Л. Статьи, воспоминания &c. [*by* R. *&c.*], 1922.

Radlov (Vasily Vasilevich). Средняя Зерафшанская долина. [I.R.G.O. Записки по отдѣл. этнограф., 6i]. 8º. С.-П. 1880

Radnor (Helen Matilda Pleydell-Bouverie, *ctss. of*), *wife of 5th earl, see* RADNOR (J. P.-B., *6th e. of*). Cat. of pictures in coll. of E. of R.; by H. M., ctss. of R. &c., 2p, 1909.

Radnor (Jacob Pleydell-Bouverie, *6th earl of*). Cat. of pictures in the collection of the E. of R. By H. Matilda, ctss. of R. & W. B. Squire. Pref. by Jacob, 6th e. of R. 2p. fol. *p.p. Chiswick Press.* 1909

Radò (Alex.) Führer durch d. Sowjetunion. Gesamtausgabe. Bearb. A. R. Hrsg. v. d. Gesell. f. Külturverb. d. Sowjetunion &c. s8º. 1928

Radowitz (Josef Maria von). Nachgel. Briefe u. Aufzeichn. z. Gesch, 1848–53. 8º. St. 1922

Radowitz (Joseph Maria F. W. L. v.) Aufzeichnungen &c. aus d. Leben d. Botschafters J. M. v. R. Hrsg. H. Holborn. 2B. 1, 1839–77; 2, 1878–90. 8º. St. 1925

Raduga. Радуга альманахъ пушкинскаго дома. s8º. П. 1922

Rădulescu (Andrei). Cultura jurid. romaneasca in ult. sec., *see* ACADEMIA ROM. Disc. 53, 1923.

Radulescu-Niger (N. G.) Căpitanul Ropotă. s8º. 1893

Radulfus, *Leodicensis* [RADOLFUS]. Une corr. d'écolatres du 11 s. [*i.e. R. &c.*], *see* TANNERY (P.) Mém. scient., t5, 1922.

Radziwill (*pcss.* **Catherine),** *aft. C. Kolb Danvin.*
Those I remember. 8º. [1924]

Radziwill (*prince* **Nicholas VII Christopher),** *the Orphan; 1549–1616* [RADZIVILUS]. Jerosolymitana peregrinatio. A T. Tretero in Lat. tr. sm. fol. 1753

Raeburn (Harold). Mountaineering art. 8º. [1920]

Raemaeker (Louis). Cartoons. [P2415]. s4º. [1916]

Raevskaya (Mariya Nikolaevna), *see* VOLKONSKAYA (*princess* M. N.)

Raffaelli (Jean François). Mes promenades au Musée du Louvre. Préf. de M. Barrès. 2ᵉ éd. rev. & augm. 8º. [1913]

Raffaellini (Francesco Maria).
Il genio di Napoli: serenata. [N125]. 8º. Napoli. 1707

Raffalovich (Arthur). Année écon. & financière, 1913–14. Le marché financièr. 8º. 1915
Le marché financièr, 1914–19. Les dettes publ. &c. pend. la Guerre. 8º. 1920

Raffard (Henri). Apontamentos acerca de pessoas e cousas do Brasil, *see* INSTITUTO HIST. &C. BRAZIL. Rev., t61ii, 1899.

Raffé (Walter George). Poems in black & white. la8º. [1922]

Raffi (Melikzate). Khamsayi meliqouthiunnere, 1600–1827. [*5 melik admin., in Armenian*]. 2nd impr. 8º. Tiflis. 1895
[Samouel, hist. tale, 364–400. Books 1–3. *In Armenian*]. 8º. Vienna. 1898

Raffin (Léonce). Saint-Julien de Balleuré, historien bourguignon, 1519?–93. 8º. 1926

Raffles (*Sir* **Thomas Stamford),** *see* COUPLAND (R.) R., 1781–1826.

Rafy (*Mrs.* **K. U.)** Folk-tales of the Khasis. s8º. 1920

Ragatz (Lowell Joseph). Check-list of H. of Commons sess. papers rel. to the Brit. W. Indies &c., 1763–1834. s8º. [1923]
Guide to offic. corr. of the Governors of the Brit. W.I. Colonies, 1763–1833. [*b. w. h.* Check-list, 1923]. s8º. [1923]

Ragazzoni, *The family of, see* BERNONI (D. G.) Dei Torresani, Blado e R., 1890.

Ragewin [RAHEWIN], *see* OTTO, *bp. of Frisingen.* O. & Rahewini Gesta Frid. I, 1884.

Ragg (Laura Marie), *wife of Rev. Lonsdale Ragg.*
The women artists of Bologna. 8º. [1907]

Ragg (Lonsdale).
St. Luke. With intr. & notes by L. R. 8º. [1922]

***Ragguaglio** hist. d. Guerra tra l' armi Cesaree e Ottomane dal princ. d. Ribellione degli' Ungari, 1683, *see* CACAVELAS (J.) The siege of Vienna by the Turks in 1683; tr. into Greek f. Ital. wk. publ. anon. [*w. t.* Ragguaglio &c.]; ed. &c. F. H. Marshall, 1925.

Ragimboldus, *Coloniensis.* Une corr. d'écolatres du 11 s. [*i.e. R. &c.*], *see* TANNERY (P.) Mém. scient., t5, 1922.

Ragnar, *called Lodbrok, king of Denmark.* Lodbrokar-Quida: death-song of Lodbroc. With tr., glossary &c. by J. Johnstone. s8º. *n.p.* 1782

Raguenet (François).
Hist. du Vte. de Turenne. n. éd. s8º. 1813

Ragut (Camille), *see* MÂCON. Cartul. de St.-Victor de M.; publ. par C. R., 1864.

Rahbek (Knud Lyne). De antiquiss. eccl. Danicae lingua vernacula hymnariis &c. s4º. Havniae. 1818

Rahir (Edouard). La bibliothèque de l'amateur: guide sommaire. 2ᵉ éd., rev. &c. la8º. 1924
Cat. d'une coll. unique de vol. impr. par les Elzevier &c. du 17ᵉ siècle. Rédigé par E. R., préc. d'un avant-propos par F. Brunetière & d'une lettre de A. Willems. 8º. 1896

Rahlfs (Alfred). Verzeichnis d. griech. Hss. d. Alten Testaments, *see* KÖNIGL. GESELLS. ZU GÖTTINGEN. Nachrichten, 1914, Beiheft.
see LÜTKEMANN (L.) & A. R. Hexaplar. Randnoten zu Isaias 1–16, 1915.

Rahm (Math.) Ein edler Geigenkünstler. [4.A.] s8º. Bonn. *n.d.*

Rahn (Conrad), *see* FREY (M. v.), *ed.* Abhandlgn. ü. d. Speichel v. C. R. &c. (1851), 1890.

Rahola (Carles). En Ramón Muntaner: l'home—la crònica. Próleg. de Ll. N. d'Olwer. 8º. Barcelona. 1922

Rai (Lajpat). The problem of nat. educ. in India. s8º. [1920]

Raile (Arthur Lyon). The wild rose: poems. s8º. 1909

Railo (Eino). The haunted castle: st. of elem. of Eng. romanticism. la8º. 1927

Railway. *A Railway traveller's reasons for adopting uniformity of gauge. [P2845]. 8º. *n.p. n.d.*

Raimond (C. E.), *ps., see* ROBINS (*Miss* ELIZ.)

Rainaldi (Carlo), *see* HEMPEL (E.) C. R.; riprod. con testo e cat., 1921.

Rainaud (Armand). Le continent austral. Hypothèses & découvertes. 8º. 1893

Rainbow (Edward), *bp. of Carlisle.* Sermon preached at funeral of Anne, countess of Pembroke &c. s4º. 1677

Raine (Angelo).
Hist. of St. Peter's School, York. 8º. 1926

Raine (G. E.) Bolshevik Russia. By G. E. R. in collab. w. E. Luboff. s8º. [1920]

Raineri (Salvatore). The mastery of the Adriatic & the Jugo-Slav question. Comp. by S. R. [P2432]. 8º. 1916

Rainerus, *Sachonus, see* SACCONUS (REINERUS).

Rainey (*Lt.-Col.* **J. W.),** *see* WAR. Hist. of the Gt. War based on offic. doc.: veterinary services; ed. Sir L. J. Blenkinsop & Lt.-Col. J. W. R., 1925.

Rainis (Janis) [*i.e.* J. PLEEKSCHAN]. Joseph u. seine Brueder. Tragödie. Übers. v. A. Pleekschan. [Lett. Lit., B1]. 8º. Riga. [1921]
The sons of Jacob. [Play]. Tr. G. Rhys. s8º. 1924

Rainolds (John). Censura libr. apocryph. Vet. Test. adv. pontificios, imprimis R. Bellarminum. 2t *b. in 1.* 4º. *In nobili Oppenheimio.* 1611
Sex theses de sacra Scr. & Eccl., ut publ. in Acad. Oxon. disput. explicatæ sic ed. s8º. Londini. 1602
The Summe of the conference betweene John Rainoldes & John Hart t. the head and the faith of the church. Penned by J. R.: perused by J. Hart. Annexed: Six Conclusions by J. R. With a defence of such things as T. Stapleton & G. Martin have carped at therein. 8º. 1588

Rainolds (William) [*ps.* ROSSAEUS (G. G.); REGINALDUS (GUL.)] Calvino-Turcismus. Id est Calvinisticæ perfidiæ cum Mahumetana collatio. [*Completed & ed. by* G. Giffordus]. s8º. Antverpiæ. 1597
*De justa reipub. Christianae in reges impios & haereticos authoritate: justissimaque cathol. ad Henr. Navarr. &c. repellendum confœd., liber. s8º. Parisiis. 1590

Rainolds (William) [*continued*].
A refutation of sundry reprehensions &c. by wh. M. Whitaker laboureth to deface the late Eng. tr. & Catholic annot. of the New Test. &c. s8°. Paris. 1583
see WHITAKER (W.), *D.D.* An answere to a certeine booke by W. R. entituled A refutation &c., 1585.

Rainwater (Clarence Elmer). The play movement in the U.S.: community recreation. s8°. Chicago. 1922

Raison du Cleuziou (Alain). La Bretagne, de l'orig. à la réunion. 3e éd. 8°. Saint-Brieuc. 1925

Raisuni, *El* [MULAI AHMED], *see* FORBES (R.) El R., the sultan of the mountains: h. life story, 1924.

Rait (Robert Sangster).
A hist. of the U.K., 1707–1919. s8°. 1920
Mem. of A. V. Dicey, letters & diaries. Ed. R. S. R. 8°. 1925
Outline of Brit. hist., *see* BUCHAN (J.), *ed.* Nations of to-day, Gt. Brit., v1, 1923.
The parliaments of Scotland. 8°. Glasgow. 1924
see DICEY (A. V.) & R. S. R. Thoughts on the Union betw. Eng. & Scotland, 1920.
—— **& A. I. Cameron,** *edd.* King James's secret: negotiations betw. Elizabeth & J. VI rel. to execut. of Mary Q. of Scots, f. the Warrender papers. 8°. 1927

Raithius (Balthasar). Vindiciae vers. S. Bibliorum German. M. Lutheri labore ed. s4°. Tubingae. 1676
see SCHICKARD (W.), *the elder.* Epitome Bibliorum &c.; accur. B. R., 1663.

Raitz v. Frentz (Emmerich), *S.J.* Der ehrw. Kard. R. Bellarmin, 1542–1621. [Jesuiten: Lebensbilder; hrsg. K. Kempf]. s8°. Freiburg i. B. 1921

Rajna (Pio).
see ALFONSO V. Il Padiglione di re Alfonso; *ed.* P. R., 1904.
,, DANTE ALIGHIERI. Lectura D.: c. 17 del Purgatorio esposto da P. R., 1901.

Rajputana. Rep. on sanitation, dispensaries & jails in R. for 1917, 1918, & on vaccination for 1917/18–1921/22. fol. Calcutta. 1918–22

Raketov (A.) Очеркъ эконом. и финанс. положенія современной Россіи. s8°. Ревель. 1921

Rakhov (V. O.), *see* PRUGAVIN (A. S.) Вопіющее дѣло, (дѣло В. О. Р.), 1906.

Raknes (Ola), *see* GRØNDAHL (I.) & O. R. Chapters in Norwegian lit., 1923.

Rakovsky (G. N.) Въ станѣ бѣлыхъ (отъ Орга до Новороссійска). s8°. Константинополь. 1920
Гражданская война на югѣ Россіи. Въ станѣ бѣлыхъ. s8°. Константинополь. 1920

Raleigh (George). Albania: or, certaine concernments of Great Britanny. s4°. 1641

Raleigh (*Sir* Thomas), *K.C.S.I.* Annals of the Ch. in Scotland, by Sir T. R., w. h. autobiog. notes & some remin. by Sir H. R. Reichel. 8°. 1921

Raleigh (*Sir* Walter).
The ballad of Sir W. R. his lamentation [1618]. Reprod. w. translit. [*a. c. in* P2417]. fol. [O.] 1919
Historie of the world. fol. 1652
Poems of R.; w. those of Sir H. Wotton, & o. courtly poets, 1540–1650. Ed. J. Hannah. [Aldine ed.] s8°. 1891
see CUST (*Sir* L.) Portraits of Sir W. R., 1920.
,, FIRTH (*Sir* C. H.) Sir W. R.'s Hist. of the world, 1918.
,, PEMBERTON (H.) Shakespere & Sir W. R., 1914.
,, WALDMAN (M.) Sir W. R., 1928.

Raleigh (*Sir* Walter), *M.A.*
Laughter f. a cloud. Foreword by H. Raleigh. 8°. 1923
Letters (1879–1922). Ed. Lady Raleigh. Pref. by D. N. Smith. 2v. 8°. [1926]
On writing & writers. Sel. & ed. G. Gordon. 8°. 1926
Romance. 2 lect., Princeton Univ., 1915. s8°. Princeton. 1916
Shakespeare & England, *see* BRIT. ACADEMY. Proc[s]., 1917–18.
Some authors: lit. essays, 1896–1916. 8°. O. 1923
Style. 14th impr. 8°. 1923
Wordsworth. 8th imp. s8°. 1921
see WAR. The War in the air, v1 by W. R., 1922.

Ralli (*Mrs.* Pantia). Particulars of the estate of Ashtead Park, for sale by Knight &c., 8th Oct. 1924. [By dir. of Mrs. P. R. P2752]. fol. 1924

Ram (Pierre François Xavier de). Disq. hist. de iis quae contra Lutherum Lovanienses theologi egerunt a. 1519. 4°. Brux. 1843

Rám Rāj. Essay on the architecture of the Hindús. R. Asiatic Soc.] 4°. 1834

Ramaekers (Georges). Eugène Demolder. s8°. Turnhout. 1920
Georges Rodenbach. s8°. Turnhout. 1920
Le gr. card. belge, D. J. Mercier, 1851–1926. Préf. du r. p. M. Lekeux. s8°. Brux. [1926]

Ramakrishna, *1833–86.*
*Life of Sri R. 8°. Mayavati, Almora. 1925

Ramakrishna Ayyar (T. V.) South Indian Coccidae, *see* AGRIC. RES. INST., *Pusa.* Bulletin 87, 1919.
Weevil fauna of S. India, *see* AGRIC. RES. INST., *Pusa.* Bulletin 125, 1922.

Ramal (Walter), *see* DE LA MARE (W.)

Ramanujan (Srinivasa), *Aiyangar.* Coll. papers. Ed. G. H. Hardy, P. V. Seshu Aiyar & B. M. Wilson. la8°. C. 1927

Ramaprasad Chanda. Archaeology & Vaishnava tradition, *see* INDIA: ARCH. SURVEY. Mem. No. 5, 1920.
The begin. of art in E. India, *see* INDIA: ARCH. SURVEY. Mem. No. 30, 1927.
Dates of the votive inscr. on the stupas at Sanchi, *see* INDIA: ARCH. SURVEY. Mem. No. 1, 1919.
The Indus Valley in Vedic per., *see* INDIA: ARCH. SURVEY. Mem. 31, 1926.

***Ramassis,** c. 1783, *see* LA ROCHEFOUCAULD (*le vte.* J. F. DE).

Ramayana, *see also* TULSI DÁS.

Rambach (Johann Jacob), *prof. of theology at Giessen.*
Betracht. ü. d. 7 Verheiss. i. d. apocalypt. Briefen. [*b. w.* Francke (A. H.) Comm. de scopo &c., 1724]. s8°. Halle. 1733
Colleg. introd. hist.-theolog., oder Hist. Einleit. in d. Streitigkeiten d. Evangel. u. Röm.-Kathol. Kirchen, &c. 2t *in* 1v. s4°. Halle [t2, Franckfurth]. 1738
Diss. qua pellis ovina Socinianis detracta sistitur. s4°. Halae. 1731
Exercitationes hermeneuticae, sive pars altera Instit. hermeneut. ed. nova. s8°. Bremae. 1741
Hist. & theolog. Einleitung in die Religions-Strittigkeiten d. Evang.-Luther. Kirche mit d. Socinianern. Mit Vorrede, Anmerk. &c. v. C. Hecht. 2t *in* 1v. s4°. Coburg. 1745
Instit. hermeneuticae sacrae. Cum praef. J. F. Buddei. ed. 4a recog. s8°. Jenae. 1732
see LUTHER (M.) Auserl. Schriften, mit Einl. dargel. v. R., 1743.
,, RECKENBERGER (J. L.) Nexus canonum exeget. ex J. J. R. Instit. hermeneut., 1736.

Rambaldi (Pier Liberale). Castel Pietra offerto alla rep. di Venezia, 1455. [Nozze Pieri—Stavole. N.121]. s8°. Padova. 1896
La chiesa d. Ss. Gio. e Paolo e la cappella d. Rosario in Venezia. s8°. Venezia. 1913

Rambaud, *de Vaqueiras.* Epistole al marchese Bonifazio I, di Monferrato. [Ed. & annot.] A. Schultz-Gora. Tr. G. del Noce. s8°. Firenze. 1898

Rambaud (Alfred N.) La domination française en Allemagne. 3e éd. corr. [t1]. s8°. 1883
[1], Les Français sur le Rhin, 1792–1804.

Ramburtius (Abrahamus). Disputationes, *see* DU MOULIN (P.) Thesaurus disput., v2, 1661.

Ram Chandra Kak, *Pandit, B.A.*, *see* SANCHI. Cat. of the Museum of Archeol. at S., Bhopal, 1922.

Rameau (Jean), *ps.* [*i.e.* L. LABAIGT]. L'arrivée aux étoiles. (Essai vers l'au-delà). s8°. [1922]
L'inoubliable. s8°. [1923]

Ramel (*le gén.* Jean Pierre), *see* PRAVIEL (A.) Massacre de R., récit, 1927.

Ramin (Henri). Notre très vieux Paris. 3e éd. la8°. *n.d.*
Vocabulaire anglais-franç. & fr.-angl. des industries du livre. 8°. [1920 ?]

Ramione (Vincenzo Palizzolo Gravina, *barone* **di),** *see* PALIZZOLO GRAVINA (V.)

Rammohun Roy, *Rajah* [RĀMAMOHANA RĀYA], *see* MARSHMAN (J.) A def. of the deity of J. C., in reply to R. R., 1822.

Ramond de Carbonnières (*le baron* Louis François Elisabeth), *see* MONGLOND (A.) La jeunesse de R., 1926.

Ramón Gomez de la Serna, *see* GOMEZ DE LA SERNA (R.)

Ramón Mélida (José). Cat. mon. de España. Prov. de Cáceres, 1914–16. 3t (Texto, 2t *&* Laminas). 8°. [1924]
Escorial. [Art in Spain, 8. Hispanic Soc.] s8°. Barcelona. *n.d.*
Iberia arqueológica ante-romana. Discursos, R. Acad. de la Hist. la8°. 1906

Ramos (Juan P.) Folklore Argentino: proyecto d. Dr. R. Instrucciones a los maestros. [Consejo Nac. de Educ. P2532]. 8°. 1921

Rampegollis (Antonius de). [Biblia aurea. *fol. 2a* [*table*] Abstinentia valet ad multa; *fol. 15a* Liber manualis ac introductorius in biblie historias &c. *fol. 159a* Vigore in-

Rampegollis (Antonius de) [*continued*].
finiti entis explicit lib'bon' & perutilis Aurea biblia, appelat'. Vlm p. Johãnem zeiner de Rütlingen].
fol. [Ulm, *Joh. Zainer de Rütlingen.* 1475]
Without tp. pagin. or signat. 160 leaves, first and last blank, the latter wanting.
*Biblia aurea veteris ac novi testamẽti vocitatus. [*f2a* Incipit liber manualis ac introductorius in biblie historias &c. *f136a* Peracta est Biblea aurea veteris &c.]
s4°. [Strassburg, *J. (Reinhard) Grüninger.* Mccccixv. 1495]
140 leaves, the last blank. 2–136 *numbered fol.* 2–126 *w. many errors.*

Ramperti (Marco). La corona di cristallo. 8°. 1926

Ramsay (*Miss* A. A. W.) Idealism & foreign policy: rel. of Gt. Brit. w. Germany & France, 1860–78. 8°. 1925

Ramsay (Allan), *the elder, 1686–1758.*
The gentle shepherd. s8°. E. 1776
see Mackail (J. W.) A. R. & the romantic revival, 1924.

Ramsay (*Sir* Andrew Crombie). Geol. of N. Wales, 2nd ed., *see* Geolog. Survey of Eng. &c. Mem. v3, 1881.
Passages in the hist. of geology. [P2658]. 8°. 1848
The physical geol. & geog. of Gt. Brit. 6th ed. Ed. H. B. Woodward. 8°. 1894
——, **W. T. Aveline & E. Hull.** Geology of parts of Wilts. & Gloucs. Lists of fossils by R. Etheridge. [Mems. of G.S.] 8°. 1858

Ramsay (*Sir* James Henry), *of Bamff, 10th bart.* Hist. of the revenues of the kings of Eng., 1066–1399. 2v. 8°. O. 1925
see Tout (T. F.) Sir J. H. R., 1832–1925, 1926.

Ramsay (*Sir* William Mitchell). Anatolian studies. [*By var. wr.*] Presented to Sir W. M. R. Ed. W. H. Buckler & W. M. Calder. [Univ. of M'ter Publ.] la8°. M'ter. 1923
Asianic elements in Greek civilis. [Gifford lect., 1915–16]. la8°. 1927

Ramsbottom (John), *see* Brit. Mus. of Nat. Hist.: Botany. Hdbk. of larger Brit. fungi; by J. R., 1923.

Ramsey (Robert W.) Dante & St. Louis, *see* Roy. Soc. of Lit. Essays, v4, 1924.

Ramsey (Stanley Churchill) & J. D. M. Harvey. Small houses of the late Georgian period, 1750–1820. v2, Details & interiors. sm. fol. 1923

Ramshausen (Franz Wilhelm). Exercit. theol. Eccl. Copticae ortum, progr. &c. repraes. Præs. J. E. Gerhardo. [P2644]. s4°. [Jena. 1666]

Ramstedt (G. I.) Этимологія имени Ойратъ. [*Extr. f.* I.R.G.O. Зап. по отд. Этн., t34. P2532]. 8°. [С.-П. 1908]

Ramus (Joannes Daniel). De ancilibus Romanorum. Resp. G. Kyngio. [P2587]. s4°. [Hafn.] 1706

Ramus (Petrus) [†La Ramée (Pierre de)].
see Graves (F. P.) P. R. & the educ. reform. of the 16th c., 1912.
,, Richardson (A.) Logician's schoolmaster: or, comm. upon R.'s Logick &c., 1657.
,, Serres (J. de). *The three partes of commentaries, disc. of the civill warres of Fraunce &c. [*erroneously attrib. to R.*], 1574.

Ramus (Pierre). F. Ferrer, s. Leben u. s. Werk. 2e, verm. A., mit Nachwort v. E. H. Schmitt. 8°. Wien. 1921

Ramuz (Charles Ferdinand).
Joie dans le ciel. [Cahiers verts, 56]. s8°. 1925

Ranby (John), *F.R.S.* A narr. of the last illness of the Earl of Orford. [*b. w.* Walpole (*Sir* R.) Authentick copy of last will, 1745]. 8°. 1745

Rance (Charles E. de), *see* De Rance (C. E.)

Rand (Benjamin), *Ph.D., Harvard Univ., see* Locke (J.) Corresp. of J. L. & E. Clarke; ed. &c. B. R., 1927.

Rand (Edward Kennard). Ovid & h. infl. [Our debt to Greece & Rome]. 8°. [1926]
see Lowe (E. A.) & E. K. Rand. A 6th-c. fragment of Letters of Pliny the Younger: a st. &c., 1922.

Randall (Henry Stephens).
The life of Thomas Jefferson. 3v. 8°. N.Y. 1858

Randall-MacIver (David). The Etruscans. 8°. O. 1927
The iron age in Italy. Aspects wh. are neither Villanovan nor Etruscan. 4°. O. 1927
Villanovans & early Etruscans: early iron age in Italy. 4°. O. 1924

Randerson (William). Albert Kahn Travelling Fellowships. Report by W. R., 1923–24. 8°. 1926

Randles (Marshall).
Design & use of Holy Scr. Fernley lect. 8°. 1892

Randolph (Edmund), *governor of Virginia, see* Bemis (S. F.), *ed.* Amer. Secretaries of State, v2, R., by D. R. Anderson, 1927.

Randolph (Paschal Beverley).
Pre-Adamite man. 6th ed. 8°. Toledo, Ohio. 1888

Randolph (Thomas), *dramatist, see* Hemings (W.) Elegy on R.'s finger (c. 1630); intr. &c. G. C. M. Smith, 1923.

Ranera (Alejandro Gomez), *see* Gomez Ranera (A.)

Ranessøn (Sigurd).
S. R.'s proces. Udg. af G. Storm. 8°. 1877

Rangabé (Alexander Rhizos). [Golden rods. *In Armenian.* Tr. M. Maqsouteantz. *Extr. f.* Banaser. P2817]. 8°. Paris. 1906

Ranga-Pillai, *see* Harischandra, *k. of Ayodhya.* Arichandra, tr. [*chiefly f. version ascr. to R.-P.*], 1863.

Ranger-Gull (Cyril Arthur Edward) [*ps.* Guy Thorne].
Muriel wins through. s8°. [1923]

Rango (Conrad Tiburtius). Diss. de gigantibus. Praes. A. Sennerto. s4°. [Wittenbergae]. 1663
Vita Romuli. Praes. C. T., resp. V. Gadebusch. [P445]. s4°. Francofurti a. O. 1661

Rangoni (Claudio), *bp. of Reggio-Emilia.* Ragguagli di C. R., Nunzio in Polonia, 1599–1605, *see* Scuola Rom. di Roma. Diplomat. Ital., v1, 1925.

Ranieri (Vincenzo). Memorie stor. per s. alla vita di Fra Sabba Castiglioni. s8°. Lugo. 1821

Ranjitsinhji (*Prince* K. S.), *Maharajah of Nawanagar, see* Fry (C. B.) Key-book of the League of Nations, w. ch. on the disarmament q. by Prince R., 1923.

Ranke (Ernst). Fragm. antiq. Evangelii Lucani vers. Lat. e membranis Curiens. 4°. Vindobonae. 1873
Par palimpsestorum Wirceburg. Antiq. Vet. Test. vers. Lat. fragm. Ed. E. R. Acc. duae tabulae. 4°. Vindobonae. 1871
Specimen codicis N. Test. Fuldensis. 4°. Marburgi. 1860
see Bible: New Test. (Latin). Codex Fuld. &c.; ed. E. R., 1868.

Ranke (Friedrich), *ed., see* Tristram. Tristan u. Isolde, 1925.

Ranke (Hermann), *see* Erman (A.) Aegypten u. aegypt. Leben in Altertum; neu bearb. v. H. R., 1923.

Ranke (Leopold v.) Zur Kritik neu. Geschichtschreiber. [*b. w. h.* Gesch. d. rom. &c. Völker, 1885]. 3e A. 8°. L. 1884
Translations.
Hist. of the Popes dur. 16th & 17th cent. Tr. E. Foster. 3v. s8°. *Bohn.* 1896–1902
Hist. of Servia & the Servian Revolution. Tr. Mrs. A. Kerr. Add. The Slave Provinces of Turkey, chiefly f. the Fr. of C. Robert. s8°. *Bohn.* 1853

Rankin (Robert A. S.)
Idiomatic Italian composition. 8°. 1912

Rankin (Thomas). *A brief narr. of the rival religion in Virginia. 3rd ed. s8°. 1786

Rannie (David Watson). Scenery in Shakespeare's plays & o. st. With mem. by h. wife & apprec. by D. Macgregor. 8°. O. 1926

Ransom (Caroline Louise). Studies in anc. furniture. Couches & beds of the Greeks, Etruscans & Romans. 4°. Chicago. 1905

Ransom (Samuel). A Hebrew grammar. 8°. 1843

Ransome (Arthur). The Chinese puzzle. s8°. [1927]

Ransome (Cyril). Advanced hist. of Eng. 2p *in* 1v [*1, 6th ed., 9th impr.; 2, 9th ed., 10th impr.*] s8°. 1923–25

Ranst (Frans van). Veritas in medio; seu D. Thomas propositiones omnes circa theoriam & praxim &c., versantes à Baianis usque ad Quesnellianas 101 prædamnans: Inserta est vita Baii, Jansenii &c. s8°. Antverpiæ. 1715

Rantzau (Ulrich K. Brockdorff-, *Graf* v.), *see* Brockdorff-Rantzau.

Ranworth, *Norfolk.* Ranworth rood screen. Drawn by R. O. Pearson. fol. *n.d.*

Ranyard (*Mrs.* Ellen), *see* Book (The) & its missions, 1856–57.

Ranza (Giovanni Antonio Francesco Maria), *see* Roberti (G.) Il Cittadino R.: ricerche doc., 1892.

Ranzoni (Daniele), *see* Carrà (C.) D. R., w. 33 reprods. in phototype, 1924.

Ranzovius (Henricus) [*ps.* Christianus Cilicius, *Cimber*]. Dithmarsici belli historia, *see* Krantz (A.) Regnorum Aquilonarium &c. chronica, 1583.

Raoul de Cambrai: e. altfr. Heldenlied; übers. v. F. Settegast, *see* Archiv f. d. St. d. neu. Spr., B70, 1883.
R. de C. Old French feudal epic. Tr. J. Crossland. [Medieval Lib.; ed. I. Gollancz]. s8°. 1926

Raper (Elizabeth). Receipt book & portion of cipher journal. Ed. B. Grant. Wr. 1756–70. 8°. Soho, *Nonesuch Press.* 1924

Rapetti (Pierre Nicholas). La défection de Marmont en 1814; suivi de docs. inéd. &c. 8°. 1858

Raphael, *the painter.*

La favola di Psiche disegnata da R., colla spiegaz. in ottava rima. obl.4°. Roma, *C. Losi.* 1774

see CARTWRIGHT (J.) R., re-issued, 1914.

„ OJETTI (U.) R. e altre leggi, 1921.

see RICCI (C.) Raffaello, 1920.

„ SCHNEIDER (F.) Un peu de théologie à p. d. R., 1896.

„ —— Theologisches zu R., Disputa - Transfiguration, 1896.

„ VICTORIA & A. MUS. Picture bk. of R. cartoons, 1927.

Raphael (Gaston).
Le roi de la Ruhr: H. Stinnes. 8°. 1924
Tirpitz. Préf. du Vice-Am. Ronarc'h. s8°. 1922

Raphael (*Mrs.* **Louis**). Cat. of old French furniture &c., prop. of Mrs. L. R. &c. Sold by Christie, May 18, 1927. [*Illust.* P2873]. 8°. 1927
Cat. of pictures by old masters, prop. of Mrs. L. R. &c., sold by Christie, May 20, 1927. [Illust.] 8°. 1927

Raphel (Georg) [RAPHELIUS]. Annots. in Sacram Scr., ex Xenophonte, Polybio, Arriano & Herodoto coll. Praef. est B. L. Raphelius. ed. nova. [Acc. Semicenturia annot. philol. in Nov. Test. ex Eusebio coll. & J. Chrysostomi Comm. &c. in Epist. P. ad Philemonem &c.] 2t. s8°. Lugd. Batav. 1747
„ „ Ed. nova auct. & emend. 2t. s8°. Lugd. Batav. 1750

Raphon (Hans) [RAPHUN], *see* STUTTMANN (F.) H. R., 1925.

Raphson (—), *see* BAXTER (R.) Catholick Communion: animadv. on R.'s book &c., 1684.

Rappard (A. C. P. G., *Ritter* **van),** *see* WIEDER (F. C.) De stichting van New York, 1625, reconstr. en nieuwe gegevens ontleend aan de van R. doc., 1925.

Rappard (Carl von).
Studien u. Phantasien. [*Plates*]. atl. fol. München. 1897

Rappolt (Friedrich). Opera theolog., exeget., didact., polem. Cur. J. B. Carpzovio. 2t *in* 1v [*pagin. cont.*] s4°. Lipsiae. 1693

Rappolt (Gottfried Christian). Diss. de Regulo. Praes. J. H. Ernesti. [P445]. s4°. Lipsiae. 1684

Rappoport (Angelo S.) Dict. of socialism. 8°. 1924

Rapports. *R. entre la langue sanscrit & la langue russe, 1811, *see* ADELUNG (F. v.)

Rapson (Edward James), *ed., see* CAMBRIDGE (THE) HIST. OF INDIA, v1, 1922.

***Rare** triumphes (The) of love & fortune, 1589, *see* COLLIER (J. P.), *ed.* Five old plays, 1851.

Rasavāhinī, *see* VEDEHATHERA.

Raschdau (Ludwig), *ed., see* BISMARCK (O., *Fürst* v.) Polit. Berichte, 1859–62, 2B, 1920.

Raschl (Thiemo) & R. Strelli. Das Benediktinerstift St. Paul in Kärnten. s8°. Wien. [1922]

Ras chung pa [RÉTCHUNG]. Le poète tibétain Milarépa, ses crimes—ses épreuves—son Nirvāna. Tr. avec intr. &c. par J. Bacot. 8°. 1925

Rashdall (Hastings), *dean of Carlisle.* Jesus, human & divine. 3 sermons w. essay. s8°. 1922
The metaphysic of Mr. F. H. Bradley, 1912, *see* BRIT. ACAD. Proc., 1911–12.
Principles & precepts. Sel. & ed. by H. D. A. Major & F. L. Cross. 8°. O. 1927
see MATHESON (P. E.) Life of H. R., 1928.

Rashi [†SOLOMON *ben Isaac, of Troyes, also called Isaaki & Jarchi*]. Comm. Hebr. in librr. Josuæ, Judicum, Ruth, Samuelis, Regum, Chronicorum, Esræ, Nehemiæ & Estheræ item in Salomonis Proverbia, Ecclesiasten & Canticum Canticorum. Lat. vers. &c., à J. F. Breithaupto. s4°. Gothae. 1714
Comm. Hebr. in Prophetas, Hiobum & Psalmos. Lat. vers. cum 2 codicibus collatus &c., à J. F. Breithaupto. s4°. Gothae. 1713
Comm. Hebraicus in quinque libros Mosis. Lat. versus, notis illust. &c., à J. F. Breithaupto. s4°. Gothae. 1713

Rashid ('Abd ul-), *see* 'ABD UL-RASHĪD IBN 'ABD UL-GHAFŪR, *Husainī.*

Rashīd-al-Dīn (Fazl Allāh). Исторія Монголовъ. Ист. Гингизъ-хана. Персидскій текстъ & Русскій переводъ. [2p. I.R.A.O. Труды Восточ. отд., 13.] 8°. С.-П. 1868

Rasi (—). *L'ape patria: racc. stor. degli avvenimenti celebri di Ravenna [*attrib. to R.*], 1845, *see* RAVENNA.

Rask (Rasmus Christian). A grammar of the Anglo-Saxon tongue. n. ed. enlarged; tr. by B. Thorpe. [*a. c. b. w.* Bosworth (J.) Anglo-Saxon tongue, 1823]. 8°. Copenhagen. 1830
Method of learning the old Norsk tongue or Icelandic lang. With reader &c., by H. Lund. 2nd corr. ed. s8°. 1869
Nonnulla de pleno systemate sibilantium in linguis montanis &c. s4°. Havniae. 1832
Ræsonn. Lapp. Sproglære. En Omarbejdelse af K. Leems Lappiske Gramm. 8°. København. 1832
Singalesisk Skriftlære. [P2654]. 8°. Kolombo. 1821

Rask-Ørstedfond, *see* COPTICA; consilio & impensis Inst. Rask-O. ed., v2, 3, 1922–25.
see MUNCH (P.), *ed.* Les origines & l'œuvre de la Soc. des Nations; publ. par R.-O., t1, 2, 1923–24.

Rasmussen (Knud). Across Arctic America: narr. of the 5th Thule Exped. la8°. N.Y. 1927
Eskimo folk-tales. Ed. & rendered into Eng. by W. Worster. la8°. 1921
Greenland by the Polar Sea. Thule Exped. f. Melville Bay to Cape Morris Jesup. Tr. A. & R. Kenney. Pref. by Adm. Sir L. Beaumont. la8°. 1921

Rasmussen (Vilhelm). Child psychology. [Tr.] Pref. by H. Høffding. [v]1–3. s8°. [1920–23]

Rasori (Giovanni). Ricordi di prigionia, mem. autobiog. e frammenti poeti, *see* REGIA DEP. S. GLI STUDI DI STORIA PATRIA. Bibl., v9, 1921.

Raspe (Rudolf Erich). The travels of Baron Münchausen. Ed. W. Rose, w. intr. [Broadway Tr.] s8°. [1923]
Wunderbare Reisen &c. d. Freyherrn v. Münchhausen. s8°. Cöln. 1810

Rasputin (Grigory Efimovich).
see BELETSKY (S. P.) Г. Р. 1923.
„ DJANOUMOVA (H.) Mes rencontres avec R.; tr. A. Pierre, 1923.
„ FÜLÖP-MILLER (R.) Der heilige Teufel: R. u. d. Frauen, 1927.
„ PURICHKEVICH (V.) Comment j'ai tué R.: pages du journal; tr., 1924.
„ RODZYANKO (M. V.) Reign of R.: An Empire's collapse; tr., 1927.

Rassegna d'arte antica & mod. Dir. da C. Ricci. Anno 7–9. la8°. 1920–22
Monogr. 1, 2. 4°. 1923
see GIACOMO (S. DI). V. Gemito, 1923. [1.]
„ OZZOLA (L.) La litogr. ital., 1805–70, 1923. [2.]

Rastadt. *Antidote au Congrès de R., 1798, *see* PRADT (D. D. DE).

Rastal (William), *see* RASTELL (W.)

Rastall (Robert Heron).
Geology of the metalliferous deposits. 8°. C. 1923
Molybdenum ores. [Imp. Inst. Monogr.] 8°. [1922]
see LAKE (P.) & R. H. R. Textbook of geology, 3rd ed., 1922.

—— & W. H. Wilcockson.
Tungsten ores. [Imp. Inst. Monogr.] 8°. 1920

Rastell (John), *printer, see* REED (A. W.) Early Tudor drama: Medwall, the Rastells &c., 1926.

Rastell (William), *Justice of the Court of Queen's Bench.* *Les termes de la ley: obscure words &c. of laws of this realm expl. [*Ascr. to W. R.*] corr. & enl. 8°. 1721

Ratan Tata Foundation: *University of London, see* TAWNEY (R. H.) St. in the minimum wage &c., 3v, 1914–15.

Ratberto, *monk, of Locedio.* La Vita ratbertiana di S. Bononio nei mss. dell' abbate G. Grandi, *see* ARCHIVIO STOR. ITAL. Anno 83, v1, 1925.

Ratcliffe (Samuel Kerkham). Sir W. Wedderburn & the Ind. reform movement. s8°. [1923]

Raterius, *bp. of Verona, see* RATHERIUS.

Rathbone (Eleanor Florence). The disinherited family: plea for the endowment of the family. s8°. 1924
„ „ ....2nd impr. s8°. 1924

Rathbun (*Miss* **Mary Jane).** Decapod crustaceans f. the Panama region. [S.I.: U.S. Nat. Mus., Bull. 193]. 8°. Wash. 1918
Fossil stalk-eyed Crustacea of the Pacific slope of N. America. [S.I.: U.S. Nat. Mus., Bull. 138]. 8°. Wash. 1926
Spider crabs of America. [S.I.: U.S. Nat. Mus., Bull. 129]. 8°. Wash. 1925

Rathbun (Seward Hume).
A background to architecture. 8°. New Haven, *Yale.* 1926

Rathenau (Walther).
Briefe.
2e A. 2B. 8o. Dresden. 1926
,, Neue Folge. 8o. Dresden. 1928
Cannes u. Genua. 4 Reden z. Reparationsproblem. 8o. 1922
Gesamm. Reden. s8o. 1924
Kunstphilos. u. Ästhetik. Zusammengestellt &c. v. W. Schumann. s8o. München. 1923
Nach d. Flut. s8o. 1923
Der neue Staat [*& Arb.*] 8o. 1922
Was wird werden? s8o. 1920
TRANSLATIONS.
In days to come. Tr. E. & C. Paul. 8o. [1921]
The new society. Tr. s8o. 1921
see FEDERN-KOHLHAAS (E.) W. R., s. Leben u. Wirken. 2e A., 1928.
,, SCHMOLLER (G.) W. R. u. H. Preuss, 1922.

Ratherius [RATERIUS], *bp. of Verona, see* PAVANI (G.) Un vescovo belga in Italia nel sec. 10: R. di Verona, 1920.

Rathschlag, *see* RATSCHLAG.

Ratio. *Ratio atque instit. studiorum, 1591, *see* JESUITS.
*Ratio educationis &c. per regn. Hungariae, tl, 1777, *see* SZERDAHÉLYI (G. A. v.)
*Ratio sacra: or an appeal about revealed religion &c., 1710, *see* BLACKWELL (T.), *the elder.*

***Rational** (A) disc. of transubstantiation, *for ans. to this work, see* BAXTER (R.) Roman tradition exam., 1676.

Rationale. Rationale diuinorum officioru̅ &c., 1482, *see* DURANDUS (G.), *bp. of Mende.*
Rationale (The) of ceremonial, 1540–43. With notes & app. & essay on the regul. of ceremonial dur. r. of Henry VIII by C. S. Cobb. [Alcuin Club Coll., 18]. la8o. 1910

Ratisbon [RATISPONA].
DIET &c., 1541.
Acta colloquii in comitiis Imperii R. habiti, 1541, *see* BUCER (M.)
Acta in Conventu R. &c. s4o. [Vitebergae, *J. Klug.* 1541]
Actes (The) of the disputacio̅ in the cowncell of the Empyre at Regenspurg [1541]: all the artycles conc. the Christen relygion &c. Prefacys of P. Melancton; set forth by M. Bucere & P. Melancton. Tr. owt of Latyne. By Mylys Coverdale. [The testimony of Eccius *begins fresh pagin.*] s8o. [Geneva ?]. 1542
Commonly known as the "Ratisbon Book."
Actorum colloquii R. ultimi &c. narratio. Jussu Cae. Ma. conscr. & edita. s4o. Ingolstadii, *A. Vueissenhorn.* 1546
,, ,, ...[*a. ed.*] s8o. Lovanii, *M. Rotarius.* 1547
Alle Handlungen u. Schr., zu vergleichung der Relig. auff Reichstag zu Regenspurg, 1541 ?, *see* BUCER (M.)
DISPUTATION, 1601.
Acta Colloquii R. de norma doctrinae cathol. & controversiarum relig. judice &c., 1601. s4o. Monachii. 1602
,, ,, ...ed. 2a [*w. t.* Actorum &c.] s4o. Monachii. 1602
Colloquium de norma doctrinae & controv. relig. judice R. habitum 1601. s4o. Lavingae. 1602
Relatio de initio, progressu & fine Colloq. R., a. 1601 instit., 1602, *see* TANNER (A.)

Ratisbonne (Marie Théodore).
Hist. de S. Bernard & de s. siècle. 11e éd. 2t. s8o. 1903

Ratouis de Limay (Paul), *see* VAILLAT (L.) & P. R. DE L. J. B. Perronneau, sa vie &c., 1923.

Ratramnus, *monachus Corbiensis* [BERTRAM]. The Book of Bertram conc. the body & the blood of the Lord, in Lat. w. a n. Engl. tr. Also An histor. diss. conc. the author. [By W. Hopkins]. s8o. 1686
The book of Bertram the priest conc. the body & blood of Christ in the Sacrament. Tr. in 1549. 3rd ed. s8o. 1686
see CLAUDE (J.) The Cath. doctr. of the Eucharist; added, acc. of the Book of the Body &c. of our Lord, publ. under name of Bertram [*i.e.* R.], 1684.

Ratschlag. *Ratschlag ains der v. hertzen begerdt das gnu̍g beschech d. Römischen st ls wirdigkait, u. darzu̍ d. Christenlichen standts frid. [*Attrib. by some to Erasmus, by others to Zwingli.*] s4o. [Augsburg, *S. Grimm.* 1521]
*Ratschlag halltender Disput. zu Bernn. [*With Schlussreden by F. Kolb & B. Haller*]. s4o. *n.p.* [1528]

Ratti (Achille), *see* PIUS XI, *pope.*

Rattray (*Capt.* **Robert Sutherland).** Ashanti. 8o. O. 1923
Religion & art in Ashanti. With ch. by G. T. Bennett, V. Blake &c. 8o. O. 1927

Ratzel (Friedrich). Polit. Geographie. 3e A., ergänzt v. E. Oberhummer. 8o. München. 1923

Rau (David Wilhelm). Diss. de pari nexu civitatum imperialium cum S. R. Imperio. Præs. G. Schwedero. [P2641]. s4o. Tubingae. [1714]

Rau (Joachim Justus). Diatribe de philos. Justini Martyris & Athenagorae. Praes. J. J. R., resp. J. C. Kallio. [P597]. s4o. Jenae. [1733]

Raucat (Thomas). Loin des blondes. 15e éd. s8o. [1928]

Rauchenegger (B.) Papstthum u. deut. Kaiserthum. [P2696]. 8o. Paderborn. 1875

Rauchhaupt (Friedrich Wilhelm v.)
Gesch. d. span. Gesetzesquellen. 8o. Heidelberg. 1923

Raulich (Italo). Storia del Risorgimento politico d' Italia (1815–49). 5v. 8o. Bologna. [1920–26]

Raulin (Joannes), *prédicateur français, 1443–1514.* Itinerariu̅ Paradisi complecte̅s sermones de penite̅tia &c. de matrimonio ac viduitate. [*b. w. h.* Sermones de Eucharistia, 1519]. 8o. Parisiis, *Jehan Petit.* [1518]
Sermones de Eucharistia. 8o. [Paris], *Jehan Petit.* 1519

Raulin (Joannes Facundus), *see* MENEZES (A. DE). Hist. Eccl. Malabaricae &c., 1745.

Raumer (Leopold Wilhelm Friedrich). Diss. de usu pract. tituli Instit. de adoptionibus. Præs. C. Thomasio. [P2741]. s4o. Hagiae Magd. 1737

Raunkiær (Christen). *Works in* KONG. DAN. VIDENSKAB. SELSKAB. Biolog. Medd.
Eremitageslettens Tjørne Isoreagentstudier 1, 1925. [5.]
Nitratindholdet hos Anemone nemorosa paa forsk. standpladser, 1926. [5.]
Recherches statist. sur les formations végétales, 1917–19. [1.]

Raupach (Bernhard). Evangelisches Oesterreich; das ist Histor. Nachricht v. d. Schicksahlen d. Evangel. Luther. Kirchen in Oesterreich. s4o. Hamburg. 1732
,, ,, Erläutertes evangel. Oesterr.: Fortgesetzte histor. Nachr. [*&* Fortsetz. 2, 3]. 3T. s4o. Hamburg. 1736–40
,, ,, Presbyterologia Austriaca. [*b. w. h* Evangel. Oest., 1732]. s4o. Hamburg. 1741
,, ,, Zwiefache Zugabe zu d. Evang. Oest. [*b. w. h.* Evang. Oest., 1732]. s4o. Hamburg. 1744
Teil 1 *of* Erläut. evangel. Oesterr., 1736, *has addit. general tp.* 1741, *covering all the vol. Each vol. has* Beylagen, *w. sep. pagin.*

Rauwenhoff (Ludwig Wilhelm Ernst). Religionsphilosophie. Übers. u. hrsg. v. J. R. Hanne. 2e A. 8o. Braunschweig. 1894

Rauwolff (Leonhard), *c. 1535–96?, see* LEGRÉ (L.) La botanique en Provence au 16e s.: L. R. &c., 1900.

Ravà (Aldo). Un arlecchino naturalista. [F. Zanuzzi. Estr. d. Boll. d. Museo di Bassano, a. 5. P2837]. la8o. [Bassano. 1909]
Contrib. alla bibliogr. di Giacomo Casanova. [Estr. d. Giorn. stor. d. lett. ital., v55. P2838]. 8o. Torino. 1910
Contrib. alla biogr. di P. Longhi. [Estr. d. Rassegna contemp., a. 4. P2838]. 8o. 1911
Il fallimento di un console Veneto a Trieste e una lettera di Casanova. [Estr. d. Ateneo Veneto, a. 33. P2838]. 8o. Venezia. 1910
Haydn a Venezia. [Estr. d. Ateneo Veneto, a. 32, fasc. 2. P2836]. 8o. Venezia. 1909

Ravagli (Francesco). Il Cortona (Domenico Cecchi). [Nozze Furiosi—Fabbri. N123]. 4o. Città di Castello. [1896]

Ravaillac (François) [RAVAILLARD; RAVILLIACK]. Procès du parricide F. R. Publ. P... D[eschamps]. [Trésors des pièces rares &c.] s8o. 1858
see THARAUD (J.) & J. THARAUD. Tragédie de R., 1913; 1922.

Ravaille (Antoine), *see* REGINALD (A.)

Ravalet (Marguerite de), *aft. wife of Jean Lefebvre, 1586–1603, see* MARTEL (T.) Julien & M. de R., 1920.

Ravel (Maurice), *see* REVUE MUSICALE, avr. 1925, No. spéc., 1925.

Raven (Charles Earle). Apollinarianism. s8o. C. 1923
Christian socialism, 1848–54. 8o. 1920
The Creator Spirit: Xtn. doctrine in light of biology, psychology &c. Hulsean Lect., 1926–27 &c. App. on biochemistry &c. by J. Needham. 8o. 1927

Raven-Hill (Leonard). Indian sketch-book. la8o. [1903]

Ravenna. *L'ape patria: ossia breve racc. stor. d. avvenimenti celebri d. città di Ravenna. [*Attrib. to Rasi ?*]. 8o. Ravenna. 1845
*Diss. epistolare s. letteratura Ravennate. 8o. Ravenna. 1749
Gli statuti di R., 1868, *see* PASOLINI (P. D.)

Ravenscroft (Edward).
Dame Dobson, a comedy. s4o. 1684
The London cuckolds (1681), *see* SUMMERS (M.), *ed.* Restor. comedies, 1921.

Ravenscroft (Thomas). The whole booke of Psalmes: w. the hymnes. With tunes. newly corr. & enl. s8o. *Harper.* 1633

Ravensperger (Hermann). De causa Dei adv. turmam Racov. in Polonia quam nunc ducit V. Smalzius. Ed. alt. melior. s8o. Bremae. 1621

Ravenstein (Ernst Georg). Birthplaces of the people &c. [Repr. f. Geog. mag.] [P2756]. s8°. 1876

Ravesteyn (Jodocus). Epistola [de gratiae et liberi arbitrii concordia], *see* REGINALD (A.) De mente Conc. Trid., 1706.

Ravignan (Gustave Fr. X de La Croix de), *see* LA CROIX DE RAVIGNAN (G. F. X. DE).

Ravitsch (S.), *see* NEVSKY (V. I.) & S. R. Arbeiter-u. Bauern-universitäten in Sowjetrussland, 1921.

Ravius (Christianus), *orientalist.* Orthographiae & analogiae Ebraicae delin. s4°. Amstelodami. 1646
Spolium orientis, catal. MSS. [P2744]. s4°. Kiloni. 1669

Ravn (J. P. J.) De irreg. Echinider, *see* KONG. DAN. VID. SELSK. Skr., Række 8, B11, 1927.

Ravnopravnost. Равноправность женщины, *n.d.*, *see* RUSSIA: ANON. WKS.

Rawlins (*Mrs.* **Pleasant),** *see* SWENDSEN (H.) The tryals of H. S. &c. for stealing Mrs. P. R., 1703.

Rawlinson (*Lt.-Col. Sir* **Alfred).** Adventures in the Near East, 1918–22. Intr. by L. C. Dunsterville &c. & gen. intr. by Sir P. Scott. 8°. 1923
Adventures on the Western Front, Aug. 1914–June 1915. 8°. 1925
The defence of London, 1915–18. Intr. by Sir P. Scott. 8°. 1923

Rawlinson (Alfred Edward John).
Authority & freedom. Bp. Paddock Lect., 1923. s8°. 1924
Catholicism w. freedom: paper at Anglo-Cath. Congr., B'ham, 22 June 1922. [P2690]. s8°. 1922
Essays on the Trinity & the Incarnation. By members of the Angl. Communion. Ed. R. 8°. 1928
The New Test. doctrine of the Christ. Bampton Lects., 1926. 8°. 1926
St. Mark. With intr., comm. & add. notes. [Westminster Comm.] 8°. 1925

Rawlinson (George), *prof. of anc. hist. in Univ. of Oxford.* Anc. Egypt. By R., w. collab. of A. Gilman. 10th ed. 8°. *n.d.*

Rawlinson (Henry Seymour, *1st baron*), *of Trent.* The life of Gen. Lord R. of Trent f. h. journals & letters. Ed. Sir F. Maurice. 8°. 1928

Rawlinson (Hugh George), *M.A.* Brit. beginnings in W. India, 1597–1657. Early days of Brit. Factory of Surat. 8°. O. 1920
Intercourse betw. India & the W. world, to the fall of Rome. 2nd ed. 8°. C. 1926

Rawlinson (Richard), *LL.D.*
see LENGLET DU FRESNOY (N.) New method of studying hist.; tr. &c. by F. R., 2v, 1728.
„ TUCKETT (J. E. S.) R. & the masonic entries in E. Ashmole's diary, 1912.
„ WOOD (A. À) & R. R. Parochial coll., by W. & R., 2p, 1920–22.

Rawnsley (Hardwicke Drummond).
A nation's heritage. s8°. [1920]

Rawnsley (Willingham Franklin), *see* FRANKLIN (J., *Lady*). Life, diaries & corresp.; ed. W. F. R., 1923.

Rawson (Graham). The Golden Hind. Play. s8°. [1928]

Ray Society. *Publications.* 8°. 1928
see GÖBEL (C. V.) W. Hofmeister: work & life; tr., 1926.
„ GROVES (J.) & G. R. BULLOCK-WEBSTER. Brit. Charophyta, 2v, 1920–24.
„ MACINTOSH (W. C.) Monogr. of the Brit. marine Annelids, v4, 2p, 1922–23.
„ SOAR (C. D.) & W. WILLIAMSON. Brit. Hydracarina, v1, 2, 1925–27.
„ STEPHENSON (T. A.) The Brit. sea anemones, v1, 1928.
„ WEST (W.) & G. S. WEST. Monogr. of the Brit. Desmidiaceæ, v5, by N. Carter, 1923.

Ray (James), *of Whitehaven.* Compleat hist. of the Rebellion, 1745–46. s8°. *pr. for a.* M'ter. [1760]

Ray (John).
The wisdom of God in the works of the creation. s8°. 1827

Ray (John Arthur). Drake dans la poésie espagnole (1570–1732). Thèse &c. 8°. 1906

Ray (Martha), *see* HACKMAN (*Rev.* J.) *Love & madness; hist. of Rev. J. H. & M. R., 1805.

Ray (Sidney Herbert). A comp. study of the Melanesian Island languages. 8°. C. 1926
Notes on Sir R. C. Temple's theory of universal grammar. [Fr. Indian Antiq., v31. P2414]. 4°. Bombay. 1902

Ray (William), *see* TOWLER (W. G.) & W. R. Socialism, 1920.

Raye (N. N.) Annals of the early Eng. settlement in Bihar. 8°. Calcutta. [1927]

Rayleigh (John William Strutt, *3rd baron*).
Scientific papers. v6, 1911–19. la8°. C. 1920
see RAYLEIGH (R. J. S., *4th b.*) J. W. S., 3rd Baron R., 1924.

Rayleigh (Robert John Strutt, *4th baron*).
J. W. Strutt, 3rd Baron Rayleigh, O.M., F.R.S. 8°. 1924

Raymond (*Father*), *see* POINCY (L. DE). Hist. of the Caribby-Islands; w. a Caribbian vocab. [by R.], 1666.

Raymond (Alexandre M.), *architecte.* Une ville célèbre, Angora; l'ant. Ancyre. la8°. [1926]

Raymond (Dora Neill), *Ph.D.* Brit. policy & opinion dur. Franco-Prussian War. [Columbia Univ.] 8°. N.Y. 1921

Raymond (E. T.), *ps.* [*i.e.* EDWARD RAYMOND THOMPSON].
All & sundry. 8°. [1919]
Disraeli: the alien patriot. 8°. [1925]
The man of promise, Lord Rosebery. 8°. [1923]
Mr. Balfour. 8°. [1920]
Mr. Lloyd George. 8°. [1922]
Portraits of the new cent. (1st 10 yrs.) 8°. [1928]
Portraits of the nineties. 8°. [1921]

Raymond (Ernest).
Damascus Gate. s8°. [1923]
Daphne Bruno. s8°. [1925]
Morris in the dance. s8°. [1927]
The old tree blossomed. s8°. [1928]
Rossenal. s8°. [1922]
Tell England. s8°. [1922]
Wanderlight. s8°. [1924]

Raymond (George Lansing).
An art-philosopher's cabinet. Passages sel. by M. M. Miller. 8°. N.Y. [1915]
The Aztec god & o. dramas. 4th ed. rev. s8°. N.Y. [1916]
Ballads & o. poems. 4th ed. rev. s8°. N.Y. [1916]
Dante & o. verse. 2nd ed. rev. s8°. N.Y. [1916]
The essentials of æsthetics. 3rd ed. rev. 8°. N.Y. [1921]
Ethics & natural law. 2nd ed. rev. 8°. N.Y. [1920]
A life in song. 4th ed. rev. s8°. N.Y. [1916]
Poetry as represent. art. 7th ed. rev. 8°. N.Y. *n.d.*
A poet's cabinet. Passages f. works of G. L. R. sel. by M. M. Miller. 8°. N.Y. [1914]

Raymond (John), *traveller.* An itinerary cont. a voyage made thr. Italy, 1646–47. [*Engr. tp. begins* Il Mercurio italiano]. s8°. 1648

Raymond (Marcel). Bibliographie crit. de Ronsard en France (1550–1585). la8°. 1927
L'influence de Ronsard sur la poésie franç., 1550–85. 2t. la8°. 1927

Raymond (Maud Wotring) *& others.* The archit. &c. of the Panama-Pacific Internat. Expos. Intr. by L. C. Mullgardt. [2nd ed.] 8°. San Francisco. [1915]

Raymond (Paul), *see* SORDE. Cartul. de l'abbaye de St. Jean de S.; publ. P. R., 1873.

Raynal (*l'abbé* **Guillaume Thomas F.)** Hist. of the settlements & trade of the Europeans in the East & West Indies. Tr. J. O. Justamond. 8v. 8°. 1788
see FEUGÈRE (A.) L'abbé R., 1713–96, 1922.

Raynal (Maurice). Ossip Zadkine. s8°. Rome. 1921

Raynal (Paul).
Le tombeau sous l'Arc de Triomphe: tragédie. 8°. 1928

Raynalde (Thomas) [RAYNOLD; RAYNOLDE], *see* POWER (*Sir* D'A.) The birth of mankind: bibliog. st., 1927.

Raynaud (Ernest). Ch. Baudelaire, étude biogr. &c. s8°. 1922
La mêlée symboliste, 1890–1900. Portraits & souv. [s]2. s8°. [1920]

Raynaud (Georges). Les dieux, les héros & les hommes de l'anc. Guatémala d'ap. Le livre du conseil [Popol-vuh]. [H.E., Sci. relig., 41]. 8°. 1925

Raynaudet (Jacques), *b. c. 1540*, *see* LEGRÉ (L.) La botanique en Provence au 16e s.: L. Rauwolff & J. R., 1900.

Rayne (*Maj.* **H.)**
Sun, sand & Somals. Brit. Somaliland. 8°. 1921

Rayner (*Hon.* **Isidor).** Addresses. Comp. by W. B. Rayner. Ed. J. F. Essary. 8°. Baltimore. 1914

Raynolde (Thomas), *see* RAYNALDE.

Raynouard (François Juste Marie). Rapp. s. le projet de loi rel. à la liberté de la presse. [Chambre des Députés, Août, 1814. *No tp.* P2772]. 8°. [1814]
see LEVY (E.) Provenzal. Suppl.-Wörterbuch; Bericht. u. Ergänz. zu R. Lexique Roman, B7, 8, 1915–24.

Raz (Ram), *see* RÁM RAJ.

Razelière (A. Batard-), *see* BATARD-RAZELIÈRE (A.)

Razzolini (Luigi) & A. Bacchi della Lega. Bibliografia dei testi di lingua a stampa citati d. Accad. d. Crusca. 8°. Bologna. 1878

Rea (*Rt. Hon.* **Russell).** The triumph of free trade, & o. essays. Intr. C. F. G. Masterman. 8°. 1920

Read (*Sir* **Alfred**), *see* *COASTWISE trade of U.K. [*intr. by* A. R.], 1925.
Read (Archibald), *see* TEBBUTT (C. G.), A. R. &c. Skating, 1897.
Read (Carveth). Man & h. superstitions. 2nd ed. [*of 2nd part of h.* Origin of man &c.] 8°. C. 1925
The origin of man & of his superstitions. 8°. C. 1920
„ „ 2nd ed. rev. & enl. [*cont.* Orig. of man *only* ; *see* Man &c. *above for* " his superstitions "]. 8°. C. 1925
Read (*Sir* **Charles Hercules).** C. H. R., tribute on h. retirement f. Brit. Mus., & record of chief add. &c. of Brit. & med. antiq. & ethnogr. dur. h. keepership, 1896–1921. 4°. 1921
Read (Conyers).
England & America. [P2509]. 8°. Chicago. [1918]
Mr. Secretary Walsingham & the policy of Queen Elizabeth. 3v. 8°. O. 1925
Read (Elizabeth F.) Internat. law & i. relations. [Amer. Foundation]. s8°. 1925
Read (Herbert). English prose style. 8°. 1928
Reason & romanticism: essays in lit. crit. 8°. [1926]
English stained glass. 4°. [1926]
see RACKHAM (B.) & H. R. English pottery, 1924.
Read (William A.) Louisiana place-names of Indian origin. [Louisiana State Univ. &c.] 8°. Baton Rouge. 1927
Read (William Roebuck). Birdham: village life & nat. hist. [1922–26]. s8°. Chichester. [1927]
Reade (Aleyn Lyell).
Johnsonian gleanings. p3–5. 8°. *p.p.* 1922–28
The Mellards & their descendants, includ. the Bibbys of Liverpool; w. mems. of D. M. Mulock & T. M. Reade. 4°. *p.p.* 1915
Reade (Charles).
The cloister & the hearth. [Biog. note by H. Bennett]. [repr.] s8°. 1903
It is never too late to mend. lib. ed. s8°. 1925
Peg Woffington. s8°. 1853
Peg Woffington. [Temple Classics]. s8°. 1901
see PHILLIPS (W. C.) Dickens, R. & Collins, sensation novelists, 1919.
Reade (Hubert G. R.) Sidelights on the Thirty Years War. 3v. 8°. 1924
Reade (Robert), *bp. of Chichester, see* REDE (R.)
Reade (Thomas Mellard), *see* READE (A. L.) The Mellards &c., w. mem. of T. M. R., 1915.
Reade (William Henry Vincent). A criticism of Einstein & h. problem. s8°. O. 1922
Reade (William Winwood). The martyrdom of man. Intr. by F. Legge. 26th ed. s8°. *n.d.*
Readers' guide to periodical literature. Author & subj. index to periodicals & reports. v4–6 (1915–24); ed. E. J. Sherwood &c. la8°. N.Y. 1919–25
„ „ Suppl., v2, 3, 1916–24; ed. E. J. Sherwood &c. la8°. N.Y. 1920–24
v3 *has title* Internat. index to period[s].
Reading.
MUSEUM & ART GALLERY, *see* MAY (T.) Pottery found at Silchester, depos. in R. Museum, 1916.
UNIVERSITY.
Calendar, 1926–27—1928–29. s8°. [Reading]. 1926–28
Reading Abbey. Octocent. of Reading Abbey, 1121–1921. Hdbk. of the celebration. [P2525]. 8°. [Reading]. 1921
Reading (Rufus Daniel Isaacs, *1st earl*), *see* STREET (C. J. C.) Lord R., 1928.
Readings in indust. society, 1920, *see* MARSHALL (L. C.)
Readwin (Thomas Allison). Acc. of the charities of Wokingham, fr. orig. doc[s]. &c. s8°. Wokingham. 1845
Real Academia de Bellas Artes de San Fernando. [*List of members, publications &c.*], Febrero 1921. s8°. 1921
see ALBA (J. S. F., *17th duke*). Discurso, 1924.
Real Academia de Ciencias Exactas, Fisicas y Naturales. [*List of members, report &c.*], 1921. s8°. 1921
Real Academia de Ciencias Morales y Politicas. [*List of members, p bl. &c.*], 1921, 1922. s8°. 1921–22
Real Academia de la Historia.
Coleccion de obras aráb. de hist. y geog. t1. la8°. 1867
see AJBAR MACHMUÂ. Crónica anón. d. s. xi; tr. &c., 1867. [1.]
[*List of members* &c.], 1922. s8°. 1922
Memorial historico español. t48. 8°. 1918
see JUSUÉ (E.) Tablas abrev. para la reducción del cómputo árabe y del hebr. al cristiano &c., 1918. [48.]
REFERENCES.
see CEDILLO (J. L. DE A. A., *conde* DE). El card. Cisneros, 1921.
„ COLECCIÓN DE docs. inéd. rel. al descubr. &c. de las ant. posesiones esp. de Ultramar, s2, t1–19, 1885–1926.
„ COLUMBUS (C.) Los restos de C., 1879.

Real Academia de la Historia [*continued*].
REFERENCES [*continued*].
see LUCAS, *bp. of Tuy.* Crón. de España, 1926.
„ MERINO ALVAREZ (A.) La sociedad abulense dur. el sig. 16, 1926.
„ RAMON MÉLIDA (J.) Iberia arqueológ. ante-romana, 1906.
„ SANTA CRUZ (A. DE). Crón. del Emp. Carlos V, 5t, 1920–25.
„ VIVES Y ESCUDERO (A.) La moneda Hispánica & Atlas, 1924–26.
Real Academia Española.
Biblioteca sel. de clas. españ., 2[a] ser., *see* CASTRO (G. DE). Obras, 2t, 1925–26.
Dicc. de la lengua castellana; [comp.] por la R.A.E. 14[a] ed. fol. 1914
Dicc. de la lengua española. [15[a] ed.] fol. 1925
Discursos leidos ante S. M. el Rey &c. 7. centenario del nacim. del rey Alfonso el Sabio [*by* W. Ribera &c.] [P2577]. 8°. 1921
Gram. de la lengua castellana. n. ed. 8°. 1895
[*List of members, publ. &c.*], 1921. s8°. 1921
Memorias. t11, 12. 8°. 1914–26
t11, 12 *contain* Pérez Pastor (C.) Noticias y docs. rel. a la hist. y lit. españolas, t2, 3.
Prontuario de ortografía castellana. 26[a] ed. s8°. 1918
see ARTIGAS (M.) Don L. de Góngora y Argote, 1925.
„ GARCIA SORIANO (J.) El humanista F. Cascales, 1924.
„ RIBERA (J.) La musica de las cantigas, 1922.
„ VEGA (L. DE). Obras, t14, 15, 1913.
Real Armería, *Madrid, see* VALENCIA DE DON JUAN (*conde* V. DE). Cat. hist.-descr. de la R. A. de Madrid, 1898.
Real Automóvil Club de España.
Guía oficial de carreteras. [2t]. 8°. [1919]
Reale Accademia dei Lincei. [R. ACCAD. NAZIONALE D. LINCEI]. Monumenti antichi. Vol. 1, 2, 4–7, 10, 14–18, 20–31. 4°. Milano. 1892–1926
v4 *has* Atlante, obl. fol.
Anti (C.) Athena marina e alata, 1920. [26.]
—— Esplor. arch. n. Licia e n. Panfilia. [29.]
—— Mon. Policletei, 1920. [26.]
Barnabei (F.) Comment. dei ludi secol. augustei e severiani, 1890. [1.]
—— Diploma milit. scop. pr. il ponte Palat., 1890. [1.]
——, Cozza & Pasqui. Scavi nel territ. falisco (Narce &c.) & Atlante (obl. fol.), 1894–95. [4.]
Barocelli (P.) Albintimilium, 1923. [29.]
Bartoli (A.) Horrea Agrippiana e la diaconia di S. Teodoro, 1921. [27.]
Bendinelli (G.) Antichità Tudertine di Villa Giulia, 1914. [23.]
—— Bronzi votivi ital. d. Museo di Villa Giulia, 1920. [26.]
—— Mon. Lanuvina, 1921. [27.]
—— Mon. sepolcr. d. Aureli al viale Manzoni, Roma, 1922. [28.]
—— Il mon. sotterraneo di Porta Maggiore in Roma, 1926. [31.]
—— Tomba &c. (5 c. B.C.) n. necrop. di Todi, 1916. [24.]
Bianchi Bandinelli (R.) Clusium, 1925. [30.]
Brizio (E.) Necrop. di Novilara, 1895. [5.]
—— Scavi a Marzabotto pr. Bologna, 1888–89, 1890. [1.]
Caetani Lovatelli (*cssa.* E.) Piccola larva convivale in bronzo, 1895. [5.]
Cafici (C.) Staz. preist. di Tre Fontane e Poggio Rosso, 1914. [23.]
Calza (G.) Preminenza dell' " insula " n. edilizia romana, 1914. [23.]
—— Scavi rec. nell' abitato di Ostia, 1920. [26.]
Castelfranco (P.) & G. Patroni. Stazione palus. di Campo Castellaro pr. Piadena, 1916. [24.]
Comparetti (D.) Nuovi framm. d'iscriz. nel Pythion, 1890. [1.]
Cozza (A.) & V. Mariani. Nuovi scavi d. stadio palatino, 1895. [5.]
Cultrera (G.) Vasi dipinti d. Museo di Villa Giulia, 1916. [24.]
Della Corte (M.) Groma, 1922. [29.]
—— Librae Pompeianae, 1912. [21.]
Della Seta (A.) Vasi di Campagnano, 1914. [23.]
Ducati (P.) Framm. di rilievo in argento, Bologna, 1912. [21.]
—— Pietre funerarie felsinee, 1910. [20.]
—— La sedia Corsini, 1916. [24.]
Gàbrici (E.) Bolsena, scavi nel sacellum d. dea Nortia sul Pozzarello, 1906. [16.]
—— Cuma [& Tavole], 1913. [22.]
—— Necrop. di età ellenistica a Teano dei Sidicini, 1910. [20.]
—— Rud. rom. alla Piazza d. Vittorio in Palermo, 1921. [27.]
Galli (E.) Fidia in Etruria, 1921. [27.]
—— Mura e vestigia di ant. mon. sacri sull'Acropoli di Fiesole, 1910. [20.]
—— Sarcof. etrusco di Torre S. Severo &c., 1916. [24.]
—— Sepolcreto visentino d. " Buccace," 1912. [21.]
Gamurrini (G. F.) Della libbra etrusca, 1890. [1.]
Gatti (G.) Ogetti scop. n. scavi d. Stadio Palatino, 1895. [5.]
Ghirardini (G.) Scavi d. palazzo di Teodorico, Ravenna, 1916. [24.]
—— La situla ital. prim., 1893–1901. [2, 7, 10.]
Halbherr (F.) Scavi del tempio d'Apollo Pythio in Gortyna, 1890. [1.]

Reale Accademia dei Lincei [*continued*].
Helbig (W.) Busto d'Alessandro Magno a Ptolemais, 1895. [6.]
—— Rilievo Torlonia completata da framm. nel Museo di Berlino, 1890. [1.]
—— Ritratti di Fulvia e di Ottavia, 1890. [1.]
Jatta (M.) Vasi dipinti d. Italia merid., 1906. [16.]
Lanciani (R.) Antichità d. territ. Laurentino di Castelporziano, 1906. [16.]
—— Itin. di Einsiedeln e l'ord. di Benedetto canonico, 1890. [1.]
Levi (A.) Bassorilievi trov. in Villazzano, 1920. [26.]
—— Camere sepolcrali scop. in Napoli &c., 1926. [31.]
—— L'Iside Barberini, 1922. [28.]
—— Ruderi di terme a Baja, 1922. [28.]
Libertini (G.) Scop. n. necropoli di S. Luigi a Caltagirone, 1922. [28.]
Loewy (E.) Venere in bronzo d. coll. Tyszkiewicz, 1890. [1.]
Lovatelli (E.) Mano votiva in bronzo, 1890. [1.]
Lugli (G.) La Villa Sabina di Orazio, 1926. [31.]
Macchioro (V.) Terme romane di Agnano, 1912. [21.]
Marchetti (D.) Relaz. int. allo scavo rel. ai ludi secol., 1890. [1.]
Marconi (P.) Antinoo, 1923. [29.]
Mariani (L.) Antichità cretesi, 1895. [6.]
—— Aufidena, 1901. [10.]
—— Statue mutile di Teseo ed il Minotauro, 1897. [7.]
Mauceri (L.) Topog. di Imera e tempio di Bonfornello, 1907. [18.]
Milani (L. A.) Piombo scr. di Magliano, 1893. [2.]
—— Reliquie di Firenze ant., 1895. [6.]
Minto (A.) Lamine a Sbalzo di arte paleoetrusca, 1922. [28.]
—— Terme rom. di Massaciuccoli, 1921. [27.]
Mommsen (T.) Comment. ludorum saec. quint., imp. Augusto, 1890. [1.]
Mosso (A.) Necrop. di Molfetta, 1910. [20.]
—— Villaggi preist. di Caldare e Cannatello pr. Girgenti, 1907. [18.]
Orsi (P.) Anathemata di una citta siculo-greca a Terravecchia di Grammichele (Catania), 1907. [18.]
—— Anon. città siculo-greca pr. Caltagirone, 1910. [20.]
—— Camarina, 1899–1903, 1904. [14.]
—— Caulonia, (1) campagne archeol, 1912–5, (2), mem. [23, 29.]
—— Città greca a Terravecchia pr. Granmichele, 1897. [7.]
—— Gela, 1900–5, *&* Tavole, 1906. [17.]
—— Megara Hyblaea, 1917–21, 1921. [27.]
—— Messana: necrop. rom. di S. Placido &c., 1916. [24.]
—— Necropoli preellen. calabresi di Torre Galli &c., 1926. [31.]
—— Necrop. sicula di Pantalica, *&* di M. Dessueri, 1912. [21.]
—— Necrop. sicula pr. Siracusa, 1893. [2.]
—— Scavi int. a l'Athenaion di Siracusa (1912–17), 1918. [25.]
—— Thapsos, 1895. [6.]
—— Urne funeb. cretesi dipinte nel stile di Micene, 1890. [1.]
—— & F. S. Cavallari. Megara Hyblaea, 1890. [1.]
Pace (B.) Basilica di Salemi, 1916. [24.]
—— Richerche cartaginesi, 1925. [30.]
—— Tempio di Giove Olimpico in Agrigento, 1922. [28.]
—— Vasi fig. con rifl. d. Pittura di Parrasio, 1922. [28.]
Paribeni (R.) Luogo dell' antica Adulis, 1907. [18.]
—— Necrop. barbar. di Nocera Umbra, 1918. [25.]
—— Necrop. del territ. capenate, 1906. [16.]
—— 4 tempietti di Ostia, 1914. [23.]
—— Ricerche nel sepolc. di Haghia Triada pr. Phaestos, 1904. [14.]
—— Vasi ined. d. Museo Kircheriano, 1904. [14.]
—— & P. Romanelli. Stud. &c. nell' Anatolia merid., 1914. [23.]
Pasqui (A.) Ant. letto di osso scop. in Norcia, 1890. [1.]
—— Villa pompeiana d. Pisanell pr. Boscoreale, 1897. [7.]
Patricolo (G.) Nuova metopa selinuntina, 1890. [1.]
Patroni (G.) Nora, colonia fenicia in Sardegna, 1904. [14.]
—— Vasi arcaici d. Puglie, 1895. [6.]
Pernier (L.) Scavi d. missione ital. a Phaestos, 1902–3, 1904. [14.]
—— Tumulo con tomba mon. al Sodo presso Cortona, 1925. [30.]
Pettazzoni (R.) Stazioni preist., prov. di Bologna, 1916. [24.]
Pigorini (L.) Terramara Castellazzo di Fontanellato, 1890. [1.]
Pinza (G.) Mon. prim. di Roma e d. Lazio ant., 1905. [15.]
—— Topog. di Cartagine punica, 1925. [30.]
Quagliati (Q.) Deposito sepolcr. con vasi preist. in Crispiano presso Taranto, 1920. [26.]
—— & Ridola. Necrop. ad incin. pr. Timmari nel Materano, 1906. [16.]
Rellini (U.) Caverna di Latrònico, 1916. [24.]
—— Cavernette e ripari preist. nell' agro Falisco, 1920. [26.]
—— La grotta d. Felci a Capri, 1923. [29.]
Ricci (S.) Misc. epigrafica, 1893. [2.]
—— Pretorio di Gortyna, 1893. [2.]
—— "Testamento d'Epikteta," 1893. [2.]
Rizzo (G. E.) Vasi greci d. Sicilia, 1904. [14.]
Robert (C.) Iscriz. greca arcaica in bronzo, 1890. [1.]
Salinas (A.) Nuove metope arc. selinuntine, 1890. [1.]
Savignoni (L.) Bronzetto dell' Acrop. di Atene &c., 1897. [7.]
—— Scavi e scop. n. necrop. di Phaestos, 1904. [14.]

Reale Accademia dei Lincei [*continued*].
Savignoni (L.) De Sanctis & Paribeni. Nuovi st. & scop. in Gortyna, 1907.
Scialoja (V.) & G. de Petra. Framm. di legge romana scop. a Taranto, 1895. [6.]
Sogliano (A.) Dipinto murale rinven. in tomba cumana, 1890. [1.]
—— L'Efebo in bronzo rinven. in Pompei, 1901. [10.]
—— Epigrafe di P. Plozio Faustino, 1890. [1.]
—— Tempio nel Foro triangolare di Pompei, 1890. [1.]
Taramelli (A.) Altipiano d. Giara di Gesturi in Sardegna [by A. T. & F. Nissardi], 1907. [18.]
—— Fortezze &c. preromane di Bonorva, 1918. [25.]
—— Gonnesa: indag. n. cittadella nurag. di Serrucci, 1916. [24.]
—— Necrop. punica di predio Ibba a S. Avendrace, 1912. [21.]
—— Il nuraghe Lugherras, 1910. [20.]
—— Ripost. d. bronzi nuragici di Monte Sa Idda, 1921. [27.]
—— Sarrok, 1926. [31.]
—— Tempio nurag. di S. Anastasia in Sardara, 1918. [25.]
—— Tempio nurag. & i mon. di S. Vittoria di Serri, 1914. [23.]
Ugolini (L. M.) La Panighina. [29.]
REFERENCES.
see FIORENTINA. Consigli d. Repubblica F.; p. c. di B. Barbadoro, v1, 1301–7, 1921.
„ FRIULANO. Parlamento F.; p. c. di. P. S. Leicht, v1, 1228–1429, p1, 1917.
„ SICILIANO. Parlamento S.; p. c. di L. Genuardi, v1; 1924.
„ VINCI (L. DA). Il Codice atlantico di L. da V.; ripr., 4v, 1894–1904.
„ VOLTA (*c.* A.) Opere, v2–6, 1923–28.

Reale Accademia delle Scienze di Torino. Dante e il Piemonte. [Misc. di studi Danteschi. *By var. a.*] 8°. Torino. 1922
see LUZIO (A.) Inizi del regno di Carlo Alberto, 1923.

Reale Commissione pe' testi di lingua n. Prov. dell' Emilia. Coll. di opere ined. &c., *see* BOIARDO (M. M.) Orlando innamorato; riscontrato &c. da F. Fòffano, 3v, 1906–7.

Reale Commissione Vinciana, *see* VINCI (L. DA). Mss. e disegni; pubbl. d. R.C.V., 1923–28.

Reale Deputazione Veneta di Storia Patria, *see* FAVARO (A.) Bibliog. d. Studio di Padova [1500–1920], 2p, 1922.

Reale Istituto di Studi Superiori Pratici e di Perfezionamento, *Firenze.*
see LE-KE. Il Li-ki &c.; tr., &c. di C. Puini, 1883.
„ —— 3 capitoli del "Li-ki" conc. la relig.; tr. &c. di C. Puini, 1886.
„ LIBERTINI (G.) Le isole Eolie nell' ant. greca e rom., 1921.
„ MINTO (A.) Populonia, la necropoli arcaica, 1922.
„ PUINI (C.) Contrib. per lo st. compar. d. istituz. soc. n. ant. civiltà, 1886.
„ —— Orig. d. civiltà &c., 1891.

Reale Istituto Lombardo di Scienze e Lettere.
Rendiconti. s2. v50–58. 8°. Milano. 1917–25
see VINCI (L. DA). Il Codice di L. da V., 1909.

Reale Istituto Veneto. [IMPERIALE REGIO ISTITUTO VENETO DI SCIENZE, LETTERE ED ARTI]. Atti. S3, t12–13 (Nov. 1866–Ott. 1868). 8°. Venezia. 1866–68
see PADOVA. Monogr. stor. s. Studio di P.; contrib. del R. Ist. Veneto &c., 1922.

Reale Società Geografica, *see* SOCIETÀ GEOGRAFICA ITALIANA (REALE).

Reale Società Romana di Storia Patria.
Archivio. v39–44. 8°. 1916–21
Miscellanea. v[7]. 8°. 1919
see FERRAJOLI (A.) La congiura dei cardinali contro Leone X, 1919. [7.]

Real-Encyklopädie. Real-Encyklopädie für protestant. Theologie &c. Hrsg. J. J. Herzog, *see* SCHAFF (P.), *ed.* Relig. encyclopædia; based on R.-Encyklop. of H., 3v, 1883–84.

Realism. Essays in crit. r., 1920, *see* DRAKE (D.)

Reallexikon d. Vorgeschichte, 1924–28, *see* EBERT (M.), *ed.*

***Reasonable** (A) acc. why some nonconform. ministers &c., 1679, *see* COLLINGES (J.), *D.D.*

***Reasonableness** of a toleration enquir'd into &c., 1705, *see* SAGE (J.)

Réau (Louis).
L'art français sur le Rhin au 18e s. 8°. 1922
L'art russe des orig. à Pierre le Grand. la8°. 1921
Etienne Maurice Falconet. 2t. 4°. 1922
La gravure d'illustration. [La grav. en Fr. au 18e s.] 4°. 1928
Saint-Pétersbourg. la8°. 1913
see FALCONET (E. M.) Corresp. de F. avec Catherine II; publ. avec intr. &c. par L. R., 1921.
„ LOUVRE. La peinture, école allem., par L. R., 1927.

Réaumur (R. A.) [†FERCHAULT DE RÉAUMUR (RENÉ ANT.)] Abhandl. ü. Thermometrie v. Fahrenheit, R. &c., 1894, *see* ÖTTINGEN (A. J. v.), *ed.*
Nat. hist. of ants. Tr. & annot. by W. M. Wheeler [*w. text*]. la8°. N.Y. 1926
*Nat. hist. of bees. Tr. 8°. 1744
Rebellion (The) of 1837–38: bibliog. of sources of inform. in Publ. Ref. Lib. of Toronto, 1924, *see* TORONTO.
Rebiczek (Franz). Der Wiener Volks- u. Bänkelgesang, 1800–48. s8°. Wien. [1913]
Rébora (Piero).
The immortal in Dante. Lect. [P2576]. 8°. Liv'l. 1922
L'Italia nel dramma inglese, 1558–1642. 8°. Milano. 1925
Reboul (*le comm.* **Frédéric**). Campagne de 1813: les préliminaires. [Publ. s. dir. de Sect. Hist. de l'Etat-Major de l'Armée]. t1, 2 [*no more publ.*] la8°. 1910–12
1, Le commandement de Murat, déc. 1812–jan. 1813.
2, Le commandement du Pr. Eugène, 1re pér., De Posen à Berlin.
see HANOTAUX (G.) Hist. de la nation franç., t7, Hist. milit. & navale, par F. R. &c., 1925.
Reboux (Paul), *ps.* [*i.e.* PAUL AMILLET].
Les drapeaux. 2[t]. s8°. [1921]
Trio, roman, *see* ŒUVRES libres, 34, 1924.
Rebuffi (Pierre). Privilegia universitatum, collegiorum, bibliopolarum &c. s8°. Francofurti. 1585
see LUDOVICI (J. F.) Obs. de privilegiis studiosorum ad P. R., 1705.
Récamier (*Mme.* **Jeanne F. J. Adélaïde**), *see* LAUNAY (L. DE). Un amoureux de Mme. R.: journal de J. J. Ampère, 1927.
Récamier (Joseph Claude Anthelme), *see* TRIAIRE (P.) R. & ses contemporains, 1774–1852, 1899.
Récéjac (E.) Essay on the bases of the mystic knowledge. Tr. S. C. Upton. 8°. 1899
Recent Eng. domestic archit., v5, 1920, *see* MACARTNEY (M. E.), *ed.*
Rechabites. Independent Order of R. Friendly Soc. Jubilee record. Proc. at Exeter 1885. 8°. [Exeter. 1885]
Réchad (Nihad). L'accord franco-turc. [P2712]. 8°. 1921
Rechenberg (Adam). Sirenum fabulam, praeses J. Stohrius & resp. A. R. submittent. [P2741]. s4°. *n.p.* [1663]
Summarium hist. eccl. ed. 3[a]. s8°. Lipsiæ. 1700
see ETTENHUSIUS (J. B.) Epistola ad R., 1698.
***Recherche** des antiquités &c. de Lyon, 1673, *see* SPON (J.)
Recherches. *Recherches philos. sur les Américains, 3t, 1770; 3t, 1771, *see* PAUW (C.)
***Recht-evangel.** (Eines) treumeinenden Dieners unparthey. Nachricht den Pietismum in Halle betreffend, 1708, *see* PIETISMUS.
Recit. *Recit de ce qui s'est faict &c. en Savoye &c. entre sa Majesté Catholique &c., 1616, *see* SAVOYE.
*Récit du sanglant &c. massacre dans la ville de Moscou; tr. par le prince A. Galitzin, 1869, *see* RUSSELL (W.)
Reckenberger (Johann Leonhard). Nexus canonum exeget. naturalis ex J. J. Rambachi Institut. hermen. sacrae &c. [*b. w.* Rambach (J. J.) Exercit., 1741]. s8°. Jenae. 1736
Reckendorf (Hermann). Arab. Syntax. la8°. Heidelberg. 1921
Reckitt (Harold J.) V.R. 76, a French military hospital. Hist. of the Fondation Johnstone-Reckitt. Arr. & ed. M. S. Turner. 8°. 1921
Reckitt (*Sir* **James**), *see* CHAPMAN-HUSTON (D.) Sir J. R., 1927.
Reckitt (Maurice Benington) & C. E. Bechhofer-Roberts. The meaning of national guilds. 2nd rev. ed., w. new pref. &c. s8°. [1920]
Recknagel (Arthur Bernhard). Forests of New York State. Intr. by L. H. Bailey. s8°. N.Y. 1923
Reclus (Onésime). L'Allemagne en morceaux. Paix draconienne. [P2734]. s8°. [1915]
Recollections. *R. of a chaperon, n. ed.; ed. Lady Dacre, 3v, 1833, *see* SULLIVAN (A. J.)
*R. of Caulincourt, duke of Vicenza; tr., 2v, 1838, *see* EILLEAUX (*ctsse.* DE).
*R. of the 1st camp. west of the Indus &c. under Sir W. Nott., 1845, *see* INDUS.
***Reconcileableness** (The) of God's prescience of sins of men &c., 1677, *see* HOWE (J.)
Reconstruction. Reconstruction (The) epoch: offic. proc. of the Nat. Rep. Conventions of 1868, 72, 76, 80, repr. 1903, *see* UNITED STATES: NAT. REPUB. CONVENT.

Record Office (Public). Cat. of MSS. &c. in the Museum of the P.R.O., w. descr. &c. notes by Sir H. C. Maxwell Lyte. 9th ed. 8°. 1922
„ „ ....10th ed. 8°. 1924
Lists & indexes, No. 46–50. fol. 1921–26
46, Lists of the records of the Treasury, Paymaster Generals' Off., Exchequer & Audit Dept. & Board of trade to 1837.
47, Index of Chancery procs. (ser. 1), James I, v1, A–K.
48, 50, List of early Chancery proc[s]., v6, 7.
49, List of diplom. doc., Scot. doc. & Papal Bulls.
see ANDREWS (C. M.) Guide to materials for Amer. hist., to 1783, in P.R.O., 2v, 1912–14.
„ CHANCERY, *Court of.* Index of persons named in early Ch. proc., pres. in P.R.O., p1, 1927.
„ COMMISSIONERS FOR TRADE & PLANTATIONS. Journal, 1704–22; in P.R.O., 1920–25.
„ COURT OF KING'S BENCH. Curia Regis rolls of r. of Rich. I & John pres. in P.R.O., 1922–26.
„ FEUDAL. Inquisitions &c. rel. to F. Aids; w. o. doc. in P.R.O., 1284–1431, 1899 &c.
„ GIUSEPPI (M. S.) Guide to the MSS. in P.R.O., v1, 2, 1923–24.
„ HIGHAM (C. S. S.) Colonial entry-books, bef. 1696, 1921.
„ KHAN (S. A.) Doc. on 17th c. Brit. India in P.R.O., 1924.
Record Office (Public), of Ireland, *see* WOOD (H.) Guide to P.R. Office of I., 1919.
Record Office, Scotland, *see* SCOTLAND.
Record Society for the Publication of Orig. Documents rel. to Lancashire & Cheshire. v74–78. 8°. 1920–28
see CHESTER. Index to wills & admin. in Probate Registry, C., 1811–20; ed. W. A. Tonge, p1, 1928. [78.]
„ —— Marriage licences gr. within Archdeaconry of C.; ed. W. F. Irvine, v8, 1691–1700, 1924. [77.]
„ LANCASHIRE. Calendar of persons commem. in monumental inscr. &c., comp. & ed. by F. C. Beazley. [76.]
„ RICHMOND. Marriage bonds for the deaneries of Lonsdale &c., archdeaconry of R., 1648–1710; ed. J. Brownbill, p2, 1711–22; ed. R. Stewart-Brown, 1920–21. [74, 75.]
Record (Robert) [RECORDE], *see* SMITH (D. E.) New inform. resp. R. R., 1921.
Recorder, *ps.* Bibliog. of mod. poetry; comp. & ed. by R., 1920, *see* BIBLIOGRAPHY.
Records. Records of the rels. betw. Siam & for. countries in 17th c., 5v, 1915–21, *see* SIAM.
Recouly (Raymond).
La bataille de Foch. s8°. 1920
Foch, h. character & leadership. 8°. 1920
Le printemps rouge: épisode de guerre & de révol. en Russie. s8°. [1925]
La Ruhr. s8°. [1923]
La Troisième Républ. 8°. [1927]
***Recruiting** officer (The): comedy, 1764, *see* FARQUHAR (G.)
Recueil.
*R. de cantiques pour les assemblées de culte &c. s8°. Lyon. 1878
R. de doc. [*&* Nouv. rec.] p. s. à l'hist. de Montreuil-sur-Mer, 1000–1782, 2t, 1907–10, *see* MONTREUIL-SUR-MER.
R. de doc. rel. à l'hist. de l'industrie drapière en Flandre, p1, t1–4, 1906–24, *see* ESPINAS (G.) & H. PIRENNE, *edd.*
R. de pièces authent. sur le captif de Ste.-Hélene, 12t, 1821–25, *see* NAPOLEON I.
R. de pièces histor. impr. s. le r. de Louis XI, 2t, 1923, *see* PICOT (E.) & H. STEIN, *edd.*
R. de piéces importantes conc. la rupture entre la cour de Rome & celle de Portugal, *see* PORTUGAL. Recueil de decrets &c. Suite, 1760.
R. de pièces, p. s. d'addition &c. à la Relation abregée &c., *see* PORTUGAL. Recueil de decrets apostol. &c., p1, 1758; 2e éd., p1, 1761.
R. de pièces qui n'avoient pas encore paru en France, conc. le procès des Jésuites, *see* PORTUGAL. Recueil des decrets apostol. &c., p2, 1761.
R. de pièces rarissimes rel. au Siège de Montpellier, 1622, 1875, *see* MONTPELLIER.
R. de textes landais, 1910, *see* MILLARDET (G.), *ed.*
R. de voyages au Nord, 1725–38, *see* BERNARD (J. F.), *ed.*
R. des chartes de l'abbaye de St.-Benoît-sur-Loire, t1, 2i, 1900–12, *see* SAINT-BENOÎT-SUR-LOIRE.
R. des chartes de l'abbaye royale de Montmartre; publ. &c. E. de Barthélemy, 1883, *see* MONTMARTRE.
R. des decrets apost. &c. du roi de Portugal &c., 2t *&* Suite, 1758–61; 2e ed., 1761, *see* PORTUGAL.
R. des historiens de la France. Publ. par l'Acad. des Inscr. & Belles-Lettres. 4°. 1923
Obituaires. Obit. de la Province de Sens, t4.
4, Diocèses de Meaux & de Troyes; publ. B. du Retail & P. de St.-Aubin sous la dir. & avec préf. de A. Longnon.
Pouillés, t8. Publ. sous la dir. de M. Prou par E. Clouzot.
8, Prov. d'Aix, d'Arles & d'Embrun.

Recueil [*continued*].
R. des instructions données aux ambassadeurs & ministres de France dep. les traités de Westphalie j. la Révol. Publ. sous les ausp. de la Comm. des Archives Diplom. t19–23. la8°. 1912–24
19, Florence, Modène, Gênes; par E. Driault, 1912.
20, Rome; par G. Hanotaux, t3, 1724–91. Intr. & notes par J. Hanoteau, 1913.
21–23, Hollande. Intr. &c. par L. André & E. Bourgeois, 1648–1788, 3t, 1922–24.
R. des traités &c. conc. la Pologne, 1762–1862, 1862, *see* ANGEBERG (*cte.* D').
R. Milliet. Textes grecs & lat. rel. à l'hist. de la peinture anc.; publ., tr. & comm. par A. Reinach, t1, 1921, *see* MILLIET (P.)
Second R. de pièces conc. les usurp. des Jésuites dans l'Amérique Espagnole & Portugaise, *see* PORTUGAL. R. de decrets apostol. &c., p1, 1758.

Redan (Pierre), *see* ANDRÉ (*capt.* P. J.)

Reddan (*Miss* **Minnie**), *see* LONDON. Survey of L., v9, Parish of St. Helen, Bishopsgate, p1; by M. R. &c., 1924.

Reddaway (William Fiddian).
Baltic Provinces, *see* BUCHAN (J.), *ed.* Nations, 1923.
Introd. to the Study of Russ. hist. [P2420]. s8°. 1920

Rede (Leman Thomas). York Castle in the 19th cent.: an acc. of princ. offences in Yorks. fr. 1800 &c. 8°. 1831

Rede (Robert), *bp. of Chichester* [READE (R.)] Episcopal register, 1397–1415. Summarized & ed. by C. Deedes. [Sussex Rec. Soc., v8, 11]. 2p. 8°. 1908–10

Redemptus, *Saint, bp. of Ferento*, *see* ASSEMANUS (J. S.) De Bonifacio ac R., diss., 1745.

Redfield (Arthur Huber). Brazil: study of econ. cond. since 1913, 1920, *see* UNITED STATES: COMMERCE.

Redfield (H. V.)
Homicide, North & South, U.S. s8°. Phila. 1880

Redfield (William Cox). Dependent America: econ. basis of our internat. relations. 8°. 1926

Redgrave (Gilbert R.) Cat. of coll. of incunabula, early woodcuts &c. Sold by Sotheby, May 1926. [Illust. P2853]. la8°. 1926
see POLLARD (A. W.) Short-title cat. of bks. pr. in Eng., Scotland, & Ireland &c., 1475–1640, 1926.

Redgrove (H. Stanley) & I. M. L. Redgrove. Joannes Baptista van Helmont, alchemist &c. s8°. 1922

Redgrove (I. M. L.), *see* REDGROVE (H. S.) & I. M. L. R. J. B. van Helmont, 1922.

Redhouse (*Sir* **James William**). Gramm. raisonnée de la langue ottomane. Suivie d'un app. 8°. Paris. 1846
Turkish dict. Eng.-T. & T.-Eng. 2nd ed. rev. &c. by C. Wells. 8°. 1880

Redi (Francesco). Raccolta d. poesie. s8°. Londra. 1781

Redier (Antoine Jean Louis). La guerre des femmes: Hist. de Louise de Bettignies & de s. compagnes. s8°. 1924
The story of L. de Bettignies. Tr. O. Hall. 8°. [1926]

Reding (Augustinus). *Oecumenica cathedrae apostol. authoritas. fol. *n.p.* 1689

Redlich (Edwin Basil).
Hist. of Teigh in Rutland. 8°. Long Compton. 1926

Redlich (Joseph). Österreich. Regierung u. Verwaltung im Weltkriege. [C.E. for Int. Peace]. la8°. Wien. 1925
Das österreich. Staats-u. Reichsproblem. Bli, ii, 2. 8°. L. 1920–26

Redlich (Oswald). Gesch. Österreichs, B6, 1921, *see* GESCH. D. EUROPÄ. STAATEN.

Redlich (Virgil). Johann Rode, e. deut. Reformabt d. 15. Jhdts. 8°. Münster. 1923

Redman (John). De justificatione opus. Huic acc. hymnus &c. [*b. w.* Fitzherbert (T.) Reply &c., 1614]. s8°. Antverpiae. 1555

Redman (William). Illust. hdbk. of pewter & Sheffield plate. 8°. Bradford. 1903

Redmayne (*Sir* **Richard Augustine Studdert**). Brit. coalmining industry dur. the War. [C.E. for Internat. Peace]. la8°. O. 1923
Mod. practice in mining. v1–4 [1, 2, 3rd ed.; 3, 4, n. impr.] 8°. 1922–25
—— **& G. Stone.** The ownership & valuation of mineral property in the U.K. 8°. 1920

Redmond (John Edward). Ireland & the War. Extr. f. speeches. [P2719]. 8°. D. 1915
Some arguments for Home Rule: speeches, 1907. Pref. & notes by J. G. S. MacNeill. [P2706]. 8°. D. 1908
see GWYNN (S. L.) J. R.'s last years, 1919.

Redon (Odilon). A soi-même; journal (1867–1915). Notes sur la vie, l'art & les artistes. Intr. de J. Morland. 8°. 1922

***Reds** in America, 1924, *see* WHITNEY (R. M.)

Red Sea. Red Sea &c. pilot, 7th ed. & Suppl., 1921–22, *see* ADMIRALTY.

Redslob (Edwin). Alt-Dänemark. [Archit. &c. d. Ausl., B2]. 3e A. 4°. München. [1922]

Redwood (*Sir* **Boverton**), *see* THOMSON (*capt.* J. H.) & *Sir* B. R. Hdbk. on petroleum, 1913.

Rée (Paul). Ursprung d. moral. Empfindungen. [P2474]. 8°. Chemnitz. 1877

Reeb (Wilhelm).
German. Namen auf rhein. Inschr. 4°. Mainz. 1895

Reed (The) of Pan: Eng. renderings of Greek epigrams &c., 1922, *see* BENSON (A. C.)

Reed (Amy Louise). The background of Gray's Elegy: taste for melancholy poetry, 1700–51. [Columbia Univ.] 8°. N.Y. 1924

Reed (Anna Yeomans) & W. Woelpper.
Junior wage earners. s8°. N.Y. 1920

Reed (Arthur William). Beginnings of the Eng. secular & romantic drama. [Shakespeare Assoc. Papers, No. 7. P2621]. 8°. [1922]
Early Tudor drama: Medwall, the Rastells, Heywood & the More circle. 8°. [1926]

Reed (*Sir* **Charles**). *An hist. narrative of the orig. & constit. of the Irish Soc. s8°. [1865]

Reed (Edward Charles). The free heart. 2nd ed. s8°. [1927]
Mrs. Ormesby's proposal. s8°. [1925]

Reed (*Sir* **Edward James**). Japan: its hist. &c. With narr. of visit, 1879. 2nd ed. 2v. 8°. 1880
Shipbuilding in iron & steel. 8°. 1869

Reed (Frederick Richard Cowper).
Geology of the Brit. Empire. 8°. 1921

Reed (Isaac), *see* NICHOLS (J.) *Biog. anecdotes of W. Hogarth [*by N. assisted by G. Steevens & I. R.*], 1781; 1783; 1785.

Reed (J. Hammond), *see* STONE (A. H.) & J. H. R. Historic Lushan, 1921.

Reed (John). Ten days that shook the world. [Intr. by N. Lenin]. 8°. N.Y. 1922

Reeger (*Fr.* **von**). Versteigerung mehrerer Porzellanssamml. des Nachlasses Dr. v. R., v. Gemälden &c. aus Privatbes., 25–27 Feb. 1920, Wien, Glückselig u. Wärndorfer. [*Illust. b. w.* Kolisch (R.) Versteig., 1921]. 4°. Wien. 1920

Reepen (H. v. Buttel-), *see* BUTTEL-REEPEN (H. v.)

Rees (Arthur J.) The Moon Rock. s8°. [1922]

Rees (J. Aubrey). The W. Co. of Grocers, 1345–1923. 8°. 1923

Rees (J. Morgan). Trusts in Brit. industry, 1914–21. 8°. 1922

Rees (James Frederick). A short fiscal & financial hist. of England, 1815–1918. s8°. [1921]

Rees (Wilhelmus van). Disput. de usu Eucharistiæ medico. Sub præs. D. Gerdesii. [P2638]. s4°. Duisburgi. 1728

Rees (Willem Adriaan van) & M. T. H. Perelaer. Nederlandsch-Indie. Teekeningen door J. C. Rappard. [4p]. fol. Leiden. 1881–83
Batavia; door W. A. van R. Buitenzorg—De Buitenbezittingen—Java; door M. T. H. P.

Rees (William), *D.Sc.* South Wales & the March, 1284–1415: a soc. & agrarian study. 8°. 1924

Reeve (Frank H.) Important ship models, 18th to 19th cent. &c. Sold, Anderson Gall. [*Illust.* P2854]. la8°. N.Y. [1925]

Reeve (Henry), *C.B.*, *see* GREVILLE (C. C. F.) Letters of C. Greville & H. Reeve, 1836–65; ed. A. H. Johnson, 1924.

Reeve (Henry Fenwick). The black republic: Liberia, polit. & social condit. to-day. Intr. by Sir A. Sharpe. 8°. 1923

Reeve (John), *hymn writer.*
Spiritual hymns upon Solomon's Song. s8°. 1693
—— **& L. Muggleton.** A list of the books &c. wr. by R. & M. [P2421]. s8°. 1843

Reeve (Sidney Armor). Modern economic tendencies: an econ. hist. of America. la8°. N.Y. [1921]

Reeve (William), *1757–1815.* Overture to the Turnpike Gate, arr. for piano forte. [*b. w.* Corelli (A.) Twelve concertos, 1790?]. 4°. [1799]

Reeve (William), *of the London Missionary Soc.* A dict., Canarese & Eng. Rev. & enl. by D. Sanderson. 8°. Bangalore. 1858

Reeves' Dict. of musicians. Ed. & partly re-wr. by E. Duncan, w. add. s8°. [1926]

Reeves (Edward Ayearst). Hints to travellers. Ed. for Royal Geog. Soc. by A. E. R. 10th ed. 2v. s8°. 1921

Reeves (John), *F.R.S.* A collat. of the Hebrew & Greek texts of the Psalms. 8°. 1800

Reeves (William), *bp. of Down.* Essay on the right use of the Fathers, *see* APOSTOLIC. The A. Fathers; tr., v2, 1889; 1909.

Reeves (*Hon.* William Pember).

The great powers & the East. Xtns., *see* ANGLO-HELLENIC LEAGUE. No. 49, 1922.

The long white cloud (Ao Tea Roa). 3rd ed. rev. &c., added a sketch of rec. events in N.Z. by C. J. Wray. 8°. [1924]

Reference Catalogue of current literature. 3v. [v1, Index]. 8°. *J. Whitaker.* 1920

Reflections. *R. & resolutions proper for the gentlemen of Ireland, 1738, *see* MADDEN (S.)

*R. on His Majesty's reasons f. withdrawing fr. Rochester, 1689, *see* BURNET (G.), *bp.*

*R. on the present state of British India, 1829, *see* INDIA.

*R. upon the late great Revolution. Wr. by a Lay-Hand in the country. [P2652]. s4°. 1689

Reflector (The). Publ. by James Stephen. v1, Nos. 1–17 (Jan. 1–Apr. 21, 1888). [*no tp.*] s4°. 1888

Reflexiones. *R. privatae de linguae Lat. usu &c., 1845, *see* RÁCZ (A.)

*R. super introducendo linguae ungaricae usu, 1806, *see* UNGARICAE.

Reforçat *de Tres, troubadour, see* BERTONI (G.) Sordello e R., 1915.

Reformační sbornik. Práce z dějin československého života náboženského. Vydávají F. Bednář &c. 1. 1921. 4°. v Praze. [1921]

Reformation. *La défense de la R., 1673, *see* CLAUDE (J.)

Reform Club. Catalogue of Panizzi pamphlets. Issued by the Library Comm. 8°. 1920

***Reformed** (The) bishop or XIX articles &c., 1680, *see* GORDON (J.)

Regan (Charles Tate). Fishes *&* Larval & post-larval fishes, *see* BRIT. ANTARCTIC EXPED., 1910–13. Zoology, v1, 1914–16.

Regenfus (Vitus Hieronymus). Diss. de philosophia Adami putatitia. Præs. J. W. Feuerlino. [P2634]. s4°. Altorfii. [1715]

Regensburg. Das Rathaus zu R. [*By var. wr.* Heinisch &c. Unter d. Leitung v. O. Hupp. Vorwort v. K. Th. v. Heigel]. fol. Regensburg. 1910

Regenvolscius (Adrianus), *ps.* [*i.e.* JĘDRZEY WĘGIERSKI]. Systema hist.-chronol. eccl. Slavonic. Libris 6 adornatum. s4°. Trajecti a. R. 1652

Regesta.

R. episc. Constant. (R. z. Gesch. d. Bischöfe v. Constantz, 517–1496). Hrsg. v. d. Badischen Hist. Comm. B3, 1384–1436. 4°. Innsbruck. 1913–26

R. Habsburgica &c., Abt. 1, 3, 1905–24, *see* HAPSBURG.

R. Pontificum Roman., 1911–27, *see* KEHR (P. F.)

Regesten.

R. d. Bischöfe v. Eichstätt, 1915–27, *see* EICHSTÄTT.

R. d. Bischöfe v. Strassburg, &c., B1, 2, 1908–28, *see* STRASSBURG.

R. d. Kaiserurkunden d. oström. Reiches, 565–1453; Dölger, *see* CORPUS d. griech. Urkunden d. M.-a. &c., Abt. 1, 1924.

R. d. Markgrafen v. Baden &c.; hrsg. v. Bad. Hist. Comm., 1892–1915, *see* BADEN.

Reggius (Honorius), *ps., see* HORNIUS (GEORGIUS).

Regia Deputazione di Storia Patria [REGIA DEPUT. SOVRA GLI STUDI DI STORIA PATRIA]. Atti, 20 apr. 1833 al 1 agosto 1880 [*&* Ind.], 1882 [*in* Miscellanea, *below*, t20].

Miscellanea di storia ital. ed. per cura d. R. D. &c. t1–52, 54. [t1–15; 2a ser. 1–16; 3a ser. 1–21, 23]. la8°. Torino. 1862–1928

t11 *cont.* Indice dei 10 primi t. *With ser. 3 the title was changed to* Regia Deput. sovra gli Studi di Storia Patria.

Acqua (C. dell'). Del piede Liutprando detto anche Aliprando &c., 1883. [21.]

Adami (V.) Magistratura dei confini n. ant. domini di casa Savoia, 1915. [48.]

Adriani (G. B.) Della vita &c. d. Card. P. Santa Croce, 1868. [5.]

Alessandria, *Piedmont.* Alcuni capit. ined. d. statuti di A., 1902. [38.]

Alghero. Statuti dei Gremi artig. di A., 1924. [51.]

Amadeus VI, *of Savoy.* Nuova ediz. d. statuti d. 1379 di A. VI di S., 1884. [22.]

Amat di San Filippo (P.) Della schiavitù e d. servaggio in Sardegna, 1895. [33.]

—— Indagini e studi s. storia econ. di Sardegna, 1903. [39.]

Regia Deputazione di Storia Patria [*continued*].

Miscellanea [*continued*].

Ambrogio, *da Paullo.* Cronaca milanese, 1476–1515, 1871. [13.]

Aosta. Cartul. de l'évêché d'A. (13e s.), 1884. [23.]

—— Livre des cens de l'évêché d'A. (1305), 1898. [35.]

Arborio (*card.* M.) Testamento 1529, 1879. [18.]

—— Vite &c., con note &c., 1915. [48.]

Bandini (A. M.) B. in Piemonte: diario, nov. 1778, 1910. [45.]

Bazzoni (A.) Una storiografo cesareo del sec. 18 arrestato nei pressi di Vienna [*G. B. Comazzi*], 1895. [33.]

Beccaria (A.) A. M. Bandini in Piemonte, nov. 1778, 1910. [45.]

Belgrano (L. T.) Della dedizione dei Genovesi a Luigi XII di Francia, 1862. [1.]

Benaglio (M. A.) Rel. d. carestia e d. peste di Bergamo, 1629 e 1630, 1865. [6.]

Bergamo. Ant. Calendarii d. chiesa di B., 1871. [13.]

—— Breves chronicae B. [1117–1512], 1868. [5.]

Bernardi (J.) Della pubbl. d. cartario dell' ant. abbadia d'Oulx fatta da Berta e Rivautella, e del codice Peralda, 1882. [20.]

Bertolotti (A.) Convenzioni e statuti pell' estirpamento d. berrovieri e de' ladri dal Monferrato &c. nei sec. 13 e 14, 1871. [12.]

Bigot de Sainte-Croix (C. L.) Relaz. d. Piemonte (Mém. hist. sur la maison roy. de Savoie &c. sous Ch. Emanuel III & de Victor Amédée III); annot. da A. Manno, 1877. [16.]

Blondel (L. A.) Mem. aneddot. s. corte di Sardegna, 1871. [13.]

Bogino (G. L.), P. Balbo &c. Lettere a G. Ferrari, 1883. [21.]

Bollati (E.) Di un ined. doc. s. Tregua di Dio, 1879. [18.]

Bollati di Saint-Pierre (F. E.) Doc. ined. s. casa di Savoia, 1884. [22.]

—— Frammento (Articuli &c. super substractione Benedicti XIII), 1882. [20.]

Bollea (L. C.) Assedio di Bricherasio dato da Carlo Eman. di Savoia, 1594, 1907. [43.]

Bornate (C.) Guerra di Pietrasanta (1484–5), 1922. [50.]

Boselli (P.) Commem. d. G. Rossi, 1915. [48.]

—— Il ministro Vallesa e l'ambasc. Dalberg nel 1817, 1893. [30.]

Bosio (*il cav.* A.) Due mon. ined. d. Piemonte illust., 1874. [15.]

—— Not. sui sepolcri di Bianca di Monferrato e di L. Portoneria in Carignano, e sul passaggio in Piemonte di Carlo VIII, re di Fr., 1870. [10.]

Bozzola (A.) Un capitano di guerra &c. Gugl. VII di Monferrato, 1922. [50.]

Brosso. Statuti minerari d. valle di B. d. sec. 15, 1870. [11.]

Bruzza (L.) Not. int. alla patria &c. d. pittore G. A. Bazzi, 1862. [1.]

Buttet (M. C. de). Victoire de Pr. Emmanuel Philibert [*poem,* 1561], 1915. [48.]

Caffaro (A.) L'arte d. lanificio in Pinerolo &c., 1893. [30.]

—— Avvisi rig. la guerra in Piemonte &c., 1642, 1893. [30.]

Caire (P.) Monografie novaresi, Mem. 2a, Sigilli e medaglie, 1880. [19.]

Cais de Pierlas (*le c.* E.) I conti di Ventimiglia, il priorato di S. Michele ed il principato di Seborga, 1884. [23.]

—— Le fief de Châteauneuf du 11e au 15e siècle, 1892. [29.]

—— Gli statuti d. gabella di Nizza sotto i conti di Provenza, 1894. [31.]

Calligaris (G.) Due pretese dominaz. straniere in Sardegna nel sec. 8, 1896. [34.]

Calvi (F.) Gius. Cossa: commem., 1887. [25.]

Cambiano (G.), *di Ruffia.* Memorabili, 1542–1611, 1870. [9.]

Camus (J.) Prem. autographes de la maison de Savoie, 1906. [42.]

—— La venue en France de Valentine Visconti, dsse. d'Orléans, & l'invent. de ses joyaux apportés de Lombardie, 1900. [36.]

Canina (A. G.) Finanza d. Piemonte (1559–80), 1924. [52.]

Carena (A. P. F.) Consid. sopra una nuova divis. d. prov. e diocesi d. stati di S. M. il Re di Sardegna, 1878. [17.]

Carnesecchi (P.) Estratto del processo di P. C., 1870. [10.]

Carpasio. Ant. statuti di C. (1433); [*ed. V. Poggi*], 1904. [40.]

Carrard (H.) Une commune vaudoise au 13e s.: les statuts de Pierre de Savoie & la charte de Moudon, 1887. [25.]

Carutti (D.) Il barone Gius. M. di S. Giovanni, 1887. [26.]

—— Il Canonico E. Bérard, 1890. [28.]

—— Il Conte della Roche d'Allery e il Col. Fresen all' assedio di Verrua (1704–5), 1901. [37.]

—— Il conte G. Porro Lambertenghi, 1887. [25.]

—— Della famiglia di Gaetano Pugnani, 1895. [33.]

—— In mem. d. Senatore C. Negroni, 1896. [34.]

—— Mgr. J. Bernardi, 1900. [36.]

—— L'on. Q. Sella, 1884. [23.]

—— Suppl. ai "Regesta comitum Sabaudiae &c. ad an. 1253," 1904. [40.]

Casti (G. B.) Lettere polit. scr. da Vienna 1793, 1883. [21.]

Caviglia (A.) C. de Seyssel, 1928. [54.]

Cerasoli (F.), C. Cipolla &c., *edd.* Clemente VI e Casa Savoia: doc. Vaticani *&* App., Nuovi doc., 1900. [36.]

—— ——, *edd.* Innocenzo VI e Casa Savoia: doc. dell' Arch. Vaticano, 1902. [38.]

Ceruti (A.) Ant. mura milanesi di Massimiano, 1869. [7.]

—— Commem. dell' avv. G. Casanova, 1889. [27.]

—— Statuta Soc. S. Iohannis Baptistae Augustae Taurin., 1389, 1870. [11.]

Regia Deputazione di Storia Patria [*continued*].
Miscellanea [*continued*].
Chiapusso (F.) Di uno statuto concesso d. duca Ludovico di Savoia alla città di Susa nel 2 luglio 1462, 1880. [19.]
—— Relaz. ant. d. stato di Piemonte e Savoia, 1571; *ed.* F. C., 1890. [28.]
Chiuso (T.) Saggio di ant. doc. dell' Archivio Arcivesc. di Torino, 1879. [18.]
Cipolla (C.) A. M. Bandini a Verona [1778], 1913. [47.]
—— Commem. del prof. C. Merkel, 1900. [36.]
—— Di Audace, vesc. di Asti, e di due doc., 1889. [27.]
—— Di Brunengo, vesc. di Asti, e di tre doc. ined., 1890. [28.]
—— Inventari trascr. da pergamene Bobbiesi dei sec. 13–14, 1909. [44.]
—— Un Italiano n. Polonia e n. Svezia tra il 16 e 17 sec. [*A. Guagninus*], 1887. [26.]
—— Nuovo doc. rig. Aless. Guagnini, 1904. [40.]
—— La pergamena orig. del trattato conchiuso nel 1188 tra Berengario I, Marchese di Busca, e il comune di Asti, 1900. [36.]
—— La pergamena rappres. le ant. pitture d. Basilica di S. Eusebio in Vercelli, 1901. [37.]
—— Quattro doc. astesi conserv. n. Bibl. di Sua Maestà in Torino (955–1078), 1887. [25.]
—— Taddeo del Branca e una tradiz. leggend. sull' Alighieri, 1887. [25.]
Cittadella (L. N.) Istrumento di divis., 12 sett. 1493, tra le sorelle Angela ed Ippolita Sforza Visconti, 1863. [4.]
Claretta (G.) Commem. d. conte A. Franchi-Verney, 1883. [21.]
—— Lettere di illust. personaggi, 1862. [1.]
—— I reali di Savoia, munifici fautori d. arti, sec. 18, 1893. [30.]
Collino (G.) Sui cartolari d. prevostura d'Oulx, 1904. [40.]
Colombo (E.) Iolanda, dssa. di Savoia (1465–78), 1894. [31.]
Colombo (G.) Not. e doc. s. vita di G. F. Bonomi, 1879. [18.]
Columbus (D.) Mem. con nota s. bolla di Aless. VI di 4 maggio 1493, di V. Promis, 1870. [9.]
Comino (F.) Il conte L. Montagnini, cenni, 1885. [24.]
Commendone (G. F.), *card.* Lettere n. nunziatura di Germania; [*ed. G. Finazzi*], 1865. [6.]
Contessa (C.) Decadenza d. diplom. ital. nel sec. 17 &c., 1906. [42.]
—— Progetti econ. d. 2ª Madama Reale di Savoia, 1678–82, 1915. [48.]
Cordero di Pamparato (S.) Doc. per la storia del Piemonte (1265–1300), 1904. [40.]
Cresci (M.) Storia ital. [1524–46], 1907. [43.]
Cuneo. Cronache ant. al sec. 17 conc. la storia di C. &c. (Chron. Cunei libri 3—Cronaca dal 1484 al 1570 di Grasso Dalmazzo—De gestis Antonii Torresani brevis narr.), 1871. [12.]
Dallari (U.) L'occupaz. francese di Reggio (1702–6), 1904. [40.]
Dalmasso (L.) Piemontesi alla guerra di Candia, 1644–69, 1909. [44.]
Danna (C.) Biografia doc. di C. Combetti, 1882. [20.]
—— Commem. d. Teol. Cav. A. Bosio, 1882. [20.]
Dell'Acqua (C.) In mem. d. Prof. C. Magenta, 1895. [33.]
Demaria (G.) La guerra di Castro e la spediz. de' presidii (1639–49), 1898. [35.]
Desimoni (C.) Commem. di M. Remondini, 1889. [27.]
De Vit (V.) Mem. dell' ant. castello di Matarella, 1890. [28.]
Dionisotti (C.) La Cappella d. Corte d'Appello di Torino, 1892. [29.]
—— Commem. d. Comm. C. Danna, 1885. [24.]
Du Bois-Melly (C.) Relat. de Sardaigne & de Genève, 1754–73, 1890. [28.]
Duc (J. A.) A quelle date est mort St. Bernard de Menthon?, 1894. [31.]
—— Doc. sur l'hist. eccl. du m. â., 1885. [24.]
Dufour (A. H.) & F. Rabut. Renonciat. du Comte Amédée VI de Savoie au mariage arrêté entre lui & la Pcsse. Jeanne de Bourgogne, 1878. [17.]
Durandi (J.) Ricerche s. il diritto pubbl. d. Vercellese e d. Lombardia; comp. da F. Rondolino, 1887. [25.]
Dutto (A.) Relaz. sull' assedio di Cuneo del 1557, 1905. [41.]
Fè d'Ostiani (L. F.) Commem. d. Conte Fr. Bettoni, 1901. [37.]
Ferrero (E.) V. Promis e i suoi studii numismatici, 1892. [29.]
Filippi (G.) Il comune di Firenze ed il ritorno d. S. Sede in Roma, 1367, 1887. [26.]
Finazzi (G.) Di alcuni mss. conc. la storia d. Co. di Trento, 1865. [6.]
Fiorani (P. L.) Territorio &c. di Mombrione, 1912. [46.]
Flamma (G. de la). Chron. extravagans et Chron. maius, 1869. [7.]
Fontana (L.) Commem. d. Comm. C. Dionisotti, 1901. [37.]
—— Commem. d. Conte C. Bon-Compagni, 1882. [20.]
Fracchia (F.) Stor. polit. &c. di Dogliani, 1924. [51.]
Fulcheri (B.) I monti frumentari d. Sardegna, 1905. [41.]
Gabotto (F.) Doc. ined. s. storia d. Piemonte (1383–1418), 1896. [34.]
—— L'età del Conte Verde in Piemonte (1350–83), 1895. [33.]
—— Invent. e regesto dell' Archivio comunale di Moncalieri, 1418, 1900. [36.]
Genova. Capitoli d. consortia d. forestieri d. chiesa d. Servi in G., 1393, 1870. [11.]

Regia Deputazione di Storia Patria [*continued*].
Miscellanea [*continued*].
Gerbaix di Sonnaz (C. A. de). Rel. fra Savoia & Portogallo, 1146–1849, 1910. [45.]
—— Ult. anni di regno di Vitt. Amedeo III, 1918. [49.]
Gerbaldo (G. G.) Mem. d. guerra, carestia e peste del Piemonte, 1629–31, 1868. [5.]
Germonius (A.) Lettere, pubbl. F. Comino, 1870. [10.]
Gerolamo (B.) Inquisitori ed eretici lombardi (1292–1318), 1922. [50.]
Giacosa (P.) Un inventario di un castello piemont. (1511), 1890. [28.]
Giustiniani (A.) Relaz. dell' attacco e difesa di Scio n. 1431 [*poem*], 1865. [6.]
Goselini (G.) Compendio stor. d. guerra di Parma e d. Piemonte, 1548–53, 1878. [17.]
Granvelle (*le card.* de). Lettere al duca di Savoia, Emanuele Filiberto, 1880. [19.]
Henrietta Maria, *q. c. of Charles I.* Lettres à Christine, dsse. de Savoie [1628–66], 1882. [20.]
Intra (G. B.) G. Braghiroli, cenni biog., 1885. [24.]
La Rocca (L.) Cessione del regno di Sardegna alla casa Sabauda, 1905. [41.]
Lattes (A.) F. de Aguirre e S. Maffei, 1909. [44.]
Lazari (V.) Del traffico e d. condiz. d. schiavi in Venezia nei tempi di mezzo, 1862. [1.]
Lemmi (F.) Diplomatici sardi (1789–96), 1922. [50.]
Liber Marchiane ruine: poema storico d. sec. 14, 1868. [5.]
Lodi. Statuta caligariorum et sartorum civit. Laudae, 1869. [7.]
Lumbroso (G.) Notizie s. vita di Cassiano Dal Pozzo, 1874. [15.]
Lupi (M.) Mem. p. s. alla vita d. m. m. D. Lupi, 1865. [6.]
Luserna (C. F. M., *conte* di). Memorie, 1551–1631, 1879. [18.]
Magenta (C.) Alfonso Corradi: commem., 1893. [30.]
Maiocchi (R.) Un diploma ined. di Re Lotario rig. Como (20 agosto 949), 1896. [34.]
—— F. Barbavara dur. la reggenza di Caterina Visconti, 1898. [35.]
Manfroni (C.) Ginevra, Berna e Carlo Eman. I (1589–92) &c., 1894. [31.]
Manno (A.) Alcuni cat. di ant. librerie piemontesi, 1880. [19.]
—— Annali e scritti di G. Spano, 1879. [18.]
—— E. Cais di Pierlas, 1904. [40.]
—— E. Ferrero, commem., 1909. [44.]
—— L. Fontana, ricordi, 1909. [44.]
—— Il lavoro quadragen. d. Barone G. Claretta, 1900. [36.]
—— P. Micca ed il gen. conte Solaro della Margarita, 1883. [21.]
—— Relaz. e doc. sull' assedio di Torino, 1706, 1878. [17.]
—— Sull' assedio di Torino nel 1706: ricerche 2, 1880. [19.]
Manuel di San Giovanni (G.) Un episodio d. storia d. Piemonte n. sec. 13 &c., 1874. [15.]
—— Not. e doc. rig. la chiesa e prepositura di S. Maria di Vezzolano nel Monferrato, 1862. [1.]
—— Not. stor. di Pagno e Valle Bronda, presso Saluzzo, 1889. [27.]
—— Tre doc. rig. G. Benso di Santena, mercatante di Chieri n. sec. 16, 1869. [7.]
Manzoni (G.) Annali tipogr. torinesi del sec. 15, 1863. [4.]
Marengo (E.) Un' ant. pergamene d. R. Archivio di Stato in Genova, 1915. [48.]
Mareschal de Luciane (F. C. de). Les prem. maréchaux de Savoie, 1887. [26.]
—— Savoyards à la bataille de Bulgnéville (1431), 1918. [49.]
Marini (R. A.) Medaglie &c. sabaudi d. Rinascimento, 1912. [46.]
Mazarin (*le card.*) Lettere a G. Giustiniani, 1863. [4.]
Mellarède (P.) Rel. s. corte d'Inghilterra, 1885. [24.]
Merkel (C.) Una pretesa dominaz. provenzale in Piemonte nel sec. 13, 1887. [26.]
Messina. Pandetta d. gabelle e dei diritti d. curia di M., 1870. [10.]
Milano. *Chronica di M. dal 948 al 1487, 1869. [8.]
—— Statuti d. strade ed acque d. contado di M., fatti 1346, 1869. [7.]
Milano (E.) Leggenda e storia del luogo di Auçabech, 1906. [42.]
Minucci (A.), *of Serravalle.* Descr. di un viaggio, 1549, da Venezia a Parigi, con cenni biogr. &c. dell' ab. J. Bernardi, 1862. [1.]
Minuti (A.) Vita di M. A. Sforza, 1869. [7.]
Miolo (G.), *di Lombriasco.* Cronaca [*985–1569. Latin*], 1862. [1.]
Monferrato (B., *dssa.* di). Inventario dei beni mobili di B. [1519], 1906. [42.]
Montagnini (C. I.) Dell' ant. legislaz. ital. s. manimorte, 1880. [19.]
Montet (A. de). Extr. de docs. rel. à l'hist. de Vevey, j. 1565, 1884. [22.]
Morone (G.) Lettere ed oraz. latine, 1863. [2.]
Müller (J.) Doc. conc. la vita pubbl. di G. Morone, 1865. [3.]
Muratori (G. F.) Iscrizioni rom. dei Vagienni, 1869. [8.]
Muratori (L. A.) Indice sistem. d. Cron. astesi (Muratori, R. I. S., XI) di O. Alfieri, G. e S. Ventura, comp. da C. Merkel &c., 1884. [23, App.]
—— Indice sistem. d. Hist. rerum in Italia gest. (Muratori, R. I. S., IX) di Ferreto de' Ferreti, comp. G. Filippi &c., 1884. [23, App.]
—— Lettere ined. (1695–1755), 1879. [18.]
—— Lettere ined. di L. A. M., 1890. [28.]
—— Lettere ined.; tratte d. autogr. d. Bibl. Ambrosiana da A. Ceruti, 1869. [8.]
—— Rerum Ital. Scr.: indices chronolog., 1885. [24, App.]

Regia Deputazione di Storia Patria [*continued*].
Miscellanea [*continued*].
Nice. Obituaire de l'anc. cathédrale de N., 1896. [34.]
Nubilonio (C.) Cronaca di Vigevano, 1584, 1892. [29.]
Orfinus, *Laudensis*. Poema de regimine et sapientia potestatis; ed. A. Caruti, 1869. [7.]
Pacciotto (F.) Lettere a Guidobaldo II, duca d'Urbino, ed. C. Promis, 1871. [12.]
Pandiani (E.) Cacciata d. Austriaci da Genova, 1746, 1924. [51.]
Paoli (*il gen*. P. de'). Lettere ined.; con. avvert. &c. di N. Bianchi, 1880. [19.]
Pastè (R.) Storia doc. dell' abbazia di S. Andrea di Vercelli, 1219–1466, 1902. [38.]
Pélissier (L. G.) L'alliance milano-allem. à la fin du 15 s.: l'ambass. d'H. Brasca à Maximilien (1498), 1898. [35.]
Pera. Statuti d. colonia genovese di P., 1870. [11.]
Peragallo (P.) Colonia ital. in Portogallo, sec. 14–16, 1904. [40.]
Perrin (A.) De l'assoc. des monnayeurs du St. Empire rom. & des ateliers de Piémont, 1871. [13.]
—— Le trésor de la chapelle du château des Échelles, Command. de St. Jean de Jérusalem—Docs. sur la prise du château par Lesdiguieres, 1896. [34.]
Pesente (G. M.) La battaglia navale di Malaga (24 agosto 1704), 1900. [36.]
Philip II, *d. of Savoy*. La ribellione di Filippo Senza Terra narrata da un contemp., 1877. [16.]
Podesta (F.) I Genovesi e le peschere di corallo nei mari di Sardegna, 1901. [37.]
Poggi (V.) L'atto di fondaz. d. mon. di S. Quintino di Spigno (991), 1901. [37.]
—— Commem. di M. Staglieno, 1910. [45.]
—— Cronotassi dei princ. magistrati che ressero &c. il comune di Savona, 1905–13. [41, 45, 47.]
—— I presunti avanzi d. mausoleo di Gastone di Foix in Savona, 1894. [31.]
Porro-Lambertenghi (G.) Breve commem. d. socio C. Morbio, 1882. [20.]
Promis (C.) Biog. di ingegneri milit. ital. d. sec. 14 alla metà d. 18, 1874. [14.]
—— Gl'ingegneri e gli scrittori milit. bolognesi d. 15 e 16 sec., 1863. [4.]
—— Gl'ingegneri milit. d. Marca d'Ancona, 1550–1650, 1865. [6.]
—— Gl'ingegneri milit. in Piemonte, 1300–1650, 1871. [12.]
—— L'Oratorio del Sacramento in Torino, con alcuni mon. archit. del Piemonte e de' sec. 15 e 16, 1871. [13.]
—— Vita di F. Paciotto da Urbino, 1863. [4.]
—— Vita di Girolamo Maggi d'Anghiari, 1862. [1.]
Promis (D. C.) Dell' orig. d. zecca di Genova e di alcune sue monete ined., 1870. [11.]
—— Illust. di un medaglia di Claudio di Seyssel, e n. ricerche sull' Ordine del Collare di Savoia, 1871. [13.]
—— Monete d. abati di S. Benigno di Fruttuaria, 1870. [10.]
—— Monete di zecche ital. ined., Mem. 2, 3, 1869–71. [7, 12.]
—— Monete e medaglie ital., 1871. [13.]
—— Monete ined. del Piemonte, Suppl., 1868. [5.]
—— Sigilli ital. illust., 1870. [9.]
Promis (V.) Ambasciata di C. F. Manfredi di Luserna a Praga nel 1604, 1877. [16.]
—— Brevi sceni s. vita &c. del p. G. Colombo, Barnabita, 1884. [23.]
—— Cento lettere conc. la storia del Piemonte, 1544–92; ed. V. P., 1870. [9.]
—— Cronachette astesi [*Latin*]; ed. V. P., 1870. [9.]
—— Due inventari del sec. 17; ed. V. P., 1880. [19.]
—— Lettere di illust. Italiani; ed. V. P., 1870. [11.]
—— Monete di zecche ital. ined. o corr., Mem. 4, 1883. [21.]
—— Sigilli ital., 1874. [15.]
—— Su un soffitto ant. nel palazzo di S. Giovanni in Torino, 1880. [19.]
—— Tasse per rifiuto a diverse cariche n. Repubb. Fiorentina n. sec. 15, 1877. [16.]
Provana di Collegno (L.) Donazione di Teutcario, ossia Cumiana, sec. 9 al 15, 1885. [24.]
Provana di Collegno (S.) Notizie e doc. d'alcune Certose d. Piemonte, 2v, 1895–1901. [32, 37.]
Pugliese (S.) Condiz. econ. & finanz. d. Lombardia (1700–50), 1924. [52.]
Regis (P.) Piverone borgo franco (1202–1379), 1906. [42.]
Ricotti (E.) Breve commem. d. c. F. Sclopis, 1879. [18.]
Rivoli. Mem. di un terrazzano di R., 1535–86, 1865. [6.]
Roberti (G.) B. Patono di Meirano (1763–1830) &c., 1905. [41.]
—— Il Cittadino Ranza, 1892. [29.]
Robolotti (F.) Pergamene e casi di Cremona avanti il mille, 1862. [1.]
Rondolino (F.) P. Bello, sua vita e suoi scritti, 1890. [28.]
Rossi (G.) Doc. ined. rig. la chiesa di Ventimiglia, 1906. [42.]
—— Glossario medioevale ligure, 1898. [35.]
—— Glossario medioevale ligure: app., 1909. [44.]
—— I Grimaldi in Ventimiglia, 1900. [36.]
—— Maria Luigia Gabriella di Savoia &c. in Nizza, nel sett. 1701, 1895. [33.]

Regia Deputazione di Storia Patria [*continued*].
Miscellanea [*continued*].
Rossi (G.) Sopra un poemetto sul preteso diritto cosciatico [*by A. Panizzi*], 1906. [42.]
—— Sulla fondaz. di Airole, 1868. [5.]
—— La Valle di Diano (Liguria), 1902. [38.]
Sala (A.) La milizia &c. d. Spagnuoli n. stato di Milano, sec. 16: doc., 1862. [1.]
Saluzzo di Castellar (G. A.) Memoriale, 1482–1528, 1869. [8.]
San Giorgio (B.) Testamento, 1885. [24.]
Sant' Ambrogio (D.) Priorato cluniac. di S. Pietro di Castelletto, 1909. [44.]
Saraceno (F.) Doc. ined. del regno di Lodovico, duca di Savoia, 1874. [15.]
—— Nota sopra un ms. fals. attrib. a G. M. Pingon, 1887. [25.]
—— Regesto dei principi di casa d'Acaja, 1295–1418, 1882. [20.]
Sauli (D.) Autobiografia; ed. G. P. Lambertenghi, 1878. [17.]
Savio (F.) I dittici del canone ambros. e del canon rom., 1906. [42.]
—— Il monastero di S. Teofredo di Cervere ed il culto di S. T., 1896. [34.]
—— I primi conti di Savoia, 1887. [26.]
Scaglia (F. G.), *conte di Verrua*. Avvertimenti polit. per entrare in corte—5 dispacci s. quest. d. marchesata di Saluzzo, 1862. [1.]
Sclopis (*il c*. F.) Di alcuni diplomatici piemont., 1887. [25.]
Segre (A.) D. Carutti di Cantogno, 1913. [47.]
—— Doc. di storia sabauda, 1510–36, 1903. [39.]
—— Reg. di lettere d. card. E. Gonzaga (1535–36), 1913. [47.]
Seregni (G.) Del luogo di Arosio e de' suoi statuti nei sec. 12–13 &c., 1902. [38.]
Sforza (C.) Un missionario piemont. in Cina [A. Vagnoni], 1906. [42.]
Sforza (G.) Antenati di Nap. I in Lunigiana, 1915. [48.]
—— Distruz. di Luni n. leggenda &c., 1922. [50.]
—— Princ. Eugenio Fr. di Savoia &c., 1909. [44.]
Silva (G. A.) Relaz. dell' ingresso d. Infanta Caterina d'Austria in Torino, 1585, 1874. [15.]
Sommi-Picenardi (G.) Tentativo fatto dai Francesi per impadronirsi del Castello di Cremona nel 1537, 1885. [24.]
Sopetto (E.) Margherita di Savoia, 1295–1313, 1907. [43.]
Spata (G.) Diplomi greci ined. [*Gr. & Ital.*], 2s, 1870–71. [9, 12.]
Spotorno (G. B.) Illust. di un ant. martirologio ventimig. &c., 1868. [5.]
Staglieno (M.) Due doc. di Tedisio, vescovo di Torino, 1300–19, 1902. [38.]
Strickland (J.), *S.J.* Ricerche stor. sopra il B. Bonifacio di Savoia, arcivesco di Cantorbery, 1207–70, 1895. [32.]
Telluccini (A.) La real chiesa di Soperga, 1912. [46.]
—— Translaz. d. salme di 2 psse. di Savoia, 1909. [44.]
—— Viaggio di ritorno d. Sicilia d. Vittorio Amedeo II, 1910. [45.]
Terraneo (G. T.) Dei primi conti Savoia &c., 1877. [16.]
Tiraboschi (G.) Carmen saphicum de laud. Bergom. &c., 1865. [6.]
Torelli (P.) Patti d. liberaz. dell' arcivescovo C. di Magonza, 1909. [44.]
[Torino.] Diario dell' assedio di T. del 1640 di anon. contemp., 1885. [24.]
Turletti (C.) La rivol. del 1797 in Fossano e Racconigi e la sollevaz. d. truppa francese in Torino, 1896. [34.]
Vaccarone (L.) Bianca M. di Challant e il suo corredo, 1898. [35.]
—— Emanuele Filiberto, pr. di Piemonte, alla Corte Cesarea di Carlo V imp. (1545–51), 1900. [36.]
Valle (D.) P. Monod &c., 1910. [45.]
Vannutelli (L.) Casa di Savoia e l'ord. d. Giarrettiera, 1910. [45.]
Varatella. Chron. vet. monast. S. Petri de V. &c., 1870. [11.]
Vassalli-Eandi (A. M.) Notice abr. de la vie & des écrits de L. Langrange, 1871. [12.]
Vassallo (C.) F. Maramaldo e gli Agostiniani in Asti, 1890. [28.]
Vayra (P.) Un anno di vita pubbl. del comune di Asti (1441), 1889. [27.]
—— Lettere e arti alla corte di Savoia nel sec. 15: inventari dei castelli di Ciamberi, di Torino e di Ponte d'Ain, 1497–98, 1884. [23.]
Vesme (A.) Sull' acquisto fatto da Carlo Eman. III, re di Sardegna, d. quadreria d. Pr. Eugenio di Savoia, 1887. [25.]
—— Torquato Tasso e il Piemonte, 1889. [27.]
—— Van Dyck, peintre de portr. des princes de Savoie, 1885. [24.]
Victor Amadeus II, *k. of Sardinia*. Lettere a G. M., conte di Morozzo, ambasc. a Madrid, 1713–17, 1887. [26.]
—— I primi atti costit. dell' augusta casa di Savoia ordin. in Palermo . . . V. A. regnante; ric. G. Spata, 1870. [10.]
Vidari (G.) Le carte stor. di Pavia, 1889. [27.]
Vignati (C.) Commem. di F. Robolotti, 1887. [25.]
Villafranca Piemonte. Statuti (1384) &c., 1918. [49.]
Visconti (B.), *d. of Milan*. Trattato fra B. V., il conte Ant. di Montefeltro, la Repubb. di Firenze, e le comunità d'Urbino e Cagli, 1 febb. 1375, 1884. [23.]
Vivanet (F.) La Sardegna n. archivi &c. d. Spagna, 1909. [44.]
Vuij (J.) Adémar Fabri, prince-évêque de Genève, 1889. [27.]
Zeno (G.) Relaz. d. Z. G., ambasc. straord. d. Repubb. Veneta a Ladislao VII, re di Polonia, nel 1638, 1894. [31.]
Zucchi (M.) Delle orig. d. nome de Sannazzaro de' Burgondi, 1906. [42.]
—— Lomello (476–1796), 1904. [40.]
—— Titolo di princ. di Piemonte, 1912. [46.]

Regia Deputazione sovra gli Studi di Storia Patria per le Antiche Provincie e la Lombardia. Biblioteca di storia ital. recente, 1800–70. v5–12. la8°. Torino. 1913–28
Charles Albert, *king of Sardinia &c.* Lettere al Cav. L. B. di Barbania, 1926. [12.]
Degli Alberti (M.) Polit estera del Piemonte secondo il carteggio diplomat. d. Conte di Sambuy, 3t, 1913–19. [5–7.]
Frati (C.) Ricordi di prigionia &c. di G. Rasori, 1921. [9.]
Gallavresi (G.) &c. Le Maréchal Sallier de La Tour: mém. & lettres, p1, 1917. [8.]
Lemmi (F.) &c., *edd.* La rivol. piemontese, 1821, 1923. [11.]
Passamonti (E.) C. Balbo e la rivol. d. 1821 in Piem., 1926. [12.]
Prato (G.) Fatti e dottrine econ. alla vigilia d. 1848 &c., 1921. [9.]
Saluzzo (A. di). Carlo Alberto d. restaur. all' avvenimento al trono, 1926. [12.]
Segre (A.) Il primo anno d. min. Vallesa (1814–15), 1928. [10.]
Sforza (G.) Costit. napoletana d. 1848 &c., 1921. [9.]

Regia Deputazione Toscana, *see* DOCUMENTI. D. di storia ital., v11, 13, 1899–1916.

Régiments (Les) de gardes d'honneur, 1813–14. Notes & doc. 8°. 1894

Reginald (Antonin), *formerly Ravaille.* De mente S. Concilii Trident. circa gratiam efficacem. Acc. Animadv. in 25 propos. L. Molinae autore J. Le Bossu & Epistolae Petri Soto, R. Tapperi, L. J. Ravestein de gratiae & liberi arbitrii concordia. fol. Antverpiae. 1706
Doctrinae T. Aquinatis tria principia &c. s8°. Tolosae. 1670

Reginaldus (Gulielmus), *see* RAINOLDS (W.)

Reginaldus (Publius Valerius), *Jesuit.*
De prudentia & caeteris in confessario requisitis tractatus. ed. 2ª corr. s8°. Coloniae Agrippinae. 1622

Regino, *Prumiensis.* Chronicon cum cont. Treverensi [*by* Adalbert, *abp. of Magdeburg*]. Rec. F. Kurze. [Script. rerum Germ. in usum schol. ex Mon.-Germ. Hist. recusi]. 8°. Hannoverae. 1890
R. P. de disciplina eccl. veterum præsertim Germanorum, libri duo. Opera &c. J. Hildebrandi. s4°. Helmæstadi. 1659
see ECOLE (L') des Chartes. Bibl., t81, L'œuvre canonique de R., 1920.

Regis (Léon). Le grande pénitence, comédie, *see* ŒUVRES libres, 69, 1927.
—— **& F. de Veynes.** Bastos le hardi: comédie. [Répert. du vieux-colombier]. 4e éd. s8°. [1923]

Regis (Pietro). Piverone borgo franco (1202–1379), *see* REGIA DEPUT. Miscellanea, t42, 1906.

Régis de Trobriand (*cte.*), *see* TROBRIAND (P.-R.-D. DE KEREDERN, *comte* DE).

Regismanset (Charles).
Couronné par l'Académie Goncourt. Roman. s8°. [1924]
see CARIO (L.) & C. R. La pensée franç., 1921.

Registrar-General of Births, Deaths & Marriages. Lists of non-parochial registers & records in custody of the R.-G. fol. 1841

Regius (Urbanus), *see* RHEGIUS (U.)

Regling (Kurt Ludwig).
Die antike Münze als Kunstwerk. la8°. 1924

Regnard (Jean François). Les folies amoureuses, *see* THÉÂTRE choisi du 18e s., t1, 1914.
The residuary legatee; tr., *see* ALDINGTON (R.) Fr. comedies of 18th c., 1923.

Regnault (*Général*).
La conquête d'Athènes, juin-juil. 1917. 2e éd. 8°. 1920

Regnault-Warin (Jean Baptiste J. I. P.) Cinq mois de l'hist. de France ou fin de la vie polit. de Napoléon. 8°. 1815
Hist. du Gén. Lafayette en Amérique, préc. d'une notice sur sa vie. 8°. 1832

***Regni** Chinensis descriptio &c., 1639, *see* TRIGAULT (N.)

Regnier (Claude), *1718–90.* Tractatus de eccl. Christi, *see* MIGNE (J. P.), *ed.* Theol. cursus, t4, 1859.

Regnier (Henri de), *b. 1864.*
L'Altana ou la vie vénitienne, 1899–1924. 2e éd. 2v. s8°. 1928
Les bonheurs perdus. 11e éd. s8°. 1924
„ „ [Livre mod. illust.] 8°. 1925
Le divertissement provincial. s8°. [1925]
La double maîtresse. 42e éd. s8°. 1925
L'entrevue. Roman. 8°. 1925
L'escapade. 9e éd. s8°. 1926
L'escapade. 13e éd. s8°. 1926
Esquisses vénitiennes. 9e éd., rev. & augm. s8°. 1920
La pécheresse. 9e éd. s8°. 1920
„ „ 22e éd. s8°. 1920
Proses datées. 9e éd. s8°. 1925
Les rencontres de M. de Bréot. 18e éd. s8°. 1922
Vestigia flammæ. Poémes. 4e éd. s8°. 1921
„ „ 7e éd. s8°. 1921
see HONNERT (R.) H. de R. & s. œuvre, 1923.

Regnier de la Planche (Louis). Hist. de l'estat de France, 1559–60—Livres des marchands, *see* BUCHON (J. A. C.) Choix de chron., 1884.

Regulae [REGULE]. Regule ad cognoscendum quo-rūq; nominū genera comodissie. s4°. *n.p. n.d.* [c. 1490 ?]
20 leaves; A⁸, BC⁶.
Regule grãmaticales antiquorum cum earūdem declaratiõibus & multis argumẽtis positis circa unamquãq; regulam in speciali. 8°. Argentine, [*Mathias Hüpfüff*]. 1502
A fragm. of 18 leaves, viz. sig. A, E, F in sixes, sig. B, C, D are missing, & all after F6.
Regulae Soc. Jesu, 1604, *see* JESUITS.

Regulations. R. & instructions rel. to H.M.'s service at sea. 5th ed., 1745, *see* NAVY.

Regulus (Marcus Atilius), *see* RAPPOLT (G. C.) Diss. de R. in legatione ad Romanos &c., 1684.

Reh (Hans). Zur mittelalterl. Kulturgesch.: Staat u. Kirche im Ma. s8°. Würzburg. 1920

***Rehearsal** (The) transpros'd, 1672, *see* MARVELL (A.)

Rehm (Albert). *Works in* KÖNIGL. AKAD. D. WISS. ZU MÜNCHEN. Phil. Kl., Sitz.
Griech. Windrosen, 1916.
Neue Beitr. z. Kenntnis d. ant. Wasseruhren, 1920.
Das 7. Buch d. Naturales Quaestiones d. Seneca u. d. Kometentheorie d. Poseidonios, 1921.
Zur Chronologie d. miles. Inschr. d. 2. Jhdts. v. Chr., 1923.

Rehm (Hermann Siegfried). Das Buch d. Marionetten. Beitr. z. Gesch. d. Theaters aller Völker. la8°. [1905]
Deutsches Lachen: 700 Jahre deut. Humordichtung zusammengetragen v. R. 3. A. 4°. [1920]

Rehm (Pierre Louis). De Bergen à Cythère, nouvelle, *see* ŒUVRES LIBRES, 59, 1926.

Rehtmeier (Philipp Julius) [RETHMEIER]. De oblatis eucharisticis quae hostiae vocari solent. Praes. J. A. Schmidio. [P437]. s4°. Helmstadii. [1702]

Reich (Emil), *historical writer.*
Handbook of geography. re-issued. 8°. 1912

Reich (Nathaniel). Papyri jurist. Inhalts in hierat. u. demot. Schr. aus d. Brit. Mus., 1, Text, Transcr. u. Übers. mit Komm., 1914, *see* KAIS. AKAD. D. W. ZU WIEN. Denkschr., B55, 1917.

Reichard (Heinrich Aug. Ottokar). An itinerary of France & Belgium. n. ed. corr. s8°. 1822

Reiche (Fritz). The quantum theory. Tr. H. S. Hatfield & H. L. Brose. 8°. [1922]

Reichel (Johann Gottlob). Vitam, fata & scripta V. Weigelii praes. J. Z. Hilligero submittit resp. J. G. R. [P599]. s4°. Wittenbergae. [1721]

Reichel (Oswald Joseph).
The canon law of church institutions. v1. 8°. 1922

Reichelt (Hans), *see* GRUNDRISS d. indogerm. Sprach- u. Altertumskunde, Abt. 2, B4ii, Iranisch, v. H. R., 1927.

Reichelt (Julius). Astronomia Hebraeorum. Praes. B. Scheidio. [P427]. s4°. Argentorati. 1660

Reichelt (Karl Ludvig). Truth & tradition in Chinese Buddhism. Tr. K. van Wagenen Bugge. 8°. Shanghai. 1927

Reichenau. Kultur d. Abtei R., 2 Halbb., 1925, *see* BEYERLE (K.), *ed.*

Reichenauer (Constantin) *v. Reichenau.* Adel v. Siebenbürgen; begonnen v. C. R. &c., *see* SIBMACHER (J.), *ed.* Wappenbuch B4xii, 1898.

Reichenbach (Giulio). Un gentiluomo poeta del quattrocento: M. A. Boiardo. pl. s8°. Ferrara. [1923]

Reichensperger (August).
Verm. Schriften ü. christl. Kunst. 8°. L. 1856

Reichental (Ulrich v.), *see* CONSTANCE, *Council of.* Concilium Constant., 1414–18, *facs. of drawings illust. R.'s Chron.*, 1874.

Reichmann (Jacob). De Sibyllis, disput. J. R. & P. P Röberus. [P1035]. s4°. [Witteberg]. 165[illegible]

Reichs-Marine-Amt, *see* GERMANY: GOVT. PUBL.

Reichstadt (Napoléon F. C. J., *duc de*), *1811–32.*
see FLEISCHMANN (H.) Le Roi de Rome & les femmes, 1910
„ MONTBEL (*le b.* G. I.) Le Duc de R., 1832.

Reichstag, *see* GERMANY.

Reichsverkehrsministerium, *see* GERMANY: GOVT. PUBL.

Reichs-Versicherungsamt. *Gesch. u. Wirkungskreis d. R.-V Verm. Sonderdruck aus d. Hdbch. d. Unfallversich.? 3. A. B3. Hrsg. v. Mitgliedern d. R.-V. la8°. L. 191[illegible]

Reichwein (Adolf). China & Europe: intellectual &c. contacts in 18th c. [Tr. J. C. Powell]. 8°. 192[illegible]

Reid (Clement), *F.G.S.*
The works below are Mems. of Geol. Survey.
Geol. of co. around Bognor. 8°. 1897
Geol. of co. around Cromer, w. notes by H. B. Woodward. 8°. 1882
Geol. of co. around Dorchester. 8°. 1899
Geol. of co. around Eastbourne. 8°. 1898
Geol. of co. around Mevagissey, w. petrolog. contrib. by J. J. H. Teall. 8°. 1907
Geol. of co. around Ringwood, w. contrib. by F. J. Bennett &c. 8°. 1902
Geol. of co. around Salisbury, w. contrib. by H. B. Woodward &c. 8°. 1903
Geol. of co. around Southampton, w. contrib. by W. Whitaker. 8°. 1902
Geol. of co. near Chichester, w. contrib. by G. W. Lamplugh & A. J. Jukes-Browne. 8°. 1903
Geol. of Holderness & adj. parts of Yorks. & Lincs. 8°. 1885
see Fox-Strangways (C. E.), C. R. & G. Barrow. Geol. of Eskdale &c., 1885.
„ Whitaker (W.) & C. R. Water-supply of Sussex &c., 1899.
——, G. Barrow &c. Geol. of Dartmoor, w. contribs. by J. S. Flett. 8°. 1912
——, —— &c. Geol. of the co. around Tavistock & Launceston. [*b. w. h.* Geol. of Dartmoor, 1912]. 8°. 1911
——, —— & H. Dewey. Geol. of the co. around Padstow & Camelford, w. contribs. by J. S. Flett &c. [*b. w. h.* Geol. of Dartmoor, 1912]. 8°. 1910
—— & J. S. Flett. Geol. of the Land's End distr., w. contribs. by B. S. N. Wilkinson &c. Mining app. by D. A. MacAlister. 8°. 1907
—— & J. B. Scrivenor. The geology of the co. near Newquay, w. contribs. by J. S. Flett &c. [*b. w.* Reid (C.) Geol. of Land's End, 1907]. 8°. 1906
Reid (Eleanor). Marrying Madeleine. s8°. [1922]
Reid (*Mrs.* **Eleanor Mary**), *see* Brit. Mus. of Nat. Hist.: Geology. Cainozoic plants in Dept. of G., v1, Bembridge flora; by E. M. R. &c., 1926.
Reid (Forrest). Apostate. 8°. [1926]
Reid (*Sir* **George Archdall O'Brien**). Prevention of venereal disease. Intr. ch. by Sir H. B. Donkin. s8°. [1920]
Reid (Gilbert), *A.M., D.D.* China, captive or free. 8°. [1922]
Reid (John), *Gardener.* The Scots gard'ner, w. The gard'ners kalendar (1683). Ed. A. H. Hyatt; w. apprec. by the Earl of Rosebery. s8°. 1907
Reid (John), *of Glasgow.* Bibliotheca Scoto-Celtica; acc. of books pr. in the Gaelic lang. 8°. Glasgow. 1832
Reid (Louis Arnaud).
Knowledge & truth: an epistemolog. essay. 8°. 1923
Reid (Rachel R.), *D.Lit.*
The King's Council in the North. 8°. 1921
Polit. influence of " the North parts " under the later Tudors, *see* Pollard (A. F.) Tudor studies, 1924.
Reid (Whitelaw). Gt. Brit. & the U.S. need each other. Addr. [P2702]. la8°. 1907
Our foremost friend in Gt. Brit. Addr., in mem. of E. Burke. [P2702]. la8°. 1908
The " practical side " of Amer. educ.: J. Bright & the Civil War. Addr. [P2702]. la8°. 1907
Thackeray in America. Addr. [Fr. The Book Monthly, Dec. 1907. P2702]. la8°. [1907]
see Cortissoz (R.) The life of W. R., 2v, 1921.
Reid-Robertson, *Barons, of Straloch, see* Robertson (J.) Barons R.-R., 1887.
Reiff (Jakob Friedrich). Ueber e. wicht. Punkte in d. Philos. [P2471]. 8°. Tübingen. 1843
Reiffenberg (Friedrich v.), *Jesuit* [*ps.* Sarpedonius (Mirtisbus)]. De divina gratia &c., *see* Maffei (*il march* F. S.) Hist. theolog., 1756.
M. Sarpedonii de vera Atticorum pronunciatione diss. [P2648]. 8°. Romae. 1750
Reiffenstuel (Anacletus). De beneficiis eccl., jure patronatus &c.—De immunitate eccl., *see* Migne (J. P.), *ed.* Theol. cursus, t18, 1862.
Reihing (Jacob), *Jesuit.* Excubiae angelicae civit. sanctae pro defensione 12 fundamentorum cathol. &c. s4°. Neoburgi ad Danubium. 1617
see Wolfgang William, *count Palatine of Neuburg.* Muri civitatis sanctae &c., explicata à J. R., 1615.
Reilly (Charles Herbert).
Some Liverpool streets & buildings in 1921. 8°. Liv'l. 1921
Reilly (William). A mem. of the ministerial life of the Rev. Gideon Ouseley. s8°. 1847

Reimann (Jacob Friedrich), *see* Reimmann (J. F.)
Reimar, *der Alte, see* Reinmar *von Hagenau.*
Reimbold (Diedericus). De Coptorum sacramentis baptismi atque Eucharistiae. [P427]. s4°. [Lipsiae. 1736]
Reimmann (Jacob Friedrich). Accessiones uberiores ad Catal. bibl. theologiae, a sect. 1 ad sect. 6. Ed. a J. W. Reimmanno. s8°. Brunsvigae. 1747
Hist. liter. Babyloniorum & Sinensium. [Hist. philos. Sin. *w. sep. tp. & pagin.*] s8°. Brunsvigae. 1741
Hist. univ. atheismi & atheorum apud Judaeos, Ethnicos, Christianos & Muhamedanos. Acc. Idea compend. theol. &c. s8°. Hildesiae. 1725
Introd. in hist. vocabul. ling. Latinae &c. s8°. Halae Magdeb. 1718
Reims (*l'archeveque duc de*), *1668–1710, see* Le Tellier (C. M.)
Rein (Adolf), *see* Geschichte d. aussereurop. Staaten. America: der Kampf Westeuropas um Nordamer., 15.–16. Jhdt. v. A. R., 1925.
Rein (Gabriel).
De loco, quo, arma Tavastis illaturus, appulerit Birgerus dux, disq. Resp. W. Boxström. 8°. Helsingforsiae. [1833]
Disquis. annum quo verbum crucis contra Carelios praedicari jusserit pontif. expos. Expos. G. R. & H. A. Mechelin & [p2], G. R. & J. G. Fabritius. [2p *in* 1v, *pagin. contin.*] s4°. Helsingforsiae. [1835]
Diss. de rerum Fennic. scriptoribus ante cond. acad. Aboensem &c. Resp. M. Akiander [J. H. Keckman; B. W. Brouou; H. J. Hjorth. *4tp. pagin. contin.*] s4°. Aboae. [1828]
Periculum hist. de Curonibus, saec. 12 & 13 Fenniam infestantibus. [4p *in* 1v., *pagin. contin.*] 8°. Helsingforsiae. [1829]
Rein (Gustav Kurt).
Abessinien. Eine Landeskunde. B2, 3. la8°. 1919–20
Rein (Joseph Friederich). Das gesamte Augspurg. Evangel. Ministerium in Bildern u. Schriften v. d. Reformation Lutheri bis auf 1748. [*Foll. by* Eigentl. Abbildung derer sowohl Alt- als Neuen Evangel. Kirchen in Augspurg &c.] s4°. [Augspurg]. 1748–49
Reinach (Adolphe J.) Textes grecs & lat. rel. à l'hist. de la peinture anc.; publ., tr. & comm. par A. R., t1, 1920, *see* Milliet (P.) Recueil M., 1920.
see Hellénisation. L'h. du monde ant.; leçons faites à l'Ecole des Hautes Et. Soc. par A. R. &c., 1914.
Reinach (Joseph). L'année de la paix. s8°. 1920
Reinach (Salomon).
Bibliog. de S. R., 1874–1903. [P2790]. la8°. Angers. 1903
„ „ 1874–1922. *&* Suppl. [*in* 1v]. la8°. [Angers]. 1922–27
Cornélie, ou le latin sans pleurs. 3e éd. rév. s8°. 1920
Cultes, mythes & religions. t5. 8°. 1923
2 nouv. statues d'Aphrodite, *see* Acad. des Inscr. &c. Fond. Piot. Mons., 1924.
Ephémérides d'Alesia: hist., fouilles, &c. la8°. 1925
Eulalie, ou le grec sans larmes. 4e éd. s8°. 1920
Glozel: la découv., la controv. &c. 5e éd. s8°. 1928
Lettres à Zoé sur l'hist. des philos. 3[t]. s8°. [1926]
Monuments nouv. de l'art antique. t1, 2. la8°. [1924–25]
Répertoire de la statuaire grecque & romaine. t5, v1, 2. s8°. 1924
Répertoire de peintures grec. & rom. la8°. 1922
Répertoire de peintures, 1280–1580. t4–6. s8°. 1918–23
Représ. du galop dans l'art anc. & mod. [n. éd. augm.] la8°. 1925
Short hist. of Xty. [Tr.] F. Simmonds. 8°. 1922
Sidonie, ou le français sans peine. s8°. 1921
Statuette en bronze trouvée en 1913 à Bavai (Nord), *see* Acad. des Inscr. Fond. Piot. Mons. &c., t28, 1925–26.
Strongylion. [*Extr.* f. Revue archéol., s4, t3. P2790]. la8°. [1904]
Xerxès et l'Hellespont. [*Extr. f.* Revue archéol., s4, t6; P2790]. la8°. 1905
see Pottier (E.) & S. R. La nécropole de Myrina, 2t, 1888.
„ Tunisie. Atlas archéolog.; texte rédigé par S. R. &c., 1893–1913.
Reinach (Théodore). Un conte babylonien dans la litt. juive. Le roman d'Akhikhar. [Extr. de la Revue des ét. juives, 1899. P2813]. 8°. 1899
Le judaïsme prophétique & les espérances actuelles de l'humanité. [*Extr. f.* Rev. des ét. juives, t70, 1920. P2497]. la8°. 1920
see Hellénisation. L'h. du monde ant., par T. R. &c., 1914.
„ Waddington (W. H.) Rec. gén. d. monnaies grecques d'Asie mineure, cont. par T. R. &c., 2e éd., t1i, 1925.
Reinach Foussemagne (*Ctsse.* **H. de**). Charlotte de Belgique, Impératrice du Mexique. Préf. de P. de La Gorce. 8°. [1925]
Une fidèle: la marquise de Lâge de Volude, 1764–1842, d'ap. des docs. inéd. 8°. 1908
Reinacher (Eduard). Die Hochzeit d. Todes. Erzählungen u. Verse. s8°. St. 1921

Reincking (Theodor), *see* Reinking (T.)

Reindl (Johann Nepomuk). Die Altkatholiken od. Döllinger's Anhang aus Klerus u. Volk. [P2694]. 8°. Amberg. 1872

Reineccius (Christianus). Concordia Germanico-Latina, ad optima &c. exemplaria edita. Cum approb. 3 facultatum theolog. Acad. Lips. Witteberg. & Rostochiens. Studio C. R. [*Lat. & Germ.*] 8°. Lipsiae. 1735

Reineccius (Jacobus) [Reneccius (J.)] Clavis sacrosanctae theologiae duobus libris &c. Acc. libri duo theologiae &c. [*w. sep. pagin.*] s4°. Lubecae. 1621

Reineck (Reinerus), *ed., see* Chronicon Hierosolymitanum, 1584.

Reinecke (Leopold). Mineral deposits betw. Lillooet & Prince George, B.C. [Canada: Geol. Survey. P2513]. 8°. Ottawa. 1920

Road materials in the vicinity of Regina, Saskatchewan. [Canada: Geol. Survey. P2513]. 8°. Ottawa. 1919

Reiner (Julius).

Hugo Grotius u. d. Weltschiedsgericht. s8°. 1922

Reiners (Heribert). Das Gebetbuch d. Herzogin Sibylla v. Cleve, *see* München. Miniaturen; hrsg. G. Leidinger, H7, 1924.

Der Kölner Malerschule. la8°. Bonn. 1925

Reinerth (Hans).

Pfahlbauten am Bodensee. 8°. Augsburg. 1922

Reinhard (Conrad Fridericus). Comment. in qua fabula de Ludovici Thuringiae comitis ex arce Gibichensteinensi saltu refellitur. D. F. Wideburg rec. &c. [P428]. s4°. Halae. Magdeb. 1737

Reinhard (Franz Volkmar). Epitome theol. Xtianae e. F. V. R. acroasibus academ. descr., obs. aucta a J. G. C. Hoepfnero. ed. 2ª. s8°. Lipsiae. 1819

Opuscula academica. 2v. 8°. Lipsiae. 1808–9

Reinhard (J. Müller-), *see* Müller-Reinhard (J.)

Reinhard (Lorenz). Comm. de vita &c. J. Jonae & M. Lutheri. [*Foll. by* Unumstössl. Beweis dass P. Melanchthon mit J. Jona weg. d. Confess. sich zu Augspurg unterredet &c., *w. sep. tp. &c.*] [*b. w.* Fabricius (J. A.) Centifolium, 1728–30; *a. c. b. w.* Herrnschmid (J. D.) Comm. de vita Lutheri, 1742]. s8°. Altenburgi. 1731

Instit. styli Latini. Acc. orationes duae &c. s8°. Erfurti. 1728

Reinhard (Luise). Die Anakoluthe bei Platon, *see* Kiessling (A.) & U. v. W.-M. Philolog. Untersuch., H25, 1920.

Reinhard (Michael Heinrich), *the elder.* Diss. qua liturgia eccl. Evangel. adv. Renaudotii object. vindicatur. Præs. J. G. Jano. [P2639]. s4°. Vitembergae. [1721]

Reinhardt (Carl). Poseidonios. la8°. München. 1921

Reinheimer (Hermann).

Evolution at the crossways. s8°. [1924]

Reinick (Robert). Märchen-, Lieder- u. Geschichtenbuch. 5ᵉ A. 8°. Bielefeld. 1880

see Rethel (A.) Auch e. Todtentanz, 1848; Text v. R. R., 1925.

Reinisch (Simon Leo). Das persönl. Fürwort u. d. Verbalflexion in d. chamito-semit. Spr. [Kaiserl. Akad. der Wissen.] 8°. Wien. 1909

Reinke (Georg). Frankreich u. Papst Johann XXIII. Diss. [P2726]. 8°. Münster. 1900

Reinkens (Joseph Hubert), *bp. of the Old Catholics.*

Die päpstl. Dekrete v. 18. Juli 1870. 6H *in* 1v [H2 *wanting*]. s8°. Münster. 1871

Über päpstl. Unfehlbarkeit, *see* Katholisch. Stimmen aus d. K. Kirche, B2, 1870.

see Bernard, *Saint, abbot of Clairvaux.* Papst u. Papstthum: Übers. u. Erläut. s. Schr. " De consideratione," v. J. H. R., 1870.

Reinking (Theodor) [Reincking]. Das Leben d. Seelen im Tode, *see* Disquisitiones theol. de anima &c., 2p, 1730.

„ „ *a. ed., see* Fasciculus rar. & curios. scr., 1692.

Reinmar *von Hagenau* [Reimar *der Alte*], *d. 1215.* Lieder [hrsg.] C. v. Kraus, 3T, 1919, *see* Königl. Akad. d. W. zu M nchen. Abhdlgn., B30, 1920.

Reinoldius (Joannes), *canon of Exeter.* Hist. Graec. & Latin. literarum diss. Acc. Ἡροδότος ὁ Ἁλικαρνασσεὺς περὶ Ὁμήρου γεν σιος καὶ ἡλικίης, καὶ βιοτῆς. [Coll. cum ms. cod. Bibl. Bodl. Interp. C. Heresbachio, recogn. H. Stephano. *Gr. & Lat. w. sep. pagin.*] 4°. Etonae. 1752

Reinsberg-Düringsfeld (Otto, *Frhr.* **v.)** Das festliche Jahr. In Sitten &c. d. german. Völker. s8°. L. 1863

Reinsch (Paul Samuel).

An Amer. diplomat in China. 8°. [1922]

Reisch (Emil), *see* Dörpfeld (W.) & E. R. Das griech. Theater, 1896.

Reiser (Anton). Vindiciae evangelico-Thomisticae, quibus T. de Aquino, contra T. Leonhardi iteratò exhibetur. Subj. Append. Anti-Thomistica contra A. Zennerum. s4°. Ulmae. 1669

Reiske (Justus Christoph). Annulum pastoralem, praes. J. A. Schmidt, diss. delin. voluit J. C. R. [P2637]. s4°. Helmstadii. 1705

Reiskius (Joannes). Diss. de scr. Rom. Judaicam circa hist. falsis narratiunculis, 1691, *see* Schläger (C. J.) Diss. fasc. 1, 1742.

Progr. quo nimbum divinum comm., 1683, *see* Schläger (C. J.) Diss. fasc. novus, 1744.

Reisner (George Andrew) & A. C. Mace. The early dynastic cemeteries of Naga-ed-Dêr. [Univ. of California. Publ.: Egypt. arch., v2, 3 (Hearst Eg. Exped.)] 2p. fol. Leipzig. 1908–9

——, C. S. Fisher & D. G. Lyon. Harvard excav. at Samaria, 1908–10. [Harvard Semitic Ser.] 2v. fol. Camb. [Mass.] 1924

Reisner (M.)

Что такое советская власть? [P2459]. 8°. Москва. 1918

Reiss (R. A.) The comitadji question in S. Serbia. s8°. 1924

Reiter (Virginia), *see* Levi (C.) V. R., 1920.

Reithmayer (Eduard). Die Burg Aggstein an der Donau in Niederösterreich. la8°. Wien. 1911

Reitlinger (Henry Scipio).

Old master drawings: handbook. 4°. 1922

Reitperger (Stephanus) [P. F. Stephanus], *see* Conradus, *Schirensis.* Chron. Schir., a P. F. Stephano auctum, 1716.

Reitterer (Theodor).

Leben u. Werke Peter Pindars (J. Wolcot). 8°. Wien. 1900

Reitz (Johann Friedrich). De ambiguis, mediis & contrariis, sive de signific. verborum ac phrasium ambigua. s8°. Trajecti ad Rhenum. 1752

Reitzenstein (Richard). Alchemist. Lehrschr. u. Märchen bei d. Arabern, *see* Heliodorus. Carmina, 1923.

Des Athanasius Werk ü. d. Leben d. Antonius. [Sitz. d. Heidelberger Akad., 1914, Abh. 8]. 8°. Heidelberg. 1914

Das iran. Erlösungsmysterium. 8°. Bonn a. Rh. 1921

Reitzenstein (Sigismund Carl Johann v.), *1766–1847, see* Schnabel (F.) S. v. R., d. Begründer d. bad. Staates, 1927.

Reizen in Zuid-Afrika in de Hollandse tijd, d1–3, 1916–22, *see* Molsbergen (E. C. G.), *ed.*

Relacion.

*R. del auto partic. de fé de la Inquisit. de Sevilla, 1723, 1723, *see* Sevilla.

R. de los autos de fé Valladolid, Cordova y Zaragoza, 1723, *see* Valladolid.

R. del suceso, 1565 *& other naval reprints*, 1565–83, *see* Bauer Landauer (I.) F. de Benavides, 1921.

Relaciones. R. hist. de America, sig. 16, 1916, *see* Serrano y Sanz (M.), *ed.*

Reland (Adrian). Diss. de inscr. nummorum Samaritan. [*b. w. h.* Diss. misc. p. 1, 1706]. s8°. Amstelodami. 1702

Diss. de marmoribus Arabicis Puteolanis &c. [*b. w. h.* Diss. misc. p. 1, 1706]. s8°. Amstelodami. [1704]

Diss. miscell. pars prima [& tertia]. s8°. Trajecti ad Rhenum. 1706–8

***Relatio** nuperi itineris Jesuitar., 1619, *see* Jesuits.

Relation.

*Exact r. (An) of the persecut. &c. sustained by the Protest. of Killmare, 1869, *see* Orpen (R.)

*Full & exact r. of the duel betw. James, duke of Hamilton & Lord Mohun, 1713, *see* Hamilton (J. H., *4th duke of*).

*R.: Aller Fürnemmen u. gedenckwürdigen Historien in Teutschland &c. 1609 (*facs.*), *see* Freytag (G.) Bilder, B4, 1925.

*R. aus dem Vatican zu Rom. [P2468]. s4°. Londen [*sic*]. 1681

*R. de la grande Tartarie dressée sur les mém. orig. des suedois prisonniers en Siberie, 1737, *see* Tartarie.

*R. de la Louisianne, 1734, *see* Louisiana.

*R. des missions des évesques franç. aux royaumes de Siam, de la Cochinchine, de Camboye, & du Tonkin &c. 4p [*in* 1v. *pagin. cont.*] 8°. 1674

*R. fidèle &c. de l'arrest. de Mme., duchesse de Berry, 1832, *see* Guibourg (A.)

*R. (A) of the great &c. success of the Fleet &c. at Vigo under Ormond & Rooke, 1702. [*Single sheet, b. w.* London Gazette, Nov. 2, 1702, *& w.* Post man *after* No. 1046, Nov. 1702]. fol. *E. Jones.* 1702

*R. (A) of the voyage to Siam, by six Jesuits &c.; tr., 1688, *see* Tachard (G.)

Relazione. R. &c. s. porto di L., 1874, *see* LIDO.
*R. verid. d. modo che si tiene nel creare il Gastaldo grande de' Niccolotti pescatori &c. [P2835]. 8°. Venezia. 1762
***Religio** medici &c., 1652, *see* BROWNE (*Sir* T.)
Religion.
*Consultation (A) about r. &c., 1693, *see* CONSULTATION.
Education & r.: lect., 1924, *see* BURROUGHS (E. A.), *ed.*
*R. (La) des Jésuites, 1689, *see* JURIEU (P.)
*R. of nature delineated, 1726, *see* WOLLASTON (W.)
Religions of the Empire: a conference, 1924. Ed. W. L. Hare, w. intr. by Sir E. D. Ross. 8°. [1925]
Religionsgeschichtliche Versuche u. Vorarbeiten.
B16ii, 17i, ii, 18i, 19i–iii, 20i, ii. 8°. Giessen. 1919–26
see CASEL (O.) De philosophorum Graec. silentio mystico, 1919. [16ii.]
,, CLEMEN (C.) Die griech. u. latein. Nachrichten ü. d. pers. Relig., 1920. [17i.]
,, HELIODORUS. Carmina 4 ad fidem cod. Casselani, 1923. [19ii.]
,, MENSCHING (G.) Das heil. Schweigen, 1926. [20ii.]
,, OPPERMANN (H.) Zeus Panamaros, 1924. [19iii.]
,, REITZENSTEIN (R.) Alchemist. Lehrschr. u. Märchen bei d. Arabern, 1923. [19ii.]
,, SCHMITT (J.) Freiwill. Opfertod bei Euripides &c., 1921. [17ii.]
,, VORDEMFELDE (H.) Die german. Relig. in d. deut. Volksrechten, Halbb. 1, 1923. [18i.]
,, WILLIGER (E.) Hagios, 1922. [19i.]
,, WUNDERLICH (E.) Bedeut. d. roten Farbe im Kultus d. Griech. u. Römer, 1925. [20i.]
Religious. R. encyclopædia; based on Real-Encyklop. of Herzog, 3v, 1883–84, *see* SCHAFF (P.), *ed.*
R. lyrics of the 14th c., 1924, *see* BROWN (C.), *ed.*
Reliquary (The). New ser., v3–5. la8°. 1897–99
Rellini (Ugo). *Works in* REALE ACCAD. D. LINCEI. Mon. ant.
La caverna di Latrònico e il culto d. acque salut. nell' età d. bronzo, 1916. [24.]
Cavernette e ripari preist. nell' agro Falisco, 1920. [26.]
La grotta d. Felci a Capri, 1923. [29.]
Relly (James) & John Relly. Christian hymns &c. [2p *in* 1v, p1, by James R.; p2, by John R.] s8°. 1758
,, ,, ...s8°. 1777
Relly (John), *see* RELLY (JAMES) & J. R.
Relton (Herbert Maurice). The new Prayer Book: lect[s]. [*by var. a.*] Ed. H. M. R. s8°. [1927]
Some postulates of a Xtn. philos. s8°. 1925
Remacle (L.), *of Liège.* Dict. wallon-français.
2e éd. corr. & augm. 2t. 8°. Liège. [1857]
Remarkable.
*Lives of the most r. criminals, 3v, 1725, *see* LIVES.
R. trials & interesting mem. of criminals convicted at the Assizes &c., 2v, 1765, *see* TRIALS.
Remarks.
*R. conc. the encroachments on the Thames &c., 1771, *see* SHARP (G.)
*R. on Lord Curzon's speech on May 5, 1921 on ratific. of Hung. Peace treaty of the Trianon. By a Transylvanian lady teacher. [P2578]. 8°. 1921
*R. on the Essays on the principles of morality, &c., 1758, *see* EDWARDS (J.)
*R. upon a late pamph. entitl. A brief & full acc. of Tate's & Brady's new vers. of the Psalms. By a divine of the Ch. of E. [*b. w.* Phillips (J.) Daveidos, 1698]. s8°. 1699
*Some r. upon Sir J. Dalrymple's hist. coll., 1714, *see* GILLANE (J.)
Remarques.
*R. crit. s. le livre de M. Lestocq, 1714, *see* L'ETOILE (P. DE).
*R. d'un théologien sur le "Traité histor." &c. par Maimbourg, 1688, *see* BOILEAU (J.)
*R. sur la protestation des Jésuites &c., 1709, *see* LE GOBIEN (C.)
Rembert, *Saint, abp. of Hamburg & bp. of Bremen* [RIMBERTUS].
S. Anscharii vita gemina, una orat. prosa, scr. per S. R., altera metrica, ut putatur per Gualdonem & prioris vitae versio vetus Suecica quam. dedit S. Nicolaus, Lincop. episc.; cum P. Lambecii annot. Ed. C. Arrhenius. [*b. w.* Arrhenius (C.) Hist. Sueonum eccl., 1689]. s4°. Holmiae. 1677
Anskar, the apostle of the North, 801–865. Tr. f. Vita Anskarii by R., by C. H. Robinson. s8°. 1921
Vita Anskarii. Acc. Vita Rimberti. Rec. G. Waitz. [Scr. rerum Germ. in usum schol.] 8°. Hannoverae. 1884
Rembrandt, *the painter.*
*Rembrandt als Erzieher, von einem Deutschen, 1890, *see* VERBEHN (J.)
Rembrandt: wiedergefundene Gemälde, 1910–20: Hrsg. W. R. Valentiner. la8°. St. 1921
see BURLINGTON FINE ARTS CLUB. Etched work of R., w. intr. remarks, 1877.
,, ISRAELS (J.) R., 1909.
,, KRAMÁŘ (V.) Mariae Verkündigung v. R., 1926.

Rembrandt [*continued*].
see LUDWIG (E.) Kunst u. Schicksal (R. &c.), 1927.
,, MELDRUM (D. S.) R.'s paintings, w. essay on h. life & work, 1923.
see SIMMEL (G.) R.: e. kunstphilos. Versuch. 2e A., 1919.
,, VAN DYKE (J. C.) R. & h. school: crit. st., 1923.
Remedios (Mendes dos), *see* DOS REMEDIOS (M.)
***Remedy** (A) against superstition, 1667, *see* CROMPTON (W.)
***Remember** the Sabbath day, 1745?, *see* WESLEY (J.)
Remembrancer (The); or, Impartial repository &c.
[*another issue*]. v1. 8°. 1775
Remey (Charles Mason).
The Bahai revel. & reconstruction. s8°. [Chicago]. 1919
The peace of the world. s8°. [Chicago]. 1919
Twelve articles intr. to st. of the Baha'i teachings.
s8°. [Firenze. 1925]
The universal consciousness of the Bahá'i religion.
s8°. [Firenze]. 1925
Remezov (Semen). Приложеніе къ Чертежной книгѣ Сибири составл. Р. въ 1701. 8°. C.-П. 1882
Чертежная книга Сибири составл. &c. С. Р. въ 1701. [*Facs. reprod.* Изд. Арх. Комм.] atlas fol. C.-П. 1882
Reminiscences. *R. of a Chinese official: revel. of offic. life under the Manchus. Repr. f. the Peking Gazette &c.
la8°. Tientsin. 1922
*R. of school & army life, 1839–59, 1875, *see* BAYLEY (J. A.)
Remizov (Aleksei Mikhailovich).
Ахру, повѣсть. s8°. Берлинъ. 1922
Зга: волшебные рассказы. s8°. Прага. 1925
Огненная Россія. s8°. Ревель. [1921]
Шумы города. 8°. Ревель. [1921]
TRANSLATIONS.
The clock. Auth. tr. by J. Cournos. s8°. 1924
The fifth pestilence, w. The hist. of the tinkling cymbal &c. Tr. &c. A. Brown. s8°. 1927
Rémond (Georges). La route de l'Abbaï Noir: souvenirs d'Abyssinie. s8°. 1924
Remondini (Marcello), *see* DESIMONI (C.) Commem. di M. R., 1889.
Remonstrance.
*Dispassionate (A) r. of the nature &c. of the laws for the reduction of interest. [P2783]. 8°. 1751
*R. (A) of all good Protestants agst. deposing James II, 1689, *see* JAMES II.
*Très-humble r. à de Precipiano, 1695, *see* ARNAULD (A.)
Remonstrantes. Antapologià sive animadvers. in 16. priora capita Apologiae Remonstrantium, 1640, *see* JUNIUS (I.)
*Confessio sive declar. sentent. pastorum, qui in Belgio R. vocantur, 1622, *see* BELGIUM.
see HAGIENSIS. Scripta advers. collat. H., 1615.
Remos y Rubio (Juan J.)
Hist. de la lit. cubana. t1. s8°. Habana. 1925
Remsen (Ira). Inorganic chemistry. [5th ed.] 8°. [1898]
Intr. to study of compounds of carbon; or organic chemistry.
5th rev. s8°. Boston [Mass.] [1909]
Remy (Gabriel). Un précieux de province au 17e s.; René Le Pays. la8°. 1925
Renaissance. The coming r.; [*by var. wr.*], 1923, *see* MARCHANT (*Sir* J.), *ed.*
Renan (Henriette), *see* RENAN (J. E.) & H. R. Nouv. lettres intimes, 1846–50, 1923.
Renan (J. Ernest).
Le Cantique des Cantiques. Tr. avec étude. 5e éd. rev. 8°. 1884
Corr., 1846–71. [2e éd.] [t]1. 8°. [1926]
Pages françaises. s8°. 1921
Souvenirs d'enfance & de jeunesse. [Coll. Nelson]. s8°. [1912]
TRANSLATIONS.
The Apostles. [Tr.] 8°. 1890
Lectures on the influence of the institutions &c. of Rome on Christianity & the development of the Catholic Ch. Tr. C. Beard [Hibbert Lectures]. 8°. 1884
Life of Jesus. [Tr.] comp. ed. 8°. 1891
see BARRÈS (M.) Dante, Pascal & R., 1923.
see BARRÈS (M.) Taine & R.: pages perdues, 1922.
,, FRAZER (*Sir* J. G.) Sur E. R., 1923.
,, GIRARD (H.) & H. MONCEL. Bibliogr. des œ. de E. R., 1923.
,, LASSERRE (P.) La jeunesse d'E. R., t1, 2, 1925.
,, —— R. & nous, 1923.
,, MOTT (L. F.) Ernest Renan, 1921.
,, POINCARÉ (R. N. L.) E. R., 1923.
,, POMMIER (J.) R., d'après des doc. inéd., 2e éd., 1923.
,, PSICHARI (J. N.) E. R., jugements & souvenirs, 1925.
,, SÉGUR (N.) Mr. R. devant l'amour: roman, 1923.
—— & H. Renan. Nouv. lettres intimes, 1846–50. 8°. 1923

Renard (Edgard). Toponymie de la Commune de Dolembreux, d'Esneux & de Villers-aux-Tours, *see* SOC. DE LITT. WALLONE, Bull., t61, 1926.
Renard (Edmund). Clemens August, Kurfürst v. Köln. la8°. Bielefeld. 1927
Renard (Georges) & G. Weulersse. Life & work in mod. Europe, 15th–18th cent. Foreword by E. Power. [Tr. M. Richards]. 8°. 1926
Le travail dans l'Europe moderne. 8°. 1920
Renard (Jules), *1864–1910.*
Les cloportes — Chroniques, 1885–93 [*sep. tp. & pagin.* Œ.] 8°. [1926]
Comédies. La Bigote—Huit jours à la Campagne—Le Cousin de Rose, suiv. de Propos de théâtre. [Œ.] 8°. [1927]
Comédies. Le plasir de rompre—Le pain de ménage—M. Vernet. [Œ.] 8°. [1926]
Coquecigrues suiv. de Bucoliques. [Œ.] 8°. 1926
Corresp. inéd. (1880–99). [Œ.] 2t [t2, suiv. d'Inédits div.] 8°. [1927]
Débuts litt., 1883–90. Préf.: par H. Bachelin. [Œ.] 8°. 1925
L'écornifleur, suivi de La lanterne sourde. [*sep. tp. & pagin.* Œ.] 8°. [1926]
Hist. naturelles, *see* Poil de Carotte &c. *below.*
Journal inéd., 1887[–1910] [Œ.] [5v]. 8°. 1925–27
La lanterne sourde, *see* L'écornifleur *above.*
Nos frères farouches. Ragotte—Les Philippe. s8°. [1921]
L'œil clair, suiv. de Chron. théâtr. &c. [Œ.] 8°. [1927]
Poil de Carotte (Le roman & la pièce), suivi des Hist. naturelles. [Œ.] 8°. [1926]
Ragotte, suivi de La maîtresse [*w. sep. tp. & pagin.* Œ.] 8°. [1926]
Le vigneron dans sa vigne; suivi de propos littér. & mots d'écrit. [Œ.] 8°. [1927]
Renard (Maurice).
Le Docteur Lerne, sous-dieu. s8°. 1919
L'homme qui voulait être invisible, *see* ŒUVRES libres, 19, 1923.
M. d'Outremort &c. s8°. *n.d.*
Le péril bleu. s8°. 1920
Le voyage immobile, suivi d'autres hist. singulières. s8°. 1919
Renart (Jean). Galeran de Bretagne: roman du 13e s. Ed. L. Foulet. [Classiques Fr. du m. âge]. 8°. 1925
see FÄRBER (E.) Sprache der dem J. R. zugeschr. Werke "Lai de l'Ombre" &c., 1915.
Renata, *von Lothringen, see* RENÉE, *de Lorraine.*
Renato, *d'Angiò, see* RENÉ [*d'Anjou*], *king of Naples & Sicily.*
Renaudot (Eusèbe), *the younger.*
Liturgiarum orient. coll. 2t. 4°. Parisiis. 1716
see REINHARD (M. H.) Diss. qua liturgia eccl. Evangel. adv. E. R. object. vindic., 1721.
Rency (Georges), *see* LIEBRECHT (H.) & G. R. Hist. illust. de la litt. belge, 1926.
Rendall (Gerald Henry).
The Epistle of St. James & Judaic Xty. 8°. C. 1927
Rendle (Alfred Barton).
The classific. of flowering plants. v2. 8°. C. 1925
see BRIT. MUS. OF NAT. HIST.: BOTANY. Flora of Jamaica; by W. Fawcett & A. B. R., v5, 1926.
René [*d'Anjou*], *king of Naples & Sicily, see* FARAGLIA (N. F.) Storia d. lotta tra Alfonso V d'Aragona e R. d'A., 1908.
Reneccius (Jacobus), *see* REINECCIUS (J.)
Renée, *de Lorraine, Consort of William V, duke of Bavaria, see* CRIGNIS-MENTELBERG (A. DE). Herzogin Renata, 1912.
Renfrew. Archæological & hist. coll. rel. to the county of R. Parish of Lochwinnoch [House of Sempill &c.] 2v. 4°. Paisley. 1885–90
Reni (Guido), *see* MALAGUZZI VALERI (F.) G. R., 1921.
Renier (Rodolfo). La Vita nuova e La fiammetta. Studio crit. s8°. Torino. 1879
Renieri (Antonio), *see* PALLAVICINO (C.) Versi et regole de la nuova poesia toscana [A. R. &c.], 1539.
Renner (Heinrich). Durch Bosnien u. d. Hercegovina. 2e ergänzte &c. A. la8°. 1897
Renneville (R. A. Constantin de). L'inquisition française: ou l'hist. de la Bastille. [v1. *tp. mutilated*]. s8°. Amsterdam. 1715]
Renneville (*Mme.* **Sophie de).** Stanislas, roi de Pologne: roman hist., suivi d'un abr. de l'hist. de Pologne & de Lorraine. 3t *in* 2v. [*pagin. contin.*] s8°. 1807
Rennie (George), R. Broun & J. Shirreff. Gen. view of agric. of the W. Riding of Yorks. &c. s4°. 1794
Rennie (James), *prof. of Zoology in King's Coll., London.*
The hand-book of gardening. n. ed. enl. s8°. 1834
Renoir (Auguste), *see* FOSCA (F.) R., 1923; tr., 1925.
„ RIVIÈRE (G.) R. & ses amis, 1921.
„ VOLLARD (A.) A. R., 1841–1919, 1920.

Renouard (Antoine Auguste).
Annales de l'imprimerie des Estienne. 2p *in* 1v. 8°. 1837–38
Renouard (Philippe). Bibliogr. des impressions & des œ. de J. Badius Ascensius, 1462–1535. 3t. la8°. 1908
Les marques typogr. paris. des 15e & 16e siècles. fasc. 1–4. sm. fol. 1926–28
Renoult (Jean Baptiste). Dispute entre Mr. R. & un mission. papiste sur le retranchement de la Coupe. [*b. w. h.* Rép. de Mr. R., 1699]. s8°. Amsterdam. 1699
Hist. des variations de l'Eglise Gallicane en forme de lettres écr. à Mr. de Meaux [Bossuet]. s8°. Amsterdam. 1703
Rép. de Mr. R. à son père pour se justifier d'hérésie &c. s8°. Amsterdam. 1699
see *TAXE de la Chancellerie romaine &c., 1744.
Renouvin (Pierre). Les formes du gouvernement de guerre. [C.E. for Internat. Peace]. la8°. [1926]
The forms of war government in France. [Tr. & abr. ser. C.E. for Internat. Peace]. la8°. New Haven, *Yale.* 1927
Les orig. immédiates de la Guerre, 28 juin–4 août 1914. 8°. 1925
Renshaw (Graham). More animal romances. la8°. 1911
Rensi (Giuseppe).
La filosofia dell' autorità. 8°. Palermo. [1920]
Renström (Eric). Hist. Sueo-Gothica, Exerc. sub praes. A. A. Scarin. pl. s4°. Aboae. [1736]
Renti (Gaston Jean Baptiste de) [RENTY].
see JACKSON (T.) Lib. of Xtn. biog., v6, M. de R., by J. Wesley, 1838.
„ WESLEY (J.) An extr. of the life of M. de R., 3rd ed., 1760.
Renton-Denning (John).
Delhi, the Imperial city. 8°. Bombay. 1911
Rentoul (James Alexander), *K.C.*
Stray thoughts & memories. Ed. L. Rentoul. 8°. [1921]
Renwick (Robert) & *Sir* **J. Lindsay.**
Hist. of Glasgow. v1. 8°. Glasgow. 1921
Renwick (William Lindsay).
Edmund Spenser: essay on renaiss. poetry. 8°. 1925
Reparation Commission.
Reparation Comm. 1–3 [*in* 1v]. 8°. 1922
1, Statement of Germany's obligations.
2, Agreements conc. deliveries in kind.
3, Official docs. rel. to amount of payments to be effected by Germany, v1 (May 1, 1921–July 1, 1922).
Rep. of first Com. of Experts—Letter f. the chairman [*C. G. Dawes*] to the Reparation Comm. [*French & Eng.*] sm. fol. Paris. 1924
Repelin (Joseph), *see* BOUCHES-DU-RHÔNE; encyclop. départ., t12, Géog. phys., par R. &c., 1914.
Répertoire gén. des traités &c., 1895–1920, *see* TRAITÉS.
Répertoire archéolog. de la France. Publ. par ordre du Min. de l'Instr. Publ. &c. 4°. 1875
Nièvre, par le Cte de Soultrait.
Répertoire bibliograph. de l'hist. de France. Publ. de la Soc. Franç. de Bibliog. t1, 1920–21, par P. Caron & H. Stein. la8°. 1923
Répertoire d'art & d'archéologie; dépouillement des périod. & des catalogues de ventes franç. & étr. [Publ. de la bibl. d'art &c. de l'Univ. de Paris]. 5e année (1914)–1924. [1914–19 *in* 2 fasc. (21, 22) *b. together*]. s4°. 1914–25
„ „ [Index alphabét], 1914–19 (fasc. 23). s4°. 1921
Repertorio das ordenações, e leis do reino de Portugal, 4t, 1795, *see* PORTUGAL. Coll. da legisl. &c. do reino de P. &c.
Repertory of arts, manufactures & agriculture.
2nd ser., v16, 17, 22, 23, 28, 29, 32–35. 8°. 1810–19
The title of the 1st ser. is, "R. of a. & m." v29 *wants* Sept. No.; v17, 23, 29, 32, 35 *have no tps.*
***Repetitio** brevis orthod. confessionis quam amplectuntur eccl. Anhaltini &c., 1581, *see* ANHALT.
Repin (Ilya Yefimovich). The I.R. exhib. Intr. & cat. of the paintings, by C. Brinton. la8°. [N.Y.] 1921
Repington (*Lieut.-Col.* **Charles à Court).**
After the War. Diary. 8°. [1922]
The first World War, 1914–18. Personal experiences. 2v. 8°. 1920
„ „ ....3rd imp. 2v. 8°. 1920
Policy & arms. 8°. 1924
Reply. *Reply (The) of T. F. in defence of h. Suppl. to discussion &c., 1614, *see* FITZHERBERT (T.)
*Reply (A) to the mischief of impositions &c., 1681, *see* CLAGETT (W.)

Réponse [RESPONSES].
*R. à l'Hist. des Oracles &c. 1709, *see* BALTUS (J. F.)
*R. au discours de Stanhope, sur l'occup. de la France &c., 1818, *see* DUPIN (C.)
*R. aux remarques de M*** sur la protestation du père le Gobien, 1700, *see* LE GOBIEN (C.)
*Responses aux Lettres Provinciales &c., 1668, *see* NOUET (J.), F. ANNAT *& others.*

Repplier (Agnes) & J. W. White. Germany & democracy: the real issue. Reply to Doctor Dernburg. [P2465]. 8°. Phila. [1914]

Representaciones populares: [textes]; publ. N. Alonso Cortes, *see* REVUE HISPANIQUE, t60, 1924.

Representation. *Brief (A) & true r. of the posture of our affairs: acc. of the dangers f. the present invasion &c. [P2780]. 8°. 1745
R. of the People Acts, 1918–21, 1922, *see* FRASER (*Sir* H.)

Representative. R. poems, American & Eng., 1886, *see* LATHROP (G. P.)

Repsold (Joh. A.) Zur Gesch. d. astronom. Messwerkzeuge, 1450[-1900]. [2B]. 4°. L. 1908–14

Repubblica Fiorentina, *see* FIORENTINA.

Republican National Conventions, *see* UNITED STATES: REPUB. NAT. CONVENT.

Requejo (Gerardo). El Cavallero del Leon. Novela. s8°. [1926]

Requesenius (Josephus Maria). Select. disput. in primam secundae Thomae lib. 4. fol. Panormi. 1659

Reresby (*Sir* John), *2nd bart.*
Travels & memoirs. [*la. paper*]. la8°. 1813

Rerum. Rerum Æthiop. scr. occid. ined. a saec 16 ad 19; cur. C. B., 15v, 1903–17, *see* BECCARI (C.)
Rerum Anglic. scriptores post Bedam praecipui, 1596, *see* SAVILE (*Sir* H.), *ed.*
*Rerum Germanic. 1617–43 gestarum epitome, 1655, *see* PAPPUS (L.)

Resca (Stanislas), *see* LANS (J.) *Spongia qua absterg. convitia &c. Equitis Poloni contra Jesuitas [*ed.* S. R.], 1591.

Reschal (Antonin). L'ornière. s8°. *n.d.*

Reschidi, *see* 'ABD UL-RASHĪD IBN 'ABD UL-GHAFŪR, *Ḥusainī.*

Rescius (Stanislaus). De atheismis et Phalarismis Evangel. libri duo &c. 8°. Neapoli. 1596

Resen (Peder). Edda Islandorum, opera P. J. R., 1665, *see* EDDA. PROSE EDDA.

Resende (Antonio Telles da Silva, *marq.* de). Correspondencia, 1823–34, *see* INSTITUTO HIST. &C. BRAZIL. Rev., t80, 1917.

Resende (Garcia de). Cancioneiro geral. n. ed., prep. pelo A. J. Gonçálvez Guimarãis. 5t. 8°. Coímbra. 1910–17

Rešetar (Milan).
Slike staroga Dubrovnika. la8°. Zagreb. 1924

***Resisting** (Of) the lawfull magistrate under colour of relig. &c., 1747, *see* HAMMOND (H.)

***Resoconto** autentico d. disputa, Roma, 19 febb. 1872 fra sacerdoti cattol. e ministri evang. int. alla venuta di San Pietro in Roma. 2ª ed. [P2693]. 8°. Roma. 1872
„ „ Tr. [*w. t.* Authentic rep. &c.] by W. Arthur. [P504]. s8°. 1872

***Resolution** (The) of this case of conscience, whether the Ch. of Engl. symbolizing &c. w. the Ch. of Rome makes it unlawful to hold communion w. the Ch. of Engl., 1683, *see* FOWLER (E.), *bp.*

Resolutiones. Extractus benign. normalium resolut. &c., 1846, *see* EXTRACTUS.

Resources of the Empire. Survey prep. by Federation of Brit. Industries. Foreword by Pr. of Wales. 10v [*in* 12. v1, 8 *have 2p each*]. 4°. 1924
see AINSWORTH-DAVIS (J. R.) Crops & fruits, 1924. [1i.]
„ —— Meat, fish, & dairy produce, 1924. [1ii.]
„ ANDREW (G. W.) Fuel, 1924. [4.]
„ ASHE (A. W.) & H. G. T. BOORMAN. Chemicals, 1924. [7.]
„ BIRKETT (M. S.) Ferrous metals, 1924. [8i.]
„ BOLTON (E. R.) & R. G. PELLY. Oils, fats, waxes, & resins, 1924. [9.]
„ DULY (S. J.) Timber & timber products &c., 1924. [2.]
„ MACLAREN (W. A.) Rubber, tea & cacao &c., 1924. [5.]
„ PENZER (N. M.) Non-ferrous metals & o. minerals, 1924. [8ii.]
„ SNOW (E. C.) Leather, hides, skins & tanning materials, 1924. [6.]
„ STEPHENSON (W. T.) Communications, 1924. [10.]
„ WARD (J. S. M.) Textile fibres & yarns, 1924. [3.]

***Responsio** hist.-theolog. ad Cleri Gallicani de potestate eccl. declarationem &c., 1683, *see* DU BOIS (N.)

***Respublica** Moscovia &c., 1630, *see* MOSCOVIA.

Rességuier (*cte.* Jules de), *see* ASSE (E.) Les petits romantiques: J. de R. &c., 1900.

Ressel (Josef), *see* LIPSKÝ (E.) J. R., 1924.

Ressich (John). The triumph of a fool. s8°. [1926]

Restif (Edme), *see* RESTIF DE LA BRETONNE (N. E.) Vie de mon père, 1924.

Restif de la Bretonne (Nicolas Edme). Les contemporains mêlées. Intr. & notes de P. L. Rousseau. s8°. *n.d.*
La dern. aventure d'un homme de 45 ans. Intr. & notes de H. d'Alméras. s8°. *n.d.*
Monsieur Nicolas; ou, Le coeur human dévoilé. Réimp. s. l'éd., 1796. 14t. 8°. 1883
13, Mon calendrier. 14, Mes ouvrages *&* Index.
Monsieur Nicolas. Ed. abrégée, avec intr. &c. par J. Grand-Carteret. [3t]. s8°. *n.d.*
Le Palais-Royal. Intr. & notes par H. d'Alméras. s8°. *n.d.*
La vie de mon père. Intr. & notes de M. Boisson. 8°. 1924
see GRASILIER (L.) R. de La B. inconnu, 1927.
„ PALACHE (J. G.) Four novelists &c.; Crébillon, R. de La B. &c., 1926.

Restoration comedies, 1921, *see* SUMMERS (M.), *ed.*

Retana (Wenceslao Emilio). Diccion. de Filipinismos, *see* REVUE HISPAN., t51, 1921.

Rétchung, *see* RAS CHUNG PA.

Rethel (Alfred). Auch e. Todtentanz, 1848; gezeichnet v. A. R., mit Text v. R. Reinick (*facs.*), *see* FREYTAG (G.) Bilder, B5, 1925.

Reti (Richard). Mod. ideas in chess. Tr. J. Hart. 8°. 1923
Die neu. Ideen im Schachspiel. s8°. Wien. 1922

Rétif (Edme), *see* RESTIF (E.)

Retinger (J. H.)
Morones of Mexico: hist. of the labour movt. s8°. 1926

Retreat. *A spiritual retreat for one day in every month &c., 1698, *see* CROISET (J.)

***Return** (The) of Alfred, 1922, *see* JENKINS (H.)

Retz (*le card.* de), *1614–79.* Œuvres. n. éd., rev. Suppl. à la corr. [Ed. &c.] par C. Cochin. 8°. 1920
see BATIFFOL (L.) Le Card. de R., 1927.
„ SCHLUMBERGER (J.) Le lion [*i.e.* Card. R.] devenu vieux [*fiction*], 2ᵉ éd., 1924.

Retzsch (Friedr. Aug. Moritz). 8 Umrisse zu Schiller's Fridolin. Andeutungen v. C. A. Böttiger. obl.4°. St. 1824

Reuchlin (Johann) [REUCHLINUS].
De arte cabalistica libri 3, *see* PISTORIUS (J.) Artis Cabalist. t1, 1587.
De Cabala, *see* COLUMNA (P.), *Galatinus.* De arcanis Cathol. veritatis libri 12, 1603.
De Verbo mirifico libri tres, emaculatius quam antehac excusi &c. s8°. Colonię, *Ex officina Eucharii.* 1532
In septem psalmos pœnitētiales hebraicos interpretatio de verbo ad verbum, ad discendum linguam hebr. s8°. [Tubingæ, *T. Anshelmus.* 1512]
Liber Congestorum de arte praedicandi. s4°. [Phorce (*Pforzheim*). 1504]
Liber de verbo mirifico. s8°. Lugduni. 1552
see LUTHER (M.) Duo M. L. fragm., ad R. De arte caballistica lib. 3, 1517 &c., 1730.

Reuden (Michael) [REUDENIUS (M.)] Discursus in welchem zehen d. weitberuffene Keyser Carls Badt &c. betreff. Fragen erörtert &c. werden. [*b. w. h.* Obs. Carolinae, 1611]. s8°. Jehna. 1618
Obs. Carolinæ: Darinnen von Natur des Keyser Carlsbads u. denen Kranckheiten. Aus M. R. vol. obs. zusammen u. verdeutscht durch M. Rathmirum. s8°. Jena. 1611

Reul (Paul de). The centenary of Shelley, *see* ROY. SOC. OF LIT. Essays, N.S., v3, 1923.
L'œuvre de Swinburne. 8°. Brux. 1922

Reumert (Elith).
Hans Andersen the man. Tr. J. Bröchner. 8°. [1927]

Reumont (Alfred v.) Frauenschicksale in d. Renaissance. [Hrsg. E. Schaeffer]. 2B. s8°. Dresden. [1927]

***Reuniting** (The) of Christianity. Wr. in French by a learned Protest. divine. Tr. by P. A. Gent. [*Attrib. to d'Huisseau*]. s8°. 1673

Reusch (Franz Heinrich). Das Verfahren deut. Bischöfe bez. der d. Altkatholiken z. Mitgebrauch eingeräumten Kirchen. [P2695]. 8°. Bonn. 1875

Reusch (Johann Peter). Annotat. in J. G. Baieri Compend. theolog. positivae. s8°. Jenae. 1757
Introd. in theologiam revelatam. s8°. Jenae. 1784
Theologia moralis. Ed. &c. C. G. Mullerus. s8°. Jenae. 1760

Reusner (Nicolaus).
Epistol. Turcic. variorum authorum libri 5. Ex rec. N. R. [Cont., libri 6–14].
[4p *in* 1v]. s4°. Francofurti ad Moenum. 1598–1600
Ethica philosophica & Christiana. Cui acc. Politicarum disput. libell. sing. Praeterea Doct. de virtutibus &c. ex var. auctoribus [*w. sep. tp. & pagin.*] [*b. w.* Strigelius (V.) In P. Melanchthonis lib. de anima, 1590]. s8°. Jenae. 1590
Icones sive imagines virorum literis illustrium &c. Add. eorundem elogiis divers. auct. Ex 2ª recognitione N. R.
s8°. Argentorati. 1590
„ „ A T. Stimmero pict. expr. & N. R. cum descr. ed. Nunc cura C. A. Z. s8°. Francofurti a. M. 1719
Symbola heroica.
ed. 9ª [3p *in* 1v, *each w. sep. tp.*] s8°. Londini. [1650]

Reuss, *House of, see* SCHMIDT (B.) Gesch. d. Reussenlandes, 1923–27.

Reuss (Eduard W. E.)
Bibl. Novi Test. Graeci. 8°. Brunsvigae. 1872
Fragments litt. & crit. rel. à l'hist. de la Bible franç. [*No tp.*; *extr. f.* Revue de théol., 1851–66]. 8°. [1851–66]

Reuss (Jeremias Friedrich), *see* WARTH (J. F.) Diss. de eccl. Ruthenica; praes. J. F. R., 1752.

Reuss (Johann Joachim). Exercit. de Eutycheismo Lutheranis theologis falso impacto. Præs. G. Wegnero.
[P2632]. s4°. Regiomonti. 1699

Reuss (Rudolf).
Hist. de Strasbourg dep. ses origines j. nos jours. 8°. 1922

Reussner (André), *see* TRAMOND (J.) & A. REUSSNER. Elém. d'hist. maritime &c. contemp., 1924.

Reuter (Edward Byron). Population problems. s8°. Phila. 1923

Reuter (Fritz). Aus d. Franzosenzeit. Hochdeutsch v. F. J. Kleemeier. 8°. München. [1909]

Reuter (*Vizeadmiral* Ludwig v.)
Scapa Flow: Das Grab d. deut. Flotte. [Anhang]. 8°. L. 1921

Reuterskiöld (Carl Axel). Den svenska förvaltningsrättens system, *see* KUNG. HUM. VET.-SAMF. I UPPSALA. Skr., B24, 1927.

Reuther (Oskar). Ocheïdir. Nach Aufnahmen v. Mitgliedern d. Babylon-Exped. d. Deut. Orient-Gesell. [Deut. Orient-Gesell., Wiss. Veröffentl., 20]. fol. L. 1912
see WIEGAND (T.) Baalbek: Ergebnisse d. Ausgrab. u. Unters., 1898 bis 1905, B3, v. O. R. &c., 1925.

Révai (Miklós János). Elaboratior grammatica Hungarica.
v1, 2 [*No more published*]. 8°. Pestini. 1806

Reval. *The importance of the port of R.
[P2735]. 8°. Reval. 1921

Réveil (Achille), *see* DUCHESNE (J.) Museum of painting &c.: princ. paintings &c. in galleries of Europe, drawn & etched by R., v1–6, 1828–30.

Reveirs-Hopkins (A. E.), *see* BLAKE (J. P.) & A. E. R.-H. Little bks. about old furniture, v1–4, 1919–20.

***Revelation** exam. w. candour, 3v, 1732–63, *see* DELANY (P.)

Revelli (Paolo). L'Italia n. Divina Commedia. fol. Milano. 1922

Revellus (Georgius). De Rupella ter obsessa, dedita, demum capta, subacta libri 3. s8°. Amsterodami. 1649

Revels. The King's Office of the R., 1610–22, doc., 1925, *see* MARCHAM (F.)

Reventlow (*Graf* Ernst zu). Minister Stresemann als Staatsmann &c. 3. A. s8°. München. 1925

Rever (Marie François Gilles), *Deputy to the Assemblée Législative, see* DUBREUIL (L.) F. R., 1753–1828, 1924.

Révérend Du Mesnil (Edmond). Armorial hist. de Bresse, Bugey &c., avec remarques crit. de P. Collet. 4°. Lyon. 1872

Révész (Imre). Dévay Bíró Mátyás elsö magyar reformátor életrajza és irodalmi müvei. 8°. Pest. 1863
Erdösi J. Magyar protestáns reformátor &c.
8°. Debrecenben. 1859

Revett (Nicholas), *see* STUART (J.) Antiq. of Athens & o. mon. of Greece, 2nd ed., 1841.

Review. *R. (A) & consider. of two late pamphlets &c., 1706, *see* FORRESTER (T.)
R. of missions overseas, 1921, *see* CHURCH. Official Year Book of the Ch. of Eng., 1921.

Review (The) of English studies. Quarterly journal of Eng. lit. &c. Ed. R. B. M'Kerrow. v1–3. 8°. 1925–27

Review (A) of the affairs of France. v2, No. 59, July 19, 1705. [*b. w.* Post Man, 1704–8]. 8°. 1705

Review of the foreign press. The economic review w. wh. is incorp. the Political review. v2–15. fol. [1920–27]

Revilla Marcos (Angel). J. M. Gabriel y Galán. Est. crit. Prólogo de M. de Unamuno. s8°. 1923

Revilliod (Gustave); *see* ARIANA, *Musée de l'.* Cat. offic., *founded by G. R.*, 1905.

Révillout (Eugène). Les Blemmyes d'ap. div. doc. coptes &c. [*Extr. f.* Comptes-rendus de l'Acad. des Inscr. &c., jan.-fév., 1871. P2686]. 8°. [1871]

Revista de archivos, bibliotecas y museos.
3ª epoca. año 19. t32, 33 (Enero-Dic. 1915). 8°. 1916

Revista de Filología Española. Anejo 1, 7, 8. 8°. 1925–27
see BOHIGAS BALAGUER (P.) Los textos esp. &c. de la Demanda d. S. Grial, 1925. [7.]
„ MENÉNDEZ PIDAL (R.) Oríg. del Español, 1926. [1.]
„ VALERA (D. DE). Crónica de los Reyes Católicos; ed. &c. J. de M. Carriazo, 1927. [8.]

Revista trimensal do Instituto Hist. e Geogr. Brazileiro, *see* INSTITUTO HIST. E GEOGR. BRAZILEIRO.

Revius (Jacobus), *see* BELGIUM. Eccl. B. confess., interp. J. R., 1638.

Revival. Account of the remark. r. of the wk. of God in Cornwall, 1814, *see* CORNWALL.

Revolution. *Old stories wh. were the fore-runners of the R. in 88, 1711, *see* STORIES.
*Reflections upon the late great R., 1689, *see* REFLECTIONS.
Revolution f. 1789 to 1906, 1920, *see* POSTGATE (R. W.), *ed.*

Revolutionary radicalism; hist. &c., 1920, *see* NEW YORK.

Revon (Maxime). Claude Farrère: s. œuvre. 8°. 1924
—— & P. Billotey.
L'Académie Française de 1895 à 1920. s4°. [1922]

Revon (Michel).
Japan. Lit.: Gesch. &c. s8°. Fr. am M. [1926 ?]

***Revue** polit. de l'Europe en 1825, *see* BOURGUIGNON D'HERBIGNY (P. F. X.)

Revue (La). Revue mondiale. (Ancienne "Revue des revues"). v134–180 [*new enumeration*], 1920–27. 8°. 1920–27

Revue archéologique. Nouv. sér., t25–28 [*tps. & Jan. 1874 wanting*], s5, t15–26. 8°. 1873–1927

Revue bénédictine. 38ᵉ, 39ᵉ année[s]. 8°. Maredsous. 1926–27

Revue bleue. Année 58–65. 8°. 1920–27

Revue celtique. t38–43. 8°. 1920–26

Revue critique d'hist. & de litt.
Année 54–61 (Nouv. sér. 87–95). 8°. 1920–27

Revue de droit international & de législation comparée.
sér. 3, t1–8. la8°. Brux. 1920–27

Revue de Genève. t9, 10 (Jan.–Déc.), 1924. 8°. Genève. [1924]
Déc. *has t.* Bibliothèque univ. & Revue de Genève, *q.v. for continuation.*

Revue de l'art ancien & moderne. Directeur: A. Dezarrois &c.
t37–53. fol. 1920–28
„ „ Suppl. bi-mensuel: Bulletin de l'art anc. & mod., 1920–27. la8°. 1920–27

Revue de l'art chrétien.
t64, livr. 1–3 (jan.–juin 1914). [*No more publ.*] 4°. 1914

Revue de linguistique & de philologie comparée. t1. 8°. 1867

Revue de métaphysique & de morale. Année 27–34. 8°. 1920–27
see PASCAL (B.) Etudes sur P., par M. Blondel &c., 1923.

Revue de Paris. Année 28–35 [*each in* 6t.] 8°. 1921–28

Revue de philologie, de litt. & d'hist. anciennes.
Nouv. sér., année & tome 43–50, s3, t1, 2. 8°. 1919–28

Revue des deux mondes.
Période VI, t55–65. Pér. VII, t1–46. 8°. 1920–28
„ „ Table. 6ᵉ période, 1911–21. 8°. 1921

Revue des études arméniennes. t1–4(1920–24). 8°. [1920]–24

Revue des études hongroises & finno-ougriennes. Dir. par Z. Baranyai &c. [Acad. Hongr. des Sci.]
Année 1–5 (1923–27). 8°. 1923–27

Revue des études Rabelaisiennes. [Publ. de la Soc. des Et. Rabelaisiennes]. Tables gén. t1–10. Par E. Clouzot & H. Martin. 8°. 1924

Revue des livres anciens. Doc. d'hist. litt., de bibliog. &c. Dir. P. Louÿs; réd. L. Loviot. 2v. 8°. 1913–17

Revue d'histoire littéraire de la France.
Année 27–34. 8°. 1920–27

Revue du monde musulman. Publ. par la Mission Sci. du Maroc, t37, t51, 52.
see BOLCHEVISME (LE) & l'Islam, 2t, 1922.
„ MARTY (P.) Et. sur l'Islam & les tribus du Soudan, 4t, 1918–21.

Revue du seizième siècle. [Publ. de la Soc. des Etudes Rabelaisiennes. N.S.] t9–13. 8°. 1922–26

Revue (La) hebdomadaire.
Année[s] 30–37. [*Each* année *in* 12t *bound in* 6]. s8°. 1921–28
Suppl. Coll. nouv. de la France dramat.
No. 1–16 [*1–12 in 1v*]. 8°. 1922–23
Amiel (D.) & A. Obey. La souriante Mme. Beudet, 1922. [7.]
Bernard (J. J.) Le feu qui reprend mal, 1922. [5.]
Bourdet (E.) L'heure du berger, 1922. [12.]
Boussac de St.-Marc (A.) Le loup de Gubbio, 1922. [8.]
Calderon de la Barca (P.) Le vie est un songe ; tr., 1922. [10.]
Chekhov (A.) Une demande en mariage ; tr., 1922. [11.]
Duvernois (H.) La dame de bronze & le monsieur de cristal, 1922. [2.]
Géraldy (P.) Aimer, 1922. [3.]
Ghéon (H.) Le débat de Nicolazic &c., 1922. [4.]
Jeromski (S.) Plus blanc que neige ; tr., 1923. [14.]
Marcel (G.) L'iconoclaste, 1923. [13.]
Nigond (G.) Sophie Arnould, 1922. [6.]
Piéchaud (Martial). Mlle. Pascal, 1922. [1.]
—— Le sommeil des amants, 1923. [15.]
Schneider (E.) Le dieu d'argile, 1923. [16.]
Variot (J.) La belle de Haguenau, 1922. [9.]

Revue hispanique. Dir. par R. Foulché-Delbosc.
t46–71. 8°. N.Y. 1919–27
„ „ Tables des t1–50 (1894–1920) [*b. w.* t50].
8°. N.Y. 1920

Revue historique. t133–157. 8°. 1920–28
„ „ ......8e Table gén., t106–136, 1911–20. 8°. 1922
„ „ ......9e Table gén., t136–151, 1921–26. 8°. 1928

Revue historique de la Révolution Française.
t14, 15. la8°. 1919–[23]
From Jan. 1924 *this* Revue *gave place to* Annales hist. de la Révol. Franç., *q.v.*

Revue (La) musicale. Directeur H. Prunières.
Année 1–7 (Nov. 1920–1926). la8°. 1920–26
Most Nos. have a Suppl. musical. *Some Nos. are devoted to separate musicians.*

Revue philosophique de la France & de l'étranger.
Année 45–53 (89–105). 8°. 1920–28

Revue rétrospective, ou Archives secrètes du dern. gouvernement. 1830–48. [31 Nos. *in* 1v]. la8°. 1848

Rex. Annuaire généalog. de la noblesse de France.
6e année, 1914. 8°. 1914

Rey (Abel). La philosophie mod. s8°. 1921

Rey (Charles Fernand).
Unconquered Abyssinia as it is to-day. 8°. 1923

Rey (Etienne), *see* CAILLAVET (G. A. DE), R. DE FLERS & E. R. La belle aventure, 1920.

Rey (Léon). Obs. sur les premiers habitats de la Macédoine ; rec. par le Service Arch. de l'Armée d'Orient, 1916–19, *see* ECOLES FRANÇ. D'ATHÈNES &C. Bull., Année[s] 41–43, 1917–19, 1921.

Rey (Raymond). Les vielles églises fortifiées du midi de la France. la8°. 1925

Rey (Robert). Gauguin. 8°. 1923
Gauguin. Tr. F. C. de Sumichrast. 8°. [1924]
Suzanne Valadon. 28 reprod., préc. d'une ét. crit. s8°. [1922]

Reyburn (Hugh A.) The ethical theory of Hegel. s8°. O. 1921

Reydon, *The family of, see* ROYDON.

Reyer (Ernest), *see* CURZON (H. DE). E. R., sa vie & s. œuvres, 1823–1909, 1924.

Reyes (Alfonso). Cuestiones Gongorinas. 8°. 1927

Reyes (Antonio de La Peña y), *see* PEÑA Y REYES (A. DE LA).

Reyes (Matías de los). Para algunos de M. de los R. 8°. 1640

Reyles (Carlos).
Beba. s8°. [1895]
El extraño. s8°. 1897
Primitivo. s8°. Montevideo. [1896]
La race de Caïn. Roman. Tr. F. de Miomandre. s8°. *n.d.*
La raza de Caín. 2a ed. s8°. Paris. [1911]
El sueño de rapiña. s8°. Montevideo. [1898]

Reymond (Arnold). Hist. of the sciences in Gr.-Rom. antiq. Tr. R. G. de Bray. 8°. [1927]

Reymond (Marcel). Michel-Ange : biog. crit. 8°. [1920]

Reymont (Władysław St.)
L'apostolat du knout en Pologne : notes de voyage au pays de Chelm. Tr. P. Cazin. s8°. 1912
Autumn. [The peasants, v1]. s8°. 1925
Die polnischen Bauern. [Der Bauernspiegel. Übers. v. J. P. d'Ardeschah]. B1, 2. 8°. Jena. 1912
Spring. [The peasants, v3. Tr. M. H. Dziewicki]. s8°. [1926]
Summer. [The peasants, v4. Tr. M. H. Dziewicki]. s8°. [1926]
Winter. [The peasants, v2]. s8°. 1925
see LORENTOWICZ (J.) Ladislas R., 1924.
„ SCHOELL (F. L.) Les paysans de L. R., 1925.

Reynard, *the Fox.* The Cambridge Reinaert fragments (Culemann fragm.) Ed., w. intr. & bibliog., by K. Breul.
8°. C. 1927
The epic of the beast. Eng. tr. of The hist. of R. the Fox (Caxton, 1481) & Physiologus. Intr. by W. Rose. [Broadway Trans.] s8°. [1924]
The hist. of R. the Fox. Tr. & pr. by W. Caxton, 1481. Ed. E. Goldsmid. [Bibl. curiosa]. 2v. s8°. *p.p.* E. 1884
Reinke de Vos, nach d. A. v. F. Prien, neu hrsg. v. A. Leitzmann. Einl. v. K. Voretzsch. s8°. Halle/Saale. 1925

Reynaud (L.)
L'influence allemande en France au 18e & 19e siècle. 8°. 1922

Reyner (Edward). Precepts for Christian practice.
13th ed. corr. & amen. s8°. 1668

Reynès-Monlaur, *see* MONLAUR (R.)

Reynold (Gonzague de). Charles Baudelaire. 8°. 1920
Comment se forme une nation : la Suisse, sa terre & s. hist., *see* BRIT. ACADEMY : Proc., 1918.

Reynolds (Edward), *bp. of Norwich.* *The humble proposals of sundry learned & pious divines, conc. the engagement to be imposed for their subscriptions. s4°. 1650
Works cont. three treatises &c. w. a coll. of 30 sermons.
fol. 1678
The whole works coll. [by J. R. Pitman] w. h. funeral sermon by B. Rively. Pref. a memoir of the author by R. Chalmers.
6v. 8°. 1826
see DURY (J.) Just re-proposals to humble proposals [by R.], 1650.

Reynolds (Frederick).
Works in †INCHBALD (*Mrs.* E.) Mod. theatre, 1808–11.
The delinquent. [2.]
The dramatist. [20.]
Folly as it flies. [2.]
Fortune's fool. [2.]
How to grow rich. [1.]
Laugh when you can. [2.]
Life. [1.]
Notoriety. [1.]
The rage. [1.]
Speculation. [2.]
Werter. [3.]
The will. [1.]

Reynolds (John H.), *see* GLEICHEN (*Lord* E.) & J. H. R. Alphabets of for. lang. transcr. into Eng., 1921.

Reynolds (*Sir* Joshua).
Fifteen disc. deliv. in the R. Acad. [Intr. by L. M. Phillipps. Everyman's Lib.] s8°. *n.d.*
Johnson & Garrick : 2 dialogues. Intr. by R. Brimley Johnson. 8°. *Cayme Press.* 1927
Literary works. Pref., mem. &c. by H. W. Beechey. 2v. s8°. 1835
see GROSVENOR GALLERY. Cat. of works of J. R. exhib. at G. G., 1883–4, 1884.
„ HUTH (L.) Cat. of mezzotint portraits aft. R. &c., 1905.
„ WESTON (A. A.) Cat. of engr. portraits aft. R. &c., 1904.

Reynolds (Osborne), *see* HARTMANN (J.) Flow of water & mercury in pipes : R.'s law of similarity, 1926.

Reynolds (Paul Kenneth Baillie).
The Vigiles of Imperial Rome. 8°. 1926

Reynolds (Stephen). How 'twas. 8°. 1912
Letters. Ed. H. Wright. 8°. 1923

Reynolds-Ball (Eustace Alfred), *see* BALL (E. A. R.)

Rhaïs (Elissa).
Les Juifs ou la fille d'Eléazar. Roman. s8°. [1921]
Petits pachas en exil, *see* ŒUVRES libres, 77, 1927.

Rhead (G. Woolliscroft). Hist. of the fan. fol. 1910

Rhegenius (Paulus Michael). Summaria diss. de oeconomia redemtionis nostrae ; controversiae inter nos & Unitarios [vulgò Socinianos] circa peccatum originale &c.
s8°. Lipsiae. 1688

Rhegius (Urbanus) [REGIUS ; RIEGER ; *ps.* HEINRICH PHOENICEUS].
Opera. Cum vita & praef. E. Regii.
3p. *b. in* 1v. fol. Noribergae. 1562
Anzaygung das die Romisch Bull mercklichen schaden in gewissin manicher menschen gebracht hab, u. nit Doctor Luthers leer.
s4°. *n.p.* [1522]
Catechismus minor puerorum. Recens ab aut. recog. & locupl.
s8°. [Vitebergæ, *J. Clug*]. 1540
De angelis. [*b. w.* Sarcerius (E.) Catechismus, 1539].
s8°. *n.p.* [Lipsiae ?]. 1543
Formulae quaedam de praecipuis Xtnae. doct.
[P1042]. s8°. [Pfortzheimiae]. 1559
Nova doctrina. s8°. *n.p.* 1526
see VEIEL (E.) & J. P. ROTH. U. R. memoria & merita &c., 1683.

Rhein. Farbige Franzosen am R. : ein Notschrei deut. Frauen, 3e A., 1921, *see* FARBIGE.

Rheinischer Merkur. Nro. 1, den 23. Jan. 1814 (*facs.*), *see* FREYTAG (G.) Bilder, B5, 1925.

Rheinlandabkommen (Das) sowie die Verordnungen d. Hohen Komm. [d. Interalliierten Rheinlandkommission] in Coblenz. Dreisprach. Textausg. [*Germ., Fr. & Eng.*] mit Erläut. v. H. u. W. Vogels. [2B]. 8º. Bonn. 1920–21

Rheinsch (Erika), *see* SPANN (E.)

Rheinisches Museum f. Philologie, Geschichte u. griechische Philosophie. Rheinisches Museum f. Philologie. N.F., B69–76. 8º. Frankfurt am Main. 1914–27

Rhénanie, La. La R.: conférences [*by*] F. Baldensperger, J. Bardoux &c. Préf. de P. Tirard. s8º. 1922

Rhine [RHIN]. Strategic geography. Theatres of war of the Rhine & Danube. s8º. 1891

Vues pittoresques du Rhin, *n.d.*, *see* BLEULER (L.), *publ.*

Rhineland High Commission, *see* RHEINLANDABKOMMEN (Das) sowie d. Verordnungen d. Hohen Komm. in Coblenz, *Germ., Fr. & Eng.*, 2B, 1920–21.

Rho (Edmondo). Lorenzo il Magnifico. 8º. Bari. 1926

Rhoades (James). Words by the wayside. [*Poems*]. s8º. 1915

Rhodes (Alexandre de), *Jesuit missionary.*

Catechismus pro iis, qui volunt suscipere baptismum, in 8 dies div. [*Lat. & Tonkinese*]. s4º. Romae. [1651]

Dict. Annnamiticum [*sic*], Lusitanum, & Latinum ope Sacrae Congreg. de Propag. fide. [*Foll. by* Ling. Annam. brevis declar., *w. sep. pagin.*] 2p *in* 1v. s4º. 1651

Tunchinensis hist. libri duo (1, status temporalis hujus regni; 2, mirabiles Evang. prædicationis progressus). 2p [*in 1v*]. s4º. Lugduni. 1652

see JESUITS. Voyages &c., t2, Mission de la Cochinchine &c. [A. de R. &c.], 1858.

,, MACHAULT (J. DE). Hist. of the mission of the S.J. establ. in Persia by A. of R.; tr. Sir A. T. Wilson, 1925.

,, WILSON (*Sir* A. T.) Hist. of Fathers of S.J. in China &c. [*extr. f.* R.'s " Divers voy.," 1681], 1926.

Rhodes (*Rt. Hon.* **Cecil J.**), *see* WILLIAMS (A. F. B.) C. R., 1921.

Rhodes (Geoffrey), *see* MACKENZIE (H. G. G.) & G. R. Health & the mind, 1921.

Rhodes (James Ford). The McKinley & Roosevelt admin., 1897–1909. 8º. N.Y. 1922

Rhodes (Kathlyn).

The city of palms. s8º. [1919]
Desert lovers. s8º. [1922]
The golden apple. s8º. [1920]
The golden journey. s8º. [1926]
Under the orange trees. s8º. [1925]
Who is Sylvia? s8º. [1924]

Rhodes (Raymond Crompton).

Shakespeare's first folio: a study. 8º. O. 1923

The stagery of Shakespeare. s8º. B'ham. 1922

Rhodesia. Colony of S.R. Official year book, No. 1, 1924. 8º. Salisbury, S. Rhodesia. 1924

S.R. Handbook for settlers. [P2762]. 8º. [1924]

Rhodius (Henricus), *see* ROTH (H.)

Rhodius (Johannes), *of Rockenhausen, see* RÖDINGER (J.)

Rhodokanakis (Nikolaus). Der Grundsatz d. Öffentlichkeit in d. südarab. Urkunden, 1915, *see* KAIS. AKAD. D. W. ZU WIEN. Sitz., B177, 1917.

Die Inschriften an d. Mauer v. Kohlān-Timnaʿ, *see* KAISERL. AKAD. D. WISS. ZU WIEN. Sitz., B200, 1924.

Kataban. Texte z. Bodenwirtschaft, 1919, *see* KAIS. AKAD. D. W. ZU WIEN. Sitz., B194, 1923.

St. z. Lexikographie u. Gramm. d. Altsüdarabischen, 1, 2, 1915–17, *see* KAISERL. AKAD. D. W. ZU WIEN. Sitz., 178, 185, 1916–18.

see NIELSEN (D.), *ed.* Hdbch. d. altarab. Altertumskunde, B1, 1927.

Rhondda (David Alfred Thomas, *1st baron*). Growth & direction of our foreign trade in coal dur. last half cent. [Extr. f. Roy. Statist. Soc. Journal, 1903]. 8º. *p.f.p.c.* 1903

see RHONDDA (M. H. M., *2nd vtss.*) D. A. T., Viscount R., 1921.

Rhondda (Margaret Haig Mackworth, *2nd viscountess*), *form. Thomas, wife of Sir H. Mackworth.* D. A. Thomas, Viscount Rhondda. By h. daughter [*i.e.* Viscountess R.] & others. 8º. 1921

Rhoon (Willem Bentinck, *heer* **v.),** *see* BENTINCK (W.)

Rhys (Ernest). Frederic Ld. Leighton, h. life & work. [3rd ed., repr.] 8º. 1900

Mod. Eng. essays [1870–1920. Ed. E. R.] 5v [v3 repr.] s8º. 1922–23

The old country: bk. of love & praise of England. Ed. E. R. s8º. [1917]

—— & C. A. Dawson-Scott.

Tales of mystery. Ed. R. & D.-S. s8º. [1927]

Rhys (*Rt. Hon. Sir* **John).** Celtic inscr. of Gaul: add. &c., 1911, *see* BRIT. ACADEMY. Proc., 1911–12.

The Coligny Calendar, 1910, *see* BRIT. ACAD. Proc., 1909–10.

see JONES (*Sir* J. M.-) Sir J. R. [R. Mem. Lect.], 1926.

—— & D. Brynmor-Jones.

The Welsh people. [6th impr.] 8º. 1923

Riat (Georges). Paris. 4e éd., rev. par P. Vitry. la8º. 1923

Ribadeneira (Pedro de), *Jesuit* [RIVADENEYRA]. Appendix Schismatis Anglicani &c. Ex Hisp. in Lat. convers. s8º. Coloniae Agripp. 1610

Vita Ignatia Loiolae. Nunc scholiis illust. à C. Simone. s8º. *n.p.* 1598

Ribas (Anselmo), *see* NETTO (COELHO), *ps.*

Riba y Garcia (Carlos), *see* COLECCION de docs. para el estudio de la hist. de Aragon, t10, Carta de poblacion de la ciudad de Santa Maria de Albarracin; est. y transcr. de C. R. y G., 1915.

Ribbeck (August Ferdinand). Anselmi Cantuar. doctrina de S. Spiritu. Diss. 4º. Berolini. [1838]

Ribbeck (Otto). Sophokles u. s. Tragödien, *see* VIRCHOW (R.) & F. v. HOLTZENDORFF. Samml., H83, 1869.

Ribblesdale (Thomas Lister, *4th baron*).

Impressions & memories. Pref. by Lady Wilson. 8º. [1927]

Ribeiro (Bernardim), *1482–1552* **& C. Falcão.** Obras. n. ed., prep. &c. por A. B. Freire e pref. por C. M. de Vasconcelos. 2v. s8º. Coimbra. 1923

Ribeiro (Patrocinio). A nacionalidade portuguesa de Cristovam Colombo. [*w. Eng. tr. by* A. Cruz]. 8º. Lisboa. [1927]

Ribemont. Cartul. de l'anc. abbaye de Saint Nicolas des Prés, sous Ribemont. Publ. par H. Stein. [Extr. des Mém. de la Soc. Acad. de St.-Quentin, s4, t5]. 8º. Saint-Quentin. 1884

Ribemont-Dessaignes (G.) Le bar du lendemain. s8º. 1927

Ribera (Almerico). Filippo Carcano, pittore. 52 tavole con intr. di A. R. la8º. Torino. 1916

Ribera (Francisco de), *Jesuit.* In Ioannis Apocalypsin comm. Adj., Quinque libri de templo &c. [*wanting*]. s8º. Antverpiae. 1603

see LÖW (J. F.) Brev. stricturae in F. R. scriptum antapologet., 1753.

Ribera (Fulgencio Afan de), *see* AFAN DE RIBERA (F.)

Ribera (José de), *called* "*Spagnoletto,*" *see* CONTE (E.) R. (Maîtres anc. & mod.), 1924.

Ribera (Julian). La musica de las cantigas [*of* Alfonso el Sabio]: est. sobre su origen &c. con. reprod. del texto y transcripcion mod. [Real Acad. Esp.] 4º. 1922

see REAL ACAD. ESPAÑOLA. Discursos &c. 7 centen. del nacim. del rey Alfonso el Sabio [*by* J. R. &c.], 1921.

Ribero (Diego). The 2nd Borgian map of D. R., Seville, 1529. Reprod. in facs. [Maps 2]. obl. folio [folded]. *n.d.*

Ribetti (Pietro Antonio). Tractatus de interdicto S. Pauli V Papæ, *see* PAUL V, *pope.* Controversiae, 1607.

Ribezzo (Francesco). La lingua d. antichi Messapii. Intr. storica.—Ermeneutica. 8º. Napoli. 1907

Ribini (Joannes). Memorabilia August. Conf. in r. Hungariae a Ferd. I usque ad III [*&* A Leopoldo M. usque ad Carolum VI]. 2v. 8º. Ponsonii. 1787–89

Ribot (Alexandre F. J.)

see CAMBON (J.) Disc. pour la récept. de J. C. (Rép. de A. R.), 1919.

,, GOYAU (G.) Séance de l'Acad. Franç.: disc. de récept. de G. G., éloge de D. Cochin, Réponse de R., 1923.

,, LAURENT (M.) Nos gouvernements de Guerre: R. &c., 1920.

,, ROBERT (H.) Disc. pour la récept. de H. R. [*on* A. R.], 1924.

Ribot (Théodule Armand).

L'évolution des idées générales. 5e éd. la8º. 1919

La psychologie allemande contemp. 4e éd. 8º. 1892

Riboudeault (Philippus) [RIBOUDEALDUS]. Sacrum Dei oraculum Urim & Thummim, a var. J. Spenceri excogitat. liberum. s8º. Genevae. 1685

R.I.C., *see* ROYAL IRISH CONSTABULARY.

Ricard (*mgr.* **Antoine).**

Sainte Claire d'Assise. éd. illust. la8º. 1895

Ricard (Auguste). L'ouvreuse de loges. 5t. s8º. 1832

Ricardo (David). Three letters on the price of gold, 1809. [J. H. Univ. P2619]. 8º. [Baltimore. 1903]

Ricardo (Halsey). The perfect citizen. 8º. 1920

Ricardus, *Anglicus, Medicus.* Anatomia vivorum [c. 1225; tr.], *see* CORNER (G. W.) Anatom. texts of earlier M. A., 1927.

Ricardus, *Corinensis, Monachus Westmonasteriensis, see* CIRENCESTER (RICHARD, *of*).

Ricardus *de San-Germano.* Chronica priora ; ed. A. Gaudenzi, adj. ejusdem R. Chron. post. ex ed. G. Pertzii, *see* FERRARIA. Ignoti monachi Cisterc. Chron. &c., 1888.

Ricasoli (*il barone* **Bettino),** *see* HANCOCK (W. K.) R. & the Risorgimento in Tuscany, 1926.

Riccardi (Antonio Ricci-) *see* RICCI-RICCARDI (A.)

Riccho (Antonio). Opere, int. Fior de Delia. Stãpata nouamente. s8º. [Venetiis. 1508]

Ricci (Corrado).

Baukunst u. dekor. Skulptur d. Barockzeit in Italien. 4º. St. 1912

Beatrice Cenci. 2v. 8º. Milano. 1923

Beatrice Cenci. 8º. Milano. 1925

Beatrice Cenci. Tr. M. Bishop & H. L. Stuart. 2v. 8º. [1926]

Béatrice Cenci. Tr. M. Hélys. 8º. 1926

Figure e figuri del mondo teatrale. 8º. Milano. 1920

Ore ed ombre dantesche. s8º. Firenze. [1921]

Raffaello. fol. Milano. 1920

Ravenna. [Italia artist., 1]. 5ª ed. la8º. Bergamo. 1905

Ravenna e i suoi dintorni. s8º. Ravenna. 1878

La statua di Guidarello Guidarelli. [P2870]. 3ª ed. la8º. Ravenna. 1897

L'ultimo rifugio di Dante. 2ª ed. s4º. Milano. 1921

Umbria santa. 8º. Milano. 1926

„ „ Tr. H. C. Stewart. 8º. [1927]

see DANTE ALIGHIERI. La Divina Commedia ; a cura di C. R., 3v, 1921.

„ —— Lect. D. : c. 5 dell' Inferno letta da C. R., 1899.

Ricci (Serafino).

Works in REALE ACCAD. D. LINCEI. Mon. ant., v2, 1893.

Miscellanea epigrafica.

Il pretorio di Gortyna sec. un disegno &c. d. sec. 16.

Il " Testamento d'Epikteta," con testo, tr. &c.

Ricci (Seymour de).

The book collector's guide. Pract. hdbk. of Brit. & Amer. bibl. 8º. Phila. 1921

Cat. d'une coll. des éditions orig. de Ronsard. [*w.* Suppl. Maggs Bros.] la8º. [1925]

Les chasses royales de Louis XV : Peintures par J.-B. Oudry. [P2524]. s8º. 1921

Les mss. de la coll. H. Y. Thompson, *see* SOC. FRANÇ. DE REPROD. DE MSS. &c. Bull., Ann. 10, 1926.

A note on the Robert Schuhmann coll. of 18th c. French books. [P2428]. 8º. Phila. [1920]

Un nouv. ms. épigraph. de Peiresc. [*Extr. f.* Revue Arch., 1900. P2870]. 8º. 1900

Der Stil Louis XVI. Mobiliar u. Raumkunst. Hrsg. S. de R. 4º. St. [1913]

see AMHERST OF HACKNEY (W. A. T.-A., *1st b.*) Hand-list of coll. of books & MSS. ; comp. by S. de R., 1906.

Riccio (David) [RIZZIO], *see* STEUART (A. F.) Seigneur Davie : life of D. R., 1922.

Ricci Paternò Castello (Maria). Nuove poesie. 8º. Firenze. 1885

Poesie. s8º. Firenze. 1880

Ricci-Riccardi (Antonio). Galileo Galilei e fra Tommaso Caccini. Il processo d. G. nel 1616 &c. 8º. Firenze. 1902

Ricciuti (Vittorio).

Vincenzo Gemito. [*a. c. in* P2517]. la8º. Milano. 1920

Riccobaldi del Bava (Giuseppe Maria). Diss. d. Etrusca nazione e d. città di Volterra &c. 8º. Firenze. 1758

Riccoboni (*Mme.* **Marie Jeanne),** Letters f. E. S. de Valiere to L. H. de Canteleu. Tr. Maceuen. 2v. s8º. 1772

see CROSBY (E. A.) Une romancière oubliée, Mme. R. : sa vie, s. œuvres &c., 1924.

Rice (Elmer L.)

The adding machine. Foreword by P. Moeller. s8º. 1923

Rice (James), *M.A.* Relativity. Systematic treatment of Einstein's theory. 8º. 1923

Rice (R. Garraway), *ed., see* SUSSEX. S. apprentices & masters, 1710–52, 1924.

Rice (Stanley), *see* MAHĀBHĀRATA. Tales f. the M. [*verse*], by S. R., 1924.

Rice (William Gorham).

Carillons of Belgium & Holland. 8º. 1915

Ricemarch, *the Wise, bp. of St. David's* [RHYGYFARCH]. Life of St. David (11 c.) [Tr., w. sel. f. o. lives, & notes] by A. W. Wade-Evans. s8º. 1923

Rice-Oxley (Leonard), *see* ANTI-JACOBIN (THE) : poetry of the A.-J. ; ed. &c. L. R.-O., 1924.

Rich (Henry), *earl of Holland, see* HOLLAND (H. R., *e. of*).

Rich (Wesley Everett). Hist. of the U.S. post office, to 1829. [Harvard Econ. St., v27]. 8º. C., Mass. 1924

Richard, *of Cluny* [RICHARD *of Poictiers*], *see* SCHNACK (I.) Richard von C., s. Chronik u. s. Kloster, 1921.

Richard I, *king of England.*

see AYTOUN (W. E.) Life & times of R. I. 1840.

„ COURT OF KING'S BENCH. Curia Regis rolls, R. I &c., 1922.

„ NORGATE (K.) R. the Lion Heart, 1924.

„ PIPE ROLLS. Great Roll of the P. for 2nd–5th year[s] of R. I, 1190–93 ; ed. D. M. Stenton, 1925–27.

Richard II, *king of England.*

see CLOSE ROLLS. Cal. of C.R., R. II, v2–6, 1381–99, 1920–27.

„ CURTIS (E.) R. II in Ireland, 1394–95, 1927.

„ FINE ROLLS. Cal. of Fine Rolls, v9, 1377–83, 1926.

„ ZIEPEL (C.) The reign of R. II, & comments upon an allit. poem on deposition, 1874.

Richard III, *king of England.*

see CAMPBELL (O. J.) Position of the *Roode en Witte Roos* in the saga of King Richard III, 1919.

„ MORE (*Sir* T.) Latina opera (Hist. R. III &c.), 1566.

Richard, *of Poictiers, see* RICHARD, *of Cluny.*

Richard, *de Saint Victor.* Trattato de' quattro gradi d. carità, volgariz., *see* BELCARI (F.) Prose, v3, 1843.

Richard (Camille). Le Comité de Salut Public & les fabricat. de guerre sous la Terreur. la8º. 1922

Richard (Henry), *1812–1888, see* APPLETON (L.) H. R., apostle of peace, 1889.

Richard (Jules Marie). La vie privée dans une prov. de l'Ouest. Laval au 17e & 18e s. 8º. 1922

Richard (Pierre P. J.)

Le poète Louis Le Cardonnel. 8º. Avignon. 1925

Richard (René). *La vie du véritable père Josef, Capucin ; cont. l'hist. anecdote du card. de Richelieu. s8º. La Haye. 1705

Richard (Timothy), *see* SOOTHILL (W. E.) T. R. of China, 1924.

Richard O'Monroy (*le vte.*), *ps.* A grandes guides. s8º. *n.d.*

Richards (Charles Russell).

Industrial art & the museum. 8º. N.Y. 1927

Richards (Francis Shakespeare). Note on the age of the temple of Ammon at Karnak. [Survey of Egypt.] la8º. Cairo. 1921

Richards (Grant). Double life. s8º. 1920

Richards (H. Grahame). The leper. s8º. [1920]

Richards (Herbert Paul). Aristotelica. 8º. 1915

Notes on Xenophon & others. 8º. 1907

Richards (Ivor Armstrong).

Principles of lit. criticism. 8º. 1925

Science & poetry. s8º. 1926

see OGDEN (C. K.) & I. A. R. The meaning of meaning, 1923.

Richards (Laura Elizabeth). Marie. 8º. Boston [U.S. 1894]

Melody. 8º. 1896

Richards (Thomas), *M.A., D.Litt.* The relig. census of 1676, *see* CYMMRODORION SOC. Trans. 1925–26, Suppl., 1927.

Richards (Thomas Bingham), *see* WESTWOOD (A.) M. Boulton's medal on reconq. of Naples, 1799, & events, by [T. B. R.], 1926.

Richards (Walter). Her Majesty's Army. Descr. acc. of var. regiments &c. 3v. 4º. [1888–91]

Richards (Wm. Urmston Searle Glanville-), *see* GLANVILLE-RICHARDS (W. U. S.)

Richardson (Albert Edward) & H. D. Eberlein.

The Eng. inn past & present. 8º. [1925]

The smaller English house of the later Renaissance, 1660–1830. 4º. [1925]

Richardson (Albert Edward) & C. L. Gill. Regional architecture in West of England. 4º. 1924

Richardson (Alexander). The logicians school-master : a comm. on Ramus Logick. Added h. prelections on Ramus his Grammar ; Taleus his Rhetorick ; also notes on physicks &c. [*Prelect. on gramm. beg. sep. pagin.*] s8º. 1657

Richardson (Caroline Francis).

Eng. preachers & preaching, 1640–70. 8º. 1928

Richardson (Charles), *Wesleyan, see* COULSON (J. E.) The peasant preacher : mems. of C. R., 1867.

Richardson (Dorothy). The book of Blanche. s8º. [1924]

Richardson (Dorothy M.) [*Mrs.* ALAN ODLE].

Deadlock. s8º. [1921]

Revolving lights. s8º. [1923]

Richardson (E. C.) The ski-runner. 8º. [1910]

see HOEK (H.) & E. C. R. Der Ski u. s. sportl. Benutzung, 2e A., 1907.

„ SOMERVILLE (D. M. M. C.), W. R. RICKMERS & E. C. R. Ski-running, 1904 ; 2nd ed., 1905.

Richardson (*Lt.-Col.* **Edwin Hautonville).**
Watch-dogs: their training & management. 2nd ed. 8º. 1924

Richardson (*Mrs.* **Ethel Mary).** The lion & the rose. (The great Howard story). Norfolk line, 957–1646. Suffolk line, 1603–1917. 2v. 8º. [1923]
Next door neighbours (at 9 & 10 Grafton St., W.) [*i.e.* Hon. Mrs. Calvert, Helen, Lady Stronge &c.] 8º. 1926

Richardson (Gwen).
On the diamond trail in Brit. Guiana. s8º. [1925]

Richardson (*Mrs.* **Hannah),** *see* WESLEY (C.) A short acc. of the death of H. R., 1766; 1775.

Richardson (Henry Handel).
Maurice Guest. [3rd impr.] s8º. 1922

Richardson (Holden Chester). Hydromechanic experiments w. flying boat hulls, 1914, *see* SMITHSONIAN INST.: Misc. coll., v62, 1923.

Richardson (Hubert N. B.) A dict. of Napoleon & h. times, w. maps &c. & bibliog. la8º. 1920

Richardson (James), *the African traveller, 1806–51, see* PETERMANN (A. H.) Acc. of exped. to C. Africa, under R. &c., 1850–53, 1854.

Richardson (James), *vicar of Huntingdon.* Popery brought to the test &c. A review of the declar. of the R. Cath. bps. &c. in Gt. Brit. 8º. 1827
Popery unmasked. Ans. to T. Baddeley's Sure way &c. John Fox defended. 8º. 1825

Richardson (*Major* **John),** *see* RIDDELL (W. R.) J. R., 1923.

Richardson (John), *bp. of Ardagh.* Choice obs. & explan. upon the Old Test. &c. Added, larger obs. upon Genesis [*w. sep. pagin.*] fol. 1655

Richardson (John), *B.D., fellow of Emmanuel College.* Canon of the New Test. vindicated; in ans. to J. T[oland] in h. Amyntor. 2nd ed., corr. w. add. s8º. 1701

Richardson (John), *F.S.A.* A diss. on the lang., lit. & manners of Eastern nations. Added p2. 2nd ed. 8º. O. 1778
Gram. of the Arabick lang. s4º. 1776

Richardson (Joseph), *Barrister-at-law.* The fugitive, *see* †INCHBALD (E.) Mod. th., v8, 1811.

Richardson (Robert Douglas). Causes of the pres. conflict of ideals in Ch. of England. s8º. 1923

Richardson (William), *print-seller, see* GRANGER (J.) Cat. of R.'s coll. of Eng. portraits, *n.d.*

Richardson (William), *prof. of humanity in the Univ. of Glasgow, see* GRAHAM (P.) Essay on authenticity of poems of Ossian &c.; added, essay on mythology of O.'s poems, 1807.

Richarz (Carl). Die Wikinger-Fahrt der "Tinto." s8º. [1917]

***Richborough:** the anc. Rutupiæ. By W. D. 3rd ed. [P2878]. s8º. Deal. 1919

Richelieu (*le card. duc* **de).** Méms. Publ. [sous la dir., de L. Delavaud *&c.*, par R. Gaucheron, E. Dermenghem &c. [Soc. de l'Hist. de F.] t5–8 (1625–1628). 8º. 1921–[27]
Rapports & notices sur l'éd. des Méms. du card. de R. Prép. sous la dir. de J. Lair &c. [Soc. de l'Hist. de Fr.] t3. 8º. 1922
Traité de la perfection du Chrestien. n. éd. s8º. [Rouen]. 1671
see RICHARD (R.) Vie du père Josef; cont. l'hist. anecdote du card. de R., 1705.
„ TOUCHARD-LAFOSSE (G.) Rollicking chron., v1, According to the Cardinal; tr., 1928.
„ VAISSIÈRE (P. DE). L'affaire du Maréchal de Marillac, 1630–32 [un gr. procès sous R.], 1924.
„ VALLE (D.) P. Monod e le sue relaz. col Card. R., 1910.

Richelieu (*le maréchal duc* **de)** [†DUPLESSIS (LOUIS F. A.)]
Mém. Notes &c. par F. Barrière. 2t [*in* 1v]. s8º. 1889

Richelieu (Armand Emmanuel S. S. Du Plessis, *duc* **de).** Corr. & doc. inéd., 1766–1822, publ. M. Polovtsoff, *see* †IMPERATORSKOE RUSSK. IST. OBSCH. Sbornik, v54, 1887.
see JORISSEN (TH.) Hist. Karakters, 1, R. en Maria de Medicis, 1912.

Richelieu (François Du Plessis, *seigneur* **de),** *gr. prévost de France; 1548–90, see* DELOCHE (M.) Les Richelieu: le père du Cardinal: F. du P.: doc. inéd., 1923.

Richepin (Jean). Les glas. Poèmes. s8º. [1922]
Théatre en vers. [t1–3]. s8º. [1919–21]
1, L'étoile—Nana-Sahib—Mons. Scapin—Le flibustier.
2, Par le glaive—Vers la joie. 3, La martyre—Le chemineau.

Richer (A.) Les Touareg du Niger (région de Tombouctou-Gao); les Oulliminden. Lettre-préf. du Maréchal Joffre. Préf. de M. Delafosse. la8º. 1924

Richer (Edmond) [RICHERIUS (EDMUNDUS)]. *Apologia pro J. Gersonio pro suprema Eccl. & Concilii auctoritate &c. Per E. R. D. T. P. [*i.e.* Edm. Richerius, Div. Theol. Prof.] s4º. Lugduni Batav. 1676

Richer (Paul).
Nouv. anatomie artistique. Les animaux. [t]1. 8º. 1910
Nouv. anatomie artistique du corps humain. [t]1–5. 8º. 1920–26
1, Cours pratique: élém[s]. d'anatomie, l'homme.
2, Cours supérieur: morphologie, la femme.
3, Physiologie, attitudes & mouvements.
4, 5, Cours supérieur: le nu dans l'art, [t1, 2].

Richert (Gertrud). Barcelona. la8º. Hamburg. 1927

Richertz (Lorenz Dieterich). Diss. de Sam. Huberi vita, fatis & doctrina. Praes. J. A. Schmidio. [P596]. s4º. Helmstadii. 1708

Richet (Charles). Dict. de physiologie. t10. la8º. 1928
L'intelligence & l'homme. 8º. 1927
Le savant. [Caractères de ce temps]. s8º. [1923]
30 years of psychical research: treatise on metaphysics. Tr. S. de Brath. 8º. [1923]
Traité de métapsychique. la8º. 1922

Richey (James Alexander). Grants-in-aid to schools in Brit. India. Ed. J. A. R. [Bureau of Educ., India. P2739]. 8º. Calcutta. 1923
see INDIA: EDUCATION. Progress of educ. in I., 1917–22; by J. A. R., 2v, 1923–24.

Richey (James Ernest), G. V. Wilson & E. M. Anderson. Econ. geology of the Ayrshire coal fields. [Geol. Survey, Scotland]. 2v. 8º. E. 1925
Area 1, Kilbirnie, Dalry, & Kilmaurs; by J. E. R., G. V. W. & E. M. A., w. contrib. by C. H. Dinham.
Area 2, Kilmarnock Basin &c.; by E. M. A., w. contrib. by G. V. W.

Richey (Margaret F.) Gahmuret Anschevin: contrib. to study of W. von Eschenbach. 8º. O. 1923

Richie (James), *M.D.* The peculiar doctrines of revelation rel. to piacular sacrifices, redemption by Christ &c. 2v *in* 1. s4º. Warrington. 1764

Richkov (Petr Ivanovich). Топографія или описаніе Оренбургской губ. [*Extr. f.* Соч., 1762, ч2]. [*b. w.* Müller (G. F.) О началѣ &c. Козаковъ, 1760]. s8º. [1762]

Richmond. *Guide to R., incl. Wensleydale & Rokeby. *b. w.* Stevenson's Hist. of Leighton Buzzard, 1850]. s8º. Richmond. 1860
*Hist. of R., 1814, *see* CLARKSON (C.)
Marriage bonds for the deaneries of Lonsdale, Kendal, Furness & Copeland, archdeaconry of R., now preserved at Lancaster, 1648–1710. Ed. J. Brownbill, 1711–22. Ed. R. Stewart-Brown. [Record Soc. for Lancs. & Cheshire, v74, 75]. [2p]. 8º. 1920–21

Richmond Park. Extr. f. the recs. of Parl. &c. rel. to the transfer & possess. of R.P. by the city of London, 1649–60. Ed., w. intr., by Sir T. J. Nelson. la8º. 1883

Richmond, *dukes of, see* KENT (J.) Recs. &c. of Goodwood & dukes of R., 1896.

Richmond (Charles Lennox, *3rd duke of***),** *see* GLENIE (J.) Obs. on the duke of R.'s extensive plans of fortification, 1794.

Richmond (*Mrs.* **Cora L. V.),** *see* HATCH (C. L. V.), *aft. (1) Tappan, (2) Richmond.*

Richmond (Ernest Tatham). Moslem architecture, 623–1516; causes &c. [Roy. A. Soc.] la8º. 1926

Richmond (George), *R.A.*
see BINYON (L.) Followers of W. Blake: G. R. &c., 1925.
„ STIRLING (A. M. W.) The Richmond papers f. corr. & MSS. of G. R. &c., 1926.

Richmond (*vice-adm. Sir* **Herbert William).** National policy & naval strength. [Raleigh lect. From Proc. of Brit. Acad., v11. P2717]. 8º. [1923]
„ „ & o. essays. Foreword by Lord Sydenham. 8º. 1928
The Navy in the war of *1739–48.* 3v. 8º. 1920

Richmond (Ian Archibald). Rel. of the Praetorian Camp to Aurelian's Wall of Rome, *see* BRIT. SCHOOL AT ROME. Papers, v10, 1927.
see CORDINGLEY (R. A.) & I. A. R. The Mausoleum of Augustus, 1927.

Richmond (Leonard) & J. Littlejohns. The art of painting in pastel. Introd. by F. Brangwyn. 4º. [1920]
The technique of water-colour painting. 4º. 1925

Richmond (W. D.)
The grammar of lithography. 6th ed. rev. 8º. 1886

Richmond (Wilfrid), *see* HOLLAND (H. S.) Philos. of faith & The 4th Gospel; ed. W. R., 1920.
Richmond (*Sir* William Blake), *K.C.B.*
Democracy, false or true? s8°. [1920]
see STIRLING (A. M. W.) The Richmond papers f. corr. & MSS. of G. R. & h. son Sir W. R., 1926.
Richmond & Lennox (Frances Teresa Stuart, *duchess of*), *wife of 3rd duke of Richmond & Lennox, see* STUART (F. T.), *duchess of Richmond & Lennox.*
Richter (A. Ludwig), *see* HOFFMANN (L.) L. R. als Radierer, 1921.
Richter (Adolph Friedrich) & A. J. Ballmann. Illyr.-deut. u. deut.-illyr. Handwörterbuch.
2T[2, bearb. v. R. Fröhlich]. 8°. Wien. 1839–40
Richter (Albert). Quellenbuch. Für d. Unterricht in d. deut. Gesch. Hrsg. E. Kornrumpf. 7e A. 8°. L. 1912
Richter (Gisela M. A.) Anc. furniture: Greek, Etruscan & Roman. App. by A. W. Barker. 4°. O. 1926
Richter (Helene).
Gesch. d. engl. Romantik. B2i. 8°. Halle a. S. 1916
Richter (Jean Paul), *see* NORTHBROOK (T. G. B., *1st e.*) Descr. cat. of coll. of pictures; Ital. & Span. schools, by R., 1889.
Richter (Jean Paul F.) [JEAN PAUL]. Briefe, 1780–1804. Hrsg. u. erläut. v. E. Berend. 4B. 8°. München. 1922–26
Leben des Quintus Fixlein &c. s8°. L. *n.d.*
see HARICH (W.) Jean Paul, 1925.
Richter (Johann Georg). Sing. quasdam M. Lutheri de matrimonio sententias examinat J. G. R.
[P2633]. s4°. Lipsiae. 1752
Richter (L.) & A. E. Marshner, *edd.* Alte u. neue Studenten Lieder, mit Bildern & Singweisen. s8°. L. [1844]
Richter (Matthäus) [M. JUDEX].
see MAGDEBURG CENTURIES. Centuriae Magdeb. [*by M. J. & others*], 4v, 1757–65.
„ WIGAND (J.) & M. R. Syntagma seu corpus doctrinae Christi, ex Novo Test., 1575.
„ —— & —— Syntagma seu corpus doctrinæ veri &c. Dei ex Vet. Test., *n.d.*
Richter (Paul). Der Rheingau. la8°. Wiesbaden. 1913
Richter (Raoul).
F. Nietzsche, s. Leben u. s. Werk. 4te A. 8°. L. 1922
Richthofen (Manfred, *Frhr.* **von).**
Der rote Kampfflieger. 101. bis 150. Tausend. s8°. 1917
Ricius (Paulus). De cœlesti agricultura libri 4, *see* PISTORIUS (J.) Artis Cabalist. t1, 1587.
Lepida & literę vndiq. concinna in psalmū Beatus vir meditatio. Concisa de modo orandi in nomine Tetragrammaton responsio.
s4°. [Augustae Vindelic., *S. Grimm. & M. Wirsung.* 1519]
Rickaby (Joseph), *S.J.*, *see* BRAYE (A. T. T. V.-C., *5th b.*) Lutterworth lect. on Xty. & lang. by var. a. (J. R. &c.), 1913.
Rickard (*Mrs.* Victor) [RICKARD (JESSIE LOUISA)].
A bird of strange plumage. s8°. [1927]
Blindfold. s8°. [1922]
A reckless puritan. s8°. [1920]
Upstairs. s8°. 1925
Rickards (Edith C.)
Bishop Moorhouse of Melbourne & Manchester. 8°. 1920
Rickert (Edith). Early Eng. romances in verse: done into mod. Eng.: romances of love. s8°. 1908
see MANLY (J. M.) & E. R. Contemp. American lit., 1922.
Rickert (Heinrich). Die Philos. d. Lebens. Darstellung u. Kritik. d. philos. Modeströmungen uns. Zeit.
8°. Tübingen. 1920
Ricketts (Charles S.), *see* LEGROS (A.) Cat. of paintings &c. by A. L., f. coll. of F. E. Bliss; w. apprec. by C. R., 1922.
Rickman (Anne), *aft. Lefroy, see* LEFROY (*Mrs.* A.)
Rickmers (W. Rickmer), *see* SOMERVILLE (D. M. M. C.), W. R. R. &c. Ski-running, 1904; 2nd ed., 1905.
Rickword (Edgell). Rimbaud: the boy & the poet. 8°. [1924]
Ricotti (Ercola). Breve commem. d. c. F. Sclopis, *see* REGIA DEP. DI STORIA PATRIA. Misc., t18, 1879.
Riddell (Agnes Rutherford). Flaubert & Maupassant: a literary relationship. 8°. Chicago, Ill. 1920
Riddell (Florence). Out of the mist. s8°. [1925]
Riddell (George Allardice Riddell, *1st baron*).
Dame Louisa Aldrich-Blake. 8°. [1926]
Ethical, legal & med. aspects of abortion. [*b. w. h.* Legal resp., 1925]. 8°. [1927]
The law & ethics of med. confidences. [*b. w. h.* legal resp., 1925]. 8°. [1927]

Riddell (George Allardice Riddell, *1st baron*) [*continued*].
The legal responsibility of the surgeon. 8°. [1925]
More things that matter. 8°. 1925
Some things that matter. 8°. 1922
Riddell (Walter Alexander).
The rise of eccl. control in Quebec. 8°. N.Y. 1916
Riddell (William Renwick).
John Richardson. s8°. Toronto. [1923]
William Kirby. [Poems, w. biog., apprec. &c.]
s8°. Toronto. [1923]
Ridder (Alfred de), *ed.*, *see* NOBLESSE BELGE (LA), 1913.
Ridder (André de).
La litt. flamande contemp. (1890–1923). 8°. Anvers. 1923
—— & W. Deonna.
L'art en Grèce. [L'évol. de l'humanité]. 8°. 1924
Art in Greece. [Tr. V. C. C. Collum]. 8°. 1927
Ridding (*Lady* Laura Elizabeth), *eldest d. of 1st e. of Selborne.*
The life of Robert Palmer, 1886–1916. 8°. [1921]
Rider (Cardanus). Rider's sheet almanack, 1777. [*b. w.* Royal Kalender, 1777]. s8°. [1776]
Rider (Dan).
Ten years' adventures am. landlords & tenants. 8°. [1927]
Rider Court. Reg. of Church of R.C., 1700–38. Ed. W. & S. Minet. [Huguenot Soc. of London, v30]. 4°. Frome. 1927
Ridgaway (Henry B.), *D.D.*
The life of E. S. Janes, D.D. s8°. N.Y. 1882
Ridge (William Pett). Ernest escaping. s8°. [1926]
Miss Mannering. s8°. [1923]
Richard triumphant. s8°. [1922]
A story teller: 40 yrs. in London. 8°. [1923]
Ridges (Edward Wavell).
Constit. law of Eng. 3rd ed. [ed.] S. E. Williams. 8°. 1922
Ridgley (Douglas Clay).
The geography of Illinois. s8°. Chicago. 1921
Ridgway (Cecile de), *see* EDWARD III. Letter for pardon to C. de R., 1358, 1822.
Ridgway (Robert). The birds of North & Middle America. [S.I.: U.S. Nat. Mus., Bull. 50]. p8. 8°. Wash. 1919
Diagnoses of some new genera of birds, *see* SMITHSONIAN INST.: Misc. coll., v72, 1922.
Ridgway's peerage of the United Kingdom, 1846. s8°. 1846
Riding (Laura) & R. Graves.
A survey of modernist poetry. s8°. 1927
Ridinger (Fr.) Taschenb. für Einspänner. s8°. L. 1826
Ridley (Glocester). Life of Dr. N. Ridley. 4°. 1763
Ridley (Henry N.) Flora of the Malay Peninsula. 5v. 8°. 1922–25
Ridley (Nicholas), *bp. of London.* A brief declar. of the Lord's Supper. Repr., w. intr. &c. & a life by H. C. G. Moule.
s8°. 1895
De Coena Dominica assertio contra sceleratam illam transubstãtiationis haeresim, quam è carcere author scripserat. [*Foll. by* Praefatio &c. habitae in scholis publ. Oxonii, 1555. *sep. signatures*]. s8°. Genevæ. 1556
see LANGDALE (A.) Catholica confut. impiae cuiusdam determinat. N. R., 1556.
„ RIDLEY (G.) Life of Dr. N. R., 1763.
Ridola (Domenico), *see* QUAGLIATI (Q.) & D. R. Necrop. ad incineraz. pr. Timmari nel Materano, 1906.
Ridolfi (*il cav.* Carlo). Le maraviglie dell' arte, ouero le vite degli illust. pittori veneti &c. 2p [*in 1v*]. 8°. Venetia. 1648
„ „ Hrsg. v. Detlev Frhr. v. Hadeln.
2p. 8°. Berlin. 1914–24
Ridolphinus (Petrus). De ordine procedendi in judiciis in Romana curia praxis recentior. Access. constit. Eugeniana, Innocentiana, Gregoriana, Urbana, Decretum Camerale, Reformationes tribunalium urbis, Facultates Populi Romani.
4a ed. purgata. fol. Coloniae Agrippinae. 1680
Ridpath (George), *minister of Stitchill.* Border hist. of Eng. & Scotland, to the Union. Rev. by P. Ridpath.
n. ed. 4°. Berwick. 1848
Diary, 1755–61. Ed. w. notes & intr. by Sir J. B. Paul. [Scot. Hist. Soc., s3, v2]. 8°. E. 1922
Ridpath (George), *pamphleteer.* *An answer to the Scotch Presbyterian eloquence. s8°. 1789
Corr. betw. G. R. & R. Wodrow (1706–19), *see* ABBOTSFORD CLUB: Misc., v1, 1837.
Riebeek (Jan Anthony van), *see* MOLSBERGEN (E. C. G.) De stichter v. Hollands Zuid-Afrika, J. v. R., 1912.
Riedel (Ch. V.) Teplitz & ses charmes. s8°. Prague. 1834

Riederer (Johann Bartholomäus). Nachrichten z. Kirchen-Gelehrten u. Bücher-Gesch. ausgedr. u. ungedr. Schr. gesammlet. v. J. B. R. 4B *in* 2v. s8°. Altdorf. 1764–68
Riedl (Richard). Sandschakbahn u. Transversallinie. [P2735]. 8°. Wien. [1908]
Rieger (Erwin). Stefan Zweig. s8°. 1928
Rieger (Georg Conrad). Die alte u. neue Böhmische Brüder als deren merckwürdige u. erbaul. Hist. zu e. verlangten Fortsetzung d. ehemal. Saltz-Bundes &c. 24 Stücke *&* Anhang [*in* 3v]. s8°. Züllichau. 1734–40
Rieger (Martin). Ein Predig v. d. verborgnen Schatz u. köstl. Perlein, Matth. 13. [P2613]. s4°. Tübingen. 1587
Rieger (U.), *see* Rhegius (U.)
Riegger (Joseph Anton Stephan von). *Amoenitates literariae Friburg. [De J. Wimphelingo &c.] 3 fasc. *in* 1v. [*pagin. cont.*] 8°. Ulmae. 1775–76
Riegl (Alois). Die Entstehung d. Barockkunst in Rom. Hrsg. A. Burda u. M. Dvořák. 2e A. 8°. Wien. 1923
Die spätröm. Kunst-Industrie nach d. Funden in Österreich-Ungarn. [Österr. Arch. Inst.] 2T. la. fol. Wien. 1901–23
T2 *has t.* Kunstgewerbe d. frühen M.-A.: auf Grundlage d. nachgelass. Materials A. R.; bearbt. E. H. Zimmermann.
Spätrömische Kunstindustrie. [n. A.] 8°. Wien. [1927]
Riehl (Alois).
Fr. Nietzsche, Künstler u. Denker. [P2477]. 8°. St. 1898
Riemann (Bernhard). Gesammelte mathemat. Werke u. wissenschaftl. Nachlass. Hrsg. v. H. Weber. 2e A. la8°. L. 1892
Riemann (Hugo). Analysis of Bach's Wohltemperirtes Clavier. Tr. J. S. Shedlock. 3rd ed. pl. 8°. [1890]
Riemsdijk (B. W. F. van). Hist. beschr. van het Klooster van Sinte Agatha met het Prinsenhof te Delft, benevens een Catal. d. Verzameling & e. lijst d. boeken in de Hist. Zaal aanwezig. 3e Druk. 8°. 's-Gravenhage. 1912
Ries (Franz Ulrich). Tract. de asylis sive urbibus refugii V. T. [P2666]. s4°. Marburgi. 1753
Riesch (Helene). Die heil. Hildegard v. Bingen. 2e u. 3e verb. A. s8°. Freiburg i. B. [1920]
Riesemann (Oskar von). Monographien z. russ. Musik. B1, 2. 8°. München. 1923–26
1, Die Musik in Russland vor Glinka.—Glinka.—Dargomyshski.—Sseroff. 2, M. P. Mussorgski.
Riess (Ludwig). Engl. Verfassungsurkunden d. 12. u. 13. Jhdts.; hrsg. v. L. R., *see* Kleine Texte, T155, 1926.
Rietschel (Georg). Weihnachten in Kirche, Kunst u. Volksleben. la8°. Bielefeld. 1902
Rietstap (Johannes Baptist). Armorial général. Suppl. par V. H. Rolland. 2t. 8°. 1926
t1 *includes* prelim. fasc. 1–4 & App. 1, 2 [*each w. sep. pagin.*]
Planches de l'Armorial gén. de J.-B. R. Par. V. Rolland. t4, 5 [L–S]. 4°. 1912–21
Riezler (Sigmund). Die Landnahme d. Baiuwaren, *see* Königl. Akad. d. W. zu München. Phil. Kl., Sitz., 1920.
—— **& C. v. Wallmenich.** Akten z. Gesch. d. bair. Bauernaufstandes, 1705–6, 3T, 1912–15, *see* Königl. Akad. d. W. zu München, Abhdlgn. d. phil. Kl., B26, 29, 1914–18.
Rifat (Mansur M.) Die Ahmadia-Sekte [*&* Anhang: Der Verrat d. Ahmadis an Heimat u. Relig. P2733]. 8°. 1923
Rigaud (Hyacinthe), *see* Roujon (H.) H. R., 1913.
Rigaudie (Pierre Chilhaud de la), *see* Chilhaud de La Rigaudie (P.)
Rigeway (Cecile), *see* Ridgway (C. de).
Rigg (Caroline E.) In mem. Caroline Rigg. *p.f.p.c.* s8°. 1892
Rigg (Caroline), *wife of J. H. Rigg, see* Rigg (C. E.) In mem. C. R., 1892.
Rigg (James Harrison).
The character &c. of Dr. Pusey. s8°. 1883
Congreg. independency & Wesleyan connexionalism contrasted. [P2538, 2585]. s8°. 1851
Essays for the times on eccl. & soc. subjects. 8°. 1866
Mem. of the Rev. John Rigg. [Extr. f. The Wesleyan-Methodist mag. P601]. *f.p.c.* 8°. 1859
The principles of Wesleyan Methodism &c. s8°. 1850
The Sabbath & the Sabbath law. [P2523]. 8°. 1869
Rigg (John).
How to conduct a meeting. [repr.] s8°. [1923]
How to take the chair. s8°. [1925]
Rigg (*Rev.* John), *see* Rigg (J. H.) Mem. of J. R., 1859.
Riggenbach (Christoph Johannes), *see* Evangelical Alliance. 7e Hauptversammlung, Basel; hrsg. C. J. R., B1, 1879.
Riggenbach (Eduard). Der trinitär. Taufbefehl. [P2791]. 8°. Gütersloh. 1903

Riggieri (*Mesdemoiselles*), *actresses, dit Colombe, see* Colombe.
Rigging. *A treatise on r.: wr. about 1625, f. a MS. at Petworth House. Ed. by R. C. Anderson. [Soc. for Naut. Research]. [P2525]. 8°. 1921
Riggs (Elias), *D.D.* A manual of the Chaldee lang. 2nd ed. rev. 8°. N.Y. 1858
Righetti (Pietro). Descr. del Campidoglio. 2t. fol. 1833–36
Righi (Ettore Scipione). Iscrizioni stor.-lapid. per la città e prov. di Verona. [Nozze Bertani-Peloso. N127]. 8°. [Verona. 1865]
Right. *Right & wrong in the Ruhr valley, 1923, *see* Ruhr.
*Right (The) divine of kings to govern wrong, 1821, *see* Hone (William).
Rignano (Eugenio).
Biol. memory. Tr. w. intr. by E. W. MacBride. 8°. 1926
Psychologie du raisonnement. 8°. 1920
The psychology of reasoning. Auth. tr. by W. A. Holl. 8°. 1923
The social significance of death duties. Adapted f. Dr. Schultz's tr. by Sir J. Stamp. s8°. [1925]
Rigobon (Pietro). Di Nicolò e Francesco Donà Veneziani del settecento. [Estr. d. Annuario d. R. S. Sup. di Comm. P2836]. la8°. Venezia. 1910
Rigomer, Les mervelles de, *see* Jean, *author of R.*
Riguet (*l'abbé*). St. Patrice. s8°. 1911
Rigutini (Giuseppe). Diz. lat.-ital. e ital.-lat. 3a ed. riv. &c. 8°. Firenze. [1910]
Riley (Franklin Lafayette). General Robert E. Lee after Appomattox. Ed. F. L. R. 8°. N.Y. 1922
Riley (J.), *B.Sc.* The age of power: 1st book of energy, its sources &c. s8°. [1921]
Riley (N. D.) & A. G. Gabriel, *see* Brit. Museum: Zoology. Cat. of type specimens of Lepidoptera Rhopalocera in B.M., pl, 2, 1924–25.
Riley (William). The lady of the lawn. s8°. 1921
A village in Craven: sk. f. the Yorks. Pennines. 8°. 1925
Riley (Woodbridge), F. W. Peabody & C. E. Humiston. Faith, falsity & failure of Christian Science. 8°. [1926]
Rilke (Rainer Maria).
Die Aufzeichnungen d. Malte Laurids Brigge. s8°. L. 1926
Duineser Elegien. 8°. L. 1923
Erzählungen u. Skizzen aus d. Frühzeit. s8°. L. 1928
Die frühen Gedichte. 8°. L. 1922
[Gesamm. Werke]. 6B. s8°. L. 1927
1–3, Gedichte. 4, 5, Schr. in Prosa. 6, Ubertragungen.
Geschichten v. lieben Gott. s8°. L. 1927
Die Weise v. Liebe u. Tod d. Cornets Christoph Rilke. s8°. L. [1926]
see Bianquis (G.) Poésie autrich., 1926.
,, Jaloux (E.) R. M. R., 1927.
Rimbaud (Isabelle).
Reliques. [Rimbaud mourant &c.] 2é éd. s8°. 1921
Rimbaud (Jean Nicolas Arthur).
see Carré (J. M.) Vie aventureuse de J. A. R., 1926.
,, Coulon (M.) Le problème de R., poète maudit, 1923.
,, Delahaye (E.) R.: l'artiste & l'être moral, 1923.
see Rickword (E.) R.: the boy & the poet, 1924.
,, Rimbaud (I.) Reliques (R. mourant &c.), 1921.
Rime.
De le rime di div. nobili poeti toscani, 1565, *see* Atanagi (D.)
Rime ant. d'autori faentini, 1846, *see* Zambrini (F. S.)
Rime di diversi celeb. poeti &c., 1587, *see* Licino (G. B.)
Rime di diversi eccellenti autori bresciani, 1553, *see* Ruscelli (G.)
Rime di poeti ital. del sec. 16, 1873, *see* Ceruti (A.), *ed.*
Rime di var. autori bresciani viventi, 1761, *see* Roncalli Parolino (C.)
Rime diverse di molti eccell. auttori nuov. racc., libro primo, 1545, *see* Domenichi (L.)
Rime e prose d. buon sec., 1852, *see* Bini (T.), *ed.*
*Rime scelte de' poeti Ferraresi ant. e mod. Agg. brevi notizie istor. s4°. Ferrara. 1713
Saggio di rime di div. buoni autori, 14–18 sec., 1825, *see* Saggio.
Rimington-Wilson (Reginald Henry). Cat. of chess lib., w. sel. f. sporting & gen. lib., prop. of R.-W. Sold by Sotheby, Feb. 1928. la8°. 1928
Rimius (Heinrich). A cand. narr. of the rise & progr. of the Herrnhuters, called Moravians, with acc. of th. doctrines &c. 2nd ed. 8°. 1753
,, ,, Suppl. [*b. w. h.* Cand. narr., 2nd ed., 1753]. 8°. 1755
Memoirs of the House of Brunswick, to the end of the r. of George I. Added, 8 tables. 4°. 1750

Rimius (Heinrich) [*continued*].
A solemn call on Ct. Zinzendorf, to answer charge brought in Candid narr. &c. 2nd ed. [*b. w. h.* Cand. narr., 2nd ed., 1753]. 8º. 1754
„ „ A second solemn call on Mr. Zinzendorf &c. 2p. [*b. w. h.* Cand. narr., 2nd ed., 1753]. 8º. 1757
Rimmer (W. B.) Luminosities & parallaxes of 500 stars. [Repr. f. Mem. of Roy. Astrom. Soc., v62]. [P2701]. 4º. 1923
Luminosities & parallaxes of 525 stars, types Fo to Mb. [Repr. f. Mem. of Roy. Astron. Soc., v64. P2768]. 4º. 1925
Rimscha (Hans v.)
Russland jenseits d. Grenzen, 1921–26. 8º. Jena. 1927
Rimsky-Korsakov (Nikolai Andreevich). My musical life. Tr. by J. A. Joffe, ed. w. intr. by C. Van Vechten. 8º. 1924
Principes d'orchestration, avec exemples &c. Réd. de M. Steinberg. Tr. M. D. Calvocoressi. 2[t]. la8º. 1914
Rinaldis (Aldo de). Bernardo Cavallino ; 26 riprod. con testo e catalogo. 8º. [1921]
Rinaudo (Costanzo). Corso di storia gen. v2–5. [v2, 4ª ed., v3, 7ª ed., v4, 5, 6ª ed.] s8º. Firenze. 1899–1900
Cronologia d. stor. d'Italia. 2ª ed. s8º. Firenze. 1900
Rinck (Eucharius Gottlieb). Bibliotheca Rinckiana, seu supellex librorum tam impress. quam Mss. &c. Cum praef. A. F. Glafey. 8º. Lipsiae. [1747]
Rinckhard (Martin). Monetarius seditiosus sive incendia rusticorum bellica & reliqua ejus lustri memorabilia. Der Müntzerische Bawrenkrieg so a. 1525 &c. [*drama in verse*]. s8º. L. [1625]
Rindom (Erik). Minder fra Studenterdagene. [*By* O. Bloch &c.] Red. E. R. 8º. København. 1924
Rinehart (Mary Roberts). The amazing interlude. s8º. 1918
Lost ecstasy. s8º. [1927]
The mystery lamp. s8º. [1925]
Ring (Walter), *see* AVERDUNK (H.) & W. R. Gesch. d. Stadt-Duisburg ; hrsg. v. W. R., 1927.
Ringholz (Odilo), *O.S.B.* Der selige Markgraf Bernhard v. Baden in s. Leben u. Verehrung. 8º. Freiburg im Br. 1892
Rinieri (Ilario). Della rovina di una monarchia. Rel. stor. tra Pio VI e la corte di Napoli, 1776–99, sec. doc. ined. dell' archivo Vaticano. la8º. Torino. 1901
see CONSALVI (E.) & B. PACCA. Corr. ined. dei card. C. e. P., 1814–15 ; corr. di sommarii e note, prec. da una st. stor. sugli stati d'Europa &c. [*by*] I. R., 1903.
Rink (Johann). Diss. de origine & progressu tritheismi. Praes. J. G. Walchio. [P434]. s4º. [Jenae. 1732]
Rintelenses. *Brevis relat. colloq. inter theologos Marpurg. & Rintel. &c., 1662 ?, *see* MARBURG.
Rintoul (Leonora Jeffrey), *see* BAXTER (E. V.) & L. J. R. Some Scot. breeding duck &c., 1922.
Rinuccini (Ottavio). Poesie. 8º. Firenze. 1622
Rio (Ignacio Jordan de Asso y del), *see* ASSO Y DEL RIO (I. J. DE).
Rio de Janeiro. Cat. da mappotheca do Min. das Rel. Exteriores, p1, Limites do Brasil. la8º. Rio de Janeiro. 1926
BIBLIOTHECA NACIONAL.
Annaes da B.N. do Rio de Janeiro ; publ. sob. a admin. do M. C. Peregrino da Silva. v38–42. la8º. Rio de Janeiro. 1920–25
Each vol. also cont. the ann. rep. of the Bibl. Nac.
38, Conferencias 1914—Hist. ou Annaes dos feitos da Co. Priv. das Indias Occid., até ao fim de 1636 por J. de Laet ; tr. J. H. D. Pereira e P. Souto Maior, livros 8–10.
39, Inventario dos doc. rel. ao Brasil, Archivo de Marinha e Ultramar ; organ. por E. de Castro e Almeida, [t]6.
40, Idéa de população da capitania de Pernambuco &c., 1774, do J. C. de Menezes—Conferencias 1915.
41, 42, Hist. ou Annaes dos feitos da Co. Priv. das Indias Occid., liv. 11–13—Cat. da Expos. biblio-iconog. commem. do 6° Cent. de Dante.
Boletim bibliog. Anno 1, 3, 1918, 1920. la8º. Rio de Janeiro. 1918–24
Cat. da Expos. biblio-iconogr. commem. do 6. centen. de Dante. la8º. Rio de Janeiro. 1925
Rioja (Antonio Perez), *see* PEREZ RIOJA (A.)
Riordan (Edward J.) Modern Irish trade & industry. With hist. intr. by G. O'Brien. s8º. [1920]
Ripalda (Juan Martinez de), *see* MARTINEZ DE RIPALDA (J.)
Ripert (Emile). L'or des ruines. s8º. [1921]
Ripley (George), *misc. writer, see* FROTHINGHAM (O. B.) G. R., 1882.
Ripley (William Zebina).
Main Street & Wall Street. 8º. [1927]
The races of Europe. A sociol. study. [repr.] 8º. *n.d.*
Ripman (Walter). The sounds of spoken English. n. version, rewr., w. add. s8º. 1921
Ripon. *Hist. of R.: w. descr. of Studley-Royal, Fountains' Abbey &c. 2nd ed. s8º. Ripon. 1806
Ripon (George F. S. Robinson, *1st marq. of*), *see* WOLF (L.) Life of 1st Marq. of R., 2v, 1921.
Rippy (J. Fred.) The United States & Mexico. 8º. N.Y. 1926
Risch (Adolf). Luthers Bibelverdeutschung. [Verein f. Ref.-gesch. Schr., Jhrg. 40 (Nr. 135)]. 8º. L. 1922
Risco (Alberto), *S.J.* Mil hombres. Rasgos biog. del Gen. D. F. de P. Romero y Palomeque. 2ª ed. s8º. 1920
Risdon (P. J.) Wireless. Intr. by J. A. Fleming. 8º. [1924]
Rising (Lawrence). She who was Helena Cass. s8º. [1920]
Risorgimento. Catalogo d. oggetti del R. ital. [p3], Documenti. [Esp. Ital. di Torino 1884]. sm. fol. Milano. 1894
Riss (Petr) [RYSS]. L'expérience russe. Tr. & préf. de R. Labry. s8º. 1922
Rist (Charles). Les finances de guerre de l'Allemagne. 8º. 1921
see GIDE (C.) & C. R. Hist. des doctrines écon., 4ᵉ éd., 1922.
„ —— & —— Hist. of econ. doctrines ; tr., 1917.
Rist (Johann), *see* KERN (O.) J. R. als weltlicher Lyriker, 1919.
Ristori (Rodolfo Jacuzio).
Pozza, e il Guerin Meschino. la8º. Milano. 1920
***Ristretto** d. vita dell' apost. S. Francesco Xaverio, 1622, *see* SCORTIA (F.)
Rita, *ps.* [*i.e. Mrs.* ELIZA M. J. VON BOOTH, *aft. Mrs.* W. DESMOND HUMPHREYS].
Conjugal rights & o. s. s8º. [1922]
Daphne. s8º. Phila. 1888
Diana of the Ephesians. new & rev. ed. s8º. [1927]
The farm of Melchizedek. s8º. [1924]
Our Miss Acadee. s8º. [1926]
The ungrown-ups. s8º. [1923]
Ritchie, *The family of, see* RITCHIE (G.) The Ritchies in India, 1920.
Ritchie (A. E.) The Kent coalfield. s8º. [1920]
Ritchie (Arthur David). Scientific method : inq. into character &c. of natural laws. 8º. 1923
Ritchie (Elizabeth). *Authentic narr. of departure of late J. Wesley, 1791. [Signed E. R. P2658]. 8º. Bristol. 1791
Ritchie (Gerald). The Ritchies in India. Extr. f. corresp. of Will. Ritchie, 1817–62 ; Personal remin. of G. R. Comp. & ed. by G. R. 8º. 1920
Ritchie (James). The influence of man on animal life in Scotland, a study in faunal evolution. 8º. C. 1920
Ritchie (Leitch), *see* TURNER (J. M. W.) Liber fluviorum, or, river scenery in France : letter-press by R., 1857.
Ritchie (Moore). A woman of the desert. s8º. [1921]
Ritchie (*Mrs.* **Richmond Thackeray)** [†THACKERAY (ANNE ISABELLA)]. Letters, w. 42 addit. letters f. W. M. Thackeray. Sel. & ed. H. Ritchie. 8º. 1924
„ „ ....[repr.] 8º. 1924
Old Kensington. 8º. 1891
Ritchie (Robert Lindsay Graeme), *see* ALEXANDER, *the Gt.* Buik (The) of A. ; ed., w. intr., notes &c., by R. L. G. R., v1–3, 1921–27.
Ritchie (William), *of the Calcutta Bar & Inner Temple* ; 1817–62, *see* RITCHIE (G.) The Ritchies of India : extr. f. corresp. of W. R., 1817–62 &c., 1920.
Ritius (Michael). De regibus Francorum—Hispaniæ—Hierosolymorũ—Neapolis & Siciliæ—Ungariæ lib. s8º. Basileæ in officina Frob. 1534
De regibus Hisp., *see* HISPANICA. Rer. Hisp. scr., t2, 1579.
Ritmeier (Christoph Heinrich). Progr. de hodierno Xtnorum Graecorum statu &c. [P2644]. s4º. Helmstadii. 1710
Ritschel (George), *1616–83, see* YOUNG (R. F.) Bohemian philos. at Oxf. : G. R., 1925.
Ritschl (Albrecht). De ira Dei. [P2655]. 4º. Bonnae. 1859
Ritschl (Friedrich Wilhelm), *see* CORPUS inscr. Lat., v1, Tabulae lithographae : Priscae Lat. mon. epigraphica ; ed. F. R., 1862.
Ritson (Joseph), *ed.* *Robin Hood : coll. of all poems &c. rel. to [R. H.] ; pref., hist. anecd. of h. life. [repr., w. abridged notes]. s8º. 1820
Robin Hood : a coll. of all poems &c. rel. to [R. H.] ; pref., hist. anecd. of h. life. *large paper copy.* la8º. 1885
Rittangel (Johann Stephan). Bilibra veritatis & rationis de verbo Dei librae &c. s8º. Freistadii. 1700
Rittenhouse (Jessie B.), *editor.* The little book of modern verse. Sel. f. work of contemp. Amer. poets. Ed. J. B. R. s8º. Boston. [1913]

Ritter (Eugène), *of Geneva*. La famille & la jeunesse de J. J. Rousseau, *see* SOC. JEAN-JACQUES ROUSSEAU. Annales, t16, 1926.

Ritter (Johann Balthasar). Eigentl. Beschreib. d. Lebens &c. Mat. Flacii Illyr. [*b. w.* Fischer (E. R.) Vita I. Gerhardi, 1723]. s8°. Franckfurth a. M. 1723

Ritter (Johann Daniel). Tract. de pago Steding & Stedingis seculi 13 haereticis. [P2641]. s4°. Wittebergae. 1751

Ritter (Moriz).
Die Entwicklung d. Geschichtswiss. 8°. München. 1919

Ritter (Otto).
Vermischte Beitr. z. engl. Sprachgesch. 8°. Halle (Saale). 1922

Ritter (William). Smetana. 8°. 1907

Ritual of the Methodist Episc. Church, 1851, *see* METHODIST.

Rituale.
R. eccl. &c. co-ordin. a B. Sannig. ed. 7ª corr. s8°. Coloniae. 1756
R. eccl. Dunelm.; n. & rev. ed., 1927, *see* DURHAM.
R. Romanum, 1628, *see* PONTANUS (G. B.) Aureum diurnale &c., 1629.
R. Rom. Urbani VIII jussu ed. Illyrica lingua. s4°. Romae. 1640
R. Rom. Benedicti XIV jussu editum, & auctum, perpetuis comm. exorn. &c. Auctore J. Catalano. 2t. fol. Romae. 1757
R. Rom. Pauli V jussu ed., nunc a Benedicto XIV auctum &c. 8°. Venetiis. 1757
R. Rom. Pauli V jussu ed. ed. ult. aucta &c. s8°. Tarascone. 1820
R. Rom. Pauli V Pont. Max. jussu ed. & a Benedicto XIV auctum &c. Acc. benedictionum & instruct. app. Nov. ed. Romana. 8°. Romae. 1874
R. Trangambaricum. [*Lutheran liturgy in Tamil, w. append.* De bapt. infant., *w. sep. pagin.*] s8°. [Tranquebar. 1781]

Ritz (Joseph Maria).
Unterfränk. Barockschlösser la8°. Augsburg. 1925
Das unterfränk. Dorf. la8°. Augsburg. 1924

Rivadeneyra (Manuel). Biblioteca de autores españoles, desde la formacion del lenguaje hasta nuestros dias. [repr.] t27. la8°. 1926

Rivander (Zacharias), *ps.* [*i.e.* ZACHARIAS BACHMANN]. Interrogatoria, Darauff Petrus Streuberus v. e. jeden dessen consilium oder auxilium er auff s. Christlich Gutachten &c. begeret, befraget &c. [P2438]. s4°. Franckfurt a/O. 1591
Lupus excoriatus oder d. offentl. u. heiml. Calvinisten u. aller Sacramentierer Wölffner Schaffspeltz &c. s4°. [Wittenberg?]. 1591

Rivarol (Antoine), *1754–1801* [A., *cte.* DE RIVAROL], *see* LATZARUS (L.) La vie paresseuse de R., 1926.

Rivas (Angel de Saavedra, *duque* **de).**
see MARTINEZ RUIZ (J.) R. y Larra, 1921.
,, PEERS (E. A.) A. de S., crit. study, 1923.
,, —— R. & romanticism in Spain, 1923.

Rivas (Jose Pablo), *see* ESTEVA (A. A.) & J. P. R. Parnaso mexicano: antología con notas biogr., 2t, *n.d.*

Rivera (Fadrique Enriquez de), *see* ENRIQUEZ DE RIVERA (F.)

Rivers (John). Figaro: the life of Beaumarchais. 8°. [1922]

Rivers (William Halse Rivers).
Conflict & dream. Pref. by G. E. Smith. 8°. 1923
Dreams & primitive culture. [Repr. f. Bull. of J. Rylands Lib., v4]. 8°. M'ter. 1917–18
Essays on the depopul. of Melanesia. [*By var. wr.*] Ed. W. H. R. R., w. pref. by Sir E. Im Thurn. s8°. C. 1922
Instinct & the unconscious. Contrib. to biolog. theory of the psycho-neuroses. 8°. C. 1920
,, ,, ...2nd ed. 8°. C. 1922
Medicine, magic, & religion. FitzPatrick Lect. Pref. by G. E. Smith. 8°. 1924
Psychology & ethnology. Ed. w. pref. &c. by G. E. Smith. 8°. 1926
Psychology & politics & o. essays. Pref. note by G. E. Smith, & an apprec. by C. S. Myers. 8°. 1923
Social organization. Ed. W. J. Perry. 8°. 1924
see HEAD (H.) Studies in neurology; by H. H. in conjunction w. W. H. R. R. &c., 2v, 1920.

Rivet (André).
see GROTIUS (H.) Testament of hooftpunten getrocken wt sijn jongste antwoort aen D. R. (1645), *n.d.*
,, —— Votum pro pace eccl. contra examen A. R. &c., 1642.

Rivet (Charles). Chez les Slaves libérés. [2] Des Alliés de demain: les Tchécoslovaques. s8°. 1921

Rivett (Albert Cherbury David). The phase rule & the study of heterogeneous equilibria. s8°. O. 1923

Rivière (Georges). Renoir & ses amis. s4°. 1921

Rivière (Jacques). Aimée. 24ᵉ éd. s8°. 1922

Rivière (Jacques) & P. Claudel.
Corr., 1907–14. [Le roseau d'or, Œ. &c., 6]. 8°. 1926

Rivington (Charles Robert). 1403–1903: short acc. of the W. Co. of Stationers &c. fol. 1903

Rivington (Septimus).
Hist. of Tonbridge School, f. 1553. 4th ed. rev. 8°. 1925

Rivinus (Andreas). Περὶ τῆς τοῦ πεταλισμοῦ ἰατρείας πολιτικῆς, 1654, *see* SCHLÄGER (C. J.) Diss. fasc. nov., 1744.

Rivinus (Tilemann Andreas). Hodegetici ad artem concionatoriam Carpzoviani uberior explan. [*b. w.* Carpzov (J. B.) Hodegeticum, 1689]. s8°. Lipsiae. 1686

Rivius (Joannes), *of Attendorn*. De instaurata renovataque doct. eccl. libellus. [*b. w.* Bucer (M.) Scripta duo, 1544]. s4°. Lipsiae. 1541
De perpetuo in terris gaudio piorū libellus &c. s8°. Basileæ. [1550]

Rivoira (G. Teresio). La Chiesa del Santo Sepolcro in Gerusalemme. [P2699]. 4°. 1916
Roman architecture under the Empire; w. app. on the dome to 17 c. Tr. G. M. Rushforth. 4°. O. 1925

Rivoli. *Memorie di un terrazzano di R., 1535–86; [*ed. D. C. Promis*], *see* REGIA DEP. DI STORIA PATRIA. Misc., t6, 1865.

Rivosecchi (Mario). La basilica di Tolentino. [*With Fr., Span. & Eng. tr.*] s8°. Firenze. 1927

Rizal (José), *see* RUSSELL (C. E.) & E. B. RODRIGUEZ. Hero of the Filipinos: J. R., 1924.

Rizo (Juan Pablo Martir), *see* MARTIR RIZO (J. P.)

Rizzetti (*il conte* **Luigi).**
Riforma de' carri di quattro ruote. 8°. Trevigi. 1785

Rizzi (Ignazio Neumann), *see* NEUMANN RIZZI (I.)

Rizzio (David), *see* RICCIO (D.)

Rizzo (Giulio Emanuele). Vasi greci d. Sicilia, *see* REALE ACCAD. D. LINCEI. Mon. ant., v14, 1904.

Rizzo (Valentino), *see* MANCHESTER (C. M., *1st d. of*). *Letters conc. h. embassy to Venice*, 1697; ed. V. R., 1890.

Roa (Armando). Span. business grammar. 8°. N.Y. 1924

Roach (Edward Keith-), *see* KEITH-ROACH (E.)

Road, *Somerset*. *Road (The) murder [of F. S. Kent]. By a Barrister-at-Law. [P2827]. 8°. 1860

Roadbuilder, *ps.*, *see* MACKENDRICK (*Lt.-Col.* W. G.)

Roaf (Herbert Eldon). Biological chemistry. s8°. 1921

Roback (Abraham Aaron), *Ph.D.*
Behaviorism & psychology. s8°. Cambridge [U.S.] 1923

Robar (Heinrich) [ROBARIUS]. Compendium elencticum relig. inter no Reformats & ils Papâls. s8°. Scuol. 1721
Compendium relig. Christ. Tschanta & miss in nos ling. tras H. R. s8°. Strada. 1693

Robarts (Henry), *attached to court of James I, see* ROBERTS (H.)

Robb (Alfred Arthur).
The absolute relations of time & space. 8°. C. 1921

Robbers (Herman).
De bruidstijd van Annie de Boogh. 7ᵉ dr. 8°. 1917
De gelukkige familie. [De roman van een gezin, 1]. 4ᵉ dr. s8°. A. 1919
Eén voor één. [De roman van een gezin, 2]. 3ᵉ dr. s8°. A. 1916

Robbertsen (Jan). Herders-Zanghen, *see* AMSTERDAM. A. Pegasus, 1627.

Robbia (Giovanni della), *see* DELLA ROBBIA (G.)

Robbins (*Sir* **Alfred Farthing).**
Parnell: the last 5 years. 8°. [1926]
The Press. s8°. [1928]
see PETER (C. H.), O. B. PETER & A. F. R. Launceston & Dunheved, 1925.

Robbins (Edwin Clyde). Railway conductors: st. in organ. labor. 8°. N.Y., *Columbia Univ.* 1914

Robbins (Frank Egleston), *see* NICOMACHUS, *Gerasinus*. Intr. to arithmetic; tr. M. L. D'Ooge, w. st. in Greek a. by F. E. R. &c., 1926.

Röber (Johann Friedrich) [ROEBERUS]. Diss. de magorum in Persia dominatione. [P2671]. s4°. Marburgi Catt. [1707]

Röber (Paul) & J. Stegmann. Disput. de indulgentiis pontificis: Propositiones quas 1517 promulgavit M. Lutherus &c. Præs. W. Franzio. [P2629]. s4°. Lipsiae. 1702

Röber (Paul Gottfried). Titulum pontif. Rom. Servi. servorum, disput., sub. praes. J. F. Mayeri. [P2670]. s4°. Wittenbergæ. 1715

Robert (*d'Artois*], *cte. de Beaumont-le-Roger, see* ALMÉRAS (H. D'). Un procès de faux &c. au m. â. [R. d'A.], 1927.

Robert II, *de Bellême, seign. d'Alençon &c., b. 1056, see* DU MOTEY (*vte.*) Le champion de la Normandie: R. II de B., 1923.

Robert, *de Clari.* La conquête de Constantinople. Ed. P. Lauer. [Classiques fr. du m-â]. s8º. 1924

Robert [*Curthose*], *duke of Normandy, see* DAVID (C. W.) R. C., duke of N., 1920.

Robert, *de Luzarches, see* BOUCHER (E.) R. de L.: discours, 1903.

Robert, *de L'Omme.* Le miroir de vie & de mort, 1266; [*ed.*] &c. A. Långfors, *see* ROMANIA, t47, 1921.

Robert (Carl), *prof. in Berlin.* Archäolog. Miszellen, *see* KÖNIGL. AKAD. D. W. ZU MÜNCHEN. Phil. Kl., Sitz., 1916.
see PRELLER (L.) Gr. Mythologie, 4e A., von C. R., 2i–iii, 1920–26.

Robert (Charles), *priest of the Oratory at Rennes.*
1795. Expéd. des émigrés à Quiberon. Le comte d'Artois à l'île d'Yeu. Préf. de A. de La Borderie. 8º. 1899

Robert (Henri).
L'avocat. s8º. [1923]
Un avocat en 1830. s8º. [1928]
Disc. pour la récept. de H. R. [*on* A. Ribot. Rép. de L. Barthou. Acad. Fr., 12 juin 1924. P2869]. 4º. 1924
L'effort de Paris. [P2718]. 8º. 1917
Les grands procès de l'hist. Préf. de M. L. Barthou. s1–6. s8º. 1922–28
Nos raisons de croire. Suivi d'une alloc. de G. Hanotaux. [P2758]. s8º. 1918

Robert (Louis de). L'amour un soir d'été. s8º. [1923]
Octavie, *see* ŒUVRES libres, 37, 1924.
Paroles d'un solitaire, souv., *see* ŒUVRES libres, 26, 1923.

Robert (Maurice). Le Katanga physique. 8º. Brux. 1927

Robert (Paul). Zur Herrschaft d. Seele. [P2491]. 8º. L. 1892

Robert (Ulysse). Inventaire des cartul. dans bibliothèques de Paris &c., suivi d'une bibliog. des cartul. publ. en France dep. 1840. 8º. 1878
,, ,, ...Suppl. [*b. w. above*]. 8º. 1879

Robert de Dreux (*le père*). Voyage en Turquie & en Grèce, 1665–69. Publ. &c. H. Pernot. 8º. 1925

Roberti (Guiseppe). Benedetto Patono di Meirano (1763–1830) e i suoi Mém. p. s. à l'hist. de la dern. guerre des Alpes, *see* REGIA DEPUT. Miscellanea, t41, 1905.
Il Cittadino Ranza, *see* REGIA DEPUT. Misc., t29, 1892.

Roberti (Joannes). Controversiae J. R. & J. Cujacii, *see* CUJAS (J. DE). Opera, t10, 1782.

Roberto (Federico de).
L'albero d. scienza. n. ed. s8º. Milano. 1911
La sorte. 3a ed. s8º. Milano. [1919]
Spasimo. Romanzo. n. ed. s8º. Milano. 1925
I vicerè. Romanzo. n. ed. 2v. s8º. Milano. 1920

Roberts (A. O.) Cloudbreak, *see* CLARKE (A. K.) 3 one-act plays, 1925.

Roberts (Askew) & E. Woodall. Gossiping guide to Wales (N. Wales & Aberystwyth). Popular ed. s8º. 1914

Roberts (C. E. Bechhofer-), *see* BECHHOFER-ROBERTS (C. E.)

Roberts (Cecil). Little Mrs. Manington. s8º. [1926]
Sagusto. s8º. [1927]
Sails of sunset. s8º. 1924

Roberts (Charles George Douglas). The house in the water: a bk. of animal life. 8º. [1908]

Roberts (David), *R.A.*
Picturesque sk. in Spain. atlas fol. 1837

Roberts (Francis). Clavis Bibliorum. Added metrical version of Bk. of Psalms. 4th ed. fol. 1675

Roberts (*Lt.-Col.* **Francis**). The Patmos Record. 8º. *n.d.*

Roberts (Frederick Sleigh Roberts, *1st earl*). Campaign speeches in cont. of Message to the Nation. [P2591]. 8º. 1913
Extracts f. division orders (Kabul). [P2593]. s8º. 1885
Letters wr. dur. the Mutiny. Pref. by Ctss. Roberts. 8º. 1924
Message to the Nation. [P2591]. 8º. 1912

Roberts (George), *of Lyme Regis.*
Hist. of Lyme Regis. s8º. Sherborne. 1823

Roberts (*Col.* **H. Harrington**).
Mem. of four-score years. la8º. *p.f.p.c.o.* 1920

Roberts (Harry). England: a national policy for labour. [Intr. by J. R. Clynes]. [P2485]. s8º. 1920

Roberts (Helen H.) & D. Jenness. Songs of the Copper Eskimos, *see* CANADIAN ARCTIC EXPED. Rep., v14, 1925.

Roberts (Henry), *attached to court of James I* [ROBARTS]. A most friendly farewell to Sir F. Drake. Transcr. w. intr. by E. M. Blackie. 8º. Cambridge, *U.S.* 1924

Roberts (Henry), *F.S.A.* The dwellings of the labouring classes &c. la8º. [1850]

Roberts (Henry David). The story of the Royal Pavilion, Brighton. [P2523]. 8º. 1915

Roberts (John), *D.I.C., F.G.S.* Coal carbonization. 8º. 1927

Roberts (*Rev.* **John**), *missionary, see* OLDEN (S. E.) Shoshone folk lore as disc. f. J. R. on Wind River Ind. Reserv. in Wyoming, 1923.

Roberts (Joseph), *M.R.A.S.* Oriental illust. of the Scriptures f. customs of the Hindoos. 2nd ed. corr. 8º. 1844

Roberts (Kenneth Lewis). Florida. 8º. N.Y. 1925

Roberts (Lawrence Graeme Allan). Brit. hist. traced f. Egypt & Palestine also the Anglo-Saxon original. 8º. 1919
Palestine into Britain, scripturally &c. consid. [*b. w. h.* Brit. hist. &c., 1919]. 8º. 1910

Roberts (Lydia Jane). Nutrit. & care of children in a mtn. co. of Kentucky, 1922, *see* UNITED STATES: LABOR.
What is malnutrition? *see* UNITED STATES: LAB. Children's Bur., No. 59 (rev.), 1927.
see HUGHES (E.) & L. J. R. Children of preschool age in Gary, Ind., 1922.

Roberts (Morley). Hearts of women. s8º. 1919
Rachel Marr. n. ed. s8º. 1925
Warfare in the human body. Essays on method, malignity, repair &c. Intr. by Prof. A. Keith. 8º. [1920]
W. H. Hudson: a portrait. 8º. [1924]

Roberts (Paul Ernest).
see INDIAN. I. viceroyalty, 1858–1921; [*by* P. E. R.], 1922.
,, LUCAS (*Sir* C. P.) Hist. geography of Brit. Dependencies, v7, India, p2, Hist. by P. E. R., 1920.

Roberts (Richard Arthur).
The reports of the Hist. MSS. Comm. s8º. 1920

Roberts (Robert E.), *D.D.*
The theology of Tertullian. 8º. 1924

Roberts (Stephen H.), *M.A.*
Population problems of the Pacific. 8º. 1927

Roberts (Sydney Castle). Doctor Johnson in Cambridge: essays in Boswellian imitation. [re-issued]. s8º. C. [1926]
Hist. of the Cambridge Univ. Press, 1521–1921. 8º. C. 1921
Picture book of Brit. history. Comp. by S. C. R. v2, 1485–1688. 4º. C. 1915

Roberts (Thomas). *Wesleyan minister, 1786–1832.*
Hymnology. 8º. Bristol. 1808

Roberts (William), *writer on English bookselling &c.* The cries of London. Intr. by C. R. Grundy. With 13 plates [by F. Wheatley]. 4º. 1924

Roberts (William James).
Literary landmarks of Torquay. 8º. 1905

Robertsbridge, *Sussex.* Calendar of charters & docs. rel. to Abbey of R., preserved at Penshurst am. muniments of Lord De Lisle & Dudley. 8º. 1873

Robertson, *The family of.*
see AIRD (G.) Geneal. of fam. of Douglas & Robertson of Kindeace, 1895.
,, ROBERTSON (J. A.) Comitatus de Atholia: possess. of fam. & th. desc. the R., 1860.

Robertson (Ainslie John). The laws of the kings of England from Edmund to Henry I. Ed. & tr. A. J. R. 8º. C. 1925

Robertson (Alexander). The life of Sir R. Moray. 8º. 1922

Robertson (Archibald), *of Charles St., St. James' Square.*
Topograph. survey of the great road f. London to Bath & Bristol. [2p *in* 1v.] 8º. 1792

Robertson (Archibald Thomas), *D.D.* Luke the historian in the light of research. 8º. E. 1920
Syllabus for New Test. study. [5th ed. rev. &c.] 8º. [1923]

Robertson (*Sir* **Benjamin**), *K.C.M.G.*
The famine in Russia. Report. [P2563]. 8º. 1922

Robertson (Charles Grant). England under the Hanoverians. [Hist. of England; ed. C. Oman, v6]. 6th ed. 8º. [1923]

Robertson (David), *M.A.* Brief acc. of the Clan Donnachaidh, w. notes on its hist. &c. 8º. Glasgow. 1894

Robertson (Dennis Holme). The control of industry. Intr. by J. M. Keynes. s8º. [1923]
Ebb & flow of unemployment. s8º. [1924]
Money. Intr. by J. M. Keynes. s8º. C. [1922]

Robertson (Eric Sutherland). Old St. Andrews. s8º. 1923

Robertson (Frederick Ewart). Arabic vocab. for Egypt: Arabic by Lûtfi Yûssef Ayrût. s8º. 1898

Robertson (*Sir* **George Scott**). Basic slags & rock phosphates. Pref. by E. J. Russell. 8º. C. 1922
Káfiristán & its people. [*no tp.*] fol. [1895]

Robertson (George Stuart). The law of copyright. Suppl. to Dec. 31, 1915. 8º. O. 1916

Robertson (George William). Rise &c. of the South Australian Protestant emigration community &c. [*w. map*]. 8º. 1837

Robertson (Howard).
Architecture explained. [2nd ed.] s8º. 1927
see ARCHITECTURAL ASSOC. SCHOOL. Book of design; intr. essays by R. Atkinson, H. R. &c., 1924.

Robertson (J. E. P.), *ed., see* JENNER-FUST (*Sir* H.) Stone altar case, 1845.

Robertson (James), *minister of Glenmuick & Glengairn, 1699–1748.* The barons Reid-Robertson of Straloch. s8º. Blairgowrie. 1887

Robertson (James A.) Comitatus de Atholia. Earldom of Atholl: possess. of fam. & th. desc. the Robertsons. 8º. *p.p.* [E.] 1860
Concise hist. proofs resp. the Gael of Alban; or, highlanders of Scotland. 2nd ed. s8º. 1866
see JOHNSTON (T. B.) & J. A. R. Hist. geog. of clans of Scot., 1872.

Robertson (James Alexander), *D.D., see* JESUS CHRIST. The sayings of Jesus of Nazareth; pref. by J. A. R., 1920.

Robertson (James Craigie).
Hist. of the Xtn. Church. 3rd ed. rev. 4v. 8º. 1864–73

Robertson (John George). The gods of Greece in German poetry. [Taylorian Lect.] 8º. O. 1924
Studies in the genesis of romantic theory in the 18th c. 8º. C. 1923
see ENG. GOETHE SOC. Publs., n.s., v2, Goethe & Byron; ed. J. G. R., 1925.

Robertson (John Mackinnon).
Charles Bradlaugh. s8º. 1920
The collapse of "Tariff Reform": Mr. Chamberlain's case exposed. Intr. by Rt. Hon. R. Rea. s8º. 1911
Explorations. 8º. [1923]
Miscellanies. s8º. 1898
1, Christ & Krishna. 2, Perversion of Scotland. 3, Thomas Paine. 4, Royalism. 5, Toryism & barbarism. 6, Socialism & Malthusianism. 7, Blunders of faith.
Mr. Lloyd George & Liberalism. s8º. 1923
Mod. humanists reconsidered. 8º. 1927
The problem of the Shakespeare sonnets. 8º. 1926
The Shakespeare canon. 3p. 8º. 1922–25
1, Origination of "Henry V"—Orig. of "Julius Caesar"—Authorship of "Richard III."
2, Authorship of "The two gentlemen of Verona"—A. of "Richard II"—A. of "The comedy of errors"—Problem of "Measure for measure."
3, "Acceptance" of Shakespeare—"All's well that ends well"—"Romeo & Juliet."
Short hist. of Xty. 2nd ed. rev., w. add. 8º. 1913

Robertson (*Sir* Johnston Forbes-), *see* FORBES-ROBERTSON (*Sir* J.)

Robertson (Joseph). Oor ain braw lads frae Kilmacolm under the flag. Tribute to their patriotism &c. Ed. J. R. [3rd ed.] 8º. 1915

Robertson (Manning). Everyday architecture: essays. Intr. by H. R. Selley. 8º. [1924]

Robertson (*Barons* Reid-), *of Straloch, see* REID-ROBERTSON.

Robertson (T.), *see* EASTWOOD (T.), T. R. &c. Geol. of the co. around Birmingham, 1925.

Robertson (William), *D.D., the historian; 1721–93.* An hist. disquis. conc. the knowledge which the ancients had of India &c. 8º. Basil. 1792
see BLACK (J. B.) Art of hist., 1926.

Robertson (William), *lexicographer, of Edinburgh.* A key to the Hebrew Bible &c. [*3 pagins.*] s8º. 1656

Robertson (*Field-Marshal Sir* William Robert).
From private to field-marshal. 8º. 1921
Soldiers & statesmen, 1914–18. 2v. 8º. [1926]

Robertson (William Spence). Hispanic-Amer. relations w. the U.S. Ed. D. Kinley. [C.E. for Int. Peace]. la8º. N.Y. 1923
Hist. of the Latin-American nations. rev. ed. 8º. N.Y. 1925

Robertson-Scott (J. W.) [*ps.* HOME COUNTIES].
The dying peasant & the future of h. sons. 8º. 1926
The foundations of Japan. 8º. 1922

Robertus, *Anglicus.* Le traité du quadrant de R. A., texte lat. & anc. tr. grecque, *see* TANNERY (P.) Mém. scient., t5, 1922.

Robespierre (Augustin Bon Joseph), *see* ROBESPIERRE (F. M. J. I.) Corr. de M. & A. R.; rec. &c. G. Michon, 1926.

Robespierre (F. Maximilien J. I.) Corr. de M. & A. Robespierre. Rec. & publ. par G. Michon. la8º. 1926
Rapp. s. les rapports des idées relig. &c. avec les principes républ. &c. [Convent. Nat. P2774]. 8º. [1794]
see DUPLAY (M.) R. chez les Duplay, 1928.
„ LENOTRE (G.) Le mysticisme révol.: R. & la "Mère de Dieu," 1926.

Robillard de Beaurepaire (Eugène), *see* LE ROY (T.) Curieuses recherches du Mont-Sainct-Michel; publ., avec intr. &c. par E. de R. de B., 2t, 1878.

Robin (Léon). La pensée grecque & les orig. de l'esprit sci. [L'évol. de l'humanité]. 8º. 1923

Robin (Raymond). Des occupations milit. en dehors des occup. de guerre. la8º. 1913

Robin (Vespasien), *see* TAMIZEY DE LARROQUE. Deux jardiniers émérites—Peiresc & Vespasien Robin, 1896.

Robinet (Jean), *conservateur du Musée Carnavalet.* Les vieux hôtels du Marais & du quartier Saint-Paul. s8º. [1927]

Robinet (*le dr.* Jean Fr. Eug.) Danton émigré. Recherches sur la diplomatie de la Républ., 1793. s8º. 1887

Robins (Benjamin). Mathemat. tracts. Cont. h. New principles of gunnery. Publ. by J. Wilson. 2v. s8º. 1761
Neue Grundsätze d. Artillerie; übers. &c. L. Euler, 1745, *see* EULER (L.) Opera omnia, s2, v14, 1922.

Robins (*Miss* Elizabeth), *aft. Mrs. G. R. Parks.* [*ps.* C. E. RAIMOND].
*Ancilla's share: an indictment of sex antagonism. 8º. 1924
The messenger. s8º. [1919]
The mills of the gods. s8º. 1920
The secret that was kept. s8º. [1926]
Time is whispering. s8º. [1923]

Robins (G. M.) [*Mrs.* L. BAILLIE REYNOLDS].
His second venture. s8º. [1924]

Robins (William Palmer).
Etching craft: guide for students &c. la8º. 1922

Robinson (Amy Edith), *see* KIDDER (R.), *bp.* Life; wr. by himself; ed. A. E. R., 1924.

Robinson (Arthur H. A.)
Titanium. [Canada: Geolog. Survey]. 8º. Ottawa. 1922
see CANADA. Geolog. Survey. Mineral industries of C.; comp. by A. H. A. R. &c., 1924.

Robinson (*Comm.* Charles Napier), *R.N.* Old naval prints, th. artists & engravers. Ed. G. Holme. [Publ. by The Studio]. 4º. 1924

Robinson (Clement). A handful of pleasant delights (1584), by C. R. & divers others. Ed. H. E. Rollins. 8º. C. [Mass.] 1924

Robinson (Corinne Roosevelt).
Service & sacrifice. Poems. s8º. N.Y. 1919

Robinson (E. S. G.), *see* LOCKER LAMPSON (G. L. T.) Cat. of anc. Greek coins coll. by G. L. L.; comp. by R., 1923.

Robinson (Edward), *D.D.* A conc. view of universities & state of theol. educ. in Germany. s8º. E. 1835
Four maps to accompany the Bibl. researches in Palestine of E. R. & Eli Smith. Drawn by H. Kiepert. folded 8º. Boston. 1856
A harmony of the 4 Gospels in the author. version &c. With explan. notes. 8º. [1847]
Phys. geography of the Holy Land. 8º. 1865

Robinson (Edward Kay), *see* FINN (F.) & E. K. R. Birds of our country, 2v, 1922–23.

Robinson (Edward Stanley Gotch), *see* WOODWARD (W. H.) Anc. Greek coins in poss. of W. H. W.; cat. by R., 1928.

Robinson (Edward Stevens).
Practical psychology. 8º. N.Y. 1927

Robinson (Edwin Arlington). Collected poems. 8º. N.Y. 1922

Robinson (Forbes). Letters to h. friends. Ed., w. intr. notice by h. brother Charles. 3rd ed. *p.f.p.c.* s8º. 1905

Robinson (George), *of the Society of Friends.* A short relation from G. R. of sufferings in journey to Jerusalem &c., *see* EVANS (C.) & S. CHEEVERS. A brief hist. of the voyage &c., 1715.

Robinson (George Platt).
The comedy of Peter Taunton. s8º. [1924]
The debt. s8º. [1921]

Robinson (Gleeson Edward). Publ. authorities & legal liability. Intr. chap. on Remedies agst. the Crown, by J. H. Morgan. la8º. 1925

Robinson (Harry Perry).
Pictorial effect in photography. 4th ed. s8º. 1893

Robinson (Heaton Bowstead).
Mem. of Sir T. Picton, incl. h. corr. 2v. 8º. 1835

Robinson (*Rt. Hon. Sir* **Henry Augustus**), *bart., K.C.B.*
Further mems. of Irish life. 8º. 1924
Memories: wise & otherwise. 8º. 1923

Robinson (Henry Crabb). Corr. w. the Wordsworth circle, 1808–66. Chron. arr. & ed. w. intr. &c. by E. J. Morley. 2v. 8º. O. 1927

Robinson (Henry Wheeler).
Life & faith of the Baptists. s8º. [1927]

Robinson (Herbert C.) The birds of the Malay Peninsula. v1, The commoner birds. la8º. 1927

Robinson (Howard). The development of the Brit. Empire. Ed. J. T. Shotwell. 8º. 1923

Robinson (James Harvey). Medieval & mod. times: intr. to hist. of Western Europe. Rev. to include the Gt. War, 1914–18. s8º. [1919]
The mind in the making: rel. of intelligence to social reform. 8º. N.Y. [1921]
„ „ [n. & rev. ed.] w. intr. by H. G. Wells. 8º. [1923]
The ordeal of civilization: develop. &c. of present-day institutions &c. 8º. N.Y. 1926
see BREASTED (J. H.), J. H. R. &c. Outlines of Europ. hist., 2p, *n.d.*

—— & C. A. Beard. Development of mod. Europe: intr. to st. of current hist. 2v. w. Suppl. s8º. Boston, U.S. [1907–18]

Robinson (John), *Bengalee translator.* Dict. of law & o. terms employed in the courts of Bengal. In Eng. & Bengalee. 8º. Calcutta. 1860

Robinson (John), *Secretary to the Treasury; 1727–1802.* Parliamentary papers, 1774–84. Ed. W. T. Laprade. [Roy. Hist. Soc., III, 33]. 8º. 1922

Robinson (*Sir* **John Charles**). The early Portuguese school of painting, *see* FINE ARTS QUARTERLY REVIEW, N.S., v1, 1866.
see MALCOLM (J.) Cat. of drawings forming collect. of J. M.; by J. C. R., 1869.

Robinson (Joseph Armitage), *dean of (1) Westminster, (2) Wells.*
Barnabas, Hermas & the Didache. Donnellan Lect., 1920. s8º. 1920
The Saxon bishops of Wells, 10th cent. [Brit. Acad.: Suppl. Papers, 4]. 8º. [1919]
Somerset historical essays. la8º. 1921
The times of St. Dunstan. Ford Lect., 1922. 8º. O. 1923
Two Glastonbury legends: King Arthur & St. Joseph of Arimathea. s8º. C. 1926
An unrecognized Westminster chronicler, 1381–94 [*contin. of Higden*], 1907, *see* BRIT. ACAD. Proc., 1907–8.
see APOCRYPHA. Excl. bks. of the New Test.; intr. by J. A. R., 1927.
„ IRENAEUS, *St.* Demonstration of apostolic preaching; tr. R., 1920.

Robinson (*Sir* **Joseph Benjamin**), *Bt.* Cat. of coll. of pictures by old masters of Sir J. B. R., sold by Christie &c., July 6, 1923. [*Illust.*] la8º. 1923

Robinson (Lennox). Golden treasury of Irish verse. 8º. 1925
The whiteheaded boy. Comedy. Intr. by E. Boyd. s8º. D. 1922

Robinson (M. E.) Public finance. Intr. J. M. Keynes. 8º. [1922]

Robinson (Mark), *see* WELCH (C.) An investig. of M. R.'s Obs. on the syst. of Wesl. Methodism, 1825.

Robinson (*Mrs.* **Mary**), *poetical writer; 1758–1800* [*ps.* PERDITA], *see* BARRINGTON (E.), *ps.* The exquisite P., *fiction*, 1926.

Robinson (Mary V.) Domestic workers & th. employment rel., *see* UNITED STATES: LABOR. Women's bur., Bull. 39, 1924.

Robinson (Matthew), *vicar of Burneston, Yorks.* Autobiography, *see* MAYOR (J. E. B.) Cambridge in the 17th cent., p2, 1856.

Robinson (Peter Frederick).
Designs for farm buildings. 4º. 1830
Designs for ornamental villas. 4º. 1827
Village architecture: designs illust. of Essay on the picturesque by Sir U. Price &c. 4º. 1830

Robinson (Richard), *citizen of London, see* LELAND (J.) The assertion of King Arthure; tr. by R. R. f. L.'s Assertio inclytissimi Arturii (16c.); ed. &c. W. E. Mead, 1925.

Robinson (Rodney Porter). De fragmenti Suetoniani de gramm. & rhetor. codicum nexu & fide. [Illinois: Univ. of. Studies in lang. & lit., v6iv]. la8º. Urbana. 1922

Robinson (Rowland Evans). Vermont. 8º. Boston. 1892

Robinson (*Mrs.* **Sarah Jane**). Offic. rep. of trial of S. J. R. for murder of P. A. Freeman. Sup. Judic. Court of Mass. [1888]. 8º. Boston [Mass.] 1888

Robinson (Theodore Henry).
Outline intr. to hist. of religions. 8º. 1926
Prophecy & the prophets in anc. Israel. Bibliog. by A. S. Peake. [2nd imp.] s8º. [1925]

Robinson (Vincent J.) Eastern carpets: 12 early examples w. descr. notes by V. J. R. & pref. by Sir F. Birdwood. [2 ser.] fol. 1882–93

Robinson (Wilfrid C.) Antwerp: hist. sketch. 8º. 1904
Bruges: hist. sketch. 8º. Bruges. 1899

Robinson (William), *F.L.S.*
Alpine flowers for Eng. gardens. 3rd ed. 8º. 1879
The Eng. flower garden. 5th ed. 8º. 1897
Wood fires for the country house &c. la8º. [1924]
see VILMORIN-ANDRIEUX ET CIE. The vegetable garden; Eng. ed. publ. under dir. of W. R., 3rd ed., 1920.

Robinson (William), *LL.D., 1777–1848, see* ABRAHAMS (A.) Life & works of W. R., w. Indices to Hist. &c. of Edmonton [*& h. o. works*] by J. Ardagh, 1925.

Robinsonaden. Sammlung v. Abenteurergesch. früh. Jhdte.; bearbt. &c. v. M. Lehnert, 5B, 1916–20, *see* LEHNERT (M.)

Robiquet (Jacques), *see* PARIS: MUSÉE DE L'ARMÉE. Cat. des armes &c., par J. R., 1916.

Robison (John). The articles, Steam & steam-engines, wr. for Encyclop. Brit. by R., w. notes & add. by J. Watt, & a letter by J. Southern. 8º. E. 1818
see ANTI-JACOBIN. New lights on Jacobinism, abs. f. R.'s Hist. of free masonry, 1798.

Robles (Luis Ballesteros), *see* BALLESTEROS ROBLES (L.)

Robles (Vito Alessio), *see* ALESSIO ROBLES (V.)

Robles Pezuela (Luis), *see* MEXICO. Memoria pres. por el Ministro de Fomento, L. R. P., de los trabajos ejecut. en su ramo, 1865, 1866.

Roblot-Delondre (*Mme.* **Louise**). Portraits d'infantes, 16e siècle: èt. iconogr. 4º. 1913

Robolotti (Francesco). Pergamene e casi di Cremona avanti il mille, *see* REGIA DEP. DI STORIA PATRIA. Misc., t1, 1862.
see VIGNATI (C.) Commem. di F. R., 1887.

Robolsky (Hermann).
*Bismarck in Frankfurt. Von ***. 8º. L. 1885

Robsart (Amy), *d. 1560* [†DUDLEY (AMY), *wife of Ld. R. Dudley, aft. e. of Leicester*], *see* TIGHE (H. U.) Hist. acc. of Cumner, w. partic. resp. death of Ctss. of Leicester &c., 1821.

Robson (E. I.) A wayfarer in Provence. 8º. [1926]
A wayfarer on the Loire. s8º. [1926]

Robson (Thomas), *1798–1871, see* BEAUMONT (W.) Memoir of T. R., 1886.

Robson (William Alexander). Compulsory voting. Fabian tract, No. 209. [P2736]. 8º. 1924
Justice & administ. law: st. of Brit. constit. 8º. 1928
The relation of wealth to welfare. s8º. [1924]

Robson (William James). *Scenes f. the lives of Robson & Redpath. By J. B. [*b. w.* Palmer (W.) The Queen *v.* Palmer, 1856]. 8º. [1857]

Roby (Henry John). Grammar of Latin. 2nd ed. p2. s8º. 1875

Roca (Juan Ant. de Vera y Figueroa, *conde* **de la),** *see* VERA Y FIGUEROA (J. A. DE), *conde de la Roca.*

Roc-Amadour. Cartul. des abbayes de T. & de R.-A., par J. B. Champeval, 1903, *see* TULLE.

Rocca (Luigi), *see* DANTE ALIGHIERI. Lectura D.: c. 16 del Paradiso letto da L. R., 1912.

Rocco (Alfredo). Polit. doct. of Fascism, *see* INTERNAT. CONCILIATION, No. 223, 1926.

Rocco (Lepido). Motta di Livenza e s. dintorni. St. storico. 8º. Treviso. 1897

Rocha (Arthur Pinto da). Hist. diplom. do Brasil, s1, *see* INSTITUTO HIST. &C. BRAZIL. Rev., t77ii, 1916.

Rocha (Diego Andrés).
Brevis paraphrasis Apocalypsis. s4º. Limae. 1653

Rochdale. Report on housing condit. &c. & notes on town planning. [By] A. G. Anderson. fol. Rochdale. 1911

Roche (Aimar de la), *see* FABRI (A.), *de la Roche, bp. of Geneva.*

Roche (John), *of Dublin.* Moravian heresy. s8º. D. 1751

Rocheblave (Samuel).
Jean-Baptiste Pigalle. [Gr. sculpteurs fr. du 18e s.] 4º. [1919]

Rochechouart (*le gén. cte.* **L. V. L. de).** Memoirs, 1788–1822. Auth. tr., F. Jackson. 8º. 1920

Roche d'Allery (Pietro de Lucas, *conte* **della),** *see* CARUTTI (D.) Il Conte della R. d'A. e il Col. Fresen all' assedio di Verrua (1704–5), 1901.

Rochefort (Albert Jouvin de), *see* JOUVIN DE ROCHEFORT (A.)

Rochefort (Henri). Un coin du voile. Aperçu des événements de Paris. [P2710]. s8°. N.Y. 1874
Rochegude (*le marquis* **Felix de) & M. Dumolin.** Guide pratique à travers le vieux Paris. n. éd., ent. ref. s8°. [1923]
Rochemaure (*le duc* **de La Salle de),** *see* LA SALLE DE ROCHEMAURE (*le duc* DE).
Rochemonteix (Maxence de Chalvet, *marquis* **de).** Le Temple d'Edfou, t3, *see* MISSION ARCH. FR. AU CAIRE. Mém., t20, 1928.
Rocher (Edmond). Louis Pergaud, conteur rustique. s8°. [1923]
Rochester. Index of wills proved in R. Consistory Court, 1440–1561. Comp. by L. L. Duncan, w. intr. note & bibliog. by F. W. Cock. [Kent Arch. Soc. Records Br., v9]. la8°. Canterbury. 1924
Parish reg. & records in diocese of R.: summary of inform., w. intr. by W. E. Buckland. [Kent Arch. Soc. Kent Records]. 8°. 1912
Rochester University [NEW YORK]. Gen. catalogue [of officers & graduates] of the Univ. of R., 1850–1900. 8°. Rochester, N.Y. 1900
Rochester (Anna). Infant mortality, Baltimore, *see* UNITED STATES: LAB. Children's Bur. Publ. 119, 1923.
Rochester (John Wilmot, *2nd earl of*), *1647–80*. Coll. works. Ed. J. Hayward. la8°. *Nonesuch Pr.* 1926
see BURNET (G.), *bp*. Remarkable passages in life of R., 1813.
„ JACKSON (T.) Lib. of Xtn. biog., v9, J. W. R., by G. Burnet, 1838.
„ PRINZ (J.) J. W., e. of R.: life & wr., w. corr., bibliog. &c., 1927.
Rockefeller Foundation. Annual report, 1919–27. [With Rep. of Internat. Health Board & China Medical Board]. 8°. N.Y. [1920–28]
Rockefeller (John Davison), *see* GATES (F. T.) Truth about R. & the Merritts, *n.d.*
Rocker (Rudolf). J. Most: Leben e. Rebellen. Vorwort v. A. Berkmann. 8°. 1924
Rockinger (Ludwig). Handschriftl. Grundlage d. Ausg. d. kaiserl. Land u. Lehenrechts, 1. Drittel, *see* KÖNIGL. AKAD. D. WISS. ZU MÜNCHEN. Abhdlgn. d. phil. Klasse, B26, 1914.
Rockow (Lewis).
Contemp. political thought in England. 8°. [1925]
Rocquain (Félix).
La France & Rome p. les Guerres de Religion. la8°. 1924
Rocque (John). New & accurate survey of London & Westminster & the borough of Southwark. atlas fol. 1748
Plan of the house & gardens of the Duke of Devonshire at Chiswick, w. views &c. [London Views, C.] folded fol. [1736?]
Rod (Edouard). L'ombre s'étend sur la montagne. s8°. 1923
Roda Roda (Alexander) [*i.e.* SANDOR FRIEDR. ROSENFELD].
Irrfahrten e. Humoristen, 1914–19. s8°. München. 1923
Von Bienen, Drohnen u. Baronen. 23–27e A. s8°. Wien. 1921
Rodbertus (J. Carl), *1805–75*, *see* LASALLE (F. J. G.) Nachgelass. Briefe u. Schr., B6, Briefwechsel m. K. R., 1925.
Rodd (*Sir* **James Rennell).** Homer's Ithaca. s8°. 1927
The Italian people. Annual Ital. lect. [P2463]. 8°. [1920]
„ „ *For a. copy see* BRIT. ACAD. Proc., v9, 1919–20.
Social & diplomatic mem. [3s.] 8°. 1922–25
Rode (Joannes), *abbot of the monastery of St. Matthew, Treves*, *see* REDLICH (V.) J. R., e. deut. Reformabt d. 15 J., 1923.
Roden (Robert Jocelyn, *3rd earl of*), *see* NORMANBY (C. H. P., *m. of*). Speech on motion of R., ref. to Ireland, 1837.
Rodenbach (Albrecht). Keurgedichten. Ingeleid met e. studie door C. Verschaeve. s8°. Brugge. [1919]
Rodenbach (Georges). Œuvres. [t]1, 2. 8°. 1923–25
1, La jeunesse blanche—Vers d'amour—Le livre de Jésus—Le règne du silence.
2, Les vies encloses—Le miroir du ciel natal—Plusieurs poèmes.
Le carillonneur. [éd. compl.] s8°. 1923
see MAES (P.) G. R., 1855–98, 1926.
„ RAMAEKERS (G.) G. R., 1920.
Rodenberg (Julius). Deut. Pressen: e. Bibliographie, mit Schriftproben. la8°. Zürich. 1925
Rodenwaldt (Gerhart). Die Fresken d. Palastes, mit Beitr. v. R. Hackl &c., *see* KAISERL. DEUT. ARCH. INST. ATHEN. ABTHLG. Tiryns, B2, 1912.
Der Fries d. Megarons v. Mykenai. la4°. Halle a S. [1921]
Röder (Johann Paul) [ROEDERUS]. De Colloquio Wormatiensi, 1540, inter Protest. & Pontif. theologos disquis. Ex Mcs. Ebneriano facta per J. P. R. s4°. [Norimbergae. 1744]

Roderich-Stoltheim (Ferdinand). The riddle of the Jew's success. Tr. C. Pownall. 8°. L. 1927
Rodericius (Alphons), *Jesuit, of Valladolid*, *see* RODRIGUEZ (ALONSO).
Rodericus, *Santius*, *see* SANCIUS DE AREVALO (R.)
Roderick, *king of the Visigoths in Spain* [RODRIGO], *see* MENÉNDEZ PIDAL (RAMÓN). Floresta de leyendas heroicas esp., R., 2t, 1925–26.
Rodes (Jean). Les Chinois: psych. ethnograph. s8°. 1923
Rodiek (*Mrs.* **Georg).** Library of Hawaiiana offered for sale. [P2856]. 8°. San Francisco. [1925]
Rödiger (Emil) [ROEDIGER]. Comm. qua vulg. opinio de interpret. Arabica librorum V. T. histor. ex Graeca Alexandrina ducta refutatur. [P2655]. 4°. Halis Sax. 1828
Rodin (Auguste).
see LUDOVICI (A. M.) Personal remin. of A. R., 1926.
„ RILKE (R. M.) Gesamm. Werke, B4, 1927.
——, A. Coomaraswamy, &c.
Sculptures çivaïtes. [Ars Asiatica, 3]. fol. Brux. 1921
Rödinger (Johann), *of Rockenhausen* [RHODIUS (J.)] Ein Christl. Sermon vom heiligen Predigtampt &c. s4°. [Erffordt]. 1587
Rodionov (Iv. A.) Москва-матушка. Былина. 8°. Берлинъ. 1922
Roditschew (J. F.=Fedor Izmailovich) & A. Nossig.
Bolschewismus u. Juden. [P2689]. 8°. Wien. [1922]
Rodney (Caesar). Autograph letters & docs. &c. papers of C. R., T. Rodney & C. A. Rodney. Sold June & Oct. 1919, by S. V. Henkels. [2p *in* 1v]. la8°. Philad. 1919
Rodney (George Brydges R., *1st baron*), *see* MUNDY (G. B.) Life of R., n. ed., 1836.
Rodney (*Col.* **Thomas),** *see* RODNEY (C.) Autograph letters &c. of C. R., T. R. &c., sold 1919, 2p, 1919.
Rodo (José Enrique).
Ariel. Tr., w. intr. essay by F. J. Stimson. s8°. Boston. 1922
Rodo (Ludovic). Ex-libris & marks. Introd. by F. Brangwyn. [P2702]. la8°. 1921
Rodocanachi (Emmanuel). Byron, 1788–1824. 8°. [1924]
Hist. de Rome de 1354 à 1471. 8°. 1922
Hist. de Rome. Une cour princière au Vatican: Sixte IV—Innocent VIII—Alex. VI Borgia, 1471–1503. 4°. [1925]
The Roman Capitol in anc. & mod. times. Tr. F. Lawton. s8°. 1906
Rodolico (Niccolò). Alla vigilia d. Repubbl. napoletana d. 1799, *see* ARCHIVIO STOR. ITAL., a. 80, 1922.
Dal Comune alla Signoria. Saggio sul governo di Taddeo Pepoli in Bologna. 8°. Bologna. 1898
Rodov (Semen Abramovich). Пролетарские писатели: антология. Составил С. Р. под общей ред. П. С. Когана. 8°. Москва. [1924]
Rodrigues Ferreira (Alexandre). Diario da viagem philos. pela capitania de São-José do Rio Negro, *see* INSTITUTO HIST. E GEOG. BRAZIL. Revista, t48–51, 1885–88.
Rodrigues Giraõ (Joaõ). Elém. de la gramm. japon. tr. du Portugais par C. Landresse, préc. d'une explic. des syllabaires japonais &c. par Abel-Rémusat. [*&* Suppl. ou remarques addit., tirées de la gramm. comp. par le P. Oyanguren. Soc. Asiatique]. [2p *in* 1v]. 8°. 1825–26
Rodriguez (Alfonso), *of Zaragoza*, *see* HISP. SOC. OF AMER. MSS., B2 (Doc., 1454), 1928.
Rodriguez (Alonso), *Jesuit, of Valladolid*. Exercitium perfectionis & virtutum christian. Ex Hispan. Lat. faciebat M. Martinez. 3p *in* 1v. s4°. Coloniae Agrippinae. 1622
A treatise of the virtue of humility. 4th ed. rev. & amend. f. Lat. ed. s8°. 1733
see *THRONUS justitiae; ex 4 S. J. patribus desumptus A. R. &c., 1624.
Rodriguez (E. B.), *see* RUSSELL (C. E.) & E. B. R. Hero of the Filipinos: J. Rizal, 1924.
Rodriguez (Francisco Javier de Salas y), *see* SALAS Y RODRIGUEZ (F. J. DE).
Rodríguez (Pedro Sáinz), *see* SAÍNZ RODRÍGUEZ (P.)
Rodriguez Campomanes y Sorriba (Pedro), *see* CAMPOMANES (P. R. C. Y S., *conde* DE).
Rodriguez de Berlanga y Rosado (Manuel).
Los bronces de Osuna. la8°. Malaga. 1873
Rodriguez de Leon (Juan), *see* CARDUCHO (V.) Dialogos de la pintura &c.: sig. inform. &c. en fabor del' arte, escr. por var. insignes [*i.e.* J. R. de L. &c.], 1633.
Rodriguez García (Francisco). Crón. del señorio de Vizcaya, 1865, *see* ESPAÑA. Crón. gen., v8, 1865 &c.
Rodriguez Giraõ (J.), *see* RODRIGUES GIRAÕ (J.)

Rodríguez Marín (Francisco). Nuevos datos para biogr. de cien escritores de los s. 16 y 17. la8º. 1923
see CERVANTES. Don Quijote ; ed. F. R. M., 8t, 1911–13 & Algunos juicios, 1919.

Rodríguez y Fernández (Ildefonso).
San Jeroteo, obispo de Segovia. 2ª ed. 8º. 1919

Rody (H.) Der Altkatholicismus gerichtet durch s. Freunde. [P2694]. 8º. Mainz. 1874

Rodzyanko (M. V.) Крушеніе Имперіи : записки ; предисл. А. И. Ксюнина, *see* ARKHIV RUSS. REVOL., т17, 1926.
Reign of Rasputin : An Empire's collapse ; mem. of M. V. R. Tr. C. Zvegintzoff. Intr. by Sir B. Pares. 8º. 1927

Roe (*Mrs.* Humphrey Verdon), *see* STOPES (MARIE C.)

Roederus (Joannes Paullus), *see* RÖDER (J. P.)

Röell (Hermann Alexander). Explicatio Catecheseos Heidelberg. s4º. Trajecti ad Rhenum. 1728

Roepke, *see* RÖPKE.

Rœrich (George). Tibetan paintings. 4º. Paris. 1925

Roerich (Nicolai Konstantinovich). Adamant. [Intr. by S. Whitman & M. Highlander]. s8º. N.Y. [1923]
"The messenger" (R.'s paintings). 7 articles by F. Adney, L. Andreyev &c. 8º. [Adyar, Madras]. 1925
The N. Roerich exhibition, w. intr. & cat. of the paintings by C. Brinton. 8º. [N.Y. 1920]
see JARINTZOV (N.) N. K. R., 1920.
„ SELIVANOVA (N.) The world of R., 1923.

Rogachevsky (V. Lvov-), *see* LVOV-ROGACHEVSKY (V.)

Roger, *van Brügge.*
see HASSE (C.) R. van B., d. Meister v. Flamalle, 1904.
„ —— R. van der Weyden u. R. van B. mit i. Schulen, 1905.

Roger (Charles), *of Dundee.* Collation of the Sacred Script. The Old Test. f. the tr. of John Rogers, the bishops, &c. ; The New Test. f. Wiclif, Rogers, The Rhemes &c. 4º. Dundee. 1847

Roger (Paul André). Archives hist. & eccl. de la Picardie & de l'Artois. Publ. par P. R. [2v *in* 1]. la8º. Amiens. 1842
*Biographie gén. des Belges. la8º. Brux. 1850
„ „ *a. c. of* livre 1 (A–J.) la8º. Brux. 1849
Noblesse & chevalerie du Comté de Flandre, d'Artois & de Picardie. la8º. Amiens. 1843

Roger (Pierre), *see* CLEMENT VI, *pope.*

Roger-Marx (Claude). Charles Despiau. s8º. [1922]

Rogers (Abner), *see* BIGELOW (G. T.) & G. BEMIS. Report of trial of A. R. for murder of C. Lincoln, 1844.

Rogers (Ann), *see* JOHNSON (J.) A short acc. of A. R., 1770.

Rogers (Arthur Kenyon). A student's hist. of philosophy. n. ed. rev. s8º. N.Y. 1921
What is truth ? : essay in the theory of knowledge. 8º. New Haven, *Yale.* 1923
see DRAKE (D.) Essays in crit. realism ; by D. D., A. K. R. &c., 1920.

Rogers (Bruce), *see* WARDE (F.) B. R., designer of books, 1925.

Rogers (C. C.) Cornish silhouettes. s8º. 1924

Rogers (Cameron).
The magnificent idler : Walt Whitman. 8º. 1926

Rogers (Charles), *D.D., 1825–90.*
Book of Wallace. [Grampian Club]. 2v. la8º. E. 1889
Genealog. mem. of the fam. of Robert Burns & the Scot. house of Burnes. 8º. E. 1877
see CUPAR-ANGUS. Rental bk. of Cistercian Abbey of C.-A. ; ed. C. R., 2v, 1879–80.

Rogers (Daniel). *A practicall catechisme, or a view of princ. truths cont. in the catechisme. 3p. s4º. 1632

Rogers (Henry), *pres. of Lancs. Independent College.*
Life & character of J. Howe &c. n. ed. 8º. 1862

Rogers (Herbert Lionel) & T. R. Harley. The life of Rome. Eng. ed. rev. & amplified of Roman home life & relig. 8º. O. 1927
Roman home life & religion. A reader. s8º. O. 1923

Rogers (*Mrs.* Hester Ann). Experience & spiritual letters ; w. a sermon on her death by T. Coke. App. by her husband [J. Rogers]. s8º. 1840

Rogers (Kenneth), *O.B.E., M.D.* The Mermaid & Mitre taverns in old London. 8º. [1928]

Rogers (Leigh). Wine of fury. s8º. 1924

Rogers (Lindsay). The Amer. Senate. s8º. N.Y. 1926
see MACBAIN (H. L.) & L. R. New constit. of Europe, 1922.

Rogers (Nehemiah). The true convert : or an expos. upon 15th chap. of St. Luke's Gospell, cont. 3 parables. 3p [*in* 1v]. s4º. 1632
Each p. has diff. tp. The watchfull shepheard—The good houswife—The indulgent father.

Rogers (Robert William). Hist. of Babylonia & Assyria. 6th ed. rev. 2v. 8º. N.Y. [1915]

Rogers (Rose Annie), *wife of Rev. H. M. Rogers.*
The lonely island. [Tristan da Cunha]. 8º. [1926]

Rogers (Samuel), *the poet.* Italy. Poem. 8º. 1830
Italy. Poem. n. ed. s8º. 1838
Italy. Poem. With cuts. s8º. Paris. 1840
Poems. 8º. 1834
Poems. s8º. 1846

Rogers (Timothy).
Pract. disc. on sickness &c., in sev. sermons. s8º. 1691

Rogers (W. H.), *schoolmaster.* Guide to the New Forest. 8th ed. 8º. Southampton. [c. 1901]
see SOUTHAMPTON. Maps & plans of old S. ; ed., w. notes, by W. H. R., 1907.

Rogers (William), *Prof., Univ. of Penn.*
A circular letter on justification. repr. s8º. 1786

Rogers (Woodes). A cruising voyage round the world. Intr. & notes by G. E. Manwaring. 8º. [1928]

Roget (Peter Mark). Animal & vegetable physiology w. ref. to natural theology. 2v. 8º. 1834
Electricity, galvanism, magnetism & electro-magnetism. [*each w. sep. pagin.* Libr. of Useful Kn.] 8º. [1831]
Internat. Thesaurus of Eng. words & phrases. Founded upon & embodying R.'s work, w. add. &c. by C. O. S. Mawson. 8º. N.Y. 1925
Thesaurus of Eng. words & phrases, enl. by J. L. Roget. n. ed. rev. & enl. by S. R. Roget. 8º. 1925

Roget (Raymond). Le Maroc chez les auteurs anc. Textes tr. par R. R. Préf. de S. Gsell. [Nouv. Coll. de textes &c. ; Assoc. G. Budé]. 8º. 1924

Roget (Samuel Romilly). Travel in the 2 last cent. of 3 generations. Ed. S. R. R. 8º. [1921]

Rogge (Christian). Luther u. d. Kirchenbilder s. Zeit. [Verein f. Ref.-gesch. Schr., Jhrg. 29, Nr. 108]. 8º. L. 1912

Roggendorff (*ctsse.* Cécile de). La dern. amie de J. Casanova : C. de R. Corr. ined., 1797–98. 8º. 1926

Rogov (Ya.) Замѣтки во время плаванія по рѣкѣ Чусовой. [? *Extr. f.* Журналь Мин. Внутр. Дѣлъ, c. 1851. P560]. 8º. [С.–П. c. 1851]

Rogowski (Erich). Das deut. Volkseinkommen. 8º. 1926

Rohan (Catherine de), *duchesse de Rohan.* Apologie pour le roy Henry IV, *see* HENRY III, *king of Fr.* Rec. de div. pièces &c., 1664.

Rohan (Henri de Rohan, *duc de*), *1579–1638.* Autobiografia dettata al cav. F. Sprecher, 1637. [Ed. V. Ceresole. Nozze Comello—Totto. N129]. la8º. Venezia. 1864

Rohan (*le card. prince* Louis René Edouard de), *1734–1803* [*le card.* COLLIER], *see* MUNIER-JOLAIN (J.) Le card. Collier & Marie-Antoinette, 1927.

Rohan (Thomas). Confessions of a dealer. 8º. [1924]
Old beautiful. 8º. [1926]

Rohan-Chabot (—). Angola & Rhodesia, 1912–14. Mission Rohan-Chabot s. les auspices du Min. de l'Instruct. Publ. & de la Soc. de Géogr. t3, fasc. 1, 4, fasc. 1. 4º. 1923–25
3, fasc. 1, Linguistique : le groupe sud-ouest des langues bantoues [par L. Homburger].
4, fasc. 1, Hist. nat., Mammifères [par R. Anthony & F. Villeming, Oiseaux, Reptiles, Poissons.

Rohault de Fleury (Georges).
Les monuments de Pise au m. âge. la8º. 1866

Rohde (Eleanour Sinclair).
Garden-craft in the Bible & o. essays. 8º. [1927]
A garden of herbs. 8º. [1920]
Old Eng. gardening books. 8º. 1924
The old Eng. herbals. la8º. 1922
The old-world pleasaunce : an anthology. s8º. 1925

Rohde (Erwin). Psyche, the cult of souls & belief in immortality among the Greeks. [Tr. fr. 8th ed. by W. B. Hillis]. 8º. 1925

Rohde (Hans), *see* WESTERMANN (D.) Die Kpelle ; mit Beitr., v. H. R., 1921.

Róheim (Géza). Australian totemism : psycho-analytic st. in anthropology. Intr. by M. D. Eder. la8º. [1925]

Rohling (August).
Der Talmudjude. 4ᵉ A. [P519]. 8º. Münster. 1873

Rohmer (Sax), *ps.* [*i.e.* JOHN SARSFIELD WARD].
The devil doctor. 9th ed. s8º. [1924]
Dope. s8º. [1919]
The dream-detective. s8º. [1920]
The golden scorpion. [7th ed.] s8º. [1927]
Grey face. s8º. [1924]
Moon of madness. s8º. [1927]
The orchard of tears. s8º. [1918]
The quest of the sacred slipper. [repr.] s8º. [1926]
The romance of sorcery. 8º. [1914]

Rohr (Philipp). Pictor errans in hist. sacra. Præses P. R., resp. C. Steche. [P2638]. s4°. Eisenbergæ. 1700
Rohrbach (Paul). Der deutsche Gedanke in d. Welt. Neubearb. 8°. L. 1920
Deutschland unter d. Weltvölkern, 1899–1918. 5e A. 8°. St. 1921
Die Verantwortlichkeit am Weltkriege. [P2574]. s8°. L. 1921
Röhrich (Timotheus Wilhelm). Gesch. d. Reformation im Elsass u. bes. in Strasburg. 3T *in* 2v. s8°. Str. 1830–32
Röhrig (Friedrich Ludwig Otto) [ROEHRIG]. De Turcarum lingua, indole ac natura. s4°. Vratisloviae. 1843
Eclairc. sur quelques particularités des langues tartares & finnoises. 8°. 1845
Roht (Rudolph).
Attila Hunnorum rex. Resp. J. C. Papa. s4°. Jenae. 1671
***Roi** (Le) Flore & la belle Jeanne &c., 1923, *see* FLORE.
Roi (Pia). Il Correggio. s8°. Firenze. [1921]
Roijaards (Herman Johan) [ROYAARDS].
Compendium hist. eccl. Christ. s8°. Trajecti a. R. 1840
Roisin (Jean). Franchises, lois & coutumes de la ville de Lille. Anc. ms. cont. chartes & titres hist. conc. la Flandre. Publ. avec notes & gloss. par Brun-Lavainne. 4°. Lille. 1842
Rojas (Fernando de), *of Montalvan.* Le Celestina. [Bibl. econ. de clás. castell.] s8°. Paris. *n.d.*
Celestina, or the tragi-comedy of Calisto & Melibea. Tr. J. Mabbe, 1631. Also Interlude of Calisto & Melebea, c. 1530. Ed., w. intr. &c. by H. W. Allen. [Broadway Trans.] 8°. [1923]
Ain hipsche Tragedia, Calixstus uñ Melibia. [Übers. C. Wirsung, 1520. Argumente u. Holzschnitte in Faks. Nachwort v. T. Musper]. la8°. [Augsburg. 1923]
Rojas (Pedro de), *conde de Mora* [ROIAS].
Hist. de la Imp. Ciudad de Toledo. 2p. sm. fol. 1654–63
Rojas Zorrilla (Francisco de). Cada qual lo que le toca y La viña de Nabot. Publ. por A. Castro. [Teatro antiguo español, 2]. 8°. 1917
Rokeby (Ralph), *barrister; d. 1595, see* COWLING (G. H.) The Felon Sew: mock-heroic poem of 15th c. [1st transcr. by R. R., 1565, *w. text*], 1922.
Rokycansky (Jan Sictor), *see* SICTOR (J.)
Rokyczana (Johannes).
see OSWALDUS (J.) De J. R. famoso Calixtin. in Bohemia pontif., 1718.
,, —— Ex hist. eccl. de J. R., 1718.
Roland. Verein z. Förderung d. Stamm-, Wappen- u. Siegelkunde &c.
Bücher-Katalog. 5. verm. &c. A. 8°. 1909
,, ,, 6. verm. &c. A. [*b. w.* Roland. Vereinsbeilage, 1912–14]. 8°. 1912
Jubiläumsschrift, B1, 18 Jan. 1912. [*b. w.* Roland. Bücher-Kat., 1909]. 8°. [1912]
Vereinsbeilage. Nr. 85–141 (Juli 1909–Juni 1914). [*no tp. b. in 2v.*] la8°. [1909–14]
Monatsschrift, 1909–14, *see* ARCHIV FÜR STAMM- U. WAPPENKUNDE.
Roland (*Mme.*), *1754–93.* Lettres. Publ. par C. Perroud. nouv. sér., 1767–80. [Doc. inéd.] t2. la8°. 1915
Roland (Guibal-), *see* GUIBAL-ROLAND.
Roland Holst (Henriette), *van der Schalk.*
De nieuwe geboort. s8°. Rotterdam. 1918
Opwaartsche wegen. 3. dr. 8°. Rotterdam. 1920
Sonnetten en verzen in terzinen geschreven. 3. dr. 8°. Rotterdam. 1922
De vrouw in het woud. s8°. Rotterdam. 1917
Rólf, *Kraki, see* OLRIK (A.) Danmarks heltedigtning, d1, R. Krake og den aeldre Skjoldungfejden, 1903.
Rolfe (Frederick William S. A. L. M.) [*ps.* F. BARON CORVO], *see* SYMONS (A. J. A.) F. B. C., 1927.
Rolfe (William James). Satchel guide to Europe. 45th ed. rev. & enl. by W. D. Crockett. s8°. 1925
Rolfs (Wilhelm). Gesch. d. Malerei Neapels. 4°. L. 1910
Rolland (Romain).
L'âme enchantée. 3[t in 4p, 3i, ii. 1, 30e éd., 2, 11e éd.] s8°. [1923]
Aux peuples assassinés [1916]. [P2525]. la8°. *n.d.*
Clerambault. Hist. d'une conscience libre pend. la Guerre. s8°. 1920
Le jeu de l'amour & de la mort. s8°. [1925]
Mahatma Gandhi. s8°. 1924
Pierre & Luce. 11e éd. s8°. [1921]
Les vaincus. Drame. s8°. Anvers. 1922
Voyage musical au pays du passé. 8°. 1920

Rolland (Romain) [*continued*].
TRANSLATIONS.
Annette & Sylvie. v1 of The soul enchanted. Tr. B. R. Redman. s8°. [1927]
The forerunners. Tr. E. & C. Paul. 8°. [1920]
Mahatma Gandhi. Tr. C. D. Groth. 8°. [1924]
see BONNEROT (J.) R. R., 1921.
,, JOUVE (P. J.) R. R. vivant, 1914–19, 3e éd., 1920.
see MAXE (J.) Cahiers de l'anti-France—1, L'idole: l' "Européen" R. R., 1922.
,, ZWEIG (S.) R. R., d. Mann u. d. Werk, 1921.
,, —— R. R., the man & h. work, 1921.
Rolland (Victor H.)
see RIETSTAP (J. B.) Armorial gén.; suppl. par V. H. R., 2t, 1926.
,, —— Planches de l'Armorial gén. de R.; par V. R., t4, 5, 1912–21.
Rolle (Richard) *of Hampole.* Eng. prose treatises of R. R. de H. Ed. f. R. Thornton's MS. by G. G. Perry. [E.E.T.S., 20]. A new rev. text & glossary. 8°. (1866) 1921
,, ,, Officium. [A revised issue of pp. xv–xxxiii of orig. ed. (1866) of Eng. prose treatises. *b. w. h.* Eng. prose treatises, 1921]. 8°. [1921]
In Psalterium Davidicum &c. enarratio. fol. Coloniae. 1536
Meditatio de passione Domini. Ed. w. intr. by R. Lindkvist. 8°. Uppsala. [1917]
Some minor works. With the Privity of the Passion by S. Bonaventura. Tr. & ed. G. E. Hodgson. 8°. 1923
Rolleston (Charles J.) The age of folly. A study of imperial needs &c. [re-issue]. 8°. 1911
Rolleston (*Sir* **Humphrey Davy**). James Lind, pioneer of naval hygiene. [*Extr. fr.* Journal R. N. Medical Service, 1915, v1. P2603]. la8°. [1915]
Sir Gilbert Blane. [P2577]. 8°. 1916
Sir William Burnett, first med. director-gen. of the R.N. [Repr. f. Journal of R.N. Med. Service, v8]. [P2703]. s4°. 1922
Some medical aspects of old age. Linacre Lect., 1922. s8°. 1922
Rolleston (Thomas William Hazen).
Ireland's vanishing opportunity. [P2529]. s8°. D. 1919
Rollin (Charles). The anc. hist. of the Egyptians, Carthaginians, Assyrians, Babylonians, Medes & Persians, Grecians, & Macedonians. Tr. 18th ed. rev. 6v. 8°. 1827
Rollin (Martin). Hist. mem. of the eccl. state of the French Protestants. Tr. W. Toase. [P2543, 2658]. 8°. 1818
Rollins (Hyder Edward). Analyt. index to ballad-entries (1557–1709) in Registers of the Co. of Stationers of London. [*Extr. f.* Studies in philol., v21]. 8°. Chapel Hill, N. Car. 1924
Cavalier & Puritan ballads & broadsides, 1640–60. Ed., w. intr. &c. by H. E. R. 8°. N.Y. 1923
Old English ballads, 1553–1625, chiefly f. MSS. Ed. H. E. R. 8°. C. 1920
The pack of Autolycus: or strange & terrible news as told in broadside ballads, 1624–93. Ed. H. E. R. la8°. Cambridge, *Harvard.* 1927
A Pepysian garland. Black-letter broadside ballads 1595–1639; chiefly f. coll. of S. Pepys. 8°. C. 1922
Rollins (Philip Ashton). The cowboy: h. characteristics, h. equipment &c. 8°. N.Y. 1922
Rollock (Robert) [ROLLOK]. An expos. upon select psalmes of David. Tr. C. L. s8°. E. 1600
In selectos aliquot Psalmos D. comm. s8°. Genevae. 1599
Rolls Series, *see* †EXCHEQUER. Red Bk. of the E., 3p, 1896. [99i–iii.]
Rølvaag (O. E.) I de dage—Fortælling on Norske nykommere i Amerika. 8°. Kristiania. 1924
Roma. *Nuova guida angelica perpetua romana per visitare le chiese &c. Tr. in Armeno da Giona d'Elia. s8°. 1725
Statuti dei mercanti di Roma. Pubbl. da G. Gatti. [Accad. Storico-Giuridica]. 4°. 1885
Romagnoli (Ettore). Il trittico dell' amore e dell' ironia. Commedie. s8°. Bologna. [1920]
see DANTE ALIGHIERI. Lectura D.: c. 8 dell' Inferno letto da E. R., 1915.
Romagnoli (Gaetano), *see* BACCHI DELLA LEGA (A.) Bibliog. dei vocab. ne' dialetti Ital. racc. e poss. da G. R., 1876.
Romagny (*lieut.* **Charles**) **& Piales d'Axtrez.** Etude sommaire des batailles d'un siècle. 4°. 1890
Romain (Georges). En route pour la Grande Chartreuse. [P2588]. s8°. [1872]

Romaine. *Taxe de la Chancellerie romaine &c., 1744, *see* TAXE.

Romaine (William). *Essay on psalmody [*&* A coll. out of the Psalms. *sep. tp. pagin. cont. Pref. signed* W. R.] s8°. 1775

see HAWEIS (T.) Life of W. R., 1797.

Romains (Jules) [LOUIS FARIGOULE].

Cromedeyre-le-vieil. 4e éd. s8°. 1920

Eyeless sight: extra-retinal vision & the paroptic sense. Tr. C. K. Ogden. s8°. [1924]

Lucienne. 8e éd. s8°. 1922

,, ,, 21e éd. s8°. 1922

Le mariage de Le Trouhadec, comédie, *see* ŒUVRES libres, No. 44, 1925.

Puissances de Paris. 5e éd. s8°. 1919

Théâtre. [t1, 2] (1, 7e éd.; 2, 4e éd.) s8°. [1924–25]

1, Knock, ou le triomphe de la médecine—M. Le Trouhadec saisi par la débauche.

2, Le mariage de Le Trouhadec—La scintillante.

Le vin blanc de la villette. 6e éd. s8°. 1923

see FAURE (E.) H. Matisse; par E. F., J. R. &c., 1923.

Roman.

Roman (The) martyrologe set forth by the comm. of Gregory XIII &c.; tr., 1667, *see* MARTYROLOGY.

*Roman missal for use of the laity, *n.d.*, *see* MISSAL.

*Roman tradition examined &c., 1676, *see* BAXTER (R.)

*A short R. history. s8°. Bristol. 1773

Roman (Frederick William).

The new education in Europe. 2nd imp. 8°. 1924

Romana (Pedro Caro y Sureda, *3rd marq.* **de la),** *see* GODCHOT (S.) En Danemark: les Espagnols du Marq. de la R., 1924.

***Romanae** hist. anthol., 1631; 1661, *see* GODWIN (T.)

Romance. *Roumance (The) of the Sowdone of Babyloyne & of Ferumbras his sone, 1854, *see* FIERABRAS.

Romanceiro. R. geral portuguez, 2a ed. ampl., 3v, 1906–9, *see* BRAGA (T.)

Romancero. R. de la Bibl. Brancacciana; publ. R. Foulché-Delbosc, *see* REVUE HISPAN., t65, 1925.

Romanelli (Pietro), *see* PARIBENI (R.) & P. R. Stud. &c. nell' Anatolia merid., 1914.

Romanelli (Romano), *see* TINTI (M.) R. R., 1924.

Romanes (Charles S.) The Calls of Norfolk & Suffolk, th. Paston connect. &c. la8°. *p.p.* [E.] 1920

Románescu. *Lesicon R.-Lát. &c., 1825, *see* LEXICON.

Romanet (*le vte.* **de).** Géographie du Perche & chronol. de s. comtes; suivies de pièces justif. formant le cartul. de cette prov. [*w. sep. tp.*: Chartes &c. *& sep. pagin.*] Par le Vte. de Romanet. [Doc. sur la prov. du Perche, s2, no. 1]. [2p]. 8°. Mortagne. 1890–1902

,, ,, Table alphabét. des noms &c. cont. dans la géogr. & dans le cartul. du P. par le Vte. de Romanet. 8°. Mortagne. 1901–2

Romang (J. P.) Der neueste Pantheismus, oder d. junghegelsche Weltanschauung. [P2480]. 8°. Bern. 1848

Romani (Felice). Saul. Tragedia lirica, 1825–26. [Nozze Marigonda—Zanetti. N. 121]. s8°. Venezia. 1891

Romania: recueil trimestriel consacré à l'étude des langues et des littératures romanes. année[s] 47–55, t45–53, 1918–27. 8°. 1918–27

Românilor. Doc. priv. la ist. Românilor, v14–19, 1911–22, *see* HURMUZAKI (E. DE).

Romanin (Samuele). Storia documentata di Venezia. 2. ed. t9, 10. 8°. Venezia. 1916–21

Romanische Bibliothek. Hrsg. v. W. Förster. No. 1, 9, 10–14, 16, 17, 20, 21. s8°. Halle a. S. 1893–1921

see ADAM, *le Bossu.* Canchons u. Partures, 1900. [17.]

,, CARAVAJAL (B. DE). La Bandolera de Flandes, 1893. [9.]

,, †FOLQUET, *de Romans.* Gedichte, 1896. [12.]

,, LORCK (J. E.) Altbergamask. Sprachdenkmäler (9–15 Jhdt.), 1893. [10.]

,, †SORDELLO *di Goito.* Vita e poesie, 1896. [11.]

,, TROYES (C. DE), Cligés, 1921. [1.]

,, —— Erec u. Enide, 1909. [13.]

,, —— Wilhelm v. England (Guill. d'Angl.), 1911. [20.]

,, —— Wörterbuch zu s. Sämtl. Werken; verfasst &c. v. W. Foerster, 1914. [21.]

,, VEGA (LOPE DE). Los Guzmanes de Toral, 1899. [16.]

,, VINCENTIUS, *Bellovacensis.* La estoria de los quatro dotores de la S. Eglesia, 1897. [14.]

Romanische Forschungen. Organ für roman. Sprachen u. Mittellatein. Hrsg. v. K. Vollmöller. B32–40. 8°. Erlangen. 1913–27

Adam (J.) Übers. u. Glossar d. altspan. Poema del Cid, 1913. [32.]

Andrae (A.) Französ. Belege zu Wanderanekdoten &c., 1915. [34.]

Romanische Forschungen [*continued*].

Apollonius, *Tyrius.* Altfranz. Prosavers. d. A.-Romans, 1915. [34.]

Bardola (C.) Sonets, 1913–17. [32, 37.]

Becker (W.) Die Sage v. d. Höllenfahrt Christi in d. altfranz. Lit., 1913. [32.]

Bellezza (P.) La satira del citatore, 1915. [34.]

Bernard, *St., of Menthon, see* FOURMAN (J.)

Danne (F.) Das altfranz. Ebrulfusleben, 1913. [32.]

Decurtins (C.) Rätoroman. Chrestomathie, B10–12, 1914–19; Ergänzungsband 1, 1913. [33, 35–38.]

Färber (E.) Sprache der dem J. Renart zugeschr. Werke "Lai de l'Ombre" &c., 1915. [33.]

Fourman (J.) Über d. Sprache d. Mystère de S. Bernard de Menthon, 1913. [32.]

Heinz (H.) Gil Blas u. d. zeitgenöss. Leben in Frankreich, 1916. [35.]

Kempel (E.) Das Hs.- verhältnis u. d. Sprache d. altfranz. Heldengedichtes Maugis d'Aigremont, 1915. [33.]

Lerch (E.) Das invariable Participium praesentis d. Franz., 1915. [33.]

Leuschner (K.) Ant. Furetière u. s. Streit mit d. französ. Akad., 1915. [34.]

Löpelmann (M.) Il dilettevole essamine de' Guidoni, Furfanti &c., 1598, 1915. [34.]

—— Das Weihnachtslied d. Franz. u. d. übrigen roman. Völker, 1915. [33.]

Lote (G.) Napoléon & le romantisme franç., 1915. [33.]

Meyer (L.) Unters. ü. d. Sprache v. Einfisch im 13 Jhdt., 1915. [34.]

Ott (A. C.) Das altfranz. Eustachiusleben, 1913. [32.]

Pult (G.) Üb. Ämter u. Würden in roman. Bünden, 1913. [32.]

Rotzler (H.) Die Benennungen d. Milchstrasse im Französ., 1915. [33.]

Tignonville (G.) Tignonvillana ined.; [hrsg.] R. Eder, 1915. [33.]

Vaganay (H.) Pour l'hist. du Franç. mod., 1913. [32.]

Vega (L. de). Novelas a la señora Marcia Leonarda, 1915. [34.]

Vollmüller (C.) Bibliog. d. Rom. Forsch. &c., 1915. [33, 34.]

Romano, *Family of, see* VERCI (G. B.) Storia d. Ecelini &c., 3v, 1841.

Romano (Carolus), *bp. of Como.* Comp. d. dott. cristiana ad uso d. citta' &c. di Como. s8°. Lugano. 1855

Romano (Salvatore). A Fiume e in Dalmazia, *see* SOCIETÀ SICILIANA. Archivio &c., N.S., 43, 1921.

Romanoff, *House of* [ROMANOV].

see RUDNEV (V. M.) La vérité sur la famille impériale russe &c., 1920.

,, WILTON (R.) Last days of the R., 1920.

Romanones (*Conde* **de).** Las responsabilidades polit. d. ant. regimen, 1875–1923. 8°. [1924?]

Romans, *abbey of.* Cartul. de l'abbaye de Saint-Barnard de Romans. n. éd. compl., p1, 817–1093. [*no tp.*] 4°. Romans. 1898

Romanus, *rhetor* [ROMANUS, *Sophista*]. Περὶ ἀνειμένου. Ed. W. Camphausen. [Rhetores Graeci, v13]. s8°. Lipsiae, *Teubner.* 1922

Romanus (Carolus Fridericus). Schediasma, an dentur spectra, magi & sagæ. [P1035]. s4°. Lipsiæ. 1717

Romanus (Franciscus), *Jesuit, see* PONTANUS (G. B.) Aureum diurnale cum brevi praxi ex F. R. &c., 1629.

Romaunce, *see* ROMANCE.

Romberg (Conrad Gisbert, *Frhr.* **v.)** Falsific. of the Russian Orange Book. Tr. Maj. C. Bridge. Foreword by G. P. Gooch. 8°. 1923

Romdahl (Axel). Anders Zorn als Radierer. Hrsg. v. A. R. la8°. Dresden. 1922

Rome.

Calendar of State Papers rel. to Eng. affairs, princ. at R. in Vatican Archives &c. v2. Ed. J. M. Rigg. [C. of S.P.]. la8°. 1926

2, Eliz., 1572–78.

Cat. of the anc. sculptures in the municipal coll. of R. Sculptures of the Palazzo d. Conservatori. By members of the British School at Rome. Ed. H. S. Jones. [Plates, fol.] 8° O. 1926

*Etat (L') du siége de R., 1707, *see* FRESCHOT (C.)

Legacy of R.; essays, 1923, *see* BAILEY (C.), *ed.*

Mind (The) of R., 1926, *see* BAILEY (C.), *ed.*

*Nepotisme (Le) de R.; tr., 2p, 1664, *see* LETI (G.)

Recueil de pièces import. conc. la rupture entre la cour de R. & celle de Portugal, *see* PORTUGAL. Rec. de decrets &c., Suite, 1760.

*Rome exactly descr., under Pope Alexandre VII in 2 disc. [1, Rel. of the state of the court &c., by A. Corraro; tr. J. Bultell. 2, New rel. of R. &c., Engl. by G. Torriano; *each w. sep. tp. & pagin.*] s8° 1664

*Rome's hunting-match for 3 kingdoms. [*b. w.* Broad-sheets Misc. b.-s.] fol. 1680

Sel. coll. of views & ruins in R. & its vicinity. [*Eng. & Fr.*] 4°. [1810?]

Rome [*continued*].
Tableau de la cour de R., 1707, *see* AYMON (J.)
*Triumphs (The) of R. over despised Protestancy, 1667, *see* HALL (G.)
CHURCH OF ROME.
Brevis orthod. fidei prof. &c., 1895, *see* PROFESSIO.
*Case (The) stated, betw. Ch. of R. & Ch. of Eng., 2p, 1721, *see* MANNING (R.)
*Ch. (The) of R.: her pres. moral theology &c., 1853, *see* MACGHEE (R. J.)
Conclavi de' pontefici romani, 1688, *see* CONCLAVI.
*De suprema Rom. Pontif. autorit. hodierna eccl. Gallicanae doctrina, 2t, 1747, *see* SUARDI (V. A.)
*Doctrines (The) & practises of the Ch. of R., &c., 1686, *see* STILLINGFLEET (E.)
Litterae apostolicae divers. Rom. pontificum pro officio Inquisit. &c., 1579, *see* EYMERICUS (N.) Directorium Inquisit., 1578.
*Of the incur. scepticism of the Ch. of R., 1688, *see* LA PLACETTE (J.)
see CONGREGATIO DE PROPAGANDA FIDE.
MUSEO NAZIONALE DI VILLA GIULIA, *see* CORPUS vasorum antiq. Italia: Museo Naz. di V. G., fasc. 1–3, 1925–28.

Römer (C.) Kirchl. Gesch. Würtembergs. 2e verm. A. bearb. v. Fr. Roos. 8o. St. 1865

Römer (Johann Wilhelm). Specimen in doct. F. Hemsterhusii de natura divina. 8o. Trajecti a. R. 1839

Römer (Rudolphus Cornelius Henricus). Specimen de Gustavo I, rerum sacrarum in Suecia, saec. 16, instauratore. 8o. Trajecti a. R. 1840

Romera (Waldo Gimenez), *see* GIMENEZ ROMERA (W.)

Romero (Carlos A.), *see* THAYER OJEDA (T.) Las biog. de los 2 " C. de Molina " publ. por C. A. R., 1920.

Romero (Tomas Muñoz y), *see* MUÑOZ Y ROMERO (T.)

Romero de Terreros y Vinent (Manuel). Las artes indust. en la Nueva España. s8o. México. 1923
Bibliogr. de cronistas de la ciudad de Mexico. s8o. Mexico. 1926

Romero de Torres (Julio), *see* MARTINEZ SIERRA (G.) J. R. de T., 1919.

Romero y Palomeque (*Gen.* Francisco de Paula), *see* RISCO (A.) Mil hombres: rasgos biog. R. y P., 2a ed., 1920.

Romier (Lucien). Catholiques & Huguenots à la cour de Charles IX. 8o. 1924
La Conjuration d'Amboise. L'aurore sanglante de la liberté de conscience—Le règne & la mort de François II. 8o. 1923
Explic. de notre temps. [Les cahiers verts, 48]. s8o. 1925
Le royaume de Catharine de Médicis. La France à la veille de Guerres de Religion. 2t. 8o. 1922

Romieu (J.) Livre noir [*by R. Marchand*] & Livre jaune. s8o. 1922

Romilly (*Sir* Samuel).
see COLLINS (*Sir* W. J.) Life & work of R., 1908.
,, —— Notes on R. & E. Dumont, 1924.
,, PHILLIPSON (C.) 3 criminal law reformers: R. &c., 1923.

Rommel (Dietrich Christoph von). Abulfedea Arabiae descr. comm. perpet. illust. [P2655]. 4o. Gottingae. [1802]

Romney (George), *see* HARVEY (F.) [R.: MS. records of pictures &c.], 2v, *n.d.*

Romstorfer (Karl A.) Cetatea Sucevii, descr. pe temeiul propriilor cercetări făcute între 1895 & 1904. Publ. in Românește cu o notiță istor. de A. Lăpědatu. Ed. Acad. Române. la4o. București. 1913

Romulus, *see* RANGE (C. T.) Vita R., 1661.

Romussi (Carlo). Milano ne' suoi monumenti. 3a ed., rinnovata e compl. 2v. la8o. Milano. [1912–13]

Ronaldshay (Lawrence John Lumley Dundas, *e. of*), *2nd son of 1st marq. of Zetland.* The heart of Âryâvarta: psychol. of Indian unrest. 8o. 1925
India: a bird's-eye view. 8o. 1924
Lands of the thunderbolt: Sikhim, Chumbi & Bhutan. 8o. 1923
The life of Lord Curzon. 3v. 8o. [1928]

Ronaldson (James Henry). Coal. 8o. 1920

Ronan (Myles V.) The Reformation in Dublin, 1536–58, f. orig. sources. 8o. 1926

Ronarc'h (*Vice-Amiral*). Souvenirs de la Guerre. [t]1, Août 1914–Sept. 1915. [*no more publ.*] 8o. 1921

Roncalli Parolino (Carlo). Rime di vari autori bresciani viventi. 8o. Brescia. 1761

Ronchini (Amadio). Not. biogr. intr. a Jacopo Marmitta. [P2861]. fol. [Parma]. *n.d.*

Rondeau (*Mrs.* —), *see* WARD (*Mrs.* —)

Rondeaux, Virelais u. Balladen, 12–14ten Jhdt., 2B, 1921–27, *see* GENNRICH (F.)

Rondeletius (Gulielmus), *see* L'OBEL (M. DE). In G. R. Pharmaceuticam offic. animadv. &c., 1605.

Rondolino (Ferdinando). P. Bello, sua vita e suoi scritti, *see* REGIA DEP. DI STORIA PATRIA. Misc., t28, 1890.

Rönick (Johann Tobias). De Gunthero eremita reform. sacr. necess. teste, comment. [P596]. s4o. Gottingae. 1759

Ronan (Barry). Forty S. African years. Foreword by Sir E. H. Walton. 8o. [1923]

Ronsard (Pierre de).
Œuvres compl. Ed. crit. avec intr. &c. par P. Laumonier. [Soc. des Textes Franç. Mod.] [t]3, 4. s8o. 1921–25
3, Ode de la paix, 1550—Tombeau de Marguerite de Valois, 1551—5e livre des odes, 1552.
4, Les amours, 1552.
Œuvres compl. Texte de 1578, publ. avec compl. &c. par H. Vaganay. Intr. par P. de Nolhac. 7t. s8o. 1923–24
Œuvres inéd. [& P. de R. par G. Colletet]. Rec. &c. P. Blanchemain. [Trésor des pièces rares &c.] s8o. 1855
Chefs-d'œuvre lyriques. Choix & notice de A. Dorchain. s8o. 1920
Ronsard & s. temps. Expos. à la Bibl. Nat., jan.–fév. 1925. [Préf. de P. de Nolhac]. s8o. [1925]
see CHAMPION (P.) R. & son temps, 1924.
,, LAUMONIER (P.) R., ét. hist. & litt., 2e éd., 1923.
,, MARTELLIÈRE (J.) P. de Ronsard, 1924.
,, NOLHAC (P. DE). R. & l'humanisme, 1921.
,, —— La vie amoureuse de P. de R., 1926.
,, RAYMOND (M.) Bibliog. crit. de R. en F. (1550–85), 1927.
,, —— L'influence de R. sur la poésie franç., 1550–85, 2t, 1927.
,, RICCI (S. DE). Cat. d'une coll. unique des éd. orig. de R., 1925.
,, SCHWEINITZ (M. DE). Les épitaphes de R., 1925.
,, SORG (R.) Cassandre, ou le secret de R., 1925.

Ronzy (Pierre). Bibliog. crit. des œuvres impr. & ms. de Papire Masson (1544–1611). la8o. 1924
Un humaniste italianisant: Papire Masson (1544–1611). la8o. 1924

Rooijens (Gijsbert Jan) [ROOYENS]. Oratio de indole religionis christ. 4o. Amstelodami. 1828

Rooke (*Sir* George), *1650–1709.* New express f. Sir G. R., Sept. 15, 1704. [*Single sheet. b. w.* Post Man, 1704–8]. fol. 1704

Rooke (Noel). Woodcuts & wood engravings. Lect. la8o. 1926

Roos (Magnus Friedrich). An expos. of prophesies of Daniel &c. Tr. E. Henderson. 8o. E. 1811
Fundamenta psychologiae ex S. Script. collecta. s8o. Tubingae. 1769
Selecta capita doctrinae de ecclesia. 8o. Tubingae. 1784

Roosendaele (L. de Lauwereyns), *see* LAUWEREYNS DE ROOSENDAELE (L. DE).

Rooses (Max), *see* ANTWERP. Cat. of the Plantin-Moretus Museum, by M. R., 3rd ed., 1921.

Roosevelt (Franklin Delano). Naval & marine prints & paintings f. coll. of R. Sold, Anderson Gall. [P2859]. 8o. N.Y. 1925

Roosevelt (Theodore). New York. [Hist. towns]. 8o. 1891
Selections f. the corresp. of R. & H. C. Lodge, 1884–1918. 2v. 8o. N.Y. 1925
T. Roosevelt the child. A sketch [*by* Mrs. M. L. Storer], incl. 32 letters &c. 8o. 1921
see BISHOP (J. B.) T. R. & h. time shown in h. own letters, 2v, 1920.
,, CHARNWOOD (G. R. B., *1st b.*) T. R., 1923.
,, FOULKE (W. D.) R. & the spoilsmen, 1925.
,, HOWLAND (H. J.) T. R. & h. times, 1921.
,, RHODES (J. F.) The McKinley & R. admin., 1897–1909, 1922.

Roosval (Johnny August Emanuel). Dopfuntar i Statens Hist. Museum. Beskriv. grupperande förteckning, utg. av Konsthist. Inst. vid Stockholms Högskola genom J. R. 4o. 1917
Nya Sankt Göransstudier. 4o. [1924]
Studier i Danmark. Över 1100–talets skulptur & arkit. 4o. 1918
Svenskt konstgalleri. 500 bilder ur d. Svenska målarekonstens & skulpturens hist., med intr. text &c., utg. &c. af J. R. 4o. [1912]

Root (Elihu). The Declar. of the rights & duties of nations adopted by the Amer. Inst. of Internat. Law. [*in Eng., Fr., Span. & Portug.* P2676]. la8o. [Wash. 1916]
The effect of democracy on internat. law: addr. [C.E. for Int. Peace. P2676]. la8o. Wash. 1917
see SCOTT (J. B.) E. R.'s services to internat. law, 1925.

Root (Robert Kilburn). The MSS. of Chaucer's Troilus, w. facs., *see* CHAUCER SOC.: I., 98, 1914.
The textual trad. of Chaucer's Troilus, *see* CHAUCER SOC.: I., 99, 1916.

Rooy (Antonius de).
Elegiarum volumen. [P2651]. 8º. Arnhemiae. 1806
Rooyens (Gysbert Jan), *see* ROOIJENS (G. J.)
Roozeboom (Janus Gysbertus). Spec. philos. inaug. de idealismo. 4º. Harderovici. [1808]
Ropartz (Sigismond). Guingamp: ét. pour serv. à l'hist. du tiers-état en Brétagne. 2e éd. refond. 2t. 8º. St.-Brieuc. 1859
Portraits bretons des 17e & 18e s. s8º. Saint-Brieuc. 1857
Récits bretons. [Jacobus—Légendes révolut.—Marguerite Lenoir]. s8º. Saint-Brieuc. [1859]
Roper (Esther Gertrude), *see* BOWMAN (F. L.) & E. G. R. Traders in east & west, 1924.
Roper (R. E.)
The individual & the community. 8º. [1922]
Ropes (James Hardy), *see* FOAKES-JACKSON (F. J.) & K. LAKE, *edd.* Beginnings of Xtianity, p1, v3, Text of Acts; by J. H. R., 1926.
Röpke (Fritz). Von Gambetta bis Clémenceau: 50 Jahre franz. Politik u. Gesch. 8º. St. 1922
Ropshin (V.), *ps.* [*i.e.* B. SAVINKOV]. The black horse. Novel. Tr. w. foreword by Sir P. Dukes. s8º. [1924]
Ce qui ne fut pas. Roman. Tr. J. W. Bienstock. s8º. 1921
Open letter to the Rt. Hon. D. Lloyd George. [P2574]. s8º. [1922]
Roques (Mario). Sur 2 particularités métr. de la Vie de St. Grégoire en anc. franç. [P2731]. 8º. 1921
For o. eds., see Bibliothèque de l'Ecole des Hautes Etudes. Cinquantenaire: mélanges, 1921, *&* Romania, t48, 1922.
Roquette (Otto), *see* LISZT (F.) Legende v. d. heil. Elisabeth, Orat. nach Worten v. R., 3. A., *n.d.*
Rorarius (Hieronymus). Quod animalia bruta saepe ratione utantur melius homine libri 2, Rec. diss. &c. auxit C. H. Ribovius. s8º. Helmstadii. 1728
Rørdam (Valdemar). De dernede. Digte. 8º 1917
Roret (——), *libraire, see* TARBÉ DES SABLONS (S. A.) Nouv. man. compl. d. poids & mesures &c., 1845.
Roretz (Carl). Z. Analyse v. Kants Philosophie d. Organischen, 1922, *see* KAIS. AKAD. D. WISS. ZU WIEN. Sitzber., B193, 1922.
Rorke (J. D. M.)
A musical pilgrim's progress. Pref. by E. Walker. s8º. 1921
Rosa (G. Titta). Narratori contemporanei; a cura di R. 2v. s8º. Milano. 1921
Rosa (J. S. da Silva), *see* SILVA ROSA (J. S. DA).
Rosa (Salvatore).
see MANWARING (E. W.) Ital. landscape in 18th c. England: infl. of S. R. &c., 1925.
„ PETTORELLI (A.) S. R.: 52 tavole con introd., 1924.
Rosadi (Giovanni), *see* DANTE ALIGHIERI. Lectura D.: c. 7 dell' Inferno letto da G. R., 1915.
Rosales (Eduardo), *see* FRANCÉS (J.) E. R., 1920.
Rosarius (Simon). *Antithesis Christi & Antichristi, videlicet papae. Recens aucta &c. [*Foll. by* Vita & gesta Hildebrandi, descr. per Benonem Card.—Joannae papissae vita—Epistola de morte Pauli III Pontif. Max. *by* P. Aesquillus, *ps., i.e.* M. Flacius Illyricus]. s8º. Genevae. 1578
Rosaroll, *The family of, see* MAZZIOTTI (M.) La congiura dei R., 1920.
Rosaroll (Cesare), *see* MAZZIOTTI (M.) La congiura dei R., 1920.
Rosary. *Intr. to the celeb. devotion of the most holy Rosary &c. [*Dedic. signed* J. C., *o.p.*] s8º. 1737
Roscher (Wilhelm Heinrich), *b. 1845, ed.* Ausführliches Lexicon d. griech. u. röm. Mythologie. B4, 5. la8º. L., *Teubner.* 1909–24
„ „ Suppl. Gesch. d. klass. Mythologie u. Religionsgesch. v. O. Gruppe. la8º. L., *Teubner.* 1921
Die hippokrat. Schrift v. d. Siebenzahl u. ihr Verhältn. z. Altpythagoreismus, *see* KÖNIGL.-SÄCHS. GESELLS. D. WISS. Berichte, phil.-hist. Kl., B71, 1919.
Der Omphalosgedanke bei verschied. Völkern, *see* KÖNIGL. SÄCHS. GESELLS. Berichte, B70, 1918.
Roschmann (Anton). *Disquis. epist. Tartarottianæ de S. Ingenuini Sabion. episc. actis. p2. s4º. [Ulm. 1751]
Rosco, *ps.* *Horrida bella. Pains & penalties v. truth & justice. [*Satire in verse, in ref. to trial of Queen Caroline. Pref. sign.* Rosco]. [P425]. 8º. 1820
Roscoe (*Rt. Hon. Sir* Henry E.) & A. Harden. Inorganic chemistry for advanced students. 2nd ed. rev. s8º. 1920
—— & C. Schorlemmer. A treatise on chemistry. 5th ed., rev. by J. C. Cain. v1, Non-metallic elements. 8º. 1920
„ „ n. ed. (6th), rev. by B. M. Jones &c., v2, Metals. 2p. [*pagin. cont.*] 8º. 1923

Roscoe (*Rev.* John).
The Bagesu & o. tribes of the Uganda Protectorate: the 3rd part of the report of the Mackie Ethnolog. Exped. to Cent. Africa. 8º. C. 1924
The Bakitara or Banyoro: the 1st part of report of Mackie Ethnolog. Exped. to Cent. Africa. 8º. C. 1923
The Banyankole: the 2nd part of the report of the Mackie Ethnolog. Exped. to Cent. Africa. 8º. C. 1923
Immigrants & th. infl. in the Lake region of Cent. Africa. Frazer Lect. [P2756]. s8º. C. 1924
The Northern Bantu: some Cent. African tribes of Uganda. 8º. C. 1915
The soul of Central Africa. Gen. acc. of the Mackie Ethnolog. Exped. 8º. 1922
Twenty-five years in East Africa. 8º. C. 1921
Roscoe (Thomas). The Spanish novelists. Tr., w. crit. & biog. notices. [Chandos Classics]. s8º. [1880]
Roscoe (William). Life of Lorenzo de' Medici. 10th ed., rev. by T. Roscoe. s8º. *Bohn.* 1877
Rose, *The family of.* Domestic papers of the R. family. Ed. A. & H. Tayler. 8º. Aberdeen. 1926
Rose (Christopher Philip Godwin).
Antecedents of Christianity. 8º. 1925
Rose (Felicitas), *ps.* [*i.e.* F. R. MÖRSEBERGER].
Heideschulmeister Uwe Karsten. neue A. s8º. [1920]
Rose (Frank Herbert). Our industrial jungle. Pref. by Rt. Hon. J. R. Clynes. s8º. [1926]
Rose (Henry). Maeterlinck's symbolism: The blue bird & o. essays. s8º. 1910
Rose (Herbert Jennings). Primitive culture in Greece. s8º. [1925]
Primitive culture in Italy. 8º. [1926]
see PLUTARCH. Roman questions; tr. &c. H. J. R., 1924.
Rose (Horace Arthur). Compend. of Punjab customary law. [*v5–20*]. With repr. of Adopt. of daughter's son &c. by M. M. Shafi. 2nd ed. 2p. 8º. Lahore. 1911
Rose (James Anderson). Coll. of engraved portraits; catalogued & exhib. by J. A. R. &c. Corpor. of London, 1872. 4º. 1874
„ „ Further sel., accomp. by biog., & intr. by G. Goodwin. [2v, *pagin. cont.*] 4º. 1894
Rose (John Holland).
Chivalry & the sea, *see* ROY. SOC. OF LIT. Essays, N.S., v4, 1924.
The development of the European nations, 1870–1921, 6th ed., incl. 2 suppl. chapters by W. L. McPherson. 8º. 1923
The indecisiveness of mod. war & o. essays. 8º. 1927
Life of Napoleon I: includ. new materials f. Brit. official rec. 8th ed. rev. 8º. 1922
Lord Hood & the defence of Toulon. 8º. C. 1922
Short life of Will. Pitt. s8º. 1925
Rose (Joseph Nelson).
see BRITTON (N. L.) & J. N. R. The Cactaceae, 4v, 1919–23.
„ —— & —— Neoabbottia, new cactus genus f. Hispaniola, 1921.
Rose (Thomas), *topographical writer.* Westmorland, Cumberland, Durham & Northumberland, illust. f. orig. drawings by T. Allom &c. [*another issue in 1 vol.*] 4º. 1832
see NOBLE (T.) & T. R. Counties of Chester, Derby &c., illust. f. drawings by T. Allom, w. hist. &c. descr. by T. N. & T. R., 1836.
Rose (William), *see* FAUST (*Dr.* JOHANN). Hist. of F., 1592–94, modernised & ed. by W. R., 1925.
Rose (William), *Baillie to the 2nd Earl of Fife.*
see FIFE (J. D., *2nd earl*). Ld. F. & h. factor [*i.e.* W. R.]: corr.; ed. A. & H. Tayler, 1925.
„ ROSE, *The family of.* Domestic papers; ed. A. & H. Tayler, 1926.
Roseau (Le) d'Or. Chroniques, no. 1. [Œuvres & chron., 5]. s8º. [1925]
Rosebery (Archibald Philip Primrose, *5th earl of***).**
Miscellanies, literary & historical. 2v. 8º. [1921]
Oliver Cromwell: eulogy & appreciation. [P2524]. s8º. [1900]
see RAYMOND (E. T.) The man of promise, Ld. R.: crit. study, 1923.
Rosedale (Honyel Gough). The Spanish match in the light of rec. works & a private MS. [Sette of Odd Volumes: Opusc. 59]. s8º. 1908
Rosegger (Peter K.) Persönl. Erinnerungen an R. Hamerling. s8º. Wien. 1891
Rosehill Collection, *see* NORTHESK (D. J. C., *10th e. of*). Cat. of R. coll. of prehist. &c. objects, 1924.
Rosell (Cayetano). Crón. de la prov. de Madrid, 1865, *see* ESPAÑA. Crón. gen., v1, 1865 &c.
Roselli (Francesco), *see* CONTARINI (G. M.) Map of the world designed by C., engraved by R., 1506, 1924.

Rosen (*count* **Eric v.)** Bland Indianer: forskningar &c. i Gran Chaco. la8°. 1921
Pop. acc. of archæol. research during the Swedish Chaco-Cordillera exped. 1901–2. la8°. Stockholm. [1924]
Rosen (Erwin), *ps.* [*i.e.* E. CARLÉ].
Der grosse Krieg. 9te A. T3. s8°. St. [1918]
*In the Foreign Legion. [n. ed.] s8°. [1915]
Rosen (Franz).
Eines grossen Mannes Liebe. Roman. 7e A. s8°. 1921
Rosen (Friedrich), *orientalist.* Corporis radicum Sanscritarum prolusio. [P2600]. s8°. Berolini. 1826
Radices Sanscritae. 8°. Berolini. 1827
Rosen (Fritz).
Shumā Farsi &c. Neupers. Sprachführer. 8°. L. 1890
Rosen (*Baron* **Georg)** [ROZEN].
Жизнь за царя. Опера. [P2435]. s8°. С.–П. 1880
Rosen (*baron* **Roman Romanovich).**
Forty years of diplomacy. 2v. 8°. [1922]
Rosenbach (Abraham S. Wolf).
Books & bidders: adv. of a bibliophile. 8°. [1928]
Rosenbacher (Martin). Dreves. s8°. Hamburg. 1919
Rosenberg (C. Adolf).
Gesch. d. Kostüms. Text v. E. Heyck. sm. fol. *n.d.*
Rosenberg (Isaac). Poems. Sel. & ed. G. Bottomley. Intr. mem. by L. Binyon. s8°. 1922
Rosenberg (Jakob). M. Schongauer Handzeichnungen. Hrsg. v. J. R., mit 50 Abbild. la8°. München. 1923
Rosenberg (Marc). Der Goldschmiede Merkzeichen.
3e, erweit. u. illust. A. B1–4. la8°. Fr. a. M. 1922–28
1–3, Deutschland. 4, Ausland u. Byzanz.
Niello, bis z. J. 1000 nach Chr. *&* Seit d. J. 1000. [2v]. fol. Frankfurt a. M. 1924
see BADISCHER KUNSTGEWERBE-VEREIN. Alte u. neue Fächer [*w.* Der Fächer: geschichtl. Skizze v. M. R.], 1891.
Rosenberg (Walter). Der Kaiser u. d. Protestanten, 1537–39. [Verein f. Ref.-gesch. Schr., Jhrg. 20, Nr. 77]. 8°. Halle a. S. 1903
Rosenberger (Jesse Leonard). The Pennsylvania Germans: sk. of th. hist. &c., of the Mennonites &c. s8°. Chicago. [1923]
Through 3 centuries. Colver & Rosenberger lives & times, 1620–1922. 8°. Chicago. [1922]
Rosenbusch (Christopher), *Jesuit.* Antwort u. Ehrerrettung auff die Schmachschrifft Lucae Osiandri, Warnung vor der Jesuiter Blutdurstigen Anschlägen &c. s4°. Ingolstadt. 1586
see OSIANDER (L.), *the elder.* Verantwortung wider C. R. &c., 1586.
Rosenbusch (Hans), *see* GULAT-WELLENBURG (W. v.), H. R. &c. Physikal. Mediumismus, 1925.
Rosenfeld (Carl Georg Fr. Heyer v.), *see* HEYER V. ROSENFELD (C. G. F.)
Rosenfeld (Lev Borisovich), *see* KAMENEV (L. B.)
Rosenfeld (Sandor Friedr.), *see* RODA RODA (A.)
Rosenhagen (Hans).
Arthur Kampf. [Knackfuss, 112]. la8°. Bielefeld. 1922
Rosenmöller (Bernhard). Relig. Erkenntnis nach Bonaventura. [Beitr. z. Gesch. d. Philosophie d. M.-a., B25, H3/4]. 8°. Münster i. W. 1925
Rosenmüller (Ernst Friedrich Carl). Instit. ad fundamenta linguæ Arab. Acc. sententiæ & narr. Arab. una cum glossario Arab.-Lat. s4°. Lipsiæ. 1818
Rosenmüller (Johann Georg). Abhdlg. ü. d. Urspr. d. christl. Theol. Nebst e. Rede, &c. Übers. v. C. G. Spranger. 8°. L. 1789
De Xtnae theol. origine. Acc. oratio &c. s8°. Lipsiae. 1786
Rosenow (Emil). Wider d. Pfaffenherrschaft: Kulturbilder a. d. Religionskampfen d. 16. u. 17. Jhdts. 2B [B2 fortgeführt v. H. Ströbel]. la8°. [1904–5]
Rosenthal (Albert), *see* ROSENTHAL (M.) & A. R. List of portraits, 1923.
Rosenthal (Erwin). Dürers Buchmalereien für Pirckheimers Bibl. [Jhbh. d. Preuss. Kunstsamml., B49, Beiheft]. fol. 1928
„ „ *f. a. copy see* JAHRBUCH D. KÖN. PREUSS. KUNSTS., B49, 1928.
Giotto in d. mittelalterl. Geistesentwicklung. la8°. Augsburg. 1924
Rosenthal (Leonard). Au royaume de la perle. s8°. 1926

Rosenthal (Max) & A. Rosenthal. List of portraits, lithographs—etchings—mezzotints; by M. & A. R. 8°. *p.p.* Phila. 1923
Roseraie (La) d'Arménie; tr. préc. d'une ét. &c. par A. Tchobanian, 2t, 1918–23, *see* TCHOBANIAN (A.)
Rose-Troup (Frances).
Biog. sketch of the Rev. C. Jelinger, w. bibl. notes by J. Ingle Dredge. [Repr. f. Trans. of Devonshire Assoc. P2518]. 8°. Plymouth. 1900
Ellis Veryard, of Plymtree. [Repr. f. Devon. Assoc. P2489]. 8°. 1892
An Exeter worthy (I. Jourdain). [Repr. f. Devon. Assoc. P2489]. 8°. 1897
Honiton in 1530. [Repr. f. Devon. Assoc. P2489]. 8°. 1898
The kalenders & the Exeter trade-gilds. [Repr. f. Devon. Assoc. P2489]. 8°. 1912
The Lady of the Isle, Isabella de Fortibus, 1236–93. 8°. *p.p.* Plymouth. 1905
Lost chapels of Exeter. 8°. Exeter. 1923
Notes on the district probate registry at Exeter. [Repr. f. Devon. Assoc. P2489]. 8°. 1901
Rev. M. Mundy, I, II, III, IV. [Repr. f. Devon. Assoc. P2489]. 8°. 1894
Two book bills of Katherine Parr. [Repr. f. The Library, Jan. 1911]. [P2463]. 8°. 1911
Rosetti (Alexandre). Etude sur le rhotacisme en Roumain. Avec un App. [H.E., 240]. 8°. 1924
Rosher (*Lieut.* **Harold),** *R.N.A.S.* In the Royal Naval Air Service: War letters. Intr. by A. Bennett. [3rd impr.] s8°. 1916
Rosi (Michele). L'Italia odierna. Due secoli. v2, t1–3. la8°. Torino. 1923–26
Rosi da Porta (Petro Dominico) [ROSIUS DA PORTA].
Hist. Reformationis eccl. Ræticarum &c. 2t. s4°. Curiae Rætorum. 1772–77
Rosiglia (Marco) [ROSIGLIA *da Foligno*]. Opera noua d. M. R. & altri auct. Nou. stamp. cioe Sonetti Capituli &c.: una p̄dica damore: & una Frottola de cēto Romiti. [*no pagin. fol. l4 missing*]. s8°. [Venetia, *Georgio da Ruschōi.* 1516]
Rosimond (Claude La Rose, *sieur* **de),** *see* LA ROSE DE ROSIMOND (C.)
Rosmer (Ernst), *ps.* [*i.e. Frau* ELSA BERNSTEIN].
Dämmerung. Schauspiel. s8°. [1894]
Rosner (Carl). Der König. s8°. St. 1921
Rosny (J. H.), *aîné, ps.* [*i.e.* J. H. H. BOËX].
L'amoureuse aventure. Roman. s8°. [1920]
Le chemin d'amour. s8°. [1921]
Le cœur tendre & cruel, *see* ŒUVRES libres, 32, 1924.
La fiancée de l'ombre, nouvelle, *see* ŒUVRES libres, 46, 1925.
Une jeune fille à la page. s8°. [1926]
La juive (Rachel & l'amour). s8°. [1926]
Mém. de la vie litt.: l'Acad. Goncourt, les salons, quelques éditeurs. 8°. 1927
Les navigateurs de l'infini, *see* ŒUVRES libres, 54, 1925.
Les origines: la préhist. s8°. [1923]
Les pures & les impures. Roman de mœurs paris. 2t. s8°. [1921]
Torches & lumignons: souv. de la vie litt. s8°. 1921
Rosny (J. H.), *jne., ps.* [*i.e.* BOËX (S. J. F.)].
Les chaperons blancs. s8°. [1928]
Claire Técel, avocat à la cour. s8°. 1924
La courtisane triomphante. s8°. 1925
La désirée. s8°. [1926]
Fanchon-la-belle. s8°. [1921]
La pigeonne. s8°. [1925]
Rosny (L. Léon de). Remarques sur quelques dictionnaires japonais &c. [P2428]. 8°. 1858
Rospatt (Johann Joseph).
Die polit. Parteien Griechenlands. 8°. Trier. 1844
Ross (Alexander). Hist. sketches of anc. Ross-shire families: Munroes of Culcairn. s8°. Invergordon. 1884
Ross (*Maj.-Gen.* **Charles).** The fly-by-nights. s8°. [1921]
When the devil was sick. s8°. 1924
Ross (Colin). Die erwachende Sphinx: durch Afrika v. Kap n. Kairo. 2e A. s8°. L. 1927
Ross (David Morison), *D.D.*
The spiritual genius of St. Paul. 8°. [1925]
Ross (Edward Alsworth).
The Russian Soviet Republic. 8°. [1923]
Ross (*Sir* **Edward Denison).** Prester John & the Empire of Ethiopia, *see* NEWTON (A. P.), *ed.* Travel &c., 1926.
see 'ABD ALLÁH MUḤAMMAD. Arabic hist. of Gujarat; ed. E. D. R., 2v, 1910–21.
„ BROWNE (E. G.) A Persian anthology; tr. E. G. B.; ed. E. D. R., 1927.
„ RELIGIONS. R. of the Empire, intr. by E. D. R., 1925.
Ross (Eliza), *see* BISHOP (J.), *murderer.* *The hist. of the London Burkers, incl. life &c. of E. R., 1832.

Ross (Elizabeth N. Macbean). A lady doctor in Bakhtiari land. Ed. J. N. M. Ross. s8°. 1921
Ross (Frank Alexander), *see* United States: Census. School attendance in 1920: analysis by F. A. R., 1924.
Ross (Hugh), *see* Le Cène (C.) An essay for a new tr. of the Bible, [tr.] by H. R., 1702.
Ross (James), *of Montreal.* Cat. of pictures &c., property of J. R., sold by Christie &c., July 8, 1927. [*Illust.*] 8°. [1927]
Ross (Mrs. Janet Ann). Leaves f. our Tuscan kitchen; or, how to cook vegetables. [repr., w. add.] s8°. 1911
Ross (John), *bp. of Exeter.* *Remarks on the Bp. of E.'s &c. interpret. of Haggai. [P543]. 8°. 1786
Ross (Sir John), *Bart., Ld. Chancellor of Ireland.* Years of my pilgrimage: random remin. 8°. 1924
Ross (John), *missionary in Newchang.* The Manchus, or the reigning dynasty in China. 8°. Paisley. 1880
Ross (John D.), *LL.D.*
Who's who in Burns. s8°. Stirling. 1927
Ross (Ludwig). A journey to Cyprus (1845). Tr. C. D. Cobham. s8°. Nicosia. 1910
Ross (Malcolm). Climber in New Zealand. 8°. 1914
Ross (Robert) & C. E. Montague. Brit. artists at the front. [p]2, Sir John Lavery, w. introd. by R. R. & C. E. M. [P2700]. 4°. 1918
Ross (Sir Ronald), *K.C.B.* Memoirs, w. acc. of the gt. malaria problem & its solution. 8°. 1923
Philosophies. [*Poems*]. s8°. 1911
see Papers for the present, No. 11, Sir R. R.'s story, 1920?.
Ross (W. McGregor).
Kenya f. within: sh. polit. hist. 8°. [1927]
Ross (William), *of Aberdour.* Aberdour & Inchcolme: hist. notices of parish & monastery. 8°. E. 1885
Ross (William David). Aristotle. 8°. [1923]
Rossaeus (G. Guilelmus), *ps., see* Rainolds (William).
Rossall Register (The), 1844–1905. Ed. E. J. Deane. 8°. Liv'l. 1905
Rossato (Arturo) [*ps.* Arros].
Mussolini: colloquio intimo. la8°. Milano. 1922
Rossbach (Carl). Geschichte d. freien Reichsdörfer Sulzbach u. Soden. 8°. Bad Soden i. T. [1924]
Rosse (William Parsons, *3rd earl of***).** Scientific papers, 1800–67. Coll. & republ. by Hon. Sir C. Parsons. 4°. 1926
Rosseeuw Saint-Hilaire (Eugène F. A.) Ce qu'il faut à la France. 2e éd. [P2657]. 8°. 1861
Etudes relig. et litt. s8°. 1863
Hist. de l'Espagne, j.' à la mort de Ferd. VII. n. éd. revue & corr. 14t. 8°. Paris. 1844–79
Rosser (James), *Wesleyan minister.* The hist. of Wesleyan Methodism in the Isle of Man; w. acc. of the life &c. of bp. Wilson. s8°. Douglas, I. of M. 1849
Rossetti (Christina Georgina), *see* De la Mare (W.) C. R., 1926.
Rossetti (Dante Gabriel).
The early Italian poets, w. D.'s Vita Nuova. Tr. by D. G. R. [Ed. E. G. Gardner]. [Temple Classics]. s8°. 1904
Letters to h. publisher, F. S. Ellis. Ed. w. intr. &c. by O. Doughty. s4°. 1928
Poems & translations, 1850–70, w. the prose story "Hand & soul." [repr.] s8°. 1919
see Dupré (H.) Un Ital. d'Angl.: D. G. R., 1921.
,, Sapori (F.) Maestri, No. 27, 1921.
,, Waugh (E.) R., h. life & works, 1928.
Rossetti (Gabriele).
Discorso inaug. per la cattedra di lingua e lett. Ital. nell Coll. del Re, Londra. [P2496]. s8°. Londra. 1831
Iddio e l'uomo, salterio. s8°. Napoli. 1849
Rossetti (William Michael), *see* Dowden (E.), R. G. & W. M. R. Letters about Shelley interchanged by 3 friends—E. D., R. G. & W. M. R., 1917.
—— **& A. C. Swinburne.**
Notes on the Royal Acad. Exhib. 1868. 8°. 1868
Rossi (Benaventura de'). Istoria genealog. e cronolog. d. 2 case Adorna e Botta &c. sm. fol. Firenze. 1719
Rossi (Filippo). Mirone e Policleto. s8°. Firenze. 1922
Rossi (Giovanni Antonio de). De praecipuis caussis & momentis neglectae a nonnullis Hebr. litt. disciplinae disquis. s4°. Augustae Taurin. 1769
Rossi (Giovanni Bernardo de).
Annales hebraeo-typogr. 1501–1540. 4°. Parmae. 1799
Apparatus Hebraeo-Biblicus, seu MSS. editique codices Sacri Textus quos possidet J. B. de R. 8°. Parmae. 1782

Rossi (Giovanni Bernardo de) [*continued*].
De Corano Arab. Venetiis Paganini typis impr. sec. 16. [P2705]. 8°. Parmae. 1805
De typographia Hebræo-Ferrariensi. 8°. Parmæ. 1780
Diz. storico d. autori arabi. 8°. Parma. 1807
Diz. storico d. Ebrei e d. loro opere. 2v. 8°. Parma. 1802
Lexicon Hebraicum selectum ex ined. R. Parchonis lexico &c. [P2594]. 8°. Parmae. 1807
MSS. codices Hebraici Bibl. J. B. de Rossi, ab eodem descr. & illust. Acc. app. qua contin. MSS. codices reliqui al. linguarum. 3v. 8°. Parmae. 1803
Scholia critica in V. T. libros. Suppl. ad Varias sacri textus lectiones. [*b. w. h.* Var. lect., t4, 1788]. 4°. Parmae. 1798
Spec. var. lect. sacri textus & Chaldaica Estheris addit. cum Lat. vers. ac notis. Acc. ejusdem aut. app. de cod. tritaplo Samarit. Bibl. Barberinae. Ed. altera, auct. s8°. Tubingae. 1783
Rossi (Giovanni Vittorio), *see* Erythræus (J. N.)
Rossi (Girolamo), *1831–1914.*
Works in Regia Dep. di Storia Patria. Misc.
Doc. ined. rig. la chiesa di Ventimiglia, 1906. [42.]
Glossario medioevale ligure, 1898. [35.]
Glossario medioevale ligure: app., 1909. [44.]
I Grimaldi in Ventimiglia, 1900. [36.]
Maria Luigia Gabriella di Savoia &c. in Nizza, nel sett. 1701, 1895. [33.]
Sopra un poemetto sul preteso diritto cosciatico [*by A. Panizzi*], 1906. [42.]
Sulla fondaz. di Airole, colonia Ventimigliese: doc. d. 15 sec., 1868. [5.]
La Valle di Diano (Liguria) e i suoi statuti ant., 1902. [38.]
see Boselli (P.) Commem. d. G. R., 1915.
Rossi (Giuseppe de).
Quando il sogno è finito. . . s8°. Milano. 1925
Rossi (Michele). Lugo. 4°. Milano. *n.d.*
Rossi (Niccolò de'). Sonetti ined. Pubbl. G. Navone. [Nozze Tittoni—Antona Traversi. N139]. la8°. 1888
Rossi (Vittorio).
Storia d. letteratura ital. 7a ed. 3v. 8°. Milano. 1917–20
Rossier (L.) Hist. des protestants de Picardie. s8°. 1861
Rossiiskaya Akademiya Ist. Mater. Kulturi, *see* Rostovtsev (M. I.) Скиѳія и Боспоръ, 1925.
Rossiiskaya Akademiya Nauk, *see* Imperatorskaya Akademiya Nauk.
Rossiiskaya Kommunist. Partiya. Десятый съезд Р. К. П. Отчет 8–28 Марта 1921. la8°. Москва. 1921
Российская коммунист. партия в постановлениях ее съездов, 1903–21. Сборник резолюций &c. 8°. П. 1921
Rossiiskaya Sotsialdemokraticheskaya Raboch. Partiya.
Задачи русской Рабочей партіи. 2e изд. [P2715]. s8°. *n.p.* 1900
Къ вопросу національной автономіи &c. [P2715]. 8°. Лондонъ. 1902
Матеріалы къ Якутскому процессу. [P2715]. s8°. Женева. 1904
Программа Росс. коммун. партии 1919. [P2724]. la8°. Москва. 1919
Пролетарскій праздникъ. [P2715]. 8°. *n.p.* [1903]
Проэктъ программы. [P2715]. s8°. Catford. *n.d.*
V-ый съѣздъ *& o. pamphlets & leaflets.* [P2716]. s8°. Лондонъ. 1903 &c.
Рабочее дѣло въ Россіи. [P2716]. s8°. Женева. 1899
see Akimov (Vl. P.) Матерьялы, 1905.
,, Cherevanin. Организац. вопросъ, 1904.
,, Lydin (M.) Mat. z. Erl. d. Parteikrise &c., 1904.
,, Panin (M.) Кустарничество &c., 1904.
,, Trotsky (N.) Второй съѣздъ Р. С.-Д. Р. П., 1903.
Rossiiskaya Sotsialisticheskaya Federat. Sovetskaya Respublika, *see* Sbornik. Сборник договоров, B1–4, 1921–23.
Rossini (Gioacchino Antonio).
see Beyle (M. H.) Vie de R., 2t, 1922.
,, Curzon (H. de). R., 1920.
Rossiter (William Sidney). Increase of populat. in U.S., 1910–20, 1922, *see* United States: Census.
Rössler (Emil Franz).
Die Gründung d. Univ. Göttingen. 8°. Göttingen. 1855
Rösslin (Eucharius), *see* Power (*Sir* D'A.) Birth of mankind [by R.], 1927.
Rosslyn (Robert Francis St. Clair-Erskine, *4th earl of***).**
Sonnets. 2nd ed. s8°. 1890
Ross-of-Bladensburg (Sir John F. G.) The Coldstream Guards, 1914–18. 2v & Maps [*bound sep.*] la8°. 1928
Rost (Friedrich Wilhelm Ehrenfried) [Rostius]. De divino spiritu eorum quae Lutherus & amici pro emend. relig. statu fecerunt uno auctore. Oratio. [P2627]. s4°. Lipsiae. [1817]
Was hat die Leipziger Thomasschule für die Reformation gethan? [P2649]. s4°. Leipzig. [1817]
Rost (Pirro). Bruno Corra. la8°. Milano. 1921
Luigi Pirandello. la8°. Milano. 1921

Rostagni (Augusto).
Ibis. Storia di un poemetto greco. la8°. Firenze. 1920
Rostan (Jean Louis), *1807–59, see* LELIÈVRE (M.) The Alpine missionary, 1869.
Rostand (Edmond).
Le cantique de l'aile. 8°. 1922
Cyrano de Bergerac. Comédie. s8°. N.Y. *n.d.*
Cyrano de Bergerac. [Tr.] B. Hooker. Pref. by C. Hamilton. 8°. [1924]
La dernière nuit de Don Juan. Poème dramat. 8°. 1921
Un rève : poème inéd., *see* ŒUVRES libres, t1, 1921.
Les romanesques. Comédie. 32e mille. s8°. 1905
see BÉDIER (J.) Discours sur l'œuvre d'E. R., 1921.
Rostand (*Mme.* Edmond), *see* GÉRARD (R.)
Rostand (Jean).
De la vanité & de quelq. autres sujets. s8°. 1925
Les familiotes, *see* ŒUVRES libres, 38, 1924.
Julien ou une conscience. s8°. 1928
La loi des riches. 5e éd. s8°. 1921
Pendant qu'on souffre encore. s8°. 1921
La perle & le poulet, fantaisie, *see* ŒUVRES libres, 12, 1922.
Rostand (Maurice).
L'ange du suicide, *see* ŒUVRES libres, 59, 1926.
La gloire. Pièce. s8°. [1922]
L'homme que j'ai tué : roman, *see* ŒUVRES libres, 3, 1921.
Le pilori. Roman. s8°. [1921]
La solitude passionnée, nouvelle, *see* ŒUVRES libres, 44, 1925.
Rosteutscher (Waldemar).
Deutschlands Herz im Frühling 1813. 8°. Kattowitz. 1913
Rosthorn (Arthur v.) Die Anfänge d. chines. Geschichtschreibung, 1920, *see* KAIS. AKAD. D. WISS. ZU WIEN. Sitzber., B193, 1922.
Gesch. Chinas. 8°. St. 1923
Das Tsch'un-tsch'iu u. s. Verfasser, 1919, *see* KAISERL. AKAD. D. W. ZU WIEN. Sitz., B189, 1919.
Rostislavov (A.) А. П. Рябушкинъ. [Grabar (I.) Русс. художники, 4]. 4°. Москва. [1913 ?]
Rostock. Beiträge z. Gesch. d. Univ. R.; hrsg. v. Verein für R. Altertümer. 8°. Rostock. 1919
*Declaratio vanitatis &c. libelli, Colloquium inter theologos Acad. Rostoch. &c. expon., De controv. Coenae Dominicae &c. s8°. Witebergae. 1587
Deutschlands Städtebau: R. [*by* Dehn &c.] Hrsg. v. Rat d. Seestadt Rostock. 4°. *Dari.* 1922
Rostomov (Ivan P.) Картвельское племя. [*In Georgian & Russian*]. obl.4°. Тифлисъ. 1896
Rostovtsev (Mikhail Ivanovich).
Скиѳія и Боспоръ. [Р. Акад. Ист. Матер. Культуры]. la8°. [Ленинград]. 1925
Hist. of the anc. world. Tr. J. D. Duff. v1, 2. la8°. O. 1926–27
Iranians & Greeks in S. Russia. 4°. O. 1922
Mystic Italy. Brown Univ. Colver lect. 8°. N.Y. [1928]
Social & econ. hist. of the Roman Empire. la8°. O. 1926
Statuette d'un cavalier de la coll. de Mme. J. D. Rockefeller, *see* ACAD. DES INSCR.: FOND. PIOT. Mons. &c., t28, 1925–26.
Une trouvaille de l'époque gréco-sarmate de Kertch au Louvre & au Musée de St.-Germain, *see* ACAD. DES INSCR.: FOND. PIOT. Mon. &c., t26, 1923.
Rostrevor (George). Bergson & future philosophy. s8°. 1921
Roswitha. Abraham. Tr. into Eng. prose by R. S. Lambert. 8°. 1922
Callimachus. Tr. into Eng. prose by R. S. Lambert. 8°. 1923
Plays. Tr. H. J. W. Tillyard. 8°. 1923
Rota. Sacrae Rotae Romanae decisiones a F. de Albertis coll. fol. Romae. 1783
Rota (A.) Hossfeld's new pract. method for learning the Italian lang. n. ed. 8°. [1887]
Rota (Andrea). L'idolatra. Romanzo. s8°. Milano. 1920
Rota (Berardino).
Egloghe pescatorie. [Ed. S. Ammirato]. s8°. Vinegia. 1566
Rota (Pietro), *see* NOZZE. Francesconi—Bariola; Ronda-album. [Contrib. by P. R. &c.], 1885.
Rotarides (János) [*ps.* HUNGARUS (H. M.), *or* M. (H.), *Hungarus*]. Hist. Hungar. literar. lineamenta &c. s4°. Altonaviae. 1745
Rotarius (Thomas Franciscus). Apparatus univ. theologiæ moralis &c. s8°. Francofurti. 1706
Rotelande (Hue de), *see* HUE, *de Rotelande.*
Rotenhan (Sebastian von), *see* EYRING (L. S.) Vita S. de R., 1739.
Roth (Carl). Sozial- u. Kulturgesch. d. byzantin. Reiches. [Samml. Göschen]. s8°. 1919
Roth (Cecil). The last Florentine republic. 8°. [1925]
Roth (David), *R.C. bp. of Ossory.* *Analecta sacra nova & mira de rebus Catholic. in Hibernia. 3p *in* 2v. s8°. Coloniae. 1617–19
Roth (Friedrich). Der Einfluss d. Humanismus u. d. Reformation &c. [Verein f. Ref.-gesch. Schr., Jhrg. 15, Nr. 60]. 8°. Halle. 1898
Leonhard Kaiser. [Verein f. Ref.-gesch. Schr., Jhrg. 18, Nr. 66]. 8°. Halle. 1900
Wilibald Pirkheimer. [Verein f. Ref.-gesch. Schr., Jhrg. 5, Nr. 21]. 8°. Halle. 1887
Roth (Georges). La couronne poét. de Byron. Textes choisis & publ. par G. R. s8°. [1924]
Roth (Heinrich), *of Eisleben, see* MENZEL (J.), H. R. &c. Auff die Verleumbdung Spangenbergs &c., 1573.
Roth (Johann Paul), *see* VEIEL (E.) & J. P. R. Urbani Regii memoria & merita &c., 1683.
Roth (Leon). The science of morals. s8°. [1928]
Spinoza, Descartes & Maimonides. s8°. O. 1924
Roth (Paul), *see* BENEDICT (F. G.), W. R. MILES, P. R. &c. Human vitality &c., 1919.
Roth (Victor). Gesch. d. deut. Kunstgewerbes in Siebenbürgen. la8°. Str. 1908
Roth (Walter Edmund). Intr. study of arts, crafts & customs of the Guiana Indians, *see* SMITHSONIAN INST.: BUR. OF ETHN. Rep. 38, 1924.
Rothamsted Experimental Station. Rep. 1921–22, 1923–24, 1925–26, w. Suppl. to the "Guide to experimental plots." 8°. Harpenden. 1923–27
Rothamsted mems. on agric. science, v9–13, 1919–28, *see* LAWES (J. B.) & J. H. GILBERT.
LIBRARY.
Cat. of pr. bks. on agriculture publ. 1471–1840. Notes by M. S. Aslin. 8°. [Aberdeen. 1926]
Rothe (Peter Conrad).
De vita & gestis Anselmi, diss. s8°. Hauniae. 1840
Rothen (Christian). De libris apparenter deperditis diss. prima. s4°. Lipsiae. 1704
Rothenburg ob d. Tauber. Jubilæus Evang.-Luther.: oratio parænetica &c. 1617. [P483]. s4°. Rotemburgi. 1617
Rothenburg o. d. Tauber, ein Führer. Geleitwort v. P. Bonatz. s8°. Bad Mergentheim. [1922?]
Rothenstein (John). The artists of the 1890's. 8°. 1928
Rothenstein (William). Twenty-four portraits, w. crit. apprec. by var. hands. la8°. [1920]
W. Rothenstein. [Plates, w. descr. &c. signed H. W.] la8°. 1923
Rother, *König, hero of romance.* König. R. Hrsg. v. T. Frings & J. Kuhnt. [Rhein. Beitr. &c. z. german. Philol., 3]. 8°. Bonn. 1922
Rotherham. Sheffield & Rotherham f. 12th to 18th c.: descr. cat. of misc. charters &c.; comp. by T. W. Hall, 1916, *see* SHEFFIELD.
Rothermere (Harold Sidney Harmsworth, *1st visct.*) Solvency or downfall? Squandermania & its story. 8°. 1921
Rothery (Guy Cadogan). Eng. chimney-pieces, to 19th cent. Architect. notice by A. L. Kocher. 4°. [1927]
Furnishing a small house or flat. 8°. [1923]
Staircases & garden steps. s8°. [1912]
Rothhaupt (Wilhelm). Habari: v. schwarzen u. weissen Afrikanern. 8°. St. 1925
Rothmann (Bernhard). Eyn kortte Bekantnisse d. lere so B. R. vor d. Stat Münster predyket hefft. [*Tr. by* J. Langerman]. s4°. *n.p.* 1532
Rothmann (Max) & E. Teuber. Aus d. Anthropoidenstation auf Teneriffa, 1, v. M. R. & E. T., *see* KÖN.-PREUSS. AKAD. Abh., Phys.-math. Klasse, 1915.
Rothschild, *The family of, see* CORTI (E. C., *conte*). Der Aufstieg d. Hauses R., 1927; tr. B. & B. Lunn, 1928.
Rothschild (Alfred de), *see* CARNARVON (A., *ctss. of*). Cat. of pictures &c. (bequeathed by A. de R.), 1925.
Rothschild (*Miss* Alice de). Cat. of French furniture, objects of art & porcelain. Property of a lady [*Miss A. de R.*] Sold by Christie &c., Nov. 23, 1922. [*&* Cat. of drawings &c., the prop. of [A. de R.] Sold, Nov. 24, 1922. *b. in* 1v. la8°. [1922]
Rothschild (Constance de).
*A Buckinghamshire story of 1663. 8°. Aylesbury. 1875
Rothschild (Henri de) & L.-G. Gourraigne. La Grande Guerre d'ap. la presse parisienne. [t]3, sept.–déc. 1914. 8°. 1920
Rothschild (Meyer Amschel), *see* BERGHÖFFER (C. W.) M. A. R., d. Gründer d. Rothschild. Bankhauses, 2e A., 1923.

Rothstein (Andrew), *see* RUSSIA: SOVIET REPUBL. The Soviet constit.; ed. A. R., 1923.

Rothwell. Registers of the parish church of R., pl, 1538–1689. Ed. G. D. Lumb. [Yorks. Parish Reg. Soc., 27]. 8º. [Leeds]. *p.p.* 1906

Rothwell (J. S. S.)
English-German letter-writer. 2nd ed. s8º. St. 1875

Rothwell (*Col.* John Sutton).
The Rochelle expedition of 1627. [P2591]. s8º. D. 1893

Rotingus (Michael), *see* ROTTINGUS (M.)

Roton (*capitaine* R. de), *see* OLIVIER (E.), G. HERMAL & R. DE R. Manuel de l'amateur de reliures armoriées franç., s1–13, 1924–28.

Rotrou (Jean de). L'hypocondriaque ou le mort amoureux: tragi-comédie. s8º. 1924

Rotsaert (Arthur). Hist. du duché de Limbourg dep. la Révolution brabançonne, *see* CAHIERS (LES) BELGES, No. 29–31, 1919.

Rotscheidt (Wilhelm). Stephan Isaak, e. kölner Pfarrer &c. Sein Leben v. ihm selbst erzählt u. ergänzt v. W. R. [Quellen &c. aus d. Gesch. d. Reformationsjhdts., B14]. 8º. L. 1910

Rott (Celine). Moana ou voyage sentimental chez les Maoris &c. des Iles. 2e éd. s8º. 1923

Rott (Edouard). Hist. de la représent. diplomat. de la France auprès des Cantons Suisses, de leurs alliés & de leurs confédérés. t6–9. la8º. Berne. 1917–26
6, 1643–63. 7, 1663–76. 8, 1676–84. 9, 1684–98.

Rottenburg (Franz Johannes), *see* EPPSTEIN (G., *Frhr.* v.) Fürst Bismarcks Entlassung; nach d. Aufzeichn. d. K. H. v. Boetticher u. F. J. v. R., 1920.

Rotter (Egon), L. Gough, H. v. Buttel-Reepen & L. Armbruster. Die Biene in Ägypten jetzt u. vor 5000 Jahren. [*Extr. f.* Arch. f. Bienenkunde, Jhrg. 3]. 8º. L. 1921

Röttger (Bernh. Hermann).
Die unterfränk. Stadt. la8º. Augsburg. 1924

Rottingus (Michael) [MICHAEL ROTING]. Testimonium M. R. contra falsam A. Osiandri de justificatione sententiam. s4º. *n.p. n.d.* [1551?]

Rottmann (Alexander). London Catholic churches. s8º. 1926

Rotuli dei lettori d. Studio bolognese, 1384–1799; pubbl. U. Dalleri, 3v, 1888–1919, *see* BOLOGNA.

Rotzler (Hermann). Die Benennungen d. Milchstrasse im Französ., *see* ROMANISCHE FORSCHUNGEN, B33, 1915.

Roubaud (Louis). Les enfants de Caïn. [Cahiers verts, 49]. s8º. 1925

Roubiliac (Louis François) [ROUBILLAC], *see* ESDAILE (K. A.) R.'s work at Trinity Coll., Cambridge, 1924.

Rouchès (Gabriel). Eustache Le Sueur. 8º. 1923
see LOUVRE. La peinture, écoles ital., 16–18 s., par G. R., 1927.

Roudnieff (V. M.), *see* RUDNEV (V. M.)

Rouen. Cartul. de l'abbaye de la Sainte-Trinité du Mont de Rouen; avec notes & intr. par A. Deville, *see* †SAINT-BERTIN, *abbey*. Cartulaire &c., 1841.
Sereniss. pr. Franciae Delphino Xenia Coll. Rothomag. soc. Jesu. s4º. Rothomagi. 1639

Rouff (Marcel). Les étranglés. Roman. s8º. 1927
Les mines de charbon en France au 18e s., 1744–91. la8º. 1922

Rouffaer (G. P.), *see* BRANDES (J. L. A.) Beschr. van Tjandi Singasari &c.; benevens e. herdenking van B. door G. P. R., 1909.

Rouffiac (Jean). Recherches sur les caractères du grec dans le Nouv. Test. d'ap. les inscr. de Priène. [H. E.: Sci. relig., 24, fasc. 2]. 8º. 1911

Rougé (*vte.* Olivier C. C. Emmanuel de). Œuvres diverses. Publ. par G. Maspero. [Bibl. égyptolog., t25]. t5. la8º. 1914

Rougemont (— de).
*De l'usurpation & de la révolution. [P2764]. 8º. 1825

Roughead (William).
The fatal countess & o. studies. 8º. E. 1924
Glengarry's way & o. studies. la8º. E. 1922
The rebel earl & o. studies. 8º. E. 1926
see BURKE (W.) Burke & Hare; ed. W. R., 1921.
„ MACLACHLAN (*Mrs.* J.) Trial of J. M'L.; ed. W. R., 2nd ed., 1925.
„ NAIRN (K.) Trial of K. N.; ed. W. R., 1926.

Rougier (Louis). Philosophy & the new physics: essay on relativity theory &c. Auth. tr. by M. Masius. s8º. [1922]

Rouillé (Guillaume), *of Lyons, c. 1518–89* [ROUVILLE], *see* BAUDRIER (H. L.) Bibliog. lyonnaise, s9, 1912.

Roujon (Henry).
F. Ziem. [Peintres illustres, 50]. 8º. [1913]
H. Rigaud. [Peintres illustres, 52]. 8º. [1913]
Henner. [Peintres illustres, 40]. 8º. [1912?]
Ph. de Champaigne. [Peintres illustres, 42]. 8º. [1912?]
see BARTHOU (L.) Disc. de récep. (*on* H. R.), 1919.

Rouland (David), *of Anglesey, see* ROWLAND (D.)

Roule (Louis). Buffon & la descr. de la nature. 8º. [1924]

Roumains. Les sacrifices roumains pend. la Guerre. Les victimes civiles. [Ed. E. Antonesco]. 4º. [1919]

Roumania [ROUMANIE].
Agrarian reform in R. & the case of the Hungarian optants in Transylvania bef. the League of Nations. Opinions by A. Alvarez, H. Berthélemy &c. la8º. 1927
A hdbk. of R., 1920, *see* ADMIRALTY: NAVAL INTELL. DIV.
*Histor. churches of Transylvania & R., 1921, *see* TRANSYLVANIA.
La réforme agraire en R. & les Optants hongrois de Transylvanie dev. la Soc. des Nations. Études redigées par A. Alvarez, J. Appleton &c. la8º. 1927
La R. Conférences faites à l'Union Française. [Par Lacour-Gayet, de Martonne *& others*. Intr. par P. Gaultier]. s8º. [1920]
La R. devant le Congrès de la Paix. [P2508]. 4º. *n.p.* [1918]
„ „ Le Banat de Temeshvar. [P2508]. 4º. [1919]
„ „ La question de la Bessarabie. [Déleg. Bessarabienne. P2508]. 4º. 1919
R.: econ. hdbk. [U.S. Dept. of Commerce]. 8º. Wash. 1924

Roumanian stories [*by var. a.*]; tr., 1921, *see* BYNG (L.)

Round Table. Romans de la Table Ronde, 4t, 1922–23, *see* BOULENGER (J.)

Round Table (The). v10–18. 8º. 1919–28

Round Table Dining Club. Roster of the R.T.D.C. Pref. note by the 4th Secretary. 8º. N.Y. 1926

Round (John Horace).
see DOUBLEDAY (H. A.) Dr. R.'s "Barons & peers," 1919.
„ RYE (W.) J. H. R. & h. recent attack on W. R. &c., 1922.

Roupnel (Gaston). La ville & la campagne au 17e s. Étude sur les populations du pays dijonnais. la8º. 1922

Rouquet (Jean). Lettres de Mons. ** [*i.e.* R.] pour lui expliquer les estampes de Hogarth, 1846, *see* HOGARTH (W.)

Rouquette (Louis Fréderic). L'épopée blanche. s8º. 1926

Rous (Francis), *the elder, 1579–1659* [ROUSE; ROWSE]. Interiora regni Dei [Coelestis academia—Grande oraculum—Mysticum matrimonium quo junguntur Christus & Ecclesia, *sep. tp. & pagin.*] s8º. Londini. 1655
The mysticall marriage. s8º. 1654
*The Psalms of David in English meeter. s8º. 1646

Rous (Francis), *the younger, 1615–43?.* Archæologia Atticæ libri 7. Seven books of the Attick antiq. With add. of th. customes in marriages &c. by Z. Bogan. 7th ed., corr. [*b. w.* Godwin (T.) Moses & Aaron, 1671]. s4º. O. 1671

Rouse (Ruth) & H. C. Miller. Xtn. experience & psycholog. processes. [2nd impr.] s8º. 1920

Rousiers (Paul de).
Les grandes industries mod. [5t]. s8º. 1924–28

Rousseau (Henri), *painter, 1844–1910, see* SOUPAULT (P.) H. R., le douanier, 1927.

Rousseau (Henri Julien), *see* ZERVOS (C.) R., 1927.

Rousseau (Henry), *b. 1864.* La sculpture aux 17e and 18e s. [Coll. des gr. artistes des Pays-Bas]. 8º. Brux. 1911

Rousseau (Jean Baptiste).
Œuvres. n. éd., revue, corr. & augm. 4t. s8º. Brux. 1743
Œuvres choisies. n. éd. s8º. 1774

Rousseau (Jean Jacques).
Œuvres, avec des notes hist. 22t [t22, Suppl. cont. écrits sur sa personne & s. ouvrages]. 8º. *Lefèvre.* 1819–20
Œuvres complètes. 4t. la8º. 1852–53
Confessions. 2t. s8º. [1920]
Corresp. avec F. Coindet, 1756–68; publ. A. François, *see* SOCIÉTÉ JEAN JACQUES R. Annales, t14, 1922.
Corresp. gén. Collat., annot. & comm. par T. Dufour. t1–9. 8º. 1924–28
Emile, ou de l'éducation. 2t [*in* 4p]. 8º. 1762
Institutions chymiques; publ. M. Gautier, *see* SOCIÉTÉ JEAN JACQUES R. Annales, t12, 13, 1918–21.
Matériaux pour la corresp. de J. J. R. Publ. A. François. 8º. 1923
La nouvelle Héloïse. n. éd., avec intr. &c. par D. Mornet. [Les gr. écrivains de la Fr.] 4t. 8º. 1925

TRANSLATIONS.
Confessions. Compl. tr. without expurgation. 2v. 8º. *p.p.* 1904
Inquiry into the nature of the social contract.
„ „ The social contract. Tr., w. hist. &c. intr. & notes by H. J. Tozer. [3rd ed. repr.] s8º. [1920]
„ „ [3rd ed. repr.] s8º. [1924]
Letters on the elements of botany. Tr., w. notes & 24 addit. letters by T. Martyn. 2nd ed., w. corr. &c. 8º. 1787
„ „ Thirty-eight plates w. explan. &c. partic. adapted

Rousseau (Jean Jacques) [*continued*].
TRANSLATIONS [*continued*].
to Letters on the elements of botany. By T. Martyn. 8°. 1788
A project of perpet. peace. [*Fr. & Eng.*] Tr. E. M. Nuttall. Intr. by G. L. Dickinson. s8°. [1927]
The reveries of a solitary. Tr. w. intr. by J. G. Fletcher. 8°. [1927]
see BABBITT (I.) R. & romanticism, 1919.
„ BENEDETTO (L. F.) Mme. de Warens, la "Maman" de R., 1922.
„ BUFFENOIR (H.) Rousseau, ami des chiens & des chats, 1927.
„ COURTOIS (L. J.) Chronolog. crit. de vie & œuvres de J. J. R., 1923.
„ DUCROS (L.) J.-J. R., v2, 3, 1917–18.
„ FAGUET (E.) R. penseur, 1912.
see IZOULET (J.) De J. J. R. utrum misopolis fuerit an philopolis, 1894.
„ JAMMES (F.) Œuvres, t4, Notes sur R. & Mme. de Warens &c., 1924.
„ MARITAIN (J.) 3 réformateurs: Luther, R. &c., 1925.
„ MERCIER (L. S.) De J. J. R., consid. comme l'un des prem. auteurs de la Révol., 2t, 1791.
„ PARIS: UNIVERSITY OF. Censure de la Fac. de Théol. de P. contre Emile (1762), 1862.
„ RITTER (E.) Famille & jeunesse de J. J. R., 1926.
„ SEILLIÈRE (E.) J. J. R., 1921.
„ SOCIÉTÉ JEAN - JACQUES ROUSSEAU.

Rousseau (Samuel). The book of knowledge or, a gramm. of the Persian lang. s4°. 1805
Rousseau (Victor), *sculptor, see* DES OMBIAUX (M.) V. R., 1908.
Roussel (Jules). La Normandie. 5 cartes. [Atlas mon. de la France]. fol. *n.d.*
Roussel (Louis). Gramm. descr. du roméique litt. [Ec. Franç. d'Athènes & de Rome, 122]. 8°. [1922]
Roussel (Pierre). Délos, colonie athénienne. [Ec. Franç. d'Athènes & de Rome, 111]. 8°. 1916
Rousset (Camille F. M.)
Les volontaires, 1791–94. 4e éd. s8°. 1882
see LOUIS XV, *king of France.* Corr. de L. XV & du Maréchal de Noailles; publ. avec intr. by C. R., 2t, 1865.
Roustan (Marius). Pioneers of the French Revol. Tr. F. Whyte. Intr. by H. J. Laski. 8°. 1926
Rout (Ettie A.) Maori symbolism: origin, migration &c. of N. Zealand Maori. Rep. by E. A. R. f. evidence of Hohepa Te Rake. Pref. by Sir W. A. Lane. 8°. 1926
Routh (Enid Maud Grace). Lady Margaret: a memoir of Lady M. Beaufort. s8°. 1924
Routh (Harold Victor). God, man, & epic poetry; st. in comp. lit. 2v. 8°. C. 1927
This world's idea of the next, *see* ENG. ASSOC. Essays &c., v11, 1925.
Rouveyre (André). Souvenirs de mon commerce. Gourmont-Apollinaire-Moréas-Soury. 8°. 1921
Rouveyre (Edouard). Analyse & compréhension des œuvres & objets d'art. [2t]. 8°. 1924–25
Comment discerner les styles enseigné par l'image. [7v]. la8°. [1922]
1, Le style Piranesi. 2, Le style empire. 3, Le mobilier. 4, La dentelle. 5, La ferronnerie. 6, Le luminaire. 7, Les plafonds.
Rouville (Guillaume), *see* ROUILLÉ.
Rouvre (Charles de). L'amoureuse hist. d'A. Comte & de C. de Vaux. [3e éd.] s8°. [1920]
Roux (André). Hongkong, colonie anglaise: ét. polit. & écon. &c. Thèse. 8°. Poitiers. 1903
Roux (François). Carte du Se-tch'ouan occid. levée en 1908–10 par F. R., *see* VARIÉTÉS sinolog., N°. 43, 1915.
Roux (Joseph). Recueil des princ. plans des ports & rades de la mer Mediterranée. obl. s8°. Marseille. 1764
Roux (Louis). La marine marchande. L'avenir de la construction navale & de l'armement maritime en France. 8°. 1923
Roux (*le marquis* **Marie de),** *b. 1878.* La Révolution à Poitiers & dans la Vienne. la8°. 1912
Rouxeau (Alfred). Laënnec après 1806 (1806–26) d'ap. des docs. inéd. 8°. 1920
Rouziès (Urbain), *see* BAUDRILLART (A.), U. R. &c. Dict. d'hist. & de géog. eccl.; publ. sous la dir. de A. B. &c., t3, 1924.
Rovenius (Philippus), *bp. of Philippi.*
Tractatus de missionibus. s8°. Lovanii. 1624
Rover (W. W.) Abr. Lincoln in 1848 secessionist. [P2758]. s8°. [Burnsville, N.C.] *n.d.*

Rovetta (Gerolamo).
La Baraonda. 16a ristampa. s8°. Milano. 1919
La moglie di Sua Eccellenza. Romanzo. s8°. Milano. 1905
Rovinsky (Dmitry Aleksandrovich). Словарь русскихъ гравировъ. портретовъ. [I. Akad. Nauk. Записки, t21]. 8°. С.-П. 1872
Rovito (Teodoro). Letterati e giornalisti ital. contemp. Diz. bio-bibliog. 2a ed. 8°. Napoli. 1922
Row (Charles Adolphus). Christian theism. 2nd ed. s8°. 1890
A manual of Christian evidences. 5th ed. s8°. 1892
Row (William), *of Ceres, see* BLAIR (R.) Life, 1593–1636, w. suppl. & cont. of hist. to 1680 by W. R., 1848.
Rowbotham (John Frederick).
The epic of God & the devil. 8°. Worcester. *n.d.*
The epic of London. 8°. *n.d.*
The epic of Semiramis. 8°. 1920
The epic of the cross. 8°. [1926]
The epic of the Empire. 8°. 1914
The epic of the globe. 8°. 1921
The human epic. 8°. *n.d.*
Rowe (Eleanor).
Pract. wood-carving. 2nd ed. rev. pl. 8°. [1918]
Wood carvings f. the S. Kensington Mus. folios 1–3 [fol. 1 *wants some plates*]. la. fol. [1889]
Rowe (*Mrs.* **Elizabeth).** Devout exercises of the heart, &c. Review'd & publ. by I. Watts. 4th ed. s8°. 1743
Misc. works in prose & verse. Added poems on sev. occ. by T. Rowe, & lives of authors. 2v. s8°. 1739
see JACKSON (T.) Lib. of Xtn. biog., v10, 1839.
Rowe (George Stringer). The life of John Hunt. s8°. 1866
see BUNTING (T. P.) Life of J. Bunting; v2, compl. by G. S. R., 1887.
„ BUNTING (W. M.) Mem. of W. M. B.; ed. G. S. R., 1870.
Rowe (Leo Stanton). Early effects of the War upon the finance &c. of Peru. [C.E. f. Int. Peace.] la8°. N.Y. 1920
The federal system of the Argentine Republic. la8°. Wash. 1921
Rowe (Nicholas).
Fair penitent, *see* INCHBALD (*Mrs* E.) Brit. th., v10, 1808.
Jane Shore. [Dolby's Brit. th.] s8°. [1824]
„ „ *For a. ed., see* INCHBALD. Brit. th., v10, 1808.
Lady Jane Grey, *see* INCHBALD. Brit. th., v10, 1808.
Tamerlane: a tragedy. s8°. 1766
„ „ *For a. ed., see* INCHBALD. Brit. th., v10, 1808.
Rowe (Thomas), *see* ROWE (*Mrs.* E.) Misc. works, w. poems of T. Rowe, 2v, 1739.
Rowell (Newton Wesley).
The Brit. Empire & world peace. 8°. Toronto. 1922
Rowfant Library, *see* BIRRELL (*Rt. Hon.* A.) F. Locker-Lampson; w. bibl. notes on bks. formerly in R. L., 1920.
Rowland (David), *of Anglesey* [ROULAND], *see* HURTADO DE MENDOZA (D.) Pleasaunt hist. of Lazarillo de Tormes, drawn out of Spanish by D. R., 1586; ed. Crofts, 1924.
Rowland (Dunbar). Jefferson Davis's place in hist. [P2717]. 8°. Jackson, Miss. [1923]
Rowlands (Ernest Bowen-), *see* BOWEN-ROWLANDS (E.)
Rowlands (M. J.) Open-air pig breeding. s8°. 1923
Rowlandson (Thomas), *see* OPPÉ (A. P.) T. R., h. drawings & water-colours, 1923.
Rowles (William F.) The garden under glass. 8°. [1914]
Rowley (Henry). The story of the Univ. Mission to C. Africa. 2nd ed. 8°. 1867
Rowley (Richard). County Down songs. [2nd impr.] 8°. [1925]
Rowley (William), *dramatist, see* MIDDLETON (T.) & W. R. The Spanish gipsy (1661); ed. w. crit. essay &c. by H. B. Clarke, 1914.
Rowntree (Arnold Stephenson).
Woodbrooke: its hist. & aims. s8°. 1923
Rowntree (Benjamin Seebohm).
The human factor in business. s8°. 1921
—— & F. D. Stuart. The responsibility of women workers for dependants. 8°. O. 1921
Rowsell (Herbert). Biblical stumbling-blocks. s8°. 1920
Roxas (Alvarus de). Comm. in Apocalypsin &c. Opus posth. fol. Hispali. 1732
Roxas (Pedro de), *see* ROJAS (P. DE).
Roxburghe Club.
see APULEIUS *Barbarus.* Herbal of A. B. f. early 12th cent. MS.; descr. by R. T. Gunther, 1926.
„ BIBLE: GENESIS. Illust. of the Bk. of Genesis; reprod. of MS. B.M., Egerton, 1894, w. intr. by M. R. James, 1921.
„ ——: PSALMS. Two East Angl. Psalters, 1926.
„ ——: REVELATION. Apocalypse in Lat. & French (Bodleian MS. Douce 180); descr. by M. R. James, 1922.

Roxburghe Club [*continued*].
see BIBLE: SPANISH. O.T. Tr. into Castilian by M. Arragel (1422–33 ?), 2v, 1918–21.
,, COLLIER (J. P.) Five old plays illust. early progress of Eng. drama, 1851.
,, EDWARD, *the Confessor*. La estoire de St. Ædward le Rei &c.; intr. by M. R. James, 1920.
,, FIERABRAS. *Romaunce of the Sowdone of Babyloyne & of Ferumbras his sone, 1854.
,, GEORGE III. Sel. f. papers, 1781–3; ed. J. Fortescue, 2v, 1927.
,, HORMAN (W.) Vulgaria, 1519; repr., w. intr. by M. R. James, 1926.
,, JAMES II, *of Gt. Brit.* Papers of devotion; intr. by G. Davies, 1925.
,, PETERBOROUGH PSALTER. P. Ps. & bestiary; descr. by M. R. James, 1921.
,, SHERBORNE MISSAL (The): reprod. f. Missal executed betw. 1396 & 1407; w. intr. by J. A. Herbert, 1920.
,, WRIGHT (C. T. H.) N. Fabri de Peiresc, 1926.

Roy (Hippolyte). La vie, la mode & le costume au 17e s. La cour de Lorraine. Préf. de C. Pfister. la8°. 1924
Roy (James Alexander). Pole & Czech in Silesia. s8°. 1921
Roy (Just Jean Etienne).
Hist. de l'Algérie. 3e éd. s8°. Tours. 1870
Roy (Maurice). Philibert de Lorme à Paris (1546–59), *see* SOCIÉTÉ DE L'HIST. DE PARIS &c. Mém., t47, 1924.
Roy (Pierre Georges), *see* QUEBEC. Rapp. de l'archiviste [*i.e.* P. G. R.], 1924–25, 1925.
Roy (Sarat Chandra). The Birhors: jungle tribe of Chota Nagpur. s8°. Ranchi. 1925
Roy (William), *Franciscan friar*, **& J. Barlow.** *"Rede me & be nott wrothe," 1528 [&] A proper dyaloge betwene a gentillman & a husbandman [*a. uncertain*]; *w.* *A compendious olde treatyse shewynge howe that we ought to have the Scripture in Englysshe, 1530 [*a. uncertain*]. Ed. E. Arber. [Eng. repr[s].] s8°. 1871
Royaards (Herman Johan), *see* ROIJAARDS (H. J.)
Royal. Royal Comm. for the Exhib. of 1851: its activities &c., 1924, *see* EXHIBITIONS: LONDON.
Royal gallery of Brit. art, 1851, *see* FINDEN (E.) & W. F.
*Royal investigation; or authentic doc. cont. acquittal of H.R.H. the P—ss of W—s, 1808, *see* CAROLINE, *q. c.*
Royal Academy.
Exhib. of Brit. prim. paintings, 12th to early 16th cent. Oct. & Nov. 1923. [Foreword by Visc. Lee. Intr. by W. G. Constable]. 4°. O. 1924
Exhib. of Flemish & Belgian art, 1300–1900, organiz. by the Anglo-Belgian Union. [Cat.] 2nd ed. 8°. 1927
,, ,, ...Illust. souvenir. la8°. 1927
Exhib. of works by Old Masters & deceased masters of the Brit. School. Winter Exhibition, 1907. [P2429]. 8°. 1907
Winter Exhibition, 1913, *see* ALMA TADEMA (*Sir* L.) Exhib., 1913.
see ROSSETTI (W. M.) & A. C. SWINBURNE. Notes on R. Acad. Exhib., 1868.
,, SARGENT (J. S.) Illust. of the S. exhib., R.A., 1926.
Royal Agricultural & Commercial Society of British Guiana.
Timehri; journal of the Roy. Agric. &c. Soc. of B.G., v4, 5, N.S., 1, 2 (1885–88), s3, v7, Progressive vol. 8°. *&* la8°. Demerara [1885–1921]
Royal Agricultural Society of England.
Agricultural research in 1925, 1926. 8°. 1926–27
Journal. v81–88. 8°. 1920–27
Royal Air Force, *see* AIR MINISTRY.
Royal Archaeological Institute. Journal. v74–80. 8°. 1917–23
Royal Artillery. List of officers of the Roy. Reg. of A., 1763 to pres. time, 1815, *see* KANE (J.)
Royal Asiatic Society of Gt. Britain & Ireland. Centenary vol., 1823–1923. [*Cont.* Hist. of the Soc., Indexes &c.] Comp. & ed. F. E. Pargiter. 8°. 1923
Journal, 1920–27. 8°. 1920–27
,, ,, Centenary suppl., Oct. 1924. 8°. 1924
Monographs. v17–19. 8°. 1915–24
see ALGAZZALI. Mishkāt al-Anwār; tr. W. H. T. Gairdner, 1924. [19.]
,, BAILEY (T. G.) Linguistic st. f. the Himalayas, 1915. [18 *wrongly numb.* 17.]
,, LALLĀ YOGISWARĪ. Lallā-Vākyāni; ed. Sir G. Grierson & L. D. Barnett, 1920. [17.]
CHINA BRANCH [NORTH C. BR.]
Journal. n.s. v27i, ii (1892–93), 29, 32–36 (1897–1905), 47 (1916)–56 (1925). 8°. Shanghai. 1894–1925
2 *parts only to* v27 & 1 *part only to* v29, 32 & 34 *published.*
,, ,, Index to v1–54, comp. by P. B. Ferguson. 8°. Shanghai. 1924

Royal Asiatic Society of Gt. Britain & Ireland [*continued*].
CHINA BRANCH [NORTH C. BR.] [*continued*].
Extra vol. 2–4. 8°. 1923–25
see SHIROKOGOROV (S. M.) Anthropology of East China & Kwangtung prov., 1925. [4.]
,, —— Anthrop. of N. China, 1923. [2.]
,, —— Soc. organ. of the Manchus, 1924. [3.]
MALAYAN BRANCH. v3. p2. 8°. Singapore. 1925
see MILLS (L. A.) Brit. Malaya, 1824–67, 1925.
REFERENCES.
see BAILEY (T. G.) Grammar of the Shina (Ṣiṇā) language, 1924.
,, GIBB (H. A. R.) Arab conquests in Cent. Asia, 1923.
,, RÁM RĀJ. Essay on the archit. of the Hindús, 1834.
,, RICHMOND (E. T.) Moslem architecture, 623–1516, 1926.
,, SCHERBATSKY (T.) Central conception of Buddhism &c., 1923.
Royal Astronomical Society.
Cat. of Grove-Hills library of R.A.S. 8°. 1924
Monthly notices. v80–87. 8°. 1920–27
,, ,, Geophys. suppl. v1 (N°s. 1–10, 1922–28). 8°. 1928
Suppl. cat. of Library of the R.A.S., 1898–1925. 8°. 1926
Royal blue book, 1925, 1926. s8°. 1925–26
Royal Celtic Society, *see* WATSON (W. J.) Hist. of Celtic place-names of Scotland, 1926.
Royal College of Physicians of London. Descr. cat. of portraits, busts, silver &c. in R.C. of P. 8°. 1926
List of fellows, members, extra-licentiates & licentiates, 1921–1923. 8°. 1921–23
Royal Colonial Institute. Sel. list of rec. publs. in Lib. of R.C.I., illust. constit. rels. betw. var. parts of the Brit. Emp. Comp. by E. Lewin. [R.C.I. Bibliog., No. 2]. 8°. 1926
United Empire. The R.C.I. Journal. N.S., v11–16 (1920–25). 8°. 1920–25
see LUCAS (C. P.) The Empire at war, 5v, 1921–26.
Royal Commission on [Anc. &] Historical Monuments (England). An inventory of the hist. monuments in Essex. 4v. 4°. 1916–23
An inventory of the hist. monuments in Huntingdonshire. 4°. 1926
Inventory of hist. monuments in London. v1, 2. 4°. 1924–25
1, Westminster Abbey. 2, West London.
Royal Commission on Ancient & Historical Monuments &c. (Scotland). 2nd rep. & Inventory of mon. &c. on Co. of Sutherland. 8°. E. 1911
7th rep., w. inventory of mon. &c. in co. of Dumfries. 4°. E. 1920
8th rep., w. inventory of mon. &c. in co. of East Lothian. 4°. E. 1924
9th rep., w. inventory of mon. &c. in the outer Hebrides, Skye & the small isles. 4°. E. 1928
Royal Commission on Anc. & Hist. Monuments &c. (Wales & Monmouthshire). An inventory of the anc. monuments in Wales & M. [v]2, 6, 7. fol. 1912–25
2, Co. of Flint. 6, Co. of Merioneth. 7, Co. of Pembroke.
Royal Commission on Historical Manuscripts, *see* HISTORICAL MANUSCRIPTS COMMISSION.
Royal Dublin Society. The Dublin Society's Weekly observations. v1. s8°. D. 1739
,, ,, [*a. copy, w. title:* Essays & obs.] 8°. D. 1740
Scientific proceedings. New Ser., v14–17. 4°. 1913–24
see COOTE (*Sir* C.) Statist. survey of county of Armagh, 1802–3, under dir. of the D.S., 1804.
,, THOMPSON (R.) Stat. survey of Co. of Meath, 1802.
Royal Engineers. Corps archæologia No. 1–4 [*in* 2v]. [Repr. f. The Royal Engineers Journal]. 8°. Chatham. 1895–1903
The work of the R.E. in the European War, 1914–19. Publ. by the Secretary, R.E. [6v.] la8°. Chatham. 1921–22
Bridging—Geolog. work on the West. Front—Military mining—Signal service in the Europ. War (France), by R. E. Priestley—Supply of engineer stores & equipment—Water supply.
see AIDE-MÉMOIRE to milit. sci.; ed. by a Comm. of R.E., 1853–62.
Royal Flying Corps. The work & training of the R.F.C. [*Intr. by* Lord Hugh Cecil. P2417]. fol. *n.d.*
Royal Geographical Society.
First general list of Europ. names. [P2502]. 8°. 1921
First list of names in Tanganyika territory. [P2565]. 8°. 1922

Royal Geographical Society [*continued*].
Geographical journal. v54–71. 8°. 1919–28
„ „ ....Gen. index, 1893–1902, 1903–1912. [2v]. 8°. 1906–25
Suppl. to the Geogr. journal. Recent geogr. lit., maps & photogr. added to the Soc.'s coll. No. 1–13 [*in* 1v]. 8°. 1918–23
Suppl. 14 & onwards are bound w. the Journal for the corresp. year (2 to each year).
see GLEICHEN (*Lord* E.) & J. H. REYNOLDS. Alphabets of for. langs. trscr. into Eng. acc. to R.G.S. system, 1921.
„ REEVES (E. A.) Hints to travellers, 10th ed., 2v, 1921.
„ YOUNG (A. E.) Some investigations in theory of map projections, 1920.

Royal Historical Research Society, *Bangkok, see* VAJIRAÑĀNA NATIONAL LIBRARY.

Royal Historical Society. List & index of the publ. of the Roy. Hist. Soc., 1871–1924, & of the Camden Soc., 1840–97. Ed. H. Hall. 8°. 1925
Transactions. Ser. 4, v3–10. 8°. 1920–27
[Publications]. Camden Series. 3rd ser. v31–38. 8°. 1922–27
see BRITISH. Brit. diplomatic instructions, 1689–1789, v1–4, 1922–27. [III, 32, 35, 36, 38.]
„ CAMDEN MISCELLANY, v13, 14, 1924–26. [III, 34, 37.]
„ NICHOLAS (*Sir* E.) Nicholas papers: corr. of Sir E. N.; ed. G. F. Warner, v4, 1920. [III, 31.]
„ ROBINSON (J.) Parl. papers of J. R., 1774–84; ed. W. T. Laprade, 1922. [III, 33.]
REFERENCE.
see HALL (H.) Repertory of Brit. Archives: comp. for the R. Hist. Soc. by H. H., p1, 1920.

Royal Horticultural Society. Journal. v45–52. 8°. [1920–27]
Report of the 3rd Internat. Conf., on genetics. Ed. W. Wilks. 8°. [1906]

Royal Institute of British Architects, *see* CORNFORD (L. C.) Designers of our buildings, 1921.

Royal Institute of International Affairs [*form.* BRIT. INST. OF INTERNAT. AFF.], *see* TOYNBEE (A. J.) Survey of internat. affairs, 1920–26, 1925–28.

Royal Institution of Great Britain. Notices of proceedings. v24, 1923–25, w. index to v13–24. 8°. 1925

Royal Irish Academy. Abstracts of Minutes. Session[s] 1908/9–1926/27. 8°. *n.p.* [1909–27]
Dict. of Irish language. Publ. by R. I. A. under ed. of C. J. S. Marstrander. fasc. 1, D-degoír. [*No more publ.*] 4°. D. 1913
List of members, 1910, 1911, 1921. 8°. 1910–21
Proceedings. v35, 36. la8°. D. 1918–24
These vol. are in 3 sections (A, Mathemat., astronom. & phys. science; B, Biolog., geolog. & chem. science; C, Archaeology, linguistic & literature).
TODD LECTURE SERIES.
see GWYNN (E.) Metrical Dindshenchas, p4, 1924. [11.]

Royal Irish Constabulary. *Tales of the R.I.C. s8°. E. 1921

Royal (The) kalendar, or correct ann. register for Eng., Scot. & Ireland, 1777. s8°. 1777
For Rider's sheet almanack (often considered part of the R.K.), see RIDER (C.)

Royal Mail Line. Die Gesch. d. Wanderungen. Verfasst f. d. Royal Mail Line v. S. Altman. 8. erweit. A. 8°. [1926]

Royal Meteorological Society. Bibliography of meteorolog. lit. [v1]. Nos. 1–10. la8°. [1922–26]
List of fellows, March 1924. 8°. [1924]
Memoirs. v1, Nos. 1–6. 8°. [1926–27]
Quarterly journal. v44–53. la8°. 1918–27
„ „ ....Index, v27–51 [1901–25]. la8°. 1928
see PHYSICAL SOC. OF LONDON &c. Discussion on ionization in the atmosphere &c., 1924.

Royal Microscopical Society, *see* MILLETT (F. W.) Rep. on Foraminifera of Malay Archipel. [Extr. f. R.M.S. journal], 1898–1904.

Royal military calendar, 2v, 1815, *see* PHILIPPART (*Sir* J.)

Royal military chronicle (The); or, British officer's monthly register &c. v1–7; N.S., v1–6 (Nov. 1810–Apr. 1817). la8°. 1810–17

Royal Naval Air Service. The work & training of the R.N.A.S. [*Intr.* by Sir E. Geddes. P2417]. fol. *n.d.*

Royal Naval Exhibition, *Chelsea, 1891, see* EXHIBITIONS.

Royal Naval Reserve. *The work of the R.N.R. [Yachting Monthly. P2416]. la8°. [1918]

Royal Photographic Society of Gt. Brit., *see* HURTER (F.) & V. C. DRIFFIELD. Photographic researches; ed. W. B. Ferguson [R.P. Soc.: Memorial vol.], 1920.

Royal Scottish Academy. Centenary exhib. of painting, sculpture &c., 1826–1926. [Catalogue]. s8°. [1926]

Royal Scottish Geographical Society, *see* GLASGOW. The City of G., its growth &c., 1921.

Royal Society of Antiquaries of Ireland.
Journal. 6th ser., v9–17 (1919–27). 8°. 1920–28
EXTRA VOLUMES.
see †CLONMACNOISE. Annals of C., to 1408; tr. 1627, by C. Mageoghagan; ed. D. Murphy, 1896.
„ GORMANSTON. Cal. of G. register (c. 1175–1397), 1916.
„ IRELAND. *Advertisements for Ireland (1623); ed. G. O'Brien, 1923.
„ PETRIE (G.) Christian inscr. in the Ir. lang., 2v, 1872–78.

Royal Society of Arts.
Journal. v69–75 (Nov. 1920–Nov. 1927). 8°. 1921–27
„ Index, v41–50 (1892–1902), 51–60 (1902–12), 61–70 (1912–22). 8°. 1904–24
see BALDWIN (*Rt. Hon.* S.) Preserv. of anc. cottages, 1927.
„ HART (E.) Lect. on Japanese art work, 1887.

Royal Society of British Artists, *see* MORRISON (A.) Exhib. of Japanese screens, Illust. cat., 1910.

Royal Society of Literature of the United Kingdom. Essays by divers hands: Transactions of the Roy. Soc. of Lit. N.S., v1–7. Ed. Sir H. Newbolt &c. 8°. 1921–27
Altamira y Grevea (R.) Span. drama as an elem. of moral educ., 1925. [N.S., 5.]
Austen (J.), *see* Spurgeon (C. F. E.)
Bailey (J. C.) Unpopularity of Landor, 1925. [N.S., 5.]
Baker (A. T.) Saints' lives wr. in Anglo-French, 1924. [N.S., 4.]
Barker (H. Granville-). On translating plays, 1925. [N.S., 5.]
—— Some tasks for dramatic scholarship, 1923. [N.S., 3.]
Baudelaire (C. P.), *see* Nicolson (*Hon.* H.)
Benson (A. C.) Art of the biographer, 1926. [N.S., 6.]
Bond (R. W.) Art of narrative-poetry, 1924. [N.S., 4.]
Buchan (J.) The old & new in lit., 1925. [N.S., 5.]
Charnwood (G. R. B., *1st b.*) Walt Whitman & Amer. [N.S., 1.]
Chesterton (G. K.) Will. Cobbett, 1923. [N.S., 3.]
Cippico (A.) An all-embracing genius: L. da Vinci. [N.S., 1.]
Cobbett (W.), *see* Chesterton (G. K.)
Collins (W.), *see* Mackail (J. W.)
Cory (W.), *see* Drinkwater (J.)
Cowper (W. C., *1st earl*), *see* Imbert-Terry (*Sir* H. M.)
Crewe (R. O. A. C.-M., *1st m. of*). The R.S. of L., 1926. [N.S., 6.]
Dante Alighieri, *see* Ramsey (R. W.)
De la Mare (W.) Christina Rossetti, 1926. [N.S., 6.]
Ditchfield (P. H.) The parson in lit. [N.S., 1.]
Drinkwater (J.) Will. Cory, 1924. [N.S., 4.]
Fagg (E.) Naturalistic motive in mod. pictures, 1923. [N.S., 3.]
Gaster (M.) Yiddish lit. of the M.A., 1927. [N.S., 7.]
Gotch (J. A.) Inigo Jones: a mod. view, 1927. [N.S., 7.]
Grey (E. G., *1st visct.*) The pleasure of reading, 1925. [N.S., 5.]
Hood (Robin), *see* Newbolt (*Sir* H. J.)
Imbert-Terry (*Sir* H. M.) Reminisc. of a Chancellor & h. wife, 1927. [N.S., 7.]
Jones (Inigo), *see* Gotch (J. A.)
Kipling (R.) Address, 1926. [N.S., 6.]
Landor (W. S.), *see* Bailey (J. C.)
Louis IX, of France, *see* Ramsey (R. W.)
Mackail (J. W.) Collins, & the Eng. lyric in 18th c. [N.S., 1.]
Manly (J. M.) The miracle play in med. Eng., 1927. [N.S., 7.]
Newbolt (*Sir* H. J.) Future of Eng. lang., 1923. [N.S., 3.]
—— Peacock, Scott & Robin Hood, 1924. [N.S., 4.]
—— Some poets & th. scenery, 1925. [N.S., 5.]
Nicolson (*Hon.* H.) Swinburne & Baudelaire, 1926. [N.S., 6.]
Noyes (A.) Some characteristics of mod. lit., 1923. [N.S., 3.]
Peacock (T. L.), *see* Newbolt (*Sir* H. J.)
Ramsey (R. W.) Dante & St. Louis, 1924. [N.S., 4.]
Reul (P. de). Centenary of Shelley, 1923. [N.S., 3.]
Rose (J. H.) Chivalry & the sea, 1924. [N.S., 4.]
Rossetti (C.), *see* De la Mare (W.)
Sackville-West (V.) Some tendencies of mod. Eng. poetry, 1927. [N.S., 7.]
Scott (*Sir* W.), *see* Newbolt (*Sir* H. J.)
Shelley (P. B.), *see* Reul (P. de).
Spurgeon (C. F. E.) Jane Austen, 1927. [N.S., 7.]
Swinburne (A. C.), *see* Nicolson (*Hon.* H.)
Underhill (E.) A Franciscan poet, J. da Todi, 1926. [N.S., 6.]
Watson (F.) J. L. Vives, 1492–1540. [N.S., 1.]
Woods (M. L.) Ballads, 1926. [N.S., 6.]
Younghusband (*Sir* F. E.) Culture as the bond of empire, 1921. [N.S., 1.]

Royal Society of London. Cat. of printed bks. Sold by Sotheby, May 1925. [P2853]. la8°. 1925
Cat. of sci. papers. 4th ser. (1884–1900). v17–19. 4°. C. 1921–25
Philosophical transactions. Ser. A, v221. Ser. B, v210. 4°. 192

Royal Society of London [*continued*].
Proceedings. 91A & B, 92A & B, 93A, 94A, 95A, 96B, 97A, 98A. la8°. 1915–21
Each vol. has 2 ser., A & B.
Reports to the Evolution Comm. Rep. 5 (Exper. st. in physiology of heredity). 8°. 1909
Yearbook. No. 25, 1921, No. 27, 1923. 8°. 1921–23
see DIXEY (F. A.) Early connex. of the R.S. w. Wadham Coll. &c., 1912.
,, KEMPEN (M. v.) Charismatum sacr. trias, cum app. de Regia Soc. Londin., 1677.
,, MUDGE (*Col.* W.) Acc. of operations for accompl. trigonometrical survey of Eng. &c.; rev. f. Philos. Trans., 3v, 1799–1811.

Royal Society of New South Wales [*form.* PHILOSOPHICAL SOCIETY]. Journal & proc. v9–58 (1875–1924). 8°. Sydney. 1876–1925
v9, *h. title* Transactions & proc.

Royal Society of Van Diemen's Land [*aft.* ROYAL SOC. OF TASMANIA]. Papers & proceedings, 1851–52, 1863–66. [3v]. 8°. Hobart. 1851–67
Report, 1852, 1863–66. [*b. w. above*]. 8°. Hobart. 1853–67

Royal Statistical Society of London.
Cat. of the Lib. of the S.S. 8°. 1921
Journal. v83–90. 8°. 1920–27

Royal United Service Institution.
Journal. v65–72. 8°. 1920–27
Offic. cat. of the R.U.S. Mus. Comp. by Lt.-Col. A. Leetham & B. E. Sargeaunt. 3rd ed. s8°. 1908

Royallieu. Cartul. de Royallieu. [*Ed. w.* Intr.] par P. Guynemer. 4°. Compiègne. 1911

Royan. Chartes du prieuré de Saint-Nicolas de Royan. Publ. par A. Dupré. [Extr. du t19 des Archives hist. de Saintonge &c. P2469]. 8°. [1891]

Royce (Alice Carrington), *see* GOODWIN (M. W.) Hist. New York; [*by var. wr.*]; ed. M. W. G., A. C. R. &c., 2v, 1899.

Royce (Josiah). Fugitive essays. Intr. by J. Loewenberg. 8°. Cambridge [Mass.] 1920
Lect. on mod. idealism. 8°. New Haven, *Yale.* 1919
Studies of good & evil. s8°. N.Y. 1899
see ARONSON (M. J.) La philos. morale de J. R., 1927.
,, SANTAYANA (G.) Character & opinion in the U.S., w. rem. of W. James & J. R. &c., 1920.

Royce (William Stapleton), *see* OULD (C. W.) W. S. R.: a memoir, 1925.

Royde-Smith (Naomi). The housemaid. s8°. [1926]
Skin-deep. s8°. 1927
The tortoiseshell cat. s8°. 1925

Royden (Agnes Maude).
Sex & common sense. 5th ed. s8°. [1922]

Royden (E. B.) Three Roydon families. [Pref. signed E. B. R. Arranged &c. by J. Brownbill]. 4°. E. 1924

Roydon, *The family of* [REYDON], *see* ROYDEN (E. B.) 3 Roydon families, 1924.

Royère (Jean). Mallarmé. Préc. d'une lettre sur M. de P. Valéry. 8°. [1927]
Poésies. s8°. Amiens. 1924

Roylance (William G.), *see* PLUMB (G. E.) & W. G. R. Indust. democracy, 1923.

Roz (Firmin). L'age d'homme. Roman. [3e éd.] s8°. [1922]

Rozanov (Vasily Vasilevich), *1856–1919.*
Легенда о великом инквизиторе Ф. М. Достоевского: опыт критич. комментария. s8°. Берлин. 1924
Опавшіе листья. s8°. С.-П. 1913
Solitaria. With abr. acc. of a.'s life by E. Gollerbach. Other biog. material, & matter f. The apocalypse of our times. Tr. S. S. Koteliansky. 8°. 1927
see SHKLOVSKY (V.) Розанов, 1921.

Rozen (Valer. Sigism.) Synopsis actorum Colloquii Thoruniensis, 1645. s8°. Amstelodami. 1646

Ruarus (Martimus), *1588–1657.* Epist. centuriae duae, *see* ZELTNER (G. G.) Hist. Crypto-Socinismi, 1729.

Rubakin (Nikolai Aleksandrovich).
Среди борцовъ. Очерки. 8°. С.-П. 1906

Rubbiani (Alfonso). Commemor. di A.R., promossa dal comitato per Bologna Storico-Artistica &c. [Discorsi]. [P2497]. 8°. Bologna. 1915
Di Bologna riabbellita. [P2497]. 8°. [Bologna]. 1913
Modelli &c. per la integraz. d. facciata quattrocentesca del salone del Podestà in Bologna. [P2516]. la8°. Bologna. 1910

Rube (Johann Christoph). Problema juridicum an haeresis sit crimen? Præs. C. Thomasio. [P2632]. s4°. Halæ. [1697]

Rubens (*Sir* Peter Paul). Palazzi di Genova. [*Plates without letterpress except dedication &c.*] 2p. fol. [Antverpiæ]. [1622]
see BURCKHARDT (J.) Erinnerungen aus R., 3e A., 1918.

Ruberti (Guido). Il teatro contemp. in Europa. 2v. s8°. Bologna. 1920–21

Rubertis (Achille de).
Doc. Manzoniani. s8°. Napoli. 1926
V. Gioberti e la Costituente di G. Montanelli, *see* ARCHIVIO STOR. ITAL., anno 79, v2, 1923.
V. Gioberti e la vertenza tosco-piemont. d. Lunigiana, *see* ARCHIVIO STOR. ITAL., anno 85, v2, 1927.

Rübezahl, *see* PRÄTORIUS (J.) Bekannte &c. Historien v. d. R., 1926.

Rubino (Joannes a), *see* JOANNES *a Rubino.*

Rubinstein (Anton). Die Musik u. ihre Meister. s8°. L. 1891

Rubinstein (Harold Frederick). The house. Play. s8°. 1926
Isabel's eleven. Comedy. s8°. 1927
— & H. Glover. Exodus. Dram. sequence. s8°. 1923

Rubió y Lluch (Antonio). Docs. per l'hist. de la cultura catalana mig-eval. Publ. per A. R. y L. [Inst. d'Estudis Catalans]. v2. 4°. Barcelona. 1921

Rubius (Johann) [JO. RU. LONGI.] Solutiones ac responsa wit[tenbergensium] Doctorum in publica disputatiōe Lipsica cōtra fulmīa Eckiana parū ꝑ futura tumorꝗ advētus & hūilitas eorū recessus per Jo. Ru. Longi cōportata. [P2444]. s4°. [Leipzig. 1519?]

Rubner (Max). Üb. d. Wasserbindung in Kolloiden, *see* KÖN.-PREUSS. AKAD. Abh., Phys.-math. Klasse, 1922.

Rubruquis (Gulielmus de) [RUBRUK]. Bericht ü. s. Reise in d. Innere Asiens, 1253–55. Übers &c. v. H. Herbst. s8°. L. 1925
see BATTON (A.) W. v. R. u. s. Sendung in d. Land d. Tataren, 1921.

Ruchat (Abraham). Hist. de la Réformation de la Suisse &c. éd. avec app. & notice sur R. par L. Vulliemin. 7t. 8°. Nyon. 1835–38
Hist. of the Reformation in Switzerland; Abr. f. Fr. by J. Collinson. s8°. 1845

Ruchon (François). Jules Laforgue, 1860–87: sa vie, s. œuvre. Préf. de G. J. Aubry. 8°. Genève. 1924

Ruck (Berta), *aft. wife of O. Onions.*
The dancing star. s8°. [1923]
The post-war girl & o. stories. s8°. [1922]
Under false pretences. s8°. [1922]

Rücker-Embden (Oscar). Chines. Frühkeramik. 4°. L. 1922

Rückersfelder (Abraham Friedrich). Disput. theol. de juribus Satanae in genus humanum. s4°. Bremae. [1748]

Rückert (Friedrich).
Weisheit d. Brahmanen: e. Lehrgedicht. s8°. L. 1843

Rudberg (Gunnar). Forsch. zu Poseidonios, *see* KUNG. HUM. VET.-SAMF. I UPPSALA. Skr., B20, 1918.

Rudd, *The family of, see* RUDD (M. A.) Records of the R. family, 1920.

Rudd (Charles). Early hist. of the 17th (North) Middlesex Volunteer Rifles, 1859–89. 8°. 1895

Rudd (Mary Amelia). Records of the Rudd family. Coll. & arr. by M. A. R. la8°. Bristol. 1920

Rudder (May de). César Franck. s8°. Turnhout. 1920
Guido Gezelle. s8°. Turnhout. 1919

Rude (Anna Elizabeth). Physical status of preschool children, Gary, Ind., 1922, *see* UNITED STATES: LAB.

Rudenschold (Madeleine de), *see* DAUDET (E.) Un drame d'amour à la cour de Suède, 1784–95 [Baron d'Armfelt & M. de R.], 1913.

Rüder (Friedrich August). Leben, Thaten u. Ende d. Kaisers Napoleon. s8°. Ilmenau. 1827

Rüdinger (Esrom), *see* EXEGESIS perspicua & ferme integra controv. de Sacra Cœna [*By* E. R.?], 1574.

Rudimenta. *R. fidei Xtianae sive Catechismus, 1575, *see* CALVIN (J.)
*R. ling. Coptae sive Ægyptiacae, 1778, *see* TUKI (R.)

Rudin (A.) Что говорятъ русскіе соціалдемократы "Деревенской бѣднотѣ." [*a. c. in* P848]. s8°. Москва. 1905

Rudkin (Olive D.) Thomas Spence & h. connections. 8°. 1927

Rudler (Frederick William), *F.G.S.* Hdbk. to coll. of minerals of the Brit. Isl.: mostly sel. f. the Ludlam coll. in Museum of Pract. Geology. 8°. 1905

Rudler (Gustave).
Michelet, historien de Jeanne d'Arc. 2t. 8º. 1926
Les techniques de la critique & de l'hist. litt. en litt. franç. mod. 8º. O. 1923

Rudmose-Brown (Robert Neal), *see* Brown (R. N. R.)

Rudnev (Andrei D.) О происхожденіи Финновъ. (Библіограф. замѣтка). [*Extr. fr.* "Финляндія." P2532]. 8º. С.-П. 1910

Rudnev (V. M.) [Roudnieff]. La vérité sur la famille impériale russe &c. Avant-propos &c. de M. D. Netchvolodoff. [P2426]. 8º. 1920

Rudolf (Robert de Montjoie), *see* Clapham & the Clapham Sect. ; [*by* R. &c.], 1927.

Rudolph, *Crown Prince of Austria, see* Mayerling. *Das Drama v. M. [Tod. d. Kronpr. R. &c.], 1921.

Rudolph IV, *duke of Austria, see* Zahn (J. v.) Austro-Friulana Actenstücken z. Gesch. d. Conflictes R. IV mit d. Patriarche v. Aquileja, 1358–65, 1877.

Rudolph II, *emp. of Germany.* Investiture of Siena granted by R., 1604, *see* Hisp. Soc. of Amer. MSS., 1928.

Rudolphi (E. Camillo). Die Buchdrucker-Familie Froschauer in Zürich, 1521–95. Verz. d. Druckwerke. 8º. Zürich. 1869

Rudyerd (*Sir* Benjamin), *see* Pembroke (W. H., *3rd earl of*). Poems of P. & Sir B. R., 2nd ed., 1817.

Rueda (Lope de), *see* Lomba y Pedraja (J. R.) Teatro ant. a L. de Vega, 1924.

Ruedinger (Esrom), *see* Rüdinger (E.)

Rueff, *see* Rüff.

Rues (Simeon Friedrich). Aufrichtige Nachrichten v. d. gegenw. Zustande d. Mennoniten, wie auch d. Collegianten od. Reinsburger &c. s8º. Jena. 1743

Ruet (Noël). L'escarpolette fleurie. Poèmes. 8º. Brux. 1925
L'urne penchée. 8º. Seraing. *n.d.*

Ruever Groneman (Sarus Adrian Jacob de). Diatribe in J. Wicliffi vitam, ingenium, scripta. 8º. Trajecti a. Rh. 1837

Rufer (Alfred), *ed.* Der Freistaat d. III Bünde u. d. Frage d. Veltlins, 1796–97, 2B, 1916–17, *see* Quellen z. Schweizer Gesch., N.F., Abtlg. 3, B3, 4, 1916–17.

Rüff (Hans) [Rueff]. Das rhein. Osterspiel d. Berl. Hs. MS. Germ. fol. 1219, 1925, *see* Königl. Gesell. d. W. zu Göttingen. Abh., N.F., 18, 1926.

Ruffec (Anne Toussainte de Volvire de), *see* Volvire de Ruffec (A. T. de).

Ruffer (Ernest). Cat. of mod. pictures &c., property of E. R., pictures by H. Fantin-Latour, property of Mrs. R. A. Workman, sold by Christie &c., May 9, 1924. [*Illust.*] 8º. 1924

Ruffer (*Sir* Marc Armand). Studies in the palaeopathology of Egypt. Ed. R. L. Moodie. 8º. Chicago. [1921]

Rufini (Alessandro). Diz. etimolog.-stor. d. strade, piazze, borghi e vicoli di Roma. s8º. Roma. 1847

Rufinus (Licinius), *see* Collatio. Lex Dei sive Mosaic. & Rom. legum collatio *attrib. to L. R.*, 1833.

Rufinus (Tyrannius) [Ruffinus ; T. R. Aquileiensis].
see Fontanini (G.) Hist. lit. Aquilej., lib. 5 [R. &c.], 1742.
,, Kimmel (E. J.) De R. Eusebii interp. lib. 2, diss., 1838.

Rufo (Juan) [†Rufo de Gutierrez (J.)] Las seiscientas apotegmas y o. obras en verso [1596. *Ed.* A. G. de Amezúa. Soc. de Bibliofilos Esp., 42]. 8º. 1923

Rufus (Vitruvius). Un nouv. texte des traités d'arpentage & de géom. d'Epaphroditus & de V. R., *see* Tannery (P.) Mém. scient., t5, 1922.

Rugby School. The book of Rugby School: its hist. & daily life. [*By var. wr.* Ed. w. pref. by E. M. Goulburn]. la8º. *p.p.* [Rugby]. 1856

Ruge (Arnold). Staat oder Papst ? V. e. Weltgeistlichen im Münsterlande. Hrsg. A. R. s8º. Elberfeld. 1876

Ruge (Sophus) & A. Arstal. Norwegen. 2e A. bearb. v. Yngvar Nielsen. 3e A. bearb. v. A. Arstal. la8º. Bielefeld. 1913

Ruge (W.) Älteres kartograph. Material in deut. Bibl., *see* Königl. Gesells. d. Wiss. zu Göttingen. Nachr., phil.-hist. Kl., 1904, 1906, 1911, 1916.

Ruggeri (Ruggero), *see* Manzini (A.) R. R., 1920.

Ruggiero (Ettore de). Diz. epigrafico di antichità romane. v2, p3 [*pagin. cont.*], v3. 8º. Roma, Spoleto. 1922

Ruggiero (Guido de). Il pensiero polit. meridionale nei sec. 18 & 19. 8º. Bari. 1922
Sommario di storia d. filosofia. 8º. Bari. 1927
Storia d. filosofia, p1, La filosofia greca. 2a ed. corr. 2v. 8º. Bari. 1921

Ruggiero (Guido de) [*continued*].
Storia d. filosofia, p2, La filosofia del Cristianesimo. 3v. 8º. Bari. 1920
Translations.
Hist. of Europ. liberalism. Tr. R. G. Collingwood. 8º. 1927
Modern philosophy. Tr. A. H. Hannay & R. G. Collingwood. 8º. [1921]

Ruggles-Brise (*Sir* Evelyn John).
The English prison system. 8º. 1921
Prison reform at home & abroad, since 1872. 8º. 1924

Ruggles-Brise (*Maj.* Harold Goodeve), *see* Guards' Brigade. Offic. rec. of the G.B. in S. Africa ; [pref. by R.-B.], 1904.

Rugman (Jonas). Saml. av isländska talesätt (17 c.) ; utg. G. Kallstenius, *see* Kung. Hum. Vet.-Samf. i Uppsala. Skr., B22, 1927.

Ruhel (Conrad). Dogmata & argumenta, de papa e Bellarmini &c. libris coll., exam. & refut. s8º. Witebergae. 1604

Ruhig (Paul Friedrich), *the younger, see* Mielcke (C. G.) Anfangs-Gründe e. Littau. Sprachlehre ; v. R. hrsg. Gramm. z. Grunde gelegt &c., 1800.

Ruhig (Philipp), *see* Mielcke (C. G.) Littau.— deut. &c. Wbch., v. R., 1800.

Ruhl (Arthur). New masters of the Baltic. 8º. N.Y. [1921]

Ruhr.
*Right & wrong in the Ruhr valley: legal aspect of Franco-Belg. occupation. By ****. [P2733]. 8º. 1923
Ruhrgebiet (Das) nebst Wupper u. Niederrhein, 1923, *see* Zobeltitz (H. C. v.), *ed.*
*Ruhr (The) raid. Facts & doc. [P2719]. 8º. Berlin. 1923

Ruinart (Thierry). Acta martyrum. Acc. Acta SS. Firmi & Rustici. fol. Veronae. 1731
Vita J. Mabillonii. In Lat. tr. 8º. Patavii. 1714

Ruiz (Antonio), *Jesuit, see* Ruiz de Montoya (A).

Ruiz (Juan), *archpriest of Hita.*
Libro de buen amor. s8º. Paris. *n.d.*

Ruiz de Montoya (Antonio). Conquista espiritual hecha por los religiosos de la Compañia de Jesus, en las prov. del Paraguay, Parana, Uruguay y Tape, &c. s4º. 1639

Ruiz de Vergara y Alava (Francisco). Regla y establecimientos nuevos de la Orden y Cavalleria del glorioso Apostol Santiago &c. reimpr. sm. fol. 1752

Ruiz Morcuende (Federico).
La novela picaresca. Seleccion. s8º. 1922

Ruland (Wilhelm).
Rhein. Sagenbuch. 41–47 Aufl. s8º. Köln. 1925

Rule (Gilbert), *principal of the Univ. of Edinburgh.*
see Forrester (T.) Causa episcopatus: confut. of J. S.'s Vindic. of princ. of Cyprianic Age [a reply to G. R.'s Cyprianic Bishop exam.], 1706.
,, Sage (J.) A vindication of a disc., being a reply to G. R.'s Cyprianic bishop examin'd, 1701.

Rule (William Harris).
Celebrated Jesuits. 2v. s8º. 1852
1, Xavier—Laynez—Garnet. 2, Bellarmino—Schall—Gruber.
Los Cuatro Evanjelios ; tr. é ilust. con notas por R. 8º. [Gibraltar]. 1841
Las Epístolas: Gálatas—Revelacion ; tr. y anot. por R. 8º. Londres. 1880
Los Hechos de los Apóstoles y las Epístolas à los Romanos y Corintios ; tr. al Español, y anot. por R. 8º. Londres. 1877
Himnos para las congregac. esp. de la Iglesia metodista (*comp.* by G. H. R.) s8º. Gibraltar. 1842
An hist. expos. of Daniel. 8º. 1869
Hist. of the Inquisition. 2v. 8º. 1874
Mem. of a mission to Gibraltar & Spain &c. s8º. 1844
Recoll. of my life. s8º. 1886
Wesleyan Methodism. s8º. 1846

Rülf (J.) Wissenschaft d. Weltgedankens u. d. Gedankenwelt. T2. 8º. L. 1888

Rulhière (Claude Carloman de), *see* Saldern (de). Hist. de la vie de Pierre III: [*Reply to* R.'s Anecd. sur la révol. en Russie, en 1762], 1802.

Rumania, *see* Roumania.

Rümann (Arthur). Honoré Daumier, s. Holzschnittwerk Text u. Katalog. 4º. München. 1914

Ruml (Bohuslav), *see* Butter (O.) & B. R. Tschechoslowak Republ., 1921.

Rumohr (Carl F. L. F. v.) Briefe an Bunsen ü. Erwerbungen für d. Berliner Museum ; mitgeteilt v. F. Stock, *see* Jahrbuch d. Preuss. Kunstsammlungen, B46, 1925.

Rumold, *Saint, bp. of Dublin, see* Wachtendonck (J. van) Vita &c. S. R., 1638.

Rump (Hermann). Die Unfehlbarkeit d. Papstes &c. [P2657]. 8°. Münster. 1870

Rumpel (Johann). Lexicon Theocriteum. la8°. Lipsiae. 1879

Rumsey (Frances). Mr. Cushing & Mlle. Du Chastel. s8°. 1918

Runciman (*Sir* **Walter**), *bart.* Before the mast—& after: autobiog. of a sailor & shipowner. [2nd impr.] 8°. [1924]

Rundall (Lionel Bickersteth). The Ibex of Shā-ping, & o. Himalayan studies. la8°. 1915

Runeberg (Johan Ludvig). Samlade skrifter. 6b. [1–3, 5e Uppl.] 8°. Örebro & Stockholm. 1858–69

Runge (Carl), *prof. at (1) Hannover, (2) Göttingen.* Vector analysis. Tr. H. Levy. 8°. [1923]

Rungius (David). Bericht u. Erinn. v. d. Tyrann. Bäpst. verfolgung dess H. Evangelii, in Steyermarckt, Kärndten u. Krain. Die Clementin. Bull v. Jubeljahr &c. s4°. Wittenberg. 1601

Disput. de duarum naturarum Christi unione personali. Præs. D. R., def. J. Huswedelius. [P2612]. s4°. Witebergae. 1600

Disput. 8 ex symbolo Apostol., de adscensu Christi in coelum &c. Praes. D. R., propugn. J. G. Hochstaterus. [P2612]. s4°. Witebergae. 1601

Doct. de baptismo. Praes. D. R., ad disput. proposita à B. Batto. [P2673]. s4°. Witebergae. 1596

Theses de ascensu Christi in coelum &c. Praes. D. R. Propugn. D. Stangius &c. ed. 2a corr. [P2612]. s4°. [Witebergae]. 1598

Rupert, *crown-prince of Bavaria, see* Krafft v. Dellmensingen. Die Führung d. Kronpr. R., Aug. 1914, 1925.

Rupert, *duke of Bingen, Saint* [Ruprecht], *see* Köbel (J.) Die Legende d. R., 1524, 1887.

Rupert, *prince, son of Frederick I, k. of Bohemia, see* True. *True & punct. rel. of sev. skirmishes &c. under Pr. R., 1643, repr., 1868.

Rupert, *emperor of Germany.* Fragen d. Königs R. ü. d. Femgerichte (*facs. c.* 1408), *see* Freytag (G.) Bilder, B2, 1924.

Ruperti (F. A.) Gesch. d. Dogmen. 8°. 1831

Ruperti (Georg Alex.), *see* Velthusen (J. C.), C. T. Kuinoel & G. A. R., *edd.* Comm. theologicae, 6v, 1794–99.

Rupertus, *abbot of St. Heribert* [Rupertus, *Juicensis*]. De victoria verbi Dei libri tredecim. s8°. Norimbergae, *Jo. Petreius.* 1524

Ruppersberg (Albert).
Gesch. d. Saargebietes. 8°. Saarbrücken. 1923

Ruppin (Arthur). Agric. colonisation of the Zionist organis. in Palestine. Tr. R. J. Feiwel. 8°. 1926

Ruprecht (Franz Johann). Гео-ботанич. изслѣдованія о Черноземѣ. [I. Akad. Nauk. Записки, t10]. 8°. С.-П. 1866

Rural life. Rep. prep. by Copec Contin. Comm. s8°. 1927

Rus (Johann Reinhard) [Rusius]. Digressio, de descensu Christi ad inferos &c. s8°. Jenae. 1730

Ruscelli (Girolamo). I fiori d. rime de' poeti ill., nuov. racc. &c. da G. R., con annot. &c. s8°. Venetia. 1558

Rime di diversi autori bresciani, nuov. racc. &c. da G. R.; rime d. sign. V. Gambara & di P. Barignano &c. s8°. Venetia. 1553

Rusch (Adolf). Die Stellung d. Osiris im theolog. System v. Heliopolis, *see* Alte Orient, B24, 1925.

Rusconi (Arturo Jahn).
Assisi. [Ital. Artist., 89]. 4°. Bergamo. [1927]

Ruses (Les) innocentes; par F[rère] F. F., 1688, *see* Fortin (F.)

Rush (James), *M.D.* The philosophy of the human voice &c. 3rd ed. enl. 8°. Phila. 1845

Rush (James Blomfield). Intr. narr. & rev. report of the trial &c. of J. B. R. for the murder of I. Jermy, of Stanfield Hall, & of h. son. 8°. Norwich. 1849

Rushbury (Henry), *see* Hall (*Mrs.* E. C.) Draughtsmen: E. C. H., H. R. &c., 1924.

Rushen (Percy C.)
Hist. & antiq. of Chipping Campden. 8°. Woodbridge. 1899

Rushforth (Frank Victor). The Indian exchange problem. [2nd impr. P2524]. s8°. 1921

Rushton (William Lowes).
Shakespeare's euphuism. 8°. 1871
Shakespeare's testamentary language. s8°. 1869

Rusiñol (Santiago), *see* Martínez Sierra (G.) S. R., 1918.

Ruskin (John).

The art of England. Lect. 1, 2 *in* 1v. la8°. Orpington. 1883

The laws of Fésole. 2nd thousand, v1 [*no more publ.*] 8°. O. 1882

Letters to W. Ward. With sh. biog. of W. W. by W. C. Ward, & intr. by A. M. Brooks. 8°. 1922

Modern painters. compl. ed. 5v. la8°. *la. paper copy.* Orpington. 1888

„ „ Gen. index, bibliog. & notes. la8°. *la. paper copy.* Orpington. 1888

Mornings in Florence. s8°. 1901

Notes on S. Prout & W. Hunt. [*Illust.*] 4°. 1880

Notes on some of the princ. pict. exhib. in the R. Acad. No. 2. 3rd ed., w. postscript. 8°. 1856

Poems. Ed., w. notes &c. by W. G. Collingwood. 2v. la8°. *la. paper copy.* Orpington. 1891

The poetry of architecture. la8°. *la. paper copy.* Orpington. 1893

Sels. f. the writings of R. s8°. *Smith, Elder & Co.* 1862

Sesame & lilies. [Works, v1]. 3rd ed. 8°. O. 1876

Stones of Venice. 4th ed. 3v. la8°. *la. paper copy.* Orpington. 1886

see Graham (J. W.) Harvest of R., 1920.

„ Mather (M.) J. R., 3rd ed., 1890.

„ Maurois (A.) Études angl., R. & Wilde, 1927.

„ —— Quatre études angl., De R. à Wilde &c., 1927.

„ Shaw (G. B.) Ruskin's politics, 1921.

„ Shepherd (R. H.) Bibliog. of R., 1834–79, 4th ed., rev. & enl., *n.d.*

„ Whitehouse (J. H.), *ed.* R. the prophet &c.; by J. Masefield &c., 1920.

„ Wise (T. J.) & J. P. Smart. Compl. bibliog. of writings of J. R., 2v, 1893.

Ruspoli (Francesco). Sonetti. Col comm. di A. Cavalcanti. [Ed. A. Bacchi della Lega]. s8°. Bologna. 1876

Russ (Hans Löwenfeld-), *see* Löwenfeld-Russ (H.)

Russan (Ashmore).
see Russan (L.) & A. R. Hist. streets of London: alphabet. hdbk., 1923.
„ —— & —— Old London city, 1924.

Russan (Lilian) & A. Russan. Hist. streets of London: an alphabetical hdbk. s8°. 1923
Old London city: a handbook. s8°. 1924

Russe [Russes]. Interrogatoires des ministres, conseillers &c. de la Cour Imp. Russe par la Comm. Extr. du Gouvt. Prov. de 1917; tr., 1927, *see* Maklakov (V. A.), *ed.*

Un livre noir: diplomatie d'avant-guerre d'ap. les doc. russes, 1910–14, 2t, 1922, *see* Marchand (R.)

Russell (A.) A tour through the Australian colonies in 1839, w. notes &c. of a voy. round the globe. s8°. Glasgow. 1840

Russell (A. J.) God's prodigal. s8°. [1922]

Russell (Alexander David). Legends of the Bocas, Trinidad. Intr. by Sir J. Chancellor. la8°. 1922

see Ibn Abū Zayd. First steps in Muslim jurisprud. &c.; Arabic text, Eng. tr., notes &c. by R. &c., 1906.

Russell (Alexander Smith). Intr. to the chemistry of radioactive substances. s8°. 1922

W. Thomson Lord Kelvin. Oration. [P2738]. 8°. Glasgow. 1924

see Streeter (B. H.) Adventure; by B. H. S., A. S. R. &c., 1927.

Russell (*Hon.* **Bertrand A. W.)**

The ABC of atoms. s8°. 1923

The ABC of relativity. 8°. 1925

Analysis of matter. 8°. 1927

The analysis of mind. 8°. [1921]

„ „ [repr.] 8°. [1922]

Free thought & official propaganda. [2nd impr.] s8°. 1922

Icarus, or, the future of science. s8°. 1924

Justice in war time. [reissued]. 8°. [1924]

On education, espec. in early childhood. s8°. [1926]

Our knowledge of the external world as a field for sci. method in philos. [reissue]. 8°. [1922]

„ „ [n. ed. rev.] 8°. [1926]

Outline of philos. 8°. [1927]

The practice & theory of Bolshevism. s8°. [1920]

„ [repr.] s8°. [1921]

The problem of China. 8°. [1922]

The problems of philosophy. [Home Univ. Lib.] n. & rev. ed. s8°. [1927]

Prospects of indust. civilization. By B. R. in collab. w. D. Russell. s8°. [1923]

Roads to freedom: socialism, anarchism & syndicalism. 3rd ed. s8°. [1920]

What I believe. s8°. 1925

see Kirchwey (F.), *ed.* Our changing morality; [*by* B. R. &c.], 1925.

Russell (C. H. St. L.)
The tradition of the Roman Empire. s8°. 1921

Russell (Charles E.)
Eng. mezzotint portraits & th. states. 2v. fol. & la8°. 1926
1, From invent. of mezzotinting until 19th c.
2, Cat. of corr. of & add. to C. Smith's "Brit. mezzotint portraits."

Russell (*Major* **Charles Edmund).**
True adventures of the Secret Service. 8°. 1924

Russell (Charles Edward) & E. B. Rodriguez. The hero of the Filipinos: story of José Rizal. 8º. 1924
Russell (Charles William) & J. P. Prendergast. The Carte MSS. in the Bodleian Lib.: rep. pres. to Lord Romilly, Master of the Rolls. 8º. 1871
Russell (David), *see* PRAYER. The power of prayer: sel. of Walker Trust essays; ed. W. P. Paterson & D. R., 1920.
Russell (David), *M.D.* The evolution of continuity in the natural world. 8º. [1922]
Russell (Dora Winifred), *wife of Hon. Bertrand Russell.*
Hypatia, or woman & knowledge. [2nd. impr.] s8º. 1925
see RUSSELL (*Hon.* B. A. W.) Prospects of indust. civilization; by B. R. in collab. w. D. R., 1923.
Russell (*Admiral* Edward), *see* ORFORD (E. R., *earl of*).
Russell (*Sir* Edward John), *D.Sc., F.R.S.*
Farm soil & its improvement. 8º. 1923
Manuring for higher crop production. 3rd ed. 8º. C. 1921
Russell (George William) [*ps.* A. E.]
*Imaginations & reveries. [2nd ed.] s8º. 1921
The inner & the outer Ireland. Repr. f. Pearson's Mag., U.S.A. [P2529]. s8º. D. 1921
*The interpreters. By A. E. 8º. 1922
Ireland & the Empire at the court of conscience. [P2560, 2706]. s8º. D. 1921
A plea for justice. Attacks on co-operative societies in Ireland. [P2529]. s8º. D. [1921]
*Voices of the stones. 8º. 1925
Russell (*Lady* Georgina Adelaide), *daughter of 1st Earl Russell, see* PEEL (*Lady* G. A.)
Russell (*Capt.* Harry T.)
A French-Eng. milit. vocabulary. s8º. 1905
Notes on strategy & milit. hist. s8º. [1904]
Russell (John). In dark places. s8º. [1923]
Where the pavement ends. 4th impr. s8º. 1921
,, ,, ...5th impr. s8º. 1921
Russell (*Lord* John), *3rd son of 6th Duke of Bedford; aft. 1st earl Russell; 1792–1878.*
Don Carlos. Tragedy. [P2863]. 8º. 1822
The later corresp. of Lord John Russell, 1840–78. Ed. G. P. Gooch. 2v. 8º. 1925
Letter to the electors of Stroud on the princ. of the Reform Act. [P2556]. 8º. 1839
Russell (*Sir* John), *D.Sc., F.R.S., see* RUSSELL (*Sir* ED. J.)
Russell (John Francis Stanley Russell, *2nd earl*).
My life & adventures. 8º. 1923
Russell (Michael).
View of anc. & mod. Egypt. 2nd ed. rev. s8º. E. 1832
Russell (Percy). Sir H. Irving. 8º. [1895]
Russell (Phillips). Benjamin Franklin. 8º. 1927
Russell (Richard), *novelist.*
Fate's a fiddler, life's a dance. s8º. 1889
Russell (Robert), *F.G.S., see* GREEN (A. H.), R. R. *& others.* Geol. of the Yorkshire coalfield, 1878.
Russell (Thomas). Poet. works. Coll. by T. Park. [*b. w.* Moore (J. H.) Poet. works, 1808]. s8º. 1808
Russell (William), *Agent at Moscow for the Dutch merchants.*
*Récit du sanglant &c. massacre dans la ville de Moscou &c., 1606. Tr. [f. Eng. of W. R.] par le prince A. Galitzin. s8º. 1869
Russell-Cotes (*Sir* Merton), *J.P.* Home & abroad: autobiog. of an octogenarian. 2v. *p.f.p.c.* la8º. Bournemouth. 1921
Russia.
ANONYMOUS WORKS.
*Famine (The) in R., 1922, *see* FAMINE.
Greetings to the new R.: Addr. at a meeting, N.Y. [C.E. for Int. Peace. P2676]. la8º. Wash. 1917
*Hdbk. of Siberia & A.R., 1920, *see* ADMIRALTY: NAVAL INTELL. DIV.
*How the War began in 1914: diary of Russian For. Office, July 3–20, 1914. Tr. by W. C. Bridge; foreword by S. D. Sazonov; intr. by Bar. M. F. Schilling. 8º. [1925]
*Letters f. a lady who resided in R., 1775, *see* WARD (*Mrs.* —).
*Obs. & reflect. on a war w. Russia. 8º. 1791
*Orig. letters f. R., 1825–28, 1878, *see* DISBROWE (C. A. A.), *ed.*
*Russia in resurrection: views &c. of a new party. By an Eng. Europasian. 8º. 1928
R. self-condemned: secret &c. doc.; tr. &c., 1854, *see* MORELL (J. R.), *ed.*
*Strategical (The) aspect of the western frontiers of R. [P2579]. 8º. 1888
*Treaty of peace betw. R. & Esthonia. [P2710]. s8º. *n.d.*
RUSSIAN ANONYMOUS WORKS [*see also* SOVIET REP. *below*].
Борьба за Россiю, 1926–27, *see* BORBA ZA ROSSIYU.
Буржуазия накануне Феврал. Револ., 1927, *see* GRAVE (B. B.), *ed.*

Russia [*continued*].
RUSSIAN ANONYMOUS WORKS [*continued*].
*Всходы. Изъ жизни полит. ссыльныхъ. [P2715]. s8º. Берлинъ. [1903]
Древне-русскiе повѣсти и романы, 1895, *see* GLAZUNOV (I. I.), *ed.*
Из эпохи "Звезды" и "Правды" (1911–14), 1921, *see* OLMINSKY (M.), *ed.*
Избiенiе русской молодежи. Документальныя подробности студенческихъ безпорядковъ въ Петербургѣ, Москвѣ и Кiевѣ. Съ письмомъ П. Карповича. [P2389]. s8º. Берлинъ. 1902
Извлеч. изъ программы Социал.-Общинниковъ. [P2824]. s8º. Женева. 1883
Историко-статист. обзоръ промышленности Россiи, t1, 1883, *see* TIMIRYAZEV (D. A.), *ed.*
Итоги и перспективы. Сборникъ статей Вл. Громана, Поля Луи, П. Маслова &c. &c. [P2447]. 8º. Москва. 1906
Какiе нужны порядки, 1906, *see* U. (V.)
Константинополь и Проливы, 2т, 1925–26, *see* ADAMOV (E. A.), *ed.*
Мат. по ист. франко-русских отношений за 1910–14. Сборникъ секретн. дипломат. док. la8º. Москва. 1922
*Марсельеза—Пѣсни рабочихъ. [P2453]. 8º. С.–П. *n.d.*
Министръ финансовъ и государств. Совѣтъ о финансовомъ положенiи Россiи. [P2445]. 8º. Stuttgart. 1903
Народное образование и социализм. Перечень избранной лит., 1918–19. [P2723]. 8º. Москва. 1919
*Объ аристократiи, въ особенности русской. Письмо. s8º. Лейпцигъ. 1874
Обвинительный актъ по дѣлу о революцiонной пропагандѣ въ имперiи. sm. fol. [С.–П. 1877]
Обществ. движенiе въ Россiи въ началѣ 20º вѣка, 2t, 1909–10, *see* MARTOV (L.) &c., *edd.*
Очередной вопросъ революц. дѣла. Изд. Аграрно-соц. лиги. [P2715]. s8º. London. 1900
Очеркъ исторiи Мин. Иностранныхъ Дѣлъ, 1802–1902. fol. С.–П. 1902
Падение царск. режима; отчеты допросов &c., т1–7, 1924–27, *see* SCHEGOLEV (P. E.), *ed.*
Полный Малороссiйскiй пѣсенникъ. s8º. Москва. 1874
Присутственный день уголовной палаты. Судебныя сцены. [*b. w.* Объ аристократiи, 1874]. s8º. Лейпцигъ. 1874
Пѣсни русскаго народа, 5ч., 1838–39, *see* SAKHAROV (I. P.), *ed.*
Работа Эсеров заграницей. la8º. Москва. 1922
Равноправность женщины. Русская женщина. Къ крестьянкамъ и работникамъ. [P2445]. 8º. Москва. *n.d.*
Россiя и Европа въ эпоху Крым. Войны, 1886, *see* JOMINI (A. DE).
Россiя и Италiя. Сборникъ истор. матерiаловъ &c. Изд. И. А. Н. т3ii, 4. la8º. П. 1915–27
Россiя и Латинство, Статьи, 1923, *see* BITSILLI (P. M.) *& others.*
Россiя и революцiя, 1906, *see* HELPHAND (A.)
Русская зарубежная книга, 1924, *see* KOMITET RUSSKOI KNIGI.
Русская промышленность в 1921 &c. [Высший Совет Народн. Хоз.] la8º. [Москва. 1921]
Русскiя завѣтныя сказки. 2ºе изд. s8º. Валаамъ. *n.d.*
Самодержавiе и стачки. Записка Мин. Финансовъ о разрѣшенiи стачекъ. Съ прилож. статьи Л. Мартова. [P2716]. s8º. Женева. 1902
Сборникъ донесенiй о Большевизмѣ въ Р., (Англ. Бѣлая книга), 1919, *see* ENGLAND.
Тайные док. восточной политики (1881–90), 1904, *see* S. (P.)
Тайные общества в России в начале 19 ст. Сборн. материалов, статей &c. [*By* В. Петров, И Звавич &c. Ист.-револ. библ., кн. 13.] la8º. Москва. 1926
Труды русскихъ ученыхъ за границей, t1, 1922, *see* KAMINKA (A. I.), *ed.*
Хроника социалистич. движенiя въ Россiи 1878–87. Официальный отчетъ. la8º. Москва. 1906
Царская Россия в мировой Войне. т1, с предисл. М. Н. Покровского [Центрархив]. la8º. Ленинград. 1925
,, ,, *For German tr., see* RUSSLAND. Das Zarist. R., 1927.
Чтецъ декламаторъ, 1922, *see* CHTETS.
Что нужно крестьянину? [P848]. s8º. С.–П 1906
Штаба Туркестанск. Военнаго Округа: свѣдѣнiя, вып. 24–35 1901–03, *see* TURKESTAN.
SOVIET REPUBLIC.
Админист.-полит. строение С.С.С.Р., 2ч., 1924, *see* SULKEVICH (S. I.)
Англо-советские отношения, 1921–27. Ноты и док. 8º. Москва. 192
Большевики! [*Leaflet.* P2459]. 8º. *n.p. n.d.*
Враги ли Евреи рабочимъ и крестьянамъ. [P2499]. 8º. П. 191
Высшие учебные заведения и рабочие факультеты С.С.С.Р. [P2861]. 4º. 192
Государств. Об. Азербайджанской Нефтяной промышленности Доклад. [P2822]. la8º. Баку. 192
Европейские державы и Греция (Народн. ком. по Иностр. Делам) 1922, *see* ADAMOV (E. A.), *ed.*
Земельный кодекс Р.С.Ф.С.Р. [P2823]. 8º. Ленинград. 192
Земледелие в Советской России. Сборник статей. [P2724]. la8º. Москва. 191

Russia [*continued*].
Soviet Republic [*continued*].
К Казакам &c. [P2723]. 8°. Москва. 1919
Казачий отдел. (Краткий очерк). [P2723]. 8°. Москва. 1919
Классификация труда по степени опасности и вредности для трудящихся. [P2459]. 8°. П. 1919
Кодекс законов о труде, 1922 г. [P2823]. 8°. Москва. 1922
Комитет Северн. Морского Пути. Северный морской путь. Под ред. Ф. А. Шольц. [P2822]. la8°. Омск. 1921
Конституция Р. С. Ф. С. Республики, 1918. [P2723]. 8°. Москва. 1919
,, ...[*a. ed.*] 8°. Лондон. 1921
Красноармейцы! конецъ гражданской войны насталъ! [*single sheet.* P2499]. fol. *n.p. n.d.*
Красный архив: истор. журнал, Центр. Архив, 1923 &c., *see* Krasnii arkhiv.
Литература профессионал. движения. [P2823]. 8°. Москва. 1923
Международное рабочее движение. Двухнедельный орган под редак. А. Лозовского. N. 1–2, Мая 1920. [P2459]. 8°. Москва. [1920]
Міровая бойня и міровая революція. [P2458]. 8°. Москва. 1918
Московское потребительское общество. [*b. w.* Russia. Статист. труда, 1918–19]. fol. Москва. 1919
Народный Ком. по дѣлам Національностей. Отчет 1917–18, 1921. [P2822]. la8°. Москва. 1918–21
Народный Ком. Финансов С.С.С.Р. Народное и государств. хозяйство, 1922–23. la8°. Москва. 1923
Народное образование в Р.С.Ф.С.Р. Под ред. К. А. Коноваловой. [P2822]. la8°. Москва. 1923
Народное хозяйство России за 1921 г. 8°. Берлин. 1922
Новое законодательство в области промышленности и торговли. Сборник 1921–1922. [Высший Совет Народ. Хозяйства]. 2в. la8°. Москва. 1922
Нормальный устав сельскохозяйств. коммун. [P2458]. 8°. Москва. 1919
О концессиях. Декрет совета народных комиссаров 1920. [P2822]. la8°. Москва. 1921
Октябрьские дни в Москве и районах. [Московский Ком. Р. К. П.] 8°. Москва. 1922
Особая ком. по разслѣдованію злодѣяній большевиковъ. [20 *leaflets*]. [2459]. 8°. 1919
,, ,, вЗ, Большевики въ Царицынѣ. [P2459]. 8°. Ростовъ н. Д. 1919
Отчет по иностранным делам, 1918–19. [P2724]. la8°. Москва. 1919
По совѣтской Россіи. [P2723]. 8°. Москва. 1918
Постановления первого общекооперат. С'езда Д. В. Р. [P2822]. la8°. Чита. 1921
Програм руске ком. партије. [Комунист. библ. No. 6. P2458]. 8°. Москва. 1919
5 лет власти Советов. fol. [Москва]. 1922
Росс. коммуинст. партия 1903–21: сборникъ резолюций &c., 1921, *see* Rossiiskaya.
[Russian Newspapers &c. *Odd numbers publ. in Moscow or Petrograd except where otherwise mentioned, in* 1v]. la. fol. 1918–20
1918.
Бюллетень газеты "Извѣстія" Грозн. Совдепа, Окт. 1918 [*3 Nos.*]
Декларация прав &c. трудящихся [1918].
Извѣстія. Грозненск. района, Окт. 1918.
Извѣстія северо-кавказской республики, Нояб. 1918.
Извѣстія центр. исполнит. Ком., Июня 1918.
Коммунар, Дек. 1918. (Кавказъ) [*2 Nos.*]
Красный солдатъ, Нояб. 1918 (Кавказъ).
Правда, Мая 1918.
Прикубанская правда, Июля–Авг. 1918 [*3 Nos.*]
Революционный фронтовик, Июня, & Июля 1918 (Кавказъ) [*3 Nos.*]
Терская правда, Июля 1918 (Владикавказъ).
Утро, Іюля 1918 (Новороссійск).
Черноморская газета, Іюня 1918 (Новороссійскъ).
1919.
Вечерніе Огни, Окт. 1919 (Кіевъ).
Всероссійскій Союзъ Торговли &c. Бюллетень 2, 1919 (Ростовъ на Дону).
Горская Бѣднота, Янв. 1919 (Владикавказъ) [*3 Nos.*]
Еженедѣльный обзоръ Кубанск. отд., Нояб. 1919.
Известия, Янв.–Мая 1919 [*Various, 10 Nos.*]
Клич трудовыхъ казаковъ, Янв. 1919.
Красная звезда, Июня 1919 (Харьковъ).
Путь Соц.-Демократа, Июня 1919 [*2 Nos.*]
Русь, Окт. 1919.
Слово, Жовтня 1919 (Київ).
1920.
Великая Россія, Сент. 1920 (Севастополь) [*15 Nos.*]
Вечерніе Слово, Мая, Іюня, Сент. 1920 (Севастополь) [*odd dates, 16 Nos.*]

Russia [*continued*].
Soviet Republic [*continued*].
Время, 24 Сент. 1920 (Симферополь).
Заря Россіи, Мая, Сент 1920 (Севастополь) [*7 Nos.*]
Красноармейцы! Конецъ гражданской войны насталъ! *n.d.*
Красный Боец, Мая 1920.
Крестянскій путь, Сент. 1920 (Симферополь) [*7 Nos.*]
Крымскій Вѣстникъ, Сент. 1920 (Севастополь).
Профессиональное Движеніе, Янв.–Июня 1920 [*14 Nos.*]
Родина, Іюля 1920.
Русскій Теремъ *n.d.*
Убійство Царской семьи, Іюля 1920.
Югъ Россіи, Мая, Іюня, Сент. 1920 (Севастополь) [*14 Nos.*]
Ялтинскій Вечеръ, 23 Сент. 1920.
Сборник декретов &c. по внешней торговле по Іюня 1922. 2в. 8°. Москва. 1922
Сборник декретов &c. по народн. хозяйству. [Высший Совет]. B2, 1918–19, 3, 1919. la8°. Москва. 1920–21
Сборник декретов &c. по народн. хозяйству за Январь 1924. [Изд. "Экон. Жизнь"] No. 4. la8°. Москва. 1924
Сборникъ докладовъ &c. 1° Се'зда партии револ. коммунизма. [P2521]. 8°. [1920]
Сборник действующ. договоров &c. заключ. Р.С.Ф.С.Р. с иностранн. государств. [1920–22]. B1–5 [B1, 2^{oe} изд.] 8°. П. *&* Москва. 1921–23
,, ,, 1925–26. B3. la8°. Москва. 1927
Сборник материалов для агитаторов, 1921, *see* Sbornik.
Собрание кодексов Р.С.Ф.С.Р. [Изд. официал.] 8°. Москва. 1923
,, ,, ...2^{oe} изд. t1. 8°. Москва. 1923
Собрание постановлений &c. Моск. Совета. Дополнит. сборник, 1° Мая–31 Июля 1918 г.; No. 1, 2, 3, 5, 6, 10, 12, 14, 1° Авг. 1918–30 Сент. 1919. [*b. in 1v*]. 8°. Москва. [1918–19]
Собрание узаконений &c. рабочего и крестьянск. правительства. Систем. сборник важнейщих декратов 1917–20. la8°. Москва. 1920
Справочник Народн. Ком. по делам национальностей. [P2823]. 8°. Москва. 1921
Статистика труда, журналъ, 4–13. fol. Москва. 1918–19
Статистич. ежегодник—Annuaire statist. [*in Russian & French*], 1921. [Труды Централ. Стат. Управл., t8iii, iv]. 4°. 2B *in* 1v. Москва. 1922
Статист. отдѣл. народн. комиссаріата труда. B4, 5 [P2459]. 8°. Москва. [1918]
Стенограф. отчеты Московск. Совета Рабочих &c. Депутатовъ 1919, No. 15–18, 21–23 (1920), No. 1–4. [*b. w.* Статист. труда, 1918–19]. fol. Москва. 1919–1920
Стрѣлковая инструкція для красно-армейцевъ. [P2455]. s8°. Москва. 1918
Тезисы о снабжении Красной Армии 1919 [*no tp.*, P2459]. 8°. *n.p.* [1919]
Теорія и практика совѣтскаго строя. вып. 1, Республика совѣтовъ. [*By* B. Kamkov & A. Shreider]. 8°. Берлинъ. [1919 ?]
Финансовая политика 1920–21. [Нар. Ком. Фин.] 8°. [Москва.] 1921
Школьно-санитарное дело в Р.С.Ф.С.Р. Сборник. 8°. Москва. 1919
see Ejenedelnik Sovetskoi Yustitsii, 1922.
,, Izvestiya Tsentr. Kom. Известия центральн. ком. Р. К. П., 1920–21.
——: English Anon. Works &c. [*For French works in the titles of which "Russie" appears, see* Russie; *for German, see* Russland].
Bibliog. of indust. & labour quest. in Soviet R., 1922, *see* Internat. Labour Office.
Code bolchevik du mariage. 2e éd. s8°. 1920
Conf. de Moscou pour la limit. des armements (1922), 1923, *see* Moscou.
Constitution of the Russ. Soc. Federal Sov. Rep. [P2824]. s8°. 1919
Criminal (The) code of S.R. Tr. O. T. Rayner. [P2849]. 8°. 1925
The first code of laws of the R.S. Federal S.R. Ed. by the Peoples Comm. of Justice. [P2464]. 8°. Петроград. 1919
Labour Code; tr., 1922, *see* Internat. Lab. Office.
Labour condit. in Soviet Russia, 1920, *see* Internat. Labour Office.
*Marriage laws of Soviet R. [P2496]. s8°. N.Y. 1921
Mem. on personal rights &c. of citizens. Publ. by the People's Commiss. of Justice. [P2682]. 8°. [Genova. 1922 ?]
Restoration (The) of agriculture in the famine area of Russia. Interim report of State Econ. Planning Comm. Tr. by E. & C. Paul. 8°. 1922
Russia: official rep. of the Brit. Trades Union delegation, 1924. 8°. 1925
Russian Code of labour laws. [Pref. by E. Sylvia Pankhurst. P2824]. s8°. 1920
Russian (The) plan of the League of nations. Russ. Soviet Govt.'s peace proposals sent by Tchicherine to Pres. Wilson. [P2381]. s8°. [1918]
The Soviet constitution. Ed. A. Rothstein. s8°. [1923]

Russia [*continued*].
SOVIET REP.: ENGLISH ANON. WORKS &c. [*continued*].
Soviet R.: legal & econ. condit. &c., 1924, *see* APOSTOL (P.) &c.
Soviet R.: var. polit. units existing on Russian territ., app. the Constit. of the U. of S.S.R. of July 6, 1923. [For. Office. *a. c. in* P2822]. 8°. 1924
10 Jahre Sowjetmacht: Manifest d. Zentralexekutivkom. &c., 1927, *see* RYKOV (A. I.)
Russia: a journal of Anglo-Russian trade. [v1–3i. *no more publ.*] 8°. [1917–18]
Russia Societies, *see* UNITED RUSSIA SOCIETIES ASSOC.
Russian.
Directory for R. & foreign businessmen, 1924, *see* MAKOVETSKY (H), *ed.*
*From a R. diary 1917–20. By an Englishwoman. 8°. 1921
Lives of eminent R. prelates: Nikon [comp. by R. Thornton], Saint Demetrius, Michael [tr. by R. W. Blackmore]. s8°. 1854
Mod. R. poetry: anthology, 1923, *see* DEUTSCH (B.) & A. YARMOLINSKY, *edd.*
Narr. of the R. milit. exped. to Khiva, 1839; tr., 1867, *see* PEROVSKY (*Gen.* V. A.)
Russian-American relations, 1917–20: doc. &c., *see* CUMMING (C. K.) & W. W. PETTIT.
Russian (The) Catechism; tr., 1725, *see* CATECHISM.
*Russian invasion of Poland, 1563; tr. of contemp. acc. in Lat. publ. at Douay, *see* AUNGERVYLE Soc. Reprints, s2, 1884.
Russian Orange book, *see* ROMBERG (C. G., *Frhr.* v.) Falsifications of the R.O. bk.; tr., 1923.
„ „ *see* STIEVE (F.) R. Orangebuch u. d. Kriegsausbr. m. d. Türkei, 1926.
Russian tales; tr., 1927, *see* MAUDE (A.)
Russian Commonwealth (The). Publ. by the Union "Russ. Commonwealth." Ed. S. Poliakoff-Litovtzeff. v1, No. 1–14 (Nov. 1918–Jan. 1920). [*no more publ.*] 8°. 1918–20
Russian information & review.
v1–6 (Oct. 1921–May 1925). [v1, 5, 6 *no tp. issued*]. 4°. 1921–25
v6 [*no more publ.*], *has title* The Soviet Union review.
Russian Liberation Committee (The), *see* NEW RUSSIA (THE), 1920.
Russie.
*Admin. Centrale Statistique de la Russie. Publ. t1i, Résultats provisoires du recensement de la population le 28 août 1920. [P2605]. fol. Москва. 1920
*Chronique du mouvement soc. en Russie 1878–89, 1890, *see* CHRONIQUE.
*Essai s. le commerce de R., 1777, *see* MARBAULT.
*Hist. de R. sous Pierre le Grand, 2t, 1759, *see* VOLTAIRE.
Livre Rouge. Doc. & corresp. diplomat. russo-finn. conc. la Carélie orientale. 8°. Moscou. 1922
Livre Rouge. Recueil des doc. diplomat. rel. aux relat. entre la R. & la Pologne 1918–20. [P2466]. 8°. Moscou. 1920
Pour la Russie Socialiste. Recueil d'articles: R. Marchand, Lettre —E. Préobrajensky, Le front de l'Oural—Z., Vandervelde &c. [P2396]. 8°. Berne. 1918
Réclamations (Les) de la Russie aux Etats responsables de l'intervention & du blocus. [Matériaux & doc. sur l'intervention, v4]. [P2700]. 4°. Gênes. 1922
*Russie (La) sous la régime communiste: rép. au rapp. de la Délég. des Trades Unions Brit., 1926, *see* FEDOROV (M.), *ed.*
Russische. *Wahrheit ü. d. r. Dorf, 1927, *see* WAHRHEIT.
Russkaya, *see* RUSSIA.
Russkaya Kniga. Русская книга. 1921 (No. 1–9), 1922 (12 Nos.), 1923 (No. 1–6). 8°. Берлинъ. 1921–23
1922, 1923 *have title* Новая Русская книга.
Russkaya Starina. Русская старина: ежемѣсячное историч. изданіе. т27 (Jan. 1880)–159i (July 1914) [*wanting* t29, 49–56, 76, 155i (July 1913), 156i (Oct. 1913), 158ii (May 1914)]. 8°. С.-П. 1880–1914
„ „ Систематич. указатель, 1891–96, 1897–1902 [*in 1v*]. 8°. С.-П. 1897–1903
Russkii. Русскій календарь на 1905, *see* SUVORIN (A.), *publ.*
Русскій парнассъ. Составили А. и Д. Элiасбергъ. 8°. L. [1920]
Русскій сборникъ. [*By* И. А. Бунинъ, А. И. Купринъ &c..] Изд. Ком. Помощи Русс. Лит. Пучепымъ. 4°. Парижъ. 1920
Русскій сборникъ. Двухнедѣльный журналъ. No. 1. [P2458]. 8°. [Севастополъ.] 1920
Russkoe Geograficheskoe Obschestvo, *see* IMPERATORSKOE RUSSKOE GEOGR. OBSCHESTVO.
Russkoe iskusstvo. Русское искусство. No. 1–3. 4°. 1923
Russko-Yaponskaya voina, *see* RUSSO-JAPANESE WAR.
Russland.
Arbeitsgesetzbuch (Das) Sowjetrusslands. Ausgabe 1922. Hrsg. &c. H. Freund. s8°. [1923]
*Justizwesen (Das) d. Sowjetrep. (Gesetze u. Verordnungen). Hrsg. v. Generalsekretariat z. Stud. d. Bolschewismus. [P2569; 2620]. 8°. 1920
*Kulturwerk (Das) Sowjet-Russlands. 8°. Wien. 1920

Russland [*continued*].
Programm (Das) d. kommunist. Partei R. [Einführung v. K. Radek]. [P2492]. 8°. Zürich. 1920
*Sowjet-Russland u. d. Völker d. Welt. Reden auf d. Internat. Versammlung in Petrograd, 19 Dez. 1918. Mit Vorwort v. M. Gorki. [P2459]. 8°. Petrograd. [1919]
*Veränderte (Das) R., 3T, 1739–44, *see* WEBER (F. C.)
Zarist. (Das) R. im Weltkriege. Dok. aus d. russ. Staatsarch. ü. d. Eintr. d. Türkei &c. in d. Weltkrieg. Übers., mit Vorwort v. A. v. Wegerer. [Beitr. z. Schuldfrage, H6]. 8°. 1927
Russo (Domenico). Mussolini & le Fascisme. s8°. [1923]
Russo (Joseph Louis). Lorenzo da Ponte, poet & adventurer. [Columbia Univ.] 8°. N.Y. 1922
Russo (Luigi). Metastasio. 8°. Bari. 1921
Russo (Rosario). La polit. d. Vaticano n. Dieta di Ratisbona, 1630, *see* ARCHIVIO STOR. ITAL., a. 84i, 1926.
Russo-Japanese War, *1904–5.*
ENGLISH HISTORIES.
Official hist. (naval & military). Prep. by Hist. Section of Committee of Imp. Defence. v3, *&* App. & Maps. la8°. 1920
3, San-de-pu, Mukden, The Sea of Japan.
RUSSIAN HISTORIES &C.
[*Coll. of Russian popular accounts, stories & verses on the R.-J. War, by var. authors.* P847]. s8°. 1904–5
Guerre R.-Japon., 1904–5. Historique, rédigé à l'Etat-major général de l'armée russe. [Tr.] t5ii. 8°. 1914 [1920]
5ii, Bataille de Moukden.
*Русско-Японская война. [P2454]. 8°. Москва. 1904
„ „ ....Японія, Корея &c. Составилъ Н. Т. [P2454]. 8°. Москва. 1904
„ „ ....изд. 2ое. [P2454]. 8°. Москва. 1904
Русско-Япон. война, 1905, *see* VOLONTER, *ps.*
Rust (George), *bp. of Dromore.* *Letter of resolution conc. Origen & the chief of his opinions. s8°. 1661
Rust (Werner). Verzeichnis v. unklaren Titelkürzungen deut. u. ausländ. Zeitschr. la8°. L. 1927
Rustem, *Pasha, 1500–61.*
Osman. Chronik. [Übers. &c. v. L. Forrer.] s8°. L. 1923
***Rustick** rampant (The) &c., 1687, *see* CLEVELAND (J.)
Rustico di Filippo [RUSTICO BARBUTO]. Le rime di R. di F., rimatore fiorent. del sec. 13. Racc. &c. da V. Federici. 8°. Bergamo. 1899
Rüstow (F. Wilhelm). Die ersten Feldzüge Nap. Bonaparte's in Ital. u. Deut., 1796 u. 1797. 8°. Zürich. 1867
Rutebeuf [RUSTEBUEF]. Le miracle de Théophile. Ed. G. Frank. [Class fr. du m-â., 49]. s8°. 1925
see LEO (U.) Studien z. R. &c., 1922.
Rutgers (Antonius), *see* 'ĀMIR IBN MUḤAMMAD, *al-Ru'āmī.* Hist. Jemanae sub Hasano Pascha; quam ed. &c. A. R., 1838.
Rüther (*Dr.* **E.**) Napoleon I u. Polen, 1806–12. [Prog.] 2T[*in* 1v]. 4°. Hamburg. 1901–2
Rutherford (Samuel). Lex Rex or the law & the prince, *see* PRESBYTERIAN. Presbyterian's armoury, v3, 1843.
see COTTON (J.) The way of congregational churches cleared f. misconstructions of R., 1648.
Rutherford (Vickerman Henzell). Mod. India, its problems & th. solution. 8°. [1927]
Rutherforth (Thomas). A letter to Mr. Kennicott, Samaritan Pentateuch &c. 8°. C. 1761
A 2nd letter to Dr. Kennicott. [*b. w. h.* A letter to K. &c., 1761]. 8°. C. 1762
see COCKBURN (C.) Remarks upon the princ. of R.'s Essay on virtue, 1747.
„ DAWSON (B.) *An exam. of Dr. R.'s argument: clergy to subscribe to an establ. confess. &c., 1766.
Ruth-Sommer (Hermann). Alte Musikinstrumente: e. Leitfaden für Sammler. 2e erweit. A. 8°. 1920
Rütjes (Heinrich G.)
Für die Jesuiten! [P519]. 8°. Emmerich. 1872
Rutland. Visitation of R., begun by F. Burghill & G. King, finished by T. May. Ed. W. H. Rylands & W. B. Bannerman. [Harleian Soc., 73]. la8°. 1922
Rutland (John James Robert Manners, *7th duke of*), *b. 1818.*
Notes of an Irish tour in 1846. n. ed. s8°. E. 1881
see WHIBLEY (C.) Lord J. Manners & h. friends, 2v, 1925.
Rutlandus (Joannes Caspar), *Brettanus.* Loci communes theolog. qui hodie potiss. in controversia agitantur. s8°. [Dilingae]. 1559
„ „ [*a. ed. b. w.* Eck (J. v.) Enchiridion, 1573]. s8°. Coloniae. 1572

Rutledge (Jean Jacques) [*ps*[s]. Le Ch. R***; *Docteur* Stearne]. *La quinzaine angloise à Paris. Ouvrage posthume du Dr. Stearne, tr. par un Observateur [*or rather orig. wk. by R.*] s8°. Londres. 1777

Rutley (Frank), *F.G.S.*
The eruptive rocks of Brent Tor &c. [Mems. of G.S.] 8°. 1878
The felsitic lavas of Eng. & Wales &c. [Mems. of Geolog. Survey &c.] 8°. 1885

Rutlinger (John), *see* Farquhar (H.) J. R. & the phœnix badge of Q. Eliz., 1923.

Rutter (Frank). Evol. in mod. art: st. of mod. painting, 1870–1925. 8°. [1926]
The old masters. s8°. [1926]
Wilson & Farington. s8°. [1923]

Rutter (Owen). Brit. North Borneo; hist., resources & native tribes. Intr. by Sir W. Ridgeway. 8°. 1922
The new Baltic states & th. future. 8°. [1925]
Thr. Formosa: acc. of Japan's island colony. 8°. [1923]
see Chapman-Huston (*Maj.* D.) & O. R. Gen. Sir J. Cowans, 2v, 1924.

Ruud (Martin Brown). Thomas Chaucer. [Univ. of Minnesota]. 8°. Minneapolis. 1926

Ruville (Albert v.) Die Kreuzzüge. 8°. Bonn. 1920

Ruville (Brossard de), *see* Brossard de Ruville.

Ruys (H. J. A.), *see* Petit (L. D.) Rep. d. verhandel. &c. betr. de gesch. d. Vaderlands, d3, 1911–20; bewerkt door R., 1928.

Ruysbroeck (Jan van). Œuvres. Tr. par les Bénédictins de S. Paul de Wisques. [t1–3, 1, 3e éd., 2, 2e éd.] s8°. Brux. 1920–22
1, Miroir du salut éternel—Les 7 clôtures—Les 7 degrés de l'échelle. 2, Le livre du royaume des amants de Dieu—Le livre de la plus haute vérité. 3, L'ornement des noces spirituelles—L'anneau ou la pierre brillante.
The book of the 12 Béguines. Tr. J. Francis, w. intr. &c. s8°. 1913
see Wautier d'Aygalliers (A.) R. the Admirable; tr., 1925.

Ruzzante, *ps.*, *see* Mortier (A.) Dramaturge pop. de la Renaiss. ital., R., 2t [t2, *cont.* Œuvres compl., tr.], 1925–26.

Ryabushkin (Andrei Petrovich) [Рябушкинъ], *see* Rostislavov (A.) А. П. Р.: жизнь и творчество, 1913 ?.

Ryan (Desmond).
J. Connolly. Pref. by H. W. Nevinson. s8°. D. 1924

Ryan (John), *see* Kennedy (J.) Report of trials of J. K., J. R. &c. for the murder of E. Butler, at Carrickshock, 14th Dec. 1831, 1832.

Ryazanov (D.) Karl Marx. A symposium ed. D. R. [Tr. by E. & C. Paul]. 8°. [1927]

Ryba (Gustav). Der Gaskampf u. d. Gasschutzgeräte im Weltkriege 1914–18. [P2700]. 4°. Teplitz-Schönau. 1921

Ryccardus *de San Germano*, *see* Ricardus *de San-Germano*.

Ryckel (Josephus Geldolphus à). Hodoeporicon Marianum sive itinera sacra B. M. Virg. in terris agentis. Item diurnale M. cultus ejusdem Virg. per menses atque hebdomadas distinctus. s8°. *typis Coenestenii.* 1634

Ryckman de Betz (F. de). La politique extérieure de la Belgique (1830–1914), *se* Cahiers (Les) belges, No. 27, 1919.

Rydberg (A. Viktor).
Faust och Fauststudier. [Skrifter, 2]. 9e uppl. s8°. 1921
Fribytaren pa Östersjön. [Skrifter, 4]. 12e uppl. s8°. [1922]
Medeltidens magi—[Jehovatjänsten hos Hebréerna—Urpatriarkernas Släkttvla. Skrifter, 11]. 8e uppl. s8°. 1921
Varia. [Skrifter, 13–14]. 4e uppl. 2v. s8°. [1921]
1, Filosof., histor., språk-vetenskapliga uppsatser.
2, Tal.—Valda uppsatser och anför. i kyrkliga, teolog., polit. &c. ämnen.
see Warburg (C.) V. R., h. levnad och diktning, 1913.

Rydell (Carl). Adv. of C. R. Autobiog. of a seafaring man. Ed. E. Green. 8°. 1924

Rydgeway (Cicely de), *see* Ridgway (C. de).

Rye (Reginald Arthur). Cat. of the MSS. & autograph letters in the Univ. libr., 1921, *see* London University.
Students' guide to the libraries of London. 3rd ed. rev. & enl. 8°. 1927

Rye (Walter).
Dr. J. H. Round & h. recent attack on W. R., as to the Colchester Chron., Norwich Castle & o. matters. [P2684]. s8°. *p.p.* Norwich. 1922
The false pedigree & arms of the family of Bacon of Suffolk, the ancestors of Sir N. Bacon &c. [P2428]. 8°. Norwich. 1919
The later hist. of the family of Walpole of Norfolk &c. [P2490]. 8°. Norwich. 1920
Some early Eng. inscr. in Norfolk bef. 1600. 8°. [1923]
Some hist. essays chiefly rel. to Norfolk. p2–5 [*pagin. cont.*] 8°. Norwich. 1926–27
p1 *has t.:* Two Cromwellian myths, 1925, *see below*.
Some new facts as to the life of St. Thomas à Becket, connected w. Norfolk. 8°. Norwich. 1924
Two Cromwellian myths: the alleged royal descent of O. Cromwell & the Squire letters. 8°. Norwich. 1925
see Tourist's Guides. Norfolk, by W. R., 2nd ed., 1880.

Ryerson (Egerton). The loyalists of America & their times, 1620–1816. 2v [*v1 wanting*]. 8°. Toronto. 1880

Rygeway (Cecilia de), *see* Ridgway (C. de).

Rykov (Aleksei Ivanovich). Resultate d. aufbauenden Tätigkeit d. Sowjetregierung. [P2570]. s8°. L. 1921
10 Jahre Sowjetmacht: Manifest d. Zentralexekutivkom.—Rede R.'s 8°. 1927
—— **& L. Trotsky.** Die Wirtschaft in Sowjetrussland u. in Westeuropa. [P2457; 2502]. 8°. 1920

Ryland (Frederick).
Victoria, 1837–1901. Events. 2nd ed. s8°. 1901

Ryland (John Collett). The character of J. Hervey &c. [*Folld. by* a series of letters f. J. H. to J. R. (1752–56) *w. sep. pagin.*] 8°. 1790

Rylands (George Humphrey Wolfestan).
Words & poetry. Intr. by L. Strachey. 8°. 1928

Ryley (Arthur Beresford). Old paste. 4°. [1913]

Ryley (William), *Lancaster Herald: d. 1667*, *see* Oxfordshire. Some pedigrees f. the visitation of O., made by J. Philipott & W. R., 1634, 1913.

Rypins (Stanley). Three old Eng. prose texts in MS. Cotton Vitellius A xv [Letter of Alexander the Great to Aristotle—Wonders of the East—Life of St. Christopher]. [E.E.T.S., 161]. 8°. 1924

Ryss (Pierre), *see* Riss (P.)

Ryssel (Johann Jacob à), *see* Vossius (G.) De philosophorum sectis; cum cont. &c. J. J. à R., 1690.

Ryssen (Leonard van). Veritas sec. pietatem de lusu aleae, a G. Amesio defensa, & nunc ab impugnationibus T. Gattakeri vindic. s8°. Ultrajecti. 1660

Rythiner (Heinrich). Bekantnuss unsers heyl. Christl. gloubens, wie es di Kilch zu Basel haltet; [*signed H. R.*], 1534, *see* Basel.

Ryuminsky (V.) Духовенство и народъ. (Церковь и государство). [P2446]. s8°. С.-П. 1906

Ryves (Bruno). *Mercurius Rusticus, w. chronology of the war to Mar. 1646 [*w. sep. tp.:* *Mercurius Belgicus]. s8°. 1685
see Barwick (J.) *Querela Cantab. [*attrib. to R.*], 1647; 1685.

S

S. (A.) [Agricola Sophocardius]. *I. G.: De rebus auspic. Caroli Regis &c. sub imp. J. Montisros. March. gestis, comm.; interp. A. S., 1647, *see* Wishart (G.)

S. (A. C.) *The Swintons of that Ilk &c., 1883, *see* Swinton (A. C.)

S. (A. G.), *ed.* Betty Stevenson, 2nd impr., 1920, *see* Stevenson (B. G.)

S. (C. G. R.), *ed.* Betty Stevenson, 2nd impr., 1920, *see* Stevenson (B. G.)

S. (C. K.) C. K. S.: autobiog., 1927, *see* Shorter (C. K.)

S. (D. M.) Beasts royal &c., 1923, *see* Stuart (D. M.), *ps.*

S. (*Meister* E.) Die Kupferstiche d. Meisters E. S. Hrsg. M. Geisberg. fol. 1924
see Albert (P. P.) Der Meister E. S.: Funde u. Vermutungen, 1911.

S. (F.) *Dizionario biog. [*comp. by* F. S., *i.e.* F. Scifoni], 1840–49, *see* Dizionario.

S. (F. R.), *ps.* *Calculus made easy, 1910, *see* Thompson (S. P.)

S. (F. R. C.) *Glimpses of anc. Hackney & Stoke Newington, 1894, *see* Clarke (B.)

S. (G.) *Guide to service, 1840, *see* Stephen (*Sir* G.)

S. (H.) Bk. of the words of glees, madrigals &c.; [pref. *signed* H. S.], 1880, *see* CITY GLEE CLUB.
S. (H. C.) Bibliotheca chemico-mathematica, 2v, 1921, *see* ZEITLINGER (H.) & H. C. SOTHERAN.
S. (J.) *Hist. of monastical conventions &c., 1686, *see* MONASTICAL.
S. (J.) Vindic. of principles of Cyprianic age, 1701, *see* SAGE (J.)
S. (M.), *D. of Exeter.* *Unmasking of a masse-monger, 1626, *see* SUTCLIFFE (M.)
S. (M.), *V.* *Christianismi restitutio, 1553, repr., *n.d.*, *see* SERVETUS (M.)
S. (P.) *Тайные док. "восточной политики" (1881–90). [P2716]. s8°. Женева. 1904
S. (R.) *Life &c. of Peter Wilkins (1751), 1925, *see* PALTOCK (R.)
S. (R.), *LL.D.*, *see* SHARROCK (R.)
S. (T.) Faithful acc. of sickness, death &c. of W. Bedlow, 1680, *see* BEDLOE (W.)
S. (T. I.) *Violin & vendetta, 1891, *see* VIOLIN.
Sa (Emmanuel), *Jesuit.* Aphorismi confessariorum ex doctorum sententijs collecti. Ed. corr. Per A. Victorellum illustrati & aucti. s8°. Duaci. 1618
Sa (José Custodio de), *see* SA E FARIA.
Saad Eddin, *see* SA'D AL-DĪN ḤASANJ[illegible]N, *called Khojah Efendi.*
Saadiah, *ben Joseph Fayumi, Gaon, see* MALTHER (H.) Saadia Gaon, h. life & works, 1921.
Saargebiet (Das). *Das Saargebiet unter d. Herrschaft d. Waffenstillstandsabkommens u. d. Vertrags v. Versailles. la8°. 1921
Saat u. Ernte: d. deut. Lyrik um 1925, 1924, *see* SERGEL (A.), *ed.*
Saavedra (Angel de), *duque de Rivas, see* RIVAS (A. DE S., *duque* DE).
Saavedra Fajardo (Diego de), *1584–1648.*
Las empresas políticas. 2t. s8°. Paris. *n.d.*
Idea de un principe politico Christiano, repres. en cien empreses. 4°. Amberes. 1655
Sabaeus (Faustus).
Epigrammatum F. S. lib. 5. s8°. Romae. 1556
Sabalich (Gius.) Vecchie storie Zaratine. la8°. Zara. 1913
Sabanin (A.), *see* KLUCHNIKOV (YU. V.) & A. S. Международн. политика, 2ч, 1925–26.
Sabarthés (*abbé* **Antoine**), *see* DICTIONNAIRE topog. de la France; Aude, par l'abbé S., 1912.
Sabatier (Pierre). L'esthétique des Goncourt. la8°. 1920
Sabatier-Ungher (F.) Salon de 1851. [P2654]. 8°. 1851
Sabatini (Rafael).
The banner of the bull. Cesare Borgia. [*repr.*] s8°. [1927 ?]
Bardelys the magnificent. [9th ed.] s8°. [1926]
Bellarion the fortunate. s8°. [1926]
Captain Blood, his Odyssey. 12th ed. s8°. *n.d.*
The Carolinian. s8°. [1925]
Fortune's fool. 3rd ed. s8°. [1923]
The historical nights' entertainment. 8°. [1917]
The lion's skin. 11th ed. s8°. [1926]
The nuptials of Corbal. 8°. [1927]
St. Martin's summer. s8°. [1924]
Scaramouche. 2nd ed. s8°. [1922]
The tavern knight. 8th ed. s8°. [1924]
Torquemada & the Span. Inquisition. [n. ed.] 8°. [1924]
The trampling of the lilies. s8°. [1924]
***Sabbath** (The): an essay, *n.d.*, *see* GRIFFITH (W.)
Sabbathier (Pierre) [SABATIER], *see* BIBLE: LATIN. Bibl. Sacr. Lat. vers. antiq. &c.; opera &c. P. S., 1743–49.
Sabbatini (Luigi Antonio). Trattato sopra le fughe musicali. Corr. da saggi del p. F. A. Vallotti. pl. 4°. Venezia. 1802
La vera idea d. musicale numeriche segnature. 4°. Venezia. 1799
Sabbe (Maurice). Christophe Plantin. s8°. Turnhout. 1920
see PLANTIN (C.) 7 études publ. [sous la dir. de M. S.] à l'occas. du 4e cent. du célèb. impr. C. P., 1920.
Sabine (*Sir* **Edward**), *ed.*
see NORTH GEORGIA GAZETTE (1819–20), 1821.
„ SAINT HELENA. Obs. at the Magnetical &c. observatory at St. H.; pr. under sup. of E. S., 1847.
„ WRANGEL (*Adm.* F. v.) Narr. of exped. to polar seas; ed. E. S., 1844.
Sabord (Noël). Le buisson d'épines. Roman. s8°. 1921
Sabran (Louis), *see* SHERLOCK (W.) A vindic. of the Preservative, in ans. to cavils of L. S., 1688.
Sabry (Moustapha). La question d'Egypte dep. Bonaparte j. la Révol. de 1919. s8°. 1920
La Révolution égypt. p2, d'ap. des doc. authent. &c. Lettre-préf. de A. Aulard. s8°. 1921

Saccano (Metelle), *Jesuit.* Relation des progrez de la foy au Cochinchine, 1646–47. [Tr. J. de Machault]. s8°. 1653
Sacchetti (Angelo). La Garibaldiade: framm. di un poema. [Nozze Sacchetto-Ragazzini. N127]. 8°. Padova. 1866
Sacchetti (Franco). Novelle. 2p. 8°. Firenze. 1724
see GIGLI (G.) F. S.: vita e opere, 1918.
Sacchi (Andrea), *see* POSSE (H.) Der röm. Maler A. S., 1925.
Sacchini (Francesco), *see* ORLANDINUS (N.) Hist. Soc. Jesu, p1, *ed.* S., p2, auctore S., 1620.
Sacconus (Reinerus) [RAINERUS, *Sachonus*], *see* GIESELER (J. C. L.) De R. S. Summa de Catharis & Leonistis, 1834.
Sacerdotale Romanum. s4°. Venetiis. 1585
Sacerdoti (Giulio). Donne avvocate? [Estr. d. Gazzetta di Venezia]. [P2860]. obl.8°. Venezia. 1884
Sachau (Carl Eduard).
Works in KÖNIGL. PREUSS. AKAD. Abhdl. (Phil-hist. Kl.)
Die Chronik v. Arbela [*by* Meschîchâ-Sechâ; *Germ. tr. w.* Einleitung &c.]: e. Beitrag z. Kenntnis d. ält. Christentums im Orient, 1915.
Ein Verzeichnis muhammedan. Dynastien, 1923.
Vom Klosterbuch d. Šâbuštî, 1919.
Zur Ausbreitung d. Christentums in Asien, 1919.
see UNGNAD (A.) Aramä. Papyrus aus Elephantine, kl. A. unter Zugrundlegung v. E. S.'s Erstausg., 1911.
Sacheverell (Henry), *see* *WOLF stript &c., by a Salopian gentleman, 1710.
Sacheverell (William), *Governor of I. of Man.* An acc. of the I. of Man, w. voyage to I-Columb-Kill. Added, diss. about Mona of Cæsar &c. by T. Brown. s8°. 1702
Sachonus, *Rainerus, see* SACCONUS (R.)
Sachs (Curt). Altägypt. Musikinstrumente, *see* ALTE ORIENT (DER), Jhrg. 21, 1920.
Die Musikinstrumente Birmas u. Assams im K. Ethn. Mus. zu München, *see* KÖNIGL. AKAD. D. W. ZU MÜNCHEN. Phil. Kl., Sitz., 1917.
Die Musikinstrumente d. alt. Ägyptens. [Staatl. Mus. zu Berlin]. fol. 1921
Sachs (Hans). Die Wittenbergisch Nachtigall (1523, *facs.*), *see* FREYTAG (G.) Bilder, B3, T1, 1924.
see KAWERAU (W.) H. S. u. d. Reformation, 1889.
„ STIEFEL (A. L.) Zu d. Quellen d. H. S. Schwänke, *n.d.*
Sachsen. Christl. Bekentnis d. Kirchen Gottes in S. Landen von d. heil. Nachtmal d. Herrn Christi, *see* Kurtze Christl. &c. widerholung, 1571, *below.*
Kurtze Christl. u. Einfeltige widerholung d. Bekentnis, der Kirchen Gottes, In d. Churfürsten zu S. Landen, Von dem Heilig. Nachtmahl &c. s4°. Dressden. 1571
„ „ [*a. ed. in 2p., p2 having sep. tp. beg.:* Christliche Bekentnis &c.] s4°. Witteberg. 1571
Unterricht d. Visitatorn an die Pfarhern zu S., *see* SAXONY.
Visitation of Saxon Ref. Church, 1527–28; ed. R. Laurence, 1839.
Sachsen (Johann Georg, *Herzog zu*), *see* JOHN GEORGE, *duke of Saxony.*
Sachsenspiegel.
see PALZ (A.) & H. VOLTELINI. Forsch. z. deut. Rechtsbüchern, 3, Der S. u. d. Zeitgesch, 1924.
„ STEFFENHAGEN (E.) Entwickl. d. Landrechtsglosse d. S., 11, 12, 1922–23.
Sächsische Weltchronik, *see* PFALZ (A.) & H. VOLTELINI. Forsch. z. d. deut. Rechtsbüchern, 2, Der Verfasser d. s. W., 1924.
Sächsische Akademie d. Wissenschaften, *see* KÖNIGLICH-SÄCHSISCHE GESELLSCHAFT D. WISS. ZU LEIPZIG.
Sachsse (*Kapitän*) & *Oberleutnant* **Cossmann.**
Kriegsgefangen in Skipton. 8°. München. [1920]
Sackville, *The family of, see* SACKVILLE-WEST (V.) Knole & the Sackvilles, 1922.
Sackville (Thomas), *1st earl of Dorset* **& T. Norton.** The tragidie of [Gorboduc; or of] Ferrex & Porrex, *see* ADAMS (J. Q.) Chief pre-Shakespearian dramas, 1925.
Sackville West (Edward). Piano quintet. s8°. 1925
The ruin, a Gothic novel. s8°. 192[illegible]
Sackville-West (Lionel).
Knole House. n. ed. 8°. *p.p.* Sevenoaks. 190[illegible]
Sackville-West (Victoria), *aft. wife of Hon. Harold G. Nicolson*
The dragon in shallow waters. s8°. [1921]
Grey wethers. s8°. [1923]
The heir. s8°. 1922
Heritage. s8°. N.Y. [1919]
Knole & the Sackvilles. la8°. 192[illegible]
The land. [Poem]. s8°. 192[illegible]

Sackville-West (Victoria) [*continued*].
Orchard & vineyard. [Poems]. 8°. 1921
Passenger to Teheran. 8°. 1926
Seducers in Ecuador. s8°. 1924
Some tendencies of mod. Eng. poetry, *see* Roy. Soc. of Lit. Essays, N.S., v7, 1927.

Sacontalá, *see* Kālidasā.

Sacra Congregatio de Propaganda Fide, *see* Congregatio (Sacra) de Prop. Fide.

Sacramentarium [Sacramentaria; Sacramentary]. The Sacramentary: hist. & liturg. notes, 3v, 1924–27, *see* Schuster (I.)

***Sacrarum** literarum memoriale, 1544, *see* Petrus *de Rosenheim.*

Sacred. *Sacred harmony, 1761?; 1789?, *see* Wesley (J.) & C. Wesley.
Sacred songs & solos, w. standard hymns. Comp. &c. by I. D. Sankey. 8°. *n.d.*
Sacred tree (The); 2nd part of " The tale of the Genji "; tr., A. D. Waley, 1926, *see* Murasaki (*Lady*).

Sacred books of the Buddhists tr. by var. oriental scholars & ed. by T. W. Rhys Davids. v4–6. 8°. 1921–27
4–6, Dialogues of the Buddha, p3; tr. f. Pali of the Dīgha Nikāya by T. W. & C. A. F. Rhys Davids. p4, 5, Further dial. tr. f. Pali of the Majjhima Nikāya, by Lord Chalmers, 2v.

Sacrifice. *Great (The) sacrifice of the new law, 1676, *see* Dymock (J.)
*Sacrifice (The) of Spring: masque, 1927, *see* Haberly (L.)
*Sacrifice, or The daughter of the sun, 1920, *see* Strickland (*Sir* W. W.)

Sacrifices (Les) roumains pend. la Guerre &c.; éd. E. Antonesco, 1919, *see* Roumains.

***Sacrobaccanali (I)** festegg. di Firenze, 1808, *see* Fabroni (G. V.)

Sacy (Claude Louis Michel de).
Hist. générale de Hongrie. 2t. s8°. 1778

Sacy (Isaac Louis Le Maistre de), *see* Le Maistre de Sacy (I. L.)

Sa'd Al-Dīn Ḥasanjān, *called Khojah Efendi.* Annales de l'Emp. Ottoman. [*Extr.* Prise de Cple.], *see* Buchon (J. A. C.) Choix de chron. &c., 1875.

Saddharmapuṇḍaríka, *see* Saunders (K.) The gospel for Asia: st. of Gita, Lotus &c., 1928.

Saddington (John). The articles of true faith.
Printed 1830 repr. [P2434]. s8°. Walthamstow. 1880

Sade (*le marq.* **Donatien Alphonse François de),** *see* Dawes (C. R.) The Marq. de S., life & works, 1927.

Sadée (Emil). Das römische Bonn. 8°. Bonn. 1925

Sadeel (Antoine).
De legitima vocatione pastorum Eccl. reformatae. [*b. w. h.* Sophismata &c., 1577]. s8°. Morgiis. 1583
De sacramentali manducatione corporis Christi &c. [*b. w. h.* De spirituali manduc. &c., 1589]. s8°. [Geneva]. 1589
De spirituali manduc. corporis Christi &c. in sacra Coena Domini. s8°. [Geneva]. 1589
De vera peccatorum remissione. [*b. w. h.* Locus de verbo Dei, &c., 1582]. ed. 2ª repurgata. s8°. Morgiis. 1583
De veritate humanae naturae Jesu Christi disput. s8°. [Paris ?], *Le Preux.* 1585
Locus de unico Christi sacerdotio & sacrificio. [*b. w. h.* Locus de verbo Dei &c., 1582]. s8°. Morgiis. 1583
Locus de verbo Dei scripto adv. humanas traditiones. s8°. Morgiis. 1582
Posnaniensium assertionum de Christi in terris Ecclesia, propositarum in Coll. Posnaniensi a monachis Soc. Jesu refut. [*b. w. h.* Sophismata &c., 1577]. s8°. Genevae. 1583
Sophismata F. Turriani: coll. ex eius libro De Eccl. & ordin. ministrorum. Subjecta solutio. Authore A. S. s8°. [Genevae ?]. 1577
see Hutter (L.) Sadeel elenchomenos disput. 2, 1601.
,, Turrianus (F.) Index repetitionum &c.; authore A. S., 1583.
,, Valentia (G. de). Redargutio inscitiarum & fraudum qui nonnulli theologici subsid. A. S. &c., 1590.

Sadeur (Nicolas), *ps.*, *see* Foigny (Gabriel de).

Sadhu, *The, see* Sundar Singh, *Sadhu.*

Sa'dī [Moslicheddin Sadi: *Cheikh* Moslih-Eddin-Sadi].
Badāyi': odes. Ed. & tr. by Sir L. W. King. Intr. by R. A. Nicholson. 8°. Berlin. [1925 ?]
Translations.
The 'Iqd-i Gul, or The rose-necklace. Sel. f. the Gulistān & the Anwār-i Suhailī [*of* Ḥusain Vā'iz Kashifī]. Tr. w. notes by Adālat Khān. 4th ed. rev. & corr. 8°. Calcutta. 1900
The secret rose garden. [Tr.] w. intr. by F. Lederer. s8°. 1920

Sadleir (Michael) [Sadler (M. T. H.)]
The anchor. s8°. [1918]
Desolate splendour. s8°. 1923
Excursions in Victorian bibliography. 8°. 1922
Hyssop. s8°. [1915]
The noblest frailty. s8°. 1925
,, ,, [2nd impr.] s8°. 1925
Privilege. s8°. 1921

Sadleir (Michael) [*continued*].
Trollope. Commentary. 8°. 1927
The water-colours of C. J. Holmes, w. foreword by M. S. [Studio Spec. No. *b. w.* Salaman (C.) Charm of the etcher's art, 1920]. obl.4°. 1920

Sadleir (Thomas Ulick).
see Dublin Univ.: Trinity Coll. Alumni Dublin.: reg. of students &c.; ed. G. D. Burtchaell & T. U. S., 1924.
,, Wilmot (C.) An Irish peer on the Continent, 1801–3: narr. of tour of Stephen, 2nd Earl Mt. Cashell, thr. France &c.; ed. T. U. S., 1920.

Sadler (Gilbert Thomas). A new world by a new vision. s8°. [1925]
Our enemy the state: plea for an unarmed commonwealth. s8°. 1922

Sadler (Henry). Masonic reprints & hist. revelations. Intr. chapter by W. J. C. Crawley. 8°. 1898

Sadler (M. T. H.), *see* Sadleir (Michael).

Sadler (*Sir* **Michael Ernest).**
Our public elem. schools. s8°. [1926]
Rep. on secondary & higher educ. in Essex. [Administ. Co. of Essex. Educ. Comm.] la8°. Chelmsford. 1906

Sadoleto (*il card.* **Jacopo).** Epistolarum appendix. Acc. Hieronymi Nigri & Pauli Sadoleti vitae ac rariora mon. &c. s8°. Romae. 1767

Sadoleto (Paolo), *bp. of Carpentras, see* Sadoleto (*il card.* J.) Epistol. append., P. S. vitae, epist. &c., 1767.

Sadoveanu (Mihail). Poezia populară, *see* Academia Rom. Disc., 56, 1923.

Sadovnikov (Dmitri Nikolaevich.)
Сказки и преданія Самарск. края. Собр. &c. Д. Н. С. [I.R.G.O. Зап. по отд. этнографіи, т12]. 8°. С. П. 1884

Sá e Faria (José Custodio de). Diario da viagem, 1774–75, *see* Instituto Hist. e Geog. Brazil. Rev., t39, 1876.

Saelden Hort (Der). Alemann. Gedicht v. Leben Jesu, Johannes d. Täufers u. d. Magdalena. Hrsg. H. Adrian. [Deut. Texte d. M.-A., B26]. la8°. 1927

Saenger, *see* Sänger.

Sæwulf, *see* Boulting (W.) 4 pilgrims [S. &c.], 1920.

Šafařík (Pavel Josef) [Schaffarik (P. J.)]
Gesch. d. slaw. Spr. u. Lit. 8°. Ofen. 1826
,, ,, ...2er Abdr. 8°. Prag. 1869
Gesch. d. Südslaw. Lit. Hrsg. v. J. Jireček. 3B. [B3ii *wanting*]. 8°. Prag. 1864–65
1, Slowen. u. glagolit. Schriftthum. 2, Illir. u. kroat. Lit. 3, Serb. Lit., Abt. 1.
Slowansky národopis. Třetí wydáni. s8°. w. Praze. 1849
Über die Abkunft d. Slawen, nach L. Surowiecki. 8°. Ofen. 1828

Safar Nameh. Persian pictures, 1894, *see* Bell (*Miss* G. L.)

Safroni-Middleton (A.) Gabrielle of the Lagoon. Romance of the South Seas. s8°. 1919
Ragged romance. s8°. [1923]
South sea foam. 8°. [1919]
A vagabond's Odyssey: remin. of a wandering sailor-troubadour. 8°. 1916

Sagarriga (Luigi), *see* Paglia (L.) Ist. d. Giovenazzo, con vita d. N. Paglia &c., *by* L. S., 1700.

Sage (John), *abp. of the Episc. Ch. in Scot.* *The reasonableness of a toleration enquir'd into. In sev. letters. [*Foll. by* A sermon preached agst. the toler. of episcopacy, by G. Meldrum. *w. sep. pagin.*] s8°. 1705
*A vindication of a disc. The principles of the Cyprianic age, being a reply to G. Rule's Cyprianic bishop examin'd &c. s4°. 1701
see Dalrymple (*Sir* J.), *bart.* A vindic., in ans. to pamph. [by J. G.] intit. The life of the Rev. J. S., 1714.
,, Forrester (T.) Causa episcopatus: confut. of J. S.'s Vindic. &c., 1706.
,, Gillane (J.) Life of J. S., 1714.

Sageret (Emile). Le Morbihan & la Chouannerie morbihan. sous le Consulat. 4t [in 5. 2i, ii]. 8°. 1911–18

Sagern (Friedrich v.)
Die Wundmale. Roman. 2B. s8°. L. 1919

Saggio. Saggio di rime di div. buoni autori, 14–18 sec. 8°. Firenze. 1825

Sagittarius (Caspar). De martyrum cruciatibus in primitiva eccl. liber &c. s4°. Jenae. 1673
Diss. pro doct. Lutheri de missa; sive confut. calumniae ab abbate [de Cordemoy] in tract. 1684, tit Recit. colloquii diaboli cum Luthero. [P2629]. s4°. Jenae. [1684]
Introd. in hist. eccl., sive notitia script. &c. [t2, exhib. supplem. tomi 1 & ejusdem contin. de Conciliis & Colloquiis curante J. A. Schmidio]. 2t. s4°. Jenae. 1718

Sagittarius (Joannes Christfriedus). Disput. acad. s4°. Alteburgi. 1671

Saglio (Edmond), *see* DAREMBERG (C. V.) & E. S., *edd.* Dict. des antiq. grec. & rom., t5, 1919.

Sagnac (Philippe), *see* LAVISSE (E.) Hist. de France contemp., t1, La Révolution, 1789–92, par P. S., 1920.

Sagra (Ramon de la).
L'âme, démonstration de sa réalité &c. s8°. 1868
see NÚÑEZ DE ARENAS (M.) R. de la S., reformador social, 1924.

Sagredo (*il conte* Agostino). G. Mazarini ritratto da un suo contemp., prec. da una nota stor. di A. S. [Nozze Treves dei Bonfili–Todros. N130]. la8°. Padova. 1844

Sahagun (Bernardino de). Einige Kapitel aus d. Geschichtswerk d. Fray B. de S. aus d. Aztek. übers. v. E. Seller [*w. text*]. Hrsg. v. C. Seler-Sachs &c. la8°. St. 1927

Sahak, *see* ISAAC, *the Gt., patriarch of Armenia.*

Sahl (Laurentius). Paraphrasis in priorem Epist. ad Corinthios, obs. illust. s4°. Hauniae. 1779

Saꜣ ḥu-reᶜ, *king of Egypt, see* BORCHARDT (L.) Grabdenkmal d. Königs S., 2B, 1910–13.

Saiffert (Jean Geoffroy) [SAYFFERT], *see* CABANÈS (A.) La Psse. de Lamballe intime, d'ap. s. médecin [*i.e.* S.], *n.d.*

Saifulina (Lola-Khan), *see* SEIFULLINA (L. N.)

Saige (M. J. J. Gustave). Doc. histor. rel. à Monaco dep. le 15ᵉ s. Rec. & publ. par ordre de Pr. Charles III par G. S. t2, 3 *&* Intr. *to* t1. 4°. Monaco. 1888–91
see FONTENAY LE MARMION. Cartul. de la seigneurie de F. le M.; publ. G. D., 1895.

Ṣaijâd (Eṣ) we ibnoh, ḥikâje maṣryje. [P2754]. 8°. Maṣr el qâhira. [1898]

Sailer (Anton Franz Xavier Sebastian), *see* LACH (R.) S. S.'s "Schöpfung" in d. Musik, 1916.

***Sailors** & saints; by the a.ˢ of the "Naval sketch book," 3v, 1829, *see* GLASCOCK (W. N.)

Sainéan (Lazare). Le langage parisien au 19ᵉ s. la8°. 1920
La langue de Rabelais. 2t. la8°. 1922–23
Problèmes litt. du 16ᵉ s.: le Cinquième livre, le Moyen de parvenir, les Joyeux devis. 8°. 1927

Sainliens (Claude de) [†DESAINLIENS; CLAUDIUS HOLLYBAND]. The Elizabethan home in 2 dialogues [by C. Hollyband & P. Erondell. Ed. M. St. C. Byrne. Haslewood Bks.] 8°. [1925]

Sainmore (Adrien Michel Hyacinthe Blin de), *see* BLIN DE SAINMORE (A. M. H.)

Sainsbury (Ethel Bruce), *see* EAST INDIA CO. Cal. of court minutes, v6, 7 (1660–67), by E. B. S., 1922–25.

Sainsbury (Geoffrey). Polarity. s8°. 1922

Saint. *Churches ded. to a saint will be found under the city, town &c. in which they are; except in the case of London.*

Saint Alban, *Holborn.* [Extr. f. S. Albans Monthly paper, The Treasury &c., cont. notices &c. of R. A. J. Suckling, A. H. Stanton & Souv. of present. to Father Stanton, June 1907 &c.] 8°. [1907–18]

Saint-André, *abbey of, near Bruges, see* GOETHALS (A.) Chronica &c., 1844.

Saint Andrews. Eccl. records. Sels. f. minutes of the presbyteries of St. Andrews & Cupar, 1641–98. [Ed. G. R. Kinloch. Abbotsford Club]. 4°. E. 1837
Liber cartarum Prioratus S. A. in Scotia. E reg. ipso in archivis Baronum de Panmure hodie asservato. [Ed. T. Thomson. Bannatyne Club]. 4°. E. 1841
Liber offic. S. A.: curie metrop. S. A. sententiarum in causis consistor. que extant. [Abbotsford Club]. 4°. E. 1845
UNIVERSITY OF.
Early records of the Univ. of St. A. Graduation Roll, 1413–1579 & Matric. Roll, 1473–1579. Transcr. & ed. J. M. Anderson. [Scottish Hist. Soc., s3, v8]. 8°. E. 1926
St. Andrews. 2 poems by R. Kipling & W. De la Mare, w. drawings & etchings by M. Patterson. 8°. [1926]
Publications. No. 10, 14, 16, 19, 20, 23, 24. 8°. O. 1912–27
see LINDSAY (W. M.) Early Welsh script, 1912. [10.]
,, —— Palaeogr. Lat., p1–5, 1922–27. [14, 16, 19, 20, 23.]
,, MILL (A. J.) Med. plays in Scot., 1927. [24.]

Saint Anne & St. Agnes, *Aldersgate, see* MACMURRAY (W.), *ed.* Records of 2 City parishes: docs. &c. f. 12th cent., 1925.

Saint-Barnard de Romans, *abbey, see* ROMANS.

Saint Bartholomew, *Smithfield.* The book of the foundation of St. B.'s Church in London. [Eng. tr., c. 1400]. Ed. Sir N. Moore. [E.E.T.S., 163]. 8°. 1923
*The Church of St. B.: foundation &c. 7th ed. s8°. 1912
The order of the hospitalls of K. Henry VIII & Edw. VI, 1557; repr. c. 1700 ?, *see* LONDON: CIVIC &C. INSTITUTIONS.

Saint Bartholomew [*continued*].
Special appeal. [P2732]. 8°. 1905
see NORMANUS, *ps.* Illust. acc. of St. B.'s Priory Church &c., 1874.
,, WEBB (E. A.) Records of St. Bartholomew's Priory, & of the church & parish, 1921.

Saint-Benoît-sur-Loire, *Abbey.* Recueil des chartes de l'abbaye de St.-B.-s.-L. Publ. &c. par M. Prou & A. Vidier. [Soc. Hist. &c. du Gatinais, 5, 6]. t1 [Intr. & 2 fasc.], t2 [fasc. 1 *only*]. 8°. 1900–12

Saint Bertin, *abbey of, at Sithiu.* Annales Bertiniani [p2, auct. Prudentio, p3, auct. Hincmaro]. Rec. G. Waitz. [Scr. rerum Germ. in usum schol.] 8°. Hannoverae. 1883

Saint Catherine, *of Alexandria, Convent of, Provins, see* BURLUGUAY (J.) Toilette de M. l'archevesque de Sens ou réponse au Factum [*by* A. Varet] des Filles Ste.-Cathérine &c., 1669.

Saint Catherine of Siena, *Convent of, Edinburgh, see* EDINBURGH.

Saint Christopher *le Stocks, London.* Accomptes of the churchwardens of the paryshe of St. C., 1575 [–1685]. Ed. E. Freshfield. 2p [*in* 1v]. 4°. *p.p.* 1885–95
p2 *has title* Account bk. of the parish of S. C. &c.
Register book of the parish of St. C. le Stocks. Ed. E. Freshfield. 3v [*in* 1]. 4°. 1882

Saint-Corneille de Compiègne, *abbey, see* COMPIÈGNE.

Saint-Domingue. *Consid. sur l'état prés. de la colonie franç. de St.-D., 2t, 1776, *see* HILLIARD D'AUBERTEUIL (M. R.)
Hist. de la catastrophe de St.-D., 1824, *see* BOUVET DE CRESSÉ (A. J. B.), *ed.*

Sainte-Geneviève, *Paris.* Cat. des œuvres d'art de la Bibl. S.-G., par A. Boinet, *see* SOCIÉTÉ DE L'HIST. DE PARIS &C. Mém., t47, 1924.
see SOC. FRANÇ. DE REPROD. DE MSS. À PEINTURES. Bull., Année 5, Les mss. à peintures de la Bibl. Ste.-G. de Paris, 1921.

Sainte-Hoïlde, *Bar-le-Duc, abbey.* Cartul. de l'abbaye de Ste.-H Publ. par A. Jacob. 8°. Bar-le-Duc. 188

Saint Ethelburga, *Bishopsgate.* The registers of the churc of St. E. the Virgin, within Bishopsgate. [Ed.] W. F. Cobb s8°. Bishopsgate. 191

Sainte-Trinité, *abbey, Rouen, see* ROUEN.

Saint Giles, *Edinburgh.* Charter by Provost &c. of Edinb of an aisle altar &c. in kirk of St. G. in favor of Will. d Prestoune, 1454, *see* MAIDMENT (J.) & R. PITCAIRN. Nuga derelictae, 1822.

Saint Helena. Obs. at the magnetical & meteorol. observator at St. H. Printed under sup. of E. Sabine. v1. 4°. 184

Saint James, *Duke's Place.* Marriages, 1668–1837; ec W. P. W. Phillimore &c., 4v, 1900–2, *see* †LONDON. I parish registers, v1–4, 1900–2.

Saint James's Evening Post. Nᵒˢ. 841 (Oct. 8–11, 1720), 85 (Nov. 5–8, 1720). [*b. w.* Post Man, 1820–24]. fol. 172

Saint James's Park. *Descr. (A) of the machine for firework exhib. in St. J.'s P., on acc. of the gen. peace, 1749, *se* DESCRIPTION.

Saint John of Jerusalem, Order of. Arms of the Grand Maste of the Order of St. John to 1799. Compiled &c. by W Dickinson. [*MS. b. w.* Tettoni (L.) &c. Dict., *n.d.*] fol. *n.*
Rep. by Comm. of Brit. Red Cross Socʸ. & O. of St. J. voluntary aid rend. to sick & wounded &c. (1914–19), 192 *see* BRITISH RED CROSS SOCIETY.
*Short hist. of gate & priory of St. John of J., Clerkenwell. [P2576]. 8°. *n.*

Saint John Zachary, *London, see* MACMURRAY (W.), Records of 2 City parishes: docs. &c. f. 12th cent., 1925.

Saint Lawrence, *river.* St. L. pilot, 8th ed., 2v, *&* Suppl. 1916–22, *see* ADMIRALTY.

Saint Margaret, *Church of, Lee, Kent, see* LEE.

Saint Margaret, *Lothbury.* Vestry minute book of St. M. 1571–1677. Ed. E. Freshfield. 4°. *p.p.* 18

Saint Martin-in-the-Fields. *St. M. in the F., 1925, JOHNSTON (H.)

Saint Maur, *Benedictine Congregation of.*
see COTELERIUS (J. B.) Ecclesiae Gr. mon., t4, Ex MS eruerunt, Lat. verterunt &c. Monachi Bened. Congr S. M., 1688.
,, MARAN (P.) *Divinitas Jesu Christi &c.; operâ unius ex monachis Congreg. S. Mauri, 1746.

Saint-Michel du Tréport, *abbey of, see* TRÉPORT (LE).

Saint-Mihiel, *abbey.* Chron. & chartes de l'abbaye, publ. A. Lesort, 1909–12, *see* Soc. Nat. des Antiq. de Fr. Mettensia, t6, 1912.

Saint Nicolas des Prés, *abbey, see* Ribemont.

Saint Olave's. *St. Olave's, Southwark. An acc. of the hist. assoc. [L.C.C. P2590]. s8º. 1918

Saint-Omer. L'arrondissement de S.-O. dans le passé &c. [*By var. wr.*] Préf. de E. Lefebvre du Preÿ. 8º. Saint-Omer. 1924

Saint Peter, *abbey church of, see* Westminster Abbey.

Saint Peter at Gowts, *Lincoln, see* Lincoln.

Saint Petersburg [Petrograd ; Leningrad].

Борьба за Петроград 1919, 1920, *see* Zinovev (G.)

Крат. Каталогъ соб. грузинск. рукописей, Имп. Публ. Библ. Сост. Н. Я. Марръ. [P2798]. la8º. С.–П. 1900

*Наши фабрики и заводы. Фабрика Максвеля. Изд. С. П. Союза &c. [P2716]. s8º. *n.p.* 1899

Обвинительный актъ о членахъ сообщества: С. Петербургскій общегородской Совѣтъ рабочихъ депутатовъ. Съ предисловіемъ Л. М. [P2448]. 8º. С.-П. 1906

Петрогуботкомхоз в 1922 г. Отчетные данные. la8º. [П.] 1923

Brit. labour delegates in red P., 1920, *see* British.

Library.

Палеограф. снимки съ нѣкоторыхъ греческихъ, латинскихъ и славянскихъ рукописей Имп. Публ. Библ. atl. fol. С.–П. 1914

see Korf (*c.* M. A.) Жизнь Графа Сперанскаго; Изд. И. Публ. Библ., 2t, 1861.

Museum of Alexander III.

Русскій музей Имп. Александра III. Живопись и скульптура. Составилъ Н. Врангель. 2t. 4º. С.-П. 1904

University.

Отчетъ о состояніи &c. С. П. Унив. за 1913 &c. [*3 pagin.*] 8º. С.–П. 1914

Первое двадцатипятилѣтіе Имп. С.–П. Унив. Историч. записка. 8º. С.–П. 1844

Тексты и разысканія по армяно-груз. филологіи. кн. 1, 3–5, 9–11. la8º. С.–П. 1902–8

[кн. 1–4 *form part of* No. 5 *of* Изд. Фак. восточ. языковъ].

see Adonts (N. G.) Арменія въ эпоху Юстиніана, 1908. [11.]

,, Antiochus [Stratig]. Плѣненіе Іерусалима Персами въ 614 г.; изд. &c. Н. Марръ, 1909. [9.]

,, Ephraim *Syrus.* О дняхъ празднов. рождества; изд. Марръ, 1900. [1.]

,, Hippolytus, *St.* Толкованіе Пѣсни пѣсней, груз. текстъ; изд. &c. Н. Марръ, 1901. [3.]

,, Marr (N. Ya.) Древнегруз. одописцы (12. в.), 1902. [4.]

,, —— Критика &c., 1903. [5.]

,, —— О раскопкахъ &c. въ Ани, 1906, 1907. [10.]

Saint-Pons. Chartrier de l' abbaye de S.-P. hors les murs de Nice. Publ. par le cte. E. Cais de Pierlas, cont. & augm. &c. par G. Saige. [Coll. de doc. hist. publ. par ordre de Pr. Albert I de Monaco]. 4º. Monaco. 1913

Saint-Vaast, *Abbey of, at Arras.* Annales Vedastini [873–900], *see* Xanten. Annales Xanten & Ann. Vedast.; rec. B. de Simson, 1909.

Saint Werburgh, *abbey of, Chester.* The chartulary or register of the Abbey of St. Werburgh, C. Ed. w. intr. & notes by J. Tait. [Chetham Soc., N.S., 79, 82]. 2p. s4º. [M'ter.] 1920–23

Saint Aignan (Paul Hippolyte de Beauvilliers, *duc* **de),** *see* Beauvilliers (P. H. de), *duc de St. Aignan.*

Saint Amour (Louis Gorin de) [†Gorin de St. Amour].

Journal cont. acc. of transactions conc. propositions controv. betw. Jansenists & Molinists. Rendred out of French. [*With* A coll. of sundry tracts, letters &c., *w. sep. pag.*] fol. 1664

Sainte-Ange (Jacques Forton, *sieur* **de),** *see* Jovy (E.) Et. pascaliennes, t1, P. & St.-Ange, 1927.

Saint-Aubin (Augustin de), *see* Dacier (E.) Expos. des St. A.: cat. raisonné, 7–29 avr. 1925.

Saint-Aubin (Charles Germain de), *see* Dacier (E.) Expos. des St. A.: cat. raisonné, 7–29 avr. 1925.

Saint-Aubin (Gabriel J. de), *see* Dacier (E.) Expos. des St. A.: cat. raisonné, 7–29 avr. 1925.

Saint Blancard (François de Gautier, *sieur* **de),** *see* Gautier (F. de).

Saint-Chamant (Henri Couderc de), *see* Couderc de Saint-Chamant.

Saint-Clair, *The family of, see* Saint-Clair (R. W.) The S.-C. of the Isles, 1898.

Saint Clair (James). *Authentic acc. of exped. to Bretagne cond. by R. Lestock & J. St. C., 1747, *see* Lestock (*adm.* R.)

Saint Clair (Roland). Analecta. 8º. 1925

Saint-Clair (Roland William). The Saint-Clairs of the Isles: hist. of the sea-kings of Orkney & th. Scot. successors Sinclair. s4º. Auckland, N.Z. 1898

Saint-Clair-Erskine (*Lady* **Harriet E.),** *1831–67.* Dainty dishes. 10th ed. s8º. [1884]

Saint-Cricq (Laurent) [*ps.* Paul Marcoy].

A journey across S. America. Half-v3. fol. 1873

Sainte-Aulaire (*le cte.* **Louis Clair de),** *1778–1854.* Souvenirs. (Vienne, 1832–41); publ. M. Thiébaut. 8º. [1927]

Sainte-Beuve (Charles Augustine).

Le Clou d'Or—La Pendule—Madame de Pontivy—Christel. Préf. de J. Troubat. s8º. 1921

see Bellessort (A.) Sainte-B. & le 19 s., 1927.

,, Brémond (H.) Le roman &c. d'une conversion: U. Guttinguer & S.-B., corr. inéd., 1925.

,, Choisy (L. F.) Sainte-B., l'homme &c., 1921.

see Maurras (C.) Romantisme &c., éd. déf., S., 1922.

,, Michaut (G. M. A.) Ste.-B. [Gr. ecriv. fr.], 1921.

,, Séché (L.) Le cénacle de Joseph Delorme (1827-30), 2t, 1912.

,, Vinet (A.) Et. sur la litt. franç. au 19e s., t3, Ste.-B. &c., 1924.

Sainte-Beuve (Jacques de). Tract. de sacramento Unctionis infirmorum extremæ, *see* Migne (J. P.), *ed.* Theol. cursus, t24, 1860.

Sainte-Croix (Claude Louis Bigot de), *see* Bigot de Sainte-Croix (C. L.)

Sainte-Croix (G. E. J. Guilhem de Clermont-Lodève, *baron* **de),** *see* Mémoires. Mém. hist. & géogr. sur les pays situés entre la Mer Noire &c. [*Extr. f.* Mém. de G. E. J. de Ste-Croix &c.], 3p, 1797.

Sainte-Foy-de-Peyrolières. Le cartul. de Ste.-Foy-de-Peyrolières. [Intr. &c.] par. J. Contrasty. la8º. Toulouse. 1919

Sainte-Hélène de Pontis (*comte* **de),** *ps., see* Coignard (P.)

Sainte-Marie-Perrin (Antoine).

Bâle, Berne & Genève. la8º. 1909

Sainte-Marie-Perrin (E.) La belle vie de Sainte Colette de Corbie, 1381–1447. Préf. de P. Claudel. [5e éd.] s8º. [1921]

Intr. à l'œuvre de P. Claudel, avec des textes. s8º. 1926

St. Colette & h. reform. Tr. Mrs. C. Maguire. Ed., w. pref. by G. O'Neill. s8º. [1923]

Sainte-Marthe (Scévole de), *the elder; 1536–1623, see* Plattard (J.) La vie & l'œuvre de S.-M., 1924.

Saint-Evremond (Charles Marguetel de Saint-Denis, *seigneur* **de)** [Marguetel]. Œuvres. Mises en ordre &c. avec intr. par R. de Planhol. 3t. 8º. 1927

Critique littéraire. Intr. & notes de M. Wilmotte. s8º. 1921

Misc. essays. With a character by a person of honour [*Dr. K. Chetwood?*] Contin. by Mr. Dryden. [v1]. s8º. 1692

Saint-Gélais (Mellin de), *see* Becker (P. A.) M. de S.-G., 1924.

Saint-Genis (Victor de).

Hist. de Savoie, j. l'annexation. 2t. 8º. Chambéry. 1868

Saint Germans (Edward Granville Eliot, *3rd earl***),** *see* Eliot, *The family of.* Genealog. mem. rel. to fam. of E. &c., in poss. of Earl of St. G., 1868.

Saint-Glain (Dominique de), *see* Lucas (J. M.) Oldest biog. of Spinoza [*i.e.* La vie de Mr. de S., *sometimes attr. to S.-G.*], 1927.

Saint-Helme (V. de). The unknown Ireland, or "Ruby-Laura." Tr. M. A. Harte. s8º. D. [1922]

Saint-Hyacinthe de Charrières (Isabelle Agnète). Four tales by Zelide. Tr. S. M. S. [*i.e.* Scott, w. intr. by G. Scott]. 8º. 1925

see Scott (Geoffrey). The portrait of Zélide, 1925.

Saintine (X. B.), *ps.* Picciola. [Tr. P2460]. 8º. *n.d.*

Saint John (Harold). A botanical explor. of the north shore of the Gulf of St. Lawrence, includ. list of vascular plants. [Canada: Geol. Survey. P2624]. 8º. Ottawa. 1922

Saint John (*Hon.* **John).** Mary Queen of Scots, *see* †Inchbald (*Mrs.* E.) Mod. theatre, v8, 1811.

Saint-John (Oliver), *Lord Chief Justice of the Court of Common Pleas.* Speech to the Lords, Jan. 7, 1640, conc. Ship-money. s4º. 1640

Saint-Johnston (Thomas Reginald). The Islanders of the Pacific, or The children of the sun. 8º. [1921]

The Lau Islands (Fiji) & th. fairy tales & folk-lore. 8º. 1918

South Sea reminiscences. 8º. [1922]

Saint Julien (Clemens Gundacker), *Graf. v. Walsee.* Miscellen über Falknerei. 8°. Linz. 1876

Saint-Julien (Pierre de) [SAINT-JULIEN DE BALLEURE], *see* RAFFIN (L.) St.-J. de B., historien, 1519?–93, 1926.

Saint-Just (Louis Antoine de), *see* LENÉRU (M.) S.-J., 1922.

Saint-Leu (Saint Maurice de), *see* SAINT MAURICE DE SAINT LEU (—).

Saint-Marc (André Boussac de), *see* BOUSSAC DE SAINT-MARC (A.)

Saint Maurice de Saint Leu (—). *Etat actuel de l'art &c. milit. à la Chine ; [*by* St. M. de St.-L. &c.], 1773, *see* CHINE.

Saint-Maxent (—). Monette (La caleuse). 3e éd. s8°. 1881

Saint-Phale (*Mademoiselle* de). *The hist. of Mdlle. de S.-P. : conversion to reformed religion &c. Tr. 8th ed. s8°. 1761

Saint-Pierre (*l'abbé* de), *1658–1743* [†CASTEL DE SAINT PIERRE (C. I.), *abbé de Tiron*]. Annales politiques, 1658–1740, n. éd., avec intr. &c. par J. Drouet. la8°. 1912
see GOUMY (E.) Et. sur la vie & les écrits de l'abbé de St.-P., 1859.

Saint-Pierre (J. H. Bernardin de).
Œuvres choisies, Paul & Virginie &c. s8°. 1843
Pablo y Virginia. Tr. s8°. 1798
see COLLIN DE PLANCY (J. A. S.), *ed.* Petit dict. d'hist. nat., par St.-P. &c., 2t, 1827.

Saint-Réal (C. V. de). Conjuration des Espagnols contre la républ. de Venise, 1618. Intr. & notes de A. Lombard. [Coll. de chefs-d'œuvre méconn.] s8°. 1922
see DULONG (G.) L'abbé de Saint-Réal &c., 1921.

Saint-René Taillandier (*Mme.*) Madame de Maintenon : l'énigme de sa vie auprès du Grand Roi. Préf. de P. Bourget. 8°. [1920]
Madame de Maintenon. Tr. Lady M. Loyd. Pref. by P. Bourget. 8°. 1922
La princesse der Ursins. 8°. [1926]

Saint-René Taillandier (René G. E. T.)
Scot Erigène et la phil. scholast. 8°. *n.d.*

Saint-Romain (Violante), *form. V. de Batz de Castro, see* PRAVIEL (A.) L'hist. tragique de la belle Violante, 1924.

Saint-Roman (*la ctsse.* de), *née de Castelbajac, see* VILLENEUVE (L. DE). Roman de l'Occitanienne & de Chateaubriand ; publ. par la ctsse. de S.-R., 1925.

Saints. The book of saints : a dict. Comp. by the Benedictine Monks of St. Augustine's Abbey, Ramsgate. 8°. 1921
Varq eu vkayabanouthiunq srbotz : [Lives &c. of the saints. *In Armenian*], 2v, 1874, *see* LIVES.

Saint-Samson (Louis La Vicomterie de), *see* LA VICOMTERIE DE SAINT-SAMSON (L.)

Saint-Sauveur (Hector). Les beaux jardins de France. Introd. de R. Ed. André. fol. [1922]

Saintsbury (George E. B.)
Coll. essays & papers, 1875–1923. 4v. 8°. 1923–24
Hist. character of Eng. lyric : Warton lect., *see* BRIT. ACAD. Proc., 1911–12.
Hist. of criticism & literary taste in Europe. 4th ed. 3v [v3, 3rd ed.] 8°. 1917–22
Hist. of Elizabethan lit. [repr.] s8°. 1910
A last scrap book. s8°. 1924
A letter book : sel. w. intr. on hist. & art of letter-writing. s8°. 1922
Minor poets of the Caroline period. Ed. G. S. v3. 8°. O. 1921
Notes on a cellar-book. s8°. 1920
„ „ . . . .[repr.] s8°. 1921
A scrap book. s8°. 1922
A second scrap book. s8°. 1923
Short hist. of Eng. lit. [repr., w. corr.] s8°. 1919
„ „ . . . . s8°. 1922
Short hist. of French lit. 7th ed. 8°. O. 1917
Trollope revisited, *see* ENGLISH ASSOC. Essays &c., v6, 1920.

Saint-Simon (*le duc* de), *1675–1755.* La cour de Louis XIV. [*Extr. f.* Mém.] Intr. par C. Sarolea. s8°. *Nelson.* [1911]
Mémoires. n. éd., augm. des add. de Saint-S. au journal de Dangeau, & de notes & app. par A. de Boislisle &c. [Gr. Ecrivains de la France]. t29–40. 8°. 1918–28
Le Régent, ses filles, ses maitresses &c., d'ap. S.-S. &c. Notes &c. par A. Meyrac. 2s. 8°. [1923–25?]

Saint-Simon (*le cte.* Claude Henri de).
see BRUNET (G.) Mysticisme soc. de S.-S., 1925.
„ BUTLER (E. M.) The St.-Simonian relig. in Germany, 1926.
„ LEROY (M.) Vie vérit. de S., 1925.
—— **& J. N. A. Thierry.** De la réorganisation de la soc. europ. (Oct. 1814). Intr. par A. Pereire. Préf. de H. de Jouvenel. s8°. [1925]

Saint-Vincent (*Mme.* de) [†FAURIS DE SAINT-VINCENT (JULIE), *marchioness*], *see* SOULIÉ (M.) La présidente de S.-V., 1928.

Saint Vincent (John Jervis, *1st earl of*). Letters whilst First Lord of the Admiralty, 1801–4. Ed. D. B. Smith. [Navy Records Soc., v55, 61]. 2v. 8°. 1922–27

Saint-Yves (Georges) & J. Fournier. Le département des Bouches-du Rhône, 1800–10. 8°. 1899

Saintyves (P.), *ps.* [*i.e.* E. NOURRY]. Les contes de Perrault & les récits parallèles : leurs orig. &c. la8°. 1923
Les reliques & les images légendaires. s8°. 1912

Sáinz Rodríguez (Pedro). B. J. Gallardo y la crit. lit. de su tiempo, *see* REVUE HISPAN., t51, 1921.
Intr. a la hist. de la lit. mística en Esp. 8°. [1927]

Sait (Edward M'Chesney).
Government & polit. of France. s8°. 1920

Saitov (V. I.)
Соболевский друг Пушкина. Со статьей В. И. С. 8°. 1922

Sajnovics (Joannes). Demonstratio. Idioma Ungar. et Lapponum idem esse. fol. Tyrnaviae. 1770

Sakhansky (V. A.)
Очеркъ Амурской области &c. la4°. С.–П. 1909

Sakharov (Fedor). Литература исторіи &c. русскаго раскола. 2в *in* 1v. 8°. Тамбовъ & С.–П. 1887–1892

Sakharov (Ivan Petrovich), *editor.* Записки русскихъ людей. Событія временъ Петра Великаго. [ч1]. 8°. С.–П. 1841
Gordon (P.)—Jelyabujsky (I. A.)—Krekshin (P. N.)—Matveev (A. A.)—Medvedev (S.).
Пѣсни русскаго народа. 5ч. s8°. С.–П. 1838–39

Sakharov (*Gen.-Leut.* Konstantin v.) Das weisse Sibirien, [1918–20]. Übers. v. L. Müller-Bulyghin. Bearb. v. A. Frhrn. v. Engelhardt. 8°. München. 1925

Sakulin (P. N.) Некрасов. s8°. Москва. 1928

Sala (Aristide). La milizia ed il governo d. Spagnuoli n. Milano n. 2a metà d. sec. 16 : doc., *see* REGIA DEP. DI STORIA PATRIA. Misc., t1, 1862.

Sala (Robert), *see* BONA (*card.* J.) Epist. selectae &c. ; coll. &c. R. S., 1755.

Saladini (F.), *see* TETTONI (L.) & F. S. Dict. of heraldic terms —Ital. armory &c. ; comp. f. T. & S.'s " Teatro araldico " by W. Dickinson, *n.d.*

Salagius (Stephanus). De statu Eccl. Pannonicae libri vi [3–7 *wanting*]. s4°. Quinque-Ecclesiis. 1777–180

Salaman (Malcolm Charles).
Anders Zorn. Intr. by M. C. S. [Studio]. obl.4°. 1925
Brit. book illustration, yesterday & to-day, w. comm. Ed. G. Holme. [Studio]. la8°. 1923
The charm of the etcher's art. Plates by Sir F. Short, D. Y. Cameron *& others.* [Studio]. 3p [*in* 1v]. obl.4°. 1920
Frank Brangwyn, R.A. Intr. by M. C. S. [Studio]. obl.4°. 1924
J. L. Forain. Intr. by M. C. S. [Studio]. obl.4°. 1925
James McBey. Intr. by M. C. S [Studio]. obl.4°. 192
Londoners then & now &c With comm. by M. C. S Ed. G. Holme. [Studio]. 4°. 192
Sir Frank Short. Intr. b M. C. S. [Studio]. obl.8°. 192
The woodcut of to-day. la8°. *Studio.* 192
see WHITMAN (A.) Print-co lector's handbook ; rev & enl. by M. C. S., 1921.

Salaman (Nina). Rahel Morpurgo & contemp. Hebrew poet in Italy. Foreword by the Chief Rabbi. s8°. 192

Salaman (Redcliffe N.) Potato varieties. la8°. C. 192

Salamon (Josephus). De statu eccl. Evang.-reformatae i Transsilvania comm. 8°. Claudiopoli. 184

Salanus. *Magni theol. Salani Hist. crit. theologiae dogma & moralis, 1724, *see* BUDDEUS (J. F.)

Salas y Rodriguez (Francisco Javier de). Marina española d la edad media. 2a ed. t1. 8°. 192

Salazar (Ambrosio de). Inventaire general des plus curieus recherches des royaumes d'Espagne. Nouv. comp. pa A. de S. & mis en François par luy mesme. [*Foll. by* Guid des chemins, *without pagin.*] s8°. 16

Salazar (Angel Allende), *see* ALLENDE SALAZAR.

Salazar (Fanny Zampini). Margherita of Savoy, 1st Quee of Italy. Her life & times. Pref. by R. Bagot. 8°. [191

Salazar (Julian de Pinedo y), *see* PINEDO Y SALAZAR (J. DE).

Salazar (Lope García de), *see* GARCÍA DE SALAZAR (L.)

Salazaro (Demetrio). Studi sui mon. d. Italia merid. dal al 13° s. 2p *in* 1v. la. fol. Napoli. 1871–
„ „ App. *w. t.* L'arte romana al medio evo. la. fol. Napoli. 18

Salazar y Castro (Luis de). Hist. genealóg. de la casa Haro. Ed. S. de Ispizúa. t1, libro 2, Los prim. soberan de Vizcaya. 8°. 19
Hist. genealogica de la Casa de Lara, justif. con instrument y escritores. 3t. fol. 1696–

Salazar y Castro (Luis de) [*continued*].
Hist. genealog. de la casa de Silva. 2p. sm. fol. 1685
Pruebas de la hist. de la Casa de Lara, sacadas de los instrumentos de div. iglesias &c. fol. 1694

Salcedo y Ruiz (Angel).
La época de Goya. [1700–1808]. 4°. 1924

Salchlin (Johann Rudolph) [†SALCHLINUS]. Stricturae & obs. in C. M. Pfaffii diss. de Formula consensus Helvetica. [P598]. s4°. [Bern]. 1723

Saldanha (João Carlos de S. de Oliviera e Daun, *duque* de).
[Hist. de la vie du Maréchal, Duc de S. Extr. de l'Hist. gén. biog. & généalog., Genève. Additions *have sep. pagin.*] fol. [Genève]. *n.d.*

Saldanha da Gama (*card.* Francisco de). Mandement au sujet d' l'expulsion des Jésuites, *see* PORTUGAL. Recueil de decrets apostol. &c., p2, 1759.
see BENEDICT XIV. Lettres par lesquelles il établit F. de S. visiteur &c. de la Cie de Jesus &c., 1758.

Salden (Willem). De libris varioque eorum usu & abusu libri 2. s8°. Amstelodami. 1688

Saldern (— de). Hist. de la vie de Pierre III. [*Reply to* Rulhière's " Anecd. sur la révol. de Russie, en 1762 "]. 8°. Metz. 1802

Sale (Antonio Giulio Brignole), *see* BRIGNOLE SALE (A. G.)

Saleeby (Caleb Williams).
Eugenic prospect: national & racial. 8°. [1921]

Salemann (Georg). De molitionibus Anabaptistarum in Suecia. Resp. A. J. Knüpffer. [P443]. s4°. Wittenbergae. [1694]

Sales (François de), *Saint, bp. of Geneva, see* FRANCIS, *Saint, de Sales.*

Salford. Records of some Salford portmoots in the 16th c.; ed. J. Tait, *see* CHETHAM misc., N.S., v4, 1921.
Taxation in Salford Hundred, 1524–1802. Ed. w. intr. & notes by J. Tait. [Chetham Soc., N.S., v83]. s4°. [M'ter.] 1924

Salgado (Antonio Pereda y), *see* PEREDA Y SALGADO.

Salic Law. Antiq. legis Sal. textus, *see* SCHILTER (J.) Thesaurus antiq., t2, 1727.

Salig (Christian August). De Eutychianismo ante Eutychen. s4°. Wolffenbuttelae. 1723

Salinas (Antonino). Dei sigilli di Creta rinvenuti a Selinunte nel Museo Nazionale di Palermo. [Estr. d. Notizie d. scavi, 1883]. la8°. 1883

Salinas (Joannes), *see* POSSIDIUS, *St.* S. A. Augustini Hipp. Episc. vita rec. notisque illust. op. J. S., 1764.

Salis (Rachel de), *see* DE SALIS (R.)

Salisburi (Sion), *see* ELLIS (R.), *ed.* An Elizab. broadside, brief, 1591, to S., 1904.

Salisbury [*Town & Cathedral*]. Services (The) of the church, w. rubrical directions acc. to the use of Sarum. [Psalms, *w. sep. pagin.*] 2nd ed. s8°. *n.d.*

Salisbury (Mary Catherine, *marchioness of*), *wife of 2nd marq., aft. wife of 15th earl of Derby, 1824–1900.* Cat. of the paintings at Hatfield House. [P2605]. 4°. *p.p.* 1865
see WELLINGTON (A. W., *1st duke of*). A gt. man's friendship: letters of W. to M., Marchioness of S., 1850–52 &c., 1927.

Salisbury (Robert Arthur T. Gascoyne-Cecil, *3rd marq. of*), *see* CECIL (*Lady* G.) Life of Robert Marq. of S., 2v, 1921.

Salisbury (Rollin D.), *see* CHAMBERLIN (T. C.) & R. D. S. Geology, 1921.

Salis-Marschlins (Meta *von*). Philosoph u. Edelmensch. Beitrag z. Charakteristik F. Nietzsche's. 8°. L. 1897

Salkauskis (Stasys). Sur les confins de deux mondes. Essai sur le probl. de la civilis. nat. en Lituanie. la8°. Genève. [1919]

Sallier de La Tour (*le maréchal* Victor Amédee), *see* GALLAVRESI (G.) & V. SALLIER DE LA TOUR DE CORDON, *edd.* Le Maréchal S. de La T.: mém. & lettres, p1, 1917.

Sallier de La Tour de Cordon (V.), *see* GALLAVRESI (G.) & V. S. DE LA T. DE C., *edd.* Le Maréchal Sallier de La Tour: mém. & lettres, p1, 1917.

Sallust.
C. S. cum vet. historicorum fragm. [Ed. M. Q. Boxhorn]. s8°. Lugduni Batav., *Off. Elzevir.* 1634
,, ,, ...[*Engr. tp.*] s8°. Amstelodami, *Elzevir.* 1658
C. C. S. & L. Annaeus Florus. 4°. Birminghamiae, *Baskerville.* 1773
,, ,, ...s8°. Birminghamiæ, *Baskerville.* 1774
TRANSLATIONS.
Des hochberompten Latin. historischreibers S. zwo schon historien: von des Catilinē u. auch des Jugurthen kriegen: auch d. Oration d. Cicero &c. Durch Dieterichen von Pleningen getheutscht. fol. [Landsshüt, *Johan Weyssenbarger.* 1515]
S. made English; pref. life & character. By J. Rowe. s8°. 1709

Sallust [*continued*].
Della congiura Catilinaria e d. guerra Giugurtina libri 2. Volgarizzati da Fr. Bartolommeo da S. Concordio. 2ª ed. s8°. Milano. 1828
S., w. Eng. tr. by J. C. Rolfe. [Loeb Class. Lib.] s8°. 1921
Conjuration de Catilina—Guerre de Jugurtha. Texte établi par B. Ornstein & tr. par J. Roman. [Coll. des univ. de Fr.] 8°. 1924
The conspiracy of Catiline & the war of Jugurtha. Tr. T. Heywood, 1608. Intr. by C. Whibley. [Tudor transl. s2i]. 8°. 1924

Sallust, *the Platonist.* Conc. the gods & the universe. Ed. w. proleg. & tr. by A. D. Nock. 8°. C. 1926

Salm (*Comtes* de), *see* SCHAUDEL (L.) Les Comtes de S. et l'Abbaye de Senones, 1921.

Salmasius (Cl.) [†SAUMAISE (CLAUDE DE); *ps.* VERINUS SIMPLICIUS].
C. S. ad Johannem Miltonum responsio. s8°. Londini. 1660
De Hellenistica comment., controversium de ling. Hellenist. decidens & pertract. orig. & dialectos Graecae ling. s8°. Lugduni Batav. 1643
De modo usurarum liber. s8°. Lugd. Bat. 1639
De Transsubstantiatione liber Simplicio Verino auctore. Ad. J. Pacium contra H. Grotium. s8°. Hagiopoli. 1646
*Defensio regia, pro Carolo I. s8°. *Sumptibus regiis.* [Leyden]. 1649
*Funus linguae Hellenisticae, sive confutatio exercit. [M. Schoockii] de Hellenistis & lingua Hellen. s8°. Lugd. Batav. 1643
,, ,, [*a. c. b. w. h.* De Hellenist. comm., 1643.]
see KORTHOLT (C.) Disquisitiones anti-Baronianae &c., exercit. anti-Salmasiana &c., 1708.
,, MILTON (J.) Pro Populo Angl. def. contra Cl. S. def. regiam, 1651.

Salmon André.
L'art vivant. s8°. 1920
E. O. Friesz. Peintures &c., préc. d'une ét. crit. s8°. 1920
L'entrepreneur d'illuminations. 4e éd. s8°. 1921
La négresse du Sacré-Cœur. éd. orig. s8°. 1920
,, ,, ...3e éd. s8°. 1920
Prikaz. s8°. 1919
Tendres canailles. 5e éd. s8°. 1921

Salmon (Arthur Leslie). Dorset. s8°. C. 1910
Plymouth. s8°. 1920

Salmon (Edward), *a. of "The story of the Empire."* Literature of the Empire—Art of the Empire by Maj. A. A. Longden. [Brit. Emp.: a survey; ed. H. Gunn]. 8°. [1924]

Salmon (François). Traité de l'étude des Conciles & de leurs collections, div. en 3 parties, avec un cat. des principaux auteurs &c. 4°. P. 1724

Salmon (George), *Provost of T. C., D.* Martin Luther. Sermon, T. C., D., Nov. 11th, 1883. 2nd ed. [P601]. 8°. D. 1883

Salmon (Lucy Maynard).
The newspaper & the historian. 8°. 1923

Salmon (Nathaniel). Short view of the families of the present Eng. nobility. 2nd ed. s8°. 1758

Salmon (Thomas), *Historical writer.* An impartial exam. of Bp. Burnet's Hist. 2v [*pagin. cont. beg. w. 291*]. 8°. 1724

Salmon (William), *M.D.*
Botanologia. The Eng. herbal. [Lib. 1]. fol. 1710

Salmony (Alfred). Die Chines. Landschaftsmalerei. [Orbis Pictus, 4]. la8°. *n.d.*

Salmuth (Heinrich), *Pfarrer zu Leipzig.* [Catechismus Crypto-Calviniano-Saxonicus jussu Nicolai Crellii Cancellarii ed. per Salmuthum. *In German. Beg.* Fragstück christl. warer Lehre. *tp. supplied in MS.*] s8°. [Witebergae. c. 1590]

Salmuth (Johann).
see BIBLE, *German. Genesis–Chronicles, Luth. vers. annot. by J. S.*, 1590–93.
,, CONSTANTIUS (F.) Biblia L. S.'s d. Calvinisten, 1592.

Salnar (—). *An harmony of the confessions &c.; tr., 1586, *see* CONFESSIONS.

Salome, *daughter of Herodias, see* DAFFNER (H.) S.: i. Gestalt in Gesch. u. Kunst, 1912.

Salomon (Felix).
Die deut. Parteiprogramme. 2e A. 2H [*in* 1v]. s8°. L. 1912

Salomon (Henry). L'incident Hohenzollern. s8°. 1922

Salomon (Ludwig). Die Gesch. e. Geige. s8°. Halle. *n.d.*

Salomon (William). De luxe illust. cat. of art. of French 18th c. & Ital. renaissance belong. to W. S. Sold by Amer. Art Assoc. [Apr. 4th–7th, 1923]. fol. N.Y. 1923

Salomon (*Mrs.* William). 18th cent. French art. Coll. belonging to Mrs. S. Sold, Amer. Art Assoc. [Catalogue. *Illust.*] 4°. N.Y. 1928

Salomone-Marino (Salvatore).
Canti pop. siciliani. s8°. Palermo. 1867

Salomons (*Sir* David), *1st bart., 1797–1873.* A new method of signalling on railways. 2nd ed. [P2845]. 8°. Southborough. 1834

Salomons (*Sir* David Lionel), *2nd bart., b. 1851.*
Breguet, 1747–1823. 8°. 1921
„ „ ....Suppl. 8°. 1921

Salon (Le) [EXPOSITION DES BEAUX-ARTS]. Catalogue illustré du Salon. Années 4–6, 8–11, 14, 16–18, 1882–84, 1886–89, 1892, 1894–96, 1899. 8°. 1882–[99]
Année 4 *has Eng. title* Illust. cat. of the Paris Salon. Années 4–8, publ. sous la dir. de F. G. Dumas. *From* 1887 *onwards title beg.* Exposition des Beaux-arts.
see SOCIÉTÉ DES ARTISTES FRANÇAIS. Explic. des ouvr. de peintre &c., 1921.

Salons. Les grands salons litt., 17e & 18e siècles : confér. du Musée Carnavalet, 1928, *see* CARNAVALET.

Salopian Gentleman, *ps.*, *see* *WOLF stript &c., by a S. g., 1710.

Saloustios, *see* SALLUST, *the Platonist.*

Salt (Henry Stephens). The call of the wildflower. s8°. [1922]
Seventy years among savages. 8°. [1921]

Salt (William). A mem. of the Methodist New Connection & acc. of the M. mission to Ireland. s8°. Nottingham. 1827

Salter (Emma Gurney), *see* THOMAS, *de Eccleston.* Coming of the Friars Minor to Eng. & Germany : chron. of T. of E. &c. ; tr. E. G. S., 1926.

Salter (Frank Reyner).
Karl Marx & modern socialism. s8°. 1921
Some early tracts on poor relief. Ed. S. Pref. by S. Webb. s8°. [1926]

Salter (Herbert Edward).
Chapters of the Augustinian canons. Ed. S. [Canterbury & York Soc., v29]. 8°. 1922
„ „ *a. ed.* [Oxf. Hist. Soc., 74]. 8°. O. 1922
The historic names of the streets & lanes of Oxford. Intra muros. Pref. by R. Bridges. 8°. O. 1921
Oxford City properties. [Oxford Hist. Soc., v83]. 8°. O. 1926
Snappe's formulary & o. records. [Oxford Hist. Soc., v80]. 8°. O. 1924
Surveys & tokens. Survey of Oxford in 1772—Sport &c. in Stuart Oxford [by P. Manning]—Subsidies in 1543, 1544, 1648 [& 1667]—Hearth tax, 1665—Poll tax, 1667—Oxford tradesmen's tokens [by E. T. Leeds]. Ed. S. [Oxf. Hist. Soc., 75]. 8°. O. 1923
see OXFORD : ANON. WKS. Liber albus civitatis Oxon. : intr. & notes by S., 1909.
„ —— Mediaeval archives of Univ. of O. ; ed. S., v1, 2, 1920–21.
„ —— Munimenta Civitatis Oxonie ; ed. S., 1920.
„ —— Records of mediæval O. ; ed. S., 1912.
„ —— : MERTON COLLEGE. Registrum annalium Coll. M., 1483–1521 ; ed. S., 1923.

Salter (*Sir* James Arthur). Allied shipping control ; an experiment in internat. administ. [C.E. for Int. Peace]. la8°. O. 1921
see LEAGUE OF NATIONS. Econ. conseq. of the League ; intr. by S., 1927.

Salter (John William), *see* GEOLOG. SURVEY OF ENG. Mem., v3, Geol. of N. Wales, by A. C. Ramsay, w. app. on fossils, by S., 1881.

Saltero, *Don.* A cat. of the rarities at Don S.'s coffee-house in Chelsea &c. [*no tp.*] 39th ed. 8°. [1786?]

Saltikov (*prince* Aleksei Dmitrievich) [†SALTUIKOV].
Путешествіе въ Персію. Письма. fol. Москва. 1849

Saltikov (Mikhail Evgrafovich) [*ps.* SCHEDRIN (N.)]
Какъ высѣкли дѣйствит. статскаго совѣтника или Ташкентцы &c. [P846]. 3e изд. 8°. Carouge. 1896
Орелъ-меценатъ. Сказка. [P846]. 8°. Carouge. 1898
Письма къ тетенькѣ. [P846]. 8°. Genève. *n.d.*
„ „ ....3e изд. [P846]. 8°. Carouge. 1895
Полное собраніе сочиненій. Съ Мат. для біог. С., К. К. Арсеньева. 12т. 8°. С.-П. 1905–6
TRANSLATIONS.
The Gollovlev family. Tr. by A. Ridgway. s8°. [1924]
see MILITSINA (E. D.) & M. E. S. Village priest &c., tr., 1918.

Saltini (Guglielmo Enrico). A. Giustinian e i suoi dispacci come ambasc. veneto in Roma 1502–5. [Estr. d. Arch. Stor. Ital., t26. P2852]. 8°. Firenze. 1877

Saltmarshe (*Col.* Philip), *see* SOLLOWAY (J.) & P. S. Hist. guide to York pageant, 1909.

Salto (Felipe Arévalo), *see* ARÉVALO SALTO (F.)

Saltzburg, *see* SALZBURG.

Salutati (Lino Coluccio *di Piero*). De tyranno [*tr.*], *see* EMERTON (E.) Humanism & tyranny, 1925.
Letters in defence of lib. studies [*tr.*], *see* EMERTON (E.) Humanism & tyranny, 1925.

Saluzzo (Alessandro di), *conte di Monesiglio ; 1775–1851.* Carlo Alberto dalla restaur. n. mem. ined. di A. di S. ; [ed.] M. Zucchi, *see* REGIA DEP. S. GLI STUDI DI STORIA PATRIA &c. Bibl., v12, 1926.

Saluzzo di Castellar (Giov. Andrea). Memoriale, 1482–1528 ; ed. V. Promis, *see* REGIA DEP. DI STORIA PATRIA. Misc., t8, 1869.

Salvador-Daniel (Francesco), *see* DANIEL (F. S.)

Salvagnoli-Marchetti (Vincenzo), *see* DORIA (A.) Un Giobertiano di Toscana : V. S., 1922.

Salvator, *see* JOHN SALVATOR, *archduke of Austria.*

Salvatorelli (Luigi). Nazionalfascismo. s8°. Torino. 1923

Salve, *Saint, bp. of Amiens, d. 613, see* L'ETOILE (P. DE). *L'ombre de M. Thiers &c., avec crit. de la vie de S. S., 1712.

Salvemini (Gaetano). The Fascist dictatorship in Italy, v1, Origins & practices. 8°. [1928]
Mazzini. s8°. 1920
La politica estera di F. Crispi. s8°. [1919]
see MARANELLI (C.) & G. S. La questione dell' Adriatico, 2a ed., 1919.
„ SILVA (P.) Chi e G. S.?, 1919.

Salvetti Antelminelli (Giovanni). Banchetto fatto dal Re n. Sala di Westminster il 23 apr. [1661]. [*Ed.* J. del Badia]. [Nozze Danyell de' Tassinari—Colnaghi. N123]. la8°. Firenze. [1896]

Salvianus, *Massiliensis, Presbyter.* De gubernatione Dei libri 8. Ejusdem epist. lib. 1. Timothei nomine ad Eccl. Catholic. lib. 4 &c. [*w.* Annot. in Salviani loca, autore J. A. Brassicano]. s8°. Oxoniæ. 1633

Salviati (Cassandre), *aft. wife of Jean de Peigné, see* SORG (R.) C., ou le secret de Ronsard, 1925.

Salviati (Leonardo). Il primo libro d. Orazioni d. Cavalier L. S. [*Includ.* Tr. d'una oraz. da M. P. Vettorii, Delle lode d. seren. Giovanna d'Austria]. Nouv. racc. [*Ed.* S. Razzi]. s4°. Firenze. 1575
The colophon is dated 1574.

Salvini (Tommaso), *see* JARRO, *ps.* Vita aneddotica de T. S., 1908.

Salvo (*le marq.* Carlo de). Consid. sur les dern. révolutions de l'Europe, *see* CONSTANT (B.) &c. Mél. hist., t1, 1829.

Salvo-Cozzo (Giuseppe). Giunte e corr. alla lett. A d. Bibliog. siciliana di G. M. Mira. [*Repr. f.* Arch. stor. sicil.] 8°. Palermo. 1881

Salwey (Jasper). The art of drawing in lead pencil. 8°. 1921

Salza (Abd-el-Kader). L'ab. Antonio Conti e le sue tragedie. [Estr. d. Annali d. R. Scuola Normale Sup. di Pisa, v13]. 8°. Pisa. 1898

Salzburg [SALTZBURG].
*Account (An) of the sufferings of the persecuted protestants in S. With their conf. of faith &c. s8°. 1732
Kurtze Hist. d. Evangel. Emigranten aus d. Ertz-Stifft S. s8°. Memmingen. 1733
Sequenz v. unser lieben Frowen d. Mönchs v. S. (*facs.*, 1480), *see* FREYTAG (G.) Bilder, B2, 1924.

Salzman (Louis Francis).
England in Tudor times. 8°. [1926]
Eng. industries of the M.A. n. ed. 8°. O. 1923
English life in the M.A. 8°. O. 1926
More medieval byways. s8°. [1926]
see SELE. Chartulary of the Priory of St. Peter at S. ; ed. L. F. S., 1923.
„ SUSSEX. Abstract of Feet of fines rel. to S. ; comp. by L. F. S., v3, 1916.

Salzmann (Erich v.) Das revolutionäre China. 8°. 1913

Samaddar (J. N.) The glories of Magadha. [Patna Univ. Lect.] 2nd ed. 8°. [Patna]. 1927

Samain (Albert). Au jardin de l'Infante ; augm. de plusieurs poèmes. 117e éd. s8°. 1922
see BERSAUCOURT (A. DE). A. S., s. œuvre, 1925.
„ BONNEAU (G.) A. S., poète symboliste, 2e éd., 1925.
„ †LOWELL (A.) Six French poets, S. &c., 1915.

Samaran (Charles).
Jacques Casanova vénitien. [4e ed.] s8°. 1914
see MANDROT (B. DE). Dépêches des ambassadeurs milanais en France &c., t4 (1465–66), par C. S., 1923.

Samarin (Yury Fedorovich), *see* GERSHENSON (M. O.) Исторические записки (Ю. Ф. С. &c.), 1923.

Samaritan. The S. liturgy. Ed. A. E. Cowley. 2v [*pagin. cont.*] 8°. O. 1909

Samassumukin, *king of Babylonia, see* LEHMANN-HAUPT (C. F. S. König v. B., 668–648 v. Chr., 1892.

Samazeuilh (Gustave). Paul Dukas. s8°. 1913

Śambhala [SAMBALA]. Der Weg nach Śambhala (Śambâlai lam vig) d. 3en Gross-Lama v. bkra śis lhun &c.: aus d. tibet. Orig. übers. u. mit d. Texte hrsg. v. A. Grünwedel, 1915, *see* KÖNIGL. AKAD. D. WISS. ZU MÜNCHEN. Abhdlgn., B29, 1918.

Sambin (J.), *Jesuit.* Hist. du Concile du Vatican, 1869–70, suivie du texte des Constit. Dei Filius &c. 8°. Lyon. 1872

Sambuy (*il conte* **Vittorio Amedeo Balbo Bertone di).** Politica estera del Piemonte secondo il carteggio diplomat. del Conte di S., 1835–46, 3t, *see* REGIA DEP. S. GLI STUDI DI STORIA PATRIA. Bibl., v5–7, 1913–19.

Samfund til udgivelse af gammel nordisk litteratur. v18, 31, 35, 45–49, 52. 8°. 1887–1927

see ALFRÆÐI ÍSLENZK; udg. ved K. Kålund, rimtol 3, 1917–18. [45.]
,, FÓSTBRŒÐRA SAGA. F. s.; udg. ved B. K. Þorolfsson, 1925–27. [49.]
,, HARVARAR-SAGA. H. saga; udg. J. Helgason, 1924. [48.]
,, HÁVARÐAR SAGA. Hávarðar saga Ísfirðings, 1923. [47.]
,, HEITHARVIGA SAGA; udg. ved K. Kålund, 1904. [31.]
,, JÓNSSON (F.) AM 623, 4°, Helgensagaer, 1927. [52.]
,, —— Rímnasafn: samling af de ældste islandske rimer, B2, 1913–22. [35.]
,, LORENZEN (M.) Gammeldanske krøniker; udg. M. L., 1887–1913. [18.]
,, SOGUR DANAKONUNGA; utg. av C. af Petersens &c., 1919–25. [46.]

Sammelbuch griech. Urkunden aus Ägypten, 1915 &c., *see* PREISIGKE (F.), *ed.*

Sammlung. Fortgesetzte S. v. alt. u. neu. theolog. Sachen, 1720–50, *see* UNSCHULDIGE NACHRICHTEN. V. ALT. U. NEU. THEOLOG. SACHEN.

*S. derjenigen Schriften welche bey Gelegenheit d. wertheim. Bibelwerks zum Vorschein gekommen sind &c. [*b. w.* Sinnhold (J. N.) Ausführl. Hist. d. Wertheim. Bibel, 1739]. s4°. Frankfurt. 1738

S. german. Elementar- u. Hdbücher. [German. Bibl.; hrsg. v. W. Streitberg]. Reihe 1, B9, 11, 16, Abt. 2, B22. s8°. Heidelberg. 1923–27

see DER MEER (M. J.) Hist. Gramm. d. niederländ. Spr., 1927. [16.]
,, HEMPEL (H.) Nibelungenstudien, B1, 1926. [Abt. 2, B22.]
,, JESPERSEN (O.) Mod. Eng. grammar, p3, 1927. [9.]
,, JÓHANNESSON (A.) Gramm. d. urnord. Runeninschr., 1923. [11.]

S. roman. Element- u. Handbücher. Hrsg. W. Meyer-Lübke. Reihe 3iii, 5vii. 8°. Heidelberg. 1920–25

see MEYER-LÜBKE (W.) Das Katalan., 1925. [5vii.]
,, —— Roman. etymolog. Wörterbuch, 1920. [3iii.]

S. slavischer Lehr- u. Handbücher. Reihe 1: Grammatiken. B3. 8°. Heidelberg. 1913

see MIKKOLA (J. J.) Urslav. Gram., T1, 1913. [1iii.]

S. symbol. Bücher d. reform. Kirche, 1828–46, *see* MESS (J. J.)

Samné (George). La Syrie. Préf. de Chekri Ganem. 8°. 1920

Samodães (*Conde* **de),** *see* AZEVEDO (*Conde* DE). Cat. da livraria que pert. aos Condes de A. e de S., 2p, 1921.

Samoyedes. Beschryvinghe van der Samoyeden Landt (1612); uitg. door S. P. L'Honoré Naber, 1924, *see* GERRITSZOON (H.)

Sampere (Antonio Cuyás y), *see* CUYÁS Y SAMPERE (A.)

Sampson (George), *M.A.* Cambridge book of prose & verse (7th–15th cent.) Ed. G. S. 8°. C. 1924

English for the English. s8°. C. 1921

On playing the sedulous ape, *see* ENGLISH ASSOC. Essays &c., v6, 1920.

Rhythm: its powers & neglect. 8°. [1919]

Sampson (Hugh Charles), *C.I.E.* Rep. on crops suitable in E. Africa &c. [Empire Cotton Growing Corpor. P2870]. 8°. 1927

Sampson (John). A contemp. light upon John Donne, *see* ENGLISH ASSOC. Essays &c., v7, 1921.

Dialect of the Gypsies of Wales: older form of Brit. Romani pres. in speech of the clan of Abram Wood. la8°. O. 1926

Sampson (*rear-admiral* **William Thomas),** *of U.S. Navy, see* GOODE (W. A. M.) With S. thr. the war: naval oper. of N. Atlantic Squadron dur. Span.-Amer. War of 1898; w. ch. by S. &c., 1899.

Samson, *Saint, bp. of Dol, d. 565, see* TAYLOR (T.) Life of St. S. of Dol: [tr. of "Vita Sanctis Samsonis" (7 c.), w. intr.], 1925.

Samson (Hillel).

The island set apart. 8°. *Cayme Press.* 1924

Sir Humphrey Gilbert a record & surmise. s8°. Kensington. 1921

The story of Francis Horatio [Jago] & his 3 companions. s8°. 1912

Samson (Joseph Isidore).

L'art théâtral. [*Poem*]. 2p [*in* 1v]. 8°. 1863–65

see VEBER (P. E.) S., 1925.

Samson (Thomas), *postmaster of Lincoln.* A narr. of the late popish plot in Ireland, with tryal of the Earl of Tyrone &c. [P525]. sm. fol. 1680

Samuel, *presbyter Aniensis.* [Hist. *& contin. In Armenian.* Ed. A. Ter-Miqelean]. 8°. Vagharshapat. 1893

Tables chronol., *see* BROSSET (M. F.) Coll. d'hist. arm., t2, 1876.

Samuel, *Marochitanus.* Qvod Judæi Messiam, qui venit, ceu venturum, temere expectent. s8°. [Argentorati, *J. Hervagius*]. 1523

Samuel (Peter). The Wesleyan-Methodist missions in Jamaica & Honduras. 8°. 1850

Samuels (Arthur Purefoy Irwin). Early life, corr. & wr. of Rt. Hon. Ed. Burke, w. transcript of minute bk. of the Debating "Club," Trinity Coll., Dublin. Intr. & Suppl. ch. by A. W. Samuels. 8°. C. 1923

Samuelsson (Johan). Ad Valerium Flaccum, *see* KUNG. HUM. VET.-SAMF. I UPPSALA. Skr., B24, 1927.

Sanazzo (Giggi), *see* ZANAZZO (G.)

Sanchez (Francisco), *of Salamanca* [EL BROCENSE], *1523-1601.*

see BELL (A. F. G.) F. S., El Brocense, 1925.
,, GONZALEZ DE LA CALLE (P. U.) Ensayo biog.: F. S. de las Brozas, 1922.

Sánchez (José Rogerio). Hist. de la lengua y lit. españolas. 3a ed. s8°. 1921

see MENÉNDEZ Y PELAYO (M.) Antología, t14, Boscán y Garcilaso de La Vega, con est. crít. por S., 1916.

Sánchez (Juan M.)

Bibliografía aragonesa del s. 16. 2t. sm. fol. 1913–14

*Bibliografía zaragozana del s. 15. Por un bibliófilo aragonés. la8°. 1908

Impresores y libros impr. en Aragón en el s. 16. 8°. 1908

Sanchez (*Mrs.* **Nellie Van de Grift).**

The life of Mrs. R. L. Stevenson. 8°. 1920

Sanchez (Thomas). Compend. totius tract. de s. matrimonii sacramento T. S. [ab E. L. Soarez] ordine alphab. dispos., *see* MIGNE (J. P.), *ed.* Theol. cursus, t25, 1860.

Sánchez-Albornoz y Menduiña (Claudio). Estampas de la vida en Leon dur. el siglo 10. Prólogo por R. Menéndez Pidal. 8°. 1926

Sanchez Alonso (B.) Fuentes de la hist. española. Prólogo de R. Altamira. la8°. 1919

Sánchez Cantón (F. J.) Los Arfes, escultores de plata y oro, 1501–1603. s8°. 1920

Fuentes lit. para la hist. del arte español. t1. la8°. 1923

see INST. DE VALENCIA DE DON JUAN. Cat. de las armas por J. M. Florit y Arizcun; compl. por F. J. S. C., 1927.
,, —— Cat. de las pinturas; por F. J. S. C., 1923.

Sanchez de Feria y Morales (Bartholemé). Palestra sagrada, o mem. de santos de Cordoba, con notas &c. 4t (4, Apend., Descr. de Cordoba &c.) 8°. Cordoba. 1772

Sanchez de las Brozas (Francisco), *see* SANCHEZ (F.)

Sanchi. Cat. of the Museum of Archaeol. at Sanchi, Bhopal. By Maulvi Muhammad Hamid, Ram Chandra Kak & Ramaprasad Chanda. Foreword by Sir J. Marshall. [Arch. Survey of India]. 4°. Calcutta. 1922

Sancho IV, *king of Castile & Leon, called the Brave, see* GAIBROIS DE BALLESTEROS (M.) Hist. del reinado de S. IV, t1, 1922.

Sancho Ramirez, *7th king of Aragon.* Docs. corresp. al reinado de S. R., v2, 1063–94, *see* COLECCION de doc. para el est. de la hist. de Aragon, t9, 1913.

Sancius de Arevalo (Rodericus) [R., *Santius &c.*] Hist. Hisp., *see* HISPANICA. Rer. Hisp. scr., t1, 1579.

Sancroft (William), *abp. of Canterbury.* Lex ignea. Sermon on fast app. for late fire in London. [P2572]. s4°. 1666

The proc. & tryal in case of abp. of C., bp. of St. Asaph, bp. of Ely, bp. of Chichester, bp. of Bath & Wells, bp. of Peterborough & bp. of Bristol. In court of King's Bench, 1688. [*Ed.* T. Basset & T. Fox. *a. c. in* P2606]. 4°. 1689

Sancta Clara (Franciscus a), *see* DAVENPORT (CHR.)

Sancta Teresia (Alexander a), *see* ALEXANDER *a Sancta Teresia*

Sanctio Pragmatica. *Discursus de successione foeminea in regna & prov. Austriacas occasione S.P. publ., 1733, *see* DISCURSUS.

Sanctis (Francesco de), *prof. in Univ. of Naples.*
Manzoni: studi e lezioni. A cura di G. Gentile. s8º. Bari. 1922
Mazzini. 5 lezioni. 8º. Bari. 1920
Teoria e storia d. lett. A cura di B. Croce. 2v. 8º. Bari. 1926
see CROCE (B.) Gli scritti di F. de S. &c.: saggio bibliog., 1917.
,, —— Ricerche &c. Desanctisiani, 9, 10, 1915–17.

Sanctis (Gaetano de). Storia dei Romani. v4i. la8º. Torino. 1923
4, La fondazione dell' Impero.
see SAVIGNONI (L.), G. DE S. &C. Nuovi st. & scop. in Gortyna, 1907.

Sanctis (Sante de). La conversione religiosa: st. bio-psicologico. 8º. Bologna. [1924]
Religious conversion: bio-psychol. st. Tr. H. Augur. 8º. 1927
see MORSELLI (E.) & S. DE S. Biografia di un bandito, G. Musolino, 1903.

Sancto-Elia (Macarius a), *see* MACARIUS, *a Sancto Elia.*

Sancy (Nicolas Harlay de) [†HARLAY DE SANCY (N.)], *see* AUBIGNÉ (T. A. D'). *La confession de M. de S., 1664.

Sand (Aurore). Encarnacion. s8º. 1923

Sand (Christoph), *see* BAIER (J. W.) Diss. qua Concilii Nicaeni primi auctoritas à crimin. D. Zwickeri & C. S. defend., 1695.

Sand (George), *ps.*
Cadio. 3e éd. s8º. 1870
Journal intime. Publ. par A. Sand. s8º. 1926
Mauprat. n. éd. s8º. 1862
TRANSLATIONS.
The devil's pool & François the waif. [repr.] s8º. [1923]
François the waif, *for a. tr. see* The devil's pool &c. *above.*
The George Sand-Gustave Flaubert letters. Tr. A. L. McKenzie. w. intr. by S. P Sherman. la8º. [1922]
REFERENCES.
see KARÉNINE (W.) S., sa vie & s. œuvres; t4, 1848–76, 1926.
,, MAURRAS (C.) Les amants de Venise, S. & Musset, 28e éd., *n.d.*
,, SANDARS (M. F.) G. S., 1927.
,, SCHERMERHORN (E. W.) Seven strings of the lyre: G. S., 1804–76, 1927.
,, SEILLIÈRE (E.) G. S. mystique de la passion &c., 1920.

Sand (Maurice), *ps.* [*i.e.* M. DUDEVANT].
The hist. of the harlequinade. 2v. 8º. [1915]

Sandalgian (Joseph). Les inscr. cunéiformes urartiques transcr. avec tr. en arm. class., lat. & fr., gloss. & gram. Mém. prés. à l'Acad. d. Inscr. la8º. Venise. 1900

San Daniele. Statuta terrae S. Danielis. [Nozze Minisini—Menchini]. 8º. [Sandaniele. 1859]

Sandars (Edmund). A bird book for the pocket. s8º. O. 1927

Sandars (Horace). Weapons of the Iberians. With Suppl. cont. texts f. class. historians, Eng. by E. J. Forsdyke. [*Fr.* Archaeologia, v54]. 4º. O. 1913

Sandars (*Miss* Mary Frances). George Sand. 8º. 1927

Sanday (William). The lang. of vindictiveness, *see* EMMET (C. W.), C. F. BURNEY & W. S. Use of the Psalter, 1918.
The position of liberal theology. Exam. of Bp. of Zanzibar's "The Christ & His critics." [P2618]. 8º. 1920
see IRENAEUS, *St.* Novum Test. Sancti I.: quotations in Old-Lat. version; ed. w. intr. &c. by W. S., &c., 1924.
—— & C. W. Emmet. The Psalms explained: compan. to the Prayer-Bk. Psalter. With contrib. f. C. F. Burney. s8º. O. 1918

Sandburg (Carl).
Abraham Lincoln: the Prairie years. 2v. la8º. [1926]
The Chicago race riots, July 1919. With introd. note by W. Lippmann. [P2427]. s8º. N.Y. 1919
Smoke & steel. [*Poems.*] s8º. N.Y. 1920

Sandel (Cora). Alberte & Jakob. Roman. 8º. Oslo. 1926

Sandeman (George). A gardener of paradise [*i.e.* P. Geddes], *see* PAPERS for the present, No. 10, 1920 ?.

Sandeman (Robert). *Letters on Theron & Aspasio. Addr. to the auth. [James Hervey] of that work. W. 2 pref., & 2 append. 4th ed. 2v. 8º. 1768

Sandeman (*Sir* Robert Groves), *see* TUCKER (A. L. P.) Sir R. G. S., 1921.

Sanden (Maximilian van den), *S.J.* [SANDAEUS (MAXIMILIANUS)].
Epist. de dissidio protestantium Holland. [*b. w.* Crutius (G.) Monita calvin, 1617]. s8º. Herbipoli. 1617

Sander (Anton), *1586–1664.* Flandria illustrata. Acced. Hagiologium Flandriæ. 3t. fol. Hagae Com. 1735

Sander (Nicholas), *see* SANDERS (N.)

Sanders (Ella Katharine).
Jacques Bénigne Bossuet: a study. 8º. 1921

Sanders (Henry Arthur) & C. Schmidt. The Minor Prophets in the Freer coll. & the Berlin fragm. of Genesis. [Univ. of Michigan, Humanist. ser., 21]. la8º. N.Y. 1927

Sanders (Nicholas). De orig. &c. schismatis Anglicani libri tres. Auct. per E. Rishtonum. s8º. Romæ. 1586
De visibili monarchia Eccl. libri 8. Acc. de Clave David, seu de regno Christi, libri 6 (contra calumnias Acleri). [*w. sep. tp. & pagin. & preface by* F. dalla Sega]. fol. Wirceburgi. 1592
Some letters & papers, 1562–80; contrib. by J. B. Wainewright, *see* CATHOLIC REC. SOC. Misc., v13, 1926.
see FULKE (W.) A retentive &c., also A discov. of the dangerous rocke of the Popish Ch. by N. S., 1580.
,, WHITAKER (W.) Ad N. S. demonstrationes 40 responsio, 1583.

Sanders (*General* Otto K. V. Liman von), *see* LIMAN VON SANDERS (*Gen.* O. K. V.)

Sanders (Richard), *see* COLLIER (T.) Font-guard routed; w. ans. to R. S.'s A balm to heal relig. wounds &c., 1652.

Sanderson (Daniel). Katha Sangraha or Canarese selections. Prose. Comp. by D. S. 8º. Bangalore. 1863
see LAKSHMĪSA, *Dévapura.* Jaimini Bharata, w. tr. &c. by D. S., 1852.

Sanderson (Edgar).
Hist. of the world f. earliest hist. time. [8º. 1898]

Sanderson (Frederick William), *headmaster of Oundle School.*
Sanderson of Oundle. [*By var. wr.*] 8º. 1923
see WELLS (H. G.) Story of a great schoolmaster: life & ideas of S. of Oundle, 1924.

Sanderson (Ghetal, *Lady*), *wife of Sir J. S. Burdon Sanderson, form. Herschell.* Sir J. Burdon Sanderson. Mem. by Lady B. S. Completed & ed. by h. nephew [J. S. Haldane] &c., w. sel. f. h. papers &c. 8º. O. 1911

Sanderson (*Sir* John Scott Burdon), *see* SANDERSON (G., *Lady*). Sir J. B. S., 1911.

Sanderson (Robert), *bp. of Lincoln.* Episcopacy (as establ. by law in England) not prejudicial to regal power. [*b. w.* Stebbing (H.) A defence, 1718]. 3rd ed. s8º. 1683
Seven lect. conc. the oblig. of promissory oathes. Tr. s8º. 1655
36 sermons. 8th ed. corr. Added, the life of the a. by I. Walton. [*w. sep. tp.*] fol. 1686
see JACKSON (T.) Lib. of Xtn. biog., v10, R. S., by I. Walton, 1839.

Sandes (*Maj.* Edward Warren Caulfeild).
Tales of Turkey. s8º. [1924]

Sandford (Francis), *Lancaster Herald.* Hist. of the coronation of James II & Queen Mary. fol. 1687
The order & ceremonies used for interment of George, duke of Albemarle. obl. fol. 1670

Sandiford (Peter). Comparative education: st. of educ. systems of 6 mod. nations. By H. W. Foght, A. H. Hope &c. Ed. P. Sandiford. [repr.] 8º. [1927]

Sandiford (Roberto).
Note di diritto marittimo di guerra. 8º. 1925
La Siria sotto ill mandato d. Francia. [Est. d. Rivista maritt., Dic. 1925. P2852]. la8º. 1925

Sandinus (Antonius). Vitae pontificum Roman. ed. 5a. Ital. auct. 2p *in* 1v. [*pagin. contin.*] s8º. Ferrariae. 1775

Sandius (Christophorus), *the younger.* Bibliotheca anti-Trinitariorum sive cat. script. & narr. Acc. alia scripta. s8º. Freistadii. 1684
Nucleus hist. eccl. Praef.: Tract. de vet. script. eccl. 3 lib. *in* 1v. *w. sep. pagin.* s8º. Cosmopoli. 1669
,, ,, 2a ed. [w. pref. by C. Sandius, the elder *&* App. *w. sep. pagin.*] s4º. Coloniae. 1676–78
Tract. de origine animae. s8º. Cosmopoli. 1671
see BALDER (J.) Conflictus de Georgio martyre, adv. C. C. S., 1685.
,, BEBEL (B.) Adv. præexistentiam animarum humanarum, errorem C. S., 1675.

Sandoval (Adolfo de). A la sombra de la Catedral. Prol. d. F. Perrino y Lopez. s8º. [1922]
Ante todo lo amado (2a p. de "A la sombra de la Catedrale"). Pról. d. José Luis de S. Teresa de Jesús. s8º. [1922]
Toda hermosa. Novela. s8º. [1926]

Sandow (Eugen).
Life is movement. Physical reconstruction &c. s4º. [1919]

Sandre (Thierry). Les yeux fermés. Roman. s8º. [1928]

Sandri (Mario). Alfredo Testoni. la8º. Milano. 1919
Matilde Serao. la8º. Milano. 1920

Sandringham. Arms & armour at S. Indian coll., also Asiatic, African &c. weapons. fol. 1910
*S. the royal home of sport. Repr. fr. " Land & Water illustr." fol. [1905]
Sands (Percy Cooper).
Literary genius of the Old Test. s8°. O. 1924
Sandukht, *Virgin, see* THADDAEUS, *St.* [*Martyrdom &c. of St. T. & S., *in Armenian*], 1853.
Sandwich Islands, *see* HAWAII.
Sandwich (Edward Montagu, *1st earl of*), *see* HISPANIA. Hispania illustrata, 1667–78, in letters f. S., also treat. [*by the same*] conc. the advant. of a nearer union w. that crown, 1703.
Sandwith (Humphry). Mem. of Rev. T. Powell. [Extr. f. The Wesleyan-Methodist mag., 1852. P601]. *p.f.p.c.* 8°. 1852
Sandy (Isabelle). Andorra ou les hommes d'airain. s8°. [1923]
Dans la ronde des Faunes. s8°. [1921]
L'heure folle. s8°. [1922]
Sandys (George). A paraphr. upon the Psalms of D. Set to new tunes by H. Lawes. Ed. rev. by J. Playford. s8°. 1676
A relation of a journey begun A.D. 1610. 4 bookes. Cont. descr. of Turkish Empire, Egypt &c. [*tp. & portrait of author wanting*]. fol. *Pr. f. W. Barrett.* 1615
Sandys (*Sir* **John Edwin).**
A companion to Latin studies. 3rd ed. 8°. C. 1921
A hist. of class. scholarship. 3rd ed. v1. s8°. C. 1921
James P. Steele, 1836–1917, *see* BRIT. SCHOOL AT ROME, v9, 1920.
Latin epigraphy. 2nd ed., rev. by S. G. Campbell. 8°. C. 1927
Sandys (Oliver). The crimson ramblers. s8°. [1927]
Tilly-make-haste. s8°. [1924]
Sandys (P.) Polit. diaries, 1847–49, *see* PUNJAB. P. govt. rec., v6, 1915.
Sanesi (Ireneo). Spàlato e la questione dalmatica, *see* QUADERNI geograf., N5, 1918.
Sanfermo (*il conte* **Rocco).** Due dispacci, 1791–92, sull' agric. e s. commercio del Piemonte. Con note [*by* A. Marcello. Nozze Remondini-Albrizzi. N123]. la8°. Venezia. 1856
Sänger (Alwin) [SAENGER]. Die Schuld d. deut. Regierung am Kriege. Nachtrag zu Meine Lond. Mission, v. Fürst Lichnowsky. [P2406]. s8°. *n.d.*
Sanger ("*Lord*" **George).** Seventy years a showman. Intr. by K. Grahame. s8°. 1926
Sänger (Konrad) [SAENGER]. Die Verfassung des deut. Reichs v. 11. Aug. 1919. Erläut. &c. v. K. S. s8°. 1920
Sanger (Margaret), *ed., see* WORLD POPULATION CONF. Proceedings, 1927, 1927.
San Germano. Die Aktenstücke z. Frieden v. S. Germano, 1230, 1926, *see* HAMPE (C.), *ed.*
San Giorgio (Benvenuto). Testamento (1513); ed. V. Promis, *see* REGIA DEP. DI STORIA PATRIA. Misc., t24, 1885.
San Giovanni (Giuseppe Manuel di), *see* MANUEL DI SAN GIOVANNI (G.)
Sangnier (Marc), *see* MAURRAS (C.) Le démocratie relig.: le dilemme de M. S. &c., 1921.
Sangorrin y Diest-Garcés (Damasco), *see* COLECCION de docs. para el estudio de la hist. de Aragon. El libro de la Cadena del Concejo de Jaca (Docs. real., episcop. y municip. sigl. 10–14). Transcrip. y notas de D. S., t12, 1920.
Sangroniz (José Antonio de), *see* ANTONIO DE SANGRONIZ (J.)
San Joseph Queiroz (*Fr.* **João de),** *bp. of Grão-Pará, see* QUEIROZ DA SILVEIRA (J. DE).
Sankey (Ira David), *see* SACRED songs & solos &c.; comp. & sung by I. D. S., *n.d.*
Sankey (*Sir* **John),** *judge of the King's Bench Division, see* SUBSTANCE or shadow?; warning agst. S. scheme, 1920?.
Sankt Gallen, *Monk of, see* CHARLEMAGNE, *for the work on C. by the "Monk of St. G." & for all refs.*
Sankt Lambrecht. Die beiden ält. Todtenbücher d. Benedictinerstiftes St. L. in Obersteier; mitgetheilt v. M. Pangerl, *see* FONTES RERUM AUSTRIAC., B29, 1869.
Sankt Paul, *in Kärnten.* Urkundenbuch d. Benedict.-Stiftes St. P.; hrsg. v. B. Schroll, *see* FONTES RERUM AUSTRIAC., B39, 1876.
Sankt Peter, *abbey, Erfurt.* Mon. Erphesfurt. saec. 12–14. [Annales, Cronica, Cronica minor &c.] Ed. O. Holder-Egger. [Scr. rerum Germ. in usum schol.] 8°. Hannoverae. 1899
San Marco, *Venezia, see* VENEZIA.
San Martín (*General* **José de),** *see* MITRE (B.) Hist. de San M. y de la emancip. Sudamericana, 3ª ed., 6t, *n.d.*

Sannazaro (Jacopo). L'Arcadia. s8°. Londra. 1781
Opere volgari. 2t. s8°. Venezia. 1741
Sonetti e canzoni. 8°. [Roma. 1530]
" " ....s8°. Vinegia. 1549
Sannazzaro, *The family of, see* ZUCCHI (M.) Delle orig. del nome di S. de' Burgondi in Lomellina e. d. fam. di J. S., 1906.
Sannikov (G.), *see* KAZIN (V.), N. LYASHKO & G. S. Цветы труда, 1923.
Sano di Pietro [ANSANO; SANO DI PIETRO DI MENICO], *see* GAILLARD (E.) Un peintre siennois au 15ᵉ s.: S. di P., 1406–81, 1923.
San Pedro (Diego de). Carcel de amor (Sevilla, 1492). [*Ed. R. Foulché-Delbosc.* Bibl. Hispanica]. s8°. Barcelona. 1904
Carcer d'amore, tr. d. Lelio de Mãfredi de idioma Spagnolo & nov. corr. s8°. [Venetia. 1530]
San Pedro de Galatino (*duque* **de),** *see* BENALÚA (*conde* DE), *duque de S. P. de Galatino.*
Sanpere y Miquel (Salvador). La pintura mig-eval Catalana. 2v [*in* 3, 2i, ii]. 8°. Barcelona. 1921–*n.d.*
1, L'art barbre. 2, Els Trescentistes, p1 per S. y M., p2 per J. Gudiol.
Sanquhar, *Barony of.* Award by James VI as to succession to barony of S., *see* ABBOTSFORD CLUB. Misc., v1, 1837.
San Secondo (Rossi di). La donna che può capire, capisca. Romanzo. s8°. Milano. 1923
La festa delle rose. Romanzo. s8°. Milano. 1920
Sanson (*r. p.* **—).** Confér. de Notre-Dame de Paris. Carême 1926: l'inquiétude humaine & le christianisme. 7 Nos. [*in* 1v]. s8°. [1926]
Sansone (Alfonso). I moniti di un veggente, *see* SOCIETÀ SICIL. Arch., N.S., 44, 1922.
Santuario del patriottismo, *see* SOCIETÀ SICILIANA. Archivio &c., N.S., 43, 1921.
Sansovino (Francesco).
Gl' Annali Turcheschi &c. s4°. Venetia. 1573
L'hist. di Casa Orsina con 4 lib. de gli huomini illust. d. fam. [*w. sep. tp. & pagin.*] la8°. in Venetia. 1565
Osservationi d. lingua volgare di div. huomini illustri: Bembo, Gabriello, Fortunio, Ascarisio et altri scrittori. [Ed. F. S. *pagin. irregular*]. s8°. Venetia. 1562
Santacana y Mensayas (Emilio).
Antiguo y moderno Algeciras. 8°. Algeciras. 1901
Santa Clara, *Sevilla, Convent of, see* HISP. SOC. OF AMER. Manuscripts: Nuns of S. C. & J. Rodriguez de Guzman, 1403, MS. B6, 1927.
Santa Croce, *The family of, see* CICCARELLI (A.) De orig., antiq. &c. illust. domus S. (16c.), 1868.
Santa Croce (*Card.* **Prospero),** *see* ADRIANI (G. B.) Della vita e d. nunziature d. Card. P. S. C. (Sanctacrucii de vita & rebus gestis, 1514–67 &c.), 1868.
Santa Cruz (Alonso de). Crónica del Emp. Carlos V. Publ. R. Beltrán y Rózpide & A. Blázquez y Delgado-Aguilera, con prologo d. F. de Laiglesia y Auser. [Real Acad. de la Hist.] 5t. la8°. 1920–25
Libro de las longitudines &c. Publ. bajo la dir. d. D. A. Blázquez y Delgado Aguilera. [Bibl. Colon. Amer., t5]. 8°. Sevilla. 1921
Santa Cruz do Castello. Registo da freguesia de S. C. do C., 1536–1628. Publ. com intr. &c. por E. Prestage e P. d'Azevedo. 4°. Coimbra. 1913
Santa Maria de Albarracin, *see* ALBARRACIN.
Santa Maria Jaboatam (Antonio de). Catalogo geneal. das princ. familias proced. de Albuquerques e Cavalcantes em Pernambuco, e Caramurús na Bahia, *see* INSTITUTO HIST. E GEOG. BRAZIL. Revista, t52, 1889.
Sant' Ambrogio (Diego). Priorato cluniac. di S. Pietro di Castelletto in prov. di Vercelli, *see* REGIA DEPUT. Miscellanea, t44, 1909.
Santander (Carlos Antonio de la Serna), *see* SERNA SANTANDER (C. A. DE LA).
Santander (Juan de), *see* BENAVIDES (A. DE). Relatio quam Philippo IV exhibuit J. de S. &c., 1634.
Santangelo (G. B.) Alcuni versi siciliani, seg. da una lettera sull' inno a S. Sofia di T. Mamiani. [P2770]. 8°. Palermo. 1878
Santanna (Girolamo Maria di), *see* GIROLAMO MARIA, *di Sant' Anna, Carmelite.*
Santarem (M. F. Barros e S. de M. de M. L. e C., *visc.* **de),** *1790–1856.* A statement of facts proving right of Portugal to territories on W. coast of Africa &c. Tr. [P2846]. 8°. 1877

Santayana (George).
Character & opinion in the U.S., w. remin. of W. James & J. Royce & Academic life in Amer. 8°. 1920
Dialogues in limbo. 8°. 1925
Little essays drawn f. wr. of G. S. by L. P. Smith, w. collab. of the a. 8°. 1920
Philosophical opinion in America, *see* BRIT. ACADEMY. Procs., 1917–18.
Platonism & the spiritual life. 8°. 1927
Poems. Sel. by the a. & rev. [Spec. signed ed.] s8°. [1922]
The realm of essence: book 1st of Realms of being. 8°. 1928
Scepticism & animal faith: intr. to a system of philosophy. 8°. [1923]
Soliloquies in England & later soliloquies. 8°. [1922]
Three philosophical poets: Lucretius, Dante & Goethe. [Harvard Sts. in Comp. Lit., 1. 3rd impr.] 8°. Cambridge [Mass.] 1922
The unknowable. Herbert Spencer lect. [P2717]. 8°. O. 1923
see DRAKE (D.) Essays in crit. realism; by D. D., G. S. &c., 1920.

Santen (Hermann von). *Die Champagne Herbstschlacht, 1915. Bearb. u. hrsg. v. Armee-Oberkommando 3. s8°. *n.p.* [1916]

Sant-Fahagun (Juan de), *see* UHAGON (F. R. DE). Libros de cetreria, noticias, 1889.

Santiago (Diogo Lopes de). Hist. da guerra de Pernambuco e feitos do J. Fernandes Vieira, *see* INSTITUTO HIST. E GEOG. BRAZIL. Rev., t38–43, 1875–80.

Santiago de Compostela. Constituciones Sinodales; dadas y publ. por J. Martin de Herrera &c., en el Sínodo Diocesano, 12–14 Julio, 1909, *see* MARTIN DE HERRERA (*Card.* J.), *abp.*

Santi Bartoli (Pietro), *see* BELLORI (G. P.) Pitture ant. del sepolcro de' Nasonii n. via Flaminia disegnate &c. da P. S. B., 1680.

Sāntideva [ÇANTIDEVA]. La marche à la lumière: Bodhicaryavatara. Poème sanscrit tr. avec intr. par L. Finot. 8°. 1920
Sikshā-Samuccaya: a compendium of Buddhist doctrine. Comp. by S. Tr. C. Bendall & W. H. D. Rouse. 8°. 1922

Santillana (Iñigo Lopez de Mendoza, *marq.* **de),** *1398–1458.*
Bias contra Fortũa. Hecho por coplas. [Hispanic Soc. of America]. 8°. [Sevilla. 1502. facs. repr. *De Vinne press.* 1902]
Letter to Don Peter, Constable of Portugal [c. 1449]. Intr. & notes by A. R. Pastor & E. Prestage. 8°. O. 1927
Poesías. s8°. Paris. *n.d.*

Santini (Pietro). Antiche riforme superstiti dei Costituti fiorentini &c., *see* ARCHIVIO STOR. ITAL. Anno 79, v2, 1923.

Santius (Rodericus), *see* SANCIUS DE AREVALO (R.)

Santo Domingo, *island.* Span. narr. of Eng. attack on S. D., 1655; transcr., tr. &c. by I. A. Wright, *see* CAMDEN MISC., v14, 1926.

Santo Domingo (Joseph Hippolyte, *comte* **de).**
London wie es ist &c. Übers. v. M—r. s8°. L. 1826

Santos (José dos), *see* DOS SANTOS (J.)

Santoyo (Enrique). Crón. de la prov. de Almeria, 1869, *see* ESPAÑA. Crón. gen., v9, 1865 &c.

Sanusi, *see* FUḌĀLĪ. Muhammedan. Glaubenslehre: d. Katechismen d. F. u. d. S.; übers. &c. M. Horten, 1916.

Sanuto (Marino), *the younger* [M. SANUDO; M. SANUTUS]. La spedizione di Carlo VIII in Italia. Publ. R. Fulin. [Arch. ven., a. 3]. 8°. Venezia. 1873

Sanyutta-Nikaya. The Book of the Kindred Sayings (Sanyutta-Nikāya) or grouped Suttas. p2, Tr. Mrs. Rhys Davids, ass. by F. H. Woodward. p3, Tr. F. L. Woodward; ed. Mrs. Rhys Davids. [Pali Text Soc., Transl. Ser., No. 10, 13]. p2, 3. 8°. [1922–24]

Sanz Arizmendi (Cl.) Indice del Tumbo de los Reyes Católicos, *see* REVUE HISPANIQUE, t62, 1924.

Sapir (Edward). Language: intr. s8°. [1921]
Takelma language of S.-W. Oregon, *see* BOAS (F.) Hdbk. of Amer. Ind. langs., p2, 1922.
see BARBEAU (M.) & E. S. Folk songs of French Canada, 1925.

Sapori (Armando). Beneficenza d. compagnie mercant. del trecento, *see* ARCHIVIO STOR. ITAL., a. 83ii, 1925.
Le compagnie d. Bardi e d. Peruzzi in Inghilterra n. sec. 13 e 14, *see* ARCHIVIO STOR. ITAL., a. 80, 1922.
Rassegna crit.: pubbl. dantesche ital. del centenario, *see* ARCHIVIO STOR. ITAL. Anno 79, v1, 1921.

Sapori (Francesco). I maestri dell' arte. Monografie d' artisti ital. mod. No. 19–27 [*in 2v*]. s8°. Torino. [1920–21]
Amendola (G. B.) [20.]
Baccarini (D.) [25.]
Biondi (E.) [23.]
Cannicci (N.) [24.]
Canova (A.) [26.]
Fracassini (C.) [21.]
Gamba (E.) [22.]
Pellizza (G.) [19.]
Rossetti (D. G.) [27.]

Saporta (*le marq.* **Gaston de).**
Le monde des plantes avant l'homme. la8°. 1879

Saposs (David J.), *see* COMMONS (J. R.), D. L. S. &C. Hist. of labour in the U.S., 2v, 1918.

Sapper, *ps.* [*i.e.* H. CYRIL MACNEILE].
The Black Gang. s8°. [1922]
Bull-dog Drummond. s8°. [1920]
The dinner club. s8°. [1923]
The final count. s8°. [1926]
Jim Maitland. s8°. [1923]
*Out of the blue. [3rd ed.] 8°. [1925]
The saving clause. s8°. [1927]
Shorty Bill. s8°. [1926]
The third round. [repr.] s8°. [1924]
Word of honour. s8°. [1926]

Sapper (Johann Georg). Diss. de culpa schismatis Eccl. Evangel. immerito imputata. Praes. J. Frickius. [P484]. s4°. Ulmae. [1717]

Sapper (Carl). Mexico. 2e A. 8°. Wien. 1928

Sappho.
Fragments of lyrical poems. Ed. E. Lobel. s8°. O. 1925
Poems. With hist. & crit. notes, tr., & a bibliog. by E. M. Cox. 8°. 1924
Poems & fragments. Text w. Eng. tr. by C. R. Haines, & intr., notes &c. [Broadway Trans.] 8°. [1926]
see ANACREON. Les odes d'A. & de S. en vers franç. par Sans Fard, 1712.
see ARNOLD (B.) S., Vortrag, 1871.
,, DIEHL (E.) Anthol. lyrica, v1, 1925.
,, —— Suppl. lyricum, 3e A., 1917.
,, LYRA Graeca; ed. & tr. by J. M. Edmonds, v1, S. &c., 1922.
,, STEBBING (W.) Greek & Lat. anthology, p3, Gr. epigrams & S., 1923.

Sapre (B. G.) The growth of Indian constit. & administ. 8°. [Sangli]. 1924

Sapte (William), *Jr.* A century's sensations. s8°. *n.d.*

Sarabyanov (Vladimir N.)
Металлопромышленность России. [P2698]. 8°. [Москва]. 1921

Saracenica sive Moamethica, 1595, *see* SYLBURGIUS (F.), *ed.*

Saracenisch, Türckisch, u. Mahometisch Glaub, &c. Durch einen Sibenbürger umb 1436, selb erfaren u. beschriben. s4°. [Strassburg, *Christ. Egenolphen.* 1530]

Saraceno (Filippo).
Works in REGIA DEP. DI STORIA PATRIA. Misc.
Doc. ined. del regno di Lodovico, duca di Savoia, 1874. [15.]
Nota sopra un ms. fals. attrib. a G. M. Pingon, 1887. [25.]
Regesto dei principi di Casa d'Acaja, 1295–1418, 1882. [20.]

Sarasin (J. G.) The black glove. s8°. 1925
The lost duchess. s8°. [1927]
Romance of three ladies. s8°. [1925]

Sarasin (Jean François). Œuvres. Rass. par P. Festugière. 2t. (1, Poésies. 2, Prose). 8°. 1926

Sarasin (Paul). Helios u. Keraunos, oder Gott u. Geist: Versuch e. Erklär. d. Trias in d. vergl. Religionsgesch. 8°. Innsbruck. 1924

Sarauw (Chr.)
Works in KONGELIGT DAN. VID. SELSK. Hist.-fil. Med.
Die Entstehungsgesch. d. Goethischen Faust, 1917–18. [1.]
Goethes Augen, 1918. [2.]
Goethes Faust i aarene, 1788–89, 1918–19. [2.]
Niederdeutsche Forschungen, 1, 2, 1921–25. [5, 10.]
Zur Faustchronol., 1924–25. [10.]

Saravia (Hadrianus), *see* BEZA (T.) Ad tract. de ministrorum Evang. gradibus ab H. S. ed. resp., 1593.

Sarcerius (Erasmus). Catechismus per omnes quaestiones &c., in usum praedicatorum. s8°. [Lipsiae]. 1539
In Evangelia Dominicalia postilla &c. s8°. Marpurgi. 1541
Methodus Scripturæ Divinæ, Ad nuda Didactici generis præcepta &c. s8°. Marpurgi. [1539]

Sarcey (Yvonne). La route du bonheur. 15e éd. s8°. *n.d.*

Sarcone (Michele). Cerere placata: festa teatrale data da il Duca d'Arcos. [N126]. 8°. Napoli. 1772

Sardini (Giovanni Battista Domenico), *see* LAZZARESCHI (E.) Ambasciatore lucchese a Vienna: G. B. D. S., 1918.

Sardis. Sardis. Publ. of the Amer. Soc. f. the Excav. of Sardis. v1, 10. la4°. Leyden *&* C. 1922–26
1, The excavations, p1, 1910–14, by H. C. Butler.
10, Terra-cottas, p1, Architectural by T. L. Shear.

Sarfatti (Margherita G.) Dux [Mussolini]. 8°. Milano. 1926
Life of B. Mussolini. Pref. by B. M. Tr. F. Whyte. 8°. 1925
Tunisiaca. la8°. Milano. [1924]

Sarga (Wadi), *see* WADI SARGA.

Sargant (Jane Alice). Life of Cranmer. s8°. 1829

Sargeaunt (John). Hist. of Bedford school. Ed. & compl. by E. Hockliffe. 8°. 1925
The pronunciation of Eng. words derived f. the Latin. Pref. & notes by H. Bradley. [S.P.E. Tract No. 4]. 8°. O. 1920
Westminster verses, w. a mem. by J. Gow. 8°. [1922]

Sargent, *Family of.*
see JOHNSON (J. M.) Publications of descendants of Epes Sargent, 1923.
„ MANN (C. E.) S. family & old S. homes, 1919.
„ SARGENT (E. W.) Epes Sargent of Gloucester & h. descendants, 1923.
„ SARGENT (W.) Early Sargents of New England, 1922.

Sargent (Charles Sprague), *see* SARGENT (E. W.) Epes Sargent & h. descendants, w. biog. notes by C. S. S., 1923.

Sargent (Emma Worcester), *wife of Winthrop Sargent.* Epes Sargent of Gloucester & h. descendants. Arranged by E. W. S. w. biog. notes by C. S. Sargent. la8°. Boston [Mass.] 1923

Sargent (Epes), *see* SARGENT (E. W.) E. S. of Gloucester & h. descendants, 1923.

Sargent (John Singer), *R.A.* Cat. of pictures & water colour drawings by S. &c., sold by Christie, July 1925. 8°. [1925]
Illust. of the Sargent exhib., Royal Academy, 1926. la8°. 1926
see CHARTERIS (*Hon.* E.) J. S., 1927.

Sargent (John Young).
Outlines of Norwegian grammar. s8°. 1865

Sargent (*Col.* Paul Dudley), *see* SARGENT (W.) Col. P. D. S., 1745–1827, 1920.

Sargent (Winthrop).
Col. P. D. Sargent, 1745–1827. 8°. *p.f.p.c.* [1920]
Early Sargents of New England. 8°. *p.p.* [Phila.] 1922

Sargis, *general* [SERGIUS], *see* NERSES *Shnorhali.* [Life of St. S. (& of h. son Martiros) tr. by N., *in Armenian*], 1854.

Sargis, *Shnorhali* [SERKIS]. [Book of comm. on the 7 catholic epistles. *In Armenian*]. s4°. i K.-polis. 1192 [=1743]

Sargis (Petros di). Дневникъ осады Испагани Афганами, 1722 и 1723. Переводъ &c. К. Патканова. [I. Akad. Nauk. Записки, t17]. 8°. С.-П. 1870

Sargisean (Barsel).
[The fable of the 3 Magi in Arm. sources. *In Armenian.* P2803]. 8°. Venetik. 1910
[The hist. of Sylvester & the sources of Moses of Khoren. *In Armenian, w. Arm. & Greek text*]. 8°. Venetik. 1893
[Study of the Manichaean Paulicians. *In Armenian.* P2799]. la8°. Venetik. 1893
see ABRAHAM, *bp. of Mamigona.* A. & h. letter to Vatchagan (*in Arm.*); ed. B. S., 1899.
see ANANIAS, *the translator.* A. & h. works: Jonah &c. (*in Arm.*); ed. B. S., 1899.
„ ARMENIAN. Ananoun zamanakagrouthiun (anon. chron.); ed. B. S., 1904.
„ EVAGRIUS *Ponticus.* [Life & works: *in Armenian* by P. V. S.], 1907.

Sarkar (Jadunath), *M.A., prof. at Patna Coll.*
Hist. of Aurangzib, based on orig. sources. v4, 5. s8°. Calcutta. 1919–24
Shivaji & h. times. 2nd ed. rev. & enl. s8°. 1920
see IRVINE (W.) Later Mughals; ed. & augm. w. hist. of Nadir Shah's invasion, by J. S., 2v, 1922.
„ KRISHNADAS KAVIRAJ. Chaitanya's pilgrimages &c.; fr. contemp. Bengali biog.; tr. J. S., 1913.

Sarkisean (Barsel), *see* SARGISEAN.

Sarment (Jean).
La couronne de carton—Le pêcheur d'ombres. [3e éd.] 8°. 1921
Facilité, comédie, *see* ŒUVRES libres, 17, 1922.
Je suis trop grand pour moi. Pièce. la8°. 1924
Le mariage d'Hamlet. Pièce. [6e éd.] 8°. 1923

Sarmiento (Domingo Faustino), *pres. of the Argentine Confederation.* Facundo. 4a ed. s8°. Buenos Aires. 1917
Recuerdos de provincia. s8°. Buenos Aires. *n.d.*

Sarn (Petrus von).
De galeis vet. Diss. [P2744]. s4°. Duisburgi. 1724

Sarnelli (Pompeo), *bp. of Bisceglia.* Memorie de' Vescovi di Biseglia e d. stessa città. 8°. Napoli. 1593

Sarnthein (Ludwig, *Graf* v.), *see* DALLA TORRE (C. W. v.) & L., *Graf* v. S. Flora d. Grafschaft Tirol &c., 6B, 1900–26.

Sarolea (Charles). Anthologie des poètes lyriques franç. Intr. par C. S. [Coll. Nelson]. s8°. [1911]
Impressions of Soviet Russia. 8°. [1924]

Sarpedonius (Mirtisbus), *ps., see* REIFFENBERG (F. v.)

Sarpi (*Fra* Paolo).
Apologia adv. oppositiones factas ab card. Bellarmino ad Tractatus &c. Joh. Gersonis [& Responsio ad alterum Gersonis opusculorum &c.] circa valorem ex communicationum, 1606, *see* PAUL V, *pope.* Controversiæ mem., 1607.
Consid. supra Censuris S. Pauli V papae contra Venetiarum rempublicam, *see* PAUL V, *pope,* Controversiae, 1607.
Hist. Concilii Trident. libri 8. Ed. 5a & ultima. s4°. Gorinchemi. 1658

Sarpi (*Fra* Paolo) [*continued*].
Hist. du Concile de Trente. Tr. avec des notes par P. F. Le Courayer [*w. portrait*]. 2t. 4°. Amsterdam. 1736
Opere, v6. [*b. w.* Minucci (M.) Hist. degli Uscochi, 1683]. s8°. Venezia. 1685
Dominio del Mar' Adriatico di Venetia.
Dominio dell' Mar' Adriatico e sue raggioni per il jus belli &c.
Allegatione in jure contro l'autor degl' Annali Eccles. &c.
Opinione del P. Paolo Servita come debba governarsi Venetia.
A treat. of matters beneficiary. Tr. out of Ital. [by W. Denton]. [P529]. fol. 1680
see AMELOT DE LA HOUSSAYE (A. N. DE). P. S. Polanus in Hist. Concil. Trident. opere &c. defensus, 1686.
„ A-VALLE (C.) Elogio di P. S., 1867.
„ BALZANI (U.) Di alcuni doc. rel. al. cadavere di P. S., 1895.
„ GRISELINI (F.) *Sciocche &c. impost. per denigr. l'illust. mem. di P. S., 1770.
„ LORENZETTI (G.) P. S., cenni biogr., 1867.
„ —— P. S., dramma, 1867.
„ MICANZIO (F.) *Vita del Padre P. &c., 1658.
„ MINUCCI (M.) Hist. degli Uscochi, –1602, e contin. dal P. M. Paolo, –1616, 1683.
„ MOSCHINI (G. A.) & E. A. CIGOGNA. Trasporto d. osse di P. S. a San Michele di Murano, 1828.
„ PALLAVICINO (*il card.* S.) Vera Conc. Tridentini hist., contra falsam P. Suavis Polani narr., 3t, 1670.

Sarrail (*Général* Maurice Paul Emmanuel).
Mon commandement en Orient, 1916–18. s8°. [1920]
see PERCIN (A.) Deux hommes de Guerre: S. & Gallieni, 1919.
„ TERRAIL (G.) Le commandement unique, p2, S. & les armées d'Orient, 1920.

Sarrasin (Jean), *chamberlain to Louis IX.* Lettre à Nicolas Arrode (1249). Ed. A. L. Foulet. [Classiques fr. du m-â.] s8°. 1924

Sarratt (J. H.)
New treatise on the game of chess. 2v [*in* 1]. 8°. 1821
Treatise on the game of chess. n. ed. 8°. 1822

Sarraut (Albert).
La mise en valeur des colonies franç. 8°. 1923

Sarre (Friedrich). Die Keramik v. Samarra; unter Mitwirk. v. E. Herzfeld. [Forsch. z. islam. Kunst, 2, Die Ausgrab. v. Samarra, B2]. 4°. 1925
Die Kunst d. alt. Persien. [Die Kunst d. Ostens; hrsg. W. Cohn, B5]. la8°. 1922
see HERZFELD (E.) Die Malereien v. Samarra, 1927.
„ —— Der Wandschmuck d. Bauten v. Samarra &c., 1923.
„ LAMM (C. J.) Das Glas v. Samarra, 1928.
—— & E. Herzfeld. Archäolog. Reise im Euphrat- u. Tigris-Gebiet. [Forsch. z. islam. Kunst; hrsg. F. Sarre, 1]. 4B. fol. 1911–20
B1, mit Beitr.: Arab. Inschriften, v. M. van Berchem. B2, mit Beitr.: Rusāfah, v. S. Guyer. B3, Tafelband.
Iranische Felsreliefs. Aufnahmen u. Untersuch. v. Denkmälern aus alt- u. mittelpers. Zeit. fol. 1910

Sarrocchi (Margherita).
La Scanderbeide, poema heroico. s4°. 1606

Sartiaux (Félix). Troie—La guerre de Troie &c. s8°. 1915

Satineau (Maurice). Hist. de la Guadeloupe sous l'Ancien Régime, 1635–1789. 8°. 1928

Sarton (George).
Intr. to hist. of science. [C.I. of Wash.] v1. la8°. 1927
1, From Homer to Omar Khayyam.

Sartor (Johann). Ein Predig: Wie man Christum lieben sol &c. [P2613]. s4°. Tübingen. 1587

Sartori Borotto (Marco). Le ferrovie strategiche d. Veneto. [P2841]. 8°. Venezia. 1908

Sartorius (Carl Friedrich). Caussarum cur Christus scripti nihil reliq. disq. [P1041]. s8°. Lips. [1815]

Sartorius (Christoph Friedrich). Compend. theologiae dogmat. Iter. curis. s8°. Stutgardiae. 1782

Sartorius (Friedrich Wilhelm). Ruinam superstit. paganae var. obs. ex hist. ecclesiae saec. 4 & 5 illust., praes. J. G. Hoffmanno, ed. F. W. S. [P2638]. s4°. Vitembergae. 1738

Sartorius von Waltershausen (A.)
Deutsche Wirtschaftsgesch. 1815–1914. la8°. Jena. 1920

Sartorius v. Waltershausen (Bodo, *Frhr.*), *see* BÄUMKER (C.) & B. S. v. W. Glossen d. Jepa z. Isagoge d. Porphyrius, 1924.

Sasnetzi (Karapet), *see* KARAPET, *Sasnetzi.*

Sasso (Pamfilo). Opera: Sonetti 407. Capituli 38. Egloghe 5. 8°. [Venetiis. 1519]

Sassoon (Siegfried). Satirical poems. s8°. 1926

Sastri (*Rao Bahadur* **H. Krishna).** Two statues of Pallava kings &c. at Mahabalipuram, *see* INDIA: ARCH. SURVEY. Mem. 26, 1926.

Sastri (Hirananda) [SHASTRI (H.)]
Works in INDIA: ARCH. SURVEY. Mem.
Bhasa & authorship of 13 Trivandrum plays, 1926. [28.]
The origin & cult of Tārā, 1925. [20.]
Some recently added sculptures in the Prov. Mus., Lucknow, 1922. [11.]

***Satan** disrob'd; or the Quakers last shift, 2nd ed., 1698, *see* LESLIE (C.)

Sathyanatha Aiyar (R.), *see* AIYAR (R. S.)

Satire Menippée [†MENIPPEAN SATIRE]. Satyre M. de la vertu du Catholicon d'Espagne, & la tenue des Etats de Paris &c. s8º. Ratisbonne. 1664
Satyre M. de la vertu du Catholicon d'Espagne, & de la tenue des Etats de Paris &c. Krit. &c. Text mit Einleit. &c. v. J. Frank. 8º. Oppeln. 1884
Satyre M. de la vertu du Catholicon de Rome & de la Sainte Ligue du Sacré Cœur. [*A mod. skit in imit. of the S. M.*] s8º. 1877

Satomi (Kishio). Japanese civilization: Nichirenism & Japan. national princ. 8º. 1923

Satow (*Rt. Hon. Sir* **Ernest Mason).**
A diplomat in Japan. 8º. 1921
Guide to diplomatic practice. 2nd & rev. ed. 2v. 8º. 1922
International congresses, *see* FOREIGN OFFICE. Handbooks, No. 151, 1920.
The Jesuit Mission Press in Japan, 1591–1610. [*facs. ed.*] 4º. *p.p.* 1888. [repr. Tokyo. 1926]
Kuaiwa hen. 25 exercises dans le dialecte de Yédo, avec notes par E. S. Tr. D. Larrieu &c. 3p. s8º. *n.p.* [1873]

Sattler (Maximilian Vincenz). Grundr. d. deut. Gesch., nebst e. Specialgesch. Baierns. 2ᵉ A. 8º. München. 1872

***Satura** diss., orat. epist. & obs. theol.-hist.-philologic. [*by var. a.*] 4p *in* 1v [*pagin. cont.*] s8º. Tiguri. 1741–43

Saturday (The) Review. v129–145. fol. 1920–28

Satya Kama Shaivya. Der Führer im Geistigen. Übertr. F. Hartmann. [*b. w.* Schott (S.) Von menschl. Schwächen. 1865]. s8º. L. *n.d.*

Saubert (Johann), *the younger, see* JACOB JUDAH ARYEH. J. J. Leonis de Templo Hierosol. libri 4, rec. a J. S., 1665.

Saubole (Roger de Comminges, *sieur* **de),** *see* COMMINGES (R. DE).

Saudek (Robert). The psychology of handwriting. [Illust. suppl. *in pocket*]. la8º. [1925]

Sauer (Carl Marquard) & S. C. Kordgien. Portugies. Konversations-Gramm. 8º. Heidelberg. 1887

Sauerbrei (Moritz). Die ital. Politik König Sigmunds bis z. Beginn d. Constanzer Concils, 1410–15. Diss. [P2725]. 8º. Halle a S. 1893

Sauerland (Heinrich Volbert) & A. Haseloff. Der Psalter Erzbischof Egberts v. Trier, Cod. Gertrudianus, in Cividale. [Tafeln *in case*]. 4º. Trier. 1901

Sauerlandt (Max).
Deut. Porzellanfiguren d. 18. Jhdts. 8º. Köln. 1923

Sauerwein (Jules). Cinq ans d'erreurs, impress. d'Allemagne (1919–25), *see* ŒUVRES libres, 49, 1925.

Sauli (Domenico). Autobiografia; ed. G. P. Lambertenghi, *see* REGIA DEP. DI STORIA PATRIA. Misc., t17, 1878.

Saulnier (Eugène) & A. Martin. Bibliog. des travaux publ. 1866–97 sur l'hist. de la France, 1500–1789. fasc. 1. la8º. 1927

Saulnier (René), *see* DUCHARTRE (P. L.) & R. S. L'imagerie pop., 1925.

Saundby (Robert). Medical ethics. 2nd ed. 8º. 1907

Saunders (A. M. Carr-), *see* CARR-SAUNDERS (A. M.)

Saunders (Arthur Leslie). The religions of India. s8º. 1925

Saunders (*maj.-gen.* **Edward Augustus).**
Recruiting without conscription. [P2845]. s8º. 1875

Saunders (Erasmus). A domestick charge, or, the duty of household-governours. s8º. O. 1701

Saunders (Frederick). *Pastime papers. 8º. 1885

Saunders (Kenneth). The gospel for Asia: st. of Gita, Lotus, & 4th Gospel. 8º. 1928

Saunders (Trelawney). Sketch of mountains & river basins of India. [P535]. la8º. 1870
see CONDER (C. R.) & H. H. KITCHENER. Map. of W. Palestine, spec. ed. by T. S., 1882.

Saunier (Charles). Barye. 8º. 1925
Bordeaux. [Villes d'art célèbres]. 2ᵉ éd. la8º. 1925

Saunier de Beaumont (—). *Lettres philosoph., sérieuses, crit. & amusantes &c. [Epistre *signed* L. C. D. T.] s8º. 1733

Saurat (Denis). La pensée de Milton. la8º. 1920

Saurīndramohana Thākura [SOURINDRO MOHUN TAGORE]. A few specimens of Indian songs. 8º. Calcutta. 1879

Saussay (André du), *bp. of Toul, see* DU SAUSSAY (A.)

Saussure (Horace Benedict de) [DESAUSSURE], *see* FRESHFIELD (D. W.) Life of H. B. de S., 1920.

Saussure (Léopold de). L'orig. des noms de Mer Rouge, Mer Blanche & Mer Noire. [*Extr. f.* Le Globe, t63. P2784]. 8º. [1925]

Sautaï (Maurice). La bataille de Malplaquet d'après les corr. du Duc du Maine à l'Armée de Flandre. [Etat-Major de l'Armée]. 8º. 1904
L'œuvre de Vauban à Lille. [Etat-Major de l'Armée]. 8º. 1911
Une opération milit. d'Eugène & de Marlborough. Le forcement du passage de l'Escaut en 1708. [Etat-Major de l'Armée]. 8º. 1905
Les préliminaires de la Guerre de la Succession d'Autriche. [Etat-Major de l'Armée]. 8º. 1907

Sautel (Joseph).
Vaison dans l'antiquité. 2t. la8º. Avignon. 1926
1, Hist. de la cité. 2, Cat. des objets rom. trouv. à V.
„ „ Rec. doc. illustré. s4º. Lyon. 1926

Sauvage (Jean). Mém. du voiage en Russie en 1586. Suivi de l'expéd. de Fr. Drake en Amér. Publ. L. Lacour. [Trésor des pièces rares]. s8º. 1855

Sauvageot (Claude). Palais, châteaux & maisons de France, 15ᵉ–18ᵉ siècle. fol. 1867

Sauvigny (Louis Edme Billardon de), *see* BILLARDON DE SAUVIGNY (L. E.)

Sauzey (*le lt.-col.* **Camille).** Les Allemands sous les aigles françaises: essai sur les troupes de la Conféd. du Rhin, 1806–13. [t]5, Nos alliés les Bavarois. 8º. 1910

Savadjian (Léon). La Bulgarie en guerre. Préf. de M. Muret & lettre de G. Fazy. [P2432]. 8º. Genève. 1917
Thrace orientale. 8º. 1922

Savaète (Arthur). La main noire. s8º. 1898

Savage Club, *see* WARD (E. A.) Recoll. of a Savage, 1923.

Savage (*Mrs.* **Ethel M.),** *wife of Col. G. T. Savage, see* DELL (ETHEL M.)

Savage (F. G.) Flora & folk lore of Shakespeare. s8º. Cheltenham. [1923]

Savage (Henry).
Richard Middleton, the man & h. work. 8º. [1922]
see HARLEIAN MISCELLANY (THE): an entertaining sel., arr. & ed. by H. S., 1924.

Savage (Henry L.), *ed., see* ERKENWALD, *St.* St. E.: Mid. Eng. poem, 1926.

Savage (James), *of Howden, 1767–1845.*
Hist. of Dorchester. s8º. Dorchester. [1823]

Savage (Marmion W.) *The bachelor of the Albany. Intr. by B. Dobrée. s8º. 1927

Savage (Minot Judson). Can telepathy explain? s8º. N.Y. 1902

Savage (Raymond). Allenby of Armageddon. Pref. by D. Lloyd George. 8º. [1925]

Savage (Richard), *d. 1743, see* JOHNSON (S.) *Life of R. S. &c., 1769.

Savage (William George).
Canned foods in rel. to health, 1923. 8º. C. 1923

Savarensky (N.) Экономич. движеніе крестьянства, *see* GORN (VL.), V. MECH & CHEREVANIN. Борьба обществ. силъ, в3, 1907.

Savarese (*il baron* **Giacomo),** *see* ANZILOTTI (A.) Un amico napolet. di G. P. Vieusseux: il baron G. S., 1921.

Savarese (Giovanni Battista). La civiltà moderna difesa contro la riposta al libro La nuova Italia ed i vecchi zelanti [*by* C. M. Curci]. 8º. Napoli. 1881
Idea cristiana d. politica ragione, ed il clero cattolico sostenitore del popolo. 8º. Napoli. 1881

Savary (Claude Étienne). Gramm. de la langue arabe aug. de q. contes arabes par l'éditeur. [L. M. Langlès]. 4º. 1813
Letters on Egypt &c. Tr. 2v. 8º. 1786

***Saved** by a woman, 3v, 1872, *see* JOHNS (B. G.)

Savelev (Pavel Stepanovich). Дополненія къ описанію саманидскихъ монетъ. *see* IMPERAT. RUSS. ARCH. OBSCH. Труды Восточ. отд., ч1, 1855.
Изъ писемъ Дорджи Банзарова, *see* IMP. RUSS. ARCH. OBSCH. Труды Восточ отд., ч3, 1858.
Монеты джучидскія, джагатайскія &c. обращ. въ Золотой Ордѣ въ эпоху Тохтамыша, *see* IMP. RUSS. ARCH. OBSCH. Труды Восточ. отд., ч3, 1858.

Savelsberg (Joseph). De digammo &c. diss. pl. [*b. w.* Longard (L. C.) Symbola &c., 1837]. 4º. Aquisgrani. 1854

Saverien (Alexandre). Diz. ist. &c. di marina. Tr. d. Francese. [2 *pagin.*] s4º. Venezia. 1769

Savi (Ethel Winifred). The beauty market. s8º. [1927]
A fateful escapade. s8º. [1925]
Fruits of desire. s8º. [1926]
Vagrant love. s8º. [1927]

Savich (G. G.)
Новый государственный строй Россіи. 8º. С.-П. 1907

Savignac (Raphael).
see MISSION ARCHÉOLOG. EN ARABIE. II, El-'Ela, d'Hégra à Teima, Harrah de Tebouk, par S. &c., 1914; Suppl., Coutumes des Fuqarâ, par S. &c., 1914.
,, MISSION ARCHÉOLOG. EN ARABIE. III, Les châteaux arabes de Qeṣeir 'Amra, Ḫarâneh & Ṭûba, par S. &c., 1922.

Savignon (André). La tristesse d'Elsie. s8º. [1924]
Vieille madame, *see* ŒUVRES libres, 32, 1924.

Savignoni (Luigi).
Works in REALE ACCAD. D. LINCEI. Mon. ant.
Bronzetto dell' Acrop. di Atene e classe di tripodi greco-orient., 1897. [7.]
Nuovi studii e scop. in Gortyna, *by* L. S., G. de Sanctis & R. Paribeni, 1907. [18.]
Scavi e scop. n. necropoli di Phaestos, 1904. [14.]

Savigny (Friedrich Carl v.) The hist. of the Roman law during the M.A. Tr. by E. Cathcart. v1. [*No more publ.*] 8º. E. 1829

Savigny (Jean Bapt. Henri) & A. Corréard. Narr. of a voyage to Senegal in 1816, compr. acc. of shipwreck of the Medusa &c. Notes by M. Bredif. [2nd ed.] 8º. 1818

Savigny-Stiftung für Rechtsgeschichte, *see* VOCABULARIUM jurisprudentiae Romanae; jussu Inst. Savigniani compos., t1, 1903.

Savile (Frank). The River of the Giraffe: desert, stream & forest shooting in S. Sudan. 8º. 1925

Savile (*Capt.* Henry). True rel. of the engagement of H.M.'s fleet w. the Dutch fleet, May 28, 1672. 8º. 1672

Savile (*Sir* Henry), *1549–1622.* Rerum Anglicarum scriptores post Bedam præcipui. fol. Londini. 1596

Savina (Jean). Nos vieux grands chemins & la corvée, en Cornouaille & en Léon. 8º. 1925

Savina (Mariya Gavrilovna). Горести и скитания: записки, 1854–77. С пред. &c. А. М. Брянского. s8º. Ленинград. 1927

Savinkov (Boris), *see* ROPSHIN (V.), *ps.*

Savinsky (A.) Recoll. of a Russian diplomat. 8º. [1927]

Savio (Domenico) [SOAVE], *see* BOSCO (G.) Der Diener Gottes D. S., Zögling d. Salesian. Oratoriums in Turin, 2e A., 1925.

Savio (Fedele).
Works in REGIA DEPUT. Misc.
I dittici del canone ambrosiano e del canone rom., 1906. [42.]
Il monastero di S. Teofredo di Cervere ed il culto di S. Teofredo in Piemonte, 1896. [34.]
I primi conti di Savoia, 1887. [26.]

Savoir (Alfred). L'homme, comédie, see ŒUVRES libres, 56, 1926.

—— & R. Gignoux. Vertu . . . Vertu!: comédie, *see* ŒUVRES libres, 52, 1925.

Savonarola (Girolamo) [JERONIMUS, *Ferrariensis*].
De simplicitate Christianae vitae libri 5. Acc. ejusdem Expos. Dominicae Orationis & Sermo in Vigilia nativ. Domini &c. Cur. C. Besoldo. s8º. [Argentoriti]. 1615
Scritti. A cura di V. Piccoli. s8º. Milano. [1921]
Die weil sich in vil Christglaubigen menschē in disen zeyten yrrige u. parteysche hanndlung begeben. Psalm. Miserere mei deus. mitt auszlegung in disem büechlein. s4º. *n.p.* 1522
see CLARK (W. R.) S., h. life & times, 1896.
,, FERRARA (M.) 2 sonetti contro il S., 1922.
,, GIORGI (CARLO). Della storia del P. G. S., 1782.
,, GOBINEAU (*le c.* J. A. DE). La fleur d'or [S. &c.], 1923.
,, OLSCHKI (L. S.) Bibl. S.; œuvres de C. S., Cat. 39, 1898.
,, PORTIGLIOTTI (G.) Un grande monomane: S., 1902.
,, SCHNITZER (J.) P. Delfin, 1444–1525: Kirchenreform Alex. VI u. S., 1926.
,, —— S.: e. Kulturbild aus d. Zeit d. Renaissance, 2B, 1924.

Savorgnan (*conte* Giuseppe di Brazza). Enrico, duca, S. Paolino, patriarca, Paolo, Diacono, Sec. 8. [P2841]. la8º. Udine. 1903

Savorgnan de Brazza (Pierre Paul F. C.), *see* BROUSSEAU (G.) Souvs. de la mission S. de B., 1925.

Savory (Theodore H.)
Brit. spiders, th. haunts & habits. s8º. O. 1926

Savoy [SAVOYE]. *Recit de ce qui s'est faict & passé en S. en ceste presente année 1616 entre sa Majesté Catholique, & son Altesse [de Savoye]. s8º. 1616

Savoy Church, *see* FRENCH CHURCH, *Savoy.*

Savoy, *House of.*
*Delle accoglienze ai principi di Savoia fatte dai Veneziani, 1367–1722, 1868, *see* BAROZZI (N.) & G. BERCHET.
Doc. ined. sulla casa di S.; [*ed.* F. E. Bollati di Saint-Pierre], *see* REGIA DEP. Misc., t22, 1884.
I primi atti costit. ordin. in Palermo, Victor Amadeus regn.; ric. G. Spata, *see* REGIA DEP. Misc., t10, 1870.
Suppl. ai " Regesta comitum Sabaudiae &c. ad an. 1253 "; [*ed.* D. Carutti], *see* REGIA DEP. Misc., t40, 1904.
see CAMUS (J.) Prem. autographes de la maison de S., 1906.
,, CHIESA (*il conte* L. DELLA). Dell' hist. di Piemonte &c., con la orig. d. casa di S., 1608.
,, CLARETTA (*il b.* G.) I reali di S., munifici fautori d. arti, sec. 18, 1893.
,, CORELLI (P.) La stella d'Italia o 9 secoli di Casa Savoia, 5v, 1863.
,, SAVIO (F.) I primi conti di S., 1887.
,, VESME (A. DE). Van Dyck, peintre de portraits des princes de S., 1885.

Savoy (Ludovico, *duke of***),** *d. 1465, see* LOUIS, *duke of Savoy.*

Savoy (Yolanda, *duchess of***),** *1434–78, see* YOLANDA, *duchess of Savoy.*

Savoye, *see* SAVOY.

Sawarkar (D. S.) Visual instr. in Baroda. [Bureau of Educ., India]. [P2497]. 8º. Calcutta. 1921

Sawyer (Charles J.) & F. J. H. Darton. Eng. books, 1475–1900: signpost for collectors. 2v. 8º. Westminster. 1927

Sawyer (Edmund), *see* WINWOOD (*Sir* RALPH). Mems. of aff. of state, coll. f. papers of Sir R. W., 3v, 1725.

Sawyer (Thomas). Antigamus: or, a satire agst. marriage, *see* OXFORD packet, 1714.

Sax (Carl *Ritter* v.) Die Wahrheit ü. d. serb. Frage &c. [P2735]. 8º. Wien. [1909]

Saxby (Henry). The British customs: hist. &c. acc. of each branch of that revenue. 8º. 1757

Saxby (I. B.) The education of behaviour: psychological study. s8º. 1921

Saxe (*le maréchal* de).
see HART (B. H. L.) Gt. captains unveiled, 1927.
,, THORNTON (L. H.) Campaigners, 1925.

Saxe (Charles de), *duke of Courland, see* CHARLES [*de Saxe*], *d. of C.*

Saxe (*le prince* Xavier de), *cte. de Lusace, see* SAXONY (F. A. X., *prince of*).

Saxo, *Grammaticus.* Erläut. zu d. ersten 9 Büchern d. Danischen Gesch. d. S. v. P. Herrmann. 2T. 8º. L. 1901–22
see GOLLANCZ (I.) Sources of Hamlet [*Lat. text & tr. f.* Hist. Dan.], 1926.

Saxony.
Articuli visitat. eccl. Christiani de Sacra Coena &c. relig. Zwinglio-Calvinianae [1594] decursi ex mandato elect. S. &c., 1662, *see* HEINRICI (D.)
Conf. doctrinae Saxonic. eccl. Synodo Tridentinae oblata a. 1541, *see* CONFESSIONES fidei Xtnae tres, 1553.
Conf. doctrinae Saxonic. eccl. Synodo Tridentinae oblata 1551 &c. s8º. [Basileae, *J. Oporinus*]. 1552
Conf. fidei de Eucharistiae Sacramento in qua ministri eccl. Saxoniae astruunt corporis &c. Domini praesentiam, & de libro J. Calvini ipsis dedicato respondent. s8º. Magdeburgae. 1557
Conf. S., *see* EDZARDI (S.) Ex conf. minist. Saxon., 1705.
The visitation of the Saxon reformed church in 1527–28. [Articuli de quibus egerunt per visitatores in regione Saxoniae, *Latin & German*]. w. introd. & remarks on Newman's Lectures on justification by R. Laurence. 8º. D. 1839

Saxony (Franz August Xavier, *prince of***),** *count of the Lausitz* [†AUGUSTUS ALBERT FRANCIS XAVIER BENEDICT], *see* BROGLIE (V. F., *duc de*). Corr. avec. le pr. Xavier de Saxe (1759–61), 4t, 1903–5.

Saya (Emilio). La lett. ital. dal 1870 ad oggi. 8º. 1928

Sayago (C. M.) Hist. de Copiapó. la8º. Copiapó. 1874

Sayce (Archibald Henry).
The Hittites. rev. & enl. ed. s8º. 1925
Primer of Assyriology. rev. ed. s8º. 1925
Races of the Old Test. rev. ed. s8º. 1925
Reminiscences. 8º. 1923

Sayers (James). Hints to J. Nollekens on h. modelling a bust of Lord G******le. [P2577]. 8º. 1808

Sayers (William C. Berwick).
Manual of classification for librarians &c. 8º. 1926
Story of Croydon: intr. hist. s8º. Croydon. 1925
see BROWN (J. D.) Man. of lib. econ., 3rd. ed. rev. & rewr. by S., 1920.

Sayffert (Jean Geoffroy), *see* SAIFFERT (J. G.)

Sayle (A.) Houses of the workers. Ed. J. A. Rosevear, who contrib. chap. 19. 8º. [1924]

Sayler (Oliver Martin). The Moscow Art Theatre ser. of Russ. plays. Ed. O. M. S. s1–2. s8º. 1923–24
s1, Tsar Fyodor Ivanovich, by Count A. Tolstoy—The lower depths, by M. Gorky—The cherry orchard—The 3 sisters—Uncle Vanya, by A. Tchekhoff. Tr. J. Covan.
2, The brothers Karamazoff, by F. Dostoievsky [tr. J. Covan]—The mistress of the inn, by C. Goldoni [tr. M. Pierson]—Ivanoff, by A. Tchekhoff [tr. M. Fell]—An enemy of the people, by H. Ibsen [tr. E. Marx-Aveling]—Enough stupidity in every wise man, by A. Ostrovsky [tr. P. Kasherman], *each w. sep. pagin.*

Sayn-Wittgenstein (Carolyne), *princess, wife of Pr. Nikolaus Sayn-Wittgenstein, b. 1819, see* WALLACE (W.) Liszt, Wagner & the Princess [*i.e.* C. S.-W.], 1927.

Sazonov (Sergei Dmitrievich). Fateful years, 1909–16: remin. [Tr. M. A. Duddington]. 8º. [1928]
see MARCHAND (R.) Un livre noir: diplomatie d'avant-guerre, 1910–14, t2, Rapports de S. &c., 1923.

Sbarbi (José María). Monogr. sobre los refranes, adagios y proverbios castell. la8º. 1891

Sbírka českých národních písní, 1845, *see* SWOBODA (W. A.)

Sbornik.
Сборник действующих договоров &c., 1921–23, *see* RUSSIA.
Сборникъ донесеній о Большевизмѣ въ Россіи (Англ. Бѣлая книга), 1919, *see* ENGLAND.
Сборникъ за народни умотворения и народописъ. Издава Българската Акад. на Наукитѣ. кн. 25i–iii, 27–29. la8º. София. 1909–14
Сборникъ "Извѣстій крестьянскихъ депутатовъ" и "Трудовой Россіи." [P2448]. 8º. Москва. 1906
Сборник материалов для агитаторов, No. 1. la8º. [Москва.] 1921
Сборникъ матеріаловъ для описанія мѣстностей и племенъ Кавказа. Изд. Управл. Кавказ. Учебн. Округа. вып. 1–39. 8º. Тифлисъ. [1881]–1908
Вып. 1 *has no tp.* вып. 2 *has engr. tp.* Матеріалы &c.
Сборникъ матеріаловъ для статистики Сыръ-Дарьинскаго Области, 1892–1902, *see* SIR-DARIÂ.
Сборникъ народныхъ юридич. обычаевъ. t1 (3 отд., *4 pagin.*) [I. R. G. O. Зап. по отд. этнографіи, т8]. 8º. С.–П. 1878
Сборникъ новѣйшихъ пѣсень и романсовъ "Чуркинъ." [P848]. s8º. С.–П. 1906
Сборникъ по хозяйств. статистикѣ полтавской губ., t3–7, 1884–88, *see* POLTAVA.
Сборникъ программъ полит. партій въ Россіи. Съ предисловіемъ В. В. Водовозова. Изд. "Нашей Жизни." B1–5. s8º. [С.–П.] 1906
Сборникъ свѣдѣній о кавказскихъ горцахъ, в3, 1870, *see* CAUCASUS.
Сборникъ статей въ честь гр. П. С. У., 1916, *see* UVAROVA (*Ctss.* P. S.)
Сборникъ товарищества "Знаніе." кн. 1–5. 8º. С.–П. 1904–5

Scaglia (Filiberto Gerardo), *conte di Verrua.* Avvertimenti polit. per entrare in corte—Cinque dispacci sulla quest. d. marchesato di Saluzzo; publ. per cura di D. Carutti, *see* REGIA DEP. DI STORIA PATRIA. Misc., t1, 1862.

Scaliger (Joseph J.), *1540–1609.*
Autobiog., w. sel. f. h. letters, h. test. & fun. orations by D. Heinsius & D. Baudius. Tr. w. intr. &c. by G. W. Robinson. 8º. C. 1927
Emendationes ad Theocriti Moschi & Bionis Idyllia 1596, &c., *see* THEOCRITUS, 1603.
Epistola de vetustate & splendore gentis Scaligerae, & Jul. C. Scaligeri vita. J. C. Scaligeri oratio in luctu filioli Audecti. Item testimonia de gente Scaligera & J. C. Scaligero. s4º. Lugd. Batav. 1594
Thesaurus temporum (Animadversiones in chronologica Eusebii &c.), 1606, *see* EUSEBIUS, *Pamphili.*
see LYDIAT (T.) Def. tract. de var. annorum formis, contra J. S. obtrect., 1607.

Scaliger (Julius Caesar). De causis linguae Latinae libri 13. s8º. *In Bibliopolio Commeliano.* 1623
see SCALIGER (J. J.) Epist. de vetustate gentis S. & J. C. S. vita, 1594.

Scaliger (Paulus), *see* DELLA SCALA (P.)

Scanaroli (Antonio). Disputatio, Bologna, 1498, *facs., see* SUDHOFF (C.) Earliest pr. lit. on syphilis, 1925.

Scanderbeg, *see* RADA (G. DE). Poesie albanesi, v2–5 (Scanderbeccu i pa-faan), 1872–75.

Scannell (Florence). Peter's predicament. s8º. [1919]

Scapula (Joannes). Lexicon Graeco-Latinum novum. Ed. ult., locupl. & corr. cum auctario dialectorum à J. Zuingero. [App. *w. sep. pagin.*] fol. Genevae. 1628

Scarabelli (Luciano).
see DANTE ALIGHIERI. Codice framment. d. D.C.; ed. L. S., 1869.
,, FRATI (C.) L. S. &c. e i. "Paralipomeni di st. piemontese," 1919.

Scarborough (Harold E.) The immortals. s8º. [1924]

Scarborough (William). A coll. of Chinese proverbs, rev. & enl. by add. of 600 proverbs by C. W. Allan. 8º. Shanghai. 1926

Scargill-Bird (S. R.), *see* GIUSEPPI (M. S.) Guide to MSS. in Public Rec. Office, v1, Legal records &c., by S.-B., 1923.

Scarlatti (Americo).
"Et ab hic et ab hoc." [v]1–5. 8º. Torino. 1920–27
1, Amenità lett. 2, Il castello dei sogni. 3, Corpus inscriptionum. 4, Altre iscriz. eclettiche. 5, Iscriz. di edifici.

Scarron (Paul). L'écolier de Salamanque—Le marquis ridicule, *see* FOURNEL (V.) Contemp. de Molière, t3, 1875.
see MAGNE (E.) S. & s. milieu, 1924.
,, MORILLOT (P.) S. & le genre grotesque, 1888.

***Scarronides**: or Le Virgile Travesty, 1664, *see* COTTON (C.)

Scarthoe, *Lincolnshire.* Parish reg. of S. Giles' Church, S. (1562–1837), w. hist. notes by E. E. Crake. 8º. Lincoln. 1926

Scatcherd (Norrisson). "Gleanings" after Eugene Aram. [*b. w. h.* Memoirs, 2nd ed., 1838]. s8º. 1836
Memoirs of Eugene Aram, w. some acc. of h. family &c. 2nd ed. s8º. 1838

Scattergood (Anthony), *see* PEARSON (J.) Critici sacri sive clar. virorum annot. &c. [ed. by J. P., A. S. &c.], 9t, 1698.

Scaturro (Ignazio). La Contessa normanna Giulietta di Sciacca, *see* SOCIETÀ SICILIANA. Archivio, N.S., 43, 1921.

Scelle (Georges). Une crise de la Soc. des Nations, mars-sept. 1926. s8º. [1927]

Scelte poesie liriche ital. s8º. Padova. 1826

Scelti versi sciolti italiani. s8º. Padova. 1826

Scève (Maurice), *see* AYNARD (J.), *ed.* Les poëtes lyonnais, 1924.

Schaack (Michael J.) Anarchy & anarchists. Chicago Haymarket conspiracy. la8º. Chicago. 1889

Schaaf (Carl). Lex. Syriacum concordantiale, omnes N. Test. Syriaci voces complectens. ed. 2ª. s4º. Lugd. Batav. 1717

Schachtzabel (Alfred). Im Hochland v. Angola: Studienreise. 8º. Dresden. 1923

Schaeffer (Asa Arthur).
Ameboid movement. 8º. Princeton. 1920

Schaetzke, *see* SCHÄTZKE.

Schäfer (Dietrich).
Kolonialgesch. 4ᵉ A. 2B [*in 1v*]. s8º. 1921
Osteuropa u. wir Deutschen. 8º. 1924

Schäfer (Ernst). Sevilla u. Valladolid, d. evangel. Gemeinden Span. im Ref.-zeitalter. [Verein f. Ref.-gesch. Schr., Jhrg. 21, Nr. 78]. 8º. Halle. 1903

Schäfer (Gustav).
Gesch. d. sächsichen Postwesens. 8º. Dresden. 1879

Schäfer (Heinrich). Nubische Texte im Dialekte d. Kunûzi (Mundart v. Abuhôr), *see* KÖNIGL. PREUSS. AKAD. Abhdl. (Phil.-hist. Kl.), 1917.
Priestergräber &c. vom Totentempel des Ne-user-reᶜ. [Deut. Orient-Gesell., Wiss. Veröffentl., 8]. fol. L. 1908
Sinn u. Aufgaben d. Berliner Ägypt. Museums, *see* ALTE ORIENT (DER), Jhrg. 22, 1920.
Von ägypt. Kunst bes. d. Zeichenkunst. 2ᵉ stark verm. A. 8º. L. 1922

Schäfer (Theobald v.) Tannenberg. [Schlachten d. Weltkrieges, B19]. 8º. Oldenburg. 1927

Schäfer (Wilhelm).
Rheinsagen. Erzählt v. W. S. s8º. München. 1927

Schaff (Philipp). Relig. encyclopædia: or dict. of Biblical, hist. &c. theology. Ed. P. S. &c. 3v. la8º. E. 1883–84
—— **& S. M. Jackson.** Encyclopedia of living divines & Xtian workers of all denom. in Europe & America. Suppl. to Schaff-Herzog, Encycl. of relig. knowledge. la8º. E. 1887

Schaffarik (Paul Joseph), *see* ŠAFAŘIK (PAVEL JOSEF).

Schäffer (Albrecht). Helianth. 3B. s8º. L. 1924

Schaffner (Jakob). Johannes. Roman e. Jugend. 6ᵉ A. 2B [*in 1v*]. s8º. St. [1922]
Kinder d. Schicksals. Roman. 6. A. s8º. St. [1925?]
Die Weisheit d. Liebe. Roman. s8º. St. [1925?]
Das Wunderbare. Roman. [7. Aufl.] 8º. St. [1924]

Schaible (Carl Heinrich). Deutsche Stich- u. Hieb-worte. 2e A. [P2507]. 8o. Str. 1885

Schairer (Reinhold) & C. Hoffmann. Die Universitätsideale d. Kulturvölker. Hrsg. v. S. & H. s8o. L. 1925

Schalk (Henriette Roland Holst van der), *see* ROLAND HOLST (H.)

Schall (Joannes Adamus) [*Father* JOHN ADAMS]. Hist. narr., de initio & progr. missionis Soc. Jesu apud Chinenses, ex litteris S. coll. s8o. Viennae Austriae. 1665

„ „ ed. 2a., aucta geogr. regni Chin. &c. [*by* P. Intorcetta]. s8o. Ratisbonae. 1672

see RULE (W. H.) Celebr. Jesuits, v2, 1853.

Schallenberg (Christof von). C. v. S. Ein österr. Lyriker d. 16 Jhdts. Hrsg. H. Hurch. [Lit. V. in St., 253]. 8o. Tübingen. 1910

Schaller (Felix). Exam. scrupulorum circa Luther. Jubiléum 1630 celeb. Sub praes. J. Himmelii. [P442]. s4o. Jenae. 1631

Schamelius (Johann Martin). Evangel. Lieder-Comment., d. gloss. Naumburg. Gesangb. verbess. &c. Dabey erscheinet d. Abdruck d. allerersten Gesang-Buchs Lutheri &c. [*w. sep. pag.*] s8o. L. 1724

Schamm (Josef). *Liturgik oder Erklärung d. gottesdienstl. Handlungen d. Kathol. Kirche z. Gebrauche f. d. Gymnasien im österr. Kaiserstaate. [Bearb. v. J. S. Umarb. v. I. Frencl.] 8o. Prag. 1857

Schannat (Johann Friedrich). Dioecesis Fuldensis cum annexa sua hierarchia. Acc. varii religios. ordinum coetus &c. fol. Francofurti ad Moenum. 1727

Hist. Fuldensis in tres partes div. Acc. Codex probationum & index abbatum. [*2 pagin.*] fol. Francofurti ad Moenum. 1729

Vindiciae quorundam archivi Fuld. diplomatum a J. G. ab Eckhart impugn. &c. [*b. w.* Eckhart (J. G.) Animadv. hist., 1727]. fol. Francofurti ad Moenum. 1728

see ECKHART (J. G.) Animadv. hist. in J. F. S. Dioecesin &c. Fuld., 1727.

Scharbau (Heinrich). Obs. sacrae, quibus varia sacri codicis utriusque Foederis loca ill. 3p [p2 & 3 *have sep. tps. dated 1733 & 1737 ; pagin. cont.*] s4o. Lubecae. 1759

Schärer (Emanuel). Beiträge z. Erkenntniss d. Wesens d. Philos. 8o. Zürich. 1846

Scharf (David). De notariis eccl. Diss. 1. Praes. J. A. Schmidio. [P432]. s4o. Helmstadii. [1715]

Scharf (Johann). Pædia theologica &c. s4o. Wittebergae. 1658

Protestatio adv. atrocia G. Calixti scandala. [P2647]. s4o. Wittenbergae. 1652

Scharff (Alexander).

Grundzüge d. ägypt. Vorgesch. 8o. L. 1927

Scharlieb (Mary Dacomb), *M.D.*

Psychol. of childhood, normal & abnormal. 8o. 1927

Reminiscences. 8o. 1924

Scharpius (Joannes), *see* SHARP (JOHN).

Scharr (Erwin). Xenophons Staats- u. Gesellschaftsideal u. s. Zeit. 8o. Halle (Saale). 1919

Scharten (Carel) & M. Scharten-Antink.

Een huis vol menschen. 10e dr. s8o. A. [1921]

Scharten-Antink (Margo). Sprotje. 3e dr. s8o. *n.d.*

see SCHARTEN (C.) & M. S.-A. Een huis vol menschen, 10e dr., 1921.

Schatz (Albert). L'entreprise gouvernementale et son admin. Préf. de H. Fayol. s8o. 1922

Schätzke (Viktor).

Greiffenstein. 2. u. 3. A. [P2878]. s8o. Schweidnitz. 1927

Schaudel (Louis). Les Comtes de Salm et l'Abbaye de Senones aux 12e & 13e siècles. Contrib. à l'hist. de Senones, Pierre-Percée, Badonviller, Blamont, Deneuvre. 8o. Nancy. 1921

Schäufelein (Hans Leonhard), *see* PINDER (U.) Speculum passionis &c. cum figuris [*by H. L. S.*], 1507.

Schauffler (Robert Haven). Sel. poems. 8o. 1922

Schauman (August), *see* ALCENIUS (C. A.) & A. SCHAUMAN. De scholis Fenniae, 1848–49.

Schaumann (August Ludolf Friedrich). On the road w. Wellington. Diary of a war commissary. Ed. & tr. A. M. Ludovici. 8o. 1924

Schaumberg (Silvester v.), *see* KIPP (F.) S. v. S., d. Freund Luthers: e. Lebensbild, 1911.

Schaumburg (Paul), *see* BURG (P.), *ps.*

Schauroth (*Freifrau* Charlotte v.), *see* DORNAU (C. v.), *ps.*

Schauspiele. Drei S. vom sterbenden Menschen, 1927, *see* BOLTE (J.)

Schaw (Janet). *Journal of a lady of quality. Narr. of a journey f. Scotland to the W. Indies, N. Carolina & Portugal, 1774–1776. Ed. E. W. Andrews, in collab. w. C. McL. Andrews. [Yale Hist. Publ., MSS. &c., 6]. 8o. New Haven. 1921

Schébéko (*Gen.* —), *ed.*, *see* CHRONIQUE. Chron. du mouv. social. en Russie, 1878–87, 1890.

Schebel (Friedrich). Disput. de propos. Paulina: Arbitramur justificari hominem fide. [*b. w.* Schweickhard (E.) Disp., 1569]. s4o. Tubingae. 1569

Schechsius (Paulus). Kurtzer, warhafftiger &c. Bericht, auf Calumnien &c. d. jetzigen Calvin. Predicanten zu Heidelberg. Ein stück Pfaltzgrave Ludwigen S. G. Testaments, die Religion betreffend &c. [P2437]. s4o. *n.p.* [c. 1585]

Scheckius (Jacobus), *see* SCHEGKIUS (J.)

Schedel (Hartmann). [*Nuremberg Chronicle. *f1 Woodcut title*]: Registrum huius operis libri cronicarum cū figuris et ymagībus ab inicio mūdi. fol. [Nürnberg. 1493]

Wanting fol. 27 (Numbered fol. 7), fol. 259–261 (blanks), 319 & 320 (numb. 298 & 299), 321 (Fol. 1 of De Sarmacia*), & 326 (blank).*

Schedius (Elias). De Dis Germanis, sive veteri Germanorum, Gallorum, Britannorum, Vandalorum religione, syngrammata quatuor. s8o. Amsterodami. 1648

Schedius (Johannes). Commentariolus in oraculum Johannæum, cap. 8, v25. s4o. Wittebergae. 1688

Scheeben (Matthias Joseph). Hdbch. d. kathol. Dogmatik. B1 [Abt. 3 *wanting*]. 8o. Freiburg im Breisgau. 1873

Scheel (Otto). Entwicklung Luthers [-1516]. [Verein f. Ref.-Gesch. Schr., Jhrg. 27 (Nr. 100)]. 8o. L. 1910

Scheffauer (Herman George).

The new vision in the German arts. s8o. 1924

Scheffel (Joseph Victor v.) Werke. Hrsg. F. Panzer. Krit. durchgesehene u. erläut. A. s8o. L. *n.d.*

Ekkehard. Gesch. aus d. 10en Jhdt. 81e A. s8o. St. 1885

Scheffer (David), *see* MÖHR (A.), B. STAUB & D. S. Amphib. beatitudinis &c., 1663.

Scheffer (Johannes).

Lapponia. s4o. Francofurti. 1673

Suecia literata, seu de scriptis & scriptoribus gentis Sueciae. Op. postum. s8o. Holmiae. 1680

Suecia litt., *see* MOLLER (J.) Bibl. septentr. eruditi, 1699.

see KUNUNGA ok höfdinga styrilse; in Lat. vertit &c., J. S., 1669.

Scheffler (Carl).

Deutsche Maler u. Zeichner im 19ten Jhrh. 8o. L. 1920

Der Geist d. Gotik. 8o. L. 1922

Scheffler (Hermann).

Körper u. Geist. 8o. Braunschweig. 1862

Scheffler (Johann) [*ps.* JOANNES ANGELUS SILESIUS]. Cherubin. Wandersmann. Nach d. A. 1675 hrsg. u. m. e. St. "Über d. Wert d. Mystik f. uns. Zeit" eingel. v. W. Bölsche. s8o. Jena. 1921

Der Cherubin. Wandersmann. Geistreiche Sinn.- u. Schlussreime. Hrsg. &c. B. Funck. s8o. München. 1921

Heilige Seelen-Lust, oder Hirten-Lieder &c. mit Melodeyen. s8o. Bresslaw. 1668

Heilige Seelenlust. Geistl. Lieder v. A. S. Bearb. &c. v. W. Winterer & H. Sprenger. s8o. Mannheim. 1838

Sämtl. poet. Werke. Hrsg. H. L. Held. 2B. s8o. München. 1922

Schegkius (Jacobus), *the elder.* Admonitio de comment. suis in Topica Aristotelis &c. [P445]. s4o. Tubingae. 1585

Antilogia, qua refellit 27 propos. Servetianæ hæreseωs. s4o. Tubingæ. 1568

*Declaratio eorum quæ in libello J. Scheckii De una persona &c. Christi nonnullis obscuriora &c. sunt visa. [Pref. *by* S. Simonius. *b. w.* Grynæus (J. J.) Synopsis &c., 1579]. s8o. Genevæ. 1566

Responsio ad libellum anon. interpretis libri sui De una persona & duabus naturis in Christo. [P2504]. s4o. Tubingæ. 1586

Schegolev (P. E.)

Дуэль и смерть Пушкина. изд. 3e. la8o. Москва. 1928

Мария Волконская. s8o. С.-П. 1922

Отречение Николая II: воспом. очевидцев, док. Ред. П. Е. Щ. Статьи Л. Китаева и М. Е. Кольцова. 8o. Ленинград. 1927

Падение царского режима. Отчеты допросов &c. данных в 1917 г. Чрезвычайной Следств. Ком. Врем. Правительства. Ред. П. Е. Щ. т1–7. 8o. Ленинград. 1924–27

For abr. Fr. tr., see MAKLAKOV (V. A.), *ed.*

Scheidemann (Philipp). Der Zusammenbruch. 8º. 1921
see LIEBIG (H. v.) Bethmann-Hollweg, S. &c. (Reichsverderber, T1), 1922.

Scheidewin (Wolfgang). The burden of milit. occup. in the Rhineland. Pref. by A. v. Gwinner. [P2719]. 8º. Leipzig. 1923

Scheidler (Carl Hermann). Grundlinien d. Hodegetik oder Methodik d. akad. Studiums &c. 2^{e} verm. A. 8º. Jena. 1839

Scheidlin (Andreas). De Sanctorum sive Apostolorum sortibus ex inspectione Bibliorum &c. Praes. H. Lincken, disput. A. S. [*b. w.* Ryssen (L. van) Veritas de lusu aleae &c., 1660]. s8º. Norica. 1686

Scheil (Vincent). Mission en Susiane : sous la dir. de R. de Mecquenem & V. S. : textes de comptabilité proto-élamites, nouv. sér., par V. S., *see* DÉLÉGATION EN PERSE, t17, 1923.

Scheler (Auguste) [†SCHELER (JEAN AUGUSTE UDALRIC)]. Mém. sur la conjugaison franç. [*Extr.* Acad. Roy. de Belgique, t19]. [P2527]. 4º. [Brux. 1845]

Scheler (Max). Die Ursachen d. Deutschenhasses : e. nationalpädagog. Erörterung. [2e verm. A. P2458]. 8º. L. [1917]

Schelgov (Ivan). Наивные вопросы. [P2445]. 8º. С.-П. 1903

Schelguigius (Samuel), *see* SCHELWIG (S.)

Schelhasse (Ferdinand), *see* WESTFALEN. Bau- u. Kunstdenkm., 37, Kreis Lippstadt, gesch. Einl. v. F. S., 1912.

Schell (Franz Jakob). S. Hrabani Mauri de sacramentis eccles. doct. coll. v. F. J. S. [P558]. 4º. Fulda. 1845

Scheller (Immanuel Johann Gerhard), *see* CHMEL (J.) Latein.-Böhm.-Deutsches Wörterbuch nach S.'s etym. Grundlage verm. u. hrsg. v. J. C., 1830.

Schellhorn (Johann Georg). De antiquiss. Lat. Bibliorum editione. s4º. Ulmae. 1760
Ergötzlichkeiten aus d. Kirchenhist. u. Literatur. 12 St. *in* 3B. [*pagin. cont.*] s8º. Ulm. 1762–64

Schellig (Konrad). Consilium (Heidelberg, 1495/6) *facs.*, *see* SUDHOFF (C.) Earliest pr. lit. on syphilis, 1925.

Schelling (Felix Emanuel). Appraisements & asperities as to some contemp. writers. 8º. Phila. 1922
Elizabethan playwrights : Eng. drama f. mediæval times to 1642. 8º. N.Y. 1925
Foreign influences in Elizabethan plays. 8º. N.Y. 1923
Poetic & verse criticism of the reign of Eliz. 8º. Phila. 1891
Shakespeare & "demi-science": papers on Elizabethan topics. 8º. Phila. 1927
Typical Elizabethan plays. Ed. f. early ed. by F. E. S. 8º. N.Y. 1926

Schelling (Friedrich Wilhelm Joseph v.) De Marcione Paullinarum Epistolarum emendatore. Praes. G. C. Storr. [P427]. s4º. Tubingae. 1795
Philosoph. Untersuchungen ü. d. Wesen d. menschl. Freiheit &c. [P2486]. s8º. Reutlingen. 1834
see FRANTZ (C.) S.'s posit. Philos., 3T, 1879–80.
„ HOFFMANN (F.) F. v. Baader in s. Verhältniss zu Hegel u. S., 1850.

Schellwien (Robert). Das Gesetz d. Causalität in d. Natur. [*b. w. h.* Sein u. Bewusstsein, 1863]. 8º. 1876
Max Stirner u. Fr. Nietzsche. [P2478]. 8º. L. 1892
Philos. u. Leben. [P2481]. 8º. L. 1898
Sein u. Bewusstsein. 8º. 1863
Der Wille, d. Lebensgrundmacht. T1 [*no more publ^{d}. b. w. h.* Sein u. Bewusstsein, 1863]. 8º. 1879

Schelstrate (Emmanuel a). Antiquitas eccl. diss., mon. ac notis illustr. 2t. fol. Romae. 1692–97

Scheltema (C. S. Adama van), *see* ADAMA VAN SCHELTEMA (C. S.)

Scheltema (Jacobus). Rusland & de Nederlanden. 4d. 8º. Amsterdam. 1817–19

Schelven (A. A. van), *ed.*, *see* DUTCH CHURCH, *Austin Friars.* Kerkeraads-protocollen, 1560–63, 1921.

Schelwig (Samuel) [SCHELGUIGIUS (S.)]. De Concilio Gangrensi exercit. [P2647]. s4º. Gedani. 1690
Synopsis controv. sub pietatis praetextu motarum &c. ed. 3^{a}. auct. s8º. Gedani. 1705
see ZIEROLD (J. W.) Synopsis verit. divin. opposita Synopsi controv. S. S., 1706.

Schemann (Carl Ludwig). Quellen u. Untersuchungen z. Leben Gobineaus. B2. 8º. 1919

Schenck (Jacob), *Reformer, of Freiberg.* Von warhafftiger Christlicher Buss, Wider die falsche un-christilche [*sic*] buss, so Georgius Witzel leret. s4º. [Wittemberg, *J. Klug*]. 1539

Schencke (Johann Christian). De Christi scriptis. Praes. G. H. Goezio. [P2645]. s4º. Wittebergae. [1687]

Schenck von Stauffenberg (Jacob). Sendtbrieff an seyne Geschwyhen. s4º. *n.p.* 1524

Schendel (Arthur van). Ein zwerver verdwaald. [3^{e} dr.] s8º. A. 1917
Een zwerver verliefd. [5^{e} dr.] s8º. A. 1917

Schenk (Pieter). Nov. Regni Scotiae tabula. [Maps, 6]. folded fol. *n.p.* 1708

Schenkl (Heinrich). Beitr. z. Textgesch. d. Reden d. Themistios, 1919, *see* KAIS. AKAD. D. W. z. WIEN. Sitz., B192, 1921.

Schepkina-Kupernik (T. L.) Стихи. s8º. Berlin. 1923

Scherbakivsky (Danilo), *see* SCHERBAKIVSKY (V.) & D. S. L'art de l'Ukraïne, t2 [*by* D. S.], 1926.

Scherbakivsky (Vadim) & D. Scherbakivsky [SHTCHERBAKIVSKY]. L'art de l'Ukraïne [*Russ. & Fr.*] [t]2 [*by* D. S.] 4º. Kiev. 1926
2, Les églises de bois en Boukovine & Galicie &c.

Scherbatov (*prince* Aleksandr Grigorevich).
[*Russian leaflets on land, politics & working classes.* P2449]. 8º. 1906–7
Only those w. tp. are catalogued separately below.
Государств.-народное хозяйство Россiи въ ближайшемъ будущемъ. [P2452]. 8º. Москва. 1910
Государств. оборона Россiи. [P2452]. 8º. Москва. 1912
Землеустройство. [*no tp.* P2452]. 8º. *n.p.* [1913]
О значенiи русско-японской войны. [P2449]. 8º. Москва. 1905
Обновленная Россiя. [P2452]. 8º. Москва. 1908
Приходъ и его значенiе. [P2449]. 8º. Москва. 1905
Рѣчи, 1906, *see* VOSTORGOV (I.) & *prince* A. G. S.
Сообщенiе о государств. думѣ. [P2449]. 8º. Москва. 1906
Способы увеличить производительность крестьянск. хозяйства. [P2449]. 8º. Москва. 1905
Хорошее управленiе денежн. обращенiемъ есть основанiе государств. и народн. богатства. [P2452]. 8º. Москва. 1908

Scherbatsky (Theodor) [STCHERBATSKY]. The central conception of Buddhism & the meaning of the word "Dharma." [Roy. Asiatic Soc.] 8º. 1923
La théorie de la connaissance & la logique chez les Bouddhistes tardifs. Tr. I. de Manziarly & P. Masson-Oursel. [Annales du Musée Guimet. Bibl. d'Études, t36]. la8º. 1926

Scherbinin (Mikhail Pavlovich).
Бiографiя Ген.-Фельдмар. кн. М. С. Воронцова. la8º. С.-П. 1858

Scheremetew, *see* SHEREMETEV.

Scherer (Georg), *Jesuit.*
Antwort auff d. zwey Famos Schandt u. Lästercharten M. A. Utzingers, wider Julium Bischoffen zu Würzburg u. Hertzogen zu Francken &c. aussgeworffen. s4º. Ingolstadt. 1589
Catholische Glossa oder Erleutterung G. S.'s auff ein Epistel d. Ubiquentlerischen Predicanten &c. zu Tübingen an Griech. Patriarchen zu Constantinopel. [P2437]. s4º. Ingolstadt, *David Sartorius.* 1584
Der Luther. Bettler Mantel. s4º. Ingolstatt. 1588
Zwo Christliche Predigen. [P2437]. s4º. Ingolstadt. 1585
see OSIANDER (L.) Verantwortung wider G. S. &c., 1586.

Scherer (Georg), *of Stuttgart.*
Illustr. deut. Kinderbuch &c. B2. s4º. L. 1869

Scherffig (Paul). Friedrich Mekum v. Lichtenfels. [Quellen &c. aus d. Gesch. d. Reformationsjhdts., B12]. 8º. L. 1909

Scherillo (Michele). Ippolito Pindemonte e la poesia bardita. s8º. Messina. [1920]
Le orig. e lo svolgimento d. lett. ital. 2, Il Rinascimento, p1, L'Umanesimo—Pontano—Poliziano. s8º. Milano. 1926
see MANZONI (A.) Manzoni intimo, v1, 2, a cura di M. S., 1923.

Schering (Arnold). Gesch. d. Oratoriums. 8º. L. 1911

Scherman (Lucian). Zur altchines. Plastik, Neuzugänge im Münchener Ethnogr. Mus., *see* KÖNIGL. AKAD. D. WISS. ZU MÜNCHEN. Phil. Classe, Sitz., 1915.

Schermerhorn (Elizabeth W.) Benjamin Constant, h. private life & h. contrib. to liberal govt. in France, 1767–1830. Pref. by F. Baldensperger. 8º. [1924]
The seven strings of the lyre : life of G. Sand, 1804–76. 8º. [1927]

Scherz (Johann Georg) [SCHERZIUS]. Glossarium Germanicum medii aevi, potiss. dial. Suevicae. Ed., illustr., Supplevit J. J. Oberlinus. 2t. *b. in* 1. fol. Argentorati. 1781–84

Scherzenfeldt (Brigitta), *1684–1736*, *see* LEIJONHUFVUD (S.) Två Kvinnoöden, 1907.

Scherzer (Carl v.) Smyrne. En collab. avec C. Humann &c. 2e éd. 8º. Leipzig. [1873–1880]

Schesaeus (Christianus). Ruinae Pannonicae libri 4, statum rei publ. & relig. in Ungaria & Transsilvania temp. I. S. Zápolya complexi ex ed. Wittemberg. 1561 recusi. Acc. Notitia liter. de Schesaeo &c. opera I. C. Eder. [Scr. rer. Transsilvan., t1, v1]. 4º. Cibinii. 1797

Schetelig (Christoph Heinrich) [SCHETELIGIUS], *see* WILDESHAUSEN (J. F.) Bibl. disputationum ; studio &c. C. H. S., 1736–37.

Schetelig (Haakon). Arkeol. tidsbestemmelser av ældre Norske Runeindskr., *see* BUGGE (S.), *ed.* Norges indskr., B3, 1914–24.

see OSEBERGFUNDET ; utg. av d. Norske Stat under redaktion av A. W. Brøgger, H. S. &c., 3B, 1917–28.

Schetinin (*prince* B. A.)
Въ московскомъ университетѣ. [P2722]. 8°. Москва. 1906

Schetky (John Christian), *see* SCHETKY (S. F. L.) Ninety years, 1877.

Schetky (S. F. L.) Ninety years of work & play. Sk. f. career of J. C. Schetky, by h. daughter [*i.e.* S. F. L. S.] s8°. E. 1877

Scheuermeier (Paul). Ein. Bezeichnungen für d. Begriff Höhle in d. roman. Alpendialekten. [Zeitschr. f. roman. Philologie, Beih., 69]. 8°. Halle a. S. 1920

Scheufflerus (Joannes Gottfridus). De articulis Svobac. August. Conf. fundamento. [*b. w.* Layritius (J. J.) De articulis Svobac., 1719]. s4°. Wittenbergae. 1719

Scheurleer (C. W. Lunsingh), *see* CORPUS vasorum antiq. : Pays-Bas, fasc. 1, Musée Scheurleer (La Haye), fasc. 1, 1927.

Schevichaven (Herman Diederik Johan van) [*ps.* J. LARWOOD], *see* †LARWOOD (J.), *ps.*

Schevill (Ferdinand). The Balkan Peninsula & the Near East : hist. f. earliest times to pres. day. 8°. 1922

Schiafenato (Giovanni Battista).
Rime. [*no pagin.*] s8°. [Vinegia. 1534]

Schiaffini (Alfredo). Chiese non parrocchiali nel M. E., *see* ARCHIVIO STOR. ITAL., Anno 81, 1925.

"Parochia" e "Plebs," *see* ARCHIVIO STOR. ITAL., a. 80, 1922.

Schiaparelli (Attilio). Leonardo ritrattista. 8°. Milano. 1921

Schiaparelli (Luigi). Il codice 490 d. Bibl. Capitolare di Lucca e la scuola scrittoria lucchese (sec. 8–9). 8°. 1924

Note paleogr. &c., *see* ARCHIVIO STORICO ITAL., Anno 82, v1, 2, a. 84, v1, 1924–26.

La scrittura latina nell' età romana ; note paleogr. 8°. Como. 1921

Schickard (Wilhelm), *the elder* [SCHIKARDUS (W.)] Bechinath happeruschim : exam. comm. rabbinic. in Mosen prodromus &c. [*b. w. h.* Tarich, 1628]. s4°. Tubingae. 1624
Following the pref., there is a 2nd tp., dated 1621.

Epitome Bibliorum : Vet. Test. testimonia uspiam in Nov. Test. citata ; sub titulo Eclogarum sacr. Ebræo-Lat. Vet. Test. ed. 1633. Accur. B. Raithio. [*b. w.* Moses ben J. Kimchi, 'Οδοιπορία &c., 1631]. s8°. Tubingae. 1663

Tarich, h. e. series regum Persiae. Ex fide MS. vol., vestita comm. ex aliis Arabum & Hebr. libris &c. s4°. Tubingae. 1628

Schickele (René).
Ein Erbe am Rhein. 2B. s8°. München. [1925]
Die Genfer Reise. s8°. 1919

Schieber (Anna). "Und hätte der Liebe nicht," Weihnachtl. Geschichten. s8°. Heilbronn. [1912]

Schieferdecker (Johann David). De Sibyllis diss., præs. J. Michaele. [P1035]. s4°. Cizæ. [1690]

Schiefner (Franz Anton v.) [SHIFNER].
Осетинскіе тексты собр. Д. Чонкадзе и В. Цораевымъ. [I. Akad. Nauk. Записки, t14]. 8°. С.-П. 1868

Schiemann (Theodor). Deutschlands u. Kaiser Wilhelms II angebliche Schuld am Ausbruch d. Weltkrieges : e. Entgegnung an C. Kautsky. [P2492]. 8°. 1921

Schiern (Frederik Eginhard). Origines & migrationes Cimbrorum. Diss. 8°. Havniae. [1842]

Schiess (Traugott). J. Kesslers Sabbata, St. Galler Reformationschronik, 1523–39. [Verein f. Ref.-Gesch., Schr., Jhrg. 28 (Nr. 103/4)]. 8°. L. 1911

Schiffer (Sinai). Die Aramäer : hist.-geograph. Untersuchungen. 8°. L. 1911

Schiffmann (Konrad). Das Land ob d. Enns, eine altbaier. Landschaft in d. Namen i. Siedlungen, Berge, Flüsse u. Seen. 8°. München. 1922

Schikardus (Wilhelmus), *see* SCHICKARD (W.)

Schill (Johann Gottfried), *see* ZWICK (H. A.) Calmuc Tartary, journey by Z. & S. ; tr., 1831.

Schiller (Ferdinand Canning Scott).
Eugenics & politics : essays. 8°. 1926
Hypothesis, *see* SINGER (C.), *ed.* St. in hist. &c. of sci., v2, 1921.
Problems of belief. s8°. [1924]
Tantalus, or, the future of man. s8°. 1924

Schiller (J. C. Friedrich v.)
Werke. Hrsg. H. Kurz. Krit. durchges. A. 8B. s8°. L., *Bibliog. Inst. n.d.*
Schillergabe für Deutschlands Jugend hrsg. v. d. Lit. Verein d. Berl. Lehrervereins mit Einl. v. Dr. Jonas. s8°. Düsseldorf. [1905]

SINGLE WORKS.
Die Jungfrau v. Orleans. Tragödie. s8°. St. 1861
Die Räuber. Trauerspiel. Ed. [w. intr.] by L. A. Willoughby. 8°. 1922
Wallenstein. 2T [*in* 1v]. s8°. L. *n.d.*
Wilhelm Tell. Notes &c. by A. J. Ulrich. s8°. *n.d.*

TRANSLATIONS.
Gli artisti ; ital. d. V. Talamini. [Nozze Danieli — Salamon. N. 127]. 8°. Belluno. 1864
Dram. works. Wallenstein & W. Tell. Tr. S. T. Coleridge, J. Churchill & T. Martin. [repr.] s8°. *Bohn.* 1901
Early dramas & romances. Tr. [repr.] s8°. *Bohn.* 1901
Essays æsthetical & philosoph. Tr. [repr.] s8°. *Bohn.* 1900
[Hist.] dramas : Don Carlos &c. Tr. R. D. Boylan, J. Mellish, A. Swanwick & A. Lodge. [repr.] s8°. *Bohn.* 1901

TRANSLATIONS [*continued*].
Hist. of the 30 Years War. Tr. A. J. W. Morrison. [repr.] s8°. *Bohn.* 1901
Poems. Tr. E. A. Bowring. [Works, v5]. s8°. *Bohn.* 1902
Revolt of the Netherlands—The disturbances in France prec. r. of Hen. IV. Tr. A. J. W. Morrison & L. D. Schmitz. [Works, v2]. s8°. *Bohn.* 1897

see CASSIRER (E.) Idee u. Gestalt: S. &c., 2. A., 1924.
" GÜNTTER (O. v.) S., Leben u. Dicht., Abbildungen, 1925.
" HAMANN (CHR.) F. S. als Mensch u. Dichter, 2e A., 1903.
" KÖRNER (J.) Romantiker u. Klassiker : d. Brüder Schlegel in i. Bezieh. zu S. u. Goethe, 1924.
" RETZSCH (F. A. M.) 8 Umrisse zu S.'s Fridolin, 1824.
" SCHWEIZER (P.) Die Wallenstein-Frage in Gesch. u. im Drama (S.'s W.-Trilogie &c.), 1899.

Schillmann (Fritz). Viterbo u. Orvieto. [Berühmte Kunststätten, 55]. s8°. L. 1911

Schilter (Johann). Disput. de syllogismo topico. Praes. Æ. Strauchio. [P522]. s4°. Witebergae. 1608

Schilter (Johann), *of Strassburg.* Instit. juris Canonici. ed. 3a. corr. s8°. Jenæ. 1699

Thesaurus antiq. Teutonic. 3t. fol. Ulmae. 1727–28
1, Otfried von Weissenburg, Vol. Evangel.—Notker *Labeo*, Psalterium Davidic.—Willeram *abbot*, In Canticum Canticorum—Kero monachus, Interpretatio regulae St. Benedicti—Poetae anon, Rhythmus de Annone.
2, Antiq. legis Salicae textus—Jus provinc. Alemann.—Stricker, Rhythmus de Caroli magni exped. Hispan.—Charlemagne, Anon. fragm. de bello Caroli contra Saracenos. — Louis *King of France*, Επινικιόν, 1383 — Tyrol, Paraeneses antiq. Germ. Tyrolis &c. ut & Winsbeckii ad filium—Tatian, Harmonia Evang.
3, Glossarium Germanic. [*for a copy, see* SCHERZ (J. G.) Gloss. Teut., 1781–84].
Each work has a sep. tp. & sep. pagin. In vol. 1 the tps. are all dated 1726 ; in vol. 2, 1727.

Schimmelpenninck (Rutger Jan), *see* COLENBRANDER (H. T.) S. & Koning Lodewijk, 1911.

Schindler (Valentin). Lexicon pentaglotton, Hebr., Chald., Syr., Talmudico-Rabbinicum, & Arab. &c. [Pref. by E. Engels]. fol. Hanoviae. 1612
" " ....[*a. ed.*] fol. Londini. 1635

Schindler (Vinzenz), *see* VIENNA. Quellen z. Gesch. d. Stadt Wien ; Abtlg. 1, B9, bearb. v. V. S., 1921.

Schiner (*Card.* Matthäus), *bp. of Sion* [SCHINNER]. Korresp. u. Akten z. Gesch. d. Kard. M. S. ; gesammelt u. hrsg. v. A. Büchi, 2B, 1489–1527, *see* QUELLEN z. SCHWEIZER GESCH., N.F., Abtlg. 3, B5, 6, 1920–25.

see BÜCHI (A.) Kard. M. S. als Staatsmann u. Kirchenfürst, T1 (bis 1514), 1923.
" KALKOFF (P.) Kard. Schiner &c. auf d. Wormser Reichstage, 1919.

Schinmeier (Johann Adolph). Versuch e. Gesch. d. Schwed. Bibel-Uebersetzungen u. Ausgaben. Nebst Anhänge. 4 Stück & 2 Beyl. & Fortsetz. [*b. in* 1v.] 4°. Flensburg. 1777–82
The Beylagen *include* Finn. Bibel Uebersetz.

Schinz (Albert). Anti-pragmatism : resp. rights of intellectual aristocracy & soc. democracy. 8°. 1910

Schipa (Michelangelo). Nobili e popolani in Napoli nel medioevo, *see* ARCHIVIO STOR. ITAL., anno 83, v1, 1925.

Schirmbeck (Adam), *see* JESUITS. Messis Paraquariensis a patribus S. J. in Paraquaria coll. 1638–43 ; conscr. à p. A. S., 1649.

Schirmer (Walter F.) Antike, Renaissance u. Puritanismus : St. z. engl. Literaturgesch. d. 16. u. 17. Jhdts. la8°. München. 1924

Schirmesterus (Wolffgang), *see* QUAESTIONES. In hoc libello exponuntur quaestiones 5 [*by* W. S. &c.], 1544.

Schiwietz (Stephan).
Das morgenländ. Mönchtum. B2. 8°. Mainz. 1913
2, Das Mönchtum auf Sinai u. in Palästina in 4ten Jhdt.

Schjelderup (Harald K.) Filosofiens hist. fra Renaissancen til nutiden. 2en forøkede utg. 8°. Oslo. 1925
Hauptlinien d. Entwicklung d. Philos. v. Mitte d. 19. Jhdt. bis z. Gegenwart. [Videnskapsselskapets Skr. II, Hist.-filos. Kl. 1919]. la8°. Kristiania. 1920

Schlachten. Schlachten d. Weltkrieges in Einzeldarstell. bearb. u. hrsg. unter Mitwirkung d. Reichsarchivs. B1–7, 9–13, 16–24 [1, 2, 3, 6, 2. A. 9, 3. A. (1 = 8 *of* 1. A., 2 = 9 *of* 1. A., 4 = 8 *of* 2. A.)] 8°. Oldenburg. 1921–28
see BETTAG (F.) Die Eroberung v. Nowo Georgiewsk, 1921. [4.]
,, BEUMELBURG (W.) Douaumont, 1925. [1.]
,, —— Loretto, 1927. [17.]
,, —— Ypern, 1914, 1926. [10.]
,, BOSE (T. v.) Das Marnedrama, 1914, T1–3i, 1928. [22–24.]
,, DIETERICH (—) Weltkriegsende, mazedon. Front, 1926. [11.]
,, FRIEDEBURG (F. v.) Karpathen- u. Dnjester-Schlacht, 1915, 1925. [2.]
,, GEBSATTEL (L. v.) Von Nancy bis z. Camp des Romains, 1914, 1924. [6.]
,, GOLD (L.) Die Tragödie v. Verdun, 1916, 1926. [13.]
,, HEYDEMANN (K.) Schlacht bei St. Quentin 1914, 2. A., 2T, 1924–25. [7.]
,, KRAFFT V. DELLMENSINGEN. Der Durchbruch am Isonzo, 2T, 1926. [12a, b.]
,, MÜHLMANN (C.) Kampf um d. Dardanellen, 1915, 1927. [16.]
,, SCHÄFER (T. v.) Tannenberg, 1927. [19.]
,, SCHMIDT (E.) Argonnen, 1927. [18.]
,, STOSCH (A. v.) Somme-Nord, Juli, 1916, 1927. [20, 21.]
,, STRUTZ (G.) Erstürmung d. Brückenkopfes v. Jakobstadt, 1917, 1927. [9.]
,, —— Herbstschlacht in Macedonien, 1916, 1925. [5.]
,, TSCHISCHWITZ (E. v.) Antwerpen, 1914, 1925. [3.]
,, VOGEL (W.) Kämpfe um Baranowitschi, 1916, 1927. [9.]

*Schlachten (Die) u. Gefechte d. Grossen Krieges, 1914–18. Quellenwerk nach d. amtl. Bezeichn. zusammengest. v. Grossen Generalstab. 8°. 1919

Schlachter (Alois). Der Globus: s. Entst. u. Verwendung in d. Ant. Hrsg. F. Gisinger. [Stoicheia. St.] 8°. L., *Teubner*. 1927

Schläger (Carl Julius). Diss. rariorum de antiq. sacris & profanis fasc. [1] & novus [*in 1v.*] s4°. Helmaestadii. 1742–44

Schlager (Patricius). Der heilige Antonius v. Padua in Kunst u. Legende. la8°. M. Gladbach. [1923]

Schlatter (Daniel). Bruchstücke aus e. Reisen nach d. südl. Russland, 1822–28. 8°. St. Gallen. 1836

Schlegel (August Wilhelm v.) Réflexions sur l'étude des langues asiat. 8°. Bonn. 1832
see KÖRNER (J.) Romantiker u. Klassiker: d. Brüder S. in i. Bezieh. zu Schiller u. Goethe, 1924.

Schlegel (C. W. Friedrich v.)
Lucinde. T1. [*No more publ.*] s8°. 1799
see KÖRNER (J.) Romantiker u. Klassiker: d. Brüder S. in i. Bezieh. zu Schiller u. Goethe, 1924.

Schlegel (Christian). Hist. vitae Georgii Spalatini. Praes. C. Sagittarius, resp. C. S. s4°. Jenae. 1693

Schleich (Martin). *L'infaillibilité expliquée &c. Tr. de l'allem. [P504]. s8°. Bruxelles. 1872

Schleicher (August).
Краткій очеркъ доисторич. жизни сѣверо-восточн. отд. Индо-Германск. Языковъ. [I. Akad. Nauk. Записки, t8]. 8°. С.–П. 1865
Склоненіе основъ на "у" въ слав. языкахъ. [I. Akad. Nauk. Записки, t11]. 8°. С.–П. 1867
Тэмы именъ числительныхъ въ литво-славянскомъ и нѣмецкомъ языкахъ. [I. Akad. Nauk. Записки, t10]. 8°. С.–П. 1866

Schleichert (Bonifacius).
Institutiones Patrologiae. s8°. Pragae. 1777

Schleiden (Matthais Jacob).
Studien. Populäre Vorträge. 2e verm. A. 8°. L. 1857

Schleiermacher (Friedrich D. E.) Monologen. s8°. L. [1874?]
Brief outline of the study of theology. Pref. remin. of S. by F. Lücke. Tr. by W. Farrer. s8°. E. 1850
see KAPPSTEIN (T.) S.'s Weltbild &c., 1921.

Schleifer (J.) Sahid. Bibel-Fragm. aus d. Brit. Mus., 3, Psalmenfragmente, *see* KAIS. AKAD. D. WISS. ZU WIEN. Sitzb., B173, 1914.

Schleinitz (Johann von), *bp. of Meissen.*
see LUTHER (MARTIN). Ad Schedulam inhibitiōis sub nom. episcopi Misneñ ed. responsio, [1520].
,, PALLAS (C.) Briefe u. Akten z. Visitationsreise d. Bisch. J. VII. v. M. im Kurf. Sachsen, 1522, 1908.

Schleiter (Frederick). Religion & culture. s8°. N.Y. 1919

Schlender (Ida Hedwig). German. Mythologie: Relig. u. Leben uns. Urväter. 4e, neubearb. A. 8°. Dresden. 1925

Schlenther (Paul). Gerhart Hauptmann. Leben u. Wke. Neue A. umgearb. u. erw. v. A. Eloesser. s8°. 1922

Schlesien, *see also* OBERSCHLESIEN.

Schlesinger (Arthur Meier). The colonial merchants & the Amer. revol., 1763–76. 8°. N.Y., *Columbia Univ.* 1917

Schlesinger (M. L.) Land u. Leute in Sowjetrussland. 3e, neubearb. A. s8°. [1927]

Schlesische. *Gesch. (Die) d. Berggeist Gnome auf d. s. Sudetengebirge. [P2588]. s8°. Dresden. *n.d.*

Schleswig. Bekanntmachungen d. Internat. Kommission für S. [*In Germ. & Dan.*] Stück 1–18 (20 Jan.–16 Juni 1920) *in* 1v. [*a. c. in* P2380]. 4°. *n.p.* 1920
,, ,, Auszug aus d. Bekanntm. Nr. 1–5 (20 Mai–16 Juni 1920). [P2380]. 4°. [Flensburg]. 1920

Schleswig-Holstein-Sonderburg-Beck (Frederick Paul Leopold, *duke of*), *see* CHRISTIAN X, *of Denmark.* C. IX's Forældre, 1918.

Schleuning (Johannes). Aus tiefster Not. Schicksale d. deut. Kolonisten in Russland. 8°. 1922

Schleunitz (Joachim Daniel). Philologemata medica, ex Ebraea &c. linguis decerpta. Praes. C. B. Michaelis. [P431]. s4°. Halae Magdeb. [1758]

Schlicht (*Frhr.* v.), *ps.* [*i.e.* WOLF, *Graf* v. BAUDISSIN].
Unsere Feldgrauen. Erzählungen. 3e A. s8°. 1915

Schlichting (Jonas), *see* SZLICHTING (J.)

Schlick (Moritz). Space & time in contemp. physics: intr. to theory of relativity &c. [Tr.] H. L. Brose, w. intr. by F. A. Lindemann. 8°. O. 1920

Schlickeysen (F. W. A.) Erklaerung d. Abkuerzungen auf Muenzen d. neu. Zeit d. M.-a. u. d. Alterthums &c. 3e A., bearbt. v. R. Pallmann. 8°. 1896

Schlieffen (Limbrecht W., *Graf* **v.)**, *see* FÖRSTER (W.) Graf S. u. d. Weltkrieg, 3T, 1921.

Schlienz (Christoph Friedrich). Views on the improvement of the Maltese lang. s8°. Malta. 1838

Schlitter (Hanns).
Gründ. d. kaiserl. Akad. d. Wiss., *see* KAIS. AKAD. D. WISS. ZU WIEN. Sitzber, B197, 1922.
Pius VI u. Josef II, 1782–84, *see* FONTES RERUM AUSTRIAC., B47ii, 1894.
Die Reise d. Papstes Pius VI nach Wien u. s. Aufenthalt daselbst &c., *see* FONTES RERUM AUSTRIAC., B47i, 1892.
see BEELEN-BERTHOLFF (*baron* DE). Berichte d. ersten Agenten Österr. in d. Verein. St. v. Amerika B. de B.-B., 1784–89, 1891.
,, MARY CHRISTINE, *archd. of Austria.* Briefe an Leopold II. &c., 1896.

Schlobies (Hans). Der akkad. Wettergott in Mesopotamien. [Altorient. Gesell. Mitteil., B1iii]. 8°. L. 1925

Schlomann (Alfred), *ed.*, *see* TECHNICAL dictionaries in 6 lang.; [ed.] A. S., v11–13, 1911–20.

Schlömp (Felix).
Das Gespensterbuch. Hrsg. F. S. 8°. München. 1920
Das unheimliche Buch. Hrsg. F. S. Vorw. v. K. H. Strobl. 8°. München. 1920

Schlosser (Joannes Ludovicus). Lutherus Lutheranus Luthero reformato J. M. Mommers oppositus. Acc. Lutherus Lutheranus de SS. Coena itemque App. gemina [*w. sep. pagin.*] 8°. Hamburgi. 1739

Schlosser (Julius).
Die Kunstliteratur: Hdbch. z. Quellenkunde d. neu. Kunstgesch. la8°. Wien. 1924
Materialien z. Quellenkunde d. Kunstgesch. [*Extr. f.* Sitz. d. K. Akad. d. Wiss. in Wien, B177, 179, 180, 184, 189, 192, 195, 196]. 10H *in* 1v. 8°. Wien. 1915–20
,, ,, *f. a. copy, see* KAIS. AKAD. D. WISS. ZU WIEN. Sitzungsb., 1915–20.
Präludien. Vorträge u. Aufsätze. 8°. [1927
Die Sammlung alt. Musikinstrumente. Beschreib. Verzeichnis v. J. S. [Kunsthist. Museum in Wien.] 4°. Wien. 192[illegible]
Unsere Musikinstrumente: e. Einführ. in ihre Gesch. la8°. Wien. 192[illegible]
see WICKHOFF (F.) Beschreib. Verzeichnis d. illum. Hss. in Österreich, B8 hrsg. J. S. &c., 1923–27.

Schlözer (August Ludwig v.), *ed.* Isländische Litteratur u. Gesch. T1 [*no more publ.*] s8°. Göttingen. 177[illegible]
see NESTOR, *the annalist.* Russ. Annalen; übers. u. erklär[illegible] v. A. L. S., 4T, 1802–5.

Schlözer (Carl F. E. v.) Menschen u. Landschaften aus d[illegible] Skizzenbuch e. Diplomaten. Hrsg. L. v. Schlözer. 8°. St. 192[illegible]

Schlözer (Kurd v.) Letzte röm. Briefe, 1882–94. Hrsg. L. v. Schlözer. 8°. St. 1924
Römische Briefe, 1864–69. Hrsg. K. v. Schlözer. [13. & 14. Aufl.] 8°. St. 1924

Schlumberger (Gustave L.) Byzance & Croisades. la8°. 1927
Un empereur de Byzance [*i.e.* Manuel II] à Paris & à Londres. 8°. 1916
Les Iles des Princes—Le palais & l'église des Blachernes—La grande muraille de Byzance. 2e éd. s8°. 1925
Jean de Chateaumorand, un des princ. héros franç. des arrière-croisades en Orient &c. 8°. 1919
Mélanges offerts à G. S. (17 oct. 1924). [*By var. a. Ed.* A. Blanchet &c.] 2t. 4°. 1924
t1, Hist. du Bas-Empire, de l'Empire byzantin &c.—Philol. byzant.
t2, Numismatique & sigillographie, archéologie.
Récits de Byzance & des Croisades. 2s. s8°. 1922–23
Voyage dans les Abruzzes & les Pouilles, 3–17 mai 1914. 8°. 1916

Schlumberger (Jean). Le camarade infidèle. 7e éd. s8°. 1922
Le lion devenu vieux. 2e éd. s8°. [1924]
La mort de Sparte. Drame. [Répert. du vieux-colombier]. s8°. [1921]

Schlupp (William F.) The destruction of rodents. [P2820]. 8°. Pretoria. 1921

Schlüsselburg.
*Жизнь въ Шлиссельбургской крѣпости. s8°. Берлинъ. [1904]

Schlüsselburg (Conrad). Haereticorum cat. Omnium nostri seculi Hereticorum index. s8°. Francofurti. 1597–99
lib. 1–13 [*in* 8v. l. 2–13 *have t.* Catalogi hæret. lib. 2 &c.]

Schmal (Felix).
Führer durch Dalmatien. [2e A.] s8°. Wien. [1926]

Schmalenbach (Hermann). Leibniz. la8°. München. 1921

Schmalkald, *Articles of.* Artikel der Evangel. Lere, so da hetten sollen auf's Concilium [Mantua] überantwortet werden, wo es sein würde. Gestellet auff dem Tage zu Schmalkalden a. 1537. [Vorrede *signed* J. Stolzius *&* J. Aurifaber]. [P2442]. s4°. *n.p.* 1553
see LUTHER (M.) Die S. Artikel, 1537 &c.; hrsg. K. Zangemeister, 1883.

Schmalkald, *League of, 1531–37.* Causae quare synodum indictam a Paulo III recusarint principes, status & civitates Imperii, profitentes puram & cath. Evangelii doct. [*engraved border to tp.*] s4°. Vitebergae. 1537
Ursachenn warumb das Concilium [Mantua] so Paulus III aussgeschriben &c. allen Christen die den auffgang d. Reichs J. C. &c. begeren &c. Durch die Churfürsten &c. zu Schmalkalden, 1537, versamlet an die Christl. Künig &c. geschriben &c. s4°. [Strassburg, *Wendel Rihel.* 1537]
„ „ *a. ed.* [Ursachen, *independ. tr.*] s4°. Smalkalden. 1537

Schmaltz (Carl). Mater ecclesiarum: Die Grabeskirche in Jerusalem. la8°. Str. 1918

Schmalz (Friedrich). Grossrumänien, wirtschaftl., polit. u. kulturell. 8°. Gotha. 1921

Schmarsow (August). Das Franciscusfenster in Königsfelden u. d. Freskenzyklus in Assisi, *see* KÖNIGL.-SÄCHS. GESELLS. D. WISS. Berichte, phil.-hist. Kl., B71, 1919.
Ital. Kunst im Zeitalter Dantes. [*Plates b. sep.*] 4°. Augsburg. 1928

Schmeil (Otto) & J. Fitschen. Flora v. Deutschland. Hilfsbuch. 29. A. bearb. v. J. Fitschen. s8°. L. 1922

Schmeizel (Martin). De statu eccl. Lutheranorum in Transilvania, diss. [*a. c. in* P484]. s4°. Jenae. 1722
Quaest. an Elector Saxon. Johannes in castra Pontif. transiverit? Resp. M. C. Othone. [P444]. s4°. Jenae. [1718]

Schmelzer (Anton Andreas), *see* WELLESZ (E.) Die Ballet-Suiten v. J. Heinrich u. A. A. S., 1914.

Schmersahl (Elias Friedrich). Gesch. jeztlebender [*sic*] Gottesgelehrten. 8 St. [*in* 1 v. *pagin. cont.*] s8°. Langensalza. 1751–55
Neue Nachrichten v. jüngstverstorb. Gelehrten. 2B. s8°. L. 1753–56
Verm. Beyträge z. Gesch. jüngstverstorb. Gelehrten. St. 1. [*b. w. h.* Neue Nachr., B2, 1756]. s8°. Zelle. 1756
Zuverlässige Nachrichten v. jüngstverstorb. Gelehrten. 2B. s8°. Zelle. 1748–53

Schmid (Christian Friedrich), *prof. of philos. at Leipzig.* Philol. u. krit. Bibliothek. 10 St. *in* 2B. s8°. L. 1770–72

Schmid (Christian Heinrich) & H. C. G. Walz. Simonides, seu de theologia poetarum. 8°. L. [1767]

Schmid (Christoph v.), *see* SCHMID (JOHANN CHRISTOPH v.)

Schmid (Daniel Friedrich) [SCHMIDIUS]. Disput. P. C. Scipionis Africani Majoris vitam exhibens. Praes. J. Simonis. [P445]. s4°. Francofurti a. O. 1662

Schmid (Frenzolf). Die Wahrheit ü. d. Wunder v. Konnersreuth. [T. Neumann]. 8°. [1927]

Schmid (Friedrich), *the botanist.* Reisen im Amur-Lande u. auf d. Ins. Sachalin. Botan. Theil. [Acad. Imp. d. Sci. de St. Pétersbourg. Mém., s7, t12ii]. 4°. St. Pétersbourg. 1868

Schmid (Friedrich August). *Abrégé chronolog. de l'hist. de Pologne. s8°. Varsovie. 1763

Schmid (Georg). Urkunden &c. aus d. Dekanats-Archive Stilfes, 1300–1810. Hrsg. G. S. 8°. Innsbruck. 1912

Schmid (Heinrich Alfred). Deutschtum u. bild. Kunst, *see* DEUTSCHE Reden in schwerer Zeit, 25, 1915.

Schmid (Johann), *of Kreuznach.* De Christianorum saeculi I vita & moribus. 8°. Lingæ. 1752

Schmid (Johann Andreas), *see* SCHMIDT (J. A.)

Schmid (Johann Christoph v.), *Domcapitular zu Augsburg.* Erinnerungen aus m. Leben. [B3 & 4 hrsg. v. A. Werfer.] 4B *in* 2v. s8°. Augsburg. 1853–57

Schmid (Johann Wilhelm), *Prof. of theology at Jena.* Theologische Moral. 8°. Jena. 1793

Schmid (Joseph), *see* SLEUMER (A.) Kirchenlatein. Wbch., 2. A. unter Mitwirk. v. J. S. hrsg. v. A. S., 1926.

Schmid (Ludwig Christian). Disput. de oblig. ad cedendum in via publ. Sub præs. C. A. Beckii. [P2746]. s4°. Jenae. [1728]

Schmid (Otto), *prof. at Univ. of Gratz.* Über verschied. Eintheilungen d. Heil. Schrift insbes. ü. d. Capitel-Eintheil. S. Langtons im 13. Jhdt. la8°. Graz. 1892

Schmid (Sebastian), *prof. of theology at Strassburg.*
Annot. in libellum Ruth. s4°. Argentorati. 1696
Collectaneorum Talmudicorum libri duo. [*b. w. h.* Tract. de circumcisione &c., 1700]. s4°. Lipsiae. 1670
Comm. in librum Ieremiæ. 2t. s4°. Francofurti ad Mœnum. 1706
Comm. in primam Joannis epistolam. s4°. Francofurti. 1707
Comm. supra prophetias Jesaiæ una cum annot. in 8 priora cap. libri Josuæ. s4°. Hamburgi. 1693
De principiis præsentiæ corporis & sanguis Christi in sacra coena tract. [*b. w. h.* Tract. de circumcisione &c., 1700]. ed. 2a. s4°. Argentorati. 1699
Fasciculus disput. super—1. Epist. Jacobi—2. Epist. ad Ephesios—3. Concionem Xti Matth. v, vi, vii.—4. Canticum Zachariae. 4p [*sep. tps. & pagins.*] [*b. w. h.* Resolutio Evang. Joh., 1699]. s4°. Argentorati. 1685
In epist. P. ad Hebræos comm. 2a ed. correctior. s4°. Lipsiae. 1698
In librum Ecclesiastes dictum comm. [*b. w. h.* Annot. in Ruth, 1696]. s4°. Argentorati. 1691
In librum Jjobi comm. ed. 2a. s4°. Argentorati. 1705
In librum Judicum comm. &c. s4°. Argentorati. 1706
In librum priorem [-post.] Samuelis comm. 2t. s4°. Argentorati. 1687
In librum Salomonis regis, Ecclesiastes dictum, comm. [*b. w. h.* Resol. Psalmorum prophetic. &c. 1688]. 8°. Argentorati. 1691
In Pauli ad Coloss. epist. comm. Acc. ejusdem Paraphrases in cap. 7–11 Epist. ad. Romanos &c. [*b. w. h.* Resolutio Evang. Joh., 1699]. s4°. Hamburgi. 1696
In prophetam Hoseam comm. [*b. w h.* Annot. in Ruth, 1696]. s4°. Francofurti ad Mœnum. 1687
In Prophetas minores comm. cum F. Balduini In tres post. prophetas comm. ed. 2a. Praemittitur autoris vita. s4°. Lipsiae. 1698
Resol. cum paraphrasi verborum ac notis Psalmorum prophetic. de Christo 14 disput. auct. & praes. S. S. &c. Acc. app. Psalmorum [*w. sep. pagin.*] 8°. Argentorati. 1688
Resolutio brevis cum paraphrasi verborum Evangelii Johannis. 2a ed. s4°. Argentorati. 1699
Succinctae &c. de Cherubim, Seraphim &c. totoque Angelorum choro & ordine diatribae. s8°. 1696
Super Mosis librum primum, Genesis dictum annot. s4°. Argentorati. 1697
Tractatus de circumcisione primo Vet. Test. sacramento. ed. 2a. s4°. Argentorati. 1700
Tractatus de Paschate altero Vet. Test. sacramento. 2p *in* 1v [*pagin. cont.*] s4°. Francofurti ad Mœnum. 1685

Schmid (Ulrich). Otto v. Lonsdorf, Bischof zu Passau, 1254–65. la8°. Würzburg. 1903

Schmidel (Johann). De mandragora, disput. Praes. J. Thomasio, 1655. Recusa & aucta. [P447]. s4°. Lipsiae. [1671]

Schmidius (Christianus Fridericus), *see* SCHMIDT (C. F.)

Schmidkunz (Hans). Psychologie d. Suggestion. . . . Mit ärztlich-psycholog. Ergänzungen v. F. C. Gerster. 8°. St. 1892

Schmidlin (Johannes Christophorus). Diss. de originibus domus Würtembergicae. s4°. Tubingæ. 1765

Schmidt (Adolf), *Direktor d. Landesbibl. zu Darmstadt.* Bucheinbände a. d. 14–19 Jhdt. in d. Landesbibl. zu Darmstadt. fol. L. 1921

Schmidt (Alfred).
Drogen u. Drogenhandel im Altertum. la8°. L. 1924

Schmidt (Berthold). Gesch. d. Reussenlandes. [2 Halbbande *in* 1B]. 8°. Gera-Reuss. 1923–27

Schmidt (Carl), *Privatdocent an d. Univ. Berlin.*
see EPISTOLA Apost.: Gespräche Jesu mit s. Jüngern nach d. Auferstehung; hrsg., übers. &c. v. C. S., 1919.
„ SANDERS (H. A.) & C. S. The Minor Prophets in the Freer coll. &c., 1927.

Schmidt (Carl Christian Gottlieb). Des Johannes Wesley Leben u. Wirken. 8°. Halle. 1849

Schmidt (Carl Eugen). Séville. Tr. & adapté par H. Peyre. [Villes d'art célèbres]. la8°. 1907

Schmidt (Christian Friedrich), *prof. of theol. at Wittenberg.*
Annot. in Ep. Pauli ad Romanos. 8°. Lipsiae. 1777
Hist. antiqua & vindic. canonis sacri Vet. Novique Test. 8°. Lipsiae. 1775

Schmidt (Erasmus). Opus sacrum posth. in quo cont. versio N. Test nova ad Graec. verit. emend., & notae &c. Acc. Sacer contextus Graec. itemque Orat. de Sibyllis. fol. Norimbergae. 1658

Schmidt (*Major* Ernst). Argonnen. [Schlachten d. Weltkrieges, B18]. 8°. Oldenburg i O. 1927

Schmidt (F. A.), *M.D.* **& Eustace H. Miles.**
The training of the body. 8°. 1901

Schmidt (Ferdinand Jakob). Das heilige Vermächtnis uns. gefallenen Helden, *see* DEUTSCHE Reden in schwerer Zeit, 31, 1915.

Schmidt (Franz), *executioner.* A hangman's diary. Journal of S., public executioner of Nuremberg, 1573–1617. Ed., w. intr. by A. Keller, & tr. C. Calvert &c. 8°. 1928

Schmidt (Harry). Relativity & the universe: intr. to Einstein's theory of space & time. Tr. C. Wichmann. s8°. [1921]

Schmidt (Hermann), *Director d. Gymn. zu Wittenberg.* Narr. de morbo obituque Melanthonis &c. [P2672]. 4°. Vitebergae. 1860

Schmidt (Immanuel), *of Lichterfelde, see* FLÜGEL (F.) Flügel-Schmidt-Tanger: dict. of Eng. & Germ. lang., 8th ed., 2p, 1913–14.

Schmidt (Isaac Jacob), *1779–1847.* Forschungen im Gebiete d. älteren relig., polit. u. literar. Bildungsgesch. der Völker Mittel-Asiens, vorzüglich d. Mongolen u. Tibeter. 8°. St. Petersburg. 1824
Gramm. d. mongol. Sprache. 4°. St. Petersburg. 1831
Ueb. d. Verwandtschaft d. gnost.-theosoph. Lehren. [P558]. 4°. L. 1828
see ARGHÚN KHÁN, *Ilkhán of Persia.* 2 mongol. Orig.-Briefen d. Könige v. Persien A. u. Öldshäitu an Philipp d. Schönen; hrsg. I. J. S., 1824.

Schmidt (Johann Andreas), *of Helmstadt.*
Compend. hist. eccl. ed. 2ª. s4°. Helmstadi. 1704
Exercit. hist.-theol. triga. 1, De missa sicca. 2, De muliere in eccl. 3, De cultu Evangeliorum. s8°. Jenae. 1692
Prolusionum Marianarum quarta de Mariae partu, actis &c. s4°. Helmstadii. 1713

Schmidt (Johann Andreas), *abbot of Marienthal.*
Compend. theol. dogmat. [*b. w.* Baier (J. W.) Compend. theol. mor., 1698]. s8°. Helmstadii. 1699
Decas diss. hist.-theolog. s4°. Helmstadii. 1714
Fragmenta lexici eccl. majoris, *see* VIVORUM &c. molimina theolog., 1761.
Hist. festorum & dominicarum rev. & aucta. s8°. Helmstadii. 1729
Hist. interimistica libellus. Ed. ab auct. fil. C. A. Schmidt. s8°. Helmstadii. 1730
Progr. de Catechesi Racoviensi, disput. 15. publ. Anti-Socinianis &c. [P440]. s4°. Helmstadii. 1724
Progr. de corporibus doct. Philippicae &c. [P2649]. s4°. Helmstadii. 1706

Schmidt (Johann Lorenz). *Die göttl. Schriften vor d. Zeiten des Messie Jesus. T1, die Gesetze d. Jisraelen. [*No more publ.*] s4°. Wertheim. 1735

Schmidt (Johannes). Distrib. of fresh-water eels, 2, Indo-Pacific region, *see* KONG. DAN. VID. SELSK. Skrifter, Række 8, B10, 1925–26.

Schmidt (Leopold Valentin), *1824–92.* Antiquit. Graecarum capita duo. 4°. Marburgi. [1867]

Schmidt (Ludwig). Gesch. d. deut. Stämme. Abt. 2, Gesch. d. Westgermanen. 8°. 1918
see FIEBIGER (O.) & L. S. Inschriftensammlung z. Gesch. d. Ostgermanen, 1917.

Schmidt (Max), *a. of "The Ego," see* STIRNER (M.), *ps.*

Schmidt (Max), *of Steglitz, & Museum f. Völkerkunde, Berlin.*
Grundriss d. ethnolog. Volkswirtschaftslehre. 2B. la8°. St. 1920
Primitive races of mankind: st. in ethnology. Tr. A. K. Dallas. 8°. [1926]

Schmidt (Otto Eduard). Die Bergstadt Freiberg i. Sa. u. i. Umgebung; bearb. O. E. S., *see* DEUTSCHLAND. D. Städtebau, 1926.
Minister Graf Brühl u. K. H. v. Heinecken. Briefe u. Akten. &c. z. sachs. Gesch., 1733–63. 8°. L. 1921

Schmidt (Richard). Der Volkswille als realer Faktor d. Verfassungslebens u. D. Defoe, *see* KÖNIGL. SÄCHS. AKAD. Ber., B76, 1925.

Schmidt (*Dr.* Richard), *of Prague.* Der polit. Bezirk Skt. Joachimsthal, *see* BOHEMIA. Topog. d. hist.- u. Kunst-Denkmale, B40, 1913.

Schmidt (Robert).
100 Jahre österreich. Glaskunst. 4°. Wien. [1925]

Schmidt (S.) Om Reaktionen mellem Toksin & Antitoksin (Difteri), *see* KONG. DAN. VIDENSKAB. SELSKAB. Biolog. Medd., 5, 1926.

Schmidt (Sebastian), *see* SCHMID (S.)

Schmidt (V. A. Jager-), *see* JAGER-SCHMIDT (V. A.)

Schmidt (W.), *bookseller, see* LIPPERT & SCHMIDT.

Schmidt (Wilhelm), *Oberlehrer am Leipniz-Gymn.* Kirchen- u. Schulvisitation im sächs. Kurkreise, 1555. [Verein f. Ref.-gesch. Schr., Jhrg. 24, Nr. 90, 92]. 2H. 8°. Halle a. d. S. 1906

Schmidt (Wilhelm), *S.V.D., b. 1868.* Die Personalpronomina in d. austral. Sprachen, 1919, *see* KAISERL. AKAD. D. WISS. ZU W. Denschr., B64, 1920.
Die Sprachfamilien u. Sprachenkreise d. Erde. 8°. Heidelberg. 1926
„ „ ....atlas fol. Heidelberg. 1926

Schmidt-Klugkist (Wilhelm) & C. Grotewold. Argentinien in geogr., geschichtl. &c. Beziehung. 2ᵉ verm. A. 8°. Hannover. 1919

Schmidtmeyer (Peter). Travels into Chile, over the Andes, 1820–21. 4°. 1824

Schmiedel (Paul Wilhelm). Jungfraugeburt u. Taufbefehl. [*Extr. f.* Prot. Monatshefte, 6 Jahrg. P2790]. la8°. *n.p. n.d.*

Schmiterlöw (Bernhard v.) Aus d. Leben d. Generalfeldm. Frhr. v. d. Goltz-Pascha, nach Briefen. 8°. 1926

Schmitt (Charles Henry). The Hungarian revolution; tr. M. P. Shiel. [P2756]. s8°. [1919?]

Schmitt (Johanna). Freiwilliger Opfertod bei Euripides: Beitr. z. s. dramat. Technik. [Religionsgesch. Versuche, u. Vorarbeiten, 17ii]. 8°. Giessen. 1921

Schmitt (Ludwig Julius Carl). Das Religionsgespräch zu Marburg, 1529. 8°. Marburg. 1840

Schmitthenner (Heinrich).
Chines. Landschaften u. Städte. 8°. St. 1925

Schmitz (Clemens). Ist der Papst persönlich unfehlbar? 1870, *see* KATHOLISCH. Stimmen aus d. K. Kirche, B1, 1870.

Schmitz (Hermann). Bildteppiche: Gesch. d. Gobelinwirkerei. [Hrsg. im Auftrage d. Staatl. Kunstgewerbe-Museums, Berlin &c.] [2ᵉ A.] 8°. 1921
Encyclopaedia of furniture: outline hist., to middle of 19th cent. Comp. under dir. of H. S., w. intr. by H. P. Shapland. fol. [1926]
Hans Baldung. [Knackfuss, 113]. la8°. Bielefeld. 1922
Soest. [Berühmte Kunststätten, 45]. s8°. L. 1908
see FALKE (O. v.) & H. S. Deutsche Möbel, 3B, 1923–24.
„ VIENNA. Tapestries of the V. Imp. Court [*by* H. S. &c.], 1922.

Schmitz (Oscar A. H.) Die Kunst d. Politik. 8°. 1911
"Wenn wir Frauen erwachen": Sittenroman. [5. A.] 8°. München. 1913

Schmitz-Kallenberg (Ludwig). Urkundenlehre, T2, Papsturkunden, 2ᵉ A, 1913, *see* GRUNDR. D. GESCHICHTSWISS.; Meister, 1ii, 1913.
see JANSEN (M.) & L. S.-K. Historiographie u. Quellen d. deut. Gesch. bis 1500, 1914.

Schmoger (F.)
München in alt. u. neu. Zeit. Hrsg. v. F. S. s8°. [1926]

Schmoller (Gustav).
Preuss. Verfassungs-, &c. u. Finanzgesch. 8°. 1921
W. Rathenau u. H. Preuss. s8°. München. 1922
see HINTZE (O.) Gedächtnisrede auf G. v. S., 1918.

Schmucker (Samuel Simon). Elements of pop. theology w. spec. ref. to diet at Augsburg, 1530. 2nd ed. 8°. N.Y. 1834

Schnabel (Carl). Handbook of metallurgy. Tr. H. Louis. 3rd ed. rev. v1. la8°. 1921

Schnabel (Franz). Sigismund v. Reitzenstein, d. Begründer d. bad. Staates. 8°. Heidelberg. 1927

Schnabel (Paul). Berossos u. d. babylon.-hellen. Lit. [Berosi Babyloniac. libr. 3 fragm.] 8°. 1923

Schnack (Ingeborg). Richard von Cluny, seine Chronik u. s. Kloster &c. [Historische Studien, H146]. 8°. 1921

Schnee (Albert Hermann Heinrich). Deut. Kolonial-Lexikon. Hrsg. H. S. 3B. la8°. L. [1920]
German colonization past & future. [*Tr.*] Intr. by W. H. Dawson. 8°. [1926]

Schneeberger (A.) Conteurs catalans: choix de nouvelles &c. des écr. mod. s8°. 1926

Schneider (C.), *Pfarrer in Kirn.* Gesch. d. Wild- u. Rheingräfl. Hauses, Volkes u. Landes auf d. Hundsrücken. 8°. Kreuznach. 1854

Schneider (Christian Wilhelm), *ed.*
see ACTA HIST.-ECCL. nostri temporis, 1776–86.
,, ACTEN, Urkunden u. Nachrichten &c., 1788–93.

Schneider (Edouard).
The Benedictines. Tr. J. Liljencrants. 8°. [1926]
Le dieu d'argile: pièce, see REVUE (LA) HEBDOMADAIRE. Suppl.: coll. nouv. &c., No. 16, 1923.
Fra Angelico da Fiesole, 1387–1455. 4°. [1924]
Sur les traces de St.-François. [4e éd.] s8°. 1926

Schneider (Fedor).
Rom u. Romgedanke im Mittelalter. 8°. München. 1926

Schneider (Friedrich). Kaiser Heinrich VII. 2H *in* 1v. 8°. Greiz i. V. 1924–26
Un peu de théologie à propos de Raphael. Tr. T. Richard. [*Extr. f.* Der Katholik. P2837]. 8°. 1896
Die St. Paulus-Kirche zu Worms. [Fest-Gabe z. Eröffn. d. Paulus-Mus.] 4°. [Mainz. 1881]
Theologisches zu Raffael. [Abd. aus Der Katholik. P2840]. 8°. Mainz. 1896

Schneider (Georg).
Handbuch d. Bibliographie. 2e A. 8°. L. 1924

Schneider (Georg Heinrich). Prof. Jäger's Entdeckung d. Seele. [P2476]. 8°. L. 1879

Schneider (Hermann). Heldendichtung, Geistlichendicht., Ritterdicht. [Gesch. d. deut. Lit. hrsg. Köster & Petersen, B1]. 8°. Heidelberg. 1925
Uhland u. d. deut. Heldensage, see KÖNIGL. PREUSS. AKAD. Abhdl. (Phil.-hist. Kl.), 1918.

Schneider (Léon Lévy-), see LÉVY-SCHNEIDER (L.)

Schneider (Louis), *b. 1861.*
Massenet (1842–1912). s8°. 1926
Un précurseur de la musique ital. aux 16e & 17e s.: C. Monteverdi, 1567–1643. 8°. 1921

Schneider (Maximilian). Deut. Titelbuch. 2e, verb. A. 8°. 1927

Schneier (Christophor Wilhelm). Theologia Musaeo-Baieriana in tabulas red. fol. Jenae. 1697
see HEIDER (W.) Biga schediasmatum bina dicteria Schul-Fuchss & Kalmeuser [*by* C. W. S.], 1728.

Schnell (Anselmus). Cursus theologiae polemicae abbr. ed. 3a auct. 2p *in* 1v. s8°. Lincii. 1747

Schnell (Heinrich). Heinrich V, d. Friedfertige, Herzog v. Mecklenburg, 1503–52. [Verein f. Ref.-gesch. Schr., Jhrg. 19, Nr. 72]. 8°. Halle. 1902

Schnell (Sebald). Disput. theol. quâ, quae I. Abravanel Hebraeus ad cap. 34. Esaiae, & Obadiae prophetiam contra fidem Xtianam scripsit, expenduntur. s8°. Altdorphi. 1647

Schnepff (Johann Theodorich). Disput. de justificatione hominis peccatoris coram Deo. [P2437]. s4°. Tubingæ. 1589

Schnepff (Theodorich) [SCHNEPFIUS (TH.); SNEPFF].
Disput. de propos. Paulina: Arbitramur justificari hominem fide. Praes. T. S., resp. F. Schebelio. [P2626]. s4°. Tubingae. 1569
Disput. de sacro baptismate. Praes. T. S., def. A. Pouchenius. [P2673]. s4°. Tubingae. 1584
Disput. peccatum originis non rectè dici substantiam. Præs. T. S., G. Wildius resp. [P2626]. s4°. Tubingæ. 1581
Propositiones de peccato orig. Præs. T. S., P. Leiser resp. [P2626]. s4°. Tubingæ. 1576
Refut. Sotici scripti, see CHRISTOPH, *Herzog zu Würtemberg.* Confessio, t2, 1561.

Schnerich (Alfred). Joseph Haydn u. s. Sendung. Stilkrit. Anh. v. W. Fischer. 2e verm. A. 8°. Zürich. 1926

Schnering (Marcus). Jus tertii orthodoxi circa caussam Jesuitico-Jansenianum; dissert. sub præs. Æ. Strauchii, def. M. S. [P2630]. s4°. Wittebergae. 1663

Schnettler (Otto). Die Veme. Enstehung &c. d. Frei- u. heiml. Gerichte Westfalens. s8°. Dortmund. 1921

Schnippel (E.) Die engl. Kalenderstäbe. [Beitr. z. engl. Philol., H5]. 8°. L. 1926

Schnitler (Carl W.), see EIDSVOLD, 1814: med bidrag av C. W. S. &c., 1914.

Schnitzer (Joseph). Peter Delfin, Gen. d. Camaldulenserordens, 1444–1525. Beitr. z. Gesch. d. Kirchenreform Alex. VI u. Savonarolas. 8°. München. 1926
Savonarola: e. Kulturbild aus d. Zeit d. Renaissance. 2B. la8°. München. 1924

Schnitzer (Manuel) [*ps.* M. NUËL]. Goethes Josephbilder, Goethes Josephdichtung. s8°. Hamburg. 1921

Schnitzler (Arthur).
Casanovas Heimfahrt. Novelle. [16e A.] s8°. 1919
Dämmerseelen. Novellen. s8°. 1920
Der einsame Weg. Schauspiel. s8°. 1921
Die Frau d. Richters. Novelle. s8°. [1925]
Fräulein Else. Novelle. s8°. 1925
Der Gang zum Weiher. Dram. Dichtung. 8°. 1926
Die griechische Tänzerin u. a. Novellen. 56–61. A. s8°. [1921]
Komödie der Verführung. 8°. 1924
Komödie der Worte. 3 Einakter. s8°. 1915
Das Märchen. Schauspiel. s8°. 1923
Professor Bernhardi. Komödie. [20e bis 22e A.] s8°. 1925
Spiel im Morgengrauen. Novelle. s8°. [1927]
Therese. [Gesamm. Werke]. s8°. 1928
Traumnovelle. s8°. 1926
Der Weg ins Freie. Roman. s8°. 1922
TRANSLATIONS.
Anatol: sequence of dialogues. Paraphrased for Eng. stage by G. Barker. [4th impr.] s8°. 1917
Beatrice & o. s. Tr. A. Jacques & E. M. Lang. 8°. 1926
Casanova's homecoming. [Tr. E. & C. Paul]. 8°. [1923]
Fräulein Else. Tr. F. H. Lyon. s8°. [1925]
Playing with love. Tr. P. M. Shand—The prologue to Anatol; by H. v. Hofmannsthal; Eng. verse by T. Blakemore. s8°. 1914

Schnitzler (J. M.) Hossfeld's method for learning the Dutch language. 2nd ed. s8°. *n.d.*

Schnizer (Georg Matthias).
De officio clavium. [P2649]. s4°. Erlangae. [1770]

Schnizlin (Johann Georg Christoph). Diss. de Arnoldo Brixiensi. Praes. J. D. Koelero. [P595]. s4°. Gottingae. 1742
Diss. de haeresi Pauli Samosateni. Sub Praes. J. G. Feverlini. [P434]. s4°. Gottingae. [1741]

Schnorhali (Nerses), see NERSES, *Shnorhali.*

Schnöring (Wilhelm). Johannes Blankenfeld. [Verein f. Ref.-gesch. Schr., Jhrg. 23, Nr. 86]. 8°. Halle a. d. S. 1905

Schnorr v. Carolsfeld (Ludwig). Porzellan d. europ. Fabriken d. 18. Jhdts. 3e A. 8°. 1920

Schnurrer (Christian Friedrich).
De eccl. Maronitica. [*sometimes attrib. to* C. C. v. Flatt. Festum natalit., 2p. P2594]. s4°. Tubingae. 1810–11
De Pentateucho Arabico polyglotto disput. Praes. C. F. S., def. C. F. Reinhard *& others.* [P2671]. s4°. Tubingae. [1780]
Disput. ad Esaiae cap. 27. Præs. S. [*b. w. h.* Obs. ad vatic. Jeremiae, 1793]. s4°. Tubingae. [1785]
Diss. philol.-crit. [*on the Old Test.*] Ed. C. F. S. 8°. Gothae. 1790
Erläuter. d. Würtemberg. Kirchen-Reformations- u. Gelehrten-Gesch. 8°. Tübingen. 1798
Observ. ad vaticinia Jeremiae. Præs. S. 4p *in* 1v. s4°. Tubingae. [1793–97]
Observ. ad vaticinia Jesaiae. Praes. S. [*b. w. h.* Obs. ad vatic. Jeremiae, 1793]. s4°. Tubingae. [1781]
Orationum acad. delectus posthumus. Add. praef. biograph. Ed. H. E. G. Paulus. 8°. Tubingae. 1828
Slav. Bücherdruck in Würtemberg im 16. Jhdt. 8°. Tübingen. 1799
see THANCHUM *ben* JOSEPH, *of Jerusalem.* Ad libros Vet. Test. comm. Arab. spec. unacum annotat. in aliquot loca libri Judic., 1791.

Schôber (David Gottfried). Ausführl. Ber. v. alt. deut. geschrieb. Bibeln vor Erfind. d. Buchdruckerey &c. s8°. Schleiz. 1763

Schobser (Hans), see SCHOTTENLOHER (CARL). Der Münchener Buchdrucker H. S., 1500–30, 1925.

Schoell (Frank L.) Les paysans de Ladislas Reymont. (Prix Nobel, 1925). 8°. [1925]

Schoengen (M.), see VOECHT (J. VAN). Narr.; uitg. M. S., 1908.

Schoenhof (Jacob). Destructive influence of the tariff &c. 2nd ed. s8°. N.Y. 1885

Schoenrich (Otto). Former Senator Burton's trip to S. Amer., 1915. [C.E. for Int. Peace. P2676]. la8º. Wash. 1915

Schoff (Wilfred Harvey). The ship "Tyre": symbol of the fate of conquerors as prophesied by Isaiah &c.; st. in commerce of the Bible. 8º. N.Y. 1920

see ISIDORUS, *Characenus.* Parthian stations; w. tr. & comm. by W. H. S., 1914.

Schöffer (Peter). *Volētes ūbi oparare infrascriptos libros &c. (1469, *facs.*), *see* FREYTAG (G.) Bilder, B3, T1, 1924.

Schofield (Alfred Taylor). Nervousness. 8º. 1910

Schofield (Stephen). The marble god & o. plays. The house with twisty windows, by M. Pakington—The net, by C. M. Nesbit—Incorrigible, by A. J. Talbot—The marble god, by S. S. s8º. O. 1926

Schofield (Stuart James). Geol. & ore deposits of Ainsworth mining camp, B.C. [Canada: Geol. Survey. P2513]. 8º. Ottawa. 1920

—— & G. Hanson. Geology & ore deposits of Salmon River Distr., B.C. [Canada: Geol. Survey. P2713]. 8º. Ottawa. 1922

Schofield (William Henry). Mythical bards & the life of William Wallace. [Harvard St. in Comp. Lit., v5]. 8º. Camb. [U.S.] 1920

Source &c. of the 7th novel of the 7th day in the Decameron, *see* HARVARD UNIV. St. &c. in philology &c., v2, 1893.

Schogolev (Yakob Ivanovich).
Вѣрсклo. Лірна поэзія. la8º. Харьківъ. 1883

Schola Salernitana. L'art de conserver sa santé, composé par l'Ecole de S. Tr. en vers fr. par M. B[ruzen de] L[a] M[artinière]. Augm. d'un traité [Secrets] sur la conserv. de la beauté des dames &c. s8º. 1766

L'école de Salerne avec la tr. burlesque du Dr. Martin (1650). n. éd., rev. &c. par P. Le Duc. s8º. 1875

Regimen sanctatis Salerni &c. Reviewed, corr. &c. by P. H. [*i.e.* Philemon Holland] &c. s4º. 1649

The school of Salernum. Eng. version by Sir J. Harington (1608). Hist. of school by F. R. Packard, & note on prehist. of Regimen sanitatis by F. H. Garrison. 8º. 1922

2nd Salern. anat. demonstr.; tr., *see* CORNER (G. W.) Anat. texts, 1927.

Scholastika, *Sister, Cistercian Order, see* DEODATA (M.), *ps.*

Scholderer (Victor). Printing at Venice, to 1481. [Repr. f. Trans. of Bibliog. Soc.] 8º. 1924

Scholefield (James), *reg. prof. of Greek at Cambridge.* Hints for an improved transl. of the N. Test. 2nd. ed. w. adds. 8º. C. 1836

Scholem (Gerhard). Bibliographia Kabbalistica. Mit e. Anhang, Bibl. d. Zohar u. s. Komm. la8º. L. 1927

Scholes (Percy Alfred). Compl. bk. of the great musicians. Intr. by Sir H. P. Allen. [3 bks. *in* 1v.] s8º. 1926

Listener's hist. of music. Notes by Sir W. H. Hadow &c. 2nd ed. v1. s8º. 1925

Scholia Hellenistica in Nova Test., 2t, 1848, *see* BIBLE: NEW TEST.: GREEK.

Schöll (Fritz), *see* HEIDELBERG UNIV. H. Professoren aus d. 19. Jhdt. [Vorrede *by* F. S.], 1903.

Scholliner (Hermann). Praelect. theologicae de Deo &c. s4º. Salisburgi. 1764

Scholtz (Christian).
Gramm. Aegypt. Ed. C. G. Woide. 4º. Oxonii. 1778

Scholz (Adolf Heinrich Wilhelm v.) Erlebnisse u. Gespräche mit Bismarck. Hrsg. v. W. v. Scholz. 8º. St. 1922

Scholz (Heinrich). Die Religionsphilos. d. Als-ob: e. Nachprüfung Kants u. d. idealist. Positivismus. la8º. L. 1921

Scholz (Richard). Die Publizistik z. Zeit Philipps d. Schönen u. Bonifaz' VIII. 8º. St. 1903

Schomberg (Arthur). Dugdale of Seend. Ed. A. S. [P2730]. la8º. Devizes. 1924

Schomer (Justus Christoph). Collegium Anti-Calvinianum &c. Subjuncta B. Proavi Meditatione Eucharistica. Ed. H. A. Engelcke. s4º. Rostochii. 1708

Collegium Anti-Socinianum; public. disput. 13, præm. diss., De damnabili Socinianismi gangræna. [Resp. S. Krüger] &c. Ed. noviss. H. A. Engelcke. [3 *pagin.*] s4º. Rostochii. 1724–25

Collegium noviss. controversiarum in univ. theologiam. Praem.: J. Fechtii praef. isagogica &c. Ed. 3ª H. A. Engelke. s4º. Rostochii. 1711

Schön (Eyn) hübsch lesen v. etl. insslen, *see* COLUMBUS (C.)

Schön (Friedrich). Gesch. d. deut. Mundartdichtung. 2T *in* 1v. 8º. Freiburg i. B. 1920–21

Schön (Jacob Friedrich). Gramm. of the Hausa lang. 8º. 1862

Schön (Wilhelm Ed., *Frhr.* **von).** Erlebtes. Beitr. z. polit. Gesch. d. neuest. Zeit. 8º. St. 1921

Memoirs of an ambassador: contrib. to polit. hist. of mod. times. Tr. C. Vesey. 8º. [1922]

Schönbeck (Jacob Christian). Diss. de jure postarum hereditario. Praes. J. P. Ludwig. [P2746]. s4º. Halæ Hermund. [1704]

Schönberg (Arnold), *see* WELLESZ (E.) A. S.; tr., 1928.

Schöne (Carl), *Evangelischer Pfarrer.*
Tabulae hist. eccl. fol. Berolini. 1828

Schöne Literatur (Die): Beilage z. Lit. Centralblatt f. Deutschland. Jhrg. 1–28. la8º. & 8º. L. 1900–27
Jhrg. 1–23, hrsg. E. Zarncke, are b. w. the Lit. Centr. f. Deut., Jhrg. 1900–22; Jhrg. 24–28, hrsg. W. Vesper, are b. separately.

Schönemann (Carl Philipp Christian). Hundert Merkwürdigk. d. Herzogl. Bibl. z. Wolfenbüttel. 8º. Hannover. 1849

Schonfield (Hugh J.), *see* BIBLE: MATTHEW. An old Heb. text of St. M.'s G.; tr. &c. H. J. S., 1927.

Schongauer (Martin), *d. 1491.*
see LEHRS (M.) Kat. d. Kupferstiche M. S., 1925.
,, ROSENBERG (J.) M. S. Handzeichnungen; mit 50 Abbild., 1923.

Schönherr (Carl). Der Kampf. Drama. s8º. L. 1920

Schonland (S.) Phanerogamic flora of the divisions of Uitenhage & Port Elizabeth. [Botan. Survey of S. Africa., Mem. 1]. [P2565]. 8º. Pretoria. 1919

Schönleben (Johann Ludwig). Carniola antiq. & nova: Annales sacro-profani.
t1i–iii [*in* 1v. *2 pagin. no more publ.*] fol. Labaci. 1680–81

Schoock (Marten) [SCHOOCKIUS (MARTINUS)].
De ecstasi tract. sing. s4º. Groningae Fris. 1661
Exercitat. variae de divers. materiis. ed. nova. s4º. Trajecti a. R. 1663
see SALMASIUS (CL.) *Funus ling. Hellen., sive confutat. exercit. [M. S.], 1643.

School. *School (The) for wives, comedy, 1811, *see* KELLY (H.)
*School, The, of Venus; or, the lady's misc. 2nd ed. s8º. 1739
Cont. Art of dress [by J. D. de Breval]; The patch, by Hauksbee; The hoop-petticoat, by J. Gay.

School of Oriental Studies. Bulletin. v1–4. 8º. 1917–28
see RELIGIONS. R. of the Empire, conf.; ed. W. L. Hare, 1925.

Schooling (*Sir* **William).**
Alliance Assurance, 1824–1924. 8º. 1924
see HILL (*Sir* N.) &c. War & insurance, 1927.
,, INWOOD (W.) Tables of interest &c. for estates &c.; rev. &c. by Sir W. S., 32nd ed. rev. &c., 1924.

Schools (The) of Eng.: *by. var. wr.*, 1928, *see* WILSON (J. D.), *ed.*

Schoonaerts (Gregorius). Examen confessariorum per univ. theologiam moralem &c. 2ª ed. s8º. Antverpiæ. 1721

Schoorle (Jan van), *see* SCOREL (J. VAN).

Schopenhauer (Arthur).

TRANSLATIONS.
Sel. essays. W. biog. intr. & sk. of h. philos. by E. B. Bax. s8º. *Bohn.* 1900
see KEYSERLING (H., *Graf.* v.) Menschen als Sinnbilder, 1926.
,, KÖBER (R.) S.'s Erlösungslehre, 1881.
,, LABAN (F.) Die Schopenhauer-Lit., 1880.
see MEYER (J. B.) A. S. als Mensch u. Denker, 1872.
,, NIETZSCHE (F. W.) Unzeitgemässe Betrachtungen, B3, S. als Erzieher, 1874.
,, PAULSEN (F.) S. &c.: Aufsätze z. Naturgesch. d. Pessimismus, 1926.
,, PENZIG (R.) S. u. d. menschl. Willensfreiheit, 1879.

Schöpflin (Johann Daniel) [SCHOEPFLINUS].
Vindiciae typographicae. s4º. Argentorati. 1760

Schoppe (Caspar) [*ps.* VARGAS (ALPHONSUS DE)].
*Arcana Soc. Jesu publico bono vulgata. Cum append. s8º. 1635
Classicum belli sacri, sive Heldus redivivus, hoc est: Ad Carolum V., suasoria. s4º. Ticini. 1619
Ecclesiasticus auctoritati Jacobi Mag. Brit. regis oppositus. s4º. Hartbergae. 1611
*Mysteria Patrum Jesuitarum ex ipsorum scriptis. ed. noviss. auctior &c.: App.: Epistola Constantinopoli missa e Græco in Lat. tr. &c. [*by* Gregory, the Patriarchal Exarch]. s8º. Lampropoli [Leyden ?]. 1632
Relatio ad reges &c., de stratagematis & sophismatis polit. Soc. Jesu &c. [*Foll. by* Sedis apost. censura, 1631–2—Urbani VIII suppressio J., 1632—Soc. J. novum fidei symbolum, *each w. sep. tp.*] 8º. [Padua ?]. 1636
,, ,, ...[*a. ed.*] s8º. [Cologne ?]. 1641

Schopper (Jacob). Oratio de encomio sacrae theologiae studii &c. altera oratio: J. Cappelii De republica lit. s4°. Witebergae. 1594

Theses de justificatione. Præs. J. S., G. Schmid resp. [P2626]. s4°. Heidelbergae. 1583

Theses de sacramento baptismi. Praes. J. S., resp. A. Brem. [P2673]. s4°. Noribergae. 1606

Schorel (Jan van), *see* Scorel (J. van).

Schorer (Christoph), *see* Hartig (O.) C. S. u. s. "Sprachverderber" (1643), 1921.

Schorlemmer (Carl), *see* Roscoe (*Sir* H. E.) & C. S. Treatise on chemistry, 5th ed., v1, 1920; n. ed. (6th) v2, 2p, 1923.

Schorn (W. C.) Alphab. index to names of places &c. in map of Turkestan. 6th ed. fol. Calcutta. 1884

Schotanus (Meinardus), *see* Voet (G.) Oratio funebris in obit. M. S., 1644.

Schott (Andreas Heinrich). Diss. de orig. cognitionis humanæ. pars 1. Praes. A. H. S., def. D. J. Ebensperger [*& others*. P2746]. s4°. Tubingæ. [1809]

Diss. de Spinozismo. Praes. A. H. S., def. F. G. Schoder [*and others*]. [2746]. s4°. Tubingæ. [1804]

Diss. de variis pantheismi formis. Præs. A. H. S., def. C. L. Liesching &c. [P2746]. s4°. Tubingæ. [1805]

Mem. P. Melanchthonis meritorumque illius in artium lib. & philos. studia. [P597]. s4°. Tubingae. [1717]

Schott (Gaspar). Physica curiosa, sive mirabilia naturæ & artis libris 12 comprehensa. ed. 3ª. s4°. Herbipoli. 1697

Schott (Gerhard).

Geographie d. Atlant. Ozeans. la8°. Hamburg. 1912

Schott (Heinrich August). Opuscula exegetica, critica, dogmatica. 2t. *in* 1v. 8°. Jenae. 1817–18

Schott (Sigmund).

Von menschl. Schwächen. s8°. Breslau. 1865

Schott (Theodor). Die Aufhebung d. Ediktes v. Nantes, 1685. [Verein f. Ref.-gesch. Schr., Jhrg. 3, Nr. 10]. 8°. Halle. 1885

Die Kirche d. Wüste, 1715–87. [Verein f. Ref.-gesch. Schr., Jhrg. 11, Nr. 43/44]. 8°. Halle. 1893

Schott (Wilhelm), *orientalist.* De indole linguae Sinicae diss. s8°. Halis. Saxon. [1826]

Versuch ü. d. Tatar. Sprachen. 4°. 1836

Schottenloher (Carl). Das alte Buch. 8°. 1919

Flugblatt u. Zeitung. Wegweiser durch d. gedr. Tagesschrifttum. 8°. 1922

Der Münchner Buchdrucker Hans Schobser, 1500–30. Mit Anhang: Wer ist Johann Locher v. München? 4°. München. 1925

Schöttgen (Christian), *1687–1751.* Vita et agon C. T. Waltheri per annos 15 missionarii Danici apud Trangambarienses &c. s4°. Halae. 1742

Schottus (Franciscus) [F. Schott; F. Scoto].

Itinerario d'Italia. s8°. Padova. 1659

Schoulguine (Vassili Vitalievitch), *see* Shulgin (V. V.)

Schoultz (G. von). With the British Battle Fleet: War recoll. Tr. A. Chambers. 8°. [1925]

Schrader (Bruno). Franz Liszt. 2e A. la8°. [1921]

Die röm. Campagna. [Berühmte Kunststätten, 49]. s8°. L. 1910

Schrader (Frederick F.), *see* England. E. on the witness stand [*by var. a.*; intr. by S.], 1915.

Schrader (Hans). Über Phidias. [Sonderabdr. a. d. Jahresh. d. Österr. Arch. Inst., B14]. la8°. [Wien. 1911]

Schrader (Otto). Reallexikon d. indogerman. Altertumskunde. 2e verm. u. umgearb. A. hrsg. v. A. Nehring. B1. 8°. Str. 1917–23

Schrader (Rudolf), *see* Westfalen. Bau- u. Kunstdenkm., 22, Kreis Bielefeld-Stadt, gesch, Einl. v. R. S., 1906.

Schrader-Breymann (Henriette J. J.), *form. Breymann, see* Breymann (H. J. J. S.-)

Schradin (Johann). Expostulation das ist Klag u. Verwiss Germanie des Teütschenlands gegen Carolo Quinto dem Keiser des unbillichen bekriegens. s4°. Tübingen, *Ulrich Morhart.* 1546

Schram (Dominicus). Analysis operum S. S. Patrum, & script. Eccl. 18t. s8°. Augustae Vindelic. 1780–96

Compendium theologiae dogmat. &c. 3t. s8°. Augustae Vindelic. 1768

Schramb (Anselm). Ethica seu philosophia moralis. ed. posterior. [*b. w. h.* Pia desideria Davidica, 1707]. s8°. Viennae. 1705

Pia desideria Davidica, seu Psalterium Davidicum metro exceptum. s8°. Viennae. 1707

Schramek (Thomas). "Frhr. v. Egloffstein" [*i.e.* L. Örthel. Aussenseiter d. Gesell., B11]. s8°. [1925]

Schramm (Jonas Conrad) [Schrammius]. Disput. de Symboli Apostolici in Talmude ruderibus. Praes. J. A. Schmidt. [P433]. s4°. Helmstadi. [1706]

Schreber (Johann David). Diss. de correptione concionatoria. Sub præs. J. Olearii. [P2638]. s4°. *n.p.* 1729

Schreiben an d. ungen. Verf. d. Abh. vom Schlaf d. Seele nach d. Tode. [*b. w. the* Abhandlung, 1754]. s8°. Franckfurt. 1754

Schreiber (Heinrich), *of Erfurt.* Johann Albrecht I, Herzog v. Mecklenburg. [Verein f. Ref.-gesch. Schr., Jhrg. 16, Nr. 64]. 8°. Halle. 1899

Die Reformation Lübecks. [Verein f. Ref.-gesch. Schr., Jhrg. 20, Nr. 74]. 8°. Halle. 1902

Schreiber (Theodor), *see* Sieglin (E. v.) Exped. E. v. S.: Ausgrabgn. in Alexandria, unter Leitung v. T. S., B1, 2iii, 1908–13.

Schreiber (Wilhelm Ludwig), *see* Cube (J. v.) Hortus sanitatis (1485); *facs.*, *w.* Nachtrag *ent.* Die Kräuterbücher d. 15. u. 16. Jhdts., *by* W. L. S., 1924.

Schreiner (Olive) [*ps.* Ralph Iron; *wife of S. C. Cronwright-Schreiner*].

From man to man. Intr. by S. C. Cronwright-Schreiner. s8°. [1926]

Letters, 1876–1920. Ed. S. C. Cronwright-Schreiner. [2nd impr.] 8°. [1924]

The story of an African farm. Intr. by S. C. Cronwright-Schreiner. s8°. [1924]

„ „ ....s8°. [1925]

Thoughts on South Africa. 8°. 1923

see Cronwright-Schreiner (S. C.) Life of O. S., 1924.

„ Findlay (F. R. N.) Big game shooting &c. in S.-E. Africa; w. chapters by O. S. &c., 1903.

Schrenck (Leopold von) [Shrenk (L. I.)]

О теченіяхъ Охотскаго, Японскаго &c. морей. [I. Akad. Nauk. Записки, t23]. 8°. С.-П. 1874

Очеркъ физической географіи Сѣверо-Японскаго моря. [I. Akad. Nauk. Записки, t16]. 8°. С.-П. 1869

Schretlen (M. J.) Dutch & Flemish woodcuts of the 15th cent. Foreword by M. J. Friedlaender. 4°. 1925

Schrevelius (Cornelius).

Greek lexicon. Ed. J. R. Major. 7th ed. 8°. 1847

Schrijver (Pieter) [Petrus Scriverius]. Principes Hollandiae & Westfrisiæ, aeri omnes incisi & descr., auspiciis P. S. la. fol. Harlemi. 1650

Schröckh (Johann Matthias). Compend. hist. catholicae &c. Latine vertit F. G. Born. s8°. Lipsiae. 1797

Schröder (Bruno). Der Sport im Altertum. la8°. 1927

Schröder (Edward). Der Dichter d. deut. "Eraclius": Beitr. z. altbayer. Literaturgesch., *see* Königl. Akad. d. Wiss. zu München. Phil. Kl., Sitz., 1924.

Schröder (Franz), *of Venice.* Repertorio genealog. d. famiglie conferm. nobili &c. esist. n. prov. venete. 2v. 8°. Venezia. 1830

Schröder (Franz Rolf). Germanentum u. Hellenismus. [German. Bibl., Abt. 2, B17]. 8°. Heidelberg. 1924

Die Parzivalfrage. 8°. München. 1928

Schröder (Heinrich Eilhard), *see* Gesner (J. M.) Memoria H. E. S., 1753.

Schröder (Herbert). Russland u. d. Ostsee. 8°. Riga. 1927

Schröder (Johan Henrik). Incunabula artis typograph. in Suecia. 4°. Upsaliae. 1842

Schröder (Johann Joachim). Thesaurus linguae Armenicae. [Diss. de antiq. &c. *w. sep. pagin.*] s4°. Amstelodami. 1660

Schröder (Nicolaus Gulielmus). Quatuor prima capita Geneseos Turcice & Lat. Lat. vertit &c. N. G. S. s4°. Lipsiae. 1739

Schröder (Otto). Keilschrifttexte aus Assur hist. Inhalts, H2, Autographien v. O. S., *see* Messerschmidt (L.) & O. S. Keilschrifttexte, 2H, 1911–22.

Keilschrifttexte aus Assur verschied. Inhalts. [Deut. Orient-Gesells. Wiss. Veröff., 35i]. fol. L. 1920

Novae comoediae fragm. in papyris reperta exceptis Menandreis ed. O. S., *see* Kleine Texte, T135, 1915.

Pindars Pythien. Erklärt v. O. S. 8°. L., *Teubner.* 1922

Schröder (Philipp Richard). Diss. de eo quod justum est circa vota novi anni. Præs. P. R. S., resp. M. Henckio. Iterum recusa. [P2746]. s4°. Vitembergae. 1734

Schroeder (Henry), *of New Jersey.* Hist. of electric light, 1923, *see* Smithsonian Inst. Misc. Coll[s]., v76, 1925.

Schroll (Beda), *ed.* Urkundenbuch d. Benedictiner-Stiftes St. Paul in Kärnten; hrsg. v. B. S., *see* Fontes rerum Austriac., B39, 1876.

Schropp (Jacob). Acta oecumenici Concilii habiti super controversia de Coena Domini. s4°. Tubingae. 1581

Schröter (Carl). Das Pflanzenleben d. Alpen. Unter Mitwirk. v. H. & M. Brockmann-Jerosch &c.
2. verm. Aufl. la8°. Zürich. 1926

Schröter (Johann Samuel), *see* ACTEN, Urkunden u. Nachrichten &c., 1788–93.

Schrÿver (*Col.* A. de).
La bataille de Liége (août 1914). 8°. Liége. 1922

Schubart (Wilhelm).
Ägypten v. Alexander d. Gr. bis auf Mohammed. 8°. 1922
Die Griechen in Ägypten, *see* ALTE ORIENT (DER). Beihefte, H10, 1927.
Papyri Graecae Berolin. [Tabulæ in usum schol.; ed. J. Lietzmann, 2]. la8°. Bonnae. 1911
Das Weltbild Jesu. [Morgenland, H13]. 8°. L. 1927

Schubert (Alois). Augustins Lex-aeterna-Lehre. [Beitr. z. Gesch. d. Philos. d. M-a.'s, B24ii]. 8°. Münster i. W. 1924

Schubert (Anton). Urkunden-Regesten aus d. ehemal. Archiv. der v. Joseph II aufgehob. Klöster Böhmens.
4°. Innsbruck. 1901

Schubert (Franz). Kammermusik. [Quartett 1–8, Trio 1, 2, Quintett A-dur, C-dur, F-dur, *each w. sep. tp. & pagin.*]
s8°. L. *n.d.*
[*Scores, w. sep. tp. & pag., b. in 1v. & arr. as below.* 4°. L. *n.d.*
C—dur Symphonie, Unvollend. Symph. u. Andante a. d. Tragischen Symph., [3p]—Duos, trios &c. [Octett (Op. 166)—Quintetto (Op. 163)—Quartette (9)—Trios (Op. 99, 100)—Rondeau brillant (Op. 70)—Sonate (Op. 137, No. 1–3)].
Songs [*w. music*]. Tr. A. H. Fox Strangeways & S. Wilson.
s8°. [1924]
see GÉROLD (T.) S., 1923.
„ LANDORMY (P.) La vie de S., 1928.
„ PITROU (R.) F. S., vie intime, 1928.

Schubert (Gotthilf Heinrich von). Die Gesch. v. Bayern. f. Schulen. 3e verm. A. s8°. München. 1864

Schubert (Hans v.)
Anfänge d. evangel. Bekenntnisbildung, 1529/30. [Verein f. Ref.-Gesch. Schr., Jhrg. 45, Nr. 143]. 8°. L. 1928
Bündnis u. Bekenntnis, 1529/30. [Ver. f. Ref.-gesch. Schr., Jhrg. 26, Nr. 98]. 8°. L. 1908
Gesch. d. christl. Kirche im Frühmittelalter. la8°. Tübingen. 1921
Luthers Frühentwicklung (bis 1517/9). [Ver. f. Ref.-gesch. Schr., 34, Nr. 124]. 8°. L. 1916
Roms Kampf um d. Weltherrschaft. [Ver. f. Ref.-gesch. Schr., Jhrg. 6, Nr. 23]. 8°. Halle. 1888

Schubert (Johann Ernst).
Compend. theologiae dogmat. s8°. Helmstadii. 1760
Consideratio articulorum fidei. s8°. Jenae. 1751
Gedanken v. d. Leben u. d. Zustande d. Seelen nach d. Tode.
s4°. Jena. 1742
Heilige Reden. Andre u. verm. A. 2T. s8°. Jena. 1753–56
Institutionum theologiae polemicae pars prima [—quarta].
4t. s8°. Jenae. 1756–58

Schubring (Paul). Gioia del Colle. [*Extr. f.* Ztschr. f. bild. Kunst]. [P2699]. 4°. Leipzig. *n.d.*
Ital. Renaissanceplastik: Burl. Fine Arts Club, London, 1912.
[*Extr.* P2699]. 4°. [1912]
Urbano da Cortona. Beitr. z. Kenntnis d. Schule Donatellos &c. nebst e. Anhang: A. Guardi. la8°. Str. 1903

Schubring (Walther). Das Mahānisīha-Sutta, *see* KÖNIGL.-PREUSS. AKAD. Abhdl. (Phil.-hist. Kl.), 1918.

Schuchardt (Hugo E. M.) *Works in* KAIS. AKAD. D. WISS. ZU WIEN. Sitz. Phil.-hist. Kl.
Das Baskische u. d. Sprachwiss, 1925. [202.]
Berber. Hiatustilgung, 1916. [182.]
Die roman. Lehnwörter im Berber., 1918. [188.]
Primitiae ling. Vasconum: Einführung ins Baskische.
la8°. Halle. 1923
Zur Kenntnis d. Baskischen v. Sara (Labourd), *see* KÖNIGL. PREUSS. AKAD. Abhdl. (Phil.-hist. Kl.), 1922.

Schuchert (Charles). A lower Cambrian Edrioasterid, *see* SMITHSONIAN INSTIT. Misc. coll., v70, 1919.

Schuchhardt (Carl). Die sogen Trajanswälle in d. Dobrudscha, *see* KÖNIGL. PREUSS. AKAD. D. WISS. Abhdl. (Phil.-hist. Klasse), 1918.

Schucht (Ludwig). Die Fabrikation des Superphosphats &c.
3e verm. &c. A. 8°. Braunschweig. 1909

Schück (J. Henrik E.) Hist. de la litt. suédoise. Tr., avec un avant-propos, par L. Maury. 8°. 1923

—— & C. Warburg.
Huvuddragen av Sveriges litt. 3 avd. 8°. 1917–18

Schücking (Levin Ludwig).
Character problems in Shakespeare's plays. 8°. [1922]
Die Charakterprobleme bei Shakespeare.
2e verb. A. 8°. L. 1927

Schücking (Walther). The internat. union of the Hague Conf. Tr. C. G. Fenwick. [C.E. for Int. Peace]. la8°. O. 1918
see KAUTSKY (C.) Deut. Dokumente z. Kriegsausbruch; hrsg. v. M. Montgelas u. W. S., 4B, 1919; (*Fr.*) tr. C. Jordan, 4t, 1922; (*Eng.*) tr., 1924.

—— & H. Wehberg. Die Satzung d. Völkerbundes, kommentiert v. W. S. & H. W. la8°. 1921

Schudt (Johann Jacob). Comp. hist. Judaicæ, ad ductum Justini Hist. libr. 36. Acc. app. De ratione proced. in promov. conversione hominis Judæi.
s8°. Francofurti ad Moenum. 1700
De Essenis Judaeorum ascetis. Sub praes. J. H. Willemeri.
[P2666]. s4°. [Wittenberg. 1680]
Deliciæ Hebræo-philologicæ. Cum app. De adventu Messiæ, ex vatic. Malach. III, 1. [*b. w. h.* Comp. hist. Jud., 1700].
s8°. Francofurti ad Moenum. 1700
Genius & indoles linguae sanctae. s8°. Francofurti a. M. 1713

Schudt (Ludwig), *ed.*, *see* MANCINI (G.) Viaggio per Roma, 1923.

Schuermans (H.) Verres à courses de chars (de Couvin). [Extr. du t20 des Ann. de Soc. Archéol. de Namur. P2498].
8°. Namur. 1893

Schuhmann (Robert), *see* RICCI (S. DE). R. S. coll. of 18th c. French books, 1920.

Schuicker (Petrus), *see* SCHWICKERIUS (P.)

Schukin (Nikolai Semenovich).
Очеркъ забайкальской области [?*Extr. f.* Журналъ Мин. Внутр. Дѣлъ, c. 1851]. [P560]. 8°. [С.-П. c. 1851]

Schulenburg-Klosterrode (Friedrich A., *Graf.* v. d.)
*Die Herzogin v. Ahlden. 8°. L. 1852

Schuler (Jacobus), *see* LUTHARD (C.) Disput. Bernensis, 1528, explic. &c. adv. J. S. &c., 1660.

Schüller (Richard), *see* GRATZ (G.) & R. S. Die äussere Wirtschaftspolitik Österreich-Ungarns, 1925.

Schultcordes (Johann). Diss. de primis initiis Xtnae. inter Russos relig. [P2644]. s4°. Halae Magdeb. [1762]

Schulte (Aloys). Gesch. d. gr. Ravensburger Handelsgesellschaft, 1380–1530. 3B. la8°. St. 1923
Der hohe Adel im Leben d. mittelalt. Köln, *see* KÖNIGL. AKAD. D. WISS. ZU MÜNCHEN. Phil. Kl., Sitz., 1919.
Tausend Jahre deut. Gesch. u. d. Kultur am Rhein. Im Auftrage d. Provinzialausschusses d. Rheinprov. bearb. v. M. Braubach &c., hrsg. v. A. 8°. Düsseldorf. 1925

Schulte (Johann Bernhard). De Synodo Tremoniensi sub Henrico II habita. Praes. J. G. Jochio.
[P2647]. s4°. Tremoniae. [1715]

Schulte (Johann Friedrich, *Ritter* von).
Denkschr. ü. d. Verhältniss d. Staates zu d. Sätzen d. päpstl. Constitut. v. 18. Juli 1870. [P2695]. 8°. Prag. 1871
Handbuch d. kathol. Eherechts. 8°. Giessen. 1855
Die Macht d. röm. Päpste über Fürsten, Länder, Völker &c., seit Gregor VII z. Würdigung ihr. Unfehlbarkeit &c.
2e verm. A. [P2657]. 8°. Prag. 1871
Die neueren kathol. Orden u. Congreg., besonders in Deutschland.
[P2657]. 8°. 1872
The power of the Roman popes over princes, countries &c. Tr. by A. Sommers. [P2506]. 8°. Adelaide. 1871
Die Rechtsfrage d. Einflusses d. Regierung bei d. Bischofswahlen in Preussen &c. [P2695]. 8°. Giessen. 1869
Die Stelling d. Concilien, Päbste u. Bischöfe u. d. päbstl. Constit. vom 18. Juli 1870. 8°. Prag. 1871
Das Unfehlbarkeits-Decret v. 18. Juli 1870.
[P2693]. 8°. Prag. 1871
see FESSLER (J.) True & false infallibility of the popes, reply to S.; tr., 1875.

Schulten (Adolf). Hispania (geogr., etnol., hist.) Tr. P. Bosch Gimpera, M. Artigas Ferrando. Con apéndice, La arqueología prerromana hisp. por P. Bosch Gimpera.
8°. Barcelona. 1920
Numantia. Die Ergebnisse d. Ausgrabungen, 1905–12. Unter Mitw. v. W. Barthel, H. Dragendorff &c.
B3 [*w.* 46 Pläne &c.] 4°. & la. fol. München. 1927
3, Die Lager d. Scipio; v. A. Schulten.
Panorama v. Numantia. Gezeichnet v. H. Hofmann, mit Text v. A. S. obl.4°. München. 1922

Schultens (Albert).
De defectibus hodiernis linguae Hebrææ, &c.
s4°. Francquerae. 1731
Instit. ad fundamenta linguae Hebraeae.
ed. altera. s4°. Lugduni Batav. 1756

Schultens (Albert) [*continued*].
Op. minora. Animadv. in Jobum, et ad varia loca V.T.
4°. Lugduni Batav. 1769
Origines Hebrææ sive Hebrææ linguæ antiq. natura & indoles ex Arabiae penetralibus revocata; cui adjectum opusc. de defectibus hodiernis linguæ Hebr. [Oratio prima (—altera) de linguae Arabicae origine &c.] 2a ed. 4°. Lugduni Batavorum. 1761
see ERPENIUS (T.) Gramm. Arab.; acc. excerpta anthologiae, ed. &c. A. S., 1748.
Schultetus (David). De feminis prima aetate eruditione ac scriptis illust. Praes. D. S., resp. [1] J. H. Langschmidius, [2] J. D. Starckius. [2p. P444]. s4°. Vitembergae. [1703]
Schultetus (Samuel). Eccl. Muhammedana. Sub praes. J. Dannhaueri. [P427]. s4°. Argentorati. 1668
Schulthess (H.) Europäischer Geschichtskalendar, N.F. Jhrg. 32–40, 42 (d. ganzen Reihe, B57–65, 67), 1916–1924, 1926.
8°. München. 1920–28
N.F., Jhrg. 32, hrsg. E. Jäckh u. K. Hönn, *in* 2T, *sep. pagin.*; 33–36, hrsg. W. Stahl; 37–40, 42, hrsg. U. Thürauf.
Schulthess (Johann). De charismatibus Spiritus sancti. pl, De vi &c. dotis linguarum. [*no more publ.*] 8°. Lipsiae. 1818
De uno argumento pro divinitate &c. Jesu. 8°. Turici. 1828
Schulthess-Rechberg (Gustav v.) Heinr. Bullinger, d. Nachfolger Zwinglis. [Verein f. Ref.-gesch. Schr., Jhrg. 22, Nr. 82]. 8°. Halle a. S. 1904
Schultingius (Cornelius). Eccl. disciplinæ libri sex.
s8°. Coloniae Agrippinae. 1598
Schultz (Georg). De Epistola Christi ad Abgarum &c. Praes. G. S., resp. C. Hein. [P426]. s4°. Regiomonti. [1706]
Schultz (Johannes Heinrich). Hypnose u. Suggestion, *see* HATTINGBERG (H. v.), *ed.* Nerv. Mensch, B12, 1924.
Nervosität u. erbl. Belastung, *see* HATTINGBERG (H. v.), *ed.* Nerv. Mensch, B4, 1924.
Schultze (Benjamin).
Catechismus Tellugicus minor, interp. B. S.
s8°. Halae Magdeb. 1746
Compendiaria Alcorani refut. Indostanice. Ed. J. H. Callenberg.
s8°. Halae. 1744
*Conjecturae hist.-crit. Sadducæorum. 8°. Halae ad Salam. 1779
Grammatica Hindostanica. Ed. J. H. Callenberg.
s4°. Halae Saxon. 1745
Hymnologia Damulica, ex Germanico &c. a B. S., 1723, *see* HYMNOLOGIA.
Mores vitamque Xtn°. dignam delin. regulae centum. In ling. Telugicam tr. Interp. B. S. s8°. Halae. 1747
*Perspicua explic. doct. Xtnae. sec. ord. 5 cap. Catechismi maioris; ex Tamulica in Telugicam versa a B. S. s8°. Halae Magd. 1747
Sermam da bemaventurança dos fieis o dia das exequias da sepultura do J. E. Grundler. s8°. Tranquebar. 1720
Via sive ordo salutis. In ling. Telugicam tr. Interp. B. S.
s8°. Halae. 1746
Schultze (Ernst). Die geistige Hebung d. Volksmassen in England. 8°. München. 1912
Ruhrbesetzung u. Weltwirtschaft. [*By var. a.*] Hrsg. E. S.
8°. L. 1927
Volksbildung u. Volkswohlfahrt in England. 8°. München. 1912
Schultze (Gretel), *see* NOBEL (A.) Hdbch. d. Staatsmanns; Personalreg. d. Polit. d. Welt, v. G. S., 1923.
Schultze (Martin). Hdbch. d. ebräischen Mythologie.
8°. Nordhausen. 1876
Schultze (Walther), *Dr. phil.*
Die Marneschlacht. 2e umgearb. A. 8°. 1923
Schultze (Wilhelm Herm.), *see* ARMINIUS (W.), *form. W. H. S.*
Schultze-Galléra (Siegmar).
Gesch. d. Stadt Halle. B1. 8°. Halle a. d. S. 1925
Schultz-Schultzenstein (C. H.) Leben—Gesundheit—Krankheit—Heilung. [*Imperf. b. w.* Körner (F.) Menschengeist, 1870]. 2e A. 8°. Basel. 1873
Schulz (Benjamin), *see* SCHULTZE (B.)
Schulz (Bruno), *see* WIEGAND (T.) Baalbek: Ergebnisse d. Ausgrabungen &c., 1898 bis 1905, B1, v. B. S. &c., 1921.
Schulz (Friedrich), *prof. of history at Mitau.* Aphorismen aus d. Menschen-Kunde u. Lebens-Philos.; Fr. u. deutsch hrsg. v. F. Schulz. Eine Nachlese zu de la Rochefoucault's Werke. s8°. Königsberg. 1793
Schulz (Hans). Wallenstein u. d. Zeit d. 30. Jähr. Krieges.
la8°. Bielefeld. 1898
Schulz (Johann Gottfried). Hist. Antinomorum sec. Lutheri ecclesiam turbantium. Diss. 1, praes. H. L. Schurzfleischio; diss. 2, resp. G. Thürmann. [P440]. s4°. Vitembergae. [1708]
Schulz (Johann Gottlob). Gesch. d. Sachsenlandes u. s. Regenten. s8°. L. 1795
Schulz (Otto Th.) Der Sinn d. Antike u. Spenglers neue Lehre. Antrittsvorl. 2e verm. A. [P2580]. 8°. St. 1922
Schulz (Ph. Walter). Die pers.-islam. Miniaturmalerei. Beitrag z. Kunstgesch. Irans.
2B [1, Text. 2, Tafeln]. 4°. L. 1914
Schulze (Carl), *of Göttingen.* Deut. Spruchweisheit auf Münzen &c., *see* ARCHIV F. D. ST. D. NEU. SPR., B56–58, 1876–77.
Schulze (Friedrich), *Superint. of the Diocese of Naumburg & Zeitz.* Disput. de rationibus theol. quibus electio J. Pflugii episc. Numburg. impugnata & propugnata est. Praes. J. E. Schuberto. [P598]. s4°. Helmstadii. [1750]
Schulze (Georg). Ewerharz. Zitter: harz. Gedichte mit Gram. u. Wbch., *see* ARCHIV F. D. ST. D. NEU. SPR., B60, 61, 1878–79.
Schulze (Gottlob Ernst). Encyklopädie d. philosoph. Wissenschaften. 3e A. 8°. Göttingen. 1823
Schulze (Hanns). Die Werke Angelo Bronzinos. la8°. Str. 1911
Schulze-Berghof (Paul). Die schöne Sabine. Ein friederizian. Roman aus d. Rheinsberger Tagen. B3 d. Trilogie.
8°. München. [1916]
Schumacher (Carl). Der Ackerbau in vorröm. u. röm. Zeit.
[P2617]. s8°. Mainz. 1922
Siedelungs- u. Kulturgesch. d. Rheinlande.
3B. la8°. Mainz. 1921–25
Schumacher (Peder), *see* GRIFFENFELD (P., *Graf* v.)
Schumann (Clara).
see LITZMANN (B.) C. S., e. Kunstlerleben, 4. A. &c., 3B, 1910.
„ SCHUMANN (E.) Memoirs; tr., 1927.
—— & J. Brahms.
Briefe, 1853–96. Hrsg. B. Litzmann. 2B. 8°. L. 1927
Letters, 1853–96. Ed. B. Litzmann. [Tr.] 2v. 8°. 1927
Schumann (Eugenie), *d. of R. Schumann.*
Memoirs. Tr. M. Busch. 8°. 1927
Schumann (Gustav Adolph).
Vita Mosis. pl, De infantia Mosis. s8°. Lipsiae. 1826
Schumann (Harry). Karl Liebknecht, ein Stück unpolit. Weltanschauung. s8°. Dresden. 1923
Schumann (Robert A.), *see* FULLER-MAITLAND (J. A.) S., n. ed., 1923.
Schur (Werner). Die Orientpolitik d. Kaisers Nero. [Klio, Beiheft 15]. 8°. L. 1923
Schuré (Édouard). L'âme celtique et le génie de la France à trav. les âges. s8°. 1921
Le drame musical. 2t [1, 12e éd.; 2, 14e éd.] s8°. 1920
1, Hist. de drame musical.
2, R. Wagner, s. œuvre & s. idée.
From Sphinx to Christ. Tr. E. Martin. 8°. [1928]
Merlin l'enchanteur. Légende dramatique. s8°. 1924
Schuricht (Richard). Auszug aus d. Tagebuche e. Materialisten. [*b. w.* Stirner (M.) D. Einzige u. s. Eigenthum, 1845]. 8°. Hamburg. 1860
Schürmann (Anna Maria v.) Opuscula.
ed. 3a, auct. &c. s8°. Trajecti ad Rhenum. 1652
Schürmann (H.) Petrus u. Papstthum. Mit e. Anhange: Louise Lateau. s8°. Barmen. 1875
Schürmann (Willem), *1876–1915.*
De Berkelmans. 6e dr. 8°. Rotterdam. 1920
De beul. 8°. Rotterdam. *n.d.*
Schurovsky (Grigory Efimovich) [†SHCHUROVSKY (G. E.)]
Уральскій хребетъ въ физико-географ. отношеніяхъ. 8°. Москва. 1841
Schürr (Friedrich). Romagnolische Dialektst., 1, 2, 1918–19, *see* KAISERL. AKAD. D. WISS. ZU WIEN. Sitzungsber., B187, 188, 1918–19.
Romagnol. Mundarten, 1917, *see* KAIS. AKAD. D. W. ZU WIEN. Phil.-hist. Kl., Sitz., B181, 1928.
Schurz (Wilhelm). De mutationibus in Imperio Rom. ordin. ab Imp. Hadriano factis. pl. [P2466]. 8°. Bonnae. 1883
Schurzfleisch (Conrad Samuel). Hist. eccl. Ed. opera &c. G. Wageneri. s4°. Vittembergae. 1744
Opera historica politica. *b. in* 2v. 4°. Berolini. 1699
Engr. tp. dated 1699; pr. tp. dated in error 1599.
Schüssler (Wilhelm). Bismarcks Sturz. 3e verb. A. 8°. L. 1922
Schuster (Ildefonso). The Sacramentary (Liber Sacrament.) Hist. & liturg. notes on the Roman Missal. Tr. A. Levelis-Marke. 3v. 8°. 1924–27
Schütte (Gudmund). Jysk og Østdansk Artikelbrug, *see* KONG. DAN. VID. SELSK. Hist.-fil. Med., B7, 1921–22.
Schütz (Heinrich), *prof. of hist. in Univ. of Ingolstadt.* Comm. crit. de scriptis & scriptor. historicis. s4°. Ulmae. 1763

Schütz (Johann), *Pfarrer zu Rhiestedt.* Fünfftzig erhebliche Ursachen darumb d. Luther. Christen zu d. Sacramentierern oder Calvinisten nicht tretten &c. sollen. Sampt 12 angeh. erschreckl. Sünden &c. [*b. w. h.* Serpens antiquus, 1580]. s8°. Eisleben. 1580
Serpens antiquus. Die alte Schlange. Das ist d. Sacraments Teuffel, d. reine Luther. Lere, v. Nachtmal &c. s8°. Eisleben. 1580
Schütz (Otto Friedrich). De vita D. Chytraei comment. libri 4. 2t *in* 1v. [App. *w. sep. pagin.*] s8°. Hamburgi. 1720–22
Schütz (Roland). Apostel u. Jünger. 8°. Giessen. 1921
Schuyler (George L.) Corr. & remarks upon Bancroft's Hist. of the Northern campaign of 1777, & the character of Maj.-Gen. P. Schuyler. [P2623]. 8°. 1867
Schuyler (Montgomery). Westward the course of Empire. "Out West" & "Back East" on "Los Angeles Ltd." s8°. N.Y. 1906
Schuyler (*gen.* **Philip John),** *see* SCHUYLER (G. L.) Corr. upon Bancroft's Hist. & the Character of P. J. S., 1867.
Schuyler (Robert Livingston).
The constit. of the U.S.: hist. survey. 8°. N.Y. 1923
Schüz (Gottfried). Diss. de infallibilitate pontif. Rom. αὐτοκατακρίτω. Praes. S. J. Baumgarten. [P436]. s4°. Halae Magdeb. [1740]
Schüz (Henricus), *see* SCHÜTZ (HEINRICH).
Schüz (Joh. Christoph), *see* KNÖBEL (J. B.) & J. C. S. Examen quietismi, 1715.
Schwab (Johann Christoph). Diss., *see* PAP (J.) Disp., 1784.
Schwab (Raymond). La conquête de la joie. Préc. d'une note sur l'auteur par Fœmina (J. Vontade). [Cahiers verts, 9]. s8°. 1922
Schwabe (A.) Courte hist. agraire de la Lettonie. [P2877]. 8°. Riga. 1926
Schwabe (Johannes). Diss. theol. de relig. ritibusque eccl. Moscovitarum. [*a. c. in* P2443]. s4°. Jenae. 1665
Schwabe (Ludwig). Die Kaiserl. Decennalien u. die Alexandrin. Münzen. [P2518]. la8°. Tübingen. 1896
Schwabe (Randolph).
see HALL (*Mrs.* E. C.) Draughtsmen: E. C. H., R. S. &c., 1924.
„ KELLY (F. M.) & R. S. Historic costume, 1925.
Schwalbe (Gustav). Die Abstammung d. Menschen &c., *see* HINNEBERG (P.) Die Kultur d. Gegenwart, T3v, 1923.
Schwandtnerus (Joannes Georgius), *ed.* Scriptores rerum Hungaric. veteres ac genuini. 3p. 4°. Vindobonae. 1766–68
Schwann (Theodor). Mein Gutachten ü. d. Stigmatis. Louise Lateau. [P601]. 8°. Köln. 1875
Schwartz (Christian Friedrich) [SWARTZ (C. F.)], *1726–98.*
*The life of C. F. Swartz, miss. at Travancore, 1750–98. s8°. 1855
Remains: letters & journals, w. sk. of h. life. 2nd ed. 8°. 1826
see JAENICKE (J. D.) Mem. of J., a fellow labourer of S. at Tanjore, 1833.
„ PAGE (J.) S. of Tanjore, 1921.
Schwartz (Eduard). Eine fing. Korresp. mit Paulus d. Samosatener, *w. text, see* KÖN. AKAD. D. W. ZU MÜNCHEN. Phil. &c. Kl., Sitz., 1927.
Die sog. Gegenanathematismen d. Nestorius—Zur Schriftstellerei Theodorets, *see* KÖNIGL. AKAD. D. W. ZU MÜNCHEN. Phil. Kl., Sitz., 1922.
Der sog. Sermo major de fide d. Athanasius, *see* KÖNIGL. AKAD. D. W. ZU MÜNCHEN. Phil. Kl., Sitz., 1924.
see EPHESUS, *Synod of, 431.* Neue Aktenstücke; [hrsg.] E. S., 1920.
Schwartzerdt (Georg), *b. 1500–1, see* MÜLLER (N.) G. S., d. Bruder Melanchthons, 1908.
***Schwarz-**Wildpret-Jagd o. d. neu. Jesuiten-Hetze, 1872, *see* JESUITS.
Schwarz (Arthur Zacharias). Die hebrä. Hss. d. Hofbibl. zu Wien: (Erwerb. seit 1851), 1914, *see* KAIS. AKAD. D. W. ZU WIEN. Sitz., B175, 1916.
Schwarz (Bernhard). Kard. Otto Truchsess v. Waldburg, bis zur Wahl als Fürstbischof v. Augsburg (1514–43). 8°. Hildesheim. 1923
Schwarz (Ernest H. L.) The Kalahari, or Thirstland redemption. 8°. Cape Town. [1919?]
Schwarz (Franz v.) Turkestan, d. Wiege d. indogerman. Völker. 8°. Freiburg im Br. 1900
Schwarz (Friedrich Immanuel). De legato Acad. Lips. ad Concil. Basileense [N. Weygel] tract. [P2643]. s4°. Lipsiae. [1786]
De silentio Lutheri. s4°. Lipsiae. [1778]

Schwarz (H. W. Carl), *1812–85.*
De sancta Trinitate &c. 8°. Halis. 1842
Schwarz (Heinrich). Salzburg u. d. Salzkammergut, in 100 Bildern d. 19ten Jhdts. la8°. Wien. 1926
Schwarz (Ignaz), *see* LANGER (E.) Bibliographie d. österr. Drucke, B1, H1, mit Anh.: Aus d. ersten Zeit d. Wiener Buchdr.; v. I. S., 1913.
Schwarz (J. C. E.)
Das erste Jahrzehnd d. Univ. Jena. 8°. Jena. 1858
Schwarz (Johann), *pastor at Querfurt.* Summulae theol., totus Christianismus &c. s8°. Isleb. 1703
Schwarz (Osias L.) General types of superior men: a philos.-psycholog. st. of genius &c. Pref. by J. London, & intr. letter by M. Nordau. 8°. Boston [U.S. 1916]
Schwarz (Sibylle), *see* GASSEN (K.) S. S., e. pommersche Dichterin, 1621–38, 1921.
Schwarze (Der) Tod: e. Chronik d. Pest, 1348–1720, 1924, *see* NOHL (J.), *ed.*
Schwarzseher (Ein), *ps., see* WILLIAM II, *G. emp.* W. II u. d. S., Nachdruck v. "Unser Kaiser u. s. Volk, v. e. S.," 1919.
Schwarzwald (Der) in Farbenphotographien. Hrsg. d. Bad. u. Württ. Schwarzwaldvereins. Text v. K. Brunner, E. Burger *& others.* fol. Freiburg im Br. [1911]
Schwegelbaur (Gustav), *see* HÖRLE (E.) & G. S. Unser schönes Stuttgart, 1926.
Schweickhard (Erhard) [SCHWEICKHARDUS (E.)]
Disp. contra purgatorium &c. s4°. Tubingae. 1569
Schweiger-Lerchenfeld (Amand, *Frhr* **v.)** Die Donau als Völkerweg, Schiffahrtsstrasse u. Reiseroute. 8°. Wien. 1896
Schweighäuser (Jean-Geoffroi), *1776–1844, see* PFISTER (C.) Les S. &c., 1927.
Schweighäuser (Johannes), *1742–1830* [SCHWEIGHAEUSERUS], *see* PFISTER (C.) Les S. & la chaire de litt. grec. de Strasbourg (1770–1855), 1927.
Schweinitz (*Gen.* **Hans Lothar v.)** Briefwechsel. 8°. [1928]
Denkwürdigkeiten d. Botschafters Gen. v. S. [Vorwort d. Hrsg., W. v. Schweinitz]. 2B. 8°. 1927
Schweinitz (Johann Siegmund von). Diss. de Caes. Maximiliano I, pontif. max. affectante. Praes. E. S. Cypriano, 1710. Recusa. [P597]. s4°. Jenae. 1716
Schweinitz (Margaret de).
Les épitaphes de Ronsard: ét. hist. & litt. 8°. [1925]
Schweitzer (Albert).
Christianity & the religions of the world. Lect. Tr. J. Powers, w. foreword by N. Micklem. [repr.] s8°. [1924]
Civilization & ethics. Tr. J. Naish. [Dale Mem. Lect., 1922]. 8°. 1923
Decay & restoration of civilization. Tr. T. Campion. [Dale Mem. Lect., 1922]. 8°. 1923
Kultur u. Ethik. 8°. München. [1923]
Memoirs of childhood & youth. Tr. C. T. Campion. s8°. [1924]
The mystery of the Kingdom of God: secret of Jesus' Messiahship & Passion. Tr. w. intr. by W. Lowrie. 8°. 1925
On the edge of the primeval forest &c., Equatorial Africa. Tr. C. T. Campion. s8°. 1922
„ „ ....[repr.] s8°. 1923
The quest of the hist. Jesus. Crit. study of its progress f. Reimarus to Wrede. Tr. W. Montgomery. Pref. by F. C. Burkitt. 2nd Eng. ed. [*repr.*] 8°. 1922
Verfall u. Wiederaufbau d. Kultur. 8°. München. [1923]
Schweitzer (Bernhard). Herakles. Aufsätze z. griech. Relig. u. Sagengesch. la8°. Tübingen. 1922
Schweizer Alpenclub. Jahrbuch. 1–58, 1864–1923. [1903 *wanting*]. 8°. *&* la8°. Bern. 1864–1924
B1–45 (*except* 1, 9, 20 & 39) *have* Artist. Beilagen (Carten, Panorama &c.), *b. sep., some maps missing.*
„ „ Repertorium u. Ortsreg. f. Jhbr. 1–20. Von O. v. Bülow. s8°. Bern. 1886
Schweizer (Paul).
Gesch. d. schweizer. Neutralität. 8°. Frauenfeld. 1895
Die Wallenstein-Frage in d. Gesch. u. im Drama. 8°. Zürich. 1899
Schweizerisches. Zeitgenossen-Lexikon; hrsg. v. H. Aellen &c., 1921, *see* AELLEN (H.)
Schweizerisches Landes-Museum, *see* ZURICH: MUSÉE NAT. SUISSE.
Schwemer (Richard). Gesch. d. Freien Stadt Frankfurt a. M., 1814–66. 3B [*in* 4v. 3i, ii]. 8°. Frankfurt a. M. 1910–18
Schwenckfeld (Caspar). Bekantnuss vō H. Sacrament des leibs u. blůts Christi, auff frag uñ antwort gestellet. s8°. Strassburg, [*H. Schweintzer.* 1530]
Summarium d. Christl. streyts vom bösen u. güten gewissen &c. s8°. [Nürnberg, *H. Schöffler*]. 1533

Schwenckfeld (Caspar) [*continued*].
see AGRICOLA (T.) Kurtze antwurt auf das Büchlein, M. Flacius wider C. S. &c., 1556.
,, BUSÆUS (J.) 30 paradoxa G. S. haeresiarchae de toto Christo Deo & Homine &c., 1595.
,, HOORNBEEK (J.) De paradoxis, & heterodoxis Weigelianis; ubi et de Swencfeldo, 1694.
,, WIGAND (J.) De Schwenckfeldismo &c., 1586.

Schwendener (Simon), *see* HABERLANDT (G.) Gedächtnisrede auf S. S., 1919.

Schwender (Friedrich). De excelso & divino Lutheri animo. [P1041]. s8°. Jenae. [1827]

Schwendi (Lazarus, *Frhr.* **v.),** *see* KRONE (R.) L. v. S., 1522–84, s. kirchenpolit. Tätigkeit &c., 1912.

Schwenke (*Dr.* **Paul),** *see* ANDERSON (A.) P. S., 1922.

Schwerdfeger (Josef).
Vienna gloriosa: Bilder &c. s8°. [Wien]. 1923

Schwerin (Claudius, *Frhr.* **von).** Deut. Rechtgesch., 1912, *see* GRUNDR. D. GESCHICHTSWISS.; Meister, 2v, 1912.

Schwertfeger (Bernhard). Die diplomat. Akten d. Auswärtigen Amtes, 1871–1914. Ein Wegweiser durch d. gr. Aktenwerk d. Deut. Regierung.
5T *in* 8v [4i, ii, 5i–iii]. la8°. 1923–27
,, ,, [*a. set.* T1, 4ii, 5i, 3. A.; 3, 4i, 2. A.] la8°. 1924–27
1, Die Bismarck-Epoche, 1871–1890.
2, Der Neue Kurs, 1890–99.
3, Die Politik d. Freien Hand, 1899–1904.
4, Die Isolierung d. Mittelmächte, 1904–8, 2H.
5, Weltpolit. Komplikationen, 1908–14, 3 Abtlg.
Der Fehlspruch v. Versailles. Abschliess. Prüfung d. Brüsseler Aktenstücke. la8°. 1921
Der Irrtum d. Marschalls Foch. Die Gründe d. deut. Kapitul. v. 11, Nov. 1918. 3. A. 8°. 1920
Zur europaischen Politik. Unveröffentl. Dokumente in amtl. Auftrage hrsg. unter Leitung v. B. S. B1–5. 8°. 1919
1, 1897–1904: Zweibund—Eng.-Deut. Gegensatz, bearb. v. W. Köhler.
2, 1905–1907: Marokkokrisis—König Eduard VII, bearb. v. B. S.
3, 1908–1911: Bosnische Krise—Agadir—Albanien, bearb. v. A. Doren.
4, 1912–1914: Kriegstreibereien u. Kriegsrüstungen, bearb. v. A. Doren.
5, [1885–1894]: Revanche-Idee u. Panslawismus, bearb. v. W. Köhler.
see GERMANY: REICHSTAG. Ursachen d. Zusammenbruchs: Entst. d. Offensive v. 1918; Gutachten d. Ober. S. &c., 1923.

Schwestermiller (Conrad). Pestregiment (*facs.* 1484), *see* FREYTAG (G.) Bilder, B2, 1924.

Schwetz (J.), *Médecin inspecteur au Congo belge.* Études &c. d'entomol. médicale sur le Katanga. 8°. Brux. 1927

Schwicker (Johann Heinrich). Die Katholiken-Autonomie in Ungarn. Wesen, Gesch. &c. [P2656]. 8°. Pest. 1870

Schwickerius (Petrus) [SCHUICKER]. P. S. sita in septem penitentium Psalmos elucidatio.
s4°. Lanndszhut, *Joannes Weyssenburger.* [1514]

Schwietering (Julius). Die Demutsformel mittelhochdeut. Dichter, 1921, *see* KÖNIGL. GESELL. D. W. z. GÖTT. Abhlgn., N.F., 17, 1921.

Schwindel (Georg Jacob) [*ps.* SINCERUS (THEOPHILUS)].
Notitia hist.-crit. librorum vet. rar. Oder: Neue Nachr. &c. s4°. L. 1753

Schwob (Marcel). Le parnasse satyrique du 15e s. Anthologie publ. par M. S. s8°. 1905
see CHAMPION (P.) M. S. & son temps, 1927.

Schwob (René). Profondeurs de l'Espagne. [Cahiers verts, n.s., 10]. s8°. 1928

Schwob (Sigismund) [SIGISMUNDUS SUEVUS]. Register Deudsch u. Latin. aller Bücher u. Schrifften M. Lutheri &c. [2p, p2 *w. sep. tp.* Index omnium librorum &c.]
fol. Wittemberg. 1573
Speculum extremi judicii. Spiegel des jüngsten Gerichts. [*b. w.* Mechler (Æ.) Catechismus &c., 1574].
s8°. [Leipzig. 1582]

Schybergson (Magnus Gottfrid), *see* GESCH. D. EUROP. STAATEN: Finnland, 1809–1919, v. S., 1925.

Schyn (Herman). Hist. Christianorum qui in Belgio Fœderato inter Protestantes Mennonitæ appellantur &c.
s8°. Amstelodami. 1723
Hist. Mennonitarum plenior deductio. [Pref. by J. van Zanten. *a. ed. b. w. h.* Hist. Christianorum, 1723].
s8°. Amstelaedami. 1729

Scialoja (Vittorio). Framm. di legge rom. scop. a Taranto, *see* REALE ACCAD. D. LINCEI. Mon. ant., v6, 1895.

Scicluna (Hannibal P.) Doc. of the archives of the Order of St. John of Jerusalem & Malta. Extr. f. "Archivum Melitense," Sept. 1912. [P2516]. la8°. Malta. 1912
Doc. rel. to the French occup. of Malta in 1798–1800.
[v]1. la8°. Malta. 1923

Scidmore (Eliza Ruhamah). Westward to the Far East: guide to China & Japan. Issued by C.P.R. Co.
5th ed. [P2830]. 8°. [Montreal?]. 1894

Science.
Outline of science, 2v, 1921–2, *see* THOMSON (J. A.), *ed.*
Science & civiliz.: essays [*by var. a.*], 1923, *see* MARVIN (F. S.), *ed.*
Science & educ. [repr.], ed. Sir E. Ray Lankester, 1917, *see* LECTURES.
Science & labour: addresses, 1924, *see* HUMBERSTONE (T. L.), *ed.*
Science for all. [*By var. wr.*] Intr. by Sir C. S. Sherrington. 8°. 1926
Science, religion & reality; [by] Earl Balfour &c., 1925, *see* NEEDHAM (J.), *ed.*

Science Abstracts.
Sect. A, Physics. v23–28 (1920–25). 8°. [1920–25]
Sect. B, Electrical engineering. v23–30 (1920–27). 8°. [1920–27]

Science Library, *South Kensington.* Catalogue. la8°. 1891
Classification for works on pure & appl. science. 2nd ed. 8°. 1921
List of current period. Ed. S. C. Bradford. 4th ed. 8°. 1926

Science Progress in the 20th century. Ed. Sir R. Ross &c.
v14–22. 8°. 1920–28

Scientia. (Rivista de scienza). Organo internaz. di sintesi scientifica [*in var. lang.*]
v27–43, Anno 14–22. 8°. Bologna. [1920–28]

Scientific American. The journal of practical information. v124–138 (Jan. 1921–June 1928) [v124 *&* 127 *want tp.*]
4°. [N.Y. 1921–28]

Scientific & Industrial Research, *Dept. of, see* CLEANING (THE) & restoration of museum exhibits, 3rd rep., 1926.

Scientific magazine (The), & Freemasons' repository.
[v8]. Jan.–June 1797. [*Incomplete*]. 8°. 1797
Earlier vol. had title Freemasons' Magazine.

Scifoni (Felice) [F. S.], *see* DIZIONARIO biografico univ. [*tr. & compiled f.* Biog. Univ. *by* F. S.], 5v, 1840–49.

Scinde. Gazetteer of the Province of Sind.
[vol. A], Bi–vii. 8°. Karachi & Bombay. 1907–20
A, comp. by E. H. Aitken. Bi, Karachi Distr., ii, Hyderabad Distr., iii, Sukkur Distr., iv, Larkana Distr., v, Nawabshah Distr., vi, Thar & Parkar Distr., vii, Upper Sind Frontier Distr.; comp. by J. W. Smyth.

***Sciocche** &c. impost. per denigr. l'illust. mem. di Paolo Servita, 1770, *see* GRISELINI (F.)

Scioppius (Gasparus), *see* SCHOPPE (CASPAR).

Scipio (Publius Cornelius), *Africanus, Major, 235–183 B.C.*
see HART (B. H. L.) A greater than Napoleon: S. A., 1926.
,, SCHMID (D. F.) Disput. S. vitam exhib., 1662.

Scipio Æmilianus (Publius Cornelius), *Africanus, Minor, see* SCHULTEN (A.) Numantia: Ausgrab., 1905–12, B3, Die Lager d. S., 1927.

Scize (Pierre).
Works in ŒUVRES libres.
Aux vendanges de Bourgogne, 1923. [28.]
Europe, ma voisine . . ., 1922. [11.]
Fêtes d'art à Orange, 1924. [37.]
La seconde jeunesse de Bonaparte, 1927. [73.]

Sclater (William), *Vicar of Pitminster Somers.* An expos. w. notes upon Thessalonians. 2p *in* 1v. [p2, 3rd ed.] s4°. 1630–32

Sclater (William Lutley), *the younger, see* WRIGHT (A.) & W. L. S. Sterne's Eliza, 1922.

Sclopis (*il conte* **Federigo).** Di alcuni diplomatici piemontesi: lettera ined. al b. D. Carutti, *see* REGIA DEP. DI STORIA PATRIA. Misc., t25, 1887.
see RICOTTI (E.) Breve commem. d. c. F. S., 1879.

Şcoala Româna din Roma, *see* SCUOLA ROMENA DI ROMA.

Scobell (Henry), *see* PARLIAMENT: GEN. COLL. Cat. &c. of ordinances &c., 1653–54 [*comp. by H. S.*], 1654.

Scofield (Cora Louise), *Ph.D.*
Life & reign of Edward IV. 2v. 8°. 1923

Scolari (Filippo), *dottore in legge.* La chiesa di S. Maria d. Pianto in Venezia. [P2835]. 8°. Venezia. [1851]

Scone. *Sconiana. Mem. of the antiq., curiosities &c. of S. 4°. E. 1807

Score (G. F.) Guide to Wimborne Minster. s8°. 1910

Scorel (Jan van) [SCHOREL; SCHOORLE], *see* HOOGEWERFF (G. J.) J. van S., peintre de la renaissance holland., 1923.

Scortia, *see also* SCORZA.

Scortia (Francesco), *Jesuit.* *Ristretto d. vita dell' apost. S. Francesco Xaverio. [*b. w.* Sgambati (S.) Vita di Maria Maddalena, 1654]. s8°. Bologna. [1622]

Scorza, *The family of* [SCORTIA], *see* SCORZA (A.) Arbor sive genealogia fam. S. &c. *&* Suppl., 1611 ; Ital. tr., 1611.

Scorza (Alessandro). Albero o genealogia d. famiglia Scorza &c. Tr. d. Dr. P. Vincenti, *&* Aggiuntione. [*b. w. h.* Arbor &c., 1611]. [*var. tp.*] 4°. Neapoli. 1611

Arbor sive genealogia familiæ Scortiæ, *&* aliarum Comitum Lavaniae *&* Suppl. iterum impr. [*var. tp*s.] 4°. Neapoli. 1611

Scorza (Angelo M. G.)

Libro d'oro d. nobiltà di Genova. fol. Genova. 1920

Scot (D. Hugh). *Sportsman's & tourist's hdbk. to Iceland. 2nd ed. s8°. 1900

Scot (Neil). The riding light. s8°. [1926]

Scotch. Old Scotch songs & poems, 1927, *see* WILSON (*Sir* J.), *ed.*

*Scotch Presbyterian eloquence display'd &c., by R. C.?, 1789, *see* CALDER (R.)

Scotland.

ANON. WORKS &c.

Ancient laws & customs of the burghs of S. [Ed. C. Innes, Scott. Burgh Records Soc.] v1, 1124–1424. 4°. E. 1868

Answer (The) of the Commiss. of S. to Parl. upon the new propos. of peace &c. [*imperfect, last leaf wanting.* P2571]. s8°. 1647

For reply, see SCOTTISH mist dispel'd, 1648.

*Assertion (An) of the govt. of the Church of S. &c., 1644, *see* GILLESPIE (G.)

Collectanea de rebus Albanicis: papers &c. rel. to Highlands &c. of S., 1847, *see* IONA CLUB.

Coll. of epitaphs & mon. inscr. chiefly in S. s8°. Glasgow. 1834

*Declaration (A) f. nobility of S., th. resolution conc. the Kings Majesty &c. [P2571]. s8°. 1647

Declaration (The) of kingdomes of Eng. & S. &c. agst. the Popish &c. party &c., 1643, *see* ENGLAND.

Declaration (A) of Parl. of Eng. conc. settlement of S., 1652, *see* PARLIAMENT.

Declaration (A) of the Comm. of Estates of S. agst. the forces of Charles II &c. repr. s8°. 1649

*Declaration of the inhabitants of the hill countreys of S., 1653, *see* MAIDMENT (J.), *ed.* Hist. fragm., p3, 1833.

Declaratioun (Ane) of the just &c. causis, moving us of the nobillitie of S. &c. ye Kings subjectis to repair to h. presence &c. for resisting of pres. daingeris to Goddis trew religion &c. s8°. Striuiling. 1582 [repr., ed. J. Maidment. 1822]

*Discourse (A) upon the uniting S. w. Eng., 1702, *see* FAIRFAX (B.)

*Dispute (A) agst. the English-Popish ceremonies obtruded upon the Ch. of S. &c., 1660, *see* GILLESPIE (G.)

*Hist. & tradit. tales in prose & verse conn. w. the S. of Scotland. s8°. Kirkcudbright. 1843

*Impartial (An) acc. of some transactions in S. conc. the Earl of Broadalban &c. 8°. 1695

*Landlords, land laws & land leagues in S. being a contrib. to contemp. politics. By Aliquis. [P2429]. 8°. E. 1881

*Letter (A) f. a gentleman at Edinburgh conc. affairs in S.: acc. of the Highlands, w. copy of the Pr—d—r's declaration. [P2779]. 8°. 1745

Letters f. the Ctte. of Estates at Newcastle, & the Comm. of S. to both Houses &c., also letters betw. Comm. of E. &c. & Gen. Poyntz. s8°. 1646

*Newes from S.: life & death of Dr. Fian, a noted sorcerer &c. (1591), *see* JAMES I, *k. of Gr. Brit.* Dæmonologie, 1924.

Papers rel. to the regalia of S. [Incl. repr. of A true acc. of the preserv. of the regalia of S., by Sir G. Ogilvie. Ed. W. Bell. Bannatyne Club]. 4°. E. 1829

*Peace againe in Sion &c., England & S. united &c., 1641, *see* PEACE.

*Present state of S., 1738, *see* MIEGE (G.) Pres. state of Gt. Brit., 8th ed., 1738.

*Proposal (A) for uniformity of weights &c. in S., 1779; 2nd ed., 1789, *see* SWINTON (J.)

*Satire agst. S. (1617). [*Signed* Johne E., *sometimes ascr. to Sir Ant. Weldon & to J. Howel*], *&* Answer, *see* ABBOTSFORD CLUB. Misc., v1, 1837.

*Scotlands alarme: or, consid. to demonstrate necessitie of marching to assist. of our brethren in Eng. &c., w. letter, Nov. 29, 1643. repr. [P2571]. s8°. 1643

Some papers of the Commiss. of S., given in lately to Parl., conc. the proposit. of peace. [P2571]. s4°. 1646

*State (The) of the weights &c. of S. & Eng. [*b. w.* Swinton (J.) Proposal, 1779]. *broadsheet.* la8°. E. 1706

West coast of S. pilot, 7th ed., 2v, *&* Suppl. 1, 1921–22, *see* ADMIRALTY.

RECORDS (PUBLIC).

Indexes, No. 4, 5. Ind. to register of deeds, 1665–66. v5, 6. fol. E. 1921

Scots. *Defence (A) of the Scots settlement at Darien, 1699, *see* FLETCHER (A.)

*Enquiry (An) into causes of miscarriage of the Scots colony at Darien, 1700, *see* DARIEN, *Scots colony.*

Scots Company, *see* DARIEN COMPANY.

Scots Philosophical Club, *see* ARISTOTELIAN Soc. Suppl. vol. 3, Relativity, logic &c.: papers, 1923.

Scott (Abraham). A diss. on the eternal sonship of Christ. [P2543]. 8°. Sheffield. 1828

Scott (Alexander), *D.Sc., see* ENNOS (F. R.) & A. S. Refractory minerals: fireclays &c., 1924.

Scott (Alexander MacCallum).

Barbary: romance of the nearest East. 8°. [1921]

Scott (Alice A.) Betty Paoli, an Austrian poetess of the 19th cent. 8°. [1926]

Scott (Andrew), *A.L.S., see* JOHNSTONE (J.), A. S. &c. The marine plankton, 1924.

Scott (*Mrs.* **Anna M.)** Day dawn in Africa: Prot. Episc. Mission at Cape Palmas, W. Africa. s8°. N.Y. 1858

Scott (Arthur Pearson).

Introd. to the peace treaties. s8°. Chicago. [1920]

see MACLAUGHLIN (A. C.), W. E. DODD &c. Source prob. in U.S. hist., by M. &c. & A. P. Scott, 1918.

Scott (Charles A. Anderson), *D.D.*

Christianity acc. to St. Paul. 8°. C. 1927

Scott (Charles Kennedy), *see* MASSÉ (H. J. L. J.) & C. K. S. Bk. of old carols, v1, 1910.

Scott (Cyril), *see* HULL (A. E.) C. S., composer, poet &c., 2nd ed., 1919.

Scott (Dukinfield Henry).

Extinct plants & problems of evolution. 8°. 1924

Intr. to structural botany (flowering plants). 3rd ed. s8°. 1895

Scott (Duncan Campbell). Poems. 8°. 1927

Scott (Ernest). History & hist. problems. s8°. O. 1925

Men & thought in mod. hist. 8°. Melbourne. 1920

Short hist. of Australia. 4th ed. s8°. Melbourne. 1920

Scott (Ernest Findlay). The Epistle to the Hebrews: its doctr. &c. 8°. E. 1922

Ethical teaching of Jesus. s8°. [1925]

First age of Xty. s8°. [1926]

Scott (Evelyn). The narrow house. s8°. 1921

Scott (Fred Newton). Amer. slang, *see* JESPERSEN (O.) Notes on relative clauses &c., 1927.

Scott (G. E., *lady*), *wife of Sir J. G. Scott, see* MITTON (G. E.)

Scott (Geoffrey).

The portrait of Zélide [Mme. de Charrières]. 8°. 1925

Scott (George Erving). Waterloo. Poem, Chancellor's medal, 1820. 8°. [*p.p.* C. 1820]

Scott (*Col.* **H. L.)** Military dictionary. 8°. N.Y. 1862

Scott (Harold).

English song book. Coll. & ed. by H. S. 8°. 1925

Scott (Henry Harold), *see* BALFOUR (A.) & H. H. S. Health prob. of the Empire, 1924.

Scott (Hew). Fasti Ecclesiæ Scoticanæ. Succession of ministers in Ch. of Scotland f. the Reformation. n. ed. rev. v3–7. la8°. E. 1920–28

3, Synod of Glasgow & Ayr. 4, Synods of Argyll, & of Perth & Stirling. 5, Synods of Fife, & of Angus & Mearns. 6, Synods of Aberdeen & of Moray. 7, Synods of Ross, Sutherland & Caithness, Glenelg, Orkney & of Shetland, The Ch. in England & Overseas.

Scott (James), *senior minister of Perth.*

A hist. of the Prot. reformers in Scotland. 8°. E. 1810

Scott (James B.)

Short acc. of the Wheelwrights' Co. la8°. *p.f.p.c.* 1884

Scott (James Brown).

Autonomy & federat. within empire: the Brit. self-govern. dominions. Prep. under S. [C.E. for Int. Peace.] la8°. Wash. 1921

The controversy over neutral rights betw. the U.S. & France 1797–1800. Coll. of Amer. State papers &c. [C.E. for Int. Peace]. la8°. N.Y. 1917

The Declaration of Independence—The Articles of Confederation—The constit. of the U.S. Ed. w. intr. note by S. [C.E. for Int. Peace]. la8°. N.Y. 1917

Elihu Root's services to internat. law, *see* INTERNAT. CONCILIATION, 207, 1925.

An Internat. Court of Justice. Letter & mem., 1914. [C.E. for Int. Peace]. 8°. N.Y. 1916

Judicial settlement of controversies betw. States of the Amer. Union: cases decided in Supreme Court of U.S. [C.E. for Int. Peace.] 2v. la8°. N.Y. 1918

" " ....Analysis. la8°. O. 1919

Offic. statements of war aims & peace proposals, Dec. 1916–Nov. 1918. Prep. under S. [C.E. for Int. Peace]. la8°. Wash. 1921

Prize cases decided in the U.S. Supreme Court, 1789–1918. Prep. under S. [C.E. for Int. Peace]. 3v. la8°. O. 1923

Scott (James Brown) [*continued*].
The project of a Permanent Court of Internat. Justice & Resolut. of the Advisory Comm. of jurists. Rep. & comm. by S. [C.E. for Int. Peace]. la8°. Wash. 1920
The Recommend. of Habana conc. internat. organiz. Addr. & comm., by S. [C.E. for Int. Peace]. la8°. N.Y. 1917
Sovereign states & suits before arbitral tribunals & courts of justice. 8°. N.Y. 1925
The status of the Internat. Court of Justice. With an app. of addr. & docs. [C.E. for Int. Peace]. 8°. N.Y. 1916
The U.S. of Amer.: a st. in internat. organiz. [C.E. for Int. Peace]. s4°. N.Y. 1920
see BEMIS (S. F.), *ed.* Amer. Secr. of State, v1, Hist. intr. by S., 1927.
,, HAGUE (THE). The H. convent. & declar. of 1899 & 1907; ed. S., 3rd ed., 1918.
,, —— The H. Court reports; ed., w. intr. by S., 1916.
,, —— Instr. to Amer. deleg. to the H. Peace Conf. & their reps.; ed., w. intr. by S., 1916.
,, —— Rep. to the H. Conf. 1899 & 1907; ed., w. intr. by S., 1917.
,, INSTITUTE OF INTERNAT. LAW. Resolutions dealing w. law of nations &c.; ed. S., 1916.
,, LADD (W.) An essay on a congress of nations, repr. f. ed. of 1840, w. intr. by S., 1916.
,, LONDON, DECLAR. OF. D. of L.: coll. of offic. papers & docs.; ed. S., 1919.
,, MADISON (J.) Debates in the Fed. Convent. of 1787 &c.; G. Hunt & S., eds., 1920.
,, PAN AMERICAN SCIENTIFIC CONGRESS (SECOND). Recomm. on internat. law &c.; ed., w. intr. matter, by S., 1916.
,, UNITED STATES: FOR. AFFAIRS. Treaties for the advancement of peace, negot. by Hon. W. J. Bryan; w. intr. by S., 1920.

Scott (*Sir* James George) [SHWAY YOE].
Burma: a hdbk. of information. 3rd ed. rev. 8°. 1921
Burma f. earliest times to pres. day. 8°. [1924]
,, ,, ... 8°. N.Y. 1924
see MITTON (G. E.) & *Sir* J. G. S. A frontier man, 1923.

Scott (*Col.* John), *of Long Island; 1634?–96? see* ABBOTT (W. C.) Col. J. S. of Long Island, 1918.

Scott (John), *poet, of Amwell; 1730–83.*
Poet. works. Coll. by T. Park. s8°. 1808

Scott (John Adams).
The unity of Homer. 8°. Berkeley, Cal. 1921

Scott (John Waugh).
Karl Marx on value. [A criticism]. la8°. 1920

Scott (Leslie Frederic) & A. Hildesley. The case of requisition. *In re* a Petition of right of De Keyser's Royal Hotel Ltd. De K.'s Roy. Hotel Ltd. *v.* The King. Intr. by Sir J. Simon. 8°. O. 1920

Scott (Melville). The message of Hosea. 8°. 1921
Textual discoveries in Proverbs, Psalms & Isaiah. 8°. [1927]

Scott (Michael), *of Glasgow.* The cruise of the Midge. Illust. by F. Brangwyn. 2v. s8°. [1894]

Scott (*Adm. Sir* Percy).
Fifty years in the Royal Navy. 8°. 1919

Scott (R. L.) Cat. of the coll. of European arms & armour formed at Greenock by R. L. S. Descr. by F. Joubert. 3v. fol. [*p.f.p.c.* Glasgow]. 1924

Scott (Ralph). A soldier's diary. s8°. [1923]

Scott (Robert), *dean of Rochester, see* LIDDELL (H. G.) & R. S. Greek-Eng. lex., n. ed., pl, 2, 1925–26.

Scott (Robert Falcon).
see BRITISH (TERRA NOVA) ANTARCTIC EXPEDITION, 1910–13.
,, EVANS (*capt.* E. R. G. R.) South w. S., 1921.
,, SIMPSON (G. C.) S.'s Polar journey & the weather, 1926.

Scott (*Mrs.* Sarah), *see* MONTAGU (*Lady* B.) & *Mrs.* S. S. *Descr. of Millenium Hall, 1762.

Scott (Sidney Herbert).
Anglo-Catholicism & re-union. s8°. 1923
Gen. Councils & Anglican claims in the light of the Council of Ephesus. Intr. by Rev. S. Jones. 2nd impr. s8°. [1927]

Scott (Stanley).
The human side of crook & convict life. 8°. [1925]

Scott (Thomas), *of Ipswich.*
Lyric poems, devotional & moral. s8°. 1773

Scott (*Sir* Walter), *1771–1832.*
Poet. works w. a.'s introd. & notes. Ed. J. L. Robertson. [Oxford compl. ed. *Thin*]. s8°. 1904
Waverley Novels. [n. ed., w. the a.'s notes]. 48v. s8°. E., *R. Cadell.* 1829–33
Waverley novels. [Bouverie ed.] 25v. 8°. *Daily News.* 1901

SINGLE WORKS.
The field of Waterloo; a poem. 8°. E. 1815
Life of Napoleon. [Prose works, v6]. la8°. Paris. *n.d.*
Minstrelsy of the Scottish Border. 4v *in* 2 [v3, 4 *wanting*]. s8°. E. 1873
*Paul's letters to h. kinsfolk. 8°. E. 1816

Scott (*Sir* Walter) [*continued*].
SINGLE WORKS [*continued*].
*Waverley. 6th ed. 3v. s8°. D. 1816
Woodstock. [Everyman's Lib.] repr. s8°. [1912]

REFERENCES.
see BUCHAN (J.) Some notes on Sir W. S., 1924.
,, GREY (H.) Key to Waverley novels, 1882.
,, MACCRIE (T.) Vindic. of the Covenanters, in a rev. of

REFERENCES [*continued*].
"Tales of my landlord," 1845.
see MILLER (F.) A. Crosbie: a reputed orig. of Paulus Pleydell in "Guy Mannering," 1919; 2nd ed., 1925.
,, NEWBOLT (*Sir* H. J.) Peacock, S. & Robin Hood, 1924.
,, ROUGHEAD (W.) Glengarry's way &c., 1922.

Scott (William), *of Venice.* A glance at the hist. doc. rel. to S. Mark in Venice. la8°. Venetia. 1887

Scott (William Robert), *D.Phil., Litt.D.* Alfred Marshall, 1842–1924. [From Proc. of Brit. Acad. P2821]. 8°. [1926]
see JONES (D. T.) &c. Rural Scotland dur. the war; by D. T. J., W. R. S. &c., 1926.
—— & J. Cunnison. Industries of the Clyde Valley dur. the War. [C.E. for Int. Peace]. la8°. O. 1924

Scott (Winifred Mary), *see* WYNNE (P.), *ps.*

Scotti (Francesco).
Il nuovo itinerario d'Italia, ora corr. &c. s8°. 1717

Scotti (Tommaso Gius. Gallarati-), *see* GALLARATI-SCOTTI (T. G.)

Scottish [SCOTCH; *see also* SCOTS].
Anc. Scottish prayers, 1912, *see* SMALL (A. H.), *ed.*
Examples of Sc. architecture f. 12th to 17th c. Reprod. f. Nat. Art Survey drawings &c. Ed. Sir R. R. Anderson, T. Ross &c. [Nat. Art. S. of S., v1]. fol. [E.] 1921
Hist. fragm. rel. to Scotish affairs, 1635–64, 3p, 1833, *see* MAIDMENT (J.), *ed.*
940 Scottish proverbs, 1675, *see* FERGUSSON (D.)
*Sc. (The) hist. of James IV, 1598, 1921, *see* GREENE (R.)
*Sc. (The) mist dispel'd: or, a reply to Ans. of the Commiss. of Scot. to Parl.; upon the new proposit. for peace &c. By an Eng. Covenanter. [P2571]. s4°. 1648
*Truths discovery of a black cloud in the North: anti-parl. &c. proc. of the Scotch army, 1646, *see* TRUTHS.

Scottish Burgh Records Society.
see ABERDEEN. Extr. f. Council Reg. of A., 2v, 1871–72.
,, EDINBURGH. Extr. f. the rec. of the Burgh of E., 1403–[1571], 3v, 1869–75.
,, GLASGOW. Charters & o. doc. rel. to G., 1175–[1707], 2v, 1894–1906.
,, —— Extracts f. records of the burgh of G., 1573–[1833], 11v, 1876–1916.
,, PEEBLES. Charters & docs. rel. to the Burgh of P., w. extr. f. rec., 1165–1710, 1872.
,, SCOTLAND. Anc. laws & customs of burghs of S., v1, 1124–1424, 1868.

Scottish (The) geographical magazine. Publ. by the Scottish Geograph. Soc. v36–43. la8°. E. 1920–27

Scottish (The) historical review. v17–25. 8°. G. 1920–28

Scottish History Society. s3, v1–11. 8°. E. 1921–28
Miscellany. v4, 1926. [III, 9.]
Cordara's Comm. on exped. to Scotland made by Charles Edward Stuart.
MS. Hist. of Craignish [by A. Campbell].
Misc. charters, 1165–1300, f. transcripts in coll. of Sir W. Fraser.
see CUNINGHAM (T.) Journal, 1640–54, 1928. [III, 11.]
,, DARIEN COMPANY. Papers rel. to ships & voyages of Co. of Scotland Trading to Africa &c., 1696–1707, 1924. [III, 6.]
,, EDINBURGH. Reg. of consultations of ministers of E., v1, 1652–57, 1921. [III, 1.]
,, FRASER (*Sir* W.) Papers f. coll. of F., 1924. [III, 5.]
,, MARY, *of Lorraine.* Foreign corr. with M., 1537–[57], 2v, 1923–25. [III, 4, 7.]
,, —— Scot. corr. of M. of L., 1542–60, 1927. [III, 10.]
,, MARY, *queen of Scots.* M. & the Babington plot, 1922. [III, 3.]
,, RIDPATH (G.) Diary of G. R., 1755–1761, 1922. [III, 2.]
,, SAINT ANDREWS. Early records of the Univ., 1926. [III, 8.]

Scottish Record Society. [*Publications*]. 8°. E. 1920–27
see EDINBURGH. Reg. of marriages, 1751–1800, 1922.
,, FOULIS (J.) & N. THOUNIS. Protocol books, 1546–53 & 1559–64, 1927.
,, GLASGOW. The burgesses & guild brethren of G., 1573–1750, 1925.
,, HUNTER, *of Hunterston, Family of.* Some family papers; ed. M. S. Shaw, 1925.
,, JOHNSOUN (T.) Protocol books, 1528–78, 1920.

Scottish Text Society.
[PUBLICATIONS]. N.S. 9–21. 8°. E. 1921–27
see ALEXANDER, *the Gt., king of Macedon.* Buik of A., v1–3, 1921–27. [N.S., 12, 17, 21.]
,, ASLOAN (J.) Asloan MS.: misc. in prose &c., 2v, 1923–25. [N.S., 14, 16.]

Scottish Text Society [*continued*].
see BISSET (H.) Rolment of courtis, 3v, 1920–26. [N.S., 10, 13, 18.]
,, FERGUSSON (D.) Scottish proverbs &c., 1924. [N.S., 15.]
,, IRLAND (J.) The meroure of wyssdom, 1926. [N.S., 19.]
,, MAITLAND (*Sir* R.) M. folio MS., v2, 1927. [N.S., 20.]
,, —— The M. 4°. MS., 1920. [N.S., 9.]
,, STIRLING (W. A.) Poetical works, v1, 1921. [N.S., 11.]

Scott-Mitchell (Frederick). Pract. stencil work. s8°. 1906

Scott-Moncrieff (Charles Kenneth). Marcel Proust. An English tribute; by J. Conrad, A. Bennett &c. Coll. by S.-M. s8°. 1923

Scotus (Andreas), *see* SCHOTTUS (A.)

Scotus (Joannes), *Erigena.*
De divisione naturae libri 5. Acc. app. ex ambiguis S. Maximi Gr. et Lat. [*w. sep. pagin.*] fol. Oxonii. 1681
see BETT (H.) J. S. Erigena, 1925.
,, CLAUDE (J.) Catholick doct. of the Eucharist; add. an acc. of Book &c. by Bertram, & of authority of J. S. or E., 6 bks.; tr. by J. R. R., 2p, 1683–84.
,, MEUSEL (C. H.) Doctr. J. Scoti E. quae cont. libris De divisione cum Xtiana comparavit C. H. M., 1869.
,, SAINT-RENÉ TAILLANDIER (R. G. E. T.) Scot E. & la phil. scholast, *n.d.*
,, TRAUBE (H.) Palaeol. Forsch., T5, Autographa d. J. Scotus, 1912.

Scotus (Romoaldus). Summarium rationum, quibus cancellarius Angliæ & prolocutor Puckeringius Elisabethae persuaserunt occidendam esse Mariam Stuartam &c. Add. Supplicium & mors reginae Scotiae &c. opera R. S. [*Foll. by* Epistola J. Pistorii qua demonst. Zwinglianam non esse veram eccl.] s8°. Ingolstadii. 1588

Scougal (Henry). *The life of God in the soul of man. Abridged by J. Wesley. 2nd ed. [P2534]. s8°. Bristol. 1748
,, ,, ...4th ed. [P2542]. s8°. 1777

Scoville (Joseph A.), *see* BARRETT (W.), *ps.*

Scriabin (Aleksandr Nikolaevich) [SKRYABIN].
see LAPSHIN (I. I.) Заветные думы С., 1922.
,, YAKOVLEV (V.) А. Н. Скрябин, 1925.

Scribner's Magazine. vols. 66–82. 8°. N.Y. 1919–27

***Scrinium** antiq. sive Misc. Groning., t1–2, 1748–51, *see* MISCELLANEA GRONINGANA.

Scriptores. Scr. eccl. de musica sacra, 3t, 1784, *see* GERBERT (M.), *ed.*
Scr. eccl. minores s. 4–6. [Corpus scr. eccl. Lat., 45]. fasc. 1. 8°. Vindobonae. 1904
1, Evagrii altercatio legis inter Simonem Judaeum & Theophilum Christianum. Rec. E. Bratke.
Scr. historiae Augustae, *see* HISTORIAE &C.
Scr. rerum Germanicarum, *see* MONUMENTA GERM. HIST.
Scr. rerum Hungaric. vet. ac genuini, 3p, 1766–68, *see* SCHWANDTNERUS (J. G.), *ed.*
Scr. rer. Transsilvanarum. t1, 2i, ii. 4°. Cibinii. 1797–1840
see SCHESAEUS (C.) Ruinae Pannonicae, 1797. [1.]
,, SIMIGIANUS (A.) Hist. rer. Ungar. & Transsilv., 1440–1606, 2v, 1800–1840. [2i, ii.]

***Scriptural** (The) unity of the Protestant Churches exhib. in their confessions. s8°. D. 1835

Scrivener (Frederick Henry A.) A plain introd. to the criticism of the N.T. 8°. C. 1861
see BIBLE: GOSPELS. Bezae cod. Cantab., ed. F. H. S., 1864.

Scrivener (Matthew). A course of divinity as prof. by the Ch. of Eng. fol. 1674

Scrivenor (J. B.), *see* REID (C.) & J. B. S. Geology of the co. near Newquay, 1906.

Scriverius (Petrus), *see* SCHRIJVER (PIETER).

Scrob (Carol). Poesii complecte. s8°. Bucuresci. 1883

Scrofani (Saverio) [SCROFANI (XAVIER)]. Voyage en Grèce, 1794–95. Tr. J. F. C. Blanvillain. 3t *in* 2. 8°. 1801

Scroggs (*Sir* William). Articles of impeachment of high treason &c. against Sir W. S. [P525]. sm. fol. 1680

Scrutator, *ps.* *Odds at Monte Carlo; analysed by Scrutator, 1924, *see* MONTE CARLO.

Scrymgeour (Daniel).
Poetry & poets of Brit. n. ed. s8°. E. 1866

Scudamore (Frank), *war correspondent.*
A sheaf of memories. 8°. [1925]

Scudder (Henry).
The Christian's daily walke. 8th ed. corr. s8°. 1642

Scudder (Vida Dunton). Le morte Darthur of Sir T. Malory: the book & its sources. 8°. 1921

Scudéry (George de). Alaric, ou Rome vaincue. Poème héroique. s8°. Rouen. 1659

Scudéry (*Mlle.* Madeleine de). Isabelle Grimaldi, princesse de Monaco. Avant-propos & notes du baron E. Seillière. 2e éd. s8°. 1923

Scullard (Herbert Hayes). The ethics of the Gospel & ethics of nature. Pref. by A. E. Garvie. 8°. 1927

Sculptors, Painters & Gravers, International Soc. of.
Cat. of 29th London exhib. s8°. 1925

Scultetus (Abraham).
Annalium Evangelii per Europam renovati, decas prima [*& secunda*], 1516–36. 2p *in* 1v. s8°. Heidelbergae. 1618–20
Concio secularis [2 Reg. 23] habita 2. Nov. 1617 in templo Sp. Sancti e Germ. in Lat. tr. à Chr. Kyferto. [*pages 81–132*]. s4°. *n.p.* [1617]
Concio secularis de Evangelii doctrina instaurata, &c. In Lat. tr. C. Kyfertus. [P483]. s4°. Heidelbergae. 1618
see OSIANDER (L.) Scultetus atheus, 1620.
,, THUMM (T.) Scultetus cacodoxus, 1621.
,, —— Scultetus iconoclastes, 1620.

Scultetus (Johann Friedrich). Diss. de computo vet. Romanorum. Sub praes. Æ. Strauchii. ed. 2a. s4°. Wittebergae. 1661

Scultetus (Severinus), *see* WAGNER (M.), T. FABRI & S. S. Examen thesium. &c. Zuingl. &c., 1586.

Scuola Romena di Roma [SCOALA ROMÂNĂ DIN ROMA]. Diplomatarium Italicum. Doc. racc. n. archivi ital. v1. la8°. 1925
Ephemeris Dacoromana. Annuario. v1–3. la8°. 1923–25

Scupoli (Lorenzo). The spiritual combat: w. the path of Paradise. new tr. s8°. 1875

Sé. Registo da freguesia da Sé, 1563–1610. Publ. com intr. &c. por E. Prestage e P. d'Azevedo. 2v. 4°. Coimbra. 1924–27

Sea songs & ballads; by Dibdin &c., 1865, *see* DIBDIN (C.)

Seabrook (W. B.) Adventures in Arabia. 8°. [1928]

Seacome (John). *Memoirs, cont. acc. of the House of Stanley to 1735; also descr. of the Isle of Man &c. s4°. M'ter. 1783
,, ,, *another ed. w. t.* *Hist. of the House of Stanley to 1776. Added, Compl. hist. of the Isle of Man [*w. sep. tp. & pagin.*] 8°. M'ter. 1821

Seager (Henry Rogers), *see* HOTCHKISS (W. E.) & H. R. S. Hist. of Shipbuilding Labor Adjust. Board, 1917–19, 1921.

Seager (J. Renwick). The Reform Act of 1918. Text w. notes by S. Foreword by J. M. Robertson, & acc. of the Speaker's conference by Sir W. H. Dickinson. 8°. 1918

Séailles (Gabriel). Eugène Carrière, l'homme & l'artiste. 8°. 1901

Seal (Horace Samuel).
Help for the pleasure-ethics &c. [P2521]. 8°. 1913
Sovereignty & the State. [P2521]. 8°. 1907
The state: true & false. [P2521; 2773]. 8°. 1921

Sealy (Thomas Henry). *The porcelain tower; 9 stories of China. Comp. by "T. T. T." [*i.e.* S.] 8°. 1841

Seaman (Cleora Augusta), *M.D.*, *see* BAINBRIDGE (L. S.) One of the pioneer women in medicine, 1921.

Seaman (*Sir* Owen).
Made in England; verses. [repr.] s8°. [1916]

Seaman (William). Gramm. ling. Turcicae. 5p. s4°. O. 1670

Seamark, *ps.*, *see* SMALL (A. J.)

Seami, *Japanese actor-author, 14th c.*, *see* WALEY (A. D.) The Nō plays of Japan [works of S. &c., tr. w. intr.] by A. D. W., 1921.

Search (John). Consid. on the law of libel, as rel. to publ. on religion. [P2552]. 8°. 1833

Sears (Fred Coleman).
Productive small fruit culture. 8°. Phila. [1920]

Sears (Louis Martin). Jefferson & the Embargo. 8°. Durham, N. Carolina. 1927

Sears (Minnie Earl), *see* MUDGE (I. G.) & M. E. S. A George Eliot dict., 1924.

Season (Henry), *see* SPECULUM ANNI: or, Season on the seasons, 1800–8.

Seaton (Ethel). Marlowe's map, *see* ENGLISH ASSOC. Essays &c., v10, 1924.

Sebastian, *king of Portugal*, *see* FIGUEIREDO (A. DE). Don S., 1554–78, 6a ed., 1925.

Sebastian (Lewis Boyd). The manor of Pellipar. [Sette of Odd Vol. Opusc. 70]. s8°. *p.p.* 1919
An old City company. The Skinners' Co. of London. [Sette of Odd Vol. Opusc. 54]. s8°. *p.p.* 1906

Sebastianus (Antonius) [MINTURNUS]. L'arte poetica, con la dottrina de' sonetti & ogni sorte di rime thoscane &c. Con le postille del Dr. Valvassori. 8°. [Venetia]. 1563
see CALDERISI (R.) Saggio crit.: A. S. M., vita e opere, 1921.

Sebeos, *bp. of the Pakradouni* [SEPEOS]. Hist. d'Héraclius. Tr. de l'Arménien & annot. par F. Macler. la8°. 1904
Patmouthiun i Herakln [Hist. of Heraclius, *in Armenian*]. s8°. i Kostantnoupolis. 1851
,, ,, [*a. ed. Ed.* Kh. Resten-Patkanean, *foll. by* Hist. *by* Mekhitar Anetz *w. sep. tp. & pagin.*] 8°. S. Peterbourg. 1879
Pseudo-Sebéos, texte arm. tr. & annot. par F. Macler. [*Extr. du* Journ. Asiat. P2791]. 8°. 1905
see ADONTS (N. G.) Начал. исторiя Арменiи у С. &c., 1901.

Seber (Wolfgang). Hortulus Biblicus, sive loci theol. Praef. J. Gerhardi. s8°. Schleusingae. 1636

Seberianus, *see* SEVERIAN, *bp. of Gabalis.*

Seccombe (Thomas), *M.A.* Lives of twelve bad men; by var. hands. Ed. T. S. 2nd ed. 8°. 1894

Seccombe (*Lt.-Col.* **Thomas Strong).**
Comic sketches f. English hist. obl.8°. 1884

Séché (Alphonse). Paroles pour notre bonheur. s8°. [1922]

Séché (Léon). Le cénacle de Joseph Delorme. [2t]. s8°. 1912]
1, Victor Hugo & les poètes.
2, Victor Hugo & les artistes.

Seckendorff (Curt, *Graf* **v.)**
Napoleon I u. Pius VII. [P2696]. 8°. 1873

Seckendorf (Friedrich Heinrich, *Graf* **v.),** *see* BELLAMINTES, *ps.* Mém. de F. H. c. de S., 1739.

Secker (Thomas), *abp. of Canterbury.*
Sermon on pres. rebellion in Scotland. [P2780]. 8°. 1745

Secker (William), *M.A.* The nonsuch professor. 7 sermons. Added, The wedding-ring, a sermon. n. ed. rev. by M. Wilks. s8°. 1829
A wedding ring: or the salve of divinity on the sore of humanity. Sermon. s8°. 1658

Seco de Lucena (Luis). La Alhambra. 2ª ed. s8°. Granada. 1920

Second. Second (The) Belgian Grey Book, p1 & p2 (sect. 10), 1915. *see* BELGIQUE.
*Second narr. (A) of the signal victory under Duke of York, 3rd June 1665, 1665, *see* JAMES II, *k. of Gt. Brit.*

Secord (Arthur Wellesley). St. in the narrative method of Defoe. [Illinois, Univ. of. Stˢ., v9i]. la8°. [Urbana]. 1924

Secret. *Secret hist. of the Geertruydenberg Negociation &c., 1712, *see* GEERTRUYDENBERG.
*Secret (The) policy of the Eng. Soc. of J., 1715, *see* JESUITS.

Secreta, *see* BACON (R.) Opera hactenus ined., fasc. 5, Secretum secretorum; ed. R. Steele, 1920.
*Secreta monita Soc. Jesu, 2nd ed., 1746, *see* ZAOROWSKY (J.)

Secretan (E.) Cat. of the coll. of paintings formed by E. S., sold July 1 &c., 1889. [S. coll., v2. *Illust.*] fol. Paris. 1889

Secretan (H. A.), *see* EAGAR (W. McG.) & H. A. S. Unemployment among boys, 1925.

Secrets. *Secrets (Les) les plus cachés de la philos. des anciens; par M. Crosset de la Haumerie, 1722, *see* COLONNA (F. M. P.)
Secrets pour la conserv. de la beauté des dames &c., *see* SCHOLA SALERN. L'art de conserv. sa santé, tr., 1766.

Secundus, *the Sophist, see* DASHEAN (H.) Short bibliog. st., in Armenian, p1, S. &c., 1895.

Secundus (Joannes). *Kisses: fragm. &c. on the kiss (1803), *see* AUNGERVYLE SOC. Reprints, s2, 1884.

***Security** (The) of Englishmens lives &c., 1682, *see* SOMERS (J. S., *baron*).

Sedaine (Michel Jean). Le philosophe sans le savoir—La gageure imprévue, *see* THÉÂTRE choisi du 18ᵉ s., t2, 1914.

Sedan. *From S. to Saarbruck, 1870, *see* KNOLLYS (H.)

Seddal (Henry). E. Nangle, the apostle of Achill. Introd. by Lord Plunket, bp. of Meath. s8°. 1884

Sedeyn (Emile). Petites villes de France. s8°. [1922]

Sedgefield (Walter John). An Anglo-Saxon verse-book. [Univ. of Manchester]. s8°. M'ter. 1922

Sedgwick (Anne Douglas), *aft. Mrs. Basil de Selincourt.*
Adrienne Toner. s8°. 1921
Autumn crocuses. s8°. [1920]
A childhood in Brittany 80 years ago. 8°. 1919
The little French girl. s8°. 1924
The old countess. s8°. [1927]
The third window. s8°. [1920]

Sedgwick (*Capt.* **Francis Roger).** The Indian Mutiny of 1857. Sketch of princ. milit. events. 8°. 1909
The Russo-Japanese war on land. 2nd rev. ed. 8°. [1908]

Sedgwick (Henry Dwight). Cortes the conqueror. 8°. [1927]
Ignatius Loyola: an attempt at impartial biog. 8°. 1923
Marcus Aurelius. Biog., w. some acc. of the Stoic relig. & an expos. of attempt to suppress Christianity. 8°. New Haven. 1921
Spain, a sh. hist. Pref. by J. D. M. Ford. 8°. [1925]

Sedgwick (James), *barrister-at-law.* *Hints to the public &c. on Evangel. preaching. By a Barrister. 5p *in* 1v. 8°. 1811–12

Sedgwick (Obadiah). Christs counsell to his languishing church of Sardis. s8°. 1640

Sedgwick (*Mrs.* **William T.)** Acoma, the sky city. St. in Pueblo-Indian hist. & civilisation. 8°. Camb., *Mass.* 1926

Sedláček (Johann), *see* MAREŠ (F.) & J. S. Topogr. d. hist. u. Kunstdenkm. Polit. Bez. Wittingau, 1904.

Sedley (*Sir* **Charles),** *bart.* [SIDLEY], *see* PINTO (V. DE S.) Sir C. S., 1927.

Sedrakean (Aristakes), *bp.* [The Armenian Church's veneration of images. *In Armenian*]. v1. la8°. S.-Peterbourg. 1904

Sedulius (Coelius). The Easter song, being the 1st epic of Xtndom. With intr., verse-tr. & app. incl. schedule of Milton's "debts," by G. Sigerson. 8°. D. 1922

See (Chong Su). The foreign trade of China. 8°. N.Y., *Columbia Univ.* 1919

Sée (Edmond). Henry Becque ou servitude & grandeur dramat. s8°. [1926]

Sée (Henri). Esquisse d'une hist. du régime agraire en Europe aux 18ᵉ & 19ᵉ s. 8°. 1921
La France écon. & sociale au 18ᵉ siècle. s8°. 1925
Les idées polit. en France au 17ᵉ s. 8°. 1923
,, ,, au 18ᵉ s. 8°. 1920
Science & philos. de l'hist. s8°. 1928

Seeberg (Reinhold). Lehrbuch d. Dogmengesch. 2ᵗᵉ u. 3ᵗᵉ A. B1, 3, 4i, ii [B1, 3ᵗᵉ verm. A.] 8°. L. 1913–22
4i *has sep. tp.* Die Lehre Luthers.

Seebohm (Frederic). The crisis of emancipation in America to the assas. of Lincoln. [P2523]. 8°. 1865
The Eng. village community. Repr. f. 4th ed. (1905). 8°. 1915
The era of the Protestant revolution. n. ed. s8°. 1889
Tribal custom in Anglo-Saxon law. 8°. 1911

Seebohm (Henry). The distribution of the family Charadriidæ, or the plovers, sandpipers, snipes, & their allies. 4°. [1888]

Seebohm (Mabel E.), *see* CHRISTIE (*Mrs.* M. E.)

Seeck (Otto K.)
Entwicklungs Gesch. d. Christentums. s8°. St. 1921
Gesch. d. Untergangs d. antiken Welt. B6 *&* Anhang z. B6 [*w. sep. tp., pagin. cont.*] s8°. St. 1920–21

Seed (Jeremiah). Posthumous works: sermons, letters &c. Publ. by J. Hall. 2nd ed. 2v. 8°. 1752

Seeger (Johann Friedrich). August. Confess. hist. &c. Praes. G. Wernsdorfius. [P484]. s4°. Vitembergae. [1705]

Seeholzer (Henri). Raymond Poincaré. 8°. Zurich. 1922

Seeker (John), *see* JOUBERT (—). *Un projet gigant. en Languedoc au 18ᵉ s., publ. J. S., 1873.

Seekers. *Anon. epistola de nova secta Quaerentium, vulgo Seekers, in Anglia exorta. [*Progr.* P2594]. s4°. Gottingae. 1814

Seelen (Johann Heinrich v.)
Meditationes exegeticae. 3p *in* 2v. s8°. Lubecae. 1730–37
Miscellanea: commentationes &c. 3p *in* 1v. s8°. Lubecae. 1734–39
Stromata Lutherana, sive var. script. ad Sacrorum emend., August. Confess., versionem Bibl., Articulos Smalcald., syntagma. 5p *in* 1v. s8°. Lubecae. 1740

Seelen-Wurzgarten. [*Beg. fol. 1ᵇ*: Hie volget nach ein lieplich vnd nützliche materi vnd wirt genant der seelen wurczgart &c. *Ends fol. 173ᵃ*. Gedrucket vnd seliglichen vollendet dises buch von Conrado Dinckmůt zu Ulm &c.] fol. [Ulm, *C. Dinckmut.* 1483]
174 leaves. 4 without sign. A–V in eights. X1–10. fol. 174 (blank) pasted on cover.

Seeley (*Sir* **John Robert).**
see ABBOTT (E. A.) & *Sir* J. R. S. Eng. lessons, 1917.
,, GAZEAU (J.) L'impérialisme angl.: S. &c., 1903.

Seelye (Kate Chambers), *see* ABŪ-MANSŪR 'ABD-AL-KĀHIR IBN-TĀHIR, *al-Baghdādī.* Moslem schisms &c.; tr. S., p1, 1920.

Seemüller (Joseph). Deutsche Mundarten, 5, 1918, *see* KAIS. AKAD. D. WISS. ZU WIEN. Sitz., B187, 1918.

Seetaram, *Soobadar, see* SITARAMA, *Subahdar.*

Sefton-Jones (Margaret).
Old Devonshire House, by Bishopsgate. 8°. [1923]

Segalen (Victor).
see GILBERT DE VOISINS (A.) Écrit en Chine [*&* Souv. de S.], 2t, 1923.
,, GUIMET. Bulletin archéolog., 1, Missions E. Chavannes, V. S. &c., 1921.

Segard (Achille). Jean Gossart, dit Mabuse. 4°. Brux. 1923

Segarizzi (Arnaldo). Biblioteca Querini Stampalia. Rel. [P2841]. 8°. Venezia. 1907
R. Predelli. [Estr. d. Archivio Trentino, a. 24. P2838]. 8°. Trento. 1909

Segers (Johann Ernst). Exercit. de symbolo heroico. Sub præs. B. v. Sanden. [P2638]. s4°. Regiomonti. 1692

Segni (Bernardo). Istorie fiorentine, 1527–55. Pubbl. p. c. di G. Gargani. s8°. Firenze. 1857

Segonzag (André Dunoyer de), *see* DUNOYER DE SEGONZAG (A.)

Segre (Arturo). Il primo anno d. min. Vallesa (1814–15), *see* REGIA DEPUT. Bibl. d. st. rec., v10, 1928.
Works in REGIA DEPUT. Miscellanea.
D. Carutti di Cantogno, 1913. [47.]
Doc. di storia sabauda, 1510–36, prec. da una intr., 1903. [39.]
Un registro di lettere d. card. Ercole Gonzaga (1535–36), con app. di doc. ined. (1520–48) 1913. [47.]

Ségu (Frédéric). Un maître de Balzac méconnu, H. de Latouche. s8°. 1928

Seguenza (Giuseppe). Costituz. geolog. d. terreni terz. d. distr. di Messina [*&* Descr. dei Foraminiferi monotulamici]. Diss. &c. 2p *in* 1v. 4°. Messina. 1862

Ségur (*la csse.* **Eugène de**), *1799–1874* [†SÉGUR (SOPHIE DE)].
Le général Dourakine. 8e éd. s8°. 1876
„ „ .... 26e éd. s8°. 1921

Ségur (*le cte.* **Louis Philippe de**), *1753–1832.* Mémoires, ou souvenirs et anecdotes. 3t. 8°. 1824–26

Ségur (Nicolas).
L'anneau charnel, *see* ŒUVRES libres, 71, 1927.
Conversations avec Anatole France. s8°. 1925
Une île d'amour. s8°. 1921
Mr. Renan devant l'amour. Roman. s8°. 1923

Ségur (Noël), *see* DUMERSAN (T. M.) & N. S. Chansons nat. & pop. de France, 2t, 1866.

Ségur (*le gén. cte.* **Philippe Paul de**), *1780–1873, see* GOURGAUD (*le baron* G.) Napoléon &c., ou exam. de l'ouvr. de P. de S., 3e éd., 1826.

Ségur (*marquis* **Pierre de**). Marie-Antoinette. [2e éd.] 8°. [1920]
see FLERS (R. DE). Disc. de récep. (*on S.*), 1921.

Segura (Francisco de P.), *see* CALVA (E.) Instit. de derecho civil ; por E. C. y colab. de S., 2t, 1874–75.

Šegvić (Cherubino). Tommaso archidiacono di Spalato, *see* BULLETTINO DI ARCH. &C. DALM., 37, Suppl., 1914.

Sehling (Emil). Gesch. d. protestant. Kirchenverfass., *see* GRUNDR. D. GESCHICHTSWISS., 2viii, 1913.

Sehrt (Edward H.) Vollständ. Wörterbuch z. Heliand u. z. altsächs. Genesis. [Hesperia ; hrsg. v. H. Collitz. Nr. 14]. 8°. Göttingen. 1925

Seidel (August).
German grammar for use of Englishmen. s8°. *n.d.*
Gramm. d. Litauischen Sprache. s8°. Wien. [1915]
Trotzdem. Der Zukunft Morgenrot. s8°. Naumburg (Saale). 1919

Seidel (Christoph Timotheus), *see* ABHANDLUNG. Abhandl. v. Schlafe d. Seelen nach d. Tode als eine Widerleg. d. Sch. d. T. S., 1754.

Seidel (Ina). Weltinnigkeit. Neue Gedichte. s8°. 1919

Seidel (Richard). Klassenarmee u. Volkswehr. [P2569]. 8°. 1919

Seidelius (Martinus), *see* SOCINUS (F.) Disput. inter F. S. & C. Francken de adoratione Christi &c. & M. S. epistolae, 1618.

Seifert (Eva). Die Proparoxytona im Galloromanischen. [Zeitschr. f. roman. Philol., Beiheft 74]. 8°. Halle (Saale). 1923

Seifert (Josef Leo). Literaturgesch. d. Čechoslowaken, Südslawen u. Bulgaren. s8°. München. [1922]

Seiffert (Max). Gesch. d. Klaviermusik. Hrsg. als 3e A. v. C. F. Weitzmann's Gesch. Nebst. Anhange Gesch. d. Klaviers v. O. Fleischer. Bl. la8°. L. 1899

Seifferth (B.) Church constit. [Ratio disciplinae] of the Bohemian & Moravian Brethren. Lat. w. tr., notes & introd. by B. S. 8°. 1864

Seifullina (Lidya Nikolaevna) [SAIFULINA (LOLA-KHAN)].
Виринея. [Соб. соч., т3, 2ое изд.] 8°. Москва. 1927
Золотые буквы. s8°. Москва. [1927]
Правонарушители. [Соб. соч., т1, 2ое изд.] 8°. Москва. 1927
Путники. Роман. s8°. Москва. 1925

Seignobos (Charles). Hist. polit. de l'Europe contemp. : évol. des partis & des formes polit., 1814–1914. 7e éd., refondue & augm. 2t. la8°. 1924–26
see LAVISSE (E.) Hist. de France contemp., t6, 7, 8 ; par C. S., 1921.

Seiler (Franciscus), *see* BODENSTEIN (A.) Von geweychtem wasser &c. wider F. S., 1520.

Seiler (Georg Friedrich). Die Relig. nach Vernunft u. Bibel. s8°. Erlangen. 1798
Theologia dogmat.-polemica. Cum compendio hist. dogmatum. ed. 2a. s8°. Erlangae. 1780
Uebers. d. Neuen Test. mit Erklärungen. 2T. 8°. Erlangen. 1806

Seillière (*le baron* **Achille**). Cat. of portion of lib. of S. Sold by Sotheby, Feb. 1887. [*MS. prices.* P2747]. 8°. 1887

Seillière (Ernest Ant. Aimé Léon, *baron*).
Une académie à l'époque romantique. [Acad. des Sci. Morales &c.]. s4°. 1926
Alexandre Vinet. App. sur H. F. Amiel. 8°. 1925
Le cœur & la raison de Mme. Swetchine. s8°. 1924
George Sand, mystique de la passion &c. s8°. 1920
Jean Jacques Rousseau. 8°. 1921
Les orig. romanesques de la morale & de la polit. romantiques. 8°. [1920]
Portraits de femmes. 8°. 1923
Pour le centenaire du romantisme. Un examen de conscience. la8°. 1927
Le romancier du grand Condé : Gautier de Coste, Sieur de la Calprenède. 8°. 1921

Seisen (D.) Gesch. d. Reformation zu Heidelberg. 8°. Heidelberg. 1846

Seitenstetten. Urkundenbuch d. Benedictiner-Stiftes S., *see* FONTES RERUM AUSTRIAC., B33, 1870.

Seitz (Don Carlos). Newfoundland. 8°. [1927]

Seitz (Otto), *ed., see* ECK (J. v.) Der authent. Text d. Leipziger Disput. (1519), 1903.

Seitz (Theodor). Südafrika im Weltkriege &c. 8°. 1920

Seivert (Johann). Nachr. v. siebenbürg. Gelehrten u. ihren Schr. [*with* Beytr. z. künft. Biogr. d. Verf. v. K. G. v. Windisch]. s8°. Pressburg. 1785

Sekino (T.), *see* COREA. Arch. researches on anc. Lolang Distr. ; by T. S. &c., 1925–27.

Selbie (William Boothby). Congregationalism. s8°. [1927]
The psychology of religion. 8°. O. 1924
see MANSFIELD COLL., *Oxford.* M. Coll. &c. ; by S. *& others,* 1890.

Selborne (William Waldegrave Palmer, *2nd earl of*). The Selborne Memorandum. Review of mutual relations of the Brit. S. African Colonies in 1907. Intr. by B. Williams. 8°. O. 1925

Selby-Bigge (*Sir* **Lewis Amherst**).
The Board of Education. 8°. [1927]

Selden Society. Publications. v37–44. 4°. 1920–27
Public works in mediaeval law. Ed. C. T. Flower. v2, 1923. [40.]
Vacarius, *magister.* Liber pauperum. Ed. F. de Zulueta. 4°. 1927. [44.]
Year Books of Edward II. v9, 14i, ii, 16–18 (1311–15). Ed. Sir P. Vinogradoff, W. C. Bolland &c., 1920–27. [37–39, 41–43.]
see SELDEN (J.) Table talk ; ed. for S. S. by Sir F. Pollock, 1927.

Selden (John) [SELDENUS].
Ad Fletam diss. Repr. f. ed. of 1647 w. parallel tr., intr. & notes by D. Ogg. [Camb. St. in Eng. Legal Hist.] 8°. C. 1925
„ „ *for a. ed., see* HOFFMANN (C. G.) Hist. jur., v1, 1734.
Analecton Anglobritannicon libri duo. s4°. Francofurti. 1615
De dis Syris syntagmata 2. s8°. Londini. 1617
De synedriis & praefecturis juridicis veterum Ebraeorum libri 3. ed. noviss. s4°. Francofurti. 1696
Of the judicature in parliaments. s8°. [1690 ?]
Table-talk, relating espec. to religion & state. 2nd ed. s8°. 1696
„ „ 3rd ed. s8°. 1716
„ „ n. ed., corr., w. biog. pref. s8°. Chiswick. 1818
„ „ Ed. for Selden Soc. by Sir F. Pollock. With acc. of Selden by Sir E. Fry. 8°. 1927
Θεάνθρωποσ : or God made man. Nativity of our Saviour on 25 Dec. s8°. 1661
see DRAYTON (M.) Poly-olbion [*w.* "*Illustrations*" *or notes by J. S.*], 1612.
„ PRIDEAUX (H.) Marmora Oxon., ex Arundel., S. aliisque conflata, 1676.

Sele. Chartulary of the Priory of St. Peter at Sele. [Tr. Ed. L. F. Salzman. 8°. *Issued to subscribers.* C. 1923

Select.
*Sel. & impartial acc. of the lives &c. of the most remark. convicts 2nd ed. corr. 3v. [1 & 3 *wanting*]. s8°. 174
Sel. British doc. of the Canadian war of 1812, v1–3 ; 1920–26, *see* WOOD (W.), *ed.*
Sel. constit. of the world, 1922, *see* CONSTITUTIONS.
Sel. fables, w. cuts by T. & J. Bewick, 1822, *see* BEWICK (T. & J.)
Sel. hymns, w. tunes annext, for Methodists, 3rd ed., 1770, *see* WESLEY (J.)
Sel. letters betw. the Duchess of Somerset, Lady Luxborough &c 2v, 1778, *see* HULL (T.), *ed.*
Sel. naval docs., 1922, *see* HODGES (H. W.) & E. A. HUGHES, *eds.*
Sel. trials, 1720–41, 2nd ed., 4v, 1742, *see* TRIALS.
„ „ 1741–64, 4v, 1764, *see* TRIALS.

***Selection** (A) of catches, glees, &c., 1884, *see* Bath York-House Catch Club.

Selections.
Second sel. f. modern poets, 1924, *see* Squire (J. C.)
Sel. f. mod. poets, 1921, *see* Squire (J. C.), *ed.*
Sel. f. the lives of the holy fathers &c., 1623 ; tr., 1905, *see* Libro. L. d'oro (Il).
*Sel. f. the publ. docs. of the province of N.S. ; ed. T. B. Akins, 1869, *see* Nova Scotia.

Seler (Eduard).
Works in Königl. Preuss. Akad. d. Wiss. Abhdl. (Phil.-hist. Kl.)
Beobacht. u. Studien in d. Ruinen v. Palenque, 1915.
Die Quetzalcouatl-Fassaden yukatek. Bauten, 1916.
Die Ruinen v. Uxmal, 1917.

Selgas y Carrasco (José). Escenas fantásticas. 8°. 1876
Poesías. [Obras, 1, 2]. 2[t]. s8°. 1882–83

Seligman (Edwin R. A.) The shifting & incidence of taxation. 2nd ed. rev. & enl. 8°. N.Y. 1899

Seligman (G. Saville) & E. T. Hughes. Domestic needlework: orig. & customs thr. the cent. fol. [1926]

Seligman (Vincent J.) The Salonica side-show. 8°. [1919]

Selincourt. Cartul. de l'abbaye de S., 1131–1513 ; par G. Beaurain, *see* Soc. des Antiq. de Picardie. Mém., s4, t10, 1925.

Selivanova (Nina). The world of Roerich. 8°. N.Y. [1923]

Sell (Carl), *D.D., b. 1845.* Philipp Melanchthon u. d. deut. Reformation bis 1531. [Verein f. Ref.-gesch. Schr., Jhrg. 14, Nr. 56]. 8°. Halle. 1897

Sella (*conde* de la Vega del), *see* Vega del Sella.

Sella (Pietro). Costituzioni d. Stato d. Chiesa anter. alla riforma albornoziana, *see* Archivio stor. ital., anno 85, v1, 1927.
Costituzioni per la Romagna pubbl. n. Parl. di Cesena, 1289, *see* Archivio stor. ital., a. 83ii, 1925.

Sella (Quintino), *see* Carutti (D.) L'on. Q. S., 1884.

Sellars (Roy Wood).
Evolutionary naturalism. 8°. Chicago. 1922
see Drake (D.) Essays in crit. realism ; by D., S. &c., 1920.

Sellen (Caspar Heinrich). Exercit. de ant. funerum ritu. Praes. J. Cellario. [P2635]. s4°. Helmestadi. [1682]

Sellers (Robert Victor). Eustathius of Antioch & h. place in early hist. of Xtn. doctrine. s8°. C. 1928

Selley (Ernest). The Eng. public house as it is. 8°. 1927

Sellier (Henri). La crise du logement & l'intervention publ. en matière d'habitation pop. dans l'agglomér. paris. 4°. 1921
—— **& A. Bruggeman.** Le problème du logement. [C.E. for Internat. Peace]. 8°. [1927]
——, —— **& M. Poëte.** Paris pend. la Guerre. [C.E. for Internat. Peace]. la8°. [1926]

Selliers di Moranville (Luigi), *ed.* Rime ant. o. poesie lir. ital. de' sec. 13–15. 4°. Vienna. 1845

Sellin (Ernst). Der alttestamentl. Prophetismus. 3 Studien. 8°. L. 1912
Intr. to the Old Test. Tr. W. Montgomery. Intr. & bibliog. by A. S. Peake. 8°. 1923
—— **& C. Watzinger.** Jericho ; d. Ergebnisse d. Ausgrabungen. [Deut. Orient-Gesell., Wiss. Veröffentl., 22]. fol. L. 1913

Sells (Dorothy). Brit. Trade Boards system. 8°. 1923

Selneccerus (Nicolaus) [Selnecker].
Annot. in Genesin. Add. Isagoge in Exodum &c. fol. Lipsiae. 1578
Recitationes aliquot. s4°. Lipsiae. [1581]
Sententiae consolatoriae ex sacra coll. &c. [*b. w.* Loss (L.) Catechismus, 1553]. s8°. Norinbergae. 1553
Theophania. Comoedia nova, de primorum parentum cond. &c. s8°. Witebergae. 1560
see Anhalt. Das die 42 Anhalt. Argument wider der Ubiquisten Trewme noch fest stehen, Verantw. uff S. &c., 1584.
,, Kirchner (T.), N. S. & M. Chemnitz. Apologia &c. d. christl. Concordien Buchs, 1583.
,, Stenius (S.) Examen recitationum N. S. de libro Concordiae, 1582.

Selous (Edmund). Realities of bird life. Intr. by J. S. Huxley. 8°. 1927
The romance of insect life. 4th ed. 8°. 1921
Romance of the animal world. 8°. 1921

Selow-Serman (K. Emil). Blockade-Brecher. s8°. 1917

Seltman (Charles Theodore). Athens: hist. & coinage bef. the Persian invasion. 4°. C. 1924

Selvagius (Julius Laurentius). Antiq. Christian. instit. Ed. altera Patavina. [A. M. Kalephati de J. L. S. vita & scriptis comm.] 4 libri *in* 2v. [*pagin. of lib. 3 & 4 contin.*] 4°. Patavii. 1780

Selvelli (Cesare). Fano. [P2860]. 4°. Milano. *n.d.*

Selver (Paul).
Mod. Czech poetry. Sel. texts, w. tr. & an intr. by R. S. s8°. 1920
One, two, three. s8°. 1926
Otakar Březina: study in Czech lit. s8°. O. 1921
Schooling. s8°. 1924
see Čísař (J.) Czechoslovak Republ., its econ. resources ; by P. S. &c., 1920.

Selwyn (Edward Gordon). The approach to Xty. 8°. 1925
Essays, Catholic & critical. By members of the Anglican Communion [E. O. James, A. E. Taylor, A. E. J. Rawlinson &c.] Ed. E. G. S. 8°. 1926

Selwyn (George Augustus), *bp. of (1) New Zealand (2) Lichfield ; 1809–78, see* Creighton (*Mrs.* L.) G. A. S., 1923.

Sembritzki (Johannes). Gesch. d. königl. preuss. See-und Handelsstadt Memel. 2. A. 8°. Memel. 1926

Semeinii.
Семейный календарь на 1922 г. s8°. Берлинъ. 1922

Semennikov (V. P.)
За кулисами царизма. Архив тибетского врача Бадмаева. Ред. В. П. С. 8°. Ленинград. 1925
Монархия перед крушением, 1914–17. Бумаги Николая II &c. 8°. Москва. 1927
Политика Романовых накануне Революции по новым документам. 8°. Москва. 1926

Semenov (Lev).
Диктаторъ. Политич. фантазія. [P2446] 8°. Москва. 1907

Semenov (Petr. Petrovich). Живописная Россія. t12 ii Восточныя окраины Россіи. Приморская и Амурская области. fol. С.-П. 1895

Semenov (Sergei). Предварительная могила. s8°. Ленинград. [1927 ?]

Semenov (Vladimir). Расплата. 8°. С.-П. 1907

Sémer (Madeleine), *see* Klein (*l'abbé* F.) M. S., convertie & mystique, 1874–1921, 11e éd., 1923.

Semevsky (Mikhail Ivanovich). Царица Катерина Алексѣевна, Анна и Виллимъ Монсъ, 1692–1724. [Очерки и разсказы изъ русс. ист. 18в., 3]. изд. 2[oe]. 8°. С.-П. 1884

Séminaire des Missions Etrangères. Lettre de Messieurs des Missions Etr. au Pape sur les idolatries &c. chinoises [*& o. p.*] s8°. Cologne. 1700

Semiramis, *queen of Assyria, see* Walch (J. G.) Parerga acad., 1721.

Semler (Johann Salomo).
Abh. ü. d. rechtmäss. Freiheit d. acad. theol. Lehrart in Antw. auf Danovs Sendschr. &c. [*b. w.* Mosheim (J. L.) & J. M. Gesner. Epist., 1770]. s8°. Halle. 1771
Apparat. ad libros symbolicos eccl. Lútheranae. 8°. Halae Magdeb. 1775
Apparatus ad Vet. Test. interpret. s8°. Halae. 1773
Comm. de daemoniacis. ed. 4[a]. s8°. Halae. 1779
Comm. hist. de ant. Christianorum statu. t1, 2i [in 1v. *No more publ.*] 8°. Halae Magdeb. 1771–72
Eigne histor. theolog. Abhandlungen. 2 Samml. [*in* 1v]. s8°. Halle im Magdeb. 1760–62
Hist. eccl. sel. capita. Cum epitome canonum &c. 3t. 8°. Halae. 1767–69
Institutio brevior ad liberalem erudit. theologicam. 2 lib. *in* 1v. s8°. Halae. 1765–66
Neuer Versuch d. Auslegung &c. d. N. Test. zu befördern. s8°. Halle. 1786
Nov. observ., hist. & relig. Xtn[ae] usque ad Constantinum M. s8°. Halae. 1784
Paraphrasis in I Cor., cum notis & Lat. tr. excerptis. s8°. Halae Magdeb. 1770
Versuch christl. Jahrbücher. 2T. 8°. Halle. 1783–86
Versuch: Gebrauch d. Quellen i. d. Staats- u. Kirchengesch. d. mitl. Zeiten. s8°. Halle. 1761
see Göze (J. M.) Ausführl. Vertheid. d. N. T. ; z. Widerleg. d. D. S., 1766–69.
,, —— Vertheid. d. Complutens. Bibel, geg. d. S. Beschuld., 1765.
,, Meyer (L.) *Philosophia Script. interpres, ed. S., 1776.

Semmt (Johann Gottlob). Judicium Lutheri de vi obligandi, quam Decalogus habeat. Disput. [P1041]. s8°. Vitebergae. [1791]

Semon (*Sir* Felix). Autobiography. Ed. by H. C. Semon & T. A. McIntyre. 8°. [1926]

Semon (Richard). The Mneme. [Tr. L. Simon]. 8°. [1921]
Mnemic psychology. Tr. by B. Duffy, w. intr. by V. Lee. 8°. [1923]

Semper (Hans). Michael u. Fr. Pacher, i. Kreis u. i. Nachfolger. 8°. Eszlingen a. N. 1911

Sempere y Guarinos (Juan). Hist. del luxo y de las leyes suntuarias de España. 2t [*in 1v*]. s8º. 1788

Sempill, *House of, see* RENFREW. Arch. & hist. coll. rel. to Co. of R., Parish of Lochwinnoch. [H. of S. &c.], 2v, 1885–90.

Sempill (*Sir* **James),** *see* ADIAPHORA. De adiaphoris Scoti τοῦ τυχόντος aphorismi [*attrib. to Sir J. S.*], 1622.

Semple (Robert), *governor of the Red River Colony; 1766–1816.* Obs. on a journey thr. Spain & Italy to Naples & thence to Smyrna &c. 2nd ed., w. add. &c.; prefixed, Span. post guide. 2v. s8º. 1808

Sen (Dinesh Chandra).
Chaitanya & h. companions. 8º. Calcutta. 1917
see BEHULA: the Indian "Pilgrim's progress"; tr. f. Bengali by D. C. S., by J. W. Petavel &c., 1923.

Sénancour (Etienne Pivert de). Aldomen ou le bonheur dans l'obscurité. Préc. d'une étude par A. Monglond. s8º. 1925
see BROOKS (VAN W.) Malady of the ideal: Obermann, &c., 1913.
,, POURTALÈS (G. DE). De Hamlet à Swann, ét s. S. &c., 1924.

Senarctaeus (Claudius). Hist. vera de morte Joannis Diazii Hispani &c. cum praef. M. Buceri [*& Christianae relig. summa, I. D. auctore*]. s8º. [Basel ?]. 1546

Sendbrief [SENDBRIEFFE]. *Ein neuer Sendbrieff v. d. bosen geystlichen geschickt tzu yrem rechten herrenn. Einn Antwort vonn yrem erbhern. s4º. [Erfurt ?]. 1521
*Sendbrieffe (Ein) an e. fürnemen Thumbherren d. Stiffts Eychstat v. D. J. Cochles &c., 1544, *see* COCHLAEUS (J.)

Sendivogius (Michael) [SENDIVOG; SANDIVOGIUS]. New chemical light; add., treatise conc. sulphur, *see* HERMETIC MUSEUM, v2, 1893.
A new light of alchymie &c. Also Nine books of the nature of things, wr. by Paracelsus [*w. sep. tp. & pagin.*] All tr. by J. F., M. D. s4º. 1650

Seneca (Lucius Annaeus).
Opera omnia et M. A. Senecae rhetoris quae extant [*w. sep. tp. & pagin.*] s8º. Amsterodami. 1628
Apocolocyntosis, *see* PETRONIUS ARBITER (T.) Cena Trimalchionis &c.; ed. W. B. Sedgwick, 1925.
D. Claudii apotheosis, Apocolocyntosis; ed. O. Rossbach, *see* KLEINE TEXTE, T154, 1926.
De morte Claudii Cesaris, cum scholiis B. Rhenani, *see* ERASMUS (D.) Moriæ encomium, 1551.
Index verborum quae in S. fabulis necnon in octavia praetexta reperiuntur a G. A. Oldfather, A. S. Pease &c. confectus. [Univ. of Illinois. St., v4ii–iv]. p1–3. la8º. [Urbana]. 1918
L. A. S. flores, sive sententiae excerptae per Erasmum Rot. Item L. A. S. tragici, sententiae. [Vita L. A. S. incerto autore]. s8º. Amsterodami, *L. Elzevir.* 1642
TRANSLATIONS.
Ad Lucilium epistulæ morales. With Eng. tr. by R. M. Gummere. [Loeb Class. Lib.] [v]2, 3. s8º. 1920–25
Apocolocyntosis; w. Eng. tr. by W. H. D. Rouse, *see* PETRONIUS ARBITER (T.) P.; w. Eng. tr. by M. Heseltine &c., repr., 1916.
Apocolocyntosis. Einführung &c., Übers. O. Weinreich. 8º. 1923
De la clémence. Texte établi & tr. par F. Préchac. [Coll. des univ. de France]. 8º. 1921
Des bienfaits. Texte établi & tr. par F. Préchac. [Coll. des univ. de Fr.] 2t. 8º. 1926–27
Dialogues. Texte établi & tr. par A. Bourgery [*& R. Waltz*]. t1–4. 8º. 1922–27
Moral essays. [Text] w. Eng. tr. by J. W. Basore. [Loeb Class. Lib.] s8º. 1928
Philosoph. Schriften. Übers., mit Einleit. &c. v. O. Apelt. B1–4. s8º. L., *Meiner.* 1923–24
Seneca, his tenne tragedies. Tr. Ed. T. Newton, 1541. Intr. by T. S. Eliot. [Tudor Tr., s2, 11, 12]. 2v. 8º. 1927
Tragédies. Texte établi & tr. par L. Herrmann. [Coll. des univ. de France]. 2t [t2 *incl.* Pseudo-Sénèque: Octavie]. 8º. 1924–26
see ALBERTINI (E.) La composition dans les ouvrages philos. de S., 1923.
,, ELIOT (T. S.) Shakespeare & the stoicism of S., 1927.
,, FAIDER (P.) Etudes sur S. &c., 1921.
,, GUMMERE (R. M.) S., & his mod. message, 1922.
,, LE GRAND (A.) Man without passion, acc. to the sentiments of S., 1675.
,, L'HERMITE (F. T.) La mort de S.: tragédie, 1919.
,, LUCAS (F. L.) S. & Eliz. trag., 1922.
,, REHM (A.) Das 7. Buch d. Nat. Quaest. u. d. Kometentheorie d. Poseidonios, 1921.

Seneca (Marcus Annaeus), *father of L. A. Seneca* [SENECA (LUCIUS A.), *the elder*]. The Suasoriae. Intr. essay, text, tr., explan. notes &c., by W. A. Edward. 8º. C. 1928
Suasoriae, Controversiae &c., *see* SENECA (L. A.) Opera, 1628.

Senefelder Club, *see* DODGSON (C.) & J. PENNELL. The S. Club, 1922.

Senese. Statuti S. scritti in volg. ne' sec. 13–14. Pubbl. p. c. di F.-L. Polidori [& L. Banchi]. 3v. 8º. Bologna. 1863–77

Senet, *wife of Antefoker, vizier of Sesostris I, see* DAVIES (N. DE G.) Tomb of Antefoker, & of h. wife, S., 1920.

Senff (Martin). Ignem Johannæum, praes. J. C. Zeumer, diss. expendet M. S. [P447]. s4º. Jenae. [1699]

Seng-houei, *see* TRIPITAKA. Cinq cents contes &c., extr. du T. chinois [*of S.-h. &c.*] & tr. E. Chavannes, 3t, 1910–11.

Senior (William), *barrister-at-law.* Doctors' Commons & the old Court of Admiralty. s8º. 1922
Naval hist. in the Law Courts: sel. of old maritime cases. 8º. 1927

Sennacherib, *king of Assyria.*
see HONOR (L. L.) S.'s invasion of Palestine, 1927.
,, LUCKENBILL (D. D.) Annals of S., 1924.
,, SMITH (S.) First campaign of S., 1921.

Sennertus (Andreas). Diss. de Cabbala: maxime Ebraeorum &c. [P431]. s4º. Wittenbergae. 1655
Ebraismus, Chaldaismus, Syriasmus, Arabismus, necnon Rabbinismus. Praecepta gramm. Add. De idiotismis &c. diss. &c. *7 parts in 1v.* s4º. Wittenbergae. 1666
Each part has a sep. tp. w. dates 1663–66. Part 2 has tp. M. Trosti Gramm. Ebraea &c. 1663. *Part 6 has tp.* Libellus anon de Lusu illustr. à A. Pfeiffern, 1665.

Senogallia [SINIGAGLIA]. Statutorum & reformat. Civitatis S. volumen. In 6 libros &c. [Assistente & curam agente c. dict. imp. praesbitero don Ventura de Civit. Castelli.] [*Bk. 6 in Italian*]. fol. [Pesaro.] 1537

Sens. Obituaires de la Prov. de S., *see* RECUEIL des hist. de la Fr., Obituaires, t4, 1923.

Sensier (Alfred). La vie & l'œuvre de J. F. Millet. 4º. 1881

Sentenach (Narciso). The painters of the school of Seville. [Tr. f. MS. by Mrs. Steuart Erskine]. 8º. [1920]

Sententia de divina praedestinatione &c., *n.d.* [c. 1619], *see* DORT.

Sentimens [SENTIMENT]. *Sentimens de quelques théologiens de Hollande sur l'Hist. crit. du Vieux Test. par R. Simon, 1685, *see* LE CLERC (J.)
Sentiment d'un jurisconsulte envoyé à son amy, 1700, *see* JESUITS.

***Sentimental** celibate (The); by The husband of one wife, 1922, *see* BENNETTS (H. J. T.)

Sentinus (Jacobus), *Riccinensis.* De quibusdam lyricis versibus, *see* MATURANZIO (F.) De compon. versibus &c., 1520.

Sepeos, *bp. of the Pakradounians, see* SEBEOS.

Sepher.
ספר לב טהור [*w. Span. tr. by I. Nieto*]. s8º. Livorno. 1753

Sepp (Johann Nepomuk).
Deutschland u. d. Vatikan. s8º. München. 1872

Sepúlveda (Juan Ginés de), *see* BELL (A. F. G.) J. G. de S., 1925.

Sepúlveda (Ricardo), *see* GUERRERO (T.) & R. S. Pleito del matrimonio entre T. G. y R. S. &c., 1880.

Sequeira (Matos).
Tempo passado: crónicas alfacinhas. la8º. 1923

Sequenz v. unser lieben Frowen d. Mönchs v. Salzburg (*facs.*, 1480), *see* FREYTAG (G.) Bilder, B2, 1924.

Serafimovich (A.), *ps.* [Александръ Серафимовичъ Поповъ]. Въ пути—Заяцъ. *see* SBORNIK. Сб. товар. "Знание" 1, 5, 1904–5.

Serafini (Camillo). Le monete e le bolle plumbee pontif. del medagliere Vaticano. v4. 4º. Milano. 1928
4, Onorio I (625–638)—Pio XI (1922)—Aggiunte, Ind. &c.

Serafino, *Aquilano, see* AQUILANO (S.)

Serampore. *Memoir of the S. translations for 1813 &c. 8º. Kettering. 1815
Specimens (Lord's prayer) of eds. of the Script. in eastern langs. Tr. by brethren of the S. mission. s4º. Serampore. 1818

Serao (Matilde) [*i.e. Mdme.* EDOUARD SCARFOGLIO].
La ballerina. 2v *in* 1. s8º. Catania. 1899
Ella non rispose. s8º. Milano. [1920]
Mors tua. . . . s8º. Milano. 1926
TRANSLATIONS.
Après le pardon. Tr. G. Hérelle. [3e éd.] s8º. *n.d.*
see SANDRI (M.) M. S., 1920.

Seraphino, *Aquilano, see* AQUILANO (S.)

Serarius (Nicolaus).
De Lutheri magistro &c. libri 2. s8º. Moguntiae. 1604
S. Kiliani Franciae Orientalis, apostoli, gesta, variis cum notationibus. s8º. Wirceburgi. 1598
see BALDUIN (F.) Hyperaspistes Lutheri adv. orationem N. S. &c., 1603.

Serban (Nicolas) [SERBANESCO].
Pierre Loti. Sa vie & son œuvre. s8°. 1920
,, ,, ...[2e éd. rev. & augm.] s8°. 1924

Serbia [SERVIA]. A hdbk. of S., Montenegro &c., 1920, *see* ADMIRALTY: NAVAL INTELL. DIV.
Serbia & Europe, 1914–20, 1920, *see* MARCOVITCH (L.), *ed.*

Serbians. Memorandum pres. to Peace Conf. conc. S. &c., 1919, *see* PEACE.

Séré (Octave), *ps.* [*i.e.* M. O. G. JEAN POUEIGH].
Musiciens franç. d'aujourd'hui. 6e éd. s8°. 1921

Serebryakova (Zinaida Evgenievna), *form.* LANSERE, *see* ERNST (S.) З. Е. С., 1922.

Seregni (Giovanni). Del luogo di Arosio e de' suoi statuti nei sec. 12–13 &c., *see* REGIA DEP. DI STORIA PATRIA. Misc., t38, 1902.

***Serena** Blandish or the difficulty of getting married; by a Lady of Quality, 1925, *see* JONES (ENID, *Lady*).

Serena (Augusto). Un insigne Scotista trevig., *see* PADOVA. Monogr. s. Studio di Padova, 1922.

Serene, *see* ELEDUS. Le roman d'E. & S., 1923.

Serenius (Jacob), *bp. of Strengnäs.* Dict. Anglo-Suethico-Lat. Collegit. J. S. Præm. E. Benzelii de nova Ulphilae ed. &c. s4°. Hamburgi. 1734
Dict. Suethico-Anglo-Lat. Collegit. J. S. [*b. w. h.* Dict. Anglo-Suethico-Lat., 1734]. s4°. Stockholmiae. 1741
Engl. & Swedish dict. 2nd ed. 4°. Nykoping. 1757

Sergeant. *Mem. of a s. in 43rd L. I., 1839, *see* MEMOIRS.

Sergeant (John), *Roman Cath. writer, see* FALKNER (W.) Two treatises: answer to J. Serjeant's Surefooting &c., 1684.

Sergeant (Philip Walsingham), *B.A.*
Life of Anne Boleyn. 8°. 1923

Sergeant (Richard). Letters f. Jamaica. s8°. 1843

Sergeevich (Vasily Ivanovich).
Русскія юридич. древности. t1, 2i. 8°. С.–П. 1890–93

Sergeevsky (N. D.) Бшь меня, собака. (Наша главная болѣзнь). [P2446]. s8°. С.–П. 1907

Sergeev-Tsensky (S.)
Кукушка.—Сумерки. [P2499]. s8°. Москва. 1917

Sergel (Albert). Saat u. Ernte: d. deut. Lyrik um 1925. Hrsg. A. Sergel. 8°. 1924

Sergio (Giovanni Antonio). Orazione alla Maestà Carlo Borbone, re di Napoli &c. nel nasc. d. s. primogenito Filippo. [P2766]. 8°. Napoli. 1747

Sergius, *see also* SARGIS.

Sergius, *Saint, of Radonez, 1315–92, see* KLUCHEVSKY (V. O.) Значеніе С. для русскаго народа &c., 1915.

***Seria ludo**; by a dilettante, 1903, *see* DARLING (*Sir* C. J.)

***Series** (A) of picturesque views of castles &c. in Yorks. &c., 1885, *see* YORKSHIRE.

Sérignan (*le cte.* **Arthur de Lort de**), *see* LORT DE SÉRIGNAN.

Serious. *Serious consid. conc. doctrines of election & reprobation. Extr. fr. a late author. [P2533]. s8°. 1740
*Serious consid. on absolute predestination, 1741, *see* BARCLAY (R.)
*Serious thoughts in r. to the publick disorders. By a country J.P. [P2783]. 8°. [1750?]

Serís (Homero). La colección Cervantina de la Soc. Hispánica de Amér. Intr. &c. por H. S. [Univ. of Illinois. Sts. in lang. &c., v6i]. la8°. [Urbana]. 1918

Serjeant (John), *R.C. writer, see* SERGEANT (J.)

Serkis, *see* SARGIS.

Serle (Ambrose), *of the Transport Office.* Horæ solitariæ: the names & titles of Jesus Christ & the Holy Spirit in the O. & N. Test. Ann. Essay on the Trinity &c. 8°. 1868

Serman (K. E. Selow-), *see* SELOW-SERMAN (K. E.)

***Sermo** pedestris. [*Verse.* P2568]. sm. fol. 1739

Sermon. *S. (A) no lesse fruitfull then [*sic*] famous (1388), 1579, *see* WIMBLEDON (R.)
*Tröstliche (Ein) S.: Christenmensch am todtbette &c., 1523, *see* TRÖSTLICHE Sermon &c.

Sermoneta (Hieronymo Bordonio de), *see* BORDONIO (H.)

Sermons. Compleat (A) coll. of farewell s. pr. by Mr. Calamy, Dr. M. &c., 1663, *see* COLLECTION.

Serna (Juan Hurtado y J. de la), *see* HURTADO Y J. DE LA S. (J.)

Serna (Ramón Gomez de la), *see* GOMEZ DE LA SERNA (R.)

Serna Santander (Carlos Antonio de la). Dict. bibliogr. choisi du 15e s. Préc. d'un essai sur l'orig. de l'imprimerie &c. 3p [p1, Essai &c. *wanting*]. 8°. Brux. 1805–7

Serov (Aleksandr Nikolaevich) [Сѣровъ].
Критическія статьи. 4t. la8°. С.-П. 1892–95
see RIESEMANN (O. v.) Monographien z. russ. Musik, B1, 1923.

Serov (Valentin Aleksandrovich).
see ERNST (S.) В. А. С., 1921.
,, MAKOVSKY (S.) В. С., 1922.

Serra (*il marchese* **Girolamo).** La storia d. ant. Liguria e di Genova. 4t. Capolago. 1835

Serra (Luigi). Il Domenichino. s8°. Firenze. [1921]
Guida di Urbino. s8°. Milano. [1920]

Serra (Renato). Esame di coscienza di un letterato. Seguìto da ult. lettere dal campo; a cura di G. de Robertis &c. s8°. Milano. [1919]
Scritti ined. [Opere, v4]. 8°. Firenze. 1923
Eman. Kant—R. Kipling—G. d'Annunzio &c.—G. Ferrero—A. Oriani.

Serrano (Luciano), *O.S.B.*
D. Mauricio, obispo de Burgos. la8°. 1922
La Liga de Lepanto entre España, Venecia y la S. Sede (1570–73). 2t. la8°. 1918–20
El real monast. de Santo Domingo de Silos (Burgos). s8°. Burgos. [1926]

Serrano y Sanz (Manuel). Relaciones histór. de America, prim. mitad d. sig. 16. [Publ. Soc. de Bibliofilas esp., 39]. 8°. 1916

Serranus (Joannes), *see* SERRES (J. DE).

Serres (Etienne), *de Montpellier.* Un déporté pour la foi. 4 lettres &c. Publ. sur l'éd. de 1688 par M. Lelièvre. s8°. 1881

Serres (Jean de). *Comm. de statu religionis & reipublicæ in regno Galliæ regibus Henrico II, Francisco II & Carolo IX. 4p *in* 2v. s8°. *n.p.* 1572–75
p1 *is an abridgment of La Place's Commentaires.*
Psalm. aliquot Davidis metaphrasis Graeca &c. Ed. F. Okely. s8°. 1770
*The three partes [*sep. pagin.*] of commentaries, cont. the discourse of the civill warres of France under Henry II, Frances II &c. [*erroneously attrib. by the translator to Petrus Ramus*]; w. add. of the murther of the Admirall Chastilion &c., 1572 [*w. sep. pagin.*] Tr. by T. Timme. [pp. 89–96 & 297, 298 of p3 *wanting*]. 8°. 1574

Serres (Paul). Le diable au village. s8°. [1922]

Serretta (Enrico). Tina di Lorenzo. la8°. Milano. 1920

Serry (Jacques Hyacinthe) [*ps.* AUGUSTIN LE BLANC]. Hist. congregationum de auxiliis divinae gratiae sub Clemente VIII & Paulo V in 4 libros distrib. Acc. Liber 5 Super. libr. Apologeticus autore J. H. Serry. [*w.* Appendix *w. sep. pagin.*] fol. Venetiis. 1740

Sertürner (Friedrich Wilhelm Adam). F. W. Sertürner, d. Entdecker d. Morphiums. Neudr. d. Orig.-Morphiumarbeiten, hrsg. v. F. Krömeke. 8°. Jena. 1925

Seruzier (*le baron* **Th. J. J.)**
Mém. milit. Réd. par Le Miere de Corvey. 8°. 1823

Servantio (Gregorio), *bp. of Treviso.* Difesa d. potestà et immunità eccl. contro le otto propos. di un dottore incogn. [G. Marsilio] sopra il Breve di censure d. papa Paulo V, contro li signori Venetiani. 8°. Bologna. 1606

Servetus (Michael).
*Christianismi restitutio. [*Signed* M. S. V. *i.e.* M. Servetus Villanovanus]. 8°. *n.p.* 1553. [repr.] *n.d.*
Dialogorum de Trinitate libri 2. De justicia regni Christi, capitula 4. s8°. [Hagenau]. 1532
*An impartial hist. of M. Servetus, burnt alive at Geneva for heresie. [*Attrib. in a MS. note on tp. to Sir B. Hodges*]. s8°. 1724
see ALLWÖRDEN (H. v.) Hist. M. S. &c., 1727.
,, BLAIR (P.), *M.D.* Thoughts on nature & relig.: right of priv. judgment maintained by M. S. in h. ans. to J. Calvin, 1774.
,, CALVIN (J.) Defensio orthod. fidei contra M. S., 1554.
,, CHAUFFEPIÉ (J. G. DE). Life of S.; tr., 1771.
see CUTHBERTSON (D.) A tragedy of the Reform.: hist. &c. of the "Christianismi restitutio," 1553, w. acc. of controv. betw. S. & Calvin, 1912.
,, DRUMMOND (W. H.) The life of M. S., 1848.
,, KIS (S.) Assertio vera de Trinitate contra deliramenta ex S. &c. opinionibus, 1573.
,, MACKALL (L. L.) S. notes, 1919.
,, SCHEGKIUS (J.) Antilogia, qua refellit 27 propos. S. hæres, 1568.
,, SCHLÜSSELBURG (C.) Haeretic. catal. lib. 11, De Servetianis, 1599.
,, WRIGHT (R.) Apology for M. S., incl. life, 1806.

Servia, *see* SERBIA.

Service des Antiquités de l'Egypte. Annales. Impr. de l'Institut Franç. d'Arch. Orientale. t13–27. la8°. Le Caire. 1914–27
,, ,, ...Index des t11–22. la8°. Le Caire. 1921

Service des Antiquités de l'Egypte [*continued*].
Temples immergés de la Nubie. Doc. sur l'état anc. des monuments. [*Ed.* G. Maspero & P. Lacau].
tl [1, Brit. Mus.] fol. Le Caire. 1920
see GAUTHIER (H.) Le temple d'Amada, 1913.
„ QUIBELL (J. E.) & A. G. K. HAYTER. Excav. at Saqqara: Teti Pyramid, N. side, 1927.
Service (Robert William). Ballads of a Bohemian. s8º. [1921]
The house of fear. s8º. 1927
The master of microbe. [2nd impr.] s8º. [1926]
Services of the church, acc. to use of Sarum, 2nd ed., *n.d.*, *see* SALISBURY.
Servier (André). Islam & the psychology of the Musulman. Tr. A. S. Moss-Blundell. Pref. by L. Bertrand. 8º. 1924
Servières (Georges). Dresde, Freiberg & Meissen. [Les villes d'art célèbres]. la8º. 1911
Weber. s8º. [1922]
Servius (Philippus), *Jesuit.* Amicus fidelis usque ad mortem sive modus invandi moribundos, ægris sanisque perinde utilis ed. noviss. s8º. Antverpiæ. 1649
Servius Maurus Honoratus [S. GRAMMATICUS]. S. Grammatici qui feruntur in Vergilii carmina comm. Rec. G. Thilo & H. Hagen. 3v [*in* 4. 3i, ii]. 8º. L., *Teubner.* 1887–1923
3ii, App. Serviana ceteros comm. cont. rec. H. Hagen.
Servois (Jean Pierre). Notice sur la vie &c. du dr. Samuel Johnson. s8º. Cambrai. 1823
Sestan (Ernesto). Ricerche int. ai primi podestà toscani, *see* ARCHIVIO STORICO ITAL., Anno 82, v2, 1924.
Setchell (William Albert). American Samoa: Vegetation of Tutuila Isl.—Ethnobotany of the Samoans—Veg. of Rose Atoll. [C.I. of Wash.] la8º. Wash. 1924
Seth (Andrew), *aft. A. Seth Pringle-Pattison.* The idea of God in the light of recent philos. Gifford Lect^s.
2nd ed. rev. 8º. N.Y. 1920
The idea of immortality. Gifford Lect. 8º. O. 1922
The philos. of hist. [Brit. Acad. P2731]. 8º. [1924]
Seth (Ephrem), *Vardapet.* Patmutheanz Hamarôtuthiun. [*Summary of hist. of the 4 empires. In Armen.*]
s8º. Venice. 1833
Seth (James). Essays in ethics & relig., w. o. p. Ed. w. mem. by A. S. Pringle-Pattison. 8º. E. 1926
Seth (Mesrovb J.)
Hist. of the Armenians in India. s8º. Calcutta. 1895
Sethe (Kurt Heinrich). Die Ächtung feindl. Fürsten, Völker u. Dinge auf altägypt. Tongefässscherben d. mittl. Reiches; hrsg. &c. v. K. S., *see* KÖNIGL.-PREUSS. AKAD. Abhandl., Phil.-hist. Kl., 1926.
Die Ägyptologie, *see* ALTE ORIENT (DER), Jhrg. 23, 1921.
Die altaegypt. Pyramidentexte, nach d. Papierabdrücken &c. d. Berliner Museums. Neu hrsg. & erläut. v. K. S.
4B. la8º. L. 1908–22
Imhotep, d. Asklepios d. Aegypter aus d. Zeit d. Königs Ḏoser. [Unters. z. Gesch. &c. Aegyptens, B2iv]. la8º. L. 1902
Die neuentdeckte Sinaischrift u. d. Entsteh. d. semit. Schr., *see* KÖN. GESELL. D. W. ZU GÖTTINGEN. Nachr., Phil.-hist. Kl., 1917, 1918.
Sarapis u. d. sogen, κάτοχοι d. Sarapis, 1913, *see* KÖNIGL. GESELL. D. W. Z. GÖTT. Abhlgn., N.F., 14, 1913.
Untersuch. z. Gesch. u. Altertumskunde Aegyptens. Hrsg. v. S. B2iv, 7. la8º. L. 1902–17
see BONNET (H.) Ägypt. Tracht, 1917. [7.]
„ SETHE (K. H.) Imhotep, 1902. [2iv.]
Seton, *The family of, see* SETON (G.) Hist. of the fam. of S. dur. 8 cent., 2v, 1896.
Seton (George), *advocate.* Hist. of the family of Seton dur. 8 cent. 2v [*pagin. cont.*] 4º. *p.p.* E. 1896
Seton (George), *5th earl of Winton, see* WINTON (GEORGE, *earl of*).
Seton (*Sir* **Malcolm Cotter Cariston),** *K.C.B.*
The India Office. s8º. 1926
Seton (Robert), *abp. of Heliopolis.*
Mem. of many years, 1839–1922. 8º. 1923
Seton (Walter W.) Nicholas Glassberger & h. works, w. text of h. Major chron. Boemorum mod., 1200–1310. [Brit. Soc. of Franciscan St., v11]. 8º. M'ter. 1923
see DE BEER (E. S.) & W. S. Byroniana: archives of the London Greek Com., 1926.
Seton-Thompson (Ernest E.), *ps.* [*i.e.* ERNEST THOMPSON SETON]. The trail of the Sandhill stag. 8º. 1914
Seton-Thompson (Grace Gallatin), *ps.* [*i.e. Mrs.* ERNEST THOMPSON SETON, *née Gallatin*]. Chinese lanterns. 8º. 1924

Seton-Watson (Robert William) [*ps.* SCOTUS VIATOR].
The Abbot Trithemius, *see* POLLARD (A. F.) Tudor studies, 1924.
The Balkans, Italy and the Adriatic. 2nd ed. [P2485]. 8º. [1916]
The future of Bohemia. Lecture. [P2485]. 8º. 1915
The historian as a polit. force in Cent. Europe.
[P2688]. 8º. [1922]
Sarajevo: st. in orig. of the Gt. War. 8º. [1926]
see POLLARD (A. F.) Tudor studies; pres. by Bd. of Studies in Hist. in Univ. of London to A. F. P.; ed. R. W. S.-W., 1924.
Settimelli (Emilio). Virgilio Talli. la8º. Milano. 1921
Settle (Elkanah).
Cambyses, king of Persia: a tragedy. 4th ed. s4º. 1692
*Compleat mem. of the life of that notorious impostor W. Morrell, alias Bowyer, alias Wickham, died, Jan. 3, 169½.
s8º. 1694
The empress of Morocco: a tragedy. s4º. 1698
Love & revenge: a tragedy. s4º. 1675
Seuffert (Bernhard). Prolegomena zu e. Wieland-Ausgabe, 7, *see* KÖNIGL.-PREUSS. AKAD. Abh., Phil.-hist. Kl., 1921.
Seume (Johann Gottfried). Zeitgemässes u. Politisches aus S.'s Werken. Hrsg. v. G. Hennig. n. A. 8º. Jena. [1924]
Seurat (Claude Ambroise). Acc. of the living skeleton. [*Extr. f.* The Medical Adviser]. [P524]. 8º. [1825]
Seurat (Georges Pierre), *see* COQUIOT (G.) S., 1924.
see COUSTURIER (L.) S., 1921.
Seutter (Matthaeus), *engraver.* [*2 maps,* Marchia sive Electoratus Brandenburgicus &c., *&* Belgium foederatum. Maps 7].
folded fol. *n.p.* [c. 1730]
Seutter de Loezen (Matthaeus). Diss. de jure navali civitatis Lindavgiae. 8º. Erlangae. 1764
Sevagi, *prince of Bijapur, see* SHIVĀJĪ.
Sevelinges (Charles Louis de), *1767–1832.* *La dernière heure des Turcs, ou rétabl. de l'équilibre en Europe. Tr. du Baron de B*** par M. L. de S. [*Ed.* R. Puaux].
[P2430]. 8º. 1920
Seven. *Seven ages: narr. of the pilgrimage of the human mind &c. By a. of "The mirrors of Downing St." s8º. [1923]
Seven Sages. Il libro dei setti savj di Roma. Testo del buon sec. d. lingua. [I sette savj nel Tûtî Nâmah di Nakhshabî del E. Brockhaus. Tr. e giunte di E. Teza. Ed. A. d'Ancona. *b. w.* Velletti (A.) St. di G. d. Almieri, 1863]. la8º. Pisa. 1864
see TEZA (E.) Il lib. dei 7 savi nella lett. arm., 1906.
Seventy American hist. nuggets, 1920, *see* AMERICAN.
Severian, *bp. of Gabalis* [SEBERIANUS]. Homiliae nunc primum ed. ex ant. vers. Arm. in Lat. serm. tr. per J. B. Aucher. [*Arm. & Lat.*] 8º. Venetiis. 1827
Severini (Joannes). Conspectus hist. Hungaricae.
2p *in* 1v. [p1, ed. alt^a]. s8º. Posonii. 1775–78
see COMPENDIOLUM regnorum Slavoniae &c. [*comp. fr. S.'s ed. of Szasky's Introd.*], 1792.
Severus, *patriarch of Antioch.* A coll. of letters of S. f. Syriac MSS.; ed. & tr. by E. W. Brooks, p2, *see* GRAFFIN (R.) & F. NAU. Pat. Or., t14, 1920.
Les homiliae cathédrales de S. Homélie 77. Texte grec éd. & tr. en Franç., vers. syr., par M. A. Kugener & E. Triffaux, *see* GRAFFIN (R.) & F. NAU. Patr. orient., t16, 1922.
The 6th bk. of the sel. letters of S., in the Syr. version of Athanasius of Nisibis. Ed. & tr. by E. W. Brooks. [Text & Trans. Soc.] 2v *in* 4p. 8º. 1902–4
Severus (Sulpicius). Historia sacra: collata & recog. [*Folld. by* Contin. ex Sleydano. *pagin. cont.*]
s8º. Lugd. Batav., *Elsevir.* 1635
Saint Martin: récits de S. S., mis en Fr. avec intr. par P. Monceaux. 8º. 1926
„ „ Eng. by M. C. Watt. 8º. 1928
see ECKHARD (T.) Codices manuscripti Quedlinburg. &c., 1723.
Sévigné (*Mme. de***)** [*i.e.* MARIE DE RABUTIN-CHANTAL, *aft. marquise de Sévigné*].
Letters, to h. daughter & h. friends. Sel., w. intr. essay by R. Aldington. [Tr.] 2v. 8º. 1927
see CELARIÉ (H.) Mme. de S., sa famille & s. amis, 1925.
„ DORBEC (P.) L'Hôtel Carnavalet & la Marq. de S., 1916.
„ HALLAYS (A.) Mme. de S., 1921.
see HERON-ALLEN (E.) Memoranda of memorabilia in corr. of Marq. de S. & h. friends, 1928.
„ LEMOINE (J.) Mme. de S., sa famille & s. amis, t1, 1926.
„ MONTIGNY (M.) En voyageant avec Mme. de S., 1920.

Sevilla. La Estrella de S., 1920, *see* ESTRELLA.
*Relacion del auto particular de fé que celebro el santo officio de la Inquisicion de Sevilla, 1723. 8º. [1723]

Seward (Albert Charles). A summer in Greenland. s8°. C. 1922
see GEOLOG. SURVEY OF SCOTLAND. Memoirs. Tertiary &c. geology of Mull, Loch Aline &c.; w. Palæobotany by A. C. &c., 1924.

Seward (William), *1747–99, see* GRAVES (R.) Recoll. of W. Shenstone [*attrib. to W. S.*], 1788.

Seward (William Henry), *see* ADAMS (C. F.) Addr. on life &c. of W. H. S., 1873.

Sewel (Willem) [SEWELL]. Compendious guide to Low-Dutch [Korte Wegwyzer &c.] 3rd ed., w. add. s8°. Amsterdam. 1747
Hist. of the Quakers. By S. & by himself tr. fol. 1722

Sewell (Alfred Joseph). The dog's medical dictionary. 2nd ed. rev. (5th impr.) 8°. [1923]

Sewell (Anna). Black Beauty. [*Italian*]. Tr. di E. Cavazza, riv. da A. da Treppio. s8°. Boston [*Mass.* 1891]
"Rabe": Lebensgesch. e. Pferdes. Deut. Bearb. d. eng. Schr.: "Black Beauty." 6er Abdr. s8°. St. [1902]
Schwarzfellchen. Nach A. S.'s "Black Beauty." s8°. 1906

Sewell (R. B. Seymour). Cercariæ Indicæ, *see* INDIAN JOURNAL OF MEDICAL RESEARCH, v10, Suppl. No., 1922.

Sewell (Robert), *Madras C.S.* Sir Walter Elliot of Wolfelee; sketch of his life & extr. f. h. note books. [*Extr. f.* Imp. & Asiatic Quarterly Rev.] 8°. E. 1896

Sew Prasad, *Bania, called Lalla, see* GANGARAM, *Brahmin.* Trial of G. & S. P., 1927.

Sewruk (P.) Genossenschaftswesen in d. Sowjetunion. Übertr. v. I. Jannsen. 8°. [1925]

Sexby (Edward) [*ps.* WILLIAM ALLEN]. Traicté polit. composé par W. A. et tr. en Franç. [*by J. Carpentier de Marigny ?*]. Prouvé par Moyse &c. que tuer un tyran n'est pas un meurtre. [*Ascr. to Silas Titus*]. s8°. Lugduni. 1658

Sexton (George). Portraiture of mormonism. s8°. 1849

Sexton (John Joseph O'Brien), *see* BINYON (L.) & J. J. O'B. S. Japanese colour prints, 1923.

Sextus decretal. liber per Bonifacium VIII &c., 1569, *see* DECRETALES.

Sextus, *Empiricus.* Adv. mathematicos libri 10, *Gr. & Lat.*, *see* THEOLOGIA. *De primis scient. elementis, 1734.

Seybert Commission on Spiritualism. Prelim. rep. of Comm. app. by Univ. of Pa. Foreword by H. H. Furness. 8°. Phila. 1920

Seybert (Henry), *see* SEYBERT COMM. ON SPIRITUALISM.

Seybolt (Robert Francis), *see* MANUALE Scholarium &c.; tr. S., 1921.

Seydlitz (Ernst von). Handbuch d. Geographie. 26. Bearb. d. "Grossen S." Hrsg. v. E. Oehlmann. la8°. Breslau. 1914

Seyffarth (Gustav). De sonis literarum Graec. Cum epist. G. Hermanni. 8°. Lipsiae. 1824

Seyfried (Wilhelm). Diss. de J. Hussi martyris ortu, educ. &c. Praes. W. S., resp. G. Seyfried. ed. 3a. s4°. Jenae. 1729

Seyler (F.), *see* SEILER (F.)

Seyler (Gustav Adelbert). Gesch. d. Heraldik, *see* SIBMACHER (J.), *ed.* Wappenbuch, Band A, 1885.
see SIBMACHER (J.), *ed.* Wappenbuch, B1–7, 1856–1912; *list of contents for var. parts* bearb. v. G. A. S.

Seymour (Beatrice Kean). Invisible tides. 2nd ed. s8°. 1919
The romantic tradition. s8°. 1925
Three wives. s8°. 1927

Seymour (Bert). All about golf. s8°. 1924

Seymour (Charles). Woodrow Wilson & the World War. [Chron. of Amer. ser., v48]. 8°. New Haven, *Yale.* 1921
see HOUSE (E. M.) Intimate papers; arr. as a narr. by C. S., 2v, 1926.
,, —— & C. S., *edd.* What really happened at Paris, 1921.

Seymour (Horatio), *see* CROLY (D. G.) S. & Blair: th. lives & services, 1868.

Seymour (Michael Hobart).
Noches con los Romanistas. Tr. s8°. Nueva York. [1855 ?]

Seymour (St. John Drelincourt). The Puritans in Ireland 1647–61. [Oxford hist. &c. studies, v12]. 8°. O. 1921
Tales of King Solomon. s8°. 1924

Seyn (Eugène de). Dict. hist. & géogr. des communes belges. 2t. la8°. Brux. 1924–25

Seyppel (Johann Jacob). Diss. de ritu flagellandi apud Romanos. Praes. J. J. S., resp. J. Kirchhoff. ed. 2a. [P445]. s4°. Wittenbergae. 1670
Diss. ritum flagellandi apud Judaeos, sub præs. Æ. Strauchii exponit J. J. S. [P445]. s4°. Wittenbergae. 1670

Seyssel (Claude de), *bp. of Marseilles & abp. of Turin; 1450–1520.*
see CAVIGLIA (A.) C. de S., vita n. stor. de' s. tempi, 1928.
,, PROMIS (D. C.) Illust. di un medaglia di C. di S. &c., 1871.

Seytres (Joseph de), *marq. de Caumont, see* CAUMONT.

Sfinge, *ps.* [CODRONCHI ARGELI (EUGENIA)].
L'onore. Novelle. s8°. Rocca San Casciano. 1914

Sfondrati (*il card.* **Celestino).** *Legatio Romam Marchionis Lavardini &c. cum Rom. Pontifice [Innocentio XI] dissidium. s8°. [Rome?]. 1688
Nodus praedestinationis dissolutus. [Append., *w. sep. tp. & pagin.*] 2p *in* 1v. s8°. Coloniae. 1698

Sforza (Angela), *wife of Ercole d'Este, see* CITTADELLA (L. N.), *ed.* Istrumento di divis., 12 sett. 1493 tra le sorelle A. ed Ippolita Sforza Visconti, 1863.

Sforza (Carlo). Un missionario e sinologo piemont. in Cina [A. Vagnoni] nel sec. 17, *see* REGIA DEPUT. Miscellanea, t42, 1906.

Sforza (Costanzo), *see* PERTICARI (G.) Delle nozze di C. S. e Camilla d'Aragona, 1919.

Sforza (Francesco I), *duke of Milan, see* MANDROT (B. DE), *ed.* Dépêches des ambassadeurs milanais en France sous Louis XI & F. S., t3, 4 (1465–66), 1920–23.

Sforza (Giovanni).
Gli antenati di Napoleone I in Lunigiana, *see* REGIA DEPUT. Misc., t48, 1915.
La costit. napoletana del 1848 e la giornata del 15 maggio, *see* REGIA DEPUT. Bibl., v9, 1921.
La distruzione di Luni n. leggenda e n. storia, *see* REGIA DEPUT. Misc., t50, 1922.
Necrologia, *see* ARCHIVO STOR. ITAL., a. 82, v2, 1924.
Il princ. Eugenio Francesco di Savoia, c. di Soissons e il suo fidanz. con Maria T. Cybo dssa di Massa, *see* REGIA DEPUT. Misc., t44, 1909.
Storia di Pontremoli d. orig. al 1500. 8°. Firenze. 1904
see AZEGLIO (M. D'). M. d'A. alla Guerra dell' Indipend. nel '48; note &c. di G. S., 1911.

Sforza (Ippolita), *see* CITTADELLA (L. N.), *ed.* Istrumento di divis. 12 sett. 1493 tra le sorelle Angela ed I. Sforza Visconti, 1863.

Sforza (Isabella), *see* LANDI (O.) *Lettere di molte valorose donne [I. S. &c.], 1548.

Sforza (Lodovico Maria) [LODOVICO IL MORO; †LOUIS MARIA [SFORZA], *called the Moor, duke of Milan*], *see* MALAGUZZI VALERI (F.) La corte di Lodovico il Moro, v3, 4, 1917–23.

Sforza (Muzio) [†ATTENDOLI (M.), *called Sforza*], *see* MINUTI (A.) Vita di M. A. S.; ed. G. Porro Lambertenghi, 1869.

Sgrilli (Bernardo Sansone). Descr. d. regia villa, fontane, e fabbriche di Pratolino. fol. [Firenze. 1742]

Sgulmero (Pietro). Fazioni imp. e Veneta e l'orig. d. mon. a S. Marco in Verona (1509–24). [P2770]. 8°. Verona. 1886
Per la critica lapidaria Veronese del 16s. [Nozze Salvi—Clementi. N122]. 8°. Verona. 1890

Shackleton (*Sir* **Ernest Henry).**
see HURLEY (F.) Argonauts of the South: in the Antarctic w. Sir E. S. &c., 1925.
,, MILL (H. R.) Life of Sir E. S., 1923.

Shadwell (Arthur).
The breakdown of socialism. 8°. 1926
The Communist movt.: a personal investig. 8°. 1925
Drink in 1914–22: a lesson in control. 8°. 1923
The London water supply. s8°. 1899.
The revolutionary movement in Gt. Brit. Repr. f. The Times, w. add. Pref. by W. A. Appleton. [P2500]. s8°. 1921
The Socialist Movt., 1824–1924. 2p. s8°. [1925]

Shadwell (John Emilius Lancelot), *see* WRIGHT (R. S.) & J. E. L. S. Golden treasury of Greek prose, 1870.

Shadwell (Thomas), *Poet Laureate.*
Compl. works. Ed. M. Summers. 5v. la8°. 1927

Shafaat Ahmad Khan, *see* KHAN (S. A.)

Shafi (M. Muhammad), *see* ROSE (H. A.) Compend. of Punjab custom. law; w. repr. of Adopt. of daughter's son in P. by M. M. S., 2p, 1911.

Shaftesbury (Anthony Ashley Cooper, *3rd earl of*), *1671–1713*, *see* BROWN (J.) Essays on the Characteristics, 5th ed., 1764.

Shaftesbury (Anthony Ashley Cooper, *7th earl of*), *1801–85* [LORD ASHLEY]. Speeches upon subjects rel. to the claims &c. of the labouring class [1838–1867]. 8°. 1868
see BREADY (J. W.) Ld. S. & social-indust. progress, 1926.
,, HAMMOND (J. L. LE B.) & B. HAMMOND. Ld. S., 1923.

Shaginyan (Marietta). Советская Армения. в1. 8°. Москва. 1923

Shah (K. T.) Trade, tariffs & transport in India. la8°. Bombay. 1923

Shahazizean (Smbat). [Jubilee anniversary. *In Armenian*]. 8°. Moskona. 1893

Shāhjahān, *emperor of India, see* BANKIPORE. Reprod. of illust. f. 3 Persian MSS. [Bâdshâh Namah: lives of Jahangir & S. &c.] in Publ. Libr. at B., 1920.

Shah Nâmah, *see* FIRDAUSI.

Shahu Chhatrapati, *see* KOLHAPUR (*Shri* S. C., *Mah. of*).

Shakespear (*Lieut.-Col.* **John).** The thirty-fourth division, 1915–19. Ripon to the Rhine. 8°. 1921

Shakespeare Association. Ser. of papers on S. & the theatre, w. papers on E. Alleyn & early rec. illust. pers. life of S. By members of the S.A. 8°. 1927

Studies in the First Folio, wr. for the S.A. by M. H. Spielmann, J. D. Wilson *& o. wr.* Intr. by Sir I. Gollancz. la8°. 1924

see DYBOSKI (R.) Rise & fall in S.'s dram. art, 1923.

,, NICOLL (A.) Dryden as an adapter of S., 1922.

,, PARROTT (T. M.) Problem of Timon of Athens, 1923.

,, REED (A. W.) Beginnings of Eng. secular & romantic drama, 1922.

,, SPIELMANN (M. H.) Title-page of the 1st folio of S.'s plays, 1924.

,, STOPES (C. C.) The 17th cent. acc. of the Masters of the Revels, 1922.

Shakespeare-Jahrbuch, *see* DEUT. SHAKESPEARE-GESELLSCHAFT.

Shakespeare Society, *see* SHAKESPEARE (W.) Merry wives: the first sketch; ed. J. O. Halliwell, 1842.

Shakespeare (William).

Works. Publ. by Mr. Pope & Dr. Sewell. 10v. s8°. 1728

Works. Rev. & corr. [by Sir T. Hanmer, w. Mr. Pope's Pref., & Some acc. of the life of S. by Mr. Rowe. [*Illust.*] 6v. 4°. O. 1743–44

Dram. works. Rev. by G. Steevens. [Ed. J. Boydell. *Illust.*] 9v. fol. 1802

Plays of S. Pr. f. text of corr. copy left by G. Steevens, w. gloss. notes. [*With* Life of S. *by* Mr. Rowe *&* Dr. Johnson's Pref.] 10v. s8°. 1803

Plays & poems. [Pref. by S. Johnson]. s8°. *Pickering.* 1825

Dram. works: w. life & sel. of notes &c. by W. Harness. Added Poems. 8v. 8°. 1830

Complete works. Rev. f. orig. ed. w. hist. &c. intrs.; also notes &c. by J. O. Halliwell [*unauthorised*] &c. [Ed. H. Tyrrell]. [4v. v4 *wanting.* v2, 3 *b. together*]. la8°. [c. 1853]

Works. Imperial ed. ed. by C. Knight. Illust. on steel. [*Foll. by* Biog. by C. Knight rev. *w. sep. tp. & pagin.*] 2v. fol. [1873–76]

Dram. works, text of 1st. ed. [Ed. J. Heminge & H. Condell, 1623. Repr.] 8v. 8°. *Chatto & Windus.* 1885

Works. Ed. H. A. Doubleday, w. assist. of T. G. Foster & R. Elson. [The Whitehall S.] v2, 3. 8°. 1893–94

A new variorum ed. of S.; ed. H. H. Furness. [v20], Coriolanus. la8°. Phila. 1928

,, ,, ...5th ed. v3, 4, 12. la8°. Phila. *n.d.*
3, 4, Hamlet, 2v. 12, Much adoe about nothing.

,, ,, ...Student's ed. v1, 2. 8°. *Dent.* 1898
1, Romeo & Juliet. 2, Macbeth.

Works. [The Arden S.] 8°. *Methuen.* [1911–24]
As you like it. Ed. J. W. Holme. 2nd ed.
Coriolanus. Ed. W. J. Craig & R. H. Case.
Henry IV, p2. Ed. R. P. Cowl.
Macbeth. Ed. H. Cunningham. 2nd ed.
Merchant of Venice. Ed. C. K. Pooler. 4th ed.
Much ado about nothing. Ed. G. R. Trenery.
Poems. Venus & Adonis—Lucrece—The passionate pilgrim—Sonnets &c. Ed. C. K. Pooler.

Works. Ed. for the Syndics of the Camb. Univ. Press by Sir A. Quiller-Couch & J. D. Wilson. [v1–11]. s8°. C. 1921–28
1, The tempest.
2, The two gentlemen of Verona.
3, The merry wives of Windsor.
4, Measure for measure.
5, The comedy of errors.
6, Much ado about nothing.
7, Love's labour's lost.
8, Midsummer-nights dream.
9, The merchant of Venice.
10, As you like it.
11, The taming of the shrew.

FACSIMILES.

Much adoe about nothing, 1600. 8°. *n.p. n.d.*

Sonnets. Never before impr., 1609. [Noel Douglas replicas]. 8°. [1926]

The Tempest. Reduced Dallastype facs. f. first folio, 1623, & mod. text. Intr. by F. J. Furnivall. Ed. w. index by F. A. Hyndman & D. C. Dallas. fol. 1895

Shakespeare (William) [*continued*].

PLAYS. (*Single editions in alphabetical order.*)

The comedie of errors. Ed. W. G. Boswell-Stone. [Old-spelling S.] 8°. 1908

Hamlet, Prince of Denmark. Collated. 8°. *Bowyer & Nichols.* 1773

,, ,, Text f. Folio of 1623, w. notices. 8°. 1864

The 1st quarto ed. of S.'s Hamlet. Ed. w. intr. & notes by F. G. Hubbard. 8°. Madison. 1920

The trag. hist. of Hamlet, 1603. [Bodley Head Quartos; ed. G. B. Harrison]. s8°. [1923]

Julius Caesar. Ed. S. G. Dunn. [Longman's Ind. Ser.] s8°. 1912

The merry wives of Windsor; First sketch. Ed. J. O. Halliwell. [Shakespeare Soc.] 8°. 1842

Much ado about nothing. [P2582]. s8°. *Lacy.* [1858]

First quarto ed. of Romeo & Juliet. Ed. w. intr. & notes by F. G. Hubbard. 8°. Madison. 1924

The taming of the shrew. Ed. W. G. Boswell-Stone. [Old-spelling S.] 8°. 1907

The two gentlemen of Verona. Ed. W. G. Boswell-Stone. [Old-spelling S.] 8°. 1907

POEMS.

Poems. [*Mem. by A. Dyce.* Aldine ed.] s8°. 1832

Poems. [*Mem. by A. Dyce.* Aldine ed.] s8°. 1887

SMALLER COLLS. &C.

Dolby's Brit. theatre. With pref. remarks, biog. sketches, stage directions &c. [*b. in* 2v]. s8°. 1823–24
As you like it—Cymbeline—Julius Caesar—King Henry IV, p1—King Henry VIII—King John—King Lear—King Richard III—Macbeth—Much ado about nothing—Othello—Romeo & Juliet—The winter's tale.

see INCHBALD (*Mrs.* E.) Brit. Theatre, v1–5, 1808.

SONNETS.

Sonnets & A Lover's complaint. Repr. of orig. ed., 1609. 8°. 1870

,, ,, Intr. by W. H. Hadow. s8°. O. 1907

Sonnets; ed. f. Quarto of 1609, w. intr. & comm. by T. G. Tucker. s4°. C. 1924

TRANSLATIONS.

Antoine & Cléopatre. Tr. par A. Gidé. n. éd. s8°. [1925]

Carmina, Sonnets latine redd. ab A. T. Barton, ed. cur. J. Harrower. la8°. *Riccardi Press.* 1913

Hamlet. Wedeug tekstu Polskiego J. Paszkowskiego &c. 8°. Kraków. 1905

Macbeth. Testo ital., note ed app. di A. de Stefani. 8°. Torino. 1922

Les sonnets. Tr. de C. M. Garnier. s8°. 1922

REFERENCES.

see ACHESON (A.) S.'s lost years in London, 1586–92, 1920.

,, —— S.'s sonnet story, 1592–98 &c., 1922.

,, ADAMS (J. Q.) A life of W. S., 1923.

,, BARKER (H. G.) From Henry V to Hamlet, 1925.

,, —— Prefaces to S., s1, 1927.

,, BARTLETT (H. C.) Mr. W. S.: orig. & early ed. of h. quartos &c., 1922.

,, BEAMONT (W.) Henry IV, p1, 1876.

,, BEECHING (H. C.) Character of S., 1917.

,, BEYLE (M. H.) Racine & S., 2t, 1925.

,, BIERFREUND (T.) Palemon og Arcite: literaturhist. Undersøgelse som bidrag til S.-kritiken, 1891.

,, BLOOM (J. H.) S.'s church, 1902.

,, BOADEN (J.) Inquiry into authenticity of var. pictures & prints &c. of S., 1824.

,, BOAS (F. S.) S. & the universities &c., 1923.

,, BRADLEY (A. C.) Shakespearean tragedy, 2nd ed., 16th impr., 1922.

,, BRANDL (A.) S.: Leben &c., n. A., 1922.

,, —— S. & Germany, 1913.

,, BRIDGE (*Sir* F.) S. music in the plays & early operas, 1923.

,, BRIDGES (R.) Coll. essays &c., 1, Infl. of audience on S.'s drama, 1927.

,, BURTON (R. F.) Shakespeareana, sold, 1920.

,, CHAMBERS (*Sir* E. K.) Disintegrat. of S., 1924.

,, —— S.: a survey, 1925.

,, CHAMBRUN (C. L. DE). S. actor-poet; tr., 1927.

,, †CHESTER (R.) Loves martyr, 1601; w. its suppl. "Diverse poet. essaies" on the Turtle & Phœnix by S. &c.; ed. &c. A. B. Grosart, 1878.

Shakespeare (William) [*continued*].
REFERENCES [*continued*].
see CHEVRILLON (A.) 3 ét. de litt. angl., S. et l'âme angl. &c., 1921; tr., 1923.
,, CLUTTON-BROCK (A.) S.'s "Hamlet," 1922.
,, COLLISON-MORLEY (L.) S. in Italy, 1916.
,, CONNES (G.) Le mystère shakespearien, 1926.
,, CRAIK (G. L.) The English of S. illust. in philol. comm. on h. Julius Cæsar, 5th ed., 1875.
,, CROCE (B.) Ariosto, S. e Corneille, 1920; tr., 1920.
,, CRUICKSHANK (A. H.) Massinger & "The two noble kinsmen," 1922.
,, CUSHING (M. G.) Pierre Le Tourneur [*tr. of S.*], 1908.
,, CUST (L.) Arden of Feversham, 1920.
,, DANE (C.) Will Shakespeare: [*play*], 1922.
,, DAVIES (R.) Notes upon some of S.'s sonnets, 1927.
,, DAWTREY (J.) Falstaff saga: N. Dawtrey as Falstaff, 1927.
,, DOWDEN (E.) S. [Lit. primers], 1877.
,, DUDLEY (*Sir* H. B.) & M., *lady* D. *Passages on trial of Vortigern &c., v1–3, 1796?–98.
,, DYBOSKI (R.) Rise & fall in S.'s dram. art, 1923.
,, EAGLE (R. L.) New light on enigmas of S.'s sonnets, 1916.
,, ELIOT (T. S.) S. & the stoicism of Seneca, 1927.
,, FISCHER (R.) Quellen zu Romeo u. Julia, 1922.
,, FORT (J. A.) Two dated sonnets, 1924.
,, FRIEDLANDER (G.) S. & the Jew, 1921.
,, FRIPP (E. I.) Master R. Quyny, friend of S., 1924.
,, —— S.'s Stratford, 1928.
,, GARROD (H. W.) Milton's lines on S., 1926.
,, GOLDSWORTHY (W. L.) S.'s heraldic emblems, 1928.
,, GOLLANCZ (*Sir* I.) Sources of Hamlet, 1926.
,, GORDON (G. S.) S.'s English, 1928.
,, GRAY (A.) Chapter in the early life of S.: Polesworth in Arden, 1926.
,, GREENWOOD (*Sir* G. G.) Ben Jonson & S., 1921.
,, —— S.'s handwriting, 1920.
,, —— Shakespeare's law, 1920.
,, —— S. signatures & "Sir Thomas More," 1924.
,, GUNDOLF (F.) S. u. d. deut. Geist, 5e A., 1920.
,, HARRISON (G. B.) S.'s fellows, 1923.
,, HAZLITT (W.) Characters of S.'s plays, 1818.
,, HEIDRICH (H.) John Davies of Hereford u. s. Bild v. S.'s Umgebung, 1924.
,, HERFORD (C. H.) Normality of S. illust. in h. treatment of love & marriage, 1920.
,, —— S.'s treatment of love & marriage &c., 1921.
,, —— Sk. of rec. S. investigation, 1893–1923, 1923.
,, HICKSON (S. A. E.) The prince of poets, 1926.
,, HOLINSHED (R.) H.'s Chron. as used in S.'s plays; ed. w. intr. by A. & J. Nicoll, 1927.
,, HOOKHAM (G.) Will o' the wisp, or the elusive S., 1922.
,, JAMESON (*Mrs.* A.) Characteristics of women, 2nd ed., 2v, 1833.
,, JOHNSON (S.) J. on S.: essays &c.; sel. W. Raleigh, repr., 1916.
,, JONES (E.) Psycho-analytic study of Hamlet, 1922; 1923.
,, JONES (H. A.) S. & Germany, 1916.
,, JUSSERAND (J. J.) "What to expect of S.": S. lect., Brit. Acad., 1911.
,, KEMPLING (W. B.) S. memorials of London, 1923.
,, LAMBORN (E. A. G.) & G. B. HARRISON. S., the man & h. stage, 1923.
,, LAW (E.) S.'s garden, Stratford-upon-Avon, 1922.
,, LEE (*Sir* S.) Life of W. S., 1922.
,, LEGOUIS (E.) Bacchic elem. in S.'s plays, 1926.
,, LEWIS (W.) The lion & the fox; hero in S.'s plays, 1927.
,, LORENZO (G. DE). S. e il dolore del mondo, 1921.
,, MACKAIL (J. W.) S. after 300 years, 1916.
,, MACKENZIE (A. M.) Women in S.'s plays, 1924.
,, MACKENZIE (J. S.) Arrows of desire: essays (Henry V—Character of S. &c.), 1920.
,, MAGGS *Bros.* S. & Shakespeareana, 1923; 1927.
,, MASEFIELD (J.) S. & spiritual life, 1924.
,, MATHEW (F.) An image of S., 1922.
,, MOULTON (R. G.) S. as a dramatic thinker, 1924.
,, MURRAY (G. G. A.) Hamlet & Orestes, 1914.
,, MURRY (J. M.) Keats & S., 1925.
,, NICOLL (A.) Dryden as an adapter of S., 1922.

Shakespeare (William) [*continued*].
REFERENCES [*continued*].
see NICOLL (A.) Studies in S., 1927.
,, NICOLL (*Mrs.* A.) S. in Poland, 1923.
,, NOBLE (R. S. H.) S.'s use of song, w. the text of the princ. songs, 1923.
,, ODELL (G. C. D.) S. f. Betterton to Irving, 2v, 1920.
,, ORD (H.) Chaucer & the rival poet in S.'s sonnets, 1921.
,, ØSTERBERG (V.) Prince Hamlet's age, 1924.
,, —— Studier over Hamlet-teksterne, 1, 1920.
,, PARROTT (T. M.) Problem of Timon of Athens, 1923.
,, PARSONS (J. D.) The great taboo &c., 1919.
,, —— Sir Sidney Lee & absolute proof, 1920.
,, —— Stratford upon Avon gravestones & inscriptions, 1920.
,, —— W. S. "Another's name," 1920.
,, PAULSEN (F.) Schopenhauer—Hamlet &c.: Aufsätze z. Naturgesch. d. Pessimismus, 1926.
,, PEMBERTON (H.) S. & Sir W. Ralegh, 1914.
,, PERRY (W.) Treatise on the identity of Herne's oak, 1867.
,, POLLARD (A. W.) The foundat. of S.'s text, 1923.
,, —— S.'s fight w. the pirates & the problems of the transmission of his text, 2nd ed. rev., 1920.
,, —— S.'s hand in the play of Sir T. More: papers by A. W. P., W. W. Greg &c., 1923.
,, POURTALÈS (G. DE). De Hamlet à Swann, 1924.
,, QUILLER-COUCH (*Sir* A. T.) S.'s workmanship, 4th impr., 1923.
,, RALEIGH (*Sir* W.) S. & England, 1918.
,, RANNIE (D. W.) Scenery in Shakespeare's plays, 1926.
,, RHODES (R. C.) S.'s first folio: a study, 1923.
,, —— Stagery of S., 1922.
,, ROBERTSON (J. M.) The problem of the S. sonnets, 1926.
,, —— The Shakespeare canon, 3p, 1922–25.
,, RUSHTON (W. L.) S.'s euphuism, 1871.
,, —— S.'s testamentary lang., 1869.
,, SAVAGE (F. G.) Flora & folk lore of S., 1923.
,, SCHELLING (F. E.) S. & "demi-science," 1927.
,, SCHÜCKING (L. L.) Character problems in S.'s plays, 1922.
,, —— Die Charakterprobleme bei S., 2e A., 1927.
,, SHAKESPEARE ASSOC. *Papers.*
,, —— St. in the First Folio, *by var. wr.*, 1925.
,, SHERMAN (L. A.) On certain new elucid. of S., 1919.
,, SIME (A. H. M.) S.: h. music & song, 1917.
,, SINGLETON (E.) The S. garden, 1922.
,, SMART (J. S.) S. truth & tradition, 1928.
,, SPENCER (H.) S. improved: Restoration versions &c., 1927.
,, SPIELMANN (M. H.) Title-page of the 1st folio of S.'s plays: comp. st. of Droeshout portrait & Stratford monument, 1924.
,, STATIONERS Co. In commem. of the 1st folio tercent. &c., w. cat. of Shakespeariana &c., 1923.
,, STILL (C.) S.'s mystery play, "The Tempest," 1921.
,, STOLL (E. E.) Hamlet: hist. & comp. study, 1919.
,, —— Othello: hist. & comp. study, 1915.
,, STOPES (C. C.) Life of Henry, 3rd earl of Southampton, Shakespeare's patron, 1922.
,, SUARÈS (A.) Poète tragique, 1921.
,, SUGDEN (E. H.) Topog. dict. to works of S. &c., 1925.
,, SYKES (H. D.) Authorship of "The Taming of a Shrew," "The fam. vict. of Henry V" &c., 1920.
,, TANNENBAUM (S. A.) Problems in S.'s penmanship, 1927.
,, TAYLOR (G. C.) S.'s debt to Montaigne, 1925.
,, THALER (A.) S. to Sheridan, 1922.
,, THOMAS (H.) S. in Spain, 1922.
,, THORN-DRURY (G.) Some 17th c. allusions to S., 1920; More 17th c. allusions, 1924.
,, TREE (*Sir* H. B.) Hamlet f. an actor's prompt bk., 1897.
,, WALCH (G. T.) S.: hdbk. of information, 1923.
,, WARD (*Col.* B. R.) Mystery of "Mr. W. H.": [*S. identified w. Ed. de Vere, 17th Earl of Oxford*], 1923.
,, WILSON (J. D.) Spellings & misprints in 2nd Quarto of Hamlet, 1924.
,, WINSTANLEY (L.) Hamlet & the Scot. succession, 1921.
,, —— Macbeth, King Lear & contemp. hist. &c., 1922.
,, —— "Othello" as the tragedy of Italy, 1924.
,, WIVELL (A.) Inq. into hist., authenticity &c. of the S. portraits, 1827.

Shakhmatov (Aleksei Aleksandrovich), *see* Imperat. Akad. Nauk. Извѣстія отд. русс. яз. &c., т25 (Посвящается памяти А. А. Ш.), 1922.

Shakhovskoi (*prince* Yakov Petrovich), *1705–77.* Записки. 2ч. *b. in* 1v. 8°. въ Москвѣ. 1810

Shakspearean miscellany (The): coll. of tracts &c., 1802, *see* Waldron (F. G.)

Shalyapin (Fedor Ivanovich), *see* Chaliapin (F. I.)

Shamurin (Ѵury).
Подмосковныя. 2 кн. (кн 1, 2ое изд. исправл.) 8°. Москва. 1914
Ростовъ Великій. Троице—Сергіева Лавра. 8°. Москва. 1913
Старая Варшава &c. 8°. Москва. 1915

—— & Z. Shamurina.
Калуга. Тверь. Тула. Торжокъ. 8°. Москва. [1914 ?]
Третьяковская Галлерея. sm. fol. Москва. 1914

Shamurina (Z.) Кіевъ. 8°. Москва. 1912
see also Shamurin (Yu.) & Z. S.

Shan States. Rep. on admin., 1901–2. fol. Rangoon. 1902

Shanahan (E. W.)
South America: econ. & regional geography. 8°. [1927]

Shand (Alexander Faulkner Shand).
The foundations of character. [2nd ed.] 8°. 1920

Shand (P. Morton). A book of wine. 8°. 1926

Shanfara ibn Aus. Schanfarà-Studien, v. G. Jacob, *w. text & tr.*, T1, 2, *see* Königl. Akad. d. Wiss. zu München, Phil. Kl., Sitz., 1914–15.

Shanks (Edward).
Coll. poems, 1909–25. s8°. [1926]
First essays on lit. 8°. [1923]
The island of youth. s8°. [1921]
The people of the ruins. s8°. [1920]
Second essays on literature. 8°. [1927]
see Mandell (C. C.) & E. S. H. Belloc, 1916.

Shanks (Robert), *see* Du Moulin (P.) The anatomy of the mass; pref., concise hist. of the Eucharist, by R. S., 1833.

Shann (George). The evolution of knowledge. s8°. 1922
see Cadbury (E.) & G. S. Sweating, 1908.

Shannon (Earl V.) The minerals of Idaho. [S.I.: U.S. Nat. Mus., Bull. 131]. 8°. Wash. 1926

Shao-Kwan Chen, *see* Chen (S.-K.)

Shapland (H. P.) Pract. decoration of furniture. 3v. 4°. 1926–27

Sharakan.
Sharaknotz. [*Armenian hymnal*]. s8°. Echmiadzin. 1664
Шараканъ богослужебные каноны и пѣсни Армянской восточной церкви. Перевелъ съ древне-армянск. языка Н. Эминъ. Подъ редакціей К. Т. Костанянца. [Lazarevsky Inst. Vostoch. Yaz.] 2ое изд. Москва. 1914

Sharif (Ja'far), *see* Ja'far Sharif.

Sharman (T. T.) Kannada poets mentioned in inscriptions [*in Kanarese*], *see* India: Arch. Survey. Mem. 13, 1924.

Sharmanov (V. G.) Жизнь Красной арміи. Сборник статей под ред. В. Г. Ш. [P2724]. la8°. Москва. 1919
Строительство Красной арміи. Сборник статей под ред. В. Г. Ш. [P2724]. la8°. Москва. 1919

Sharp (Cecil J.) The country dance book. p2, 3, 5, 6. [2, 3rd ed., 3, 6, 2nd ed.] s8°. 1918–27
2, 3, 6, Dances f. The Eng. dancing master [by J. Playford]; 5, The running set coll. in Kentucky, by S. & M. Karpeles.

—— & A. P. Oppé. The dance, an hist. survey of dancing in Europe. 4°. 1924

Sharp (*Mrs.* Eliz. Amelia). Women poets of the Victorian era. Ed. &c. by Mrs. W. S. s8°. [1890]

Sharp (Evelyn). Hertha Ayrton, 1854–1923. 8°. 1926
The London child. 8°. [1927]

Sharp (Granville), *philanthropist.* *Remarks conc. the encroachments on the Thames nr. Durham-Yard. 2p [*in* 1v]. s8°. 1771

Sharp (Henry). Notes on vernacular educ. in Ceylon. [Bureau of Educ., India. Pamph. No. 5. P2412]. 8°. Calcutta. 1919

Sharp (Hilda Mary). A pawn in pawn. s8°. [1920]

Sharp (J. Alfred), *see* Wesleyan Methodist Conference. Cat. of MSS. &c. [comp. by J. A. S.], 1921.

Sharp (John), *Scotch divine, 1572 ?–1648* [Scharpius (J.)] Cursus theologicus: controversiae de fidei dogmatibus, hoc sec. exagit.; & ad Bellarmini argumenta resp. ed. 2a. aucta. 2t *in* 1v. 8°. Genevae. 1620

Sharp (Thomas). New poems. 8°. 1925

Sharp (Thomas), *archdeacon of Northumberland.* Mr. Hutchinson's exposition of Cherubim examined. 8°. 1755
Two diss. conc. the etymology & script.-meaning of the Hebr. words Elohim & Berith. [P490]. 8°. 1751

Sharp (Walter Rice), *see* Ogg (F. E.) Economic develop. of mod. Europe, suppl. chap. by S., 1926.

Sharp (William), *1856–1905* [*ps.* Fiona Macleod]. The silence of Amor—Where the forest murmurs. s8°. [repr.] 1919
Vistas. The gypsy Christ & o. prose imaginings. Sel. & arr. by Mrs. W. Sharp. 8°. 1921

Sharpe (*Sir* Alfred). The backbone of Africa. Travel dur. the Gt. War. With suggestions for admin. reform. 8°. 1921

Sharpe (Charles Kirkpatrick). A ballad book. Ballads of Scotland; coll. by C. K. S. Ed. E. Goldsmid. 2v. s8°. E. 1891

Sharpe (Edmund). The ornamentation of the transit. per. of Brit. archit., 1145–90. No. 1. 4°. 1871

Sharpe (Horatio), *see* Edgar (M., *Lady*). Colonial governor in Maryland; H. S. & his times (1753–1773), 1912.

Sharpe (Sutton), *see* Gunnell (D.) S. S. & s. amis franç., avec des lettres inéd., 1925.

Sharpley (Ada).
The poets' year. Anthology. s8°. C. 1922

Sharr (Francis John). The inspiration of the Holy Scr. Fernley lect. 8°. 1891

Sharrock (Robert). *De finibus virtutis Christianæ. The ends of Christian religion. By R. S. s4°. O. 1673

Shastri (Hirananda), *see* Sastri (Hirananda).

Shaver, The, *ps.*, *see* Macgowan (J.)

Shavtel [Chawthel]. Пѣвецъ Давида Строителя [*Abdulmessia*] (Georgian text &c.), *see* Marr (N. Ya.) Древнегруз. одописцы (12в.), 1902.

Shaw, *The family of*, *see* Shaw (W. G.) Mem. of clan S., 1871.

Shaw (Barnabas), *Wesleyan missionary, 1788–1857.*
Memorials of S. Africa. 8°. 1841
see Moister (W.) B. S., h. life &c., 1877.

Shaw (Cuthbert). Poet. works. Coll. by T. Park. s8°. 1807

Shaw (G. Bernard).
Androcles & the lion—Overruled—Pygmalion. [repr.] s8°. 1925
Back to Methuselah. A metabiolog. pentateuch. s8°. 1921
B. S. & Fascism. [*Letters &c. by G. B. S. & o. wr.*] [P2877]. 8°. [1927]
Common sense about the War, w. Replies by A. Bennett &c. 8°. N.Y. 1914
The doctor's dilemma, Getting married, & The shewing-up of Blanco Posnet. [5th impr.] s8°. 1920
Dramatic opinions & essays [*&*] A word on the dramatic o. & e. of B. S. by J. Huneker. [repr.] 2v. 8°. N.Y. 1922
Fanny's first play. s8°. 1924
*The great fight. [Repr. f. The Nation, Dec. 13, 1919. P2523]. 8°. 1921
The intelligent woman's guide to socialism & capitalism. 8°. 1928
,, ,, [repr.] 8°. 1928
John Bull's other island. s8°. 1921
John Bull's other island, & Major Barbara: also How he lied to her husband. [6th impr.] s8°. 1920
La maison des cœurs brisés, *see* Œuvres libres, 83, 1928.
The perfect Wagnerite; comm. on the Ring. [4th ed.] s8°. 1923
Ruskin's politics. s8°. 1921
Saint Joan. A chronicle play. s8°. 1924
,, ,, [2nd impr.] s8°. 1924
Statement of evidence before the Joint-Committee on Stage Plays. s8°. *p.p.* 1909
Table-talk. Conversations betw. B. S. & h. biographer, A. Henderson. 8°. 1925
Translations & tomfooleries. s8°. 1926
see Castrén (G.) G. B. S., 1906.
,, Collis (J. S.) S., 1925.
,, Duffin (H. C.) The quintessence of B. S., 1920.
,, Harris (F.) O. Wilde, [w. mem. of O. W., by G. B. S.], 2v, 1918.
,, Owen (H.) Common sense about the Shaw: crit. of "Common sense about the War" by B. S., 1915.

Shaw (George). Our Filey fishermen. s8°. 1867
Rambles round Filey. [2nd ed.] s8°. [1886]

Shaw (Henry), *F.S.A.* Decorative arts eccl. & civil of the Middle Ages. fol. 1851

Shaw (Lachlan). Hist. of the province of Moray. 4°. E. 1775

Shaw (*Sir* Napier), *see* Shaw (*Sir* Will. N.)

Shaw (R. C.), *see* Simpson (F. G.) & R. C. S. The purpose &c. of the Vallum &c., 1922.

Shaw (Robert). An expos. of the confess. of faith of the Westminster Assembly. Introd. essay by W. M. Hetherington. 8th ed. s8°. 1857

Shaw (*Maj.* Samuel). Journals of S. S., 1st Amer. Consul at Canton. With life of the a. by J. Quincy. 8°. Boston. 1847

Shaw (Samuel), *Writer in Edinburgh.* Alphabet. index of the registered entails in Scot., 1685–1784. 4°. E. 1784

Shaw (Thomas Shaw, *baron*). The law of the kinsmen. Foreword by W. H. Taft. 8º. [1923]
Letters to Isabel. 8º. 1921
The other bundle. 8º. [1927]
Shaw (Vero) & M. H. Hayes. Dogs for hot climates. 2nd ed. rev. &c. by W. S. Burke. s8º. 1908
Shaw (William), *M.A.* Enquiry into the authenticity of the poems ascr. to Ossian. s8º. 1781
Shaw (William), *Wesleyan missionary, 1798–1872.* Letter to the Earl of Aberdeen on the late irruption of the Caffres into Albany, S. Africa. [P527]. 8º. 1735 [*i.e.* 1835]
The story of my mission in S.E. Africa &c. s8º. 1860
see BOYCE (W. B.) Mem. of W. S., 1874.
Shaw (William Arthur). Letters of denization & Acts of naturaliz. for aliens in Eng. & Ireland, 1701–1800. Ed. W. A. S. [Huguenot Soc. of London, 27]. 4º. M'ter. 1923
Shaw (William George). Memorials of the clan Shaw. 8º. *p.f.p.c.* Forfar. 1871
Shaw (*Sir* William Napier).
The air & its ways. Rede Lect. la8º. C. 1923
Manual of meteorology. By Sir N. S. w. assist. of E. Austin. v1, 2. la8º. C. 1926–28
Shay (Frank).
The bibliography of Walt Whitman. s8º. N.Y. 1920
Shchedrin (N. E.), *ps.*, *see* SALTIKOV (M. E.)
Shea (John Gilmary). Discovery & explor. of the Mississippi valley; w. orig. narr. of Marquette, Allouez, Membré, Hennepin, [Leclerq] & A. Douay. 8º. N.Y. 1852
Hist. of Cathol. missions among Indian tribes of the U.S., 1529–1854. s8º. N.Y. 1855
Mem. of 1st cent. of Georgetown College, D.C., compr. a Hist. of Georgetown Univ. by S. &c. 4º. Wash. 1891
Sheaf (A) of Greek folk songs &c., 1922, *see* GREEK.
Sheahan (James W.) & G. P. Upton. The great conflagration: Chicago, past, pres. &c., & statement of all gt. fires of the world. 8º. Chicago. 1871
Shear (Theodore Leslie), *see* SARDIS. Publ. of Amer. Soc. for Excav., v10, p1, Architect. terra-cottas by T. L. S., 1926.
Shearman (Montague), *barrister*, *see* PRESS. Press laws of for. countries; ed. M. S. &c., 1926.
Shearwood (Joseph Alexander). Short hist. of Russia. s8º. 1888
Sheba, *The queen of.* The Queen of Sheba. Tr. into Fr. f. h. Arabic text by J. C. Mardrus. Eng. version by E. Powys Mathers. s8º. [1924]
see KEBRA NAGAST. The Q. of S. & h. only son Menyelek; tr., Budge, 1922.
Sheehan (Daniel Desmond). Ireland since Parnell. 8º. 1921
Sheehy (P.) Union a plague. In ans. to Mackenna's Mem. on the projected union. [P2555]. 8º. D. 1799
Sheffield, *town & university.*
Descr. cat. of charters, Copy Court rolls & deeds, part of the Wheat coll. &c. With abstr. of S. wills, 1560–6 & genealogies. Comp. by T. W. Hall. la8º. Sheffield. 1920
Descr. cat. of S. manorial records f. 8th year of Richard I to Restoration. Comp. &c. by T. W. Hall. 2v. la8º. Sheffield. 1926–28
Mappin Art Gallery Cat. 7th ed. 8º. Sheffield. 1914
Material for the hist. of Wincobank, S., 1523–1750. Fr. Wheat coll., w. abstract of wills &c. of Fam. of Greaves; comp. by T. W. Hall. 8º. Sheffield. 1922
Parish Register of S. Transcr. & ed. by C. Drury & T. W. Hall &c. [Hunter Arch. Soc.] p3–5. 8º. *p.p.* Sheffield. 1921–27
S. & Rotherham f. 12th to 18th cent. Descr. cat. of misc. charters &c., w. abstracts of S. wills, 1554–60 &c.; comp. by T. W. Hall. la8º. Sheffield. 1916
S. & environs, 13th–17th c. Descr. cat. of land charters &c., w. article on Hawksyard. Comp. by T. W. Hall. la8º. Sheffield. 1922
Sheffield (T.) Story of the Settlement, w. sketch of Grahamstown &c., w. list of settlers &c. 2nd ed. enl. &c. [*MS. index*]. s8º. Grahamstown. 1884
Shein (Pavel Vasilevich). Дополненія &c. къ Словарю Даля. [Imp. Akad. Nauk. Записки, т22]. 8º. С-П. 1873
She King [SCHĪ-KING; SHI KING; SHIH CHING; SHIH KING]. The S. K.; tr., w. annot. by W. Jennings. 8º. 1891
Shelden (Edward Stevens). Origin of the Eng. names of the letters of the alphabet—Further notes, *see* HARVARD UNIV. St. &c. in philology &c., v1, 2, 1892–93.
Sheldon (H. P.) The practice & law of banking. 8º. 1920
Sheldon (Ralph Edward), *see* PARKER (G. H.) & R. E. S. The sense of smell in fishes, 1913.
Shelgunov (Vasily Andreevich). Воспоминанія, *see* BLAGOEV (D.) От группы Благоева &c., 1921.

Shelley (Henry Charles).
Majorca. Intr. by A. S. M. Hutchinson. 8º. [1926]
Shelley (*Mrs.* Mary Wollstonecraft), *wife of P. B. Shelley.*
Proserpine & Midas. 2 unpubl. dramas. Ed., w. intr. by A. Koszul. s8º. 1922
Shelley (Percy Bysshe) [*ps.* THE HERMIT OF MARLOW].
*Address to the people on the death of Pss. Charlotte; by The hermit of Marlow (1817), *see* AUNGERVYLE Soc. Reprints, s2, 1883.
A defense of poetry. Ed., w. intr. & notes by A. S. Cook. s8º. Boston [U.S.] 1890
Defence of poetry, *see* PEACOCK (T. L.) Four ages of poetry &c.; ed. H. F. B. Brett-Smith, 1921.
A philosoph. view of reform. Now pr. for 1st time, w. intr. & app. by T. W. Rolleston. 8º. 1920
Poet works. Ed. Mrs. Shelley. 3v. s8º. 1853
The Shelley corr. in the Bodleian Library, f. coll. pres. by Lady Shelley in 1892. Ed. R. H. Hill. la8º. O. 1926
see BLUNDEN (E.) S. & Keats as they struck their contemporaries, 1925.
„ BROWNING (R.) Essay on Shelley &c., ed. H. F. B. Brett-Smith, 1921.
„ CAMPBELL (O. W.) S. & the unromantics, 1924.
„ CARPENTER (E.) & G. BARNEFIELD. Psychology of S., 1925.
see CLUTTON-BROCK (A.) S., the man & the poet, 2nd ed., 1923.
„ COURTEN (M. L. G. DE). P. B. S. e l'Italia, 1923.
„ DOWDEN (E.), R. GARNETT & W. M. ROSSETTI. Letters about S. interchanged by 3 friends; ed. &c. R. S. Garnett, 1917.
„ GORDON (G.) S. & oppressors of mankind, 1922.
„ HIME (H. W. L.) Greek materials of Adonais, 1888.
„ HITCHENER (E.) Letters to P. B. S., 1926.
„ LIPTZIN (S.) S. in Germany, 1924.
„ MADARIAGA (S. DE). S. & Calderon & o. essays, 1920.
„ MAUROIS (A.) Ariel; ou, la vie de S., 1923.
„ —— Ariel: a S. romance; tr., 1924.
„ MOORE (T. V.) P. B. S.: intr. to the study of character, 1922.
„ REUL (P. DE). Centenary of S., 1923.
„ STRONG (A. T.) Three st. in S. &c., 1921.
Shengeli (Georgy). Трактат о русском стихе. изд. 2ое. ч1, органич. метрика. 8º. Москва. 1923
Shenk (Hiram Herr), *see* MARTIN (A. E.) & H. H. S. Pennsylvania hist., 1925.
Shennan (*Capt.* Kenneth Gordon Woodbine), *see* ARTHUR (*Sir* G.) Story of the Household Cavalry, v3, by Sir G. A. assist. by Capt. S., 1926.
Shenstone. S. charters; [ed.] H. E. Savage, *see* STAFFORDSHIRE. Coll., 1923, 1924.
Shenstone, *The family of*, *see* GRAZEBROOK (H. S.) Fam. of S., 1890.
Shenstone (William), *the poet.*
Works in prose & verse. 2v. s8º. E. 1768
Poet. works. Coll. by T. Park. 2v. s8º. 1806
The School-mistress, 1742. [*fasc.* repr.] 8º. O. [1924]
T. Percy u. W. S.: e. Briefwechsel; hrsg. v. H. Hecht, 1909, *see* PERCY (T.)
see GRAVES (R.) *Recoll. of some particulars in the life of the late W. S., 1788.
see GRAZEBROOK (H. S.) Family of S., 1890.
„ HULL (T.), *ed.* Sel. letters betw. the Duchess of Somerset, W. S. &c., 2v, 1778.
„ LUXBOROUGH (H., *Lady*). Letters to S., [1739–56], 1775.
„ WILLIAMS (I. A.) 7 18th cent. bibliog., W. S. &c., 1924.
Shepard (Arthur MacCartney). Sea power in anc. hist. Foreword by W. Moffett. 8º. 1925
Shepard (Thomas), *the elder* [SHEPHARD]. Certain select cases resolved. [*b. w. h.* Theses Sabbaticæ, 1650]. s8º. 1650
Theses Sabbaticæ: or the doct. of the sabbath. 4p [*in* 1v. *2 pagin.*] s8º. 1650
Shephard (Gordon S.) Mem. Ed. S. Leslie. 8º. *p.p.* 1924
Shepheard-Walwyn (H. W.) The spirit of the wild. Intr. by P. Chalmers Mitchell. 8º. [1924]
Shepherd (Richard Herne), *misc. writer; 1842–95.* Bibliography of Ruskin, 1834–79. 4th ed. rev. & enl. s8º. *n.d.*
Shepherd (Thomas), *see* MASON (J.) Spiritual songs, & Penitential cries by T. S., 1859.
Shepherd (William Robert).
The story of New Amsterdam. 8º. N.Y. 1926
Sheppard (Eric William).
Short hist. of the Brit. army to 1914. 8º. 1926
Sheppard (James William ffranck) [*ps.* W. FFRANCK].
Urijah the Hittite. Tragedy. s8º. 1927
Sheppard (John G.) & L. Evans.
Notes on Thucydides. Bks. 1, 2 & 3. n. ed. 8º. 1889

Sheppard (John Tresidder). Greek tragedy. [repr.] s8°. C. 1920
The pattern of the Iliad. s8°. [1922]
Richard Croke a 16th c. don. [P2424]. 8°. C. 1919
Sheppard (William Fleetwood).
From determinant to tensor. s8°. O. 1923
Sherap (Paul) [Dorje Zödba]. A Tibetan on Tibet; w. an introd. chap. on Buddhism &c. by G. A. Combe. 8°. [1926]
Sherard (Robert Harborough). Life, work & evil fate of G. de Maupassant. 8°. 1926
Sherborn (Charles Davies). Index animalium sive index nominum quae ab 1758 generibus et speciebus animalium imposita sunt. [Brit. Museum].
Sect. 2, Jan. 1801–Dec. 1850. p1–14 [*pagin. contin.*] 8°. 1922–27
Sherborne Missal (The). Reproductions of full pages & details of ornament f. Missal executed betw. 1396 & 1407 for Sherborne Abbey Church & now in lib. of the Duke of Northumberland at Alnwick Castle. With intr. by J. A. Herbert. [Roxburghe Club]. la. fol. O. 1920
Sherbrooke (Robert Lowe, *viscount***).** Obs. sugg. by A few more words [by W. G. Ward] in support of [Tract] No. 90. [P2788]. 8°. O. 1841
Poems of a life. s8°. 1885
Sheremetev (*Graf* **Boris Petrovich)** [Chérémétef]. Journal du voy. à Cracovie, Venise &c., 1697–99. [Tr. A. Galitzin]. s8°. 1859
see Müller (G. F.) Lebensbeschr. d. Gen.-Feldm. Graf B. P. S. &c., 1789.
Sherer (John). Classic lands of Europe: Italy, Sicily & Greece &c. 2v. 4°. [1879–81]
Sheridan, *The family of.*
see Harvey (F.) Genealog. table of fam. of S. &c., 1875.
,, Sheridan (*Mrs.* C.) Nuda veritas, 1927.
Sheridan (*Mrs.* **Clare).**
Across Europe w. Satanella. 8°. [1925]
Make believe. s8°. [1926]
Nuda veritas. [2nd impr.] 8°. [1927]
Russian portraits. 8°. [1921]
Stella defiant. [3rd impr.] s8°. [1924]
The thirteenth. s8°. [1925]
Sheridan (Edward), *M.D.*
see Burrowes (P.) Speeches on trials of S. &c., under the Convent. Act &c., 1812.
,, Bushe (C. K.) Speeches in cases of S. &c., 1812.
Sheridan (*Mrs.* **Frances),** *wife of Thomas Sheridan.*
*The discovery, a comedy. 2nd ed. 8°. 1763
,, ,, Adapted for mod. stage by A. Huxley. s8°. 1924
*The dupe, a comedy. 8°. 1764
*The hist. of Nourjahad. By the Ed. of Sidney Bidulph. 8°. 1927
see Lefanu (A.) Memoirs of Mrs. F. S. &c., 1824.
Sheridan (*Rt. Hon.* **Richard Brinsley B.)**
Dramatic works. s8°. *Cassell.* [1887]
Duenna, *see* Inchbald (E.) Brit. th., v19, 1808.
An ode to scandal, w. A portrait. Ed. R. C. Rhodes. 8°. 1927
Plays; w. intr. by H. Morley. 6th ed. s8°. 1885
Plays. [Everyman's Lib.] repr. 8°. [1907]
Plays. Ed., w. intr. by I. A. Williams. 8°. 1926
Rivals, *see* Inchbald (E.) Brit. th., v19, 1808.
A trip to Scarborough. [Dolby's Brit. theatre]. s8°. 1823
A trip to Scarborough, *see* †Inchbald (E.) Mod. th., v7, 1811.
see Cobbett (W.) The polit. Proteus: public character &c. of R. B. S., 1804.
,, Thaler (A.) Shakspere to S., 1922.
,, Watkins (J.) Mem. of public & private life of R. B. S., 2nd ed., 2v, 1817.
,, Williams (I. A.) 7 18th cent. bibliog., S. &c., 1924.
Sheringham (George). Drawings in pen & pencil f. Dürer's day to ours. Notes &c. by G. S. Ed. G. Holme. [Studio]. la8°. 1922
Figure painting in water-colours by contemp. Brit. artists. Foreword by G. S. Ed. G. Holme. [Studio]. la8°. 1923
—— **& J. Laver.** Design in the theatre. With contrib. by E. G. Craig, C. B. Cochran &c. Ed. G. Holme. [The Studio]. la8°. 1927
—— **& R. B. Morrison.** Robes of Thespis: costume designs. [*By var. a*[s]*.*] Ed. for R. Mason by G. S. & R. B. M. 4°. 1928
Sherlock (Paul) [†Sherlogus (Paulus)].
Antiq. Hebraic. dioptra. fol. Lugduni. 1651
Sherlock (Richard), *D.D.* The practical Christian. 3rd ed. enl. & corr. 4p [*in* 1v. *pagin. cont.*] s8°. 1682
Sherlock (Robert Lionel). Geol. of co. around Aylesbury & Hemel Hampstead. With contrib. by J. Pringle, C. R. Chatwin &c. [Mem. of G.S.] 8°. 1922
Gypsum &c. by S. &c., 2nd ed., *see* Geolog. Survey of Eng. &c. Spec. rep. on min. resources, 3, 1918.
Man as a geological agent. Foreword by A. S. Woodward. 8°. 1922
Rock-salt &c., *see* Geolog. Survey of Eng. &c. Spec. rep. on min. resources, 18, 1921.
see Wright (W. B.), R. L. S. &c. Geol. of the Rossendale Anticline, 1927.
—— **& A. H. Noble.** Geol. of the co. around Beaconsfield. With contrib. by J. Pringle. [Mem. of G.S.] 8°. 1922
—— **& R. W. Pocock.** Geol. of the co. around Hertford. With contrib. by J. Pringle & C. P. Chatwin. [Mem. of G.S. Explan. of sheet 239]. 8°. 1924
Sherlock (Thomas), *bp. of (1) Bangor, (2) Salisbury, (3) London.*
The use & intent of prophecy. Add. 4 diss. 3rd ed. 8°. 1732
Sherlock (William), *Dean of St. Paul's.*
An answer to A friendly debate betw. Satan & S. wr. by T. Danson. [P2653]. s4°. 1677
*A disc. about church-unity being a defence of Dr. Stillingfleet's Unreasonableness of separation in ans. to Dr. Owen & Mr. Baxter. By a Presbyter of the Ch. of E. s8°. 1681
A disc. conc. the knowledge of Jesus Christ &c. 2nd ed. corr. s8°. 1674
A pract. disc. conc. a future judgment. 2nd ed. s8°. 1692
A pract. disc. conc. death. s8°. 1739
A preservative against popery. 2p [*b. w.* Stillingfleet (E.) Doctrines &c. of the Ch. of Rome, 1686]. s4°. 1688
A vindication of the Preservative in ans. to cavils of L. Sabran. [*b. w. above*]. s4°. 1688
A vindic. of the rights of eccl. authority. s8°. 1685
see Giles (W.) Defence of S.'s Preservative, 1688.
,, South (R.) *Animadv. upon S.'s Vindic. of Trinity, 1693.
,, —— Tritheism charged upon Dr. S.'s new notion of the Trinity &c., 1695.
Sherlogus (Paulus), *see* Sherlock (P.)
Sherman (James), *dissenting minister, 1796–1862.*
Mem. of W. Allen. s8°. 1851
The pastor's wife. Mrs. Sherman. By her husband. s8°. 1853
Psalms & hymns. Sel. s8°. 1841
see Allon (H.) Mem., incl. autobiog., 1863.
Sherman (Lucius Adelno). On certain new elucid. of Shakespeare, *see* Nebraska Univ. Studies, v19, 1919.
Sherman (Martha), *wife of James Sherman, see* Sherman (J.) The pastor's wife, 1853.
Sherman (Stuart Pratt).
see Camb. hist. of Eng. lit. Suppl.: Hist. of Amer. lit.; ed. W. P. Trent, S. P. S. &c., v3, 4, 1921.
,, —— Suppl.: Short hist. of Amer. lit.; ed. W. P. Trent, S. P. S. &c., 1924.
Sherrill (Charles Hitchcock). Korea & Shantung *v.* the white peril, by S.—The anti-Japanese agitation in California; by J. P. Irish. [P2503]. s8°. Seoul. 1920
Stained glass tours in Germany, Austria & the Rhine lands. 8°. [1927]
Stained glass tours in Spain & Flanders. 8°. [1924]
Sherrington (*Sir* **Charles Scott).**
The assaying of Brabantius, & o. verse. s8°. O. 1925
see Science for all: [*by var. wr.*]; intr. by Sir C. S., 1926.
Sher Shah [Farid], *Sultan of Delhi, see* Temple (*Sir* R. C.) A new view of Sher Shah Sur, 1922.
Shershenevich (G. F.) Программа конституціонно-демократ. партіи въ общедоступномъ изложеніи. [P848]. s8°. Казань. 1905
Sherson (Erroll). London's lost theatres of the 19th cent., w. notes on plays & players. Foreword by Mrs. Kendal. 8°. [1925]
Sherwell (Arthur). Life in West London. 3rd ed. s8°. 1901
Sherwood (William Edward).
Oxford yesterday: mems. of 70 yrs. ago. 8°. O. 1927
Shestov (Leon). Les révélations de la mort: Dostoïevsky—Tolstoï. Préf. & tr. de B. de Schlœzer. s8°. [1923]
Shetland. Statist. acc. of the S. Islands. By the ministers of the parishes. 8°. E. 1841
Shevchenko (Taras Grigorevich), *1814–61.* Повне видання творів. [t1 *contains* Life & Criticism]. 5t. 8°. Коломия. [1912]
Shevirev (Stepan). Исторія Московскаго университета, 1755–1855. la8°. Москва. 1855
Shia Imami Ismailia Council, *see* Ismailia Council.
Shiel (Matthew Phipps).
How the old woman got home. s8°. [1927]
Shier (John). Rep. on starch-producing plants of Brit. Guiana. [P2846]. 8°. Demerara. 1847

Shifner (Anton Antonovich), *see* Schiefner (F. A. v.)

Shilder (Nikolai Karlovich).
Графъ Эдуардъ Ивановичъ Тотлебенъ, его жизнь и дѣятельность. 2t [*pagin. cont.* Приложенія *w. sep. pagin.*] 8º. С.-П. 1885–86

Shillito (Elizabeth Helen). Dorothea Beale, 1858–1906. s8º. 1920

Shilov (Aleksei A.), *ed.*, *see* Lopatin (H. A.) Г. А. Лопатин (1845–1918): автобиог. &c., 1922.

Shimun (Benyamin *Mar*), *see* Surma *d' Bait Mar Shimun.* Assyrian church customs & the murder of M. S., 1920.

Shinto. Die hist. Quellen d. Shinto-Relig.; aus d. Altjapan. u. Chin. übers. u. erkl. v. K. F., 1919, *see* Florenz (C. A.)

Shipley (*Sir* Arthur Everett). Cambridge cameos. 8º. [1924]
Hunting under the microscope. Ed. C. F. A. Pantin. s8º. [1928]
Islands, West Indian-Aegean. 8º. 1924
Life. Book for students. s8º. C. 1923

Shipov (D. N.)
Воспоминанія и думы о пережитомъ. 8º. Москва. 1918

Shippee (Lester Burrell). Recent Amer. hist. 8º. N.Y. 1924

Shire-Horse Society. Stud book. v1–43 (1883–1922).
[v1–4, a re-issue, *b. together.* v5 *wanting*]. 8º. 1885–1922
„ „ Index, v1–13. 8º. 1893

Shirley, *The family of*, *see* Shirley (E. P.) Stemmata Shirleiana; annals of the S. fam. of Nether Etindon, Warw. & of Shirley in Co. of Derby, 1841.

Shirley (Evelyn Philip). *Stemmata Shirleiana, or annals of the Shirley family, lords of Nether Etindon &c. 4º. *p.p.* 1841

Shirley (James). The royal master (1638); ed. w. crit. essay &c., by A. W. Ward, *see* Gayley (C. M.) Repres. Eng. comedies, v3, 1914.

Shirley (Walter Waddington). Cat. of the extant Lat. works of Wyclif. Rev. by J. Loserth. [Wyclif Soc.] 8º. [O. 1924]

Shirley (William), *dramatist.*
Edward the Black Prince. Tragedy. [P2575]. 8º. 1779
„ „ *see* Inchbald (E.) Brit. th., v14, 1808.

Shirley (William), *Gov. of Massachusetts*, *see* Wood (G. A.) W. S., 1741–56, v1, 1920.

Shirokogorov (S. M.) Anthropology of East. China & Kwangtung prov. [Roy. As. Soc. N. China Br. Extra vol. 4]. la8º. Shanghai. 1925
Anthropology of N. China. [Roy. As. Soc. N. China Br. Extra vol. 2]. la8º. Shanghai. 1923
Social organiz. of the Manchus. [Roy. As. Soc. N. China Br. Extra vol. 3]. la8º. Shanghai. 1924

Shirras (George Findlay). Price of silver, *see* Internat. Financial Conf., Paper 14, 1920.
The science of public finance. 8º. 1924

Shirreff (John), *see* Rennie (G.), R. Broun & J. S. Gen. view of the agric. of Yorks., 1794.

Shivâji, *the Maráthá, prince of Bijapur; c. 1627–80.*
see Orléans (*le père* P. J. d'). Hist. des deux conq. tartares qui ont subjugué la Chine [*&* Hist. de S. &c.], 1690.
„ Sarkar (J.) S. & h. times, 2nd ed., 1920.
„ Takakhav (N. S.) Life of S., 1921.

Shklovsky (Viktor).
Розанов. Из книги "Сюжет как явление стиля." s8º. [П.] 1921

Shleikher (A.), *see* Schleicher (August).

Shlyapkin (Ilya Aleksandrovich).
Старинныя дѣйства и комедіи Петровск. врем., извлеч. изъ рукоп. &c. Ш., *see* Imp. Akad. Nauk. Сборникъ, т97, 1921.

Shlyapnikov (A.) Семнадцатый год. [Истпарт: Ком. по ист. Окт. револ.] кн. 1, 2. [1, изд. 2ое]. 8º. Москва. *n.d.*–1925

Shmavon, *see* Simeon, *bp. in Persia.*

Shmelev (Ivan S.) Голуби, *see* Russkii. Р. сборникъ, 1920.

Shmidt (O. Yu.), *ed.*, *see* Encyclopaedia. Большая совет. э., 1926 &c.

Shmurlo (E.) Исторія Россіи, 862–1917. 8º. Мюнхенъ. 1922

Shnorhali (Nerses), *see* Nerses, *Shnorhali.*

Shnorhali (Sargis), *see* Sargis, *Shnorhali.*

Shoin Yoshida, *see* Tokutomi (I.) Life of S. Y.; tr., 1917.

Sholts (F. A.), *see* Russia: Soviet Republic. Ком. Северн. Морск. Пути: Северн. морской путь; под ред. Ф. А. Ш., 1921.

Shoo-King, *see* Pelliot (P.) Le Chou king en caractères anc. &c., 1916.

Shopkeeper's & tradesman's assistant: list of stage-coaches, carriers &c., acc. of inns in London &c. s8º. *H. Kent.* 1768

Shore (W. Teignmouth), *see* Cream (T. N.) Trial; ed. W. T. S., 1923.

Short.
*Short (A) acc. of E. Swedenborg, 1787, *see* Swedenborg (E.)
*Short (A) acc. of Eliz. Flook, *n.d.*, *see* Flook (E.)

Short [*continued*].
*Short (A) acc. of God's dealings w. John Haime, 1785, *see* Wesley (J.)
*Short (A) acc. of the death of M. Langson, 1775, *see* Wesley (J.)
*Short (A) acc. of the 1st settlement of the prov. of Virginia, Maryland, New-York &c. by the English; annexed, Map of Maryland &c., 1630. [Amer. Geogr. Soc.] 8º. 1735 [repr. 1922]
*Short (A) acc. of the late J. Wesley dur. the two last weeks of h. life, 1791, *see* Wesley (J.)
*Short (A) acc. of the life & death of Jane Newland, 1790, *see* Wesley (J.)
*Short (A) & easie method w. the Deists, 4th ed., 1711, *see* Leslie (C.)
*Short (A) & easie method w. the Jews, 4th ed., 1715, *see* Leslie (C.)
*Short (A) hist. of Bristol's Little Theatre, 1925, *see* Bristol.
*Short (A) introd. to Eng. grammar, 1787, *see* Lowth (R.)
*Short obs. on a commut. of tithes for gov. annuities, 1798, *see* Tithes.
*Short (A) Roman hist., 1773, *see* Roman.

Short (Ernest Henry). The house of God: hist. of relig. architecture & symbolism. 8º. 1925

Short (*Sir* Frank), *see* Salaman (M. C.) Sir F. S., 1925.

Shorter (Clement King). C. K. S.: autobiog. [*w.* Bibliog.] Ed. J. M. Bulloch. 8º. *p.p.* 1927

Shorter (Lewis Arthur Hurst). Echoes afar. [Poems]. s8º. 1925
Essays & sketches. s8º. 1925
The golden gateway. A tale of old Winchelsea. [*Poem*]. s8º. 1922
Sunshine & Jack. s8º. 1923
The talisman & o. poems. s8º. 1921

Shorthose (*Capt.* William John Townsend), *D.S.O.* Sport & adv. in Africa: 12 yrs. of big game hunting, campaigning &c. in tropical Africa. 8º. 1923

Shortt (Adam), *see* Canada: Canadian Archives. Docs. rel. to Canadian currency &c. dur. French per.; sel. & ed. A. S., 2v, 1925.

Shota Rustaweli. Vephkhis-tqaosani. [Man in the tiger-skin. *In Georgian.* Ed. D. Karitchamvili]. 8º. Tiflis. 1903
see Sbornik. Сборн. матер. для опис. Кавказа, в. 4 (О. Варсовой Кожѣ Р.: рѣчи Н. Гулака), 1884.

Shotwell (James Thompson). Plans & protocols to end war, *see* Internat. Conciliation, 208, 1925.
see Acad. of Polit. Science, *N.Y.* Proc., v12, No. 1, Internat. problems &c.; ed. S., 1926.

Shotwell (Walter Gaston).
The Civil War in America. 2v. 8º. 1923

Shovel (*Adm. Sir* Cloudesley), *see* Allyn (R.) Narr. of victory obt. by Eng. &c. fleet, La-Hogue, 1692, & acc. drawn up by Sir C. S.'s dir., 1744.

Shower (John), *1657–1715*, *see* Jackson (T.) Lib. of Xtn. biog., v4, J. S., by W. Tong, 1838.

Shpet (Gustav). Философское мировоззрение Герцена. 8º. П. 1921

Shreider (Aleksandr), *see* Russia: Soviet Rep. Теорія и практика совѣтскаго строя, в1, 1919.

Shreve (Forrest). Growth record in trees, *see* MacDougal (D. T.) & F. S. Growth in trees &c., 1924.

Shrewsbury (George Talbot, *6th earl of*), *d. 1590*, *see* Lodge (E.) Illust. of Brit. hist.; cont. great part of corr. of Eliz. w. S., 3v, 1791.

Shrewsbury (Ralph, *of*), *bp. of Bath & Wells.* Household roll, 1337–38, *see* Somerset Record Soc. Collectanea 1, 1924.

Shrewsbury (William James), *see* Parl.: H. of Commons. Auth. rep. of debate, June 1825, rel. to demolition of Methodist Chapel in Barbadoes & expulsion of S. &c., 1825.

Shrimpton (A. W.) & A. E. Mulgan.
Maori & Pakeha. A hist. of New Zealand. s8º. [1921]

Shropshire Parish Register Society.
8º. [Shrewsbury]. *p.p.* 1912–22
Hereford Diocese, v13–18ii.
Lichfield Diocese, v13–17.
Nonconformist & Roman Catholic registers. [*b. in 3v*].
St. Asaph Diocese, v5–8.

Shtein (B. E.) Торговая политика и торгов. договоры Советской России 1917–22. la8º. Москва. 1923
—— & A. Ya. Kantorovich. Русский экспорт и внешние рынки. [2ч *in* 1]. la8º. Москва. 1923

Shteinberg (Isaak). Отъ Февраля по Октябрь 1917. [Проблемы русской револ., в1]. 8º. Berlin. [1919]

Shuckford (Samuel). Sacred & profane hist. of the world connected &c., w. treatise on the creation & fall of man. [n. ed.] 2v. [3v *in* 2]. 8º. O. 1848

Shulgin (Varsily Vitalievich) "1920 г." очерки. 8°. Софія. 1921
Три столицы: путеш. въ Красную Россію. 8°. [Berlin. 1926]
La résurrection de la Russie: mon voy. secret en R. soviét. Tr. Ph. Pouget. [Coll. d'études &c. pour servir à l'hist. de notre temps]. 8°. 1927

Shunjō *Hōin.* Honen the Buddhist saint. Tr., hist. intr. &c., by H. H. Coates & R. Ishizuka. 8°. Kyoto. 1925

Shunshō (Katsuawa) [HARUAKI], *see* SUCCO (F.) K. S., 1922.

Shushan, *daughter of Vardan* [SUSAN]. [*Martyrdom of St. S. *In Armenian.* Soferq Hayk., v9]. *b. w.* Thaddaeus, *St.* Martyrdom]. s8°. i Venetik. 1853

Shuster (William Morgan).
The strangling of Persia. [repr.] 8°. N.Y. 1920

Shvetsov (A. I.)
Денежная реформа и кооперация. [P2823]. 8°. Москва. 1924

Shvittau (G. G.) Революция и народное хозяйство в России, 1917–21. 8°. [в Лейпциге]. 1922

Siam. Full (A) & true rel. of the revolution in Siam, & the expulsion of the Jesuits & soldiers of the French nation. Substance of letters wr. in Oct. 1688 &c. & now tr. s4°. 1690
Records of the rels. betw. S. & for. countries in the 17th c. From papers in India Office. [Vajirañāṇa Nat. Lib.] 5v. la8°. Bangkok. 1915–21
*Rel. des missions des évesques franç. au S. &c., 1674, *see* RELATION.
*Rel. (A) of voyage to Siam by 6 Jesuits; tr., 1688, *see* TACHARD (G.)

Sianda (Giovanni). Lexicon polemicum in quo potiorum haeretic. vita perstringitur &c. 2t [*2 pag. in* t2]. fol. Romae. 1733–34

Siang (Song Ong), *see* SONG ONG SIANG.

Siano (Francesco de). Brevi notizie di storia nat. e civile dell' isola d'Ischia. s8°. [Naples ?. 1800 ?]

Sibbald (*Mrs.* **Susan**), *wife of Lt.-Col. Will. Sibbald, form. Mein; 1783–1866.* Memoirs, 1783–1812. Ed. F. P. Hett. 8°. [1926]

Sibbern (Nicolaus Petrus). Bibl. hist. Dano-Norvegica. [*Foll. by* Lex regia (1665) *w. sep. tp.*] s8°. Hamburgi. 1716

Sibbes (Richard) [SIBBS; SIBS]. Bowels opened: or a discovery of the neare & deare love &c. betwixt Christ & the church, in div. sermons on the Canticles. [Ed. T. Goodwin & P. Nye]. s4°. 1641
A learned comm. upon the first chapter of the 2nd Epistle of S. Paul to the Corinthians &c. Publ. by P. Manton. sm. fol. 1655
The saint's cordialls; sundry sermons [*w. sep. tp.*: Josiah's reformation &c.] fol. 1637
The soul's conflict w. itself. s8°. [1830 ?]

Siber (Urbanus Godofridus). S. Spyridionis episcop. vitam &c. examinat &c. S. s4°. Lips. 1718

Siberia [Сибирь &c.]
*Древняя пословица Сибирь золотое дно. [*Extr. no tp.* P2867]. s8°. *n.p.* [1761]
Лѣтопись сибирская, повѣствованіе о взятіи Сибирскія земли Русскими &c. Изд. XVIIв. 8°. С.-П. 1821
Сибирскія лѣтописи. [*Latin summary of Siberian history c. 1680. Extr. fr.* Отечеств. Записокъ 1849]. 8°. [St. Petersb. 1848 ?]
" " Изд. И. Археографич. коммиссіи. la8°. С.-П. 1907
Сибирь ея соврем. состояніе &c.: сборникъ статей, *see* MELNIK (I. S.), *ed.*
East coasts of Korea & S. & Sea of Okhotsk pilot, & Suppl. 7, 1913–22, *see* ADMIRALTY.
Hdbk. (A) of S. & Arctic Russia, 1920, *see* ADMIRALTY: NAVAL INTELL. DIV.

Siberus (Urban Gottfried). De Caesareae Palaestinae episcopis. [P2742]. s4°. Lipsiae. [1734]
Hist. melodorum Eccl. Graec. eorumque theol. poet. [P427]. s4°. [Lipsiae.] 1714

Sibir, *see* SIBERIA.

Sibiryakov (Vladimir Dmitrievich Vilensky-), *see* VILENSKY-SIBIRYAKOV.

Sibly (Thomas Franklin). Iron ores &c., *see* GEOLOG. SURVEY OF ENG. &c. Spec. rep. on min. resources, 10, 1919.

Sibmacher (Johann) [SIEBMACHER]. J. Siebmacher's grosses u. allg. Wappenbuch in Verbindung mit Mehreren. Neu hrsg., mit hist. &c. Notizen v. O. T. v. Hefner. B1–7iii [*in progr.*] 4°. Nürnberg. 1856–1925
Each Band is in var. parts. Contents as under. The missing parts are not yet publ.
Band A.: Gesch. d. Heraldik: bearbt. v. G. A. Seyler, 1885.
B1, Abthlg. 1, [T1], Wappen d. Souveraine d. deut. Bundesstaaten; v. O. T. v. Hefner.

Sibmacher (Johann) [*continued*].
J. S.'s gr. &c. Wappenbuch [*continued*].
B1, Abthlg. 1, T2–4, Wappen d. deut. Souveraine u. Lande, N. F.; v. G. A. Seyler.
" 2, Wappen d. ausserdeut. Souveraine u. Staaten; v. O. T. v. Hefner.
" 3, Reihe 1, Mediat. Fürstengeschlechter in Deut.; v. O. T. v. Hefner &c.
" " " 2, Erlaucht. Grafengeschlechter in Deut.; durch A. M. F. Gritzner.
" " " 3, A, Fürsten d. H. Röm. Reiches, M–Z; v. M. Gritzner.
" " " " B, Die durch deut. Bundesfürsten in d. Fürstenstand erhob. Geschlechter; v. M. Gritzner.
" " " " C, Europ. Fürstengeschlechter nicht Röm.-Kaiserl. &c. Extraction; v. M. Gritzner.
" 4, Städtewappen; v. O. T. Hefner &c., 2B.
" 5, Reihe 1, Bisthümer; v. G. A. Seyler.
" " " 2, Klöster; v. G. A. Seyler.
" 6, Flaggen; v. A. M. Gritzner.
" 7, Berufswappen; v. G. A. Seyler.
" 8, Siegel d. deut. Universitäten &c.; v. E. Gritzner &c. [*b. w.* Abthlg. 7].
B2, Abthlg. 1, Adel d. König. Bayern; v. O. T. v. Hefner.
" 2, Adel d. Herzog. Braunschweig; v. A. M. Hildebrandt.
" 3, Adel d. König. Sachsen; v. O. T. v. Hefner. [*b. w.* 2.]
" 4, Wappen d. Schwarzburger u. Waldecker Adels; v. O. T. v. Hefner. [*b. w.* 2.]
" 5, Wappen d. Württemberger Adels; v. O. T. v. Hefner.
" 6, Adel in Baden, nebst Anhang &c.; v. C. A. Frhr. v. Grass. [*b. w.* 5.]
" 7, Wappen d. Nassauer Adels; v. O. T. v. Hefner [*b. w.* 5.]
" 8, Adel d. freien Stadt Frankfurt; v. O. T. v. Hefner. [*b. w.* 5.]
" 9, Hannöver. Adel; v. A. M. Hildebrandt. [*b. w.* 5.]
" 10, Adel d. Elsass; v. M. Gritzner.
" 11, Adel Deut.-Lothringens; v. M. F. A. Gritzner. [*b. w.* 10.]
B3, Abthlg. 1, [B1], Adel d. König. Preussen; v. O. T. v. Hefner.
" " B2, Preuss. Adel: Frhrn. u. Grafen; v. G. A. v. Mülverstedt.
" 2, [B1], Blühende Adel d. König. Preussen: Edelleute A–L; v. O. T. Hefner &c.
" " B2, Preuss. Adel: Edelleute, Nachträge &c.; v. G. A. v. Mülverstedt. [*b. w.* Abthlg. 1, B2.]
" 3, Adel d. freien Städte Hamburg, Bremen u. Lübeck; v. M. Gritzner.
" 4, Adel d. Kurfürsten., Grossherzog. &c. Hessen; v. O. T. v. Hefner. [*b. w.* 3.]
" 5, Adel d. Grossherzog. Oldenburg; v. M. F. A. Gritzner. [*b. w.* 3.]
" 6, Wappen d. Mecklenburger Adels; v. O. T. v. Hefner.
" 7, Adel d. Herzog. Anhalt; v. A. M. Hildebrandt. [*b. w.* 6.]
" 8, Blühende Adel d. Herzog. Schleswig-Holstein-Lauenburg; v. M. F. A. Gritzner. [*b. w.* 6.]
" 9, Luxemburg. Adel; v. M. Gritzner. [*b. w.* 6.]
" 10, Adel d. Fürsten. Lippe u. Schaumburg-Lippe; v. M. F. A. Gritzner. [*b. w.* 6.]
" 11, Adel d. russ. Ostseeprovinzen; v. M. Gritzner, 2T.
B4, Abthlg. 1, Adel d. gefürsteten Grafschaft Tirol; v. O. T. v. Hefner.
" 2, Adel d. Herzog. Krain u. d. Grafschaften Görz u. Gradiska; v. O. T. v. Hefner. [*b. w.* 1.]
" 3, Adel d. König. Dalmatien &c.; v. C. G. F. H. v. Rosenfeld. [*b. w.* 1.]
" 4, [2T], Niederösterreich. Adel, A–R, v. J. E. Kirnbauer v. Erzstätt, S–Z, v. J. B. Witting.
" 5, Oberoesterreich. Adel; v. Alois, Frhr. v. Starkenfels &c.
" 6, Salzburg. Adel; v. M. M. Edlen v. Weittenhiller.
" 8, Kärntner Adel; v. A. M. Hildebrandt.
" 9, Böhm. Adel; v. R. J. Gf. Meraviglia.
" 10, Mähr. Adel; v. H. E. v. Kadich &c.
" 11, Adel v. oesterr. Schlesien; v. K. Blažek.
" 12, Adel v. Siebenbürgen; v. C. R. v. Reichenau.
" 13, Adel v. Kroatien u. Slavonien; v. I. v. Bojnicic &c.
" 14, Adel v. Galizien, Lodomerien u. d. Bukowina; v. F. Heyer v. Rosenfeld.
" 15, Adel v. Ungarn &c.; v. G. v. Csergheö [*b. in* 2v]: & Suppl.; v. G. v. C. u. J. v. Csoma.
B5, Abthlg. 1–12, Bürgerl. Wappen. [*var. edd.*]
B6, Abthlg. 1, Abgestorbener bayer. Adel; v. G. A. Seyler, 3T.
" 2, " württemberg. Adel; v. G. A. Seyler.
" 4, " preuss. Adel; v. G. A. Mülverstedt.

Sibmacher (Johann) [*continued*].
J. S.'s gr. &c. Wappenbuch [*continued*].
B6, Abthlg. 5, Abgestorbene Adel d. Prov. u Mark Brandenburg; v. G. A. v. Mülverstedt.
„ 6, Ausgestorbener preuss. Adel, Prov. Sachsen; v. G. A. v. Mülverstedt. [*b. w.* Abthlg. 5.]
„ 7, Abgestorbene nassau. Adel; v. H. v. Goeckingk.
„ 8, Abgestorbene Adel d. preuss. Prov. Schlesien; v. C. Blažek, 3T. [T1, *b. w.* Abthlg. 7. 2 & 3 *b. in* 1v.]
„ 9, Ausgestorbener preuss. Adel, Prov. Pommern; v. G. A. v. Mülverstedt.
„ 10, Ausgestorbener meklenburg. Adel; v. G. A. Mülverstedt.
„ 11, „ anhalt. Adel; v. G. A. v. Mülverstedt. [*b. w.* 10.]
„ 12, „ Adel d. saechs. Herzogthümer; v. G. A. Mülverstedt. [*b. w.* 10.]
„ 13, „ Adel d. Fürsten. Schwarzburg &c.; v. G. A. v. Mülverstedt. [*b. w.* 10.]
B7, Abthlg. 1, Ergänzungsband, enthalt. d. Nachträge &c. zu d. Staatenwappen v. Russland u. Baden &c.; v. O. T. v. Hefner.
„ 2, Ergänzungsband, Preuss. Grafen u. Freiherren; v. C. Blažek. [*b. w.* 1.]
„ 3, Ausgestorbener preuss. Adel, Prov. Ost-u. Westpreussen, Suppl.; v. G. A. Mülverstedt. [*b. w.* 1.]
„ „ ....Index. [*MS.*] fol. 2v. [1909]
see HEFNER (O. T. v.) Grund-Saeze d. Wappenkunst, 1855.

Sibona (Mario). Genova attraverso i secoli. 8º. Genova. [1925]

Siborne (William). Hist. of the war in France & Belgium, 1815. 3rd & rev. ed., w. remarks upon Gleig's "Story of Waterloo." 8º. 1848

Sibour (M. Augustin D.), *bp. of Digne, abp. of Paris, see* BOUCHARDON (M. P. G.) L'assassinat de l'archévêque, 1926.

Sibree (James), *missionary.* Fifty years in Madagascar: personal exper. of mission life. 8º. [1924]

Sibree (John) & M. Caston. Independency in Warwickshire; hist., cont. biog. notices &c. 8º. 1855

Sibylla [*von Cleve*], *wife of John Frederick I, elector of Saxony, 1512–54.* Gebetbuch d. Herzogin S.; unters. u. erläut. v. H. Reiners, *see* MÜNCHEN. Miniaturen; hrsg. G. Leidinger, H7, 1924.

Sibylline Oracles. Fragm. librorum Sibyllin. quæ apud Lactantium reperiuntur. Ed. C. L. Struve. [*Progr.*] 8º. Regiomonti. 1817

Sicard (*l'abbé*) [†CUCURRON-SICARD (ROCH AMBROISE)], *see* MÉMOIRES sur les journées de sept. 1792, par S. &c.; avec notes par F. Barrière, 1881.

Sicard (*l'abbé* **Augustin**). Le clergé de France pend. la Révol. t2, La lutte relig. 8º. 1927

Sich (Alexander Ernest), *see* HILL (*Sir* N.) &c. War & insurance, 1927.

Sichardus (Johannes), *see* LEHMANN (P.) J. S., u. d. v. ihm benutzt. Bibliotheken u. Hss., 1911.

Sichart (Emma v.) Prakt. Kostümkunde: nach C. Köhler, bearb. v. E. v. S. 2 Halbb. [*pagin. contin.*] s8º. München. 1926

Sichel (Walter). Sands of time: recoll. &c. 8º. 1923
Types & characters. 8º. [1925]

Sichem (Christoffel van), *the younger?*. De Kindsheyd onses Heeren Iesu Christi. Gesneden door C. v. S. s8º. *n.p.* 1617

Sichevsky (—). Историч. записка о китайской границѣ, составл. С. въ 1846г. Сообщаетъ В. Н. Басшнъ. Изд. Имп. Общ. Ист. при Москов Унив. la8º. Москва. 1875

Sicilia. I diplomi greci ed arabi di S., v1, 1868, *see* CUSA (S.)
*S. (La) in prospettiva, 1709, *see* MASSA (G. A.)

Siciliano. Parlamento siciliano. Per cura di L. Genuardi. [R. Accad. dei Lincei.] v1, p1, 1034–1282. la8º. Bologna. 1924

Sickel (Theodor v.) Erläuter. zu d. Diplomen Otto III. [*Extr. f.* Inst. f. österr. Gesch., Mitthlg. 12. P2729]. 8º. [1891]
G. Waitz u. T. S.: Briefwechsel; *ed.* W. Erben, *see* KÖNIGL. GESELLS. D. W. ZU GÖTT., Nachr., 1926.

Sickingen (Franz von). Eyn Sendbrieff so F. v. S. seynem Schweher, dem Edlen Diethern vō Henschuchssheym tzu geschickt halt. Missive H. von Cronenberg an F. v. S. [*Decor. border to tp.* P2539]. s4º. Wittemberg. 1522

Sictor (Jan), *Rokycansky, 1593–1652, see* YOUNG (R. F.) Czech humanist in London: J. S. R., 1926; *& Czech tr.,* 1926.

Siddhi-Kûr, *see* GOLSTUNSKY (K. F.) Крит. замѣчанія на изд. Юльга: "Die Märchen d. S.-K.," 1867.

Siddonius (Johannes). Confessionis Calvinianorum in colloquio Thoruniensi anno 1645 exhib. artic. IV antithes. VI de Divina nostri ad vitam æternam prædestinatione. s4º. *n.p.* 1655

Siddons (Henry). Time's a tell-tale, *see* †INCHBALD (*Mrs.* E.) Mod. theatre, v10, 1811.

Sidersky (David). Etude sur la chronol. assyro-babylon., *see* ACAD. DES INSCR. Mém., s1, t13i, 1923.

Sidgwick (*Mrs.* **Alfred**) [CECILY W. SIDGWICK; *ps. Mrs.* ANDREW DEAN].
The bride's prelude. s8º. [1927]
Humming bird. s8º. [1925]
Law & outlaw. s8º. [1921]
London mixture. s8º. [1924]
None-go-by. s8º. [1923]
Sack & sugar. s8º. [1926]
Victorian. s8º. [1922]

Sidgwick (*Mrs.* **Eleanor Mildred**). Exam. &c. of cases of telepathy pr. in Journ. of Soc. for Psychical Research since publ. of "Phantasms of the living" by Gurney &c. [1886–1920], *see* SOC. FOR PSYCHICAL RESEARCH. Proc., v32, 1923.

Sidgwick (Ethel). Hatchways. s8º. [1916]
Restoration. s8º. 1923

Sidler (Godefroy), *see* ARIANA, *Musée.* Cat. offic., par G. S., 1905.

Sidney, *the family of, see* HIST. MSS. COMM. Rep. on MSS. at Penshurst Place, v1, 1925.

Sidney (Edwin). The life of Sir Richard Hill, Bt., M.P. 8º. 1839
The life of the Rev. S. Walker of Truro. 2nd ed. rev. 8º. 1838

Sidney (*Sir* **Philip**).
Apologie for poetry, 1595. Ed. E. Arber. s8º. 1868
Corresp. of P. S. & H. Languet. Ed. W. A. Bradley. 8º. Boston, *Merrymount Press.* 1912
The countesse of Pembrokes Arcadia. 8th time publ. w. new add. *&* Suppl. of a defect by Sir W. A., added a 6th booke by R. B. [*Imperf.*] sm. fol. 1633
„ „ 9th time publ. [*made up copy,* Suppl. by J. Johnstoun *wanting*]. fol. 1638
„ „ orig. version. Ed. A. Feuillerat. [Camb. Eng. classics]. 8º. C. 1926
The defence of poesie—Letter to Q. Elizabeth—Defence of Leicester. Ed. G. E. Woodberry. 8º. Boston, *Merrymount Press.* 1908
„ „ Polit. discourses — Corresp. — Translations. Ed. A. Feuillerat. [Camb. Eng. classics]. 8º. C. 1923
Last part of the Countesse of Pembroke's Arcadia—Astrophel & Stella, & o. p., the lady of May. Ed. A. Feuillerat. [Camb. Eng. classics]. s8º. C. 1922
Valour anatomized in a fancie, 1581, *see* COTTON (*Sir* R. B.) Cottoni posthuma, 1651; 1672.
see HARMAN (E. G.) The Ctsse. of Pembrokes Arcadia exam. & discussed, 1924.

Sido [SYDO]. Epistola (c. 1196), *see* HELMOLDUS. Cron. Slav.; ed. 2ª; rec. B. Schmeidler, 1909.

Sidonia von Bork, d. Klosterhexe, 2B, 1924, *see* MEINHOLD (J. W.)

Sidorov (N. P.), *see* BRODSKY (N. L.), N. M. MENDELSON & N. P. S. Хрестоматия, ч1–3, 1922–23.

Sieber (Siegfried).
J. M. von Loen, Goethe's Grossoheim (1694–1776). s8º. L. 1922

Siebert (Benno von). Diplomat. Aktenstücke z. Gesch. d. Ententepolitik d. Vorkriegsjahre. Hrsgb. v. B. v. S. 8º. 1921
Einkreisung? [P2689]. la8º. L. 1922
Entente diplomacy & the world: matrix of hist. of Europe, 1909–14. Tr. f. orig. texts by B. de S. Ed. &c. G. A. Schreiner. 8º. [1923]
see GEBHARDT (A.) Polit. Gespr., 5, Was enthüllt v. S. in London?, 1921.

Siebert (Carl).
Verzeichnis d. Werke d. Malers G. Cornelius. la8º. Str. 1914

Siebmacher (Johann), *see* SIBMACHER (J.)

Siebs (Theodor), *see* UNWERTH (W. v.) & T. S. Gesch. d. deut. Lit. bis z. Mitte d. 11ten Jhdts., 1920.

Siegfried (André).
America comes of age. Tr. H. H. & D. Hemming. 8º. [1927]
L'Angleterre d'aujourd'hui: s. évol. écon. & polit. s8º. 1924
Les Etats-Unis d'aujourd'hui. 3e éd. 8º. 1927

Sieglin (Ernst von). Expedition E. v. S. Ausgrabungen in Alexandria, unter Leitung v. T. Schreiber. Hrsg. v. E. v. S. B1, 2iii [*no more publ.*] fol. L. 1908–13
1, Die Nekropole v. Kôm-esch-Schukâfa; hrsg. v. E. v. S., bearb. v. T. S. *w. sep. Tafelband.*
2iii, Die griech.-ägypt. Samml. E. v. S., T3, Die Gefässe in Stein u. Ton-Knochenschnitzereien; v. R. Pagenstecher.

Siegling (W.), *see* BAINES (*Sir* J. A.) Ethnography; w. list of wks. on Ind. e. by W. S., 1912.

Siemens (Georg v.), *see* HELFFERICH (C.) G. v. S., 3B, 1921–23.

Siena [*see also* SENESE]. Altfranz. Liederhs. v. S.; ed. G. Steffens, *see* ARCHIV F. D. ST. D. NEU. SPR., B88, 1892.

Sienes. Meister d. trecento in d. Gemäldegalerie zu S., 1907, *see* JACOBSEN (E.)

Siena (Lodovico).
Storia d. città di Sinigaglia &c. 8°. Sinigaglia. 1746

Sienkiewicz (Henryk), *see* GARDNER (M. M.) The patriot novelist of Poland, H. S., 1926.

Sieper (Ernst). Die altenglische Elegie. 8°. Str. 1915
Die Kultur d. mod. England in Einzeldarstellungen. Hrsg. v. E. S. B1–6. 8°. München. 1912–14
see BERLEPSCH-VALENDÀS (H. E. v.) Die Gartenstadtbewegung in Eng., 1912. [3.]
„ SCHULTZE (E.) Die geistige Hebung d. Volksmassen in Eng., 1912. [1.]
„ —— Volksbildung u. Volkswohlfahrt in Eng., 1912. [2.]
„ SINGER (H. W.) Der Prae-Raphaelitismus in Eng., 1912. [4.]
„ STAHL (E. L.) Das engl. Theater im 19. Jhdt., 1914. [5.]
„ WALTER (H. A.) Die neuere engl. Sozialpolitik, 1914. [6.]

Sierk (Hartich) [SYRCK]. Die Bauernchronik d. H. S. (1615–64). Mit Einltg. &c. hrsg. v. O. Mensing. s8°. Flensburg. 1925

Sieroszewski (Wacław).
Jos. Pilsudski. [P2503]. s8°. Varsovie. 1921

Sierra (Lorenzo), *see* ALCALDE DEL RIO (H.), H. BREUIL & L. S. Les cavernes de la rég. Cantabrique, 1911.

Sierra Leone. An acc. of the colony of S. L. f. its establ. in 1793, report to the proprietors. [*2 tps.*] 8°. 1795

Sierra y Mariscal (Francisco de). Idéas geraes sobre a revol. do Brazil &c. [P2876]. la8°. Rio de Janeiro. 1926

Sieveking (Heinrich). Grundzüge d. neu. Wirtschaftsgesch. v. 17. Jhdt. b. z. Gegenwart, 3te A., 1921, *see* GRUNDR. D. GESCHICHTSWISS.; Meister, 2ii, 1921.

Sieveking (Johannes). Hermeneut. Reliefstudien, *see* KÖNIGL. AKAD. D. W. ZU MÜNCHEN. Phil. Kl., Sitz., 1920.
Röm. Soldatenrelief, *see* KÖNIGL. AKAD. D. W. ZU MÜNCHEN. Phil. Kl., Sitz., 1919.

Sieveking (L. de Giberne). Stampede. s8°. *Cayme Press.* 1924

Sievers (Eduard). Altslaw. ē u. ja, *see* KÖNIGL.-SÄCHS. GESELLS. Berichte, B77, 1925.
Die altslaw. Verstexte v. Kiew u. Freising, im Verein m. G. Gerullis u. M. Vasmer hrsg. v. E. S., *see* KÖNIGL.-SÄCHS. GESELLS. Ber., B76, 1925.
Deut. Sagversdichtungen des 9.–11. Jhdts., nebst e. Anhang: die gotische Bergpredigt. [Germ. Bibl.; hrsg. W. Streitberg, II, 6]. 8°. Heidelberg. 1924
see IGOR, *Prince.* Das Igorlied; bearb. v. E. S., 1926.

Sifre, *Midrash, see* KITTEL (G.) S. zu Deuteronomium, L. 1, 1922.

Siga (Peter Augustin, *bp. of***),** *see* BAINES (P. A.)

Sigebertus, *Gemblacensis.* Des cript. eccl., *see* LE MIRE (A.) Bibl. eccl., 1639.

Sigel (Georg). Explan. prior. 5 cap. primi Evang. Joannis vers., de divinitate J. C., &c. Thesibus, resp. J. Wolckero. [P2612]. s4°. Altorphii. [1587]

Siger, *v. Brabant.* Neuaufgefund. Quaestionen Sigers z. d. Werken d. Aristoteles, hrsg. M. Grabmann, *see* EHRLE (F.) Miscell., v1, 1924.
see GRABMANN (M.) Neu aufgef. Werke d. S. v. B. &c., 1924.

Sigerist (Henry E.)
see BRUNSCHWIG (H.) Book of cirurgia, 1497, w. study by H. E. S., 1923.
„ MONUMENTA medica; under the gen. ed. of H. E. S., v1, 1924.

Sigerson (George), *see* SEDULIUS (C.) The Easter song; w. intr., verse-tr. &c., by G. S., 1922.

Sighinolfi (Lino). La signoria di Giov. da Oleggio in Bologna, 1355–60. 8°. Bologna. 1905
L'architettura Bentivolesca in Bologna e il Palazzo del Podestà. 8°. Bologna. 1909

Sigismund, *emperor.*
see KAGELMACHER (E.) F. M. Visconti u. König S., 1413–31, 1885.
„ SAUERBREI (M.) Die ital. Politik K. S. bis z. Beginn d. Constanzer Concils, 1410–15, 1893.

Signac (Paul). Jongkind (1819–91). la8°. [1927]

Signer (Paul). Ernst Toller, e. Studie. s8°. 1924

Signet Library, *see* SOCIETY OF WRITERS TO THE SIGNET.

Signorelli (Luca).
see VENTURI (A.) L. S., 1922.
„ —— L. S. interprete di Dante, 1921.

Sigogne (*Sieur* **de).** Œuvres satyriques. Avec un discours prélim. &c., par F. Fleuret & L. Perceau. 8°. 1920

Sigonius (Carolus) [†SIGONIO (CAROLO)]. De antiquo jure populi Romani libri 11. Acc. Animadvers. J. G. Graevii. Nova diss. Thomasiana de usu vario studii antiq. &c. 2t *in* 1v. s8°. Lipsiae. 1715
De episcopis Bonon. libri 5. 8°. Bononiae. 1586
De republica Hebreorum. s8°. Medioburgi. 1678

Sigston (James). Mem. of William Bramwell. s8°. [1839]

Sigwart (Johann Georg), *see* TÜBINGEN, UNIV. Jubilæum in mem. liberat. doct. evang. [*8 orat. by J. G. S. & others*], 1617.

Šihāb ad-Dīn Aḥmad bin Mājid, *see* IBN MĀJID.

Sihler (Ernest Gottlieb). From Augustus to Augustine: contact & conflict of classic paganism & Xty. 8°. C. 1923

Sikes (Edward Ernest). Roman poetry. s8°. [1923]

Silas (Ellis). A primitive Arcadia: impress. of an artist in Papua. 8°. [1926]

Silberer (Herbert). Problems of mysticism & its symbolism. Tr. S. E. Jelliffe. 8°. N.Y. 1917

Silbernagel (Endres). *For all books on* "The Master E. S." [*sometimes identified w. E. S.*], *see* S. (*The Master* E.)

Silberrad (Una L.)
Blackstones. s8°. [1926]
The book of Sanchia Stapleton. s8°. [1927]
The honest man. s8°. [1922]
Jim Robinson. s8°. [1920]
Joe, a simple soul. s8°. [1924]
The letters of Jean Armiter. s8°. [1923]
The success of Mark Wyngate. s8°. Westminster. 1902
The vow of Micah Jordan. s8°. [1925]

Silberstein (Lodovico) [*ps.* LEO GILBERT]. Relativitätsprinzip, d. jüng. Modenarrheit d. Wiss. 8°. Brackwede i. W. 1914
The theory of relativity. 2nd ed. enl. 8°. 1924

Sild (Olaf). Das altchristl. Martyrium in Berücksicht. d. rechtl. Grundlage d. Christenverfolgung. la8°. Dorpat. 1920

Siler (*Lt.-Col.* **Joseph F.),** *see* UNITED STATES: ARMY. Med. Dept. of U.S. army in the World War, v9, Communicable & o. diseases, by S., 1928.

Silesia. *The economic value of Upper S. for Poland & Germany respectively. [P2464]. 8°. [1920]

Silesius (Angelus), *see* SCHEFFLER (J.)

***Siliad** (The) or the siege of the seats, *n.d.*, *see* DOWTY (A. A.) & S. O. BEETON.

Silingardi (Gasparo), *bp. of Modena; 1537–1607.* Les négociations du nonce S. rel. à la publ. du Co. de Trente en France, 1599–1601. Doc. Thèse par V. Martin. la8°. 1919

Sillem (C. H. Wilhelm). Die Einführung d. Reformation in Hamburg. [Verein f. Ref.-gesch. Schr., Jhrg. 4, Nr. 16]. 8°. Halle. 1886

Sillib (Rudolf) & C. Lohmeyer. Heidelberg. s8°. L. [1927]

Sillig (David). De synagogis vet. Ebraeorum. Præs. C. Bornitius. [P2587]. s4°. Wittebergae. 1650

Šilović (Slade). Anarhija u Trogiru, 1797, *see* BULLETTINO DI ARCH. &C. DALM., 37, Suppl., 1914.

Siltzer (Frank). Newmarket: its sport & personalities. 8°. 1923
Story of Brit. sporting prints. 8°. [1925]

Silva, *the family of, see* SALAZAR Y CASTRO (L. DE). Hist. geneal. de la casa de Silva, 2p, 1685.

Silva (Antonio Telles da), *marq. de Resende, see* RESENDE (A. T. DA S., *marq.* DE).

Silva (Giovanni Angela). Relaz. dell' ingresso d. Infanta Caterina d'Austria in Torino, 10 agosto 1585; pubbl. da A. Angelucci, con note &c., *see* REGIA DEP. DI STORIA PATRIA. Misc., t15, 1874.

Silva (José Asuncion), *1865–96, see* KING (G. G.) A citizen of the twilight: J. A. S., 1921.

Silva (Pietro). Chi e Gaetano Salvemini. [P2431]. s8°. 1919

Silva Alvarez de Toledo (María del Pilar Teresa Cayetana de), *duquesa de Alba, see* ALBA.

Silvain (Eugène). Frédérick Lemaître. 8°. 1926

Silva Rosa (J. S. da). Gesch. d. Portugeesche Joden te Amsterdam, 1593–1925. 8°. A. 1925

Silva y Figueroa (Garcia de). L'ambassade de G. de Silva Figveroa en Perse [1617–24]. Tr. de l'Espagnol par M. de Wicqfort. s4°. 1667

Silveira (João de Queiroz da), *see* QUEIROZ DA SILVEIRA.

Silveira (Miguel de) [SILVEYRA].
El Macabeo. Poema heroyco. n. impr. s8°. 1731

Silver treasury of English lyrics, *see* WELBY (T. E.)

Silvestre (Charles). Aimée Villard, fille de France. s8°. [1924]
Prodige du cœur. s8°. [1926]

Silvestro (Tommaso di). Diario (1482–1514), *see* MURATORI (L. A.) Rerum Ital. scr., t15v, 1920.

Silveyra (Miguel de), *see* SILVEIRA (M. DE).

Sim (Frances Mary) [*Mrs.* W. A. SIM]. Robert Browning, poet & philosopher, 1850–89. 8º. [1923]
Robert Browning, the poet & the man, 1833–46. 8º. [1923]
Simancas (Jacobus) [DIDACUS DE S.], *bp.* Enchiridion judicum violatæ religionis, ad extirpandas hæreses. Acc. Annotat. in Zanchinum & De dignitate episcopali. s8º. Antverpiæ. 1573
Simcoe (*Lt.-Governor* **John Graves**). Corr. of S., w. allied docs. rel. to h. admin. of govt. of Upper Canada. Coll. & ed. by Brig.-Gen. E. A. Cruikshank. [Ontario Hist. Soc.] 2v. la8º. Toronto. 1923–24
1, 1789–93. 2, 1793–94.
Sime (A. H. Moncur).
Shakespeare: h. music & song. s8º. [1917]
Simeon, *bp. in Persia* [SHMAVON]. [Life of S. & Oration on Eastern martyrs (? by Ephraim). *In Armenian.* Soferq Hayk., v20]. s8º. i Venetik. 1854
Simeon, *Stylites, Saint, the elder.*
see BALL (H.) Byzantin. Christentum: 3 Heiligenleben [*i.e.* S. &c.], 1923.
,, DELEHAYE (H.) Saints stylites, 1923.
,, MARUKAS, *Saint, bp. of Tagrit.* Acta Sanctorum martyrum. Acc. Acta S. Simeonis Stylitae &c., 1748.
,, †UHLEMANN (F.) Symeon d. erste Säulenheilige in Syrien, u. s. Einfluss auf d. Verbreitung d. Christenthums im Orient, 1846.
Simeon, *Stylites, the younger, see* DELEHAYE (H.) Saints stylites, 1923.
Simeon (Charles). Memorial sketches of the Rev. D. Brown, w. sermons [& extr. f. journal &c.] 8º. 1816
Simeoni (Gabriele) [SYMEONI]. Le satire alla Berniesca con un elegia sopra alla morte del re Francesco primo &c. 8º. [Turino]. 1549
Simigianus (Ambrosius). Hist. rer. Ungar. & Transsilv., 1440–1606. [Script. rer. Transsilvan., adcur. I. C. Eder & J. B. de Mildenberg, t2i, ii]. 2v. 4º. Cibinii. 1800–1840
Simionescu (Ioan). Studii geolog. & paleont. din Dobrogea, *see* ACADEMIA ROMÂNA. Publ. Fond. V. Adamachi, t4, 5, 1910–13.
Simler (Josias). De æterno Dei Filio Domino & Servatore nostro J. C. & de Spiritu Sancto adv. Antitrinitarios &c. Acc. H. Bullinger, Praef. s8º. Tiguri. 1582
Simmel (Ernst), *see* FERENCZI (S.) Psycho-analysis & the war neuroses; by S. F., E. S. &c., 1921.
Simmel (Georg). Philos. Kultur. Gesammelte Essais. 3e A. 8º. Potsdam. [1923]
Rembrandt: e. kunstphilos. Versuch. 2e A. 8º. L. 1919
Simmonds (Thomas C.)
The art of modelling in clay & wax. 2nd ed. s8º. *n.d.*
Simmonite (William Joseph). Complete arcana of astral philosophy. n. ed. by J. Story. 8º. 1890
Simmons (Lucretia van Tuyl). Goethe's lyric poems in Eng. tr. prior to 1860. [Univ. of Wisconsin]. 8º. Madison. 1919
Simmons (Thomas Frederick), *deputy judge advocate.* The constitution & practice of Courts Martial. 7th ed. cont. by T. F. S., junr. 8º. 1875
Simms (Henry), *called Gentleman Harry.* The life of H. S.; narr. of robberies &c. Wr. by himself. [P2828]. s8º. 1747
Simms (William Gilmore).
*Beauchampe: or, the Kentucky tragedy. 8º. 1843
Simnett (W. E.) Books & reading. s8º. [1926]
Simon, *Magus.* *The anatomy of S. M., or, the sin of simony laid open. s8º. 1700
see HELWIG (J. A.) Diss. de S. M., 1711.
,, MEAD (G. R. S.) S. Magus, 1892.
Simon, *Sir, ps., see* PARLIAMENT, *Anon. Works.* A vindication of the last P., 1711.
Simon, *of Sudbury, abp. of Canterbury, see* SUDBURY (SIMON *of*).
Simon (*Prof.*) Sowjet-Russland. s8º. [1925]
Simon (André Louis). The blood of the grape: wine trade text book. 8º. [1920]
Bottlescrew days: wine drinking in Eng. dur. 18th cent. 8º. 1926
Simon (Ernest Darwin). A city council from within. Pref. by G. Wallas. 8º. 1926
The inheritance of riches. [P2848]. 8º. 1925
—— **& M. Fitzgerald.**
The smokeless city. Pref. by Ld. Newton. 8º. 1922

Simon (Gustave M. S. C.) L'enfance de V. Hugo avec des fragm. d' " Irtamène " & de ses prem. poésies inéd. s8º. 1904
Hist. d'une collaboration: Alexandre Dumas & Auguste Maquet. s8º. 1919
La vie d'une femme [Mme. V. Hugo]. s8º. 1914
Simon (Henri), *engraver.*
Armorial gén. de l'empire française. t1. fol. 1812
Simon (James), *see* BORCHARDT (L.) Der Porträtkopf d. Königin Teje im Besitz v. J. S. in Berlin, 1911.
Simon (Johann). Synopsis hist. eccl. sec. 18. loco supplem. ad J. A. Turrettini compend. [*b. w.* Baier (J. W.) Compend., 1750]. s8º. Halae Magdeb. 1750
Simon (*Rt. Hon. Sir* **John**). 3 speeches on the General Strike, w. intr. diary of events &c. 8º. 1926
Simon (John Smith).
John Wesley & the advance of Methodism. la8º. [1925]
Simon (Pedro). Noticias hist. de las conquistas de tierra firme en las Indias Occident. 3p [*in* 5t. t1 *wanting*]. 8º. Bogota. 1891–92
Simon (Richard), *Hebraist.* Crit. enquiries into the var. eds. of the Bible, w. animadv. upon tr. of I. Vossius conc. Sybils [*w. sep. tp.*] I. Vossius conc. the Oracles of the Sybils. Wr. orig. in Lat., tr. by N. S. [Transl. address to the reader is signed M. R.] s4º. 1684
Hist. crit. Vet. Test. In Lat. versa a N. A. de Versé. [*2 pagins.*] s4º. Parisiis. 1681
see LE CLERC (J.) Sentimens sur l'Hist. crit. du Vieux Test. par R. S., 1685.
,, MAJUS (J. H.) Repet. examen Hist. crit. textus N.T. a R. S. &c., 1708.
Simon (Th.), *see* TERMAN (L. M.) Measurement of intelligence: Stanford revision of Binet-S. intell. scale, repr., 1922.
Simond (Émile). Hist. de la Troisième République, 1887–94 [1894–96, 1897–99, 1899–1906]. [t1–4]. 8º. 1913–22
Simonds (Cecil Barrow). Hints on milit. mapping. s8º. 1904
Simonds (Frank Herbert).
How Europe made peace without America. la8º. 1927
Simone (Luigi Giuseppe de). Architectonica. s8º. Lecce. 1879
Simonetti (Cesare), *da Fano.* Rime. 8º. Padova. 1579
Rime. s8º. Padoua. 1586
Rime scelte. 8º. Fano. 1831
Simonides, *of Ceos, the poet.*
see LYRA. Lyra Graeca; ed. & tr. by J. M. Edmonds, v2, S. &c., 1924.
,, SCHMID (C. H.) & H. C. G. WALZ: S., 1767.
Simonis (Johann), *prof. at Halle.* Arcanum formarum nominum Hebr. ling. [*b. w. h.* Onomasticum, 1741]. 2p *in* 1v. [*pagin. contin.*] s4º. Halae Magdeb. 1735
Onomasticum Novi Test. & libr. V T. Apocr. Acced. biga dissert. 8º. Halae Magdeb. 1762
Onomasticum Vet. Test. s4º. Halae Magdeb. 1741
Simonis (Josephus), *see* SIMONS (J.)
Simonius (Joannes). Triumphus secularis. Oratio: per minist. M. Lutheri liberat. eccl. [P483]. s4º. Rostochi. 1618
Simonov (Matvei Terentevich) [*ps.* NOMIS (M.)]
Українські приказки, прислівья &c.; спорудив М. Номис, 1864, *see* MARKOVICH (O. V.)
Simons (Joseph) [SIMONIS (J.)]
Zeno, tragoedia. s8º. Romae. 1648
Simons (Menno).
see LASCO (J. A). Def. verae &c. doct. de Christi incarnatione adv. M. S., 1545.
,, SCHYN (H.) Hist. Mennonitarum plenior deductio, 1729.
,, ZEIDLER (C. G.) Hist. M. &c., 1696.
Simons (Walther). Der Friedensvertrag u. s. finanziellen Folgen. [P2457]. 8º. 1920
Simonsfeld (Henry). Eine deut. Colonie zu Treviso im spät. M.-a. [Aus K. Bay. Akad. d. Wiss. Abhlg. III. Cl., 19. B. P2843]. 4º. München. 1890
Sulle scoperte d. R. Galli n. Cronaca Altinate. Risposta. [*Extr. fr.* Archivio Veneto, t35. P2835]. 8º. Venezia. 1888
Simons-Mees (Josina A.)
Atie's huwelijk. Tooneelspel. 3e dr. s8º. A. [1916]
Levensstroomingen. Tooneelspel. s8º. [A.] 1917
De veroveraar. Spel. 3e dr. s8º. A. *n.d.*
Simonson (George A.) Francesco Guardi (1712–93). [Estr. da Pro Cultura, Anno liii. P2841]. 8º. [1910]
Simowycz (Wassyl).
Prakt. Gram. d. ukraïn. Spr. s8º. Wien. [1921]
Simplicien (*le père*), *ps., see* LUCAS (PAUL).

Simplicissimus. Adv. of S., *var. ed. & tr.*, *see* GRIMMELSHAUSEN (H. J. C. v.)

Simplicissimus. Begründet v. A. Langen & T. T. Heine. 6. Jahrgang (April 1901–März 1902). fol. München. 1901–2

Simplicius, *of Cilicia*, *see* EPICTETUS. Morals, w. S. his comment; tr., 4th ed., 1721.

Simpson (Alex.), *consul in the Sandwich Isl.*, *see* FRENCH (W.) In Chancery: estate of W. F. & F. J. Greenway, in liquidation w. A. S., 1845.

Simpson (Bertram Lenox), *see* WEALE (B. L. P.), *ps.*

Simpson (Charles), *R.I.* El rodeo (1924). Intr. by R. B. Cunninghame Graham & descr. letterpress by the artist. 4°. 1925

Simpson (*Col.* **Charles Napier).** The eyes & ears of the artillery. Pref. by Sir W. G. Knox. s8°. 1905

Simpson (David), *minister of Christ Church, Macclesfield.* A plea for the deity of Jesus, & the doct. of the Trinity. Memoir of the a. by E. Parsons. 8°. 1812

Simpson (Evelyn M.)
A study of the prose works of John Donne. 8°. O. 1924

Simpson (F. Gerald) & R. C. Shaw. The purpose & date of the Vallum & its crossings. [Repr. f. Cumberland & Westmorland Antiq. Soc. Trans., n.s., v22]. [P2705]. 8°. Kendal. 1922

Simpson (Frederick Arthur). Louis Napoleon & the recovery of France, 1848–56. 8°. 1923

Simpson (George Clarke). Meteorology, 3v, *see* BRIT. ANTARCTIC EXPED., 1910–13, 1919–23.
Scott's Polar journey & the weather. Halley Lect., 1923. 8°. O. 1926

Simpson (Gertrude Sparrow) & W. S. Simpson.
Life & legend of S. Vedast. 8°. 1896

Simpson (Henry Cuthbert Connell Dunlop).
Manual of volunteer position Artillery. 2nd ed. s8°. 1890

Simpson (James Young), *b. 1873.* Landmarks in the struggle betw. science & relig. s8°. [1925]
Man & the attainment of immortality. 8°. [1922]
The spiritual interpret. of nature. n. ed. rev. &c. s8°. 1923

Simpson (*Sir* **John William),** *president of Roy. Inst. of Brit. Architects.* Essays & memorials. Pref. by H. Barnes. 8°. 1923
Paris rosemary for rememb. of bygone scenes &c. 8°. 1927
see WARD (W. H.) Archit of the Renaiss. in Fr., 2nd ed. rev., 1927.

Simpson (Joseph). Hist. of Newport Pagnell & neighbourhood. 8°. Newport Pagnell. 1868

Simpson (Matthew), *bp. of the Methodist Episc. Ch., 1811–84.* Cyclopædia of Methodism &c. Ed. M. S. rev. ed. la8°. Phila. 1880
see CROOKS (G. R.) Life of S., 1890; 1891.

Simpson (Melville W. Hilton-), *see* HILTON-SIMPSON (M. W.)

Simpson (Percy). Designs by I. Jones for masques & plays at Court: descr. cat. of drawings &c.; intr. & notes by P. S. &c., *see* WALPOLE SOC., v12, 1924.
The 1604 text of Marlowe's "Doctor Faustus," *see* ENGLISH ASSOC. Essays &c., v7, 1921.
see JONSON (B.) B. J.; ed. C. H. Herford & P. S., v1–3, 1925–27.

Simpson (Richard), *murderer.* The trial of R. S. for murder of h. mother, Aug. 1845. Repr. f. Westmorland Gazette. [P2828]. s8°. Kendal. 1845

Simpson (W. Douglas).
The historical St. Columba. la8°. Aberdeen. 1927
Origins of Xty. in Aberdeenshire. la8°. Aberdeen. 1925

Simpson (William), *R.I.; M.R.A.S.* The Jonah legend; suggestion of interpretation. 8°. 1899

Simpson (William John Sparrow).
Archbishop Bramhall. 8°. 1927
The Catholic conception of the Church. 8°. 1914
The diocesan synod. [P2488]. s8°. 1920

Simpson (William Sparrow), *see* SIMPSON (G. S.) & W. S. S. Life & legend of S. Vedast, 1896.

Simpson (William Overend), *1831–81*, *see* BUSH (J.), *ed.* W. O. S., early life &c., by S. Wray; mission life, by R. Stephenson, 1886.

Simrock (Carl Joseph). Deutsche Weihnachtslieder. s8°. L. 1859

Sims (George Robert). Mary Jane's memoirs. n. impr. s8°. 1913

Sims (*Rev.* **Thomas),** *see* PEYRAN (J. R.) Hist. defence of the Waldenses; w. intr. & app^{s}. by T. S., 1826.

Sims (*Rear-Adm.* **William Sowden),** *U.S. Navy.* The victory at sea. By Rear-Adm. S. in collab. w. B. J. Hendrick. 8°. 1920
" " ....[repr.] 8°. 1921

Simson (Robert), *M.D.* Sectionum conicarum libri 5. ed. 2^{a}, emend. & auctior. s4°. Edinburgi. 1750

Sîn. Ming sîn paó Kiân, *n.d.*, *see* MING.

Sinapius (Joannes). Adversus ignaviam, & sordes eorum qui literas humaniores negligunt aut cōtemnunt &c. declamatio. s8°. [Haganoæ, *J. Secerius.* 1530]

Sinarum. *Icon regia monarchæ Sinarum nunc regnantis, 1699, *see* BOUVET (J.)

Sincerus (Theophilus), *ps.*, *see* SCHWINDEL (GEORG JACOB).

Sinclair, *The family of*, *see* SAINT-CLAIR (R. W.) The Saint-Clairs of the Isles & th. Scot. successors of sirname S., 1898.

Sinclair (Bertha Muzzy), *wife of Bertrand W. S.*, *see* BOWER (B. M.)

Sinclair (Bertrand William). Burned bridges. s8°. [1920]

Sinclair (*Rt. Hon. Sir* **John),** *1st bart.; 1754–1835.* Diss. on authenticity of Ossian's poems, *see* OSSIAN. Poems in orig. Gaelic &c., v1, 1807.

Sinclair (Mary L.), *wife of J. E. Sinclair.* Windows of the parish ch. of the House of Commons. 6th ed. rev. [P2503]. s8°. [1906]

Sinclair (May).
The Allinghams. s8°. [1927]
Anne Severn & the Fieldings. s8°. [1922]
Arnold Waterlow, a life. 4th ed. s8°. [1924]
A cure of souls. s8°. [1924]
" " 2nd ed. s8°. [1924]
Far End. 4th ed. s8°. [1926]
The life & death of Harriett Frean. s8°. [1922]
Mr. Waddington of Wyck. s8°. [1921]
The new idealism. 8°. 1922
The rector of Wyck. s8°. [1925]
The romantic. s8°. [1920]
Uncanny stories. s8°. [1924]

Sinclair (Upton). The goose-step: st. of Amer. education. rev. ed. s8°. Pasadena, California. [1923]
Oil! A novel. [3rd pr.] s8°. [1927]

Sinclair-Cowan (Bertha Muzzy), *see* BOWER (B. M.)

Sindall (Robert Walter), *F.C.S.* Paper technology. 8°. 1906

Sindercomb (Miles) [SUNDERCOMBE; FISH]. The triall of M. S. f. conspiring agst. the life of the Lord Protector, Feb. 9, 1656, *see* *FURTHER (A) narr. of these times, 1658.

Sindral (Jacques). Attirance de la mort. s8°. 1924
Talleyrand. 6e éd. s8°. 1926
La ville éphémère. Roman. s8°. 1922

Sinenses [SINENSIUM]. *Acta causae rituum seu ceremon. Sinens., 1715, *see* ACTA.
*Hist. cultus Sinens. &c., 1700, *see* FATINELLI (G. G.), *ed.*

***Singaleesch** belydenis boekje, na kerken-ordre behoorlyk gerevideert. 2 druk door den vertalder. s8°. Colombo. 1742

Singapore. 100 yrs. of S., 1819–1919, 2v, 1921, *see* MAKEPEACE (W.), G. E. BROOKE &c., *edd.*

Singer (Charles).
Early Eng. magic & med., *see* BRIT. ACAD. Proc., v9, 1919–20.
The evolution of anatomy. Fitzpatrick lect. 8°. 1925
From magic to science. la8°. 1928
Greek biology & Gr. medicine. s8°. O. 1922
Short hist. of medicine. 8°. O. 1928
Studies in hist. & method of science. Ed. C. S. v2. la8°. O. 1921
2 *cont.*, Cole (F. J.) Hist. of anatomical injections.
Fahie (J. J.) Sci. works of Galileo, 1564–1642.
Hopstock (H.) Leonardo as anatomist; tr. E. A. Fleming.
Schiller (F. C. S.) Hypothesis.
Singer (C.) Greek biology & its rel. to rise of mod. b.
—— Steps leading to invention of first optical apparatus.
Steele (R. R.) R. Bacon & the state of sci. in 13th c. *& o. papers by var. a.*
see BEVAN (E. R.) & C. S., *edd.* The legacy of Israel, 1927.
" FASCICULO. Fasc. di medicina, 1493, w. intr. by C. S., 1925.
" SUDHOFF (C.) Essays on hist. of medicine; pres. to S. by Sir T. C. Allbutt &c.; ed. C. S. &c., 1924.

Singer (*Mrs.* **Dorothea Waley),** *see* UNION ACAD. INTERNAT. Cat. des mss. alchim. grecs, t3, Mss. des Iles Brit., décr. par D. W. S., 1924.

Singer (Hans Wolfgang). Jakob Christoffel Le Blon. [Sonderabdr. aus d. Mitth., Gesells. f. vervielfält. Kunst]. fol. Wien. 1901
Der Kupferstich. la8°. Bielefeld. 1922
Der Prae-Raphaelitismus in England. [Sieper (E.), *ed.* Kultur d. mod. Eng., B4]. 8°. München. 1912

Singer (Heinrich). Die Dekretalensammlung d. Bernardus Compostellanus antiquus, *see* KAIS. AKAD. D. WISS ZU WIEN. Sitzb. B171, 1914.
Neue Beitr. ü. d. Dekretalensamml. vor u. nach Bernhard v. Pavia, 1913, *see* KAIS. AKAD. D. WISS. ZU WIEN. Sitzb., B171, 1914.

Singer (Samuel). Arab. u. europ. Poesie im M.-a., *see* KÖNIGL. PREUSS. AKAD. Abhdl. (Phil.-hist. Kl.), 1918.
Die Dichterschule v. St. Gallen, mit e. Beitrag v. P. Wagner, St. Gallen in d. Musikgesch. s8°. L. 1922
Wolfram's Stil u. der Stoff d. Parzival, 1916, *see* KAISERL. AKAD. D. W. ZU WIEN. Sitz., B180, 1917.

Singer (Simeon), *see* TEPHILOTH. Auth. daily prayer book of the U. Hebrew Congr.; n. tr. by S., 9th ed., 1912.

***Singhalese** (A) primer. s8°. Colombo. 1819

***Singi-boekoe** vo da Evangel. Broeder-Gemeente na Suriname-Kondre. 8°. Bautzen. 1867

Singleton (Esther). The Shakespeare garden. 8°. N.Y. 1922

Sinica. Noviss. Sinica historiam nostri temporis illust. [*Incl.* Libertas evang. annunc. *by* J. Suarez *&* Icon regia Monarchae Sin. à J. Bouveto *w. sep. tp. & pag.*] Ed. G. G. L[eibnitio]. 2^a ed. s8°. [Leipzig?]. 1699

Sinigaglia (Giorgio).
De' Vivarini, pittori da Murano. 8°. Bergamo. 1905

Siniscalchi (Liborio), *see* LOYOLA (I.) Spirit. exercises, w. med. &c. by Father L. S.; tr., 1864.

Sinnhold (Johann Nicolaus). Ausführl. Hist. d. Wertheim. Bibel, 1735. Vorrede v. J. G. Walch. s4°. Erfurt. 1739

Sinowjew (G.), *see* ZINOVEV (G.)

Sintenis (Carl Heinrich). Widerlegung d. Tellerschen u. Richterschen Erinn. wider d. Hannöver. Katechismus &c. [P1042]. s8°. Zittau. 1794

Sintenis (Christian Friedrich) [*ps.* ELPIZON]. Elpizon an s. Freunde. 2er Anhang z. "Elpizon." 2^e A. s8°. L. 1810
Elpizon; oder ueb. m. Fortdauer im Tode. 3 everbesserte A. 3T [*in* 4v]. s8°. L. 1810–11
[T3 *is in* 2 Abthl. *each of which has 2nd tp.*: "Was steht vom Zustande nach d. Tode in d. Bibel?"]

Sinton (Thomas). Family & genealog. sketches [Stewarts &c.] la8°. *f.p.c.* Inverness. 1911

Sinués y Urbiola (J.), *see* JIMÉNEZ CATALÁN (M.) & J. S. Y U. Hist. de la Univ. de Zaragoza, 2t, 1922–24.

Sinyanki (J. E.) Notes on some passages of Script. orig. & sel. f. rabbinical sources. 8°. 1852

Sinzheimer (Ludwig), E. Francke & W. Lotz. Die geistigen Arbeiter. [V. f. Sozialpol., B152i, ii]. 2T. 8°. München. 1922
1, Freies Schriftstellertum u. Lit. Verlag; hrsg. L. Sinzheimer.
2, Journalisten u. bild. Kunstler; hrsg. E. Francke & W. Lotz.

Sionita (Gabriel), *see* GABRIEL, *Sionita.*

***Sion's** prospect in its first view: by a minister of Christ, R. M., 1653, *see* MOSSOM (R.)

Siraudin (Paul), A. Delacour & A. Choler. Après le bal. Comédie en un acte. 2e éd. [P2583]. s8°. 1864

Sircar (Mahendranath). The system of Vedantic thought & culture. 8°. Calcutta. 1925

Sir-Daria. Сборникъ матеріаловъ для статистики. Сыръ-Дарьинской области. Изд. Сыръ-Дарьинскаго Областнаго Статист. Ком. Подъ ред. Н. Н. Гейера &c. т2–10. 8°. Ташкентъ. 1892–1902
Each vol. except 7 & 8 has отд. 2, Этнограф. матеріалы, собранные А. А. Диваевымъ, *w. sep. pagin.*

Sirdel (Claude). L'aventure virtuelle, *see* ŒUVRES libres, 79, 1928.

Sire Degarre: metrical romance of 13th c., 1849, *see* DEGORE.

Sirén (Oswald). Chinese sculpture, f. 5th to 14th cent. 4v. sm. fol. 1925
Don Lorenzo Monaco. la8°. Str. 1905
Toskan. Maler im 13. Jhdt. la8°. 1922

Sir Galahad, *ps., see* GALAHAD, *Sir, ps.*

Siri (Johann Jacob). Zinzendorfiana dogmata rei Xtnae. noxia. Praes. F. A. Hallbauero. [P2632]. s4°. Jenae. [1748]

Siricius, *pope, see* ORICHOVIUS (S.) De lege cœlibatus contra S., 1551.

Siricius (Michael). Beata animae humanae immortalitas. 8°. Gissae Hass. 1669

Sirku (P. A.), *see* USPENSKY (P.) Путеш. въ монаст. въ Өессаліи; подъ ред. П. А. С., 1896.

Sirmond (Jacques), *Jesuit, see* NIEMEIER (J. B.) Tract. de disciplina eccl. &c.; acc. J. S. Hist. poenitentiae publicae, 1703.

Siroechkovsky (B. E.) Междуцарствие 1825 года и восстание декабристов в переписке и мем. членов царской семьи [Nicholas I &c.] Подгот. к печати Б. Е. С. la8°. Москва. 1926

Sirtema de Grovestins (*baron* **Charles Frédéric).** Hist. des luttes & rivalités polit. entre des puissances maritimes & la France dur. la 2e moitié du 17e s. 8[t]. 8°. 1851–54

Sisam (Kenneth). Fourteenth century verse & prose. Ed. K. S. s8°. O. 1921
,, ,, [repr., *w.* Middle Eng. vocab., by J. R. R. Tolkien, *w. sep. tp.*, 1922, *& sep. pagin.*] s8°. O. 1923

Sisianos, *vardapet of Armenia, 11th cent.* [Praise of 40 Saints *of Sebaste. In Armenian.* Soferq Hayk., v12]. s8°. i Venetik. 1854

Sisley (Alfred), *see* GEFFROY (G.) S., 1923.

Sisson (Joseph Lawson).
The elements of Anglo-Saxon gram. s8°. Leeds. 1819

Sisto, *da Siena, a Dominican Monk* [SIXTUS *Senensis*]. Bibliotheca sancta a S. ex praecipuis Cathol. Eccl. autoribus coll. et in 8 libros digesta. ed. 3^a. fol. Coloniae. 1586

Sitārāma, *Sūbahdār* [SEETARAM]. From Sepoy to Subadar: life & adv. of a native officer of the Bengal Army. Tr. Lt.-Col. Norgate. 3rd ed. Ed. D. C. Phillott. 8°. Calcutta. 1911
From Sepoy to Subadar, *for a retr. into Hindustani & Eng. tr., see* PHILLOTT (*Lt.-Col.* D. C.) Khwab o Khiyal &c., 1911.

Sitges (J. B.)
Las mujeres del rey D. Pedro I, de Castilla. 8°. 1910

Sitte (Heinrich). Ein vergessenes Parthenonbild — Karl Domanig v. A. Octav v. Loehr. fol. Wien. 1915
Zu Phidias: biog. Beitrag. 8°. Innsbruck. [1924]

Šittler (Ed.), *see* BOHEMIA. Topogr. d. hist. & Kunstdenkm., *for vol*^{s}. *by S. &c. on* Karolinenthal, Mühlhausen, Prag & Selčan, 1899–1904.

***Situation** (The) in Ireland, 1920, *see* IRELAND, ANON. WORKS.

Sitwell (Edith). Bucolic comedies. s8°. [1923]
Poetry & criticism. 8°. 1925
Rustic elegies. s8°. 1927
see MÉGROZ (R. L.) The 3 Sitwells: biog. & crit. study, 1927.

Sitwell (*Sir* **George Reresby),** *4th bart.* Country life in the 17th cent. Note upon Ld. Macaulay's caricature of the country squires &c. 8°. Scarborough. 1901
see YEATMAN (J. P.), *Sir* G. R. S. &c. Feudal hist. of Co. of Derby, 5v, 1886–1907.

Sitwell (Osbert).
Argonaut & Juggernaut. [*Poems*]. s8°. 1919
Before the bombardment. s8°. 1926
Discursions on travel, art & life. [repr.] 8°. 1925
Triple fugue. [repr.] 8°. [1924]
see MÉGROZ (R. L.) The 3 Sitwells: biog. & crit. study, 1927.

—— **& S. Sitwell.** All at sea. With A few days in an author's life, by O. S. 8°. 1927

Sitwell (Sacheverell).
All summer in a day: autobiog. fantasia. 8°. 1926
The cyder feast & o. p. 8°. 1927
German Baroque art. la8°. 1927
Southern Baroque art: painting, architecture & music in Italy & Spain of 17th & 18th cent. 8°. 1924
see MÉGROZ (R. L.) The 3 Sitwells: biog. & crit. study, 1927.
,, SITWELL (O.) *&* S. S. All at sea, 1927.

Sitwell (*Brig.-Gen.* **William Henry).** The Border f. a soldier's point of view. 8°. Newcastle-upon-Tyne. [1927]

Siurmelean (Khatchatour), *see* AVEDICHIAN (G.), K. S. &c. New dict. of Armenian, 2v, 1836–37.

Sivadesa. Vetālapañcaviṃsálikā (Die) d. S., 1914, *see* VETĀLAPAÑCAVIṂSALIKĀ.

Sivo (Giacinto de), *see* CROCE (B.) F. P. Bozzelli & G. de S., 1918.

Six. *Six days' tour thr. the Isle of Man, 1836, *see* MAN, *Isle of.*

Six (J.) Altgriech. Gewebemuster u. Webetechnik. [Aus d. Jahresh. d. Österr. Archäolog. Inst., B15, 1912]. [P2501]. la8°. [1912]
Apelleisches. [Aus. d. Jhbch. d. K. Deut. Archäolog. Inst., 25, 26. P2516]. la8°. 1910
Theon. [Sonderabdr. aus: Mitt. d. Deut. Arch. Inst. Röm. Abt., B32. P2502]. 8°. 1917

Sixle. Transcripts of charters rel. to the Gilbertine houses of S., Ormsby &c., 1922, *see* STENTON (F. M.), *ed.*

Sixt (Johann Andreas) [SIXTUS]. Comment. de Methodio Tyri quondam episcopo. [P597]. s4°. Altorfii. [1787]
Duorum fragm. S. cod. Hebraei descr. &c. s4°. Altorfii. [1772]

Sixtus IV, *pope.*
see DALLA SANTA (G.) Appellaz. d. rep. d. Venez. d. scomun. d. S. IV &c., 1899.
,, RODOCANACHI (E.) Hist. de Rome: une cour princière au Vatican: S. IV &c., 1925.

Sixtus V, *pope.* Brutum fulmen adv. Henricum, Regem Navarre & Henricum Borbonium &c. s8°. *n.p.* 1585
Declaratio contra Henricum Borbonium assertum regem Navarræ &c. [P2510]. s8°. Romæ. 1585

Sixtus V, *pope* [*continued*].
see Leti (G.) La vie de S. V, tr., 2t, 1698.
,, Maffei (G. P.) Hist. ab excessu Greg. XIII libri 3, S. V pontific. compl., 1747.
Sixtus *Senensis, see* Sisto *da Siena*.
Sjögren (Andreas Johan). Osset. Sprachlehre nebst kurzem osset.-deut. & deut.-osset. Wörterbuche. 4°. St. Petersburg. 1844
Sjögren (Håkan). Ad Ciceronis Epist. ad Atticum adnot., *see* Kung. Hum. Vet.-Samf. i Uppsala. Skr., B24, 1927.
Sjöstedt (Carolus Gustavus). Obs. in doct. grammaticorum de formis verborum linguae Russicae. Respond. J. F. Evander, 1824. 8°. Aboae. [1824]
Skabichevsky (Aleksandr Mikhailovich). Ист. новѣйшей русской литературы 1848–1906. 6°° изд. 8°. С.-П. 1906
Skagerrak. Die Seeschlacht am S. [Deut. Geschichtskal. Sonderheft. *b. w.* Europäische Krieg in aktenmäss. Darst., B4, 1916]. 8°. L. 1916
Skalbe (Karlis). Winter-Märchen. Übers. v. W. Christiani u. O. Schönhoff. 8°. Riga. [1921]
see Blaumanis (R.) Builders of new Rome & o. Lettish tales; [by] R. B., K. S. &c., 1924.
Skalweit (August). Die deut. Kriegsernährungswirtschaft. [C.E. for Int. Peace]. 8°. St. 1927
Skar (O.) Под красное знамя союза. [P2722]. s8°. Москва. 1919
Skating. Poetry of skating: coll. of verses, *see* Syers (E. W.), *ed.*
*Simple skating club figures, as skated at St. Moritz. [*Intr. signed* C. G.] 8°. *p.f.p.c.* 1893
Skeat (Walter William). Evol. of the Canterbury tales, *see* Philol. Soc. Trans., 1907.
see Morris (R.) Spec. of early Eng., 4th ed., p2, 1898.
Skeats (Herbert S.) Hist. of the Free Churches of Eng., 1688–1851. 2nd ed. 8°. 1869
Skeel (Caroline Anne James). Wales under Henry VII, *see* Pollard (A. F.) Tudor studies, 1924.
Skeet, *Family of.* *Hist. of the families of Skeet, Somerscales, Widdrington, Wilby, Murray, Blake, Grimshaw, & others. By a connection of the same. 4°. 1906
Skeet (Francis). A hist. of the parish of Angmering, Sussex. Acc. of manors, churches &c. 4°. Arundel. [1921]
Skelton (John), *poet laureate; 1460?–1529.* Poems. 8°. 1924
Skelton (Oscar Douglas). The Canadian Dominion. Our northern neighbour. [Chron. of Amer. ser., v49]. 8°. New Haven, *Yale.* 1919
Life & letters of Sir Wilfrid Laurier. 2v. 8°. 1922
Skendo (Lumo). Pritmi i Sqiperise. [P2684]. s8°. Sofje. 1915
Skene, *of Skene, Family of.*
*Descent of the fam. of S. [*folded*]. la8°. *n.p. n.d.*
Skene (*Sir* John). Memorabilia Scotica, 1475–1612 & revisals of Regiam Majestatem. Ed. w. intr. by G. Neilson. 8°. Glasgow. 1923
Skene (MacGregor). Biology of flowering plants. 8°. 1924
Trees. [Home Univ. Lib.] s8°. [1927]
Škerlj (Stanko). Syntaxe du participe prés. & du gérondif en vieil ital. &c., avec. intr. sur l'emploi en latin. [H.E., fasc., 249]. 8°. 1926
Skertchly (Sydney B. J.), *F.G.S.*
The geol. of the Fenland. [Mems. of G.S.] 8°. 1877
On the manufacture of gun-flints &c.—The connex. betw. Neolithic art & the gun-flint trade. [Mems. of G.S.] 8°. 1879
see Whitaker (W.), S. B. J. S. & A. J. Jukes-Browne. Geol. of S.-W. Norfolk &c., 1893.
Sketch. *Sk. of the defences of the W. & Swiss frontiers of Germany, 1888, *see* Germany.
*Sk. (A) of the hist. & proc. of the deputies app. to protect the civil rights of the protest. dissenters &c., 1814, *see* Dissenters.
Sketches. *Sk. & mem. of works for tunnel under the Thames, 1828, *see* Thames.
*Sk. of Persia, 2v, 1827, *see* Malcolm (*Sir* J.)
Skevratzi (Gregory), *see* Gregory, *Skevratzi.*
Skewes (Joseph Henry). A complete &c. digest of the polity of Methodism. s8°. 1869
Ski Club of Gt. Britain. Year-book, 1905–11. 8°. [1905–11]
see British Ski year book, 1926.
Skilbeck (Clement O.), *see* Dearmer (P.) Illust. of the Liturgy: 13 drawings of celeb. of Holy Communion by C. O. S.; notes &c. by P. D., 1912.
Skillington (S. H.) A hist. of Leicester. 8°. Leicester. 1923
Short hist. of Leicester. s8°. 1924
see Fosbrooke (T. H.) & S. H. S. The Old Town Hall, Leicester, 1925.
Skinner (Alanson). Notes on Iroquois archeology. [Hispanic Soc. of Amer.] s8°. N.Y. 1921
Skinner (Constance Lindsay). Adventurers of Oregon. Fur trade. [Chron. of Amer. ser., v22]. 8°. New Haven, *Yale*, 1920
Skinner (John), *bp. of Scot. Episc. Ch. in Aberdeen.* Primitive truth & order vindicated, w. a def. of episcopacy, particularly that of Scotland, agst. Dr. Campbell. 8°. Aberdeen. 1803
Skinner (John), *prof. at the Presbyterian Coll., London.*
Prophecy & religion: st. in the life of Jeremiah. 8°. C. 1922
Skinner (M. L.), *see* Lawrence (D. H.) & M. L. S. The boy in the bush, 1924.
Skinner (Mary E.), *see* Williams (D.) & M. E. S. Work of children on Illinois farms, 1926.
Skinner (*Major* Thomas), *1800?–43.*
Excursions in India. 2v. 8°. 1832
Skinner (Walter E.), *see* Mining manual (The), 1926.
Skinner's Company, *London, see* Sebastian (L. B.) An old City co., 1906.
Skipton. Parish reg. of Skipton-in-Craven, 1592–1680. Ed. W. J. Stavert. 8°. Skipton. 1894
Skitalets (—). Стихотворенія — Памяти Чехова — Кандалы, *see* Sbornik. Сб. товар. "Знаніе" 2, 3, 5, 1904–5.
Skobelev (*Gen.* Mikhail Dmitrievich).
see Gradovsky (G. K.) М. Д. С., 1884.
,, Grodekov (N. I.) Война въ Туркменіи: походъ Скобелева, 1880–81, 4t, 1883–84.
Skok (Petar). Ime grada Splita, *see* Bullettino di arch. &c. dalm., 39, Suppl., 1919.
Skolaster (Hermann). Die Pallottiner in Kamerun: 25 Jahre Missionsarbeit. 8°. Limburg. [1924]
Skorov (A.) Сборникъ узаконеній &с. относящ. до крестьянск. общ. управленія &с. Состав. А. С. 8°. Москва. 1883
Skovoroda (Grigory Savvich), *1722–94.*
see Ern (V.) Г. С. С., 1922.
,, Kovalensky (M. I.) Житіе Сковороды, 1886.
Skowronnek (Fritz). Die Jagd. la8°. Bielefeld. 1901
Das Masurenbuch. 8°. [1916]
Skrine (Clarmont Percival). Chinese Central Asia. Intr. by Sir F. Younghusband. 8°. [1926]
Skrine (Francis Henry B.)
Democratize education! Address. [P2423]. s8°. 1920
The Irish Brigades, 1689–1745. Lect. [P2562]. 8°. 1921
see Hawkins (L. M.) Gossip about Dr. Johnson &c.: chapters f. Mems. of H.; ed. F. H. S., 1926.
Skrine (Henry).
Two successive tours throughout Wales &c. 8°. 1798
Skrine (Mary J. H.) Shepherd Easton's daughter. s8°. 1925
,, ,, ... pop. ed. s8°. 1926
,, ,, ... pop. ed. [repr.] s8°. [1927]
Skrine (*Mrs.* Nesta), *form. Higginson, see* †O'Neill (Moira), *ps.*
Skryabin (A. N.), *see* Scriabin (A. N.)
Skues (G. E. M.) The way of a trout with a fly. la8°. 1921
Skulerud (Olai). Cat. of Norse MSS. in Edinb., Dublin & Manchester. [Norske Hist. K.] 8°. Kristiania. 1918
Slack (*Mrs*). The pleasing instructor &c., 1806, *see* Fisher (A.), *ps.*
Slade (Felix), *see* Nesbitt (A.) Notes on hist. of glass-making; prep. as intr. to cat. of coll. formed by F. S., 1869.
Slade (William Adams), *see* MacLaughlin (A. C.), W. A. S. &c. Writings on Amer. hist., 1903, 1905.
Sládek (Josef V.) Selské písně a české znělky. s8°. v Praze. 1890
Směska, nové starosvětské písničky. [*b. w. h.* Sel. písne, 1890]. s8°. v Praze. 1891
Starosvětské písničky a jiné písne. [*b. w. h.* Sel. písne, 1890]. s8°. v Praze. [1891]
Sladen (Douglas Brooke Wheelton). Fair Inez. s8°. [1918]
How to see Italy by rail. 2nd ed. s8°. 1912
see Cosmos: scheme f. co-op. betw. cap. & lab.; ed. D. S., 1920.
Slataper (Scipio). Il mio carso. 4ª ed. s8°. 1920
Slater (Catherine Ponton). Marget Pow. s8°. E. [1925]
Slater (David A.) Towards a text of the Metamorphosis of Ovid. la8°. O. 1927
Slater (Francis Carey). Centenary book of S. African verse, 1820–1925. Chosen by F. C. S. 8°. 1925
Slater (Gilbert). Dravidian element in Indian culture. Foreword by H. J. Fleure. 8°. 1924
The making of mod. England. [repr.] s8°. 1921

Slater (Herbert Edward), *see* CANTERBURY. Reg. of St. Augustine's Abbey ; ed. G. J. Turner & H. E. S., p2, 1924.

Slater (J. Herbert), *barrister*. Book collecting : guide for amateurs. [la. paper ed.] s8°. 1892
Engravings & th. value. 5th ed. rev. & enl. 8°. 1921
The library manual. 3rd & enl. ed. 8°. 1892
Problems of the borderland. s8°. 1915

Slater (John), *F.R.I.B.A.*, *see* SMITH (T. R.) & J. S. Architecture, classic & early Xtn., 1886.

Slater (William F.)
The faith & life of the early church. s8°. 1892
Methodism in the light of the early church. Fernley Lect. 8°. 1885

Slater's, *publishers*. S.'s Manchester, Salford & suburban directory, 1917. la8°. [1917]

Slavery. Analysis of rep. of Comm. of House of Commons on extinction of s., w. notes. 8°. 1833

Slavische. *Grammatik d. Slav. Spr. in Krain, Kärnten u. Steyermark, 1808, *see* KOPITAR (B.)

Slavonia. *Comp. regnorum Slavoniae &c., 1792, *see* COMPENDIOLUM.

Slavonic review (The). v1–6. 8°. 1922–28

Slee (Jacob Cornelis van). De Kloostervereeniging v. Windesheim, eene filiaalstichting v. de Broeders van het Gemeene Leven. 8°. Leiden. 1874
see MULLER (F.) Cat. diss. &c. ab a. 1650 ad 1850 in academiis Neerlandiae &c. coll. a F. M. ; acc. 2 indices, cur. J. G. van S., 1867.

Sleepy Hollow Cemetery, 1866, *see* TARRYTOWN.

Sleidanus (Joannes) [†PHILIPPSON (J.), *Sleidanus*], *see* SEVERUS (S.) Hist. sacra, contin. ex Sleydano, 1635.

Sleigh (R. S.) The sufficiency of Xty. ; w. spec. ref. to relig. philos. of E. Troeltsch. Intr. by W. Fulton. 8°. [1923]

Slesser (*Sir* Henry). Trade unionism. s8°. [1913]
—— & C. Baker. Trade union law. 2nd ed., w. suppl. 8°. [1926]
—— & W. S. Clark. The legal position of trade unions. 8°. 1912

Sleumer (Albert). Kirchenlatein. Wbch. 2. verm. A. d. " Liturg. Lexikons " unter Mitarbeit v. J. Schmid, hrsg. v. A. S. 8°. Limburg a. d. Lahn. 1926

Slevogt (Georg Gabriel). De jurisprudentia per emendat. relig. reformata. Praes. C. A. Beckio. [P484]. s4°. Jenae. [1717]

Slevogt (Johann Philipp). Comm. de divisione eccl. & beneficiorum. [P2636]. s4°. Jenae. 1746

Slevogt (Max), *see* ALTEN (W. v.) M. S. [Knackfuss], 1926.

Slipper (Stanley Eades). Sheep River gas & oil field, Alberta. [Canada : Geolog. Survey. P2514]. 8°. Ottawa. 1921
see DOWLING (D. B.), S. E. S. & F. H. McLEARN. Investig. in the gas & oil fields of Alberta &c., 1919.

Sloane (*Sir* Hans), *bart.* Voyage to Madera, Barbados &c. & Jamaica w. the natural hist. of the last ; prefix'd, acc. of the inhabitants &c. 2v. fol. 1707–25

Sloane (William Milligan).
Greater France in Africa. 8°. N.Y. 1924

Slonim (Marc). Le Bolchévisme vu par un Russe. s8°. 1921

Sloss (D. J.), *see* BLAKE (W.) Prophetic writings ; ed., w. gen. intr. &c., by D. J. S. &c., 2v, 1926.

Slosson (Edwin Emery). The American spirit in education. 8°. New Haven, *Yale*. 1921
Chats on science. 8°. 1924
Easy lessons in Einstein. With an article by A. E. s8°. 1920
Keeping up w. science : notes on rec. progress. [*By var. wr.*] Ed. E. E. S. 8°. [1924]

Slotty (Friedrich). Vulgärlatein. Übungsbuch ; hrsg. F. S., *see* KLEINE TEXTE, T143, 1918.

Słotwinski (Felix).
De immunitate eccl. [P2757]. s8°. Cracoviae. 1833

Slouschz (Nahum). Hebræo-Phéniciens & Judéo-Berbères : intr. à l'hist. des Juifs & du Judaïsme en Afrique, *see* MISSION SCIENT. DU MAROC. Archives, v14, 1908.

Słowacki (Juliusz). Pisma. s8°. Lipsk. 1875–76

Slyunin (Nikolai Vasilevich). Соврем. положеніе нашего дальняго Востока. [*3 pagin.*] 8°. [illegible] 1908

Small (Albion Woodbury). Americans & the world-crisis. [Univ. of Chicago. P2509]. 8°. Chicago. 1918

Small (Annie H.)
Anc. Scottish prayers, w. intr. by A. H. S. s8°. 1912

Small (Austin J.) [*ps.* SEAMARK]. Pearls of desire. s8°. [1924]

Smaller (The) house : sel. examples of mod. Eng. domestic archit. fol. 1924

Smallwood (J. R.) Coaker of Newfoundland. s8°. [1927]

Smalz (Valentin), *1572–1622*. Diarium vitae, *see* ZELTNER (G. G.) Hist. Crypto-Socinismi, 1729.
see RAVENSPERGER (H.) De causa Dei &c. adv. turmam Racov. q. ducit V. S., 1621.

Smart (Christopher). A song to David. s8°. 1895
A song to David w. o. poems. Chosen w. biog. &c. pref. & notes by E. Blunden. 8°. [1924]
A transl. of the Psalms of David. [Hymns & spiritual songs for the fasts & festivals of the Church of Eng.—A song to David]. 4°. 1765

Smart (James P.), *see* WISE (T. J.) & J. P. S. Compl. bibliog. of writings of J. Ruskin, 2v, 1893.

Smart (John Semple). Shakespeare truth & tradition. With mem. by W. M. Dixon. 8°. 1928
Tragedy, *see* ENGLISH ASSOC. Essays &c., v8, 1922.

Smeaton (John), *see* *TOUCHSTONE (The) of the reformed gospel &c. [by J. S. ?], 1685 (?).

Smeding (Alie). Achter het Anker. 8°. Rotterdam. 1924

Smedley (Alfred), *of Belper*. Some remin. by A. S. Miss Wood in Derbyshire : exper. seances &c. reported by W. P. Adshead ; also an acc. of Miss Wood's mediumship by T. P. Barkas. s8°. 1900

Smedley (Edward), *fellow of Sidney Sussex Coll., Cambridge.* Jonah. Poem. [*b. w.* Scott (G. E.) Waterloo, 1820]. 8°. 1815

Smedley (Francis E.) Frank Fairlegh, or scenes f. the life of a private pupil. 8°. 1899

Smeeks (Henrik). A Dutch source for Robinson Crusoe. The narr. of the El-Ho " Sjouke Gabbes," by H. S., 1708. Tr. f. the Dutch & compared w. story of R. C. by L. L. Hubbard. 8°. Ann Arbor. 1921

Smelingus (Tilmannus), *Segebergensis*. De septem sacramentis liber unus. Ab auctore recogn. &c. s8°. Coloniæ, *Melchior Novesianus*. 1546

Smena Vekh. Смѣна Вѣхъ. Сборникъ статей : Ю. В. Ключникова &c. 2[oe] изд. 8°. Прага. 1922
О Смене Вех. 1, А. С. Изгоев. ; 2, I. Clemens ; 3, П. К. Губер ; 4, А. Б Петрищев. 8°. [П.] 1922

Smend (Julius). Das evangel. Lied v. 1524. [Verein f. Ref.-gesch. Schr., Jhrg. 42 (Nr. 137)]. 8°. L. 1924

Smetana (Bedřich), *1824–84*.
see NEJEDLÝ (Z.) F. S., 1924.
,, RITTER (W.) S., 1907.

Smethurst (Thomas), *M.D.*, *see* NEWTON (A.) The case of T. S., his trial &c., 1859.

Smidelinus (Jacobus), *see* ANDREÆ (J.), *called Schmidtlein*.

Smilg-Benario (Michael). Ein Jahr in Dienste d. russ. Sowjet-Republik. 8°. 1920

Smillie (Robert), *M.P.* My life for labour. Foreword by J. R. Macdonald. s8°. [1924]

Smirnov (Alexis). Sclirène. Roman byzantin. Tr. Halpérine-Kaminsky. Préf. du Comte Prozor. s8°. 1921

Smirnov (Petr Semenovich).
Исторія христіанской православной церкви. s8°. Берлинъ. *n.d.*

Smirnov (S. S.)
Рабочие и крестьяне Украины &c. [P2722]. s8°. Москва. 1919

Smital (Ottokar), *see* ZIMMERMAN (H.), A. HANDLIRSCH & O. S. Die beiden Hofmuseen u. d. Hofbibliothek, 1920.

Smith, *The family of*, *see* SMITH (A. J.) True &c. hist. of fam. of S., orig. cradled at Wiverton &c., 1861.

Smith, *of Glasshouse, The family of*, *see* NUTTALL-SMITH (G. N.) Chron. of Puritan family in Ireland, 1923.

Smith (A. Duncan), *ed.*, *see* SMITH (*Miss* M. H.) Trial of M. S., 1921.

Smith (Adam), *LL.D., F.R.S. ; 1723–90*. Inquiry into the nature & causes of the wealth of nations. Ed. w. intr. &c. by E. Cannan. 4th ed. 2v. 8°. [1925]
Unters. ü. d. Wesen &c. d. Nationalreichtums ; übers. v. M. Stirner, *see* JASTROW (I.) Textbücher &c., B3, 1920.

Smith (Albert R.) The adv. of Mr. Ledbury & his friend Jack Johnson. Illust. by J. Leech. la8°. 1886
The Marchioness of Brinvilliers. [Illust. by J. Leech]. la8°. 1886

Smith (*Capt.* Alex.) Compl. hist. of lives & robberies of notorious highwaymen, footpads &c. Ed. A. L. Hayward. la8°. 1926
The hist. of the lives of the most noted highway-men, footpads, &c. 3rd ed. corr. [v1]. s8°. 1714

Smith (Alex.), *poet, 1830–67*.
Poet. works. Ed. w. intr. by W. Sinclair. s8°. E. 1909

Smith (Alfred Owen), *ed., see* SMITH (GERVASE). The Rev. G. Smith, 1882.
Smith (Alice R. Huger) & D. E. H. Smith.
Charles Fraser. la8º. N.Y. 1924
Smith (Annie Lorrain). Lichens. la8º. C. 1921
see BRITISH MUSEUM OF NAT. HIST.: BOTANY. Monogr. of Brit. lichens, p2, by A. L. S., 2nd ed., 1926.
Smith (Arthur Douglas Howden).
Commodore Vanderbilt. 8º. 1928
Smith (Arthur Hamilton). Notes on a tour in Asia Minor. [Repr. f. the Journal of Hellenic St.] 8º. 1887
see CORPUS vasorum antiq. Gt. Brit.: Brit. Museum, fasc. 1, 2; by A. H. S. &c., 1925–26.
,, YARBOROUGH (C., *Earl of*). Cat. of antiquities, by A. H. S., 1897.
Smith (Arthur Henderson), *missionary.*
China in convulsion. 2v. 8º. N.Y. 1901
Smith (Arthur Lionel), *1850–1924, see* SMITH (*Mrs.* M. F.) A. L. S., master of Balliol (1916–24), 1928.
Smith (Augustus John). True &c. hist. of the family of Smith, orig. cradled at Wiverton & Cropwell-Butler, more rec. establ. at Nottingham. sm. fol. 1861
Smith (Benjamin), *Wesleyan Minister.*
Methodism in Macclesfield. s8º. 1875
Smith (Bernard), *architect.* Sketches abroad, Germany & Switz., 1876. fol. [1880]
Sketches in Spain. fol. 1883
Smith (Bernard), *F.G.S.*
see GEOLOG. SURVEY. Spec. rep. on min. resources. 8, Iron ores &c. 19, Lead & Zinc ores &c., by S. &c. 23, Lead & Zinc ores &c., by S. &c., 1919–22.
,, LAMPLUGH (G. W.) & B. S. The water supply of Notts., 1914.
,, WEDD (C. B.), B. S. &c. Geol. of Liverpool &c., 1923.
,, —— —— Geol. of co. around Wrexham, p1, 1927.
Smith (Bertram). Running wild. Pref. by W. Muir. s8º. [1920]
Smith (Buckingham), *see* SMITH (THOMAS BUCKINGHAM).
Smith (Cades Alfred Middleton), *M.Sc.*
The British in China & Far Eastern trade. 8º. 1920
Smith (Cecil). A Proto-Attic vase. [Repr. f. Journal of Hellenic st., v22. P2516]. la8º. 1902
Smith (Chaloner), *see* SMITH (JOHN CHALONER).
Smith (Charles Card), *see* MASSACHUSETTS HIST. SOC. Sh. acc. of the M.H.S.; orig. prep. by C. C. S. &c., 1918.
Smith (Charles Edward), *surgeon of the whale-ship Diana.*
From the deep of the sea: diary of C. E. S. Ed. by h. son, C. E. Smith Harris. 8º. 1922
Smith (Charles Henry), *see* CHAMBERLAIN (J. L.) Universities & th. sons; spec. ed., Yale, C. H. S. &c., 5v, 1898–1900.
Smith (*Mrs.* Charlotte), *wife of Benj. Smith; 1749–1806.*
*What is she?: comedy, *see* †INCHBALD (*Mrs.* E.) Mod. theatre, v10, 1811.
Smith (Cicely Fox). A book of shanties. 8º. [1927]
The return of the "Cutty Sark." 8º. [1924]
Ships & folks. s8º. 1920
Smith (Clifford Pabody). Christian science: its legal status. s8º. Boston, U.S. [1914]
Smith (Constance I.) [*ps.* ISABEL BEAUMONT].
Storm dust. s8º. [1925]
Smith (D. E. Huger), *see* SMITH (A. R. H.) & D. E. H. S. Charles Fraser, 1924.
Smith (David Baird). Some French bibliophiles. [Fr. Glasgow Bibliogr. Soc. Trans. P2851]. 4º. Glasgow. 1920
Smith (David Eugene). Computing jetons. [Amer. Num. Soc. Notes &c., No. 9]. s8º. N.Y. 1921
Hist. of mathematics. 2v. 8º. Boston. [1923–25]
Mathematics. Intr. by Sir T. L. Heath. s8º. [1923]
New inform. resp. R. Recorde. [Repr. f. The Amer. math. monthly, v28, 1921. P2740]. la8º. [1921]
Smith (E. A. Wyke). The second chance. s8º. [1923]
Smith (Edgar A.), *see* BRIT. ANTARCTIC EXPED., 1910–13: Zoology, v2, Mollusca, p1; by S., 1914–20.
Smith (Edward H.) Famous Amer. poison mysteries. 8º. [1927]
Smith (Edwin W.) The golden stool: conflict of cultures in mod. Africa. Foreword by Sir F. D. Lugard. [Hartley lect., 3rd ed.] 8º. 1927
—— **& A. M. Dale.**
The Ila-speaking peoples of N. Rhodesia. 2v. 8º. 1920
Smith (Egerton). Princ. of Eng. metre. s8º. 1923
Smith (Eli), *see* ROBINSON (E.) Maps to accompany Bibl. researches in Palestine of E. R. & E. S., 1856.
Smith (Eli) & H. G. O. Dwight. Missionary researches in Armenia &c. Pref. mem. by the a. of "The mod. traveller." 8º. 1834
Smith (Erasmus Peshine). Manual of polit. econ. s8º. N.Y. 1868
Smith (Eric Montague). The investig. of mind in animals. [2nd ed.] s8º. C. 1923
Smith (Essex). The revolving fates. s8º. [1922]
Smith (Frank), *lecturer in educ., Univ. Coll., Aberystwyth.*
Life & work of Sir J. Kay-Shuttleworth. Intr. by Sir M. Sadler, & a chapter by Ld. Shuttleworth. 8º. 1923
Smith (Frank Herron). The other side of the Korean question. [P2427]. s8º. Seoul. 1920
Smith (Franklin H.) Teak in Siam & Indo-China, 1915, *see* UNITED STATES: COMMERCE.
Smith (Frederic), *poetical writer.*
A chest of viols & o. v. s8º. 1896
Smith (*Sir* Frederick Edwin), *see* BIRKENHEAD (F. E. S., *1st e.*)
Smith (G. Abbott-), *see* ABBOTT-SMITH (G.)
Smith (Geoffrey Watkins), *fellow of New Coll., O.*
Primitive animals. s8º. C. 1911
Smith (George), *C.I.E., LL.D., see* GRANT (A.), *F.R.S.* Physician & friend: A. G., autobiog. &c., ed. G. S., 1902.
Smith (George), *F.A.S., 1800–68.*
The Cassiterides: commercial op. of the Phoenicians in W. Europe, w. ref. to Brit. tin trade. 8º. 1863
The doctrine of the cherubim &c. 8º. 1850
The doctrine of the pastorate. 8º. 1851
The harmony of divine dispensations. 8º. 1856
The life & reign of David, King of Israel. 8º. 1867
Perilous times: or the aggressions of antichrist. error. 8º. 1845
The relig. of Anc. Brit. [–1066]. 8º. 1844
Smith (George), *of Messrs. Ellis, New Bond St., see* ELLIS, *bookseller.* Coll. of armorial bookbindings; descr. by G. S., 1927.
Smith (*Sir* George Adam).
Jeremiah. Baird Lect., 1922. s8º. [1923]
see BEVAN (E. R.) & C. SINGER, *edd.* The legacy of Israel: essays by S. &c., 1927.
,, BIBLE. Expositor's B.: Isaiah; G. A. S., 2v, 1890.
Smith (George Barnett). Heroes of the 19th cent. Wellington—Garibaldi—Grant—Gordon. 8º. 1899
Smith (George Charles Moore).
College plays in the Univ. of Camb. s8º. C. 1923
Smith (George D.), *bookseller.* Selections f. purchases &c. Sold, Anderson Gall., N.Y. p2–7. 8º. N.Y. 1920–21
Smith (George Joseph).
Trial of G. J. S. Ed. E. R. Watson. 8º. E. [1922]
Smith (George Nuttall), *aft. Nuttall-Smith, see* NUTTALL-SMITH (G. N.)
Smith (George Tulloch Bisset-), *see* BISSET-SMITH (G. T.)
Smith (Gerrit), *see* FROTHINGHAM (O. B.) G. S., 1878.
Smith (Gervase), *1821–82.* The Rev. Gervase Smith. A mem. volume. Ed. A. O. Smith. [Hist. sk. by S. Lees]. s8º. 1882
Smith (Goldwin). False hopes; or fallacies, socialistic &c. answered. An address. s8º. 1886
Smith (Grafton Elliot).
The anc. Egyptians & the origin of civiliz. n. & rev. ed. s8º. 1923
Elephants & ethnologists. la8º. 1924
The evolution of man. Essays. 8º. 1924
,, ,, [repr.] 8º. [1924]
The evolution of man. 2nd ed. 8º. 1927
Primitive man, 1916, *see* BRIT. ACAD. Proc., 1915–16.
Tutankhamen & the discovery of h. tomb by the Earl of Carnarvon & Mr. H. Carter. s8º. 1923
—— **& W. R. Dawson.** Egyptian mummies. 4º. [1924]
Smith (H. Guthrie-), *see* GUTHRIE-SMITH (H.)
Smith (*Maj.* H. Marriot). The hist. of the 13th Batt., R.F. Artillery, 1759–1913. 8º. 1913
Smith (Harlan Ingersoll). Album of prehist. Canadian art, *see* CANADA: GEOLOG. SURVEY. Museum bull., no. 37, 1923.
Smith (Harold), *D.D.* Hist. of the parish of Havering-atte-Bower, Essex. 8º. Colchester. 1925
Smith (Harold Clifford), *see* VICTORIA & ALBERT MUSEUM. Cat. of Eng. furniture & woodwork; by H. C. S., v1, 1923.
Smith (Harry B. Allin). Represent. wages &c. in Gt. Brit., *see* UNITED STATES: COMMERCE. Trade inform. bull., 91, 1923.
Smith (Harry Bradley). Industrial hist. s8º. N.Y. 1923
Smith (Hastings Bertrand Lees-), *see* LEES-SMITH (H. B.)
Smith (*Mlle.* Hélène), *medium, see* FLOURNOY (T.) Des Indes à la planète Mars, 4e éd., 1910.

Smith (Henry), *minister of St. Clement Danes.*
The affinitie of the faithfull. Sermon. [*b. w. h.* Prep. to mariage, 1591]. s8°. 1591
The benefite of contentation. [*all missing after sig. B7. b. w. h.* Prep. to mariage, 1591]. s8°. 1591
The Christians sacrifice. [*b. w. h.* Prep. to mariage, 1591]. s8°. 1589
A fruitfull sermon, upon 5 Chap. of 1st Thessalonians. [*b. w. h.* Prep. to mariage, 1591]. s8°. 1591
A preparative to mariage [*sic*]. Annexed a treatise of the Lord's Supper: & a. of Usurie. [*&* Three Praiers]. Corr. & augm. by author. [*4p. sep. tps. one pagin.*] s8°. 1591
Seven godly & learned sermons. [*b. w. h.* Prep. to mariage, 1591]. s8°. 1591
The trumpet of the soule. [*b. w. h.* Prep. to mariage, 1591]. s8°. 1591
The wedding garment. [*b. w. h.* Prep. to mariage, 1591]. s8°. 1591
Smith (Henry Bompas). The nation's schools: th. task & th. importance. 8°. 1927
Smith (Henry Monmouth), *see* BENEDICT (F. G.), W. R. MILES, P. ROTH & H. M. S. Human vitality &c., 1919.
Smith (Herbert Maynard). Frank, Bp. of Zanzibar: life of F. Weston, D.D., 1871–1924. 8°. 1926
see EVELYN (J.) Early life & educ., w. a comm. by H. M. S., 1920.
Smith (Hj.), *see* PREBENSEN (N.) & HJ. S. Christian V norske Lov, 1687, 1887.
Smith (*Sir* Hubert Llewellyn).
The economic laws of art production. s8°. 1924
Smith (James), *of Melbourne.*
Wilton & its associations. 8°. Salisbury. 1851
Smith (James Haldane). Collectivist economics. 8°. 1925
Smith (James Reuel). Springs & wells in Gr. & Rom. lit.; legends & locat. 8°. N.Y. 1922
Smith (John), *of the Inner Temple.* Iconographia Scotica: or portraits of illust. persons of Scotland, w. their lives &c. la8°. [1798]
Smith (John), *fellow of Queen's Coll., Camb.* Extracts f. works, *see* WESLEY (J.) Xtn. lib., v19, 20, 1752–53.
Smith (John), *missionary to Demerara.* The London Miss. Soc.'s report of the proc. agst. J. S., tried under martial law on a charge of aiding &c. in a rebellion of Negro slaves. With app. 8°. 1824
Smith (John), *of Montague Close, Southwark.* The mystery of rhetorick unveil'd. s8°. 1688
Smith (John), *governor of Virginia; 1580–1631.*
see ASHTON (J.) Adv. & discourses of Capt. J. S., 1883.
,, CHATTERTON (E. K.) Capt. J. S., 1927.
Smith (John Alexander). Knowing & acting. Inaug. lect., Oxford, 26 Nov. 1910. [P2506]. 8°. O. 1910
Smith (John Benjamin), *see* PETERLOO. Three accounts of P. by eyewitnesses: J. B. S. &c., 1921.
Smith (John Chaloner), *see* RUSSELL (C. E.) Eng. mezzotint portraits, v2, Cat. of corr. & add. to C. S.'s "Brit. mezzotint port.," 1926.
Smith (John George). Organised produce markets. 8°. 1922
Smith (John Jay). *Celeb. trials of all countries, & remark. cases of crim. jurisprudence. Sel. by a Member of the Philadelphia Bar. 8°. Phila. 1835
Smith (John Pye), *D.D.* An answer to Manifesto of the Xtn. Evidence Soc., 3rd ed. Add., A rejoinder to a pamph. by the same a., Rob. Taylor, entitled Syntagma of the evidences. [P2543]. 8°. 1829
Smith (John Russel), *publisher & bookseller.* Bibl. Americana. Cat. of books &c. illust. the hist. & geogr. of N. & S. America & the W. Ind. [*&* Suppl.] 8°. 1865–67
Smith (John Thomas), *keeper of the prints in the Brit. Museum, 1766–1833.* The celeb. 12 etchings [1815] of itin. traders &c. in London. [*2 plates wanting. no tp.*] 8°. *n.d.*
The cries of London: exhib. itinerant traders, copied f. engravings &c. 4°. 1839
Nollekens & his times &c. Ed. & annot. by W. Whitten. 2v. 8°. 1920
Smith (Joseph Russell). North America, its people &c. 8°. [1925]
Smith (Logan Pearsall).
English idioms. [S.P.E., Tract No. 12]. 8°. 1923
The Eng. language. [Home Univ. Lib.] [repr.] s8°. [1921]
A few practical suggestions. [S.P.E., 3]. 8°. O. 1920
4 words, romantic, originality, creative, genius. [S.P.E., Tract No. 17]. 8°. 1924
More Trivia. s8°. 1922
Words & idioms. 8°. 1925
Smith (Lucien). The wife of Evelyn Strode. s8°. [1927]

Smith (Lucy Margaret).
The early hist. of the monastery of Cluny. 8°. 1920
Smith (Madeleine Hamilton). Trial for alleged poisoning of P. E. L'Angelier: spec. verbatim rep. 8°. E. 1857
Trial of M. S. Ed. A. D. Smith. 8°. E. [1921]
Smith (Malcolm), *see* BRIT. MUS. OF NAT. HIST.: ZOOLOGY. Monogr. of sea-snakes; by M. S., 1926.
Smith (Marion Elmina). Une Anglaise intellect. en France s. la Restauration: Miss M. Clarke [*aft.* Mohl]. 8°. 1927
Smith (*Mrs.* Mary Ann), *daughter of A. Clarke, wife of Richard Smith.* The life of the Rev. Henry Moore, incl. Autobiog. & cont. by Mrs. R. S. 8°. 1844
see CLARKE (A.) Acc. of life of A. C., 3v [v2, 3, by a member of h. family (M. A. S.)], 1833.
Smith (*Mrs.* Mary Florence), *form. Baird, wife of A. L. S.*
A. L. Smith. Biog. & remin. 8°. [1928]
Smith (Maurice Hamblin).
The psychology of the criminal. 8°. [1922]
Smith (May), *M.A.* St. in the laundry trade, *see* INDUST. FATIGUE RESEARCH BD, Rep., 22, 1922.
Smith (Montague Bentley Talbot Paske-), *see* PASKE-SMITH (M. B. T.)
Smith (Munroe). Militarism & statecraft. s8°. N.Y. 1918
Smith (Nora Archibald).
Kate Douglas Wiggin as her sister knew her. 8°. 1925
Smith (Norman Kemp). Comm. on Kant's "Critique of pure reason." 2nd ed. rev. & enl. 8°. 1923
Prolegomena to an idealist theory of knowledge. 8°. 1924
Smith (Paul Jordan-), *see* JORDAN-SMITH (P.)
Smith (Pauline). The beadle. [2nd impr.] 8°. [1926]
The little Karoo. Intr. by A. Bennett. s8°. [1925]
Smith (Percival Gardner-), *see* GARDNER-SMITH (P.)
Smith (Philip Vernon), *b. 1845.* The Fourth Gospel: its hist. importance. Pref. by J. M. Wilson. s8°. 1926
Smith (Preserved). The age of the Reformation. [Amer. Hist. Ser.] 8°. N.Y. 1920
Erasmus, h. life, ideals & place in hist. 8°. N.Y. 1923
Smith (Reginald A.), *F.S.A.*, *see* BRIT. MUS.: ANTIQ. Guide to Anglo-Saxon &c. antiqs.; by R. A. S., 1923.
Smith (Reginald Heber) & J. S. Bradway. Growth of legal aid work in tbe U.S., *see* UNITED STATES: LAB. Bull. No. 398, 1926.
Smith (Richard), *D.D., Dean of St. Peter's Church, Douay, 1500–63* [SMYTHAEUS (R.)] [A defence of the sacrifice of the Masse]. [*tp. & 7 leaves missing*]. s8°. [*W. Myddylton.* 1547]
Diatriba de hominis justificatione ædita Oxoniae in Anglia, a. 1550 adv. Petrum Martyrē nunc apostatā in Anglia Oxoniæ. s8°. Lovanii. 1551
see CRANMER (T.), *abp. of Canterbury.* Answer unto Gardiner, also answered places in the booke of R. S., 1551.
Smith (*Mrs.* Richard), *see* SMITH (*Mrs.* M. A.)
Smith (Robert), *D.D., master of Trinity Coll., Cambridge; 1689–1768.* Compleat system of opticks. 2v [*pagin. cont., but* Author's remarks *w. sep. pagin.*] la8°. C. 1738
Smith (Robert), *of Maryland, see* BEMIS (S. F.), *ed.* Amer. Secr. of State, v3, S., by C. C. Tansill, 1927.
Smith (Robinson). Research papers.
Nos. 1, 3–8, 11, 12. [P2501, 2751]. la8°. *n.d.*–1923
Smith (*Sir* Ross). 14,000 miles through the air. 8°. 1922
Smith (S. Percy). Lore of the Whare-wānanga, or teachings of the Maori College. Wr. down by H. T. Whatahoro f. teachings of Te Matorohanga &c. Tr. &c. S. P. S. [Polynesian Soc. Mem., v3, 4]. 2p. 8°. New Plymouth, N.Z. 1913–15
Smith (Samuel), *of Burlington, N.J.* The hist. of the colony of Nova-Cæsaria, or New Jersey &c. 8°. Burlington in N.J. 1765
Smith (Samuel), *of Liverpool, M.P.*
The Franco-German war. [P2831]. 8°. 1870
Smith (Sidney), *M.A.* Babylonian histor. texts rel. to capture &c. of Babylon. Tr. S. S. 8°. [1924]
Early hist. of Assyria to 1000 B.C. la8°. 1928
The first campaign of Sennacherib, king of Assyria, 705–681. Assyrian text ed. w. translit., tr. & notes. 8°. 1921
Smith (Solomon Charles Kaines). Cotman. s8°. [1926]
Crome, w. note on the Norwich school. Intr. by C. H. C. Baker. s8°. [1923]
Looking at pictures. 2nd ed. s8°. [1921]
—— **& H. C. Bemrose.** Wright of Derby. s8°. [1922]
Smith (Spenser Theyre).
Happy pair. Comedietta. [P2583]. s8°. *French.* [1868]

Smith (Stanley). Lead & zinc ores of Northumberland & Alston Moor, *see* GEOLOG. SURVEY OF ENGLAND &c. Spec. rep. on mineral resources &c., v25, 1923.
Smith (*Sir* Swire). The real German rivalry. 8º. [1916]
see SNOWDEN (K.) The master spinner: life of Sir S. S., 1921.
Smith (Sybil Cormack).
That which was written. 2nd ed. s8º. [1913]
Smith (Sydney), *canon of S. Paul's; 1771–1845.* Letter to the electors upon the Cath. question.
2nd ed. [P2552]. 8º. York. 1826
Sermons. 2nd ed. 2v. s8º. 1801
see HOLLAND (S., *Lady*). Mem. of S. S. by h. daughter Lady H.; w. sel. f. h. letters, ed. Mrs. Austin, n. ed., 1878.
Smith (Theodore Clarke). Life & letters of J. A. Garfield.
2v. la8º. New Haven, *Yale.* 1925
Smith (Thomas), *F.S.A.* The assize of Jerusalem. Read before Leic. Lit. Soc. 8º. Leicester. 1842
Marculfus. la8º. Leicester. 1836
Smith (*Sir* Thomas), *c. 1558–1625, governor of the E. I. Co.*
*Sir Thomas Smithes voiage & entertainment in Rushia [*sic*].
s4º. 1605
Smith (Thomas), *master of Foxhounds.* The life of a fox, by himself. Intr. by Lord Willoughby de Broke. n. ed. la8º. 1920
Smith (Thomas), *fellow of Magd. Coll., Oxford, 1638–1710.*
De Græcæ Eccl. hodierno statu epistola.
ed. 2ª auctior. s8º. Londini. 1678
Epistolae quatuor: duae de moribus &c. Turcarum, duae septem Asiae eccl. & Constantinopoleos notitiam cont.
s8º. Oxonii. 1674
Miscellanea: Praemonitio—Def. libri de Gr. Ecclesiae statu—De vita &c. Cyrilli Lucarii &c. s8º. Londini. 1686
Smith (Thomas), *of Mary-le-bone.*
Histor. recoll. of Hyde Park. s8º. 1836
Smith (Thomas), *pastor, Portland, U.S.* Journals of Rev. T. S. & Rev. S. Deane w. notes & summ. hist. of Portland by W. Willis. 8º. Portland [*U.S.A.*] 1849
Smith (*Sir* Thomas), *Sec. of State; 1513–77.* The Commonwealth of England, & manner of govt. thereof. s8º. 1601
The Commonwealth of England; w. new add. of the chiefe Courts &c. s8º. 1635
,, ,, ... s8º. 1640
Smith (*Rt. Hon.* Thomas Berry Cusack), *Master of the Rolls in Ireland.* *Letter to S. &c. suggest. propriety of extending to Ireland reforms rec. adopted in Eng. [P2554]. 8º. D. 1844
Smith (Thomas Buckingham). Coleccion de var. doc. para la hist. de la Florida y tierras adyacentes.
t1. [*No more publ.*] 4º. Londres. [1857]
Smith (Thomas Grigg-), *see* GRIGG-SMITH (T.)
Smith (Thomas Roger).
Architecture, Gothic & Renaissance. 8º. 1884
—— **& J. Slater.** Architecture, classic & early Xtn. 8º. 1886
Smith (Thornley). Mem. of J. Whittle Appleyard. s8º. 1881
see WESLEY (J.) Xtn. theology; w. biogr. sketch by T. S., 1872.
Smith (Vincent Arthur), *M.R.A.S.* Early hist. of India f. 600 B.C. to the Muhammadan conquest incl. the invasion of Alex. the Great. 4th ed., rev by S. M. Edwardes. 8º. O. 1924
Indian constitut. reform. s8º. O. 1919
The Oxford hist. of India to 1911. 2nd ed., rev. & cont. to 1921 by S. M. Edwardes. s8º. O. 1923
Smith (W. C.) Short hist. of Irish Sea herring fisheries dur. 18th & 19th c. [Port Erin Biolog. Station. Publ., No. 1].
8º. Liv'l. 1923
Smith (W. Thomas), *see* FURST (H. E. A.) The mod. woodcut, w. ch. on practice of xylography by W. T. S., 1924.
Smith (W. Whately). A theory of the mechanism of survival: 4th dimension & its applic. 8º. 1920
see HART (M. D.) & W. W. S. Princ. of sound signalling, 1925.
Smith (Walter Chalmers).
*Borland Hall. 2nd ed. s8º. Glasgow. 1874
Hilda among the broken gods. [*Poem*].
3rd ed. s8º. Glasgow. 1882
Smith (Wilfred), *tutor in geography, Univ. of Liverpool.* Geogr. study of coal & iron in China. Intr. by P. M. Roxby. 8º. 1926
Smith (Willard M.) Gloves past & present. 8º. N.Y. 1918
Smith (*Rev.* William), *rector of Catwick.* Ancient springs & streams of the East Riding of Yorkshire. s8º. 1923
Smith (*Sir* William), *LL.D.* Dict. of Greek & Roman antiq.
2nd ed., impr. & enl. 8º. 1865
Dict. of Greek & Roman biography & mythology.
3v. 8º. 1862–64
Dict. of Greek & Roman geography. 2v. la8º. 1856–57

Smith (William), *chief justice of New York.* The hist. of the prov. of New York to 1732. 4º. 1757
Smith (William), *Sec. of Post Office Dept., Canada.* The hist. of the post office in Brit. N. America, 1639–1870. 8º. C. 1920
Smith (William), *potter & farmer, 1790–1858, see* BOURNE (G.) W. S., 1920.
Smith (William Carlson). The Ao Naga tribe of Assam. Intr. by J. H. Hutton. 8º. 1925
Smith (William H.), *see* TREFETHEN (J. A.) & W. H. S. Trial of T. & S. for murder of D. J. Davis, 1895.
Smith (William Ramsay). In southern seas: wanderings of a naturalist. 8º. [1924]
Smith (William Robertson). Kinship & marriage in early Arabia. n. ed. w. notes by the a. & by Prof. I. Goldziher.
8º. 1903
Lects. on the relig. of the Semites. The fundamental institutions. 3rd ed., w. intr. & add. notes by S. A. Cook.
8º. 1927
Smith (William Wesley). Pork-production; w. chap. on prevention of hog disease, by R. A. Craig. s8º. N.Y. 1920
Smith (Worthington George), *F.L.S.* Outlines of Brit. fungology. Suppl. [*to* Berkeley's Outlines of Brit. f., 1860].
8º. 1891
see FITCH (W. H.) & W. G. S. Illust. of Brit. flora, 1880.
Smith-Dampier (E. M.) Danish ballads. Tr. S.-D. s8º. C. 1920
Smith-Dorrien (*Gen. Sir* Horace Lockwood).
Mem. of 48 years' service. 8º. 1925
Smith, Elder & Co., *publishers, see* HUXLEY (L.) *The House of Smith Elder, 1923.
Smithells (Arthur), *see* CLERK (*Sir* D.), A. S. &c. Rep. on coal-gas & electr. supply indust[s]. of U.K., 1919.
Smithsonian Institution. Annals of the Astrophys. Obs. of the S.I.; by C. G. Abbot, F. E. Fowle & L. B. Aldrich.
v4. 4º. W. 1922
Ann. report of Board of Regents, 1919–1927. 8º. Wash. 1920–27
Each Rep. is in 2p, of which one is Rep. of U.S. National Museum.
Conference on the future of the S.I., Feb. 11, 1927.
8º. Wash. 1927
Explorations & field-work of the S.I. in 1918–26, *see* SMITHSONIAN INST. Misc. coll., v70, 72, 74, 76–78, 1919–27.
Misc. collections.
v58ii, 62, 67, 69–72, 74, 76–79. 8º. Wash. 1912–27
Abbot (C. G.) Distrib. of energy over the sun's disk, 1926. [78.]
—— On periodicity in solar variation, 1918. [69.]
—— Provision. solar-constant values, Aug. 1920 to Nov. 1924, 1925. [77.]
—— Solar variation & forecasting, 1925. [77.]
—— & A. F. Moore. Obs. of the total solar eclipse of May 29, 1919, 1920. [71.]
—— F. E. Fowle & L. B. Aldrich. Distrib. of energy in the spectra of the sun & stars, 1923. [74.]
Adams (E. P.) Smithsonian math. formulae, 1922. [74i.]
Aldrich (L. B.) The melikeron—an approx. black-body pyranometer, 1922. [72.]
—— Reflecting power of clouds, 1919. [69.]
—— Smithsonian eclipse exped. of June 8, 1918, 1919. [69.]
Britton (N. L.) & J. N. Rose. Neoabbottia, new cactus genus f. Hispaniola, 1921. [72.]
Candolle (C. de). Begoniaceae Centrali-Amer. & Ecuadorenses, 1919, 1921. [69.]
—— New species of Piper from Panama, 1920. [71.]
Clark (A. H.) Echinoderms as aberrant arthropods, 1921. [72.]
—— Sea-lilies & feather-stars, 1921. [72.]
Clayton (H. H.) Solar activity & long-per. weather changes, 1926. [78.]
—— Solar radiation & weather, 1925. [77.]
—— Variation in solar radiation & the weather, 1920. [71.]
—— World weather records; collected by Dr. F. Exner, Sir G. Walker &c., 1927. [79.]
Cushman (J. A.) Introd. to morphol. & classif. of Foraminifera, 1925. [77.]
Densmore (F.) Music of the Tule Indians of Panama, 1926. [77.]
Dixon (H. N.) Mosses coll. by Smithsonian African exped., 1909–10, 1918. [69.]
—— Rep. on 2 coll. of mosses f. Brit. East Afr., 1920. [72.]
—— Uganda mosses coll. by R. Dümmer & o., 1918. [69.]
[England]. Rep. on aircraft supply of Gt. Brit. &c., 1918, 1921. [69.]
Fewkes (J. W.) Add. designs on prehist. Mimbres pottery, 1924. [76.]
—— Archeolog. coll. f. Young's Canyon, nr. Flagstaff, Arizona, 1926. [77.]
—— Designs on prehist. pottery f. Mimbres valley, New Mexico, 1923. [74.]
—— Prelim. archeolog. explor. at Weeden Is., Florida, 1924. [76.]

Smithsonian Institution [*continued*].
Misc. collections [*continued*].
Fisher (W. J.) Brightness of lunar eclipses, 1860–1922, 1924. [76.]
Foote (J. S.) Circulatory system in bone, 1921. [72.]
Fowle (F. E.) Atmospheric scattering of light, 1918. [69.]
—— Smithsonian physical tables, 7th rev. ed., 1920. [71.]
Gilmore (C. W.) Fossil footprints f. the Grand Canyon, 1926. [77.]
—— New Sauropod dinosaur f. Ojo Alamo formation of New Mexico, 1922. [72.]
Goddard (R. H.) Method of reaching extreme altitudes, 1919. [71.]
Goldman (E. A.) Mammals of Panama, 1920. [69.]
Helland-Hansen (B.) & F. Nansen. Temperature variations in N. Atlantic & in the atmosphere, 1920. [70.]
Hess (F. L.) & E. Hess. Bibliog. of geology &c. of tin, 1912. [58ii.]
Hippisley (R. L.) Tables of elliptic functions, 1922. [74i.]
Hoxmark (G.) Solar rad. & weekly weather forecast of Argentine Meteorolog. Service, 1925. [77.]
Hrdlička (A.) The races of Russia, 1919. [69.]
Hunsaker (J. C.) Dynamical stability of aeroplanes, 1916. [62.]
—— E. Buckingham &c. Rep. on wind tunnel experiments &c., 1916. [62.]
Judd (N. M.) Archeolog. investig. at Paragonah, Utah, 1919. [70.]
Kellogg (R.) Appar. new toothed Cetacean f. S. Carolina, 1923. [76.]
Langley Ærodynamical Laboratory. Advisory Comm., 1913. [62.]
Lee (W. T.) Early mesozoic physiography of S. Rocky Mts., 1918. [69.]
Maxon (W. R.) New Selaginellas f. West. U.S., 1920. [72.]
Merriam (C. H.) Classific. & distrib. of Pit River Indian tribes of California, 1926. [78.]
Miller (G. S.), *jr.* Remains of mammals f. caves in Haiti, 1922. [74.]
—— Telescoping of the Cetacean skull, 1923. [76.]
Mitman (C. W.) Some pract. aspects of fuel economy, 1923. [76.]
Moore (A. F.) & L. H. Abbot. The brightness of the sky, 1920. [71.]
Oberholser (H. C.) New East Indian birds, Turdidae &c., 1923. [76.]
—— New Timaline birds f. E. Indies, 1922. [74.]
Palmer (H.) Freshfield glacier, 1924. [76.]
Richardson (H. C.) Hydromechanic experiments w. flying boat hulls, 1914. [62.]
Ridgway (R.) Diagnoses of some new genera of birds, 1920. [72.]
Schroeder (H.) Hist. of electric light, 1923. [76.]
Schuchert (C.) A lower Cambrian Edrioasterid, Stromatocystites walcotti, 1919. [70.]
[S.I.] Explorations & field-work of the S.I. in 1918–26, 1919–27. [70, 72, 74, 76–78.]
—— Report on coop. educat. & research work, 1923. [76.]
Smithsonian meteorological tables, 4th rev. ed., 1918. [69.]
Snodgrass (R. E.) Morphol. of insect sense organs &c., 1926. [77.]
Snyder (T. E.) "Adaptations" to soc. life: the Termites (Isoptera), 1924. [76.]
Springer (F.) On the fossil crinoid family Catillocrinidae, 1923. [76.]
Standley (P. C.) Flora of Barro Colorado Is., Panama, 1927. [78.]
Stejneger (L.) Chap. in hist. of zoolog. nomenclature, 1924. [77.]
Thériot (I.) Mexican mosses coll. by A. Brouard, 1926. [78.]
Thorington (J. M.) Lyell & Freshfield glaciers, Canadian Rocky Mts., 1926. [78.]
Walcott (C. D.) Cambrian geology & paleontology, IV, 1924. [67.]
Wetmore (A.) Body temperature of birds, 1921. [72.]
—— Remains of birds f. caves in Haiti, 1922. [74.]
Winge (H.) Review of interrelationships of the Cetacea; tr., 1921. [72.]
Zahm (A. F.) Rep. on European aeronautical laboratories, 1914. [62.]

References.
see Gilbert (C. G.) Sources of nitrogen compounds in U.S., 1916.
,, Jewett (C. C.) On the construction of catalogues &c., 1853.

Bureau of Ethnology.
Bulletins 40, 58, 67, 68, 70–83, 85. 8º. Wash. 1914–27
List of publications of the B. of Amer. Ethnology, w. index to authors & titles. [58.]
see Boas (F.) Hdbk. of Amer. Ind. languages, p2, 1922. [40.]
,, Bushnell (D. I.), *jr.* Burials of the Algonquian, Siouan &c. tribes, 1927. [83.]
,, —— Native cemeteries &c. E. of Mississippi, 1920. [71.]
,, —— Native villages &c. E. of the Mississippi, 1919. [69.]

Smithsonian Institution [*continued*].
Bureau of Ethnology [*continued*].
Bulletins [*continued*].
see Bushnell (D. I.) Villages of Algonquian &c. tribes W. of Mississippi, 1922. [77.]
,, Densmore (F.) Mandan & Hidatsa music, 1923. [80.]
,, —— Northern Ute music, 1922. [75.]
,, Fewkes (J. W.) Prehist. villages, castles &c. of S.-W. Colorado, 1919. [70.]
,, Fowke (G.) Archeolog. investig., 1922. [76.]
,, Frachtenberg (L. J.) Alsea texts & myths, 1920. [67.]
,, Jeancon (J. A.) Excav. in the Chama Valley, New Mexico, 1923. [81.]
,, Judd (N. M.) Archeolog. obs. N. of the Rio Colorado, 1926. [82.]
,, Karsten (R.) Blood revenge &c. am. Jibaro Indians of E. Ecuador, 1923. [79.]
,, Kroeber (A. L.) Hdbk. of the Indians of Cal., 1925. [78.]
,, Michelson (T.) Contrib. to Fox ethnology, 1927. [85.]
,, —— The Owl sacred pack of the Fox Indians, 1921. [72.]
,, Swanton (J. R.) Early hist. of the Creek Indians &c., 1922. [73.]
,, —— Struct. &c. comparison of the Tunica, Chitimacha & Atakapa lang., 1919. [68.]
,, Tozzer (A. M.) Excav. of a site at Santiago Ahuitzotla, D. F. Mexico, 1921. [74.]

Report (Annual), 33rd–40th (1911–19). la8º. Wash. 1919–25
Boas (F.) Ethnology of the Kwakiutl, based on data coll. by G. Hunt, 2p, 1921. [35.]
Fewkes (J. W.) Designs on prehist. Hopi pottery, 1919. [33.]
—— A prehistor. island culture area of Amer. [34.]
Gilmore (M. R.) Uses of plants by Indians of Missouri River Region, 1919. [33.]
Haleole (S. N.) Hawaiian romance of Laieikawai; intr. & tr. by M. W. Beckwith, 1919. [33.]
La Flesche (F.) The Osage tribe: rite of chiefs &c., 1921. [36.]
—— The Osage: rite of vigil, 1925. [39.]
Michelson (T.) Autobiog. of a Fox Ind. woman, 1925. [40.]
—— Mythical orig. of White Buffalo Dance of Fox Indians, 1925. [40.]
—— Notes on Fox mortuary customs & beliefs, 1925. [40.]
—— Notes on Fox society known as "Those who worship the Little Spotted Buffalo," 1925. [40.]
—— Tradit. origin of the Fox society known as "The singing around rite," 1925. [40.]
Morris (E. H.) Prelim. rep. of antiq. of region betw. Mancos & La Plata Rivers in S.-W. Colorado, 1919. [33.]
Radin (P.) The Winnebago tribe, 1923. [37.]
Roth (W. E.) Intr. study of arts, crafts, & customs of the Guiana Indians, 1924. [38.]

Study of Natural Resources.
see Wyer (S. S.) Niagara Falls, 1925.

United States National Museum.
Bulletins 39, 50, 82, 99, 100iii–v, 102–104, 106, 108–127, 129–141 & Spec. bull. 8º. Wash. 1919–28
Bull. 39 *has gen. tp.:* Directions for collecting & preserving specimens, *by var. a.* [p. C, F, J, L, N, *wanting*].
Bull. 103 *has gen. tp.:* Contrib. to the geol. &c. of the Canal Zone, Panama &c., *by var. a. whose contrib. are catalogued separately.*
see Banks (N.) Revision of the Nearctic termites, 1920. [108.]
,, Bartsch (P.) A monograph of Amer. shipworms, 1922. [122.]
,, Bent (A. C.) Life hist. of N. Amer. gulls & their terns, 1921. [113.]
,, —— Life hist. of N. Amer. marsh birds, 1926. [135.]
,, —— Life hist. of N. Amer. petrels &c., 1922. [121.]
,, —— Life hist. of N. Amer. wild fowl: Order Anseres (pt.), 1923–25. [126, 130.]
,, Berry (E. W.) The fossil higher plants f. the Canal Zone, 1918. [103.]
,, Blanchard (F. N.) Revision of the king snakes: Genus Lampropeltis, 1921. [114.]
,, Canu (F.) & R. S. Bassler. Bryozoa of the Canal Zone &c., 1918. [103.]
,, —— & —— North Amer. early Tertiary Bryozoa, 1920. [106.]
,, —— & —— North Amer. later Tertiary &c. Bryozoa, 1923. [125.]
,, Chapman (F. M.) Distrib. of bird life in Urubamba valley of Peru. [117.]
,, Clark (A. H.) Monog. of existing Crinoids, v1, p2, 1921. [82.]
,, Cram (E. B.) Bird parasites of the Nematode suborders Strongylata &c., 1927. [140.]
,, Cushman (J. A.) Foraminifera of the Atlantic Ocean, p1–5, 1918–24. [104.]
,, —— Foraminifera of Philippine & adjac. seas, 1921. [100iv.]
,, —— Larger fossil Foraminifera of the Panama Canal Zone, 1918. [103.]
,, —— Smaller fossil Foraminifera of the Panama Canal Zone, 1918. [103.]

Smithsonian Institution [*continued*].
United States National Museum [*continued*].
Bulletins [*continued*].
see Dall (W. H.) Summ. of the marine shellbearing mollusks of the N.W. coast of America, 1921. [112.]
,, Densmore (F.) Hdbk. of coll. of musical instruments in U.S. Nat. Mus., 1927. [136.]
,, Fisher (W. K.) Biol. of Philippine Archip. &c.: starfishes, 1919. [100iii.]
,, Gahan (A. B.) & M. M. Fagan. Type species of the genera of Chalcidoidea, 1923. [124.]
,, Gilbert (C. G.), J. E. Pogue & S. S. Wyer. Mineral indust. of the U.S., 8p, 1917–23. [102.]
,, Gilmore (C. W.) Osteology of the carnivorous Dinosauria in U.S. Nat. Mus., 1920. [110.]
,, Heinrich (C.) Revis. of the N. Amer. moths of subfam. Eucosminae of fam. Olethreutidae, 1923. [123.]
,, —— Revision of N. Amer. moths &c., 1926. [132.]
,, Henderson (J. B.) A monograph of the East Amer. Scaphopod mollusks, 1920. [111.]
,, Hollister (N.) E. Afr. mammals, p1–3, 1918–24. [99.]
,, Hough (W.) Coll. of heating &c. utensils in U.S. Nat. Mus., 1928. [141.]
,, —— Fire as an agent in human culture, 1926. [139.]
,, Howe (M. A.) On some fossil & rec. Lithothamnieae of the Panama Canal Zone, 1918. [103.]
,, Jackson (R. T.) Fossil Echini of the Panama Canal Zone & Costa Rica, 1918. [103.]
,, Koehler (R.) Ophiurans of the Philippine Seas & adj. waters; tr., 1922. [100v.]
,, Krieger (H. W.) Material culture of people of S.-E. Panama, 1926. [134.]
,, —— Prim. weapons & armor of the Philippine Is., 1926. [137.]
,, MacDonald (D. F.) Sediment. format. of the Panama Canal Zone, 1919. [103.]
,, Merrill (G. P.), *ed.* Contrib. to a hist. of Amer. state &c. surveys, 1920. [109.]
,, —— Handbook & descr. cat. of coll. of gems &c. in U.S. Nat. Mus., 1922. [118.]
,, Metcalf (M. M.) The Opalinid ciliate infusorians, 1923. [120.]
,, Mitman (C. W.) Cat. of the mechan. engineering coll. in the U.S. Nat. Mus.: motors, locomot. & self-propell. vehicles, 1922. [119.]
,, —— Cat. of watercraft coll. in U.S. Nat. Mus., 1923. [127.]
,, Nutting (C. C.) Amer. hydroids, p3, The Campanularidæ & the Bonneviellidæ, 1915. [Spec. bull.]
,, Pilsbry (H. A.) Cirripedia f. the Panama Canal Zone, 1918. [103.]
,, Rathbun (M. J.) Decapod crustaceans f. the Panama region, 1918. [103.]
,, —— Fossil stalk-eyed Crustacea of Pacific slope of N. Amer., 1926. [138.]
,, —— Spider crabs of America, 1925. [129.]
,, Ridgway (R.) Birds of N. & Middle America, p8, 1919. [50.]
,, Shannon (E. V.) Minerals of Idaho, 1926. [131.]
,, Springer (F.) The fossil crinoid genus Dolatocrinus & its allies, 1921. [115.]
,, Van Duzee (M. C.), F. R. Cole & J. M. Aldrich. The dipterous genus Dolichopus Latreille in N. America, 1921. [116.]
,, Vaughan (T. W.) Biologic character &c. of the sediment. format. of Panama, 1919. [103.]
,, —— Fossil corals f. C. Amer., Cuba & Porto Rico, 1919. [103.]
,, Wetmore (A.) Obs. on birds of Argentina &c., 1926. [133.]
Proceedings. v55–71. 8º. Wash. 1920–28

Smits (Andreas).
The theory of allotropy. Tr. J. S. Thomas. 8º. 1922

Smoke rings & roundelays, 1924, *see* Partington (W.), *ed.*

Smoke Alley, *see* Dublin.

Smolensky (Mikhail). Троцкiй. [P2570; 2850]. s8º. Берлинъ. 1921

Smolensky (S.) Крымская катастрофа. [P2526]. 8º. Софiя. 1921

Smollett (Tobias George).
Ferdinand Count Fathom. 2v. s8º. O. 1925
Humphry Clinker. 2v. s8º. O. 1925
Peregrine Pickle. Illust. by G. Cruikshank. 2v. s8º. 1831
,, ,, 2v. s8º. *Bohn.* 1895
,, ,, 4v. s8º. O. 1925
Poet. works. Coll. by T. Park. s8º. 1807
Roderick Random. 2v. s8º. O. 1925–26
Roderick Random. [Intr. by H. W. Hodges. Everyman's Lib.] s8º. [1927]
Sir Launcelot Greaves, w. The hist. & adv. of an Atom. s8º. O. 1926
see Buck (H. S.) S. as poet, 1927.
,, Melville (L.) Life & letters of T. S., 1721–71, 1926.

Smon-lam-btschu-tham &c., *see* Tübetisches. T. Gebetbuch, 1835.

Smout (Adriaan) [Smoutius]. Nicolaus Grevinchovius, Heautontimorumenos &c. s4º. Amsterodami. 1617

Smuts (*Gen. Rt. Hon.* **Jan Christiaan).**
Holism & evolution. 8º. 1926

Smyth (*Mrs.* **Agnes).** The Christian's triumph. s8º. 1783

Smyth (Charles Hugh Egerton). Cranmer & the Reformation under Edward VI. Thirlwall &c. Prize Essay, 1925. 8º. C. 1926

Smyth (Edward), *minister of Bethesda chapel, Dublin.* An acc. of the trial of E. S. [P2667]. s8º. D. 1777
see *Dialogue (A) betw. the pulpit & reading desk [*sometimes attrib. to E. S.*], 1786; 1795.

Smyth (*Mrs.* **Eleanor C.)**
An essay on Chaucer. [P2736]. 8º. [1924]

Smyth (Ethel). A final burning of boats &c. [*includ.* Two comedies]. 8º. 1928
Streaks of life. 8º. 1921
A three-legged tour in Greece, 1925. 8º. 1927

Smyth (Herbert Weir).
Æschylean tragedy. 8º. Berkeley, *California.* 1924

Smyth (John Paterson) [Paterson-Smyth (J.)]
The gospel of the hereafter. 21st ed. 8º. *n.d.*
The story of St. Paul's life & letters. 3rd ed. s8º. [1921?]

Smyth (John William), *see* Scinde. Gazetteer, vol. Bi–vii; comp. by J. W. S., 1919–20.

Smyth (*Capt.* **Ralph)** & *Capt.* **E. H. L. Thuilier.** A manual of surveying for India. Prep. for use of Survey Dept. Comp. by R. S. & E. H. L. T. 8º. Calcutta. 1851

Smyth (Richard), *D.D., Dean of St. Peter's Church, Douay, see* Smith (R.)

Smyth (William), *prof. of mod. hist. in the univ. of Cambridge, 1765–1849.* A list of books recomm. in lect. on mod. hist. by S. 8º. C. 1823

Smyth (*Rear-Admiral* **William Henry),** *1788–1865.* The cycle of celestial objects cont. at Hartwell Observatory to 1859 &c. 4º. *f.p.c.* 1860
Descr. cat. of a cabinet of Roman imperial large-brass medals. 4º. Bedford. 1834
Synopsis of the publ. & priv. printed works of S. 4º. *f.p.c.* 1864

Smythaeus (Ricardus), *see* Smith (Richard).

Smythe (Lionel Percy), *R.A., see* Whitlaw (R. M.) & W. L. Wyllie. L. P. S., 1923.

Smythe (*Mrs.* **S. M.),** *wife of Col. W. J. Smythe.* Ten months in the Fiji Islands. With an intr. by Col. W. J. Smythe. 8º. O. 1864

Smythe (William Ellsworth).
City homes on country lanes. 8º. N.Y. 1921

Snaffle, *ps.* *The impossible island: Corsica &c. 8º. 1923

Snaith (John Collis).
The adventurous lady. s8º. [1920]
The council of seven. s8º. [1921]
The hoop. s8º. [1927]
Thus far. s8º. [1925]
The Van Roon. s8º. 1922
What is to be. s8º. [1926]

Snape (R. H.)
Eng. monastic finances in the later M.A. 8º. C. 1926

Snappe (John), *see* Salter (H. E.) S.'s formulary &c. (14 c.), 1924.

Snavely (Tipton Ray), *see* United States: Labor. Negro migration in 1916–17: reps. by R. H. Leavell, T. R. S. &c., 1919.

Snegirev (Ivan Mikhailovich).
Рускiе въ своихъ пословицахъ. 4кн. s8º. Москва. 1831–34
Рускiе простонародные праздники и суевѣрные обряды. 2в. 8º. Москва. 1837–38

Snell (Bruno). Die Ausdr. f. d. Begriff d. Wissens in d. vorplaton. Philos., *see* Kiessling (A.) & U. v. Wilamowitz-Möllendorf. Philol. Unters., H29, 1924.

Snell (Carl).
Die Streitfrage d. Materialismus. [P2491]. 8º. Jena. 1858

Snell (Frederick John), *M.A.*
The age of Alfred, 664–1154. s8º. 1912
Blundell's: sh. hist. 8º. [1928]
The Celtic borderland. s8º. [1928]
King Arthur's country. 8º. 1926

Snell (*Maj.* **S.)** Story of railway pioneers: inventions &c. of I. & T. W. Dodds. 8º. [1921]

Snellius (Willebrodus), *see* Jacchaeus (G.) Oratio in obit. W. S., 1626.

Snepff (Theodorich), *see* Schnepff (T.)

Snesarev (*capt.*), *see* Turkestan. Штаба Т. Военн. Округа: Свѣдѣнiя; сост. С. &c., вып. 24–35, 1901–3.

Sneyd (Ralph). Cat. of old Eng. & Fr. furniture, porcelain &c.: portion of S. heirlooms; also the property of Mrs. J. A. Mango &c. Sold by Christie, June 26, 1924. [*Illust.* P2748]. 8°. 1924
Cat. of silver & silver-gilt plate, portion of the S. heirlooms. Sold by Christie, June 24, 1924. [*Illust.* P2748]. 8°. 1924
Snider (Denton Jacques). The redemption of the Hamlets: drama. s8°. St. Louis. 1923
Snift (*Dean*), *of Brazen-Nose, ps.*, see HILL (B. E.)
Snodgrass (Robert Evans). Morphology of insect sense organs &c., see SMITHSONIAN INST. Misc. colls., v77, 1926.
Snoilsky (*grefve* **Carl Johann Gustaf),** *see* WARBURG (C.) C. S., hans lefnad och skaldskap, 1905.
Snorri, *Sturlason.*
see EDDA *for the prose Edda* [*Snorre Edda*].
,, WACHTER (F.) Heimskringlae &c., illust. specimen, 1834.
Snow (A. J.) Matter & gravity in Newton's physical philosophy. 8°. 1926
Snow (Alpheus Henry). The American philosophy of government. Essays. 8°. N.Y. 1921
The question of aborigines in the law & practice of nations. 8°. N.Y. 1921
Snow (E. C.) Leather, hides, skins & tanning materials. Intr. by Sir E. Geddes & Sir S. Barrow. [Resources of the Empire, v6]. 4°. 1924
Snowden (*Mrs.* **Ethel),** *wife of Philip Snowden.*
A political pilgrim in Europe. 8°. 1921
Through Bolshevik Russia. 8°. 1920
——, **J. H. Thomas, R. Williams** *& others.*
What we want & why. s8°. [1922]
Snowden (Keighley) [SNOWDEN (JAMES)]. The master spinner. A life of Sir Swire Smith, LL.D., M.P. 8°. [1921]
Snowden (Philip). Labour & the new world. s8°. 1921
Wages & prices. s8°. 1920
Snowden (*Mrs.* **Philip),** *see* SNOWDEN (*Mrs.* ETHEL).
Snowdon. The mountains of Snowdonia, 1925, *see* CARR (H. R. C.) & G. A. LISTER, *edd.*
Snoy (Reynerius) [SNOYGOUDANUS]. Psalterium paraphrasibus ill. Autore R. Snoy. s8°. Coloniae. 1536
,, ,, ...s8°. Parisiis. 1551
Snyder (Edward Douglas).
The Celtic revival in Eng. lit., 1760–1800. 8°. C. 1923
Snyder (Thomas Elliott). "Adaptations" to social life: the Termites (Isoptera), 1924, *see* SMITHSONIAN INST. Misc. Coll., v76, 1925.
see BANKS (N.) Revision of the Nearctic termites, w. notes on biology & geogr. distrib. by T. E. S., 1920.
Snyder (William Henry), *see* DAVIS (W. M.) Physical geography; by W. M. D. ass. by W. H. S., 1898.
Soames (Henry). The Anglo-Saxon Church. 2nd ed. 8°. 1838
Soane (*Sir* **John),** *1753–1837,* **& Soane Museum.**
An account of the sarcophagus of Seti I. By E. A. W. Budge. s8°. 1908
Descr. of the house & museum, Lincoln's Inn Fields, residence of Sir J. S. Ed. f. orig. "Descr.," 1835, by A. T. Bolton. 10th ed. of offic. hdbk. of Sir J. Soane Museum. 8°. O. 1920
Designs for public improvements in London & Westminster. fol. 1827
Souvenir of Sir J. S., 1753–1837. [Soane Mus. Publ., No. 5. P2740]. la8°. *n.d.*
The works of Sir J. S. [Ed. A. T. Bolton. Soane Museum Publ., No. 8]. 4°. [1924]
see BIRNSTINGL (H. J.) Sir J. S., 1925.
,, BOLTON (A. T.) Archit. & decor. of R. Adam & Sir J. S. (1758–1837), 1920.
,, —— Archit. educ. a cent. ago: office of Sir J. S. &c., 1924.
,, —— Eng. 18th c. sculptures in Sir J. S.'s mus., *n.d.*
,, —— Life & work a cent. ago: career of Sir J. S., 1923.
,, HOFLAND (B.) Pop. descr. of house, museum & library; ed. A. T. Bolton, 1919.
Soar (Charles D.) & W. Williamson. The Brit. Hydracarina. [Ray Soc., 110, 112]. v1, 2. 8°. 1925–27
Soares (José Carlos de Macedo), *see* MACEDO SOARES (J. C. DE).
Soares de Souza (Gabriel). Tratado descr. do Brasil em 1587; ed. F. A. de Varnhagen, 2ª ed., *see* INSTITUTO HIST. E GEOG. BRAZIL. Rev., t14 (1851), 1879.
Soarez (Cyprianus), *Jesuit.* De arte rhetorica libri 3 ex Aristotele, Cicerone & Quinctiliano praecipue deprompti. s8°. Coloniæ. 1584
Soarez (Emanuel Laurentius), *see* SANCHEZ (T.) Compend. totius tract. de s. matrimonii sacramento T. S. [ab E. L. S.] ordine alphabet. dispos., 1860.
Soave (Dominic), *see* SAVIO (D.)
Soba (Rudolf). Oberschlesien u. s. Bedeutung insbes. für Breslau. Vorwort v. F. Kleiner. [P2526]. 8°. Breslau. [1921]
***Sober** (A) & temperate disc. conc. the interest of words in prayer. The just antiq. &c. of liturgies. By H. D[aubney ?], M.A. s8°. 1661
Sobieski (*Princess* **Clementina),** *see* MARIA CLEMENTINA.
Sobieski (Jakob), *marshal of the Polish Diet, see* LISKE (J.) Viajes de extranjeros por España &c.: J. S. (1611) &c., 1878.
Sobieski (John), *ps., see* †ALLAN (JOHN HAY).
Sobius (Jacobus), *see* LIVY. Hist. Romani &c.; castigatiores autore J. S., 1525.
Sobolevsky (Sergei Aleksandrovich), *see* SAITOV (V. I.) С. друг Пушкина, 1922.
Sobranie. Собраніе актовъ относящ. къ. обозр. ист. армянск. народа, 1833–38, *see* ARMENIA.
*Собраніе запрещенныхъ стиховъ и прозы.
изд. 6ое [*b. w.* Объ аристократіи, 1874]. s8°. Лейпцигъ. [1874 ?]
Social. Social & polit. ideas of gt. thinkers of the Renaissance &c., 1925, *see* HEARNSHAW (F. J. C.), *ed.*
Social problems & social policy; [*by var. wr.*], 1924, *see* FORD (J.), *ed.*
Socialists-Revolutionists. The twelve who are to die. [*By* W. Woitinsky]. Trial of the Soc.-Rev. in Moscow. [Pref. K. Kautsky]. s8°. Berlin. 1922
For Russian ed., see SOTSIALISTI-REVOLYUTSIONERI.
Sociedad de Amigos del Arte, *see* ARTE ESPAÑOL, 1912–.
Sociedad de Bibliófilos Andaluces, *see* VILLA (A. M.) Reseña hist. de la Univ. de Sevilla &c., 1886.
Sociedad de Bibliófilos Españoles.
[*Publications*]. 8°. 1914–27
see CUEVA (J. DE LA). Comedias y tragedias, 2t, 1917.
,, HAEDO (D. DE). Topog. e hist. gen. de Argel, t1, 1927.
,, PORREÑO (B.) Dos trat. hist. toc. al card. Ximenez de Cisneros, 1918.
,, RUFO (J.) Las seiscientas apotegmas &c., 1923.
,, SERRANO Y SANZ (M.) Relaciones hist. de Amer., sig. 16, 1916.
,, SUAREZ DE FIGUEROA (C.) El passagero, 1914.
,, ULLOA Y PEREIRA (L. DE). Memorias &c., 1925.
Società Dantesca Italiana.
Bullettino. N.S., v25–28. [*no more publ.*] 8°. Firenze. 1918–21
see DANTE ALIGHIERI. Opere: testo crit. d. Soc. D. Ital.; a cura di M. Barbi, 1921.
Società di Mutuo Soccorso fra Barcajuoli di Venezia.
Monografia. [P2835]. 8°. Venezia. 1892
Società Filologica Romana, *see* MONACI (E.) Studj romanzi, v10–13, 1913–17.
Società Geografica Italiana (Reale), *see* UGOLINI (L. M.) Albania antica, v1, 1927.
Società Napoletana di Storia Patria. Monumenti storici. ser. 1. Cronache.
see FERRARIA. Ignoti monachi Cisterc. S. Mariae de F. Chron. &c.; ed. A. Gaudenzi, 1888.
Società Siciliana per la Storia Patria. Archivio storico siciliano. N.S., 43–46. la8°. Palermo. 1921–25
Abbadessa (G.) Le aspirazioni ital. nei canti dei poeti irredenti, 1921. [N.S., 43.]
Amatucci (A. G.) L'Eneide di Virgilio e la Sicilia, 1924. [N.S., 45.]
Garufi (C. A.) Contrib. alla storia dell' Inquis. de Sicilia nei sec. 16 e 17, 1921. [N.S., 43.]
Giordano (N.) Il diritto marittimo sicil. d. orig. al s. 14, 1921–22. [N.S., 43, 44.]
Natoli (L.) Il primo sogg. di G. Balsamo a Parigi &c., 1925. [N.S., 46.]
Niceforo (N.) La Sicilia e la costit. del 1812, 1922–25. [N.S., 44–46.]
Orlando (V. E.) Contrib. alla storia di Partinico, 1922. [N.S., 44.]
Quinci (G. B.) Un breve soggiorno di Maria Carolina in Mazara, 1924. [N.S., 45.]
Romano (S.) A Fiume e in Dalmazia, 1921. [N.S., 43.]
Sansone (A.) I moniti di un veggente, 1922. [N.S., 44.]
—— Santuario del patriottismo, 1921. [N.S., 43.]
Scaturro (I.) La Contessa normanna Giulietta di Sciacca, 1921. [N.S., 43.]
Societàd reto-romantscha.
Annalas. Annada 15, 17–20, 25–29. la8°. Coira. 1901–15
Societas Latina Jenensis, *see* EICHSTÄDT (H. C. A.) Acroasis pro S. L. J. instauratione, 1800.
Societas Spinozana.
see FREUDENTHAL (J.) S.: Leben u. Lehre; hrsg. C. Gebhardt, 1927.
,, SPINOZA (B. DE). Chronicon S. [*by var. a.*], 3t, 1921–23.
,, —— Spinozana, 1897–1922, 1922.

Société Académique de l'Oise.
Publications. Documents, t4, 6. la8°. 1919–21
see BEAUVAIS. Cartul. de l'Hôtel-Dieu de B.; [publ. &c.] V. Leblond, 1919. [t4.]
,, LEBLOND (V.) L'art & les artistes en Ile-de-France, 16e s. (Beauvais & Beauvaisis), 1921. [t6.]

Société Archéologique de Montpellier, *see* GUILLEMS, *Seigneurs de Montpellier.* Liber instrument. memorialium &c., 1884–86.

Société Archéologique d'Eure-et-Loir, *see* TIRON. Cartul. de l'abbaye de la Ste.-Trinité de T.; publ. &c. par L. Merlet, 2t, 1883.

Société Archéologique du Midi de la France.
Mémoires. t17, livr. 1. [*no more publ.*] 4°. Toulouse. 1919

Société Archéologique et Historique de la Charente.
Cartulaires de l'Angoumois. t1. 4°. Angoulême. 1867
see BAIGNE. Cartul. de l'abbaye de St-Etienne de B., 1867. [1.]

Société Archéologique et Historique de l'Orléanais.
see BAUGENCY. Cartul. de l'abbaye de Notre-Dame de B., 1879.

Société Artistique des Amateurs, *see* DACIER (E.) Expos. des Saint-Aubin organ. par la Soc. A. des A., 1925, 1925.

Société Asiatique. Chrestomathie chinoise. 4°. 1833
see EL MASUDI. M.: le livre de l'avertissement & de la revision; tr., 1896.
,, KLAPROTH (H. J. v.) Vocab. & gramm. de la langue géorgienne, pl, 1827.
,, TRIPITAKA. 500 contes &c., extr. du Tripitaka chinois; tr., 3t, 1910–11.

Société d'Archéologie de la Drôme, *see* BOURG-LÈS-VALENCE. Cartul. du prieuré de St.-Pierre du B.-lès-Valence, 1875.

Société d'Avocats, *ps.* *Causes crimin. célèbres du 19e siècle, réd. par une Soc. d'A., 4t, 1827–28, *see* CAUSES.

Société de Géographie, *see* ROHAN-CHABOT. Angola & Rhodesia: mission R.-C., 1923–25.

Société de Législation Comparée. Annuaire de législ. étrangère. Publ. par la S. de L. C. 1919–25 (s2, année 17–23, 47–53 de la Coll.) la8°. 1920–26
Annuaire de législ. franç. Publ. par la S. de L. C. 1920–1922, 1924–1926, année 40–42, 44–46. la8°. 1921–27
Bulletin. t46–56. la8°. 1917–27

Société de l'Histoire de France.
Annuaire-Bulletin, année 1919–26. 8°. 1919–26
see FLEURANGE. Mém., 1505–25, 2t, 1913–24.
,, FRANCE. Les grandes chroniques de F., t1–4, 1920–27.
,, —— Les grandes chron. de F.: Chron. des règnes de Jean II & de Charles V, t3, 4, 1920.
,, MANDROT (B. DE), *ed.* Dépêches des ambassadeurs milanais en France sous Louis XI & F. Sforza, t3, 4 (1465–66), 1920–23.
,, PETRUS, *Sarnensis.* Hyst. Albigensis, t1, 1926.
,, RICHELIEU (*le card. duc* DE). Méms., t5–8, 1921–27.
,, —— Rapports &c. sur l'éd. des mém. de R., t3, 1922.
,, VIVONNE (L. V. DE R., *maréchal duc* DE). Corr. rel. à l'expéd. de Messine, t2, 1676–78, 1911.

Société de l'Histoire de la Guerre.
Publications. sér. 1. t1–3. 8°. 1921–22
see BIBLIOTHÈQUE & MUSÉE DE LA GUERRE. Cat. méthod., t1–3, 1921–22.

Société de l'Histoire de l'Art Français.
Bulletin. Année 1920–1926. 8°. 1920–26
Nouvelles archives de l'art français. Nouv. période, *w. t.* Archives de l'art franç. t11–14. 8°. 1921–27
Bibl. Nat. Cat. des ouvrages rel. aux beaux-arts du cabinet des estampes de la Bibl. Nat., t1; intr. par F. Courboin. [11.]
Courteault (P.) La Place Royale de Bordeaux, 1922. [12.]
Guiffrey (J.) L'œuvre de P. P. Prud'hon, 1924. [13.]
see ACADÉMIE ROYALE D'ARCHITECTURE. Procès-verbaux, 1671–1793, t6–8, 1744–79, 1920–24.
,, ACADÉMIE ROY. DE PEINTURE &C. Le Salon de 1725, 1924.
,, GUIFFREY (J. J.) Les dessins de l'hist. des rois de France par N. Houel, 1920.

Société de l'Histoire de l'Inde Française.
see PONDICHÉRY. Cat. des mss. des anc. archives de l'Inde franç., t2, 1924.
,, —— Corresp. du Conseil Supérieur de P. & de la Comp., t1, 2, 1920.

Société de l'Histoire de Normandie, *see* HENRY VI, *king of England.* Actes de la Chancellerie d'H. VI conc. la Normandie, 1422–35, t2, 1908.

Société de l'Histoire de Paris & de l'Ile de France.
Bulletin. Année 43–54, 1916–27. 8°. 1916–28
Mémoires. t47, 48. 8°. 1924–25
t48 *cont.* Mélanges publ. à l'occasion du cinquantenaire de la Soc., 1.
Anchel (R.) La commém. des rois de France à Paris pend. la Restauration, 1924. [47.]
Dumolin (M.) Notes sur les vieux guides de Paris, 1924. [47.]
Mirot (L.) Une propriété rurale de la famille Gobelin: la Cour-Roland, 1924. [47.]
Roy (M.) Philibert de Lorme à Paris (1546–59), 1924. [47.]
Sainte-Geneviève, *Paris.* Cat. des œuvres d'art de la Bibl. S.-G., 1924. [47.]
Vallet (F.) Rel. inéd. des obsèques de François I, 1924. [47.]

Société de l'Histoire des Colonies Françaises.
see LA BISSACHÈRE (P. J. L. DE). Rel. sur le Tonkin & la Cochinchine (1807), 1920.
,, MARTINEAU (A.) Dupleix & l'Inde fr., 1722–1749, 2t, 1920–23.

Société de Linguistique de Paris.
see GRAMMONT (M.) Le vers franç., 1923.
,, LANGUES (Les) du monde; Meillet & Cohen, 1924.
,, MAROUZEAU (J.) L'ordre des mots dans la phrase lat., 1, Les groupes nominaux, 1922.
,, MEILLET (A.) Ling. hist. &c., 1921.
,, —— Le slave commun, 1924.

Société de Littérature Wallonne. Annuaire, 1920, 1921–22, 1923, 1924–25. s8°. Liège. 1920–24
Bulletin, t56–62. 8°. Liège. 1922–28
Bull. du dict. gén. de la langue wallonne. 11–13 année (1921–25). [*no tp.*] 8°. Liège. [1922–25]

Société d'Emulation de Bruges.
see GOETHALS (A.) Chron. monast. St. Andreae juxta Brugas, 1844.
,, STOOP (P. DE). Not. sur l'abbaye de Loo, & invent. de ses archives, 1843.

Société des Amateurs de Jardins, *see* GAZETTE ILLUSTRÉE DES AMATEURS DE JARDINS.

Société des Anciens Textes Français. Bulletin. Année 40, No. 1, 48–52 (1914, 1922–26). 8°. 1914–27
Liste des membres. 8°. 1926
Publications.
see DOON, *de Laroche.* Chanson de geste, 1921.
,, LORRIS (G. DE) & J. DE MEUNG. Roman de la rose, t2–4, 1920–22.
,, MACHAULT (G. DE). Œuvres, t3, 1921.
,, PONTIEU. La fille du Comte de Pontieu, 1923.

Société des Antiquaires de la Morinie, *see* TÉROUANE. Cartul. de l'église de T., 1881.

Société des Antiquaires de Picardie.
Sér. 4, t8–10 [38–40]. 8°. 1914–25

Société des Archives Historiques de la Gironde, *see* DAX. Le Livre noir & les Etablissements de D.; [*ed. &c.*] F. Abbadie, 1902.

Société des Archives Historiques du Maine. Archives hist. du Maine. [t]4, 10. 8°. au Mans. 1903–13
see LE MANS. Cartul. du Chapitre Royal de St.-Pierre-de-la-Cour, *& Introd.*: Le Chap. Royal &c., 1903–10. [4, 10.]
,, —— Cartul. de l'évêché du M., 965–1786, 1908. [10.]
,, TOURS. Chartes de St.-Julien de T., 1002–1300; publ. L. J. Denis, 2 fasc., 1912–13. [12.]

Société des Artistes Français. Explic. des ouvr. de peintre, sculpture &c. exposés au Grand Palais des Champs-Elysées. [Le Salon, 1921]. 8°. 1921

Société des Bibliophiles Belges, *Mons, see* LENGHERAND (G.) Voyage à Venise &c., 1485–86, 1861.

Société des Bibliophiles Français.
see PICOT (E.) & H. STEIN, *edd.* Rec. de pièces histor. impr. s. le règne de Louis XI, 2t, 1923.
,, PORTALIS (*le b.* R.) H. P. Danloux, & s. journal, 1793–1809, 1910.

Société des Bibliophiles Languedociens.
see AIGREFEUILLE (C. D'). Hist. de Montpellier, n. éd., 4t, 1875–82.
,, JOUBERT. Un projet gigant. en Languedoc au 18e s., 1873.
,, MONTPELLIER. Rec. de pièces rel. au Siège de M., 1622, 1875.

Société des Bollandistes, *see* DELEHAYE (H.) L'œuvre des B., 1615–1915, 1920.
SUBSIDIA HAGIOGRAPHICA.
see DELEHAYE (H.) Les saints stylites, 1923. [14.]
,, PLUMMER (C.) Misc. hagiogr. Hibern., 1925. [15.]

Société des Etudes Rabelaisiennes.
see REVUE DES ET. RABELAISIENNES. Tables, 1924.
,, REVUE DU SEIZ. SIÈCLE, 1922–.

Société des Etudes Robespierristes.
see ANNALES HIST. DE LA RÉVOL. FRANÇ. Organe de la Soc. des Et. R., n. sér., t1–, 1924–.
,, ROBESPIERRE (F. M. J. I.) Corr. de M. & A. Robespierre ; rec. & publ. G. Michon, 1926.

Société des Langues Romanes.
see MILLARDET (G.) Linguistique & dialectologie romanes, 1923. [28.]

Société des Lettres, Sciences & Arts des Alpes-Maritimes, *see* LÉRINS, *abbey of*. Cartul. de l'abbaye de L., p1, 1883.

Société des Missions-Étrangères, *see* LAUNAY (A.) Mémorial de la Soc. des M.-é., 2p, 1912–16.

Société des Textes Français Modernes.
see DU BELLAY (J.) Divers jeux rustiques, 1923.
,, —— Œuvres poét., t5, 1923.
,, LE METEL DE BOIS-ROBERT (F.) Epistres en vers, t1, 1921.
,, L'HERMITE (F. T.) La mort de Seneque, 1919.
,, RONSARD (P. DE). Œuvres compl., t1–4, 1914–25.

Société d'Etudes des Hautes-Alpes, *see* BERTAUD. Chartes de N.-D. de B., 1888.

Société d'Histoire Contemporaine.
see FRANCE : CONVENTION NATIONALE. Actes du gouvt. révol. : rec. de doc., t1, 1920. [62.]

Société d'Histoire Moderne, *see* CARON (P.) Concordance des calendriers républ. & grégor., 1905.

Société Ernest Renan. Publ. v1. 8°. 1923
see GIRARD (H.) & H. MONCEL. Bibliogr. des œuvres de Renan, 1923. [1.]

Société Finlandaise d'Archéologie [SUOMEN MUINAISMUISTO-YHDISTYS]. Inscr. de l'Iénissei. Rec. & publ. par la Soc. F. d'A. fol. Helsingfors. 1889

Société Française de Bibliographie.
see MORTET (C.) Orig. & débuts de l'imprimerie, 1922.
,, RÉPERTOIRE BIBLIOGRAPH. DE L'HIST. DE FRANCE, t1, 1923.

Société Française de Philosophie, *see* LALANDE (A.) Vocab. de la philos., n. éd., 2t, 1928.

Société Française de Reproductions de Manuscripts à Peintures.
Bulletin. Année 1–11, 1911–27 [Année 4, 1914–20]. 4°. 1911–27
see BIBLE. La Bible moralisée : reprod. du ms. du 13e s., 5t, 1911–27.
,, BLOCHET (E.) Peintures des mss. orient. de la Bibl. Nat., 1914–20.
,, BYVANCK (A. W.) Les princ. mss. à peintures de la Bibl. Roy. des Pays-Bas &c., 1924.
,, DURRIEU (*le c.* P.) Livre d'heures peint par J. Foucquet, 45e feuillet, 1923.
,, —— Les très belles Heures de Notre Dame du Duc J. de Berry, 1922.
,, FAWTIER (R.) La Bible hist. toute figurée de la John Rylands Library, 1924.
,, HEVESY (A. DE). La bibliothèque du roi M. Corvin, 1923.

Société Historique de Compiègne.
see COMPIÈGNE. Cartul. de l'abbaye de St.-Corneille de C., t1, 1904.
,, ROYALLIEU. Cartul., 1911.

Société Historique & Archéologique du Gatinais, *see* SAINT-BENOÎT-SUR-LOIRE. Rec. des chartes de l'abbaye de St.-B.-sur-L., t1, 2i, 1900–12.

Société Historique & Archéologique de Langres, *see* VIGNORY. Cartul. du prieuré de St.-Etienne de V., 1882.

Société Hollandaise des Sciences, *see* HUYGENS (C.) Œuvres compl., 14t, 1888–1920.

Société Jean-Jacques Rousseau.
Annales. t10–16 (1914–25). 8°. Genève. [1915–26]
t12, 13 *cont.* Les institutions chym. de R. ; publ. M. Gautier.
t14 *cont.* Corresp. de R. avec F. Coindet, 1756–68 ; publ. A. François.
t15 *cont.* Chronolog. crit. de vie & œuvres de J. J. R. par L. J. Courtois.
t16 *cont.* La famille & la jeunesse de J. J. R. ; par E. Ritter.

Société Nationale des Antiquaires de France [SOC. IMPÉR. &c.]
Bulletin, 1857–67, 1869, 1872–84 [*b. w.* Mém., s3, t4–s5, t5]. 8°. 1859–84
Mémoires. Nouv. sér. t10 ; sér. 3, 10t ; sér. 4, 10t ; sér. 5, 10t ; sér. 6, 10t [t7 *wanting*] ; sér. 7, 10t ; sér. 8, t1–6 [*also numbered* t20–76 (57 *wanting*)]. 8°. 1850–1924

Société Nationale des Antiquaires des France [*continued*].
Mettensia. Mém. & doc. publ. par la Soc. Fond. A. Prost. t1–8. 8°. 1897–[1927]
Bar-le-Duc. Coll. Cloüet-Buvignier s. l'hist. du Verdunois ; publ. P. Marichal, 1923–27. [8.]
Gorze, *abbey*. Cartul. ; publ. A. d'Herbomez, 1898–1901. [2.]
Marichal (P.) Remarques sur la Cartul. de Gorze, 1902. [3.]
Metz. Cartul. de l'Evêché de M. ; P. Marichal, 1903–8. [4, 5.]
—— Coll. sur l'hist. de M. &c. à la Bibl. Nat. ; Omont, 1919. [7.]
Prost (A.) A. P., vie, œuvres, coll., 1897. [1.]
Saint-Mihiel, *abbey*. Chron. & chartes ; A. Lesort, 1909–12. [6.]
Tables alphabét. des publ. de l'Acad. Celt. & de la Soc. des Ant. de Fr., 1807–89. Red. sous la dir. de R. de Lasteyrie par M. Prou. 8°. 1894

Société Nationale des Beaux-Arts [*see also* SALON (LE)].
Cat. de l'expos. d'art polonais. [P2496]. s8°. 1921
Cat. des ouvr. exposés au Grand Palais, 1921. s8°. Evreux. [1921]

Société pour l'Etude des Langues Romanes [*Montpellier*], *see* DURANTE, *Ser.* Il Fiore, poème ital. du 13e s. &c., 1881. [9.]

Société Royale de Géographie d'Egypte.
see DEVONSHIRE (*Mme.* R. L.) 80 mosquées &c. du Caire, 1925.
,, DRIAULT (E.) Mohamed Aly & Napoléon, 1807–14, 1925.
,, LA RONCIÈRE (C. B. DE). La découverte de l'Afrique au moyen âge, 3t, 1924–27. [Mém., 5, 6, 13].
,, LORIN (H.) L'Égypte d'aujourd'hui, 1926.

Société Royale des Beaux-Arts, Bruxelles, *see* LAMBOTTE (P.) Œuvre de A. Stevens ; cat. de l'expos. org. par la Soc., 1907.

Société Royale pour l'Encouragement des Sciences &c., *see* ACADÉMIE D'ARRAS.

Société Sultanieh de Géographie. Mém. prés. & publ. s. les auspices de Ahmed Fouad. t2. fol. Le Caire. 1921
see JONDET (G.) Atlas hist. de la ville & des ports d'Alexandrie, 1921. [2.]

Société Vaudoise d'Histoire & d'Archéologie, *see* MOTTAZ (E.) Dict. hist., géogr. & statist. du Canton de Vaud, 2v, 1914–21.

Societies for the Reformation of Manners.
see CHANDLER (E.), *abp.* Sermon &c., 1724.
,, GIBSON (E.), *bp.* Sermon &c., 1725.
,, GREENE (T.), *bp.* Sermon &c., 1727.
,, HEYLYN (J.) Sermon &c., 1729.

Society for Equitable Assurances.
Deed of settlement &c. 8°. 1811
,, ,, w. bye-laws &c., & 9 addresses by W. Morgan. 8°. 1833

Society for Nautical Research. Journal, *see* MARINER'S MIRROR, v6–13, 1920–27.
see RIGGING. A treatise on r., *c.* 1625 ; ed. R. C. Anderson, 1921.

Society for Old Testament Study. O.T. essays. Papers read bef. the Soc. at 18th meeting, Keble Coll., Oxf., 1927. [*By var. a.* Foreword by D. C. Simpson]. 8°. 1927

Society for Psychical Research. Journal. v19–23. 8°. [1920–26]
Proceedings. v30–37. 8°. 1920–28
37, Library catalogue.

Society for Pure English. Index to Tracts, 1–19, w. list of members. Comp. by A. M. Savage. [S.P.E., Tract 20]. 8°. 1926
Prelim. announcement & list of members, Oct. 1919. [S.P.E., Tract No. 1]. 8°. 1919
Tracts. Nos. 1–30. 8°. 1919–28
see AIKIN (W. A.) Eng. vowel-sounds &c., 1927. [26.]
,, B. (E.), H. W. FOWLER &c. Metaphor [& Misc. notes &c.], 1922. [11.]
,, BARBIER (P.) Eng. infl. on French vocab., 2p, 1921–23. [7, 13.]
,, BARNES (M.) What is pure French, 1922. [8.]
,, BRADLEY (H.) & R. BRIDGES. On the terms Briton, British, Britisher—Preposition at end, by H. W. Fowler, 1923. [14.]
,, BRIDGES (R.) Eng. handwriting, contin. f. tract 23, 1927. [28.]
,, —— On Eng. homophones, 1919. [2.]
,, —— The Society's work, 1927. [21.]
,, †CRAIGIE (W. A.) The study of Amer. English, 1927. [27.]
,, FOWLER (H. W.) On grammat. inversions [*&* Rep. of Soc.—Amer. invitation], 1922. [10.]
,, —— On hyphens & shall & will, should & would, in the newspapers of to-day, 1921. [6.]
,, —— The split infinitive—Pictorial, picturesque, by R. Bridges, 1923. [15.]
,, —— Subjunctives—Poetry in schools, by R. Bridges &c., 1924. [18.]
,, FRY (R. E.) & E. A. LOWE. Eng. handwriting, w. 34 facs. &c., 1926. [23.]

Society for Pure English [*continued*].
Tracts [*continued*].
see GORDON (G. S.) Medium aevum & the middle age, 1925. [19.]
,, —— Shakespeare's English, 1928. [29.]
,, JESPERSEN (O.) Logic & grammar—Gt. & Little Brit. by D. MacRitchie &c., 1924. [16.]
,, JESPERSEN (O.) Notes on relative clauses &c., 1926. [24.]
,, —— Some disputed points in Eng. gram., 1926. [25.]
,, KURATH (H.) Amer. pronunc.—Words f. the French—é, ée, by M. Barnes—Pronunc. of clothes &c., by R. Bridges, 1928. [30.]
,, MATTHEWS (J. B.) Englishing of French words, 1921. [5.]
,, MORTON (W. C.) Lang. of anatomy, 1922. [9.]
,, PAGET (*Sir* R. A. S.) The nature of human speech &c., 1925. [22.]
,, SARGEAUNT (J.) The pronunc. of Eng. words derived f. the Latin, 1920. [4.]
,, SMITH (L. P.) Eng. idioms, 1923. [12.]
,, —— A few pract. suggestions, 1920. [3.]
,, —— 4 words, romantic, originality, creative, genius, 1924. [17.]
,, SOC. FOR PURE ENG. Index to Tracts, 1–19, 1926. [20.]

Society for the Diffusion of Political Knowledge, *see* HANDBOOK of the democracy, 1864.

Society for the Diffusion of Useful Knowledge.
Maps. v1. fol. 1844

Society for the Discharge & Relief of Persons imprisoned for Small Debts. Acc. of rise & pres. state of the Soc. 6th ed. s8º. 1783

Society for the Mitigation & Abolition of Slavery &c. Report [*&* 2nd *&* 3rd Rep.] of Comm. of Soc., read at meeting[s], 1824–25. [P2761]. 8º. 1824–26
see PARLIAMENT: H. OF COMMONS. Substance of debate, May 1923, w. pref. [*on* Soc.], 1823.

Society for the Preservation of New England Antiquities.
Bulletin. v1–10 [*in* 1v], 18 (1910–28). la8º. Boston, Mass. 1925–28

Society for the Preservation of the Wild Fauna of the Empire.
Journal. v2, 4, 5. 8º. 1905–9

Society for the Promotion of Hellenic Studies. Classified catalogue of books, pamph. & maps in lib. of S. f. P. of H. & Roman Studies. la8º. 1924
see ANTIQUITY. Claim of ant., w. annot. list of bks., 1922.
,, JOURNAL OF HELLENIC STUDIES, 1920–.

Society for the Promotion of Roman Studies.
see ANTIQUITY. Claim of ant., w. annot. list of bks., 1922.
,, SOC. FOR PROMOTION OF HELLENIC ST. Classified cat. of books &c., in lib. of S. f. P. of H. & Rom. St., 1924.

Society for the Propagation of the Gospel, *see* HUMPHREYS (D.) Histor. acc., 1730.

Society for the Protection of Anc. Buildings. 1st–50th Annual report[s]. [5th–10th, 13th, 30th, 35th, 36th, 43rd, 45th, & 48th *wanting*]. s8º. 1878–1927
,, ,, Index, 1878–1916; 1878–1927 [b. *in* 1v]. s8º. [1916–27]
An old cottage saved. Prep. by the secretary [A. R. Powys], w. intr. by A. H. Powell. s8º. 1921
Report on treatment of old cottages. By A. H. Powell *& others*. s8º. *n.d.*

Society for the Publication of Oriental Texts.
see ATHANASIUS, *St.* Festal letters, Syriac vers., 1848.
,, EUSEBIUS, *Pamphili*. Theophania, Syriac vers., 1842.

Society of Antiquaries of London. The Antiquaries Journal. Journal of the Soc. of Antiq. of L. [*incl.* Proceedings]. v1–7. la8º. 1921–27
Archaeologia; or, miscellaneous tracts rel. to antiquity. v70–77. 4º. O. 1920–28
Proceedings. s2, v32 (Nov. 1919–June 1920). [*Contin. in* Antiquaries journal, *above*]. 8º. [1921]
Reports of Research Committee. No. 4–6. la8º. O. 1916–26
see BUSHE-FOX (J. P.) Excav. of late-Celtic urn-field at Swarling, Kent, 1925. [5.]
,, —— Excav. of Roman fort at Richborough, Kent, 1926. [6.]
,, —— Excav. on site of Roman town at Wroxeter, 1914, 1916. [4.]

Society of Antiquaries of Newcastle-upon-Tyne. Archæologia Æliana. s3, v17–21. s4, v1–5. 8º. Kendal *&* N.-u.-T. 1920–28
s4, v3 *cont.* Greenwell (W.) The Greenwell deeds preserved in Publ. Lib., N.-u.-T.; calendared by J. Walton, 1927. [*w. sep. tp.*]
Cat. of the inscribed & sculptured stones of the Roman period, preserved in the Black-Gate Museum. 3rd ed., by R. Blair. 8º. Kendal. 1920
Proceedings. s3, v9, 10. s4, v1, 2. 8º. Kendal. 1921–27

Society of Antiquaries of Scotland.
Proceedings. v49–59 (1914/15–25). s4º. E. 1915–25
see STUART (J.), *ed.* Rec. of priory of Isle of May, 1868.

Society of Army Historical Research. Journal. v1–6. 8º. 1921–27
v1 has spec. Nº.: Tangier, 1680, diary of Sir J. Halkett [*b. w.* v1].
v2 has spec. Nº.: Orderly book of Ld. Ogilvy's Regt., army of Pr. Ch. Ed. Stuart, 1745–6; notes by Sir B. Seton [*b. w.* v2].

Society of Authors, *see* BESANT (*Sir* W.) The Soc. of A.: record, 1893.

Society of British Artists. Exhibition, 1–17, 1824–40. [Catalogues]. [*b. in* 2v]. 8º. [1824–40]
Winter exhib., 1–3, 1832–34. Cat. [1832 *b. w.* Exhib., 1–9; 1833–34 *b. w.* Exhib., 10–17]. 8º. [1832–34]

Society of Civil Servants, *see* CIVIL. Develop. of the Civil Service: lect., Soc. of C. S., 1920–21, 1922.

Society of Comparative Legislation. Journal. s3, v2–9. 8º. 1920–27

Society of Friends of Russian Freedom, *see* FREE RUSSIA, 1890–1910.

Society of Hebrew Literature.
Miscellany of Hebrew lit. v1. 8º. 1872

Society of Merchant Venturers of Bristol, *see* LATIMER (J.) Hist. of Soc. of M.V., 1903.

Society of the Sons of St. George. Hist. sketch of the orig. & progress of the Soc. 8º. Phila. 1897

Society of Writers to the Signet. Cat. of the Lib. of the W. to H.M.'s S. 4º. E. 1805
List of books added to Lib. of Soc. in 1920–1927. 4º. E. 1921–28

Socin (Albert). Die neu-aram. Dialekte v. Urmia bis Mosul. Texte u. Übers. hrsg. v. A. S. 4º. Tübingen. 1882
see PRYM (H. E.) & A. S. Kurd. Samml., 2 Abt., 1887–90.

Socinus (Faustus), *Senensis.*
Assertiones theol. de trino et uno Deo, adv. nov. Samosatenicos. Ex praelect. Coll. Posnan. excerpt.; unà cum animadvers. F. S. [*a. c. b. w. h.* Breves tract., 1618]. ed. 3ª. s8º. Racoviae. 1618
Breves quidam de div. materiis ad Christianam relig. pertin. tractatus. s8º. Racoviae. 1618
De Coena Domini tract. brevis, unà c. ejusdem adv. scr. J. Niemojevii defensione &c. [*b. w. h.* Breves tractatus, 1618]. s8º. Racoviae. 1618
De Sacrae Scr. auctoritate. [*wrongly attrib. on the tp. to D. Lopez, Jesuit*]. s8º. Hispali. 1588
Disput. inter F. S. & C. Francken de adoratione Christi &c. [*&* M. Seidelii epistolae]. s8º. Racoviae. 1618
Fragmenta duorum script., &c. [*b. w. h.* Breves tractatus, 1618]. s8º. Racoviae. 1619
Miscellanea: scripta theolog. de div. materiis. s8º. Racoviae. 1611
Tract. de Eccl. s8º. Racoviae. 1611
Tract. de justificatione. [*b. w. h.* Breves tractatus, 1618]. s8º. Racoviae. 1611
see ASHWELL (G.) De Socino &c., 1680.
,, DAVID (FERENCZ). De non invoc. Jesu Christo, propos. F. S., 1595.
,, JOHANNIS (E.) De unigeniti Filii Dei existentia inter E. J. & F. S. disput., 1595.
,, PRZYPKOWSKI (S.) *The life of F. S. S. &c.; tr. 1653.
,, —— Vita F. S., cum cat. operum, 1651.

Socinus (Laelius). In haereticis coercendis &c., 1577, *attrib. to L. S., see* CELSUS (M.), *ps.*
Symbolarum ad vitam L. S. illustr., 1826, *see* ILLGEN (C. F.)

Socio (Nobile). Le miserie de li amanti. [*Sig. y4 & z1, 2 wanting*]. 4º. [Vinegia. 1533]

Sociological review (The). v8, 1915. v11–14, 1919–22. la8º. 1915–22
Monograph Suppl. 1, *see* GEDDES (P.) Survey of Edinburgh, 1919.

Socolovius (Stanislaus), *see* SOKOŁOWSKI (STANISŁAW).

Socrates [SOCRATE; SOKRATES].
see DUPRÉEL (E.) Légende S. & les sources de Platon, 1922.
,, GROTE (G.) Plato & o. companions of S., 3v, 1865; 3rd ed., 3v, 1867.
see LÖNBORG (S.) Dike & Eros, d2, Den Vise [S.], 1920.
,, TAYLOR (A. E.) Plato's biog. of S., 1917.
,, WALTERS (H. B.) Statuette of S., 1925.

Socrates, *Scholasticus.* Eccl. hist.; tr. M. Hanmer, *see* EUSEBIUS, *Pamphili*. Anc. eccl. histories &c., 1607.
[Eccl. hist. & Life of St. Sylvester. *In Armenian.* Ed. M. Ter Movsesean]. 8º. Vagharshapat. 1897
,, ,, [*a. enl. ed. w. notes &c.; half-title in Greek.* 2v *in* 1. *b. w. above*]. 8º. Vagharshapat. 1897
Eccl. hist. of S., Sozomen & Theodorit. Abridg'd by S

Socrates [*continued*].
Parker. Added, Letter to Mr. Bold conc. resurrection of the same body [*w. sep. tp. & pagin.*] 2p. s8°. 1707–12
see EUSEBIUS. Eccles. hist. of E., S. &c.; tr. Parker, 3rd ed. rev., 1729.

Sod. סוד ישרים* [2p], 1652, *see* MODENA (L.)

Soddy (Frederick). The interpret. of radium & the structure of the atom. 4th ed. rev. & enl. 8°. 1920
Inversion of science &c. [P2732]. 8°. 1924

Soden (Hermann, *Frhr.* v.) Die Schriften d. N. Test. in i. ältesten erreichbaren Textgestalt hergest. auf Grund i. Text-gesch.
2T *in* 4v. [1i–iii *pagin. cont.*] la8°. Göttingen. 1911–13
1, Untersuchungen, 2e unveränd. A.
2, Text u. Apparat. Sonderausg.

Söderberg (Hjalmar). Skrifter. 10d. s8°. [1919–21]
1, Förvillelser, 5e uppl.
2, Preludier—Historietter.
3, Martin Bircks ungdom, 5e uppl.
4, Samtidsnoveller.
5, Doktor Glas., 6e uppl.
6, Gertrud—Aftonstjärnan.
7, Hjärtats oro.
8, Den allvarsamma leken.
9, Forntid och saga.
10, Vers och varia.

Söderblom (Nathan), *abp. of Upsala, see* TIELE (C. P.) Tiele-Söderbloms Kompendium d. Religionsgesch., 5e A., 1920.

Sodoma [SODDOMA; †BAZZI (GIOV. ANTONIO), *called Il Soddoma*], *see* BRUZZA (L.) Not. int. alla patria e ai primi studi d. pittore G. A. B., 1862.

Soergel (Albert), *see* SÖRGEL (A.)

Soettler (Joannes Gaspar), *see* SÖTTLER (J. G.)

Soffici (Ardengo). Battaglia fra due vittorie, prec. da un ragguaglio s. stato d. intellettuali risp. al Fascismo di C. Suckert. s8°. Firenze. 1923
Bïf§zf+18. Simultaneità e chimismi lirici.
n. ed. accresc. 8°. Firenze. [1919]
see CARRÀ (C.) A. S., avec 32 reprod., 1922.

Sofi, *dynasty, see* ZACHARIAS, *the deacon.* Mém. sur les Sofis (–17 c.), 1876.

Søfrenssøn (Søfren). Memorialbog, 1564–99. Udg. ved A. E. Erichsen. 8°. 1898

Sogliano (Ant.) L'Efebo in bronzo rinven. in Pompei, *see* REALE ACCAD. D. LINCEI. Mon. ant., v10, 1901.

Sǫgur Danakonunga. 1, Sǫgubrot af fornkonungum. 2, Knytlinga saga. Utg. av C. af Petersens & E. Olson. [Samfund t. u. a. g. n. l., 46]. s8°. 1919–25

Sohnrey (Heinrich), *see* KÜCK (E.) & H. S. Feste u. Spiele, 1925.

Soho. Twenty yrs. in Soho. Review of work, St. Anne's, Soho. [*By var. wr. Pref. signed* J. H. Cardwell]. 8°. 1911

Sohr (Frédéric). Le port d'Anvers, *see* CAHIERS (LES) BELGES, No. 32, 1919.

Sohr (Theoph. Sigfrid.) Notata de comitibus Palatinis Saxoniae. [P2641]. s4°. Lipsiae. [1785]

Soissons (Guy Jean R. E. Ch. Eman. de Savoie-Carignan, *cte.* de). The true story of the Empress Eugénie. 8°. 1921

Sokirko (Ded).
Труд, капитал и советская власть. [P2722]. s8°. Москва. 1919

Sokolnikov (G. Ya.)
Государств. капитализм и новая финансовая поштика.
[P2698]. 8°. [Москва]. 1922
Денежная реформа &c. [P2823]. la8°. Москва. [1924]

Sokolov (Boris M.) Наука въ совѣтской Россіи. s8°. 1921
М. Н. Раевская кн. Волконская в жизни и поэзии Пушкина.
s4°. Москва. 1922
Le voyage de Cachin & de Frossard dans la Russie des Soviets. Faits & Doc. Tr. L. Krestovsky. 2e éd. 8°. [1921]

Sokolov (Dimitri).
Ученіе о богослуженіи православной церква. изд. 3e 8°. С.–П. 1878

Sokolov (K. N.) Правленіе ген. Деникина. 8°. Софія. 1921

Sokolov (Nikolai Alekseevich). Enquête judic. sur l'assassinat de la famille imp. russe. 8°. 1924

Sokolovitch (P. P. de).
Pierre I de Serbie & ses calomniateurs. [P535]. la8°. 1909

Sokołowski (Stanisław) [SOCOLOVIUS (STANISLAUS)]. Ad Wirtemberg. theologorum invectivam, quam actis &c. cum Hieremia patriarcha Const. de Aug. Conf. per eos ed. praefixerunt, brevis resp. s4°. Ingolstadii. 1585

Solano (E. John). Field entrenchments. Wr. by an officer. Ed. E. J. S. [Introd. by G. K. Scott-Moncrieff].
[repr.] s8°. 1915
Labour as an internat. problem. Essays by G. N. Barnes, A. Thomas &c. Ed. E. J. S. 8°. 1920

Solano (E. John) [*continued*].
Musketry. Wr. by an officer of the reg. army. Ed. E. J. S. [Pref. by Gen. Sir O'M. Creagh]. s8°. 1915
Signalling. Wr. by an officer of the reg. army. Ed. by E. J. S. s8°. 1915

Sola Pinto (Vivian de), *see* PINTO (V. DE S.)

Solar Correa (E.) Poetas de Hispano-América: sel. y notas de E. S. C. 8°. [Santiago, *Chile.* 1926]

Solaro della Margarita (*il conte* Giuseppe Maria), *see* MANNO (A.) P. Micca ed il gen. conte S. della M.: richerche sull' assedio di Torino del 1706, 1883.

Solaro della Margherita (*il conte* Clemente). Mem. stor. polit. per gli affari esteri del Re Carlo Alberto, 1835–47.
la8°. Torino. 1851

Soldati (Mario), *see* TORINO. Cat. d. Galleria d'arte mod. d. Museo Civico; comp. da M. S., 1927.

Soldiers' marching songs. [P2758]. s8°. *n.d.*

Soldus (Organtinus). Epistola de rebus Ind., *see* JESUITS. Rerum a Soc. Iesu in Oriente gest. vol., 1574.

Solemn League & Covenant [*see also* COVENANT].
*Burning of the S.L. & C., May 29, 1662, *see* MAIDMENT (J.), *ed.* Hist. fragm., p2, 1833.

Soler (Mariano Cubí y), *see* CUBÍ Y SOLER (M.)

Solera, *Marquises of, see* BENAVIDES.

Solerius (Hugo), *see* SOLIER (H. DE).

Solesmes. Les principaux mss. de chant Grégorien &c. publ. par les Bénédictins de S., 11v, 1900–12, *see* PALÉOGRAPHIE MUSICALE.

Solf (Ferdinand E.) 1934: Deutschlands Auferstehung. Geleitwort v. Ob. Bauer. s8°. Naumburg a. d. S. 1921

Solicitor (A), *ps.* *The Magna Charta of Methodism invalid &c., 1835, *see* METHODISM.

Solicitors. *Concerning s. By one of them. Pref. by A. Birrell. 8°. 1920

Solida. Solida decisio 4 illor. inter aliquos theolog. Aug. Conf. controv. capit. &c., 1624, *see* JOHN GEORGE, *d. of Saxony.*
*Solida refut. compil. Cinglianae & Calvin., 1584, *see* ANDREAE (J.)

Solier (Hugues de), *b. 1547* [†SOLERIUS (HUGO)], *see* LEGRÉ (L.) La botanique en Provence au 16e s.: H. de S., 1899.

Solis (Antonio de) [†SOLIS Y RIBADENEYRA (A. DE)]. Hist. de la conq. de Méjico. s8°. Madrid. 1829

Solito (Domenico). Notizie del S. Cataldo, protettore d. città di Taranto. [P2561]. 8°. Napoli. 1850

Sollas (William Johnson). Ancient hunters & th. mod. representatives. [3rd ed.] 8°. 1924

Sollogub (*c.* Vladimir Aleksandrovich), *see* SOLOGUB (*c.* V. A.)

Solloway (John) & *Col.* P. Saltmarshe. Hist. &c. guide to the York pageant, 1909. s4°. York. [1909]

Solly (J. Raymond). A cynic's breviary: 120 pensées "rosses" chosen & tr. by J. R. S. s8°. 1925
Free will & determinism. s8°. 1922

Solmi (Arrigo).
Making of mod. Italy. Intr. by Arundell del Re. 8°. 1925
Stato e chiesa nel pensiero di Dante, *see* ARCHIVIO STOR. ITAL. Anno 79, vl, 1921.

Solmi (Edmondo), *see* VINCI (L. DA). L. da V.: conferenze fiorentine: La resurrezione dell' opera di Leonardo, by E. S., 1910.

Solmsen (Felix). Indogerm. Eigennamen als Spiegel d. Kulturgesch. Hrsg. v. E. Fraenkel. [Indogerm. Bibl., 4te Abt. 2]. s8°. Heidelberg. 1922

Solo (Petrus à), *see* BRENTZ (J.) Op., t8, Polemica scr. contra P. à S., 1590.

Sologub (Fedor), *ps.* [*i.e.* F. KUZMICH TETERNIKOV].
Костер дорожный. s8°. Москва. 1922
Небо голубое: стихи. s8°. Ревель. [1921]
Свирель. s8°. П. 1922
Сочтенные дни. 8°. Ревель. [1921]
Чародейная чаша, стихи. 8°. П. 1922
Фимиамы. s8°. П 1921

Sologub (*count* Vladimir Aleksandrovich).
Вчера и сегодня. Литерат. сборникъ. Изд. А. Смирданымъ.
2кн. *in* 1v. 8°. С.–П. 1845–46
Тарантас: путевые впечатления. s8°. Москва. 1923

Solomon, *king of Israel.*
Sapientia S. [*In Greek, Armen. & Lat.*] s8°. i Venetik. 1827
*Solomon & Abiathar &c., 1692, *see* HILL (S.)
The testament of S. Ed. w. introd. by C. C. McGown. 8°. Leipzig. 1922
see BOSSUET (J. B.) ŒUVRES,

Solomon, *king of Israel* [*continued*].
t2, Libri S. Proverba, Ecclesiastes, Sapientia &c., cum notis, 1815.
see CARRIÈRE (A.) De psalt. Salomonis, 1870.
see LEVERTIN (O.) Kung S. och Morolf: dikter, 1919.
,, PINEDA (J. DE). In S. comm., 1609.
,, SEYMOUR (ST. J. D.) Tales of King S., 1924.

Solomon ben Abraham ben Adreth, *1235–1310, see* EPSTEIN (I.) The "Responsa" of S., 1925.

Solomon ben Abraham ben Parchon, *see* ROSSI (G. B. DE). Lexicon Hebr. select. ex R. P. lexico &c., 1807.

Solomon ben Isaac, *of Troyes, called Rashi* [JARCHI], *see* RASHI.

Solomon Tsebi, *Ufhausen* [SALOMON ZEVI].
יודישר טירייאק. [P1015]. s4°. Altdorfi. 1680
see BRENZ (S. F.) Theriaca Judaica, scripta S. F. B. & S. Z., 1681.

Solomon (Joseph). Bergson. [4th impr.] s8°. [1922]

Solomon (W. E. Gladstone).
Bombay revival of Indian art. 8°. [Bombay. 1924]

Solon, *see* FREEMAN (K.) Work & life of S., w. tr. of h. poems, 1926.

Soloviev (Sergei Mikhailovich) [Соловьевъ].
Учебная книга русской исторіи. изд. 8ое. 8°. Москва. 1880

Soloviev (Vladimir Sergeevich).
L'idée russe. [*a. c. in* P2498]. 8°. 1888

Soloviev (Vsevolod S.) Вольтерьянецъ. Романъ (продолженіе "Сергѣй Горбатовъ"). 2ч. [*in* 1v. *pagin. cont.*] 8°. С.-П. 1883
Сергѣй Горбатовъ. Романъ. 2ч. [*in* 1v. *pagin. cont.*] 8°. С.-П. 1882

Solsky (Vladimir). Ленинъ. s8°. Берлинъ. 1921

Soltau (Roger Henry). Pascal. 8°. 1927

Soltre [SOUTRA]. Registrum Domus de Soltre, necnon Eccl. Coll. S. Trinitatis prope Edinburgh. Charters of the Hospital of Soltre &c. [Ed. D. Laing. Bannatyne Club]. 4°. E. 1861

Soltyk (*count* **Roman).** Rel. des opér. de l'armée aux ordres du Prince J. Poniatowski pend. la campagne de 1809 en Pologne c. les Autrichiens. 8°. 1841

Somadeva (Bhaṭṭa). L'hist. romanesque d'Udayana, Roi de Vatsa. Extr. du Kathâ-sarit-sâgara de S. Tr. avec intr. & notes par F. Lacôte. 8°. 1924
The ocean of story. C. H. Tawney's tr. of S.'s Kathā Sarit Sāgara. Ed., w. intr., notes & terminal essay by N. M. Penzer. Foreword by Sir R. C. Temple. 10v (v10, App. & Index). la8°. *p.p.f.s.o.* 1924–28

Somal (Placido Sukias), *abp. of Siunia.* Quadro d. storia letteraria di Armenia. 8°. Venezia. 1829

Somalean (Vardapet). Hnakhosuthiun ashkharhagrakan Hayastaneaytz. [Geograph. antiquity of Armenia. *In Armenian*]. 3v. la8°. Venice. 1835

Sombart (Werner). Der moderne Kapitalismus. 4e unveränd. A. 3B *in* 6 [*each B in* 2, *pagin. cont.*] la8°. München. 1921
B3 *has t.:* Das Wirtschaftsleben im Za. d. Hochkapitalismus.
Der proletarische Sozialismus ("Marxismus"). 10e neugearb. A. d. "Sozialismus u. soz. Bewegung." 2B. 8°. Jena. 1924

Somborn (Carl). Das venezian. Volkslied: Die Villotta [*w. Germ. tr.*] 8°. Heidelberg. 1901

Sombreuil (Marie-Maurille Vireau [VIROT] **de),** *1767–1823, see* DUCHEMIN (P. V.) Mdlle. de Sombreuil, 1925.

Some.
*Some acc. of the experience of E. J., 1770?, *see* WESLEY (J.)
*Some acc. of the Reformed church of France, 1819, *see* COBBIN (I.)
*Some data illust. the devel. of Swedish indust. life &c. [*Eng. & Swed.*], 1923, *see* SWEDISH.
*Some disc. upon Dr. Burnet & Dr. Tillotson, 1695, *see* HICKES (G.)
*Some primit. doctrines reviv'd: or The intermediate state &c., 1713, *see* CAMPBELL (A.), *bp. of Aberdeen.*
*Some queries to Protestants answ., 1686, *see* ALTHAM (M.)
*Some reflections upon the Pr. of Oranges declaration, 1688, *see* WILLIAM III, *k. of Eng.*
*Some remarks on the dialogue between Philalethes & Philotimus [on the questions betw. churchmen & dissenters], & the cont. of the dialogue & James Lacy's answer. [*w. sep. tp. & pagin.*] s8°. 1705
*Some remarks upon Sir J. Dalrymple's Hist. coll., 1714, *see* GILLANE (J.)
*Some seasonable advice f. an honest sailor, 1746, *see* VERNON (*adm.* E.)
*Some verses comp. upon the insurrect. of the Jacobites &c., 1746, *see* TURNBULL (W.)

Somers (John Somers, *baron*), *1651–1716.* *The security of English-mens lives, or the trust, power &c. of Grand Jurys &c. s8°. 1682

Somerscales, *Family of, see* SKEET, *Family of.* Hist. of the families of S. &c., 1906.

Somerset. Calendar of customs, superstitions &c. conn. w. Co. of S. Foreword & index by W. G. W. Watson. [Repr. f. Somerset County Herald]. s8°. 1920
Parish registers, v1, *see* DWELLY (E.) Parish records, v8, 1921.
Quarter Sessions records for Co. of Somerset. [Somerset Rec. Soc., 34]. v4. s4°. 1919
4, Charles II, 1666–77.
Somersetshire pleas f. Rolls of the itinerant justices (41 Henry III to end of h. reign). v2, 3. Ed. L. Landon. [Somerset Rec. Soc., 36, 41]. s4°. 1923–26

Somerset Record Society. v33–41. 8°. 1917–26
Collectanea 1. Coll. of doc. f. var. sources. Arr. by T. F. Palmer, 1924. [39.]
see BATH. Accounts of Chamberlains of City of B., 1568–1602; ed. F. D. Wardle, 1923. [38.]
,, BEAUCHAMP, *The family of.* 2 registers; ed. Sir H. C. Maxwell-Lyte, 1920. [35.]
,, DUNSTER. Doc. & extracts illust. hist. of Honour of D.; sel. & ed. Sir H. C. Maxwell-Lyte, 1917–18. [33.]
,, KIDDER (R.), *bp.* Life; wr. by himself; ed. A. E. Robinson, 1924. [37.]
,, SOMERSET. Quarter Sessions records for S., v4, 1666–77, 1919. [34.]
,, —— S. pleas f. Rolls of the itinerant justices, v2, 3; ed. L. Landon, 1923–26. [36, 41.]
,, WELLS. Mediaeval wills f. W., 1543–56; ed. D. O. Shilton &c., 1925. [40.]

Somerset (Henry), *1st marquis of Worcester, see* WORCESTER (H. S., *m. of*).

Somerset (*Lady* **Henry),** *wife of Rt. Hon. Ld. Henry R. C. Somerset, form. Lady Isabel Somers Cocks, see* FITZPATRICK (K.) Lady H. S., 1923.

Somerset (*Lord* **Henry Richard Charles).**
Songs of adieu. 8°. 1889

Somervell (David Churchill). Disraeli & Gladstone. 8°. 1925
A short hist. of our religion: f. Moses to the present day. s8°. 1922
Studies in statesmanship. 8°. 1923

Somerville (Alexander).
Hist. of the Brit. Legion, & war in Spain. 8°. 1839

Somerville (D. M. M. Crichton), W. R. Rickmers & E. C. Richardson. Ski-running. Ed. E. C. Richardson. 8°. 1904
,, ,, ...2nd ed. 8°. 1905

Somerville (Edith Œ.) [*ps.* G. HERRING] & *Miss* **Violet Martin** [*ps.* MARTIN ROSS].
The big house of Inver. s8°. [1925]
An enthusiast. s8°. 1921
French leave. s8°. [1928]
An Irish cousin. n. & rev. 7th impr. s8°. 1922
Mount music. s8°. 1919
Some experiences of an Irish R.M. n. imp. s8°. 1920
Stray-aways. 8°. 1920

Somerville (*Vice-Adm.* **Henry Boyle Townshend).**
The chart-makers. 8°. E. 1928

Somerville (William), *F.L.S.* How a tree grows. 8°. 1927

Somerville (William), *the poet.*
The chace. A poem. [*tp. missing*]. 8°. *n.d.*
Hobbinol, or, the rural games. A poem. [*b. w. h.* The chace, *n.d.*] 8°. 1740
Hobbinol, or the rural games: burlesque poem. 3rd ed. [P2778]. 8°. 1740
Poet. works. Coll. by T. Park. 2v. s8°. 1805

Sommer (Hermann Ruth-), *see* RUTH-SOMMER (H.)

Sommerfeld (Arnold). Atombau u. Spektrallinien. 3e umgearb. A. 8°. Braunschweig. 1922

Sommi (Maladobato). Dell' assedio di Cremona (1446). Cronaca in ed. [Ed. G. S. P.] [P2839]. s8°. Firenze. 1880

Sommi-Picenardi (Guido). Del gran priorato d. ord. Gerosolimit. in Venezia. [Estr. d. Nuovo arch. veneto, t4]. la8°. Venezia. 1892
Di un tentativo fatto dai Francesi per impadronirsi del Castello di Cremona nel 1537, *see* REGIA DEP. DI STORIA PATRIA. Misc., t24, 1885.
Don Giovanni de Medici gov. d. esercito Veneto nel Friuli (1565–1612). [Estr. d. Nuovo Arch. Veneto, N.S., v13]. 8°. Venezia. 1907

Somov (Konstantin Andreevich), *see* ERNST (S.) К. А. С., 1918.

Sonal (Marc), *see* BISSON (A.) & M. S. Le coup du berger, 1911.

Sones de la lira inglesa, 1920, *see* ZÉNDEGUI (G. DE).
Sonetti, burleschi e realistici, 2v, 1920, *see* MASSÈRA (A. F.), *ed.*
Song (The) of Lewes; ed. &c. C. L. Kingsford, 1890, *see* LEWES.
Songes. La clef des songes. Facs. &c. par M. Hélin, 1925, *see* DANIEL, *the prophet, ps.*
Song Ong Siang. 100 years hist. of the Chinese in Singapore, 1819–1919. 8°. 1923
Songs. Songs of society, 1880, *see* ADAMS (W. D.), *ed.*
Songs of the Xtn. creed & life, 1876, *see* MACGILL (H. M.)
Songster's (The) favourite companion. [*tp. torn*]. s8°. *n.d.*
Songy, *ps., see* PANGE (*ctsse.* J. DE).
Sonnenschein (Edward Adolf).
The soul of grammar. 8°. C. 1927
What is rhythm? Acc. by append. on exper. syllable-measurement. s8°. O. 1925
Sonnenschein (William Swan). The best books: reader's guide. 3rd ed. rewr. p1–4. 8°. 1910–[26]
Sonnentaller (Johannes). Ursach warumb der vermeint geystlich huff mit yren patronē das Euangelion Iesu Christi nit annimpt. s4°. *n.p.* 1524
Sonnois (Etienne Marie Alphonse), *abp. of Cambrai, see* CHEVALLIER (G.) Mgr. S.: sa vie—s. œuvre, 1920.
Sonntag (Christoph).
Gyonismus confutatus. [P443]. s4°. Altorfii. 1717
Stricturae Anti-Becanianae adv. lib. 1 Manualis controversiarum disput. Praes. C. S., resp. C. F. Bischoff. [P432]. s4°. Altdorfi. [1708]
Sonntag (Johannes Michael). De excommunicatione tympanitica Græcorum. Disput. Praes. J. M. S. & resp. C. Sonntag. [P433]. s4°. Altdorfi. [1698]
Sonolet (Louis). La vie & l'œuvre de Paul Deschanel, 1855–1922. 8°. [1926]
see FLEURY (*cte.* M. DE) & L. S. La société du Second Empire, t4, *n.d.*
Sontsov (Dmitry Petrovich).
Роспись древней русской утвари. 2 вып. *in* 1v. fol. Москва. 1857–58
Soobroya (Teroovercaudoo), *Modelliar, see* TEROOVERCAUDOO SOOBROYA.
Soothill (William Edward). China & England. 8°. O. 1928
China & the West. 8°. O. 1925
A mission in China. 8°. E. 1907
The 3 religions of China. Lect. 2nd ed. 8°. O. 1923
Timothy Richard of China. Foreword by Sir J. N. Jordan. 8°. 1924
Sopetto (Elvira). Margherita di Savoia, march. di Monferrato, 1295–1313, *see* REGIA DEPUT. Miscellanea, t43, 1907.
Sophia Dorothea, *consort of George I, see* SCHULENBURG-KLOSTERRODE (F. A., *Graf.* v. D.) *Die Herzogin v. Ahlden, 1852.
Sophocardius (Agricola), *see* WISHART (G.)
Sophocles.
Fabulae. Rec. &c. A. C. Pearson. s8°. O. 1924
Quae extant omnia cum vet. gram. scholiis. Rec., versione & notis illust., fragmenta collegit R. F. P. Brunck. v2. [*3 pagin.*] 4°. Argentorati. 1786
Quae exstant omnia, cum vet. scholiis. Rec. &c. R. F. P. Brunck. Acc. excerpta ex var. lect. quam continet ed. C. G. A. Erfurdt &c. 4t. 8°. Lond. 1824
Vol. 3 *contains* Scholia *&* Versio latina *w. sep. pagin.* v4 *has tp.* C. G. A. Erfurdtii Annot. integræ in S. tragoedias.
Sophocles: the plays & fragments. With crit. notes, comm., & tr. by R. C. Jebb. 2nd ed. p1, 2. 8°. C. 1887–89
TRANSLATIONS.
Tragedies. New tr., w. biog. essay, by E. H. Plumptre. s8°. 1880
Sophocle. Texte établi & tr. par P. Masqueray. [Coll. des univ. de Fr.] 2t. 8°. 1922–24
1, Ajax—Antigone—Œdipe Roi—Electre.
2, Les Trachiniennes — Philoctète — Œdipe à Colone — Les Limiers.
—— SINGLE PLAYS.
Antigone. Tr. H. Macnaghten. s8°. C. 1926
Antigone. Tr. R. C. Trevelyan. 8°. Liv'l. 1924
Elektra (1639), *see* VONDEL (J. VAN DEN). Werken, d7, *n.d.*
Herkules in Trachin; verduitscht door J. v. Vondel (1668), *see* VONDEL (J. VAN DEN). Werken, d28, *n.d.*
King Œdipus: a vers. for the mod. stage by W. B. Yeats. s8°. 1928
Koning Edipus (1660), *see* VONDEL (J. VAN DEN). Werken, d23, *n.d.*
Oedipus Tyrannus. Tr. J. T. Sheppard. s8°. C. 1922
see ÆSCHYLUS. Tragœdiæ selectæ Æschyli, S., Euripidis &c., 1567.
,, BETHE (E.) Die Ichneutai d. S., 1919.
,, DINDORF (C. W.) Poet. scenic. Graec. fabulae &c., ed. 5ª, 1869.
,, ERFURDT (C. G. A.) Annot. integrae in S. tragoedias, 1824.
,, RIBBECK (O.) S. u. s. Tragödien, 1869.

Sophocles [*continued*].
see TUDEER (L. O. TH.) De vocab. quibus S. in Ichneutis fabula satyrica usus est, 1916.
,, WILAMOWITZ-MÖLLENDORFF (U. V.) Gr. Tragoedien, B4, Philoktetes, 1923.
Sophocles (Evangelinus Apostolides).
A Romaic grammar, accomp. by a chrestomathy, w. vocab. s8°. Hartford (Conn.) 1842
Sophronius, *patriarch of Alexandria, see* THEODOSIUS, *of Alexandria.* Canones, S¹. excerpta; rec. A. Hilgard, 1894.
Soprani (Raffaello). Li scrittori d. Liguria, e partic. d. Maritima. 8°. Genova. 1667
Sopron [ŒDENBURG, *Hungary*]. Acta Comitialia Hungarica Sopron. [*Foll. by* Gravamina evangelic., 1681; Serius exhib. suppl. actorum; Articuli dominic. praelat &c., 1681; *each w. sep. pagin.*] s4°. *n.p.* [1681]
Sorabji (R. K.) Facilities for Indian students in America & Japan. [Bureau of Educ., India. Pamph. No. 7]. [P2412]. 8°. Calcutta. 1920
Soranus II, *of Ephesus.* Gynaeciorum libri 4—De signis fracturarum—De fasciis—Vita Hippocratis; ed. J. Ilberg, *see* CORPUS medic. Graec. &c., v4, 1927.
Soranzo (Alvise). Rel. d. battaglia di Lepanto 1571. [Nozze Mocenigo-Soranzo—Soresina-Vidoni. N. 131]. 8°. Venezia. 1852
Soranzo (Giacomo). Diario d. viaggio da Venezia a Costantinopoli fatto da J. S. ambasc. al Murad III &c., 1575. [Nozze Trieste—Vivante. N. 129]. 8°. Venezia. 1856
Soranzo (Girolamo). Bibliografia veneziana, in agg. &c. d. Saggio di E. A. Cicogna. la8°. Venezia. 1885
Sorapure (Victor Edgar).
The Oxford index of therapeutics. 8°. [1921]
Sorbelli (Albano).
Le croniche bolognesi del sec. 14. 8°. Bologna. 1900
Le marche tipogr. bolognesi nel sec. 16. 4°. Milano. *n.d.*
La signoria di Giov. Visconti a Bologna e le sue rel. con la Toscana. 8°. Bologna. 1901
see BAROZZI (G.) Mem. e studi int. a J. B. [*by* A. S. &c.], 1908.
,, MAZZATINTI (G.) & A. S. Inventari dei mss. d. biblioteche d'Italia, v26–38, 1918–28.
Sorber (Johann Jacob) [SORBERUS]. Comment. de institutis sacris populorum German. &c. s8°. Marburgi. 1791
Sorbonne, *see* PARIS: UNIVERSITY.
Sorde. Cartul. de l'abbaye de Saint Jean de S. Publ. P. Raymond. la8°. 1873
Sordello, *see* BERTONI (G.) S. e Reforzat, 1915.
Sordet (*le gén.* **Jean François André**), *see* BOUCHERIE (*col.*) Hist. du corps de cavalerie S.; rédigé sous la dir. du Gén. S., 1923.
Sordini (Giuseppe).
A prop. del restauro d. trifora n. facciata di S. Gregorio in Spoleto. [Extr. d. Boll. d'Arte, 1908. P2605]. fol. Roma. 1908
Alla ricerca d. tomba di un uomo celebre. [Extr. d. Atti d. Accad. Spoletina, 1901. P2599]. 8°. Spoleto. 1903
La cappella d. reliquie nel Duomo di Spoleto. [Estr. da L'Arte. anno 6. P2605]. fol. Roma. 1903
Dei sepolcri dei Tacito in Terni. [Extr. d. Boll. d'Arte, 1908]. [P2605]. fol. Roma. 1908
Di alc. ant. pitture di Spoleto. [Estr. d. Boll. d. R. D. di Storia patriâ per l'Umbria, v3]. [P2599]. 8°. *n.d.*
Di alc. lavori nel duomo di Spoleto, 1904–5. [P2599]. 8°. Perugia. 1906
Di un grossolano errore topogr. n. storia umbra. [Estr. dal Boll. d. Regia Deput. per l'Umbria, v13]. [P2703]. la8°. Perugia. 1908
Di un sunto ined. di storia Spoletina, sec. 10. [P2599]. 8°. Perugia. 1906
Di una ignorata cappella depinta in Spoleto da Giovanni Spagna. [Estr. d. Rassegna d'Arte 1907. P2599]. 8°. Milano. 1907
Il duomo di Spoleto. [P2599]. 8°. Spoleto. 1908
Piero de' Medici e Pierleone Leoni. [P2599]. s8°. Firenze. 1906
La pretesa descr. d. palazzo duc. di Spoleto. [P2599]. 8°. Perugia. 1908
Il sepolcro di G. Garofoli da Spoleto. [P2599]. 8°. Firenze. 1895
La tomba di fra Filippo Lippi nel duomo di Spoleto. [Estr. d. Illustratore Fiorentino, 1905. P2599]. s8°. Firenze. 1904
Sorel (Albert), *b. 1842.* L'Europe & la Révol. Fr. 8p [1, 4ᵉ éd., 2–5, 3ᵉ éd., 6, 7, 5ᵉ éd.] 8°. 1895–1904
La grande falaise, 1785–99. [Roman]. [repr.] s8°. [1920]
Notes & portraits cont. des pages inéd. Rec. &c. A. E. Sorel. s8°. 1909
Sorel (Albert Emile), *b. 1876.* L'autre blessure, *see* ŒUVRES libres, 83, 1928.
Sorel (Cécile). La vie amoureuse d'A. Lecouvreur. s8°. [1925]

Sorel (Charles). La jeunesse de Francion. Texte de 1626. Intr. & notes de A. Thérive. s8°. 1922
*La maison des jeux académiques. s8°. 1665
Sorel (Georges). La décomposition du Marxisme. 2e éd. s8°. 1910
Soret (Frédéric Jacob). Неизд. восточ. тонеты, *see* IMP. RUSS. ARCH. OBSCH. Труды Восточ. отд., ч4, 1859.
Sorg (Roger).
Cassandre [Salviati], ou le secret de Ronsard. 8°. 1925
Sorgato (Antonio Cesare). Venezia a Lord J. W. 1862. [*Verse.* Nozze Emo Capodilista—Venier. N127]. 8°. Padova. 1867
Sörgel (Albert). Dichtung u. Dichter d. Zeit. Eine Schilderung d. deut. Literatur d. letzten Jahrzehnte. 9. A. la8°. L. [1919]
Soriano (José del Castillo y), *see* CASTILLO Y SORIANO (J. DEL).
Soriano (Justo Garcia), *see* GARCIA SORIANO (J.)
Sóriga (Renato). Pavia e la Certosa. [Italia artistica, 88]. la8°. Bergamo. [1926]
Sorley (Charles). The letters of C. S.; w. a chapter of biography. 8°. 1919
Sorley (William Ritchie).
The moral life & moral worth. s8°. 1911
Moral values & the idea of God. Gifford Lect. 2nd ed. 8°. C. 1921
Spinoza, *see* BRIT. ACADEMY. Proc., 1918.
Tradition. [H. Spencer lect.] 8°. O. 1926
Sorokin (Pitirim A.)
Leaves from a Russian diary [1917–22]. 8°. [1925]
Современое состоянie Россiи. 8°. Прага. 1922
Sorolla y Bastida (Joaquin). Columbus leaving Palos—Portraits—Prov. of Spain, 2v—Scenes, *see* HISP. SOC. OF AMERICA. Cat. ser., 5v, 1926.
see BERUETE (AURELIANO DE). J. S., 1919.
,, WILLIAMS (L.) Art of J. S., 1926.
Sotela (Rogelio).
Valores literarios de Costa Rica. 8°. San Jose, C.R. 1920
Sotheby (Samuel Leigh). Principia typographica. Block-books issued in Holland, Flanders & Germany dur. 15th cent., &c. Added, char. of paper-marks of the period. 3v. fol. 1858
Unpubl. doc. marginal notes &c. in the autograph of P. Melanchthon & of M. Luther. With facs. fol. 1840
Sotheran, *The family of, see* SOTHERAN (C.) Genealog. mem., 1871.
Sotheran (Charles). *Genealog. mem. rel. to fam. of Sotheron, of Durham, Northumberland &c., & to the sept of Macmanus. 2p *in* 1v. 4°. *p.p.* 1871[–73]
Sotheran (Henry Cecil), *see* ZEITLINGER (H.) & H. C. S. Bibl. chemico-mathem., 2v, 1921.
Sotheron, *The family of, see* SOTHERAN (C.) Genealog. mem., 1871.
Soto (Ferdinando de) [FERNÃDO DE SOUTO; HERNANDO DE SOTO]. Rel. d. trabalhos q̃ ho F. de S. &c. pass. no descob. da Frolida [*sic*], 1557, *see* COLLECÇÃO de opusc. reimpr., 1875.
Soto (Petrus de). De conciliat. gratiae & liberi arbitrii, *see* REGINALD (A.) De mente Conc. Trid., 1706.
see CHRISTOPH, *Herzog zu Würtemberg.* Confessio &c. [Refut. Sotici scr.], 1561.
,, HOSIUS (S.) Confut. proleg. Brentii adv. S. &c., 1561.
Sotomaior (Antonio a). Index librorum prohibit. & expurg. pro catholicis Hispan. regnis Philippi IV, 1667, *see* INDEX.
Sotomayor (Fernando A. de), *see* ABRIL (M.) F. A. de S., 1920.
Sotsialisticheskaya Akademiya. Вестник Социалист. Акад. N. 1, 3 (Нояб. 1922. Фев. 1923). 8°. Москва. 1922–23
Sotsialisti-Revolyutsioneri [Партiя Соц. Револ.]
Двѣнадцать смертниковъ. Судъ надъ Соц.-Рев. въ Москвѣ. 8°. Берлинъ. 1922
For Eng. tr., see SOCIALISTS-REVOLUTIONISTS.
Ко всѣмъ Работникамъ въ Россiи. [P2715]. s8°. *n.p.* 1902
Матросы Черного Моря. [P2716]. s8°. *n.p.* 1905
Процесс П. С.-Р. Речи защитников Уленова &c. Последние слова подсудимых. [*Pref. by L. Trotsky*]. 8°. Москва. 1922
Царь-голодъ. [*a. c. in* P810]. s8°. *n.p.* 1902
Эволюцiя русской соцiалист. мысли. [P2715]. 8°. *n.p.* [1903 ?]
Эхъ, пора вы, братцы, взяться вамъ за умъ *& o. p.* [P810, 2706]. s8°. *n.p.* 1889–1905
see KHILKOV (D.) О свободы, *n.d.*
,, NICHOLAS II. *Царь; переводъ съ англ., 1905.
,, THUN (A.) Ист. револ. движенiя въ Россiи, 1903.
Sottas (Henri). Statuettes funéraires de la 18e dynastie, *see* ACAD. D. INSCR.: FOND. PIOT. Mon., t25, 1921–22.
Sottas (Jules), *see* ANTHIAUME (A.) & J. S. L'astrolabe-quadrant du Musée des Antiq. de Rouen, 1910.
Söttler (Joannes Gaspar) [†SOETTLER (J. G.)] De officiis sacerdot. & pastoral., *see* MIGNE (J. P.), *ed.* Theol. cursus, t25, 1860.
Soubies (Albert). Les membres de l'Acad. des Beaux-Arts dep. la fond. de l'Institut. s4 (4, 1876–1901). 8°. 1917
Souday (Paul).
André Gide. 3e éd. s8°. [1927]
Les livres du temps. 2s. [s1, 4e éd.; s2, 2e éd.] s8°. 1913–14
Marcel Proust. 3e éd. s8°. [1927]
Paul Valéry. 3e éd. s8°. [1927]
see VOLTAIRE. Mem., préc. de V. démiurge, par P. S., 1927.
Soufflot (Jacques Germain), *1713–80.* Corresp. avec les directeurs des bâtiments conc. la manufacture des Gobelins (1756–80). Publ. J. Mondain-Monval. la8°. 1918
see MONVAL (J.) S.: sa vie, son œuvre &c., 1918.
Soul (The) of harmony: being a coll. of the most admired glees, & catches, duets &c. s8°. Norwich. [1804]
Soulaine (Pierre). La rue de la Paix. Roman. s8°. [1922]
Soulas d'Allainval (Léonor Jean C.) L'école des bourgeois, *see* THÉÂTRE choisi du 18e s., t1, 1914.
Soule (George). The accumul. of capital. [P2734]. s8°. N.Y. 1924
Soule (Winsor). Spanish farm houses & minor public buildings. Photographs &c. by W. S. Intr. by R. A. Cram. la8°. N.Y. 1924
Soulié (Georges) [G. SOULIÉ DE MORANT]. Exterritorialité & intérêts étrangers en Chine. Préf. par S. Pichon. la8°. 1925
Florilège des poèmes Song, 960–1277 après J.-C. Tr. du chin. par G. S. s8°. [1923]
Hist. de l'art chinois. la8°. 1928
see HAOU KEW CHUEN. La brise au clair de lune: roman chinois [*by* Ming-tsiao tchong-jenn]; tr. G. S. de M., 1925.
Soulié (Maurice). La grande aventure, le roman d'une Parisienne [Marie de La Tour] au Canada (1640–50). s8°. 1927
La présidente de Saint-Vincent, *see* ŒUVRES libres, 81, 1928.
Soulier (—), *prêtre.* Hist. des édits de pacification &c. s8°. 1682
see BERNARD (P.) L'explic. de l'Edit de Nantes, avec de nouv. obs. par M. S., 1683.
Souligné (— de). *The desolation of France demonstrated. By a person of quality, a native of France. s8°. 1697
The polit. mischiefs of popery. By a person of quality, a native of France. [Tr. G. Ridpath]. s8°. 1698
Soult (*le maréchal* **Nicolas Jean-de-Dieu),** *duc de Dalmatie.*
Mémoires. Publ. par s. fils. p1, Hist. des Guerres de la Révolution. 3t. 8°. 1854
Soultrait (*le comte* **Georges de).** Nièvre, *see* RÉPERTOIRE ARCHÉOL. DE LA FR., 1875.
Soupault (Philippe). A la dérive. Roman. s8°. [1923]
En joue! . . . Roman. s8°. 1925
Henri Rousseau, le douanier. la8°. [1927]
Souriau (Maurice). Hist. du romantisme en France. 2t [t1 *in* 2p]. la8°. [1927]
Soury (Jules), *see* ROUVEYRE (A.) Souv. de mon commerce: Gourmont &c., S., 1921.
Sousa (Gabriel Soares de), *see* SOARES DE SOUZA (G.)
Sousa (Luiz de), *Dominican* [†SOUSA COUTINHO (MANOEL DE)], *see* CACEGAS (L. DE). Vida de Bertolameu dos Martyres; reformada e ampliada &c. por L. de S., 3t, 1890; 2a ed., t1, 1921.
Sousa Costa (Alberto de). Regresso á Felicidade. s8°. 1916
Sousa Coutinho (Francisco de). Corresp. diplomát. dur. a sua embaixada em Holanda. Publ. E. Prestage & P. de Azevedo. vol. 1, 2 (1643–48). 4°. Coimbra. 1920–26
Sousa Coutinho (Manoel de), *see* SOUSA (L. DE).
Sousa Ferreira (João). America abreviada, em particular Maranhão [1693], *see* INSTITUTO HIST. E GEOG. BRAZIL. Revista, t57, 1894.
Sousa Silva Costa Lobo (A. de), *see* COSTA LOBO (A. DE S. S.)
Soutar (Andrew). Corinthian days. s8°. [1923]
Dear fools. s8°. [1927]
Hornets Nest. s8°. 1922
Souter (Alexander). Character & hist. of Pelagius' comm. on the Epistles of St. Paul, 1916, *see* BRIT. ACAD. Proc., 1915–16.
Hints on the study of Latin (A.D. 125–750). [P2420]. s8°. 1920
Hints on transl. fr. Latin into Engl. [P2420; 2867]. s8°. 1920
see TEXTS & STUDIES, v9i, ii, Pelagius's expos. of 13 epistles of St. Paul: intr. [by A. S.], 1922–26.

South (Robert), *D.D.* *Animadv. upon Dr. Sherlock's bk. A vindic. of the Trinity &c. By a divine of the Church of Engl. s4°. 1693
*Tritheism charged upon Dr. Sherlock's new notion of the Trinity &c. By a divine of the Church of England [*i.e.* R. S. Pref. *signed* A. A.] 8°. 1695
South African. Centenary bk. of S. Afr. verse, 1820–1925, 1925, *see* SLATER (F. C.), *ed.*
South African Christian watchman & missionary magazine. v1, 2, 1846–47. [*No more publ.*] 8°. Graham's Town. [1846]–47
South African News. Weekly ed. v1–3 [*in 4.* June 1899–Oct. 1901]. fol. Cape Town. [1899–1901]
South American handbook, 1926–28. Ed. J. A. Hunter. s8°. [1925–27]
South & East African (The) year book & guide, 1914 &c., *see* BROWN (A. S.) & G. G. BROWN.
Southampton. Assembly books of S. Ed., w. intr., notes &c. by J. W. Horrocks. [S. Rec. Soc.] v2–4. 1609–16. la8°. S. 1920–25
The Assize of Bread book, 1477–1517. Ed. R. C. Anderson. [S. Rec. Soc.] la8°. S. 1923
The book of remembrance of S. Ed. w. intr., notes &c. by H. W. Gidden. [South. Rec. Soc.] v1 (1440–1620). la8°. S. 1927
Court Leet records. Transcr. & ed. F. J. C. & D. M. Hearnshaw. [S. Record Soc.] v1, 3p, 1550[–1634. *pagin. cont.*] la8°. S. 1905–7
„ „ Suppl. to v1, cont. Glossary, notes on syntax & dialect & indexes. [S. Record Soc.] la8°. S. 1908
Maps & plans of old S. Ed., w. notes by W. H. Rogers. [S. Record Soc.] fol. S. [1907]
Southampton Record Society. Publications, *see* SOUTHAMPTON.
Southampton (Henry Wriothesley, *3rd earl of***),** *see* STOPES (C. C.) Life of S., 1922.
South Australia. *New (The) Brit. prov. of S.A., 2nd ed., 1835, *see* WAKEFIELD (E. G.)
South Australian Protestant Emigration Community, *see* ROBERTSON (G. W.) Rise &c., 1837.
South Downs (The). By the Tramp. s8°. [1916]
Southern. *Southern (The) Passion; ed. w. intr. &c. by B. D. Brown, 1927, *see* JESUS CHRIST.
Southerne (Thomas). Isabella, or the fatal marriage, *see* INCHBALD (*Mrs.* E.) Brit. theatre, v7, 1808.
Oroonoko. Tragedy. [P2575]. 8°. 1778
Oroonoko, *see* INCHBALD (*Mrs.* E.) Brit. theatre, v7, 1808.
Southern review (The). [Ed. A. T. Bledsoe]. v1–8 (1867–70). 8°. Baltimore. 1867–70
Southey (Robert).
The book of the Church. 2nd ed. 2v. 8°. 1824
Joan of Arc, ballads, lyrics, & minor poems. s8°. [1878]
Life of Nelson. Ed. w. intr. & crit. notes by G. Callender. 8°. 1922
Life of Wesley. Notes by S. T. Coleridge, & remarks on J. Wesley by A. Knox; ed. w. intr. & notes by M. H. Fitzgerald. 2v. s8°. O. 1925
Lives & works of the uneducated poets [*w.* John Jones, an old servant: an acc. of h. life wr. by himself]. Ed. J. S. Childers. s8°. 1925
A love story. Fragm. f. "The doctor." Ed. J. W. Warter. [*b. w.* Forster (J.) De Foe &c., 1855]. s8°. 1853
Madoc. Poem. 4°. 1805
Poems. Ed. M. H. Fitzgerald. Oxford ed. s8°. 1909
Sel. lives of Cromwell & Bunyan. n. ed. s8°. 1849
see WATSON (R.) Obs. on S.'s Life of Wesley, 1821.
Southey (Rosamond). The last bout. s8°. [1918]
South Kensington Museum, *see* VICTORIA & ALBERT MUSEUM.
South Place Institute, *see* MEADMORE (W. S.) S.P. Sunday pop. concerts (1887–1927), 1927.
South Wales Ports. [2nd annual No.] Produced &c. by H. N. Appleby. By arrangement w. Gt. West. Railway Co. la8°. 1924
Southwark. *Morning Exercise (The) agst. popery, preached in S., 1675, *see* MORNING-EXERCISE.
Southwell (Robert). Marie Magdalen's funerall teares for the death of our Saviour. [1634]. repr. s8°. 1823
Souto (Fernãdo de), *see* SOTO (FERDINANDO DE).
Soutra, *see* SOLTRE.
Souvenirs. Souv. de guerre d'un sous-officier allemand Feldwebel C., 1914–16. Publ. avec préf. par L. P. Alaux.
„ „ *Eng. tr. w. t.*, The diary of a German soldier. s8°. N.Y. 1919
*Souv. d'un officier ayant servi dans le Caucase, 1835–38, *see* BROSSET (M. F.) Coll. d'histor. arm., t2, 1876.
Souza (Augusto Fausto de). A bahia do Rio de Janeiro, *see* INSTITUTO HIST. E GEOG. BRAZIL. Revista, t44, 1881.
Souza (*Count* **Baretto de).** Advanced equitation. 8°. 1927
Souza (Gabriel Soares de), *see* SOARES DE SOUZA (G.)
Souza (Robert de). Un débat sur la poésie, *see* BRÉMOND (H.) La poésie pure &c., 1926.
Souza Pinto (—). Nouv. dict. portugais-franç. & franç.-portugais. [2p]. s8°. 1899
Souza Silva (Joaquim Norberto). Mem. das aldeias de Indios da prov. do Rio de Janeiro, 1852, *see* INSTITUTO HIST. E GEOG. BRAZIL. Rev., t17 (1854), 1894.
Sovetsky.
Совѣтскій букварь для взрослыхъ. [P2459]. 8°. Москва. 1919
Soviet Union monthly. v1 (Feb.–Dec., 1926). sm. fol. 1926
Soviet Union review, *formerly publ. as* RUSSIAN INFORMATION & REVIEW [*no more publ. aft. May 1925*], *see* RUSSIAN INFORMATION.
Soviet Union year-book, 1926. Comp. & ed. L. Segal & A. A. Santalov. s8°. 1926
1st issue, 1925, *had t.:* Commercial year-bk. of the Soviet Union.
Sovremenniya Zapiski. Современныя записки. Обществ.-полит. и лит. журналъ. 1–23. [Annales contemp.] 8°. Парижъ. 1920–25
Sowerby (Arthur de Carle).
Fur & feather in N. China. 8°. Tientsin. 1914
The naturalist in Manchuria. v1–3 [2 & 3 *b. together, sep. pagin.*] la8°. Tientsin. 1922–23
A naturalist's holiday by the sea. 8°. 1923
A naturalist's note-book in China. la8°. Shanghai. 1925
Sowerby (Githa). Rutherford & Son, *see* PLAYS of to-day, v2, 1925.
Sowers (Don Conger). Financial hist. of New York state, 1789–1912. 8°. N.Y., *Columbia Univ.* 1914
Sowjet-Russland. *S.-R. u. d. Völker d. Welt: Reden, 19 Dez. 1918, 1919, *see* RUSSIA: SOVIET REP.
Sowjetrussland u. Polen. Reden v. Kamenev, Lenin, Trotzki &c., 5 Mai 1920. [P2462]. 8°. 1920
Sozialdemokratische Partei Deutschlands, *see* BESTREBUNGEN (DIE) für e. Annäherung Deutschlands u. Oesterreich-Ungarns; hrsg. v. S.P.D., 1916.
Sozomenus (Hermias) [SOZOMENE], *see* EUSEBIUS. Eccl. hist. of E., Socrates, S.; tr. Parker, 3rd ed. rev., 1729.
see SOCRATES, *Scholasticus*. Eccl. hist. of Socrates, S. &c.; abridg'd by S. Parker, 2p, 1707–12.
Spaan (Theodorus). Diss., *see* PAP (J.) Disp., 1784.
Spaccini (Gio. Batt.) Cronaca Modenese (1588–1636). A cura di G. Bertoni, T. Sandonnini &c. [Mon. di stor. patria d. prov. Mod. Ser. d. cron., t16]. sm. fol. Modena. 1911
Spaight (James Molony). Air power & war rights. 8°. 1924
Spain. *Travels thr. S. & part of Portugal, 2v, 1808, *see* WHITTINGTON (*Rev.* —).
West coast of S. & Portugal pilot, & Suppl. 1, 1921–22, *see* ADMIRALTY.
Spalatin (Georg) [†BURCKARD (G.), *Spalatinus*; BURKHARDT (G.)] Spalatiniana. Hrsg. G. Berbig. [Quellen &c. aus d. Gesch. d. Reformationsjhdts., B5]. 8°. L. 1908
Tröstung inn tods nöten, d. mehrern teils aus Thome Venatorii Buchlin durch G. Spalatinum gezogen. s8°. [Wittemberg, *G. Rhaw*]. *n.d.* [*c.* 1530]
see BERBIG (G.) G. S. u. s. Verhältnis zu M. Luther auf Grund i. Briefwechsels 1525, 1906.
„ SCHLEGEL (C.) Hist. vitae G. S., 1693.
Spalding (Kenneth Jay). Desire & reason: origin &c. of intellect. principles. 8°. 1922
Spalding (William Frederick).
The London money market. s8°. 1922
Spallicci (Maria). La poesia popolare romagnola. 8°. 1921
Spampanato (Vinc.) Vita di Giordano Bruno. Con doc. 2v [*pagin. cont.*] 8°. Messina. 1921
Spang (William) [*ps.* PHILALETHES (IRENAEUS), *Eleutherius*]. Rerum nuper in regno Scot. gest. hist.; Addita est Eccl. Scot. ad Helvet. reformatas epist. &c. 8°. Dantisci. 1641
Spangenberg (August Gottlieb). An acc. of the manner in which the Unitas Fratrum or United Brethren preach the Gospel &c. 8°. 1788
Expos. of Xtn. doct. as taught in the church of the United Brethren. Pref. by B. La Trobe. 8°. 1784
„ „ ....2nd ed. 8°. 1796
Leben d. Herrn Nicolaus Ludwig, Grafen &c. v. Zinzendorf. 8T [*in 6v. pagin. cont.*] s8°. [1773–]75

Spangenberg (Cyriacus).
Antwort S. auff d. schreckl. Landlügen &c. [P2665]. s4°. Eisleben. 1572
Catechismus die fünff Heuptstück der Christl. Lehre &c. s4°. Erfford. 1547
Ehespiegel d. i. alles was v. d. heyligē Ehestande &c. mag gesagt werden &c. s8°. Strassburg. 1578
Hist. Manichæorum &c. ex eccl. historiis & Patrum scriptis coll. s4°. Ursellis. 1578
Kurtze &c. Bekentnis v. etlichen Religions Articklen. [P2665]. s4°. [Mansfelt]. 1573
Warhafftige gewisse bestendige d. heil Schr. gemesse &c. Lere v. d. Erbsünde &c. [P2665]. s4°. Eisleben. 1572
see HESHUSIUS (T.) Gründl. Beweisung &c. samt Widerlegung d. Schr. C. S. v. d. Erbsünde, 1574.
,, PRAETORIUS (Z.) Antwort auff S. Gegenbericht, 1572.

Spangenberg (Wolfhart). Anbind-oder Fangbriefe. Hrsg. F. Behrend. [Lit. V. in St. 262]. 8°. Tübingen. 1914

Spanheim (Ezechiel, *Frhr.* v.), *see* LOEWE (V.) Ein Diplomat u. Gelehrter, E. S., 1629–1710: mit Anhang: Aus d. Briefwechsel zw. S. u. Leibniz, 1924.

Spanheim (Friedrich), *the elder, see* DAILLÉ (J.) Apolog. pro 2 eccl. in Gallia protest. synodis &c.; adv. F. S. exercit. de gratia univ., 2t, 1655.

Spanheim (Friedrich), *the younger, 1632–1701.*
De Papa foemina inter Leonem IV & Benedictum III disq. s8°. Lugduni Batav. 1691
Diss. hist. argumenti quaternio. 1, De Petri in urbem Romam profectione. 2, De æra conversionis Paulinæ &c. s8°. Lugd. Batav. 1679
Eccl. annals, to Reformation. Pref. geogr. descr. of Palestine. Tr. compress. &c. by G. Wright. 2nd ed. corr. 8°. 1840
Hist. de la Papesse Jeanne. Tirée de la diss. lat. 2e éd. 2t. s8°. La Haye. 1720
Hist. imaginum restituta, praecipue adv. Gallos scriptores L. Maimburg & N. Alexandrum. s8°. Lugduni Batav. 1686
Select. de relig. controv., elenchus hist.-theol. s8°. Lugduni Batav. 1687
Summa hist. eccles. ad saec. 16. inchoatum. Praem. Doctrina temporum, cum oratione de Christianismo degenere [*w. sep. pagin.*] 2t. [*pagin. cont.*] s8°. Lugd. Batav. 1689
,, ,, Cont. usque ad 1740, à C. a Velzen. [*w. t.* Introd. ad hist. eccles.] s8°. Groningae. 1740

Spanish.
Sp. ballads, 1920, *see* LE STRANGE (G.)
Sp. (A) Franciscan's narr. of a journey to the Holy Land. Tr. f. 16th cent. MS. & ed. by H. C. Luke [Palestine Explor. F.] 8°. 1927
Sp. Grail fragments; ed. K. Pietsch, 2v, 1924–25, *see* GRAIL.
*Sp. pictures, 1870, *see* MANNING (S.)
*Sp. tragedy (The), w. add., 1602, 1925, *see* KYD (T.)
Ten Sp. farces of 16th-18th c., 1924, *see* NORTHUP (G. T.), *ed.*

Spann (Erika) [*ps.* E. RHEINSCH; E. SPANN-RHEINSCH].
Parazelsus u. s. Jünger: Dichtung. la8°. Reichenberg. [1921]

Spann (Othmar).
Tote u. lebendige Wissenschaft. 2e A. s8°. Jena. 1925
Der wahre Staat. Vorles. üb. Abbruch u. Neubau d. Gesellschaft. 2. durchgeseh. A. 8°. L. 1923

Spanner (Harry) & S. Guyer. Ruṣâfa, die Wallfahrtsstadt d. hlgn. Sergios. [Forsch. z. islam. Kunst; hrsg. F. Sarre, 4]. 4°. 1926

Spann-Rheinsch (Erika), *see* SPANN (E.)

Spano (Giovanni), *see* MANNO (A.) Annali e scr. di G. S., 1879.

Spanyik (Glycerius). Compend. hist. regni Hungariae usque ad nostra tempora. 2t [*in* 1v]. s8°. Pesthini. 1816

Spargo (John). "The greatest failure in all history." Crit. exam. of Bolshevism in Russia. s8°. N.Y. [1920]
Mem. on trade w. Soviet Russia. [P2492]. 8°. N.Y. [1921]

Spark (Michael), *see* VERSES. V. on man's mortalitie &c.; repr. f. M. S.'s Crums of comfort &c., 1628, 1925.

Sparling (H. Halliday). The Kelmscott Press & W. Morris, master-craftsman. 8°. 1924

Sparrow (Anthony), *bp. of* (*1*) *Exeter,* (*2*) *Norwich.* [Coll. of articles, injunctions, canons &c. w. o. publ. records of the Ch. of Eng., chiefly Edw. VI to Ch. I. *Gen. tp. wanting. The contents are same as the first part of Sparrow's Coll.*] s4°. [1661 ?]

Sparrow (Walter Shaw).
Angling in Brit. art thr. 5 c. Foreword by H. T. Sheringham. 4°. 1923
Brit. sporting artists f. Barlow to Herring. Foreword by Sir T. Cook. 4°. [1922]
The Fifth Army in March 1918. Intr. by Gen. Sir H. Gough. 8°. 1921
The Fifth Army in March 1918. [3rd ed., w. new intr.] 8°. [1923]
John Lavery & h. work. Pref. by R. B. Cunninghame Graham. la8°. [1922]
see BRANGWYN (F.) & W. S. S. A book of bridges, 1920.
,, BRITISH home (The); ed. W. S. S., 1904.

Spartacus.
*Ce que veut le parti de S. [P2487]. s8°. Moscou. 1919
Spartakus (Das) Programm, 1919, *see* BOUSSET (H.)
*Was will d. Spartakusbund. Hrsg. v. d. Kommunist. Partei Deutschlands. [P2484]. 8°. 1919

Spas. The spas of Brit., 1924, *see* BRIT. SPA FEDERATION.

Spasovic (Vladimir Danilovich), *see* PYPIN (A. N.) & V. D. S. Исторія славянскихъ лит., изд. 2ое, т1, 1879.

Spassky (Grigory Ivanovich). Свѣдѣнія Русскихъ о рѣкѣ Амура въ xvii ст. [*Extract.* P2532]. 8°. *n.p.* [1830 ?]

Spata (Giuseppe). Diplomi greci ined. ric. da alcuni mss. d. Bibl. Com. di Palermo; tr. da G. S. [*Gr. & Ital.*], 2s, *see* REGIA DEP. DI STORIA PATRIA. Misc., t9, 12, 1870–71.

Spathary (Nikolai Gavrilovich).
Описаніе первыя части вселенныя именуемой Азіи, в ней же состоитъ Китаиское Государство. Церковно-слав. текстъ [*mostly tr. f. Martini*], съ біог. Н. Г. С. напис. А. И. Яцимирскимъ, предисл. и указ. Н. Θ. Катанова &c. fol. Казань. 1910
Сказаніе о великой рѣкѣ Амурѣ, *see* TITOV (A. A.) Сибирь въ xvii вѣкѣ, 1890.
Статейный списокъ посольства Н. Спаѳарія въ Китай (1675–78). [*Ed.* Ю. В. Арсеньевъ]. la8°. С.-П. 1906
see ARSENEV (YU.) Новыя данныя о службѣ Н. С., 1900.
,, GREBENSCHIKOV (A. V.) Къ ист. русско-маньчжур. отношій, 1, посольство С., 1912.

Spaventa (Bertrando), *see* GENTILE (G.) B. S., 1924.

Spaventa (Silvio). Lettere polit., 1861–93. Ed. G. Castellano. 8°. Bari. 1926

Spaventa Filippi (Silvio).
Tre uomini e una farfalla. Romanzo. s8°. Milano. 1921

Speakman (Martha Travilla). Games for organized play, *see* UNITED STATES: LAB. Children's Bur., 113, 1923.
Recreation for blind children, *see* UNITED STATES: LAB. Children's Bur., 172, 1927.

Speare (Morris Edmund).
The polit. novel in England & America. 8°. N.Y. 1924

Spearing (Joseph). The true state of the question: whether admissibility of Romanists to the higher offices of the State be compatible w. Brit. Constit. 8°. Cork. 1816

Spearman (Charles E.) The abilities of man. 8°. 1927
The nature of "intelligence" & the princ. of cognition. 8°. 1923

Spearman (*Capt.* James Morton).
The British gunner. 2nd ed. s8°. 1828
Notes on milit. educ. [P2593]. s8°. 1853

Spears (*Mrs.* Mary), *wife of Brig.-Gen. E. L. Spears, see* BORDEN (M.)

Specht (F. A.) Die Frauenkirche in München. 8°. München. 1894

Specht (Richard). Richard Strauss u. s. Werk. 2B. la8°. L. 1921

***Specimen** of naked truth f. a Brit. sailor, 1746, *see* VERNON (*adm.* E.)

Speckter (Otto), *see* HEY (W.) Noch 50 Fabeln; in Bildern gezeichnet v. O. S., 1837 ?.

***Spectacle** de la nature: or Nature display'd; tr., 7v, 1736–48, *see* PLUCHE (N. A.)

Spectator (The), *see* ADDISON (J.) Days w. Sir Roger de Coverley; repr. f. the S., 3rd ed., 1892.

Spectator (The). v124–140. fol. [1920–28]
see MASSINGHAM (H. J.) *Dogs, birds, & others. Nat. hist. letters f. S., 1921.
,, STRACHEY (J. ST. L.) Adv. of living, 1922.

Spectator, *ps.*
*Die Gesch. d. Berliner Fünftageregierung. s8°. L. 1920

Spectator, *ps.*, Labour, cap. & finance, 1920, *see* WALL (W. W.)

Speculum. *Magnum speculum exemplorum excerptum ab Anonymo quodam, qui c. A.D. 1480 vixisse deprehenditur. Vindic., variis notis &c. illust. per quendam patrem e Soc. Jesu [*i.e.* J. Major] &c. 2a ed. castigatior. 2t. s4°. Duaci. 1605
*Speculum Beatae virginis, 1686, *see* HICKES (G.)
*Speculum humane salvatōis. [*Lat. & Germ. w. a metrical summary by Frater Johannes of the Monastery of S. S. Ulrich & Afra. fol. 2a.* Incipit ꝓhemium libri sequentis. *Ends fol. 270b.* Explicit humaneq. salutis sūmula plane a me fratre Iohanne tui pater ordinis alme vir bn̄dicte quasi minimo monacho]. fol. [Augsburg, *Günther Zainer.* 1473]
270 leaves, first, a blank, missing; sig. A-Z, A-D10.
Speculum humanæ salvationis. Reprod. of Ital. MS. of the 14th cent. Descr. & pref. by M. R. James, w. discussion of the school & date by B. Berenson. sm. fol. O. *p.f.p.c.* 1926
*Speculum humanae salvationis, *see* BERJEAU (J. P.) Essai bibliogr., 1862.
Spiegel d. menschl. Heils, 1924, *see* CONRAD, *von Helmsdorf.*

Speculum anni: or, Season on the seasons, 1800–8. By H. Season. [1804 *wanting*. *b. w.* Gentleman's diary, 1800–8]. s8°. 1800–8

Spedizione Italiana de Filippi nell' Himàlaia, Caracorùm &c., 1913–14, *see* FILIPPI (F. DE).

Spee (Friedrich v.), *1591–1635* [SPE]. Cautio criminalis, seu de process. contra sagas liber. Locuplet. per A.D.M.C.A. s8°. Augustæ Vindelic. 1731
Trutz-Nachtigall. Hrsg. P. L. Willmes. s8°. Köln. 1812
„ „ ....[a. ed.] s8°. Berlin. 1817

Speed (Harold). Science & practice of oil painting. 8°. 1924

Speedy (Thomas). The natural hist. of sport in Scotland with rod & gun. s4°. 1920

Speelman (Cornelis). Journaal der reis van den gezant der O. I. Compagnie J. Cunaeus naar Perzië, 1651–52. Uitg. door A. Hotz. [Hist. Genoots. Werken, s3, 26]. 8°. A. 1908

Speer (Victor). *Mem. of a gt. detective, J. W. Murray. 8°. 1904
„ „ Comp. by V. S. 8°. Toronto. 1905

Speight (Harry). Chronicles & stories of old Bingley. s8°. 1898

Speight (Robert), *see* PHILOS. INST. OF CANTERBURY [*N.Z.*] Nat. hist. of C.; ed. R. S., 1927.

Speke (Hugh). *By His Highness Will. Henry, Pr. of Orange: a 3rd declaration [given at Sherbourne, Nov. 1688. *Wr. by H. S.* P2572. *a. issue in* England. Coll. of papers, 1688]. s8°. 1688

Speke (John Hanning). Journal of the discovery of the source of the Nile. [Everyman's Lib.] [repr.] s8°. 1908

Spelman (*Sir* Henry). Tithes too hot to be touched. Treatises. [3p *in* 1v]. s4°. [1646]
1, Larger worke. 2, An apology &c. 3, An answer &c. (Resol. of a doubt). *p1 & 3 have sep. pagin. p2 has none. p3 wants all after page 24.*

Spelsbury. Churchwardens' acc., 1925, *see* MARSTON.

Spence (Hugh S.) Barium & strontium in Canada. [Canada: Mines Br. P2624]. 8°. Ottawa. 1922
Bentonite. [Canada: Mines Br. P2771]. 8°. Ottawa. 1924
Graphite. [Canada: Mines Br.] 8°. Ottawa. 1920
Phosphate in Canada. [Canada: Mines Br.] 8°. Ottawa. 1920
Talc & soapstone in Canada. [Canada: Mines Br. P2713]. 8°. Ottawa. 1922

Spence (John). Shetland folk-lore. s8°. Lerwick. 1899

Spence (Lewis).
Atlantis in America. 8°. 1925
The gods of Mexico. 8°. [1923]
Hero tales & legends of the Rhine. 8°. 1915
An introd. to mythology. 8°. [1921]
Legends & romances of Spain. 8°. [1920]
Myths & legends of ancient Egypt. [repr.] 8°. [1922]
The problem of Atlantis. 8°. 1924

Spence (Patrick), *see* ABBOT (R.) A mirrour of Popish subtilties &c. which a Papist in the behalfe of P. S. hath gathered &c., 1594.

Spence (Robert), *bookseller, 1758–1824.*
see BURDEKIN (R.) Mem. of R. S. &c., 1840.
„ HYMN. *A pocket h. book, pr. for R. S., 1786.
„ PSALMS. *A coll. of ps. & hymns for Xtn., pr. for R. S., 1781.

Spence (Thomas). Real rights of man, *see* BEER (M.) Pioneers of land reform, 1920.

Spence (Thomas), *bookseller*, *see* RUDKIN (O. D.) T. S., 1927.

Spencer (Albert Edward John Spencer, *7th earl*). Spencer House, St. James's Place. [Repr. f. "Country Life"]. 4°. [1926]

Spencer (Arthur Marshman), *see* THOMPSON (E. J.) & A. M. S. Bengali relig. lyrics; sel. & tr. by E. J. T. & A. M. S., 1923.

Spencer (*Sir* Baldwin) & F. J. Gillen.
The Arunta: st. of a Stone Age people. 2v. 8°. 1927

Spencer (Frederick Augustus Morland).
Civilization remade by Christ. 8°. 1928
Ethics of the Gospel. 8°. [1925]

Spencer (George John Spencer, *2nd earl*). Private papers of S., 1st Ld. of the Admiralty, 1794–1801. Ed. Rear-Adm. H. W. Richmond. [Navy Record Soc., v58, 59]. v3, 4. 8°. 1924

Spencer (Harold Sherwood). Democracy or Shylocracy? Pref. by Dr. J. H. Clarke. 3rd ed. 8°. 1922

Spencer (Hazelton). Shakespeare improved. The Restoration versions in quarto & on the stage. la8°. Cambridge, *Harvard*. 1927

Spencer (Herbert).
Descriptive sociology. No. 3, 11 [3, new ed.] fol. 1925
3, Lowest races: Negrito races, Malayo-Polynesian races; by Prof. Duncan; ed. H. R. Tedder.
11, Ancient Egyptians; by Sir W. F. Petrie.
First principles. 4th impr. pop. ed. 2v. 8°. 1911

Spencer (Herbert Ritchie). The renaissance of midwifery. Lloyd Roberts lect., 1924. [*b. w. h.* W. Harvey, 1921]. 8°. [1924]
W. Harvey, obstetric physician &c. Harveian oration, 1921. 8°. 1921

Spencer (John), *dean of Ely, 1630–93*, *see* RIBOUDEAULT (P.) Sacrum Dei oraculum Urim & Thummim, a var. J. S. excog. liberum, 1685.

Spencer (John), *Jesuit* [SPENSER]. Scripture mistaken the ground of Protestants &c. agst. the anc. catholicke relig. of Eng. s8°. Antwerpe. 1655

Spencer (John), *Librarian of Sion College*. Καινὰ καὶ παλαιά. Things new & old. Similies, sentences, allegories . . . &c. [*Ed.* T. Fuller]. fol. 1658

Spencer (Leonard James). The world's minerals, w. app. by W. D. Hamman. 8°. N.Y. [1916]

Spencer (Sanders).
The pig. Breeding, rearing & marketing. s8°. 1921

Spencer (Walter George). The "Epitome" of Vesalius on vellum in the B.M. Lib. [Repr. f. Essays pres. to K. Sudhoff. P2754]. 8°. [1923]
Vesalius: h. delin. of the framework of the human body in the "Fabrica" & "Epitome." 4th Vicary Lect., 1922. [Repr. f. Brit. journ. of surgery, v10]. [P2703]. la8°. Bristol. 1923
Westminster Hospital: its hist. 8°. 1924

Spencer (Walter Thomas). Forty years in my bookshop. Ed., w. intr., by T. Moult. 8°. 1923

Spender (Constance) & E. Thompson.
Bath. [Intr. F. Harrison]. s8°. 1922

Spender (E. Harold). Byron & Greece. 8°. 1924
Men & mansions. 8°. [1924]
The resurrection of Greece, 1921, *see* ANGLO-HELLENIC LEAGUE, No. 44, 1921.
The sacrifice of Greece, *see* ANGLO-HELLENIC LEAGUE, No. 47, 1922.

Spender (Edith), *see* SPENDER (H. F.) & E. S. The awakening, 1922.

Spender (Hugh F.) The banner. s8°. [1920]
see EUROPA YEAR BOOK; ed. H. F. S. &c., 1926 &c.
—— **& E. Spender.** The awakening. s8°. 1922

Spender (John Alfred). The changing East. 8°. [1926]
Life, journalism & politics. 2v. 8°. [1927]
Life of the Rt. Hon. Sir H. Campbell-Bannerman. 2v. 8°. [1923]
The public life. 2v. 8°. [1925]

Spener (Philipp Jacob).
Consilia & judicia theolog. Latina. 3p *in* 1v. s4°. Francofurti a. M. 1709
Litterarum a S. ad H. A. Franckium datarum spec. 1 & 2. Exhib. A. Tholuckius. [P2603; *a. c. of* spec. 2 *in* P2672]. 4°. Halis. 1854–57
Philosophema de conform. creaturae rationalis ad Creatorem, T. Hobbei ψευδογραφήμασι oppos. [P443]. s4°. Lipsiae. 1716
Pia desideria, oder hertzl. Verlangen &c. s8°. Franckfurt a. M. 1676
see ALBERTI (V.) Ausführl. Gegen-Antwort auff S.'s Vertheid., 1696.
„ BLANCKENBERG (CONRAD GOTTFRIED). Das Leben der Glaubigen, Leichenpredigt &c., 1705.
„ CANSTEIN (C. H. v.) Das Muster e. rechtschaff. Lebens &c., 1740.
„ JÄGER (J. W.) Exam. Quietismi &c.; adj. S. judicium, 1715.
„ LANGE (J.) Antibarbarus &c., & controv. adv. S., 2p, 1709–11.
„ MÜLLER (A. L.) Gradus damnationis aeternae, u. Tractat S., 1735.
„ WÄCHTLER (J.) Arcana chiliasmi moderni, &c. aus Schr. &c., 1695.

Spengler (Lazarus). Bekendnis. Mit Vorrhede D. Mart. Luth[eri]. s4°. Wittemberg [*Joseph Klug*]. 1535
*Ein Kurtzer ausszug, aus dem Bepstlichen rechten der Decret u. Decretalen. s4°. *n.p.* 1530 [1584]

Spengler (Oswald).
Neubau des deutschen Reiches. 8°. München. 1924
Pessimismus? [P2564]. 8°. 1921
Preussentum u. Sozialismus. 8°. München. 1920
„ „ 8°. München. 1921
Der Untergang d. Abendlandes. B2. 16e bis 30e A. 8°. München. 1922
The decline of the West. Auth. tr. w. notes by C. F. Atkinson. la8°. [1926]

Spengler (Oswald) [*continued*].
see EMMEL (F.) Tod d. Abendlandes: gegen S.'s Philos., 1920.
,, GODDARD (E. H.) & P. A. GIBBONS. Civilisation &c.: S. philos. of hist., 1926.
,, HEIM (C.) & R. H. GRÜTZMACHER. O. S. u. d. Christentum, 1921.
see KEYSERLING (H., *Graf* v.) Menschen als Sinnbilder (S. d. Tatsachenmensch), 1926.
,, MESSER (A.) O. S. als Philosoph, 1922.
,, MEYER (E.) S.'s Untergang d. Abendlandes, 1925.
,, SCHULZ (O. TH.) Der Sinn d. Antike u. S.'s neue Lehre, 1922.

Spens (Janet). Chapman's ethical thought, *see* ENG. ASSOC. Essays &c., v11, 1925.
Elizabethan drama. s8º. [1922]

Spenser (Edmund) [SPENCER].
Lyric poems. Ed. E. Rhys. s8º. [1895]
Poet. works. [Life by J. P. Collier. Aldine ed.] 5v. s8º. 1888
The Shepheardes calender. Orig. ed. of 1579 in facs., w. intr. by H. O. Sommer. 4º. 1890
see CARPENTER (F. I.) Reference guide to E. S., 1923.
,, HENLEY (P.) S. in Ireland, 1928.
,, JACK (A. A.) Poetry of Chaucer & S., 1920.
see JONES (H. S. V.) S.'s defence of Ld. Grey, 1919.
,, LEGOUIS (E.) E. S., 1923.
,, —— S., lect., 1926.
,, NOTCUTT (H. C.) The Faerie Queene & its critics, 1926.
,, OSGOOD (C. G.) Concordance to poems of E. S., 1915.
,, RENWICK (W. L.) E. S., essay on renaiss. poetry, 1925.

Spenser (John), *Jesuit, see* SPENCER (J.)
Spéransky (*Countess*), *née* GRANT, *see* CANTACUZÈNE (*Princess*).
Speransky (*Count* **Mikhail Mikhailovich),** *1772–1839, see* KORF (*c.* M. A.) Жизнь графа С., 2t, 1861.
Speratus (Paul), *see* TSCHACKERT (P.) P. S. v. Rötlen, evangel. Bischof v. Pomesanien, 1891.
Sperl (August). Pfalzgraf Philipp Ludwig v. Neuburg, s. Sohn Wolfgang Wilhelm u. d. Jesuiten. [Verein f. Ref.-gesch. Schr., Jhrg. 12, Nr. 48]. 8º. Halle. 1895
Sperl (Hans), *see* LAMMASCH (M.) & H. S. H. Lammasch, &c., 1922.
Sperling (Otto), *the younger.* De Danicæ linguæ & nominis ant. gloria &c. comment. [P2641]. s4º. Hafniae. 1694
Spettmann (Hieronymus), *O.F.M.* Die Psychologie d. J. Pecham. [Beitr. z. Gesch. d. Philos. d. M.-a., B20vi]. 8º. Münster i. W. 1919
Speusippus. Liber de Platonis definit. &c., *see* IAMBLICHUS *of Chalcis.* De mysteriis &c., 1497.
see ACTA Iberica SS. tergemin. martyrum S. &c.; ed. &c. N. Marr, 1906.
Speyer [SPIRES]. *Eyn Christenl. Ratschlag &c., Reichstag zu S., 1526, *see* CHRISTLICH.
Speyer (Jacob Samuel). Vedische u. Sanskrit-Syntax. [Grundr. d. indo-ar. Phil., B1, H6]. la8º. Str. 1896
Speyer (Wilhelm).
Charlott etwas verrückt. Roman. 8º. [1927]
Sphyris (Konstantin D.) Griechenland u. Italien. Polit.-geogr. Betrachtungen. 8º. Dresden. 1916
Spicer (Ernest Evan). The money market in rel. to trade &c. 3rd ed. rev. 8º. 1922
Spiegel (Friedrich). Chrestomathia Persica. Ed. & gloss. explan. F. S. 8º. Lipsiae. 1846
Spiegel (Friedrich Theodor). Arminii Cheruscorum ducis vitam &c. disput., sub praes. P. Hachenberg, proponet F. T. S. [P2647]. s4º. Heidelberg. [1679]
Spiegel (Laurens Pieter van de), *see* MEULEN (A. J. VAN DER). Studies over het ministerie van Van de S., 1905.
Spiegelberg (Wilhelm).
Works in KÖNIGL. AKAD. D. W. ZU MÜNCHEN. Phil. Kl., Sitz. Ägyptolog. Mitteilungen, 1925.
Beitr. z. Erklär. d. neu. dreisprach. Priesterdekretes zu Ehren d. Ptolemaios Philopator, 1925.
Demotica 1, 1925.
Credibility of Herodotus' acc. of Egypt in light of Egypt. monuments. W. add. notes by tr. A. M. Blackman. 8º. O. 1927
Koptisches Handwörterbuch. la8º. Heidelberg. 1921
—— **& W. Otto.** Eine neue Urkunde zu d. Siegesfeier d. Ptolemaios IV u. d. Frage d. ägypt. Priestersynoden, *see* KÖNIGL. AKAD. D. W. ZU MÜNCHEN. Phil. Kl., Sitz., 1926.
Spiegel v. u. zu Peckelsheim (Hermann P. R., *Frhr.*) Oberheizer Zenne, der letzte Mann d. "Wiesbaden". s8º. [1917]
Spielhagen (Friedrich). Sturmflut. 5e A. 2B. s8º. L. 1883

Spielmann (*Sir* **Isidore),** *F.S.A.* The Brit. Govt. exhibit at the New Zealand Internat. Exhib. (1906–7). Comp. by Sir I. S. Pref. by the High Comm. for N.Z. sm. fol. 1908
Spielmann (Marion Harry). The iconography of Andreas Vesalius, 1514–1564. la8º. 1925
The title-page of the 1st folio of Shakespeare's plays: comp. st. of Droeshout portrait & Stratford monument. Wr. for Shakespeare Assoc., 1923. la8º. 1924
see SHAKESPEARE ASSOC. St. in the First Folio, 1925.
Spiers (R. A. H.)
*Round about "The Mitre" at Oxford. 8º. O. [1924]
Spiers (William). The Sabbath for man. 8º. 1890
Spiller (Gustav), *see* RACES CONGRESS (UNIVERSAL). Papers on inter-racial problems &c.: ed. G. S., 1911.
Spillman (William Jasper) & E. Lang. The law of diminishing returns. p1, Law of d. increment by S., p2, Law of the soil by L. s8º. [1925]
Spilsbury (John). Coll. of 50 prints f. ant. gems, in coll. of Earl Percy, Hon. C. F. Greville & T. M. Slade. Engr. by J. S. 4º. *Boydell.* [1785]
Spina (Claudius de), *see* PETRUS, *Lombardus.* Epitome in 4 lib. sententiarum M. P. L.; authore F. C. Spinaeo, 1551.
Spinden (Herbert Joseph). Anc. civilizations of Mexico & Cent. America. [Amer. Mus. of Nat. Hist. Hdbk. ser., No. 3]. s8º. N.Y. 1917
Spindler (*Kapitän* **Carl).** Das geheimnisvolle Schiff: d. Fahrt d. "Libau" z. irischen Revol. s8º. 1921
Gun running for Casement in the Easter rebellion, 1916. Tr. W. Montgomery & E. H. McGrath. s8º. [1921]
Spindler (Robert), *see* *COURT (The) of sapience; krit. Textausg. &c. v. R. S., 1927.
Spinelli (Aless. Gius.), *see* BAROZZI (G.) Mem. e studi int. a J. B. [*by* A. G. S. &c.], 1908.
Spinelli (Nino). Diz. commerciale, ital.-ingl. e ingl.-ital. p1, Ital.-ingl. 8º. Torino-Genova. [1925]
Spinelli (Salvatore). Caltanissetta. [P2860]. 4º. Milano. *n.d.*
Spingarn (Joel Elias). Poems. 8º. N.Y. 1924
Scholarship & criticism in the U.S. Repr. f. "Civilization in the U.S." [P2705]. 8º. N.Y. 1922
The younger generation, 1922. [P2773]. 8º. *p.p.* N.Y. 1925
Spink & Son, *Ltd.* The milled silver coinage of England f. Charles II to pres. day, w. chap. on Maundy money. Repr. f. Num. circular, 1924. la8º. 1925
Spinola, *The family of, see* DEZA (M.) Ist. d. fam. S., 1694.
Spinola (Carlo), *see* SPINOLA (F. A.) Vita C. S. &c., 1630.
Spinola (Fabio Ambroglio). Vita Caroli Spinolae S. J. pro Xtiana relig. in Iaponia mortui. Lat. redd. a H. Hugone. s8º. Antverpiae. 1630
Spinola (Francesco), *of Milan, see* †FLAMINIO (M. A.) Psalmi a F. & S. Lat. versibus expr., 1559.
Spinola (Gio. Battista). Due lettere d. balì G. B. S. gen. d. galere di Malta, 1700. [Nozze Spinola—d'Ondes Reggio. N. 135]. la8º. 1894
Spinoza (Benedictus de).
Chronicon Spinozanum [*by var. a.* Soc. Spinozana]. 3t. 8º. Hag. Com. 1921–23
Opera. Recog. J. van Vloten et J. P. N. Land. ed. 3ª. 4t. 8º. Hagae Com. 1913–14
Opera. Im Auftr. d. Heidelberger Akad. d. Wiss., hrsg. v. C. Gebhardt. 4[v]. s4º. Heidelberg. [1925]
Spinozana, 1897–1922. Benevens een Levensb. omt. Dr. W. Meijer & Lijst v. d. Geschr. [Bibl. Spinozana, t1. Soc. Spinoz.] 8º. Heidelberg. 1922
Tract. de Deo & homine &c. lineamenta & adnot. ad tract. theol. polit. Ed. E. Boehmer. 4º. Halae ad Salam. 1852
Tract. theol.-politicus. s4º. Hamburgi. 1670
TRANSLATIONS.
Chief works, tr. w. intr. by R. H. M. Elwes. v1, Intr., Tract. theol. politicus, Tract. politicus. rev. ed. s8º. *Bohn.* 1900
Corr. Tr. & ed. w. intr. &c. by A. Wolf. 8º. [1928]
TRANSLATIONS [*continued*].
Ethic. Tr. W. H. White. 4th ed. rev. & corr. 8º. 1910
Oeuvres. Tr. & annot. par C. Appuhn. t2. s8º. [1921] 2, Traité théologico-polit.
see ALEXANDER (S.) S. & time, 1921.
,, BARUCH (S.) S., 1914.
,, BILFINGER (G. B.) In B. S. method. explic. Script. S., 1739.
,, CAROLINE LOUISE. Baruch v. S.; drama, 1855.
,, COLERUS (J.) La vie de B. de S., 1706.
,, —— La verité de la résurection de Jésus Christ def. contre B. de S., 1706.
,, CONSTANS (L. A.), *ps.* De jure eccles. [*attrib. to S. &c.*], 1665.
,, FÉNÉLON (F. DE S. DE LA M.) Réfut. des erreurs de B. de S. &c., 1703.
,, FREUDENTHAL (J.) S.: Leben u. Lehre [Bibl. Spinoz., 5], 1927.
,, HÖFFDING (H.) S.'s Ethica: Analyse &c., 1924.

Spinoza (Benedictus de) [*continued*].
see KELLERMANN (B.) Die Ethik Sp.'s: ü. Gott u. Geist, 1922.
,, LÉVÊQUE (R.) Problème de la vérité dans la philos. de S., 1923.
,, LUCAS (J. M.) Oldest biog. of S. [*i.e.* La vie de feu Mr. de S., *attr. to J. M. L.*], 1927.
,, MARBACH (G. O.) Gedächtnissrede auf B. v. S., 1831.
,, MEIJER (W.) S.: levensbeeld, 1915.
see MUSÆUS (J.) Spinosismus, 1708.
,, POLLOCK (*Rt. Hon. Sir* F.) Sp.'s polit. doct. &c., 1921.
,, ROTH (L.) S., Descartes & Maimonides, 1924.
,, SCHOTT (A. H.) Diss. de Spinozismo, 1804.
,, —— Diss. de variis pantheismi formis, 1805.
,, SORLEY (W. R.) S., 1918.
,, STUMPF (C.) Spinozastudien, 1919.
,, WERDER (J. F.) Diss. de Spinozismo ante S., 1701.

Spinster lady, *ps.* *Notebooks of a spinster lady, 1878–1903, 1919, *see* HOLLAND (*Miss* C.)

Spinula (Francesco), *of Milan, see* SPINOLA (F.)

Spir (African) [*ps.* PRAIS].
Empirie u. Philos. [P2482]. 8°. L. 1876
Gesammelte Schriften. 3e A. 4B [*in 3v*]. s8°. L. 1884–5
1, 2, Denken u. Wirklichkeit, 2T.
3, Moralität u. Religion—Recht u. Unrecht.
4, Schriften vermischten Inhalts.
Moralität u. Religion. 2e neubearbt. A. [P2461]. s8°. L. 1878
Recht u. Unrecht. 2e mit Vorwort verm. A. [P2482]. 8°. L. 1883
Sinn u. Folgen d. mod. Geistesströmung. 2e A. [P2473]. s8°. L. 1878
Ueber Idealismus u. Pessimismus. [P2482]. 8°. L. 1879
*Ueber Religion. 2e A. [P2473]. 8°. L. 1883
Vier Grundfragen. [P2482]. 8°. L. 1880
Die Wahrheit. [2473]. s8°. L. 1867
*Die Wahrheit in i. Hauptzügen dargestellt v. Prais. [P2473]. s8°. L. 1866
see FINDEL (J. G.) *Spir u. d. Bedeutung s. Philos., 1881.

Spira (Joannes de), *see* DENIS (J. N. C. M.) Suffragium pro J. de S., 1794.

Spiridion, *Saint, bp. of Trimithus* [S., *Thaumaturgus*], *see* SIBER (U. G.) S. Spyridionis ep. Trimith. vitam examinat S., 1718.

Spiridovich (A. I.) Исторія большевизма въ Россіи, 1883–1917. Съ приложеніемъ док. 8°. Парижъ. 1922

Spirit. The Spirit. God & h. rel. to man. [By] A. S. Pringle-Pattison, L. Dougall [*& o. wr.*], & B. H. Streeter, ed. [repr.] 8°. 1921
Spirit (The) of St. Louis: 100 poems, 1927, *see* VALE (C.), *ed.*
Spirit (The) of the New Thought movement: essays &c., 1917, *see* DRESSER (H. W.), *ed.*

Spirit (The) of the fair. No. 1–17. [*no more publ.*] 4°. N.Y. [1864]

Spiriti (*il. march.* Salvatore). Mem. d. scrittori cosentini. [*Foll. by* Per l'avvent. nascimento di Filippo A. di Borbone pr. reale d. Due Sicile, canto genetliaco. *w. sep. tp.*] 8°. Napoli. 1750

Spiritual. *Sp. (A) retreat for one day in every month; tr., 1698, *see* CROISET (J.)
*Sp. songs &c., 1685, *see* MASON (J.)
*Sp. songs or, holy poems, 1686, *see* SYMSON (A.)

Spiritualism. Prelim. report of Comm. app. by Univ. of Pa. to investigate mod. sp., 1920, *see* SEYBERT COMM. ON SPIRITUALISM.
Sp.: its present-day meaning, 1920, *see* CARTER (H.), *ed.*

Spiritu Sancto (Joseph à), *see* JOSEPH, *del Espiritu Santo.*

Spiro (Socrates). An Eng.-Arabic vocab. of mod. & colloq. Arabic of Egypt. 8°. Cairo. 1897

Spitta (Carl Johann Philipp).
Lyra domestica. Tr. R. Massie. s8°. 1860

Spitta (Friedrich). Die Bekenntnisschriften d. Herzogs Albrecht v. Preussen, *see* ARCHIV F. REFORMATIONSGESCH., Jhrg. 6, 1909.

Spittal (John Ker). Contemp. criticisms of Dr. S. Johnson, h. works, & h. biographers. Coll. & ed. J. K. S. 8°. 1923

Spittel (R. L.) Wild Ceylon; descr. lives of pres. day Veddas &c. 8°. Ceylon. 1924

Spitteler (Carl). Balladen. 4. A. s8°. Zürich. 1916
Glockenlieder. 8°. Jena. 1921
Laughing truths. Tr. J. F. Muirhead. s8°. 1927
Prometheus u. Epimetheus. Ein Gleichnis. 8°. Jena. 1920

Spitzel (Gottlieb) [SPIZELIUS (THEOPHILUS)]. Templum honoris reseratum, sive illustr. aevi hujus theolog. & philolog. imagines ac elogia. Acc. A. Reiseri epistola &c. s4°. Augustae Vindel. 1673

Spitzer (Frédéric). La collection S. t4–5. fol. 1892

Spitzer (Leo). Die Umschreibungen d. Begriffes "Hunger" im Italien. [Zeitschr. f. roman. Philologie, Beih., 68]. 8°. Halle a. S. 1920

Spitzweg (Carl), *see* BÖHN (M.) C. S., 1921.
see UHDE-BERNAYS (H.) C. S.: d. Meisters Leben u. Werk, 5e A., 1919.

Splendour of the heavens, 1923, *see* HUTCHINSON & Co.

Spohn (Klemens). Der Stellungskrieg im Westen u. d. Kämpfe bis 2. März 1915, H3, 4, *see* KAISER-WILHELM-DANK. Kriegschr., H79, 80, 1917.

***Spoil'd child** (The): farce, 1792, *see* BICKERSTAFFE (I.)

Spon (Jacob). *Recherche des antiq. &c. de la ville de Lyon &c. s8°. Lyon. 1673

Sponde (Henri de), *bp. of Pamiers.*
Annales sacri. [*3 pag.*] fol. Coloniae Agripp. 1640

***Spongia** qua absterguntur convitia &c. Equitis Poloni contra Jesuitas, 1591, *see* LANS (J.)

Spont (Henry). Psychologie de la guerre. s8°. 1920

Spontone (Ciro) [SPONTONI]. La corona del principe. [*Foll. by* Commenti di M. Ficino sopra i 10 dialoghi di Platone del giusto; tr. S.] s4°. Verona. 1590
La metoposcopia, overo commensuratione d. linee d. fronte. Nuov. ristamp. [*b. w.* Dolce (L.) Dialogo, 1586]. s8°. Venetia. 1642

Spoor (Johann Friedrich). De ll. Ebræorum contra magiam ratione &c. Præs. J. J. Zentgravio, resp. J. F. S. [P2744]. s4°. Argentorati. 1694

Sporschil (Johann). Wanderungen durch d. sächs. Schweiz &c. 2e A. 8°. L. *n.d.*

Sporting magazine. Pictures in old Sporting magazines, 1792–1870. [Index of engravers &c. comp. by F. S. Banks. Ed. W. Gilbey]. 8°. [1892]

Spotorno (Giovanni Battista). Illust. di un ant. martirologio ventimigliese, coll' aggiunta di un Necrologia e di note d. Prof. Rossi, *see* REGIA DEP. DI STORIA PATRIA. Misc., t5, 1868.

Spotswood, *family of, see* MACCARTHY (S. T.) Three Kerry families, 1925.

Spottiswoode (John), *abp. of St. Andrews, see* CALDERWOOD (D.) Altare Damascenum &c., adj. Epistola H. Philadelphi de Regimine Eccl. Scot. ejusque vindic. contra calumnias J. S. per anonymum, 1623; 1708.

Sprague (William Buell).
Annals of the Amer. pulpit. 7v. 8°. N.Y. 1859–61
v7, *has tp.:* Annals of Amer. Methodist pulpit &c.

Spranger (Eduard). Die wiss. Grundlagen d. Schulverfassungslehre &c., *see* KÖN.-PREUSS. AKAD. Abh., Phil.-hist. Kl., 1927.

Sprat (Thomas), *bp. of Rochester.* *A letter f. the bp. of Rochester to the earl of Dorset conc. his sitting in the late eccl. Comm. & Second letter. [P2653]. s4°. *in the Savoy.* 1688–89

Spravochnaya Kniga. Справочная книга. Спутникъ избирателя на 1906г. Освободит. движеніе и его формы. s8°. С.-П. [1906]

Sprecher (Johann Andreas v.) Gesch. d. Republik d. drei Bünde (Graubünden) im 18. Jhdt. &c. 2B [B2 *wants tp.*] 8°. Chur. 1873–75

Sprengel (Christian Conrad). Das entdeckte Geheimniss d. Natur im Bau u. in d. Befruchtung d. Blumen (1793). Hrsg. v. P. Knuth. 4B. 8°. L. 1894

Sprengel (Kurt P. J.) Intr. to the study of cryptogamous plants. Tr. [C. D. E. Kœnig]. 8°. 1807

Sprenger (Balthasar), *see* HÜMMERICH (F.) Quellen &c. z. Fahrt d. erst. Deutschen (B. S. &c.) nach d. portugies. Indien, 1505–6, *w. text*, 1918.

Sprenger (Jacob) & H. Institor. Der Hexenhammer. [Malleus maleficarum]. Ins Deut. übertr. u. eingeleitet v. J. W. R. Schmidt. 3e A. 3T. 8°. 1923

Sprenger (Johann Theodor). Polonia nov-antiqua. Ex antiq. & nov. Poloniae scr. excerpta &c. s8°. Francofurti. 1656

Spreul (John), *town clerk of Glasgow.* Some remarkable passages of the Lord's Providence towards J. S., 1635–64, 1832, *see* MAIDMENT (J.), *ed.* Hist. fragm., p2, 1833.

Sprietsma (Cargill).
Louis Bertrand, dit Aloysius B., 1807–41. 8°. 1926

Sprigg (W. Stanhope). The British blockade. [Repr. f. Pearson's Mag.] [P2415]. la8°. *n.d.*

Sprigge (*Sir* Samuel Squire). Physic & fiction. 8°. [1921]

Spring, *The family of, see* MACCLENAGHAN (B.) S. of Lavenham &c., 1924.

Spring (Agnes Wright).
Caspar Collins: Indian fighter. 8°. N.Y. 1927

Spring (Leverett Wilson).
A hist. of Williams College. 8°. Boston. 1917

Springer (Anton Heinrich). Paris au 13e s. Tr. avec intr. &c. par [V. F.] [Trésor des pièces rares &c.] s8°. 1860

Springer (Balthasar). Die Merfart ün erfarung nüwer Schiffung &c. (*facs.* 1509), *see* Freytag (G.) Bilder, B3, T2, 1924.

Springer (Ethel M.) Children deprived of parental care, 1921, *see* United States: Labor.

Springer (Frank). The fossil crinoid genus Dolatocrinus & its allies. [S.I.: U.S. Nat. Mus., Bull. 115]. 8°. Wash. 1921
On the fossil crinoid family Catillocrinidae, 1923, *see* Smithsonian Inst. Misc. Coll., v76, 1925.

Springer (Max).
Loslösungsbestrebungen am Rhein (1918–24). 8°. 1924

Springer (Norman). Fire Mountain. s8°. [1924]

Springett, *The family of, see* Demetriadi (*Sir* S.) The S. family of Kent & Sussex, 1924.

Springett (Bernard H.) Secret sects of Syria & the Lebanon. Origin, creeds & conn. w. mod. freemasonry. 8°. [1922]

Spring Rice (*Sir* Cecil Arthur). Poems. s8°. 1920

Sprint (John), *vicar of Thornbury.* Propositions, tending to proove the necessarie use of the Christian Sabbaoth, or Lord's Day &c. s4°. 1607

Sprott (George W.), *ed., see* Prayer-Book. The Booke of C.P. &c., 1871.

Sprotta (Gottfried). Insignia 4 Evangel. Praes. J. T., resp. G. Sprotta, 1667. Ed. nova. [P430]. s4°. Wittebergae. [1667]

Spruner (Carl v.), *see* Koeppen (A. L.) The world in the Middle Ages &c., w. maps f. S., 1854.

Spuler (Arnold), *see* Hofmann (E.) Die Raupen d. Schmetterlinge Europas, 2^{e} A., [v. A. S.], 1904.

Spunda (Franz). Paracelsus. 8°. Wien. [1925]

Spurgeon (Caroline Frances Eleanor). 500 yrs. of Chaucer criticism & allusion, 1357–1900, 5p, 1914–22, *see* Chaucer Soc., s2, 48–50, 52–54, 1914–22.
,, ,, Suppl., Addit. entries, 1868–1900. 8°. *p.p.* 1920
Jane Austen, *see* Roy. Soc. of Lit. Essays, N.S., v7, 1927.

Spurgeon (Charles Haddon). A catechism with proofs. s8°. 1879

Spurrell (Herbert George Flaxman).
Patriotism: a biological study. s8°. 1911

" Spy," *of Vanity Fair, see* Ward (*Sir* L.)

Spyker (H. J.) Specimen de pretio Institut. divinis Lactantii statuendo. 4°. Lugduni Batav. 1826

Spyridion, *Saint, Thaumaturgus, see* Spiridion.

Spyridon, *of the Laura, Mt. Athos, monk, see* Athos. Cat. of Greek MSS. in library of the Laura on Mt. A.; by S. &c., 1925.

Squier (George Owen). The pres. status of milit. aëronautics. [Repr. f. Journal of Amer. Soc. of Mechan. Engineers]. 8°. [1908]

Squire papers, *see* Rye (W.) 2 Cromwellian myths: the Squire letters &c., 1925.

Squire (John Collings).
The Cambridge book of lesser poets. Comp. by J. C. S. s8°. C. 1927
Coll. parodies. 8°. [1921]
The comic muse. Anthology of humorous verse. s8°. [1925]
Essays on poetry. 8°. [1925]
The Grub Street nights entertainments. s8°. [1924]
Life at the Mermaid [& o. essays]. s8°. [1927]
Poems. s2. 8°. 1922
Second selections f. modern poets. s8°. [1924]
Selections f. mod. poets. s8°. [1921]
,, ,, 4th impr. s8°. [1923]
see Williams (I. A.) Bibliographies of mod. a., No. 4, J. C. S. &c., 1922.

Squire (Samuel), *bp. of St. David's.* Indifference for religion inexcusable. 2nd ed. s8°. 1759

Squire (William Barclay). A monastery [Hosios Loukas] of the Levant. [Repr. f. " The Pilot." P2862]. 8°. 1897
see Radnor (J. P.-B., *6th e. of*). Cat. of pictures in coll. of E. of R.; by H. M., ctss. of R. & W. B. S., 2p, 1909.

Squires (Benjamin Mark). Operation of the Indust. Disputes Investig. Act of Canada, *see* United States: Labor. Bull. 233, 1918.

***Squitinio** d. liberta veneta, 1612, *see* Veneta.

Srbik (Heinrich, *Ritter* **v.)** Metternich, d. Staatsmann u. d. Mensch. 2B. la8°. München. [1925]
Ein Schüler Niebuhrs: W. H. Grauert, 1914, *see* Kaiserl. Akad. d. W. zu Wien. Sitz., B176, 1916.

Sreznevsky (Ismail Ivanovich). Матеріалы для словаря древне-русс. языка по письменн. памят. [И. Акад. Наукъ]. 3т. 4°. С.–П. 1893–1912
Свѣдѣнія &c. о малоизвѣстныхъ &c. памятникахъ. [I. Akad. Nauk. Записки, т9, 11, 20, 22]. 8°. С.–П. 1866–73
Чтенія о древн. русск. лѣтописяхъ. [I. Akad. Nauk. Записки, т2]. 8°. С.–П. 1862

Sreznevsky (V. I.) Описаніе рукописей и книгъ, собр. для Имп. Акад. Наукъ въ Олонецкомъ краѣ. la8°. С.–П. 1913

Srinivasa Ramanujan, *Aiyangar, see* Ramanujan (S.)

Sserow, *see* Serov (A. N.)

St. (G. T.), *see* Tersteegen (Gerhard).

Staaf (Erik Schöne). Sur une lauda de Jacopone da Todi, *see* Kung. Hum. Vet.-Samf. i Uppsala. Skr., B24, 1927.

***Staat** (Der) u. d. allgem. Concil, 1873, *see* Friedberg (E.)

Staatliche Museen, *Berlin, see* Königliches Museum &c.

Staatliches Kunstgewerbemuseum, *Berlin, see* Königl. Kunstgewerbemuseum.

Staatsarchiv (Das). Sammlung d. offiz. Aktenstücke z. Gesch. d. Gegenwart. B84–86, N.F., B1. 8°. München & L. 1914–28

Staatsblad van het Koningrijk der Nederlanden. 1813–1922. [1906, 1913 *wanting*]. 8°. 's Gravenhage. 1813–1922
The first 2 vols. (1813–15) *have t.:* Staatsblad d. vereenigde Nederlanden.
,, ,, Register [Alphab. Reg.], 1813–22, 1823–32, 1833–42, 1813–92, 1901–10. [5v]. 8°. 's Gravenhage. 1823–1911

Stace (Walter Terence). The philos. of Hegel. 8°. 1924

Stäckel (Paul). Gauss als Geometer, *see* Gauss (C. F.) Werke, B10ii, Abh. 4, 1923.

Stackelberg (*Graf* Ernst von), *see* Gagarin (*pr.* G. G.) Le Caucase pittoresque dessiné par G.; avec intr. & texte par le comte E. S., 1847.

Stackhouse (Thomas), *Vicar of Beenham.* A complete body of divinity &c. 2nd ed. corr. fol. 1734
*The miseries &c. of the inferiour clergy in & about London. 8°. 1722

Stacpoole (George, *duke* **de),** *see* De Stacpoole (G., *d.*)

Stacpoole (Henry de Vere).
The blue lagoon. [23rd impr.] s8°. [1920]
The city in the sea. s8°. [1926]
The garden of God. s8°. [1923]
The gates of morning. s8°. [1925]
Goblin market. s8°. [1927]
Golden ballast. s8°. [1924]
The house of crimson shadows. s8°. [1925]
A man of the islands. s8°. [1920]
Men, women, & beasts. s8°. [1922]
The mystery of Uncle Bollard. s8°. [1927]
Vanderdecken. s8°. [1923]

Stacpoole (William Henry). The coronation regalia. s8°. 1911

Stade. *Gesch. d. Reg.-Bez. Stade. 3p *in* 1v. s8°. Bremerhaven. 1924–26
1, Die sächs. Gaue; v. E. R. Jungclaus. 2, Die Karolingerzeit; v. R. Cappelle. 3, Von d. Sächs. Kaisern bis z. Ausgange d. Staufer; v. R. Cappelle.
Stade. [*By var.* a^{s}.] Hrsg. unter Mitwirk. d. Magistrats d. Stadt S. &c. sm. fol. Hannover. 1927

Stade (Dietrich v.) Specimen lect. antiq. Francic. ex Olfridi mon. libris Evangel. &c. coll. cum interp. Lat. 4°. Stadae. 1708

Staden (Johann von), *voyager* [Hans Stade]. Relação dos uzos e costumes dos Tupinambas, (1557); tr. por T. de Alencar Araripe, *see* Instituto Hist. e. Geog. Brazil. Revista, t55, 1892.
Warhaftige Hist. u. beschr. eyner Landtschafft d. wilden &c. Menschfresser-Leuthen in d. Newenwelt America gelegen (1557). Faksimile. Begleitschr. v. R. N. Wegner. 2e verm. A. 8°. Frankfurt a. M. 1927

Stadtmüller (Hugo), *ed.* Anthologia Graeca, v3i, 1906, *see* Anthologia Graeca.

Staël (*Mme.* de), *1776–1817.*
see Haggard (*Lt.-Col.* A. C. P.) Mme. de S.: her trials & triumphs, 1922.
,, Haussonville (G. P. O. de C., *cte.* d'). Mme. de S. et Necker, d'après corr. inéd., 1925.
,, Kohler (P.) Mme. de S. & la Suisse: ét. biogr. & litt., 1916.
,, Larg (D. G.) Mme. de S. (1766–1800), 1920.
see Leuridant (F.) Le Pr. de Ligne, Mme. de S. &c., 1920.
,, Mistler (J.) Mme. de S. & M. O'Donnell, 1805–17, 1926.
,, Turquan (J.) Mme. de S., sa vie amoureuse, polit. &c., 1926.
,, Whitford (R. C.) Mme. de S.'s literary reput. in Eng., 1918.

Staerkodder, *see* Starkad, *hero of romance.*

Stafford. A register of S. & o. local wills (1537–83), *see* STAFFORDSHIRE. Coll., 1928.
Staffordshire. Coll. for a hist. of S. [William Salt Arch. Soc.] 8°. Kendal. 1920–28
The numbering of the vol. has now ceased.
Bridgeman (C. G. O.) Anc. earthwork at Huntley Hall, near Cheadle. [1928.]
—— Betley Morris dance window, 1924. [1923.]
—— Forest pleas in Staffs. Pipe Roll of 13 Hen. II, 1166–7, 1924. [1923.]
—— Some unidentified Domesday vills. [1923.]
—— & G. P. Mander. The Staffs. hidation. [1920.]
Carter (W. F.) Notes on Staffs. families. [1925.]
Chancery, *Court of.* C. proceedings, temp. Eliz. (1560–78). [1928.]
Cornford (M. E.) & E. B. Miller. Cal. of MSS. in Will. Salt Library, Stafford. [1921.]
King (G.) Staff. note book, 1679–80. [1920.]
Lichfield. Gt. register of L. Cathedral. [1924.]
Mander (G. P.), *see* Bridgeman (C. G. O.) & G. P. M.
—— & T. Pape. Some Ridware armorial glass. [1923.]
Murray (D. S.) Notes on early hist. of Blithfield. [1920.]
[Shenstone]. S. Charters. [1923.]
Stafford. Reg. of S. & o. local wills. [1928.]
Staffordshire. Lay subsidy hearth tax. [1921, 1923, 1925.]
—— Two early S. charters; notes by Rev. C. Swynnerton. [1928.]
Wedgwood (J. C.) Staffs. Parliamentary hist., v2, 1603–1832, 1920–22. [1920, 1922.]
Lay subsidy hearth tax, Co. Stafford, *see* STAFFORDSHIRE Coll.
Two early S. charters, w. notes by Rev. C. Swynnerton, *see* STAFFORDSHIRE. Coll., 1928.
Staffortsches Buch, *see* ERNEST FREDERICK, *Margrave of Baden.* Christlichs Bedencken u. Motiven dess Herrn E. F. &c., 1590.
Staglieno (Marcello), *1829–1909.* Due doc. di Tedisio, vescovo di Torino, 1300–19, *see* REGIA DEP. DI STORIA PATRIA. Misc., t38, 1902.
see POGGI (V.) Commem. di M. S., 1910.
Stahel (Ludwig), *publisher.* Thesaurus librorum rei Catholicæ. Hdbch. d. Bücherkunde &c. 2B *in* 1v. 8°. Würzburg. 1848–50
Stähelin (Felix). Das älteste Basel. 2ᵉ, verb. A. 8°. Basel. 1922
Stähelin (Rudolf). H. Zwingli u. s. Reformationswerk. [Verein f. Ref.-gesch. Schr., Jhrg. 1, Nr. 3]. 8°. Halle. 1883
Stahl (Eduard), *see* BERLEPSCH (H. E. v.) Motive d. deut. Architektur; hrsg. v. A. Lambert u. E. S., Abtlg. 1, 1890.
Stahl (Ernst Leopold). Das engl. Theater im 19. Jhdt.: s. Bühnenkunst u. Lit. [Sieper (E.), *ed.* Kultur d. mod. Eng., 5]. 8°. München. 1914
Stählin (Carl). Gesch. Russlands. B1. 8°. St. 1923
Jacob v. Stählin. [Quellen &c. z. russ. Gesch., H1]. s8°. L. [1920]
Stählin (Friedrich). Das hellen. Thessalien. 8°. St. 1924
Stählin-Storcksburg (Jacob v.) [JACQUES DE STAEHLIN], *see* STÄHLIN (C.) J. v. S.: biogr. Beitrag &c., 1920.
Stainer (*Sir* John). The music of the Bible; w. acc. of development of mod. mus. instruments. s8°. [1879]
Stainton (Henry Tibbatts).
Manual of Brit. butterflies & moths. 2v. s8°. 1857–59
Stalenus (Joannes). Papissa monstrosa & mera fabula. Opposita calumniis E. Grim. s8°. Coloniae Agrippinæ. 1639
Staley (Edgcumbe). Franz Hals. [*b. w.* Israels (J.) Rembrandt, 1909]. 8°. [1909]
Stalin (Josif), *form. Djugashirli.* Ленинизм или Троцкизм?, *see* TROTSKY (L.) 1917, 1924.
Leninism. Tr. E. & C. Paul. 8°. [1928]
Stalker (James). Life of Jesus Christ. n. ed. s8°. E. 1891
Stalker (John) & G. Parker.
Treatise of japaning & varnishing &c. fol. O. 1688
Stallbaum (Johann Gottfried). De instaur. sacrorum per Lutherum facta vitae civilis emendatrice oratio. [P1041]. 8°. Lipsiae. 1840
De P. Melanchthone librorum sacr. interprete praestantiss. Oratio &c. [P2672]. 4°. Lipsiae. [1856]
Stamford (Henri Guillaume de), *see* WEIL (M. H.) Le gén. de St. d'ap. s. corresp. inéd., 1923.
Stammler (Rudolf). Die Gerechtigkeit in d. Gesch., *see* DEUTSCHE Reden in Schwerer Zeit, 22, 1915.
Stamp (*Sir* Josiah Charles). British incomes & property. With suppl. tables, 1914–18. 8°. 1920
The Christian ethic as an econ. factor. 8°. [1926]
The fundamental princ. of taxation: in the light of mod. develop. [Newmarch Lectˢ., 1919]. 8°. 1921

Stamp (*Sir* Josiah Charles) [*continued*].
On stimulus in the economic life. Rede lect., 1927. s8°. C. 1927
Studies in current problems in finance & government & "The wealth & income of the chief powers." 8°. 1924
Wealth & taxable capacity. Newmarch lectˢ., 1920–21. 8°. 1922
see BOWLEY (A. L.) & *Sir* J. S. The nat. income, 1924, 1927.
,, RIGNANO (E.) Social signif. of death duties; adapted f. Dr. Schultz's tr. by Sir J. S., 1925.
Stamp (William W.) Hist. notices of Wesleyan methodism in Bradford &c. s8°. 1841
Stampa (Baldassare). Rime, *see* STAMPA (G.) Rime di G. S. e di B. S. &c., 1738.
Stampa (Gaspara). Rime di G. S.; con alcune altre di Collaltino, e di Vinciguerra, Conti di Collalto: e di B. Stampa. [Ed. L. Bergalli]. s8°. Venezia. 1738
see DONADONI (E.) G. S., vita e opere, 1919.
Stampe. Raccolta de parti prese in div. tempi: in materia di s. (1517–1697), *see* VENEZIA.
Stampe (William). A treatise on spiritual infatuation, the pres. visible disease of the Eng. nation &c. s8°. Haguæ. [1650]
Stampini (Ettore). Nel mondo latino. Studi di lett. e filologia. s2, con App. di scritti ital. e lat. 8°. Torino. 1921 [1920]
s1 h. t.: Studi di lett. &c. lat.
Stampioen (Johan), *the younger, b. 1610,* *see* DESCARTES (R.) Corr. of D. & C. Huygens, 1635–47, (The S.-Waessenaer affair, 1639 &c.); ed. L. Roth, 1926.
Stanberger (Baltasar). Ein sendt brieff B. S. von der lieb gotz u. des nechsten.
[*Woodcut on tp.* P2539]. s4°. [Weimar ?. 1523]
Stancari (Francesco). *Epistolae duae ad Eccl. Polonicas scr. à Tigur. eccl. ministris de negotio Stancariano &c., 1561, *see* ZÜRICH.
Suae Ebreæ grammaticæ comp. s8°. Basileæ. 1547
see ORICHOVIUS (S.) Chimæra: sive de Stancari funesta regno Poloniæ secta, 1562; 1563.
Standage (H. C.) The leather worker's manual. 8°. 1900
***Standing** (The) rules & orders of the Commons &c. of Dublin &c., 1838, *see* DUBLIN.
Standish, *The family of,* *see* PORTEUS (T. C.) Capt. Myles S. &c., 1920.
Standish (Miles), *see* PORTEUS (T. C.) Capt. M. S.: h. lost lands & Lancs. connections, 1920.
Standley (Paul Carpenter). Flora of Barro Colorado Is., Panama, *see* SMITHSONIAN INST. Misc. coll., v78, 1927.
Staney (William). A treatise of penance w. an explic. of the rule of the 3rd order of S. Francis. Added, epistle &c., w. a cat. of this order &c. s8°. Douay. 1617
Tp. missing & otherwise imperfect.
Stanfield (William), *see* MANCHESTER: ART GALLERY. Cat. of pictures, w. descr. notes &c.; compiled by W. S., 1894.
Stanford, *publ. firm.* Compend. of geog. & travel. Europe. Ed. B. C. Wallis. 2v. 8°. [1924]
Map of China & Japan, w. adjacent parts of the Russian Emp. &c. [*folded*]. s8°. 1903
Map of Spain & Portugal. s8°. *n.d.*
Stanford (Charles Thomas-), *see* THOMAS-STANFORD (C.)
Stanford (*Sir* Charles Villiers) & C. Forsyth.
A history of music. [repr.] s8°. N.Y. 1918
Stange (Alfred). Deut. Kunst um 1400. 8°. München. 1923
Die Entw. d. deut. mittelalt. Plastik. 8°. München. 1923
Stanghellini (Arturo). Introd. alla vita mediocre. Pref. di U. Ojetti. 2ª ed. s8°. Milano. 1921
Quando gli assenti ritornano. Romanzo. s8°. Milano. 1923
Stanhope (*Rt. Hon.* Edward). The British Army & our defensive posit. in 1892. With pref. by E. S. s8°. 1892
Stanhope (*Lady* Hester L.), *d. of 3rd earl Stanhope; d. 1839,* *see* BORDEAUX (P. HENRY-). Lady S. en Orient, 2t, 1924–26.
Stanhope (James Stanhope, *1st earl***),** *see* EDWARDS (F. L.) J., 1st Earl S. & Brit. for. policy, 1925.
Stanhope (Philip Henry Stanhope, *4th earl***).**
see DUPIN (C.) *Réponse au discours de S., sur l'occup. de la France &c., 1818.
,, JUBÉ DE LA PERRELLE (A.) Lettre d'un français à Lord S., 1818.
Stanhope (Philip Henry Stanhope, *5th earl***),** *1805–75* [*Lord* MAHON]. The French retreat f. Moscow, & o. hist. essays. s8°. 1876
Stanihurst (William), *Jesuit.* Vet. hominis per expensa quatuor noviss. metamorphosis & novi genesis. s8°. Coloniae. 1624

Stanislaus *a Placentia.* Augustini & Scoti de gratia Christi consensus. Acc. S. Prosperi Aquitani opusculo. 2v. s4°. Venetiis. 1768

Stanislaus I [LESZCZYNSKI], *king of Poland.*
see BOYÉ (P.) Le roi St. grand-père, 1922.
,, RENNEVILLE (*Mme.* S. DE). S., roman hist., 3v, 1807.

Stanislaus Augustus [PONIATOWSKI], *king of Poland, see* †CATHERINE II, *emp. of Russia.* Corr. of C. II, & letters f. Count P.; tr., 1928.

Stanislavsky (Konstantin), *ps.* [*i.e.* K. S. ALEKSEEV].
My life in art. Tr. J. J. Robbins. 8°. [1925]

Stankevich (Vladimir Benediktovich).
Судьбы народовъ Россіи. 8°. Берлинъ. 1921

Stanley, *The family of, see* SEACOME (J.) *Mem., cont. acc. of the House of S. &c., 1783; 1821.

Stanley (Arthur Penrhyn), *dean of Westminster.*
The Athanasian Creed, w. pref. s8°. 1871
Lects. on hist. of Eastern Church. With intr. on study of eccl. hist. n. ed. s8°. 1889
Lect. on hist. of Jewish Church. 3p. [p1, 4th ed., p2, 2nd ed.] 8°. 1866–76
The third part is given as "series 3" on its tp.
[MS. of speech on Wesley at the Children's Home, May 1st, 1877]. 8°. [1877]
Sinai & Palestine. 4th ed. 8°. 1857
,, ,, ...n. ed. 8°. 1866
Whether states &c. tend to decay. Prize essay. [P2850]. s8°. O. 1840
see BREWER (J. S.) Athanasian Creed vindic. f. obj. of S. &c., 1871.

Stanley (*Lady* **Augusta Frederica Elizabeth),** *wife of A. P. S., dean of Westminster.* Letters, 1849–63. Ed. by the Dean of Windsor [*i.e. A. Baillie*] & H. Bolitho. 8°. 1927

Stanley (Dorothy), *Lady Stanley, wife of Sir H. M. Stanley.*
Miss Pim's camouflage. s8°. 1918

Stanley (Edward), *bp. of Norwich, see* PETERLOO. Three accounts of P. by eyewitnesses, Bp. S. &c., 1921.

Stanley (Henry Edw. John Stanley, *3rd baron*), *see* CHINESE. *C. manual; recueil de phrases chinoises; ed. w. Eng. tr. by S., 1854.

Stanley (Jacob). An orig. essay on memory. [P601]. 8°. 1824

Stanley (*Hon.* **Oliver Frederick George),** *see* BOOTHBY (R. J. G.) &c. Industry & the state, 1927.

Stanley (Rupert), *B.A.*
Text-book on wireless telegraphy. 2nd ed. v2. 8°. 1923

Stanley (Rupert), *ps., see* GWATKIN-WILLIAMS (RUPERT STANLEY).

Stanley-Stone (A. C.) The Worshipful Co. of Turners of London, origin & hist. 8°. 1925

Stannard (Harold Martin). The fabric of Europe: hist. survey of internat. relations. 8°. [1923]
Gambetta & the found. of the 3rd Rep. 8°. [1921]
Rome & her monuments. 8°. [1923]

Stannus (*Mrs.* **Graydon).**
Old Irish glass. n. ed. rev. & enl. 4°. 1921

Stanojević (Gjorgje M.) [STANOÏÉWITCH]. Le bombardement de l'Univ. de Belgrade. Préf. de L. Poincaré. [P2700]. 4°. 1915

Stanoyevich (Milivoy Stoyan). Early Jugoslav. lit. (1000–1800). [Columbia Univ.] 8°. N.Y. 1922

Stanton (Arthur Henry), *see* SAINT ALBAN, *Holborn.* Extr. f. S.A. Monthly paper &c. cont. mem. notices &c. of S., 1907–18.

Stanton (Coralie) & H. Hosken. The oldest land. s8°. [1926]

Stanton (*Mrs.* **Eliz. Cady),** *see* HISTORY. Hist. of woman suffrage, v3; ed. E. C. S. &c., 1886.

Stanton (Vincent Henry).
The Gospels as hist. documents. p3. 8°. C. 1920

Stanway (Kate).
For Valour, a complete record of the V.C. s8°. [1904]

Stanyukovich (K. M.)
Отплата. Между своими. Утро. [P2499]. s8°. Москва. 1917

Stanzaic (A) life of Christ: comp. f. Higden's Polychronicon &c.; ed. F. A. Foster, *see* CHRIST.

tapfer (Johann Friedrich). Instit. theologiae polemicae univ. 5t. [*pagin. of* t1, 2 *contin.*] s8°. Tiguri. 1743–47

Staphylus (Fridericus), *the elder.*
Apologia recens aucta & recogn. De vero germanóq; scr. sacræ intellectu — De sacr. Bibliorum tralatione — De Lutheran. concionatorum consensione. [*b. w. h.* Theol. Luther. epitome &c. 1558]. s8°. Coloniae. 1562
,, ,, ...[*a. ed.*] s8°. Coloniae. 1563
The apologie of F. S. intreating Of the true & right understanding of Holy Scr.—Of the transl. of the Bible—Of disagreement in doctrine amonge the Protestants. Tr. by T. Stapleton. 8°. Antwerp. 1565

Staphylus (Fridericus), *the elder* [*continued*].
Defensio pro trimembri theologia M. Lutheri contra ædificatores Babylonicæ turris: P. Melanthonem; Schwenckfeldianum Longinum, A. Musculum, M. F. Illyricum, J. A. Shmidelinum &c. s4°. [Dillingae]. 1559
Prodromus in defens. Apologiae suae &c. Lat. redd. per F. L. Surium. Adv. J. Smidelinum. [*b. w. h.* Apologia, 1563]. s8°. Coloniae. 1563
Theologiae M. Lutheri trimembris epitome. Nuper coll. Wormatiae dur. colloquio. s8°. Nissae. 1558
,, ,, *a. ed. w. t.:* Theologiae Lutheranae trim. epit. s8°. Coloniae. 1558
Theologiae Lutheranæ trimembris epitome &c., *see* LINDANUS (W. D.) Tabulae hæreseon &c., 1562.
see MUSCULUS (A.) Resp. ad. script. ex meris calumniis &c. conflatum F. S., 1558.
,, STROBEL (G. T.) Miscell. lit. [Leben S. &c.], 1778–79.

Staples (John). Notes on St. Botolph, without Aldersgate, London. 8°. *p.f.p.c.* 1881

Stapleton (Alan). London alleys, byways & courts. 8°. 1924

Stapleton (Joseph Whitaker). The great crime of 1860: the murder committed at Road. With app. cont. evidence. 8°. 1861

Stapleton (Thomas), *prof. at Louvain.*
Promptuarium catholicum, ad instruct. concionatorum contra haereticos, super Evangelia totius anni dominicalia quam de festis. 2p. [*b. w. h.* Prompt. cath. super Evang. ferialia &c., 1594]. s8°. Coloniae Agrippinae. 1594
Promptuarium catholicum ad instruct. concionatorum contra haereses, super Evangelia ferialia. s8°. Coloniae Agrippinae. 1594
Tres Thomae, seu de S. Thomae Apostoli rebus gestis. De S. Thoma archiep. Cantuar. & martyre. De Thomae Mori vita. His adj. est oratio funebris in laudem A. de Ganthois. [*2 pagin.*] s8°. Duaci. 1588
see RAINOLDS (J.) Summe of the conference between J. R. & J. H. &c., w. def. *agst.* T. S., 1588.
,, WHITAKER (W.) Disput. de S. Scriptura, contra R. B. & T. St. &c., 1588.

Stapleton-Bretherton (Evelyn), *see* BLÜCHER (E., *princess*).

Stapley (Mildred), *aft. wife of Arthur Byne, see* BYNE (*Mrs.* M. S.)

Star (Maria), *ps., see* STERN (*Mme.* E.)

Star Chamber (Court of). Abstr. of Star Ch. proc. rel. to Sussex. Hen. VII—Philip & Mary. Transcr. & ed. P. D. Mundy. [Sussex Rec. Soc., v16]. 8°. 1913

Stargardt (J.) Druckannalen der Fürstl. Buchdruckerei zu Barth in Pommern. 8°. [1860]

Stark (Francis Raymond). Abolit. of privateering & the Declar. of Paris. 8°. N.Y., *Columbia Univ.* 1897

Starie gody. Старые годы. 1914, 1915. 8°. 1914–15

Staring (Antoni Christiaan Winand) [STARING VAN DEN WILDENBOSCH]. Gedichten. Med inleid. uitg. door N. Beets. Volksuitgave, 12e dr. s8°. Zutphen. *n.d.*

Stark (Carl Bernhard). J. J. Winckelmann, *for a. copy see* VIRCHOW (R.) & F. v. HOLTZENDORFF. Sammlung, H42, 1867.

Starkad, *hero of romance* [STAERKODDER], *see* OLRIK (A.) Danmarks heltedigtning, d2, S. den gamle og den yngre Skjoldungraekke, 1910.

Starkenfels (Alois, *Frhr.* **v.)** Oberoesterr. Adel; bearbt. v. A. Frhr. v. S., *see* SIBMACHER (J.), *ed.* Wappenbuch, B4v, 1885–1904.

Starkey (George) [*ps.,* EIRENÆUS PHILOPONOS PHILALETHES]. *The marrow of alchemy, being an experimental treatise [*in verse*]. [*Pref. to p1 signed* "Egregius Christo"; the advertisement *in p2* "Vir gregis Custos"; *both anagrams on author's name*]. 2p [in 1v]. s8°. 1654–55
Three treatises, *see* HERMETIC MUSEUM, v2, 1893.

Starkey (William), *D.D.* Apology for the laws eccl. establ. that command public exercise in relig. &c. s8°. 1675

Starkie (Walter). Jacinto Benavente. 8°. 1924
Luigi Pirandello. 8°. 1926

Starling (Ernest Henry). Action of alcohol on man. With essays by R. Hutchison, F. W. Mott, R. Pearl. 8°. 1923
see UNIV. COLL., *London.* Centenary addresses [by S. &c.], 1927.

Starling (Sydney G.) Electricity. 8°. 1922
see DUNCAN (J.) & S. G. S. Text book of physics, 1919.

Starowolski (Szymon). Tractatus tres, 1, Polonia, 2, Sarmatiae bellatores, 3, Script. Polon. Ἑκατοντας. [*each w. sep. pagin. & half tp. dated 1733*]. Ed. nova. 4°. Wratislaviae. 1734

State. *State (The) & sexual morality. [P2584]. s8°. [1920]
*State (The) of weights &c. of Scot. & Eng., 1706, *see* SCOTLAND.

State Papers. British & Foreign Papers. v110–120 (1916–24). 8º. 1920–27
v115, Gen. index, chron. & alphabet., 1900–21.
[Calendar of] letters & papers, foreign & domestic, of r. of Henry VIII. 2nd ed. rev. &c. by R. H. Brodie.
v1 (1509–14) [*in 3p. p2, 3 pagin. cont.*] la8º. 1920
Calendar of S.P.: Colonial Series. Ed. C. Headlam. [C. of S.P.] [v24–27]. la8º. 1922–26
24, Amer. & W. Indies, June 1708–9. 25, 1710–June 1711. 26, July 1711–June 1712. 27, July 1712–July 1714.
Calendar of S.P.: Domestic Series [of r. of Charles II]. Ed. F. H. B. Daniell. [C. of S.P.] v22 (1680–81). la8º. 1921
Calendar of S.P.: Domestic Series, of r. of William III. Ed. W. J. Hardy. [Cal. of S.P.] [v8], 1697. la8º. 1927
Calendar of S.P.: Domestic Series [of r. of Anne]. Ed. R. P. Mahaffy. v2 (1703–4). la8º. 1924
Calendar of S.P.: Foreign Series of r. of Elizabeth. v20, 21, pl. Ed. S. C. Lomas. [C. of S.P.] la8º. 1921–27
20 Sept. 1585–May 1586. 21, pl, June 1586–June 1588.
State Police, *see* COMMITTEE FOR STATE POLICE.
Statens Historiska Museum och Myntkabinett, *Stockholm, see* ROOSVAL (J.) Dopfuntar i Statens Hist. Mus., 1917.
Statesman's year-book (The). 1921–28. s8º. 1921–28
Statham, *The family of, see* STATHAM (S. P. H.) Descent of family of S., 1925.
Statham (Edward Phillips). A Jacobean letter-writer: life & times of John Chamberlain. 8º. [1920]
Statham (Francis Reginald).
The Zulu iniquity. [P2832]. 8º. 1884
Statham (*Col.* **John Charles Barron).**
Through Angola. 8º. E. 1922
Statham (Samuel Percy Hammond).
Descent of the family of Statham. 8º. [1925]
Stationers' Company. In commem. of the 1st folio tercent.: a re-setting of the prelim. matter, w. cat. of Shakespeariana exhib. &c., & intr. by Sir I. Gollancz. la8º. 1923
To all printers, booke-sellers, booke-binders, free-men of the Co. of S. [Dated 13 June 1645. *b. w.* London printers lamentation, 1660]. s8º. [1645]
*To the High Court of Parliament: the humble remonstrance of the Co. of S., London. [By H. Parker. *b. w.* London printers lamentation, 1660]. s8º. [1843]
see RIVINGTON (C. R.) 1403–1903: short acc. of the W. Co. of S. &c., 1903.
,, ROLLINS (H. E.) Analyt. index to ballad-entries (1557–1709) in Reg^s^. of Co. of S., 1924.
Statistical & Social Inquiry Society of Ireland.
Journal. v13 (1913–19)–15. 8º. D. 1924–27
Statisticheskii. Статистич. ежегодник—Annuaire statist. [*in Russian & French*], 1921, *see* RUSSIA: SOVIET REPUBL.
Statistics. Guide to current statistics. [Perm. Consult. Comm. on Off. Statistics]. v1–5 (1922–26). 8º. 1924–27
*Statistics of Protest. missionary societies, 1872–73, 1874, *see* BOYCE (W. B.)
Statistisches Handbuch für d. Republik Österreich. Hrsg. v. d. Statist. Zentralkommission. Jhrg. 1–2. la8º. Wien. 1920–21
Statistisches Jahrbuch für d. Deutsche Reich. Hrsg. v. Statist. Reichsamt. Jhrg. 1921/22, 1923, 1926, 1927. 8º. 1922–27
Statius (Publius Papinius). S. [Works. Text] w. Eng. tr. by J. H. Mozley. [Loeb Class. Lib.] 2v. s8º. 1928
1, Silvae—Thebaid 1–4. 2, Thebaid 5–12—Achilleid.
Silvae. Rec. &c. J. S. Phillimore. 2ª ed. corr. s8º. O. [1918]
Thebais & Achilleis. Rec. &c. H. W. Garrod. s8º. [1906]
Togail na Tebe. Thebaid. Irish text. Ed. f. 2 MSS. w. intr., tr. &c. by G. Calder. 8º. C. 1922
Staton (James Taylor). Rays fro th' Loominary: comic Lancashire tales. [P2850]. s8º. M'ter. [1866]
Status. *Status cathol. & evangel. relig. in regno Hungariae &c., 1790, *see* HUNGARIA.
*Status eccl. Gallic., or the eccl. hist. of France, 1676, *see* GEAVES (G.)
Statuti. S. d. Rep. Fiorentina, v1, 2, 1910–21, *see* FIORENTINA.
S. Senesi scr. in volg. ne' sec. 13–14, 1863–67, *see* SENESE.
Statutorum & reformat. magn. civit. Senogallie, 1537, *see* SENOGALLIA.
Staub (Burchard), *see* MÖHR (A.), B. S. &c. Amphib. beatitud. &c., 1663.
Staub (Franz), *see* VIENNA. Quellen z. Gesch. d. Stadt Wien, Abt. 3, B3i, bearb. F. S., 1923.
Staudacher (Benedictus Andreas). Jonas vates Æthiopicè & Latinè, cum gloss. Ed. a B. A. S. s4º. Francofurti a. M. 1706

Staufenberg (Peter v.) [†DIMRINGER (PETER) *von Staufenberg*], *see* CRAON (M. DE). 2 altdeut. Rittermaeren: M. v. C.—P. v. S. [*by* Egenolt: *texts*]; n. hrsg. E. Schröder, 3e A., 1920.
Stauff (Argula von), *see* GRUMBACH (A. v.)
Staunton (Howard).
The chess-player's companion. s8º. 1889
The chess-player's hdbk. s8º. 1889
Chess praxis. s8º. 1891
The chess tournament, a coll. of games. s8º. 1873
Laws & practice of chess. Ed. R. B. Wormald. n. ed. 8º. 1881
Staupitz (Johann von).
Eyn buchleyn von der nachfolgung des willigen sterbens Christi. s4º. [Leipzic]. 1523
Võ der Liebe gottes. Bewert u. approbiert durch Do. M. Luther. s4º. *n.p.* [München, *J. Schobser.* 1518]
see GEUDER (A. D.) Vita J. S., 1837.
see GRIMM (C. L. W.) De J. S. in sacr. Xtn. instaur. meritis, 1835.
,, KOLDE (T.) Deut. Augustiner-Congreg. u. J. v. S., 1879.
,, STUSS (J. H.) Progr. de J. Staupitii meritis in relig. evang., 1732.
Stavanger. Stavanger Domkapitels protokol 1571–1630. Udg. ved A. Brandrud. [Norske Hist. K.] 8º. 1901
Stave (Erik). Om källorna till 1526 års öfversattning af Nya Test., 1893, *see* KUNGL. HUMAN. VET.-SAMF. Skr., B3i, 1893.
Staveley (Thomas). The Romish horseleech or acc. of the intolerable charge of popery &c. Ann. An essay of the supremacy of the King of Eng. s8º. 1769
Stawell (F. Melian). Conrad, *see* ENGLISH ASSOC. Essays & studies, v6, 1920.
—— **& F. S. Marvin.** The making of the Western mind: sh. survey of European culture. s8º. [1923]
Staygmayr (Hans). Ain kurtze underrichtung von der waren Christl. brüderschaft &c. s4º. *n.p.* 1524
Stcherbatsky (Th.), *see* SCHERBATSKY (TH.)
Stead (William Thomas). If Christ came to Chicago! s8º. 1894
Josephine Butler. s8º. 1887
see WHYTE (F.) Life of W. T. S., 2v, 1925.
Stearne (*Docteur*), *ps., see* RUTLEDGE (J. J.)
Stearns (Harold Edmund). Civiliz. in the U.S. Enquiry by 30 Americans. Ed. S. 8º. [1922]
Steavenson (William Herbert), *see* HUTCHINSON & Co., *publishers.* Splendour of the heavens; ed. T. E. R. Phillips & W. H. S., 1923.
Stebbing (Edward Percy).
Commercial forestry in Britain. s8º. 1919
The forests of India. 3v. 8º. 1922–[26]
On insects that affect forestry. No. 3. la8º. Calcutta. 1906
Stebbing (George). Story of the Catholic Church. 8º. [1915]
Stebbing (Henry), *D.D., F.R.S., Rector of St. Nicholas Cole Abbey, London.* The Christian in Palestine or scenes of sacred hist. Illustr. by W. H. Bartlett. 4º. [1847]
Stebbing (Henry), *archdeacon of Wilts.* *A defence of the first head of the charge of the C^tee^ of Convocation agst. the Bp. of Bangor: being remarks &c. wherein is shown that his Lordship hath denied &c. all authority to the church. s8º. 1718
Polemical tracts; or a coll. of papers wr. in defence of the doctrines &c. of the Ch. of E. [5p *in* 1v]. fol. C. 1727
Stebbing (William). Greek & Lat. anthology thought into Eng. verse. 3p. s8º. [1923]
1, Greek masterpieces. 2, Lat. masterpieces. 3, Greek epigrams & Sappho.
Steber (Bartholomäus). A malafranczos praeservatio &c., Viennae, 1498, *facs., see* SUDHOFF (C.) Earliest pr. lit. on syphilis, 1925.
Stebler (Friedrich G.) Sonnige Halden am Lötschberg. [Beilage zum Jahrbh. des Schweizer Alpenclub, B49]. la8º. Bern. 1913
Stebnitsky (Ieronim Ivanovich).
Объ отклоненіи отвѣсныхъ линій притяженіемъ Кавказскихъ горъ. [I. Akad. Nauk. Записки, т17]. 8º. С.-П. 1870
Stebnitzky (N.), *ps., see* LESKOV (N. S.)
Stechau (Ludolph Otto), *see* WONNA (G.) Exercit. de geniis; publ. exam. sistet L. O. S. &c., 1663.
Steche (Christian Friedrich). Explorat. spiritus Brendeliani. Praes. G. Wernsdorfio. [P595]. s4º. Vitembergae. [1717]
Stecher (Gilbert E.) Cork: its origin & indust. uses. 8º. 1914
Stedingk (*Count* **Kurt v.),** *Field-Marshal, see* BREVERN DE LA GARDE (*ctsse.*) Un ambassadeur de Suède à la Cour de Cath. II: Cte. de S., 1790–96, 2t, 1919.

Stedman (John W.), *see* NORWICH, *Conn.* Norwich Jubilee; rep. of celebr. &c. comp. by J. W. S., 1859.
Steeb (Johann Gottlieb). Diss. de Inquisitione. Praes. J. F. Cotta. [P437]. s4°. Tubingae. [1766]
Steed (Henry Wickham).
The Hapsburg monarchy. 3rd ed., w. new pref. 8°. 1914
Through 30 years, 1892–1922: a personal narrative. [n. impr.] 2v. 8°. 1924
——, **C. Bouglé &c.** Les démocraties modernes. Par W. S., C. Bouglé, H. Bois, E. Doumergue, G. Lanson &c. [Avant-propos par P. Doumergue]. s8°. 1921
Steel (David). Steel's naval chronologist of the late war, 1793–1801. 3rd ed. corr. s8°. *n.d.*
Steel (*Mrs.* Flora Annie). The law of the threshold. s8°. [1924]
Tales of the tides & o. s. s8°. 1923
Steel (*Col.* John Philip).
see CUMBERLAND, *County.* Feet of fines, C. dur. the r. of Edward VI &c., *n.d.*
,, ——, ——. Feet of fines, C. dur. the reign of Henry VIII, 1913.
Steele (Anne) [*ps.* THEODOSIA].
Poems on subjects chiefly devotional. 2v. s8°. 1760
Steele (Glenn). Infant mortality in Pittsburgh, 1920, 1921, *see* UNITED STATES: LABOR.
Maternity & infant care, Georgia, *see* UNITED STATES: LABOR. Children's bureau. Publ. 120, 1923.
Steele (James Peddie), *1836–1917*, *see* SANDYS (*Sir* J. E.) J. P. S., 1920.
Steele (James W.) Frontier army sketches. 8°. Chicago. 1883
Steele (Mary Susan). Plays & masques at court dur. reign of Eliz., James & Charles. [Cornell St. in Eng.] 8°. New Haven, *Yale.* 1926
Steele (*Sir* Richard). Conscious lovers, *see* INCHBALD (*Mrs.* E.) Brit. th., v12, 1808.
see CERRI (U.) Acc. of state of Rom. Cath. relig.; tr. &c. by R. S. (*or rather* Bp. Hoadly), 1715.
Steele (Robert Reynolds). Dies Aegyptiaci. [Repr. f. Proc. of Royal Soc. of Med., v13. [P2707]. la8°. 1920
The earliest arithmetics in English. Ed. w. intr. by R. R. S. [E.E.T.S. E. S., 118]. 8°. 1922
Roger Bacon & the state of science in the 13th c., *see* SINGER (C.), *ed.* St. in hist. &c. of sci., v2, 1921.
Steep (Thomas). Chinese fantastics. 8°. [1926]
Steevens (George).
see NICHOLS (J.) *Biog. anecdotes of W. Hogarth [*by N. assisted by G. S. &c.*], 1781; 1783; 1785.
,, —— & G. S. Genuine works of W. Hogarth, w. biog. anecdotes &c., 1808.
Stefan (Ludolf Eduardovich).
Нимбъ и лучезарный вѣнецъ въ произведеніяхъ древн. искусства. [I. Akad. Nauk. Записки, т4]. 8°. С.–П. 1863
Stefan (Paul). Gustav Mahler: e. Studie ü. Persönlichkeit u. Werk. n., verm. &c. A. 8°. München. 1920
Stefanelli (Teodor V.) Doc. din vechiul ocol al Câmpulungului Moldovenesc culese, adnot. şi publ. de T. V. S. Ed. Acad. Române. la8°. Bucuresti. 1915
Stefani (Alberto de). La legisl. econ. d. Guerra. [C.E. for Int. Peace]. la8°. Bari. 1926
Stefani (Alessandro de), *see* SHAKESPEARE (W.) Tragedia di Macbeth; teste ital., note ed app. di A. de S., 1922.
Stefani (Eduardo Luigi de). Etymologicum Gudianum rec. &c. fasc. 2 litteras Bω–Ze cont. la8°. Lipsiæ. 1920
Stefani (Federico). Cordignano e i. suoi signori. [Nozze Cays de Pierlas—Mocenigo. N121]. s8°. Venezia. 1884
Stefanini (Giuseppe). Descr. of fossils f. S. Arabia &c., *see* LITTLE (O. H.) Geogr. &c. of Makalla, 1925.
Fossili d. secondario e d. terziario, *see* FILIPPI (F. DE). Rel. sci d. Spediz. Ital. de F. n. Himàlaia &c., s2, v6, 1928.
Stefánsson (Viljálmur). The adventure of Wrangel Island. Wr. by V. S. w. collab. of J. I. Knight upon diary of E. L. Knight. Foreword by L. S. Amery. 8°. 1926
The friendly Arctic. 5 years in Polar regions. 8°. N.Y. 1922
Hunters of the great North. 8°. [1923]
The northward course of empire. Intr. by E. W. Nelson. 8°. [1922]
Steffen (Richard). Forntiden, medeltiden, Reformationstiden, *see* SVENSKA litt. hist., d1, 1919.
Steffenhagen (Emil). Die Entwicklung d. Landrechtsglosse d. Sachsenspiegels, 11, 12, 1922–23, *see* KAIS. AKAD. D. WISS. ZU WIEN. Sitzber., B194, 195, 1923.

Stegemann (Hermann). Gesch. des Krieges. B4. 8°. St. 1921
The mirage of Versailles. Tr. R. T. Clark. 8°. [1928]
Steger (Wolfgang).
De Interim August. diss. [P2642]. s4°. Lipsiae. 1683
Stegmann (Joachim). *Brev. disquis., an & quomodo Evangelici Pontificios, ac nominatim Val. Magni de Acatholicorum credendi regula judicium refutare queant. [*b. w.* Przypkowski (S.) Vita F. Socini, 1651]. s8°. Eleutheropoli. 1633
Stegmann (Josua). Studii pietatis icon, Christognosia &c. 2p *in* 1v. s4°. Lipsiae. 1689
see RÖBER (P.) & J. S. Disput. de indulgentiis pontif., 1702.
Stehelin (Johann Samuel). Diss. de hierologia seu benedictione sacerdotali in matrimonii negotio usitata. Præs. P. Müllero, prop. J. S. S. [P2633]. s4°. Jenæ. 1680
Stehelin (John Peter). Rabinical literature: or, the traditions of the Jews &c. 2v. 8°. 1748
Stehr (Hermann). Auf Leben u. Tod. 2 Erzählungen. s8°. 1898
Drei Nächte. Roman. s8°. 1920
Der Heiligenhof. Roman. 2B. s8°. 1920
see MERIDIES (W.), *ed.* H. S.: s. Werk u. s. Welt [*by var. a.*], 1924.
Steiermark. Beiträge z. Kunde steiermärk. Geschichtsquellen, 1864–1906, *see* HISTORISCHER VEREIN F. STEIERMARK.
Steiger (Hugo). Euripides, s. Dichtung &c. 8°. L. 1912
Steilen (Diedrich). Die Niederweser. la8°. Bielefeld. 1928
Stein (Abraham).
Thalmud. Terminologie. Nebst e. Vorworte. 8°. Prag. 1869
Stein (Erwin), *see* LUTHER (H.), P. MITZLAFF & E. S., *edd.* Die Zukunftsaufgaben d. deut. Städte, 1922.
Stein (Friedrich v.), *ps.*, *see* WREDE (F. E. I., *Furst* v.)
Stein (Gertrude). Composition as explanation. [Hogarth essays, s2]. s8°. 1926
Stein (H. F. Carl, *Frhr.* vom und zum), *1757–1831*, *see* FORD (G. S.) S. & the era of reform in Prussia, 1807–15, 1922.
Stein (Henri). Les architectes des cathédrales gothiques. Ét. crit. 8°. [1909]
Charles de France, frère de Louis XI. [Ecole des Chartes]. la8°. 1919
see PICOT (E.) & H. STEIN. Rec. de pièces histor. impr. s. le règne de Louis XI, avec comm. par E. P. & H. S., 2t, 1923.
,, RÉPERTOIRE BIBL. DE L'HIST. DE FRANCE, t1, par P. Caron & H. S., 1923.
,, RIBEMONT. Cartul. de l'anc. abbaye de St. Nicolas des Prés, sous R.; publ. par H. S., 1884.
Stein (Leonard). Syria. s8°. 1926
Stein (*Sir* Marc Aurel). The desert crossing of Hsüan-tsang, 630 A.D. Repr. f. Ind. Antiq., v50. [P2875]. 4°. Bombay. 1921
Memoir on maps of Chinese Turkistan & Kansu f. surveys made dur. Sir A. S.'s explor., 1900–15. App. by Maj. K. Mason & J. de G. Hunter. [Records of Survey of India, v17. Maps *in case sep.*] fol. Dehra Dun. 1923
Serindia. Rep. of explor. in Cent. Asia & West. China. Carried out &c. under orders of Ind. Govt. With lists of antiq. by F. H. Andrews, F. M. G. Lorimer & others. App. 5v. 4°. O. 1921
The thousand Buddhas: anc. Buddhist paintings f. cave-temples of Tun-Huang on west. frontier of China. Recovered & descr. by A. S. Intr. essay by L. Binyon. Text [*& Plates.* 1–33 *in case*, atlas fol. Plates 34–48 *b. w.* Text]. fol. 1921
see HĀTIM TILAWŌNᵘ. H.'s tales &c.; recorded w. the assist. of G. Kaul by Sir A. S., 1923.
,, KHAROṢṬHĪ. K. inscr. discov. by Sir A. S. in Chinese Turkestan, 2p, 1920–27.
Stein (Otto). Megasthenes u. Kautilya. 1921, *see* KAIS. AKAD. D. WISS. ZU WIEN. Sitzber., B191, 1922.
Stein (Walther). Bismarck. Leben in Bildern nebst e. Einführ. Hrsg. W. S. la8°. Siegen. 1915
Stein (Wilhelm). Nietzsche u. d. bild. Kunst. [Beil. zu H1, 2 d. Archivs f. Gesch. d. Phil., B30. Bibl. f. Phil., B28]. 8°. 1925
Stein (Wolfgang), *see* STEYN (W.)
Steinacker (Carl). Die Stadt Braunschweig. s8°. St. 1924
Steinacker (Harold), *see* HAPSBURG. Regesta Habsburgica &c., Abt. 1, bearb. v. H. S., 1905.
Steinberg (I.), *see* SHTEINBERG (I.)
Steineg (Theodor Meyer), *see* MEYER-STEINEG (T.)

Steiner (Friedrich). Notenbankpolitik u. staatl. Anleihepolitik in d. österr.-ungar. Nachfolgestaaten. [V. f. Sozialpol., B166i]. 8°. München. 1924
Steiner (Gustav), *see* OCHS (P.) Korr.: hrsg. G. S., B1, 1927.
Steiner (Paul). Röm. Landhäuser (villae) im Trierer Bezirk. 8°. 1923
Steiner (Rudolf). Goethe as the founder of a new sci. of æsthetics. Tr. G. Metaxa. Ed. H. Collison. [P2718]. 8°. 1922
Le mystère chrét. & les mystères antiq. Tr. & préc. d'une intr. par E. Schuré. s8°. 1908
Die Rätsel d. Philos. in i. Gesch. als Umriss dargestellt. Zugleich n. A. d. Werkes: Welt-u. Lebensanschau. im 19. Jhdt. 2B. s8°. [1914]
see LAUER (H. E.) R. S.'s Lebenswerk, 1926.
Steinhausen (Georg). Kulturgesch. d. Deutschen im Mittelalter. 3e neub. A. s8°. L. 1921
Die Schuld d. Heimat. [P2406]. s8°. 1919
Steinhausen (Heinrich).
Irmela, eine Gesch. aus alt. Zeit. 5e A. s8°. L. 1883
Steinhauser (Walter). Beitr. z. Kunde d. bairisch-österreich. Mundarten, H2, 1922, *see* KAIS. AKAD. D. WISS. ZU WIEN. Sitzungsber., B195, 1923.
Steinheil (*Mme.* **Marguerite).** My memoirs. 8°. 1912
Steinhoffer (Johann Ulrich). Græcia sacra: ritus &c. vet. Græc. s8°. Tubingæ. 1784
Steinle (Mich.) Mit d. Nord-China-Expedition. s8°. Hamburg. [1921]
Steinmann (Ernst).
Botticelli's "Tempelscene" in d. Cappella Sistina. [Abdr. aus Repertorium f. Kunstwiss., B18i. P2842]. la8°. [St. 1895]
Der Jeremias d. Michelangelo. [*Extr. f.* Repertorium f. Kunstwiss., B17. P2837]. 8°. [St. 1894]
Der Palast v. San Marco in Rom. [Abd. aus Zentralblatt f. Kunstwiss. Lit., H. 6. P2838]. 8°. 1909
Terrakotta-modelle Berninis im Mus. zu Schwerin. [Abdr. aus Münch. Jhrb. d. Kunst. P2860]. 4°. München. 1907
Die Tituli u. d. Kirchl. Wandmalerei im Abenlande, 5. bis z. 11. Jhrdt. [Beiträge z. Kunstgesch., N.F., 19]. 8°. L. 1892
Steinmann (Olga), *wife of E. Steinmann, born O. v. Gerstfeldt.* Venus und Violante. [*Extr. f.* Monatshefte f. Kunstwiss. Jahrg. 3. P2842]. 4°. L. 1910
Steinmeyer (E. Elias v.) Die klein. althochdeut. Sprachdenkmäler. Hrsg. v. E. v. S. 8°. 1916
Steinmüller (Paul). Einführ. d. Reformation in d. Kurmark Brandenburg durch Joachim II. [Verein. f. Ref.-gesch. Schr., Jhrg. 20, Nr. 76]. 8°. Halle. 1903
Steinschneider (Moritz). Bibliogr. Hdbch. ü. d. Lit. für hebr. Sprachkunde. Anhang zu Gesenius Gesch. 8°. L. 1859
Gesammelte Schriften. Hrsg. H. Malter u. A. Marx. B1. 8°. 1925
Jewish literature, 8th–18th cent. w. introd. on Talmud & Midrash. From the Germ. [by W. Spottiswoode], rev. by auth. 8°. 1857
Steirische Zeitschrift f. Geschichte, 1903–18, *see* HISTORISCHER VEREIN F. STEIERMARK.
Stejneger (Leonhard). Chap. in hist. of zoolog. nomenclature, 1924, *see* SMITHSONIAN INST. Misc. colls., v77, 1926.
Steklov (Yurii) [STEKLOW (G.)]
A. J. Herzen: e. Biographie. s8°. 1920
М. А. Бакунин, его жизнь и деятельность. 4т. 8°. Москва. 1920–27
Stella (Didacus de), *see* ESTELLA (DIEGO DE).
Stelling (C. David). Yea & nay. Lect. & counter-lect. at London Sch. of Econ. [Ed. C. D. S.] s8°. [1923]
Stemplinger (Eduard). Antike u. mod. Volksmedizin. 8°. L. 1925
Horaz in Urteil d. Jhdte. 8°. L. 1921
Sten (Simon), *see* STENIUS (S.)
Stencel-Lensky (Z.)
Co-oper. in Soviet Russia. [P2464]. 8°. 1920
Stender-Petersen (Ad.) Die Schulkomödien d. Paters F. Bohomolec. 8°. Heidelberg. 1923
Stengel (Carl). Hierologia: loca sacra. s4°. Ingolstadii. 1653
Stengel (Carl, *Frhr.* **v.)** Wörterbuch d. deut. Staats- u. Verwaltungsrechts; begründet v. S. 2e, völlig neu gearb. u. erweit. A. hrsg. v. M. Fleischmann. B3. la8°. Tübingen. 1914
Stengel (Edmund E.) Nova Alamanniae. Urkunden, Briefe u. a. Quellen bes. z. deut. Gesch. d. 14. J. hrsg. S. 1. Hälfte. [*no more publ.*] la8°. 1921
Stengel (Johann). Apparatus librorum theolog., Das ist: Vorrath theolog. Bücher, &c. s8°. Ulm. 1724
Stengel (Walter). Signaturenkunde. [Sonderabdr. a. d. Museumskunde, B6, 7.] [P2701]. 4°. *n.d.*
Stenhammar (Christian). Äminnelse—Tal öfver Nils Dalberg. [P2672]. 4°. Linköping. 1822

Stenhouse (Anthony Maitland). Marriage & anti-waste; genesitic primer of political econ. 3rd ed. [P2584]. s8°. Plymouth. [1922]
Marriage as a wealth distributor. 2nd ed. [P2757]. s8°. 1918
Stenhouse (Ernest). Simple lessons on the weather. s8°. 1921
Stenius (Simon) [*ps.* BALEUS (JOANNES); LITHUS (CHR. SIMON), *Misenus*]. Examen recitationum N. Selnecceri de libro Concordiae, admonitionem Neustadianum confirm. [*b. w.* Selneccerus (N.) Recit., 1581]. s4°. Neapoli Nemetum. 1582
Oratio qua publicè in Acad. Heidelberg. Casparis Peuceri manibus parentatum est a S. S. [P2611]. s4°. Servestae. 1603
see GRETSER (J.) Panegyricus Misenicus [*ans. to* S.'s "Gretserus Triumphatus"—Stigma frontis Misenicae] &c., 1606.
Stenton (Frank Merry).
The development of the castle in Eng. & Wales. [Hist Assoc., Leaflet 22. P2706]. 8°. 1910
Doc. illust. of soc. & econ. hist. of the Danelaw f. var. coll. Ed. F. M. S. [Brit. Acad. Rec. of soc. &c. hist. of Eng. &c. v5]. la8°. 1920
Transcripts of charters rel. to the Gilbertine houses of Sixle, Ormsby, Catley, Bullington & Alvingham. Ed., w. a tr. by F. M. S. [Lincoln Rec. Soc., v18]. la8°. Horncastle. 1922
see MAWER (A.) & F. M. S., *edd.* Intr. to survey of Eng. place-names, p1, 1924.
,, —— & —— Place-names of Beds. & Hunts., 1926.
,, —— & —— Place-names of Buckinghamshire, 1925.
,, —— & —— Place-names of Worcestershire, 1927.
Stenzel (Alfred). Seekriegsgesch. T6, 1910–20, von H. Kirchhoff. 8°. Hannover. 1921
Step [STEPPE]. Степъ. Херсонськый беллетристычный сбирныкъ. Херсонъ. 1886. 8°. С.-П. 1886
Step (Edward).
Animal life of the Brit. Isles. s8°. 1921
Brit. insect life: pop. intr. to entomology. 8°. [1921]
Go to the ant. Nat. hist. of ants. 8°. 1924
Herbs of healing: bk. of Brit. simples. 8°. [1926]
Wayside & woodland blossoms. n. ed. 2s. s8°. [1923]
Wayside & woodland trees: guide to Brit. sylva. 2nd impr. s8°. 1904
see KNIGHT (A. E.) & E. S. Hutchinson's pop. botany, 2v, 1912.
,, —— & —— Living plant, *n.d.*
Stepanov (Aleksii Vasilevich). Екатерина II ея происхожденіе &c. [P2388]. s8°. Лондонъ. 1897
Елизавета Петровна, ея происхожденіе &c. [P2388]. s8°. Лондонъ. 1899
Stepanov (Ivan).
О "живой церкви." [P2682]. 8°. Москва. 1922
Stéphan (L.) Notice sur Notre-Dame du Mur, patronne de Morlaix. s8°. Morlaix. 1895
Stéphane (Gaston).
Cannes: notes & croquis. 2e éd. la8°. Cannes. [1923]
Stephani, *see* ESTIENNE, *Family of.*
Stephanopoli (Dimo) & N. Stephanopoli. Voyage en Grèce (1797–98). Rédigé par un des profess. du Prytanée [*i.e.* A. Sérieys. *Added* Mém. & pièces justific. *&* Voyage à Maina, poème ital., de D. S. *w.* tr.] [Tr.] 2t. 8°. [1800]
Stephanopoli (Nicolo), *see* STEPHANOPOLI (D.) & N. S. Voyage en Grèce (1797–98); tr., 2t, 1800.
Stephanus, *bp. of Siuniq, fl. 1287, see* ORBELIAN (S.)
Stephanus, *of Taron, Asolik.* [Hist. of the world. *In Armenian. Ed.* S. Malkhaseantz]. 2nd ed. 8°. i S. Peterbourg. 1885
Stephanus, *bp. of Tournay.* Epistolæ, 1159–96, *see* SYLVESTER II, *pope.* Epistolæ, 1611.
Stephanus, *Winton., see* GARDINER (S.), *bp. of Winchester.*
Stephanus (P. F.), *see* REITPERGER (STEPHANUS).
Stephanus (Robert), *see* ESTIENNE (R.)
Stephen [*Bathory*], *king of Poland, see* BATHORY (I.)
Stephen, *of Taron, Asolik, see* STEPHANUS, *of Taron.*
Stephen (Barbara, *Lady***),** *wife of Sir H. L. Stephen.*
Emily Davies & Girton College. 8°. 1927
Stephen (Dorothea). Jeremiah the prophet of hope. s8°. 1923
Stephen (*Sir* **George),** [*ps.* CAVEAT EMPTOR]. *The adv. of a gentleman in search of a horse. By Caveat Emptor. 2nd ed. s8°. 1836
*The guide to service. The groom. s8°. 1840
Stephen (George A.) Borrow House museum: life of G. Borrow & h. Norwich home. 8°. Norwich. 1927
Stephen (Henry John), *Serjeant at Law.* Comm. on the laws of England. 17th ed., rev. &c. under gen. editorship of E. Jenks. 4v. 8°. 1922

Stephen (*Sir* **James Fitzjames**). A digest of the criminal law (Crimes & punishments). 4th ed. 8°. 1887

Stephen (Karin). The misuse of mind. A study of Bergson's attack on intellectualism. W. pref. letter by H. Bergson. 8°. 1922

Stephen (*Sir* **Leslie**), *K.C.B.* Some early impressions. 8°. 1924

Stephens (Edward). *A disc. conc. the original of the Powder-Plot with a rel. of the conspiracies agst. Q. Elizabeth & the persecutions of the protestants in France to the death of Henry IV &c. s4°. 1674

Stephens (James).
The charwoman's daughter. [repr.]. s8°. 1927
Coll. poems. 8°. 1926
The crock of gold. [repr.] s8°. 1924
„ „ [repr.] s8°. [1926]
The demi-gods. [repr.] s8°. 1922
Insurrection in Dublin. n. ed. 8°. D. 1919
Irish fairy tales. 8°. 1920
A poetry recital. 8°. 1925
see WILLIAMS (I. A.) Bibliographies of mod. a., No. 4, J. S. &c., 1922.

Stephens (John). Stephens's rep. of Dr. Warren's case in Vice-Chanc.'s court, 1835, conc. the suspens. of Dr. W. &c. [P527]. 8°. 1835
see WARREN (SAMUEL) & J. STEPHENS. Chron. of Wesleyan Methodism, 2v, 1827.

Stephens (Winifred), *aft. wife of G. Whale.*
Women of the French Revol. 8°. 1922

Stephenson (H. W.) The author of Nearer, my God, to Thee: Sarah Flower Adams. s8°. 1922

Stephenson (James).
Princ. & practice of commerce. 8°. *Pitman.* [1915]

Stephenson (Mill). List of monumental brasses in the Brit. Isles. la8°. 1926

Stephenson (Nathaniel Wright).
Lincoln, an acc. of his personal life &c. 8°. 1924
Texas & the Mexican War. [Chron. of Amer. Ser., v24]. 8°. New Haven, *Yale.* 1921

Stephenson (Robert), *civil engineer; 1803–59, see* WARREN (J. G. H.) Cent. of locomotive building by R. S. & Co., 1823–1923, 1923.

Stephenson (Robert), *Wesleyan minister, see* BUSH (JOSEPH). W. O. Simpson, Methodist minister, mission life, by R. S., 1886.

Stephenson (T. A.)
The British sea anemones. [Ray Soc., 113]. v1. 8°. 1928

Stephenson (W. Tetley). Communications. Intr. by Sir E. Geddes & Sir F. W. Lewis. [Resources of the Empire, v10]. 4°. 1924

Stepney. Customs & privileges of the manors of S. & Hackney, prefix'd an act [of 21 James I] for establ. of the said customs. s8°. 1736

Stepniak (S.), *ps.* [*i.e.* SERGIUS KRAVTCHINSKY].
Подпольная Россія. s8°. 1893
*С. П. Бардина. [P2824]. s8°. Genève. 1883
„ „ ....[P2400]. s8°. Carouge (Genève). 1900

Sterling (Andrew). Orissa. Added, a hist. of the Baptist Miss. in the prov., by J. Peggs. 8°. 1846

Stern (Alfred).
Gesch. Europas 1815–71. B7-10. 8°. St. 1916–24
7-10 [Abtlg. 3, 4B], 1848–71.

Stern (Boris). Works council movement in Germany, *see* UNITED STATES: LABOR. Bull. 383, 1925.

Stern (*Mme.* **Ernesta**) [*ps.* MARIA STAR].
Terre des symboles. fol. 1903

Stern (Gladys Bronwyn), *wife of Geoffrey L. Holdsworth.*
The back seat. s8°. 1923
Bouquet. s8°. 1927
Children of no man's land. s8°. [1919]
A deputy was king. s8°. 1926
Jack a' Manory. s8°. 1927
The Matriarch, *see* Tents of Israel, *below.*
The room. s8°. 1922
Smoke rings. s8°. 1923
Tents of Israel. 2nd impr. s8°. 1924
„ „ 3rd impr. s8°. 1924
„ „ *another ed. w. t.* The Matriarch. [6th pr.] s8°. N.Y. 1925
Thunderstorm. s8°. 1925

Stern (Jean). Les courses de Chantilly sous la Monarchie de Juillet. la8°. [1913]
Mesdemoiselles Colombe de la Comédie-Ital., 1751–1841. Préf. de R. de Flers. s8°. 1923

Stern (William). Die menschl. Persönlichkeit. 3. A. mit e. Begleitwort. 8°. L. 1923
Psychology of early childhood. Suppl. by extr. f. Diaries of Clara Stern. Tr. f. 3rd ed. by A. Barwell. 8°. [1924]

Sternberg (Caspar M., *Graf* **v.),** *see* BRETHOLZ (B.) Z. Gesch. d. kais. Akad. d. Wiss. in Wien: e. Gutachten d. Grafen K. v. S., 1914.

Sterne (Henry). Statement of facts, submitted to Ld. Glenelg, w. exposure of pres. system of Jamaica apprenticeship. 8°. 1837

Sterne (Laurence).
Works. With life by himself. 4v. 8°. 1808
„ „ ......[1v]. 8°. 1839
*A sentimental journey thr. France & Italy. By Mr. Yorick. 2v. s8°. 1782
„ „ w. contin. by Eugenius. s8°. 1792
„ „ ....s8°. 1794
Sentimental journey & Journal to Eliza. [Intr. by G. Saintsbury. Everyman's Lib.] s8°. [1927]
Seven letters by S. & h. friends hitherto unpubl. Ed. W. D. Cooper. [P2777]. s8°. *f.p.c.* 1844
Tristram Shandy, & A sentimental journey thr. France & Italy. 2v. 8°. 1911
Viaggio sentimentale di Yorick. Tr. di D. Chierico. [*b. w.* Foscolo (N. U.) Ult. lettere di J. Ortis, 1817]. s8°. Italia. 1818
„ „ tr. U. Foscolo, *see* FOSCOLO (N. U.) Prose, v3, 1920.
see CROSS (W. L.) Life & times of S., n. ed., 2v, 1925.
„ RABIZZANI (G.) S. in Italia: riflessi nostrani dell' umorismo sentimentale, 1920.
„ WRIGHT (A.) & W. L. SCLATER. Sterne's Eliza, 1922.

Sternfeld (Richard). Kaiser Wilhelm I in uns. Zeit, *see* KAISER-WILHELM-DANK. Kriegsschr., H47, 1916.

Sternheim (Carl).
Bürger Schippel. Komödie. 8°. L. 1913
Chronik v. d. 20ten Jhdt.'s Beginn. 2B *in* 1v. s8°. München. 1923
Der entfesselte Zeitgenosse. Lustspiel. s8°. München. 1920
Europa. Roman. 2B. s8°. München. [1919–20]
Die Hose. Bürgerl. Lustspiel. 2e A. 8°. L. 1919
Die Kassette. Komödie. 8°. L. 1912
Perleberg. Komödie. 8°. L. 1917
Der Snob. Komödie. 8°. München. 1920
Tabula rasa. Schauspiel. [2e A.] 8°. L. *n.d.*

Sternhold (Thomas) & J. Hopkins, *see* BIBLE: PSALMS. The Booke of Psalmes, coll. into Eng. meeter, *var. eds.*

Stesichorus, *fl. c. 608 B.C., see* LYRA. Lyra Graeca; ed. & tr. by J. M. Edmonds, v2, S. &c., 1924.

Stetson (John Batterson). The Oscar Wilde coll. of S. Sold, Apr. 23, Anderson Gall. [P2856]. 8°. N.Y. 1920

Stettbacher (Hans), *see* PESTALOZZI (J. H.) P. & h. times; intr. by H. S., 1928.

Stettinger (Gottfried). Geschichtlichkeit d. Johanneischen Abschiedsreden. Gegen K. Clemen. 8°. Wien. 1919

Steuart (Archibald Francis).
Seigneur Davie: sk. life of D. Riccio. s8°. 1922
see MARY, *queen of Scots.* Trial; ed. A. F. S., 1923.

Steuart (*Sir* **Henry**), *1st bart.* The genealogy of the Stewarts refuted. [*a. c. b. w.* Stuart (A.) Genealog. hist., 1798]. 4°. E. 1799

Steuart (John Alex.) Robert Louis Stevenson, man & writer: a crit. biog. 2v. 8°. [1924]

Steuart (Walter), *of Pardovan.* Coll. & obs. conc. the worship, discipline &c. of the Ch. of Scotland, 4th ed., *see* CHURCH OF SCOTLAND. Compendium of laws, p1, 1830.

Stevanović (Borislav P.) Experimental st. of the mental processes involved in judgment. Thesis. [Brit. Journal of Psych., Monogr. Suppl., 12]. la8°. C. 1927

Stevartius (Petrus). Comm. in Epistol. Pauli ad Philippenses &c. [*b. w. h.* Exegesis in Ep. Pauli ad Ephesios, 1593]. s4°. Ingolstadii. [1595]
Exegesis in Epist. Pauli ad Ephesios &c. s4°. Ingolstadii. 1593

Steven (Alexander Gordon). Coll. poems. 8°. Melbourne. [1925]

Steven (William).
A brief view of the Dutch eccl. establ. 3rd ed. 8°. E. 1839
The hist. of the Scottish church, Rotterdam. Subj. Notices of o. Brit. churches in Netherlands &c. [*engr. tp. dated* 1832]. 8°. E. 1833

Steveni (James William Barnes). Europe's great calamity: the Russian famine. [P2585]. s8°. 1922
Unknown Sweden. 8°. [1925]

Stevens (Abel), *LL.D.*
Hist. of Methodism. v3. la8°. N.Y. [1861]
Life & times of Nathan Bangs. s8°. N.Y. 1863
Mem. of the early progress of Methodism in the Eastern States. 2nd ser. s8°. Boston [Mass.] 1852
Mem. of the introd. of Methodism into the Eastern States. s8°. N.Y. 1854

Stevens (Alfred), *see* LAMBOTTE (P.) L'œuvre de A. S.: cat. de l'expos., avr.-juin 1907; ét. illust., 1907.

Stevens (Benj. Franklin), *see* FENN (G. M.) Mem. of B. F. S., [*& h.* Intr. to Catalogue index of Amer. MSS.], 1903.

Stevens (C. L. McCluer). Famous crimes & criminals. 8°. [1924]

Stevens (*Maj.* Edward James). Field telephones & telegraphs for army use. 6th ed. rev. & enl. s8°. 1918

Stevens (Ethel Stefana), *aft. Mrs. Edwin Mortimer Drower.* By Tigris & Euphrates. 8°. 1923

Stevens (Frank). Stonehenge to-day & yesterday. s8°. 1919

Stevens (Frederick Haller), *see* HALL (H. S.) & F. H. S. A shorter school geometry, 2p, 1924.

Stevens (George Alexander). The dramatic hist. of Master Edward, Miss Ann, & others. Coll. f. Zaphaniel's orig. papers. n. ed. s8°. 1785

Stevens (Gerald Philip). Ramblings of a rolling stone. 8°. [1924]

Stevens (Henry), *auctioneer, see* ALLINGHAM (E. G.) Romance of the rostrum: business life of H. S. & hist. of 38 King St. &c., 1924.

Stevens (Henry), *F.S.A., of Vermont.* Histor. & geogr. notes, 1453–1869, *see* TEHUANTEPEC. T. Rly., 1869.

see HUMPHREYS (A. L.) Old decorative maps &c.; w. cat. of atlases &c. in coll. of H. S., 1926.

Stevens (*Capt.* John). Hist. acc. of all taxes f. the Conquest to death of George I. 2nd ed. 8°. 1733

*A new coll. of voyages & travels into several parts of the world, none before pr. in English. [*Each w. sep. pagin.* Ed. by J. S.] 2v [v1 *wanting*]. s4°. 1711

2, Mouëtte (G.) Travels in kingdoms of Fez & Morocco.—Teixeira (P.) Travels f. India to Italy by land.—Cauche (F.) Voyage to Madagascar &c.—Tellez (B.) Travels of Jesuits in Ethiopia &c., *w. sep. tp.*, 1710.

see MEMOIRS of the antiq. of Gt. Brittain &c.; w. remarks on Stevens' first addit. vol. to Dugdale's Monastichon &c., 1713.

Stevens (Kathleen L.), *ed., see* BOOK-AUCTION RECORDS. 2nd gen. index, 1912–23; ed. S., 1928.

Stevens (Simon), *see* TEHUANTEPEC. The T. Railway &c. [*prep. by S.*], 1869.

Stevens (Thomas Palmer).
Story of Southwark Cathedral. s8°. [1922]

Stevens (William Oliver) & A. Westcott.
Hist. of sea power. 8°. N.Y. [1920]

Stevenson (A. G.), *ed., see* STEVENSON (B. G.) Betty S., 1920.

Stevenson (Betty G.) Betty Stevenson, Y.M.C.A., Sept. 1896–May 1918. Ed. C. G. R. S. & A. G. S. 2nd impr. s8°. 1920

Stevenson (C. G. R.), *ed., see* STEVENSON (B. G.) Betty S., 1920.

Stevenson (Edward Luther). Facsimiles of portolan charts. Intr. by E. L. S. [Hispanic Soc. of Amer.] atlas fol. N.Y. 1916

Terrestrial & celestial globes; hist. &c. [Hispanic Soc. of Amer.] 2v. 8°. 1921

see FREDUCCI (C. DE O.) Portolan atlas, 1537: facs.; intr. by E. L. S., 1915.

,, MARTINES (J.) Portolan atlas; 1582; facs. w. intr. by E. L. S., 1915.

Stevenson (Fanny Van de Grift), *wife of R. L. Stevenson, see* SANCHEZ (N. VAN DE G.) Life of Mrs. R. L. S., 1920.

Stevenson (George John).
The Methodist hymnbook & its assoc. &c. s8°. 1870

Stevenson (Gertrude Scott). Charles I in captivity. From contemp. sources [Sir T. Herbert &c.] ed. w. intr., by G. S. S. 8°. 1927

Stevenson (*Sir* John Andrew), *1760?–1833.* Faithless Emma. Words by G. A., of Dublin. [*b. w.* Corelli (A.) Twelve concertos, 1790 ?]. 4°. *n.d.*

Stevenson (*Hon.* John White). Speech, U.S. Senate, 1875. The supremacy of the constit. essential to civil liberty. [P2625]. 8°. W. 1875

Stevenson (Joseph). Early hist. of Leighton Buzzard. pl. s8°. Leighton Buzzard. 1850

Stevenson (Lilian). A child's bookshelf: suggestions on children's reading, w. list of books &c. 5th ed. s8°. 1922

Stevenson (Paul Huston). The Chinese-Tibetan borderland & its peoples. [Bull. of Peking Soc. of Nat. Hist., v11, p2]. la8°. Peking. 1927

Stevenson (Robert Louis).

Cat. of unpubl. autogr. letters of R. L. S. & MS. of "Monmouth." Auction by Christie, July 11, 1922. [P2747]. 8°. [1922]

Dr. Jekyll & Mr. Hyde. 6th ed. s8°. 1886

,, ,, w. o. fables. n. impr. s8°. 1911

,, ,, n. impr. s8°. 1920

Stevenson (Robert Louis) [*continued*].

Essays of travel. [4th impr.] s8°. 1912

Father Damien. [repr.] s8°. Indiana. [1927]

Further memories. s8°. [1924]

An inland voyage. [n. impr.] s8°. 1919

Memories & portraits. n. impr. s8°. 1919

Moral emblems & o. p. illust. w. woodcuts. 1st pr. by L. Osbourne & w. pref. by same. s8°. 1921

New Arabian nights. n. impr. s8°. 1912

Poems, incl. Underwoods, Ballads, Songs of travel. s8°. 1912

Prince Otto. n. impr. s8°. 1912

Tales & fantasies. 3rd impr. s8°. 1910

Travels w. a donkey in the Cevennes. n. impr. s8°. 1920

Treasure Island. [illust. ed.] s8°. *n.d.*

Twenty-two poems. s8°. [1923]

Virginibus puerisque & o. papers. n. impr. s8°. 1919

TRANSLATION.

Сентъ-Ивъ. St. Ives. Переводъ Е. М. Чистяковой-Вэръ. 8°. Спб. [1914]

see BALFOUR (G.) Life of R. L. S., 2nd ed., 2v, 1901.

,, BAY (J. C.) Echoes of R. L. S., 1920.

,, BLAND (H. M.) S.'s California, 1924.

,, CHESTERTON (G. K.) R. L. S., 1927.

,, CUNNINGHAM (A.) Cummy's diary: diary kept by R. L. S.'s nurse on the Continent dur. 1863, 1926.

,, FLETCHER (C. B.) S.'s Germany, 1920.

,, GUTHRIE (C. J. G., *Ld.*) R. L. S.: personal remin., 1920.

,, MACCULLOCH (J. A.) R. L. S. & the Bridge of Allan &c., 1927.

,, STEUART (J. A.) R. L. S., man & writer: a crit. biog., 2v, 1924.

,, SWINNERTON (F. A.) R. L. S.: a crit. study, n. ed., 1924.

,, WILLIAMS (*Mrs.* I.) Cat. of books, Stevensoniana, property of L. Osbourne, 1923.

—— & F. Van De Grift Stevenson. More New Arabian nights. The dynamiter. n. ed. s8°. 1885

—— & Lloyd Osborne. The wrong box. n. imp. s8°. 1911

Stevenson (*Mrs.* Sinclair) [form. MARGARET ADAMS]. The rites of the twice-born. Foreword by A. A. Macdonell. 8°. O. 1920

Stevenson (Thomas George). Bibliog. of J. Maidment, 1817–78 [*w.* App., Notices of sale of Maidment coll., 1880]. 8°. E. [*f.p.c.*] 1883

Stevenson (William B.), *D.Litt.*
Grammar of Palestinian Jewish Aramaic. s8°. O. 1924

Stevenson (William Henry), *see* MACRITCHIE (D.) & W. H. S. Great & Little Britain, 1924.

Steward (George), *1803–66.* Mediatorial sovereignty, mystery of Christ & revel. of O. & N. Test. 2v. 8°. E. 1863

*Mem. of G. S. 8°. 1868

The principles of Church govt. & their applic. to Methodism. 8°. 1853

Stewart, *The family of* [*see also* STUART], *see* SINTON (T.) Fam. & genealog. sketches [S. &c.], 1911.

see STEWART (C. E.) Stewarts book-plates, 2p, 1907–11.

Stewart (Alexander). A Highland parish: or the hist. of Fortingall. 8°. Glasgow. 1928

Stewart (Alexander M.) Science & gossip: annals of the countryside. s8°. [1923]

Stewart (Alfred Walter). Recent advances in organic chemistry. Intr. by J. N. Collie. 4th ed. 8°. 1920

,, ,, ...5th ed. 2v. 8°. 1927

Recent advances in physical & inorganic chemistry. Intr. by Sir W. Ramsay. 4th ed. 8°. 1920

,, ,, ...5th ed. 8°. 1926

Stewart (Andrew). "Once I was blind——" s8°. [1926]

Stewart (Archibald), *minister at Glasserton.* Hist. vindicated in the case of the Wigtown martyrs. 2nd ed. 8°. E. 1869

Stewart (Basil). Japanese colour-prints. la8°. 1920

Stewart (C. G.), *see* BROWNE (G. L.) & C. G. S. Rep. of trials f. murder by poisoning, 1883.

Stewart (C. J.), *bookseller in London.* Bibles & Biblical literature &c. on sale, w. prices affixed. [*w.* Suppl. *pagin. cont.*] s8°. *n.d.*

Cat. of Bibles & Biblical lit. On sale by C. J. S. 8°. 1849

Cat. of books in all branches of theology &c. On sale by C. J. S. [*&* Suppl. *in* 1v]. 8°. 1846–47

Cat. of writers of the 16th [& 17th] cent. &c. On sale by C. J. S. 2p *in* 1v. s8°. *n.d.*

,, ,, ...Suppl. 1–3 *in* 1v. s8°. *n.d.*

General cat. of the stock of C. J. S. [3p *in* 1v]. s8°. [1880–81]

Rom. cathol. theology &c. 8°. 1871

see also HOWELL & STEWART, *Messrs.*

Stewart (Charles Edward).
The Stewarts book plates. 2p. [P2603]. 4°. *n.p.* [1907–11 ?]

Stewart (Charles Poyntz). The Roman Church & heresy w. spec. ref. to the infl. of the Vatican, w. foreword by W. A. Limbrick. 8°. [1925]

Stewart (David James).
On the architect. hist. of Ely Cathedral. 8°. 1868

Stewart (Estelle M.) Cost of Amer. almshouses, *see* UNITED STATES: LABOR. Bull. 386, 1925.

Stewart (Herbert Leslie).
Questions of the day in philos. & psychol. 8°. 1912

Stewart (Horace). Hist. of the W. Co. of Gold & Silver Wyre-Drawers &c. la8°. 1891

Stewart (Hugh Fraser). Francis Jenkinson. 8°. C. 1926

—— **& P. Desjardins.** French patriotism in the 19th c., 1814–33. 8°. C. 1923

—— **& A. Tilley.** The French romanticists. Anthol., sel. & annot. by H. F. S. & A. T. s8°. C. 1914

The romantic movt. in French lit. traced by a ser. of texts. Sel. & ed. by H. F. S. & A. T. [repr.] s8°. C. 1917

Stewart (Irvin). Consular privileges & immunities. [Columbia Univ.] 8°. N.Y. 1926

Stewart (Isabel Maitland), *see* DOCK (L. L.) Sh. hist. of nursing; by L. L. D. in collab. w. I. M. S., 1920.

Stewart (*Lt.-col.* J.) & J. Buchan.
The 15th (Scottish) Division, 1914–19. la8°. 1926

Stewart (*Sir* James) *of Goodtrees* **&** *Rev.* **J. Stirling.** Naphtali, or the wrestlings of the Church of Scotland, f. Reformation to 1667. With speeches &c. of some who have died since 1660. s8°. E. 1761

Stewart (James Douglas), *see* BERMONDSEY. Cat. of prints & drawings in B. Public Lib. illust. B.; comp. by J. D. S., 1927.

Stewart (John). Bread & bread baking. s8°. [1924]

Stewart (John), *4th earl of Atholl, see* ATHOLL.

Stewart (John A.), *writer on heraldry, see* MACMILLAN (W.) & J. A. S. Story of the Scot. flag, 1925.

Stewart (Joseph Spencer). Geology of the disturbed belt of Southwestern Alberta. [Canada. Geol. Survey. P2514]. 8°. Ottawa. 1919

Stewart (Matthew), *4th earl of Lennox, see* LENNOX.

Stewart (Robert Walter). The tent and the Khan: a journey to Sinai & Palestine. 8°. E. 1857

Stewart (William). The first Glasgow newspaper: "The Glasgow courant" aft. "The West-country intelligence." s4°. Glasgow. 1924

J. Keir Hardie. Intr. by J. R. Macdonald. 8°. [1921]

Stewart (William M.)
Analysis of the functions of money. s8°. W. 1898

Stewart-Brown (Ronald), *M.A.* Birkenhead Priory & the Mersey ferry. Chap. on the monastic buildings by H. Brakspear. 8°. Liverpool. 1925

Isaac Greene, a Lancashire lawyer of 18th cent., w. diary of Ireland Greene (Mrs. I. Blackburne of Hale), 1748–49. 8°. Liv'l. 1921

Stewart's hand book of the Pacific Islands, 1920, *see* ALLEN (P. S.)

Steyert (André). Nouv. hist. de Lyon &c. 3t. la8°. Lyon. 1895–99

Steyn (Wolfgang). Ob dz allerhochwirdigeste Sacrament, des leibs u. blutes Christi, anders benenhet moge werden dan eyn getrew Testament. . . . Eine newe Disputation zw. den Barfuessern zu Weimmar u. W. St. . . . s4°. *n.p.* [1523 ?]

Stibbe (D. G.), *ed., see* ENCYCLOPÆDIE van Ned.-Indië, 2e druk, d4, 1921.

Stickel (Johann Gustav) & C. F. Bogenhard. De morali primaevorum Christ. conditione. Ed. J. F. Roehr. 8°. Neostadtii ad Orlam. 1826

Stickers (Joe). Die absolute Vereindeutl. d. philos. Terminologie. [Beilage zu H3/4 d. Archivs f. system. Philos., B28. Bibl. f. Philos., B25]. 8°. 1924

Stieda (Wilhelm). J. Bernoulli in s. Bezieh. z. preuss. Herrscherhause u. z. Akad. d. Wiss., *see* KÖN.-PREUSS. AKAD. Abhdln., Phil.-hist. Kl., 1925.

Prof. F. Leubnitz, d. Vater d. Philosophen, *see* KÖNIGL. SÄCHS. GESELLS. Berichte, B69, 1917.

Stiefel (Arthur Ludwig). Zu d. Quellen d. Hans Sachsischen Schwänke. [P2463]. 8°. *n.d.*

Stieler (Adolf). Hand-Atlas: 100 Karten &c. Hrsg. v. J. Perthes' Geog. Anstalt. 9e A., 10er bericht. Abdr. fol. Gotha. 1919/20

Hand-Atlas. 10e A. unter Leitung v. H. Haack. [*w.* Namenverzeichnis]. fol. Gotha. 1925

Stieler (Georg). Nikolaus Malebranche. 8°. St. 1925

Stier (Ewald Rudolf).
Altes u. Neues in deut. Bibel. Oder Vergleichung d. Bibelverdeutschung Luthers mit i. Berichtigung durch Meyer. [P2651]. 8°. Basel. 1828

The words of the angels. s8°. 1862

The words of the Apostles expounded by R. S. Tr. G. H. Venables. 8°. E., *Clark.* 1869

The words of the Lord Jesus. Tr. f. 2nd ed. by W. B. Pope. 8v. 8°. E., *Clark.* 1855–58

The words of the risen Saviour, & comm. on the Epistle of St. James. Tr. W. B. Pope. 8°. E., *Clark.* 1869

Stier (G.) Ungar. Volksmärchen. Nach. d. aus G. Gaals Nachlass hrsg. Urschrift übers. v. G. S. s8°. Pesth. [1857]

Stiernhielm (Georg) [STIERNHIELMIUS; †STJERNHJELM].
Hercules. Jämte motsvarande partier av F. Tamms Glossar. 4de uppl., utg. av A. Noreen. 8°. Uppsala. 1921

see JUNIUS (F.), 1589–1677. Glossarium Ulphila-Gothicum; illust. per G. S., 1671.

,, ULFILAS. Evangelia ab U., nunc cum vers. Sueo-Goth., Norrænâ, seu Island., & vulg. Lat. ed. [*by* G. S.], 1671.

Stieve (Friedrich). Isvolsky & the World War. Based on docs. publ. by the German Foreign Office. Tr. E. W. Dickes. 8°. [1926]

Iswolski u. d. Weltkrieg. la8°. 1924

Russ. Orangebuch u. d. Kriegsausbruch mit der Türkei. Seine Falschungen &c. Hrsg. F. S. 8°. 1926

see IZVOLSKY (A. P.) I. im Weltkriege, dipl. Schriftwechsel, 1914–17, nebst Komm., v. F. S., 1925.

Stifel (Michael), *1487–1567* [STYFEL]. Arithmetica integra. Cum praef. P. Melanchthonis. s4°. Norimbergae. 1544

*Ein sehr wunderbarliche wortrechnūg etlicher zalen Danielis u. d. Offenbarung Sanct Johannis. [*Decor. border to tp.*] s4°. *n.p.* 1553

see GUDDAS (A.) M. S., 1922.

Stigand (Chauncey Hugh). Equatoria: the Lado Enclave. Introd. mem. by Sir R. Wingate. 8°. 1923

Stigel (Johann). De viro sancto M. Luthero &c. Auff das Christl. absterben D. M. L. [*Lat. & Germ. verse*]. s4°. *n.p.* 1546

Stiles (Percy Goldthwait). Dreams. 8°. Camb., *Harvard.* 1927

Stilfes. Urkunden u. Akten-Registen aus d. Dekanats-Archive Stilfes, 1300–1810, 1912, *see* SCHMID (G.), *ed.*

Stilgebauer (Edward). Götz Kraffts Wanderzeit. 2B. s8°. [1921]

The ship of death. [Auth. tr.] s8°. 1918

Still (Colin). Shakespeare's mystery play, a study of "The Tempest." 8°. [1921]

Still (Dorothea). Poems of motherhood. s8°. O. 1920

Still (J. Ironside), *D.D.* St. Paul on trial: a new reading of the hist. in Bk. of Acts & Pauline Epistles. s8°. 1923

Stillingfleet (Edward), *bp. of Worcester.*
Ans. to Locke's Second letter; wherein h. notion of ideas is prov'd to be inconsistent &c. s8°. 1698

*A disc. conc. the illegality of the late Eccl. Comm. [P529]. fol. 1689

*The doctrines &c. of the Ch. of Rome, in ans. to A papist misrepresented, &c. [*by J. Gother*]. 2nd ed. s4°. 1686

Epistola ad Deistam. A. A. Hochstetterus in Lat. serm. convertit &c. [*b. w.* Fecht (J.) Lect. theolog., 1722]. s8°. Ulmae. 1695

Origines sacrae: or a rational acc. of the grounds of religion. 7th ed. [2p *in* 1v. 1, Xtn. faith, 1701; 2, Religion, 1701]. fol. C. 1702

" " ....8th ed. fol. 1709

Rational acc. of the grounds of Prot. relig.: vindic. of [Laud's] Rel. of a Conference &c. f. the ans. of T. C[arwell]. 2nd ed. fol. 1681

A rel. of a conf. &c. w. some gentlemen of the Church of Rome. [P2664]. s4°. 1687

see BAXTER (R.) Catholick communion: survey of defender of S. &c., 1684.

,, CLAGETT (W.) *A reply to the mischief of impositions &c., 1681.

,, SHERLOCK (W.) *A disc. about church-unity: def. of S., 1681.

,, WHITBY (D.) A disc. conc. the idolatry of the Ch. of Rome: refut. of S.'s Disc. answered, 1674.

Stillman (John Maxson).
The story of early chemistry. 8°. N.Y. 1924

Theophrastus Bombastus von Hohenheim called Paracelsus, h. personality & influence. 8°. Chicago. 1920

Stilson (Charles B.) A cavalier of Navarre. s8°. [1925]

Stilwell (Arthur Edward). The light that never failed. s8°. [1921]

Stimmen aus d. Kathol. Kirche &c., 2B, 1870, *see* KATHOLISCH.

Stimmen aus Maria-Laach. Kathol. Monatschrift. B1–22. [B1v *wanting*]. 8°. Freiburg i. B. 1882

B7–22 *have sub-title:* Kathol. Blätter. *For earlier series entitled* Das ökumen. Concil, *see under* VATICAN COUNCIL.

see also †PIUS IX. Die Encycl. P., 1865–69.

Stimmer (Tobias), *see* Reusner (N.) Icones vir. lit. illust. sec. 15 &c.; a T. S. pict. expr., 1719.

Stimson (Julia C.), *see* United States: Army. Med. Dept. of U.S. Army in the World War, v13, The Army Nurse Corps; by S., 1927.

Stinde (Julius) [*ps.* Alfred de Valmy].
Die Familie Buchholz. 58^{e} A. 8°. 1886

Stinnes (Hugo).
see Brinckmeyer (H.) H. S., 4^{e} A., 1921; tr., 1921.
,, Heinig (K.) S. u. s. 600000 Arbeiter, 1921.
,, Ortner (E.) Gott Stinnes, 1922.
,, Raphael (G.) Le roi de la Ruhr; H. S., 1924.

Stintzing (Roderich v.)
Hugo Donellus in Altdorf. [P2683]. 8°. Erlangen. 1869

Stirke (D. W.) Barotseland: 8 yrs. among the Barotse. Intr. chap. by H. Johnston. 8°. 1922

Stirling (*Mrs.* **Anna Maria Wilhelmina),** *wife of Charles G. Stirling.* Life's little day: tales & reminiscences. 8°. [1924]
The Richmond papers f. corr. & MSS. of G. Richmond, & h. son Sir W. Richmond. 8°. [1926]
William de Morgan & h. wife. Pref. by Sir W. Richmond. 8°. [1922]

Stirling (D. M.) A hist. of Newton-Abbot & Newton-Bushel & neighbourhood &c. s8°. Newton-Abbot. 1830

Stirling (Fanny) [Stirling (*Mrs.* Mary Anne), *form.* Hehl, *aft. Lady* Gregory], *see* Allen (P.) Stage life of Mrs. S. &c., 1922.

Stirling (*Rev.* **James),** *of Paisley, see* Stewart (*Sir* J.) & J. S. Naphtali, or the wrestlings of the Church of Scotland &c., 1761.

Stirling (*Mrs.* **Mary Anne)** [*aft. Lady* Gregory], *see* Stirling (Fanny).

Stirling (William Alexander, *earl of***),** *d. 1640.* *The complaint of the muses upon Sir W. A. [*probably wr. to dictation of King James*], *see* Abbotsford Club. Misc., v1, 1837.
Poetical works. Ed. by L. E. Kastner & H. B. Charlton. [Scot. Text Soc., N.S., 11]. v1. 8°. E. 1921
1, Dramatic works, w. intr. essay on growth of Senecan tradition in Renaissance tragedy.
,, ,, [*a. issue*]. [Univ. of M'ter. Eng. ser., 10]. v1. 8°. M'ter. 1921
see Sidney (*Sir* P.) Countesse of Pembrokes Arcadia, w. suppl. of a defect by Sir W. A., 1633.

Stirling-Maxwell (*Sir* **William),** *9th bart., see* Coeck (P.) The Turks in 1533: drawings &c. publ. 1553; reprod., w. intr. by Sir W. S.-M., 1873.

Stirner (Max), *ps.* [*i.e.* Max Schmidt].
Der Einzige u. s. Eigenthum. 8°. L. 1845
Kleinere Schriften u. s. Entgegn. auf d. Kritik s. Werkes: "Der Einzige &c." Hrsg. v. J. H. Mackay. [P2480]. 8°. 1898
see Duboc (J.) Das Ich u. d. Uebrigen (für u. wider M. S.), 1897.
,, Schellwien (R.) M. S. u. Fr. Nietzsche, 1892.

Stix (Alfred), *see* Vienna. Die Einblattdrucke d. 15. Jhdts. in d. Kupferstichsammlung d. Hofbibliothek zu Wien, B2, Die Holzschnitte; bearbt. v. A. S., 1920.

Stjerna (Knut Martin). Essays on questions conn. w. the old Eng. poem Beowulf. Tr. & ed. J. R. C. Hall. [Viking Club. Extra ser., v3]. la8°. Coventry. 1912

Stjernhjelm (Georg), *see* Stiernhielm (G.)

Stjernstedt (Marika). Fröken Liwin. Roman. s8°. [1925]

Stobart (*Mrs.* **St. Clair),** *aft. Mrs.* Stobart Greenhalg. Anc. lights: or, the Bible, the Church, & psychic science. Intr. &c. by Sir O. Lodge. 8°. 1923
Torchbearers of spiritualism. 8°. [1925]

Stock (Alfred). The structure of atoms. Tr. S. Sugden. rev. & enl. 8°. [1923]

Stock (Joseph), *bp. of (1) Killala, (2) Waterford.* The book of Isaiah in Hebrew & English w. notes. 4°. Bath. 1803

Stock (Leo Francis). Proc. & debates of Brit. Parliaments resp. N. Amer. Ed. L. F. S. [C. Inst. of Wash.] v1, 2 (1, 1542–1688; 2, 1689–1702). la8°. Wash. 1924–27

Stock (Ralph). The cruise of the dream ship. 8°. 1921

Stock (Richard). A learned &c. comm. upon the prophesie of Malachy. Added, an exercitation by S. Torshell [*w. sep. tp. & pagin.*] fol. 1641

Stockbridge (John C.), *see* Brown University. Anthony memorial: cat. of Harris Coll. of Amer. poetry, w. biog. &c. notes by J. C. S., 1886.

Stockdale (Percival), *see* Waller (E.) Works; pref., Life by P. S., 1772.

Stöcker (W.) Die grosse Zeit 1914: Volks- u. Soldatenlieder. 2^{e} A. [P2711]. s8°. [1914]

Stockert (G. *or* **C.)** Le monete d. comune di Spalato, *see* Bullettino di arch. &c. dalm., 40–42, Suppl., 1919–22.

Stock Exchange year-book. 1915, 1923. 8°. [1915–22]

Stockhausen (Juliana v.) Brennendes Land: Roman d. Barock in d. Pfalz. s8°. München. 1921
Die Soldaten d. Kaiserin. Roman. s8°. München. 1925

Stockholm. The S. Conference, 1925. Offic. rep. of Univ. Xtn. Conf. on life & work. Ed. G. K. A. Bell. 8°. O. 1926
S. pittoreskt album. [*Letterpress by* P. Niboyet]. obl.4°. [1857]
National Museum.
Från Nationalmuseum. Taflor af Svenska Konstnärer. la8°. 1899
see Statens Historiska Museum och Myntkabinett, *Stockholm.*

Stocking (Charles Francis).
Carmen Ariza. [16th pr.] 8°. Chicago. 1920

Stöckl (Albert). Die Infallibilität d. Oberhauptes d. Kirche &c. [P2694]. 8°. Münster. 1870

Stockley (Cynthia). Ponjola. s8°. 1923

Stockmann (Alois).
Die deutsche Romantik. s8°. Freiburg im Br. 1921

Stockmann (Paul).
Elucidarius hæresium, schismatum &c. s8°. L. 1692

Stocks (C. de Beauvoir). Folk-lore & customs of the Lap-chas of Sikhim. [From Journal &c., As. Soc. of Bengal, N.S., v21]. 8°. [1927]

Stocks (Helen), *see* Leicester. Records of the borough of L.; extr. f. archives of the Corpor., 1603–88; ed. H. S., 1923.

Stocks (John Edward).
see Leicester. Old Town Hall Library of L., Cat. &c., by S. &c., 1919.
,, Market Harborough. Parish records, to 1837; by J. E. S. &c., 2v, 1890–1926.

Stocks (John Leofric). Aristotelianism. s8°. [1926]
Patriotism & the Super-State. s8°. 1920
The voice of the people: essay on representative democracy. s8°. [1920]
see Leicester. Old Town Hall Library; cat. &c. comp. by C. Deedes, J. L. S. &c., 1919.

Stocks (Theodor). Das Flussgebiet d. Pinnau. 8°. St. 1926

Stoddard (Lothrop) [Stoddard (Theodore Lothrop)].
The French Revol. in San Domingo. 8°. Boston [U.S.] 1914
The new world of Islam. 8°. 1921
Racial realities in Europe. 8°. 1924
The revolt agst. civiliz. Menace of the under-man. 8°. 1922
Re-forging America. 8°. 1927
The rising tide of color agst. white world-supremacy. Intr. by M. Grant. 8°. 1920
,, ,, [repr.] 8°. 1923
Scientific humanism. 8°. 1926

Stoddard (Richard Henry). Recoll., personal & literary. Ed. R. Hitchcock, w. intr. by E. C. Stedman. 8°. N.Y. 1903

Stoddart (Amos).
Sketches, hist. & descr., of Louisiana. 8°. Phila. 1812

Stöer (Joachim Christoph).
De vindice sanguinis. [P1015]. s4°. [Leipzig ? 1694]

Stogdon (John Hubert), *see* Harrow. Harrow School reg.; ed. J. H. S., s2, 2v, 1925.

Stoglav. Le Stoglav ou les 100 chapitres. Rec. des décisions de l'Assemblée eccl. de Moscou, 1551. Tr., avec intr. & comm. par E. D. 8°. 1920

Stöhr (August) [Stoehr]. Deutsche Fayencen u. deut. Steingut. Hdbh. 8°. [1920]

Stoicheia. Στοίχεια. St. z. Gesch. d. ant. Weltbildes &c. Begründet v. F. Boll. H8. 8°. L., *Teubner.* 1927
see Schlachter (A.) Der Globus, 1927. [8.]

Stoicorum veterum fragm. coll. I. ab Arnim, v1, 4, 1903–24, *see* Arnim (H. v.)

Stoke (Melis). Rijmkroniek. Uitg. door W. G. Brill. [Hist. Genoots. Werken., N.S., 40, 42, Bronnen &c.] 2d. 8°. Utrecht. 1885

Stoke Newington. *Glimpses of anc. Hackney & S. N.; by F. R. C. S., 1894, *see* Clarke (B.)

Stoker (Bram) [*i.e.* Abraham Stoker].
Dracula. 17th ed. s8°. 1927

Stokes (A. G. Folliott-), *see* Folliott-Stokes (A. G.)

Stokes (Adrian), *R.A.* Landscape painting. 8°. 1925
The thread of Ariadne. Intr. by J. M. Murry. 8°. 1925

Stokes (George Thomas), *D.D., prof. of Eccles. Hist. in Dublin.* Ireland & the Celtic Church: hist. of Ireland from St. Patrick to 1172. s8°. 1886
,, ,, ...7th ed., rev. by H. J. Lawlor. 8°. 1928

Stokes (H. F. Scott). Annals of Glastonbury Corpor., 1705–1834. Repr. f. the Central Somerset Gazette. s8°. [Glastonbury]. 1925
Perseus; or, of dragons. s8°. 1924

Stokes (Henry Paine).
Ceremonies of the Univ. of Cambridge. 8°. C. 1927
A sh. hist. of the Jews in England. s8°. 1921

Stokes (Hugh). Girtin & Bonington. s8°. [1922]
James Holland (1800–70). [Walker's Quarterly, No. 23]. 8°. [1927]
Thomas Gainsborough. s8°. [1925]

Stokes (*Miss* **Margaret McN.),** *see* PETRIE (G.) Xtian inscr. in the Irish lang.; ed. M. S., 2v, 1872–78.

Stokoe (F. W.) German infl. in Eng. romantic period, 1788–1818, w. spec. ref. to Scott, Coleridge &c. 8°. C. 1926
Tollkopf on dreams & o. poems. s8°. C. 1922

Stolberg (Balthasar). Exercitat. Graecae ling. tract. de soloecismis &c. Graecae Novi Foederis dictioni tributis &c. Acc. Disput., cum praef. C. S. Schurzfleischii. s4°. Francofurti. 1688

Stolinski (Sigismond).
Les Allemands en Pologne. 8°. Varsovie. 1927

Stolipin (P.) [STOLYPIN].
Проектъ о порядкѣ изданія касающ. Финляндіи законовъ &c. (*&* объяснительная записка) [*no tp.*] la8°. *n.p.* [1910]

Stolitsa i usadba. Столица и усадьба. Nos. 6, 8–18, 21, 22, 24, 25, 27, 33–35, 38–59, 62–65, 68, 69, 71, 73–78 (15 Мар. 1914–30 Мар. 1917). 4°. С.–П. 1914–17

Stoll (Elmer Edgar). Hamlet: hist. & comparative study. [Minnesota Univ. *b. w. h.* Othello, 1915]. 8°. Minneapolis. 1919
Othello: hist. & comparative study. [Minnesota Univ.] 8°. Minneapolis. 1915

Stolper (Gustav). Deutsch.-Österreich. Hrsg. v. G. S., mit Beitr. v. M. Sokal &c. [V. f. Sozialpol., B162]. 8°. München. 1921

Stolpyansky (P. N.) Старый Петербург. [3v *in* 1]. 8°. С.–П. *&* Москва. 1922–23
Дворец труда.
Колыбель русской свободы (Дело 1 Марта 1881).
Петропавловская крепость.

Stoltheim (Ferdinand Roderich-), *see* RODERICH-STOLTHEIM (F.)

Stoltze (Johann Gottlob). Diatribe [*&* Diatr. altera] de Eusebio Pamphili. Praes. J. C. Ernesti. [P595]. s4°. Wittebergae. 1689

Stolypin, *see* STOLIPIN.

Stolz (Heinz). Düsseldorf. s8°. L. [1914]

Stolze (Wilhelm). Bauernkrieg u. Reformation. [V. f. Ref.-gesch., Jahr. 44, H2 (Nr. 141)]. 8°. L. 1926

Stolzius (Johannes) [†STOLZ], *see* SCHMALKALD. Artikel d. Evangel. Lere &c., Vorrede *by* J. S. &c., 1553.

Stolzmann (Walter).
Die letzten Acht v. S. M. S. "Frauenlob." s8°. St. [1917]

Stone (A. C. Stanley-), *see* STANLEY-STONE (A. C.)

Stone (Albert H.) & J. H. Reed. Historic Lushan: the Kuling Mountains. Ed. by A. H. S. & J. H. R. 8°. Hankow. 1921

Stone (Darwell). Holy Baptism. n. impr. 8°. 1917

Stone (E. Herbert), *F.S.A.* The stones of Stonehenge. 4°. 1924

Stone (Edna L.) List of ref. on minimum wage for women, U.S. & Canada, *see* UNITED STATES: LABOR. Women's bur., Bull. 42, 1925.

Stone (Frederick D.), *see* MACMASTER (J. B.) & F. D. S., *edd.* Pennsylvania & the Federal Constit., 1787–88, 1888.

Stone (Gilbert). A hist. of labour. 8°. [1921]
see REDMAYNE (*Sir* R. A. S.) & G. S. Ownership & valuation of mineral property in the U.K., 1920.

Stone (J. Harris), *M.A.*
England's Riviera: Land's End &c. 2nd ed. 8°. [1923]

Stone (Percy Goddard). Alassio: its life story. s8°. Siena. 1924

Stone (William Leete), *the younger.* Mem. of the centen. celebr. of Burgoyne's surrender, held at Schuylerville, N.Y., 17th Oct., 1877. Prep. by W. L. S. 8°. Albany. 1878

Stonehill (C. A.) & H. W. Stonehill. Bibliographies of mod. authors. Comp. &c. C. A. & H. W. S. s2. 8°. 1925
Ser. 1 is by H. Danielson, *q.v.*

Stonehill (H. W.), *see* STONEHILL (C. A.) & H. W. S. Bibliog. of mod. authors, s2, 1925.

Stonhouse (*Sir* **James),** *bart., M.D., see* ORTON (J.) & *Sir* J. S. Letters to T. Stedman, 1800.

Stonor, *The family of.* Suppl. S. letters & papers (1314–1482); [ed.] C. L. Kingsford, 1923, *see* CAMDEN MISCELLANY (THE), v13, 1924.

Stonyhurst (The) pageants. Ed. w. intr. by C. Brown. 8°. Göttingen. 1920

Stoop (P. de). Notice sur l'abbaye de Loo, & invent. de ses archives. [Soc. d'Emulation de Bruges. Rec., s1. *b. w.* Goethals (A.) Chronica &c., 1844]. 4°. Bruges. 1843

Stopes (*Mrs.* **Charlotte Carmichael).** Life of Henry, 3rd earl of Southampton, Shakespeare's patron. 8°. C. 1922
The 17th cent. accounts of the Masters of the Revels. [Shakespeare Assoc. P2683]. 8°. [1922]

Stopes (Marie Carmichael).
Married love. 11th ed. rev. s8°. [1923]
Radiant motherhood. s8°. 1920
see MAUDE (A.) Authorized life of M. C. S., 1924.
—— **& R. V. Wheeler.**
Monogr. on the constit. of coal. la8°. 1918

Stopford (Francis).
The romance of the jewel. 4°. *p.f.p.c. Mappin & Webb.* 1920

Storck (Carl). Gesch. d. Musik. 4ᵉ, verm. A. 2B. la8°. St. 1921
Der Tanz. la8°. Bielefeld. 1903

Storer (Edward), *see* NOVELLE. Il Novellino; tr. E. S., 1925.

Storer (James Sargant) & J. Greig. *Antiquarian & topograph. cabinet. Views of objects of curiosity in Gt. Brit., w. descr. 10v. 8°. 1807–11

Storer (Malcolm). Numismatics of Mass. [Mass. Hist. Soc. Coll., v76]. la8°. [Camb., *Mass.*] 1923

Storer (Maria Longworth), *wife of Bellamy Storer, see* ROOSEVELT (T.) T. R. the child: sketch [*by* Mrs. M. L. S.] &c., 1921.

Storer (Tracy Irwin), *see* GRINNELL (J.) & T. I. S. Animal life in the Yosemite, 1924.

Storey (Charles Ambrose). Persian lit.: bio-bibliog. survey. p1, Qur'ānic lit. 8°. 1927

Storey (F. W.) & K. M. Wright.
South African botany. 2nd ed. s8°. 1922

Storia. Storia letteraria d'Italia. Scr. da una soc. di prof. la8°. Milano. [1910]
see BERTONI (G.) I. Duecento, 1910.
Storia polit. d'Italia scritta da una società di professori. [*Publ.* F. Vallardi]. la8°. Milano. *n.d.*
see FIORINI (V.) & F. LEMMI. Periodo napoleonico, 1799–1814.
,, GIOVAGNOLI (R.) Risorgimento ital., 1815–48.

Stories. Great s. of all nations, 1927, *see* LIEBER (M.) & B. C. WILLIAMS, *edd.*
Great short stories of the world, 1926, *see* CLARK (B. H.) & M. LIEBER, *edd.*
*Old stories wh. were the fore-runners of the Revolution in 88. s8°. 1711
Stories & ballads of the far past; tr. f. the Norse, 1921, *see* KERSHAW (N.), *ed.*
*Stories f. the lips of the teacher; retold by a disciple, 5th ed., 1876, *see* FROTHINGHAM (O. B.)

Storm (Ernst).
Gesch. d. deut. Kohlenwirtschaft, 1913–26. 8°. [1926]

Storm (Gustav).
Historisk-topogr. Skrifter om Norge &c. forfattede in Norge i d. 16 Aarh (Om Norgis rige, af A. P. Beyer &c.) Udg. ved G. S. [Norske Hist. K.] 8°. 1895
Islanske Annaler indtil 1578. Udg. ved G. S. [Norske Hist. K.] 8°. 1888
Monumenta hist. Norveg. Latinske Kildeskr. til Norges hist. i Middelalderen. [Norske Hist. K.] 8°. 1880
Otte brudstykker af d. aeldste saga om Olav den Hellige. [Norske Hist. K.] 4°. 1893
Regesta Norvegica. Kronolog. fortegn. over dok. vedkomm. Norge, Nordmaend og d. norske Kirkeprovins. 1, 991–1263. [Norske Hist. K.] 8°. 1898

Storm (Lesley). Lady, what of life? [2nd impr.] s8°. [1927]

Storr (Gottlob Christian). Annotat. quaedam theologic. ad philosophicam Kantii de religione doctrinam. s4°. Tubingae. 1793
Diss. de Evangeliis Arabicis. Def. G. C. S., resp. J. F. Roos. [P427]. s4°. Tubingae. [1775]
Doctr. Xtnae. pars theoretica. Ed. alt. emend. s8°. Stuttgardiae. 1807
Opuscula acad. ad interpret. librorum sacrorum [*of the New Test.*] 3v. s8°. Tubingae. 1796–1803

Storr (Vernon Faithfull), *see* ANGLICAN EVANG. GROUP MOVT. Pamphlets, by S. &c., 1923–24.

Storrie (James). The message of the king, Ad Britannos, & o. p. 8°. Paisley. 1913

Stort (R. van Genderen), *see* GENDEREN STORT (R. VAN).

Story (Thomas), *1662–1742, see* LOGAN (J.) Corresp. of J. L. & T. S., 1724–41, 1927.

Stosch (Albrecht v.) Somme-Nord: Juli, 1916. [Schlachten d. Weltkrieges, B20, 21]. 2T. 8°. Oldenburg. 1927

Stosch (Eberhard Heinrich Daniel). Comm. de librorum N.T. canone. Praem. diss. de cura vet. eccl. circa libros N.T. s8°. Francofurti ad Viadrum. 1755

Introd. in theolog. dogmaticam. 8°. Francofurti. 1778

Stoss (Veit), *see* DAUN (B.) V. S. u. s. Schule in Deutschland, Polen, Ungarn &c., 2e A., 1916.

Stott (M. Boole). Rep. on pres. position of vocational guidance & selection. [P2786]. 8°. [1925]

Stotz (A.), *see* MANEK (F.), G. PEKMEZI & A. S. Albanes. Bibliographie, 1909.

Stötzner (Walther). Ins unerforschte Tibet: Tagebuch d. deut. Exped. Stötzner, 1914. 8°. L. 1924

Stoughton (John), *of Kensington.* Ages of Christendom bef. the Reformation. s8°. 1857

A mem. of the Rev. Thomas Binney. Ed. J. S. s8°. 1874

Windsor: hist. & descr. of Castle & town. 8°. 1862

Stourdza (Alexandre de). Consid. sur la doctrine et l'esprit de l'Eglise orthodoxe. 8°. St. 1816

Stourton (Charles, *baron*). The Stourton tragedy, acc. of murder of the Hartgills, 1557. [P2710]. repr. s8°. Wincanton. 1901

Stout (George Frederick). The nature of universals & propositions. [Brit. Acad.] [P2565]. 8°. 1921

Stow (John), *historian & antiquary.* Survey of London [1603. With App. cont. Libellum de situ &c. Londini, by W. Fitzstephen. Ed. H. B. Wheatley. Everyman's Lib.] s8°. [1912]

Stowe. *Descr. of the gardens of Lord Visct. Cobham at S. in Buckinghamshire. 6th ed. corr. & enl. [P2781]. 8°. Northampton. 1749

Stowe (*Mrs.* Harriet Eliz. Beecher).

A Key to Uncle Tom's Cabin. la8°. 1853

see HENSON (J.) Life [Mrs. H. B. S.'s " Uncle Tom "], 1852.

Stowe (Richard Temple, *4th bart.*), *visct. Cobham, see* COBHAM (R. T., *visct.*)

Stowell (Ellery Cory).

Intervention in internat. law. 8°. Wash. 1921

Stowell (Thora). Strange wheat. s8°. [1925]

Stowell (William Hendry). Mem. of R. W. Hamilton. 8°. 1850

Stoyanovitch (Costa).

Economic problems of Serbia. 8°. Paris. 1919

Strabo. Rerum geograph. lib. XVII. Graece et Latine, animadv., annot. &c. adj. T. Falconer. Subjic. Chrestomathiae Graece et Latinae. 2t. fol. Oxonii. 1807

TRANSLATIONS.

S. on the Troad, Bk. 13, cap. 1. Ed. w. tr. & comm. by W. Leaf. 8°. C. 1923

Geography. [Text], w. Eng. tr. by H. L. Jones. [Loeb Class. Lib.] v2–5. s8°. 1923–28

see DUSSAUD (R.) La digue du lac de Homs & le " mur égypt." de S., 1921–22.

,, GRONOVIUS (A.) Varia geographica; acc. Animadv. in Strabonis Γεωγραφικῶν libros 9, 1739.

Strabo (Walafridus). Hortulus or the little garden. 9th cent. poem [done into Eng. by R. S. Lambert &c.] la8°. *Stanton Press.* [1924]

see BIBLE: *Latin.* Biblia Sacra cum glossa ordin. a S. coll., 1634.

Strachan-Davidson (James Leigh), *see* MACKAIL (J. W.) J. L. S.-D., Master of Balliol, 1925.

Strache (Hans). Eklektizismus des Antiochus v. Askalon, 1921, *see* KIESSLING (A.) & U. v. WILAMOWITZ-MÖLLENDORFF. Philolog. Unters., H26, 1921.

Strachey (Constance, *Lady*), *see* LEAR (E.) Queery Leary nonsense; ed. Lady S., 1911.

Strachey (Giles Lytton).

Books & characters. French & English. 8°. 1922

Eminent Victorians: Cardinal Manning, Florence Nightingale, Dr Arnold, Gen. Gordon. [9th impr.] 8°. [1920]

,, ,, ...[n. ed.] 8°. [1921]

Landmarks in French lit. [Home Univ. Lib.] [repr.] s8°. [1923]

Pope. L. Stephen Lect. 8°. C. 1925

Queen Victoria. 8°. 1921

,, ,, [2nd impr.] 8°. 1921

,, ,, 3rd impr. 8°. 1921

Strachey (John St. Loe).

The adventure of living: a subjective autobiog. 8°. [1922]

,, ,, [3rd ed.] 8°. [1922]

Amer. soundings. 8°. [1926]

Economics of the hour. 8°. [1923]

The referendum: a hdbk. to the poll of the people &c. 8°. [1924]

The Madonna of the Barricades: mems. of George, Ld. Chertsey, 1847–9. s8°. [1925]

The river of life. s8°. [1924]

Strachey (Marjorie). The counterfeits. s8°. 1927

The nightingale (A life of Chopin). [*Fiction*]. s8°. 1925

Strachey (Ray). Marching on. s8°. [1923]

Strack (Herman Leberecht). Jüdische Geheimgesetze.? Mit 3 Anhängen. 6e unveränd. A. [P2502]. 8°. 1921

Jüdischdeutsche Texte. Lesebuch. [*b. w. h.* Jüd. Wbch., 1916]. 8°. L. 1917

—— **& P. Billerbeck.** Komm. z. Neu. Test. aus Talmud u. Midrasch. 3B. 8°. München. 1922–26

Stracke (Ernst). Luthers grosses Selbstzeugnis 1545 ü. s. Entwick. z. Reform. [V. f. Ref.-gesch. Jahr. 44, H1 (Nr. 140)]. 8°. L. 1926

Strada (Famianus). De bello Belgico. 2p. fol. Romae. [1632–47]

Strada (Octavius de) *a Rosberg, the Elder.* De vitis Imperat. & Caesarum Roman. &c. usque ad Caesarem Matthiam. Cura authoris filii. fol. Frankofurti ad Moenum. 1615

Stradivari (Antonio), *see* FÉTIS (F. J.) Notice of A. S. &c.; tr., 1864.

Strafford (Thomas Wentworth, *earl of*), *1593–1641.* A briefe & perfect relation, of the answeres &c. of S. to the articles exhib. agst. him by the Hse. of Commons, Apr. 1641. s4°. 1647

The Earle of S.'s last speech on the scaffold &c. [*no tp.; woodcut*]. s8°. [1641 ?]

see O'GRADY (H.) S. & Ireland: hist. of h. Vice-Royalty w. acc. of h. trial, 2v, 1923.

Strahan (*Sir* Aubrey), *F.G.S.*

The following are Mems. of Geol. S.

Geol. of the coasts adj. Rhyl, Abergele & Colwyn, w. notes by R. H. Tiddeman. 8°. 1885

Geol. of the Isle of Purbeck & Weymouth. 8°. 1898

Geol. of the neighb. of Chester. 8°. 1882

Geol. of the neighb. of Flint, Mold & Ruthin, w. parts by C. E. De Rance. [*& Suppl.*, 1898]. 8°. 1890–98

Geol. of the Thames Valley nr. Goring. 8°. 1924

Guide to the geolog. model of Ingleborough & dist. 8°. 1910

Guide to geolog. model of Isle of Purbeck. 8°. 1906

Works in GEOLOG. SURVEY OF ENG. &c. Spec. rep. on min. resources.

Iron ores &c., by A. S. &c., 1920. [13.]

Lead & zinc ores of Durham, Yorks. &c.; by R. G. Carruthers & Sir A. S., 1923. [26.]

Mineral oil &c., by A. S. &c., 1920. [7.]

Potash-felspar &c., by A. S. &c., 1917. [5.]

——, **T. C. Cantrill** *& others.* Geol. of the South Wales coalfield. By A. S. *& others.* [Mems. of G.S. of Eng. &c.] pl, 3–5, 9–13. [pl, 3, 4, 2nd ed.] 8°. 1909–21

1, Newport. 3, Cardiff. 4, Pontypridd &c. 5, Merthyr Tydfil. 9, W. Gower & Pembrey. 10, Carmarthen. 11, Haverfordwest. 12, Milford, by T. C. Cantrill &c. 13, Pembroke &c., by E. E. L. Dixon.

——, **T. V. Holmes** *& others.* On the thicknesses of strata in the co. of Eng. & Wales exclusive of rocks older than the permian. [Mems. of G.S.] 8°. 1916

—— **& W. Pollard.** The coals of South Wales w. spec. ref. to anthracite. [Mems. of G.S.] 2nd ed. 8°. 1915

Strahan (James), *D.D.* God in history. 8°. [1923]

Strahl (Hans) & E. Ballmann. Embryonalhüllen u. Plazenta v. Putorius furo, *see* KÖN.-PREUSS. AKAD. Abh., Phys.-math. Klasse, 1915.

Straight (Willard Dickerman), *see* CROLY (H.) W. S., 1924.

***Strange** (A) Delilah. By B. B. s8°. 1921

Strange (Edward Fairbrother).

The colour-prints of Hiroshige. 4°. [1925]

Japanese colour prints. [V. & A. Mus. Hdbks.] [4th ed.] s8°. 1913

,, ,, ...[5th ed.] s8°. 1923

see VICTORIA & ALBERT MUSEUM. Cat. of Japanese lacquer, by E. F. S., 2p, 1924–25.

Strange (Thomas Arthur). Hist. guide to French interiors, furniture, decoration &c. dur. last half of the 17th, the 18th, & part of 19th c. 4°. [1923]

Stranger (A), *ps.* *Six days' tour thr. the Isle of Man, 1836, *see* MAN, *Isle of.*

Stransky (Paulus). Respublica Bojema. s8°. Lugd. Batav. 1643

Straparola (Giovanni Francesco). Le piacevoli notti. A cura di G. Rua. [2t]. 8°. Bari. 1927

Strasburger (Eduard). Text-book of botany. Re-wr. by H. Fitting, L. Jost &c. 5th Eng. ed. rev. w. 14th German ed. by W. H. Lang. 8°. 1921

Strass (Johann Friedrich von der). Memoria Thaumasiandri Lutheri renovata. Sub praes. J. C. Dannhaweri. s4°. Argentorati. 1661

Strassburg [ARGENTORATUM]. Bekandtnuss der vier Frey u. Reichstätt, Strassburg, Costantz, Memmingen u Lindaw, uff dem Reichstag zu Augspurg im XXX. Jar gehalten, ihres glaubens &c. rechenschafft gethan haben &c. s4°. [Strassburg, *Johann Schweintzer*. 1531]

Conf. religionis Christianæ Imp. Carolo V 1530 per legatos civitatum Argentorati, Constantiæ, Memmingæ & Lindaviae exhibita. s4°. [Argentorati, *Georg Ulricher*]. 1531

Doc. hist. rel. à l'hist. de France tirés des archives de S., 2t, 1918–19, *see* KENTZINGER (A. DE).

Regesten d. Bischöfe v. S. Veröff. v. d. Komm. z. Hrsgbe Elsäss. Geschichtsquellen. B1, 2. 4°. Innsbruck. 1908–28

1, Die elsäss. Annalen v. Stauferzeit: Einleitung, v. H. Bloch. —Regesten, bis z. 1202, v. P. Wentzcke.
2, Regesten, 1202–1305; hrsg. A. Hessel u. M. Krebs.

Teutsch Kirchēampt mit lobgsengen, uñ götl. psalmen, wie es die gemein zu Strassburg singt. Getruckt by Wolff Köpphel [1525] [Lithogr. facsimile ed. K. Rheinthaler; *b. w.* Enchiridion oder ein Handbuchlein &c., 1848]. s8°. [Erfurt. 1848]

***Strategems** of Chess, 1817, *see* MONTIGNY (—).

***Strategical (The)** aspect of the western frontiers of Russia, 1888, *see* RUSSIA.

Stratford-upon-Avon. Minutes & accts. of the Corp. of S.-upon-A. & o. records, 1553–1620. Transcr. by R. Savage. Intr. & notes by E. I. Fripp. [Dugdale Soc., v1, 3, 5]. v1–3. la8°. O. 1921–26

Rep. of Conf. on new ideals in educ., S.-on-A., 1915, *see* CONFERENCE.

Stratford (Barbara Wingfield-), *see* WINGFIELD-STRATFORD (B.)

Strathspey (Trevor Ogilvie-Grant of Grant, *Baron*). The case for colonial represent. in Parl. Hist. notes &c. by L. G. Redmond-Howard. s8°. [1923]

Stratico (Simone). Bibliografia di marina. la8°. Milano. 1823

Relaz. d. Publ. Libreria di Padova, 1773. [*Ed.* G. A. Fioravanti-Onesti. Nozze Dondi dall' Orologio—Fedrigotti. N127]. 8°. *n.p.* [Padua ? 1850]

Vocab. di marina in 3 lingue [ital.-franc.-ingl.] 3v. la8°. Milano. 1813–14

t2 *has tp. in French,* t3 *in English. App. in each vol.*

Stratton (Arthur). The life, work, & infl. of Sir C. Wren. An essay. fol. *p.f.p.c.* Liv'l. 1897

Stratton (John Proudfoot).

*Chitor & the Mewar family. 8°. [Allahabad]. 1881

Stratton Porter (Gene).

A daughter of the land. s8°. 1918
Homing with the birds. 8°. 1919
Let us highly resolve. s8°. [1927]
The magic garden. s8°. [1927]
Tales you won't believe. s8°. [1926]

Stratz (Carl Heinrich).

Die Rassenschönheit d. Weibes. 16.–17. verm. A. 8°. St. 1922

Stratz (Rudolph).

Das deutsche Wunder. Roman. s8°. 1918
Friede auf Erden. s8°. [1918]
Herzblut. s8°. St. 1922
Die kleine Elten. Roman. 12e–14e A. s8°. St. 1922
König und Kärrner. Roman. s8°. 1921
Liebestrank. Roman. 21.–26. A. s8°. St. 1920
Das Schiff ohne Steuer. s8°. [1921]

Strauch (Ægidius), *prof. of theology, Dantzig.* Consensus repetitus fidei vere Lutheranae, a calumniis &c. F. U. Calixti vindicatus. s4°. Wittebergae. 1668

Jus tertii orthodoxi c. causam Jesuitico-Jansenianam. [P443]. s4°. Wittebergae. 1663

Straus (Oscar Solomon).

Roger Williams the pioneer of relig. liberty. 8°. 1894

Under 4 admin. f. Cleveland to Taft. Recoll. [3rd impr.] 8°. Boston. [1922]

Straus (Ralph). Pengard awake. s8°. [1920]

The unspeakable Curll: acc. of E. Curll, bookseller, added, list of h. books. 8°. 1927

Volcano. s8°. [1922]

Strauss (Bettina).

La culture franç. à Francfort au 18e s. 8°. 1914

Strauss (David Friedrich). Sendschreiben an Bürgermeister Hirzel &c. 2e A. [P2495]. 8°. Zürich. 1839

Strauss (Jacob).

Auffrur Zwitracht u. Uneinigkeijt, zw. woren Evangel. Christen fürzukommen &c. [*Imperfect*]. s4°. *n.p.* 1525

Das der war leyb Christi im Sacramēt gegenwertig sey, erklerūg auff das new büchleyn D. Joh. Hauszscheyn. s4°. *n.p.* 1527

Häubtstück u. artickel christenlicher leer wider den unchrystenlychē wuecher, darumb etlych pfaffen tzue Eyssenach sogar unrywig u. bemyet sint. s4°. [Erfurt ?. 1523 ?]

Ein kurtz Christenlich vnterricht des grossen irrthumbs, so im heiligthüm zů eren gehalten &c. [*Woodcut on tp.* P2539]. s4°. *n.p.* 1523

Eyn Sermō In d' deutlich angezeigt uñ gelert ist die pfaffen Ee, yn Evangelischer leer nitt zu d'freiheyt des fleischs &c. gefundiert. [*Decor. border to tp.* P2539]. s4°. [Erffurdt. 1523]

Eyn Sermon uber das Euangelium Luce am XIX. Gepredigет zu Eyssenach, 1523. [*b. w. h.* Underricht, 1522]. s4°. *n.p.* 1523

Underricht D. J. S. wartzů die Brůderschafften nütz seyen, wie man sy biszher gehaltē hat &c. s4°. *n.p.* 1522

Eyn verstendig trostlich leer uber das wort Sanct Paulus: Der mensch sol sich selbs probieren u. alsso von dem brott essen &c. [*Decor. border to tp. a. c. in* P2539]. s4°. [Wyttemberg]. 1522

Strauss (Johann), *1825–99, see* DECSEY (E.) J. S.: ein Wiener Buch, 1922.

Strauss (Richard), *musician.* Corr. betw. R. C. & H. v. Hofmannsthal, 1907–18. Tr. P. England. 8°. 1927

see SPECHT (R.) R. S. u. s. Werk, 2B, 1921.

Stravinsky (Igor), *see* REVUE MUSICALE, déc. 1923.

Strawberry Hill.

see WALPOLE (H.) Journal of the printing-office at S. Hill, w. notes by P. Toynbee, 1923.

,, —— S. H. accounts: record of expenditure &c. kept by H. W., 1747–95; notes &c. by P. Toynbee, 1927.

Strean (Thomas). The Strean will case. Report of celeb. will case of Kelly & os. *v.* Armstrong &c., Dublin, 1874. 8°. Newtownards. 1875

Streatfeild (Richard Alexander). The opera. Sk. of development &c. Intr. by J. A. Fuller-Maitland. 5th ed., rev., enl. &c. by E. J. Dent. 8°. 1925

Streatfield (Thomas). *Lympsfield & its environs, & The old oak chair, a ballad. 8°. Westerham. 1838

Strebel (Georgius Sigismundus). De antiq. Judaeorum ritibus & moribus. [P2587]. s4°. [Wittenberg ?]. 1664

Strebski (Martinus) [STREPUS], *see* MARTINUS [*Strepus*].

Streck (Maximilian). Die alte Landschaft Babylonien nach d. arab. Geographen. 2T *in* 1v. [*pagin. cont.*] 8°. Leiden. 1900–1

Strecker (Carl), *critic.* Nietzsche u. Strindberg; mit i. Briefwechsel. s8°. München. 1921

Stredowsky (Joannes Georgius). Sacra Moraviae hist. sive vita SS. Cyrilli & Methudii &c. s4°. Solisbaci. 1710

Street (Cecil John Charles). Hungary & democracy. Foreword by T. P. O'Connor. 8°. [1923]

Lord Reading. 8°. [1928]

Street (George Edmund). Unpubl. notes & repr. papers. With essay by G. G. King. [Hispanic Soc. of Amer.] 8°. 1916

Street (George Slythe). At home in the War. s8°. [1918]

The London Assurance, 1720–1920. 8°. *p.f.p.c.* 1920

Street (John). Makt. Övers. H. Vallentin. 8°. [1914]

Street (Julian). Mysterious Japan. s8°. 1922

Streeter (Burnett Hillman). Adventure: faith of science & sci. of faith. By B. H. S., C. M. Chilcott, J. Macmurray & A. S. Russell. 8°. 1927

The four Gospels, a study of origins. 8°. 1924

Reality: new correlation of science & relig. 8°. 1926

,, ,, ...[repr.] 8°. 1927

see ANGLICAN EVANG. GROUP MOVT. Pamphlets, by S. &c., 1923–24.

,, SPIRIT, The; God & h. relation to man &c.; [by] A. S. Pringle-Pattison; B. H. S. ed., 1921.

—— **& A. J. Appasamy.** The Sadhu. St. in mysticism & pract. religion. s8°. 1921

Streitberg (Wilhelm).

see GRUNDRISS d. indogerman. Sprach- u. Altertumskunde; hrsg. W. S., 1916–27.

,, SAMMLUNG german. Elementar- u. Hdbücher. (Germanische Bibl.); hrsg. v. W. S.

Streitwolf (Fridericus Gulielmus) & R. E. Klener. Libri symbolici eccl. catholicae. 2t. 8°. Gottingae. 1838

,, ,, *a. issue omitting* Confessio Romano-Catholica in Hungaria *from App.* 2t. Gottingae. 1846

Strelli (Richard), *see* RASCHL (T.) & R. S. Das Benediktinerstift St. Paul in Kärnten, 1922.

Strengnaees. Bibliotheca Templi Cathedralis St. Descr. ab H. Aminson. [Suppl. *wanting*]. 8°. Stockholmiae. 1863

***Strenne** nuziali del secolo 14, 1873, *see* TARGIONI TOZZETTI (O.), *ed.*

Stresemann (Gustav), *see* REVENTLOW (*Graf* E. ZU). S. als Staatsmann &c., 2. A., 1925.

Stretch (L. M.)
The beauties of history. 2v. [v2 *wanting*]. s8°. 1770

Streuber (Peter). Christl. Gutachten, Wie etwan der schwere Streit, v. d. Person u. heiligen Abendmal nach anleitung Göttl. Worts u. der Augspurg. Conf. könte auffgehaben &c. werden. [P2438]. s4°. *n.p.* 1591
see RIVANDER (Z.) Interrogatoria, Darauff P. S. &c., 1591.

Streuvels (Stijn), *ps.* [*i.e.* P. F. M. FRANK LATEUR].
Lenteleven. 7e dr. s8°. A. *n.d.*
Minnehandel. 2e dr. 2d. s8°. A. *n.d.*
De vlaschaard. 7e dr. 2d. s8°. A. *n.d.*

Stribling (Thomas Sigismund). Birthright. Novel. s8°. [1925]

Strich (Fritz). Deut. Klassik u. Romantik. 8°. München. 1922
Die Mythologie in d. deut. Lit., v. Klopstock bis Wagner. 2B. 8°. Halle. 1910

Stricker. Rhythmus antiq. German. de Caroli magni exped. Hispan.; ed. J. G. Scherzius, *see* SCHILTER (J.) Thesaurus antiq., t2, 1727.

Strickland (Claude Francis). Intr. to co-oper. in India. s8°. 1922

Strickland (Joseph), *S.J.* Ricerche storiche sopra il B. Bonifacio di Savoia, arcivesco di Cantorbery, 1207–70, *see* REGIA DEP. DI STORIA PATRIA. Misc., t32, 1895.

Strickland (Samuel). Twenty-seven years in Canada West. Ed. by Agnes Strickland. 2v *in* 1. s8°. 1853

Strickland (*Sir* Walter William), *9th Bt.* [*ps.* THELGAR VANICORO]. Il ragno Attis e i suoi occhi meravigliosi. [P2485]. s8°. Genova. 1920
*Sacrifice, or The daughter of the sun. Prehist. Arctic tragi-comedy. s8°. Genoa. [1920]

Strickland (William Peter). Hist. of the American Bible Soc. Introd. by N. L. Rice. 8°. N.Y. 1849
The pioneer bishop; or, the life &c. of Francis Asbury. Introd. by N. Bangs. s8°. N.Y. [1858]
,, ,, Eng. ed. w. intr. by S. W. Christophers. 8°. 1860

***Strictures** on passages in Napier's Hist. of Peninsular War &c., 1835, *see* NAPIER (*Gen. Sir* W. F. P.)

Striebe (Friedrich). Der jüd. Schekel. [P2758]. s8°. Brüx. 1923

Strieder (Jacob). Studien z. Gesch. kapitalist. Organisationsformen. 2e A. 8°. München. 1925
see JANSEN (M.) & J. S. St. z. Fugger-Gesch., H6, 7, 1915–23.

Striegel (J.) "Wozu" dienen Vernunft-Anlagen im Hinblick auf d. Schluss v. Fr. v. Hellwald's "Kulturgesch.," u. Ed. v. Hartmann's "Philos. d. Unbewussten." [*b. w.* Liebmann (O.) Ged. u. Thats., B2ii, 1901]. 8°. L. [1896]

Strigelius (Victorinus).
Arithmeticus libellus. s8°. Lipsiæ. [1563]
In Epitomen philosophiæ moralis P. Melanchthonis, ὑπομνήματα. Ed. opera C. Pezelii. s8°. Neapoli Nemetum. 1582
In P. Melanchthonis libellum de anima notae. Acc. F. Vicomercati De anima rationali peripatetica discept. Item V. S. in primam Tuscul. quaest. Cicer. comm. s8°. Lipsiae. 1590
Liber Iob ad Ebraicam veritatem recogn. &c. & illust. s8°. Lipsiae. [1575]
Libri duo Maccabæorum interprete V. S. [*b. w. h.* Liber Iob &c., 1575]. s8°. Lipsiae. [c. 1575]
Loci theologici quibus loci communes P. Melanthonis illustrantur &c. Labore &c. C. Pezelii. 4p *in* 2v. s4°. Neapoli Nemetum. 1582–84
Ὑπομνήματα in omnes libros N. Test., quibus & genus sermonis explicatur, &c. 2t *in* 1v. s8°. Lipsiae. 1565
Tp of t2 reads: Ὑπομνήματα in omnes Epistolas &c.
see MERZ (H.) Hist. vitae & controv. V. S., 1732.

***Strike** nights in Printing House Square, 1926, *see* TIMES (THE).

Strindberg (August).
Kronbruden. 8°. [1917]
Märchenspiele, e. Traumspiel. Verdeut. v. E. Schering. 5e A. 8°. München. 1916
Mäster Olof. 8°. [1923]
Nach Damaskus. 3T *in* 1v. 8°. München. 1926
Påsk: skådespel. 8°. [1921]
see ERDMANN (N.) A. S.: en kämpande och lidande själs historia, 2v, 1920.
,, HEDÉN (E.) S., ledtråd vid stud. av h. verk, 1921.
,, STRECKER (C.) Nietzsche u. S., 1921.

Stringher (Bonaldo). Relaz. al XVI congresso d. "Dante Alighieri." [P2843]. la8°. 1905

Strobel (Georg Theodor). Miscellaneen literar. Innhalts &c. [Leben Staphyli &c.] 2 Samml. *in* 1v. s8°. Nürnberg. 1778–79
see CAMERARIUS (J.) De vita Melanchthonis; rec., notas, doc., bibl. libr. M. aliaque add. G. T. S., 1777.

Ströbel (Heinrich). Die deut. Revolution, i. Unglück u. i. Rettung. 8°. [1920]
The German Revolution & after. Tr. H. J. Stenning. 8°. [1923]
Socialisation in theory & practice. Tr. by H. J. Stenning. s8°. 1922
see ROSENOW (E.) Wider d. Pfaffenherrschaft, B2 fortgeführt v. H. S., 1904–5.

Strobl (Carl Hans). Die alten Türme. Roman. s8°. L. 1922

Stroganov, *The family of, see* USTRYALOV (N. G.) Именитые люди С., 1842.

Stroganov (Grigory Dmitrievich), *see* USTRYALOV (N. G.) Имен. люди С. (Жалов. грам. Г. Д. С., 1692), 1842.

Stroganovskoe Tsentraln. Uchilische. Мотивы орнаментовъ (12–17c) снятые со старинн. русск. произведенiй. Изд. С. Ц. У. Bl. fol. 1887

Ströhl (Hugo Gerard).
Russ.-asiat. Wappenrolle. [*no tp.*] la8°. *n.p. n.d.*
Die Wappen d. Äbte d. Prämonstratenser-Stiftes Schlägl. [K. k. herald. Gesells. "Adler" in Wien. *b. w. h.* Russ.-asiat. Wappenrolle, *n.d.*] la8°. Wien. 1893
Das Wappen d. Fürstentums Liechtenstein. [Sep.-Abdr. aus d. "Schweizer. Archiv. f. Heraldik," 1913, H3. *b. w. h.* Russ.-asiat. Wappenrolle, *n.d.*] la8°. [1913]
Die Wappen u. Siegel d. Orte Vorarlbergs. [K. k. herald. Gesells. "Adler" in Wien. *b. w. h.* Russ.-asiat. Wappenrolle, *n.d.*] la8°. Wien. 1893

Stromeyer (M. Carl Ludwig). De fidei justificantis ratione formali, Arminianis opposita. s8°. Wittebergae. 1667

Strong (Archibald Thomas). A short hist. of Eng. Lit. 8°. 1921
Three studies in Shelley & an essay on nature in Wordsworth & Meredith. 8°. 1921

Strong (Charles Augustus). A theory of knowledge. s8°. 1923
see DRAKE (D.) Essays in crit. realism; D. D., C. A. S. &c., 1920.

Strong (*Mrs.* Eugénie) [*Mrs.* ARTHUR STRONG].
A bronze plaque in the Rosenheim coll., *see* BRIT. SCHOOL AT ROME. Papers, v9, 1920.
La Chiesa Nuova (S. Maria in Vallicella), con un saggio biog. sopra S. Filippo Neri, di P. Misciattelli. s8°. [1923]
Note on a copy of the Responsiones of R. Parsons, *see* BRIT. SCH. AT ROME. Papers, v9, 1920.
Roman sculpture, f. Augustus to Constantine. [*re-issue*]. 2v. 8°. [1911]
Sepulchral relief of a priest of Bellona, *see* BRIT. SCH. AT ROME. Papers, v9, 1920.

Strong (Harrington). The spider's den. s8°. [1926]

Strong (Hilda Arthurs).
A sketch of Chinese arts & crafts. s8°. Peking. 1926

Strong (John), *see* MACCLINTOCK (J.) & J. STRONG. Cyclop. of Bibl., theol. & eccles. lit., 12v, 1867–87.

Strong (Richard Pearson), *see* AMERICAN RED CROSS. Rep., Medical Research Comm.; prep. by R. P. S., 1918.

Strong (Thomas Banks), *bp. of Ripon.*
Religion, philosophy & history. 4 lect. s8°. O. 1923

Strong (William), *LL.D.* Two lect. upon the relations of civil law to Church polity &c. s8°. N.Y. [1875]

Stronge (Helen, *Lady*), *wife of Sir James Stronge, Bart., aft.* HOLMES, *see* RICHARDSON (E. M.) Next door neighbours [*i.e.* Lady S. &c.], 1926.

Strongylion, *the sculptor, 5. cent.* B.C., *see* REINACH (S.) S., 1904.

Strood. Churchwardens' accounts of St. Nicholas, Strood. Transcr. w. intr. by H. R. Plomer. [Kent Arch. Soc. Records Br., v5]. 2p [*in* 1v], 1555–1662. 8°. 1927

Strowski (Fortunat).
La renaiss. litt. de la France contemp. s8°. [1922]
Saint François de Sales; intr. à l'hist. du sentiment relig. en France. n. éd. rev. & corr. 8°. 1928
see HANOTAUX (G.) Hist. de la nation franç., t13, Hist. des lettres, v2, De Ronsard à nos jours, par F. S., 1923.

Strozzi (Bernardo), *see* FIOCCO (G.) B. S., 1921.

Strozzi (Giovanni Battista), *il Cieco.* Madrigali. 8°. Firenze. 1593

Strozzi (Lorenzo di Filippo). Le vite d. uomini ill. d. Casa Strozzi. Con ragion. ined. di F. Zeffi. 8°. Firenze. 1892

Strozzi (Luigi), *see* ALAZARD (J.) L'abbé L. S., 1924.

Strozzi (Piero di Andrea), *1483–1523, see* UZIELLI (G.) P. di A. S., viaggiatore fiorent., 1895.

Struben (A. M. A.), *O.B.E.* Tidal power. s8°. 1921

Struck (Ernst). Im Fesselballon. s8°. [1918]

Struckmeyer (O. K.)
Croce & literary criticism. [P2573]. s8°. 1921

Strümpell (Ludwig Heinrich). Die Einl. in die Philos. v. Standpunkte d. Gesch. d. Philos. 8º. L. 1886
Erläut. zu Herbarts Philos. H1. 8º. Göttingen. 1834
Vorschule d. Ethik. 8º. Mitau. 1844
Strunz (Franz). Albertus Magnus: Weisheit u. Naturforsch. im M.-A. 8º. Wien. [1926]
Struthers (Gavin). The hist. of the rise of the Relief Church, *see* THOMSON (A.) Hist. sketch of orig. of the Secession Ch. &c., 1848.
Struthers (John), *M.D.* On the study of medicine: intr. address. [P2651]. 8º. E. 1856
Strutt (Robert John), *4th baron Rayleigh, see* RAYLEIGH.
Strutz (Georg). Die Erstürmung d. Brückenkopfes v. Jakobstadt, Sept. 1917. [Schlachten d. Weltkrieges, B9. *b. w.* Vogel (W.) Kämpfe um Baranowitschi, 1927]. 8º. Oldenburg. 1927
Herbstschlacht in Macedonien, Cernabogen, 1916. [Schlachten d. Weltkrieges, B5]. 10.–12. A. 8º. Oldenburg. 1925
Struve (Burcard Gotthelff) [STRUVIUS]. Acta litteraria ex MSS. eruta & coll. cura B. G. S. 2t. s8º. Jenae. 1706–17
T1 has a 2nd or gen. tp.: B. G. Struvii Collectanea MSS. in decem fasc. digesta. Jenae, 1713.
Ausführl. Bericht v. d. Pfältz. Kirchen-Hist. &c. s4º. Frankfurt. 1721
Struve (Carl Ludwig), *see* SIBYLLINE ORACLES. Fragm. quæ apud Lactantium reperiuntur; ed. C. L. S., 1817.
Struve (Friedrich Gottlieb). Tractatus de pace domestica. Acc. 2 diss. (1) G. A. Struvii De juribus palatii princ. (2) G. Beyeri De violatione pacis domest. s4º. Jenae. 1713
Struve (Georg). Neue Elem. d. inn. Saturnstrabanten, *see* KÖN.-PREUSS. AKAD. Abh., Phys.-math. Klasse, 1918.
Struve (Heinrich v.)
Zur Entstehung d. Seele. [P2471]. 8º. Tübingen. 1862
Struve (Petr Bernhardovich), *ed.* Матеріалы по университетскому вопросу. в1, 2. [P2391]. 8º. St. 1902–4
Struys (Jan). Reysen door Italien, Griekenlandt, Lijflandt, Moscovien, Tattarijen &c. 8º. A. 1676
Stryienski (Casimir). The eighteenth century. Tr. H. N. Dickinson. Intr. by J. E. C. Bodley. 8º. [1916]
Stryker (*Gen.* **William Scudder).** The Battle of Monmouth. Ed. W. S. Myers. 8º. Princeton, [N.J.] 1927
Strykius (Johann Samuel). De incommodis festorum. [*no tp. b. w.* Wagner (C. L.) De jure Sabathi, 1702]. s4º. [Halae Magdeb. 1702]
Strype (John). The abridgment of the life of T. Cranmer compos. by J. S. Done by J. C. S. Hölling. s8º. Hanover. 1725
*Hist. of the life &c. of E. Grindal. [*w.*] app. of MSS. fol. 1710
Life & acts of T. Whitgift; w. app. of papers. fol. 1718
Mem. of T. Cranmer. 3 bks. *in* 1v. fol. 1694
Strzygowski (Josef).
Kleinarmen. Miniaturmalerei: Miniat. d. Tübinger Evangeliars. [P2805]. 4º. [Tübingen. 1906]
Die Landschaft in d. nord. Kunst. s8º. L. [1922]
Der Norden in d. bild. Kunst Westeuropas. Heidn. u. Christl. um d. Jahr 1000. Unter Mitwirk. v. B. Brehm &c., hrsg. J. S. la8º. Wien. 1926
Origin of Xtn. church art. 8 lect., added, ch. on Xtn. art in Brit. Tr. O. M. Dalton & H. J. Braunholtz. la8º. O. 1923
Studien z. Kunst d. Ostens. J. St. z. 60sten Geburtstage v. s. Freunden u. Schülern. [Hrsg. H. Glück]. 4º. Wien. [1923]
Ursprung d. christl. Kirchenkunst. 8 Vorträge. 8º. L. 1920
Stuart, *The house of* [*including* STUART PAPERS; *see also* STEWART]. Stuart Papers, v6, 7, 1916–23, *see* HIST. MSS. COMM.
see CRAWFURD (G.) Genealog. hist. of royal family of the S., 1710.
,, FARQUHAR (H.) Portraiture of our S. monarchs on their coins &c., 7p [in 1v], 1909–16.
,, KENNEDY (M.) Chronolog., genealog. &c. diss. of Roy. fam. of S., 1705.
,, NOBLE (M.) An hist. genealogy, 1795.
Stuart (Alex. Moody). The Song of Songs. Expos. of the Song of Solomon. 2nd ed. 8º. 1860
Stuart (Andrew), *d. 1801.* Genealog. hist. of the Stewarts: Suppl., w. corr. & add. & ans. to "The g. h. of the S. refuted." [*b. w.* Genealog. hist., 1798]. 4º. 1799
Stuart (*Lady* **Arabella),** *see* LEFUSE (M.) Life & times of A. S., 1913.
Stuart (*Sir* **Campbell),** *K.B.E.* Secrets of Crewe House. s8º. 1920
Stuart (*Gen. Sir* **Charles),** *4th son of 3rd Earl of Bute; 1753–1801, see* STUART-WORTLEY (*Hon. Mrs.* V.) A prime minister & h. son, f. corresp. of 3rd Earl of Bute & Lt.-Gen. Sir C. S., 1925.

Stuart (Dorothy Margaret), *ps.* [*i.e.* DOROTHY MARGARET STUART BROWNE]. Beasts royal & o. poems. s8º. 1923
The boy through the ages. 8º. [1926]
Horace Walpole. [Eng. Men of Letters]. 8º. 1927
Stuart (E. J.), *J.P.* Land of opportunities: exped. to north. territories of Australia. 8º. [1923]
Stuart (Frances Teresa), *aft. wife of 3rd duke of Richmond & Lennox; 1647–1702* [LA BELLE STUART], *see* HARTMANN (C. H.) La belle Stuart: mem. of court &c., 1924.
Stuart (Frank D.), *see* ROWNTREE (B. S.) & F. D. S. Responsibility of women workers for dependants, 1921.
Stuart (Gilbert). *Histor. diss. conc. the antiq. of the Eng. constit. 8º. Edinburgh. 1768
Stuart (Graham Henry). The governmental system of Peru. [C.I. of Wash.] la8º. Wash. 1925
Stuart (James), *F.R.S.* ["Athenian Stuart"] **& N. Revett.** The antiq. of Athens & o. mon. of Greece. 2nd ed. s8º. 1841
Stuart (John), *LL.D.* Records of the priory of the Isle of May. Ed. J. S. [Soc. of Ant. of Scot.] 4º. E. 1868
Stuart (Leonard).
The great god Pan. An all-time story. 8º. N.Y. 1913
Stuart (*Lady* **Louisa),** *d. of 3rd earl of Bute.*
Letters. Sel. w. intr. by R. B. Johnson. 8º. [1926]
Stuart (Muriel). Poems. s8º. 1922
Stuart (Murray). The Srimgal earthquake of 8th July 1918, *see* INDIA: Geol. Survey, Memoirs, v46i, 1920.
Stuart de Rothesay (Charles Stuart, *1st baron***),** *1779–1845, see* STUART-WORTLEY (*Hon. Mrs.* V.) Highcliffe & the Stuarts, 1927.
Stuart of Wortley (Charles Beilby Stuart-Wortley, *1st baron***),** *see* GROSVENOR (C.) & *Lord* S. OF W. The 1st Lady Wharncliffe & h. fam. (1779–1856), 2v, 1927.
Stuart-Wortley, *The family of.*
see GROSVENOR (C.) & *Lord* STUART OF WORTLEY. The 1st Lady Wharncliffe & h. fam. (1779–1856), 2v, 1927.
,, STUART-WORTLEY (*Hon. Mrs.* V.) Highcliffe & the Stuarts, 1927.
Stuart-Wortley (*Hon. Mrs.* **Violet),** *wife of Hon. Ed. Stuart-Wortley.* Highcliffe & the Stuarts. 8º. [1927]
A prime minister & h. son, f. corresp. of the 3rd Earl of Bute & Lt.-Gen. the Hon. Sir C. Stuart. Intr. by Sir R. Rodd. 8º. 1925
Stub (Nils). Optegnelsesbøger fra Oslo Lagthing 1572–80, udg. ved H. J. Huitfeldt-Kaas. [Norske Hist. K.] 8º. 1895
Stubbs, *publishing firm.* Stubb's Directory. Manufacturers, shippers &c., Brit. & foreign, 1923, 1925, 1927, 1928. la8º. [1923–28]
Stubbs (Charles William), *dean of Ely, aft. bp. of Truro.*
Christ & economics in light of Sermon on the Mount. 8º. 1894
Stubenberg, *The House of, see* LOSERTH (J.) Archiv des Hauses S., 1906.
Stuck (Gottlieb Heinrich). Verzeichniss v. Land- u. Reisebeschreib. Mit e. Realregister u. Vorrede v. J. E. Fabri. 2T *&* Nachtr. *in* 1v. s8º. Halle. 1884–87
Stückelberg (Ernst Alfred).
Langobardische Plastik. 2e verm. A. la8º. Kempten. 1909
Stucken (Rudolf). Die wertbeständ. Anleihen in finanzwirtschaftl. Betrachtung. [V. f. Sozialpol., B166iii]. 8º. München. 1924
Student [STUDENT'S]. *Student-life at Harvard, 1876, *see* TRIPP (G. H.)
Student's hdbk. to the Univ. & Colls. of Cambridge, 20th ed., 1921, *see* CAMBRIDGE.
Studer (Paul). The study of Anglo-Norman. Inaug. lecture &c. [P2526]. 8º. O. 1920
—— **& J. Evans.** Anglo-Norman lapidaries. 8º. Paris. 1924
Studien. St. zur Engl. Philologie; hrsg. v. L. Morsbach. H62. 8º. Halle. 1922
see LEOPOLD (W.) Die relig. Wurzel v. Carlyles liter. Wirksamkeit, dargest. an s. "State of Germ. lit. (1827)," 1922.
St. z. Kunst d. Ostens: J. St. z. 60sten Geburtstage [hrsg. H. Glück], 1923, *see* STRZYGOWSKI (J.)
St. z. spätant. Kunstgesch. Hrsg. R. Delbrück u. H. Lietzmann. [B]1, 2. 4º. & la. fol. 1925–26
see BEYER (H. W.) Der syr. Kirchenbau, 1925. [1.]
,, DELBRÜCK (R.) Die Consulardiptychen, 1926. [2.]
Studiengesellschaft f. sociale Folgen d. Krieges [SELSKABET F. SOC. FORSKEN AF KRIGENS FØLGER], *see* DÖRING (C.) Bevölkerungsbewegung im Weltkrieg, 2H, 1919.

Studies. Studies & notes in philol. & lit., v1, 2, 8, 9, 1892–1903, *see* HARVARD UNIVERSITY.

*Studies in gardening: articles repr. f. the Times. [Mar. 1907 to May 1908]. 8°. [1908]

Studio (The): an illust. magazine of fine & applied art. v79–95. la8°. 1920–28

Graphic arts folios. No. 1–3. obl.4°. 1920

see SALAMAN (M. C.), *ed.* Charm of the etcher's art, 3p, 1920.

Mod. masters of etching. No. 1–5. obl.4°. 1924–25

see SALAMAN (M. C.) Anders Zorn, 1925. [3.]
,, —— Frank Brangwyn, 1924. [1.]
,, —— J. L. Forain, 1925. [4.]
,, —— James McBey, 1924. [2.]
,, —— Sir F. Short, 1925. [5.]

Year-book of decorative art, 1921–1927. la8°. 1921–27
1921 *has t.* Year-book of applied art; 1926, 1927 *have t.* Decorative art, 1926, 1927: The Studio year-book.

SPECIAL NUMBERS &c.

see BALDRY (A. L.) Contemp. figure painters, 1925.
,, BAUD-BOVY (D.) Peasant art in Switzerland; tr., 1924.
,, BELLOC (H.) The highway & its vehicles, 1926.
,, BERUETE Y MORET (A. DE). Span. painting, 1921.
,, BINYON (L.) Drawings & engravings of W. Blake, 1922.
,, BRINTON (S.) Venice, 1925.
,, CANE (P. S.) Mod. gardens, 1926.
,, CHATTERTON (E. K.) Ship-models, 1923.
,, COX (D.) Treatise of landscape painting (1813), repr., 1922.
,, CUNDALL (H. M.) Masters of water-colour painting, 1922–23.
,, —— The Norwich school, 1920.
,, DODGSON (C.) Etchings of C. Meryon, 1921.
,, —— Etchings of J. McN. Whistler, 1922.
,, EISLER (M.) J. Israëls, 1924.
,, GAUNT (W.) Rome, 1926.
,, HOLME (G.) Brit. water-colour painting of to-day, 1921.
,, JONES (S. R.) Art & publicity, 1925.
,, —— Posters & publicity, 1926.
,, —— Posters & th. designers, 1924.
,, KENDRICK (A. F.) Book of old embroidery &c., 1921.
,, LAMBOTTE (*Sir* P.) Flemish painting bef. 18th cent., 1927.
,, NEVILL (R. H.) Old Eng. sporting prints & th. hist., 1923.
,, OPPÉ (A. P.) T. Rowlandson, h. drawings &c., 1923.
,, —— Water-colour drawings of J. S. Cotman, 1923.
,, PICHON (L.) The new book-illustr. in France; tr., 1924.
,, ROBINSON (C. N.) Old naval prints, 1924.
,, SADLER (M. T. H.) The water-colours of C. J. Holmes, 1920.
,, SALAMAN (M. C.) Brit. bk. illustration, 1923.
,, —— Londoners then & now; ed. G. Holme, 1920.
,, —— Woodcut of to-day, 1927.
,, SHERINGHAM (G.) Drawings in pen & pencil &c., 1922.
,, —— Figure painting in water-colours by contemp. Brit. artists, 1923.
,, —— & J. LAVER. Design in the theatre, 1927.
,, SULLIVAN (*Sir* E.) The Book of Kells, 2nd ed., 1920.
,, WHITLEY (W. T.) Art coll. of the nation, 1920.

Studland, *Dorset.* *Anc. church of S. Nicholas of Myra, S. [P2877]. 8°. [1925]

Studniczka (Franz). Der farnes. Stier u. d. Dirkegruppe d. Apollonios u. Tauriskos. Brief an G. Treu. [Sonderdr. aus d. Ztschr. f. bild. Kunst, N.F. 14. P2699]. 4°. L. [1903]

Das Symposion Ptolemaios II n. d. Beschr. d. Kallixeinos wiederhergest. [Königl. Sächs. Gesell. d. Wiss. Phil.-hist. Kl. Abhdlgn., B30ii]. la8°. L. 1914

Tropaeum Traiani. [Kön. Sächs. Gesells. d. Wiss. Abh. d. phil.-hist. Cl., B22iv]. la8°. L. 1904

Stuffken (Jan Hendrik). Diss. de Theodosii Magni in rem Christianam meritis &c. 8°. Lugd. Batav. 1828

Stuhlfauth (Georg). Die apokryphen Petrusgesch. in d. altchristl. Kunst. la8°. 1925

Stuhr (Peter Feddersen). Die chines. Reichsrelig. u. d. Systeme d. ind. Philos. in i. Verhältniss zu Offenbarungslehren. 8°. 1835

Stulli (Joakim). Lexicon lat.-ital.-illyricum. [2t]. 4°. Budæ. 1801

Rjecsoslòxje &c. Illir. Ital. Lat. csast drùga. 2 razdjelki. 4°. u Dubrovniku. 1806

Stülpnagel (Otto v.) Die Wahrheit üb. d. deut. Kriegsverbrechen. 4e ungekürzte A. 8°. 1921

Stumpf (Arnold), *see* MÖHR (A.) & A. S. Graphis theol. human. ad mentem J. Duns Scoti deducta &c., 1665.

Stumpf (Carl). Die deut. Kolonien im Schwarzmeergebiet, d. früh. Neu- (Süd-) Russland. 8°. St. 1922

Works in KÖNIGL. PREUSS. AKAD. Abhdl. (Phil.-hist. Kl.)
Die Attribute d. Gesichtsempfindungen, 1917.
Empfindung u. Vorstellung, 1918.
Spinozastudien, 1919.

Stunica (Jacobus Lopis), *see* LOPIS STUNICA (J.)

Stur (J.) Die slaw. Sprachelemente in d. Ortsnamen d. deutsch-österr. Alpenländer zw. Donau u. Drau, 1914, *see* KAISERL. AKAD. D. W. ZU WIEN. Sitz., B176, 1916.

Sturdy (H. F.) Potterspury Lodge, Stony Stratford. Sold by Collins, 19th July 1921. [By dir. of H. F. S. P2752]. fol. 1921

Sturge (*Miss* M. Carta). Opposite things. [Intr. to philos. of Hegel]. s8°. Bristol. 1927

Sturgeon (William). Scientific researches in electricity, magnetism &c. 4°. Bury. 1850

Sturges (Octavius) & Sidney Coupland. The natural hist. & relat. of pneumonia. 2nd ed. s8°. 1890

Stürgkh (Josef, *Graf* v.)
Im deut. Grossen Hauptquartier. 8°. L. 1921

Sturm (Christoph Christian). Hdbch. z. Kenntniss d. theolog. Schriftsteller unter d. Deutschen. T1, vor d. 16ten Jhrh. [*No more publ.*] s8°. Halle i. Magdeb. 1770

Reflections; tr., *see* CLARKE (A). Misc. wks., v3 & 4, 1836.

Sturm (G.) Animals in ornament. Coll. of designs. la. fol. [1894]

Stürmer (Franz). Die Rhapsodien d. Odyssee, 1921, *see* DRERUP (E.) Homer. Poetik, B3, 1921.

Sturmhoefel (Conrad H.) Kurfürstin Anna v. Sachsen: e. polit. &c. Lebensbild aus d. 16. Jhdt. 8°. Halle. [1905]

Sturmius (Joannes), *Sleidanus.*

Conf. Augustana, Argentin. Epistolarum Eucharistic. libri primi epist. 4a. s4°. Neustadii in Palatinatu. 1581

De instit. scholastica opusc. Rec. & auxit F. A. Hallbauer. [*b. w.* Vockerodt (G.) Consultationes, 1705]. s8°. Jenae. 1730

De periodis libellus &c. Ed. cura F. A. Hallbaueri. [*b. w.* Vockerodt (G.) Consultationes, 1705]. ed. 2a. s8°. Jenae. 1734

Epistola apologetica contra J. Andream. s4°. Neustadii in Palatinatu. 1581

Epistol. Eucharistic. libri secundi epistola secunda. Ambrosia, ad J. Pappum. s4°. Neapoli Casimiriana. 1581

see MANES. Sturmiani sive epicedia scr. in obitum I. S., 1590.
,, ZANCHIUS (H.) Ad cujusdam Ariani lib. &c.; resp. ad J. S., 1586.

Sturmy (Samuel). The mariners magazine, stor'd w. mathematical arts &c. With tables of logarithms [*w. sep. tp. & pagin.*] 3rd ed. rev. &c. by J. Colson. [*3 pagin.*] sm. fol. 1684

Sturt (George), *see* BOURNE (G.), *ps.*

Sturt (Henry). Human value: an ethical essay. s8°. C. 1923

Sturt (Mary). The psychology of time. 8°. 1925

Sturzo (Luigi). Italy & Fascismo. Tr. B. B. Carter. Pref. by G. Murray. 8°. 1926

Popolarismo e Fascismo. 8°. Torino. 1924

Stuss (Johann Heinrich). Progr. de J. Staupitii meritis in relig. evangelicam. [P600]. s4°. [Gothae. 1732]

Stutfield (Hugh E. M.) Mysticism & Catholicism. 8°. [1925]

Priestcraft. 8°. 1921

The sovranty of society. s8°. 1909

Stuttgarter (Das) Passionale, 1923, *see* BÖCKLER (A.)

Stuttmann (Ferdinand). Hans Raphon. 8°. Bremen. 1925

Stutz (Ulrich). Die päpstl. Diplomatie unter Leo XIII, nach d. Denkwürd. d. Kard. D. Ferrata, *see* KÖN.-PREUSS. AKAD. Abhdln., Phil.-hist. Kl., 1925.

Styfel (Michael), *see* STIFEL (M.)

Styra (Robert).
Das poln. Parteiwesen u. s. Presse. 8°. Plauen i V. 1926

Styx (Pierre Maurice de).
Chants de Grenade & du Maghreb. s8°. 1923

Suabia [SCHWABEN]. *Genotigter u. fremdt eingetragener schrifft auch mislichens dewtens d. wort des abentmals Christi. Syngramma (das ist) Vorsammelte schriffte &c. der predigere [J. Lachman &c.] ynn Schwaben so sich darüber besprochen, zu Oecolampadio. [Vorrede *by* M. Luther]. s8°. Wittemberg. 1526

Suardi (Victore Amedeo). *De suprema Romani Pontificis autoritate hodierna eccl. Gallicanae doctrina. Autore *** in Regia Univ. Taurin. doctore. 2t [*in* 1v.] 4°. Avenione. 1747

Suarès (André). Poète tragique. [Essai sur Prospéro]. 8°. 1921

Xénies. s8°. 1923

Suarez (Franciscus) *e Soc. Jesu.*

De horis canonicis & laude Dei per cantum & psalmodiam, *see* MIGNE (J. P.), *ed.* Theol. cursus, t18, 1862.

De simonia—De oratione in communi—De oratione mentali ac devot.—De oratione vocali privata, *see* MIGNE (J. P.) Theol. cursus, t17, 1860.

Defensio fidei Catholicae &c. adv. Anglicanae sectae errores. sm. fol. Conimbricae. 1613

Juris naturæ & gentium princ. & offic., cum notis Guarini, *see* MIGNE (J. P.) Theol. cursus, t15, 1861.

Suarez (Franciscus) [*continued*].
Tract. de legibus, & legislatore Deo, *see* MIGNE (J. P.) Theol. cursus, t12, 13, 1861.
see DOMINIS (M. A. DE). De republica eccl., v2: add. Responsio ad partem Defensionis Fidei P. F. S., 1620.

Suarez (Joseph), *Jesuit.* Libertas evang. annunc., *see* SINICA. Noviss. Sin. hist. &c., 1699.

Suarez (P. Blanco), *see* BLANCO SUAREZ (P.)

Suarez (Victoriano), *see* ARCHIVO BIBLIOG. HISP.-AMER.; publ. V. S., 1925–.

Suarez de Figueroa (Cristóbal). El passagero [1617]. [*Ed.* R. S. Rose. Soc. de Bibliofilos Esp., 38]. 8°. 1914

Suavis (Petrus), *Polanus, ps., see* SARPI (*Fra* P.)

***Subaltern** (The), 1825, *see* GLEIG (G. R.)

Subedar (M.), *see* ANDERSON (G.) & M. S. Development of an Indian policy, 1921.

Subercaseaux (Guillermo). Monetary & banking policy of Chile. Ed. D. Kinley. [C.E. for Int. Peace]. la8°. O. 1922
Le papier-monnaie. 8°. 1920

Subiaco. Chron. Sublacense, 593–1369; a cura di R. Morghen, *see* MURATORI. Rerum Ital. Script., t24, p6, 1927.

***Substance** or shadow? A warning agst. the Sankey scheme. By a practical miner. [P2484]. 8°. *n.p.* [1920 ?]

Subversion (The) of Robert Parsons his worke &c., 1606, *see* SUTCLIFFE (M.)

Successi d. armi venete in Levante, 1685, 1686, *see* VENETE.

***Succinct** (A) & impartial hist. of all regencies, protectorships &c. of England since the Conquest. [P2783]. 8°. 1751

Succo (Friedrich). Katsukawa Shunshō (Haruaki). 4°. Plauen im Vogtlande. 1922

Suchomlinoff, *see* SUKHOMLINOV.

Suchtelen (Nico van).
Quia absurdum. Roman. 4e dr. s8°. A. *n.d.*

Suckling (Florence Horatia). The brotherhood of love: stories of the saints & th. animal friends. s8°. 1910
The humane educator & reciter. 8°. [1891]
The humane play-book: coll. of dialogues, action pieces &c. 8°. 1900
The Saxon town of King's Somborne. [Repr. f. Hampshire Chron. P2862]. s8°. 1920

Suckling (Robert Alfred), *see* WILLIAMS (I.) A short mem. of R. A. S., 3rd ed., 1853.

Suckling (Robert Alfred John), *see* SAINT ALBAN, *Holborn.* Extr. f. S. A. Monthly papers &c. cont. mem. notices of S. &c., 1907–18.

Sucquet (Antonius). Piae consid. ad declinandum à malo &c., cum inconibus viæ vitæ aeternæ. s8°. Viennae. 1672
see PONTANUS (G. B.) Aureum diurnale cum brevi praxi ex A. S. &c., 1629.

Südamerika. Handbuch d. Ostküste Südamerikas. 2e A. 2T [*&* Ergänzungen *&* Nachtrag, 1911–21 *in* 1v]. 8°. 1911–21
1, Brasilien. 2, Die La Plata Staaten.

Sudan. Penal & criminal procedure codes of the S. 8°. 1924

Sudan notes & records. v3–9. la8°. Khartoum. 1920–26
„ „ ....Index, v1–6. la8°. Khartoum. 1925

Sudbury, *Suffolk.* Allegations for marriage licences in the archdeaconry of S., 1782–[1839]. Ed. W. B. & G. G. B. Bannerman. [Harleian Soc., 71, 72]. p3, 4. la8°. 1920–21

Sudbury (Simon *of*), *bp. of London, aft. abp. of Canterbury; d. 1381* [SIMON THEBAUD; SIMON THEOBALD]. Registrum Simonis de Sudbiria, Dioc. London., 1362–75. Transcr. & ed. R. C. Fowler. [Canterbury & York Soc.] v1. 8°. 1927

Südekum (Albert).
Kapital-u. Gewinnbeteiligung. [P2522]. 8°. 1921

Sudermann (Hermann).
Das Bilderbuch meiner Jugend. s8°. St. 1922
The book of my youth. Tr. W. Harding. 8°. [1924]
Das deutsche Schicksal. Eine vaterländ. Dramenreihe. Heilige Zeit.—Opfer.—Notruf. s8°. St. 1921
Frau Sorge. 63e A. s8°. St. 1902
Litauische Geschichten. 40.–60. A. 8°. St. 1918
Die Raschhoffs. Schauspiel. 6.–8. Auflage. s8°. St. 1920
Der tolle Professor. 8°. 1926
see BUSSE (K.) H. S., s. Werk u. s. Wesen, 1927.

Sudhoff (Carl), *the younger; b. 1853.* The earliest pr. literature on syphilis, being 10 tractates, 1495–98. In facsimile, w. intr. &c. by K. S., adapted by C. Singer. [Monumenta medica, v3]. la8°. Florence. 1925
1, Schellig. 2, 3, Grünpeck. 4, Leoniceno. 5, Torrella. 6, Widmann. 7, Gilino. 8, Steber. 9, Montesauro. 10, Scanaroli.
Essays on the hist. of medicine. Pres. to S. on h. 70th

Sudhoff (Carl) [*continued*].
birthday. By Sir T. C. Allbutt, A. Castiglioni &c. Ed. C. Singer & H. E. Sigerist. la8°. 1924
K. S. z. 70. Geburtstage: [Festschrift] hrsg. v. E. Ebstein u. R. Stein, *see* ARCHIV FÜR GESCH. D. MED., B15, 1923.
see MEYER-STEINEG (T.) & C. S. Gesch. d. Medizin, 2° durchges. A., 1922.

Suecia. *Sueciae hist. pragmat., 1731, *see* WILDE (J.)

Suède. Législ. ouvrière et prévoyance sociale en S. 8°. Stockholm. 1921

Suess (Eduard). La face de la terre. Tr. sous la dir. de. E. de Margerie. 2e tir. or. éd. t3ii–iv [*pagin. contin.*] *&* Tables gén. la8°. [1921]–24
The face of the earth. Tr. H. B. C. Sollas under dir. of W. J. Sollas. v5, Indexes & maps. la8°. O. 1924
El porvenir de la plata. Tr. E. Santibanez. 8°. México. 1894

Suess (Franz Eduard), *see* NEUMAYR (M.) Erdgesch., 3te A. neu bearb. v. F. E. S., B1, 1920.

Suetonius Tranquillus (Caius). Hist. of twelve Caesars. Tr. P. Holland, 1606. Ed. J. H. Freese. [Broadway Trans.] 8°. [1924]
see HOWARD (A. A.) & C. N. JACKSON. Index verborum C. S. T., 1922.
„ ROBINSON (R. P.) De fragm. S. de gramm. & rhetor. cod. nexu & fide, 1922.

Suevus (Sigismundus), *see* SCHWOB (S.)

Šufflay (Milan v.) Städte u. Burgen Albaniens hauptsächl. währ. d. Mittelalters, *see* KAISERL. AKAD. D. W. ZU WIEN. Denkschr., B63, 1924.

Suffolk. S. manorial families, being Co. visit. & o. pedigrees. Ed., w. add. by J. J. Muskett. [v3 cont. by F. Johnson]. v1–3iii. 4°. *p.p.* Exeter. 1900–14

Suffolk (Henrietta Howard, *countess of*), *wife of 9th earl, see* MELVILLE (L.) Lady S. & h. circle, 1924.

Suffolk County, *Massachusetts.* Professional & industrial hist. [*By var. wr.*] 3v [v1, Hist. of the bench & bar, by W. T. Davies]. 8°. Boston, Mass. 1894

Suffragette, The. The official organ of the Women's Social & Polit. Union. v1, 2 (Oct. 18, 1912–Apr. 10, 1914). fol. 1912–14

Suffridus (Petrus), *see* PETRUS (S.)

Sufi, *dynasty, see* SOFI.

Sugana (Luigi).
La ricostruzione d. Bucintoro. [P2836]. la8°. [Venezia. 1900]

Sugden (Edward H.) Topog. dict. to the works of Shakespeare & h. fellow dramatists. la8°. M'ter. 1925

Sugenheim (Samuel). Gesch. d. Aufhebung d. Leibeigenschaft u. Hörigkeit in Europa. 8°. St. Petersburg. 1861

Suginomori Nobumori, *see* CHIKAMATSU MONZAÉMON, *ps.*

Suhr (Werner). Der künstlerische Tanz. s8°. L. [1922]

Suicerus (Joannes Caspar). Thesaurus eccl. e patribus Græcis ordine alphabetico. 2t. fol. Amstelædami. 1682

Suida (Wilhelm). Österreichs Malerei i. d. Zeit Ernst d. Eisernen u. König Albrecht II. sm. fol. Wien. 1926

Suidas, *see* WALTER (J. A.) Cod. in S. mendax de Jesu, 1724.

Suisse [SUISSES]. *Quelques peintres suisses: Hodler, Burnand, Forestier, Giacometti, Ihly, Menn, Pahnke, Vibert. [*Illust.*] 4°. 1921

***Suite** de la réponse à l'Hist. des Oracles &c., 1709, *see* BALTUS (J. F.)

Sukhanov (Nikolai).
Записки о революции. кн. 1–7. s8°. Берлин. 1922–23

Sukhomlinov (Mikhail Ivanovich). Повѣсть о судѣ Шемяки. [I. Akad. Nauk. Записки, т22]. 8°. С.-П. 1873

Sukhomlinov (*Adj.-Gen.* **Vladimir Aleksandrovich),** *Russian War Minister.* Воспоминанія. la8°. Берлин. 1924
Erinnerungen. Deut. A. 8°. 1924
see GEBHARDT (A.) Polit. Gespr., Nr. 7, Was beweist d. S.-Prozess? 1921.

Sukhotin (L. M.)
Любовь въ русской лирикѣ 19в. 8°. Белградъ. 1927

Sukias Somal (Placido), *see* SOMAL (P. S.)

Sulaimán II, *called the Magnificent, sultan of Turkey.*
see BIZARI (P.) Cyprium bellum, inter Venetos & S. gestum, 1573.
„ —— Pannonicum bellum, sub Max. II & S. gest., 1573.
„ KARABACEK (J. v.) Z. orient. Altertumskunde, 7 (Gesch. S.'s], 1917.
„ LYBYER (A. H.) The govt. of the Ottoman Empire in the time of S., 1913.

Sulaimān ibn Aḥmad, *al-Mahri, the merchant.* Le pilote des mers de l'Inde, de la Chine &c., see FERRAND (G.) Instruct. naut., t2, 1925.
Voyage du marchant arabe Sulaymân en Inde & en Chine, rédigé en 851. Suivi de remarques par Abû Zayd Hasan (vers 916). Tr. de l'Arabe &c. par G. Ferrand. 8°. 1922
Sulaimán ibn Yakúb, see NEGRI (SALOMON).
Sulkevich (S. I.)
Администр.-политич. строение С.С.С.Р. 2ч. la8°. Ленинград. 1924
Sulla (Lucius Cornelius), *dictator of Rome* [*Sylla*].
see BAKER (G. P.) S. the fortunate, 1927.
„ DAUDET (L.) S. & son destin, 1922.
Sullivan (Arabella Jane), *wife of Rev. Frederick Sullivan, form. Wilmot.* *Recoll. of a chaperon. Ed. Lady Dacre. n. ed. 3v. s8°. 1833
*Tales of the peerage & the peasantry. Ed. Lady Dacre. s8°. 1849
Sullivan (*Sir* Arthur Seymour).
see CHURCH hymns; ed. A. S., 1874.
„ SULLIVAN (H.) & N. FLOWER. Sir A. S.: h. life, letters & diaries, 1927.
„ WYNDHAM (H. S.) A. S. S. (1842–1900), 1926.
Sullivan (*Sir* Edward), *2nd bart., of Garryduff.* The Book of Kells. Descr. by Sir E. S. & illust. w. 24 plates in colours. 2nd ed. sm. fol. *Studio.* 1920
Cat. of books, bindings &c., prop. of S. &c. Sold by Sotheby, 13 Dec. 1926. [Illust. P2857]. 8°. 1926
Sullivan (Herbert) & N. Flower. Sir A. Sullivan: h. life, letters & diaries. Intr. by A. Bennett. 8°. [1927]
Sullivan (James), *governor of Massachusetts.* Hist. of the district of Maine. 8°. Boston [U.S.] 1795
Sullivan (*Maj.-Gen.* John), see AMORY (T. C.) Milit. services & public life of S., of Amer. Revol. army, 1868.
Sullivan (John William Navin).
Aspects of science. 2 ser. 8°. [1923–26]
Atoms & electrons. s8°. [1924]
Beethoven, h. spiritual development. 8°. [1927]
Hist. of mathematics in Europe. s8°. 1925
Three men discuss relativity. s8°. [1925]
Sullivan (Mark). The gt. adventure at Washington: story of the Conference. 8°. 1922
Sullivan (Timothy Daniel). Poems. 4th ed. 8°. D. [1882]
Sully (Maximilien de Béthune, *duc* **de).** Grand design of Henry IV, f. Mem. of S. [Tr.] w. intr. by D. Ogg. [Grotius Soc. Publ., No. 2]. s8°. 1921
Memoirs. Tr. by C. Lennox. n. ed. rev. &c. & brief hist. intr. 5v. 8°. 1810
Sully (Thomas), *1783–1872,* see PENNSYLVANIA ACAD. OF THE FINE ARTS. Cat. of memorial exhib. of portraits by T. S., 1922.
Sully Prudhomme (R. F. A.), see DESCHANEL (P.) Disc. de récep.; réponse de S. P., 1900.
Sulzberger (A.) Erklärung d. Glaubensartikel &c. d. Methodistenkirche. s8°. Bremen. [1879]
***Sumario** del concilio provinc. en la ciudad de los reyes (*i.e.* Lima), 1614, see LIMA.
Sumarokov (Aleksandr Petrovich). Письма, see GROT (YA. K.) Письма Л. и С. &c., 1862.
see POKROVSKY (V.) А. П. С., его жизнь и сочиненія, изд. 2ᵉ, 1911.
Sumérien. Le poème s. du Paradis, 1919, see LANGDON (S.)
Summa. *Summa der godliker schriftueren, oft een Duytsche Theologie. 2p *in* 1v. s8° *n.p.* [c. 1556]
*Die Summa der heil. Schrift [1523 &c.] Hrsg. K. Benrath. s8°. 1880
*Summa doctrinæ Christianæ &c., 1554, see CANISIUS (P.)
*Summa univ. theol. Christ. sec. Unitarios. [*Attrib. to G. Markos, or to S. Lazal, or to M. Lombard*]. 8°. Claudiopoli. 1787
Summary. *Summary acc. &c. of diff. Europ. armies, engaged in late war; tr., 1803, see EUROPEAN.
Summary of Brit. official rep. on the metric system, arranged by J. H. T., 1908, see BRITISH.
***Summer's** tale (The), mus. comedy, 1765, see CUMBERLAND (R.)
Summers (A. Leonard). Anthracite. s8°. [1922]
Summers (James), *ed.*, see CHINESE & JAP. REPOSITORY (THE) &c., 1863–65.
Summers (Montague).
The geography of witchcraft. la8°. 1927
Hist. of witchcraft & demonology. 8°. 1926
Restoration comedies. The parson's wedding, The London cuckolds, & Sir Courtly Nice, or, It cannot be. Intr. & notes by M. S. 8°. 1921
Summers (Thomas O.), *ed.* *Coll. (A) of hymns for public &c. worship, 1860, see HYMNS.
Summers (Walter Coventry). The silver age of Latin lit., f. Tiberius to Trajan. s8°. [1920]
Summo (Maladobatus de), see SOMMI (MALADOBATO).
Sumner (Charles).
Prophetic voices conc. America. s8°. Boston. 1874
Sumner (Helen Laura), see ADAMS (T. S.) & H. L. S. Labor problems, 1920.
—— **& E. E. Hanks.** Admin. of child labor laws, 2p, 1915–17, see UNITED STATES: LABOR.
Sumner (Heywood), *F.S.A.* Excav. at East Grimstead, Wiltshire: desc. of a Roman villa &c. 8°. 1924
Sumner (William Graham).
Coll. essays in polit. & social sci. 8°. N.Y. 1885
Folkways: study of the sociol. importance of usages, manners &c. 8°. Boston, Mass. [1906]
——, **A. G. Keller & M. R. Davie.** The science of society. 4v [v1–3, *pagin. contin.*] 8°. New Haven, *Yale.* 1927
Sumtsov (Nikolai Fedorovich).
Досвѣтки и посидѣлки. [P535]. la8°. Кіевъ. 1886
Изученіе колядокъ и щедривокъ. [P535]. 8°. Кіевъ. 1886
Малорусскія пьяницкія пѣсни. [P535]. la8°. Кіевъ. 1886
Мѣстныя названія въ украинской народной словесности. [P535]. 8°. Кіевъ. 1886
Sun Fire Office, see BAUMER (E.) The early days of the S.F.O., 1910.
Sunavala (A. J.) Vijaya Dharma Sūri, h. life & work. With pref. note by F. W. Thomas. s8°. C. 1922
Sundar Singh, *Sadhu.*
see HEILER (F.) S. S. S., ein Apostel des Ostens u. Westens, 1924; abr. tr. [Gospel of S. S.], 1927.
„ STREETER (B. H.) & A. J. APPASAMY. The Sadhu: st. in mysticism & pract. relig., 1921.
Sundercombe (Miles), see SINDERCOMB (M.)
Sunderland (Frederick Harold). Marmaduke, Ld. Langdale & some events of h. time, 1598–1661. 8°. 1926
Sunderland (Robert Spencer, *2nd earl of*), see HISPANIA. Hispania illust., 1667–78, in letters f. the Earl of S. &c., 1703.
Sundt (Einar). Imagination, labour, civilization. Bibliogr. intr. by S. C. Hammer. 8°. 1920
Sunity Devee, *Maharani of Cooch Behar,* see COOCH BEHAR, *Maharani of.*
Sunodikon. Συνοδικόν, sive Pandectae canonum SS. Apost. &c. ab eccl. Gr. recept., 2t, 1672, see BEVERIDGE (W.)
***Sunto** storico d. princ. contee di Gorizia e Gradisca, 1853, see GORIZIA.
Sun Yat-Sen, *president of the Chinese Republic.* The internat. development of China. 8°. Shanghai. 1920
Suomalaisen Kirjallisuuden Seura.
see AGRICOLA (M.), *bp.* Käsikirja & messu, 1893.
„ CHRISTOPHER III, *k. of Denmark.* Maanlaki, H. Martin Suomeksi kääntämä, 1905.
„ HURT (J.) Setukeste laulud, 1904.
„ LÖNNROT (E.) Kanteletar, 1864.
„ PIPPING (F. W.) Förteckning öfver i tryck utgifna skrifter på Finska &c., 1856–57.
„ PORTHAN (H. G.) Opera selecta, d1, 2, 1859–62.
***Suomen** historia. Suomentanut G. C. s8°. Turussa. 1858
Suomen Muinaismuistoyhdistys, see SOCIÉTÉ FINLANDAISE D'ARCHÉOLOGIE.
Supino (Igino Benvenuto).
La basilica di San Francesco d'Assisi. fol. Bologna. [1924]
La costruzione del Duomo di Pisa. [2p]. [*Extr.* Mem. R. A. d. Sc. di Bologna S1, 7, 8]. [P2604]. 4°. Bologna. 1913–14
Giotto. [2v. 1, Testo; 2, Tavole]. fol. Firenze. 1920
Jacopo dalla Quercia. 4°. Bologna. 1926
La pala d'altare di Iacobello e Pier Paolo dalle Masegne n. Chiesa di S. Francesco in Bologna. [P2699]. 4°. Bologna. 1915
La patria di Niccola Pisano. [P2699]. 4°. Bologna. 1916
Pisa. [Italia artist., 16]. 2ª ed. la8°. Bergamo. 1910
Supplement, The. May 19 *&* July 14, 1708. [*b. w.* Postman, 1704–8]. fol. 1708
Supplementum epigraph. Graecum. Adjuv. P. Roussel, A. Salač &c., red. curavit J. J. E. Hondius. v1, 2. 8°. Lugd. Bat. 1923–25
Supplex. *Libellus supplex Imp. Majestati &c., 1570, see BELGAE.
*Supplex exhortatio ad Carolum V &c., 1543, see CALVIN (J.)
***Supplicatio** ad Imperatorem &c. super causis Gen. Conc. convocandi: contra Paulum V, 1613, see BECANUS (M.)

***Supplication** (The) of certaine masse-priests falsely called Catholikes directed to the King's Maj. Publ. w. glosse & answer. [P2660]. s4°. 1604

***Supplicationes,** Erklärungen u. Protest., der Churf. Fürsten u. Stände d. Augspurg. Conf. verwandt, die Freystellung d. Geistlichen belangend &c. Item, Ferdinandi Declaration. s4°. *n.p.* 1579

Surdus (Henricus), *see* HENRICUS, *Surdus, de Selbach.*

Suremain (*le lt.-gén.* **J. B. de**). Mémoires, 1794–1815. 8°. 1902

Surendranath Das Gupta, *see* DASGUPTA (SURENDRANATH).

Surenhusius (Guilielmus). Βίβλος καταλλαγῆς in quo sec. vet. theolog. Hebr. formulas allegandi &c. conciliantur loca ex V. & N.T. allegata. s4°. Amstelaedami. 1713

Surgères (*le comte* **J. Fr. de**), *vicomte de La Rochefoucauld, see* LA ROCHEFOUCAULD (*le vte.* J. F. DE).

Suriano (Christoforo), *see* LIONELLO (G. B.) Brieven van L. & S. uit Den Haag aan Doge &c. v. Venetie, 1616–18, 1883.

Surinam [SURINAME]. *Gesch. d. Kolonie van S. door een Gezelschap van geleerde joodsche mannen [M. Pereira de Leon *& others*]. 8°. 1791

Singi-boekoe vo da Evangel. Broeder-Gemeente na S.-Kondre, 1867, *see* *SINGI-BOEKOE.

Surius (Laurentius). Comm. brevis rerum in orbe gestarum, 1500–1568, congestus & nunc auctus per L. S. Carthusianum. s8°. Coloniae. 1568

Surma *d'Bait Mar Shimun.* Assyrian church customs & the murder of Mar Shimun. Intr. by Abp. of Canterbury. Glossary by W. A. Wigram. s8°. 1920

Surowiecki (Lorenz), *see* ŠAFAŘÍK (P. J.) Üb. d. Abkunft d. Slawen, nach L. S., 1828.

Surr (Thomas Skinner). A winter in London: or, sketches of fashion. 9th ed. 3v. s8°. 1807

***Surrendered:** naval War secrets, 1927, *see* GRIFF, *ps.*

Surrey. Co. of S. Abstract of parish rec., civil & eccl. Comp. by D. L. Powell. Ed. H. Jenkinson. 8°. Kingston. 1928

Surrey Archaeological Society.
Surrey Archaeological Collections. v33–37. 8°. 1920–27

Surrey (**Henry Howard,** *earl of*), *1517 ?–47.* Poems, pr. f. a correct copy. With poems of Sir T. Wiat, & o. Added, Mem. of h. life & wr. 8°. 1717
Poems. [Aldine ed.] s8°. [1866 ?]
Poems. [Pref., intr. &c. by] F. M. Padelford. [Univ. of Wash.] la8°. Seattle. 1920

Surtees Society.
Publications. v132–139. 8°. Durham. 1920–26
see CORBRIDGE (TH. *of*), *abp. of York.* Register, 1300–4, p1, 1925. [138.]
,, DURHAM. D. Protestations, 1641/2, for maintenance of Protestant relig. &c., 1922. [135.]
,, —— Fasti Dunelm.: rec. of beneficed clergy, to 1548, 1926. [139.]
,, —— Liber vitae Eccl. Dunelm.: facs., w. intr. essays &c., v1, 1923. [136.]
,, —— Rituale eccles. Dunelmensis; n. & rev. ed., 1927. [140.]
,, ENGLAND. Visitations of the North, p2, 1921. [133.]
,, NEWCASTLE [*upon Tyne*]. Early deeds, 1924. [137.]
,, PERCY, *Family of.* P. bailiff's rolls of the 15th c., 1921. [134.]
,, YORK. Horae Eboracenses: Prymer or Hours of the Blessed Virgin Mary &c., 1920. [132.]

Surtees (Robert Smith) [*ps.* **JOHN JORROCKS**]. Robert Smith Surtees (creator of "Jorrocks"), 1803–64. By himself & E. D. Cuming. 8°. E. 1924
Thoughts on hunting &c. 8°. 1925

Survey (The) of the Memorials of Greater London [LONDON SURVEY COMM.]
Monograph[s] of The Committee. 7. 4°. [1921]
see NORMAN (P.) East Acton Manor House, 1921. [7.]
Survey of London, 1921–27, *see* LONDON.

Surya (G. W.) [*i.e.* DEMETER GEORGIEVITZ-WEITZER].
Sammlung okkulte Medizin. 2. A. B1–5 [in 1v]. 8°. 1923
1, Der Mensch im Spiegel d. Schulweisheit u. im Lichte d. Geheimwiss.
2, Makrokosmos u. Mikrokosmos.
3, Ursachen d. Krankheiten u. Wesen d. Leides &c.
4, Astrologie u. Medizin. 5, Okkulte Diagnostik u. Prognostik.

Susan, *see also* SHUSHAN.

Susanin (Ivan Osipovich), *see* DOROGOBUJINOV. Костромской крестьянинъ И. С., 1882.

Susannah, *see* WETSTEIN (J. R.) De hist. S., 1691.

Sushkova (Ekaterina A) [KHVOSTOVA (E. A.)]. Записки, 1812–41. Ред. &c. Ю. Г. Оксмана. s8°. Ленинград. 1928

Süskind (Friedrich Gottlieb v.) Diss. theol. Quonam sensu suam Jesus doct. divinam perhibuerit ? [Resp. A. F. Heyd *& others*]. 2p *in* 1v. s4°. Tubingae. [1798–1801]
Symbolarum ad illust. quaedam Evangeliorum loca pars 1[–3]. Præs. S. 3p *in* 1v. s4°. Tubingae. [1802–4]

Suso (Heinrich). Opera (quæ quidem haberi potuerunt) omnia tr. per F. Laurentium Surium Carthusianum. [Appendix quarundam sublimium quaestionum; H. Susonis, vita &c.] s8°. Coloniae. 1555

Süss (Eduard), *see* SUESS (E.)

Süss (Wilhelm). De Graecorum fabulis satyricis, *see* DORPAT UNIV. Acta &c., B–v5, 1924.

Sussex. Abstract of Feet of fines rel. to S. Comp. by L. F. Salzmann. [S. Rec. Soc., v23]. [v3], 1 Ed. II–24 Hen. VII. 8°. 1916
Abstracts of S. deeds & doc. f. muniments of H. C. Lane, of Middleton Manor, Westmeston. Prep. & ed. by W. Budgen. [S. Rec. Soc., 29]. 8°. C. 1924
Cal. of S. marriage licences. By E. H. W. Dunkin. [v25, 26, ed. E. W. D. Penfold, v32, ed. D. Macleod]. [S. Rec. Soc., v6, 9, 12, 25, 26, 32]. [6v]. 8°. 1906–26
Chichester, Archdeaconry of, 1575–1774. [9, 32.]
,, Deanery of, 1582/3–1730. [12.]
Lewes, Archdeaconry of, 1670–1728–29. [6.]
,, ,, ,, 1772–1837. [25, 26.]
Pagham & Tarring, Deaneries of, 1579/80–1730. [12.]
South Malling, Deanery, 1620–1732. [6.]
,, ,, 1772–1837. [25, 26.]
Misc. records, includ. Eccl. returns in E. S., 1603—Poll for election of knights, 1705—Cal. of ref. to S. in Harleian MSS.—Extr. f. Episc. reg. of Bp. Praty, 1438–45. [S. Rec. Soc., v4]. 8°. Lewes. 1905
Notes of post mortem inquisitions taken in S., I Hen. VII to 1649 &c. Abstr. & tr. by F. W. T. Attree. [S. Rec. Soc., v14]. 8°. 1912
Star Chamber proc. rel. to S., 1913, *see* STAR CHAMBER.
Sussex apprentices & masters, 1710–52. Extr. f. Apprenticeship bks., & ed. &c. R. G. Rice. [S. Rec. Soc., 28]. 8°. 1924
Sussex Inquisitions: extr. f. Rawlinson MS. B. 433 in Bodl. Lib. Ed. M. S. Holgate. [S. Rec. Soc., 33]. 8°. C. 1927
Sussex manors, advowsons &c. rec. in Feet of fines, 1509–1833. Arr. & ed. by E. H. W. Dunkin. [S. Rec. Soc., v19, 20]. 2v. 8°. 1914–15
Thirteen custumals of the S. manors of the Bp. of Chichester & o. doc. f. lib. P. & C. of the Episc. MSS. Tr. & ed. W. D. Peckham. [S. Rec. Soc., 31]. 8°. C. 1925
Three earliest subsidies for S., 1296, 1327, 1332. Transcr. & ed. W. Hudson. [S. Rec. Soc., v10]. 8°. 1910
West S. protestation returns, 1641–42. Transcr., ed. &c. by R. G. Rice. [S. Rec. Soc., v5]. 8°. Lewes. 1906

Sussex Archaeological Society.
Sussex Archaeolog. Collections. v61–69. 8°. C. 1920–28

Sussex Record Society [Publications].
v4–6, 8–33. 8°. [4, 5, Lewes; 29–33, C.] 1905–27
see ANGMERING. Parish reg., 1st bk., 1562–1687, 1913. [18.]
,, ARDINGLY. Parish reg., 1558–1812, 1913. [17.]
,, BOLNEY. Parish reg., 1541–1812, 1912. [15.]
,, COWFOLD. Parish reg., 1558–1812, 1916. [22.]
,, CUCKFIELD. Parish reg., 1598–1699, 1911. [13.]
,, EAST GRINSTEAD. Parish reg., 1558–1661, 1917. [24.]
,, GLYNDE. Parish reg. of G., 1558–1812, 1924. [30.]
,, HORSHAM. Parish reg., 1541–1635, 1915. [21.]
,, PRESTON. Abstract of Court rolls of the manor of P., 1921. [27.]
,, REDE (R.), *bp.* Episc. reg., 1397–1415, 2p, 1908–10. [8, 11.]
,, STAR CHAMBER (COURT OF). Abstr. of Star Ch. proc. rel. to Sussex, 1913. [16.]
,, SUSSEX, *for other works catalogued under this heading.*

Sutcliffe (Emerson Grant). Emerson's theories of lit. expressions. [Illinois, Univ. of: St. in lang. & lit., v8i]. la8°. Urbana. 1923

Sutcliffe (Halliwell). The master passion. s8°. [1926]
Storm. 3rd ed. s8°. [1925]
The winds of March. s8°. [1927]

Sutcliffe (J. T.)
A hist. of trade unionism in Australia. s8°. Melbourne. 1921

Sutcliffe (Joseph), *Methodist, ed., see* VALTON (J.) The life & labours of J. V., by himself, 1830.

Sutcliffe (Matthew). *The subversion of Robert Parsons his worke, A treatise of three conversions of England &c. s4°. 1606
*The unmasking of a masse-monger, who hath cunningly crept into the closets of many Eng. ladies. Or the vindication

Sutcliffe (Matthew) [*continued*].
of S. Augustine's Conf., f. the calumniations of a late noted Apostate [*i.e. Sir T. Matthew*]. s4°. 1626

Sutherland, *The earldom of, see* FRASER (*Sir* W.) The S. book, 3v, 1892.

Sutherland (Halliday Gibson). Birth control: statement of Xtn. doctrine agst. Neo-Malthusians. s8°. 1922

Sutherland (Joan). Behind the curtain. s8°. [1928]
Onslaught. s8°. [1927]
Told at random. s8°. [1927]
Unquenchable fire. s8°. [1926]
Wings of the morning. 8°. [1919]

Sutherland (John). The bonds of society. 8°. [1914]

Sutherland (*Sir* William), *M.P.* Nineteen sixteen–Nineteen twenty. The Lloyd George Coalition in war & peace. Intr. by W. S. s8°. [1920]

Suthers (Robert B.) Money made easy. [P2733]. 8°. *n.d.*

Sutra. Пратимокша-сутра, 1869, *see* PĀTIMOKKHA-SUTRA.

Sutro (Alfred).
Far above rubies. Comedy. s8°. 1924
Five little plays. [The man in the stalls—A marriage has been arranged—The man on the kerb—The open door—The bracelet]. [6th impr.] s8°. [1922]
The great well. Play. s8°. [1923]
John Glayde's honour. Play. s8°. 1907
The laughing lady. Comedy. s8°. [1922]
A man with a heart. Play. s8°. [1925]
Mollentrave on women. Comedy. s8°. 1905

Sutro (Esther).
Nicholas Poussin. Intr. by W. Rothenstein. 8°. [1923]

Suttapitaka, *see* AṄGUTTARA-NIKĀYA.

Sutton (Amos). Narr. of the miss. at Orissa. With introd. ess. by J. C. Ewing. 2nd ed. s8°. Glasgow. 1836

Sutton (Thomas), *founder of the Charterhouse, see* HERNE (S.) Domus Carthusiana; w. the life of T. S., 1677.

***Suum** cuique. Die Verfassung d. Kirche nach ihrer Trennung v. Staate. [P2695]. 8°. Breslau. 1872

Suvorin (Aleksei Sergeevich).
Дневник (1893–1907). Ред. &c. М. Кричевского. 8°. Москва. 1923
Русскій календарь на 1878, 1905, 1907, 1911, 1912. 8°. С.–П. 1878–1911

Suvorov (*Field-Marshal*), *see* BLEASE (W. L.) Suvorof, 1920.

Svechnikov (M. S.) Революция и гражданская война в Финляндии, 1917–18. Воспом. и материалы. 8°. Москва. 1923

Svedeniya. Свѣдѣнія касающіяся странъ &c., 1901–3, *see* TURKESTAN.

Svedstrup (Alexander).
Syn og meninger. 8°. København. [1919]

Svenska. Svenska litt. hist. Av F. Böök, G. Castrén, R. Steffen, E. Sylwan. Under redaktion av E. Sylwan. 3d. la8°. 1919–21
1, Forntiden, medeltiden, Reformationstiden av R. Steffen, Stormaktstiden av G. Castrén, Sjuttonhundratalet av E. Sylwan.
2, Den romantiska tidsåldern av F. Böök, Liberalismens tidsålder av O. Sylwan.
3, Sveriges mod. litt. av F. Böök, samt tillägg och register.

Svenska Akademi, *Stockholm.* Ordbok öfver svenska språket. Utg. af Sv. Akad. B4–9. s4°. Lund. [1916–28]
B4–9, Betacka-Föttling.
see WARBURG (C. J.) Olof Dalin, 1884.

Svenske (Carl Fedorovich). Мат. для ист. состав. Атласа Росс. Имп., изд. 1745. [I. Akad. Nauk. Записки, т9]. 8°. С.–П. 1866

Sventramento (Lo) di V., 1887, *see* VENEZIA.

Sverdlov (V. M.) Доклад. о положении русских железных дорог. &c. [P2458]. 8°. Москва. 1920

Sverige [SVERIGES]. Sveriges ekon. & soc. hist. [1914–25], d1, 1926, *see* HECKSCHER (E. F.), *ed.*
Sveriges hist. intill tjugonde seklet; under medverkan af O. Montelius &c., 10 Afd., 1903–10, *see* HILDEBRAND (E.), *ed.*
Sveriges skönaste folkvisor, 1882, *see* QVANTEN (E. v.), *ed.*

Sveriges Offentliga Bibliotek: Stockholm, Uppsala, Lund, Göteberg. Accessions-katalog. Utgivet av Kungl. Bibl. genom S. Hallberg. v33–41. 8°. 1920–28
,, ,, Tioårs-Register, 1906–15. H1, A–K, H2, L–O. 8°. 1919–20

Sverris saga. Utg. ved G. Indrebø. [Norske Hist. K.] 8°. 1920

Svevo (Italo).
La coscienza di Zeno: romanzo. s8°. Bologna. [1923]

Svinin (Pavel Petrovich).
Sketches of Russia. [Tr.] 2nd ed. 8°. 1831

Svoronos (Jean N.) Les monnaies d'Athènes. Terminé par B. Pick. fol. Münich. 1923–26
Νέαι ἑρμηνεῖαι ἀρχαίων ἀναγλύφων. [P2699]. 4°. Ἀθῆναι. 1910
Paris, cité protohellén. [*Fr.* L'Acropole, v1]. [P2793]. la8°. [Athènes. 1921]
Synopsis de 1000 coins faux du faussaire C. Christodoulos. la8°. Athènes. 1922

Svyatitsky (N.) Соврем. состояние наших трестов. Под редакц. П. Богданова. [P2823]. 8°. Москва. 1923

Svyatlovsky (V.) Професcіон. движеніе въ Россіи. 8°. С.–П. 1907

Svyatopolk-Mirsky (*prince* D.), *see* MIRSKY (*pr.* D. SVYATOPOLK-).

Swain (Joseph), *Baptist minister.* Experimental essays on divine subjects in verse & prose. 3rd ed. [*b. w. h.* Walworth hymns]. s8°. 1804
Walworth hymns. Subj. Essay on church fellowship &c. 2nd ed. corr. s8°. 1796

Swainson (Charles Anthony). The Athanasian creed & its usages in the Engl. Ch. &c. s8°. 1870

Swakeleys. Partic. of estate known as "Swakeleys," nr. Uxbridge, f. sale, 5th July 1922. Auctioneers, Humbert & Flint. [P2752]. fol. 1922

Swallow (J. Albert). Methodism in the light of the Eng. lit. of the last cent. 8°. Erlangen. 1895

Swallow (Robert W.) Sidelights on Peking life. Intr. by H. Jowett. la8°. Peking. 1927

Swalue (Edelhardus Bernardus). Disput. acad. de discidio Eccl. Xtnae. in Graecam & Lat. Photii auctoritate maturato. 8°. Lugduni Batav. 1829

Swamikannu Pillai (Lewis Dominic). Indian ephemeris, 700–1799. [Madras. Govt. Publ.] v1, p1, v6. fol. Madras. 1922
1i, Gen. princ. & tables (rev. &c. ed. of "Ind. chronology, 1911."). 6, 1600–1799.

Swan (Albert D.), *see* GOODWIN (H. K.) Trial of G. for murder of A. D. S., 1887.

Swan (C. G.) & H. Granström.
English & Finnish dict. 8°. Helsingissä. 1904

Swan (Tom).
Edward Carpenter, the man & h. message. s8°. 1922

Swann (Harry Kirke).
Two ornithologists on the Lower Danube. 8°. 1925
see MULLENS (W. H.) & H. K. S. Bibliog. of Brit. ornithology, Suppl., Chronolog. list of Brit. birds by H. K. S., 1923.
,, ——, H. K. S. &c. Geograph. bibliog. of Brit. ornithology, 1920.

Swanson (Margaret) & A. MacBeth. Educational needlework. Pref. by M. McMillan. n. ed. 8°. 1913

Swanton (John Reed). Early hist. of the Creek Indians & their neighbors. [S.I.: Bur. of Ethn., Bull. 73]. 8°. W. 1922
Structural & lexical comparison of the Tunica, Chitimacha & Atakapa languages. [S.I.: Bur. of Ethn., Bull. 68]. 8°. W. 1919

Swarth (Hélène) [LAPIDOTH-SWARTH (H.)]
Gedichten. s8°. A. *n.d.*
Verzen. s8°. A. *n.d.*

Swartz (Christian Friedrich), *see* SCHWARTZ (C. F.)

Swarzenski (Georg). Nicolo Pisano. la8°. Fr. am Main. 1926

Swaythling (Samuel Montagu, *1st baron***).** Cat. of coll. of silversmith's work formed by M., 1st Ld. S. Sold by Christie, May 6, 1924. [*Illust.*] la8°. [1924]
Cat. of objects of art & porcelain, property of M., 1st Ld. S. &c. Sold by Christie, May 8, 1924. [*Illust.* P2748]. 8°. 1924

Swedberg (Jesper), *bp. of Skara, see* †SVEDBERG (J.)

Sweden.
Economic review; comp. by Swedish Bd. of Trade, 1922–, *see* SWEDISH ECON. REVIEW.
Hdbk. (A) of Norway & S., 1920, *see* ADMIRALTY: NAVAL INTELL. DIV.
*Histor. &c. Untersuchung d. Uhrsachen [*sic*] durch welche d. zw. Dennemarck u. S. vorgefall. Streitigkeiten &c., 1715, *see* AMTHOR (C. H.)
Housing (The) question in S. [*b. w.* Suède. Législ. ouvr., 1921]. 8°. [Stockholm. 1920]
Industry in S. [Tr.] 8°. [1927]
Seafaring-trade (The) in Sweden. [*b. w.* Suède. Législ. ouvr., 1921]. 8°. [Stockholm. 1920]

Swedenborg (Emmanuel).
The Apocalypse revealed. Tr. 8°. 1876
Conc. the White Horse in Rev. 19 &c. Tr. [*b. w.* Swedenborg (E.) Short acc. of E. S., 1787]. s8°. 1788

Swedenborg (Emmanuel) [*continued*].
Conjugial love &c. [Tr. A. H. Searle. Swedenborg Soc.] 8°. 1891
Heaven & its wonders, & hell: From things heard & seen. Tr. s8°. [1909]
The heavenly doct. of the New Jerusalem. Tr. [*b. w.* Swedenborg (E.) Short acc. of E. S., 1787]. 3rd ed. s8°. 1787
On marriages in Heaven &c. Extr. [*b. w.* Swedenborg (E.) Short acc. of E. S., 1787]. s8°. 1789
*A short acc. of E. S. & his theolog. writings. s8°. 1787
see Hodgetts (E. A. B.) Reasonable relig.: E. S., h. message &c., 1923.
,, Ireland (W. W.) Thr. the ivory gate [S. *& others*], 1889.
,, James (H.) The secret of S., 1869.
,, Lamm (M.) S.: st. öfver hans utveckling till mystiker och andeskådare, 1915.
,, Whitehead (J.) Study of S.'s psychical states &c., 1909.

Swedish.
*Some data illust. the devel. of Swedish indust. life. [*Eng. & Swed.* P2749]. 8°. 1923
Swedish (The) agricult. labourer. [*b. w.* Suède. Législ. ouvr., 1921]. 8°. [Stockholm. 1921]
*Swedish ports; harbours & trade conditions. la8°. Stockholm. [1923]
Swedish (The) rite; tr. of "Handbok för Svenska Kyrkan," by E. E. Yelverton, 1921, *see* Handbok &c.

Swedish economic review (The) [Sweden: Economic review]. Comp. by the Swedish Bd. of Trade. 1922–1927. 8°. [1922–27]

Swedish (The) Year Book, 1921, 1923, 1925. s8°. [1921–25]

Sweeney (Charles Patrick). Adult working-class educ. in Gt. Brit. & the U.S., *see* United States: Lab. Bull. 271, 1920.

Sweet & Maxwell, *Ltd.* Compl. law book catalogue. v1. 8°. 1925
1, Bibliog. of Eng. law to 1650, incl. bks. dealing w. that period, pr. 1480–1925. Compiled by W. H. Maxwell.

Sweet (Henry). A new Engl. grammar, logical & histor. 2p. s8°. O. 1900–3
Second Middle Eng. primer. Extracts fr. Chaucer. With grammar &c. 2nd ed. s8°. O. 1905
see Aelfric, *abbot.* Sel. homilies; ed. H. S., 2nd ed., 1901.
,, Orosius (P.) Extracts fr. Alfred's O., ed. H. S., 2nd ed., 1901.

Sweeting (Walter Debenham). The cathedral church of Peterborough. [2nd ed., repr.] s8°. [1922]

Sweetman (Edward). Australian constit. development. Intr. by E. Scott. 8°. Melbourne. 1925

Sweetman (George). Hist. of Wincanton, Somerset. 8°. 1903

Swencfeldus (Casparus), *see* Schwenckfeld (Caspar).

Swendsen (Haagen). The tryals of H. Swendson, S. Baynton, J. Hartwell & J. Spurr for stealing Mrs. P. Rawlins, w. intent to cause P. R. to marry H. S., 1702. [P2606]. fol. 1703

Swetchine (*Mme.*) [†Svyechina (Sofiya)], *see* Seillière (E.) Le cœur & la raison de Mme. S., 1924.

Swete (Henry Barclay).
The parables of the Kingdom. Lect. s8°. 1920

Swift (Benjamin), *ps.* [*i.e.* William Romaine Paterson]. Sudden love. s8°. [1922]

Swift (Jonathan), *dean of St. Patrick's.*
Works. Arr. by T. Sheridan, w. notes. n. ed., corr. & rev. by J. Nichols. 24v. s8°. 1803
[Gulliver's travels]. *Travels into several remote nations. By Lemuel Gulliver. v1 [p1, 2 *pagin. cont.*] s8°. 1731
p2 *has a 2nd tp. dated* "1627."
,, ,, [Temple Classics]. s8°. [1896]
*Poet. works. [Works, v2]. s8°. D. 1747
,, ,, Coll. by T. Park. 4v. s8°. 1806
,, ,, [Life by J. Mitford. Aldine ed.] 3v. s8°. [1866]
*A tale of a tub &c. 3rd ed. corr. s8°. 1704
,, ,, added an acc. of battle betw. the books; w. Author's Apology & notes by W. Wotton. s8°. 1811
Translation.
Voyages de Gulliver. Tr. B. H. Gausseron. [*la. paper, pap. du Japan*]. la8°. [1884]
see Eddy (W. A.) Gulliver's travels: crit. st., 1923.
,, Firth (C. H.) Polit. significance of "Gulliver's travels," 1920.
,, Pilkington (*Mrs.* L.) Memoirs, 1712–50 [anecdotes of S. &c.], 1928.
,, Teerink (J.) Hist. of John Bull: re-issued f. orig. pamphlets (Law is a bottomless pit &c.), 1712, w. investig. into its composition & authorship, 1925.
,, Vanhomrigh (*Miss* H.) Vanessa & h. corresp. w. J. S.; letters ed. &c. by A. M. Freeman, 1921.

Swinburne (Algernon Charles).
Atalanta in Calydon. s8°. 1865
Ballads of the English Border. Ed. w. intr., gloss. &c. by W. A. MacInnes. 8°. [1925]
Chastelard. [2nd issue]. s8°. 1866
Note of an Eng. republican on the Muscovite crusade. s8°. 1876

Swinburne (Algernon Charles) [*continued*].
Poems & ballads. [1st ser.] s8°. *Hotten.* 1866
,, ,, 2nd ser. 3rd ed. s8°. 1880
Sel. f. the poet. works of S. 5th ed. s8°. 1894
A song of Italy. s8°. 1867
Translation.
Poèmes & ballades. [Tr.] G. Mourey. Notes sur S. par G. de Maupassant. 2e éd. s8°. 1891
see Gosse (*Sir* E.) S., 1925.
,, Grierson (H. J. C.) Ld. Byron: Arnold & S., 1920.
,, Nicolson (H.) S. [Eng. Men of Letters], 1926.
,, —— S. & Baudelaire, 1926.
see Reul (P. de). L'œuvre de S., 1922.
,, Rossetti (W. M.) & A. C. S. Notes on R. Acad. Exhib., 1868.
,, Vettermann (E.) Balen-Dichtungen u. i. Quellen, 1918.
,, Watts-Dunton (C.) Home life of S., 1922.
,, Wise (T. J.) The Ashley Library: cat. of pr. books &c. coll. by T. J. W., v6, 7, 1925.
,, —— Bibliog. of writings in prose & verse of A. C. S., v2, 1920.

Swinburne (Henry), *Vendue Master at Trinidad.* Travels in the 2 Sicilies, 1777–80. 2nd ed. 4v. 8°. 1790

Swinburne (James), *F.R.S.*
Population & the social problem. 8°. [1924]

Swinden (Henry).
Hist. & antiq. of Gt. Yarmouth. 4°. Norwich. 1772

Swinglehurst (H. E.) Patriotic poems. s8°. [1915]

Swinnerton (Frank Arthur).
Coquette. s8°. [1921]
The elder sister. s8°. [1925]
,, ,, 2nd ed. s8°. *n.d.*
,, ,, s8°. N.Y. [1925]
George Gissing: a crit. study. [n. ed.] 8°. 1924
R. L. Stevenson: a crit. study. [n. ed.] 8°. 1924
Summer storm. s8°. [1926]
The three lovers. s8°. [1923]
Young Felix. s8°. [1923]

Swinnerton (Henry Hurd). Outlines of palæontology. 8°. 1923

Swinstead (John Howard).
The Swedish Church & ours. s8°. 1921

Swinton, *The family of, see* Swinton (A. C.) The S. of that ilk, 1883.

Swinton (Archibald Campbell), *of Kimmerghame.* *The Swintons of that ilk & th. cadets. [*Pref. signed* A. C. S.] 4°. E. 1883

Swinton (John), *Senator of the College of Justice.* *Proposal for uniformity of weights & measures in Scotland. 8°. E. 1779
,, ,, ...2nd ed. [*b. w.* 1779 ed.] 8°. E. 1789

Swiss travel almanac, 1923. Ed. by Swiss Tourist Inform. Office. 8°. Olten. 1923

Switzerland. Message from the Federal Council of S. to Fed. Assembly of S. conc. the question of accession of S. to the League of Nations, 1919. Tr. 8°. C. [1920]

Swoboda (Carl M.)
Römische u. roman. Paläste. 2e A. 4°. Wien. 1924

Swoboda (Wáclaw Alois). Sbírka českých národních písní. Sammlung böhm. National-Lieder. [*Coll. by S. Czech & Germ.*] [P2605]. 4°. Prag. 1845

Sybel (Heinrich C. L. v.) Klerikale Politik im 19ten Jhdt. [P2696]. 8°. Bonn. 1874
Vorträge u. Aufsätze. 8°. 1874

Sybilla (Bartholomæus). Speculum peregrinarum quæstionum. Rev. per C. Guidum. s8°. Venetiis. 1609

Sydenham, *The family of, see* Sydenham (G. F.) Hist. of S. family; ed. A. T. Cameron, 1928.

Sydenham (Edward A.) Aes grave: cast coinages of Rome & Cent. Italy. la8°. 1926
see Mattingly (H.) & E. A. S. Roman imperial coinage, v1, 2, 1923–26.

Sydenham (George Francis). Hist. of the Sydenham family, coll. f. fam. docs. &c. Ed. A. T. Cameron. la8°. *p.p.* East Molesey. 1928

Sydenham (Humphrey). Five sermons [*each w. sep. tp., pagin. cont.*] s4°. 1627
Sermons [3, *each w. sep. tp. & pagin.*] [*b. w. h.* Five sermons, 1627]. s4°. 1630

Sydenham (Thomas), *M.D.*
Whole works. Tr. by J. Pechy. 3rd ed. 8°. 1701

Sydenham of Combe (George Sydenham Clarke, *1st Baron*).
The Jewish world problem. [Repr. f. Nineteenth cent., Nov. 1921. P2564]. 8°. 1921

Sydo, *see* Sido.

Sydow (Eckart v.) Kunst u. Religion d. Naturvölker. 4°. Oldenburg i. O. [1926]

Sydserf (Thomas), *comedian, see* Murray (M.) Trial of M. for assaulting S., 1669, 1837.

Syers (Edgar Wood). The poetry of skating. Coll. of verses by var. hands. 8°. 1905
Sykes (Arthur Ashley). Paraphrase & notes upon the Epistle to the Hebrews &c. 4°. 1755
Sykes (*Maj.* Clement Arthur). Service & sport on the tropical Nile. 8°. 1903
Sykes (*Maj.-Gen. Sir* Frederick Hugh).
Aviation in peace & war. 8°. 1922
Sykes (George), *1761–1826, see* GREENWOOD (W.) *Mem. of the life &c. of G. S., 1827.
Sykes (H. Dugdale). The authorship of "The Taming of a Shrew," "The famous vict. of Henry V," & the add. to Marlowe's "Faustus." [Shakesp. Assoc., Feb. 1919]. [P2463]. 8°. [1920]
Sidelights on Elizabethan drama: authorship of 16th & 17th cent. plays. 8°. 1924
Sykes (*Sir* Mark), *6th Bart., see* LESLIE (S.) M. S., h. life & letters, 1923.
Sykes (Norman). Edmund Gibson, Bp. of London, 1669–1748: st. in politics & relig. in 18th cent. 8°. 1926
Sykes (*Sir* Percy Molesworth) [NURULLAH KHAN, *ps.*]
Hist. of Persia. 2nd ed. 2v. 8°. 1921
Persia. s8°. O. 1922
Persian manners & customs, *see* PERSIA SOCIETY. Lect., 1913.
The Rt. Hon. Sir M. Durand. 8°. 1926
Sylburgius (Fridericus). Cat. libr. mss. Graec. in Bibl. Elect. Palat., *see* MIEG (J. R.) Monumenta, 1701.
Saracenica sive Moamethica. Ex Euthymii Zigabeni Panoplia &c. Græce et Lat. ed. &c. opera F. S. s8°. *Ex typ. H. Commelini.* 1595
see BELGIUM. Eccl. Belgic. confess., interp. J. Revio; & Catechesis; interp. F. S., 1638.
Sylhet. S. District records. Ed. W. K. Firminger. v4, 1788–91. [India: Govt. Publ.] 4°. Shillong. 1919
***Sylph** (The); a novel, 2v, 1783, *see* DEVONSHIRE (G. C., *duch. of*).
Sylvester I, *Saint, pope.* *Life of St. S., *in Armenian, see* SOCRATES, *Scholast.* Eccles. hist.; *ed.* M. Ter Movsesean, 1897.
see ALTUS (H.) Donatio Constant. facta (ut ajunt) S., 1703.
„ SARGISEAN (B.) Hist. of S. & sources of Moses of Choren (*in Arm., w. Arm. & Gr. texts*), 1893.
Sylvester II [GERBERTUS], *pope.* Epistolæ. Acc. Decret. electionis ejus a. D. 998. Epistolæ Joannis Saresberiensis, 1154–80. Epistolæ Stephani, 1159–96. Ed. e bibl. P. Massoni [*by* J. Massonus]. s4°. Parisiis. 1611
Œuvres collat. sur les mss. préc. de biog., suivies de notes par A. Olleris. 4°. Clermont-Fd. 1867
see LA SALLE DE ROCHEMAURE (*le duc* DE). Gerbert, S. II, 1914.
Sylvester (György). Nonnulla ad hist. &c. Unitariorum in Transsylvania pertin. [*Letter f. G. S. &c.*] [*Progr.*] s4°. Gottingae. 1818
Sylvester (János) [ERDÖSI (J.)], *see* RÉVÉSZ (I.) Erdösi János, &c., 1859.
Sylvester (Tipping), *see* WHEATLAND (S.) & T. S. The Psalms of D., 1754.
Sylwan (Otto). Liberalismans tidsålder, *see* SVENSKA litt. hist., d2, 1919.
Sjuttonhundratalet, *see* SVENSKA litt. hist., d1, 1919.
Symbolae literariae, ad incrementum scientiarum omne genus a variis amice collatae. 3t. s8°. Bremae. 1744–49
„ „ Symbolarum &c. coll. altera. s8°. Halae. 1754
Symbolae litterariae Haganae, ad incrementum scientiarum omne genus. [*Contin. of* Bibl. Hag.] Ed. N. Barkey. 2 classes [*in 6 fasc., each w. sep. tp.*] s8°. Hagae Comitum. 1777–81
Symbolae litt. ex Haganis factae Duisburgenses. Cur. J. P. Berg. 2t. s8°. Hagae Comitum. 1783–84
Symbolici. Eccl. evang. Libri s., 1730, *see* PFAFF (C. M.), *ed.* Libri symbolici eccl. cathol., 2t, 1838, *see* STREITWOLF (F. G.) & R. E. KLENER.
Symbolische. Sammlung symbol. Bücher d. reform. Kirche, 1828–46, *see* MESS (J. J.)
Symbol. Bücher d. evangel.-luther. Kirche, 3e A., 1868, *see* MÜLLER (J. T.)
Syme (J.) Nine years in Van Diemen's Land. s8°. Dundee. 1848
Syme (Patrick). Pract. directions for learning flower-drawing. 4°. E. 1813
Symeoni (Gabriello), *see* SIMEONI (G.)
Symes (John Elliotson). The evol. of the New Test. 8°. 1921

Symington (Lindsay), *see* MAQUARIE (A.) The Uffizi A.B.C.; drawn by L. S., 1908.
Symmons (Charles), *D.D.*
The life of John Milton. 3rd ed. 8°. 1822
Symon (James D.) Byron in perspective. 8°. [1924]
The press & its story. 8°. 1914
Symonds (Charlotte Mary), *see* LEAF (*Mrs.* W.)
Symonds (Janet Catherine), *w. of J. A. Symonds, the younger, see* SYMONDS (M.) Out of the past, w. acc. of J. C. S. by Mrs. W. Leaf, 1925.
Symonds (John Addington), *the younger; 1840–93.*
Letters & papers. Coll. & ed. by H. F. Brown. 8°. 1923
Studies of the Greek poets. 3rd ed. [repr.] 2v. 8°. 1902
A Venetian painter, P. Longhi. 4°. 1889
see BABINGTON (P. L.) Bibliog. of writings of J. A. S., 1925.
„ SYMONDS (M.) Last days of J. A. S., 1906.
„ —— Out of the past, 1925.
—— & Emily Hickey.
The poetry of Hon. Roden Noel. *pr. pr.* s8°. *n.p.* 1901
Symonds (Margaret), *aft. Mrs. W. W. Vaughan.*
A child of the Alps. s8°. [1920]
The last days of J. A. Symonds. s8°. Portland, Maine. 1906
Out of the past. With an acc. of Janet C. Symonds by Mrs. W. Leaf. 8°. 1925
Symonds (R. W.) Old Eng. walnut & lacquer furniture. Foreword by P. D. Griffiths. 4°. 1923
The present state of old Eng. furniture. 4°. [1921]
„ „ ....[cheap ed.] 4°. [1927]
Symonds (William), *of Magdalen Coll., Oxford.* A heavenly voyce. A sermon to call the people f. among the Rom. Babylonians. [P2660]. s4°. 1606
Symons (A. J. A.) Frederick Baron Corvo. [Sette of Odd Volumes, Opusc., 81]. s8°. *p.p.* 1927
Symons (Arthur).
Charles Baudelaire. A study. s8°. 1920
Eleanora Duse. 8°. 1926
Intr. to Browning. n. ed. rev. & enl. s8°. 1916
Notes on J. Conrad, w. unpubl. letters. 8°. 1925
Poems. [repr.] 2v. 8°. 1924
The symbolist movement in lit. [2nd ed., 2nd impr.] 8°. 1911
see DOWSON (E. C.) Poems & prose; mem. by A. S., 1919.
Symons (J. H.) Love & the cardinal. s8°. [1919]
Symons (Jellinger Cookson).
District farm schools &c. [P2558]. 8°. 1850
Symons (M. Travers). Britain & Egypt: the rise of Egyptian nationalism. 8°. [1925]
Symons (R.) The Rev. John Wesley's ministerial itineraries in Cornwall 1743–89. Added, Statistics of Methodism in Cornwall. s8°. Truro. 1879
Symons-Jeune (John Frederic), *see* JEUNE (J. F. S.-).
Sympher (Arthur Leo). Die Wasserwirtschaft Deutschlands u. ihre Aufgaben. Hrsg. v. A. L. S. Schriftleiter: Soldan. [2B]. fol. 1922
Symson (Andrew). *Spiritual songs or holy poems. Tr. into Engl. meeter. Digested into 6 bks. [*w. sep. tps. pagin. cont.*] s8°. E. 1686
The 1st & 6th bk. are 2nd ed. 2nd bk. is 3rd ed.
Tripatriarchicon, Lives of Abraham, Isaac & Jacob. Engl. verse. s8°. E. 1705
see GALLOWAY. Reg. of the Synod of G., 1664–71; [wr. by A. S.], 1856.
Symson (Patrick).
The historie of the Church. 3rd ed. corr. & inlarged. sm. fol. 1634
Symsoun (James). Cowmpt of ye geir yat J. S. & J. Chalmers hes in yair keipping belong. to the Abbacie of Lindores, 1530, *see* MAIDMENT (J.) & R. PITCAIRN. Nugae derelictae, 1822.
Synaxarium [SYNAXAIRE]. The book of the saints of the Ethiopian Church. Tr. of the Ethiopic Synaxarium [Maṣḥafa Sĕnkĕsâr] f. MSS. in B.M. by Sir E. A. W. Budge. 4v. 8°. C. 1928
Le s. arabe jacobite (rédaction copte); texte arabe publ., tr. & annoté par R. Basset, p4, 5, *see* GRAFFIN (R.) & F. NAU. Patr. orient., t16, 17, 1922–23.
Le s. éthiopien: les mois Taḥschasch, Ṭer & Yakatit; publ. & tr. par S. Grébaut, p4, *see* GRAFFIN (R.) & F. NAU. Patr. orient., t15, 1927.
Le s. géorgien (rédaction arméno-géorg.); publ. & tr. par N. Marr, *see* GRAFFIN (R.) & F. NAU. Patr. orient., t19, 1926.

Synesius, *of Cyrene, bp. of Ptolemais.* De laudibus calvitii, J. Phrea interp., cum scholiis B. Rhenani, *see* ERASMUS (D.) Moriæ encomium, 1551.
De somniis, *see* IAMBLICHUS, *of Chalcis.* De mysteriis &c., 1497.
TRANSLATIONS.
Letters. Tr. w. intr. & notes by A. FitzGerald. 8°. 1926
Traumbuch. Übers. u. Analyse v. W. Lang. 8°. Tübingen. 1926
see THILO (J. K.) Comm. ad Synesii hymnum secundum &c., 1842–43.

Synge (Edward), *bp. of Raphoe, archbp. of Tuam.* An essay tow. making the knowledge of relig. easy. [*b. w.* Hanway (J.) Acc. of the Marine Soc., 1759]. 8°. 1759

Synnott (Nicholas J.) Notes on the family of De Lacy in Ireland. [Repr. f. R. Soc. of Antiq. of Ir., v49. P2432]. 8°. [D. 1919]

***Synodus** Anglicana: or, the constit. &c. of an Eng. convocation, 1702, *see* GIBSON (E.)

Synopsis. *S. Papismi, that is a gen. view of papistrie, 1614, *see* WILLET (A.)

Syrbius (Johann Jacob). Sententiam theologorum nostratium de determinata futur. contingentium veritate adsertam, disquisitioni submittit J. J. S. [P436]. s4°. Jenae. [1738]

Syrck (Hartich), *see* SIERK (H.)

Syrett (Netta). As the stars come out. s8°. [1925]
Lady Jem. s8°. [1923]
The mystery of Jenifer. s8°. [1926]
The path to the sun. s8°. [1923]

Syria. A hdbk. of S. incl. Palestine, 1920, *see* ADMIRALTY: NAVAL INTELL. DIV.
*Syria reborn, 1919, *see* CEDAR OF LEBANON, *ps.*
HAUT-COMMISSARIAT DE LA RÉPUBL. FRANÇAISE EN SYRIE & AU LIBAN. Bibl. archéol. & hist. t2–4, 7, 8. la8°. & 4°. 1922–27
see CONTENAU (G.) La glyptique syro-hittite, 1922. [2.]
,, DUSSAUD (R.) Topog. hist. de la Syrie ant. & méd., 1927. [4.]
,, ENLART (C.) Les mons. des Croisés dans le Royaume de Jérusalem, 1925–27. [7, 8.]
,, GAUDEFROY-DEMEMBYNES (M.) La Syrie à l'époque des Mamelouks, 1923. [3.]

Syria. Revue d'art oriental & d'archéologie. t1–8. 4°. 1920–27

Syricius, *see* SIRICIUS, *pope.*

Syrienne. La question syr., exposée par les Syriens. [*Pref. signed* Chekri Ganem]. [P2502]. 8°. 1919

System. System of elem. books for use of Tamil schools, 1820, *see* TAMIL.
*System (A) of magick, 1728, *see* DEFOE (D.)

***Système** (Du) adopté pour arriver au minist., en rép. à C., 1818, *see* CHATEAUBRIAND (F. R. DE).

Szabó (Ladislas). Documents secrets de la propagande bolchéviste. Publ. L. S. [P2430]. 8°. Berne. 1920

Szalay (László). Magyarország' története. K.1–6 (884–1711). 8°. Lipcse & Pest. 1852–59
A Tatárjárás Magyarországon, 1241–42. 8^{ld} Kiadás. [P2394]. s8°. 1905

Szamuelly (Tibor), *see* BIZONY (L.) 133 Tage ungar. Bolschewismus: die Herrschaft B. Kuns u. T. S. &c., 1920.

Szántó (Béla). Klassenkämpfe u. d. Diktatur d. Proletariats in Ungarn. Vorwort v. K. Radek. [P2457]. 8°. 1919

Szaszky (Joannes Tomka) [TOMKA SZASZKY], *see* COMPENDIOLUM regnorum Slavoniae &c. [*comp. fr.* J. Severin's *ed. of* S.'s Introd.], 1792.

Szczucka (*Mme.* **Sophia Kossak-),** *see* KOSSAK (S.)

Szeberinyi (Janos). Corpus maxime memorab. Synodorum evangelic. Augustanae conf. in Hungaria. Ed. J. Sz. 8°. Pesthini. 1848

Széchenyi (*Gróf* **István),** *see* GAAL (M.) S. I. vagy Magyar. ujjaszületése, 1899.

Szegedin (Stephan), *see* KIS (STEPHANUS), *Szegedinus.*

Szeliga (Emilian v. Żernicki-), *see* ŻERNICKI-SZELIGA (E. v.)

Szentiványi (Márton), *Jesuit.* Diss. haeresiologico-polemica. De haeresiarchis & haeresibus &c. s8°. Tyrnaviae. 1701

Szerdahelyi (Gábor). Celebriorum Hungariæ urbium celebriora. p1, Pannoniam vet. complexa. s4°. Tyrnaviae. 1801

Szerdahélyi (Georg Alois v.) *Ratio educationis totiusque rei liter. per regn. Hungariae & provincias eidem adnexas. t1. [*No more publ.*] 8°. Vindobonae. 1777

Szilágyi (Sándor). Rajzok a forradalom utáni idokböl. 8°. 1876

Szilassy (*Baron* **Julius von)** [SZILAS U. PILLS]. Der Untergang d. Donau-Monarchie. Diplomat. Erinnerungen. 8°. 1921

Szinnyei (József). Die Herkunft d. Ungarn, ihre Sprache u. Urkultur. [P2466]. 8°. 1920

Szlichting (Jonas) [SCHLICHTING (J.)]
Belydenisse d. Christel. Geloofs [*w. comm. by J. S.*], 1643; *& Lat. ed.* Confessio, 1642, *see* APOSTLES' CREED.
Epistola apologetica. [*b. w.* Apostle's Creed, &c., 1651]. s8°. *n.p. n.d.*
Notae in G. Vechneri concionem, super initium Evang. Joannis. [*b. w.* Apostle's Creed, Confessio &c., 2ª ed., 1651]. s8°. Racoviae. 1644
see CICHOWSKI (M.) Confess. Xtnae. ad rogum damnatae & combustae manium N. C., sui vindices [*by* J. S.], 1652.

Szlupas (John). Essay on the past, present & future of Lithuania. s8°. Stockholm. [1918]

Szögyény-Marich (László), *1806–93.* Idösb Szögyény-Marich L. országbiró emlékiratai. k.1. 1836–48. 8°. 1903

Szpotanski (Stanislas).
Adam Mickiewicz & le romantisme. s8°. [1923]
La Pologne nouvelle & Joseph Pilsudski. s8°. 1920

T

T. (A. D.) Cours élém. de langue flamande, p1, 1895, *see* FLAMANDE.

T. (D.) *Grammaire gén. & raisonnée [par le sieur D. T.], n. éd., 1676, *see* LANCELOT (C.)

T. (D. N. E.) *Dict. Lat.-Armen., 1695, *see* NIERSZESOVICZ (D.)

T. (H.) *On the use of Jehovah & Elohim in the Pentateuch, 1869, *see* TERRELL (F. A. H.)

T. (H.) Manuel of controversies, 1654, *see* TURBERVILLE (HENRY).

T. (J.) *Old halls, manors, & families of Derbyshire, 4v, 1892–93, *see* TILLEY (J.)

T. (J. H.) Summary of Brit. official rep. on the metric system, 1908, *see* BRITISH.

T. (L. C. D.) *Lettres philos., serieuses &c., 1733, *see* SAUNIER DE BEAUMONT (—).

T. (M. de). La muger grande, vida meditada de S. T. de J., 3t, 1807, *see* THERESA *de Jesus, Saint.*

T. (N.) Русско-японская война, 1904; изд. 2ое, 1904, *see* RUSSKO-YAPONSKAYA VOINA.

T. (P.), *pastore arcade.* *La gara d. virtù ne' trionfi di Carlo, 1745, *see* CHARLES III, *of Spain.*

T. (P.), *S.J.* *Caesarea legatio ad Portam Ottoman, 1668, *see* TAVERNER (P.)

T. (T. T.) *The porcelain tower, 1841, *see* SEALY (T. H.)

Taafe, *Family of.*
*Mem. of the f. of T. [*Not publ.*] 8°. Vienna. 1856

Taanith, *see* TALMUD.

Tabarant (A.) Pissarro. Tr. J. L. May. 8°. 1925

Tabaraud (Mathieu Mathurin).
De la réunion des communions chrét. 8°. 1808

Ṭabari ('Ali), *see* 'ALI ṬABARI.

Tabarrini (Marco), *see* AZEGLIO (M. D'). Vita italiana: bozzetti; intr. di M. T., 1910.

Tableau. Tableau de la cour de Rome, 1707, *see* AYMON (J.)
*Tableau gén. de la Russie mod., par V. C***, 1807, *see* DELPUECH DE COMEIRAS (V.)

Table-Talk. Table-talk of a Mesopotamian judge (10 c.); ed. D. S. Margoliouth, 1921; tr., 1922, *see* ABU 'ALĪ AL-MUḤASSIN AL-TANŪKHĪ.

Tabor (Margaret E.) The City churches. Intr. by L. C. Cornford. [3rd impr.] s8°. [1919]
Octavia Hill. [P2878]. s8°. [1927]

Tabourot (Etienne) [*ps.* DES ACCORDS, *seigneur*; GAULARD, *Le sieur*]. [Les bigarrures, avec les Apophtegmes du Sieur Gaulard, les Escraignes dijonnoises, & avec les Contes facecieux du Sieur Gaulard].
[5p, *gen. tp. wanting.* p2–5 *have sep. tp. & pagin.*] s8°. [1663]

Tabourot (Jean) [*ps.* THOINOT ARBEAU]. Orchesography: treatise in form of dialogue whereby persons may acquire exercise of dancing. Tr. f. orig. ed., 1588, by C. W. Beaumont. 8°. 1925

Tabula [TABULAE]. Tabulae in usum scholarum. Ed. sub cura J. Lietzmann. v1–9. la8°. Bonnae &c. 1910–27
see DELBRÜCK (R.) Antike Porträts, 1912. [6.]
,, DIEHL (E.) Inscriptiones Latinae, 1912. [4.]
,, EHRLE (F.) & P. LIEBAERT. Spec. codicum Lat. Vaticanorum, ed. 2ª, 1927. [3.]
,, FRANCHI DE' CAVALIERI (P.) & J. LIETZMANN. Specimina codicum Graec. Vatican., 1910. [1.]
,, HULSHOF (A.) Deut. u. lat. Schrift in d. Niederlanden, 1350–1650, 1918. [9.]
,, KERN (O.) Inscr. Graecae, 1913. [7.]
,, MENTZ (G.) Hss. d. Reformationszeit, 1912. [5.]
,, SCHUBART (W.) Papyri Graecae Berolin., 1911. [2.]
,, TISSERANT (E.) Specimina cod. orient., 1914. [8.]

Tachard (Gui). *A relation of the voyage to Siam. Tr. s8°. 1688
29 plates with French inscriptions are inserted.

Tachibana (S.) The ethics of Buddhism. 8°. 1926

Tacitus (Marcus Cornelius), *emperor of Rome, see* SORDINI (G.) Dei sepolcri d. T., 1908.

Tacitus (Publius Cornelius).
C. C. T. quae exstant opera. Rec. J. N. Lallemand. 3t. s8°. Parisiis. 1760
Historiarum libri I, II. Publ. avec notes &c. par H. Goelzer. 5e éd. rev. s8°. 1920
TRANSLATIONS.
Annales, livres 1–16. Texte établi & tr. par H. Goelzer. [Coll. des univ. de France]. 3t. 8°. 1923–25
Histoires. Texte établi & tr. par H. Goelzer. [Coll. des univ. de Fr.] 2t. 8°. 1921
Histories. [Text], w. Eng. tr. by C. H. Moore. [Loeb Class. Lib.] v1. s8°. 1925
Opere. Volgar. da L. Valeriani. 3v. 8°. Pavia. 1810
Tacite. Dialogue des orateurs—Vie d'Agricola—La Germanie. Texte établi & tr. par H. Goelzer, H. Bornecque &c. [Coll. des univ. de Fr.] 8°. 1922
see LAMPUGNANUS (P.) J. Lipsi in C. C. T. notæ cum cod. Mirandulano coll. a P. L., 1602.
,, LIPSIUS (J.) Dispunctio notarum Mirandulani cod. ad T., 1602.
,, PERSSON (P.) Bemerk. zu d. kl. Schr. d. T., 1927.
,, TOFFANIN (G.) Machiavelli e il "Tacitismo," 1921.

Tackaberry (Fossey), *1796–1847, see* HUSTON (R.) Life &c. of F. T., 1860.

Tadra (Ferdinand). Briefe Albrechts v. Waldstein an Karl v. Harach (1625–27); hrsg. v. F. T., *see* FONTES RERUM AUSTRIAC., B41ii, 1879.

Tafel (Gottlieb Lucas Friedrich). Hist. Thessalonica ad annum 904. [P558]. 4°. Tubingae. 1835

Tafrali (Oreste). Les fresques de l'église St.-Nicolas de Courtéa-de-Argeš, *see* ACAD. DES INSCR.: FOND. PIOT. Mon., t23, 1918–19.
Le trésor byzantin & roumain du monastère de Poutna. Texte *&* Atlas. 4°. 1925

Taft (William Howard), *pres. of the U.S.* The Anti-Trust Act & the Supreme Court. s8°. N.Y. 1914
Liberty under law: interp. of princ. of our constit. govt. s8°. New Haven, *U.S.* 1922
Taft papers on League of Nations. Ed. T. Marburg & H. E. Flack. 8°. N.Y. 1920

Tafur (Pero). Andanças é viajes, 1435–39. [*Ed. w. notes &c.* M. Jimenez de la Espada]. s8°. 1874
Travels & adv., 1435–39. Tr. & ed. w. intr. by M. Letts. [Broadway travellers]. 8°. [1926]

Tagle (José Vazquez), *see* VAZQUEZ TAGLE (J.)

Taglioni (Philipp). Die neue Amazone. Feen-Ballet. [P2588]. s8°. *n.d.*
Die Sylphide. Ballet. [P2588]. s8°. *n.d.*

Tagore (*Sir* Rabindranath).
Broken ties & o. stories. s8°. 1925
Creative unity. 8°. 1922
Glimpses of Bengal sel. f. the letters of R. T., 1885–95. s8°. 1921
Gora. s8°. [1924]
Hungry stones & o. stories. Tr. by var. wr. [repr.] 8°. 1922
Red oleanders. Drama. 8°. 1925
The wreck. s8°. 1921
see KALIDASA. Sakuntala: n. vers. wr. by L. Binyon, introd. essay by R. T., 1920.
,, THOMPSON (E. J.) R. T., h. life & work, 1921.

Taheiti. *Te aebi no Taheiti. [*b. w.* Vhael (B. G.) Gram. Fenn., 1733]. s8°. *Miss. Soc.* 1810

Tāhir, *Bābā, called* 'URYĀN, *Hamadānī.* The Lament. Pers. text ed. &c. by E. Heron-Allen & rendered into Eng. verse by E. C. Brenton. 8°. 1902

Tahourdin (C. B.) Native orchids of Britain. 8°. Croydon. [1925]

Tailhade (Laurent).
Carnet intime. s8°. 1920
De Célimène à Diafoirus. Misanthropie & misanthropes—La pharmacopée au temps de Molière. s8°. 1913
Lettres familières. s8°. 1904
La médaille qui s'efface. s8°. 1924
Platres & marbres. s8°. [1913]
Poèmes aristophanesques. 7e éd. s8°. 1915
Poémes élégiaques. 6e éd. s8°. 1922

Taillandier (*Mme.* Saint-René), *see* SAINT-RENÉ TAILLANDIER (*Mme.*)

Tailliart (Charles). L'Algérie dans la litt. franç. Bibliog., j. 1924. 8°. 1925

Tailor (Thomas), *see* TAYLOR (T.)

Taine (Hippolyte A.) Carnets de voyage: notes sur la province, 1863–65. 2e éd. s8°. 1913
see BARRÈS (M.) T. & Renan: pages perdues, 1922.

Tainie. Тайныя общества въ Россіи въ нач. 19 ст., 1926, *see* RUSSIA.

Tait (James). The study of early municipal hist. in Eng. [*From* Proc. of Brit. Acad., v10. P2737]. 8°. [1922]
see BALLARD (A.) & J. T., *edd.* Brit. borough charters, 1216–1307, 1923.
,, SALFORD. Taxation in S. Hundred, 1524–1802, 1924.

Tait (Peter Guthrie). Scient. papers. 2v. 4°. C. 1898–1900
see KELVIN (W. T., *baron*) & P. G. T. Sketch of elem. dynamics, 1864.

Tait (William C.) The birds of Portugal. 8°. 1924

Takaishvili (E. S.), *see* MARR (N. YA.) Отзывъ о сочиненіи Е. С. Т., 1908.

Takakhav (Nilkanth Sadashiv).
Life of Shivaji Maharaj. 8°. Bombay. 1921

Takata (Tadasuke). Hsiao Ku Fu Fan. [*Hist. of the development of Chinese characters & writing. In Chinese.* 8p *in* 7 *in case*]. 8°. [Tokyo]. *n.d.*
Ku Chou Pien. [*Coll. of anc. Chinese characters & letters.* 100p *in* 10 cases]. 8°. [Tokyo]. *n.d.*
,, ,, [*Index to orig. characters.* 2p *Index to classical characters.* 7p *in case*]. 8°. [Tokyo]. *n.d.*
,, ,, [*Index, by* Tsai Ting-Kan]. 8°. [Tokyo. 1927]
Ku Chou Pien Pu. [*Suppl. to above.* 10p *in* 2 *in case*]. 8°. [Tokyo]. *n.d.*

Taki (R. S.) Amourism or premâmrita. s8°. [Bombay]. 1922

Talæus (Audomarus), *see* RICHARDSON (A.) Logicians school-master &c.; added prelections on T. his Rhetorick, 1657.

Talaran phoqrik, *n.d., see* BALTASAR, *Armenian scribe.*

Talavera. *The battles of T., poem, 8th ed., 1810, *see* CROKER (*Rt. Hon.* J. W.)

Talbot (A. J.) Incorrigible, *see* SCHOFIELD (S.) The marble god & o. plays, 1926.

Talbot (*Lady* Cecil Chetwynd), *afterwards wife of 7th Marquess of Lothian, see* LOTHIAN (C. C., *marchioness of*).

Talbot (Frederick Arthur Ambrose).
Motor-cars & th. story. la8°. 1912
New garden of Canada: by pack-horse &c. thr. undeveloped new Brit. Columbia. 8°. 1911

Talbot (Hayden), *see* COLLINS (M.) M. C.'s own story; told by H. T., 1923.

Talbot (Matthew), *of Leeds.*
An analysis of the Holy Bible. 4°. Leeds. [1800]

Talbot (Neville Stuart), *bp. of Pretoria.*
The returning tide of faith. s8°. [1923]

Talbot (Percy Amaury). Life in Southern Nigeria: magic, beliefs &c. of the Ibibio tribe. 8°. 1923
The peoples of Southern Nigeria. 4v. 8°. O. 1926
Some Nigerian fertility cults. 8°. 1927

Talbot (Thomas), *see* KELLY (R.) Report of trial of R. K. for murder of Head-Constable T., 1873.

Talbot (William), *bp. of (1) Oxford, (2) Salisbury, (3) Durham, see* LAURENCE (R.) The Bishop of Oxford's charge considered &c., 1712.

Talbot (William Henry Fox).
The pencil of nature. No. 2. 4°. 1844

***Tale** (The) of Beatrice; tr., 1927, *see* BEATRICE.

Tales. Tales of mystery, 1927, *see* RHYS (E.) & C. A. DAWSON-SCOTT, *edd.*
*Tales of the peerage & the peasantry; ed. Lady Dacre, 1849, *see* SULLIVAN (A. J.)
*Tales of the R.I.C., 1921, *see* ROYAL IRISH CONSTABULARY.

Taliesin, *the Bard, see* EVANS (J. G.) Taliesin: or the critic [*i.e.* Sir J. Morris-Jones] criticised, 1924.

Tallemant des Réaux (Gédéon) [†TALLEMANT (G.), *sieur des Réaux*].
see GOSSE (*Sir* E.) Tallemant des Réaux, 1925.
„ MAGNE (E.) La fin troublée de T. des Réaux, 1922.
„ —— Joyeuse jeunesse de T. d. R., 1921.

Tallents (T. F.) Hist. of Lithuania, *see* BUCHAN (J.), *ed.* Nations of to-day, Baltic & Caucasian States, 1923.

Talleyrand (*le prince* de), *1754–1838.*
see JAUCOURT (A. F.) Corr. du Cte. de J. avec le p. de T., pend. le Congrès de Vienne, 1905.
„ PALÉOLOGUE (G. M.) Romantic diplomat, T. &c.; tr., 1926.
„ —— T., Metternich &c., 1924.
„ SINDRAL (J.) T., 6e éd., 1926.

Tallgren (Aarne Michael). La Pontide préscyth. ap. l'intr. des métaux. [Eurasia Septentr. Ant., 2]. la8º. Helsinki. 1926

Talli (Virgilio), *see* SETTIMELLI (E.) V. T., 1921.

Tallis (John). Tallis's London street views (1839). Bond Street, Div. 1. [Repr. for London Topog. Soc.] obl. s8º. [1921]

Tallow Chandlers, Company of, *London.* Records of the W. Co. of T.C., London. Ed. under dir. of M. F. Monier-Williams. [Coll. & arr. by A. S. Maskelyne &c.] 8º. 1897

Talmay (*sire de*), *maréchal de Bourgogne, see* PONTAILLER (G. DE).

Talmud (*see also* TOSEFTA).
מסכת ברכות [— נדה] עם פירוש רשי &c. [*Each mischath has sep. tp. & pagin. b. in* 12v.] 4º. Amsterdam, *Benveniste.* [1644–48]
The Babylonian Talmūd: Tractate Berākōt. Tr., w. intr., comm. &c. by A. Cohen. 8º. C. 1921
Compendium d. Hierosolymitan. u. Babylon. T. Uebers. &c. v. M. Pinner. [*Heb. & Germ. with 2nd tp., in Hebrew*]. Bl. 4º. 1832
Talmudis Babylon. cod. Succa, sive de tabernaculorum festo &c. Lat. don. &c. F. B. Dachs. [*Heb. & Lat.*] Acc. J. J. Crameri in eundem tract. comm. posth. Cum praef. D. Millii. s4º. Trajecti ad Rhenum. 1726
A tr. of the treatise Taanith (On the public fasts). From the Palestinian Talmud by A. W. Greenup. s8º. 1918
see DALMAN (G. H.) Aram.-neuhebr. Hdwch. zu Targum, T. u. Midrasch, 1922.
„ FRANKEL (Z.) Introd. in T. Hieros., 1870.
„ HERSHON (P. I.) Genesis, w. a Talmudical comm.; tr., 1883.
„ MONUMENTA Hebr.-mon. T., 1913–1914.
„ NETTER (N.) Israël & s. T. à trav. l'hist., 1926.
„ SCHMID (S.) Collectan. T. lib. duo, 1670.
„ STEHELIN (J. P.) Rabin. lit.: or, the traditions of the Jews cont. in the T. &c., 1748.
„ STRACK (H. L.) & P. BILLERBECK. Komm. z. Neu. Test. aus T. &c., 3B, 1922–26.

Talon (Denis), *see* SFONDRATI (*card.* C.) Legatio M. Lavardini Romam &c., ubi refutantur rationes Lavardini advocato [*i.e. D. T.*], 1688.

Tamarati (Michel). Hist. du catholicisme en Géorgie [*in Georgian*], avec doc. [*in Lat., Ital. &c.*], 13–20 s. la8º. Tiflis. 1902
Ricerche stor. in risp. agli scritt. armeni che negano l'esistenza dei Giorgiani cattolici. [*In Georgian*]. 8º. Tiflis. 1904

Tamaro (Attilio). Italiani e Slavi nell' Adriatico. 8º. 1915
Storia di Trieste. 2v. la8º. 1924
La Vénétie Julienne & la Dalmatie. 3t. la8º. Rome. 1918–19

Tamayo y Baus (Manuel). A new drama (Un drama nuevo), tragedy. Tr. by J. D. Fitz-Gerald & T. H. Guild w. intr. by J. D. F.-G. [Hispanic Soc. of America, 90]. 8º. N.Y. 1915

Tambour (Ernest). Les Gondi & le château de Noisy, 1568–1732. Compl. & publ. par L. Pierre-Bonnet. Préf. de M. Prou. s8º. 1925

Tamburinus (Thomas). De sacrificio missæ expedite celebrando libri 3. n. ed. in Germania. s8º. Coloniae Agrippinae. 1657

Tamil. Christian hymns in T., used by Tranquebar German Mission. 8º. [Madras. 1820]
System of elem. books for the use of Tamil schools. [5 bks. *in* 1v]. 8º. Vepery. 1820
[*Tamil hymns f. the German; tp. in Tamil*]. s8º. [Madras. 1774]

Tamilia (Donato). De Timothei christiani et Aquilæ Judaei dialogo. [P2790]. la8º. Romae. 1901

Tamizey de Larroque (Jacques Philippe). Deux jardiniers émérites: Peiresc & V. Robin. [P2847]. 8º. Aix. 1896
Notice inéd. sur le livre de raison du muet de Laincel d'ap. les mss. de Peiresc. [P2847]. 8º. Digne. 1895
Peiresc, abbé de Guitres. Suppl. à la not. d'A. de Lantenay. [Extr. de la Revue Cath. de Bordeaux]. la8º. 1893
—— & A. Mouttet.
Autour de Peiresc. [P2833]. 8º. Aix-en-Prov. 1898

Tanagra. *Die Mädchen v. T.: griech. Terrakotten u. gr. Verse. la8º. L. 1925

Tananarive, 1923. Madagascar écon. 1e foire commerciale. [*Fr. & Eng.*] 8º. [? Tananarive. 1923]

Tanchum, *Hierosolymitanus, see* THANCHUM *ben Joseph, of Jerusalem.*

Tancoigne (J. M.) Narr. of a journey into Persia [*under Gen. Gardane*]. From the Fr. 8º. 1820

T'ang (Leang-Li). China in revolt. Foreword by Dr. Tsai Yuan-Pei. Pref. by Hon. B. Russell. 8º. [1927]

Tanger (Gustav), *see* FLÜGEL (F.) Flügel-Schmidt-Tanger: dict. of Eng. & Germ. lang., 8th ed., 2p, 1913–14.

Tangl (Michael). Bonifatiusfragen, *see* KÖNIGL. PREUSS. AKAD. D. WISS. Abhdl. (Phil.-hist. Klasse), 1919.
Die sogen. Brevis nota ü. das Lyoner Concil v. 1245. [*Extr. f.* Inst. f. österr. Gesch., Mitthlg. 12. P2729]. 8º. [1891]

Tangutanum. Alphabetum T., sive Tibetanum, 1773, *see* ALPHABETUM.

Tanizaki [TANIZAKI JUNICHIRO]. Puisque je l'aime (Aisureba koso). [Tr., suivi d'un Panorama de la litt. jap. contemp. par S. Elisséev. Cahiers du mois, 14]. 8º. [1925]

Tank (G.), *ed.* Akershusregisteret af 1622. Fortegnelse optaget af Gregers Krabbe og Mogens Høg &c. [Norske Hist. K.] 8º. 1916

Tank (Roar), *see* EIDSVOLD 1814: med bidrag av R. T. &c., 1914.

Tannenbaum (Samuel Aaron). Problems in Shakspere's penmanship, includ. a study of the poet's will. [Mod. Lang. Assoc. of Amer.] 8º. N.Y. 1927

Tanner (Adam), *Jesuit.* Relatio de initio, processu & fine Colloquii Ratisbon. &c. [*b. w.* Ratisbon. Acta Colloquii, 1602]. s4º. Monachii. 1602
„ „ ed. 2a. [*b. w.* Ratisbon. Act. Colloq. R., ed. 2a, 1602]. s4º. Monachii. 1602

Tanner (Jack). The social general strike. [P2419]. s8º. 1919

Tanner (Joseph Robson). English constit. conflicts of the 17th cent., 1603–89. 8º. C. 1928
Mr. Pepys: intr. to the Diary w. sk. of h. later life. s8º. 1925
Tudor constit. doc., 1485–1603, w. histor. comm. 8º. C. 1922

Tanner (Lawrence E.) Westminster Abbey—The music of Westminster by E. H. Fellowes. s8º. 1927
Westminster School &c. s8º. [1923]

Tanner (Thomas), *bp. of St. Asaph.* Notitia monastica, relig. houses in Eng. & Wales. 8º. O. 1695

Tannery (Jules), *see* PICARD (E.) La vie & l'œuvre de J. T., 1926.

Tannery (Paul). Mémoires scientif. Publ. par J. L. Heiberg & H. G. Zeuthen. 5t. s8º. Toulouse. 1912–22
1–3, Sci. exactes dans l'antiq.; publ. par H. & Z.
4, Chez. les Byzantins; publ. par H.
5, Au m. â.; publ. par H.

Tanquerey (Frédéric Joseph). L'évol. du verbe en Anglo-Français (12e–14e s.) la8º. 1915

Tansill (Charles Callan). Robert Smith, *see* BEMIS (S. F.), *ed.* Amer. Secr. of State, v3, 1927.

Tansillo (Luigi). L'egloga e i poemetti. Intr. e note di F. Flamini. 8º. Napoli. 1893
Le lagrime di San Pietro; con Le lagrime d. Maddalena d. E. da Valuasone, di nuovo ristamp. Et agg. L'Eccellenze d. gloriosa Vergine Maria d. H. Guarguante da Soncino [*&* Capitolo al Crocifisso, d. A. Grillo]. s8º. Venetia. 1592
Poesie. s8º. Londra. 1782
Il sofista: comedia. Nuov. posta in luce. s8º. Vicenza. 1610

Tansley (Arthur George).
Elements of plant biology. 8º. [1922]
The new psychology & its rel. to life. [3rd impr.] 8º. [1921]

Tante Amanda, *ps.*
Eine Häschen- u. e. Kätzchengesch. 4º. [1872]

Tanton (T. L.) The Harricanan-Turgeon basin, N. Quebec. [Canada. Geol. Survey. P2514]. 8º. Ottawa. 1919

Tappan (*Mrs.* Cora L. V.), *see* HATCH (C. L. V.), *aft.* (1) *Tappan,* (2) *Richmond.*

Tappen (*Generalleut.* Adolf).
Bis zur Marne, 1914. [P2492]. 8º. Oldenburg i. O. 1920

Tapper (Ruard) [TAPPART].
Opera. 2t *in* 1v. fol. Coloniæ Agrippinæ. 1582–83
De conciliat. gratiae & liberi arbitrii, *see* REGINALD (A.) De mente Conc. Trid., 1706.
Explicationis articulorum Facult. Sacrae Theologiae gen.

Tapper (Ruard) [TAPPART] [*continued*].
Studii Lovaniensis, circa dogmata eccl. ab annis 34 controversa, una cum responsione.
2t *in* 1v [*wanting tp. to t2*]. fol. Lovanii. 1565
see GELDORPIUS (H.) D. R. T. Haeretica pravit. primi & postremi per Belgium inquisitoris apotheosis, 1643.

Tappius (Eberhardus). Germanic. adagiorum cum Lat. & Gr. collat., centuriæ septem.
s8°. Ex libera Argentina, *W. Rihelius*. 1539

Taques (Pedro) [PEDRO TAQUES DE ALMEIDA PAES LEME].
Nobiliarchia paulistana, hist. e genealog., 2ª ed., com biog. de P. T. &c. por A. d'E. Taunay &c., *see* INSTITUTO HIST. &C. DE BRAZIL. Revista, tomo esp., 1926.
see TAUNAY (A. DE E.) P. T. e seu tempo, 1922.

Taraknath Das, *see* DAS (TARAKNATH).

Taramelli (Antonio).
Works in REALE ACCAD. D. LINCEI. Mon. ant.
Fortezze &c. e necropoli prerom. nell' agro di Bonorva, 1918. [25.]
Gonnesa : indagini n. cittadella nurag. di Serrucci, 1916. [24.]
La necropoli punica di predio Ibba a S. Avendrace, 1921. [21.]
Il nuraghe Lugherras presso Paulilatino, 1910. [20.]
Il ripostiglio d. bronzi nuragici di Monte Sa Idda di Decimoputzu, 1921. [27.]
Sarrok : scavi nel nuraghe Sa Domu 'e s'Orcu, 1926. [31.]
Il tempio nuragico di S. Anastasia in Sardara, 1918. [25.]
Il tempio nuragico & i mon. prim. di S. Vittoria di Serri, 1914. [23.]

—— **& F. Nissardi.** L'altipiano d. Giara di Gesturi in Sardegna, *see* REALE ACCAD. D. LINCEI. Mon. ant., v18, 1907.

Taramelli (Torquato). Il Massiccio del Grappa, *see* QUADERNI geograf., N. 6, 1918.

Tarapha (Franciscus), *see* TARRAFA (F.)

Tarbé (Prosper). Recherches sur l'hist. du lang. & des patois de Champagne. [papier de couleur]. 2t *in* 1v. 8°. Reims. 1851

Tarbé des Sablons (Sébastien André).
Nouv. manuel des poids & mesures &c. n. éd. s8°. 1845

Tarchi (Ugo). L'architettura e l'arte musulmana in Egitto e n. Palestina. fol. Torino. [1923]

Tarchiani (Nello). Italia medievale. la8°. Bologna. 1925
see PITTI, *Palace*. La pittura ital., Palazzo P.; [*by*] U. Ojetti, N. T. &c., 1924.

Tarde (Gabriel). Underground man. Tr. C. Brereton. Pref. by H. G. Wells. s8°. 1905

Tardieu (André). Devant l'obstacle : l'Amér. & nous. 8°. 1927
The truth about the Treaty. Foreword by E. M. House. Intr. by G. Clemenceau. 8°. 1921

Tardif (Edmond). Nature, orig. & valeur de la connaissance humaine. 8°. Aix. 1903

Tarentum (Stephen Joseph Alexander Macdonald, *duke of*), *see* MACDONALD (S. J. A.)

Targioni Tozzetti (Ottaviano). Antol. d. poesia ital. 9ª ed., cur. da F. C. Pellegrini. 8°. Livorno. 1904
Strenne nuziali del secolo 14. [*Ed.* O. T. T.] [Nozze Catemario—Sansoni. N124]. 8°. Livorno. 1873

Targum [THARGUM]. T. hoc est paraphrasis Onkeli Chaldaica, 1546 &c., *see* ONKELOS.

Tarich, h. e. series regum Persiae, 1628, *see* SCHICKARD (W.), *the elder*.

Tarifa (Fadrique Enriquez de Rivera, *marq.* **de),** *see* ENRIQUEZ DE RIVERA (F.)

Tarkington (Booth). Alice Adams. s8°. [1921]
Penrod. s8°. [1920]
Ramsey Milholland. s8°. [1919]
Women. s8°. 1926

Tarn (William Woodthorpe). Hellenistic civilisation. 8°. 1927
see BURY (J. B.) Hellenistic age; by J. B. B., W. W. T. &c., 1923.

Tarnovius (Johannes), *prof. of theology at Rostock*. Tres Eliæ: comparatio Eliæ Thesbitæ, Johannis Baptistæ, M. Lutheri &c. [P483]. s4°. Rostochii. 1618
Tuba Jubilæi Lutherani &c.; resp. H. Lonero. [P483]. s4°. Rostochii. 1618

Tarnovius (Paulus). Panegyr. Acad. Rostoch., occas. Jubilæi Luther., de visitat. per M. Lutheri ministerium &c. [P483]. s4°. Rostochi. 1618

Tarnowska (*countess* **Marie),** *see* VIVANTI (A.) M. T., 1915.

Tarrafa (Franciscus) [TARAPHA]. De origine & rebus gestis regum Hispaniae liber. s8°. Antverpiae. 1553
„ „ *for a. ed., see* HISPANICA. Rer. Hisp. scr., t2, 1579.

Tarrhaeus, *see* LUCILLUS, *of Tarrha*.

Tarrytown. Sleepy Hollow Cemetery, at T., Hudson river. [P2686]. 8°. N.Y. 1866

Tarsia (Pablo Antonio de). Vida de Don Francisco de Quevedo y Villegas. s8°. 1663

Tartarie. *Rel. de la grande T. dresse'e sur les mém. orig. des Suedois prisonniers en Siberie. s8°. Amsterdam. 1737
„ „ *for a. ed., see* BERNARD (J. F.), *ed.* Recueil, t10, 1738.

Tartarotti [GIROLAMO], *see* ROSCHMANN (A.) Disq. epist. T. de S. Ingenuini actis, p2, 1751.

Tartu, *see* DORPAT.

Tarvisium, *see* TREVISO.

Taschenbuch d. Kriegsflotten, 16. Jhrg., 1915. Hrsg. v. B. Weyer. s8°. München. 1915

Tashean (Hagovpos), *see* DASHIAN (H.)

Tasman (Abel Janszoon). De reizen v. T. & F. J. Visscher ter nadere ontdekking van het Zuidland in 1642/3 & 1644. Uitg. door R. P. Meyjes. [Linschoten-Vereeniging, 17]. 8°. 's-Gravenhage. 1919

Tasso, *Family of*, *see* VAERINI (B.) Scritt. di Bergamo d. fam. Medolago e T., pubbl. A. Alessandri, 1873.

Tasso (Bernardo).
Libro primo de gli Amori di B. T. s4°. [Vinegia. 1531]
see PASOLINI DALL' ONDA (P. D.) Genitori di T. Tasso: [*w.* Lettere scelte di B. Tasso &c.], 1895.

Tasso (Torquato).
L'Aminta. [*Ital. & Eng.*] 2nd ed. s8°. O. [1650 ?]
Aminta. [*Engr. by Lapi*]. s8°. Londra. 1780
„ „ Ed., w. essay on Renaiss. pastoral drama & prose tr., by E. Grillo. s8°. 1924
La Gerusalemme liberata. Con gli argomenti &c. di B. Barbato, le annot. di S. Gentile &c., & le notitie hist. di L. Pignoria. s4°. Padova. 1628
Il Goffredo, ovvere Gerusalemme liberata. n. ed. arrich. di figure e d'annot. colla vita dell' a. 2t *in* 1v. fol. Venezia. 1760–61
La Gerusalemme liberata. [*Engr. by Lapi*]. 2t. s8°. Londra. 1778
Scritti ined. Pubbl. C. Cavedoni. [Nozze Toldo—Faella. N128]. 8°. Faenza. [1851]
Le sette giorn. d. Mondo creato. s8°. Londra. 1780
see CARDUCCI (G.) Il "Torrismondo" di T., 1894.
„ COMPAGNONI (G.) Les veillées du Tasse [*or rather C.*] &c., 1800.
„ GALILEO. Consid. al T. di G. e disc. di G. Iseo sopra il poema di T. &c., 1793.
„ PASOLINI DALL' ONDA (P. D.) I genitori di T. T.: note stor. [*w.* Rime di T. in vita &c. di Porzia de' Rossi &c.], 1895.
„ VESME (A.) T. T. e il Piemonte, 1889.

Tassoni (*il conte* **Alessandro).** Lettere ined. al can. Barisoni di Padova. [1616–20. Nozze Belgrado-Breda. N127]. 8°. Padova. 1866
La secchia rapita. s8°. Londra. 1779
La secchia rapita e altre poesie. 2ª ed. s8°. Firenze. 1861

Tata (Jamshedji Nusserwanji).
see FRASER (L.) Iron & steel in India: chap. f. life of J. N. T., 1919.
„ HARRIS (F. R.) J. N. T., life, 1925.

Tate Gallery ["NAT. GALLERY OF BRIT. ART"; NATIONAL GALLERY, MILLBANK]. Cat.: book illust. of the sixties, 1923. [P2754]. 8°. [1923]
Cat., Brit. school. 22nd ed. 8°. 1921
Record of 10 yrs., 1917–27. 4°. 1927

Tate (Nahum).
see BIBLE: PSALMS. New version of the Ps., *var. ed.*
„ *BRIEF (A) & full acc. of Tate's & Brady's new vers. of the Psalms &c., 1698.
„ *REMARKS upon a late pamph.: A brief & full acc. &c., 1699.

Tatham (Edward Henry Ralph). Francesco Petrarca, h. life & corresp., 1304–47. 2v. la8°. 1925–26

Tatham (*Mrs.* **Mary),** *see* BEAUMONT (J.) Mem., 1838.

Tatian. Harmonia Evangel. tr. in ling. Theotiscam J. Schilteri recens.; acc. Fragm. Theotiscum, *see* SCHILTER (J.) Thesaurus antiq., t2, 1727.
Perfection according to the Saviour. [Tr.] Ed. R. Harris. [Repr. f. Bull. of John Rylands Library, v8, No. 1]. la8°. M'ter. 1923
„ „ *For a. copy see* JOHN RYLANDS LIBRARY. Bull., v8, 1924.
see EPHRAIM, *St.* Works in Arm., v2, Comm. on Harmony of the Gospels, 1836.

Tatischev (Vasily Nikitich).
see PEKARSKY (P. P.) Новыя извѣстія о В. Н. Т., 1864.

Tatlock (John Strong Perry). The scene of the Franklin's tale visited, *see* CHAUCER SOC., s2, 51, 1914.

Tatlock (John Strong Perry) & A. G. Kennedy. Concordance to compl. works of G. Chaucer & to the Romaunt of the rose. [C.I. of Wash.] 4º. 1927

Tatlock (Robert Rattray), R. Tyler *& others.* Spanish art. [Burlington Mag. monogr., 2]. 4º. 1927

Tatlow (A. H.), *ed., see* NATAL, *Colony.* N. province ; descr. guide & official hd-bk., 1911.

Tatrosi (John).
The Hungarians of Moldavia. [P2567]. s8º. 1920

Tattersall (C. E. C.) Notes on carpet-knotting & weaving. [Victoria & Albert Mus.] [2nd ed.] s8º. [1927]
see KENDRICK (A. F.) & C. E. C. T. Hand-woven carpets, 2v, 1922.

Tattersall (William Medley).
see BRIT. ANTARCTIC EXPED., 1910–13 : ZOOLOGY, v3, Crustacea, p6, 7 ; by T., 1915–23.
„ LANCASHIRE (THE) & Cheshire naturalist, 1919–25.

Taube (Heinrich), *see* HENRICUS, *Surdus, de Selbach.*

Taube (*Baron* **Mikhail Aleksandrovich)** [TAUBE (*Baron* M. DE)]. La polit. russe d'avant-guerre & la fin de l'empire des Tsars (1904–17). Mémoires. 8º. 1928

Taube (Otto, *Frhr.* **v.)** Das Opferfest. Roman. s8º. L. 1926
Verse. s8º. [1907]

Taubert (Agnes), *aft. Hartmann, see* HARTSEN (*Fr.* A. v.) Moral d. Pessimismus, nach Veranl. v. T.'s " Der Pessimismus u. s. Gegner," 1874.

Täubler (Eugen). Die Archaeologie d. Thukydides. 8º. L. 1927

Tauff (Das) buchlin verdeutscht durch M. Luther, 1523, *see* LUTHER (M.)

Tauler (Johann) [THAULERE]. Les exercices sur la vie &c. de Jesus-Christ. Tr. par Jacques Talon. s8º. 1670
Exercitia super vita & passione Jesu Christi ex Germ. in Lat. nuper versa. Alia prorsus divina access. auct. N. Eschio. s8º. Antwerpiae. 1565
„ „ ....[*a. ed.*] s8º. Lugduni. 1572
Homiliȩ, operaq. sm. fol. Coloniae. 1553
Institutions ; tr., *see* BUCHON (J. A. C.) Choix d'ouvr. myst., 1840.
Nachfolge d. armen Lebens Christi. Bearb. u. hrsg. N. Casseder. 2e verb. &c. A. s8º. Fr. am M. 1824

Taunay (Affonso de E.)
Works in MUSEU PAULISTA. Annaes, t1, 1922.
Aspectos da vida setecent. Brasileira, sobretudo em S. Paulo.
Um grande bandeirante : B. Paes de Abreu (1674–1738).
Pedro Taques e seu tempo.

Taunt (Henry William). Fairford church, Lechlade & district. 3rd ed. enl. s8º. Fairford. *n.d.*

Taunton. Cal. of wills &c. in Court of the Archdeacon of T., p3, 4, *see* BRIT. RECORD SOC. : Index Library, v53, 1921.

Taunus. *Offiz. Taunus- Führer. Hrsg. v. T.-Klub. 4e A. s8º. Frankfurt a. M. [1905]

Taurellus (Nicolaus). Carmina funebria. [*b. w. h.* Emblemata, 1602]. s8º. Noribergae. 1602
Emblemata physico-ethica. ed. 2a. s8º. Noribergae. 1602

Tauroggen, Convention of. Urkunde d. Konvent. v. T., 30 Dez. 1812 (*facs.*), *see* FREYTAG (G.) Bilder, B5, 1925.

Taussig (Frank William). International trade. 8º. N.Y. 1927

Tauxier (Louis). Nègres Gouro & Gagou (centre de la Côte d'Ivoire). [Et. Soudanaises]. la8º. 1924
Le Noir de Bondoukou. Koulangos—Dyoulas—Abrons &c. [Et. Soudanaises]. la8º. 1921
La relig. Bambara. [Et. Soudanaises]. 8º. 1927

Tavannes (Jacques de Saulx, *cte.* **de).**
Mémoires. s8º. Cologne. 1691

Taverner (Paul), *S.J.* *Cæsarea legatio quam mand. Imp. Leopoldo I ad Portam Ottoman. suscepit &c. W. comes de Leslie. Expos. a r.p. P. T., *S.J.* [*w. portrait*]. s8º. Viennae. 1668

Taverner (Percy Algernon). Birds of Eastern Canada. [Canada : Geol. Survey]. 8º. Ottawa. 1919
Hawks of the Canadian Prairie Provs. in rel. to agric., *see* CANADA : GEOL. SURVEY. Mus. bull., 28, 1918.

Tawney (Charles Henry), *see* SOMADEVA (B.) The ocean of story ; C. H. T.'s tr. of S.'s Kathā Sarit Sāgara, 10v, 1924–28.

Tawney (Richard Henry).
The acquisitive society. s8º. 1921
„ „ ....[repr.] s8º. 1922
Religion & the rise of capitalism. Holland Mem. Lect. Pref. note by Dr. C. Gore. 8º. 1926

Tawney (Richard Henry) [*continued*].
Secondary educ. for all. Ed. for Educ. Advisory Comm. of Labour Party by R. H. T. s8º. [1922]
Studies in the minimum wage. [Ratan Tata Found.] 3v. s8º. 1914–15
1, Chain making indust. 2, Tailoring indust. 3, Boxmaking indust. ; by M. E. Bulkley, w. intr. by R. H. T.
see BLAND (A. E.), R. H. T. &C., *edd.* Eng. econ. hist. ; sel. doc., 1921.
„ WILSON (*Sir* T.) Disc. upon usury (1572) ; hist. intr. by R. H. T., 1925.
—— **& E. Power,** *edd.* Tudor econ. doc. : sel. doc. illust. econ. & soc. hist. [London Univ.] 3v. 8º. 1924
1, Agric. & industry. 2, Commerce, finance & the poor law. 3, Pamphlets, memoranda, & lit. extracts.

***Taxation** no tyranny &c., 1775, *see* JOHNSON (S.)

***Taxe** de la Chancellerie romaine, ou la banque du pape &c. Tr. [*by A. du Pinet. Pref. by J. B. Rénoult*]. n. éd. [App. *has sep. pagin.*] s8º. Rome. 1744

***Taxes** on knowledge. Reduction of newspaper stamp-duty ? [P2782]. 8º. 1836

Tayler (Alistair).
see FIFE (J. D., *2nd earl*). Ld. Fife & h. factor : corr. &c. ; ed. A. & H. T., 1925.
„ ROSE, *The family of.* Domestic papers ; ed. A. & H. T., 1926.

Tayler (Charles Benj.)
Mem. of Eng. martyrs. n. & rev. ed. 8º. [1867]

Taylor (Alexander S.), *see* BROWNE (J. R.) Resources of the Pacific Slope, w. sk. of settlement &c. of Lower California [by A. S. T.], 1869.

Taylor (Alfred Edward).
Comm. on Plato's Timaeus. 8º. O. 1928
David Hume & the miraculous. s8º. C. 1927
Elements of metaphysics. 2nd ed. 8º. [1909]
F. H. Bradley. [Brit. Acad. P2834]. 8º. [1926]
Francis Bacon. [Brit. Acad. P2870]. 8º. [1926]
Plato, the man & h. work. 8º. [1926]
Platonism & its influence. s8º. [1925]
Plato's biography of Socrates, *see* BRIT. ACADEMY. Proc., 1917–18.
St. Thomas Aquinas as a philosopher. 8º. O. 1924

Taylor (Andrew Thomas), *architect.* The towers & steeples designed by Sir C. Wren. 8º. 1881

Taylor (Charles Carlisle). The life of Admiral Mahan. 8º. 1920

Taylor (*Mrs.* **Clare).** Hymns. s8º. 1859

Taylor (Duncan). The compos. of matter & the evol. of mind. Immortality a certainty. s8º. 1912

Taylor (Eva G. R.), *see* UNSTEAD (J. F.) Gen. & regional geography for students, 1916.

Taylor (Francis Edward). Wit & wisdom of the S. Lancs. dialect. [P2867]. s8º. M'ter. 1901

Taylor (Frank). The wars of Marlborough, 1702–9. Ed. G. W. Taylor. Intr. by J. W. Fortescue. 2v. 8º. O. 1921

Taylor (Frederick Lewis).
The art of war in Italy, 1494–1529. 8º. C. 1921

Taylor (Frederick Winslow).
see COPLEY (F. B.) F. W. T., father of sci. management, 2v 1923.
„ LORENZ (S.) T.-system u. Arbeiterschaft, 1921.

Taylor (George), *of Ballywalter, Ireland.* An hist. of the rebellion in the co. of Wexford, in 1798 &c. 2nd ed. corr. 8º. D. 180[illegible]

Taylor (George), *M.A., see* UNWIN (G.) S. Oldknow & the Arkwrights ; w. chaps. by A. Hulme & G. T., 1924.

Taylor (George Coffin). Shakespere's debt to Montaigne. 8º. Cambridge, *Mass.* 192[illegible]

Taylor (George Robert Stirling). Oliver Cromwell. 8º. [1928

Taylor (George Watson), *see* WATSON (G.), *aft. Taylor.*

Taylor (Griffith). Environment & race. 8º. O. 192[illegible]
Physiography of the M'Murdo Sound & Granite Harbou[r] region, 1922, *see* BRIT. ANTARCTIC EXPED., 1910–13.

Taylor (Henry), *Rector of Crawley, 1711–85.* *The apology o[f] Benjamin ben Mordecai for embracing Christianity, in [...] letters. [*With an 8th letter, w. tp.* : An inquiry into opinion[s] on the generation of Jesus Christ]. 4p *in* 1v. 4º. 1771–7[illegible]
Consid. on anc. & mod. creeds compared &c. Publ. by h[is] son, H. Taylor. With a Treat. on the existence &c. of th[e] soul. By —— ——, Esq. s8º. 178[illegible]

Taylor (*Sir* **Henry),** *1800–86, see* TAYLOR (U.) Guests [&] memories, 1924.

Taylor (Henry Charles). Agricult. economics. 8º. N.Y. 191[illegible]

Taylor (Henry Osborn).
Freedom of the mind in history. s8°. 1923
Greek biology & medicine. s8°. [1923]
Human values & verities. 8°. 1928
Thought & expression in the 16th c. 2v. 8°. N.Y. 1920
Taylor (Hugh). Conditions of nat. success. s8°. O. 1923
Taylor (Isaac), *of Stanford Rivers.*
Consid. on the Pentateuch. 2nd ed. [P2658]. 8°. 1863
Taylor (J. Lionel). The stages of human life. 8°. 1921
Taylor (J. Traill). Optics of photography & photographic lenses. s8°. 1892
Taylor (Jane), *of Ongar.*
Prose & poetry. Intr. by F. V. Barry. s8°. 1925
Taylor (Jeremy).
*Disc. of auxiliary beauty &c. [*by J. T.?*], 1656, *see* DISCOURSE.
A disc. of the liberty of prophesying. s4°. 1647
The Great Exemplar: life &c. of Jesus Christ. 4th ed. 3p [*sep. tp.*] sm. fol. 1667
Rule & exercises of holy dying. s8°. *Pickering.* 1840
„ „ ......s8°. [C. 1864]
Rule & exercises of holy living [& dying, *w. sep. tp. & pagin.*] 11th ed. s8°. 1676
„ „ s8°. [C. 1864]
„ „ ....8°. [1890]
Via intelligentiæ, a sermon, Univ. of Dublin. 4°. 1662
„ „ Der Weg d. Friedens. Nebst Vorrede &c., in teut. Spr. überlief. [P2644]. s4°. Franckfurt. 1728
The worthy communicant. Together with cases of conscience, devotions &c. s8°. 1660
see JEANES (H.) 2nd part of mixture of scholast. divinity &c.: annexed, letters of a. & J. T. conc. orig. sin &c., 1660.
„ WHITE (N. J. D.) Four good men, J. T. &c., 1927.
Taylor (John), *D.D., of Norwich, see* HAMPTON (G.) Candid remarks upon T.'s disc. The doct. of atonement, 1753.
Taylor (John), *publisher.* Catechisms of the currency & exchanges. n. ed. enl. [*3 pagin.*] s8°. 1836
Taylor (Leila S.), *see* WHITE (A.) & L. S. T. Shakerism, 1904.
Taylor (*Col.* Lemesurier), *see* GOODRICH-FREER (A.) & JOHN, *3rd marq. of* BUTE, *edd.* Alleged haunting of B—— House; incl. journal dur. tenancy of Col. L. T., 1899.
Taylor (Lily Ross). Local cults in Etruria. [Papers &c. of Amer. Acad. in Rome, v2]. 8°. [Rome]. 1923
Taylor (Rachel Annand). Aspects of the Ital. Renaissance. Pref. by G. Murray. 8°. 1923
Leonardo the Florentine. la8°. [1927]
Taylor (Reynell G.) Polit. diaries, 1847–49, *see* PUNJAB. P. govt. rec., v6, 1915.
Taylor (*Rev.* Richard). *Hist. of union betw. presbyterian & congregational ministers &c. 2nd ed. [P2653]. 8°. 1698
Taylor (Richard), *F.R.S., F.S.A.; 1781–1858, see* SCIENTIFIC MEMOIRS, sel. f. trans. of for. academies &c.; ed. R. T., 5v, 1837–52.
Taylor (Robert), *A.B., see* SMITH (J. P.) Ans. to "Manifesto of the Xtn. Evidence Soc.," by R. T. &c., 1829.
Taylor (*capt.* Robert), *see* BOMBAY: SEL. F. RECORDS. Hist. &c. conn. w. prov. of Oman, Muskat &c.; prep. by R. T. &c., 1856.
Taylor (Thomas), *B.D.* Life of St. Samson of Dol. [Tr. of "Vita Sanctis Samsonis" (7 c), w. intr. Trans. of Xtn. doc.] s8°. 1925
Taylor (Thomas) [TAILOR], *D.D., 1576–1633, fellow of Christ's College, Cambridge.*
Christ revealed, or the Old Test. explained. s4°. 1635
Christ's victory over the dragon. Expos. of the 12th chap. of Revelation. [Ed. W. Jemmat]. s4°. 1633
A comm. upon Titus. s4°. C. 1619
The parable of the Sower & of the Seed. 8°. 1621
„ „ Add. A mappe of Rome in 5 sermons on 5th Nov. [*w. sep. pagin. & tp.*] 3rd ed. s4°. 1634
Regula vitæ. The rule of the law under the Gospel. A discovery of Libertines, Antinomians &c. s8°. 1635
Taylor (Thomas), *Wesleyan minister.*
An answer to the 1st [& 2nd] part[s] of the Age of reason. [2p *in* 1v]. s8°. M'ter. 1796
*An appeal to the public whether a Calvinist can be a minister of the Ch. of Eng. [*b. w. h.* Redeeming grace &c., 1785]. s8°. *n.p.* 1780
A defence of the Methodists. [P2667]. s8°. Liv'l. 1792
Redeeming grace displayed: acc. of God's dealings w. T. T. [*Foll. by sermons, w. sep. pagin. & tps.*] 4th ed. s8°. Leeds. 1785
see CALVINISTICUS, *ps.* Calvinism defended &c. or remarks on pamph. by Philalethes, ent. Solemn caution agst. ten horns of Calvinism [*attrib. to T. T.*], 1780.

Taylor (Thomas N.), *see* THERESA, *St., of Lisieux.* St. T. of L.; rev. tr. of Autobiog. &c. w. st. of h. canonization &c.; by T. N. T., 1927.
Taylor (Tom).
*Plot & passion. Drama. [P2582]. s8°. *Lacy.* [1853?]
A sheep in wolf's clothing. Drama. [P2582]. s8°. *Lacy.* [1857?]
see FOSTER (B.) Pict. of Eng. landscape; w. pict. in words by T. T., 1863.
—— & A. W. Dubourg.
New men & old acres. Comedy. [P2583]. s8°. *French.* [1869]
Taylor (*Miss* Una). Guests & memories. 8°. 1924
Taylor (Vincent). Behind the 3rd Gospel: Proto-Luke hypothesis. 8°. O. 1926
Hist. evidence for the Virgin Birth. 8°. O. 1920
Taylor (William), *antiquary.*
The antiq. of King's Lynn, Norfolk. la8°. Lynn. 1844
Taylor (William), *missionary bp. of Africa.*
Christian adventures in S. Africa. 8°. [1867]
Ten years of missions in India. s8°. N.Y. 1882
Taylor (William Cooke). Notes of a visit to the model schools in Dublin &c. [P2558]. 8°. D. 1847
Taylor (William Franklin). Technique & expression in pianoforte playing. la8°. [1897]
Tchakhroukhadzé, *see* CHAKHRUKHADZE.
Tchamtchean (Miqael) [CHAMCHEAN; TSCHAMTSCHEAN]. Patmouthiun Hayoy. [Hist. of the Armenians, *in Armenian*]. 3v. [*Tables &c. in v3 have sep. pagin.*] la8°. i Venetik. 1784–86
Tchang (Mathias), *S.J.* Tombeau des Liang, famille Siao, p1, Siao Choen-tche, *see* VARIÉTÉS SINOLOG., No. 33, 1912.
—— & P. de Prunelé. Le père S. A. Cunha (Ou Li Yu-chan), *see* VARIÉTÉS SINOLOG., No. 37, 1914.
Tchang-Tche-tong, *see* CHANG-CHIH-TUNG.
Tchang Yi-Tchou & J. Hackin. La peinture chinoise au Musée Guimet. [Annales du Musée Guimet: Bibl. d'Art, t4]. obl.4°. 1910
Tchaykovsky (Nicholas), *see* GREEN (J. F.) N. T., 1850–1926, 1926.
Tchécoslovaque. Miscellanea de la Républ. Tch. Quelques aspects de la nature de l'état Tchéco-Slov. [P2426]. 8°. Prague. 1919
Tche-ka, *see* CHE-KA.
Tcheou Fou. Kiao-ou ki-lio: resumé des affaires relig. [*comp. by Li Kang-ki*] publ. par ordre de T. F.; tr., comm. & doc. par J. Tobar, *see* VARIÉTÉS sinolog., No. 47, 1917.
Tcherakian (Cherubin), *see* TCHRAQEAN (Q. A.)
Tcherkinsky (M.), *see* CHERKINSKY (M.)
Tchernoff (Olga Kolbassine-), *see* KOLBASSINE-TCHERNOFF (O.)
Tchernov, *see* CHERNOV.
Tchmshkean (Simeon Bahanaye). [Poem on the death of Loris-Melikov, 7 Jan. 1889. *In Armenian.* P2812]. 8°. Tiflis. 1889
Tchoang-tzeu, *see* WIEGER (L.) Taoïsme, t2, Les pères du système t., T. &c., [*Chinese & French*], 1913.
Tchobanian (Archag). La roseraie d'Arménie. Tr. préc. d'une ét. &c. par A. T. 2t. la8°. 1918–23
1, Arakel de Sunik. Pages choisies: Visions de l'enfer & du ciel—Le livre d'Adam &c.
2, Poèmes de Nersès le Gracieux, Sarkis, Constantin d'Erzenga &c.
Tchoubinof (David), *see* CHUBINOV (D.)
Tchou-Kia-Kien. Le théatre chinois. Peintures &c. d'Alexandre Jacovleff. Texte de T.-K.-K. fol. 1922
Tchraqean (Qerobe A.) [TCHERAKIAN (CHERUBIN)].
see APOCRYPHA. Apoc. acts of the Apostles (*in Arm.* Coll. of Arm. lit., ed. T., v3), 1904.
„ HESYCHIUS, *of Jerusalem.* Expos. of Job (*in Arm.* Coll. of Arm. lit., ed. T., v5), 1913.
„ NANA. Expos. of Gospel of John (*in Arm.* Coll. of Arm. lit., ed. T., v7), 1920.
Tead (Ordway) & H. C. Metcalf.
Personnel administration: princ. & practice. 8°. N.Y. 1920
Teatro. Teatro antiguo español: textos y estudios. [t]1–6. 8°. 1916–25
see ROJAS ZORRILLA (F. DE). Cada qual lo que le toca y La viña de Nabot; publ. por Américo Castro, 1917. [2.]
„ VEGA (L. DE). La corona merecida; publ. J. F. Montesinos, 1923. [5.]
„ —— El cuerdo loco, 1922. [4.]
„ —— El Marqués de las Navas, 1925. [6.]

Teatro [*continued*].
see Vélez de Guevara (L.) El rey en su imaginación; publ. J. Gómez Ocerin, 1920. [3.]
,, —— La serrana de la vera; publ. por R. Menéndez Pidal & Ma. Goyri de Menéndez Pidal, 1916. [1.]
Teatro classico ital., ant. e mod. Con illust. biogr., istor. e crit. [*b. in* 2v]. 8°. Lipsia. 1829–[1832]
Tebaldeo, *see* Tibaldeo.
Tebbitt (Charles), *see* Lloyd (F.) & C. T. How to utilise the Volunteers, 1879.
Tebbs (Louisa A.) The art of bobbin lace. la8°. 1907
,, ,, Suppl., by L. A. T. & R. Tebbs. la8°. 1911
The new lace embroidery (punto tagliato). 8°. 1905
Tebbs (Rosa), *see* Tebbs (L. A.) The art of bobbin lace; Suppl. by L. A. & R. T., 1911.
Tebbutt (Arnold), *see* Tebbutt (C. G.), A. Reid, & A. T. Skating, 1897.
Tebbutt (C. G.), A. Read, & A. Tebbutt. Skating. s8°. 1897
Technical dictionaries in 6 languages. [Schlomann-Oldenberg Ser.] [Ed.] A. Schlomann. v11–13. s8°. [1911–20]
11, Metallurgy of iron; compiled by W. Venator & C. Ross.
12, Hydraulics—Aerology—Refrigeration.
13, Constructional building.
Techo (Nicolaus del). Hist. de la prov. del Paraguay de la Comp. de Jesus. Version por M. Serrano y Sanz. Prol. de B. Garay. 5t. s8°. 1897
Techov (Fritz). Das Rote Armee. 8°. 1925
Tecklenburg (August) & K. Dageförde.
Gesch. d. Provinz Hannover. 3e A. 8°. Hannover. 1921
Tedder (Henry Richard). The Athenaeum, 1824–1924. Cent. record. [P2738, 2785]. 8°. 1924
see Ward (T. H.) Hist. of the Athenaeum, 1824–1925; [mat. coll. by H. R. T.], 1926.
Teding van Berkhout (B. L.), *see* Hossfeld (C.) H.'s Eng.-Dutch & Dutch-Eng. dict.; by B. L. T. v. B., *n.d.*
Tedisio di Camilla, *bp. of Turin*, *see* Camilla (T. di).
Teerink (H.) The history of John Bull. Re-issued f. orig. pamphlets, 1712, w. investig. into its compos. &c. 8°. [1925]
Teesdale. *Tour (A) in T. &c., 1828, *see* Garland (R.)
Teffi, *ps.*
Юмористическiе разсказы. [P2392]. s8°. Москва. 1917
Tegani (Ulderico).
Fanfara di pifferi. Novelle. s8°. Milano. [1923]
Sinfonia d. morte. Novelle. s8°. Milano. [1923]
Tegernsee. Die Tegernseer Briefsamml., *see* Froumundus.
Tegethoff (Ernst).
Märchen, Schwänke u. Fabeln. 8°. [München]. 1925
Tegg (Thomas). Chronology, or the historian's companion. 7th ed. s8°. 1831
Teggart (Frederick John). Prolegomena to history. Rel. of hist. to lit., philos. &c. [Univ. of California]. 8°. Berkeley. 1916
Tegnér (Elof). Gustaf M. Armfelt. Studier ur A.'s efterlemnade papper &c. 3[B]. 8°. [1883–87]
Tegnér (Esaias), *bp. of Wexiö.* Frithiofssage. Hrsg. v. G. V. Leinburg. Urschr. u. Uebertragung in Prosa. s8°. Frankfurt am Main. 1846
,, ,, Med Oversættelse af A. E. Boye. s8°. København. 1850
,, ,, ...11e uppl. 8°. Stockholm. 1852
Samlade skrifter. Ny krit. upplaga. Uttg. af E. Wrangel & F. Böök. 6d. s8°. 1918–22
see Böök (E.) E. T., d1, till 1814, 1917.
Tehuantepec. The T. Railway, its locat., features & advant. under the La Sere grant of 1869. [*Prep. by S. Stevens. Foll. by* Hist. & geog. notes, 1453–1869; by H. Stevens, *w. sep. tp. & pagin.*] 8°. N.Y. 1869
Teichman (Eric). Travels of a consular officer in E. Tibet; w. hist. of rels. betw. China, Tibet & India. la8°. C. 1922
Travels of a consular officer in N.-W. China. 8°. C. 1921
Teichman (*Capt.* **Oskar).** The Cambridge undergraduate 100 yrs. ago. Comp., w. extr. f. contemp. sources by O. T. s8°. C. 1926
Diary of a Yeomanry M. O., Egypt, Gallipoli, Palestine & Italy. 8°. [1921]
The life & letters of an Ansbach Ranger [*i.e.* J. G. Teichmann], 1676–1737. Ed. O. T. 8°. *f.p.c.* 1927
Pandour Trenck, 1710–49. 8°. [1927]
Teichmann (Johann George) [Deichmann], *see* Teichman (O.) The life & letters of an Ansbach Ranger [*i.e.* J. G. T.], 1676–1737, 1927.

Teichmüller (Gustav). Neue Grundlegung d. Psych. u. Logik. Hrsg. v. J. Ohse. 8°. Breslau. 1889
Religionsphilosophie. 8°. Breslau. 1886
Ueb. d. Unsterblichkeit d. Seele. [*b. w. h.* Wesen d. Liebe, 1879]. 2e A. 8°. L. 1879
Ueb. d. Wesen d. Liebe. 8°. L. 1879
Die wirkl. u. d. scheinbare Welt. Grundl. d. Metaphysik. [*b. w. h.* Grundl. d. Psych. &c., 1889]. 8°. Breslau. 1882
Teignmouth (*Comm.* **Henry Noel Shore,** *5th baron*), *R.N.*, **& C. G. Harper.** The smugglers: ch. in hist. of contraband. 2v. 8°. 1923
Teignmouth (John Shore, *1st baron*), *see* Jones (W.) Letters f. Lord T.'s coll., 2v, 1821.
Teijo [*Heizo*], *see* Hall (J. C.) T.'s family instruction, 1763, 1916.
Teillard (Jean). Les emprunts de guerre. 8°. 1921
Teirlinck (Herman).
Het ivoren aapje. Roman van Brusselsch leven. 7e dr. s8°. A. [1921]
Ik dien: spel ter verheerl. van Zuster Beatrijs. 2. dr. 8°. Arnhem. 1924
De vertraagde film: drama. s8°. [A.] 1922
Teissier (Antoine), *see* Thou (J. A. de). Les éloges des hommes savans; avec des add. [& Nouv. add.] cont. l'abrégé de leur vie, &c. par A. T., 1683–1704.
Teixeira (Pedro). Travels f. India to Italy by land, *see* Stevens (J.) New coll. of voyages &c., v2, 1711.
see Edmundson (G.) Voy. of P. T. on the Amazon &c., 1637–39, 1920.
Teixeira Botelho (J. J.)
Hist. popular da guerra da Península. 8°. Porto. 1915
Tejada (Miguel M. Lerda de), *see* Lerda de Tejada (M. M.)
Teje, *queen of Egypt*, *see* Borchardt (L.) Der Porträtkopf d. Königin T. in Besitz v. J. Simon, 1911.
Tejera (José Pío) & R. de Moncada. Biblioteca del Murciano o ensayo de un dicc. biog. y bibliog. de la lit. en Murcia. [t1]. la8°. 1922
Teksti. Тексты и разысканія по арм.-груз. филол., 1902–8, *see* Saint-Petersburg: Univ.
Tekusch (Johann Michael). *Kurze Gesch. d. evang. luther. Kirche in Ungarn. Nebst d. neuest. Religions-Gesetze. 8°. Göttingen. 1794
Teleki (*Gróf* **László),** *1811–61.* Levelei (1849–54), *see* Klapka (G.) Emlékeimböl &c., 1886.
Teleki (*Gróf* **Paul).**
Ethnogr. map of Hungary. [P2751]. obl.8°. Hague. 1920
The evolution of Hungary & its place in Europ. hist. 8°. N.Y. 1923
Telepnev (Boris).
Freemasonry in Russia. [*From* Trs. Quatuor Coronati Lodge, v35. P2768]. la8°. [1922]
О происхожденіи соврем. франкмасонства. [P2849]. 8°. Лондонъ. 1926
Rosicrucians in Germany in 18th cent. [P2871]. 8°. *f.p.c.* [1926]
Rosicrucians in Russia. [P2733]. 8°. *p.p.* 1924
Russian masons. [*no tp.*] s8°. [1925]
Some asp. of Russ. freemasonry dur. reign of Alexander I. [*no tp.*] la8°. [1926 ?]
Teleshov (Nikolai Dmitrievich). Между двухъ Береговъ-Черною ночью, *see* Sbornik. Сб. товар. "Знаніе," 1, 5, 1904–5.
Telesius (Bernardinus) [Telesio], *see* Gentile (G.) B. T. con app. bibliog., 1911.
Telford (Thomas). Descr. of bridge over Menai Strait &c. [P2595]. s8°. Bangor. 184[illegible]
Tell (Wilhelm), *see* Lang (P.) Die schweiz. Tellspiele, 1924.
Tellegen (B. D. H.) De wedergeboorte van Nederland. 2 (verm.) dr. bez. door H. T. Colenbrander. 8°. Groningen. 191[illegible]
Teller (Johann Friedrich).
De apodixi Scripturae sacrae. s4°. Erlangae. 177[illegible]
De paradoxia sacra. [*b. w. h.* De apodixi, 1773]. s4°. Erlangae. 177[illegible]
Jesum Christum ob oculos pridem depictum Galatis ce[illegible] crucifixum ex data ad eos epist. [*b. w. h.* De apodixi &c. 1773]. 4°. Erlangae. [1773
Teller (Romanus). De tribus sacrae morum doctrina[illegible] methodis. s8°. Lipsiae. 174[illegible]
Teller (Wilhelm Abraham). Opuscula varii argumenti. s8°. Francofurti ad Viadrum. 178[illegible]
see Sintenis (C. H.) Widerlegung d. T. u. Richter. Erinn[illegible] wider d. Hannöver. Katech. &c., 1794.

Telles da Silva (Antonio), *marq. de Resende, see* RESENDE (A. T. DA S., *marq. de*).

Tellez (Balthazar). Travels of the Jesuits in Ethiopia; tr., 1710, *see* STEVENS (J.) New coll. of voyages &c., v2, 1711.

Tellez (Joaquin).
Ratos perdidos, compos. en verso. 8°. México. 1873

Telluccini (Augusto).
Works in REGIA DEPUT. Miscellanea.
La real chiesa di Soperga, 1912. [46.]
La translaz. d. salme di 2 psse. di Savoia, 1909. [44.]
Viaggio di ritorno d. Sicilia d. re Vittorio Amedeo II, 1910. [45.]

Teluccini (Mario), *called Il Bernia.* Le pazzie amorose di Rodomonte Secondo. 8°. Parma. 1568

Telyakovsky (V. A.) Воспоминания, 1898–1917. s8°. П. 1924
Императ. театры и 1905 год. Под ред. Е. М. Кузнецова с пред. А. А. Гвоздева. s8°. Ленинград. 1926
Мой сослуживец Шаляпин. Под ред. Е. Кузнецова. s8°. Ленинград. 1927

Temirdjipashean (E.) Nor keanq. [New life, 1, Nat. lang. *In Armenian.* P2815]. s8°. K.-polis. 1879

Temmam (Hamasa Abi), *see* HABIB IBN AUS (ABU TAMMAM), *al-Tai.*

Temnitsky (Voldemar) & Joseph Burachinsky. Les atrocités polonaises en Galicie ukrainienne. [P2401]. 8°. 1919
Polish atrocities in Ukrainian Galicia. [P2401]. 8°. N.Y. 1919

***Témoignage** (Du) de la vérité dans l'Église, 1714, *see* LA BORDE (V. DE).

Temperance. Handbook for speakers &c. on the t. q. [Freedom Assoc.] 5th ed. rev. 8°. 1920
True t. monographs, 1921, *see* TRUE TEMPERANCE ASSOC.

Temperley (Harold William Vazeille).
The foreign policy of Canning, 1822–27. 8°. 1925
Hist. of the Peace Conf. of Paris. [*By var. wr.*] Ed. H. W. V. T. Publ. Inst. of Internat. Affairs. 6v. la8°. 1920–24
The second year of the League. s8°. [1922]
2 legends conn. w. T. Gray, *see* WARD (*Sir* A. W.) In memoriam, 1924.
The Victorian age in politics &c. Lect. s8°. C. 1928
see BRITISH. Brit. docs. on orig. of the War, 1898–1914; ed. G. P. Gooch & H. T., v1, 2, 11, 1926–27.
,, GRANT (A. J.) & H. W. V. T. Europe in 19th c., 1927.
,, LIEVEN (*princess* D. K.) Diary &c., ed. H. W. V. T., 1925.

Tempest's Dundalk annual, 1919. 8°. Dundalk. 1919

Templars [TEMPLIERS]. Cartul. gén. de l'ordre du Temple, 1119?–50: rec. des chartes &c., 1913; fasc. compl. cont. table &c., 1922, *see* †ALBON (*le marq.* D').
Dossier (Le) de l'affaire des T.; éd. & tr. par G. Lizerand, 1923, *see* LIZERAND (G.)
Hist. & cartul. des T. de Provins &c., 1919, *see* PROVINS.

Temple, *The family of, see* TEMPLE (*Col.* J. A.) The T. memoirs: acc. of family, w. biog. sk. &c., 1925.

Temple (Daniel), *Missionary in Western Asia, see* TEMPLE (D. H.) Life & letters of D. T., 1855.

Temple (Daniel H.) Life & letters of D. Temple, a missionary of the A.B.C.F.M. in W. Asia. s8°. Boston [Mass.] 1855

Temple (Harald Markham), *see* TEMPLE (*Col.* J. A.) The T. mem., 1925.

Temple (Joan). The widow's cruise. Comedy. s8°. 1926

Temple (*Sir* John), *1600–77.* The Irish rebellion or an hist. of the beginnings &c. of the rebellion in 1641. s8°. 1679

Temple (*Col.* John Alexander). The Temple memoirs: acc. of family, w. biog. sk. &c. By J. A. T. assisted by H. M. Temple. la8°. 1925

Temple (Michael). Shallowdale. s8°. 1922

Temple (O.) Notes on the tribes, prov., emirates & states of the n. prov. of Nigeria. Ed. C. L. Temple. 2nd ed. 8°. Lagos. 1922

Temple (Richard), *visct. Cobham, 4th bart. of Stowe; 1669?–1749, see* COBHAM (R. T., *visct.*)

Temple (*Sir* Richard Carnac), *2nd bart.*
Note.—I.A.=Indian Antiquary.
Admin. value of anthropology. [*Repr.* Brit. Assoc.] [P2423]. 8°. 1913
The advent of Islam into S. India. Repr. f. "I.A.," v51. [P2701]. 4°. Bombay. 1922
Andamanese in Penang. [Repr. f. "I.A.," v49, P2501]. la8°. Bombay. 1920
A brief sketch of Malayan hist. [Repr. f. "I.A.," v48–49, 1919–20. P2501]. la8°. Bombay. 1920
Buddermokan. [Extr. f. Jl. of Burma Res. Soc., v15. P2851]. 4°. Rangoon. 1925

Temple (*Sir* Richard Carnac), *2nd bart.* [*continued*].
Colour symbolism. [Repr. f. "I.A.," v52. P2730]. la8°. Bombay. 1923
Currency & coinage am. the Burmese. [Repr. f. "I.A.," v48. P2875]. 4°. Bombay. 1921
A factor's complaint f. Porakâd in 1665. Repr. f. "I.A.," v51. [P2875]. 4°. Bombay. 1922
Fifty years of "The Ind. Antiq." [P2584]. s8°. Hertford. 1921
A fixed Easter & reform of the Xtn. Calendar. [Repr. f. "I.A.," v53. P2851]. 4°. Bombay. 1924
In the cent. before the Mutiny. [Repr. f. "I.A.," v52. P2730]. la8°. Bombay. 1923
The Indian folk-heroine &c. [P2423]. 8°. 1899
A new view of Sher Shah Sur. Repr. f. "I.A.," v51. [P2701]. 4°. Bombay. 1922
On the pract. value of anthropology. [From Camb. Antiq. Soc., v11. P2424]. 8°. [C.] 1904
The projected illust. Mahabharata. [Repr. f. "I.A.," v52. P2730]. la8°. Bombay. 1923
Regarding the Christians of St. Thomas in S. India. Repr. f. "I.A.," v52. [P2875]. 4°. Bombay. 1923
The sequel to Hir & Ranjha. Repr. f. "I.A.," v55. [P2875]. 4°. Bombay. 1926
Sketch of S. Ind. culture. [Repr. f. "I.A.," v53. P2851]. 4°. Bombay. 1924
Some comments on Barbosa. (As ed. by M. L. Dames.) [Repr. f. "I.A.," v52. P2730]. la8°. Bombay. 1923
Topaz—Topass. Repr. f. "I.A.," v50. [P2701]. 4°. Bombay. 1921
Waddell on Phoenician origins. [Repr. f. "I.A.," v54. P2851]. 4°. Bombay. 1925
The women of India. [P2429]. 8°. 1899
see DRAKE (*Sir* F.) The world encompassed &c.; w. apprec. by Sir R. C. T., 1926.
,, INDIA: CENSUS, 1901. C. of I., v3, Andaman &c. Isl.; by Sir R. C. T., 1903.
,, LALLĀ YOGISWARĪ. The word of L. the prophetess; Eng. verse & annot. by Sir R. C. T., 1924.
,, RAY (S. H.) T.'s theory of univ. grammar, 1902.

Temple (William), *bp. of Manchester.*
Christianity & the State. s8°. 1928
Christus veritas: an essay. [repr.] 8°. 1925
Essays in Xtn. politics &c. 8°. 1927
Life of Bishop Percival. 8°. 1921
The Prayer Book crisis: rep. to Sir W. Joynson Hicks. s8°. 1928

Temple Bar.
v100, List of titles of articles in prev. 99 vol. 8°. 1894

***Temple Bar:** the city Golgotha, 1853, *see* WILSON (J. H.)

Temple-Leader (John), *see* BULLER (*Sir* J. Y.) *Sir J. Y. B.'s motion: letter addr. to J. T.-L., 1840.

Templemoyle. Report of Agricultural Seminary, 1836, 41, 43. [P2558]. 8°. Derry. 1836–43

Templeton (Jesse). The eternal conflict. s8°. [1925]

Ten. Ten learned personages lately converted (in France) &c.; tr. by W. B., 1601, *see* FRANCE.
*Ten (The) pleasures of marriage & 2nd pt. Confession of the new married couple, 1922, *see* BEHN (A.)

Ten Broeke (James). Moral life & religion. s8°. N.Y. 1922

Tencin (*Mme.* de) [†GUÉRIN DE TENCIN (CLAUDINE A.)
Œuvres complètes. 4t. s8°. 1812
1, Mém. du comte de Comminges.—Siège de Calais. 2, Siège de Calais.—Malheurs de l'amour. 3, Malheurs de l'amour.—Régne d'Edouard II. 4, Régne d'Edouard II. Corresp. avec M. de Richelieu.

Tenison (Eva Mabel). Alastair Gordon, R.N. 8°. 1921
Louise Imogen Guiney, an appreciation. [P2509]. 8°. 1921
Louise Imogen Guiney, h. life & works. 8°. 1923
The order of Saint John of Jerusalem. [2nd ed.] s8°. [1922]
The valiant heart. [*Amer. ed. of* "The Unknown God," *publ. under ps.*] s8°. N.Y. 1920

Tennant (A. E.) Studies in Polish life & hist. 8°. [1924]

Tennant (Frederick Robert). Philosophical theology. v1, The soul & its faculties. la8°. C. 1928

Tennant (*Lt.-Col.* John Edward), *D.S.O.* In the clouds above Baghdad: records of an Air Commander. 8°. 1920

Tennessee, *State of.* Introd. to the resources of T.; by J. B. Killebrew ass. by J. M. Safford. [Tenn. Bur. of Agric., 1st & 2nd rep.] 8°. Nashville, Tenn. 1874

Tenniel (*Sir* John). Cartoons f. Punch. 4°. [1864]

Tennyson (Alfred Tennyson, *1st baron*).
Works. [repr.] 8°. 1890
"Crossing the Bar" & o. translations. [*Lat. & Gr.*] By H. M. B. Not publ. 8°. [C.] 1890
Idylls of the King. s8°. 1859
In memoriam. 2nd ed. s8°. 1850
Poems. 19th ed. s8°. 1868
The Princess. 4th ed. s8°. 1851
Suppressed poems, 1830–68. Ed. by J. C. Thomson. s8°. 1910
see FAUSSET (H. I'A.) T., a mod. portrait, 1923.
,, JONES (HENRY). T. [*lect.*], 1909.

Tennyson (Alfred Tennyson, *1st baron***)** [*continued*].
see LESTER (G.) Lord T. & the Bible, 1891.
,, NICOLSON (H.) T.: aspects of h. life &c., 1923.
,, PATERSON (A. H.) The homes of T., painted by H. Allingham, 1905.
,, POSTMA (J.) T. as seen by h. parodists, 1926.
see PYRE (J. F. A.) Formation of T.'s style: versific. of early poems, 1921.
,, TENNYSON (H. T., *2nd baron*). A., Lord T.: a mem., 1906.
,, VETTERMANN (E.) Balen-Dichtungen u. i. Quellen, 1918.

Tennyson (Hallam Tennyson, *2nd baron***).**
Alfred, Lord Tennyson: a mem. [repr.] 8º. 1906

Ténot (Eugène). Les nouvelles défenses de la France: la frontière, 1870–1882. la8º. Bordeaux. 1882

Tenreiro (Ramon Maria). Libros de caballerías. [Amadis de Gaula—Palmerin de Inglaterra]. Sel. por T. 8º. 1924
El loco amor. s8º. 1921

Tenterden, *Kent.* Kentish mon. inscr. Inscr. at Tenterden. Ed. L. L. Duncan. [Kent Arch. Soc., Records Br.] 8º. Blackheath. [1919]

Tentori (Cristoforo). Saggio s. storia &c. d. repub. di Venezia. 12t. s8º. Venezia. 1785–90
t5 *wants tp. & contents*; t12 *wants* pp. 513–28.

Tentzelius (Jacobus). Disput. de jure pontificis circa elect. imperatoris Rom. Præs. J. Meisnero. [P2670]. s4º. Wittebergæ. 1657

Teodoret, *see* THEODORET.

Teodozije, *see* THEODOSIUS.

Teofredo, *Saint, see* THEOFREDUS, *St.*

Teonge (Henry). Diary of T., chaplain on board H.M.'s S. Assistance, Bristol & Royal Oak, 1675–79. Transcr. & ed. w. intr. &c. by G. E. Manwaring. 8º. [1927]

Tephiloth. The authorised daily prayer book of the United Hebrew Congr. of the Brit. Emp. New tr. by S. Singer [*w. Hebrew text & 2nd tp. in Hebrew*]. 9th ed. s8º. 1912
The form of prayers acc. to the custom of the Spanish & Portuguese Jews. Tr. by D. Levi. s8º. A.M. 5549 [1789]
Forms of prayer acc. to custom of Span. & Portuguese Jews, w. Eng. tr. by D. A. De Sola. Added, tables forming Hebrew almanac, 5596–5646 [1836–86]. 3v. 8º. 5596–97 [1836–37]
Gebete d. hochdeut. u. poln. Juden. Übers. v. I. A. Euchel. s8º. Wien. 1815
Orden de ros-asanah y kipur, nuev. corr. s8º. Amsterdam, *Yshak de Cordova.* 5466 [*i.e.* 1700]

Teplov (P.) Ист. Якутскаго протеста (дѣло "Романовцевъ") [1904]. s8º. С.-П. [1905]

Tepp (Max). Tandaradei. Neue Tänze hrsg. v. M. T. Lautensatz v. B. Schneider. obl.8º. L. 1922

Terence [†TERENTIUS (PUBLIUS), *Afer*].
Comoediae sex. Ex rec. Heinsiana. s8º. Lugd. Bat., *Elzevir.* 1635
Comœdiae sex. Ex rec. F. Lindenbrogii cum lect. & obs. atque Donati, Eugraphii &c. comm. 2t. 8º. Londini. 1820
,, ,, Ed. J. A. Phillips. 8º. D. 1846
TRANSLATIONS.
Comedies: made Eng., w. h. life & remarks by L. Echard &c. Rev. & corr. by Dr. Echard & Sir R. L'Estrange. 8th ed. s8º. 1733
Eunuchus. Übers. v. Hans Neidhardt, 1486. Hrsg. H. Fischer. [Lit. V. in St. 265]. 8º. Tübingen. 1915
TRANSLATIONS [*continued*].
Plays. Tr. into parallel Eng. metres, by W. Ritchie [*w. text*]. la8º. 1927
see AUSTIN (J. C.) The significant name in T., 1922.
,, CRAIG (J. D.) Jovialis & the Callop. text of T., 1927.
,, LAWTON (H. W.) T. en France au 16e s.: éds. & trs., 1926.
,, LEFFINGWELL (G. W.) Social &c. life at Rome in time of Plautus & T., 1918.
,, NORWOOD (G.) Art of T., 1923.

Tereschenko (Aleksandr). Бытъ русск. народа. 7ч. 8º. С.-П. 1848

Térey (Gabriel v.), *see* BUDA-PEST. Die Gemäldegalerie d. Museums f. bild. Künste; beschr. Kat., bearb. v. G. v. T., Abt. 1, 1926.

Terman (Lewis Madison). Genetic studies of genius. [Ed. L. M. T.] v1, 2. 8º. [Berkeley, Cal.] 1925–26
1, Mental & physical traits of 1000 gifted children; [by] L. M. T., assisted by B. T. Baldwin, E. Bronson &c.
2, Early mental traits of 300 geniuses; by C. M. Cox, assisted by L. O. Gillan &c.
The intelligence of school children. s8º. [1921]
The measurement of intelligence: Stanford revision Binet-Simon scale. Intr. by J. J. Findlay. [repr.] s8º. [1922]

***Termes** (Les) de la ley: obscure words &c. of laws expl., 1721, *see* RASTELL (W.)

Ter Meulen, *see* LEAGUE OF NATIONS. Internat. credits (The "T. M." scheme), 1921.

Ter-Mikaëlian (Nerses).
Das arm. Hymnarium: gesch. Entwicklung. 8º. L. 1905

Ter-Movsesean (Mesrop) [MESROP, *episkopos*]. Рукоп. отрывки армянской версіи Ветхаго Завѣта лапидарн. письмомъ. Изд. епископъ Месропъ. [*a. tp. in Armenian.* Bibl. Arm.-Georgica, 5]. la8º. П. 1915

Terne (A. M.) [TÖRNE (A. M.)]
Въ царствѣ Ленина. Очерки. 2oe. изд. 8º. Berlin. 1922

Ternier (Louis). Nos oiseaux de mer, de rivière & de marais. La sauvagine en Fr. 8º. [1898]

Ternovetz (Boris). G. De Chirico. s8º. Milano. 1928

Teroovercaudoo Soobroya *Modelliar.*
A Tamel expositor. s4º. Madras. 1811

Térouane [THÉROUANNE]. Cartul. de l'église de Térouane. Publ. par T. Duchet & A. Giry. [Soc. des Antiq. de la Morinie]. 4º. Saint-Omer. 1881

Terpander, *see* LYRA Graeca; ed. & tr. by J. M. Edmonds, v1, T. &c., 1922.

Terracina (Laura). Quarte rime. [*b. w. h.* Rime, 1560]. s8º. Vinegia, *Valvassorio.* 1550
Quinte rime. [*b. w. h.* Rime, 1560]. s8º. Vinegia, *Valvassorio.* 1552
Rime. [*Pref. by* L. Domenichi. *Foll. by* Rime d'alcuni ingegni in lode de L. T.] s8º. Vinegia, *Giolito.* 1548
,, di nuovo corr. e ristamp. s8º. Vinegia, *Giolito.* 1560
,, Con il Discorso [*in verse*] sopra il princ. di tutti i canti d'Orlando Furioso [*of Ariosto*] &c. [*w. sep. tp. & pagin.*] s8º. Vinegia. 1566
Rime seconde. [*Foll*d. *by* Rime di div. ingegni &c.] s8º. Fiorenza. 1549

Terrail (Gabriel) [*ps.* MERMEIX; X*** DU FIGARO].
Au sein des commissions. 8º. 1924
Le combat des trois. Notes & docs. s. la Confér. de la paix. 6e éd. s8º. 1922
Le commandement unique. 2p. [1, 6e éd., 2, 2e éd.] s8º. 1920
1, Foch & les armées d'Occident. 2, Sarrail & les armées d'Orient.
Le Ralliement et l'Action Française. s8º. [1927]

Terraneo (Giovanni Tommaso). Dei primi conti di Savoia e d. loro signoria s. valle d'Aosta; [*ed. E. Bollati*], *see* REGIA DEP. DI STORIA PATRIA. Misc., t16, 1877.

Terra Nova Expedition, *see* BRITISH ANTARCTIC [TERRA NOVA] EXPED., 1910–13.

Terrasse (Charles), *see* LOUVRE. La peinture, école franç., 17 s., par C. T., 1927.

Terrell (Francis A. Hull). *On the use of Jehovah & Elohim in the Pentateuch. By H. T. 8º. 1869

Terreros y Vinent (Manuel Romero de), *see* ROMERO DE TERREROS Y VINENT (M.)

***Terrific** (The) register, or record of crimes &c. 2v. 8º. 1825

Terrington. The registers of T., Co. York, 1599–1812. Transcr. &c. by W. Brigg. [Yorks. Parish Reg. Soc., 29]. 8º. [Leeds]. *p.p.* 1907

Terror. Бѣлый терроръ или выстрѣлъ, 1865, *n.d.*, *see* BELII.

Terry (Charles Sanford). Bach's chorals. p3. 8º. C. 1921
The Forty-five: narr. of last Jacobite rising, by contemp. hands. Ed. C. S. T. 8º. C. 1922
A hist. of Scotland to 1843. 8º. C. 1920
The Jacobites & the Union: narr., 1708, 15, 19, by contemp. hands. Ed. C. S. T. 8º. C. 1922
see BACH (J. S.) Cantata texts: w. reconstruct. of the Leipzig Liturgy of h. period [& intr. &c.] by C. S. T., 1926.

Terry (Michael), *F.R.G.S.* Across unknown Australia. 8º. 1925

Terry (*Sir* **Richard Runciman).** On music's borders. 8º. 1927
see FOSS (H. J.), *ed.* Heritage of music: essays, by R. R. T. &c., 1927.

Terry (William H.) The Insurrection. 8º. *Cayme Press.* 1927
The Interregnum: 3 plays. [The great crime—The power of the sword—The return of the gown]. 8º. *Cayme Press.* 1928

Tersian (Tommaso R.) Arsace II: trag. lir. in 4 atti. [*In Armenian.* P2800]. s8º. Kostantnopolis. 1871

Tersteegen (Gerhard), *1697–1769.* *Auserlesene Lebensbeschr. heiliger Seelen &c. [*Pref. signed:* G. T. St.] 3B. s8º. Franckfurt u. Leipzig. 1733–43
Life &c. of G. T. w. sel. fr. h. letters & writings. Tr. by S. Jackson, 4th ed. s8º. 1846

Tertullian [TERTULLIEN; †TERTULLIAN (QUINTUS SEPTIMUS FLORENS)].

Opera, per Beatum Rhenanum eruta, adiectis singulorum lib. argumentis adnotat. &c. fol. Parisiis, *C. Guillard.* 1545

De praescriptionibus adv. haereticos, *see* MIGNE (J. P.), *ed.* Theologiae cursus, t1, 1860.

TRANSLATIONS.

The apology of T.; tr. & annot. by W. Reeve: & the Meditations of Marcus Aurelius Antoninus; tr. J. Collier. 8°. [1889]

Conc. the resurrection of the flesh. [Tr., w. intr. & notes] by A. Souter. [Trans. of Xtn. lit., s2, Lat. texts]. s8°. 1922

see HOPPE (H.) Syntax u. Stil d. T., 1903.

,, KAYE (J.) Eccl. hist. of the 2nd & 3rd c. illust. f. T., 1889.

,, MORGAN (*Rev.* J.) Importance of T. in develop. of Xtn. dogma, 1928.

,, NÖSSELT (J. A.) Opusc. fasc. 3 (De vera aetate &c. script. T. disput), 1817.

,, ROBERTS (R. E.) Theol. of T., 1924.

,, ZIMMERMANN (M.) Diss. ad illud T. Apol. cap. 18: Fiunt &c. Xtn., 1662.

Tervishean (Serovbe). [Indo-European prim. language. *In Armenian*]. 8°. K. Polis. 1885

Tesdorpf (Oscar L.), *see* MEYER (E. L.) & O. L. T. Hamburg. Wappen u. Genealogien: [*enl. ed.*], 1890.

Tesi-Passerini (Carlo). Pio IX e il suo tempo. Collab. P. Zannelli. 3v. sm. fol. Firenze. 1877–81

Tesoro dei novellieri ital. scelti dal 13 al 19 sec. e pubbl. p. c. di G. Zirardini. 2p. 8°. Parigi. 1847

Tessier (Andrea), *ed.* Sette lettere ined. d'illustri Italiani dei sec. 18 e 19. [Nozze Peregalli—Albrizzi. N124]. 8°. Rovigo. 1856

see GUALANDI (M. A.) Lettera di M. G. e risposta di A. T. int. a. G. Gherardini &c., 1855.

Tessmann (Günter). Die Bubi auf Fernando Poo. Völkerkundl. Einzelbeschr. Hrsg. O. Reche. 4°. Hagen i W. 1923

Tesson (L.) Le Mont Valérien: hist., 1400–1845, *see* PARIS: COMMISSION MUNIC. DE VIEUX P. Procès-verbaux, 1921.

Testa de Nevill. Liber feodorum. The book of fees T. de N. Reformed f. the earliest MSS. by the deputy keeper of the Records. 2p. la8°. 1920–23

Testamenta Leodiensia. Wills of Leeds, Pontefract, Wakefield &c., 1539–53. Extr. & ed. by G. D. Lumb. [Thoresby Soc., 19]. 8°. *p.p.* Leeds. 1913

Testi (*il conte* **Fulvio Lodovico),** *1593–1646.* L'Arsinda. Dramma. [*b. w.* Opere, 1656]. s8°. 1659

Opere. [Rime-Poesie lir. [1], 2, 3—L'Arsinda]. Poesie lir. p2, 3 *have sep. tps.* 1652 & 1655. s8°. Venetia. 1656

Testimonies, *Books of, see* HARRIS (J. R.) Testimonies; by H. w. assist. of V. Burch, p2, 1920.

Testoni (Alfredo).

see SANDRI (M.) A. T., 1919.

,, TREBBI (O.) A. T., 1926.

Tettelbach (Henricus). Propos. de verbis Jehovae Exod. 20. Non facies tibi sculptile &c. Præs. D. Rungio. [P2640]. s4°. Wittebergae. 1597

Tettoni (Leone) & F. Saladini. Dict. of heraldic terms in Lat., Ital., Fr. & Eng. [*& Ital. armory &c. of families*]. Comp. f. T. & S.'s "Teatro araldico" by W. Dickinson. [*MS.*] fol. *n.d.*

Tetzel (Johann) [TEZELIUS (J.)], *see* MAYER (J. F.) De J. T., 1717.

Teuber (Christian Andreas). Tract. de utilitate linguæ Anglicanæ in explic. Scripturæ &c. s8°. Lipsiæ. 1733

Wahrscheinl. Muthmassung v. d. jüd. Oster-Liede: Ein Zickelein &c. [P431]. s4°. L. 1732

Teuber (E.), *see* ROTHMANN (M.) & E. T. Aus d. Anthropoidenstation auf Teneriffa, 1, v. M. R. & E. T., 1915.

Teudecarius, *see* PROVANA DI COLLEGNO (L.) Donazione di T. (810), ossia Cumiana dal sec. 9 al 15, 1885.

Teufelsdröckh *Junior, ps.*

Gladstone government. [P2560]. 8°. [1885]

Teufenbach, *Family of, see* MELL (A.) Regesten z. Gesch. d. Fam. v. T. in Steiermark, 1074–1547, 1905.

Teutleben (Valentin), *bp. of Hildesheim, see* CHARLES V, *Emp. of Germany.* Röm. K. M. u. gemein. Stende des heil. Reichs Ordnungen &c., 1538.

Teutsch [TEUTSCHE]. *Ein new Klaglied Teutsche Michel genannt wider alle Sprachverderber, [1637? *facs.*], *see* FREYTAG (G.) Bilder, B4, 1925.

Teutsch Kircheampt &c., 1525, 1848, *see* STRASSBURG.

Teutsch (Friedrich). Gesch. d. ev. Kirche in Siebenbürgen. [1150–1907]. 2B. 8°. Hermannstadt. 1921–22

Te Winkel (Jan). De Ontwikkelingsgang der Nederl. Letterkunde. 5d. *in* 6v. [4i, ii]. la8°. Haarlem. 1908–21

Texas, *University of, see* BYRON (*Ld.*) Descr. cat. of exhib. of MSS. & 1st ed. of B., Univ. of T., 1924; comp. &c. by R. H. Griffith &c., 1924.

Text & Translation Society.

see CONYBEARE (F. C.) The Armenian version of Revelation & Cyril of Alexandria's Scholia on the Incarnation &c., 1907.

,, EPHRAIM, *St.* Prose refut. of Mani &c.; transcr. C. W. Mitchell, v2, 1921.

,, SEVERUS, *pat. of Antioch.* 6th bk. of the sel. letters of S.; ed. & tr. E. W. Brooks, 4p, 1902–4.

Texte u. Forschungen z. Byzantinisch-Neugriech. Philologie, 1922 &c., *see* BYZANTINISCH-NEUGRIECH. JAHRBÜCHER, Beihefte, 1922 &c.

Texte und Untersuchungen z. Gesch. d. altchristl. Litt. Hrsg. v. Gebhardt u. Harnack. B36iii, 43, 44v. N.F., 5iii. 8°. L. 1900–24

see HARNACK (C. G. A. v.) Die Pfaff'schen Irenäus-Fragmente als Fälschungen nachgewiesen &c., 1900. [N.F., 5iii.]

,, IRENAEUS, *St.* Armen. Irenaeusfragmente m. deut. Übers. hrsg. v. H. Jordan, 1913. [36iii.]

,, JESUS CHRIST. Gespräche Jesu mit s. Jüngern nach d. Auferstehung; hrsg. &c. C. Schmidt, 1919. [43.]

,, LOOFS (F.) Paulus v. Samosata, 1924. [44v.]

Textor (Johann Wolfgang). Synopsis juris gentium (1680). [C.I. of Wash.] 2v. la8°. Wash. 1916

Texts & studies: contrib. to Biblical & patristic literature. Ed. J. A. Robinson. v9i, ii. 8°. C. 1922–26

9i, ii. Pelagius's expos. of 13 epistles of St. Paul: intr. [by A. Souter] & Text.

Teza (Emilio).

Armenia: discorso. [Atti d. R. Istit. Ven., s7, t5. P2795]. 8°. Venezia. 1894

Cose armene: discorso. [Estr. d. Atti d. R. Istit. Ven., s7, t1. P2795]. 8°. Venezia. 1890

Del Saule Alfieriano; tr. in Armeno dal P. A. Bagratuni: nota. [Dagli Atti &c. d. R. Accad. di Padova, v11. P2795]. 8°. Padova. 1895

Dell' "Essaemero" di Giorgio Piside sec. la ant. vers. arm. [R. Accad. d. Lincei, Estr. d. Rend., v2, 1893. P2795]. 8°. 1893

Delle sentenze morali di filosofi greci scelte e tr. da Armeni. [R. Accad. d. Lincei, Estr. d. Rend., 1893. P2795]. 8°. 1893

Le geste di S. Cristoforo n. tradiz. armena. [Estr. d. Atti d. R. Istit. Veneto di Sci. &c., s7, t6. P2795]. 8°. Venezia. 1895

Il libro dei 7 savi n. lett. armena. [Atti d. R. Istit. Veneto di Sci. &c., t65, p2. P2803]. 8°. Venezia. 1906

La natura dell'uomo di Nemesio e le vecch. tr. in Ital. & Armeno. [Estr. d. Atti d. R. Istit. Veneto, s7, t3. P2795]. 8°. Venezia. 1895

Nemesiana. [R. Accad. d. Lincei, Estr. d. Rend., v2. P2795]. 8°. 1893

La storia dei Vardaniani di Eliseo. [R. Accad. d. Lincei. Sci. morali &c. Estr. d. v2. P2795]. 8°. 1893

Thabaud de Latouche (Hyacinthe Joseph Alexander) [HENRI DE LATOUCHE], *see* SÉGU (F.) Un maître de Balzac méconnu, H. de L., 1928.

Thach (Charles Coleman), *Jr.* The creation of the presidency, 1775–89. [Johns Hopkins Univ.] 8°. Baltimore. 1922

Thackeray (Henry St. John). The Septuagint & Jewish worship: study in origins. Schweich lect. [Brit. Acad.] la8°. 1921

Some aspects of the Greek Old Test. Foreword by M. Gaster. s8°. [1927]

Thackeray (William Makepeace).

Works. 26v. 8°. 1887–94

The book of snobs—Christmas books—Sketches & travels in London [*each w. sep. tp. & pagin.*] s8°. 1900

Contribs. to Punch &c. s8°. 1900

The English humourists of the 18c. 2nd ed. rev. 8°. 1853

Essays, reviews &c. s8°. 1900

Hist. of Henry Esmond. 3rd ed. 3v. s8°. 1853

,, ,, [New Cent. Lib.] s8°. 1902

,, ,, Ed., w. intr. & notes by T. C. & W. Snow. Intr. by G. Saintsbury. 2nd ed. s8°. O. 1915

The Kickleburys on the Rhine. s8°. 1866

The landscape painters of Eng.: steel engravings by L. Marvy. Notices by T. 4°. [1850]

The Newcomes. s8°. 1906

The Paris sketch book—The Irish sk. bk.—Notes of a journey f. Cornhill to Grand Cairo [*each w. sep. tp. & pagin.*] s8°. 1900

Pendennis. s8°. 1906

Thackeray centenary, 1911. Exhibition. Pr. for the Titmarsh Club. [P2867]. s8°. [1911]

The Virginians. s8°. 1905

TRANSLATIONS.

Gesch. d. S. Titmarsh u. d. gross. Hoggarty-Diamanten. [Einführ. *by* W. Miessner. Tr. Bücher d. Deut. Hauses, R1, B7]. s8°. 1908

Das Snobsbuch. Übers. v. E. U. Witte. s8°. L. [1913?]

see CHANCELLOR (E. B.) The London of T., 1923.

Thackeray (William Makepeace) [*continued*].

see Furniss (H.) How &c. I illustrated T., 1912.

,, Hall (T.) Ill. cat. of notable first eds., w. Baxter coll. of T. letters, 1921.

,, Reid (W.) Th. in America, 1907.

see Ritchie (*Mrs.* R. T.) Letters, w. 42 addit. letters f. T., 1924.

,, Van Duzer (H. S.) A T. library, 1922.

Thaddaeus, *Saint, Apostle* [Addaeus ; †Jude]. [*Martyrdom & invention of relics of St. Th. & Sandukht. *In Armenian.* Soferq Hayk., v8]. s8°. i Venetik. 1853

see Dashean (H.) [Doct. of the Apostles, Canons of T. &c. : comm. & text *in Armen.*], 1896.

Thalbitzer (William). The Ammassalik Eskimo: contrib. to ethnology of East Greenland natives. Ed. W. T. 2p. la8°. Copenhagen. 1914–23

1, Results of G. Holm's exped., 1883–5 & G. Amdrup's exped., 1898–1900, in papers by G. Holm, S. Hansen, H. Rink &c. 2, H. Thuren, On Eskimo music in Greenland—W. Thalbitzer & H. Thuren, Melodies f. E. Greenland—W. Thalbitzer, Language & folklore.

Thaler (Alwin). Shakspere to Sheridan: the theatre of yesterday & to-day. 8°. Camb. [Mass.] 1922

Thallóczy (Ludwig v.) Bruchstücke aus d. Gesch. d. nordwestl. Balkanländer. [Sep.-Abdr. aus Wiss. Mittheil. aus Bosnien &c., B3. P1789]. la8°. Wien. 1895

Thalyaeus (Martinus Z.) Anatome Samosatenianismi, sive censura resp. &c. ad argumenta Orthodoxorum de doct. S. S. Trinitatis &c. s8°. Lugd. Batav. 1634

Thamar, *queen of Georgia, d. 1212/13* [Tamara], *see* Chakhrukhadze. Пѣвецъ Т. (*12c. Georgian text &c.*) ; изд. Н. Марръ, 1902.

Thamer (Johann Heinrich). Schediasma de orig. &c. pericoparum quae Evangelia & Epistolae vocantur atque diebus Dominicis, Festis &c. praeleguntur &c. s4°. Jenae. 1734

Thames.

Lithographic sketch of N. bank of Thames f. Westminster Bridge to London Br. shewing prop. quay &c. suggested by Lt.-Col. Trench. obl.4°. 1825

*Pilot's guide for the river T., S.-E. coast, & Strait of Dover. 3rd ed. 8°. 1913

*Remarks conc. the encroachments on the T., 1771, *see* Sharp (G.)

*Sketches & mem. of works for tunnel under the T. f. Rotherhithe to Wapping. s8°. [*w. folded plan*]. 1828

T. Conservancy. Bye-laws &c. [P2873]. 8°. 1902

Thanchum, *ben Joseph, of Jerusalem* [Tanchum]. Ad libros Vet. Test. comm. Arab. spec. unacum annotat. in aliquot loca libri Judicum. Praes. C. F. Schnurrer, resp. A. F. Fischer. [P427]. s4°. Tubingae. [1791]

Thane (Elswyth). Echo answers. s8°. [1927]

Tharau (Hans). Kloster Rossdyk. Palette u. Krone. 2 Novellen. s8°. Bielefeld. 1871

Tharaud (Charles), *see* Tharaud (Jean).

Tharaud (Ernest), *see* Tharaud (Jérôme).

Tharaud (Jérôme) [*i.e.* Ernest] **& Jean** [*i.e.* Charles] **Tharaud.**

L'an prochain à Jérusalem ! s8°. [1924]

La bataille à Scutari. [27e éd.] s8°. [1926]

Le chemin de Damas. s8°. [1923]

,, ,, s8°. [1925 ?]

Un grand maître [Barrès] n'est plus. 8°. [1927]

La maîtresse servante. 8°. 1922

Mes années chez Barrès. s8°. [1928]

Notre cher Péguy. 2[t]. s8°. [1926]

L'ombre de la croix. s8°. [1920]

Petite hist. des Juifs. [26e éd.] s8°. [1927]

Quand Israël est roi. s8°. [1921]

La randonnée de Samba Diouf. s8°. [1922]

Une relève. s8°. [1924]

Rendez-vous Espagnols. s8°. [1925]

La rose de Sâron. s8°. [1927]

Un royaume de Dieu. s8°. [1920]

La tragédie de Ravaillac. [repr.] s8°. [1922]

La vie & la mort de Déroulède. s8°. [1925]

see Bonnerot (J.) J. & J. T., leur œuvre, 1927.

Thargum, *see* Targum.

Thauler (Johann), *see* Tauler (J.)

Thaw (Harry K.)

Trial of H. T. Ed. F. A. Mackenzie. 8°. [1928]

Thayer (Alexander Wheelock). The life of Ludwig van Beethoven. Ed., rev. &c. by H. E. Krehbiel. 3v. la8°. N.Y. 1921

Thayer (John). An acc. of the conversion of the Rev. J. Thayer. Wr. by himself. [*2 tps., Eng. & Port.*] s8°. Lisbon. 1788

Thayer (William Roscoe). George Washington. 8°. [1922]

see Chamberlain (J. L.) Universities & th. sons; spec. eds., Harvard, W. R. T. &c., 5v, 1898–1900.

Thayer Ojeda (Tomás). Apuntes para la hist. ecón. y soc. de Chile, 1540–65. la8°. Santiago de Chile. 1920

Las biog. de los dos " Cristóbales de Molina," publ. por C. A. Romero. la8°. Santiago. 1920

Ensayo crít. s. alg. obras hist. utiliz. para el estudio de la conq. de Chile. la8°. Santiago de Chile. 1917

Reseña hist.-biog. de los eclesiásticos en el descubr. y conq. de Chile. 8°. Santiago de Chile. 1921

Theal (George MacCall). Cat. of books &c. rel. to Africa south of the Zambesi, in coll. of T. &c., w. notes. 8°. Capetown. [1912]

S. Africa. [Story of the Nations]. [12th impr.] 8°. [1925]

Theatre [Théâtre]. T. choisi du 18e s., choix de pièces d. meilleurs aut.: Regnard, Le Sage, Destouches, Dancourt, Collin d'Harleville, Piron, Gresset, Sedaine &c. 2t. s8°. [1914]

T. de l'Hermitage de Catherine II, 1799, *see* Catherine II, *emp. of Russia.*

*T. (The) of Iaponia's constancy &c., 1624, *see* Japonia.

***Theatrum** amoris divini & humani, emblematis &c. expressi Lat. Gall. Hispan. Flandricis versibus illust. [*Engr. tp. reads* Amoris div. & hum. antipathia, ed. 3, 1670]. s8°. Antverpiae. 1655

Thebaldeo, *da Ferrara, see* Tibaldeo (A.)

Thebaud (Simon), *bp. of London, aft. abp. of Canterbury, see* Sudbury (Simon *of*).

Thédenat (Henry). Pompéi: vie publique. [Villes d'art célèbres]. n. éd. la8°. 1910

see Héron de Villefosse (A.) & H. T. Cachets d'oculistes romains, t1, 1882.

Thedisius, *bp. of Turin, see* Camilla (Tedisio di).

Theele (Josef). Rheinische Buchkunst. la8°. Köln. 1925

Theiner (Augustin). Hist. du Pontificat de Clément XIV. Tr. par P. de Geslin. 2t. 8°. 1852

Vetera mon. Poloniae et Lithuaniae gentiumque finit. historiam illustr. 4t. fol. Romae. 1860–64

1, 1217–1409. 2, 1410–1572. 3, 1585–1696. 4, 1697–1775.

Theiner (Johann Anton). De Pseudo-Isidoriana canonum coll. Diss. 8°. Vratislaviae. 1827

Thelwall (Algernon Sidney), *editor.* Proc. of the Anti-Maynooth conf. of 1845. W. an hist. introd. &c. [*2 pag.*] 8°. 1845

Themistius, *Euphrada, see* Schenkl (H.) Beitr. z. Textgesch. d. Reden d. T., 1919.

Thengberg (Pehr Adrian), *see* Alander (P. A.) De relig. Xtna. in Vestrogotiam introd., 1839.

Theobald (Leonhard). Das Leben u. Wirken d. Tendenzdramatikers d. Reformationszeit, T. Naogeorgus seit s. Flucht aus Sachsen. [Quellen &c. aus d. Gesch. d. Reformationsjhdts., B4]. 8°. L. 1908

Theobald (Simon *of*), *bp. of London, aft. abp. of Canterbury, see* Sudbury (Simon *of*).

Theobald (Zacharias). Bellum Hussiticum, quo J. Hussii vita &c. comprehenditur &c. fol. Francofurti. 1621

Salomonis Kirchenbraut: Erkl. d Hohenlieds &c. s4°. Nürnberg. 1622

Widertaufferischer Geist. Das ist: Bericht was Jammer &c. die alten Widertauffer gestifftet &c. s4°. Nürnberg. 1623

Theocritus. Θεοκρίτου, Μόσχου, Βίωνος, Σιμμίου τὰ σωζόμενα. Omnia cum interpret. Lat. Acc. notae &c. J. Scaligeri, I. Casauboni, D. Heinsii. 4p. [*each w. sep. pagin. & tp. dated* 1603, 1596, 1596, 1601]. s8°. *In Bibliopolio Commeliniano* [Heidelberg]. 1603

Idylls. Ed. w. intr. &c. R. J. Cholmeley. New ed. rev. 8°. 1919

Translations.

Bucoliques grecs ; texte établi & tr. par E. Legrand, t1, T., t2, Pseudo-T. &c., 1925–27, *see* Bucolic Poets.

Idylls. Tr. R. C. Trevelyan. la8°. *Casanova Soc.* 1925

Idylls of T., w. Bion & Moschus. Tr. by J. H. Hallard. [Broadway tr.] 4th ed. (rev. &c.) s8°. [1924]

T., Bion & Moschus. Rendered into prose, w. essay by A. Lang. [repr.] s8°. 1920

see Broughton (L. N.) Theocritean element in works of W. Wordsworth, 1920.

,, Rumpel (J.) Lexicon T., 1879.

,, Wendel (C.) Überlief. &c. d. T.-Scholien, 1920.

Theodericus, *Nidarholm* [Theodricus]. Hist. de antiq. regum Norwag., *see* Storm (G.) Monumenta, 1880.

Theodore, *abp. of Canterbury, Saint, see* Browne (G. F.) T. & Wilfrith, 1897.

Theodore, *Khertenavor &c., see* John IV, *of Otzun &c. Works (in Arm.)*, 1833.

Theodore, *bp. of Mopsuestia.*
see DUBOIS (H.) Ét. sur les princ. travaux exégét., en partic. sur ceux de T. de M., 1858.
,, PATTERSON (L.) T. of M. & mod. thought, 1926.
Theodore, *Prodromus.* Sur le grand & le petit (à Italicos), texte grec & notice, *see* TANNERY (P.) Mém. scient., t4, 1920.
Theodore, *Studita, Saint.* Enkomion auf d. hlgn. Arsenios [*Greek,* hrsg. Th. Nissen], *see* BYZANTINISCH-NEUGRIECH. JHBR., B1, 1920.
Theodore Alekseevich, *see* FEODOR ALEKSEEVICH.
Theodoret, *bp. of Cyrus.*
see EUSEBIUS. Eccl. hist. of E., T. &c.; tr. Parker, 3rd ed. rev., 1729.
,, SCHWARTZ (E.) Zur Schriftstellerei T.'s, 1922.
,, SOCRATES, *Scholasticus.* Eccl. hist. of S., T. &c.; abridg'd by S. Parker, 2p, 1707–12.
Theodoricus (Cunradus). Theses theol. de bonis operibus. Præs. J. Molthero. [P2626]. s4°. Marpurgi Catt. 1597
Theodoricus (Vitus), *see* DIETRICH (V.)
Theodorus, *archiep. Ultraject., see* CROON (T. V. D.)
Theodosia, *ps., see* STEELE (A.)
Theodosianus. Codex T., rec. P. Krueger, 1923 &c., *see* CODEX.
Theodosius, *of Alexandria, the grammarian.* Th. A. Canones, G. Choerobosci Scholia, Sophronii patriarchae Alexandrini excerpta. Rec. & apparatum crit. &c. adj. A. Hilgard. [Grammatici Graeci, p4i, ii]. 2v. 8°. Lipsiae, *Teubner.* 1894
Theodosius, *bp. of Nona, aft. abp. of Spalato (879–892), see* PEROJEVIĆ (M.) Ninski biskup T., 1922.
Theodosius I, *emperor of Rome, the Great* [*T. Magnus*], *see* STUFFKEN (J. H.) Diss. de T. M. in rem. Xtn. meritis &c., 1828.
Theodotus, *bp. of Ancyra.* Homélies [*Grec & Lat.*], *see* MARY, *the Virgin.* Homélies mariales byz.; éd. &c. M. Jugie, p2, 1926.
Theodricus, *see* THEODERICUS, *Nidarholm.*
Theofredus, *Saint, see* SAVIO (F.) Il monastero di S. T. di Cervere ed il culto di S. T. in Piemonte, 1896.
Theognis. Sententiae elegiacae, cum interpret. &c. Eliae Vineti. Acc. et opera sententiosa Phocylidis, Pythagoræ, Solonis &c. s8°. Basileæ. [1561]
see DIEHL (F.) Anthol. lyrica, v1, 1925.
,, FRERE (*Rt. Hon.* J. H.) Works, 2nd ed., v3, Tr. f. Aristophanes & T., 1874.
Theognostus, *monachus.* Homélie [*Grec & Lat.*], *see* MARY, *the Virgin.* Homélies mariales byz.; éd. &c. M. Jugie, 1922.
Theologi. Theologorum aliquot Græcorum veterum orthodoxorum libri Græci & iidem Latinitate donati &c. [*Ed. E. Gesner ?*]. 6p [*sep. tps. & pagins.*] fol. [Zürich]. 1560
1, Canones Sanctorum Apostolorum.
2, Ignatius, *bp. of Antioch.* Epistolæ 12; interp. I. Brunnero, 1559.
3, Athenagoras. Apologia pro Christianis &c., 1559.
4, —— De mortuorum resurrectione &c., 1560.
5, Aeneas Gazæus. Theophrastus sive de animarum immortalitate &c., 1559.
6, Cydonius. De contemnenda morte oratio, Hermiae Irrisio gentilium philos. &c., 1559.
Theologia. *De primis scientiarum elementis seu theologia naturalis. App.: De summo bono. Acc. Sexti Empyrici Adv. mathematicos decem modorum ἐποχῆς &c. [*4 pagins.*] fol. Regiomonti. 1734
Theologia Germanica, libellus aureus. Ed. nova accur. J. G. Pritio. s8°. Lipsiae. 1630
***Théologie** morale des Jesuites & nouv. casuistes &c., 1666, *see* JESUITS.
Theologische [THEOLOGISCHES]. Auserlesene theol. Bibl., 1780–92, *see* DÖDERLEIN (J. C.)
Neue [*&* Neuste] theol. Bibl. &c., 1760–76, *see* ERNESTI (J. A.)
Neues [*&* Neuestes] theol. Journal, 1793–1803, *see* NEUES THEOLOG. JOURNAL.
Theologische Annales d. 1e [-5e] Decennium d. 18 s.: oder Begriff d. Unschuld. Nachrichten, 1701–10, 1711–20, 1721–30, 1731–40, 1741–50. Nebst Suppl. &c. [*An epitome, comp. by* V. E. Löscher &c. *of the* Unschuldige Nachrichten, 1701–50, *q.v.*] s8°. L. 1715[-54]
Theologische Berichte v. neuen Büchern u. Schriften v. e. Gesellschaft zu Danzig ausgefertigt. [*Ed.* E. A. Bertling]. 110 Stücke [*in* 10v]. s8°. Danzig. 1764–73
Theologische Büchersaal darinnen v. d. Inhalte d. neu. theolog. Bücher &c. Nachr. gegeben wird. Vorrede v. J. G. Walch. B1, Jahr 1749. s8°. Jena. 1749
Theologische Literaturzeitung. Jhrg. 45–52. fol. L. 1920–27
Bibliogr. Beiblatt. Jhrg. 1–6. Die theolog. Lit. Bearb. v. K. D. Schmidt. 8°. L. [1922–27]
Theologische Monatschrift, 1801, 1802. Hrsg. J. C. W. Augusti. [*Each Jahr in 2B, w. sep. pagin., b. in 1v*]. s8°. Jena. 1801–2
Theology (The) & philos. in Cicero's Somnium Scipionis expl., 1751, *see* HORNE (G.)
Theology. A monthly journal of hist. Xty. Ed. E. G. Selwyn. v1–16. 8°. [1920–28]
Theon, *of Samos, Greek painter, see* SIX (J.) Theon, 1917.
Theon (Ælius). Progymnasmata emendata &c. Acc. interpret. Lat. [*Ed.* D. Heinsius]. [*b. w.* Theocritus, 1603]. s8°. Lugd. Batav. 1626
Theophanes, *called Isaacius, Saint* [*T. Confessor*; *T. Monachus*], *c. 758–818, see* METHODIUS, *Saint.* Vita S. Th. confess. [*in Greek*), ed. B. Latyšev, 1918.
Théophile [*de Viau*], *Sieur.* Œuvres poét. Texte choisi & ét. par L. R. Lefèvre, avec intr. & bibl. s8°. 1926
Theophilus, *of Adana, Saint.* Das niederdeut. Spiel v. T.; krit. Ausg. v. C. Sarauw, *see* KONG. DAN. VID. SELSK. Hist.-fil. Med., B8, 1923–24.
Theophrastus.
Characteres. Rec. H. Diels. s8°. O. [1909]
Characters. With tr. into Latin & notes &c. by R. Newton. 8°. O. 1754
Expositio Prisciani & Marsilii in T. de sensu ac phantasia & intellecti, *see* IAMBLICHUS *of Chalcis.* De mysteriis &c., 1497.
TRANSLATIONS.
Caractères. Texte établi & tr. par. O. Navarre. [Coll. des univ. de France]. s8°. 1920
Moral characters. Tr. W. Rayner. [*b. w.* †Hierocles. Comm., 1797]. 8°. Norwich. 1797
T. Moralische Charaktere. Übers. &c. v. J. D. Büchling. [*b. w.* Palaephatus v. den unglaubl. Begebenheiten, 1791]. s8°. Halle. 1791
see ALDINGTON (R.), *ed.* Bk. of "Characters" f. T. &c.; tr., 1924.
Theophrastus redivivus, *ps.* [*Citador; *tr. f. MS. in Latin. tp. wanting.* P468]. s8°. *n.p. n.d.*
Theophylactus, *abp. of Achrida.* Opera omnia [*w. tr. by* J. Œcolampadius; J. Lonicer; L. Sifanus; B. Finetti & A. Bongiovanni] cum prævia dissertatione [*by* G. F. B. M. de Rubeis] de ipsius T. gestis ac doctrina [Acc. Euthymii Zigabeni Comm. in Psalmos &c. opera A. Bongiovanni *w. sep. pagin.*] *Gr. & Lat.* 4t. fol. Venetiis. 1754–63
Libellus de iis in quibus Latini accusantur, *see* MINGARELLI (G. L.) Anecdotorum fasc., 1756.
Theopompos, *of Chios, the historian, see* HELLENICA Oxyrhynchia cum T. & Cratippi fragm., 1909.
***Theory** (The) of presumptive proof; includ. exam. of evid. of trial of Capt. Donnellan. 8°. 1815
Theosophical Society, *see* LÉVY (E.) Mrs. Besant & the pres. crisis in the Th. Soc.; tr., 1913.
Theosophy. *Introduction (An) to th. &c., v1, 1855, *see* WALTON (C.)
Théot (Catherine) [*ps.* "MÈRE DE DIEU"], *see* LENOTRE (G.) Le mysticisme révol.: Robespierre & la "Mère de Dieu," 1926.
Theotisca. *Incerti monachi Weissenburg. Catechesis Theotisca sec. 9 conscr., 1713, *see* CATECHESIS.
Theotocopuli (Domenico), *called El Greco.*
see COSSIO (M. B.) El Greco, *n.d.*
,, —— Lo que sabe de la vida del Greco, 1914.
,, DOMÉNECH (R.) The House of El Greco, *n.d.*
,, HISP. SOC. OF AMER. El G. in coll. of H.S., 1927.
,, MAYER (A. L.) El Greco, 2e A., 1916.
see MAYER (A. L.) Il Greco, 1921.
,, MEIER-GRAFE (J.) Spanische Reise, 1923; tr., 1926.
,, TRAPIER (E. DU G.) El Greco, 1925.
,, WILLUMSEN (J. F.) La jeunesse du peintre El G., 2t, 1927.
Theotokes (Nicephorus), *abp. of (1) Slavensk & Cherson, (2) Astrachan.* Σειρὰ ἑνὸς καὶ πεντήκοντα ὑπομνηματίστων εἰς τὴν Ὀκτάτευχον καὶ τὰ τῶν Βασιλείων. [*With Gr. text*]. Τύποις ἐκδόθεισα ἐπιμελείᾳ N. τοῦ Θ. 2t. fol. ἐν Λειψίᾳ. 1772–73
Theragāthā [THERA-THERĪ-GĀTHĀ]. Psalms of the early Buddhists (Thera-therī-gāthā). [Tr., w. intr.] by Mrs. Rhys Davids. [Pali Text Soc.] 2[v]. 8°. 1909–13
1, Psalms of the Sisters, w. chron. f. Comm. by Dhammapāla ent. "The elucidation of the highest meaning."
2, Psalms of the Brethren, w. sel. f. chron. in Dhammapāla's Comm. ent. "Paramattha-Dīpanī" (p5).
Theresa, *d'Avila, Saint, see* THERESA [*de Cepeda*], *de Jesus, Saint.*

Theresa [*de Cepeda*], *de Jesus, Saint.*

Letters. Compl. ed., tr. & annot. Intr. by Card. Gasquet. 4v. 8º. 1919–24
The life of S. T., wr. by herself. Tr. D. Lewis. 8º. 1870
*La muger grande; vida de S. Teresa con exemplos y doctrina, por el F. M. de T. 3t. 8º. 1807
Obras escogidas. Prec. de una carta del Fr. L. de Leon. s8º. Barcelona. *n.d.*

see BERTRAND (L. M. E.) Ste. T., 1927.
,, CAZAL (E.) Sainte Thérèse, 1921.
,, GALZY (J.) Ste. T. d'Avila, 1927.
,, GRAHAM (G. C.) Santa T.: su vida y su época; *tr.*, 1927.

Theresa, *de Jesus, Mother; 1576–1622, see* ALEXIA [*Le Clerc*].
Theresa, *St., of Lisieux; 1873–97* [MARIE FRANÇOISE THÉRÈSE MARTIN]. Saint Thérèse of Lisieux. Rev. tr. of Autobiog. & letters, w. st. of h. canonization &c. By T. N. Taylor. 8º. 1927
Theresa Christina Maria, *consort of Peter II, emp. of Brazil.* Trasladação dos restos mortaes de D. Pedro II e de D. T. C., *see* INSTITUTO HIST. &C. BRAZIL. Revista, tomos esp., 1925.
Théret (Auguste). Littérat. du Berry. Poésie. Le 19e s. avec H. de Latouche & E. Deschamps. 8º. 1902
Thériot (I.) Mexican mosses coll. by A. Brouard; tr., *see* SMITHSONIAN INST. Misc. coll., v78, 1926.
Thérive (André).

L'expatrié. s8º. 1921
Le français langue morte? . . . s8º. [1923]
Le plus grand péché. [Cahiers verts, 36]. s8º. 1924
,, ,, [20e éd.] s8º. 1924
Le retour d'Amazan, ou une hist. de la litt. fr. s8º. [1926]
Sans âme. s8º. 1928
Le voyage de M. Renan. Roman. s8º. 1922

Théroigne (Anne Josèphe), *de Méricourt, see* LACOUR (L.) 3 femmes de la Révol., 1900.
Thérouanne, *see* TÉROUANE.
Therry (John Joseph), *see* O'BRIEN (E. M.) Life & letters of J. J. T., 1922.
Théry (Edmond). Conséquences écon. de la Guerre pour la France. s8º. 1922
Therzean, *see* TERSIAN.
***Thesaurarium** trilingue publicum: being an introd. to Eng., Latin & Greek, 1689, *see* HOGARTH (RICHARD).
Thesaurus [THESAURI].
Thesauri consiliorum &c. 3v, 1671, *see* DEDEKENNUS (G.)
Th. disputat. theolog. in alma Sedanensi Acad., 2t, 1661, *see* DU MOULIN (P.)
Th. librorum rei Cath.: Hdbch. d. Bücherkunde &c., 2B, 1848–50, *see* STAHEL (L.)
Th. linguae Lat. Ed. auct. & cons. Acad. 5 german. Berolin. Gotting. Lips. Monac. Vindobon. v6, pl. 4º. L., *Teubner.* 1912–26
Th. temporum: Eusebii Chron. canon. hist. &c., 1606, *see* EUSEBIUS *Pamphili.*
Th. Theutonicae linguae. Schat d. Neder-duytscher spraken &c. dict Flameng tr. en Franç & en Lat. [*Pref. in French by* C. Plantin]. 4º. Antverpiae. 1573
These eventful years: 20th cent. in the making, 2v, 1924, *see* EVENTFUL.
Thesiger (Ernest). Practically true. 8º. 1927
Thespian dictionary (The), or dram. biog. of the present age. 2nd ed. w. addˢ. s8º. 1805
Theuriet (André). La chanoinesse. s8º. *Nelson.* [1912]
Reine des bois. s8º. 1921
Thévenin (Denis), *ps., see* DUHAMEL (G.)
Thévenin (Léon). Le retour d'Ariel. Roman. s8º. 1921
—— **& Georges Lemierre.** Les étapes d'un livre. 8º. 1922
Thevenot (E. H.) Essai hist. sur le vitrail. [P2505]. s8º. 1837
Thian (Raphael P.), *see* UNITED STATES. ARMY. Legisl. hist. of Gen. Staff, 1775–1901; comp. by R. P. T., 1901.
Thibaudet (Albert).

Le Bergsonisme. 3e éd. 8º. 2t. [1923]
La campagne avec Thucydide. 4e éd. s8º. 1922
Cluny. 8º. 1928
Gustave Flaubert, 1821–80. Sa vie—s. romans—s. style. s8º. [1922]
Les idées de Charles Maurras. 6e éd. s8º. 1920
Intérieurs: Baudelaire—Fromentin—Amiel. 8º. [1924]
Les princes lorrains [Barrès & Poincaré. Cahiers verts, 35]. s8º. 1924
La république des professeurs. s8º. 1927
La vie de M. Barrès. 3e éd. 8º. 1921

Thibaudet (Paul).
Paul Valéry. [Les cahiers verts, 25]. s8º. 1923
Thibault (G.), *see* DROZ (E.) & G. T. Poètes & musiciens du 15e s., 1924.
Thibaut (Georg Friedrich Wilhelm). Astronomie, Astrol. u. Mathematik. [Grundr. d. indo-ar. Phil., B3, H9. *no tp.*] la8º. Str. [1899]
Thibaw, *king of Burmah, see* MANDALAY. M. massacres: Upper Burma dur. reign of King T., 1884.
Thicknesse (Ralph). Poems. s8º. O. 1924
Thiele (Johann Carl Günther), *see* GÜNTHER THIELE (J. C.)
Thielle (Petrus Henricus de). Illustres ex Brit. hist. controversiae. s8º. Argentorati. [1731]
Thieme (Friedrich Wilhelm). Eng.-Germ. & Germ.-Eng. dict. Stereotyp-A. [2p *in* 1v]. 8º. *n.d.*
Thieme (Ulrich) & F. Becker. Allgem. Lexikon d. bildenden Künstler v. d. Antike b. zur Gegenwart. Begründet v. T. u. B. Hrsg. v. T. B11–22, Erman-Leitch. la8º. L. 1915–28
B14, 15, hrsg. U. T. u. F. C. Willis; 16–22, hrsg. v. H. Vollmer.
Thierry (A. Augustin) [A. AUGUSTIN-THIERRY]. Augustin Thierry, 1795–1856, d'ap. sa corresp. &c. Préf. de G. Hanotaux. 8º. 1922
La princesse Belgiojoso. 5e éd. 8º. 1926
Thierry (Albert). Le sourire blessé. 7e éd. s8º. 1922
Thierry (J. N. Augustin), *1795–1856.* 1er [2e *&* 3e] récit des temps mérovingiens, avec 6 dessins de J. P. Laurens. [3t]. atlas fol. 1881–83
see SAINT-SIMON (*le cte.* C. H. DE) & J. N. A. T. De la réörganis. de la soc. européenne, 1925.
,, THIERRY (A. A.) A. T., 1795–1856, d'ap. sa corresp. &c., 1922.
Thiers (Jean Bapt.), *see* L'ETOILE (P. DE). *L'ombre de M. T., ou rép. à la diss. de M. Lestocq s. la transl. de S. Firmin &c., 1712.
Thiers (L. Adolphe), *president of the French Republic.* The Mississippi Bubble: mem. of J. Law. Added, Auth. acc. of the Darien Exped. &c. Tr. & ed. F. S. Fiske. s8º. N.Y. 1864
see ALLISON (J. M. S.) T. & the French monarchy, 1926.
,, DOSNE (*Mme.* S. E.) Mémoires (1832–69), 2t, 1928.
,, HALÉVY (D.) Le courrier de M. Thiers, 1921.
Thiéry (*gén.* **Alfred)** [*ps.* CONSTITUTIONNEL SALARIÉ].
*Le ministère venge, ou apolog. de la nécess. d'une lég. de la presse &c. Par un constit. salarié. [*A. T.*] [P2553; 2772]. 8º. 1818
Thies (Louis), *see* HARVARD UNIVERSITY. Cat. of coll. of engravings bequeathed to H. Coll. by F. C. Gray; by L. T., 1869.
Thiess (Frank). Die Verdammten: Roman. s8º. St. 1924
Thijm (Joseph Albert Alderdingk).
*J. A. Alberdingk Thijm; door A. J. 8º. A. 1893
Thilo (Johann Karl). Comm. ad Synesii hymnum secundum, v1–24. [P558]. v22–24. [P2655]. 4º. Halis. 1842–43
Thimme (Margarete). Marlowe's "Jew of Malta," Stil- u. Echtheitsfragen. 8º. Halle. 1921
Thinet (Louis). Le non-lieu du fils à papa, *see* ŒUVRES libres, 68, 1927.
***Things** I shouldn't tell. By the a. of "Uncensored recollections." [2nd ed.] 8º. [1924]
Third. The 3rd winter of unemployment, 1922, *see* UNEMPLOYMENT.
Thiriakian (H. [J.]) [THIREAQEAN], *see* ARTAXERXES I. Artashir Babakan Karnamak; tr. H. Th., 1906.
Thirlwall (Connop), *bp. of St. David's.* Primitiæ; or, Essays & poems &c. By C. T., 11 years of age. Pref. by T. Thirlwall. s8º. 1809
Thirring (*Dr.* **Gustav).** West-Hungary. [East Europ. problems, No. 6. P2567]. s8º. 1920
Thirring (J. Hans). The ideas of Einstein's theory. Tr. R. A. B. Russell. s8º. [1921]
Thirsk. The parish register of T., Co. of York, 1556–1721. Transcr. & ed. by Col. J. Parker. [Yorks. Parish Reg. Soc., 42]. *p.p.* 8º. [Leeds]. 1911
***This** day's madness. By the a. of The house made with hands. 8º. [1926]
Thistle, *The Order of the.* Statutes of the O. of the T. [Ed. &c. N. H. Nicolas]. 4º. 1828
Thlkourantzin (Hovhannes), *see* JOHN *of Thlkouran.*
Thokhathzeti, *see* YONAN *Vardapet of Tokat.*
Tholuck (F. August G.)
Comm. on the Gospel of St. John. Tr. [C. P. Krauth]. 8º. E., *Clark.* 1860
Comm. on the Sermon on the Mount. Tr. R. L. Brown. 8º. E., *Clark.* 1860

Tholuck (F. August G.) [*continued*].
Disput. de Thoma Aquinate & Abaelardo interp. N. Test. [*Progr.* P558]. 4°. Halis. 1842
Der Geist d. luther. Theologen Wittenbergs im Verlaufe d. 17. Jhdts. 8°. Hamburg. 1852
Lebenszeugen d. luther. Kirche, vor u. währ. d. 30j. Krieges. 8°. 1859
Spicilegium ex commercio epistolico J. Gerhardi. [P2672]. 4°. Halae. 1864
see CALVIN (J.) Comm. on Joshua; tr. H. Beveridge; T.'s diss &c., 1854.
,, SPENER (P. J.) Litterarum a S. ad H. A. Franckium datarum spec. 1 *&* 2, 1854–57.

Thom (Douglas Armour). Child management, *see* UNITED STATES: LAB. Children's Bur., Publ. 143, 1925.
Habit clinics for the child of preschool age, *see* UNITED STATES: LAB. Children's bureau, Publ. 135, 1924.

Thoma (Franciscus). Sponsa Christi: wie das Wort, Catholisch, eine Nota d. Röm. Apost. kirchen &c. s4°. München. 1586

Thoma (Hans), *see* OSTINI (F., *Baron* v.) T. [Knackfuss, 46], 3e A., 1923.

Thomaeus (Nicolaus Leonicus), *see* LEONICO TOMEO (N.)

Thomas, *Ardzrouni.* [Hist. of the Ardzrouni. *In Armenian. Ed.* K. Patkanov]. la8°. S. Peterbourg. 1887
Hist. des Ardzrouni (10 c.); *tr., see* BROSSET (M. F.) Coll. d'histor. arm., t1, 1874.

Thomas, *de Celano.*
see LITTLE (A. G.) Some recently disc. Franciscan doc. & th. rel. to the 2nd life by C., &c., 1926.
,, WARREN (C. F. S.) Authorship &c. of the hymn Dies Irae [*attrib. to T. de C.*], 1902.

Thomas, *ex Charmes.* Comp. theologiæ dogmaticæ. 2a ed. Hispana. s8°. Matriti. 1825
Comp. theologiæ moralis. 2a ed. Hispana. s8°. Matriti. 1824
De castitate in usu matrimonii servanda, *see* MIGNE (J. P.), *ed.* Theol. cursus, t25, 1860.

Thomas *de Cobham, see* COBHAM (T. DE).

Thomas, *of Corbridge, abp. of York, see* CORBRIDGE (THOMAS *of*).

Thomas, *de Eccleston.* The coming of the Friars Minor to Eng. & Germany. Chron. of Br. T. of E. & Br. Jordan of Giano. Tr. f. crit. ed. of A. G. Little & H. Boehmer by E. G. Salter. 8°. 1926

Thomas, *a Jesu* [DIEGO DE AVILA]. De unione schismat. cum. eccl. cath. procuranda, *see* MIGNE (J. P.), *ed.* Theol. cursus, t5, 1841.

Thomas, *a Jesu, Span. Carmelite, d. 1627.* Thesaurus sapientiae divinæ, in gentium omnium salute procuranda. 8°. Antwerpiæ. 1613

Thomas, *of Jesus* [T. ALVARES DE ANDRADE], *see* THOMÉ *de Jesus.*

Thomas, *of Medzoph, monk* [THOVMA *Medjophetzov*]. [Hist. of Tamerlane &c. *In Armenian.* Galérie hist. armén. *Ed.* G. V. Chahnazarian. *b. w.* Moses *Kalank.* Hist., v2, 1860]. s8°. [Paris]. 1860
[Hist., 1441–43 &c. *In Armenian.* Ed. &c. K. Kostaneantz. P2806]. s8°. Tiflis. 1892

Thomas, *Saint & Apostle* [T. DIDYMUS: T. THE TWIN].
see D'CRUZ (F. A.) St. Thomas in India, 1922.
,, GERMANN (W.) Die Kirche d. Thomaschriften, 1877.
,, STAPLETON (J.) Tres Thomae, 1588.

Thomas, *Saint, Martyr, see* BECKET (THOMAS), *Saint.*

Thomas, *archdeacon, aft. abp. of Spalato, 1200–1268, see* ŠEGVIĆ (C.) Tommaso archid. di Spalato, 1914.

Thomas *of Villanova, Saint, abp. of Valentia, see* CORTE (C.) D. T. de V., 1658.

Thomas (A. Hermann).
see LONDON. Cal. of early mayor's court rolls, 1298–1307; ed. A. H. T., 1924.
,, —— Calendar of Plea & Memoranda Rolls, 1323–64; ed. A. H. T., 1926.

Thomas (Albert), *see* SOLANO (E. J.), *ed.* Labour as an internat. problem: essays by G. N. Barnes, A. T. &c., 1920.

Thomas (André).
Psychothérapie. Intr. de Prof. Dejerine. s8°. 1912

Thomas (Antoine), *archiviste paléographe.* Notice sur le ms. lat. 4788 du Vatican cont. une tr. franç. avec comm. par Maître Pierre de Paris, de la Consolatio philos. de Boèce, *see* BIBLIOTHÈQUE NAT. Notices, t41.
Nouv. essais de philologie franç. .... 8°. 1904

Thomas (Antoine Léonard), *1732–85, see* MICARD (E. J. P. N.) Écrivain acad. au 18s., A. L. T., 1924.

Thomas (David). A biblical liturgy, for use of evang. churches & homes. 5th ed. s8°. [c. 1861]

Thomas (David Yancey). One hundred years of the Monroe doctrine, 1823–1923. 8°. N.Y. 1923

Thomas (Edgar). The economics of small holdings. Pref. by C. S. Orwin. s8°. C. 1927

Thomas (Edward). Cloud Castle & o. papers. Foreword by W. H. Hudson. 8°. [1922]
Coll. poems. Forew. by W. De la Mare. 8°. 1920
Richard Jefferies, h. life & work. [repr.] s8°. [1911]
This England. An anthology. Comp. by E. T. s8°. 1915

Thomas (Ferdinandus), *M.D.* Conjecturae de orig., prima sede & lingua Hungarorum. s8°. Pestini. 1802

Thomas (Flora).
The builders of Milford. 8°. Haverfordwest. [1920]

Thomas (Frederick William), *see* EPIGRAPHIA INDICA; ed. F. W. T. &c., 1917–.

Thomas (Gabriel). Acc. of Pennsylvania & West New Jersey. Repr. f. orig. ed. of 1698. Intr. by C. T. Brady. 8°. Cleveland, *Ohio.* 1903

Thomas (Gilbert Oliver). Sparks fr. the fire: essays. s8°. 1923

Thomas (Harrison Cook). Return of the Democratic party to power in 1884. 8°. N.Y., *Columbia Univ.* 1919

Thomas (Henry), *D.Litt.* Shakespeare & Spain. 8°. O. 1922
Spanish 16th-cent. printing. la8°. 1926
see BRITISH MUSEUM. Sh.-title cat. of bks. pr. in France &c., 1924.
,, —— Sh.-title cat. of books pr. in Spain &c., 1921.

Thomas (Herbert Henry). Refractory materials: ganister, petrography &c., by T. &c., *see* GEOLOG. SURVEY. Spec. rep. on Min. resources, 16, 1920.
see GEOLOG. SURVEY OF SCOT. Memoirs. Tertiary &c. geology of Mull, Loch Aline &c.; w. Petrology by H. H. T. &c., 1924.

Thomas (Hubertus), *Leodius.* De Palatinarum orig. &c., *see* FREHER (M.) Orig. Palatin. comm., 1599.

Thomas (Isaiah). Hist. of printing in America, w. a biog. of printers & an acc. of newspapers &c. 2v. 8°. Worcester, [Mass.] 1810

Thomas (Ivor). Brit. carboniferous Orthotetinae, *see* GEOLOG. SURVEY OF ENG. &C. Mem.: Palaeontology, v1i, 1910.
Brit. carboniferous Producti, 1, Genera Pustula & Overtonia, *see* GEOLOG. SURVEY. OF ENG. &C. Mem.: Palæontology, v1iv, 1914.

Thomas (Jacob), *see* THOMASIUS (J.)

Thomas (*Rt. Hon.* James Henry), *M.P.*
When Labour rules. 8°. [1920]
see SNOWDEN (*Mrs.* E.), J. H. T. &c. What we want & why, 1922.

Thomas (Lowell). Beyond Khyber Pass. 8°. [1926]
With Lawrence in Arabia. 8°. N.Y. [1924]
,, ,, ...4th ed. 8°. [1925]
,, ,, ...16th ed. 8°. [1927]

Thomas (Margaret Haig), *see* RHONDDA (M. H. M., *2nd viscountess*).

Thomas (Norman), *see* LAIDLER (H. W.) & N. T., *edd.* New tactics in soc. conflict, 1926.

Thomas (Percy Goronwy).
English lit. before Chaucer. 8°. 1924

Thomas (R. Hughes), *see* BOMBAY: SEL. F. RECORDS. Hist. &c. conn. w. prov. of Oman, Muskat &c.; comp. by R. H. T., 1856.

Thomas (S. Evelyn). The principles & arithmetic of foreign exchange. 8°. 1921

Thomas (Shipley), *capt.* History of the A.E.F. 8°. N.Y. [1921]

Thomas (Thomas), *lexicographer, see* THOMASIUS (T.)

Thomas (W. N.) The development of bridges. s8°. Ealing. [1920]

Thomas (William), *clerk of the Council to Edward VI, see* ADAIR (E. R.) W. T., 1924.

Thomas (*Sir* William Beach).
How England becomes prairie. s8°. 1927

Thomasin (Simon). Rec. des figures, groupes, thermes, vases &c. de Versailles. Gravé par S. T. [*w. explan. notes in Fr., Lat., Ital. & Flem.*] s4°. Amsterdam. 1695

Thomasius (Christian). Delin. hist. jur. civ., *see* HOFFMANN (C. G.) Hist. jur. Rom.-Justin., v1ii, 1734.

Thomasius (Gottfried), *prof. at Leipzig, see* SPROTTA (G.) Insignia 4 Evangelistarum, præs. G. T., 1667.

Thomasius (Jacobus), *prof. at Leipzig.*
Curiöser Tractat von Zigeunern. Aus d. Lat. übers. v. M. M. [P2684]. s8°. Dressden. 1702
Diss. 63, mag. partem ad hist. philos. & eccl. pertin. Nunc ed. à C. Thomasio. s8°. Halae Magd. 1693
Thomasius (Thomas), *lexicographer.*
Dict. summa fide &c. emendatum. 11ª ed. s8°. 1619
Thomassin (Louis), *prêtre de l'Oratoire.* De adventu Christi, *see* MIGNE (J. P.), *ed.* Theol. cursus, t8, 1860.
Thomas-Stanford (Charles). Early editions of Euclid's Elements. [Bibliogr. Soc.] 4°. 1926
Wick: a contrib. to the hist. of Hove. 8°. Hove. 1923
see PRESTON. Abstract of Court rolls of the manor of P.; by C. T.-S., 1921.
Thomé, *de Jesus* [THOMÉ ALVARES DE ANDRADE]. The sufferings of the Son of God. Tr. R. Welton. v1. 8°. 1720
Thomle (E. A.), *ed.* Norske Herredags-Dombøger. Raekke 1 (1578–1604), 1–6, Navne Reg. 1–6; 2 (1607–23), 1–4. [Norske Hist. K.] 8°. 1893–1911
Thommen (Rudolf). Urkundenlehre, T1, Grundbegriffe Königs- u. Kaiserurkunden, 2ᵉ A., 1913, *see* GRUNDR. D. GESCHICHTSWISS.; Meister, 1ii, 1913.
Thompson (Alexander Hamilton).
Cathedral churches of England. 8°. 1925
Mystical elem. in Eng. poetry, *see* ENGLISH ASSOC. Essays &c., v8, 1922.
A short bibliog. of local hist. [Hist. Assoc. Leaflet, 72]. 8°. 1928
York Minster hist. tracts, 627–1927. [*By var. wr.*] Ed. A. H. T. 8°. 1927
Thompson (Benjamin), *dramatist.* The stranger, *see* INCHBALD (*Mrs.* E.) Brit. theatre, v24, 1808.
Thompson (Charles John S.) Mysteries of hist., w. acc. of some remark. characters &c. 8°. [1928]
The mystery & lure of perfume. 8°. [1927]
Thompson (Charles Manfred), *see* BOGART (E. L.) & C. M. T. The indust. state 1870–1893, 1920.
Thompson (Charles Thaddeus). The Peace Conf. day by day. With intr. letter by E. M. House. 8°. N.Y. [1920]
Thompson (*Maj.-Gen.* **Charles William).** Records of the Dorset Yeomanry. (Queen's Own, 1914–19). 8°. Sherborne. 1921
Thompson (David), *geographer etc. of N.W. Company, see* COCHRANE (C. N.) D. Thompson, explorer, 1924.
Thompson (Edith).
Conc. Sir John Crosby & h. hall. [P2877]. 8°. [1927]
Hist. of Eng. n. ed. rev. to 1923. s8°. 1923
see SPENDER (C.) & E. T. Bath, 1922.
Thompson (*Mrs.* **Edith)**, *see* BYWATERS (F.) & E. T. Trial of F. B. & E. T.; ed. F. Young, 1923.
Thompson (Edmund). *A mem. of E. T. formerly of Armin, late of Scarborough. 8°. *p.f.p.c.* 1855
Thompson (Edward Herbert), *Amer. archaeologist, see* WILLARD (T. A.) City of the sacred well: discov. & excav. of E. H. T. in Chi-chen Itza, 1926.
Thompson (Edward John).
An Indian day. [2nd impr.] 8°. 1927
Krishna Kumari. Hist. drama. s8°. 1924
The other side of the medal. s8°. 1925
Rabindranath Tagore, h. life & work. s8°. Calcutta. 1921
Suttee: Hindu rite of widow-burning. s8°. [1928]
These men thy friends. s8°. 1927
,, ,, [3rd impr.] s8°. 1927
—— **& A. M. Spencer.** Bengali relig. lyrics, Sākta. Sel. & tr. by E. J. T. & A. M. S. s8°. Calcutta. 1923
Thompson (Edward Raymond), *see* RAYMOND (E. T.), *ps.*
Thompson (Elbert Nevius Sebring). Literary bypaths of the Renaissance. 8°. New Haven, *Yale.* 1924
Thompson (F. W. Butt-), *see* BUTT-THOMPSON (F. W.)
Thompson (Francis), *poet.* Health & holiness. s8°. [1905]
see MÉGROZ (R. L.) F. T., the poet of earth in heaven, 1927.
,, STONEHILL (C. A.) &c. Bibliog. of mod. a., s2, 1925.
Thompson (*Rev.* **George)**, *LL.B., see* THOMSON (*Rev.* G.)
Thompson (George), *of York, see* FRANCISCO *de los Santos.* Descr. of the royal palace &c., the Escurial &c.; tr. G. T., 1760.
Thompson (George Carslake). A neglected aspect of the land question. [P2590]. s8°. 1883
Thompson (Henry Yates). Cat. of 14 illuminated MSS. & 15 early pr. bks. &c. prop. of H. Y. T., sold by Sotheby 22 June 1921. [*Illust.*] la8°. 1921
Thompson (Henry Yates) [*continued*].
Illust. cat. of pictures & portraits now at 19 Portman Square. la8°. *p.p.* 1921
Les mss. de la coll. H. Y. T.; [*by*] S. de Ricci, *see* SOC. FRANÇ. DE REPROD. DE MSS. Bull., Ann. 10, 1926.
Thompson (Herbert M.) An amateur's study of Llandaff Cathedral, w. bibliog. la8°. *p.f.p.c.* 1924
The purse & the conscience. Connection betw. economics & ethics. s8°. 1891
The theory of wages & its applic. to the 8 hours question &c. s8°. 1892
Thompson (Holland). The age of invention. [Chron. of Amer. Ser., v37]. 8°. New Haven, *Yale.* 1921
The new South. Social & industrial evolution. [Chron. of Amer. Ser., v42]. 8°. New Haven, *Yale.* 1919
Thompson (James Westfall).
Feudal Germany. la8°. Chicago. 1928
Reference studies in medieval hist. [rev. & enl. ed.] 3p. 8°. Chicago. 1923–24
Thompson (Joe), *fictitious character.* *The life & adv. of Joe Thompson. Wr. by himself. 2v. s8°. 1750
Thompson (Laura Amelia). Laws rel. to "mothers' pensions" in U.S., Canada, Denmark & N. Zealand, 1919, *see* UNITED STATES: LABOR.
Ref. on child labor &c., 1916–24, *see* UNITED STATES: LAB. Children's Bur., Publ. 147, 1925.
Thompson (Nathaniel). The tryal of N. Thompson, J. Farewell, W. Pain, June 1682. For wr. scandalous letters in rel. to death of Sir Edmund-Bury Godfrey. [P2606]. fol. 1682
Thompson (Nesta M.) Arno Holz & the origins of the new poetry. Naturalism & the dream motive in works of Gerhart Hauptmann. [Repr. f. Washington Univ. Studies, v8. P2518]. la8°. [Wash.] 1920
Thompson (Norcliffe G.) & F. L. Cannan. Hand-in-hand figure-skating. Intr. by J. H. Thomson. s8°. 1896
——, —— & *Visc.* **Doneraile.**
Combined hand-in-hand figure-skating. s8°. 1904
Thompson (P. A.) Lions led by donkeys: how victory in the Gt. War was achieved &c. 8°. [1927]
Thompson (Reginald Campbell).
Assyrian herbal: monogr. on Assyr. vegetable drugs, comm. in paper to Roy. Med. Soc., March 1924. [*MS., stencilled*]. fol. 1924
Assyrian medical texts f. originals in Brit. Museum. fol. 1923
Assyrian medical texts. [2p. Repr. f. Proc. of Roy. Soc. of Med., v17, 19. P2740]. la8°. 1924–26
The Brit. Mus. excav. at Abu Shahrain in Mesopotamia in 1918. [From Archæologia, v70. P2700]. 4°. O. 1920
Some notes on mod. Babylonia. [*From* J.R.A.S., Apr. 1923. P2686]. 8°. 1923
see GILGAMISH. Epic of G.; new tr. f. collation of cuneiform tablets in Brit. Mus. into Eng. hexameters by R. C. T., 1928.
Thompson (Robert), *of Oatland.*
Statist. survey of Co. of Meath. 8°. D. 1802
Thompson (Silvanus Phillips) [*ps.* F. R. S.]
*Calculus made easy. By F. R. S. s8°. 1910
Calculus made easy. 2nd ed. enl. s8°. 1921
The family & arms of Gilbert of Colchester. [P2618]. 8°. 1904
The manufacture of light. Lect. s8°. 1906
Thompson (Slason). Life of Eugene Field. 8°. N.Y. 1927
Thompson (Sylvia). The hounds of spring. [n. impr.] s8°. [1926]
The rough crossing. s8°. O. 1921
Thompson (Thomas), *of Boston, Mass., see* EAVES (L.) Legacy to wage-earning women, Brattleboro, Vermont, T. T. Trust, 1925.
Thompson (Thomas), *banker, of Hull, F.S.A.* Reasons for giving land to cottagers. [*b. w. h.* Tithes indef., 3rd ed., 1796]. 8°. Hull. [1803]
Tithes indefensible. 3rd ed. w. app. on commut. of tithes &c. 8°. York. 1796
Thompson (Thomas), *B.D., minister of Montgomery.*
Antichrist arraigned. With the tryall of Guides. 2p. [p2 *wanting*]. s4°. 1618
Thompson (Thomas Perronet). *Catechism on the corn laws. 14th ed. rev. & corr. Added, the art. on free trade, f. the Westminster review, No. 23 [Jan. 1830]. By a member of the Univ. of Camb. 8°. [1830]
,, ,, ...16th ed. [P2782]. 8°. 1832
Thompson (Warren Simpson). Population: st. in Mathusianism. 8°. N.Y., *Columbia Univ.* 1915

Thompson (William), *methodist preacher?.* *Extract of a letter f. a gent. in Ireland; to Mr. W. T. [Rebellion in Wexford]. [P2667]. s8°. 1798

Thompson (William), *dean of Raphoe.*
Poet. works. Coll. by T. Park. s8°. 1807
Sickness. A poem in 3 bks. [Bks. 2, 3 *wanting*]. 4°. 1745

Thom's Irish who's who, 1923. s8°. D. [1923]

Thomsen (Grimur). Ljóđmæli. s8°. Reykjavík. 1880

Thomsen (Hermann). Danzigs Handel u. Industrie. [P2565]. 8°. Danzig. 1921

Thomsen (Vilhelm). Den gotiske sprogklasses indflydelse på d. finske. 8°. København. 1869
Une inscr. de la trouvaille d'or de Nagy-Szent-Miklós, *see* KONGELIGT DAN. VID. SELSK. Hist.-fil. Med., B1, 1917–18.

Thomson, *The family of, see* THOMSON (T. R.) Hist. of family of T. of Corstorphine, 1926.

Thomson (A. Landsborough).
Problems of bird-migration. 8°. 1926

Thomson (*Rev.* **Adam**), *minister at Coldstream.* A compar. view of the Eng. & Scot. dissenters. s8°. E. 1830

Thomson (Andrew), *D.D., minister of St. George's, Edinburgh.*
Slavery condemned by Xty. s8°. E. [1847]

Thomson (Andrew), *D.D., of the U. Presbyt. Ch., Edinburgh.*
Hist. sketch of the orig. of the Secession Ch., by A. T. & The hist. of the rise of the Relief Ch., by G. Struthers. s8°. E. 1848

Thomson (*Sir* **Basil**). The criminal. 8°. [1925]
Queer people. 8°. [1922]

Thomson (*Brig.-Gen.* **Christopher Birdwood**).
Old Europe's suicide, 1912–19. s8°. [1920]
Victors & vanquished: new balance of power in Cent. & S.-E. Europe. s8°. [1924]

Thomson (David), *gardener.*
Handy book of the flower-garden. 3rd ed. 8°. E. 1876

Thomson (Ellis), *see* COLLINS (W. H.), T. T. QUIRKE & E. T. Michipicoten iron ranges, 1926.

Thomson (*Rev.* **George**), *LL.B., vicar of St. Gennys* [THOMPSON]. *Original sacred hymns. s8°. 1776

Thomson (*Hon.* **George M.**) The naturalisation of animals & plants in New Zealand. la8°. C. 1922

Thomson (Gladys Scott). Lords Lieutenants in the 16th cent.: st. in Tudor local admin. 8°. 1923

Thomson (Godfrey Hilton), *D.Sc.* Instinct, intelligence & character: an educ. psychology. 8°. [1924]
see BROWN (W.) & G. H. T. Essentials of mental measurement, 1921.

Thomson (Henry John), *see* LINDSAY (W. M.) & H. J. T. Anc. lore in med. Latin gloss., 1921.

Thomson (J. Maitland).
The public records of Scotland. 8°. Glasgow. 1922

Thomson (J. Stuart). The animal kingdom. s8°. 1923

Thomson (James), *D.Sc., LL.D.* Coll. papers in physics & engineering. Sel. & arr. &c. by Sir J. Larmor &c. 8°. C. 1912

Thomson (James), *F.S.A.Scot.*
The book of Silchester. 2v. 4°. 1924

Thomson (James), *the poet, 1700–48.*
Britannia, poem, 1729 [facs. repr.] fol. [O. 1925]
Poet. works. Coll. by T. Park. 2v. s8°. 1805
„ „ 2v. s8°. *Pickering.* 1830
Poet. works. [Mem. by Sir H. Nicolas. Aldine ed.] 2v. s8°. *n.d.*
Tancred & Sigismunda, *see* INCHBALD (E.) Brit. th., v13, 1808.

Thomson (James Alex. Kerr). Greeks & Barbarians. 8°. [1921]
Irony. 8°. [1926]

Thomson (*capt.* **Jocelyn Home**). Guide to the Explosives Act, 1875 &c. 3rd ed. s8°. 1917
see CUNDILL (J. P.) Dict. of explosives, entirely re-arr. &c. by J. H. T., 1895.
—— & *Sir* **B. Redwood.** Hdbk. on petroleum. 3rd ed. rev. & added to by A. Cooper-Key &c. 8°. 1913

Thomson (John Arthur).
Biology of birds. 8°. 1923
Concerning evolution. 8°. New Haven. 1925
The control of life. s8°. 1921
Everyday biology. s8°. [1923]
The haunts of life. 8°. 1921
Mountain & moorland. s8°. 1921
Nature all the year round. la8°. [1921]
Outline of science. Ed. J. A. T. 2v [*pagin. cont.*] la8°. [1921–2]
Science & religion. 8°. [1925]
The system of animate nature. Gifford Lect. 2v. 8°. 1920
Ways of living, nature & man. [*By var. wr.*] Ed. J. A. T. s8°. [1926]
What is man? s8°. [1923]
see GEDDES (P.) & J. A. T. Biology, 1925.
„ MARCHANT (*Sir* J.), *ed.* Control of parenthood, 1920.

Thomson (*Sir* **Joseph John**).
Beyond the electron. Lect. s8°. C. 1928
The electron in chemistry. Lect. 8°. Phila. 1923

Thomson (Mary R. H.), *see* EVANS (I. B. POLE), M. R. H. T. &c. Wastage in export citrus fruits f. S. Africa, 1921.
——, **V. A. Putterill &c.** Investig. on export citrus fruit f. S. Africa dur. 1921. [Union of S. Afr., Dept. of Agric., Bull. 1. P2820]. 8°. Pretoria. 1922

Thomson (N. H.) The Emerald Coast & Brittany. [4th ed.] s8°. Dinard. 1923

Thomson (Spencer).
Wanderings am. wild flowers &c. 3rd ed. s8°. 1856

Thomson (Theodore Radford). Hist. of the family of Thomson of Corstorphine. 8°. E. 1926

Thomson (William Burns), *medic. missionary.*
A mem. of W. J. Elmslie &c. 3rd ed. s8°. 1881

Thorburn (Archibald), *F.Z.S.* British mammals. Wr. & illustr. by A. T. 2v. 4°. 1920–21

Thorburn (John M.) Art & the unconscious. 8°. 1925

Thordarson (Olaf) [THORÐARSON]. Málhljóða—og málskrúðsrit: gram.-ret. afh.; udg. F. Jónsson, *see* KONG. DAN. VID. SELSK. Hist.-fil. Medd., B13, 1927.

Thorel (Oct.), *see* LE GRAS (N.) Vérit. discours: ét. hist. &c. par O. T., 1916.

Thoresby Society. Miscellanea. [Thoresby Soc., 2, 4, 9, 11, 15, 22, 24]. 7v. 8°. Leeds. 1891–1917
Publications. v1–24. 8°. Leeds. 1891–1917
see ADEL, *Yorks.* Reg. of parish ch. of A., 1606–1812 &c., 1895. [5.]
„ CALVERLEY. C. charters; transcr. by S. Margerison &c., v1, 1904. [6.]
„ COLMAN (F. S.) Hist. of parish of Barwick-in-Elmet, in Co. of York, 1908. [17.]
„ HOPE (*Sir* W. H. ST. J.) & J. BILSON. Architect. descr. of Kirkstall Abbey, 1907. [16.]
„ KIRSTALL, *abbey.* Coucher book of Cistercian abbey of K., 1904. [8.]
„ LEEDS. Parish Church reg., 1572–1757, 6v, 1891–1914. [1, 3, 7, 10, 13, 20.]
„ —— Reg. of chapels of parish ch., 1724–63, 1916. [23.]
„ LEEDS GRAMMAR SCHOOL. Admission books; ed. &c. E. Wilson, 1906. [14.]
„ METHLEY, *Yorks.* Registers, 1560–1812, 1903. [12.]
„ MOORMAN (F. W.) Place-names of West Riding of Yorkshire, 1910. [18.]
„ TESTAMENTA LEODIENSIA: wills of Leeds, Pontefract &c., 1539–53; ed. G. D. Lumb, 1913. [19.]
„ THORESBY (R.) Letters addr. to R. T., 1912. [21.]
„ THORESBY SOC., *above.* Miscellanea, 7v, 1891–1917. [2, 4, 9, 11, 15, 22, 24.]

Thoresby (Ralph), *F.R.S.* Letters addr. to R. T. Pr. f. orig. in poss. of Yorks. Arch. Soc. Ed. W. T. Lancaster. [Thoresby Soc., 21]. 8°. *p.p.* Leeds. 1912

Thorington (J. Monroe). Lyell & Freshfield glaciers, 1926, *see* SMITHSONIAN INST. Misc. coll., v78, 1927.

Thorlacius (Theodorus), *see* THORLÁKSSON (THÓRÐUR), *bp. of Skálholt.*

Thorláksson (Guđmundr), *bp. of Holar, see* HERMANNSSON (H.) 2 cartographers: G. T. &c., 1926.

Thorláksson (Thórður), *bp. of Skálholt* [THORLACIUS (THEODORUS)]. Diss. de Islandia &c. Sub praes. Æ. Strauch., 1666. ed. 2ª. [P444]. s4°. Wittebergae. 1670
see HERMANNSSON (H.) 2 cartographers: T. T. &c., 1926.

Thorn [THORUNIENSIS]. Acta Conventus Thorun., pro ineunda ratione componend. dissid. in relig., per regnum Poloniae. s4°. Varsaviae. 1646
Scripta partis reformatae in Colloquio Thorun., 1645, parti Romano-cathol. exhib. &c. Cum declar. partis Romano-cathol. de regula fidei &c. s4°. Berolini. 1646

Thorndike (Ashley Horace).
Literature in a changing age. 8°. N.Y. 1920

Thorndike (Herbert). A disc. of the right of the church in a state. [*Added,* A review, *w. sep. pagin.*] s8°. 1670
Just weights & measures. The present state of religion &c. s4°. 1662
Of the gov. of churches. s8°. C. 1641
Origines eccl.: sive de jure et potestate eccl. Christianæ. fol. Londini. 1674

Thorndike (Lynn). Hist. of magic & experimental science dur. the 1st 13 c. 2v. 8°. 1923
Medieval Europe: its development &c. 8°. 1920
A short hist. of civilization. la8°. [1927]

Thorndike (Russell). The Slype. s8°. 1927

Thorn-Drury (George). A little ark cont. pieces of 17th-c. verse. Coll. & ed. G. T.-D. 8°. 1921

*Some 17th cent. allusions to Shakespeare & h. works. 8°. 1920

„ „ More 17th cent. allusions to Shakespeare & h. works. [*b. w. above*]. 8°. 1924

Thorne. *Hist. & antiq. of Thorne, w. acc. of the drainage of Hatfield Chase. s8°. Thorne. 1829

Thorne (Atwood). Pink lustre pottery: hdbk. for collectors. Pref. by M. A. Buckmaster. la8°. 1926

Thörnell (Gustaf) [Thörnell (Per Gösta)]. Ad Scriptores Hist. Augustae & Ammianum Marcellinum adnot., *see* Kung. Hum. Vet.-Samf. i Uppsala. Skr., B24, 1927.

Thorneus (Eduardus), *see* Heshusius (T.) Gratiarum actio pro conversione E. T., 1567.

Thornhill. Reg. of the parish of T., 1580–1812. Ed. J. Charlesworth. [Yorks. Parish Reg. Soc., 28, 40]. 2p. 8°. [Wakefield]. *p.p.* 1907–11

Thorning-Engelstoft (Christian), *see* Engelstoft (C. T.)

Thornley (Isobel D.), *M.A.* The destruction of sanctuary, *see* Pollard (A. F.) Tudor studies, 1924.

Thornton (Abraham).

*Affecting case of Mary Ashford, includ. Trial of A. T. for the murder of M. A., at Warwick Assizes, Aug. 1817. 8°. 1817

Trial of A. T. Ed. Sir J. Hall. 8°. E. [1926]

see Holroyd (E.) Obs. on the case of A. T. &c., 1819.

Thornton (Frederic Du Pre) & R. A. Nicholson. Elem. Arabic first reading book. s8°. C. 1907

Thornton (*Lt.-Col.* Leslie Heber). Campaigners grave & gay: 4 soldiers of the 18th & 19th c. [M. de Saxe—Sir R. R. Gillespie—Lord Peterborough—J. Wolfe]. 8°. C. 1925

Light & shade in bygone India: st. of the soldier in I. [Career of Sir D. Baird]. 8°. 1927

Thornton (Robinson), *archd. of Midd.* Life of Nikon, *see* Russian. Lives of eminent prelates, 1854.

Thornton (W. Pugin), *see* Canterbury. Descr. &c. cat. of 2 old Dutch painted &c. windows in Roy. Museum &c., 1899.

Thoroddsen (Thorvaldr). Gesch. d. isländ. Vulkane, *see* Kong. Dan. Vid. Selsk. Skrifter, Række 8, B9, 1925.

Thorold (Anthony Wilson), *bp. of (1) Rochester, (2) Winchester.* The gospel of work. s8°. 1893

Thorp (Willard L.) Integration of indust. operation &c., 1924, *see* United States: Census.

Thorp (William), *dissenting minister of Bristol.* Catholic emancipation: an enquiry &c. [*b. w.* Kenyon (G. K., *b.*) Obs., 1810]. 8°. Bristol. 1813

Thorpe (Arthur Winton), *see* Burke (*Sir* J. B.) B.'s handbook to the Order of the Brit. Empire; ed. A. W. T., 1921.

Thorpe (Benjamin), *see* †Exeter Book. Codex Exoniensis: coll. of Anglo-Saxon poetry, w. Engl. tr. &c. by T., 1842.

Thorpe (*Sir* Thomas Edward).

Dict. of applied chemistry. rev. & enl. ed. 7v. 8°. 1921–27

Hist. of chemistry. 2v [*in* 1]. s8°. 1921

Thorpe (W. A.) Eng. & Irish glass. With intr. s4°. [1927]

Thorschmid (Justus Christian). Hesychio Milesio locum inter Xtianos vindic. J. C. T., defend. J. H. Rephunio. [P596]. s4°. Vitembergae. [1716]

Thorschmid (Urban Gottlob).

Crit. Lebensgesch. Anton Collins &c. s8°. Dresden. 1755

Versuch e. engelländ. Freydenker-Bibl. 4T. [*b. in* 2v]. s8°. Halle & Cassel. 1765–67

Thorsøe (Alex.)

Fra Kong Kristian IX's yngre dage. 8°. Kjøbenhavn. 1913

Kong Christian IX. 2. udg. 8°. København. [1906]

Thortharson, *see* Thordarson.

Thorunium, *see* Thorn.

Thou (Jacques Auguste de), *the elder, 1553–1617.* Les éloges des hommes savans tirez de l'Hist. de M. de Thou [*tr. f. Latin*]. Avec des adds. cont. l'abrégé de leur vie, le jugement & le cat. de leurs ouvrages, par A. Teissier. 3p *in* 2v. s8°. Genève & Berlin. 1683–1704

p3 *has t.:* Nouv. adds. aux Eloges, t3.

Posteritati J. A. Thuani poematium in quo argutias criticorum [J. B. Gallus (*i.e. J. Machault*) &c.] refellit. Opera I. Melanchthonis [*ps., i.e. P. de Chambrun. b. w.* Jonstonus (J.), *M.D.* De communione, 1658]. s8°. Amstelodami. 1722

A true narr. of conspiracy against King James &c. called the gun-powder-treason. Rendred into Engl. [by E. Stephens. *Foll. by*: The hist. of the massacres of the protestants at Paris &c., 1572 [*sep. pagin.*] [*b. w.* Stephens (E.) A discourse, 1674]. s4°. 1674

see Christie-Miller (S. R.) Cat. of a series of books f. lib. of J. A. de T., 1553–1617, 1920.

„ Stephens (E.) *A discourse conc. the original of the Powder-Plot &c. coll. out of Thuanus &c., 1674.

Thoughts. *Thoughts in the cloister & the crowd, 1835, *see* Helps (*Sir* A.)

*Thoughts on nature & religion, or an apology for the right of private judgment &c., 1774, *see* Blair (P.), *M.D.*

*Thoughts on the importance of religion. [P2467]. s8°. Stockport. 1814

Thouless (Robert Henry). The control of the mind. 8°. [1927]

Intr. to the psychology of religion. s8°. C. 1923

The Lady Julian: psycholog. study. 8°. 1924

Thoulouse, *see* Toulouse.

Thounis (Nicol), *see* Foulis (J.) & N. T. Protocol books, 1546–53 & 1559–64, 1927.

***Thousand** (A) Amer. men of mark of to-day, 1916, *see* American.

Thouvenin (*capitaine* L.) L'artillerie nouv.: munitions—tir—matériels. s8°. 1924

Thovez (Enrico). L'opera pittorica di V. Avondo. 28 tavole con intr. d. E. T. la8°. Torino. 1912

Thrace. Mémoire sur la T., adr. à la Soc. des Nations par le Comité Turc de la T. (30 avril 1922). [P2682]. 8°. Constantinople. 1922

Thrasher (Frederic M.) The gang: st. of 1313 gangs in Chicago. 8°. Chicago. [1927]

Three.

*Three godly &c. treatises, 1632, *see* Preston (J.)

Three great portrait painters, *see* Israels (J.) Rembrandt [*foll. by* F. Hals & Velasquez], 1909.

*The three ladies of London, 1584 [*ascr. to Robert Wilson*], *see* Collier (J. P.), *ed.* Five old plays, 1851.

*Three letters addr. to Visc. Melbourne, &c. on pres. state of parties, 1835, *see* Wallace (T.)

*The three lords & three ladies of London, 1590 [*ascr. to Robert Wilson*], *see* Collier (J. P.), *ed.* Five old plays, 1851.

Three months' visit. by the bp. of Capetown, 1856, *see* Gray (R.)

Thresh (John Clough), *see* Whitaker (W.) & J. C. T. Water supply of Essex f. underground sources, 1916.

***Thronus** justitiae: quomodo anima viri iusti se ipsam iudicet &c. Ex 4 Soc. Jesu patribus desumptus: P. L. de Ponte, P. J. A. de Paz, P. J. Pelecyo, P. Alfonso Rodriquez. s8°. Coloniae Agrippinae. 1624

Thucydides.

Hist. belli Peloponnesiaci cum tr. Lat. F. Hasii. Acced. Marcellini vita, &c. [*sep. pagin.*] [ed. J. F. Dübner]. la8°. Parisiis, *Didot.* 1869

Historiae. Rec. &c. H. S. Jones. 2t. s8°. O. [1898–1902]

Translations.

Hist. of the Peloponnesian War. Tr. W. Smith. 2v. 4°. 1753

„ „ Ann. 3 prelim. disc. Pref. The life &c. of the translator. 4th ed. 2v *in* 1. 8°. 1805

Hist. New & lit. version by D. Dale. 2v. s8°. *Bohn.* 1852–59

Thucydides. [v]2–4, Hist. of the Peloponnesian War. Bks. 3–8. With Eng. tr. by C. F. Smith. [Loeb Class. Lib.] s8°. 1920–23

Orationes plaeraeque in Lat. serm. conv., *see* Della Casa (G.) Carmina &c., 1610.

see Abbott (G. F.), T., 1925.

„ Bauer (C.) De lect. T. optima interpret. disciplina, 1753.

„ Gerstinger (H.) Bruchstücke e. ant. Komm. z. Archäologie d. T., 1925.

„ Henderson (B. W.) The gt. war betw. Athens & Sparta: companion to the milit. hist. of T., 1927.

„ Sheppard (J. G.) & L. Evans. Notes on T., bks. 1–3, n. ed., 1889.

„ Täubler (E.) Archaeologie d. T., 1927.

„ Thibaudet (A.) La campagne avec Th., 1922.

Thuilier (*Capt.* Edward Henry Landor), *see* Smyth (*Capt.* R.) & E. H. L. T. Manual of surveying for India, 1851.

Thülemeyer (Heinrich Günther von). Dépêches, 1763–88. In de bewerking van R. Fruin; ingeleid &c. door H. T. Colenbrander. [Hist. Genoots. Werken, s3, 30]. 8°. A. 1912

Thulié (Henry). La lutte contre la dégénérescence & la criminalité. 2e éd. [P2564]. 8°. 1912

Thumb, *Family of, architects, see* Werneburg (R.) P. T. u. s. Familie, 1916.

Thumb (Albert). Die griech. Sprache, *see* Grundriss d. indogerm. Sprach-u. Altertumskunde, Abt. 2, B1, 1916.

Thumb (Peter), *see* Werneburg (R.) P. T. u. s. Familie, 1916.

Thumm (Theodor).
Disquis. de jubilæo antichristiano & indulgentiis pontif. &c. [P437]. s4°. Tubingae. 1625
Scultetus cacodoxus. Praes. T. T., resp. J. Falcone. [P599]. s4°. Tubingae. 1621
Scultetus iconclastes. Sub praes. T. T., resp. J. Falcone. [P599]. s4°. Tubingae. 1620
Tract. theolog. de bello &c. ed. 2a. [P444]. s4°. Tubingae. 1668
Tractatus, de bonis eccl. s4°. Tubingae. 1621

Thummerer (Johannes). Krämer u. Seelen. Ein deut. Grossstadtroman. s8°. L. 1920

Thun (Alphons). Ист. револ. движенія въ Россіи. Переводъ съ нѣмецкаго. Подъ ред. А. Э. Шишко. [P810]. s8°. *n.p.* 1903

Thun (*Graf* Joseph Maria von), *bp. of Gurck, see* Österreich. Oesterreich u. d. Papstwahl 1740: Samml. u. d. Acta legationis Rom. Josephi Episc. Gurcensis, 1875.

Thunmann (Johann Erich), *see* Schlözer (A. L. v.), *ed.* Isländ. Litt. &c., T1, 3 Anmerkungen gegen T., 1773.

Thura (Albert). Idea hist. litt. Danorum. s8°. Hamburgi. 1723

Thureau-Dangin (François). La chronologie des dynasties de Sumer & d'Accad. la8°. 1918
Recherches s. l'orig. de l'écriture cunéiforme. pl & Suppl. *in* 1v [*no more publ.*] 8°. 1898–99
Recueil de tablettes chaldéennes. la8°. 1903
Statuettes de Tello, *see* Acad. des Inscr. &c.: Fond. Piot. Mons. &c., t27, 1924.

Thuren (Hjalmar). On the Eskimo music in Greenland &c., *see* Thalbitzer (W.), *ed.* The Ammassalik Eskimo, p2, 1923.

Thurneysen (Eduard). Dostojewski. 8°. München. 1921

Thurneysen (Rudolf).
Die irische Helden- u. Königsage bis zum 17ten Jhdt. 2T [*in 1v. pagin. cont.*] 8°. Halle (Saale). 1921
Die kelt. Sprachen, *see* Grundriss d. indogerman. Sprach- u. Altertumskunde, Abt. 2, B1, 1916.
Zu irisch. Hss. u. Litteraturdenkmälern, 2 Ser., 1912–13, *see* Königl. Gesells. d. Wiss. z. Gött. Abhlgn., N.F., 14, 1913.
see Cōic conara fugill &c.; hrsg. &c. v. R. T., 1925.
,, Indogerman. Forsch., B45 (Festschr. f. R. T.), 1927.

Thurn und Taxis, *House of, see* Görs (G. F. A.) Thurn- u. T. Postwesen, 1907.

Thurn und Taxis (*Graf* Lamoral v.) Bekanntmachung d. Kaiserl. u. Span. Generaloberpostmeisters u. d. Verbesserungen im Postverkehr zw. England u. d. Kontinent [*in English*], (*facs.* c. 1660), *see* Freytag (G.) Bilder, B4, 1925.

Thurnwald (Richard). Die Gemeinde d. Bánaro. Forschungsreise, 1913–15. [Sonderausg. aus d. Zeitschr. f. vergl. Rechtswiss., B28, 29]. 8°. St. 1921

Thurston (Carl Hammond Philander). Art of looking at pictures: intr. to old masters. [repr.] s8°. N.Y. 1924

Thurston (Ernest Temple).
The Blue Peter. Play. s8°. [1924]
Charmeuse. [repr.] s8°. [1924]
The eye of the wift. s8°. [1922]
The forest fire: & o. stories. s8°. [1919]
The goose-feather bed. s8°. [1926]
The green bough. s8°. [1921]
Jane Carroll. s8°. [1927]
Judas Iscariot. Play. [*Signed copy*]. s8°. [1923]
The miracle. s8°. [1922]
Mr. Bottleby does something. s8°. [1925]
A roof & four walls. Comedy. s8°. [1923]

Thurston (Herbert), *S.J.*
Some inexactitudes of Mr. G. G. Coulton. s8°. [1927]

Thurtell (John).
see Egan (P.) Acc. of trial of J. T. &c., w. Recoll. of T., 1824.
,, Weare (W.) Compl. hist. of murder of Mr. W. by T. T. &c., 1824.
—— & J. Hunt. Trial. Ed. E. R. Watson. 8°. [1920]

Thynne (Roger). Churches of Rome. s8°. 1924

Thyraeus (Gulielmus). Discursus panegyrici de nominibus, tribulat. &c. S. Patricii; cum exhort. ad persec. ferendas. [*Ed.* P. Donovanus]. s8°. Duaci. 1617

Thyræus (Petrus). Daemoniaci, hoc est: de obsessis & spiritibus daemoniorum hominibus liber unus. Ed. 2a. corr. auct. s4°. Coloniæ Agripp. 1598

Thyrén (Johan Carl Wilhelm). Den första väpnade neutraliteten. Svensk-danska förbunden af 1690, 1691 & 1693 &c. [*Extr. f.* Lund Univ. Årsskr., T21, 22]. 4°. *n.d.*

Thysanodes (Georgius Nicolai), *ps., see* Csipkes (György).

Tibaldeo (Antonio) [Tebaldeo; Thebaldeo *da Ferrara*].
Opere del thebaldeo da Ferrara cū tabula. Sonetti 283, Dialogo 1, Epistole 3, Egloge 4, Desperata 1, Capituli 19. [132 leaves, *fol. Ai & last leaf* (*blank*) *wanting*]. 8°. *n.p. n.d.* [Venice, *C. de Pensis.* 1500 ?]
Opere. Sonetti, Dialoghi, Disperata, Epistole, Egloghe, Capitoli &c. 8°. [Venetia, *A. de Bindonis.* 1511]

Tibet. *Описаніе Тивета въ нынѣшнемъ его состояніи; переводъ съ Китайскаго, 1828, *see* Bichurin (J.)

Tibetan [Tübetisches]. 3 T. mysteries: Tchrimekundan, Nansal, Djroazanmo; tr. f. French version of J. Bacot &c., 1924, *see* Woolf (H. I.), *ed.*
Tibetan Book of the Dead, by W. Y. Evans-Wentz, 1927, *see* Bardo Thödol.
Tibetan tales f. Indian sources, tr. f. the Kahgyur, n. ed., 1926, *see* Bkah-Hgyur.
Tübet. (Ein) Gebetbuch. [Smon-lam-btschu &c.] 8°. L. 1835

Tibetanum. Alphabetum Tangu. sive T., 1773, *see* Alphabetum.

Tibullus (Albius). T. aliorumque carminum libri tres. Rec. &c. J. P. Postgate. 2a ed. s8°. O. [1914]
T. & les auteurs du Corpus Tibullianum. Text établi & tr. par M. Ponchont. [Coll. des univ. de Fr.] 8°. 1924
see Catullus (C. V.) C., T., Propertius, 1529; Opera, 1772.
,, —— C.; [w. tr. by F. W. Cornish]—T.; [w. tr. by J. P. Postgate] &c., 1919.
,, Pichard (L.) T. & les auteurs du Corpus Tibullianum; texte établi &c. par L. P., 1924.

Tichborne Case. In the Queen's Bench. The Q. agst. Castro, alias Orton, alias Tichborne. [T. v. Lushington &c.] [4v.] fol. *n.p.* [1871–72]
The T. romance: report of trial, T. v. Lushington, May 10 to July 7, 1871. 8°. [1871]
Trial at bar of Sir R. C. D. T. for perjury. Ed. Dr. Kenealy. Pref. Biog. sketch. Intr. *&* 8v. fol. 1875–80
see Brown (Joseph). The T.C. comp. w. prev. impostures, 1874.

Tichler (Jacob). Diss. de indole sacrorum emendat., a Zwinglio instit. s8°. Trajecti ad Rhenum. 1827

Tickell (Thomas). *Kensington garden. [*Poem*]. 4°. 1722
Poet. works. Coll. by T. Park. s8°. 1807

Ticknor (George). Letters to P. de Gayangos, f. orig. in coll. of Hisp. Soc. of Amer. Ed. C. L. Penney. s8°. N.Y. 1927

Tiddeman (Richard Hill). The water-supply of Oxfordshire, w. contrib. on rainfall by H. R. Mill. [Mems. of G.S.] 8°. 1910
see Dakyns (J. R.), R. H. T. &c. Geol. of the co. around Ingleborough, 1890.
,, —— Geol. of the co. around Mallerstang &c., 1891.
,, —— & J. G. Goodchild. Geol. of co. betw. Appleby, Ullswater & Haweswater, 1897.

Tiddy (Reginald John Elliott). The mummers' play. [Hist. &c., w. 33 unpubl. mumming plays]. With a mem. [Ed. D. R. Pye]. 8°. O. 1923

Tieck (J. Ludwig).
see Jost (W.) Von L. T. zu E. T. A. Hoffmann, 1921.
,, Lüdeke (H.) L. T. u. d. alte engl. Theater, 1922.

Tiele (Cornelius Petrus). Tiele-Söderbloms Kompendium d. Religionsgesch. 5e A. [Vorwort v. N. Söderblom]. s8°. 1920

Tiele (Pieter Anton). De Europeërs in d. Maleischen Archipel, 1509–1623, *see* Bijdragen tot de taal &c. v. Ned. Ind., volg. 4, dl, 3–6, 8, volg. 5, dl, 2, 1877–87.

Tielrooy (Johannes).
Conrad Busken Huet & la litt. franç. s8°. Haarlem. 1923

Tien (Anton).
Levant interpreter: polyglot dialogue book. s8°. 1879
Manual of colloquial Arabic. n. & rev. ed. s8°. 1891

Tiepolo (Giacomo).
Sopra Dante Allighieri. Disc. 8°. Venezia. 1864

Tiepolo (Lorenzo). Rel. dei consolati di Alessandria e di Soria, 1552–60. [*Ed.* D. Canal. Nozze Passi—Valier-Tiepolo. N124]. 8°. Venezia. 1857

Tiepolo (Paolo), *1523–85*. Commissione data d. doge Alvise Mocenigo a P. T. ambasc. a Roma, 1571, in prop. d. lega contro il Turco. [G. Moroni pubbl. *Ed.* E. A. Cicogna. Nozze Giustinian—Michiel. N134]. 8°. Venezia. 1845

Tiersot (Julien). Les Couperin. 8°. 1926
La musique dans la comédie de Molière. s8°. [1922]

Tietze (Hans). Alt-Wien in Wort u. Bild. Hrsg. v. H. T. 2. verm. A. 4°. Wien. 1926
Die Kunstsammlungen d. Stadt Salzburg. [Österr. Kunsttopographie, B16]. 4°. Wien. 1919
Michael Pacher u. s. Kreis. s8°. L. [1921]

Tighe (Hugh Usher). Hist. acc. of Cumner, w. partic. &c. resp. death of Ctss. of Leicester, also extr. f. Ashmole's Antiq. of Berks. 2nd ed. 8°. O. 1821

Tignonville (Guillaume). Tignonvillana ined.; [hrsg.] R. Eder, *see* Romanische Forschungen, B33, 1915.

Tigurinae. Orthodoxa T. eccl. ministrorum confessio &c., 1545, *see* Zürich.

Tihoti, *ps., see* Calderon (G.)

Tijdschrift voor Indische taal-, land- en volkenkunde, uitgeg. door het Bataviaasch Genootschap van Kunsten en Wetenschappen. dl–39. 8°. Batavia. 1853–95
d4–6 are also numbered N.S., dl–3; 7–9, s3, dl–3; 10–14, s4, dl–5; 15–17, s5, dl–3; 18–20, s6, dl–3.

Tikhomirov (Dmitry Ivanovich).
Книга для церковнослав. чтенія. изд. 11ое. чl. 8°. Москва. 1895

Tikhomirov (Lev Aleksandrovich).
Монархич. государственность. чl–3. *b. in* 1. 8°. Москва. 1905

Tikhonov (Tit. Ivanovich).
Земство въ Россіи и на окраинахъ. [P2450]. 8°. С.–П. 1907

Tikhoretskii. *Изъ соврем. жизни. Тихорѣцкій погромъ &c. [P2716]. s8°. [Genève]. 1902

Til (Salomon van). Comm. analyt. in var. libros prophet., cum justa rerum hist. collatos &c. Adj. diss. phil.-theol. & Acta Apostol. ad annales revocata. 3t. s4°. Lugduni Batav. 1744
Methodus concionandi &c. s8°. Francofurti ad Moenum. 1716

Ṭiḷak (Nārāyaṇ Vāman), *see* WINSLOW (J. C.) N. V. T., the Xtn. poet of Maharashtra, 1923.

Tilby (A. Wyatt). The evol. of consciousness. 8°. [1922]
The quest of reality. 8°. 1927

Tild (Jean). Goya. 8°. 1921

Tilden (Samuel Jones). Writings & speeches. Ed. J. Bigelow. vl. 8°. N.Y. 1885
see GIBSON (A. M.) A polit. crime [*i.e.* Hayes-T. disputed election], 1885.
,, HAWORTH (P. L.) Hayes-T. disputed presidential election of 1876, 1906.

Tilden (*Sir* William Augustus). Chemical discovery & invent. in 20th c. [4th ed.] 8°. [1922]
The elements: nature & origin. s8°. 1910
Famous chemists: the men & their work. 8°. 1921

Tilden (William T.) The art of lawn tennis. 3rd ed. 8°. [1921]

Tildesley (Miriam L.) Sir Thomas Browne: h. skull, portraits & ancestry. Intr. note by Sir A. Keith & rep. of the endocranial cast by G. E. Smith. [Repr. f. Biometrika, v15]. la8°. *Issued to subscribers only.* [C. 1923]

Tilemann (Joannes), *called* SCHENCK. Vitae profess. theol. qui in Acad. Marburg. docuerunt. Acc. W. Dilichii MS. s4°. Marburgi Cattorum. 1727

Tilenus (Daniel), *see* CALDERWOOD (D.) Altare Damascenum &c., interserta Confut. Paræneseos T. ad Scotos &c., 1623; 1708.

Tilgher (Adriano). Ricognizioni. Profili di scrittori &c. contemp. ital. 8°. 1924

Tiling (Eberhard). Disquis. de ratione inscript. 15 Psalmorum, qui dicuntur Cantici adscensionum. 8°. Bremae. 1765

Tilke (Max). Oriental costumes, th. designs & colors. [Tr. L. Hamilton]. 4°. [1923]

Till (Salomon van), *see* TIL (S. v.)

Tillett (Ben). The Ruhr. By B. T. *& others.* Rep. of Deput. f. Transport &c. Union. [P2719]. 8°. 1923

Tilley (Arthur).
Medieval France. [*By var. a.* (C. V. Langlois &c.)] 8°. C. 1922
Modern France. Ed. A. T. [*By* H. Hauser &c.] 8°. C. 1922
Molière. 8°. C. 1921
St. in the French Renaissance. 8°. C. 1922
see STEWART (H. F.) & A. T. The French romanticists; anthol., 1914.
,, —— & —— Romantic movt. in French lit., 1917.

Tilley (Joseph). *Old halls, manors & families of Derbyshire. By J. T. [*i.e.* Tilley]. 4v. 4°. 1892–1902

Tillier (Claude), *1801–44.* Ergänz. z. Werken (*French*); *ed.* M. Cornicelius, *see* ARCHIV F. D. ST. D. NEU. SPR., B109, 1902.

Tillion (Lucien), *see* MONMARCHÉ (M.) & L. T., *edd.* Le pays de France, 3t, 1925.

Tillotson (John), *abp. of Canterbury.* Twenty disc. (19 of them abp. T.'s) abrdgd. by D. Henry. s8°. 1743
see HICKES (G.) *Some disc. upon Dr. Burnet & Dr. T. &c., 1695.

Tilly (Joan Tserclaes, *Graf* von), *see* MAGDEBURG. Aussführliche Bericht, Warnungsschreiben &c., 1631.

Tillyard (Eustace Mandeville Wetenhall). The Hope vases. A cat. & discussion of the H. Coll. of Greek vases, w. intr. &c. 4°. C. 1923

Tillyard (Frank). The worker & the state: wages, hours, safety & health. 8°. 1923

Tilmannus, *Segebergensis, see* SMELINGUS (T.)

Tilney All Saints. Transcript of churchwardens' accounts of parish of Tilney All Saints, Norfolk, 1443–1589. Transcr. by A. D. Stallard. 8°. 1922

Tiltman (H. Hessell), *see* ETHERTON (P. T.) & H. H. T. The Pacific, 1928.

Tilton (William Frederic). Die Katastrophe d. span. Armada, 1588. 8°. Freiburg i. B. 1894

Timaeus, *Locrus.* Trattato di Timeo da Locri, tr. in lingua Toscana da D. Bembo. [*b. w.* Plato. Protagora. 1833]. 8°. Roma. 1833

Timehri: journal of the Roy. Agric. &c. Soc. of Brit. Guiana, v4, 5, N.S., 1, 2, s3, v7, 1885–1921, *see* ROYAL AGRIC. &c. SOC. OF BRIT. GUIANA.

Times (The). 1920–28. la. fol. 1920–28
Official index, Apr. 1920–June 1928. 8°. [1920–28]
*Strike nights in Printing House Square. An episode in the Hist. of The Times. f. priv. rec. 8°. 1926
Survey atlas of the world. Prep. under dir. of J. G. Bartholomew. fol. 1922
Tercentenary handlist of Eng. & Welsh newspapers, magazines & reviews (1620–1920). la8°. 1920
The T. Hist. of the War. v21, 22, la8°. 1920–21
Weekly ed. v39–42. fol. 1915–18
see COPPLESTONE (B.) Moberly Bell & h. times, 1925.
,, HOLLAND (*Sir* T. E.) Letters to "The Times" upon war & neutrality, 1881–1920, 3rd ed., 1921.
,, STUDIES in gardening; articles repr. f. the T., 1908.

Times Book Club.
see MACMILLAN (*Sir* F.) Net book Agreement, 1899 &c., incl. narr. of dispute betw. T.B.C. & Publishers' Assoc., by E. Bell, 1924.

Times (The) of India, *see* INDIAN. I. viceroyalty, 1858–1921; iss. w. "T. of I.", 1922.

Timiryazev (Dmitry Arkadievich). Историко-статист. обзоръ промышленности Россіи. Подъ ред. Т. tl [*4 pagin.*] la8°. С.–П. 1883

Timkovsky (Egor Fedorovich) [TIMKOVSKI (GEORGE)]. Voyage à Péking à travers la Mongolie. Tr. du Russe; publié avec des corrs. [Aperçu statist. &c.] par M. J. Klaproth. atlas 4°. 1827

Timme (Paul). Tell el-Amarna vor d. deut. Ausgrabung im Jahre 1911. [Deut. Orient-Gesell., Wiss. Veröff., 31. *b. w.* Borchardt (L.) Porträtkopf d. K. Teje, 1911]. fol. L. 1917

Timmermans (Felix).
Het Kindeken Jezus in Vlaanderen. 4e dr. s8°. A. *n.d.*
Pallieter. 9e dr. s8°. A. *n.d.*

Timmling (Walter). Kunstgesch. u. Kunstwiss. Mit e. Abhdl.: Meinungen ü. Herkunft u. Wesen d. Gotik v. P. Frankl. s8°. L. 1923

Timochenko (Woldemar). Rel. écon. entre l'Ukraine et la France. [P2402]. 4°. 1919
L'Ukraine et la Russie dans leurs rapports écon. [P2402]. 4°. 1919

Timofeev (P. G.) Краткий курс эконом. географии С.С.С.Р. 8°. Москва. [1924]

Timon (Samuel), *S.J.* Epitome chronol. rerum Hungar. [969–1736]. s4°. Claudiopoli. 1764

Timoneda (Juan de). El sobremesa y alivio de caminantes, 1569. Reprod., acosta de M. García. s8°. 1917

Timotheos, *of Miletus.* Der Timotheos-Papyrus gefunden bei Abusir am 1. Feb. 1902. Hrsg. v. W.-M. Lichtdruck-Ausgabe. [Deut. Orient-Gesell., Wiss. Veröff., 3. *a. c. b. w.* Koldewey (R.) Hettit. Inschr., 1900]. fol. L. 1903
see LYRA Graeca; ed. & tr. J. M. Edmonds, v3, 1927.

Timotheus Verinus, *character in controv. works on Pietism, see* LÖSCHER (V. E.)

Timothy, *see* TAMILIA (D.) De T. Xtni. et Aquilæ Judaei dialogo, 1901.

Timothy I, *bp. of Alexandria, 381–85, see* AKINEAN (N.) Timotheos Kouz (*Ælurus*); *in Armenian, w. app. on T. I,* 1909.

Timothy, *Ælurus, patriarch of Alexandria, d. 477, see* AKINEAN (N.) T. Kouz (*in Armenian*), 1909.

Timperley (Charles H.) Encyclop. of lit. & typograph. anecdote. 2nd ed., added, a cont. & a manual of printing. [*sep. tp. dated* 1838 *& sep. pag.*] 8°. 1842

Timúr, *khan of the Mongols.*
see BANKIPORE. Reprod. of illust. f. 3 Persian MSS. [Tîmûr-Nâmah: hist. of family of T. &c.], in Publ. Libr. at B., 1920.
,, THOMAS, *of Medzob.* Hist. of Tamerlane &c. [*In Armenian*], 1860.

Tinan (Jean L. de), *see* LEBEY (A.) J. L. de T., 1921.

Tinayre (*Mme.* Marcelle).
Le bouclier d'Alexandre. s8°. 1922
Un drame de famille. s8°. 1925
Figures dans la nuit. s8°. 1926
Les lampes voilées. Lawrence-Valentine. s8°. 1921
Madeleine at her mirror. Tr. W. Stephens. s8°. 1913
Perséphone. s8°. 1920
Priscille Séverac. s8°. 1922
La vie amoureuse de Mme. de Pompadour. s8°. [1924]

Tinctoris (Joannes). Terminorum musicae diffinitorium, *see* HAMILTON (J. A.) Dict., *n.d.*

Tindall (Edwin H.) The Wesleyan Methodist atlas of Eng. & Wales. la. fol. *n.d.*

Tindall (Henry). Gramm. & vocab. of Namaqua-Hottentot lang. 8°. [Cape Town]. *n.d.*

Ting-Fang (Wu), *see* WU TING-FANG.

Tingry (Pierre François). Painter & varnisher's guide. 8°. 1804

Tinker (Chauncey Brewster). Young Boswell: chapters on James Boswell the biographer. la8°. Boston [U.S. 1922]

Tinker (Edward Larocque).
Lafcadio Hearn's American days. 8°. 1925

Tinley (George F.), T. Humphreys & W. Irving. Colour planning of the garden. Intr. by G. Jekyll. 4°. 1924

Tino (Antonio de). Epitalamio [Il giubilo d. Sebeto. Nozze Caracciolo—Caracciolo]. [N125]. 8°. Napoli. 1717

Tinseau (Léon de). Jeanne la mystérieuse. s8°. 1921

Tinti (Mario).
Il Bachiacca. [Testo ital., fr., eng.] s8°. Firenze. 1925
Romano Romanelli. la8°. Firenze. 1924

Tinworth (George), *see* GOSSE (*Sir* E.) Crit. essay on life & works of G. T., w. descr. cat., 1883.

Tinyanov (Yury). Кюхля: повесть о декабристе. изд. 2ое. 8°. Ленинград. 1927

Tipper (Harry). The new business. 8°. *Pitman.* [1916]

Tipperary. *Mad Tipperary. [P2560]. 8°. D. 1890

Tipping (Henry Avray).
Eng. furniture of the Cabriole period. la8°. [1922]
English gardens. fol. 1925
English homes. Period 1, v1; Period 2, v1; Period 3, v1, 2; Period 4, v2; Period 5, v1; Period 6, v1. fol. 1921–28
1, v1, Norman & Plantagenet, 1066–1485.
2, v1, Early Tudor, 1485–1558.
3, v1, 2, Late Tudor & early Stuart, 1558–1649.
4, v2, Work of Sir J. Vanburgh & h. school, 1699–1736; by T. & C. Hussey.
5, v1, Early Georgian, 1714–60.
6, v1, Late Georgian, 1760–1820.

Tippoo, *sultan*, *see* MYSORE. Narr. sketches of the conq. of M. & death of T., 1803.

Tiraboschi (Giacomo), *of Bergamo* [TIRABUSCUS (JACOBUS)].
Carmen saphicum de laudibus Bergom. contra externos; a I. Finazzi ed., *see* REGIA DEP. DI STORIA PATRIA. Misc., t6, 1865.

Tirinus (Jacobus), *see* BIBLE: LATIN. Biblia maxima, cum annot. J. T. &c., 19t, 1660.
see DESMARETS (S.) Theol. elenchticae nova synopsis controv. fidei ex Scripturis à J. T. concinn. & censura auctus per S. M., 2t, 1646–48.

Tiron. Cartul. de l'abbaye de la Ste.-Trinité de T. Publ. & annoté par L. Merlet. [Soc. Arch. d'Eure-et-Loir]. 2t. 4°. Chartres. 1883

Tirpitz (*Gross-Admiral* Alfred v.)
Der Aufbau d. deut. Weltmacht. 8°. St. 1924
Erinnerungen. n. A. 8°. L. 1920
see DELBRÜCK (H.) Ludendorff, T. &c., 1920.
,, RAPHAËL (G.) Tirpitz, préf. du Vice-Am. Ronarc'h, 1922.

Tischendorf (Lobegott F. Constantin). De evangel. apocryphorum origine & usu. [Haagsche Genootschap, Verhand., d12]. 8°. Hagae Com. 1851
De Israelitarum per Mare Rubrum transitu. [P527]. 8°. Lipsiae. 1847
When were our Gospels written? With narr. of discov. of Sinaitic MS. [*Tr.*] 8°. [1866]
,, ,, ...2nd ed. s8°. 1867
see BIBLE. NEW TESTAMENT. [GREEK]. Nov. Test. Sinaiticum; [*ed.*] G. F. C. T., 1863.
,, ——: PAUL. Codex Claromontanus; ed. C. T., 1852.
,, ——: SEPTUAGINT. Vet. Test. Gr. juxta 70 interp.: Text. Vat. ed. &c. C. T., 5a ed., 2t, 1875.

Tischner (Rudolf). Telepathy & clairvoyance. Tr. W. D. Hutchinson, w. intr. by E. J. Dingwall. 8°. 1925

Tisserand (Ernest). Gilles Normand. s8°. 1922
Pour les finances d'un dictateur. s8°. 1920
Un second cabinet de portraits. 6e éd. s8°. [1925]

Tisserant (Eugène). Specimina codicum orient. [Tab. in usum schol.; ed. J. Lietzmann]. la8°. Bonnae. 1914

Tisseur (Clair) [*called* NIZIER DU PUITSPELU]. Le Littré de la Grand' Côte. Préf. par E. Leroudier. la8°. Lyon. 1926

Tissot (Ernest). Le livre des reines. La reine Victoria. L'imp. Frédéric. L'imp. Elisabeth. La reine Marguerite de Savoie. s8°. 1896
N. A. Nekrassov. [*Extr. f.* Revue internat., t28. P643]. 8°. *n.d.*

Tissot (Joseph James). Life of Jesus Christ. Compos. f. the Gospels, w. notes & explan. drawings. Notes tr. Mrs. A. Bell. [*Lat. & Eng.*] people's ed. 2v. 4°. [1897]

Tisza (*Count* István).
Briefe, 1914–18. Hrsg. O. v. Wertheimer. Bl. 8°. [1928]
see HERCZEG (F.) Graf Stephan T., 1926.

Titelman (Franciscus). Libri duo de authoritate Libri Apocalypsis adv. eos [*Erasmus & others*] qui Canon. hujus scripturæ authoritate derogarunt &c. s8°. Antverpiæ, *M. Hillenius.* 1530

Tithes [TYTHES]. *Essay (An) conc. the divine right of tythes, 1700, *see* LESLIE (C.)
*Letter (A) [Second & Third letter] to the people of Ireland, on tythes. By a friend to the Constitution. [P2669]. s8°. D. 1758
*Short obs. on a commutation of tithes for gov. annuities. [*b. w.* Thompson (T.) Tithes indef., 3rd ed., 1796]. 8°. Hull. 1798

Tithing. Decimarum &c. tabula: a t. table &c., 1676, *see* CRASHAW (W.)

Titian.
see BURLINGTON FINE ARTS CLUB. Venetian school: T. &c., 1915.
,, STEINMANN (O.) Venus & Violante, 1910.
,, WEDMORE (F.) Notes on Velasquez & T. in the etchings of R. W. Macbeth, 1888.

Titius (Arthur). Natur u. Gott: Verständigung zw. Naturwiss. u. Theologie. 8°. Göttingen. 1926

Titius (Gerhard), *see* CALIXTUS (G.) Epitome theolog.; acc. quorundam locorum declaratio, autore G. T., 1653; 1661.

Titov (Andrei Aleksandrovich). Лѣтопись Великоустюжская. Изд. А. К. Трапезникова. 8°. Москва. [1889]
Сибирь въ xvii в. Сборникъ старинныхъ русскихъ статей о Сибири &c. Издалъ Г. Юдинъ. 8°. Москва. 1890
This contains (1) О человѣцѣхъ пезнаемыхъ на восточной странѣ &c. (15c.). (2) Роспись Сибирскимъ городамъ и острогамъ (c. 1640). (3) Чертежъ всей Сибири (c. 1667). (4) Списокъ съ чертежа Сибирскія земли (c. 1672). (5) Описаніе новыя земли, сирѣчь Сибирск. царства (1683). (6) Сказаніе о великой рѣкѣ Амурѣ (c. 1689. *By* N. Spathary). (7) Historia de Siberia (c. 1680. *By* Yury Krijanich), *with translation.*

Titov (Feodor I.) Типографія Кіево-Печерской Лавры. Состав. Ѳ. Т. т1, 1606–1721 & Приложенія. la8°. Кіевъ. 1916–18

Tittmann (Carl Christian). De vestigiis Gnosticorum in N. Test. s8°. Lipsiae. 1773
Opuscula theologica. 8°. Lipsiae. 1803

Tittmann (Johann August Heinrich). De summis principiis August. Confess. [*Progr.* P2648]. s4°. [Lipsiae. 1830]

Tittoni (Tommaso). Modern Italy, its intellect., cultural &c. aspects. 8°. 1922

Titus, *emp. of Rome*, *see* HENDERSON (B. W.) 5 Roman emperors, 1927.

Titz (Heinrich Gottlieb). Disquis. de libro poet. Theuerdanck. ed. nova. s4°. Altdorfii. 1737

Tivaroni (Carlo). Storia crit. del risorgimento ital: L'Italia prima d. Rivoluzione Francese, 1735–89. s8°. Torino. 1888

Tiverton (*Miss*), *ps.* *Miss T. goes out, 1925, *see* MISS.

Tizac (Jean Henri d'Ardenne de), *see* ARDENNE DE TIZAC (J. H. D').

Tizard (Thomas Henry), *see* ADMIRALTY. Yangtse Kiang pilot, 1914.

Tizengauzen (*baron* Vladimir Gustavovich). О саманидскихъ монетахъ, *see* IMPERAT. RUSS. ARCH. OBSCH. Труды Восточ. отд., ч1, 1855.

Tluchowski (Oscar Skarbek).
Adamo Mickiewicz. 48°. Roma. 1922

Tlukaanti (David). [Christian doctrine. *In Georgian.* P2816]. s8°. [Rome]. 1741

„ „ 2ª ed. *w. add. t.* Dottrina cristiana per usu d. missioni d. Giorgia ; tr. d. ling. ital. in ling. civ. giorg. s8°. Roma. 1797

*To a lady on her passion for old china, 1725 ; repr., 1925, *see* GAY (J.)

Toase (William), *Methodist minister.* *Mem. of W. J.: extr. f. h. journals & corr. Methodism in France & the Channel Islands. Comp. by a friend. Intr. by W. Arthur. s8°. 1874

The Wesleyan mission in France. [P2538]. s8°. 1835

Tobar (Jérôme), *see* TCHEOU FOU. Kiao-ou ki-lio; tr. &c. par J. T., 1917.

Tobias, *see* MARTYN (F.) Homilies on Bk. of T., 1822.

Tobilevich (Ivan Karpov.), *see* KARPENKO-KARY.

Tobin (John), *dramatic writer.* Honey moon, *see* INCHBALD (E.) Brit. th., v25, 1808.

Tobler (Friedrich). Kolonialbotanik. s8°. L. [1907]

Tocco (Vittorio). Un progetto di confed. ital. (G. Muzio, 1572), *see* ARCHIVIO STOR. ITAL. Anno 82, v1, 1924.

Tocilescu (Gr. G.) Monumentele epigrafice şi sculpturali ale Mus. Nat. de Antichitati. Publ. sub ausp. Acad. Romane. v1 [*wants tp. in 2p, pagin. cont.*] sm. fol. Bucuresci. 1902–8

Tocqueville (Alexis de). Etudes écon., polit. & litt. 8°. 1866

Tod (*Lieut.-Col.* **James).** Annals & antiq. of Rajasthan, or the C. & W. Rajput States of India. Ed. w. intr. & notes by W. Crooke. 3v. s8°. 1920

Tod (William Montgomery). Hints on feeding for the farmer, dairyman & pig-keeper. 2nd ed. rev. & enl. 8°. [1924]

Todd (Henry John), *1763–1845.*

A vindic. of our auth. tr. of the Bible &c.: occ. by object. by Bellamy & Burges. s8°. 1819

A vindic. of T. Cranmer &c. 2nd ed. s8°. 1826

Todd (James Henthorn), *1805–69.* The search after infallibility. Remarks on the testimony of the Fathers to the Roman dogma. 8°. 1848

Todd (John Alton).

The mechanism of exchange. [2nd ed.] 8°. 1919

Toderini (Giovanni Battista). Litteratur d. Türken. Aus d. Ital. mit Zusätzen &c. v. P. W. G. Hausleutner. 2T. s8°. Königsberg. 1790

Todi (Luiza Rosa de Aguiar), *Portuguese singer, 1753–1833, see* N. (N.) Lettera &c., 1791.

Todischus (Thomas Radinus), *see* RADINUS TODISCHUS (T.)

Toffanin (Giuseppe). La fine dell' Umanesimo. 8°. Milano. 1920

Machiavelli e il " Tacitismo." 8°. Padova. 1921

Togni (Luigi) [TOGNI (ALOISIUS)].

Instructio pro sacris Eccl. ministris. s8°. Oeniponte. 1856

***Toilet** (The) of Flora: methods of prep. baths, essences &c., w. receipts for cosmetics &c. n. ed., impr. s8°. 1784

***Toilette** de M. l'archevesque de Sens &c., 1669, *see* BURLUGUAY (J.)

Toke, *The family of, see* LODGE (E. C.) Acc. bk. of Kentish estate, 1616–1704: [Cheynecourt &c., T. fam. e.]; ed. E. C. L., 1927.

Tököly (Imre), *count.* *Austriaca Austeritas, in qua ostenditur: quibus modis & quo jure, Hungariae Regnum a. 1670 armis Regiis infestatum a Ferdinando I everti coeperit &c. ab authore anonymo [*i.e.* I. T.] s4°. Venetiis. [1671]

Tokutomi (*Hon.* **Iichiro).**

Jap.-Amer. relations. Tr. by S. Yanagiwara. s8°. N.Y. 1922

The life of Shoin Yoshida. [Tr.] H. E. Coleman, *see* ASIATIC SOC. OF JAPAN. Trans., v45i, 1917.

Toland (John). Hist. of the Druids; w. life &c. by R. Huddleston. n. ed. 8°. Montrose. 1814

see LUNGERSHAUSEN (J. J.) Diss. prior [*&* posterior]: mysteria Christianismi contra [T.'s] Xtny. not mysterious, 1713–14.

„ MOSHEIM (J. L. v.) Vindiciae antiq. Xtnorum discipl. adv. J. T.; acc. De vita, &c. J. T. comm., ed. 2ª., 1722.

„ RICHARDSON (J.) Canon of New Test. vindic.; in ans. to J. T., 2nd ed., 1701.

„ WAGSTAFFE (T.) *Def. of the Vindic. of Charles, in ans. to Amyntor, 1699.

Toldo (Vittorio de). L'art ital. de la reliure du livre (15–16 siècle). la8°. Milano. 1924

Toledo. Les canons des conciles de T., de Meaux, de Mayence, d'Oxfort & de Constance: advis & censures de la faculté de théol. de Paris: arrests du Parl. de Paris &c. Propositions d'un livre [*by* N. Eymericus] intitulé Directorium Inquisit. &c. [*Ed.* S. Vigor]. [2p]. 8°. [Paris ?]. 1615

Toletani. SS. PP. Toletanorum opera, 1782–97, *see* LORENZANA Y BUITRON (F. A.), *ed.*

Toletus (Franciscus), *Cardinal.* D. F. Toleti in Joannis Evang. comm. [2t *in* 1v]. fol. Coloniae Agrippinae. 1599

Tolhausen (Louis). Neues span.-deut. u. deut.-span. Wörterbuch. 2B. la8°. L. 1913

Tolkien (John Ronald Renel). Middle Eng. vocab., 1922, *see* SISAM (K.) 14th c. verse &c., repr., 1923.

Tolkowsky (S.)

The gateway of Palestine, a hist. of Jaffa. 8°. 1924

Tollemache (Bentley Lyonel John Tollemache, *3rd baron*).

Croquet. 8°. [1914]

Tollenaer (Joos de). Sommige Brieven ofte Belijdingen geschreven van J. de T. ghevangen om de ewige Wahrheyt &c. [*foll. by* Een Testament v. J. T. *b. w.* Offer. Dit B. w. genaemt: Het offer des Heerē &c.] s8°. Harlinghen. 1599

Tollenarius (Joannes), *see* JESUITS. Imago primi saeculi soc. J. &c. [*by* J. T. &c.], 1640.

Toller (Ernst).

Der entfesselte Wotan. Komödie. 8°. Potsdam. 1924

Hoppla, wir leben! Vorspiel. s8°. Potsdam. 1927

Die Maschinenstürmer. Drama aus d. Zeit d. Ludditenbewegung in England. s8°. L. 1924

Masse-Mensch. s8°. Potsdam. 1925

Die Rache des verhöhnten Liebhabers. Puppenspiel. 8°. 1925

Das Schwalbenbuch. 8°. Potsdam. [1924]

Tag d. Proletariats—Requiem d. gemordeten Brüdern: 2 Sprechchöre. s8°. Potsdam. [1925]

Die Wandlung. s8°. Potsdam. 1924

TRANSLATIONS.

Brokenbrow. Tragedy. Tr. V. Mendel, w. drawings by G. Grosz. 8°. *Nonesuch Press.* 1926

The machine-wreckers: drama of the Eng. Luddites. Eng. by A. Dukes. s8°. 1923

Masses & man. Fragm. of the soc. revol. of the 20th c. [*Play.*] Tr. V. Mendel. s8°. 1923

The swallow-book. [Poems.] Eng. by A. Dukes. s8°. 1924

see SIGNER (P.) E. T., e. Studie, 1924.

Toller (T. Northcote), *fellow of Christ's Coll., Cambridge.*

see BOSWORTH (J.) Anglo-Saxon dict.; Supplement by T., 1921.

Tolley (Charles H.) Complete income tax &c. Chart of rates &c. for 1927–28 &c. 12th ed. 8°. 1927

Töllner (Joh. Gottlieb). Unterricht v. symbol. Büchern überhaupt. s8°. Züllichau. 1769

Tollnerus (Car. Lud.), *see* TOLNERUS (C. L.)

Tolly (Colin). Horizons at dawn & dusk. [Poems]. s8°. 1918

Knowledge & dream: & o. p. s8°. 1926

Tolnay (Cornel de). Hungarian railways & territ. integrity. [P2524]. s8°. Budapest. 1919

Tolner (Carl Ludwig) [TOLNERUS]. Hist. Palatina. Adj. Codex Diplomat. [*w. sep. tp. & pagin.*] fol. Francofurti ad Moenum. 1700

„ „ Additiones, ad object. G. C. Joannis resp. fol. Heidelbergae. 1709

Tolpo (Martinus).

De initiis rei lit. in Svethia. s4°. Aboae. 1750

Tolstoy, *The family of, see* MAUDE (A.) Family views of T.; tr., 1926.

Tolstoy (*ctss.* **Aleksandra Andreevna).** Erinnerungen an L. N. Tolstoi [Einl. *by* A. Hess]. s8°. L. [1920 ?]

Tolstoy (Aleksandra Lvovna). Tolstojs Flucht u. Tod, geschild. v. s. Tochter Alexandra, mit Briefen &c. v. L. T. &c. Hrsg. v. R. Fülöp-Miller &c. [Übers. v. Mitrofanoff-Demelič]. s8°. [1925]

Tolstoy (*count* **Aleksei Konstantinovich).**

Сонъ статскаго совѣтника Попова. [P2434]. 8°. Berlin. 1878

TRANSLATIONS.

Czar Feodor Ioannovitch, drama. Eng. by A. Hayes. Pref. &c. by C. Nabokoff. 8°. 1924

„ „ *for a. ed. see* SAYLER (O. M.) Moscow Art Theatre ser. of Russ. plays; tr., 1923.

The death of Ivan the Terrible. [Tr.] A. Hayes. Pref. by C. Nabokoff. s8°. 1926

Tolstoy (*count* **Aleksei N.)**

Аэлита. Романъ. s8°. Берлинъ. 1923

Любовь, *see* RUSSKII. Р. сборникъ, 1920.

Навожденіе. s8°. Парижъ. 1921

Хожденіе по мукамъ. Романъ. s8°. Берлинъ. *n.d.*

Tolstoy (*count* **Ivan Ivanovich) & N. P. Kondakov.** Русскія древности въ памятн. искусства. вып. 2, 6. la8°. С.-П. 1889–99
2, Древн. Скиѳо-сарматскія.
6, Памятники Владиміра, Новгорода и Пскова.

Tolstoy (*count* **Lev Lvovich).**
La vérité sur mon père. s8°. 1923

Tolstoy (*count* **Lev Nikolaevich).**
Аггей, пьеса, *see* GUSEV (N. N.) & V. CHERTKOV. Толстой &c. сб. 2, 1926.
Власть тьмы. Драма. s8°. Москва. 1887
Гоненіе на Христіянъ въ Россіи. Письмо. Изд. М. К. Элпидина. [P643]. s8°. Carouge-Genève. 1896
Деньги. 2oe изд. [P643]. 8°. Genève. 1890
Живой трупъ. Драма. 8°. Berlin. *n.d.*
Живой трупъ. Изд. А. Л. Толстой. s8°. [Москва. 1912]
Законъ насилія и законъ любви. Подъ. ред. В. Г. Черткова. [P2757]. s8°. Москва. 1917
К столетию Л. Н. Т. Сборник Комиссии. la8°. Москва. 1926
Конецъ вѣка. [P2715]. s8°. Christchurch. 1905
Не могу молчать. [*a. c. in* P849]. s8°. Berlin. [1908]
О Землѣ. [P810]. s8°. *n.p.* 1902
О Значеніи русской революціи. [P849]. s8°. Москва. *n.d.*
Отвѣтъ Синоду (1901). [P2722]. s8°. *n.d.*
Отвѣтъ Т. на постановленіе Синода отъ 20–22 Февр. 1901. [P643]. s8°. Onex près Genève. 1901
Письма по поводу Кишинева, *see* GORKY (M.) Протестъ., *n.d.*
Family happiness. Russ. text w. intr., notes &c. by J. D. Duff. pl. s8°. C. 1923
"Солдатская памятка." изд. 2oe. [P810]. s8°. *n.p.* 1903
Ученіе 12 Апостоловъ. Изд. М. К. Элпидина. [P643]. s8°. Genève. 1892
Ходите въ свѣтѣ пока есть свѣтъ &c. Повѣсть. [P643]. 8°. Genève. 1892

ENGLISH TRANSLATIONS.
"And all with one consent began to make excuses." [Free Age Press Leaflets, No. 3. P643]. s8°. [Maldon]. *n.d.*
Bethink yourselves. Tr. V. Tchertkoff & I. F. M. [*a. c. in* P847]. s8°. [1904]
Christianity & patriotism. Tr. C. Garnett. 8°. [1922]
The Devil. Tr. A. Maude. s8°. [1926]
The division of labour! [P643]. s8°. [Maldon]. *n.d.*
How to read the Gospels &c. [Tr. A. Maude. P643]. s8°. [Maldon]. *n.d.*
In the name of God stop a moment. [P643]. s8°. [Maldon]. *n.d.*
The Kreutzer sonata & o. s. [Family happiness; tr. J. D. Duff—Polikushka; tr. L. & A. Maude]. Ed. A. Maude. s8°. O. 1924
Love letters. With study on autobiog. elements in T.'s work by P. Biryukov. Tr. S. S. Koteliansky & V. Woolf. s8°. Richmond. 1923
The martyrdom of the world. [P643]. s8°. [Maldon]. *n.d.*
My reply to the Synod's edict of excommunication &c. [*a. c. in* P643]. s8°. Christchurch. 1901
On flogged and floggers. With comments by J. Prelooker. [P846]. 8°. 1899
Plays. Tr. L. & A. Maude. compl. ed., incl. posthumous plays. s8°. [1923]
Private diary, 1853–57. Ed. A. Maude. Tr. L. & A. Maude. 8°. 1927
The religious educ. of the young. [P643]. s8°. [Maldon]. *n.d.*
Stories & dramas. Tr. L. Turin, H. M. Lucas &c. 8°. [1926]
"Thou shalt not kill." [Tr. L. Maude. P643]. s8°. [Maldon]. *n.d.*
Twenty-three tales. Tr. L. & A. Maude. [repr.] s8°. [1921]
War & peace. Tr. L. & A. Maude 3v. s8°. [1923]
What is to be done, then? [P643]. s8°. [Maldon]. *n.d.*

FRENCH TRANSLATIONS.
Hadji Mourad & a. contes. Tr. J.-W. Bienstock. s8°. *Nelson.* [1912]
Journal intime 1895–99. Tr. par N. Rostowa & J. Debrit. Préf. & comm. de P. Birukoff. s8°. [1910]
Lettres inéd. à Botkine, *see* ŒUVRES libres, 66, 1926.
La lumière luit dans les ténèbres, *see* ŒUVRES libres, 42, 1924.
Pages inéd.; tr. J. W. Bienstock, *see* ŒUVRES libres, 10, 1922.
Sonate à Kreutzer. Tr. E. Halpérine-Kaminsky. s8°. [1890]

GERMAN TRANSLATION.
Ich kann nicht schweigen, Deut. v. E. Rot. 3e A. [P849]. s8°. [1908]

REFERENCES.
see BAUDOUIN (C.) T.: the teacher; tr., 1923.
,, BEHRS (S. A.) Воспоминанія о Т., 1893.
,, BIRYUKOV (P. I.) Л. Н. Т., 3t, 1921.
,, BOURDEAU (J.) T., Lénine & la Révol. Russe, 1921.
,, BULGAKOV (V. F.) T., la tragédie de ses dern. jours, 1924.
,, CHERTKOV (V. G.) Уход Толстого. 1922.
,, —— Last days of T.; tr., 1922.
,, FAUSSET (H. I'A.) T., inner drama, 1927.
,, GOLDENVEIZER (A. B.) Вблизи Т., 2t, 1922–23.
,, —— Talks w. T.; tr., 1923.
,, GORKY (M.) Remin. of T., 1920.
,, GUSEV (A. F.) Любовь &c. въ ученіи Т., 1892.
,, GUSEV (N. N.) Жизнь Л. Н. Т.: молодой Т., 1828–62, 1927.
,, —— "Замолчанное о Т.," ответ, 1926.
,, —— & V. CHERTKOV. Толстой и о Толстом, нов. материалы, 1–3, 1924–27.

Tolstoy (*count* **Lev Nikolaevich)** [*continued*].
REFERENCES [*continued*].
see GYURKOVECHKY (V. v.) Warum T. Liebe verachtet &c., 1892.
,, KUZMINSKAYA (T. A.) Моя жизнь дома и в Ясной Поляне, 2oe изд., 1927.
,, —— Ma vie; revu & corr. par L. T., 1923.
,, LAVRIN (J.) T.: a psycho-crit. study, 1924.
,, MAKLAKOV (V. A.) T. и большевизмъ, 1921.
,, MAUDE (A.), *ed.* Family views of T.; tr., 1926.
,, —— The teaching of T., 1900.
,, MEREJKOVSKY (D. S.) Le règne de l'Antéchrist [T. & le Bolchevisme &c.], 1921.
,, OVSYANIKO-KULIKOVSKY (D. N.) Л. Н. Т., в1, 1899.
see *PLODI. Плоды ученія Л. Н. Т., 2кн., 1896.
,, SHESTOV (L.) Révélations de la mort: Dostoïevsky—T., 1923.
,, TOLSTOY (*ctss.* A. A.) Erinnerungen an L. N. T., 1920?.
,, TOLSTOY (A. L.) T.'s Flucht u. Tod geschild. v. s. Tochter A.; übers., 1925.
,, TOLSTOY (*c.* L. L.) La vérité sur mon père, 1923.
,, YU. (B.) Нѣсколько словъ по поводу письма Т. о способахъ борьбы съ голодомъ, 1891.
,, YUSUPOV (N. B.) Нѣчто объ исповѣда &c. T., 1883.
,, ZAKOSKIN (N.) Т. и его студенч. годы, 1894.

Tolstoy (*ctss.* **Sofi Andreevna),** *wife of count L. N. Tolstoy.*
Autobiography. Pref. & notes by V. Spiridonov. Tr. S. S. Koteliansky & L. Woolf. s8°. 1922
see AIKHENVALD (Y. I.) Двѣ жены, Т. и Достоевская, 1925.

Tolstoy (Yakob Nikolaevich), *1791–1867.*
Революция 1848 г. во Франции. (Донесения Я. Т.) Под ред. &c. Г. Зайделя и С. Красного. [Центрархив]. la8°. Ленинград. 1925

Toltz (Johann), *see* DOELSCHIUS (I.)

Tom. Loving mad Tom, 1927, *see* LINDSAY (J.), *ed.*

Tomashevsky (B.)
Пушкин. s8°. Ленинград. 1925

Tomasi (*card.* **Giuseppe Maria)** [*ps.* CARUS (J. M.)]
Sacrorum Bibliorum juxta ed. seu 70 interpretum seu B. Hieronymi vet. tituli. Ed. studio J. M. Cari. 2p *in* 1v. 8°. Romae. 1688
see FRONTEAU (J.) Epistolae & diss. eccl. &c.: Calend. Rom. emend. per card. Thomasium, 1733.

Tomasin (Pietro). Remin. storiche di Trieste dal sec. 4 al 19. 2v. la8°. Trieste. 1900

Tomassetti (Francesco), *see* TOMASSETTI (G.) & F. T. La Campagna Romana, v4, 1926.

Tomassetti (Giuseppe) & F. Tomassetti.
La Campagna Romana antica, med. e mod. v4. la8°. 1926

Tombes (John), *B.D.*, *see* BAXTER (R.) More proofs of infants' church-membership &c.; confut. of T., &c., 1675.

Tombo hist. geneal. de Portugal, v1, 2, 1911–14, *see* DORNELLAS (A. DE) & A. DE G. NAVARRO.

Tomek (Václav Vladivoj).
Gesch. d. Prager Univ. 8°. Prag. 1849

Tomeo (Nicola Leonico), *see* LEONICO TOMEO (N.)

Tomka Szaszky (Joannes), *see* SZASZKY (JOANNES TOMKA).

***Tom K——g's**: or, the Paphian grove, 2nd ed., 1738, *see* KING (T.)

Tomkinson (G. S.) A sel. bibliog. of the princ. mod. presses in Gt. Brit. & Ireland. Intr. by B. H. Newdigate. [First Edition Club]. la8°. 1928

Tomkinson (W. S.) The teaching of English. s8°. O. 1921
see PHILLIPS (M.) & W. S. T. Eng. women in life & letters, 1926.

Tomlinson (Everett T.)
Stories of the Amer. Revol. s8°. N.Y. 1923

Tomlinson (H. M.) Gallion's Reach. s8°. [1927]
,, ,, ...[n. impr.] s8°. [1927]
Gifts of fortune, w. hints for those about to travel. 8°. 1926
London river. 8°. 1921
Tidemarks: records of journey to the beaches of the Moluccas & the forest of Malaya in 1923. 8°. [1924]

Tommaseo (Niccolò). Diz. dei sinonimi d. lingua ital. n. ed. corr. 8°. Milano. 1913
N. T. e G. Capponi. Carteggio ined., 1833–74. Per cura di I. Del Lungo e P. Prunas. v2–4i. s8°. Bologna. [1914–23]
—— & B. Bellini. Diz. d. lingua italiana. 4v [*in 8p, each part b. sep., w. sep. tp., pagin. cont.*] 4°. [1861–79]

Tompkins (Albert Edward). Turbines. 3rd ed. rev. s8°. 1921

Tompkins (Benjamin). Springs of water & how to discover them by the divining-rod. 3rd & enl. ed. 8°. [1925]

Tompson (Benjamin), *poet, 1642–1714*, *see* MURDOCK (K. B.), *ed.* Handkerchiefs f. Paul: Verses, by B. T. &c., 1927.

Tomsky (Mikhail). Принципы организац. строительства професс. союзов. [P2458]. 8°. Москва. 1919
Tonaphetean (P.) [Armenia by Lynch. *In Armenian*]. s8°. London. 1902
Tonatzoytz: [Armenian church calendar; *in Armenian*], 1774; 1782, *see* ARMENIAN.
Tonelli (Luigi). Manzoni. 8°. Milano. 1928
Tonge (William Asheton), *ed.*, *see* CHESTER. Index to wills &c. in Probate Reg., C., 1811–20, p1, 1928.
Toni (Giovanni Battista de). Le pianti e gli animali in Leonardo da Vinci. 8°. Bologna. 1922
Spigolature Aldrovandiane, 19, il botanico padov. G. A. Cortuso &c., *see* PADOVA. Monogr. s. Studio di Padova, 1922.
Toniolo (Antonio Renato).
Il Tirolo unità geografica? s8°. Firenze. 1921
Tonnelat (Ernest). La Chanson des Nibelungen: compos. & form. [Univ. de Strasbourg]. 8°. 1926
Tönnies (Ferdinand).
Gemeinschaft u. Gesellschaft. 4e u. 5e A. 8°. 1922
T. Hobbes Leben u. Lehre. 3e verm. A. 8°. St. 1925
Tonti (Henri de). Rel. de la Louisianne et du Mississipi (1678–90), *see* BERNARD (J. F.), *ed.* Recueil, t5, 1734.
Tony, *ps.*, *see* BERGMANN (A.)
Tooke (John Horne). Mem. to J. H. T., unveiled by the New Eng. Soc. of Brooklyn, N.Y., in St. Mary's Church, Ealing, 1919; w. intr. statement, addr. &c. Comp. by H. Putnam. [P2501]. la8°. [Brooklyn]. 1920
Tooke (Thomas), *merchant.* A letter to Lord Grenville on the effects ascr. to the resumption of cash payments on the value of the currency. [P448]. 8°. 1829
Tooley (Marian J.) The authorship of the Defensor pacis, *see* ROY. HIST. SOC. Trans., s4, v9, 1926.
Tooley (*Mrs.* Sarah A.) Personal life of Queen Victoria. 8°. 1896
Toorenenbergen (Johann Justus van), *see* OECONOMICA. Hed oudste Nederl. verboden boek 1523 uitg. door J. J. van T., 1882.
Tootell (Hugh) [TOOTLE; *ps.* CHARLES DODD]. *An apology for the Church hist. of Eng., 1500–1688, pr. in 1737. Reply to A spec. of amendments &c. under fict. name Clerophilus Alethes [*i.e.* Constable]. 8°. *n.p.* 1742
see CONSTABLE (J.) Spec. of amendments proposed to compiler [H. T.] of The Church-hist. of Eng., 1500–1688, 1741.
Topass (Jan). L'art & les artistes en Pologne. 8°. 1926
Topelius (Zacharias), *1818–98*, *see* LAGERLÖF (S.) Z. T., utveckling och mognad, 1920.
Topham (*Major* Edward).
The life of John Elwes. 6th ed. 8°. 1790
„ „ ....10th ed. 8°. 1791
Toplady (Augustus M.)
*Church (The) of England vindic. f. the charge of Arminianism in a letter to Dr. Nowell. By a presbyter of the Ch. of Engl. 8°. 1769
Hymns & sacred poems. s8°. 1860
A letter to John Wesley rel. to his Abridgment of Zanchius on predestination. 2nd ed. enl. [*b. w. h.* Ch. of Eng. vindic., 1769]. 8°. 1771
More work for John Wesley; or, A vindic. of the decrees &c. of God f. the defamations of a paper, "The consequence proved." [*b. w. h.* Ch. of Eng. vindic., 1769]. 8°. 1772
Psalms & hymns. s8°. 1776
Topolev (I.) Нужна ли рабочим &c. своя армия &c. [P2722]. s8°. Москва. 1919
Toppino (Giuseppe). Il dialetto di Castellinaldo, p2, *see* MONACI (E.) Studj romanzi, v10, 1913.
p1 *appeared in* Archivio glottolog. ital.
Topsell (Edward). The Elizabethan Zoo: bk. of beasts, fabulous & authentic. [Sel. f. P. Holland's tr. of Pliny, 1601, & E. T.'s "Hist. of foure-footed beastes," 1607, & h. "Hist. of serpents," 1608. Ed. M. St. C. Byrne. Haslewood Bks.] la8°. 1926
Torau-Bayle (X.) La campagne des Dardanelles. Doc. diplomat. &c. s8°. 1920
Torche (*l'abbe* de). *Chien (Le) de Boulogne, ou l'amant fidelle. s8°. 1668
Torczyner (Harry). Altbabylon. Tempelrechnungen, 1913, *see* KAIS. AKAD. D. W. ZU WIEN. Denkschr., B55, 1917.
Torday (E.) Causeries congolaises. s8°. 1925
On the trail of the Bushongo. 8°. 1925
Torelli (Giuseppi), *1721–81.* Poesie ital.: con alcune prose lat. 8° .Verona. 1795

Torelli (Guasparri). Rime. [*Ed.* L. Domenichi. *tp. wanting. b. w.* Paschale (L.) Rime, 1549]. s8°. [Lucca. 1561]
Torelli (Luigi).
Manuale topogr. archeol. dell' Italia. 8°. Venezia. 1872
Torelli (Pietro). Patti d. liberaz. dell' arcivescovo Cristiano di Magonza prigione dei marchesi di Monferrato, *see* REGIA DEPUT. Miscellanea, t44, 1909.
Torelli (Pomponio).
Rime. Di nuovo ristamp. & corr. s8°. Parma. 1586
Rime amorose. 4°. Parma. 1575
Il Tancredi. Per cura di L. Cappelletti. [*Repr. of Parma ed. of 1597.* Scelta di curiosità lett., 147]. s8°. Bologna. 1875
Torfaeus (Thormodus). Comm. hist. de rebus gestis Færeyensium s. Faröensium. s8°. Havniae. 1695
Orcades, seu rerum Orcad. hist. libri tres. fol. Havniae. 1697
Torgau. *Apologia modesta & Christiana ad acta conventus 15 theologorum Torgæ nuper habiti. De Sacra Coena &c. [*a. c. b. w.* Exegesis perspicua &c., 1574]. s4°. Genevæ. 1575
*Kurtz Bekentnis u. Artickel v. heiligen Abendmal des Leibs u. Bluts Christi. Ubergeben u. gehandelt in jüngsten Landtag zu Torgaw. s8°. Wittenberg. 1574
see BALTHASAR (J. H.) Hist. d. T. Buchs, 1741–44.
Toribio Medina (José), *see* MEDINA (J. T.)
Tories. *Proper lessons for the T. (1716), *see* AUNGERVYLE Soc. Repr., s2, 1883.
Torino. Cat. d. Galleria d'arte mod. d. Museo Civico di T. Comp. da M. Soldati. 8°. 1927
*Diario dell' assedio di Torino del 1640 di anon. contemp.; pubbl. da A. Manno, *see* REGIA DEP. DI STORIA PATRIA. Misc., t24, 1885.
Tormay (Cécile). The old house. Tr. E. Torday. s8°. [1921]
An outlaw's diary. Foreword by Duke of Northumberland. [2p]. 8°. [1923]
Tormo y Monzó (Elias). The monastery of Guadalupe. [Hispanic Soc.] s8°. Barcelona. *n.d.*
Törne (A. M.), *see* TERNE (A. M.)
Tornquist (Alexander), *see* HÖRSTEL (W.) Die Oberitalien. Seen, mit e. geogr.-geolog. Übersicht v. A. T., 1910.
Tornquist (Ernesto) & Co., *Ltd.* Econ. development of the Argentine Rep. in the last 50 years. 8°. Buenos Aires. 1919
Toro (Alfonso).
Compend. de hist. de México. [3t]. 8°. Mexico. 1926
Toronto.
Canadian books: a study outline. Comp. by T. Publ. Lib. [P2740]. la8°. [1923]
A cat. of periodicals (incl. publs. &c. of societies) in libraries of T. la8°. Toronto. 1924
Map. coll. of Public Ref. Library, T. [Comp. by M. MacLachlan]. 8°. Toronto. 1923
The Rebellion of 1837–38: bibliog. of sources of inform. in Publ. Ref. Lib. of T. [P2740]. la8°. Toronto. 1924
Toro y Gisbert (Miguel de). Curso práct. de gramática y correccion del estilo. 8°. Paris. 1916
Voces andaluzas &c., *see* REVUE HISPAN., t49, 1920.
Torp (Alf), *see* HÆGSTAD (M.) & A. T. Gamalnorsk Ordbok &c., 1909.
Torquemada (Juan de), *Cardinal*, *see* TURRECREMATA (J. DE), *Cardinal.*
Torquemada (Thomas de), *Grand Inquisitor*, *see* SABATINI (R.) T. & the Span. Inquisition, 1924.
Torquet (Charles). Paris en huit jours, choses vues, *see* ŒUVRES libres, 16, 1922.
Torr (Cecil). Hannibal crosses the Alps. s8°. C. 1924
Jésus & S. Jean dans l'art &c. [*Extr. f.* Revue arch., s3, t40; P2790]. la8°. [1902]
Small talk at Wreyland. s2, 3. 8°. C. 1921–23
„ „ ....abr. ed. s8°. C. 1926
Torraca (Francesco). Le donne ital. n. poesia provenzale—Su la "Treva" di G. de la Tor. s8°. Firenze. 1901
Nuovi studi Danteschi. 8°. Napoli. 1921
Torrance (David Watt), *see* LIVINGSTONE (W. P.) A Galilee doctor: career of Dr. D. W. T., 1923.
Torrance (William). Obs. on soil erosion. [Union of S. Afr., Dept. of Agric., Bull. 4. P2820]. 8°. Pretoria. 1919
Torre (Carlo). Il ritratto di Milano. s4°. Milano. 1674
Torregiani (*card.* Luigi Maria), *see* ACCIAJUOLI (*card.* F.) *Réponse [*attrib. to F. de Almada e Mendonça*] à la Relation envoyée par le Card. T. aux ministres étr. résidents à Rome &c., 1760.
Torre Hermosa (*Marqués* de). Nos regeneramos? 8°. 1899

Torrella (Caspare) [†TORRELLA (GASPAR), *titular bp. of Santa Giusta*]. Tractatus, (Romae), 1497, *facs.*, *see* SUDHOFF (C.) Earliest pr. lit. on syphilis, 1925.

Torrend (J.) Specimens of Bantu folklore f. N. Rhodesia. Texts & Eng. trs. 8°. 1921

Torres (Francisco Caro de), *see* CARO DE TORRES (F.)

Torres (Giuseppe). Cenni sul monast. cisterc. di Follina (Treviso). [P2843]. fol. Mestre. 1900

Torres (Julio Romero de), *see* ROMERO DE TORRES (J.)

Torres Amat (Felix), *bp. of Astorga*, *see* BIBLE: SPANISH. La Sagrada Biblia nuev. tr. por F. T. A., 6t (t6, Notes), 1832–35.

Torresani, *The family of*, *see* BERNONI (D. G.) Dei Torresani &c., 1890.

Torresano (Antonio). De gestis A. T. brevis narr., ed. D. Promis, *see* REGIA DEP. DI STORIA PATRIA. Misc., t12, 1871.

Torres Bernal (José de), *see* OLMET (LUIS ANTON DEL) & J. DE T. B. Los grandes Españoles, t11, 12, 1919–20.

Torres Lanzas (Pedro).
see ARCHIVO GEN. DE INDIAS. Cat.: cuadro gen. de la document., por P. T. L. &c., 1918.
,, —— Cat. de legajos del A. G. de I., por P. T. L., 1919–22.
,, —— Rel. de mapas &c.; por P. T. L., 1897–1906.

Torres Naharro (Bartolomé de). Comedia soldadesca, *see* LOMBA Y PEDRAJA (J. R.) Teatro ant. a L. de Vega, 1924.

Torrey (Samuel), *of Weymouth, Mass., 1631–1707*, *see* MURDOCK (K. B.), *ed.* Handkerchiefs f. Paul: verses, by T. &c., 1927.

Torriano (Giovanni). New relation of Rome &c., Engl. by T., 1664, *see* ROME exactly descr., 1664.

Torriente (Cosme de la), *see* LUGO-VINA (R. DE). Internac. repr.: T., 1924.

Torsellino (Orazio) [TURSELLINUS]. De vita S. Francisci Xaverii libri 6. s8°. Coloniæ Agripp. 1610
,, ,, ... s8°. Augustæ Vind. 1752
Hist. ab origine mundi usque ad 1598 epitome. Acc. eiusdem Epitomes cont. ad 1658 operâ R. P. P. B. S. I. Belgae [*sep. pagin.*] s8°. Parisiis. 1659
Lauretanæ hist. libri 5. s4°. Romæ. 1597

Torshell (Samuel). An exercit. upon the prophecie of Malachy, 1640, *see* STOCK (R.) Comm. upon Malachy, 1641.

Torsiello (I. E.) Gli ult. giorni di Fiume Dannunziana. Cronache e doc. &c. s8°. Bologna. [1921]

Tortelli (Giovanni), *see* MANCINI (G.) G. T. cooperatore di Niccolò V nel fondare la Bibl. Vaticana, 1920.

Tortus (Matthæus), *ps.*, *see* BELLARMINO (*card.* R. F. R.)

Tory. Ten yrs. of T. govt., 1895–1905, *see* LIBERAL PUBL. DEPT.

Toscana. La Toscana alla fine del Granducato: Conferenze di O. Bacci—P. Barbèra *& others.* s8°. Firenze. 1909

Toscanelli (Paolo).
see BANDINI (A. M.) Vita di A. Vespucci—bibliogr. d. opere conc. P. T. &c. per G. Fumagalli, 1898.
,, VIGNAUD (H.) The Columbian tradition on discov. of Amer. & part played by T. &c., 1920.

Tosefta [TOSEPHTA]. Der Tosephtatraktat roš haššana in vokalis. Text, mit Bemerkungen v. P. Fiebig, *see* KLEINE TEXTE, T130, 1914.
Tractate Berakoth, Mishna & Tosephta; tr. &c. A. L. Williams, 1921, *see* MISHNAH.

Tosi (Arturo), *see* BERNASCONI (U.) A. T., 1925.

Tosi (Pier Francesco). Obs. on the florid song. Tr. by [J. E.] Galliard. s8°. 1742

Tossanus (Daniel).
De Pelagianismo &c. Theses. [P434]. s4°. Heidelbergæ. 1595
Doctr. cathol. orthod. de sanct. spirituum veneratione: Per theses explic. Resp. H. Iekelmannus. [P437]. s4°. Heidelbergae. 1587
see CANCERINUS (N.) Rettung d. Augspurg. Conf. wider das fürgeben D. T., 1579.

***Total** (The) eclipse: a grand polit.-astron. phenomenon, 1820; w. a ser. of engravings [by I. R. Cruikshank] &c. [P425]. 8°. [1820]

Totleben (Eduard Ivanovich, cte. de). Défense de Sébastopol. 2t. [*Each t. has 2p, w. sep. tp., t1 pagin. cont., but* Pièces justific. *have sep. pagin.*] 4°. Saint Pétersbourg. 1863–74
,, ,, Exposé de la guerre souterraine, 1854–55; rédigé sous la dir. du Gén. T. par M. M. Frolow. 4°. Saint-Pétersbourg. 1870
,, ,, App., Service sanitaire des hôpitaux russes pend. la guerre de Crimée, 1854–56; par le Dr. Hubbeneth. [*b. w.* Exposé &c. *above*]. 4°. Saint-Pétersbourg. 1870
see SHILDER (N. K.) Графъ Э. И. Т., 2t, 1885–86.

Totomianz (Vachan Fomič). Anthologie coopérative. [*By var. a.* Préf. de C. Gide]. s8°. [1921]
Der Internat. Genossenschaftsbund, *see* UNTERSUCHUNGEN ü. Konsumvereine, 1924.
Die Konsumvereine in Russland, *see* UNTERSUCHUNGEN ü. Konsumvereine, 1922.

Touatânkhamanou, *see* TUTANKHAMEN.

Touchard (Albert). La mort du loup. Roman. s8°. 1924

Touchard-Lafosse (G.) The rollicking chronicles of T.-L. v1, According to the Cardinal. Tr. G. S. Taylor. 8°. [1928]

Touchet (George). *Histor. colls. out of Protestant historians, conc. relig., in the r. of Henry VIII &c.; w. add. of Sir W. Dugdale's Antiq. of Warwickshire, rel. to the abbies &c. Appendix. s8°. 1686

***Touch-stone** (The) of the reformed gospel: tenents [*sic*] of the Protest. doctrine refuted &c. [By J. Smeaton? *Imperf.*] s8°. *n.p.* [1685 ?]

Tough (Douglas Leonard Walton). The last years of a frontier: hist. of Borders dur. reign of Eliz. 8°. O. 1928

Toulorge (*le col.*)
Le service d'état-major en campagne. pl-3 [*in* 2t.] 8°. 1912

Touloubre (Louis Ventre, *seigneur* **de la)**, *dit Artefeuil*, *see* ARTEFEUIL.

Toulouse [THOULOUSE]. *Arrest du Parlement de T. contre la prétendue déclaration &c. de foy de Mr. de Candales [4 Feb. 1616. *b. w.* Candale (H. *duc de*). Déclaration 1616]. s8°. [Toulouse]. 1616

T'oung pao: archives pour servir à l'étude de l'hist., des langues, de la géographie &c. de l'Asie or. Dir. par H. Cordier & E. Chavannes. [Sér. 2], v15–25. 8°. Leide. 1914–27
20–24, dir. par H. Cordier & P. Pelliot. 25, dir. par P. Pelliot.

Tour. *Tour (A) in Teesdale incl. Rokeby &c., 1828, *see* GARLAND (R.)
*Tour (A) through the whole island of Gt. Britain, 3rd ed., 4v, 1742, *see* DEFOE (D.)

Tourane. Les sculptures chames au Musée de T., 1922, *see* PARMENTIER (H.)

Tourangeau (André du Chesne), *see* DU CHESNE (A.)

Tourean (Elishe). [Course of wr. lang. *In Armenian.* 2nd year. 2nd ed.] 8°. K. Polis. 1896

Touring Club Italiano. Carta d'Italia. Pubbl. dir. da L. V. Bertarelli. fogli 1–56 [*in* 1v, f13 *in* 2p. Indici *issued w. each fogl. b. in 1v.*] s8°. fol. Milano. [1907–18]
,, ,, Indice gen. d. carta &c. Compilato s. la dir. di L. V. Bertarelli. la8°. [Milano. 1916]

***Tourist's** (The) companion, or a guide to the steam & canal boats, Edinb. & London smacks &c. s8°. E. 1822

Tourist's guides [*publ. by Stanford*].
Norfolk; by W. Rye. 2nd ed. s8°. 1880

Tournai. A declar. of the princ. pointes of Christian doctrine, out of diverse Catechismes, & set forth by the English priests in Tournay-Colledge. s8°. Paris. 1647

Tournament. *The Eglinton T., 1839, 1840, *see* EGLINTON CASTLE.

Tournély (Honoré). De baptismo, *see* MIGNE (J. P.), *ed.* Theol. cursus, t21, 1841.
—— **& P. Collet.** De subjecto sacramentorum, *see* MIGNE (J. P.), *ed.* Theol. cursus, t21, 1841.

Tournès (René). L'hist. militaire. 8°. 1922
—— **&** *Capt.* **H. Berthemet.** La Bataille des Flandres d'ap. le journal de marche &c. de la IVe armée allemande. (9–30 avril, 1918). Tr., comm. & notes. la8°. 1925

Tourneur-Aumont (J. M.) Etudes de cartographie hist. sur l'Alémanie. Régions du haut Rhin & du haut Danube du 3e au 8e s. la8°. 1918

Tourneux (Maurice). La Tour. Biog. crit. 8°. [1904]

Tournon (*le card.* **de)** [†MAILLARD DE TOURNON (CHARLES T.)]
*Vera ac sincera hist. actorum patriarchae Antiocheni [*i.e.* C. T. M. de T.] in Sinarum imperio &c. circa Sinenses ritus. Auctore quodam Sinensi missionario veritatis amante. s4°. [Paris ? 1708]
see GONZAGA (F.), *bp. of Mantua.* Relatio pretiosæ mortis C. T. Maillard de Tournon &c., 1712.

Tours. Chartes de Saint-Julien de T., 1002–1300. Publ. L. J. Denis. [Soc. des Archives Hist. du Maine]. 2 fasc. 8°. au Mans. 1912–13

Tourte (François), *violin-maker*, *see* FÉTIS (F. J.) Notice of A. Stradivari &c.: foll. by remarks on F. T.; tr., 1864.

Tourtoulon (Charles de) & O. Bringuier. La limite géograph. de la Langue d'oc et la Langue d'oil. [Extr. des Arch. des miss. scient. &c., s3, t3]. 8°. 1876

Tout (Thomas Frederick).
An advanced hist. of Eng. n. ed., reissue. s8º. 1925
Beginnings of a mod. capital: London & Westminster in 14 c. [Raleigh lect.; f. Proc. of Brit. Acad., v11. P2731; 2737]. 8º. [1923]
The captivity & death of Edward of Carnarvon. [Repr. f. Bull. of John Rylands Lib.] 8º. M'ter. 1920
Chapters in the admin. hist. of med. England. The Wardrobe, the Chamber, & the Small Seals. [Univ. of M'ter. Hist. ser., 48, 49]. v3, 4. 8º. M'ter. 1928
Essays in medieval history: presented to T. F. T. Ed. A. G. Little & F. M. Powicke. la8º. *p.p.* M'ter. 1925
France & England: their relations in Middle Ages & now. 8º. M'ter. 1922
Hist. of Eng., 1216–1377. [Polit. Hist. of Eng., v3]. n. ed. 8º. 1920
Medieval & mod. warfare. Repr. f. Bulletin of John Rylands Lib. [P2416]. la8º. M'ter. 1919
Mediaeval forgers & forgeries. Repr. f. Bull. of John Rylands Lib. [P2416]. la8º. M'ter. 1920
Mediæval town planning. Lect. Repr. f. Bull. of John Rylands Lib. la8º. M'ter. 1917
Sir A. W. Ward, 1837–1924. [Brit. Acad. P2821]. 8º. [1926]
Sir J. H. Ramsay, 1832–1925. [Brit. Acad. P2821]. 8º. [1926]
Study of mediaeval chronicles. [Repr. f. Bull. of John Rylands Lib.] 8º. 1922
see AQUINAS (T.), *St.* St. T. A.: papers; by T. &c., 1925.

Toutain (Jules), *member of the École Franç. de Rome.* Les cultes païens dans l'Empire romain. [H. E.: Sci. Relig., 31]. p1, t3. la8º. 1920
p1, Les provinces latines. t3, Les cultes indigènes nat. & locaux.

Touzé-Bocage (Pierre François), *see* BOCAGE (P. F.)

Touzeau (James). The rise & progress of Liverpool, 1551–1835. 2v. la8º. Liv'l. 1910

Tovey (Donald Francis). Essays in mus. analysis. [p]2, A great sonata by Haydn &c. [P2705]. 8º. *n.d.*

Tower Bridge. Opening ceremony. Rep. f. Bridge-house Estates Com. fol. 1894

Tower of London. Illust. guide to the Armouries. By Visct. Dillon. 8º. 1910

Towers (William Samuel).
Version of the Psalms [*in verse*]. 8º. 1811

Towgood (Micaiah). A dissent f. the Church of England &c. Being the dissenting gentleman's Three letters &c. in ans. to the letters of Mr. White &c. 6th ed. w. corr. & add. 8º. 1787

Towle (Matthew). The young gentleman & lady's private tutor. 3p [*in* 1v]. s8º. O. 1770

Towler (W. G.)
The nationalis. of British industries. [P2484]. 8º. [1919]
—— & W. Ray. Socialism; its promise & failure. s8º. [1920]

Town. *View (A) of London & Westminster: or, the town spy, 2p, 1728, *see* LONDON.

Towne (Charles Hanson), *see* MAUDE (C.) & G. H. T. The actor in room 931, 1927.

Towne (Edward Cornelius).
The story of money. s8º. N.Y. [1900]

Towneley MSS., *see* COATES (*Sir* E. F.) Cat. of T. mysteries, sold, 1922.

Towneley (John). Cat. of coll. of Brit. portraits, illust. of Granger; formed by J. T. Sold by Mr. Evans, 1828. [*MS. prices*]. la8º. [1828]

Towner (Rutherford Hamilton).
Philosophy of civiliz. 2v. 8º. N.Y. 1923

Townley (James) *D.D., Wesleyan minister, 1774–1833.*
Essays on var. subjects of eccl. hist. & antiq. 8º. 1824
Illust. of Biblical lit., hist. &c. of the Sacred writings &c. 3v. 8º. 1821
see HOOLE (E.) Mem. of J. T., 1835.

Townley (*Lady* Susan Mary).
"Indiscretions" of Lady Susan. [2nd impr.] 8º. [1922]

Townroe (Bernard Stephen). Handbook of housing. 8º. [1924]
A wayfarer in Alsace. s8º. [1926]

Townsend (Charles F.)
Chemistry for photographers. 2nd ed. rev. s8º. 1899

Townsend (George), *canon of Durham.* The accusations of hist. agst. the Church of Rome examined, in remarks on C. Butler's work, "Book of the R. Cath. Ch." n. ed., rev. & corr. by J. E. Cox. s8º. 1845
*Life & defence &c. of E. Bonner, bp. of London. By A Tractarian Brit. critic. 8º. 1842
The New Test. arranged in chronol. & hist. order &c. 4th ed. 2v. 8º. 1838

Townsend (George), *canon of Durham* [*continued*].
The Old Test. arranged in hist. & chronol. order &c. 2nd ed. 2v. 8º. 1826
see BUTLER (C.) Vindic. of "The Book of the Rom. Cath. Church" agst. T. &c., 2nd ed., 1826.

Townsend (George E.) Pract. rabbit keeping. s8º. [1924]

Townsend (Richard), *fellow of Trinity Coll., Dublin.*
Chapters on mod. geometry of point, line & circle. 2v. 8º. D. 1863–65

Townsend (William G. Paulson).
Mod. decorative art in England. v1. fol. [1922]
1, Woven &c. fabrics, wall-papers, lace & embroidery.
Plant & floral studies for designers. la8º. 1901

Townshend papers. Cat. of pr. books & doc. comprising the T. papers, Eng. bookbindings the prop. of H. H. Mulliner &c. Auction by Sotheby, July 1924. [*Illust.* P2747]. 8º. [1924]

Townshend (*Rt. Hon.* Charles).
*National thoughts. By a landowner. [P2783]. 8º. [1767]

Townshend (*Maj.-Gen. Sir* Charles Vere Ferrers).
My campaign in Mesopotamia. 8º. [1920]

Townshend (Dorothea), *wife of R. B. Townshend.*
George Digby, 2nd Earl of Bristol. 8º. [1924]

Townshend (*Brig.-Gen.* George), *see* NORTHCLIFFE (A. C. W. H., *1st baron*). The N. Coll. [papers of T. &c.]; pres. to Govt. of Canada, 1926.

Townshend (Richard Baxter).
Last memories of a tenderfoot. 8º. [1926]
A tenderfoot in Colorado. 8º. [1923]
The tenderfoot in New Mexico. 8º. [1923]

Townson (Thomas), *D.D.*
Disc. on the 4 Gospels &c. s4º. O. 1778
Practical discourses. [*Pref. signed* John Limerick, *i.e.* J. Jebb, *bound as* Jebb (J.) Works, v4]. *not publ.* 8º. 1828

Towse (J. Wrench), *see* FISHMONGERS' Co. Sh. acc. of portraits &c. in poss. of the Co.; by T., 1907.

Toye (Nina). The shadow of fear. s8º. 1921

Toynbee (Arnold Joseph). Greek civilisation & character. [*Extracts*]. Intr. & tr. by A. J. T. s8º. 1924
Greek hist. thought f. Homer to age of Heraclius. [*Extracts*]. With 2 pieces newly tr. by G. Murray. s8º. 1924
The place of mediaeval & mod. Greece in hist. Pref. statement by J. Gennadius. [P2416]. s4º. 1919
Survey of internat. affairs, 1920–23. [Brit. Inst. of Int. Affairs]. la8º. 1925
,, ,, 1924. Pref. by H. A. L. Fisher. la8º. 1926
,, ,, 1925. v1, The Islamic world since the Peace Settlement. 8º. 1927
,, ,, 1926. 8º. O. 1928
The Western question in Greece & Turkey. 8º. 1922
The world after the Peace Conf. la8º. 1925
see MÉLAS (G. M.) The Turk as he is; ans. to a libel: [*Crit. of Western question in Greece & Turkey, by T.*], 1922.
—— & K. P. Kirkwood.
Turkey. 8º. 1926

Toynbee (Paget Jackson). The bearing of the cursus on the text of Dante's De vulgari eloquentia. [Brit. Acad. P2683]. 8º. [1923]
Britain's tribute to Dante in lit. & art (c. 1380–1920). [Brit. Acad.] la8º. 1921
Dante in Eng. art, *see* DANTE SOC., *Camb., Mass.* 38th rep., 1921.
Dante studies. [*Includ.* Chronolog. list of Eng. translations]. 8º. O. 1921
Epistolae: the letters of Dante. Emended text w. intr., tr., notes, & indices, & app. on the cursus. 8º. O. 1920
The Oxford Dante. [Fr. Rep. of Dante Soc. P2849]. 8º. [Camb., U.S.A. 1926]
see OXFORD DANTE SOC. A record of 44 years, 1876–1920; comp. by P. T., 1920.

Toynbee (William). Glimpses of the twenties. 8º. 1909

Tozzer (Alfred Marston). Excav. of a site at Santiago Ahuitzotla, D. F. Mexico. [S.I., Bur. of Ethn., Bull. 74]. 8º. W. 1921

Tozzi (Federigo).
Con gli occhi chiusi. Romanzo. s8º. Milano. 1919
Gli egoisti. Romanzo—L'incalco. Dramma. Con nota di G. A. Borgese. s8º. [1923]
Giovani. Novelle. s8º. Milano. 1920
Il podere. Romanzo. s8º. Milano. 1921
Tre croci. Romanzo. s8º. Milano. 1920
Three crosses. [Tr. R. Capellero]. s8º. [1921]

Traber-Amiel (August).
Das Buch für mod. Tänze. [2B]. 8º. [1922]

Trackenbar, *see* TRANQUEBAR.
Tractarian British critic, *ps.* *Life &c. of E. Bonner, 1842, *see* TOWNSEND (G.)
***Tractat** (Ein) in dem kürtzlich durch die heyligen geschrifft angezaygt wirdt, wie der inwendig u. auszwendig mensch, wider-einander u. bey einander sein. s4°. *n.p.* 1524
Tractätlein. *Eyn edles schönes lieplichs T., c. 1524, *see* MARSHALCK (H.)
Tractatus.
Tr. curiosus [theolog.], 1691–92, *see* FASCICULUS rar. & cur. script. theol., 1692.
Tr. de schismate &c., 1718, *see* LONGUEVAL (J.)
Tr. Graeci de re metrica ined., 1922, *see* KOSTER (W. J. W.), *ed.*
*Tr. novi. de potu caphe &c., 1685, *see* DUFOUR (P. S.)
Tr. sollennis de arte & vero modo predicandi ex diversis sacror. doctor. scripturis & p̄ncipaliter doctoris Thome de Aquino ex parvo suo quodā tractatulo recollectus [*supposititious work*]. 8°. [Memming, *A. Kunne de duderstat*]. 1483
12 leaves, 1st blank, double columns, 32 ll. to a full col. Sig. A, B in sixes].
Tracts for the times, No. 67, 68, 69. Scriptural views of baptism by E. B. Pusey [*separate issue*]. 8°. 1836
,, ,, No. 75. On the Roman Breviary &c. [*by J. H. Newman*]. 8°. [1836]
,, ,, Some doc. &c. conn. w. Tract No. 90 [*incl.* Newman's Letter to the Vice-Chancellor. P2788]. 8°. O. 1841
see CROLY (D.) An index to the Tracts for the times, 1842.
,, PUSEY (E. B.) Articles in T. 90 reconsid., 1841.
Tracy (Hiram A.), *see* BENEDICT (W. A.) & H. A. T. Hist. of Sutton, Mass., 1878.
Tracy (Joseph). The great awakening: revival of relig. in the time of Edwards & Whitefield. 8°. Boston, Mass. 1842
Hist. of the Amer. Board of Comm. for foreign missions. 2nd ed. 8°. N.Y. 1842
Tracy (Louis). The law of the talon. s8°. [1926]
The Park Lane mystery. s8°. [1924]
Tracy (Stanley J.), *see* CLARK (L. D.) & S. J. T. *for works wr. in collab.*
Trade. *Essays & observ. on t. &c.; publ. by a Soc. of gentlemen in Dublin, 1740, *see* ESSAYS.
Trade & industry of Finland, 1922, *see* FINLAND.
*Trade revival & the reparations muddle. [P2708]. 8°. [1922]
Trade Conference (International). Proceedings of Int. T. Conf., New York, Dec. 6–8, 1915. 8°. N.Y. [1916]
Tradescant (John), *the elder, see* GUNTHER (R. T.) Early Brit. botanists &c., based on unpubl. wr. of T., 1922.
Tradescant (John), *the younger.* Musæum Tradescantianum: or, a coll. of rarities at South-Lambeth, 1656. [Prep. by R. T. Gunther. Old Ashmolean repr., 1]. s8°. [O. 1925]
Trades Union, *see* BRITISH TRADES UNION.
Träger (Paul). Die Deutschen in d. Dobrudscha. [Schr. d. Deut. Ausland-Inst. Stuttgart, A, Kulturhist. Reihe, B6]. 8°. St. 1922
Tragett (*Mrs.* R. C.), *see* LARMINIE (M.R.), *ps.*
Traggia (Joaquin), *see* ASTARLOA Y AGUIRRE (P. P. DE).
Apología de la lengua Bascongada &c. en resp. á los reparos propuestos [*by* J. T.] &c., 1803.
***Tragi-comicall** (A) hist. of our times; tr., 1627, *see* AUDIGUIER (V. D').
Trahard (Pierre).
La jeunesse de P. Mérimée (1803–34). 2t. 8°. 1925
Le Romantisme défini par "Le Globe." s8°. [1925]
Traherne (Thomas), *B.D.; 1636?–74, see* WILLETT (G. E.) T.: essay, 1919.
Trail (William), *M.A., of M'ter.* The literary characteristics &c. of the Bible. 8°. E. 1863
Traill (Peter), *see* MORTON (M.) & P. T. Woman to woman, 1924.
Traill (Robert). Select pract. writings. s8°. E. 1845
Train (Arthur). High winds. [2nd ed.] s8°. 1927
His children's children. s8°. 1923
True stories of crime f. the Distr. Attorney's Office. 8°. 1908
Traité [TRAICTÉ; TRAITTÉ]. Traicté polit.: prouvé par Moyse &c. que tuer un tyran n'est pas un meurtre, 1658, *see* SEXBY (E.)
*Traité de la comédie &c., 1669, *see* CONTI (A. DE B., *pr.* DE).
*Traité de l'autorité du pape &c., 1720, *see* LEVESQUE DE BURIGNY (J.)
*Traité de l'étude des Conciles &c., 1724, *see* SALMON (F.)
*Traité des anc. cérémonies &c., 1673, *see* PORRÉE (J.)
*Traitté de l'origine des cardinaux &c., 1665, *see* DUPEYRAT (G.)

Traités. Répertoire gén. des traités &c., 1895–1920. [Inst. Interméd. Internat., La Haye]. 8°. Harlem. 1926
Traités & conventions en vigueur entre la Fr. & les puissances étr., t3, 4, 1920–22, *see* FRANCE: STATE DEPT., MINISTÈRE DES AFFAIRES ETR.
Trajan, *emperor of Rome.*
see BONI (G.) T.'s column, 1907.
,, HENDERSON (B. W.) 5 Roman emperors, 1927.
,, STUDNICZKA (F.) Tropaeum Traiani, 1904.
Trajectense. Bullarium T.; coll. & ausp. Soc. Hist. Rheno-Traj. ed. G. Brom, 2v, 1891–96, *see* BULLARIUM.
Quedam narracio de Groninghe, de Thrente, de Covordia et de diversis aliis sub div. episc. Tr. [Gesta episc. Traj.] Uitg. door C. Pijnacker Hordijk. [Hist. Genoots. Werken., N.S., 49]. 8°. Utrecht. 1888
Tramerye (Pierre L'Espagnol de la), *see* LA TRAMERYE (P. L'E. DE).
Tramond (Joannès). Manuel d'hist. maritime de la France, à 1815. 2e éd., rev. & augm. 8°. 1927
—— **& A. Reussner.** Elém. d'hist. maritime & colon. contemp., 1815–1914. 8°. 1924
Tranchère (J. Hovyn de), *see* HOVYN DE TRANCHÈRE (J.)
Tranckenbar, *see* TRANQUEBAR.
Trancoso (Gonçalo Fernandez), *see* FERNANDEZ TRANCOSO (G.)
Tranér (Johannes). Imperii & litt. Germanicae sub Suevis imperat. fortuna. [2p. P2641]. s4°. Upsaliae. [1816]
Tranquebar [TRANCKENBAR; TRANGAMBAR]. A explĩcaçaõ da doutr. Christaã, pelos Padres Missionarios de Trangambar, 1762, *see* EXPLĨCAÇAÕ.
Kurtzgefassete Nachr. v. d. gegenwärt. Zustande d. hier z. Tranckenbar angericht. Königl. Dänischen Mission, 1754, 1767, 1770–73, 77, 1780, 81, 86. [*in* 1v.] 8°. nachgedr. Halle. 1755–87
***Transalpine** memoirs: or, anecdotes &c. of Italy; by an Eng. Catholic, 1826, *see* BESTE (J. R. D.)
Transvaal.
Hdbk to the municipal laws of the T. 8°. 1903
List of farms in Bethal district, T., w. names of owners. fol. Pretoria. 1900–1
Foll. by lists of farms in following districts, all w. sep. tp. & pagin.

Bloemhof.	Middelburg.	Utrecht.
Carolina.	Middelburg (Mapocks Gronden).	Vryheid.
Ermelo.		Wakkerstroom.
Heidelberg.	Piet Retief.	Waterberg.
Krugersdorp.	Potchefstroom.	Wolmaransstad.
Lichtenburg.	Pretoria.	Zoutpansberg.
Lydenburg.	Rustenburg.	
Marico.	Standerton.	

The statute law of the T. Tr. by S. H. Barber, W. A. Macfadyen & J. H. L. Findlay. la8°. 1901
Transvaal (Maj. Jackson's ser.) [Maps]. Sheets 1–57 (5, 11, 14, 16, 20, 21, 29, 33, 34, 44, 47, 50, 52, 53b wanting). *folded* s8°. Pretoria. 1901–2
Sheets 36, 38, 38a, 39 & 39a *are lettered* Natal.
T. & Orange River Colony. Public educ. Rep. of Director of educ., 1900–4. n. ed. 8°. 1905
T. Colony proclamations, 1900–1902. la8°. 1902
Transvaal (The) agricultural journal; issued by Agric. Dept., v3–7, 1904–9, *see* AFRICA: UNION OF SOUTH A. Journal of Dept. of Agric.
Transylvania [TRANSYLVANICA].
Acta & epist. T. &c., v1, 1914, *see* VERESS (A.), *ed.*
*Confessio fidei Christianae sec. Unitarios, inter 4 in T. religiones receptas numerata &c. [*by J. Kermötzi*]. s4°. [Cibinii. 1782]
Epist. & acta Jesuitarum T. (1571–1613); ed. A. Veress, 2v, 1911–13, *see* JESUITS.
Fontes rerum T., *see* FONTES R. T.
*The histor. churches of T. & Roumania. [P2576]. 8°. Budapest. 1921
Pictures of T., 1920, *see* MAKOLDY (J. DE).
T. under the rule of Roumania. Rep. of Amer. Unitarian Comm. 2nd ed. [P2578]. 8°. Budapest. 1921
Transylvanian Lady Teacher, *ps.* Remarks on Lord Curzon's speech on ratific. of Hung. Peace treaty of the Trianon, 1921, *see* REMARKS.
Transylvanus Viator, *ps.* In Transylvania. [P2567]. s8°. 1921
Trant, *The family of, see* MACCARTHY (S. T.) Trant family, 1924; Suppl., 1926.
Trant (Clarissa Sandford).
Journal, 1800–32. Ed. C. G. Luard. 8°. [1925]
Trapesnikoff (Trifon). Porträtdarstellungen d. Mediceer d. 15. Jhdts. la8°. Str. 1909
Trapier (Elizabeth Du Gue).
El Greco. [Hispanic Soc. of Amer.] s8°. N.Y. 1925

Trapp (John), *vicar of Weston-upon- Avon.*
Annot. upon the Old & New Test. With a Treatise "The Righteous Man's Recompense. . . ." With a Decad of Divine Disc. &c. fol. 5v. [v5 *wanting*; v1, 2nd ed.] 1654–62
Only v1 *has above gen. tp. Each vol. has tp. beg.* A comm. or expos. &c.; v1–3 *have 2 pagin. For earlier issue of contents of* v5, *see* Comm. &c. *below.*
A clavis to the Bible: or a comm. upon the Pentateuch. [3 *pagin.*] s4º. 1650
A comm. or expos. upon all the Epistles, & the Revelation of John the Divine. With a decad of commonplaces. [*w. sep. tp.*] s4º. 1647
A comm. or expos. upon the 4 Evangelists & the Acts of the Apostles. [3 *pagin.*] s4º. 1647

Trapp (Joseph), *D.D.* The Ch. of Engl. defended agst. Ch. of Rome. In ans. to England's conversion &c. [*by* R. Manning]. s8º. 1727

Trapp (*Fregattenkapitän* **Robert).** Reconciliation betw. Germany & England: key to G.'s fut. for. policy. [Tr.] s8º. Berlin. [1920]

Trappes-Lomax (Richard). Hist. of the township & manor of Clayton-le-Moors, Co. Lancaster. [Chetham Soc., N.S., 85]. 8º. M'ter. 1926

Traprock (Walter E.), *ps.* [*i.e.* George Shepard Chappell]. The cruise of the Kawa. Wanderings in the South Seas. 8º. [1921]

Traquair (Ramsay). Frankish archit. in Greece. [Repr. f. Journal of R.I.B.A., v31. Byzant. Research Fund. P2730] [2p *in* 1v]. la8º. 1923

Tratado de paz, concl. entre el Rey de Fr. &c. en Vienna 18 Nov. 1738, 1739, *see* Vienna.

Traube (Ludwig). Palaeog. Forschungen, T5, Autographa d. Jo. Scotus, *see* Königliche Akad. d. Wiss. zu München. Abhdlgn. d. phil. Klasse, B26, 1914.
Quellen u. Untersuchungen z. latein. Philologie d. M.-A. Begr. v. L. T. Hrsg. v. P. Lehmann. B3i–iv, 4i, ii, 5i, ii. 8º. München. 1908–20
see Becker (J.) Textgesch. Liudprands v. Cremona, 1908. [3ii.]
,, Beeson (C. H.) Isidor-Studien, 1913. [4ii.]
,, Frenken (G.) Die Exempla d. Jacob v. Vitry 1914. [5i.]
,, Lehmann (P.) F. Modius als Handschriftenforscher, 1908. [3i.]
,, —— J. Sichardus, 1911. [4i.]
,, —— Vom M.-A. u. d. latein. Philol. d. M.-A., 1914. [5i.]
,, Lowe (E. A.) Ält. Kalendar. aus Monte Cassino, 1908. [3iii.]
,, Paulus, *diaconus.* Gedichte, 1908. [3iv.]
,, Walther (H.) Das Streitgedicht in d. latein. Lit. d. M.-A., 1920. [5ii.]
Vorlesungen u. Abhandlungen. Hrsg. v. F. Boll. B3. la8º. München. 1920
3, Kl. Schriften; hrsg. v. S. Brandt.

Trausch (Joseph Franz), *see* Massa (S.) Chronicon Fuchsio-Lupino-Oltardinum &c., ed. J. F. T., 1847–48.

Trautwein (Theodor). Führer durch München &c. 33e A. s8º. München. [1927]

Travaginus (Franciscus). Super observat. a se factis temp. ult. terraemotuum, ac potiss. Ragusiani, disquis. [P447]. s4º. Venetiis. 1673

Travaux tactiques publ. par le Journal des Sciences militaires. Thèmes & solutions. Préf. de Gén. H. Bonnal. 3s. 8º. 1909–13

Travel & travellers of the Middle Ages, 1926, *see* Newton (A. P.), *ed.*

Traveller (A), *ps.*, *see* Hugman (J.) Orig. poems, 14th ed., 1833.

Traveller's Club (The), *see* Fitzroy (*Sir* A. W.) Hist. of the T.C., 1927.

***Travels** through Spain & part of Portugal, 2v, 1808, *see* Whittington (*Rev.*)

Travers (Ben). Mischief. s8º. [1925]
Rookery Nook. s8º. [1923]

Travers (John), *ps.* [*i.e. Mrs.* G. H. Bell].
In the long run. s8º. [1925]
A servant when he reigneth. s8º. [1921]

Travers (Joseph), *& Co.*
A few records of an old firm. 8º. [1924]

Travers-Borgstroem (Arthur). Mutualism; a synthesis. [P2488]. s8º. *pr. impr.* Clarens. 1918

Traz (Robert de). Dépaysements. [Vienne, Hongrie, Berlin &c. Les cahiers verts, 29]. s8º. 1923

Treasury (The) of American sacred song, 1896, *see* Horder (W. G.), *ed.*

Treasury [Government Office]. Calendar of T. Books. Prep. by W. A. Shaw. [C. of S.P.] v8. 4p. la8º. 1923
8, 1685–89.
see Heath (*Sir* T. L.) The T., 1927.

Treaties (The) of peace, 1919–23. Maps comp. & summary of legal basis of the new boundaries by Lt.-Col. L. Martin. [C.E. for Int. Peace]. 2v. 8º. N.Y. 1924
1, Treat[ies] of Versailles, St. Germain-en-Laye & Trianon.
2, Treaties of Neuilly & Sèvres, Treaties betw. U.S. & Germany, Austria & Hungary, & Treaty of Lausanne &c.

Treatise. *T. conc. the fulnesse of Xt., 1656, *see* Jeanes (H.)
*T. (A) of the nature of a minister, 1670, *see* Lucy (W.), *bp. of St. David's.*
*T. (A) on rigging, c. 1625; ed. R. C. Anderson, 1921, *see* Rigging.

Treaty of peace betw. Russia & Esthonia, *n.d.*, *see* Russia.

Trebbi (Oreste). Alfredo Testoni. s8º. 1926

Trebitsch (Siegfried). Die Frau ohne Dienstag. s8º. 1919

Treble (H. A.) Eng. prose, narr., descr. & dramatic. Comp. by H. A. T. [repr.] s8º. [1921]

Trébutien (François Guillaume Stanislas). Caen: hist., monuments &c. Guide. 3e éd. s8º. Caen. [1881]

Treby (George), *see* Popish. Coll. of letters &c. rel. to P. plot &c.; pr. f. originals in hands of G. T., 1681.

Tredgold (Alfred Frank).
Mental deficiency (Amentia). 3rd ed. rev. & enl. 8º. 1920

Tree (*Sir* **Herbert Beerbohm).**
Hamlet f. an actor's prompt book. Lect. s8º. 1897
The imaginative faculty. Lect. s8º. 1893
Thoughts & after-thoughts. 8º. 1913
see Beerbohn (M.) H. B. T.; memories &c. coll. by M. B., 1921.

Treen (Albert Edward).
Hist. & antiq. of vicinity of Rugby. v1. s8º. Rugby. 1909

Trefethen (James Albert) & William H. Smith. Condensed rep. of trial of J. A. T. & W. H. S. for murder of D. J. Davis. Sup. Court of Mass. [1892]. 8º. Boston [Mass.] 1895

Treffel (Georges), *see* Larousse, *publ. firm.* Atlas départ. Larousse: texte par G. T., 1914.

Treffry (Richard), *the elder.*
Mem. of the Rev. Joseph Benson. s8º. 1840
Mem. of the Rev. Richard Treffry, jun. App. sel. remains. By his father. 3rd ed. s8º. 1854
A treatise on secret & soc. prayer. s8º. 1841

Treffry (Richard), *the younger, 1804–38, see* Treffry (R.), *elder.* Mem. of R. T., jun., 1854.

Trefnant (John), *bp. of Hereford; d. 1404.* Registrum J. T., episc. Hereford., 1389–1404. Ed. W. W. Capes. [Canterbury & York Soc.] 8º. 1916

Trégain (*le comte* **E. de).**
Hist. du royaume des Deux-Siciles. 8º. 1854

Tregarthen (Greville). Australian Commonwealth. Add. chap. by P. E. G. Bayley. [2nd ed.] 8º. [1924]

Tregarthen (John Coulson). Life story of a badger. 8º. [1925]

Treherne (Geo. Gilbert Treherne) & J. H. D. Goldie. Record of the University Boat Race, 1829–80, & of Commem. dinner, 1881. la8º. 1883

Treiber (Johann Philipp). Comm. de excussione fenestrarum. Adj. opusc. A. R. I. Bünemanni de studiosis bacchantibus &c. [P2746]. s4º. Halae Sax. 1736

Trelawny (Edward John). Adv. of a younger son. Intr. by H. N. Brailsford. 2v. s8º. 1914

Trelawny (*Sir* **John Salusbury),** *bart.* Analysis of the evidence before Contagious Diseases Comm. s8º. 1872

Trelawny (*Sir* **Jonathan),** *3rd bart., bp. of (1) Bristol, (2) Exeter, (3) Winchester, see* Sancroft (W.) Proc. & tryal in case of abp. of Canterbury, bp. of B. &c., 1688, 1689.

Tremearne (*Major* **Arthur John Newman).** The ban of the Bori. Demons & demon-dancing in W. & N. Africa. 8º. [1914]

Tremellius (Immanuel).
סֵפֶר חִנּוּךְ בְּחִירֵי יָהּ. s8º. לונדן. [1820]
see Bible: New Test.: Greek. Ἡ Καινὴ Διαθήκη; interp. Syr. N.T., Hebr. typ. descr.; aut. I. T., cujus Gramm. Chald. & Syra adj., 1569.

Trench (*Col.* **Frederic Chenevix).** Manœuvre orders 1914. Ed. Lt.-Col. B. M. Bateman. 8th ed. rev. & augm. s8º. 1907
,, ,, ...12th ed. rev. s8º. 1914

Trench (*Sir* **Frederick William).** Lithogr. sk. of N. bank of Thames f. Westminster Br. to London Br. shewing prop. quay &c. suggested by Lt.-Col. T., 1825, *see* Thames.

Trench (Herbert).
Poems w. fables in prose. [2nd impr.] s8º. 1919

Trench (Richard Chenevix), *abp. of Dublin.* Lects. on medieval Church hist. 2nd ed. rev. & impr. 8º. 1886
Notes on the miracles of our Lord. 10th ed. rev. 8º. 1874
Notes on the parables of our Lord. 12th ed. rev. 8º. 1874
Synonyms of the New Test. 7th ed. rev. & enl. 8º. 1871

Trenchard (John) & W. Moyle. *An argument, shewing that a standing army is inconsistent w. a free govt. &c. s4º. 1697

Trenck (Franz, *Frhr.* v. der), *1710–49, see* TEICHMAN (*Capt.* O.) Pandour T., 1927.

Trenck (Friedrich, *Frhr.* v. der).
see DU JEU (*Vte.* E.) A Prussian Casanova [Baron F. v. d. T.]; tr., 1924.
,, LINGUET (S. N. H.) Mém. &c., & fragm. conc. captivité du Baron de T., 1884.

Trend (John Brande).
Alfonso the sage & o. Span. essays. 8º. 1926
Luis Milan & the vihuelistas. [Hispanic Soc. of Amer.] s8º. O. 1925
The music of Span. hist. to 1600. [Hispanic Soc. of Amer.] s8º. 1926
Picture of mod. Spain, men & music. 8º. [1921]
Spain f. the South. 8º. [1928]

Trendelenburg (F. Adolf), *see* WACH (J.) Typenlehre T., 1926.

Trendell (Herbert A. P.), *ed.*
Dress worn at H.M.'s court. 2p [*in* 1v]. 8º. 1912

Treneer (Anne). The sea in Eng. lit. f. Beowulf to Donne. s8º. Liv'l. 1926

Trent, *Council of.*
Acta Co. T. quorum cat. in sequent. habetur paginis. s8º. Antverpiae. 1546
Acta Co. T. 1562 & 63 &c. a G. Paleotto descr. Ed. J. Mendham. 8º. Londini. 1842
Canones, & decreta C.T. sub Paulo III, Julio III, Pio IIII. fol. Romae. 1564
Canones & decreta, P. Chiffletii praefatio. ed. noviss[a]. s8º. Lugduni. 1677
Canones & decreta C.T. sub Paulo III, Julio III, Pio IIII celebrati juxta exemplar authenticum Romæ 1564 ed. opera J. Le Plat. 4º. Antverpiæ. 1779
Canones & decreta. Cur. A. Bisping. 8º. Monasterii Guestphal. 1845
Canones & decreta C.T. ex ed. Romana a. 1834 repetiti. Ed. Æ. L. Richter. 8º. Lipsiae. 1853
Catechismus, ex decreto C.T., ad Parochos, Pii V Pont. Max. jussu ed. sm. fol. 1566
Catechismus ex decreto C.T. s8º. Lovanii. 1567
Catechismus catholicus. Per Georg. Eder. s8º. Coloniae. 1569
Catechismus Romanus ex decreto C.T. jussu Pii V. s8º. Utini. 1706
Catechismus C.T. Opera P. D. L. H. P. [*i.e.* P. de la Haye]. s8º. Parisiis. 1830
Catechismus ex decreto C.T. ed. ster. 8[a]. s8º. Lipsiae. 1865
*Causae cur electores &c. Aug. Conf. ad Concilium a Pio IIII Tridenti indictum, non accedant &c., 1564; 1664, *see* AUGSBURG CONFESSION.
Concilinum Tridentinum. Cum Indice librorum prohib. [*w. sep. tp.*] s8º. Venetiis. 1589
Concilium Tridentinum. t8–10. 4º. Friburgi. 1916–24
8, Actorum p5, Acta, 1562 a prima ad sextam. Coll. &c. S. Ehses.
9, Actorum p6, Acta, 17. Sept. 1562–4. Dec. 1563. Coll. &c. S. Ehses.
10, Epist. p1, 5. Mart. 1545 ad 11. Mart. 1547. Coll. &c. G. Buschbell.
Decretum Salviconductus in SS. Oecumenica, & gen. T. Synodo approbatum. s4º. Venetiis. 1562
Recusatio T. Synodi a. 1546 a Statibus August. Conf. Germanicè evulgata, & nunc Lat. ed. Rationes item [*by M. Flacius Illyricus*], cur ejusmodi Synodi devitandae sint. s8º. Basileæ. *n.d.* [1550 ?]
Sacrosanctum Concilium Tridentium. Cum citationibus ex utroque Test. &c. s8º. Patavii. 1758
,, ,, ...s8º. Bassani. 1791

TRANSLATIONS.
Canons & decrees of the C. of T. Tr. s4º. 1687
Canons & decrees. Tr. J. Waterworth. 8º. 1848
The Catechism for the curats compos. by the decree of the C. of T. Tr. s8º. 1687
Catecismo del santo Concilio de Trento &c. Tr. segun la impresion de 1761. 4º. Valencia. 1782
The Catechism by decree of the C. of T. Tr. J. Donovan. [*Lat. & Engl.*] 2v. 8º. Rome. 1839
Zwey Decret des T. C. Warauff die Lere u. haltung jrer Kirchen stehen solle. [P2439]. s4º. *n.p.* 1546
see ANTON (P.) C.T. ad eoque et pontific. doctr. publ. &c., 1738.
,, CHEMNITZ (M.) Examen decret. C.T., 1566; *a. ed.*, 1707.
,, CRAMP (J. M.) *The c. of T. &c., 1839.

Trent, *Council of* [*continued*].
TRANSLATIONS [*continued*].
see GENTILLET (J.) Examen C.T. &c., 1586.
,, GROTIUS (H. DE). Via ad pacem &c. confess. fidei secund. C.T. &c., 1642.
,, NAUMBURG. Adv. Synodi T. restit., 1565.

Trent (Paul). Delilah. s8º. 1920
The peacemaker. s8º. 1927

Trent (William Peterfield).
see CAMB. HIST. OF ENG. LIT. Suppl.: Hist. of Amer. lit.; ed. W. P. T. &c., v3, 4, 1921.
,, —— Suppl.: Short hist. of Amer. lit.; ed. W. P. T. &c., 1924.

Trent Otter (The), *ps., see* MARTIN (J. W.)

Tréport (Le), *abbey of.* Cartul. de l'abbaye de Saint-Michel du T. (Ordre de St. Benoît). [Publ.] par P. Laffleur de Kermaingant. 4º. 1880
,, ,, ...Planches. atlas fol. 1880

Tres. Libro de los Tres Reyes de Oríente, 1904, *see* LIBRO.

*Trés oratiunculae hab. in domo Convoc. Oxon., 1743, *see* KING (W.)

Trésal (J.) Les orig. du schisme anglican (1509–71). s8º. 1908

Trescot (William Henry).
The diplomacy of the Revolution. s8º. N.Y. 1852

Tresham, *The family of, see* BELL (T.) Ruins of Liveden, w. notices of fam. of T., 1847.

Tresham (*Sir* Thomas), *1543 (?)–1605, see* GOTCH (J. A.) Compl. acc. of bldgs. erected in Northants. by Sir T. T. &c., 1883.

Trèsor des pièces rares ou inédites. [20v]. s8º. 1855–62
The vol[s]. in this series have been catalogued separately under the foll. authors &c.

†Baude (H.)	Guillebert, *de Metz.*	Ravaillac (F.)
Bordier (H. L.)	Journée.	Ronsard (P. de).
Bretaigne.	La Force (C. R. de C. de).	†Sauvage (J.)
Brézé (J. de).	Le Roux de Lincy (A. J. V.)	†Sicile.
Bury (R. de).	Loix.	Springer (A. H.
Du Lis (C.)	Margaret [*de Valois*].	Virey (C. E.)
Ferrières (G. de).		
Fournival (R. de).		

Tressan (Louis Elisabeth de La Vergne, *cte.* de), *see* JACOUBET (H.) Le Comte de T. & les orig[s]. du genre troubadour, 1923.

Treston (Hubert Joseph).
Poine: st. in anc. Greek blood-vengeance. 8º. 1923

Treter (Mieczysław), *see* BACHOWSKI (W.) & M. T. Wystawa miniatur i sylwetek &c., 1912.

Treterus (Thomas). Index in Q. Horatium Flacc. olim quidem coll. a T. T., deinde omnib. edd. accomod. a D. Aveman, auctus &c. ab I. Verburgio. [*Extr. f.* Horace. Eclogae, 1809, *q.v. for a. copy*]. 8º. [Londini. 1809]

Tretyakov Gallery. Московская Городская Худож. Галлерея П. и С. М. Третьяковыхъ. Текстъ И. С. Остроухова и С. Глаголя подъ общей ред. И. С. Остроухова [*& Plates*]. [2t]. la. fol. Москва. 1909
see SHAMURINY (YU.) & Z. SHAMURINY. T. Г., 1914.

Tretz (Jean François de Gaufridi, *baron* de), *see* GAUFRIDI (J. F. DE).

Treu (Georg Dan. C.) Hellen. Stimmungen i. d. Bildhauerei v. einst u. jetzt. la8º. L. 1910

Treuer (Gottlieb Samuel). Untersuch. d. Ursprungs u. d. Bedeut. d. Märtens-Mannes &c. [P444]. s4º. Helmstädt. 1733

Treuvé (Simon Michel). *Instruction sur les dispos. qu'on doit aporter aux sacremens de pénitence &c. s8º. 1712

Trevaskis (Hugh Kennedy). The land of the five rivers: econ. hist. of the Punjab to 1890. 8º. 1928

Trévédy (J.) Essai sur l'hist. de Concarneau. la8º. Saint-Brieuc. 1908

Trevelyan (George Macaulay).
British hist. in the 19th c. (1782–1901). 8º. 1922
England in the age of Wycliffe. n. impr. 8º. 1912
,, ,, n. impr. 8º. 1920
Eng. under the Stuarts. 11th ed. 8º. [1924]
,, ,, 12th ed. rev. 8º. [1925]
Garibaldi & the making of Italy. 6th impr. 8º. 1919
Hist. causes of pres. state of affairs in Italy. [P2733]. 8º. 1923
Hist. of England. 8º. 1926
Manin & the Venetian Revolution of 1848. 8º. 1923
The present position of hist. Inaug. lect., Cambridge. 8º. 1927
The two-party system in Eng. polit. hist. [Romanes lect.] 8º. O. 1926

Trevelyan (*Rt. Hon. Sir* George Otto), *Bart.*
Early hist. of C. J. Fox. s8º. *Nelson. n.d.*
Life & letters of Lord Macaulay. enl. & compl. ed. (1908), n. impr. 2v. 8º. 1923

Trevelyan (H. B.) The dark angel. Play. 8º. 1928

Trevelyan (Janet Penrose), *wife of G. M. Trevelyan.*
Life of Mrs. Humphry Ward. 8º. [1923]
Trevelyan (Robert Calverley). The Deluge & o. poems. 8º. 1926
The Pterodamozels: an operatic fable. *pr.f.a.* 8º. [1917]
Thamyris, or is there a future for poetry? s8º. [1925]
Trevena (John), *ps.* [*i.e.* ERNEST G. HENHAM].
The custom of the manor. s8º. [1924]
Trévern (J. F. M. Le Pappe de), *see* LE PAPPE DE TRÉVERN.
Treves. *Hist. Trevir. diplomat. &c., 3t, 1750, *see* FEBRONIUS (J.), *ps.*
Treves, *Fratelli.* Handbooks. Rome & the environs. n. ed. rev. &c. s8º. Milan. [1908]
Treves (*Sir* Frederick), *bart.*
The elephant man & o. remin. 8º. 1923
Highways & byways in Dorset. 8º. 1914
The lake of Geneva. 8º. 1922
The Riviera of the Corniche Road. 8º. 1921
The War in South Africa. [*Newspaper cuttings*]. s8º. *n.d.*
—— **& J. Hutchinson.** Student's hdbk. of surgical operations. 4th ed. enl. s8º. 1924
Trevirus (Gaspar Olevianus), *see* OLEVIANUS (C.)
Trevisa (John). Dialogus inter militem & clericum [*by* Occam] — R. FitzRalph's sermon: "Defensio curatorum — & Methodius": þe bygynnyng of þe world &c. [Tr.] by J. T. Intr. by A. J. Perry. [E.E.T.S., 167]. 8º. 1925
Trevisano (Girolamo), *Envoy Extraord. of Venice*, *see* LIONELLO (G. B.) Brieven v. L. &c. uit Den Haag, benevens verslag v. T. betref. zijne zending naar Holland in 1620, 1883.
Treviso [TARVISIUM]. Chron. marchiae Tarvisinae &c., 1207–70, *see* MURATORI. Rerum Ital. scr., t8iii, 1916.
Codex Trivis., 996–1318. Chronolog. ordine per regesta; cur. A. S. Minotto. [Acta & diplom. e R. Tabulario Veneto; st. &c. A. S. M., v2, sect. 3]. 8º. Venetiis. 1874[–75]
Trevor (*Col.* George Herbert). Rhymes of Rajputana. 8º. 1894
Trevor (John). The Reforming press & reformers &c. [P2782]. 8º. [Carnarvon. 1835]
The Sheriffs of Carnarvonshire & Merionethshire. Carnarvon municipal affairs &c. [P2782]. 8º. [Carnarvon. 1835]
Trevor (John), *ps.*, *see* BENSON (A. C.)
Trevor (*Sir* John), *speaker of the H. of C.*, *see* PARLIAMENT. II, HOUSE OF COMMONS. PROCEED. REL. TO SPEC. SUBJ. Abstr. of several exam. deliv. to H. of C. rep. by Sir J. T., 1680.
Trevor (John B.) Analysis of Amer. Immigration Act of 1924, *see* INTERNAT. CONCILIATION, No. 202, 1924.
Trew (Christoph Jacob). Plantae sel., quarum imagines &c. pinxit G. D. Ehret, in aes incidit & vivis coloribus repraes. J. J. Haid. Decuria 1[–10 *in* 1v]. fol. [Nuremberg]. 1750
Trewhertzige, notwendige u. ernste Warnung &c., 1598, *see* HERBORN.
Trewman (Harry Frederick). Electrific. of railways. s8º. 1920
Trézel (*le col.*) Notice s. le Ghilan & le Mazenderan, *see* JAUBERT (*le cte.* P. A. E. P.) Voy. en Arménie &c., 1821.
Trezzo (Jacopo da) [NIZZOLA (J.)], *see* BABELON (J.) J. da T. & la construction de l'Escurial, 1519–89, 1922.
Triaire (Paul). Récamier et ses contemporains, 1774–1852. Et. d'hist. de la médecine aux 18 & 19 s. 8º. 1899
Trial (J. E. Louis).
Jean-Jacques Gourd, 1850–1909. 8º. Nîmes. 1914
Trials [TRYAL].
*Celeb. trials &c., 1835, *see* SMITH (J. J.)
*Exact (An) abridg. of all the trials which have been publ. since 1678 rel. to the Popish &c. plots in the r. of Charles II & James II [*by* P. N.] s8º. 1690
[Newspaper cuttings &c. rel. to trials & crimes, 1842–65]. 3v. 8º. [1842–65]
Remarkable trials & interesting mem. of criminals convicted at the Assizes, King's-Bench Bar &c. 2v [v2 *wanting*]. s8º. 1765
Select trials for murders, robberies &c., at the Sessions-House in the Old Bailey; Dec. 1720–Sept. 1741. 2nd ed. 4v. s8º. 1742
,, ,, 1741–64. 4v [v1 *wanting, its place being taken by* Remarkable trials, v1, 1765]. s8º. 1764
Tryal (A) of witches at the assizes, Bury St. Edmonds, 10 March 1664, before Sir M. Hale &c. s8º. 1682
Tribbechov (Adam). De doctoribus scholasticis. Acc. C. A. Heumanni praefatio, Vita Tribbechovii &c. s8º. Jenae. 1719
Exercit. ad Baronii Annales, *see* KORTHOLT (C.), *the elder.* Disq. anti-Baronianae &c., 1708.
Tribunaux. *Chronique des tribunaux, ou choix des causes &c. dans l'Europe. 3t. 8º. Brux. & La Haye. 1835–36
Tribune almanac (The) & political register, 1838–1914. [1878–86, 1890 *wanting.* 1838–77 *b. in* 3v]. s8º. N.Y. 1868–1914
Early yrs. h. t.: T. A.: the politicians reg. & The Whig almanac.

Tridentinum Concilium, *see* TRENT, *Council of.*
Tridon (André). Psychoanalysis: its hist., theory & practice. s8º. [1919]
,, ,, ...[6th ed.] s8º. N.Y. 1923
Triepel (Heinrich).
Konterbande, Blockade u. Seesperre. [P2490]. 8º. 1918
see MARTENS (G. F. v.) Nouv. rec. gén. de traités &c.; cont. du grand rec. de M. par T., s3, t8–17, 1915–27.
Trigault (Nicolas) [TRIGAUTIUS]. De Christianis apud Japonios triumphis, 1612–20. Ex annuis Soc. Jesu litteris contin. hist. serie distrib. Cum Raderi auctario & iconibus. s4º. Monachii. 1623
*Regni Chinensis descr. ex variis auctor. s8º. Lugduni Batav. 1639
see JESUITS. Litterae Soc. Jesu e regno Sinarum 1610–11; auctore N. T., 1615.
,, —— Rei Chr. apud Jap. comm.; auctore N. T., 1615.
Triger (Robert). Notes d'hist. & d'archéol.: Vivoin, Ballon. [Extr. de la Revue hist. du Maine, s2, t2]. [P2703]. 8º. Le Mans. 1922
Triggs (H. Inigo). The art of garden design in Italy. fol. 1906
Trigland (Jacobus), *the younger*, *see* MORDECAI, B. NISAN. Notitia Karaeorum &c., acc. J. T. diss. de K., 1714.
Trigo (Felipe).
El amor en la vida y en los libros. s8º. [1907]
Del frio al fuego. 6ª ed. 8º. *n.d.*
Las Evas del paraiso. Novela. 4ª ed. 8º. 1920
Jarrapellejos. 8º. 1921
Las posadas del amor—Mi prima me odia—Además del frac—Mi media naranja. Novelas. 3ª ed. s8º. 1919
Triller (Caspar Ernst), *see* BIBLE: GERMAN. Eine Übersetsunge d. N.T., v. C. E. T., 1703.
Trilussa (Salustri Carlo Alb.), *see* FRATTINI (A.) T., 1920.
Trimberg (Hugo v.) Der Renner. Hrsg. G. Ehrismann. [Lit. V. in St., 252, 256]. B3, 4. 8º. Tübingen. 1909–1912
Trimble (William Copeland). The hist. of Enniskillen w. ref. to manors in Co. Fermanagh. v3. 8º. Enniskillen. 1921
Trimen (Andrew). Church & chapel architecture, w. an acc. of the Hebrew church &c. 8º. 1849
Trimmer (*Mrs.* Sarah), *1741–1810* [*form. Kirby*].
The history of the robins. 8º. [1868?]
Trinity College, *Toronto.* Year bk. & calendar of the Faculty of Divinity, 1916–17, 1918–19. s8º. Toronto. 1916–18
Triomphe d'argent [16 c.]; *ed.* G. Schmilinsky, *see* ARCHIV. F. D. ST. D. NEU. SPR., B95, 1895.
Trionfi. Tutti i t., carri, mascherate &c. andati per Firenze, 2ª ed., 2p, 1750, *see* †FIRENZE.
Tripiṭaka. Cinq cents contes & apologues, extr. du T. chinois [*of* Seng-houei *&c.*] & tr. par E. Chavannes. [Soc. Asiat.] 3t. 8º. 1910–11
Tripp (George Henry).
*Student-life at Harvard. s8º. Boston. 1876
Trissino (Giovanni Giorgio).
L'Italia liberata dai Goti. 3t. s8º. Londra. 1779
Rime del Trissinω. 8º. [Vicenza. 1529]
Tristan, *see* L'HERMITE (F. TRISTAN).
Tristram, *knight of the Round Table.* Le roman de T. [par] Béroul. Poème du 12ᵉ s. Ed. E. Muret. [Class. fr. du m. â.] s8º. 1913
Tristan u. Isolde. [*French, Germ. & Icelandic texts. Hrsg.*] v. F. Ranke. 8º. München. 1925
see KELEMINA (J.) Gesch. d. Tristansage nach d. Dichtungen d. M.-a., 1923.
,, LOOMIS (R. S.) Illust. of med. romance [*i.e.* T. &c.] on tiles f. Chertsey Abbey, 1916.
,, MASEFIELD (J.) T. & Isolt, play, 1927.
,, VINAVER (E.) Etudes s. le "Tristan" en prose, sources, mss., bibliog., 1925.
Tristram, *The family of.* *Pedigree of the fam. of T., of Belbroughton, Worcs. 4º. *p.p.* 1904
Tristram (Henry Baker), *the younger, b. 1822.* The land of Moab; w. chap. on the Persian palace of Mashita by J. Fergusson. 2nd ed. 8º. 1874
Tritheim (Johann) [TRITEMIUS; TRITHEMIUS *Spanhemensis*].
De origine gentis &c. Bavarorum comm. s8º. Francofurti. 1549
Res gestae Friderici Palatini electoris primi. Acc. P. Antonii De dignitate principum liber. [*Ed.* M. Freher. *a. c. b. w.* Freher (M.) Orig. Palat. comm., 1599]. s4º. Heidelbergae. 1602
see SETON-WATSON (R. W.) The Abbot T., 1924.
***Tritheism** charged upon Dr. Sherlock's new notion of the Trinity &c., 1695, *see* SOUTH (R.)
Tritton (A. S.) Rise of the Imams of Sanaa. 8º. 1925

Tritton (Joseph). Bapt. Miss. Soc. Rise &c. of work on the Congo river. By the Treasurer. 2nd ed. s8°. 1885

***Triumphs** (The) of Rome over despised Protestancy, 1667, *see* HALL (G.)

Trivett (Edward). Hymns & spiritual songs. s8°. 1755

Triviño Valdivia (Francisco). Del Marruecos español. Prólogo de J. Ortega Munilla. 8°. [1920]

Trivisianus, *see* TREVISO.

Trivulziana. Cat. dei codici manoscr. d. T. Ed. p. c. di G. Porro. la8°. Torino. 1884

Trobriand (Philippe-Régis-Denis de Keredern, *comte* de). Vie milit. dans le Dakota. Notes &c., 1867–69. la8°. 1926

Trofimov (M. V.) & D. Jones.
Pronunciation of Russian. s8°. C. 1923

Troie, *see* TROY.

Trolard (Eugène). Pèlerinage aux champs de bataille franç. d'Italie. s2, De Rivoli à Marengo & à Solferino. s8°. 1893

Trollope (Anthony).

The American senator. n. ed. s8°. 1886
Autobiography. Intr. by M. Sadleir. s8°. [1923]
Barchester Towers. s8°. 1909
„ „ ....s8°. 1913
The Claverings. s8°. [1924]
Doctor Thorne. [Everyman's Lib. repr.] s8°. [1915]
Framley Parsonage. [Everyman's Lib.] s8°. [1907]
„ „ [illust. ed.] 8°. [1927]
Miss Mackenzie. s8°. [1924]
The noble jilt. Comedy. Ed. w. pref. by M. Sadleir. 8°. 1923
Thackeray. [Eng. Men of Letters]. s8°. 1880
The Warden. [Everyman's Lib.] s8°. [1907]
The Warden. Intr. by F. Harrison. [Barsetshire novels, 1]. s8°. 1923
see SADLEIR (M. T. H.) T., comm., 1927.
„ SAINTSBURY (G. E. B.) T. revisited, 1920.
„ WALPOLE (H.) A. T. [Eng. Men of Letters], 1928.

Trollope (*Mrs.* Frances), *1780–1863 ; wife of Thomas Anthony Trollope.* Domestic manners of the Americans. Intr. by M. Sadleir. [repr. f. 5th (1839) ed.] 8°. [1927]
One fault. 8°. Paris. 1840

Trollope & Colls, *Ltd.* Buildings of to-day & to-morrow. Review of mod. construction. fol. [1924]

Tröltsch (Ernst).
Aufsätze z. Geistesgesch. u. Religionssoziologie. Hrsg. H. Baron. [Gesamm. Schr., 4.] 8°. Tübingen. 1925
Der Berg d. Läuterung. Rede, 600 jhrg. Todestag. Dantes. [P2564]. 8°. 1921
Xtn. thought, its hist. & application. Lect. Tr. by var. hands, & ed. w. intr. &c. by Baron F. v. Hügel. s8°. 1923
Der Historismus u. s. Probleme. Buch 1, Das logische Problem d. Geschichtsphilos. [Gesamm. Schr., B3]. 8°. Tübingen. 1922
Der Kulturkrieg, *see* DEUTSCHE Reden in schwerer Zeit, 27, 1915.
Zur relig. Lage, Religionsphilos. u. Ethik. [Gesam. Schr. B2]. 2. A. 8°. Tübingen. 1922
see SLEIGH (R. S.) Sufficiency of Xty. : enq. conc. nature &c. of Xtn. relig., w. spec. ref. to relig. philos. of E. T., 1923.

Trombetti (Alfredo). Elementi di glottologia. [R. Accad. d. Sci. dell' Ist. di Bologna]. la8°. Bologna. 1923
La lingua etrusca : gramm., testi con comm., saggi di tr. interlin. &c. 4°. Firenze. 1928
L'unità d'origine del linguaggio. 8°. Bologna. 1905

Trömel (Paul), *ed., see* BROCKHAUS (F. A.) Bibl. amér., 1861.

Tromm (Abraham). Concordantiae Graecae vers. LXX interpretum &c. Ed. B. de Montfaucon. 2t. fol. Amstelodami. 1718
t2 *incl.* Index Hebraeus & Chaldaeus, & Lexicon Graecum ad Hexapla Origenis, *both w. sep. pagin.*

Trommler (Carl Heinrich). Abbild. d. Jacobit. o. Copt. Kirche, mit Urkunden erl. Nebst e. Vorrede J. G. Walchs. s8°. Jena. 1749

Tromnau (Friedrich). Gesch. d. deut. Ritterordens. 14e A. [P2580]. 8°. L. 1921

Tron (Nicolò). Rel. d. ingresso in Londra, 1715. [Nozze Zasso—Tosca. N133]. 8°. Venezia. 1886

Troostembergh (*Baron* Maximilien de). Les sires d'Héverlé, 1125–1446. [Extr. de l'Annuaire de la Noblesse Belge, N.S., p1, t1 (1910)]. n. éd. rev. & corr. 8°. Louvain. [1924]
see NOBLESSE BELGE (LA), 1913, p1, publ. s. la dir. du Baron de T., 1913.

***Trophées** (Les) de Damas : controverse jud.-chrét. du 7e siécle ; texte grec éd. & tr. par G. Brady, *see* GRAFFIN (R.) & F. NAU. Patr. orient., t15, 1927.

Troppmann (Jean-Baptiste). *Troppmann. [Acc. of murders by T. *no tp.* P2826]. s8°. [Sceaux]. *n.d.*

Trostius (Martinus). Gramm. Ebraea : acc. Comp. Lexici Ebraei autore A. Sennert, 1663, *see* SENNERT (A.) Ebraismus &c., 1666.

***Tröstliche** (Ein) Sermon : wesz sich der Christenmensch hab am todtbette zû haltē etc. s4°. [Zwickaw, *Jörg Gastell*]. 1523

Trotsky (L.) [*i.e.* LEV DAVIDOVICH BRONSTEIN].

Куда идет Англия ? 8°. Москва. 1925
Новый этап, мировое положение и наши задачи. 8°. [Москва]. 1921
Совѣтская власть и международный имперіализмъ. [P2459]. 8°. П. 1918
1917 : уроки Октября. 8°. [Берлин. 1924]
1917 : уроки Октября—Каменев и Сталин, Ленинизм или Троцкизм ? Ответ Троцкому [*w. sep. pagin.*] 8°. [Berlin. 1924]
TRANSLATIONS.
Der Charakter d. Russ. Revolution. [P2526]. 8°. Wien. 1921
The defence of terrorism. Reply to K. Kautsky. Pref. by H. N. Brailsford. s8°. 1921
Die Fragen d. Arbeiterbewegung in Frankreich u. d. kommunist. Internat. 2 Reden, &c. [P2685]. 8°. Hamburg. 1921
Lenin. auth. tr. 8°. [1925]
Literature & revolution. Tr. R. Strunsky. 8°. [1925]
Meine Flucht aus Sibirien. Übers. v. H. Ruoff. s8°. 1922
Die neue Etappe. Die Weltlage u. uns. Aufgaben. 8°. Hamburg. 1921
Die Organisierung d. Roten Armee, *see* LENIN (N.) Die Rote Armee, 1920.
Problems of life. Tr. Z. Vengerova. Intr. by N. Minsky. s8°. [1924]
TRANSLATIONS [*continued*].
Die rote Armee d. Sowjet-Republik auf d. Wacht. [P2689]. la8°. Hamburg. 1922
Terrorismus u. Kommunismus : Anti-Kautsky. 8°. Wien. 1920
Towards socialism or capitalism ? Tr. R. S. Townsend & Z. Vengerova. s8°. 1926
Where is Britain going ? s8°. [1926]
see DRAHN (E.) Brest-Litowsk ; Reden &c. T. &c., 1920.
„ EASTMAN (M.) L. T. : portrait of a youth, 1926.
„ KAUTSKY (C.) Von d. Demokratie z. Staats-Sklaverei : e. Auseinandersetzung mit T., 1921.
„ LEVY (R.) T., 1920.
„ MORIZET (A.) Chez Lénine & T., Moscou 1921, 1922.
„ RYKOW (A. I.) & L. T. Die Wirtschaft in Sowjetruss. &c., 1920.
„ SMOLENSKY (M.) Троцкій, 1921.
„ SOWJETRUSSLAND u. Polen ; Reden v. Kamenev, Lenin, T. &c., 1920.
„ ZINOVEV (G.) & L. T. О мятежѣ лѣвыхъ С.-р., 1918.
„ —— & —— Karl Liebknecht u. R. Luxemburg, 1920.
„ ZIV (G. A.) T. : характеристика, 1921.

Trotsky (N.) Второй съѣздъ Р.С.-Д.Р. Партіи. Отчетъ Сибирской делегаціи. [P2715]. s8°. Женева. 1903

Trotter (Catherine), *aft. Cockburn, see* COCKBURN (C.)

Trotter (F. M.), *see* DIXON (E. E. L.), J. MADEN, F. M. T. &c. Geol. of the Carlisle &c. district, 1926.

Trotter (Jacqueline T.) Valour & vision. Poems of the War, 1914–18. Coll. & ed. J. T. [n. & enl. ed.] 8°. 1923

Trotter (Thomas Henry Yorke). Music & mind. s8°. 1924

Trotter (W.)
Instincts of the herd in peace & war. s8°. [1916]
„ „ ....[3rd impr.] s8°. [1917]
„ „ ....[2nd ed.] s8°. [1919]
„ „ ....[6th impr.] 8°. [1921]

Troubadour (Un), *ps.* *D'Anacharsis, ou Lettres d'un troubadour sur cet ouvrage &c., 1789, *see* BÉRENGER (L. P.)

Troup (*Sir* Charles Edward). The Home Office. 8°. [1925]

Troup (Robert Scott). Silvicultural systems. la8°. O. 1928
The silviculture of Indian trees. 3v. 4°. O. 1921

Trout (C.), *ps., see* CHRYSTAL (*Maj.* R. A.)

Troward (Thomas).
The creative process in the individual. s8°. [1921]
The Edinburgh lect. on mental science. s8°. 1921

Trowbridge (J. M.) Cider makers' hand book. s8°. N.Y. 1920

Trowbridge (John Townsend). The South : tour of its battle-fields & ruined cities. 8°. Hartford, Conn. 1866

Trowbridge (William Rutherford Hayes).
In the sun w. a passport. 8°. [1925]

Trower (Harold Edward).
Book of Capri. 8°. Naples. 1906
„ „ ....2nd ed. s8°. Naples. 1924

Troy [TROIE]. Der Göttweiger Trojanerkrieg [*attrib. to* Wolfram v. Eschenbach]. Hrsg. A. Koppitz. [Deut. Texte d. M.-a ; hrsg. v. d. Preuss. Akad. d. Wiss., B29]. la8°. 1926
Le roman de Troie en prose. Ed. L. Constans & E. Faral. [Class. fr. du m.-â.] t1. s8°. 1922
The seege or batayle of Troye. A Middle Eng. metrical romance. Ed. M. E. Barnicle. [E.E.T.S., 172]. 8°. 1927

Troya d'Assigny (Louis), *see* FOURQUEVAUX (J. B. R. DE P. DE) & L. T. D'A. Catéchisme hist. & dogmat., 1750–68.

Troyes. Collection des princ. cartul. du diocèse de T., t3, 6, 7, 1878–90, *see* COLLECTION.

*Mém. hist. & crit. pour l'hist. de Troyes, t1, 1774, *see* GROSLEY (P. J.)

see RECUEIL. R. des hist. de la France, Obituaires, t4, O. de la Prov. de Sens, t4 [Diocèse de Meaux & de T.], 1923.

Troyes (Chrestien de) [CHRISTIAN VON TROIES]. Cligés. Textausg. hrsg. v. W. Förster. 4te verkürzte A. besorgt v. A. Hilka. [Roman. Bibl., 1]. s8°. Halle a. S. 1921

Erec u. Enide. Hrsg. v. W. Foerster. 2te umgearb. u. verm. A. [Roman. Bibl., 13]. s8°. Halle a. S. 1909

Erec & Enide—Le Chevalier au Lion. Tr. A. Mary. 8°. [1923]

Erec & Enide. Roman d'aventures du 12e siècle. Tr. M. Lot-Borodine. s8°. 1924

see KLOSE (M.) Der Roman v. Claris u. Laris, bes. Berücks. d. Werke d. C. v. T., 1916.

Truber (Primosh). Die fürnämpsten Hauptartickel christl. Lehre, auss d. Lat. &c. in die Crobat. verdolmetscht [*by* Anton *Dalmatin* & S. Consul *Istrian*] u. mit Cyrul. Buchstaben getruckt. s4°. Tübingen. 1562

,, ,, [*another ed.*, mit Crobat. (*i.e. Glagolitic*) Buchstaben getruckt]. s4°. Tübingen. 1562

Trubetskoi (*prince* **Evgenii).** Смыслъ жизни. 8°. Берлинъ. 1922

Truc (Gonzague). Paul Claudel. 8°. [1925]

Tibériade. [Roman]. s8°. [1921]

Truchsess von Waldburg (Otto), *Card. Prince, see* WALDBURG (O. v.)

Truchy (Henri). Les finances de guerre de la France. [C.E. for Int. Peace]. 8°. [1926]

Trudi. Труды русскихъ ученыхъ за границей: сборникъ, t1, 1922, *see* KAMINKA (A. I.)

Trüdinger (Carl). Studien z. Gesch. d. griech.-röm. Ethnographie. 8°. Basel. 1918

True.

*A true & authentic acc. of A. Frey, tr. f. the German, 1753, *see* FREY (A.)

*True (A) & authentick narr. of action betw. the Northumberland & 3 French men of war, w. acc. of the behaviour of Capt. Watson &c. By an Eye-Witness. [P2778]. 8°. 1745

True (A) & exact cat. of all plays &c. pr. in Eng., 1732, *see* CATALOGUE.

*True &c. narr.; or sundry &c. injuries &c. wh. the Hollanders have exercised agst. the English &c., 1665, *see* DARELL (J.)

*True & punctuall rel. of sev. skirmishes betw. Northamptonshire forces & King's Horse &c. under Pr. Rupert, 1643, repr., *see* HARTSHORNE (E. S.) Mem. of Holdenby, 1868.

*True (A) rep. of disputation &c. in Tower of Lond. w. E. Campion, 1583, *see* CAMPION (E.)

*True (A) represent. of the absurd &c. principles of the Muggletonians, 1694, *see* WILLIAMS (J.), *bp.*

True informer (The), or monthly mercury. Being the certain intelligence of Mercurius militaris, Oct. 7–Nov. 8, 1648. Communicating enterprises &c. of army under Lord Fairfax. No. 1. [*no more publ.*] 8°. 1648

True Temperance Association. True temperance monographs. By 12 writers. Intr. by the Earl of Halsbury. 8°. 1921

True (Ronald). Trial of R. T. Ed. D. Carswell. 8°. E. [1925]

Truesdell (Leon Edgar).

see UNITED STATES: CENSUS. Farm population; by T., 1926.

,, —:— Farm tenancy, by T. &c., 1924.

Truffi (Ferruccio).

Commemor. di A. Pascolato. [P2411]. 8°. Venezia. 1907

Truffier (Jules). Mélingue: le comédien &c. 8°. 1925

Truman (Joseph). Poems. s8°. 1859

Trumbull (John), *painter, see* MORGAN (J. H.) Paintings by J. T., 1926.

Trumbull (*Sir* **William),** *1639–1716*. Papers, *see* HIST. MSS. COMM. Downshire, *m. of*, v1, 1924.

Trumper (*Lt.-Com.* **Victor L.),** *R.N.R.* Hist. sites, Palestine, w. sh. acc. of Napoleon's exped. to Syria. s8°. Cairo. [1921]

Truschet (Olivier) & G. Hoyau. Plan de Paris sous Henri II, *see* PARIS. Reprod. d'anc. plans de P., 1908.

Trusler (John). Hogarth moralized; added, intr. essay & notes by J. Major. n. ed. rev. 8°. 1841

Trussel (John), *see* DANIEL (S.) Coll. of the hist. of Eng., w. contin. by J. T., 1685.

Trustee (A), *ps.* Other people's money, 2nd ed., 1921, *see* OTHER.

Trustee's (The) handbook. Extr. f. "Snell's Principles of equity," "Williams on Real property." 2nd ed. 8°. 1926

Truth.

*The naked truth, p2, 3, 1681, *see* HICKERINGILL (E.)

*Truth about an author, 1903; 1914, *see* BENNETT (E. ARNOLD).

*Truth about Ireland, 1921, *see* JUNIUS *junior, ps.*

*Truth (The) about "The Protocols" [publ. by S. Nilus, *founded on* Joly's Dialogue]. From the Times of Aug. 16, 17, & 18, 1921. 8°. [1921?]

*Truth brought to light, 1692, *see* JAMES I.

***Truths** discovery of a black cloud in the North: anti-parl. &c. proc. of the Scotch army agst. the well-affected in N. of Eng. [*no tp.*] s8°. [1646]

Tsagareli (Aleksandr Antonovich).

Мингрельскіе этюды. 2 вып *in* 1v. 8°. С.-П. 1880

О граммат. литературѣ грузинск. языка. 8°. С.-П. 1873

Свѣдѣнія о памяникахъ грузинской письменности. вып.1 [*b. w. h.* О грамм. лит., 1873]. 8°. С.-П. 1886

Ts'aou Seuĕ-k'in. Hung lou meng; or, The dream of the Red Chamber. [Chinese novel wr. c. 17th c. *In Chinese*]. 2v. s8°. [c. 1840]

Tsar. *Царь Iудейскій: драма, изд. 2oe, 1914, *see* CONSTANTINE CONSTANTINOVICH.

Tsarskaya. Царская Россия в Мир. Войне, t1, 1925, *see* RUSSIA.

Tsarskoe Selo. Notice sur le Musée de T.-S. &c. la coll. d'armes. 8°. St.-Pétersbourg. 1860

Tschaadajew, *see* CHAADAEV.

Tschackert (Paul). Analecta Corviniana. Quellen z. Gesch. d. niedersächs. Reformators A. Corvinus (†1553). Gesammelt u. hrsg. &c. P. T. [Quellen &c. aus d. Gesch. d. Reformationsjhdts., B16]. 8°. L. 1910

Herzog Albrecht v. Preussen. [Verein f. Ref.-gesch. Schr., Jhrg. 11, Nr. 45]. 8°. Halle. 1894

P. Speratus v. Rötlen, evangel. Bischof v. Pomesanien. [Verein f. Ref.-gesch. Schr., Jhrg. 8, Nr. 33]. 8°. Halle. 1891

see AUGSBURG CONFESSION. Die unveränderte A. Konf., deut. u. lat. &c.; krit. A. v. P. T., 1901.

Tschamtschean (Miqael), *see* TCHAMTCHEAN (M.)

Tschepe (Albert). Hist. des 3 royaumes Han (423–230), Wei (423–209) & Tchao (403–222), *see* VARIÉTÉS sinolog., No. 31, 1910.

Hist. du royaume de Ts'in, [2p], *see* VARIÉTÉS sinolog., No. 27, 30, 1909–10.

Tscherikower (V.) Hellenist. Städtegründungen v. Alexander d. Gr. bis a. d. Römerzeit. [Philologus, Suppl.-Band 19, H1]. 8°. L. 1927

Tschernow (Viktor), *see* CHERNOV (V.)

Tschischwitz (Erich v.) Antwerpen, 1914. [Schlachten d. Weltkrieges, B3]. Bearb. E. v. T. 2. A. 8°. Oldenburg. 1925

Tschischwitz (W. von). Rules for the conduct of the war-game. Comp. [& tr. f. W. v. T.'s "Anleitung z. Kriegsspiel"], by E. Baring. 8°. [1872]

Tschitscherin (C. W.), *see* CHICHERIN (C. W.)

Tschouansher, *see* DSCHOUANSHER.

Tschudi (Aegidius). De prisca ac vera Alpina Rhætia, cum cætero Alpinarum gentium tractu descr. [*Tr. by S. Münster*]. s4°. Basileæ. 1538

Tschudi (Clara). Augusta, Tysk Keiserinde og Dronning af Preussen. [Efter 3e Udg.] s8°. 1912

Tschudi (Friedrich von). Les Alpes. Descr. de la nature & de la faune. [Tr.] 8°. Berne. 1859

Tsch'un-tsch'iu, *see* ROSTHORN (A. v.) Das Tsch'un-tsch'iu u. s. Verfasser, 1919.

Tsebrikova (M.)

Письмо Александру III. [P2390]. s8°. Carouge-Genève. 1898

Tsederbaum (Yuly O.), *see* MARTOV (L.), *ps.*

Tsekh. Цехъ поэтовъ. [t]1–3 *in* 2v. s8°. Берлинъ. [1923]

Tsenker (Ernst Viktor), *see* ZENKER (E. V.)

Tsen Tsonming.

Essai hist. sur la poésie chinoise. la8°. Lyon. 1922

Tsetkin (Klara), A. Kollontai, Yu. Markhlevsky & P. Levi.

Роза Люксембург. Сборник статей. 8°. [Москва]. 1921

Tsingovatov (A. Ya.)

А. А. Блок: жизнь и творчество. 8°. Москва. 1926

Tsion (I. v.), *see* CYON (E. DE).

Tsiperovich (G.) [Цыперович]. Чему учит опыт? Петроградский союз рабочих швейной промышленности &c. [P2697]. 8°. П. 1921

Tsonming (Tsen), *see* TSEN TSONMING.

Tsui Schi, *see* KUHN (F.) Dschong lun d. T. S. (2 Jahrh. n. Chr.), 1914.

Tsvetaeva (Marina). Версты. Стихи. s8°. Москва. 1921
Психея романтика. s8°. Берлинъ. 1923
Стихи къ Блоку. s8°. Берлинъ. 1922

Tsvetkov (Aleksandr Aleksandrovich).
Образцы древней русской словесности. 8°. С.-П. 1879
Пушкинскій періодъ. Образцы новой русской словесности. Собралъ А. Ц. отдѣлъ 3. 8°. С.-П. 1881

Tsyavlovsky (M.), *see* MOSKOVSKY PUSHKINIST. М. П., 1, 1837–1927: статьи, под ред. М. Ц., 1927.

T. T. T., *ps.* *The porcelain tower, 1841, *see* SEALY (T. H.)

Tübetisches, *see* TIBETAN.

Tübingen, *University.* Jubilæum Acad. Tub. in mem. liberationis; restaurata̧que in Germania, operâ Lutheri doctr. evang., 1617. [*8 orat. by J. G. Sigwart & others*]. [P483]. s4°. Tubingae. 1617
Systemat.-alphabet. Hauptkat. d. königl. Universitätsbibl. M, Hss., a, orient. xiii. Verz. d. arm. Hss. v. F. N. Finck u. L. Gjandschezian. 4°. Tübingen. 1907
see HALLER (J.) Anfänge d. Univ. T., 1477–1537, 1927.

Tucci (Raffaele di). Cagliari. [P2860]. 4°. Milano. *n.d.*

Tuck (Stephen). Wesleyan Methodism in Frome, Somersets. s8°. Frome. 1837

Tucker (Alexander Lauzan Pendock).
Sir Robert G. Sandeman, K.C.S.I. 8°. 1921

Tucker (Charles Louis). Offic. rep. of trial of T. for murder of Mabel Page. Sup. Court of Mass., [1905]. 2v. 8°. Boston [Mass.] 1907

Tucker (Gilbert Milligan). American English. 8°. N.Y. 1921

Tucker (John), *murderer, see* HAMPSTEAD. The H. murder [murder of Deloraine by J. T.], 1845.

Tucker (Sarah). Abbeokuta: origin &c. of the Yoruba mission. 2nd ed. s8°. 1853

Tucker (Stephen Isaacson).
Pedigree of the fam. of Chauncy. priv. repr. 4°. 1884
see PALMER (C. J.) & S. T., *edd.* Palgrave fam. mem., 1878.

Tucker (Thomas George), *ed., see* SHAKESPEARE (W.) Sonnets, 1609, 1924.

Tucker (William), *of Chard, Somerset, see* BROCAS (T.) Calvinism unmasked: ans. to T.'s Predestination &c., 1812.

Tuckett (James Edward Shum). Napoleon I & freemasonry. [*No tp.* Repr. f. Trans. Quatuor Coronati Lodge, v27, 1914. P2730]. la8°. *n.p.* [1914]
Dr. R. Rawlinson & the masonic entries in E. Ashmole's diary. [*No tp.; repr. f.* Trans. Quatuor Coronati Lodge, v25, 1912. P2730]. la8°. *n.p.* [1912]

Tuckney (Anthony), *D.D.* The day of the churches peace & rest improved [A good day well improved]. Annexed, A forme of sound words. s8°. 1656

Tudeer (Lauri O. Th.) De vocabulis quibus Sophocles in Ichneutis fabula satyrica usus est. [Annales Acad. Sci. Fenn., ser. B, t14. P2621]. 8°. Helsingforsiae. 1916
Remarks on the letters of Euripides. [Expr. ex Annal. Acad. scient. Fennicae]. [P2703]. la8°. [Helsinki. 1921]

Tudesq (André). Keepsake à la Japonaise, choses vues, *see* ŒUVRES libres, 20, 1923.

Tudor. Tudor constit. doc., 1485–1603, 1922, *see* TANNER (J. R.)
Tudor econ. doc., 3v, 1924, *see* TAWNEY (R. H.) & E. POWER, *edd.*
Tudor studies; pres. to A. F. Pollard, Univ. of London, 1924, *see* POLLARD (A. F.)

Tudor-Craig (*Sir* Algernon Tudor). Armorial porcelain of the 18th cent. Foreword by Sir H. F. Burke. 4°. 1925

Tuesch, *see* TÜSCH.

Tuetey (Alexandre), *see* FRANCE: STATE DEP. &C.: MIN. DE L'INTÉR. Corr. &c., 1792; publ. & annot. par A. T., 1917.

Tuffrau (Paul). La légende de Guillaume d'Orange. Renouvelée par P. T. 6e éd. s8°. [1920]
Le merveilleux voyage de S. Brandan: légende lat. du 9e s. renouv. par. P. T. s8°. 1925

Tuglas (Friedebert), *Estonian novelist, see* KALLAS (A. J. M.) An Est. novelist: F. T., 1927.

Tuileries. *Hist. du cabinet des T. dep. le 20 mars 1815, *see* GUILLIÉ (S.)

Tukārāma, *Marathi poet, c. 1608–1649, see* NELSON (J. F.) & J. E. EDWARDS. Life & teaching of T., 1922.

Tuke (Anthony W.), *ed., see* MATTHEWS (P. W.) Hist. of Barclay's Bank, Ltd., 1926.

Tuke (John). Gen. view of the agric. of the N. Riding of Yorks. &c. [*b. w.* Rennie (G.) &c. Gen. view, 1794]. s4°. 1794

Tuki (Raphael), *bp. of Arsinoe.* *Rudimenta linguae Coptae sive Ægyptiacae. 4°. Romae. 1778

Tulane University of Louisiana. Tribes & temples: rec. of exped. to Middle America cond. by the T. Univ. of Louisiana, 1925. [By F. Blom & O. La Farge]. 2v. la8°. New Orleans. 1926–27

Tulle. Cartul. des abbayes de T. & de Roc-Amadour, par J. B. Champeval. la8°. Brive. 1903

Tulsi Dás. Rámáyana. Tr. f. the Hindi by F. S. Growse. 6th ed. rev. 8°. Allahabad. 1922

Tumiati (Domenico). La badia di Pomposa. Lirica. 3a ed. [P2844]. s8°. Bologna. 1901
La regina Ginevra: tragedia. s4°. Milano. [1925]

Tumulty (Joseph Patrick).
Woodrow Wilson as I know him. 8°. 1922

Tunbridge Wells. *The visitor's guide to T. W. s8°. Tunbridge Wells. 1827

Tundale. Incipit libellus de raptu anime Tundali & eius visione Tractans de penis inferni & gaudiis paradisi [*w. woodcuts*]. s4°. [Speier. *Johann & Conrad Hist.* 1483]
30 leaves incl. blanks at beg. & end, without pagin. or signatures, 29 lines to a full page.

Tüneewa (A. N.) Miniaturausgaben in d. Staatsbibl. in Odessa. la8°. L. 1926

Tunisie. Atlas archéolog. de la T. Ed. spéc. des cartes topog. publ. par le Min. de la Guerre. Accomp. d'un explic. rédigé par E. Babelon, R. Cagnat, S. Reinach. [Min. de l'Instr. Publ.] la. fol. 1893[–1913]
,, ,, 2e sér., livr. 1–3. Accomp. d'un texte explic. par R. Cagnat & A. Merlin. la. fol. 1914–26

Tupling (G. H.) The econ. hist. of Rossendale. [Chetham Soc., N.S., v86]. 8°. M'ter. 1927

***Tuppy**: autobiog. of a donkey. By the a. of "Tiny stories" &c. [*Folld. by*: The ass, by E. Carrington, *w. sep. pagin.*] s8°. 1903

Turanians. Manual on the T. & Pan.-Turanianism, 1921, *see* ADMIRALTY: NAVAL INTELLIGENCE DIVISION.

Turati (Filippo), *see* BOLZA (G.) T., 1919.

Turbervill (Edward), *of Skerr.* The information of E. T. deliv. at the bar of the H. of Commons. [P525]. sm. fol. 1680

Turberville (Arthur Stanley).
Eng. men & manners in the 18th cent. 8°. O. 1926
The House of Lords in the 18th cent. 8°. O. 1927
Mediæval heresy & the Inquisition. 8°. 1920
— & F. A. Howe.
Great Brit. in the latest age. s8°. 1921

Turberville (Henry). *A manuel of controversies demonstrating the truth of the Catholique religion &c. By H. T. s8°. Doway. 1654

Turchi (Nicola).
Manuale di storia delle religioni. 8°. Torino. 1922

Türck (Hermann). Fr. Nietzsche u. s. philosoph. Irrwege. 3e A. [P2478]. 8°. Dresden. 1891
see ZERBST (M.) Nein u. Ja! Antwort auf H. T.'s Friedrich Nietzsche, 1892.

Türckisch, *see* TÜRKISCH.

Turcograeciae libri 8, 1584, *see* CRUSIUS (M.)

Turenne (Henri de La Tour d'Auvergne, *maréchal vte.* **de),** *1611–75, see* RAGUENET (F.) Hist. du Vte. de T., n. éd., 1813.

Turfan-Expedition, *see* KÖNIGLICH PREUSSISCHE TURFAN-EXPED.

Turgenev (Aleksandr Ivanovich), *see* VYAZEMSKY (*pr.* P. A.) Остафьевскій архивъ, т1–4, переписка кн. П. А. В. съ А. И. Т., 1812–45, 1899–1908.

Turgenev (Ivan Sergeevich).
Попъ: эротическая поэма. [P846]. 8°. Genève. *n.d.*
TRANSLATIONS.
Dimitri Roudine; suiv. du Journal d'un homme de trop & de Trois rencontres. 4e éd. s8°. *n.d.*
Knock, knock, knock & o. stories. Tr. by C. Garnett. s8°. 1922
Une nichée de gentilshommes. s8°. *Nelson.* [1911]
Plays. Tr. M. S. Mandell. Intr. by W. L. Phelps. 8°. [1924]
Récits d'un chasseur. Tr. & intr. de E. Halpérine-Kaminsky. s8°. [1926]
The two friends & o. s. Tr. C. Garnett. s8°. 1921
see GERSHENZON (M.) Мечта &c. И. С. Т., 1919.
,, GONCHAROV (I. A.) И. А. Г. и И. С. Т., 1923.
,, GREVS (I. M.) Ист. одной любви: Т. и Полина Виардо, 1927.
,, NIKOLSKY (YU.) Т. и Достоевскій, 1921.
,, PIKSANOV (N. K.) Тургеневскій кружокъ, Тургеневскій сборникъ, & библіогр., 1922.
,, UTEVSKY (L. S.) Смерть Т., 1923.
,, YARMOLINSKY (A.) T., the man, h. art & age, 1926.

Turgot (Anne Robert Jacques), *baron de l'Aulne.*
Œuvres de T. & docs. Avec. biog. & notes par G. Schelle. t4, 5. 8º. 1922–23
see ADAMS (J.) Defence of constit. of govt. of U.S. agst. attack of T., 3v, 1798.

Turgot (Michel Étienne). Plan de Paris [dit Plan de T.], 1734–39, *see* PARIS. Reprod. d'anc. plans, 1908.

Turin. Saggio di ant. doc. dell' Arch. Arcivesc. di Torino; pubbl. T. Chiuso, *see* REGIA DEP. DI STORIA PATRIA. Misc., t18, 1879.
Statuta Soc. S. Iohannis Bapt. Augustae Taurin., 1389, nunc primum ed. A. Ceruti, *see* REGIA DEP. DI STORIA PATRIA. Misc., t11, 1870.
BIBLIOTECA REALE.
see VINCI (L.) Mss. e disegni, v2, Fogli manc. al cod. nella B. R., 1926.

Turina (Joaquín). Enciclopedia abrev. de musica. [Prólogo de M. de Falla]. 2t. s8º. 1917

Turique (Julien de Berr), *see* BERR DE TURIQUE (J.)

Türkenkalendar. Eyn manūg d cristēheit widd die durkē (1454, *facs.*), *see* FREYTAG (G.) Bilder, B3, T1, 1924.

Turkestan. Штаба Туркестанск. Военнаго Округа. Свѣдѣнія касающіяся странъ &c. Составилъ кап. Снѣсаревъ &c. вып. 24–35 *in* 1v. 8º. Ташкентъ. 1901–3

Turkey.
Greek atrocities in Turkey. 2v. 8º. Constantinople. 1921
A hdbk. of T. in Europe, 1920, *see* ADMIRALTY: NAVAL INTELL. DIV.
*The minorities in Turkey. [P2712]. 8º. Lausanne. 1920

Türkisch [TÜRCKISCH; TÜRKISCHE]. *Eher Türckisch als Päpstisch: Die alte &c. Rede. [P2670]. 8º. 1627
Türk. Nachrichten &c.; zusamm. v. A. Ungnad, 1916, *see* KLEINE TEXTE, T136, 1916.
Türk. Volkstümliche u. Volkspoesie, 1917, *see* KLEINE TEXTE, T140, 1917.

Turkish. [Explan. of T. writing. *Specimens*]. obl. s8º. [Cple.?. 1291=1874]
Turkish proverbs [*in Armen. characters &*] tr. into Eng. s8º. Venice. 1844

Turlerus (Hieronymus). De peregrinatione & agro Neapolitano lib. 2, *see* PYRCKMAIR (H.) De arte peregrin., 1591.

Turletti (Casimiro). La rivol. del 1797 in Fossano e Racconigi e la sollevaz. d. truppa francese in Torino, narr. da contemporanei, *see* REGIA DEP. DI STORIA PATRIA. Misc., t34, 1896.

Turmann (Max). La Suisse pend. la Guerre. L'aide aux victimes—Les difficultés écon. s8º. 1917

Turnbull (George Henry). Samuel Hartlib. Sketch of h. life & h. rel. to J. A. Comenius. 8º. 1920

Turnbull (James) [JACOBUS DE TORNABULA; GIACOMO DI TORNBULL], *d. 1496, see* BOSIO (*il cav.* A.) Due mon. ined. d. Piemonte illust. (Urna sepolcr. d. Scozzese G. di T.), 1874.

Turnbull (Monica Peveril). A short day's work. Orig. verses, tr. f. Heine, & essays. 2nd ed. 8º. 1902

Turnbull (Walter). *Some verses upon the insurrect. of the Jacobites &c. [P536]. s8º. Newcastle upon Tyne. 1746

Turnelius (Honoratus), *see* TOURNÉLY (H.)

Turner (*Sir* Alfred Edward). The retreat from Moscow & the passage of the Beresina. [P2598]. 8º. Woolwich. 1898

Turner (Anthony), *see* WHITE (T.) Last speeches of the 5 traitors: A. T. &c., 1679.

Turner (Cuthbert Hamilton).
The early printed eds. of the Greek Test. 8º. O. 1924
The study of the New Test., 1883–1920. 8º. O. 1920
see IRENAEUS, *St.* Novum Test. Sancti I.: quotations in Old Lat. version; ed., w. intrs. &c. by W. Sanday & C. H. T., 1924.
,, WORCESTER. Early W. MSS.; ed., w. transcr., intr. &c. by C. H. T., 1916.

Turner (Dawson), *1775–1858, see* COTMAN (J. S.) Archit. antiq. of Normandy; notices by D. T., 2v, 1822.
—— & Lewis W. Dillwyn. The botanist's guide thr. England & Wales. 2v. s8º. 1805

Turner (*Miss* E. L.) Broadland birds. la8º. 1924

Turner (E. M.), *see* FAWCETT (M. G.) & E. M. T. J. Butler, 1927.

Turner (Edward Raymond). Europe, 1450–1789. 8º. 1924
Europe since 1870. 8º. 1922
The Privy Council of Eng., 1603–1784. [Johns Hopkins Univ. Semicent. publs.] 2v. 8º. Baltimore. 1927–28

Turner (Francis), *bp. of (1) Rochester, (2) Ely, see* SANCROFT (W.) Proc. & tryal in case of abp. of Canterbury, bp. of E. &c., 1688, 1689.

Turner (Francis McDougall Charlewood).
The element of irony in Eng. lit. s8º. C. 1926

Turner (Fred.), *F.L.S.*
Australian grasses & pasture plants. s8º. Melbourne. [1921]

Turner (Fred), *F.R.Hist.S.*
Hist. & antiq. of Brentford. la8º. Brentford. 1922

Turner (Frederic). Egham, Surrey: hist. 8º. Egham. 1926

Turner (Frederick Jackson).
The frontier in American history. s8º. N.Y. 1920

Turner (G. D.) Main events in Persia, Oct. 1912 to Oct. 1913, *see* PERSIA SOCIETY. Lect., 1913.

Turner (G. J.), *see* CANTERBURY. Reg. of St. Augustine's Abbey; ed. G. J. T. &c., p2, 1924.

Turner (George), *Wesleyan minister.*
The constit. & discipline of Wesleyan Methodism. s8º. 1841

Turner (George Albert), *see* MAYNARD (G. D.) & G. A. T. Anthropol. notes on Bantu natives, 1914.

Turner (J. E.) Personality & reality. 8º. [1926]
Philosophic basis of moral obligation: study in ethics. 8º. 1924
A theory of direct realism & the rel. of r. to idealism. 8º. [1925]

Turner (James), *called Colonel Turner.* *The life & death of J. T., executed Jan. 21, 1663, for a burglary &c. [P2828]. s8º. 1663

Turner (John G.)
The pioneer missionary: life of N. Turner. 8º. 1872

Turner (Joseph Horsfall). Anc. Bingley. 8º. Bingley. 1897
Haworth past & present. s8º. Brighouse. 1879
see COLLYER (R.) & J. H. TURNER. Ilkley, 1885.

Turner (Joseph Mallord William). Liber fluviorum; or, river scenery in France. Engr. f. drawings by T. Letter-press by L. Ritchie. Biog. sk. by A. A. Watts. la8º. 1857
Picturesque views of Eng. & Wales, f. drawings by T. w. descr. &c. illust. by H. E. Lloyd. 2v. fol. 1832–38
see ASHBY (T.) T.'s visions of Rome, 1925.

Turner (Laurence), *F.S.A.* Decorative plasterwork in Gt. Brit. Intr. by A. T. Bolton. fol. [1927]

Turner (Nathaniel), *see* TURNER (J. G.) The pioneer missionary: life of N. T., 1872.

Turner (Richard), *LL.D., the elder.* A view of the earth: being a system of mod. geography, &c. Added, a descr. of the terrestial globe. [P2568]. sm. fol. 1762

Turner (Robert), *prof. in the university of Ingolstadt.*
Epistolæ. [*b. w. h.* Orationum vol. 1 & 2, 1615]. s8º. Coloniae Agrippinae. 1615
Orationum vol. 1 & 2 [*in 1v*]. Acc. Edmundi Campiani opuscula omnia [*w. sep. tp.*] s8º. Coloniæ Agrippinae. 1615
see BARNESTAPOLIUS (O.), *ps.* Maria Stuarta, martyr eccl. &c., *sometimes attrib. to T.*, 1588.

Turner (Samuel). My climbing adventures in 4 continents. [2nd impr.] s8º. [1913]
The conquest of the New Zealand Alps. 8º. [1922]
Short statement on need of a tariff &c. [P2732]. 8º. [1923]

Turner (Samuel Hulbeart). Biog. notices of Jewish rabbies &c. & transl. of portions of th. Commentaries &c. s8º. N.Y. 1847

Turner (T. S.)
*Hist. of Aldborough & Boroughbridge. s8º. 1853

Turner (W. J.) [TURNER (WALTER JAMES REDFERN)].
The aesthetes. s8º. 1927
Beethoven. 8º. 1927
Landscape of Cytherea. [*Poems*]. s8º. 1923
The man who ate the popomack. Tragi-comedy. s8º. 1922
Orpheus or the music of the future. s8º. [1926]
Variations on the theme of music. 8º. [1924]

Turner (William), *F.S.S.* The ceramics of Swansea & Nantgarw. App. on mannerisms of the artists, by R. Drane. la8º. 1897

Turpin (François). Georges Courteline, s. œuvre. 8º. [1925]

Turpin (François René). Hist. of Siam. Tr. by B. O. Cartwright. [Vajirañāna Nat. Lib.] s8º. Bangkok. 1908

Turpin (J. M.) Anne-Toussante de Volvire de Ruffec, demoiselle du Bois de la Roche. s8º. Nantes. 1906

Turquan (Joseph). Madame de Staël, sa vie amoureuse, polit. &c., 1766–1817. 8º. 1926
La reine Hortense, d'ap. les témoignages des contemp. 2t. 8º. [1927]
—— & L. Ellis. La belle Pamela (Lady Edward FitzGerald), 1773–1831, d'ap. des corr. & mém. inéd. &c. 2t. 8º. 1923–24

Turquet-Milnes (G.) Some modern French writers: a study in Bergsonism. s8º. 1921

Turquie. *La Turquie moderne. Réponse à calomniateurs. [P2712]. 8º. Genève. 1919

Turrecremata (Joannes de), *Cardinal, b. 1388, see* ZAPF (G. W.) Ueb. e. Ausg. v. J. de T. Explan. in Psalterium, 1803.

Turretin (Benedict). Theses theol. de infinitate Dei. [*b. w.* Arminius (J.) Theses, 1603]. s8º. Lugd. Bat. 1605

Turretini (Jean Alphonse). Dilucidationes philos.-theolog.-dogm.-morales &c. Acc. Orationes, Commercium epist. &c. 3v. 8º. Lugd. Bat. 1748
Hist. eccl. compend. Ed. altera. s8º. Geneva. 1736
see SIMON (J.) Synop. hist. eccl. sec. 18. loco suppl. ad J. A. T. compend., 1750.

Turretinus (Franciscus). De necessaria secessione ab Eccl. Romana, disput. Disput. misc. decas. Acc. De satisfactione Xti. &c. [Opera v4]. 8º. E. 1748
Institutio theologiae elencticae. Acc. B. Picteti oratio de vita & obitu authoris. [Opera v1–3]. 3p. 8º. E. 1847

Turri (Vittorio). Dante (1265–1321). s8º. Firenze. 1907

Turrianus (Franciscus).
Index ἐλεγκτικός repetitionum & ταυτολογίων Turriani ex tertio eius libro coll. Authore A. Sadeele. [*b. w.* Sadeel (A.) Sophismata &c., 1577.] s8º. Morgiis. 1583
see SADEEL (A.) Sophismata F. T.: coll. ex eius libro De Eccl. & ordin. ministrorum: subjecta solutio, 1577.

Turro (R.) Les origines de la connaissance. 8º. 1914

Tursellinus (Horatius), *see* TORSELLINO (ORAZIO).

Turton (Thomas), *bp. of Ely* [*ps.* CRITO CANTABRIGIENSIS].
Obs. on Dr. Wiseman's reply to Dr. Turton's Roman Cath. doct. of the Eucharist considered &c. 8º. C. 1839

Turville-Petre (Francis). Researches in prehist. Galilee, 1925–26, w. sect. by D. M. Bate & C. Baynes, & A report on the Galilee skull by Sir A. Keith. [Brit. Sch. of Arch. in Jerusalem]. 4º. 1927

Tusca. Tusca &c.; übers. v. A. Grünwedel, 1922, *see* GRÜNWEDEL (A.)

Tüsch (Hans Ehrart) [DÜSCH; TUESCH]. Chron. rimée des guerres de Bourgogne, Strasb., 1477, facs. & tr., *see* PICOT (E.) & H. STEIN. Recueil, 1923.

Tutânkhâmen, *king of Egypt.*
see BUDGE (*Sir* E. A. T. W.) T.: Amenism, Atenism &c., 1923.
,, CAPART (J.) The tomb of T.; tr., 1923.
,, CARTER (H.) & A. C. MACE. Tomb of T.-a.-A., 2v, 1923–27.
,, †DAVIS (T. M.) Excav.: Bibân el Molûk; tombs of Harmhabi & T., 1912.
,, SMITH (G. E.) T. & the discovery of h. tomb, 1923.
,, WEIGALL (A. E. P.) T. & o. essays, 1923.

Tutschek (Charles) & Lorenz Tutschek. Dict. of the Galla lang. 2p *in* 1v (p2, by L. T.) 8º. München. 1844–45
Gramm. of the Galla lang. Ed. L. Tutschek. [*tr. by* M. J. Smead. *b. w. h.* Dict. 1844–45]. 8º. Munich. 1845

Tuttle (Hudson).
Arcana of spiritualism. s8º. Boston [Mass.] 1871

Tutton (Alfred Edwin Howard). Crystallography & pract. crystal measurement. [2nd ed.] 2v. 8º. 1922
The natural hist. of crystals. 8º. 1924
Natural hist. of ice & snow illust. f. the Alps. 8º. 1927

Tuxen (Poul). Forestillingen om Sjælen i Rigveda, *see* KONGELIGT DAN. VID. SELSK. Hist.-fil. Med., B2, 1918–19.

Tverdokhlebov (V. N.) Новейшие финансовые проблемы. la8º. П. 1923

Twain (Mark), *ps.*
Adventures of Huckleberry Finn. n. impr. s8º. 1920
,, ,, ...s8º. [1924]
Autobiography. Intr. by A. B. Paine. 2v. la8º. N.Y. 1924
A double-barrelled detective story. [*tp. wanting*]. s8º. [1902]
The prince & the pauper. n. impr. s8º. 1920
What is man? s8º. 1910
see BROOKS (VAN W.) Ordeal of M. T., 1922.

Tweedale (*Mrs.* Violet). Ghosts I have seen: & other psychic experiences. s8º. 1920

Tweedie (*Mrs.* Alec), *form. Ethel B. Harley.*
America as I saw it. 8º. 1913
A woman on 4 battlefronts. [P2518]. la8º. 1919

Twelve (The) who are to die: trial of Socialists-Revolut. in Moscow, 1922, *see* SOCIALISTS-REVOLUTIONISTS.

Twesten (Carl). Machiavelli: Vortrag, *for a. c., see* VIRCHOW (R.) & HOLTZENDORFF. Samml., s3, H49, 1868.

Twietmeyer (Johann Heinrich). Ex hist. eccl. de conciliis Lateran. Praes. P. F. Hane. [P440]. s4º. Kiliae. [1726]

***Twilight** & candle-shades, 1888, *see* EXUL, *ps.*

"Twin," *ps., see* PHILLIMORE (JOHN).

Twiss (*Sir* Travers), *see* CHAFFERS (A.) The T. libel case, 1872.

***Two** letters, conc. farther advantages &c. nec. on taking Cape Breton, 1746, *see* BRETON, *Cape.*

Twynam (*Sir* William Crofton).
Rep. on Ceylon pearl fisheries. sm. fol. Colombo. 1900

Twysden (*Sir* Roger), *2nd bart.* The Twysden Lieutenancy papers, 1583–1668. Ed. w. intr. by G. S. Thomson. [Kent Arch. Soc.] 8º. [Ashford. 1926]
see ANNE [*Bullen*]. Acc. of Queen A. B., f. MS. in wr. of R. T., 1815.

Tyas (Robert). Flowers & heraldry. s8º. 1851

Tyau (Min-Ch'ien T. Z.) China awakened. 8º. N.Y. 1922

Tyburn. Malefactor's register, or the Newgate & T. cal., 1700–79, 1779, *see* MALEFACTOR's register.
*Tyburn (The) chronicle. 4v. 8º. [1768]

Tyerman (Daniel), *see* MONTGOMERY (J.) Journal of voyages &c. by D. T. &c., 1821–29, 2v, 1831.

Tyerman (Luke).
The life of George Whitefield. 2nd ed. 2v. 8º. 1890
Wesley's designated successor: life &c. of J. W. Fletcher (1729–85). 8º. 1882

Tyler (John Mason).
The new stone age in Northern Europe. 8º. 1921

Tyler (Royall).
see PEIRCE (H.) & R. T. Byzantine art, 1926.
,, TATLOCK (R. R.), R. T. &c. Spanish art, 1927.

Tyler (Thomas). Jehovah, the Redeemer God: script. interp. of div. name. s8º. 1861

Tyler (Wat), *see* CLEVELAND (J.) Revived poems &c. [*incl.* *The rustic rampant &c. in the insurrect. of W. T.], 1687.

Tyndale (Walter), *see* BROWN (H. F.) Dalmatia, painted by W. T., 1925.

Tyndale (William). The works of the Eng. reformers: William Tyndale & John Frith. Ed. by T. Russell. 3v. 8º. 1831
see BIBLE: NEW TEST. 1st N.T. in Eng. lang. (1525 or 26); tr. W. T., 1862.
,, —— The first printed Eng. New Test., tr. T.; photo-lithographed f. the fragment in the Brit. Mus.; E. Arber, 1871.
,, —— The N.T., 1526; tr. W. T., 1836.
,, JOHN RYLANDS LIBRARY. Cat. of exhib. illust. hist. of transmission of the Bible, in commem. of 400th ann. of publ. of T.'s New Test., 1525, 1925.
,, MORE (*Sir* T.) Dialogue conc. T. (1528); ed. W. E. Campbell, 1927.

Tyndall (John). The glaciers of the Alps: Mountaineering in 1861. [Everyman's Lib. repr.] s8º. [1906]

Tyrol. Paraenesis antiq. Germ. Tyrolis regis Scotorum &c. ut Winsbeckii ad filium ac Winsbeckiae ad filiam; ed. M. H. Goldastus &c., *see* SCHILTER (J.) Thesaurus antiq., t2, 1727.

Tyrrell (Henry) & H. A. Haukeil.
Hist. of Russia, to 1878. 3v. la8º. [1879–80]

Tyrrell (Robert Yelverton), *see* KOTTABOS. Trin. Coll., Dublin; ed. R. Y. T. (1869–95), 1873–95.

Tyrrell-Green (Edmund), *see* GREEN (E. T.)

Tysilio, *episcopus Gaeliae, see* PETRIE (W. M. P.) Neglected Brit. hist. [*i.e.* T.'s Chron.], 1917.

Tyssot de Patot (Simon), *see* LACHÈVRE (F.) Les successeurs de Cyrano de Bergerac [T. de P. &c.], 1922.

Tythes, *see* TITHES.

Tyttery, *The family of, see* GRAZEBROOK (H. S.) Coll. for a genealogy of noble families of T. &c., 1877.

Tyumenets (Vasily), *see* POKROVSKY (F. T.) Путешествіе въ Монголію &c., 1914.

Tyutchev (Theodor Ivanovich). Тютчевіана. Эпиграммы &c. Предисловіе Г. Чулкова. 8º. Москва. 1922

Tyzack, *The family of, see* GRAZEBROOK (H. S.) Coll. for a genealogy of noble families of T. &c., 1877.

Tzebrikova (M.), *see* TSEBRIKOVA (M.)

Tzetzes (Isaac). De metris Pindaricis comm.; ed. A. B. Drachmann, *see* KONG. DAN. VID. SELSK. Hist.-fil. Medd., 9, 1924–25.

Tzolakean (T. I. Kh.) [TZOLAKIDES (D. I. KH.)]
[New dict. Armenian & Greek]. s8º. K.-polis. 1868

Tzu-ssu, *grandson of Confucius, born c. 500 B.C.* *The Chung-Yung, or The centre, the common. [Wr. by T.-s. to record the teachings of Confucius]. Tr. L. A. Lyall & King Chien-Kün. 8º. 1927

U

U. (E. B.) *Christian missions in East & West, 1792–1872, 1873, *see* UNDERHILL (E. B.)

U. (V.) Какіе нужны порядки. [P848]. s8°. Москва. 1906

Ubaghs (Gérard Casimir).
Logicae elem. ed. 4ª aucta. 8°. Lovanii. 1844
Theodicæ seu theologiae nat. elementa. ed. 2ª aucta. 8°. Lovanii. 1845

Ubaldini, *The family of, see* UBALDINI (G. B.) Istoria, 1588.

Ubaldini (Giovanni Battista). Istoria d. casa d. Ubaldini, e de' fatti d'alcuni di quella famiglia. Libro primo. E la vita di N. Acciaioli, descr. da M. Palmieri. s4°. Firenze. 1588

Ubbo Philippi, *see* PHILIPPS (UBBO).

Ubertini (Francesco d'Albertino), *see* BACHIACCA (IL).

***U-Boote** im Eismeer. s8°. [1917]

Uccelli (Raffaello).
Contrib. alla bibliografia d. Toscana. la8°. Firenze. 1922

Udale (James). Handy book on pruning, grafting & budding. 4th ed. s8°. Evesham. 1920

Udall (Nicholas). Roister Doister. Ed. E. Arber. [Eng. repr. *a. c. b. w.* Howell (J.) Instructions &c., 1868]. s8°. [1869]
Roister Doister, *see* ADAMS (J. Q.) Chief pre-Shakespearian dramas, 1925.

Ude (Johann). Psych. d. Strebevermögens im Sinne d. Scholastik. [P2479]. 8°. Graz. 1907

Ufhausen (Solomon Tsebi), *see* SOLOMON TSEBI, *Ufhausen.*

Uganda. Hdbk. of the U. Protectorate, 1920, *see* ADMIRALTY: NAVAL INTELL. DIV.

Uganda Railway (The), Brit. E. Africa, f. Mombasa to Lake Victoria Nyanza. 8°. *n.d.*

Ughelli (Ferdinando) [UGHELLUS]. Italia sacra, sive de episcopis Italiæ &c. ed. 2ª, aucta & emend. cura N. Coleti. 10t *in* 9v. fol. Venetiis. 1717–22
t10 *includes* Anecdota Ughelliana, *w. sep. pagin.*

Uglow (W. L.)
see JOHNSTONE (W. A.) & W. L. U. Placer & vein gold dep. of Barkerville, 1926.
„ YOUNG (G. A.) & W. L. U. Iron ores of Canada, v1, 1926.

Ugolini (Luigi M.)
Albania antica. Pref. di R. Paribena. v1. sm. fol. 1927
La Panighina: fonte sacra preist., *see* REALE ACCAD. D. LINCEI. Mon. ant., v29, 1923.

Uhagon (Francisco R. de). Los libros de cetreria d. P. Lopez de Ayala, de J. de Sant-Fahagun y de F. de Zuñiga y Sotomayor. Noticias. 8°. 1889

Uhde-Bernays (Hermann). Carl Spitzweg: d. Meisters Leben u. Werk [*incl.* Gedichte]. 5e verm. A. la8°. München. 1919

Uhland (J. Ludwig). Gedichte. 5e A. s8°. St. 1857
see SCHNEIDER (H.) U. u. d. deut. Heldensage, 1918.

Uhland (Ludwig Joseph). Disput. de fide haereticis servanda. Præs. D. Maichelio. [P2632]. s4°. Tubingæ. [1741]

Uhlhorn (Johann Gerhard W.) Ant. Corvinus. Vortrag. [Verein f. Ref.-gesch. Schr., Jhrg. 9, Nr. 37]. 8°. Halle. 1892

Uhlirz (Mathilde). Die Genesis d. 4 Prager Artikel, 1914, *see* KAIS. AKAD. D. WISS. ZU WIEN. Sitzb., B175, 1916.

Uhrström (W.) Pickpocket, turnkey, wrap-rascal, & similar formations in English. s8°. Stockholm. [1918]

Uisel, *see* USSEL.

Ujfalvy (Károly Jenö). Iconographie & anthropologie irano-ind. 1, L'Irân. [Extr. de l'Anthropologie, 1900]. la8°. 1900
—— **& R. Hertzberg.** Gramm. finnoise d'après les princ. d'Eurén, suiv. de morceaux choisis. 8°. 1876

Ukers (William Harrison). All about coffee. la8°. N.Y. 1922

Ukhtanes, *see* OUKHTANES.

Ukraina [UKRAINE].
*Chronologie des princ. événements en U., 1917–19. [P2401]. 8°. [1919]
Mém. sur l'indépendance de l'U. prés. à la Conf. de la Paix par la délég. de la Répub. ukr. fol. 1919
*Ukraine. Résumé hist. & polit. [P2401]. 8°. La Haye. 1919
L'U. Sovietiste. 4 années de guerre & de blocus. Doc. off. d'ap. les livres rouges ukrain. la8°. Berlin. 1922
Ukrainian problems Nos. 1–6. [P2402]. 4°. *n.p.* 1919
No. 1 *is the French ed.*: Les questions ukr.

Ukrainskaya Sotsialist. Sovetskaya Respublika.
[*Leaflets* (10). P2455]. s8°. Kueb. 1919

Ulbrecht (Johann Gottfried), *see* HASSEN (M.) & J. G. U. Characteres tyranni in O. Cromwello, 1712.

Ulbrich (Josef). Die rechtl. Natur d. österreich.-ungar. Monarchie. la8°. Prag. 1879

Ule (Otto). Die Wunder d. Sternenwelt. Neu hrsg. H. H. Kritzinger. 7e verb. A. 8°. [1923]

Ulenberg (Caspar). Hist. de vita, moribus &c. prædicantium Lutheranorum, M. Lutheri, P. Melanchthonis, M. Flacii Illyrici, G. Majoris et A. Osiandri. [*Ed.* A. Meshovius]. [2v]. s8°. Coloniae Agripp. 1622
v2 *has title* Hist. de vita &c. P. Melanchthonis, M. Flacii Illyr. &c.
see BADIUS (J.) Gründl. u. bestendige Ableynung d. vermeynt. Antwort C. U., 1592.

Ulenov (—). Процесс П. С.-Р. Речи защитников Уленова &c., 1922, *see* SOTSIALISTI-REVOLYUTSIONERI.

Ulfilas [*see also* BIBLE: ANGLO-SAXON & GOTHIC].
Evangelia ab U. ex Graeco Gothicè tr., nunc. cum parallelis vers., Sueo-Goth., Norrænâ, seu Islandicâ, & vulg. Lat. ed. [*by* G. Stiernhielm]. s4°. Stockholmiae. 1671
U. Die heil. Schriften Alten u. Neuen Bundes in goth. Spr. Mit griech. u. lat. Texte, Wbch. u. Einl. v. H. F. Massmann. 8°. St. 1857
U. Gothica versio Epist. ad Corinthios secundae. Ed. C. O. Castillionaeus. [P2527]. 4°. Mediolani. 1829
U. partium ined. ab A. Maio repert. specimen conjunctis curis ejusdem Maii et C. O. Castillionaei ed. [P2527]. 4°. Mediolani. 1819
see HEUPEL (G. F.) De U., seu vers. 4 Evang. Gothica, 1693.
„ IHRE (J.) Scripta versionem Ulphilanam & ling. Mæso-Gothicam illust., 1773.

Ulger, *bp. of Angers, d. 1149, see* URSEAU (C.) Tombe de l'évêque U. à la cath. d'A., 1925.

Ulin, *see* ULLIN *the bard.*

Ullathorne (William Bernard), *bp. of (1) Hetalona, (2) Birmingham, see* BUTLER (E. C.) Life & times of Bp. U., 1806–89, 2v, 1926.

Ullin *the bard* [ULIN], *see* OSSIAN. Poems of Ossian, Orran, U., & o. bards; ed. by H. & J. M'Callum, 1816.

Ulloa (Francisco de). Rel. d. viaje, por la costa de Nueva Esp., 1540, *see* SERRANO Y SANZ (M.) Rel. hist., 1916.

Ulloa (Juan de). De primis et ult. temporibus. [*2 pagin.*] fol. Augustae Vindelic. 1719
Theologia scholastica. 5t. fol. Augustae Vindelic. 1719

Ulloa y Pereira (Luis de). Memorias familiares y lit. [*Ed.* M. Artigas]. Publ. la Soc. de Bibl. Esp. 8°. 1925

Ullswater (James William Lowther, *1st visc.***)**
A speaker's commentaries. 2v. 8°. 1925

Ulmann (Heinrich). Leben d. deut. Volks bei Beginn d. Neuzeit. [Verein f. Ref.-gesch. Schr., Jhrg. 10, Nr. 41]. 8°. Halle. 1893

Ulmer (Friedrich Ferdinand). Diss. de calendario vet. Hebraeorum. Praes. J. A. Nagel. [P446]. s4°. Altorfii Noric. [1746]

Ulric, *saint, bp. of Augsburg* [HULRICUS; OUDALRICH].
Epistola ad Nicolaum I pro defensione conjugii sacerdotum scripta &c. s8°. Magdeburgi, *M. Lotther.* [1521 ?]
see GULLMANN (B.) Ex hist. Augustan. de S. U., 1693.

Ulrich, *Engelberti, of Strassburg, see* ENGELBERTI (U.)

Ulrich (Hermann).
Die besten deut. Geschichtswerke. s8°. L. 1923
see WESTPHAL (M.) Die besten deut. Memoiren &c.; mit Abh. ü. d. Entwickl. d. deut. Selbstbiog., v. H. U., 1923.

Ulrich (Johann Daniel). Diss. de autoritate Lutheri in eccl. A. C. professa. Praes. J. M. Lorenz. [P442]. s4°. Argentorati. [1748]

Ulster. Hdbk. of the U. question. Issued by the North Eastern Boundary Bureau. 8°. 1923
The plea of presbytery in behalf of ordination, gov. &c. of the Xtn. Church in a reply to A. Boyd On Episcopacy by ministers of the General Synod of U. [W. D. Killen & others]. 3rd ed. contains a reply to A. Boyd's Episcopacy & Presbytery & Reprint of Mene Tekel. 8°. Belfast. 1843
Ulster; [*by var. wr.* Prov. of Ireland], 1921, *see* FLETCHER (G.), *ed.*
Ulster songs & ballads, 1925, *see* HAYWARD (H. R.), *ed.*

Ultrajectensis. Acta & decreta 2ae synodi prov. U., 1763, 1764, *see* UTRECHT.

Ultrajectinae. Acta quaedam eccl. U. &c., 1737, *see* CROON (T. V. D.)

Ultramar. Coleccion de docs. inéd. rel al descubr. &c. de las ant. posesiones esp. de U., s2, t1–19, 1885–1926, *see* COLECCIÓN.

Ultramontane's (An) reply to Mr. Gladstone's expostul. [P2576]. 8°. 1874

Ulugh Beg, *aft. Don Juan of Persia, see* JUAN (*Don*), *of Persia.*

Ulugh Beg ibn Shahrukh, *Mīrzā, see* BARTOLD (V. V.) У. и его время, 1918.

Umanskij (Konstantin). Neue Kunst in Russland, 1914–19. Vorwort v. L. Zahn. la8°. Potsdam. 1920

'Umarī, Al-, *see* AḤMAD IBN YAḤYĀ.

'Umar Khayyám, *see* OMAR KHAYYAM.

Umbra Oxoniensis. Results of the " Expostulation " of W. E. Gladstone, in rel. to the unity of Roman Catholicism. By U. O. s8°. 1875

Umbreit (Paul) & C. Lorenz. Der Krieg u. d. Arbeitsverhältnisse. [C.E. for Int. Peace.] 8°. St. 1928

Umlauft (Friedrich), *see* HANNAK (E.) & F. U. Hist. Schulatlas, 2T., 1920.

Umpffenbach (Heinrich). Diss. de chiliasmo apocalyptico fanaticorum comm. contrario. [P2632]. s4°. Argentorati. [1674]

Unamuno (Miguel de).
Andanzas y visiones españolas. s8°. 1922
De Fuerteventura a Paris : diario vert. en sonetos. s8°. Paris. 1925
Sensaciones de Bilbao. s8°. 1922
Tres novelas ejemplares y un prólogo. s8°. 1920
TRANSLATIONS.
Brouillard. Tr. N. Larthe. s8°. [1926]
" " ....[4e éd.] s8°. [1926]
Essays & soliloquies. Tr. w. intr. essay by J. E. C. Flitch. 8°. [1925]
The life of Don Quixote & Sancho acc. to Cervantes expounded w. comm. by U. Tr. H. P. Earle. 8°. 1927
The tragic sense of life in men & in peoples. Tr. J. E. C. Flitch. Intr. essay by S. de Madariaga. 8°. 1921
Trois nouvelles exemplaires & un prologue. Tr. de J. Cassou & M. Pomès. Intr. de Valery Larbaud. 4e éd. s8°. [1925]

Uncensored. *Uncensored letters from the Dardanelles, 1916, *see* DARDANELLES.
*Uncensored recollections. [2nd ed.] 8°. [1924]

Uncinariasis Commission to the Orient, 1915–17, *see* DARLING (S. T.) &c. Hookworm & malaria research in Malaya &c., 1920.

***Under** Eastern skies, 1901, *see* MIMOSA, *ps.*

Underhill (Edward Bean). *Christian missions in the East & West, in conn. w. Baptist Miss. Soc., 1792–1872. [*Pref. signed E. B. U.*] s8°. 1873

Underhill (Evelyn) [*aft. Mrs.* STUART-MOORE].
The essentials of mysticism & o. essays. s8°. 1920
A Franciscan poet : Jacopone da Todi, *see* ROY. SOC. OF LIT. Essays &c., n.s., v6, 1926.
Immanence. Bk. of verses. [repr.] s8°. [1920]
The life of the spirit & the life of to-day. s8°. [1922]
The life of the spirit & the life of to-day. 3rd ed. s8°. [1923]
Man & the supernatural. 8°. [1927]
Mysticism. 2nd ed. 8°. [1911]
The mystics of the Church. 8°. [1925]
Theophanies. Bk. of verses. s8°. 1916

Underhill (George Edward). Hist. [of Romania], by U. &c., *see* BUCHAN (J.), *ed.* Nations of to-day, 1924.

Underwood (Leon), *see* HALL (*Mrs.* E. C.) Draughtsmen : E. C. H., L. U. &c., 1924.

Underwood (Reginald Edward).
Elements of actuarial science. s8°. 1922

Undset (Ingvald). Études sur l'âge de bronze de la Hongrie. 1, Avant-propos, fibules, épées. la8°. Christiania. 1880

Undset (Sigrid).
Kristin Lavransdatter. Husfrue. s8°. 1921
" " Korset. s8°. 1922
" " Kransen. s8°. 1923
Olav Audunssøn i Hestviken. 2[B]. 8°. Oslo. 1925
TRANSLATIONS.
The cross. Tr. C. Archer. 8°. 1927
The garland. 8°. 1922
The mistress of Husaby. 2v. s8°. 1925

Unemployment. Is u. inevitable ? An analysis & a forecast. Cont. of investig. s8°. 1924
The 3rd winter of u. Rep. of Enquiry, autumn, 1922. s8°. 1923
U. in its nat. & internat. aspects, 1924, *see* INTERNAT. LABOUR OFFICE.
*U. insurance in Gt. Brit. : crit. examin. 8°. 1925

***Unexpected** tidings of the War & of the future, 1915, *see* FOX (R. J.), *ed.*

Ungar (Hermann). Die Ermordung d. Hauptmanns Hanika. s8°. [1925]

Ungarelli (Luigi Maria) [ALOISIUS M. U.] Praelect. de N.T. & hist. Vulgatae Bibl. ed. 8°. Romae. 1847

Ungaria, *see* HUNGARIA.

Ungaricae. *Reflexiones super introduc. linguae ungaricae in administ. Regni usu. [P2622]. s8°. Vindebonae. 1806

Ungarische Rundschau für hist. u. soz. Wissenschaften. Hrsg. v. G. Heinrich. Jhrg. 2, H1–3. la8°. München. 1913

Ungarn [UNGAREN].
*Gesch. d. evangel. Kirche in U. v. Anfange d. Reformation bis 1850, mit Rücksicht auf Siebenbürgen. Einl. v. Merle d'Aubigné. 8°. 1854
*Gesch. d. Generalsynoden beider evang. Confessionen in Ungarn v. 1791, von CLVI. 8°. Jena. 1858
*Kurze Gesch. d. evang. luther. Kirche in U., 1794, *see* TEKUSCH (J. M.)
*Kurtzer u. warhafft. Bericht v. d. letzten Verfolgung d. evang. Prediger in Ungaren &c. aus d. Holländ. ins Teutsche übers. durch C.A.O.R. s8°. *n.p.* 1683
*Nothwendige Gedancken d. evang. Prediger in Teutschland üb. d. Exulanten auss. U. &c. Ins Teutsche übers. [*b.w.* Kurtzer u. warhafft. Bericht &c., 1683]. s8°. *n.p.* 1683

Unger (Arthur Wilhelm). Die Herstellung v. Büchern, Illustrationen, Akzidenzen usw. 2e verm. A. 8°. Halle a. S. 1910

Unger (Carl Richard). Oldnorsk Læsebog med Gloss. 8°. 1863

Unger (Johann Gottfried). De papyro frutice. Praes. J. G. U.; resp. I. E. Hahnio. [P428]. s4°. Lipsiae. [1731]

Unger (W. S.) Bronnen tot de gesch. v. Middelburg in d. landsheerlijken tijd. Uitg. v. W. S. U. [Rijks Gesch. Publ., 54, 61]. d1, 2. la8°. 's-Gravenhage. 1923–26

Ungerer (Alfred). Les horloges d'édifice. la8°. [1926]

Ungher (F. Sabatier-), *see* SABATIER-UNGHER (F.)

Ungnad (Arthur). Aramä. Papyrus aus Elephantine. Kl. A. unter Zugrundlegung v. E. Sachau's Erstausg. Bearb. v. A. U. 8°. L. 1911
Türk. Nachrichten aus Zeitungen zusamm. mit Anmerk. versehen v. A. U., *see* KLEINE TEXTE, T136, 1916.

Unheimliche (Das) Buch, 1920, *see* SCHLÖMP (F.)

***Uniformes** (Les) de l'armée allemande. s8°. 1877

Unigenitus. *An abstract of what is nec. to be known conc. the Constit. U. &c. [By D***]. Tr. f. the Fr. s8°. *n.p* 1724

Union Académique Internationale. Cat. des mss. alchimiques grecs. Publ. J. Bidez, F. Cumont &c. t1–3. 8°. Brux. 1924–27
1, Les Parisini, décr. par H. Lebègue. App., mss. des Coeranides &c.
2, Mss. ital., décr. par C. O. Zuretti, O. Lagercrantz &c. App., mss. des Coeranides &c.
3, Mss. des Iles Brit., décr. par D. W. Singer &c. App., recettes alchim. du Codex Holkhamicus, éd. par O. Lagercrantz.
Classif. des céramiques antiq. Par C. Dugas [*& o. wr.*] 12p [*in 1v*]. 8°. [1921?–27]
see CORPUS vasorum antiq., 1922–28. Organisation, 1921.

Union Française, *see* ROUMANIE. La R. : Conf. faites à l'U. F., 1920.

Union Intellectuelle Franco-Italienne, *see* DANTE ALIGHIERI. D. : mélanges de crit. & d'érudition franç. &c., 1921.

***Unione** (De) personali duarum in una persona Domini nostri J. C. naturarum &c., 1587, *see* HASSIA.

Unions-Conferenz, *see* BONN. Bericht ü. d. U.-C., 1875.

Unitarii. *Conf. fidei Xtnae. sec. U. in Transylvania &c. [*by J. Kermötzi*], 1782, *see* TRANSYLVANIA.
*Summa univ. theol. Christ. sec. Unitarios, 1787, *see* SUMMA.

Unitè des Frères. *Briève & fidèle expos. de l'orig. de la doct. des constit. &c. de l'Église de l'U. des F., 1758, *see* BOHEMIA.

United Brethren. Coll. of hymns ; for use of Brethren's Church, 2p, 1754, *see* HYMNS.
Liturgic hymns of the U.B., 1811, *see* LITURGIC.
Liturgy &c. for U.B., n. ed., 1849, *see* LITURGY.

United Foreign Missionary Society, *see* AMERICAN MISSION. REGISTER, w. proc. of U.F.M.S., v1, 1821.

United Ireland on Spencer, Trevelyan & Gladstone. Value of W. O'Brien's denials. [P2560]. 8°. D. 1888

United Russia Societies Association. U.R.S.A. Proceedings. v1 (1917–18). 8°. 1919

United Service (The) Magazine.
N.S., v61 (Apr.–June 1920). la8°. 1920
On & after Oct. 1920, *incorp. w.* The Army Quarterly, *q.v.*

United States.
Anonymous Works & Misc. Govt. Publs.
Amer. & Brit. claims arbitration under agreem., Aug. 18, 1910: Rep., 1926, *see* NIELSEN (F. K.)
Civilization in the U.S., 1922, *see* STEARNS (H. E.), *ed.*

United States [*continued*].

Anonymous Works & Misc. Govt. Publs. [*continued*].

Constit. of the U.S., w. amendments: Added Jefferson's Manual of parliament. practice &c. & Barclay's Digest. [*w. sep. tp. & pagin.*] 8°. W. [1871]

Diplom. corr. of the U.S. conc. independ. of Lat.-Amer. nations, v1–3, 1925, *see* MANNING (W. R.), *ed.*

East coast of U.S. pilot, 3rd ed., 2v, *&* Suppl. 1, 1921–22, *see* ADMIRALTY.

*Englishman's (The) guide to the U.S. & Canada. [n. ed.] s8°. 1884

Foreign policy of the U.S.; addr., 1899, *see* AMER. ACAD. OF POLIT. &C. SCI.

Fredonia; or the U.S. of N. Amer. &c. [map], 1830, *see* LAURIE (R. H.) *publ.*

N. Atlantic Coast Fisheries Tribunal of arbitr., Jan. 1909, betw. U.S. & Gt. Brit., 1910, *see* HAGUE (THE): PERM. COURT OF ARBITR.

Public treaties of the U.S. in force 1 Dec. 1873. [*b. w.* U.S. Rev. statutes rel. to Dist. of Columbia, 1875]. sm. fol. Wash. 1875

Army, *see also* WAR DEPT. *below.*

Legisl. hist. of the Gen. Staff of the Army, 1775–1901. Comp. &c. by R. P. Thian. 8°. Wash. 1901

The Medical Dept. of the U.S. Army in the World War. Prep. under dir. of Maj.-Gen. M. W. Ireland. v1, 2, 5–9, 11, 13, 14, 15, p1, 2. la8°. Wash. 1921–28

1, Surgeon General's Office; by C. Lynch, F. W. Weed, L. M'Afee.
2, Administration, Amer. Expedit. Forces; by J. H. Ford.
5, Military hospitals in the U.S.; by F. W. Weed.
6, Sanitation, In U.S., by W. P. Chamberlain, In Amer. Exped. Force, by F. W. Weed.
7, Training; by W. N. Bispham.
8, Field operations; by C. Lynch, J. H. Ford, F. W. Weed.
9, Communicable and other diseases; by J. F. Siler.
11i, ii, Surgery; p1, under dir. of M. W. Ireland, p2, by E. K. Dunham, R. H. Ivy, *& others.*
13, Physical reconstr. & vocational educ.; by A. G. Crane—The Army Nurse Corps; by J. C. Stimson.
14, Med. aspects of gas warfare; by W. D. Bancroft &c.
15i, ii, Statistics: 1, Army anthropology; by C. B. Davenport & A. G. Love. 2, Medical & casualty statistics; by A. G. Love.

Official army reg., 1906, 1908, 1913, 1914, 1916. 8°. Wash. 1905–16

Census.

Birth statistics for the birth registr. of the U.S. 1918, 1921. 4th, 7th Annual rep. 4°. W. 1920–23

Century (A) of population growth, 1790–1900. 4°. W. 1909

Disc. (A) of increase of population. Prep. under superv. of W. F. Willcox. [Bull. 4. P2604.] 4°. W. 1903

Mortality statistics 1918, 1920, 19th, 21st Ann. rep. 4°. W. 1920–22

Wealth, debt & taxation, 1913. 2v. 4°. W. 1915

9th Census, 1870.

Compendium of 9th C. Comp. by F. A. Walker. 8°. Wash. 1872

13th Census, 1910.

Abstract. 4°. W. 1914

Indian population in the U.S. & Alaska. 4°. Wash. 1915

14th Census, 1920. v2, 3, 6i–iii, 7, 8–11. 4°. W. 1922–23

Agriculture. [6i–iii.]
Irrigation & drainage. [7.]
Manufactures. [8–10.]
Mines & quarries, 1919. [11.]
Population, 1920: compos. & character of pop. by States. [3.]
„ „ : gen. report & analytical tables. [2.]

Blind in the U.S., 1920. 4°. W. 1923

Carpenter (N.) Immigrants & th. children, 1920. [Census monogr., 7.] la8°. Wash. 1927

Deaf-mutes in the U.S., 1920. 4°. W. 1923

Edwards (A. M.) Children in gainful occupations. 4°. Wash. 1924

Financial statistics of cities having population of over 30,000, 1921. 4°. Wash. 1922

Goldenweiser (E. A.) & L. E. Truesdell. Farm tenancy in U.S. [Census monogr. 4.] la8°. Wash. 1924

Mortgages on homes. [Census monogr. 2.] la8°. Wash. 1923

Ross (F. A.) School attendance in 1920: an analysis. [Census monogr., 5.] la8°. Wash. 1924

Rossiter (W. S.) Increase of pop. in U.S., 1910–20. [Census monogr., 1.] 8°. Wash. 1922

Thorp (W. L.) Integration of indust. operation. [Census monogr. 3.] la8°. Wash. 1924

Truesdell (L. E.) Farm population of the U.S.: anal. of 1920 figures &c. [Census monogr., 6.] la8°. Wash. 1926

see NIENBURG (B. M.) Woman home-maker, Rochester, N.Y., 1920, 1923.

Coast Survey.

Davidson (G.) Methods & results. Voyages of discovery &c. on the N.W. coast of America, 1539–1603. [App. No. 7, Rep. 1886.] [P2604.] 4°. W. 1887

Gulf Stream explor.: obs. of currents, 1888–9. Report by J. E. Pillsbury. App. No. 16. 4°. W. 1890

United States [*continued*].

Commerce, Dept. of. [*See also* **Statistics** *below.*]

Annual Conference (1st to 11th) on the weights and measures of the U.S. 1905–16. [*b. in 2v. 8th Ann. Conf. wanting.*] 8°. W. 1906–17

Annual report of the Sec. of Commerce, 1919, 1920. 8°. W. 1919–20

Bur. of Standards, Circular No. 95, Inks. la8°. Wash. 1920

Clements (J. M.) China: automotive condit. & the good roads movement. [P2679]. 8°. Wash. 1922

—— Gold placer area in Mongolia, China. [P2679]. 8°. Wash. 1922

Coblentz (W. W.) Instruments & methods used in radiometry, p1–3. [Bureau of Standards Reprs. 85, 188 & 319. P2704.] la8°. Wash. 1907–18

Condit. of industries in Soviet Russia. Tr. f. the Bolsh. newspaper, Econ. life. [P2679]. 8°. Wash. 1922

Factors in foreign trade. Language, currency, weights, &c. [P2679]. 8°. W. 1912

Ferrin (A. W.) Chinese currency & finance. [P2679]. 8°. W. 1919

Foreign commerce & navig. of the U.S. 1919. 4°. W. 1920

Fowler (J. A.) Cotton-goods markets of the Netherlands E. Indies. [P2679]. 8°. Wash. 1922

French Transportation Act of 1921. Tr. W. C. Huntington. [P2679]. 8°. Wash. 1922

Geringer (V. A.) & E. P. Herman. Commerce & finance in Czechoslovakia. [P2679]. 8°. Wash. 1922

Jones (E. L.) Elements of chart making. 8°. Wash. 1916

Jones (G. M.) Navigation laws: comp. study. Prep. by G. M. J. [P2680]. 8°. W. 1916

Kendall (W. C.) The pikes (app. 5 to Rep. of U.S. Comm. of Fisheries). [P2679]. 8°. Wash. 1917

Lee (F. E.) The Russian co-operative movement. [P2679]. 8°. W. 1920

MacGuire (J. W.) Geog. dict. of the Virgin Islands of the U.S. 8°. W. 1925

Mitchell (W. C.) Internat. price comparisons, by W. C. M., assisted by M. L. Goldsmith & F. K. Middaugh. 8°. W. 1919

Moore (B. F.) Econ. aspects of the commerce &c. of the Netherlands, 1912–18. [P2679]. 8°. W. 1919

Oxholm (A. H.) Forest resources, lumber industry &c. of Norway. [P2679]. 8°. Wash. 1922

Paton (W. A.) The econ. position of the U.K., 1912–18. [P2679]. 8°. W. 1919

Peters (O. S.) Protect. of life & property against lightning. Techn. papers, No. 56. [P2704]. la8°. Wash. 1916

Radcliffe (L.) Caviar. [P2679]. 8°. Wash. 1916

Redfield (A. H.) Brazil: econ. conditions since 1913, by A. H. R., ass. by H. Watkins. [P2679]. 8°. W. 1920

Smith (F. H.) Teak in Siam & Indo-China. [P2679]. 8°. Wash. 1915

Smith (H. B. A.) Representative wages &c. in Gt. Brit. [Trade inform. bull., 91. P2763.] 8°. Wash. 1923

Trade of the U.S. with the world, 1917–8. 2p *in* 1v. 8°. W. 1919

Whitney (E.) Statist. record of progr. of the U.S. 1800–1920, &c. [P2680]. 8°. W. 1920

Wright (A. H.) Frogs: nat. hist. & utilization. [App. 6 to Rep. of U.S. Comm. of Fisheries, 1919. P2680.] 8°. W. 1920

see ARNOLD (J. H.) &c. Commercial hdbk. of China, 2v, 1919–20.
„ ROUMANIA. Rumania: econ. hdbk., 1924.

Congress.

Congressional globe (The): cont. sketches of the debates & proc. of Congress. 23rd–42nd Congress (Dec. 7, 1833–March 3, 1873). [109v *incl.* Indexes *b. sep.*] 4°. Wash. 1835–73
Most vols. have App., *w. sep. pagin. Cont. as* Congressional record, *q.v.*

Congressional record: cont. the proc. & debates of Congress. 43rd–55th Congress (March 4, 1873–July 14, 1897). [165v *incl.* Indexes *b. sep.*] 4°. Wash. 1873–97
Most vols. have App., *w. sep. pagin.*

Journals of the Continental Congress, 1774–89. Ed. f. orig. records in Library of Congress by W. C. Ford [*&* G. Hunt]. v1–25 (1774–83). la8°. Wash. 1904–22

Letters of members of the Continental C., v1–3, 1774–78, 1921–26, *see* BURNETT (E. C.), *ed.*

Consular Reports.

Baker (Henry D.) Brit. India, w. notes on Ceylon &c. [Special C. rep. No. 72.] 8°. W. 1915

Currency & Banks.

Comptroller of the Currency. Annual rep., 1919–27. 8°. Wash. 1920–27

Education.

Annusson (J.) Public instr. in Estonia. Tr. [P2872]. 8°. [Wash. 1926]

Guerrier (E.) The Federal executive depts. as sources of inform. for libraries. [U.S. Bureau of Educ., Bull. 74.] 8°. Wash. 1919

Kandel (I. L.) Educ. in Gt. Brit. & Ireland. [Bull., 1919, No. 9. P2763.] 8°. W. 1919

Pearson (P. H.) Schools of Scandinavia &c. [Bull., 1919, No. 29. P2763.] 8°. W. 1919

United States [*continued*].
Foreign Affairs.
Diplom. corr. betw. the U.S. & bellig. govt. rel. to neutral rights & commerce. [3v. Suppl. to the Amer. journal of internat. law, v9, 1915, v10, 1916, v11, 1917.] 8°. N.Y. 1915–17
Treaties for the advancement of peace betw. the U.S. & o. powers, negot. by the Hon. W. J. Bryan. Intr. by J. B. Scott. [C.E. for Int. Peace.] la8°. N.Y. 1920
Geological [& Geographical] Survey.
Bulletin. No. 360, 611–4. 8°. Wash. 1909–15
360, Pre-Cambrian geology of North Amer.; by C. R. Van Hise & C. K. Leith.
611–4, Guidebook of the Western U.S., *by M. R. Campbell & others*, pA–D. [*By var. wr.*]
Monographs of the U.S.G.S. No. 43, 52. 4°. Wash. 1903–11
see LEITH (C. K.) The Mesabi iron-bearing district of Minnesota, 1903. [43.]
„ VAN HISE (C. R.) & C. K. LEITH. Geology of the Lake Superior region, 1911. [52.]
Interior, Dept. of.
Capen (S. P.) Facilities for for. students in Amer. colleges & univ. [P2680]. 8°. Wash. 1921
Joint report upon the survey & demarcation of the boundary betw. the U.S. & Canada f. the source of the St. Croix River to the St. Lawrence River. [U.S. Dept. of the Interior]. 4°. Wash. 1925
„ „ Triangulation & precise traverse sketches to accomp. Report. 4°. Wash. 1924
Labor, *see also* **Census**, *above*.
Abbott (E.) & S. P. Breckinridge. Admin. of the aid-to-mothers law in Illinois. [P2678]. 8°. Wash. 1921
Bloodgood (R.) Federal courts & the delinquent child. [P2681]. 8°. Wash. 1922
Bulletin of Bureau of L. Statistics. No. 106ii–450. [109, 111, 114, 117, 118, 121–124, 126–131, 133–135, 140, 147, 150, 152, 155, 157, 166, 167, 169, 173, 175, 176, 179, 180, 183, 185, 186, 189, 190, 194, 195, 200, 201, 213, 216, 227, 234, 273, 277, 284 *wanting*]. 8°. Wash. 1912–27
No. 106ii *onwards are divided into series as under:*
Conciliation & arbitration ser. [139, 144, 145, 191, 198, 233, 303, 341].
Employment & unemployment ser. [192, 196, 202, 206, 220, 235, 241, 247, 310, 311, 337, 355, 400, 409, 414].
Foreign labor laws ser. [142].
Indust. accidents & hygiene ser. [120, 141, 165, 188, 205, 207, 209, 219, 221, 230, 231, 236, 251, 253, 256, 267, 276, 280, 291, 293, 298, 306, 339, 392, 405, 425–428].
Indust. rel. & lab. cond. ser. [399].
Labor as affected by the War ser. [237, 249, 255, 283, 287].
Labor laws of U.S. ser. [112, 148i, ii, 211, 224, 229, 244, 246, 257, 258, 285, 290, 292, 308, 309, 321, 322, 330, 343, 344, 370, 391, 403, 408, 417, 434, 444].
Misc. ser. [158, 159, 162, 170, 172, 174, 208, 222, 242, 250, 254, 263, 266, 268, 271, 282, 295, 299, 307, 313, 314, 319, 323, 326, 340, 342, 346, 347, 349, 361, 368, 372, 380, 383, 384, 386, 389, 393, 397, 398, 401, 402, 411, 419, 420, 424, 429, 437, 439, 448, 449].
Productivity of labor. [441].
Retail prices & cost of living ser. [106ii, 108, 110, 113, 115, 125, 132, 136, 138, 156, 164, 184, 197, 228, 270, 300, 315, 334, 357, 366, 369, 396, 418, 445].
Safety code ser. [331, 336, 338, 350, 364, 375, 378, 382, 410, 430, 433, 436, 447].
Vocational education ser. [199].
Wages & hours of labor ser. [137, 143, 146, 151, 153, 154, 161, 163, 168, 171, 177, 178, 187, 204, 214, 218, 225, 232, 238, 239, 245, 252, 259, 260, 261, 262, 265, 274, 278, 279, 286, 288, 289, 294, 297, 302, 305, 316, 317, 324, 325, 327–9, 345, 348, 353, 354, 356, 358, 360, 362, 363, 365, 371, 373, 374, 376, 377, 381, 387, 388, 394, 404, 407, 412, 413, 416, 421, 422, 431, 435, 438, 442, 443, 446, 450].
Wholesale prices ser. [149, 181, 226, 269, 296, 320, 335, 367, 390, 415, 440].
Women in industry ser. [116, 119, 160, 182, 193, 215, 223].
Workmen's insurance & compensation ser. [107, 203, 210, 212, 217, 240, 243, 248, 264, 272, 275, 281, 301, 304, 312, 332, 333, 359, 379, 385, 395, 406, 423, 432].
Child labor in the U.S.: compar. of state & fed. child-labor standards &c. [P2681]. 8°. [Wash. 1923]
Children's Bureau. No. 59 (rev.), 93 (rev.), 106, 113, 115–180. 8°. Wash. 1922–27
Some earlier numbers have been catalogued separately, above & below.
Chute (C. L.) Probation in children's courts. [P2678]. 8°. Wash. 1921
Conf. on juvenile-court standards, Proc. [P2678]. 8°. Wash. 1922
Commissioner of Labor. 10th annual report, 1894. 2v. 8°. W. 1896
10, Strikes & Lockouts.
County organiz. for child care & protect. [P2681]. 8°. Wash. 1922
Economics of the construction industry. [Div. of public works &c.] 8°. Wash. 1919

United States [*continued*].
Labor [*continued*].
The employment-certificate system. [Children's Bureau. P2677]. 8°. Wash. 1919
Flexner (B.) & R. Oppenheimer. Legal aspect of the juvenile court. [P2681]. 8°. Wash. 1922
Healy (W.) Pract. value of scient. study of juvenile delinquents. [P2678]. 8°. Wash. 1922
Hughes (E.) Infant mortality, Gary, Ind. [P2678]. 8°. Wash. 1923
Illegitimacy as a child-welfare problem. p2, Boston & Mass., by E. O. Lundberg & K. F. Lenroot. [P2681]. 8°. Wash. 1921
„ „ *for* p3, *see* Children's Bureau, *above*, No. 128, 1924.
Industrial home work of children. [P2681]. 8°. Wash. 1922
Kalet (A.) Effect of the War on working children in Germany. [*From* Monthly labor review, July 1921. *no tp.* P2677]. 8°. [Wash. 1921]
MacGill (N.) Infant-welfare work in Europe. [P2677]. 8°. Wash. 1921
Marcus (J.) Labor condit. in Porto Rico. [P2679]. 8°. Wash. 1919
Mediat. & arbitrat. laws of the U.S. [P2680]. 8°. Wash. 1913
Negro migration in 1916–17. Reps. by R. H. Leavell, T. R. Snavely &c. Intr. by J. H. Dillard. [P2680]. 8°. Wash. 1919
Paradise (V. I.) Child labor & work of mothers in oyster & shrimp canning, Gulf Coast. [P2678]. 8°. Wash. 1922
Physical standards for working children. [P2678]. 8°. Wash. 1921
Proc. of the 1st Indust. Conference, Oct. 6 to 23, 1919. 8°. Wash. 1920
Reports of the Dept. of Labor: Sec. & Bureaus, 1913–1920. 8°. W. 1914–21
Roberts (L.) Nutrit. & care of children in a mountain co. of Kentucky. [P2681]. 8°. Wash. 1922
Rude (A. E.) Physical status of pre-school children, Gary, Ind. [P2681]. 8°. Wash. 1922
Springer (E. M.) Children deprived of parental care. [P2678]. 8°. Wash. 1921
Standards of legal protect. for children born out of wedlock. [P2678]. 8°. Wash. 1921
Steele (G.) Infant mortality in Pittsburgh, 1920. [P2681]. 8°. Wash. 1921
Sumner (H. L.) & E. E. Hanks. Admin. of child labor laws. [P2677]. 2p. 8°. Wash. 1915–17
Thompson (L. A.) Laws rel. to "mothers' pensions" in U.S., Canada, Denmark, & N. Zealand. [Children's Bureau. Legal ser. No. 4]. 8°. Wash. 1919
Wolfe (S. H.) Care of dependents of enlisted men in Canada. [P2677]. 8°. Wash. 1917
—— Govt. provis. in the U.S. & for. countries for members of milit. forces & th. depend. [P2677]. 8°. Wash. 1917
Women's bureau. Bulletins Nos. 11–60. [*b. in* 5v, 56 *wanting*]. 8°. Wash. 1920–26
see MONTHLY LABOR REVIEW, 1921–.
Laws, Constitution & Arbitration.
The debates in the Fed. Convent. of 1787 wh. framed the constit. of the U.S., 1920, *see* MADISON (J.)
Labor laws, w. decisions of courts, *see* UNITED STATES: LABOR. Bull. 370, 1925.
Laws of the U.S. rel. to loans & the currency, coinage & banking. 8°. Wash. 1886
Laws rel. to payment of wages, *see* UNITED STATES: LABOR. Bull. 408, 1926.
Mediat. & arbitrat. l. of the U.S., 1913, *see* LABOR, *above*.
Revised statutes, 1873–74. 2nd ed. sm. fol. Wash. 1878
„ „ Suppl., 2nd ed., v1, 1874–91. sm. fol. Wash. 1891
Revised statutes rel. to Dist. of Columbia & post roads, 1873–74 &c. sm. fol. Wash. 1875
Statutes at large. v22–[27]. (47th–52nd Congr., Dec. 1881–93). sm. fol. Wash. 1883–93
see BUCKALEW (C. R.) Speech, 1868, upon bill to abolish appell. jurisd. of sup. court in cases of hab. corp. &c.
„ CUMMINGS (J. P.) Argument of C. C. Whittelsey, 1865, on appeal of J. P. C.
„ ELDRIDGE (C. A.) Against employment of the bayonet at the ballot box by C. A. E. &c., 1871.
„ GLOVER (S. T.) Argument of C. C. Whittelsey, 1866, on appeal of S. T. G.
Library of Congress.
Fitzpatrick (J. C.) List of the Washington MSS., 1592–1775. Prepared by J. C. F. 8°. Wash. 1919
Hanson (J. C. M.) Amer. & Eng. genealogies. Comp. under dir. of [H.] la8°. W. 1919
Jacobs (Katharine). A list of Amer. doctoral diss. pr. in 1917, 1918. Prep. by K. J. 8°. W. 1921
MacNair (M. W.) List. of Amer. doctoral diss. pr. in 1919–1926. 8°. Wash. 1921–28
Meyer (H. H. B.) List of ref. on dyestuffs. la8°. W. 1919
—— List of recent ref. on income tax. [P2750]. la8°. Wash. 1921
—— List of ref. on the treaty-making power. Comp. under dir. of M. la8°. W. 1920
—— Sel. list of refs. on economic reconstruction. [P2415]. la8°. W. 1919

United States [*continued*].
Library of Congress [*continued*].
Meyer (H. H. B.) List of ref. on shipping & shipbuilding. Comp. under dir. of M. la8°. Wash. 1919
Phillips (Philip Lee). A list of geograph. atlases in the Lib. of C. Comp. under dir. of P. L. P. v4. la8°. W. 1920
Report of Librarian of C. &c., 1920–27. 8°. Wash. 1920–27
see U.S.: CONGRESS, *above*. Journals of the Continental Congress, 1774–89; ed. f. orig. records in L. of C. by W. C. Ford, v1–25, 1904–22.
Messages of Presidents.
A message of the President (Washington) rel. to France & Gt. Britain, Dec. 5, 1793. 8°. Phila. 1793
Message f. the Presid. of the U.S. to both Houses of Congress [*&* Documents]. 13–20th, 25th Congress. [*b. in* 7v]. 8°. W. 1814–37
Veto Messages of the Presidents of the U.S. w. the action of Congress thereon. la8°. W. 1886
see WILLIAMS (E.) Statesman's manual: pres. messages, 1789–1851, 3v, 1854.
Republican National Convention.
The Reconstruct. epoch. Offic. proc. of the N.R.C. of 1868, 72, 76, 80. repr. 8°. Minneapolis. 1903
Revenue.
Rates of duty on imports into the U.S., 1789–1890, w. statistics. Prep. by the Comm. on Finance. [51st Congress]. 8°. Wash. 1891
Senate.
Eulogies deliv. in Senate on J. C. Calhoun, H. Clay & D. Webster, 1853, *see* FOSTER (T.) & G. COCHRAN, *edd.*
see STEVENSON (J. W.) Speech of J. W. S., 1875, suprem. of const. essential to civil liberty, 1875.
Statistics.
Foreign & domestic commerce. Statistical abstract of the U.S., 1919. 8°. W. 1920
Nimmo (J.) Compar. rates of wages in U.S. & in for. countries. [P2686]. 8°. Wash. 1882
Young (E.) The cost of labor & subsistence in the U.S., 1869, as comp. w. prev. yrs. [P2686]. 8°. Wash. 1870
Surgeon General's Office, *see* **Army,** *above.*
War Dept., *see also* **Army,** *above.*
Annual reports, 1905–13, 1915, 1916. 8°. Wash. 1905–17
No. of vols. & contents vary in diff. years. The following vols. are wanting: 1905, v3, 9; 1906, v1, 2, 4–6; 1907, v5, 6; 1908, v6; 1910, v1, 3, 4; 1911, v1, 3, 4.
Report of the Chief, Div. of Militia Affairs rel. to organized militia of U.S., 1912–15. 8°. Wash. 1912–15
Source-book of milit. law & war-time legis. Prep. by War Dept. Comm. on Educ. & Spec. Training. 8°. St. Paul, Minnesota. 1919
see CROSS (T.) Milit. laws of the U.S. &c., 1825; 1838; 1846.
United States Catalog (The). Books in print, 1912. Ed. M. E. Potter. 3rd ed. 4°. N.Y. 1912
„ „ Suppl.: Books publ. 1912–17. Ed. M. E. Potter&c. 4°. N.Y. 1918
„ „ Suppl.: Books publ. 1918–21. Ed. E. E. Hawkins & E. E. Painter. la8°. N.Y. 1921
„ „ Suppl., 1921–24. Ed. E. E. Hawkins. la8°. N.Y. 1924
United States Christian Commission, *see* Moss (L.) Annals, 1868.
Unity. *The Scriptural u. of the Protestant Churches &c., 1835, *see* SCRIPTURAL.
Universal (A new) history of arts & sciences. 2v. 4°. 1769
Universal Christian Conference on Life & Work, *see* STOCKHOLM. The S. Conf., 1925, 1926.
Universal Races Congress, *see* RACES CONGRESS (UNIV.)
Universities. 3rd Congress of the U. of the Empire, 1926. Rep. of proc. Ed. A. Hill. la8°. 1926
Univ. & th. sons, 5v, 1898–1900, *see* CHAMBERLAIN (J. L.), *ed.*
Universities Bureau of the Empire, *see* YEARBOOK OF THE UNIVERSITIES OF THE EMPIRE.
University College, *Galway.* Cat. of the library of Univ. Coll., Galway. Comp. by V. Steinberger. la8°. Galway. 1913
University College, *London.*
Calendar, 1926/27–1928/29. 8°. 1926–28
Centenary addresses, bound in 1v. By Dr. E. H. Starling, Sir O. Lodge &c. [*each w. sep. tp. & pagin.*] Pref. by R. W. Chambers. 8°. 1927
DEPARTMENT OF APPLIED STATISTICS.
Questions of the day & of the fray. Nos. 9–12 [10 & 11 *in* 1v]. 8°. & la8°. [1914–23]
Pearson (K.) Charles Darwin, 1809–82, 1923. [12.]
—— Francis Galton, 1822–1922, 1922. [11.]
—— Mendelism & the problem of mental defect, 3, 1914. [9.]
—— The science of man: its needs & prospects, 1920. [10.]
see PETRIE (*Sir* W. M. F.) Amulets: illust. by Egypt. Coll. in Univ. Coll., 1914.
„ —— Anc. weights & measures, 1926.
„ —— Buttons & design scarabs, 1925.
University College, *London* [*continued*].
see PETRIE (*Sir* W. M. F.) Glass stamps & weights, 1926.
„ —— Objects of daily use, 1927.
„ —— Prehist. Egypt, 1920.
University College of Wales, *Aberystwyth.*
Aberystwyth Studies. v10. la8°. 1928
see HOWEL, "*the Good.*" The Hywel Dda millen. vol., 1928. [10.]
University of Hokkaido, *see* HOKKAIDO IMPERIAL UNIVERSITY.
Unkovsky (Ivan). Посольство къ зюнгарскому хунъ-тайчжи Цэванъ Рабтану и путевой журналъ, 1722–24. Док. изд. Н. Ив. Веселовскаго. [*From* I.R.G.O. Зап. по отд. этног., т10]. 8°. С.–П. 1887
***Unmasking** (The) of a masse-monger &c., 1626, *see* SUTCLIFFE (M.)
Unpartheyische Kirchenhist. Alten u. Neuen Test. bis 1730 (–1750) [nach d. Methode J. Hübners. T1, 2 *by* J. G. Heinsius, E. Stockmann & J. A. Fabricius, T3 *by* J. A. Fabricius, W. E. Kraft, C. W. Becker & J. C. Mylius]. 3T *in* 4v. [T3, 1730–50]. 4°. Jena. 1735–54
***Unreality:** a romance, 1920, *see* BARTIMEUS, *ps.*
Unruh (Fritz v.) Flügel d. Nike: Buch e. Reise. 8°. Frankfurt a. M. 1925
The way of sacrifice. [Tr. C. A. Macartney]. s8°. 1928
Unschuldige Nachrichten v. alt. u. neu. theolog. Sachen, 1701–19. s8°. L. 1701–19
1701 *has title* Altes u. neues aus d. Schatz theolog. Wissenschaften, *& was pr. at Wittenberg.*
„ „ *contin. as* Fortgesetzte Sammlung v. alt. u. neu. theolog. Sachen, 1720–50. s8°. L. 1720–50
„ „ *contin. as* Neue Beyträge v. alt. u. neu. theolog. Sachen, 1751–61. s8°. L. 1751–61
„ „ Vollständige Register, 1701–10; 1711–20; 1721–30; 1731–40; 1741–50. [5v]. s8°. L. 1721–55
see AMMON (J. C.) Kernhaffter Auszug d. besten &c. Schrifften &c. aus d. 40 B. de U. N., 5T, 1745–58.
„ BORNIUS (B.) Neueröffnete Schatz-Kammer aller theol. Wiss. aus d. unschuld. Nachr. fortgesetzten Samml. &c., 4T, 1746–47.
„ FRÜHAUFGELESENE Früchte d. theol. Sammlung. v. Alten u. Neuen &c., 1735–41.
„ LANGE (J.) Auffricht. Nachricht v. d. Unrichtigkeit d. sog. U. N., &c., 1707–8.
„ THEOLOG. ANNALES, 1701–50, *epitome of* U. N., 5B, 1715–54.
Unselt (Daniel Joannes). Disputatio de chao mundi. s4°. Vitembergæ. [c. 1725]
Unstead (John Frederick) & E. G. R. Taylor. General & regional geography for students. 5th ed. 8°. 1916
Unter englischem Feuer: Zerstör. in Flandern u. Nordfrankreich. obl. s8°. [1918]
Untermeyer (Louis). Modern American poetry. 8°. [1921]
Mod. Brit. poetry. Ed. L. U. s8°. N.Y. 1920
Unterricht d. Visitatorn an die Pfarhern ym Kurfürstenthum zu Sachssen, *see* SAXONY. Visitation of Saxon Ref. Church, 1527–28; *ed.* R. Laurence, 1839.
Untersuchung. *Histor. &c. U. d. Uhrsachen [*sic*] durch welche d. zw. Dennemarck u. Schweden vorgefall. Streitigkeiten &c., 1715, *see* AMTHOR (C. H.)
Untersuchungen. Unters. über Konsumvereine. [V. f. Sozialpol., B150ii–v, 151iii]. 8°. München. 1919–24
150ii, Russland; v. B. Totomianz; mit e. Geleitwort v. R. Wilbrandt.
150iii, Holland, Japan, Österreich u. d. Schweiz; v. G. J. W. C. Goedhart &c.
150iv, Deutschland; v. T. O. Cassau.
150v, Frankreich u. in d. Ver. Staaten; v. C. Gide u. J. P. Warbasse—Der Internat. Genossenschaftsbund; v. B. Totomianz.
151iii, Der Stand d. Gesetzgeb. ü. Erwerbs- u. Wirtschaftsgenossenschaften bei Kriegsanbruch 1914; v. L. Waldecker.
Unters. ü. Preisbildung. [V. f. Sozialpol., B145iv, 146i, ii]. 8°. München. 1915–20
Abt. C. [3], Löhne u. Lebenskosten in Westeuropa im 19. J., v. C. v. Tyszka.
„ [4], Ost- u. Norddeutschland, T2; m. Beitr. v. E. Meyer-Pollack &c.
„ [5], Lebenskosten in d. Schweiz; m. Beitr. v. E. Ackermann &c., hrsg. v. S. Bauer.
„ [6], Lebenshalt. d. Mittelstandes, v. A. Gunther; Beitr. v. H. Neumann.
Unwerth (Wolf v.) Proben deutschruss. Mundarten aus d. Wolgakolonien u. d. Gouvt. Cherson, *see* KÖNIGL. PREUSS. AKAD. Abhdl. (Phil.-hist. Kl.), 1918.
—— **& T. Siebs.** Gesch. der deut. Lit. bis zur Mitte d. 11ten Jhdts. [Grundriss d. deut. Literaturgesch., 1]. 8°. 1920

Unwin (George), *lect., Univ. of Edinburgh.* S. Oldknow & the Arkwrights: Indust. revol. at Stockport & Marple. By G. U., w. chaps. by A. Hulme & G. Taylor. [Univ. of M'ter.] 8°. M'ter. 1924
Studies in econ. hist.: coll. papers. Ed. w. intr. mem. by R. H. Tawney. 8°. 1927
Unwin (Stanley). The truth about publishing. 8°. [1926]
Unwin (William Cawthorne).
Short logarithmic & o. tables. 6th ed. 8°. 1917
Upanishads. 60 Upanishad's d. Veda. Übers., Einleit. &c. v. P. Deussen. 3e A. 8°. L. 1921
The 13 princ. U. Tr. f. the Sanskrit, w. an outline of the philos. of the U. & an annot. bibliogr., by R. E. Hume. 8°. O. 1921
see KEITH (*Sir* A. B.) Relig. & philos. of Veda & U., 2v, 1925.
„ RADHAKRISHNAN (S.) Phil. of the U., 1924.
Uparpilli. Inscriptions at Uparpilli, *see* HYDERABAD Arch. Ser., No. 3, 1919.
Upcher (Arthur Charles Wodehouse), *see* HINGHAM. Hist. of H., Norfolk &c. [pref. by U.], 1921.
Up De Graff (Fritz W.) Head-hunters of the Amazon. Intr. R. B. C. Graham. 8°. 1923
Updike (Daniel Berkeley). Printing types: hist., forms & use. [repr.] 2v. 8°. Camb. [*Mass.*] 1927
Uppström (Andreas), *ed., see* BIBLE: ANGLO-SAXON & GOTHIC. Codex argenteus, 1854–57.
Upright (Blanche). The valley of content. s8°. [1924]
Upsala.
KONGL. UNIVERSITET I U.
U. Univ. Matrikel, höstterminen 1926, av T. Fries & E. v. Döbeln. 8°. Uppsala. 1927
see KUNG. HUM. VET.-SAMF. I U. Skr., B24, Festskr. tilläg. U. U. vid. d. 450-årsjubileum, 1927.
Upton (Charles Barnes).
Dr. Martineau's philosophy: a survey. rev. ed. 8°. 1905
Upton (Florence K.), *see* LYTTELTON (E. S.) F. U., painter, 1926.
Upton (George P.), *see* SHEAHAN (J. W.) & G. P. U. Great conflagration: Chicago &c., 1871.
Upton (Jacob Kendrick). Money in politics. Intr. by E. Atkinson. s8°. Boston. [1885]
Ur excavations. v1, Al-'Ubaid. Rep. on work for B.M., 1919, & for Joint Exped. [B.M. & Mus. of Univ. of Penn.], 1923–24. By H. R. Hall & C. L. Woolley. With ch. by C. J. Gadd & Sir A. Keith. sm. fol. 1927
Urban II, *pope, see* LEIB (B.) Rome, Kiev & Byzance; rapports relig. des Latins &c. sous U. II, 1088–99. 1924.
Urban VIII, *pope.* *Passionate remonstrance upon the late proc. & gt. Covenant of Scotland &c., w. reply of Card. De Barbarini &c. [*satire,* 1641), *see* AUNGERVYLE SOC. Reprints, s2, 1884.
Suppressio prætensæ congreg. Jesuit. [13 Jan. 1631]. s4°. [Romae]. 1636
„ „ *for a. ed., see* SCHOPPE (C.) Rel., 1636; 1641.
Urban (J.) De iis quae theologici catholici praestare possint ac debeant erga eccl. Russicam. [P2424]. 8°. Pragae. 1907
Urbani (Giuseppe Marino). Guida d. Scuola di S. Giovanni Evangelista in Venezia. [P2844]. 8°. Venezia. 1895
La "Nuova Sirena" [Faustina Bordoni Hasse] e il "Caro Saffone" [G. A. Hasse], note biogr. 8°. Venezia. 1890
Urbanitzky (Grete v.), *ps.* [*i.e.* G. PASSINI]. Das andere Blut: Roman. [3. bis 7. Taus.] s8°. L. 1920
Urbano *da Cortona, see* SCHUBRING (P.) U. da C.: Beitr. z. Kenntnis d. Schule Donatellos &c., 1903.
Urbevetanae. Ephemerides U. dal Cod. Vaticano Urbinate 1745 (1342–69); a cura di L. Fumi, v1, *see* MURATORI (L. A.) Rerum Ital. Scr., t15v, 1920.
Urbiciani (Bonagiunta), *da Lucca* [ORBICCIANI], *see* LUISO (F. P.) Per la biog. di B. O., 1927.
Urbinas. Tractatus U., *see* KOSTER (W. J. W.), *ed.* Tract. Graeci, 1922.
Urbini (Giulio). Le chiese perugine del medioevo e del rinascimento. s8°. Firenze. 1922
Urbino (Guidobaldo II, *duke of*), *see* GUIDOBALDO II, *d. of Urbino.*
Urbiola (J. Sinués y), *see* SINUÉS Y URBIOLA (J.)
Ure (James) *of Shargarton.* Rising at Bothwell bridge (1679), *see* †VEITCH (W.) Memoirs, 1825.
Ure (Percy Neville). The Greek renaissance. s8°. [1921]
The origin of tyranny. 8°. C. 1922
Venizelos & h. fellow-countrymen, *see* ANGLO-HELLENIC LEAGUE. Publ^s., No. 30, 1917.

Urechiĕ (Grigoriŭ) [URECHI (GRÉGOIRE)]. Chronique de Moldavie dep. le milieu du 14e s. j. 1594. Texte roumain, avec tr. fr., notes &c. par E. Picot. la8°. 1878
Ureña (Pedro Henriquez), *see* HENRIQUEZ UREÑA (P.)
Urfé (Honoré d'). Astrea. Tr. by a person of quality. [*Pref. signed* J. D.] 3v [*in 1, tp. of v1 mutilated*]. sm. fol. 1657–58
L'Astrée de H. d'Urfé. [Bibl. Romanica. Publ. par H. Vaganay]. p1 (Livres 1–12) *in* 3v. s8°. [Strasbourg. 1921]
L'Astrée. n. éd., publ. par H. Vaganay. Préf. de L. Mercier. p1–4. 8°. Lyon. 1925–27
see BONAFOUS (N. A.) Etudes sur l'Astrée & sur H. d'U., 1846.
„ MAGENDIE (M.) Du nouv. sur l'Astrée, 1927.
Urgeschichte. *Zur Urgesch. d. Armenier, 1854, *see* LAGARDE (P. A. DE).
Uri (Johannes).
Pharus artis gram. Heb. [P543]. 8°. Oxonii. 1784
Uribe Angel (Manuel). Geogr. gen. y compendio hist. del estado de Antioquia en Colombia. la8°. Paris. 1885
Uriburu (José Evaristo).
Hist. del Gen. Arenales, 1770–1831. la8°. Londres. 1924
Uriendt (Justa de), *see* FORNEAU (J. DE).
Urkunden. Urkunden d. deut. Könige u. Kaiser. Hrsg. v. d. Gesellschaft f. Ält. Deut. Geschichtskunde. B5, T1, 8. 4°. 1926–27
5i, Heinrich III, 1039–47; hrsg. H. Bresslau.
8, Die Urkunden Lothars III u. d. Kaiserin Richenza; hrsg. E. v. Ottenthal u. H. Hirsch.
Urkunden-Regesten aus d. Klöster Böhmens, 1901, *see* SCHUBERT (A.)
Urkunden u. Aktenstücke z. Gesch. d. inn. Politik d. Kurfürsten Fr. Wilhelm v. Brandenburg, T1i, 2, 1895–1908, *see* FREDERICK WILLIAM, *elector of Brandenburg.*
Urkundenbuch d. Univ. Wittenberg, T1, 2, 1926–27, *see* WITTENBERG UNIVERSITY.
Urquhart (David). The Abyssinian War. [P745]. 8°. 1868
Ad summum pontificem ut jus gentium restauretur appellatio. Lat. redd. 8°. Londini. 1869
The rebellion of India. [P2858]. 8°. 1857
Urquiza (Justo José de), *president of the Argentine Republic.* Urquiza, el juicio de la posteridad. [*Comp. by* M. Leguizamón. [Comisión Nac. del Homenaje]. 2p [*pagin. cont.*] la8°. Buenos Aires. 1921
Ursachen des Zusammenbruchs: Entst. &c. d. Offensive v. 1918, 1923, *see* GERMANY: REICHSTAG.
Ursachenn warumb das Concilium so Paulus III ausgeschriben &c., 1537, *see* SCHMALKALD, *League,* 1531–1537.
Urseau (Charles). Le tombe de l'évêque Ulger à la cath. d'Angers, *see* ACAD. DES INSCR.: FOND. PIOT. Mons. & méms., t28, 1925–26.
Ursin (Johann Heinrich). De eccl. Germanic. orig. et progr. ad Carolum Magnum. s8°. Norimbergae. 1664
Von d. Zustand d. glaubigen Seelen welche durch d. zeitl. Todt in warem Glauben &c. abgeschieden &c. s8°. Franckfurt am Mayn. 1663
Ursinus (Joachimus), *ps., see* BERINGER (J.)
Ursinus (Zacharias). Opera theolog. tributa in tres tomos. Ed. studio Q. Reuteri. [*Foll. by* Misc. catechetica D. Parei *w. sep. pag.*] 3t *b. in* 1v. fol. Heidelbergae. 1612
Comm. on the Heidelberg Catechism. Tr. G. W. Williard. 3rd Amer. ed. la8°. Cincinnati. [1851]
Corpus doctrinæ orthodoxæ. Opus D. Parei opera recogn. Adj. Misc. catechet. [*w. sep. tp. & pag.*] ed. nova. s8°. Heidelbergae. 1612
The summe of Xtian religion &c. Tr. by H. Parry. s8°. O. 1589
see HEIDELBERG CATECHISM. Catechismus &c., item.: Antwort auf 6 Fragen, durch Z. U., 1596.
Ursuline (The) manual or a coll. of prayers &c. s8°. D. 1835
Ursyn-Pruszyński (*Ritter* v.)
Die Japan. Armee im Jahre 1910. 8°. Wien. 1910
Urtheil. *Geistliches Urtheil v. Lotterie-Wesen &c., 1723, *see* GEISTLICHES.
Uruch Beg, *aft. Don Juan of Persia, see* JUAN (*Don*) *of Persia.*
Uruguay. Anuario estadístico de la Rep. Or. del U. Lib. 27–34 (1917–25). 4°. Montevideo. 1919–27
Urwick (Edward Johns). The message of Plato. Re-interp. of the "Republic." 8°. [1920]
A philosophy of social progress. 2nd ed. rev. 8°. [1920]
The social good. 8°. [1927]
Usener (Hermann), *see* DIETERICH (A.) H. U., 1905.

Uses (The) of libraries [lect.]; ed. E. A. Baker, *see* BAKER (E. A.)

Usher (Abbot Payson).
Intr. to the indust. hist. of England. 8°. [1921]

Usher (James), *abp., see* USSHER (J.)

Usher (James M.), *see* BROOKS (C.) Hist. of Medford, Mass., 1630–1855; rev., enl. &c. to 1885 by J. M. U., 1886.

Uspensky (A. I.) В. М. Васнецовъ. 8°. Москва. 1906

Uspensky (P. D.) [OUSPENSKY]. Tertium organum: a key to the enigmas of the world. Tr. N. Bessaraboff & C. Bragdon, w. intr. by C. B. 8°. Rochester, N.Y. 1920

Uspensky (Porfiry). Путешествіе въ Метеорскіе и Осоолимпійскіе монастыри въ Θессаліи. Изд. Имп. Акад. Наук подъ ред. П. А. Сырку. 4°. С.-П. 1896

Uspensky (V. M.) О бассейнѣ Лобъ-Нора. [I.R.G.O. Записки по отдѣл. этнограф., 6i]. 8°. С.-П. 1880
Страна Кукэ-норъ, съ прибавленіемъ ист. Ойратовъ и Монголовъ. [I.R.G.O. Записки по отдѣл. этнограф., 6ii]. 8°. С.-П. 1880

Ussani (Vicenzo), *see* DANTE ALIGHIERI. Lectura D., D. e Lucano; conf. da V. U., 1917.

Ussel [UISEL]. Les poésies des 4 troubadours d'Ussel. [Guy, Eble, Elias & Pierre d'Ussel]. Publ. d'ap. les MSS. par J. Audiau. s8°. 1922

Ussher (James), *bp. of Meath; abp. of Armagh, 1581–1656.*
Annales Vet. Test. una cum rerum Asiatic. & Ægypt. chronico. 2p *in* 1t. sm. fol. 1650
A body of divinity or the summe &c. of Christian religion. Adj. Immanuel or the mystery of the incarnation of the Son of God &c. sm. fol. 1649
Britannic. eccl. antiq. Inserta est pestiferae à Pelagio in Eccl. inductae haereseos hist. Acc. Graviss. quaestionis de Christ. eccl. successione &c. histor. explicatio *w. sep. pagin. & tp.* fol. Londini. 1687
Chronologia sacra—De Macedonum & Asian. anno solari, *see* PETAU (D.) Rationarium temporum, 1741.
Gotteschalci, & praedestinationae controv. ab eo motae, hist. &c. s8°. Dublinii. 1631
Orig. &c. instit. of Corbes, Erenachs, & Termon lands, 1609, *see* VALLANCEY (C.) Coll. de rebus Hibernicis, v1, 1774.
Veterum epistol. Hibernic. sylloge. s4°. Herbornæ Nassov. 1696
see ELRINGTON (C. R.) The life of J. U., w. acc. of h. wr., 1848.
,, HOYLE (J.) Rejoynder to Master Malone's reply [to J. U.] conc. Reall Presence, 1641.
,, JACKSON (T.) Lib. of Xtn. biog., v. 12, J. U., by N. Bernard, 1840.

Ussher (Percy Arland), *see* MERRIMAN (B.) The midnight court [*by* B. M.] & The adv. of a luckless fellow [*by* D. Macnamara]; tr. f. Gaelic by P. A. U., 1926.

Ussher (William Augustus Edward).
The following works are Mem[s]. of the Geol. Survey.
Geol. of co. around Exeter, w. notes on petrology by J. J. H. Teall. 8°. 1902
Geol. of co. around Ivybridge &c., w. chap. on altered rocks, by G. Barrow. 8°. 1912
Geol. of co. around Kingsbridge &c. 8°. 1904
Geol. of co. around Plymouth &c., w. notes on petrology by J. S. Flett. 8°. 1907
Geol. of co. around Newton Abbot. With contribs. by C. Reid &c. [*b. w.* Reid (C.) Geol. of Dartmoor, 1912]. 8°. 1913
Geol. of co. around Torquay. 8°. 1903
Geol. of parts of N. Lincs. & S. Yorks. By U. [*& others*]. 8°. 1890
Geol. of the Quantock Hills, Taunton & Bridgwater. 8°. 1908

Ussher (William Augustus Edward), G. Barrow & D. A. MacAlister. Geol. of the co. around Bodmin & St. Austell. [*b. w.* Reid (C.) &c. Geol. of Land's End, 1907]. 8°. 1909

Ustryalov (Nikolai Gerasimov). Именитые люди Строгановы. [*includ.* Жалов. граммата Г. Д. Строганову, 1692]. 8°. С.-П. 1842

***Usurpation** (De l') & de la révolution, 1825, *see* ROUGEMONT (DE).

Utenbogaert (Johannes) [WTENBOGAERT]. Brieven en onuitg. stukken, 1584[–1644]. Verzameld en met aanteeken. uitg. door H. C. Rogge. [Hist. Genoots. Werken, N.S., 11, 12, 15, 17, 19, 20, 22]. 3d [*in* 7p, 2i, ii, 3i–iv]. 8°. Utrecht. 1868–75

Utenhove (Jan). Simplex & fidelis narr. de instituta ac demum dissipata Belgarum aliorumque peregrinorum in Anglia eccl. &c. [*With short pref. by J. a Lasco*]. s8°. [Basileæ]. 1560

Utevsky (L. S.) Смерть Тургенева, 1883–1923. s8°. П. 1923

Utrecht.
Acta & decreta secundae synodi prov. Ultraject., 1763. s8°. Ultrajecti. 1764
*Actes, mém. & autres pièces authent. conc. la paix d'U. [*Sometimes attrib. to* C. Freschot]. 6t [t1, 2e éd., augm. & corrig.] s8°. Utrecht. 1713–15
De registers & rekeningen van het Bisdom U., 1325–36. [Schuldregister &c. v. Hubert v. Budel]. Uitg. door S. Muller. [Hist. Genoots. Werken., N.S. 53, 54]. 2d. 8°. Utrecht [d2, 'sGravenhage]. 1889–91
Rekeningen van het bisdom U., 1378–1573. Uitg. K. Heeringa. [Hist. Genootschap te Utrecht. Werken, s3, 50]. d1, 2 stuk [*pagin. cont.*] 8°. Utrecht. 1926
Resolutiën van de Vroedschap van U. betref. de Academie. Uitg. door J. A. Wijnne & L. Miedema. [Hist. Genoots. Werken, N.S., 52]. 8°. Utrecht. 1900
Verslagen van kerkvisitatiën in het bisdom U. uit de 16de eeuw. Uitg. door F. A. L. ridder Van Rappard & S. Muller. [Hist. Genoots. Werken, s3, 29]. 8°. A. 1911

Utrillo (Maurice).
see CARCO (F. C.) La légende & la vie d'U., 1928.
,, —— M. U., reprod. de peintures &c. & ét. crit., 1921.

Utzinger (Alexander). Notwendige Errinnerung v. d. grossen Abfalle u. geringer bestendigkeit, so sich newlich in d. Fränck. Verfolgung ereugnet. Erörterung 4 fürnemer Fragen &c. s4°. [Schmalkalden]. 1588
see SCHERER (G.), *Jesuit.* Antwort auff d. Lästercharten A. U. wider Julium Bischoff. z. Würzburg &c. aussgeworffen, 1589.

Utzinger (Rudolf). Masken. [Orbis pictus; hrsg. P. Westheim, 13]. la8°. [1922 ?]

Utzschneider (Simon), *publ., see* BIBLE: PSALMS. Harpffen Davids mit Teutschen Saiten &c., 1669.

Uvarova (*countess* **Praskovya Sergeevna).**
Сборникъ статей въ честь гр. П. С. У. [1885–1915. *By var. a. Intr. by D. N. Anuchin*]. la8°. [Москва. 1916]

Uxkull (*Baron* **Woldemar v.)**
Lucie Bertier. Roman. s8°. Dresden. 1920

Uxkull-Gyllenband (*Graf* **Woldemar).**
Frühgriech. Plastik. [Orbis Pictus, 3]. la8°. [1920]
Griech. Kultur-Entstehungslehren. [Beilage zu H3/4 d. Archivs f. Gesch. d. Philos., B36. Bibl. f. Philos., B26]. 8°. 1924

Uzanne (Octave). Pietro Longhi. s8°. [1924]

Uzielli (Gustavo). Piero di Andrea Strozzi, viaggiatore fiorentino. [*No tp.; extr. f.* Soc. Geogr. Ital., Mem., v5, 1895. P2686]. 8°. [1895]
Richerche intorno a L. da Vinci. s2. 8°. 1884

Uzureau (*l'abbé* **François Constant),** *see* DENIAU (F.) Hist. de la guerre de la Vendée; t5, 6, par D., U. &c., 1911–12.

V

"V," *ps., see* GARVIN (*Mrs.* J. L.)

V. (*le sieur* **A. D.),** *see* AUBERT DE VERSÉ (NOËL).

V. (L.) *The language & sentiment of flowers, 1866, *see* FLOWERS.

V* (M.)** *Joujou (Le) des demoiselles, augm. de plusieurs contes de M. V***, 1773, *see* JOUJOU.

V* (M. D.)** *Lettres écr. de Londres sur les Anglois, 1734, *see* VOLTAIRE.

V. (S. M.) *Christianismi restitutio, 1553, repr., *n.d.*, *see* SERVETUS (M.)

Vacandard (*l'abbé* **E.)** Abélard, sa lutte avec St. Bernard, sa doctrine, sa méthode. s8°. 1881
St. Victrice. 2e éd. s8°. 1903

Vacant (Jean Michel Alfred), *see* DICTIONNAIRE. D. de théologie catholique, dir. de A. V., cont. de E. Mangenot, t6–8, 1920–25.

Vacarius, *magister.* Lib. pauperum; ed. F. de Zulueta, *see* SELDEN Soc., v44, 1927.
see WENCK (C. F. C.) Magister Vacarius primus juris Romani in Anglia professor, 1820.

Vaccari (Antonio), *see* Béguinot (A.) & A. V. Contrib. [*& 2o* contrib.] alla flora d. Libia, 1912–13.

Vaccaro (Mich. Angelo). La lotta per l'esistenza e i suoi effetti nell' umanità. 5a ed. 8o. Torino. 1921

Vaccarone (Luigi). Bianca Maria di Challant e il suo corredo, *see* Regia Dep. di Storia Patria. Misc., t35, 1898.

Emanuele Filiberto, pr. di Piemonte, alla Corte Cesarea di Carlo V imp. (1545–51), *see* Regia Dep. Misc., t36, 1900.

Vachell (Horace Annesley).

Blinkers. s8o. [1921]
Change partners. s8o. [1922]
Dew of the sea & o. s. s8o. [1927]
Fellow-travellers. 8o. 1923
The fourth dimension. s8o. 1920
Leaves from Arcady. s8o. [1924]
Miss Torrobin's experiment. s8o. [1927]
Quinney's adventures. s8o. [1924]
Watling's for worth. s8o. [1925]
Whitewash. s8o. [1920]
The Yard. s8o. [1923]

—— **& A. Marshall.** Mr. Allen. s8o. [1926]

Vacquerie (Auguste). Jean Baudry. n. éd. s8o. 1881

Vadianus (Joachim) [†Watt (J. von)]. Epitome trium terrae partium, Asiae, Africae et Europae compendiariam locorum descr. cont. præcipue quorum in Actis Lucas &c. meminere. Acc. tabulæ. s8o. Tiguri *apud Frosch.* [1535]

Pro veritate carnis triumphantis Christi &c. s8o. Tiguri *apud Frosch.* [1541]

see Götzinger (E.) J. V., d. Reformator u. Geschichtsschr. v. St. Gallen, 1895.

Vadius, *see* Wade.

Vadivelu (A.) The aristocracy of South. India. 8o. Madras. 1903

Vaenius (Otho), *see* Veen (Otto van).

Vaerini (Barnaba). Gli scrittori di Bergamo d. famiglie Medolago e Tasso. Pubbl. A. Alessandri. [Nozze Medolago—Calori. N123]. la8o. Bergamo. 1873

Væsarti (Agellius). Chronicon propheticum a resurr. Christi ex musæo A. V. [*Foll. by* Methodus introd. in veram Danielis expos. *pagin. cont.*] s8o. Amstelodami. 1682

Vaeth (Joseph Anthony). Tirant lo Blanch. St. of its authorship, sources &c. [Columbia Univ.] 8o. N.Y. 1918

Vagabond songs & ballads of Scotland, 1899, *see* Ford (R.)

Vaganay (Hugues). Pour l'hist. du Français mod., *see* Roman. Forsch., B32, 1913.

Vagantenlieder aus d. lat. Dichtung d. 12. u. 13. Jhdts. &c., 1927, *see* Carmina Burana.

Vagnone (Filippo), *poeta laureato, d. 1499, see* Bosio (*il cav.* A.) Due mon. ined. d. Piemonte illust. (Urna sepolcr. di F. V. &c.), 1874.

Vagnoni (Antonio), *d. 1640, see* Sforza (C.) Un missionario e sinologo piemont. in Cina: A. V., 1906.

Vahan, *of Golthn (Koghthen), d. 737.* Martyrdom, *see* Armenia. Lamentations for the ills of A. *in Armenian,* 1854.

Vahl (Martin). Growth-forms of some plant-formations of S. Norway, *see* Kong. Dan. Vid. Selsk., Biol. Med., B1, 1917–19.

Vahlen (Johann). Gesammelte philol. Schriften. T2. la8o. L. 1923

Vaihinger (Hans). Die Philos. des Als Ob. Mit Anhang ü. Kant u. Nietzsche. 8o. 1911

,, ,, ...Volksausgabe. s8o. L. 1923

The philosophy of "As if." Tr. C. K. Ogden. 8o. 1924

Vaillant, *French poet, c. 1450, see* Winkler (E.) Französ. Dichter d. M.-a., 1, V., 1918.

Vaillant (A.), *see* Meillet (A.) & A. V. Gramm. de la langue serbo-croate, 1924.

Vaillant-Couturier (Paul), *see* Maxe (J.) Cahiers de l'anti-France, 4, "Clarté," s. initiateurs, V.-C. &c., 1922.

Vaillat (Léandre). La femme inconnue. s8o. [1922]

—— **& P. Ratouis de Limay.** J. B. Perronneau, 1715–83, sa vie & s. œuvre. 2e éd. rev. & augm. la8o. 1923

Vaina (Eugenio). La nazione albanese. 2a ed. aumentata d'uno scritto di G. d'Acandia su E. V. &c. 8o. Catania. 1917

Vair (Gabrielle), *see* Grimpret (B.) & G. V. Etudiantes, 1921.

Vairasse (Denis) [Veiras (D.)], *see* Lachèvre (F.) Les successeurs de Cyrano de Bergerac [D. V. &c.], 1922.

Vaisons (*le cte.* **de**), *see* Aubry (O.) Le roi perdu (Louis XVII retrouvé: mém. inéd. du Cte. de V.; publ. [*or rather wr. by* O. A.], 1924.

Vaissière (Pierre de). L'affaire du Maréchal de Marillac, 1630–32. Préf. de F. Funck-Brentano. 8o. 1924

Messieurs de Joyeuse (1560–1615). 8o. [1926]

Vajirañāṇa National Library. [*Publications*].

see Batavia. Dutch papers: extr. f. the "Dagh register," 1624–42, 1915.

,, Burney (*Capt.* H.) Burney papers [1822–49], v1–5i, 1910–14.

,, Crawfurd (J.) C. papers: mission to Siam, 1821, 1915.

,, Siam. Records of the rel. betw. S. & for. countries in 17th c., 5v, 1915–21.

,, Turpin (F. R.) Hist. of Siam; tr. by B. O. Cartwright, 1908.

Vaka (Demetra) [*Mrs.* Kenneth Brown].

The heart of the Balkans. s8o. Boston. 1917

Valadon (*Mme.* **Suzanne),** *see* Rey (R.) S. V.: 28 reprod., préc. d'une ét. crit., 1922.

Valbuena (Bernardo de), *bp. of Porto Rico, see* Balbuena.

Valck (Gerard), *see* Valk (G.)

Valcombe (Madeleine de). Métempsycose. . . . Hist. mauresque. Suppl. au Monde nouveau du 1 Oct. 1922. s8o. 1922

Valdagne (Pierre).

Constance, ma tendre amie. Roman. s8o. [1922]

Variations sur le même air. Roman. s8o. 1896

Works in Œuvres libres.

Constance, ma tendre amie, 1922. [9.]
Pour sauver Francis, 1926. [61.]
Le rétour à la maison, 1927. [76.]
Le secret qui démange, 1921. [3.]
Si jeunesse savait . . . 47, 1925. [47.]
Une vie de patachon, roman, 1923. [27.]

Valdenebro y Cisneros (José Maria de). La imprenta en Córdoba: ensayo bibliog. la8o. 1900

Valdenses, *see* Waldenses.

Valdés (A. P.) [†Palacio Valdes (Armando)].

Los cármenes de Granada. Novela. s8o. [1927]

Santa Rogelia (de la leyenda de oro). s8o. 1926

see Olmet (L. A. de) & J. de Torres Bernal. Los grandes Españoles, [v11], P. V., 1919.

Valdés (Juan de), *the Spanish reformer, see* Heep (J.) J. de V., s. Relig., s. Werden &c., 1909.

Valdesio (Ferdinando), *ps., see* Muratori (L. A.)

Valdés Leal (Juan de). Exposición V. L. y de arte retrospectivo, Sevilla, Mayo, 1922. Catálogo. la8o. Sevilla. 1923

Valdivia (Francisco Triviño), *see* Triviño Valdivia (F.)

Valdivia (Pedro de), *see* Graham (R. B. C.) P. de V., conqueror of Chile, 1926.

Vale (Charles). The spirit of St. Louis. 100 poems. Ed. C. V. 8o. N.Y. [1927]

Vale (Edmund). By shank & by crank. 8o. E. 1924

Valence. Chartes de l'église de V., *see* Vienne. Chartes de St.-Maurice de V. &c.; publ. U. Chevalier, 1912.

Valencia de Don Juan, Inst. de, *see* Instituto de Valencia de Don Juan, *Madrid.*

Valencia de Don Juan (*conde Vdo* **de).** Cat. hist.-descr. de la Real Armería de Madrid. sm. fol. 1898

Valendàs (Hans Eduard v. Berlepsch-), *see* Berlepsch-Valendàs.

Valens (Petrus). M. Paulli Boudot Burgundi laurus theologica. [P2510]. s8o. Parisiis. 1604

Valensi (R.-H.), *see* Clouzot (H.) & R.-H. V. Le Paris de la Comédie humaine, 1926.

Valentia (Gregarius de), *Jesuit.*

Apologia de S. S. missae sacrificio adv. cavillationes J. Herbrandi &c. s8o. Ingolstadii. 1581

Confut. calumniarum, quas Heerbrandus Spongia quadam sua, ut appellat, complexus est, & in Apologeticum de idolatria, effudit. s4o. Ingolstadii. 1579

Contra fundamenta duarum sectarum Ubiquetariæ & Sacramentariæ pro vera Christi præsentia disputatio. s4o. Ingolstadii. 1582

De sacrosancto missae sacrificio contra impiam disput. Tubingę nuper à J. Herbrando propositam &c. [*b. w. h.* Apologia, 1581]. s8o. Ingolstadii. 1580

Redargutio inscitiarum & fraudum, quibus nonnulli theologi &c. Genev. subsidarii A. Sadeelis itemque F. Crellius, eum librum cavillati sunt &c. s4o. Ingolstadii. 1590

see Heerbrand (J.) Explic. causarum cur cum G. de Valentia non sit disputandum, 1580.

,, —— Refut. tract. G. de V. de prophana missa pontificia, 1581.

,, Osiander (A.), *the younger.* Apologia contra mendacia &c. cujusdam Ingolstad. [*i.e. G. de V.*], 1595.

,, —— Defensio Responsi ad Analysin G. V., 1594.

,, —— Resp. ad Analysin G. V. de ecclesia, 1593.

Valentin, *bp. of Hildesheim, see* Teutleben (Valentin).

Valentine (Charles Wilfrid), *see* Gill (C.) Govt. & people; by C. G. w. collab. of C. W. V., 1921.

Valentine (Douglas), *see* Williams (V.)

Valentinelli (Giuseppe). Diplomatarium Portusnaonense (1276–1514) &c.; cura J. V., *see* Fontes rerum Austriac., B24, 1865.

Specimen bibliog. de Dalmatia et Agro Labeatium. 8º. Venetiis. 1842

Valentiner (Max). 300,000 Tonnen versenkt! Meine U-Boots-Fahrten. s8º. 1917

Valentiner (Wilhelm Reinhold). The art of the Low Countries: studies. Tr. Mrs. Schuyler van Rensselaer. 8º. 1920

Nicolaes Maes. la8º. St. 1924

see Rembrandt, *the painter*. R.: wiedergefundene Gemälde, 1910–20; hrsg. W. R. V., 1921.

Valentini (Enzo), *conte di Laviano*. Letters & drawings of E. V., Ital. volunteer. Tr. F. Bellachioma. s8º. 1917

Valentinov (N.), *ps.* [*i.e.* Nik. Vladisl. Volsky].

Сношения с союзниками по военн. вопросам во время воины 1914–18. Сост. Н. В. ч1. la8º. Москва. 1920

Valentinus (Basilius), *Benedictine monk* [B. Valentin].

Practica, w. 12 keys & app., *see* Hermetic museum, v1, 1893.

Valenziano (Luca). Opere volgari, 1532. 8º. [Parigi. 1816]

Valera (Diego de) [Valera (Mosen Diego de)]. Crónica de los Reyes Católicos. Ed. &c. por J. de M. Carriazo. [Revista de Filología Esp., Anejo 8]. la8º. 1927

Valera (Eamonn De), *see* De Valera (E.)

Valera (Juan). Obras completas. t36–46. s8º. [1915–17]

35–36, Estudios crit. s. filos. y relig., 1863–88, 1883–89.
37–40, Hist. y polit., 1859–68, 1869–87, 1892–98, 1896–1903.
41–44, Cartas americanas, 1888–1900.
45–46, Miscelánea.

***Valerie,** ou lettres de G. de Linar, 1804, *see* Krüdener (B. J. v.)

Valeriis (Valerius de), *see* Lully (R.) Opera; acc. V. de V. aureum in artem Lulli gen. opus, 1617.

Valerius Flaccus (Caius), *see* Samuelsson (J.) Ad. V. F., 1927.

Valerius Maximus.

Dictorum factorumque mem. lib. 9. s8º. Amsterodami. 1626

Factorum dictorumque memorabilium libri 9. Illust. a J. Vorstio. [2p. p2, Notae, *w. sep. pagin.*] s8º. Berlini. 1672

Œuvres compl. Tr. C. A. F. Frémion [*w. text*]. n. éd. rev. par P. Charpentier. 2t. s8º. *n.d.*

Valerj (G. B.), *ed.* Cose notabili occorse in Padova (1606–7). [Nozze Oltran—Pavan. N134]. 8º. [Padova]. 1860

Valéry (Paul).

Album de vers anciens, 1890–1900. [5e cahier]. la8º. 1920

Album de vers anciens. 8º. [1927]

L'âme & la danse, *see* Revue mus., déc. 1921.

Charmes. s8º. [1926]

Disc. de réception [*on* R. Boylesve. Acad. Fr.] 8º. 1927

Eupalinos ou l'architecte, préc. de L'âme & la danse. 5e éd. s8º. [1924]

Introd. à la méthode de Léonard de Vinci. 8º. [1919]

Lettre à Mme. C[roiza]. [Les amis des Cahiers verts, 1]. 8º. [1928]

Monsieur Teste. 8º. [1927]

P. V. [*By var. a.* R. Boylesve &c. Les contemporains. Et. &c.] 8º. [1926]

Le serpent. With tr. into Eng. by M. Wardle & intr. by T. S. Eliot. 8º. London. 1924

Variété [*includ.* Intr. à la méthode de L. de Vinci]. 4e éd. s8º. [1924]

see Droin (A.) P. V. & la tradit. poét. franç., 1924.
,, Fisher (*Rt. Hon.* H. A. L.) P. V., 1927.
,, Hanotaux (G.) Rép. au disc. de P. V., 1927.
,, Porché (F.) P. V. & la poésie pure, 1926.
,, Souday (P.) P. V., 1927.
,, Thibaudet (P.) P. V., 1923.

Valikhanov (Chokan Chingisovich), *1837–66*. Сочиненія. Изд. подъ редак. Н. И. Веселовскаго. [I.R.G.O. Зап. по отд. этногр., т29]. la8º. С.–П. 1904

Valin (Lucien).

Le duc de Normandie & sa cour, 912–1204. la8º. 1910

Valk (Gerard) [Valck]. Provinces Unies des Pays-Bas &c. [Maps, 7]. folded fol. [1690?]

Valla (Laurentius). De rebus a Ferdinando Aragoniæ rege gestis libri 3, *see* Hispanica. Rer. Hisp. scr., t2, 1579.

Treatise on the Donation of Constantine. [De falso cred. & ement. Const. Don. declam.] Text & tr. [by] C. B. Coleman. 8º. New Haven. 1922

Valladolid. Anales univ.: hist. de la Univ. de V., 4t, 1918–22, *see* Alcocer Martinez (M.)

*Relacion de los autos de fé, que han celebrado las inquisiciones de V. y la de Cordova, y la de Zaragoza, Junio, 1723. 8º. Madrid. 1723

Vallalobos (Ruy López de), *see* Colección de docs. inéd. de Ultramar, s2, t2, Filipinas, Exped. de V. (1541–43) &c., 1886.

Vallance (Aymer). The old colleges of Oxford, th. architectural hist. &c. fol. [1912]

Vallancey (Charles).

Collectanea de rebus Hibernicis. 6v. 8º. D. 1770–1804

Beauford (W.) Ant. topog. of Ireland, 1783. [3.]
—— Druidism revived—Orig. & language of the Irish, 1781. [2.]
Davies (*Sir* J.) Letter to the Earl of Salisbury (1606), 1774. [1.]
Ledwich (E.) Dunamase & Shean Castle, 1781. [2.]
—— Hist. & antiq. of Irishtown & Kilkenny, 1781. [2.]
—— Obs. on Irish antiq., 1783. [3.]
—— Round towers in Ireland, 1781. [2.]
—— St. of Irish antiq., 1781. [2.]
O'Conor (C.) Reflect. on hist. of Ireland dur. heathenism, 1782. [3.]
—— 2nd [*&* 3rd] letter on heathen state &c. of Ireland, 1783–4. [3, 4.]
Piers (*Sir* H.) Chorogr. descr. of Co. of West-Meath (1682), 1770. [1.]
Pownall (T.) Ship-temple, nr. Dundalk &c., 1782. [3.]
Ussher (J.) Orig. &c. instit. of Corbes, Erenachs &c. (1609), 1774. [1.]
Vallancey (C.) Acc. of an extraord. carn &c., 1804. [6.]
—— Acc. of 2 anc. instruments, 1774. [1.]
—— All hallow Eve—Gule of August, or Lammas Day—Banqueting-hall of Tamar—Kiss of salutation—Conclusion misc., 1783. [3.]
—— Antiq. of Irish lang., 2nd ed., &, Remarks, 1772 [*signed* Celticus], 1781. [2.]
—— Astronomy of the anc. Irish, 1804. [6.]
—— Brehon laws of Ireland, 1775–82. [1–3.]
—— Cabiric or Mithratic caves in Ireland, 1804. [6.]
—— Chin. lang. collated w. the Irish, 1782. [3.]
—— Dioscuri & Cabiri, 1804. [6.]
—— Diss. conc. ant. Irish laws, 2p, 1774–5. [1.]
—— First inhabitants of Ireland, 1781. [2.]
—— Golden implements &c. found in Ireland, 1804. [6.]
—— Japon. lang. collated w. the Irish, 1782. [3.]
—— Lang. of Gypsies of Bohemia, England &c., 1804. [6.]
—— Lit. of Irish after establ. of Xty., 1781. [2.]
—— Lit. of Ir. nation in heathenish times, 1781. [2.]
—— Money of anc. Irish, 1804. [6.]
—— Ogham inscriptions, 1804. [6.]
—— Orig. of alphab. writing, 1790. [5.]
—— Orig. of feudal system of govt., 1790. [5.]
—— Round towers of Ireland, 1782–1804. [3, 6.]
—— Terms of the Brehon-Amhan laws expl. &c., 1790. [5.]
—— Uraikeft, or Bk. of Oghams, a fragm. w. tr. &c., 1790. [5.]
—— Vindic. [*&* Further vindic.] of anc. hist. of Ireland, 1786–1804. [4, 6.]

Vallardi (Francesco), *publisher*, *see* Enciclopedia mod. illust., 10v, 1898–1904.

Vallaux (Camille), *see* Brunhes (Jean) & C. V. Géog. de l'hist., 1921.

Valle (Adrián del). Parnaso cubano. Sel. compos. poet. col. por A. del V. Con un prólogo. n. ed. aum. s8º. Barcelona. 1920

Valle (Carlo a), *see* Avalle (C.)

Valle (Domenico). P. Monod e le sue relaz. col Card. Richelieu, con doc., *see* Regia Deput. Miscellanea, t45, 1910.

Valle-Inclán (Ramón del). La corte de los milagros. [El ruedo ibérico, s1, t1]. s8º. [1927]

El embrujado. Tragedia. s8º. [1913]

The pleasant mem. of the Marquis de Bradomín. Tr. M. H. Broun & T. Walsh. 8º. [1925]

Sonata de primavera: memorias del Marq. de Bradomin. s8º. [1922]

Tirano Banderas. s8º. [1926]

Vallentin (Rupert), *see* Boyson (V. F.) The Falkland Islands, w. notes on natural hist. by R. V., 1924.

Vallery-Radot (Jean). La Cathédrale de Bayeux. s8º. [1922]

Loches. s8º. 1926

Vallery-Radot (René). Le duc d'Aumale, d'ap. sa corresp. avec Cuvillier-Fleury. [t1] 1840–71. 8º. 1922

Vallery-Radot (Robert). Anthol. de la poésie catholique. Publ. &c. par R. V.-R. s8º. 1916

Valles (*vte.* H. Charles Bernard Théodore Médéric de). Beaumarchais magistrat (doc. inéd.) Préf. de H. Robert. s8º. [1928]

Vallès (Jules). Jacques Vingtras: le bachelier. s8º. 1921

Jacques Vingtras: l'enfant. s8º. 1921

Vallesa (Alessandro Carlo Filiberto, *barone* **di),** *conte di Montaldo*, *see* Boselli (P.) Il ministro V. e l'ambasc. Dalberg nel 1817, 1893.

Vallet (François), *Guienne herald*. Rel. inéd. des obsèques de François I; *ed.* L. Royer, *see* Société de l'Hist. de Paris. Mém., t47, 1924.

Vallette (*Mme.* **Alfred**), *formerly Mlle. M. Eymery* [*ps.* RACHILDE &c.] Alfred Jarry. [6e éd.] s8o. [1928]
L'animale. 4e éd. s8o. 1923
Le château des deux amants. s8o. [1923]
La haine amoureuse. s8o. [1924]
La Marquise de Sade. s8o. 1887
see DAVID (A.) Rachilde [*i.e. Mme.* V.], homme de lettres, s. œuvre, 1924.
Valli (Luigi), *see* DANTE ALIGHIERI. Lectura D.: c. 4 dell' Inferno, da L. V., 1914.
Vallings (Gabrielle). The forge of democracy. s8o. [1921]
Vallois (G. M.)
Antiques & curios in our homes. [2nd ed.] 8o. [1922]
Vallois (René). Les portiques au Sud du Hièron, pl, Le portique de Philippe; par R. V. avec collab. de G. Poulsen &c., *see* ECOLE FRANÇ. D'ATHÈNES. Explor. archéol. de Délos &c., fasc. 7i, 1923.
Vallon (— de), *see* MÖRL (G. P.) Vindic. doct. Lutheran. de gratia praedest.; nuper Dom. de V. impugn. suscepit, 1702.
Vallon (Marie Anne, *called* **Annette),** *see* LEGOUIS (E.) W. Wordsworth & A. V., 1922.
Vallotti (Francesco Antonio), *see* SABBATINI (L. A.) Tratt. sopra le fughe musicali; corr. da saggi d. p. V., pl, 1802.
Vallotton (Benjamin). Achille & Cie. s8o. 1922
A tâtons. s8o. 1921
Valmaggi (Luigi). I cicisbei: costume ital. n. sec. 18. Pref. &c. di L. Piccioni. 8o. Torino. 1927
Vālmiki. Yajńadattabada, ou la mort d'Yadjnadatta, épisode extr. du Ramâyana. Donné avec texte, analyse gramm., tr. franç. & notes par A. L. Chezy & suivie d'une tr. lat. par J. L. Burnhouf. [Soc. Asiatique]. 4o. 1826
see TULSI DÁS. Rámáyana; tr. f. Hindi by F. S. Growse, 6th ed., 1922.
Valori (Gino). Notari. la8o. Milano. 1920
Valour & vision: poems of the War, 1914–18, *see* TROTTER (J. T.), *ed.*
Valperga di Caluso (Tommaso) [*ps.* DIDYMUS TAURINENSIS]. Literaturae Copticae rudimentum. 8o. Parmae. 1783
Valrose (Pierre de). Le péché dont on meurt. Roman. s8o. 1922
Valsalva (Antonius Maria), *see* MORGAGNI (G. B.) Epistolæ anatomicæ 22 ad scripta pertin. A. M. V. &c., 2p, 1764.
Valsecchi (Antonino). De spiritu philosophico, *see* MIGNE (J. P.), *ed.* Theol. cursus, t6, 1862.
see HOOKE (L. J.) De vera religione, 2p, & App. (V. &c.), 1861–62.
Valsecchi (Virginio). Epist. de vet. Pisan. civ. constitutis, *see* HOFFMANN (C. G.) Hist. jur. Rom.-Justin., v1ii, 1734.
Valton (John), *Methodist.* The life & labours of J. Valton, wr. by himself; ed. by J. Sutcliffe. s8o. 1830
Valuev (*graf* **Petr. Aleksandrovich),** *1814–90.* Дневникъ (1880). [*Extr. fr.* Вѣстникъ Европы. P2445]. 8o. [1907]
Valvasone (Erasmo di), *1532–93.*
Angeleida. 8o. Venetia. 1590
Le lagrime d. Maddalena, *see* TANSILLO (L.) Le lagrime di San Pietro, 1592.
Valyi (Felix). Europe in Asia Minor. 2nd ed. [P2580]. 8o. 1922
Vambéry (Armin). Alt-osman. Sprachstudien mit e. Azerbaižan. Texte. 8o. Leiden. 1901
La lutte fut. pour la possession de l'Inde: progrès de la Russie dans l'Asie cent. s8o. [1886]
A török faj. Ethnolog. és ethnogr. tekintetben. [M. Tud. Akad.] 8o. 1885
La Turquie d'aujourd'hui d'avant 40 ans. Tr. G. Tirard. [P2620]. 8o. 1898
Voyages d'un faux derviche dans l'Asie centrale. Tr. E. D. Forgues. 8o. 1865
***Vampyre** (The); a tale, 1819, *see* POLIDORI (J. W.)
Van. *Van den olden eñ nieuwen God geloove ende leere. [*b. w.* Summa d. godl. schr., c. 1556]. s8o. *n.p.* [*Magnus van den Merberghe.* 1556]
Van Amringe (John Howard), *see* CHAMBERLAIN (J. L.) Universities & th. sons; spec. ed., Columbia, J. H. van A., &c., 5v, 1898–1900.
Van Antwerp (William Clarkson). Illustr. cat. of early pr. books &c., Sold, Amer. Art. Assoc. [P2859]. la8o. N.Y. 1922
Van Bastelaer (René).
Les estampes de P. Bruegel l'anc. 4o. Brux. 1908
Van Bemmel (*le baron* **Eugène P. P.)** La Belgique illust. Publ. sur la dir. de E. Van B. 2t. 4o. Brux. [1878–82]
Van Bever (Ad.), *see* VERLAINE (P.) Corresp.; publ., avec une préf. & des notes, par A. van B., t1, 2, 1922–23.
Van Biervliet (J.-J.) La psychologie d'aujourd'hui. s8o. 1927
Vanbrugh (*Sir* **John).** Compl. works. Plays ed. B. Dobrée: Letters ed. G. Webb. 4v. la8o. *Nonesuch Press.* 1927–28
Provoked wife, *see* INCHBALD (*Mrs.* E.) Brit. theatre, v9, 1808.
see DOBRÉE (B.) Essays in biog., 1680–1726, 1925.
,, TIPPING (H. A.) Eng. homes, Period 4, v2, Work of Sir J. V. &c., 1699–1736, 1928.
—— & C. Cibber.
The provok'd husband. [P2865]. s8o. 1765
,, ,, *a. ed.* [Dolby's Brit. theatre]. s8o. 1823
,, ,, *for a. ed., see* INCHBALD (*Mrs.* E.) Brit. theatre, v9, 1808.
Van Buren (E. Douglas), *wife of A. W. Van Buren.* Figurative terra-cotta revetments in Etruria & Latium in 6. & 5. c. B.C. la8o. 1921
Greek fictile revetments in the archaic period. la8o. 1926
Van Buren (Martin), *president of the United States.* Autobiography; ed. J. C. Fitzpatrick, *see* AMER. HIST. ASSOC. Ann. rep., 1918, v2, 1920.
Van Cauwenbergh (Etienne). Les pèlerinages expiat. & judic. dans le droit communal de la Belg. au m.-â. [Univ. de Louvain]. 8o. Louvain. 1922
see LOUVAIN. L'Univ. de L.: ét. hist.; avec le concours de E. van C. &c., 1927.
Vance (Andrew), *barrister.* The green book: acc. of princ. rep. decisions at law &c., on the Irish statutes &c.(1224–1860). 8o. Dublin. 1862
Vance (John G.) & *Sir* **J. W. Fortescue.**
Adrian Fortescue: a memoir. la8o. 1924
Vance (Louis Joseph). The dead ride hard. s8o. [1927]
Vancini (Oreste). Bologna d. chiesa, 1360–76. [Estr. d. Atti &c. d. R. Deput. di St. Patria, s3, v23, 25]. 8o. Bologna. 1906
La rivolta dei Bolognesi al gov. dei vicari d. chiesa, 1376–77. 8o. Bologna. 1906
Vancouver (George), *see* MENZIES (A.) Journal of V.'s voyage, Apr. to Oct., 1792; ed. &c. C. F. Newcombe, 1923.
Vancsa (Max). Gesch. Nieder- u. Oberösterreichs. [Deut. Landesgesch.; hrsg. A. Tille, 6]. B2, 1283–1522. 8o. St. 1927
Vandal (Albert). L'avènement de Bonaparte. Intr. par Lord Rosebery. 2t. s8o. *Nelson.* [1912]
Le Pacha Bonneval. 8o. 1885
Vandelli (Giuseppe), *see* DANTE ALIGHIERI. Lectura D.: c. 28 del Paradiso da G. V., 1904.
Van Deman (Esther Boise).
The Atrium Vestae. [C.I. of Wash.] la8o. Wash. 1908
Van den Bergh (Henry). The Incas & their industries. s8o. 1921
Vanden Bergh (Leonard John). On the trail of the Pigmies. Anthropolog. explor. Foreword by R. H. Lowie. 8o. 1922
Van den Borren (Charles). Guillaume Dufay: s. import. dans l'évol. de la musique au 15e s. la8o. Brux. 1925
Sources of keyboard music in England. Tr. J. E. Matthew. 8o. [1913]
Van den Heuvel (Jules). The statesmanship of Benedict XV. Tr. J. C. Burns. [P2734]. s8o. 1923
Vandenhoven (Hubert). La langue flamande, son passé et son avenir. 8o. Brux. 1844
Van de Put (Albert). The Monypenny breviary. With note by F. C. Eeles. [Repr. f. Proc. of Soc. of Antiq. of Scot., v6]. [P2703]. la8o. E. 1922
Vanderbilt (Cornelius), *see* SMITH (A. D. H.) Commodore V., 1928.
Van der Chijs (Jacob Anne), *see* CHIJS (J. A. VAN DER).
Vandercom (Joseph Fitzwilliam), *see* HABERDASHERS' COMPANY. Manual for use of court assistants, comp. by J. F. V. &c., 1828.
Van der Croon (Theodorus), *see* CROON (THEODORUS VAN DER).
Van der Does (Franck), *see* DOES (F. VAN DER).
Vandérem (Fernand). La cendre. 2e éd. s8o. 1894
Van der Essen (Léon). Une instit. d'enseignement sup. sous l'anc. régime: L'Univ. de Louvain (1425–1797). s8o. Brux. 1921
see LOUVAIN. L'Univ. de L.: ét. hist., 1927.
Van der Flier (M. J.), *LL.D.* War finances in the Netherlands up to 1918. [C.E. for Internat. Peace]. la8o. O. 1923
Van der Goes (Hugo), *see* GOES (H. v. D.)
Van der Hoop (J. H.) Character & the unconscious: crit. exposit. of the psychology of Freud & of Jung. Auth. tr. by E. Trevelyan. 8o. 1923

Van der Horst (Didericus Gertrudus). Disp. de Hussi vita praesertimque illius condemnati causis. 8°. Amstelodami. 1837
Van der Kabel (Adriaan), *see* KABEL (A. V. D.)
Van der Kemp (Joannes Theodorus), *see* KEMP (J. T. VAN DER).
Van der Linden (Fritz).
Le Congo, les noirs & nous. 2e éd. la8°. 1910
Vander Linden (Herman), *see* LANNOY (C. DE) & H. V. L. Hist. de l'expansion colon., Néerlande & Danemark, 1911.
Vanderlint (Jacob). Money answers all things, 1734. [J. H. Univ. Repr. of econ. tracts. P2619]. 8°. [Baltimore. 1914]
Van der Meulen (A. J.), *see* MEULEN (A. J. VAN DER).
Van der Meulen (R.), *see* MEULEN (R. VAN DER).
Vanderpol (Alfred).
La doctrine scolastique du droit de guerre. la8°. 1919
Vandervelde (Émile). Le collectivisme & l'évolution industrielle. n. éd. s8°. 1921
Vandervelde (Lalla), *wife of Émile Vandervelde.*
Monarchs & millionaires. 8°. [1925]
Vandervell (Henry Eugene). The figure skate &c. s8°. 1901
—— **& T. M. Witham.**
A system of figure-skating. s8°. 1869
„ „ ....4th ed. [*by T. M. W.*] s8°. 1893
Van de Velde, *The family of, see* ZÖGE VON MANTEUFFEL (K.) Die Künstlerfam. Van de V., 1927.
Van de Weyer (Sylvain) [†WEYER (S. VAN DE)]. *Letter on the Belgic Revolution. [Tr.] [P2782]. 8°. 1831
Van Dieren (Bernard).
Epstein. With 50 reproductions. 4°. 1920
Van Dine (S. S.) The Canary murder case. s8°. 1927
Van Dongen (Kees), *see* DONGEN (K. VAN).
Van Doren (Carl). The American novel. s8°. N.Y. 1921
see CAMB. HIST. OF ENG. LIT. Suppl.: Short hist. of Amer. lit.; ed. W. P. Trent &c., w. intr. by C. v. D., 1924.
Van Doren (Louis O.) Fishes of the East Atlantic coast, incl. Fishes of the East coast of Florida by S. C. Clarke. 8°. N.Y. 1884
Van Doren (Mark). The poetry of John Dryden. 8°. N.Y. 1920
Van Drunen (James). Adolphe Quetelet. s8°. Turnhout. 1919
Van Druten (John). The return of the soldier. Play by J. Van D. Adapted f. R. West's novel. s8°. 1928
Van Duzee (Millard C.), F. R. Cole & J. M. Aldrich. The dipterous genus Dolichopus Latreille in N. America. [S.I.: U.S. Nat. Mus., Bull. 116]. 8°. Wash. 1921
Van Duzer (Henry Sayre). A Thackeray library coll. by V. D. Sold, Feb. 1922, Anderson Gall. [P2856] 8°. N.Y. 1922
Van Dyck (*Sir* **Anthony),** *see* VESME (A. DE). Van D., peintre de portraits des princes de Savoie, 1885.
Van Dyk (Harry Stoe).
Theatrical portraits w. other poems. s8°. 1822
Van Dyke (John Charles). The new New York: place & people. Illust. by J. Pennell. 8°. N.Y. 1909
Rembrandt & h. school: crit. st. of the master & h. pupils &c. 4°. N.Y. 1923
Van Dyke (Paul). Catherine de Médicis. 2v. 8°. 1923
Vane (Sutton). Outward bound. [Play]. 8°. 1924
Vane (Thomas), *see* CHISENHALE (E.) Cath. hist.; occas. by a bk. by T. V., 1653.
Vanessa, *ps., see* VANHOMRIGH (*Miss* H.)
Van Eyrie (John H.) White supremacy & negro subordination &c. With an app. 2nd ed. s8°. N.Y. 1870
1st ed. h. t.: Negroes & negro slavery.
Vangerow (Wilhelm Gottlieb). Diss. μετεμψύχωσιν veterum sistens. Sub moderam. J. F. Stiebritz. [P445]. s4°. Halae Magdeb. 1765
Van Hise (Charles Richard). Concentration & control: trust problem in the U.S. rev. [ed.] 8°. N.Y. 1914
—— **& C. K. Leith.** Geology of the Lake Superior region. [U.S. Geolog. Survey]. 4°. Wash. 1911
Pre-Cambrian geology of North Amer., *see* UNITED STATES: GEOLOG. SURVEY. Bull. 360, 1909.
Vanhomrigh (*Miss* **Hester)** [*ps.* VANESSA]. Vanessa & h. correspondence w. J. Swift. Letters ed., w. intr. by A. M. Freeman. s8°. [1921]
Vanity Fair: a weekly show of polit., soc. & lit. wares. v1–[88]. Nov. 7, 1868–Dec. 31, 1913. fol. 1868–1913
2v for each year b. together. The vol. for 1888–1913 mostly have no tp. & are lettered Vanity Fair Album *& cont. plates w. relative letterpress only. The vol. for 1888 has tp.* Vanity Fair Album, v20.
see WARD (*Sir* L.) 40 yrs. of "Spy," 1917.

Van Keymeulen (L.), *see* HOLLANDE (La), par L. van K. *& o. authors,* 1909.
Van Kleeck (Mary). What industry means to women workers, *see* UNITED STATES: LABOR. Women's Bur., Bull. 31, 1923.
Van Laer (Arnold Johan Ferdinand), *see* HENRY E. HUNTINGTON LIBRARY. Doc. rel. to New Netherland, 1624–26; tr. & ed. A. J. F. van L., 1924.
Vanlande (René). Avec le Gén. Niessel en Prusse & en Lithuanie. Préf. de Mme. J. Adam. 8°. 1921
Van Langenhove (Fernand). L'action du Gouvernement belge en matière écon. pend. la Guerre. [C.E. for Internat. Peace]. 8°. 1927
Van Lerberghe (Charles). Les flaireurs. 2e éd. s8°. Brux. 1894
Van Marle (Raimond), *see* MARLE (R. V.)
Van Metre (Thurman William), *see* JOHNSON (E. R.) Hist. of domestic &c. commerce of the U.S.; by E. R. J., T. W. Van M. &c., 2v, 1922.
Vannérus (Jules), *see* LUXEMBOURG. Dénombrements des feux des duché de L. & comté de Chiny; publ. avec adds. &c. de J. V., t1, 1921.
Vanni de' Quaranta, *see* QUARANTA (VANNI DE').
Vannier (Antonin). La clarté française. L'art de composer, d'écrire & de se corriger. 6e éd. rev. & corr. s8°. 1920
Vannius (Valentin). De missa integra hist. ex evangelistis, apostolis &c. congesta. Adv. librum I. Fabri de opinata &c. evangelica missa. 2t *in* 1v. s4°. Tubingæ. 1563
Van Noppen (Leonard).
The challenge: war chants of the Allies. s8°. 1918
Vannozzi (Bonifacio), *see* CANCELLIERI (F.) Osserv. int. alla quest. prom. dal V. &c. s. l'origin. d. Div. Comm., 1814.
Vannozzo (Francesco). Due sonetti ined. d. 1387. [P2870]. 8°. [Padova. 1866]
Rime. [Nozze Zacco-Valvasori]. [N138]. fol. Padova. 1825
Vannucci Pinacoteca, *see* PERUGIA.
Vannutelli (Luigi). La Casa di Savoia e l'ord. d. Giarrettiera, *see* REGIA DEPUT. Miscellanea, t45, 1910.
Van Oost (Joseph). Notes sur le T'oemet, *see* VARIÉTÉS sinolog., No. 53, 1922.
Van Overbergh (Cyr.), *see* GAUD (F.) & C. VAN O. Les Mandja (Congo franç.), 1911.
—— **& E. de Jonghe.** Les Bangala (Etat ind. du Congo). Sociologie descriptive. la8°. Brux. 1907
Vansteenberghe (Edmond).
Le Cardinal N. de Cues, 1401–64. la8°. 1920
Van Tieghem (Paul).
Le mouvt. romantique 2e éd. rev. & augm. 8°. 1923
Van Tyne (Claude Halstead). Causes of the War of Independence, being v1 of a hist. of founding of the Amer. Republ. 8°. [1922]
England & America: rivals in Amer. Revol. 8°. C. 1927
India in ferment. 8°. N.Y. 1923
—— **& W. G. Leland.** Guide to the archives of the govt. of the U.S. in Washington. 2nd ed. rev. & enl. by W. G. Leland. [C.I. of Wash.] la8°. Wash. 1907
Van Vechten (Carl). Firecrackers. s8°. N.Y. 1925
Nigger heaven. [7th impr.] s8°. [1927]
The tiger in the house. 8°. 1921
Van Vlijmen (Bernard Reiner Frans), *see* VLIJMEN (B. R. F. VAN).
Van Vorst (*Miss* **Marie).** Sunrise. s8°. [1924]
Van Waters (Miriam).
Youth in conflict. Intr. by Sir E. Ruggles-Brise. 8°. [1926]
Vanzype (Gustave). Henri de Braekeleer. 4°. Brux. 1923
Vermeer de Delft. n. éd. rev. & corr. la8°. 1925
Vararuchi. The Pràkrita-Prakásá, or, Prákrit-Gramm. w. comm. of Bhámaha. Orig. text, w. notes & Eng. tr. &c. by E. B. Cowell. la8°. Hereford. 1854
Varatella. Chronicon vet. monast. S. Petri de V. in Albinganensi diocesi, ed. H. de Rubeis, *see* REGIA DEP. DI STORIA PATRIA. Misc., t11, 1870.
Varchi (Benedetto). Opere. Con disc. di A. Racheli int. a. filologia del sec. 16. Agg. le lettere di G. B. Busini sopra l'assedio di Firenze. 2v. la8°. Trieste. 1858–59
Componimenti pastorali. Nuovamente in quel modo stampati. [*tp. wanting*]. 4°. [Bologna. 1576]
Sonetti. s8°. Venetia. 1555
Storia fiorentina. 2v. s8°. Firenze. 1888
Varè (Daniele). Storia d'Inghilterra. v1, 2. 8°. Firenze. [1923]

Varendonck (Julien). The psychology of day-dreams. Intr. by S. Freud. 8°. [1921]
The evolution of the conscious faculties. 8°. [1923]
Varenius (Augustus).
Breviarium theolog. [*2 pagin.*] s4°. Rostochi. 1682
Gemmae Salomonis: Liber Koheleth &c. s4°. Rostochi. 1659
Varenius (Bernardus). Descr. regni Japoniæ. 2p. [p2 *w. sep. tp.* Tract. de Jap. relig. &c.] s8°. Amstelodami. 1649
Varesi (Masud Ali). 'Umar Khayyám. s8°. 1922
Varet (Alexandre), *see* BURLUGUAY (J.) *Toilette de M. l'archevesque de Sens ou réponse au Factum [*by A. V. &c.*], 1669.
Varga (Eugen). Sozialismus u. Kapitalismus in Sowjet-Russland. [P2758]. s8°. L. 1921
Vargas (Alphonsus de), *ps.*, *see* SCHOPPE (C.)
Vargas (Francisco de). Lettres & mém. de F. de V., de P. de Malvenda & de quelques évêques d'Espagne t. le Concile de Trente tr. M. Le Vassor. 8°. Amsterdam. 1700
Vargas Machuca (Bernardo), *see* LAS CASAS (B. DE). Destruc. de las Indias *&* Refut. de Las C. [by B. V. M.], *n.d.*
Variétés sinologiques. Nos. 26–56. 8°. Chang-hai. 1909–25
26, K'iuen-his p'ien: exhortations à l'étude; par Tchang Tche-tong, n. éd. par J. Tobar.
27, Hist. du royaume de Ts'in (777–207 av. J. C.); par A. Tschepe.
28i, ii, Cat. des tremblements de terre sign. en Chine d'ap. sources chin., par P. Hoang, 2t.
29, Concordance des chronologies néoméniques, chin. & europ.; par P. Hoang.
30, Hist. du royaume de Tsin (1106–452); par A. Tschepe.
31, Hist. des 3 royaumes Han, Wei & Tchao; par A. Tschepe.
32i, ii, Recherches sur les superstitions en Chine; par H. Doré, t1, 2.
33, Tombeau des Liang, famille Siao, p1, Siao Choen-tche; par M. Tchang.
34i, ii, Rech. s. les superstitions en Chine; par H. Doré, t3, 4.
35, Carte des préfectures de Chine & de leur popul. chrét. en 1911; [par] J. de Moidrey.
36, Rech. s. les superstitions en Chine; par H. Doré, t5.
37, Le père S. A. Cunha; par M. Tchang & P. de Prunelé.
38, La hiérarchie catholique en Chine, en Corée & au Japon; par J. de Moidrey.
39, Rech. s. les superstitions en Chine; par H. Doré, t6.
40, Notice histor. sur les T'oan ou cercles du Siu-tcheou Fou; par E. Zi.
41, 42, Rech. s. les superstitions en Chine; par H. Doré, t7, 8.
43, Carte du Se-tch'ouan occidental levée en 1908–10 par F. Roux.
44–46, Rech. s. les superstitions en Chine; par H. Doré, t9–11.
47, Kiao-ou Ki-lio: affaires relig.; tr. &c. par J. Tobar.
48, 49, Rech. s. les superstitions en Chine; par H. Doré, t12, 13.
50, Dictons & proverbes des Chinois habit. la Mongolie sud-ouest; par J. van Oost.
51, Rech. s. les superstitions en Chine; par H. Doré, t14.
52, Mélanges sur la chronologie chin.; par pp. Havret, Chambeau & Hoang.
53, Notes sur le T'oemet; par J. van Oost.
54, Carte de la prov. du Kiang-sou; par H. Dugout, feuille 1.
55, Manuel du code chinois; par G. Boulais.
56, Catalogue des éclipses de soleil & de lune rel. dans doc. chin. &c.; par P. Hoang.
Varillas (Antoine). Histoire de Charles IX. 2t. s8°. 1684
see BURNET (G.) Reflections on V.'s Hist. of revolutions &c., 1686.
,, WACHTER (G.) Hist. Aug. Confess. a corruptelis A. V., 1730; 1737.
Väring (Astrid). Frosten. Skildring från 1860–talets Västerbotten. s8°. [1926]
Variot (Jean). La belle de Haguenau: comédie, *see* REVUE HEBDOM. Suppl.; coll. nouv. &c., No. 9, 1922.
Le sang des autres. s8°. 1919
Varisco (Bernardino).
Know thyself. Tr. G. Salvadori. 8°. 1915
Varlet (Théo).
see JONCQUEL (O.) & T. V. L'agonie de la terre, 1922.
,, —— & —— Les Titans du ciel, 1921.
Varlet de la Grange (Charles).
*C. V. de la G. & son registre. 8°. 1876
Varley (Telford). Hampshire. s8°. C. 1922
Isle of Wight. s8°. C. 1924
Varnhagen (Hermann). Über e. Sammlung alter ital. Drucke der Erlanger Universitätsbibl. Beitr. z. Kenntnis d. ital. Lit. d. 14. u. 15. Jhrdts. [P2380]. 4°. Erlangen. 1892
Varnhagen von Ense (Carl August L. P.), *see* HOUGHTON (R. M. M., *1st baron*). Briefe an V. v. E. (1844–54); hrsg. W. Fischer, 1922.
Varnhagen von Ense (*Frau* Rahel A. F.), *wife of C. A. Varnhagen von Ense; 1771–1833.* R. u. Alexander v. d. Marwitz in i. Briefen [1809–13]. Hrsg. v. H. Meisner. 8°. Gotha. 1925
Varotari (Dario). Il vespaio stuzzicato. Satire veneziane. s8°. Venezia. 1671
Varro (Marcus Terentius). De lingua Latina &c., *see* GODEFROY (D.) Auctores Lat. ling. &c., 1585.
see AGRONOMES (Les) latins: Caton, V. &c. (Lat. & Fr.); Nisard, 1877.
Vars (Émilie de). Les ultra-catholiques. s8°. 1870
Vartan [VARDAN], *called the Great.* La domination arabe en Arménie. Extr. de l'Hist. univ. de V. Tr. & annoté, étude de crit. text. & litt. par J. Muyldermans. 8°. Louvain. 1927
Сборники притчъ Вардана. Матеріалы; *ed.* Н. Марръ. 3ч *in* 1v. la8°. С.–П. 1894–99
v2 *has t. in Armenian:* Coll. of the fables of Vardan. v3, Приложенія.
[Univ. hist. *In Armenian.* Ed. M. Emin]. 8°. Moskva. 1861
,, ,, ...[*a. ed.*] 8°. i Venetik. 1862
see ELISHA *Vartabed.* Hist. of V. &c., *in Armenian*; ed. Kh. Hovhannisean, 1892.
,, JOHN, *the Deacon.* [Panegyrics of Gregory the Illuminator, by J., V. &c., *in Armenian*], 1853.
Varthema (Lodovico), *see* BOULTING (W.) 4 pilgrims [L. V. &c.], 1920.
Vasaeus (Joannes). Rerum Hisp. chron., *see* HISPANICA. Rer. Hisp. scr., t1, 1579.
Vasari Society (The) for the reprod. of drawings by old masters. Reproductions, p10 (1914–15) & Index to p1–10. fol. [1914]
Vasca. Biblioteca de hist. Vasca, t1–7, 1919–23, *see* BIBLIOTECA.
Vaschalde (*le capitaine* J.)
Marine & guerre navale. Préf. de J. Cels. s8°. 1920
Vasconcellos (Carolina de), *see* MICHAELIS (C.), *aft. Vasconcellos.*
Vasconcellos (Ernesto Julio de Carvalho e), *see* CARVALHO E VASCONCELLOS (E. J. DE).
Vasconcellos (Jorge Ferreira de), *see* FERREIRA DE VASCONCELLOS (J.)
Vasey (Mary Jane), *wife of T. Vasey.*
The life of Th. Vasey. By his widow. s8°. 1874
Vasey (Thomas), *1814–71*, *see* VASEY (M. J.) Life of T. V.; by h. widow, 1874.
Vasi (Mariano). Itinéraire de Rome &c. Revu &c. par A. Nibby. 2t [t1 *wanting*]. 8°. Rome. 1826
Vasilev (Aleksandr Aleksandrovich). Византія и Арабы. Полит. отнош. В. и А. за время Македонской дин. Имп. Василія I, Левъ VI, и Константинъ VII, 867–959. 8°. С.–П. 1902
Поѣздка на Синай, 1902. 8°. С.–П. 1904
Vasilev (Aleksandr Vasilevich). Space, time, motion: hist. intr. to gen. theory of relativity. Tr. H. M. Lucas & C. P. Sanger, w. intr. by B. Russell. s8°. 1924
Vasilev (Ivan Ivanovich).
Археолог. указатель г. Пскова, &c. la8°. С.–П. 1898
la8°. 1921
Vasilev (N.) Карская экспедиція.
Vasilev (Vasily Pavlovich), *1818–1900.* Записка о надписяхъ на скалѣ Тыръ, близъ устья Амура. [*Extr. f.* Извѣстія I. А. Н., 1896, t4. P2752]. la8°. 1896
Исторія и древности восточ. части Средней Азіи, 10–13в., *see* IMP. RUSS. ARCH. OBSCH. Труды Восточ. отд., ч4, 1859.
Открытіе Китая. 8°. С.–П. 1900
Vasnetsov (Viktor Mikhailovich).
see BAYE (*le baron* J. DE). L'œuvre de V. W. dev. l'école mod. de peinture en Russie, 2e éd., 1896.
,, USPENSKY (A. I.) В. М. В., 1906.
Vassal (Gabrielle M.) Life in French Congo. 8°. [1925]
Vassali (Michele Antonio). Mylsen Phoenico-Punicum sive gramm. Melitensis. 8°. Romae. 1791
Vassalli-Eandi (Antonio Maria). Notice abr. de la vie & des écrits de L. Lagrange; [*ed. D. C. Promis*], *see* REGIA DEP. DI STORIA PATRIA. Misc., t12, 1871.
Vassallo (Carlo). F. Maramaldo e gli Agostiniani in Asti, *see* REGIA DEP. Misc., t28, 1890.
Vasselot (Jean J. Marquet de), *see* MARQUET DE VASSELOT (J. J.)
Vasubandhu. Vijñaptimātratāsiddhi. 2 traités: Viṃśatikā (La Vingtaine), accomp. d'une explic. en prose, & Triṃśikā (La Trentaine) avec comm. de Sthiramati. Publ. S. Lévi. [H.E., 245]. pl. 8°. 1925

Vatablus (Franciscus). Annot. in Psalmos, subjunct. H. Grotii notis, quibus obs. crit. adspersit G. I. L. Vogel. 8°. Halae Magdeb. 1767

Vater (Johann Severin).
Anbau d. neuesten Kirchengesch. 2B. s8°. 1820–22
Synchron. Tafeln. d. Kirchengesch. Hrsg. v. A. H. Niemeyer. 5e A. fol. Halle. 1828

Vatican. *Relation aus dem V. zu Rom, 1681, *see* RELATION.

Vatican Council.
Acta & decreta sacr. œcumenici Co. V. 8°. Romae. 1872
Acta officialia Conc. Magni V. [*Lat. & Ital.*] 2p *in* 1v. 8°. Torino. 1869–70
Aktenstücke d. Ordinariates d. Erzb. München u. Freising betreff. d. Allgem. Vatic. Conc. B1 [*no more publ.*] 8°. Regensburg. 1871
*Ce qui se passe au Concile. 3e éd. 8°. 1870
Le Concile du V. & le mouvement anti-infaillibiliste en Allemagne. 2p [p1 *in* P2506]. 8°. Brux. 1871–74
1, L'excomm. du prof. J. Friedrich & sa réponse.
2, L'excomm. du chan. Dr. v. Doellinger & sa déclar.
Decreta & canones Co. V., cum interpret. Gallica. s8°. Paris. 1872
*La dern. heure du Concile. [P2691]. 8°. München. 1870
Ökumen. (Das) Concil. Stimmen aus Maria Laach. Neue Folge. Hrsg. v. F. Riess & K. v. Weber. 8°. Freiburg. im Br. 1869–71
7, Das Concil u. d. Neu Jansenismus.
8, Das Concil. u. d. Neu Gallicanismus.
9, Die dogmat. Constit. v. 24. April 1870.
10, Die päbstliche Unfehlbarkeit u. d. alte Glaube der Kirche.
11, Die Janus-Gläubigen n. d. vatikan. Entscheidung v. 18. Juli 1870.
12, Fortschreitende Klärung in Sachen d. Concils u. s. Gegner.
*Wie es auf d. Concil zugeht, *see* KATHOLISCH. Stimmen aus d. K. Kirche, B2, 1870.
see FRIEDBERG (E.) Sammlung der Aktenstücke z. 1. V. Concil mit e. Grundrisse der Gesch., 1872.
,, GUÉRIN (P.) Concile œcumén. du V. : hist., décisions &c., 1871.
,, MARTIN (C.), *bp.* Omnium Co. V. quae ad doct. &c. pert. doc. coll., 1873.

Vatican Library. Calendar of State Papers rel. to Eng. affairs at Rome in V. Archives &c., v2, 1926, *see* ROME.
Mon. V. di paleografia musicale latina. Racc. e illust. da E. M. Bannister. [Codices e Vaticanis sel., v12]. atlas fol. [Tavole *in case, sep.*] Lipsia. 1913
Specimina cod. Lat. V., ed. 2a, 1927, *see* EHRLE (F.) & P. LIEBAERT, *edd.*
see BROM (G.) & A. H. L. HENSEN, *edd.* Rom. Bronnen v. d. kerk.-staatk. toestand d. Ned. in de 16de eeuw, 1922.
,, FRANCHI DE' CAVALIERI (P.) &c. Specimina codicum Graec. Vat., 1910.
,, MANZI (G.) Testi di lingua ined. tr. da codici d. Bibl. Vat., 1816.
,, PROVENZALISCHE (Die) Liederhs. Cod. 5232 d. V. Bibl., 1873.

Vaticana [VATICANO], *see* MASSI (E.) Descr. compend. dei musei dell' ant. scultura gr. e rom. nel V., 3a ed., 1888.

Vatnsdœla saga; hrsg. W. H. Vogt. [Altnord. Saga-Bibl., H16]. 8°. Halle (Saale). 1921

Vatopedi, *monastery, see* ATHOS.

Vattel (Emerich de) [VATEL ; WATTEL]. Le droit des gens &c. [C. Inst. of Wash.] 3v. la8°. Wash. 1916
1, 2, [Text]; w. intr. by A. de Lapradelle. 3, Tr., by C. G. Fenwick.

Vauban (*le maréchal* **de).** Lettres intimes (inéd.) adr. au Marq. de Puyzieulx, 1699–1705. Intr. &c. de H. de Landosle. [Coll. des chefs-d'œ. méconnus]. s8°. 1924
see HALÉVY (D.) V., 1923.
,, ——— V., builder of fortresses ; tr. w. notes &c., 1924.
,, SAUTAI (M.) L'œuvre de V. à Lille, 1911.

Vaucher (Paul).
La crise du ministère Walpole en 1733–34. 8°. [1924]
Robert Walpole & la politique de Fleury (1731–42). 8°. [1924]

Vaudon (Jean). Une âme de jeune fille. n. éd. s8°. [1905]

Vaudoyer (Jean Louis).
L'amie du mort, nouvelle, *see* ŒUVRES libres, 21, 1923.
Beautés de la Provence. [Les cahiers verts, 66]. s8°. 1926
Le dernier rendez-vous. s8°. [1920]
Nouv. beautés de la Provence. [Cahiers verts, 66]. s8°. 1928
Raymonde Mangematin, roman, *see* ŒUVRES libres, 45, 1925.
Un vieil été, roman, *see* ŒUVRES libres, 61, 1926.

Vaughan (Bernard John), *S.J., see* MARTINDALE (C. C.) B. V., S.J., 1923.

Vaughan (Charles Edwyn). Studies in hist. of polit. philosophy Ed. A. G. Little. [Univ. of M'ter.] 2v. 8°. 1925
1, Hobbes to Hume. 2, Burke to Mazzini, w. list of wr. of V. by H. B. Charlton.

Vaughan (Charles John), *dean of Llandaff.* The Epistle to the Hebrews [*Greek*], w. notes. s8°. 1891

Vaughan (*Paymaster lt.* **H. R. H.),** *R.N.* A compar. table of naval hist. [*Repr. f.* The naval review, Nov. 1922. P2682]. 8°. [1922]

Vaughan (*Dame* **Helen Charlotte Isabella Gwynne-),** *see* GWYNNE-VAUGHAN.

Vaughan (Henry), *the Silurist, 1622–95.* Poems from *Poems, Olor Iscanus, Silex scintillans, Thalia rediviva*—An essay from *The mount of olives*—Two letters. la8°. Soho, *Nonesuch Press.* 1924
Secular poems, incl. a few pieces by Thos. [Vaughan]. Sel. &c. by J. R. Tutin. s8°. Hull. 1893
Silex Scintillans: sacred poems &c. [With mem. by H. F. Lyte]. s8°. 1858
,, ,, Facs. of 1st ed. w. intr. by W. Clare. s8°. 1885
,, ,, W. mem. by H. F. Lyte. s8°. 1890
,, ,, Intr. by W. A. L. Bettany. s8°. [1905]
see BLUNDEN (E.) On poems of H. V. ; w. princ. Latin p. tr. into Eng. verse by E. B., 1927.

Vaughan (Herbert Millingchamp). The South Wales squires: Welsh picture of soc. life. 8°. [1926]
see WALKER (G.) Voyages ; intr. &c. by V., 1928.

Vaughan (Herbert Stanley). Notes on the earliest records of Malta victualling yard. [P2709]. 8°. *p.p.* Malta. 1921

Vaughan (J. D.) The manners & customs of the Chinese of the Straits Settlements. 8°. Singapore. 1879

Vaughan (James).
Psalms & hymns. Sel. by J. V. 4th ed. s8°. 1853

Vaughan (John). The music of wild flowers. s8°. 1920

Vaughan (Robert Alfred), *1823–57.*
Hours w. the mystics. 2nd ed. rev. & augm. 2v. s8°. 1860
,, ,, ...7th ed. 2v *in* 1. s8°. 1895

Vaughan (Thomas Wayland). Biologic character &c. of the sediment. format. of Panama. [S.I.: U.S. Nat. Mus., Bull. 103]. 8°. Wash. 1919
Fossil corals f. Central America, Cuba, Porto Rico. [S.I.: U.S. Nat. Mus., Bull. 103]. 8°. Wash. 1919
see BOSWORTH (T. O.) Geology of tertiary &c. periods in N.W. Peru ; w. acc. of palaeontology by V. &c., 1922.

Vaughan (*Mrs.* **W. W.),** *see* SYMONDS (M.), *aft. Mrs. W. W. V.*

Vauquelin (Nicolas), *seigneur de Yveteaux, 1567–1649.* Œuvres complètes. Publ. G. Mongrédien. la8°. 1921
see MONGRÉDIEN (G.) Étude sur la vie & l'œ. de N. V., 1921.

Vauquelin (Pierre Guitet-), *see* GUITET-VAUQUELIN (P.)

Vautel (Clément). L'amour à la parisienne. s8°. [1927]
Je suis un affreux bourgeois. Roman. s8°. [1926]
Mon curé chez les pauvres. s8°. [1925]
Mon curé chez les riches. s8°. [1923]
Mons. Palémon chez les dingos, *see* ŒUVRES libres, 8, 1922.

Vauthier (M.), *see* PIRENNE (J.) & M. V. Législ. &c. allemandes en Belgique, 1926.

Vauvenargues (Luc de Clapiers, *marq.* **de),** *see* MERLANT (J.) De Montaigne à V., 1914.

Vaux (Clotilde de), *see* ROUVRE (C. DE). L'amoureuse hist. d'A. Comte & de C. de V., 1920.

Vaux (*le baron* **Ludovic de).** Les duels célèbres. Préf. par A. Scholl. la8°. 1884

Vaux (Pierre), *instituteur à Longepierre, see* BUCHOT (A.) & C. G. Gauthey. Hist. de P. V., 1889.

Vauxcelles (Louis), *see* FONTAINAS (A.) & L. V. Hist. gén. de l'art franç., 1922.

Vaux de Foletier (François de). Galiot de Genouillac, maître de l'artillerie de France, 1465–1546. 8°. 1925

Vavala (Evelyn Sandberg). La pittura veronese d. trecento e d. primo quattrocento. la8°. Verona. 1926

Vayer (François de la Mothe le), *see* LA MOTHE LE VAYER.

Vayra (Pietro). Un anno di vita pubbl. del comune di Asti (1441): doc. e note, *see* REGIA DEP. DI STORIA PATRIA. Misc., t27, 1889.
Lettere e arti alla corte di Savoia nel sec. 15: inventari dei castelli di Ciamberì, di Torino e di Ponte d'Ain, 1497–98, *see* REGIA DEP. Misc., t22, 1884.

Vayssière (Albert), *see* BOUCHES-DU-RHÔNE ; encyclop. départ., t12, Biogéog., par V., 1914.

Vazir (The) of Lankuran: play ; tr., 1911 ; 1919 ; 1920, *see* FATH 'ALI AKHUNDZĀDAH, *Mirzā.*

Vazquez Tagle (José), *see* PALLARES (J.) Legisl. federal complement. del derecho civil mexicano: col. formada por J. V. T. &c., 1897 ; App., 1898.

Veatch (Arthur Clifford). Quito to Bogota. Intr. by Ld. Murray of Elibank. 8°. 1917 [1923]

Veber (Pierre Eugène). Amour, amour. . . . s8°. 1903

Le rebut d'humanité, see ŒUVRES libres, 30, 1923.

Samson. [Acteurs &c. d'autrefois]. 8°. 1925

Vecchi (Augusto Vittorio) [JACK LA BOLINA]. Cronachette del risorgimento italiano. s8°. Firenze. 1920

Storia gen. d. marina militare. 2ª ed. riv., corr. &c. 3v. 8°. Livorna. 1895

Vecchia (Pierro). Idea cronografica sopra la correzione del calendario romano. [*MS.*] fol. 1759

Vecchio-Veneziani (Augusta del). La vita e l'opera di A. C. de Meis. s8°. Bologna. [1921]

Veccus (Joannes), see ALLACCI (L.) Graeciae orthodoxae scr., N. Blemmida, J. V. [&c.], 2t, 1652–59.

Vecelli (Cesare). Corona d. nobili e virtuose donne, Libro quinto, dissegni. [Facsimile d. 1596. Intr. *by* U. de Gheltof]. fol. Venezia. [1891]

Vechnerus (Georgius), see SZLICHTING (J.) Notae in G. V. concionem, super init. Evang. Joan., 1644.

Veckenstedt (Edmund). Die Mythen, Sagen u. Legenden der Zamaiten (Litauer). Gesamm. u. hrsg. E. V. 2B *in* 1v. 8°. Heidelberg. 1883

Vedanta Desika (*Sri*), see DESIKA (*Sri* V.)

Vedas.

Rig-Veda. Übers. u. mit krit. &c. Anmerkungen versehen v. H. Grassmann. Tl. 8°. L. 1876

see BLOOMFIELD (M.) Atharva-veda, 1899.

„ GRISWOLD (H. D.) The religion of the Rigveda, 1923.

„ JONES (*Sir* W.) Works, vol. 6, Extracts from the Vedas, 1799.

see KEITH (*Sir* A. B.) Relig. & philos. of the V. & Upanishads, 2v, 1925.

„ OLDENBERG (H.) Rgveda; Textkritik u. exeget. Noten, 7es bis 10es Buch, 1912.

„ TUXEN (P.) Forestillingen om Sjælen i Rigveda &c., 1919.

Vedast, *Saint.* Carmina Vedastina. Coll. & ed. W. S. Simpson. [*b. w.* Simpson (G. S. & W. S.) Life of S. Vedast, 1896]. 8°. 1895

Tragico-comoedia de S. V. Ed. f. MSS. at Arras by W. S. Simpson. [*b. w.* Simpson (G. S. & W. S.) Life of S. Vedast, 1896]. 8°. 1895

see JONAS, *Elnon.* Vitae SS. Columbani, V. &c.; rec. B. Krusch, 1905.

„ SIMPSON (G. S.) & W. S. SIMPSON. Life & legend of S. V., 1896.

Vedehathera. 2. Dekade d. Rasavāhinī, *text & tr.; ed.* M. u. W. Geiger, see KÖNIGL. AKAD. D. WISS. ZU MÜNCHEN. Phil. Kl., Sitz., 1918.

Vedel-Petersen (Knud Otto), see DUMAS (S.) & K. O. V.-P. Losses of life caused by war, 1923.

Veder (Gulielmus Robertus).

Diss. de Anselmo Cantuar. 8°. Lugd. Batav. 1832

Veen (Otto van) [VAENIUS (OTHO)]. Emblemata Horatiana, Lat., German., Gall. & Belgico carmine illust. [*Add. engr. tp.*] s8°. Amstelaedami. 1684

see GUYON (*Mme.* J. M.) L'ame amante de son Dieu représ. dans les emblèmes d'O. V. &c., 1790.

Veesenmeyer (Georg). Lit.-bibliogr. Nachrichten v. evangel. catechet. Schriften u. Catechismen &c. s8°. Ulm. 1830

Vega (Andreas).

De justificatione doctr. universa lib. xv. fol. Coloniae. 1572

Vega (Lope de).

Obras. Publ. por la R. Acad. Española. t14, 15. 4°. 1913

14, 15, Comedias novelescas, Sección 2, 3.

La corona merecida. Publ. J. F. Montesinos. 8°. 1923

El cuerdo loco. Publ. por José F. Montesinos. [Teatro ant. esp.] 8°. 1922

Los Guzmanes de Toral. Commedie spagn. sec. 17, pubbl. A. Restori. [Roman. Bibl., 16]. s8°. Halle a. S. 1899

El Marqués de las Navas. Publ. J. F. Montesinos. [Teatro ant. esp.] 8°. [1925]

Novelas a la señora Marcia Leonarda; *ed.* J. D. & L. A. Fitz-Gerald, see ROMANISCHE FORSCH., B34, 1915.

TRANSLATIONS.

Œuvres dramatiques. Tr. E. Baret. 2t. s8°. 1874

see CARDUCHO (V.) Dialogos de la pintura &c.: sig. inform. &c. en fabor del' arte, escr. por varones insignes [*i.e.* L. de V. &c.], 1633.

„ ESTRELLA. La E. de Sevilla [*attrib. to L. de V.*], 1920.

Vega del Sella (*conde* **de la**), see OBERMAIER (H.) & LA V. Cueva del Buxu, 1918.

Vega Inclan (Miguel de la), J. de Castro y Lopez & M. Astorga. Rel. hist. de la últ. campaña del Marq. del Duero. Intr. por J. Gomez de Arteche. 8°. 1874

Veheyne (Cherry). The journal of Henry Bulver. s8°. [1921]

Veiel (Elias). Exercit. de eccl. Graecanica hodierna, L. Allatio, P. Arcudio & B. Nihusio opposita. [*b. w.* Hesterberg (J.) Eccl. Waldens., 1668]. s4°. Argentorati. 1666

—— **& J. P. Roth.** Urbani Regii memoria & meritis, disput. [P598]. s4°. Ulmae. [1683]

Veiras (Denis), see VAIRASSE (DENIS).

Veit (Andreas Ludwig). Kirche u. Kirchenreform in d. Erzdiözese Mainz, 1517–1618, see PASTOR (L. v.) Erläut. &c. zu Janssens Gesch. d. deut. Volkes, B10, H3, 1920.

Veitch (Marion), *wife of Wm. Veitch,* see MEMOIRS of Mrs. W. Veitch, T. Hog, &c., 1846.

Veith (Georg), see KROMAYER (J.) Antike Schlachtfelder, B4i, ii, v. J. K. u. G. V., 1924–26.

Vekhi. Вѣхи. Сборникъ статей о русской интеллигенціи Н. А. Бердчева, С. Н. Булгакова, М. О. Гершензона &c. 2е изд. 8°. Москва. 1909

Vela (Vincenzo), *1820–91,* see CALDERINI (M.) V. V., sculptore: 50 tavole con intr., 1920.

Velasco (Alfonso Luis). Geografía y estadística de la Rep. Mexicana. 14t *in* 3v. 8°. Mexico. 1889–93

Velasco y Fernandez de La Cuesta (Ladislao de). Los Euskaros en Álava, Guipúzcoa y Vizcaya. 8°. Barcelona. 1879

Velasquez, *the painter.*

The masterpieces of V. 60 reprod. s8°. 1907

see BENSUSAN (S. L.) V., 1909.

„ BERUETE Y MORET (A. DE). V. in the Prado Mus., *n.d.*

see HISP. SOC. OF AMERICA. Cat. ser., 1925.

„ WEDMORE (F.) Notes on V. & Titian in the etchings of R. W. Macbeth, 1888.

„ WILLIAMSON (G. C.) V., 1904.

Velasquez de Figueroa (Vicente). Libro de Bezerro [1757], see ALCOCER MARTINEZ (M.) Anales universit.: hist. de la Univ. de Valladolid, t1, 1918.

Velasti (Thomas Stanislaus).

Diss. de litt. Graec. pronuntiatione. 4°. Romae. 1751

Vélez de Guevara (Luis). El rey en su imaginación. Publ. por J. Gómez Ocerin. [Teatro ant. esp.] 8°. 1920

La serrana de la vera. Publ. por R. Menéndez Pidal y Ma. Goyri de Menéndez Pidal. [Teatro ant. esp.] 8°. 1916

see HURTADO DE MENDOZA (D.) L. de Tormes; El diablo cojuelo [*by L. V. de G.*], *n.d.*

***Velitationes** polemicæ, 1652, see DOUGHTY (J.)

Velius (Caspar Ursinus) [†URSINUS VELIUS (C.)] De bello Pannonico libri 10. In lucem prolati studio &c. A. F. Kollarii. s4°. Vindobonae. 1762

Velius (Theodorus). Chronyk van Hoorn, tot 1630. 4en dr. met Aanteken. verm. door S. Centen. [Bladwyzer & Burgermeesteren &c. *have sep. pagin.*] s4°. Hoorn. 1740

Westfrisia. [*Lat. & Dutch. 2 tps. b. w. h.* Chronyk, 1740]. s4°. Hoorn. 1740

Vellacott (Paul Cairn). Struggle of James II w. the Univ. of Cambridge, see WARD (*Sir* A. W.) In memoriam, 1924.

Velleius Paterculus (Caius). M. V. P., cum notis G. Vossii. [*w. sep. pagin.*] s8°. Lugd. Bat. 1654

Compendium of Roman hist.—Res gestae divi Augusti. With Eng. tr. by F. W. Shipley. [Loeb Class. Lib.] s8°. 1924

Velletti (Agostino). La storia di Ginevra degli Almieri che fu sepolta viva in Firenze. Riprod. [w. pref. by A. d'Ancona], sulle ant. stampe. la8°. Pisa. 1863

Velserus (Marcus), see VENETA. Squitinio d. liberta v. [*attr. to M. V.*], 1612.

Velsius (Justus). Apologia contra haereticae pravitatis appellatos Inquisitores &c. [*b. w.* Sarcenius (E.) In Evangelia Dominic. postilla, 1541]. s8°. *n.p.* 1546

Epistolae, aliaque quaedam scripta [*wanting all after page 174. b. w.* Sarcenius (E.) In Evangelia Dominic. postilla, 1541]. s8°. *n.p.* 1547

Velthusen (Johann Caspar), C. T. Kuinoel & G. A. Ruperti, *edd.* Comm. theologicae. [*Incl. diss. by each of edd.*] 6v. 8°. L. 1794–99

see BREMISCHES U. VERDISCHES THEOLOG. MAGAZIN, 1795–98.

Velthuysen (Lambert van) [VELTHUSIUS].

see BROWN (J.), *of Wamphray.* Libri 2 &c.; in post. L. Velthusii sententia de idololatria &c. confut., 1670.

„ —— Libertino-Erastianae L. Velthusii Sententiae &c. confut., 1670.

Veltkirch (Joannes). Confut. inepti & impii Libelli F. August. Alveld. Franciscani Lipsici, pro D. M. Luthero. s4°. Vuittenbergæ, *M. Lotther.* 1520

Velyaminov-Zernov (Vladimir Vladimirovich).
Works in Imp. Russ. Arch. Obsch. Труды Босточ. отд.
Изслѣдованіе о Касимовскихъ царяхъ &c. ч3, 1864. [11.]
Монеты Бухарскія и Хивинскія, 1859. [4.]
Памятникъ съ араб.-татар. надписью въ Башкиріи, 1859. [4.]
Источники дея изученія Тарханства, жалованнаго Башкирамъ. [I. Akad. Nauk. Записки, т4]. 8°. С.–П. 1864
Unters. ü. d. kasimofschen Zaren u. Zarewitsche. Übers. v. J. Th. Zenker. [Beitr. z. Gesch. d. Völker Mittelasiens, B1]. T1 [*no more publ. ?*] 8°. L. 1867

Velzen (Cornelius a), *see* Spanheim (F.), *the younger*. Summa hist. eccl.; contin. *as* Introd. ad hist. eccl. N.T., 1740], 1689.

Venatorius (Thomas), *see* Gechauf (T.), *surnamed Venatorius*.

Vence, ses mons., s. saints &c. [*Pref. signed* J. D. P2503]. s8°. [1914]

Vendekaabe (Povel), *see* Eliae (P.)

Vendelinus (Gottfried), *see* Musaeus (J.) Collegium controversiarum Becano, Wendelino &c. oppos., 1701.

Vendetta (Cesare). Serenata a 3 voci. [N125]. s8°. Napoli. 1704

Vendramin (Andrea), *fl. 1648, see* Borenius (T.) Picture gallery of A. V., 1923.

Vendryes (Joseph). Le langage. Intr. linguist. à l'hist. 8°. 1921
Language. Tr. P. Radin. 8°. 1925

Veneer (John). Expos. on the 39 articles of the Ch. of Eng. 2nd ed. 2v. 8°. 1730

Venema (Hermann). Diss. sacrarum lib. 3. s4°. Harlingae. 1731
Diss. sel. ad sacram scr. V. & N. Test. t1i, ii, diss. ad lib. Geneseos. [*in* 1v. *No more publ. ?*] s4°. Leovardiae. 1747–50

Venerius (Johannes Antonius).
De oraculis & divin. antiq. [P2741]. s4°. 1628

Veneroni (Giovanni). Compl. Ital. master; rules for attaining that lang. Tr. f. Dutch ed., rev., w. add. s8°. 1763

Veneta [Venete; Veneti].
Capitolare d. Maggior Conseglio. Stampato ad intellig. di cadaun nobile d. Rep. Veneta (1577–1740). la8°. [Venezia]. *n.d.*
Chronicon Venetum vulgo Altinate, *see* Simonsfeld (H.) Sulle scoperte d. R. Galli n. Cron. Alt., 1888.
Nuove ricerche sul Chronicon Altinate, 1908, *see* Besta (E.)
*Squitinio d. libertà Veneta. [*Sometimes attrib. to* (1) A. Albizzi, (2) Gualdo, (3) Pignoria, (4) Peireschio, (5) A. della Cueva, (6) M. Velsero].
For tr., see †Venise. Examen de la liberté orig. de V., 1677.
Storia arcana ed aneddot. d'Italia racc. dai veneti ambasciatori, 3v, 1855–58, *see* Mutinelli (F.)
Successi d. armi V. in Levante, 1685, sotto F. Morosini. s8°. Venetia. 1686
Another copy with 2 plates *wanting*.

Veneto, Patrizio, *see* Patrizio Veneto.

Veneto (Nicolao), *see* Conti (Niccolò de').

Venetus (Paulus), *see* Sarpi (P.)

Venezia [Venetia].
*Le arti che vanno per via n. città di V., 1803, *see* Zompini (G.)
*Avviso di Parnaso nel q. si racc. la povertà &c. dove è giunta la republ. di V. & il duca di Savoia, [tr.] con annot. per Valerio Fulvio Savoiano. [*b. w.* Veneta. Squit. d. libertà, 1612]. s8°. *n.p.* "In Antopoli." 1621
*Basilica (La) di S. Marco in V. [P2842]. la8°. Venezia. 1883
Basilica (La) di San Marco, illust. n. storia &c. da scr. venez. sotto dir di C. B., 1888–1893, *see* Boito (C.)
Basilica di S. Marco in V.: Direz. dei restauri &c. Condiz. stat. d. Basilica. [*Signed* M. E. Manfredi &c.] la8°. Venezia. 1904
„ Opere di restauro. [*Signed* M. E. Manfredi &c.] la8°. Venezia. 1908
*Campanile (Il) di San M. Cenni storici. [P2838]. 8°. Venezia. 1902
*Chiesa (La) ducale di S. M., 2t, 1753, *see* Meschinello (G.)
*Dell' orig. d. barbari, che distrussero &c. l'imperio di Roma onde hebbe principio V., 1557. *For reprint, see* Zeno (N.) Dell' orig. di V., 1558.
Doc per la storia di San Marco in V., d. 9. sec. s. a. 18. [F. Ongania editore. Pref. *signed* B. Cecchetti]. fol. Venezia. 1886
Dogi (I) di V. [*list.* P2850]. s8°. Venezia. 1871
Forestiere istruito n. cose più pregevoli &c. di Venezia. Nouv. comp. &c. s8°. Venezia. 1819
*Frammenti su V. [Nozze Oliva-Mazzarotto. N34]. la8°. Rovigo. 1864
Iconografia d. trente parrocchie di V., 1821, *see* Paganuzzi (G. B.), *ed.*
Inventario d. Archivio di Stato in V. Saggio. 4°. Venezia. 1881
Leggi d. elezioni, [1273–1775. P2842]. la8°. *n.p. n.d.*
Notte (La) del Redentore a V. [Nozze Donà-Marzari]. [Nozze 33]. 8°. [Vicenza]. [1862]
Ordini et capitoli d. Collegio de gli Spetiali d. V., 1565. [P2840]. 8°. Venezia. 1891
Parte presa n. Conseglio di X, 1611, in materia di Condanne &c. [P2858]. 8°. [Venezia. 1611]
Parte presa n. Conseglio di Pregadi, 1621, in materia di Contrabandi. [P2858]. 8°. [Venezia. 1621]

Venezia [Venetia] [*continued*].
Parte presa n. Maggior Conseglio 1697 in materia di proibizion de Brogli, preghiere &c. [*b. w.* Veneta. Capitolare (1577–1740), *n.d.*] 8°. [Venezia. 1697 ?]
Per il restauro d. Capella d. Rosario n. SS. Giovanni e Paolo. [L. Marangoni, relatore. P2843]. fol. [Venezia. 1910]
Per la ricostruzione d. Campanile. Deliberazioni &c. d. Comm. tecnico-artistica. [P2841]. 8°. Venezia. 1906
Raccolta de parti prese [d. Signoria di Venetia]. In materia di Stampe [1517–1697]. 8°. [Venezia]. *n.d.*
Sententia d. Eccelso Conf. di X contra Ridolfo Poma &c. [*b. w.* Veneta. Capitolare (1577–1740), *n.d.*] 8°. Venezia. 1607
*Sventramento (Lo) di V. Polemica. Progetti—Delendae Ven. di P. G. Molmenti &c. [P2836]. 8°. Venezia. [1887]
Le 3 Venezie, Tridentina, Propria, Giulia. Carta in due fogli. 2ª ed. *folded* la8°. Novaro. 1915
V. e le sue lagune. 2v [*in 4p, w. sep. tp. & pagin.* v2i *&* ii *b. sep.*] la8°. Venezia. 1847
V. nei secoli 18–19: espos. apr.-maggio 1919, Parigi, 1919, *see* Palais des Beaux-Arts.

Veneziani (Carlo). Antonio Gandusio. la8°. Milano. 1919
Armando Falconi. la8°. Milano. 1921

Veneziano. Settecento Veneziano, 1925, *see* Illustrazione Italiana, Suppl., 1925.

Vengerov (Semen Afanasevich). Основныя черты ист. нов. русс. литературы. 2e изд. Съ прибавлен. этюда "Побѣдители или побѣжденные? *b. w.* Skabichevsky (A. M.) Ист. нов. русс. лит., 6oe изд., 1906]. 8°. С.–П. 1909

Venice. Calendar of State Papers & MSS. rel. to Eng. affairs, existing in the Archives & coll. of V. & o. libraries of N. Italy. v22–28; ed. A. B. Hinds. la8°. 1919–27
22, 1629–32; 23, 1632–36; 24, 1636–39; 25, 1640–42; 26, 1642–43; 27, 1643–47; 28, 1647–52.
Biblioteca Nazionale Marciana.
Deux registres de prêts de mss. de la Bibl. de St. Marc (1545–59). [*Ed.* H. Omont. Extr. de la Bibl. de l'Éc. des chartes, 1887. P2835]. 8°. 1888
see Pittoni (L.) Lib. di S. M., 1903.
Biblioteca Querini Stampalia.
see Segarizzi (A.) B. Q. S., 1907.

Venier (Gerolimo). Relazione 1697, *see* Manchester (C. M., *1st duke*).

Venise. *Hist. de la républ. de V., par l'abbé L., 12t, 1758–68, *see* Laugier (M. A.)
*Mém. hist. & polit. sur la républ. de V., 2p, 1795, *see* Curti (L.)
*Mém. justif. de l'a. des Mém. hist. &c. de V., 1796, *see* Curti (L.)

Veni Vidi, *ps.* Ludendorff in Bayern: d. Novemberputsch. [P2735]. 8°. L. 1924

Venizelos (Eleftherios).
England's welcome to V., Nov. 1917: speeches &c., *see* Anglo-Hellenic League. Publ., No. 35, 1917.
The internal situation in Greece & h. amnesty of political offenders. Tr. [P2426]. 8°. 1920
Speech to the people, Aug. 27, 1916, *see* Anglo-Hellenic League, No. 28, 1916.
see Box (P. H.) Three master builders &c., 1925.
„ Chester (S. B.) Life of V., 1921.
„ Ure (P. N.) V. and h. fellow countrymen, 1917.

Venkatanàtha, *see* Desika (*Sri* V.)

Venn (Henry), *vicar of Huddersfield*. The life & a sel. f. the letters of H. V. Mem. drawn up by John Venn. Ed. by Henry Venn, B.D. 6th ed. s8°. 1839

Venn (John), *fellow & president of Caius Coll., Camb.* **& J. A. Venn.** Alumni Cantabrigienses: biog. list of students, graduates & holders of office at Univ. of Cambridge, to 1900. p1, 4v. la8°. C. 1922–27
p1, From earliest times to 1751.

Venn (John), *M.A., see* Venn (Henry). The life & a sel. f. letters of H. V.; Mem. by J. V., 1839.

Venn (John Archibald).
Foundations of agricultural economics. 8°. C. 1923
see Venn (J.) & J. A. V. Alumni Cantab.: biog. list of students &c., to 1900, p1, 4v., 1922–27.

Venner (Tobias). Via recta ad vitam longam. Annexed a Treatise of the baths of Bathe. Also Treatise conc. tobacco. s4°. 1637

Vent (Heinrich Wilhelm). De causis quibusdam Reformationem Lutheri praeparantibus. Oratio. [P1041]. s8°. Jenae. [1816]

Ventilatio confutatoria glossae pontificiae. Erleuterung &c. d. bäpstischen Gloss: ü. das zu Lawingen getruckte Gebet. [*In verse.* P2608]. s4°. *n.p.* 1615

Ventimiglia, *The Counts of, see* Cais de Pierlas (*le c.* E.) Il conti di V., il priorato di S. Michele ed il principato di Seborga, 1884.

Ventre (Louis), *seigneur de la Touloubre, dit Artefeuil, see* Artefeuil.

Ventura (Gulielmus). Indice d. Cron. astesi (Muratori, R. I. S., XI) di G. e S. V., comp. C. Merkel &c., *see* Regia Dep. Misc., t23, App., 1884.

Ventura (Secundinus). Indice d. Chron. astesi (Muratori, R. I. S., XI) di G. e S. V., comp. C. Merkel &c., *see* Regia Dep. Misc., t23, App., 1884.

Venturi (Adolfo).

L'arte ital.: disegno storico. 8°. Bologna. [1924]
Il Botticelli, interprete di Dante. 8°. Firenze. 1921
Filippo Brunelleschi. 32 riprod. con testo e cat. 8°. [1923]
Grandi artisti italiani. Celebrazioni e tributi. 4°. Bologna. [1925]
Leon Batt. Alberti. 26 riprod. con testo e cat. 8°. [1923]
Leonardo da Vinci, pittore. 8°. Bologna. [1920]
Luca Signorelli. [Grandi maestri]. la8°. Firenze. [1922]
Luca Signorelli interprete di Dante. 8°. Firenze. 1921
La miniatura ferrarese n. sec. 15 e il Decretum Gratiani. [Estr. (con agg.) da Le gallerie ital., anno 4]. fol. 1900
Piero della Francesca. la8°. Firenze. [1922]
Storia dell' arte italiana. v8i, ii, 9i–iii. la8°. Milano. 1923–28
8i, ii, L'architettura del quattrocento, p1, 2.
9i–iii, La pittura del cinquecento, 3p.
Studi dal vero. Attrav. le racc. artist. d'Europa. la8°. Milano. 1927

Translations.
Botticelli. [Tr.] la8°. 1927
Short hist. of Ital. art. Tr. E. Hutton. 8°. 1926

Venturi (Lionello). Il Caravaggio; 32 riprod. con testo e cat. 8°. [1921]
Il gusto dei primitivi. 8°. Bologna. [1926]

Venturi (Pietro Tacchi).
Storia d. Co. di Gesù in Italia. v2. la8°. 1922

Venturini (Luigi). Milano ne' suoi storici settecenteschi. 8°. 1921

Venudo (Giovanni), *1811–90, see* Bernardi (J.) Commem. di G. V., 1890.

Venukoff (M.), *see* Venyukov.

Venuti (Ridolfino). Accurata, e succinta descr. di Roma moderna. 2t. 4°. 1766
Descr. topograf. d. antichità di Roma. ed. 2ª. 2p [*in* 1v]. 4°. 1803

Venyukov (Mikhail Ivanovich). Списокъ русскихъ путешественниковъ по Азіи 1854–80. [P2499]. s8°. [Москва. 1881]

Venzky (Georg). *Gesch. d. Menschen in s. Zwischenzustande v. Tode b. zu s. Auferstehung. s8°. Bützow. 1762

Veo (Ettore). L'on. Federzoni. la8°. Milano. 1919

***Vera,** ac sincera hist. actorum patriarchae Antiocheni &c. in Sinarum imperio &c.; auctore quodam Sinensi missionario veritatis amante, 1708, *see* Tournon (*card.* de).

***Vera**; by a. of "Elizabeth & h. German garden," 1921, *see* Arnim (*countess* v.)

Véra (Augusto). Introd. to speculative logic & philos. [P2479]. 8°. St. Louis. 1873

***Veränderte** Russland (Das), 3T, 1739–44, *see* Weber (F. C.)

Verax (*Mons.*), *bachelier en théologie.* Difficultez sur l'ordonnance &c. de l'archévêque de Cambrai, t. le fameux Cas de conscience. [P2659]. s8°. Nancy. 1705

Vera y Figueroa (Juan Antonio de), *conde de la Roca.* *L'hist. du ministère du comte-duc [d'Olivarez], avec des réflex. polit. &c. [Tr.] s8°. Cologne. 1673

Verband der deutschen Akademien, *see* Deutsch. D. biograph. Jahrbuch, hrsg. v. V. d. deut. A., 1925 &c.

Verbehn (Julius). *Rembrandt als Erzieher. Von e. Deutschen. 18ᵉ A. 8°. L. 1890

Verbelis (K.) La Lituanie russe. Considér. statist. & ethnograph. Tr. d'A. Viscont. 8°. Genève. [1919]

Verbiest (*Father* **Ferdinand**). Epistola, 1678. [*b. w. h.* Lettre écr. de la cour de Pekin &c., 1684. *no tp.*] 8°. [1678?]
Lettre écrite de la cour de Pekin sur un voyage que l'Emp. de la Chine a fait l'an 1683, dans la Tartarie occid. 8°. 1684
Voy. de l'emp. de la Chine dans la Tartarie or., 1682, *see* Bernard (J. F.), *ed.* Recueil, t3, 1715; t4, 1732.

Vercelli Codex. Il Codice V. con omelie e poesie in lingua Anglosassone. A cura d. Bibl. Vaticana con intr. del Prof. M. Foerster. la8°. Roma. 1913

Verci (Giovanni Battista). Notizie int. alla vita e alle opere de' pittori, scultori e intagliatori d. città di Bassano. s8°. Venezia. 1775
Storia d. Ecelini. 3v [*in* 1]. 8°. Venezia. 1841
Storia d. Marca Trivigiana e Veronese. 20t [t20, Index]. s8°. Venezia. 1786–91

Verdam (Jakob). Middelnederl. handwoordenboek. la8°. 's-Gravenhage. [1911]

Verdegay y Fiscowich (Eduardo). Hist. del correo. Con un ap. compr. la legisl. la8°. 1894

Verdellay (Joannes de). Questiones cum suis argumētis in oppositum formatis supra evāgelia dominic. et solennium festivitatum. Item et casus conscientie &c. [*b. w.* Gulielmus, *Paris.* Postilla, 1508]. 8°. [Lugd., *J. de Place & T. de Cloches.* 1508]

***Verdeutscht** (Die) antwort, der, die Eck in s. Sendbrieff an d. Bischoff zu Meyssen hat die ungelarten Luther. Thumhern genandt, 1520, *see* Oecolampadius (J.)

Verdi (Giuseppe).
see Luzio (A.) Garibaldi, Cavour, V., 1924.
,, Werfel (F.) V., Roman, 1924.

Verdier (Aymar) & F. Cattois. Architecture civile & domest. au m. âge & à la Renaissance. 2t. 4°. 1858

Verdizotti (Francesco). De' fatti Veneti. 3v (1, –1504; 2, 1504–70; 3, 1570–1644). fol. Venetia. 1674–98

Vere (Edward de), *17th earl of Oxford, see* Oxford.

Vereenigde Doopgezinde Gemeente te Amsterdam, *see* Amsterdam.

Verein für Geographie und Statistik, *see* Frankfurter Verein für Geographie und Statistik.

Verein für Geschichte d. Stadt Wien, *see* Vienna. Quellen zur Gesch. d. S. W.; hrsg. v. V. f. G. d. S. W., 1895–1921.

Verein für Hamburgische Geschichte.
Veröffentlichungen. B3. 8°. Hamburg. 1922
see Finder (E.) Die Vierlande, 2T, 1922. [3.]

Verein für Meklenburgische Geschichte u. Alterthumskunde, *see* Mecklenburg. Meklenburg. Urkundenbuch, 11B, 1863–78.

Verein für Reformationsgeschichte.
Schriften. Jhrg. 1–45 [Nr. 1–143]. 8°. Halle a. S. [1883–1928]
see Albrecht (O.) Luthers Katechismen, 1915. [33 (Nr. 121/22).]
,, Aleandro (*card.* G.) Depeschen d. A. vom Wormser Reichstage 1521; übers. &c. P. Kalkoff. [4 (Nr. 17).]
,, Anrich (G.) Die Strassburger Reformation, 1918. [36 (Nr. 130).]
,, Arbusow (L.) Wolter v. Plettenberg u. d. Untergang d. Deut. Ordens in Preussen, 1919. [36 (Nr. 131).]
,, Arnold (C. F.) Ausrottung d. Protestant. in Salzburg &c., 2H, 1900–1. [18 (Nr. 67, 69).]
,, Bahlow (F.) J. Knipstro, 1898. [16 (Nr. 62).]
,, Bauer (C.) Die Beziehungen Calvins zu Frankfurt a. M., 1920. [38 (Nr. 133).]
,, —— Luther u. d. Papst, 1910. [27 (Nr. 100).]
,, Baumgarten (H.) Karl V. u. d. deut. R., 1889. [7 (Nr. 27).]
,, Beck (H.) Kaspar Klee v. Gerolzhofen, 1901. [19 (Nr. 71).]
,, Benrath (C.) Gesch. d. R. in Venedig, 1887. [5 (Nr. 18).]
,, —— Julia Gonzaga, 1900. [16 (Nr. 65).]
,, —— Luther im Kloster, 1505–25, 1905. [23 (Nr. 87).]
,, Bogler (W.) Hartmuth v. Kronberg, 1897. [14 (Nr. 57).]
,, Bossert (G.) Das Interim in Württemberg, 1895. [12 (Nr. 46/47).]
,, —— Württemberg u. Janssen, 2T, 1884. [2 (Nr. 5, 6).]
,, Brandenburg (E.) & G. Eberlein. Vorträge &c., 1901. [19 (Nr. 70).]
,, Buddenseig (R.) J. Wiclif u. s. Zeit, 1885. [2 (Nr. 8 u. 9).]
,, Bürckstummer (C.) Gesch. d. R. u. Gegenref. in Dinkelsbühl, 2T, 1914–15. [31, 32 (Nr. 115/16, 119/20).]
,, Cohrs (F.) P. Melanchthon, 1897. [14 (Nr. 55).]
,, Drews (P.) P. Canisius, 1892. [10 (Nr. 38).]
,, Egelhaaf (G.) Gustav Adolf in Deutschland, 1630–32, 1901. [18 (Nr. 68).]
,, —— & W. Diehl. Landgraf Philipp v. Hessen—Butzers Bedeutung f. d. kirchl. Leben in Hessen, 1904. [22 (Nr. 83).]
,, Erdmann (D.) Luther u. s. Beziehungen zu Schlesien, insbes. zu Breslau, 1887. [5 (Nr. 19).]
,, Ficker (J.) Luther, 1517: Rede, 1918. [36 (Nr. 130).]
,, Friedensburg (W.) Fortschritte in Kenntnis &c. d. Ref.-gesch., 1910. [27 (Nr. 100).]
,, Gauss (C.) Ref.-versuche in Pruntrut, 1913. [31 (Nr. 114).]
,, Gothein (E.) Ignatius v. Loyola, 1885. [3 (Nr. 11).]
,, Götzinger (E.) J. Vadian, 1895. [13 (Nr. 50).]
,, Gurlitt (C.) Kunst u. Künstler am Vorabend d. R., 1890. [7 (Nr. 29).]
,, Herrmann (F.) Evangel. Regungen zu Mainz, 1910. [27 (Nr. 100).]
,, Haussherr (H.) Der Staat in Calvins Gedankenwelt, 1923. [41 (Nr. 136).]
,, Hering (H.) Dr. Pomeranus, J. Bugenhagen, 1888. [6 (Nr. 22).]
,, Hermelink (H.) Toleranzgedanke im Ref.-zeitalter, 1908. [26 (Nr. 98).]

Verein für Reformationsgeschichte. Schriften [*continued*].
see HEROLD (R.) Gesch. d. R. in d. Grafschaft Oettingen, 1522–69, 1902. [20 (Nr. 75).]
,, HOLMQUIST (H. F.) Die schwed. R., 1523–31, 1925. [43 (Nr. 139).]
,, HOLSTEIN (H.) Die R. im Spiegelbilde d. dramat. Litt. d. 16. Jhdts., 1886. [4 (Nr. 14/15).]
,, IKEN (J. F.) Heinrich v. Zütphen, 1886. [3 (Nr. 12).]
,, JACOBI (F.) Das Thorner Blutgericht 1724, 1896. [13 (Nr. 51/52).]
,, JACOBS (E.) H. Winckel u. d. R. im süd. Niedersachsen, 1896. [13 (Nr. 53).]
,, KALKOFF (P.) Anfänge d. Gegenref. in d. Niederlanden, 2T, 1903. [21 (Nr. 79, 81).]
,, —— Briefe, Depeschen &c. ü. Luther v. Wormser Reichstage 1521, 1898. [15 (Nr. 59).]
,, —— Erasmus, Luther u. Fried. d. Weise, 1919. [37 (Nr. 132).]
,, KAWERAU (G.) H. Emser, 1898. [15 (Nr. 61).]
,, —— Luther in kath. Beleuchtung, 1911. [29 (Nr. 105).]
,, —— Luthers Schriften nach d. Reihenfolge d. Jahre verzeichnet &c., 1917. [35 (Nr. 129).]
,, —— P. Gerhardt, 1907. [24 (Nr. 93).]
,, —— Die Versuche, Melanchthon z. kath. Kirche zurückzuführen, 1902. [19 (Nr. 73).]
,, KAWERAU (W.) H. Sachs u. d. R., 1889. [7 (Nr. 26).]
,, —— Die R. u. d. Ehe, 1892. [10 (Nr. 39).]
,, —— T. Murner u. d. deut. R., 1891. [8 (Nr. 32).]
,, —— T. Murner u. d. Kirche d. M.-a., 1890. [8 (Nr. 30).]
,, KÖHLER (W.) Luther u. d. Lüge, 1912. [30 (Nr. 109/10).]
,, —— Wie Luther d. Deutschen d. Leben Jesu erzählt hat, 1917. [35 (Nr. 127/8).]
,, KOLDE (T.) Luther u. d. Reichstag zu Worms, 1521, 1883. [1 (Nr. 1).]
,, —— Relig. Leben in Erfurt &c., 1898. [16 (Nr. 63).]
,, KOLDEWEY (F.) Heinz v. Wolfenbüttel, 1883. [1 (Nr. 2).]
,, KONRAD (P.) Dr. A. Moibanus, 1891. [9 (Nr. 34).]
,, KÖRBER (K.) Kirchengüterfrage u. schmalkald. Bund, 1912. [30 (Nr. 111/112).]
,, KORTE (A.) Konzilspolitik Karls V, 1538–43, 1905. [22 (Nr. 85).]
,, KRONE (R.) Lazarus v. Schwendi, 1522-84, 1912. [29 (Nr. 106/7).]
,, LANG (A.) Der Heidelberger Katechismus, 1913. [31 (Nr. 113).]
,, —— J. Calvin: e. Lebensbild &c., 1909. [26 (Nr. 99).]
,, LECHLER (G. V.) J. Hus, 1889. [7 (Nr. 28).]
,, LENZ (M.) Geschichtsschreib. u. Geschichtsauffass. in Elsass &c., 1895. [12 (Nr. 49).]
,, —— Luthers Tat in Worms, 1921. [39 (Nr. 134).]
,, LÖSCHE (G.) Zur Gegenref. in Schlesien, 2T, 1915–16. [32, 33 (Nr. 117/18, 123).]
,, LÖSCHER (F. H.) Schule, Kirche u. Obrigkeit im R.-Jhdt., 1925. [43 (Nr. 138).]
,, LUTHER (M.) An d. christl. Adel deut. Nation &c., 1884. [1 (Nr. 4).]
,, MEYER VON KNONAU (G.) Die evangel. Kantone u. d. Waldenser, 1663–64, 1911. [28 (Nr. 103/4).]
,, MÜLLER (L.) Der Kommunismus d. mähr. Wiedertäufer, 1927. [45 (Nr. 142).]
,, MÜLLER (N.) G. Schwartzerdt, d. Bruder Melanchthons, 1908. [25 (Nr. 96/97).]
,, MULOT (R.) John Knox, 1505–72, 1904. [22 (Nr. 84).]
,, NEY (J.) Pfalzgraf Wolfgang, Herzog v. Zweibrücken &c., 1912. [29 (Nr. 106/107).]
,, —— Die R. in Trier 1559, 2H, 1906–7. [23, 25 (Nr. 88/89, 94).]
,, NIEMÖLLER (H.) Ref.-gesch. v. Lippstadt, 1906. [24 (Nr. 91).]
,, PREGER (C.) Pankraz v. Freyberg auf Hohenaschau, 1893. [10 (Nr. 40).]
,, RISCH (A.) Luthers Bibelverdeutschung, 1922. [40 (Nr. 135).]
,, ROGGE (C.) Luther u. d. Kirchenbilder s. Zeit, 1912. [29 (Nr. 108).]
,, ROSENBERG (W.) Der Kaiser u. d. Protest., 1537–9, 1903. [20 (Nr. 77).]
,, ROTH (F.) Einfluss d. Humanismus u. d. R. &c., 1898. [15 (Nr. 60).]
,, —— L. Kaiser, 1900. [18 (Nr. 66).]
,, —— W. Pirkheimer, 1887. [5 (Nr. 21).]
,, SCHÄFER (E.) Sevilla u. Valladolid, 1903. [21 (Nr. 78).]
,, SCHEEL (O.) Entwicklung Luthers, [–1516], 1910. [27 (Nr. 100).]
,, SCHIESS (T.) J. Kesslers Sabbata, St. Galler Ref.-chron., 1523–39, 1911. [28 Nr. (103/4).]
,, SCHMIDT (W.) Kirchen- u. Schulvisitation im sächs. Kurkreise, 1555, 1906. [24 (Nr. 90).]
,, SCHNELL (H.) Heinrich V, d. Friedfertige, Herzog v. Mecklenburg, 1902. [19 (Nr. 72).]
,, SCHNÖRING (W.) J. Blankenfeld, 1905. [23 (Nr. 86).]

Verein für Reformationsgeschichte. Schriften [*continued*].
see SCHOTT (T.) Aufhebung d. Ediktes v. Nantes, 1685, 1885. [3 (Nr. 10).]
,, —— Die Kirche d. Wüste, 1715–87, 1893. [11 (Nr. 43/44).]
,, SCHREIBER (H.) Johann Albrecht I., Herzog v. Mecklenburg, 1899. [16 (Nr. 64).]
,, —— Die Reform. Lübecks, 1902. [20 (Nr. 74).]
,, SCHUBERT (H. v.) Anfänge d. evangel. Bekenntnisbild., 1529/30, 1928. [45, H2 (Nr. 143).]
,, —— Bündnis u. Bekenntnis, 1529/30: Vortrag, 1908. [26 (Nr. 98).]
,, —— Luthers Frühentwicklung—Luthers Gedanken ü. d. Krieg, v. G. Kawerau, 1916. [34 (Nr. 124).]
,, —— Roms Kampf um d. Weltherrschaft, 1888. [6 (Nr. 23).]
,, SCHULTHESS-RECHBERG (G. v.) H. Bullinger, 1904. [22 (Nr. 82).]
,, SELL (C.) P. Melanchthon u. d. deut. R. bis 1531. [14 (Nr. 56).]
,, SILLEM (C. H. W.) Die Einführung d. R. in Hamburg, 1886. [4 (Nr. 16).]
,, SMEND (J.) Das evangel. Lied v. 1524, 1924. [42 (Nr. 137).]
,, SPERL (A.) Pfalzgraf Philipp Ludwig v. Neuburg &c., 1895. [12 (Nr. 48).]
,, STÄHELIN (R.) H. Zwingli u. s. Reformationswerk, 1883. [1 (Nr. 3).]
,, STEINMÜLLER (P.) Einführ. d. Ref. in Brandenburg durch Joachim II, 1903. [20 (Nr. 76).]
,, STOLZE (W.) Bauernkrieg u. Reformation, 1926. [44 (Nr. 141).]
,, STRACKE (E.) Luthers grosses Selbstzeugnis, 1545, 1926. [44 (Nr. 140).]
,, TSCHACKERT (P.) Herzog Albrecht v. Preussen, 1894. [11 (Nr. 45).]
,, —— P. Speratus v. Rötlen, 1891. [8 (Nr. 33).]
,, UHLHORN (J. G. W.) A. Corvinus, 1892. [9 (Nr. 37).]
,, ULMANN (H.) Leben d. deut. Volks bei Beginn d. Neuzeit, 1893. [10 (Nr. 41).]
,, VOGT (W.) Vorgesch. d. Bauernkrieges, 1887. [5 (Nr. 20).]
,, VORBERG (A.) Einführ. d. R. in Rostock, 1897. [15 (Nr. 58).]
,, WALDENMAIER (H.) Entstehung d. evangel. Gottesdienstordnungen Süddeut., 1916. [34 (Nr. 125/26).]
,, WALTHER (W.) Luther im neu. röm. Gericht, 4H, 1884–92. [2, 3, 8, 9 (Nr. 7, 13, 31, 35).]
,, WESTPHAL (F.) Fürst Georg zu Anhalt, 1907. [25 (Nr. 95).]
,, WIESE (H. v.) Der Kampf um Glatz, 1896. [14 (Nr. 54).]
,, WINTER (F. J.) J. Arndt, d. Verf. d. Wahren Christentums, 1911. [28 (Nr. 101/102).]
,, WINTZINGERODA-KNORR (L. G. C. W., *Frhr.* v.) Kämpfe u. Leiden d. Evangelisten auf d. Eichsfelde, 2H, 1892–3. [9, 11 (Nr. 36, 42).]
,, WREDE (A.) Ernst d. Bekenner, Herzog v. Braunschweig &c., 1888. [6 (Nr. 25).]
,, ZAHN (W.) Die Altmark im 30-jähr. Kriege, 1904. [21 (Nr. 80).]
,, ZIEGLER (H.) Gegenreform. in Schlesien, 1888. [6 (Nr. 24).]
,, ZUCKER (M.) A. Dürer, 1900. [17.]
see ARCHIV FÜR REFORMATIONSGESCH., in Verbindung mit d. V. f. R., 1904–14.
,, BRANDENBURG (E.) & G. EBERLEIN. Vorträge gehalten auf d. 6. Gen.-versamml. d. V. f. Ref.-gesch., 1901.

Verein für Rostocks Altertümer, *see* ROSTOCK. Beiträge z. Gesch. d. Universität R.; hrsg. v. V. für R. A., 1919.

Verein für Sozialpolitik. Schriften. B145iv, 146i, ii, 147v, 150ii–v, 151iii, 152i, ii, 156ii, iii, 157ii, 158–163, 164i, ii, 165i–iv, 166i–iii, 167i, ii, 168i, ii, 169, 170, 171i, ii, 172, 173i, ii. 8º. München. 1919–28
,, ,, [*List*], B1–170, 1873–1914. s8º. München. 1924
Verhandlungen d. Generalversamml. 1919, 1920, 1922, 1924. [159, 161, 163, 170.]
1919, Wirtschaftl. Bez. zw. d. Deut. Reich u. Deut.-Österr.—Prob. d. Sozialisierung.
1920, Die Reform d. Staatswiss. Studien, T2. [*For T1, see* Jastrow (I.)].
1922, Die Zukunft d. Sozialpolitik—Die Not d. geist. Arbeiter.
1924, Theorie d. Klassenkampfs—Handelspolitik—Währungsfrage.
Verhandlungen d. Vereins f. S. in Wien, 1926. Krisis d. Weltwirtschaft—Übervölkerung Westeuropas—Steuerüberwälzung. Hrsg. F. Boese. [172.]
see AMONN (A.) & M. v. BERNATSKY. Währungsreform, Tschechoslowakei u. Russland, 1924. [165iv.]
,, ANSIEDELUNG (DIE) v. Europäern in d. Tropen, T5, 1915. [147v.]
,, BUNZEL (J.), *ed.* Geldentwert. &c., Einfl. auf die sozial. Entwickl. in Österr., 1925. [169.]
,, COHEN (A.) Besteuerung u. Geldentwertung, 1924. [168ii.]
,, DIETZEL (H.) Engl. u. preuss. Steuerveranlagung, 1919. [157ii.]
,, EULENBURG (F.), *ed.* Neue Grundlagen d. Handelspolitik, 2T, 1925. [171i, ii.]

Verein für Sozialpolitik [*continued*].
see FALKNER (S. A.) Das Papiergeld d. französ. Revol., 1789–97, 1924. [165iii.]
,, GERLOFF (W.) Steuerbelast. u. Wiedergutmachen, 1924. [168i.]
,, HAINISCH (M.), *ed.* Wirtschaftl. Verhält. Deut.-Österr., 1919. [158.]
,, HERTZ (F.) Zahlungsbilanz u. Lebensfähigkeit Österr., 1925. [167ii.]
,, HOFMANN (V.) Die Devalv. d. österr. Papiergeldes, 1811, 1923. [165i.]
,, JASTROW (I.) Die Reform d. staatswiss. Studien, 1920. [160.]
,, LANSBURGH (A.) Die Politik d. Reichsbank &c., 1924. [166ii.]
,, LOTZ (W.) Valutafrage u. öffentl. Finanzen in Deutschl., 1923. [164i.]
,, MEERWARTH (R.) &c. Probleme d. deut. Zahlungsbilanz, 1924. [167i.]
,, MISES (L.) & F. KLEIN. Geldtheoret. u. geldrechtl. Seite d. Stabilisierungsproblems, 1923. [164ii.]
,, NEUORDNUNG (DIE) d. deut. Finanzwirtschaft; hrsg. v. H. Herkner, T2, 3, 1918. [156ii, iii.]
,, PLÄNE u. Versuche z. Währungssanierung, 1923. [165ii.]
,, SINZHEIMER (L.) &c. Die geist. Arbeiter, 2T, 1922. [152i, ii.]
,, STEINER (F.) Notenbankpolitik u. staatl. Anleihepol. in d. österr.-ungar. Nachfolgestaaten, 1924. [166.]
,, STOLPER (G.), *ed.* Deutsch-Österreich, 1921. [162.]
,, STUCKEN (R.) Die wertbeständ. Anleihen, 1924. [166iii.]
,, UNTERSUCHUNGEN ü. Konsumvereine, 1919–24. [150ii–v, 151iii.]
,, WIRTSCHAFTSTHEORIE. Beiträge z. W.; hrsg. K. Diehl, T1, 2, 1926–28. [173i, ii.]

Verein "Herold," [VEREIN F. SIEGEL- U. WAPPENKUNDE], *see* DEUTSCHER HEROLD (DER): Organ d. V. für S.- u. W. zu Berlin: Jhrg. 1–10, 1870–79.

Vereinigung z. Erhaltung deutscher Burgen, *see* BURGWART (DER), 1909–12.

Veresaev (Vikenty Vikentevich), *ps.* [*i.e.* V. V. SMIDOVICH].
Передъ завѣсой, *see* SBORNIK. Сб. товар. "Знаніе," 1, 1904.

Vereschagin (Vasily Vasilevich), *1842–1904.* Voyage dans les provinces du Caucase. Tr. par Mme. & M. Le Barbier, 1864–65. [*Part of* t17 *of* Le Tour du Monde]. fol. [1868]

Veress (Andreas), *ed.* Acta & epist. rel. Transylvaniae Hungariaeque cum Moldavia & Valachia. [Fontes rer. Transyl., t4]. v1. la8°. Budapest. 1914
see HUNGARI. Matricula &c. Hungarorum in univ. Ital. stud.; ed. A. V., 2v, 1915–17.
,, JESUITS. Epist. &c. Jesuitarum Transylvaniae (1571–1613); ed. A. V., 2v, 1911–13.

Verfasser (Julius).
The half-tone process; photo-engraving. 2nd ed. s8°. 1896

Verfassung (Die) d. Deutschen Reiches v. 11. Aug. 1919, 1920, *see* DEUTSCH.

Verga (Giovanni). Cavalleria rusticana & o. s. Tr. w. intr. by D. H. Lawrence. 8°. [1928]
Little novels of Sicily. Tr. D. H. Lawrence. s8°. O. 1925
Mastro-Don Gesualdo. Romanzo. s8°. Milano. [1920]
,, ,, Tr. D. H. Lawrence. s8°. [1925]

Vergara y Martin (Gabriel María).
Atlas geográf. de España. obl.8°. 1925

Verger (Jean Louis), *see* BOUCHARDON (P.) L'assassinat de l'archévêque (1856), 1926.

Vergerio (Pietro Paolo), *the younger, bp. of (1) Modrusch; (2) Capo d'Istria, c. 1498–1565.*
see HOSIUS (S.) Confut. prolegomenon Brentii adv. P. à Soto deinde P. P. Vergerius &c., 1561.
,, PERTHEL (E. T.) Oratio de P. P. V., 1842.

Vergessenen (Die): 100 deut. Gedichte d. 17. u. 18. Jhdts., 1926, *see* FISCHER (H.)

Vergilius (Polydorus). An abridgement of the notable worke of P. V. cont. the devisers &c. of artes, ministeries, rites &c. used in the churche &c. gathered by T. Langley. s8°. *n.p.* 1551
De rerum inventoribus libri 8. Acc. Pars altera Auctorum qui a Polydoro relicta pertractant &c. s8°. Coloniae Agrippinae. 1626

Vergniaud (Pierre Victurnien), *see* LINTILHAC (E.) V.: le drame des Girondins, 1920.

Verhaegen (Paul). La Belgique sous la domination franç., 1792–1814. 2t. la8°. Brux. 1922–24

Verhaeren (Emile). An aesthetic interpretation of Belgium's past [*French*], *see* BRIT. ACADEMY. Proc., 1917–18.
Choix de poèmes. Préf. d'A. Heumann, bibliog. &c. 14e éd. s8°. 1917
Les heures du soir &c. 4e éd. s8°. 1921
Toute la Flandre. 3t [1, 8e éd.; 2, 3, 7e éd.] s8°. 1920
see JONES (H. M.) E. V.: devel. of h. art & ideas, 1926.

Verheerlykt (Het) Nederland, 1745–74, *see* NEDERLAND.

Verheiden (Jacobus). Praestantium aliquot theologorum qui Rom. Antichristum praecipuè oppugnarunt effigies; quibus addita elogia, librorumque cat. fol. Halae Com. 1602

Veridicus (Theodorus), *ps., see* BATE (GEORGE), *M.D.*

Verinus (Simplicius), *ps., see* SALMASIUS (CL.)

Verinus (Timotheus), *character in controv. works on Pietism, see* LÖSCHER (V. E.)

***Veritas** toti mundo declarata; S. C. Regiamque Majest. non obligari &c., 1721, *see* BARSONY (G.), *bp.*

***Vérité** (La) sur les Cent Jours; par Un citoyen de la Corse, 1825, *see* DELFICO (M.)

Verjuys (Joannes Baptista).
Pastorale missionarum. [*tp. wanting*]. s8°. Brux. 1664

Verkhovsky (Yury Nikandrovich).
Баронъ Дельвигъ. Мат. біограф. и литерат. собр. Ю. В. 8°. П. 1922
Поэты-декабристы. Сборник под ред. Ю. Н. В. 8°. Москва. 1926
Поэты пушкинской поры сборникъ стиховъ. Подъ редакц. Ю. Н. В. s8°. Москва. 1919

Verkooren (Alphonse). Invent. des chartes & cartul. des duchés de Brabant & de Limbourg & des pays d'Outre-Meuse. pl, t6, 7. 8°. Brux. 1917
Invent. des chartes & cartul. du Luxembourg. t2–4. Brux. 1915–17

Verlaine (Paul). Correspondance. Publ. sur les mss. orig. avec une préf. & des notes, par A. Van Bever. t1, 2. s8°. 1922–23
see CAZALS (F. A.) & G. LE ROUGE. Les derniers jours de P. V., n. éd., 1923.
,, DELAHAYE (E.) V., 1910.
,, NICOLSON (H.) P. V., 1921.

Verlot (Jean Baptiste). Les plantes alpines. 2e éd. la8°. 1873

Vermeylen (August).
De wandelende Jood. 3e dr. 8°. Bussum. 1918

Vermigli (Caterina), *wife of P. Martyr, reformer, see* HUBERTUS (C.) *Hist. de vita M. Buceri &c.; item hist. C. V., 1562.

Vermorel (V.) & R. Danguy. Les vins du Beaujolais, du Mâconnais & Chalonnais. 8°. Dijon. [1893]

Vermuyden (*Sir* **Cornelius**), *see* KORTHALS-ALTES (J.) Sir C. V.: lifework in land-reclamation & drainage, 1925.

Vernadsky (Georgy Vlad.), *see* KONDAKOV (N. P.) Rec. d'études déd. à la mém. de K. (*w. life by G. V. V.*), 1926.

Verne (Jules).
Cinq semaines en ballon. n. éd. s8°. 1923
Five weeks in a balloon. [Tr.] s8°. *n.d.*
Hist. des grands voyages & des grands voyageurs. 6t [1, 14e éd., 3, 4, 4e éd., 5, 2e éd.] s8°. *n.d.*
On the track. s8°. *n.d.*
see ALLOTTE DE LA FUŸE (M.) J. V., sa vie, s. œuvre, 1928.

Verneau (René), *see* GRIMALDI. Grottes de G., t2i, Anthropologie; par R. V., 1906.

Vernède (Robert Ernest). War poems & o. verses. Intr. note by E. Gosse. [n. impr.] s8°. [1918]

Verner (William Willoughby Cole), *see* BREUIL (H.), H. OBERMAIER & *Col.* W. V. La Pileta à Benaojan, 1915.

Vernet (Carle) [VERNET (ANT. CHARLES HORACE)]. [Les cris de Paris. *99 coloured plates after C. V.* Lithog. de F. Delpech. *no tp.*] 4°. *n.d.*

Vernet (Jean Jacob). Selecta opuscula. s8°. Genevae. 1784

Verney (*il conte* **Alessandro Franchi-**), *see* FRANCHI-VERNEY (*il c.* A.)

Verney (Richard Greville), *19th baron Willoughby de Broke, see* WILLOUGHBY DE BROKE.

Vernierus (Benedictus). Magnum & universale concilium eccl. militantis super veritate div. Eucharistiæ sacramenti. s8°. Parisiis. 1554

Vernon MS., *see* ARCHIV F. D. ST. D. NEU. SPR., B56, Altengl. Marienlegenden aus MS. V., B57, Die Evangelien Gesch. d. Homiliensamml., B81, Proprium sanctorum, Zusatz-Homilien; hrsg. C. Horstmann, 1876–88.

Vernon (*Admiral* **Edward**). *Some seasonable advice f. an honest sailor. [P607]. s8°. 1746
*A specimen of naked truth f. a Brit. sailor [*i.e. letters f. V.*] [P607; 2778]. 8°. 1746
see WAGER (*adm. sir* C.) *Orig. letters to an honest sailor [*i.e.* Adm. V.], 1746.

Vernon (Frank).
The 20th century theatre. Intr. by J. Drinkwater. s8°. [1924]

Vernon (George), *Rector of Burton-on-the-Water, see* BARNARD (J.) Theologico-Historicus &c. wr. to correct errors of [G. V.] &c., 1683.

Vernon (George Middleton), *see* INDUST. FATIGUE RESEARCH BOARD. Rep. 1, 5, 6, 18, 19; by H. M. V., 1919–22.
Vernon (Horace Middleton), *see* INDUSTRIAL FATIGUE RESEARCH BOARD. Reports, by H. M. V. *& others*, 1919–26.
Vernünftigen (Die) Tadlerinnen, 1725, *see* GOTTSCHED (J. C.)
***Vero** (Il) successo occorso n. città di Parigi contra l'Armiraglio &c., 1572, *see* PARIS.
Véron (François). De regula fidei cathol. &c., *see* MIGNE (J. P.) Theol. cursus, t1, 1860.
Methodus compendiaria prætensam Reform. erroris convincendi, *see* MIGNE (J. P.) Theol. cursus, t5, 1841.
The rule of Catholick faith. Tr. by E. S. [*i.e. Ed. Sheldon*]. s8°. Paris. 1660
„ „ ....Tr. J. Waterworth. 8°. B'ham. 1833
see MESTREZAT (J.) & F. V. Actes d'une conférence &c., 1655.
Verona. Cat. descritt. dei manoscritti d. Bibl. Comunale di V. [*By* G. Biadego]. 8°. Verona. 1892
Storia d. Bibl. Comunale di V., 1892, *see* BIADEGO (G.)
La V. illustrata, 1771, *see* MAFFEI (F. S.)
Veronae rythmica descr.; a cura di L. Simeoni, *see* MURATORI (L. A.) Rerum Ital. Scr., t2i, 1920.
Verona (Guido da).
Azyadèh, la donna pallida. s8°. Firenze. [1927]
Cléo robes & manteaux. s8°. Firenze. 1926
Lettera d'amore alle sartine d'Italia. s8°. Milano. 1924
La mia vita in un raggio di sole. Romanzo. s8°. Firenze. 1922
La vita comincia domani. 8ª ed. s8°. Firenze. 1920
Veronese (Angela). Varie poesie. s8°. Venezia. 1804
Veronica, *Saint, of Jerusalem.* Die mittelniederdeut. V.; *ed.* K. Euling, *see* ARCHIV F. D. ST. D. NEU. SPR., B81, 1888.
Verplanck (Gulian Crommelin), *see* DALY (C. P.) G. C. V., 1870.
Verpoorten (Albrecht Meno). Comm. hist. de Martino Bucero, ejusque De coena Domini &c. Acc. Buceri ad Urbanum Regium epistola &c. s8°. Coburgi. 1709
Verpoorten (Philippus Theodorus). De urbe Nino et rebus Assyriis. Praes. A. M. Verpoortenn, resp. P. T. V. [P2587]. s4°. Witembergae. 1696
Verrall (Arthur Woolgar), *see* HOERNLE (E. S.) Problem of the Agamemnon: crit. of Dr. V.'s theory of the plot; & Dr. V.'s reply, 1921.
Verraux (*le général*). La bataille des Flandres en 1917. s8°. 1920
Verri (Aless.) The life of Erostratus. [Ital.], w. lit. & interlineal tr. on princ. of Hamiltonian system. Prefixed, Epitome of Ital. grammar by A. Gentili. s8°. 1842
see VERRI (P.) & A. V. Carteggio [1766–97]; a cura di F. Novati &c., v2–4, 1910–19.
Verri (Pietro). Storia di Milano, cont. fino al 1792 da P. Custodi: Disc. s. vita &c. di Verri per G. Carcano. 2v. s8°. Firenze. 1890
see OTTOLINI (A.) P. V. e i suoi tempi, con ristampa dei s. scritti ined., 1921.
—— **& A. Verri.** Carteggio [1766–97]. A cura di F. Novati e d'E. Greppi. v2–4, 1768[–71]. 8°. Milano. 1910–19
Verriest (Léo). Invent. du fonds de la cour des mortemains de Hainaut. [Invent. des archives de la Belg.] 8°. Brux. 1915
Verrill (A. Hyatt). Islands & th. mysteries. Pref. by J. A. Thomson. s8°. [1922]
Verrill (Charles H.), *see* HAMILTON (A.) Hygiene of the printing trades, 1917.
Verrua (Filiberto Gerardo Scaglia, *conte* **di),** *see* SCAGLIA (F. G.)
Verrua (Pietro). Orazio Nelson nel pensiero e nell' arte del Foscolo e del Canova. [P2516]. la8°. Padova. 1919
Versailles, *Treaty of.* Antwort d. Alliierten u. Assoz. Mächte (16. Juni 1919). Amtl. Text. [*Ed.* U. Rauscher]. [P2409]. 8°. 1919
Der Friede v. Versailles. [*b. w.* Bucharest. Friede v. B., 1918]. 8°. L. [1919]
Friedensbedingungen (Die) d. Alliierten u. Assoz. Regierungen, mit Einl. Anhang &c. 8°. 1919
Materialien betr. die Friedensverhandlungen, 1919. Amtl. Text. Autor. Ausg. T1–12 [8 *wanting*] *&* Beih. 1. 8°. & s4°. Charlottenburg. 1919–21
1, 2, Der Notenkampf. Reden u. Noten, T1, 2.
3, Die deut. Gegenvorschläge.
4, Mantelnote u. Antwort.
5, Zusammenstellung d. Änderungen &c.
6, Das deut. Weissbuch ü. die Schuld am Kriege.
7, Der Friedensvertrag in 3 Sprachen.
8, Der Friedensvertrag zw. Deutschland u. d. Entente. [*wanting.*]

Versailles, *Treaty of* [*continued*].
9, Der Notenwechsel bis z. Unterzeichnung d. Friedensvertrages.
10, Sachverzeichnis z. Friedensvertrage.
11, Friedensvertrag zw. Bulgarien u. d. Alliierten u. Assoz. Mächten.
12, Die acht Verträge v. Sèvres.
Beiheft 1, Die amtlichen Karten. [*b. w.* T7.]
Das Saargebiet unter d. Herrschaft d. Waffenstillstandsabkommens u. d. Vertrags v. V., 1921, *see* SAARGEBIET.
see TREATIES. T. of peace, 1919–23, v1, Treaty of V. &c., 1924.
Versé (Noël Aubert de), *see* AUBERT DE VERSÉ (NOËL).
Versegi (Ferencz) [VERSEGHY]. Diss. de versione Hungarica Script. sacrae. s4°. Budae. 1822
Versen (Max von). Hist. da guerra do Paraguai; tr. M. T. Alves Nogueira; notas pelo gen. E. A. da Cunha Mattos, *see* INSTITUTO HIST. &C. BRAZIL. Rev., t76ii, 1914.
Verses. *Verses on man's mortalitie [Like as the damaske rose] &c. [Repr. f. M. Spark's Crums of comfort &c., 7th ed., 1628]. 8°. Long Crendon. 1925
*Verses on var. occas. for friends, 1843, *see* JOWETT (W.)
Versicherungsamt, *see* REICHS-VERSICHERUNGSAMT.
Versteigerung.
*V. e. Gemäldesammlung v. altem Mobil. &c. aus Privatbesitz. Okt. 1919 [Mai 1920, Okt. 1920, Jan. 1921], Wien, Glückselig u. Wärndorfer. [4p *in* 1v. *Illust.*] 4°. Wien. 1919–21
Versti. Версты. Под ред. кн. Д. П. Святополк-Мирского &c. N. 1–3. la8°. Париж. 1926–28
1, *cont.* Житие Аввакума, *w. sep. pagin.*
Verstraeten (Fr.) & Em. Doms. Cours complet de la langue flamande. 5e éd. s8°. Cologne. 1883
***Verteütschtē** (Die) Text aus den Bebstlichen Rechten, c. 1530, *see* PÄPSTLICHE.
Vertot (René de). Hist. des chevaliers hospital. de S. Jean de Jerusalem. 4t [*t4 has 3 pagin.*] 4°. 1726
Hist. des révol. de Portugal. s8°. Amsterdam. 1712
Hist. of the revols. of Portugal. [Tr.] 4th ed. rev. & enl. 8°. 1735
Vertrauen: *Kein Vertrauen zur deutschen Regierung, 1920, *see* KEIN.
Vertue (George). A descr. of the works of W. Hollar, w. some acc. of h. life. 2nd ed., w. add. s4°. 1759
see CHARLES I, *of Gt. Brit.* Cat. &c. of King C.'s coll. of pictures &c.; transcr. &c. by Mr. V., 1757.
„ HOUBRAKEN (J.) & G. V. Heads of illust. persons of Gt. Brit., engr. by H. & V., n. ed., 1813.
, WALPOLE (H.) Cat. of engravers, digested by W. f. MSS. of V. [w. life of V.], 1762.
„ —— A cat. of engravers f. MSS. of G. V., added acc. of life & works of latter, 1786.
Verus (Gratianus), *ps.*, *see* GELDORPIUS (H.)
Verwey (Albert). Inleiding tot de nieuwe nederl. Dichtkunst, 1880–1900. 4e dr. s8°. [A. 1914]
Verzamelde gedichten. 3d. s8°. A. 1911–12
Verwijs (Eelco), *see* ALBERT I, *duke of Bavaria.* De oorlogen van A. met de Friezen &c.; naar onuitg. bescheiden door E. V., 1869.
Veryard (Ellis), *see* ROSE-TROUP (F.) E. V., 1892.
Vesalius (Andreas).
see SPENCER (W. G.) The "Epitome" of V. on vellum in the B.M. Lib., 1923.
„ —— V.: h. delin. of the framew. of the hum. body in the "Fabrica" & "Epitome," 1923.
„ SPIELMANN (M. H.) Iconography of A. V., 1925.
Vesely (Artem), *ps.* [*i.e.* NIK. KOCHKUROV].
Дикое сердце. s8°. Москва. [1926?]
Vesme (Alessandro).
Works in REGIA DEP. DI STORIA PATRIA. Misc.
Sull' acquisto fatto da Carlo Emanuele III, re di Sardegna, d. quadreria del Pr. Eugenio di Savoia, 1887. [25.]
Torquato Tasso e il Piemonte, 1889. [27.]
Van Dyck, peintre de portraits des princes de Savoie, 1885. [24.]
Vesnitch (Milenko R.), *see* FRANCE-AMERICA SOC., *New York.* Addresses, Feb. 2, 1918, 1918.
Vespasian, *emp. of Rome, see* HENDERSON (B. W.) 5 Roman emperors, 1927.
Vesper (Will). Die Jahresernte: Auswahl jüngster deut. Dichtung, hrsg. v. W. V. Jhrg. 1–5, 1923–27. s8°. L. [1923–27]
Vespucci (Amerigo), *see* BANDINI (A. M.) Vita di A. V.; illust. &c. da G. Uzielli—bibliogr. d. opere conc. P. Toscanelli & A. V. per G. Fumagalli, 1898.

Vesterinen (Emil). Agricult. conditions in Esthonia. 2nd ed. enl. [P2708]. 8°. Helsinki. 1923
Vestnik. Вестник Социалист. Акад., 1922–23, see SOTSIALISTICHESKAYA AKAD.
Vestris (*Madame*) [LUCIA ELIZABETH MATHEWS], see PEARCE (C. E.) Madame V. & h. times, 1923.
Vesuvio. *Diss. dell' estatico int. all' erruzioni [*sic*] del Vesuvio. [*b. w.* Alsario dalla Croce (V.) Vesuvius, 1632]. 8°. [c. 1753]
Vetālapañcaviṃśalikā (Die) d. Śivadāsa; [hrsg.] H. Uhle, see KÖNIGL. SÄCHS. GESELLS. Berichte, B66, 1914.
***Veterum** aliquot Galliae theol. scripta, 1586, see GALLIA.
Vethake (Henry). Princ. of polit. econ. 8°. Phila. 1838
Vetik (Ahmad), see AHMAD VETIK.
Vetsera (Helene, *baroness* **von),** see MAYERLING. *Das Drama v. M. [Tod d. Kronpr. Rudolf u. d. Bsse M. Vetsera: Denkschr. d. Baronin H. V. &c.], 1921.
Vetta. Su la v., pagine d'arte &c., 3v, 1920, see PELLIZZARI (A.), *ed.*
Vetter (Paul). [Armenian studies. *In Armenian*. Tr. &c. H. Dashean]. s8°. Vienna. 1895
Die armen. apokr. Apostelakten. [*Greek & Arm. Extr. f.* Oriens Christianus, 1.–2. Jhg. P2804]. pl, 2ii. la8°. [Roma. 1901–2?]
1, Das gnost. martyrium Petri.
2, Die Akten d. Petrus u. Paulus [*last part only*].
Nerses Schnorhali's Kirchenlieder. [*Extr. f.* Theol. Quartalschrift. P2794]. 8°. [Tübingen. 1899]
Vettermann (E.) Die Balen-Dichtungen u. i. Quellen. [Zeitschr. f. rom. Phil. Beih. 60]. 8°. Halle a. S. 1918
Vettori (Pietro), *the elder* [VICTORIUS (PETRUS)]. Orazione d. lode d. seren. Giovanna d'Austria &c., tr., 1566, see SALVIATI (L.) Primo libro d. Oraz., 1575.
***Vetus** disciplina monastica seu coll. auctorum ord. S. Benedicti max. partem ined., 1726, see BENEDICTINES.
Veuillot (Louis).
Rome pendant le Concile (1869–1870). t1. 8°. 1872
Vevers (William). An appeal to the Wesleyan Societies on the attempt now made to subvert their constit. 6th ed. [P2531]. s8°. 1834
Vevey (H. de), see GALBREATH (D. L.) & H. DE V. Manuel d'héraldique, 1922.
Veynes (François de), see REGIS (L.) & F. DE V. Bastos le hardi, 4e éd., 1923.
Veyrat (Jean-Pierre), see BERTHIER (A.) Le poète Savoyard, J.-P. V., 1810–44, 1920.
Veyssière de La Croze (Mathurin), see LA CROZE (M. V. DE).
Vhael (Bartholdus G.) Gramm. Fennica. s8°. Aboae. 1733
Via (Joannes à) [†WEGE (JOHANN ZU)]. Jugis eccl. catholicae sacrificii &c.: defensio & assertio contra calumnias &c. J. Andreæ Smidelini. s8°. Coloniae. 1570
Viaene (Ernest), see HALKIN (J.) & E. V. Les Ababua (Congo belge), 1911.
Viallate (Achille). La vie polit. dans les deux mondes. Publ. sous la dir. de A. V. & M. Caudel. 9, La Grande Guerre, 2 août 1914–11 nov. 1918. 8°. 1922
Vialleton (Louis Marius).
Éléments de morphologie des vertébrés. la8°. 1911
Vial-Mazel (G.)
Le Rhin, victoire allemande. [2e éd.] s8°. [1923 ?]
Viane (Franciscus van) & Christianus Lupus. Relatio doctorum F. v. V. & C. L. de iis quae 1677 in sua ad Innocentium XI deputatione peracta sunt. [P2659]. s8°. Lovanii. 1693
Vianello (Pietro), *ed.* Un Atto nuziale d. 1324. [Nozze Brunetta d'Usseaux-Pontini. N136]. obl.8°. Padova. 1873
Viani (Lorenzo). Parigi. s8°. Milano. 1925
I vàgeri. s8°. Milano. [1926 ?]
Viard (Jules), see FRANCE. Les grandes chroniques de F.; publ. par J. V., t1–4, 1920–27.
Viard (Paul Emile). André Alciat, 1492–1550. la8°. 1926
Viardot (*Mme.* **Pauline)** [†VIARDOT-GARCIA (M. F. P.)], see GREVS (I. M.) Ист. одной любви: Тургенев и П. В., 1927.
Viaud (Samuel).
see LOTI (P.) Un jeune officier pauvre, fragm. rassemblés par son fils S. V., 1923.
,, —— & S. V. Suprêmes visions d'Orient, 1921.
Vibart (Hugh Henry Rose).
Family allowances in practice. 8°. 1926
Vibert (R. Laurent-), see LAURENT-VIBERT (R.)
Vibius Sequester, see GRONOVIUS (A.) Varia geogr. & L. T. Gronovii animadv. in V. S., 1739.

Vic (Jean). La litt. de Guerre. Manuel des publ. de langue franç, 1914–18. Préf. de G. Lanson. 5t. [t1, 2, n. éd.] s8°. 1923
1, 2, Prem. pér., 1914–16, 2t [*pagin. contin.*], 3–5, 2e pér. 1916–18, 3t [*pagin. contin.*]
Vicaire (Gabriel). Émaux bressans. 8°. Lyon. 1919
Vicaire (Georges).
Bibliogr. gastronom. Préf. de P. Ginisty. 8°. 1890
Vicat (Béat Philippe). Vocabularium juris utriusque, opera & studio B. P. V. 3t. 8°. *Ex officina Bousquetiana.* 1759
Vicelinus, *bp. of Altenburg, d. 1154.* Versus de vita Vicelini, see HELMOLDUS. Cron. Slav.; ed. 2a; rec. B. Schmeidler, 1909.
Vicente (Gil). Obras. Com. revisão, pref. e notas de Mendes dos Remedios. 3t. 8°. Coimbra. 1907–14
Auto de la Sibila Casandra. Conforme a la ed. de 1562, con prólogo &c. de A. Giráldez. s8°. 1921
Auto da Sibilla Cassandra, see LOMBA Y PEDRAJA (J. R.) Teatro ant. a L. de Vega, 1924.
Autos portugueses de G. V. y de la escuela Vicentina. Ed. facs. con introd. de C. M. de Vasconcellos. 4°. Madrid. 1922
Four plays [Auto da alma—Exhortação da guerra—Farsa dos almocreves—Tragicomedia pastoril da Serra da Estrella]. Ed. f. ed. princ. (1562), w. tr. & notes, by A. F. G. Bell. la8°. C. 1920
Lyrics. [Tr., w. notes by] A. F. G. Bell. [3rd ed.] s8°. *n.p.* 1925
see BELL (A. F. G.) G. V., 1921.
,, KING (G. G.) Play of the Sibyl Cassandra *by V.*, 1921.
Vicentina. Legge suntuaria V., 1882, see FASOLO (G.), *ed.*
Vicenza (Armand Augustin Louis de Caulaincourt, *duke of***),** see EILLEAUX (*ctsse.* **d'**). *Recoll. of Caulincourt, duke of V.; tr., 2v, 1838.
***Vices** & virtues: being a soul's confession of its sins, w. Reason's description of the virtues, a Middle Eng. dialogue ab. 1200. Ed., w. intr., tr., notes & gloss. by F. Holthausen. [E.E.T.S., 159]. p2, Notes & gloss. 8°. 1921
Vicetia (Antonio Maria a), see ANTONIO MARIA *da Vicenza.*
Vichy-Chamrond (Marie de), *marquise du Deffand,* see DU DEFFAND.
Vick (Charles J.), see WHITE (A. V.) Water powers of Brit. Columbia, by A. V. W. asst. by C. J. V., 1919.
Vickers (Kenneth Hotham). England in the later Middle Ages. [Hist. of Eng., ed. C. Oman, v3]. 3rd ed. 8°. [1921]
Parishes of Carham, Branxton &c., see NORTHUMBERLAND. Hist. of N., v11, 1922.
Vico (Giovanni Battista). G. B. V. Volume commem. n. 2° cent. d. pubbl. d. "Scienza nuova" (1725–1925). A cura d. A. Gemelli. la8°. Milano. [1926]
see CROCE (B.) Le fonti d. gnoseologia Vichiana, 1912.
,, LONGO (M.) G. V., 1921.
,, NAPLES, *University.* In Reg. Caroli Borboni & Amaliae Saxonicae nuptis; [Orat. J. B. V. &c.], 1738.
,, NICOLINI (F.) Per la biog. di G.-B. V., 1925.
Vicomercatus (Franciscus), see STRIGELIUS (V.) In P. Melanchthonis libellum de anima notae &c.; acc. F. V. De anima rationali discept., 1590.
Victor, *ps.*, see DUCANGE (V. H. J. B., *dit*).
Victor Amadeus II, *king of Sardinia.* I primi atti costit. dell' augusta casa di Savoia ordin. in Palermo . . . V. A. regnante; ric. G. Spata, see REGIA DEP. DI STORIA PATRIA. Misc., t10, 1870.
Lettere a G. M., conte di Morozzo, ambasc. a Madrid, 1713–17; pubbl. E. Morozzo della Rocca, see REGIA DEP. DI STORIA PATRIA. Misc., t26, 1887.
see TELLUCCINI (A.) Viaggio di ritorno d. Sicilia d. re V. A. II, 1910.
Victor Amadeus III, *king of Sardinia,* see GERBAIX DI SONNAZ (C. A. DE). Ult. anni di regno di V. A. III re di S. (1789–96), 1918.
Victor Emmanuel II, *King of Italy,* see FORESTER (C. S.) V. E. II & union of I., 1927.
Victoria & Albert Museum.
Bookbindings & rubbings of bindings in Nat. Art Library; by W. H. J. Weale. [Dept. of Sci. &c.] 2[p *in* 1v]. 8°. 1894–98
Carvings in ivory; by M. H. Longhurst. pl. 8°. 1927
Constantine A. Ionides Collection, v1. By B. Long. la8°. 1925
1, Paintings in oil, tempera & water-colour.
Drawings of old London in Victoria & Albert Museum. By P. Norman. [P2565]. 8°. 1921
Eng. furniture & woodwork. v1, 3. la8°. 1923–27
1, Gothic & early Tudor; by H. C. Smith.
3, Late Stuart to Queen Anne; by O. Brackett.

Victoria and Albert Museum [*continued*].
Eng. silversmiths' work &c., civil & domestic. Intr. by W. W. Watts. 8º. 1920
Flat ornament: sel. f. S. Kens. Mus. by A. J. Lee. sl (*50 plates*). fol. 1910
Herbert Allen coll. of Eng. porcelain; by B. Rackham. 2nd ed. 8º. 1923
Italian plaquettes; by E. Maclagan. la8º. 1924
Japanese lacquer; by E. F. Strange. 2p. la8º. 1924–25
Jones Coll. 3p. 8º. 1922–24
1, Furniture; by O. Brackett.
2, Ceramics, ormolu, goldsmiths' work &c.
3, Paintings & miniatures; by B. S. Long.
Maps, plans, & views of London & Westminster, coll. by F. Crace, lent by J. G. Crace. s8º. 1879
Notes on printing & bookbinding. Guide to exhib. of tools & materials &c., by S. T. Prideaux. [P2500]. s8º. 1921
Pastoral staves. By W. W. Watts. la8º. 1924
Picture book of bookbindings. 2p *in* 1v. s8º. [1927]
Picture bk. of medieval enamels. s8º. [1927]
Picture bk. of portrait busts. s8º. [1927]
Picture bk. of the Raphael cartoons. s8º. [1927]
Review of principal acquisitions, 1918, 1924, illust. la8º. 1920–26
Special loan coll. of scientific apparatus, 1876. 8º. [1876]
Textiles f. burying-grounds in Egypt; by A. F. Kendrick. v1. la8º. 1920
Water colour paintings by Brit. artists &c. rev. ed. 8º. 1927
see Eccles (H.) & B. Rackham. Analysed spec. of Eng. porcelain, 1922.
,, †Gardner (J. S.) Ironwork &c., 3p, 1893–1922.
,, Rowe (E.) Wood carvings, fol. 1–3, 1889.
,, Strange (E. F.) Japanese colour prints, 1904; 4th ed., 1913; 5th ed., 1923.
,, Tattersall (C. E. C.) Notes on carpet-knotting &c., 2nd ed., 1927.

Victoria history (The) of the counties of England. sm. fol. 1924–28
Berkshire, v3, 4, 1924; Index, 1927.
Buckingham; v3, 4, 1925–27.
Durham; v3, 1928.
Hertford; Index, 1923.
Huntingdon; v1, 1926.
Kent; v2, 1926.
Worcester; v4, 1924; Index, 1926.
York, North Riding; v2, 1923; Index, 1925.
Yorkshire; Index. sm. fol. 1925

Victoria Institute (The), or Philosophical Soc. of Gt. Brit.
Journal of the Transactions. v45–58. 8º. 1913–26

Victoria Memorial, *Calcutta, see* Calcutta.

Victoria Memorial Museum, *Ottawa, see* Canada: Geolog. Survey.

Victoria, *queen of Gt. Brit. & Ireland.*
[Coll. of portraits &c. of V., h. family &c.] fol. *n.d.*
*A diary of royal movements & of personal events &c. in life of V. v1. [*no more publ.*] 8º. 1883
Letters. Ser. 2. Sel. f. corr. & journ., 1862–85. Ed. G. E. Buckle. 3v. 8º. 1926–28
see Humphrey (F. P.) The Queen at Balmoral, 1893.
,, Martin (A. P.) The Q. in the I. of Wight, 1898.
see Maxwell (*Sir* H. E.) 60 years a Queen, 1897.
,, Ryland (F.) V., 1837–1901: events, 1901.
,, Strachey (G. L.) Queen V., 1921.
,, Tissot (E.) Le livre des reines: la reine V. &c., 1896.
,, Tooley (S. A.) Personal life, 1896.

Victoria Adelaide Mary Louise, *consort of Frederick III, German Emp., see* Tissot (E.) Le livre des reines: l'impératrice F. &c., 1896.

Victoria (Franciscus de), *see* Franciscus, *a Victoria.*

Victorinus, *Saint, of Pettau.* Opera. Rec., comm. crit. instr. &c. J. Haussleiter. [Corpus scr. eccl. Lat., 49]. 8º. Vindobonae. 1916

Victricius, *Saint, see* Vacanard (É.) St. Victrice, 2e éd., 1903.

Vicuña Mackenna (Benjamin).
El libro de la plata. la8º. Santiago de Chile. 1882

Vida (Girolamo) [Vida (Hieronimo)]. Il Sileno, dialogo. Con le sue rime &c. et con l'interpret. d. O. de' Belli. s8º. Vicenza. [1589]

Vida (Marcus Hieron), *bp. of Alba.*
Opera. s8º. Antverpiae. 1558
The game of chess. Done into Eng. &c. by R. S. Lambert. Intr. by R. C. Lambert. [*With text*]. 4º. *p.p. Stanton Press.* 1921
Poetics, w. tr. f. the Latin of Lowth, Gray & o. by J. Hampson. 8º. Sunderland. 1793

Vidal (C.)
Charles-Albert & le Risorgimento ital. (1831–48). 8º. 1927

Vidal (J.), *see* Jouvin (G.) & *Capt.* Gillet. Marches & chansons des soldats de France; rec. par J. V., 1919.

Vidal (Pierre), *bibliothécaire de Perpignan, see* Calmette (J.) & P. V. Hist. de Roussillon, 1923.

Vidal de La Blache (Paul). Hist. & géogr. Atlas gén. Vidal-Leblache. n. éd. conforme aux Traités de Paix. fol. 1922
—— & L. Gallois. Le bassin de la Sarre. Clauses du Traité de Versailles. la8º. [1919]

Vidalenc (G.) L'art norvégien contemp. s8º. 1921
William Morris. 8º. 1920

Vidania (Diego Vincencio de), *see* Vincencio de Vidania (D.)

Vidari (Giovanni). Le carte storiche di Pavia, *see* Regia Dep. di Storia Patria. Misc., t27, 1889.

Videman (Ferd. Ivanovich), *see* Wiedemann (F. J.)

Videnskabs Selskab [*Christiania*]. Register til Forhandlinger & Skrifter, 1858–1924. 8º. 1925
see Mowinckel (S.) Psalmenstudien, 1, 2, 1921–22.
,, Schjelderup (H. K.) Hauptlinien d. Entwicklung d. Philos. v. Mitte d. 19. Jhdt., bis z. Gegenwart, 1920.

Vie.
*Vie de Jacques Cathelineau, 1821, *see* Genoude (A. E.)
*Vie de Napoléon, 1822, *see* Napoleon I, *emp. of the French.*
*Vie (La) du véritable père Josef, Capucin &c., 1705, *see* Richard (R.)
Vie (La) polit. dans les deux mondes, 9, La Grande Guerre, 2 août 1914–11 nov. 1918, 1922, *see* Viallate (A.)

Viebig (Clara), *ps.*
Eine Handvoll Erde. Roman. s8º. 1915
Der einsame Mann: Roman. s8º. St. 1925
Die Passion. s8º. St. 1925
Das rote Meer. Roman. [5e A.] s8º. 1920
Töchter d. Hekuba. Roman. [34e A:] s8º. 1920
Unter d. Freiheitsbaum. Roman. 1.–10. A. s8º. St. 1922
Translation.
Daughters of Hecuba. Tr. A. Barwell. s8º. [1922]

Vieillard (Camille). Gilles de Corbeil, 1140–1224? Préf. de Ch.-V. Langlois. 8º. 1909

Vieira (Afonso Lopes), *see* Lopes Vieira (A.)

Vieira (Antonio), *Jesuit, see* Carel (E.) V., sa vie & s. œuvres, 1879.

Vieira Castrioto (João Fernandes), *see* Santiago (D. L. de). Hist. da guerra de Pernambuco e feitos do J. F. V., 1875–80.

Vieira Fazanda (José). Antiq. e memorias do Rio de Janeiro, *see* Inst. Hist. e Geogr. Brazileiro. Revista trimensal, t88, 89, 1923–24.

Viel-Castel (*le cte.* **Horace de).** Méms. s. le r. de Napoléon III, 1851–64. 3e éd. [5, 6, 2e éd.] 6t. 8º. 1883–85

Vielé-Griffin (Francis).
Choix de poèmes. Intr. par J. de Cours. Bibl. s8º 1923
Œuvres. 2[t]. 8º. 1924–26

Vielliard (Jeanne). Le Latin des diplômes roy. & chartes privées de l'époque méroving. [H.E., 251]. 8º. 1927

Vienna [Vienne; Wien]. Actes & doc. de la Conf. Germano-Polon., tenue à Vienne du 30 avr.–30 août 1924, 1925, *see* Actes.
Album v. Objecten aus d. Sammlung Kunstindustrieller Gegenstände d. Kaiserhauses. Arbeiten d. Goldschmiede-u. Steinschlifftechnik. Erläut. Text v. A. Ilg. fol. Wien. 1895
Die Einblattdrucke d. 15. Jhdts. in d. Kupferstichsammlung d. Hofbibl. zu Wien. Hrsg. F. M. Haberditzl. 2B. fol. Wien. 1920
1, Die Holzschnitte; bearbt. v. F. M. Haberditzl.
2, Die Schrotschnitte; bearbt. v. A. Stix.
Die illum. Hss. u. Inkunabeln d. Nationalbibl. in Wien; beschr. v. H. J. Hermann, 3T, *see* Wickhoff (F.), *ed.* Beschreib. Verzeichnis d. illum. Hss. in Österreich, B8, 1923–27.
Österreich. Galerie, Wien. Das Barockmuseum im Unteren Belvedere. [*Foreword signed* F. M. Haberditzl]. la8º. Wien. 1923
Quellen zur Gesch. d. Stadt Wien. Hrsg. v. Verein f. Gesch d. Stadt Wien. Abt. 1, B7i, 8, 9; Abt. 2, B4, 5i; Abt. 3, B3i. 4º. Wien. 1914–23
I, B7i, 8, Regesten aus in- u. ausländ Archiven, B7, 8, redigirt v. J. Lampel.
,, B9, Regesten aus d. Zentralarchive d. deut. Ritterordens zu Wien; bearbt. v. V. Schindler.
II, B4, Regesten d. Originalurkunden d. stadt. Hauptarchivs bearb. v. J. Lampel.
,, B5i, Regesten d. Originalurkunden d. ehemal. W. Burger spitalarchivs, 1264–1529, bearb. v. H. Hango & G. A. Ressel.
III, B3, Grundbücher d. Stadt Wien; 3, Satzbuch A1, 1373–88; bearb. F. Staub, T1, Texte u. Reg.
Tapestries of the Vienna Imp. Court. [*Cont.* H. Schmitz The Vienna coll. &c.—E. W. Braun: the Boucher Gobelin —Plates]. 4º. Vienna. 192

Vienna [*continued*].
Tratado de paz, concl. entre el Rey de Fr., el Emperador &c. en V. 18 Nov. 1738. Con la accession de el Rey [Carlos] al Tratado, 1739. [P2766]. 8°. Napoles. 1739
KUNSTHIST. INSTITUT D. K. K. UNIV. WIEN.
see DIEZ (E.) Churasan. Baudenkmäler, B1, 1918.
,, WICKHOFF (F.), *ed.* Beschreib. Verzeichnis d. illum. Hss. in Österreich., B8, 3T, 1923–27.
see KAISERLICH-KÖN. KUNSTHIST. HOFMUS.
,, KAISERLICH-KÖN. MÜNZ- &c. KABINET.
,, MEKHITARISTS. Cat. d. armen. Hss. in d. Mechit.-Bibl. v. J. Dashian, 1895.

Vienna Union (The), *see* INTERNAT. CONFERENCE. 2nd & 3rd Internat. & the V.U., Offic. rep., 1922.

Vienne. Chartes de Saint-Maurice de V., de l'abbaye de Léoncel & de l'église de Valence. Suppl. aux recueils impr. publ. par U. Chevalier. [Coll. de cartul. dauphinois, t10, livr. 1. *b. w.* Dauphiné. Choix de doc. &c., 1874]. la8°. 1912

Viénot (John). Hist. de la Réforme franç., des orig. à l'Édit de Nantes. la8°. 1926
Pages de défense protestante, publ. sous la dir. de J. V. t1 [*no more publ.*] la8°. [1923]
La vie ecclés. & relig. dans Montbéliard au 18e s. Thèse, Paris. la8°. Audincourt. 1895

Vient de paraître. Revue bibliog. mensuelle—Revue du mois scientif. 1924 (mars–déc.), 1925–1927. 4°. London. 1924–27
1925 *has* Numéro spéc. *w. t.* Les arts décor. mod., 1925.

Vier Documente a. röm. Archiven, 1872, *see* DRESSEL (A. R. M.)

Viera y Clavijo (José de). Noticias de la hist. gen. de las Islas Canarias. n. ed. corr. y aument. por el autor. 4t. 8°. Santa Cruz de Tenerife. 1858–63

Vierlingh (Andries). Tractaet van dyckagie. Uitg. door J. de Hullu en A. G. Verhoeven. [Rijks Gesch. Publ.; uitg. in opdracht v. d. Min. v. Onderwijs &c., Kleine ser., 20, 20A]. [Platen, *b. sep.*] la8°. 's-Gravenhage. 1920

Vies. *Vies des papes Alexandre VI & Léon X; par D. B., 1751, *see* DU BOULAY (N.)
*Vies (Les) des pères des déserts & des saintes solitaires, 4t, 1714, *see* VILLEFORE (J. F. B. DE).

Viëtor (Carl). Gesch. d. deut. Ode. 8°. München. 1923
Die Lyrik Hölderlins. 8°. Frankfurt a. M. 1921

Viets (Edward).
Ad somnum & o. poems. s8°. Boston [U.S. 1924]

Vieusseux (Giovanno Pietro), *see* ANZILOTTI (A.) Un amico napolet. di G. P. V.: il barone G. Savarese, 1921.

Vieux manoirs, vieilles maisons, s1, 1927, *see* QUEBEC.

Vieuxtemps (Henry), *see* BERGMANS (P.) H. V., 1920.

View.
*View (A) of London & Westminster, 2p, 1725–28, *see* LONDON.
*View (A) of some exceptions made by a Romanist to the Ld. viscount Falkland's Disc. of the infallibilitie of the Ch. of R., 1646, *see* HAMMOND (H.)
*View (A) of the new directory &c., 1645; 1646, *see* HAMMOND (H.)
*View of the origin &c. of freemasonry, 1830, *see* FREEMASONRY.

Vieyra (Anthony), *prof. of Spanish in Dublin Univ.* Novo dicc. portatil das linguas Portugueza e Ingl. n. ed., rev. e augm. por J. P. Aillaud. 2v [*in* 1]. s8°. Pariz. 1873

Vifquain (J. B.) Carte de la navig. de la Belgique &c. Ann. au Rapp. de l'Inspecteur des Ponts &c., J. B. V. folded 8°. 1842

Viganò (*Gen.* **Ettore**). La nostra Guerra, sino al Nov. 1917. 8°. Firenze. 1920

Vigée Le Brun (*Mme.*)
Memoirs, 1755–89. Tr. G. Shelley. 8°. [1927]

Vigener (Fritz). Drei Gestalten aus d. mod. Katholizismus: Möhler, Diepenbrock, Döllinger. [Hist. Zeitschrift, Beiheft 7]. 8°. München. 1926

Vigeois. Cartul. de l'abbaye de V. en Limousin, 954–1167. Publ. par M. de Montégut. la8°. Limoges. 1907

Viger (A.) L'atmosphère. 8°. [1925]

Vigerus (Franciscus). De præcipuis Græcæ dictionis idiotismis. 10a ed. s8°. Londini. 1647

Vigier (*le cte.* **Henri**). Davout, (1770–1823). Intr. de M. F. Masson. 2e éd. 2t. 8°. 1898

Vigil (Christianus), *ps.*, *see* GESENIUS (FRIEDRICH).

Vigil (Francisco de Paula G.) Carta al Papa y analisis del breve 10 Junio 1851. [*b. w. h.* Compendio, 1852]. 2a ed. 8°. Lima. 1852
Compendio de la defensa de la autoridad de los gobiernos contra las pretensiones de la Curia Romana. 8°. Lima. 1852

Vigil (José María). Flores de Anahuac. Compos. dramaticas. 8°. Guadalajara. 1867

Vigilis (Christianus), *ps.*, *see* GESENIUS (F.)

Vigilius, *Saint, bp. of Trent.* B. V. martyris &c. opera. Ad hæc Comment. de duabus in Christo naturis &c. G. Cassandri [*w. sep. tp. & pagin.*] s8°. Coloniæ. 1555
Contra Eutychianam confusionem duarum naturarum, damnatam in Synodo Chalcedonensi. s8°. *n.p. in officina Voegeliana. n.d.*

Viglione (Francesco).
Ugo Foscolo in Inghilterra. la8°. Catania. 1910

Vignali (*l'abbé* **Ange Paul**). Descr. of the V. Coll. of relics of Napoleon. [P2753]. 8°. Phila. 1924

Vignat (G.), *see* BAUGENCY. Cartul. de l'abbaye de Notre-Dame de B.; publ. G. V., 1879.

Vignati (Cesare). Commem. di F. Robolotti, *see* REGIA DEP. DI STORIA PATRIA. Misc., t25, 1887.
Storie lodigiane. 8°. Milano. 1847

Vignaud (Henry). The Columbian tradition on the discovery of America & the part played therein by Toscanelli. Mem. addr. to H. Wagner & C. Errera. 8°. O. 1920

Vignay (Jean de), *see* FRERE (W. H.), *ed.* Expos. de la Messe f. La legende dorée of J. de V., 1899.

***Vigne** (La) florissante du Japon, 1620, *see* JAPON.

Vigneul - Marville (— de), *ps.* [*i.e.* NOËL BONAVENTURE D'ARGONNE]. De optima legendorum eccl. patrum methodo. Ex Gall. tr. &c. interp. J. F. R. 8°. Augustae Taurin. 1742

Vignola (Il), *see* BAROZZI (G.), *called Il Vignola.*

Vignoli (Carlo). Il folk-lore di Castro dei Volsci, *see* MONACI (E.) Studj romanzi, v13, 1917.

Vignon (Marie-Louise).
Le cœur ardent & grave. Poèmes. s8°. 1924

Vignon (Paul).
The shroud of Christ. Tr. f. the Fr. 4°. Westminster. 1902

Vignory. Cartul. du prieuré de Saint-Etienne de V. Publ. de Soc. Hist. &c. de Langres, avec intr. &c. par J. d'Arbaumont. 8°. Langres. 1882

Vigny (*le cte.* **Alfred de**). Chatterton—La Maréchale d'Ancre—Quitte pour la peur—Shylock. [Théâtre, 1]. s8°. *Nelson.* [1915]
Cinq-Mars, préc. de réflexions sur la verité dans l'art, suiv. du disc. de récept. à l'Acad. Fr. &c. 10e éd. s8°. 1852
Journal d'un poète. n. éd. rev. & augm. par F. Baldensperger. 8°. 1928
see DUPUY (E.) Jeunesse d. romantiques, V. Hugo & A. de V., 1905.
,, FRANCE (A.) Œuvres compl., t1, A. de V.: étude &c., 1925.

Vigo (Pietro). Montenero. Guida. 8°. Livorno. 1902
Necrologia, *see* ARCHIVIO STOR. ITAL., a. 78, v1, 1920.

Vigor (*Mrs.* —), *see* WARD (*Mrs.* —).

Vigor (Simon), *abp. of Narbonne, see* ACTES. Acts of the dispute & conf., Paris, 1566, betw. [S. V. & C. de Sainctes] & 2 ministers; tr., 1602.

Viguerius (Joannes). Instit. ad Christ. theologiam, sacr. lit., universaliumque concil. authoritate. fol. Antverpiae. 1565

Vijaya Dharma Suri [SHASTRA-VISHARADA JAIN ACHARYA SHRI VIJAYA DHARMA SURI], *see* SUNAVALA (A. J.) V. D. S., h. life & work, 1922.

Vijaya Pala, *prince, of Ceylon, see* PIERIS (P. E.) Pr. V. P. of C., 1927.

Viking Club. Extra ser. v3. la8°. Coventry. 1912
see STJERNA (K.) Essays on questions conn. w. Beowulf; tr. & ed. J. R. C. Hall, 1912. [3.]

Vikramāditya, *king of Ujjayinī.* Vikrama's adventures, or, The 32 tales of the throne. Ed. & tr. w. intr. by F. Edgerton. [Harvard Orient. Ser., v26, 27]. 2p. la8°. Cambridge, *Mass.* 1926

Viladrich (Miguel), *see* PEREZ DE AYALA (R.) M. V., 1920.

Vilains (Des) ou Des xxiii manieries de vilains; *ed.* E. Faral, *see* ROMANIA, t48, 1922.

Vilarrasa y Costa (Eduardo Maria) & J. I. Gatell. Hist. de la Revolucion de Setiembre. t1. 8°. Barcelona. 1875

Vilate (J.) Causes secr. de la Révol. du 9 au 10 Thermidor [*& Contin.* P2774]. 8°. an 3. [1794]
Les mystères de la mère de Dieu dévoilés; 3e vol. des Causes secr. [P2774]. 8°. an 3. [1794]

Vildrac (Charles).
Chants du désespéré, 1914–20. 2e éd. s8°. 1920
,, ,, ... 4e éd. s8°. 1920

Vildrac (Charles) [*continued*].
Découvertes. 5e éd. s8º. 1923
Michel Auclair—Le pèlerin. Pièce[s]. 2e éd. s8º. 1923
Le paquebot Tenacity. Comédie. 3e éd. s8º. 1920

Vilenkin (Grigory Abr.)
Государств. и экономич. строй соврем. Япони. 8º. С.-П. 1908

Vilenkin (Nikolai Mikhailovich), *see* MINSKY (N. M.)

Vilensky-Sibiryakov (Vladimir Dmitrievich).
Черная годана Сибирской реакции. [P2723]. 8º. Москва. 1919

Viles (Edward) & F. J. Furnivall, *edd.* Rogues & vagabonds of Shakespeare's youth: Awdeley's "Fraternitye of vacabondes" & Harman's "Caveat" &c. 8º. 1907

Vilgelms (Alfred) [Вильгельмъ; WILLHELMS].
Русь великая или Руй-бель. Изысканіе обрусѣвшаго финскаго Шведа по пѣснямъ "исландской Едды" &c. ч1. [P2452]. 8º. С.-П. 1908

Villa (Antonio Martin). Reseña hist. de la Univ. de Sevilla y descr. de su iglesia. [Soc. de Bibliófilos Andaluces]. 8º. Sevilla. 1886

Villa-Amil (Genaro Perez de), *see* ESCOSURA (P. DE LA). España artistica y mon.: obra dirigada &c. por G. P. de V.-A., 3t, 1842–50.

Villa-Amil y Castro (José). Crón. de la prov. de Lugo, 1866, *see* ESPAÑA. Crón. gen., v2, 1865 &c.

Villada (Zacarias Garcia). Paleografía española. Prec. de una intr. sobre la paleogr. lat. 2[v] (1, Texto; 2, Album). 8º. & obl.4º. 1923

Villaespesa (Francisco). El espejo encantado. Poesías. 8º. 1911

Villafranca Piemonte. Statuti di V. P. (1384) con altri doc. e mem. (1001–1620); *ed.* R. A. Marini, *see* REGIA DEPUT. Miscellanea, t49, 1918.

Village. Village educ. in India: rep. of Comm. of Inquiry, 1920, *see* INDIA.

*Village lawyer (The): farce, 1792, *see* MACREADY (W.)

Villain (Georges). Le Palais, 1922, *see* PARIS. COMM. MUNIC. DU VIEUX P. Procès-verb., Année 1922, 1925.

Villalpando (Juan Bautista), *see* PRADO (H.) & J. B. V. In Ezechielem explanat. &c., 1596–1604.

Villalva (Federico). Crón. de la prov. de Palencia, 1867, *see* ESPAÑA. Crón. gen., v6, 1865 &c.

Villamediana (J. de Tassis, *conde* **de)**, *see* HURTADO DE MENDOZA (A.) Fiestas de Aranjuez [*a prose summary of the* "Comedia de la gloria de Niquea" *of V. &c.*]; tr. by Sir R. Fanshawe, 1670.

Villamil (*Lt.-Col.* **Richard de)**, *see* DE VILLAMIL (*Lt.-Col.* R.)

Villani (Carlo). Scrittori ed artisti pugliesi. la8º. Trani. 1904

Villanis (Luigi Alberto).
L'arte del clavicembalo. 8º. Torino. 1901

Villanova (*il conte* **Francesco Alberti di)**, *see* ALBERTI DI VILLANOVA (*il conte* F.)

Villanueva (Joaquin Lorenzo). De la leccion de la Sagrada Escr. en lenguas vulgares. 4º. Valencia. 1791

Villard (Léonie). Jane Austen: a French appreciation. Tr. V. Lucas. With a new study of Jane Austen by R. B. Johnson. 8º. 1924

Villaret (Claude), *see* VOLTAIRE. L'esprit de V. [*ed.* C. V.], 1760.

Villari (Luigi).
The awakening of Italy: the Fascista regen. 8º [1924]
La campagna di Macedonia. 8º. Bologna. [1922]
Development of polit. ideas in Italy in 19th cent. [Brit. Acad. P2834]. 8º. [1926]

Villari (Pasquale). La "Dante Alighieri" a Siena. [Nuova Antologia, Dec. 1902. P2841]. 8º. 1902
Donatello u. s. Werke. Festrede. Übers. v. H. N.-D. A. [P2507]. 8º. Jena. 1887
L'Italia giudicata da un meridionale. [P2837]. 8º. *n.p. n.d.*
see PANELLA (A.) Commem. di P. V. e bibliog., 1918.

Villarosa (Francesca de), *comtesse d'Orsay*, *see* ORSAY.

Villars (*l'abbé* **de)** [†MONTFAUCON DE VILLARS (-DE)]. *Le comte de Gabalis, ou entretiens sur les sciences secrètes (1670). Préc. de Magie & dilettantisme &c. par R. L. Doyon & L'ésotérisme de Gabalis par P. Marteau. s8º. 1921

Villars (Louis Hector de), *marshal of France*, *see* MORRIS (W. O'C.) V., 1892.

Villars (Meg). The broken laugh. s8º. 1920

Villault (Nicolas), *Sieur de Bellefond* [†VILLAUT (NICOLAS)]. Rel. des costes d'Afrique, appelle'es Guine'e, avec descr. &c. s8º. 1669

Villa-Urrutia (Wenceslao Ramírez, *marq.* **de).** Fernando VII rey constit. Hist. diplom., 1820–23. 8º. [1922]
La reina de Etruria, Doña Maria Luisa de Borbon. 8º. [1923]

Villaut (Nicolas), *Sieur de Bellefond*, *see* VILLAULT.

Ville (Pierre de la), *see* LA VILLE (P. DE).

Villedieu (Alexander de), *see* ALEXANDER, *grammaticus.*

Villefore (Joseph François Bourgoing de) [†BOURGOING DE VILLEFORE]. *Les vies des pères des déserts & des saintes solitaires. 4t [t4 *wanting*]. s8º. Anvers. 1714

Villehervé (Bertran de la), *see* LA VILLEHERVÉ (B. DE).

Villèle (A. de). Mirage d'amour. Roman. s8º. 1922

Villemarqué (*le vte.* **Hersart de la)**, *see* LA VILLEMARQUÉ.

Villène (Georges Lanoë-), *see* LANOË-VILLÈNE (G.)

Villeneuve (François Alberti de), *see* ALBERTI DI VILLANOVA (*il conte* F.)

Villeneuve (L. de), *see* GRIMALDI. Grottes de G., t1i, Hist. & descr. par L. de V., 1906.

Villeneuve (Léontine de), *aft. comtesse de Castelbajac.* Le roman de l'Occitanienne & de Chateaubriand. Publ. par la comtesse de Saint-Roman, avec 70 lettres inéd. de C. Préf. de R. de Flers. s8º. [1925]

Villeroi (Nic. de Neufville *sieur* **de)**, *see* MATTHIEU (P.) Remarques d'estat de V., 1652.

Villeroy (Madeleine Angélique de Neufville de), *aft. dsse. de Luxembourg*, *see* LUXEMBOURG.

Villers (Charles François Dominique de). Essay on the spirit &c. of the Reformation &c. Added Life of Luther. Tr. by B. Lambert. 2nd ed. 8º. 1806

Villes & tribus du Maroc: doc. &c., t4–7, 1918–21, *see* MISSIONS SCIENTIFIQUES DU MAROC.

Villetard (Pierre).
L'aventure de Marise. s8º. 1923
Le château sous les roses. Roman. s8º. 1921
Marise chez Tante Loulou, roman, *see* ŒUVRES libres, 21, 1923.
Un ménage d'autrefois, nouvelle, *see* ŒUVRES libres, 40, 1924.
Mon. Bille dans la tourmente. s8º. 1920
Les poupées se cassent. Roman. s8º. [1919]

Villette (*Rev.* **John).** The annals of Newgate, or malefactors register: by Rev. J. V. & others. 4v. 8º. 1776

Villey (Pierre). Marot & Rabelais, avec table chron. des œuvres de M. 8º. 1923
see MONTAIGNE (M. DE). Les Essais, t4, Les sources des Essais, &c. par P. V., 1920.

Villiers (Cosme de) [†VILLIERS DE ST.-ETIENNE]. Bibliotheca Carmelitana, notis crit. & dissert. illust. (1752). Add. nova praef. & suppl. cur. G. Wessels. 2t [*in* 1v]. fol. Romae. 1927

Villiers (Frederic). Villiers: his 5 decades of adv. 2v. 8º. 1921

Villiers (Henry Montague).
Charms of the consular career. 8º. [1925]

Villiers (J. de), *actor, d. 1861.* La vengeance des marquis (1663)—Les Costeaux (1665), *see* FOURNEL (V.) Contemp. de Molière, t1, 1863.

Villiers (M. de), *see* DE VILLIERS (M.)

Villiers de L'Isle Adam (*le comte* **Philippe Auguste M. de).**
Œuvres complètes. 4[t]. 8º. 1922–23

Villiers du Terrage (*le b.* **Marc de).** La découv. du Missouri & l'hist. du Fort d'Orléans (1673–1728). la8º. 1925

Villiers-Wardell (*Mrs.* **Janie).** Spain of the Spanish. s8º. 1909

Villon [*i.e.* FRANÇOIS CORBUEIL, *dit Villon*].
Les ballades en jargon du ms. de Stockholm. Essai de restit. &c., intr., notes & comm. &c. par R. F. Guillon. 8º. Groningen. 1920
Le grant testament villon et le petit. Son codicille. Le iargon & ses balades. [*facs.* 1489. Notice par P. Champion]. s8º. [1924]
Œuvres. Publ. avec notes & gloss. par P. Lacroix. s8º. *n.d.*
Œuvres. Ed. A. Longnon. [Classiques fr. du m.-â.] 2e éd. rev. par L. Foulet. s8º. 1914
Œuvres. Ed. crit. avec notices & gloss. par L. Thuasne. 3t. 8º. 1923
Œuvres compl. Publ. avec intr. &c. par L. Dimier. s8º. 1927
Poems. Done into Eng. verse by J. Payne. 8º. 1881
see CARCO (F. C., *dit*). Le roman de F. V., 1926.
,, LEWIS (D. B. W.) F. V., doc. survey, 1928.
,, VITU (A. C. J.) Notice sur F. V., 1873.

Villot (Frédéric), *see* LOUVRE. Notice des tableaux, 3p, 1873–74.

Villuga (Pedro Juan). Reportorio de todos los camínos de España. [Hispanic Soc. of America]. s8º. 1546. [facs. repr. *De Vinne Press*, 1902]

Vilmorin-Andrieux et Cie. The vegetable garden. Eng. ed. publ. under dir. of W. Robinson. Addendum by W. P. Thomson. 3rd ed. 8º. 1920

Vilna (The) problem. P2749]. 8º. [1922]

Vimer (Rudolf). Malta ili Mljet—Ne Mljet već Malta, *see* BULLETTINO DI ARCH. &C. DALM., 36, Suppl., 1913.
Vina (Ruy de Lugo), *see* LUGO-VINA.
Vinacke (Harold Monk).
Modern constit. develop. in China. 8°. Princeton. 1920
Problems of indust. development in China. 8°. Princeton. 1926
Vinaver (Eugène). Etudes sur le "Tristan" en prose. la8°. 1925
Vince (*Mrs.* Millicent).
Decoration & care of the home. 8°. [1923]
Vincencio de Vidania (Diego). Francisco de Benavides: servicios heredados &c. y los de su hijos, D. de Benavides y L. de Benavides &c. fol. Napoles. 1696
Vincent [Ferrer], *Saint.* *Un hombre de acción: San Vicente Ferrer, su vido &c. s8°. [1925]
see GORCE (M. M.) St. V. F. (1350–1419), 1924.
Vincent, *of Lerins, Saint.* Adv. prophanas haereseωn novationes libellus. Item E. Campiani oblati certaminis in causa fidei rationes decem. [*tp. wanting*]. s8°. Coloniae. 1600
Commonitorium adv. haereses. Adnexa: J. B. Bossuet Doctrinae catholicae, expos. [*w. sep. pagin.*] s8°. Vetero-Pragae. *n.d.*
Commonitorium, *see* MIGNE (J. P.), *ed.* Theologiæ cursus compl., t1, 1860.
Peregrini [*i.e.* Vincent] pro cath. fidei commonitoria duo, *see* GALLIA. *Vet. aliq. G. theol. scripta, 1586.
Vincent (Arthur), *ps.* The defence of India. 2nd imp. s8°. 1923
Twelve bad women. [*By var. wr.*] Ed. A. V. [3rd impr.] 8°. [1911]
Vincent (*Sir* Edgar), *aft. Baron D'Abernon,* **& T. G. Dickson.**
Hdbk. to modern Greek. 2nd ed. rev. s8°. 1893
see MARRIOTT (*Sir* W. T.) The Khedivial family: corresp. betw. M. & E. V., 1889.
Vincent (John Hayle). The Chautauqua movement. Introd. by L. Miller. s8°. Boston [U.S.A.] 1886
Vincent (José). Théodore Aubanel, la vie & l'homme, le poète. 8°. Avignon. [1924]
Vincent (L. H.) & E. J. H. Mackay. Hébron: le Ḥaram el-Khalîl, sépulture des Patriarches. Par L. H. V. & E. J. H. M. avec collab. de F. M. Abel. fol. 1923
,, ,, Album des planches. fol. 1923
Vincenti (Giuseppe Oggeri), *see* MURATORI (L. A.) Annali d'Italia, cont. d. V., 1789–90.
Vincentiis (Emma de). Caduta d. monarchia borbon. in un' op. ined. di L. Bianchini, *see* ARCHIVIO STOR. ITAL., a. 83ii, 1925.
Vincentius, *Bellovacensis* [VINCENT VON BEAUVAIS]. La estoria de los quatro dotores de la S. Eglesia. Hrsg. v. F. Lauchert. [Roman. Bibl., 14]. s8°. Halle a. S. 1897
Vinci (Leonardo da). Il Codice atlantico di L. da V., n. Bibl., Ambrosiana; riprod. e pubbl. d. Regia Accad. d. Lincei, trascriz. diplom. e. crit. d. G. Piumati. Testo 2v. Tavole 2v. la. fol. Milano. 1894–1904
Il Codice di L. da V. d. Bibl. di Lord Leicester in Holkham Hall. Pubbl. G. Calvi. [R. Istit. Lombardo]. la. fol. Milano. 1909
L. da V. Conferenze fiorentine. [*By*] E. Solmi [*& others*]. la8°. Milano. 1910
I manoscritti e i disegni di L. da V. Pubbl. d. R. Comm. Vinciana. Disegni. fasc. 1. atlas fol. 1928
,, ,, Manoscritti. v1i, ii, 2. fol. 1923–26
1, Il Codice Arundel 263, p1, 2.
2, I fogli manc. al cod. su'l volo d. uccelli n. Bibl. R., Torino.
Raccolta Vinciana. Presso l'Archivio Stor. del Comune di Milano. fasc. 1–12 (1905–25). 8°. Milano. [1906]–26
TRANSLATIONS.
Thoughts on art & life. Tr. M. Baring. 8°. Boston, *Merrymount Press.* 1906
Treatise on painting. Tr. J. F. Rigaud. Life of [V.] by J. W. Brown. s8°. 1887
see CALVI (G.) I manoscritti di L. da V., 1925.
,, CIPPICO (A.) An all-embracing genius: L. da V., 1921.
,, COOK (*Sir* T. A.) L. da V., sculptor: illust. essay on Albrizzi Madonna, 1923.
,, HART (I. B.) Mechanical investig. of L. da V., 1925.
,, HOLMES (*Sir* C. J.) L. da V.: lect., 1919.
,, HOPSTOCK (H.) L. as anatomist; tr., 1921.
,, LORENZO (G. DE). L. da V. e la geologia, 1920.
,, MACCURDY (E.) L. & war, 1919.
,, —— L. da V., 1920.
,, —— Mind of L. da V., 1928.

Vinci (Leonardo da) [*continued*].
see MALAGUZZI VALERI (F.) L. da V. e la scultura, 1922.
,, SCHIAPARELLI (A.) L. ritrattista, 1921.
,, TAYLOR (R. A.) L. the Florentine, 1927.
,, TONI (G. B. DE). Le pianti e gli animali in L. da Vinci, 1922.
,, UZIELLI (G.) Richerche int. a L. da V., s2, 1884.
,, VALÉRY (P.) Introd. à la méthode de L. de V., 1919.
,, —— Variété [*incl.* Intr. à la méthode de L. de V.], 1924.
,, VENTURI (A.) L. da V., pittore, 1920.
Vinciguerra (Antonio). Opera nova. s8°. [Venetiis. 1527]
Vinçotte (Thomas), *see* DEVIGNE (M.) T. V., 1919.
Vindication.
*Full (A) v. of the 11 accused Members &c., 1647, *see* HOLLES (D. H., *1st baron*).
*Just (A) & modest v. of the Scots design &c., 1699, *see* DARIEN.
*V. (A) of a book, int., Brief acc. of persec. of Quakers, 1737; 1741, *see* BESSE (J.)
*V. (A) of a disc. The principles of the Cyprianic age, 1701, *see* SAGE (J.)
*V. of Lady Byron, 1871, *see* FOX (J.)
*V. (A) of Mr Wesley's last Minutes &c., 1771, *see* FLETCHER (J. W.)
V. (A) of the imprisoned &c. Members of the H. of Commons, 1649, *see* PRYNNE (W.)
V. (A) of the last Parl., 1711, *see* PARLIAMENT, *Anon. Works.*
Vindicta Salvatoris, mitteleng. Gedicht d. 13. Jhdts.; hrsg. R. Fischer, *see* ARCHIV F. D. ST. D. NEU. SPR., B111–112, 1903–4.
Vinent (Antonio de Hoyos y), *see* HOYOS Y VINENT (A. DE).
Viner (Jacob). Dumping: a problem in internat. trade. 8°. Chicago. 1923
Vines (Richard), *presbyterian divine.* H.M. concessions to Bill of abolition of abps. & bps. &c. [1648]. [P2662]. s4°. 1660
Vines (Sherard). The Pyramid. Pref. verses by E. Blunden & Y. Noguchi. 8°. [1926]
Vinet (Alexandre R.)
Disc. sur quelques sujets relig. 3e éd. revue. 8°. 1836
Études sur la litt. franç. au 19e s. Texte de l'éd. de 1848, rev. & compl. & préc. d'une préf. par P. Sirven. t2, 3. 8°. [1916–24]
2, Lamartine & Victor Hugo.
3, Sainte-Beuve, E. Quinet, Michelet &c.
Outlines of philosophy & lit. [Sel. & tr. Ed. J. F. Astié]. 8°. 1877
Outlines of theology. [Sel. by J. F. Astié. Tr.] 2nd ed. s8°. 1866
Philosophie morale & sociale. Rec. d'essais &c. publ. par P. Bridel avec la collab. de P. Bonnard. t2. 8°. Lausanne. [1916]
see SEILLIÈRE (*b.* E. A. A. L.) A. V., 1925.
Vingboons (Johannes). MS. atlas, c. 1660, *see* WIEDER (F. C.) Mon. cartograph., v1, 1925.
Vingtrinier (Emmanuel). La Contre-Révolution, prem. période, 1789–91. 2t. 8°. 1924
Vining (*Maj.* L. E.) Held by the Bolsheviks: diary of Brit. officer in Russia, 1919–20. la8°. [1924]
Vinogradoff (A. K.)
Мериме въ письмах к Соболевскому. la8°. Москва. 1928
Vinogradoff (*Sir* Paul). Custom & right. s8°. Oslo. 1925
The growth of the manor. [3rd ed.] 8°. [1920]
Outlines of hist. jurisprudence. v1, 2. 8°. 1920–22
1, Intr.—Tribal law.
2, Jurisprudence of the Greek city.
Oxford studies in social & legal hist. Ed. P. V. v6–9. 8°. O. 1921–27
Each work has separate pagin.
6, Studies in the hundred rolls; aspects of 13th cent. admin.; by H. M. Cam.—Proc. agst. the crown (1216–1377); by L. Ehrlich.
7, Early treat. on the practice of Justices of the Peace in 15th & 16th cent.; by B. H. Putnam.
8, Studies in the period of Baronial reform & rebellion, 1258–67; by E. F. Jacob.
9, Social structure of medieval E. Anglia; by D. C. Douglas.
see FISHER (H. A. L.) P. V., a mem., 1927.
,, HOLDSWORTH (W. S.) Prof. Sir. P. V., 1926.
Vinokurov (A.) Социальное обеспечение в советской России. Сборник статей. [P2578]. la8°. Москва. 1919
Vinsauf (Geoffrey). Poetria nova *& o. works,* *see* FARAL (E.) Les arts poét. du 12 & 13 s., 1924.
Vinson (Auguste). Voyage à Madagascar au couronnement de Radama II. la8°. 1865
Vintimile du Luc (Charles G. G. de), *(1) bp. of Marseille, (2) abp. of Aix, (3) abp. of Paris,* *see* PARIS (F. DE). Éclaircissemens sur les miracles operez par P.; rép., 1733.

Vio (Thomas de), *Cardinal.* Jentacula. Praeclar. 64 notabilium sententiarum N. Test. literalis expos. &c. [*b. w. h.* Summula, 1530]. s8°. Lugduni. 1550
Summula Caietani. De peccatis summula [per Joannem Danielis castigata &c.] s8°. Lugduni. 1530
„ „ ....[*a. ed. incl.* Jentacula]. s8°. Lugd. 1581

Violet (Bruno), *see* EZRA. Die Apokalypse d. Esra &c.; hrsg. B. V., 1924.

***Violin** & vendetta. By T. I. S. s8°. Bristol. [1891]

Viollet-Le-Duc (Eugène Emmanuel).
La cité de Carcassonne. 8°. 1881

Viollis (Jean), *ps.* [*i.e.* J. H. D'ARDENNE DE TIZAC, *q.v. for h. works on art*]. L'Auvergnate, nouvelle, *see* ŒUVRES libres, 15, 1922.
Bonne-fille, roman, *see* ŒUVRES libres, 44, 1925.

Vioux (Marcelle).
L'ami de cœur, *see* ŒUVRES libres, 36, 1924.
Amour de printemps, *see* ŒUVRES libres, 11, 1922.
Une enlisée. Roman. s8°. 1920
La grotte de Saint-Honnorat, *see* ŒUVRES libres, 83, 1928.
Ma route: roman. s8°. 1928
Une repentie (Marie-Magdelaine). Roman. s8°. 1922
La Sunamite, *see* ŒUVRES libres, 55, 1926.

Vipper (R. Yu.) Иван Грозный. 8°. [Москва]. 1922

Virchow (Hans). Gesichtsmuskeln d. Schimpansen, *see* KÖN.-PREUSS. AKAD. Abh., Phys.-math. Klasse, 1915.

Virck (F. W.) Lübeck, *see* DEUTSCHLAND. D.'s Städtebau, 1921.

Vireau de Sombreuil (Marie-Maurille), *see* SOMBREUIL (M.-M. V. DE).

Virey (Claude Enoch), *secrétaire du Henry II, prince de Condé.* L'enlèvement innocent, ou la retraite clandestine de Msgr. le Prince avec la Psse. sa femme, 1609–10. Vers &c. Publ. E. Halphen. [Trésor des pièces rares &c.] s8°. 1859

Virey (Jean). L'abbaye de Cluny. s8°. [1921]

***Virgidemiarum :** satires by J. H. . . . (1602), 1825, *see* HALL (J.)

Virgilius Maro (Publius).
Opera. Una cum annotat. P. Melanchthonis. 8°. Tiguri. 1547
„ P. Melanchthonis & aliorum scholiis &c. illust. s8°. Tiguri. 1567
Bucolica, Georgica & Æneis. [*Ed.* H. Laughton]. 4°. Cantabrigiae. 1701
Opera; ad fidem ed. C. G. Heyne. s8°. Londini. 1824
„ Ed. &c. T. Jarrett. 8°. Cantab. 1866
„ Rec. &c. F. A. Hirtzel. s8°. O. [1900]

ÆNEIS.
Æneid, bks. iv–vi. Ed., w. intr. & notes by T. L. Papillon & A. E. Haigh. 8°. O. 1890
Aeneid: books 1[–12]. Ed. w. intr. & notes by T. E. Page. [repr. 2v.] s8°. 1914–20
Aeneis Buch 6. [*Lat. & Germ.*]; erklärt v. E. Norden. 2. A. la8°. L. 1916
The sixth Book of the Æneid. With intr. & notes by H. E. Butler. s8°. O. 1920

BUCOLICA & GEORGICA.
Bucolica; ed. C. Hosius, *see* KLEINE TEXTE, T134, 1915.
Bucolica & Georgica: w. intr. & notes by T. E. Page. [repr.] s8°. 1920

Translations.
Works. Tr. J. Ogilby. Adorn'd w. sculptur I. Drapentier. [*engr. tp.*] s8°. *n.p.* [1684 ?]
Works. Cont. Pastorals, Georgics, & Æneis. Tr. into Eng. verse by Mr. Dryden. fol. 1697
V.; w. an Eng. tr. by H. R. Fairclough. [Loeb Class. Lib.] [repr.] 2[v]. s8°. 1922
[Œuvres]. Texte établi. & tr. par H. Goelzer. [Coll. des univ. de France]. [t1–3]. 8°. [1925–26]
Wercken (1646–60), *see* VONDEL (J. VAN DEN). Werken, d12, 13, 21, 22, *n.d.*

ÆNEIS.
L'Eneide. [Tr.] A. Caro. 2t. 8°. Parigi. 1760
Eneide travestita di G. B. Lalli. 2t. s8°. Venezia. 1796
Æneid in Eng. verse by A. S. Way [*w. text*]. v2, Bk. IV–VI. s8°.1924

BUCOLICA & GEORGICA.
[Georgics. *Tr. into Armenian by* A. K. Bagratouni]. 4°. i Venetik. 1847

REFERENCES.
see AMATUCCI (A. G.) L'Eneide di V. e la Sicilia, 1924.
„ BOISSIER (G.) Nouv. promenades archéol.: Horace & V., 5e éd., 1904.
„ CARCOPINO (J.) V. & les origs. d'Ostie, 1919.
„ CRUMP (M. M.) Growth of the Æneid, 1920.
„ DE WITT (N. W.) V.'s Biogr. litt., 1923.
„ DREW (D. L.) The allegory of the Æneid, 1927.
„ —— Culex: sources & th. bearing on problem of authorship, 1925.

Virgilius Maro (Publius) [*continued*].
REFERENCES [*continued*].
see FOWLER (W. W.) Æneas at the site of Rome: obs. on 8th bk. of the Aeneid, 2nd ed., 1918.
„ FRANK (T.) Vergil, biog., 1922.
„ HENLEY (S.) Obs. on 4th Ecl., 3rd Georgic &c., 1788.
„ KÖHLER (J. G. W.) Disput. de cod. V. adhuc incogn., 1771.
„ MACKAIL (J. W.) V. & h. meaning to the world to-day, 1923.
„ MAZZONE DI MIGLIONICO (M. A.) Fiori d. poesia dich. &c. da l'op. di V. &c., 1593.
„ MERGUET (H.) Lexikon zu V., mit Angabe sämtl. Stellen, 1912.
„ SERVIUS MAURUS HONORATUS. In V. carmina comment., 3v, 1887–1923.
„ WARREN (*Sir* T. H.) V. in rel. to place of Rome, 1921.
„ WEBER (W.) Der Prophet u. s. Gott: St. z. 4. Ekloge V., 1925.
„ ZABUGHIN (V.) V. nel rinascimento ital., 2v, 1921–23.

Virginia.
*A brief narr. of rival relig. in V., 3rd ed., 1786, *see* RANKIN (T.)
*Hist. (The) of V., 1722, *see* BEVERLEY (R.)
Plymouth copy of 1st Charter of V., 1920, *see* HARRIS (J. R.) Souv. of the "Mayflower" tercent., No. 4, 1920.
Proc. of 126th annual comm. of Grand Lodge of V., 1903, *see* FREEMASONS.
*Short acc. of the 1st settlement of prov. of V., Maryland &c., 1735, 1922, *see* SHORT.
Virginia campaign of 1862 under Gen. P., 1886; 1895, *see* POPE (*maj.-gen.* J.)

***Viri** docti anon. judicium de S. M. Joanna papissa restituta, 1705, *see* JOAN, *pope.*

Virorum quondam eruditissim. molimina theologica, seu opuscula sel., ad antiq. Christ. &c. spectantia. s8°. Halae. 1761
Contains Schmidt (J. A.) Fragmenta lexici; Bose (G. C.) De anathemate; Zorn (P.) Delineatio theologiae; Losius (J. J.) De defectu judicii logici; Hardt (H. v. d.) Exegesis 4 Evangelist.

Virot de Sombreuil (Marie-Maurille), *see* SOMBREUIL.

Virubova (Anna) [VIROUBOVA-TANAIEVA].
Journal secret, 1909–17. Tr. M. Vaneix. 8°. 1928
Memories of the Russian court. 8°. 1923

Virza (Ed.) La litt. lettone. 8°. Riga. [1926 ?]

Vis (Eelco M.) Dutch tiles, 15–18 cent. Coll. of E. M. V. [Sale, Nov. 9 & 10, 1927, Amer. Art Assoc.] 8°. N.Y. 1927

Vischer (Friedrich Theodor). Auch einer. 95–99 A. s8°. St. 1918
see HESNARD (O.) F. T. V., 1921.
„ —— F. T. V.: étude bibliogr., 1921.

Vischer (Peter), *the elder, see* MELLER (S.) P. V. u. s. Werkstatt, 1925.

Vischer (Xystus), *see* FÖRER (L.) Septem characteres M. Lutheri &c. resp. X. V., 1626.

Viscont (Antoine). La Lituanie & la Guerre. 8°. Genève. 1917

Visconti, *The family of.*
see FOLIGNO (C.) Di alcuni doc. V. in bibl. ingl., 1905.
„ MUIR (D.) Hist. of Milan under the V., 1924.

Visconti (Bernabò), *duke of Milan.* Trattato fra B. V., il conte Ant. di Montefeltro, la Repubb. di Firenze e le comunità d'Urbino e Cagli, 1 febb. 1375; [*ed. G. Sommi-Picenardi*], *see* REGIA DEP. DI STORIA PATRIA. Misc., t23, 1884.

Visconti (Filippo Maria), *duke of Milan, see* KAGELMACHER (E.) F. M. V. u. König Sigismund, 1413–31, 1885.

Visconti (Galeazzo II de'), *d. 1378, see* LAVAGNO (F.) Convito nuziale dato da G. V., 1368, 1884.

Visconti (Giovanni), *da Oleggio, see* OLEGGIO (G. V.)

Visconti (Louis Tullius Joachim), *see* NAPOLEON I. Tombeau de N., érigé dans le dome des Invalides par V., 1853.

Visher (Stephen Sargent), *see* HUNTINGTON (E.) & S. S. V. Climatic changes, 1922.

Vishnu, *see* BIDYABINOD (B. B.) Varieties of the V. image, 1920.

Vishṇugupta, *see* KAUṬILYA.

***Visible** pursuit of a foreign interest in opp. to the int. of England, 1745, *see* ENGLAND.

Vising (Johan). Anglo-Norman lang. & lit. s8°. 1923

Visitation of Eng. & Wales, v21, 1921, *see* HOWARD (J. J.) & F. A. CRISP, *edd.*

***Visitor's (The)** guide to Tunbridge Wells, 1827, *see* TUNBRIDGE WELLS.

Visscher (Franchoys Jacobszoon), *see* TASMAN (A. J.) De reizen v. T. & F. J. V. ter nadere ontdekking van het Zuitland in 1642/3 & 1644, 1919.

Visscher (Nikolaas), *the elder* [CLAS JANSZ VISSCHER]. Brabantiae Ducatus cum adj. prov. per N. V. [Maps, 6]. folded fol. *Schenk*, [Amsterdam. 1715 ?]
London. [*View of river &c.*] repr. fol. *n.d.*
Nieuwe kaart van t'Baljuwschap van Kennemerland &c. [Maps, 7]. folded fol. *Schenk*, [? Amsterdam]. *n.d.*

Visser (M.), *see* BOSMANS (C. J. E.) & M. V. Répertoire des traités & des engagements internat. du 20s. conc. les Pays-Bas, 1921.

Visser (Marinus Willem de).
Arhats in China & Japan. 4°. Berlin. 1923

Visvesvaraya (*Sir* Mokshagundum).
Reconstructing India. s8°. 1920

Viswanatha (S. V.) Racial synthesis in Hindu culture. 8°. 1928

Vit (Vincenzo de), *see* DE VIT (V.)

Vita (La) britannica. Rivista bimestrale; ed. dall' Ist. Britannico di Firenze. Anno 1, 2 (1918–19). 8°. Firenze. [1918–19]

Vitae. Vitae sanct. Danorum. nov. ed. crit. curavit M. Cl. Gertz. la8°. København. 1908–12
For an earlier ed., see Langebek (J.), *ed.* Scr. rerum Dan. medii aevi, t1.

Vitale (Vito). Il dominio d. Parte Guelfa in Bologna, 1280–1327. 8°. Bologna. 1901

Vitalis (Léon). *V., la femme coupée en morceaux [1877]. [*no tp.* P2826]. s8°. [Sceaux. *n.d.*]

Vitense (Otto). Gesch. v. Mecklenburg. [Deut. Landesgesch., Werk 11]. 8°. Gotha. 1920

Viterbo. Per l'inaugur. del Museo Civico di V. [*By* C. Pinzi *& others*]. [P2699]. 4°. Viterbo. 1912

Vitevsky (Vladimir Nikolaevich). Расколъ въ уральскомъ войскѣ &c. въ 18 и 19 в. [*2 pagin.*] 8°. Казань. 1878

Vitringa (Campegius), *the elder.* De synagoga vetere lib 3. ed altera emend. s4°. Leucopetrae. 1726
Obs. sacrarum libri sex. Ed. nov., cui acc. auctoris Geographica sacra &c. & praemissa est vita. [*3 pagin.*] s4°. Jenae. 1723

Vitrolles (E. F. A. d'Arnaud, *baron* **de).** Souv. autobiog. d'un émigré, 1790–1800. Publ. avec intr., notes &c. par E. Forgues. 8°. 1924

Vitruvius Pollio (Marcus), *see* BIRNBAUM (A.) V. u. d. griech. Architektur, 1914.

Vitry (Aubert de), *see* AUBERT DE VITRY (F. J. P.)

Vitry (Jacques de), *see* FRENKEN (G.) Die Exempla d. J. v. V., *w. text*, 1914.

Vitry (Paul). Un fragm. du tombeau de St. Lazare d'Autun au Musée du Louvre, *see* ACAD. DES INSCR.: FOND. PIOT. Mons. &c., t26, 1923.
La "Vierge d'Isenheim," *see* ACAD. DES INSCR.: FOND. PIOT. Mons., t27, 1924.

Vittorio Veneto. Royal Italian Army. Rep. by the Comando Supremo on the battle of V. V., 24 Oct.–4 Nov. 1918. [P2700]. 4°. *n.d.*

Vitu (Auguste C. J.) Notice sur F. Villon, d'ap. des docs. nouv. & inéd. &c. 8°. 1873

Vitzthum von Eckstädt (Carl Friedrich, *count*). The Emperor William at Baden-Baden. Personal recolls., 1881–87. [P2605]. 4°. Paris. 1889

Viva (Domenico), *Jesuit.* Appendix theologicae Trutinae damnatarum thesium ab Alex. VII, Innoc. XI & Alex. VIII &c. á V. elucubratae. [*Ed.* M. A. Mutius]. s8°. Neapoli. 1710
Damnatae theses ab Alexandro VII, Innocentio XI & Alex. VIII necnon Jansenii ad theol. Trutinam revocatae juxta pondus Sanctuarii. ed. 14ª. t1, p1–3 [*in* 1v]. s4°. Patavii. 1749
De jubilæo praesertim anni sancti, ac de indulgentiis univ. enchiridion &c. [*b. w. h.* Damnatae theses &c., t1, 1749]. s4°. Patavii. 1749
Quesnellianae theses a Clemente XI confixae ad theolog. Trutinam revocatae juxta pondus. ed. 4ª. T2, Trutinae theologicae p4. s4°. Beneventi. 1724

Viva (Isaac). Vindex sanguinis, *see* BRENZ (S. F.) Thoriaca Judaica, 1681.

Vivanet (Filippo). La Sardegna n. archivi &c. della Spagna; pubbl. da S. Lippi, *see* REGIA DEPUT. Miscellanea, t44, 1909.

Vivante (Leone). Intelligence in expression, w. essay: Originality of thought &c. Tr. by Prof. Brodrick-Bullock. Foreword by H. W. Carr. 8°. [1925]

Vivanti (Annie), *aft. Mrs. Chartres.*
The devourers. [2nd impr.] s8°. 1910
Gioia! Novelle. s8°. Firenze. 1921
Lirica. Pref. e nota di G. Carducci. n. ed. s8°. Firenze. 1921
Marie Tarnowska. Intr. letter by L. M. Bossi. 8°. [1915]
Naja tripudians. Romanzo. s8°. Firenze. 1921
Perdonate Eglantina. s8°. Milano. 1926
Vae victis! 9ª ed. s8°. Milano. [1923]
" " [Tr.] s8°. 1917

Vivarini, *The family of, see* SINIGAGLIA (G.) De' V., pittori da Murano, 1905.

Vivell (Cölestin). Comm. anon. in Micrologum Guidonis Aretini, 1917, *see* KAISERL. AKAD. D. W. ZU WIEN. Sitz., B185, 1918.
see FRUTOLF, *Benedictine monk.* F. Breviarium de musica & Tonarius, veröff. v. C. V., 1916.

Vivenel (Antoine), *see* COMPIÈGNE: MUSÉE VIVENEL.

Vives (Joannes Ludovicus). Colloquia sive exercit. Latinae linguae J. T. Freigii notis illustr. [*Pref. dated* 1582]. s8°. Noribergae, [*P. Kauffmann*]. *n.d.*
" " [*a. ed., pref. dated* 1582]. s8°. Noribergae, *S. Halbmayer. n.d.*
De subventione pauperum; tr., *see* SALTER (F. R.), *ed.* Some early tracts on poor relief, 1926.
see WATSON (F.) L. Vives, 1922.
" —— J. L. V.: scholar of the Renascence, 1492–1540, 1921.

Vives y Escudero (Antonio).
La moneda Hispánica. [R. Acad. de la Hist.] la8°. 1926
" " .... Atlas. 8°. 1924

Vivian (*Hon.* Claud Hamilton).
Richard Hussey Vivian, 1st Baron Vivian. 8°. 1897

Vivian (E. Charles). Hist. of aeronautics, w. sect. on progress in aeroplane design by Lt.-Col. W. L. Marsh. 8°. [1921]

Vivian (George). Scenery of Portugal & Spain. On stone by L. Haghe. fol. 1839
Spanish scenery. [L. Haghe lith.] fol. 1838

Vivian (Herbert), *M.A.* Secret societies old & new. 8°. [1927]

Vivian (*Sir* Richard Hussey, *1st baron*), *see* VIVIAN (*Hon.* C. H.) R. H. V., 1st Baron V., 1897.

Viviani (Quirico). Dizionario, *see* DANTE ALIGHIERI. La Div. Commedia, v3ii, 1828.

Viviani (René). As we see it. France & the truth about the War. Tr. T. R. Ybarra. 8°. [1923]
see LAURENT (M.) Nos gouvernements de Guerre: V. &c., 1920.

Viviani (Ugo). Curiosità storiche e lett. aretine. 8°. Arezzo. 1921

Vivien, *Chevalerie.* La Chevalerie Vivien. Chanson de geste. Publ. A. L. Terracher. Texts. 8°. 1923

Vivonne (Louis Victor de Rochechouart, *maréchal duc* **de).** Corr. rel. à l'expédition de Messine. Publ. par J. Cordey. [S. de l'H. F.] t2, 1676–78. 8°. 1914

Vizcaya, Diputación de. Ensayo de un cat. de la sección Vascongada por D. de Areitio. Prólogo de C. de Echegaray. Authores. 8°. Bilbao. 1919

Vizetelly (Ernest Alfred). Loves of the poets. 8°. 1915

Vjesnik za arheologiju i hist. dalmatinsku, *see* BULLETTINO DI ARCHEOL. E. STORIA DALM., 1911–22.

Vlaamsche. De algemeene Belydenissen d. vereen. V. &c., Doopsgezinde, 1739, *see* BAPTIST.

Vlachos (Angelos), *see* BLACHOS (A.)

Vladimir, *Saint, called the Great, Grand Duke of Russia, see* BONIFACE, *St., Apostle of Russia.* Témoignage sur St. V.; publ. par le pr. A. Galitzin, 1861.

Vladimir (Paul), *of Cracow, see* PAUL VLADIMIR.

Vladimirescu (Tudor), *see* IORGA (N.) Izvoarele contemp. asupra mişcării lui T. V., 1821, 1921.

Vladimirov (Vsevolod). The revolution in Finland under prince John Obolensky. From the Russian. [P2451]. 8°. 1911

Vladimirsky (M.)
Организация Советской власти на местох. la8°. [Москва]. 1921

Vladimirsky-Budanov (Mikhail Fleg.)
Исторія университета Св. Владимира. t1. la8°. Кіевъ. 1884

Vladislaus VII, *king of Poland, see* ZENO (G.) Relaz., ambasc. d. Repubb. Veneta a Ladislao VII, nel 1638; pubbl. G. Ferraro, 1894.

Vladislavlev (I. V.) Русские писатели. Опыт библиогр. пособия, 19–20 ст. 4ᵉ изд. la8°. Москва. 1924

Vlaminck (Maurice de), *see* CARCO (F. C.) M. de V.: reprods. de peintures &c., *&* ét. crit., 1920.

Vlasák (František). Der altböhm. Adel u. s. Nachkommenschaft nach d. 30 jähr. Kriege. Aus d. Böhm. übers. u. verbess. s8°. Prag. [1866?]

Vlijmen (Bernard Reiner Frans van). Vers la Bérésina, 1812. 8°. 1908

Vloten (Johan van), *see* MIDDELBURG. Onderzoek van's Konings wege ingesteld omtrent de M. beroerten, 1566–67; uitg. door J. van V., 1873.

Vluchtig (Piet), *ps.* [*i.e.* E. G. F. H. SMIT KLEINE]. De Madonna van Duinlust & a. verhalen. s8°. 's Gravenhage. 1882

Vocabolario di marina in 3 lingue, 3v, 1813–14, *see* STRATICO (S.), *ed.*

Vocabularies. V.: Eng., Arabic, Persian, Turk., Armen., Kurdish, Syriac, 1920, *see* ADMIRALTY: NAVAL INTELL. DIV.

V.: Eng., German, Magyar, Serbian &c., 1920, *see* ADMIRALTY: NAVAL INTELL. DIV.

Vocabularium jurisprudentiae Romanae. Jussu Instit. Savigniani compos. [O. Gradenwitz, B. Kuebler &c.] t1, A–C. la8°. Berolini. 1903

Vocino (Michele). Foggia e la Capitanata. [P2860]. 4°. Milano. *n.d.*

Vockerodt (Gottfried). Comm. de erudit. societatibus &c. [*b. w. h.* Consultationes &c., 1705]. s8°. Gothae. 1704

Consultationes de litterarum studiis &c. Acc. comm. de vera, & falsa eruditione &c. [*w. sep. pagin.*] s8°. Gothae. 1705

Disput. hist. de societatibus literariis. G. V. præses, A. Günther resp. [P1035]. s4°. Jenæ. 1687

Sermones panegyrici. [*b. w. h.* Consultationes, 1705]. s8°. Gothae. 1705

Vodovozov (Vasily Vasilevich). Всеобщее избирательное право. B1. [*b. w.* Сборникъ программъ полит. партій, 1906]. s8°. С.-П. 1906

Voecht (Jacobus de) [JACOBUS, *Trajecti*]. Narr. de inchoatione domus clericorum in Zwollis, met Akten & Bescheiden betref. dit Fraterhuis. Uitg. door M. Schoengen. [Hist. Genoots. Werken, s3, 13]. 8°. Amsterdam. 1908

Voersio (Francesco), *see* FRANCESCO [*Voersio*], *da Cherasco, Carmelite.*

Voet (Gijsbert) [VOETIUS (G.)] Examen disput. primae G. Voetii quam proposuit in Gymn. Ultrajectino a. 1634. [*b. w.* Belgium. Confessio &c., 1622]. s4°. [Ultrajecti?]. 1634

Oratio funebr. in obit. Meinardi Schotani, 1644. [P598]. s4°. Ultrajecti. [1644]

Voet (Johannes). Oratio funebr. in obitum A. Matthaei, 14th Sept. 1710. [P2672]. 4°. Lugduni Batav. 1710

Oratio funebr. in obit. Andreae Essenii, 1677. [P595]. s4°. Ultrajecti. 1677

Vogau (Boris Andreevich), *see* PILNYAK (B.), *ps.*

Vogel (Albrecht), *prof. zu Wien.* Beiträge z. Herstellung d. alt. lat. Bibel-Übersetzung &c. 8°. Wien. 1868

Vogel (Eberhard). Taschen-Wbch. d. katalan. u. deut. Sprache &c. T1, Katalan.-deut. s8°. [1911]

Vogel (Emil Ferdinand). Lexicon lit. acad.-juridicae quo tituli diss. &c. ab Academiarum initiis ad 1835 ed. &c. cont. Cui praef. praemisit E. F. V. 2t *w. suppl. cont. Index w. sep. tp., pag. cont.* 8°. Lips. 1836–38

Vogel (Ernst Gustav). Bibl. biograph. Lutherana. Uebersicht d. Luther betreff. biogr. Schriften. 8°. Halle. 1851

Vogel (Georg Wolfgang). Exercit. de tonsura clericorum, sub præs. C. Ziegleri. [P2635]. s4°. Wittenbergæ. 1685

Vogel (J. Ph.) Antiq. of Chamba state. p1, Inscr. of pre-Muhammadan period. [Arch. Survey of India. New Imp. ser., v36]. 4°. Calcutta. 1911

Indian serpent-lore, or the Nāgas in Hindu legend & art. la8°. 1926

Tile-mosaics of the Lahore Fort. Ed. Sir J. Marshall. [Arch. Survey of India. New Imp. ser., v41]. 4°. Calcutta. 1920

Vogel (Julius). Otto Greiner. [Künstler-Monographien, 114]. la8°. Bielefeld. 1925

Vogel (Julius L. F.) Unemployment: its causes and cure. Foreword by Sir A. Balfour. s8°. 1925

Vogel (Walther), *historian.* Gesch. der deut. Seeschiffahrt. B1. 8°. 1915

1, Von d. Urzeit bis z. Ende 15. Jhdts.

Hugo Grotius u. d. Urspr. d. Schlagworts v. d. Freiheit d. Meere. [Meereskunde, H136. P2408]. 8°. 1918

Vogel (*Major* Walther). Die Kämpfe um Baranowitschi, 1916. [Schlachten d. Weltkrieges, B9]. 3. A. 8°. Oldenburg. 1927

Vogels (Heinrich), *see* RHEINLANDABKOMMEN (DAS) sowie d. Verordnungen d. Hohen Komm. in Coblenz; Textausg. [*Germ., Fr. & Eng.*] mit Erläut. v. H. u. W. V., 2B, 1920–21.

Vogl (Carl). Sowjet-Russland. 8°. L. 1927

Vogler (Georg). Catechismus in aüsserlesenen Exempeln, kürtzen Fragen, schönen Gesängern &c. gestelt. s8°. Würtzburg. 1625

Vogler (Josephus), *Jesuit.* Juris-cultor theol. c. obligat. restitutionis in gen. &c., *see* MIGNE (J. P.), *ed.* Theol. cursus, t15, 1861.

Vogt (Edouard), *see* CHIQUITO DE CAMBO, *ps.*, G. BÉNAC & E. V. La pelote basque, 1924.

Vogt (Friedrich). Gesch. d. mittelhochdeut. Lit. [Grundr. d. deut. Lit.-gesch., 2]. 3e umgearb. A. T1. 8°. 1922

—— & M. Koch. Gesch. d. deut. Literatur. 4e neubearb. A. 3B. la8°. L. 1918–20

Vogt (Johannes), *Pastor at Bremen.* Bibl. hist. hæresiolog. select. doct. virorum diss. hæreticorum hæresiumque hist. exponentes complectens. Coll. rec., notis illust. J. V. T1 & t2, fasc. 1. [*in* 1v. *No more publ.*] s8°. Hamb. 1723–29

see LOCHNER (J. H.) & J. V. Observ. Anglic. delectum primum submitt., 1714.

Vogt (Joseph). Röm. Politik in Ägypten, *see* ALTE ORIENT, Beih. 2, 1924.

Vogt (Wilhelm), *Dr. phil.* Die Vorgesch. d. Bauernkrieges. [Verein f. Ref.-gesch. Schr., Jhrg. 5, Nr. 20]. 8°. Halle. 1887

Vogué (Charles Jean Melchior de), *marquis, see* FOCH (*mar.* F.) Disc. de récep. (*on* V.), 1920.

Vogüé (*le vte.* E. Melchior de). Lettres à Armand & Henri de Pontmartin (1867–1909). s8°. [1922]

Les morts qui parlent. Intr. par V. Giraud. s8°. *Nelson.* [1910]

Voigt (Christoph). Schiffs-Æsthetik. Die Schönheit d. Schiffes &c. 4°. 1922

Voigt (Johann Georg). Comm. de theoria Augustiniana, Pelagiana, Semipelagiana & Synergistica in doctr. de peccato originali, gratia & libero arbitrio. [*Progr.* P2648]. s4°. Gottingae. [1829]

Voigt (Johannes). Deut. Hofleben zur Zeit d. Reformation. [Hrsg. E. Schaeffer]. s8°. Dresden. [1927]

Voinov (Vsevolod), *see* KUZMIN (M.) & V. V. Д. И. Митрохин, 1922.

Voisins (A. Gilbert de), *see* GILBERT DE VOISINS (A.)

Voit a Berg (Christoph. Ferd.), *see* BRUNQUELL (J. S.) Diss. de pictura famosa: exam. subm. C. F. Voit a B., 1733.

Voiture (Vincent), *see* MAGNE (E.) V. & les années de gloire de l'Hôtel de Rambouillet, 1635–48, 1912.

Voladimirus (Paulus), *see* PAUL VLADIMIR, *of Cracow.*

Voland (*Mlle.* Sophie), *see* VOLLAND (*Mlle.* S.)

Volbach (Wolfgang Fritz). Mittelalterl. Elfenbeinarbeiten. [Orbis Pictus, 11]. la8°. [1922]

see WULFF (O.) Altchristl. u. mittelalterl. byzantin. u. ital. Bildwerke; bearbt. v. O. W. u. W. F. V., Ergänzungsband, 1923.

Volbeding (Johann Ernst). Index diss. &c. quibus hist. N.T. & antiq. eccl. loci illust. 8°. L. 1849

Volbertal (J. H.) Ermenonville, s. sites, s. curiosités, s. hist. 8°. 1923

Volcamerus (Christophorus Theophilus). Iridis admiranda. Praes. J. C. Sturmio. s4°. Noribergae. 1699

Völckener (Johann). Diss. de christianismo Graecorum hodiern. Praeses J. N. Quistorp. s4°. Rostochi. 1665

Volckmann (Erwin). German. Handel u. Verkehr: v. d. Urzeit bis 1600. la8°. Würzburg. 1925

Volckmar (Johannes Georg). De eccl. triumphante in coelis disput. 2. De sanctorum in vita aeterna beatitudine [*by V.*] De Sanctorum cultu [*by* D. Cramerus]. s4°. Witebergae. 1595

Volentes. *Volētes oparare infrascriptos libros (1469), *see* SCHÖFFER (P.)

Volf (Josef). Gesch. d. Buchdrucks in Böhmen u. Mähren bis 1848. s8°. Weimar. 1928

Volkenshtein (N. V.), *see* KRANDIEVSKAYA (N. V.)

Volkenshtein (Vladimir Mikhailovich). Спартак: трагедия. 8°. [Москва]. 1921

Völker (Ambrosius). Ist d. menschl. Wille frei? [P2476]. 8°. St. 1880

Völker (Carl). Mysterium u. Agape: d. gemeinsamen Mahlzeiten in d. alt. Kirche. 8°. Gotha. 1927

Völkerkrieg (Der). Chronik d. Ereignisse seit d. 1. Juli 1914. Bearb. u. hrsg. C. H. Baer. B22–28. 8°. St. [1920–23]

Völkerrechtlichen (Die) Urkunden d. Weltkrieges; hrsg. T. Niemeyer &c., B4, 6, *see* JAHRBUCH D. VÖLKERRECHTS, B6, 8, 1920–22.

Volkert (August). Statist. Karte v. Bayern; zugl. Post-Karte v. Süd-west-Deutschland. Vervollst. hrsg. v. Piloty u. Loehle. *folded* 8°. München. [1852?]

Volkhovsky (Feliks Vladimirovich). Какъ мужикъ у всѣхъ въ долгу остался. Сказка. [*a. c. in* P848]. s8°. С.–П. 1906

Volkmann (Erich Otto). Der grosse Krieg 1914–18, auf Grund d. amtl. Quellen d. Reichsarchivs. 8°. 1922

Volkmann (Hans). Emanuel d'Astorga. B2. s8°. L. 1919

Volkna (Johann), *ps., see* FREDERICK II, *king of Prussia.*

Volkonskaya (*princess* **Mariya Nikolaevna),** *1805–63, form. M. N. Raevskaya.*
see SCHEGOLEV (P. E.) М. В., 1922.
,, SOKOLOV (B. M.) М. Н. Раевская, кн. В., 1922.

Volkonsky (*prince* **Aleksandr**) [WOLKONSKY]. The Ukraine question: hist. truth versus the Separatist propaganda. Tr. under dir. of W. Gibson. s8°. Rome. 1920

Volkonsky (*prince* **Grigory M.)** Взглядъ на соврем. положеніе Россіи. [P2715]. 8°. Stuttgart. 1903

Volkonsky (*prince* **Sergei Grigorevich),** *see* VOLKONSKY (*pr.* S. M.) О Декабристахъ, по семейн. воспом. [S. G. V. &c.], 1921.

Volkonsky (*prince* **Sergei Mikh.)** Мои воспоминанія, [1] Лавры, [2] Странствія, [3] Родина *in* 2t. 8°. [Berlin. 1923]
My reminiscences. Tr. A. E. Chamot. 2v. 8°. [1925]
О Декабристахъ, по семейн. воспом. [S. G. V. &c.] 8°. Парижъ. [1921]

Volkov (E. Z.) Аграрно-экономич. статистика России (1865–1922). la8°. Москва. 1922

Volkov (Nikolai). Александр Блок и театр. [Государст. Акад. Худож. Наук]. 8°. Москва. 1926

Volkov (S.) & M. Bereznyakov. Общій уставъ росс. желѣзныхъ дорогъ по 1901. [*b. in 2v*]. изд. 3ᵉ. 8°. С.–П. 1901

Volksliederbuch. Illust. V.: e. Sammlung. s8°. Lahr. *n.d.*

Volkswirtschaftliche Chronik: Abdruck aus d. Jahrbüchen für Nationalökonomie u. Statistik, 1914, 1915, 1919–1926. la8°. Jena. 1915–26

Volland (*Mlle.* **Sophie)** [VOLAND], *see* LEDIEU (P.) Diderot & S. V., 1925.

Vollandus (Christianus Guil.) Vindiciae Chrysostomi contra J. Harduinum. [P2743]. s4°. Lipsiae. 1714

Vollandus (Joannes Ignatius). Merita P. Melanchthonis in rem literariam Noribergensium &c. [P597]. s4°. Altorfii. [1719]

Vollard (Ambroise). Auguste Renoir, 1841–1919. s8°. 1920
Degas (1834–1917). [4ᵉ éd.] s8°. 1924
Paul Cézanne. Tr. H. L. Van Doren. 8°. [1924]

Vollenhoven (Janus Jacobus van). Spec. theolog. de Cyrilli Hierosolymitani catechesibus. 8°. Amstelodami. 1837

Vollerthun (*Konteradmiral* **Waldemar).** Der Kampf um Tsingtau. Eine Episode 1914–18. 8°. L. 1920

Vollmann (Remigius).
Flurnamensammlung. 3ᵉ Aufl. 8°. München. 1924

Vollmer (Friedrich). *Works in* KÖNIGL. AKAD. DER WISS. ZU MÜNCHEN. Phil. Kl., Sitz.
Kürzung durch Tonanschluss im alt. Latein, 1917.
Lesungen u. Deutungen, 2, 3, 1918–19.
Die Prosodie d. lat. Komposita mit pro- u. re-, 1922.
Studien zu d. röm. Kochbuche v. Apicius, 1920.
Üb. d. sog. Iambenkürzung bei d. sken. Dichtern d. Römer, 1924.
Zur Gesch. d. lat. Hexameters: kurze Endsilben in arsi, 1917.
see BÄHRENS (E.) Poetæ Lat. minores, post Æ. Baehrens rec. F. V., v2ii, 1923.

Vollmer (Hans), *see* THIEME (U.) & F. BECKER. Allgem. Lexikon d. bild. Künstler &c., B16–22, hrsg. v. H. V., 1922–28.

Vollmüller (Carl). Bibliog. d. Roman. Forsch. &c., *see* ROMANISCHE FORSCH., B33, 34, 1915.

Volney (C. F.) Les ruines, ou, Médit. s. les révol. des empires. s8°. 1792
,, ,, 3ᵉ éd. corr. & augm. du Catéchisme du Citoyen français. 8°. an VII. [?1798]
see AMAT (F.) Meditationes [in Palmyrae ruinas], 1833.

Volnov (Ivan). Le train, *see* ŒUVRES libres, No. 77, 1927.

Volny (Ivan).
За вѣру, царя и отечество. Разсказъ. [P810]. s8°. С.–П. 1902

Volonakis (Michael D.) Greece on the eve of resurrection. Pref. by A. J. Toynbee. Intr. letter by J. Gennadius. [P2465]. 8°. 1920
The Island of Roses & her eleven sisters; or, The Dodecanese f. earliest time to pres. day. Intr. by J. L. Myres. 8°. 1922

Volonakis (Michael D.) [*continued*].
The national claims of the Dodecanese, *see* ANGLO-HELLENIC LEAGUE, No. 46, 1922.
Saint Sophia & Constantinople. With proleg. by G. Murray. [P2432]. 8°. 1920

Volonter, *pseud.* Русско-японская война. [P2445]. s8°. С.–П. 1905

Voloshin (Maksimilian).
Демоны глухонемые. 2. изд. s8°. в Берлине. 1923
Стихи о терроре. s8°. в Берлине. 1923

Volpe (Gioacchino). Lunigiana medievale. Storia di Vescovi signori &c., sec. 11–15. 8°. Firenze. 1923
Medio evo italiano. s8°. Firenze. [1923]
Volterra. Storia di Vescovi signori &c. sec. 11–15. 8°. Firenze. 1923

Volpi (Elia). Gothic & Renaissance Italian works of art. Coll. of E. V. [Sale, Amer. Art. Assoc., Apr. 1927]. la8°. N.Y. 1927

Volsky (Nikolai Vladislavovich), *see* VALENTINOV (N.)

Volsky (Stanislav). Dans le royaume de la famine &c.: la Russ. bolchev. s8°. 1920

Volta (*il conte* **Alessandro).** Le opere di A. V. Ed. naz. sotto gli auspici d. R. Accad. dei Lincei &c. v2–6. 4°. Milano. 1923–28
L'opera di A. V. Scelta di scrit. orig. racc. &c. d. F. Massardi. Con monografie. la8°. Milano. 1927

Voltaire.
Œuvres. t7, 8, Dict. philosoph. &c. la8°. *Firmin Didot.* 1876
*Candide, ou l'optimisme. Tr. Dr. Ralph. s8°. Genève. 1761
,, ,, ...s8°. [1877]
Dict. philosophique. s8°. [1912 ?]
L'esprit de M. de V. [*Ed.* C. Villaret]. s8°. 1760
Hist. de Charles XII. Publ. par E. Brochard-Dauteuille, w. Fr.-Eng. vocab. by G. Masson. n. éd. s8°. 1903
*Hist. de Russie sous Pierre le Grand. Par l'a. de l'hist. de Charles XII. 2t. 8°. 1759
,, ,, n. éd., rev. &c. par L. T. Ventouillac. 2t. s8°. Londres. 1825
Mém. écrits par lui-même. s8°. Londres. 1784
Mémoires, suiv. de mélanges div. & préc. de Voltaire démiurge, par P. Souday. 8°. [1927]
*Le philosophe ignorant. Avec un avis au public sur les parricides imputés aux Calas & aux Sirven. [*a. ed.*] 8°. *n.p.* 1766
La Pucelle d'Orléans. Stér. d'Herhan. 8°. 1808
Romans, suivis de s. contes en vers. n. éd. rev. s8°. [1920]
Théâtre. 8t. s8°. Londres. 1782
*Traité sur la tolérance. [*a. c. b. w. h.* Le philos. ignor., 1766]. 8°. *n.p.* 1763
LETTERS.
Lettres choisies, c le traitéave de la connaiss. des beautés &c. de la poésie &c. dans la langue franç. Préc. d'une notice par L. Moland. 2t. s8°. 1923
*Lettres écrites de Londres sur les Anglois &c. Par M. D. V***. s8°. Basle. 1734
Lettres philosoph. Ed. crit. avec intr. & comm. par G. Lanson. [Soc. des Textes Fr. Mod.] 3ᵉ éd. 2t. 8°. 1924
TRANSLATIONS.
The age of Louis XIV. Tr. M. P. Pollack. [Everyman's lib.] s8°. [1926]
TRANSLATIONS [*continued*].
Candide. Tr. w. intr. by H. Morley. Illust. A. Odle. 4°. [1922]
An essay on univ. hist.; manners & spirit of nations; w. Suppl. Tr., w. add. notes &c. by Mr Nugent. n. ed. rev. 4v. s8°. E. 1777
Letters conc. the Eng. nation. Intr. by C. Whibley. 8°. 1926
Letters of V. & Frederick the Great (1736–78). Sel. & tr. w. intr. by R. Aldington. [Broadway Lib. of 18c. Fr. lit.] 8°. [1927]
Mahomet. [*Tr.*] J. Millar, *see* INCHBALD (*Mrs.* E.) Brit. theatre, v13, 1808.
La Pucelle, The Maid of Orleans: heroic-comical poem. New tr., rev. &c. f. tr. of W. H. Ireland & of Lady Charleville, now tr. by E. Dowson. 2v. 8°. 1899
A treatise on religious toleration. Occas. by exec. of J. Calas. Tr. 8°. 1764
Zadig, & o. romances. Tr. by H. I. Woolf; w. intr. & notes. [Broadway tr.] s8°. *n.d.*
REFERENCES.
see ALDINGTON (R.) Voltaire, 1925.
,, ANTI-JACOBIN, *ps.* New lights on Jacobinism, 1798.
,, BELLESSORT (A.) Essai sur V., 1925.
,, BERTAUT (J.) V., 1911.
,, BLACK (J. B.) Art. of hist., 1926.
,, FREDERICK II, *king of Prussia.* Briefwechsel F. mit V., t3, 1911; Nachträge, 1917.
,, †LOUISA DOROTHEA, *dss. of Sachsen-Gotha.* Briefe an V. (1751–67) [*in Fr.*], 1893–94.
,, MERIAN-GENAST (E.) V. u. d. Entwicklung d. Idee d. Weltlit., 1927.

Voltelini (Hans), *see* PFALZ (A.) & H. V. Forsch. z. d. deut. Rechtsbüchern, 1–3, 1919–24.

Völtzkow (Alfred). Reise in Ostafrika in d. Jahren 1903–5 ausgeführt v. A. V. B1, Abt. 1, Reisebericht, T2. 4°. St. 1923
1i, Reisebericht, T2, Witu-Inseln u. Zanzibar-Archipel, v. A. V.

Volude (*la marquise* **Béatrix Stéphanie Lâge de**), *see* LÂGE DE VOLUDE.

Volunteer. The V. Force & the V. Training Corps dur. the Great War, 1920, *see* CENTRAL ASSOC. VOLUNTEER REGT.

Volvire de Ruffec (Anne-Toussainte de), *see* TURPIN (J. M.) A.-T. de V. de R., 1906.

Volz (Wilhelm). Im Dämmer d. Rimba. Sumatras Urwald u. Urmensch. 8°. Breslau. 1921
see BUSCHAN (G.), *ed.* Illust. Völkerkunde, B2i, 1923.

Vom [VON]. Vom Altertum zur Gegenwart &c. Skizzen v. F. Boll, U. Curtius *& others*, 1919, *see* ALTERTUM.

*Von den fier ketzeren Prediger ordẽs &c., 1510, *see* MURNER (T.)

Vonck (Cornelius Hugo). Oratio in funere Joannis van den Broeck. [P600]. s4°. Amstelædami. 1739

Vondel (Joost van den). Werken. Uitg. door J. van Lennep. Herzien en bijgewerkt door J. H. W. Unger. [30d]. s8°. Leiden, *Sijthoff. n.d.*

The following are the princ. works as mentioned on tp. Smaller poems are scattered in various vol. acc. to date of issue.

Adam in Ballingschap.	[27.]	Jeptha.	[20.]
Adonias.	[24.]	Joannes de Boetgezant.	[25.]
Altaergeheimenissen.	[11.]	Josef of Sofompaneas.	[6.]
Amsteldamsche Hecuba (De).	[4.]	Joseph in Dothan.	[8.]
		Joseph in Egypten.	[8.]
Batavische Gebroeders.	[26.]	Koning David herstelt.	[23.]
Bespiegelingen.	[24, 25.]	Koning David in Ballingschap.	[23.]
Brieven der Heilige Maeghden.	[10.]	Koning Davids Harpzangen.	[18–20.]
Elektra.	[7.]		
Faëton.	[26.]	Koning Edipus.	[23.]
Feniciaensche.	[28.]	Leeuwendalers (De).	[14.]
Gebroeders.	[8.]	Lucifer.	[17.]
Grotius. Testament.	[10.]	Maeghden.	[7.]
Gulden Winckel (Den).	[1.]	Maria Stuart.	[14.]
Gysbreght van Aemstel.	[7.]	Noah.	[14.]
Heerlyckheit der Kercke (De).	[26.]	Ovidius. Herscheppinge.	[28–30.]
Heerlyckheyd van Salomon (De).	[3.]	Palamedes.	[4.]
		Pascha (Het).	[1.]
Helden Godes (De).	[3.]	Peter en Pauwels.	[9.]
Heldinnebrieven.	[9.]	Salmoneus.	[18.]
Herkules in Trachin.	[28.]	Salomon.	[15.]
Hierusalem verwoest.	[3.]	Samson.	[24.]
Hippolytus of Rampsalige Kuyscheyd.	[5.]	Vaderen (De).	[1.]
		Virgilius. Wercken.	[12, 13, 21, 22.]
Horatius. Lierzangen.	[16.]		
Ifigenie in Tauren.	[27.]	Vorstelycke Warande der Dieren.	[2.]
Inwydinge van 't Stadthuis t'Amsterdam.	[17.]	Zungchin.	[27.]

see BAKHUIZEN VAN DEN BRINK (R. C.) V. met Roskam en Rommelpot, 3e druk, 1886.
,, BARNOUW (A. J.) V., 1925.

Von der Osten (H. H.)
Explor. in Hittite Asia Minor. la8°. Chicago. [1927]

Von Donop (*Capt.* **Stanley Brenton**). Notes on mechanism as applied to artillery. 8°. [1902]

Vorberg (Axel). Die Einführ. d. Reformation in Rostock. [Verein f. Ref.-gesch. Schr., Jhrg. 15, Nr. 58]. 8°. Halle. 1897

Vordemfelde (Hans). Die german. Religion in d. deut. Volksrechten. Halbb. 1, Der relig. Glaube. [Religionsgeschichtl. Versuche &c.; hrsg. Wünsch u. Deubner, B18i]. 8°. Giessen. 1923

Vorländer (O.), *see* BORRMANN (R.), *ed.* Aufnahmen mittelalterl. Wand- u. Deckenmalereien in Deut.: unter Mitw. v. O. V. &c., 2B, 1897–1914.

Vorläufer des neueren Sozialismus.
B2–4 [2, 6e A.; 3, 4, 2e A.] s8°. St. 1921–22
2, D. Kommunismus in d. deut. Reform.; v. K. Kautsky.
3, Die beiden ersten grossen Utopisten: T. More, v. K. Kautsky; T. Campanella, v. P. Lafargue; Der Jesuitenstaat in Paraguay, v. P. Lafargue.
4i, D. Sozialismus in Frankreich im 17 u. 18 Jhdt.; v. H. Lindemann.
4ii, D. utop. Sozialismus &c. in d. Verein. Staaten Nordamer.; v. M. Hillquit.

Voronoff (Serge). Vivre. Etude des moyens de relever l'énergie vitale et de prolonger la vie. s8°. [1920]

Voronovich (N.) Сборник матеріаловъ &c. "Зеленая книга". Ист. крестьянскаго движенія в черноморской губ. Собрал Н. В. 8°. [Praha]. 1921

Vorontsov (*prince* **Mikhail Semenovich**), *1782–1856*, *see* SCHERBININ (M. P.) Біографія Ген.-фельдмар. М. С. В., 1858.

Vorontsov-Dashkov (*graf* **Ilarion Ivanovich**).
Записка объ уничтоженіи крестьянской общины &c. (1893). [P2445]. s8°. Carouge-Genève. 1900

Vorovsky (V.)
В мире мерзости запустения. [P2722]. s8°. Москва. 1919

Vorovsky (Watzlaw), *commercial agent of Soviet Govt., see* AUBERT (T.) L'affaire Conradi [*i.e.* Assassination of V. by C.]: plaidoirie devant le Tribunal Criminel, 14 & 15 nov. 1923, 1924.

Vorsokratiker. Fragm. d. V., 3B, 1922, *see* DIELS (H.)

Vorst (Conrad), *see* DORT. The judgement of the Synode at D.; also their sentence t. C. V., 1619.

Vorst (Johann) [VORSTIUS]. De Hebraismis N.T. comm. Acc. praeter ejusdem cogita de stylo N.T. & diatr. de adagiis N.T., H. Vitringae animadv. Cur. J. F. Fischerus. 8°. Lipsiae. 1778
De Latinitate falso suspecta. s8°. Lipsiae. 1722
see VALERIUS MAXIMUS. Factorum dictorumque memorabilium libri ix; illust. a J. V., 2p, 1672.

Vortigern. *Passages sel. on trial of V. &c., v1–3, 1796 ?–98, *see* DUDLEY (H. B.) & M. D.

Vosbergen (Gaspar van). Verbaal van de ambassade van V. bij den Koning v. Denemarken, d. Neder-Sax. Kreits en d. Koning v. Zweden, 1625. [Hist. Genoots. Werken, N.S. 9]. 8°. Utrecht. 1867

Voskresenskaya letopis. Лѣтопись по воскресен. списку. [*includ.* Среднiй текстъ лѣт. Нестора. Полное соб. русс. лѣтописей, изд. Археогр. Ком., т7]. 4°. С.–П. 1856

Vosmaer (Carel).
Nanno, e. griek. Idylle. 4e dr. 8°. 'sGravenhage. 1913
see DEKKER (E. D.) Verzam. werken van Multatuli, d1, Studien over M. door C. Vosmaer, 1916.

Vosmerus (Michael). Principes Hollandiae & Zelandiae, domini Frisiae. [*b. w.* Martin (C.) Genealogies &c., 1580]. sm. fol. Antverpiae. 1578

Voss (Hermann). Giuseppe M. Crespi; 29 riprod. con testo e catologo. [Bibl. d'arte ital. sI, fasc. 5]. 8°. [1921]
Die Malerei d. Barock in Rom. 4°. [1924]
Die Malerei d. Spätrenaissance in Rom u. Florenz. 2B [*pagin. cont.*] 8°. 1920

Voss (Richard). Die Erlösung. s8°. St. 1922
Das grosse Wunder. Roman. s8°. St. [1915]
Villa Falconieri. s8°. 1923
Zwei Menschen. Roman. s8°. St. 1921

Vossius (Gerardus), *canon of Canterbury* [G. JOANNES V.]
De philosophia et philosophorum sectis lib. 2. s4°. Hagae-Com. 1656–57
De philosoph. sectis *has a sep. tp. & sep. pagin.*
De philosophorum sectis lib. Cum cont. &c. J. J. à Ryssel. s4°. Lipsiae. 1690
De theologia gentili & physiologia Xt., libri 1 & 2. [*b. w.* Maimonides, De idolatria, 1662]. s4°. Amsterdami. 1662
,, ,, [*a. ed.*] libri 9 [*in* 1v. lib. 5–9 *have 2nd tp.,* Amstel., 1669]. s4°. Francofurti ad M. 1675
De vitiis sermonis, et glossematis latino-barbaris, lib. 4. s4°. Amstelodami. 1645
Hist. de controversiis, quae Pelagius ejusque reliquiae moverunt, lib. 7. 2a ed. s4°. Amstelodami. 1655

Vossius (Isaac). De Septuaginta diss. *&* Appendix [*w. sep. pag.*] s4°. Hagae. 1661–63
De Sibyllinis &c. Acc. ejusdem responsio [*w. sep. pagin.*] s8°. Lugd. Batav. 1680
see SIMON (R.) Crit. enq. into the var. eds. of the Bible w. animadv. on treat. of I. V. on Sibylls, &c., 1684.

Vossler (Carl).
Dante als religiöser Dichter. 8°. Bern. 1921
Works in KÖNIGL. AKAD. D. WISS. ZU MÜNCHEN. Phil. Kl., Sitz.
Der Minnesang d. Bernhard v. Ventadorn, 1918.
Peire Cardinal, Satiriker aus d. Za. d. Albigenserkriege, 1916.
Sprachgemeinschaft u. Interessengemeinschaft, 1914.

Vossler (Otto). Mazzinis polit. Denken u. Wollen &c. [Hist. Zeitschrift. Beih. 11]. 8°. München. 1927

Vostochni Institut. Извѣстія. Приложеніе. Каталогъ Библ. В. И. ч2, вып. 1. Сост. Е. Г. Спальвинъ. 8°. Владивостокъ. 1913

Vostorgov (Ioann Joannovich) & *prince* **A. G. Scherbatov.**
Рѣчи на Всеросс. Съѣздѣ 6° Апр. 1906. [P2449]. 8°. Москва. 1906

Vote, The. The organ. of the Women's Freedom League. v1–3, 5, 6, No. 1 (Oct. 30, 1909–Apr. 20, 1912). sm. fol. 1909–12

Votes for women. Ed. F. & E. Pethick Lawrence. v3–7 (Oct. 1909–Sept. 1914) [*b. in* 6v]. fol. 1909–14

Voullième (Ernst). Der Buchdruck Kölns bis z. Ende d. 15. Jhdts. [Gesells. f. Rhein. Geschichtskunde, 24]. 8°. Bonn. 1903
Die deut. Drucker d. 15. Jhdt. 2e A. la8°. 1922

Vowles (Alfred), *F.R.G.S.* Wanderings w. a camera in Mesopotamia. s8º. 1920
Vowles (Hugh P.) Under new management. Book for business men & o. s8º. [1922]
Vox stellarum: or, A loyal almanack, 1800–8. By F. Moore. [1804 *wanting. b. w.* Gentleman's diary, 1800–8]. s8º. 1800–8
Voyage.
*Late v. (A) to Holland, 1681, *see* HOLLAND.
*V. à la Louisiane, 1794–98 &c., 1802, *see* BAUDRY DE LOZIÈRES (L. N.)
*V. aux pays rouges, par un Conservateur, 1873, *see* BESLAY (F.)
*V. (The) of adm. G. Carlton, in search of loyalty, 1820, *see* CARLTON (G.)
Voyages. Earliest v. round the world, 1519–1617, 1916, *see* ALEXANDER (P. F.), *ed.*
V. &c. des miss. de la Cie de Jésus, 2t, 1857–58, *see* JESUITS.
Vozrojdenie. *Возрожденіе. (Еврейскій пролетаріатъ и національная проблема. Сборникъ статей.) [P2446]. 8º. 1905
Vrangel, *see* WRANGEL.
Vriemoet (Emo Lucius).
Athenarum Frisiac. libri 2. [*3 pagin.*] s4º. Leovardiae. 1758
Vries (Matthias de), L. A. Te Winkel *& others, edd.* Woordenboek der Nederlandsche taal. d3iii [*pagin. cont.*], 7i, 8ii [*pagin. cont.*], 9, 13. la8º. 's-Gravenhage en Leiden. 1913–26
Vries (Simon de). Diss. crit. de Priscillianistis &c. s4º. Trajecti ad Rhenum. 1745
Vrij (M. P.) Internat. rivers. Reply to L. W. Lyde. [P2423]. 8º. 1920
Vsevolodsky-Gerngross (Vsevol Nikolaevich).
Теория русской речевой интонации. 8º. П. 1922
Vues pittoresques du Rhin, *n.d.*, *see* BLEULER (L.), *publ.*
Vugman (I. S.) 95 лет жизни &c. Одесской госуд. библ. (1830–1925). [P2870]. 8º. Ленинград. 1926
Vuice (Georgius). Homiliæ duæ de eccl. mysteriis Baptismo & Eucharistia &c. s8º. Lipsiæ, *N. Wolrab.* 1538
Oratio eccl. de pastoribus ovium Christi. s8º. Lipsiae. 1537
Vuicelius (Georgius), *see* WITZEL (GEORG).
Vuij (Jules). Adémar Fabri, prince-évêque de Genève, *see* REGIA DEP. DI STORIA PATRIA. Misc., t27, 1889.
Vuillemin (Louis). L'héroique pastorale. Variations au grand air 1914–18. Préf. de R. Dorgelès. s8º. 1920
Vuitry (Adolphe). Etudes sur le régime financier de la France avant la Révol. de 1789. 8º. 1878
,, ,, ...nouv. sér. 2t. 8º. 1883

Vujić (Michael) [WUITSCH]. Über Substanz u. Causalität. Inaug.-Diss. [P2491]. 8º. L. 1879
Vulcanius (Bonaventura) *of Bruges.* De literis & lingua Getarum sive Gothorum. Item De notis Lombardicis &c. s8º. Lugd. Batav. 1597
Vullers (Johann August). Instit. linguae Persicae, cum Sanscrita & Zendica compar. 8º. Gissae. 1840
Vulliamy (Colwyn Edward).
Immortal man: funeral customs &c. s8º. [1926]
Our prehistoric forerunners. 8º. [1925]
Unknown Cornwall. 8º. [1925]
Vulliamy (Lewis). Examples of classic ornament f. Greece & Rome. Drawn by L. V. 20 plates sel. f. orig. wk., w. intr. &c. notes by R. P. Spiers. la. fol. 1907
Vulliaud (Paul). Joseph de Maistre, franc-maçon. 8º. 1926
Vulliet (Auguste). Scènes de la révocation de l'Édit de Nantes, 1685. s8º. Lausanne. [1885]
Vulpesco (Michel). Les coutumes roumaines périodiques. Préf. par A. Van Gennep. la8º. 1927
Vulson (Marc de), *sieur de La Colombière.* Portraits des hommes illust. franç., dans le gallerie du Palais Card. de Richelieu, avec leurs actions &c., desseignez &c. par Heince & Bignon, leurs vies, composez par V. la. fol. 1650
Les vies des hommes illustres &c. s8º. 1700
Vuy (Jules), *see* VUIJ (J.)
Vyazemsky, *The family of, see* VYAZEMSKY (*pr.* P. A.) Остафьевскій архивъ, 1899–1913.
Vyazemsky (*pr.* **Boris Leonidovich).**
Верховный Тайный Совѣтъ. 8º. С.–П. 1909
Vyazemsky (*pr.* **Petr Andreevich),** *1792–1878.*
Остафьевскій архивъ князей В. Изд. гр. С. Д. Шереметева. Подъ ред. В. И. Саитова. 5т [т5 *in 2p*]. la8º. С.–П. 1899–1913
1–4, Переписка кн. П. А. В. съ А. И. Тургеневымъ, 1812–45.
Полное собраніе сочиненій. Изд. гр. С. Д. Шереметева. la8º. С.–П. 1878–96
1, 2, 7, Лит., крит. и біограф. очерки, 1810–77, 3т.
3, 4, 11, 12, Стихотворенія, 4т.
5, Фонъ-Визинъ.
6, Lettres d'un Vétéran russe de 1812, sur la question d'Orient; publ. P. d'Ostafievo [*French & Russ.*]
8–10, Старая записная книжка, 3т.
Фонъ-Визинъ. 8º. С.–П. 1848

W

W. (A.) *Mary Queen of Scots, 1889, *see* WALKER (A.)
W. (D.) *Horae subsecivae; or treat. showing grounds necess. our sanguinary laws agst. the papists, 1664, *see* DENTON (W.)
W. (D. T.) *Hall marks on gold & silver articles, 1925, *see* HALL.
W. (H.) J. Epstein: [*intr. ent.* The sculpture of J. E., *signed* H. W., 1925, *see* EPSTEIN (J.)
W. Rothenstein: [*descr. &c. signed* H. W.], 1923, *see* ROTHENSTEIN (W.)
W. (J. V.) *Vita &c. S. Rumoldi, 1638, *see* WACHTENDONCK (J. VAN).
W. (P.) *Grammaire albanaise, 1887, *see* ALBANAISE.
W. (R. H.) Draughtsmen: E. C. Hall, H. Rushbury &c.: [*intr. signed* R. H. W.], 1924, *see* HALL (*Mrs.* E. C.)
W. (S.) Athenian Oracle, 1704, *see* WESLEY (S.)
W. (T.) *The anker of Xtn. doctrine, 1622, *see* WORTHINGTON (THOMAS).
W. (T.) *Queries offered by T. W. [*i.e.* Thomas Ward] to Protestants, 1688, *see* CLAGETT (W.)
W. (W.), *B.D.* A modest plea for infants baptism, 1677, *see* WALKER (W.)
W. (W.), *gent.* *Brief rel. of the persec. agst. Catholike Xtns. in Japonia; tr. W. W., 1619, *see* JESUITS.
W. (W. G.) *A few words in support of No. 90 of Tracts for the Times &c., 1841, *see* WARD (W. G.)
Wace (Alan John Bayard). A Cretan statuette in the Fitzwilliam Museum. Study in Minoan costume. 4º. C. 1927
Wace (Henry), *D.D.* Xty. & morality; corresp. of Gospel w. moral nature of man. 7th ed. s8º. 1887
Wace (Robert). La vie de Sainte Marguerite, poème inéd., préc. de l'hist. de s. transform[s]. & suivi de textes &c. & de l'analyse du Mystère de Ste. M. par A Joly. [Extr. des Mém. de la Soc. des Antiq. de Normandie]. 8º. 1879
see PHILPOT (J. H.) Maistre W., 1925.
Wach (Joachim). Die Typenlehre Trendelenburgs u. i. Einfl. auf Dilthey. 8º. Tübingen. 1926
Wachstein (Bernhard). Hebräische Grabsteine aus d. 13.–15. Jhdt. in Wien &c., 1916, *see* KAIS. AKAD. D. W. IN WIEN. Phil.-hist. Kl. Sitz., B181, 1928.
Wachtendonck (Jan van). *Vita, passio & miracula S. Rumoldi, apostoli Mechlin., & martyris. [*tp. mutilated*]. s4º. [Mechliniae. 1638]
Wächter (Alfred v. Kiderlen-), *see* KIDERLEN-WÄCHTER (A. v.)
Wachter (Ferdinand). Heimskringlae ill. & Germ. hist. illust. specimen. 8º. Jenae. 1834
Wachter (Georg). Hist. August. Confess. a corruptelis A. Varillasii. Disput. [P484]. s4º. Altorfii Noric. [1730]
,, ,, [*a. copy w. add. pref. dated* 1737. P2642].
Wachthausen (René), *see* BIRABEAU (A.) & R. W. Plaire [*in* Œuvres (Les) libres, t63, 1926].
Wächtler (Jacob). Arcana chiliasmi moderni, d. i. 21 sonderbare Hauptgründe, aus Schr. P. J. Speners u. J. W. Petersens. [*b. w.* Gebhardi (V. C.) De chiliasmo, 1691]. s4º. L. 1695
Wackernagel (Carl Eduard Philipp).
Das deutsche Kirchenlied. s4º. St. 1841
Wackernagel (Jacob), *see* GRUNDRISS. G. d. indo-ar. Philol. u. Altertumskunde; hrsg. v. H. Lüders u. J. W., 3B, 1896–1920.
Wackernagel (Rudolf).
Gesch. der Stadt Basel. B2ii, 3. la8º. Basel. 1916–24
Waddell (Helen Jane). The wandering scholars. 8º. 1927

Waddell (Lawrence Austine).
Aryan origin of the alphabet. 8°. 1927
Indo-Sumerian seals deciphered. 8°. 1925
Phoenician origin of Britons, Scots & Anglo-Saxons. 8°. 1924
A Sumer-Aryan dict. Etymolog. lexicon of Eng. & o. Aryan lang. & Sumerian orig. of Egyptian & its hieroglyphs. pl. 8°. 1927
see TEMPLE (*Sir* R. C.) W. on Phoenician origins, 1925.

Waddesworth (James) [†WADSWORTH (J.)] Copies of certaine letters &c. betweene Spain & England in matter of religion. Betw. J. W. & W. Bedell. s4°. 1624
see BURNET (G.), *bp.* Life of W. Bedell [*&* copies of cert. letters betw. J. W. & W. B., *w. sep. tp.*], 1685.

Waddington (Albert). Hist. de Prusse. t2. [1688–1740]. 8°. [1922]

Waddington (William Henry). Recueil gén. des monnaies grecques d'Asie mineure. Commencé par W. H. W., cont. & compl. par E. Babelon & T. Reinach. [Acad. des Inscr. & Belles-Lettres (Fond. Piot)]. 2e éd. t1i. 4°. 1925
Ii, Pont & Paphlagonie.

Wade [*VADIUS], *see* MICHEL (F.) Wade: lettre s. une tradit. du moyen âge, 1837.

Wade (Arthur Shepherd). Cotton spinning. s8°. [1921]

Wade (George Woosung), *D.D.* New Test. hist. With contrib. by J. H. Wade. 8°. [1922]

Wade (M. S.), *M.D.*
Mackenzie of Canada: life & adv. 8°. E. 1927

Wade (Thomas Callander), *see* BOROUGHS (*Sir* J.) Sovereignty of the Brit. seas wr. in year 1633; ed. &c. by T. C. W., 1920.

Wade-Evans (Arthur Wade), *see* RICEMARCH, *the Wise.* Life of St. David; [tr., w. sels. f. o. lives, & notes] by A. W. W.-E., 1923.

Wadia (Ardaser Sorabjee N.) The call of the world: remin. of a year's tour. s8°. 1918

Wadi Sarga. Coptic & Greek texts f. the excav. [at W. S.] by the Byzantine Research Acc. Ed. W. E. Crum & H. I. Bell, w. intr. by R. C. Thompson. [Coptica, 3]. 8°. Hauniae. 1922

Wadmore (Beauchamp).
The earthworks of Bedfordshire. 4°. Bedford. 1920

Wadsley (Olive).
Almond-blossom. s8°. [1921]
Belonging. s8°. [1920]
Fair game. s8°. [1927]
Shutters. [2nd impr.] s8°. [1926]
Sometimes. s8°. [1923]
You & I. s8°. [1924]

Wadstein (Elis). Fries. Lehnwörter im Nordischen, *see* KUNG. HUM. VET.-SAMF. I UPPSALA. Skr., B21, 1922.
On the orig. of the English, *see* KUNG. HUM. VET.-SAMF. I UPPSALA. Skr., B24, 1927.

Waepenaert (Ed. Dhont de), *see* DHONT DE WAEPENAERT (E.)

Waerland (Are). Die Diktatur d. Proletariats. Übers. d. 3en schwed. A. v. F. Arnheim. 8°. [Gotha]. 1921
Idealism och materialism. s8°. Uppsala. [1924]

Waessenaer (Jacobus á), *see* DESCARTES (R.) Corr. of D. & C. Huygens, 1635–47, (The Stampioen-W. affair, 1639 &c.); ed. L. Roth, 1926.

Waffenstillstand. Vom W. z. Frieden v. Versailles, Okt. 1918–Juni 1919. [Deut. Geschichtskal. Hrsg. F. Purlitz]. 8°. L. [1919]
Zwischen W. u. Frieden (Juni 1919–Jan. 1920). [Deut. Geschichtskal., Lief. 67; *b. w.* Vom Waffenstillstand &c., 1919]. 8°. L. [1920]

Wagemann (Ernst). Die deut. Kolonisten im brasil. Staate Espirito Santo, *see* ANSIEDELUNG (DIE) v. Europäern in d. Tropen, 1915.

Wagenbronner (Georg Christian). Ergo notio illa animam mortui esse & dici in Evangeliis daemonem &c. [*b. w.* Caspari (J. B.) Not. δαιμονίου &c., 1761]. s4°. Jenae. 1762

Wagenseil (Johann Christoph), *b. 1633.* Exercit. sex varii argumenti. [P1015]. s4°. Altdorfi Noric. 1687
„ „ Acc. vita & consignatio scr. autoris cura F. Roth-Scholtzii. s4°. Norimbergae. 1719
Tela ignea Satanae. Hoc est arcani &c. Judaeorum adv. Christum Deum &c. libri ἀνεκδοτοι, R. Lipmanni Carmen Memoriale *&* Liber Nizzachon—Acta disput. R. Jechielis cum quodam Nicolao—Acta disput. R. Mosis Nachmanidis cum Fr. Paulo Christiani & Fr. R. Martini—R. Isaaci Liber Chissuk emuna—Libellus Toldos Jeschu. Acc. Mantissa de LXX hebdomadibus Danielis adv. J. Marshami explic. [*6 pagin.*] s4°. Altdorfi Noricorum. 1681
see MISHNAH. J. C. W. Sota; hoc est liber Mishnicus &c., 1674.

Wager (*adm. sir* **Charles).** *Orig. letters to an honest sailor [*i.e.* Adm. Vernon, f. Sir C. W., W. Pulteney, the Duke of Newcastle, Vere Beauclerk &c.] [P607]. s8°. [1746]

Wager (William) [WAYER]. Enough is as good as a feast (c. 1565). Intr. note by S. de Ricci. [H. E. Huntington Facs. Repr., 2]. 8°. N.Y. 1920

Wages. *Wages, prices & profits. Report prep. by Labour Research Dept. Pref. by S. Webb. la8°. 1922

Waggaman (Mary T.) Family allowances in for. countries, *see* UNITED STATES: LABOR. Bull. 401, 1926.

Waggett (Philip Napier). Knowledge & virtue. Hulsean Lect., 1920–21. 8°. O. 1924

Wagner (Christoph), *see* FAUST (*Dr.* J.) Hist. &c. of J. F., contg. deeds of W. (1594); ed. W. Rose, 1925.

Wagner (Conrad Ludwig).
De jure Sabathi, diss. jur. eccl. s4°. Halae. [1702]

Wagner (Gottfried), *of Leipzig.*
De originibus Americanis diss. s4°. Lipsiae. [1669]

Wagner (Harr), *see* BASHFORD (H.) & H. W. A man unafraid: J. C. Frémont, 1927.

Wagner (Henry Raup). Sir F. Drake's voyage around the world, its aims &c. 4°. San Francisco, Cal. 1926

Wagner (Leopold). London inns & taverns. 8°. [1924]
A new book about London. 8°. [1921]

Wagner (Martin), T. Fabri & S. Scultetus. Examen thesium & regularum Zuinglianarum de Coena Domini vulgatarum per C. Pilcium. Script. opera M. W., T. F. & S. S. s8°. Bartphae. [c. 1586]

Wagner (Richard).
Sämtliche Schriften u. Dichtungen. 5e A. B11, 12. 8°. L. *n.d.*
Das Liebesverbot, oder Die Novize v. Palermo. Komische Oper. s8°. L. [1922]
[*Orchestral scores of var. works, w. sep. tp. & pag.; b. in 1v & arr. as below*]. 4°. Berlin *&* L. *n.d.*
Ouverture zu Flieg. Holländer—Ouverture zu Tannhäuser—Vorspiel *&* Einl. zu Lohengrin — Tristan u. Isolde: Vorspiel u. Isoldens Liebestod — Meistersinger: Vorspiel — Ritt d. Walküren — Wotans Abschied, aus d. Walküre — Trauermarsch aus Gotterdämmerung — Siegfried-Idyll — Liebesmahl d. Apostel—Kaisermarsch [*w.* Volks-Gesang, *orch. & vocal score*].
[Sonaten, Lieder *& o. pieces* für d. Pianoforte, *includ.* Aus R. W.'s Opern, Transcr. v. F. Liszt. *Coll. in 1v. each w. sep. tp. & pagin.*] 4°. *n.p. n.d.*
TRANSLATIONS.
Œuvres en prose. Tr. J. G. Prod'homme &c. t3, 4, 5, 10–13. s8°. [1913–25]
3, 1849–50. 4, 5, Opéra & Drame. 10, 1869–71. 11, 1872–73. 12, 1874–78. 13, 1879–83—Index gén.
Letters. Sel. & ed. W. Altmann. Tr. M. M. Bozman. 2v. 8°. 1927
"The music of the future." Letter. Tr. by E. Dannreuther. [P2862]. 8°. 1873
The Valkyrie [w. German text]. Tr. H. & F. Corder. s8°. Mayence. *n.d.*
see BARTHOLONI (J.) W. & le recul du temps, 1924.
„ CORBETT-SMITH (A.). Nat. opera hdbks., 1–4 (Parsifal, Master-singers, Tristan & Isolda, Ring of the Nibelungs), 1922.
„ FOUQUE (O.) Révolutionnaires de la musique, 1882.
„ FOURCAUD (L. DE). R. W., sa vie, sa pensée & s. art, 1923.
„ HIGHT (G. A.) R. W., crit. biog., 2v, 1925.
„ KOCH (M.) R. W., 2T, 1907–15.
„ NEWMAN (E.) W. as man & artist, 2nd Amer. ed., 1924.
„ NIETZSCHE (F. W.) Nietzsche-W. corr.; ed. E. Foerster Nietzsche; tr. C. V. Kerr, 1922.
„ —— Unzeitgemässe Betrachtungen, B4, W. in Bayreuth, 1876
„ REVUE MUSICALE, oct. 1923, No. spéc., W. & la France, 1923
„ SCHURÉ (E.) Le drame musical, t2, R. W., s. oeuvre &c., 1920.
„ SHAW (G. B.) The perfect Wagnerite: comm. on the Ring. 4th ed., 1923.
„ WALLACE (W.) Liszt, W. & the Princess, 1927.
„ —— R. W. as he lived, 1925.
„ WILSON (P. C.) W.'s dramas & Greek tragedy, 1919.

Wagner (Tobias). Inquisitio theolog. in acta henotica. s4°. Tubingae. 1666

Wagstaffe (Thomas), *the elder.* *A defence of the Vindication of Charles the Martyr. In ans. to Amyntor [by John Toland]. [P2652]. s4°. 1699

Wahl (Adalbert).
Vom Bismarck d. 70er Jahre. 8°. Tübingen. 1920

Wahl (Jean). Les philosophies pluralistes d'Angleterre & d'Amérique. 8°. 1920

Wahl (Josef). Andreas v. Regensburg, e. Geschichtsschr. d. 15. Jhdts. [P2728]. 8°. Altaville. 1882

Wahl (Maurice). Nouv. géogr. gén. de la France. la8°. *n.d.*
Les prem. années de la Révolution à Lyon, 1788–92. 8°. 1894

Wahlberg (Olaus). Diss. præstantiam & hist. idiomatis Sueo-Gothorum evolvens. Præses O. W., resp. G. Psilander. s4°. Gryphisw. 1726

Wahle (Richard). Gehirn u. Bewusstsein. [*b. w.* Zimmermann (R.) Anthroposophie, 1882]. 8°. Wien. 1884

Wahlius (Johannes).
Diss. de Thoma Moro. s4°. Altenburgi. 1686

Wahlsprüche. Die Wahl-u. Denksprüche, Feldgeschreie &c., 1884, *see* DIELITZ (J.)

Wahrhaftiger, *see* WARHAFFTE &C.

*Wahrheit (Die) ü. d. russ. Dorf. [P2878]. s8°. [1927]

Waife (Geraldine). Colleagues. s8°. 1923

Waight (George). Allhallows' Church, Tottenham. 8°. 1876

Wailes (George Herbert), *see* CASH (J.) & G. H. W. Brit. freshwater Rhizopoda &c.; v5, Heliozoa by G. H. W., 1921.

Wainwright (Gerald A.) Balabish. Pref. by T. Whittemore. [Egypt Explor. Fund]. 4°. 1920

Wainwright (Henry) & T. G. Wainwright. Trial of the Wainwrights. Ed. H. B. Irving, w. apprec. of the Editor by Sir E. Marshall Hall. 8°. E. [1920]

Wainwright (Thomas George), *see* WAINWRIGHT (H.) & T. G. W. Trial of the Wainwrights; ed. H. B. Irving, 1920.

Wait (W. E.)
Manual of the birds of Ceylon. la8°. [Colombo]. 1925

Waite (Arthur Edward).
The Brotherhood of the Rosy Cross: records of the House of the Holy Spirit. 8°. 1924
Emblematic freemasonry. 8°. 1925
A new encyclopædia of freemasonry. 2v. 8°. 1921
Raymund Lully. s8°. 1922
The secret tradition in alchemy. la8°. 1926
see HERMETIC MUSEUM; ed. A. E. W., 2v, 1893.

Waitz (Georg). G. W. u. Th. Sickel: Briefwechsel; *ed.* W. Erben, *see* KÖNIGL. GESELLS. D. W. ZU GÖTT. Nachr., 1926.

Waitz (Theodor). Lehrbuch d. Psychologie als Naturwiss. 8°. Braunschweig. 1849

Wake (Joan), *ed.*, *see* NORTHAMPTON. Quarter Sessions rec. (1630, 1657–58), 1924.

Wake (William), *bp. of Lincoln, abp. of Canterbury.*
The genuine epistles of the apostol. Fathers, Barnabas—Clement—Ignatius—Polycarp—the Shepherd of Hermas; & martyrdoms of Ignatius & Polycarp. Tr. w. disc. by [W.] 3rd ed. s8°. 1719
see MAICHELIUS (D.) Lucubrationes Lambetanae: monumenta lit. ex Bibl. Gul. W. coll. &c., 1729.

Wakefield (Edward Gibbon).
*The new Brit. prov. of S. Australia. 2nd ed. s8°. 1835
Sir C. Metcalfe in Canada (1844), *see* WRONG (E. M.) C. Buller &c., 1926.

Wakefield (Gilbert). A new transl. of the Gospel of St. Matthew; w. notes. 4°. Warrington. 1782
A new transl. of those parts only of the N.T. wrongly transl. 8°. 1789

Wakefield (H. R.)
They return at evening. Ghost stories. s8°. [1928]

Wakefield (Priscilla).
Excursions in N. America. 3rd ed. s8°. 1819

Wakeley (Joseph B.) Anecdotes of George Whitefield, w. biogr. sketch. 4th ed. s8°. Douglas, Isle of Man. 1875
Anecdotes of the Wesleys. Introd. by J. M'Clintock. s8°. [1869]
The heroes of Methodism, sk. of ministers &c. s8°. N.Y. [1856]

Wakeman (Anna R.), *wife of Geo. Wakeman.*
In memoriam: George Wakeman. 8°. N.Y. 1870

Wakeman (George), *see* WAKEMAN (A. R.) In memoriam: G. W., 1870.

Walbe (Heinrich). Die Kunstdenkmäler d. Kreises Giessen. B2, Kloster Arnsburg mit Altenburg. Bearbt. v. H. W. Geschichtl. Teil v. K. Ebel. Mit e. Anhang. la8°. Darmstadt. 1919

Walbran (John Richard). Guide to Ripon, Harrogate, Fountains Abbey, Bolton Priory &c. 5th ed. 8°. Ripon. 1851

Walbrook (Henry Mackinnon).
J. M. Barrie & the theatre. s8°. 1922

Walch (Charlotta Catharina), *wife of J. G. Walch, form. Buddein.* *Ehren Gedächtnis d. wohlseel. Frau Kirchenräthin C. C. W. [*w.* Gedichte *on* C. C. W. &c. *by var. a., pagin. cont. b. w.* Walch (J. G.) Leben, 1777]. 4°. Jena. 1766

Walch (Christian Wilhelm Franz).
Breviarium theologiae symbolicae eccl. Lutheranae. ed. 2ª aucta. s8°. Goettingae. 1781
Comm. de Luthero disputatore. [P442]. s4°. [Göttingae. 1754]
Compendium hist. eccl. Compendio hist. eccl. Gothano suppl. s8°. Gothæ. 1757
A compend. hist. of the popes. Tr. 8°. 1759
De Deo Ebraeorum Montano. Praes. C. G. F. W., resp. C. H. Kirchnerus. [P2666]. s4°. Jenae. 1746
Grundsäze d. natürl. Gottesgelahrheit. 2ᵉ A. s8°. Göttingen. 1779
Hist. Adoptianorum. s8°. Göttingae. 1755
Monimenta medii ævi. Ex Bibl. Regia Hanoverana. 6 fasc. [2v *in* 3]. s8°. Gottingæ. 1757–64

Walch (Gérard). Anthol. des poètes fr. contemp. (1866–1925). Préf. de S. Prudhomme. n. éd. t1. s8°. 1925
Poètes d'hier & d'aujourd'hui. Suppl. à l'Anthologie des poètes franç. contemp. n. éd., remaniée & augm. s8°. 1925

Walch (George T.) Shakespeare: a hdbk. of information. [P2758]. s8°. 1923

Walch (George Turner). The engineering works of the Kistna Delta: descr. &c. acc. 2v. la8°. Madras. 1899

Walch (Johann Ernst Immanuel).
Antiq. symbolicae. s8°. Jenae. 1772
Christianorum sub Diocletiano in Hispania persequutio. s8°. Jenae. 1751
Comm. qua antiq. Xtianorum doctorum de jurejurando sententiae percensentur &c. [P433]. s4°. Jenae. 1744
Diss. in Acta Apostolorum. 3v *in* 1. [v1, 2, ed. 3ª]. s4°. Jenae. 1761–66
Sacrorum Acad. Jenensis secularium hist. [P444]. s4°. Jenae. 1759

Walch (Johann Georg).
Bibl. patristica. 8°. Jenae. 1770
Compendium antiq. eccl. Acc. C. S. Schurzfleischii Controversiae &c. antiq. eccl. s8°. Lipsiae. 1733
Einl. in d. theolog. Wissenschaften. 2ᵉ verm. A. s8°. Jena. 1753
Hist. crit. Latinae linguae. ed. nova. s8°. L. 1729
Hist. eccl. N. Test. variis observ. illust. s4°. Jenae. 1744
Hist. u. theolog. Einl. in d. Relig.-Streitigkeiten d. Evangel.-Luther. Kirchen. Hrsg. &c. W. 2ᵉ A. 5T. s8°. Jena. 1733[–39]
Hist. u. theolog. Einl. in d. Relig.-Streitigkeiten welche sonderlich ausser d. Evangel.-Luther. Kirche entstanden. Hrsg. W. 3ᵉ A. 5T. s8°. Jena. 1733–36
Introd. in libros eccl. luther. symbolicos &c. s4°. Jenae. [1732]
Jubelgedächtnis d. W. gestiftet. s4°. Jena. 1768
*Leben u. Character d. wohlseel. Herrn Kirchenraths J. G. W. 4°. Jena. 1777
Miscellanea sacra, sive comm. ad hist. eccl. sanctioresque disciplinas pertin. coll. 4°. Amstelodami. 1744
Obs. in Novi Foederis libros. [*b. w.* Buddeus (J. F.) Eccl. Apostolica, 1779]. s8°. Jenae. 1727
Parerga academica ex histor. mon. coll. s8°. Lipsiae. 1721
see BOSIUS (J. A.) Intr. in notit. scr. eccl. J. F. Buddei &c.; coll. & ed. cura J. G. W., 1723.
,, THEOLOGISCHER BÜCHERSAAL, B1, 1749.

Walcott (Charles Doolittle). The Cambrian faunas of China, *see* WILLIS (B.), E. BLACKWELDER &C. Research in China, v3, 1913.
Cambrian geology & paleontology, IV, 1924, *see* SMITHSONIAN INSTITUTION. Misc. coll., v67, 1924.

Walcott (Mackenzie Edward Charles).
Mem. of Stamford. 2nd ed. rev. & corr. 8°. Stamford. 1888
William of Wykeham & h. colleges. 8°. Winchester. 1852

Wald (Samuel Gottlieb). *De haeresi abjuranda quid statuat eccl. Rom.-Cath. [P2644]. s4°. Regiomonti. 1721
De vita, scriptis & systemato mystico Seb. Franci. [P596]. s4°. Erlangae. 1793
Theologiae symbolicae Lutheranae descr. [*b. w.* Walch (C. F. W.) Breviarium, 1781]. s8°. Halae Sax. 1786

Waldburg (Otto v.), *Fürstbischof v. Augsburg* [†TRUCHSESS v. WALDBURG (O.), *Card. Prince*], *see* SCHWARZ (B.) Kard. O., bis zur Wahl als Fürstbischof v. Augsburg (1514–43), 1923.

Walde (Alois). Die ital. Sprachen, *see* GRUNDRISS d. indogerman. Sprach-u. Altertumskunde, Abt. 2, B1, 1916.

Waldecker (Ludwig). Stand d. Gesetzgeb. ü. Erwerbs-u. Wirtschaftsgenossenschaften, 1914, *see* UNTERSUCHUNGEN ü. Konsumvereine, 1919.

Waldef. The Romance of Waldef [*Lat. & Eng.*]; ed. &c. J. G. Smyly, *see* HERMATHENA, v18, 1919.

Waldenmaier (Hermann). Entstehung d. evangel. Gottesdienstordn. Süddeutschlands im Za. d. Reformation. [Verein f. Ref.-gesch. Schr., Jhrg. 34 (Nr. 125/26)]. 8°. L. 1916

Waldenses. *Apologia verae doctrinae eorum qui vulgo appellantur Waldenses, vel Picardi. J. Hussitae doct., cum scr. sanctis consenc. &c. Aucta & recognita. [Tr. e Bohemico in lat. *b. w.* Bohemia. Confessio, 1535]. s4°. [Vitebergę, *G. Rhaw*]. 1538
In hoc vol. haec continentur: Duplex cōfessio Valdensiū ad Regem [Wladislaw II] Ungarie missa, Augustini de Olomucz Epistole cōtra perfidiam Valdensium. Eiusdem bine Littere de heresi Vald. Excusacio Vald. contra binas litteras Doctoris Augustini, Jacobi Zigleri contra heresim Valdensium Libri 5. sm. fol. [Lypsiae, *Melchior Loterus.* 1512]

Waldere, *king, see* BEOWULF. Widsith—Beowulf—Waldere &c.; Eng. by C. Scott-Moncrieff, 1921.

Waldersee (*Graf* **Alfred v.)** Aus d. Briefwechsel d. Gen.-Feldmar. A. Graf. v. W. Hrsg. H. O. Meisner. B1, Die Berliner Jahre, 1886–91. la8°. 1928
Denkwürdigkeiten. Bearb. u. hrsg. H. O. Meisner. 3B. 8°. St. 1923
A field-marshal's memoirs: f. diary, corr. &c. of W. Condensed & tr. by F. Whyte. 8°. 1924
see †RAUCH (F. v.) Mit Graf W. in China, 1907.

Waldersee (*Gräfin* **Elisabeth v.)** Von Klarheit zu Klarheit! Gräfin M. E. v. Waldersee, geb. Lee, 1837–1914: e. Lebensbild. 8°. St. 1915

Waldersee (*Gräfin* **Marie Esther v.),** *wife of (1) Pr. Friedrich v. Noer, (2) Graf A. H. K. L. v. Waldersee, form. Lee, see* WALDERSEE (*Gräfin* E. v.) Von Klarheit zu Klarheit!; Gräfin M. E. v. W.: e. Lebensbild, 1915.

Waldeyer (Wilhelm) [WALDEYER-HARTZ (H. WILHELM G. v.)] Gedächtnisrede auf A. Brauer, *see* KÖN.-PREUSS. AKAD. Abh., Phys.-math. Klasse, 1918.
Die im Weltkriege stehenden Völker in anthropolog. Betrachtung, *see* DEUTSCHE Reden in schwerer Zeit, 32, 1915.
Die Intraparietalnähte, *see* KÖN.-PREUSS. AKAD. Abh., Phys.-math. Klasse, 1917.

Waldman (Louis), *see* NEW YORK: ASSEMBLY. Proc. of the Judic. Comm. of the Assembly in investig. as to qualif. of L. W. &c. to retain their seats, 1920.

Waldman (Milton). Americana: the lit. of Amer. hist. 8°. 1926
Sir W. Raleigh. 8°. [1928]

Waldmann (Emil). Albrecht Altdorfer. la8°. 1923
Edouard Manet. 4°. Berlin. 1923

Waldo (Fullerton Leonard). Down the Mackenzie thr. the gt. lone land. 8°. N.Y. 1923

Waldron (Francis Godolphin). The Shakspearean misc.: coll. of tracts, biog. anecdotes of theatrical performers &c. [*4 pagin.*] s4°. 1802

Waldschmidt (Ernst) & W. Lentz. Die Stellung Jesu im Manichäismus, *see* KÖNIGL.-PREUSS. AKAD. Abhandl., Phil.-hist. Kl., 1926.

Waldstein (Albrecht v.), *duke of Friedland.* Briefe an C. v. Harrach (1625–27); hrsg. v. F. Tadra, *see* FONTES RERUM AUSTRIAC., B41ii, 1879.

Waldstein (*Sir* **Charles),** *aft. Walston.* Alcamenes & the establ. of the classical type in Greek art. la8°. C. 1926
Harmonism & conscious evolution. 8°. 1922
Notes on Greek sculpture. la8°. C. 1927

Walenburch (Adrian van), *bp. of Adrianople,* **& P. van Walenburch.** Tractatus gen. de controversiis fidei. 2t (t1 *has 2*; t2 *3 pagin.*) fol. Coloniae Agripp. 1669–71
De controv. tract. gen. s8°. Parisiis. 1768
De controv. tract. gen.—Professio fidei cathol., *see* MIGNE (J. P.), *ed.* Theol. cursus, t1, 1860.
Methodus Augustiniana defendendi &c. fidem catholicam, ex solo Verbo Dei. s8°. Coloniæ Agrippinæ. 1645

Walenburch (Pieter van), *bp. of Mysia, see* WALENBURCH (A. VAN) & P. VAN W., *for works wr. in collaboration.*

Wales. Ancient laws & institutes of Wales; compr. laws supposed to be by Howel the Good &c. With indexes & glossary. [Ed. Aneurin Owen]. [Public Rec. Comm.] 2v. la8°. 1841
Reports of Comm. on Inq. into State of Educ. in W. 8°. 1848

Wales (Hubert).
The purpose: reflections & digressions. s8°. 1913

Waley (Adolf). A pageant of India. 8°. 1927

Waley (Arthur David).
Intr. to the study of Chinese painting. 4°. 1923
The Nō plays of Japan. [*Works of Seami &c. tr., w. intr.*] by A. D. W. With letters by O. Sickert. 8°. [1921]
The temple & o. p. Tr. A. W., w. intr. essay on early Chinese poetry &c. 8°. [1923]

Waley (Arthur David) [*continued*].
see BRITISH MUSEUM. Index of Chinese artists repres. in Dept. of Prints &c., by W., 1922.
,, MURASAKI (*Lady*). Tale of Genji; tr. A. W., v1–4, 1925–28.

Walford (Edward), *M.A., see* WALFORD'S COUNTY FAMILIES &c.; by E. W., 1865.

Walford's county families of the United Kingdom. By E. Walford. 3rd ed. enl. la8°. 1865

Waliszewski (Kasimir). La Russie il y a 100 ans: le règne d'Alex. Ier. [3t]. 8°. 1923–25

Walker Art Gallery, *Liverpool.* Cat. Ed. w. intr. &c. by C. Dyall. la8°. [1907 ?]

Walker Trust essays, *see* PRAYER. The power of prayer: sel. of Walker Trust essays &c.; ed. W. P. Paterson &c., 1920.

Walker (A. Jamieson), *ed., see* HOLLEMAN (A. F.) Text-book of organic chemistry, 1920.

Walker (Alexander) [*ps.* ELDER OF THE CHURCH OF SCOTLAND].
*Mary Queen of Scots: a narr. & defence. By an elder of the Ch. of Scotland. [Foreword signed A. W.] 8°. Aberdeen. 1889

Walker (Anthony), *D.D., see* HOLLINGWORTH (R.) Dr. H.'s defence of Charles I bk. Εἰκὼν Βασιλική; agst. assaults of Dr. W., 1692.

Walker (Charles), *of Brighton.*
The ritual reason why. Ed. C. W. [2nd ed.] s8°. [1869]
The server's handbook: manner of serving at celebrations of the Holy Eucharist &c. s8°. 1871

Walker (Cyril Tollemache Harley). The construction of the world in terms of fact & value. s8°. O. 1919

Walker (Donald). Walker's manly exercises. Rev., or wr., by "Craven." 9th ed. s8°. *Bohn.* 1855

Walker (Eric Anderson).
Hist. atlas of S. Africa. fol. Cape Town. 1922
Hist. of South Africa. 8°. 1928
Lord de Villiers & h. times: S. Africa, 1842–1914. 8°. 1925

Walker (Ernest), *D.Mus.* Hist. of music in Eng. 2nd ed. 8°. 1924

Walker (Francis), *Ph.D.*
Double taxation in the U.S. 8°. N.Y., *Columbia Univ.* 1895

Walker (Francis Amasa). Discussions in economics & statistics. Ed. D. R. Dewey. 2v. 8°. N.Y. 1899
see UNITED STATES. 9TH CENSUS, 1870. Compendium; comp. by F. A. W., 1872.

Walker (George), *commodore.* Voyages & cruises. Intr. &c. by H. S. Vaughan. 8°. [1928]

Walker (George), *novelist, 1772–1847.* Walker's coll. of dances, No. 2, 8. [*b. w.* Corelli (A.) Twelve concertos, 1790 ?]. 4°. [1795 ?]

Walker (George), *stockbroker.* Chess studies. 8°. 1844

Walker (*Maj.-Gen.* **George Townsend Forestier-),** *see* FORESTIER-WALKER.

Walker (*Sir* **Gilbert),** *see* CLAYTON (H. H.), *ed.* World weather records; coll. by W. &c., 1927.

Walker (Hugh). English satire & satirists. 8°. [1925]
The revelation of England thr. her poetry, *see* BRIT. ACADEMY. Proc., 1917–18.
Sel. Eng. short stories (19 c.) Intr. by H. Walker. [repr.] s8°. 1921

Walker (J. F.) Geology & min. deposits of Windermere map-area, B. Columbia. [Canada. Geolog. Survey]. 8°. Ottawa. 1926

Walker (James Barr). *Philosophy of the plan of salvation. By an American citizen. s8°. 1847

Walker (James Thomas). Map of Turkestan &c. Comp. under orders of J. T. Walker, chiefly by G. W. E. Atkinson. [In 4 sheets. Sheet 3, 6th ed.] *folded* la8°. Dehra Dun. 1883

Walker (John), *the philologist.* A key to the class. pronunc. of Greek, Latin & Scripture proper names. 7th ed. 8°. 1822
Rhyming dict. rev. & enl. L. H. Dawson. 8°. [1924]

Walker (John), *vicar of Hornchurch, Essex.*
*Oxoniana. 4v. s8°. [1807 ?]

Walker (John William), *O.B.E., F.S.A.,* **& M. I. Walker.**
The church plate of Berkshire. la8°. *p.p.* [Winchester]. 1927

Walker (Leslie Joseph), *S.J.*
The problem of reunion, 7 essays. 8°. 1920
see COULTON (G. G.) Medieval st. No. 17, Roman Cath. truth: open discussion betw. G. G. C. & L. J. W., 1924.

Walker (Margaret I.), *see* WALKER (J. W.) & M. I. W. Church plate of Berks., 1927.

Walker (Obadiah). *Disc. of auxiliary beauty &c. [*by bp. Jeremy Taylor ? or rather O. W. ?*], 1656, *see* DISCOURSE.
*Of educ., espec. of young gentlemen. 3rd impr., w. adds. s8°. 1677

Walker (Richard Johnson Bernard). Addenda scenica: treatment (suppl. to Nauck's) of the fragments of the Trag. Min. Graeci &c. la8°. Paris. 1923
Essay on the date of Aristophanes' Ecclesiazusae. 8°. Monaco. 1925
3 inscriptions f. Crete. Tr. & ed. R. J. W. 8°. *pr. for a.* Monaco. 1925
Walker (Samuel), *of Truro, 1714–61, see* SIDNEY (E.) Life of S. W., 1838.
Walker (Samuel Abraham). Missions in W. Africa among the Soosoos, Bulloms &c. 8°. D. 1845
Walker (Thomas), *D.D.* What Jesus read, His dependence & independence. s8°. [1925]
Walker (William), *B.D., schoolmaster of Grantham.* *A modest plea for infants baptism. By W. W. s8°. C. 1677
Some improvements to the art of teaching Latin &c. 9th ed. corr. s8°. 1730
A treatise of Engl. particles &c. 10th ed. s8°. 1691
Walker-Tisdale (Charles William) & J. Jones.
Butter & cheese. s8°. [1920]
Walkley (Arthur Bingham). More prejudice. 8°. 1923
Pastiche & prejudice. [repr.] 8°. 1921
Still more prejudice. 8°. 1925
Wall (Edward John).
Dict. of photography. 6th ed. re-wr. & enl. s8°. 1895
Dict. of photography. Rev. by T. Bolas. 8th ed. enl. s8°. 1902
Wall (*Lt.-Col.* **Frank),** *C.M.G.* Ophidia Taprobanica or the snakes of Ceylon. 8°. Colombo. 1921
Wall (Herman van de). Diss. de pileis & tiaris sacerdotum &c. Hebr. [P2744]. s4°. *n.p. n.d.*
Wall (J. Charles). Mediaeval wall paintings. s8°. [1914]
Wall (John Clifford). Kelmarsh: parochial hist. 8°. Market Harborough. [1927]
Wall (Walter W.) [*ps.* SPECTATOR].
Labour, capital & finance. s8°. 1920
Wall (William), *D.D.* The hist. of infant baptism. 2v. 8°. [1889]
Wallace Collection. Cat. of paintings. 11th ed. 8°. 1910
European armour & arms in W.C. By G. F. Laking. s8°. 1900
" " ....4th ed. s8°. 1910
" " ....[5th ed., rewr.] 2p. 8°. 1924
Objects of art (illust.) 8°. 1924
Wallace, *The family of, see* ROGERS (C.) Bk. of W., 2v, 1889.
Wallace (Alfred Russel), *O.M.* Narr. of travels on the Amazon & Rio Negro, w. acc. of native tribes. Ed., w. intr., by G. T. Bettany. 4th ed. s8°. 1892
Wallace (Dillon). Troop one of the Labrador. 8°. [1926]
Wallace (*Sir* **Donald Mackenzie).** [*MS. notes on 1st & 2nd Duma & Revolutionary movement, includ. Outline sketch on Revolution. movement wr. for Edward VII & Chronicle of Events, 1861–1906*]. 2v. obl.8°. [1906–11]
Wallace (Edgar).
The Black Abbot. s8°. [1926]
The brigand. s8°. [1927]
The door with seven locks. s8°. [1926]
The double. s8°. [1928]
The feathered serpent. s8°. [1928]
The fellowship of the frog. [repr.]. s8°. [1926]
Flat 2. s8°. [1927]
The gaunt stranger. s8°. [1925]
The law of the four just men. s8°. [1921]
The man from Morocco. s8°. [1926]
The mixer. s8°. [1927]
The Northing tramp. s8°. [1926]
People: a sh. autobiog. 8°. [1926]
Sanders. s8°. [1926]
The sinister man. s8°. *n.d.*
The square emerald. s8°. [1926]
The Squeaker. s8°. [1927]
Terror Keep. s8°. [1927]
The three oak mystery. s8°. [1925]
The Traitor's Gate. s8°. [1927]
The Twister. s8°. [1928]
Wallace (Frederick William).
Wooden ships & iron men. [2nd impr.] 8°. [1924]
Wallace (*Col.* **James).** Rising at Pentland (1666), *see* †VEITCH (W.) Memoirs, 1825.
Wallace (John). Hist. of Blyth. s8°. Blyth. 1862
Wallace (*Sir* **Richard),** *bart., see* WALLACE COLLECTION.
Wallace (Thomas). *A letter to Visc. Melbourne &c. on admin. of Earl Mulgrave, in rel. to defective applic. of the law &c. By a Conservative Whig. [P2556]. 8°. 1836
*Three letters addr. to Visc. Melbourne, & Sir R. Peel on pres. state of parties, urging necessity of union &c. By a Conservative Whig. [P2556]. 8°. 1835
Wallace (William), *M.A., Fellow of Merton.* Index of Greek ligatures & contractions. [Repr. f. Journ. of Hellenic St., v43. P2740]. la8°. 1923
Wallace (William), *musician.*
Liszt, Wagner & the Princess. 8°. 1927
R. Wagner as he lived. 8°. 1925
Wallace (*Sir* **William).**
see ROGERS (C.) Bk. of Wallace, 2v, 1889.
" SCHOFIELD (W. H.) Mythical bards & the life of W. W., 1920.
Wallace (William Kay). The passing of politics. 8°. [1924]
Thirty years of mod. hist. 8°. [1926]
The trend of history: orig. of 20th c. problems. 8°. N.Y. 1922
Wallace-Dunlop (Madeline A.), *see* DUNLOP (M. A. W.)
Wallas (Graham). The art of thought. 8°. [1926]
The great society. A psycholog. analysis. s8°. N.Y. 1920
Our social heritage. 8°. [1921]
W. J. Fox (1786–1864). [Conway Lect.] s8°. 1924
Wallaszky (Paulus). Conspectus reipubl. litt. in Hungaria. ed. altera. 8°. Budae. 1808
Tentamen hist. litt. sub M. Corvino. s4°. Lipsiae. 1769
Wallen (James). Things that live forever: office equipment. 8°. Jamestown, N.Y. [1921]
Wallenstein [†WALDSTEIN (ALBRECHT W. E. VON), *duke of Friedland*].
*Eigendliche Beschreibung/Was sich mit dem General Wallenstein/den 15. Febr. zu Eger begeben &c., 1634 [Zeitung aus Franckfurt &c. *facs.*], *see* FREYTAG (G.) Bilder, B4, 1925.
see DÖBLIN (A.) Wallenstein: Roman, 2B, 1922.
" HART (B. H. L.) Gt. captains unveiled, 1927.
see HUCH (R.) W.: e. Charakterstudie, 1920.
" KUGLER (B.) W., Vortrag, 1873.
" MITCHELL (*Maj.-Gen.* JOHN). Life of W., 1841.
" SCHULZ (H.) W. u. d. Zeit d. 30. Jähr. Krieges, 1898.
" SCHWEIZER (P.) Die W.-Frage in d. Gesch. u. im Drama, 1899.
Waller (Edmund), *the poet.*
Poems &c. 9th ed., w. add. & life. s8°. 1712
Poet. works. Coll. by T. Park. 2v. s8°. 1806
Works. Pref., Life of the a. by P. Stockdale. s8°. 1772
Waller (*Sir* **William),** *see* PRANCE (M.) Ans. to Mrs. Cellier's libel &c., likewise a vindic. of Sir W. W. f. Popish scandals, 1680.
Wallez (Jean Baptiste). Précis hist. des négoc. entre France & St.-Domingue &c.; suivi de pièces justif. & d'une notice biog. sur Gén. Boyer. 8°. 1826
Wallgren (Hjalmar). Sveriges bageriidkareförening och Stockholms bageriidkareförening. Minnesskrift. [*&* Bilaga: Jubileum, 1924]. la8°. 1925
Wallich (Nathanael), *see* COPENHAGEN. Cat. libr. Sanskrit., quos bibl. Univ. Havn. vel dedit vel paravit N.W., 1821.
Wallin (Benjamin). Evangel. hymns & songs. 8°. 1750
Wallis (Albert), *see* WALLIS (P.) & A. W. Prices & wages, 1921.
Wallis (Ann), *aft. wife of J. Blencowe, see* BLENCOWE (*Mrs.* A.)
Wallis (Bertie Cotterell).
Technique of examining children. s8°. 1927
see STANFORD, *publ. firm.* Compend. of geog. & travel, 2v, 1924.
Wallis (E.), *publ.* *Brighton as it is. s8°. Brighton. [1828]
Wallis (George August), *1768–1847, see* BAUDISSIN (C. v.) G. A. W., 1924.
Wallis (Henry), *R.W.S.* Notes on examples of early Persian lustre ware. No. 3. fol. 1889
Persian lustre vases. *p.f.p.c.* fol. 1899
Wallis (Henry Richard). The hdbk. of Uganda. 2nd ed. 8°. 1920
Wallis (J. P. R.), *see* BLAKE (W.) Prophetic writings; ed., w. gen. intr. &c. by D. J. Sloss & J. P. R. W., 2v, 1926.
Wallis (John), *D.D., Savilian prof.* A defense of infant-baptism. [P2652]. s4°. O. 1697
A defense of the Xtn. Sabbath. [P2653]. s4°. 1692
The doctrine of the blessed Trinity: 8 Letter[s] to a friend. [*each w. sep. tp. & pagin. b. w. h.* Three sermons, 1691]. s4°. 1690–92
Three sermons conc. the sacred Trinity. s4°. 1691
Wallis (John Eyre Winstanley). Eng. regnal years & titles. [Helps for students: Eng. time-books, v1]. s8°. 1921
Wallis (Norbert Hardy). Ethics of criticism & o. essays. 8°. 1924
Wallis (Percy) & A. Wallis. Prices & wages: investig. of dynamic forces in soc. economics. la8°. 1921
Wallis (Richard). Londons armory, 1677, *see* WELCH (C.) Coat-armour of the London Livery Co. &c., 1914.
Wallmenich (Carl v.), *see* RIEZLER (S.) & C. v. W., *edd.* Akten z. Gesch. d. bair. Bauernaufstandes 1705/6, 3T, 1912–15.

Wallon (Henri A.) Les représentants du peuple en mission & la justice révolutionnaire dans les départements en l'an II (1793–94). 5t. 8º. 1889–90

Wallop, *Family of, see* WATNEY (V. J.) The W. fam. &c., 4v, 1928.

Walls (Ernest). Progressive copartnership. 8º. [1921]

Walmesley (Charles), *bp. of Rama* [*ps.* SIGNOR PASTORINI].
The gen. hist. of the Christian Church &c. s8º. *n.p.* 1771
„ „ ....5th ed. w. adds. 8º. D. 1812

Walmisley (Claude Atherstone), *see* CHANCERY, *Court of.* Ind. of persons named in early Ch. proc.; ed. C. A. W., pl, 1927.

Walpole Society. 9th–16th annual vol. Ed. A. J. Finberg. 4º. O. 1921–28
v12 cont. Jones (Inigo). Designs for masques & plays at Court: descr. cat. of drawings &c. in coll. of the Duke of Devonshire; intr. & notes by P. Simpson & C. F. Bell [*w. sep. tp.*]

Walpole, *Family of, see* RYE (W.) Later hist. of f. of W. of Norfolk, 1920.

Walpole (Arthur Sumner). Early Latin hymns. With intr. & notes by A. S. W. 8º. C. 1922

Walpole (George). Text-book of shorthand. 8º. 1921

Walpole (Horace), *4th earl of Orford, 1717–1797.*
Castle of Otranto. [Sk. of life by Lord Dover]. s8º. 1834
A cat. of engravers, who have been born or resided in Eng., digested by W. f. MSS. of G. Vertue, repr. f. ed. of Strawberry-Hill. [With life of G. V.] s8º. [1762]
„ „ s8º. 1786
Journal of the printing-office at Strawberry Hill. Now 1st pr., w. notes by P. Toynbee. la8º. 1923
Journals of visits to country seats; ed. P. Toynbee, *see* WALPOLE SOC. 16th ann. vol., 1928
Letters to G. Montagu, 1736–70. 4º. 1818
Strawberry Hill accounts: record of expenditure &c. kept by H. W., 1747–95. Now first pr., w. notes &c. by P. Toynbee. 4º. O. 1927
Suppl. to Letters. Chron. arr. & ed. w. notes &c. by P. Toynbee. v3. s8º. O. 1925
see MASON (W.) Satirical poems, w. notes by H. W. (1779); ed. P. Toynbee, 1926.
„ MAUROIS (A.) Études angl., W. &c., 1927.
„ —— Quatre études angl., W. &c., 1927.
„ STUART (D. M.) H. W. [Eng. Men of Letters], 1927.
„ YVON (P.) Vie d'un dilettante, H. W., 1924.

Walpole (Hugh).
A. Trollope. [Eng. Men of Letters]. 8º. 1928
The captives. s8º. 1920
The cathedral. s8º. 1922
The English novel. Rede Lect. 1925. 8º. C. 1925
Harmer John. s8º. 1926
Jeremy & Hamlet. s8º. [1923]
Jeremy at Crale. s8º. [1927]
Mr. Perrin & Mr. Traill. n. ed. [repr.] s8º. 1925
The old ladies. s8º. 1924
Portrait of a man with red hair. s8º. 1925
The prelude to adventure. n. ed. s8º. 1919
The secret city. [n. ed.] s8º. 1922
The thirteen travellers. s8º. [1921]
„ „ ....4th ed. s8º. *n.d.*
The young enchanted. s8º. 1921

Walpole (*Sir* Robert), *aft. 1st earl of Orford.* *An authentick copy of last will & test. of R****** E—l of O***** w. remarks. 8º. [1745]
see RANBY (J.) Narr. of last illness, 1745.
„ VAUCHER (P.) Crise du ministère W., 1924.
„ —— R. W. & la polit. de Fleury, 1924.

Walramus, *of Schwarzenberg, bp. of Naumburg, d. 1111.* Liber de unitate eccl. conservanda. Rec. W. Schwenkenbecher. [Scr. rerum Germ. in usum schol.] 8º. Hannoverae. 1883

Walsee (Clemens Gundacker St. Julien, *Graf* **v.),** *see* SAINT JULIEN (C. G.), *Graf v. W.*

Walsh (A.) Scandinavian rel. w. Ireland dur. the Viking period. s8º. D. 1922

Walsh (Paul). Leabhar Chlainne Suibhne. Acc. of the MacSweeney families in Ireland, w. pedigrees. Ed., w. intr. & notes by P. W. s8º. D. 1920

Walsh (Robert), *ed. of American review, see* AMERICAN (THE) REGISTER; ed. R. W., v1, 1817.

Walsh (Thomas), *critic.* Hispanic anthology. Poems tr. f. Spanish by Eng. & N. Amer. poets. Coll. &c. by T. W. [Hispanic Soc. of Amer.] s8º. N.Y. 1920

Walsh (*Capt.* Thomas), *93rd Foot.* Journal of the late campaign in Egypt: incl. descr. of country. With app. cont. official papers & doc. 2nd ed. 4º. 1803

Walsh (Thomas), *Wesleyan preacher, see* MORGAN (J.) The life & death of T. W., 1762.

Walsh (William Sebastian).
The psychology of dreams. 8º. N.Y. 1920

Walsingham (*Sir* Francis). Sir F. W.'s anatomizing of honesty, ambition & fortitude, 1590, *see* COTTON (*Sir* R. B.) Cottoni posthuma, 1651; 1672.
see READ (C.) Mr. Secretary W. & the policy of Q. Elizabeth, 3v, 1925.

Walston (*Sir* Charles), *see* WALDSTEIN (*Sir* C.)

Walter, *of Chatillon, see* GAUTIER (P.)

Walter *de Wenlok, see* WENLOK (WALTER DE).

Walter (Emil). Der Flussaal. Biolog. u. fischereiwirts. Monographie. 8º. Neudamm. 1910

Walter (Félix). La litt. portugaise en Angleterre à l'époque romant. 8º. 1927

Walter (Hans A.) Die neuere engl. Sozialpolitik. [Sieper (E.), *ed.* Kultur d. mod. Eng., 6]. 8º. München. 1914

Walter (Hubert Conrad).
Mod. foreign exchange. 2nd ed. s8º. [1924]

Walter (Johann Andreas).
Codex in Suida mendax de Jesu. [P598]. s4º. Lipsiae. [1724]

Walter (Julius). Gesch. d. Ästhetik im Altertum. 8º. L. 1893

Walter (K.), *see* AGRICULTURAL. A. co-operation in its applic. to the farmer in the Brit. Empire, [Survey, ed. K. W.], 1925.

Walter (Richard), *naval chaplain, see* ANSON (G. A., *b.*) Voyage 1740–44; comp. by R. W., 15th ed., 1776.

Walters (F. Y.)
Money & money's worth. Pref. by J. R. Clynes. s8º. [1925]

Walters (Henry Beauchamp).
Art of the Romans. la8º. [1911]
A portrait statuette of Socrates. [Repr. f. J. of Hellenic st., v45. P2851]. la8º. 1925
see BRIT. MUSEUM: ANTIQ. Engraved gems & cameos, Greek, Etruscan &c.; by H. B. W., rev. ed., 1926.
„ ——: —— Greek & Roman lamps; by H. B. W., 1914.
„ ——: —— Silver plate &c. in B.M., 1921.

Walters (L. D'O.)
Irish poets of to-day. An anthology. 8º. [1921]

Walters (*Dr.* M.), *Latvian minister at Rome.* Lettland, s. Entwicklung z. Staat u. d. balt. Fragen. 8º. [Rome]. 1923
Le peuple letton. 8º. Riga [Brux., pr.] 1926
Protect. des minorités en Lettonie, 1922, *see* LEAGUE OF NATIONS.

Waltershausen (Sartorius von), *see* SARTORIUS VON W.

Walthamstow Antiq. Soc. Publ. No. 6, 7, 9. 4º. 1919–21
see BOSWORTH (G. F.) Manor of Higham Bensted, 1919. [6.]
„ —— Manors of Low Hall & Salisbury Hall, 1920. [7.]
„ FRY (G. S.) Abstracts of wills &c. (1335–1559), 1921. [9.]

Walther *v. d. Vogelweide, see* HALBACH (K.) W. v. d. V. u d. Dichter v. Minnesangs Frühling, 1927.

Walther (Bernhard), *von Walthersweil, see* WALTHERUS (B.)

Walther (Christian), *see* MAIMONIDES (M.) Exerc. acad.: M. tract. De circumcisione, cum interpret. Lat. & annot. exhib. C. W., 1705.

Walther (Christoph), *of Wittemberg.* Bericht v. d. falschen nachdrucken d. Deutschen Biblien.
[P2436]. s4º. Wittemberg, *Hans Lufft.* 1569
Bericht von unterscheid der Biblien u. a. M. Lutheri Bücher so zu Wittemberg &c. gedruckt werden. s4º. Wittemberg. 1563

Walther (Christoph Theodosius), *1699–1741.* Obs. gramm., linguae Tamul. idioma vulgare. [*b. w.* Beschius (C. J.) Gramm. Lat.-Tamulica, 1738]. s8º. Trangambariae. 1739
see SCHÖTTGEN (C.) Vita et agon C. T. W., 1742.

Walther (Friedrich Wilhelm). Disput. de librorum prohibit. indicibus. Praes. J. C. Schrammio.
[P437]. s4º. Helmstadii. [1708]

Walther (Hans). Das Streitgedicht in d. latein. Lit. d. M-A. [Quellen &c. z. latein. Philol. d. M-A., B5ii]. 8º. München. 1920

Walther (Heinrich Andreas). Ex antiq. orientali de Zabiis. Praes. J. H. Maio. [P431]. s4º. Giessae Hass. [1716]

Walther (Michael), *the elder.* Manichæismi recensionem hist. quam sub praes. Æ. Strauchii exhibet M. W.
ed. 2a. s4º. Wittebergae. 1661

Walther (Rudolph), *the elder* [GUALTHERUS (RODOLPHUS)].
D. Joannes Evangelista. R. Gualtheri in Evangelium secund. Joannem homiliae 180. [*b. w. h.* D. Marcus Evang.]
fol. Tiguri. 1575
D. Marcus Evangelista. R. Gualtheri in Evang. secund. Marcum homiliae 139. Acc. Praefatio authoris &c.
fol. Tiguri. 1577
In Acta Apostolorum homiliae 175. sm. fol. Tiguri. 1577

Walther (Rudolph) [*continued*].
In Ioannis Epistolam Canonicam homiliæ 37. In ejusdem Apostoli duas poster. homiliarum Sylvæ. s8º. Tiguri, *Froschouer*. 1553
Οἰκέτης, sive servus ecclesiasticus: oratio, 1548. s4º. Tiguri. [1548]

Walther (Wilh.) Luther im neu. röm. Gericht. [Verein f. Ref.-gesch. Schr., Jhrg. 2, 3, 8, 9, Nr. 7, 13, 31, 35]. 4H. 8º. Halle. 1884–92
H3 *has title* Luthers Beruf. 4, Luthers Glaubensgewissheit.

Waltherus (Bernardus), *Jurisconsultus, c. 1516–84* [Walther v. Walthersweil]. Miscellaneorum ad jus pert. libri duo. [*b. w.* Polanus (A.) De æterna Dei prædestin., 1660]. s8º. Coloniae Agripp. 1596
see Pfaff (I.) B. W. v. Walthersweil als Romanist, 1918.

Walton (Brian), *bp. of Chester*. Introd. ad lectionem linguarum oriental. ed. 2ª. emend. s8º. Londini. 1655
see Barnes (W. E.) B. W., ed. of the London Polyglot, 1924.

Walton (Charles Livesey), *see* Flattely (F. W.) & C. L. W. Biology of the sea-shore, 1922.

Walton (Christopher). *An introd. to Theosophy, or the science of the "mystery of Christ." v1. [*no more publ.*] s8º. [1855]
Also attributed to J. F. Fortescue.

Walton (Izaak).
The complete angler. [2p, p2 *by* C. Cotton, prefixed, Some acc. of life &c. of C. C. signed W. O. [*i.e.* Will. Oldys], *w. sep. pagin.*] s8º. 1760
" " Mem. & notes by Sir H. Nicolas. 2nd ed. 2v. la8º. 1860
" " [Intr. by A. Lang. Everyman's Lib.] s8º. [1906]
" " By I. W. & C. Cotton. Intr. & bibliog. by R. B. Marston. s8º. 1915
Lives of Donne, Wotton, Hooker, Herbert. To wh. are added letters. [4p *in* 1v, *each w. sep. tp. & pagin.*] s8º. 1670
" " Intr. by G. Saintsbury. [World's classics]. s8º. [1927]
see Donne (J.) Love poems; w. some acc. of h. life taken f. wr^s. in 1639 of I. W., 1923.
" Lambert (L.) I. W. & the royal deanery of Stafford, 1926.
" Wotton (*Sir* H.) Reliquiæ, life by I. W., 3rd ed., 1672.

Walton (Joseph), *see* Greenwell (W.) The G. deeds; calendared by J. W., 1927.

Walton (Leslie Bannister). Pérez Galdós & the Span. novel of the 19th cent. 8º. 1927

Waltzemüller (Martin Hylacomylus), *see* Hylacomylus (M.)

Walwyn (B.) *Chit chat, or Penance for polygamy, *see* Dublin. Vol. of farces, 1792.

Walwyn (H. W. Shepheard-), *see* Shepheard-Walwyn (H. W.)

Walz (Heinrich Car. Gottlob), *see* Schmid (C. H.) & H. C. G. W. Simonides, 1767.

Walzel (Oskar Franz).
Die deut. Dichtung seit Goethes Tod. 2ᵉ A. 8º. 1920

Wambaugh (Sarah). Monograph on plebiscites, w. coll. of offic. doc. [C.E. for Internat. Peace]. la8º. N.Y. 1920

Wander (Otto). Fremdwörterbuch. 17ᵉ A. s8º. L. 1857

***Wanderings (The)** of Asaf, *see* Afghan, *ps.*

Wandsworth. Registers of the parish of W., Surrey, 1603–1787. Transcr. by J. T. Squire. la8º. Lymington. 1889

Wanine (J.) Contrib. à l'hist. &c. d'une révol. prolétarienne (Nov. 1917–Nov. 1918). [P2397]. 8º. Genève. [1919 ?]

Wanklyn (C.) Lyme Regis. 8º. 1922
" " ....2nd ed. rev. & enl. s4º. 1927

Wanless (Harold R.) The stratigraphy of the White River beds of South Dakota. [*From* Proc. of Amer. Philos. Soc., v62, 1923. P2737]. 8º. Phila. 1923

Wanley (Humphrey). Acc. of the common grounds of Coventry, copied f. orig. rec. by H. W. [P2781]. 8º. 1778

Wanley (Nathaniel), *see* Martin (L. C.) A forgotten poet of the 17th cent. [*i.e.* N. W.], 1925.

Wannemakerus (Philippus). Funus Justæ Urientiæ uxoris Joannis de Forneau. [P2510]. s8º. Lovani. 1614

Wansbrough (Charles E.), *see* Methodist Conference. Hdbk. & Index of the Minutes, 1744–1890, by C. E. W., 1890.

Wansleben (Johann Michael) [Vansleb (J. M.)] Hist. de l'église d'Alexandrie: Jacobites-Coptes d'Egypte. s8º. 1677

Wäntig (Heinrich).
Zusammenbruch u. Wiederaufbau. 8º. Bonn. 1920

Wappen und Flaggen d. Deutschen Reiches nach d. neu. Verordnungen, 1920 ?, *see* Deutsch.

Wappen-Almanach d. Souverainen Regenten Europa's. Lithogr. Druck. s4º. Rostock, *Tiedemann*. [1840]

Wappensammler (Der), 1900–1, *see* Archiv für Stamm-u. Wappenkunde.

Wappensammlung. Wappenbeschr. zu d. W. in Buntdruck. Ser. 3, Blatt 1–40 (A. Weller's Verlag, Kahla), Ser. 4, Blatt 1–40 (Gebr. Vogt, Verlag &c.) [*&* Alphab. Verzeichnis, Ser. 1–5 *in* 1v]. la8º. Kahla &c. 1902 *& n.d.*

Waquet (Henri). Vieilles pierres bretonnes. 8º. Quimper. 1920

War.
Brit. docs. on the orig. of the War, 1898–1914; ed. G. P. Gooch &c., v1, 2, 11, 1926–27, *see* British.
Cat. of War lit. issued by H.M. Govt., 1914–19. Incl. posters, publ. bearing upon the War &c. 8º. 1921
Hist. of the Great War based on offic. doc. Comp. under dir. of Hist. Sect. of Comm. of Imp. Defence.
The Campaign in Mesopotamia, 1914–18, by Brig.-Gen. F. J. Moberly. 4v. 8º. 1923–27
Medical services.
Gen. hist. by Maj.-Gen. Sir W. Macpherson. 3v. 8º. 1921–24
Surgery. Ed. Maj.-Gen. Sir W. Macpherson, Sir A. A. Bowlby &c. v1, 2. 8º. 1922
The merchant navy, by A. Hurd. v1, 2. 8º. 1921–23
Military oper., Egypt & Palestine. [v1]. to June 1917. By Sir G. MacMunn & C. Falls. [*maps b. sep.*] 8º. 1928
Military oper., France & Belgium, 1914[–15]. By Brig.-Gen. J. E. Edmonds [4v. *maps to each v. b. sep.*] 8º. 1922–28
v3, comp. by J. E. E. & G. C. Wynne.
Naval operations. By Sir J. S. Corbett. v1–3. [Maps of v1 & 3 *b. sep.*] 8º. 1920–23
Principal events, 1914–18. Compl. by Hist. Sect. of Comm. of Imp. Defence. fol. 1922
Seaborne trade. By C. E. Fayle. 3v [*maps b. sep.*] 8º. 1920–24
Veterinary services. Ed. Maj.-Gen. Sir L. J. Blenkinsop & Lt.-Col. J. W. Rainey. la8º. 1925
The War in the air; story of part played by Royal Air Force. 2v (v1, by W. Raleigh; v2, by H. A. Jones). 8º. O. 1922–28
*How the War began in 1914: diary of Russian For. Office, July 3–20, 1914, 1925, *see* Russia.
Mem. of the late war, 2v, 1828, *see* Memorials.
*Patiala & the Great War, 1923, *see* Patiala.
Statistics of the military effort of the Brit. Empire dur. the Gt. War, 1914–20. [War Office]. fol. 1922

War & peace. A Norman Angell monthly. v1, 2 (Oct. 1913–Dec. 1914) [*in* 1v]. 4º. [1913–14]

War Office.
Alphab. list of period. & newspapers taken by W.O., 1st Jan. 1921. [*No tp.* P2687]. fol. [1921]
Animal management, 1908. Prep. in the Vet. Dept. &c. repr. s8º. 1914
Animal management, 1923. s8º. 1923
Army manual of sanitation, 1926. s8º. 1926
Artillery. 2v. s8º. 1923–24
Cat. of maps publ. by the Geograph. Section, General Staff. [P2418]. 8º. 1920
Cat. of W.O. Lib. Subject-index, p3, 9th–16th ann. suppl., 1920–27. Comp. by F. J. Hudleston. 8º. 1921–28
Drill regulations of the German Field Artillery 1899. Rev. by J. H. V. Crowe. s8º. 1901
Field service pocket book. p1, Countries other than India. s8º. 1926
Field service regulations. 2v. s8º. 1923–24
Handbook for the ·303-in. Vickers machine gun. s8º. 1923
Handbook of the 4·5-in. Q.F. Howitzer. Land service. 8º. 1915
Infantry training. v2. s8º. 1926
King's regul. for the Army &c., 1923. 8º. 1923
Machine gun training, 1925. s8º. 1925
Manual of field works (all arms). s8º. 1925
Manual of hydraulics for Garrison Artillery. 8º. 1895
Milit. engineering (Technical training). v1. 8º. 1925
Milit rep. on Brit. Somaliland (incl. notes on French & Italian S.) v1. s8º. 1925
Milit. report on Gambia. v2. s8º. 1926
Notes on ammunition. [Orig. comp. by Maj. Barlow]. 5th ed. Corr. up to Feb. 1881. [Ed. E. H. Cameron]. 8º. [1881]
Officers died in the Great War, 1914–19. 2p [*in* 1v]. la8º. 1919
Regul. for care &c. of artillery equipments. s8º. 1925
Regul. for engineer services—Peace. p1. s8º. 1924
Regul. for the equipment of the army. p1. s8º. 1923
Rep. on the propaganda library. [*By P. C. Mitchell. No tp.*; P2687]. fol. [1917]
Roy. A.M.C. training, 1925. s8º. 1925
Roy. A.S.C. training. p2, Supplies. s8º. 1922
Royal warrant for the pay &c. of the Army, 1922, 1926. s8º. 1922–26
Staff duties. [Prep. by F. C. H. Clarke, rev. & corr. by J. S. Rothwell]. s8º. 1890
Text book of gunnery. [By G. Mackinlay]. 8º. 1897
Titles &c. of formations &c. of the Territorial army. s8º. 1927
Training & manœuvre regul., 1923. s8º. 1923
see Callwell (C. E.) Armed strength of Roumania, 1888.
" Daily extracts from the foreign press, 1 June 1915–6 Aug. 1919, 1915–19.
" Du Boulay (N. W. H.) Epitome of the Chino-Japanese war, 1894–5, 1896.

War Office [*continued*].
see GRIERSON (J. M.) Armed strength of German Empire, 2p, 1888.
,, —— Armed strength of Japan, 1886.
,, KING (L. N. F. I.) Graphical methods of plotting f. air photographs, 1925.
,, LEFROY (J. H.) Report on regimental &c. schools of the army, 1859.
,, LIST (A) of the officers of the Army & Royal Marines, 1784–1867.
,, MAURICE (J. F.) Milit. hist. of Campaign of 1882 in Egypt, 1908.
,, MOSER (*Gen.* O. v.) Prepar. &c. of tactical rides &c.; tr., 1911.
,, TSCHISCHWITZ (W. v.) Rules for the conduct of the War-Game; [trans.] &c. by E. Baring, 1872.
,, WAR. Statistics of milit. effort of Brit. Empire dur. the Gt. War, 1914–20, 1922.
,, WATSON (*Maj.* A. J.) Armed strength of United Bulgaria, 1887.

Waræus (Jacobus), *see* WARE (*Sir* JAMES).

Warbasse (James Peter). Konsumgenossenschaftsbewegung in d. Ver. St. v. Amer., *see* UNTERSUCHUNGEN ü. Konsumvereine, 1924.

Warburg (Carl).
Carl Snoilsky, hans lefnad och skaldskap. s8°. [1905]
V. Rydberg, h. levnad och diktning. ny förkortad uppl. s8°. [1913]
see SCHÜCK (J. H. E.) & C. W. Huvuddragen av Sveriges litt., 3 avd., 1917–18.

Warburg (Carl Johan). Olof Dalin. Hans lif och gerning. [Svenska Akad. Handlingar, 69]. 8°. 1884

Warburg (*Comm.* Harold Dreyer), *R.N.*
Tides & tidal streams. 8°. C. 1922

Warburton (William), *bp. of Gloucester.* The alliance betw. Church & State, or the necessity &c. of an establ. religion & a Test law. 8°. 1736
Misc. trans. in prose & verse f. Roman poets &c. s8°. 1724
see COCKBURN (C.) *Remarks upon Rutherforth's Essay, publ. by W., 1747.

Warcollier (R.), *see* DUCHATEL (E.) & R. W. Les miracles de la volonté, 1914.

Ward, Lock & Co., *publishers.* Channel Islands, w. excursions to Brittany & Normandy. 20th ed. rev. s8°. [1926]
Pictorial & descr. guide to the Thames f. Putney to Cricklade. With notes on navigation &c. 2nd ed. rev. s8°. [1920]

Ward (*Mrs.*) *aft. Rondeau, aft. Vigor.* *Letters f. a lady who resided in Russia, w. hist. notes. s8°. 1775

Ward (A. C.) Twentieth-cent. lit.: age of interrog., 1901–25. s8°. [1928]

Ward (*Sir* Adolphus William).
Coll. papers, hist., lit., travel & misc. 5v. 8°. C. 1921
In memoriam, A. W. W. [*By var. wr.* Life by P. Giles]. 8°. C. 1924
Shakespeare & the makers of Virginia, *for a. copy, see* BRIT. ACAD. Proc., v9, 1919–1920.
see CAMBRIDGE (THE) HIST. OF BRIT. FOREIGN POLICY 1783–1919; ed. A. W. W. &c., 3v, 1922–23.
,, MILTON (J.) Tercent. of M.'s birth, 1908.
,, TOUT (T. F.) Sir A. W. W., 1837–1924, 1926.

Ward (Bernard Mordaunt). The 17th Earl of Oxford, 1550–1604. Fr. contemp. docs. 8°. [1928]

Ward (*Col.* Bernard Rowland). The mystery of "Mr. W. H." [*identified w. W. Hall, & attributing the authorship of the Sonnets to the Earl of Oxford*]. 8°. 1923

Ward (C. S.), *see* BADDELEY (M. J. B.) & W., *edd.* Thorough Guide Series.

Ward (Charles Augustus), *see* CUNNINGHAM (P.) Hdbk. of London, n. ed. [*with MS. addit. by C. A. W.*], 8v, 1850.

Ward (Charles Hamble Dudley). Hist. of the Welsh Guards. Intr. by Sir F. Lloyd. 8°. 1920
A romance of the 19th c. comp. f. the letters &c. of Baliol, Visct. Esher. 8°. 1923

Ward (E. M.) English coastal evolution. 8°. [1922]

Ward (Edward) [NED W.], *author of "The London Spy."*
The London spy. Vanities &c. of the town exposed. Ed. w. notes by A. L. Hayward. 8°. [1927]
*Secret (The) hist. of the Calves-Head Club. 5th ed., w. add., corr. [w.] a vindic. of the Royal Martyr, by Mr. Buttler [*sic*] w. a character of a Presbyterian by Sir J. Denham. s8°. 1705
,, ,, ...6th ed. [*a. c. w. diff. frontispiece*]. 8°. 1707
see *HUDIBRASTICK. The H. brewer &c., a satyr upon the suppos'd author [E. W.] of the Republ. procession, 1714.

Ward (Edwin A.) Recoll. of a Savage. 8°. 1923

Ward (*Hon.* Emily). Three travellers in N. Africa; w. ch. on South. Tunisia by Ld. Leigh. Pref. by Hon. A. Leigh. s8°. 1921
see JERSEY (M. E., *dowager ctss. of*) & *Hon.* E. W. Hannibal's tribunal, 1927.

Ward (Emma F.) Phosphorus necrosis in mf. of fireworks &c., *see* UNITED STATES: LABOR. Bull. 405, 1926.

Ward (Francis). Animal life under water. 8°. 1919
,, ,, ...[repr.] 8°. [1921]

Ward (Francis Kingdon).
From China to Hkamti Long. 8°. 1924
In farthest Burma. 8°. 1921
Mystery rivers of Tibet. 8°. 1923
The riddle of the Tsangpo gorges. With contrib. by Earl of Cawdor. 8°. 1926

Ward (Fred. W.) The 23rd (Service) Batt. Royal Fusiliers (1st Sportsman's). Record of services in Gt. War, 1914–19. 8°. 1920

Ward (George Whiteley). Wall paper, its orig. development & manufacture. s8°. [1922]

Ward (Harry Frederick). The new social order: princ. & programs. s8°. N.Y. 1922

Ward (*Mrs.* Henrietta Mary Ada) [*Mrs.* E. M. WARD].
Memories of 90 years. Ed. I. G. McAllister. 8°. [1924]

Ward (Henry Snowden), *F.R.P.S., b. 1865.* Figures, facts & formulæ of photography. 8°. 1903

Ward (*Mrs.* Humphry). Engeland's krachtsinspanning. Brieven aan e. vriend in Amerika. 8°. A. [1916]
Harvest. s8°. [1920]
see TREVELYAN (J. P.) Life of Mrs. H. W., 1923.

Ward (J. Clifton), *F.G.S.* The geology of the northern part of the English Lake district. [Mems. of G.S.] 8°. 1876

Ward (James), *artist.* Hist. & methods of anc. & mod. painting. v3, 4. 8°. 1920–21
3, 4, Ital. painting f. 15th to 18th cent.
Progressive design for students. 8°. 1902

Ward (James), *prof. of Mental Philos., Univ. of Camb.* Essays in philos. With mem. of the a. by O. W. Campbell. 8°. C. 1927
Psychology applied to education. Lects. Ed. G. D. Hicks. la8°. C. 1926
A study of Kant. 8°. C. 1922
see MUIRHEAD (J. H.), *ed.* Contemp. Brit. philos.: personal statements by J. W. &c., s2, 1925.

Ward (John), *Wesleyan minister.*
Skipton Castle. [2nd ed.] s8°. Skipton. [1877]

Ward (John Sebastien Marlow). Freemasonry & the ancient gods. Intr. by Sir J. A. Cockburn. 8°. [1921]
Textile fibres & yarns. Intr. by Sir E. Geddes, Ld. Barnby &c. [Resources of the Empire, v3]. 4°. 1924

Ward (Josephine M.) [*i.e. Mrs.* WILFRED WARD].
Not known here. s8°. 1920
The plague of his own heart. s8°. [1925]
The shadow of Mussolini. s8°. [1927]

Ward (*Sir* Leslie) ["SPY," *of Vanity Fair*].
Forty years of "Spy." [n. ed.] 8°. [1917]

Ward (Richard), *M.A.* Theolog. questions, dogmat. obs. &c. upon the Gospel acc. to St. Matthew. fol. 1640

Ward (Rowland). Records of big game w. th. distrib. &c. 8th ed., ed. J. G. Dollman & J. B. Burlace. la8°. 1922

Ward (Samuel), *B.D., of Ipswich, see* WARNING-PIECE to drunkards, coll. f. works of S. W. &c., 1682.

Ward (Thomas), *schoolmaster.* The controv. of ordination, as far as it concerns the Ch. of E. [P504]. s8°. 1719
England's Reformation. Poem. 8°. 1716
,, ,, ...[*a. ed. illust.*] 2v. s8°. 1747
The errata to the Protestant Bible, or the truth of their Engl. transl. exam. fol. 1688
see CLAGETT (W.) *Queries offered by T. W. &c., 1688.
,, GRIER (R.) An answer to W.'s errata of the Protest. Bible &c., 1812.

Ward (Thomas Humphry). *Brasenose ale: verses pres. on Shrove Tuesday. s8°. Boston. *p.p.* 1878
Hist. of the Athenaeum, 1824–1925. [Based on materials coll. by H. R. Tedder]. la8°. *pr. for the Club.* 1926

Ward (Valentine). A miniature of Methodism; hist., doctrines &c. 6th ed. s8°. 1834

Ward (W. H.) Architecture of the Renaissance in France: building, decor. & garden design, 1495–1830. 2nd ed., rev. [*by* Sir J. W. Simpson]. 2v. 8°. [1926]

Ward (W. J.) [*ps.* ANDROCLUS].
Government blight, or blighters. [P2419]. s8°. 1919

Ward (Wilfred Philip). The Oxford movement. s8°. [1913]

Ward (William), *pupil of Ruskin, 1829–1908, see* RUSKIN (J.) Letters to W. W., w. sh. biog. of W. W. by W. C. Ward &c., 1922.

Ward (William George). A few more words in support of No. 90 of Tracts for the Times. [P2788]. 8°. O. 1841
„ „ App. in ans. to Mr. Lowe's pamphlet. [P2788]. 8°. O. 1841
*A few words in support of No. 90 of Tracts for the Times, partly w. ref. to Mr. Wilson's letter. [*Signed* W. G. W. P2788]. 8°. O. 1841
see SHERBROOKE (R. L., *visct.*) Obs. sugg. by A few more words [by W. G. W.], 1841.
Ward (William Hayes). The seal cylinders of Western Asia. [C.I. of Wash., Publ. 100]. la8°. Wash. 1900
Wardale (Edith Elizabeth).
An old English grammar. s8°. [1922]
Wardan, see VARTAN.
Warde (Frederic). Bruce Rogers, designer of books, w. list of bks. pr. under R.'s superv. 8°. Cambridge [*Mass.*] 1925
Wardell (Janie Villiers-), see VILLIERS-WARDELL (J.)
Warden (Florence), *ps.* [*i.e. Mrs.* JAMES]. Lilith. s8°. 1923
Warden (Francis), see BOMBAY: SEL. F. RECORDS &c. Hist. &c. conn. w. prov. of Oman, Muskat &c.; prep. by F. W. &c., 1856.
Wardin (Ivan). Die Partei d. Menschewiki i. d. Russ. Revolution. s8°. Hamburg. 1922
Wardlaw (Ralph), *D.D.*
Disc. on Socinian controv. 4th ed. enl. 8°. 1828
„ „ ....5th ed. 8°. 1837
Unitarianism: a reply to J. Yates. 8°. 1816
Wardrop (Oliver). Georgian MSS. at the Iberian mon. on Mt. Athos. [*Extr. f.* J. of Theolog. St., v12. P2847]. 8°. 1911
Ware (Edith Ellen). Polit. opinion in Mass. dur. Civil War & reconstruct. 8°. N.Y., *Columbia Univ.* 1916
Ware (J. Redding). The Isle of Wight. 8°. 1869
Ware (*Sir* James). The antiq. & hist. of Ireland. Cont^g. Inquiries into antiq. of I., Annals of I., Comm. of prelates of I., 2 books of writers of I.; added, Disc. of Sir J. Davis of cause why I. was no sooner reduced to obedience &c. [*each w. sep. tp. & pagin.* Tr.] sm. fol. [1704]–5
De Hibernia & antiq. ejus. disquis. s8°. Londini. 1654
The hunting of the Romish fox & the quenching of sectarian firebrands. Coll. by W. Publ. by R. Ware. s8°. D. 1683
Ware (William Rotch). The Amer. Vignola. pl, The 5 orders. 3rd ed. 8°. Scranton [U.S.] 1904
Wareham. Illust. guide to anc. town of W. [Pref. by F. Pidsley]. 8°. [1900]
Warelius (Andreas). Beitr. z. Kenntniss Finnlands in ethnograph. Beziehung. [Aus B13 d. Beitr. z. Kenntn. d. Russ. Reich, hrsg. v. Baer u. Helmersen]. 8°. St. Petersburg. 1849
Warens (Louise Françoise E. de), see BENEDETTO (L. F.) Mme. de W., la "Maman" de Rousseau, 1922.
Warfield (Benjamin Breckenridge).
An introd. to the textual crit. of the New Test. s8°. 1889
Warhaffte [WAHRHAFFTIGER; WARHAFFTIGE].
Warhaffte christl. &c. Widerlegung d. Prediger zu Bremen &c., 1583, see BREMEN.
*Warhaffte u. Christl. verantwortung d. Prediger zu Bremen &c., 1581, see BREMEN.
*Warhafftige erzelung der Geschicht, was sich Hertzog Henrich von Braunschweigs &c. halben, dises gegenwertigen Jars zugetragen &c. s4°. [Warpurg, *Andres Kolben*]. 1545
*Warhafftige Zeitung aus Praag, 1618, see PRAGUE.
Warhafftiger Unterricht &c., 1537, see JOHN FREDERICK, *duke of Saxony* &c.
Waring (Edward), *1734–98,* see HARDY (G. H.) Some famous problems of theory of numbers, in partic. W. Problem, 1920.
Waring (L. F.) Hist. of Montenegro, see BUCHAN (J.), *ed.* Nations of to-day, Yugoslavia, 1923.
Waring (Samuel James Waring, *1st baron*). Illust. particulars &c. of outlying portions of the Gopsall estate, sale by Knight, Frank & Rutley, Feb. 1927. By dir. of Lord W. sm. fol. [1927]
Warlock (Peter). The Eng. ayre. s8°. 1926
Warmington (Eric Herbert).
The commerce betw. the Roman Empire & India. 8°. C. 1928
Warnecke (Friedrich). The Treaty: comments of Wilson, Keynes, Lansing & others. [*& Wörterbuch, b. w. it*]. s8°. Leipzig. 1924
Warner (*Sir* Frank), *K.B.E.*
Silk indust. of the U.K., its orig. & develop. la8°. [1921]
Warner (*Sir* George Frederick), see BRIT. MUSEUM: MSS. Cat. of Western MSS. in the old Royal & King's Coll.; by Sir G. F. W. &c., 4v, 1921.
Warner (George Townsend), *M.A.*
How wars were won: st. of Napoleon's times. 8°. 1915
Landmarks in Eng. indust. hist. 15th ed. s8°. *n.d.*
—— **& C. H. K. Marten.**
Groundwork of Brit. hist. [repr.] 8°. [1923]
Warner (Langdon). The long old road in China. 8°. [1927]
Warner (Pelham Francis). The fight for the ashes in 1926. Australian tour in Eng. 8°. [1926]
see BADMINTON LIBRARY. Cricket by W. &c., 1920.
Warner (Richard), *rector of Chelwood.*
Excursions from Bath. 8°. Bath. 1801
Hist. of the Isle of Wight. Added, View of its agriculture. 8°. S'ton. 1795
Warner (Richard Hyett). Hist. of Thorney abbey; w. notice of the mod. parish & bap. reg. of French Colony, 1658–1724 [*w. sep. pagin.*] 8°. Wisbech. 1879
Warner (S. G.), see HILL (*Sir* N.) &c. War & insurance, 1927.
Warner (Stephen Alfred). Oxford Cathedral. 8°. 1924
St. Paul's Cathedral. 8°. 1926
Warner (*Miss* Susan) [*ps.* ELIZABETH WETHERELL].
The wide, wide world. n. ed. s8°. 1871
Warner (Sylvia Townsend). Lolly Willowes. s8°. 1926
Mr. Fortune's maggot. s8°. 1927
Warnes (Arthur R.) Building stones: properties, decay & preservation. 8°. 1926
Warning-piece (A) to all drunkards & health-drinkers: coll. f. the works of S. Ward, S. Clark & others &c. 8°. 1682
Warnod (André). Trois petites filles dans la rue, nouvelle, see ŒUVRES libres, 14, 1922.
Warongo (The) or Japanese Analects, 1917, see KATO (G.)
Warrack (Alexander). Scots dialect dict., words in use f. latter part of 17th cent. Intr. &c. by W. Grant. 8°. 1911
Warrack (Grace). Dal cor gentil d'Italia: folk songs f. Venetia to Sardinia. Chosen & tr. by G. W. 8°. O. 1925
Florilegio di canti toscani: folk songs of the Tuscan hills, w. Eng. renderings by G. W. 8°. 1914
Warrack (John). Domestic life in Scotland, 1488–1688. Rhind lect. s8°. [1920]
Warrand (Duncan), see CULLODEN PAPERS. More C.P., 1626–1745; ed. D. W., 3v, 1923–27.
Warre (Edmond), *D.D., Headmaster of Eton,* see FLETCHER (C. R. L.) E. W., 1922.
Warren (Arthur), 1860–.
London days. Book of reminisc. 8°. 1921
Warren (Arthur), *bibliographer.* The Charles Whittinghams, printers. [Grolier Club]. la8°. N.Y. 1896
Warren (Charles), 1868–.
The Supreme Court & sovereign states. 8°. Princeton. 1924
Warren (*Sir* Charles), see WILLIAMS (R. C.) Brit. lion in Bechuanaland: exped. under Sir C. W., 1885.
Warren (Charles F. S.) Authorship, text, & hist. of the hymn Dies Irae. re-issue. 8°. 1902
Warren (E. P.), see BEAZLEY (J. D.) The Lewes House coll. of anc. gems [property of E. P. W.], 1920.
Warren (Howard Crosby).
Hist. of the association psychology. 8°. 1921
Warren (J. G. H.)
A century of locomotive building by R. Stephenson & Co., 1823–1923. 4°. Newcastle upon Tyne. 1923
Warren (Samuel), *barrister.*
Works. 5v. s8°. E. 1854–55
1, Passages f. the diary of a late physician.
2, 3, Ten thousand a-year, 2v.
4, Now & then—The lily & the bee—The intellectual & moral develop. of the pres. age.
5, Miscellanies.
Warren (Samuel), *LL.D., of Manchester, 1781–1862.* A digest of the laws &c. of the Methodists, w. app. s8°. 1835
see CUBITT (G.) Obs. on W.'s pamph., agst. the Wesleyan Instit., 1834.
„ STEPHENS (S.) St.'s rep. of Dr. Warren's case &c., 1835.
—— **& J. Stephens,** *Wesleyan minister.*
Chron. of Wesleyan Methodism. 2v. s8°. 1827
1, A digest of all its laws & regulations &c., by S. W.
2, An alphabetic. arrangement of circuits in Eng., Wales & Scot. w. names of preachers &c., by J. S.
Warren (*Sir* Thomas Herbert).
Encaenia, 1919. Creweian oration. Tr. [P2487]. s8°. O. 1919
Oratio Creweiana, 1919. [P2488]. s8°. [O. 1919]
Virgil in relation to the place of Rome in hist. of civilization. Lect. [P2576]. 8°. O. [1921]

Warren (Whitney).
The just claims of Italy. [P2502]. 8º. [1917 ?]
Warrender Papers, *see* RAIT (R. S.) & A. I. CAMERON, *edd.* King James's secret, f. the W. p., 1927.
Warrington & Altrincham Junction Railway.
Map; Session 1851. folded 8º. 1851
Warsaw [WARSZAWA]. Album reprod. obrazów z wystawy "Sto lat malarstwa Polskiego" z. prywatnych zbiorów Warszawskich w. Pałacu Łazienkowskim. 8º. Warszawa. 1919
Warschauer (Joseph). The histor. life of Christ. Pref. by F. C. Burkitt. 8º. [1927]
Wartburg (Walther v.) Zur Benennung d. Schafes in d. roman. Sprachen, *see* KÖNIGL. PREUSS. AKAD. D. WISS. Abhdl. (Phil.-hist. Klasse), 1918.
Warth (Johannes Friedrich). Diss. de eccl. Ruthenica. Praes. J. F. Reussio. [P427]. s4º. Tubingae. [1752]
Wartmann (W.) Tafelbilder d. 15. u. 16. Jhdt.'s 1430–1530: Schweiz u. angrenz. Gebiete. [P2701]. 4º. Zürich. [1921]
Warton (Joseph). Poet. works. Coll. by T. Park. [*b. w.* Johnson (S.) Poet. works, 1805]. s8º. 1805
see MORLEY (E. J.) J. W.: compar. of h. Essay on Pope w. h. ed. of P.'s works, 1924.
Warton (Thomas), *poet laureate.*
Poet. works. Coll. by T. Park. s8º. 1805
Warwick. Abstr. of the bailiffs' accounts of monastic & o. estates in the Co. of W., 1547. Tr. by W. B. Bickley. Intr. by W. F. Carter. [Dugdale Soc. Publ., v2]. 8º. 1923
Descr. of the Beauchamp Chapel at W., & the mon. of Earls of Warwick. la8º. 1804
Warwick, *Earldom, see* WARWICK. Descr. of Beauchamp Chapel, & mon. of Earls of W., 1804.
Warwick (Robert Rich, *earl of*). True rel. of W.'s passage thr. the Spanish Armatho, 1627, *see* ABBOTSFORD CLUB. Misc., v1, 1837.
Warwickshire. Lay Subsidy Roll for W. of Ed. III (1332). Tr. & ed. w. intr. by W. F. Carter. With app. cont. 3 Subsidy Rolls for Stratford-upon-Avon &c.; ed. F. C. Wellstood. [Dugdale Soc., v6]. la8º. 1926
Was.
*Was bedeutet Landsturm u. Landwehr, 1813, *see* ARNDT (E. M.)
Was der ausszug zu Bepstlicher hailigkeit verordnet &c., 1523 ?, *see* ADRIAN VI, *pope.*
*Was ist der Nihilismus ? 1881, *see* NIHILISMUS.
Was kann Deutschland leisten ? 1920, *see* DEUTSCHLAND.
Wäsche (Hans). Grundzüge zu e. Logik d. Arithmetik. [Bibl. f. Philos., B29]. [T1]. 8º. 1926
Waschnitius (Viktor). Perht, Holda u. verandte Gestalten. Beitr. z. deutsch. Religionsgesch., 1913, *see* KAIS. AKAD. D. WISS. ZU WIEN. Sitzb., B174, 1915.
Washburn, *The family of, see* HUNT (G.) Israel, Elihu & Cadwallader W., 1925.
Washburn (Cadwallader Colden), *see* HUNT (G.) I., E. & C. Washburn, 1925.
Washburn (Claude Carlos), *see* MAUROIS (A.) Les Anglais; préc. d'une opin. sur les Franç. par C. W., tr. A. M., 1927.
Washburn (Israel), *see* HUNT (G.) I., E. & C. Washburn, 1925.
Washburne (Carleton W.) Common science. s8º. 1923
Washburne (Elihu Benjamin), *see* HUNT (G.) I., E. & C. Washburn, 1925.
Washington. *The mirrors of W. 8º. N.Y. 1921
W. & Berlin. Corr. betw. Count Bernstorff & Berlin, w. docs. on German peace proposal of 1916. 8º. Amsterdam. 1920
see PARKER (D. W.) Cal. of papers in W. archives rel. to territories of the U.S. (to 1873), 1911.
,, WHITE HOUSE.
Washington, *The family of, see* LONGDEN (H. I.) Hist. of the W. family, 1927.
Washington (George), *president of the U.S.* Life, by himself, comp. h. mems. & corr., incl. sev. letters now first pr.; ed. C. W. Upham. 2nd ed. s8º. 1852
Message of the President rel. to France & Gt. Brit., Dec. 5, 1793, *see* UNITED STATES, MESSAGES.
see BOSTON ATHENAEUM. Cat. of the W. Coll.; comp. &c. by A. P. C. Griffin, 1897.
,, JONES (C. S.) Short life of W., 1920.
,, OSBORN (L. P.) W. speaks for himself, 1927.
,, THAYER (W. R.) G. W., 1922.
,, UNITED STATES: LIB. OF CONGRESS. Fitzpatrick (J. C.) List of the W. MSS., 1592–1775, 1919.

Washington (George) [*continued*].
see WEEMS (M. L.) Life of W., 1828.
,, WOODWARD (W. E.) G. W., the image & the man, 1928.
,, WRONG (G. M.) W. & h. comrades in arms, 1921.
Wasielewski (Joseph Wilhelm v.) Die Violine u. i. Meister. 6e verm. A. v. W. v. Wasielewski. 8º. L. 1920
Wasilewski (Léon). La paix avec l'Ukraine. Podlachie & Chelm. [P2426]. 8º. Genève. [1918]
Wasnetzoff (Victor), *see* VASNETSOV (V. M.)
Wassenaar-Duivenvoorde (Jacob van). Verbaal van de buitengewone ambassade van J. van W.-D., A. van Citters en E. van Weede van Dijkveld naar Engeland in 1685. [Hist. Genoots. te Utrecht. Werken, N.S., 2]. 8º. Utrecht. 1863
Wassenaer (Nicolaas van), *see* NEW YORK. Papers rel. to 1st settlement by the Dutch, cont. Desc. &c. of New Netherland f. "W.'s Hist. van Europa," v2, 1888.
Wassenaer-Obdam (*Adm.* **Jacob van)** [†WASSENAAR (JAKOB VAN)]. Journalen van de admiralen Van W.-O., 1658–59 & De Ruyter, 1659–60. Uitg. door G. L. Grove. [Hist. Genoots. Werken, 23]. 8º. A. 1907
Wassermann (Dieterich). Ein Predigt v. d. heil. Tauff &c. [P2613]. s4º. [Nürnberg.] 1591
Wassermann (Jakob).
Der Aufruhr um d. Junker Ernst. Erzählung. [16. bis 25. A.] s8º. [1926]
Christian Wahnschaffe. Roman. 2B. s8º. 1920
Der Fall Maurizius. 8º. 1928
Das Gänsemännchen. Roman. s8º. 1917
Laudin u. d. Seinen. [21.–30. A.] 8º. [1925]
Der Mann von vierzig Jahren. s8º. 1918
Die Schwestern. 3 Novellen. s8º. 1918
The triumph of youth. [Tr.] s8º. [1928]
Der Wendekreis. 4B. s8º. 1921–[24]
The world's illusion. Tr. L. Lewisohn. 2v. s8º. 1921
Watarai (Toshiharu). Nationaliz. of railways in Japan. 8º. N.Y., *Columbia Univ.* 1915
Watelin (Louis Charles). La Perse immobile: paysages &c. Préf. de J. Dieulafoy. 8º. 1921
Waterfall (Edith Anna). The day contin. school in England: its function & future. s8º. [1923]
Waterfield (*Mrs.* **Lina Duff),** *née Gordon* [WATERFIELD (*Mrs.* AUBREY)]. Bemporad's concise guide to Florence. s8º. Florence. 1920
Waterford & South-East of Ireland Archaeological Society. v18, 19i. 8º. Waterford. [1915–20]
Waterhouse (Edward) *of Sion College.* The gentlemans monitor; rise & decay of men & families &c. s8º. 1665
Waterhouse (Eric S.)
The philos. of relig. experience. 8º. [1923]
Waterhouse (Gilbert), *see* YEARBOOK OF MODERN LANGUAGES, 1920; ed. G. W., 1920.
Waterhouse (Joseph). The King & the people of Fiji: cont. a life of Thakombau. s8º. 1866
Waterhouse (Paul), *see* WREN (*Sir* C.) Sir C. W., 1632–1723; contrib. by P. W. &c., 1923.
Waterland (Daniel). A crit. hist. of the Athanasian creed. n. ed. rev. by J. R. King. s8º. O. 1870
Works. Life &c. by W. Van Mildert. 2nd ed. 6v. 8º. O. 1843
Waterman (William Randall).
Frances Wright. [Columbia Univ.] 8º. N.Y. 1924
Waters (Arthur W.), *see* DAVIS (W. J.) & A. W. W. Tickets & passes of Gt. Brit. & Ireland, 1922.
Waters (Charlotte M.) Econ. hist. of Eng., 1066–1874. s8º. 1925
Waters (*lt.-col.* **George),** *surgeon.* On charity. Lect., Wilson College, Bombay, 1895. [P2622]. s8º. Bombay. 1895
Plague in Bombay, 1896–1900. [P2877]. 8º. 1900
Persia: people & lang., *see* PERSIA SOCIETY: Lect., 1912.
Rep. on relapsing fever &c. in H.M. common prison, Bombay, 1899. [P2877]. 8º. [1900]
Three years medical hist. of the Persian Gulf. 8º. Bombay. 1878
Waters (Helena L.)
French & Italian Rivieras. s8º. [1924]
Waters (*Capt.* **R. S.)**
Simple tactical schemes, w. solutions. 2nd ed. rev. 8º. 1913
Waters (*Brig.-Gen.* **Wallscourt Hely Hutchinson).**
"Private & personal": further exper. 8º. [1928]
"Secret & confidential": exper. of a milit. attaché. 8º. 1926
Waters (William George).
Traveller's joy. Comp. by W. G. W. s8º. 1906
Waterston (James), *see* BRITISH ANTARCTIC EXPED., 1910–13. Zoology, v3, Insecta, by G. H. Carpenter & J. W., 1915–23.

Waterton (Charles). Wanderings in S. America, the N.W. of the U.S., & the Antilles, 1812, 16, 20, 24. 4°. 1825

Watkin (Absalom).
Extracts f. journal, 1814–56. Ed. A. E. Watkin. 8°. [1920]

Watkin-Jones (Howard).
The Holy Spirit in the mediaeval Church. 8°. [1922]

Watkins (Alfred). Early Brit. trackways, moats, mounds &c. Lect., 1921. 8°. Hereford. 1922
The old straight track, its mounds, beacons &c. 8°. [1925]

Watkins (George Pendleton).
Welfare as an economic quantity. 8°. Boston. 1915

Watkins (Gordon S.)
Intr. to the study of labor problems. 8°. [1922]

Watkins (John), *LL.D.* Important results of investig. into case of E. Fenning, incl. rep. of h. trial. With 30 letters wr. in prison [*w. sep. pagin. a. copy b. w.* Theory. T. of presumptive proof, 1815]. 8°. 1815
Mem. of the public & private life of Rt. Hon. R. B. Sheridan &c. 2nd ed. 2v. 8°. 1817
Universal biog. & hist. dict. 8°. 1800
„ „ ....n. ed. 8°. 1821
see LEFANU (A.) Memoirs of the life &c. of Mrs. F. Sheridan, w. remarks upon a late life [*by* J. W.] of R. B. Sheridan &c., 1824.

Watkins (John), *of Whitby.*
Life & career of George Chambers. s8°. 1841
Life, poetry & letters of E. Elliott, the corn-law rhymer. s8°. 1850
see MYERS (J.) Remains, w. acc. of his life by J. W., 1830.

Watkins (L. T.) Libraries in Indian high schools. [Bureau of Educ., India. P2497]. 8°. Calcutta. 1920

Watkins (William), *a. of The fall of Carthage.* *Anomaliae: desultory essays on misc. subjects. s8°. Whitby. 1798

Watkinson (William L.), *Wesleyan minister.* The influence of scepticism on character. Fernley Lect. 8°. 1890
The transfigured sackcloth & o. sermons. s8°. 1893

Watmough (A.) Methodism in Gt. Yarmouth &c. s8°. 1826

Watney (Vernon James). The Wallop family and th. ancestry. 4v. sm. fol. O. 1928

Watson (Aaron), *see* BURT (T.) Autobiog.; w. suppl. chapters by A. W. &c., 1924.

Watson (*Sir* Alfred William), *K.C.B., see* HILL (*Sir* N.) &c. War & insurance, 1927.

Watson (*Maj.* Arthur John). The armed strength of United Bulgaria. [War Office. P2830]. 8°. 1887

Watson (*Col. Sir* Charles Moore).
Universal service &c. [P2503]. s8°. 1909

Watson (Edmund Henry Lacon). Rudolf Strange. s8°. [1927]

Watson (Elliot Lovegood Grant). Innocent desires. s8°. [1924]
The mainland. [reissued]. s8°. [1921]

Watson (Eric Russell).
see BECK (A.) A. B. (1877–1904); ed. E. R. W., 1924.
„ SMITH (G. J.) Trial of G. J. S.; ed. E. R. W., 1922.
„ THURTELL (J.) & J. HUNT. Trial, 1920.

Watson (Ernest Bradlee). Sheridan to Robertson: st. of the 19th cent. London stage. 8°. C. 1926

Watson (Forbes). Flowers & gardens. Ed., w. pref. by Canon Ellacombe. 8°. 1901

Watson (Foster). Juan Luis Vives, 1492–1540, *see* ROY. SOC. OF LIT. Essays &c.: Trans., N.S., v1, 1921.
Luis Vives, el gran Valenciano (1492–1540). [Hispanic Soc. Hisp. notes &c., 4]. s8°. O. 1922
Richard Hakluyt. s8°. 1924

Watson (Frederick). Pandora's young men. s8°. [1920]

Watson (George), *aft. G. W. Taylor.* England preserved, *see* † INCHBALD (*Mrs.* E.) Mod. th., v8, 1811.

Watson (*Sir* George), *see* BRYCE (J. B., *vct.*) St. of Amer. hist. &c., 1921.

Watson (George Neville). Treatise on the theory of Bessel functions. la8°. C. 1922
see WHITTAKER (E. T.) & G. N. W. Course of mod. analysis, 3rd ed., 1920.

Watson (Gilbert). The amazing guest. s8°. [1925]

Watson (Henry Brereton Marriott).
The skirts of happy chance. n. ed. s8°. [1905]

Watson (Herbert Armstrong).
The Incarnation & personality. 8°. 1920

Watson (James), *printer at Edinburgh.*
*The hist. of printing, in Europe &c. s8°. 1713

Watson (James A. S.) & J. A. More. Agriculture: the science & practice of Brit. farming. 8°. E. 1924

Watson (Janet), *ed., see* HALYBURTON (T.) Mem. of life of T. H., 1848 ?.

Watson (*Capt.* John), *see* *TRUE &c. narr., 1745.

Watson (John Broadus). Behaviorism. 8°. [1928]
Psychology f. the standpoint of a behaviorist. 2nd ed. 8°. Phila. [1924]

Watson (Joseph Yelloly). Tendring Hundred in the olden time. 8°. Colchester. [1877]

Watson (*Mrs.* Lucy Eleanor), *form. Gillman.*
Coleridge at Highgate. 8°. 1925

Watson (Richard), *D.D.* The Rt. Rev. John Cosin, bp. of Durham, his opinion for communicating rather w. Geneva than Rome &c. s8°. 1684

Watson (Richard), *Wesleyan minister.*
Works cont. Mem. of the author [by T. Jackson]. 13v. [v1–6, 5th ed.; v7–13, 6th ed.] 8°. 1847–48
A defence of the Wesleyan Methodist missions in the W. Indies &c. 8°. 1817
The life of John Wesley. 2nd ed. s8°. 1831
„ „ ....10th ed. s8°. 1861
Obs. on Southey's Life of Wesley: being a defence of Wesley. 2nd ed. 8°. 1821
Vie du Rév. Jean Wesley avec détails sur C. Wesley, morceaux sur les ancêtres de Wesley du Rév. H. Moore & du dr. [R.] Southey. Tr. sur la 4e éd. angl. 2v *in* 1. 8°. Jersey. 1843
see JACKSON (T.) Mem. of the life & wr. of R. W., 1834.
„ WESLEYAN classics, or biogr. sketches of the orators &c. of the Wesleyan Church, pl (R. W.), 1870.

Watson (Robert), *rector of Saltwood.* Ætiologia R. W., in qua explicatur, quare deprehensus annum unum & menses penè quatuor propter Evangeliū incarceratus fuit &c. s8°. [Londini?]. 1556

Watson (Robert Addison). In the Apostolic age: the churches & the doctrine. s8°. 1894

Watson (William), *poet writer.*
Coll. poems. [2nd ed.] s8°. 1899
Ireland arisen. [P2560]. 8°. 1921
Ireland unfreed, poems &c. s8°. 1921
Ode on the day of the coron. of Edward VII. 8°. 1902
Poems brief & new. s8°. [1925]

Watson (William), *priest.* *Important consid. wh. ought to move all true &c. Catholicks &c., 1601, repr. 1688, *see* JESUITS. Brief hist. acc., 1689.

Watson (William George Willis). Chronological hist. of Somerset. [Somerset folk ser., No. 21]. pl. s8°. 1925
see SOMERSET. Cal. of customs &c., conn. w. Co. of S.; foreword & index by W., 1920.

Watson (William John). Hist. of the Celtic place-names of Scotland. Rhind lect. (expanded). [Royal Celtic Soc.] 8°. 1926
Ross & Cromarty. s8°. C. 1924

Watt (Francis), *see* BARTON (*Sir* D. P.), C. BENHAM & F. W. Story of our Inns of Court, 1924.

Watt (James), *the engineer, see* ROBISON (J.) The articles Steam & steam-engines, wr. by R., w. notes & add. by J. W., 1818.

Watt (Lauchlan Maclean). Douglas's Æneid. 8°. C. 1920
Scottish life & poetry. 8°. 1912

Watt (Rachel Stuart). In the heart of savagedom: mission. labours in wilds of E. Equat. Africa. Ed. by h. husband. 3rd ed. s8°. [1923]

Watt (Wellstood A.) Study of social morality. 8°. E. 1901

Watteau (Antoine).
see HIND (A. M.) W., Boucher & the Fr. engravers, 1911.
„ HOURTICQ (L.) De Poussin à W., 1921.
„ MAUCLAIR (C.) A. W., 1684–1721, 1920.

Watters (Thomas). Guide to the tablets in a temple of Confucius. 8°. Shanghai. 1879
Lao-Tzū, a study in Chinese philosophy. s8°. Hongkong. 1870

Watteville (Jean de), *see* BOREL (T.) L'abbé de Watteville & sa mission en Suisse, 1923.

Watts (Alaric Alfred), *see* TURNER (J. M. W.) Liber fluviorum; or, river scenery in France: biog. sk. by W., 1857.

Watts (Arthur P.) Hist. des colonies anglaises aux Antilles, 1649–60. 8°. [1924]
Nevis & St. Christopher's, 1782–84. (Unpubl. doc.) 8°. Paris. *n.d.*

Watts (Frank). Educ. for self-realis. & soc. service. s8°. 1920
Intr. to psycholog. problems of industry. 8°. [1921]

Watts (Henry Edward). Spain, f. Moorish conquest to fall of Granada, 711–1492. [Story of the Nations]. 3rd ed. 8°. *n.d.*
see QUEVEDO (F. DE). Pablo de Segovia, w. essay on life &c. of Q. by H. E. W., 1892.

Watts (Isaac).
Divine songs for children. s8°. 1805
Evangelical disc. Added an essay on flesh & spirit. 8°. 1747
Horae lyricae. Poems. 8th ed. corr. s8°. 1743
„ „ Poems in 3 bks. 10th ed. corr. s8°. 1758
Hymns & spiritual songs. 5th ed. s8°. 1716
„ „ ....7th ed. s8°. 1720
The improvement of the mind: or a suppl. to the Art of logic. 2nd ed. pl. 8°. 1743
„ „ [*a. ed.* 2p.] Also his posthum. wks. Publ. by D. Jennings & P. Doddridge. s8°. Edinburgh. 1792
Poet. works. Coll. by T. Park. 2v. s8°. 1807
Psalms of David imitated. [*Verse*]. s8°. 1719
The Psalms of David in the lang. of the N.T. [*w.* Tunes *imperfect, sep. pagin.*] 6th ed. s8°. 1727
„ „ ....With pref. & notes. s8°. 1772
Reliquiæ juveniles. Misc. thoughts, prose & verse. new ed. corr. s8°. 1789
see CONDER (J.) The poet of the sanctuary: cent. comm. of W., 1851.
„ JACKSON (T.) Lib. of Xtn. biog., v1, I. W. fr. Mem. of Dr. Gibbons, 1837.
„ MILNER (T.) Life, times & corresp. of I. W., 1845.

Watts (*Mrs.* Mary Stanbery).
The Boardman family. s8°. N.Y. 1918

Watts (W. W.), *F.S.A.* Old English silver. 4°. 1924
see VICTORIA & ALBERT MUSEUM. Cat. of Eng. silversmiths' work; intr. by W. W. W., 1920.
„ —— Cat. of pastoral staves; by W. W. W., 1924.
„ YEANDLE (W. H.) Hist. of churches in Mortlake &c.; in collab. w. W. W. W., 1925.

Watts (Walter Henry), *see* †ANNUAL BIOG. & obituary; [ed. W. H. W.], 21v, 1817–37.

Watts (William B.), *see* ELDRIDGE (B. P.) & W. B. W. Our rival the rascal, 1897.

Watts (William Lord). Across the Vatna Jökull; or, Scenes in Iceland. s8°. 1876

Watts-Dunton (Clara), *wife of T. Watts-Dunton.*
The home life of Swinburne. 8°. 1922

Watzinger (Carl). Griech. Holzsarkophage aus d. Zeit Alex. d. Gr. [Deut. Orient-Gesell., Wiss. Veröffentl., 6. *b. w.* Koldewey (R.) Hettit. Inschr., 1900]. fol. L. 1905
see BACHMANN (W.), C. W. &c. Petra, 1921.
„ KOHL (H.) & C. W. Antike Synagogen in Galilaea, 1916.
„ SELLIN (E.) & C. W. Jericho, 1913.
„ WULZINGER (C.) & C. W. Damaskus, d. islam. Stadt, 1924.
—— **& C. Wulzinger.** Damaskus d. ant. Stadt. [Wiss. Veröff. d. deut.-türk. Denkmalschutz-Kommandos, H4]. fol. 1921

Waugh (Alec). Kept. s8°. 1925
The last chukka: stories of East & West. s8°. 1928
The lonely unicorn. s8°. 1922
Pleasure. s8°. 1921
Public school life. s8°. [1922]

Waugh (Coulton). Rare ship models &c. Sold, Anderson Gall. [Illustr.] [P2854]. la8°. N.Y. [1925]

Waugh (Edwin). The barrel organ. s8°. M'ter. *n.d.*
Besom Ben. s8°. M'ter. [1894]
Owd Bodle. [*b. w. h.* Barrel organ, *n.d.*] s8°. M'ter. 1865
Yeth-Bobs an' scaplins. [*b. w. h.* Barrel organ, *n.d.*] s8°. M'ter. *n.d.*

Waugh (Evelyn). Rossetti, h. life & works. 8°. 1928

Waugh (Francis Gledstanes).
The Athenæum Club & its associations. s8°. *p.f.p.c.* [? 1894]
„ „ ....enl. ed., illust. 8°. *p.f.p.c.* [? 1897]

Waugh (William Templeton). Machinery of Empire, *see* BUCHAN (J.), *ed.* Nations of to-day, Gt. Brit., v2, 1923.

Wauters (Alphonse). Les libertés communales: orig. &c. en Belgique, le nord de la France & les bords du Rhin. 2p. [*in* 1v. *pagin. cont.*] la8°. 1878

Wauters (Alphonse Jules).
La peinture flamande. n. éd. 8°. [1883]

Wautier d'Aygalliers (A.) Ruysbroeck the Admirable. Auth. tr. by F. Rothwell. 8°. 1925

*Waverley, 6th ed., 3v, 1816, *see* SCOTT (*Sir* W.)

Wavre (Philippus van). Apologia contra impugnatores constitut.: Unigenitus, signanter pro Unigeniti salvatoris gratia. [P2659]. s8°. Lovanii. 1719
Assert. theolog. de justitia contractuum, quas præs. P. v. W. sustinebit R. B. Aerts. [P2659]. s8°. Lovanii. 1682
Justitia quam justo aequitatis libramento exam., praes. P. v. W., sustinere tentabit M. van Aultre. [P2659]. s8°. Lovanii. 1681
Peregrinus Jerichuntinus, praes. P. v. W., respond. G. de Visser. [P2659]. s8°. Lovanii. 1685

Waxman (Meyer). The philosophy of Don Hasdai Crescas. [Columbia Univ.] 8°. N.Y. 1920

Waxman (Samuel Montefiore).
Antoine & the Théâtre-Libre. 8°. Cambridge, *Mass.* 1926

Wayland (Francis), *the elder.*
Elements of polit. economy. 8°. N.Y. 1837
see WAYLAND (F.), *the younger,* & H. L. WAYLAND. Mem. of life &c. of F. W., 1867.

Wayland (Francis), *the younger,* **& H. L. Wayland.** Mem. of life &c. of Francis Wayland. 2v. s8°. N.Y. 1867

Wayland (H. L.), *see* WAYLAND (F.), *the younger,* & H. L. W. Mem. of F. Wayland, 1867.

Wayland Smith [*Legend of*], *see* BUCK (K. M.) The saga of Dietrich of Bern &c., prec. by that of W. S., pl, v1-6, 1924–27.

Ways of living, nature & man, 1926, *see* THOMSON (J. A.), *ed.*

Wazir, *see* VAZIR.

Waziristan. Operations in W., 1919–20. Comp. by Gen. Staff, Army Headquarters, India. 8°. Calcutta. 1921

Weale (B. L. Putnam), *ps.* [*i.e.* BERTRAM LENOX SIMPSON].
The eternal priestess. s8°. [1914]
An indiscreet chronicle f. the Pacific. 8°. [1923]
The truth about China & Japan. s8°. [1921]
The vanished empire. 8°. 1926
Wang the ninth. s8°. [1920]
Why China sees red. 8°. 1926

Weale (John).
Letter on the defence of the country. [P2831]. 8°. 1847

Weale (W. H. James).
see BRITISH MUSEUM: MSS. Early stamped bookbindings in B.M.; descr., mainly by W., 1922.
„ NORTHBROOK (T. G. B., *1st e.*) Descr. cat. of coll. of pictures; Dutch, Flemish &c. schools, by W., 1889.
„ VICTORIA & ALBERT MUSEUM. Bookbindings &c. in Nat. Art Library; by W. H. J. W., 2p, 1894–98.

Weare (William). Compl. hist. &c. of murder of Mr. W. [by J. Thurtell, J. Hunt &c., *w.* App. *&* Hist. of gaming houses, *each w. sep. pagin.*] 8°. 1824

Weathers (John). The bulb book. 8°. 1911
My garden book. la8°. 1924
Practical guide to garden plants, also fruit & vegetables &c. 8°. 1901

Weaver (Edward Ebenezer). Mind & health, w. an exam. of some systems of divine healing. Intr. by G. Stanley Hall. s8°. N.Y. 1913

Weaver (*Sir* Lawrence).
Cottages: th. planning, design &c. 8°. 1926
Lutyens houses & gardens. 8°. 1921
Small country houses of to-day. 3rd ed. rev. v1. 4°. 1922
„ „ *For* v3, *see* PHILLIPS (R. R.)
Sir C. Wren, scientist, scholar & architect. s8°. 1923
see JEKYLL (G.) & L. W. Gardens for small country houses, 5th ed., 1924.

Weaver (Raymond Melbourne).
Herman Melville, mariner & mystic. 8°. N.Y. [1921]

Weaving. Minerva, or, the art of weaving, by R. C., 1677, *see* MINERVA.

Webb (*Mrs.* Beatrice) [POTTER (B.), *aft. Webb*].
My apprenticeship. 8°. 1926
see WEBB (S.) & *Mrs.* B. WEBB, *for works wr. in collab.*

Webb (Clement Charles Julian).
A century of Anglican theology & o. lect. 8°. O. 1923
Kant's philos. of relig. 8°. O. 1926
Philosophy & the Christian religion. [P2424]. 8°. O. 1920

Webb (Daniel), *of Bath, see* HECHT (H.) D. W., mit Abdruck d. Remarks on the beauties of poetry (1762), 1920.

Webb (Edward). Character & intelligence. Attempt at exact st. of character. Thesis. [Brit. journ. of psychol.: Monogr. suppl. 3]. la8°. C. 1915

Webb (Edward Alfred), *F.S.A.* Records of St. Bartholomew's Priory, & of the church & parish of St. Bartholomew the Great, West Smithfield. 2v. la8°. O. 1921

Webb (*Mrs.* Henry Bertram Law), *see* WEBB (M.)

Webb (John), *collector, see* CRAGG (*Mrs.* E.) Cat. of old French & Eng. furniture &c., prop. of Mrs. C., coll. by J. W., sold by Christie, 1925.

Webb (*Mrs.* Mary), *wife of Henry B. L. Webb, née Meredith.*
The golden arrow. [re-issue]. s8°. [1928]
Gone to earth. Intr. by J. Buchan. s8°. [1928]
The house in Dormer forest. Intr. by H. R. L. Sheppard. s8°. [1928]
Precious bane. [Travellers' lib.] s8°. [1927]

Webb (Sidney). Grants in aid: a criticism & a proposal. n. ed. rev. & enl. 8°. 1920
The story of the Durham miners (1662–1921). s8°. 1921
*Wages, prices & profits, pref. by S. W., 1922, *see* WAGES.
The works manager to-day. [2nd impr.] s8°. 1918
—— & *Mrs.* **Beatrice Webb.** A constit. for the socialist commonwealth of Gt. Brit. 8°. 1920
The consumers' co-operative movement. 8°. 1921
The decay of capitalist civilisation. 8°. 1923
[Eng. local govt.] [v4, 6, 7]. 8°. 1922–27
4, Statutory authorities for spec. purposes.
6, Eng. prisons; pref. by B. Shaw
7, Eng. poor law hist. pl, The old poor law.
Industrial democracy. Ed. of 1920, w. new intr. 8°. 1920

Webbe (Edward). E. W.: his trauailes, 1590. Ed. E. Goldsmid. s8°. *p.p.* E. 1885

Webb-Johnson (Alfred Edward). Notes on a tour of princ. hospitals & medical schools of the U.S. & Canada. 8°. *p.p.* 1923

Webb-Johnson (S.) Digest of Ind. law cases &c. 1922–1925. Comp. by S. W.-J. la8°. Calcutta. 1925–27
„ „ Index of cases (1910–21). la8°. Calcutta. 1925
For previous vol., see BOSE (B. D.)

Weber (Adolf). Der Kampf zwischen Kapital u. Arbeit. 3e u. 4e A. 8°. Tübingen. 1921

Weber (Albrecht), *see* KAUṬILYA. Abhdlg. d. Hrn. W. über 100 Sprüche d. C.; [*w. text & tr.*], 1864.

Weber (Alfred). Hist. de la philos. européenne. 8e éd. augm. d'une app. bibliograph. 8°. 1914

Weber (Anatole). L'enseignement de la prévoyance. 8°. 1911

Weber (Beda), *see* BRENTANO (C.), J. v. GÖRRES & B. W. A. K. Emmerich, M. v. Mörl u. D. Lazzaris, 1874.

Weber (Carl Maria Friedrich Ernst v.)
see LUDWIG (E.) Kunst u. Schicksal (W. &c.), 1927.
„ SERVIÈRES (G.) W., 1922.

Weber (Ernst Heinrich).
Tastsinn u. Gemeingefühl. Hrsg. v. E. Hering. 8°. L. 1905
Ü. d. Anwendung d. Wellenlehre auf d. Lehre v. Kreislaufe d. Blutes &c. (1850). Hrsg. v. M. v. Frey. 2. A. 8°. L. 1921

Weber (Friedrich Christian). *Das veränderte Russland. 3T *in* 1v. [T1, neu-verb. A.] s4°. Franckfurth. 1739–44

Weber (*Sir* Hermann).
The Weber Coll. v1–3i [*& Plates, b. sep.*] la8°. 1922–26
1–3, Greek coins; by L. Forrer.

Weber (J. C.) Die Fische Deutschlands u. d. Schweiz. Abbildn. v. J. C. Weber. Text v. C. A. Kranz. 2e A. s8°. München. 1870

Weber (Marianne).
Max Weber, e. Lebensbild. 8°. Tübingen. 1926

Weber (Max). Gen. econ. hist. Tr. F. H. Knight. 8°. [1927]
Gesammelte Aufsätze z. Religionssoziologie. 2e A. 3[B]. 8°. Tübingen. 1922–23
Gesammelte Aufsätze z. Soziologie u. Sozialpolitik. 8°. Tübingen. 1924
Gesammelte Aufsätze z. Sozial- u. Wirtschaftsgesch. 8°. Tübingen. 1924
Gesammelte Aufsätze z. Wissenschaftslehre. 8°. Tübingen. 1922
Gesammelte polit. Schriften. 8°. München. 1921
see GRUNDRISS D. SOZIALÖKONOMIK, Abt. 3, Wirtschaft u. Gesellschaft, bearb. v. M. W., 1922.
„ WEBER (M.) M. W., e. Lebensbild, 1926.

Weber (Melchior). Secta Pietistarum dissecta gladio Verbi Dei &c. s8°. Coloniae Agripp. 1714

Weber (Michael). De conjugiis in codice sacro vere prohib. [P2649]. s4°. Vitebergae. [1812]

Weber (Otto). Altoriental. Siegelbilder, 2B, *see* ALTE ORIENT (DER), Jhrg. 17, 18, 1922.
L'art hittite. Tr. G. Taboulet. la8°. 1922
Assyrische Kunst. la8°. [1924]
Die Kunst d. Hethiter. 8°. [1922]

Weber (Ottocar). Die Quadrupel-Allianz v. Jahre 1718. Beitrag z. Gesch. d. Diplomatie in 18. Jhdt. 8°. Wien. 1887

Weber (Peter Xaver).
Der Pilatus u. s. Gesch. s8°. Luzern. 1913

Weber (Siegfried).
Fiorenzo di Lorenzo, e. Kunsthist. Studie. la8°. Str. 1904

Weber (Simon). Die kathol. Kirche in Armenien: ihre Begründ. u. Entwicklung vor d. Trennung. 8°. Freiburg i. B. 1903

Weber (Theodor), *prof. of philosophy at Breslau.* Die erste altkathol. Synode u. i. Reformen. Vortrag, 1874. [P2693]. 8°. Breslau. 1874
Die Ziele d. altkathol. Bewegung. Vortr., 1873. [P2694]. 8°. Breslau. 1874
Staat u. Kirche nach d. Zeichnung &c. d. Ultramontanismus. [P2656]. 8°. Breslau. 1873

Weber (Wilhelm). Der Prophet u. s. Gott: St. z. 4. Ekloge Vergils, *see* ALTE ORIENT. Beih. 3, 1925.

Webling (Peggy).
Comedy corner. s8°. [1920]
The fruitless orchard. s8°. [1921]
In our street. s8°. 1918
The life of Isobel Erne. s8°. [1922]
The scent shop. s8°. [1919]

Webster (A. D.) Hardy ornamental flowering trees & shrubs. 3rd ed. 8°. 1908
London trees. 8°. 1920

Webster (Charles Kingsley). Brit. diplomacy, 1813–15. Sel. doc. dealing w. reconstruction of Europe. Ed. C. K. W. 8°. 1921
England & the Polish-Saxon problem at the Congress of Vienna. [Repr. f. Trans. of R. Hist. Soc., s3, v7]. [P2495]. 8°. 1913
Foreign policy of Castlereagh, 1815–22: Britain & the Europ. Alliance. 8°. 1925

Webster (Daniel). Works. 4th ed. 6v. 8°. Boston. 1853
see BURNHAM (G. W.) Proc. at inaug. of statue of D. W. erected by B., 1876.
„ FOSTER (T.) & G. COCHRAN, *edd.* *Eulogies on D. W. &c., 1853.

Webster (George Russell Bullock-), *see* BULLOCK-WEBSTER.

Webster (Hutton). Rest days: a study in early law & morality. 8°. N.Y. 1916

Webster (John), *poet.*
Complete works. Ed. F. L. Lucas. 4v. 8°. 1927
Works: notes &c. by A. Dyce. n. ed. rev. & corr. la8°. 1859

Webster (John White). Report of the case of J. W. W. indicted for the murder of G. Parkman. By G. Bemis. la8°. Boston, *Mass.* 1850
Trial of Prof. J. W. W. Intr. by G. Dilnot. 8°. [1928]

Webster (Kate) [*i.e.* CATHERINE LAWLER].
Trial of K. W. Ed. E. O'Donnell. 8°. E. [1925]

Webster (*Mrs.* Nesta H.), *wife of Arthur Webster.*
The French Revolution. A study in democracy. [repr.] 8°. 1920
„ „ [3rd ed.] 8°. 1922
Secret societies & subversive movements. 8°. 1924
Secret societies & subversive movements. 2nd ed. 8° 1924
The socialist network. 8°. 1926
World revolution: the plot agst. civiliz. 8°. 1921

Webster (Noah). New internat. dict. of the Eng. lang., based on the Internat. dict. of 1890 & 1900. Compl. rev., incl. dict. of geog. & biog. Ed. in chief W. T. Harris. Gen. ed. F. S. Allen. [9th ed.] 4°. 1927

Webster (Wentworth). *Les loisirs d'un étranger au Pays Basque. 8°. Chalon-sur-Saone. 1901

Webster (William Clarence). Recent centralizing tendencies in state educat. admin. 8°. N.Y., *Columbia Univ.* 1897

Webster's Royal red book: or, Court & fashionable register. Jan. 1903; Jan. 1921, 1922, 1923; May 1925; Jan. 1926; Jan. 1927; Jan. 1928. s8°. [1903–28]

Wechselmann (Heinr. Jul. Hans), *see* WENDEN (H.), *ps.*

Weck (Rudolf). Die Erwerbslosenfürsorge nach d. neuesten Stande. s8°. 1921

Wecklein (Nikolaus).
Works in KÖNIGL. AKAD. D. W. ZU MÜNCHEN. Phil. Kl., Sitz.
Epikrit. z. Homer. Frage, 1923.
Die Homer. Hymnen u. d. griech. Tragiker, 1920.
Textkrit. Studien zu d. griech. Tragikern, 1921.
Textkrit. Stud. z. Ilias, 1917.
Textkrit. Studien z. Odyssee, 1915.
Üb. Zenodot u. Aristarch, 1919.
Üb. Zusätze u. Auslassung v. Versen im Homer. Texte, 1918.

Wedd (Charles Bertie), *see* GIBSON (W.) & C. B. W. Geol. of N. part of Derbys. coal-field &c., 1913.
—— & **W. B. R. King.** Geol. of the co. around Flint, Hawarden & Caergwrle. By C. B. W. & W. B. R. K., w. contrib. by G. W. Lamplugh, H. H. Thomas &c. [Mem. of G.S. &c.] 8°. 1924
——, **B. Smith** *& others.* Geol. of Liverpool, w. Wirral & part of the Flintshire coalfield. [Mem. of G.S.] 8°. 1923
——, —— & **L. J. Wills.** Geol. of the co. around Wrexham. W. a contrib. by G. W. Lamplugh. [Mem. of G.S.] pl. 8°. 1927

Wedderburn, *The family of, see* Hume (D.) De familia Humia W., 1839.

Wedderburn (*Sir* **William),** *Bart., see* Ratcliffe (S. K.) Sir W. W. & the Ind. reform movement, 1923.

Wedderkamp (Johann Heinrich). Hist. sec. primi fabulis variorum maculata. Praes. J. A. Schmidt. [P432, 2645]. s4°. Helmstadii. 1700

Wedekind (Eduard). Studentenleben in d. Biedermeierzeit: Tagebuch, 1824. Hrsg. H. H. Houben. 2. & 3. A. s8°. Göttingen. 1927

Wedekind (Frank).
Der Marquis v. Keith. Schauspiel. s8°. München. 1921
Mine-Haha. Aus Helene Engels schriftl. Nachlass hrsg. F. W. s8°. München. 1919
see Fechter (P.) F. W., d. Mensch u. d. Werk, 1920.
,, Kutscher (A.) F. W.: Leben u. Werke, 2B, 1922–27.

Wedel (Theodore Otto). The mediæval attitude toward astrology partic. in England. Diss. [Yale st[s]. in Eng., 60]. 8°. New Haven, *Yale.* 1920

Wedelius (Georgius Wolfgangus). Centuria exercitat. medico-philolog. sacr. & profan. s4°. Jenae. [1686–1711]
Centuria prima has 10 Decades; 1 & 2 in 1 w. cont. pagin., 3–10 w. sep. tp. & pagin., 1686–99; tp. of Decas 10 wanting. Centuria secunda has 3 Decades w. sep. pagin., 1705–11.

Wedel-Jarlsberg (*baron* **Fredrik Wilhelm af).** *Abhandlung ü. d. ältere scandinav. Gesch. v. d. Cimbrern u. d. scand. Gothen. Von F. W. Frhr. v. W. J. 2T [*in 1v. pagin. cont.*] 8°. Copenhagen. 1781

Wedgwood (Josiah), *the elder, see* Burton (W.) J. W. & his pottery, 1922.

Wedgwood (*Col. the Rt. Hon.* **Josiah Clement).**
Essays & adventures of a labour M.P. 8°. [1924]
The seventh dominion. s8°. [1928]
Staffordshire Parl. hist., v2i, 1603–1832, *see* Staffordshire. Coll., N.S., 1920–22.

Weditz (Annette).
Bilder aus d. Kinderleben. Erzählungen. s8°. 1879

Wedmore (*Sir* **Frederick).** Notes on Velasquez & Titian in the etchings of R. W. Macbeth. s8°. 1888

Wedovius (Matthias). Τριάς paradoxorum chronolog., c. veram mundi cond. epocham occurr. Praeses M. C. Reinhartus. Resp. M. W. [P2438]. s4°. Wittebergæ. 1631

Weeber (J. Chr.) & Friedrich Krauss.
Liedersammlung. 5H [*in* 1v]. s8°. St. 1852–54

Weed (*Lt.-Col.* **Frank W.),** *U.S. Army, see* United States: Army. Medical Dept. in the World War, v5, 6, 8, by W. &c., 1923–26.

Weedall (Henry), *see* Husebeth (F. C.) Life of Monsig. W., 1860.

Weeden (William Babcock). War government, federal & state, in Mass., New York, Penn. & Indiana, 1861–65. 8°. Boston. 1906

Weede van Dijkveld (Everard van), *see* Dijkveld (E. van W. van).

Weege (Fritz). Etrusk. Malerei. 4°. Halle (Saale). 1921
Der Tanz in d. Antike. 4°. Halle, Saale. 1926

Weekes (Agnes Russell) [*ps.* Pryde (Anthony)].
Spanish sunlight. s8°. [1925]
—— & R. K. Weekes. *The city of lilies. By a. of "Jenny Essenden" [*i.e.* A. R. W.] & R. K. W. s8°. 1923

Weekes (Rose Kirkpatrick), *see* Weekes (A. R.) & R. W. W. *The city of lilies, 1923.

Weekley (Ernest).
An etymolog. dict. of modern English. la8°. 1921
More words, anc. & mod. 8°. [1927]
Words anc. & mod. 8°. [1926]

Weekly Account, The. No. 4. (July 25, 1702). [*b. w.* Daily Courant, No. 85 &c., 1702–3]. fol. 1702

Weekly Journal, The, or British Gazetteer. Dec. 24, 1720. [*b. w.* Post Man, 1720–24]. fol. 1720

Weekly Pacquet of Advice from Rome, *see* Popery. Hist. of Popery: [abstract, w. improvements, of Weekly Pacquet &c.], 2v, 1735–36.

Weekly review (The). v5 (July–Sept. 1921). 4°. N.Y. [1921]
Afterwards (*i.e. f. Oct. 1921 onwards*) *incorpor. w.* The Independent, *w. t.* The Independent & The weekly review, *q.v.*

Weeks (John H.) Among Congo cannibals: 30 yrs. amongst the Boloki & o. Congo tribes. 8°. 1913

Weemes (John), *of Lathocher.* The Christian synagogue: the diverse reading, tr. &c. of Scripture: w. customs of the Hebrewes &c. 4th ed. corr. & am. s4°. 1633
An explan. of the judiciall lawes of Moses. W. 2 treatises. s4°. 1632

Weems (Mason L.)
The life of G. Washington; w. anecdotes. s8°. Phila. 1828

Weemse (John), *see* Weemes (J.)

Weert (Sebald de). Wijdtloopigh verhael van tgene de 5 schepen, 1598–99, *see* Wieder (F. C.) De reis v. Mahu &c., d1, 1923.

Weetman (*Capt.* **W. C. C.)** The Sherwood Foresters in the Great War, 1914–19. 1/8th Batt. Intr. by Brig.-Gen. C. T. Shipley. s8°. Nottingham. 1920

Weg (Der) z. Zusammenbruch, T1, 1919, *see* Diplomatische Enthüllungen, H2, 1919.

Weg (Tobias).
Disput. de precatione. [P2436]. s4°. Tubingæ. 1576

Wege (Johann zu), *see* Via (Joannes à).

Wegehaupt (Hans). Der Florentiner Plutarchpalimpsest, *w. facs., see* Kön.-Preuss. Akad. Abhdln., Phil.-hist. Kl., 1914

Wegelin (Johann Christoph.) Diss. de dominio maris Suevici vulgo lacus Bodamici. [*b. w.* Seutter de Loezen (M.) Diss., 1764]. 8°. *n.p.* 1742

Wegelin (Thomas). Rel. v. d. theolog. Discurs zw. Georg Frider. Marggraven zu Baden u. Frantzen Hertzogen auss Lothringen &c. zu Durlach &c. [P2608]. s4°. Str. 1614

Wegener (Albert Ben).
Church & community recreation. 8°. N.Y. 1924

Wegener (Alfred). Die Entstehung d. Kontinente u. Ozeane. 3e A. 8°. Braunschweig. 1922
The origin of continents & oceans. Tr. f. 3rd Germ. ed. by J. G. A. Skerl. Intr. by J. W. Evans. 8°. [1924]

Wegg (Jervis).
The decline of Antwerp under Philip of Spain. 8°. [1924]

Węgierski (Jędrzey), *ps., see* Regenvolscius (Adrianus).

Weglinus (Thomas). Prodromus disput. public. in Johannem, cont. proleg. in omnes Evangelistas &c. [*b. w.* Calixtus (G.) Quatuor Evang. Scr. concordia, 1624]. s4°. Argentorati. 1624

Wegner (Gottfried). Ad M. Lutheri versionem Bibliorum German. obs. s8°. *n.p.* 1701

Wegscheider (Julius August Ludwig). P. Melanchthonis epistolae 13. [P2672]. 4°. Halis Sax. [1827]

Wehberg (Hans). The limitation of armaments. [C.E. for Int. Peace]. la8°. Wash. 1921
Problem of an Internat. Court of Justice. Tr. C. G. Fenwick. [C.E. for Int. Peace]. la8°. O. 1918
Wider d. Aufruf d. 93! [P2502]. 8°. Charlottenburg. 1920
see Schücking (W.) & H. W. Die Satzung d. Völkerbundes, 1921.

***Wehklage** [*for the death of Gustavus Adolphus, 1632, facs.*], *see* Freytag (G.) Bilder, B4, 1925.

Wehrli (Gustav A.) Der zürcher Stadtarzt Dr. C. Clauser u. s. Stellung z. Reform. d. Heilkunde im 16. Jhdt. 8°. Zürich. 1924

Wei (Wen Pin).
Currency problem in China. 8°. N.Y., *Columbia Univ.* 1914

Weickhmann (Joachim).
see E. (J. A.) *Unparthey. Gedanken ü. d. Wort-Streit W. mit Willenberg v. d. Polygamie, 1716.
,, Willenberg (S. F.) Iterata praes. juris div. pro def. thesium de polygamia simultanea J. W. oppos., 1714.

Weickhmann (Joachim Samuel). De Concilio Tridentino ex morte Lutheri triumphante & parentalia M. Luthero adornata. [P2627]. s4°. Vitembergae. 1746
De schola Origenis sacra ex Greg. Thaumaturgo informata comment. [P432]. s4°. Vitembergae. 1744

Weidenfeld (Christian Franz). Diss. de eo quod circa decimas novales in Germania, & præcipue in dioecesi &c. Colon. justum est. s4°. Bonnæ. 1782

Weigall (Arthur Edward Pearse Brome).
Ancient Egyptian works of art. 4°. [1924]
Bedouin love. s8°. [1922]
The Garden of Paradise. s8°. [1923]
The glory of the Pharaohs. 8°. 1923
Hist. of the Pharaohs. v1, 2. 8°. [1925–27]
Life & times of Akhnaton, Pharaoh of Egypt. n. & rev. ed. 8°. [1922]
Life & times of Cleopatra, queen of Egypt. n. & rev. ed. 8°. [1923]
Madeline of the desert. s8°. [1920]

Weigall (Arthur Edward Pearse Brome) [*continued*].

The paganism in our Christianity. s8°. [1928]
Saturnalia in Room 23. s8°. [1927]
Tutankhamen & o. essays. 8°. [1923]
Wanderings in Anglo-Saxon Britain. 8°. [1927]
Wanderings in Roman Britain. 8°. [1926]
" " [4th impr.] s8°. [1927]
The way of the East. s8°. [1924]

Weigall (Rachel). Lady Rose Weigall. A mem. based on h. corr. &c. 8°. 1923

Weigall (*Lady* Rose Sophia Mary), *see* WEIGALL (R.) Lady R. W.: a mem. based on h. corr. &c., 1923.

Weigand (Gustav).
Albanes.-deut. u. deut.-albanes. Wbch. s8°. L. 1914
Ethnographie von Makedonien. 8°. L. 1924

Weigand (Wilhelm).
Fr. Nietzsche. Psycholog. Versuch. [P2478]. 8°. München. 1893
Die Löffelstelze. Roman. 8°. München. 1919

Weigel (Johann August Gottlieb). Apparatus literarius. Index libr. quos emtur. offert W. 4°. Lipsiae. 1821

Weigel (Theodor Oswald), *bookseller.*
Katalog d. Bücherlagers. 8°. L. [1852]
" d. Antiq. Lagers. 8°. L. 1865

Weigel (Valentin).
see HOORNBEEK (J.) De paradoxis, & heterodoxis Weigelianis &c., 1694.
" REICHEL (J. G.) Vita, fata & scripta V. W., 1721.

Weigelt (Curt H.) Duccio di Buoninsegna. Frühsienes. Tafelmalerei. la8°. L. 1911

Weighver, Th' owd, *ps.*, *see* CLEGG (J. T.)

Weik (Jesse William), *see* HERNDON (W. H.) & J. W. W. H.'s Lincoln, 3v, *n.d.*

Weil (Ernst).
Die deut. Druckerzeichen d. 15. Jhdts. s4°. München. 1924
Der Ulmer Holzschnitt in 15. Jhdt. la8°. 1923

Weil (Friedrich). Tschechoslowakei. 8°. St. 1924

Weil (*Lt.-Col.* Lucien), *see* NOGARO (B.) & L. W. La main-d'œuvre étr. & coloniale pend. la Guerre, 1926.

Weil (Maurice Henri). Campagne de 1813. La cavalerie des armées alliées. 8°. 1886
Le gén. de Stamford d'ap. sa corresp. inéd. (1793–1806). 8°. 1923
see GENTZ (FRIEDRICH v.) D'Ulm à Iéna: corr. inéd. du Chev. de G. avec F. J. Jackson, 1921.

Weil (Rudolf). La cité de David. Compte rendu des fouilles exécutées, à Jérusalem sur le site de la ville prim. Campagne de 1913–14. [*Extr. f.* Revue des ét. juives, t69–71]. 8°. [1919–20]
" " ....Planches. 4°. [1920]

Weill (David).
Coll. D. W. Notices par G. Henriot. 2t. fol. 1926–27
1, Peintures. 2, Pastels, aquarelles, gouaches, tableaux mod.

Weill (Georges). Hist. de l'enseignement secondaire en France, 1802–1920. s8°. 1921
Les théories sur le pouvoir royal en France pend. les guerres de religion. 8°. 1892

Weill (Raymond). Figurines funéraires des 19e & 20e dynasties, *see* ACAD. D. INSCR.: FOND. PIOT. Mon., t25, 1921–22.

Weimar. Confession u. Bekentnis d. Glaubens d. Fürsten Joh. Frid. &c., ubergeben zu W., 1549, 1550?, *see* JOHN FREDERICK II, *d. of Saxony.*

Weimarer historisch-genealog. Taschenbuch d. gesamten Adels jehudä. Ursprunges, 1912. s8°. Weimar. 1912

Weinberg (Christian Gottfried).
De clerico cambiante &c. [P2639]. s4°. Vitembergae. [1739]

Weingartner (Josef). Der Geist d. Barock. 4°. Augsburg. 1925

Weinhagen (Napoleon). Die päpstl. Bulle "De salute animarum," 16. Juli 1821 &c. 8°. Köln. 1872

Weinhold (Carl). Altnordisches Leben. 8°. 1856

Weininger (Otto). Geschlecht u. Charakter. 4e A. 8°. Wien. 1905
see LUCKA (E.) O. W., s. Werk u. s. Persönlichkeit, 1905.

Weinreich (Otto), *see* SENECA (L. A.) Apocolocyntosis; Einführ., Analyse u. Untersuch., Übers. v. O. W., 1923.

Weir (Archibald). The anthropol. point of view. s8°. 1924

Weisbach (Werner). Die Kunst d. Barock in Italien, Frankreich, Deutschland u. Spanien. la8°. 1924

Weismann (Christian Eberhard). Instit. theologicæ exegetico-dogmat. &c. 4°. Tubingæ. 1739
Introd. in memorabilia eccl. hist. sacrae N. Test. ad juvandam notitiam regni Dei &c.
Rev. & emend. & aucta. 2t. s4°. Halae Magdeburg. 1745
Typus noviss. theol. Societatis Trementium. Praes. C. E. W.; resp. G. J. Klein & J. F. Martin. [P443]. s4°. Tubingae. 1746

Weiss (Charles), *prof. au Lycée Bonaparte.* Hist. of the French Protestant refugees. Tr. F. Hardman. 8°. E. 1854

Weiss (Gabriel), *see* WELLS (G.)

Weiss (Gottfried). Diss. chiliasmum subtilem exhib., sub præs. J. Fechtii. [P2632]. s4°. Rostochii. [1693]

Weiss (J. Bernard). Gliding & soaring flight. Pref. by C. G. Grey & app. by W. H. Sayers. s8°. [1923]

Weiss (Johannes), *Prof. d. Theologie zu Heidelberg.* Die Schriften d. N. Test., neu übers. u. erklärt v. O. Baumgarten, W. Bousset &c. Hrsg. v. J. W. 3e, verb. u. verm. A.; hrsg. v. W. Bousset u. W. Heitmüller. 4B. 8°. Göttingen. 1917–18
1, Die drei ält. Evangelien. 2, Die paulin. Briefe u. d. Pastoralbriefe. 3, Die Apostelgesch., d. Hebräerbrief u. d. kathol. Briefe. 4, Das Johannes-Evangelium, d. Johannes-Briefe u. d. Offenbarung d. Johannes. Sachregister z. ganzen Werke [*w. sep. pagin.*]

Weiss (L. Georg). Electorum Saxoniae Lutheran. symbola heroica, coll. & ed. studio L. G. W. [P440]. s4°. Dresdae. *n.d.*

Weiss (Leopold).
Unromant. Morgenland. 8°. Frankfurt a. M. 1924

Weiss (Renzo), *see* ARANO (A.) R. W., 1923.

Weissbach (Franz H.) Babylon. Miscellen. Hrsg. v. W. [Deut. Orient-Gesell., Wiss. Veröffentl., 4. *b. w.* Koldewey (R.) Hettit. Inschr., 1900]. fol. L. 1903
Die Denkmäler u. Inschr. an d. Münd. d. Nahr el-Kelb. [Deutsch-Türkisches Denkmal-Schutz-Kommando]. fol. 1922
Die Inschr. Nebukadnezars II im Wâdi Brîsā u. am Nahr el-Kelb. Hrsg. u. übers. v. W. [Deut. Orient-Gesell. *b. w.* Koldewey (R.) Hettit. Inschr., 1900]. fol. L. 1906

Weisse (Christian Felix). Briefe an K. W. Ramler [1762–97], mitget. v. K. Schüddekopf, *see* ARCHIV F. D. ST. D. NEU. SPR., B77, 79, 82, 1887–89.

Weisse (Christian Heinrich) [†WEISSIUS]. Antiq. Misnico-Saxonic. singularia. s8°. Chemnitii. 1727
De stylo Romano lib. 5. s8°. Chemnitii. 1724

Weisse (Christian Hermann).
Grundzüge d. Metaphysik. 8°. Hamburg. 1835
Psych. u. Unsterblichkeitslehre; nebst Vorles. ü. d. Materialismus &c. Zu.-gest. v. R. Seydel. 8°. L. 1869

Weissenborn (Johann). Delineatio atheismi et enthusiasmi, cum notis ad Quakerismum pernosc. fac. [P2630]. s4°. Jenae. 1694

Weissenburg. Annales W. [705–1147], *see* LAMBERTUS, *Hersfeld.* Opera; rec. O. Holder-Egger, acced. An. W., 1894.
*Incerti monachi W. Catechesis Theotisca sec. 9 conscr., 1713, *see* CATECHESIS.

Weissenburger (Wolfgang). Antilogia Papæ; hoc est, de corrupto eccl. statu &c., scripta aliquot vet. authorum plus nunc primum in lucem eruta. [Scriptum Scholae Paris. de periculis Eccles., 1389; Marsilii de Padua, de transl. Imperii; Aureum Speculum Papae &c.] Cum praef. W. W. s8°. [Basileæ. 1555]

Weissig (Carl Wilhelm). Diss. de regeneratione monastica. Praes. J. S. Semler. [P437]. s4°. Halae. [1754]

Weissmann (Adolf). Giacomo Puccini. 8°. 1922
Problems of modern music. Tr. M. M. Bozman. Intr. by E. J. Dent. 8°. 1925

Weitbrecht (John James), *see* WEITBRECHT (*Mrs.* M.) Mem. of the Rev. J. J. W., 1854.

Weitbrecht (*Mrs.* Mary), *wife of J. J. W.* Mem. of the Rev. J. J. Weitbrecht, comp. f. h. journal & letters by h. widow. Introd. by the editor A. M. W. Christopher. 2nd ed. 8°. 1854

Weittenhiller (Moriz Maria *Edlen* v.) Salzburg. Adel, *see* SIBMACHER (J.) Wappenbuch, B4vi, 1883.

Weitz (Hans Philipp). G. Engel, s. Werk u. s. Zeit. s8°. St. [1923]

Weitzel (Carl), *see* BOCK (H.) & C. W. Der hist. Roman, 1921.

Weitzer (Demeter Georgievitz), *see* SURYA (G. W.)

Weitzmann (Carl Friedrich), *see* SEIFFERT (M.) Gesch. d. Klaviermusik; hrsg. als 3e A. v. C. F. W.'s Gesch. d. Klavierspiels &c., B1, 1899.

Weixlgärtner (Arpad). August Pettenkofen. Hrsg. v. K. K. Min. für Kultus &c. 2T. 4°. Wien. 191

Welbeck Abbey. Cat. of pictures belong. to D. of Portland, at W.A. &c., 1894, *see* PORTLAND.
see WILLIAM III, *k. of Eng.* Corr. v. W. III en H. W. Bentinck; ged. 1, Archief v. W.A., dl, 1927.

Welbourne (Edward). The Miners' Unions of Northumberland & Durham. s8°. C. 192

Welby (Thomas Earle). The silver treasury of Eng. lyrics, ed. T. E. W. 8°. 1925

Welby (Victoria, *Lady*) [VICTORIA A. M. L., *wife of Sir W. E. Welby-Gregory*]. Links & clues. 2nd ed. 8°. 1883

Welch (Adam C.), *D.D.* The Psalter in life, worship & hist. [4 essays]. s8°. O. 1926
The relig. of Israel under the Kingdom. Kerr Lects., 1911–12. 8°. E. 1912
Welch (Charles). An investig. of M. Robinson's Obs. on the system of Wesleyan Methodism. 8°. 1825
The Wesleyan polity. s8°. 1829
Welch (Charles), *F.S.A.* City guilds & th. rel. to commerce & educ. Lect. [P2773]. 8°. [1902]
Coat-armour of the London Livery Companies. With bibliog. list & reprod. of R. Wallis's "Londons armory," publ. 1677. 4°. *p.f.p.subs.* 1914
Hist. of the Cutlers' Co. of London &c., w. biog. notices of early London cutlers. v2, From 1500 to mod. times. 4°. *p.p.* 1923
Hist. of the Worshipful Co. of Gardeners. 2nd ed. 8°. 1900
Welchman (Edward).
The 39 articles, w. notes &c. Tr. 13th ed. 8°. 1823
Weld (Herbert), *see* LANGDON (S.) Excav. at Kish: the H. W. & Field Museum Exped. to Mesopotamia, v1, 1924.
Weld (Louis Dwight Harvell).
The marketing of farm products. [repr.] s8°. N.Y. 1924
Weld-Blundell (Charles J.)
What's wrong w. England? 8°. [Newcastle-upon-Tyne. 1921?]
Weld-Blundell (Herbert Joseph), *see* ABYSSINIA. The Royal Chronicle of A. 1769–1840, w. tr. & notes by H. W.-B., 1922.
Weldon (*Sir* Anthony). *Satire agst. Scotland (1617) [*sometimes ascr. to Sir A. W.*], *&* Answer, *see* ABBOTSFORD CLUB. Misc., v1, 1837.
Weldon (John), *1676–1736.* Hope thou nurse: duet. [*b. w.* Corelli (A.) Twelve concertos, 1790?]. 4°. *Andrews. n.d.*
Welhaven (Johann Sebastian Cammermejer).
Samlede Digterverker. 3e udg. 4b. s8°. 1921
Welie (Antoon van), *see* MAUCLAIR (C.) Un peintre hollandais contemp.: A. van W., 1924.
Weljaminof-Zernof, *see* VELYAMINOV-ZERNOV.
Wellander (Johan), *see* LEVERTIN (O.) J. W., 2a uppl., 1908.
Wellbeloved (Robert).
Treatise on the law rel. to highways &c. 8°. 1829
Wellcome Historical Medical Museum. Research studies in medical history. No. 1, 3. la8°. 1922–25
see ARDERNE (J.) De arte phisicali & de cirurgia (1412); tr. Sir D'Arcy Power, 1922. [1.]
,, SPIELMANN (M. H.) Iconogr. of A. Vesalius, 1925. [3.]
Wellcome (Henry S.)
*Antient Cymric medicine. [P2878]. s8°. [1903]
Welldon (James Edward Cowell), *bp. of Calcutta, aft. dean of (1) Manchester, (2) Durham.* The English Church. 8°. [1926]
Wellenburg (W. v. Gulat-), *see* GULAT-WELLENBURG (W. v.)
Weller (A.), *publisher, see* WAPPENSAMMLUNG. Wappenbeschreibungen zu d. W. in Buntdruck, Ser. 3, Blatt 1–40 (A. W.'s Verlag), 1902 &c.
Weller (Edward), *F.R.G.S.*
Map of Gt. Brit., railways, canals &c. folded 8°. *n.d.*
Weller (Emil). Die ersten deut. Zeitungen; hrsg. mit e. Bibliog. (1505–99) v. E. W. [Lit. V. in St., 111]. 8°. [Tübingen]. 1872
Weller (Hieronymus). Ratio formandi studii theologici. Item de modo & ratione concionandi. s8°. Norибergæ. 1562
Weller (Stuart), *geologist.* A report on ordovician fossils coll. in E. Asia, 1903–4, *see* WILLIS (B.), E. BLACKWELDER &c. Research in China, v3, 1913.
Wellers Archiv für Stamm-u. Wappenkunde, 1901–3, *see* ARCHIV FÜR STAMM-U. WAPPENKUNDE.
Wellesley (Francis) & M. Wellesley. Hand-list of miniatures & portraits in plumbago or pencil belong. to F. & M. W. Foreword by G. C. Williamson. 8°. O. 1914
Wellesley (Henry), *D.D.* Cat. of drawings by old masters & coll. of engravings formed by W., sold by Sotheby, 25th June &c., 1866. [*b. w. h.* Cat. of library, 1866]. 8°. 1866
Cat. of the coll. of MSS. formed by W., incl. Ital. works &c., sold by Sotheby 3rd August 1866. [*b. w. h.* Cat. of library, 1866]. 8°. 1866
Cat. of the library of W., sold by Sotheby, 8th Nov. &c., 1866. 8°. 1866
Wellesley (Minnie), *see* WELLESLEY (F.) & M. W. Hand-list of miniatures &c. in plumbago &c. belong. to F. & M. W., 1914.
Wellesley (Richard Colley Wellesley, *marquess***).** Despatches, minutes & corr. of W. dur. h. admin. in India. Ed. M. Martin. v1. 8°. 1836

Wellesz (Egon).
Arnold Schönberg. Tr. W. H. Kerridge. s8°. [1928]
Die Ballet-Suiten v. J. Heinrich u. A. A. Schmelzer: Musik a. österr. Hofe i. 17. Jhdt., 1914, *see* KAISERL. AKAD. D. WISS. ZU WIEN. Sitzungsber., B176, 1916.
Byzantin. Musik. 8°. Breslau. 1927
Wellhausen (Julius). Das Evangelium Johannis. 8°. 1908
Krit. Anal. d. Apostelgesch., 1914, *see* KÖNIGL. GESELLS. D. WISS., *Göttingen*. Abh., Phil.-hist. Kl., B15, 1917.
Die Pharisäer u. d. Sadducäer. 2. unveränd. A. 8°. Hannover. 1924
see KEGEL (M.) Away f. Wellhausen; tr. M. Nolloth, 1924.
,, MÖLLER (W.) Hist.-krit. Bedenken gegen d. Graf-Wellhausen. Hypothese, 1899.
Welling (James Clarke).
Addresses, lect. & o. papers. s8°. Camb. [Mass.] 1904
Wellington (Arthur Wellesley, *1st duke of***).**
Dispatches of W., dur. h. var. campaigns. Comp. by Col. Gurwood. [enlarged ed.] v7. 8°. 1845
A great man's friendship: letters of W. to Mary, Marchioness of Salisbury, 1850–52. Ed. Lady Burghclere, w. biog. sk. of Lady S. 8°. 1927
see APSLEY HOUSE. Descr. & hist. cat. of coll. of pictures &c. at A. H. [formed by W.]; by E. Wellington, 2v, 1901.
,, BEATSON (*Maj.-Gen.* F. C.) W.: the crossing of the Gaves & the Battle of Orthez, 1925.
see BEATSON (*Maj.-Gen.* F. C.) With W. in the Pyrenees, 1813, 1914.
,, FORTESCUE (*Hon.* J. W.) W., 1925.
,, GLEIG (G. R.) Life of W., rev. ed., 1873.
,, HOOPER (G.) W., repr., 1913.
,, MAXWELL (*Rt. Hon. Sir* H. E.) Life of W., 3rd ed., 2v, 1900.
,, PROUDHON (P. J.) Comm. sur les Méms. de Fouché, [*&*] parallèle entre Napoléon & W., 3e éd., 1900.
,, SMITH (G. B.) Heroes of the 19th c.: W. &c., 1899.
Wellington (Evelyn), *see* APSLEY HOUSE. Descr. & hist. cat. of coll. of pictures &c. at A.H.; by E. W., 2v, 1901.
Wellmann (Maximilian). Die Georgika d. Demokritos, *see* KÖNIGL.-PREUSS. AKAD. Abhandl., Philos.-hist. Klasse, 1921.
Wells. Medieval wills f. Wells, in Diocesan Registry, 1543–56. Ed. D. O. Shilton & R. Holworthy. [Somerset Rec. Soc., v40]. 8°. *p.f.s.o.* 1925
Wells Cathedral. Archit. details f. W. Cath. &c. Photogr. by Cundall, Downes & Co. la. fol. [1865]
Wells (David Ames).
The theory & practice of taxation. 8°. N.Y. 1900
Wells (Edward), *D.D.* Controv. treatises agst. the dissenters [*incl.* Copy of letter by Mr. Dowley *wh. has sep. tp. & begins 2nd pagin.*] 6th ed. s8°. 1716
Wells (Gabriel) [*form.* G. WEISS].
Arbitration. [P2849]. 8°. N.Y. 1925
Are we a democracy? [P2870]. 8°. N.Y. 1927
If I were France. [P2849]. 8°. N.Y. 1926
Wells (Geoffrey H.) A bibliography of the works of H. G. Wells, 1893–1925. la8°. 1925
Wells (H. G.) [HERBERT GEORGE WELLS].
Boon, The mind of the race &c. Being a first selec. f. the lit. remains of George Boon. Prep. for publ. by R. Bliss. Introd. by W. the author. [2nd ed.] s8°. [1920]
Christina Alberta's father. s8°. [1925]
The dream. s8°. [1924]
Meanwhile. s8°. 1927
Men like gods. s8°. [1923]
Mr. Belloc objects to "The outline of history." [Forum ser.] [2nd impr.] s8°. 1926
The new teaching of history. [P2520]. 8°. 1921
The outline of history. Wr. w. editorial help of E. Barker, Sir H. H. Johnston &c rev. & corr. ed. la8°. 1920
,, ,, [repr.] la8°. [1921]
,, ,, def. ed., rev. &c. la8°. [1923]
Russia in the shadows. s8°. [1920]
The salvaging of civilization. s8°. 1921
The secret places of the heart. s8°. [1922]
A short hist. of the world. s4°. 1922
,, ,, ...s8°. 1924
Short stories. [3rd impr.] s8°. 1927
The story of a great schoolmaster: life & ideas of Sanderson of Oundle. s8°. 1924
The time machine. [pop. ed.] s8°. 1920
Washington & the hope of peace. s8°. [1922]
The way the world is going. s8°. [1928]
The world of William Clissold. [3v, *pagin. cont.*] s8°. [1926]
see BELLOC (H.) Companion to W.'s Outline of hist., 1926.
,, —— Mr. B. still objects to Mr. W.'s "Outline of hist.," 1926.
,, BROWN (I. J. C.) H. G. W., 1923.
,, CONNES (G. A.) Dict. of characters & scenes in the novels &c. of H. G. W., 1926.

Wells (H. G.) [*continued*].

see CRAUFORD (A. H. G.) Relig. of H. G. W. & o. essays, 1909.
„ DARK (S.) Outline of H. G. W., 1922.
„ GOMME (A. W.) Mr. W. as historian: inq. into parts of W.'s Outline of hist. wh. deal w. Greece & Rome, 1921.
see GUYOT (E.) H. G. W., 1920.
„ WELLS (G. H.) Bibliog. of works of H. G. W., 1893–1925, 1925.

Wells (John Edwin). A manual of the writings in Mid. English, 1050–1400, 2nd Suppl. to Jan. 1923, 3rd Suppl. to June 1926. [2v]. 8°. New Haven. 1923–26

Wells (Joseph), *warden of Wadham College.* Studies in Herodotus. 8°. O. 1923

Wells (Rollin J.) Hagar. Dramatic poem. s8°. N.Y. 1903

Wells (Warre Bradley). An Irish apologia: Anglo-Irish rels. & the War. [*a. c. in* P2529]. s8°. D. 1917

Wells (William), *Florist.* Culture of the chrysanthemum. rev. & enl. s8°. 1920

Wels (Paul). Gesch. d. Klosters Leubus u. s. Bedeutung f. Schlesien. [P2565]. 8°. Liegnitz. 1921

Welsford (Enid). The court masque. 8°. C. 1927

Welsh. *How to learn Welsh; Eng.-W. vocab. s8°. Wrexham. *n.d.*

*Welsh (The) embassador (c. 1623). [Prep. H. Littledale & W. W. Greg. Malone Soc.] s4°. [O.] 1920 [1921]

Welsh in educ. & life. Rep. of Dept. Comm. app. by Bd. of Educ. s8°. 1927

Welsh Folk Song Society. Cylchgrawn Cymdeithas Alawon Gwerin Cymru. Journal of the W.F.S. Soc. v1–2. 8°. [1909–25]

Welsh (David). Acc. of the life & wr. of T. Brown. 8°. E. 1825

Elements of Church hist. v1, Hist. dur. first 3 cent. [*no more published*]. 8°. Edinb. 1844

Welsh (James C.), *M.P.* The Morlocks. s8°. [1924]

Welsh (R. Ethol) & F. G. Edwards. Romance of Psalter & hymnal: authors & composers. 8°. 1889

Welsh-Mason (Charles Henry Alan), see MASON (C. W.)

Welshmen. Facs. of letters of Oxford W., 1903, *see* OXFORD.

Weltgeschichte in Umrissen, 6e A., 1901, *see* YORCK V. WARTENBURG (M., *Graf* v.)

Weltkrieg. *Nächste (Der) W., 1916, *see* WENCKER (F.)

Weltkrieg (Der), 1914 bis 1918. Bearb. im Reichsarchiv. B1–4. la8°. 1925–26

1–4, Milit. Operationen zu Lande.
1, Grenzschlachten im Westen.
2, Befreiung Ostpreussens.
3, Der Marne-Feldzug v. d. Sambre z. Marne.
4, Der Marne-Feldzug: d. Schlacht.

Weltprotest (Der) gegen d. Versailler Frieden, 1920, *see* FRIED (A. H.)

Weltzien (Otto). Celler Geschichte. 8°. Celle. 1926

Wely (F. P. H. Prick van), *see* PRICK VAN WELY (F. P. H.)

Wemyss (Francis Wemyss Charteris-Douglas, *9th earl***).** London Scottish Volunteer Rifles, Speech, July 4. [P2831]. 8°. 1859

Wemyss of Wemyss, *The family of, see* FRASER (*Sir* W.) Memorials of the family of W. of W., 3v, 1888.

Wenceslaus, *of Liegnitz, bp. of Breslau, d. 1420.* Statuta synodalia a W. 1410, publ., nunc primum ed a J. C. Friedrich. [P2755]. 8°. Hannoverae. 1827

Wenck (Carl Friedrich Christian). Magister Vacarius primus juris Rom. in Anglia prof. ex mon. &c. illust. 8°. Lipsiae. 1820

Wencker (Friedrich). *Der nächste Weltkrieg. Prophezeiung e. neutr. Diplomaten. [P2685]. 8°. [1916]

Wend (Jacob Joachim). Ex hist. eccl. de Ebionitis, contra G. Arnoldum. Praes. S. Schelguigio, resp. J. J. W. [P434]. s4°. Gedani. [1700]

Wendal (Carl). Überlief. u. Entsteh. d. Theokrit-Scholien, 1920, *see* KÖNIGL. GESELL. D. WISS. Z. GÖTT. Abhlgn., N.F., 17, 1921.

Wendel (Hermann). Der Kampf d. Südslawen um Freiheit u. Einheit. 8°. Fr. am M. 1925

Südslaw. Silhouetten. 8°. Fr. am Main. 1924

Wendelinus, *see* VENDELINUS.

Wendell (Barrett). Cotton Mather, the Puritan priest. 8°. Cambridge, *Mass.* 1926

see BOSTON ATHENAEUM. Influence & hist. &c.; by B. W. &c., 1907.

Wenden (Henry), *ps.* [*i.e.* H. J. H. WECHSELMANN]. Ich kenne keine Parteien mehr! Kriegsroman. 3e A. s8°. 1915

Wendland (Paul). Die hellenist.-röm. Kultur in i. Bezieh. zu Judentum u. Christentum—Die urchristl. Literaturformen, *see* LIETZMANN (H.), *ed.* Hdbch. z. Neu. Test., B1, T2, 3, 1912.

Krit. u. exeget. Bemerk. zu Philo. [Sonder-Abdr. aus d. Rhein. Mus., B52, 53. P2794]. 8°. [Frankfurt a. M.] 1897–98

Wendler (Johann Christoph). Prodromus bibl. Biblicae, exhib. hist. crit. comment. in Epist. Paulinas &c. s8°. Jenae. 1721

Wendt (Hans Hinrich). Die Johannesbriefe u. d. johann. Christentum. la8°. Halle. 1925

Wenger (Leopold).
Works in KÖNIGL. AKAD. D. W. ZU MÜNCHEN. Philos.-philol. Kl., Sitz.

Praetor u. Formel, 1926.
Üb. Papyri u. Gesetzesrecht, 1914.
Zum cippus Abellanus, 1915.

Wengerscius (Andreas). Libri 4 Slavoniae reformatae &c. Add. App. var. monument. ad res eccl. Slavoniae pert. s4°. Amstelodami. 1679

Weniger (Ludwig). Altgriech. Baumkultus. [Das Erbe d. Alten, N.F., H2]. 8°. L. 1919

Wenkebach (Ernst). John Clement: engl. Humanist u. Arzt d. 16. Jhdts. la8°. L. 1925

Works in KÖNIGL.-PREUSS. AKAD. Abhandl. (Phil.-hist. Klasse).

Das Proömium d. Komm. Galens zu d. Epidemien d. Hippokrates, 1918.
Pseudogalen. Komm. zu d. Epidemien d. Hippokrates, 1917.
Unters. ü. Galens Komm. zu d. Epidemien d. Hippokrates, 1925.

Wenlok (Walter de), *abbot of Westminster, d. 1307, see* PEARCE (E. H.) W. de W., 1920.

Wen Pin Wei, *see* WEI (W. P.)

Wenrich (Johann Georg). De auctorum Graec. vers. & commentariis Syr., Arab., Armen. & Pers. comm. 8°. Lipsiae. 1842

Wentworth (*Sir* John), *see* MAYO (L. S.) J. W., gov. of New Hampshire, 1767–75, 1921.

Wentworth (Patricia) [*ps. Mrs.* DILLON].
The amazing chance. s8°. [1926]
Anne Belinda. s8°. [1927]
The black cabinet. s8°. [1926]

Wentzcke (Paul). Die deut. Farben, *see* HAUPT (H.) Quellen &c. z. Gesch. d. Burschenschaft &c., B9, 1927.

Gesch. d. deut. Burschenschaft, B1, *see* HAUPT (H.) Quellen &c., B6, 1919.

see STRASSBURG. Regesten d. Bischöfe, B1, Reg., bis z. 1202, v. P. W., 1908.

Wenzel (Johann Heinrich). Disput. jubilaea de Conf. August. lenitate. Praes. C. A. Heumanno. [P484]. s4°. Hanoverae. 1730

Wenzig (Joseph). Westslaw. Märchenschatz: e. Charakterbild d. Böhmen, Mährer &c. Deut. bearbt. v. J. W. 8°. L. 1857

Weobly (Charles), *see* MEDLAND (W. M.) & C. W. Coll. of remark. criminal trials, 3v, 1803–5.

Wer ist's? Unsere Zeitgenossen; hrsg. v. H. A. L. Degener. 8e A. 8°. L. 1922
„ „ ....9e A. 8°. L. 1928

Werder (Johann Friedrich). Diss. de Spinozismo ante Spinozam. Praes. J. F. Buddeo, resp. J. F. W. [P599]. s4°. Halae Magdeb. [1701]

Werdin (Joannes Philippus), *see* PAULINUS, *a Sancto Bartholemaeo.*

Werenfels (Samuel). Diss. theolog. sylloge. s8°. 1709

Opusc. theolog. philos. & philol. Ed. 3a. aucta Diss. de Div. Script. origine. 2t. 4°. Lugduni Batav. 1772

Werfel (Franz).
Der Abiturientag: Gesch. e. Jugendschuld. s8°. 1928
Beschwörungen. [Gedichte]. 8°. München. [1923]
Einander. [4e A.] 8°. München. 1920
Geheimnis e. Menschen. Novellen. s8°. 1927
Der Gerichtstag. la8°. [L. 1919]
Juarez u. Maximilian. Dramat. Hist. s8°. 1924
Paulus unter d. Juden. Dram. Legende. 8°. 1926
Der Tod des Kleinbürgers. Novelle. s8°. 1927
Verdi. Roman d. Oper. s8°. 1924

Wergeland (Henrik Arnold), *1808–45.* Samlede skrifter. Utgit av H. Jaeger og D. A. Seip. la8°. 1920–[28]

II, Digterverker, B2–6.
IV, Avhandlinger, Oplysningskrifter, B1–6, 1829–45.

see LAACHE (R.) H. W. & h. strid med Prokurator Praëm, B1, 1828–31, 1927.

Werkmann (*Baron* Carl von).
Tragedy of Charles of Habsburg. 8°. [1924]

Werminghoff (Albert).
Conrad Celtis u. s. Buch ü. Nürnberg. 8°. Freiburg i. B. 1921
Verfassungsgesch. d. deut. Kirche im M.-a., 2e A, 1913, *see* GRUNDR. D. GESCHICHTSWISS; Meister, 2vi, 1913.

Werndly (Georg Henrik). Maleische Spraakkunst; Aanhangsel v. 2 Boekzalen. 8°. Amsterdam. 1736

Werneburg (Rudolf). Peter Thumb u. s. Familie: Beitr. z. süddeut. Kirchenbaukunst. la8°. Str. 1916

Werner (*Miss* Alice), *see* MYTHOLOGY of all races, v7, African; by A. W., 1925.

Werner (Andreas Conrad).
Liber Ruth illustr. s4°. Hamburgi. 1740

Werner (E. T. Chalmers).
Myths & legends of China. [repr]. 8°. [1924]

Werner (Heinz). Die melodische Erfindung im frühen Kindesalter (43. Mitt. d. Phonogramm-Archivs-Komm.), 1917, *see* KAISERL. AKAD. D. WISS. ZU WIEN. Sitz., B182, 1918.

Werner (Joachim Melchior). Diss. sistens examen doct. Quesnellianae de eccl. &c. Præs. M. Chladenio. [P2630]. s4°. Vitembergae. 1717

Werner (Johann), *Vratislav.*
Johannes Hus, martyr. s4°. Lipsiae. 1671

Werner (Michael Meinhard). Disput. de Jubilaeo Romano. Sub praes. B. v. Sanden. [2p. P446]. s4°. Regiomonti. [1700]

Wernert (Paul), *see* OBERMAIER (H.) & P. W. Las pinturas rupestres del barranco de Valltorta, 1919.

Wernher, *Swiss poet.* Das Marienleben d. Schweizers Wernher. [Bearbtg. d. Vita beate virginis Marie et salvatoris rhythmica]. Aus d. Heidelberger Hs. hrsg. v. M. Päpke, zu Ende geführt v. A. Hübner. [Deut. Texte d. Ma.; Preuss. Akad., 27]. la8°. 1920

Wernher (Joannes Balthasarus).
Principia juris eccl. Protestantium. s8°. Lipsiae. 1749

Wernigerode. Index Bibliorum &c. in Christiano-Ernestina Bibl. ed. 3a. 8°. Halae Magdeb. [1766]

Wernlé (Gabriel), *see* WULFSOHN (L.) & G. W. L'évasion des capitaux allemands, 1923.

Wernle (Paul). Der evangel. Glaube nach d. Hauptschriften d. Reformatoren. 3[B]. 8°. Tübingen. 1918–19
1, Luther. 2, Calvin. 3, Zwingli.

Wernsdorf (Ernst Friedrich). De vet. eccl. diebus festis anniversariis liberationis a periculo comm. [P2635]. s4°. Vitebergae. 1767
Exerc. de sacerdote Lat. lingua ad altare cantillante. [P437]. s4°. Vitebergae. 1761
Liturgia Lutherana servans exemplum ant. eccl. Exercit. I. [P2629]. s4°. Vitebergae. *n.d.*

Wernsdorf (Gottlieb), *the elder* [WERNSSDORFF]. De Montanistis sec. 2 comm. [P2632]. s4°. Gedani. 1751
Diss. de Constit. Apostol. orig., contra G. Whistonum. [P433]. s4°. Wittebergae. 1739
Hist. Confess. Tetrapolitanae. Resp. M. R. Reinhardo. ed. 4a. [P441]. s4°. Wittenbergae. 1721
Schrifftmässige Gedancken v. Zustande d. abgeschied. Seelen. Übers. s8°. Wittenberg. 1726

Wernsdorf (Gottlieb), *the younger.* Comm. hist.-crit. de fide histor. libr. Maccabaicorum &c. s4°. Wratislaviae. 1747

Wernsdorf (Johann Christian).
Diss. 1–4 de Hypatia, philosopha Alexandrina. [1, Praes. J. D. Rittero, 2–4, Praes. J. C. W., *var. resp.*] [P600]. s4°. Vitembergae. 1747–48

Wertenbaker (Thomas J.) The planters of colonial Virginia. 8°. Princeton [N.J.] 1922

Werth (Léon). Ghislaine, roman, *see* ŒUVRES libres, 62, 1926.

Wertheimer (Max). 3 Abhandlgn. z. Gestalttheorie. Neuhrsg. 8°. Erlangen. 1925

Wertheimische. *Samlung derjen. Schriften bey Gelegenheit d. w. Bibelwerks &c., 1738, *see* SAMMLUNG.

Werther (Hans Friedrich v.) Hist. episcop. Numburg. [*sic*]. Præs. C. Sagittario. [P2646]. s4°. Halae. 1736

Wesenbeccius (Joannes). Disput. de unione personali in Christo &c. Præs. T. Schnepffio, J. W. def. [P2626]. s4°. Tubingæ. 1577

Wesenberg-Lund (Carl Jørgensen).
Works in KONG. DAN. VID. SELSK. Skr., Række 8.
Biol. & morphology of genus Daphnia, 1926. [11.]
Biol. of the Danish Culicidæ, 1920–25. [7.]
Contrib. to biology of the Rotifera, 1, 1918–23. [4.]
Contrib. to biol. of Zoothamnium geniculatum Ayrton, 1925–26. [10.]
Furesøstudier, en bathymetr., botan., zoolog. Undersøgelse of Mølleaaens Søer, 1917. [3.]

Wesley, *The family of.* The bards of Epworth or poetic gems f. the Wesley cabinet. s8°. 1856
see CLARKE (A.) Misc. wks., v1 & 2, Mem. of the W. family, 1838–39.
,, WAKELEY (J. B.) Anecdotes of the W., 1869.

Wesley (Charles), *M.A.*
C. W. seen in his poems. s8°. N.Y. 1878
An epistle to the Rev. Mr. J. Wesley. [*In verse. repr.* P449]. s8°. 1785
Finer & less known poems. [Ed. F. M. Bird]. 8°. N.Y. 1878
*Gloria Patri &c., or Hymns to the Trinity. 2nd ed. [P2547]. s8°. Bristol. 1749
,, ,, 4th ed. [P2545]. s8°. Bristol. 1764
A guide to syllogism, or, a manual of logic. s8°. 1832
Hymns & sacred poems. 2v. s8°. Bristol. 1749
,, ,, 2nd ed. 2v. s8°. Bristol. 1755–56
,, ,, *see also* WESLEY (JOHN) & C. W.
Hymns for use of families &c. [P2545, 2550]. s8°. Bristol. 1767
Journal, appended sel. f. h. corresp. & poetry. Intr. & notes by T. Jackson. 2v. s8°. [1849]
A sermon preached on April 4, 1742; bef. Univ. of Oxford. 10th ed. [P2551]. s8°. Bristol. 1745
,, ,, 21st ed. [P2535]. s8°. 1767
A short acc. of the death of Mrs. H. Richardson. 9th ed. [P2675]. s8°. Bristol. 1766
,, ,, 10th ed. [P2542]. s8°. 1775
Short hymns on sel. passages of Holy Scr. 2v. s8°. Bristol. 1762
see MOORE (H.) Life of J. W. & C. W., 2v, 1824.
,, WATSON (R.) Vie du Rév. J. W. avec détails sur C. W., 1843.
,, WESLEY (J.) Books publ. by J. & Charles W., 1750.
,, —— & C. W. *for works wr. in collab.*

Wesley (John).
Works. 32v. s8°. Bristol. 1771–74
An address to the clergy. [P2622]. s8°. 1756
Advice to Methodists w. regard to dress. [P2536]. s8°. 1780
The almost Christian: A sermon, Oxford, 1741. 6th ed. [P2551]. s8°. Bristol. 1747
,, ,, 11th ed. [P2535]. s8°. 1766
*An answer to a letter publ. in the Bath Journal, 1749, sign'd N.D. [P2534]. s8°. Bristol. 1749
The beauties of J. W. Prefixed mem. of h. life &c. s8°. Nottingham. 1802
*A blow at the root: or Christ stabbed &c. 2nd ed. [P2535] s8°. 1762
Books publ. by J. & Charles Wesley. s8°. [1750]
A call to backsliders: sermon on Ps. lxxvii, 7, 8. 4th ed. [P2536]. s8°. 1778
A calm address to our American colonies. s8°. 1775
,, ,, ...s8°. *n.d.*
,, ,, n. ed. corr. s8°. *n.d.* [1776 ?]
The character of a Methodist. 5th ed. [P2551]. s8°. 1745
,, ,, 7th ed. [P2542]. s8°. D. 1804
A Christian library. Extr. f. & abridgments of the choicest pieces of pract. divinity publ. in Eng. tongue. 50v. [v26, 27, 49 & 50 *are* Lives of emin. persons]. s8°. Bristol. 1749–55
Christian perfection: sermon. 2nd ed. [P2534]. s8°. Newcastle. 1743
Christian theology; passages in the wr. of J. W. With biogr. sk. by T. Smith. s8°. [1872]
Coll. of forms of prayer for every day in the week. 8th ed. [P2534]. s8°. Bristol. 1745
A coll. of hymns for the use of Methodists. 2nd ed. s8°. 1781
A coll. of hymns for the use of Methodists. w. a Suppl. 8°. 1832
,, ,, w. new Suppl. 8°. 1876
,, ,, w. new Suppl. ed. w. tunes. 8°. 1877
,, ,, Suppl. s8°. 1831
A coll. of hymns for use of M. Episc. Church. Princ. f. coll. of W. rev. & corr., w. Suppl. s8°. N.Y. 1840
A coll. of moral & sacred poems fr. Engl. authors. Publ. by J. W. 3v. s8°. Bristol. 1744
A coll. of prayers for families. [*tp. wanting.* P2534]. s8°. *n.p. n.d.* [1746 ?]
,, ,, 23rd ed. [P2595]. s8°. 1813
Coll. of Psalms & hymns. Charles-town, 1737. w. pref. by G. Osborn. [*Facsimile repr.*] s8°. [1882]
A coll. of tunes set to music. [*b. w. h.* Coll. of Psalms &c. facs. repr., 1882]. s8°. 1742 [repr. 1882 ?]
*A coll. of tunes set to music as sung at the Foundery Lond. 1742 [*facs. repr.*] [*b. w. h.* Coll. of Psalms &c., facs. repr., 1882]. s8°. *n.d.*
A companion for the altar. Extr. f. T. à Kempis. 5th ed. [*b. w.* Wesley (J. & C.) Coll. of Ps. & hymns, 5th ed., 1760]. s8°. 1755
The complete Engl. dict. 3rd ed. s8°. 1777
A concise hist. of England, to death of George II. 4v. s8°. [1775]–76
*The cure of evil-speaking: sermon on Matt. xviii, 15–17. [P2535]. s8°. Bristol. 1777
,, ,, [P2536]. s8°. 1784
Dialogue betw. an Antinomian & h. friend. 2nd ed. [P2533]. s8°. 1745
,, ,, 2nd dial. [P2533]. s8°. 1745
*The dignity of human nature. [P2536]. s8°. 1786
Directions conc. pronunciation & gesture. [P2542]. s8°. 1811

Wesley (John) *[continued]*.
Directions for renewing our covenant w. God.
3rd ed. [P2536]. s8°. 1787
A disc. on sin in believers.
2nd ed. [P2525]. s8°. Bristol. *n.d.*
The doctrine of original sin.
s8°. Bristol. 1757
„ „ [repr.] s8°. *Wesl. Conf. Office. n.d.*
*The doctrine of salvation &c. Extr. f. Homilies of Ch. of Eng. 9th ed. [P2534].
s8°. Bristol. 1748
„ „ 11th ed. [P2536].
s8°. Bristol. 1770
*The duty & advantage of early rising. [Sermon].
[P2535]. s8°. 1783
„ „ [a. ed. P2536].
s8°. 1786
An earnest appeal to men of reason &c. 3rd. ed. [P2533].
s8°. Bristol. 1744
*An estimate of the manners of the pres. times.
[P2535]. s8°. 1782
Explan. notes on the New Test. [*with text*]. s4°. 1755
„ „ 2nd ed. s4°. 1757
„ „ 4th ed. s4°. Bristol. 1768
„ „ 11th ed. w. corr.
2v. 8°. 1831
Explan. notes upon the Old Test. [*with text*] [Version of 1611]. 3v. 4°. Bristol. 1765
An extr. of the life &c. of John Janeway. [P2542]. s8°. 1753
An extr. of the life &c. of T. Haliburton.
5th ed. [P2675]. s8°. 1777
An extr. of the life of D. Brainerd. 3rd ed. s8°. 1793
„ „ ....s8°. 1825
An extr. of the life of M. de Renty. 3rd ed. [P2675].
s8°. Bristol. 1760
An extr. of the life of Madam Guion. [*b. w. h.* Life of D. Brainerd, 3rd ed. 1793].
s8°. 1776
An extract of W.'s Journal f. h. embarking for Georgia to h. return to London.
s8°. Bristol. [1740 ?]
Extract of W.'s Journal. [No.] 18–20, Jan. 1, 1776–June 28, 1786. s8°. 1788–91
*A faithful warning to followers of J. W. &c.
[P2535]. s8°. 1774
A farther appeal to men of reason & religion.
[P2533]. s8°. 1745
„ „ 4th ed. [P2533].
s8°. 1746
Free grace. Sermon, Bristol.
[P2551]. s8°. 1740
„ „ 3rd ed. [P2533]
s8°. 1741
God's love to fallen man, Sermon. [P2595]. s8°. 1791
The great assize: sermon on Rom. xiv, 10.
[P2535]. s8°. 1782
Hymns &c., *see* WESLEY (J.) & C. W.
The important question. Sermon on Matt. xvi, 26.
[P2536]. s8°. 1783
*Jesus, altogether lovely. Letter.
[P2536]. s8°. 1780
Journal. [Intr. by F. W. Macdonald. Everyman's lib.]
4v. s8°. [1906]
„ *see also* Extract *above*.
A letter to a friend conc. tea.
2nd ed. [P2535]. s8°. Bristol. 1749
*A letter to a person joined w. the Quakers.
[P2533]. s8°. 1748
*A letter to Rev. Conyers Middleton, occas. by h. late Free inquiry. 2nd ed. [P2534].
s8°. Bristol. 1749
*The life of J. Wesley. [Comp. f. var. mem.] s8°. 1856
*Lines in memory of J. W.
[P2701]. 4°. Sheffield. 1791
The Lord our righteousness: sermon. [P2535]. s8°. 1766
The manners of the ancient Christians. Extr. f. a French a. [P2535]. s8°. Bristol. 1749
„ „ 2nd ed. [P2551].
s8°. Bristol. 1749
„ „ 3rd ed. [P2536].
s8°. Bristol. 1771
Minutes of conversations betw. J. W. & preachers &c. cont. form of discipline in Methodist Soc. s8°. 1779
Modern Christianity.
2nd ed. [P2667]. s8°. 1745
*Mr. W.'s dangerous tenets exposed. [*Poem. no tp.*]
s8°. *n.p. n.d.*
Orig. letters of J. W. & his friends illust. of h. early hist., w. o. papers (Acc. of strange noises &c.). Pref. Address by J. Priestley.
8°. Birmingham. 1791
*A plain acc. of genuine Xty.
[P490]. s8°. Bristol. 1761
*A plain acc. of the Methodists.
[P2535]. s8°. Bristol. 1749
„ „ 9th ed. [P2542].
s8°. D. 1810
*A pocket hymn book for the use of Christians &c. s8°. 1785
„ „ [*A different coll. f. that of 1785*]. s8°. 1787
„ „ 2nd ed. s8°. 1788
„ „ 10th ed. s8°. D. 1794
Popery calmly considered.
[P2535]. s8°. E. 1779
„ „ 3rd ed. [P2536].
s8°. 1779
Predestination calmly considered. s8°. MDDCCLII. [1752]
A preservative agst. unsettled notions in religion.
s8°. Bristol. 1758
Primitive physic.
13th ed. s8°. 1768
„ „ 29th ed. s8°. 1820
*The question, What is an Arminian? By a lover of free grace [*i.e.* J. W.].
[P2537]. s8°. 1770
*Remember the Sabbath day.
[*no tp.* P2534]. s8°. *n.p. n.d.* [1745 ?]
Scriptural Xtny.: sermon St. Mary's, Oxf. [P2535].
s8°. Newcastle-u.-Tyne. 1744
„ „ 4th ed. [P2551].
s8°. 1744
Scripture doctrine conc. predestination &c. Extr. fr. a late a. [P2533]. s8°. 1741
[P2536]. s8°. 1775
*The scripture-doctrine of imputed righteousness, asserted &c. by J. W. Added, remarks on W.'s inconsistency &c. [*attrib. on tp. to Martin Madan. Also attrib. to Wm. Mason*]. 2nd ed. [P2535].
s8°. 1763
Sel. hymns, w. tunes annext, for use of Methodists.
3rd ed. s8°. Bristol. 1770
Serious thoughts occas. by the earthquake at Lisbon.
6th ed. [P2536]. s8°. 1756
Sermon, Nov. 12, 1775. For benefit of widows &c. of soldiers who fell in New Eng. [2 Sam. xxiv, 27].
[P2667]. s8°. 1775
A Sermon on Romans viii, 29, 30.
[P2536]. s8°. Bristol. 1776
A sermon on salvation by faith.
9th ed. [P2551].
s8°. Newcastle. 1745
„ „ [P2535]. s8°. Bristol. 1761
Sermon on the death of George Whitefield. [P2622]. s8°. 1770
Sermon preached before Soc. for Reformation of Manners.
[P2536]. s8°. 1778
Sermon preached in Lewisham Ch. bef. the Humane Soc.
[P2536]. s8°. 1777
Sermons on several occasions.
s8°. Bristol. 1760
„ „ ....3v. 8°. 1863
*A short acc. of God's dealings w. John Haime.
[P2675]. s8°. 1785
*A short acc. of the death of Mary Langson.
[P2675]. s8°. 1775
*A short acc. of the late J. W. Added, a sh. sketch of h. character. [P2675]. s8°. 1791
*A short acc. of the life &c. of Jane Newland, of Dublin.
[P2675]. s8°. 1790
*A short acc. of the life &c. of N. Othen, shot 1757.
[P2542]. s8°. Bristol. *n.d.* [1757 ?]
*Some acc. of the experience of E. J. s8°. [1770 ?]
*Some remarks on a defence of the preface to Edin. ed. of Aspasio vindicated.
[P2535]. s8°. E. 1766
Some remarks on Mr. Hill's Review of all the doctrines taught by W. [*tp. missing.* P2533]. s8°. [Bristol. 1772]
*A survey of the wisdom of God in the Creation; or a compendium of natural philosophy. 2v. s8°. Bristol 1763
„ „ 3rd ed. enl. 5v. s8°.1777
*Swear not at all. [*no tp.* P2534
s8°. *n.p. n.d.* [1745 ?]
Thoughts on a single life.
[P2535]. s8°. Bristol. 1770
Thoughts on marriage & a single life. 2nd ed. [P2533].
s8°. Bristol. 1743
Thoughts on the imputed righteousness of Christ.
[P2537]. s8°. 1779
Thoughts upon slavery.
repr. [P2535]. s8°. Phila. 1774
A treatise on justification extr. fr. J. Goodwin.
3rd ed. s8°. 1836
Wandering thoughts: sermon.
2nd ed. [P2667]. s8°. Bristol. 1763
„ „ [*a. ed.* P2536].
s8°. 1786
Wesley his own biographer. Sel. fr. journals. s4°. 1891
The Wesley memorial vol. [*By var. a.*] Ed. by J. O. A. Clark. 8°. N.Y. 1881
Wesley: the man &c. Sermons &c. in comm. of J. W.'s death. [*With acc. of the* Allan Library]. 8°. 1891
Wesley's house. Sermons &c. Revised by the authors.
s8°. 1898
The witness of the Spirit. Sermon on Rom. viii, 16.
[P2535]. s8°. Bristol. 1767
*A word in season: or, advice to a soldier. [*no tp.* P2534].
s8°. *n.p. n.d.* [c. 1745]
*A word in season: or, advice to an Englishman.
8th ed. [P2534]. s8°. 1745
A word of advice to saints & sinners.
10th ed. [P2536]. s8°. 1782
*A word to a drunkard.
[P2534]. s8°. *n.p.* 1748
*A word to a freeholder &c.
[P2534]. s8°. *n.p.* 1748
A word to a Protestant.
8th ed. [P2534]. s8°. 1745
*A word to a street-walker.
[P2534]. s8°. *n.p.* 1748

REFERENCES.
see BARCLAY (R.) Serious consid. on predestination; extr. f. a late a. [*i.e.* R. B., *by* J. W.], 1741.
„ BAXTER (R.) Extr. of B.'s aphorisms of justific.; publ. J. W., 2nd ed., 1745, 3rd ed., 1784.
„ BENEZET (A.) View of Amer. slavery: A. B., J. W., 1858.
„ BURKHARDT (J. G.) Vollst. Gesch. d. Methodisten, nebst Lebensbeschr. J. W. &c., 1795.
„ EAYRS (G.) J. W., Xtn. philosopher &c., 1926.
„ FLETCHER (J. W.) Vindic. of Mr. W.'s last Minutes &c., 1771.
„ HAMPSON (S.) Memoirs of J. W., 3v. 1791.
„ HERVEY (J.) Eleven letters to J. W. &c., 1765.
„ HOLMES (D.) The Wesley offering; or, W. & his times, 1858.
„ HUTTON (W. H.) J. W. [Gt. Eng. Churchmen], 1927.
„ KENTON (J.) A token to J. W., 1791.
„ LAW (W.) The nature & design of Christianity; extr. f. a late a. [*i.e.* W. L., *by* J. W.], 9th ed., 1771.
„ LEFEVRE (*Mrs.*) An extr. of letters by Mrs. L. [by J. W.], 1773.
„ LUNN (*Sir* H. S.) J. W.: prize essay, 1885.
„ —— Reunion & Lambeth; J. W.'s [*supposed*] message to the bishops, 1920; intr. letter by L., 1920.
„ MANNERS (N.) Remarks on writings of W., 1788.
„ METHODISM unmasked: W.'s doct. proved false &c., 1828.
„ MOORE (H.) Life of J. W., 2v, 1824.
„ NORRIS (J.) Treatise on Xtn. prudence; extr. f. N. by J. W., 3rd ed., 1749.
„ PIETTE (M.) La réaction de J. W. dans l'évol. du Protestantisme, 2e éd., 1927.
„ RITCHIE (E.) *Authentic narr. of departure of late J. W., 1791, 1791.
„ SCHMIDT (C. C. G.) J. W. Leben &c., 1849.
„ SCOUGAL (H.) *Life of God in soul of man; abridged by J. W., 1748; 1777.
„ SIMON (J. S.) J. W. & the advance of Methodism, 1925.
„ SOUTHEY (R.) Life of W.; notes by S. T. Coleridge &c., ed. M. H. Fitzgerald, 2v, 1925.
„ STANLEY (A. P.) Speech on W. at Children's Home, May 1st 1877.

Wesley (John) *[continued]*.
REFERENCES *[continued]*.
see SYMONS (R.) W.'s ministerial itineraries in Cornwall, 1879.
,, TOPLADY (A. M.) Letter to J. W., 1771.
,, —— More work for J. W., 1772.
,, WATSON (R.) The life of J. W., 2nd ed., 1831; 10th ed., 1861.
,, —— Obs. on Southey's Life of W.: def. of W., 1821.
see WATSON (R.) Vie du Rév. J. W. &c., 1843.
,, —— Works, v5, Life of J. W. & Obs. on Southey's Life, 5th ed., 1847.
,, WESLEY (C.) An epistle to J. W. *[verse]*, repr., 1785.
,, WESLEYAN METHODIST CONFERENCE. Cat. of MSS. &c., 1921.
,, WHITEHEAD (J.) A disc. at the funeral of J. W., 1791.

—— & Charles Wesley.
Coll. of Psalms & hymns. 2nd ed. 1743
,, ,, 5th ed. s8º. Bristol. 1760
,, ,, 6th ed. [P2549]. s8º. 1756
,, ,, 8th ed. [P2546]. s8º. Bristol. 1771
,, ,, 10th ed. s8º. 1779
,, ,, 15th ed. s8º. 1818
Funeral hymns. [P2550]. s8º. Bristol. 1769
,, ,, 2nd ed. [P2550]. s8º. *n.p. n.d.*
,, ,, 3rd ed. [P2545]. s8º. D. 1747
Graces before meat. *[no tp. 2 issues.* P2545, 2550] s8º. [1762 ?]
,, ,, *[a. ed. no tp.* P2542]. s8º. [1775 ?]
Hymns & sacred poems. Publ. by J. & C. W. *[tp supplied in MS.]* s8º. 1739
,, ,, 4th ed. s8º. Bristol. 1743
,, ,, 5th ed. s8º. 1756
Hymns & sacred poems. Publ. by J. & C. W. *[diff. f. the 1739 coll.]* s8º. Bristol. 1742
,, ,, 2nd ed. s8º. Bristol. 1743
,, ,, 2nd ed. *[reissue]*. s8º. Bristol. 1745
*Hymns & spiritual songs. 4th ed. s8º. 1756
,, ,, 14th ed. s8º. Bristol. 1770
,, ,, 20th ed. [P2548]. s8º. 1776
*Hymns for Ascension-day. 2nd ed. [P2547]. s8º. Bristol. 1747
,, ,, *[a. ed.* P2545]. s8º. 1775
*Hymns for children & others of riper years. 2nd ed. [P2546]. s8º. Bristol. 1768
,, ,, 4th ed. [P2548]. s8º. 1784
Hymns for New-Year's day. [P2547]. s8º. 1752
,, ,, [P2545]. s8º. Bristol. 1761
*Hymns for our Lord's Resurrection. 3rd ed. [P2547]. s8º. Bristol. 1748
,, ,, 5th ed. [P2545]. s8º. Bristol. 1769
Hymns for the fast day. [P2548]. s8º. 1780
*Hymns for the nation. [P2548]. s8º. 1782
*Hymns for the nativity of our Lord. 10th ed. [P2547]. s8º. 1750
,, ,, *[a. ed.]* [P2545]. s8º. Bristol. 1768
*Hymns for the public Thanksgiving-day, Oct. 9, 1746. [P2548]. s8º. 1746
,, ,, *[a. ed.* P2545]. s8º. Bristol. 1769
*Hymns for the watch night. *[no tp.* P2547]. s8º. *n.p.* [1746?]
*Hymns for the year 1756. Particularly for the fast-day, Feb. 6th. [P2545]. s8º. D. 1756
*Hymns for those that seek redemption in the blood of Jesus Christ. 3rd ed. [P2547]. s8º. Bristol. 1749
,, ,, 8th ed. [P2545]. s8º. Bristol. 1768
Hymns for those to whom Christ is all in all. [P2549]. s8º. Bristol. 1765
Hymns for times of trouble. *[12 pp.* P2550]. s8º. *n.p. n.d.*
Hymns for times of trouble & persecution. 2nd ed. repr. [P2550]. s8º. Bristol. 1745
,, ,, 3rd ed. [P2546]. s8º. 1756
Hymns occasioned by the earthquake. 2p. [p1, 2nd ed. P2548]. s8º. 1750
,, ,, 2nd ed. 2p. [P2546]. s8º. Bristol. 1756
*Hymns of intercess. for all mankind. [P2545]. s8º. D. 1759
,, ,, *[a. ed.*P2548]. s8º. *n.d.*
Hymns of petition & thanksgiving for the promise of the Father. 2nd ed. [P2547]. s8º. Bristol. 1747
,, ,, *[a. ed.* P2545]. s8º. Bristol. 1768
*Hymns on God's everlasting love. 3rd ed. [P2546, 2547]. s8º. Bristol. 1770
*Hymns on the expected invasion, 1779. *[no tp.* P2545, 2548]. s8º. [1779]
*Hymns on the great festivals &c. [Tunes by J. F. Lampe]. 2nd ed. 4º. 1753
Hymns on the Lord's Supper. *[a. ed. tp. wanting.* P2549]. s8º. *n.d.*
,, ,, With pref. conc. the Sacrament f. Dr. Brevint. 4th ed. *[b. w.* Coll. of Ps. & h., 5th ed., 1760]. s8º. 1757
,, ,, 9th ed. *[b. w.* Coll. of Ps. & hymns, 10th ed., 1779]. s8º. 1786
*Hymns on the Trinity. [P2547]. s8º. Bristol. 1767
*Hymns wr. in the time of the tumults, June 1780. [P2545, 2548]. s8º. Bristol. 1780
The nature &c. of the Methodist societies. [P449]. s8º. D. 1818
*Preparation for death, in sev. hymns. [P2545, 2550]. s8º. 1772
*The Protestant association, wr. in the midst of the tumults, June 1780. [P2548, 2667]. s8º. 1781
*Sacred harmony, or a choice coll. of psalms & hymns, set to music. *[Engraved]*. s8º. [1761 ?]
,, ,, *[a. ed.]* s8º. [1789 ?]
A short view of the difference betw. the Moravian Brethren & J. & C. W. Extr. f. a late journal. [By J. & C. W.] [P2533]. s8º. 1745
see KIRK (J.) Orig. titles of hymns, & names of a., 1854.

Wesley (Samuel), *the elder.* *The Athenian Oracle: coll. of questions & ans. in the old Athenian Mercuries &c. By a Member of the Athenian Soc. *[Pref. signed* S. W. *Also attrib. to J. Dunton]*. 2nd ed. corr. v1, 2. 8º. 1704
,, ,, *Suppl.: pref., hist. of the Athenian Soc. &c. By a Member of the Athenian Soc. [*i.e.* S. W.] 8º. 1710
The life of Jesus Christ. An heroic poem. Prefat. disc. conc. heroic poetry. fol. 1693
,, ,, ...2nd ed. rev. fol. 1697

***Wesleyan** classics, or biogr. sketches of the orators, poets, &c. of the W. Church. By Oxonian. pl [Richard Watson]. 8º. Leamington. 1870

Wesleyan Methodist. Alphabet. (An) arrangement of all the W.M. ministers, missionaries &c. on trial. By the late W. Hill. 6th–19th ed. (6–10, ed. J. P. Haswell; 11–14, ed. M. C. Osborn; 15–19, ed. D. J. Waller). [14v]. 8º. 1847–1900
*Handbook (A) of script. church principles & of W.M. polity & hist. 2p *in* 1v. 8º. 1888

Wesleyan Methodist Conference. Cat. of MSS. & relics, books & pamphlets &c. belong. to W.M. Conf., w. princ. books &c. in poss. of United M. Ch. *[Comp. by* J. A. Sharp]. 8º. [1921]

Wesleyan Methodist Local Preachers Mutual Aid Assoc., *see* LOCAL PREACHERS MAGAZINE.

Wesleyan Methodist Missionary Society. Exam. of sources f. which income is derived. [P2538]. s8º. 1851
Report[s], 1812–1900 [1891–94 *wanting*]. 8º. 1814–1900
The Reports *for* 1812–17 *have title* The annual rep. of the state of the missions, conducted by the Conference &c.
see MISSIONARY controversy: discussion &c., 1890.

Wesleyan Missionary notices, rel. princ. to the foreign missions. v1–s5, v3 (1816–80). 8º. 1816–80
v1–9 (1816–38) *have t.* Missionary notices rel. princ. to for. missions &c. *The earlier vol. include* Papers rel. to Wesleyan missions, *w. sep. pagin.*

Wesleyan Theological Institution. A cat. of books & MSS. [coll. by Rev. T. Jackson] presented to the W. Th. Inst. in 1859, by J. Heald. 8º. [1859]

Wessel (Johann) [GANSFORT]. De causis Incarnationis. De magnitudine &c. Dñicę passionis libri 2. s8º. *n.p. n.d.*
Opera omnia. Acc. Jacobi de Paradyso tractatus aliquot. Publ. J. M. F. Lydius. s4º. Amstelodami. 1617
see HYMA (A.) The Xtn. Renaissance: hist. of the "Devotio Moderna," 1925.
,, MUURLING (W.) Comm. de W. Gansfortii vita &c., p1, 1831.

Wessel (Johann), *of Lübeck.* Fasciculus diss. in loca V. & N. T. Concionum in Jesaiae 54 &c. [1692–1743]. Ed. C. de Feyfer. s4º. Groningae. 1756
Nestorianismus & Adoptianismus redivivus confutatus &c. s4º. Roterodami. 1727

Wessels (C.), *S.J.* Early Jesuit travellers in C. Asia, 1603–1721. [App. Azevedo's acc. of journey to Tibet (1631–32), Letter of Stephen Cacella, Oct. 4, 1627 &c.] 8º. Hague. 1924

Wesselski (Albert). Märchen d. Mittelalters. 8º. 1925

Wessely (Carl). Les plus anc. mon. du christianisme écrits sur papyrus; textes éd., tr. & annotés par C. W., [p]2, *see* GRAFFIN (R.) & F. NAU. Pat. Or., t18, 1924.
Sahid. Papyrusfragmente d. paulin. Briefe, *see* KAIS. AKAD. D. WISS. ZU WIEN. Sitzb., B174, 1915.

Wessenberg (Ignaz Heinrich, *Baron* **v.)** *Reformation in the Cathol. church of Germany &c., corresp. w. the court of Rome, on the nomination of Baron v. W. as success. in diocese of Constance &c., accomp. by docs. & introd. *[by* I. Rudhart]. Tr. 8º. 1819

West Kent Cricket Club, *orig. Prince's Plain C.C., see* NORMAN (P.) Scores &c. of W.K.C.C., 1897.

West Wales historical records. Annual mag. of the Hist. Soc. of W.W. Ed. F. Green. v1–12 (1910–27). 8º. Carmarthen. 1912–27

West (*Rt. Hon. Sir* **Algernon).**
Contemporary portraits. 8º. [1920]
Polit. England: chron. of the 19th c. 8º. [1922]
Private diaries. Ed. H. G. Hutchinson. 8º. 1922

West (Arthur George Bainbridge). The church & parish of St. Dunstan in the East, Gt. Tower St., E.C. 8º. [1923]

West (*Sir* **Edward).** The applic. of capital to land &c., 1815. [J. H. Univ. Repr. of econ. tracts. P2619]. 8º. [Baltimore. 1903]

West (Edward Sackville), *see* SACKVILLE WEST (E.)

West (Francis Athon), *see* EVERETT (J.) Test law of '35: w. letters in reply [f. W.], 1851.

West (George). Further contrib. to comp. st. of the flora of aquatic habit in Scottish lakes. [*Extr. f.* Proc. of Roy. Soc. of Edin., v30]. la8°. [1910]

West (*Maj.* George F. M. Cornwallis-), *see* CORNWALLIS-WEST (G. F. M.)

West (George Herbert). Gothic architecture in Eng. & France. 2nd & rev. ed. s8°. 1927

West (George Stephen), *see* WEST (W.) & G. S. W. Monogr. of the Brit. Desmidiaceæ, v5, by N. Carter, 1923.

West (John E.) Cathedral organists: a record, w. biog. notes &c. 8°. 1899

West (Julius). Hist. of the Chartist movement. Intr. mem. by J. C. Squire. 8°. [1920]

West (Lionel Sackville), *see* SACKVILLE-WEST (L.)

West (Michael). Bilingualism, w. spec. ref. to Bengal. [Bureau of Educ., India]. la8°. Calcutta. 1926

West (Rebecca), *ps.* [*i.e. Miss* FAIRFIELD].
The judge. Novel. s8°. [1922]
" " ....2nd ed. s8°. [1922]
" " ....3rd ed. s8°. [1922]
see VAN DRUTEN (J.) The return of the soldier: play, adapted f. R. W.'s novel, 1928.

West (Robert Athow).
Sketches of Wesleyan preachers. s8°. 1849

West (*Capt.* Temple). Defence agst. vice-adm. Lestock's charge rel. to his conduct off Toulon. [P608]. s8°. 1746

West (V. Sackville-), *see* SACKVILLE-WEST (V.)

West (William), *F.L.S.* **& G. S. West.** A monograph of the Brit. Desmidiaceæ. [Ray Soc.] v5, by N. Carter. 8°. 1923

Westaway (F. W.)
Scient. method: its philos. &c. n. ed. 8°. 1919

Westcott (Allan), *see* STEVENS (W. O.) & A. W. Hist. of sea power, 1920.

Westcott (Brooke Foss), *bp. of Durham.* Epistles of John. Gr. text w. notes & essays by W. 2nd ed. 8°. C. 1886

Westcott (Frederick Brooke). St. Paul's Letter to the Colossians: a paraphrase &c. [A letter to Asia]. s8°. 1914

West-country (The) intelligence, *see* GLASGOW (THE) COURANT.

Westen (Thomas von), *see* HAMMOND (H.) Den nord. Missions-hist. &c., 1787.

Westergaard (Harald). Econ. development in Denmark before & dur. the World War. [C.E. for Internat. Peace]. la8°. O. 1922

Westergaard (Niels Ludwig). On the connexion betw. Sanskrit & Icelandic. [*Extract*]. 8°. [1840]

Westerman (Percy F.) King of Kilba. s8°. 1926
The riddle of the air. s8°. [1926]

Westermann (Dietrich). Die Kpelle, ein Negerstamm in Liberia. Mit 2 Nachtr.: Texte in d. Golaspr. u. Kpelle-Beitr. v. H. Rohde. la8°. Göttingen. 1921

Westermarck (Edward Alexander).
The goodness of gods. s8°. 1926
The hist. of human marriage. 5th ed. rewr. 3v. 8°. 1921
Origin & development of moral ideas. 2nd ed. v2. 8°. 1917
Ritual & belief in Morocco. 2v. 8°. 1926

Westermayer (Anton). *Dr. A. W. u. P. Petrus Hötzl. Von e. kathol. Geistlichen. [P601]. 8°. München. 1870

Western (August). Norsk riksmåls-grammatikk. 8°. 1921

Western (*Col.* Charles Maximilian). The pract. science of billiards & its pointer. 8°. 1911

Western (*Col.* John Sutton Edward).
Remin. of an Indian cavalry officer. 8°. [1922]

Western (R. W.) Graphic chronology. s8°. 1892

Wester Wemyss (*Adm.* Rosslyn Erskine Wemyss), *G.C.B., 1st baron Wemyss.* The Navy in the Dardanelles campaign. 8°. [1924]

Westfalen. Die Bau- u. Kunstdenkmäler v. Westfalen. Hrsg. v. Provinzial-Verbande d. Prov. W., bearb. v. A. Ludorff. [T22, 23, 25, 26, 29–32, 34–37]. 4°. Münster i. W. 1906–12
Each " Kreis " *has* Geschichtl. Einleit. *by sep. author as given below*:—

Altena; Kuemmel. [36.]	Halle; Nitzsch. [30.]
Bielefeld-Stadt; Schrader. [22.]	Hattingen; Darpe. [31.]
Bochum-Land; Darpe. [25.]	Herford; Jellinghaus. [26.]
Gelsenkirchen-Stadt: Darpe. [29.]	Lippstadt; Schelhasse. [37.]
	Tecklenburg; Brennecke. [23.]
Hagen-Stadt; Darpe. [34.]	Wittenstadt; Darpe. [32.]
Hagen-Land; Darpe. [35.]	

Westfälisch [WESTPHÄLISCH]. Album v. Autographen d. westphäl. Friedensschlusses (1648). fol. L. 1849

Westfälische Kommission für Heimatschutz, *see* KERCKERINCK ZUR BORG (E., *Frhr.* v.) & R. KLAPHECK. Alt-Westfalen, 1912.

Westheim (Paul). Indische Baukunst. [Orbis pictus; hrsg. P. Westheim, 1]. la8°. [1920]
Klassizismus in Frankreich. [Orbis pictus; hrsg. P. Westheim, 15]. la8°. 1923

West Indies. W.I. pilot, 3v, Suppl. 1, 6, *&* Not. to mariners, 1912–22, *see* ADMIRALTY.

West-Indische Compagnie (Dutch), *see* DE LAET (J.) Hist. (-1636), tr. [*in Portuguese*], 2v, 1916–25.

Westlake (Herbert Francis).
Westminster Abbey. 2v. [*pagin. cont.*] fol. 1923
Westminster Abbey: last days of the monastery as shown by the life &c. of Abbot John Islip, 1464–1532. s8°. [1921]
see HORNCHURCH PRIORY. Kalendar of doc. in poss. of New Coll., Oxford; intr. &c. by H. F. W., 1923.

Westman (Carl Gustaf). Häradsnämnd & häradsrätt [17–18 c.] *see* KUNG. HUM. VET.-SELSK. I UPPSALA. Skr., B24, 1927.

Westminster. *View (A) of London & W. &c., 2p, 1725–28, *see* LONDON.

Westminster Abbey. *Hist. of the Abbey Church of St. Peter's, 2v, 1812, *see* COMBE (W.)
see †ROBINSON (J. A.) & M. R. JAMES. The MSS. of W.A., 1909.

Westminster Assembly. Minutes of the Sessions of the W.A. while engaged in preparing their Directory, Confession of faith (1644–49) &c. Ed. by A. F. Mitchell & J. Struthers. 8°. E. 1874
see BIBLE: GEN. COMM. &C. *Annot. upon all the books of O. & N. Test. by [J. Ley *& others of the W.A.*], 1645.

Westminster Confession.
Conf. fidei in conventu theolog. authoritate Parliamenti Angl., unà cum catechismo duplici majori, minorique. In Lat. versa. s8°. Cantab. 1656
C. (The) of faith & the larger & shorter catechisme first agreed upon by the Assembly of Divines at Westminster. [*Imperfect*]. s8°. E. 1649
C. (The) of the faith w. the larger & lesser catechismes. [The humble advice &c. *sep. tps. & pagins. n.d. &* 1658]. s4°. [1658 ?]
" " ....[*a. ed.*] s8°. E. 1810
" " ....[*a. ed.*] s8°. E. 1827
" " ....[*a. ed.*] la8°. E. 1855
W. (The) c. of faith. Introd. by J. Macpherson. 2nd ed. s8°. E. [1882]
see PARKER (WILLIAM). The late Assembly of Divines C. &c. [*w. text*], 1651.

Westminster gazette, *see* GOULD (F. C.) W. cartoons, 1895–1903, 1895–1904.

Westminster (Hugh Richard Arthur Grosvenor, *2nd duke of***).** Cat. of pictures of Ital. & Flemish schools, the property of the D. of W. &c. Sold by Christie, July 4, 1924. [*Illust.* P2748]. 8°. 1924

Weston (A. Anderdon). Cat. of engr. portraits after Reynolds &c., formed by J. H. Anderdon, prop. of A. A. W., sold by Christie. [*Priced.* P2849]. 8°. 1904

Weston (F.) & M. Weston.
Camera pictures of Malta. 4°. Malta. [1924]

Weston (Frank), *bp. of Zanzibar &c.*
see SANDAY (W.) Position of liberal theol.; exam. of Bp. of Z.'s "The Christ & His critics," 1920.
" SMITH (H. M.) F., Bp. of Zanzibar, 1926.

Weston (H. Claude). St. of efficiency in fine linen weaving, *see* INDUST. FATIGUE RESEARCH BD. Rep., 20, 1922.

Weston (Jessie Laidlay).
King Arthur & his knights. [P2586]. s8°. 1899

Weston (M.), *see* WESTON (F.) & M. W. Camera pictures of Malta, 1924.

Weston (Walter). A wayfarer in unfamiliar Japan. 8°. [1925]

Westphal (F.) Zur Erinnerung an Fürst Georg d. Gottseligen zu Anhalt. [Verein f. Ref.-gesch. Schr., Jhrg. 25, Nr. 95]. 8°. L. 1907

Westphal (Joachim).
Confut. sophistici Adiaphoristarum scripti Lyps: editi. Cum duabus praefatiunculis Illyr: [*i.e.* M. Flacius, Illyricus]. s8°. *n.p. n.d.* [c. 1551]
Cur in eccl. Dei ritus processionum & circuitus abrogatus sit &c. s8°. [Magdeburgae, *Mich. Lotther*]. 1553
Duo scripta de rebus paruis & non necessariis &c. [P2528]. s8°. *n.p.* 1549
Explicatio gen. sententiae, Quod e duobus malis minus sit eligendum, in praes. de adiaphoris controversia &c. [P2528]. s8°. *n.p.* 1549
Hist. v. güldenen Kalbe Aaronis, *see* HAMBURG. Ein Brieff der Prediger &c., 1549.

Westphal (Joachim) [*continued*].
Hist. vituli aurei Aaronis ad nostra tempora & controversias accomodata. [P2528]. s8°. *n.p.* 1549
Verlegung des gründl. Berichts d. Adiaphoristen. Mit e. Praefation Illy: [*i.e.* M. Flacius Illyricus]. [P2441]. s4°. [Magdeburg]. 1551
see CALVIN (J.) Ultima admonitio ad J. W. &c., 1557.
„ LUTHER (M.) Sententia M. L. de adiaphoris, coll. per J. W., 1549.
„ MELANCHTHON (P.) Sententia de coena coll. per J. W., 1557.
„ WIGAND (J.) De bonis operibus, & argumenta J. Westphal, 1568.

Westphal (Max). Die besten deut. Memorien &c. aus 7 Jhdten. Mit e. Abh. ü. d. Entwickl. d. deut. Selbstbiog., v. H. Ulrich. s8°. L. 1923

Westphälisch, *see* WESTFÄLISCH.

Westron (Charles W.) Combe Hamlet. s8°. [1923]

Westropp (M. S. Dudley), *M.R.I.A.* Irish glass. Account of glass-making in Ireland from 16th c. to pres. day. 4°. [1920]

Westropp (Thomas Johnson).
The beginnings of hist. tradition & survival of Celtic mythology in Ireland. [*Fr.* Journal of Galway Arch. & Hist. Soc., v11]. [P2463]. 8°. Galway. [1920]
Clare Island survey, p2, Hist. & archaeol. [*Extr. f.* Roy. Ir. Acad., Proc., v31. P2751]. la8°. D. 1911
Folklore on the coast of Connacht. [*Extr. f.* Folklore, v32. *For prev. p., see* Folklore, v29]. [P2755]. 8°. [1922]
The later pagan sanctuaries in Co. Limerick. [*Fr.* N. Munster Archaelog. Soc., 4]. [P2433]. 8°. *n.p.* [1918]
The marriages of the gods at the sanctuary of Tailltiu. [*Repr. f.* Folk-Lore, June 1920]. [P2433]. 8°. 1920
Notes on sev. forts in Dunkellin & o. parts of co. Galway. [*Repr. f.* Roy. Soc. of Antiq. of Ir., v49, *no tp.* P2497]. 8°. [1919]
Promontory forts & traditions of Beare & Bantry, co. Cork. [*Repr. f.* Roy. Soc. of Antiq. of Ir., v51. *no tp.* P2579]. 3p. 8°. 1921
Temair Erann, an anc. cemetery of the Ernai on Slievereagh, Co. Limerick. [*Extr. f.* R. S. of Antiq. of Ireland, Journal, v48ii. P2418]. 8°. 1918

Westrup (Margaret) [*i.e.* SYDNEY STACEY].
The blue hat. s8°. [1921]

West Ukrainian Press Agency, *see* GALICIA. Eastern G., Nos. 1-4, 1920?.

Westwood (Arthur). M. Boulton's medal on the reconquest of Naples in 1799, & events in conn., by a Birmingham observer [T. B. Richards], also Nelson's reception, 1802. 4°. B'ham. 1926

Westwood (John Obadiah). Facs-similes of the miniatures & ornaments of Anglo-Saxon & Irish MSS. atlas fol. 1868
Lapidarium Walliæ: early inscr. &c. stones of Wales. [Cambrian Arch. Assoc.] 4°. O. 1876–79
Palaeographia sacra pictoria: illust. of anc. vers. of the Bible f. illum. MSS., 4th-16th cent. 4°. 1843–45

Weterus (David). Testimonia. De præcipuis Xtnae. relig. capitibus &c. [*b. w.* Aretius (B.) Sermones tres, 1578]. s8°. Sangalli. 1579

Wé-than-da-ya, *see* Goss (L. A.) Story of W.: sk. f. Burmese vers. of Pali text, 1886.

Wethered (Florence Thomas). St. Mary's, Hurley, in the Middle Ages, based on charters &c. 8°. 1898

Wethered (Herbert Newton). From Giotto to John: the development of painting. 8°. [1926]
Mediæval craftsmanship & the mod. amateur more partic. w. ref. to metal & enamel. 8°. 1923

Wetmore (Alexander). Body temperature of birds, *see* SMITHSONIAN INST. Misc. coll., v72, 1922.
Obs. on the birds of Argentina, Paraguay, Uruguay, & Chile. [S.I.: U.S. Nat. Mus., Bull. 133]. 8°. Wash. 1926
Remains of birds f. caves in Haiti, 1922, *see* SMITHSONIAN INST. Misc. Coll., 74, 1925.

Wetstein (Johann Jacob). Ἡ Καινὴ Διαθήκη: Nov. Test. Graec., cum lect. variant., & comm. pleniore, opera & studio J. J. W. 2t. fol. Amstelaedami. 1751–52
see GÖZE (J. M.) Vertheid. d. Complutens. Bibel, geg. d. W. Beschuldig., 1765.

Wetstein (Johann Rodolph).
De hist. Susannae. [P2587]. s4°. Basileae. 1691

Wetsten (Johann Jacob), *see* WETSTEIN (J. J.)

Wette (Gottfried Albin v.) Evangel. Jena. Mit Vorrede v. J. F. Hirt. 2T. *in* 1v [*pagin. cont.*] s8°. Jena. 1756

Wetter (Gillis P: son). Phōs; e. Unters. ü. hellenist. Frömmigkeit, Manichäismus. [*Extr. f.* Kungl. Human. Vetensk.-Samf., Skr., B17]. 8°. Uppsala. [1915]

Wetzel (Friedrich). Alt-Sachsen: heim. Bau- u. Raumkunst. Vorwort v. C. Gurlitt. 4°. Dresden. 1923
Islam. Grabbauten in Indien, 1320–1540. [Deut. Orient-Gesell., Wiss. Veröffentl., 33]. fol. L. 1918

Wetzel (Johann Caspar). Hymnopœographia, oder histor. Lebensbeschreibung d. berühmt. Lieder-Dichter. 4T. *b. in* 2*v.* s8°. Herrnstadt. 1719–28
Hymnopoeographia *is omitted f. tp. of T2–4. T1 has 2 pag. w.* 1es & 2es Opffer; *T2 has 2p. w.* 3es & 4es Opffer. 5es Opffer *is in* T3 pp. 477–496.

Weulersse (Georges).
see RENARD (G.) & G. W. Life & work in mod. Europe; tr., 1926.
„ —— & ——. Travail dans l'Europe moderne, 1920.

Wewetzer (Adolph). De antinomismo J. Agricolae, diss. [P600]. s4°. Sundiae. 1829

Wey (Francis). Rome: descr. & souvenirs. la4°. 1872

Weyden (Goossen van der), *see* ENGHIEN, *Hôpital d'.* Vente du triptyque [*attrib. to W.*], 1926.

Weyden (Roger van der) [*or* ROGER DE LA PASTURE].
see BURGER (W.) R. v. d. W., 1923.
„ FRIEDLÄNDER (M. J.) Altniederl. Malerei, B2, 1924.
„ HASSE (C.) R. van der W. u. R. van Brügge mit i. Schulen, 1905.
„ WINKLER (F.) Der Meister von Flémalle u. R. van der W., 1913.

Weygandt (Cornelius).
A century of the English novel. 8°. [1927]

Weygel (Nicolaus), *see* SCHWARZ (F. I.) De legato Acad. Lips. ad Concil. Basil. [N. W.] tract., 1786.

Weyl (Hermann).
Space—time—matter. Tr. H. L. Brose. 8°. [1922]
see LORENTZ (H. A.), A. EINSTEIN, H. W. &c. Princ. of relativity; tr., 1923.

Weyman (Carl). Beitr. z. Gesch. d. christlich-lat. Poesie. la8°. München. 1926

Weyman (Henry T.)
The glass in Ludlow Church. [P2495]. 8°. Ludlow. 1905

Weyman (Stanley John). Ovington's Bank. s8°. 1922
Queen's Folly. s8°. [1925]
The traveller in the fur cloak. s8°. [1924]

Whale (*Mrs.* Winifred), *see* STEPHENS (W.)

Whall (W. B.)
Handy bk. of the tides, w. charts. 10th ed. obl.8°. *n.d.*

Wharncliffe (*Lady* Elizabeth Caroline Mary), *form. Creighton, wife of James A. Stuart Wortley, 1st baron Wharncliffe, see* GROSVENOR (C.) & *Lord* STUART OF WORTLEY. The 1st Lady Wharncliffe &c., 2v, 1927.

Wharton (Anthony) [*ps.* LYNN BROCK].
Be good, sweet maid. s8°. [1924]
Colonel Gore's second case. s8°. [1925]
Colonel Gore's third case, the kink. s8°. [1927]

Wharton (Edith).
The age of innocence. s8°. 1920
The glimpses of the moon. s8°. 1922
The greater inclination. s8°. 1906
Here & beyond. 8°. 1926
In Morocco. 8°. 1920
The mother's recompense. s8°. N.Y. [1925]
Old New York. s8°. N.Y. 1924
The old maid (The 'fifties).
The spark (The 'sixties).
New Year's day (The 'seventies).
A son at the front. s8°. 1923
Tales of men & ghosts. s8°. N.Y. 1910
Twilight sleep. 8°. 1927

Wharton (Henry), *vicar of Chartham* [*ps.* ANTHONY HARMER].
*A defence of pluralities. s8°. 1692

Wharton (Philip W., *duke of), 1698–1731, see* CHANCELLOR (E. B.) Col. Charteris & the Duke of W. [Lives of the Rakes], 1925.

Wharton (*Sir* William James Lloyd). Hydrograph. surveying. 4th ed. rev. & enl. by Adm. Sir M. Field. 8°. 1920

***What** is she?: comedy, 1811, *see* SMITH (*Mrs.* C.)

Whatahoro (H. T.), *see* SMITH (S. P.) Lore of the Whare-wānanga; wr. down by H. T. W. &c., 2p, 1913–15.

Whately (Richard), *abp. of Dublin.* Elements of logic: substance of article in Encyclop. Metropol., w. add. 8°. 1826
*Historic doubts rel. to Napoleon Buonaparte. 8°. 1819

Whately (William), *vicar of Banbury.* Prototypes; or the primarie precedent presidents out of Genesis. [With W. W.'s life & death. Publ. by E. Leigh & H. Scudder. *3 pagin.*] sm. fol. 1640

Wheat (J. B.), *see* SHEFFIELD. Descr. cat. of charters &c., part of W. coll. at Publ. Ref. Lib., S., 1920.

Wheater (William).
Temple Newsam: hist. & antiq. 3rd ed. la8°. Leeds. 1889
Wheatland (Stephen) & Tipping Sylvester. The Psalms of David, tr. into heroic verse &c. s8°. 1754
Wheatley Manuscript (The). Coll. of middle Eng. verse & prose &c. Ed. w. intr. & notes by M. Day. [E.E.T.S. 155]. 8°. 1921
Wheatley (Francis), *R.A., 1747–1801, see* ROBERTS (W.) Cries of London; with 13 plates [by F. W.], 1924.
Wheatley (Henry Benjamin). The Adelphi & its site. la8°. 1885
Samuel Pepys & the world he lived in. 5th ed. 8°. 1907
Wheatley (John). A letter to Lord Grenville on the distress of the country. [P2428]. 8°. 1816
Wheatly (Charles). A rational illust. of the Bk. of C. Prayer. n. ed. 8°. 1845
" " ....n. ed., impr. 8°. 1863
Wheatley-Crowe (Henry Stuart).
Royalist revelations & the truth about Charles I. 8°. 1922
Wheeler (Daniel), *the elder, of the Soc. of Friends.* Extr. f. the letters & journal of D. W., now engaged in a relig. visit to the islands of the Pacific Ocean &c. [4p *in* 1v]. 8°. 1839
Wheeler (G. Owen).
Old Eng. furniture of 15th–18th c. 3rd ed., rewr. 8°. 1924
Wheeler (Geo. Wm.), *ed., see* BODLEY (*Sir* T.) Letters, 1926–27.
Wheeler (James Talboys).
Mem. on Afghanistan affairs f. 1700. sm. fol. Calcutta. 1869
Mem. on Afghan-Turkistan. [*tp. wanting*]. fol. [Calcutta. 1869]
Mem. on Persian affairs, w. suppl. note on Turkomans &c. fol. Calcutta. 1871
Mem. on the records in the Foreign Dept. la8°. Calcutta. 1865
Wheeler (Olive Annie). Bergson & education. Foreword by J. L. Paton. [M'ter Univ.] s8°. M'ter. 1922
Wheeler (Owen Edlestone). Practical photography. 8°. [1881]
Wheeler (R. E. Mortimer).
Prehist. & Roman Wales. 8°. O. 1925
The Roman fort near Brecon, *see* CYMMRODORION. Y Cymmrodor, v37, 1926.
Segontium & the Roman occup. of Wales, *see* CYMMRODORION. Y Cymmrodor, v33, 1923.
Wheeler (R. V.), *see* STOPES (M. C.) & R. V. W. Monogr. on constitut. of coal, 1918.
Wheeler (Stephen).
see ORIENTAL CLUB. Annals, 1824–58; ed. S. W., 1925.
,, WISE (T. J.) & S. W. Bibliog. of writings of W. S. Landor, 1919.
Wheeler (William Henry). The sea-coast. (1) Destruction. (2) Littoral drift. (3) Protection. 8°. 1902
Wheeler (William Morton).
The social insects: orig. and evol. 8°. 1928
Social life among the insects. 8°. [1923]
Wheeler-Bennett (John Wheeler), *Junr.* Information on the reduct. of armaments. Intr. by Sir N. L. Malcolm. 8°. [1925]
—— & F. E. Langermann. Information on the problem of security, 1917–26. Intr. by H. A. L. Fisher. 8°. [1927]
Wheelwrights' Company, *see* SCOTT (J. B.) Short acc. of the W.C., 1884.
Whelan (William) & Co. Hist., gazetteer & directory of Northamptonshire &c. & diocese of Peterborough. 8°. 1849
Whelpley (James Davenport). Brit.-Amer. relations. Intr. by Hon. G. Harvey. 8°. 1924
Reconstruction. 8°. N.Y. 1925
***When** Cupid wins none lose, 1927, *see* HABERLY (L.)
***Where** freedom falters, 1927, *see* LYON (L.)
Wherry (Edith). The red lantern. [3rd ed.] s8°. 1911
Wherry (George Edward). Cambridge & Ch. Lamb. Ed. G. W. [4 essays: Cambridge Lamb dinners, by G. W.; Camb. & C. L., by E. V. Lucas; The earliest C. L. dinner, by Sir E. Gosse; G. Dyer & "Dyer's Frend," by G. W.] s8°. C. 1925
Whetham (Margaret Dampier), *see* WHETHAM (W. C. D.) & M. D. W., *edd.* Cambridge readings in the lit. of science, 1924.
Whetham (William Cecil Dampier). Matter & change: intr. to physical & chemical science. s8°. C. 1924
Politics & the land. 8°. C. 1927
The recent development of physical science. [5th ed.] 8°. [1924]
—— & M. D. Whetham, *edd.*
Cambridge readings in the lit. of science. 8°. C. 1924
Whetstone (George). Historye of Promos & Cassandra, *& o. plays, see* †SIX old plays, 1779.
Metrical life of G. Gascoigne, the poet (1577). [repr.] 8°. Bristol. 1815

Whibley (Charles). Literary portraits. [repr.] 8°. 1920
Lord John Manners & h. friends. 2v. 8°. E. 1925
Political portraits. s2. 8°. 1923
Whichcot (Benjamin) [WHICHCOTE].
Several discourses. 4v [v1, 2nd ed.] 8°. 1702–7
Whieldon (Thomas), *see* PRICE (R. K.) Astbury, W. & Ralph Wood figures, & Toby jugs, 1922.
Whig (The) almanac & U.S. register.
1843–49 [*in* 1v]. s8°. N.Y. 1843–49
Whipple (George Chandler). Vital statistics: intr. to sci. of demography. 2nd ed. s8°. N.Y. 1923
Whish (John Charles). The first cause: or, a treatise upon the being & attributes of God. 8°. 1855
***Whispering gallery** (The), 1926, *see* PEARSON (H.)
Whistler (Hugh), *F.Z.S.* In the high Himalayas. 8°. 1924
Pop. handbook of Indian birds. 8°. 1928
Whistler (James A. McNeill). Illust. cat. of drawings &c. by W. &c. Sold, Jan. 13, 1922, Amer. Art. Assoc. [P2855]. 8°. N.Y. 1922
see BROOKS (A. M.) From Holbein to W.: notes on drawing & engraving, 1920.
,, DODGSON (C.) Etchings of J. McN. W., 1922.
,, HUNTER (F. W.) Coll. of books &c. rel. to W., 1920.
,, PENNELL (J.) & E. R. PENNELL. The W. journal, 1921.
Whiston (William), *M.A.*
Astronom. princ. of religion &c. s8°. 1717
Coll. of authentick records belonging to the O. & N. Test. Tr. 2p. [*pagin. cont. tp. &c. of p2 wanting*]. 8°. 1727
An essay on the Revelation of St. John. 2nd ed. 4°. 1744
Six diss. Testimonies of Josephus conc. Jesus &c. s8°. 1734
see CARPZOV (J. G.) Defence of Heb. Bible in ans. to W. &c.; tr., 1729.
,, WERNSDORF (G.) Diss. de Const. Apostolic. origines, contra G. W., 1739.
,, WORKENIUS (F.) Christianismus prim. quem G. W. dictitat, 1729.
Whitacre (Aelred), *O.P., see* AQUINAS (T.), *saint.* Papers read at 6th centenary, 1924, by A. W. &c., 1925.
Whitaker, *The family of, see* WHITAKER (R. S.) W. of Hesley Hall &c., 1907.
Whitaker (Herman). The settler of Silver Creek. 8°. [1921]
Whitaker (J.), *F.Z.S.* Nimrod, ramrod, fishing-rod & nature tales. 8°. Nottingham. 1909
Notes on the birds of Notts. 8°. Nottingham. 1907
Whitaker (Joseph).
Almanack, 1870–73, 77, 1921–28. s8°. [1869–1927]
Whitaker (Joseph I. S.)
Motya, a Phoenician colony in Sicily. la8°. 1921
Whitaker (Robert Sanderson). Whitaker of Hesley Hall &c., & Palermo. Fam. records. 4°. 1907
Whitaker (Thomas Dunham). Hist. & antiq. of the deanery of Craven, co. York. 4°. 1805
Whitaker (William), *D.D.* Ad N. Sanderi demonstr. quadraginta, in octavo libro Visibilis Monarchiae positas, quibus Romanum pontificem non esse Antichristum docere instituit responsio. Acc. Ejusdem thesis de Antichristo &c. s8°. Londini. 1583
An answere to a certeine booke wr. by W. Rainolds entit. A refut. of sundrie reprehensions, cavils &c. s8°. *T. Chard.* 1585
Cygnea cantio: ultima concio ad clerum [*w.* Vita]. [*b. w. h.* Praelectiones, 1599]. s8°. Herbornae Nassov. 1599
Disput. de Sacra Scr. contra hujus temp. Papistas, imprimis R. Bellarminum &c. s4°. Cantabrigiæ. 1588
" " ....s8°. Herbornae. 1590
Praelectiones in quibus tractatur controversia de Eccl. contra Pontificios &c. Operâ & curâ J. Allenson. s8°. Herbornae Nassov. 1599
Praelectiones W. in controv. de Romano pontifice. Operâ & curâ J. Allenson. s8°. Hanoviae. 1608
Responsionis ad decem illas rationes, quibus fretus E. Campianus certamen Eccl. Angl. ministris obtulit in causa fidei, Defensio contra confut. J. Duræi &c. s8°. Londini. 1583
see DURIE (J.), *Jesuit.* Confut. Resp. G. W. ad rationes &c., 1582.
,, RAINOLDS (W.) Refut. of sundry reprehensions &c. by wh. W. laboureth to deface the late Eng. tr. & Catholic annot. of the N.T. &c., 1583.

Whitaker (William), *F.G.S.*
The following are Mem^{s}. of the Geol. Survey.
Geol. of co. around Ipswich, Hadleigh & Felixstow. 8°. 1885
Geol. of Southwold & of the Suffolk Coast. 8°. 1887
Geol. of the Eastern end of Essex (Walton Naze & Harwich). 8°. 1877
The water supply of Bucks. & Herts. &c. 8°. 1921
The water-supply of Cambridgeshire, Hunts. & Rutland &c. 8°. 1922
The water-supply of Hampshire, includ. the Isle of Wight, w. records of sinkings &c.; w. contrib. by H. R. Mill &c. 8°. 1910
The water supply of Kent; w. records of sinkings & borings. Contrib. by H. F. Parsons *& others.* 8°. 1908
The water-supply of Norfolk &c. 8°. 1921
The water-supply of Suffolk &c.: w. rec. of sinkings & borings, w. contrib. by H. F. Parsons &c. 8°. 1906
The water-supply of Surrey &c., w. contrib. on rainfall by H. R. Mill. 8°. 1912
——, F. J. Bennett & J. H. Blake.
Geology of the neighb. of Stowmarket. 8°. 1881
—— & W. H. Dalton.
Geology of co. around Halesworth & Harleston. 8°. 1887
—— & F. H. Edmunds.
The water supply of Wiltshire f. underground sources. 8°. 1925
Wells & springs of Dorset. 8°. 1926
—— & A. J. Jukes-Browne.
Geology of the borders of the Wash. 8°. 1899
—— W. H. Penning &c.
Geol. of the N.W. part of Essex & the N.E. part of Herts. &c. 8°. 1878
—— & C. Reid.
The water supply of Sussex &c. 8°. 1899
——, S. B. J. Skertchly & A. J. Jukes-Browne.
Geol. of S.-W. Norfolk & of N. Cambridgeshire. 8°. 1893
—— & J. C. Thresh.
The water supply of Essex &c. Rainfall by H. R. Mill. 8°. 1916
—— H. B. Woodward, &c.
Geol. of parts of Cambridgeshire & of Suffolk (Ely, Mildenhall, Thetford). 8°. 1891

Whitaker's cumulative book list, 1925. la8°. 1926

Whitbread & Co. Ltd. Whitbread's Brewery, 1740–1920. Illust. hist. [P2508]. 4°. [1920]

Whitby (Daniel). Addit. annot. to the New Test.; w. 7 disc. & app. ent. Exam. variantium lect. J. Millii in Nov. Text. [*sep. tp. & pagin.*] sm. fol. 1710
A disc. conc. the idolatry of the Church of Rome: wherein the refut. [by T. G., *i.e.* T. Godden] of Stillingfleet's Discourse is answered. s8°. 1674
A full ans. to the arguments of the Rev. J. Edwards, for the opinion of St. Austin conc. the first sin of Adam &c. s8°. 1712
*An hist. acc. of some things rel. to nature of Eng. govt. &c. [P2663]. s4°. 1690
A paraphrase & comm. on the New Test. 2v (2, A paraph. &c. upon the Epistles, 1700). sm. fol. 1700–3
Reflections on assertions &c. of Dodwell cont. in An epistolary disc. proving that the soul is a principle naturally mortal &c. s8°. 1707
see FULLWOOD (F.) *Agreement betw. the present & former govt. [*sometimes attrib. to D. W.*], 1689.

White (Albert Beebe). Making of the Eng. constit., 449–1485. 8°. N.Y. [1908]

White (Albert C.) The Irish Free State, its evolution &c. Pref. by Sir A. W. Cope. s8°. [1923]

White (Alexander). Confut. of Church-of-Englandism &c. Tr. by E. W. O'Mahoney. 8°. D. 1841

White (Andrew Dickson). Autobiog. 2v. 8°. N.Y. 1914

White (Anna) & L. S. Taylor. Shakerism: its meaning & message. 8°. Columbus. [1904]

White (Arthur Silva). Achievements of Scotsmen dur. 19th cent. in geog. explor. & research. [R. Scot. Geog. Soc. P2769]. 8°. E. 1889

White (Arthur V.) Water powers of Brit. Columbia. By A. V. W. asst. by C. J. Vick. [Canada: Comm. of Conservation]. la8°. Ottawa. 1919

White (Benjamin).
Gold, its place in the economy of mankind. s8°. [1920]

White (Bertram Lee). The barometers of business. s8°. [1918]
The things that sales are made of. 8°. [1921]

White (*Capt.* C. W.)
The army & the public. 3rd ed. [P2831]. 8°. *n.d.*

White (Charles), *of Bathurst.*
Hist. of Australian bushranging. 2v. s8°. Sydney. 1900–6

White (Charles), *genealogist.*
Compendium of the Brit. peerage. s8°. 1825

White (Dorothy V.), *wife of W. Hale White.* The Groombridge diary. [*With extracts from W. H. W.'s letters*]. 8°. 1924

White (E. M.) Woman in world-history. 8°. 1924

White (Edmund) [*ps.* JAMES BLYTHE PATTON].
The sway of Philippa. s8°. 1900

White (Edward Lucas). El Supremo. Romance of the gt. dictator of Paraguay. s8°. [1923]

White (Francis), *bp. of (1) Carlisle, (2) Norwich, (3) Ely.* The orthodox faith & way to the Church &c., *see* WHITE (J.) Works, 1624.
A replie to Jesuit Fishers answere to questions by King James. Annexed, a Conf. of the right: R. B. of St. David's w. the same Jesuit. [*w. sep. tp. & pagin.* Ans. by R[ichard] B[ayly]. *b. w.* White (John). Workes, 1624]. fol. 1624

White (Francis Buchanan White). The flora of Perthshire. Ed., w. intr. &c. by J. W. H. Trail. s8°. E. 1898

White (Fred M.) A deal in letters. s8°. [1923]

White (Freda). Mandates. Foreword by Sir F. Lugard. s8°. 1926

White (George Miles) [GEORGE BLISS].
From Boniface to bank burglar. s8°. N.Y. 1807

White (*Rev.* Gilbert). Nat. hist. of Selborne. la8°. 1911

White (Gleeson). Pract. designing. Ed. G. W. Contrib. A. Millar &c. s8°. 1893
„ „ ....[2nd ed.] s8°. 1894

White (Harold J. Osborne), *F.G.S.*
The following are Mem^{s}. of Geol. Survey.
Geol. of co. around Alresford. 8°. 1910
Geol. of co. around Bournemouth. 2nd ed. 8°. 1917
The 1st ed. (1898) *was* by C. Reid.
Geol. of co. around Hungerford & Newbury. 8°. 1907
Geol. of co. around Marlborough. 8°. 1925
Geol. of co. around Winchester & Stockbridge. 8°. 1912
Geol. of co. nr. Brighton & Worthing. 8°. 1924
Geol. of co. nr. Fareham & Havant. 8°. 1913
Geol. of co. nr. Hastings & Dungeness. 8°. 1928
Geol. of co. nr. Lewes. 8°. 1926
Geol. of co. nr. Lymington & Portsmouth. 8°. 1915
Geol. of co. S. & W. of Shaftesbury. 8°. 1923
Short acc. of geol. of the Isle of Wight. 8°. 1921
see JUKES-BROWNE (A. J.) & H. J. O. W. Geol. of co. around Henley-on-Thames &c., 1908.

White (Henry A.) Crime & criminals: remin. of the penal dept. in Victoria. 8°. Ballarat. 1890

White (Henry Julian), *see* PLATER (W. E.) & H. J. W. Grammar of the Vulgate, 1926.

White (Henry Kirke). Poet. works. [Mem. by Sir H. Nicolas. Aldine ed.] s8°. [1866 ?]

White (*Sir* Herbert Thirkell). Burma. s8°. C. 1923

White (Horace).
Money & banking illust. by Amer. hist. s8°. Boston. 1895

White (Horatio Stevens). Sketch of the life & labors of Prof. W. Fiske. 8°. Chicago. [1918]
Willard Fiske, life & corr.: biog. study. 8°. N.Y. 1925
see FISKE (W.) W. F. Memorial: papers by H. S. W. &c., 1919.

White (Hugh G. Evelyn), *see* LOGIA JESU. Sayings of Jesus f. Oxyrhynchus; ed. w. intr., comm. &c., by H. G. E. W., 1920.

White (James Dundas). Land-value policy. s8°. 1924

White (James George), *deputy of Walbrook Ward.* Hist. of the 3 Royal Exchanges, the Gresham Lects., & the Gresham Almshouses. s8°. 1896
Short hist. of the Royal Hospitals of Bridewell & Bethlem. [*2 pagin.*] 8°. *p.f.p.c.* 1899

White (*Col.* James Grove). Hist. & topog. notes &c. on Buttevant, Castletownroche, Doneraile, Mallow, & places in th. vicinity. [*Suppl. to* Journal of Cork Hist. & Arch. Soc.] v3, 4. la8°. 1913–25

White (James William), *see* REPPLIER (A.) & J. W. W. Germany & democracy, 1914.

White (John), *B.D., fellow of St. John's Coll., Camb.* The protestant Englishman guarded agst. Romish priests &c. 8°. 1753

White (John), *D.D., minister at Eccles.*
The way to the true church. s8°. 1608
Workes. Together with a defence of The Way to the true Church in ans. to a Popish treatise wr. by T. W. P[riest] entituled White died blacke; by F. White. [4p.] fol. 1624

White (John), *navigator.* Rel. de Terre-Neuve & Mém. de T.-N., et le golfe de S. Laurent, *see* BERNARD (J. F.) Recueil, t3, 1715; 1732.

White (John P.), *of the Pyghtle Works, Bedford.* Garden furniture & ornament. [Catalogue &c.] 4°. *n.d.*

White (Joseph), *Canon of Christ Church.* Actuum Apostolorum et Epistolarum versio Syriaca cum interpret. &c. [*Syr. & Lat.*] 2t [*in* 1v]. 4°. Oxonii. 1799–1803

Letter suggesting a plan for a new ed. of the LXX. Added Spec. of eastern versions. [P543]. 8°. O. 1779

Sacr. Evangel. vers. Syriaca Philoxeniana ex codd. MSS. Ridleianis. Ed. cum interpr. & annotat. [*Syr. & Lat.*] t1. 4°. Oxonii. 1778

White (Joseph Blanco).

Pract. &c. evidence agst. Catholicism. 2nd ed. rev. 8°. 1826

White (Lewis Borrett), *ed., see* EVANGELICAL ALLIANCE. The religious condition of Christendom &c., 1885.

White (Mary Helen), *see* †TOWRY (M. H.), *ps.*

White (Newport John Davis). Acc. of Abp. Marsh's library, Dublin; w. note on autographs by N. B. White. 8°. D. 1926

Four good men: L. Challoner, J. Taylor, N. Marsh, E. Bouhéreau. s8°. Dublin. 1927

Occasional verses. s8°. D. 1924

see PATRICK, *St.* Writings & life; [ed. w. intr. &c.] by W., 1920.

White (P.), *of the Gen. Excise Office, Edinburgh.* Obs. upon Scotch fisheries & interior parts of the Highlands. s8°. E. 1791

White (Percy). Mr. Bailey-Martin, O.B.E. s8°. [1923]

White (Robert), *astronomer, see* CELESTIAL ATLAS (THE), 1800–8.

White (Stewart Edward). The rose dawn. s8°. [1921]

White (Thomas) [WHITEBREAD], *Jesuit.* The last speeches of the 5 notor. traitors & jesuits: viz. T. W. &c. execut. at Tyburn, June 20, 1679 for conspir. the death of H. M. &c. [*no tp.* P529]. fol. [1679]

White (Thomas), *Roman Catholic priest.* *Betrachtung v. d. mittleren Zustand d. Seelen. [*Tr. by G. Arnold*]. s8°. Amsterdam. 1703

White (Thomas), *bp. of Peterborough, see* SANCROFT (W.) Proc. & tryal in case of abp. of Canterbury, bp. of P. &c., 1688, 1689.

White (Viola Chittenden). Horizons. [Yale ser. of younger poets]. s8°. New Haven, *Yale.* 1921

White (Walter Grainge), *F.R.G.S.* Sea gypsies of Malaya: Mawken people of Mergui Archipelago &c. Foreword by R. R. Marett. 8°. 1922

White (William Allen). Woodrow Wilson: the man, his times & task. [3rd imp.] 8°. Boston, *Mass.* 1925

White (William Hale) [*ps.* MARK RUTHERFORD; REUBEN SHAPCOTT].

Autobiography of Mark Rutherford. 15th ed. s8°. *n.d.*

Letters to 3 friends. 8°. 1924

Mark Rutherford's deliverance. s8°. [1913]

Miriam's schooling & o. p. 2nd ed. 8°. 1892

More pages f. a journal. s8°. 1910

The revolution in Tanner's Lane. [10th impr.] s8°. [1923]

see WHITE (D. V.) The Groombridge diary [*w. extracts f. W. H. W.'s letters*], 1924.

White (*Sir* William Hale-), *M.D.* Bacon, Gilbert & Harvey. Harveian Oration, 1927. s8°. 1927

White (Sir William Henry).

see MANNING (F.) Life of Sir W. W., 1923.

Whitear (Walter Henry). More Pepysiana. Notes on the diary of S. Pepys & genealogy of the family &c. 8°. 1927

Whitebread (Thomas), *Jesuit, see* WHITE (T.)

Whitechurch (Victor Lorenzo).

A bishop out of residence. 2nd impr. s8°. [1924]

,, ,, [4th impr. (pop. ed.)] s8°. [1925]

The canon's dilemma & o. s. [2nd impr.] s8°. [1924]

The crime at Diana's pool. s8°. [1927]

The Dean & Jecinora. s8°. [1926]

Downland echoes. s8°. [1924]

Whitefield (George).

Works. Sermons, tracts, letters &c. Pref. acc. of his life. 6v. 8°. 1771–72

Brief acc. of trial at Gloucester, Mar. 3, 1743, betw. Methodists & persons of Minchin-Hampton. [P2759]. 8°. 1744

A coll. of hymns &c. s8°. 1754

,, 23rd ed. s8°. 1777

Coll. of hymns for soc. worship. 14th ed. [*b. w h.* Communion mornings comp., 1767]. s8°. 1767

A communion morning's companion. 5th ed. s8°. 1767

,, ,, 7th ed. [*b. w. h.* Coll. of hymns, 23rd ed., 1777]. s8°. 1775

Letter to Dr. Durell, occas. by expulsion of six students f. Edmund Hall. 2nd ed. [P2586]. s8°. 1768

Several disc. upon pract. subjects. Added The Oxford Methodists. [3rd ed. *w. sep. tp. & pag.*] s8°. 1738

Whitefield (George) [*continued*].

A short acc. of God's dealings w. W. Wr. by himself. 4th ed. s8°. 1753

The two first parts of his life, w. h. journals, rev., corr. & abr. by G. W. s8°. 1756

see BURKHARDT (J. G.) Vollst. Gesch. d. Methodisten nebst Lebensbeschr. G. W. &c., 1795.

see ELLINGTON (E.) Reproach of Xt.: sermon occ. by death of G. W., 1770, 1771.

,, TYERMAN (L.) Life of G. W., 1890.

,, WAKELEY (J. B.) Anecdotes of G. W., w. biogr. sketch, 1875.

,, WESLEY (J.) Sermon on death of G. W., 1770.

Whiteford (James Forbes). Factory management wastes: & how to prevent them. 8°. [1919]

Whitehead (Alfred North). The principle of relativity, w. applic. to phys. sci. 8°. C. 1922

Religion in the making. Lowell Lect., 1926. 8°. C. 1926

,, ,, ...[n. impr.] 8°. C. 1927

Science & the mod. world. Lowell Lects., 1925. 8°. C. 1926

,, ,, ...[n. impr.] 8°. C. 1927

,, ,, ...[repr.] 8°. C. 1928

Symbolism. s8°. C. 1928

Whitehead (George). In the Nicobar Islands. Pref. by Sir R. C. Temple. 8°. 1924

Whitehead (Henry), *bp. of Madras.*

Indian problems in religion, educ. &c. 8°. 1924

Whitehead (John), *A.M.* Study of Swedenborg's psychical states & experiences. [P2577]. 8°. Boston. 1909

Whitehead (John), *M.D.*

A disc. at the funeral of J. Wesley. 8°. 1791

,, ,, ...4th ed. [P2595]. s8°. 1791

Whitehead (John Livesay), *M.D.*

The Undercliff of the Isle of Wight. 8°. Ventnor. 1911

Whitehead (Paul).

*The case of the Hon. Alex. Murray, Esq. [P2783]. 8°. 1751

Manners: satire. [P2568]. fol. 1739

Whitehead (Talbot Haes), E. E. L. Dixon *& others.* The country betw. Stafford & Market Drayton. [Mem. of G.S.] 8°. 1927

—— & T. Eastwood. Geol. of S. p. of S. Staffs. coalfield. With contrib. by T. Robertson. [Mem. of G.S.] 8°. 1927

see EASTWOOD (T.), T. H. W. &c. Geol. of the co. around Birmingham, 1925.

Whitehead (William), *sec. to Order of Bath.* The Roman father, *see* INCHBALD (*Mrs.* E.) Brit. th., v14, 1808.

White House, *Washington.* The White House gallery of official portraits of the presidents. la. fol. N.Y. 1906

Whitehouse (John Howard). Bembridge: an hist. &c. survey. By members of Bembridge School. Ed. J. H. W. 8°. O. 1923

Ruskin the prophet & o. centenary st. By J. Masefield, Dean Inge &c. Ed. J. H. W. 8°. [1920]

Whitelaw (Charles E.), *see* JACKSON (H. J.) European hand firearms, w. treatise on Scottish hand firearms by C. E. W., 1923.

Whitelaw (David). Madcap Betty. s8°. [1927]

Whiteley (Opal). The diary of Opal Whiteley. Intr. by Visct. Grey of Fallodon & pref. by E. Sedgwick. s8°. 1920

Whitelocke (*Lt.-Gen.* John). Trial of W., Commander in Chief of exped. agst. Buenos Ayres, by court-martial, 28th Jan. 1808. [Tipper's ed.] 8°. 1808

Whitfield (Archie Stanton). Thomas Hardy. Lecture. Intr. by Sir J. A. Cockburn. s8°. 1921

Whitford (Robert Calvin). Madame de Staël's literary reput. in England. [Univ. of Illinois]. la8°. [Urbana]. 1918

Whitgift (John), *(1) bp. of Worcester, (2) abp. of Canterbury.* The defense of the Aunswere to the admonition agst. the replie of T[homas] C[artwright]. fol. 1574

see HEARNSHAW (F. J. C.) Eccl. polity of Abp. W., 1924.

,, STRYPE (J.) Life & acts of W., 1718.

Whitham (G. I.) The guarded room. s8°. 1921

St. John of Honeylea. s8°. 1919

Whitham (J. Mills). Silas Braunton. s8°. [1923]

Stinging nettles. s8°. [1927]

The windlestraw. s8°. [1924]

Whiting, *Family of, see* MORSE (W. I.), *ed.* Genealogiae or data, 1925.

Whiting (John D.) Practical illustration. 8°. N.Y. [1920]

Whiting (Lilian). The Brownings, th. life & art. 8°. 1911

Whiting (William). War powers under the constitution of the U.S. 43rd ed. 8°. Boston. 1871

1st ed. h. t. War powers of the President &c.

Whitlaw (Rosa M.) & W. L. Wyllie.

Lionel P. Smythe, R.A. 8°. [1923]

Whitley Report, *see* LABOUR, MINISTRY OF. Industrial reports, Nos. 1–4, 1917–19.

Whitley (Mary Theodora), *see* NORSWORTHY (N.) & M. T. W. Psychology of childhood, 1920.

Whitley (William T.) The art collections of the nation: with articles by W. T. W. Ed. G. Holme. [Studio Spec. No.] la8º. 1920

Whitlock (Herbert P.) The story of minerals. [Amer. Museum of Nat. Hist.] s8º. N.Y. 1925

Whitman (Alfred). Whitman's print-collector's handbook. Rev. & enl. by M. C. Salaman. [repr.] la8º. 1921

Whitman (Walt).

Gathering of the forces. Editorials, essays, &c., wr. 1846–1847. Ed. C. Rodgers & J. Black. 2v. 8º. N.Y. 1920
Leaves of grass. s8º. 1909
Specimen days in America. Newly rev. by a., w. fresh pref. & add. note. [Camelot Ser.] s8º. 1887
Uncoll. poetry & prose. Coll. & ed. E. Holloway. 2v. 8º. Garden City, N.Y. 1921
see BAILEY (J. C.) W. W., 1926.
see CHARNWOOD (G. R. B., *1st b.*) W. W. in America, 1921.
,, HOLLOWAY (E.) W.: an interpret. in narrative, 1926.
,, KELLER (E. L.) W. W. in Mickle Street, 1921.
,, ROGERS (C.) The magnificent idler: W. W., 1926.
,, SHAY (F.) Bibliog. of W. W., 1920.

Whitmee (William).
Lent & Holy week in Rome. s8º. Roma. 1896

Whitmore (William Henry). The American genealogist: cat. of family hist. & publ. 8º. Albany. 1868
Notes conc. Peter Pelham, the earliest artist resident in New England, & his successors prior to the Revolution. [Repr. f. Proc. of Massachusetts Hist. Soc., 1866–67]. [P2623]. 8º. Cambridge [Mass.] 1867

Whitney (Caspar). The flowing road: adv. on gt. rivers of South Amer. 8º. 1912

Whitney (Edson Leone). Trade agreements, 1923–24, *see* UNITED STATES: LABOR. Bull. 393, 1925.

Whitney (Edward). Statist. record of progr. of the U.S., 1800–1920 &c., *see* UNITED STATES: COMMERCE.

Whitney (Henry M.) Hawaiian guide book. s8º. Honolulu. 1875

Whitney (Richard Merrill). *Reds in America: present status of revol. movt. in U.S. 8º. N.Y. 1924

Whittaker (Edmund Taylor) & G. N. Watson.
A course of mod. analysis. 3rd ed. la8º. C. 1920

Whittaker (John William). Enquiry into the interpret. of the Hebrew Scr., w. remarks on Bellamy's new tr. 8º. C. 1819

Whittaker (Thomas). The liberal state. 2nd ed. rev. s8º. [1928]
Macrobius, or philos., science &c. in yr. 400. s8º. C. 1923
The metaphysics of evolution, w. o. essays. 8º. 1926
The theory of abstract ethics. s8º. C. 1916

Whittaker (William Gillies). Fugitive notes on certain cantatas & the motets of J. S. Bach. 8º. [1925]

Whittelsey (Charles C.)
see CUMMINGS (J. P.) Argument on appeal of J. P. C., 1865.
,, GLOVER (S. T.) Argument on appeal of S. T. G., 1866.

Whitten (Robert Harvey).
Public admin. in Mass. 8º. N.Y., *Columbia Univ.* 1898

Whitten (Wilfred), *see* SMITH (JOHN T.) Nollekens & h. times; ed. & annot. by W. W., 2v, 1920.

Whittier (John Greenleaf).
Poems. [*engr. tp. dated 1850*]. 8º. Boston [Mass.] 1855
Poet. works. With notes &c., ed. W. G. Horder. Oxford compl. ed. s8º. 1904

Whittingham (Charles), *the elder, see* WARREN (A.) The Ch. Whittinghams, printers, 1896.

Whittingham (Charles), *the younger, see* WARREN (A.) The Ch. Whittinghams, printers, 1896.

Whittingham (George Napier). The home of fadeless splendour, or, Palestine of to-day. Foreword by Sir A. W. Money. 8º. [1921]

Whittingham (William), *dean of Durham, see* FRANKFORT ON THE MAIN. *A brieff disc. off troubles at F., 1554 [*by W. W.?*], 1575.

Whittington (*Rev.* —).
*Travels thr. Spain & part of Portugal. 2v. s8º. 1808

Whittington (*Sir* Richard), *see* BESANT (*Sir* W.) & J. RICE. W., 1905.

Whitton (*Lt.-Col.* Frederick Ernest).
The decisive battles of mod. times. 8º. 1923
Moltke. 8º. 1921

Whittuck (Edward Arthur). International canals, *see* FOREIGN OFFICE. Handbooks, No. 150, 1920.
A. c. bound separately.

Whitwell, *The family of, see* FOSTER (S. B.) Pedigrees of W. of Kendal &c., 1890.

***Who** burnt Cork city? &c., 1921, *see* CORK.

Whole. *Whole (The) art of dying. 2p [*in* 1v]. The 1st being an experimental discovery, wr. orig. in German. The 2nd is a Gen. instruction, publ. by comm. of the French king (1705). [repr.] s8º. B'ham. *n.d.*
*Whole (The) art of pen making &c. [P505]. s8º. *n.d.*
*Whole (The) duty of man &c. [With prefat. letter by H. Hammond]. s8º 1668

***Wholesome** advices f. the Blessed Virgin, 1687, *see* WIDENFELDT (A.)

Who's who. 1921–1928. 8º. [1920–27]
see also HVEM ER HVEM?; QUI ÊTES-VOUS?; WER IST'S?

Who's who in America. Ed. A. N. Marquis. v6, 1910–11; v11, 1920–21; v12, 1922–23; v14, 1926–27. s8º. & 8º. Chicago. [1910–26]

Who's who in Canada. Ed. B. M. Greene, 1927. 8º. Toronto. [1927]

Who's who in literature, 1924, 1926, 1927. A cont. of the bibliogr. sect. of the Literary year book. M. Meredith, ed. 8º. [1924–27]

Who's who in New York City & State. Ed. J. W. Leonard, 1907, 1909, 1911, 1914 [1914, ed. W. F. Mohr]. 8º. & la8º. N.Y. 1907–14

Whowell (Thomas).
An analogy of the Old & New Test. 2v. la8º. 1846

***Why** Gordon perished, 1896, *see* MACDONALD (ALEX.)

Whybrow (*Mrs.* A. N.) The day-by-day cookery book. 8º. 1900

Whymper (Edward). How to use the aneroid barometer. 8º. 1891

Whyte (A. J.) Early life & letters of Cavour, 1810–48. 8º. 1925

Whyte (Alexander), *see* BARBOUR (G. F.) Life of A. W., 1923.

Whyte (Frederic). Life of W. T. Stead. 2v. 8º. [1925]
A wayfarer in Sweden. s8º. [1926]

Whyte (L. L.) Archimedes; or, the future of physics. s8º. [1927]

Wiat (*Sir* Thomas), *see* WYATT.

Wibberley (T.) Continuous cropping & tillage dairy farming for sm. farmers. 3rd ed. s8º. 1919

Wicelinus (Georgius), *see* WITZEL (GEORG).

Wichers (J. van Buttingha), *see* BUTTINGHA WICHERS (J. VAN).

Wickenburg (Eduard, *Graf* **v.)** Fahrten u. Ritte durch d. La Plata Staaten u. Chile. 8º. München. 1924

Wickham (Humphrey), *ps., see* MORRELL (W.)

Wickham (James Douglas Clephane). Records by spade & terrier: hist. side-lights &c. garnered f. tithe-maps & registers of Holcombe-by-Mendip &c. 8º. Bath. [1912]

Wickhoff (Franz). Beschreibendes Verzeichnis d. illum. Hss. in Österreich. *[Hrsg. F. W. Publ. d. 2en. Kunsthist. Inst. d. Univ. Wien in Verbind. mit d. Österreich. Inst. f. Geschichtsforschung]. B8, T1–3, 5 [*each w. sep. tp. &c.*; hrsg. J. Schlosser u. H. J. Hermann]. fol. L. 1923–28
8, Illum. Hss. u. Inkunabeln d. Nationalbibl. in Wien; [v.] H. J. Hermann.

Wickner (Abdias). Catechesis sive summa Christianae doctrinae inventuti scholæ Rotenburg. ad Tuberum traditae. s8º. Rotenburgi, *A. Magnus. n.d.* [c. 1560]

Wickner (Conrad). Das man sich vor d. zukünfftigen sterben oder Pestilentz nicht entsetzen soll. s4º. [Nürnberg]. 1530

Wicksteed (Philip Henry). From Vita Nuova to Paradiso: 2 essays on rels. betw. Dante's successive works. [Univ. of M'ter.] s8º. M'ter. 1922
The reactions between dogma & philosophy illust. f. the works of S. Thomas Aquinas. [Hibbert Lect.] 8º. 1920

Wickwar (J. W.) Witchcraft & the black art. 8º. [1925]

Wiclif (John) [VUICLERUS].
Opera minora. Notes by J. Loserth. Eng. side-notes by F. D. Matthew. [Wyclif Soc.] 8º. 1913
Operis evangelici liber 3 & 4, sive De Antichristo liber 1 & 2. Notes by J. Loserth. Eng. side-notes by F. D. Matthew. [Wyclif Soc.] v3, 4 [*in* 1v. *pagin. cont.*] 8º. 1896
Aphorismi J. Vu., *see* FOX (J.) Commentarii, 1554.
De civili dominio liber tertius. Notes by J. Loserth. Eng. side-notes by F. D. Matthew. [Wyclif Soc.] v3, 4. 8º. 1903–4
Dialogorū libri q̄ttuor quorū primus divinitatē & ideas tractat, secūdus universarū creationē, tertius de virtutib. &c., quartus Ro. ecclesie sacramēta &c. s4º. *n.p.* [Basel]. 1525
Dialogorum libri 4. s4º. Francofurti. 1753
Miscellanea philos. Ed. M. H. Dziewicki, w. essay on W.'s philos. system. [Wyclif Soc.] 2v. 8º. 1902–5
1, De actibus anime — Replicacio de universalibus — De materia & forma.

Wiclif (John) [*continued*].
2, De universalibus — Fragmenta — Notae & quest. variae — De materia.
Tractatus de mandatis divinis, acc. Tractatus de statu innocencie. Ed. w. notes, & app. De diff. inter peccatum mortale et veniale, by J. Loserth & F. D. Matthew. [Wyclif Soc.] 8°. 1922
Tractatus de potestate papae. Ed., w. notes by J. Loserth. Eng. side-notes by F. D. Matthew. [Wyclif Soc.] 8°. 1907
see BIBLE: NEW TEST. The N.T. tr. by J. W. c. 1380, 1848.
„ BUDDENSEIG (R.) J. W. u. s. Zeit, 1885.
„ GILPIN (W.) Lives of J. W. &c., 1765.
„ LECHLER (G. V.) J. W.; tr. Lorimer, 1884.
„ LOSERTH (J.) J. von W. u. R. Grosseteste, 1918.
„ —— J. von Wiclif u. G. Peraldus, 1916.
„ PICTET (B.) W., oratio acad., 1717.
„ RUEVER GRONEMAN (S. A. J. DE). Diatribe in J. W. vitam, ingenium, scripta, 1837.
„ SHIRLEY (W. W.) Cat. of extant Lat. works of W., 1926.
„ WORKMAN (H. B.) J. W.: st. of Eng. medieval church, 2v, 1926.

Wicquefort (Abraham de). Mém. sur la guerre faite aux Prov. Unies, 1672, *see* HISTORISCH GENOOTS. TE UTRECHT. Berigten, d6i, 1857.
„ „ n. uitg. door J. A. Wijnne, *see* HIST. GENOOTS. Bijdragen, d11, 1888.

Widdrington, *Family of, see* SKEET, *Family of*. Hist. of the families of S. &c., 1906.

Widdrington (Roger), *see* FITZHERBERT (T.) *Reply in defence of h. Suppl. to the discussion &c. impugned by R. W., 1614.

Wideburgius (Joannes Bernardus), *see* WIEDEBURG (J. B.)

Widefordus (Guilielmus). Ob nichts anzūnemen sey, dañ was klar in d. hayl. geschrifft ist auss getruckt. [*Tr. by* J. D. Cochlaeus]. s4°. [Stuttgart?. 1524]

Widenfeldt (Adam). Wholesome advices f. the Blessed Virgin. [Tr. J. Taylor]. [P2664]. s4°. 1687

Widenmann (Gustav).
Magnetismus d. Menschen. [P2470]. 8°. Nürnberg. 1854

***Wider** dē haubtschalck uñ todfeind des menschē gewissen &c., [1524], *see* HAUBTSCHALCK.

Widerteuffer.
*Newe Zeytung Die W. zu Münster belangende. s8°. 1535

Widgery (Alban Gregory).
Comparative study of religions. 8°. 1923

Widmann (Johannes) [*dictus* MEICHINGER]. De pustulis (Romae, 1497) *&* Tractatus de pustulis (Strassburg, 1497), *facs., see* SUDHOFF (C.) Earliest pr. lit. on syphilis, 1925.

Widmanstadt (Johann Albrecht). Syr. linguae prima elementa, *see* BIBLE: SYRIAC. Liber Sacr. Evangelii &c., 1555.

Widowson (Henry).
Present state of Van Diemen's Land. 8°. 1829

Widsið, *see* BEOWULF. W.—Beowulf—&c.; Eng. by C. Scott Moncrieff, 1921.

Widt (Frederick de), *see* WITT (F. DE).

Widukind, *see* WITTEKINDUS.

Wied (Gustav). Die Karlsbader Reise d. leibhaft. Bosheit. [Üb. v. M. Mann]. s8°. 1919

Wied (Herman von), *see* HERMANN V [VON WIED], *abp. & elector of Cologne.*

Wiedeburg (Johann Bernhard) [WIDEBURGIUS (J. B.)] Oratio de influxu siderum in temperamentum hominis. s4°. Jenae. 1720

Wiedeburg (Johann Ernst Basilius) [WIDEBURG]. De caussis diluvii physicis. [*b. w.* Baier (J. W.) Trias quaest., 1610]. s4°. Erlangae. 1759

Wiedemann (Alfred). Das alte Ägypten. s8°. Heidelberg. 1920

Wiedemann (Ferdinand Johann).
Обзоръ прежней судьбы и нынѣшняго состоянія Ливовъ. [I. Akad. Nauk. Записки, t18]. 8°. С.-П. 1870
О происхожденіи и языкѣ Курляндскихъ Кревиновъ. [I. Akad. Nauk. Записки, t21]. 8°. С.-П. 1872
Syrjänisch-deut. Wbch., nebst e. wotjak.-deut. im Anh. u. e. deut. Register. [K. Akad. d. Wiss.] la8°. St. Petersb. 1880

Wiedenfeld (Carl Wilhelm). Diss. inaug. de exorcismi orig. &c. [P2759]. s8°. Marburgi Catt. 1824

Wieder (F. C.) Mon. cartographica: reprod. of rare maps, plans &c. in size of orig., acc. by monogr. Ed. F. C. W. v1, 2 [*pagin. contin.*] atlas fol. The Hague. 1925–26
De reis van Mahu & de Cordes door de Straat van Magalhães naar Zuid-Amerika & Japan, 1598–1600. Scheepsjournaal, rapporten, brieven, kaarten, enz. Uitg. F. C. W. [Linschoten-Vereeniging, 21, 22, 24]. 3d. 8°. 's-Gravenhage. 1923–25
1, De uitreeding & de Scheepstocht. [Wijdtloopigh verhael, beschr. door Barent Jansz. &c.]

Wieder (F. C.) [*continued*].
2, De Straat v. Magalhães. [Nieuwe volmaeckte Beschr. door Jan Outghersz. &c.]
3, Het eerste holland. schip in Japan.
De stichting van New York in Juli 1625. Reconstr. en nieuwe gegevens ontleend aan de Van Rappard doc. door F. C. W. [Linschoten-Vereeniging, 26]. la8°. 's-Gravenhage. 1925

Wiederhold (Wilhelm). Papsturkunden in Frankreich, *see* KÖNIGL. GESELLS. D. WISS. ZU GÖTTINGEN. Nachrichten, 1906, 1907, 1910, 1911, 1913, Beiheft.

Wied-Neuwied (Maximilian A. P., *Prince* **zu).** Travels into the interior of North America. [Repr. of rare Americana, 2. *Plates only*]. 2v. obl. fol. & obl. 4°. [L. 1921]

Wiegand (Conrad). Erdbeschreibung d. Kurfürstenthums Hessen. 3e verm. Aufl. s8°. Cassel. 1826

Wiegand (Theodor). Baalbek: Ergebnisse d. Ausgrabungen u. Unters., 1898 bis 1905. Hrsg. v. T. W. 3B. 4°. 1921–25
1, Von B. Schulz & H. Winnefeld, unter Mitwirkung v. O. Puchstein, D. Krencker &c. Tafeln *b. separately.*
2, Von D. Krencker, T. v. Lüpke, H. Winnefeld, unter Mitwirkung v. O. Puchstein u. B. Schulz.
3, Von H. Kohl, D. Krencker, O. Reuther, F. Sarre, M. Sobernheim.
8er vorläuf. Bericht ü. d. v. d. Staatl. Museen in Milet u. Didyma untern. Ausgrab., *see* KÖN.-PREUSS. AKAD. Abhdln., Phil.-hist. Kl., 1924.
Sinai. Mit Beitr. v. F. Frhr. Kress v. Kressenstein &c. [Wissenschaftl. Veröffentl. d. deut.-türk. Denkmalschutz-Kommandos; hrsg. v. T. Wiegand, H1]. fol. 1920
see BACHMANN (W.), C. WATZINGER & T. W. Petra, 1921.
„ WISSENSCHAFTLICHE VERÖFFENTL. d. deut.-türk. Denkmalschutz-Kommandos; hrsg. T. W., H1–6, 1921–24.

Wiegand (Wilhelm).
Friedrich d. Grosse. 2e verb. A. la8°. Bielefeld. 1909

Wiegendrucke. Gesamtkatalog d. W., 1925 &c., *see* GESAMTKATALOG.

Wieger (Léon), *S. J.* Hist. des croyances relig. & des opinions philos. en Chine. 2e éd., augm. la8°. 1922
Taoïsme [*in Chinese & French*]. 2t [*in* 1v]. 8°. [Hien-hien]. 1911–13
t1, Bibliog. gén., le canon taoïste &c.
t2, Les pères du système taoïste.

Wiehler (Rudolf). Deutsche Wirtschaftspropaganda im Weltkrieg. la8°. 1922

Wiel (Alethea).
The story of Bologna. [Med. Town ser.] s8°. 1923
The story of Verona. [Med. Town ser.] [3rd ed.] s8°. 1907
Venice. [Story of the Nations]. 4th ed. 8°. *n.d.*

Wiel (Taddeo). Francesco Cavalli (1602–76). [*Extr. f.* Musical Antiquary, v4. P2837]. la8°. 1912
Scene liriche. s8°. Venezia. 1890
I teatri musicali veneziani. Cat. d. opere in musica rappres. in Venezia, 1701–1800. [Estr. dall' Archivio Veneto, 1891–97]. 8°. Venezia. 1897
Versioni da Th. Gray, J. Keats, Ld. Byron, P. B. Shelley, R. Browning. [Eng. & Ital. Tr. & pref. by T. W.] 8°. Venezia. 1906

Wieland (Christoph Martin). Gesamm. Werke. Hrsg. v. d. Deut. Komm. d. K. Preuss. Akad. d. Wiss. Abtlg. 1, B4. 8°. 1916
Abtlg. 1, Werke.
I, 4, Prosaische Jugendwerke; hrsg. F. Homeyer u. H. Bieber.
Il poter d. Grazie. Versione. [Nozze Tergolina—Ghislanzoni. N127]. 8°. Brescia. 1832
see KURRELMEYER (W.) Doppeldrucke in i. Bedeut. f. d. Textgesch. v. W. Werken, 1913.
„ SEUFFERT (B.) Proleg. zu e. W.-Ausgabe, 7, 1921.

Wien. *Vier Wochen in W. Von Fidelis. [*in case, w. 2 maps*]. s8°. Wien. 1827

Wien (Alfred). Die Seele d. Zeit in d. Dichtung, um d. Jahrhundertwende, [1900]. 8°. L. [1921]

Wiener (Paul), *Protestant bp. in Transylvania, d. 1554, see* ELZE (TH.) P. W., Mitreformator in Krain &c., 1882.

Wiertz (Antoine) [WIERTZ (ANTOINE JOSEPH)], *see* FIERENS-GEVAERT (H.) A. W., 1920.

Wiese (Erwin Wilh. Rud. v.) Die engl. parlamentar. Opposition &c., 1740–44. Diss., Göttingen. 8°. Waldenburg i. Schl. 1883

Wiese (Hugo v.) Der Kampf um Glatz. [Verein f. Ref.-gesch. Schr., Jhrg. 14, Nr. 54]. 8°. Halle. 1896

Wieser (Friedrich v.), *see* BOLSCHEWISMUS. Staat, Recht u. Wirtschaft d. B., hrsg. v. F. v. W. &c., 1925.

Wieser (J. E.) Der Spiritismus u. d. Christenthum. Mit e. Beilage: Ueb. Fechners "Tagesansicht." [P2482]. 8°. Regensburg. 1881

Wiesinger (J. T. August). Bibl. comm. on St. Paul's Epistles to Philippians, Titus & 1st Timothy. 3rd ed. 8°. E. 1866

Wiest (Edward).
Butter industry in the U.S. 8°. N.Y., *Columbia Univ.* 1916

Wiest (Stephanus).
Instit. Patrologiae in usum acad. s8°. Ingolstadii. 1795

Wiet (Gaston), *see* MASPERO (J.) & G. W. Matériaux p. s. à la géogr. de l'Egypte, s1, 1919.

Wieten (Alida Alberdina Sibbellina). Mrs. Radcliffe: her rel. towards romanticism; w. app. on novels falsely ascr. to her. 8°. Amsterdam. 1926

Wieth-Knudsen (K. A.)
Feminism: sociolog. study. Tr. A. G. Chater. 8°. [1928]

Wietrowski (Maximilian). Hist. de Arriana hæresi in compend. reducta. 4t *in* 1v [*pagin. cont.*] fol. Vetero-Pragæ. 1723

Wigand (Curt). Unkultur. Vier Kapitel Deutschtum. 8°. 1907

Wigand (Johann).
De anabaptismo grassante ad huc in multis Germaniae, Poloniae, Prussiae, Belgicae &c. locis, dogmata & argumenta cum refutat., coll. per I. W. s4°. Lipsiae. 1582
De bonis operibus positiones. Et argumenta J. Westphal. s8°. *n.p.* 1568
De monstris novis &c. in doctrina de peccato. Commonefactio. s8°. Jenae. 1571
De sacramentariismo, dogmata &c. ex quatuor patriarchis sacramentariorum Carlstadio, Zwinglio, Oecolampadio, Calvino potissimum & quibusdam aliis. Item de schismate sacramentario &c. s4°. Lipsiæ. 1584
De Schwenckfeldismo. Dogmata &c. cum succinctis solutionibus, coll. per J. W. s4°. Lipsiae. 1586
Γνῶθι σεαυτόν. Hoc est de homine integro; corrupto; renato; glorificato &c. s8°. Francoforti. 1543
Methodus doctr. Christi sicut in eccl. Magdeburg. traditur. Add. Catechismus parvus Lutheri. s8°. Francofurti. 1561
Methodus oder Heubtartickel Christl. lere wie sie in der Kirchen zu Magdeburg &c. geleret werden. s8°. [Magdeburg. 1560]
see MAGDEBURG CENTURIES. Centuriae Magdeb. [*by J. W. & others*]. 4v. 1757–65.
,, PEZEL (C.) Apologia verae doct. de definitione Evangelii opposita praestigiis &c. J. W., 1571.

——, T. Heshusius & T. Kirchner. Erinnerung v. Coelestini Büchlin v. d. Erbsünde. [P2665]. s4°. Jhena. 1572

——, ——, J. Mörlin & M. Kemnitz. De peccato originis scripta quædam contra Manichæorum delirium. [*b. w.* FLACIUS (M.) Orthodoxa conf. de orig. peccato, 1571]. s8°. Jenæ. 1571

—— & M. Judex. *Kirchenhistoria. Durch etl. Gottfürchtige Menner zu Magdeburg [J. Wigand u. M. Judex]. Aus d. Lat. Exemplar durch die Authores verdeutscht &c. Gesch. d. nachapostol. Zeitalters d. Apostol. Kirchenlehrer, 1560. [*Ed.* Count C. Münnich]. 8°. Hamburg. 1855

—— & M. Richter. Syntagma seu corpus doctrinae Christi, ex Novo Test. [*b. w. h.* Syntagma ex Vet. T., *n.d.*] 4°. Basileae. 1575
Syntagma seu corpus doctrinae veri &c. Dei ex Vet. Test. [*Pref. dated 1563*]. 4°. Basileae. *n.d.*

Wigand (Johann Rudolph). Tractatus hist.-crit.-curiosus de nobilibus theologis. s8°. Francofurti. 1714

Wigandt (Martinus). Tribunal confessariorum &c. complectens materias theologico-morales; dogmata Thomae Aquinatis &c. opera ac studio M. W. Ed. corr. a F. Vidal. 4°. Venetiis. 1724

Wiggam (Albert Edward).
The new decalogue of science. 8°. [1925]

Wiggin (Kate Douglas). Penelope's experiences in Scotland. Illust. C. E. Brock. [9th ed.] 8°. 1900
see SMITH (*Miss* N. A.) K. D. W. as her sister knew her, 1925.

Wight, Isle of. New picture of I. of W., 1808; 1813, *see* COOKE (W. B.)

Wigram (William Ainger).
The Assyrian settlement. [P2734]. s8°. 1922
The separation of the Monophysites. 8°. 1923

Wijnne (Jan Adam). De Geschillen over de afdanking van 't krijgsvolk in de Vereenigde Nederlanden, 1649–50, & de handelingen van Prins Willem II &c. [Hist. Genoots. Werken., N.S., 41]. 8°. Utrecht. 1885

—— & L. Miedema, *see* UTRECHT. Resolutiën v. d. Vroedschap v. Utrecht betref. de Academie; uitg. door W. & M., 1900.

Wikenhauser (Alfred). Die Apostelgesch. u. ihr Geschichtswert. la8°. Münster i. W. 1921

Wiklund (Carl Bernhard). Lapp. Studien 1–3, *see* KUNG. HUM. VET.-SAMF. I UPPSALA. Skr., B24, 1927.

Wilamowitz-Möllendorff (Ulrich v.) Gesch. d. Philologie. [Einl. in d. Altertumswiss; hrsg. A. Gercke &c., B1i]. la8°. L., *Teubner*. 1921
,, ,, *f. a. c. see* GERCKE (A.) & E. NORDEN.
Die griech. Heldensage, *see* KÖN.-PREUSS. AKAD. Sitzb., 1925.
Griech. Tragoedien. Übers. v. W.-M. B4. s8°. 1923
4, Sophokles: Philoktetes—Euripides: Die Bakchen—Die gr. Tragoedie u. i. 3 Dichter.
Griech. Verskunst. la8°. 1921
Die Heimkehr des Odysseus: neue Homerische Unters. 8°. 1927
Hellenist. Dichtung in d. Zeit des Kallimachos. 2B. 8°. 1924
Das homerische Epos. Vortrag. 8°. 1927
Pherekydes, *see* KÖNIGL.-PREUSS. AKAD. Sitz., Phil.-hist. Kl., 1926.
Pindaros. 8°. 1922
Vitae Homeri et Hesiodi; ed. U. de W.-M., *see* KLEINE TEXTE, T137, 1916.
see ARISTOPHANES. Lysistrate; erklärt v. U. v. W.-M., 1927.
,, KIESSLING (A.) & U. v. W.-M. Philolog. Untersuchungen; hrsg. v. K. & W.-M., H25–30, 1920–25.
,, MENANDER. Das Schiedsgericht, erklärt &c. v. W.-M., 1925.

Wilberforce (*Ven.* Basil), *D.D.* The hope that is in me. s8°. 1909

Wilberforce (Robert Isaac). The five empires. Repr. 8°. [1889]

Wilberforce (William), *philanthropist*. A pract. view on prevailing relig. system of professed Xtns. &c. 8°. [1888]
see COUPLAND (R.) W.: a narrative, 1923.

Wilbur (Sibyl) [SIBYL WILBUR O'BRIEN].
The life of Mary Baker Eddy. 8°. Boston, U.S.A. [1913]

Wilby, *Family of, see* SKEET, *Family of.* Hist. of the families of S. &c., 1906.

Wilcken (Ulrich). Beitr. z. Gesch. d. korinth. Bundes, *see* KÖNIGL. AKAD. D. W. ZU MÜNCHEN. Phil. Kl., Sitz., 1917.
Griech. Gesch. im Rahmen d. Altertumsgesch. 8°. München. 1924

Wilcocke (Samuel Hull).
Hist. of the viceroyalty of Buenos Ayres. 8°. 1807

Wilcockson (W. H.), *see* RASTALL (R. H.) & W. H. W. Tungsten ores, 1920.

Wilcox (Arthur Marwood) & J. H. Metcalfe.
Royal descent. 8°. *p.f.p.c.* 1892

Wilcox (Delos Franklin). Municipal govt. in Michigan & Ohio. 8°. N.Y., *Columbia Univ.* 1896

Wilcox (Thomas) [WILCOCKS]. Choice drop of honey f. the Rock Christ. 41st ed. [*b. w.* Wesley (J.) Hymns & spir. songs, 4th ed., 1756]. s8°. 1755

Wild (Adam). Specimen sistens luem animarum Boehmisticam &c. [P426]. s4°. Altorfi. [1705]

Wild (Johann) [FERUS (JOANNES)]. Examen ordinandorum, quicquid ad clericorum institutionem pert. videtur. Auctoribus R. D. Jo. Fero, Jo. Althusio, ac Georgio Vuicelio. [*Ed.* Nicolaus Aurificus. Acc. 1, D. Odonis Cameracen Episc. SS. Canonis missae expos. 2, Tabula. 3, Tabula altera. 4, Epitome omnium dogmatum Cath. Eccl. 5, Opusc. de dignitate &c. clericorum [per N. Aurificum]. s8°. Venetiis. 1589
In sacrosanctum Jesu Christi sec. Joãnem Evang. comm. &c. Per M. Medinam repurgata. Acc. eiusdem authoris Paulinae Epistolae ad Romanos interpretatio. 4°. Leyva. 1578

Wild (Robert). Iter Boreale. [*MS. copy*]. s8°. [c. 1660]

Wilde (Edith E.)
The Westgate, Winchester. [P2878]. s8°. Winchester. 1927

Wilde (H.) Brussa: Entwickelungsgesch. türk. Architektur in Kleinasien unter d. erst. Osmanen. la8°. 1909

Wilde (Jacob), *historian*. *Sueciae hist. pragmatica quae vulgo jus publicum dicitur. s4°. Holmiae. 1731

Wilde (Oscar F. O'F. W.)
The Happy Prince & o. t. Illust. by C. Robinson. la8°. [1913]
,, ,, [n. ed.] s8°. [1920]
A house of pomegranates. 10th ed. s8°. [1921]
Plays. 3v. 8°. Boston [Mass]. 1905–7
Sel. poems, incl. "The ballad of Reading gaol." [2nd ed.] s8°. 1911
see CLARK (W. A.), *jr.* Lib. of W. A. C.: W. & Wildeiana, v3, 1924.
,, GIDE (A.) O. W.: In

Wilde (Oscar F. O'F. W.) [*continued*]
memoriam (souv.)—Le "De Profundis," 1925.
see HARRIS (F.) O. W., h. life &c. [*w.* mem*s*. by G. B. Shaw], 2v, 1918.
„ MAUROIS (A.) Etudes angl., Ruskin & W. 1927.
see MAUROIS (A.) Quatre études angl., De Ruskin à W., &c., 1927.
„ STETSON (J. B.) The O. W. coll., 1920.

Wilde (*Sir* William R. W.)
Irish popular superstitions. s8°. D. [1852]

Wildenauer (Johann), *Egranus, see* EGRANUS (JOHANN SYLVIUS).

Wildenbruch (Ernst Ad. v.), *see* LITZMANN (B.) E. v. W., B2, 1885–1909, 1916.

Wildenstein (Georges). Lancret. 4°. [1924]
Le peintre Aved, sa vie & son œuvre, 1702–66. 2[t]. la4°. 1922
see ACADÉMIE ROY. DE PEINTURE &c. Le salon de 1725; publ. avec notes &c. par C. W., 1924.

Wilder (George D.), *see* GEE (N. G.), L. I. MOFFETT & G. D. W. List of Chinese birds, 1926.

Wilder (Thornton Niven).
The bridge of San Luis Rey. 4th impr. s8°. 1928
The Cabala. [*Novel*]. n. ed. 8°. 1928

Wildeshausen (Jacob Friedrich). Bibl. disput. in V. & N. Testamentum. Studio &c. C. H. Scheteligii. 3p *in* 1v. s4°. Hamburgi. 1736–37

Wildgans (Anton). Armut. Trauerspiel. 8°. L. [1916]
Dies irae. Tragödie. 8°. L. 1918
Kain. Ein mythisches Gedicht. 8°. L. 1920
Liebe. Tragödie. 8°. L. [1916]

Wildridge (Oswald). Clipper folk. s8°. E. 1920

Wildt (Johann Ulrich). Eccl. Æthiopica. [*b. w.* Hesterberg (J.) Eccl. Waldens., 1668]. ed. 2a. s4°. Argentorati. 1672

Wilenski (R. H.) The modern movement in art. 8°. [1927]

Wiley (John), *American citizen.* Corr. betw. Minister of For. Rel. [Hawaii] & the U.S. Comm. on case of J. W., imprisoned &c. [P2775]. 8°. Honolulu. 1845
Corr. betw. the Secretary of State [Hawaii] & U.S. Comm. in case of J. W. [P2775]. 8°. Honolulu. 1844

Wilfrid, *Saint, of Ripon, see* WILFRID, *St., abp. of York.*

Wilfrid, *St., abp. of York, 634–709.*
see BROWNE (G. F.) Theodore & W., 1897.
„ EDDIUS, *Stephanus.* Life of Bishop W.; text, tr., &c. by Colgrave, 1927.
„ FLETCHER (J. S.) Life & work of St. W. of Ripon, 1925.

Wilhelm (Adolf). Att. Urkunden, T2, 3, 1916–25, *see* KAISERL. AKAD. D. WISS. ZU WIEN. Sitzungsber., B189, 202, 1917–25.
Neue Beitr. z. griech. Inschriftenkunde, T3, 4, 6, 1913–21, *see* KAISERL. AKAD. D. WISS. ZU WIEN. Sitzungsber., B179, 183, 1916–24.

Wilhelm (Friedrich). Zur Gesch. d. Schrifttums in Deutschland bis z. Ausg. d. 13. Jhrh. [2H *in* 1v]. la8°. München. 1920–21

Wilhelm (Richard). Chines. Volksmärchen. Übers. u. eingeleit. v. R. W. s8°. Jena. 1921

Wilhelm (Wilhelm).
Patrologia ad usus acad. s8°. Friburgi Brisg. 1775

Wilhelmina, *queen of the Netherlands, see* BARNOUW (A. J.) Holland under Queen W., 1923.

Wilibrord, *St., bp. of Utrecht* [WILLIBRORD], *see* GRIEVE (A.) W., missionary in the Netherlands, 691–739; incl. tr. of the Vita W. by Alcuin of York, 1923.

Wilke (August Lebrecht). Ὕψος scriptorum divin. e Longini excelsa disciplina expensum. [2p; p2, resp. G. C. E. Bauer]. [P427]. s4°. Vitembergae. [1758]

Wilke (Georg). Die Relig. d. Indogermanen in archäolog. Beleuchtung. la8°. L. 1923

Wilken (Friedrich), *prof. of history at Berlin.* Comm. de bellorum Cruciatorum ex Abulfeda hist. 4°. Gottingæ. [1798]

Wilkes (Charles). U.S. Exploring Exped., 1838–42. 1–5, Narr. of U.S. Explor. Exped., 1838–42. Atlas. la8°. 1845

Wilkes (John), *M.P.* Compl. coll. of gen. papers, letters &c. in the case of J. W. s8°. Paris. 1767

Wilkie (*Sir* David), *see* DODGSON (C.) The etchings of Sir D. W., 1923.

Wilkie (James). History of Fife. 8°. E. 1924

Wilkin (*Capt.* Walter Harold). Life of Sir D. Baird. 8°. 1912

Wilkins (*Sir* Charles). Gramm. of the Sanskrĭta lang. 4°. 1808

Wilkins (Ernest H.) "Il chi e il quale," *see* DANTE SOCIETY, *Cambridge, Mass.,* Report, 37, 1920.

Wilkins (Ernest Powell). Geol., antiq. & topog. of the I. of Wight. Topog. &c. by J. Brion & Sons. la8°. Newport. [1861]

Wilkins (Harold T.) Marvels of mod. mechanics: mastery of land, sea & air. 8°. [1926]

Wilkins (Henry John). Edward Colston [1636–1721]. Suppl., w. acc. of Colston Soc. &c. in Bristol. 8°. Bristol. 1925
Redland Chapel & Redland. 8°. Bristol. 1924

Wilkins (John), *bp. of Chester.* A disc. conc. the gift of prayer &c. Added, Ecclesiastes: or a disc. conc. preaching. [*w. sep. tp.*, 1675, *& sep. pagin.*] s8°. 1690
see HENDERSON (P. A. W.) Life & times of J. W., 1910.

Wilkins (W. Vaughan).
Sidelights on indust. evolution. s8°. [1925]

Wilkins (William Glyde). The Dickens coll. of W. Sold, Feb. 1922, Anderson Gall. [P2856]. 8°. N.Y. 1922

Wilkins (William Henry).
Edward the Peacemaker. 2v. 4°. [1911]

Wilkinson (Albert Edmund).
The apple. Pract. treatise. 8°. Boston [Mass. 1915]

Wilkinson (Cyril Hackett), *see* LOVELACE (R.) Poems; ed. C. H. W., 2v, 1925.

Wilkinson (Geo. Blakiston).
Repeal. Die Beschwerden Irlands gegen England. 8°. 1849

Wilkinson (Henry), *B.D., Pastor of Waddesdon, Bucks.* The debt book: or a treatise upon Rom. 13, v. 8. s8°. 1625

Wilkinson (Henry), *D.D., principal of Magdalen Hall.* Three decads of sermons. 3p *in* 1v. s4°. O. 1660

Wilkinson (Henry), *M.R.C.S.* Sketches of scenery in the Basque Prov. of Spain, w. a sel. of national music. fol. 1838

Wilkinson (Henry Spenser).
Brit. aspects of war & peace. [P2500]. s8°. [1920]
The defence of Piedmont, 1742–48. Prelude to st. of Napoleon. 8°. O. 1927

Wilkinson (Hiram Parkes).
The family in classical China. 8°. 1926

Wilkinson (Horace).
A booklet on the stained glass of H. W. [P2498]. 8°. *n.d.*

Wilkinson (John), *of Merton Coll., Oxon.* Analysis of Butler's Analogy of religion. 2nd ed. 8°. O. 1853

Wilkinson (John H.), *F.R.G.S.*
Leeds dialect glossary & lore. s8°. Leeds. 1924

Wilkinson (Joseph), *of Barnsley.*
Worsborough: hist. assoc*s*. &c. s8°. [1879]

Wilkinson (*Capt.* Nevile R.), *F.S.A.*
Wilton House guide: a hdbk. for visitors. s8°. 1908

Wilkinson (Nicholas), D. Herd &c. The trial at large of N. W., D. H. &c. for the murder of George Battersby. 5th ed. 8°. Clitheroe. 1816

Wilkinson (Robert), *D.D., see* CONJUGAL duty, a coll. of wedding-sermons [by R. W. &c.], 2p, 1732–34.

Wilkinson (Robert), *publisher.* Cat. of engr. Brit. portraits, illust. of wks. of Granger &c. Publ. by R. W. 4°. 1806

Wilkinson (William Francis).
Personal names in the Bible. s8°. 1866

Wilks (John), *assist. librarian, Univ. Coll., London, see* LONDON UNIV. Cat. of works dealing w. study of west. palaeography; compiled by J. W. &c., 1921.

Wilks (John), *junior.* A Xtn. biographical dict. s8°. 1821

Will (Georg Andreas). Beyträge z. Gesch. d. Antibaptismus in Deutschland. s8°. Nürnberg. 1773
Gesch. &c. der Univ. Altdorf. s8°. Altdorf. 1795
Nürnberg. Gelehrten-Lexicon, oder Beschreibung all. Nürnberg. Gelehrten beyderley Geschlechtes nach ihr. Leben &c. 4T [*& Suppl. in 2v*]. 8°. Nürnberg. 1755–58

Will (Ludwig). Kolloidale Substanz als Energiequelle f. d. mikroskop. Schusswaffen d. Coelenteraten, *see* KÖN.-PREUSS. AKAD. Abhdln., Phys.-math. Kl., 1914.

Will (Robert). Le culte: ét. d'hist. & de philos. relig. t1. la8°. Str. 1925
La liberté chrétienne: étude s. le principe de la piété chez Luther. la8°. Str. 1922

Willaert (Joannes Baptista). Fasc. assert. theolog., praes. J. B. W., propugn. F. Le Roy. [P2659]. s8°. Ipris. 1683

Willard (James Field). Progr. of mediaeval studies in U.S.A. Bulletin No. 3. [P2785]. 5, [P2872]. 8°. Colorado. 1925–27

Willard (Margaret Wheeler). Letters on the Amer. Revol., 1774–76. Ed. M. W. W. 8°. Boston. 1925

Willard (T. A.) The city of the sacred well. Discov. & excav. of E. H. Thompson in Chi-chen Itza, w. disc. on Mayan civilization &c. 8°. [1926]

Willart de Grécourt (Jean Bapt. Joseph), *see* GRÉCOURT (J. B. J. W. DE).

Willcock (John). A Shetland minister of the 18th c.: passages in life of J. Mill. s8°. Kirkwall. [1897]

Willcock (William J.)
The ancient masonic ring of Peterborough. s8°. 1923

Willcocks (*Gen. Sir* **James),** *G.C.M.G.*
With the Indians in France. 8°. 1920

Willcocks (Mary Patricia). Between the old world & the new: st. in lit. personality. 8°. [1925]
The keystone. s8°. [1921]
Ropes of sand. s8°. [1926]

Wille (Bruno).
Philosophie d. Befreiung durch d. reine Mittel. 8°. 1894

Wille (Jakob). Elisabeth Charlotte, Herzogin v. Orleans. 3e erweit. A. s8°. Bielefeld. 1921

Willelme. Chançon de W., *see* GUILLAUME, *d'Orange.*

Willems (Alphonse). Les Elzevier. Suppl. par G. Berghman. la8°. Stockholm. 1897
see BERGHMAN (G. S.) Et. sur la bibliog. elzevier., basées sur l'ouvr. de A. W., 1885.
,, COPINGER (H. B.) The Elzevir Press: handlist, w. refs. to W. &c., 1927.

Willenberg (Samuel Friedrich). De polygamia a Xtna. Eccl. prohib., adv. Meletium. [P2745]. s4°. Francofurti. 1714
Iterata præsidia juris div. pro def. thesium de polygamia simultanea J. Weickmanni oppos. [P2745]. s4°. Francofurti. 1714
*Vindiciae Scripturæ à pseudhermenia quae in scriptis patronorum polygamias, inprimis S. F. Willenbergs schediasmate De finibus polygamiæ licitæ committitur. Adj. schediasma Willenbergianum. [P2633]. s4°. Lipsiæ. 1713
see E. (J. A.) *Unparthey. Gedanken ü. d. Wort-Streit Weickmanns mit W. v. d. Polygamie, 1716.

Willeram, *abbot of Ebersberg.* In Canticum Canticorum paraphrasis, *see* SCHILTER (J.) Thesaurus antiq., t1, 1728.

Willert (*Sir* **Arthur).**
Aspects of Brit. foreign policy. 8°. New Haven, *Yale.* 1928

Willes (Thomas). A word in season for a warning to England. Sermon. s8°. 1659

Willet (Andrew). Hexapla in Exodum, a sixfold comm. 2p *in* 1v. [*pagin. cont. tp. placed in front of Genesis & altered to cover both works. b. w. h.* Hexapla in Genesin, 1632–33]. fol. 1633
Hexapla in Genesin, a sixfold comm. [3rd ed. rev. & enl. 2t *in* 1v. *pagin. cont.; tp. wanting*]. fol. [1632]–1633
*Synopsis Papismi, that is a gen. view of papistrie &c. [4th ed.] fol. 1614

Willett (Gladys E.) Traherne. An essay. 8°. C. 1919

Willey (Basil). Tendencies in Renaissance literary theory. [P2618]. 8°. C. 1922

Willhelms (Alfred), *see* VILGELMS (A.)

William Salt Archæological Society, *see* STAFFORDSHIRE. Coll. for a hist. of S.

William IV, *duke of Bavaria.* Turnierbuch Herzog W.'s IV [*by* H. Ostendorfer, 1541], *see* MÜNCHEN. Miniaturen; hrsg. G. Leidinger, H3, 1913.

William, *of Colchester, abbot of Westminster, see* COLCHESTER (W. DE).

William, *bp. of Coventry & Lichfield, see* LLOYD (W.)

William I, *king of England, see* HAYWARD (*Sir* J.) Hist. of W. I &c., 1618.

William II, *king of England, see* HAYWARD (*Sir* J.) Hist. of W. II &c., 1618.

William III, *king of England.* Corr. v. W. III en v. H. W. Bentinck, Graaf v. Portland. Uitg. N. Japikse. [Rijks Gesch. Publ., Kl. ser., 23].
gedeelte 1, dl. la8°. 's-Gravenhage. 1927
1i, Archief v. Welbeck Abbey.
Declar. of the Prince of Orange conc. papists, 1688 [1689]. [*b. w.* Broad-sheets. Misc. b.-s.] fol. 1689
*A friendly conf. conc. the new oath of allegiance &c. By a Divine. [P2653]. s4°. 1689
*K. W. or K. Lewis. Wherein is set forth the necessity of submitting &c. Wr. out of Cheshire by a gentleman &c. [P2663]. s4°. 1689
*Memento (A) to English-men for the special service of K. W. & Q. Mary. *no tp.* [*b. w.* Burnet (G.) Citation, 1687]. 8°. *n.p.* [1691]
The Prince of Orange, h. declar.: reasons why he invades England, w. pref. & remarks &c. [P2572]. s8°. 1688

William III, *king of England* [*continued*].
*Some reflections upon the Prince of Oranges declar. [*no tp.* P2572]. s8°. 1688
see ANGLETERRE. *Hist. des révolutions d'A. sous le régne de J. II. j. Guillaume III, 1689.
,, GREW (M. E.) Will. Bentinck & W. III, 1924.
,, GUTTRIDGE (G. H.) Colonial policy of W. III in Amer. & West Indies, 1922.
,, SPEKE (H.) *By His Highness, Will. Henry, Pr. of Orange: a 3rd declar. &c. [*wr. by H. S.*], 1688.

William, *German Crown Prince* [WILLIAM FRED. AUG. ERNEST] *1882–.* Erinnerungen. Hrsg. K. Rosner. s8°. St. 1922
Memoirs. [Tr.] 8°. 1922
My War experiences. 8°. [1922]
The 2 battles of the Marne, by W. &c., 1927, *see* JOFFRE (*le mar.* J. J. C.)
see ANKER (K.) Kronprinz W., 1919.
,, LANGE (C.) Der Kronprinz u. s. wahres Gesicht, 1921.

William I, *German Emperor.* Wilhelms I. Briefe an s. Vater, Fr. Wilh. III, 1827–39. Hrsg. P. A. Merbash. 8°. 1922
see STERNFELD (R.) Kaiser W. I in uns. Zeit, 1916.
,, VITZTHUM V. ECKSTÄDT (C. F., *c.*) Emp. W. at Baden-Baden: recoll., 1881–87, 1889.

William II, *German Emperor, 1888–1918.*
Comparative hist., 1878–1914. Tr. F. A. Holt. 8°. [1922]
Ereignisse u. Gestalten, 1878–1918. 8°. L. 1922
The Kaiser's letters to the Tsar. Copied &c. by I. D. Levine. Ed. w. intr. by N. F. Grant. 8°. [1920]
My early life. Tr. 8°. [1926]
My memoirs, 1878–1918. [Tr.] la8°. 1922
Переписка В. II с Николаем II 1894–1914. [Центрархив]. 8°. Москва. [1923]
Wilhelm II u. die Schwarzseher. Nachdruck v. "Unser Kaiser u. s. Volk," v. e. Schwarzseher." 9e A. 8°. Freib. im B. 1919
see BENTINCK (*Lady* N.) The ex-Kaiser in exile, 1921.
,, BORNHAK (C.) Deut. Gesch. unter Kaiser W. II, 1921.
,, HÖNSBRÖCH (P. *Graf* v.) W. II. Abdankun gu. Flucht, 1919.
see KAUTSKY (C.) Delbrück u. W. II, 1920.
,, —— Guilt of W. Hohenzollern, 1920.
,, LEUDET (M.) Emp. of Germany at home; tr., 1898.
,, LACOUR-GAYET (G.) Guillaume II le vaincu, 1920.
,, LUDWIG (E.) W. II, 1926; tr., 1926.
,, MURET (M.) L'évolution belliqueuse de Guill. II, 1917.
,, NIEMANN (A.) Wanderungen mit W. II, 1924.
,, NOUSSANNE (H. DE). Le véritable Guillaume II, 1904.
,, —— The Kaiser as he is; tr., 1905.
,, SCHIEMANN (T.) Deutschlands u. W. II. Schuld am Ausbruch d. Weltkrieges, 1921.

William, *bp. of Gloucester, see* NICHOLSON (W.)

William VI, *landgrave of Hesse-Cassel, see* MARBURG. *Brevis relat. colloq. authoritate W. hab., 1662 ?.

William, *St., of Monte-Vergine* [GUGLIELMO, *da Vercelli*], *d. 1142, see* COSTO (T.) Ist. dell' orig. di Montevergine, vita di S. G. &c., 1591.

William I, *king of the Netherlands, see* COLENBRANDER (H. T.) Gedenkstukken d. algem. gesch. van Nederland, 1795–1840, d10iv, v, Regeering v. W. I, 1830–40, 1921–22.

William I, *duke of Normandy; 912–43* [GUILLAUME I, *Longue-Epée*], *see* LAIR (J.) Etude sur la vie & mort de Guill. Longue-Epée, duc de N., 1893.

William I, *prince of Orange, Stadholder of the Netherlands.*
see BLOK (P. J.) Willem I &c., 2d., 1919–20.
,, RACHFAHL (F.) W. v. Oranien u. d. niederländ. Aufstand, B3, 1924.

William II, *prince of Orange, Stadholder, see* WIJNNE (J. A.) Geschillen over de afdanking van 't krijgsvolk in de Vereenigde Nederl., 1649–50, & de handelingen v. Prins W. II &c., 1885.

William IV, *prince of Orange, Stadholder.* Engelsche corr. v. Pr. W. IV & Pr. Anna, 1734–43; med. door P. Geyl, *see* HISTORISCH GENOOTS. Bijd., d45, 1924.

William V, *prince of Orange, Stadholder.* Brieven aan Baron van Lijnden van Blitterswijk &c. Uitg. onder toezicht v. F. de Bas. [Hist. Genoots. Werken, s3, 3]. 8°. s'Gravenhage. 1893

William, *of Salisbury, ps.* The Chronicle of Abomilech, king of the Isles. [*A satire on King George IV*]. [P425]. 8°. 1820

William, *prince of Sweden* [CARL WILHELM LUDWIG]. Among pygmies & gorillas: w. the Swedish Zoolog. Exped. to Central Africa, 1921. 8°. 1923
Between two continents. Notes f. journey in C. Amer. 1920. [Tr. W. Worster]. 8°. 1922

William Henry, *prince of Saxe-Eisenach.* Fürstl. Sachsen-Eisenach. Verordnung wid. d. eingeriss. Profanation d. Sabbaths &c. [P447]. s4º. Eisenach. [1731]
William (Maurice). The social interpret. of history: refut. of the Marxian econ. interp. &c. 8º. [1922]
Williams' Library [*Dr.* WILLIAMS' LIBRARY]. Author. cat. of add., 1900–21. With Suppl. cont. lists of sel. publ. soc. & connected ser. 8º. 1923
Williams (Albert Rhys).
Through the Russian Revol. 8º. N.Y. 1921
Williams (Aneurin).
Co-partnership & profit-sharing. [repr.] s8º. [1919]
Williams (Archibald). The romance of modern invention. n. ed., rev. &c. by T. W. Corbin. 8º. 1921
Williams (Arthur Frederick Basil).
The campaigns of 1917. By W. *& others.* 8º. [1918]
Cecil Rhodes. 8º. 1921
„ „ ....[2nd impr.] 8º. 1921
Williams (Arthur Lukyn), *see* BIBLE. Cambridge B.: Ecclesiastes, by W., 1922.
Williams (Ben Ames). Evered. s8º. [1921]
Williams (Benjamin Francis-), *see* FRANCIS-WILLIAMS (B.)
Williams (Blanche Colton), *see* LIEBER (M.) & B. C. W., *edd.* Gt. stories of all nations, 1927.
Williams (*Sir* Charles Hanbury). Odes. s8º. 1775
see †CATHERINE II, *emp. of Russia.* Corresp. w. Sir C. H.-W. &c.; tr., 1928.
Williams (D. J.) Capitalist combination in the coal industry. Intr. by Rt. Hon. T. Richards. s8º. [1924]
Williams (Daniel), *D.D.* A defence of Gospel truth. Reply to Chancy's First part. [*imperf.*] s4º. 1693
Man made righteous &c. 2 sermons. Also remarks on Mather's postscript. s8º. 1694
see WILLIAMS' LIBRARY. Author. cat. of add., 1900–21, 1923.
Williams (Dorothy) & M. E. Skinner. Work of children on Illinois farms, *see* UNITED STATES: LAB. Children's Bur., 168, 1926.
Williams (E.), *F.R.G.S.* Early Holborn & the legal quarter of London. 2v. la8º. 1927
Williams (Edward Huntington) & E. B. Hoag.
Our fear complexes. 8º. [1924]
Williams (Edward Thomas).
China, yesterday & to-day. 8º. [1923]
Williams (Edwin). The Statesman's manual: cont. presidents' messages, 1789–1851, w. their mems. & hist. of their admin. &c. ref. ed. enl. 3v. 8º. N.Y. 1854
Williams (*Lt.-Col.* Eliot Crawshay-), *see* CRAWSHAY-WILLIAMS (E.)
Williams (Francis Edgar).
Orokaiva magic. Foreword by R. R. Marett. 8º. O. 1928
Williams (Gertrude).
Social aspects of indust. problems. s8º. 1923
Williams (Griffith), *bp. of Ossory.* Seven treatises very necessary &c., to prevent the Seven last vials of God's wrath &c. [*3 pagin.*] fol. 1661
Williams (Gwen Mary). Mary Clifford. s8º. Bristol. 1920
Williams (Hamilton).
Britain's naval power. [2p. pl repr.] s8º. 1898–1906
Williams (Henry W.), *D.D., Wesleyan minister.*
The priesthood of Christ. [Fernley Lect.] 8º. 1876
Williams (Hugh Noel). A gallant of Lorraine: François, Seigneur de Bassompierre, Maréchal de France, 1579–1646. 2v. 8º. 1921
Last loves of Henri of Navarre. 8º. [1925]
Williams (Hugh William). Sel. views in Greece w. classical illust. 2v [*in* 1]. la8º. 1829
Williams (*Mrs.* Ignatius). Cat. of books &c. prop. of Mrs. I. W., Stevensoniana, prop. of L. Osbourne &c. Auction by Sotheby, Feb. 1923. [*Illust.* P2747]. 8º. [1923]
Williams (Iolo Aneurin). Bibliographies of mod. authors. No. 1–4 [*in* 1v]. [No. 1, *anon.*] s8º. 1921–22
1, R. Bridges. 2, J. Masefield. 3, G. Moore; pref. letter by G. M. 4, J. C. Squire & J. Stephens; pref. letter by J. C. S.
By-ways round Helicon. A kind of anthology. Intr. by J. C. Squire. s8º. 1922
Elements of book-collecting. 8º. 1927
Seven 18th cent. bibliographies: J. Armstrong, M. Akenside, O. Goldsmith, W. Shenstone, W. Collins, C. Churchill, R. B. B. Sheridan. 8º. 1924
Shorter poems of the 18th c. An anthology. Sel. & ed., w. intr. by I. A. W. s8º. 1923

Williams (Isaac), *fellow of Trin. Coll., Oxf.* The cathedral. Ed., w. notes &c. by W. Benham. 8º. 1889
A short mem. of the Rev. R. A. Suckling. 3rd ed. s8º. 1853
Williams (J. J.), *civil engineer.* El Istmo de Tehuantepec. Reconoc. para la constr. de un ferro-carril. Tr. F. de Arrangoiz. 8º. Mejico. 1852
Williams (*Rev.* James).
The Arawak Indians & t. lang. [P2851]. la8º. [La Haye. 1924]
The name "Guiana." [Extr. du Journal de la Soc. d. Américanistes, N.S., t15. P2851]. la8º. 1923
Recuerdos hist. de las Islas Canarias. Impr. en La Prensa. reimpr. la8º. *n.p.* [1926]
Williams (*Sir* John), *Bart., see* NATIONAL LIB. OF WALES. Cat. of MSS., v1, addit. MSS. in coll. of Sir J. W., 1921.
Williams (John), *bp. of Chichester.* *A true represent. of the absurd &c. principles of the Muggletonians. [P2652]. s4º. 1694
Williams (John), *of Glanmor, Denbigh.* Records of Denbigh & its lordship. 8º. Wrexham. 1860
Williams (John), *missionary, see* CAMPBELL (J.) Martyr of Erromanga: J. W., 2nd ed., 1842.
Williams (John), *sailor, see* FAIRBURN (J.) Murders in Ratcliff Highway, w. life of J. W., 1811.
Williams (*Sir* John Bickerton). Mem. of the life &c. of Sir M. Hale. 8º. 1835
Williams (*Sir* John Fischer). The Geneva Protocol of 1924. [Repr. f. Journ. of Brit. Inst. of Internat. Affairs. P2784]. 8º. [1925]
Williams (*Maj.-Gen. Sir* John Hanbury-), *see* HANBURY-WILLIAMS (*Maj.-Gen. Sir* J.)
Williams (Joseph), *of Kidderminster, 1692–1755.* Extracts f. diary, meditat., & letters. n. ed., added, orig. letters. s8º. E. 1807
Williams (Joshua). Principles of the law of real property. 24th ed. by R. A. Eastwood. 8º. 1926
Williams (Judith Blow). Guide to the printed materials for Eng. soc. & economic hist., 1750–1850. 2v. 8º. N.Y. 1926
Williams (Laurence Frederic Rushbrook), *see* INDIA: ANON. WKS. &c. India in 1920, 1921–22, 1922–23, 1923–24, 1924–25; by L. F. R. W., 1921–25.
Williams (Leonard). The art of J. Sorolla. [Hisp. Soc. of Amer.] s8º. N.Y. 1926
Williams (Leonard Llewelyn Bulkeley), *M.D.*
Middle age & old age. 8º. [1925]
Williams (M. F. Monier-), *see* MONIER-WILLIAMS (M. F.)
Williams (Mary Wilhelmine).
Social Scandinavia in the Viking age. 8º. N.Y. 1920
Williams (Max), *of N.Y.* Illust. cat. of ship models & marine prints. Sold, Mar. 1921, Amer. Art Assoc. [P2855]. 8º. N.Y. 1921
Williams (Morgan S.) Cat. of the coll. of arms & armour, early Eng. oak & tapestry formed by M. S. W. Sold by Christie, Apr. 1921. 8º. 1921
Williams (Norman Powell). Ideas of the Fall & of original sin. [Bampton Lect.] 8º. 1927
Williams (Orlo). The good Englishwoman. s8º. 1920
Some gt. Eng. novels; st. in art of fiction. 8º. 1926
Williams (Philip H.) Mod. chess problem. 3rd ed. s8º. *n.d.*
Williams (Ralph Ch.) The British lion in Bechuanaland. Exped. under Sir C. Warren. [P2832]. 8º. 1885
Williams (Ralph Hodder-), *see* HODDER-WILLIAMS (R.)
Williams (Robert), *see* SNOWDEN (*Mrs.* E.), J. H. THOMAS, R. W. &c. What we want & why, 1922.
Williams (Robert A.) The Finn episode in Beowulf. 8º. C. 1924
Williams (Roger), *see* STRAUS (O. S.) R. W. the pioneer of relig. liberty, 1894.
Williams (*Sir* Roger). Memoriën, voorafgegaan door eene verhandeling over hem, door J. T. B. Nyenhuis. [Hist. Genoots. te Utrecht. Werken., N.S., 3]. 8º. Utrecht. 1864
Williams (Roth). The League of Nations to-day, its growth & rel. to Brit. foreign policy. s8º. [1923]
The League, the Protocol, & the Empire. s8º. [1925]
Williams (Samuel Wells). Eng. & Chinese vocab. in the Court dialect. 8º. Macao. 1844
Williams (Stanley Thomas). Studies in Victorian lit. 8º. [1924]
Williams (T. G.) Methodism & Anglicanism. Intr. by W. I. Shaw. s8º. Toronto. [1891]
Williams (T. Hudson-), *see* HUDSON-WILLIAMS (T.)
Williams (Thomas), *missionary, see* FIJI & the Fijians; v1, Islands &c., by W., 1860.

Williams (Valentine) [*ps.* Douglas Valentine].
Clubfoot the avenger. s8°. 1924
The eye in attendance. s8°. [1927]
The man with the clubfoot. s8°. 1918
Mr. Ramosi. s8°. [1926]
The orange divan. s8°. 1923
The pigeon house. s8°. [1926]
The Red Mass. s8°. [1925]
The return of Clubfoot. s8°. 1923

Williams (W. H.) Burnham, Bucks: hist. sketch. s8°. 1925

Williams (William), *of Pantycelyn.* Hosannah to the Son of David. Introd. sk. by E. Morgan. s8°. 1859

Williams (William A.), *D.D.*
Evolution of man disproved. 8°. Camden, N.Y. 1925

Williams (William R.) The conservative principle in our literature. s8°. Phila. 1897

Williams-Ellis (A.) An anatomy of poetry. s8°. O. [1922]
see Williams-Ellis (C.) & A. W.-E. Pleasures of architecture, 1924.

Williams-Ellis (Clough) & A. Williams-Ellis.
Pleasures of architecture. 8°. [1924]

Williamson (Alice Muriel) [*Mrs.* C. N. W.]
Cancelled love. s8°. [1926]

Williamson (Benedict). The Bridgettine order, its foundress, hist. & spirit. Intr. by Lord Bishop of Plymouth. 8°. 1922

Williamson (Charles Norris) & A. M. Williamson.
Berry goes to Monte Carlo. s8°. [1921]
The dummy hand. s8°. [1920]

Williamson (George). Old Greenock: eccles., educ. & lit. hist. s2. 4°. Paisley. 1888

Williamson (George Charles), *Litt.D.*
Behind my library door. Authors, books & miniatures. 8°. [1921]
The book of famille rose. 4°. 1927
Curious survivals. 8°. 1923
Daniel Gardner, painter in pastel &c.: h. life & works. 4°. 1921
George, 3rd earl of Cumberland, 1558–1605, his life & voyages. 8°. C. 1920
Murillo. s8°. 1902
Stories of an expert. 8°. 1925
Velazquez. s8°. 1904
see Cumberland (E. A. W. G. F., *duke of*). Cat. of coll. of miniatures, property of Duke of C., compiled by Dr. W., 1914.
see Keats House Committee. The John Keats Mem. volume: ed. G. C. W., 1921.
,, Manners (*Lady* V.) & G. C. W. Angelica Kauffmann, h. life &c., 1924.
,, Milton (J.) Portraits, prints & writings of M.; by G. C. W., 2nd ed., 1908; repr., *large paper copy,* 1908.

Williamson (*Mrs.* Harcourt), *see* Pemberton (A. C.) The complete cyclist; by A. C. P. & Mrs. H. W. &c., 1897.

Williamson (Henry). The old stag. Stories. 8°. [1926]
,, ,, ... [repr.] 8°. [1928]
Tarka the otter. Intr. by Sir J. Fortescue. [4th ed.] 8°. 1928

Williamson (J. Bruce). Hist. of the Temple, London, to the close of the Stuart period. 8°. 1924

Williamson (J. W.) In a Persian oil field. 8°. 1927

Williamson (James A.)
The Caribbee Islands under the proprietary patents. 8°. 1926
Eng. colonies in Guiana & on the Amazon, 1604–68. 8°. O. 1923
Short hist. of Brit. expansion. 8°. 1922
Sir John Hawkins, the time & the man. 8°. O. 1927
see Belcher (*Maj.* E. A.) & J. A. W. Migration within the Empire, 1924.

Williamson (John), *see* *Advice to the officers of the Brit. Army [*by J. W.?*], 6th ed., 1783.

Williamson (John), *of Shadwell, see* Fairburn (J.) Acc. of murders of families of Marr & W., 1811.

Williamson (Robert Wood). Social & polit. systems of Cent. Polynesia. 3v. la8°. 1924

Williamson (W.), *F.L.S., see* Soar (C. D.) & W. W. Brit. Hydracarina, v1, 2, 1925–27.

Williamson (William), *shorthand writer.* Stenography: system of short-hand writing. s8°. 1775

Williams Wynn (*Rt. Hon.* Charles), *see* Williams Wynn (C., *Lady*). Corr. of Lady W. W. & h. sons, Rt. Hon. C. W. W. &c.; ed. R. Leighton, 1920.

Williams Wynn (Charlotte, *Lady*), *form. Grenville, 1754–1832.* Corr. of Lady W. W. & h. 3 sons, Sir W. W. W., Rt. Hon. C. W. W. & Sir H. W. W., 1795–1832. Ed. R. Leighton. 8°. 1920

Williams Wynn (*Sir* Henry), *K.C.B., see* Williams Wynn (C., *Lady*). Corr. of Lady W. W. & h. sons, Sir H. W. W. &c.; ed. R. Leighton, 1920.

Williams Wynn (*Sir* Watkin), *see* Williams Wynn (C., *Lady*). Corr. of Lady W. W. & h. sons, Sir W. W. W. &c.; ed. R. Leighton, 1920.

Willibaldus, *presbyter.* Vita Bonifatii, *see* Boniface, *St.* Vitae; rec. W. Levison, 1905.

Willich (Hans). Giacomo Barozzi da Vignola. la8°. Str. 1906

Williger (Eduard). Hagios: Terminologie des Heiligen in d. Hellen.-Hellenist. Religionen. [Religionsgeschichtl. Versuche &c.; hrsg. Wünsch u. Deubner, B19i]. 8°. Giessen. 1922

Willing's Press guide & advertiser's directory &c., 1924, 1926. 8°. [1924–26]

Willis (Bailey), E. Blackwelder, *& others.* Research in China. [C.I. of Wash., Publ. 54]. 3v [*in* 4. 1i, ii] *&* atlas: Geograph. & geolog. maps. 4°. [Atlas, fol.] Wash. 1906–13
1i, Descr. topog. & geol., by B. W., E. B. & R. H. Sargent.
1ii, Petrography & zoology, by E. Blackwelder—Syllabary of Chinese sounds, by F. Hirth.
2, Systematic geol., by B. Willis.
3, Cambrian faunas of China, by C. D. Walcott—Rep. on ordovician fossils coll. in E. Asia 1903–4, by S. Weller—Rep. on upper paleozoic fossils coll. in China 1903–4, by G. H. Girty.

Willis (Eola). The Charleston stage in the 18th c., w. soc. settings of the time. la8°. Columbia. 1924

Willis (Fred. Charles), *see* Thieme (U.) & F. Becker. Allgem. Lexikon d. bildenden Künstler v. d. Antike b. z. Gegenwart, B14, 15, Hrsg. U. T. u. F. C. W., 1921–22.

Willis (Irene Cooper). How we came out of the War. s8°. 1921
How we got on with the War. s8°. M'ter. [1919]
How we went into the War. s8°. M'ter. [1918]

Willis (John Christopher). Age & area, a study in geogr. distrib. & origin of species. With ch. by H. de Vries, *& others.* 8°. C. 1922
Agriculture in the tropics: elem. treatise. 3rd ed. rev. 8°. C. 1922
Dict. of flowering plants & ferns. 5th ed. rev. s8°. C. 1925
Earlier ed. have title Manual & dict. of flowering plants &c.

Willis (Nathaniel Parker). Canadian scenery illustr. Fr. drawings by W. H. Bartlett. 2v. 4°. 1842

Willis (William), *of Portland, Maine, see* Smith (T.) Journ. of T. S. & S. Deane, w. notes &c. & hist. of Portland by W. W., 1849.

Willis (William Downes). Simony, its hist. *&* effects. Puritan feoffees, 1622, & Simeon Trustees, 1836. 2nd ed. rev. 8°. 1865

Willison (John). The mother's catechism for the young child &c. [*2nd tp.,* Leabhar-Ceist &c. *Eng. & Gaelic*]. s8°. E. 1758

Willkomm (Moritz).
Suppl. Prodomi florae Hispanicae. 8°. St. 1893

Willman-Grabowska (*Mme.* H. de), *see* Meillet (A.) & H. de W.-G. Gramm. de la langue polon., 1921.

Willmott (Robert Eldridge Aris). The poets of the 19th c. Sel. & ed. by R. E. A. W. s8°. 1892

Willoby (Henry). Willobie his Avisa, 1594. With essay by G. B. Harrison. 8°. [1926]

Willoughby (Barrett). Rocking Moon. s8°. N.Y. 1925

Willoughby (Francis Willoughby, *5th baron*), *see* Harlow (V. T.), *ed.* Colonising exped. to West Indies & Guiana, 1623–67, [Lord W. &c.], 1925.

Willoughby (Leonard Ashley), *see* Schiller (J. C. F. v.) Die Räuber; ed. [w. intr.] by L. A. W., 1922.

Willoughby (Westel Woodbury). Constit. govt. in China: present condit. &c. [C.E. for Int. Peace]. la8°. Wash. 1922
Fundamental concepts of public law. 8°. N.Y. 1924
Opium as an internat. problem: the Geneva Conferences. la8°. Baltimore. 1925

Willoughby (William Charles). Race problems in the new Africa. St. of rel. of Bantu & Britons &c. 8°. O. 1923

Willoughby de Broke (Richard Greville Verney, *19th baron*).
The passing years. 8°. 1924

Willoughby-Meade (G.) Chinese ghouls & goblins. 8°. 1928

Wills (Barclay). Bypaths in Downland. 8°. [1927]

Wills (F. L.), *see* Winchester (C.) & F. L. W. Aerial photography, 1928.

Wills (Leonard Johnston), *F.G.S.*
see Barrow (G.) & L. J. W. Records of London wells, 1913.
,, Wedd (C. B.), B. Smith & L. J. W. Geol. of co. around Wrexham, p1, 1927.

Wills (William). On the princ. of circumstantial evidence. Ed. A. Wills. 6th ed. 8°. 1912

Willson (Beckles).
America's ambassadors to France, 1777–1927. 8°. [1928]
The Paris Embassy: Franco-Brit. diplom. rel., 1814–1920. 8°. 1927

Willumsen (J. F.)
La jeunesse du peintre El Greco. [2t]. la8°. 1927

Willy (Colette), *ps.* [*i.e. Mme.* GAUTHIER VILLARS, *aft. Mme.* HENRI DE JOUVENEL]. La maison de Claudine. s8°. [1922]
Mitsou. Bois orig. de Hermann-Paul. 8°. *n.d.*
Sept dialogues de bêtes. Préf. de F. Jammes. 21e éd. s8°. 1917
see LARNEC (J.) Colette, sa vie, s. œuvre, 5e éd., 1927.
Wilm (Emil Carl).
Theories of instinct. 8°. New Haven, *Yale*. 1925
Wilmart (*Dom* André), *see* BOBBIO MISSAL (THE): notes & studies; by A. W. &c., 1924.
Wilmersdörffer (Ernst), *see* PLÄNE u. Versuche z. Währungssanierung; Beitr. v. E. W. &c., 1923.
Wilmore (Albert), *F.R.G.S.*
Groundwork of mod. geography. s8°. 1925
see WOOD (L. S.) & A. W. Romance of the cotton indust. in Eng., 1927.
Wilmot (Arabella Jane), *aft. wife of Rev. Fred. Sullivan, see* SULLIVAN (A. J.)
Wilmot (Catherine). An Irish peer on the Continent, 1801–3. Narr. of tour of Stephen, 2nd Earl Mount Cashell, thr. France &c., as rel. by C. W. Ed. T. U. Sadleir. 8°. 1920
Wilmot (David), *see* GOING (C. B.) D. W., free-soiler, 1924.
Wilmot-Buxton (H. J.), *see* BUXTON (H. J. W.)
Wilms (Hieronymus), *O.P.* Gesch. d. deut. Dominikanerinnen, 1206–1916. 8°. Dülmen i. W. 1920
Wilmshurst (Walter Leslie). The meaning of masonry. 8°. 1922
Wilshire (Henry Gaylord). Wilshire editorials. 8°. N.Y. [1906]
Wilson, *The family of, see* FOSTER (S. B.) Pedigrees of W. of High Wray &c., 1890.
Wilson (A.), *M.A., of Dunedin, N.Z.* The education of girls. Addr. [P2502]. 8°. *p.c.* [Otago]. *n.d.*
The Georgian novelists. Lecture. [P2463]. 8°. Dunedin. 1894
Wilson (Albert), *M.D.* Education, personality & crime. 8°. 1908
Wilson (Alexander) & C. L. Bonaparte. American ornithology. Notes & life of Wilson by Sir W. Jardine. 3v. 8°. 1832
Wilson (Alfred W. G.) Develop. of chemical, metallurg. &c. indust. in Canada. [Canada: Dept. of Mines]. la8°. Ottawa. 1924
Potash recovery at cement plants. [Canada: Dept. of Mines. P2413]. 8°. Ottawa. 1919
Wilson (Andrew). The "ever victorious army." The Chinese campaign under Gordon &c. 8°. 1868
Wilson (Anne Campbell, *Lady*), *née Macleod, wife of Sir James Wilson.* After 5 yrs. in India: life &c. in a Punjaub district. 8°. 1895
Wilson (Anthony), *see* BROMLEY (H.), *ps.*
Wilson (*Sir* Arnold Talbot).
Early Span. & Portug. travellers in Persia. [P2833]. 8°. [1926]
Hist. of miss. of fathers of Soc. of Jesus in China &c. [*i.e. extr. f. A. de Rhodes'* Divers voy. &c., 1681, *tr. Extr. f.* Bull. of Sch. of Or. St., v4, pl. P2818]. 8°. [1926]
The Middle East. [*Extr. f.* Jl. of Brit. Inst. of Int. Aff., Mar. 1926. P2833]. la8°. [1926]
The military record &c. of the Persian Empire. [P2852]. 8°. 1926
The opium trade thr. Persian spectacles. [*Extr. f.* Asiatic Review, v21. P2784]. 8°. [1925]
The Persian Gulf: hist. sketch. Foreword by Rt. Hon. L. S. Amery. 8°. O. 1928
The Persian Gulf. [*Repr. f.* Edinb. Rev., Oct. 1924. P2773]. 8°. [1924]
Some early travellers in Persia & the Persian Gulf. [*Repr. f.* Journ of Cent. Asian Soc., v12. P2769]. 8°. *n.p.* 1925
A summary of scientific research in the Persian gulf. [*Extr. f.* Bombay Nat. Hist. Soc. Journal, v31. P2859]. la8°. 1926
A voyage up the Persian gulf. [*Repr. f.* A.P.O.C. Mag. P2851]. la8°. [1924]
Wilson (Arthur), *1595–1652.* Hist. of Gt. Britain, life &c. of James I. sm. fol. 1653
Wilson (*Adm. Sir* Arthur Knyvet), *Bart., see* BRADFORD (*Adm. Sir* E. E.) Life of Adm. Sir A. K. W., 1923.
Wilson (Charles), *D.D., see* APOCRYPHA. Bks. of the A., w. crit. &c. obs., by C. W., 1801.
Wilson (Charles Edward), *see* NIẒĀMĪ, *Ganjavī.* Haft paikar; tr., w. comm. by C. E. W., 2v, 1924.
Wilson (*Major* Charles Holmes). The relief of Ladysmith. The Artillery in Natal. s8°. 1901
Offence not defence, or Armies & fleets. s8°. 1907
Wilson (David Alec). Carlyle at his zenith, 1848–53. 8°. 1927
Carlyle on Cromwell & others, 1837–48. 8°. 1925
Carlyle till marriage, 1795–1826. 8°. 1923
Carlyle to "The French Revolution," 1826–37. 8°. 1924
Wilson (David Calder). Chinese white. s8°. [1927]
Wilson (Edmund Beecher). The cell in development & inheritance. [Columbia Univ.] 2nd ed. rev. & enl. 8°. N.Y. 1919
Wilson (Emilie I.), *aft. wife of Russell Barrington, see* BARRINGTON (*Mrs.* E. I.)
Wilson (Frank Percy).
The plague in Shakespeare's London. 8°. O. 1927
Wilson (George Francis).
Bibliography of the wr. of W. H. Hudson. 8°. 1922
Wilson (George Victor). Barytes & witherite, by W. &c., 3rd ed., *see* GEOLOG. SURVEY. Spec. rep. on min. resources, v2, 1922.
Lead, zinc &c. ores of Scotland, *see* GEOLOG. SURVEY. Spec. rep. on min. resources, 17, 1921.
see RICHEY (J. E.), G. V. W. &c. Econ. geol. of Ayrshire coalfields, 2v, 1925.
Wilson (*Sir* Guy Douglas Arthur Fleetwood).
Letters to nobody, 1908–13. 8°. 1921
Letters to somebody: a retrospect. 8°. 1922
Wilson (Harriette). Memoirs. Wr. by herself. [Repr. of 1825 ed. By J. J. Stockdale]. 2v. 8°. *p.p.* 1924
Wilson (Harry Leon). Oh, Doctor! s8°. [1923]
Wilson (Henry Austin), *see* BOBBIO MISSAL (THE): notes & studies; by A. Wilmart, H. A. W. &c., 1924.
Wilson (Henry Bristow). *Letter to T. T. Churton [on No. 90 of Tracts for the Times. *Signed* H. B. W. P2788]. 8°. O. 1841
see WARD (W. G.) Few words in support of No. 90 of Tracts for the Times, partly w. ref. to Mr. W.'s letter, 1841.
Wilson (*Sir* Henry Hughes), *see* CALLWELL (*Maj.-Gen. Sir* C. E.) Field-M. Sir H. W., 2v, 1927.
Wilson (Henry Lane).
Diplomatic episodes in Mexico, Belgium, & Chile. 8°. 1927
Wilson (Herbert Wrigley). Battleships in action. 2v. 8°. [1926]
The War guilt. 8°. [1928]
Wilson (Hill Peebles). John Brown, soldier of fortune. Critique. 8°. Boston [Mass. 1918]
Wilson (*Rt. Hon.* James), *1805–60, see* BARRINGTON (E. I.) The servant of all: pages f. the life of J. W., 2v, 1927.
Wilson (*Sir* James), *K.C.S.I.*
The dialects of Central Scotland. 8°. 1926
Old Scotch songs & poems, phonetically spelt & tr. 8°. O. 1927
Wilson (James), *M.D., see* ROBINS (B.) Mathematical tracts &c., of the late B. R.; publ. by J. W., 1761.
Wilson (James), *prof. of agriculture, R. Coll. of Sci., Dublin.* The breeding & feeding of farm stock. s8°. [1921]
Wilson (James Holbert). *Temple Bar: the city Golgotha. Hist. occurrences. By a member of the Inner Temple. 8°. 1853
Wilson (James Maurice), *canon of Worcester.* The Acts of the Apostles. Tr. f. Codex Bezæ, w. intr. on its Lucan origin &c. s8°. 1923
The figures on Edgar Tower, Worcester. 8°. Worc. 1912
Wilson (James Simpson Grant), *see* BARROW (G.), J. S. G. W. &c. Geol. of co. round Blair Atholl &c., 1905.
Wilson (John), *F.R.S., 1804–75.* An exposure of the Hindu relig., in reply to Mora Bhatta Dandekara. Prefixed a tr. of the Bhatta's Tract. 8°. Bombay. 1832
India 3,000 years ago. [*a. c. in* P524]. 8°. Bombay. 1858
The Pársé religion: as cont. in the Zand-Avastá. 8°. Bombay. 1843
A second exposure of the Hindu relig., in reply to Nárá-yana Ráo of Satárá. [*b. w. h.* An exposure, 1832]. 8°. Bombay. 1834
Wilson (John), *of New England, 1588–1667, see* MURDOCK (K. B.), *ed.* Handkerchiefs f. Paul: verses, by W. &c., 1927.
Wilson (John Cook). Statement & inference, w. o. philos. papers ed., w. mem. &c., by A. S. L. Farquharson. 2v. 8°. O. 1926
Wilson (John Dover). The schools of England. [*By var. a.*] Ed. J. D. W. Pref. by Lord Eustace Percy. 8°. 1928
Spellings & misprints in the 2nd Quarto of Hamlet, *see* ENGLISH ASSOC. Essays &c., v10, 1924.
see SHAKESPEARE ASSOC. St. in the First Folio, 1925.
Wilson (Joseph Havelock).
My stormy voy. through life. v1. 8°. 1925
Wilson (Lea). Bibles &c. in English in the coll. of L. W. 8°. *p.f.p.c.* 1845
Wilson (*Miss* M.) *Concise harmony of the 4 Gospels. W. notes. 4°. Congleton. [1888]
Wilson (Margaret). The Kenworthys. s8°. N.Y. 1925

Wilson (Morley Evans). Arnprior-Quyon & Maniwaki areas, Ontario & Quebec. [*With map.* Canada: Geolog. Survey]. 8º. Ottawa. 1924
Geol. & mineral deposits of a part of Amherst township, Quebec. [Canada: Geolog. Survey. P2514]. 8º. Ottawa. 1919
Talc deposits of Canada. [Canada: Geolog. Survey]. 8º. Ottawa. 1926
Wilson (Muriel Talbot). Hist. of the English Church in Rome, 1816–1916. 8º. [Rome. 1916]
Wilson (Pearl Cleveland). Wagner's dramas & Greek tragedy. [Columbia Univ.] 8º. N.Y. 1919
Wilson (Philip). Hunstanton & its neighbourhood. 18th ed., enl. by G. Webster. s8º. King's Lynn. 1903
Wilson (Rathmell).
A rose f. Montmartre, w. o. writings. s8º. [1919]
Wilson (Reginald Henry Rimington Rimington-), *see* RIMINGTON-WILSON.
Wilson (Richard), *R.A., see* RUTTER (F.) W. & Farington, 1923.
Wilson (Robert), *accountant.* An enquiry into the high prices of corn & labour. [P2434]. 8º. E. 1815
Wilson (Robert), *of Hawick.* Hist. of Hawick. App., mem. of the a. 2nd ed. corr. 8º. Hawick. 1841
Wilson (Robert MacNair).
The beloved physician: Sir J. Mackenzie. 8º. 1926
The care of human machinery. s8º. 1921
How our bodies are made. 8º. [1923]
Wilson (Romer). All alone: life & priv. hist. of Emily J. Brontë. 8º. 1928
The death of society. s8º. [1921]
Dragon's blood. s8º. [1926]
The grand tour. s8º. [1923]
Greenlow. s8º. [1927]
Wilson (Stanley Gordon Francis). The Univ. of London & its colleges. [With intr. by Sir S. Russell-Wells]. la8º. 1923
Wilson (Thomas), *bp. of Sodor & Man, see* ROSSER (J.) Hist. of Wesleyan Methodism; w. acc. of life &c. of bp. W., 1849.
Wilson (Thomas), *doctor of Civil Law, of Univ. of Ferrara, see* WILSON (*Sir* T.), *master of St. Catherine's Hospital.*
Wilson (Thomas), *LL.D., one of the Masters of Her Majesty's Court of Requests, see* WILSON (*Sir* T.), *master of St. Catherine's Hospital.*
Wilson (*Sir* Thomas), *master of St. Catherine's Hospital.*
Discourse upon usury (1572). Hist. intr. by R. H. Tawney. 8º. 1925
Wilson (*Mrs.* Violet Alice), *wife of Alex. R. G. Wilson, form. Morland.* Queen Elizabeth's maids of honour. 8º. 1922
Society women of Shakespeare's time. 8º. [1924]
Wilson (Wilfred), *see* BLACKWOOD (A.) & W. W. The wolves of God & o. fey stories, 1921.
Wilson (William), *bookseller, of Poughkeepsie, N.Y.*
Poems. Ed. [w. mem.] by B. J. Lossing. 3rd ed. s8º. Poughkeepsie. 1881
Wilson (William), *minister of Airlie.*
The House of Airlie. 2v. 8º. 1924
Wilson (*Sir* William James Erasmus), *see* QUAIN (J.) Anatomical plates, p2–5 by J. Q. & W. J. E. W., 1837–42.
Wilson (William L.)
The National Democratic party. 8º. Baltimore. [1888]
Wilson (William Rae). Travels in Russia &c. 2v. 8º. 1828
Wilson (Woodrow), *President of the U.S.*
College & state: educ., lit. & polit. papers, 1875–1913. Ed. R. S. Baker & W. E. Dodd. 2v. 8º. N.Y. 1925
Robert E. Lee: an appreciation. s8º. Chapel Hill. N.C. 1924
Self-determination & the rights of small nations. [P2432]. 8º. D. [1918]
see ANNIN (R. E.) W. W.: character study, 1924.
„ ARCHER (W.) The Peace-President: an apprec., 1919.
„ BAKER (R. S.) W. W. & world-settlement, 3v, 1923
„ —— W. W.: life & letters, v1, 2, 1928.
„ BOX (P. H.) Three master builders &c., 1925.
see DODD (W. E.) W. W. & his work, 1920.
„ FOREIGN OFFICE. Handbks., No. 161, Pres. W.'s policy, 1920.
„ HILL (D. J.) President's challenge to the Senate, 1919.
„ LANSING (R.) The Big Four, 1922.
„ LAWRENCE (D.) True story of W. W., 1924.
„ SEYMOUR (C.) W. W. & the World War, 1921.
„ TERRAIL (G.) Le combat des trois; la Confér. de la paix, 1922.
„ TUMULTY (J. P.) W. W. as I know him, 1922.
„ WHITE (W. A.) W. W., 3rd imp., 1925.

Wilson-Barker (*Capt. Sir* David), *R.N.R., see* CARPENTER (A.) & D. W.-B. Nature notes for ocean voyagers, 1915.
Wilson-Barkworth (Arthur Bromby). The composition of the Saxon Hundred in wh. Hull &c. were situate. 4º. Hull. [1921]
Wilson-Browne (A. E.) Cat. of coll. of books on angling, formed by A. E. W.-B. Sold by Puttick & Simpson, June 1924. 8º. 1924
Priced cat. of coll. of books on angling formed by A. E. W.-B. [*b. w. h.* Catalogue, 1924]. 8º. B'ham. 1924
Wilstach (Paul). Along the Pyrenees. la8º. [1925]
Wilton House, *see* WILKINSON (*Capt.* N. R.) W.H. guide, 1908.
Wilton (Robert). The last days of the Romanovs, from 15th March 1917. p1, Narr. by R. W. p2, Depositions of eye-witnesses. 8º. [1920]
Wiltshire Archaeological & Natural History Magazine. Publ. under dir. of the Society. v1–38. 8º. Devizes. 1854–1914
„ „ Gen. index, v1–8 [*b. w.* v8], v9–16 [*b. w.* v16], v17–24 [*b. w.* v24], v25–32 [*b. w.* v32]. 8º. 1864–1902
Wiltshire Archaeological & Natural History Society. *see* WILTSHIRE ARCH. & NAT. HIST. MAG., 1854–1914.
Wiltshire notes & queries. Illust. quarterly antiq. & genealog. mag., v1–8 (Mar. 1893–Dec. 1916). [*no more publ.*] 8º. 1896–1917
Wiltshire (Mary). The burying road. s8º. [1928]
Wimbledon. Parish reg. of W., Co. Surrey. Intr. by A. W. Hughes Clarke. la8º. 1924
Wimbledon (R.) *A sermon no lesse fruitfull then [*sic*] famous. Made in the yeare of our Lorde 1388. And founde out hyd in a wall. [Sig. A–F_4 in eights.] s8º. 1579
Wimborne (Ivor Churchill Guest, *viscount*). Cat. of old Chinese porcelain, tapestry &c., property of Visct. W., sold by Christie &c. March 6 &c., 1923. [*Illust.*] 8º. [1923]
Pictures &c. by old masters, property of Visct. W. &c., sold by Christie, March 9, 1923. [*b. w. h.* Cat. of old Chin. porcelain, 1923]. 8º. [1923]
Wimpheling (Jacob), *see* RIEGGER (J. A. S. v.) Amoenitates lit. Friburg. [De J. W. &c.], 3 fasc., 1775–76.
Winbolt (S. E.) Roman Folkestone: record of excav. of Roman villas at East Wear Bay &c. 8º. [1925]
The Roman villa at Bignor: its mosaic pavements. [P2821]. 8º. O. 1925
Winch (E.), *see* MAKGILL (J. D.) & E. W. Captain Joan, 1923.
Winchelsea. *Guide to W., 1927, *see* LEIGH (G.)
*St. of W. church, 1927, *see* LEIGH (G.)
Winchester. The anc. usages of the City of W. Fr. Anglo-Fr. vers. pres. in Winchester Coll. [w. tr.] by J. S. Furley. Glossary by E. W. Patchett. 8º. O. 1927
The Black Book of W. Ed. W. H. B. Bird. 8º. Winchester. 1925
Chartulary of W. Cath. Ed. in Eng. by A. W. Goodman. 8º. Winchester. 1927
A consuetudinary of the 14th cent. for refectory of the House of St. Swithun in Winchester. Ed. G. W. Kitchin. [Winchester Cath. Rec., No. 1]. 8º. 1886
Hist. & antiquities of W., w. charters, laws &c. [*Attrib. to T. Warton &c.*] 2v [v1 *wanting*]. s8º. Winton. 1773
Winchester College. *A manual of prayers for the use of the scholars of W. Colledge &c., 1709, *see* KEN (T.)
W.C., 1836–1906. Register; ed. J. B. Wainewright. 8º. Winchester. 1907
Winchester (Clarence). Complete aeronautics. [*By var. a.*] Ed. C. W. Foreword by Sir J. Alcock. v1. la8º. [1920]
—— & F. L. Wills. Aerial photography. Foreword by Sir A. J. Cobham. Intr. notes by Sir P. Clutterbuck & Sir F. J. C. Pole. la8º. 1928
Winckel (Heinrich), *see* JACOBS (E.) H. W. u. d. Reformation im süd. Niedersachsen, 1896.
Winckler (Georg), *see* LUTHER (M.) Trostunge an die Christen zu Halle &c., 1527.
Winckler (Hugo).
Die babylon. Geisteskultur. 2e unveränd. A. s8º. L. 1919
Winckler (Johann Dietrich). Anecdota hist.-eccl. novantiqua. s8º. Braunschweig. 1751–70
B1 *contains* 6 Stück *&* Anhang *w. sep. tps.* 1751–57. Stück 1 & 2 *publ. in* Chemnitz. *No tp. for* B2, *wh. contains* Stück 7–9. Stück 8 & 9 *publ. in* Leipzig.
Animadv. ad varia sacri codicis utriusque foederis loca pars 1. [*b. w.* Baier (J. W.) Compend., 1750]. s8º. Hildesiae. 1750
Wincobank.
Material for hist. of W.; T. W. Hall, 1922, *see* SHEFFIELD.

Windelband (Wilhelm).
Einleitung in d. Philosophie. 2e A. 8o. Tübingen. 1920
Gesch. d. abendländ. Philos. im Altertum. [Müller (I. v.) Hdbch. d. Alt.-Wiss., 5, 1i.]
4e A., bearbt. v. A. Goedeckemeyer. 8o. München. 1923
Intr. to philosophy. Tr. J. McCabe. 8o. [1921]
Die Lehren vom Zufall. [P2470]. 8o. 1870
Winder (Henry), *D.D.* A crit. & chronolog. hist. of the rise &c. of knowledge. 2v *in* 1. 4o. 1745
Windet (James). De vita functorum statu: ex Hebrae. & Graec. sententiis concinnatus. ed. 3a. s8o. 1677
Windham (*Lt.-Gen. Sir* **Charles Ash),** *see* ADYE (J. M.) Defence of Cawnpore, by the troops under W., 1858.
Windham (*Rt. Hon.* **William).** Speech in H. of Commons, May 26th, 1809; on Curwen's Bill, "for better secur. the independ. & purity of Parl. &c." [P2557]. 8o. 1810
Windisch (Hans). Der Hebräerbrief; erklärt v. H. W., *see* LIETZMANN (H.), *ed.* Handbuch z. N.T., B4iii, 1913.
Die katholischen Briefe; erkl. v. H. W., *see* LIETZMANN (H.), *ed.* Handbuch z. N.T., B4ii, 1911.
see LIETZMANN (H.) Hdbch. z. N. Test., Ergänzungsband 3, Der Barnabasbrief; erkl. v. H. W., 1920.
Windisch (Wilhelm Oscar Ernst). Gesch. d. Sanskrit-Philol. u. ind. Altertumskunde. [Grundr. d. indo-ar. Philol., B1, H1B]. 2T *in* 1v. la8o. Str. 1917–20
T2, 1920, *publ. at Berlin.*
Windischgrätz (Ludwig *Fürst* **v.)**
My memoirs. Tr. C. Vesey. 8o. [1921]
Vom roten zum schwarzen Prinzen. Mein Kampf gegen d. K. u. K. System. s8o. 1920
Windle (*Sir* **Bertram Coghill Alan).** Remains of the prehistoric age in Eng. 2nd ed. rev. 8o. [1909]
The Romans in Britain. 8o. [1923]
" " ....2nd ed. rev. 8o. [1923]
The Wessex of T. Hardy. 8o. 1912
Windle (William).
The church & home metrical psalter & hymnal. s8o. 1862
Winds (Adolf). Der Schauspieler in s. Entwicklung vom Mysterien- zum Kammerspiel. 8o. 1919
Windsor, *Victoria.* *The Windsor & Rainhill murders, 1892, *& o. p., see* DEEMING (F. B.)
Windust (Charles). Some crime stories. 8o. *n.d.*
Wines (Enoch Cobb).
Comm. on the laws of the anc. Hebrews. 8o. N.Y. 1853
Winfield (Percy Henry).
Chief sources of Eng. legal hist. 8o. Camb. [*Mass.*] 1925
The history of conspiracy & abuse of legal procedure. [Camb. studies in Engl. legal hist.] 8o. C. 1921
Wing (Tycho), *see* Ὀλύμπια δωμάτα, or, Almanack; by T. W., 1800–3, 1805.
Wingate (*Mrs.* **Alfred).** A servant of the Mightiest. s8o. [1927]
Wingate (Charles E. L.), *see* CHAMBERLAIN (J. L.) Universities & th. sons; biog. ed. C. E. L. W. &c., 5v, 1898–1900.
Wingate (Charles F.) Views & interviews on journalism. Ed. by C. F. W. 8o. N.Y. 1875
Wingate (*Sir* **Francis Reginald),** *see* STIGAND (C. H.) Equatoria; intr. mem. by Sir R. W., 1923.
Winge (Herluf). Review of interrelationships of the Cetacea; tr. G. S. Miller, Jr., *see* SMITHSONIAN INST. Misc. coll., v72, 1922.
Winger (Gottfried).
Disput. de jobeleo Lutheranorum. [P2629]. s4o. Altdorfi. 1700
Wingfield, *The family of, see* WINGFIELD (*Lt.-Col.* J. M.) Some records of the W. family (–1546), 1925.
Wingfield (*Lt.-Col.* **John Maurice).** Some records of the Wingfield family. Ed. Lt.-Col. J. M. W. 8o. 1925
Wingfield-Stratford (Barbara). India & the English. Intr. by V. S. Srinavasa Sastri. 8o. [1922]
Wingfield-Stratford (Esmé). Facing reality. 8o. [1922]
Reconstruction of mind: open way of mind-training. s8o. 1921
Wininger (Solomon). Grosse jüd. National-Biographie. B1, 2. 8o. Cernăufi. [1925–27]
Winkel (Jan te), *see* TE WINKEL (J.)
Winkelhagen (Juan).
Das Geheimnis v. Scapa Flow. 8o. München. [1923]
Winkelmann (Eduard). Acta Imperii ined. sec. 13 & 14. Urkunden u. Briefe z. Gesch. d. Kaiserreichs u. d. Königr. Sicilien. [B2], 1200–1400. la8o. Innsbruck. 1885
Winkler (Emil). Französ. Dichter d. M. a.: 1, Vaillant, 2, Marie de France, 1918, *see* KAISERL. AKAD. D. WISS. ZU WIEN. Sitzungsber., B186, 188, 1919–21.
Winkler (Friedrich). Der Meister von Flémalle u. Rogier van der Weyden. la8o. Str. 1913
Winkler (Heinrich). Die altaische Völker u. Sprachenwelt. [Osteuropa-Inst. in Breslau. Quellen &c., Abt. 6, H1]. 8o. L. 1921
Winkler (Martin). Peter J. Čaadaev. 8o. 1927
Winkles (B.) French cathedrals, f. drawings by R. Garland, w. hist. &c. acc. [*a. c. b. w.* Winkles (H.) &c. Arch. illust. &c., v3, 1842]. la8o. 1837
see WINKLES (H.) & B. W. Architect. &c. illust. of cathedral churches of Eng. & Wales, 3v, 1836–42.
Winkles (Henry) & B. Winkles. Architect. &c. illust. of cathedral churches of Eng. & Wales: the drawings f. sketches by R. Garland, w. descr. by T. Moule. 3v [*b. in* 2]. la8o. 1836–42
Winkworth (Catharine). Lyra Germanica: The Christian life. Tr., C. W. Illust. 8o. 1868
Lyra Germanica: hymns for the Xtn. year. Tr. C. W. n. ed. s8o. 1873
Winlow (R. S.) Rhodesia, 1922. Souvenir Number. [P2701]. 4o. Salisbury, Rhodesia. 1922
Winn (Wren). Timbers & th. uses. 8o. 1919
Winnefeld (Hermann), *see* WIEGAND (T.) Baalbek: Ergebnisse d. Ausgrabungen &c., 1898 bis 1905, B1, v. B. Schulz & H. W., 1921.
Winner & Waster. A good short debate betw. W. & W. An allit. poem on soc. &c. problems in 1352, w. mod. Eng. rendering. [Sel. Early Eng. poems; ed. I. Gollancz, 3]. 8o. 1920
Winnifrith (Alfred).
The fair maids of Kent. 8o. Folkestone. [1921]
Wins (Alphonse).
L'horloge à travers les âges. la8o. Mons. 1924
Winsbeke [WINSBECKIUS]. Paraenesis ad filium *&* Winsbeckiae ad filiam, *see* SCHILTER (J.) Thesaurus antiq., t2, 1727.
Winshemius (Jodocus) [WINDSHEMIUS (J.)] Christiani poenitentis conf. e decē præceptis, humanorū morū & officia & errata &c.
[*Decor. border to tp.* P2539]. s4o. Basileae, *A. Petri.* 1520
Winslow (Charles Henry). Coll. agreements in the men's clothing industry, *see* UNITED STATES: LABOR. Bull. 198, 1916.
Winslow (J. C.) Narayan Vaman Tilak, the Xtn. poet of Maharashtra. s8o. Calcutta. 1923
Winslow (Mary Nelson). Married women in industry, *see* UNITED STATES: LABOR. Women's bureau, Bull. 38, 1924.
Winsnes (A. H.)
Johan Nordahl Brun: en monografi. 8o. 1919
Winsor (Charlotte). *Life & trial of child murderess C. W. [*in* Trials, Newspaper cuttings &c., v3]. 8o. [1866]
Winstanley (Denys Arthur).
The Univ. of Cambridge in 18th century. 8o. C. 1922
Winstanley (Hamlet), *1698–1756.*
*Memoir of H. W., artist. [P2428]. 8o. Warrington. 1883
Winstanley (Henry). Book of the ground-platts, prospects of all parts of H.M.'s royal pallace of Audley End. [*Dedic. to the Earl of Suffolk & to Sir C. Wren, & plate 4* (Gen. prospect *in 2 sheets*) *wanting*]. obl.4o. [1688]
Winstanley (Lilian). Hamlet & the Scot. succession. Rel. of the play of H. to the Scot. succession & Essex conspiracy. s8o. C. 1921
Macbeth, King Lear & contemp. hist.: rel. of the play to personal hist. of James I, the Darnley murder & St. Bartholomew massacre, also of King L. as symbolic mythology. s8o. C. 1922
" Othello " as the tragedy of Italy. s8o. [1924]
Winstanley (William), *biographical writer.*
*Lives of the most famous Eng. poets. s8o. 1687
Winstedt (Richard Olaf). Malaya: the Straits Settlements & Malay States. [*By var. wr.*] Ed. R. O. W. 8o. 1923
Shaman, Saiva & Sufi: Malay magic. 8o. 1925
Winter. This winter's wonders, 1673, repr., *see* HASLEWOOD (F.) Parish of Benenden, 1889.
Winter (Cornelius), *see* JAY (W.) Mems. of the life of C. W., 1809.
Winter (Friedrich Julius). J. Arndt, d. Verf. d. Wahren Christentums. [Verein f. Ref.-Gesch. Schr., Jhrg. 28 (Nr. 101/102)]. 8o. L. 1911

Winter (*Sir* **James Spearman**), *see* NEWFOUNDLAND. French treaty rights: case for the colony stated by Sir J. S. W. &c., 1890.

Winterfeld-Platen (Leontine v.)
Vom wundersamen Wanderweg d. Lori Reck. Roman. 15e A. s8o. Schwerin i. Mecklb. 1923

Winterhalder (Theodor). Die österreich.-ungar. Kriegsmarine im Weltkriege. 8o. München. 1921

Winternitz (Moriz). Die Flutsagen d. Alt. &c. [Sonderabdr. aus d. Mitt. d. Anthrop. Gesells. in Wien, B31]. la8o. Wien. 1901
Die Frau in d. ind. Religionen. [Sonderdr. a. d. Archiv f. Frauenkunde &c., B2, 3]. T1. 8o. L. 1920
Gesch. d. ind. Litt. B2. 8o. L. 1920
see NARIMAN (G. K.) Lit. hist. of Sanskrit Buddhism, fr. W. &c., 1920.

Winterthur (Johann v.), *see* JOANNES, *Vitoduranus.*

Winthrop Papers. [Mass. Hist. Soc.] v1, 1498–1628. la8o. Camb., Mass. 1925
see also †MASSACHUSETTS HIST. SOC. Coll., s3, v9, s5, v1, 8 *for previously publ.* W. papers, 1846–82.

Winthrop, *The family of, see* WINTHROP PAPERS, v1, 1498–1628, 1925.

Winthrop (Adam). Diary, 1595–1610, *see* WINTHROP PAPERS, v1, 1925.

Wintle (W. James).
Ghost gleams: tales of the uncanny. s8o. [1921]

Winton (George Seton, *5th earl of*) [WINTOUN]. The tryal of G. earl of Wintoun, impeachment of high treason &c., 1716. [P2606]. fol. 1716

Wintringham (*Sir* **Clifton**), *Bart.* Notationes & obs. in R. Mead Monita & praecepta medica. [*b. w.* Mead (R.) Medica sacra, 1759]. 8o. Parisiis. 1773

Wintzingeroda-Knorr (Levin Georg Carl Wilhelm, *Frhr.* **v.)**
Die Kämpfe u. Leiden d. Evangelisten auf d. Eichsfelde währ. 3 Jhdte. [Verein f. Ref.-gesch. Schr., Jhrg. 9, 11, Nr. 36, 42]. 2H. 8o. Halle. 1892–93

Winwood (*Rt. Hon. Sir* **Ralph).** Mem. of affairs of state in the r. of Q. Elizabeth & K. James I, collect. from papers of Sir R. Winwood, likewise the negot. of Sir H. Neville, Sir C. Cornwallis & others at the courts of France & Spain & in Holland, Venice &c. 3v. fol. 1725

Winzer (Julius Fridericus). De daemonologia in N.T. libris comm. [P2649]. s4o. Vitebergae. 1812

Wippo [WIPO]. Werke. [*Lat.*] Hrsg. H. Bresslau. [Scr. rerum Germ. in usum schol.] 3e A. 8o. Hannover. 1915

Wirnt von Gravenberg, *see* GRAVENBERG (WIRNT v.)

Wirsüng (Johann Georg), *see* BERTELLI (D.) J. G. W., 1922.

Wirtembergici, *see* WÜRTTEMBERG.

Wirth (Albrecht). Gesch. d. russ. Reiches v. 600 v. Chr. bis 1920 n. Chr. 8o. Hamburg. 1920

Wirth (Zdeněk). Topogr. d. hist. u. Kunstdenkm., Polit. Bez. Nachod, *see* BOHEMIA. Topographie d. hist. u. Kunstdenkmale, B36, 1911.
see KAMPER (J.) & ZD. W. Topogr. d. hist. u. Kunstdenkm., Polit. Bez. Mies, 1911.

Wirtschaftstheorie. Beiträge z. W. Hrsg. K. Diehl. [Verein f. Sozialpolitik, 173i, ii]. 2T. 8o. München. 1926–28
1, Volkseinkommen u Volksvermögen: v. A. Amonn &c.
2, Konjunkturforschung &c.: Gutachten v. E. Altschul &c.

Wise (Charles), *see* KETTERING. Compotus of the manor of K., 1292, w. intr., tr. & notes by C. W., 1899.

Wise (Thomas James). The Ashley Library. Cat. of pr. books, MSS. & autograph letters coll. by T. J. W. 9v [v9 *contd. gen. index*]. la8o. *p.f.p.c.* 1922–27
A bibliog. of Keats, *see* KEATS HOUSE COMMITTEE. John Keats Mem. volume, 1921.
A bibliogr. of the wr. of A. C. Swinburne. v2. 8o. *p.f.p.c.* 1920
A bibliogr. of the wr. of J. Conrad, 1895–1920. 8o. *p.f.p.c.* 1920
Coleridgeiana. Suppl. to The bibliog. of Coleridge. [Bibliog. Soc.] 8o. 1919
A Conrad library. Cat. of pr. bks., MSS. & autograph letters by J. C. Coll. by T. J. W. la8o. *p.f.p.c.* 1928
—— **& J. P. Smart.** Complete bibliography of the wr. of J. Ruskin. Comp. by T. J. W. & J. P. S. Ed. T. J. W. 2v. 4o. *p.f.s.o.* 1893
—— **& S. Wheeler.** Bibliography of the wr. of W. S. Landor. [Bibliog. Soc.] 8o. 1919

Wiseman (Nicholas Patrick Stephen), *cardinal.* Letter on Catholic unity, addr. to the Earl of Shrewsbury. [P2788]. 8o. 1841

Wiseman (Nicholas Patrick Stephen) [*continued*].
Letter to J. H. Newman upon passages in h. letter to Dr. Jelf. 3rd ed. [P2788]. 8o. 1841
see TURTON (T.) Obs. on Dr. Wiseman's reply to Dr. Turton's Rom. Cath. doct. &c., 1839.

Wishart (George), *bp. of Edinburgh* [*ps.* SOPHOCARDIUS (AGRICOLA)]. *I. G. [*i.e.* James Graham]. De rebus auspiciis Caroli Regis &c., sub imp. J. Montisros. Marchionis &c. gestis, comm. Interp. A[gricola] S[ophocardio, *i.e.* G. W.] s8o. 1647

Wisler (Willis), *see* COMMONS (J. R.) Indust. govt. by J. R. C., W. W. &c., 1921.

Wissant (Georges de).
Cafés & cabarets. [Le Paris d'autrefois]. s8o. [1928]
Cafés qui disparaissent, *see* ŒUVRES libres, No. 77, 1927.

Wissenburgius (Wolfgangus), *see* WEISSENBURGER (W.)

Wissenschaftliche Veröffentlichungen d. deut.-türk. Denkmalschutz-Kommandos. Hrsg. v. T. Wiegand. H1–6. fol. 1921–24
see ALT (A.) Die griech. Inschr. d. Palaestina Tertia westl. d. 'Araba, 1921. [2.]
„ BACHMANN (W.), C. WATZINGER & T. W. Petra, 1921. [3.]
„ WATZINGER (C.) & C. WULZINGER. Damaskus, 1921. [4.]
„ WEISSBACH (F. H.) Denkm. &c., Nahr el-Kelb, 1922. [6.]
„ WIEGAND (T.) Sinai, 1920. [1.]
„ WULZINGER (C.) & C. WATZINGER. Damaskus, d. islam. Stadt, 1924. [5.]

Wissler (Clark). The American Indian: intr. to anthropology. 2nd ed. 8o. N.Y. 1922
North Amer. Indians of the plains. [Amer. Mus. of Nat. Hist.] 2nd ed. s8o. N.Y. 1920
Man & culture. 8o. [1923]

Wissowa (Georg). Gesamm. Abhdlg. z. röm. Religions-u. Stadtgesch. Ergänzungsb. z. Religion u. Kultus d. Römer. la8o. München. 1904

Wister (Owen). Neighbours henceforth. 8o. 1922

Wit (Augusta de). De Godin die wacht. 4e dr. s8o. A. *n.d.*

Wit (Frederick de), *see* WITT (F. DE).

Wit (Jo de). Donker geluk. 2. dr. 8o. Leiden. 1920

Witasse (Charles) [VITASSE]. Tract. de confirmatione, *see* MIGNE (J. P.), *ed.* Theol. cursus, t21, 1841.
Tract. de S. Trinitate, *see* MIGNE (J. P.), *ed.* Theol. cursus, t8, 1860.

Witebergensis, *see* WITTENBERG.

With (Carl).
Buddhist. Plastik in Japan, bis 8. Jhdt. 3. A. 4o. Wien. 1922
Chines. Steinschnitte. s8o. L. [1922]
Java. Brahman., buddhist. &c. Architectur u. Plastik auf Java. 4o. Hagen i. W. 1920
see KRAUSE (GREGOR) *&* C. W. Bali, 1922.

With (Nanna). Illust. biografisk leksikon over kjendte norske maend og kvinder. 8o. [1920]

With (Witte Corneliszoon de), *vice-adm., 1599–1659.* Leven & bedrijff; med. door S. P. L'Honoré Naber, *see* HISTORISCH GENOOTS. Bijd., d47, 1926.

Witham (Thomas Maxwell), *see* VANDERVELL (H. E.) & T. M. W. A system of figure-skating, 1869; 4th ed., by T. M. W., 1893.

Wither (George). The Psalmes of David tr. into lyrick verse &c. s8o. Impr. in the Neatherlands [*sic*]. 1632
A view of the marginal notes of the Popish Test., tr. s8o. [1588]
W.'s motto, 1621. [*repr.*] 8o. B'ham. 1814

Wither (Reginald Fitzhugh Bigg-), *see* BIGG-WITHER (R. F.)

Witherby (Harry Forbes). Pract. hdbk. of Brit. birds. Ed. H. F. W. A. of var. sect.: E. Hartert, A. C. Jackson &c. 2v [v2 *in* 2p, *pagin. cont.*] 8o. 1920–24

Withers (Hartley). Bankers & credit. s8o. [1924]
Hints about investments. 8o. 1926
The meaning of money. [repr.] s8o. 1920
„ „ ....[repr.] s8o. 1923
Stocks & shares. [2nd ed., repr.] s8o. 1921

Withers (Thomas Henry), *see* BRITISH MUSEUM OF NAT. HIST.: GEOLOGY. Machaeridia; by T. H. W., 1926.

Witherspoon (John), *see* COLLINS (V. L.) President W., 2v, 1925.

Withington (Robert). English pageantry: an hist. outline. v2. la8o. Cambridge [U.S.] 1920
"F. S., which is to say. . ." [Repr. f. St. in Philology, 22, 2, Apr. 1925. P2784]. 8o. [1925]
Mod. folk pageantry. [Repr. f. Publ. of Mod. Lang. Assoc. of Amer., v27, No. 2. P2784]. 8o. *n.p.* 1922

Withington (T.)
Remin. of ministerial life. 8o. Devonport. 1895

Witkiewicz (Stanisław). Matejko. 8°. Lwów. [1911]
Witkop (Philipp).
Deutsche Dichtung der Gegenwart. s8°. L. 1924
Die deutschen Lyriker v. Luther bis Nietzsche.
2e veränd. A. 2B. 8°. L. 1921
Witkowski (Gustav Jules).
Les licences de l'art chrétien. 8°. 1920
Wits (Herman). Aegyptiaca & De decem tribubus Israelis. Acc. Diatribe de legione fulminatrice. s4°. Amstelodami. 1683
,, ,, ...ed. 2a. s4°. Amstelodami. 1696
Exercit. sacrae in symbolum quod Apostolorum dicitur & in Orationem Dominicam.
[*2 pagin.*] ed. 3a. s4°. Amstelaedami. 1697
Miscell. sacrorum libri iv. ed. nova. 2t. s4° Lugd. Bat. 1736
t2, *cont.* Animadvers. irenicæ ad controv. quasdam Angl. &c. *&* Judaeus Christian. circa princ. fidei & SS. Trinitatem [*w. sep. pagin.*]
The oeconomy of the covenants between God & man. Tr. & rev. by W. Crookshank. 3v [*pagin. cont.*] 8°. 1763
Witsen (Nicolaas Cornelisz.), *see* NIJHOFF (M.) De Anglophobie van N. W. en verschillende redactien van zijn Scheepsbouw, 1671, 1925.
Witsius (Herman), *see* WITS (H.)
Witt (C.) Myths of Hellas. Tr. F. Younghusband.
14th impr. s8°. 1915
Witt (Frederick de) [WIDT; WIT]. Nieut kaert-boek van de 17 Nederlandse Provincie. fol. A. [1680 ?]
Witt (Jan de). Brieven. Bewerkt door R. Fruin; uitg. G. W. Kernkamp [*&* N. Japikse. Hist. Genoots. Werken, s3, 18, 25, 31, 33]. 4d. 8°. A. 1906–13
1, 1650–57; uitg. K. 2, 1658–64; uitg. J. 3, 1665–69; uitg. J. 4, 1670–72; uitg. J.
Brieven aan J. de W. Bewerkt door R. Fruin; uitg. door N. Japikse. [Hist. Genoots. Werken, s3, 42, 44].
2d. (1, 1648–60; 2, 1660–72). 8°. A. 1919–22
see JAPIKSE (N.) J. de W., 1915.
Witt (Mary Helene, *Lady*), *see* WITT (*Sir* R. C.) & *Lady* M. W. Cat. of painters &c., 1920; Suppl., 1925.
Witt (*Sir* Robert Clermont) & *Lady* Mary Witt. Cat. of painters & draughtsmen repres. in library of reprod. of pictures &c. formed by R. & M. W. 8°. *p.p.* 1920
,, ,, ...Suppl. 8°. *p.p.* 1925
Witte (Heinrich), *see* BADEN. Regesten d. Markgrafen v. Baden &c., 1050–1515, B3, bearb. v. H. W., 1907.
Witte (Hermann), *bp. of Åbo.* Exemplum non simulatae relig. in Meynardo, primo Livonorum episc. Praes. H. W., resp. T. Sculteto. [P597]. s4°. Wittenbergae. [1689]
Witte (*baron* Jehan de). Un explorateur & un apôtre du Congo franç.: Mgr. Augouard. Sa vie par J. de W., s. notes de voyage & sa corr. Intr. par Mgr. Le Roy. 8°. 1924
Witte (*count* Sergius).
Министръ финансовъ и Государств. Совѣтъ о финансовомъ положенiи Россiи, 1902. [P2391]. 8°. Stuttgart. 1903
Mémoires (1849–1915). Tr. F. Rousseau. 8°. [1921]
Memoirs. Tr. & ed. A. Yarmolinsky. 8°. 1921
see KONI (A. F.) С. Ю. Витте, 1925.
Wittek (Paul), *see* MITTEILUNGEN Z. OSMAN. GESCH.; hrsg. v. F. Kraelitz u. P. W., 1921–25.
Wittekindus [WITICHINDUS; WIDUKINDUS], *see* CRUSIUS (J. A.) W.: vita &c., 1679.
Wittels (Fritz).
An end to poverty. Tr. E. & C. Paul. s8°. [1925]
Sigmund Freud, h. personality, teaching & school. Tr. E. & C. Paul. 8°. [1924]
Wittembergische neue orient. & exeget. Bibliothek, 4t, 1776–79, *see* HIRT (J. F.)
Wittenberg [WITTEBERG; WITTEMBERG].
Abfertigung d. zu Amberg ohnlangst ausgesprengten Anleytung etl. Calvin. Blindenleyter. Antwort auff die im Anhalt ausgegang. Schr. &c. Gestellt durch d. theolog. Fac. zu W. [*b. w.* Hoym (C. v.) Erinnerungsschrifft, 1597]. s4°. Wittemberg. 1597
Ausführl. u. gründl. Wiederlegung d. deut. Arian. Catechismi, Rackaw, 1608; durch d. theolog. Facultet zu W., 1619; Lat., 1620, *see* BALDUIN (F.)
Bekentnis von d. ewig. Gnadenwahl u. verordnung Gottes z. Seligkeit, in welcher S. Hubers Calumnien wiedertrieben werden. Gestellet durch die theol. Facultet zu W. [*b. w.* Osiander (L.) Gründl. Bericht &c., 1596].
s4°. [Wittenberg ?]. 1597
*Christl. Fragstück v. d. unterschied d. zweyen Artickel, d Apostol. Glaubens Bekentnis, das Xtus gen Himel [*sic*] auffgefaren sey &c. Gestellet durch d. Theologen d. Univ. W.
s4°. [Wittenberg]. 1571

Wittenberg [*continued*].
Christl. u. wolgegründete Widerlegung d. Calvin. Testaments, so wol auch Confession, u. Leichpredigt C. Peuceri, durch d. theolog. Facultet z. W. [P2611]. s4°. Wittenberg. 1603
*Endlicher Bericht u. Erklerung der Theolog. beider Univ. Leipzig u. W. &c., 1570, *see* LEIPZIG.
Ex actis Synodicis & aliis collecta expositio eorum, quae theologi Acad. Witeberg. & alii de rebus ad religionem pert., monuerint de libro Augustano qui nominatur Interim [a decree by Charles V, 1548]. Et edita de sententia profess. Acad. W.
s4°. Witebergae. 1559
Fragstück u. Antwort oder erklerung der Theologen in Leipzig, W. u. Jhena &c., 1581, *see* LEIPZIG.
Intimatio Jubilæi Evang. ad mandat. elect. Saxon. ab Acad. Witeb. [P483]. s4°. Witebergae. 1617
Libelli Calviniani cui titulus, Tract. hist. de P. Melanthonis sententia, de controv. Coenae Domini à C. Peucero scr. Refut., concinnata à Facult. Theol. in Acad. W. s4°. Witebergae. 1597
Theolog. (Der) Facultät zu W. Beweisz dass die Calvin. Irthumb den Grund d. Glaubens betreffen &c. Nebst Anhang [*w. sep. pagin. & tp. dated* 1663]. s4°. Wittenberg. 1664
Trewhertzige, notwendige &c. Warnung &c.; gestelt durch die Theolog. Facultet zu W., 1598, *see* HERBORN.
Urkundenbuch d. Universität W. Hrsg. v. d. Hist. Komm. f. Sachsen &c. Bearb. v. W. Friedensburg.
T1, 2. la8°. Magdeburg. 1926–27
Vera, gravis &c. refutatio frivolae &c. responsionis Flaccii Illyrici. Scripta à Scholasticis Witeberg. epistolae forma. Adjecta est prima epistola Schol. Witeb. & F. defensio. [*b. w.* Diassorinus (J.) Encomium, 1558]. s4°. Wittebergae. 1558
see MELANCHTHON (P.) Kurtzer Bericht wie P. Melanthon s. Leben geendet; geschr. v. d. Professoribus d. Univ. W., 1560.
,, —— Orationes, epitaphia & scripta de morte P. M. &c., ed. à professoribus Acad. W., 1561.
Wittenberg Catechism. Catechesis cont. explic. simplicem & brevem &c.; ed. in Acad. W. &c., 1571; 1572, *see* MELANCHTHON (P.)
Einhellige Bekentnis vieler Theologen von d. newen Catechismo der newen W. &c., 1572, *see* MELISSANDER (C.)
see BRAUNSCHWEIG. Bedencken d. Theologen zu B. v. d. neue Witt. Cat. gestellet &c., 1571.
,, MANSFELD. *Der Mansfeld. Theologen Bericht u. Bekentnis v. dem W. C., 1571.
Wittgenstein (Caroline Sayn-), *princess, see* SAYN-WITTGENSTEIN.
Wittgenstein (Ludwig). Tractatus logico - philosophicus. [*Germ. & Eng.*] Intr. by B. Russell. 8°. 1922
Witting (Johann Baptist). Der niederösterreich. landständ. Adel, T2, S–Z, *see* SIBMACHER (J.) Wappenbuch, B4, Abthlg. 4, 1918.
Wittke (Carl). Hist. of Eng. parliamentary privilege. [Ohio State Univ.] 8°. Ohio. 1921
Wittmann (Michael). Ethik. la8°. München. 1923
Die Ethik d. Aristoteles. 8°. Regensburg. 1920
Wittrock (Georg). Gustaf Adolfs krigföring i Tyskland, 1632, *see* KUNG. HUM. VET.-SAMF. I UPPSALA. Skr., B24, 1927.
Wittrock (Joachim). Diss. de Reformatione Lutheri &c. Praes. J. H. v. Seelen.
Ed. 2a auct. [P484]. s4°. Lubecae. [1722]
Wittstein (Theodor). Der Streit zw. Glauben u. Wiss. auf Grundlage d. Lehre D. Hume's. [*b. w.* Zimmermann (R.) Anthroposophie, 1882]. 8°. Hanover. 1884
Witty (John). The first princ. of mod. Deism confuted. 8°. 1707
Witzel (Georg), *the elder* [VUICELIUS; WICELIUS]. Acta, wie sich es zu Eisleiben begeben hat, Uber d. tröstl. Artickel, v. d. vergebung d. Sunden. s8°. Leiptzigk, *N. Wolrab.* 1537
Retectio Lutherismi. [*Foll. by*: Querela Evangelii *&* Oratio in veterem Adam, *pagin. cont.*] s8°. Lipsiæ. 1537
Via regia, sive de controv. relig. capitibus conciliandis sententia. Acc. varia: necessitas reform. Eccl. Rom., Co. Tridentini iniquitas. H. Conringius redegit & in singula praefatus est. s4°. Helmestadii. 1650
see SCHENCK (J.) Von warhafft. Christl. Buss, wider G. W., 1539.
,, WILD (J.) Examen ordinandorum, auctoribus J. Fero, G. W. &c., 1589.
Wivell (Abraham). Inquiry into hist., authenticity &c. of the Shakespeare portraits &c. 8°. 1827
Wlassak (Moriz).
Works in KAIS. AKAD. D. WISS. ZU WIEN. Sitzber.
Anklage u. Streitbefestigung: Abwehr gegen P. Lotmar, 1923. [194.]
Anklage u. Streitbefestigung im Kriminalrecht d. Römer, 1918. [184.]
Judikationsbefehl d. röm. Prozesse &c., 1922. [197.]
Die klass. Prozessformel, T1, 1925. [202.]
Zum röm. Provinzialprozess, 1919. [190.]

Wlassics (*Baron* **Julius**). Territ. integrity of Hungary & the League of Nations. [P2524]. s8°. Budapest. 1919
Wobbermin (Georg). Das Wesen der Religion. 8°. L. 1921
Wesen u. Wahrheit d. Christentums. 8°. L. 1925
Woburn. *Hist. & descr. of W. & its abbey. n. ed. 8°. 1890
Wodderspoon (John). Hist. sites of Suffolk. With introd. verses by B. Barton. 8°. Ipswich. 1841
Wodehouse, *The family of.* The Wodehouse's of Kimberley. [*Extr. f.* Blomefield's Norfolk, v1, 1739]. *no tp.* fol. [1739]
Wodehouse (Helen). Survey of hist. of education. s8°. 1924
Wodehouse (Pelham Grenville).
Bill the Conqueror. s8°. [1924]
The clicking of Cuthbert. s8°. 1922
A damsel in distress. s8°. 1920
A gentleman of leisure. s8°. 1921
The girl on the boat. [5th pr.] s8°. [1925]
The heart of a goof. s8°. 1926
Indiscretions of Archie. s8°. 1921
The inimitable Jeeves. s8°. 1923
Jill the reckless. s8°. 1921
The man with two left feet & o. s. 9th ed. s8°. [1926]
Meet Mr. Mulliner. s8°. [1927]
Piccadilly Jim. [pop. ed.] s8°. [1925]
The small bachelor. s8°. [1927]
Ukridge. [3rd pr.] s8°. 1924
Wodrow Society.
see BLAIR (R.) Life, cont. h. autobiog. &c., 1593–1636 &c., 1848. [11.]
,, FERME (C.) Logical analysis of the Epistle to the Romans &c., 1850. [12.]
Wodrow (Robert), *minister of Eastwood.* Corr. betw. G. Ridpath & R. W. (1706–19), *see* ABBOTSFORD CLUB. Misc., v1, 1837.
Memorial & letter rel. to Alex. Henderson, 1723, *see* MAIDMENT (J.), *ed.* Hist. fragm., p3, 1833.
Woelmont (*le baron* **Henry de**) [WOELMONT DE BRUMAGNE]. Notices généalogiques. sér. 1–4. la8°. 1923–28
Woelpper (Wilson), *see* REED (A. Y.) & W. W. Junior wage earners, 1920.
Woenig (Franz), *see* WÖNIG (F.)
Woestijne (Peter Eduard Marie Karel van de), *see* KAREL VAN DE WOESTIJNE.
Wogan (Charles). Female fortitude: narr. of seizure, escape & marriage of Princess Clementina Sobiesky. s8°. 1722
Wohlenberg (Gustav), *see* ZAHN (T.) Komm. z. N. Test., B15, Der 1. u. 2. Petrusbrief u. d. Judasbrief; ausgelegt v. G. W., 1923.
Wohlgemuth (Adolph) [GUSTAV AD. W.]
Crit. exam. of psycho-analysis. 8°. [1923]
Pleasure—unpleasure: an experim. investig. on the feeling-elements. [Brit. Journal of Psych. Monogr. Supp., v6]. la8°. C. 1919
Woide (Carl Gottfried). Notitia codicis Alexandrini &c. Recudendam cur. &c. G. L. Spohn. 8°. Lipsiae. 1788
see BIBLE: NEW TEST. (GR.) Nov. Test. Gr. e cod. MS. Alexandrino descr. a W., 1786.
Wolbe (Eugen). Generalfeldmarschall Prinz Leopold v. Bayern; e. Lebensbild. Geleitwort v. Gen. Hoffmann. 8°. L. 1920
Wolbers (Julien). Geschiedenis van Suriname. la8°. 1861
Wolcot (John) [*ps.* PETER PINDAR]. Poems. s8°. 1791
see REITTERER (TH.) Leben u. Werke P. P., 1900.
***Wolf,** The, stript of his shepherd's clothing, add. to Dr. Sacheverell, by a Salopian gentleman. [P2868]. s8°. 1710
Wolf (Abraham), *M.A., D.Lit.* Essentials of logic. s8°. [1926]
Essentials of scientific method. s8°. 1925
see LUCAS (J. M.) Oldest biog. of Spinoza; ed. w. tr. by A. W., 1927.
Wolf (Friedrich August) [†WOLF (CHRISTIAN W. F. A.)], *see* CANZ (I. G.) Philos. Leibnit. & W. usus in theol., 2t, 1739.
Wolf (Georg Jacob). Altdorfer. la8°. Bielefeld. 1925
Wolf (Gustav). Deut. Gesch. d. Gegenreformation. B2, Abt. 1. [*no more publ.*] 8°. 1908
Wolf (Jacobus Gabriel).
Instit. jurisprudentiae eccl. s8°. Lipsiae. 1713
Wolf (Johann Christoph). Hist. Bogomilorum, ex Panoplia dogm. Euthymii Zigabeni &c. s4°. Vitembergae. 1712
see HIPPOLYTUS, *St.* Compend. hist. philosoph. ant. &c.; rec. &c. a J. C. W. *&* Diss., 1706.
,, MORDECAI B. NISAN. Notitia Karaeorum &c., cum vers. Lat., notis & praef. ed. J. C. W., 1714.
Wolf (Johannes). Musikal. Schrifttafeln. 4°. Bückeburg. 1923
Wolf (Joseph). Missionary journal & mem. Wr. by himself. Rev. & ed. by J. Bayford. 8°. 1824
Wolf (Lucien). The Jewish bogey, & the forged protocols of the learned elders of Zion. [P2509]. 8°. 1920
Jews in the Canary Islands. Calendar of Jewish cases extr. f. records of the Canariote Inquisition in coll. of the Marq. of Bute. Tr. & ed. w. intr. &c. by L. W. [Jewish Hist. Soc. of Eng.] 4°. 1926
Life of the 1st Marquess of Ripon, K.G., P.C. &c. 2v. 8°. 1921
Under the Duma and the Entente. The persecution of the Jews in Russia. With pref. by L. W. [P2452]. 8°. 1912
Wolf (Simon). The presidents I have known, 1860–1918. [Foreword by W. P. Stafford]. 8°. W. 1918
Wolf (Walther).
Die Bewaffnung d. altägypt. Heeres. 8°. L. 1926
Wolfart (Johann Friedrich). De P. Melanchthone eoque per Scr. Sacrae interpret. de Sacrorum instaur. optime merito. [P2672]. 4°. Jenae. 1824
Wolfe (A. T.), *see* WOLFE (FF.) & A. T. W. How to identify orient. rugs, 1927.
Wolfe (Charles), *curate of Donoughmore, Armagh.* The burial of Sir John Moore; with o. poems. Prec. by biogr. mem. [P2757]. s8°. 1825
Wolfe (ffrida) & A. T. W. How to identify oriental rugs. 4°. 1927
Wolfe (H. Ashton-), *see* ASHTON-WOLFE (H.)
Wolfe (Humbert). Labour supply & regulation. [C.E. for Int. Peace]. la8°. O. 1923
Requiem. s8°. 1927
Wolfe (*Maj.-Gen.* **James**).
see HART (B. H. L.) Gt. captains unveiled, 1927.
,, LONDON GAZETTE extraordinary. [Letter f. W. &c.], Oct. 18, 1759.
,, TEMPERLEY (H. W. V.) 2 legends conn. w. T. Gray: Wolfe & G.'s Elegy &c., 1924.
,, THORNTON (L. H.) Campaigners, 1925.
Wolfe (Samuel Herbert). Care of dependents of enlisted men in Canada, 1917, *see* UNITED STATES: LABOR.
Govt. provis. in the U.S. & for. countries for members of milit. forces & th. depend., 1917, *see* UNITED STATES: LABOR.
Wolfenbüttel, *see* SCHÖNEMANN (C. P. C.) 100 Merkwürdigkeiten d. Herzogl. Bibl. zu W., 1849.
Wolfenstein (Alfred), *see* ERHEBUNG (DIE). Jahrbuch für neue Dichtung &c.; hrsg. v. A. W., Buch 1, 2, *n.d. &* 1920.
Wolff (Caspar Friedrich). Theoria generationis (1759). Übers. u. hrsg. v. P. Samassa. 2T. 8°. L. 1896
Wolff (Christian von), *Freiherr, see* GOTTSCHED (J. C.) *Vita, fata &c. C. W., 1739.
Wolff (Elizabeth) [*form.* BETJE BEKKER] **& A. Deken.** Hist. van mejuffrouw Sara Burgerhart. Inleid. v. L. Knappert. [6e dr.] 2d. s8°. [A. 1915]
Wolff (Henry William). Co-operation in India. 2nd ed. 8°. 1927
Rural reconstruction. 8°. [1921]
see EWBANK (R. B.), *ed.* Indian co-operative studies; introd. by W., 1920.
Wolff (Johann Daniel). De legibus Ebræorum contra magiam, de maleficio magico. Præs. J. J. Zentgravio. [P2666]. s4°. Argentorati. 1694
Wolff (Johann Heinrich). Fabula Judaica de ave זיז שדי dicta. Præses J. H. W., resp. C. Schmid. [P2666]. s4°. Lipsiae. [1683]
Wolff (Joseph), *missionary to the Jews.* Missionary journal & mem. of J. W. wr. by himself. Rev. & ed. by J. Bayford. 8°. 1824
Researches & missionary labours am. the Jews, Mohammedans &c., 1831–34. 2nd ed. 8°. 1835
Wolff (Julius).
Der Rattenfänger v. Hameln, e. Aventiure. s8°. 1889
Der Sülfmeister: e. alte Stadtgesch. 2B. s8°. 1883
Wolff (Kurt). Kat. d. Incunabeln-Samml. K. W. Versteig., Okt. 1926, J. Baer & Co. T1. [*Illust.*] la8°. Frankfurt a. M. [1926]
Wolff (Paul). Unser liebes Land Thüringen. Bilder [mit Text] v. P. W. 3B. 8°. Rudolstadt. 1921
Weimar. 8°. Rudolstadt. 1923
Wolff (Philipp). Arabischer Dragomen. Gramm. &c. d. neu-arab. Spr. 2te verb. A. 8°. L. 1867
Wolff (Pierre). Les deux amants, comédie, *see* ŒUVRES libres, 16, 1922.
L'école des amants, comédie, *see* ŒUVRES libres, 26, 1923.
Wolff (Richard). Politik d. Hauses Brandenburg, 1486–99. [Veröffentl. d. Vereins für Gesch. d. Mark Brandenburg]. 8°. München. 1919

Wolff (Rudolf). Die neue Lyrik. 8°. L. 1922
Wolff (Theodor). Das Vorspiel. [B1]. 8°. München. 1925
Wolffgang, *see* WOLFGANG.
Wolffheim (Fritz).
see LAUFENBERG (H.) & F. W. Nation u. Arbeiterklasse, 1920.
,, —— & —— Revol. Volkskrieg, 1919.
Wolffheim (Werner). Versteigerung d. Musikbibl. d. Dr. W. W. T1, Testb. *&* Tafelb. *in* 1v. la8°. 1928
Wölfflin (Georg).
Disc. de Reformatione Lutheri. [P442]. s4°. Tubingae. 1619
Wölfflin (Heinrich).
Kunstgeschichtl. Grundbegriffe. 6ᵉ A. la8°. München. 1923
Wolfgang, *Graf von Hohenloe u. Langenburg, see* GRÜNDLICHER Bericht auss Göttl. Schr. v. d. furnembsten Articuln auff Befehl d. Herrn W., 1605.
Wolfgang, *Count Palatine* [WOLFFGANG, *Herzog v. Zweibrücken &c.*] Kirchenordung wie es inn d. Herrn W.'s Fürstenthumben u. Landen &c. gehalten worden. Erstlich zu Zwaypruckh 1557 &c. publicirt. Jetzund durch d. Herren Philipps Ludwigen u. Johansen, Pfaltzgraven inn Druck gegeben. [Kirchengesanng Teutsch u. Lat. &c., 1570. *w. sep. tp. & pagin.*] sm. fol. [Nürmberg]. 1570
Kirchenordnung wie es mit d. Christenl. Leer, Raichunge d. heiligen Sacramenten &c. in Wolffgangs Pf. bey Rein &c. Fürstenthumb gehalten werden sol. Erstlich ausgegangen 1557. [*Foll. by* Kirchengesanng Teutsch u. Lat. &c. *w. sep. half tp. & pagin.*] sm. fol. [Neuburg ?]. 1560
see NEY (J.) Pfalzgraf W., Herzog v. Zweibrücken &c., 1912.
Wolfgang William, *Count Palatine of Neuburg.* Muri civitatis sanctae, hoc est relig. Cathol. fundamenta 12. Dissert. explic. à J. Reihing. s4°. Coloniae Agrippinae. 1615
Wolfgang (H. F. Crohn-), *see* CROHN-WOLFGANG (H. F.)
Wolfius (Christianus), *see* WOLFF (C. v.)
Wolfradt (Willi). Lyonel Feininger. 8°. L. 1924
Wolkonsky, *see* VOLKONSKY.
Wollaston (Alexander Frederick Richmond). Life of Alfred Newton. Pref. by Sir A. Geikie. 8° 1921
Wollaston (William). *Religion of nature delineated. 4°. 1726
Wolle (Christoph) [WOLLIUS]. Ecclesia Pharisaica & Christiana in vitae morumque ἀκριβεία diversa. Acc. diss. de particul. Novi Foederis Graec. emphasi. s8°. Altonae. 1730
Schediasma de Jesu spirituali in Anglia redivivo &c.; contra T. Woolstonum. [P428]. s4°. Lipsiae. 1730
see BLACKWALL (A.) Auctores sacri classici &c. C. W. ex angl. latine vertit & Hermeneuticam N. F. dogmaticam adjunxit, 2p, 1736.
Wollebius (Joannes).
Compendium theologiae. ed. nov. s8°. Oxoniae. 1657
Wolley-Dod (Anthony Hurt). The roses of Britain. 8°. 1924
Wollheim da Fonseca (Anton Edmund). Dicc. portatif das ling. portug. e allem. 3ª ed. augm. 2t *in* 1v. s8°. Leipzig. 1883
Wollius (Christophorus), *see* WOLLE (C.)
Wollny (Franz). Ueber Freiheit u. Character. d. Menschen. [*b. w.* Schulze (G. E.) Encykl. d. philos. Wiss., 1823]. 8°. L. 1876
Wołowski (Louis F. M. R.) Mém. sur le Cours de polit. constit. de B. Constant. 8° 1862
Wolph (Erasmus). De obitu Ioan. Eckii adv. calumniam Viti Theodorici (1543); hrsg. J. Metzler, *see* CORPUS catholicorum, H2, 1921.
In obitu Joannis Eckii Epicedion. [P2439]. s4°. Ingolstadii, *A. Weissenhorn.* 1543
Wolseley (*Sir* Charles), *2nd bart.* A faithful narr. of the life &c. of John Machin &c. s8°. 1671
Wolseley (Frances Garnet, *vtess.*) Some of the smaller manor houses of Sussex. 8°. 1925
Wolseley (Garnet J. Wolseley, *viscount*). The letters of Lord & Lady W., 1870–1911. Ed. Sir G. Arthur. 8°. 1922
see MAURICE (*Maj.-Gen. Sir* F. B.) & *Sir* G. ARTHUR. Life of Ld. W., 1924.
Wolseley (Louisa, *vtess.*), *wife of Visct. Wolseley, see* WOLSELEY (G. J. W., *visct.*) Letters of Lord & Lady W., 1870–1911; ed. Sir G. Arthur, 1922.
Wolsey (Thomas), *cardinal.* Registrum T. W., Eccl. Winton. administratoris. Transcr. by F. T. Madge & H. Chitty, & ed. w. intr. by H. C. [Canterbury & York Soc., v32]. 8°. 1926
see CAVENDISH (G.) Life & death of T. W. (wr. 1557); [ed. F. S. Ellis], 1899.
,, —— Memoirs of card. Woolsey &c., 1706.
,, LAW (E.) Card. W. at Hampton Court, 1923.

Woltereck (Käthe).
Goslar, e. 1000jähr. Stadt. 8°. Hannover. 1924
Wolters (Albrecht), *see* HEIDELBERG CATECHISM. Der H. K.; hrsg. nebst d. Gesch. s. Textes im J. 1563, v. A. W., 1864.
Wolters (Friedrich), *see* BREYSIG (C.) & F. W. Gesch. d. brandenburg. Finanzen, 1640–97, 2B, 1895–1915.
Wolters (Gerardus). Oratio de lit. orient. studiis ab Arabica potius quam ab Hebraea lingua inchoandis. 4°. [Groningae. 1829]
Wolters (Paul H. A.) Archäolog. Bemerkungen, 2, *see* KÖNIGL. AKAD. D. W. ZU MÜNCHEN. Phil. Klasse, Sitz., 1915.
see MÜNCHEN. Illust. Kat. d. K. Glyptothek zu M., v. P. H. A. W., 1912.
Wolters (Richard), *see* GEYL (P.) De agent W. over de woelingen 1747 & 48 (*Eng. letters*), 1922.
Wolzogen (Ludwig v.) [WOLZOGIUS (L.)], *see* BROWN (J.), *of Wamphray.* Libri 2, in priori W., in lib. de interp. Script. causam orthod. prodidisse demons., 1670.
Womack (Laurence), *see* WOMOCK (L.)
Woman. Hist. of w. suffrage, v3–6, 1886–1922, *see* HISTORY.
Women's Freedom League, *see* VOTE, THE, 1909–12.
Women's Social & Political Union, *see* SUFFRAGETTE, THE, 1912–14.
Womock (Laurence), *bp. of St. David's* [WOMACK]. The exam. of Tilenus &c., *see* NICHOLS (J.) Calvinism & Arminianism comp., p1, 1824.
***Wonders** (The) of the East [*O. Eng. & Lat.*], 1924, *see* RYPINS (S.), *ed.*
Wong Ching-Wai. China & the nations. Draft of rep. on internat. problems prep. for People's Conf. &c., Peking, Apr. 1925. [Tr.], & ed. w. intr. &c. by I-Sen Teng & J. N. Smith. 8°. 1927
Wönig (Franz) [WOENIG].
Pflanzen im alt. Ægypten. neue billige A. 8°. L. 1897
Wonna (Georg). Exercit. de geniis deorum & hominum. Præs. G. W., publ. exam. sistet L. O. Stechau. [Exercit. 2ª, sistet J. L. Ritter]. [P1035]. s4°. *n.p. literis Krebsianis.* 1663
Wonnecke (Johann), *see* CUBE (J. v.)
Wonyan (Arsen), *see* ONIAN (A.)
Wood (Anthony à) & R. Rawlinson. Parochial collections. Made by A. à W. & R. R. Transcr. &c. by F. N. Davis. [Oxf. Rec. Soc., v2, 4]. 2p. 8°. O. 1920–22
Wood (Casey Albert) & F. H. Garrison. A physician's anthology of Eng. & Amer. poetry. Sel. & ed. C. A. W. & F. H. G. s8°. 1920
Wood (Catherine Elizabeth), *medium, see* SMEDLEY (A.) Some remin.: Miss W. in Derbyshire &c., 1900.
Wood (Frederick Augustus).
The finances of Vermont. [Columbia Univ.] 8°. N.Y. 1913
Wood (George). Combined figure skating. s8°. 1899
Wood (George Arnold). The discovery of Australia. 8°. 1922
Wood (George Arthur). William Shirley, gov. of Mass., 1741–56. [Columbia Univ.] v1. 8°. N.Y. 1920
Wood (Ge-Zay). The Shantung question. 8°. [1922]
Wood (*Mrs.* Henry). East Lynne. s8°. 1914
Wood (*Sir* Henry Evelyn).
Winnowed memories. cheap & rev. ed. 8°. 1918
Wood (Herbert), *M.E.I.A.* Guide to records depos. in the Public Record Office of Ireland. 8°. D. 1919
Wood (Herbert George) & A. E. Ball.
Tom Bryan, 1st Warden of Fircroft. s8°. [1922]
Wood (John), *see* AFRICA. Imperial map of S.A.; comp. by J. W., 5p, 1900.
Wood (John), *captain.* Discours s. le passage par le Nord-Est *&* Journal (1676), *see* BERNARD (J. F.), *ed.* Recueil, t2, 1715; 1732.
Wood (John), *of Kirkstall.* Hardy perennials & old-fashioned garden flowers. s8°. [1897]
Wood (*Sir* Kingsley), *see* BROWNE (*Sir* E.) & *Sir* K. W. Law of Nat. Health Insurance, 1919.
Wood (Leonard Southerden), *see* MORRIS (G. W.) & L. S. W. The English-speaking nations, 1924.
,, —— & ——. The golden fleece, 1922.
—— & A. Wilmore.
Romance of the cotton indust. in Eng. 8°. O. 1927
Wood (Marguerite), *see* MARY, *of Lorraine, q. c. of James V of Scotland.* Foreign corr. with M., 1537–[57]; ed. M. W., 2v, 1923–25.
Wood (*Sir* Matthew), *Bart., see* HOOK (T. E.) Tentamen, [*a satire on Sir M. W.*], 1820.

Wood (Ralph), *see* PRICE (R. K.) Astbury, Whieldon & R. W. figures, & Toby jugs, 1922.
Wood (Robert), *1787–1851.* Memorial. s8°. *f.p.c.* 1854
Wood (*Rev.* Theodore). Butterflies & moths. s8°. [1909]
Wood (Walter). Survivors' tales of famous crimes. Ed. W. W. 8°. [1916]
Wood (William). Captains of the Civil War. [Chron. of Amer. Ser., v31]. 8°. New Haven, *Yale.* 1921
Select British doc. of the Canadian war of 1812. Ed. w. intr. by W. W. [Champlain Soc. Publ., 13–15, 17]. v1–3i, ii. 8°. Toronto. 1920–28
Wood (William Alfred Rae). Hist. of Siam to 1781, w. suppl. dealing w. rec. events. 8°. 1926
Woodall (Edward), *see* ROBERTS (A.) & E. W. Gossiping guide to Wales, 1914.
Woodall (Frederick), *see* MARTIN (J.), S. PETTO & F. W. The preacher sent, 1658.
Woodall (William Otter). A coll. of reports of celeb. trials. Ed. w. introd. & notes by W. O. W. v1. 8°. 1873
Woodard (Nathaniel), *see* OTTER (*Sir* J. L.) N. W., 1925.
Woodberry (George Edward).
Appreciation of literature & Amer. in lit. 8°. 1921
Heart of man & other papers. 8°. 1920
Literary essays. 8°. 1920
Studies of a litterateur. 8°. 1921
The torch & o. lectures &c. 8°. 1920
Woodbine Willie, *ps., see* KENNEDY (G. A. STUDDERT).
Woodbridge (Benjamin Mather). Gatien de Courtilz, Sieur du Verger. [Johns Hopkins Studies]. 8°. Baltimore. 1925
Woodburn (Samuel). W.'s gallery of rare portraits, plates by Cecil, Delaram &c., w. copies f. rarest portraits, illust. of Granger's Biogr. hist. of Eng., Clarendon's Hist. &c. 2v. fol. 1816
Woodbury (Helen Sumner). Admin. of child labor laws, p5, *see* UNITED STATES: LABOR. Children's Bur., Publ. 133, 1924.
Working children of Boston. [From Monthly Labor Rev., Jan. 1921]. [P2564]. 8°. Wash. 1921
Woodbury (Robert Morse). Causal factors in infant mortality, *see* UNITED STATES: LAB. Children's Bur., Publ. 142, 1925.
Maternal mortality, *see* UNITED STATES: LAB. Children's Bur., Publ. 158, 1926.
Woodcock (William H.), *see* BLOUNT (B.) Cement; by B., ass. by W. H. W. &c., 1920.
Woodcox (Benjamin Franklin). In Cupid's chains & o. p.—Thoughts about love &c.—Spiritual evolution. [*sep. tps. & pagin.*] s8° Battle Creek, *Mich.* 1926
Woodes (Nathaniel). The conflict of conscience, 1581, *see* COLLIER (J. P.), *ed.* Five old plays, 1851.
Woodford (*Rev.* Adolphus Frederick Alexander), *ed.* Kenning's Masonic cyclopaedia & hdbk. of masonic archaeology, hist. & biog. 8°. 1878
Woodforde (James). Diary of a country parson, 1758–[92]. Ed. J. Beresford. v1–3. 8°. 1924–27
Woodhead (Henry George Wandesforde).
The truth about the Chinese Republic. 8°. [1925]
Woodhouse (Reginald Illingworth).
Sh. acc. of Merstham, Surrey. s8°. [1912 ?]
Woodhouse (Thomas) & P. Kilgour. The jute industry f. seed to cloth. s8°. 1921
Wood-Jones (Frederic), *F.Z.S.*
Arboreal man. 2nd impr. 8°. 1918
Problem of man's ancestry. s8°. 1918
***Woodland** (The) companion, 3rd ed., 1820, *see* AIKIN (JOHN).
Woodman (Lilian), *see* ALDRICH (*Mrs.* T. B.)
Woodmongers & Coal Sellers Company, *London, see* DALE (H. B.) Fellowship of Woodmongers: 6 cent. of London coal trade, 1923.
Woodring (Wendell P.) Miocene mollusks f. Bowden, Jamaica. Pelecypods & Scaphopods. [C.I. of Wash.] 8°. Wash. 1925
Woodroffe (Benjamin). Examinis, & examinantis examen, sive Reformationis &c. defensio adv. calumnias F. Foris Otrokocsi. 4°. Oxoniae. 1700
Woodroffe (*Sir* John George). Shakti & Shâkta. Essays &c. on the Shâkta Tantrashâstra. 2nd ed. rev. & enl. la8°. Madras. 1920
see also †AVALON (ARTHUR), *ps.*
Woodroofe, *The family of, see* WOODROOFE (S. M.) Pedigree of W., w. mem. &c., 1878.
Woodroofe (Selina Mary).
Pedigree of Woodroofe, w. mem. & notes. 4°. *p.p.* 1878

Woodrow (G. Marshall). The mango. [P2871]. 8°. Paisley. 1904
Woodruff (Douglas).
Plato's American republic. [Satire]. [repr.] s8°. 1926
Woodruff (Lorande Loss).
Foundations of biology. s8°. N.Y. 1922
Woods (Alice). Advance in co-educ.: articles by var. authors. Ed. A. W. Intr. by H. Lane. s8°. 1919
Educational experiments in England. s8°. [1920]
Woods (Frank Theodore), *bp. of (1) Peterborough, (2) Winchester.* The Prayer Book revised. s8°. 1927
Woods (Henry), *see* BOSWORTH (T. O.) Geol. of tertiary &c. periods in N.-W. Peru; w. acc. of palaeontology by H. W. &c., 1922.
Woods (*Sir* Henry Felix). Spunyarn: 47 years under the ensigns of Great Britain & Turkey. 2v. 8°. 1924
Woods (Hilda M.), *see* GREENWOOD (*Maj.* M.) & H. M. W. Incidence of indust. accidents &c., 1919.
Woods (Julian Edmund Tenison).
Hist. of discovery & explor. of Australia. 2v. 8°. 1865
Woods (K. S.)
The rural industries round Oxford &c. 8°. O. 1921
Woods (Leonard), *D.D., the elder, see* NEWELL (*Mrs.* H.) Memoirs: also, Sermon on h. death by L. W., 1816.
Woods (Margaret Louisa). Ballads, *see* ROY. SOC. OF LIT. Essays &c., n.s., v6, 1926.
A poet's youth [*i.e.* Wordsworth]. s8°. 1923
The Spanish lady. s8°. [1927]
Woods (Maurice). Hist. of the Tory Party in the 17th & 18th c. 8°. [1924]
Wood-turning. [Ed. J. C. S. Brough]. s8°. [1921]
Woodward (Bernard Barham), *librarian of Brit. Mus. of Nat. Hist., see* BRITISH MUSEUM OF NAT. HIST.: ZOOLOGY. Synonymy of Brit. non-marine Mollusca; by A. S. Kennard & B. B. W., 1926.
Woodward (Ernest Llewelly). The Congress of Berlin, 1878, *see* FOREIGN OFFICE. Handbooks, No. 154, 1920.
Woodward (Ezekias). A childes patrimony. Laid out upon the good nurture, or tilling over the whole man. 2p in 1v. s4°. 1640
p2 has title: A child's portion &c. *The* "Epistle to the reader" *has also a sep. tp. reading:* Vestibulum or manuduction &c.
Woodward (George Ratcliffe). The Cowley carol bk. [*w. music*]. Comp. &c. by G. R. W. rev. & enl. ed. 8°. 1912
Hymns of the Greek Church. Tr. G. R. W. [P2598]. 8°. 1922
Woodward (Horace Bolingbroke), *F.G.S.* Geol. of E. Somerset & the Bristol coal-fields. With notes by H. W. Bristow *& others* & app. by F. Rutley. [Mems. of G.S.] 8°. 1876
Geol. of the co. around Fakenham, Wells & Holt. [Mems. of G.S.] 8°. 1884
Geol. of the co. around Norwich. [Mems. of G.S.] 8°. 1881
see FOX-STRANGWAYS (C.) & H. B. W. Jurassic rocks of Britain, 5v, 1892–95.
,, WHITAKER (W.), H. B. W. &c. Geol. of parts of Cambridgeshire & Suffolk, 1891.
Woodward (Josiah). An acc. of the rise &c. of the relig. societies in London &c. s8°. 1698
Woodward (Kathleen). Queen Mary. 2nd impr. 8°. [1927]
Woodward (Matthew), *vicar of Folkestone.* The past & present of the parish church of Folkestone. 8°. 1892
Woodward (Parker). Sir Francis Bacon. 8°. 1920
Woodward (W. E.)
George Washington, the image & the man. 8°. [1928]
Woodward (William). A satirical &c. addr. to the Unitarian preachers of Belper & Mansfield. Wr. in verse. [P2511]. 8°. Nottingham. 1810
Woodward (William Harrison). Anc. Greek coins in the poss. of W. H. W. Catalogue by E. S. G. Robinson. la8°. O. 1928
Short hist. of the expansion of the Brit. Empire, 1500–1920. [4th ed.] s8°. C. 1921
Studies in educ., 1400–1600. [repr.] s8°. C. 1924
Woodwork joints, how they are set out, made &c. [Ed. J. C. S. Brough]. [2nd ed.] s8°. [1919]
Woodworth (Robert Sessions).
Psychology: st. of mental life. s8°. [1922]
Woodyatt (*Maj.-Gen.* Nigel). My sporting memories. 8°. 1923
Under 10 viceroys: remin. of a Gurkha. 8°. 1922
Woog (Carl Christian). De Melitone Sardium in Asia episcopo. [P597]. s4°. Lipsiae. 1734
Woolavington (James Buchanan, *1st baron***).** Sporting pictures at Lavington Park. [Intr. by Sir T. Cook]. 4°. *p.f.p.c.* 1927

Wooldredge (Clifton R.)
Hands up! or 12 yrs. a detective. 8°. Chicago. [1906]
Woolf (Bella Sidney), *aft. wife of Robert Heath Lock.*
How to see Ceylon. 8°. Colombo. *n.d.*
Woolf (H. I.) Three Tibetan mysteries: Tchrimekundan, Nansal, Djroazanmo. Tr. f. the French version of J. Bacot, w. intr., notes &c. [Broadway Trans.] s8°. [1924]
Woolf (Leonard Sidney). Economic imperialism. s8°. 1920
Essays on lit., hist. &c. s8°. 1927
Internat. government. Prep. for Fabian Res. Dept. Intr. by B. Shaw. [2nd ed.] 8°. [1923]
Stories of the East. s8°. 1921
Woolf (Virginia). The common reader. 8°. 1925
Jacob's room. s8°. Richmond. 1922
Kew Gardens. 2nd ed. 8°. Richmond. 1919
Mrs. Dalloway. s8°. 1925
To the lighthouse. s8°. 1927
Woollacott (Arthur P.) Mackenzie & h. voyageurs: by canoe to the Arctic &c., 1789–93. 8°. 1927
Woolley (Charles Leonard). Dead towns & living men. 8°. 1920
From Kastamuni to Kedos: exper. of prisoners of war in Turkey, 1916–18. Wr. by many hands & ed. W. la8°. O. 1921
see Brit. Museum. Carchemish: rep. on excav. at Jerablus; conducted by C. L. W. &c., p2, The town defences, 1921.
„ Peet (T. E.) & C. L. W. The city of Akhenaten, p1, 1923.
„ Ur excavations, v1, Al-'Ubaid: rep., by W. &c., 1927.
Woolley (R. V. Giffard).
Herbaceous borders for amateurs. 8°. 1926
Woolley (Reginald Maxwell). St. Hugh of Lincoln. 8°. [1927]
see Gilbertine Rite; ed. R. M. W., 2v, 1921–22.
„ Lincoln. Cat. of MSS. of L. Cath. Library, 1927.
Woolls (William), *F.L.S.*
Contrib. to the flora of Australia. 8°. Sydney. 1867
Woolman (John). Journal & Essays. Ed. w. biog. intr. by A. M. Gummere. Rancocas ed. 8°. 1922
Woolmer (Ethel A.) Story of Battersea as told to children. Foreword by Rt. Hon. J. Burns. s8°. [1924]
Woolmer (Theophilus). Wesleyan pastors & their people; or, a 3rd letter to J. B. [P449]. 8°. 1851
Woolner (Thomas).
My beautiful lady. [3rd ed. *engr. tp. dated* 1866]. s8°. 1865
Woolrich (Ellen), *see* Phillips (R. R.) & E. W. Furnishing the house, 1921.
Woolrych (Humphry William).
A series of Lords Chancellors &c. s8°. 1826
Woolston (Thomas), *see* Wolle (C.) Sched. de Jesu spirituali in Anglia redivivo &c., contra T. W. 1730.
Woolwich. Official cat. of the Museum of Artillery in the Rotunda, Woolwich. By J. H. Lefroy. s8°. 1864
A survey & record of W. & W. Kent, 1909, *see* Grinling (C. H.), T. A. Ingram *& others, edd.*
Woordenboek d. Nederlandsche taal, *in prog.*, *see* Vries (M. de), L. A. Te Winkel, *& others, edd.*
Wootton (W. H.), *see* Mandalay. M. massacres; [by W. &c.], 1884.
Worcester. Early W. MSS. Fragments of 4 books & a charter of the 8th c. belong. to W. Cathedral. Photograph. reprod. Ed., w. transcr., intr. &c. by C. H. Turner. fol. O. 1916
Worcester (Edward Somerset, *2nd marq. of*). *Inquiry into the share wh. Ch. I had in the trans. of the E. of Glamorgan &c., 1645–46, 1747, *see* Birch (T.)
Worcester (Henry Somerset, *1st marquis of*), *see* Cartwright (C.) Certamen religiosum or conf. betw. the late K. of E. & the late Marq. of W. &c., 1652.
Worcestershire Exhibition, 1882. Reports on the var. sections &c. Publ. under authority of Gen. Comm. 4°. [1882]
***Word.** *A word in season, or advice to a soldier, *n.d.*, *see* Wesley (J.)
*A word to a drunkard, 1748, *see* Wesley (J.)
*A word to a freeholder &c., 1748, *see* Wesley (J.)
*A word to a street-walker, 1748, *see* Wesley (J.)
Wordsworth, *The family of*, *see* Robinson (H. C.) Corr. w. the W. circle, 1808–66; ed. &c. E. J. Morley, 2v, 1927.
Wordsworth (Anne Caroline), *see* Harper (G. McL.) Wordsworth's French daughter, 1921.
Wordsworth (Charles), *bp. of St. Andrews.*
*A Greek primer. 2nd ed. s8°. O. 1871
Wordsworth (Christopher), *1774–1846, Master of Trin. Coll., Cam.* Eccl. biography, lives of men conn. w. the hist. of relig. in Eng. 4th ed. 4v. 8°. 1853

Wordsworth (Christopher), *1807–85, bp. of Lincoln.* Greece. n. ed., w. Characteristics of Gr. art, by G. Scharf. la8°. 1859
Sequel to letters &c. to Gondon. 2nd ed. s8°. 1848
Wordsworth (Dorothy), *see* Maclean (C. M.) D. & William W., 1927.
Wordsworth (Elizabeth), *principal of Lady Margaret Hall, Oxford.* Essays old & new. s8°. O. 1919
Wordsworth (William), *poet laureate.*
The Grasmere Wordsworth. Ed. J. Hawke. s8°. [1926]
Pref. & essays on poetry 1800–1815; ed. G. Sampson, *see* Coleridge (S. T.) Biographia lit.; ch. 1–4, 14–22, 1920.
The prelude. Ed. w. intr. &c. by E. De Selincourt. 8°. O. 1926
see Babenroth (A. C.) Eng. childhood: W.'s treatment, 1922.
„ Bardi (P.) La poesia di W., 1922.
„ Beatty (A.) W.: h. doctrine & art in their hist. rels., 1922.
„ Broughton (L. N.) Theocritean element in works of W. W., 1920.
„ Garrod (H. W.) W.: lect. &c., 1923; 2nd ed., 1927.
„ Grey (E. G., *1st visct.*) W.'s "Prelude," 1923.
see Harper (G. McL.) W.'s French daughter, 1921.
„ Legouis (E.) W. Wordsworth & A. Vallon, 1922.
„ —— W. in a new light, 1923.
„ Lyrical ballads &c. [*by* Coleridge & W.], 1798; [Noel Douglas Replicas], 1926.
„ Maclean (C. M.) Dorothy & W. W., 1927.
„ Madariaga (S. de). Shelley, &c. & o. essays [The case of W.], 1920.
„ Myers (F. W. H.) W., 1919.
„ Raleigh (*Sir* W.) W., 8th impr., 1921.
„ Robinson (H. C.) Corr. w. the W. circle, 1808–66; ed. &c. E. J. Morley, 2v, 1927.
„ Strong (A. T.) Three st. in Shelley & essay on nature in W., 1921.
„ Woods (M. L.) A poet's youth, *fiction*, 1923.
Workenius (Franciscus). Christianismus primaevus quem Guil. Whistonus modo non probando restituendam dictitat &c. [*b. w.* Zeltner (G. G.) Breviarium &c., 1719]. s8°. Wittenbergae. 1729
Working days: records of 16 working men &c., 1926, *see* Pollock (M. A.), *ed.*
***Working-man's** (The) companion: the results of machinery &c., 1831, *see* Knight (C.)
Workman (Herbert Brook). John Wiclif: st. of the Eng. medieval church. 2v. 8°. O. 1926
Workmen's. Digest of Workmen's Compensation laws, 1912. Prep. by Nat. Assoc. of Manufact. 8°. [St. Louis, Mo. 1912]
***World** (The) peace & Chinese tariff autonomy. [P2385]. s8°. [1919]
World, The, *N.Y.*, *see* Heaton (J. L.) Story of a page: 30 yrs. of N.Y. World, 1913.
World (The) almanac. 1886, 1890, 1902–17 (1905–7, 1912–14 *missing*). s8°. N.Y. 1886–1917
World Population Conference. Proceedings, Geneva, Aug. 29th to Sept. 3rd, 1927. Ed. M. Sanger. 8°. 1927
***World's** (The) mistake in O. Cromwell, 1668, *see* Bethell (S.)
Worlledge (Arthur John). Prayer. 5th impr. 8°. 1917
Worm (Christen), *bp. of Seeland.*
Hist. Sabelliana. s8°. Francofurti. 1696
Worm-Müller (Jacob S.) Norge gjennem nødsaarene: d. norske Regjeringskomm., 1807–10. la8°. 1918
Worms [Wormbs]. Abschied der gesandten Augspurg. Conf., zum Colloquio inn Wormbs [*signed* P. Melanthon, J. Brentius *&c.*] [P2442]. s4°. *n.p.* 1557
Colloquium Wormac. instit. A.D. 1540 autoritate. Imp. Caroli V ad derimendas controversias Eccl. s4°. Vitebergae, *J. Klug.* 1542
Another copy b. w. Ratisbon. Acta in Conventu, 1541.
Worrell (William Hoyt). Two Coptic homilies & a magical text in the Freer Coll. Ed. W. H. W. [Univ. of Michigan]. 4°. N.Y. 1923
Worringer (Wilhelm). Egyptian art. Tr., ed. w. pref. by B. Rackham. la8°. [1928]
Formprobleme d. Gotik. 8e bis 12e A. 8°. München. 1920
Worsfold (William Basil). Palestine of the Mandate. 8°. [1925]
Sir Bartle Frere: footnote to hist. of Brit. Empire. 8°. [1923]
Worster (W.), *see* Rasmussen (K.) Eskimo folk-tales, ed. &c. by W. W., 1921.
Wortabet (William Thomson). Arabic-Eng. dict. With collab. of J. Wortabet & H. Porter. 8°. Cairo. 1888
Wörterbuch. Wbch. d. griech. Papyrusurkunden &c., *see* Preisigke (F.), *ed.*
Worth (Claud). Yacht cruising. By C. W., w. collab. of G. Green, C. J. Bennet, & C. D. Marshall. la8°. 1910
Wortham (Hugh Evelyn). Oscar Browning. 8°. 1927

Worthington (Frank), *C.B.E.*
The witch doctor & o. Rhodesian studies. 8º. [1922]
Worthington (Thomas). An anker of Christian doctrine; princ. pointes of Cath. relig. s4º. Doway. 1622
Wortley (*Hon. Mrs.* **Edward Stuart),** *see* STUART-WORTLEY (*Hon. Mrs.* VIOLET), *wife of Hon. Ed. S.-W.*
Wortley (John Dixon). Swannington: its church, rectors & hist. 8º. Norwich. [1921]
Wortmann (Carl). Gesch. d. Deut. Vaterlands-Partei, 1917–18. 8º. Halle (Saale). 1926
Wostrowitz (Eduard B. Fleissner v.), *see* FLEISSNER v. WOSTROWITZ (E. B.)
Wotquenne (Alfred). Baldassare Galuppi, 1706–85. Et. bibliog. sur ses œuvres dramat. 8º. Brux. 1902
Wotschke (Theodor). Der Briefwechsel d. Schweizer mit d. Polen. [Archiv f. Ref.-gesch., Ergänzungsband 3]. 8º. L. 1908
Wotton (*Sir* **Henry).** The elem. of architecture. s4º. 1624
Reliquiæ Wottonianae: lives, letters, poems &c. by W. [& life of W. by I. Walton]. 3rd ed., w. add. s8º. 1672
Wotton (Mabel E.)
S. Peter's chapel, Palace St., S.W.1. [P2585]. s8º. 1918
Woude (Johanna van), *ps.* [*i.e.* SOPHIA MARGARETHA CORNELIA VAN WERMESKERKEN]. Hollandsch binnenhuisje. Geillust. door L. Raemaekers. 15e dr. 8º. Amsterdam. 1920
Woulfe (Patrick). Irish names & surnames. s8º. D. 1923
Wounded Allies' Relief Committee, The, 1914–19.
A brief record. 8º. [1920]
Wower (Joannes à). Syntagma de Gr. & Lat. Bibliorum interpret. s8º. Hamburgi. 1618
Woytinsky (Wladimir). La démocratie géorgienne. Préf. de M. E. Vandervelde. 8º. 1921
Wragg (*Mrs.* **Harriet),** *see* DUCKITT (M.) & H. W., *edd.* Sel. Eng. letters (15–19 c.), 1916.
Wrangel (*baron* **Nikolai),** *1847–1920.* From serfdom to bolshevism. Memoirs, 1847–1920. Tr. by B. & B. Lunn. 8º. 1927
Wrangel (*baron* **Nikolai Nikolaievich)** [VRANGEL], *1882–, see* SAINT PETERSBURG: RUSSIAN MUS. OF ALEX. III. РУССКІЙ МУЗЕЙ ИМП. А. III, 2т, 1904.
Wrangell (*Adm.* **Ferdinand v.)** Narr. of an exped. to the Polar Sea, 1820–23, comm. by Adm. F. v. W. [Tr.] Ed. Lt.-Col. E. Sabine. 2nd ed., w. add. s8º. 1844
Wratislaw (Albert Charles), *C.B.*
A consul in the East. 8º. E. 1924
Wray (Cecil J.), *see* REEVES (W. P.) Long white cloud, added sketch of rec. events by C. J. W., 1924.
Wray (Disney Alexander), *see* POCOCK (R. W.) & D. A. W. Geology of co. around Wem, 1925.
Wray (Samuel), *see* BUSH (J.) W. O. Simpson, early life &c., by S. W., 1886.
***Wreath (A)** of cloud: 3rd part of "The tale of Genji"; tr. A. Waley, 1927, *see* MURASAKI (*Lady*).
Wrede (Adam). Gesch. d. alt. Kölner Univ. [1388–1798]. s8º. [Köln]. 1921
Wrede (Adolf). Ernst. d. Bekenner, Herzog v. Braunschweig u. Lüneberg. [Verein f. Ref.-gesch. Schr., Jhrg. 6, Nr. 25]. 8º. Halle. 1888
Wrede (*Feldmarschall Fürst* **Carl Philipp),** *1767–1838, see* BIBL (V.) Metternich in neu. Beleuchtung: s. geheimer Briefwechsel mit W. [1831–34], 1928.
Wrede (Friedrich Egon Ignaz, *Fürst* **v.)** [*ps.* FRIEDRICH v. STEIN]. Politeia. Roman. 2e A. 8º. Darmstadt. [1925]
Wren (*Sir* **Christopher).** Sir C. W., 1632–1723. Contrib. by P. Waterhouse, Sir R. Blomfield [*& others.* Repr., w. add., from The Architects' Journal]. fol. 1923
"Tom Tower" Christ Church, Oxford. Some letters of W. to J. Fell. Set forth & annot. by W. D. Caröe. With a chap. by H. H. Turner, & another by A. Cochrane. 4º. O. 1923
see STRATTON (A.) The life, work, & infl. of Sir C. W., 1897.
,, TAYLOR (A. T.) Towers & steeples designed by Sir C. W., 1881.
,, WEAVER (*Sir* L.) Sir C. W., 1923.
Wren (Percival Christopher).
Beau Geste. [repr.] s8º. 1926
Beau Sabreur. s8º. [1926]
Wrenn Library, *Texas, see* GRIFFITH (R. H.) Great torch race; addr. at dedic. of W. Lib., 1920.

Wreszinski (Walter). Bericht ü. d. photograph. Exped. v. Kairo bis Wadi Halfa. [Königsb. Gelehrt. Gesells.] 8º. Halle a. S. 1927
Wright (Abraham). A pract. comm. &c. upon the Pentateuch. sm. fol. 1662
Wright (Albert Hazen). Frogs: nat. hist. & utilization, 1920, *see* UNITED STATES: COMMERCE.
Wright (*Sir* **Almroth Edward).** Further contrib. to st. of phenomena of intertraction. [From Roy. Soc. Proc., A, v114]. [P2876]. la8º. [1927]
Immunity. Repr. f. Encycl. Brit., 13th ed. [P2872]. 8º. [1927]
New principles in therapeutic inoculation. Repr. f. The Lancet, 1923. [P2701]. 4º. [1923]
The physiology of wounds. [Repr. f. The Medical hist. of the War. P2709]. 8º. [1923]
—— **& L. Colebrook.**
Technique of the teat & capillary glass tube. 8º. 1921
Wright (Arnold). Romance of colonis.: econ. development of Brit. Empire. 8º. [1923]
see BRAZIL. 20th c. impressions of B.: historian A. W., 1913.
—— **& W. L. Sclater.** Sterne's Eliza. Acc. of h. life in India, w. letters, 1757–74. 8º. 1922
Wright (Bryce McMurdo), *see* BRASSEY (A., *Lady*). Cat. of natural hist., ethnolog. specimens &c. coll. by Lady B., 1876–1883; by B. W., 1885.
Wright (Charles), *chairman of Lloyd's Brokers' Assoc.* **& C. E. Fayle.** A hist. of Lloyd's. la8º. 1928
Wright (Charles Henry Conrad). French classicism. [Harvard studies]. 8º. Camb. [Mass.] 1920
Wright (Charles Seymour).
Works in BRIT. ANTARCTIC EXPED., 1910–13, *q.v.*
Determinat. of gravity, 1921.
Obs. on the aurora, 1921.
Physiography of the Beardmore Glacier Region, 1923.
—— **& R. E. Priestley.** Glaciology, 1922, *see* BRIT. ANTARCTIC EXPED., 1910–13.
Wright (Charles Theodore Hagberg). La "London Library." [Extr. de la Revue des bibl.] la8º. 1925
The London Library: hist. & admin. 8º. 1926
Nicholas Fabri de Peiresc. [Roxburghe Club]. la8º. 1926
The soul's dispensary. Early yrs. of the London Library. [*Repr. f.* Nineteenth cent., March 1922]. la8º. [1922]
see LONDON LIBRARY. Cat., 2v, 1913; Suppl. (1913–20), 1920; Subject index, 2v, 1909–23.
Wright (Constance Hagberg).
Tales of Chinese magic. Ill. by D. T. Lewis. la8º. 1925
Wright (Dudley). Druidism, the anc. faith of Britain. la8º. 1924
Wright (Elizabeth Mary), *see* WRIGHT (J.) & E. M. W. Elem. Old Eng. grammar, 1923.
Wright (Frederick Adam).
The arts in Greece. 3 essays. 8º. 1923
Greek athletics. 8º. [1925]
Greek social life. [*Passages f. Gr. a.*] 8º. 1925
see ANTHOLOGIA GRAECA. The girdle of Aphrodite; tr. by F. A. W., w. intr., 1923.
,, —— Poets of the Gr. Anthology; tr. F. A. W., w. biog. & crit. pref., 1924.
Wright (Florence Swift). Industrial nursing. s8º. N.Y. 1920
Wright (Frances), *aft. Mme. d'Arusmont, see* WATERMAN (W. R.) F. W., 1924.
Wright (George Newnham). The Rhine, Italy, & Greece. Drawings by Col. Cockburn &c. With descr. by G. N. W. 2v. 4º. [1841–42]
Scenes in Ireland; w. hist. illust., legends & biograph. notices. s8º. 1834
Wright (Harold).
Population. Pref. by J. M. Keynes. s8º. [1923]
Wright (Harold J. L.), *see* DELTEIL (L.) & H. J. L. W. Cat. raisonné of etchings of C. Meryon, 1924.
Wright (Hendrick B.)
A practical treatise on labor. s8º. N.Y. 1871
Wright (Herbert). Assoc. of T. L. Peacock w. Wales, *see* ENG. ASSOC. Essays, v12, 1926.
Wright (Ichabod Charles), *1795–1871, see* BRISCOE (J. P.) A Nottingham translator of Dante & Homer, 1901.
Wright (Irene Aloha). Cuba. 8º. N.Y. 1910
Span. narratives of Eng. attack on Santo Domingo, 1655; transcr., tr. &c. by I. A. W., *see* CAMDEN MISC., v14, 1926.
Wright (John Frank). Brockville-Mallorytown map-area, Ontario. [Canada. Geolog. Survey. P2713]. 8º. Ottawa. 1923

Wright (John Kirtland). The geograph. lore of the times of the Crusades. [American Geog. Soc.] 8°. N.Y. 1925
Wright (Joseph), *A.R.A.* ["WRIGHT *of Derby*"], *see* SMITH (S. C. K.) & H. C. BEMROSE. W. of Derby, 1922.
Wright (Joseph), *D.C.L.*, **& E. M. Wright.**
Elementary Old English grammar. s8°. O. 1923
Wright (Joseph), *of Harvard Univ.* Sel. readings in municipal problems. Intr. by W. B. Monro. 8°. Boston. [1925]
Wright (K. M.), *see* STOREY (F. W.) & K. M. W. South African botany, 1922.
Wright (Lewis). Optical projection. 5th ed., re-wr. &c. by R. S. Wright. pl. s8°. 1920
A pop. handbook to the microscope. s8°. 1895
,, ,, ...2nd impr. s8°. 1905
Wright (Peter E.) At the Supreme War Council. s8°. 1921
Wright (Phillip Quincey). The control of the for. relations of the U.S. &c. [*Extr. f.* Amer. Philos. Soc. Procs., v60]. la8°. Phila. 1921
Wright (Reginald W. M.) Farleigh Castle, *see* WALPOLE SOC., v10, 1922.
Wright (Richard), *Unitarian missionary.* An apology for M. Servetus: includ. life &c. 8°. Wisbech. 1806
Wright (Richardson).
Hawkers & walkers in early America. 8°. Phila. 1927
Wright (*Sir* **Robert Samuel)** [*Mr. Justice* WRIGHT]. Golden treasury of anc. Greek poetry. 2nd ed., rev. by E. Abbott. s8°. O. 1889
—— **&** *Rt. Hon.* **H. Hobhouse.** Outline of local govt. & local taxation in Eng. & Wales (excl. London). 5th ed. 8°. 1922
—— **& J. E. L. Shadwell.**
A golden treasury of Greek prose. s8°. O. 1870
Wright (S. Fowler). The deluge. s8°. 1927
Wright (Thomas), *M.A., F.S.A.* Early Christianity in Arabia. 8°. 1855
Wright (Thomas), *principal of Cowper School, Olney.* Buckinghamshire & Northamptonshire ballads. [v1]. 8°. Olney. 1925
The life of William Cowper. 2nd ed. 8°. 1921
The romance of the shoe. 8°. 1922
Wright (Thomas Goddard). Literary culture in early New England, 1620–1730. Ed. by his wife. 8°. New Haven. 1920
Wright (W.) *Briefe rel. of the persecution agst. Catholike Xtns. in Japonia; tr. W. W., Gent., 1619, *see* JESUITS.
Wright (Walter Page). Beautiful gardens. 8°. 1907
The garden week by week. 8°. [1909]
Illust. encyclopædia of gardening. [Everyman's Lib.] s8°. [1911]
The perfect garden: how to keep it &c. [2nd ed.] 8°. 1928
Pop. garden flowers. 8°. [1911]
Wright (Willard Huntington).
What Nietzsche taught. 8°. N.Y. 1915
Wright (William Bourke), R. L. Sherlock *& others.* Geol. of the Rossendale Anticline. [Mems. of G.S.] 8°. 1927
Wright (William Josiah). Geology of the Moncton map-area. [Canada. Geolog. Survey. P2713]. 8°. Ottawa. 1922
Wrigley (M. Jackson). The film: its use in pop. educ. Foreword by Sir G. Parker. Intr. by W. A. Briscoe. s8°. 1922
Wriothesley, *The family of, see* WALPOLE SOC., v8 (W. portraits, by R. W. Goulding), 1920.
Wriothesley (Henry), *3rd earl of Southampton, see* SOUTHAMPTON (H. W., *3rd e. of*).
Wrisberg (Ernst v.)
Heer u. Heimat, 1914–18. [Erinnerungen, 2]. 8°. L. 1921
Der Weg zur Revolution, 1914–18. [Erinnerungen, 1]. s8°. L. 1921
Wehr u. Waffen, 1914–18. [Erinnerungen, 3]. 8°. L. 1922
Writers' (The) & artists' year book, 1926, 1927. Directory. Ed. A. Herbert. 19th, 20th year[s] of new issue. s8°. [1925–26]
Wrong (Edward Murray). Charles Buller & responsible govt. [*Cont.* Buller's Respons. govt. & Wakefield's Sir C. Metcalfe in Canada]. 8°. O. 1926
Wrong (George McKinnon). Washington & h. comrades in arms. [Chron. of Amer. ser., v12]. 8°. New Haven, *Yale.* 1921
Wrong (Hume). Govt. of the West Indies. 8°. O. 1923
Sir A. Mackenzie, explorer & fur-trader. s8°. Toronto. 1927
Wroot (Herbert E.), *see* KENDALL (P. F.) & H. E. W. Geol. of Yorkshire, 2v, 1924.
Wroth (Warwick William). The rearrangement of Parthian coinage. [Repr. f. Num. Chron., s3, v20]. [P2515]. 8°. 1900
Tickets of Vauxhall Gardens. [Repr. f. Num. Chron., s3, v18]. 8°. 1898

Wryde (J. Saxby). Brit. lighthouses, th. hist. &c. 8°. [1913]
Wtenbogaert (Joannes), *see* UTENBOGAERT (J.)
Wuitsch (Michael), *see* VUJIĆ (M.)
Wujek (Jakub). Zywot y nauka pana naszego Jesu Christa. Albo Ewangelia ze czterech iedna &c. s8°. w Krakowie. 1597
Wulf (Maurice de). Philosophy & civiliz. in the Middle Ages. 8°. Princeton [U.S.A.] 1922
Wulf (Max v.) Die husit. Wagenburg. Diss. [P2729]. 8°. [1889]
Wülfer (Joannes).
see BRENZ (S. F.) Theriaca Judaica, studio J. W., 1681.
,, MISHNAH. Schekalim: tract. Talmud. &c.; comm. à J. W., 1680.
Wulff (Oskar). Altchristl. u. mittelalterl. byzantin. u. ital. Bildwerke. Bearbt. v. O. W. u. W. F. Volbach. [Staatl. Museen.] Ergänzungsband. 4°. 1923
Wulfsohn (Leo) & G. Wernlé.
L'évasion des capitaux allemands. s8°. 1923
Wulfstan Collectar, *see* LEOFRIC COLLECTAR. The L. C. compared w. the Collectar of St. Wulfstan &c., v2, 1921.
Wulzinger (Carl), *see* WATZINGER (C.) & C. W. Damaskus d. ant. Stadt., 1921.
—— **& C. Watzinger.** Damaskus: d. islam. Stadt. [Wissenschaftl. Veröffentl. d. deut.-türk. Denkmalschutz-Kommandos, H5]. fol. 1924
***Wunderbarliche** (Ein sehr) wortrechnung etl. Zalen Danielis &c., 1553, *see* STIFEL (M.)
Wunderlich (Eva). Die Bedeutung d. roten Farbe im Kultus d. Griechen u. Römer &c. [Religionsgesch. Versuche &c., B20, H1]. 8°. Giessen. 1925
Wunderlich (Johann), *see* BRISSON (B.) Additamentorum ad B. B. opus de verborum &c. signific. vol. coll. J. W., 1778.
Wunderlich (Johann Georg). De Formulis Concordiae in terris Buggraviatus Norici ab eccl. doctoribus subnotatis. [P440]. s4°. Baruthi. 1783
Wundt (Max W. Aug.), *b. 1879.*
Gesch. d. griech. Ethik. 2B. 8°. L. 1908–11
Griech. Weltanschauung. 2e A. s8°. L. 1917
Wundt (Wilhelm Max), *1832–1920.* Völkerpsychologie: e. Untersuch. d. Entwicklungsgesetze v. Sprache, Mythus u. Sitte. B6–9 [6, 2e n. bearb. A.] 8°. L. 1915–18
6, Mythus u. Religion, T3. 7, 8, Die Gesellschaft, 2T.
9, Das Recht. 10, Kultur u. Geschichte.
see BEITRÄGE Z. PHIL. D. DEUT. IDEALISMUS, B2 (W. W.: eine Würdigung *by var. a.*), 1922.
,, DVORNIKOVIĆ (V.) W. W. i njegovo značenje, 1920.
Wünsche (August). Die Räthselweisheit bei den Hebräern, mit Hinblick auf a. alte Völker. [P2589]. 8°. Leipzig. 1883
Würfel (Gotthard). Englands Kohle als Kampfmittel, *see* KAISER-WILHELM-DANK. Kriegschr., H63, 64, 1916.
Wurm (Mathis), *von Geydertheym.* Balaams eselin. [*Below woodcut*]:—Von dem Bann das er umb geldtschuld uñ andre geringe sachen nit mag, Christlich gefehlt werden &c. [*wanting all after sig. a4*]. s4°. *n.p.* 1523
Jesus. Ausslegung der gschrifft inn S. Jacobs Ep. &c. s4°. [Strasburg ?] 1524
Würtenberger (Ernst).
Zeichnung, Holzschnitt u. Illustration. 8°. Basel. 1919
Württemberg [WIRTEMBERGICI; WIRTEMBERGICAE].
Abfertigung u. Widerlegung, zweier Jesuit. schmähl. Lästerschrifften. Eines durch R. Bellarminum unter dem Tittel: Iudicium R. B. de libro: Concordiae. Das ander durch P. Hansonium des Tittel: Entdeckung d. grossen Thorheit. &c. Gestellt durch die Würtemberg. Theologen. s4°. Tübingen. 1587
Acta & scripta publica Eccl. W. &c., 1720, *see* PFAFF (C. M.)
Acta et scripta theolog. W. et patriarchae Constantinop. D. Hieremiae; quae utriq. ab 1576 ad 1581, de Augustana Confess. inter se miserunt. Gr. & Lat. ed. fol. Witebergae. 1584
Actorum Huberianorum pars prior[-posterior]; Zwispalt zw. S. Huber u. d. W. Theologen &c., 2p, 1597, *see* HUBER (S.)
Ad Wirtemberg. theolog. invectivam resp., 1585, *see* SOKOLOWSKI (S.)
Christliche Erklärung d. W. Theologen Bekanndtnuss, *see* MAULBRONN. Protocoll d. Gesprächs im Apr. 1564 zů M. gehalt., 1565.
Epitome colloquii inter Illust. Pr. Friderici Palatini Elect. & Chr. Ducis, de majestate hominis Christi &c., per Wirtenb. theologos perscripta, 1564, *see* MAULBRONN.
*Gesch. v. W., 1865, *see* GUNDERT (W.)
Wirteberg. theologorum de Colloquio epitome, *see* MAULBRONN. Protocollum colloquii a. 1564, 1566.
Württemberg. Regesten, 1301–1500. Hrsg. v. d. W. Staatsarchiv in Stuttgart. 1, Altwürttemberg, T1, 2. 4°. St. 1916–27
Wurtz (Adolphe).
Atomic theory. Tr. E. Cleminshaw. 5th ed. 8°. 1888

Würzburg.
*Bilder aus alt. u. neu. Zeit. [2e A.] la8o. Würzburg. [1927]
*In disem puchleine ist czu wysen das heylthum in Wirtzpurg &c., 1483, *repr., n.d.*, see KILIAN, *Saint*.

Wurzer (Balduin). De statu relig. Xtianae in Bavaria (1517–55). Adj.: Adversaria sel. &c., quae A. Michl & F. S. Birzer [*&* F. Speer] subjiciunt. 2p. [P2646]. s4o. Ingolstadii. 1776–77

Wu Ting-Fang. Confucius & Mencius. Addr., Jan. 27, 1901. [P2710]. s8o. Phila. 1901

Wuttke (Carl Friedrich Adolph).
De Buddhaistarum disciplina. s8o. Vratislaviae. [1848]

Wyatt (Edward Gerald Penfold).
English or Roman use? [Alcuin Club Tracts, 11]. 8o. 1913

Wyatt (Horace Graham). Methods of school inspection in Eng. [Bureau of Educ., India.] [P2412]. 8o. [Calcutta. 1917]
Rural school teachers in the U.S. [Bureau of Educ., India. P2739]. 8o. Calcutta. 1923

Wyatt (*Sir* Matthew Digby). The art of illuminating: what it was—what it should be. [*imperf. no tp.*] fol. [*p.p.* 1860]

Wyatt (S.), see INDUST. FATIGUE RESEARCH BD. Rep. 7, 21, 23; by S. W., 1920–23.
—— **& J. A. Fraser.** Repetitive work, see INDUST. FATIGUE RES. BD. Rep. 32, 1925.

Wyatt (*Sir* Thomas), *the elder* [WYAT; WIAT], see SURREY (H. H., *e. of*). Poems; w. p. of Sir T. W. &c., 1717.

Wycherley (William). Complete works. Ed. M. Summers. 4v. la8o. Soho, *Nonesuch Press*. 1924
W. W. Ed. w. intr. & notes by W. C. Ward. [Mermaid ser.] [*repr.*] s8o. *n.d.*
see PERROMAT (C.) W. W., sa vie, son œuvre, 1921.

Wyclif Society, see DYMMOK (R.) Liber contra 12 errores &c. Lollardorum; ed. H. S. Cronin, 1921.
for o. publs. of this Soc., see WICLIF (J.)

Wye. *Hist. & topog. of Wye, 1842, see MORRIS (W. E.)

Wyer (Samuel S.)
Niagara Falls. [S.I.: St. of Nat. Resources]. 8o. Wash. 1925
see GILBERT (C. G.), J. E. POGUE, & S. S. W. Mineral indust. of the U.S., 8p, 1917–23.

Wykeham (William *of*), *bp. of Winchester, Ld. High Chancellor*, see WALCOTT (M. E. C.) W. of W. & h. colleges, 1852.

Wyld (Henry Cecil Kennedy). Diction & imagery in Anglo-Saxon poetry, see ENG. ASSOC. Essays &c., v11, 1925.
Eng. philology in Eng. universities. Lect. [P2502]. 8o. O. 1921
South-Eastern & S.E. Midland dialects in Middle English, see ENGLISH ASSOC. Essays & studies, v6, 1920.
Studies in Eng. rhymes f. Surrey to Pope: chapter in hist. of English. s8o. [1923]

Wyld (James). An atlas of maps to show the stations of the Protestant missionaries. 8o. 1839
Great Western Railway map. *folded* s8o. 1840
Memoir annexed to an atlas cont. plans of the principal battles, sieges &c. dur. the war in the Span. Peninsula & South of France. 4o. *J. Wyld*. 1841

Wylde (Augustus B.) Modern Abyssinia. 8o. 1900

Wylie (Elinor). Mortal image. s8o. [1927]
The Venetian glass nephew. 8o. 1926

Wylie (Ida Alena Ross).
All sorts. s8o. [1919]
Ancient fires. [repr.] s8o. 1924
Black harvest. [repr.] s8o. [1925]
Brodie & the deep sea. s8o. [1920]
The dark house. s8o. [1922]
Side shows. s8o. [1923]

Wylie (James Aitken).
The papacy; its history, dogmas &c. 8o. E. 1851

Wylie (Macleod). Bengal as a field of missions. la8o. 1854

Wyllarde (*Miss* Dolf). The second establishment. s8o. [1925]
Take your choice. s8o. [1926]
Temperament. s8o. [1920]
The water diviner. s8o. [1923]

Wyllie (William Lionel), see ALLEN (GRANT). Tidal Thames: cat. of drawings of W. L. W., 1884.
see WHITLAW (R. M.) & W. L. W. L. P. Smythe, 1923.

Wylly (*Col.* Harold Carmichael). A life of Lieut.-Gen. Sir Eyre Coote, K.B. With intr. by Gen. Sir C. Monro. 8o. O. 1922
see DAVIS (*Col.* J.) Hist. of the Queen's Royal Regt., v7, comp. by Col. H. C. W., 1925.

Wyndham (*Rt. Hon.* George), see MACKAIL (J. W.) & GUY WYNDHAM. Life & letters of G. W., 2v, 1925.

Wyndham (*Col.* Guy Percy), see MACKAIL (J. W.) & G. W. Life & letters of George Wyndham, 2v, 1925.

Wyndham (Henry Saxe).
A. S. Sullivan (1842–1900). s8o. 1926

Wyndham (Horace). Crime on the Continent. 8o. [1928]
Famous trials re-told: some society causes celeb. 8o. [1925]
The Mayfair calendar: some society causes celeb. 8o. [1925]

Wyndham (*Hon.* Hugh Archibald). Early hist. of the thoroughbred horse in S. Africa. 8o. O. 1924

Wyndham (*Hon.* Maud Mary), *wife of Hon. Hugh A. Wyndham*. Chronicles of the 18th c., founded on the corr. of Sir T. Lyttelton & h. family. 2v. 8o. 1924

Wyndham-Quin (*Col.* Windham Henry), see DUNRAVEN & MOUNTEARL (W. H. W.-Q., *5th earl*).

Wynn, *The family of.*
see NAT. LIB. OF WALES. Cal. of Wynn (of Gwydir) papers, 1515–1690, 1926.
,, †WYNNE (*Sir* J.) Hist. of the Gwydir family, 1878.

Wynn (Charlotte, *Lady* Williams), see WILLIAMS WYNN (C., *Lady*).

Wynne (Anthony). The double-thirteen mystery. s8o. [1926]
The horseman of death. s8o. [1927]
Red scar. s8o. [1928]

Wynne (Ellis) [WYN]. The sleeping bard; or, visions of the world, death & hell; tr. f. the Cambrian British by G. Borrow, 1860, see BORROW (G.) Wks., v16, 1924.

Wynne (*capt.* Graeme C.), see WAR. Hist. of Gt. War, Milit. oper., France & Belgium, v3, comp. by J. E. Edmonds & G. C. W., 1927.

Wynne (Lucy), *wife of W. R. C. Wynne*, see WYNNE (W. R. C.) Mem.: arr. & coll. by L. W., *n.d.*

Wynne (May), *ps.* [*i.e.* M. W. KNOWLES].
The spendthrift duke. s8o. [1920]

Wynne (Pamela), *ps.* [*i.e.* WINIFRED MARY SCOTT].
Mademoiselle Dahlia. s8o. [1928]

Wynne (Warren Richard Colvin), *R.E.* Memoir. [Coll. & arr. by L. Wynne]. s8o. *p.f.p.c.* Southampton. *n.d.*

Wynne-Jones (T.) Wesl. Methodism in the Brecon circuit & introd. of Eng. & Welsh methodism into the Principality. 8o. Brecon. 1888

Wynnere & Wastoure, see WINNER & WASTER.

Wyrall (Everard). The Die-Hards in the Great War: Middlesex Reg., 1914–19. v1. 8o. [1926]
The hist. of the 62nd (W. Riding) Division, 1914–19. 2v. 8o. [1924–25]
Hist. of the Somerset Light Infantry (Pr. Albert's), 1914–19. Foreword by Duke of York. la8o. [1927]

Wyse (*Sir* Thomas). Education (Ireland). Speech in H. of C., May 1835. [P2552]. 8o. D. 1835

Wyspiański (Stanisław).
Bolesław śmiały. Dramat. [*b.w.h.* Bolesław śmiały, 1910]. 8o. Kraków. 1916
Bolesław śmiały. [*Poem*]. 8o. Kraków. 1910
Daniel [Pisma pośmiertne, 1]. 8o. Kraków. 1908
Klątwa. Tragedya. [wydanie 4e]. s8o. Kraków. 1920
Meleager. Tragedya. [*b. w. h.* Daniel, 1908]. 8o. Kraków. 1916
Noc listopadowa. Sceny dramat. 8o. Kraków. 1916
Protesilas i Laodamia. Tragedya. [*b. w. h.* Daniel, 1908]. 8o. Kraków. 1910
Skałka. Dramat. [*b. w. h.* Daniel, 1908]. 8o. Kraków. 1916
Warszawianka. Pieśń z rokv 1831. [*b. w. h.* Daniel, 1908]. 8o. Kraków. 1918
Wesele. Dramat. 8o. Kraków. 1916
Wiersze—Fragmenty dramat.—Uwagi. [Pisma pośmiertne, 2]. 8o. Kraków. 1910
Wyzwolenie. Dramat. 8o. Kraków. 1918

Wyss (Johann Christoph) [WYS]. Extract historic del Velg & Nouf Test. Mo huossa miss gio in Rumaunsch træs P.p. Juvalta &c. s8o. Cuira. 1719

Wytsman (P.) Genera insectorum. Dir. par W. [v13, 23–31], (Fasc. 82–86, 144–185. fol. Brux. 1908–27

Wyttenbach (Daniel Albert). Oratio de philosophia auctore Cicerone &c. 4o. Amstelodami. 1779

Wyvern, *ps.*, see HERBERT (*Col.* A. H. C. K.)

Wyvill (*Sir* Christopher). The pretensions of the triple-crown. 2p [in 1v. *pagin. cont.*] s8o. 1672

Wyzewa (Teodor). Quelques figures de femmes, aimantes ou malheureuses. 8o. 1922

X

"X." *Myself not least: personal remin. of "X," 1925, see MYSELF.

X***. Manon, pièce, see ŒUVRES libres, No. 47, 1925.

X (*Capitaine*). Foch, 1920, see RECOULY (R.)

X . . (*Capitaine de corvette*) & C. Farrère. Journal de bord de l'expéd. des Dardanelles, see ŒUVRES libres, No. 17, 1922.

X . . . (*docteur*). *La pagaïe, choses vues, see ŒUVRES libres, 31, 1924.

X . . . (*Mr.*) Coll. de Mr. X . . . : décor., ordres franç. & étr., médailles &c., vente, 5 & 6 mars, 1924. [P2751]. 4º. 1924

Xanten. Annales X. & Annales Vedastini. Rec. B. de Simson. [Scr. rerum Germ. in usum schol.] 8º. Hannoverae. 1909

Xanthoudides (Stephanos). The vaulted tombs of Mesará: acc. of some early cemeteries of S. Crete. Tr. J. P. Droop. Pref. by Sir A. Evans. 4º. Liv'l. 1924

Xavier (Francis), *Saint.* Vita S. F. X. Indiæ & Japoniæ apostoli iconibus illust. M. Haffner sc. [*Text attrib. to J. Preiss, also to le p. de Backer*]. s8º. *n.p. n.d.* [1691 ?]
see BOUHOURS (D.) Vita S. Fr. X., 1712.
,, JESUITS. Epist. Indicae, 1566; 3ª ed., 1570.
,, LUCENA (J. DE). Vida do X., 2v, 1921.
,, RULE (W. H.) Celebr. Jesuits, v1, 1852.
,, SCORTIA (F.) *Ristretto d. vita dell' apost. S. F. X., 1622.
,, TORSELLINO (O.) De vita S. F. X. libri 6, 1610; 1752.

Xavier (Hieronymus), *Jesuit.* Hist. Christi Persice conscripta. Lat. reddita & animadv. notata a L. de Dieu. *Pers. & Lat.* s4º. Lugduni Batav. 1639
*Hist. S. Petri Pers. conscr. [*by H. X.*] Lat. reddita & animadv. notata a L. de Dieu. [*Foll. by* Narr. brevis rerum a Societate in regno magni Mogor gestarum, transcr. ex literis H. X. & E. Pigneiro]. [*b. w. h.* Hist. Christi, 1639]. s4º. Lugduni Batav. 1639
see JESUITS. Recent. de ampl. regno Chinae; item De statu rei Xtnae. apud magnum regem Mogor [ex litt. H. X. &c.], 1601.

Xavier de Saxe (François Auguste, *prince* **de),** see SAXONY (F. A. X., *pr. of*).

Xenocrates, *philosopher.* Liber de morte, see IAMBLICHUS *of Chalcis.* De mysteriis &c., 1497.

Xenophon, *monastery,* see ATHOS.

Xenophon, *the historian.* Omnia quae extant opera. Annot. H. Stephani, indicem cum Lat. interpret. [*by F. Filelfo, R. Amasaeus, B. Pirckheimer & o. w. sep. pagin.*] habebis. [p1, Gr.] fol. [Geneva], *H. Stephanus.* 1561
Opera. Ed. G. Sauppe. ed. stereot. 5t. 8º. Lipsiae. 1865–66
Each vol. has also a second special tp.
1, Cyropaedia. 2, Anabasis. 3, Commentarii & Apol. Socratis. 4, Hist. Graeca. 5, Scripta minora.

Xenophon, *the historian* [*continued*].
Opera omnia. Rec. &c. E. C. Marchant. 5t. [t2, 2ª ed.] s8º. O. [1900–20]
Gnomologiae, Parabolae, sive Similitudines. Praetereà Sententiae ex probat. cum Graecis tum Lat. autoribus excerptae per T. Beconum. s8º. Lugduni. 1559
Memorabilia Socratis, cum Apologia. Rec. J. G. Schneider. Acc. adnot. L. Dindorfii. 8º. O. 1826
TRANSLATIONS.
Anabasis, & Memorabilia. Lit. tr. by J. S. Watson; w. geogr. comm. by W. F. Ainsworth. s8º. *Bohn.* 1859
Memorabilia & Œconomicus. With Eng. tr. by E. C. Marchant. [Loeb Class. Lib.] s8º. 1923
Scripta minora. [Text], w. Eng. tr. by E. C. Marchant. [Loeb Class. Lib.] s8º. 1925
Xenophon. [Loeb Class. Lib.] [v]2, 3. s8º. 1921–22
2, Hellenica, Bks. 6, 7. Anabasis, Bks. 1–3. With Eng. tr. by C. L. Brownson.
3, Anabasis, Bks. 4–7. With Eng. tr. by C. L. Brownson, & Symposium & Apology, with Eng. tr. by O. J. Todd.
see ARNIM (H. v.) X.'s Mem. u. Apologie d. Sokrates, 1923.
,, RICHARDS (H. P.) Notes on X. &c., 1907.
,, SCHARR (E.) X.'s Staats- u. Gesellschaftsideal u. s. Zeit, 1919.

Xenos (Stephen Th.) Ἡ Κιβδηλεία ἤτοι μία ἀληθὴς ἱστορία τῶν ἡμέρων μας &c. 2t. 4º. 'εν Λονδινῳ. 1859–60

Xerxes, *King of Persia,* see REINACH (S.) X. et l'Hellespont, 1905.

Ximenez de Cisneros (*cardinal* **Francisco).**
see BAUDIER (M.) Hist. de l'admin. de X., 1635.
,, BIBLE: COMPLETE TEXTS &C. X. de C.: Vetus test. &c., 6v, 1514–17.
,, CEDILLO (*c.* DE). El card. Cisneros gobernador del reino, 1921.
,, GOMEZ DE CASTRO (A.) De rebus gest. a F. X., 1581.
,, MARSOLLIER (J.) Hist. du ministère du c. X., 1694.
,, PORREÑO (B.) Dos tratados histór. toc. al card. X. de C., 1918.

Ximenez de Quesada (Gonzalo), see JIMENEZ DE QUESADA (G.)

Ximenez de Rada (Rodrigo), *abp. of Toledo.* Opera (Hist. de rebus Hispan.—Hist. Roman.—Hist. Ostrogoth. Hist. Hunn. Vandal. &c.), see LORENZANA Y BUITRON (F. A.) PP. Tolet. opera, t3, 1793.
Ostrogotthorum hist.—Hunnorum, Vandal. &c. hist.—De rebus Hisp., see HISPANICA. Rer. Hisp. scr., t1, 1579.

Ximenez de Urrea (Pedro Manuel). Penitencia de amor (Burgos, 1514). Reimp. publ. por R. Foulché-Delbosc. [Bibl. Hispanica.] s8º. Barcelona. 1902

Y

Yadrintsev (Nikolai Mikhailovich) [JADRINZEW]. Sibirien. Geograph., ethnograph. u. hist. Studien. Nach. d. Russ. bearb. &c. v. E. Petri. 8º. Jena. 1886

Yafetichesky Institut [Инст. Яфетидолог. Изысканий Росс. Акад. Наук]. Яфетич. сборник. Recueil japhét. [*Some articles in French*]. [p]1, 2. 8º. П. 1922–23

Yagodovsky (K. P.) В стране полуночного солнца. Воспоминания о Мурманской экспедиции. 2ºᵉ изд. la8º. [Москва.] 1921

Yaḥya ibn al-Baṭrīk, *al-Anṭākī,* see YAḤYA IBN SA'ĪD IBN AL-BAṬRĪK.

Yaḥya ibn Sa'īd ibn al-Baṭrīk, *al-Anṭākī.* Hist. de Yahya-ibn Sa'īd d'Antioche cont. de Sa'īd-ibn-Bitriq; éd. & tr. en franç. par I. Kratchkovsky & A. Vasiliev, see GRAFFIN (R.) & F. NAU. Patr. orient., t18, 1924.

Yajñadattabada, see VĀLMĪKI.

Yakobson (Roman). О чешском стихе. [ч]1. 8º. [Берлин]. 1923

Yakovlev (Aleksandr), see PERESVET. Пересвет, 1, А. Я. &c., 1921.

Yakovlev (Vasily).
А. Н. Скрябин. Предисл. А. Б. Гольденвейзера. 8º. Москва. 1925

Yakushkin (—).
Государств. дума. [P2722]. 8º. Ростовъ на Дону. [1905

Yakut ibn 'Abd Allāh, *al-Ḥamawī* [YAQOUT], see BARBIER DE MEYNARD (C. A. C.) Dict. de la Perse &c. extr. du Mòdjem el-Bouldan de Y. &c., 1861.

Yale review, The. Ed. W. L. Cross. n.s. v11–17. 8º. New Haven. 1922–28
American & British verse f. the Y.R. Foreword by J. G. Fletcher. s8º. New Haven, Yale. 1920

Yale University [YALE COLLEGE]. Cat. (A) of the most valuable books in the library of Y.C. [Advt. *signed* T. Clap. *wanting tp.*] s8º. *n.p.* [1755]
Every-day ethics: Page lect. ser., 1909, Sheffield Scient. School, Y.U. [*by var. a.*] 8º. New Haven, *Yale.* 1910
Two cent. growth of Amer. law, 1701–1901. By Members of the Faculty of the Yale Law School. 8º. N.Y. 1901
see ARNOLD (M.) Unpubl. letters; ed. A. Whitridge, 1923.
,, BARBEAU (M.) & E. SAPIR. Folk songs of French Canada, 1925.
,, JAYNE (W. A.) Healing gods of anc. civilizations, 1925.
,, MORGAN (J. H.) Paintings by J. Trumbull at Y.U., 1926.
,, OSLER (*Sir* W.) Evolution of mod. medicine, 1921.
ELIZABETHAN CLUB.
see PEPYS (S.) P. on the Restoration stage, 1916.

Yangtse Kiang. Y.K. pilot, comp. by T. H. Tizard, *&* Suppl. 5, 1914–22, *see* ADMIRALTY.

Yanich (Voyeslav), *D.D.*, **& C. P. Hankey.** Lives of the Serbian saints. [Trans. of Xtn. lit., s7]. s8°. 1921

Yanitsky (N. F.)
Книжная статистика Совет. России, 1918–23. la8°. Москва. [1923]

Yanjul (Ivan Ivanovich) [Янжулъ]. Изъ воспоминаній и переписки фабричнаго инспектора. [P2448]. 8°. С.–П. 1907

Yapp (*Sir* **Arthur Keysall),** *K.B.E.*
In the service of youth. 8°. [1927]

Yaqout, *see* YAKUT.

Yarborough (Charles Alfred Worsley Anderson Pelham, *4th earl of*). Cat. of antiquities in coll. of Earl of Y. By A. H. Smith. *p.f.p.c.* la8°. 1897

Yarborough (Minnie Clare).
John Horne Tooke. [Columbia Univ.] 8°. N.Y. 1926

Yardley (Edward), *archdeacon of Cardigan, 1739–70.* Menevia sacra. Ed. F. Green. [Cambrian Arch. Assoc. Suppl. vol. for 1927]. 8°. 1927

Yarker (John). The Arcane schools; th. origin &c. w. a gen. hist. of freemasonry. 8°. Belfast. 1909
Geneal. of the fam. of Mark. Pedigree of Bowscale branch of the fam. 4°. *p.p.* M'ter. 1898

Yarmolinsky (Avrahm). Turgenev. 8°. [1926]
see DEUTSCH (B.) & A. Y. Mod. Russ. poetry; chosen & tr. by B. D. & A. Y., 1923.

Yarrell (William). Hist. of British fishes. Suppl. 2. Ed. Sir J. Richardson. 8°. 1860

Yarrow (*Sir* **Alfred Fernandez),** *see* BARNES (E. C.) A. Y., h. life & work, 1923; 2nd impr., 1924.

Yarrow (Eleanor C., *Lady*), *see* BARNES (E. C.)

Yashiro (Yukio). Sandro Botticelli. 3v. 4°. *Medici Soc.* 1925

Yastrjembsky (V. Ya). Как рабочие создают новый строй. Секция по металлу. [P2397]. 8°. П. 1918

Yates (Dornford). Valerie French. s8°. 1923

Yates (G.) *The ball; or, a glance at Almack's in 1829. 8°. 1829

Yates (Hannah). Irene in the centre. s8°. [1926]

Yates (James), *see* WARDLAW (R.) Unitarianism: reply to J. Y., 1816.

Yates (John), *B.D.*
*God's arraignement of hypocrites &c. s4°. C. 1615
Ibis ad Caesarem. In ans. to Mountagues Appeale. s4°. 1626

Yates (May). George Gissing: an appreciation. [Univ. of M'ter.] s8°. M'ter. 1922

Yates (Samuel Ashton Thompson). A compilation & notes about painted windows in cathedrals & churches of France &c. 8°. *p.f.p.c.* Liv'l. 1897

Yates (William), *D.D.*
Gramm. of the Sunscrit lang. 8°. Calcutta. 1820
Introd. to Hindoostanee lang. 8°. Calcutta. 1827
A Sunscrit vocab.; arranged in gramm. order. 8°. Calcutta. 1820
see HOBY (J.) Memoir of W. Y., D.D., of Calcutta, 1847.

Yavorsky (Stefan), *Metropolitan of Riazan, aft. Patriarch of Russia.* Disc. de poena haereticorum noviter ab eccl. se avellentium &c. ex Ruthen. serm. in Lat. idioma tr. &c. G. Bülfinger. [P426]. s4°. Tubingae. 1725
see MOSHEIM (J. L.) De poenis haeret. cum S. I. disput., 1731.

Yazdani (Ghulam). The temples at Palampet, *see* INDIA: ARCH. SURVEY. Mem., No. 6, 1922.
see EPIGRAPHIA INDO-MOSLEMICA; ed. G. Y., 1917–18—1923–24, 1921–27.

Yazikov (Nikolai Mikhailovich).
Стихотворенія. 2т. *in* 1v. s8°. С.–П. 1898

Yder. Der altfranzös. Yderroman. Hrsg. H. Gelzer. [Gesellschaft fur roman.-Lit., B31]. la8°. Dresden. 1913

Ydoine. Amadas & Ydoine: roman du 13ᵉ s.; éd. J. R. Reinhard, 1926, *see* AMADAS.

Yea & nay: lect. & counter lect. at London Sch. of Econ., 1923, *see* STELLING (C. D.), *ed.*

Yeandle (W. H.) Hist. of the churches in Mortlake & East Sheen, in collab. w. W. W. Watts. s8°. Richmond. 1925

Yearbook of Amer. poetry, *see* BRAITHWAITE (W. S.), *ed.* Anthology of magazine verse, 1926.

Yearbook of Eastern-Europe, 1923/24. Ed. F. Fodor. s8°. Budapest. [1923]

Yearbook of modern languages, 1920. Ed. for Mod. Lang. Assoc. by G. Waterhouse. 8°. 1920

Year book of photography & amateurs guide. Ed. by P. R. Salmon. s8°. 1901

Year-book of the scientific & learned societies of Gt. Brit. & Ireland. 40th, 43rd annual issue[s]. 8°. 1923–26

Yearbook (The) of the universities of the Empire. Publ. for the Universities Bureau of the Empire. 1918–20, 1923, 1924. [1924, ed. W. H. Dawson]. 8°. 1920–24

Year Books. Year Books of Probates. Abstracts of Probate Acts in the Prerogative Court of Canterbury. Ed. J. & G. F. Matthews. [v5, 6, 1650–53]. la8°. 1909–11
,, ,, [Extra vol.] Abstracts of Probates & Sentences in Prerogative Court of Canterbury, 1620–24. Ed. J. & G. F. Matthews. la8°. 1911

Year's art (The), 1918, 1923, 1924, 1926, 1927. Comp. by A. C. R. Carter. s8°. 1918–27

Year's work in Eng. studies, 1919–, *see* ENGLISH ASSOCIATION.

Yearsley (Macleod). The folklore of fairy-tale. 8°. 1924

Yeates (Thomas), *see* GORDON (E. A.) Asian Cristology & the Mahāyāna., repr. of Indian Ch. hist. by T. Y., 1921.

Yeatman (John Pym), *Sir* **G. R. Sitwell &** *Earl of* **Liverpool.** The feudal hist. of the Co. of Derby. 5v [*in 9 sect. v3, sect. 6 wanting*]. la8° [London *&* B'ham]. 1886[–1907]

Yeats (Elizabeth Corbet).
Brush work. Intr. by T. R. Ablett. obl.8°. 1896

Yeats (William Butler) [*ps.* GANCONAGH].
Autobiographies. Reveries over childhood &c. & The trembling of the veil. 8°. 1926
Four plays for dancers. 8°. 1921
*John Sherman & Dhoya. s8°. 1891
Later poems. 8°. 1922
Plays & controversies. [*Cont.* The Irish dramatic movt.—The Countess Cathleen—The land of heart's desire—4 plays for dancers]. s8°. 1923
Plays in prose & verse. Written for an Irish theatre, & gen. w. help of a friend [Lady Gregory]. 8°. 1922
The tower. [Poems]. 8°. 1928
The trembling of the veil. [Autobiog.] [priv. printed]. 8°. 1922
see GREGORY (A., *Lady*). Visions & beliefs in the West of Ireland, w. 2 essays & notes by W. B. Y., 2 ser., 1920.
,, SOPHOCLES. King Œdipus; vers. for mod. stage by W. B. Y., 1928.

Yeaxlee (Basil Alfred).
An educated nation. Pref. by A. L. Smith. s8°. 1920

Yeldham (Florence A.) Story of reckoning in the Middle Ages. Intr. by C. Singer. s8°. 1926

Yelverton (Eric Esskildsen). The Mass in Sweden: its development f. the Latin rite, 1531–1917. [Henry Bradshaw Soc., 57]. 8°. 1920

Yerbury (F. R.) Georgian details of domestic archit. 4°. 1926
see JAMES (C. H.) & F. R. Y. Mod. Eng. houses &c., 1925.
,, —— & —— Small houses for the community, 1924.

Yerkes (Robert Mearns). Almost human. 8°. [1926]
——, J. W. Bridges & R. S. Hardwick. A point scale for measuring mental ability. 8°. Baltimore. 1915

Yetts (W. Perceval). Chinese bronzes. [*Repr. f.* Burlington Mag. Monogr. ent. Chinese art; ed. R. E. Fry]. fol. 1925
The Chinese isles of the Blest. [*Repr. fr.* Folk Lore, 1919. P2601]. 8°. 1919
Discoveries of the Kozlov Exped. [*Repr. f.* Burlington Mag., Apr. 1926. P2861]. 4°. 1926
The eight Immortals *&* more notes. [*Extr. f.* R. A. Soc. Journal, 1916–1922. P2601]. 8°. 1916–22

Yglesias (H. R.) Figure skating. s8°. [1905]

Yin Ch'u Ma, *see* MA (Y. C.)

Yolanda, *duchess of Savoy; 1434–78, see* COLOMBO (E.) Iolanda, dssa. di S. (1465–78), 1894.

Yolland (Arthur Battishill). Dict. of the Hungarian & Eng. lang. p2, Hung.-Eng. 2v. 8°. Budapest. 1924

Yonan, *Vardapet of Tokat* [THÔKHATHETZI]. Dashtik dsalkal [Field of blossoms. In Armenian]. s8°. Venice. 1727

Yonge (Charlotte Mary).
Aunt Charlotte's stories of French hist. s8°. 1875
Aunt Charlotte's stories of Greek hist. s8°. 1876
A book of golden deeds. [Golden Treasury Ser.] s8°. 1893
The clever woman of the family. 8°. 1892
The daisy chain. s8°. 1886
*The herb of the field. 2nd ed. s8°. 1858
Little Lucy's wonderful globe, *see* P's & Q's &c., 1891, *below.*
P's & Q's & Little Lucy's wonderful globe. s8°. 1891

Yonge (John Eyre). An expos. of the Apostles' creed. s8°. 1888

Yorck v. Wartenburg (Maximilian, *Graf* **v.)** Weltgeschichte in Umrissen. Federzeichnungen e. Deutschen. 6ᵉ A. 8°. 1901

Yorick, *ps., see* COCCOLUTO-FERRIGNI (P.)

York, *archbishops & church.* Horae Eboracenses. The Prymer or Hours of the Blessed Virgin Mary acc. to use

York [*continued*].
of the Church of York, w. o. devotions as used in 15th & 16th c. [Ed. Canon Wordsworth. Surtees Soc., 132]. 8º. 1920
see THOMPSON (A. H.), *ed.* York Minster hist. tracts, 627–1927 ; [*by var. wr.*], 1927.
York, *city &c.* Anonimalle chronicle (The), 1333–81, f. a MS. wr. at St. Mary's Abbey, 1927, *see* ANONIMALLE.
*Antient (The) & mod. hist. of Y. ; coll. by T. G., 1730, *see* GENT (T.)
*Glorious (The) & miraculous battel at York, 1644, *see* MAIDMENT (J.), *ed.* Hist. fragm., pl, 1833.
Index of wills &c. in the York Registry. [Yorkshire Arch. Soc. Record ser.] 8º. 1920–26
1666–72. [60.]
1673–80, & wills &c. in the Peculiar of Beeford. [68.]
The parish registers of Holy Trinity Church, Goodramgate, York, 1573–1812. Transcr. & ed. by R. B. Cook. [Yorks. Parish Reg. Soc., 41]. *p.p.* 8º. [York]. 1911
York (Albert Fred. Arthur George, *duke of*), *see* ALBERT F. A. G., *d. of York.*
Yorke (Curtis), *ps.* [*i.e. Mrs.* S. RICHMOND LEE].
Her house of dreams. s8º. [1923]
The irrepressibles. s8º. [1924]
The wooing of a witch. s8º. [1926]
Yorke (*Hon. Mrs.* **Eliot Constantine).** Cat. of pictures, prop. of Mrs. Y. &c. Sold by Christie, May 1927. [Illust. P2870]. 8º. 1927
Yorkshire.
*Costume (The) of Y. illust. by 40 engravings & descr. in Eng. & French. fol. Leeds, *R. Jackson.* 1885
Feet of Fines for Co. of Y., 1218–46. Ed. J. Parker. [Y. Arch. Soc. Rec. Ser., 62, 67]. [2v]. 8º. 1921–25
*Series (A) of picturesque views of castles & country houses in Y. From sketches by E. Healey. Letterpress rev. by owners. Repr. f. Bradford Illust. Weekly Telegraph. 4º. Bradford. 1885
Y. deeds. Ed. W. Brown [*&* C. T. Clay]. [Y. Arch. Soc., Rec. Ser., v63, 65, 69]. v3–5. 8º. 1922–26
Y. Star Chamber proceedings. [Y. Arch. Soc. Rec. Ser., v70]. v4, ed. J. Lister. 8º. 1927
Yorkshire archaeological journal. Publ. under dir. of the Yorkshire Archaeolog. Soc. v25–28. 8º. Leeds. 1920–26
Yorkshire Archaeological Society.
Miscellanea. [Rec. ser. 61]. v1. 8º. 1920
Record Series. v60–70. 8º. 1920–27
see LISTER (J.), *ed.* Early Y. woollen trade : extr. f. Hull Customs' Rolls &c., 1924. [64.]
,, MONKBRETTON. Abstract of the chartularies ; ed. J. W. Walker, 1924. [66.]
,, YORK. Index of wills in the Y. Registry, 1920–26. [60, 68.]
,, YORKSHIRE. Feet of Fines, 1218–46 ; ed. J. Parker, 2v, 1921–25. [62, 67.]
,, —— Y. deeds ; ed. W. Brown, v3–5, 1922–26. [63, 65, 69.]
,, —— Y. Star Chamber proc., v4 ; ed. J. Lister, 1927. [70.]
Yorkshire Esk Fishery Association, *see* ENGLISH (T. H.) Memoir, 1925.
Yorkshire Parish Register Society.
[*Publications*]. v26–29, 31, 32, 35, 40–42, 46, 48. 8º. 1906–13
see ALLERTON MAULEVERER. Reg. of parish ch. of A.M. [1562–1812] ; transcr. by F. W. Slingsby, 1908. [31.]
,, ASKHAM RICHARD. Reg. of Askham Richard, 1579–1812 ; transcr. &c. by F. W. Slingsby, 1908. [31.]
,, GARFORTH. Reg. of parish church of G., 1631–1812 ; transcr. by G. D. Lumb, 1913. [46.]
,, HOWDEN. Reg. of parish of H. ; ed. G. E. Weddall, p3, 4, [1659]–1770, 1909–13. [40–42.]
,, KIRKLINGTON. Parish Reg. of K., 1568–1812 ; transcr. by H. B. McCall, 1909. [35.]
,, LEDSHAM. Parish reg. of L., 1539–1812 ; ed. J. W. Clay, 1906. [26.]
,, ROTHWELL. Reg. of parish of R., pl, 1538–1689 ; ed. G. D. Lumb, 1906. [27.]
,, TERRINGTON. Reg. of T., 1599–1812 ; transcr. by W. Briggs, 1907. [29.]
,, THIRSK. Parish reg. of T., 1556–1721 ; transcr. &c. J. Parker, 1911. [42.]
,, THORNHILL. Reg. of parish of T., 1580–1812 ; ed. J. Charlesworth, 2p, 1907–11. [28, 40.]
,, YORK, *city.* Parish reg. of Holy Trinity Ch., Goodramgate, York, 1573–1812 ; transcr. &c. by R. B. Cook, 1911. [41.]
Yoshida (Shoin), *see* SHOIN YOSHIDA.
Youatt (William). *The horse ; w. a treatise on draught. 8º. 1831
Youmans (Edward Livingston). The culture demanded by modern life. Essays by Tyndall *& others.* [repr.] s8º. N.Y. 1873
Young ladies' journal (The). Language of flowers. s8º. 1869

Young, *The family of*, *see* YOUNG (*Sir* G.) Young of Formosa, fam. hist., 1927.
Young (Alexander), *1800–54, D.D., of Boston, Mass.* Chron. of the first planters of Mass. Bay, 1623–36. 8º. Boston. 1846
Young (Alfred Ernest). Some investig. in the theory of map projections. [Roy. Geogr. Soc.] 8º. 1920
Young (Andrew), *see* KEYTE (J. C.) A. Y. of Shensi : adv. in medical missions, 1924.
Young (Andrew W.) Introd. to the science of govt., & compend. of the constit. &c. of the U.S. &c. 4th ed. s8º. Albany. 1840
Young (Arthur), *F.R.S.* A tour in Ireland, w. gen. obs. on pres. state, 1776–78. Sel. & ed. by C. Maxwell. s8º. C. 1925
Travels dur. 1787–89. v2. 8º. D. 1793
Travels in France & Italy, 1787–89. [Intr. by T. Okey. Everyman's Lib.] s8º. [1927]
Young (Bennett Henderson), *see* BENJAMIN (L. N.) The St. Albans raid : investig. into charges agst. Lt. B. H. Y. &c., 1864, 1865.
Young (Blamire). The Proverbs of Goya : acc. of "Los proverbios," exam. &c. by B. Y. 8º. [1923]
Young (Carl). Ordo Prophetarum. [*no tp.* Repr. f. Trans. of Wisconsin Acad. of Sci. &c., v20]. 8º. 1922
Young (David), *D.D., of Perth, see* HALYBURTON (T.) Mem. of the Rev. T. H. ; w. introd. essay by D. Y., 1824.
Young (E. Brett), *see* YOUNG (F. B.) & E. B. Y. Undergrowth, 1913.
Young (E. H.) [*i.e. Mrs.* E. H. DANIELL]. William. s8º. [1925]
Young (Edward), *chief of Bureau of Statistics.* The cost of labor & subsistence in U.S. for 1869, as comp. w. prev. yrs., 1870, *see* U.S. : STATISTICS.
Young (Edward), *the poet.*
*The centaur not fabulous : the life in vogue. 3rd ed. corr. s8º. 1755
*The complaint ; or, Night-thoughts of life, death &c. Night the 1st[–5th, *each w. sep. tp. & pagin. b. in 1v.* Night the 1st *is 2nd ed.*] la8º. 1742–43
,, ,, [*a. ed.*] 8º. 1756
,, ,, [Nights I–IV ; with illust[s]. by W. Blake ; *ed.* R. Edwards]. la. fol. 1797
Night thoughts, 1810, *see* BELLE ASSEMBLÉE (LA), v7, 1809.
An extract f. Night-thoughts. s8º. Bristol. 1770
Poet. works. Coll. by T. Park. 4v. s8º. 1806
Poet. works. [Life by J. Mitford. Aldine ed.] 2v. s8º. [1866 ?]
The revenge, *see* INCHBALD (*Mrs.* E.) Brit. theatre, v12, 1808.
Young (Edward Hilton) & N. E. Young.
The system of national finance. 2nd ed. 8º. [1924]
Young (Egerton Ryerson). By canoe & dog train among the Cree & Salteaux Indians. Introd. by M. G. Pearse. s8º. 1892
Young (Ella).
Celtic wonder tales. Re-told by E. Y. n. ed. s8º. D. 1923
Young (Ernest), *Educ. Dept., Siam.* From Russia to Siam, w. voyage down the Danube &c. 8º. 1914
Young (Everett). Custody children. s8º. 1927
Young (F. E. Mills).
Ailsa. [repr.] s8º. [1926]
The almonds of life. s8º. [1920]
The broken silence. s8º. [1926]
Dawn at Sundays River. s8º. [1922]
The future. [repr.] s8º. [1925]
Imprudence. s8º. 1920
The romantic tragedy. s8º. [1927]
Selwyn brothers. s8º. [1923]
The white locust. s8º. [1927]
The wine farm. s8º. [1924]
Young (Filson) [ALEX. BELL FILSON YOUNG]. Mastersingers. [Apprec. of music &c., w. essay on H. Berlioz]. [2nd ed.] 8º. 1908
With the battle cruisers. 8º. 1921
see ARMSTRONG (H. R.) Trial of A. ; ed. F. Y., 1927.
,, BYWATERS (F.) & E. THOMPSON. Trial of F. B. & E. T. ; ed. F. Y., 1923.
Young (Francis Brett).
The black diamond. s8º. [1921]
Cold Harbour. s8º. [1924]
The crescent moon. 3rd impr. s8º. [1919]
The key of life. s8º. [1928]
Pilgrim's rest. s8º. [1922]
Portrait of Clare. [n. impr.] 8º. [1927]
The red knight. s8º. [1921]
Sea horses. [2nd impr.] s8º. [1925]
The tragic bride. s8º. [1920]
Woodsmoke. [2nd impr.] s8º. [1924]
—— & E. Brett Young. Undergrowth. s8º. [1913]
Young (Geoffrey Winthrop).
Mountain craft. [*By var. a.*] Ed. G. W. Y. 8º. [1920]
On high hills : mem. of the Alps. 8º. [1927]
Young (*Adm. Sir* **George**), *1732–1810, see* YOUNG (*Sir* G.), *3rd bart.* Young of Formosa, 1927.

Young (*Sir* **George),** *3rd bart.*
An Eng. prosody on inductive lines. 8º. C. 1928
Young of Formosa. *Not publ.* 8º. Reading. 1927

Young (George), *b. 1872, son of Sir G. Young, 3rd bart.*
Constantinople. 8º. [1926]
Diplomacy old & new. s8º. 1921
Egypt. 8º. 1927
see KENWORTHY (*Lt.-Comm. Hon.* J. M.) & G. Y. Freedom of the seas, 1928.

Young (George), *D.D.*
A geolog. survey of the Yorkshire coast. 4º. Whitby. 1822
Life & voyages of Capt. J. Cook. s8º. 1836
A picture of Whitby &c. 2nd ed. s8º. Whitby. 1840
Scriptural geology. 8º. 1838

Young (George Albert). Geology & econ. minerals of Canada. [Canada. Geolog. Survey]. 8º. Ottawa. 1926

—— & W. L. Uglow. The iron ores of Canada, v1, Brit. Columbia & Yukon. [Canada. Geol. Survey]. 8º. Ottawa. 1926

Young (*Col.* **George Frederick),** *C.B.*
The Medici. [3rd ed., repr.] 2v. 8º. [1926]

Young (Hayward).
Short cuts to sketching. [Ed. F. Klickmann]. 4º. [1913]

Young (James H.) Mitchell's Reference & distance map of the U.S. *folded* 4º. Phila. 1836

Young (Joan). An ale-house guest. s8º. 1927

Young (John), *dean of Winchester; 1585–1654.* Diary. 1616[–45]. Extracts, transcr. & ed. by F. R. Goodman. 8º. 1928

Young (Mabel H.), *see* PIPER (T. W.) Trial of T. W. P. for murder of M. H. Y., 1887.

Young (N. E.), *see* YOUNG (E. HILTON) & N. E. Y. System of national finance, 1924.

Young (Norwood). Carlyle, h. rise & fall. 8º. [1927]

Young (Robert), *bookseller & orientalist of Edinburgh, see* ABOTH. Ethics of the Fathers; tr. w. intr. to the Talmud, by R. Y., 1852.

Young (Robert), *Wesleyan Minister.* The Southern world. Journal of a deputation to Australia & Polynesia &c. s8º. 1854

Young (Robert Fitzgibbon). A Bohemian philosopher at Oxford: G. Ritschel, 1616–83. Lect., Prague, 1924. [P2834]. 8º. [1925]
A Czech humanist in London: J. Sictor Rokycanský, 1593–1652. [P2834]. 8º. [1926]
Jan Sictor z Rokycan, 1593–1652. [P2834]. 8º. v Praze. 1926

Young (Robert Newton).
The witness of the Spirit. [Fernley Lect.] 8º. 1882

Young (Ruth). Mrs. Chapman's portrait, a beauty of Bath of the 18th cent. 8º. Bath. 1926

Young (Sidney). Hist. of the Worshipful Co. of Glass Sellers of London. 8º. 1913

Young (Thomas), *vicar of Stowmarket, Suffolk* [PHILO-KURIACES (THEOPHILUS), *Loncardiensis, ps.*] *Dies Dominica, sive succincta narr. ex S. Script. &c. testimoniis. [*w. engr. tp.*] s4º. [London ?]. 1639

Young (W. A.)
The silver & Sheffield plate collector. [2nd pr.] 8º. [1927]

Younge (Richard) [*ps.* FLORILEGIUS (JUNIUS)]. A Christian library &c. [*var. tp. & pagin.*] s8º. 1660
The odious &c. condition of a drunkard &c. [*b. w. h.* The poores advocate, 1654]. s8º. 1659
The poores advocate. 2p. *No more published* [*& other works by same a. w. sep. pagin. but wanting tp.*] s8º. [1654]
The prevention of poverty, w. the cure of melancholy. p1. [*b. w. h.* The poores advocate, 1654]. s8º. 1655

Younghusband (*Sir* **Francis Edward).**
Culture as the bond of empire, *see* ROY. SOC. OF LIT. Essays: Trans., N.S., v1, 1921.
The epic of Mt. Everest. [repr.] 8º. [1926]
The gleam. 8º. 1923
The light of experience. 8º. 1927
Wonders of the Himalaya. 8º. 1924
see PEREIRA (*Brig.-Gen.* G.) Peking to Lhasa; comp. by Sir F. Y. f. notes & diaries, 1925.

Younghusband (*Maj.-Gen. Sir* **George John).**
Forty years a soldier. 8º. 1923

Yoxall (*Sir* **James Henry).** More about collecting. 3rd ed. 8º. 1921

Yriarte (Tomás de). Compendio de la hist. de España. Rev. por J. Blazquez. s8º. Londra. 1822

Ysalguerio (Anselmus de), *see* ISALGUIER (A. D').

Ysopet, *see* ÆSOP.

Yü. Inschrift des Yü. Übers. u. erklärt v. J. v. Klaproth. [P2701]. 4º. Halle. 1811

Yu. (B.) [Б. Ю.] Нѣскольско словъ по поводу письма Толстаго о способахъ борьбы съ голодомъ. [P846]. 8º. Кіевъ. 1891

Yucatán. Col. de docs. inéd. de Ultramar, s2, t11, 13, Rels. de Y., 1898–1900, *see* COLECCIÓN.

Yūhannā ibn Abū Zakarīyā, *ibn Sabā.* La perle précieuse, traitant des sci. eccl.: texte arabe, publ. & tr. par J. Périer, *see* GRAFFIN (R.) & F. NAU. Patr. orient., t16, 1922.

Yule (George Udny). The fall of the birth-rate. Paper, Camb. Univ. Eugenics Soc. [P2490]. 8º. C. 1920
Function of statist. method, *see* INDUST. FATIGUE RES. BD. Rep. 28, 1924.

Yule (*Sir* **Henry).** Essay introd. to Capt. Gill's "The river of golden sand." [P2714]. 8º. 1880
see CORDIER (H.) Ser Marco Polo, notes & addenda to Sir H. Y.'s ed., 1920.

Yun-Kang. *Les grottes de Yun-Kang. L'art des Wei. la8º. Pékin. [1924 ?]

Yurovsky (L. N.) Currency problems & policy of the Soviet Union. [Tr.] 8º. 1925

Yushkevich (Ivan A.) Литовскія народныя пѣсни. Съ переводомъ на русс. яз. [I. Akad. Nauk. Записки, t12]. 8º. С.–П. 1867

Yushkevich (Semen Solomonovich). Голодъ. Драма. 8º. St. 1905
Еврем, *see* SBORNIK. Сб. товар. "Знаніе," 2, 1904.
Комедія брака. 8º. Berlin. [1911]

Yusupov, *Family of, see* YUSUPOV (*pr.* N. B.) О родѣ князей Ю., 2ч, 1866–67.

Yusupov (*prince* **Nikolai Borisovich).** Нѣчто объ исповѣди и истолкованіи Евангелія Л. Толстаго. [P643]. 8º. С.–П. 1883
О родѣ князей Юсуповыхъ. Собраніе жизнеописаній. 2ч *in 1v.* la8º. С.–П. 1866–67

Yuzefovich (B. M.) [Юзефовичъ].
Основы самопознанія, филос. очеркъ. [P2452]. s8º. Кіевъ. [1908]
Политич., эконом. &c. основы для реформы русск. государств. школы. 8º. С.–П. 1910
Политич. письма. Мат. для ист. русск. политич. умопомраченія (1898–1908). 3ч. [*in 1v. 2 pagin*[s]*.*] 8º. Кіевъ. 1908

Yuzefovich (I.) Очерки профессиональнаго движения Польши. [P2697]. 8º. Москва. 1921

Yver (Colette) [*i.e. Mme.* ANTOINETTE HUZARD].
Les Cervelines. Roman. 8º. *n.d.*
Dans le jardin du féminisme. s8º. [1920]
Haudequin, de Lyon. Roman. s8º. 1927
Vous serez comme des dieux. Roman. s8º. 1922

Yver (Georges), *prof. à la Faculté des lettres d'Alger, see* GSELL (S.), G. MARÇAIS & G. Y. Hist. d'Algérie, 1927.

Yves-Guyot, *see* GUYOT (Y.)

Yvoire (*le baron* **François d'),** *see* LAVAL (M. DE). Une âme de lumière: le Baron F. d'Y., 1923.

Yvon (Paul). La vie d'un dilettante: Horace Walpole (1717–97). la8º. 1924

Z

Z. (D.) *Henoticum Xtnorum, 1662, *see* ZWICKER (D.)

Z. (H.) Bibliotheca chemico-mathematica, 2v, 1921, *see* ZEITLINGER (H.) &c.

Z. (*H.* **Kar),** *see* ZARBHANALEAN (K.)

Zablotsky-Desyatovsky (Andrei Parfenevich).
Графъ П. Д. Киселевъ и его время. 4т. la8º. С.–П. 1882

Zaborowski (Sigismond) [ZABOROWSKI-MOINDRON], *see* HOLLANDE (La), par L. van Keymeulen, Z., *& o. authors,* 1909.

Zabughin (Vladimir). Vergilio nel rinascimento ital., da Dante a Torquato Tasso. 2v. 8º. Bologna. [1921–23]

Zaccagnini (Guido). La vita dei maestri e d. scolari n. Studio di Bologna nei sec. 13 e 14. Con 2 app. la8º. Genève. 1926

Zaccaria (Francesco Antonio). Antifebronius vindic. seu suprema rom. pontif. potestas &c., *see* MIGNE (J. P.), *ed.* Theol. cursus, t27, 1843.
De usu librorum liturg.—De usu inscript. xtn., *see* MIGNE (J. P.), *ed.* Theol. cursus, t5, 1841.

Zacchetti (Corrado). Lord Byron e l'Italia. s8°. Palermo. [1919]
Zachariae (Theodor). Die ind. Wörterbücher (Kośa). [Grundr. d. indo-ar. Phil., B1, H3B. *no tp.*] la8°. [Str. 1897]
Zacharias, *the deacon, 1623–1699.* Cartul. du saint asile de Iohannou-Vank (6–17 c.), *see* BROSSET (M. F.) Coll. d'hist. arm., t2, 1876.
Mémoires hist. sur les Sofis, *see* BROSSET (M. F.) Coll. d'histor. arm., t2, 1876.
Zacher (Julius). Disq. gramm. de alphabeti Gothici Ulphilani orig. &c. partic. 1. Diss., Acad. Hal. 4°. Lipsiae. 1854
Zachrisson (Robert Eugen). Eng. place-names & river-names cont. the prim. Germanic roots *vis, *vask. [Uppsala Univ. Årsskr. 1926. Filos. Språkvetenskap &c., 2]. 8°. Uppsala. [1926]
The Eng. pronunc. at Shakespeare's time as taught by W. Bullokar, w. word-lists, *see* KUNG. HUM. VET.-SAMF. I UPPSALA. Skr., B22, 1927.
Romans, Kelts & Saxons in anc. Brit. (400–600). 8°. Uppsala. [1927]
" " *for a. c., see* KUNG. HUM. VET.-SAMF. I UPPSALA. Skr., B24, 1927.
Zadkine (Ossip), *see* RAYNAL (M.) O. Z., 1921.
Zafar Hasan (*Maulvi*). Guide to Nizamu-d Dīn, *see* INDIA: ARCH. SURVEY. Mem., No. 10, 1922.
Mosque of Shaikh 'Abdu-n Nabī, *see* INDIA: ARCH. SURVEY. Mem., No. 9, 1921.
Spec. of calligraphy in Delhi Museum of Arch., *see* INDIA: ARCH. SURVEY. Mem., No. 29, 1926.
Zagaria (Riccardo).
Vita e opere di N. Amenta, 1659–1719. 8°. Bari. 1913
Zagorovsky (Nikolai Ivanovich). *Топогр. описаніе Харьковск. намѣстничества &c., *see* KHARKOV. Харьковскій сборникъ, 1888.
Zagorsky (Simon). La Rép. des Soviets. Bilan écon. 8°. 1921
Zahm (Albert Francis). Rep. on European aeronaut. laboratories, 1914, *see* SMITHSONIAN INST. Misc. coll., v62, 1923.
Zahn (Christian Gotthelff). Versuch e. Reformations-Gesch. d. Herzogthums Würtemberg. s8°. Tübingen. 1791
Zahn (Ernst). Die Clari-Marie. Roman. s8°. St. 1920
Einsamkeit. s8°. St. 1920
Frau Sixta: Roman. s8°. St. 1926
Die Hochzeit d. Gaudenz Orell. Roman. 8°. 1927
Nacht. Erzählung. s8°. St. 1919
Zahn (Joseph v.) Austro-Friulana &c.; gesamm. & hrsg. v. J. v. Z., *see* FONTES RERUM AUSTRIAC., B40, 1877.
Codex diplomaticus Austriaco-Frising.; hrsg. v. J. Z., 3B, *see* FONTES RERUM AUSTRIAC., B31, 35, 36, 1870–71.
Zahn (Theodor). Forschungen zur Gesch. d. neutest. Kanons u. d. altkirchl. Lit. T9. 8°. L. 1916
9, Die Urausgabe d. Apostelgesch. d. Lucas.
Komm. zum N. Test. Hrsg. v. T. Z. B5, 15, 18i. 8°. L. 1919–24
5, Die Apostelgesch. d. Lucas, 2H.
15, Der 1e u. 2e Petrusbrief u. d. Judasbrief; ausgelegt v. G. Wohlenberg, 3e A.
18, Die Offenbarung d. Johannes; ausgelegt v. T. Z., H1, 1e bis 3e A.
Zahn (W.) Die Altmark im 30-jähr. Kriege. [Verein f. Ref.-gesch. Schr., Jhrg. 21, Nr. 80]. 8°. Halle a. S. 1904
Zähringer (Wilhelm).
Mein Heidelberg. 8°. Bühl (Baden). [1922]
Zaitsev (Boris). Путники. s8°. Парижъ. 1921
Собраніе сочиненій. кн. 1–3, 5–7. 8°. Берлинъ. 1922–23
1, Тихія зори. 2, Сны. 3, Усадьба Ланиныхъ и другіе разсказы. 5, Земная печаль. 6, Голубая звѣзда. 7, Италія.
see PERESVET. Пересвет, 1, Б. 3. &c., 1921.
Zaitsev (Vartholomei Aleksandrovich), *1842–1882.*
*В. А. Зайцевъ. [Библ. біографій русс. револ.] [P2390]. s8°. Лондонъ. *n.d.*
Современное положеніе русской прессы. Изд. М. К. Элпидина. [P2390]. s8°. Carouge (Genève). 1902
Zakaria, *see* ZACHARIAS.
Zakavkaz. Док. и матерьялы по внѣшней политикѣ Закавказья и Грузіи. 8°. Тифлисъ. [1919]
Zakhzakhean, *see* DSCHAKHDSCHAKHEAN.
Zakoskin (Nikolai). Л. Н. Толстой и его студенческіе годы. [*Extr. f.* Истор. Вѣстникъ, t55, 1894. P643]. 8°. С.-П. 1894
Zaleski (Bronislaw). La vie des steppes Kirghizes. Descr., récits & contes. obl.4°. 1865
Zalesov (—). Colonel Ignatief's mission to Khiva & Bokhara in 1858. Tr. R. Mitchell. [P2386]. 8°. [1876]

Zalts (Alberts).
Latvian foreign trade &c. [P2877]. 8°. Riga. 1927
Zamacoïs (Miguel). Les bouffons. Pièce en vers (1907). [60e éd.] s8°. *n.d.*
Le passage de Vénus, fantaisie, *see* ŒUVRES libres, t5, 1921.
Zamakargouthiun: [Breviary of Armenian Church], 1705, *see* ARMENIAN.
Zambaur (E. de). Manuel de généalogie & de chronologie p. l'hist. de l'Islam. 4°. Hanovre. 1927
Zambeccari (Pellegrino). Sei sonetti. [Nozze Renier—Campostrini. N139]. la8°. Bologna. 1887
Zamboni (Baldassare Camillo). Vita di V. Gambara, *see* GAMBARA (V.) Rime &c., 1759.
Zambrini (Francesco Saverio). Rime ant. d'autori faentini. Pubbl. Z. 8°. Mola. 1846
see NOVELLE d'incerti autori del sec. 14; [ed. F. Z.], 1861.
Zamirailo (Viktor Dmitrievich), *see* ERNST (S.) B. 3., 1921.
Zamyatin (Evgeny). Островитяне. Повѣсть. [*Extr. f.* "Скиѳы," No. 2. P2769]. 8°. *n.p.* [1917]
Zanazzo (Giggi) [ZANAZZO (LUIGI)]. Anticaje, pietrelle e bboccaje pe'li lumi: sestine romanesche. s8°. Roma. 1887
Zanchius (Hieronymus).
·Ad cujusdam Ariani libellum: Antithesis doct. Christi & Antichristi de uno vero Deo. Resp. ad J. Sturmium [*b. w.* Grabe (J.) Isagoge &c. 1586]. s4°. Neostadii Palatinov. 1586
Ad partem prodromi V. Holderi resp. de visionibus quibus apparuit Christus [*b. w.* Grabe (J.) Isagoge &c. 1586]. s4°. Neostadii Palati. 1586
Compendium praecip. capitum doctrinae Xtnae &c. s8°. Neustadii im Palatinatu. 1598
De aperiendis in eccl. scholis &c. Oratio, 20 Maii 1578, habita. s4°. Neapoli Casimir. 1579
De Jesu Christi a mortuis resurrectione &c. Theses. [P2612]. s4°. Nevstadii in Palatin. 1581
De tribus Elohim, æterno Patre, Filio & Spiritu Sancto, uno eadem Jehova. 2p. *in* 1v. [*tp. wanting f. p1*]. fol. Neostadii. 1589
Miscellaneorum lib. 3. fol. Neaopli (*sic*) Palat. 1582
Lib. 1 & 2 have cont. pag. Lib. 3 has tp. & sep. pagin.
Theses de iis quae de J. C. post unionem praedicantur &c. Ex Ep. ad Ephes. cap. 1. Præs. H. Z., def. J. Becius. [P2612]. s4°. Neapoli Nemetum. 1582
TRANSLATIONS.
*Doctrine (The) of absolute predestination. Tr., in great measure, f. Jerom Zanchius. By the a. of The Church of Engl. vindic. f. charge of Arminianism [A. M. Toplady]. Subj. fr. Lipsius an App. conc. the fate of antients. [*b. w.* Toplady (A. M.) Ch. of Eng. vindic., 1769]. 8°. 1769
H. Z. his conf. of Christian religion &c. Englished &c. s8°. C. 1599
see PERKINS (W.) *Brief disc., out of the wr. of H. Z. &c., 1592.
" TOPLADY (A. M.) Letter to J. Wesley rel. to his Abridgment of Z. on predestination, 1771.
Zanella (Giacomo). Nature e scienza. [Nozze Boschetti—Tozzi. *a. c. in* N127]. 8°. [Padova. 1866]
Il sonno. [Nozze Fogazzaro—Valmarana. *a. c. in* N127]. 8°. Padova. 1866
La suocera al genero. [Nozze Giusti—Cittadella. N127]. 8°. [Padova]. 1863
La veglia. [Nozze Da Schio—Marcello. N127]. 8°. Padova. 1864
Versi. s8°. Firenze. 1868
Zangwill (Israel). The voice of Jerusalem. 8°. 1920
Zaniboni (E.) Alberghi italiani e viaggiatori stran., s. 13–18. 8°. Napoli. 1921
Zankow (Stefan). Die Verwaltung d. bulgar. orthodoxen Kirche. 8°. Halle (Saale). 1920
Zannelli (Pietro), *see* TESI-PASSERINI (C.) Pio IX e il suo tempo; a cura del collab. P. Z., 3p, 1877–81.
Zannolini (*cav.* **Nicola**). Nel felic. arrivo d. conte W. de Daun, idillio. [N125]. 8°. Napoli. 1713
Zanolini (Antonio). Antonio Aldini ed i suoi tempi. Narr. storica. v1. s8°. Firenze. 1864
Zanolini (Antonio), *J.U.D.* Disput. de festis & sectis Judæorum, *see* MIGNE (J. P.), *ed.* Theol. cursus, t26, 1859.
Lexicon Chaldaico-Rabbinicum. Acc. disput. de Targumin Talmude &c. Ann. hist. quaedem a A. Majemonide ex Arabica in Hebr. Rabb. tr. 4°. Patavii. 1747
Zanotti-Bianco (Umberto), *see* KOLPINSKA (A.) I precursori d. Rivol. Russa; con La Russia e il principio di nazionalità, di U. Z.-B., 1919.
Zanuzzi (Francesco), *1727–1800, see* RAVÀ (A.) Un arlecchino naturalista, 1909.
Zaorowsky (Jerome). *Secreta monita Soc. Jesu: secret instructions of the Jesuits. [*Lat. & Eng.*] 2nd ed. s8°. 1746

Zapf (Georg Wilhelm). Aelteste Buchdruckergesch. von Mainz, bis 1499. s8º. Ulm. 1790
Älteste Buchdrukergesch. Schwabens. s8º. Ulm. 1791
Augsburgs Buchdruckergesch.
2T. (1468–1530). 4º. Augsburg. 1788–1791
Ueb. e. alte Ausgabe v. d. Joannis de Turrecremata Explan. in Psalterium, u. a. typograph. Seltenheiten.
s4º. Nürnberg. 1803
Zapiski. Записки мечтателей. No. 1–6 *in* 2v. 8º. П. 1919–22
Записки русскихъ людей, 1841, *see* SAKHAROV (I. P.), *ed.*
Zapolska (*countess* Gabryela).
Frau Renas Ehe. [Übers. 4. Aufl.] s8º. [1924]
Die Hölle d. Jungfrauen. [Übers. 7. Aufl.] s8º. [1924]
Zapolsky (M. V. Dovnar-), *see* DOVNAR-ZAPOLSKY (M. V.)
Zappi (Faustina Maratti) [MARATTI (F.), *aft.* Zappi; *ps.* AGLAURA CIDONIA], *see* ZAPPI (G. B. F.) & F. M. Z. Rime, ed. 10ª, p2, 1773.
Zappi (Giov. Batt. Felice) & F. M. Zappi.
Rime. ed. 10ª. p2. s8º. Venezia. 1773
2, Alcuni rime di celeb. poeti dell' Arcadia di Roma.
Zaragozana. *Bibliografia z. del s. 15, 1908, *see* SÁNCHEZ (J. M.)
Zarbhanalean (Karekin) [KAREKIN (*le père*); H. KAR. Z.]
*Bibliographie arménienne. [*In Armenian*].
s8º. Venetik, *Mekhitharist Press.* 1883
[*Cat. des anc. traductions armén., siècles 4–13. *In Armenian*]. s8º. Venetik, *Mekhitharist Press.* 1889
*Les études arméniennes en Europe, siècles 14–19. [*In Armenian*]. s8º. Venetik. 1895
[*Hist. litt. de l'Arménie anc., siècles 4–13. *In Armenian*].
[2nd ed.] s8º. Venetik, *Mekhitar. Press.* 1886
Zarco Cuevas (Julian), *see* ESCURIAL. Cat. de los mss. castellanos de la Real Bibl. de el E., 2v, 1924–26.
Zardo (Antonio). Gasparo Gozzi n. lett. del s. tempo in Venezia. s8º. Bologna. [1923]
Zaristische (Das) Russland im Weltkriege; übers., 1927, *see* RUSSLAND.
Zarlino (Gioseffo). Dimostr. harmoniche. fol. Venetia. 1571
Le istit. harmoniche &c. 4º. Venetia. 1562
Istit. harmoniche. [4p *in* 1v. *w. cont. pagin.*] fol. Venetia. 1573
Sopplimenti musicali. [Istit. & Dimostr., t3]. fol. Venetia. 1588
Zarnitsi.
Зарницы. Лит.-полит. сборникъ. No. 2. [*2 pagin.*] 8º. С.-П. 1909
Zavie (Emile).
La maison des trois fiancées. 10e éd. s8º. [1926]
see DEFFOUX (L.) & E. Z. Le groupe de Médan: E. Zola &c., 1920.
Zayaitsky (Sergei). Баклажаны. Повесть. s8º. [Москва]. 1927
Zayas Enriquez (R. de). Avicultura práctica. [*b. w.* Mexico. Informe &c. sobre coloniz. &c., 1885]. 8º. Mexico. 1897
Zazzera (Francesco).
Della nobilità dell' Italia. 2p. fol. Napoli. 1615–28
Zbinden (Hans). Ein Künder neuer Lebenswege: Einzelbilder z. Seelenforsch. R. M. Holzapfels. [*By var. a.*] Hrsg. v. H. Z. 8º. Jena. 1923
Zdekauer (Lodovico). Necrologia, *see* ARCHIVIO STORICO ITAL. Anno 82, v2, 1924.
Studi Pistoriesi. [Fasc. 1]. 8º. Siena. 1889
Zdziarski (A. F.), *see* DMITRIEV-MAMONOV (A. I.) & A. F. Z. Guide to Gt. Siberian Rly., 1900.
Zeaeman (Georgius). Controv. de imagine Dei in primo homine &c. s4º. Campidoni. 1619
Zealous, *H.M.S.* Our journal in the Pacific; by officers of H.M.S. Zealous, 1873, *see* EARDLEY-WILMOT (*Sir* S. M.), *ed.*
Zech (Franciscus Xaverius). Rigor moderatus doctr. pontif. circa usuras à Benedicto XIV, per epist. encycl. episc. Ital. trad., *see* MIGNE (J. P.), *ed.* Theol. cursus, t16, 1859.
Zechius (Lælius), *see* MAIER (B.) De jubilæo Romano, L. Z. oppos., 1617.
Zedler (Gottfried). Von Coster zu Gutenberg: d. holländ. Frühdruck u. d. Erfindung d. Buchdrucks. 4º. L. 1921
Zedlitz-Trützschler (Robert, *Graf* v.)
Zwölf Jahre am deut. Kaiserhof. 9e u. 10e A. 8º. 1924
12 years at the Imp. German court. [Tr. A. K.] 8º. [1924]
Zeeland. De rekeningen der Grafelikheid van Zeeland onder het Henegouwsche Huis. Uitg. door H. G. Hamaker. [Hist. Genoots. te Utrecht. Werken, N.S., 29, 30].
2d. 8º. Utrecht. 1879–80
Zeibich (Christoph Heinrich). Electa hist. vitae & mortis M. Lutheri. [P2627]. s4º. Wittebergae. 1746
Schediasma de theologis ad tempus commodatis.
[P2637]. s4º. Lipsiae. 1709

Zeibig (Hartmann Joseph). Urkundenbuch d. Stiftes Klosterneuburg bis z. Ende d. 14. Jhdt., T2, *see* FONTES RERUM AUSTRIAC., B28, 1868.
Zeidler (Carl Gottlob). Hist. Mennonis ejusque asseclarum, sub praes. F. T. Kettneri, submittit C. G. Z.
[P597]. s4º. Lipsiae. [1696]
Zeiller (Jacques). Orig. del nome di Spalato, *see* BULLETTINO DI ARCH. &c. DALM., 39, Suppl., 1919.
Spalato, le palais de Dioclétien. Relevés & restaur. par E. Hébrard. Texte par J. Z. Préf. de C. Diehl. App. de G. Jéquier. fol. 1912
Zeiss (Carl), *Stiftung*, *see* AUERBACH (F.) The Z. works; tr., 1904.
Zeissberg (Heinrich v.) Todtenbuch d. Cisterc.-Stiftes Lilienfeld in Österreich; *see* FONTES RERUM AUSTRIAC., B41i, 1879.
Zeitlinger (Heinrich) & H. C. Sotheran. Bibliotheca chemico-mathematica: cat. of wks. on exact & applied science, w. a subject-index. Comp. &c. by H. Z. & H. C. S.
2v. 8º. 1921
Zeitschrift d. Deutschen Morgenländ. Gesellschaft, *see* DEUTSCHE MORGENLÄND. GESELLSCHAFT.
Zeitschrift d. Deut. u. Österreich. Alpenvereins, *see* DEUTSCHER U. ÖSTERREICH. ALPENVEREIN.
Zeitschrift d. histor. Vereines f. Steiermark, 1903–18, *see* HISTORISCHER VEREIN F. STEIERMARK.
Zeitschrift d. Savigny-Stiftung für Rechtsgeschichte.
B41–48. 8º. Weimar. 1920–28
Each Band has a Germanistische Abt. *& a* Romanistische Abt., *& each of these has sep. tp. & pagin.; but the 2 Abt. are bound together.* B41–48 *have also a* Kanonistische Abt. (10–17), 1920–28, *bound sep.*
Zeitschrift d. Vereins für Volkskunde. Jhrg. 24 (1914). Jhrg. 1920/22, 1923/24, 1925/26, 1927/28. la8º. 1914–28
Zeitschrift f. ägyptische Sprache u. Alterthumskunde.
Gegr. v. H. Brugsch. Jahrg. 24. la8º. L. 1886
Zeitschrift f. armenische Philologie. Unter Mitwirk. v. A. Joannissiany hrsg. v. F. N. Finck, E. Gjandschezian & A. Manandian. B1, 2. 8º. Marburg. 1903–4
Zeitschrift f. celtische Philologie. B13–17. 8º. 1921–28
Zeitschrift f. d. alttestamentliche Wissenschaft.
Hrsg. v. K. Marti. B37–41 (1917–23). 8º. Giessen. 1918–23
„ „ Neue Folge. Hrsg. v. H. Gressmann.
B1–4. 8º. Giessen. 1924–27
N.F. *has title* Zeitschr. f. d. alttest. Wiss. u. d. Kunde d. nachbibl. Judentums.
Zeitschrift f. d. neutestamentliche Wissenschaft u. d. Kunde d. Urchristentums. Hrsg. v. E. Preuschen.
Jhrg. 1–19. 8º. Giessen. 1900–20
Zeitschrift für Ethnologie. Organ d. Berliner Gesells. f. Anthropologie, Ethnol.- u. Urgesch. Jhrg. 46–58. la8º. 1914–26
Zeitschrift f. roman. Philologie.
B38, 40–47. 8º. Halle a. S. 1917–27
47, Festschrift für C. Appel.
Beihefte 66–75. 8º. Halle a. S. 1921–25
see APPLI (F.) Ausdrücke f. d. Tanzen in d. roman. Sprachen, 1925. [75.]
„ FERNÁNDEZ Y ÁVILA (G.) La infancia Jesu-Christo: 10 span. Weihnachtsspiele; hrsg. M. L. Wagner, 1922. [72.]
„ GARTNER (TH.) Ladin. Wörter a. d. Dolomitentälern &c., 1923. [73.]
„ LEO (U.) Studien z. Rutebeuf: Entwicklungsgesch. u. Form d. Renart le Bestourné &c., 1922. [67.]
„ LUTTA (C. M.) Der Dialekt v. Bergün &c., 1923. [71.]
„ PAR (A.) Sintaxi Catalana segons los escrits en prosa de Bernat Metge (1398), 1923. [66.]
„ SEIFERT (E.) Die Proparoxytona im Galloroman., 1923. [74.]
„ SCHEUERMEIER (P.) Ein Bezeichungen für d. Begriff Höhle in d. Alpendialekten, 1920. [69.]
„ SPITZER (L.) Die Umschreib. d. Begriffes "Hunger" im Italien., 1920. [68.]
„ ZENKER (R.) Forsch. z. Artusepik, 1, Ivainstudien, 1921. [70.]
Supplementheft 34, 35 u. 36, 44 (Bibliographie, 1909, 1910/11, 1924, v. F. Ritter). 8º. Halle a. S. 1923–27
Zeitschrift f. vergleichende Sprachforschung auf d. Gebiete d. indogerman. Sprachen. Begründet v. A. Kuhn. Neue Folge vereinigt mit d. Beiträgen z. Kunde d. indogerman. Sprachen. Hrsg. v. A. Bezzenberger &c.
Der ganzen Reihe B46–55. 8º. Göttingen. 1914–28
Zeitung [ZEYTUNG]. *Zeytung, Von der eroberung Copenhagen. Aus d. Keiserl. feldtleger vor Thurin. Von Römischer Keiserl. Mai. &c. Von Graff Heinrichen võ Nassaw &c. s4º. *n.p.* 1536

Zelion (Emma v. Brandis-), *see* BRANDIS-ZELION (E. v.)

Zeller (Gaston). La réunion de Metz à la France (1552–1648). [Univ. de Strasbourg]. pl. la8°. 1926

Zeller (Heinrich), *see* GRUNDRISS d. indogerm. Sprach- u. Altertumskunde, Abt. 2, B4ii, Armenisch, v. H. Z., 1927.

Zellinger (Johannes). Bad u. Bäder in d. altchristl. Kirche. 8°. Munchen. 1928

Zelter (Carl Friedrich), *see* GOETHE. Letters to Z., w. extr. f. those of Z. to G.; sel., tr. &c. Coleridge, 1892.

Zeltner (Gustav Georg).

Breviarium controv. cum eccl. Graeca, ac proinde etiam Ruthenica &c. s8°. Norimbergae. 1737

Breviarium controv. cum Enthusiastis & Fanaticis &c [*b. w. h.* Brev. controv. c. Remonstrantibus, 1719]. s8°. Lipsiae. 1724

Breviarium controv. cum Remonstrantibus agitatarum ad modum Schmidianorum paulloque fusius adornatum cum praef. hist. s8°. Noribergae. 1719

De P. Lautensack fanatici Noriberg. fatis &c. sched. Acc. J. Schwanhauseri ad L. epistola de sacra Coena &c. [P597]. s4°. Altorphii. 1716

Diss. de novis Bibl. versionibus German. non temere vulgandis &c. s4°. Altdorfi. 1707

Hist. Crypto-Socinismi Altorfinae quondam Acad. infesti arcana ex doc. adornata &c. Acc. V. Smalcii diarium vitae & M. Ruari epist. centuriae duae [*w. sep. pagin.*] s4°. Lipsiae. 1729

Hist. Noriberg. eccl. notabilior pericope in M. Helingi vita & fatis exhib. &c. s4°. Altorfii. 1715

Kurtz-gefasste Hist. d. gedr. Bibel-Version u. a. Schr. D. M. Lutheri, in d. Beschr. des Lebens &c. H. Luffts; auch a. Typographorum. s4°. Nürnberg. 1727

Tertullus obtrectator, h. e. diss. qua eccl. Evangel. non esse sectam ostenditur. s4°. Altdorffi. [1711]

Vitae theolog. Altorphin. s4°. Norimbergae. 1722

Zeltner (Johann Conrad). Correctorum in typographiis erudit. centuria. s8°. Norimbergae. 1716

,, ,, [*a. ed. w. t.*] Theatrum virorum erudit. Praem. vita Z. per F. Roth-Scholtzium. s8°. Norimbergae. 1720

Zen: der lebendige Buddhismus in Japan. Ausgewählte Stücke d. Z.-Textes übers. v. Schûej Ôhasama, hrsg. v. A. Faust, mit Geleitwort v. R. Otto. 8°. Gotha. 1925

Zend Avesta.

see KOSSOVICH (K. A.) Четыре статьи изъ Зендавесты, 1864.

,, MEILLET (A.) 3 conf. sur les Gâthâ de l'Avesta, 1925.

,, MITCHELL (J. M.) The Z.-A. & the relig. of the Pârsis, *n.d.*

Zéndegui (G. de). Sones de la lira inglesa. s8°. 1920

Zenker (Ernst Viktor) [Ценкер]. Анархизм. Ист. &c. анарх. учений. Переводъ съ нѣмецкаго. la8°. Москва. 1906

Zenker (Rudolf). Forsch. z. Artusepik. 1, Ivainstudien. [Z. f. roman. Phil., Beiheft, 70]. 8°. Halle. 1921

Zenne (*Oberheizer*), *see* SPIEGEL V. U. ZU PECKELSHEIM (H. P. R., *Frhr.*) O. Z., d. letzte Mann d. "Wiesbaden," 1917.

Zenner (Albert), *see* REISER (A.) Vindiciae evang.-Thomist. &c., subj. App. Anti-Thomistica contra A. Z., 1669.

Zeno, *emperor of the East, see* DIETERDT (J.) Exerc. de Henotico Zenonis &c., 1673.

Zeno (Giorgio) [ZORZI (GIORGIO)]. Relaz. d. Z. G., ambasc. straord. d. Repubb. Veneta a Ladislao VII, re di Polonia, nel 1638; pubbl. G. Ferraro, *see* REGIA DEP. DI STORIA PATRIA. Misc., t31, 1894.

Zeno (Nicolo), *the younger.* *Dell' orig. di Venetia. Libri 11. Con un cronico. Di nuovo rev. &c. [*by* F. Marcolini]. s8°. Venetia. 1558

Repr. of Orig. de' barbari, che distrussero &c. l'imperio di Roma, onde hebbe principio la città di Venetia, 1557.

Zenob, *abbot of Klag, see* HOVHANNESEAN (M.) Z. Glak (4c.) *In Armenian*, 1912.

Zenodotus, *of Ephesus, see* WECKLEIN (N.) Ü. Z. u. Aristarchus, 1919.

Zenon, *Egyptian business man, see* EDGAR (C. C.) Z. papyri, v1, 1925.

Zentgraf (Johann Joachim).

Colluvies Quackerorum. [P443, 2632]. s4°. Argentorati. 1665

De theologia mystica. Resp. J. F. Haug. [P426]. s4°. Argentorati. [1701]

Zenuno (Manfredus). Breves chronicae Bergom. [M. Z. &c. 1117–1512]; nunc primum ed. cura I. Finazzi, *see* REGIA DEP. DI STORIA PATRIA. Misc., t5, 1868.

Zenzinov (Vladimir).

Государств. переворотъ адм. Колчака въ Омскѣ, 18 Ноября 1918. Сборникъ док. Собралъ 3. 8°. Парижъ. 1919

Zeppelin (Ferdinand A. A. H., *Graf* **v.)** Das Werk Z. Eine Festgabe zu s. 75. Geburtstag v. Luftschiffbau Z., 1913. 4°. [St. 1913]

Zepper (Wilhelm).

Politia eccl. ed. 3ª. s4°. Herbornae Nassav. 1714

Von der christl. Disciplin oder Kirchenzucht &c. [*b. w.* Heidelberg Catechism. Catechismus, 1595]. s8°. Sigen. 1596

Zerbst. Wiederlegung des newlich aussgegangenen Zerbestischen Buchs &c., *see* GEDIK (S.) Von den Bildern u. Altarn &c., 1597.

Zehen starcke anzeigungen &c. das d. Dichter d. Zerbster Buchs, v. keinem guten Geiste getrieben sey, 1597, *see* HOFMANN (D.)

see also ANHALT.

Zerbst (Max). Nein u. Ja! Antwort auf H. Türck's Fr. Nietzsche. [P2478]. 8°. L. 1892

Zéréga-Fombona (A.) Le symbolisme français & la poésie espagnole mod. s8°. 1919

Zerener (Holm). Studien ü. d. beginn. Eindringen d. Luther. Bibelübersetzung i. d. deut. Lit., nebst e. Verzeichnis ü. 681 Drucke-hauptsächl. Flugschriften, 1522–25. [Archiv f. Reformationsgesch. Ergzb. 4]. 8°. L. 1911

Zereteli (Grigorii Filimonovich). Papyri russ. u. georg. Sammlungen [P. Ross.-Georg.], hrsg. G. Z. [p]1, 4. fol. Tiflis. 1925–27

1, Literar. Texte, bearb. v. G. Z. & O. Krüger.

4, Die Kome-Aphrodito Papyri d. Sammlung Lichačov; bearb. P. Jernstedt.

Żernicki-Szeliga (Emilian v.)

Der poln. Adel &c. 2B. 8°. Hamburg. 1900

Die poln. Stammwappen, i. Gesch. u. i. Sagen. 8°. Hamburg. 1904

Zernike (Elisabeth). Een vrouw als zij. 8°. Leiden. 1920

Zero, *ps.* *The secret hist. of the Coningham case, 1901, *see* CONINGHAM (A.)

Zervos (Christian). Un philosophe néoplatonicien du 11ᵉ s., M. Psellos, sa vie, s. œuvre &c. Préf. de F. Picavet. 8°. 1920

Rousseau. 4°. [1927]

Zervos (Skevos Georges).

Rhodes, capitale du Dodécanèse. 4°. 1920

Zesen (Philipp von). Des geistl. Standes Urteile wider d. Gewissenszwang in Glaubenssachen. [*b. w. h.* Des weltl. Standes Handlungen &c., 1665]. s8°. Amsterdam. 1665

Des weltl. Standes Handlungen &c. wider d. Gewissenszwang in Glaubenssachen. s8°. Amsterdam. 1665

Zettersten (Louis). City street names. 3rd ed. s8°. [1926]

Zeugnisse. *Alte u. neue Z. v. Zustande d. Seelen &c., *n.d.*, *see* ALTE.

Zeumer (Johann Caspar). Vitae profess. qui in Acad. Jenensi vixerunt & adhuc vivunt 4 class. rec. [*4 pagin.*] s8°. Jenae. 1711

Zeuthen (Hieronimus Georg). Hvorledes Mathematiken i Tiden fra Platon til Euklid blev en rationel Videnskab, *see* KONG. DANSKE VIDENSK. SELSK. Skrifter, Naturvid. Afd., Række 8, B1, 1915–17.

Zévaès (Alexandre), *ps.* [*i.e.* GUSTAVE ALEX. BOURSON]. Hist. de la 3ᵉ Républ., 1870–1926. s8°. 1926

Zevi (Salomon), *see* SOLOMON TSEBI, *Ufhausen.*

Zeytung, *see* ZEITUNG.

Zi (Etienne), *S.J.* Notice histor. sur les T'oan ou cercles du Siu-tcheou Fou, *see* VARIÉTÉS SINOLOG., No. 40, 1914.

Ziani (Pietro), *doge of Venice, 1205–29, see* LAIGUE (L. DE). S. & P. Ziani, 1906.

Ziani (Sebastiano), *doge of Venice, 1172–78.*

see DALL' ACQUA GIUSTI (A.) La loggia d. doge Z., 1880.

,, LAIGUE (L. DE). S. & P. Ziani, 1906.

Zíbrt (Čeněk). Bibliografie České historie. Sestavil C. Z. [Publ. České Akad.] díl 1–5. la8°. v Praze. 1900–12

Ziccardi (Giovanni). Le fiabe di C. Gozzi, *see* GIORNALE STORICO D. LETT. ITAL., v83, 1924.

Zichy (Géza, *Graf*), *1849–.*

Aus meinem Leben. Erinnerungen &c. 3B. 8°. St. 1911–20

Ziegenbalg (Bartholomaeus). Propag. of the Gospel in the East: an acc. of the success of 2 Danish missionaries [H. Pluetscho & B. Z.] in Malabar &c. Tr. 3p *in* 1v. s8°. 1709–14

—— **& Heinrich Plütscho.** Merckwürdige Nachricht [*& Fortsetzung*] welche Z. & P. von S. K. M. in Dennermarck &c. nach Trangebar gesandt überschrieben.

Die andere Auflage. s4°. L. 1708[–17]

15 parts w. sep. tps. in 1 vol. Cont. in add. to above, Ausführl. Bericht, 1ᵉ–12ᵉ Contin. d. Bericht., *publ. in Halle* 1710–17 [*pagin. contin.*] *Added* Symbolum Apostol. in lingua Malabarica, 1713 *unpaged.*

Ziegfeld (Arnold Hillen). Im Reiche d. Meergottes: Bilder aus d. Blühen u. Vergehen e. Kultur d. atlant. Afrika. Vorwort v. L. Frobenius. 2e A. s8o. St. [1923]

Ziegler (Bernardus), *of Leipzig* [ZIGLERUS]. Disput. duae: 1, De justicia fidei. 2, De bonis operibus. [*Presentation copy to Bugenhagen*]. s8o. Lipsiae. 1549
Oratio de conjunctione & unitate Christianorum &c. [P2528]. s8o. Lipsiae. 1549
see QUAESTIONES. In hoc libello exponuntur quaestiones 5, cui inclusa Oratio de conjunct. scol. cum ministerio [*by* B. Z.], 1544.

Ziegler (Caspar). De diaconis & diaconissis vet. eccl. s4o. Wittebergae. 1678

Ziegler (Heinrich). Die Gegenreformation in Schlesien. [Verein f. Ref.-gesch. Schr., Jhrg. 6, Nr. 24]. 8o. Halle a. S. [1888]

Ziegler (Jacobus), *of Landau.* Excusacio Valdensium cōtra binas litteras Augustini contra heresim Valdensium, libri V, *see* WALDENSES. In hoc vol. cont. &c., 1512.

Ziegler (Leo), *of Munich.* Bruchstücke e. vorhieronym. Übers. d. Pentateuch. 4o. München. 1883
Italafragm. d. Paulin. Briefe nebst Bruchstücken e. vorhieronym. Übers d. 1en Johannesbriefes. Vorwort v. E. Ranke. 4o. Marburg. 1876
Die lat. Bibelübersetzungen vor Hieronymus u. d. Itala d. Augustinus. Ein Beitrag. 4o. München. 1879

Ziegler (Leopold). Der ewige Buddho. 8o. Darmstadt. 1922
Gestaltwandel der Götter. 3e A. 2B. [*pagin. contin.*] s8o. Darmstadt. 1922

Ziegler (Theobald). Gesch. d. christl. Ethik. 8o. Str. 1886

Ziehl (Johann Conrad). Diss. de schola Jabnensi. [P427]. s4o. Altorfii. [1760]

Zieliński (Thaddaeus).
The relig. of anc. Greece. Tr. G. R. Noyes. 8o. 1926

Ziem (Félix), *see* ROUJON (H.) – F. Z., 1913.

Ziepel (C.) The reign of Richard II, & comments upon an allit. poem on the deposition of that monarch. 4o. Berlin. 1874

Zierold (Johann Wilhelm). Synopsis veritatis divinae opposita Synopsi controvers. S. Schelguigii. Praef. diss. Suff. Idea theol. Schelguig., aut. J. Langio. [*w. sep. pagin. b. w.* Schelwig (S.) Synopsis controv., 1705]. s8o. Francofurti. 1706

Ziesemer (Walther), *see* BIBLE: GERMAN. Eine ostdeut. Apostelgesch. d. 14. Jhdts.; hrsg. W. Z., 1927.

Zigler (Bernardus), *see* ZIEGLER (B.)

Zijnen (Frederik P. J. S.) Specimen hist.-dogmat. quo Anselmi & Calvini placita de redemtione inter se conferuntur &c. 8o. Schoonhoviae. 1852

Zimka (Cornelius).
T. Masaryk, wie man Präsident wird. s8o. Wien. 1923

Zimmer (Bernard). Les oiseaux, *see* ŒUVRES libres, 80, 1928.
Le veau gras, comédie, *see* ŒUVRES libres, 40, 1924.

Zimmer (George Frederick). Engineering of antiquity & technical progress in arts & crafts. 8o. [1920]

Zimmer (Heinrich). Karman: e. buddhist. Legendenkranz [Divyāvadāna]. Übers. u. hrsg. v. H. Z. 8o. München. 1925
Kunstform u. Yoga im ind. Kultbild. la8o. 1926

Zimmer (John Todd). Cat. of the Edward E. Ayer ornitholog. library, 2p, *see* FIELD COLUMBIAN MUSEUM. Zoolog. ser., v16, 1926.

Zimmermann (Alfred).
Gesch. d. preuss.-deut. Handelspolitik. 8o. Oldenburg. 1892

Zimmermann (E. Heinrich), *see* RIEGL (A.) Spätröm. Kunst.-Industrie, T2, bearbt. E. H. Z., 1923.

Zimmermann (Emil). Das deutsche Kaiserreich Mittelafrika als Grundlage e. neuen deut. Weltpolitik. [P2509]. 8o. 1917

Zimmermann (Ernst), *see* GRÄSSE (J. G. T.) & E. JÄNNICKE. Führer für Sammler v. Porzellan u. Fayence &c.; umgearb. &c. v. E. Z., 15e A., 1919.

Zimmermann (Heinrich), A. Handlirsch & O. Smital. Die beiden Hofmuseen u. d. Hofbibliothek. Vorwort v. A. Weixlgärtner. 8o. Wien. 1920

Zimmermann (Joachim). Thomas Münzer. 8o. [1925]

Zimmermann (Johann Georg, *Ritter* **von).**
Solitude [Tr.] [v1]. 8o. 1800

Zimmermann (Matthias). Diss. ad illud. Tertull. Apolog. cap. 18. Fiunt non nascuntur Christiani. s4o. Lipsiae. 1662

…mermann (Max Georg), *see* KNACKFUSS (H.) & M. G. Z. …m. Kunstgesch., B1, 3, 1910–14.

Zimmermann (Robert).
Anthroposophie in Umriss. 8o. Wien. 1882
Philos. u. Erfahrung. [*b. w. h.* Anthroposophie, 1882]. 8o. Wien. 1861
see HARTSEN (F. A. v.) Untersuch. ü. Psych.: Anmerk. zu R. Z.'s "Philosoph. Propädeutik," 1869.

Zimmern (Alfred Eckhard).
Europe in convalescence. s8o. [1922]
The Greek commonwealth: politics & economics in 5th cent. Athens. 3rd ed., rev. 8o. O. 1922
,, ,, 4th ed., rev. 8o. O. 1924
Learning & leadership. [League of N., Publ. 12Ai]. 8o. 1927
Learning & leadership: needs &c. of internat. intellectual co-op. 8o. 1928
Nationality & government: w. o. war-time essays. n. ed. s8o. 1919
The 3rd Brit. Empire. 8o. 1926

Zimmern (Heinrich), *Ph.D.* Babylon. Hymnen u. Gebete, 2e Auswahl, *see* ALTE ORIENT (DER), Jhrg. 13, 1911.
Das babylon. Neujahrsfest, *see* ALTE ORIENT (DER), Jhrg. 25, 1926.
Hethit. Gesetze aus d. Staatsarchiv v. Boghazköi (um 1300 v. Chr.) unter Mitw. v. J. Friedrich, übers. v. H. Z., *see* ALTE ORIENT (DER), Jhrg. 23, 1922.
Ištar u. Ṣaltu [*&*] K. Lipit-Ištar's Vergöttlichung, *see* KÖNIGL. SÄCHS. GESELLS. Berichte, B68, 1916.
Zum babylon. Neujahrsfest. 2er Beitrag. 8o. L. 1918

Zinano (Gabriele).
Il sogno, overo della poesia. s8o. Reggio. [1590]

Zincgreff (Julius Wilhelm). Emblematum ethico-politic. centuria. Ed. ultima. [*b. w.* Petrasanta (S.) Symbola, 1682]. s4o. Heidelbergae. 1666

Zincke (Foster Barham).
Wherstead: materials for its hist. 2nd ed. enl. 8o. 1893

Zindel (Christian Siegmund). Der Eislauf. Mit Gedichten v. Klopstock, Göthe &c. Hrsg. v. C. S. Z. s8o. Nürnberg. 1825

Zingali (Gaetano). Il riform. dei viveri dell' esercito ital., *see* BACHI (R.) L'alimentazione &c. in Italia, 1926.

Zingarelli (Nicola), *see* DANTE ALIGHIERI. Lectura D.: c. 29 dell' Inferno letto da N. Z., 1917.

Zingerle (Ignaz Vincenz). Die deutschen Sprichwörter im Mittelalter. Gesammelt v. I. V. Z. 8o. Wien. 1864

Zingerle (Oswald v.) Meinhards II. Urbare d. Grafschaft Tirol, *see* FONTES RERUM AUSTRIAC., B45i, 1890.

Zinny (Antonio). Hist. de los gobernadores de las Provincias Argentinas. ed. reord. con prol. de P. Banastre. 5v. 8o. Buenos Aires. 1920–21

Zinovev (Grigory) [Зиновьевъ].
Австрія и міровая война. [P2391]. 8o. Петроградъ. 1918
Безпартийный или коммунист. [P2723]. 8o. Москва. 1919
Борьба за Петроград 15 Окт.–6 Нояб. 1919. [*Ed.* 3.] 8o. П. 1920
Коммунист. интернационал. [P2455]. s8o. П. [1919]
Лицом к Деревне: статьи и речи. 8o. Ленинград. 1925
Мировая революция и коммунист. Интернационал. Речь 14 Окт. 1920. [P2697]. 8o. П. 1920
Н. Ленинъ. Очеркъ жизни &c. [P2723]. 8o. Москва. 1919
О роли професс. союзов. [P2698]. 8o. П. 1921
Тактика коминтерна. Послесловие к работам III. всемирного конгресса. [P2697]. 8o. П. 1921
TRANSLATIONS.
Bericht d. Exekutivkom. d. Kommunist. Internat. [P2462]. 8o. 1920
The communist party & indust. unionism. [P2487]. s8o. [1920 ?]
Gesch. d. kommunist. Partei Russlands (Bolschewiki). 8o. Hamburg. 1923
L'internationale communiste. [P2455]. s8o. Pétrograd. [1919]
TRANSLATIONS [*continued*].
Der Krieg u. d. Krise d. Sozialismus. 8o. Wien. 1924
N. Lénine. s8o. 1924
La révolution russe et le prolétariat internat. [P2455]. s8o. Petrograd. 1919
Die Rolle d. Kommunist. Partei in d. proletar. Revol. Rede. Hrsg. v. Kommunist. Internat. [*b. w. h.* Tagesfragen, 1920]. 8o. 1920
Die russ. Revolution u. d. internat. Proletariat. [P2462]. 8o. [1920]
Die Tagesfragen d. internat. Arbeiterbewegung. Hrsg. v. Kommunist. Internat. 8o. 1920
Vom Werdegang unseren Partei. Vortrag. [P2509]. 8o. 1920
Von d. bürgerl. bis z. proletar. Revolution. [P2758]. s8o. L. 1921
Was d. kommunist. Internationale bisher war &c. [P2487]. s8o. Hamburg. [1920]
Die Weltpartei d. Leninismus. [Tr.] 8o. Hamburg. 1924
Die Weltrevolution u. d. III. Kommun. Internationale. Rede. [P2462]. 8o. 1920

—— **& L. Trotzky.** Karl Liebknecht u. Rosa Luxemburg. Reden. [P2455]. s8o. Petrograd. 1920
О мятежѣ лѣвыхъ С.–Р. [P2499]. 8o. [П.] 1918

Zinzendorf (Nicolaus Ludwig, *Graf* v.) *Etwas v. Liede Mosis, u. d. Liede des Lammes, d. i.: Alt u. neuer Brüder-Gesang. [*Comp. by Z.*] s8°. London. 1753
A coll. of all the hymns ever used by the Unitas Fratrum, in chronol. order.
16 disc. on redemption of man. Tr. s8°. 1740
„ „ 2nd ed. [*w. t.*] 16 disc. on Jesus Christ. s8°. 1751
see BENNER (J. H.) Diss. de noxa homiletica Z., 1744.
„ —— Noxa catechetica Z., 1743.
„ HALLBAUER (F. A.) Animadv. in licentiam novas Germ. Sacri cod. versiones condendi quum L. de Z. suam N. Foed interpret. publicasset, 1741.
„ HYMNS. H. composed for use of Brethren; by C. Z. [*i.e.* Z.], 1749.
„ LEPELL (W. H. FERD. CARL *Graf.* v.) *Verz. d. Schr. d. Grafen L. v. Z., 1824.
„ SIRI (J. J.) Z. dogmata rei Xtnae. noxia, 1748.
„ SPANGENBERG (A. G.) Leben d. Herrn N. L., Grafen &c. v. Z., 8T, 1773–75.

Zionsharfe. Gesangbuch f. d. deutschen Wesleyan Methodisten. s8°. Cannstatt. 1878

Zipoli (Perlone), *ps.*, *see* LIPPI (LORENZO).

Zippel (Giuseppe). Il Palazzetto di Venezia. [Estr. dall' Ann. dell' Assoc. Artist. fra i Cultori di Archit., 1910]. [P2702]. la8°. 1910

Zirardini (Giuseppe), *see* TESORO dei novellieri ital. scelti dal 13 al 19 sec. e pubbl. p. c. di G. Z., 2p, 1847.

Zirato (Bruno), *see* KEY (P. V. R.) Enrico Caruso: a biog., by K., in collab. w. B. Z., 1923.

Zisca (Jan) [ZISSKA], *see* ŽIŽKA (J.)

Ziv (G. A.) [Зивъ]. Троцкій. Характеристика. 8°. Нью-Іоркъ. 1921

Zivier (Ezechiel). Neuere Gesch. Polens, B1, Die 2 letzten Jagellonen (1506–72), 1915, *see* GESCHICHTE DER EUROP. STAATEN.

Žižka (Jan) [TROCZNOWA (JOH. DE); ZISCA].
see GILPIN (W.) Lives of Wicliff, Z. &c., 1765.
„ HÄBERLIN (F. D.) Elogium J. de T. cogn. Z., 1742.

Zlatogor (Maksim).
Живая рѣчь, христоматія. 2ч. [*in* 1v]. s8°. London. 1920
По Руси очерки из русской жизни &c. [*b. w. h.* Живая рѣчь, 1920]. s8°. London. 1920
Русскій семейный письмовникъ; образцы писем &c. [*b. w. h.* Живая рѣчь, 1920]. s8°. London. 1920

Zlobin (V. A.), *see* MEREJKOVSKY (D. S.), V. A. Z. &c. Царство Антихриста, 1921.

Znanie, *see* SBORNIK. Сборникъ товар. "Знаніе," 1–5, 1904–5.

Zobeltitz (Fedor v.) Chronik d. Gesells. unter d. letzten Kaiserreich, 1894–1914. 2B. 8°. Hamburg. 1922
Heinz Stirlings Abenteuer als Kriegsfreiwilliger. 8°. 1915
Die von Schebitz. Gesch. e Adelsfamilie im Revolutionsjahr. s8°. 1920

Zobeltitz (Hanns v.)
Die Fürstin-Witwe. Roman. s8°. St. [1915]

Zobeltitz (Hans Caspar v.) Das Ruhrgebiet nebst Wupper u. Niederrhein. Hrsg. H. C. v. Z. 8°. Bielefeld. 1923

Zöckler (Otto). Die Augsburg. Conf. als symbol. Lehrgrundlage d. deut. Reformationskirche hist. &c. untersucht v. O. Z. 8°. Frankfurt a. M. 1870
Handbuch d. theolog. Wissenschaften. Hrsg. O. Z. 3B. Nördlingen. 1883–85

Zöge von Manteuffel (Helene Marie), *see* KÜGELGEN (H. M. v.)

Zöge von Manteuffel (Kurt). Die Künstlerfamilie Van de Velde. [Künstler-Monogr., 117]. la8°. Bielefeld. 1927

Zohar.
see KNORR VON ROSENOTH (C.) Kabbala denudata &c.; tr. libri Sohar, &c., 2t, 1677–84.
„ SCHOLEM (G.) Bibliogr. Kabbalistica: mit Anhang, Bibliog. d. Z. u. s. Komm., 1927.

Zola (Émile).
Germinal. [Les Rougon-Macquart]. s8°. 1904
Jean Gourdon. s8°. *n.d.*
Le ventre de Paris. [Les Rougon-Macquart]. s8°. 1903
see DEFFOUX (L.) & E. ZAVIE. Le groupe de Médan: E. Z. &c., 1920.
see MANN (H.) Macht u. Mensch, 1919.
„ PATTERSON (J. G.) Z. dict.: characters of the Rougon-Macquart novels, w. biog. &c. intr., 1912.

Zola (Giuseppe). Comm. de rebus Xtn^is^. ante Const. magnum lib. 3v. 8°. Ticini. 1780–86

Zollmann (Carl). American civil church law. [Columbia Univ.] 8°. N.Y. 1917

Zöllner (David). Stricturae libelli Cogitat. nov. de primo & secundo Adamo. [*By S. Crellius*]. [P2634]. s4°. Lipsiæ. 1702

Zollner (Johann Carl Friedrich).
Wissenschaftl. Abhandlungen. 3B [*in* 4v]. 8°. L. 1878–79
B3 *has tp.*: Die Transcendentale Physik.

Zolotarev (David Alekseevich).
Лопарская экспед., 1927. [I.R.G.O. Карельско-Мурманская Ком.] la8°. Ленинград. 1927

Zompini (Gaetano). *Le arti che vanno per via n. città di Venezia. Pub. by Lackington, Allen & Co. fol. Finsbury Sq., London. 1803

Zonaras (Joannes). Historia, nuov. tr. dal Greco per M. Emilio. 8°. Vinegia. 1560

Zonghi (Aurelio). Le marche principali d. carte Fabrianesi, 1293–1599. [P2842]. la8°. Fabriano. 1881

Zonin (A.) Долой партизанщину! Стройте красную Армию! [P2459]. 8°. [Одесса]. 1919

Zoological Society of London.
List of fellows, members &c. 1923, 1925. 8°. 1923–25
Proceedings, 1916–1925. 8°. [1916–25]
„ „ ....Index, 1911–20. 8°. 1922
Zoological record: rec. of zool. lit. Superintended by D. Sharp. v52–57 (1915–20). 8°. 1917–22

Zoophilist & Animals' Defender.
v38–46 (1918–27). 4°. [1919–27]

Zöphel (Georg), *see* DEUTSCH. Verfassung d. Deutschen Reiches v. 11. Aug. 1919; kurz erläut. &c. v. G. Z., 1920.

Zoppetti (Domenico). Disegni di mon. storici venez. esist. presso D. Z. obl.8°. [Venezia]. *n.d.*

Zorn (Anders Leonhard).
see ROMDAHL (A.) A. Z. als Radierer, 1922.
„ SALAMAN (M. C.) A. Z., 1925.

Zorn (John C. L.)
Thoughts on a capital levy. [P2732]. 8°. [1919]

Zorn (Peter). Bibliotheca antiq. &c. in Scripturam S. Vet. & Novi Test. t1, pars 1–12 [*in 1v. No more published*]. s8°. Francofurti. 1724–25
Delin. theologiae patristicae, *see* VIRORUM &c. molimina theolog., 1761.
Diss. de eunuchismo Origenis Adamantii. Praes. J. H. Majo. [P432]. s4°. Gissae Hass. 1708
Hist. Bibliorum manualium, ron denen Hand-Bibeln d. ersten Christen. s4°. Lipsiae. 1738
Hist. Bibliorum pictorum ex antiq. Ebr. & Xtn. illust. s4°. Lipsiae. 1743
Hist. eucharistiae infantium &c. s8°. Berolini. 1736
Hist. fisci Judaici sub imp. vet. Rom. &c. s8°. Altonaviae. 1734
Opuscula sacra &c. 2t. s8°. Altonaviæ. 1731
„ „ ....ed. 2^a^. t1. s8°. Altonaviæ. 1743

Zorrilla (José). Granada: poema. Prec. de la Leyenda de al-Hamar. n. ed. 2t. 8°. 1895
see CORTÉS (N. A.) Z., su vida y sus obras, t2, 3, 1918–20.

Zorzi (Giorgio), *see* ZENO (G.)

Zottmann (Ludwig). Zur Kunst d. Bassani. la8°. Str. 1908

Zouch (Richard) [ZOUCHE]. The jurisdiction of the Admiralty of England asserted. [*b. w.* Burroughs (*Sir* J.) Soveraignty &c., 1686]. fol. 1686

Zouche of Haryngworth (Mary C. Frankland, *baroness*). Cat. of library, includ. first issue of Mazarin bible. Sold by Sotheby, Nov. 1920. [Illust. P2853]. la8°. 1920

Zschokke (Johannes Heinrich D.) Les matinées suisses. Contes. Tr. A. I. & J. Cherbuliez. 4t [*in* 2v]. s8°. 1830

Zubov (Platon).
Картина Кавказскаго края. 2ч *in* 1v. s8°. С.-П. 1834–35

Zubov (*graf* Valery Aleksandrovich), *see* DUBROVIN (N. F.) Походъ В. А. З. въ Персію, 1796, 1874.

Zucchi (Mario). Carlo Alberto d. restaur. &c. n. mem. ined. di A. di Saluzzo, *see* REGIA DEPUT. S. GLI STUDI DI STORIA PATRIA &c. Bibl., v12, 1926.
Works in REGIA DEPUT. Miscellanea.
Delle orig. del nome di Sannazzaro de' Burgondi in Lomellina e d. famiglia di J. Sannazzaro, 1906. [42.]
Lomello (476–1796), 1904. [40.]
Orig. e vicende d. titolo di princ. de' Piemonte, 1912. [46.]

Zuccoli (Luciano).
Baruffa. n. ed. riv. s8°. Milano. [1921]
Le cose più grandi di lui. Romanzo. s8°. Milano. 1922
La divina fanciulla. Romanzo. s8°. Milano. 1920
Kif tebbi. Romanzo africano. s8°. Milano. 1923

Zuccoli (Luciano) [*continued*].

Il peccato e le tentazioni. s8°. Milano. [1926]
Per la sua bocca. Romanzo. s8°. Milano. [1920]
Primavera. s8°. Milano. *n.d.*
La straniera in casa. Romanzo. s8°. Milano. 1925
La vita elegante. s8°. Milano. [1925]

Zuchhold (Hans). Aus der Hölle empor: Erlebnisse e. aus russ. Kriegsgefang. Ausgetauschten. s8°. [1917]

Zucker (Markus). Albrecht Dürer. [Verein f. Ref.-gesch. Schr., Jhrg. 17]. la8°. Halle a. S. 1900

Zukunftsaufgaben (Die) d. deut. Städte, 1922, *see* LUTHER (H.), P. MITZLAFF &c., *edd.*

Zülch (Walter Carl), *see* FRANKFURTER URKUNDENBUCH z. frühgesch. d. Buchdrucks; hrsg. v. W. C. Z. &c., 1920.

Zulian (Gianfrancesco).
Torcello e la sua cattedrale. s8°. Venezia. 1885

Zuloaga (Ignacio).
*Zuloaga. [L'art & les artistes, n. sér. t11]. la8°. 1925
see MARTINEZ SIERRA (G.) I. Z., 1919.

Zulueta (Francis de), *see* VACARIUS, *magister.* Lib. pauperum; ed. F. de Z., 1927.

Zündel (Gottlob). Erzählen u. Vorlesen: Vorschläge zu gemeinsamer Lektüre &c. 4e A. s8°. L. 1923

Zuñiga y Sotomayor (Fadrique de), *see* UHAGON (F. R. DE). Libros de cetreria, noticias, 1889.

Zunz (Leopold). Die gottesdienstl. Vorträge d. Juden. 8°. 1832
Die synagogale Poesie d. Mittelalters. 2e A., hrsg. v. A. Freimann. 8°. Frankfurt a M. 1920
Die 24 Bücher d. Heil. Schrift. 1838, *see* BIBLE: OLD TEST.

Zupitza (Julius). Alt- u. mittelengl. Übungsbuch, mit e. Wörterbuch. 11e A., hrsg. J. Schipper. 8°. Wien. 1915

Zur europä. Politik, B1–5, 1919, *see* SCHWERTFEGER (B.), *ed.*

Zurara (Gomes Eannes de), *see* EANNES DE ZURARA (G.)

Zurbarán (Francisco de), *see* HISP. SOC. OF AMERICA. Cat. ser., 1925.
see KEHRER (H.) F. de Z., 1918.

Zuretti (Carlo Oreste), *see* UNION ACAD. INTERNAT. Cat. des mss. alchim. grecs, t2, mss. ital., décr. par Z., 1927.

Zürich.
*Acta oder geschicht wie es uff d. gesprech. d. 26. 27. u 28. tagen Wynmonadts in Z. ergangen ist; Anbetreffend die götze u. die Mess. s4°. Zürich [*Christoph Froschouer*]. 1523
*Epistolæ duæ ad Eccl. Polonicas scr. à Tigurinæ eccl. ministris de negotio Stancariano & mediatore Dei & hominum &c. [*a. copy b. w.* Flacius (M.) Def. sanae doct., 1570]. s8°. Tiguri. 1561
Ex chronica univ. Turic. excerpta, *see* OTTO *de S. Blasio.* Chron.; ed. A. Hofmeister, 1912.
Handlung d. versamlung inn Z. auff d. 29. tag Jeñers võ wegen d. hayl. Evangelii zw. d. botschafft v. Costentz H. Zwingli ū. gemainer priesterschafft d. gantzen gebyets d. stat Zürich vor gesessnem radt beschehen. s4°. [Zürich ?]. 1523
Musée Nat. Suisse. 28e & 30e rapports, 1919 & 1924. 8°. Zurich. 1920–25
Orthodoxa Tigurinæ eccl. ministrorum conf. &c. una cum responsione ad M. Lutheri calumnias &c. [*by* H. Bullinger]. Lat. donata, R. Gualthero interprete. s8°. Tiguri, *C. Frosch.* 1545
ZENTRALBIBLIOTHEK, *see* PESTALOZZI (J. H.) P. & h. times; pict. rec., ed. by the Zentralbibl. &c., 1928.

Zurita (Gerónimo), *see* ARGENSOLA (B. L. DE). Primera parte de los anales de Aragon que prosigue los del Secretario G. Ç., desde 1516 &c., 1630.

Zusammenbruch. Ursachen des Z.: Entst. &c. d. Offensive v. 1918, 1923, *see* GERMANY: REICHSTAG.

Zutphen (Hendrik van), *see* MULLER (H.) *van Zutphen.*

Zvezda. Звезда: лит.-обществ. &c. журнал. N°. 1. 8°. П. 1924
Из эпохи "Звезды" и "Правды" (1911–14), 1921, *see* OLMINSKY (M.)

Zwanzig Jahre alldeut. Arbeit u. Kämpfe. Hrsg. v. d. Hauptleitung d. Alldeut. Verbandes. [Vorwort v. H. Class]. 8°. L. 1910

Zwehl (*Gen.* **Hans v.)** E. v. Falkenhayn. la8°. 1926
Maubeuge, Aisne–Verdun. 7th Reserve-Korps im Weltkriege, bis Ende 1916. 8°. 1921
Die Schlachten im Sommer 1918 an d. Westfront. [P2682]. 8°. 1921

Zweibrücken, *Counts of, see* CROLLIUS (G. C.) Orig. Bipontinarum, p1, 2, 1761–69.

Zweig (Arnold).
Der Streit um d. Sergeanten Grischa. s8°. Potsdam. 1928

Zweig (Stefan).
Amok. 8°. L. 1925
[De]struction d'un cœur, *see* [Œu]VRES libres, 82, 1928.
Gesamm. Gedichte. 8°. L. 1924
Das Haus am Meer. Schauspiel. s8°. L. 1912

Zweig (Stefan) [*continued*].
Romain Rolland, d. Mann u. d. Werk. 8°. Frankfurt am M. 1921
Romain Rolland, the man & h. work. 8°. [1921]
Verwirrung der Gefühle. 3 Novellen. s8°. L. 1927
see RIEGER (E.) S. Z., der Mann u. das Werk, 1928.

Zwemer (Samuel Marinus). The influence of animism on Islam. Acc. of pop. superstitions. s8°. 1920

Zwerg (Anton Wilhelm). De pygmaeis Aethiopiae populis diss. [P2648]. s4°. Kiliae. 1727

Zwick (Heinrich August). Calmuc Tartary, or journey from Sarepta to Calmuc hordes, 1823. [Tr.] s8°. 1831

Zwicker (Daniel). *Henoticum Christianorum. Rec. à D. Z. [*b. w. h.* Irenicum, 1658]. s8°. Amsterodami. 1662
*Irenicum Irenicorum seu reconciliatoris Christianorum hodiern. norma triplex &c. s8°. *n.p.* [1658]
Irenicomastix iterato victus &c. seu novum &c. exemplum pugnae J. A. Comenii contra Irenici Irenicorum autorem &c. Ostendente I. I. autore. [*b. w. h.* Irenicum, 1658]. s8°. Amsterodami. 1662
Irenicomastix perpetuo convictus &c. Edente Irenici autore. [*b. w. h.* Irenicum, 1658]. s8°. Amsterodami. 1661
see BAIER (J. W.) Diss. qua Concilii Nicaeni primi auctoritas à crimin. D. Z. & C. Sandii defenditur, 1671; 1695.

Zwingero (Jacobo). Graecarum dialect. hypotyposis &c., *see* SCAPULA (J.) Lexicon, 1628.

Zwingli (Ulrich). Opera, partim quidem ab ipso Lat. conscr., partim verò è vernaculo sermone in Lat. tr.: omnia nov. recogn. [R. Gualtheri apologia]. 4t. fol. [Zürich, *Froschower.* 1545]
t4 has title: Quartus tomus operum H. Z. qui annot. in Evang. & Apost. scr. ex ore ejusdem per L. Judae exceptas cont.
Sämtl. Werke. Unter Mitwirkung d. Zwingli-Vereins in Zürich. Hrsg. E. Egli, G. Finsler &c. [Corpus Reformat., v91, 96]. B4, 9 (9, Briefwechsel, B3). la8°. L. 1925–27
Ad Philippenses annot., per Leonem Judæ ex ore Zwinglii excepta. [*b. w. h.* Annotatiunculae in P. ad Corinthios epist., 1528]. s8°. Tiguri, *C. Froschouer.* 1531
Amica exegesis, id est, expositio eucharistiæ negocii ad M. Lutherum. s4°. [Zürich. 1527]
Annotatiunculae per Leonem Judæ, ex ore Z. in utranq; Pauli ad Corinthios epistolam. s8°. Tiguri, *C. Froschouer.* 1528
Eyn Antwurt H. Z. uff die Epistel Joannis Pugenhag, das Nachtmal Christi betreffende. s4°. Zürich [*Christoffel Froschouer*]. 1526
Brevis & luculenta in epist. Jacobi expositio, per L. Judae ex ore ejus excepta &c. [*b. w. h.* Annotatiunculae &c. 1528]. s8°. Tiguri. 1523
Complanationis Isaiæ foetura prima, cum apologia qur quidque sic versum sit. [*w. Jerome's & Zwingli's Lat. versions*]. fol. Tiguri, *C. Froschouer.* 1529
Complanationis Ieremiae foetura prima, cum apologia quur quidque sic versum sit. [*w. Lat. version. b. w. h.* Complan. Isaiæ proph., 1529]. fol. Tiguri, *C. Froschover.* 1531
De vera & falsa religione H. Z. commentarius. s8°. Tiguri. *Chr. Froschouer,* 1525
Dise nachbestimte Artickell bekenne ich H. Z. mich In d. lobl. statt Zürich gepredigett haben &c. s4°. *n.d.* [16c.]
Ein göttlich vermanung an die Ersamen &c. Eydgnossen zu Schweytz, das sie sich vor frömden herrn hütind u. entladindt &c. s4°. [Zürich. 1522]
„ „ [*a. ed. woodcut on tp.* P2539]. s4°. [Leiptz. 1522 ?]
In Evangelicam hist. de Jesu Christo, per Matthaeum, Marcum, Lucam & Johannem conscriptam, Epistolasq; aliquot Pauli, annot. per Leonem Judae exceptae & æditæ. Adj. est Epistola Pauli ad. Hebraeos & Joannis Apostoli epistola per G. Megandrum. [*b. w. h.* Complan. Isaiæ proph., 1529]. fol. Tiguri, *C. Froschover.* 1539
Ein klare underrichtung v. Nachtmal Christi durch H. Z. tütsch &c. s8°. Zürich, *Joh. Hager.* 1526
*Nöthige &c. Unterredung: erstes Gespräche gehalten v. M. Luthero & U. Z., 1720, *see* LUTHER (M.)
The rekenynge & declaracion of the fayth & beliefe of Huldrike Zwyngly sent to Charles V that nowe is Emproure of Rome: holdynge a parlement or Counsayll at Ausbrough with the chefe Lordes & lerned men of Germanye The yere MDXXX &c. [*Marginal notes slightly cut into by binder*]. s8°. Zuryk [*R. Wyer*]. 1543
Sermonis De providentia Dei anamnema. s8°. Tiguri, *C. Froschouer.* 1530

Zwingli (Ulrich) [*continued*].
see Andreae (J.) Solida refut. comp. Cingl. & Calvin, 1584.
,, Baden, *Switzerland*. Ein gleidt so die Eydgenossen U. Z. uff die Collation zu Baden &c., 1527.
,, Bugenhagen (J.) Contra novum errorem [*of Zwingli*] de sacramento, 1525 ?.
,, Faber (J.) Christenl. beweisung über sechs Artickel d. unchristl. U. Z. &c., 1526.
,, —— Ein warlich underrichtung wie es zu Zürch by dē zwinglin uff d. 20 Jan. nest verschinē ergangen sey, 1523 ?.

Zwingli (Ulrich) [*continued*].
see Luther (M.) Wie sich M. L. u. H. Z. in d. Sum̄ Christl. leer &c., 1529.
,, Stähelin (R.) H. Z. u. s. Reformationswerk, 1883.
,, Wernle (P.) Der evangel. Glaube nach d. Hauptschr. d. Reformatoren, B2, Z., 1919.
,, Zürich. Handlung d. versamlung inn Z. zw. d. botschafft v. Costentz H. Z. &c., 1523.

Zwolle, *see* Voecht (J. de). Narratio de inchoat. Domus cleric. in Z., 1908.

Zylka (Johann). Westrussland in militärgeograph. Hinsicht, *see* Kaiser-Wilhelm-Dank. Kriegsschr., H58, 1916.

PRINTED IN GREAT BRITAIN BY NEILL AND CO., LTD., EDINBURGH.